2015

AV Market Place™

AV Market Place™
43rd Edition

Publisher
Thomas H. Hogan

Vice President, Content
Dick Kaser

Senior Director, ITI Reference Group
Owen O'Donnell

Managing Editor
Karen Hallard

Senior Editor
Mitra Purkayastha

Assistant Editor
Karen DiDario

Tampa Operations:

Manager, Tampa Editorial Operations
Debra James

Project Coordinator, Tampa Editorial
Carolyn Victor

Graphics & Production:

Production Manager
Norma Neimeister

Production
Dana Stevenson
Jackie Crawford

2015

AV Market Place™

The Complete Business Directory of Products and Services for the Audio/Video Industry

AUDIO

FILM

VIDEO

AUDIO VISUAL

PROGRAMMING

COMPUTER SYSTEMS

Information Today, Inc.

ISSN 1044-0445
ISBN 978-1-57387-502-8
Library of Congress Catalog Card Number 69-17201

Information Today, Inc.
143 Old Marlton Pike
Medford, NJ 08055-8750
Phone: 800-300-9868 (Customer Service)
800-409-4929 (Editorial)
Fax: 609-654-4309
E-mail (orders): custserv@infotoday.com
Web Site: www.infotoday.com

Printed in the United States of America

ISBN 978-1-57387-502-8

9 781573 875028

Contents

Preface

AV Market Place™, now in its 43rd edition, continues to be the one-stop guide to the ever-changing AV industry. This complete business directory of audio, audio/visual, computer systems, film, video and programming covers a broad range of services and suppliers in the U.S. and Canada. *AVMP 2015* lists almost 5,100 companies that supply more than 1,250 industry-related products and services.

Contents & Indexes

AV Market Place™ includes an alphabetical listing of all products and services in the easily accessible Products & Services Index. Following is the Products, Services & Companies section which is organized into seven major categories — Audio, Audio/Visual, Computer Systems, Film, Video, Programming and Miscellaneous. Categories are further organized by state, then alphabetically by company name. For a complete description of the organization and indexes, see "How to Use *AV Market Place*™" (page ix).

The AV Product & Service Providers section provides full contact information — address, telephone, fax, e-mail & web addresses as well as personnel information. The remaining sections of *AVMP* are devoted to support services and organizations vital to the industry. The Associations section lists entries for the audio visual trade and related organizations with AV interests. The section on Film & Television Commissions includes city, county and state agencies that provide information and services to prospective filmmakers. The Awards & Festivals section lists events open to AV producers in the U.S. and Canada. Major conventions and meetings from early 2015 through 2019 are chronologically listed in the Calendar of Events section. Preceding the Calendar of Events are two indexes. The Sponsor Index is an alphabetical list of event sponsors and the events they sponsor; the Event Index is an alphabetical list of events along with the date(s) on which they are held. Trade and consumer publications, covering the audio visual field and related media, are listed in the Periodicals for the Trade section. A select list of audio/visual reference materials is included in the Reference Books for the Trade section. Finally, the Industry Indexes cover two distinct areas of data. A Company Index includes the name, address, communications information and page reference for company listings. A separate Personnel Index includes the main personnel associated with each company appearing in the Company Index as well as the page reference number.

Compilation

While we have used our best efforts to compile an accurate, comprehensive directory, in a project of this magnitude there may be errors and omissions, and we would appreciate learning of them. Updated information or suggestions for new listings can be submitted to:

AV Market Place™
Information Today, Inc.
121 Chanlon Road, Suite G-20
New Providence, NJ 07974
Fax: 908-219-0192
Phone: 800-409-4929

Requests to have your product, service or company listed in *AVMP* should be addressed to Karen Hallard at the above address or submitted via e-mail to khallard@infotoday.com. We will then provide a listing application. Once your completed application is received, your information will be entered in our database and appear in the next possible edition of *AV Market Place*.

The editors are grateful for the assistance and cooperation of everyone whose contributions made *AV Market Place 2015* possible.

How to Use AV Market Place™

AV Market Place™ (AVMP) contains seven informational sections, the focus of which is the AV Product & Service Providers section and its Products, Services & Companies Index. The AV Product & Service Providers section lists AV product and service suppliers alphabetically and provides full listings of addresses, telecommunication information, personnel and other relevant facts. Two indexes described and illustrated below, each of which have distinctly different functions, are provided to aid the user in selecting the company that will best meet their needs.

Products & Services Index

This index alphabetically lists AV products and services that are available through the companies represented in the AV Product & Service Providers section. Here you will find over 1,250 classifications interfiled alphabetically pertaining to seven major AV categories: Audio, Audio/Visual, Computer Systems, Film, Video, Programming and Miscellaneous. Some classifications may be listed in more than one way, ensuring that the user will easily find what is required. The user must first locate the classification desired, which then refers them to a page number in the Products, Services & Companies section where they will find a list of providers of that particular product or service. This index is best suited to the user who is limiting his research to a particular segment of the industry.

This index further separates services by medium and products by company function. Where appropriate, the medium is included in parenthesis. As an example, if the user is looking for a distributor of Multimedia Workstations, the classification can be found on page 8:

Multimedia Workstation (Computer Systems)——— **classification**
—Distributors p. 278 ——————————— **page reference to the Products, Services & Companies section**
—Manufacturers p. 279
—Rentals p. 279
—Repairs p. 280

Products, Services & Companies

This section organizes the over 1,250 product and service classifications by seven major industry segments: Audio, Audio/Visual, Computer Systems, Film, Video, Programming and Miscellaneous. All of the major headings are included in the table of contents. Within each segment, the product and service classifications are listed alphabetically. Following each classification, arranged in state order, the user will find a list of companies that are providers of that particular product or service. A company name may be found under many classifications depending on the extent of its activities. This index may be utilized by the user who is interested in the products or services available for a particular segment of the AV industry.

The above user wants to locate a Multimedia Workstation distributor in California. This would be accomplished by consulting page 278 of this section which provides a list of company names arranged by state and looking under this classification until locating companies in California (page 278). Page references are included with the company names.

Multimedia Workstation——————————— **classification (begins on page 278)**
Distributors

ARIZONA

CADint, pg 816
EAR Professional Audio/Video, pg 855

CALIFORNIA ——————————————— **state**

Ametron Audio/Video, pg 785
Audio Images Corp, pg 794
Be Media, pg 804
California Tape Products Inc, pg 817
Computer Modules Inc, pg 834
Diaquest, pg 846
DiskFaktory Direct, pg 849
Electrosonic Inc, pg 859——————————— **company**
Media Fabricators Inc, page 936
MediaPOINTE, pg 938
Mobilized Tech Systems, pg 944

AV Product & Service Providers

Having chosen Electrosonic Inc from the Products, Services & Companies section, the user would then refer to the AV Product & Service Providers section, page 859, to obtain more detailed information.

Electrosonic Inc	**company name**
3320 N San Fernando Blvd, Burbank, CA 91504	**address**
Tel: 818-333-3600 *Toll Free Tel:* 888-343-3604 (sales) *Fax:* 818-230-1017	**telephone & fax**
E-mail: info@electrosonic.com	**company e-mail**
Web Site: www.electrosonic.com	**company web site**
Key Personnel	
Pres: Jim Bowie Sr Mktg Mgr: Ramzi Shakra Mktg Coord: Pamela Manlulu E-mail: pamela.manlulu@electrosonic.com	**personnel**
Founded: 1964	**year founded**
AV company providing systems integration services, engineering, project management & AV design.	**business description**
Branch Office(s)	
4501 Vineland Rd, Suite 105, Orlando, FL 32811 *Tel:* 407-839-1154 *Fax:* 407-839-2055 10320 Bren Rd E, Minnetonka, MN 55343-9048 *Tel:* 952-931-7500 *Toll Free Tel:* 800-328-6202 *Fax:* 952-938-9311 318 W 39 St, 9th fl, New York, NY 10018 *Tel:* 212-206-7711 *Fax:* 212-206-7333	**branch office(s)**
Foreign Office(s): Electrosonic Ltd, Hawley Mill, Hawley Rd, Dartford, Kent DA2 7SY, United Kingdom *Tel:* (01322) 222211 *Fax:* (01322) 282215 *Web Site:* www.electrosonic.co.uk	**foreign office**
Membership(s): AFCEA; American Institute of Architects; ASTC; IAAPA; InfoComm International®; NSCA; Themed Entertainment Association	**association membership(s)**

In review, the user should follow these three steps to locate a company offering the product or service needed:

1. Find the product or service needed in the Products & Services Index and note the page number provided.
2. Refer to that page number in the Products, Services & Companies section and select a company from the desired state and note the page number given.
3. Refer to the listing for that company in the AV Product & Service Providers section for further details.

Section Contents

AV Product & Service Providers
Entries in the AV Product & Service Providers section are arranged alphabetically by company name and generally contain address, phone and fax numbers, e-mail and web site addresses, key personnel, branch offices and catalog data. The user who is already familiar with a company, but needs contact information, should go directly to this section.

Associations
This section contains entries for AV trade related associations. Entries contain name, address, phone, fax and contact data as well as information on upcoming events (2015-2019), the purpose of the organization, publication data (with frequency) and membership data. A chronological listing of upcoming AV-related events can be found in the Calendar of Events section.

Film & Television Commissions
Listed geographically in this section are state, county and city agencies involved with providing information and services to film, TV and commercial producers. Entries contain name, address, phone, fax and personnel data, as well as descriptions of the variety and extent of the services provided.

Awards & Festivals
Listed here are sponsoring agencies of awards & festivals open to professional, educational, student and industrial media producers. In addition to name, address, phone, fax & personnel data, entries contain information on media covered, categories and types of awards, date and location of presentation or festival, closing dates and entry fees.

Calendar of Events
This section chronologically lists AV related meetings and conventions scheduled at press time from early 2015 through 2019. Entries — sorted by year, month and event name — contain name, address, phone, fax and personnel data as well as the date and location of the event. The calendar is preceded by two indexes. The Sponsor Index is an alphabetical list of event sponsors and a list of the events they sponsor. This index is helpful to the user who knows the name of the sponsor, but may not know the name of the event. The Event Index is an alphabetical list of events, along with the dates on which they are being held. This index should be consulted when the user knows the event name, but not the date on which the event is being held.

Periodicals for the Trade
AV related publications are listed with the name of the publisher, address, phone, fax and contact data. Specific data such as description of content, frequency, circulation, advertising rates and close date, trim size, subscription cost and ISSN are also included.

Reference Books for the Trade
Titles related to AV topics are listed with the name of the publisher, address, phone, fax and contact data. Specific data such as author, description of content, edition, publication date and ISBN are also included.

Industry Indexes
The Industry Indexes cover two distinct areas of data. The Company Index includes the name, address, communications information and page reference for all listings in the directory with the exception of Calendar of Events, Periodicals for the Trade and Reference Books for the Trade. The Personnel Index includes the main personnel associated with each company listed in the Company Index as well as the page reference. The Personnel Index is helpful for the user who is looking to contact a specific individual from whom the company affiliation is unknown.

Comments or suggestions regarding the content and format of *AVMP* are encouraged and can be directed to *AV Market Place*™, Information Today, Inc., 121 Chanlon Road, Suite G-20, New Providence, NJ 07974.

Abbreviations & Acronyms

The following is a list of acronyms & abbreviations used throughout *AVMP*.

AB – Alberta
ABA – American Booksellers Association
Acct(s) – Accounts
Acctg – Accounting
ACM/SIGGRAPH – The Association for Computing Machinery Special Interest Group on Computer Graphics and Interactive Techniques
Acq(s) – Acquisition(s)
Ad – Advertising
Admin – Administrative, Administration
AECT – The Association for Educational Communications and Technology
AES – Audio Engineering Society
Aff – Affairs
AFI – American Film Institute
AICP – Association of Independent Commercial Producers
AIE™ – Association of Imaging Execu tives™
AIIM – Association for Information and Image Management
AK – Alaska
AL – Alabama
ALA – American Library Association
AMPAS – The Academy of Motion Picture Arts and Sciences
appt – appointment
Apt – Apartment
AR – Arkansas
ASA – Acoustical Society of America
ASCAP – The American Society of Composers, Authors and Publishers
ASMP – American Society of Media Photographers
Assoc(s) – Associate(s)
Asst(s) – Assistant(s)
ATA – American Translators Association
ATD - Association for Talent Development
AV – Audiovisual
Ave – Avenue
AZ – Arizona

B&W – Black & White
BC – British Columbia
Bd – Board
bio – biography
Bldg – Building
Blvd – Boulevard
BMI – Broadcast Music Inc
Br – Branch
Busn – Business

CA – California
CEO – Chief Executive Officer
CFO – Chief Financial Officer
Chmn – Chairman
Chpn – Chairperson
CIO – Chief Information Officer
Circ – Circulation
CN – Canada
CO – Colorado
Co(s) – Company(-ies)
Co-edns – Co-editions
Coll(s) – College(s)
Comm – Committee
Commun(s) – Communication(s)
Comp – Compiler
Compt – Comptroller
Cont – Controller
Contrib – Contributing
COO – Chief Operating Officer
Coord(s) – Coordinator(s)
Corp – Corporate, Corporation
Coun - Counsel
CT – Connecticut
Ct – Court
CTO – Chief Technical / Technology Officer
Ctr – Center
Curr – Current
Cust – Customer
CZ – Canal Zone

DC – District of Columbia
DE – Delaware
Dept – Department
Devt – Development
DGA – Directors Guild of America
Dir(s) – Director(s)
Dist – Distributed, Distribution, Distributor
Div – Division
Dom – Domestic
Dr – Drive

ed – edition
Ed(s) – Editor(s)
Edit – Editorial
EDPA – Exhibit Designers + Producers Association
Educ – Education, Educational
Elem – Elementary
El-hi – Elementary-High School
Ency – Encyclopedia
Eng – English
Engg – Engineering
Engr – Engineer
Equip – Equipment
ESL – English as a Second Language
Est – Established
EVP – Executive Vice President
exc – except
Exec(s) – Executive(s)
Expwy – Expressway
ext – extension

Fed – Federal
Fin – Finance, Financial
fl – floor
FL – Florida
Freq – Frequency
Fwy – Freeway

GA – Georgia
Gen – General
Govt – Government
GU – Guam

HD - High-definition
HDTV - High-definition television
HeSCA – Health & Science Communications Association
HI – Hawaii
HR – Human Resources
HS – High School
Hwy – Highway

IA – Iowa
IAAVC - International Association of Audio Visual Communicators
IABC – International Association of Business Communicators
ICVM – International Christian Visual Media
ID – Idaho
IEEE – Institute of Electrical & Electronics Engineers Inc
IL – Illinois
Illus – Illustrator
IMCCA – Interactive Multimedia & Collabora tive Communications Alliance
IN – Indiana
indiv(s) – individual(s)
Indus – Industrial, Industry
Info – Information
Instl – Institutional
Instn(s) – Institution(s)
Instrl – Instructional
Intl – International
IQ – International Quorum of Motion Picture Producers
IS&T – Society for Imaging Science and Technology
ISBN – International Standard Book Number
ISSN – International Standard Serial Number
IT – Information Technology

Jr – Junior
Jt – Joint
Juv – Juvenile

K – Kindergarten
KS – Kansas
KY – Kentucky

LA – Louisiana
Lang(s) – Language(s)
Lib(s) – Library(-ies)
Libn(s) – Librarian(s)
Lit – Literature

MA – Massachusetts
MB – Manitoba
MCA-I – Media Communications Association International
MD – Maryland
Mdse – Merchandise
Mdsg – Merchandising
ME – Maine
Med – Medical
Memb(s) – Member(s)
Metro – Metropolitan
Mfg – Manufacturing
Mgmt – Management
Mgr(s) – Manager(s)
MI – Michigan
Mkt – Market
Mktg – Marketing
MN – Minnesota
Mng – Managing
MO – Missouri
MS – Mississippi
ms(s) – manuscript(s)
MT – Montana

NAB – National Association of Broadcasters
NABET-CWA – National Association of Broadcast Employees & Technicians-Communications Workers of America
NAPET – National Association of Photo Equipment Technicians
NATAS – The National Academy of Television Arts & Sciences
Natl – National
NATPE – National Association of Television Program Executives
NB – New Brunswick
NC – North Carolina
NCTA – National Cable & Telecommunications Association
ND – North Dakota
NE – Nebraska
NH – New Hampshire
NJ – New Jersey
NL – Newfoundland and Labrador
NM – New Mexico
No – Number
NOPA – National Office Products Alliance
NS – Nova Scotia
NSCA – National Systems Contractors Association
NT – Northwest Territories
NU – Nunavut
NV – Nevada
NY – New York

Off(s) – Office(s)
Offr – Officer
OH – Ohio
OK – Oklahoma
ON – Ontario
Oper(s) – Operation(s)
OR – Oregon

PA – Pennsylvania
PE – Prince Edward Island
Perms – Permissions
Photo – Photograph
Photog – Photographer, Photography
Pkwy – Parkway
pp - pages
PPA – Professional Photographers of America
PR – Public Relations
PR – Puerto Rico
Pres – President
Proc – Processing
Prod(s) – Product(s)
Prodn – Production
Prodr – Producer
Prof – Professional
Prog(s) – Program(s)
Proj(s) – Project(s)
Promo(s) – Promotion(s)
Prop – Proprietor
Pub Aff – Public Affairs
Publg – Publishing
Publr – Publisher
Pubn(s) – Publication(s)
Purch – Purchasing

QC – Quebec

R&D – Research & Development
Rd – Road
Ref – Reference
Reg – Region
Regl – Regional
Rel – Relations
Rep(s) – Representative(s)
Res – Research
RI – Rhode Island
RIAA – Recording Industry Association of America
Rm – Room
RTDNA – Radio Television Digital News Association
Rte – Route
Rts – Rights
SAG -AFTRA – Screen Actors Guild - American Federation of Television and Radio Artists
SBE – Society of Broadcast Engineers Inc
SC – South Carolina
Sci – Science
SCTE – Society of Cable Telecommunications Engineers Inc
SD – South Dakota
Secy – Secretary
Serv(s) – Service(s)
SID – Society for Information Display
SK – Saskatchewan
SMPTE – Society of Motion Picture & Television Engineers
Soc – Social, Sociology
SPARS – Society of Professional Audio Recording Services
Spec – Special
Sq – Square
Sr – Senior
St – Street, Saint
Sta – Station
Ste – Sainte
Subn(s) – Subscription(s)
Subs – Subsidiary
Supv – Supervisor
SVP – Senior Vice President
Synd – Syndicated, Syndication

Tech – Technical
Technol – Technology
Tel – Telephone
Terr – Terrace
TN – Tennessee
Tpke – Turnpike
Treas – Treasurer
TX – Texas

UK – United Kingdom
Univ – University
USITT – United States Institute for Theatre Technology Inc
UT – Utah

V – Vice
VA – Virginia
VChmn – Vice Chairman
VI – Virgin Islands
vol(s) – volume(s)
VP(s) – Vice President(s)
VT – Vermont

WA – Washington
WI – Wisconsin
WV – West Virginia
WY – Wyoming

yr – year
YT – Yukon Territory

Products & Services Index

Products & Services Index

This index interfiles over 1250 classifications throughout the AV industry. Where necessary, references are specified as being audio, video or film related, etc. It provides page references to all the headings in the Products, Services & Companies index which follows. Those who are limiting their research to a certain segment of th AV industry such as Video or Film will find the Products, Services & Companies section more convenient. The "How To Use *AV Market Place*™" section is recommended to assist in understanding the indexes.

Products, Services & Companies

Products, Services & Companies

This section combines the classifications of the Products & Services Index with the company names listed in the AV Product & Service Providers section. It also serves to help those users who are focusing on only one segment of the AV industry, as the classifications are arranged under the seven major headings of Audio, Audio/Visual, Computer Systems, Film, Video, Programming and Miscellaneous. The "How To Use AVMP" section is recommended to assist in understanding the indexes.

AUDIO

Accessory, *see* Part & Accessory

Alternative Music, *see* Music Libraries—Alternative

Amplifier Distributors

ARIZONA

Allusion Studios & Pure Wave Audio, pg 782
Arizona Cine Equipment, pg 789
EAR Professional Audio/Video, pg 855
Metropolitan Audio-Visual Inc, pg 940
Projector SuperStore LLC, pg 986
Troxell Communications Inc, pg 1045

CALIFORNIA

Ametron Audio/Video, pg 785
Amplifier Technologies Inc (ATI), pg 785
Apex Jr, pg 788
Associated Sound, pg 792
ATV Video Center Inc, pg 793
Audio Images Corp, pg 794
AV Conferencing, pg 797
Be Media, pg 804
BroadcastStore.com, pg 813
California Tape Products Inc, pg 817
Christy's Editorial, pg 826
Cibola Systems, pg 826
Cinema Equipment Sales of California Inc, pg 827
Delicate Electronics Sales Inc, pg 845
Directed Electronics, pg 848
Educational Technology Services (ETS), pg 857
Empire Wholesale Inc, pg 860
FXC Communications, pg 874
Gallien/Krueger, pg 875
Gluskin's Custom Audio Video, pg 879
Hosa Technology Inc, pg 891
Instructional Materials & Equipment Distributors (I-Med), pg 899
JD Audio Visual Inc, pg 904
L Acoustics US, pg 914
Location Sound Corp, pg 924
Lloyd F McKinney Associates Inc, pg 935
Media Control Systems LLC, pg 936
MediaMation Inc, pg 937
MediaPOINTE, pg 938
Mobilized Tech Systems, pg 944
OWI Inc, pg 966
Parasound Products Inc, pg 969
POP TV, pg 978
Related Visual Inc, pg 994
RF Specialties of California Inc, pg 995
Randall Schiller Productions, pg 1004
Signal Transport, pg 1011
SNAP, pg 1014
Sound Service Co, pg 1017
Southern California Sound Image Inc, pg 1019
SSL Industries Inc, pg 1022
Stanislaus Audio Video Inc, pg 1023
Studio 637, pg 1027
SuperVision, pg 1029
TOA Electronics Inc, pg 1041
Towards 2000 Inc, pg 1043
Tri-Ed, pg 1044
VMI Inc, pg 1060
Yanchar Design & Consulting Group, pg 1072

COLORADO

Audio Consultant Services Inc, pg 794
Daylight Productions & Rentals, pg 844
Spectrum Audio Visual Services, pg 1020
Stanco Sales LLC, pg 1023

CONNECTICUT

Connecticut Audio & Theatrical Supply, pg 835
Everett Hall Associates Inc, pg 863
HB Communications Inc, pg 886
The Music People Inc, pg 951

DELAWARE

Actors Attic, pg 775

FLORIDA

Allstar Audio Systems Inc, pg 782
A2D Solutions Inc, pg 793
AVI-SPL, pg 798
BAI Distributors Inc, pg 801
Broadcasters General Store Inc, pg 813
Digital Video Systems Inc, pg 848
General Projection Systems Inc, pg 877
Griffiths Broadcast Co Inc, pg 882
Gulf Coast Audio Visual Producers Inc, pg 883
Harmon's Audio-Visual Services, pg 885
Harris Corp, pg 885
Herman Pro AV, pg 888
Hi-Tech Enterprises Inc, pg 888
Hi-Tech Import Export Corp, pg 888
Intermark Industries Inc, pg 900
Lighting Sales Connections, pg 920
Media Concepts Inc, pg 936
Midtown Video Inc, pg 942
Photomart Cine-Video Inc, pg 975
Pro Stage Inc, pg 983
Recording Media & Equipment Inc (RM&E), pg 993
Sight & Sound Productions, pg 1010
Stereo Sales Inc, pg 1024
TAI Audio, pg 1031
Technomedia Solutions, pg 1035

GEORGIA

AVForSale, pg 798
Baker Audio Inc, pg 801
Clark, pg 829
Lighting & Production Equipment Inc, pg 920
Stage Front Presentation Systems, pg 1022

HAWAII

The Audio Visual Co (AVCO), pg 795

ILLINOIS

Allen Visual Systems Inc, pg 781
Creative Technology, pg 838
Joseph Electronics, pg 906
C V Lloyde, pg 923
Quintessence Audio Ltd, pg 989
RAM Systems LLC, pg 991
RC Communications, pg 992
Sound Vision Inc, pg 1018
Woodside Avenue Music Productions Inc, pg 1069

INDIANA

Heart Breaker Entertainment LLC, pg 887
Sensory Technologies LLC, pg 1006
SHP Electronics, pg 1010
Sweetwater Sound Inc, pg 1029

IOWA

ECS Inc, pg 856

KANSAS

Smith Audio-Visual Inc, pg 1014

KENTUCKY

Audio Visual Techniques Inc, pg 796
Axxis Inc, pg 800
Barney Miller's Inc, pg 943
NOR-COM Inc, pg 958

LOUISIANA

Intermedia Technologies, pg 900
Pace Systems, pg 966

MAINE

Headlight Audio Visual Inc, pg 887
Independent Audio Inc, pg 897

MARYLAND

Bradley Broadcast & Pro Audio, pg 811
Cardinal Sound & Video, pg 820
Human Circuit, pg 892
Kipp Visual Systems Inc, pg 911

MASSACHUSETTS

Professional Audio Design Inc, pg 985
Rule Broadcast Systems, pg 1000

MICHIGAN

Olson Anderson Co, pg 786
Ascom Communications Contractors, pg 791
City Events Group, pg 828
Digi Sign Design LLC, pg 847
On Stage Visuals, pg 963
TeL Systems, pg 1035

MINNESOTA

Advanced Audio-Visual Inc, pg 777
Alpha Video & Audio Inc, pg 782
Digital Audio Labs, pg 847
New Life Communications Inc, pg 956
Tierney Brothers Inc, pg 1040

MISSISSIPPI

Bowie Audio Visual Enterprises Inc, pg 811

MISSOURI

Communitronics Corp, pg 833
Conference Technologies Inc, pg 835
MIS Technologies, pg 944
Modern Communications Inc, pg 944
Production Support Services Inc, pg 985
Schiller's Audio-Visual, pg 1004

NEVADA

Pignose-Gorilla, pg 975

NEW HAMPSHIRE

APS Lighting-Sound-AV, pg 789
Technet® Systems Group, pg 1033

NEW JERSEY

A-V Services Inc, pg 771
Alltec Stores, a Vcom IMC Company, pg 782
Audio Visual Associates, pg 795
AV Bluebook, pg 797
Comprehensive Cable & Connectivity Co, pg 833
Diversified Systems Inc, pg 849
Earl Girls Inc, pg 855
Entel Systems Inc, pg 861
G&G Technologies Inc, pg 875
Hamilton Buhl, pg 884
The Music Place, pg 951

AUDIO

Amplifier Distributors (continued)

NEW JERSEY (continued)

National Audio-Visual Supply, pg 952
Nelson Enterprises Theatrical Supply Co, pg 954
Onkyo USA Corp, pg 963
PatchAmp, pg 970
SLD Lighting, pg 1013
Starlite Productions, pg 1024
SYMCO Inc, pg 1030
Total Video Products Inc, pg 1042
Video Corporation of America (VCA), pg 1055
Wired 4 Sound Inc, pg 1068
York Telecom, pg 1072

NEW MEXICO

Quickbeam Systems Inc (QSI), pg 989

NEW YORK

Albany Theatre Supply Co Inc, pg 780
ALTEL Systems Inc, pg 783
American Video Inc, pg 785
Audio-Video Corp, pg 795
AV Workshop, pg 797
Cadence Jazz Records, pg 816
Colortone Audio Visual, pg 832
Communication Corner Inc, pg 832
Custom Media Environments, pg 841
Design Audio Visual Inc, pg 845
General Audio-Visual Inc (GAVI), pg 876
HAVE Inc, pg 886
Hot House Professional Audio, pg 891
Indigo Productions, pg 897
Korg USA Inc, pg 913
KVL Audio Visual Services Inc, pg 914
Lee Dan® Communications Inc, pg 918
Long Island Video Enterprises Live Inc, pg 924
Magnaplan Corp, pg 928
Mark Custom Recording Service Inc, pg 931
Markertek Video Supply, pg 931
Music Hall LLC, pg 950
NorthCountry Distributors, pg 959
Presentation Products Inc, pg 981
RNJ Electronics, pg 997
Technisphere Corp, pg 1034
TecNec Distributing, pg 1035
Theatrical Services & Supplies Inc, pg 1038
Toys From The Attic, pg 1043
Visual Word Systems Inc, pg 1060
Whirlwind Music Distributors Inc, pg 1065
XTA Electronics Ltd, pg 1071
Yorkville Sound Inc, pg 1072

OHIO

Aztec Video Productions, pg 801
Copp Integrated Systems, pg 836
ITA Audio Visual Solutions, pg 902
Luminaud Inc, pg 926
Parts Express, pg 969
Jimmy Rea Electronics Inc, pg 992
Smithall Electronics Inc, pg 1014
Tri-State Audio Visual Co, pg 1044
Tri-State Visual Products, pg 1044

OREGON

Lightspeed Technologies Inc, pg 921
PLUS Corp of America, pg 977
Spectrum Systems Design, pg 1021
SuperDigital Ltd, pg 1029

PENNSYLVANIA

Advanced AV, pg 777
Audio Visions Inc, pg 795
Brodart Co, pg 813
Clair Brothers Audio Systems Inc, pg 829
J E Foss Co, pg 871
The Lerro Corp, pg 919
Morefield Communications Inc, pg 946
Sound by Fitch, pg 1017
Vistacom Inc, pg 1059
Visual Sound Inc, pg 1059
Wespen Audio Visual Co, pg 1063

RHODE ISLAND

Shanix Inc, pg 1008

SOUTH CAROLINA

DaviSound, pg 843

TENNESSEE

Advanced Sound, pg 778
Belew Enterprises, pg 804
Durrell LLC, pg 854
Lowrance Sound Co Inc, pg 925
Mr Mark's Used Musical, Stereo & Studio Equipment Store, pg 944
Spectrum Sound Inc, pg 1021
Technical Support Systems LLC, pg 1034
Zion Music Group, pg 1074

TEXAS

Astro Audio Visual, pg 792
AVES Audio Visual Systems Inc, pg 798
Crossroads Audio Inc, pg 840
Data Projections Inc, pg 843
Digital Display Solutions Inc, pg 847
FitzCo Sound Inc, pg 869
Heffernan Audio Visual, pg 887
Lubbock Audio Visual Inc, pg 925
Media Management LLC, pg 937
Pro Video & Film Equipment Co Inc, pg 983
Quality Audio Visual Service Inc, pg 988
RF Specialties of Texas LLC, pg 996
Schoolhouse Audio Visual, pg 1004
Southwest Sound & Electronics Inc, pg 1019
Tarpley Media Systems, pg 1032

UTAH

Performance Audio, pg 973
RIA Corp, pg 996

VERMONT

Production Advantage Inc, pg 984

VIRGINIA

Avitecture Inc, pg 799
Boitnott Visual Communications Corp (BVC), pg 810
Communications Specialists Inc, pg 833
Design & Production Inc, pg 845
Hoppmann Audio Visual, pg 891
Intellidyne LLC, pg 899
Lee Hartman & Sons Inc, pg 918
Old Dominion Broadcasting, pg 961
Rocktown Media, pg 998
StageSound, pg 1023
The Whitlock Group, pg 1065

WASHINGTON

CCI Solutions, pg 821
Northern Lights & Pro Audio, pg 959
Pacific Northwest Theatre Associates Inc (PNTA), pg 967

WEST VIRGINIA

United Sound & Electronics, pg 1048

WISCONSIN

Audio Visual of Milwaukee Inc, pg 795
Camera Corner Connecting Point, pg 818
Full Compass Systems, pg 874

PUERTO RICO

Audio Visual Concepts Inc, pg 795
Bonnin Electronics Inc, pg 810

ALBERTA

Infosat Communications Inc, pg 898
Matrix Video Communications Corp (MVCC), pg 934
Sharp's Audio-Visual Ltd, pg 1008
Unique Communications Ltd, pg 1048

BRITISH COLUMBIA

ADI Systems Inc, pg 776
Commercial Electronics Ltd, pg 832

MANITOBA

Advance Pro, pg 777
Inland Audio Visual Ltd, pg 898

ONTARIO

Bryston Ltd, pg 814
Cinema Stage Inc, pg 827
HD Source, pg 886
Nationwide Audio Visual Co, pg 953
Premier A/V Sales Ltd, pg 980
Sascom Marketing Group Inc, pg 1003
Westbury National Show Systems Ltd, pg 1064

QUEBEC

AVS Technologies Inc, pg 800
Concept Audio-Visual, pg 834
JAM Industries Ltd, pg 903
Panavideo Inc, pg 968
SC Media Canada, pg 1003
Sennheiser (Canada) Inc, pg 1006

Amplifier Manufacturers

ARIZONA

Adcom LLC, pg 776
Fender Musical Instruments Corp, pg 866
MTX Audio, pg 949
Radio Design Labs (RDL), pg 990

ARKANSAS

Shaker Microphones & Promotions Inc, pg 1008

CALIFORNIA

AB Systems Amplifiers, pg 772
ALTINEX Inc, pg 783
Amplifier Technologies Inc (ATI), pg 785
Audio Upgrades, pg 795
B&K Components Ltd, pg 802
BGW Systems, an Amplifier Technologies Inc Company, pg 806
Califone International Inc, pg 817
Communications & Power Industries, Satcom Division, pg 833
Digital Music Corp, pg 847
Directed Electronics, pg 848
ESE, pg 862
Extron Electronics, pg 864
FM Systems Inc, pg 870
Gallien/Krueger, pg 875
Henry Engineering, pg 888
Hosa Technology Inc, pg 891
L Acoustics US, pg 914
Manley Laboratories Inc, pg 930
Media Control Systems LLC, pg 936
Nady Systems Inc, pg 952
Opamp Labs Inc, pg 964
Orevox USA Corp, pg 965
OWI Inc, pg 966
Panasonic Broadcast & Digital Systems Co, pg 968
Panasonic Professional Audio Systems, pg 968
Parasound Products Inc, pg 969
PowerPhysics Inc, pg 979
QSC Audio Products LLC, pg 988
Renkus-Heinz Inc, pg 994
Roland Corp US, pg 998
Sherwood America Inc, pg 1009
Signal Transport, pg 1011
TASCAM, pg 1032
TeachLogic Inc, pg 1033
TOA Electronics Inc, pg 1041
Velodyne Acoustics Inc, pg 1052
Wohler Technologies Inc, pg 1069
Xantech LLC, pg 1071

COLORADO

Video Accessory Corp, pg 1054

CONNECTICUT

Earmark LLC, pg 855
Sound Control Technologies Inc, pg 1017

FLORIDA

Intermark Industries Inc, pg 900
JT Communications, pg 906
Magna-Tech Electronic Co Inc, pg 928
Tel-Test, pg 1035

ILLINOIS

AmpliVox Portable Sound Systems, pg 785
Dukane Corp, Audio Visual Products Division, pg 853
Precision Electronics Inc, pg 980
SoundTech, pg 1018
Studio Technologies Inc, pg 1027

INDIANA

Auralex Acoustics Inc, pg 796
Crown Audio Inc, pg 840

Amplifier Rentals

AUDIO

Amplifier Rentals (continued)

MISSISSIPPI

Bowie Audio Visual Enterprises Inc, pg 811

MISSOURI

Communitronics Corp, pg 833
Production Support Services Inc, pg 985
Show-Me Audio-Visual, pg 1009
Switch, pg 1030

MONTANA

Jereco Studios Inc, pg 905

NEVADA

GES Audio Visual, pg 877
Lefco Video Services Inc, pg 918

NEW HAMPSHIRE

Apertura, pg 788
APS Lighting-Sound-AV, pg 789

NEW JERSEY

Audio Visual Associates, pg 795
Earl Girls Inc, pg 855
Giant Audio Visual Inc, pg 878
International Audio Visual Inc, pg 900
Moe AV LLC, pg 945
The Music Place, pg 951
Nelson Enterprises Theatrical Supply Co, pg 954
PLS Staging, pg 977
SLD Lighting, pg 1013
Soundtracks Production Services LLC, pg 1018
Starlite Productions, pg 1024
Wired 4 Sound Inc, pg 1068

NEW MEXICO

Quickbeam Systems Inc (QSI), pg 989

NEW YORK

Albany Theatre Supply Co Inc, pg 780
American Video Inc, pg 785
Audio Visual Resources LLC, pg 795
Aura Sonic Ltd, pg 796
AV Workshop, pg 797
Colortone Audio Visual, pg 832
Communication Corner Inc, pg 832
CP Communications, pg 837
Custom Media Environments, pg 841
Design Audio Visual Inc, pg 845
Dreamhire LLC, pg 852
KVL Audio Visual Services Inc, pg 914
Long Island Video Enterprises Live Inc, pg 924
Posthorn Recordings, pg 979
See Factor Industry Inc, pg 1006
Specialized Audio-Visual Inc, pg 1020
Studio Instrument Rentals (SIR), pg 1027
TBA Global Events, pg 1032
Visual Word Systems Inc, pg 1060
WorldStage, pg 1070

NORTH CAROLINA

A&V Company, pg 772
AV Metro Inc, pg 797
Special Event Services, pg 1020
Visual Aids Electronics of North Carolina Inc, pg 1059

NORTH DAKOTA

Media Productions, pg 937

OHIO

Hughie's Event Production Services, pg 892
ITA Audio Visual Solutions, pg 902
Mills James Productions, pg 943
Ohio HD Video, pg 961
Production Solutions Inc, pg 984
R&B Communications Inc, pg 991

OKLAHOMA

PDC Productions, pg 970

PENNSYLVANIA

Advanced AV, pg 777
Audio Visions Inc, pg 795
Clair Brothers Audio Systems Inc, pg 829
FirstGeneration Audio/Visual Services, pg 869
Grise Audio Visual Center Inc, pg 882
Production Solutions Inc, pg 985
Sound by Fitch, pg 1017
Viewpoint Production Services Inc, pg 1058
Vistacom Inc, pg 1059
Visual Sound Inc, pg 1059

SOUTH CAROLINA

Sound & Images Inc, pg 1016

TENNESSEE

Brantley Sound Associates Inc, pg 812
Mr Mark's Used Musical, Stereo & Studio Equipment Store, pg 944
Technical Support Systems LLC, pg 1034
Trew Audio Inc, pg 1044

TEXAS

Alford Media Services, pg 780
Astro Audio Visual, pg 792
Bright Star Productions Inc, pg 812
Crossroads Audio Inc, pg 840
Data Display Audio Visual Co LP, pg 843
Digital Display Solutions Inc, pg 847
FitzCo Sound Inc, pg 869
Lubbock Audio Visual Inc, pg 925
Music Lab Inc, pg 950
Onstage Systems, pg 963
Padgitt's, pg 967
Power Factory Productions, pg 979
The Samuels Co, pg 1002
Stage Directions, pg 1022
Tropikal Productions, pg 1045

UTAH

Performance Audio, pg 973

VERMONT

Parlato Productions, pg 969

VIRGINIA

American AV, pg 783
Audio Visual Actions Inc (AVA), pg 795
Lee Hartman & Sons Inc, pg 918
Rainbow Rentals, pg 991
StageSound, pg 1023
The Whitlock Group, pg 1065

WASHINGTON

D A Sound, pg 842
Northern Lights & Pro Audio, pg 959
Pacific Northwest Theatre Associates Inc (PNTA), pg 967

WEST VIRGINIA

United Sound & Electronics, pg 1048

WISCONSIN

Audio Visual of Milwaukee Inc, pg 795
Camera Corner Connecting Point, pg 818
Event Essentials, pg 863
Full Compass Systems, pg 874

PUERTO RICO

Stage Crew Audiovisual Inc, pg 1022

ALBERTA

Allstar Show Industries Inc, pg 782
Cine Audio Visual Sales & Service Ltd, pg 826
Evolution Presentation Technologies, pg 863
L R Light & Sound, pg 915
Sharp's Audio-Visual Ltd, pg 1008
Unique Communications Ltd, pg 1048

BRITISH COLUMBIA

Clark's Audio Visual Services Ltd, pg 829
Commercial Electronics Ltd, pg 832
DL Sound & Lighting Productions Ltd, pg 849
MicrophoneRentals.com, pg 941

MANITOBA

Inland Audio Visual Ltd, pg 898

ONTARIO

HD Source, pg 886
Premier A/V Sales Ltd, pg 980
Westbury National Show Systems Ltd, pg 1064
ZTV Broadcast Services Inc, pg 1074

QUEBEC

Audio Visual Dynamics Ltd, pg 795
Concept Audio-Visual, pg 834
Panavideo Inc, pg 968

Amplifier Repairs

ARIZONA

Metropolitan Audio-Visual Inc, pg 940
Troxell Communications Inc, pg 1045

CALIFORNIA

AB Systems Amplifiers, pg 772
ALC (Auernheimer Labs & Co), pg 780
Ametron Audio/Video, pg 785
Audio Images Corp, pg 794
BroadcastStore.com, pg 813
Christy's Editorial, pg 826
Communications & Power Industries, Satcom Division, pg 833
Diemer Amp & Keyboard Repair, pg 846
FXC Communications, pg 874
Gluskin's Custom Audio Video, pg 879
Instructional Materials & Equipment Distributors (I-Med), pg 899
McAlister Electronics, pg 935
Parasound Products Inc, pg 969
Randall Schiller Productions, pg 1004
Sound Service Co, pg 1017
Sounds Unique, pg 1018
SSL Industries Inc, pg 1022
TOA Electronics Inc, pg 1041
Towards 2000 Inc, pg 1043

CONNECTICUT

A/V Davey, pg 797
HB Communications Inc, pg 886

DELAWARE

Actors Attic, pg 775

FLORIDA

Digital Video Systems Inc, pg 848
Hi-Tech Enterprises Inc, pg 888
JT Communications, pg 906
Phat Planet Recording Studios, pg 973
Stereo Sales Inc, pg 1024
TAI Audio, pg 1031

GEORGIA

Stage Front Presentation Systems, pg 1022

ILLINOIS

Beatty TeleVisual Productions, pg 804
Dukane Corp, Audio Visual Products Division, pg 853
C V Lloyde, pg 923
RC Communications, pg 992

INDIANA

SHP Electronics, pg 1010
Sweetwater Sound Inc, pg 1029

IOWA

ECS Inc, pg 856

KENTUCKY

Axxis Inc, pg 800
NOR-COM Inc, pg 958

MARYLAND

Cardinal Sound & Video, pg 820
Maryland Sound International Holding Co LLC, pg 933
Strauss Photo Technical Service Inc, pg 1026
Visual Aids Electronics Corp, pg 1059

MASSACHUSETTS

Professional Audio Design Inc, pg 985

MICHIGAN

Olson Anderson Co, pg 786
K&R's Recording Studios Inc, pg 908
TeL Systems, pg 1035

MISSOURI

Communitronics Corp, pg 833

NEW JERSEY

A-V Services Inc, pg 771
Audio Visual Associates, pg 795
Earl Girls Inc, pg 855
The Music Place, pg 951
Nelson Enterprises Theatrical Supply Co, pg 954
Starlite Productions, pg 1024

NEW MEXICO

Quickbeam Systems Inc (QSI), pg 989

NEW YORK

American Video Inc, pg 785
Custom Media Environments, pg 841
Design Audio Visual Inc, pg 845
Hot House Professional Audio, pg 891
Technisphere Corp, pg 1034
Toys From The Attic, pg 1043
Visual Word Systems Inc, pg 1060
Whirlwind Music Distributors Inc, pg 1065
Yorkville Sound Inc, pg 1072

OHIO

Copp Integrated Systems, pg 836
ITA Audio Visual Solutions, pg 902
Smithall Electronics Inc, pg 1014
Tri-State Audio Visual Co, pg 1044

OREGON

All Service Musical Electronics Repair, pg 780

PENNSYLVANIA

Audio Visions Inc, pg 795
Clair Brothers Audio Systems Inc, pg 829
J E Foss Co, pg 871
Right Coast Recording Inc, pg 997
Vistacom Inc, pg 1059
Wespen Audio Visual Co, pg 1063

SOUTH CAROLINA

DaviSound, pg 843

TENNESSEE

Belew Enterprises, pg 804
Technical Support Systems LLC, pg 1034
Trew Audio Inc, pg 1044

TEXAS

Astro Audio Visual, pg 792
FitzCo Sound Inc, pg 869
Industrial Audio/Video Inc, pg 897
Lubbock Audio Visual Inc, pg 925
Padgitt's, pg 967
Quality Audio Visual Service Inc, pg 988
Southwest Sound & Electronics Inc, pg 1019
Tarpley Media Systems, pg 1032

VIRGINIA

Boitnott Visual Communications Corp (BVC), pg 810
Hoppmann Audio Visual, pg 891
Lee Hartman & Sons Inc, pg 918
Old Dominion Broadcasting, pg 961
The Whitlock Group, pg 1065

WASHINGTON

Northern Lights & Pro Audio, pg 959
Pacific Northwest Theatre Associates Inc (PNTA), pg 967

WEST VIRGINIA

United Sound & Electronics, pg 1048

WISCONSIN

Audio Visual of Milwaukee Inc, pg 795
Full Compass Systems, pg 874

PUERTO RICO

Bonnin Electronics Inc, pg 810

ALBERTA

Allstar Show Industries Inc, pg 782
Infosat Communications Inc, pg 898
Sharp's Audio-Visual Ltd, pg 1008
Unique Communications Ltd, pg 1048

BRITISH COLUMBIA

Commercial Electronics Ltd, pg 832

MANITOBA

Inland Audio Visual Ltd, pg 898

ONTARIO

HD Source, pg 886
Premier A/V Sales Ltd, pg 980
Westbury National Show Systems Ltd, pg 1064

QUEBEC

Panavideo Inc, pg 968
SC Media Canada, pg 1003

Audio Editing, *see* Dubbing

Audiocassette—Blank Distributors

ALABAMA

Curtis Company, pg 841
Media Visions Inc, pg 937

ARIZONA

Troxell Communications Inc, pg 1045

CALIFORNIA

Adolph Gasser Inc, pg 776
Ametron Audio/Video, pg 785
Audio Images Corp, pg 794
Audio/Video Supply Inc, pg 795
Big Time Picture Company Inc, pg 807
Birns & Sawyer Inc, pg 808
California Tape Products Inc, pg 817
Christy's Editorial, pg 826
Dan Dugan Sound Design Inc, pg 853
Edgewise Media Inc, pg 856
Educational Technology Services (ETS), pg 857
El Mar Plastics Inc, pg 858
Express Video Supply Inc, pg 864
Gluskin's Custom Audio Video, pg 879
Instructional Materials & Equipment Distributors (I-Med), pg 899
JD Audio Visual Inc, pg 904
KABA Audio Productions, pg 907
Location Sound Corp, pg 924
Lynch Communications, pg 926
Maximus Media Inc, pg 934
Media Fabricators Inc, pg 936
On-Trax Inc, pg 963
Related Visual Inc, pg 994
Revolt Pro Media Inc, pg 995
Sound Service Co, pg 1017
Sounds Unique, pg 1018
SSL Industries Inc, pg 1022
Tri-Ed, pg 1044
Zack Electronics Inc, pg 1073

COLORADO

Audio Consultant Services Inc, pg 794
Daylight Productions & Rentals, pg 844
Rocky Mountain Audio/Video Productions Inc, pg 998
Spectrum Audio Visual Services, pg 1020
Stanco Sales LLC, pg 1023
White Swan Music Inc, pg 1065

CONNECTICUT

Concord Communications, pg 835
Connecticut Audio & Theatrical Supply, pg 835
HB Communications Inc, pg 886
MAVCO, pg 934
Rockwell Communications Inc, pg 998
T & M Digital Services, pg 1031
Trod Nossel Productions & Recording Studios, pg 1045

DELAWARE

Actors Attic, pg 775

FLORIDA

AVI-SPL, pg 798
Broadcasters General Store Inc, pg 813
Digital Video Systems Inc, pg 848
Gulf Coast Audio Visual Producers Inc, pg 883
Harris Corp, pg 885
Hi-Tech Import Export Corp, pg 888
Hunter Electronics LLC, pg 892
Industrial Strength Inc, pg 897
Media Concepts Inc, pg 936
Photosound of Orlando Inc, pg 975
Pro Stage Inc, pg 983
Recording Media & Equipment Inc (RM&E), pg 993
Sight & Sound Productions, pg 1010
Stereo Sales Inc, pg 1024
TAI Audio, pg 1031
Tallahassee Audio Visual, pg 1031
Universal Studios Florida® Production Group, pg 1049

GEORGIA

Audio Visual Resources Inc, pg 795
Lighting & Production Equipment Inc, pg 920
ON Event Services, pg 963
Technical Innovation, pg 1033
Visioneering International Inc, pg 1058

HAWAII

The Audio Visual Co (AVCO), pg 795

ILLINOIS

Central Audio-Visual Equipment Inc, pg 823
Creative Technology, pg 838
Joseph Electronics, pg 906
Major Reproductions Equipment Co, pg 929
Polyline LLC, pg 978
Tape Resources, pg 1031

INDIANA

OMNI Productions, pg 962
SHP Electronics, pg 1010

IOWA

ECS Inc, pg 856

KANSAS

KK Office Solutions Inc, pg 911
Smith Audio-Visual Inc, pg 1014
Theatrical Services Inc, pg 1038

KENTUCKY

Audio Visual Techniques Inc, pg 796
Barney Miller's Inc, pg 943
NOR-COM Inc, pg 958
Northern Kentucky University, pg 959

MAINE

Headlight Audio Visual Inc, pg 887

MARYLAND

Bradley Broadcast & Pro Audio, pg 811
Kipp Visual Systems Inc, pg 911
Nicholas P Pipino Associates Inc, pg 976
RTZ Audio Visual, pg 1000
Visual Aids Electronics Corp, pg 1059

MASSACHUSETTS

Terry Hanley Audio Systems Inc, pg 884
Hunt's Photo, Video & Digital, pg 892
University Products Inc, pg 1050

MICHIGAN

City Events Group, pg 828
TeL Systems, pg 1035

MISSISSIPPI

Bowie Audio Visual Enterprises Inc, pg 811
Jasper Ewing & Sons Inc, pg 864

MISSOURI

Audio-VideoGraphics Inc, pg 795
Communitronics Corp, pg 833

AUDIO

Audiocassette—Blank Distributors (continued)

MISSOURI (continued)

Conference Technologies Inc, pg 835
Image Technologies Corp, pg 895
Modern Communications Inc, pg 944
Schiller's Audio-Visual, pg 1004
Swank Audio Visuals, pg 1029

NEBRASKA

Video Service of America Inc (VSA), pg 1056

NEW JERSEY

Alltec Stores, a Vcom IMC Company, pg 782
Argraph Corp, pg 789
Audio Visual Dynamics®, pg 795
AV Bluebook, pg 797
Avtech Systems Inc, pg 800
Comprehensive Cable & Connectivity Co, pg 833
G&G Technologies Inc, pg 875
Hamilton Buhl, pg 884
Maxell Corp of America, pg 934
The Music Place, pg 951
National Audio-Visual Supply, pg 952
Starlite Productions, pg 1024
Tele-Measurements Inc, pg 1035
Total Media, pg 1042
Total Video Products Inc, pg 1042
Turner Engineering Inc, pg 1046
VCom International Multimedia Corp, pg 1052
Video Corporation of America (VCA), pg 1055
Wired 4 Sound Inc, pg 1068
York Telecom, pg 1072

NEW YORK

AV Workshop, pg 797
B&H Photo & Video Pro Audio, pg 802
Burlington A/V Recording Media, pg 815
Cadence Jazz Records, pg 816
Centennial Electric Sound Co Ltd, pg 822
Cine 60 Inc, pg 826
Colortone Audio Visual, pg 832
Communication Corner Inc, pg 832
Design Audio Visual Inc, pg 845
Digital Force, pg 847
Gaylord Brothers, pg 876
HAVE Inc, pg 886
Indigo Productions, pg 897
Langie Audio Visual Systems, pg 915
Long Island Video Enterprises Live Inc, pg 924
Magnaplan Corp, pg 928
Markertek Video Supply, pg 931
Saul Mineroff Electronics Inc, pg 943
Moviola, pg 948
Neptune Photo Inc, pg 954
NorthCountry Distributors, pg 959
Ray Supply Inc, pg 992
RNJ Electronics, pg 997
Sentry Industries Inc, pg 1007
Technisphere Corp, pg 1034
TecNec Distributing, pg 1035
Visual Technologies Corp, pg 1060
Visual Word Systems Inc, pg 1060
Willoughby's Imaging Center, pg 1067
WorldStage, pg 1070

NORTH CAROLINA

Camcor Inc, pg 818
Strategic Connections, pg 1026

OHIO

Aztec Video Productions, pg 801
Copp Integrated Systems, pg 836
Hughie's Event Production Services, pg 892
ITA Audio Visual Solutions, pg 902
The Little Warehouse Inc, pg 923
Lyon Video Inc, pg 927
Jimmy Rea Electronics Inc, pg 992
Tri-State Audio Visual Co, pg 1044
Tri-State Visual Products, pg 1044

PENNSYLVANIA

Advanced AV, pg 777
Bernie's Photo Center, pg 805
J E Foss Co, pg 871
Garcia Marketing Inc, pg 875
Grise Audio Visual Center Inc, pg 882
Hite Co, pg 889
The Lerro Corp, pg 919
Morefield Communications Inc, pg 946
Tape World, pg 1031
Visual Sound Inc, pg 1059
Wespen Audio Visual Co, pg 1063

RHODE ISLAND

Custom Computer Specialists Inc, pg 841

TENNESSEE

Lowrance Sound Co Inc, pg 925
Memphis Communications Corp, pg 938
Spring Arbor Distributors, pg 1022
Tennessee Visual Service Co, pg 1037

TEXAS

Astro Audio Visual, pg 792
CAM Audio Inc, pg 817
Heffernan Audio Visual, pg 887
J&S Audio Visual Inc, pg 904
Lubbock Audio Visual Inc, pg 925
Quality Audio Visual Service Inc, pg 988
RadioShack Corp, pg 990
RF Specialties of Texas LLC, pg 996

UTAH

Performance Audio, pg 973
RIA Corp, pg 996
Webb Audio Visual Communication, pg 1063

VIRGINIA

Boitnott Visual Communications Corp (BVC), pg 810
Communications Specialists Inc, pg 833
Filmdex Inc, pg 867
Lee Hartman & Sons Inc, pg 918
National Media Services Inc, pg 953
The Whitlock Group, pg 1065

WASHINGTON

CCI Solutions, pg 821
Inland Audio Visual Co, pg 898

WISCONSIN

Camera Corner Connecting Point, pg 818
Demco Inc, pg 845
Full Compass Systems, pg 874
School Specialty Inc, pg 1004

PUERTO RICO

Bonnin Electronics Inc, pg 810

ALBERTA

Infosat Communications Inc, pg 898
McBain Audio Visual Ltd, pg 935
Sharp's Audio-Visual Ltd, pg 1008
Unique Communications Ltd, pg 1048

BRITISH COLUMBIA

Commercial Electronics Ltd, pg 832
Triad Communications Ltd, pg 1044

MANITOBA

Advance Pro, pg 777
Inland Audio Visual Ltd, pg 898

ONTARIO

Carr McLean Ltd, pg 820
Edcom Multimedia Products, pg 856
HD Source, pg 886
Nationwide Audio Visual Co, pg 953
Premier A/V Sales Ltd, pg 980

QUEBEC

AVS Technologies Inc, pg 800
Concept Audio-Visual, pg 834
Panavideo Inc, pg 968

Audiocassette—Blank Manufacturers

CALIFORNIA

ACDC Audio CD & Cassette, pg 774
Ampex Data Systems Corp, pg 785
El Mar Plastics Inc, pg 858
KABA Audio Productions, pg 907
Parasound Products Inc, pg 969
Sony Electronics Inc, pg 1016
Sounds Unique, pg 1018
United Audio Video Group Inc, pg 1048

COLORADO

Rocky Mountain Audio/Video Productions Inc, pg 998

MASSACHUSETTS

Soundtrack Recording Studios, pg 1018

MISSOURI

Audio-VideoGraphics Inc, pg 795

NEW JERSEY

AV Bluebook, pg 797
CELCO-Constantine Engineering Labs Co, pg 822
Maxell Corp of America, pg 934
National Audio-Visual Supply, pg 952
Panasonic Consumer Electronics Co, pg 968

NEW YORK

Burlington A/V Recording Media, pg 815
Eastco Multimedia Solutions Inc, pg 856
FSL Media Inc, pg 873
Tapemaker, pg 1032

PENNSYLVANIA

Forge Recording LLC, pg 871
Tape World, pg 1031

TEXAS

Adams Evidence Grade Technology Inc, pg 775

UTAH

One Stop CD Shop LLC, pg 963

WISCONSIN

Full Compass Systems, pg 874

ONTARIO

Cinram Inc, pg 828

Audiocassette Duplication, *see* Duplication—Audiocassettes

Audiocassette Duplicator Distributors

ARIZONA

Troxell Communications Inc, pg 1045

CALIFORNIA

Ametron Audio/Video, pg 785
Audio Images Corp, pg 794
Instructional Materials & Equipment Distributors (I-Med), pg 899
KABA Audio Productions, pg 907
Joseph Nicoletti Consulting-Promotion/California International Records/Global Village Records, pg 957
Players Press, pg 977
QRS Software Services, pg 988

COLORADO

Audio Consultant Services Inc, pg 794

CONNECTICUT

HB Communications Inc, pg 886
The Music People Inc, pg 951

DELAWARE

Actors Attic, pg 775

FLORIDA

Allstar Audio Systems Inc, pg 782
Digital Video Systems Inc, pg 848
Harris Corp, pg 885
Intermark Industries Inc, pg 900
Lighting Sales Connections, pg 920
Media Concepts Inc, pg 936
Progressive Media & Music, pg 985

Recording Media & Equipment Inc (RM&E), pg 993
Sight & Sound Productions, pg 1010
Stereo Sales Inc, pg 1024

GEORGIA

ON Event Services, pg 963
Stage Front Presentation Systems, pg 1022

HAWAII

The Audio Visual Co (AVCO), pg 795

ILLINOIS

Allen Visual Systems Inc, pg 781
Woodside Avenue Music Productions Inc, pg 1069

INDIANA

SHP Electronics, pg 1010

IOWA

ECS Inc, pg 856

KENTUCKY

Audio Visual Techniques Inc, pg 796
Barney Miller's Inc, pg 943
NOR-COM Inc, pg 958
Northern Kentucky University, pg 959

MAINE

Headlight Audio Visual Inc, pg 887

MARYLAND

Bradley Broadcast & Pro Audio, pg 811
Kipp Visual Systems Inc, pg 911

MICHIGAN

Digi Sign Design LLC, pg 847
TeL Systems, pg 1035

MISSOURI

Modern Communications Inc, pg 944

NEW JERSEY

Alltec Stores, a Vcom IMC Company, pg 782
AV Bluebook, pg 797
Hamilton Buhl, pg 884
National Audio-Visual Supply, pg 952
Reed Presentations Inc (RPI), pg 993
Total Video Products Inc, pg 1042
Wilray Audio Visual Corp, pg 1067
York Telecom, pg 1072

NEW YORK

Audio-Video Corp, pg 795
Colortone Audio Visual, pg 832
Communication Corner Inc, pg 832
Design Audio Visual Inc, pg 845
Digital Force, pg 847
Eastco Multimedia Solutions Inc, pg 856
Gaylord Brothers, pg 876
Markertek Video Supply, pg 931
Neptune Photo Inc, pg 954
TecNec Distributing, pg 1035
Visual Word Systems Inc, pg 1060

OHIO

Aztec Video Productions, pg 801
ITA Audio Visual Solutions, pg 902
Jimmy Rea Electronics Inc, pg 992
Tri-State Audio Visual Co, pg 1044

PENNSYLVANIA

Advanced AV, pg 777
Bernie's Photo Center, pg 805
J E Foss Co, pg 871
Grise Audio Visual Center Inc, pg 882
The Lerro Corp, pg 919
Wespen Audio Visual Co, pg 1063

TENNESSEE

Durrell LLC, pg 854
Lowrance Sound Co Inc, pg 925
Technical Support Systems LLC, pg 1034

TEXAS

Astro Audio Visual, pg 792
Lubbock Audio Visual Inc, pg 925
Quality Audio Visual Service Inc, pg 988
RF Specialties of Texas LLC, pg 996
Tarpley Media Systems, pg 1032

UTAH

Performance Audio, pg 973

VIRGINIA

Lee Hartman & Sons Inc, pg 918
The Whitlock Group, pg 1065

WASHINGTON

CCI Solutions, pg 821

WISCONSIN

Full Compass Systems, pg 874

PUERTO RICO

Bonnin Electronics Inc, pg 810

ALBERTA

Matrix Video Communications Corp (MVCC), pg 934
Unique Communications Ltd, pg 1048

BRITISH COLUMBIA

Commercial Electronics Ltd, pg 832

MANITOBA

Advance Pro, pg 777
Inland Audio Visual Ltd, pg 898

ONTARIO

Premier A/V Sales Ltd, pg 980
Westbury National Show Systems Ltd, pg 1064

Audiocassette Duplicator Manufacturers

CALIFORNIA

KABA Audio Productions, pg 907
Newdoll Enterprises LLC, pg 956
Parasound Products Inc, pg 969
QRS Software Services, pg 988

FLORIDA

Progressive Media & Music, pg 985

INDIANA

Infonics Inc, pg 898

MASSACHUSETTS

Soundtrack Recording Studios, pg 1018

MINNESOTA

Telex Communications Inc, pg 1037

NEW JERSEY

Reed Presentations Inc (RPI), pg 993

NEW YORK

Chromavision Corp, pg 826
Digital Force, pg 847

BRITISH COLUMBIA

Triad Communications Ltd, pg 1044

ONTARIO

Cinram Inc, pg 828

Audiocassette Duplicator Rentals

CALIFORNIA

Ametron Audio/Video, pg 785
Express Media Inc, pg 864
JD Audio Visual Inc, pg 904
Lynch Communications, pg 926

COLORADO

Audio Consultant Services Inc, pg 794
Spectrum Audio Visual Services, pg 1020

CONNECTICUT

A/V Davey, pg 797

DELAWARE

Side Door Studio Inc, pg 1010

FLORIDA

Allstar Audio Systems Inc, pg 782
Pro Stage Inc, pg 983
Sight & Sound Productions, pg 1010

GEORGIA

Stage Front Presentation Systems, pg 1022

ILLINOIS

Allen Visual Systems Inc, pg 781
On Stage Audio, pg 963
RC Communications, pg 992
Woodside Avenue Music Productions Inc, pg 1069

KENTUCKY

Audio Visual Techniques Inc, pg 796

MASSACHUSETTS

massAV, pg 933

MICHIGAN

Digi Sign Design LLC, pg 847
K&R All Media Productions Inc, pg 908
K&R's Recording Studios Inc, pg 908

MISSOURI

Show-Me Audio-Visual, pg 1009

NEW YORK

Design Audio Visual Inc, pg 845
Visual Word Systems Inc, pg 1060

NORTH CAROLINA

Visual Aids Electronics of North Carolina Inc, pg 1059

OHIO

Hughie's Event Production Services, pg 892
ITA Audio Visual Solutions, pg 902

PENNSYLVANIA

JPL, pg 906

TENNESSEE

Mr Mark's Used Musical, Stereo & Studio Equipment Store, pg 944

TEXAS

Lubbock Audio Visual Inc, pg 925
Quality Audio Visual Service Inc, pg 988
The Samuels Co, pg 1002

UTAH

Performance Audio, pg 973

VIRGINIA

Lee Hartman & Sons Inc, pg 918

WISCONSIN

Audio Visual of Milwaukee Inc, pg 795

ALBERTA

Evolution Presentation Technologies, pg 863
Unique Communications Ltd, pg 1048

MANITOBA

Inland Audio Visual Ltd, pg 898

ONTARIO

Westbury National Show Systems Ltd, pg 1064

Audiocassette Duplicator Repairs

CALIFORNIA

Ametron Audio/Video, pg 785
Audio Images Corp, pg 794
McAlister Electronics, pg 935

CONNECTICUT

A/V Davey, pg 797
HB Communications Inc, pg 886

AUDIO

Audiocassette Duplicator Repairs (continued)

FLORIDA

AMP Services Inc, pg 785
Stereo Sales Inc, pg 1024

GEORGIA

Stage Front Presentation Systems, pg 1022

ILLINOIS

Allen Visual Systems Inc, pg 781

IOWA

ECS Inc, pg 856

KENTUCKY

Barney Miller's Inc, pg 943
NOR-COM Inc, pg 958

MAINE

Headlight Audio Visual Inc, pg 887

NEW YORK

Visual Word Systems Inc, pg 1060

OHIO

ITA Audio Visual Solutions, pg 902
Tri-State Audio Visual Co, pg 1044

OREGON

All Service Musical Electronics Repair, pg 780

PENNSYLVANIA

J E Foss Co, pg 871
Wespen Audio Visual Co, pg 1063

TEXAS

Astro Audio Visual, pg 792
Lubbock Audio Visual Inc, pg 925
Quality Audio Visual Service Inc, pg 988

VIRGINIA

Lee Hartman & Sons Inc, pg 918

WISCONSIN

Full Compass Systems, pg 874

ALBERTA

Unique Communications Ltd, pg 1048

MANITOBA

Inland Audio Visual Ltd, pg 898

ONTARIO

Premier A/V Sales Ltd, pg 980
Westbury National Show Systems Ltd, pg 1064

Audiocassette Loading Equipment Distributors

CALIFORNIA

Ametron Audio/Video, pg 785
KABA Audio Productions, pg 907
Newdoll Enterprises LLC, pg 956

DELAWARE

Actors Attic, pg 775

FLORIDA

Digital Video Systems Inc, pg 848
Recording Media & Equipment Inc (RM&E), pg 993

KENTUCKY

Axxis Inc, pg 800
NOR-COM Inc, pg 958

MARYLAND

Bradley Broadcast & Pro Audio, pg 811

NEW JERSEY

Starlite Productions, pg 1024

NEW YORK

Centennial Electric Sound Co Ltd, pg 822

OHIO

Aztec Video Productions, pg 801

PENNSYLVANIA

Advanced AV, pg 777
J E Foss Co, pg 871
The Lerro Corp, pg 919

TENNESSEE

Lowrance Sound Co Inc, pg 925

TEXAS

Tarpley Media Systems, pg 1032

PUERTO RICO

Bonnin Electronics Inc, pg 810

MANITOBA

Advance Pro, pg 777
Inland Audio Visual Ltd, pg 898

Audiocassette Loading Equipment Rentals

CONNECTICUT

Connecticut Audio & Theatrical Supply, pg 835

FLORIDA

Lighting Sales Connections, pg 920
Pro Stage Inc, pg 983

ILLINOIS

On Stage Audio, pg 963
RC Communications, pg 992

MICHIGAN

K&R All Media Productions Inc, pg 908

NEW JERSEY

Starlite Productions, pg 1024

MANITOBA

Inland Audio Visual Ltd, pg 898

Audiocassette Loading Equipment Repairs

CALIFORNIA

Ametron Audio/Video, pg 785
McAlister Electronics, pg 935

CONNECTICUT

HB Communications Inc, pg 886

KENTUCKY

Axxis Inc, pg 800
NOR-COM Inc, pg 958

OREGON

All Service Musical Electronics Repair, pg 780

MANITOBA

Inland Audio Visual Ltd, pg 898

Audiocassette Recorder & Player Distributors

ARIZONA

EAR Professional Audio/Video, pg 855
Troxell Communications Inc, pg 1045

CALIFORNIA

Ametron Audio/Video, pg 785
Audio Images Corp, pg 794
Cibola Systems, pg 826
Instructional Materials & Equipment Distributors (I-Med), pg 899
JD Audio Visual Inc, pg 904
Location Sound Corp, pg 924
Mobilized Tech Systems, pg 944
RF Specialties of California Inc, pg 995
SNAP, pg 1014
Southern California Sound Image Inc, pg 1019
Towards 2000 Inc, pg 1043

COLORADO

Audio Consultant Services Inc, pg 794
Daylight Productions & Rentals, pg 844

CONNECTICUT

Connecticut Audio & Theatrical Supply, pg 835
HB Communications Inc, pg 886
The Music People Inc, pg 951

DELAWARE

Actors Attic, pg 775

FLORIDA

Allstar Audio Systems Inc, pg 782
AVI-SPL, pg 798
BAI Distributors Inc, pg 801
Broadcasters General Store Inc, pg 813
Digital Video Systems Inc, pg 848
Harris Corp, pg 885
Intermark Industries Inc, pg 900
Lighting Sales Connections, pg 920
Media Concepts Inc, pg 936
Midtown Video Inc, pg 942
Recording Media & Equipment Inc (RM&E), pg 993
Sight & Sound Productions, pg 1010
Stereo Sales Inc, pg 1024
Technomedia Solutions, pg 1035

GEORGIA

Lighting & Production Equipment Inc, pg 920
ON Event Services, pg 963
Stage Front Presentation Systems, pg 1022

HAWAII

The Audio Visual Co (AVCO), pg 795

ILLINOIS

Joseph Electronics, pg 906
Woodside Avenue Music Productions Inc, pg 1069

INDIANA

Sensory Technologies LLC, pg 1006
SHP Electronics, pg 1010

IOWA

ECS Inc, pg 856

KENTUCKY

Audio Visual Techniques Inc, pg 796
Axxis Inc, pg 800
NOR-COM Inc, pg 958
Northern Kentucky University, pg 959

MAINE

Headlight Audio Visual Inc, pg 887

MARYLAND

Bradley Broadcast & Pro Audio, pg 811
Kipp Visual Systems Inc, pg 911

MASSACHUSETTS

Professional Audio Design Inc, pg 985
University Products Inc, pg 1050

MICHIGAN

Digi Sign Design LLC, pg 847
TeL Systems, pg 1035

MISSOURI

Modern Communications Inc, pg 944
Schiller's Audio-Visual, pg 1004

NEW HAMPSHIRE

Technet® Systems Group, pg 1033

NEW JERSEY

Alltec Stores, a Vcom IMC Company, pg 782
AV Bluebook, pg 797
Entel Systems Inc, pg 861
Hamilton Buhl, pg 884

National Audio-Visual Supply, pg 952
Nelson Enterprises Theatrical Supply Co, pg 954
Starlite Productions, pg 1024
Total Video Products Inc, pg 1042
Wilray Audio Visual Corp, pg 1067
York Telecom, pg 1072

NEW YORK

ALTEL Systems Inc, pg 783
B&H Photo & Video Pro Audio, pg 802
Cadence Jazz Records, pg 816
Colortone Audio Visual, pg 832
Design Audio Visual Inc, pg 845
Eastco Multimedia Solutions Inc, pg 856
Gaylord Brothers, pg 876
HAVE Inc, pg 886
KVL Audio Visual Services Inc, pg 914
Magnaplan Corp, pg 928
Markertek Video Supply, pg 931
Music Sales Corp, pg 951
Neptune Photo Inc, pg 954

OHIO

Aztec Video Productions, pg 801
ITA Audio Visual Solutions, pg 902
Lyon Video Inc, pg 927
Jimmy Rea Electronics Inc, pg 992
Tri-State Audio Visual Co, pg 1044

OREGON

SuperDigital Ltd, pg 1029

PENNSYLVANIA

Advanced AV, pg 777
Bernie's Photo Center, pg 805
J E Foss Co, pg 871
Grise Audio Visual Center Inc, pg 882
The Lerro Corp, pg 919

TENNESSEE

Lowrance Sound Co Inc, pg 925
Mr Mark's Used Musical, Stereo & Studio Equipment Store, pg 944
Spectrum Sound Inc, pg 1021
Spring Arbor Distributors, pg 1022
Technical Support Systems LLC, pg 1034

TEXAS

Astro Audio Visual, pg 792
AVES Audio Visual Systems Inc, pg 798
Crossroads Audio Inc, pg 840
Lubbock Audio Visual Inc, pg 925
Quality Audio Visual Service Inc, pg 988
RadioShack Corp, pg 990
RF Specialties of Texas LLC, pg 996
Schoolhouse Audio Visual, pg 1004
Tarpley Media Systems, pg 1032

UTAH

Performance Audio, pg 973

VIRGINIA

Intellidyne LLC, pg 899
Lee Hartman & Sons Inc, pg 918
The Whitlock Group, pg 1065

WASHINGTON

CCI Solutions, pg 821

WISCONSIN

Full Compass Systems, pg 874

PUERTO RICO

Bonnin Electronics Inc, pg 810

ALBERTA

Unique Communications Ltd, pg 1048

BRITISH COLUMBIA

Commercial Electronics Ltd, pg 832

MANITOBA

Advance Pro, pg 777
Inland Audio Visual Ltd, pg 898

ONTARIO

Premier A/V Sales Ltd, pg 980
Westbury National Show Systems Ltd, pg 1064

QUEBEC

AVS Technologies Inc, pg 800

Audiocassette Recorder & Player Manufacturers

CALIFORNIA

Newdoll Enterprises LLC, pg 956
Panasonic Broadcast & Digital Systems Co, pg 968
Sherwood America Inc, pg 1009

MINNESOTA

Telex Communications Inc, pg 1037

NEW JERSEY

AV Bluebook, pg 797
National Audio-Visual Supply, pg 952
Panasonic Corp, pg 968

NEW YORK

Sentry Industries Inc, pg 1007

Audiocassette Recorder & Player Rentals

ALABAMA

Audio-Video Resources Inc, pg 795

ARIZONA

Merestone, pg 938

ARKANSAS

White Diamond Productions, pg 1065

CALIFORNIA

AGF Media Services, pg 778
Ametron Audio/Video, pg 785
Audio Rents, pg 794
AV Guys, pg 797
Big Time Picture Company Inc, pg 807
Dan Dugan Sound Design Inc, pg 853
Express Media Inc, pg 864
Hollywood Sound Systems, pg 890
JD Audio Visual Inc, pg 904
Location Sound Corp, pg 924
Lynch Communications, pg 926
Maximus Media Inc, pg 934
Munday & Collins AV, pg 950
PSAV® Presentation Services, pg 986
Slate Media Group, pg 1013
Towards 2000 Inc, pg 1043
Videorama Industries LLC, pg 1057
Voice & Video Rentals, pg 1060
Warner Bros Production Sound & Video Services, pg 1062

COLORADO

Multimedia Audio Visual Inc, pg 950

CONNECTICUT

A/V Davey, pg 797
Fox Connecticut, pg 872
HB Communications Inc, pg 886

DELAWARE

Side Door Studio Inc, pg 1010

FLORIDA

Accord Productions, pg 773
Allstar Audio Systems Inc, pg 782
AVI-SPL, pg 798
Image Technical Services, pg 895
Industrial Strength Inc, pg 897
Lighting Sales Connections, pg 920
Pro Stage Inc, pg 983
Sight & Sound Productions, pg 1010
Universal Studios Florida® Production Group, pg 1049

GEORGIA

Lighting & Production Equipment Inc, pg 920
MAGNUM Companies Ltd, pg 929
ON Event Services, pg 963
Stage Front Presentation Systems, pg 1022

ILLINOIS

Allen Visual Systems Inc, pg 781
AV Chicago Inc, pg 797
On Stage Audio, pg 963
RC Communications, pg 992
Woodside Avenue Music Productions Inc, pg 1069

KENTUCKY

Audio Visual Techniques Inc, pg 796

MARYLAND

CPR MultiMedia Solutions, pg 837
Visual Aids Electronics Corp, pg 1059

MASSACHUSETTS

AVFX Inc, pg 798
massAV, pg 933
Preston Productions Inc, pg 981

MICHIGAN

Digi Sign Design LLC, pg 847
K&R All Media Productions Inc, pg 908
K&R's Recording Studios Inc, pg 908

MISSOURI

Show-Me Audio-Visual, pg 1009

NEVADA

GES Audio Visual, pg 877

NEW JERSEY

Giant Audio Visual Inc, pg 878
Moe AV LLC, pg 945
Nelson Enterprises Theatrical Supply Co, pg 954
Starlite Productions, pg 1024

NEW YORK

Colortone Audio Visual, pg 832
Design Audio Visual Inc, pg 845
Dreamhire LLC, pg 852
KVL Audio Visual Services Inc, pg 914

NORTH CAROLINA

A&V Company, pg 772
Visual Aids Electronics of North Carolina Inc, pg 1059

OHIO

Hughie's Event Production Services, pg 892
ITA Audio Visual Solutions, pg 902
Lyon Video Inc, pg 927
R&B Communications Inc, pg 991

OREGON

Northwest Film Center, pg 959

PENNSYLVANIA

Grise Audio Visual Center Inc, pg 882
Production Solutions Inc, pg 985

TENNESSEE

Mr Mark's Used Musical, Stereo & Studio Equipment Store, pg 944
Technical Support Systems LLC, pg 1034

TEXAS

Astro Audio Visual, pg 792
Crossroads Audio Inc, pg 840
Lubbock Audio Visual Inc, pg 925
Quality Audio Visual Service Inc, pg 988
The Samuels Co, pg 1002

UTAH

Performance Audio, pg 973

VIRGINIA

American AV, pg 783
D&B Television & Video Productions Inc, pg 842
Lee Hartman & Sons Inc, pg 918
Rainbow Rentals, pg 991

WISCONSIN

Full Compass Systems, pg 874

PUERTO RICO

Stage Crew Audiovisual Inc, pg 1022

ALBERTA

Evolution Presentation Technologies, pg 863
Unique Communications Ltd, pg 1048

AUDIO

Audiocassette Recorder & Player Rentals (continued)

BRITISH COLUMBIA

Commercial Electronics Ltd, pg 832

MANITOBA

Inland Audio Visual Ltd, pg 898

ONTARIO

Premier A/V Sales Ltd, pg 980
Westbury National Show Systems Ltd, pg 1064

Audiocassette Recorder & Player Repairs

ARIZONA

Troxell Communications Inc, pg 1045

CALIFORNIA

Ametron Audio/Video, pg 785
Audio Images Corp, pg 794
Dan Dugan Sound Design Inc, pg 853
Instructional Materials & Equipment Distributors (I-Med), pg 899
JD Audio Visual Inc, pg 904
Location Sound Corp, pg 924
McAlister Electronics, pg 935
Towards 2000 Inc, pg 1043

CONNECTICUT

A/V Davey, pg 797
HB Communications Inc, pg 886

FLORIDA

AMP Services Inc, pg 785
Stereo Sales Inc, pg 1024

GEORGIA

Lighting & Production Equipment Inc, pg 920
Stage Front Presentation Systems, pg 1022

ILLINOIS

Allen Visual Systems Inc, pg 781

IOWA

ECS Inc, pg 856

KENTUCKY

Axxis Inc, pg 800
NOR-COM Inc, pg 958

MAINE

Headlight Audio Visual Inc, pg 887

MARYLAND

Visual Aids Electronics Corp, pg 1059

MASSACHUSETTS

Professional Audio Design Inc, pg 985

NEW JERSEY

Nelson Enterprises Theatrical Supply Co, pg 954
Starlite Productions, pg 1024

NEW YORK

Design Audio Visual Inc, pg 845
Visual Word Systems Inc, pg 1060

OHIO

ITA Audio Visual Solutions, pg 902
Tri-State Audio Visual Co, pg 1044

OREGON

All Service Musical Electronics Repair, pg 780

PENNSYLVANIA

J E Foss Co, pg 871

TENNESSEE

Technical Support Systems LLC, pg 1034

TEXAS

Astro Audio Visual, pg 792
Lubbock Audio Visual Inc, pg 925
Quality Audio Visual Service Inc, pg 988

VIRGINIA

Lee Hartman & Sons Inc, pg 918

WISCONSIN

Full Compass Systems, pg 874

ALBERTA

Unique Communications Ltd, pg 1048

BRITISH COLUMBIA

Commercial Electronics Ltd, pg 832

MANITOBA

Inland Audio Visual Ltd, pg 898

ONTARIO

Premier A/V Sales Ltd, pg 980
Westbury National Show Systems Ltd, pg 1064

Audiotape—Blank Distributors

ALABAMA

Curtis Company, pg 841
Media Visions Inc, pg 937

ARIZONA

Troxell Communications Inc, pg 1045

CALIFORNIA

Adolph Gasser Inc, pg 776
Ametron Audio/Video, pg 785
Audio/Video Supply Inc, pg 795
Birns & Sawyer Inc, pg 808
California Tape Products Inc, pg 817
Christy's Editorial, pg 826
Dan Dugan Sound Design Inc, pg 853
Edgewise Media Inc, pg 856
Educational Technology Services (ETS), pg 857
Gluskin's Custom Audio Video, pg 879
Instructional Materials & Equipment Distributors (I-Med), pg 899
JD Audio Visual Inc, pg 904
Location Sound Corp, pg 924
Lynch Communications, pg 926
Media Fabricators Inc, pg 936
MSE Media Solutions, pg 949
QRS Software Services, pg 988
Related Visual Inc, pg 994
Revolt Pro Media Inc, pg 995
Sounds Unique, pg 1018
SSL Industries Inc, pg 1022
Tri-Ed, pg 1044

COLORADO

Audio Consultant Services Inc, pg 794
Daylight Productions & Rentals, pg 844
Rocky Mountain Audio/Video Productions Inc, pg 998
Stanco Sales LLC, pg 1023

CONNECTICUT

Concord Communications, pg 835
Connecticut Audio & Theatrical Supply, pg 835
HB Communications Inc, pg 886
MAVCO, pg 934
Rockwell Communications Inc, pg 998
T & M Digital Services, pg 1031
Trod Nossel Productions & Recording Studios, pg 1045

FLORIDA

Broadcasters General Store Inc, pg 813
Digital Video Systems Inc, pg 848
Gulf Coast Audio Visual Producers Inc, pg 883
Harris Corp, pg 885
Hi-Tech Import Export Corp, pg 888
Hunter Electronics LLC, pg 892
Industrial Strength Inc, pg 897
Media Concepts Inc, pg 936
Midtown Video Inc, pg 942
Pro Stage Inc, pg 983
Recording Media & Equipment Inc (RM&E), pg 993
Sight & Sound Productions, pg 1010
Stereo Sales Inc, pg 1024
TAI Audio, pg 1031
Tallahassee Audio Visual, pg 1031

GEORGIA

Audio Visual Resources Inc, pg 795
Technical Innovation, pg 1033
Visioneering International Inc, pg 1058

HAWAII

The Audio Visual Co (AVCO), pg 795

ILLINOIS

Allen Visual Systems Inc, pg 781
Central Audio-Visual Equipment Inc, pg 823
Creative Technology, pg 838
Major Reproductions Equipment Co, pg 929
Tape Resources, pg 1031
Woodside Avenue Music Productions Inc, pg 1069

INDIANA

OMNI Productions, pg 962
SHP Electronics, pg 1010

IOWA

ECS Inc, pg 856

KANSAS

KK Office Solutions Inc, pg 911
Smith Audio-Visual Inc, pg 1014

KENTUCKY

American Recordable Media, pg 785
Barney Miller's Inc, pg 943
NOR-COM Inc, pg 958

MARYLAND

Nicholas P Pipino Associates Inc, pg 976
RTZ Audio Visual, pg 1000
Visual Aids Electronics Corp, pg 1059

MASSACHUSETTS

University Products Inc, pg 1050

MICHIGAN

City Events Group, pg 828
TeL Systems, pg 1035

MINNESOTA

Cinequipt Inc, pg 828

MISSISSIPPI

Bowie Audio Visual Enterprises Inc, pg 811
Jasper Ewing & Sons Inc, pg 864

MISSOURI

Communitronics Corp, pg 833
Image Technologies Corp, pg 895
Modern Communications Inc, pg 944
Schiller's Audio-Visual, pg 1004
Swank Audio Visuals, pg 1029

NEBRASKA

Video Service of America Inc (VSA), pg 1056

NEW JERSEY

Argraph Corp, pg 789
Audio Visual Dynamics®, pg 795
AV Bluebook, pg 797
G&G Technologies Inc, pg 875
Hamilton Buhl, pg 884
Maxell Corp of America, pg 934
Starlite Productions, pg 1024
Tele-Measurements Inc, pg 1035
Turner Engineering Inc, pg 1046
VCom International Multimedia Corp, pg 1052
Video Corporation of America (VCA), pg 1055
Wired 4 Sound Inc, pg 1068
York Telecom, pg 1072

NEW YORK

AV Workshop, pg 797
Burlington A/V Recording Media, pg 815

Cadence Jazz Records, pg 816
Cine 60 Inc, pg 826
Colortone Audio Visual, pg 832
Communication Corner Inc, pg 832
Design Audio Visual Inc, pg 845
Digital Force, pg 847
Gaylord Brothers, pg 876
HAVE Inc, pg 886
Langie Audio Visual Systems, pg 915
Long Island Video Enterprises Live Inc, pg 924
Magnaplan Corp, pg 928
Markertek Video Supply, pg 931
Saul Mineroff Electronics Inc, pg 943
Moviola, pg 948
Neptune Photo Inc, pg 954
NorthCountry Distributors, pg 959
Ray Supply Inc, pg 992
RNJ Electronics, pg 997
Technisphere Corp, pg 1034
TecNec Distributing, pg 1035
Visual Technologies Corp, pg 1060
Willoughby's Imaging Center, pg 1067
WorldStage, pg 1070

NORTH CAROLINA

Camcor Inc, pg 818
Duke Media Services, pg 853
Strategic Connections, pg 1026

OHIO

Hughie's Event Production Services, pg 892
ITA Audio Visual Solutions, pg 902
The Little Warehouse Inc, pg 923
Lyon Video Inc, pg 927
Jimmy Rea Electronics Inc, pg 992

OREGON

SuperDigital Ltd, pg 1029

PENNSYLVANIA

Advanced AV, pg 777
Bernie's Photo Center, pg 805
J E Foss Co, pg 871
Morefield Communications Inc, pg 946
Visual Sound Inc, pg 1059

RHODE ISLAND

Custom Computer Specialists Inc, pg 841

TENNESSEE

Lowrance Sound Co Inc, pg 925
Memphis Communications Corp, pg 938
Spring Arbor Distributors, pg 1022
Trew Audio Inc, pg 1044

TEXAS

Astro Audio Visual, pg 792
Harbor House Studios, pg 884
Heffernan Audio Visual, pg 887
J&S Audio Visual Inc, pg 904
Lubbock Audio Visual Inc, pg 925
RadioShack Corp, pg 990
RF Specialties of Texas LLC, pg 996

UTAH

Performance Audio, pg 973

VIRGINIA

Communications Specialists Inc, pg 833
Filmdex Inc, pg 867
Lee Hartman & Sons Inc, pg 918
The Whitlock Group, pg 1065

WASHINGTON

Inland Audio Visual Co, pg 898

WISCONSIN

Camera Corner Connecting Point, pg 818
Full Compass Systems, pg 874

PUERTO RICO

Bonnin Electronics Inc, pg 810

ALBERTA

Infosat Communications Inc, pg 898
Matrix Video Communications Corp (MVCC), pg 934
McBain Audio Visual Ltd, pg 935
Sharp's Audio-Visual Ltd, pg 1008
Unique Communications Ltd, pg 1048

BRITISH COLUMBIA

Commercial Electronics Ltd, pg 832
Triad Communications Ltd, pg 1044

MANITOBA

Advance Pro, pg 777
Inland Audio Visual Ltd, pg 898

ONTARIO

Edcom Multimedia Products, pg 856
HD Source, pg 886
Nationwide Audio Visual Co, pg 953
Premier A/V Sales Ltd, pg 980

QUEBEC

AVS Technologies Inc, pg 800
Concept Audio-Visual, pg 834
Panavideo Inc, pg 968

Audiotape—Blank Manufacturers

CALIFORNIA

QRS Software Services, pg 988
Sony Electronics Inc, pg 1016
Sounds Unique, pg 1018

COLORADO

Rocky Mountain Audio/Video Productions Inc, pg 998

NEW JERSEY

AV Bluebook, pg 797
Maxell Corp of America, pg 934
Panasonic Consumer Electronics Co, pg 968

NEW YORK

Eastco Multimedia Solutions Inc, pg 856
Sentry Industries Inc, pg 1007

PENNSYLVANIA

Forge Recording LLC, pg 871

WISCONSIN

Full Compass Systems, pg 874

Audiotape Duplication, *see* Duplication—Audiotapes

Background Music, *see* Music Libraries—Background

Bass Synthesizer Distributors

COLORADO

Audio Consultant Services Inc, pg 794

FLORIDA

BAI Distributors Inc, pg 801
Recording Media & Equipment Inc (RM&E), pg 993

GEORGIA

Stage Front Presentation Systems, pg 1022

ILLINOIS

Woodside Avenue Music Productions Inc, pg 1069

INDIANA

Sensory Technologies LLC, pg 1006
Sweetwater Sound Inc, pg 1029

IOWA

ECS Inc, pg 856

KENTUCKY

NOR-COM Inc, pg 958

MARYLAND

Kipp Visual Systems Inc, pg 911

MASSACHUSETTS

Professional Audio Design Inc, pg 985

NEW JERSEY

Hamilton Buhl, pg 884
Starlite Productions, pg 1024

NEW YORK

Hot House Professional Audio, pg 891
MultiDyne Video & Fiber Optics Systems, pg 950

PENNSYLVANIA

Advanced AV, pg 777

TENNESSEE

Lowrance Sound Co Inc, pg 925
Mr Mark's Used Musical, Stereo & Studio Equipment Store, pg 944

TEXAS

Tarpley Media Systems, pg 1032

UTAH

Performance Audio, pg 973

WISCONSIN

Audio Visual of Milwaukee Inc, pg 795
Full Compass Systems, pg 874

MANITOBA

Advance Pro, pg 777

Bass Synthesizer Manufacturers

UTAH

Rolls Corp, pg 999

WASHINGTON

AudioControl®, pg 796

Bass Synthesizer Rentals

ARIZONA

Merestone, pg 938

ARKANSAS

White Diamond Productions, pg 1065

CALIFORNIA

Lynch Communications, pg 926
Synthesizer Rental Service, pg 1030
Synthesizer Systems Technologies (SST), pg 1030

DELAWARE

Actors Attic, pg 775

GEORGIA

Stage Front Presentation Systems, pg 1022

ILLINOIS

On Stage Audio, pg 963
QuickSet International Inc, pg 989
Woodside Avenue Music Productions Inc, pg 1069

MASSACHUSETTS

Preston Productions Inc, pg 981

MICHIGAN

K&R All Media Productions Inc, pg 908
K&R's Recording Studios Inc, pg 908

NEVADA

GES Audio Visual, pg 877

NEW JERSEY

Starlite Productions, pg 1024

NEW YORK

Dreamhire LLC, pg 852

TENNESSEE

Mr Mark's Used Musical, Stereo & Studio Equipment Store, pg 944

AUDIO

Bass Synthesizer Rentals (continued)

TEXAS

Tropikal Productions, pg 1045

UTAH

Performance Audio, pg 973

VERMONT

Parlato Productions, pg 969

BRITISH COLUMBIA

MicrophoneRentals.com, pg 941

Bass Synthesizer Repairs

CALIFORNIA

Diemer Amp & Keyboard Repair, pg 846
McAlister Electronics, pg 935

DELAWARE

Actors Attic, pg 775

FLORIDA

Phat Planet Recording Studios, pg 973

GEORGIA

Stage Front Presentation Systems, pg 1022

INDIANA

Sweetwater Sound Inc, pg 1029

IOWA

ECS Inc, pg 856

KENTUCKY

NOR-COM Inc, pg 958

MAINE

Headlight Audio Visual Inc, pg 887

MASSACHUSETTS

Professional Audio Design Inc, pg 985

NEW JERSEY

Starlite Productions, pg 1024

OREGON

All Service Musical Electronics Repair, pg 780

Blank Audiocassette, *see* Audiocassette—Blank

Blank Audiotape, *see* Audiotape—Blank

Blank Compact Disc, *see* Compact Disc—Blank

Blank Digital Audiotape, *see* Digital Audiotape—Blank

Bluegrass Music, *see* Music Libraries—Bluegrass

Blues Music, *see* Music Libraries—Blues

Bridges & Cues, *see* Music Libraries—Bridges & Cues

Broadway & Hollywood Music, *see* Music Libraries—Broadway & Hollywood

Cable Distributors

ARIZONA

Allusion Studios & Pure Wave Audio, pg 782
EAR Professional Audio/Video, pg 855
Projector SuperStore LLC, pg 986

CALIFORNIA

Adolph Gasser Inc, pg 776
Ametron Audio/Video, pg 785
Apex Jr, pg 788
ARS Electronics, pg 791
Associated Sound, pg 792
ATV Video Center Inc, pg 793
Audio Images Corp, pg 794
AV Conferencing, pg 797
California Tape Products Inc, pg 817
Christy's Editorial, pg 826
Cibola Systems, pg 826
Cinema Equipment Sales of California Inc, pg 827
Computer Modules Inc, pg 834
Delicate Electronics Sales Inc, pg 845
Edgewise Media Inc, pg 856
Empire Wholesale Inc, pg 860
FXC Communications, pg 874
GigaSonic, pg 878
Hosa Technology Inc, pg 891
Jameco Electronics, pg 903
JD Audio Visual Inc, pg 904
The LAST Factory, pg 916
Location Sound Corp, pg 924
Marshall Electronics Inc, pg 932
MediaPOINTE, pg 938
Orvac Electronics, pg 965
Pacific Radio Electronics, pg 967
POP TV, pg 978
Promax Systems, pg 986
Signal Transport, pg 1011
Sound Service Co, pg 1017
Southern California Sound Image Inc, pg 1019
Stanislaus Audio Video Inc, pg 1023
Towards 2000 Inc, pg 1043
VMI Inc, pg 1060
Zack Electronics Inc, pg 1073

COLORADO

Audio Consultant Services Inc, pg 794

CONNECTICUT

Connecticut Audio & Theatrical Supply, pg 835
Lex Products Corp, pg 919
Redco Audio Inc, pg 993

DELAWARE

Actors Attic, pg 775

FLORIDA

Allstar Audio Systems Inc, pg 782
A2D Solutions Inc, pg 793
BAI Distributors Inc, pg 801
Broadcasters General Store Inc, pg 813
Digital Video Systems Inc, pg 848
Harris Corp, pg 885
Herman Pro AV, pg 888
Hi-Tech Enterprises Inc, pg 888
Hunter Electronics LLC, pg 892
Intermark Industries Inc, pg 900
Media Concepts Inc, pg 936
Midtown Video Inc, pg 942
Photomart Cine-Video Inc, pg 975
Pro Stage Inc, pg 983
Recording Media & Equipment Inc (RM&E), pg 993
Sight & Sound Productions, pg 1010
Stereo Sales Inc, pg 1024
TAI Audio, pg 1031
Techni-Lux Inc, pg 1033
Technomedia Solutions, pg 1035

GEORGIA

Accu-Tech, pg 773
Lighting & Production Equipment Inc, pg 920
Omnimedia Inc, pg 962
Stage Front Presentation Systems, pg 1022

HAWAII

The Audio Visual Co (AVCO), pg 795

ILLINOIS

Allen Visual Systems Inc, pg 781
Anixter Inc, pg 787
Arcor Electronics Co, pg 789
Clark Wire & Cable, pg 829
Cole Wire & Cable Co Inc, pg 831
Creative Technology, pg 838
Gepco®, a General Cable brand, pg 877
Joseph Electronics, pg 906
LKG Industries Inc, pg 923
Quintessence Audio Ltd, pg 989
Sound Vision Inc, pg 1018
Waldom Electronics Corp, pg 1061
Woodside Avenue Music Productions Inc, pg 1069

INDIANA

Sensory Technologies LLC, pg 1006
SHP Electronics, pg 1010
Sweetwater Sound Inc, pg 1029

IOWA

ECS Inc, pg 856

KENTUCKY

Audio Visual Techniques Inc, pg 796
Axxis Inc, pg 800
NOR-COM Inc, pg 958

LOUISIANA

Intermedia Technologies, pg 900

MAINE

Headlight Audio Visual Inc, pg 887

MARYLAND

Bradley Broadcast & Pro Audio, pg 811
Cardinal Sound & Video, pg 820
Event Tech, pg 863
Human Circuit, pg 892
Noventri, pg 960

MASSACHUSETTS

Professional Audio Design Inc, pg 985
Rule Broadcast Systems, pg 1000
SLR Enterprises LLC, pg 1013

MICHIGAN

Olson Anderson Co, pg 786
Ascom Communications Contractors, pg 791
DAWNco, pg 843
Digi Sign Design LLC, pg 847
On Stage Visuals, pg 963
TeL Systems, pg 1035

MINNESOTA

Tierney Brothers Inc, pg 1040

MISSOURI

MIS Technologies, pg 944
The RapcoHorizon Co, pg 991
Schiller's Audio-Visual, pg 1004

NEW HAMPSHIRE

APS Lighting-Sound-AV, pg 789
Technet® Systems Group, pg 1033

NEW JERSEY

Alltec Stores, a Vcom IMC Company, pg 782
Argraph Corp, pg 789
AV Bluebook, pg 797
Diversified Systems Inc, pg 849
Earl Girls Inc, pg 855
Entel Systems Inc, pg 861
Hamilton Buhl, pg 884
Interstate Connecting Components, pg 901
National Audio-Visual Supply, pg 952
Nelson Enterprises Theatrical Supply Co, pg 954
Starlite Productions, pg 1024
Total Video Products Inc, pg 1042
Varto Technologies, pg 1052
York Telecom, pg 1072

NEW MEXICO

Quickbeam Systems Inc (QSI), pg 989

NEW YORK

Albany Theatre Supply Co Inc, pg 780
ALTEL Systems Inc, pg 783
Audio-Video Corp, pg 795

Aura Sonic Ltd, pg 796
B&H Photo & Video Pro Audio, pg 802
Barbizon Electric Co Inc, pg 802
BMI Supply, pg 810
BTX Technologies, pg 814
Colortone Audio Visual, pg 832
Creative Stage Lighting Co Inc, pg 838
Custom Media Environments, pg 841
Design Audio Visual Inc, pg 845
Gaylord Brothers, pg 876
Gotham Sound & Communications Inc, pg 881
HAVE Inc, pg 886
Hot House Professional Audio, pg 891
KVL Audio Visual Services Inc, pg 914
Mark Custom Recording Service Inc, pg 931
Markertek Video Supply, pg 931
RNJ Electronics, pg 997
Russell Industries Inc, pg 1001
TecNec Distributing, pg 1035
Toys From The Attic, pg 1043
Visual Word Systems Inc, pg 1060
Whirlwind Music Distributors Inc, pg 1065

OHIO

ITA Audio Visual Solutions, pg 902
Parts Express, pg 969
Smithall Electronics Inc, pg 1014
Tri-State Audio Visual Co, pg 1044
Tri-State Visual Products, pg 1044

OREGON

SuperDigital Ltd, pg 1029
TARA Labs, pg 1032

PENNSYLVANIA

Advanced AV, pg 777
J E Foss Co, pg 871
The Lerro Corp, pg 919
RSS Distributors, pg 1000
Techni-Tool Inc, pg 1033
Wespen Audio Visual Co, pg 1063

TENNESSEE

Belew Enterprises, pg 804
Durrell LLC, pg 854
Lowrance Sound Co Inc, pg 925
Spectrum Sound Inc, pg 1021
Technical Support Systems LLC, pg 1034
Trew Audio Inc, pg 1044

TEXAS

Crossroads Audio Inc, pg 840
Data Projections Inc, pg 843
RadioShack Corp, pg 990
RF Specialties of Texas LLC, pg 996
Tarpley Media Systems, pg 1032

UTAH

Performance Audio, pg 973

VERMONT

Artech Electronics Ltd, pg 791
Production Advantage Inc, pg 984

VIRGINIA

Avitecture Inc, pg 799
Communications Specialists Inc, pg 833
Intellidyne LLC, pg 899
Lee Hartman & Sons Inc, pg 918
Rocktown Media, pg 998
StageSound, pg 1023

WASHINGTON

CCI Solutions, pg 821
Northern Lights & Pro Audio, pg 959
Pacific Northwest Theatre Associates Inc (PNTA), pg 967

WISCONSIN

Audio Visual of Milwaukee Inc, pg 795
DH Satellite, pg 846
Full Compass Systems, pg 874

PUERTO RICO

Audio Visual Concepts Inc, pg 795
Bonnin Electronics Inc, pg 810

ALBERTA

Infosat Communications Inc, pg 898
Matrix Video Communications Corp (MVCC), pg 934
Unique Communications Ltd, pg 1048

BRITISH COLUMBIA

Commercial Electronics Ltd, pg 832
Noramco Wire & Cable, pg 958

MANITOBA

Advance Pro, pg 777

ONTARIO

Cinema Stage Inc, pg 827
Henry's Camera, pg 888
Premier A/V Sales Ltd, pg 980
Westbury National Show Systems Ltd, pg 1064

QUEBEC

JAM Industries Ltd, pg 903
SC Media Canada, pg 1003

Cable Manufacturers

ARIZONA

Covid Inc, pg 837

CALIFORNIA

Addlogix, pg 776
Adolph Gasser Inc, pg 776
ALTINEX Inc, pg 783
Ametron Audio/Video, pg 785
Apogee Electronics Corp, pg 788
Fiber Optic Cable Shop, pg 866
Gefen, pg 876
Get Organized, pg 877
Hosa Technology Inc, pg 891
Marshall Electronics Inc, pg 932
Monster Cable Products Inc, pg 945
RF Industries, pg 995
Signal Transport, pg 1011
Taperwire, pg 1032
TASCAM, pg 1032
Towards 2000 Inc, pg 1043

CONNECTICUT

Lex Products Corp, pg 919
The Music People Inc, pg 951
Redco Audio Inc, pg 993

FLORIDA

Intermark Industries Inc, pg 900
Nemal Electronics International Inc, pg 954

ILLINOIS

Arcor Electronics Co, pg 789
Clark Wire & Cable, pg 829
Gepco®, a General Cable brand, pg 877
Joseph Electronics, pg 906
SoundTech, pg 1018
Tripp Lite, pg 1045
Woodside Avenue Music Productions Inc, pg 1069

INDIANA

Belden, pg 804

MAINE

Dielectric Communications, pg 846

MARYLAND

Event Tech, pg 863
RCI Custom Products, pg 992

MASSACHUSETTS

Miranda Telecast Fiber Systems Inc, pg 944
Mohawk, pg 945
Quabbin Wire & Cable Co Inc, pg 988

MINNESOTA

Intercon 1, pg 900

MISSISSIPPI

Peavey Electronics Corp, pg 970

MISSOURI

The RapcoHorizon Co, pg 991

NEW JERSEY

Alltec Stores, a Vcom IMC Company, pg 782
Alpha Wire Co, pg 782
AV Bluebook, pg 797
Brim Electronics, pg 812
Crestron Electronics Inc, pg 839
Daburn Electronics & Cable Corp, pg 842
FSR Inc, pg 873
JSC Wire & Cable, pg 906
Kramer Electronics USA Inc, pg 913
National Audio-Visual Supply, pg 952
Starlite Productions, pg 1024
Wireworks Corp, pg 1068

NEW YORK

Creative Stage Lighting Co Inc, pg 838
Hannay Reels Inc, pg 884
HAVE Inc, pg 886
Hot House Professional Audio, pg 891
Key Digital Systems, pg 910
Laird Digital Cinema, pg 915
MultiDyne Video & Fiber Optics Systems, pg 950
Servoreeler Systems, pg 1007
TecNec Distributing, pg 1035

NORTH CAROLINA

CommScope Inc, pg 832

OHIO

Audio-Technica US Inc, pg 794

OREGON

Evidence Audio Inc, pg 863
TARA Labs, pg 1032

PENNSYLVANIA

West Penn Wire, pg 1064

RHODE ISLAND

APC by Schneider Electric, pg 788

TENNESSEE

Remote Audio Products, pg 994
Trew Audio Inc, pg 1044

WASHINGTON

D A Sound, pg 842

WISCONSIN

Intelix LLC, pg 899

ONTARIO

Westbury National Show Systems Ltd, pg 1064

Cable Repairs

CALIFORNIA

Ametron Audio/Video, pg 785
Diemer Amp & Keyboard Repair, pg 846

FLORIDA

Hi-Tech Enterprises Inc, pg 888

ILLINOIS

Joseph Electronics, pg 906

KENTUCKY

NOR-COM Inc, pg 958

MASSACHUSETTS

Professional Audio Design Inc, pg 985

MICHIGAN

On Stage Visuals, pg 963
TeL Systems, pg 1035

NEW JERSEY

Starlite Productions, pg 1024

OREGON

All Service Musical Electronics Repair, pg 780

PENNSYLVANIA

Right Coast Recording Inc, pg 997

TENNESSEE

Technical Support Systems LLC, pg 1034

TEXAS

Tarpley Media Systems, pg 1032

WASHINGTON

D A Sound, pg 842

AUDIO

Children's Music, *see* Music Libraries—Children's

Choral Music, *see* Music Libraries—Choral

Classical Music, *see* Music Libraries—Classical

Commercial Jingles, *see* Music Libraries—Commercial Jingles

Compact Disc—Blank Distributors

ARIZONA

EAR Professional Audio/Video, pg 855
Troxell Communications Inc, pg 1045

CALIFORNIA

Adolph Gasser Inc, pg 776
Ametron Audio/Video, pg 785
California Tape Products Inc, pg 817
Delicate Electronics Sales Inc, pg 845
Diversified Imaging Supply, pg 849
Edgewise Media Inc, pg 856
El Mar Plastics Inc, pg 858
JD Audio Visual Inc, pg 904
MSE Media Solutions, pg 949
New Cyberian Systems Inc, pg 955
Joseph Nicoletti Consulting-Promotion/California International Records/Global Village Records, pg 957
Pacific Audio-Visual Enterprises, pg 967
QRS Software Services, pg 988
Reel Picture, pg 994
Revolt Pro Media Inc, pg 995
Sound Service Co, pg 1017
Sounds Unique, pg 1018
TapeStockOnline.com, pg 1032

COLORADO

Alpine Media, pg 782
Audio Consultant Services Inc, pg 794
White Swan Music Inc, pg 1065

CONNECTICUT

Sennheiser Electronic Corp, pg 1006
T & M Digital Services, pg 1031

FLORIDA

BAI Distributors Inc, pg 801
Digital Video Systems Inc, pg 848
Media Concepts Inc, pg 936
Pro Stage Inc, pg 983
Progressive Media & Music, pg 985
Recording Media & Equipment Inc (RM&E), pg 993
Technomedia Solutions, pg 1035

ILLINOIS

Major Media Inc, pg 929
Major Reproductions Equipment Co, pg 929
Polyline LLC, pg 978
Tape Resources, pg 1031

INDIANA

Optical Disc Solutions Inc, pg 964
SHP Electronics, pg 1010
Sweetwater Sound Inc, pg 1029

KENTUCKY

Audio Visual Techniques Inc, pg 796
NOR-COM Inc, pg 958
Northern Kentucky University, pg 959

MAINE

Headlight Audio Visual Inc, pg 887

MARYLAND

Absolute Hollywood, pg 772

MASSACHUSETTS

Terry Hanley Audio Systems Inc, pg 884
Hunt's Photo, Video & Digital, pg 892
Professional Audio Design Inc, pg 985

MINNESOTA

Aggressive Records Audio Duplication LLC, pg 778

MISSISSIPPI

Bowie Audio Visual Enterprises Inc, pg 811

NEW JERSEY

National Audio-Visual Supply, pg 952
Starlite Productions, pg 1024
Total Media, pg 1042

NEW YORK

Aura Sonic Ltd, pg 796
Design Audio Visual Inc, pg 845
Light Impressions, pg 920
Mark Custom Recording Service Inc, pg 931

OHIO

The Little Warehouse Inc, pg 923
Midwest Photo Exchange, pg 942
Promedia Digital, pg 986
Tri-State Audio Visual Co, pg 1044

OREGON

SuperDigital Ltd, pg 1029

PENNSYLVANIA

Advanced AV, pg 777
Brodart Co, pg 813
J E Foss Co, pg 871
The Lerro Corp, pg 919
Wespen Audio Visual Co, pg 1063

TENNESSEE

Lowrance Sound Co Inc, pg 925
NTS ProMedia, pg 960

TEXAS

CAM Audio Inc, pg 817
Harbor House Studios, pg 884
RadioShack Corp, pg 990
TapeWorks Texas Inc, pg 1032

UTAH

ELS Productions Inc, pg 860

VIRGINIA

Furnace MFG, pg 874
Lee Hartman & Sons Inc, pg 918

WASHINGTON

CCI Solutions, pg 821

WISCONSIN

Audio Visual of Milwaukee Inc, pg 795

ALBERTA

Matrix Video Communications Corp (MVCC), pg 934

BRITISH COLUMBIA

Triad Communications Ltd, pg 1044

MANITOBA

Advance Pro, pg 777
Inland Audio Visual Ltd, pg 898

ONTARIO

Westbury National Show Systems Ltd, pg 1064

Compact Disc—Blank Manufacturers

ARIZONA

Tempe Tape & Disc, pg 1037

CALIFORNIA

KABA Audio Productions, pg 907
QRS Software Services, pg 988
SF Global Sourcing, pg 1007
Sony Electronics Inc, pg 1016

COLORADO

MAM-A Inc, pg 929

FLORIDA

Jordan Klein Film & Video (JKFV), pg 906
Pandisc Music Corp, pg 968
Progressive Media & Music, pg 985

ILLINOIS

Folk Era Productions Inc, pg 870

INDIANA

Crystal Clear Media Group, pg 840
Optical Disc Solutions Inc, pg 964

MARYLAND

Absolute Hollywood, pg 772

MINNESOTA

Imation Corp, pg 896

MISSOURI

Audio-VideoGraphics Inc, pg 795

NEW JERSEY

Disc Makers, pg 848
Panasonic Consumer Electronics Co, pg 968
Panasonic Corp, pg 968
Reed Presentations Inc (RPI), pg 993
Synergem, pg 1030

NEW YORK

Digital Force, pg 847
Eastco Multimedia Solutions Inc, pg 856
Entertainment One Distribution, pg 861
HAVE Inc, pg 886
Juston Records, pg 907

OHIO

QCA, pg 988

PENNSYLVANIA

Forge Recording LLC, pg 871

TEXAS

Adams Evidence Grade Technology Inc, pg 775

UTAH

HEC Reading Horizons, pg 887
One Stop CD Shop LLC, pg 963

WISCONSIN

Excel Duplication Services, pg 864

ONTARIO

Cinram Inc, pg 828

Compact Disc Duplication, *see* Duplication—Compact Discs

Compact Disc Recorder & Player Distributors

ALABAMA

Curtis Company, pg 841
Media Visions Inc, pg 937

ARIZONA

Arizona Cine Equipment, pg 789
EAR Professional Audio/Video, pg 855
Troxell Communications Inc, pg 1045

CALIFORNIA

Advanced Systems Group LLC, pg 778
Ametron Audio/Video, pg 785
Associated Sound, pg 792
Audio Images Corp, pg 794
Be Media, pg 804
Christy's Editorial, pg 826
Cibola Systems, pg 826
Computer Modules Inc, pg 834
Delicate Electronics Sales Inc, pg 845
DiskFaktory Direct, pg 849
Eiki International, pg 858
FXC Communications, pg 874
Gluskin's Custom Audio Video, pg 879

AUDIO

Compact Disc Recorder & Player Distributors (continued)

PUERTO RICO

Bonnin Electronics Inc, pg 810

ALBERTA

Sharp's Audio-Visual Ltd, pg 1008
Unique Communications Ltd, pg 1048

BRITISH COLUMBIA

Commercial Electronics Ltd, pg 832
Richmond Sound Design Ltd, pg 996

MANITOBA

Advance Pro, pg 777
Evolution Presentation Technologies, pg 863
Inland Audio Visual Ltd, pg 898

ONTARIO

HD Source, pg 886
Nationwide Audio Visual Co, pg 953
Premier A/V Sales Ltd, pg 980
Westbury National Show Systems Ltd, pg 1064

QUEBEC

AVS Technologies Inc, pg 800
Concept Audio-Visual, pg 834

Compact Disc Recorder & Player Manufacturers

CALIFORNIA

Califone International Inc, pg 817
Citizens Systems America Corp, pg 828
Colby Systems Corp, pg 831
DiskFaktory Direct, pg 849
Sherwood America Inc, pg 1009
Sony Electronics Inc, pg 1016
TASCAM, pg 1032
TEAC America Inc, pg 1033

ILLINOIS

Superscope Technologies Inc, pg 1029

NEW JERSEY

Bogen Communications Inc, pg 810
Emerson Radio Corp, pg 860
Onkyo USA Corp, pg 963
Panasonic Consumer Electronics Co, pg 968
SDI Technologies Inc, pg 1005
Technics, pg 1034

NEW YORK

Music Hall LLC, pg 950

SOUTH CAROLINA

Paso Sound Products Inc, pg 969

TENNESSEE

Adtec Digital Inc, pg 777

VIRGINIA

Lee Hartman & Sons Inc, pg 918

Compact Disc Recorder & Player Rentals

ALABAMA

Audio-Video Resources Inc, pg 795

ARIZONA

Arizona Cine Equipment, pg 789
Merestone, pg 938
Metropolitan Audio-Visual Inc, pg 940
Video West Inc, pg 1056

ARKANSAS

White Diamond Productions, pg 1065

CALIFORNIA

Absolute Rentals, pg 772
Advanced Media LLC, pg 778
AGF Media Services, pg 778
Alliant Event Services, pg 781
Ametron Audio/Video, pg 785
Associated Sound, pg 792
Audio Rents, pg 794
AV Guys, pg 797
Bexel Corp, pg 806
Big Time Picture Company Inc, pg 807
Express Media Inc, pg 864
FXC Communications, pg 874
Gold Standard Productions, pg 880
Hollywood Sound Systems, pg 890
JD Audio Visual Inc, pg 904
Lynch Communications, pg 926
Maximus Media Inc, pg 934
McCune Audio-Video-Lighting, pg 935
Munday & Collins AV, pg 950
Muse Presentation Technologies, pg 950
On-Trax Inc, pg 963
Pacific Audio-Visual Enterprises, pg 967
PSAV® Presentation Services, pg 986
Randall Schiller Productions, pg 1004
Slate Media Group, pg 1013
Sound Service Co, pg 1017
Synthesizer Rental Service, pg 1030
Towards 2000 Inc, pg 1043
Videorama Industries LLC, pg 1057
VMI Inc, pg 1060
Voice & Video Rentals, pg 1060
Warner Bros Production Sound & Video Services, pg 1062

COLORADO

Daylight Productions & Rentals, pg 844
Multimedia Audio Visual Inc, pg 950
Spectrum Audio Visual Services, pg 1020

CONNECTICUT

A/V Davey, pg 797
Fox Connecticut, pg 872

DELAWARE

Showorks Audio Visual Inc, pg 1010
Side Door Studio Inc, pg 1010

FLORIDA

Accord Productions, pg 773
Allstar Audio Systems Inc, pg 782
Image Technical Services, pg 895
Industrial Strength Inc, pg 897
Lighting Sales Connections, pg 920
Paradise Show & Design Inc, pg 969
Photosound of Orlando Inc, pg 975
Pro Stage Inc, pg 983
Sight & Sound Productions, pg 1010
TAI Audio, pg 1031
Universal Studios Florida® Production Group, pg 1049

GEORGIA

Lighting & Production Equipment Inc, pg 920
Stage Front Presentation Systems, pg 1022
Staging Directions Inc, pg 1023

HAWAII

Sight & Sound Studios, pg 1010

ILLINOIS

Audio Visual Services Corp, pg 796
AV Chicago Inc, pg 797
Backstar Creative Media Inc, pg 801
Creative Technology, pg 838
On Stage Audio, pg 963
PSAV® Presentation Services (Hotel Services Division), pg 987
QuickSet International Inc, pg 989
RC Communications, pg 992
Show Department Inc, pg 1009
Staging Resources Inc, pg 1023
Woodside Avenue Music Productions Inc, pg 1069

IOWA

ECS Inc, pg 856

KENTUCKY

Audio Visual Techniques Inc, pg 796

LOUISIANA

Clark Services Audio Visual & Exhibit Inc, pg 829

MARYLAND

Advance Audiovisual Presentation Ltd, pg 777
CPR MultiMedia Solutions, pg 837
Event Tech, pg 863
Maryland Sound International Holding Co LLC, pg 933
Visual Aids Electronics Corp, pg 1059

MASSACHUSETTS

AVFX Inc, pg 798
Terry Hanley Audio Systems Inc, pg 884
massAV, pg 933
Preston Productions Inc, pg 981

MICHIGAN

City Events Group, pg 828
K&R All Media Productions Inc, pg 908
K&R's Recording Studios Inc, pg 908

MINNESOTA

Advanced Audio-Visual Inc, pg 777

MISSISSIPPI

Bowie Audio Visual Enterprises Inc, pg 811

MISSOURI

Show-Me Audio-Visual, pg 1009

MONTANA

Jereco Studios Inc, pg 905

NEVADA

GES Audio Visual, pg 877
Lefco Video Services Inc, pg 918

NEW JERSEY

Audio Visual Associates, pg 795
Audio Visual Dynamics®, pg 795
Earl Girls Inc, pg 855
Giant Audio Visual Inc, pg 878
PLS Staging, pg 977
SLD Lighting, pg 1013
Starlite Productions, pg 1024
Wired 4 Sound Inc, pg 1068

NEW MEXICO

Quickbeam Systems Inc (QSI), pg 989

NEW YORK

Audio Visual Resources LLC, pg 795
Aura Sonic Ltd, pg 796
AV Workshop, pg 797
Colortone Audio Visual, pg 832
CP Communications, pg 837
Dreamhire LLC, pg 852
Interactive International Inc, pg 899
KVL Audio Visual Services Inc, pg 914
Long Island Video Enterprises Live Inc, pg 924
Posthorn Recordings, pg 979
SmartSource Computer & AV Rentals, pg 1014
Specialized Audio-Visual Inc, pg 1020
TBA Global Events, pg 1032
Technisphere Corp, pg 1034
WorldStage, pg 1070

NORTH CAROLINA

A&V Company, pg 772
AV Metro Inc, pg 797
Special Event Services, pg 1020
Visual Aids Electronics of North Carolina Inc, pg 1059

NORTH DAKOTA

Media Productions, pg 937

OHIO

Hughie's Event Production Services, pg 892
Lyon Video Inc, pg 927
R&B Communications Inc, pg 991

OREGON

Northwest Film Center, pg 959
Rose City Sound, pg 999

PENNSYLVANIA

Advanced AV, pg 777
Audio Visions Inc, pg 795

FMP Media Solutions Inc, pg 870
Grise Audio Visual Center Inc, pg 882
Production Solutions Inc, pg 985
Visual Sound Inc, pg 1059

TENNESSEE

Brantley Sound Associates Inc, pg 812
Love Shack Recording Studios, pg 925
Technical Support Systems LLC, pg 1034

TEXAS

Alford Media Services, pg 780
Bright Star Productions Inc, pg 812
Crossroads Audio Inc, pg 840
Data Display Audio Visual Co LP, pg 843
Lubbock Audio Visual Inc, pg 925
Music Lab Inc, pg 950
Onstage Systems, pg 963
Quality Audio Visual Service Inc, pg 988
The Samuels Co, pg 1002
Stage Directions, pg 1022

UTAH

Performance Audio, pg 973

VERMONT

Parlato Productions, pg 969

VIRGINIA

American AV, pg 783
Audio Visual Actions Inc (AVA), pg 795
D&B Television & Video Productions Inc, pg 842
Lee Hartman & Sons Inc, pg 918
Rainbow Rentals, pg 991
StageSound, pg 1023

WASHINGTON

Northern Lights & Pro Audio, pg 959

WEST VIRGINIA

United Sound & Electronics, pg 1048

WISCONSIN

Camera Corner Connecting Point, pg 818
Full Compass Systems, pg 874

WYOMING

Bridger Productions Inc, pg 812

PUERTO RICO

Stage Crew Audiovisual Inc, pg 1022

ALBERTA

Evolution Presentation Technologies, pg 863
L R Light & Sound, pg 915
Sharp's Audio-Visual Ltd, pg 1008
Unique Communications Ltd, pg 1048

BRITISH COLUMBIA

Clark's Audio Visual Services Ltd, pg 829
Commercial Electronics Ltd, pg 832

MANITOBA

Inland Audio Visual Ltd, pg 898

ONTARIO

HD Source, pg 886
Premier A/V Sales Ltd, pg 980
Westbury National Show Systems Ltd, pg 1064

QUEBEC

Audio Visual Dynamics Ltd, pg 795

Compact Disc Recorder & Player Repairs

CALIFORNIA

Advanced Media LLC, pg 778
Ametron Audio/Video, pg 785
Audio Images Corp, pg 794
Gluskin's Custom Audio Video, pg 879
McAlister Electronics, pg 935
Randall Schiller Productions, pg 1004
Sound Service Co, pg 1017
SSL Industries Inc, pg 1022
Towards 2000 Inc, pg 1043

CONNECTICUT

A/V Davey, pg 797
Sennheiser Electronic Corp, pg 1006

FLORIDA

Digital Video Systems Inc, pg 848
Hi-Tech Enterprises Inc, pg 888
JT Communications, pg 906
Stereo Sales Inc, pg 1024
TAI Audio, pg 1031

GEORGIA

Lighting & Production Equipment Inc, pg 920
Stage Front Presentation Systems, pg 1022

ILLINOIS

Beatty TeleVisual Productions, pg 804
Midwest Digital Corp, pg 942

INDIANA

Sweetwater Sound Inc, pg 1029

IOWA

ECS Inc, pg 856

KENTUCKY

Barney Miller's Inc, pg 943
NOR-COM Inc, pg 958

MARYLAND

Strauss Photo Technical Service Inc, pg 1026
Visual Aids Electronics Corp, pg 1059

MASSACHUSETTS

Professional Audio Design Inc, pg 985

MICHIGAN

City Events Group, pg 828
K&R's Recording Studios Inc, pg 908
TeL Systems, pg 1035

MINNESOTA

Microboards Technology LLC, pg 941

NEW JERSEY

A-V Services Inc, pg 771
Audio Visual Associates, pg 795
Earl Girls Inc, pg 855
Starlite Productions, pg 1024

NEW MEXICO

Quickbeam Systems Inc (QSI), pg 989

NEW YORK

Technisphere Corp, pg 1034
Toys From The Attic, pg 1043

OHIO

Copp Integrated Systems, pg 836
ITA Audio Visual Solutions, pg 902
Tri-State Audio Visual Co, pg 1044

OREGON

All Service Musical Electronics Repair, pg 780

PENNSYLVANIA

J E Foss Co, pg 871

TENNESSEE

Technical Support Systems LLC, pg 1034

TEXAS

Lubbock Audio Visual Inc, pg 925
Quality Audio Visual Service Inc, pg 988
Southwest Sound & Electronics Inc, pg 1019

VIRGINIA

Hoppmann Audio Visual, pg 891
Lee Hartman & Sons Inc, pg 918
Old Dominion Broadcasting, pg 961
The Whitlock Group, pg 1065

WASHINGTON

Northern Lights & Pro Audio, pg 959

WEST VIRGINIA

United Sound & Electronics, pg 1048

WISCONSIN

Full Compass Systems, pg 874

PUERTO RICO

Bonnin Electronics Inc, pg 810

ALBERTA

Unique Communications Ltd, pg 1048

BRITISH COLUMBIA

Commercial Electronics Ltd, pg 832

MANITOBA

Inland Audio Visual Ltd, pg 898

ONTARIO

HD Source, pg 886
Premier A/V Sales Ltd, pg 980
Westbury National Show Systems Ltd, pg 1064

Compression & Decompression Equipment Distributors

ARIZONA

Allusion Studios & Pure Wave Audio, pg 782
EAR Professional Audio/Video, pg 855
Troxell Communications Inc, pg 1045

CALIFORNIA

Ametron Audio/Video, pg 785
Associated Sound, pg 792
Audio Images Corp, pg 794
Computer Modules Inc, pg 834
Empire Wholesale Inc, pg 860
FXC Communications, pg 874
Harman Pro North America, pg 885
MediaMation Inc, pg 937
MediaPOINTE, pg 938
SNAP, pg 1014
Sound Service Co, pg 1017
Towards 2000 Inc, pg 1043
VMI Inc, pg 1060
VTP Inc, pg 1061

COLORADO

Audio Consultant Services Inc, pg 794

CONNECTICUT

Connecticut Audio & Theatrical Supply, pg 835
HB Communications Inc, pg 886
The Music People Inc, pg 951

FLORIDA

Access Media Group, pg 773
Allstar Audio Systems Inc, pg 782
Broadcasters General Store Inc, pg 813
CD ROM™ Inc, pg 822
Digital Video Systems Inc, pg 848
Harris Corp, pg 885
Intermark Industries Inc, pg 900
Midtown Video Inc, pg 942
Pro Stage Inc, pg 983
Recording Media & Equipment Inc (RM&E), pg 993
Stereo Sales Inc, pg 1024
TAI Audio, pg 1031
Technomedia Solutions, pg 1035

GEORGIA

Clark, pg 829
Lighting & Production Equipment Inc, pg 920
Stage Front Presentation Systems, pg 1022

HAWAII

The Audio Visual Co (AVCO), pg 795

AUDIO

Compression & Decompression Equipment Distributors (continued)

ILLINOIS

Joseph Electronics, pg 906

INDIANA

Sensory Technologies LLC, pg 1006
SHP Electronics, pg 1010

IOWA

ECS Inc, pg 856

KENTUCKY

NOR-COM Inc, pg 958

MAINE

Headlight Audio Visual Inc, pg 887

MARYLAND

Bradley Broadcast & Pro Audio, pg 811
Cardinal Sound & Video, pg 820
NewWave Technologies Inc, pg 957

NEW HAMPSHIRE

Technet® Systems Group, pg 1033

NEW JERSEY

Earl Girls Inc, pg 855
Starlite Productions, pg 1024
Wired 4 Sound Inc, pg 1068
York Telecom, pg 1072

NEW MEXICO

Quickbeam Systems Inc (QSI), pg 989

NEW YORK

Audio-Video Corp, pg 795
B&H Photo & Video Pro Audio, pg 802
Group One Ltd, pg 882
Markertek Video Supply, pg 931
XTA Electronics Ltd, pg 1071

OHIO

ITA Audio Visual Solutions, pg 902

OREGON

SuperDigital Ltd, pg 1029

PENNSYLVANIA

Advanced AV, pg 777
Clair Brothers Audio Systems Inc, pg 829

SOUTH CAROLINA

DaviSound, pg 843

TENNESSEE

Durrell LLC, pg 854
Lowrance Sound Co Inc, pg 925
Mr Mark's Used Musical, Stereo & Studio Equipment Store, pg 944
Technical Support Systems LLC, pg 1034
Zion Music Group, pg 1074

TEXAS

Crossroads Audio Inc, pg 840
Lubbock Audio Visual Inc, pg 925
RF Specialties of Texas LLC, pg 996
Southwest Sound & Electronics Inc, pg 1019
Tarpley Media Systems, pg 1032

UTAH

Performance Audio, pg 973

VIRGINIA

Filmdex Inc, pg 867
Intellidyne LLC, pg 899
Old Dominion Broadcasting, pg 961
Rocktown Media, pg 998

WASHINGTON

CCI Solutions, pg 821
Northern Lights & Pro Audio, pg 959

WISCONSIN

Audio Visual of Milwaukee Inc, pg 795
Camera Corner Connecting Point, pg 818
Full Compass Systems, pg 874

PUERTO RICO

Bonnin Electronics Inc, pg 810

ALBERTA

Unique Communications Ltd, pg 1048

BRITISH COLUMBIA

ADI Systems Inc, pg 776

MANITOBA

Advance Pro, pg 777

ONTARIO

Sascom Marketing Group Inc, pg 1003

QUEBEC

JAM Industries Ltd, pg 903
SC Media Canada, pg 1003

Compression & Decompression Equipment Manufacturers

ARIZONA

Applied Integration Corp, pg 789
Orban, pg 965
Radio Design Labs (RDL), pg 990

CALIFORNIA

Harman Pro North America, pg 885
Linkabit, pg 922
Manley Laboratories Inc, pg 930
Millennia Media FPC, pg 943
Physical Optics Corp, pg 975
Summit Audio Inc, pg 1028
Telestream Inc, pg 1036

FLORIDA

CD ROM™ Inc, pg 822

MARYLAND

API, pg 788

MASSACHUSETTS

Comrex Corp, pg 834

MINNESOTA

Telex Communications Inc, pg 1037

NEW JERSEY

ATI Audio, pg 793

NEW YORK

Ashly Audio Inc, pg 792
Laird Digital Cinema, pg 915
Solid State Logic Inc, pg 1015

NORTH CAROLINA

Micro Technology Unlimited, pg 941

OHIO

Telos Systems, pg 1037

SOUTH CAROLINA

DaviSound, pg 843

TENNESSEE

Adtec Digital Inc, pg 777

Compression & Decompression Equipment Rentals

ARIZONA

Merestone, pg 938
Video West Inc, pg 1056

CALIFORNIA

Ametron Audio/Video, pg 785
Associated Sound, pg 792
Audio Rents, pg 794
Express Media Inc, pg 864
Lynch Communications, pg 926
McCune Audio-Video-Lighting, pg 935
On-Trax Inc, pg 963
Sound Service Co, pg 1017
Synthesizer Rental Service, pg 1030
Total Media Group, pg 1042
Towards 2000 Inc, pg 1043
Westcoast Video Productions Inc, pg 1064

COLORADO

Audio Consultant Services Inc, pg 794
Spectrum Audio Visual Services, pg 1020

DELAWARE

Actors Attic, pg 775
Side Door Studio Inc, pg 1010

FLORIDA

Access Media Group, pg 773
Allstar Audio Systems Inc, pg 782
Image Technical Services, pg 895
Pro Stage Inc, pg 983
TAI Audio, pg 1031
Universal Studios Florida® Production Group, pg 1049

GEORGIA

Lighting & Production Equipment Inc, pg 920
Stage Front Presentation Systems, pg 1022

HAWAII

Sight & Sound Studios, pg 1010

ILLINOIS

On Stage Audio, pg 963
QuickSet International Inc, pg 989
Staging Resources Inc, pg 1023

IOWA

ECS Inc, pg 856

KENTUCKY

Audio Visual Techniques Inc, pg 796
NOR-COM Inc, pg 958

MARYLAND

CPR MultiMedia Solutions, pg 837
Event Tech, pg 863

MASSACHUSETTS

massAV, pg 933
Preston Productions Inc, pg 981

MICHIGAN

K&R All Media Productions Inc, pg 908
K&R's Recording Studios Inc, pg 908

MISSOURI

Show-Me Audio-Visual, pg 1009

NEW JERSEY

Earl Girls Inc, pg 855
Giant Audio Visual Inc, pg 878
Moe AV LLC, pg 945
PLS Staging, pg 977
Starlite Productions, pg 1024
Wired 4 Sound Inc, pg 1068

NEW MEXICO

Quickbeam Systems Inc (QSI), pg 989

NEW YORK

Aura Sonic Ltd, pg 796
CP Communications, pg 837
HB-Content, pg 886
See Factor Industry Inc, pg 1006
TBA Global Events, pg 1032

NORTH CAROLINA

A&V Company, pg 772
Special Event Services, pg 1020

OHIO

ITA Audio Visual Solutions, pg 902
Lyon Video Inc, pg 927
R&B Communications Inc, pg 991

OKLAHOMA

PDC Productions, pg 970

PENNSYLVANIA

Advanced AV, pg 777
Production Solutions Inc, pg 985

Compression & Decompression Equipment Repairs

Consulting

AUDIO

Consulting (continued)

DISTRICT OF COLUMBIA

Hillmann & Carr Inc, pg 889
O'Keefe Communications Inc, pg 961

FLORIDA

Allstar Audio Systems Inc, pg 782
Cliff Ayers Enterprises, pg 800
CD ROM™ Inc, pg 822
Steven Cohen Motion Picture Production, pg 831
Communications Concepts Inc (CCI), pg 833
Digital Video Arts, pg 848
Ed Ethridge Productions Inc, pg 863
Griffiths Broadcast Co Inc, pg 882
Gulf Coast Audio Visual Producers Inc, pg 883
JT Communications, pg 906
LHV Audio Services, pg 919
Lighting Sales Connections, pg 920
Phat Planet Recording Studios, pg 973
Pro Stage Inc, pg 983
Promidi Music, pg 986
Sight & Sound Productions, pg 1010
Stereo Sales Inc, pg 1024
Sunfire Communications Inc, pg 1028
TAI Audio, pg 1031
Top Hat Productions, pg 1042
Universal Studios Florida® Production Group, pg 1049

GEORGIA

CDAI Innovative Design Solutions, pg 822
COMPRO Productions Inc, pg 834
Guerrilla Productions LLC, pg 883
Hottrax Records, pg 891
Lighting & Production Equipment Inc, pg 920
Merck & Hill Consultants Inc, pg 938
Malcolm Neal Productions, pg 954
NorthTown Sounds Inc, pg 959
Omega Media Group Inc, pg 962
Stage Front Presentation Systems, pg 1022
Symmes Systems, pg 1030
Visioneering International Inc, pg 1058

HAWAII

DL Adams Associates Ltd, pg 775
Audio Resource Honolulu, pg 794
KHNL/KGMB, pg 910
Media Bridge Gamekids, pg 936
TV Juice Productions Inc, pg 1046

ILLINOIS

ABS Enterprises, pg 772
Accenture, pg 773
AudioTransitions, pg 796
Beatty TeleVisual Productions, pg 804
CCore Media Inc, pg 821
Communications Corporation of America, pg 833
Comtech Multimedia Marketing, pg 834
Creative Technology, pg 838
Major Media Inc, pg 929
On Site Video, pg 963
Paragon Studios Inc, pg 969
Jim Passin Productions, pg 970
The Prairie Production Group, pg 980
Sound/Video Impressions Inc, pg 1018
Sparkfactor, pg 1019
20/20 Communications Inc, pg 1047
Twisted Media Inc, pg 1047
Universal Training, pg 1049
Woodside Avenue Music Productions Inc, pg 1069

INDIANA

AVA Productions, pg 798
Bright Ideas Creative Services, pg 812
Digital Rain LLC, pg 847
Gaither Studios LLC, pg 875
Alan Johnson Recording, pg 905
OMNI Productions, pg 962
Sweetwater Sound Inc, pg 1029

IOWA

Hedquist Productions Inc, pg 887
The Production House, pg 984

KANSAS

Chapman Recording & Mastering, pg 824

KENTUCKY

Axxis Inc, pg 800
Broadway Digital, pg 813
Hammond Communications Group, pg 884
Idle Minds Productions Inc, pg 894
NOR-COM Inc, pg 958
Trusty Tuneshop Recording Studios, pg 1045

LOUISIANA

Louisiana State University Health Sciences Center - Shreveport, pg 925
Moxie Media, pg 948

MAINE

Slim Goodbody Corp, pg 1013

MARYLAND

The Ahern Group, pg 779
CPR MultiMedia Solutions, pg 837
CSPMedia.com, pg 840
The Cutting Corp, pg 841
dbF a Media Company, pg 844
Kramer Communications Video Production, pg 913
Omega Recording Studios, pg 962
Pro Cuts Editing Services, pg 982
Smolian Sound Studios, pg 1014

MASSACHUSETTS

Capron Lighting & Sound Co Inc, pg 819
Cavanaugh Tocci Associates Inc, pg 821
CommCreative, pg 832
Communications Design Associates, pg 833
Continental Recordings Inc, pg 835
Cramer Productions, pg 837
Emergency Film Group, pg 860
Green Mountain Post Films (GMP), pg 882
Terry Hanley Audio Systems Inc, pg 884
Inter-Media Electronics, pg 899
Labrecque Creative Sound, pg 915
M Works Mastering Studios, pg 927
Monadnock Media Inc, pg 945
Northeastern Digital Recording Inc, pg 959
Northern Light Productions, pg 959
Penfield Productions Ltd, pg 971
PixMix Video Services, pg 976
Preston Productions Inc, pg 981
Professional Audio Design Inc, pg 985
Soundtrack Recording Studios, pg 1018
TR Productions, pg 1043
TVN-The Video Network, pg 1046
Yellow Moon Press, pg 1072

MICHIGAN

Audio Graphic Services, pg 794
Brilliance Audio, pg 812
Digi Sign Design LLC, pg 847
GMP Music, pg 879
K&R's Recording Studios Inc, pg 908
MessageMakers, pg 939
Michigan Recording Arts Institute & Technologies, pg 941
On Stage Visuals, pg 963
Studio A Recording Inc, pg 1026

MINNESOTA

Aggressive Records Audio Duplication LLC, pg 778
Alpha Video & Audio Inc, pg 782
Big Event Productions LLC, pg 807
Digital Audio Labs, pg 847
Jamieson & Associates Inc, pg 904
Media Loft Inc, pg 937
MultiMedia, pg 950

MISSOURI

Communitronics Corp, pg 833
Production Consultants, pg 984
Show-Me Audio-Visual, pg 1009
Switch, pg 1030
Visionworks Design Services Inc, pg 1059

MONTANA

North Country Media Group, pg 959

NEVADA

Aardvark Video & Media Productions, pg 772
Encore Productions Inc, pg 861
Lefco Video Services Inc, pg 918
MeshTel-Intelite, pg 939
Stage America LLC, pg 1022
Tanglewood Productions, pg 1031

NEW HAMPSHIRE

Apertura, pg 788
Captain Fiddle Music & Publications, pg 820
Chip Taylor Communications LLC, pg 1032

NEW JERSEY

All Jersey Studios, pg 780
Audio Vistas LLC, pg 795
Audio Visual Dynamics®, pg 795
CFP Video Productions Inc, pg 823
Color Leasing Studios, pg 831
Diversified Systems Inc, pg 849
Emanuel Audiovisual Consultants, pg 860
Euro-Pacific Film & Video Productions Inc, pg 863
Jeep Jazz Media Solutions, pg 905
Laurel Video Productions, pg 916
Mia Mind Music, pg 941
MIB Mediaworks, pg 941
Milgrom Productions, pg 943
Moe AV LLC, pg 945
Oasis CD Manufacturing, pg 960
Optisonics Productions, pg 965
Outside The Box Interactive LLC, pg 966
PatchAmp, pg 970
PeopleVisionFX, pg 972
PLS Staging, pg 977
Princeton Acoustics Corp, pg 982
Reed Presentations Inc (RPI), pg 993
Starlite Productions, pg 1024
Suede Interactive, pg 1027
Telemanagement Resources International Inc (TRI), pg 1036
Varto Technologies, pg 1052
VCSvideo, pg 1052
Wired 4 Sound Inc, pg 1068

NEW MEXICO

Production Outfitters, pg 984
Quickbeam Systems Inc (QSI), pg 989

NEW YORK

Audio Visual Resources LLC, pg 795
Aura Sonic Ltd, pg 796
Aural Gratification Inc, pg 796
aurora productions, pg 797
Big Fish Productions Inc, pg 807
The Big House Group, pg 807
BZ/Rights & Permissions Inc, pg 816
Chromavision Corp, pg 826
Cohn Creative Group LLC, pg 831
CP Communications, pg 837
De Nonno Productions Inc (DPI), pg 844
Edgeware Associates/Travel Arts Syndicate, pg 856
Educational Images Ltd, pg 857
Foothill Digital Inc, pg 871
4-D Creative Media, pg 871
A Gentle Wind, pg 877
GHO Group LLC, pg 878
Granny Press LLC, pg 881
Greyfalcon House, pg 882
Gurrilla Video Solutions, pg 883
HB-Content, pg 886
Heavy Melody, pg 887
Hello World Communications, pg 888
IAI Video, pg 893
Lylofilm Productions, pg 926
Manhattan Center Studios Inc, pg 930
Mark Custom Recording Service Inc, pg 931
Neal Marshad Productions, pg 931
Mother West, pg 947
MRG Productions Inc, pg 948
No Soap Productions, pg 957
Now Hear This, pg 960
NSR Productions Inc & Capricorn Five Films, pg 960
Shelly Palmer Production, pg 968
Posthorn Recordings, pg 979
David Rapkin Audio Production, pg 991
Peter Schleger Co, pg 1004
Shen Milsom & Wilke LLC, pg 1008
Smithsonian National Museum of the American Indian, pg 1014
Synaptic Digital, pg 1030
TBA Global Events, pg 1032

VIEW Inc (Video International Entertainment World Inc), pg 1058
Visual Technologies Corp, pg 1060
Zelman Studios Ltd, pg 1073

NORTH CAROLINA

Pat Appleson Studios Inc, pg 788
Audio Art, pg 794
Lawrence Behr Associates Inc, pg 804
Camcor Inc, pg 818
The Communications Group Inc, pg 833
Duke Media Services, pg 853
Horizon Video Productions Inc, pg 891
Pamela Johnston Voice Talent, pg 906
On Location North Carolina, pg 963
Special Event Services, pg 1020
Studio B Mastering, pg 1026
Visual Aids Electronics of North Carolina Inc, pg 1059

NORTH DAKOTA

Media Productions, pg 937

OHIO

Advent Media Inc, pg 778
Challenge Productions, pg 823
Creative Technology, pg 838
EDR Media LLC, pg 857
GatesAir, pg 875
Icom Multimedia, pg 893
Lyon Video Inc, pg 927
R&B Communications Inc, pg 991
Smithall Electronics Inc, pg 1014
Tri-State Audio Visual Co, pg 1044
Vista Color Imaging Inc, pg 1059

OKLAHOMA

Digital Designs, pg 847
PDC Productions, pg 970
Piper Media Services Inc, pg 976
University of Oklahoma Academic Media & Digital Services, pg 1050

OREGON

ASC-Tube Trap, pg 791
Consolidated Communications Consultants, pg 835
Producers Studio, pg 984
Spectrum Systems Design, pg 1021

PENNSYLVANIA

AiH Group Inc, pg 779
American Artist Studio, pg 783
Berry & Homer, pg 805
Clair Brothers Audio Systems Inc, pg 829
Dreambox Media Inc, pg 852
Goodman Associates Inc, pg 880
JPL, pg 906
Kloss Studios Co, pg 912
Metropolitan Acoustics LLC, pg 940
Robin Miller, Filmaker Inc, pg 943
Right Coast Recording Inc, pg 997
Ted The Fiddler Music, pg 1035
The Videohouse Inc, pg 1057
WQED-Multimedia, pg 1070

RHODE ISLAND

A&M Productions, pg 771
Sound Advantage, pg 1016
Sound-FX-Design, pg 1017

SOUTH CAROLINA

DaviSound, pg 843

TENNESSEE

American Blackguard Inc, pg 784
Analog Man Recording Studio, pg 786
Ardent Studios Inc, pg 789
Continental Film, pg 835
Cupit Music Group, pg 841
Durrell LLC, pg 854
Fricon Entertainment Co Inc, pg 873
Love Shack Recording Studios, pg 925
Memphis Communications Corp, pg 938
Mr Mark's Used Musical, Stereo & Studio Equipment Store, pg 944
Motion Picture Services, pg 947
Spectrum Sound Inc, pg 1021
Stage Post, pg 1022
Technical Support Systems LLC, pg 1034
Zion Music Group, pg 1074

TEXAS

AVES Audio Visual Systems Inc, pg 798
Biway Media, pg 808
Bright Star Productions Inc, pg 812
Castleview Productions, pg 821
Communication Arts Multimedia Inc, pg 832
Crossroads Audio Inc, pg 840
The Editing Co, pg 857
James Loupas Associates Inc, pg 925
The Music Bakery, pg 950
Julye Newlin Productions Inc, pg 956
Onstage Systems, pg 963
Out of the BLUE Media, pg 966
Phillips MediaSource, pg 974
Planet Dallas Recording Studios, pg 976
The Samuels Co, pg 1002
The Sound Lab Inc, pg 1017
Sound Works, pg 1018
Stage Directions, pg 1022
Tarpley Media Systems, pg 1032
Texas Heart Institute Visual Communication Services, pg 1037
TopCat Records LLC, pg 1042
Tropikal Productions, pg 1045
Writer's AudioShop/Davenport Productions, pg 1070
The Yesterday USA Radio Networks, pg 1072

UTAH

ImageWorks Communications, pg 896
Performance Audio, pg 973
Spectrum Engineers, pg 1021

VERMONT

Parlato Productions, pg 969
University of Vermont, Instructional Television Dept, pg 1050

VIRGINIA

Advance Concepts Inc, pg 777
Allied Media Corp, pg 781
American AV, pg 783
AudioImage Recording, pg 796
CACI Productions Group, pg 816
CALIBRE, pg 816
CDR Communications Inc, pg 822
Design & Production Inc, pg 845
Lion Recording Services Inc, pg 922
Mark Sonder Productions Inc, pg 931
Metro Productions, pg 939
National Media Services Inc, pg 953
Studio Center Corp, pg 1026

WASHINGTON

Adams Creative & Production Services, pg 775
Jake Barner Studio, pg 803
D A Sound, pg 842
Inland Audio Visual Co, pg 898
Kostov Productions, pg 913
Laser Fantasy/HECK Industries/ Photon Manufacturing, pg 916
Media Elite Productions, pg 936
Northern Lights & Pro Audio, pg 959
Pacific Northwest Theatre Associates Inc (PNTA), pg 967
Quiet Planet LLC, pg 989
Sound Sound/Savage Fruitarian Productions, pg 1017

WISCONSIN

Audio Visual of Milwaukee Inc, pg 795
Concept Productions Inc, pg 834
Full Compass Systems, pg 874
Learning Technology Services, pg 917
Meridian Studios, pg 939
University of Wisconsin-Oshkosh Radio-TV-Film Dept, pg 1050
USAV Group Inc, pg 1050
Video Wisconsin Inc, pg 1056
Watts Communications Inc, pg 1062
Wisconsin Public Television, pg 1068

WYOMING

Bridger Productions Inc, pg 812

PUERTO RICO

Stage Crew Audiovisual Inc, pg 1022

ALBERTA

Unique Communications Ltd, pg 1048

BRITISH COLUMBIA

DWD Theatre Design & Consulting, pg 854
MicrophoneRentals.com, pg 941
North West Digital Ltd, pg 959
Pinewood Sound, pg 975

MANITOBA

daCapo Productions, pg 842

ONTARIO

ADS Media, pg 777
AMPLUS Productions, pg 786
Artaflex Inc, pg 791
Cinema Stage Inc, pg 827
DebsVoice, pg 844
Edcom Multimedia Products, pg 856
GAPC (General Assembly Production Centre), pg 875
JFB Communications, pg 905
MCS Recording Studios, pg 936
MVI Multivision Inc, pg 951
Sonic Science Inc, pg 1016
State of the Art Acoustik Inc, pg 1024
Video Excellence Productions, pg 1055
VO2 Mix Studios, pg 1060
Wanted! Sound + Picture, pg 1062
Westbury National Show Systems Ltd, pg 1064

QUEBEC

Group PVP, pg 882
Sceno Plus, pg 1004
20k, pg 1047

Continuous Recorder & Player Distributors

ALABAMA

Media Visions Inc, pg 937

ARIZONA

Arizona Cine Equipment, pg 789
Coustic Car Audio, pg 837
Troxell Communications Inc, pg 1045

CALIFORNIA

Advanced Systems Group LLC, pg 778
Ametron Audio/Video, pg 785
Be Media, pg 804
Cibola Systems, pg 826
Empire Wholesale Inc, pg 860
Lloyd F McKinney Associates Inc, pg 935
MediaPOINTE, pg 938
POP TV, pg 978
SBS Productions, pg 1003
Sound Service Co, pg 1017
Southern California Sound Image Inc, pg 1019
SSL Industries Inc, pg 1022

COLORADO

Audio Consultant Services Inc, pg 794

CONNECTICUT

MAVCO, pg 934
USI Inc, pg 1051
Vista Group International Inc, pg 1059

DELAWARE

Actors Attic, pg 775

FLORIDA

Allstar Audio Systems Inc, pg 782
BAI Distributors Inc, pg 801
Digital Video Systems Inc, pg 848
Gulf Coast Audio Visual Producers Inc, pg 883
Harris Corp, pg 885
Hi-Tech Import Export Corp, pg 888
Photomart Cine-Video Inc, pg 975
Pro Stage Inc, pg 983
Recording Media & Equipment Inc (RM&E), pg 993
Stereo Sales Inc, pg 1024
TAI Audio, pg 1031
Technomedia Solutions, pg 1035

GEORGIA

Baker Audio Inc, pg 801
Clark, pg 829

AUDIO

Continuous Recorder & Player Distributors (continued)

GEORGIA (continued)
Lighting & Production Equipment Inc, pg 920
Stage Front Presentation Systems, pg 1022

ILLINOIS
Quintessence Audio Ltd, pg 989

INDIANA
Sensory Technologies LLC, pg 1006
SHP Electronics, pg 1010
Sweetwater Sound Inc, pg 1029

IOWA
ECS Inc, pg 856

KENTUCKY
NOR-COM Inc, pg 958

MAINE
Headlight Audio Visual Inc, pg 887

MARYLAND
Bradley Broadcast & Pro Audio, pg 811
Human Circuit, pg 892
Kipp Visual Systems Inc, pg 911
NewWave Technologies Inc, pg 957
RTZ Audio Visual, pg 1000

MASSACHUSETTS
MALCO Electronics, pg 929

MICHIGAN
City Events Group, pg 828

MISSOURI
Communitronics Corp, pg 833
Conference Technologies Inc, pg 835

NEW JERSEY
Alltec Stores, a Vcom IMC Company, pg 782
Audio Visual Associates, pg 795
Hamilton Buhl, pg 884
Onkyo USA Corp, pg 963
Starlite Productions, pg 1024
Video Corporation of America (VCA), pg 1055
Wilray Audio Visual Corp, pg 1067
Wired 4 Sound Inc, pg 1068

NEW YORK
AV Workshop, pg 797
Cadence Jazz Records, pg 816
Custom Media Environments, pg 841
Design Audio Visual Inc, pg 845
Indigo Productions, pg 897
KVL Audio Visual Services Inc, pg 914
Technisphere Corp, pg 1034

OHIO
ITA Audio Visual Solutions, pg 902

PENNSYLVANIA
Advanced AV, pg 777
The Lerro Corp, pg 919
Morefield Communications Inc, pg 946

SOUTH CAROLINA
Paso Sound Products Inc, pg 969

TENNESSEE
Durrell LLC, pg 854
Lowrance Sound Co Inc, pg 925

TEXAS
AVES Audio Visual Systems Inc, pg 798
Crossroads Audio Inc, pg 840
Heffernan Audio Visual, pg 887
Lubbock Audio Visual Inc, pg 925
Schoolhouse Audio Visual, pg 1004
Tarpley Media Systems, pg 1032

UTAH
Performance Audio, pg 973

VIRGINIA
Hoppmann Audio Visual, pg 891
Intellidyne LLC, pg 899
Lee Hartman & Sons Inc, pg 918
The Whitlock Group, pg 1065

WISCONSIN
Audio Visual of Milwaukee Inc, pg 795
Full Compass Systems, pg 874

PUERTO RICO
Bonnin Electronics Inc, pg 810

ALBERTA
Unique Communications Ltd, pg 1048

BRITISH COLUMBIA
Commercial Electronics Ltd, pg 832

MANITOBA
Advance Pro, pg 777
Inland Audio Visual Ltd, pg 898

ONTARIO
Nationwide Audio Visual Co, pg 953
Technovision® Interactive Inc, pg 1035

QUEBEC
Concept Audio-Visual, pg 834

Continuous Recorder & Player Manufacturers

ARIZONA
Applied Integration Corp, pg 789
Coustic Car Audio, pg 837

CALIFORNIA
Antex Electronics Corp, pg 787
Gilderfluke & Co Inc, pg 878
Mackenzie Laboratories Inc, pg 927
Newdoll Enterprises LLC, pg 956
TASCAM, pg 1032

CONNECTICUT
Alarmco Intelligent Message Repeaters, pg 779

GEORGIA
Register Data Systems, pg 994

MINNESOTA
Digital Audio Labs, pg 847

NEW JERSEY
Onkyo USA Corp, pg 963
Panasonic Consumer Electronics Co, pg 968

NEW YORK
RCS Enterprises, pg 992

TENNESSEE
Adtec Digital Inc, pg 777

BRITISH COLUMBIA
Creation Technologies Inc, pg 838
Richmond Sound Design Ltd, pg 996

Continuous Recorder & Player Rentals

ARIZONA
Arizona Cine Equipment, pg 789
Merestone, pg 938
Metropolitan Audio-Visual Inc, pg 940

CALIFORNIA
Alliant Event Services, pg 781
Ametron Audio/Video, pg 785
Artichoke Productions, pg 791
Express Media Inc, pg 864
Lynch Communications, pg 926
McCune Audio-Video-Lighting, pg 935
Munday & Collins AV, pg 950
PSAV® Presentation Services, pg 986
Synthesizer Systems Technologies (SST), pg 1030

COLORADO
Daylight Productions & Rentals, pg 844

DELAWARE
Showorks Audio Visual Inc, pg 1010

FLORIDA
Allstar Audio Systems Inc, pg 782
Gulf Coast Audio Visual Producers Inc, pg 883
Pro Stage Inc, pg 983
TAI Audio, pg 1031

GEORGIA
Lighting & Production Equipment Inc, pg 920
Stage Front Presentation Systems, pg 1022
Staging Directions Inc, pg 1023

ILLINOIS
Backstar Creative Media Inc, pg 801
Beatty TeleVisual Productions, pg 804
On Stage Audio, pg 963
RC Communications, pg 992

IOWA
ECS Inc, pg 856

MARYLAND
CPR MultiMedia Solutions, pg 837
Event Tech, pg 863

MASSACHUSETTS
AVFX Inc, pg 798
massAV, pg 933
Preston Productions Inc, pg 981

MICHIGAN
City Events Group, pg 828
K&R All Media Productions Inc, pg 908
K&R's Recording Studios Inc, pg 908

MINNESOTA
Advanced Audio-Visual Inc, pg 777

MISSOURI
Show-Me Audio-Visual, pg 1009

NEVADA
GES Audio Visual, pg 877

NEW JERSEY
Audio Visual Associates, pg 795
Giant Audio Visual Inc, pg 878
Starlite Productions, pg 1024

NEW YORK
AV Workshop, pg 797
Design Audio Visual Inc, pg 845
KVL Audio Visual Services Inc, pg 914
TBA Global Events, pg 1032
Technisphere Corp, pg 1034
WorldStage, pg 1070

NORTH DAKOTA
Media Productions, pg 937

PENNSYLVANIA
Advanced AV, pg 777

TENNESSEE
Love Shack Recording Studios, pg 925

TEXAS
Crossroads Audio Inc, pg 840
Lubbock Audio Visual Inc, pg 925

UTAH
Performance Audio, pg 973

VIRGINIA
American AV, pg 783

WYOMING
Bridger Productions Inc, pg 812

ALBERTA

Unique Communications Ltd, pg 1048

BRITISH COLUMBIA

Commercial Electronics Ltd, pg 832
Triad Communications Ltd, pg 1044

MANITOBA

Inland Audio Visual Ltd, pg 898

Continuous Recorder & Player Repairs

CALIFORNIA

Ametron Audio/Video, pg 785
Audio Images Corp, pg 794
McAlister Electronics, pg 935
SSL Industries Inc, pg 1022

FLORIDA

Digital Video Systems Inc, pg 848
Hi-Tech Enterprises Inc, pg 888
Phat Planet Recording Studios, pg 973
Stereo Sales Inc, pg 1024
TAI Audio, pg 1031

GEORGIA

Lighting & Production Equipment Inc, pg 920
Stage Front Presentation Systems, pg 1022

ILLINOIS

Beatty TeleVisual Productions, pg 804
Midwest Digital Corp, pg 942

INDIANA

Sweetwater Sound Inc, pg 1029

IOWA

ECS Inc, pg 856

KENTUCKY

NOR-COM Inc, pg 958

MARYLAND

Strauss Photo Technical Service Inc, pg 1026

MICHIGAN

City Events Group, pg 828
K&R's Recording Studios Inc, pg 908
TeL Systems, pg 1035

NEW JERSEY

Audio Visual Associates, pg 795
Starlite Productions, pg 1024

NEW YORK

Technisphere Corp, pg 1034

OREGON

All Service Musical Electronics Repair, pg 780

TEXAS

Lubbock Audio Visual Inc, pg 925

VIRGINIA

Hoppmann Audio Visual, pg 891
The Whitlock Group, pg 1065

WISCONSIN

Full Compass Systems, pg 874

PUERTO RICO

Bonnin Electronics Inc, pg 810

BRITISH COLUMBIA

Commercial Electronics Ltd, pg 832

MANITOBA

Inland Audio Visual Ltd, pg 898

ONTARIO

Technovision® Interactive Inc, pg 1035

Control System & Equipment Distributors

ARIZONA

EAR Professional Audio/Video, pg 855
Troxell Communications Inc, pg 1045

ARKANSAS

Jay S Stanley & Associates Inc, pg 1023

CALIFORNIA

Ametron Audio/Video, pg 785
Associated Sound, pg 792
Be Media, pg 804
Cibola Systems, pg 826
Delicate Electronics Sales Inc, pg 845
Empire Wholesale Inc, pg 860
FXC Communications, pg 874
GigaSonic, pg 878
Hi-Tech Audio Systems Inc, pg 888
Instructional Materials & Equipment Distributors (I-Med), pg 899
JD Audio Visual Inc, pg 904
Kontron America, pg 913
Media Fabricators Inc, pg 936
Media Vision USA, pg 937
MediaMation Inc, pg 937
MediaPOINTE, pg 938
POP TV, pg 978
Pristine Systems Inc, pg 982
RF Specialties of California Inc, pg 995
Sound Service Co, pg 1017
Southern California Sound Image Inc, pg 1019
Stanislaus Audio Video Inc, pg 1023
Towards 2000 Inc, pg 1043
Videobotics, pg 1056
VMI Inc, pg 1060
VTP Inc, pg 1061

COLORADO

Audio Consultant Services Inc, pg 794
Daylight Productions & Rentals, pg 844

CONNECTICUT

HB Communications Inc, pg 886
The Music People Inc, pg 951
Vista Group International Inc, pg 1059

DELAWARE

Actors Attic, pg 775

FLORIDA

Access Media Group, pg 773
Alcorn McBride Inc, pg 780
Digital Video Systems Inc, pg 848
Harris Corp, pg 885
Hi-Tech Enterprises Inc, pg 888
Midtown Video Inc, pg 942
Photomart Cine-Video Inc, pg 975
Pro Stage Inc, pg 983
Recording Media & Equipment Inc (RM&E), pg 993
Stereo Sales Inc, pg 1024
Technomedia Solutions, pg 1035

GEORGIA

Lighting & Production Equipment Inc, pg 920
Stage Front Presentation Systems, pg 1022

HAWAII

The Audio Visual Co (AVCO), pg 795

ILLINOIS

Quintessence Audio Ltd, pg 989
Sound Vision Inc, pg 1018
Woodside Avenue Music Productions Inc, pg 1069

INDIANA

Sensory Technologies LLC, pg 1006
SHP Electronics, pg 1010
Sweetwater Sound Inc, pg 1029

IOWA

ECS Inc, pg 856

KENTUCKY

Axxis Inc, pg 800
NOR-COM Inc, pg 958

MAINE

Headlight Audio Visual Inc, pg 887

MARYLAND

Bradley Broadcast & Pro Audio, pg 811
Human Circuit, pg 892
Kipp Visual Systems Inc, pg 911

MASSACHUSETTS

Burk Technology Inc, pg 815

MICHIGAN

Ascom Communications Contractors, pg 791
TeL Systems, pg 1035

MINNESOTA

Tierney Brothers Inc, pg 1040

MISSOURI

MIS Technologies, pg 944

NEVADA

Midas Consoles North America, pg 942

NEW HAMPSHIRE

Technet® Systems Group, pg 1033

NEW JERSEY

Alltec Stores, a Vcom IMC Company, pg 782
Audio Visual Associates, pg 795
AV Bluebook, pg 797
Earl Girls Inc, pg 855
National Audio-Visual Supply, pg 952
SLD Lighting, pg 1013
Starlite Productions, pg 1024
Total Video Products Inc, pg 1042
Wired 4 Sound Inc, pg 1068
York Telecom, pg 1072

NEW YORK

ALTEL Systems Inc, pg 783
BMI Supply, pg 810
Colortone Audio Visual, pg 832
Custom Media Environments, pg 841
Group One Ltd, pg 882
Presentation Products Inc, pg 981
Sanako Inc, pg 1002
Visual Word Systems Inc, pg 1060

OHIO

ITA Audio Visual Solutions, pg 902
Smithall Electronics Inc, pg 1014
Tri-State Audio Visual Co, pg 1044

OREGON

Spectrum Systems Design, pg 1021

PENNSYLVANIA

Advanced AV, pg 777
The Lerro Corp, pg 919
Vistacom Inc, pg 1059

RHODE ISLAND

Shanix Inc, pg 1008

TENNESSEE

Advanced Sound, pg 778
Durrell LLC, pg 854
Lowrance Sound Co Inc, pg 925
Technical Support Systems LLC, pg 1034

TEXAS

Crossroads Audio Inc, pg 840
Data Projections Inc, pg 843
Industrial Audio/Video Inc, pg 897
Lubbock Audio Visual Inc, pg 925
Media Management LLC, pg 937
Schoolhouse Audio Visual, pg 1004
Southwest Sound & Electronics Inc, pg 1019
Tarpley Media Systems, pg 1032

UTAH

Performance Audio, pg 973

VIRGINIA

Avitecture Inc, pg 799
Intellidyne LLC, pg 899
Schafer World Communications Corp, pg 1004
The Whitlock Group, pg 1065

AUDIO

Control System & Equipment Distributors (continued)

WASHINGTON

D A Sound, pg 842
Northern Lights & Pro Audio, pg 959
Telect Inc, pg 1036

WISCONSIN

Audio Visual of Milwaukee Inc, pg 795
Full Compass Systems, pg 874
Safe Harbor Computers, pg 1001

PUERTO RICO

Bonnin Electronics Inc, pg 810

ALBERTA

Infosat Communications Inc, pg 898
Matrix Video Communications Corp (MVCC), pg 934
Unique Communications Ltd, pg 1048

BRITISH COLUMBIA

Commercial Electronics Ltd, pg 832

MANITOBA

Advance Pro, pg 777
Inland Audio Visual Ltd, pg 898

ONTARIO

Cinema Stage Inc, pg 827
Sascom Marketing Group Inc, pg 1003
Soundmaster Group, pg 1018
Westbury National Show Systems Ltd, pg 1064

QUEBEC

SC Media Canada, pg 1003

Control System & Equipment Manufacturers

ARIZONA

Adcom LLC, pg 776

CALIFORNIA

ALTINEX Inc, pg 783
Gefen, pg 876
Kontron America, pg 913
Mackenzie Laboratories Inc, pg 927
Media Control Systems LLC, pg 936
QSC Audio Products LLC, pg 988
Renkus-Heinz Inc, pg 994
Simon - Kaloi Engineering, pg 1011
TV Pro Gear, pg 1046
Videobotics, pg 1056
Xantech LLC, pg 1071
Yanchar Design & Consulting Group, pg 1072

COLORADO

Arrakis Systems, pg 790

FLORIDA

Alcorn McBride Inc, pg 780
Compuvideo Sales USA Ltd, pg 834
CTG Audio, pg 840
Z-Systems Audio Engineering, pg 1073

GEORGIA

Register Data Systems, pg 994
Simtrol Inc, pg 1011

IDAHO

Marketron Broadcast Solutions, pg 931

INDIANA

Crown Audio Inc, pg 840

MASSACHUSETTS

Burk Technology Inc, pg 815

MISSISSIPPI

Crest Audio Inc, pg 839

NEW HAMPSHIRE

Russound, pg 1001

NEW JERSEY

Crestron Electronics Inc, pg 839
FSR Inc, pg 873
Starlite Productions, pg 1024

NEW YORK

Norman N Axelrod Associates, pg 800
Harry Joseph & Associates Inc, pg 906
Monroe Electronics Inc, pg 945
Protech Audio Corp, pg 986

OREGON

BIAMP Systems, pg 806

TENNESSEE

Adtec Digital Inc, pg 777
Remote Audio Products, pg 994

UTAH

Vantage/Legrand, pg 1051

VIRGINIA

Avitecture Inc, pg 799

WASHINGTON

AudioControl®, pg 796
Conex Electro-Systems Inc, pg 835
Telect Inc, pg 1036

BRITISH COLUMBIA

Commercial Electronics Ltd, pg 832
Richmond Sound Design Ltd, pg 996

ONTARIO

McCurdy Radio Ltd, pg 935
Soundmaster Group, pg 1018

Control System & Equipment Rentals

ARIZONA

Merestone, pg 938
Video West Inc, pg 1056

CALIFORNIA

Ametron Audio/Video, pg 785
Associated Sound, pg 792
Express Media Inc, pg 864
FXC Communications, pg 874
Hi-Tech Audio Systems Inc, pg 888
JD Audio Visual Inc, pg 904
Lynch Communications, pg 926
McCune Audio-Video-Lighting, pg 935
Media Fabricators Inc, pg 936
Muse Presentation Technologies, pg 950
Sound Service Co, pg 1017
Towards 2000 Inc, pg 1043

DELAWARE

Actors Attic, pg 775

FLORIDA

Image Technical Services, pg 895
Pro Stage Inc, pg 983

GEORGIA

Lighting & Production Equipment Inc, pg 920
Stage Front Presentation Systems, pg 1022

ILLINOIS

On Stage Audio, pg 963
RC Communications, pg 992
Show Department Inc, pg 1009
Woodside Avenue Music Productions Inc, pg 1069

IOWA

ECS Inc, pg 856

KENTUCKY

Audio Visual Techniques Inc, pg 796
NOR-COM Inc, pg 958

MARYLAND

CPR MultiMedia Solutions, pg 837

MASSACHUSETTS

AVFX Inc, pg 798
massAV, pg 933
Preston Productions Inc, pg 981

MICHIGAN

K&R All Media Productions Inc, pg 908

MISSOURI

Show-Me Audio-Visual, pg 1009

NEVADA

GES Audio Visual, pg 877

NEW JERSEY

Earl Girls Inc, pg 855
PLS Staging, pg 977
SLD Lighting, pg 1013
Starlite Productions, pg 1024

NEW YORK

Custom Media Environments, pg 841
See Factor Industry Inc, pg 1006
TBA Global Events, pg 1032

NORTH CAROLINA

A&V Company, pg 772
AV Metro Inc, pg 797

OHIO

ITA Audio Visual Solutions, pg 902
Lyon Video Inc, pg 927

TENNESSEE

Technical Support Systems LLC, pg 1034

TEXAS

Crossroads Audio Inc, pg 840
Data Display Audio Visual Co LP, pg 843
Lubbock Audio Visual Inc, pg 925
The Samuels Co, pg 1002

UTAH

Performance Audio, pg 973

VIRGINIA

American AV, pg 783
Schafer World Communications Corp, pg 1004

WASHINGTON

D A Sound, pg 842
Northern Lights & Pro Audio, pg 959

WISCONSIN

Full Compass Systems, pg 874

ALBERTA

Unique Communications Ltd, pg 1048

BRITISH COLUMBIA

Commercial Electronics Ltd, pg 832

MANITOBA

Inland Audio Visual Ltd, pg 898

ONTARIO

Westbury National Show Systems Ltd, pg 1064

Control System & Equipment Repairs

CALIFORNIA

Ametron Audio/Video, pg 785
Audio Images Corp, pg 794
Diemer Amp & Keyboard Repair, pg 846
McAlister Electronics, pg 935
Sound Service Co, pg 1017
Towards 2000 Inc, pg 1043

CONNECTICUT

HB Communications Inc, pg 886

FLORIDA

Hi-Tech Enterprises Inc, pg 888
Midtown Video Inc, pg 942

Co-Production Services

AUDIO

Co-Production Services (continued)

MASSACHUSETTS

Capron Lighting & Sound Co Inc, pg 819
Emergency Film Group, pg 860
Green Mountain Post Films (GMP), pg 882
Labrecque Creative Sound, pg 915
M Works Mastering Studios, pg 927
Monadnock Media Inc, pg 945
PixMix Video Services, pg 976
Professional Audio Design Inc, pg 985
Shambhala Publications, pg 1008
Soundtrack Recording Studios, pg 1018

MICHIGAN

Audio Graphic Services, pg 794
Brilliance Audio, pg 812
Digi Sign Design LLC, pg 847
GMP Music, pg 879
K&R's Recording Studios Inc, pg 908
MessageMakers, pg 939
Michigan Recording Arts Institute & Technologies, pg 941
On Stage Visuals, pg 963
Studio A Recording Inc, pg 1026

MINNESOTA

Aggressive Records Audio Duplication LLC, pg 778
Jamieson & Associates Inc, pg 904
Winterland Studios, pg 1068

MISSOURI

Communitronics Corp, pg 833
Hardcastle Films & Video, pg 885
Production Consultants, pg 984
Visionworks Design Services Inc, pg 1059

MONTANA

North Country Media Group, pg 959

NEVADA

Encore Productions Inc, pg 861
Lefco Video Services Inc, pg 918
Stage America LLC, pg 1022

NEW HAMPSHIRE

Apertura, pg 788
Captain Fiddle Music & Publications, pg 820
Chip Taylor Communications LLC, pg 1032

NEW JERSEY

CFP Video Productions Inc, pg 823
Color Leasing Studios, pg 831
Euro-Pacific Film & Video Productions Inc, pg 863
Hogpenny Studios, pg 890
Jeep Jazz Media Solutions, pg 905
Laurel Video Productions, pg 916
Milgrom Productions, pg 943
Optisonics Productions, pg 965
Outside The Box Interactive LLC, pg 966
Starlite Productions, pg 1024
Suede Interactive, pg 1027
VCSvideo, pg 1052

NEW MEXICO

Production Outfitters, pg 984
Quickbeam Systems Inc (QSI), pg 989

NEW YORK

A&E Home Video, pg 771
Aura Sonic Ltd, pg 796
Aural Gratification Inc, pg 796
aurora productions, pg 797
The Big House Group, pg 807
De Nonno Productions Inc (DPI), pg 844
Educational Images Ltd, pg 857
4-D Creative Media, pg 871
A Gentle Wind, pg 877
Granny Press LLC, pg 881
Gurrilla Video Solutions, pg 883
HB-Content, pg 886
Heavy Melody, pg 887
Hello World Communications, pg 888
IAI Video, pg 893
Icontent, pg 893
L&P Media, pg 915
Lylofilm Productions, pg 926
Manhattan Center Studios Inc, pg 930
Neal Marshad Productions, pg 931
Mother West, pg 947
MRG Productions Inc, pg 948
No Soap Productions, pg 957
Now Hear This, pg 960
NSR Productions Inc & Capricorn Five Films, pg 960
SISU Home Entertainment Inc, pg 1012
Synaptic Digital, pg 1030
TBA Global Events, pg 1032
Tiki Recording Studios Inc, pg 1040
Visual Technologies Corp, pg 1060
Zelman Studios Ltd, pg 1073

NORTH CAROLINA

Pat Appleson Studios Inc, pg 788
The Communications Group Inc, pg 833
Duke Media Services, pg 853
Horizon Video Productions Inc, pg 891
Image Associates Inc, pg 894
On Location North Carolina, pg 963
Special Event Services, pg 1020

NORTH DAKOTA

Media Productions, pg 937

OHIO

Challenge Productions, pg 823
Cuyahoga Community College Media Center, pg 841
Icom Multimedia, pg 893
Mills James Productions, pg 943
Musicol Recording, pg 951
R&B Communications Inc, pg 991
Vista Color Imaging Inc, pg 1059

OKLAHOMA

PDC Productions, pg 970
University of Oklahoma Academic Media & Digital Services, pg 1050

OREGON

KVAL, pg 914
Rex, pg 995

PENNSYLVANIA

AiH Group Inc, pg 779
American Artist Studio, pg 783
Ivory Productions, pg 903
JPL, pg 906
Production Masters Inc (PMI), pg 984
Ted The Fiddler Music, pg 1035
The Videohouse Inc, pg 1057
WQED-Multimedia, pg 1070

RHODE ISLAND

A&M Productions, pg 771
Sound-FX-Design, pg 1017

SOUTH CAROLINA

DaviSound, pg 843
Venture Media, pg 1052

TENNESSEE

American Blackguard Inc, pg 784
Analog Man Recording Studio, pg 786
Ardent Studios Inc, pg 789
Cupit Music Group, pg 841
Durrell LLC, pg 854
Fricon Entertainment Co Inc, pg 873
Love Shack Recording Studios, pg 925
Marine Geographic, pg 931
Memphis Communications Corp, pg 938
Mr Mark's Used Musical, Stereo & Studio Equipment Store, pg 944
Motion Picture Services, pg 947
Stage Post, pg 1022
Zion Music Group, pg 1074

TEXAS

AMA Nystrom Printing/Finishing, pg 783
Audiomoxie®, pg 796
Biway Media, pg 808
Bright Star Productions Inc, pg 812
Castleview Productions, pg 821
Crossroads Audio Inc, pg 840
Dykeman Associates Inc, pg 854
The Editing Co, pg 857
The Music Bakery, pg 950
Julye Newlin Productions Inc, pg 956
Out of the BLUE Media, pg 966
Romar Learning, pg 999
The Samuels Co, pg 1002
The Sound Lab Inc, pg 1017
Sound Works, pg 1018
Stage Directions, pg 1022
Tecfilms Inc, pg 1033
Texas Heart Institute Visual Communication Services, pg 1037
TopCat Records LLC, pg 1042
Tropikal Productions, pg 1045
The Yesterday USA Radio Networks, pg 1072

UTAH

Performance Audio, pg 973

VERMONT

Parlato Productions, pg 969
University of Vermont, Instructional Television Dept, pg 1050

VIRGINIA

Advance Concepts Inc, pg 777
AudioImage Recording, pg 796
CACI Productions Group, pg 816
CALIBRE, pg 816
CDR Communications Inc, pg 822
Lion Recording Services Inc, pg 922
Metro Productions, pg 939
National Media Services Inc, pg 953

WASHINGTON

Adams Creative & Production Services, pg 775
Jake Barner Studio, pg 803
Inland Audio Visual Co, pg 898
North-by-Northwest Productions, pg 958
Sound Sound/Savage Fruitarian Productions, pg 1017
Victory Studios, pg 1054

WEST VIRGINIA

Sweetsong Productions, pg 1029

WISCONSIN

Audio Visual of Milwaukee Inc, pg 795
Concept Productions Inc, pg 834
5th Floor Recording Co, pg 867
Learning Technology Services, pg 917
Meridian Studios, pg 939
University of Wisconsin-Oshkosh Radio-TV-Film Dept, pg 1050
USAV Group Inc, pg 1050
Video Wisconsin Inc, pg 1056
Watts Communications Inc, pg 1062
Wisconsin Public Television, pg 1068

WYOMING

Bridger Productions Inc, pg 812

MANITOBA

daCapo Productions, pg 842

ONTARIO

ADS Media, pg 777
AMPLUS Productions, pg 786
DebsVoice, pg 844
GAPC (General Assembly Production Centre), pg 875
JFB Communications, pg 905
MCS Recording Studios, pg 936
VO2 Mix Studios, pg 1060
Westbury National Show Systems Ltd, pg 1064

QUEBEC

Trebas Institute, pg 1044

Country Music, *see* Music Libraries—Country

Digital Audiotape—Blank Distributors

ALABAMA

Media Visions Inc, pg 937

ARIZONA

Troxell Communications Inc, pg 1045

CALIFORNIA

Adolph Gasser Inc, pg 776
Ametron Audio/Video, pg 785
Audio Images Corp, pg 794
Big Time Picture Company Inc, pg 807
California Tape Products Inc, pg 817
Diversified Imaging Supply, pg 849
Dan Dugan Sound Design Inc, pg 853
Edgewise Media Inc, pg 856
JD Audio Visual Inc, pg 904
Location Sound Corp, pg 924
Lynch Communications, pg 926
MSE Media Solutions, pg 949
On-Trax Inc, pg 963
Pacific Audio-Visual Enterprises, pg 967
Players Press, pg 977
QRS Software Services, pg 988
Related Visual Inc, pg 994
Sound Service Co, pg 1017
TapeStockOnline.com, pg 1032

COLORADO

Audio Consultant Services Inc, pg 794

CONNECTICUT

Sennheiser Electronic Corp, pg 1006

FLORIDA

Broadcasters General Store Inc, pg 813
Digital Video Systems Inc, pg 848
Harris Corp, pg 885
Media Concepts Inc, pg 936
Photomart Cine-Video Inc, pg 975
Pro Stage Inc, pg 983
Recording Media & Equipment Inc (RM&E), pg 993
Sight & Sound Productions, pg 1010
Stereo Sales Inc, pg 1024
TAI Audio, pg 1031

GEORGIA

Lighting & Production Equipment Inc, pg 920
Stage Front Presentation Systems, pg 1022

HAWAII

The Audio Visual Co (AVCO), pg 795

ILLINOIS

Major Media Inc, pg 929
Major Reproductions Equipment Co, pg 929
Polyline LLC, pg 978
Sound Vision Inc, pg 1018
Woodside Avenue Music Productions Inc, pg 1069

INDIANA

SHP Electronics, pg 1010

IOWA

ECS Inc, pg 856

KENTUCKY

American Recordable Media, pg 785
Barney Miller's Inc, pg 943
NOR-COM Inc, pg 958
Northern Kentucky University, pg 959

MARYLAND

Bradley Broadcast & Pro Audio, pg 811
Human Circuit, pg 892
Kipp Visual Systems Inc, pg 911
RTZ Audio Visual, pg 1000

MASSACHUSETTS

Terry Hanley Audio Systems Inc, pg 884
MALCO Electronics, pg 929
Professional Audio Design Inc, pg 985

MICHIGAN

TeL Systems, pg 1035

MINNESOTA

Aggressive Records Audio Duplication LLC, pg 778

MISSOURI

Audio-VideoGraphics Inc, pg 795
Modern Communications Inc, pg 944

NEBRASKA

Video Service of America Inc (VSA), pg 1056

NEVADA

JCS Video Productions, pg 904

NEW JERSEY

Argraph Corp, pg 789
AV Bluebook, pg 797
Diversified Systems Inc, pg 849
Hamilton Buhl, pg 884
National Audio-Visual Supply, pg 952
Onkyo USA Corp, pg 963
Panasonic Consumer Electronics Co, pg 968
Starlite Productions, pg 1024
Total Media, pg 1042
Turner Engineering Inc, pg 1046
York Telecom, pg 1072

NEW YORK

Aura Sonic Ltd, pg 796
B&H Photo & Video Pro Audio, pg 802
Burlington A/V Recording Media, pg 815
Colortone Audio Visual, pg 832
Design Audio Visual Inc, pg 845
Eastco Multimedia Solutions Inc, pg 856
HAVE Inc, pg 886
Markertek Video Supply, pg 931
Moviola, pg 948
NorthCountry Distributors, pg 959
RNJ Electronics, pg 997
TecNec Distributing, pg 1035

NORTH CAROLINA

Duke Media Services, pg 853

OHIO

ITA Audio Visual Solutions, pg 902
The Little Warehouse Inc, pg 923
Lyon Video Inc, pg 927
Jimmy Rea Electronics Inc, pg 992

OREGON

SuperDigital Ltd, pg 1029

PENNSYLVANIA

Advanced AV, pg 777
Grise Audio Visual Center Inc, pg 882
The Lerro Corp, pg 919

TENNESSEE

Lowrance Sound Co Inc, pg 925
Trew Audio Inc, pg 1044

TEXAS

Heffernan Audio Visual, pg 887
Lubbock Audio Visual Inc, pg 925
RF Specialties of Texas LLC, pg 996

UTAH

Performance Audio, pg 973

VIRGINIA

Filmdex Inc, pg 867
Hoppmann Audio Visual, pg 891
Lee Hartman & Sons Inc, pg 918
The Whitlock Group, pg 1065

WISCONSIN

Camera Corner Connecting Point, pg 818
Full Compass Systems, pg 874

PUERTO RICO

Bonnin Electronics Inc, pg 810

BRITISH COLUMBIA

Commercial Electronics Ltd, pg 832
Finale Editworks, pg 868
Triad Communications Ltd, pg 1044

MANITOBA

Advance Pro, pg 777
Evolution Presentation Technologies, pg 863
Inland Audio Visual Ltd, pg 898

ONTARIO

Westbury National Show Systems Ltd, pg 1064

Digital Audiotape—Blank Manufacturers

CALIFORNIA

Bridge Publications Inc, pg 812
Panasonic Broadcast & Digital Systems Co, pg 968
Players Press, pg 977
QRS Software Services, pg 988

ILLINOIS

Woodside Avenue Music Productions Inc, pg 1069

NEW JERSEY

Onkyo USA Corp, pg 963

Digital Disc Recorder & Player Distributors

ARIZONA

Allusion Studios & Pure Wave Audio, pg 782
EAR Professional Audio/Video, pg 855
Troxell Communications Inc, pg 1045

CALIFORNIA

Ametron Audio/Video, pg 785
Associated Sound, pg 792
Audio Images Corp, pg 794
Be Media, pg 804
Cibola Systems, pg 826
Educational Technology Services (ETS), pg 857
Empire Wholesale Inc, pg 860
FXC Communications, pg 874
Instructional Materials & Equipment Distributors (I-Med), pg 899
JD Audio Visual Inc, pg 904
Location Sound Corp, pg 924
MediaPOINTE, pg 938
RF Specialties of California Inc, pg 995
SNAP, pg 1014
Sound Service Co, pg 1017
Southern California Sound Image Inc, pg 1019
Stanislaus Audio Video Inc, pg 1023
SuperVision, pg 1029
Towards 2000 Inc, pg 1043
VMI Inc, pg 1060
VTP Inc, pg 1061

COLORADO

Audio Consultant Services Inc, pg 794

CONNECTICUT

Connecticut Audio & Theatrical Supply, pg 835
HB Communications Inc, pg 886
The Music People Inc, pg 951
Vista Group International Inc, pg 1059

DELAWARE

Actors Attic, pg 775

FLORIDA

Access Media Group, pg 773
BAI Distributors Inc, pg 801
Broadcasters General Store Inc, pg 813
CD ROM™ Inc, pg 822
Digital Video Systems Inc, pg 848
Harris Corp, pg 885
Hi-Tech Enterprises Inc, pg 888
Media Concepts Inc, pg 936
Midtown Video Inc, pg 942
Pro Stage Inc, pg 983
Recording Media & Equipment Inc (RM&E), pg 993
Sight & Sound Productions, pg 1010
Stereo Sales Inc, pg 1024
TAI Audio, pg 1031
Technomedia Solutions, pg 1035

AUDIO

Digital Disc Recorder & Player Distributors (continued)

GEORGIA

Clark, pg 829
Lighting & Production Equipment Inc, pg 920
Stage Front Presentation Systems, pg 1022

ILLINOIS

Joseph Electronics, pg 906
Woodside Avenue Music Productions Inc, pg 1069

INDIANA

Sensory Technologies LLC, pg 1006
SHP Electronics, pg 1010
Sweetwater Sound Inc, pg 1029

IOWA

ECS Inc, pg 856

KENTUCKY

Axxis Inc, pg 800
Barney Miller's Inc, pg 943
NOR-COM Inc, pg 958

MARYLAND

Bradley Broadcast & Pro Audio, pg 811
Cardinal Sound & Video, pg 820
Kipp Visual Systems Inc, pg 911

MASSACHUSETTS

Avid Technology Inc, pg 799
Hunt's Photo, Video & Digital, pg 892
Professional Audio Design Inc, pg 985
Rule Broadcast Systems, pg 1000

MICHIGAN

Ascom Communications Contractors, pg 791
TeL Systems, pg 1035

MINNESOTA

Aggressive Records Audio Duplication LLC, pg 778
Alpha Video & Audio Inc, pg 782

MISSISSIPPI

Bowie Audio Visual Enterprises Inc, pg 811

MISSOURI

Conference Technologies Inc, pg 835
Modern Communications Inc, pg 944
Schiller's Audio-Visual, pg 1004

NEVADA

JCS Video Productions, pg 904

NEW HAMPSHIRE

APS Lighting-Sound-AV, pg 789
Technet® Systems Group, pg 1033

NEW JERSEY

Diversified Systems Inc, pg 849
Earl Girls Inc, pg 855
Hamilton Buhl, pg 884
National Audio-Visual Supply, pg 952
Onkyo USA Corp, pg 963
Starlite Productions, pg 1024
SYMCO Inc, pg 1030
York Telecom, pg 1072

NEW YORK

Cadence Jazz Records, pg 816
Colortone Audio Visual, pg 832
Custom Media Environments, pg 841
Design Audio Visual Inc, pg 845
Eastco Multimedia Solutions Inc, pg 856
HAVE Inc, pg 886
Hot House Professional Audio, pg 891
Image Management Systems Inc, pg 895
Korg USA Inc, pg 913
KVL Audio Visual Services Inc, pg 914
NorthCountry Distributors, pg 959
TecNec Distributing, pg 1035
Toys From The Attic, pg 1043

OHIO

ITA Audio Visual Solutions, pg 902
The Little Warehouse Inc, pg 923
Jimmy Rea Electronics Inc, pg 992
Tri-State Audio Visual Co, pg 1044

OREGON

SuperDigital Ltd, pg 1029

PENNSYLVANIA

Advanced AV, pg 777
Bernie's Photo Center, pg 805
J E Foss Co, pg 871
The Lerro Corp, pg 919

RHODE ISLAND

Akai Professional, pg 779

TENNESSEE

Advanced Sound, pg 778
Durrell LLC, pg 854
Lowrance Sound Co Inc, pg 925
Technical Support Systems LLC, pg 1034
Trew Audio Inc, pg 1044
Zion Music Group, pg 1074

TEXAS

Crossroads Audio Inc, pg 840
Data Projections Inc, pg 843
Lubbock Audio Visual Inc, pg 925
RadioShack Corp, pg 990
Replicopy Digital Media Center, pg 995
RF Specialties of Texas LLC, pg 996
Tarpley Media Systems, pg 1032

UTAH

Performance Audio, pg 973

VIRGINIA

Filmdex Inc, pg 867
Hoppmann Audio Visual, pg 891
Intellidyne LLC, pg 899
Lee Hartman & Sons Inc, pg 918
The Whitlock Group, pg 1065

WISCONSIN

Audio Visual of Milwaukee Inc, pg 795
Full Compass Systems, pg 874

PUERTO RICO

Bonnin Electronics Inc, pg 810

ALBERTA

Matrix Video Communications Corp (MVCC), pg 934

BRITISH COLUMBIA

Commercial Electronics Ltd, pg 832

MANITOBA

Advance Pro, pg 777
Inland Audio Visual Ltd, pg 898

ONTARIO

Westbury National Show Systems Ltd, pg 1064

Digital Disc Recorder & Player Manufacturers

ARIZONA

Applied Integration Corp, pg 789

CALIFORNIA

Doremi Labs, pg 851
Mackenzie Laboratories Inc, pg 927
Newdoll Enterprises LLC, pg 956
Panasonic Broadcast & Digital Systems Co, pg 968
TASCAM, pg 1032
360 Systems, pg 1039

COLORADO

Arrakis Systems, pg 790

FLORIDA

Alcorn McBride Inc, pg 780
CD ROM™ Inc, pg 822

ILLINOIS

Superscope Technologies Inc, pg 1029

MASSACHUSETTS

Avid Technology Inc, pg 799

MICHIGAN

ENCO Systems Inc, pg 860

NEW JERSEY

Onkyo USA Corp, pg 963

NEW YORK

Laird Digital Cinema, pg 915

RHODE ISLAND

Akai Professional, pg 779
M-Audio, pg 927

TENNESSEE

Adtec Digital Inc, pg 777

VIRGINIA

Schafer World Communications Corp, pg 1004

BRITISH COLUMBIA

Creation Technologies Inc, pg 838

ONTARIO

McCurdy Radio Ltd, pg 935

Digital Disc Recorder & Player Rentals

ARIZONA

Merestone, pg 938
Video West Inc, pg 1056

CALIFORNIA

Absolute Rentals, pg 772
Advanced Media LLC, pg 778
Alliant Event Services, pg 781
Ametron Audio/Video, pg 785
Associated Sound, pg 792
ATV Video Center Inc, pg 793
Audio Rents, pg 794
AV Guys, pg 797
Big Time Picture Company Inc, pg 807
Design FX Audio, pg 845
Express Media Inc, pg 864
Hollywood Sound Systems, pg 890
JD Audio Visual Inc, pg 904
Location Sound Corp, pg 924
Lynch Communications, pg 926
Maximus Media Inc, pg 934
McCune Audio-Video-Lighting, pg 935
PSAV® Presentation Services, pg 986
Alwin Sauers Audio Productions (ASAP), pg 1003
Sound Service Co, pg 1017
Synthesizer Rental Service, pg 1030
Towards 2000 Inc, pg 1043
VMI Inc, pg 1060

COLORADO

Audio Consultant Services Inc, pg 794
Spectrum Audio Visual Services, pg 1020

CONNECTICUT

A/V Davey, pg 797

FLORIDA

Accord Productions, pg 773
Phat Planet Recording Studios, pg 973
Pro Stage Inc, pg 983
Sight & Sound Productions, pg 1010
TAI Audio, pg 1031
Universal Studios Florida® Production Group, pg 1049

GEORGIA

Lighting & Production Equipment Inc, pg 920
Stage Front Presentation Systems, pg 1022

HAWAII

Audio Resource Honolulu, pg 794

ILLINOIS

Backstar Creative Media Inc, pg 801
Creative Technology, pg 838
On Stage Audio, pg 963
RC Communications, pg 992
Show Department Inc, pg 1009
Woodside Avenue Music Productions Inc, pg 1069

IOWA

ECS Inc, pg 856

KENTUCKY

Audio Visual Techniques Inc, pg 796

MARYLAND

CPR MultiMedia Solutions, pg 837
Event Tech, pg 863
Maryland Sound International Holding Co LLC, pg 933

MASSACHUSETTS

Preston Productions Inc, pg 981

MICHIGAN

K&R All Media Productions Inc, pg 908

MINNESOTA

Alpha Video & Audio Inc, pg 782

MISSISSIPPI

Bowie Audio Visual Enterprises Inc, pg 811

MISSOURI

Show-Me Audio-Visual, pg 1009

NEVADA

GES Audio Visual, pg 877

NEW HAMPSHIRE

APS Lighting-Sound-AV, pg 789

NEW JERSEY

Earl Girls Inc, pg 855
Moe AV LLC, pg 945
PLS Staging, pg 977
Starlite Productions, pg 1024

NEW YORK

CP Communications, pg 837
Design Audio Visual Inc, pg 845
Dreamhire LLC, pg 852
KVL Audio Visual Services Inc, pg 914

NORTH CAROLINA

Take One Productions Ltd, pg 1031

OHIO

Lyon Video Inc, pg 927
R&B Communications Inc, pg 991

PENNSYLVANIA

FMP Media Solutions Inc, pg 870
JPL, pg 906

TENNESSEE

Love Shack Recording Studios, pg 925
Technical Support Systems LLC, pg 1034

TEXAS

Alford Media Services, pg 780
Crossroads Audio Inc, pg 840
The Samuels Co, pg 1002
Stage Directions, pg 1022

UTAH

Performance Audio, pg 973

VERMONT

Parlato Productions, pg 969

VIRGINIA

Audio Visual Actions Inc (AVA), pg 795
Schafer World Communications Corp, pg 1004

WISCONSIN

Full Compass Systems, pg 874

PUERTO RICO

Stage Crew Audiovisual Inc, pg 1022

MANITOBA

Inland Audio Visual Ltd, pg 898

ONTARIO

Westbury National Show Systems Ltd, pg 1064

Digital Disc Recorder & Player Repairs

CALIFORNIA

Advanced Media LLC, pg 778
Ametron Audio/Video, pg 785
Audio Images Corp, pg 794
McAlister Electronics, pg 935
Sound Service Co, pg 1017
Towards 2000 Inc, pg 1043

CONNECTICUT

A/V Davey, pg 797

FLORIDA

Digital Video Systems Inc, pg 848
Hi-Tech Enterprises Inc, pg 888
Stereo Sales Inc, pg 1024
TAI Audio, pg 1031

GEORGIA

Lighting & Production Equipment Inc, pg 920
Stage Front Presentation Systems, pg 1022

ILLINOIS

Midwest Digital Corp, pg 942

INDIANA

Sweetwater Sound Inc, pg 1029

IOWA

ECS Inc, pg 856

KENTUCKY

Axxis Inc, pg 800
Barney Miller's Inc, pg 943
NOR-COM Inc, pg 958

MASSACHUSETTS

Professional Audio Design Inc, pg 985

MICHIGAN

K&R's Recording Studios Inc, pg 908
TeL Systems, pg 1035

MINNESOTA

Aggressive Records Audio Duplication LLC, pg 778

NEW JERSEY

Earl Girls Inc, pg 855
Starlite Productions, pg 1024

NEW YORK

Toys From The Attic, pg 1043

OHIO

Tri-State Audio Visual Co, pg 1044

OREGON

All Service Musical Electronics Repair, pg 780

TENNESSEE

Technical Support Systems LLC, pg 1034

VIRGINIA

Hoppmann Audio Visual, pg 891
Schafer World Communications Corp, pg 1004

WISCONSIN

Full Compass Systems, pg 874

PUERTO RICO

Bonnin Electronics Inc, pg 810

MANITOBA

Inland Audio Visual Ltd, pg 898

ONTARIO

Westbury National Show Systems Ltd, pg 1064

Digital Editor Distributors

ARIZONA

EAR Professional Audio/Video, pg 855
Troxell Communications Inc, pg 1045

CALIFORNIA

Addlogix, pg 776
ADS Technologies, pg 777
Ametron Audio/Video, pg 785
Audio Images Corp, pg 794
Bitcentral Inc, pg 808
FXC Communications, pg 874
MediaPOINTE, pg 938
Pristine Systems Inc, pg 982
RF Specialties of California Inc, pg 995
Southern California Sound Image Inc, pg 1019
VMI Inc, pg 1060
VTP Inc, pg 1061

COLORADO

Audio Consultant Services Inc, pg 794
Spectrum Audio Visual Services, pg 1020

CONNECTICUT

HB Communications Inc, pg 886

DELAWARE

Actors Attic, pg 775

FLORIDA

Access Media Group, pg 773
AVI-SPL, pg 798
Digital Video Systems Inc, pg 848
Harris Corp, pg 885
Hi-Tech Enterprises Inc, pg 888
Pro Stage Inc, pg 983
Recording Media & Equipment Inc (RM&E), pg 993
Sight & Sound Productions, pg 1010
TAI Audio, pg 1031

GEORGIA

Clark, pg 829
Stage Front Presentation Systems, pg 1022

ILLINOIS

Woodside Avenue Music Productions Inc, pg 1069

INDIANA

Heart Breaker Entertainment LLC, pg 887
Sensory Technologies LLC, pg 1006
Sweetwater Sound Inc, pg 1029

IOWA

ECS Inc, pg 856

KENTUCKY

Axxis Inc, pg 800
NOR-COM Inc, pg 958
Northern Kentucky University, pg 959

MAINE

Headlight Audio Visual Inc, pg 887
Independent Audio Inc, pg 897

MARYLAND

Bradley Broadcast & Pro Audio, pg 811
Human Circuit, pg 892
Noventri, pg 960

MASSACHUSETTS

Avid Technology Inc, pg 799
Rule Broadcast Systems, pg 1000

MICHIGAN

Digi Sign Design LLC, pg 847
TeL Systems, pg 1035

AUDIO

Digital Editor Distributors (continued)

MINNESOTA

Alpha Video & Audio Inc, pg 782
Microboards Technology LLC, pg 941

NEVADA

JCS Video Productions, pg 904

NEW JERSEY

Diversified Systems Inc, pg 849
Hamilton Buhl, pg 884
SADiE Inc, pg 1001
Starlite Productions, pg 1024
Total Video Products Inc, pg 1042
York Telecom, pg 1072

NEW YORK

Custom Media Environments, pg 841
Sanako Inc, pg 1002

OHIO

ITA Audio Visual Solutions, pg 902
Jimmy Rea Electronics Inc, pg 992

OREGON

SuperDigital Ltd, pg 1029

PENNSYLVANIA

Advanced AV, pg 777
The Lerro Corp, pg 919
Vistacom Inc, pg 1059

RHODE ISLAND

Akai Professional, pg 779

TENNESSEE

Lowrance Sound Co Inc, pg 925
Zion Music Group, pg 1074

TEXAS

Lubbock Audio Visual Inc, pg 925
Pro Video & Film Equipment Co Inc, pg 983
RF Specialties of Texas LLC, pg 996
Tarpley Media Systems, pg 1032

UTAH

Performance Audio, pg 973

VIRGINIA

Avitecture Inc, pg 799
Lee Hartman & Sons Inc, pg 918
Rocktown Media, pg 998
Schafer World Communications Corp, pg 1004
The Whitlock Group, pg 1065

WASHINGTON

CCI Solutions, pg 821

WISCONSIN

Audio Visual of Milwaukee Inc, pg 795
Full Compass Systems, pg 874
Safe Harbor Computers, pg 1001

PUERTO RICO

Bonnin Electronics Inc, pg 810

BRITISH COLUMBIA

Commercial Electronics Ltd, pg 832

MANITOBA

Advance Pro, pg 777
Inland Audio Visual Ltd, pg 898

ONTARIO

Sascom Marketing Group Inc, pg 1003
Soundmaster Group, pg 1018

QUEBEC

JAM Industries Ltd, pg 903

Digital Editor Manufacturers

CALIFORNIA

ADS Technologies, pg 777
Grande Vitesse Systems Inc (GVS), pg 881
360 Systems, pg 1039

COLORADO

Arrakis Systems, pg 790

GEORGIA

Outsource Engineering & Manufacturing Inc dba Texscan MSI, pg 966

KANSAS

GlobalStreams™ Corp, pg 879

MASSACHUSETTS

Avid Technology Inc, pg 799

NEW JERSEY

SADiE Inc, pg 1001

NEW YORK

Dalet Digital Media Systems, pg 842
Laird Digital Cinema, pg 915
Voyetra Turtle Beach, pg 1061

RHODE ISLAND

Akai Professional, pg 779

TENNESSEE

Adtec Digital Inc, pg 777

VIRGINIA

Schafer World Communications Corp, pg 1004

BRITISH COLUMBIA

Creation Technologies Inc, pg 838

ONTARIO

Soundmaster Group, pg 1018

Digital Editor Rentals

ARIZONA

Merestone, pg 938

CALIFORNIA

Absolute Rentals, pg 772
Ametron Audio/Video, pg 785
Artichoke Productions, pg 791
Audio Rents, pg 794
Bexel Corp, pg 806
Express Media Inc, pg 864
Lynch Communications, pg 926
On-Trax Inc, pg 963
Reality Check Systems, pg 992
Synthesizer Rental Service, pg 1030
Synthesizer Systems Technologies (SST), pg 1030
VMI Inc, pg 1060

COLORADO

Audio Consultant Services Inc, pg 794

DELAWARE

Side Door Studio Inc, pg 1010

FLORIDA

Pro Stage Inc, pg 983
Sight & Sound Productions, pg 1010
Universal Studios Florida® Production Group, pg 1049

GEORGIA

Stage Front Presentation Systems, pg 1022

HAWAII

Audio Resource Honolulu, pg 794

ILLINOIS

On Stage Audio, pg 963
QuickSet International Inc, pg 989
Show Department Inc, pg 1009
Woodside Avenue Music Productions Inc, pg 1069

INDIANA

Heart Breaker Entertainment LLC, pg 887

IOWA

ECS Inc, pg 856

MARYLAND

Kramer Communications Video Production, pg 913
Maryland Sound International Holding Co LLC, pg 933

MASSACHUSETTS

Preston Productions Inc, pg 981

MICHIGAN

Digi Sign Design LLC, pg 847
K&R All Media Productions Inc, pg 908

MISSOURI

Show-Me Audio-Visual, pg 1009

MONTANA

Jereco Studios Inc, pg 905

NEW JERSEY

CFP Video Productions Inc, pg 823
Jeep Jazz Media Solutions, pg 905
Starlite Productions, pg 1024

NEW YORK

HB-Content, pg 886

NORTH DAKOTA

Media Productions, pg 937

OHIO

R&B Communications Inc, pg 991

PENNSYLVANIA

The Videohouse Inc, pg 1057

SOUTH CAROLINA

Genesis Creative, pg 877

TENNESSEE

Love Shack Recording Studios, pg 925

TEXAS

Onstage Systems, pg 963
The Samuels Co, pg 1002
Stage Directions, pg 1022

UTAH

Performance Audio, pg 973

WASHINGTON

Victory Studios, pg 1054

WISCONSIN

Full Compass Systems, pg 874

BRITISH COLUMBIA

Video In Studios/Video Out Distribution, pg 1055

MANITOBA

Inland Audio Visual Ltd, pg 898

Digital Editor Repairs

CALIFORNIA

Ametron Audio/Video, pg 785
Audio Images Corp, pg 794
Diemer Amp & Keyboard Repair, pg 846
McAlister Electronics, pg 935

CONNECTICUT

HB Communications Inc, pg 886

FLORIDA

Hi-Tech Enterprises Inc, pg 888

GEORGIA

Stage Front Presentation Systems, pg 1022

ILLINOIS

Midwest Digital Corp, pg 942

INDIANA

Sweetwater Sound Inc, pg 1029

IOWA

ECS Inc, pg 856

KENTUCKY

Axxis Inc, pg 800
NOR-COM Inc, pg 958

MICHIGAN

K&R's Recording Studios Inc, pg 908
TeL Systems, pg 1035

MINNESOTA

Microboards Technology LLC, pg 941

NEW JERSEY

Starlite Productions, pg 1024

TEXAS

Pro Video & Film Equipment Co Inc, pg 983

WISCONSIN

Full Compass Systems, pg 874

MANITOBA

Inland Audio Visual Ltd, pg 898

Digital Mixer Distributors

ARIZONA

EAR Professional Audio/Video, pg 855
Troxell Communications Inc, pg 1045

CALIFORNIA

Adolph Gasser Inc, pg 776
Ametron Audio/Video, pg 785
Associated Sound, pg 792
Audio Images Corp, pg 794
Delicate Electronics Sales Inc, pg 845
Empire Wholesale Inc, pg 860
FXC Communications, pg 874
Hi-Tech Audio Systems Inc, pg 888
Location Sound Corp, pg 924
MediaPOINTE, pg 938
POP TV, pg 978
Promax Systems, pg 986
RF Specialties of California Inc, pg 995
SNAP, pg 1014
Sound Service Co, pg 1017
Southern California Sound Image Inc, pg 1019
TOA Electronics Inc, pg 1041
Videobotics, pg 1056
VMI Inc, pg 1060
VTP Inc, pg 1061

COLORADO

Audio Consultant Services Inc, pg 794
Spectrum Audio Visual Services, pg 1020

CONNECTICUT

Connecticut Audio & Theatrical Supply, pg 835
HB Communications Inc, pg 886
The Music People Inc, pg 951

DELAWARE

Actors Attic, pg 775

FLORIDA

Access Media Group, pg 773
Allstar Audio Systems Inc, pg 782
AVI-SPL, pg 798
Digital Video Systems Inc, pg 848
Griffiths Broadcast Co Inc, pg 882
Harris Corp, pg 885
Hi-Tech Enterprises Inc, pg 888
Lighting Sales Connections, pg 920
Media Concepts Inc, pg 936
Pro Stage Inc, pg 983
Recording Media & Equipment Inc (RM&E), pg 993
Sight & Sound Productions, pg 1010
TAI Audio, pg 1031

GEORGIA

Clark, pg 829
Lighting & Production Equipment Inc, pg 920
Stage Front Presentation Systems, pg 1022

ILLINOIS

Quintessence Audio Ltd, pg 989

INDIANA

Heart Breaker Entertainment LLC, pg 887
Sensory Technologies LLC, pg 1006
SHP Electronics, pg 1010
Sweetwater Sound Inc, pg 1029

IOWA

ECS Inc, pg 856

KENTUCKY

Axxis Inc, pg 800
NOR-COM Inc, pg 958

LOUISIANA

Intermedia Technologies, pg 900

MAINE

Headlight Audio Visual Inc, pg 887
Independent Audio Inc, pg 897

MARYLAND

Bradley Broadcast & Pro Audio, pg 811
Human Circuit, pg 892
Kipp Visual Systems Inc, pg 911
Noventri, pg 960

MASSACHUSETTS

Professional Audio Design Inc, pg 985
Rule Broadcast Systems, pg 1000

MICHIGAN

Ascom Communications Contractors, pg 791
Digi Sign Design LLC, pg 847
TeL Systems, pg 1035

MINNESOTA

Alpha Video & Audio Inc, pg 782

MISSOURI

Modern Communications Inc, pg 944
Schiller's Audio-Visual, pg 1004

NEBRASKA

Video Service of America Inc (VSA), pg 1056

NEW HAMPSHIRE

Technet® Systems Group, pg 1033

NEW JERSEY

Alltec Stores, a Vcom IMC Company, pg 782
Audio Visual Associates, pg 795
Diversified Systems Inc, pg 849
Hamilton Buhl, pg 884
Starlite Productions, pg 1024
Total Video Products Inc, pg 1042
York Telecom, pg 1072

NEW YORK

Albany Theatre Supply Co Inc, pg 780
ALTEL Systems Inc, pg 783
Aura Sonic Ltd, pg 796
Custom Media Environments, pg 841
Design Audio Visual Inc, pg 845
HAVE Inc, pg 886
Hot House Professional Audio, pg 891
Indigo Productions, pg 897
Posthorn Recordings, pg 979
TecNec Distributing, pg 1035

OHIO

ITA Audio Visual Solutions, pg 902
Parts Express, pg 969
Jimmy Rea Electronics Inc, pg 992

OREGON

SuperDigital Ltd, pg 1029

PENNSYLVANIA

Advanced AV, pg 777
The Lerro Corp, pg 919
Vistacom Inc, pg 1059

RHODE ISLAND

Shanix Inc, pg 1008

TENNESSEE

Durrell LLC, pg 854
Lowrance Sound Co Inc, pg 925
Mr Mark's Used Musical, Stereo & Studio Equipment Store, pg 944
Technical Support Systems LLC, pg 1034
Trew Audio Inc, pg 1044
Zion Music Group, pg 1074

TEXAS

Crossroads Audio Inc, pg 840
Industrial Audio/Video Inc, pg 897
Lubbock Audio Visual Inc, pg 925
Pro Video & Film Equipment Co Inc, pg 983
RF Specialties of Texas LLC, pg 996
Tarpley Media Systems, pg 1032

UTAH

Performance Audio, pg 973

VIRGINIA

Avitecture Inc, pg 799
Intellidyne LLC, pg 899
Lee Hartman & Sons Inc, pg 918
Rocktown Media, pg 998
The Whitlock Group, pg 1065

WASHINGTON

CCI Solutions, pg 821
Pacific Northwest Theatre Associates Inc (PNTA), pg 967

WISCONSIN

Audio Visual of Milwaukee Inc, pg 795
Full Compass Systems, pg 874
Safe Harbor Computers, pg 1001

PUERTO RICO

Bonnin Electronics Inc, pg 810

BRITISH COLUMBIA

Commercial Electronics Ltd, pg 832

MANITOBA

Advance Pro, pg 777
Inland Audio Visual Ltd, pg 898

ONTARIO

Cinema Stage Inc, pg 827
HD Source, pg 886
Westbury National Show Systems Ltd, pg 1064

QUEBEC

JAM Industries Ltd, pg 903
SC Media Canada, pg 1003

Digital Mixer Manufacturers

CALIFORNIA

Antex Electronics Corp, pg 787
Graham-Patten, pg 881
Opticomm-EMCORE, pg 964
Panasonic Broadcast & Digital Systems Co, pg 968
Roland Corp US, pg 998
Soundcraft USA, pg 1018
TASCAM, pg 1032
TOA Electronics Inc, pg 1041

CONNECTICUT

Sound Control Technologies Inc, pg 1017
Titus Technological Laboratories (TTL), pg 1041

NEW JERSEY

Bogen Communications Inc, pg 810
Sony Pro Audio (Broadcast & Professional Systems Division), pg 1016

NEW YORK

Harbro Corp, pg 884

NORTH CAROLINA

Audioarts Engineering, pg 796
Wheatstone Corp, pg 1065

PENNSYLVANIA

Aviom Inc, pg 799

TENNESSEE

Harrison Consoles, pg 885

TEXAS

Logitek Electronic Systems Inc, pg 924

BRITISH COLUMBIA

Richmond Sound Design Ltd, pg 996

AUDIO

Digital Mixer Rentals

ALABAMA

Audio-Video Resources Inc, pg 795

ARIZONA

Merestone, pg 938
Video West Inc, pg 1056

CALIFORNIA

Absolute Rentals, pg 772
AGF Media Services, pg 778
Ametron Audio/Video, pg 785
Artichoke Productions, pg 791
Associated Sound, pg 792
Audio Rents, pg 794
Bexel Corp, pg 806
Express Media Inc, pg 864
Hi-Tech Audio Systems Inc, pg 888
Location Sound Corp, pg 924
Lynch Communications, pg 926
McCune Audio-Video-Lighting, pg 935
Muse Presentation Technologies, pg 950
On-Trax Inc, pg 963
Synthesizer Systems Technologies (SST), pg 1030
VER-Video Equipment Rentals, pg 1053
Westcoast Video Productions Inc, pg 1064

COLORADO

Audio Consultant Services Inc, pg 794
Multimedia Audio Visual Inc, pg 950
Open Media Foundation, pg 964
Spectrum Audio Visual Services, pg 1020

FLORIDA

Allstar Audio Systems Inc, pg 782
Lighting Sales Connections, pg 920
Pro Stage Inc, pg 983
Sight & Sound Productions, pg 1010
TAI Audio, pg 1031
Universal Studios Florida® Production Group, pg 1049

GEORGIA

ECG Productions, pg 856
Lighting & Production Equipment Inc, pg 920
Stage Front Presentation Systems, pg 1022

ILLINOIS

On Stage Audio, pg 963
QuickSet International Inc, pg 989
RC Communications, pg 992
SCI Television Productions LLC, pg 1004
Show Department Inc, pg 1009

INDIANA

Heart Breaker Entertainment LLC, pg 887

IOWA

ECS Inc, pg 856

KENTUCKY

Audio Visual Techniques Inc, pg 796

MARYLAND

CPR MultiMedia Solutions, pg 837
Event Tech, pg 863
Maryland Sound International Holding Co LLC, pg 933
Visual Aids Electronics Corp, pg 1059

MASSACHUSETTS

Preston Productions Inc, pg 981

MICHIGAN

Digi Sign Design LLC, pg 847
K&R All Media Productions Inc, pg 908

MISSOURI

Show-Me Audio-Visual, pg 1009

MONTANA

Jereco Studios Inc, pg 905

NEW JERSEY

Audio Visual Associates, pg 795
Starlite Productions, pg 1024

NEW YORK

Aura Sonic Ltd, pg 796
CP Communications, pg 837
Dreamhire LLC, pg 852
HB-Content, pg 886
Posthorn Recordings, pg 979

NORTH CAROLINA

A&V Company, pg 772

NORTH DAKOTA

Media Productions, pg 937

OHIO

Production Solutions Inc, pg 984

OKLAHOMA

PDC Productions, pg 970

OREGON

Picture This Production Services, pg 975

PENNSYLVANIA

Advanced AV, pg 777
The Videohouse Inc, pg 1057

TENNESSEE

Love Shack Recording Studios, pg 925
Mr Mark's Used Musical, Stereo & Studio Equipment Store, pg 944
Technical Support Systems LLC, pg 1034

TEXAS

Alford Media Services, pg 780
Bright Star Productions Inc, pg 812
Crossroads Audio Inc, pg 840
Lubbock Audio Visual Inc, pg 925
Music Lab Inc, pg 950
The Samuels Co, pg 1002
Stage Directions, pg 1022

UTAH

Performance Audio, pg 973

VERMONT

Parlato Productions, pg 969

VIRGINIA

American AV, pg 783

WASHINGTON

D A Sound, pg 842
Victory Studios, pg 1054

BRITISH COLUMBIA

Finale Editworks, pg 868
Video In Studios/Video Out Distribution, pg 1055

MANITOBA

Inland Audio Visual Ltd, pg 898

ONTARIO

HD Source, pg 886
Westbury National Show Systems Ltd, pg 1064

Digital Mixer Repairs

CALIFORNIA

Ametron Audio/Video, pg 785
Audio Images Corp, pg 794
Diemer Amp & Keyboard Repair, pg 846
Location Sound Corp, pg 924
McAlister Electronics, pg 935
TOA Electronics Inc, pg 1041

CONNECTICUT

HB Communications Inc, pg 886

FLORIDA

Hi-Tech Enterprises Inc, pg 888
TAI Audio, pg 1031

GEORGIA

Lighting & Production Equipment Inc, pg 920
Stage Front Presentation Systems, pg 1022

ILLINOIS

Midwest Digital Corp, pg 942

INDIANA

Sweetwater Sound Inc, pg 1029

IOWA

ECS Inc, pg 856

KENTUCKY

Axxis Inc, pg 800
NOR-COM Inc, pg 958

MARYLAND

Visual Aids Electronics Corp, pg 1059

MASSACHUSETTS

Professional Audio Design Inc, pg 985

MICHIGAN

K&R's Recording Studios Inc, pg 908
TeL Systems, pg 1035

NEW JERSEY

Starlite Productions, pg 1024

OHIO

ITA Audio Visual Solutions, pg 902

OREGON

All Service Musical Electronics Repair, pg 780

TENNESSEE

Technical Support Systems LLC, pg 1034

TEXAS

Lubbock Audio Visual Inc, pg 925
Pro Video & Film Equipment Co Inc, pg 983

WASHINGTON

Pacific Northwest Theatre Associates Inc (PNTA), pg 967

WISCONSIN

Full Compass Systems, pg 874

MANITOBA

Inland Audio Visual Ltd, pg 898

ONTARIO

Westbury National Show Systems Ltd, pg 1064

QUEBEC

SC Media Canada, pg 1003

Digital Tape Recorder & Player Distributors

ALABAMA

Dogwood Recording Studios, pg 850

ARIZONA

Arizona Cine Equipment, pg 789
EAR Professional Audio/Video, pg 855
Troxell Communications Inc, pg 1045

CALIFORNIA

Advanced Systems Group LLC, pg 778
Ametron Audio/Video, pg 785
Audio Images Corp, pg 794
Audio/Video Supply Inc, pg 795
Delicate Electronics Sales Inc, pg 845
FXC Communications, pg 874
Gluskin's Custom Audio Video, pg 879
GMF Sound Inc, pg 879
Instructional Materials & Equipment Distributors (I-Med), pg 899
JD Audio Visual Inc, pg 904
Location Sound Corp, pg 924
MediaPOINTE, pg 938
Mobilized Tech Systems, pg 944

RF Specialties of California Inc, pg 995
SBS Productions, pg 1003
SNAP, pg 1014
Southern California Sound Image Inc, pg 1019
SSL Industries Inc, pg 1022
Stanislaus Audio Video Inc, pg 1023
TASCAM, pg 1032
Towards 2000 Inc, pg 1043
Videobotics, pg 1056
VMI Inc, pg 1060
VTP Inc, pg 1061

COLORADO

Audio Consultant Services Inc, pg 794
Spectrum Audio Visual Services, pg 1020

CONNECTICUT

Connecticut Audio & Theatrical Supply, pg 835
HB Communications Inc, pg 886
The Music People Inc, pg 951

DELAWARE

Actors Attic, pg 775

FLORIDA

Access Media Group, pg 773
Alcorn McBride Inc, pg 780
Allstar Audio Systems Inc, pg 782
BAI Distributors Inc, pg 801
Broadcasters General Store Inc, pg 813
Digital Video Systems Inc, pg 848
Harris Corp, pg 885
Hi-Tech Enterprises Inc, pg 888
Hi-Tech Import Export Corp, pg 888
Intermark Industries Inc, pg 900
Lighting Sales Connections, pg 920
Media Concepts Inc, pg 936
Midtown Video Inc, pg 942
Photomart Cine-Video Inc, pg 975
Pro Stage Inc, pg 983
Recording Media & Equipment Inc (RM&E), pg 993
Sight & Sound Productions, pg 1010
Stereo Sales Inc, pg 1024
TAI Audio, pg 1031

GEORGIA

Clark, pg 829
Lighting & Production Equipment Inc, pg 920
LT Sound Inc, pg 925
Stage Front Presentation Systems, pg 1022

HAWAII

The Audio Visual Co (AVCO), pg 795

ILLINOIS

Allen Visual Systems Inc, pg 781
C V Lloyde, pg 923
RAM Systems LLC, pg 991
RC Communications, pg 992

INDIANA

Sensory Technologies LLC, pg 1006
SHP Electronics, pg 1010
Sweetwater Sound Inc, pg 1029

IOWA

ECS Inc, pg 856

KANSAS

Smith Audio-Visual Inc, pg 1014

KENTUCKY

Barney Miller's Inc, pg 943
NOR-COM Inc, pg 958
Northern Kentucky University, pg 959

MAINE

Headlight Audio Visual Inc, pg 887
Independent Audio Inc, pg 897

MARYLAND

Bradley Broadcast & Pro Audio, pg 811
Human Circuit, pg 892
Kipp Visual Systems Inc, pg 911
RTZ Audio Visual, pg 1000

MASSACHUSETTS

Avid Technology Inc, pg 799
MALCO Electronics, pg 929
Professional Audio Design Inc, pg 985

MICHIGAN

Ascom Communications Contractors, pg 791
TeL Systems, pg 1035

MINNESOTA

Alpha Video & Audio Inc, pg 782

MISSOURI

Communitronics Corp, pg 833
Modern Communications Inc, pg 944
Schiller's Audio-Visual, pg 1004

NEBRASKA

Video Service of America Inc (VSA), pg 1056

NEW HAMPSHIRE

APS Lighting-Sound-AV, pg 789
Technet® Systems Group, pg 1033

NEW JERSEY

A-V Services Inc, pg 771
Alltec Stores, a Vcom IMC Company, pg 782
Diversified Systems Inc, pg 849
G&G Technologies Inc, pg 875
Hamilton Buhl, pg 884
The Music Place, pg 951
National Audio-Visual Supply, pg 952
Onkyo USA Corp, pg 963
Starlite Productions, pg 1024
Video Corporation of America (VCA), pg 1055
Wilray Audio Visual Corp, pg 1067
Wired 4 Sound Inc, pg 1068
York Telecom, pg 1072

NEW YORK

ALTEL Systems Inc, pg 783
American Video Inc, pg 785
Aura Sonic Ltd, pg 796
AV Workshop, pg 797
Cadence Jazz Records, pg 816
Colortone Audio Visual, pg 832
Custom Media Environments, pg 841
Design Audio Visual Inc, pg 845
HAVE Inc, pg 886
Hot House Professional Audio, pg 891
Long Island Video Enterprises Live Inc, pg 924
Mark Custom Recording Service Inc, pg 931
NorthCountry Distributors, pg 959
Posthorn Recordings, pg 979
RNJ Electronics, pg 997
Technisphere Corp, pg 1034
TecNec Distributing, pg 1035

OHIO

Aztec Video Productions, pg 801
ITA Audio Visual Solutions, pg 902
The Little Warehouse Inc, pg 923
Jimmy Rea Electronics Inc, pg 992

OREGON

SuperDigital Ltd, pg 1029

PENNSYLVANIA

Advanced AV, pg 777
The Lerro Corp, pg 919
Morefield Communications Inc, pg 946
Vistacom Inc, pg 1059

TENNESSEE

Durrell LLC, pg 854
Lowrance Sound Co Inc, pg 925
Mr Mark's Used Musical, Stereo & Studio Equipment Store, pg 944
Technical Support Systems LLC, pg 1034
Trew Audio Inc, pg 1044

TEXAS

AVES Audio Visual Systems Inc, pg 798
Crossroads Audio Inc, pg 840
FitzCo Sound Inc, pg 869
Heffernan Audio Visual, pg 887
Lubbock Audio Visual Inc, pg 925
Pro Video & Film Equipment Co Inc, pg 983
RadioShack Corp, pg 990
RF Specialties of Texas LLC, pg 996
Schoolhouse Audio Visual, pg 1004
Tarpley Media Systems, pg 1032

UTAH

Performance Audio, pg 973
RIA Corp, pg 996

VIRGINIA

Avitecture Inc, pg 799
Filmdex Inc, pg 867
Hoppmann Audio Visual, pg 891
Intellidyne LLC, pg 899
Lee Hartman & Sons Inc, pg 918
Schafer World Communications Corp, pg 1004
The Whitlock Group, pg 1065

WISCONSIN

Audio Visual of Milwaukee Inc, pg 795
Camera Corner Connecting Point, pg 818
Full Compass Systems, pg 874

PUERTO RICO

Bonnin Electronics Inc, pg 810

BRITISH COLUMBIA

Commercial Electronics Ltd, pg 832

MANITOBA

Advance Pro, pg 777
Inland Audio Visual Ltd, pg 898

ONTARIO

HD Source, pg 886
Nationwide Audio Visual Co, pg 953
Westbury National Show Systems Ltd, pg 1064

QUEBEC

AVS Technologies Inc, pg 800
Panavideo Inc, pg 968

Digital Tape Recorder & Player Manufacturers

ARIZONA

Applied Integration Corp, pg 789

CALIFORNIA

Gilderfluke & Co Inc, pg 878
Grande Vitesse Systems Inc (GVS), pg 881
Newdoll Enterprises LLC, pg 956
Panasonic Professional Audio Systems, pg 968
Sony Electronics Inc, pg 1016
TASCAM, pg 1032

MASSACHUSETTS

Avid Technology Inc, pg 799

MINNESOTA

Telex Communications Inc, pg 1037

NEW JERSEY

Onkyo USA Corp, pg 963
Panasonic Consumer Electronics Co, pg 968
Technics, pg 1034

TENNESSEE

Adtec Digital Inc, pg 777

BRITISH COLUMBIA

Richmond Sound Design Ltd, pg 996

Digital Tape Recorder & Player Rentals

ARIZONA

Arizona Cine Equipment, pg 789
Merestone, pg 938
Metropolitan Audio-Visual Inc, pg 940

ARKANSAS

White Diamond Productions, pg 1065

CALIFORNIA

Absolute Rentals, pg 772
Advanced Media LLC, pg 778

AUDIO

Digital Tape Recorder & Player Rentals (continued)

CALIFORNIA (continued)

AGF Media Services, pg 778
Ametron Audio/Video, pg 785
Artichoke Productions, pg 791
Audio Rents, pg 794
AV Guys, pg 797
Bexel Corp, pg 806
Big Time Picture Company Inc, pg 807
Design FX Audio, pg 845
Express Media Inc, pg 864
FXC Communications, pg 874
Hollywood Sound Systems, pg 890
JD Audio Visual Inc, pg 904
Location Sound Corp, pg 924
Lynch Communications, pg 926
Maximus Media Inc, pg 934
McCune Audio-Video-Lighting, pg 935
Munday & Collins AV, pg 950
On-Trax Inc, pg 963
PSAV® Presentation Services, pg 986
Pyramind Studios, pg 988
Synthesizer Systems Technologies (SST), pg 1030
Total Media Group, pg 1042
Towards 2000 Inc, pg 1043
VER-Video Equipment Rentals, pg 1053
Video Resources Inc, pg 1056
Videorama Industries LLC, pg 1057
VMI Inc, pg 1060
Warner Bros Production Sound & Video Services, pg 1062

COLORADO

Audio Consultant Services Inc, pg 794
Daylight Productions & Rentals, pg 844
Multimedia Audio Visual Inc, pg 950

CONNECTICUT

A/V Davey, pg 797
Fox Connecticut, pg 872

DELAWARE

Side Door Studio Inc, pg 1010

FLORIDA

Accord Productions, pg 773
Allstar Audio Systems Inc, pg 782
Cinema East, pg 827
Image Technical Services, pg 895
Lighting Sales Connections, pg 920
Pro Stage Inc, pg 983
Sight & Sound Productions, pg 1010
TAI Audio, pg 1031
Universal Studios Florida® Production Group, pg 1049

GEORGIA

Lighting & Production Equipment Inc, pg 920
Stage Front Presentation Systems, pg 1022
Staging Directions Inc, pg 1023

HAWAII

Audio Resource Honolulu, pg 794
Sight & Sound Studios, pg 1010

ILLINOIS

Allen Visual Systems Inc, pg 781
AV Chicago Inc, pg 797
Backstar Creative Media Inc, pg 801
Beatty TeleVisual Productions, pg 804
On Stage Audio, pg 963
QuickSet International Inc, pg 989
RBR Productions, pg 992
RC Communications, pg 992
Show Department Inc, pg 1009
Woodside Avenue Music Productions Inc, pg 1069

IOWA

ECS Inc, pg 856

KENTUCKY

Audio Visual Techniques Inc, pg 796

MARYLAND

Advance Audiovisual Presentation Ltd, pg 777
CPR MultiMedia Solutions, pg 837
Event Tech, pg 863

MASSACHUSETTS

massAV, pg 933
Preston Productions Inc, pg 981

MICHIGAN

K&R All Media Productions Inc, pg 908

MINNESOTA

Alpha Video & Audio Inc, pg 782

MISSOURI

Show-Me Audio-Visual, pg 1009

MONTANA

Jereco Studios Inc, pg 905

NEVADA

GES Audio Visual, pg 877

NEW HAMPSHIRE

APS Lighting-Sound-AV, pg 789

NEW JERSEY

Giant Audio Visual Inc, pg 878
Jeep Jazz Media Solutions, pg 905
Moe AV LLC, pg 945
Starlite Productions, pg 1024
Wired 4 Sound Inc, pg 1068

NEW MEXICO

Production Outfitters, pg 984

NEW YORK

American Video Inc, pg 785
Aura Sonic Ltd, pg 796
AV Workshop, pg 797
CP Communications, pg 837
Design Audio Visual Inc, pg 845
Dreamhire LLC, pg 852
Hello World Communications, pg 888
Manhattan Center Studios Inc, pg 930
Posthorn Recordings, pg 979
TBA Global Events, pg 1032
Technisphere Corp, pg 1034
WorldStage, pg 1070

NORTH CAROLINA

A&V Company, pg 772
Duke Media Services, pg 853
Special Event Services, pg 1020
Take One Productions Ltd, pg 1031

NORTH DAKOTA

Media Productions, pg 937

OHIO

ITA Audio Visual Solutions, pg 902
Lyon Video Inc, pg 927

OREGON

Northwest Film Center, pg 959

PENNSYLVANIA

Advanced AV, pg 777
Production Solutions Inc, pg 985
Right Coast Recording Inc, pg 997

TENNESSEE

Love Shack Recording Studios, pg 925
Mr Mark's Used Musical, Stereo & Studio Equipment Store, pg 944
Technical Support Systems LLC, pg 1034

TEXAS

Alford Media Services, pg 780
FitzCo Sound Inc, pg 869
Lubbock Audio Visual Inc, pg 925
Music Lab Inc, pg 950
Onstage Systems, pg 963
The Samuels Co, pg 1002

UTAH

Performance Audio, pg 973

VERMONT

Parlato Productions, pg 969

VIRGINIA

American AV, pg 783
Schafer World Communications Corp, pg 1004

WASHINGTON

Victory Studios, pg 1054

WISCONSIN

Full Compass Systems, pg 874

BRITISH COLUMBIA

Commercial Electronics Ltd, pg 832
Finale Editworks, pg 868

MANITOBA

Inland Audio Visual Ltd, pg 898

ONTARIO

HD Source, pg 886
Westbury National Show Systems Ltd, pg 1064

QUEBEC

Panavideo Inc, pg 968

Digital Tape Recorder & Player Repairs

CALIFORNIA

Advanced Media LLC, pg 778
Ametron Audio/Video, pg 785
Audio Images Corp, pg 794
Gluskin's Custom Audio Video, pg 879
Instructional Materials & Equipment Distributors (I-Med), pg 899
Location Sound Corp, pg 924
McAlister Electronics, pg 935
SSL Industries Inc, pg 1022
Towards 2000 Inc, pg 1043

FLORIDA

AMP Services Inc, pg 785
Hi-Tech Enterprises Inc, pg 888
Stereo Sales Inc, pg 1024
TAI Audio, pg 1031

GEORGIA

Lighting & Production Equipment Inc, pg 920
Stage Front Presentation Systems, pg 1022

ILLINOIS

Allen Visual Systems Inc, pg 781
Beatty TeleVisual Productions, pg 804
C V Lloyde, pg 923
Midwest Digital Corp, pg 942

INDIANA

Sweetwater Sound Inc, pg 1029

IOWA

ECS Inc, pg 856

KENTUCKY

Barney Miller's Inc, pg 943
NOR-COM Inc, pg 958

MARYLAND

Strauss Photo Technical Service Inc, pg 1026

MASSACHUSETTS

Professional Audio Design Inc, pg 985

MICHIGAN

K&R's Recording Studios Inc, pg 908
TeL Systems, pg 1035

MINNESOTA

Aggressive Records Audio Duplication LLC, pg 778

NEW JERSEY

A-V Services Inc, pg 771
Starlite Productions, pg 1024

NEW YORK

Technisphere Corp, pg 1034

OHIO

ITA Audio Visual Solutions, pg 902

OREGON

All Service Musical Electronics Repair, pg 780

PENNSYLVANIA

Right Coast Recording Inc, pg 997

TENNESSEE

Technical Support Systems LLC, pg 1034

TEXAS

Lubbock Audio Visual Inc, pg 925
Pro Video & Film Equipment Co Inc, pg 983

VIRGINIA

Hoppmann Audio Visual, pg 891
Schafer World Communications Corp, pg 1004

WISCONSIN

Full Compass Systems, pg 874

PUERTO RICO

Bonnin Electronics Inc, pg 810

BRITISH COLUMBIA

Commercial Electronics Ltd, pg 832

MANITOBA

Inland Audio Visual Ltd, pg 898

ONTARIO

Westbury National Show Systems Ltd, pg 1064

QUEBEC

Panavideo Inc, pg 968

Dubbing

ARIZONA

Merestone, pg 938
On-Site Video, pg 963
Phoenix VideoFilms®, pg 974
SPEAK HOUSE Audio™, pg 1019
Star Video Duplicating, pg 1024

ARKANSAS

Live'N'Loud, pg 923

CALIFORNIA

AB Audio Visual Entertainment Inc, pg 772
Access Video in Berkeley, pg 773
ACDC Audio CD & Cassette, pg 774
Adolph Gasser Inc, pg 776
AlphaDogs Inc, pg 782
Argyle Post, pg 789
Artichoke Productions, pg 791
Chace Audio by Deluxe, pg 823
Custom Video Productions Inc, pg 841
Express Media Inc, pg 864
International Contact Inc, pg 900
Juice, pg 906
The Kitchen, pg 911
Lynch Communications, pg 926
Maximus Media Inc, pg 934
Penrose Productions, pg 972
PM Productions, pg 977
Point 360, pg 978
Private Island Trax, pg 982
QRS Software Services, pg 988
Roundabout Entertainment Inc, pg 1000
Sahara Records & Filmworks Entertainment Co, pg 1001
Saturn Studios, pg 1003
SonicPool, pg 1016
Still N'Motion, pg 1025
Studio 132, pg 1027
Total Media Group, pg 1042
WalkerVision Interarts, pg 1061

COLORADO

Clear Gravy Productions, pg 829
Colorado Sound Recording Studios, pg 831
Flashback Media Productions, pg 869
Open Media Foundation, pg 964
Rocky Mountain Audio/Video Productions Inc, pg 998

CONNECTICUT

A/V Davey, pg 797
Ironik Design & Post, pg 902
T & M Digital Services, pg 1031

FLORIDA

Access Media Group, pg 773
Allegro Productions Inc, pg 781
Comtel Inc, pg 834
Eastern Video, pg 856
Home Shopping Network (HSN), pg 890
JT Communications, pg 906
Phat Planet Recording Studios, pg 973
Progressive Media & Music, pg 985
Promidi Music, pg 986
Sight & Sound Productions, pg 1010
Top Hat Productions, pg 1042
Video Techniques Inc, pg 1056

GEORGIA

Crawford Media Services, pg 838
Digital Projection, pg 847
Doppler Studios, pg 851
Guerrilla Productions LLC, pg 883
Hottrax Records, pg 891
Lighting & Production Equipment Inc, pg 920
ON Event Services, pg 963
Stage Front Presentation Systems, pg 1022

HAWAII

Audio Resource Honolulu, pg 794
Media Bridge Gamekids, pg 936

ILLINOIS

CCore Media Inc, pg 821
Comtech Multimedia Marketing, pg 834
Esoteric Sound, pg 862
IV Media Resources, pg 903
Solid Sound Recording Studio, pg 1015
Sound/Video Impressions Inc, pg 1018
20/20 Communications Inc, pg 1047
Woodside Avenue Music Productions Inc, pg 1069

INDIANA

Crystal Clear Media Group, pg 840
Sweetwater Sound Inc, pg 1029

IOWA

Duplication Media, pg 853

KANSAS

Chapman Recording & Mastering, pg 824

KENTUCKY

Audio Visual Techniques Inc, pg 796
Hammond Communications Group, pg 884
Trusty Tuneshop Recording Studios, pg 1045

LOUISIANA

Louisiana State University Health Sciences Center - Shreveport, pg 925

MARYLAND

CPR MultiMedia Solutions, pg 837
dbF a Media Company, pg 844
Omega Recording Studios, pg 962
Smolian Sound Studios, pg 1014
Welocalize, pg 1063

MASSACHUSETTS

Continental Recordings Inc, pg 835
Cramer Productions, pg 837
Linguistic Systems Inc, pg 922
Soundtrack Recording Studios, pg 1018

MICHIGAN

Audio Graphic Services, pg 794
Brilliance Audio, pg 812
The Brookwood Studio Inc, pg 814
Digi Sign Design LLC, pg 847
K&R's Recording Studios Inc, pg 908

MINNESOTA

The ADS Group, pg 777
Aggressive Records Audio Duplication LLC, pg 778
Winterland Studios, pg 1068

MISSOURI

Avatar Studios, pg 798
Hardcastle Films & Video, pg 885
Production Consultants, pg 984
Show-Me Audio-Visual, pg 1009

NEVADA

Encore Productions Inc, pg 861

NEW HAMPSHIRE

Chip Taylor Communications LLC, pg 1032

NEW JERSEY

All Jersey Studios, pg 780
CFP Video Productions Inc, pg 823
Color Leasing Studios, pg 831
DWJ Television, pg 854
Laurel Video Productions, pg 916
Midnight Media Group Inc, pg 942
Milgrom Productions, pg 943
Optisonics Productions, pg 965
Suede Interactive, pg 1027
VCSvideo, pg 1052

NEW MEXICO

Production Outfitters, pg 984

NEW YORK

Ace Video, pg 774
Aural Gratification Inc, pg 796
The Big House Group, pg 807
Burlington A/V Recording Media, pg 815
Chromavision Corp, pg 826
DuArt, pg 853
Duplication Depot Inc, pg 853
Eastco Multimedia Solutions Inc, pg 856
Fingerpaint, pg 868
Foothill Digital Inc, pg 871
HB-Content, pg 886
Heavy Melody, pg 887
InterNation Inc, pg 900
International Digital Centre, pg 901
iProbe Multilingual Solutions Inc, pg 902
Lylofilm Productions, pg 926
Manhattan Center Studios Inc, pg 930
Mark Custom Recording Service Inc, pg 931
Mood Creations Ltd, pg 946
Now Hear This, pg 960
TBA Global Events, pg 1032
Tiki Recording Studios Inc, pg 1040
Tobin Productions Inc, pg 1041
Visual Technologies Corp, pg 1060

NORTH CAROLINA

A&V Company, pg 772
Pat Appleson Studios Inc, pg 788
Duke Media Services, pg 853
Horizon Video Productions Inc, pg 891
Take One Productions Ltd, pg 1031
Unifour Productions Inc, pg 1048

NORTH DAKOTA

Media Productions, pg 937

OHIO

Curtis Inc, pg 841
EDR Media LLC, pg 857
Lyon Video Inc, pg 927
Mills James Productions, pg 943
Musicol Recording, pg 951

OKLAHOMA

PDC Productions, pg 970

PENNSYLVANIA

American Artist Studio, pg 783
Audio Visual Communications Inc, pg 795
Forge Recording LLC, pg 871
Kloss Studios Co, pg 912
Laser Video Corp, pg 916
Production Masters Inc (PMI), pg 984
The Videohouse Inc, pg 1057

RHODE ISLAND

A&M Productions, pg 771
Sound-FX-Design, pg 1017

SOUTH CAROLINA

DaviSound, pg 843
Genesis Creative, pg 877

AUDIO

Dubbing (continued)

Duplication—Audiocassettes

Duplication—Audiotapes

AUDIO

Duplication—Audiotapes (continued)

FLORIDA

Access Media Group, pg 773
Communications Concepts Inc (CCI), pg 833
Eastern Video, pg 856
Gulf Coast Audio Visual Producers Inc, pg 883
Home Shopping Network (HSN), pg 890
Mach 1 Productions, pg 927
Photosound of Orlando Inc, pg 975
Progressive Media & Music, pg 985
Sight & Sound Productions, pg 1010
Tallahassee Audio Visual, pg 1031
Video Techniques Inc, pg 1056

GEORGIA

Audio Visual Resources Inc, pg 795
Beast Atlanta, pg 804
Doppler Studios, pg 851
Lighting & Production Equipment Inc, pg 920
ON Event Services, pg 963
White Dog Studios, pg 1065

ILLINOIS

ABS Enterprises, pg 772
CCore Media Inc, pg 821
IV Media Resources, pg 903
Major Media Inc, pg 929
Major Media Productions Inc, pg 929
Paragon Studios Inc, pg 969
RBR Productions, pg 992
Woodside Avenue Music Productions Inc, pg 1069

INDIANA

Infonics Inc, pg 898
OMNI Productions, pg 962
Optical Disc Solutions Inc, pg 964
Sweetwater Sound Inc, pg 1029

IOWA

Duplication Media, pg 853
The Production House, pg 984

KANSAS

Chapman Recording & Mastering, pg 824

LOUISIANA

Louisiana State University Health Sciences Center - Shreveport, pg 925

MAINE

Headlight Audio Visual Inc, pg 887

MARYLAND

Absolute Hollywood, pg 772
The Cutting Corp, pg 841
dbF a Media Company, pg 844
Omega Recording Studios, pg 962
Optic Bindery & Packaging, pg 964
Soundtrax Optical Sound Recording, pg 1018
Video Labs, pg 1055

MASSACHUSETTS

CommCreative, pg 832
Continental Recordings Inc, pg 835
Cramer Productions, pg 837
M Works Mastering Studios, pg 927
Penfield Productions Ltd, pg 971
Soundtrack Recording Studios, pg 1018
TR Productions, pg 1043
Video Express, pg 1055

MICHIGAN

Brilliance Audio, pg 812
Digi Sign Design LLC, pg 847
K&R's Recording Studios Inc, pg 908
MessageMakers, pg 939

MINNESOTA

GMI Productions, pg 879

MISSISSIPPI

Jasper Ewing & Sons Inc, pg 864

MISSOURI

Audio-VideoGraphics Inc, pg 795
Hardcastle Films & Video, pg 885
Image Technologies Corp, pg 895
Show-Me Audio-Visual, pg 1009

MONTANA

KUSM TV, pg 914

NEW HAMPSHIRE

Academic & Campus Technology Services, pg 773
Apertura, pg 788
Chip Taylor Communications LLC, pg 1032

NEW JERSEY

All Jersey Studios, pg 780
DWJ Television, pg 854
NFL Films Music Library, pg 957
Reed Presentations Inc (RPI), pg 993
Starlite Productions, pg 1024
Suede Interactive, pg 1027
Video Corporation of America (VCA), pg 1055

NEW YORK

The Big House Group, pg 807
Burlington A/V Recording Media, pg 815
Chromavision Corp, pg 826
CMI Communications, pg 830
Digital Force, pg 847
DuArt, pg 853
Duplication Depot Inc, pg 853
Duplication Specialists Inc, pg 853
Eastco Multimedia Solutions Inc, pg 856
HAVE Inc, pg 886
HB-Content, pg 886
HOThead, pg 891
J & D Laboratories Inc, pg 903
Kamen Entertainment Group Inc, pg 908
Magno Sound & Video, pg 929
Manhattan Center Studios Inc, pg 930
Masterdisk Corp, pg 933
Mood Creations Ltd, pg 946
MRG Productions Inc, pg 948
New York Audio Productions, pg 956
Now Hear This, pg 960
Nutmeg Post, pg 960
Shelly Palmer Production, pg 968
Elliot Sokolov Music, pg 1015
Sony Music Entertainment, pg 1016
Specialized Audio-Visual Inc, pg 1020
TBA Global Events, pg 1032
Teatown Communications Group, pg 1033
Tobin Productions Inc, pg 1041
USA Studios, pg 1050
Visual Technologies Corp, pg 1060
Zelman Studios Ltd, pg 1073

NORTH CAROLINA

A&V Company, pg 772
Pat Appleson Studios Inc, pg 788
Duke Media Services, pg 853
Take One Productions Ltd, pg 1031
Trailblazer Studios®, pg 1043

OHIO

Cuyahoga Community College Media Center, pg 841
EDR Media LLC, pg 857
The Little Warehouse Inc, pg 923
Lyon Video Inc, pg 927
Mills James Productions, pg 943
Musicol Recording, pg 951
SoundSpace Inc, pg 1018

OKLAHOMA

Garman Productions LLC, pg 875
Piper Media Services Inc, pg 976
University of Oklahoma Academic Media & Digital Services, pg 1050

OREGON

Rex, pg 995

PENNSYLVANIA

American Artist Studio, pg 783
Craig Recording Studios, pg 837
FMP Media Solutions Inc, pg 870
Forge Recording LLC, pg 871
JPL, pg 906
Production Masters Inc (PMI), pg 984
The Videohouse Inc, pg 1057

RHODE ISLAND

Sound-FX-Design, pg 1017

SOUTH CAROLINA

DaviSound, pg 843

TENNESSEE

Ardent Studios Inc, pg 789
Memphis Communications Corp, pg 938
Stage Post, pg 1022

TEXAS

Astro Audio Visual, pg 792
Dub King, pg 853
Harbor House Studios, pg 884
Matson Multi-Media, pg 934
The Samuels Co, pg 1002
Sound Works, pg 1018
Stage Directions, pg 1022
Texas Heart Institute Visual Communication Services, pg 1037
U-Edit Video, pg 1047

UTAH

One Stop CD Shop LLC, pg 963

VERMONT

University of Vermont, Instructional Television Dept, pg 1050

VIRGINIA

BES Studios, pg 805
Lee Hartman & Sons Inc, pg 918
Lion Recording Services Inc, pg 922
The Whitlock Group, pg 1065

WASHINGTON

Inland Audio Visual Co, pg 898
Kostov Productions, pg 913
Pacific Multimedia Inc, pg 967
Proforma GW Marketing, pg 985
Victory Studios, pg 1054

WISCONSIN

Audio Visual of Milwaukee Inc, pg 795
5th Floor Recording Co, pg 867
USAV Group Inc, pg 1050

PUERTO RICO

Stage Crew Audiovisual Inc, pg 1022

BRITISH COLUMBIA

Pinewood Sound, pg 975
Triad Communications Ltd, pg 1044

ONTARIO

Cinram Inc, pg 828
Edcom Multimedia Products, pg 856
VO2 Mix Studios, pg 1060
Wanted! Sound + Picture, pg 1062

Duplication—Compact Discs

ALABAMA

Sound of Birmingham Productions, pg 1017

ARIZONA

Allusion Studios & Pure Wave Audio, pg 782
Film Creations Ltd, pg 867
Fire Power Music Inc, pg 868
Merestone, pg 938
On-Site Video, pg 963
SPEAK HOUSE Audio™, pg 1019
Star Video Duplicating, pg 1024
Tempe Tape & Disc, pg 1037

ARKANSAS

White Diamond Productions, pg 1065

CALIFORNIA

AB Audio Visual Entertainment Inc, pg 772
ACDC Audio CD & Cassette, pg 774
Action Video, pg 775
Adolph Gasser Inc, pg 776
AGF Media Services, pg 778
AlphaDogs Inc, pg 782
AM Productions, pg 783
The Annex, pg 787
Argyle Post, pg 789
Audio Rents, pg 794
Barbosa Video Services, pg 802

AUDIO

Duplication—Compact Discs (continued)

WASHINGTON

CCI Solutions, pg 821
Pacific Multimedia Inc, pg 967
Proforma GW Marketing, pg 985

WEST VIRGINIA

Blackwater Video Productions, pg 808

WISCONSIN

Audio Visual of Milwaukee Inc, pg 795
Concept Productions Inc, pg 834
Excel Duplication Services, pg 864
5th Floor Recording Co, pg 867
Sound Strations Audio Productions Inc, pg 1017
Watts Communications Inc, pg 1062

PUERTO RICO

Stage Crew Audiovisual Inc, pg 1022

BRITISH COLUMBIA

Finale Editworks, pg 868
Pinewood Sound, pg 975
Triad Communications Ltd, pg 1044

MANITOBA

Ironstone Technologies, pg 902

ONTARIO

ADS Media, pg 777
Music Manufacturing Services, pg 950
Purefire Communications Inc, pg 987
SLI Manufacturing Inc, pg 1013
Video Excellence Productions, pg 1055
VO2 Mix Studios, pg 1060
Wanted! Sound + Picture, pg 1062

Duplicator, *see* Tape Duplicator

Easy Listening Music, *see* Music Libraries—Easy Listening

Editing

ALABAMA

Dogwood Recording Studios, pg 850

ARIZONA

Aardvark Productions LLC, pg 772
Allusion Studios & Pure Wave Audio, pg 782
Audio Video Resources, pg 795
Fire Power Music Inc, pg 868
Forensic Video Deposition Service, pg 871
MediaWorks, pg 938
Merestone, pg 938
Metropolitan Audio-Visual Inc, pg 940
SPEAK HOUSE Audio™, pg 1019
Star Video Duplicating, pg 1024

ARKANSAS

Cedar Crest Studio, pg 822
Live'N'Loud, pg 923
White Diamond Productions, pg 1065

CALIFORNIA

AB Audio Visual Entertainment Inc, pg 772
ACDC Audio CD & Cassette, pg 774
Action Video, pg 775
Adolph Gasser Inc, pg 776
Aliso Creek Productions Inc, pg 780
AlphaDogs Inc, pg 782
AM Productions, pg 783
The Annex, pg 787
Argyle Post, pg 789
Artichoke Productions, pg 791
Audio Mechanics, pg 794
Audio Upgrades, pg 795
The Banquet Sound Studios, pg 802
Barbosa Video Services, pg 802
Berke Creative Inc, pg 805
Berkeley Sound Artists Inc, pg 805
Blaise Media, pg 809
Blue Lotus Temple Studio, pg 809
Chace Audio by Deluxe, pg 823
Creative Media Recording, pg 838
Custom Video Productions Inc, pg 841
Different Fur Recording Ltd, pg 846
Digital Jungle, pg 847
Dogma Studios, pg 850
DV Post, pg 854
Earwax Productions Inc, pg 855
ECONEWS (Environmental Television Series) & (Environmental Directions Radio Series), pg 856
Express Media Inc, pg 864
Eye & I Productions, pg 864
5 Alarm Music, pg 869
FJ Productions Inc, pg 869
48 Windows, pg 871
Full Moon & High Tide Productions & Studios, pg 874
FXC Communications, pg 874
Joe Gastwirt Mastering, pg 875
Gold Standard Productions, pg 880
Gordon Productions Inc, pg 880
Havas Edge, pg 885
iCorpTv, pg 893
Illuminate Post/Digital Finishing, pg 894
JDS Video & Media Productions Inc, pg 904
Juice, pg 906
K2B2 Records, pg 907
KABA Audio Productions, pg 907
The Kenwood Group, pg 909
KION-TV, pg 911
The Kitchen, pg 911
KVIE-Channel 6, pg 914
Ludlow Media Solutions, pg 926
Lynch Communications, pg 926
Main Street Media Inc, pg 929
Maximus Media Inc, pg 934
McCune Audio-Video-Lighting, pg 935
Media Magic, pg 937
The Media Staff Inc, pg 937
Mind Over Eye Inc, pg 943
On-Trax Inc, pg 963
Oral Tradition Sound & Music, pg 965
OTR Studios, pg 966
Pacific Audio-Visual Enterprises, pg 967
Palardo Productions, pg 968
Panorama Productions, pg 968
Penrose Productions, pg 972
piXvfm, pg 976
PM Productions, pg 977
Point 360, pg 978
Polarity Post Production, pg 978
Private Island Trax, pg 982
Pyramind Studios, pg 988
QRS Software Services, pg 988
Reality Check Systems, pg 992
Regent Press Publishers & Printers, pg 994
Roundabout Entertainment Inc, pg 1000
Saturn Studios, pg 1003
SBS Productions, pg 1003
Shapeshifter, pg 1008
Steve Shapiro Music, pg 1008
SonicPool, pg 1016
Sounds Unique, pg 1018
Staylor-Made Communications Inc, pg 1024
Kris Stevens Enterprises, pg 1024
Still N'Motion, pg 1025
Studio 132, pg 1027
Studio 637, pg 1027
Tam Communications Inc, pg 1031
Tele-Video Production Services (TVPS), pg 1036
Total Media Group, pg 1042
Trac Record Co & Recording Studio, pg 1043
United Audio Video Group Inc, pg 1048
Universal Studios, pg 1049
Video Symphony TV & Film School, pg 1056
Z-Ville Productions, pg 1073

COLORADO

Airshow Mastering, pg 779
Alpine Media, pg 782
Audio Consultant Services Inc, pg 794
blue onion, pg 810
Ceavco Audio/Visual Co, pg 822
Tim Cissell Music, pg 828
Clear Gravy Productions, pg 829
Conly Productions, pg 835
Daylight Productions & Rentals, pg 844
Flashback Media Productions, pg 869
Open Media Foundation, pg 964
Rocky Mountain Audio/Video Productions Inc, pg 998

CONNECTICUT

Antenna International, pg 787
A/V Davey, pg 797
BRB Audiovisual Productions, pg 812
Broadcast Video Productions LLC, pg 813
Cine-Med Inc, pg 826
EagleVision Inc, pg 855
The Gary-Paul Agency, pg 875
Guymark Studios LLC, pg 883
Ironik Design & Post, pg 902
New London Media, pg 956
Palace Digital Studios, pg 967
P&P Studios Inc, pg 968
Powerstation Events, pg 979
T & M Digital Services, pg 1031

DELAWARE

Ken-Del Studios, pg 909
Side Door Studio Inc, pg 1010

DISTRICT OF COLUMBIA

Hillmann & Carr Inc, pg 889
Interface Media Group, pg 900

FLORIDA

A Cut Above Video Productions Inc, pg 771
Access Media Group, pg 773
Accord Productions, pg 773
Adrenaline Films, pg 777
Allegro Productions Inc, pg 781
Audacity Creative, pg 793
Big Byte Video Productions, pg 806
CD ROM™ Inc, pg 822
Communications Concepts Inc (CCI), pg 833
Comtel Inc, pg 834
Eastern Video, pg 856
Ed Ethridge Productions Inc, pg 863
Global Video Distributors Inc, pg 879
Gulf Coast Audio Visual Producers Inc, pg 883
Home Shopping Network (HSN), pg 890
LHV Audio Services, pg 919
Media Concepts Inc, pg 936
Morrisound Recording, pg 946
New Art Miami, pg 955
Phat Planet Recording Studios, pg 973
Photosound of Orlando Inc, pg 975
Progressive Media & Music, pg 985
Promidi Music, pg 986
Shooting Stars Post Inc, pg 1009
Sight & Sound Productions, pg 1010
Style-City Music Inc, pg 1027
Sunfire Communications Inc, pg 1028
Sunrise Studios, pg 1028
Top Hat Productions, pg 1042
Universal Studios Florida® Production Group, pg 1049
WKMG-TV Channel 6, pg 1068

GEORGIA

Beast Atlanta, pg 804
Crawford Media Services, pg 838
Doppler Studios, pg 851
ECG Productions, pg 856
Encyclomedia, pg 861
Guerrilla Productions LLC, pg 883
Hottrax Records, pg 891
Lighting & Production Equipment Inc, pg 920
NorthTown Sounds Inc, pg 959
Stage Front Presentation Systems, pg 1022
White Dog Studios, pg 1065

HAWAII

Audio Resource Honolulu, pg 794
Hyperspective Studios Inc, pg 893
Media Bridge Gamekids, pg 936
TV Juice Productions Inc, pg 1046

ILLINOIS

ABS Enterprises, pg 772
Advanced Audio Technology, pg 777
Analog Free Media, pg 786
AnswersMedia, pg 787
Audio Visual Services Corp, pg 796
Big Shoulders Digital Video Productions, pg 807
CCore Media Inc, pg 821
Centrax Corp, pg 823
Comtech Multimedia Marketing, pg 834

Esoteric Sound, pg 862
IV Media Resources, pg 903
Major Media Inc, pg 929
Optimus, pg 964
Paragon Studios Inc, pg 969
The Pepper Group, pg 972
The Prairie Production Group, pg 980
PSAV® Presentation Services (Hotel Services Division), pg 987
Steven Samler Music & Sound, pg 1002
Solid Sound Recording Studio, pg 1015
Sound/Video Impressions Inc, pg 1018
20/20 Communications Inc, pg 1047
WEEK TV, pg 1063
Woodside Avenue Music Productions Inc, pg 1069

INDIANA

AVA Productions, pg 798
Bright Ideas Creative Services, pg 812
Communication Ministries, pg 833
Covenant Productions®, pg 837
Digital Rain LLC, pg 847
Alan Johnson Recording, pg 905
OMNI Productions, pg 962
Optical Disc Solutions Inc, pg 964
Sweetwater Sound Inc, pg 1029
World Media Group Inc, pg 1069

IOWA

Hedquist Productions Inc, pg 887
Iowa State University-Information Technology Services, pg 902
The Production House, pg 984

KANSAS

Chapman Recording & Mastering, pg 824

KENTUCKY

Audio Visual Techniques Inc, pg 796
Broadway Digital, pg 813
Hammond Communications Group, pg 884
Barney Miller's Inc, pg 943
Northern Kentucky University, pg 959
Trusty Tuneshop Recording Studios, pg 1045

LOUISIANA

Launch Media, pg 916
Louisiana State University Health Sciences Center - Shreveport, pg 925
Vidox Motion Imagery, pg 1057

MAINE

Headlight Audio Visual Inc, pg 887
WGME-TV, pg 1065

MARYLAND

CPR MultiMedia Solutions, pg 837
The Cutting Corp, pg 841
dbF a Media Company, pg 844
The Image Generators, pg 895
Kramer Communications Video Production, pg 913
Lion & Fox Recording Studios, pg 922
Omega Recording Studios, pg 962
Satellite Media Production, pg 1003
Sheffield Audio/Video Productions, pg 1008
Smolian Sound Studios, pg 1014
Speakeasy Productions, pg 1020
Welocalize, pg 1063

MASSACHUSETTS

CommCreative, pg 832
Continental Recordings Inc, pg 835
Extreme Reach Inc, pg 864
Labrecque Creative Sound, pg 915
M Works Mastering Studios, pg 927
Northeastern Digital Recording Inc, pg 959
Northern Light Productions, pg 959
Penfield Productions Ltd, pg 971
Soundtrack Recording Studios, pg 1018
Rik Tinory Productions, pg 1041
TR Productions, pg 1043
WGBH Production Group, pg 1065

MICHIGAN

Audio Graphic Services, pg 794
Brilliance Audio, pg 812
The Brookwood Studio Inc, pg 814
Digi Sign Design LLC, pg 847
Digital Image Studios LLC, pg 847
GMP Music, pg 879
K&R's Recording Studios Inc, pg 908
MessageMakers, pg 939
Michigan Recording Arts Institute & Technologies, pg 941
RingSide Creative, pg 997
Studio A Recording Inc, pg 1026
TGA Recording Co, pg 1038

MINNESOTA

The ADS Group, pg 777
Aggressive Records Audio Duplication LLC, pg 778
Alpha Video & Audio Inc, pg 782
Badiyan Inc, pg 801
Beyers Sound & Essay Audio, pg 806
GMI Productions, pg 879
Jamieson & Associates Inc, pg 904
Media Loft Inc, pg 937
MultiMedia, pg 950
Winterland Studios, pg 1068

MISSOURI

Avatar Studios, pg 798
Hardcastle Films & Video, pg 885
Production Consultants, pg 984
Show-Me Audio-Visual, pg 1009
Studio Worx Inc, pg 1027
Swank Audio Visuals, pg 1029

MONTANA

Jereco Studios Inc, pg 905
KUSM TV, pg 914
North Country Media Group, pg 959
ooLite Media, pg 964

NEBRASKA

JoeAudio, pg 905
Three Pillars Media, pg 1040

NEVADA

JCS Video Productions, pg 904
Stage America LLC, pg 1022
Tanglewood Productions, pg 1031
VirtualMix, pg 1058

NEW HAMPSHIRE

Apertura, pg 788
Captain Fiddle Music & Publications, pg 820
Chip Taylor Communications LLC, pg 1032

NEW JERSEY

All Jersey Studios, pg 780
CFP Video Productions Inc, pg 823
Color Leasing Studios, pg 831
Deluxe Media Services, pg 845
DWJ Television, pg 854
Euro-Pacific Film & Video Productions Inc, pg 863
Laurel Video Productions, pg 916
MIB Mediaworks, pg 941
Midnight Media Group Inc, pg 942
Milgrom Productions, pg 943
NFL Films Inc, pg 957
NFL Films Music Library, pg 957
Oasis CD Manufacturing, pg 960
Optisonics Productions, pg 965
SADiE Inc, pg 1001
Starlite Productions, pg 1024
Suede Interactive, pg 1027
VCSvideo, pg 1052

NEW MEXICO

Production Outfitters, pg 984

NEW YORK

The Audio Department Inc, pg 794
Aural Gratification Inc, pg 796
Bellin Productions, pg 805
The Big House Group, pg 807
Chromavision Corp, pg 826
Design Audio Visual Inc, pg 845
Digital Art Video Inc, pg 847
Digital Force, pg 847
dM works, pg 849
DuArt, pg 853
Duplication Depot Inc, pg 853
Eastco Multimedia Solutions Inc, pg 856
Fingerpaint, pg 868
Foothill Digital Inc, pg 871
4-D Creative Media, pg 871
Greyfalcon House, pg 882
Gurrilla Video Solutions, pg 883
HB-Content, pg 886
HBO Studio Productions, pg 886
Headroom Digital Audio, pg 887
Heavy Melody, pg 887
Hello World Communications, pg 888
HOThead, pg 891
InterNation Inc, pg 900
Jupiter Moon Productions, pg 907
Kamen Entertainment Group Inc, pg 908
KAS Music & Sound, pg 908
L A Bruell Inc, pg 914
La Paloma Films, pg 915
Loftin Productions, pg 924
Lylofilm Productions, pg 926
Manhattan Center Studios Inc, pg 930
Mark Custom Recording Service Inc, pg 931
Neal Marshad Productions, pg 931
Masterdisk Corp, pg 933
Mood Creations Ltd, pg 946
Mother West, pg 947
MRG Productions Inc, pg 948
The Napoleon Group, pg 952
New York Audio Productions, pg 956
No Soap Productions, pg 957
Now Hear This, pg 960
Nutmeg Post, pg 960
Shelly Palmer Production, pg 968
Posthorn Recordings, pg 979
RadioArt/Bob & Ray CDs & MP3 Files, pg 990
David Rapkin Audio Production, pg 991
Sear Sound, pg 1005
Elliot Sokolov Music, pg 1015
Sony Music Entertainment, pg 1016
SoundByte Productions Inc, pg 1018
Synaptic Digital, pg 1030
TBA Global Events, pg 1032
Teatown Communications Group, pg 1033
TeleTime Productions, pg 1036
Tiki Recording Studios Inc, pg 1040
Tobin Productions Inc, pg 1041
USA Studios, pg 1050
Visual Technologies Corp, pg 1060
Zelman Studios Ltd, pg 1073

NORTH CAROLINA

Pat Appleson Studios Inc, pg 788
Audio Art, pg 794
The Communications Group Inc, pg 833
Duke Media Services, pg 853
Franklin Video Inc, pg 872
Horizon Video Productions Inc, pg 891
On Location North Carolina, pg 963
Studio B Mastering, pg 1026
Take One Productions Ltd, pg 1031
Trailblazer Studios®, pg 1043
2BruceStudio, pg 1047
Unifour Productions Inc, pg 1048

NORTH DAKOTA

Media Productions, pg 937

OHIO

Advent Media Inc, pg 778
Alegra House Publishers, pg 780
Bartha, pg 803
Cinecraft Productions Inc, pg 827
Curtis Inc, pg 841
Cuyahoga Community College Media Center, pg 841
EDR Media LLC, pg 857
Lyon Video Inc, pg 927
Mills James Productions, pg 943
Musicol Recording, pg 951
R&B Communications Inc, pg 991
SoundSpace Inc, pg 1018
Vista Color Imaging Inc, pg 1059

OKLAHOMA

Garman Productions LLC, pg 875
PDC Productions, pg 970
University of Oklahoma Academic Media & Digital Services, pg 1050

OREGON

A KTVA Production LLC, pg 771
Future Disc LLC, pg 874
Intersect Video, pg 901
Odyssey Productions Inc, pg 961
Rex, pg 995

PENNSYLVANIA

AiH Group Inc, pg 779
American Artist Studio, pg 783
Audio Visual Communications Inc, pg 795
Craig Recording Studios, pg 837
FMP Media Solutions Inc, pg 870
Forge Recording LLC, pg 871
Innovision Media Group, pg 899

AUDIO

Editing (continued)

PENNSYLVANIA (continued)

Ivory Productions, pg 903
Javboy Records, pg 904
JPL, pg 906
Kloss Studios Co, pg 912
Laser Video Corp, pg 916
Robin Miller, Filmaker Inc, pg 943
Panta Rhei Media Inc, pg 968
Production Masters Inc (PMI),
 pg 984
Right Coast Recording Inc, pg 997
The Videohouse Inc, pg 1057
Visual Sound Inc, pg 1059
WHYY Inc, pg 1066

RHODE ISLAND

A&M Productions, pg 771
Sound Advantage, pg 1016
Sound-FX-Design, pg 1017

SOUTH CAROLINA

DaviSound, pg 843
Genesis Creative, pg 877
Venture Media, pg 1052

TENNESSEE

American Blackguard Inc, pg 784
Analog Man Recording Studio,
 pg 786
Anode Inc, pg 787
Ardent Music LLC, pg 789
Ardent Studios Inc, pg 789
Brantley Sound Associates Inc,
 pg 812
Continental Film, pg 835
JamSync, pg 904
Kingswood Productions, pg 911
Love Shack Recording Studios,
 pg 925
Marine Geographic, pg 931
Memphis Communications Corp,
 pg 938
Mr Mark's Used Musical, Stereo &
 Studio Equipment Store, pg 944
Motion Picture Services, pg 947
Scripps Networks, pg 1005
Stage Post, pg 1022
Technical Support Systems LLC,
 pg 1034
Zion Music Group, pg 1074

TEXAS

AMA Nystrom Printing/Finishing,
 pg 783
AMS Pictures, pg 786
Audiomoxie®, pg 796
Biway Media, pg 808
Castleview Productions, pg 821
Cerutti Productions Inc, pg 823
Communication Arts Multimedia
 Inc, pg 832
The Editing Co, pg 857
Fire Station Studios, pg 868
Freeman, pg 872
Great Recordings LLC, pg 881
Harbor House Studios, pg 884
Horizon Film + Video Productions,
 pg 891
Marx InDigital, pg 933
Matson Multi-Media, pg 934
Maverick Video Productions, pg 934
Julye Newlin Productions Inc,
 pg 956
Out of the BLUE Media, pg 966
Phillips MediaSource, pg 974

Planet Dallas Recording Studios,
 pg 976
Real to Reel Studios Inc, pg 992
Romar Learning, pg 999
The Samuels Co, pg 1002
The Sound Lab Inc, pg 1017
Sound Works, pg 1018
South Coast Film & Video, pg 1019
Stage Directions, pg 1022
Texas Heart Institute Visual
 Communication Services,
 pg 1037
TopCat Records LLC, pg 1042
Tropikal Productions, pg 1045

UTAH

ImageWorks Communications,
 pg 896
K-SAR Video & DVD Productions,
 pg 907
Performance Audio, pg 973
Soularium Recording Studios,
 pg 1016

VERMONT

University of Vermont, Instructional
 Television Dept, pg 1050

VIRGINIA

AudioImage Recording, pg 796
Bias Studios, pg 806
CACI Productions Group, pg 816
CDR Communications Inc, pg 822
Wally Cleaver's Recording Service,
 pg 830
Lion Recording Services Inc,
 pg 922
Metro Productions, pg 939
National Media Services Inc,
 pg 953
Studio Center Corp, pg 1026
The Whitlock Group, pg 1065

WASHINGTON

Jake Barner Studio, pg 803
Inland Audio Visual Co, pg 898
Kostov Productions, pg 913
North-by-Northwest Productions,
 pg 958
Pacific Multimedia Inc, pg 967
Sound Sound/Savage Fruitarian
 Productions, pg 1017
Victory Studios, pg 1054

WEST VIRGINIA

Sweetsong Productions, pg 1029

WISCONSIN

Audio Visual of Milwaukee Inc,
 pg 795
Concept Productions Inc, pg 834
5th Floor Recording Co, pg 867
Learning Technology Services,
 pg 917
Lux Mundi Production House,
 pg 926
Meridian Studios, pg 939
Sound Strations Audio Productions
 Inc, pg 1017
TBC Studios, pg 1033
University of Wisconsin-Oshkosh
 Radio-TV-Film Dept, pg 1050
USAV Group Inc, pg 1050
Video Wisconsin Inc, pg 1056
Watts Communications Inc, pg 1062
Wisconsin Public Television,
 pg 1068

PUERTO RICO

Stage Crew Audiovisual Inc,
 pg 1022

ALBERTA

Global Television, pg 879

BRITISH COLUMBIA

Finale Editworks, pg 868
North West Digital Ltd, pg 959
Pinewood Sound, pg 975
Triad Communications Ltd, pg 1044

MANITOBA

daCapo Productions, pg 842

ONTARIO

ADS Media, pg 777
AMPLUS Productions, pg 786
DebsVoice, pg 844
GAPC (General Assembly
 Production Centre), pg 875
JFB Communications, pg 905
JL Recording Studios, pg 905
MCS Recording Studios, pg 936
Metalworks Recording Studios Inc,
 pg 939
Nightingale Music Productions Inc,
 pg 957
Optix Digital Pictures & Sound,
 pg 965
Purefire Communications Inc,
 pg 987
Spence-Thomas Audio Post,
 pg 1021
Video Excellence Productions,
 pg 1055
VO2 Mix Studios, pg 1060
Wanted! Sound + Picture, pg 1062

QUEBEC

Group PVP, pg 882
Trebas Institute, pg 1044

Electronic Music, see Music Libraries— Electronic

Equalizer Distributors

ARIZONA

Allusion Studios & Pure Wave
 Audio, pg 782
EAR Professional Audio/Video,
 pg 855
Radio Design Labs (RDL), pg 990
Troxell Communications Inc,
 pg 1045

CALIFORNIA

Ametron Audio/Video, pg 785
Associated Sound, pg 792
Audio Images Corp, pg 794
Cibola Systems, pg 826
Delicate Electronics Sales Inc,
 pg 845
Empire Wholesale Inc, pg 860
FXC Communications, pg 874
Harman Pro North America, pg 885
JD Audio Visual Inc, pg 904
Location Sound Corp, pg 924
MediaMation Inc, pg 937
MediaPOINTE, pg 938
Mobilized Tech Systems, pg 944
POP TV, pg 978
SNAP, pg 1014

Sound Service Co, pg 1017
Sounds Unique, pg 1018
Southern California Sound Image
 Inc, pg 1019
Stanislaus Audio Video Inc,
 pg 1023
TOA Electronics Inc, pg 1041
Towards 2000 Inc, pg 1043
VMI Inc, pg 1060

COLORADO

Audio Consultant Services Inc,
 pg 794

CONNECTICUT

Connecticut Audio & Theatrical
 Supply, pg 835
HB Communications Inc, pg 886
The Music People Inc, pg 951

DELAWARE

Actors Attic, pg 775

FLORIDA

Access Media Group, pg 773
Allstar Audio Systems Inc, pg 782
AVI-SPL, pg 798
BAI Distributors Inc, pg 801
Broadcasters General Store Inc,
 pg 813
Digital Video Systems Inc, pg 848
Griffiths Broadcast Co Inc, pg 882
Harris Corp, pg 885
Hi-Tech Enterprises Inc, pg 888
Industrial Strength Inc, pg 897
Intermark Industries Inc, pg 900
Lighting Sales Connections, pg 920
Pro Stage Inc, pg 983
Recording Media & Equipment Inc
 (RM&E), pg 993
Sight & Sound Productions,
 pg 1010
Stereo Sales Inc, pg 1024
TAI Audio, pg 1031
Technomedia Solutions, pg 1035

GEORGIA

Clark, pg 829
Lighting & Production Equipment
 Inc, pg 920
Stage Front Presentation Systems,
 pg 1022

ILLINOIS

Allen Visual Systems Inc, pg 781
Sound Vision Inc, pg 1018
Woodside Avenue Music
 Productions Inc, pg 1069

INDIANA

Heart Breaker Entertainment LLC,
 pg 887
Sensory Technologies LLC, pg 1006
SHP Electronics, pg 1010
Sweetwater Sound Inc, pg 1029

IOWA

ECS Inc, pg 856

KENTUCKY

Axxis Inc, pg 800
Barney Miller's Inc, pg 943
NOR-COM Inc, pg 958

MAINE

Headlight Audio Visual Inc, pg 887
Independent Audio Inc, pg 897

MARYLAND

Bradley Broadcast & Pro Audio, pg 811
Cardinal Sound & Video, pg 820
Kipp Visual Systems Inc, pg 911

MASSACHUSETTS

Terry Hanley Audio Systems Inc, pg 884
Professional Audio Design Inc, pg 985
Rule Broadcast Systems, pg 1000

MICHIGAN

Ascom Communications Contractors, pg 791
Digi Sign Design LLC, pg 847
On Stage Visuals, pg 963
TeL Systems, pg 1035

MISSOURI

Production Support Services Inc, pg 985
Schiller's Audio-Visual, pg 1004

NEW HAMPSHIRE

APS Lighting-Sound-AV, pg 789
Technet® Systems Group, pg 1033

NEW JERSEY

Alltec Stores, a Vcom IMC Company, pg 782
Audio Visual Associates, pg 795
AV Bluebook, pg 797
Diversified Systems Inc, pg 849
Earl Girls Inc, pg 855
Hamilton Buhl, pg 884
National Audio-Visual Supply, pg 952
Nelson Enterprises Theatrical Supply Co, pg 954
SLD Lighting, pg 1013
Starlite Productions, pg 1024
Wired 4 Sound Inc, pg 1068
York Telecom, pg 1072

NEW MEXICO

Quickbeam Systems Inc (QSI), pg 989

NEW YORK

ALTEL Systems Inc, pg 783
Aura Sonic Ltd, pg 796
Cadence Jazz Records, pg 816
Colortone Audio Visual, pg 832
Custom Media Environments, pg 841
Design Audio Visual Inc, pg 845
Group One Ltd, pg 882
HAVE Inc, pg 886
Hot House Professional Audio, pg 891
KVL Audio Visual Services Inc, pg 914
Markertek Video Supply, pg 931
MultiDyne Video & Fiber Optics Systems, pg 950
Posthorn Recordings, pg 979
TecNec Distributing, pg 1035
Toys From The Attic, pg 1043
Visual Word Systems Inc, pg 1060
XTA Electronics Ltd, pg 1071
Yorkville Sound Inc, pg 1072

OHIO

Aztec Video Productions, pg 801
ITA Audio Visual Solutions, pg 902
Parts Express, pg 969
Jimmy Rea Electronics Inc, pg 992
Smithall Electronics Inc, pg 1014
Tri-State Audio Visual Co, pg 1044

OREGON

Spectrum Systems Design, pg 1021
SuperDigital Ltd, pg 1029

PENNSYLVANIA

Advanced AV, pg 777
Clair Brothers Audio Systems Inc, pg 829
Vistacom Inc, pg 1059

RHODE ISLAND

Shanix Inc, pg 1008

SOUTH CAROLINA

DaviSound, pg 843

TENNESSEE

Belew Enterprises, pg 804
Durrell LLC, pg 854
Lowrance Sound Co Inc, pg 925
Mr Mark's Used Musical, Stereo & Studio Equipment Store, pg 944
Spectrum Sound Inc, pg 1021
Technical Support Systems LLC, pg 1034
Zion Music Group, pg 1074

TEXAS

AVES Audio Visual Systems Inc, pg 798
CAM Audio Inc, pg 817
Crossroads Audio Inc, pg 840
Data Projections Inc, pg 843
Lubbock Audio Visual Inc, pg 925
Pro Video & Film Equipment Co Inc, pg 983
Quality Audio Visual Service Inc, pg 988
RadioShack Corp, pg 990
RF Specialties of Texas LLC, pg 996
Southwest Sound & Electronics Inc, pg 1019
Tarpley Media Systems, pg 1032

UTAH

Performance Audio, pg 973

VERMONT

Production Advantage Inc, pg 984

VIRGINIA

Avitecture Inc, pg 799
Design & Production Inc, pg 845
Intellidyne LLC, pg 899
Lee Hartman & Sons Inc, pg 918
Rocktown Media, pg 998
The Whitlock Group, pg 1065

WASHINGTON

CCI Solutions, pg 821
D A Sound, pg 842
Northern Lights & Pro Audio, pg 959

WISCONSIN

Audio Visual of Milwaukee Inc, pg 795
Full Compass Systems, pg 874

PUERTO RICO

Audio Visual Concepts Inc, pg 795
Bonnin Electronics Inc, pg 810

ALBERTA

Infosat Communications Inc, pg 898
Unique Communications Ltd, pg 1048

BRITISH COLUMBIA

ADI Systems Inc, pg 776
Commercial Electronics Ltd, pg 832

MANITOBA

Advance Pro, pg 777
Inland Audio Visual Ltd, pg 898

ONTARIO

Cinema Stage Inc, pg 827
Sascom Marketing Group Inc, pg 1003
Westbury National Show Systems Ltd, pg 1064

QUEBEC

AVS Technologies Inc, pg 800
JAM Industries Ltd, pg 903
SC Media Canada, pg 1003

Equalizer Manufacturers

ARIZONA

Radio Design Labs (RDL), pg 990

CALIFORNIA

Furman, pg 874
Graham-Patten, pg 881
Harman Pro North America, pg 885
Manley Laboratories Inc, pg 930
Martinsound Inc, pg 932
Meyer Sound Laboratories Inc, pg 940
Millennia Media FPC, pg 943
Nady Systems Inc, pg 952
Sherwood America Inc, pg 1009
Summit Audio Inc, pg 1028
TOA Electronics Inc, pg 1041

COLORADO

Video Accessory Corp, pg 1054

CONNECTICUT

Sound Control Technologies Inc, pg 1017

FLORIDA

JT Communications, pg 906
Sabine® Inc, pg 1001

ILLINOIS

Esoteric Sound, pg 862
Precision Electronics Inc, pg 980
SoundTech, pg 1018

MARYLAND

API, pg 788

MINNESOTA

Digital Audio Labs, pg 847
Great River Electronics, pg 881
Telex Communications Inc, pg 1037
Telex EVI, pg 1037

MISSISSIPPI

Peavey Electronics Corp, pg 970

NEW JERSEY

Apogee Sound International LLC, pg 788

NEW MEXICO

Lectrosonics Inc, pg 918

NEW YORK

Ashly Audio Inc, pg 792
GLI Sound Systems, pg 878
Harbro Corp, pg 884
Hot House Professional Audio, pg 891
MultiDyne Video & Fiber Optics Systems, pg 950
Yorkville Sound Inc, pg 1072

NORTH CAROLINA

Audioarts Engineering, pg 796
Micro Technology Unlimited, pg 941
Wheatstone Corp, pg 1065

OREGON

BIAMP Systems, pg 806

RHODE ISLAND

M-Audio, pg 927
Numark Industries Inc, pg 960

SOUTH CAROLINA

DaviSound, pg 843

TENNESSEE

Auratron Systems, pg 796

UTAH

Rolls Corp, pg 999

WASHINGTON

AudioControl®, pg 796
Rane, pg 991

BRITISH COLUMBIA

Richmond Sound Design Ltd, pg 996

Equalizer Rentals

ARIZONA

Merestone, pg 938
Video West Inc, pg 1056

CALIFORNIA

AGF Media Services, pg 778
Alliant Event Services, pg 781
Ametron Audio/Video, pg 785
Associated Sound, pg 792
Audio Rents, pg 794
AV Guys, pg 797
Design FX Audio, pg 845
Express Media Inc, pg 864
FXC Communications, pg 874
JD Audio Visual Inc, pg 904
Location Sound Corp, pg 924
Lynch Communications, pg 926
McCune Audio-Video-Lighting, pg 935
Muse Presentation Technologies, pg 950
On-Trax Inc, pg 963

AUDIO

Equalizer Rentals (continued)

CALIFORNIA (continued)

Slate Media Group, pg 1013
Sound Service Co, pg 1017
Stanislaus Audio Video Inc, pg 1023
Synthesizer Rental Service, pg 1030
Total Media Group, pg 1042
Towards 2000 Inc, pg 1043
Video Resources Inc, pg 1056
Videorama Industries LLC, pg 1057
VMI Inc, pg 1060

COLORADO

Audio Consultant Services Inc, pg 794
Multimedia Audio Visual Inc, pg 950
Spectrum Audio Visual Services, pg 1020

CONNECTICUT

A/V Davey, pg 797
Connecticut Audio & Theatrical Supply, pg 835
Fox Connecticut, pg 872

DELAWARE

Side Door Studio Inc, pg 1010

FLORIDA

Allstar Audio Systems Inc, pg 782
AVI-SPL, pg 798
Image Technical Services, pg 895
Industrial Strength Inc, pg 897
Lighting Sales Connections, pg 920
Pro Stage Inc, pg 983
Sight & Sound Productions, pg 1010
TAI Audio, pg 1031
Universal Studios Florida® Production Group, pg 1049

GEORGIA

Lighting & Production Equipment Inc, pg 920
MAGNUM Companies Ltd, pg 929
Stage Front Presentation Systems, pg 1022

HAWAII

Sight & Sound Studios, pg 1010

ILLINOIS

AV Chicago Inc, pg 797
On Stage Audio, pg 963
QuickSet International Inc, pg 989
RC Communications, pg 992
Show Department Inc, pg 1009
Staging Resources Inc, pg 1023
Woodside Avenue Music Productions Inc, pg 1069

IOWA

Central Lighting & Equipment Inc (CLE), pg 823
ECS Inc, pg 856

KENTUCKY

Audio Visual Techniques Inc, pg 796

MARYLAND

Advance Audiovisual Presentation Ltd, pg 777
Cardinal Sound & Video, pg 820
CPR MultiMedia Solutions, pg 837
Event Tech, pg 863
Maryland Sound International Holding Co LLC, pg 933
Visual Aids Electronics Corp, pg 1059

MASSACHUSETTS

AVFX Inc, pg 798
Terry Hanley Audio Systems Inc, pg 884
massAV, pg 933
Preston Productions Inc, pg 981

MICHIGAN

Digi Sign Design LLC, pg 847
K&R All Media Productions Inc, pg 908
K&R's Recording Studios Inc, pg 908
On Stage Visuals, pg 963

MISSOURI

Production Support Services Inc, pg 985
Show-Me Audio-Visual, pg 1009

MONTANA

Jereco Studios Inc, pg 905

NEVADA

GES Audio Visual, pg 877

NEW HAMPSHIRE

APS Lighting-Sound-AV, pg 789

NEW JERSEY

Audio Visual Associates, pg 795
Audio Visual Dynamics®, pg 795
CFP Video Productions Inc, pg 823
Earl Girls Inc, pg 855
Giant Audio Visual Inc, pg 878
Jeep Jazz Media Solutions, pg 905
Moe AV LLC, pg 945
Nelson Enterprises Theatrical Supply Co, pg 954
PLS Staging, pg 977
SLD Lighting, pg 1013
Starlite Productions, pg 1024
Wired 4 Sound Inc, pg 1068

NEW MEXICO

Quickbeam Systems Inc (QSI), pg 989

NEW YORK

Audio Visual Resources LLC, pg 795
Aura Sonic Ltd, pg 796
Colortone Audio Visual, pg 832
CP Communications, pg 837
Design Audio Visual Inc, pg 845
Dreamhire LLC, pg 852
KVL Audio Visual Services Inc, pg 914
Posthorn Recordings, pg 979
TBA Global Events, pg 1032
Visual Word Systems Inc, pg 1060

NORTH CAROLINA

A&V Company, pg 772
AV Metro Inc, pg 797
Visual Aids Electronics of North Carolina Inc, pg 1059

OHIO

ITA Audio Visual Solutions, pg 902
Lyon Video Inc, pg 927
Mills James Productions, pg 943
Production Solutions Inc, pg 984
R&B Communications Inc, pg 991
Smithall Electronics Inc, pg 1014

OKLAHOMA

PDC Productions, pg 970

OREGON

Rose City Sound, pg 999

PENNSYLVANIA

Advanced AV, pg 777
FMP Media Solutions Inc, pg 870
Production Solutions Inc, pg 985
Right Coast Recording Inc, pg 997

TENNESSEE

Mr Mark's Used Musical, Stereo & Studio Equipment Store, pg 944
Technical Support Systems LLC, pg 1034

TEXAS

Alford Media Services, pg 780
Bright Star Productions Inc, pg 812
Crossroads Audio Inc, pg 840
Data Display Audio Visual Co LP, pg 843
Lubbock Audio Visual Inc, pg 925
Music Lab Inc, pg 950
Onstage Systems, pg 963
The Samuels Co, pg 1002
Stage Directions, pg 1022

UTAH

Performance Audio, pg 973

VERMONT

Dark Star Lighting & Production, pg 842
Edgewood Studios, pg 857
Parlato Productions, pg 969

VIRGINIA

American AV, pg 783

WASHINGTON

D A Sound, pg 842
Northern Lights & Pro Audio, pg 959
Pacific Northwest Theatre Associates Inc (PNTA), pg 967
Victory Studios, pg 1054

WISCONSIN

Full Compass Systems, pg 874

PUERTO RICO

Stage Crew Audiovisual Inc, pg 1022

ALBERTA

Evolution Presentation Technologies, pg 863
Unique Communications Ltd, pg 1048

BRITISH COLUMBIA

Commercial Electronics Ltd, pg 832
DL Sound & Lighting Productions Ltd, pg 849

MANITOBA

Inland Audio Visual Ltd, pg 898

ONTARIO

RB Productions, pg 992
Westbury National Show Systems Ltd, pg 1064

Equalizer Repairs

CALIFORNIA

Ametron Audio/Video, pg 785
Audio Images Corp, pg 794
Audio Upgrades, pg 795
Diemer Amp & Keyboard Repair, pg 846
McAlister Electronics, pg 935
Sound Service Co, pg 1017
TOA Electronics Inc, pg 1041
Towards 2000 Inc, pg 1043

CONNECTICUT

HB Communications Inc, pg 886

FLORIDA

Hi-Tech Enterprises Inc, pg 888
JT Communications, pg 906
Phat Planet Recording Studios, pg 973
Stereo Sales Inc, pg 1024
TAI Audio, pg 1031

GEORGIA

Lighting & Production Equipment Inc, pg 920
Stage Front Presentation Systems, pg 1022

ILLINOIS

Midwest Digital Corp, pg 942

INDIANA

SHP Electronics, pg 1010
Sweetwater Sound Inc, pg 1029

IOWA

ECS Inc, pg 856

KENTUCKY

Axxis Inc, pg 800
Barney Miller's Inc, pg 943
NOR-COM Inc, pg 958

MARYLAND

Visual Aids Electronics Corp, pg 1059

MASSACHUSETTS

Professional Audio Design Inc, pg 985

MICHIGAN

TeL Systems, pg 1035

MINNESOTA

Aggressive Records Audio Duplication LLC, pg 778

NEW JERSEY

Earl Girls Inc, pg 855
Nelson Enterprises Theatrical Supply Co, pg 954
Starlite Productions, pg 1024

NEW MEXICO

Quickbeam Systems Inc (QSI), pg 989

NEW YORK

Design Audio Visual Inc, pg 845
Hot House Professional Audio, pg 891
Toys From The Attic, pg 1043

OHIO

ITA Audio Visual Solutions, pg 902
Smithall Electronics Inc, pg 1014
Tri-State Audio Visual Co, pg 1044

OREGON

All Service Musical Electronics Repair, pg 780

PENNSYLVANIA

Right Coast Recording Inc, pg 997

SOUTH CAROLINA

DaviSound, pg 843

TENNESSEE

Belew Enterprises, pg 804
Technical Support Systems LLC, pg 1034

TEXAS

Lubbock Audio Visual Inc, pg 925
Quality Audio Visual Service Inc, pg 988

VIRGINIA

Avitecture Inc, pg 799

WASHINGTON

Northern Lights & Pro Audio, pg 959
Pacific Northwest Theatre Associates Inc (PNTA), pg 967

WISCONSIN

Full Compass Systems, pg 874

PUERTO RICO

Bonnin Electronics Inc, pg 810

ALBERTA

Infosat Communications Inc, pg 898
Unique Communications Ltd, pg 1048

BRITISH COLUMBIA

Commercial Electronics Ltd, pg 832

MANITOBA

Inland Audio Visual Ltd, pg 898

ONTARIO

Westbury National Show Systems Ltd, pg 1064

QUEBEC

SC Media Canada, pg 1003

Ethnic Music, *see* Music Libraries—Ethnic & International

Fiber Optic Cable Distributors

ARIZONA

EAR Professional Audio/Video, pg 855
Troxell Communications Inc, pg 1045

ARKANSAS

Jay S Stanley & Associates Inc, pg 1023

CALIFORNIA

Adolph Gasser Inc, pg 776
Ametron Audio/Video, pg 785
Audio Images Corp, pg 794
Delicate Electronics Sales Inc, pg 845
FXC Communications, pg 874
Hosa Technology Inc, pg 891
Southern California Sound Image Inc, pg 1019
SSL Industries Inc, pg 1022
SuperVision, pg 1029
Towards 2000 Inc, pg 1043
Zack Electronics Inc, pg 1073

COLORADO

Audio Consultant Services Inc, pg 794

CONNECTICUT

Connecticut Audio & Theatrical Supply, pg 835
HB Communications Inc, pg 886
Redco Audio Inc, pg 993

DELAWARE

Actors Attic, pg 775

FLORIDA

Access Media Group, pg 773
Digital Video Systems Inc, pg 848
Griffiths Broadcast Co Inc, pg 882
Herman Pro AV, pg 888
Hunter Electronics LLC, pg 892
Martin Professional Inc, pg 932
Pro Stage Inc, pg 983
Sight & Sound Productions, pg 1010
Stereo Sales Inc, pg 1024

GEORGIA

Accu-Tech, pg 773
Stage Front Presentation Systems, pg 1022

ILLINOIS

Allen Visual Systems Inc, pg 781
Arcor Electronics Co, pg 789
Clark Wire & Cable, pg 829
Cole Wire & Cable Co Inc, pg 831
Gepco®, a General Cable brand, pg 877
Joseph Electronics, pg 906
Quintessence Audio Ltd, pg 989

INDIANA

Sensory Technologies LLC, pg 1006
SHP Electronics, pg 1010
Sweetwater Sound Inc, pg 1029

IOWA

ECS Inc, pg 856

KENTUCKY

Axxis Inc, pg 800
NOR-COM Inc, pg 958

MARYLAND

Bradley Broadcast & Pro Audio, pg 811
Kipp Visual Systems Inc, pg 911
TKH Security Solutions USA Inc, pg 1041

MASSACHUSETTS

Professional Audio Design Inc, pg 985
SLR Enterprises LLC, pg 1013

MICHIGAN

Ascom Communications Contractors, pg 791
DAWNco, pg 843
TeL Systems, pg 1035

MISSOURI

The RapcoHorizon Co, pg 991

NEVADA

MeshTel-Intelite, pg 939

NEW JERSEY

Alltec Stores, a Vcom IMC Company, pg 782
Argraph Corp, pg 789
Canare Corporation of America, pg 819
Diversified Systems Inc, pg 849
Fiber Optic Systems Inc (FOSI), pg 866
Interstate Connecting Components, pg 901
Onkyo USA Corp, pg 963
Starlite Productions, pg 1024
York Telecom, pg 1072

NEW YORK

Albany Theatre Supply Co Inc, pg 780
BTX Technologies, pg 814
Communications Specialties Inc, pg 833
Direct Broadcast Services Inc (DBS), pg 848
HAVE Inc, pg 886
Markertek Video Supply, pg 931
MultiDyne Video & Fiber Optics Systems, pg 950
TecNec Distributing, pg 1035

OREGON

TARA Labs, pg 1032

PENNSYLVANIA

Advanced AV, pg 777
The Lerro Corp, pg 919
Techni-Tool Inc, pg 1033

TENNESSEE

Durrell LLC, pg 854
Lowrance Sound Co Inc, pg 925

TEXAS

Lubbock Audio Visual Inc, pg 925
Sundance Systems, Fibox Products Division, pg 1028

UTAH

Performance Audio, pg 973

VERMONT

Power & Telephone Supply Co, pg 979

VIRGINIA

Avitecture Inc, pg 799
The Whitlock Group, pg 1065

WASHINGTON

Telect Inc, pg 1036

WISCONSIN

Audio Visual of Milwaukee Inc, pg 795
Full Compass Systems, pg 874

PUERTO RICO

Bonnin Electronics Inc, pg 810

ALBERTA

Infosat Communications Inc, pg 898

MANITOBA

Advance Pro, pg 777

ONTARIO

Cinema Stage Inc, pg 827

Fiber Optic Cable Manufacturers

ARIZONA

Covid Inc, pg 837

CALIFORNIA

Enright Co, pg 861
Fiber Optic Cable Shop, pg 866
Gefen, pg 876
Hosa Technology Inc, pg 891
Monster Cable Products Inc, pg 945
Opticomm-EMCORE, pg 964
Physical Optics Corp, pg 975

ILLINOIS

Joseph Electronics, pg 906

INDIANA

Belden, pg 804

MARYLAND

RCI Custom Products, pg 992

AUDIO

Fiber Optic Cable Manufacturers (continued)

MASSACHUSETTS

Miranda Telecast Fiber Systems Inc, pg 944
Mohawk, pg 945

MISSOURI

The RapcoHorizon Co, pg 991

NEVADA

MeshTel-Intelite, pg 939

NEW JERSEY

Brim Electronics, pg 812
Canare Corporation of America, pg 819
Crestron Electronics Inc, pg 839
Onkyo USA Corp, pg 963

NEW YORK

Communications Specialties Inc, pg 833
MultiDyne Video & Fiber Optics Systems, pg 950

NORTH CAROLINA

CommScope Inc, pg 832

OREGON

TARA Labs, pg 1032

PENNSYLVANIA

West Penn Wire, pg 1064

WASHINGTON

Telect Inc, pg 1036

Fiber Optic Cable Repairs

CALIFORNIA

Audio Images Corp, pg 794
McAlister Electronics, pg 935
SSL Industries Inc, pg 1022
Towards 2000 Inc, pg 1043

ILLINOIS

Allen Visual Systems Inc, pg 781
Joseph Electronics, pg 906

IOWA

ECS Inc, pg 856

KENTUCKY

Axxis Inc, pg 800
NOR-COM Inc, pg 958

MICHIGAN

K&R's Recording Studios Inc, pg 908
TeL Systems, pg 1035

ALBERTA

Infosat Communications Inc, pg 898

Folk Music, *see* Music Libraries—Folk

Headset & Headphone Distributors

ALABAMA

Curtis Company, pg 841
Media Visions Inc, pg 937

ARIZONA

Arizona Cine Equipment, pg 789
EAR Professional Audio/Video, pg 855
Metropolitan Audio-Visual Inc, pg 940
Projector SuperStore LLC, pg 986
Tempe Camera, pg 1037
Troxell Communications Inc, pg 1045

CALIFORNIA

Adolph Gasser Inc, pg 776
AKG Acoustics US, pg 779
Ametron Audio/Video, pg 785
Arkon Resources Inc, pg 790
Associated Sound, pg 792
Audio Images Corp, pg 794
Be Media, pg 804
California Tape Products Inc, pg 817
Christy's Editorial, pg 826
Cibola Systems, pg 826
Clear-Com®, pg 829
Delicate Electronics Sales Inc, pg 845
Eiki International, pg 858
Empire Wholesale Inc, pg 860
FXC Communications, pg 874
Gearhouse Broadcast LLC, pg 876
GigaSonic, pg 878
Gluskin's Custom Audio Video, pg 879
GMF Sound Inc, pg 879
Instructional Materials & Equipment Distributors (I-Med), pg 899
JD Audio Visual Inc, pg 904
Location Sound Corp, pg 924
Logitech, pg 924
Lloyd F McKinney Associates Inc, pg 935
Media Fabricators Inc, pg 936
MediaPOINTE, pg 938
Pacific Radio Electronics, pg 967
PMP Marketing Inc, pg 977
POP TV, pg 978
Premier Lighting & Production Co, pg 980
Professional Sound Corp, pg 985
Promax Systems, pg 986
Related Visual Inc, pg 994
Randall Schiller Productions, pg 1004
Sound Service Co, pg 1017
Sounds Unique, pg 1018
Southern California Sound Image Inc, pg 1019
SSL Industries Inc, pg 1022
SuperVision, pg 1029
Towards 2000 Inc, pg 1043
Tri-Ed, pg 1044
VMI Inc, pg 1060
VTP Inc, pg 1061
Zack Electronics Inc, pg 1073

COLORADO

Audio Consultant Services Inc, pg 794
Spectrum Audio Visual Services, pg 1020

CONNECTICUT

Connecticut Audio & Theatrical Supply, pg 835
HB Communications Inc, pg 886
MAVCO, pg 934
The Music People Inc, pg 951
Sennheiser Electronic Corp, pg 1006

DELAWARE

Actors Attic, pg 775

FLORIDA

Access Media Group, pg 773
Allstar Audio Systems Inc, pg 782
BAI Distributors Inc, pg 801
Broadcasters General Store Inc, pg 813
Digital Video Systems Inc, pg 848
Gulf Coast Audio Visual Producers Inc, pg 883
Harris Corp, pg 885
Herman Pro AV, pg 888
Hi-Tech Enterprises Inc, pg 888
Hi-Tech Import Export Corp, pg 888
Hunter Electronics LLC, pg 892
Industrial Strength Inc, pg 897
Intermark Industries Inc, pg 900
Lighting Sales Connections, pg 920
Media Concepts Inc, pg 936
Midtown Video Inc, pg 942
Photomart Cine-Video Inc, pg 975
Pro Stage Inc, pg 983
Recording Media & Equipment Inc (RM&E), pg 993
Sight & Sound Productions, pg 1010
Stereo Sales Inc, pg 1024
TAI Audio, pg 1031
Technomedia Solutions, pg 1035
Videoscope, pg 1057

GEORGIA

AVForSale, pg 798
Baker Audio Inc, pg 801
Lighting & Production Equipment Inc, pg 920
LT Sound Inc, pg 925
Stage Front Presentation Systems, pg 1022
Visioneering International Inc, pg 1058

HAWAII

The Audio Visual Co (AVCO), pg 795

ILLINOIS

Allen Visual Systems Inc, pg 781
Central Audio-Visual Equipment Inc, pg 823
Joseph Electronics, pg 906
LKG Industries Inc, pg 923
C V Lloyde, pg 923
Production Intercom Inc, pg 984
Quintessence Audio Ltd, pg 989
RAM Systems LLC, pg 991
RC Communications, pg 992
Waldom Electronics Corp, pg 1061
Woodside Avenue Music Productions Inc, pg 1069

INDIANA

Sensory Technologies LLC, pg 1006
SHP Electronics, pg 1010
Sweetwater Sound Inc, pg 1029

IOWA

ECS Inc, pg 856

KANSAS

Smith Audio-Visual Inc, pg 1014

KENTUCKY

Axxis Inc, pg 800
Barney Miller's Inc, pg 943
NOR-COM Inc, pg 958

LOUISIANA

Intermedia Technologies, pg 900
Pace Systems, pg 966

MAINE

Headlight Audio Visual Inc, pg 887

MARYLAND

Bradley Broadcast & Pro Audio, pg 811
Cardinal Sound & Video, pg 820
Human Circuit, pg 892
Kipp Visual Systems Inc, pg 911
Noventri, pg 960

MASSACHUSETTS

Terry Hanley Audio Systems Inc, pg 884
Hunt's Photo, Video & Digital, pg 892
Professional Audio Design Inc, pg 985
Rule Broadcast Systems, pg 1000
University Products Inc, pg 1050

MICHIGAN

Olson Anderson Co, pg 786
Ascom Communications Contractors, pg 791
City Events Group, pg 828
Digi Sign Design LLC, pg 847
TeL Systems, pg 1035

MINNESOTA

Advanced Audio-Visual Inc, pg 777
Harris Communications Inc, pg 885
New Life Communications Inc, pg 956

MISSISSIPPI

Bowie Audio Visual Enterprises Inc, pg 811

MISSOURI

Communitronics Corp, pg 833
Conference Technologies Inc, pg 835
Image Technologies Corp, pg 895
Modern Communications Inc, pg 944
Schiller's Audio-Visual, pg 1004

NEW HAMPSHIRE

APS Lighting-Sound-AV, pg 789
Technet® Systems Group, pg 1033

NEW JERSEY

Alltec Stores, a Vcom IMC Company, pg 782
Argraph Corp, pg 789
Audio Visual Associates, pg 795
Audio Visual Dynamics®, pg 795
AV Bluebook, pg 797

Comprehensive Cable & Connectivity Co, pg 833
Earl Girls Inc, pg 855
Entel Systems Inc, pg 861
Hamilton Buhl, pg 884
The Music Place, pg 951
National Audio-Visual Supply, pg 952
Nelson Enterprises Theatrical Supply Co, pg 954
Onkyo USA Corp, pg 963
PatchAmp, pg 970
SLD Lighting, pg 1013
Starlite Productions, pg 1024
Video Corporation of America (VCA), pg 1055
Wilray Audio Visual Corp, pg 1067
Wired 4 Sound Inc, pg 1068
York Telecom, pg 1072

NEW YORK

Albany Theatre Supply Co Inc, pg 780
American Video Inc, pg 785
Audio-Video Corp, pg 795
Aura Sonic Ltd, pg 796
AV Workshop, pg 797
beyerdynamic Inc, pg 806
BMI Supply, pg 810
Cadence Jazz Records, pg 816
Colortone Audio Visual, pg 832
Communication Corner Inc, pg 832
Creative Stage Lighting Co Inc, pg 838
Custom Media Environments, pg 841
Design Audio Visual Inc, pg 845
Gaylord Brothers, pg 876
Gotham Sound & Communications Inc, pg 881
HAVE Inc, pg 886
Hot House Professional Audio, pg 891
Indigo Productions, pg 897
KVL Audio Visual Services Inc, pg 914
Long Island Video Enterprises Live Inc, pg 924
Markertek Video Supply, pg 931
Neptune Photo Inc, pg 954
NorthCountry Distributors, pg 959
RNJ Electronics, pg 997
Russell Industries Inc, pg 1001
Sanako Inc, pg 1002
Sentry Industries Inc, pg 1007
SmartSource Computer & AV Rentals, pg 1014
Stampede Presentation Products Inc, pg 1023
Syracuse Scenery & Stage Lighting Co Inc, pg 1031
Technisphere Corp, pg 1034
TecNec Distributing, pg 1035
Theatrical Services & Supplies Inc, pg 1038
Visual Word Systems Inc, pg 1060
Voyetra Turtle Beach, pg 1061

NORTH CAROLINA

Innocinema, pg 898
Strategic Connections, pg 1026

OHIO

Copp Integrated Systems, pg 836
ITA Audio Visual Solutions, pg 902
Midwest Photo Exchange, pg 942
Parts Express, pg 969
Jimmy Rea Electronics Inc, pg 992
Smithall Electronics Inc, pg 1014
Tri-State Audio Visual Co, pg 1044
Tri-State Visual Products, pg 1044

OREGON

Lightspeed Technologies Inc, pg 921
SuperDigital Ltd, pg 1029

PENNSYLVANIA

Advanced AV, pg 777
Audio Visions Inc, pg 795
Brodart Co, pg 813
J E Foss Co, pg 871
Grise Audio Visual Center Inc, pg 882
The Lerro Corp, pg 919
Morefield Communications Inc, pg 946
Visual Sound Inc, pg 1059
Wespen Audio Visual Co, pg 1063

TENNESSEE

Durrell LLC, pg 854
Lowrance Sound Co Inc, pg 925
Spectrum Sound Inc, pg 1021
Technical Support Systems LLC, pg 1034
Trew Audio Inc, pg 1044
Zion Music Group, pg 1074

TEXAS

Audio Visual Technologies Group, pg 796
AVES Audio Visual Systems Inc, pg 798
CAM Audio Inc, pg 817
Crossroads Audio Inc, pg 840
FitzCo Sound Inc, pg 869
Heffernan Audio Visual, pg 887
Industrial Audio/Video Inc, pg 897
Lubbock Audio Visual Inc, pg 925
Precision Camera & Video, pg 980
Pro Video & Film Equipment Co Inc, pg 983
Quality Audio Visual Service Inc, pg 988
RadioShack Corp, pg 990
RF Specialties of Texas LLC, pg 996
Schoolhouse Audio Visual, pg 1004
Southwest Sound & Electronics Inc, pg 1019
Tarpley Media Systems, pg 1032

UTAH

Performance Audio, pg 973
RIA Corp, pg 996

VIRGINIA

Avitecture Inc, pg 799
Boitnott Visual Communications Corp (BVC), pg 810
Design & Production Inc, pg 845
Hoppmann Audio Visual, pg 891
Lee Hartman & Sons Inc, pg 918
Old Dominion Broadcasting, pg 961
StageSound, pg 1023
The Whitlock Group, pg 1065

WASHINGTON

Broadcast Supply World Wide, pg 813
CCI Solutions, pg 821
Northern Lights & Pro Audio, pg 959
Pacific Northwest Theatre Associates Inc (PNTA), pg 967

WISCONSIN

Audio Visual of Milwaukee Inc, pg 795
Camera Corner Connecting Point, pg 818
Demco Inc, pg 845
Full Compass Systems, pg 874

PUERTO RICO

Bonnin Electronics Inc, pg 810

ALBERTA

McBain Audio Visual Ltd, pg 935
Sharp's Audio-Visual Ltd, pg 1008
Unique Communications Ltd, pg 1048

BRITISH COLUMBIA

Commercial Electronics Ltd, pg 832
ProVision Video Sales & Rentals Inc, pg 986

MANITOBA

Advance Pro, pg 777
Inland Audio Visual Ltd, pg 898

ONTARIO

Edcom Multimedia Products, pg 856
HD Source, pg 886
Henry's Camera, pg 888
Nationwide Audio Visual Co, pg 953
Premier A/V Sales Ltd, pg 980
Westbury National Show Systems Ltd, pg 1064

QUEBEC

AVS Technologies Inc, pg 800
Concept Audio-Visual, pg 834
JAM Industries Ltd, pg 903
SC Media Canada, pg 1003
Sennheiser (Canada) Inc, pg 1006

Headset & Headphone Manufacturers

CALIFORNIA

AKG Acoustics US, pg 779
Anchor Audio Inc, pg 786
Arkon Resources Inc, pg 790
Califone International Inc, pg 817
Calrad Electronics, pg 817
Clear-Com®, pg 829
HM Electronics Inc (HME), pg 889
Hosa Technology Inc, pg 891
Logitech, pg 924
Nady Systems Inc, pg 952
Plantronics Inc, pg 976
Simon - Kaloi Engineering, pg 1011
Sony Electronics Inc, pg 1016
Sounds Unique, pg 1018
TEAC America Inc, pg 1033
TeachLogic Inc, pg 1033

CONNECTICUT

Earmark LLC, pg 855
Redco Audio Inc, pg 993
Vista Group International Inc, pg 1059

FLORIDA

Cobham Tactical Communications & Surveillance, pg 831
Intermark Industries Inc, pg 900

ILLINOIS

AmpliVox Portable Sound Systems, pg 785
Central Audio-Visual Equipment Inc, pg 823
Shure Inc, pg 1010
SoundTech, pg 1018
Technical Exhibits Corp, pg 1033

MASSACHUSETTS

Bose Corp, pg 811
David Clark Co Inc, pg 843

MINNESOTA

Telex Communications Inc, pg 1037
Telex EVI, pg 1037

NEW JERSEY

AV Bluebook, pg 797
National Audio-Visual Supply, pg 952
Onkyo USA Corp, pg 963
Panasonic Consumer Electronics Co, pg 968
Sony Pro Audio (Broadcast & Professional Systems Division), pg 1016

NEW MEXICO

EDCOR Electronics Corp, pg 856

NEW YORK

Benchmark Media Systems Inc, pg 805
beyerdynamic Inc, pg 806
Sentry Industries Inc, pg 1007
Television Equipment Associates Inc (TEA), pg 1036
Voyetra Turtle Beach, pg 1061

OHIO

Audio-Technica US Inc, pg 794

OREGON

Lightspeed Technologies Inc, pg 921

RHODE ISLAND

Numark Industries Inc, pg 960

TENNESSEE

Remote Audio Products, pg 994
Stanton Magnetics, pg 1023

TEXAS

Setcom Corp™, pg 1007

WISCONSIN

Koss Corp, pg 913

Headset & Headphone Rentals

ALABAMA

Audio-Video Resources Inc, pg 795

ARIZONA

Arizona Cine Equipment, pg 789
Merestone, pg 938
Metropolitan Audio-Visual Inc, pg 940
Video West Inc, pg 1056

AUDIO

Headset & Headphone Rentals (continued)

ARKANSAS

White Diamond Productions, pg 1065

CALIFORNIA

Absolute Rentals, pg 772
Alliant Event Services, pg 781
Alternative Rentals, pg 783
Ametron Audio/Video, pg 785
Artichoke Productions, pg 791
Associated Sound, pg 792
Audio Rents, pg 794
AV Guys, pg 797
Big Time Picture Company Inc, pg 807
Express Media Inc, pg 864
FXC Communications, pg 874
Golden Gate Studios, pg 880
Hollywood Sound Systems, pg 890
Imagecraft Productions, pg 896
JD Audio Visual Inc, pg 904
Location Sound Corp, pg 924
Lynch Communications, pg 926
McCune Audio-Video-Lighting, pg 935
Media Fabricators Inc, pg 936
Munday & Collins AV, pg 950
Muse Presentation Technologies, pg 950
Old School Cameras, pg 961
On-Trax Inc, pg 963
Premier Lighting & Production Co, pg 980
Pro HD Rentals, pg 983
Production Gear Rentals (PGR), pg 984
PSAV® Presentation Services, pg 986
Radiant Images, pg 990
Randall Schiller Productions, pg 1004
Shooting Star Video, pg 1009
Slate Media Group, pg 1013
Sound Service Co, pg 1017
The Studios at Paramount, pg 1027
Synthesizer Rental Service, pg 1030
Total Media Group, pg 1042
Towards 2000 Inc, pg 1043
VER-Video Equipment Rentals, pg 1053
Video Resources Inc, pg 1056
Voice & Video Rentals, pg 1060
Warner Bros Production Sound & Video Services, pg 1062
Westcoast Video Productions Inc, pg 1064

COLORADO

Audio Consultant Services Inc, pg 794
Daylight Productions & Rentals, pg 844
Multimedia Audio Visual Inc, pg 950
Spectrum Audio Visual Services, pg 1020

CONNECTICUT

A/V Davey, pg 797
Connecticut Audio & Theatrical Supply, pg 835

DELAWARE

Actors Attic, pg 775
Side Door Studio Inc, pg 1010

FLORIDA

Allstar Audio Systems Inc, pg 782
Budget Video Rentals, pg 815
Cinema East, pg 827
Gulf Coast Audio Visual Producers Inc, pg 883
Hi-Tech Enterprises Inc, pg 888
Image Technical Services, pg 895
Industrial Strength Inc, pg 897
Jordan Klein Film & Video (JKFV), pg 906
Knowles Video Inc (KVI), pg 912
Lighting Sales Connections, pg 920
Pro Stage Inc, pg 983
Sight & Sound Productions, pg 1010
Skyline Broadcast, pg 1013
TAI Audio, pg 1031
10-20 Productions, pg 1037

GEORGIA

ECG Productions, pg 856
Lighting & Production Equipment Inc, pg 920
MAGNUM Companies Ltd, pg 929
Stage Front Presentation Systems, pg 1022
Staging Directions Inc, pg 1023

HAWAII

Sight & Sound Studios, pg 1010

ILLINOIS

AV Chicago Inc, pg 797
Backstar Creative Media Inc, pg 801
Beatty TeleVisual Productions, pg 804
Central Audio-Visual Equipment Inc, pg 823
Firehouse Studios, pg 868
On Site Video, pg 963
On Stage Audio, pg 963
QuickSet International Inc, pg 989
RC Communications, pg 992
Woodside Avenue Music Productions Inc, pg 1069
Zacuto, pg 1073

INDIANA

Advanced Media Integration, pg 777

IOWA

ECS Inc, pg 856
Pro Video, pg 983

KENTUCKY

Audio Visual Techniques Inc, pg 796

LOUISIANA

Pace Systems, pg 966

MARYLAND

Advance Audiovisual Presentation Ltd, pg 777
CPR MultiMedia Solutions, pg 837
Event Tech, pg 863
Maryland Sound International Holding Co LLC, pg 933
Soundtrax Optical Sound Recording, pg 1018
Visual Aids Electronics Corp, pg 1059

MASSACHUSETTS

Terry Hanley Audio Systems Inc, pg 884
massAV, pg 933
Preston Productions Inc, pg 981

MICHIGAN

City Events Group, pg 828
Digi Sign Design LLC, pg 847
K&R All Media Productions Inc, pg 908
K&R's Recording Studios Inc, pg 908
Lowing Light & Grip Inc, pg 925

MINNESOTA

Advanced Audio-Visual Inc, pg 777
Lights On, pg 921

MISSISSIPPI

Bowie Audio Visual Enterprises Inc, pg 811

MISSOURI

Cashmark Media Inc, pg 820
Image Technologies Corp, pg 895
Show-Me Audio-Visual, pg 1009

NEVADA

GES Audio Visual, pg 877

NEW HAMPSHIRE

Apertura, pg 788
APS Lighting-Sound-AV, pg 789

NEW JERSEY

Audio Visual Associates, pg 795
Audio Visual Dynamics®, pg 795
Earl Girls Inc, pg 855
Moe AV LLC, pg 945
Nelson Enterprises Theatrical Supply Co, pg 954
PLS Staging, pg 977
Bill Quinn Productions, pg 989
SLD Lighting, pg 1013
Starlite Productions, pg 1024
Wired 4 Sound Inc, pg 1068

NEW MEXICO

Production Outfitters, pg 984

NEW YORK

Adorama Rental Co, pg 776
American Video Inc, pg 785
Audio Visual Resources LLC, pg 795
Aura Sonic Ltd, pg 796
AV Workshop, pg 797
Bond Street Studio, pg 810
CP Communications, pg 837
Design Audio Visual Inc, pg 845
Dreamhire LLC, pg 852
Gotham Sound & Communications Inc, pg 881
Hello World Communications, pg 888
Interactive International Inc, pg 899
KVL Audio Visual Services Inc, pg 914
LightHouse Films, pg 920
Long Island Video Enterprises Live Inc, pg 924
Manhattan Center Studios Inc, pg 930
SmartSource Computer & AV Rentals, pg 1014
Specialized Audio-Visual Inc, pg 1020
Syracuse Scenery & Stage Lighting Co Inc, pg 1031
TBA Global Events, pg 1032
Theatrical Services & Supplies Inc, pg 1038
Visual Word Systems Inc, pg 1060
WorldStage, pg 1070
Xtech Inc, pg 1071

NORTH CAROLINA

A&V Company, pg 772
AV Metro Inc, pg 797
Special Event Services, pg 1020

NORTH DAKOTA

Media Productions, pg 937

OHIO

Hughie's Event Production Services, pg 892
Lyon Video Inc, pg 927
Mills James Productions, pg 943
Ohio HD Video, pg 961
Smithall Electronics Inc, pg 1014

OKLAHOMA

PDC Productions, pg 970

OREGON

Northwest Film Center, pg 959
Rose City Sound, pg 999

PENNSYLVANIA

Advanced AV, pg 777
Audio Visions Inc, pg 795
Grise Audio Visual Center Inc, pg 882
Production Solutions Inc, pg 985
Right Coast Recording Inc, pg 997
The Videohouse Inc, pg 1057
Viewpoint Production Services Inc, pg 1058
Visual Sound Inc, pg 1059

TENNESSEE

Brantley Sound Associates Inc, pg 812
Mr Mark's Used Musical, Stereo & Studio Equipment Store, pg 944
Nashville Production Rentals (NPR), pg 952
Technical Support Systems LLC, pg 1034
Trew Audio Inc, pg 1044

TEXAS

Alford Media Services, pg 780
Astro Audio Visual, pg 792
Audio Visual Technologies Group, pg 796
Bright Giant Creative Group, pg 812
Crossroads Audio Inc, pg 840
Data Display Audio Visual Co LP, pg 843
Lubbock Audio Visual Inc, pg 925
Music Lab Inc, pg 950
Onstage Systems, pg 963
Stage Directions, pg 1022
Texcam Inc, pg 1038

UTAH

Performance Audio, pg 973
Redman Movies & Stories, pg 993

VERMONT

Dark Star Lighting & Production, pg 842
Edgewood Studios, pg 857
Parlato Productions, pg 969

VIRGINIA

American AV, pg 783
Boitnott Visual Communications Corp (BVC), pg 810
StageSound, pg 1023

WASHINGTON

D A Sound, pg 842
Northern Lights & Pro Audio, pg 959
Victory Studios, pg 1054

WISCONSIN

Event Essentials, pg 863
Full Compass Systems, pg 874
MKE Production Rental, pg 944

PUERTO RICO

Stage Crew Audiovisual Inc, pg 1022

ALBERTA

McBain Audio Visual Ltd, pg 935
Sharp's Audio-Visual Ltd, pg 1008
Unique Communications Ltd, pg 1048

BRITISH COLUMBIA

Clark's Audio Visual Services Ltd, pg 829
Commercial Electronics Ltd, pg 832
MicrophoneRentals.com, pg 941
ProVision Video Sales & Rentals Inc, pg 986
Video In Studios/Video Out Distribution, pg 1055

MANITOBA

Inland Audio Visual Ltd, pg 898

ONTARIO

Boxcar Studio, pg 811
Edcom Multimedia Products, pg 856
HD Source, pg 886
SIM Digital, pg 1011
Westbury National Show Systems Ltd, pg 1064

QUEBEC

Concept Audio-Visual, pg 834

Headset & Headphone Repairs

ALABAMA

Media Visions Inc, pg 937

CALIFORNIA

Ametron Audio/Video, pg 785
Audio Images Corp, pg 794
Location Sound Corp, pg 924
McAlister Electronics, pg 935
Plantronics Inc, pg 976
Randall Schiller Productions, pg 1004
Sound Service Co, pg 1017
Towards 2000 Inc, pg 1043

CONNECTICUT

HB Communications Inc, pg 886
Sennheiser Electronic Corp, pg 1006

DELAWARE

Actors Attic, pg 775

FLORIDA

Hi-Tech Enterprises Inc, pg 888
Midtown Video Inc, pg 942
Stereo Sales Inc, pg 1024
TAI Audio, pg 1031

GEORGIA

Lighting & Production Equipment Inc, pg 920
Stage Front Presentation Systems, pg 1022

ILLINOIS

Beatty TeleVisual Productions, pg 804
On Site Video, pg 963
RC Communications, pg 992

INDIANA

Sweetwater Sound Inc, pg 1029

IOWA

ECS Inc, pg 856

KENTUCKY

Axxis Inc, pg 800
NOR-COM Inc, pg 958

MARYLAND

Cardinal Sound & Video, pg 820
Visual Aids Electronics Corp, pg 1059

MICHIGAN

City Events Group, pg 828
K&R's Recording Studios Inc, pg 908
TeL Systems, pg 1035

MISSOURI

Cintrex Audio Visual, pg 828

NEW JERSEY

Earl Girls Inc, pg 855
Nelson Enterprises Theatrical Supply Co, pg 954
Starlite Productions, pg 1024

NEW YORK

beyerdynamic Inc, pg 806
Technisphere Corp, pg 1034
Xtech Inc, pg 1071

OHIO

Copp Integrated Systems, pg 836
Smithall Electronics Inc, pg 1014

OREGON

All Service Musical Electronics Repair, pg 780

PENNSYLVANIA

J E Foss Co, pg 871
Right Coast Recording Inc, pg 997

TENNESSEE

Technical Support Systems LLC, pg 1034
Trew Audio Inc, pg 1044

TEXAS

Astro Audio Visual, pg 792
Audio Visual Technologies Group, pg 796
Lubbock Audio Visual Inc, pg 925
Padgitt's, pg 967
Quality Audio Visual Service Inc, pg 988
Southwest Sound & Electronics Inc, pg 1019

VIRGINIA

Boitnott Visual Communications Corp (BVC), pg 810
Old Dominion Broadcasting, pg 961
The Whitlock Group, pg 1065

WASHINGTON

Northern Lights & Pro Audio, pg 959

WISCONSIN

Full Compass Systems, pg 874

PUERTO RICO

Bonnin Electronics Inc, pg 810

ALBERTA

Sharp's Audio-Visual Ltd, pg 1008

BRITISH COLUMBIA

Commercial Electronics Ltd, pg 832

MANITOBA

Inland Audio Visual Ltd, pg 898

ONTARIO

Edcom Multimedia Products, pg 856
HD Source, pg 886
Westbury National Show Systems Ltd, pg 1064

QUEBEC

SC Media Canada, pg 1003

Hearing Assistance System Distributors

ARIZONA

EAR Professional Audio/Video, pg 855
Troxell Communications Inc, pg 1045
David Wexler & Co, pg 1064

ARKANSAS

Jay S Stanley & Associates Inc, pg 1023

CALIFORNIA

Ametron Audio/Video, pg 785
Associated Sound, pg 792
Richard W Burden Associates, pg 815
Cibola Systems, pg 826
Cinema Equipment Sales of California Inc, pg 827
Delicate Electronics Sales Inc, pg 845
FXC Communications, pg 874
Instructional Materials & Equipment Distributors (I-Med), pg 899
JD Audio Visual Inc, pg 904
Media Vision USA, pg 937
Phonic Ear Inc (FrontRow), pg 974
Sound Service Co, pg 1017
Southern California Sound Image Inc, pg 1019
Stanislaus Audio Video Inc, pg 1023

COLORADO

Audio Consultant Services Inc, pg 794
Daylight Productions & Rentals, pg 844
Oval Window Audio, pg 966

CONNECTICUT

Connecticut Audio & Theatrical Supply, pg 835
Sennheiser Electronic Corp, pg 1006

DELAWARE

Actors Attic, pg 775

FLORIDA

Allstar Audio Systems Inc, pg 782
BAI Distributors Inc, pg 801
Cinema Equipment & Supplies Inc, pg 827
Harris Corp, pg 885
Hi-Tech Import Export Corp, pg 888
Intermark Industries Inc, pg 900
Media Concepts Inc, pg 936
Photomart Cine-Video Inc, pg 975
Pro Stage Inc, pg 983
Technomedia Solutions, pg 1035

GEORGIA

Lighting & Production Equipment Inc, pg 920
Stage Front Presentation Systems, pg 1022

HAWAII

The Audio Visual Co (AVCO), pg 795

ILLINOIS

Allen Visual Systems Inc, pg 781

INDIANA

Sensory Technologies LLC, pg 1006
SHP Electronics, pg 1010
Sweetwater Sound Inc, pg 1029

KENTUCKY

Axxis Inc, pg 800
NOR-COM Inc, pg 958

MAINE

Headlight Audio Visual Inc, pg 887

MARYLAND

Cardinal Sound & Video, pg 820

MASSACHUSETTS

Terry Hanley Audio Systems Inc, pg 884

AUDIO

Hearing Assistance System Distributors (continued)

MICHIGAN

Olson Anderson Co, pg 786
Ascom Communications Contractors, pg 791

MINNESOTA

Harris Communications Inc, pg 885

MISSOURI

MIS Technologies, pg 944
Schiller's Audio-Visual, pg 1004

NEW HAMPSHIRE

APS Lighting-Sound-AV, pg 789

NEW JERSEY

Alltec Stores, a Vcom IMC Company, pg 782
AV Bluebook, pg 797
National Audio-Visual Supply, pg 952
SLD Lighting, pg 1013
Starlite Productions, pg 1024
Wilray Audio Visual Corp, pg 1067
Wired 4 Sound Inc, pg 1068
York Telecom, pg 1072

NEW YORK

Albany Theatre Supply Co Inc, pg 780
BMI Supply, pg 810
Colortone Audio Visual, pg 832
Custom Media Environments, pg 841
Design Audio Visual Inc, pg 845
RNJ Electronics, pg 997
Sound Associates Inc, pg 1017

OHIO

ITA Audio Visual Solutions, pg 902
Jimmy Rea Electronics Inc, pg 992
Smithall Electronics Inc, pg 1014
Tri-State Audio Visual Co, pg 1044

OREGON

Lightspeed Technologies Inc, pg 921

PENNSYLVANIA

Advanced AV, pg 777
J E Foss Co, pg 871
Vistacom Inc, pg 1059

TENNESSEE

Belew Enterprises, pg 804
Durrell LLC, pg 854
Lowrance Sound Co Inc, pg 925
Spectrum Sound Inc, pg 1021
Trew Audio Inc, pg 1044
Zion Music Group, pg 1074

TEXAS

CAM Audio Inc, pg 817
Industrial Audio/Video Inc, pg 897
Media Management LLC, pg 937
RadioShack Corp, pg 990
Tarpley Media Systems, pg 1032

UTAH

Comtek Communications Technology Inc, pg 834

VIRGINIA

Intellidyne LLC, pg 899
Lee Hartman & Sons Inc, pg 918

WASHINGTON

CCI Solutions, pg 821
Pacific Northwest Theatre Associates Inc (PNTA), pg 967

WISCONSIN

Audio Visual of Milwaukee Inc, pg 795
Full Compass Systems, pg 874

PUERTO RICO

Bonnin Electronics Inc, pg 810

ALBERTA

Infosat Communications Inc, pg 898
Matrix Video Communications Corp (MVCC), pg 934

MANITOBA

Advance Pro, pg 777
Inland Audio Visual Ltd, pg 898

ONTARIO

Cinema Stage Inc, pg 827
Premier A/V Sales Ltd, pg 980
Westbury National Show Systems Ltd, pg 1064

Hearing Assistance System Manufacturers

CALIFORNIA

Anchor Audio Inc, pg 786
Calrad Electronics, pg 817
Nady Systems Inc, pg 952

COLORADO

Oval Window Audio, pg 966

CONNECTICUT

Sennheiser Electronic Corp, pg 1006
Vista Group International Inc, pg 1059

ILLINOIS

AmpliVox Portable Sound Systems, pg 785

MINNESOTA

Telex Communications Inc, pg 1037
Williams Sound Corp, pg 1067

NEW JERSEY

Bogen Communications Inc, pg 810
Crestron Electronics Inc, pg 839

NEW YORK

Sound Associates Inc, pg 1017

OHIO

R L Drake Co, pg 852

OREGON

Lightspeed Technologies Inc, pg 921

UTAH

Comtek Communications Technology Inc, pg 834
Listen Technologies Corp, pg 923

Hearing Assistance System Rentals

CALIFORNIA

Alliant Event Services, pg 781
Ametron Audio/Video, pg 785
Associated Sound, pg 792
AV Guys, pg 797
FXC Communications, pg 874
JD Audio Visual Inc, pg 904
Lynch Communications, pg 926
McCune Audio-Video-Lighting, pg 935
Sound Service Co, pg 1017
Stanislaus Audio Video Inc, pg 1023

CONNECTICUT

A/V Davey, pg 797

FLORIDA

Allstar Audio Systems Inc, pg 782
Pro Stage Inc, pg 983

GEORGIA

Stage Front Presentation Systems, pg 1022

ILLINOIS

AV Chicago Inc, pg 797
On Stage Audio, pg 963
QuickSet International Inc, pg 989

KENTUCKY

Audio Visual Techniques Inc, pg 796

MARYLAND

Cardinal Sound & Video, pg 820

MASSACHUSETTS

Terry Hanley Audio Systems Inc, pg 884

MICHIGAN

K&R All Media Productions Inc, pg 908

MISSOURI

Show-Me Audio-Visual, pg 1009

NEW HAMPSHIRE

APS Lighting-Sound-AV, pg 789

NEW JERSEY

Starlite Productions, pg 1024
Wired 4 Sound Inc, pg 1068

NEW YORK

Colortone Audio Visual, pg 832
CP Communications, pg 837
Design Audio Visual Inc, pg 845
Sound Associates Inc, pg 1017

NORTH CAROLINA

A&V Company, pg 772

OHIO

Smithall Electronics Inc, pg 1014

OREGON

Rose City Sound, pg 999

UTAH

Listen Technologies Corp, pg 923

VERMONT

Parlato Productions, pg 969

VIRGINIA

American AV, pg 783

WISCONSIN

Full Compass Systems, pg 874

MANITOBA

Inland Audio Visual Ltd, pg 898

Hearing Assistance System Repairs

CALIFORNIA

Ametron Audio/Video, pg 785
McAlister Electronics, pg 935
Phonic Ear Inc (FrontRow), pg 974
Sound Service Co, pg 1017

CONNECTICUT

HB Communications Inc, pg 886
Sennheiser Electronic Corp, pg 1006

GEORGIA

Stage Front Presentation Systems, pg 1022

ILLINOIS

Allen Visual Systems Inc, pg 781

KENTUCKY

Axxis Inc, pg 800
NOR-COM Inc, pg 958

MARYLAND

Cardinal Sound & Video, pg 820

MICHIGAN

TeL Systems, pg 1035

NEW JERSEY

Starlite Productions, pg 1024

NEW YORK

Sound Associates Inc, pg 1017

OHIO

Smithall Electronics Inc, pg 1014
Tri-State Audio Visual Co, pg 1044

OREGON

All Service Musical Electronics Repair, pg 780

AUDIO

Language Lab Carrell & Equipment Repairs (continued)

VIRGINIA

Lee Hartman & Sons Inc, pg 918
The Whitlock Group, pg 1065

WASHINGTON

Inland Audio Visual Co, pg 898

WEST VIRGINIA

United Sound & Electronics, pg 1048

PUERTO RICO

Bonnin Electronics Inc, pg 810

MANITOBA

Evolution Presentation Technologies, pg 863
Inland Audio Visual Ltd, pg 898

ONTARIO

Westbury National Show Systems Ltd, pg 1064

Magnetic Recording Equipment Distributors

ALABAMA

Media Visions Inc, pg 937

ARIZONA

Arizona Cine Equipment, pg 789
Audio Video Resources, pg 795
Troxell Communications Inc, pg 1045

ARKANSAS

Jay S Stanley & Associates Inc, pg 1023
White Diamond Productions, pg 1065

CALIFORNIA

Ametron Audio/Video, pg 785
Audio Images Corp, pg 794
Audio/Video Supply Inc, pg 795
Birns & Sawyer Inc, pg 808
California Tape Products Inc, pg 817
Educational Technology Services (ETS), pg 857
FXC Communications, pg 874
Gluskin's Custom Audio Video, pg 879
Alan Gordon Enterprises Inc, pg 880
Instructional Materials & Equipment Distributors (I-Med), pg 899
JD Audio Visual Inc, pg 904
Location Sound Corp, pg 924
Martel Electronics Sales Inc, pg 932
Media Fabricators Inc, pg 936
MediaMation Inc, pg 937
MediaPOINTE, pg 938
Mobilized Tech Systems, pg 944
Related Visual Inc, pg 994
Randall Schiller Productions, pg 1004
Sound Service Co, pg 1017
SSL Industries Inc, pg 1022
SuperVision, pg 1029
Tri-Ed, pg 1044
VTP Inc, pg 1061
Yamaha Electronics Corp, pg 1071

COLORADO

Audio Consultant Services Inc, pg 794
Ceavco Audio/Visual Co, pg 822
Spectrum Audio Visual Services, pg 1020

CONNECTICUT

Concord Communications, pg 835
HB Communications Inc, pg 886
MAVCO, pg 934
Rockwell Communications Inc, pg 998

DELAWARE

Actors Attic, pg 775

FLORIDA

Allstar Audio Systems Inc, pg 782
Broadcasters General Store Inc, pg 813
CD ROM™ Inc, pg 822
Harris Corp, pg 885
Hi-Tech Import Export Corp, pg 888
Hunter Electronics LLC, pg 892
Industrial Strength Inc, pg 897
Photomart Cine-Video Inc, pg 975
Pro Stage Inc, pg 983
Recording Media & Equipment Inc (RM&E), pg 993
Stereo Sales Inc, pg 1024
TAI Audio, pg 1031

GEORGIA

Baker Audio Inc, pg 801
Convergent Media Systems, pg 836
Lighting & Production Equipment Inc, pg 920
Stage Front Presentation Systems, pg 1022
Technical Innovation, pg 1033
Visioneering International Inc, pg 1058

ILLINOIS

Creative Technology, pg 838
International Electro-Magnetics Inc, pg 901
Major Reproductions Equipment Co, pg 929
Woodside Avenue Music Productions Inc, pg 1069

INDIANA

Sensory Technologies LLC, pg 1006

IOWA

ECS Inc, pg 856

KANSAS

Smith Audio-Visual Inc, pg 1014

KENTUCKY

Axxis Inc, pg 800
Barney Miller's Inc, pg 943
NOR-COM Inc, pg 958

MAINE

Headlight Audio Visual Inc, pg 887
Independent Audio Inc, pg 897

MARYLAND

Bradley Broadcast & Pro Audio, pg 811
Cardinal Sound & Video, pg 820
Kipp Visual Systems Inc, pg 911
Nicholas P Pipino Associates Inc, pg 976
RTZ Audio Visual, pg 1000
Visual Aids Electronics Corp, pg 1059

MASSACHUSETTS

Professional Audio Design Inc, pg 985

MICHIGAN

City Events Group, pg 828
TeL Systems, pg 1035

MINNESOTA

Advanced Audio-Visual Inc, pg 777
AVI Systems, pg 799
Cinequipt Inc, pg 828
New Life Communications Inc, pg 956

MISSISSIPPI

Jasper Ewing & Sons Inc, pg 864

MISSOURI

Communitronics Corp, pg 833
Conference Technologies Inc, pg 835
Image Technologies Corp, pg 895
Modern Communications Inc, pg 944

NEW JERSEY

Audio Visual Dynamics®, pg 795
AV Bluebook, pg 797
Comprehensive Cable & Connectivity Co, pg 833
FlagHouse, pg 869
G&G Technologies Inc, pg 875
Hamilton Buhl, pg 884
JRF Magnetic Sciences Inc, pg 906
National Audio-Visual Supply, pg 952
Onkyo USA Corp, pg 963
Starlite Productions, pg 1024
Tele-Measurements Inc, pg 1035
Turner Engineering Inc, pg 1046
VCom International Multimedia Corp, pg 1052
Video Corporation of America (VCA), pg 1055
York Telecom, pg 1072

NEW YORK

American Video Inc, pg 785
AV Workshop, pg 797
Flash Electronics Inc, pg 869
HAVE Inc, pg 886
Hot House Professional Audio, pg 891
Indigo Productions, pg 897
Langie Audio Visual Systems, pg 915
Long Island Video Enterprises Live Inc, pg 924
Markertek Video Supply, pg 931
NorthCountry Distributors, pg 959
Posthorn Recordings, pg 979
Technisphere Corp, pg 1034
Willoughby's Imaging Center, pg 1067

NORTH CAROLINA

Camcor Inc, pg 818
Strategic Connections, pg 1026

OHIO

Copp Integrated Systems, pg 836
ITA Audio Visual Solutions, pg 902
The Little Warehouse Inc, pg 923

OREGON

SuperDigital Ltd, pg 1029

PENNSYLVANIA

Advanced AV, pg 777
Audio Visual Communications Inc, pg 795
Brodart Co, pg 813
J E Foss Co, pg 871
Grise Audio Visual Center Inc, pg 882
The Lerro Corp, pg 919
Morefield Communications Inc, pg 946
Visual Sound Inc, pg 1059

RHODE ISLAND

Custom Computer Specialists Inc, pg 841

TENNESSEE

Durrell LLC, pg 854
Lowrance Sound Co Inc, pg 925
Technical Support Systems LLC, pg 1034
Tennessee Visual Service Co, pg 1037
Zion Music Group, pg 1074

TEXAS

Astro Audio Visual, pg 792
Audio Visual Technologies Group, pg 796
Crossroads Audio Inc, pg 840
FitzCo Sound Inc, pg 869
J&S Audio Visual Inc, pg 904
Lubbock Audio Visual Inc, pg 925
Pro Video & Film Equipment Co Inc, pg 983
Quality Audio Visual Service Inc, pg 988
RF Specialties of Texas LLC, pg 996
Schoolhouse Audio Visual, pg 1004
Stage Directions, pg 1022
Tarpley Media Systems, pg 1032

UTAH

Performance Audio, pg 973
RIA Corp, pg 996
Webb Audio Visual Communication, pg 1063

VIRGINIA

Communications Specialists Inc, pg 833
Hoppmann Audio Visual, pg 891
Lee Hartman & Sons Inc, pg 918
The Whitlock Group, pg 1065

WASHINGTON

Inland Audio Visual Co, pg 898

WISCONSIN

Full Compass Systems, pg 874
School Specialty Inc, pg 1004

Magnetic Recording Equipment Manufacturers

Magnetic Recording Equipment Rentals

AUDIO

Magnetic Recording Equipment Rentals (continued)

ALBERTA

McBain Audio Visual Ltd, pg 935
Sharp's Audio-Visual Ltd, pg 1008
Unique Communications Ltd, pg 1048

BRITISH COLUMBIA

Image Media Farm, pg 895

MANITOBA

Inland Audio Visual Ltd, pg 898

ONTARIO

Edcom Multimedia Products, pg 856

QUEBEC

AVW-TELAV Audio Visual Solutions, a Freeman Company, pg 800
Concept Audio-Visual, pg 834
Group PVP, pg 882

Magnetic Recording Equipment Repairs

ALABAMA

Media Visions Inc, pg 937

CALIFORNIA

Advanced Media LLC, pg 778
Ametron Audio/Video, pg 785
Audio Images Corp, pg 794
Dan Dugan Sound Design Inc, pg 853
Gluskin's Custom Audio Video, pg 879
Location Sound Corp, pg 924
McAlister Electronics, pg 935
Randall Schiller Productions, pg 1004
Sound Service Co, pg 1017
SSL Industries Inc, pg 1022
Yamaha Electronics Corp, pg 1071

CONNECTICUT

HB Communications Inc, pg 886
Rockwell Communications Inc, pg 998

FLORIDA

Phat Planet Recording Studios, pg 973
Stereo Sales Inc, pg 1024
TAI Audio, pg 1031

GEORGIA

Lighting & Production Equipment Inc, pg 920
Stage Front Presentation Systems, pg 1022

ILLINOIS

Midwest Digital Corp, pg 942
On Site Video, pg 963

IOWA

ECS Inc, pg 856

KENTUCKY

Axxis Inc, pg 800
Barney Miller's Inc, pg 943
NOR-COM Inc, pg 958

MAINE

Headlight Audio Visual Inc, pg 887

MARYLAND

RTZ Audio Visual, pg 1000
Strauss Photo Technical Service Inc, pg 1026

MASSACHUSETTS

Capron Lighting & Sound Co Inc, pg 819
Professional Audio Design Inc, pg 985

MICHIGAN

City Events Group, pg 828
K&R's Recording Studios Inc, pg 908
TeL Systems, pg 1035

MINNESOTA

AVI Systems, pg 799

NEW JERSEY

JRF Magnetic Sciences Inc, pg 906
Starlite Productions, pg 1024
Turner Engineering Inc, pg 1046

NEW YORK

Colortone Audio Visual, pg 832
Langie Audio Visual Systems, pg 915

NORTH CAROLINA

Strategic Connections, pg 1026

OHIO

Copp Integrated Systems, pg 836

OREGON

All Service Musical Electronics Repair, pg 780

PENNSYLVANIA

Audio Visual Communications Inc, pg 795
Brush Industries Inc, pg 814
J E Foss Co, pg 871

RHODE ISLAND

Custom Computer Specialists Inc, pg 841

TENNESSEE

Technical Support Systems LLC, pg 1034
Tennessee Visual Service Co, pg 1037

TEXAS

Audio Visual Technologies Group, pg 796
FitzCo Sound Inc, pg 869
Lubbock Audio Visual Inc, pg 925
Pro Video & Film Equipment Co Inc, pg 983

VIRGINIA

Hoppmann Audio Visual, pg 891
Lee Hartman & Sons Inc, pg 918

WASHINGTON

Inland Audio Visual Co, pg 898

WISCONSIN

Full Compass Systems, pg 874

PUERTO RICO

Bonnin Electronics Inc, pg 810

ALBERTA

Sharp's Audio-Visual Ltd, pg 1008
Unique Communications Ltd, pg 1048

BRITISH COLUMBIA

Commercial Electronics Ltd, pg 832

MANITOBA

Inland Audio Visual Ltd, pg 898

ONTARIO

Edcom Multimedia Products, pg 856

Magnetic Sound Recording, *see* Sound Recording—Magnetic

Microphone Distributors

ALABAMA

Curtis Company, pg 841
Media Visions Inc, pg 937

ARIZONA

Allusion Studios & Pure Wave Audio, pg 782
Arizona Cine Equipment, pg 789
Audio Video Resources, pg 795
EAR Professional Audio/Video, pg 855
Metropolitan Audio-Visual Inc, pg 940
Projector SuperStore LLC, pg 986
Tempe Camera, pg 1037
Troxell Communications Inc, pg 1045

ARKANSAS

White Diamond Productions, pg 1065

CALIFORNIA

Adolph Gasser Inc, pg 776
Advanced Systems Group LLC, pg 778
AKG Acoustics US, pg 779
Ametron Audio/Video, pg 785
ARS Electronics, pg 791
Associated Sound, pg 792
ATV Video Center Inc, pg 793
Audio Images Corp, pg 794
Audio/Video Supply Inc, pg 795
AV Conferencing, pg 797
Be Media, pg 804
Birns & Sawyer Inc, pg 808
BroadcastStore.com, pg 813
California Tape Products Inc, pg 817
Carvin Corp, pg 820
Cibola Systems, pg 826
Delicate Electronics Sales Inc, pg 845
Educational Technology Services (ETS), pg 857
Empire Wholesale Inc, pg 860
FXC Communications, pg 874
Gearhouse Broadcast LLC, pg 876
GigaSonic, pg 878
Gluskin's Custom Audio Video, pg 879
GMF Sound Inc, pg 879
Alan Gordon Enterprises Inc, pg 880
The Hollywood Edge, pg 890
Hosa Technology Inc, pg 891
IAMP Professional Audio, pg 893
Impact Group, pg 897
Instructional Materials & Equipment Distributors (I-Med), pg 899
JD Audio Visual Inc, pg 904
Location Sound Corp, pg 924
Logitech, pg 924
Marshall Electronics Inc, pg 932
Martel Electronics Sales Inc, pg 932
Lloyd F McKinney Associates Inc, pg 935
Media Fabricators Inc, pg 936
Media Vision USA, pg 937
MediaPOINTE, pg 938
Mole-Richardson Co, pg 945
Pacific Radio Electronics, pg 967
Plus 24, pg 977
POP TV, pg 978
Professional Sound Corp, pg 985
Promax Systems, pg 986
Related Visual Inc, pg 994
Randall Schiller Productions, pg 1004
SNAP, pg 1014
Sound Service Co, pg 1017
Southern California Sound Image Inc, pg 1019
SSL Industries Inc, pg 1022
Stanislaus Audio Video Inc, pg 1023
TOA Electronics Inc, pg 1041
Towards 2000 Inc, pg 1043
Tri-Ed, pg 1044
Video Gear Rentals Inc, pg 1055
VMI Inc, pg 1060
VTP Inc, pg 1061
Zack Electronics Inc, pg 1073

COLORADO

Audio Consultant Services Inc, pg 794
Daylight Productions & Rentals, pg 844
Spectrum Audio Visual Services, pg 1020

CONNECTICUT

Connecticut Audio & Theatrical Supply, pg 835
Everett Hall Associates Inc, pg 863
Gold Line/TEF, pg 880
HB Communications Inc, pg 886
MAVCO, pg 934
The Music People Inc, pg 951
Neumann USA, pg 955
Sennheiser Electronic Corp, pg 1006

DELAWARE

Actors Attic, pg 775

FLORIDA

Access Media Group, pg 773
Allstar Audio Systems Inc, pg 782
A2D Solutions Inc, pg 793

AVI-SPL, pg 798
BAI Distributors Inc, pg 801
Broadcasters General Store Inc, pg 813
Digital Video Systems Inc, pg 848
Enhanced View Services Inc, pg 861
General Projection Systems Inc, pg 877
Griffiths Broadcast Co Inc, pg 882
Gulf Coast Audio Visual Producers Inc, pg 883
Harmon's Audio-Visual Services, pg 885
Harris Corp, pg 885
Herman Pro AV, pg 888
Hi-Tech Enterprises Inc, pg 888
Hi-Tech Import Export Corp, pg 888
Hollywood Theatre Equipment Inc, pg 890
Hunter Electronics LLC, pg 892
Industrial Strength Inc, pg 897
Intermark Industries Inc, pg 900
Lighting Sales Connections, pg 920
Media Concepts Inc, pg 936
Midtown Video Inc, pg 942
Photomart Cine-Video Inc, pg 975
Photosound of Orlando Inc, pg 975
Pro Stage Inc, pg 983
Recording Media & Equipment Inc (RM&E), pg 993
Sight & Sound Productions, pg 1010
Southern Audio Visual, pg 1019
Stereo Sales Inc, pg 1024
TAI Audio, pg 1031
Tallahassee Audio Visual, pg 1031
Technomedia Solutions, pg 1035
Videoscope, pg 1057

GEORGIA

AVForSale, pg 798
Baker Audio Inc, pg 801
Clark, pg 829
Convergent Media Systems, pg 836
Lighting & Production Equipment Inc, pg 920
LT Sound Inc, pg 925
Stage Front Presentation Systems, pg 1022
Visioneering International Inc, pg 1058

HAWAII

The Audio Visual Co (AVCO), pg 795

ILLINOIS

A T Products Inc, pg 771
Allen Visual Systems Inc, pg 781
Central Audio-Visual Equipment Inc, pg 823
Joseph Electronics, pg 906
LKG Industries Inc, pg 923
C V Lloyde, pg 923
Major Media Inc, pg 929
Precision Electronics Inc, pg 980
Quintessence Audio Ltd, pg 989
RAM Systems LLC, pg 991
RC Communications, pg 992
Sound Vision Inc, pg 1018
Waldom Electronics Corp, pg 1061

INDIANA

Heart Breaker Entertainment LLC, pg 887
Jack's Camera Shop, pg 903
Sensory Technologies LLC, pg 1006
SHP Electronics, pg 1010
Sweetwater Sound Inc, pg 1029

IOWA

ECS Inc, pg 856

KANSAS

Smith Audio-Visual Inc, pg 1014

KENTUCKY

Audio Visual Techniques Inc, pg 796
Axxis Inc, pg 800
Barney Miller's Inc, pg 943
NOR-COM Inc, pg 958
Northern Kentucky University, pg 959

LOUISIANA

Intermedia Technologies, pg 900
Pace Systems, pg 966

MAINE

Headlight Audio Visual Inc, pg 887
Independent Audio Inc, pg 897

MARYLAND

Advance Audiovisual Presentation Ltd, pg 777
Bradley Broadcast & Pro Audio, pg 811
Cardinal Sound & Video, pg 820
Human Circuit, pg 892
Kipp Visual Systems Inc, pg 911
Noventri, pg 960
RTZ Audio Visual, pg 1000

MASSACHUSETTS

Terry Hanley Audio Systems Inc, pg 884
Hunt's Photo, Video & Digital, pg 892
Professional Audio Design Inc, pg 985
Rule Broadcast Systems, pg 1000

MICHIGAN

Olson Anderson Co, pg 786
Ascom Communications Contractors, pg 791
City Events Group, pg 828
On Stage Visuals, pg 963
TeL Systems, pg 1035

MINNESOTA

Advanced Audio-Visual Inc, pg 777
AVI Systems, pg 799
Cinequipt Inc, pg 828
New Life Communications Inc, pg 956
Tierney Brothers Inc, pg 1040

MISSISSIPPI

Bowie Audio Visual Enterprises Inc, pg 811
Jasper Ewing & Sons Inc, pg 864

MISSOURI

Communitronics Corp, pg 833
Conference Technologies Inc, pg 835
Image Technologies Corp, pg 895
MIS Technologies, pg 944
Modern Communications Inc, pg 944
Production Support Services Inc, pg 985
Schiller's Audio-Visual, pg 1004

NEBRASKA

Video Service of America Inc (VSA), pg 1056

NEVADA

Pignose-Gorilla, pg 975

NEW HAMPSHIRE

APS Lighting-Sound-AV, pg 789
Technet® Systems Group, pg 1033

NEW JERSEY

A-V Services Inc, pg 771
Alltec Stores, a Vcom IMC Company, pg 782
Audio Visual Associates, pg 795
Audio Visual Dynamics®, pg 795
AV Bluebook, pg 797
C-Ducer/C T Audio, pg 816
Comprehensive Cable & Connectivity Co, pg 833
Diversified Systems Inc, pg 849
Earl Girls Inc, pg 855
Euro-Pacific Film & Video Productions Inc, pg 863
FlagHouse, pg 869
G&G Technologies Inc, pg 875
Hamilton Buhl, pg 884
The Music Place, pg 951
National Audio-Visual Supply, pg 952
Nelson Enterprises Theatrical Supply Co, pg 954
PatchAmp, pg 970
SLD Lighting, pg 1013
Starlite Productions, pg 1024
Tele-Measurements Inc, pg 1035
Total Video Products Inc, pg 1042
Turner Engineering Inc, pg 1046
VCom International Multimedia Corp, pg 1052
Video Corporation of America (VCA), pg 1055
Wilray Audio Visual Corp, pg 1067
Wired 4 Sound Inc, pg 1068
York Telecom, pg 1072

NEW MEXICO

Quickbeam Systems Inc (QSI), pg 989

NEW YORK

Albany Theatre Supply Co Inc, pg 780
ALTEL Systems Inc, pg 783
American Video Inc, pg 785
Aura Sonic Ltd, pg 796
AV Workshop, pg 797
beyerdynamic Inc, pg 806
BMI Supply, pg 810
BTX Technologies, pg 814
Cadence Jazz Records, pg 816
Centennial Electric Sound Co Ltd, pg 822
Colortone Audio Visual, pg 832
Communication Corner Inc, pg 832
Custom Media Environments, pg 841
Design Audio Visual Inc, pg 845
Gaylord Brothers, pg 876
Gotham Sound & Communications Inc, pg 881
HAVE Inc, pg 886
Hot House Professional Audio, pg 891
Indigo Productions, pg 897
KVL Audio Visual Services Inc, pg 914
Lee Dan® Communications Inc, pg 918
Long Island Video Enterprises Live Inc, pg 924
Magnaplan Corp, pg 928
Mark Custom Recording Service Inc, pg 931
Markertek Video Supply, pg 931
Saul Mineroff Electronics Inc, pg 943
Neptune Photo Inc, pg 954
NorthCountry Distributors, pg 959
PicturePhone Inc, pg 975
Posthorn Recordings, pg 979
Ray Supply Inc, pg 992
RNJ Electronics, pg 997
SmartSource Computer & AV Rentals, pg 1014
Stampede Presentation Products Inc, pg 1023
Technisphere Corp, pg 1034
TecNec Distributing, pg 1035
Theatrical Services & Supplies Inc, pg 1038
Toys From The Attic, pg 1043
Videoguys, pg 1057
Visual Technologies Corp, pg 1060
Visual Word Systems Inc, pg 1060
Willoughby's Imaging Center, pg 1067
Yorkville Sound Inc, pg 1072

NORTH CAROLINA

Camcor Inc, pg 818
Innocinema, pg 898
Strategic Connections, pg 1026

OHIO

Copp Integrated Systems, pg 836
Hughie's Event Production Services, pg 892
ITA Audio Visual Solutions, pg 902
Midwest Photo Exchange, pg 942
Parts Express, pg 969
Jimmy Rea Electronics Inc, pg 992
Smithall Electronics Inc, pg 1014
Tri-State Audio Visual Co, pg 1044
Tri-State Visual Products, pg 1044
Visual Products Inc, pg 1059

OREGON

Audix Corp, pg 796
PLUS Corp of America, pg 977
SuperDigital Ltd, pg 1029

PENNSYLVANIA

Advanced AV, pg 777
Audio Visions Inc, pg 795
Clair Brothers Audio Systems Inc, pg 829
J E Foss Co, pg 871
Garcia Marketing Inc, pg 875
Grise Audio Visual Center Inc, pg 882
The Lerro Corp, pg 919
Morefield Communications Inc, pg 946
RSS Distributors, pg 1000
Sound by Fitch, pg 1017
Vistacom Inc, pg 1059
Visual Sound Inc, pg 1059
Wespen Audio Visual Co, pg 1063

RHODE ISLAND

Custom Computer Specialists Inc, pg 841
Shanix Inc, pg 1008

SOUTH CAROLINA

DaviSound, pg 843

AUDIO

Microphone Distributors (continued)

TENNESSEE

Belew Enterprises, pg 804
Durrell LLC, pg 854
Lowrance Sound Co Inc, pg 925
Memphis Communications Corp, pg 938
Mr Mark's Used Musical, Stereo & Studio Equipment Store, pg 944
Spectrum Sound Inc, pg 1021
Technical Support Systems LLC, pg 1034
Tennessee Visual Service Co, pg 1037
Trew Audio Inc, pg 1044
Zion Music Group, pg 1074

TEXAS

Astro Audio Visual, pg 792
Audio Visual Technologies Group, pg 796
AVES Audio Visual Systems Inc, pg 798
CAM Audio Inc, pg 817
Crossroads Audio Inc, pg 840
Data Projections Inc, pg 843
Digital Display Solutions Inc, pg 847
FitzCo Sound Inc, pg 869
Heffernan Audio Visual, pg 887
Industrial Audio/Video Inc, pg 897
J&S Audio Visual Inc, pg 904
Lubbock Audio Visual Inc, pg 925
Media Management LLC, pg 937
Precision Camera & Video, pg 980
Pro Video & Film Equipment Co Inc, pg 983
Quality Audio Visual Service Inc, pg 988
RadioShack Corp, pg 990
RF Specialties of Texas LLC, pg 996
Schoolhouse Audio Visual, pg 1004
Sound Works, pg 1018
Southwest Sound & Electronics Inc, pg 1019
Stage Directions, pg 1022
Tarpley Media Systems, pg 1032

UTAH

Performance Audio, pg 973
RIA Corp, pg 996
Webb Audio Visual Communication, pg 1063

VERMONT

Dark Star Lighting & Production, pg 842
Production Advantage Inc, pg 984

VIRGINIA

Avitecture Inc, pg 799
Boitnott Visual Communications Corp (BVC), pg 810
Communications Specialists Inc, pg 833
Hoppmann Audio Visual, pg 891
Intellidyne LLC, pg 899
Lee Hartman & Sons Inc, pg 918
Old Dominion Broadcasting, pg 961
Rocktown Media, pg 998
StageSound, pg 1023
The Whitlock Group, pg 1065

WASHINGTON

Broadcast Supply World Wide, pg 813
CCI Solutions, pg 821
D A Sound, pg 842
Northern Lights & Pro Audio, pg 959
Pacific Northwest Theatre Associates Inc (PNTA), pg 967

WISCONSIN

Audio Visual of Milwaukee Inc, pg 795
Camera Corner Connecting Point, pg 818
Demco Inc, pg 845
Full Compass Systems, pg 874

PUERTO RICO

Audio Visual Concepts Inc, pg 795
Bonnin Electronics Inc, pg 810

ALBERTA

Infosat Communications Inc, pg 898
Matrix Video Communications Corp (MVCC), pg 934
McBain Audio Visual Ltd, pg 935
Sharp's Audio-Visual Ltd, pg 1008
Unique Communications Ltd, pg 1048

BRITISH COLUMBIA

ADI Systems Inc, pg 776
Commercial Electronics Ltd, pg 832
ProVision Video Sales & Rentals Inc, pg 986

MANITOBA

Advance Pro, pg 777
Evolution Presentation Technologies, pg 863
Inland Audio Visual Ltd, pg 898

ONTARIO

Cinema Stage Inc, pg 827
Edcom Multimedia Products, pg 856
HD Source, pg 886
Henry's Camera, pg 888
Nationwide Audio Visual Co, pg 953
Premier A/V Sales Ltd, pg 980
Westbury National Show Systems Ltd, pg 1064

QUEBEC

AVS Technologies Inc, pg 800
Concept Audio-Visual, pg 834
JAM Industries Ltd, pg 903
Panavideo Inc, pg 968
SC Media Canada, pg 1003
Sennheiser (Canada) Inc, pg 1006

Microphone Manufacturers

ALABAMA

Media Visions Inc, pg 937

ARIZONA

Fender Musical Instruments Corp, pg 866
David Wexler & Co, pg 1064

CALIFORNIA

ACO Pacific Inc, pg 774
AKG Acoustics US, pg 779
Anchor Audio Inc, pg 786
Califone International Inc, pg 817
Calrad Electronics, pg 817
Carvin Corp, pg 820
Countryman Associates Inc, pg 837
Hosa Technology Inc, pg 891
Josephson Engineering Inc, pg 906
Logitech, pg 924
Manley Laboratories Inc, pg 930
Marshall Electronics Inc, pg 932
Millennia Media FPC, pg 943
Nady Systems Inc, pg 952
Panasonic Broadcast & Digital Systems Co, pg 968
Panasonic Professional Audio Systems, pg 968
Professional Sound Corp, pg 985
Sony Electronics Inc, pg 1016
TEAC America Inc, pg 1033
TeachLogic Inc, pg 1033
TOA Electronics Inc, pg 1041
Wohler Technologies Inc, pg 1069

CONNECTICUT

Gold Line/TEF, pg 880
The Music People Inc, pg 951
Neumann USA, pg 955
Sennheiser Electronic Corp, pg 1006
Sound Control Technologies Inc, pg 1017

FLORIDA

CTG Audio, pg 840
Intermark Industries Inc, pg 900
TAI Audio, pg 1031

ILLINOIS

A T Products Inc, pg 771
AmpliVox Portable Sound Systems, pg 785
Shure Inc, pg 1010
SoundTech, pg 1018

KENTUCKY

Innovative Electronic Designs LLC, pg 898

MINNESOTA

Telex Communications Inc, pg 1037
Telex EVI, pg 1037

MISSISSIPPI

Peavey Electronics Corp, pg 970

NEVADA

Pignose-Gorilla, pg 975

NEW HAMPSHIRE

Earthworks Inc, pg 855

NEW JERSEY

AV Bluebook, pg 797
Bogen Communications Inc, pg 810
National Audio-Visual Supply, pg 952
Oklahoma Sound Corp, pg 961
Panasonic Consumer Electronics Co, pg 968
Sony Pro Audio (Broadcast & Professional Systems Division), pg 1016

NEW YORK

beyerdynamic Inc, pg 806
Centennial Electric Sound Co Ltd, pg 822
GLI Sound Systems, pg 878
Harbro Corp, pg 884
Posthorn Recordings, pg 979
Servoreeler Systems, pg 1007
Television Equipment Associates Inc (TEA), pg 1036

OHIO

Audio-Technica US Inc, pg 794
CAD Audio, pg 816

OREGON

Audix Corp, pg 796

PENNSYLVANIA

Ac-cetera Inc, pg 772

SOUTH CAROLINA

DaviSound, pg 843
Paso Sound Products Inc, pg 969

WASHINGTON

AudioControl®, pg 796

Microphone Rentals

ALABAMA

Audio-Video Resources Inc, pg 795
Media Visions Inc, pg 937

ARIZONA

Arizona Cine Equipment, pg 789
Audio Video Resources, pg 795
AV Concepts, pg 797
Broadcast Rentals, pg 813
Merestone, pg 938
Metropolitan Audio-Visual Inc, pg 940
Tempe Camera, pg 1037
Ultimate Presentation Systems Inc, pg 1047
Video Media Productions (VMP), pg 1055
Video West Inc, pg 1056

ARKANSAS

White Diamond Productions, pg 1065

CALIFORNIA

Absolute Rentals, pg 772
Action Audio & Visual, pg 775
Adolph Gasser Inc, pg 776
AGF Media Services, pg 778
Alliant Event Services, pg 781
Alternative Rentals, pg 783
Ametron Audio/Video, pg 785
The Annex, pg 787
Artichoke Productions, pg 791
Associated Sound, pg 792
ATV Video Center Inc, pg 793
AV Conferencing, pg 797
AV Guys, pg 797
Best Bet Camera Rentals, pg 805
Bexel Corp, pg 806
Big Time Picture Company Inc, pg 807
Chater Camera Inc, pg 824
Cherry Multimedia, pg 824
Cinema Camera Rentals, pg 827
Design FX Audio, pg 845
Express Media Inc, pg 864
First Camera, pg 868
Flip 2 Media Inc, pg 870
Full Moon & High Tide Productions & Studios, pg 874
FXC Communications, pg 874

AUDIO

Microphone Rentals (continued)

NEW MEXICO

Production Outfitters, pg 984
Quickbeam Systems Inc (QSI), pg 989

NEW YORK

Ace Video, pg 774
Adorama Rental Co, pg 776
American Video Inc, pg 785
Audio Visual Resources LLC, pg 795
Aura Sonic Ltd, pg 796
AV Workshop, pg 797
Bond Street Studio, pg 810
CMI Communications, pg 830
Colortone Audio Visual, pg 832
Communication Corner Inc, pg 832
CP Communications, pg 837
CSI Rentals, pg 840
Design Audio Visual Inc, pg 845
Dreamhire LLC, pg 852
Gearhead Rentals, pg 876
Gotham Sound & Communications Inc, pg 881
Hello World Communications, pg 888
KVL Audio Visual Services Inc, pg 914
LightHouse Films, pg 920
Long Island Video Enterprises Live Inc, pg 924
Manhattan Center Studios Inc, pg 930
Posthorn Recordings, pg 979
See Factor Industry Inc, pg 1006
SmartSource Computer & AV Rentals, pg 1014
Specialized Audio-Visual Inc, pg 1020
Studio Instrument Rentals (SIR), pg 1027
TBA Global Events, pg 1032
Technisphere Corp, pg 1034
Theatrical Services & Supplies Inc, pg 1038
Visual Technologies Corp, pg 1060
Visual Word Systems Inc, pg 1060
WorldStage, pg 1070

NORTH CAROLINA

A&V Company, pg 772
AV Metro Inc, pg 797
Camcor Inc, pg 818
Duke Media Services, pg 853
Special Event Services, pg 1020
Strategic Connections, pg 1026
Take One Productions Ltd, pg 1031
Visual Aids Electronics of North Carolina Inc, pg 1059

NORTH DAKOTA

Media Productions, pg 937

OHIO

Hughie's Event Production Services, pg 892
ITA Audio Visual Solutions, pg 902
Lyon Video Inc, pg 927
Mills James Productions, pg 943
Ohio HD Video, pg 961
Production Solutions Inc, pg 984
R&B Communications Inc, pg 991
Smithall Electronics Inc, pg 1014

OKLAHOMA

PDC Productions, pg 970

OREGON

BingoLewis, pg 807
Northwest Film Center, pg 959
Picture This Production Services, pg 975
Rose City Sound, pg 999

PENNSYLVANIA

Advanced AV, pg 777
Argentine Productions Inc, pg 789
Audio Visions Inc, pg 795
Audio Visual Communications Inc, pg 795
FirstGeneration Audio/Visual Services, pg 869
FMP Media Solutions Inc, pg 870
Grise Audio Visual Center Inc, pg 882
JPL, pg 906
New York Camera & Video, pg 956
Production Solutions Inc, pg 985
Right Coast Recording Inc, pg 997
Sound by Fitch, pg 1017
The Videohouse Inc, pg 1057
Viewpoint Production Services Inc, pg 1058
Vistacom Inc, pg 1059
Visual Sound Inc, pg 1059

SOUTH CAROLINA

Sound & Images Inc, pg 1016

TENNESSEE

Belew Enterprises, pg 804
Brantley Sound Associates Inc, pg 812
Love Shack Recording Studios, pg 925
Memphis Communications Corp, pg 938
Mr Mark's Used Musical, Stereo & Studio Equipment Store, pg 944
Nashville Production Rentals (NPR), pg 952
RentACamera.com, pg 995
Technical Support Systems LLC, pg 1034
Tennessee Visual Service Co, pg 1037
Trew Audio Inc, pg 1044

TEXAS

Alford Media Services, pg 780
Astro Audio Visual, pg 792
Audio Visual Technologies Group, pg 796
Bright Giant Creative Group, pg 812
Bright Star Productions Inc, pg 812
Crossroads Audio Inc, pg 840
Data Display Audio Visual Co LP, pg 843
FitzCo Sound Inc, pg 869
GEAR Cameras & Lighting, pg 876
J&S Audio Visual Inc, pg 904
Lubbock Audio Visual Inc, pg 925
Music Lab Inc, pg 950
Omega Productions, pg 962
Onstage Systems, pg 963
Padgitt's, pg 967
Power Factory Productions, pg 979
Quality Audio Visual Service Inc, pg 988
The Samuels Co, pg 1002
South Coast Film & Video, pg 1019
Stage Directions, pg 1022
Texcam Inc, pg 1038
Video Perspective, pg 1056

UTAH

Ron Hill Imagery, pg 889
Performance Audio, pg 973
Redman Movies & Stories, pg 993
Webb Audio Visual Communication, pg 1063

VERMONT

Dark Star Lighting & Production, pg 842
Edgewood Studios, pg 857
Parlato Productions, pg 969

VIRGINIA

American AV, pg 783
Audio Visual Actions Inc (AVA), pg 795
Boitnott Visual Communications Corp (BVC), pg 810
D&B Television & Video Productions Inc, pg 842
Lee Hartman & Sons Inc, pg 918
Projection Presentation Technology, pg 985
Rainbow Rentals, pg 991
StageSound, pg 1023

WASHINGTON

D A Sound, pg 842
The House Studios, pg 891
Northern Lights & Pro Audio, pg 959
Oppenheimer Camera Products, pg 964
Pacific Northwest Theatre Associates Inc (PNTA), pg 967
Victory Studios, pg 1054

WEST VIRGINIA

United Sound & Electronics, pg 1048

WISCONSIN

Camera Corner Connecting Point, pg 818
Event Essentials, pg 863
Full Compass Systems, pg 874
MKE Production Rental, pg 944
University of Wisconsin-Oshkosh Radio-TV-Film Dept, pg 1050
USAV Group Inc, pg 1050
Wisconsin Public Television, pg 1068

WYOMING

Bridger Productions Inc, pg 812

PUERTO RICO

Stage Crew Audiovisual Inc, pg 1022

ALBERTA

Allstar Show Industries Inc, pg 782
Cine Audio Visual Sales & Service Ltd, pg 826
Evolution Presentation Technologies, pg 863
L R Light & Sound, pg 915
McBain Audio Visual Ltd, pg 935
Sharp's Audio-Visual Ltd, pg 1008
Unique Communications Ltd, pg 1048

BRITISH COLUMBIA

Clark's Audio Visual Services Ltd, pg 829
Commercial Electronics Ltd, pg 832
DL Sound & Lighting Productions Ltd, pg 849
Image Media Farm, pg 895
MicrophoneRentals.com, pg 941
ProVision Video Sales & Rentals Inc, pg 986
Video In Studios/Video Out Distribution, pg 1055

MANITOBA

Evolution Presentation Technologies, pg 863
Inland Audio Visual Ltd, pg 898

ONTARIO

Boxcar Studio, pg 811
Edcom Multimedia Products, pg 856
HD Source, pg 886
Premier A/V Sales Ltd, pg 980
RB Productions, pg 992
SIM Digital, pg 1011
Westbury National Show Systems Ltd, pg 1064
ZTV Broadcast Services Inc, pg 1074

QUEBEC

Audio Visual Dynamics Ltd, pg 795
AVW-TELAV Audio Visual Solutions, a Freeman Company, pg 800
Concept Audio-Visual, pg 834
Group PVP, pg 882
Panavideo Inc, pg 968

Microphone Repairs

ALABAMA

Media Visions Inc, pg 937

ARIZONA

Metropolitan Audio-Visual Inc, pg 940

CALIFORNIA

Ametron Audio/Video, pg 785
Audio Images Corp, pg 794
Carvin Corp, pg 820
FXC Communications, pg 874
GMF Sound Inc, pg 879
IAMP Professional Audio, pg 893
Location Sound Corp, pg 924
McAlister Electronics, pg 935
Lloyd F McKinney Associates Inc, pg 935
Randall Schiller Productions, pg 1004
Sound Service Co, pg 1017
SSL Industries Inc, pg 1022
TEK Media Group, pg 1035
TOA Electronics Inc, pg 1041
Towards 2000 Inc, pg 1043
VMI Inc, pg 1060

CONNECTICUT

HB Communications Inc, pg 886
Neumann USA, pg 955
Sennheiser Electronic Corp, pg 1006

DELAWARE

Actors Attic, pg 775

FLORIDA

Hi-Tech Enterprises Inc, pg 888
Midtown Video Inc, pg 942
Phat Planet Recording Studios, pg 973
Stereo Sales Inc, pg 1024
TAI Audio, pg 1031

GEORGIA

Lighting & Production Equipment Inc, pg 920
Stage Front Presentation Systems, pg 1022

ILLINOIS

Allen Visual Systems Inc, pg 781
Beatty TeleVisual Productions, pg 804
Central Audio-Visual Equipment Inc, pg 823
C V Lloyde, pg 923
Midwest Digital Corp, pg 942
RC Communications, pg 992

INDIANA

Sweetwater Sound Inc, pg 1029

KENTUCKY

Axxis Inc, pg 800
NOR-COM Inc, pg 958

MAINE

Headlight Audio Visual Inc, pg 887

MARYLAND

Cardinal Sound & Video, pg 820
RTZ Audio Visual, pg 1000
Visual Aids Electronics Corp, pg 1059

MASSACHUSETTS

Capron Lighting & Sound Co Inc, pg 819
Professional Audio Design Inc, pg 985

MICHIGAN

City Events Group, pg 828
K&R's Recording Studios Inc, pg 908
On Stage Visuals, pg 963
TeL Systems, pg 1035

MINNESOTA

Aggressive Records Audio Duplication LLC, pg 778
AVI Systems, pg 799

NEW JERSEY

A-V Services Inc, pg 771
Earl Girls Inc, pg 855
The Music Place, pg 951
Nelson Enterprises Theatrical Supply Co, pg 954
Starlite Productions, pg 1024

NEW MEXICO

Quickbeam Systems Inc (QSI), pg 989

NEW YORK

beyerdynamic Inc, pg 806
Design Audio Visual Inc, pg 845
Technisphere Corp, pg 1034
Toys From The Attic, pg 1043
Visual Technologies Corp, pg 1060

NORTH CAROLINA

Camcor Inc, pg 818
Strategic Connections, pg 1026

OHIO

Copp Integrated Systems, pg 836
Hughie's Event Production Services, pg 892
ITA Audio Visual Solutions, pg 902
Smithall Electronics Inc, pg 1014
Tri-State Audio Visual Co, pg 1044

OREGON

All Service Musical Electronics Repair, pg 780

PENNSYLVANIA

J E Foss Co, pg 871
Right Coast Recording Inc, pg 997
Vistacom Inc, pg 1059

SOUTH CAROLINA

DaviSound, pg 843

TENNESSEE

Belew Enterprises, pg 804
Memphis Communications Corp, pg 938
Technical Support Systems LLC, pg 1034

TEXAS

Astro Audio Visual, pg 792
Audio Visual Technologies Group, pg 796
Lubbock Audio Visual Inc, pg 925
Pro Video & Film Equipment Co Inc, pg 983
Quality Audio Visual Service Inc, pg 988
Southwest Sound & Electronics Inc, pg 1019
Tarpley Media Systems, pg 1032

VIRGINIA

Boitnott Visual Communications Corp (BVC), pg 810
Hoppmann Audio Visual, pg 891
Old Dominion Broadcasting, pg 961

WASHINGTON

Northern Lights & Pro Audio, pg 959
Pacific Northwest Theatre Associates Inc (PNTA), pg 967

WEST VIRGINIA

United Sound & Electronics, pg 1048

WISCONSIN

Full Compass Systems, pg 874

PUERTO RICO

Bonnin Electronics Inc, pg 810

ALBERTA

Allstar Show Industries Inc, pg 782
Infosat Communications Inc, pg 898
Sharp's Audio-Visual Ltd, pg 1008
Unique Communications Ltd, pg 1048

BRITISH COLUMBIA

Commercial Electronics Ltd, pg 832

MANITOBA

Evolution Presentation Technologies, pg 863
Inland Audio Visual Ltd, pg 898

ONTARIO

Edcom Multimedia Products, pg 856
HD Source, pg 886
Premier A/V Sales Ltd, pg 980
Westbury National Show Systems Ltd, pg 1064

QUEBEC

Panavideo Inc, pg 968
SC Media Canada, pg 1003

Microphone Stand, Boom & Accessory Distributors

ALABAMA

Curtis Company, pg 841

ARIZONA

Allusion Studios & Pure Wave Audio, pg 782
Arizona Cine Equipment, pg 789
EAR Professional Audio/Video, pg 855
Metropolitan Audio-Visual Inc, pg 940
Olsen Audio Group Inc, pg 962
Troxell Communications Inc, pg 1045
WindTech™ Microphone Windscreens & Accessories, pg 1067

ARKANSAS

White Diamond Productions, pg 1065

CALIFORNIA

Adolph Gasser Inc, pg 776
AKG Acoustics US, pg 779
Ametron Audio/Video, pg 785
Associated Sound, pg 792
ATV Video Center Inc, pg 793
Audio Images Corp, pg 794
BroadcastStore.com, pg 813
California Tape Products Inc, pg 817
Cibola Systems, pg 826
Delicate Electronics Sales Inc, pg 845
Empire Wholesale Inc, pg 860
Alan Gordon Enterprises Inc, pg 880
IAMP Professional Audio, pg 893
Impact Group, pg 897
Instructional Materials & Equipment Distributors (I-Med), pg 899
JD Audio Visual Inc, pg 904
Location Sound Corp, pg 924
LTM Corp of America, pg 925
Martel Electronics Sales Inc, pg 932
Lloyd F McKinney Associates Inc, pg 935
MediaPOINTE, pg 938
Mole-Richardson Co, pg 945
Pacific Radio Electronics, pg 967
POP TV, pg 978
Professional Sound Corp, pg 985
Related Visual Inc, pg 994
Randall Schiller Productions, pg 1004
Sound Service Co, pg 1017
Southern California Sound Image Inc, pg 1019
SSL Industries Inc, pg 1022
Stanislaus Audio Video Inc, pg 1023
Towards 2000 Inc, pg 1043
Tri-Ed, pg 1044
VMI Inc, pg 1060
VTP Inc, pg 1061

COLORADO

Audio Consultant Services Inc, pg 794
Daylight Productions & Rentals, pg 844
Spectrum Audio Visual Services, pg 1020
Ultimate Support Systems Inc, pg 1047

CONNECTICUT

Connecticut Audio & Theatrical Supply, pg 835
HB Communications Inc, pg 886
The Music People Inc, pg 951
Neumann USA, pg 955
Redco Audio Inc, pg 993
Sennheiser Electronic Corp, pg 1006

DELAWARE

Actors Attic, pg 775

FLORIDA

Access Media Group, pg 773
Allstar Audio Systems Inc, pg 782
AVI-SPL, pg 798
BAI Distributors Inc, pg 801
Broadcasters General Store Inc, pg 813
Digital Video Systems Inc, pg 848
Enhanced View Services Inc, pg 861
General Projection Systems Inc, pg 877
Gulf Coast Audio Visual Producers Inc, pg 883
Harris Corp, pg 885
Herman Pro AV, pg 888
Hi-Tech Enterprises Inc, pg 888
Hi-Tech Import Export Corp, pg 888
Hunter Electronics LLC, pg 892
Industrial Strength Inc, pg 897
Intermark Industries Inc, pg 900
Lighting Sales Connections, pg 920
Media Concepts Inc, pg 936
Midtown Video Inc, pg 942
Photomart Cine-Video Inc, pg 975
Pro Stage Inc, pg 983
Recording Media & Equipment Inc (RM&E), pg 993
Sight & Sound Productions, pg 1010
Stereo Sales Inc, pg 1024
TAI Audio, pg 1031
Technomedia Solutions, pg 1035

GEORGIA

Baker Audio Inc, pg 801
Clark, pg 829
Lighting & Production Equipment Inc, pg 920
Stage Front Presentation Systems, pg 1022

AUDIO

Microphone Stand, Boom & Accessory Distributors (continued)

HAWAII

The Audio Visual Co (AVCO), pg 795

ILLINOIS

Allen Visual Systems Inc, pg 781
Central Audio-Visual Equipment Inc, pg 823
Joseph Electronics, pg 906
LKG Industries Inc, pg 923
C V Lloyde, pg 923
Major Media Inc, pg 929
Quintessence Audio Ltd, pg 989
RAM Systems LLC, pg 991
Woodside Avenue Music Productions Inc, pg 1069

INDIANA

Heart Breaker Entertainment LLC, pg 887
Jack's Camera Shop, pg 903
Sensory Technologies LLC, pg 1006
SHP Electronics, pg 1010
Sweetwater Sound Inc, pg 1029

IOWA

ECS Inc, pg 856

KANSAS

Smith Audio-Visual Inc, pg 1014

KENTUCKY

Audio Visual Techniques Inc, pg 796
Axxis Inc, pg 800
Barney Miller's Inc, pg 943
NOR-COM Inc, pg 958
Northern Kentucky University, pg 959

LOUISIANA

Intermedia Technologies, pg 900

MAINE

Headlight Audio Visual Inc, pg 887

MARYLAND

Advance Audiovisual Presentation Ltd, pg 777
Bradley Broadcast & Pro Audio, pg 811
Cardinal Sound & Video, pg 820
Human Circuit, pg 892
Noventri, pg 960

MASSACHUSETTS

Terry Hanley Audio Systems Inc, pg 884
Hunt's Photo, Video & Digital, pg 892
Professional Audio Design Inc, pg 985
Rule Broadcast Systems, pg 1000

MICHIGAN

Olson Anderson Co, pg 786
Ascom Communications Contractors, pg 791
City Events Group, pg 828
On Stage Visuals, pg 963
Stedman Corp, pg 1024
TeL Systems, pg 1035

MINNESOTA

Advanced Audio-Visual Inc, pg 777
Lights On, pg 921
New Life Communications Inc, pg 956
Tierney Brothers Inc, pg 1040

MISSISSIPPI

Bowie Audio Visual Enterprises Inc, pg 811

MISSOURI

Communitronics Corp, pg 833
Conference Technologies Inc, pg 835
MIS Technologies, pg 944
Modern Communications Inc, pg 944
Production Support Services Inc, pg 985
The RapcoHorizon Co, pg 991
Schiller's Audio-Visual, pg 1004

NEW HAMPSHIRE

APS Lighting-Sound-AV, pg 789
Technet® Systems Group, pg 1033

NEW JERSEY

A-V Services Inc, pg 771
Alltec Stores, a Vcom IMC Company, pg 782
AV Bluebook, pg 797
Comprehensive Cable & Connectivity Co, pg 833
Diversified Systems Inc, pg 849
Earl Girls Inc, pg 855
Euro-Pacific Film & Video Productions Inc, pg 863
G&G Technologies Inc, pg 875
Hamilton Buhl, pg 884
Manfrotto Distribution Inc, pg 930
The Music Place, pg 951
National Audio-Visual Supply, pg 952
Nelson Enterprises Theatrical Supply Co, pg 954
Starlite Productions, pg 1024
Total Video Products Inc, pg 1042
VCom International Multimedia Corp, pg 1052
Video Corporation of America (VCA), pg 1055
Wired 4 Sound Inc, pg 1068
York Telecom, pg 1072

NEW MEXICO

Quickbeam Systems Inc (QSI), pg 989

NEW YORK

Albany Theatre Supply Co Inc, pg 780
ALTEL Systems Inc, pg 783
American Video Inc, pg 785
Audio-Video Corp, pg 795
Aura Sonic Ltd, pg 796
AV Workshop, pg 797
Barbizon Electric Co Inc, pg 802
beyerdynamic Inc, pg 806
BTX Technologies, pg 814
Colortone Audio Visual, pg 832
Communication Corner Inc, pg 832
Custom Media Environments, pg 841
Design Audio Visual Inc, pg 845
Gaylord Brothers, pg 876
Gotham Sound & Communications Inc, pg 881
HAVE Inc, pg 886
Hot House Professional Audio, pg 891
Indigo Productions, pg 897
KVL Audio Visual Services Inc, pg 914
Long Island Video Enterprises Live Inc, pg 924
Magnaplan Corp, pg 928
Mark Custom Recording Service Inc, pg 931
Markertek Video Supply, pg 931
Neptune Photo Inc, pg 954
Popless Voice Screens, pg 978
Posthorn Recordings, pg 979
Presentation Products Inc, pg 981
RNJ Electronics, pg 997
Technisphere Corp, pg 1034
TecNec Distributing, pg 1035
Theatrical Services & Supplies Inc, pg 1038
Toys From The Attic, pg 1043
Visual Technologies Corp, pg 1060
Visual Word Systems Inc, pg 1060
Yorkville Sound Inc, pg 1072

OHIO

Copp Integrated Systems, pg 836
Hughie's Event Production Services, pg 892
ITA Audio Visual Solutions, pg 902
Parts Express, pg 969
Jimmy Rea Electronics Inc, pg 992
Smithall Electronics Inc, pg 1014
Tri-State Audio Visual Co, pg 1044
Tri-State Visual Products, pg 1044

OREGON

SuperDigital Ltd, pg 1029

PENNSYLVANIA

Advanced AV, pg 777
Audio Visions Inc, pg 795
Clair Brothers Audio Systems Inc, pg 829
J E Foss Co, pg 871
Grise Audio Visual Center Inc, pg 882
The Lerro Corp, pg 919
Morefield Communications Inc, pg 946
RSS Distributors, pg 1000
Sound by Fitch, pg 1017
Vistacom Inc, pg 1059
Visual Sound Inc, pg 1059
Wespen Audio Visual Co, pg 1063

TENNESSEE

Durrell LLC, pg 854
Lowrance Sound Co Inc, pg 925
Mr Mark's Used Musical, Stereo & Studio Equipment Store, pg 944
Spectrum Sound Inc, pg 1021
Technical Support Systems LLC, pg 1034
Trew Audio Inc, pg 1044
Zion Music Group, pg 1074

TEXAS

Astro Audio Visual, pg 792
CAM Audio Inc, pg 817
Crossroads Audio Inc, pg 840
Data Projections Inc, pg 843
FitzCo Sound Inc, pg 869
Heffernan Audio Visual, pg 887
Industrial Audio/Video Inc, pg 897
Lubbock Audio Visual Inc, pg 925
Media Management LLC, pg 937
Pro Video & Film Equipment Co Inc, pg 983
Quality Audio Visual Service Inc, pg 988
RadioShack Corp, pg 990
RF Specialties of Texas LLC, pg 996
Schoolhouse Audio Visual, pg 1004
Sound Works, pg 1018
Southwest Sound & Electronics Inc, pg 1019
Stage Directions, pg 1022
Tarpley Media Systems, pg 1032

UTAH

Performance Audio, pg 973
RIA Corp, pg 996
Spectra Sonics Applied Technology Inc, pg 1020

VERMONT

Production Advantage Inc, pg 984

VIRGINIA

Avitecture Inc, pg 799
Boitnott Visual Communications Corp (BVC), pg 810
Communications Specialists Inc, pg 833
Hoppmann Audio Visual, pg 891
Intellidyne LLC, pg 899
Lee Hartman & Sons Inc, pg 918
Old Dominion Broadcasting, pg 961
Rocktown Media, pg 998
StageSound, pg 1023
The Whitlock Group, pg 1065

WASHINGTON

CCI Solutions, pg 821
D A Sound, pg 842
Northern Lights & Pro Audio, pg 959
Pacific Northwest Theatre Associates Inc (PNTA), pg 967

WEST VIRGINIA

United Sound & Electronics, pg 1048

WISCONSIN

Audio Visual of Milwaukee Inc, pg 795
Camera Corner Connecting Point, pg 818
Full Compass Systems, pg 874

PUERTO RICO

Audio Visual Concepts Inc, pg 795
Bonnin Electronics Inc, pg 810

ALBERTA

Infosat Communications Inc, pg 898
Matrix Video Communications Corp (MVCC), pg 934
McBain Audio Visual Ltd, pg 935
Sharp's Audio-Visual Ltd, pg 1008
Unique Communications Ltd, pg 1048

BRITISH COLUMBIA

Commercial Electronics Ltd, pg 832
ProVision Video Sales & Rentals Inc, pg 986

MANITOBA

Advance Pro, pg 777
Inland Audio Visual Ltd, pg 898

Microphone Stand, Boom & Accessory Manufacturers

Microphone Stand, Boom & Accessory Rentals

AUDIO

Microphone Stand, Boom & Accessory Rentals (continued)

MASSACHUSETTS

AVFX Inc, pg 798
Terry Hanley Audio Systems Inc, pg 884
massAV, pg 933
Preston Productions Inc, pg 981

MICHIGAN

Olson Anderson Co, pg 786
City Events Group, pg 828
K&R All Media Productions Inc, pg 908
K&R's Recording Studios Inc, pg 908
On Stage Visuals, pg 963
Stedman Corp, pg 1024
TeL Systems, pg 1035

MINNESOTA

Advanced Audio-Visual Inc, pg 777
Alpha Video & Audio Inc, pg 782
Lights On, pg 921

MISSISSIPPI

Bowie Audio Visual Enterprises Inc, pg 811

MISSOURI

Communitronics Corp, pg 833
Production Support Services Inc, pg 985
Schiller's Audio-Visual, pg 1004
Show-Me Audio-Visual, pg 1009
Switch, pg 1030

MONTANA

Jereco Studios Inc, pg 905

NEVADA

GES Audio Visual, pg 877
MG Studio, pg 940

NEW HAMPSHIRE

Apertura, pg 788
APS Lighting-Sound-AV, pg 789

NEW JERSEY

CFP Video Productions Inc, pg 823
Earl Girls Inc, pg 855
Euro-Pacific Film & Video Productions Inc, pg 863
Giant Audio Visual Inc, pg 878
International Audio Visual Inc, pg 900
MIB Mediaworks, pg 941
Moe AV LLC, pg 945
The Music Place, pg 951
Nelson Enterprises Theatrical Supply Co, pg 954
PLS Staging, pg 977
Starlite Productions, pg 1024
Video Corporation of America (VCA), pg 1055
Wired 4 Sound Inc, pg 1068

NEW MEXICO

Production Outfitters, pg 984
Quickbeam Systems Inc (QSI), pg 989

NEW YORK

Ace Video, pg 774
American Video Inc, pg 785
Audio Visual Resources LLC, pg 795
Aura Sonic Ltd, pg 796
AV Workshop, pg 797
Big Foot Productions Inc, pg 807
Bond Street Studio, pg 810
Camart, pg 817
Colortone Audio Visual, pg 832
Communication Corner Inc, pg 832
CP Communications, pg 837
CSI Rentals, pg 840
Design Audio Visual Inc, pg 845
Dreamhire LLC, pg 852
Gearhead Rentals, pg 876
Gotham Sound & Communications Inc, pg 881
Hello World Communications, pg 888
KVL Audio Visual Services Inc, pg 914
Long Island Video Enterprises Live Inc, pg 924
Posthorn Recordings, pg 979
See Factor Industry Inc, pg 1006
Specialized Audio-Visual Inc, pg 1020
Studio Instrument Rentals (SIR), pg 1027
TBA Global Events, pg 1032
Technisphere Corp, pg 1034
Theatrical Services & Supplies Inc, pg 1038
Visual Technologies Corp, pg 1060
Visual Word Systems Inc, pg 1060
WorldStage, pg 1070

NORTH CAROLINA

A&V Company, pg 772
AV Metro Inc, pg 797
Duke Media Services, pg 853
Special Event Services, pg 1020
Take One Productions Ltd, pg 1031
Visual Aids Electronics of North Carolina Inc, pg 1059

NORTH DAKOTA

Media Productions, pg 937

OHIO

Hughie's Event Production Services, pg 892
Lyon Video Inc, pg 927
Mills James Productions, pg 943
Production Solutions Inc, pg 984
R&B Communications Inc, pg 991
Smithall Electronics Inc, pg 1014

OKLAHOMA

PDC Productions, pg 970

OREGON

Northwest Film Center, pg 959
Picture This Production Services, pg 975
Rose City Sound, pg 999

PENNSYLVANIA

Advanced AV, pg 777
Argentine Productions Inc, pg 789
Audio Visions Inc, pg 795
Audio Visual Communications Inc, pg 795
FirstGeneration Audio/Visual Services, pg 869
FMP Media Solutions Inc, pg 870
Grise Audio Visual Center Inc, pg 882
New York Camera & Video, pg 956
Production Solutions Inc, pg 985
Right Coast Recording Inc, pg 997
Sound by Fitch, pg 1017
The Videohouse Inc, pg 1057
Viewpoint Production Services Inc, pg 1058
Vistacom Inc, pg 1059
Visual Sound Inc, pg 1059

SOUTH CAROLINA

Sound & Images Inc, pg 1016

TENNESSEE

Brantley Sound Associates Inc, pg 812
Love Shack Recording Studios, pg 925
Mr Mark's Used Musical, Stereo & Studio Equipment Store, pg 944
Technical Support Systems LLC, pg 1034
Trew Audio Inc, pg 1044

TEXAS

Alford Media Services, pg 780
Astro Audio Visual, pg 792
Bright Giant Creative Group, pg 812
Bright Star Productions Inc, pg 812
Crossroads Audio Inc, pg 840
FitzCo Sound Inc, pg 869
GEAR Cameras & Lighting, pg 876
Lubbock Audio Visual Inc, pg 925
Music Lab Inc, pg 950
Onstage Systems, pg 963
Quality Audio Visual Service Inc, pg 988
The Samuels Co, pg 1002
South Coast Film & Video, pg 1019
Stage Directions, pg 1022
Texcam Inc, pg 1038
Video Perspective, pg 1056

UTAH

Performance Audio, pg 973
Redman Movies & Stories, pg 993

VERMONT

Dark Star Lighting & Production, pg 842
Edgewood Studios, pg 857
Parlato Productions, pg 969

VIRGINIA

American AV, pg 783
Boitnott Visual Communications Corp (BVC), pg 810
D&B Television & Video Productions Inc, pg 842
Lee Hartman & Sons Inc, pg 918
Rainbow Rentals, pg 991
StageSound, pg 1023

WASHINGTON

D A Sound, pg 842
Northern Lights & Pro Audio, pg 959
Oppenheimer Camera Products, pg 964
Pacific Northwest Theatre Associates Inc (PNTA), pg 967
Victory Studios, pg 1054

WEST VIRGINIA

United Sound & Electronics, pg 1048

WISCONSIN

Camera Corner Connecting Point, pg 818
Event Essentials, pg 863
Full Compass Systems, pg 874

WYOMING

Bridger Productions Inc, pg 812

PUERTO RICO

Stage Crew Audiovisual Inc, pg 1022

ALBERTA

Allstar Show Industries Inc, pg 782
Evolution Presentation Technologies, pg 863
L R Light & Sound, pg 915
McBain Audio Visual Ltd, pg 935
Sharp's Audio-Visual Ltd, pg 1008
Unique Communications Ltd, pg 1048

BRITISH COLUMBIA

Clark's Audio Visual Services Ltd, pg 829
Commercial Electronics Ltd, pg 832
DL Sound & Lighting Productions Ltd, pg 849
Image Media Farm, pg 895
MicrophoneRentals.com, pg 941
ProVision Video Sales & Rentals Inc, pg 986
Video In Studios/Video Out Distribution, pg 1055

MANITOBA

Inland Audio Visual Ltd, pg 898

ONTARIO

HD Source, pg 886
Premier A/V Sales Ltd, pg 980
RB Productions, pg 992
Westbury National Show Systems Ltd, pg 1064

QUEBEC

Audio Visual Dynamics Ltd, pg 795
Concept Audio-Visual, pg 834
Group PVP, pg 882

Microphone Stand, Boom & Accessory Repairs

CALIFORNIA

Ametron Audio/Video, pg 785
Audio Images Corp, pg 794
Alan Gordon Enterprises Inc, pg 880
LTM Corp of America, pg 925
McAlister Electronics, pg 935
Professional Sound Corp, pg 985
Randall Schiller Productions, pg 1004
Sound Service Co, pg 1017
Towards 2000 Inc, pg 1043

CONNECTICUT

HB Communications Inc, pg 886
Sennheiser Electronic Corp, pg 1006

FLORIDA

Hi-Tech Enterprises Inc, pg 888
Phat Planet Recording Studios, pg 973

Microphone—Wireless Distributors

AUDIO

Microphone—Wireless Distributors (continued)

MASSACHUSETTS

Terry Hanley Audio Systems Inc, pg 884
Hunt's Photo, Video & Digital, pg 892
Professional Audio Design Inc, pg 985
Rule Broadcast Systems, pg 1000

MICHIGAN

Olson Anderson Co, pg 786
Ascom Communications Contractors, pg 791
City Events Group, pg 828
Digi Sign Design LLC, pg 847
On Stage Visuals, pg 963
TeL Systems, pg 1035

MINNESOTA

Advanced Audio-Visual Inc, pg 777
New Life Communications Inc, pg 956
Tierney Brothers Inc, pg 1040

MISSISSIPPI

Bowie Audio Visual Enterprises Inc, pg 811

MISSOURI

Communitronics Corp, pg 833
Conference Technologies Inc, pg 835
MIS Technologies, pg 944
Modern Communications Inc, pg 944
Production Support Services Inc, pg 985
Schiller's Audio-Visual, pg 1004

NEW HAMPSHIRE

APS Lighting-Sound-AV, pg 789
Technet® Systems Group, pg 1033

NEW JERSEY

A-V Services Inc, pg 771
Alltec Stores, a Vcom IMC Company, pg 782
Audio Visual Associates, pg 795
AV Bluebook, pg 797
Comprehensive Cable & Connectivity Co, pg 833
Diversified Systems Inc, pg 849
Earl Girls Inc, pg 855
Euro-Pacific Film & Video Productions Inc, pg 863
G&G Technologies Inc, pg 875
Hamilton Buhl, pg 884
The Music Place, pg 951
National Audio-Visual Supply, pg 952
Nelson Enterprises Theatrical Supply Co, pg 954
PatchAmp, pg 970
SLD Lighting, pg 1013
Starlite Productions, pg 1024
Total Video Products Inc, pg 1042
VCom International Multimedia Corp, pg 1052
Video Corporation of America (VCA), pg 1055
Wilray Audio Visual Corp, pg 1067
Wired 4 Sound Inc, pg 1068
York Telecom, pg 1072

NEW MEXICO

Quickbeam Systems Inc (QSI), pg 989

NEW YORK

Albany Theatre Supply Co Inc, pg 780
ALTEL Systems Inc, pg 783
American Video Inc, pg 785
Audio-Video Corp, pg 795
Aura Sonic Ltd, pg 796
AV Workshop, pg 797
beyerdynamic Inc, pg 806
BMI Supply, pg 810
BTX Technologies, pg 814
Centennial Electric Sound Co Ltd, pg 822
Colortone Audio Visual, pg 832
Communication Corner Inc, pg 832
Custom Media Environments, pg 841
Design Audio Visual Inc, pg 845
Gaylord Brothers, pg 876
Gotham Sound & Communications Inc, pg 881
HAVE Inc, pg 886
Hot House Professional Audio, pg 891
Indigo Productions, pg 897
iProbe Multilingual Solutions Inc, pg 902
KVL Audio Visual Services Inc, pg 914
Long Island Video Enterprises Live Inc, pg 924
Magnaplan Corp, pg 928
Markertek Video Supply, pg 931
Neptune Photo Inc, pg 954
PicturePhone Inc, pg 975
Posthorn Recordings, pg 979
Presentation Products Inc, pg 981
RNJ Electronics, pg 997
Samson Technologies Corp, pg 1002
SmartSource Computer & AV Rentals, pg 1014
Technisphere Corp, pg 1034
TecNec Distributing, pg 1035
Theatrical Services & Supplies Inc, pg 1038
Toys From The Attic, pg 1043
Visual Technologies Corp, pg 1060
Visual Word Systems Inc, pg 1060

NORTH CAROLINA

Innocinema, pg 898

OHIO

Copp Integrated Systems, pg 836
Hughie's Event Production Services, pg 892
ITA Audio Visual Solutions, pg 902
The Little Warehouse Inc, pg 923
Luminaud Inc, pg 926
Midwest Photo Exchange, pg 942
Parts Express, pg 969
Jimmy Rea Electronics Inc, pg 992
Smithall Electronics Inc, pg 1014
Tri-State Audio Visual Co, pg 1044
Tri-State Visual Products, pg 1044

OREGON

Audix Corp, pg 796
Lightspeed Technologies Inc, pg 921
PLUS Corp of America, pg 977
Spectrum Systems Design, pg 1021
SuperDigital Ltd, pg 1029

PENNSYLVANIA

Advanced AV, pg 777
Audio Visions Inc, pg 795
Bernie's Photo Center, pg 805
Clair Brothers Audio Systems Inc, pg 829
J E Foss Co, pg 871
Garcia Marketing Inc, pg 875
Grise Audio Visual Center Inc, pg 882
The Lerro Corp, pg 919
Morefield Communications Inc, pg 946
RSS Distributors, pg 1000
Sound by Fitch, pg 1017
Vistacom Inc, pg 1059
Visual Sound Inc, pg 1059
Wespen Audio Visual Co, pg 1063

RHODE ISLAND

Shanix Inc, pg 1008

TENNESSEE

Belew Enterprises, pg 804
Durrell LLC, pg 854
Lowrance Sound Co Inc, pg 925
Spectrum Sound Inc, pg 1021
Technical Support Systems LLC, pg 1034
Trew Audio Inc, pg 1044
Zion Music Group, pg 1074

TEXAS

Astro Audio Visual, pg 792
Audio Visual Technologies Group, pg 796
AVES Audio Visual Systems Inc, pg 798
CAM Audio Inc, pg 817
Crossroads Audio Inc, pg 840
Data Projections Inc, pg 843
Digital Display Solutions Inc, pg 847
FitzCo Sound Inc, pg 869
Heffernan Audio Visual, pg 887
Industrial Audio/Video Inc, pg 897
Lubbock Audio Visual Inc, pg 925
Media Management LLC, pg 937
Precision Camera & Video, pg 980
Pro Video & Film Equipment Co Inc, pg 983
Quality Audio Visual Service Inc, pg 988
RadioShack Corp, pg 990
RF Specialties of Texas LLC, pg 996
Schoolhouse Audio Visual, pg 1004
Sound Works, pg 1018
Southwest Sound & Electronics Inc, pg 1019
Stage Directions, pg 1022
TapeWorks Texas Inc, pg 1032
Tarpley Media Systems, pg 1032

UTAH

Comtek Communications Technology Inc, pg 834
Performance Audio, pg 973
RIA Corp, pg 996
Spectra Sonics Applied Technology Inc, pg 1020

VERMONT

Production Advantage Inc, pg 984

VIRGINIA

Avitecture Inc, pg 799
Boitnott Visual Communications Corp (BVC), pg 810
Communications Specialists Inc, pg 833
Hoppmann Audio Visual, pg 891
Intellidyne LLC, pg 899
Lee Hartman & Sons Inc, pg 918
Rocktown Media, pg 998
StageSound, pg 1023
The Whitlock Group, pg 1065

WASHINGTON

CCI Solutions, pg 821
D A Sound, pg 842
Northern Lights & Pro Audio, pg 959
Pacific Northwest Theatre Associates Inc (PNTA), pg 967

WEST VIRGINIA

United Sound & Electronics, pg 1048

WISCONSIN

Audio Visual of Milwaukee Inc, pg 795
Camera Corner Connecting Point, pg 818
Demco Inc, pg 845
Full Compass Systems, pg 874

PUERTO RICO

Audio Visual Concepts Inc, pg 795
Bonnin Electronics Inc, pg 810

ALBERTA

Infosat Communications Inc, pg 898
Matrix Video Communications Corp (MVCC), pg 934
McBain Audio Visual Ltd, pg 935
Sharp's Audio-Visual Ltd, pg 1008
Unique Communications Ltd, pg 1048

BRITISH COLUMBIA

ADI Systems Inc, pg 776
Commercial Electronics Ltd, pg 832
ProVision Video Sales & Rentals Inc, pg 986

MANITOBA

Advance Pro, pg 777
Inland Audio Visual Ltd, pg 898

ONTARIO

Cinema Stage Inc, pg 827
HD Source, pg 886
Henry's Camera, pg 888
Nationwide Audio Visual Co, pg 953
Premier A/V Sales Ltd, pg 980
Westbury National Show Systems Ltd, pg 1064

QUEBEC

Concept Audio-Visual, pg 834
JAM Industries Ltd, pg 903
Panavideo Inc, pg 968
SC Media Canada, pg 1003

Microphone—Wireless Manufacturers

CALIFORNIA

AKG Acoustics US, pg 779
Anchor Audio Inc, pg 786
Califone International Inc, pg 817
Calrad Electronics, pg 817

Countryman Associates Inc, pg 837
Nady Systems Inc, pg 952
Panasonic Broadcast & Digital Systems Co, pg 968
TeachLogic Inc, pg 1033
TOA Electronics Inc, pg 1041
Wohler Technologies Inc, pg 1069

CONNECTICUT

Sennheiser Electronic Corp, pg 1006

FLORIDA

Sabine® Inc, pg 1001

ILLINOIS

AmpliVox Portable Sound Systems, pg 785
Shure Inc, pg 1010
SoundTech, pg 1018

MINNESOTA

Telex Communications Inc, pg 1037
Telex EVI, pg 1037

MISSISSIPPI

Peavey Electronics Corp, pg 970

NEVADA

Pignose-Gorilla, pg 975

NEW JERSEY

Bogen Communications Inc, pg 810
Gemini Sound, pg 876
Oklahoma Sound Corp, pg 961
Sony Pro Audio (Broadcast & Professional Systems Division), pg 1016

NEW MEXICO

Lectrosonics Inc, pg 918

NEW YORK

beyerdynamic Inc, pg 806
MG Electronics, pg 940
Samson Technologies Corp, pg 1002

OHIO

Audio-Technica US Inc, pg 794
CAD Audio, pg 816
R L Drake Co, pg 852

OREGON

Audix Corp, pg 796
Lightspeed Technologies Inc, pg 921

RHODE ISLAND

Numark Industries Inc, pg 960

SOUTH CAROLINA

Paso Sound Products Inc, pg 969

UTAH

Comtek Communications Technology Inc, pg 834

Microphone—Wireless Rentals

ALABAMA

Audio-Video Resources Inc, pg 795

ARIZONA

Arizona Cine Equipment, pg 789
AV Concepts, pg 797
Broadcast Rentals, pg 813
Glendale Media Center, pg 878
Merestone, pg 938
Metropolitan Audio-Visual Inc, pg 940
Ultimate Presentation Systems Inc, pg 1047
Video West Inc, pg 1056

ARKANSAS

White Diamond Productions, pg 1065

CALIFORNIA

Absolute Rentals, pg 772
Adolph Gasser Inc, pg 776
AGF Media Services, pg 778
Alliant Event Services, pg 781
Ametron Audio/Video, pg 785
Artichoke Productions, pg 791
Associated Sound, pg 792
ATV Video Center Inc, pg 793
Audio Rents, pg 794
AV Conferencing, pg 797
AV Guys, pg 797
Bexel Corp, pg 806
Cherry Multimedia, pg 824
Express Media Inc, pg 864
First Camera, pg 868
Flip 2 Media Inc, pg 870
Full Moon & High Tide Productions & Studios, pg 874
FXC Communications, pg 874
Gearhouse Broadcast LLC, pg 876
Gold Standard Productions, pg 880
Golden Gate Studios, pg 880
Alan Gordon Enterprises Inc, pg 880
IAMP Professional Audio, pg 893
Imagecraft Productions, pg 896
Images in Motion Media Inc, pg 896
Impact Group, pg 897
Instructional Materials & Equipment Distributors (I-Med), pg 899
InVision Productions, pg 902
JD Audio Visual Inc, pg 904
Location Sound Corp, pg 924
Lynch Communications, pg 926
Maximus Media Inc, pg 934
McCune Audio-Video-Lighting, pg 935
Media Vision USA, pg 937
Munday & Collins AV, pg 950
Muse Presentation Technologies, pg 950
New Circuit Films LLC, pg 955
Next Arts, pg 957
North County Media Center, pg 959
Old School Cameras, pg 961
On-Trax Inc, pg 963
Pacific Audio-Visual Enterprises, pg 967
Prime Cut Productions, pg 982
Pro HD Rentals, pg 983
Production Gear Rentals (PGR), pg 984
PSAV® Presentation Services, pg 986
Pyxis Industries Inc, pg 988
Related Visual Inc, pg 994
Randall Schiller Productions, pg 1004
Shooting Star Video, pg 1009
Shoulder High Productions, pg 1009
Slate Media Group, pg 1013
SNAP, pg 1014
Sound Service Co, pg 1017
Stanislaus Audio Video Inc, pg 1023
Stray Angel Films, pg 1026
Studio 637, pg 1027
The Studios at Paramount, pg 1027
Synthesizer Systems Technologies (SST), pg 1030
Third Ear Sound Co, pg 1038
Total Media Group, pg 1042
Towards 2000 Inc, pg 1043
VER-Video Equipment Rentals, pg 1053
Video Gear Rentals Inc, pg 1055
Video Resources Inc, pg 1056
Vitruvian Entertainment, pg 1060
VMI Inc, pg 1060
Voice & Video Rentals, pg 1060
Warner Bros Entertainment Inc, pg 1062
Warner Bros Production Sound & Video Services, pg 1062
Westcoast Video Productions Inc, pg 1064

COLORADO

Audio Consultant Services Inc, pg 794
Daylight Productions & Rentals, pg 844
Denver Media Center, pg 845
Multimedia Audio Visual Inc, pg 950
Open Media Foundation, pg 964
Spectrum Audio Visual Services, pg 1020

CONNECTICUT

A/V Davey, pg 797
Connecticut Audio & Theatrical Supply, pg 835
Everett Hall Associates Inc, pg 863
Fox Connecticut, pg 872

DELAWARE

Actors Attic, pg 775
Showorks Audio Visual Inc, pg 1010

DISTRICT OF COLUMBIA

Metro Teleproductions Inc (MTI), pg 939

FLORIDA

Access Media Group, pg 773
Accord Productions, pg 773
Allstar Audio Systems Inc, pg 782
AVI-SPL, pg 798
Blackburst Entertainment, pg 808
Budget Video Rentals, pg 815
Cinema East, pg 827
Gulf Coast Audio Visual Producers Inc, pg 883
Harmon's Audio-Visual Services, pg 885
Hi-Tech Enterprises Inc, pg 888
Image Technical Services, pg 895
Industrial Strength Inc, pg 897
Knowles Video Inc (KVI), pg 912
Lighting Sales Connections, pg 920
Paradise Show & Design Inc, pg 969
Pro Stage Inc, pg 983
Sight & Sound Productions, pg 1010
TAI Audio, pg 1031
Technomedia Solutions, pg 1035
10-20 Productions, pg 1037
Universal Studios Florida® Production Group, pg 1049

GEORGIA

ECG Productions, pg 856
Lighting & Production Equipment Inc, pg 920
MAGNUM Companies Ltd, pg 929
See Production Services, pg 1006
Stage Front Presentation Systems, pg 1022
Staging Directions Inc, pg 1023
Studio Space Atlanta, pg 1027

HAWAII

Sight & Sound Studios, pg 1010

ILLINOIS

Allen Visual Systems Inc, pg 781
AV Chicago Inc, pg 797
Backstar Creative Media Inc, pg 801
Beatty TeleVisual Productions, pg 804
Central Audio-Visual Equipment Inc, pg 823
Creative Technology, pg 838
Firehouse Studios, pg 868
C V Lloyde, pg 923
Magnanimous Media, pg 928
The Meetinghouse Companies Inc, pg 938
On Stage Audio, pg 963
Product Productions, pg 984
QuickSet International Inc, pg 989
RC Communications, pg 992
SCI Television Productions LLC, pg 1004
Show Department Inc, pg 1009
Staging Resources Inc, pg 1023
Winter Productions, pg 1068
Woodside Avenue Music Productions Inc, pg 1069
Zacuto, pg 1073

INDIANA

Heart Breaker Entertainment LLC, pg 887

IOWA

Central Lighting & Equipment Inc (CLE), pg 823
ECS Inc, pg 856
Pro Video, pg 983

KANSAS

Smith Audio-Visual Inc, pg 1014

KENTUCKY

Audio Visual Techniques Inc, pg 796
Idle Minds Productions Inc, pg 894
Kentucky Grip & Lighting, pg 909
Barney Miller's Inc, pg 943

LOUISIANA

Clark Services Audio Visual & Exhibit Inc, pg 829
Pace Systems, pg 966

MAINE

Headlight Audio Visual Inc, pg 887

MARYLAND

Advance Audiovisual Presentation Ltd, pg 777
The Ahern Group, pg 779
Cardinal Sound & Video, pg 820
CPR MultiMedia Solutions, pg 837
Event Tech, pg 863
Hargrove Inc, pg 885

AUDIO

Microphone—Wireless Rentals (continued)

MARYLAND (continued)

Kramer Communications Video Production, pg 913
Maryland Sound International Holding Co LLC, pg 933
Shadowstone R & R™, pg 1008
Soundtrax Optical Sound Recording, pg 1018
Visual Aids Electronics Corp, pg 1059

MASSACHUSETTS

AVFX Inc, pg 798
Fastlane Productions LLC, pg 866
Terry Hanley Audio Systems Inc, pg 884
massAV, pg 933
Preston Productions Inc, pg 981

MICHIGAN

Olson Anderson Co, pg 786
City Events Group, pg 828
Digi Sign Design LLC, pg 847
K&R All Media Productions Inc, pg 908
K&R's Recording Studios Inc, pg 908
On Stage Visuals, pg 963
TeL Systems, pg 1035

MINNESOTA

Advanced Audio-Visual Inc, pg 777
Alpha Video & Audio Inc, pg 782
Big Event Productions LLC, pg 807
Lights On, pg 921
New Life Communications Inc, pg 956
Pro Media Productions, pg 983

MISSISSIPPI

Bowie Audio Visual Enterprises Inc, pg 811

MISSOURI

Cashmark Media Inc, pg 820
Communitronics Corp, pg 833
Production Support Services Inc, pg 985
Schiller's Audio-Visual, pg 1004
Show-Me Audio-Visual, pg 1009
Switch, pg 1030
Wise Audio Video, pg 1068

MONTANA

High Plains Films, pg 889
Jereco Studios Inc, pg 905

NEVADA

GES Audio Visual, pg 877
MG Studio, pg 940

NEW HAMPSHIRE

Apertura, pg 788
APS Lighting-Sound-AV, pg 789

NEW JERSEY

Audio Visual Associates, pg 795
CFP Video Productions Inc, pg 823
Earl Girls Inc, pg 855
Euro-Pacific Film & Video Productions Inc, pg 863
Giant Audio Visual Inc, pg 878
International Audio Visual Inc, pg 900
MIB Mediaworks, pg 941
Moe AV LLC, pg 945
The Music Place, pg 951
Nelson Enterprises Theatrical Supply Co, pg 954
PLS Staging, pg 977
SLD Lighting, pg 1013
Soundtracks Production Services LLC, pg 1018
Starlite Productions, pg 1024
Video Corporation of America (VCA), pg 1055
Wired 4 Sound Inc, pg 1068

NEW MEXICO

Production Outfitters, pg 984
Quickbeam Systems Inc (QSI), pg 989

NEW YORK

Ace Video, pg 774
American Video Inc, pg 785
Audio Visual Resources LLC, pg 795
Aura Sonic Ltd, pg 796
AV Workshop, pg 797
Big Foot Productions Inc, pg 807
Bond Street Studio, pg 810
Colortone Audio Visual, pg 832
Communication Corner Inc, pg 832
CP Communications, pg 837
CSI Rentals, pg 840
Design Audio Visual Inc, pg 845
Dreamhire LLC, pg 852
Gearhead Rentals, pg 876
Gotham Sound & Communications Inc, pg 881
Hello World Communications, pg 888
KVL Audio Visual Services Inc, pg 914
LightHouse Films, pg 920
Long Island Video Enterprises Live Inc, pg 924
Posthorn Recordings, pg 979
See Factor Industry Inc, pg 1006
SmartSource Computer & AV Rentals, pg 1014
Specialized Audio-Visual Inc, pg 1020
Studio Instrument Rentals (SIR), pg 1027
TBA Global Events, pg 1032
Technisphere Corp, pg 1034
Theatrical Services & Supplies Inc, pg 1038
Visual Technologies Corp, pg 1060
Visual Word Systems Inc, pg 1060
WorldStage, pg 1070

NORTH CAROLINA

A&V Company, pg 772
Audio & Light, pg 794
AV Metro Inc, pg 797
Duke Media Services, pg 853
Special Event Services, pg 1020
Take One Productions Ltd, pg 1031
Visual Aids Electronics of North Carolina Inc, pg 1059

NORTH DAKOTA

Media Productions, pg 937

OHIO

Hughie's Event Production Services, pg 892
ITA Audio Visual Solutions, pg 902
Lyon Video Inc, pg 927
Mills James Productions, pg 943
Production Solutions Inc, pg 984
R&B Communications Inc, pg 991
Smithall Electronics Inc, pg 1014

OKLAHOMA

PDC Productions, pg 970

OREGON

Picture This Production Services, pg 975
Rose City Sound, pg 999

PENNSYLVANIA

Advanced AV, pg 777
Argentine Productions Inc, pg 789
Audio Visions Inc, pg 795
Audio Visual Communications Inc, pg 795
FirstGeneration Audio/Visual Services, pg 869
FMP Media Solutions Inc, pg 870
Grise Audio Visual Center Inc, pg 882
JPL, pg 906
Muderick Media, pg 949
New York Camera & Video, pg 956
Production Solutions Inc, pg 985
Sound by Fitch, pg 1017
The Videohouse Inc, pg 1057
Vistacom Inc, pg 1059
Visual Sound Inc, pg 1059

SOUTH CAROLINA

Sound & Images Inc, pg 1016

TENNESSEE

Nashville Production Rentals (NPR), pg 952
RentACamera.com, pg 995
Technical Support Systems LLC, pg 1034
Trew Audio Inc, pg 1044

TEXAS

Alford Media Services, pg 780
Astro Audio Visual, pg 792
Audio Visual Technologies Group, pg 796
Bright Giant Creative Group, pg 812
Bright Star Productions Inc, pg 812
Crossroads Audio Inc, pg 840
Data Display Audio Visual Co LP, pg 843
FitzCo Sound Inc, pg 869
GEAR Cameras & Lighting, pg 876
Lubbock Audio Visual Inc, pg 925
Music Lab Inc, pg 950
Onstage Systems, pg 963
Quality Audio Visual Service Inc, pg 988
The Samuels Co, pg 1002
South Coast Film & Video, pg 1019
Stage Directions, pg 1022
Texcam Inc, pg 1038
Video Perspective, pg 1056

UTAH

Performance Audio, pg 973

VERMONT

Dark Star Lighting & Production, pg 842
Edgewood Studios, pg 857
Parlato Productions, pg 969

VIRGINIA

American AV, pg 783
Audio Visual Actions Inc (AVA), pg 795
Boitnott Visual Communications Corp (BVC), pg 810
D&B Television & Video Productions Inc, pg 842
Lee Hartman & Sons Inc, pg 918
Rainbow Rentals, pg 991
StageSound, pg 1023

WASHINGTON

D A Sound, pg 842
Northern Lights & Pro Audio, pg 959
Oppenheimer Camera Products, pg 964
Pacific Northwest Theatre Associates Inc (PNTA), pg 967
Victory Studios, pg 1054

WEST VIRGINIA

United Sound & Electronics, pg 1048

WISCONSIN

Camera Corner Connecting Point, pg 818
Event Essentials, pg 863
Full Compass Systems, pg 874
MKE Production Rental, pg 944

WYOMING

Bridger Productions Inc, pg 812

PUERTO RICO

Stage Crew Audiovisual Inc, pg 1022

ALBERTA

Allstar Show Industries Inc, pg 782
Evolution Presentation Technologies, pg 863
L R Light & Sound, pg 915
McBain Audio Visual Ltd, pg 935
Unique Communications Ltd, pg 1048

BRITISH COLUMBIA

Clark's Audio Visual Services Ltd, pg 829
Commercial Electronics Ltd, pg 832
DL Sound & Lighting Productions Ltd, pg 849
Image Media Farm, pg 895
ProVision Video Sales & Rentals Inc, pg 986

MANITOBA

Inland Audio Visual Ltd, pg 898
MidCanada Production Services Inc (MidCan), pg 942

ONTARIO

HD Source, pg 886
JIB Shots Equipment Inc, pg 905
Metalworks Recording Studios Inc, pg 939
Premier A/V Sales Ltd, pg 980
RB Productions, pg 992
Westbury National Show Systems Ltd, pg 1064
ZTV Broadcast Services Inc, pg 1074

QUEBEC

Audio Visual Dynamics Ltd, pg 795
Concept Audio-Visual, pg 834
Group PVP, pg 882
Panavideo Inc, pg 968

Microphone—Wireless Repairs

ARIZONA

Metropolitan Audio-Visual Inc, pg 940

CALIFORNIA

Ametron Audio/Video, pg 785
Audio Images Corp, pg 794
FXC Communications, pg 874
Location Sound Corp, pg 924
McAlister Electronics, pg 935
Randall Schiller Productions, pg 1004
Sound Service Co, pg 1017
SSL Industries Inc, pg 1022
TOA Electronics Inc, pg 1041
Towards 2000 Inc, pg 1043

CONNECTICUT

HB Communications Inc, pg 886
Sennheiser Electronic Corp, pg 1006

FLORIDA

Hi-Tech Enterprises Inc, pg 888
Midtown Video Inc, pg 942
Stereo Sales Inc, pg 1024
TAI Audio, pg 1031

GEORGIA

Lighting & Production Equipment Inc, pg 920
Stage Front Presentation Systems, pg 1022

ILLINOIS

Allen Visual Systems Inc, pg 781
Beatty TeleVisual Productions, pg 804
C V Lloyde, pg 923
RC Communications, pg 992

INDIANA

Sweetwater Sound Inc, pg 1029

IOWA

ECS Inc, pg 856

KENTUCKY

Axxis Inc, pg 800
Barney Miller's Inc, pg 943
NOR-COM Inc, pg 958

MAINE

Headlight Audio Visual Inc, pg 887

MARYLAND

Cardinal Sound & Video, pg 820
Visual Aids Electronics Corp, pg 1059

MICHIGAN

City Events Group, pg 828
K&R's Recording Studios Inc, pg 908
On Stage Visuals, pg 963
TeL Systems, pg 1035

NEW JERSEY

A-V Services Inc, pg 771
Earl Girls Inc, pg 855
The Music Place, pg 951
Nelson Enterprises Theatrical Supply Co, pg 954
Starlite Productions, pg 1024

NEW MEXICO

Quickbeam Systems Inc (QSI), pg 989

NEW YORK

American Video Inc, pg 785
beyerdynamic Inc, pg 806
Technisphere Corp, pg 1034
Toys From The Attic, pg 1043
Visual Technologies Corp, pg 1060

OHIO

Copp Integrated Systems, pg 836
Hughie's Event Production Services, pg 892
Smithall Electronics Inc, pg 1014
Tri-State Audio Visual Co, pg 1044

OREGON

All Service Musical Electronics Repair, pg 780

PENNSYLVANIA

Audio Visions Inc, pg 795
J E Foss Co, pg 871
Vistacom Inc, pg 1059

TENNESSEE

Belew Enterprises, pg 804
Technical Support Systems LLC, pg 1034
Trew Audio Inc, pg 1044

TEXAS

Astro Audio Visual, pg 792
Lubbock Audio Visual Inc, pg 925
Quality Audio Visual Service Inc, pg 988
Southwest Sound & Electronics Inc, pg 1019
Tarpley Media Systems, pg 1032

UTAH

Comtek Communications Technology Inc, pg 834

VIRGINIA

Boitnott Visual Communications Corp (BVC), pg 810
Hoppmann Audio Visual, pg 891
Old Dominion Broadcasting, pg 961

WASHINGTON

Northern Lights & Pro Audio, pg 959
Pacific Northwest Theatre Associates Inc (PNTA), pg 967

WEST VIRGINIA

United Sound & Electronics, pg 1048

WISCONSIN

Full Compass Systems, pg 874

ALBERTA

Allstar Show Industries Inc, pg 782
Infosat Communications Inc, pg 898
Sharp's Audio-Visual Ltd, pg 1008
Unique Communications Ltd, pg 1048

BRITISH COLUMBIA

Commercial Electronics Ltd, pg 832

MANITOBA

Inland Audio Visual Ltd, pg 898

ONTARIO

HD Source, pg 886
Westbury National Show Systems Ltd, pg 1064

QUEBEC

Panavideo Inc, pg 968
SC Media Canada, pg 1003

Mixer Distributors

ALABAMA

Media Visions Inc, pg 937

ARIZONA

Arizona Cine Equipment, pg 789
EAR Professional Audio/Video, pg 855
Metropolitan Audio-Visual Inc, pg 940
Projector SuperStore LLC, pg 986
Troxell Communications Inc, pg 1045

ARKANSAS

White Diamond Productions, pg 1065

CALIFORNIA

Adolph Gasser Inc, pg 776
American Music & Sound (AM&S), pg 785
Ametron Audio/Video, pg 785
ARS Electronics, pg 791
Associated Sound, pg 792
ATV Video Center Inc, pg 793
Audio Images Corp, pg 794
AV Conferencing, pg 797
Be Media, pg 804
Bext Inc, pg 806
BroadcastStore.com, pg 813
California Tape Products Inc, pg 817
Carvin Corp, pg 820
Christy's Editorial, pg 826
Cibola Systems, pg 826
Computer Modules Inc, pg 834
Delicate Electronics Sales Inc, pg 845
Educational Technology Services (ETS), pg 857
Empire Wholesale Inc, pg 860
Gearhouse Broadcast LLC, pg 876
GigaSonic, pg 878
GMF Sound Inc, pg 879
Hi-Tech Audio Systems Inc, pg 888
Hosa Technology Inc, pg 891
IAMP Professional Audio, pg 893
Impact Group, pg 897
Instructional Materials & Equipment Distributors (I-Med), pg 899
JD Audio Visual Inc, pg 904
Location Sound Corp, pg 924
Martel Electronics Sales Inc, pg 932
Lloyd F McKinney Associates Inc, pg 935
Media Fabricators Inc, pg 936
MediaPOINTE, pg 938
Mobilized Tech Systems, pg 944
Orvac Electronics, pg 965
Plus 24, pg 977
POP TV, pg 978
Professional Sound Corp, pg 985
Promax Systems, pg 986
Related Visual Inc, pg 994
RF Specialties of California Inc, pg 995
Randall Schiller Productions, pg 1004
SNAP, pg 1014
Sound Service Co, pg 1017
Soundcraft USA, pg 1018
Southern California Sound Image Inc, pg 1019
SSL Industries Inc, pg 1022
Stanislaus Audio Video Inc, pg 1023
TASCAM, pg 1032
TOA Electronics Inc, pg 1041
Towards 2000 Inc, pg 1043
Tri-Ed, pg 1044
Video Gear Rentals Inc, pg 1055
VMI Inc, pg 1060
VTP Inc, pg 1061

COLORADO

Audio Consultant Services Inc, pg 794
Daylight Productions & Rentals, pg 844
Spectrum Audio Visual Services, pg 1020

CONNECTICUT

Connecticut Audio & Theatrical Supply, pg 835
HB Communications Inc, pg 886
MAVCO, pg 934
The Music People Inc, pg 951

DELAWARE

Actors Attic, pg 775

FLORIDA

Access Media Group, pg 773
Allstar Audio Systems Inc, pg 782
A2D Solutions Inc, pg 793
AVI-SPL, pg 798
BAI Distributors Inc, pg 801
Broadcasters General Store Inc, pg 813
Digital Video Systems Inc, pg 848
Enhanced View Services Inc, pg 861
General Projection Systems Inc, pg 877
Griffiths Broadcast Co Inc, pg 882
Gulf Coast Audio Visual Producers Inc, pg 883
Harris Corp, pg 885
Herman Pro AV, pg 888
Hi-Tech Enterprises Inc, pg 888
Hi-Tech Import Export Corp, pg 888
Hunter Electronics LLC, pg 892
Industrial Strength Inc, pg 897
Intermark Industries Inc, pg 900
Lighting Sales Connections, pg 920
Media Concepts Inc, pg 936
Midtown Video Inc, pg 942
Photomart Cine-Video Inc, pg 975
Pro Stage Inc, pg 983
Recording Media & Equipment Inc (RM&E), pg 993

AUDIO

Mixer Distributors (continued)

FLORIDA (continued)

Sight & Sound Productions, pg 1010
Stereo Sales Inc, pg 1024
TAI Audio, pg 1031
Technomedia Solutions, pg 1035
Videoscope, pg 1057

GEORGIA

AVForSale, pg 798
Baker Audio Inc, pg 801
Clark, pg 829
Lighting & Production Equipment Inc, pg 920
LT Sound Inc, pg 925
Stage Front Presentation Systems, pg 1022
Visioneering International Inc, pg 1058

HAWAII

The Audio Visual Co (AVCO), pg 795

ILLINOIS

Allen Visual Systems Inc, pg 781
Central Audio-Visual Equipment Inc, pg 823
Joseph Electronics, pg 906
C V Lloyde, pg 923
Manning Productions, pg 930
Quintessence Audio Ltd, pg 989
RAM Systems LLC, pg 991
RC Communications, pg 992
Sound Vision Inc, pg 1018
Woodside Avenue Music Productions Inc, pg 1069

INDIANA

Heart Breaker Entertainment LLC, pg 887
Sensory Technologies LLC, pg 1006
SHP Electronics, pg 1010
Sweetwater Sound Inc, pg 1029

IOWA

ECS Inc, pg 856

KANSAS

Smith Audio-Visual Inc, pg 1014

KENTUCKY

Audio Visual Techniques Inc, pg 796
Axxis Inc, pg 800
Barney Miller's Inc, pg 943
NOR-COM Inc, pg 958
Northern Kentucky University, pg 959

LOUISIANA

Intermedia Technologies, pg 900
Pace Systems, pg 966

MAINE

Headlight Audio Visual Inc, pg 887
Independent Audio Inc, pg 897

MARYLAND

Advance Audiovisual Presentation Ltd, pg 777
Bradley Broadcast & Pro Audio, pg 811
Cardinal Sound & Video, pg 820
Human Circuit, pg 892
Noventri, pg 960

MASSACHUSETTS

Terry Hanley Audio Systems Inc, pg 884
Professional Audio Design Inc, pg 985
Rule Broadcast Systems, pg 1000

MICHIGAN

Olson Anderson Co, pg 786
Ascom Communications Contractors, pg 791
City Events Group, pg 828
On Stage Visuals, pg 963
TeL Systems, pg 1035

MINNESOTA

Advanced Audio-Visual Inc, pg 777
Alpha Video & Audio Inc, pg 782
New Life Communications Inc, pg 956

MISSISSIPPI

Bowie Audio Visual Enterprises Inc, pg 811

MISSOURI

Communitronics Corp, pg 833
Conference Technologies Inc, pg 835
Image Technologies Corp, pg 895
MIS Technologies, pg 944
Modern Communications Inc, pg 944
Schiller's Audio-Visual, pg 1004

NEBRASKA

Video Service of America Inc (VSA), pg 1056

NEVADA

Midas Consoles North America, pg 942

NEW HAMPSHIRE

APS Lighting-Sound-AV, pg 789
Technet® Systems Group, pg 1033

NEW JERSEY

A-V Services Inc, pg 771
Alltec Stores, a Vcom IMC Company, pg 782
Audio Visual Associates, pg 795
Audio Visual Dynamics®, pg 795
AV Bluebook, pg 797
Comprehensive Cable & Connectivity Co, pg 833
Diversified Systems Inc, pg 849
Earl Girls Inc, pg 855
Euro-Pacific Film & Video Productions Inc, pg 863
G&G Technologies Inc, pg 875
Hamilton Buhl, pg 884
MCCOM Inc, pg 935
The Music Place, pg 951
National Audio-Visual Supply, pg 952
Nelson Enterprises Theatrical Supply Co, pg 954
PatchAmp, pg 970
SLD Lighting, pg 1013
Starlite Productions, pg 1024
Total Video Products Inc, pg 1042
Video Corporation of America (VCA), pg 1055
Wired 4 Sound Inc, pg 1068
York Telecom, pg 1072

NEW MEXICO

Quickbeam Systems Inc (QSI), pg 989

NEW YORK

Albany Theatre Supply Co Inc, pg 780
ALTEL Systems Inc, pg 783
American Video Inc, pg 785
Audio-Video Corp, pg 795
Aura Sonic Ltd, pg 796
AV Workshop, pg 797
BTX Technologies, pg 814
Colortone Audio Visual, pg 832
Communication Corner Inc, pg 832
Custom Media Environments, pg 841
Design Audio Visual Inc, pg 845
Gotham Sound & Communications Inc, pg 881
Group One Ltd, pg 882
HAVE Inc, pg 886
Hot House Professional Audio, pg 891
Indigo Productions, pg 897
KVL Audio Visual Services Inc, pg 914
Lee Dan® Communications Inc, pg 918
Long Island Video Enterprises Live Inc, pg 924
Markertek Video Supply, pg 931
Neptune Photo Inc, pg 954
Posthorn Recordings, pg 979
RNJ Electronics, pg 997
SmartSource Computer & AV Rentals, pg 1014
Solid State Logic Inc, pg 1015
Technisphere Corp, pg 1034
TecNec Distributing, pg 1035
Theatrical Services & Supplies Inc, pg 1038
Toys From The Attic, pg 1043
Visual Word Systems Inc, pg 1060
Whirlwind Music Distributors Inc, pg 1065
Yorkville Sound Inc, pg 1072

NORTH CAROLINA

Innocinema, pg 898
Strategic Connections, pg 1026

OHIO

Copp Integrated Systems, pg 836
Hughie's Event Production Services, pg 892
ITA Audio Visual Solutions, pg 902
Midwest Photo Exchange, pg 942
Parts Express, pg 969
Jimmy Rea Electronics Inc, pg 992
Smithall Electronics Inc, pg 1014
Tri-State Audio Visual Co, pg 1044
Visual Products Inc, pg 1059

OREGON

Spectrum Systems Design, pg 1021
SuperDigital Ltd, pg 1029

PENNSYLVANIA

Advanced AV, pg 777
Audio Visions Inc, pg 795
Clair Brothers Audio Systems Inc, pg 829
J E Foss Co, pg 871
Grise Audio Visual Center Inc, pg 882
The Lerro Corp, pg 919
Morefield Communications Inc, pg 946
Sound by Fitch, pg 1017
Vistacom Inc, pg 1059
Visual Sound Inc, pg 1059
Wespen Audio Visual Co, pg 1063

RHODE ISLAND

Shanix Inc, pg 1008

SOUTH CAROLINA

DaviSound, pg 843

TENNESSEE

Belew Enterprises, pg 804
Durrell LLC, pg 854
Lowrance Sound Co Inc, pg 925
Mr Mark's Used Musical, Stereo & Studio Equipment Store, pg 944
Spectrum Sound Inc, pg 1021
Technical Support Systems LLC, pg 1034
Trew Audio Inc, pg 1044
Zion Music Group, pg 1074

TEXAS

Audio Visual Technologies Group, pg 796
AVES Audio Visual Systems Inc, pg 798
CAM Audio Inc, pg 817
Crossroads Audio Inc, pg 840
Data Projections Inc, pg 843
FitzCo Sound Inc, pg 869
Heffernan Audio Visual, pg 887
Lubbock Audio Visual Inc, pg 925
Media Management LLC, pg 937
Pro Video & Film Equipment Co Inc, pg 983
RadioShack Corp, pg 990
RF Specialties of Texas LLC, pg 996
Schoolhouse Audio Visual, pg 1004
Southwest Sound & Electronics Inc, pg 1019
Stage Directions, pg 1022
Tarpley Media Systems, pg 1032

UTAH

DigiTech, pg 848
Performance Audio, pg 973
RIA Corp, pg 996

VERMONT

Production Advantage Inc, pg 984

VIRGINIA

Avitecture Inc, pg 799
Boitnott Visual Communications Corp (BVC), pg 810
Communications Specialists Inc, pg 833
Hoppmann Audio Visual, pg 891
Intellidyne LLC, pg 899
Lee Hartman & Sons Inc, pg 918
Old Dominion Broadcasting, pg 961
Rocktown Media, pg 998
StageSound, pg 1023
The Whitlock Group, pg 1065

WASHINGTON

Broadcast Supply World Wide, pg 813
CCI Solutions, pg 821
D A Sound, pg 842
Northern Lights & Pro Audio, pg 959
Pacific Northwest Theatre Associates Inc (PNTA), pg 967

WEST VIRGINIA

United Sound & Electronics, pg 1048

WISCONSIN

Audio Visual of Milwaukee Inc, pg 795
Camera Corner Connecting Point, pg 818
Full Compass Systems, pg 874
Safe Harbor Computers, pg 1001

PUERTO RICO

Audio Visual Concepts Inc, pg 795
Bonnin Electronics Inc, pg 810

ALBERTA

Infosat Communications Inc, pg 898
Matrix Video Communications Corp (MVCC), pg 934
McBain Audio Visual Ltd, pg 935
Sharp's Audio-Visual Ltd, pg 1008
Unique Communications Ltd, pg 1048

BRITISH COLUMBIA

ADI Systems Inc, pg 776
BeachTek Inc, pg 804
Commercial Electronics Ltd, pg 832
ProVision Video Sales & Rentals Inc, pg 986

MANITOBA

Advance Pro, pg 777
Inland Audio Visual Ltd, pg 898

ONTARIO

Cinema Stage Inc, pg 827
Edcom Multimedia Products, pg 856
HD Source, pg 886
Henry's Camera, pg 888
Nationwide Audio Visual Co, pg 953
Premier A/V Sales Ltd, pg 980
Sascom Marketing Group Inc, pg 1003
Westbury National Show Systems Ltd, pg 1064

QUEBEC

Concept Audio-Visual, pg 834
JAM Industries Ltd, pg 903
Panavideo Inc, pg 968
SC Media Canada, pg 1003

Mixer Manufacturers

ARIZONA

Fender Musical Instruments Corp, pg 866
MTX Audio, pg 949
Radio Design Labs (RDL), pg 990

ARKANSAS

Autogram/Crl, pg 797

CALIFORNIA

American Music & Sound (AM&S), pg 785
Califone International Inc, pg 817
Carvin Corp, pg 820
Ensemble Designs Inc, pg 861
For-A Corp of America, pg 871
Henry Engineering, pg 888
Hosa Technology Inc, pg 891
Martinsound Inc, pg 932
Millennia Media FPC, pg 943
Nady Systems Inc, pg 952
Panasonic Professional Audio Systems, pg 968
Professional Sound Corp, pg 985
Roland Corp US, pg 998
Sony Electronics Inc, pg 1016
Sound Service Co, pg 1017
Soundcraft USA, pg 1018
Summit Audio Inc, pg 1028
TASCAM, pg 1032
TEAC America Inc, pg 1033
TOA Electronics Inc, pg 1041

COLORADO

Arrakis Systems, pg 790

CONNECTICUT

Sound Control Technologies Inc, pg 1017
Titus Technological Laboratories (TTL), pg 1041

FLORIDA

BAI Distributors Inc, pg 801
CircuitWerkes Inc, pg 828
Intermark Industries Inc, pg 900

ILLINOIS

AmpliVox Portable Sound Systems, pg 785
J K Audio Inc, pg 903
Precision Electronics Inc, pg 980
RAM Systems LLC, pg 991
Shure Inc, pg 1010
SoundTech, pg 1018
Studio Technologies Inc, pg 1027

KENTUCKY

Innovative Electronic Designs LLC, pg 898

MARYLAND

API, pg 788

MINNESOTA

Telex Communications Inc, pg 1037
Telex EVI, pg 1037

MISSISSIPPI

Crest Audio Inc, pg 839
Peavey Electronics Corp, pg 970

MISSOURI

Lowell Manufacturing, pg 925

NEW JERSEY

ATI Audio, pg 793
Bogen Communications Inc, pg 810
Gemini Sound, pg 876
Kramer Electronics USA Inc, pg 913
Radio Systems Inc, pg 990

NEW MEXICO

EDCOR Electronics Corp, pg 856
Lectrosonics Inc, pg 918

NEW YORK

Ashly Audio Inc, pg 792
Broadcast Devices Inc, pg 813
GLI Sound Systems, pg 878
Harbro Corp, pg 884
Protech Audio Corp, pg 986
Sescom Inc, pg 1007
Solid State Logic Inc, pg 1015
TecNec Distributing, pg 1035
Yorkville Sound Inc, pg 1072

NORTH CAROLINA

Audioarts Engineering, pg 796
Wheatstone Corp, pg 1065

OHIO

Audio-Technica US Inc, pg 794

OREGON

BIAMP Systems, pg 806

PENNSYLVANIA

Right Coast Recording Inc, pg 997
Rossman Audio LLC, pg 1000

RHODE ISLAND

M-Audio, pg 927
Numark Industries Inc, pg 960

SOUTH CAROLINA

DaviSound, pg 843
Paso Sound Products Inc, pg 969

TENNESSEE

Auratron Systems, pg 796
Harrison Consoles, pg 885
WhisperRoom™ Inc, pg 1065

UTAH

ClearOne Inc, pg 830
DigiTech, pg 848
Ivie Technologies Inc, pg 903
Rolls Corp, pg 999
Spectra Sonics Applied Technology Inc, pg 1020

WASHINGTON

LOUD Technologies Inc, pg 925
Rane, pg 991

WISCONSIN

Intelix LLC, pg 899

ONTARIO

McCurdy Radio Ltd, pg 935

Mixer Rentals

ALABAMA

Audio-Video Resources Inc, pg 795

ARIZONA

Arizona Cine Equipment, pg 789
Broadcast Rentals, pg 813
Glendale Media Center, pg 878
Merestone, pg 938
Metropolitan Audio-Visual Inc, pg 940
Video West Inc, pg 1056

ARKANSAS

White Diamond Productions, pg 1065

CALIFORNIA

Absolute Rentals, pg 772
Action Audio & Visual, pg 775
Adolph Gasser Inc, pg 776
AGF Media Services, pg 778
Alliant Event Services, pg 781
Ametron Audio/Video, pg 785
Artichoke Productions, pg 791
Associated Sound, pg 792
ATV Video Center Inc, pg 793
Audio Rents, pg 794
AV Guys, pg 797
Best Bet Camera Rentals, pg 805
Bexel Corp, pg 806
Big Time Picture Company Inc, pg 807
Chater Camera Inc, pg 824
Cherry Multimedia, pg 824
Express Media Inc, pg 864
First Camera, pg 868
Flip 2 Media Inc, pg 870
Gear Monkey, pg 876
Gold Standard Productions, pg 880
Golden Gate Studios, pg 880
HDrental.com, pg 886
Hi-Tech Audio Systems Inc, pg 888
Hollywood Sound Systems, pg 890
IAMP Professional Audio, pg 893
Imagecraft Productions, pg 896
Impact Group, pg 897
JD Audio Visual Inc, pg 904
Location Sound Corp, pg 924
Maximus Media Inc, pg 934
McCune Audio-Video-Lighting, pg 935
Media Fabricators Inc, pg 936
Munday & Collins AV, pg 950
Muse Presentation Technologies, pg 950
Next Arts, pg 957
Old School Cameras, pg 961
On-Trax Inc, pg 963
Pacific Audio-Visual Enterprises, pg 967
Prime Cut Productions, pg 982
PSAV® Presentation Services, pg 986
Pyxis Industries Inc, pg 988
Related Visual Inc, pg 994
Alwin Sauers Audio Productions (ASAP), pg 1003
Randall Schiller Productions, pg 1004
Shooting Star Video, pg 1009
Shoulder High Productions, pg 1009
Slate Media Group, pg 1013
SNAP, pg 1014
Sound Service Co, pg 1017
Stanislaus Audio Video Inc, pg 1023
Stray Angel Films, pg 1026
Synthesizer Rental Service, pg 1030
Synthesizer Systems Technologies (SST), pg 1030
T-stop Inc, pg 1031
Third Ear Sound Co, pg 1038
Total Media Group, pg 1042
Towards 2000 Inc, pg 1043
VER-Video Equipment Rentals, pg 1053
Video Gear Rentals Inc, pg 1055
Video Resources Inc, pg 1056
Videorama Industries LLC, pg 1057
VMI Inc, pg 1060
Voice & Video Rentals, pg 1060
Warner Bros Production Sound & Video Services, pg 1062
Westcoast Video Productions Inc, pg 1064

AUDIO

Mixer Rentals (continued)

COLORADO

Audio Consultant Services Inc, pg 794
Daylight Productions & Rentals, pg 844
Denver Media Center, pg 845
Multimedia Audio Visual Inc, pg 950
Open Media Foundation, pg 964
Spectrum Audio Visual Services, pg 1020

CONNECTICUT

A/V Davey, pg 797
Connecticut Audio & Theatrical Supply, pg 835
Everett Hall Associates Inc, pg 863
Fox Connecticut, pg 872

DELAWARE

Actors Attic, pg 775
Showorks Audio Visual Inc, pg 1010
Side Door Studio Inc, pg 1010

DISTRICT OF COLUMBIA

Metro Teleproductions Inc (MTI), pg 939

FLORIDA

Access Media Group, pg 773
All Communications Rentals Inc (ALLCOMM), pg 780
Allstar Audio Systems Inc, pg 782
AVI-SPL, pg 798
Blackburst Entertainment, pg 808
Budget Video Rentals, pg 815
Cinema East, pg 827
Gulf Coast Audio Visual Producers Inc, pg 883
Image Technical Services, pg 895
Industrial Strength Inc, pg 897
Jordan Klein Film & Video (JKFV), pg 906
Knowles Video Inc (KVI), pg 912
Lighting Sales Connections, pg 920
Paradise Show & Design Inc, pg 969
Phat Planet Recording Studios, pg 973
Pro Stage Inc, pg 983
Sight & Sound Productions, pg 1010
TAI Audio, pg 1031
Technomedia Solutions, pg 1035
10-20 Productions, pg 1037
Universal Studios Florida® Production Group, pg 1049
Zebedee Productions, pg 1073

GEORGIA

ECG Productions, pg 856
Lighting & Production Equipment Inc, pg 920
MAGNUM Companies Ltd, pg 929
See Production Services, pg 1006
Stage Front Presentation Systems, pg 1022
Staging Directions Inc, pg 1023
Studio Space Atlanta, pg 1027

HAWAII

Hawaii Sound & Vision, pg 886
Sight & Sound Studios, pg 1010

ILLINOIS

Allen Visual Systems Inc, pg 781
AV Chicago Inc, pg 797
Backstar Creative Media Inc, pg 801
Beatty TeleVisual Productions, pg 804
Central Audio-Visual Equipment Inc, pg 823
Firehouse Studios, pg 868
C V Lloyde, pg 923
The Meetinghouse Companies Inc, pg 938
On Site Video, pg 963
On Stage Audio, pg 963
QuickSet International Inc, pg 989
RC Communications, pg 992
Show Department Inc, pg 1009
Staging Resources Inc, pg 1023
Woodside Avenue Music Productions Inc, pg 1069
Zacuto, pg 1073

INDIANA

Advanced Media Integration, pg 777
Gaither Studios LLC, pg 875
Heart Breaker Entertainment LLC, pg 887

IOWA

Central Lighting & Equipment Inc (CLE), pg 823
ECS Inc, pg 856

KANSAS

Smith Audio-Visual Inc, pg 1014

KENTUCKY

Audio Visual Techniques Inc, pg 796
Idle Minds Productions Inc, pg 894
Kentucky Grip & Lighting, pg 909

LOUISIANA

Clark Services Audio Visual & Exhibit Inc, pg 829
Pace Systems, pg 966

MAINE

Headlight Audio Visual Inc, pg 887

MARYLAND

Advance Audiovisual Presentation Ltd, pg 777
Cardinal Sound & Video, pg 820
CPR MultiMedia Solutions, pg 837
CSPMedia.com, pg 840
Event Tech, pg 863
Hargrove Inc, pg 885
Kramer Communications Video Production, pg 913
Maryland Sound International Holding Co LLC, pg 933
Shadowstone R & R™, pg 1008
Soundtrax Optical Sound Recording, pg 1018
Visual Aids Electronics Corp, pg 1059

MASSACHUSETTS

AVFX Inc, pg 798
Capron Lighting & Sound Co Inc, pg 819
Terry Hanley Audio Systems Inc, pg 884
massAV, pg 933
Preston Productions Inc, pg 981

MICHIGAN

Olson Anderson Co, pg 786
City Events Group, pg 828
K&R All Media Productions Inc, pg 908
K&R's Recording Studios Inc, pg 908
On Stage Visuals, pg 963
TeL Systems, pg 1035

MINNESOTA

Advanced Audio-Visual Inc, pg 777
Alpha Video & Audio Inc, pg 782
Big Event Productions LLC, pg 807
Lights On, pg 921
New Life Communications Inc, pg 956

MISSISSIPPI

Bowie Audio Visual Enterprises Inc, pg 811

MISSOURI

Cashmark Media Inc, pg 820
Show-Me Audio-Visual, pg 1009
Switch, pg 1030
Wise Audio Video, pg 1068

MONTANA

Jereco Studios Inc, pg 905

NEVADA

GES Audio Visual, pg 877
MG Studio, pg 940

NEW HAMPSHIRE

Apertura, pg 788
APS Lighting-Sound-AV, pg 789

NEW JERSEY

Audio Visual Associates, pg 795
Audio Visual Dynamics®, pg 795
CFP Video Productions Inc, pg 823
Earl Girls Inc, pg 855
Euro-Pacific Film & Video Productions Inc, pg 863
Giant Audio Visual Inc, pg 878
International Audio Visual Inc, pg 900
Moe AV LLC, pg 945
The Music Place, pg 951
Nelson Enterprises Theatrical Supply Co, pg 954
PLS Staging, pg 977
SLD Lighting, pg 1013
Starlite Productions, pg 1024
Video Corporation of America (VCA), pg 1055
Wired 4 Sound Inc, pg 1068

NEW MEXICO

Production Outfitters, pg 984
Quickbeam Systems Inc (QSI), pg 989

NEW YORK

Adorama Rental Co, pg 776
American Video Inc, pg 785
Audio Visual Resources LLC, pg 795
Aura Sonic Ltd, pg 796
AV Workshop, pg 797
Big Foot Productions Inc, pg 807
Colortone Audio Visual, pg 832
Communication Corner Inc, pg 832
CP Communications, pg 837
Design Audio Visual Inc, pg 845
Dreamhire LLC, pg 852
Gearhead Rentals, pg 876
Gotham Sound & Communications Inc, pg 881
Hello World Communications, pg 888
KVL Audio Visual Services Inc, pg 914
LightHouse Films, pg 920
Long Island Video Enterprises Live Inc, pg 924
Posthorn Recordings, pg 979
Production Central, pg 984
See Factor Industry Inc, pg 1006
SmartSource Computer & AV Rentals, pg 1014
Specialized Audio-Visual Inc, pg 1020
Studio Instrument Rentals (SIR), pg 1027
TBA Global Events, pg 1032
Technisphere Corp, pg 1034
Theatrical Services & Supplies Inc, pg 1038
Visual Word Systems Inc, pg 1060
WorldStage, pg 1070

NORTH CAROLINA

A&V Company, pg 772
AV Metro Inc, pg 797
Duke Media Services, pg 853
Special Event Services, pg 1020
Strategic Connections, pg 1026
Take One Productions Ltd, pg 1031
Visual Aids Electronics of North Carolina Inc, pg 1059

NORTH DAKOTA

Media Productions, pg 937

OHIO

Hughie's Event Production Services, pg 892
ITA Audio Visual Solutions, pg 902
Lyon Video Inc, pg 927
Mills James Productions, pg 943
Ohio HD Video, pg 961
Production Solutions Inc, pg 984
R&B Communications Inc, pg 991
Smithall Electronics Inc, pg 1014

OKLAHOMA

PDC Productions, pg 970

OREGON

Picture This Production Services, pg 975
Rose City Sound, pg 999

PENNSYLVANIA

Advanced AV, pg 777
Audio Visions Inc, pg 795
Audio Visual Communications Inc, pg 795
FirstGeneration Audio/Visual Services, pg 869
FMP Media Solutions Inc, pg 870
Grise Audio Visual Center Inc, pg 882
JPL, pg 906
Muderick Media, pg 949
New York Camera & Video, pg 956
Production Solutions Inc, pg 985
Right Coast Recording Inc, pg 997
Sound by Fitch, pg 1017
The Videohouse Inc, pg 1057
Viewpoint Production Services Inc, pg 1058
Vistacom Inc, pg 1059
Visual Sound Inc, pg 1059

SOUTH CAROLINA

Sound & Images Inc, pg 1016

TENNESSEE

Brantley Sound Associates Inc, pg 812
Love Shack Recording Studios, pg 925
Mr Mark's Used Musical, Stereo & Studio Equipment Store, pg 944
RentACamera.com, pg 995
Technical Support Systems LLC, pg 1034
Trew Audio Inc, pg 1044

TEXAS

Alford Media Services, pg 780
Astro Audio Visual, pg 792
Audio Visual Technologies Group, pg 796
Big House Sound Inc, pg 807
Bright Star Productions Inc, pg 812
Crossroads Audio Inc, pg 840
FitzCo Sound Inc, pg 869
GEAR Cameras & Lighting, pg 876
Lubbock Audio Visual Inc, pg 925
Music Lab Inc, pg 950
Omega Productions, pg 962
Onstage Systems, pg 963
Power Factory Productions, pg 979
The Samuels Co, pg 1002
South Coast Film & Video, pg 1019
Stage Directions, pg 1022
Tropikal Productions, pg 1045
Video Perspective, pg 1056

UTAH

Ron Hill Imagery, pg 889
Performance Audio, pg 973
Redman Movies & Stories, pg 993

VERMONT

Dark Star Lighting & Production, pg 842
Edgewood Studios, pg 857
Parlato Productions, pg 969

VIRGINIA

American AV, pg 783
Audio Visual Actions Inc (AVA), pg 795
Boitnott Visual Communications Corp (BVC), pg 810
D&B Television & Video Productions Inc, pg 842
Lee Hartman & Sons Inc, pg 918
StageSound, pg 1023

WASHINGTON

D A Sound, pg 842
Northern Lights & Pro Audio, pg 959
Oppenheimer Camera Products, pg 964
Pacific Northwest Theatre Associates Inc (PNTA), pg 967
Victory Studios, pg 1054

WEST VIRGINIA

United Sound & Electronics, pg 1048

WISCONSIN

Camera Corner Connecting Point, pg 818
Event Essentials, pg 863
Full Compass Systems, pg 874

WYOMING

Bridger Productions Inc, pg 812

PUERTO RICO

Stage Crew Audiovisual Inc, pg 1022

ALBERTA

Allstar Show Industries Inc, pg 782
Cine Audio Visual Sales & Service Ltd, pg 826
Evolution Presentation Technologies, pg 863
L R Light & Sound, pg 915
McBain Audio Visual Ltd, pg 935
Sharp's Audio-Visual Ltd, pg 1008
Unique Communications Ltd, pg 1048

BRITISH COLUMBIA

Clark's Audio Visual Services Ltd, pg 829
Commercial Electronics Ltd, pg 832
DL Sound & Lighting Productions Ltd, pg 849
Finale Editworks, pg 868
Image Media Farm, pg 895
MicrophoneRentals.com, pg 941
ProVision Video Sales & Rentals Inc, pg 986
Video In Studios/Video Out Distribution, pg 1055

MANITOBA

Inland Audio Visual Ltd, pg 898
MidCanada Production Services Inc (MidCan), pg 942

ONTARIO

Edcom Multimedia Products, pg 856
HD Source, pg 886
JIB Shots Equipment Inc, pg 905
Premier A/V Sales Ltd, pg 980
RB Productions, pg 992
SIM Digital, pg 1011
Westbury National Show Systems Ltd, pg 1064
ZTV Broadcast Services Inc, pg 1074

QUEBEC

Audio Visual Dynamics Ltd, pg 795
Group PVP, pg 882
Panavideo Inc, pg 968

Mixer Repairs

CALIFORNIA

Ametron Audio/Video, pg 785
Audio Images Corp, pg 794
Audio Upgrades, pg 795
Carvin Corp, pg 820
Diemer Amp & Keyboard Repair, pg 846
Digitron Electronics, pg 848
Location Sound Corp, pg 924
McAlister Electronics, pg 935
Professional Sound Corp, pg 985
Randall Schiller Productions, pg 1004
Sound Service Co, pg 1017
SSL Industries Inc, pg 1022
TOA Electronics Inc, pg 1041
Towards 2000 Inc, pg 1043
VMI Inc, pg 1060

CONNECTICUT

HB Communications Inc, pg 886

FLORIDA

Digital Video Systems Inc, pg 848
Hi-Tech Enterprises Inc, pg 888
JT Communications, pg 906
Midtown Video Inc, pg 942
Phat Planet Recording Studios, pg 973
Stereo Sales Inc, pg 1024
TAI Audio, pg 1031
Tel-Test, pg 1035

GEORGIA

Lighting & Production Equipment Inc, pg 920
Stage Front Presentation Systems, pg 1022

ILLINOIS

Allen Visual Systems Inc, pg 781
Beatty TeleVisual Productions, pg 804
C V Lloyde, pg 923
Midwest Digital Corp, pg 942
On Site Video, pg 963
RC Communications, pg 992

INDIANA

SHP Electronics, pg 1010
Sweetwater Sound Inc, pg 1029

IOWA

ECS Inc, pg 856

KENTUCKY

Axxis Inc, pg 800
NOR-COM Inc, pg 958

MAINE

Headlight Audio Visual Inc, pg 887

MARYLAND

Cardinal Sound & Video, pg 820
Strauss Photo Technical Service Inc, pg 1026
Visual Aids Electronics Corp, pg 1059

MASSACHUSETTS

Capron Lighting & Sound Co Inc, pg 819
Professional Audio Design Inc, pg 985

MICHIGAN

City Events Group, pg 828
K&R's Recording Studios Inc, pg 908
On Stage Visuals, pg 963
TeL Systems, pg 1035

MINNESOTA

Aggressive Records Audio Duplication LLC, pg 778

NEW JERSEY

A-V Services Inc, pg 771
Earl Girls Inc, pg 855
The Music Place, pg 951
Nelson Enterprises Theatrical Supply Co, pg 954
Starlite Productions, pg 1024

NEW MEXICO

Quickbeam Systems Inc (QSI), pg 989

NEW YORK

American Video Inc, pg 785
Technisphere Corp, pg 1034
Toys From The Attic, pg 1043
Whirlwind Music Distributors Inc, pg 1065
Yorkville Sound Inc, pg 1072

NORTH CAROLINA

Strategic Connections, pg 1026

OHIO

Copp Integrated Systems, pg 836
Hughie's Event Production Services, pg 892
ITA Audio Visual Solutions, pg 902
Smithall Electronics Inc, pg 1014
Tri-State Audio Visual Co, pg 1044

OREGON

All Service Musical Electronics Repair, pg 780

PENNSYLVANIA

Audio Visions Inc, pg 795
Vistacom Inc, pg 1059

SOUTH CAROLINA

DaviSound, pg 843

TENNESSEE

Belew Enterprises, pg 804
Technical Support Systems LLC, pg 1034
Trew Audio Inc, pg 1044

TEXAS

Astro Audio Visual, pg 792
Audio Visual Technologies Group, pg 796
Lubbock Audio Visual Inc, pg 925
Music Lab Inc, pg 950
Southwest Sound & Electronics Inc, pg 1019
Tarpley Media Systems, pg 1032

VIRGINIA

Boitnott Visual Communications Corp (BVC), pg 810
Hoppmann Audio Visual, pg 891
Old Dominion Broadcasting, pg 961
The Whitlock Group, pg 1065

WASHINGTON

Northern Lights & Pro Audio, pg 959
Pacific Northwest Theatre Associates Inc (PNTA), pg 967

WEST VIRGINIA

United Sound & Electronics, pg 1048

WISCONSIN

Full Compass Systems, pg 874

PUERTO RICO

Bonnin Electronics Inc, pg 810

AUDIO

Mixer Repairs (continued)

ALBERTA

Allstar Show Industries Inc, pg 782
Infosat Communications Inc, pg 898
Sharp's Audio-Visual Ltd, pg 1008
Unique Communications Ltd, pg 1048

BRITISH COLUMBIA

Commercial Electronics Ltd, pg 832

MANITOBA

Inland Audio Visual Ltd, pg 898

ONTARIO

Edcom Multimedia Products, pg 856
HD Source, pg 886
Westbury National Show Systems Ltd, pg 1064

QUEBEC

SC Media Canada, pg 1003

Mixing—Stereo or Dolby Stereo

ALABAMA

Dogwood Recording Studios, pg 850
Sound of Birmingham Productions, pg 1017

ARIZONA

Aardvark Productions LLC, pg 772
Allusion Studios & Pure Wave Audio, pg 782
Fire Power Music Inc, pg 868
Merestone, pg 938
Metropolitan Audio-Visual Inc, pg 940

ARKANSAS

White Diamond Productions, pg 1065

CALIFORNIA

AB Audio Visual Entertainment Inc, pg 772
ACDC Audio CD & Cassette, pg 774
AlphaDogs Inc, pg 782
Argyle Post, pg 789
Artichoke Productions, pg 791
Audio Mechanics, pg 794
Audio Upgrades, pg 795
Barbosa Video Services, pg 802
Berke Creative Inc, pg 805
Creative Media Recording, pg 838
Custom Video Productions Inc, pg 841
Different Fur Recording Ltd, pg 846
Digital Jungle, pg 847
Dogma Studios, pg 850
Earwax Productions Inc, pg 855
5 Alarm Music, pg 869
48 Windows, pg 871
iCorpTv, pg 893
Juice, pg 906
The Kitchen, pg 911
Ludlow Media Solutions, pg 926
Lynch Communications, pg 926
Main Street Media Inc, pg 929
Martinsound Inc, pg 932
Maximus Media Inc, pg 934
McCune Audio-Video-Lighting, pg 935
Mind Over Eye Inc, pg 943
On-Trax Inc, pg 963
Pacific Audio-Visual Enterprises, pg 967
PACSAT, pg 967
Panorama Productions, pg 968
PM Productions, pg 977
Private Island Trax, pg 982
Pyramind Studios, pg 988
QRS Software Services, pg 988
Roundabout Entertainment Inc, pg 1000
Saturn Studios, pg 1003
Shapeshifter, pg 1008
Steve Shapiro Music, pg 1008
SonicPool, pg 1016
Kris Stevens Enterprises, pg 1024
Still N'Motion, pg 1025
Sunburst Recording, pg 1028
Tam Communications Inc, pg 1031
Timeless Productions, pg 1040
Total Media Group, pg 1042
Universal Studios, pg 1049

COLORADO

Airshow Mastering, pg 779
blue onion, pg 810
Tim Cissell Music, pg 828
Clear Gravy Productions, pg 829
Conly Productions, pg 835
Daylight Productions & Rentals, pg 844
Flashback Media Productions, pg 869
Rocky Mountain Audio/Video Productions Inc, pg 998

CONNECTICUT

BRB Audiovisual Productions, pg 812
Broadcast Video Productions LLC, pg 813
Ironik Design & Post, pg 902
Palace Digital Studios, pg 967

DELAWARE

Side Door Studio Inc, pg 1010

DISTRICT OF COLUMBIA

Interface Media Group, pg 900

FLORIDA

Access Media Group, pg 773
Allegro Productions Inc, pg 781
Allstar Audio Systems Inc, pg 782
Big Byte Video Productions, pg 806
Eastern Video, pg 856
Ed Ethridge Productions Inc, pg 863
Global Video Distributors Inc, pg 879
Home Shopping Network (HSN), pg 890
LHV Audio Services, pg 919
Morrisound Recording, pg 946
Phat Planet Recording Studios, pg 973
Progressive Media & Music, pg 985
Promidi Music, pg 986
Sight & Sound Productions, pg 1010
Stereo Sales Inc, pg 1024
Style-City Music Inc, pg 1027
Sunfire Communications Inc, pg 1028
Top Hat Productions, pg 1042
Universal Studios Florida® Production Group, pg 1049

GEORGIA

Beast Atlanta, pg 804
Crawford Media Services, pg 838
Doppler Studios, pg 851
Guerrilla Productions LLC, pg 883
Hottrax Records, pg 891
Lighting & Production Equipment Inc, pg 920
Stage Front Presentation Systems, pg 1022

HAWAII

Media Bridge Gamekids, pg 936
TV Juice Productions Inc, pg 1046

ILLINOIS

CCore Media Inc, pg 821
IV Media Resources, pg 903
Solid Sound Recording Studio, pg 1015
Sound/Video Impressions Inc, pg 1018
20/20 Communications Inc, pg 1047
Woodside Avenue Music Productions Inc, pg 1069

INDIANA

AVA Productions, pg 798
Bright Ideas Creative Services, pg 812
Alan Johnson Recording, pg 905
Sweetwater Sound Inc, pg 1029

KENTUCKY

Broadway Digital, pg 813
Trusty Tuneshop Recording Studios, pg 1045

LOUISIANA

Bay Records, pg 803
WVLA-TV, pg 1071

MARYLAND

CPR MultiMedia Solutions, pg 837
CSPMedia.com, pg 840
dbF a Media Company, pg 844
Lion & Fox Recording Studios, pg 922
Omega Recording Studios, pg 962
Sheffield Audio/Video Productions, pg 1008
Smolian Sound Studios, pg 1014
Welocalize, pg 1063

MASSACHUSETTS

Continental Recordings Inc, pg 835
Cramer Productions, pg 837
Labrecque Creative Sound, pg 915
Northern Light Productions, pg 959
Penfield Productions Ltd, pg 971
Soundtrack Recording Studios, pg 1018

MICHIGAN

Audio Graphic Services, pg 794
Brilliance Audio, pg 812
Digi Sign Design LLC, pg 847
Digital Image Studios LLC, pg 847
GMP Music, pg 879
K&R's Recording Studios Inc, pg 908
Michigan Recording Arts Institute & Technologies, pg 941
Studio A Recording Inc, pg 1026
TGA Recording Co, pg 1038

MINNESOTA

The ADS Group, pg 777
Aggressive Records Audio Duplication LLC, pg 778
Rum Jungle Media, pg 1000
Winterland Studios, pg 1068

MISSOURI

Audio-VideoGraphics Inc, pg 795
Avatar Studios, pg 798
Production Consultants, pg 984
Show-Me Audio-Visual, pg 1009

MONTANA

Jereco Studios Inc, pg 905

NEBRASKA

JoeAudio, pg 905
Three Pillars Media, pg 1040

NEVADA

JCS Video Productions, pg 904
Tanglewood Productions, pg 1031

NEW JERSEY

CFP Video Productions Inc, pg 823
Deluxe Media Services, pg 845
DWJ Television, pg 854
Jeep Jazz Media Solutions, pg 905
Laurel Video Productions, pg 916
MIB Mediaworks, pg 941
Midnight Media Group Inc, pg 942
Milgrom Productions, pg 943
Oasis CD Manufacturing, pg 960
Optisonics Productions, pg 965
Starlite Productions, pg 1024
Suede Interactive, pg 1027
VCSvideo, pg 1052
Video Ideas Productions, pg 1055

NEW MEXICO

Production Outfitters, pg 984

NEW YORK

Aura Sonic Ltd, pg 796
Aural Gratification Inc, pg 796
Big Fish Productions Inc, pg 807
The Big House Group, pg 807
Chromavision Corp, pg 826
Digital Art Video Inc, pg 847
Digital Force, pg 847
DuArt, pg 853
Eastco Multimedia Solutions Inc, pg 856
Fingerpaint, pg 868
HB-Content, pg 886
Headroom Digital Audio, pg 887
Lylofilm Productions, pg 926
Manhattan Center Studios Inc, pg 930
Mark Custom Recording Service Inc, pg 931
Mood Creations Ltd, pg 946
Mother West, pg 947
The Napoleon Group, pg 952
No Soap Productions, pg 957
Now Hear This, pg 960
Nutmeg Post, pg 960
RadioArt/Bob & Ray CDs & MP3 Files, pg 990
Sear Sound, pg 1005
TBA Global Events, pg 1032
Tobin Productions Inc, pg 1041
Visual Technologies Corp, pg 1060

Mixing—Stereo Surround or Dolby Surround

AUDIO

Mixing—Stereo Surround or Dolby Surround (continued)

NEW JERSEY (continued)

Deluxe Media Services, pg 845
Milgrom Productions, pg 943
NFL Films Inc, pg 957
Oasis CD Manufacturing, pg 960
Starlite Productions, pg 1024
Suede Interactive, pg 1027

NEW MEXICO

Production Outfitters, pg 984

NEW YORK

Aura Sonic Ltd, pg 796
Big Fish Productions Inc, pg 807
The Big House Group, pg 807
Chromavision Corp, pg 826
Digital Art Video Inc, pg 847
HB-Content, pg 886
HBO Studio Productions, pg 886
Lylofilm Productions, pg 926
Now Hear This, pg 960
Nutmeg Post, pg 960
TBA Global Events, pg 1032

NORTH CAROLINA

Pat Appleson Studios Inc, pg 788
Horizon Video Productions Inc, pg 891
Unifour Productions Inc, pg 1048

OHIO

Creative Technology, pg 838
Curtis Inc, pg 841
Mills James Productions, pg 943

OKLAHOMA

PDC Productions, pg 970

OREGON

Future Disc LLC, pg 874
Rex, pg 995

PENNSYLVANIA

Audio Visual Communications Inc, pg 795
Forge Recording LLC, pg 871
Innovision Media Group, pg 899
Ivory Productions, pg 903
Kloss Studios Co, pg 912
Laser Video Corp, pg 916
Production Masters Inc (PMI), pg 984
Right Coast Recording Inc, pg 997
The Videohouse Inc, pg 1057

RHODE ISLAND

Sound-FX-Design, pg 1017

SOUTH CAROLINA

DaviSound, pg 843
Genesis Creative, pg 877

TENNESSEE

American Blackguard Inc, pg 784
Ardent Music LLC, pg 789
Ardent Studios Inc, pg 789
Durrell LLC, pg 854
JamSync, pg 904
Love Shack Recording Studios, pg 925
Motion Picture Services, pg 947
Scripps Networks, pg 1005
Stage Post, pg 1022

TEXAS

Harbor House Studios, pg 884
The Samuels Co, pg 1002
South Coast Film & Video, pg 1019

UTAH

One Stop CD Shop LLC, pg 963
Soularium Recording Studios, pg 1016

VIRGINIA

Wally Cleaver's Recording Service, pg 830
Lion Recording Services Inc, pg 922
Metro Productions, pg 939
Studio Center Corp, pg 1026

WASHINGTON

North-by-Northwest Productions, pg 958
Victory Studios, pg 1054

WISCONSIN

5th Floor Recording Co, pg 867
Sound Strations Audio Productions Inc, pg 1017
TBC Studios, pg 1033
Video Wisconsin Inc, pg 1056

BRITISH COLUMBIA

Finale Editworks, pg 868
Pinewood Sound, pg 975

MANITOBA

daCapo Productions, pg 842

ONTARIO

ADS Media, pg 777
DebsVoice, pg 844
GAPC (General Assembly Production Centre), pg 875
Metalworks Recording Studios Inc, pg 939
Phase One Studios, pg 973
Spence-Thomas Audio Post, pg 1021
VO2 Mix Studios, pg 1060
Wanted! Sound + Picture, pg 1062

Music Libraries—Alternative

ALABAMA

Sound of Birmingham Productions, pg 1017

ARIZONA

Direct Current Video Productions, pg 848
Film Creations Ltd, pg 867
Merestone, pg 938
Productiontrax.com, pg 985

ARKANSAS

Shadowbox Video Productions, pg 1007
White Diamond Productions, pg 1065

CALIFORNIA

Aaron & Le Duc, pg 772
Artichoke Productions, pg 791
Berke Creative Inc, pg 805
Berkeley Sound Artists Inc, pg 805
Creative Support Services/CSS Music, pg 838
Diamond Dreams Music Productions, pg 846
Dogma Studios, pg 850
Eye & I Productions, pg 864
5 Alarm Music, pg 869
Kaleidosound, pg 907
Killer Tracks, pg 910
Lynch Communications, pg 926
Megatrax, pg 938
Mind Over Eye Inc, pg 943
The Music Kitchen Inc, pg 950
OGM Production Music, pg 961
Reality Check Systems, pg 992
Regent Press Publishers & Printers, pg 994
Saturn Studios, pg 1003
Steve Shapiro Music, pg 1008
Sonoton Music Library, pg 1016
Still N'Motion, pg 1025
Total Media Group, pg 1042
Visions Plus, pg 1058

COLORADO

Tim Cissell Music, pg 828
Flashback Media Productions, pg 869
Los Angeles Post Music Inc, pg 924

CONNECTICUT

Music 2 Hues, pg 951

DELAWARE

Ken-Del Productions Inc, pg 909

FLORIDA

LHV Audio Services, pg 919
Promidi Music, pg 986
Top Hat Productions, pg 1042
Universal Studios Florida® Production Group, pg 1049

GEORGIA

Continental Film & Video, pg 835
Doppler Studios, pg 851
ECG Productions, pg 856
Guerrilla Productions LLC, pg 883
Hottrax Records, pg 891

ILLINOIS

Convenience, pg 835
Twisted Media Inc, pg 1047

INDIANA

Folkcraft Instruments, pg 871

KANSAS

KAKE-TV, pg 907

MARYLAND

Adelphi Records Inc, pg 776
CPR MultiMedia Solutions, pg 837

MASSACHUSETTS

Labrecque Creative Sound, pg 915
Soundtrack Recording Studios, pg 1018

MICHIGAN

GMP Music, pg 879

MISSOURI

Production Consultants, pg 984
Show-Me Audio-Visual, pg 1009

MONTANA

Jereco Studios Inc, pg 905

NEBRASKA

JoeAudio, pg 905

NEVADA

JCS Video Productions, pg 904
Tanglewood Productions, pg 1031

NEW JERSEY

Milgrom Productions, pg 943
Oasis CD Manufacturing, pg 960
TRF Production Music Libraries, pg 1044
VCSvideo, pg 1052

NEW MEXICO

Production Outfitters, pg 984

NEW YORK

Audio Network US Inc, pg 794
Beekman Books Inc, pg 804
Heavy Melody, pg 887
Loftin Productions, pg 924
Mother West, pg 947
Now Hear This, pg 960
Omnimusic, pg 962
TBA Global Events, pg 1032
TecNec Distributing, pg 1035

NORTH CAROLINA

Pat Appleson Studios Inc, pg 788
Ladyslipper Inc, pg 915
Take One Productions Ltd, pg 1031

NORTH DAKOTA

Media Productions, pg 937

OHIO

Aztec Video Productions, pg 801
Creative Technology, pg 838
EDR Media LLC, pg 857
Mills James Productions, pg 943
R&B Communications Inc, pg 991
Take 1 Media Services, pg 1031

OKLAHOMA

PDC Productions, pg 970

OREGON

International Loving Touch Foundation Inc, pg 901

PENNSYLVANIA

BRg Music Works, pg 812
Brown Bag Imaging, pg 814
Monster Tracks, pg 945
The Videohouse Inc, pg 1057

RHODE ISLAND

Sound-FX-Design, pg 1017

SOUTH CAROLINA

Genesis Creative, pg 877
Stages Video Productions, pg 1023

TENNESSEE

Anode Inc, pg 787
Film House Inc, pg 867
Fricon Entertainment Co Inc, pg 873

TEXAS

The Editing Co, pg 857
FirstCom Music, pg 869
Mediaforce Productions, pg 937
The Music Bakery, pg 950
Julye Newlin Productions Inc, pg 956
Production Garden Music, pg 984
The Sound Lab Inc, pg 1017
South Coast Film & Video, pg 1019

VERMONT

Inner Traditions International, pg 898

VIRGINIA

CALIBRE, pg 816

WISCONSIN

5th Floor Recording Co, pg 867

ONTARIO

Canamedia Inc, pg 818
DebsVoice, pg 844
Entertainment One Distribution, pg 861
GAPC (General Assembly Production Centre), pg 875
MCS Recording Studios, pg 936
Metalworks Recording Studios Inc, pg 939
Nightingale Music Productions Inc, pg 957
Sound Ideas, pg 1017
StockMusic.com, pg 1025
Video Excellence Productions, pg 1055
VO2 Mix Studios, pg 1060
Wanted! Sound + Picture, pg 1062
Westar Music, pg 1064

Music Libraries—Background

ARIZONA

Direct Current Video Productions, pg 848
Film Creations Ltd, pg 867
Fire Power Music Inc, pg 868
Merestone, pg 938
Phoenix VideoFilms®, pg 974
Productiontrax.com, pg 985
SPEAK HOUSE Audio™, pg 1019

ARKANSAS

Shadowbox Video Productions, pg 1007
White Diamond Productions, pg 1065

CALIFORNIA

Aaron & Le Duc, pg 772
Aliso Creek Productions Inc, pg 780
Ancient Future, pg 786
Associated Production Music LLC, pg 792
Berke Creative Inc, pg 805
Berkeley Sound Artists Inc, pg 805
CCI Digital, pg 821
Creative Support Services/CSS Music, pg 838
Diamond Dreams Music Productions, pg 846
Dogma Studios, pg 850
Eye & I Productions, pg 864
5 Alarm Music, pg 869
The Hollywood Edge, pg 890
Jaguar Distribution Corp, pg 903
K2B2 Records, pg 907
Kaleidosound, pg 907
Killer Tracks, pg 910
Lynch Communications, pg 926
Megatrax, pg 938
Mind Over Eye Inc, pg 943
The Music Kitchen Inc, pg 950
Joseph Nicoletti Consulting-Promotion/California International Records/Global Village Records, pg 957
OGM Production Music, pg 961
OTR Studios, pg 966
Polarity Post Production, pg 978
Pyramind Studios, pg 988
Reality Check Systems, pg 992
RJ Video Productions, pg 997
Saturn Studios, pg 1003
Steve Shapiro Music, pg 1008
Sonoton Music Library, pg 1016
Still N'Motion, pg 1025
Timeless Productions, pg 1040
Total Media Group, pg 1042
Visions Plus, pg 1058
WalkerVision Interarts, pg 1061

COLORADO

Tim Cissell Music, pg 828
Conly Productions, pg 835
Flashback Media Productions, pg 869
Los Angeles Post Music Inc, pg 924
Transtar Entertainment Co Inc, pg 1043

CONNECTICUT

Applebox Studio, pg 788
EagleVision Inc, pg 855
Fox Connecticut, pg 872
Ironik Design & Post, pg 902
Music 2 Hues, pg 951
P&P Studios Inc, pg 968

DELAWARE

Ken-Del Productions Inc, pg 909

DISTRICT OF COLUMBIA

Smithsonian Folkways Recordings, pg 1014

FLORIDA

Cinema East, pg 827
Kat Epple Music Productions, pg 862
Gulf Coast Audio Visual Producers Inc, pg 883
Hard Hat Radio Music Service, pg 884
Home Shopping Network (HSN), pg 890
Jordan Klein Film & Video (JKFV), pg 906
LHV Audio Services, pg 919
Pandisc Music Corp, pg 968
Promidi Music, pg 986
Top Hat Productions, pg 1042
Universal Studios Florida® Production Group, pg 1049

GEORGIA

Beachwood Productions, pg 804
Doppler Studios, pg 851
ECG Productions, pg 856
Guerrilla Productions LLC, pg 883
Hottrax Records, pg 891
LT Sound Inc, pg 925
On-Line Productions, pg 963
Showcase Photo & Video, pg 1009

HAWAII

KHNL/KGMB, pg 910

ILLINOIS

Analog Free Media, pg 786
Jim Passin Productions, pg 970
Twisted Media Inc, pg 1047
WEEK TV, pg 1063
Woodside Avenue Music Productions Inc, pg 1069

INDIANA

AVA Productions, pg 798
Folkcraft Instruments, pg 871

KANSAS

Chapman Recording & Mastering, pg 824
KAKE-TV, pg 907

MAINE

Serendipity Recordings, pg 1007

MARYLAND

CAS Video Productions, pg 820
CPR MultiMedia Solutions, pg 837
CSPMedia.com, pg 840
The Cutting Corp, pg 841

MASSACHUSETTS

CommCreative, pg 832
Labrecque Creative Sound, pg 915
Manchester Music Library Inc, pg 929
Soundtrack Recording Studios, pg 1018
TR Productions, pg 1043
The Well-Tempered Music Library, pg 1063

MICHIGAN

American Music Environments Inc (AME), pg 785
GMP Music, pg 879

MINNESOTA

Media Loft Inc, pg 937
MultiMedia, pg 950

MISSOURI

Production Consultants, pg 984
Show-Me Audio-Visual, pg 1009

MONTANA

Jereco Studios Inc, pg 905
North Country Media Group, pg 959

NEBRASKA

JoeAudio, pg 905

NEVADA

DVDs4Less, pg 854
JCS Video Productions, pg 904
Tanglewood Productions, pg 1031

NEW HAMPSHIRE

Channell One Video, pg 824
The Troupe, pg 1045

NEW JERSEY

CFP Video Productions Inc, pg 823
Milbrodt/Music & Sound Design, pg 943
Milgrom Productions, pg 943
NFL Films Music Library, pg 957
Oasis CD Manufacturing, pg 960
Producer East Productions, pg 983
Bill Quinn Productions, pg 989
Richard Reiter Productions Inc, pg 994
TRF Production Music Libraries, pg 1044
VCSvideo, pg 1052

NEW MEXICO

Production Outfitters, pg 984
Uncharted Country Publishing, pg 1048

NEW YORK

The Audio Department Inc, pg 794
Big Fish Productions Inc, pg 807
Cornell Laboratory of Ornithology, pg 836
De Wolfe Music USA, pg 844
Heavy Melody, pg 887
HOThead, pg 891
Loftin Productions, pg 924
Manhattan Production Music Inc, pg 930
Mother West, pg 947
Now Hear This, pg 960
Nutmeg Post, pg 960
Omnimusic, pg 962
Shelly Palmer Production, pg 968
Patco Resources Inc, pg 970
David Rapkin Audio Production, pg 991
Sony Music Custom Marketing, pg 1016
Sony Music Entertainment, pg 1016
TBA Global Events, pg 1032
TecNec Distributing, pg 1035
WNET/NET TELECON, pg 1069

NORTH CAROLINA

Pat Appleson Studios Inc, pg 788
Baker & Taylor Inc, pg 801
Duke Media Services, pg 853
Franklin Video Inc, pg 872
NASCAR Media Group LLC, pg 952
Take One Productions Ltd, pg 1031

NORTH DAKOTA

Media Productions, pg 937

OHIO

Aztec Video Productions, pg 801
Bartha, pg 803
EDR Media LLC, pg 857
Mills James Productions, pg 943
R&B Communications Inc, pg 991
Take 1 Media Services, pg 1031
VGI Productions, pg 1053
Vista Color Imaging Inc, pg 1059

OKLAHOMA

PDC Productions, pg 970
University of Oklahoma Academic Media & Digital Services, pg 1050

OREGON

"PBTM" Music, pg 970

AUDIO

Music Libraries—Background (continued)

PENNSYLVANIA

RHODE ISLAND

SOUTH CAROLINA

TENNESSEE

TEXAS

VIRGINIA

WASHINGTON

WEST VIRGINIA

WISCONSIN

ONTARIO

QUEBEC

Music Libraries—Bluegrass

ALABAMA

ARIZONA

ARKANSAS

CALIFORNIA

COLORADO

CONNECTICUT

DELAWARE

FLORIDA

GEORGIA

ILLINOIS

INDIANA

MARYLAND

MASSACHUSETTS

MICHIGAN

MISSOURI

MONTANA

NEBRASKA

NEVADA

NEW JERSEY

NEW MEXICO

NEW YORK

NORTH CAROLINA

NORTH DAKOTA

OHIO

OKLAHOMA

OREGON

PENNSYLVANIA

RHODE ISLAND

SOUTH CAROLINA

TENNESSEE

TEXAS

Music Libraries—Blues

Music Libraries—Bridges & Cues

AUDIO

Music Libraries—Bridges & Cues (continued)

Music Libraries—Broadway & Hollywood

LHV Audio Services, pg 919
Promidi Music, pg 986
SOS Worldwide Productions Inc, pg 1016
Times-Square Fantasy Theatre, pg 1041
Top Hat Productions, pg 1042
Universal Studios Florida® Production Group, pg 1049

GEORGIA

Doppler Studios, pg 851

ILLINOIS

WEEK TV, pg 1063

KANSAS

Chapman Recording & Mastering, pg 824

MAINE

Serendipity Recordings, pg 1007

MARYLAND

CPR MultiMedia Solutions, pg 837
The Cutting Corp, pg 841

MASSACHUSETTS

Labrecque Creative Sound, pg 915
Soundtrack Recording Studios, pg 1018

MICHIGAN

GMP Music, pg 879

MINNESOTA

MultiMedia, pg 950

MISSOURI

Production Consultants, pg 984
Show-Me Audio-Visual, pg 1009

NEBRASKA

JoeAudio, pg 905

NEVADA

Tanglewood Productions, pg 1031

NEW JERSEY

CFP Video Productions Inc, pg 823
Milgrom Productions, pg 943
Oasis CD Manufacturing, pg 960
TRF Production Music Libraries, pg 1044
VCSvideo, pg 1052

NEW MEXICO

Production Outfitters, pg 984

NEW YORK

Beekman Books Inc, pg 804
DRG Records Inc, pg 852
Historic Films, pg 889
HOThead, pg 891
Kamen Entertainment Group Inc, pg 908
Loftin Productions, pg 924
Manhattan Production Music Inc, pg 930
New World Records, pg 956
Now Hear This, pg 960
Nutmeg Post, pg 960
Omnimusic, pg 962
Shelly Palmer Production, pg 968
Sony Music Entertainment, pg 1016
TBA Global Events, pg 1032
TecNec Distributing, pg 1035
WNET/NET TELECON, pg 1069

NORTH CAROLINA

Pat Appleson Studios Inc, pg 788
Baker & Taylor Inc, pg 801
Ladyslipper Inc, pg 915
Take One Productions Ltd, pg 1031

NORTH DAKOTA

Media Productions, pg 937

OHIO

Aztec Video Productions, pg 801
Creative Technology, pg 838
EDR Media LLC, pg 857
Mills James Productions, pg 943
R&B Communications Inc, pg 991
Take 1 Media Services, pg 1031

OKLAHOMA

PDC Productions, pg 970

PENNSYLVANIA

Audio Visual Communications Inc, pg 795
BRg Music Works, pg 812
Craig Recording Studios, pg 837
Fusion Brand Experiences, pg 874
The Videohouse Inc, pg 1057

SOUTH CAROLINA

Genesis Creative, pg 877
Stages Video Productions, pg 1023

TENNESSEE

Anode Inc, pg 787
Film House Inc, pg 867
Fricon Entertainment Co Inc, pg 873
Memphis Communications Corp, pg 938
WKPT-TV, pg 1068

TEXAS

The Editing Co, pg 857
FirstCom Music, pg 869
Horizon Film + Video Productions, pg 891
Mediaforce Productions, pg 937
The Music Bakery, pg 950
The Sound Lab Inc, pg 1017
Sound Works, pg 1018
South Coast Film & Video, pg 1019
Stage Directions, pg 1022
TM Studios Inc, pg 1041

VIRGINIA

CALIBRE, pg 816

WISCONSIN

5th Floor Recording Co, pg 867
ProVideo, pg 986
USAV Group Inc, pg 1050

ONTARIO

Canamedia Inc, pg 818
Entertainment One Distribution, pg 861
GAPC (General Assembly Production Centre), pg 875
MCS Recording Studios, pg 936
Metalworks Recording Studios Inc, pg 939
Morning Music Ltd, pg 946
Nightingale Music Productions Inc, pg 957
Sound Ideas, pg 1017
StockMusic.com, pg 1025
VO2 Mix Studios, pg 1060
Wanted! Sound + Picture, pg 1062
Westar Music, pg 1064

Music Libraries—Children's

ALABAMA

Sound of Birmingham Productions, pg 1017

ARIZONA

Direct Current Video Productions, pg 848
Film Creations Ltd, pg 867
Productiontrax.com, pg 985

ARKANSAS

Shadowbox Video Productions, pg 1007
White Diamond Productions, pg 1065

CALIFORNIA

Aliso Creek Productions Inc, pg 780
Associated Production Music LLC, pg 792
Berke Creative Inc, pg 805
Berkeley Sound Artists Inc, pg 805
Creative Support Services/CSS Music, pg 838
Dogma Studios, pg 850
5 Alarm Music, pg 869
Bruce Goldberg Inc, pg 880
K2B2 Records, pg 907
Kaleidosound, pg 907
Killer Tracks, pg 910
Lynch Communications, pg 926
Megatrax, pg 938
Moose School Productions, pg 946
Joseph Nicoletti Consulting-Promotion/California International Records/Global Village Records, pg 957
OGM Production Music, pg 961
OTR Studios, pg 966
Players Press, pg 977
Russ InVision Co/AbridgeClub.com, pg 1001
Steve Shapiro Music, pg 1008
Sonoton Music Library, pg 1016
Still N'Motion, pg 1025
Total Media Group, pg 1042

COLORADO

Tim Cissell Music, pg 828
Conly Productions, pg 835
Flashback Media Productions, pg 869
Los Angeles Post Music Inc, pg 924

CONNECTICUT

Music 2 Hues, pg 951

DELAWARE

Ken-Del Productions Inc, pg 909

FLORIDA

Alliance Entertainment Corp (AEC) LLC, pg 781
Gulf Coast Audio Visual Producers Inc, pg 883
Home Shopping Network (HSN), pg 890
LHV Audio Services, pg 919
Promidi Music, pg 986
SOS Worldwide Productions Inc, pg 1016
Top Hat Productions, pg 1042
Universal Studios Florida® Production Group, pg 1049

GEORGIA

Doppler Studios, pg 851

ILLINOIS

Earwig Music Co Inc, pg 855
WEEK TV, pg 1063
Woodside Avenue Music Productions Inc, pg 1069

INDIANA

Folkcraft Instruments, pg 871

MAINE

WGME-TV, pg 1065

MARYLAND

CSPMedia.com, pg 840
The Cutting Corp, pg 841
Kids on the Block Inc, pg 910

MASSACHUSETTS

Labrecque Creative Sound, pg 915
Ben Rudnick & Friends, pg 1000
Soundtrack Recording Studios, pg 1018

MICHIGAN

AirBrands Event & Marketing Group, pg 779
GMP Music, pg 879
HighScope Press, pg 889

MISSOURI

Production Consultants, pg 984
Show-Me Audio-Visual, pg 1009

NEBRASKA

JoeAudio, pg 905

NEVADA

JCS Video Productions, pg 904
Tanglewood Productions, pg 1031

NEW JERSEY

CFP Video Productions Inc, pg 823
Milbrodt/Music & Sound Design, pg 943
Milgrom Productions, pg 943
Oasis CD Manufacturing, pg 960
TRF Production Music Libraries, pg 1044
VCSvideo, pg 1052

NEW MEXICO

Production Outfitters, pg 984
SouthWest Organizing Project (SWOP), pg 1019

NEW YORK

Audio Network US Inc, pg 794
Firefly Book Club, pg 868
Greyfalcon House, pg 882
HOThead, pg 891
Irish Music Corp, pg 902
Kamen Entertainment Group Inc, pg 908
Loftin Productions, pg 924

AUDIO

Music Libraries—Children's (continued)

NEW YORK (continued)

Manhattan Center Studios Inc, pg 930
Manhattan Production Music Inc, pg 930
Now Hear This, pg 960
Nutmeg Post, pg 960
Omnimusic, pg 962
Shelly Palmer Production, pg 968
Patco Resources Inc, pg 970
Sony Music Entertainment, pg 1016
TBA Global Events, pg 1032
TecNec Distributing, pg 1035

NORTH CAROLINA

Pat Appleson Studios Inc, pg 788
Baker & Taylor Inc, pg 801
Ladyslipper Inc, pg 915
Take One Productions Ltd, pg 1031

NORTH DAKOTA

Media Productions, pg 937

OHIO

Aztec Video Productions, pg 801
EDR Media LLC, pg 857
Mills James Productions, pg 943
R&B Communications Inc, pg 991
Take 1 Media Services, pg 1031
Twin Sisters Productions LLC, pg 1047

OKLAHOMA

PDC Productions, pg 970

OREGON

International Loving Touch Foundation Inc, pg 901
"PBTM" Music, pg 970

PENNSYLVANIA

BRg Music Works, pg 812
Craig Recording Studios, pg 837
The Videohouse Inc, pg 1057

RHODE ISLAND

Sound-FX-Design, pg 1017

SOUTH CAROLINA

Stages Video Productions, pg 1023

TENNESSEE

Anode Inc, pg 787
Film House Inc, pg 867
Fricon Entertainment Co Inc, pg 873
Spring Arbor Distributors, pg 1022
WKPT-TV, pg 1068
Word Label Group, pg 1069

TEXAS

The Editing Co, pg 857
FirstCom Music, pg 869
Horizon Film + Video Productions, pg 891
The Music Bakery, pg 950
Production Garden Music, pg 984
Real to Reel Studios Inc, pg 992
The Sound Lab Inc, pg 1017
Sound Works, pg 1018
South Coast Film & Video, pg 1019

VERMONT

Multicultural Media, pg 950

VIRGINIA

Allied Media Corp, pg 781
CALIBRE, pg 816

WISCONSIN

Alliance Publications Inc (API)/ Sinsinawa Studios Productions, pg 781
5th Floor Recording Co, pg 867
USAV Group Inc, pg 1050

ONTARIO

Canamedia Inc, pg 818
DebsVoice, pg 844
Entertainment One Distribution, pg 861
GAPC (General Assembly Production Centre), pg 875
MCS Recording Studios, pg 936
Metalworks Recording Studios Inc, pg 939
Morning Music Ltd, pg 946
Nightingale Music Productions Inc, pg 957
Sound Ideas, pg 1017
StockMusic.com, pg 1025
VO2 Mix Studios, pg 1060
Wanted! Sound + Picture, pg 1062
Westar Music, pg 1064

Music Libraries—Choral

ALABAMA

Sound of Birmingham Productions, pg 1017

ARIZONA

Direct Current Video Productions, pg 848
Film Creations Ltd, pg 867
Merestone, pg 938
Productiontrax.com, pg 985

ARKANSAS

Shadowbox Video Productions, pg 1007
White Diamond Productions, pg 1065

CALIFORNIA

Associated Production Music LLC, pg 792
Berke Creative Inc, pg 805
Creative Support Services/CSS Music, pg 838
Dogma Studios, pg 850
5 Alarm Music, pg 869
Kaleidosound, pg 907
Killer Tracks, pg 910
Lynch Communications, pg 926
Megatrax, pg 938
Joseph Nicoletti Consulting-Promotion/California International Records/Global Village Records, pg 957
OGM Production Music, pg 961
OTR Studios, pg 966
Steve Shapiro Music, pg 1008
Sonoton Music Library, pg 1016
Still N'Motion, pg 1025
Total Media Group, pg 1042
WalkerVision Interarts, pg 1061

COLORADO

Tim Cissell Music, pg 828
Flashback Media Productions, pg 869

DELAWARE

Ken-Del Productions Inc, pg 909

FLORIDA

Alliance Entertainment Corp (AEC) LLC, pg 781
Catholic Books & Tapes, pg 821
Children of Mary, pg 825
Gulf Coast Audio Visual Producers Inc, pg 883
Hard Hat Radio Music Service, pg 884
Home Shopping Network (HSN), pg 890
LHV Audio Services, pg 919
Promidi Music, pg 986
Top Hat Productions, pg 1042
Universal Studios Florida® Production Group, pg 1049

GEORGIA

Doppler Studios, pg 851

ILLINOIS

Analog Free Media, pg 786
Bolchazy - Carducci Publishers Inc, pg 810
WEEK TV, pg 1063

MAINE

Serendipity Recordings, pg 1007

MARYLAND

CPR MultiMedia Solutions, pg 837

MASSACHUSETTS

Labrecque Creative Sound, pg 915
Soundtrack Recording Studios, pg 1018

MISSOURI

Production Consultants, pg 984
Show-Me Audio-Visual, pg 1009

NEBRASKA

JoeAudio, pg 905

NEVADA

Tanglewood Productions, pg 1031

NEW JERSEY

CFP Video Productions Inc, pg 823
Milgrom Productions, pg 943
Oasis CD Manufacturing, pg 960
TRF Production Music Libraries, pg 1044
VCSvideo, pg 1052

NEW MEXICO

Production Outfitters, pg 984

NEW YORK

Kamen Entertainment Group Inc, pg 908
Loftin Productions, pg 924
Manhattan Production Music Inc, pg 930
Mark Custom Recording Service Inc, pg 931
Now Hear This, pg 960
Patco Resources Inc, pg 970
Sony Music Entertainment, pg 1016
TBA Global Events, pg 1032
TecNec Distributing, pg 1035

NORTH CAROLINA

Pat Appleson Studios Inc, pg 788
Baker & Taylor Inc, pg 801
Ladyslipper Inc, pg 915
Take One Productions Ltd, pg 1031

NORTH DAKOTA

Media Productions, pg 937

OHIO

Aztec Video Productions, pg 801
EDR Media LLC, pg 857
Mills James Productions, pg 943
R&B Communications Inc, pg 991
Take 1 Media Services, pg 1031

OKLAHOMA

PDC Productions, pg 970

TENNESSEE

Anode Inc, pg 787
Film House Inc, pg 867
Fricon Entertainment Co Inc, pg 873
Spring Arbor Distributors, pg 1022
Word Label Group, pg 1069

TEXAS

FirstCom Music, pg 869
Mediaforce Productions, pg 937
The Music Bakery, pg 950
Real to Reel Studios Inc, pg 992
The Sound Lab Inc, pg 1017
Sound Works, pg 1018
South Coast Film & Video, pg 1019

VIRGINIA

CALIBRE, pg 816

WISCONSIN

Alliance Publications Inc (API)/ Sinsinawa Studios Productions, pg 781
5th Floor Recording Co, pg 867
USAV Group Inc, pg 1050

ONTARIO

Canamedia Inc, pg 818
Entertainment One Distribution, pg 861
MCS Recording Studios, pg 936
Metalworks Recording Studios Inc, pg 939
Nightingale Music Productions Inc, pg 957
StockMusic.com, pg 1025
VO2 Mix Studios, pg 1060
Wanted! Sound + Picture, pg 1062
Westar Music, pg 1064

QUEBEC

Muse Entertainment Enterprises, pg 950

Music Libraries—Classical

ALABAMA

Sound of Birmingham Productions, pg 1017

AUDIO

Music Libraries—Commercial Jingles

ALABAMA

Sound of Birmingham Productions, pg 1017

ARIZONA

Direct Current Video Productions, pg 848
Film Creations Ltd, pg 867
Merestone, pg 938
Productiontrax.com, pg 985

ARKANSAS

Shadowbox Video Productions, pg 1007
White Diamond Productions, pg 1065

CALIFORNIA

Aaron & Le Duc, pg 772
Aliso Creek Productions Inc, pg 780
Associated Production Music LLC, pg 792
Berke Creative Inc, pg 805
Bruce Chianese, pg 824
Creative Media Recording, pg 838
Creative Support Services/CSS Music, pg 838
Diamond Dreams Music Productions, pg 846
Dogma Studios, pg 850
Eye & I Productions, pg 864
5 Alarm Music, pg 869
Kaleidosound, pg 907
Killer Tracks, pg 910
Lynch Communications, pg 926
Megatrax, pg 938
Mind Over Eye Inc, pg 943
The Music Kitchen Inc, pg 950
Joseph Nicoletti Consulting-Promotion/California International Records/Global Village Records, pg 957
OTR Studios, pg 966
Polarity Post Production, pg 978
Pyramind Studios, pg 988
Reality Check Systems, pg 992
Steve Shapiro Music, pg 1008
Sonoton Music Library, pg 1016
Still N'Motion, pg 1025
Total Media Group, pg 1042

COLORADO

Tim Cissell Music, pg 828
Flashback Media Productions, pg 869
Los Angeles Post Music Inc, pg 924
Transtar Entertainment Co Inc, pg 1043

DELAWARE

Ken-Del Productions Inc, pg 909

FLORIDA

Kat Epple Music Productions, pg 862
Gulf Coast Audio Visual Producers Inc, pg 883
Home Shopping Network (HSN), pg 890
Jordan Klein Film & Video (JKFV), pg 906
LHV Audio Services, pg 919
Promidi Music, pg 986
SOS Worldwide Productions Inc, pg 1016
Top Hat Productions, pg 1042
Universal Studios Florida® Production Group, pg 1049

GEORGIA

Beachwood Productions, pg 804
Doppler Studios, pg 851
ECG Productions, pg 856
Guerrilla Productions LLC, pg 883

HAWAII

KHNL/KGMB, pg 910

ILLINOIS

Twisted Media Inc, pg 1047
WEEK TV, pg 1063
Woodside Avenue Music Productions Inc, pg 1069

KANSAS

Chapman Recording & Mastering, pg 824

LOUISIANA

Disk Productions, pg 849

MAINE

Serendipity Recordings, pg 1007

MARYLAND

CSPMedia.com, pg 840
The Cutting Corp, pg 841

MASSACHUSETTS

Labrecque Creative Sound, pg 915
Manchester Music Library Inc, pg 929
Soundtrack Recording Studios, pg 1018
The Well-Tempered Music Library, pg 1063

MINNESOTA

MultiMedia, pg 950

MISSOURI

Production Consultants, pg 984
Show-Me Audio-Visual, pg 1009

MONTANA

Jereco Studios Inc, pg 905
North Country Media Group, pg 959

NEVADA

JCS Video Productions, pg 904
Tanglewood Productions, pg 1031

NEW HAMPSHIRE

Channell One Video, pg 824

NEW JERSEY

CFP Video Productions Inc, pg 823
Milgrom Productions, pg 943
Oasis CD Manufacturing, pg 960
Richard Reiter Productions Inc, pg 994
TRF Production Music Libraries, pg 1044
VCSvideo, pg 1052

NEW MEXICO

Production Outfitters, pg 984

NEW YORK

Big Fish Productions Inc, pg 807
Heavy Melody, pg 887
HOThead, pg 891
Kamen Entertainment Group Inc, pg 908
Loftin Productions, pg 924
Manhattan Center Studios Inc, pg 930
Now Hear This, pg 960
Nutmeg Post, pg 960
Shelly Palmer Production, pg 968
Patco Resources Inc, pg 970
Sony Music Entertainment, pg 1016
TBA Global Events, pg 1032
TecNec Distributing, pg 1035
WNET/NET TELECON, pg 1069

NORTH CAROLINA

Pat Appleson Studios Inc, pg 788
Duke Media Services, pg 853
Franklin Video Inc, pg 872
NASCAR Media Group LLC, pg 952
Take One Productions Ltd, pg 1031

NORTH DAKOTA

Media Productions, pg 937

OHIO

Aztec Video Productions, pg 801
EDR Media LLC, pg 857
Mills James Productions, pg 943
R&B Communications Inc, pg 991
Take 1 Media Services, pg 1031

OKLAHOMA

PDC Productions, pg 970

OREGON

"PBTM" Music, pg 970

PENNSYLVANIA

BRg Music Works, pg 812
Monster Tracks, pg 945

RHODE ISLAND

Sound-FX-Design, pg 1017

SOUTH CAROLINA

Genesis Creative, pg 877

TENNESSEE

Anode Inc, pg 787
Film House Inc, pg 867
Fricon Entertainment Co Inc, pg 873
Memphis Communications Corp, pg 938

TEXAS

Audiomoxie®, pg 796
The Editing Co, pg 857
FirstCom Music, pg 869
Mediaforce Productions, pg 937
The Music Bakery, pg 950
Julye Newlin Productions Inc, pg 956
The Sound Lab Inc, pg 1017
Sound Works, pg 1018
South Coast Film & Video, pg 1019
Stage Directions, pg 1022
Texas Heart Institute Visual Communication Services, pg 1037
TM Studios Inc, pg 1041
Tropikal Productions, pg 1045

VIRGINIA

CALIBRE, pg 816

WEST VIRGINIA

Sweetsong Productions, pg 1029

WISCONSIN

5th Floor Recording Co, pg 867
ProVideo, pg 986
USAV Group Inc, pg 1050
Video Wisconsin Inc, pg 1056

MANITOBA

daCapo Productions, pg 842

ONTARIO

Canamedia Inc, pg 818
DebsVoice, pg 844
Entertainment One Distribution, pg 861
MCS Recording Studios, pg 936
Metalworks Recording Studios Inc, pg 939
Morning Music Ltd, pg 946
Nightingale Music Productions Inc, pg 957
Sound Ideas, pg 1017
StockMusic.com, pg 1025
VO2 Mix Studios, pg 1060
Wanted! Sound + Picture, pg 1062
Westar Music, pg 1064

Music Libraries—Country

ALABAMA

Sound of Birmingham Productions, pg 1017

ARIZONA

Direct Current Video Productions, pg 848
Film Creations Ltd, pg 867
Fire Power Music Inc, pg 868
Merestone, pg 938
Productiontrax.com, pg 985

ARKANSAS

Shadowbox Video Productions, pg 1007
White Diamond Productions, pg 1065

CALIFORNIA

Aaron & Le Duc, pg 772
Aliso Creek Productions Inc, pg 780
Associated Production Music LLC, pg 792
Berke Creative Inc, pg 805
CCI Digital, pg 821
Bruce Chianese, pg 824
Creative Support Services/CSS Music, pg 838
Dogma Studios, pg 850
5 Alarm Music, pg 869
Bruce Goldberg Inc, pg 880
The Hollywood Edge, pg 890
Kaleidosound, pg 907
Killer Tracks, pg 910
Lynch Communications, pg 926
Megatrax, pg 938
The Music Kitchen Inc, pg 950

Music Libraries—Easy Listening

AUDIO

Music Libraries—Easy Listening (continued)

CONNECTICUT

Ironik Design & Post, pg 902
Music 2 Hues, pg 951

DELAWARE

Ken-Del Productions Inc, pg 909

FLORIDA

Alliance Entertainment Corp (AEC) LLC, pg 781
Kat Epple Music Productions, pg 862
Gulf Coast Audio Visual Producers Inc, pg 883
Hard Hat Radio Music Service, pg 884
Home Shopping Network (HSN), pg 890
LHV Audio Services, pg 919
Promidi Music, pg 986
Times-Square Fantasy Theatre, pg 1041
Top Hat Productions, pg 1042
Universal Studios Florida® Production Group, pg 1049

GEORGIA

Beachwood Productions, pg 804
Doppler Studios, pg 851
ECG Productions, pg 856

ILLINOIS

Analog Free Media, pg 786
Creative Technology, pg 838
WEEK TV, pg 1063

KANSAS

Chapman Recording & Mastering, pg 824

KENTUCKY

Trusty Tuneshop Recording Studios, pg 1045

MAINE

Serendipity Recordings, pg 1007

MARYLAND

CSPMedia.com, pg 840

MASSACHUSETTS

Labrecque Creative Sound, pg 915
Soundtrack Recording Studios, pg 1018
The Well-Tempered Music Library, pg 1063

MICHIGAN

GMP Music, pg 879

MINNESOTA

MultiMedia, pg 950

MISSOURI

Production Consultants, pg 984
Show-Me Audio-Visual, pg 1009

MONTANA

Jereco Studios Inc, pg 905

NEBRASKA

JoeAudio, pg 905

NEVADA

JCS Video Productions, pg 904
Tanglewood Productions, pg 1031

NEW JERSEY

CFP Video Productions Inc, pg 823
Milgrom Productions, pg 943
Oasis CD Manufacturing, pg 960
Richard Reiter Productions Inc, pg 994
TRF Production Music Libraries, pg 1044
VCSvideo, pg 1052

NEW MEXICO

Production Outfitters, pg 984

NEW YORK

Audio Network US Inc, pg 794
DRG Records Inc, pg 852
Heavy Melody, pg 887
Kamen Entertainment Group Inc, pg 908
Loftin Productions, pg 924
Manhattan Production Music Inc, pg 930
Mother West, pg 947
Now Hear This, pg 960
Omnimusic, pg 962
Sony Music Entertainment, pg 1016
TBA Global Events, pg 1032
TecNec Distributing, pg 1035

NORTH CAROLINA

Pat Appleson Studios Inc, pg 788
Baker & Taylor Inc, pg 801
NASCAR Media Group LLC, pg 952
Take One Productions Ltd, pg 1031

NORTH DAKOTA

Media Productions, pg 937

OHIO

Aztec Video Productions, pg 801
Creative Technology, pg 838
EDR Media LLC, pg 857
Mills James Productions, pg 943
R&B Communications Inc, pg 991
Take 1 Media Services, pg 1031
Twin Sisters Productions LLC, pg 1047

OKLAHOMA

PDC Productions, pg 970
University of Oklahoma Academic Media & Digital Services, pg 1050

OREGON

"PBTM" Music, pg 970

PENNSYLVANIA

Craig Recording Studios, pg 837
The Videohouse Inc, pg 1057

RHODE ISLAND

Sound-FX-Design, pg 1017

SOUTH CAROLINA

Genesis Creative, pg 877
Stages Video Productions, pg 1023

TENNESSEE

Anode Inc, pg 787
Film House Inc, pg 867
Fricon Entertainment Co Inc, pg 873

TEXAS

The Editing Co, pg 857
FirstCom Music, pg 869
Horizon Film + Video Productions, pg 891
Mediaforce Productions, pg 937
The Music Bakery, pg 950
Julye Newlin Productions Inc, pg 956
Production Garden Music, pg 984
Real to Reel Studios Inc, pg 992
The Samuels Co, pg 1002
The Sound Lab Inc, pg 1017
Sound Works, pg 1018
South Coast Film & Video, pg 1019
TM Studios Inc, pg 1041

VIRGINIA

Allied Media Corp, pg 781
CALIBRE, pg 816

WASHINGTON

Avast! Recording Co, pg 798

WEST VIRGINIA

Sweetsong Productions, pg 1029

WISCONSIN

5th Floor Recording Co, pg 867
ProVideo, pg 986
USAV Group Inc, pg 1050

ONTARIO

Canamedia Inc, pg 818
DebsVoice, pg 844
Entertainment One Distribution, pg 861
GAPC (General Assembly Production Centre), pg 875
MCS Recording Studios, pg 936
Metalworks Recording Studios Inc, pg 939
Morning Music Ltd, pg 946
Nightingale Music Productions Inc, pg 957
Sound Ideas, pg 1017
StockMusic.com, pg 1025
Video Excellence Productions, pg 1055
VO2 Mix Studios, pg 1060
Wanted! Sound + Picture, pg 1062
Westar Music, pg 1064

Music Libraries—Electronic

ALABAMA

Sound of Birmingham Productions, pg 1017

ARIZONA

BeachWare Inc, pg 804
Direct Current Video Productions, pg 848
Film Creations Ltd, pg 867
Fire Power Music Inc, pg 868
Merestone, pg 938
Productiontrax.com, pg 985
SPEAK HOUSE Audio™, pg 1019

ARKANSAS

Shadowbox Video Productions, pg 1007
White Diamond Productions, pg 1065

CALIFORNIA

Aaron & Le Duc, pg 772
Aliso Creek Productions Inc, pg 780
Artichoke Productions, pg 791
Associated Production Music LLC, pg 792
Berke Creative Inc, pg 805
Berkeley Sound Artists Inc, pg 805
CCI Digital, pg 821
Bruce Chianese, pg 824
Creative Support Services/CSS Music, pg 838
Diamond Dreams Music Productions, pg 846
Dogma Studios, pg 850
Eye & I Productions, pg 864
5 Alarm Music, pg 869
Kaleidosound, pg 907
Killer Tracks, pg 910
Lynch Communications, pg 926
Megatrax, pg 938
Mind Over Eye Inc, pg 943
The Music Kitchen Inc, pg 950
Joseph Nicoletti Consulting-Promotion/California International Records/Global Village Records, pg 957
OGM Production Music, pg 961
OTR Studios, pg 966
Pyramind Studios, pg 988
Reality Check Systems, pg 992
Saturn Studios, pg 1003
Steve Shapiro Music, pg 1008
Sonoton Music Library, pg 1016
Still N'Motion, pg 1025
Timeless Productions, pg 1040
Total Media Group, pg 1042
WalkerVision Interarts, pg 1061

COLORADO

Tim Cissell Music, pg 828
Conly Productions, pg 835
Daylight Productions & Rentals, pg 844
Flashback Media Productions, pg 869
Los Angeles Post Music Inc, pg 924
Transtar Entertainment Co Inc, pg 1043

CONNECTICUT

Applebox Studio, pg 788
EagleVision Inc, pg 855
Ironik Design & Post, pg 902
Music 2 Hues, pg 951
P&P Studios Inc, pg 968

DELAWARE

Ken-Del Productions Inc, pg 909

FLORIDA

Alliance Entertainment Corp (AEC) LLC, pg 781
Kat Epple Music Productions, pg 862
Home Shopping Network (HSN), pg 890
LHV Audio Services, pg 919
Promidi Music, pg 986
Top Hat Productions, pg 1042
Universal Studios Florida® Production Group, pg 1049

GEORGIA

Beachwood Productions, pg 804
Continental Film & Video, pg 835
Doppler Studios, pg 851
ECG Productions, pg 856
Guerrilla Productions LLC, pg 883

ILLINOIS

Analog Free Media, pg 786
Convenience, pg 835
Jim Passin Productions, pg 970
Twisted Media Inc, pg 1047
Video Impressions, pg 1055
WEEK TV, pg 1063
Woodside Avenue Music Productions Inc, pg 1069

KANSAS

Chapman Recording & Mastering, pg 824

LOUISIANA

Centaur Records Inc, pg 822

MAINE

WGME-TV, pg 1065

MARYLAND

CPR MultiMedia Solutions, pg 837
CSPMedia.com, pg 840
The Cutting Corp, pg 841

MASSACHUSETTS

CommCreative, pg 832
Labrecque Creative Sound, pg 915
Manchester Music Library Inc, pg 929
Soundtrack Recording Studios, pg 1018
TR Productions, pg 1043
The Well-Tempered Music Library, pg 1063

MICHIGAN

GMP Music, pg 879

MINNESOTA

MultiMedia, pg 950

MISSOURI

Production Consultants, pg 984
Show-Me Audio-Visual, pg 1009

MONTANA

Jereco Studios Inc, pg 905

NEBRASKA

JoeAudio, pg 905

NEVADA

DVDs4Less, pg 854
Tanglewood Productions, pg 1031

NEW HAMPSHIRE

Channell One Video, pg 824

NEW JERSEY

CFP Video Productions Inc, pg 823
Milbrodt/Music & Sound Design, pg 943
Milgrom Productions, pg 943
NFL Films Music Library, pg 957
Oasis CD Manufacturing, pg 960
Bill Quinn Productions, pg 989
Richard Reiter Productions Inc, pg 994
TRF Production Music Libraries, pg 1044
VCSvideo, pg 1052

NEW MEXICO

Production Outfitters, pg 984

NEW YORK

Audio Network US Inc, pg 794
Aural Gratification Inc, pg 796
De Wolfe Music USA, pg 844
Heavy Melody, pg 887
HOThead, pg 891
IAI Video, pg 893
Kamen Entertainment Group Inc, pg 908
Loftin Productions, pg 924
Manhattan Production Music Inc, pg 930
Mother West, pg 947
New World Records, pg 956
Now Hear This, pg 960
Nutmeg Post, pg 960
Omnimusic, pg 962
Shelly Palmer Production, pg 968
David Rapkin Audio Production, pg 991
Sear Sound, pg 1005
Sony Music Custom Marketing, pg 1016
Sony Music Entertainment, pg 1016
TBA Global Events, pg 1032
TecNec Distributing, pg 1035

NORTH CAROLINA

Pat Appleson Studios Inc, pg 788
Baker & Taylor Inc, pg 801
The Communications Group Inc, pg 833
Franklin Video Inc, pg 872
NASCAR Media Group LLC, pg 952
Take One Productions Ltd, pg 1031

NORTH DAKOTA

Media Productions, pg 937

OHIO

Aztec Video Productions, pg 801
Creative Technology, pg 838
EDR Media LLC, pg 857
Mills James Productions, pg 943
R&B Communications Inc, pg 991
Take 1 Media Services, pg 1031
VGI Productions, pg 1053

OKLAHOMA

PDC Productions, pg 970
University of Oklahoma Academic Media & Digital Services, pg 1050

OREGON

"PBTM" Music, pg 970

PENNSYLVANIA

Audio Visual Communications Inc, pg 795
Brown Bag Imaging, pg 814
Monster Tracks, pg 945
The Videohouse Inc, pg 1057

RHODE ISLAND

Sound-FX-Design, pg 1017

SOUTH CAROLINA

DaviSound, pg 843
Genesis Creative, pg 877
Stages Video Productions, pg 1023

TENNESSEE

Anode Inc, pg 787
Film House Inc, pg 867
Fricon Entertainment Co Inc, pg 873
Memphis Communications Corp, pg 938
WKPT-TV, pg 1068

TEXAS

Audiomoxie®, pg 796
The Editing Co, pg 857
FirstCom Music, pg 869
The Music Bakery, pg 950
Julye Newlin Productions Inc, pg 956
Production Garden Music, pg 984
Real to Reel Studios Inc, pg 992
The Sound Lab Inc, pg 1017
Sound Works, pg 1018
South Coast Film & Video, pg 1019
Stage Directions, pg 1022
Texas Heart Institute Visual Communication Services, pg 1037
TM Studios Inc, pg 1041

VIRGINIA

CALIBRE, pg 816

WASHINGTON

Avast! Recording Co, pg 798

WISCONSIN

5th Floor Recording Co, pg 867
ProVideo, pg 986
USAV Group Inc, pg 1050

ONTARIO

Canamedia Inc, pg 818
DebsVoice, pg 844
Entertainment One Distribution, pg 861
GAPC (General Assembly Production Centre), pg 875
MCS Recording Studios, pg 936
Metalworks Recording Studios Inc, pg 939
Morning Music Ltd, pg 946
Nightingale Music Productions Inc, pg 957
Sound Ideas, pg 1017
StockMusic.com, pg 1025
Video Excellence Productions, pg 1055
VO2 Mix Studios, pg 1060
Wanted! Sound + Picture, pg 1062
Westar Music, pg 1064

Music Libraries—Ethnic & International

ALABAMA

Sound of Birmingham Productions, pg 1017

ARIZONA

Direct Current Video Productions, pg 848
Drumbeat Indian Arts Inc, pg 852
Film Creations Ltd, pg 867
Merestone, pg 938
Productiontrax.com, pg 985

ARKANSAS

Shadowbox Video Productions, pg 1007
White Diamond Productions, pg 1065

CALIFORNIA

Aaron & Le Duc, pg 772
Ancient Future, pg 786
Associated Production Music LLC, pg 792
Berke Creative Inc, pg 805
CCI Digital, pg 821
Bruce Chianese, pg 824
Creative Support Services/CSS Music, pg 838
Diamond Dreams Music Productions, pg 846
Dogma Studios, pg 850
Eye & I Productions, pg 864
5 Alarm Music, pg 869
Kaleidosound, pg 907
Killer Tracks, pg 910
Lynch Communications, pg 926
Megatrax, pg 938
The Music Kitchen Inc, pg 950
Joseph Nicoletti Consulting-Promotion/California International Records/Global Village Records, pg 957
OGM Production Music, pg 961
Osho Viha Information Center & Book Distributors, pg 965
OTR Studios, pg 966
Steve Shapiro Music, pg 1008
Sonoton Music Library, pg 1016
Still N'Motion, pg 1025
Total Media Group, pg 1042
Visions Plus, pg 1058
WalkerVision Interarts, pg 1061

COLORADO

Tim Cissell Music, pg 828
Daylight Productions & Rentals, pg 844
Flashback Media Productions, pg 869
Los Angeles Post Music Inc, pg 924

CONNECTICUT

Applebox Studio, pg 788
Fox Connecticut, pg 872
Ironik Design & Post, pg 902
Music 2 Hues, pg 951

DELAWARE

Ken-Del Productions Inc, pg 909

DISTRICT OF COLUMBIA

Sano Videos, pg 1002

FLORIDA

Alliance Entertainment Corp (AEC) LLC, pg 781
Kat Epple Music Productions, pg 862
Gulf Coast Audio Visual Producers Inc, pg 883
Home Shopping Network (HSN), pg 890
LHV Audio Services, pg 919
Promidi Music, pg 986
SOS Worldwide Productions Inc, pg 1016

AUDIO

Music Libraries—Ethnic & International (continued)

FLORIDA (continued)

Top Hat Productions, pg 1042
Universal Studios Florida® Production Group, pg 1049

GEORGIA

Beachwood Productions, pg 804
Doppler Studios, pg 851
Hottrax Records, pg 891

ILLINOIS

Bolchazy - Carducci Publishers Inc, pg 810
Twisted Media Inc, pg 1047
Video Impressions, pg 1055
WEEK TV, pg 1063

INDIANA

Folkcraft Instruments, pg 871

KANSAS

Chapman Recording & Mastering, pg 824

MARYLAND

Adelphi Records Inc, pg 776
CSPMedia.com, pg 840
The Cutting Corp, pg 841

MASSACHUSETTS

Labrecque Creative Sound, pg 915
Revels Records, pg 995
Soundtrack Recording Studios, pg 1018

MICHIGAN

GMP Music, pg 879
Rebirth/Wenha Records, pg 993

MISSOURI

Production Consultants, pg 984
Show-Me Audio-Visual, pg 1009

MONTANA

Jereco Studios Inc, pg 905

NEBRASKA

JoeAudio, pg 905

NEVADA

JCS Video Productions, pg 904
Tanglewood Productions, pg 1031

NEW HAMPSHIRE

French American Music Enterprises, pg 873

NEW JERSEY

Milbrodt/Music & Sound Design, pg 943
Milgrom Productions, pg 943
Oasis CD Manufacturing, pg 960
Bill Quinn Productions, pg 989
Shanachie Entertainment Corp, pg 1008
TRF Production Music Libraries, pg 1044
VCSvideo, pg 1052

NEW MEXICO

Production Outfitters, pg 984

NEW YORK

Beekman Books Inc, pg 804
Greyfalcon House, pg 882
Heavy Melody, pg 887
HOThead, pg 891
Irish Music Corp, pg 902
Kamen Entertainment Group Inc, pg 908
Loftin Productions, pg 924
Manhattan Production Music Inc, pg 930
Mother West, pg 947
Now Hear This, pg 960
Nutmeg Post, pg 960
Omnimusic, pg 962
Shelly Palmer Production, pg 968
Patco Resources Inc, pg 970
Sony Music Entertainment, pg 1016
TBA Global Events, pg 1032
TecNec Distributing, pg 1035
VIEW Inc (Video International Entertainment World Inc), pg 1058

NORTH CAROLINA

Pat Appleson Studios Inc, pg 788
Baker & Taylor Inc, pg 801
Ladyslipper Inc, pg 915
Take One Productions Ltd, pg 1031

NORTH DAKOTA

Media Productions, pg 937

OHIO

Aztec Video Productions, pg 801
EDR Media LLC, pg 857
Mills James Productions, pg 943
R&B Communications Inc, pg 991
Take 1 Media Services, pg 1031

OKLAHOMA

PDC Productions, pg 970

PENNSYLVANIA

Monster Tracks, pg 945
The Videohouse Inc, pg 1057

RHODE ISLAND

Sound-FX-Design, pg 1017

SOUTH CAROLINA

Genesis Creative, pg 877
Stages Video Productions, pg 1023

TENNESSEE

Anode Inc, pg 787
Film House Inc, pg 867
Fricon Entertainment Co Inc, pg 873
Word Label Group, pg 1069

TEXAS

Audiomoxie®, pg 796
The Editing Co, pg 857
FirstCom Music, pg 869
Horizon Film + Video Productions, pg 891
Mediaforce Productions, pg 937
The Music Bakery, pg 950
Julye Newlin Productions Inc, pg 956
Production Garden Music, pg 984
Real to Reel Studios Inc, pg 992
The Sound Lab Inc, pg 1017
Sound Works, pg 1018
South Coast Film & Video, pg 1019
TM Studios Inc, pg 1041
Tropikal Productions, pg 1045

VERMONT

Inner Traditions International, pg 898
Multicultural Media, pg 950

VIRGINIA

Allied Media Corp, pg 781
CALIBRE, pg 816

WISCONSIN

Alliance Publications Inc (API)/ Sinsinawa Studios Productions, pg 781
5th Floor Recording Co, pg 867
USAV Group Inc, pg 1050

ONTARIO

Canamedia Inc, pg 818
DebsVoice, pg 844
Entertainment One Distribution, pg 861
GAPC (General Assembly Production Centre), pg 875
MCS Recording Studios, pg 936
Metalworks Recording Studios Inc, pg 939
Morning Music Ltd, pg 946
Nightingale Music Productions Inc, pg 957
Sound Ideas, pg 1017
StockMusic.com, pg 1025
VO2 Mix Studios, pg 1060
Wanted! Sound + Picture, pg 1062
Westar Music, pg 1064

Music Libraries—Folk

ALABAMA

Sound of Birmingham Productions, pg 1017

ARIZONA

Direct Current Video Productions, pg 848
Film Creations Ltd, pg 867
Fire Power Music Inc, pg 868
Merestone, pg 938
Productiontrax.com, pg 985

ARKANSAS

Shadowbox Video Productions, pg 1007
White Diamond Productions, pg 1065

CALIFORNIA

Aaron & Le Duc, pg 772
Aliso Creek Productions Inc, pg 780
Ancient Future, pg 786
Associated Production Music LLC, pg 792
Berke Creative Inc, pg 805
Creative Support Services/CSS Music, pg 838
Diamond Dreams Music Productions, pg 846
Dogma Studios, pg 850
5 Alarm Music, pg 869
Bruce Goldberg Inc, pg 880
Kaleidosound, pg 907
Killer Tracks, pg 910
Lynch Communications, pg 926
Megatrax, pg 938
The Music Kitchen Inc, pg 950
Joseph Nicoletti Consulting-Promotion/California International Records/Global Village Records, pg 957
OGM Production Music, pg 961
OTR Studios, pg 966
Steve Shapiro Music, pg 1008
Sonoton Music Library, pg 1016
Still N'Motion, pg 1025
Total Media Group, pg 1042
Welk Music Group, pg 1063

COLORADO

Tim Cissell Music, pg 828
Conly Productions, pg 835
Flashback Media Productions, pg 869
Los Angeles Post Music Inc, pg 924
Transtar Entertainment Co Inc, pg 1043

CONNECTICUT

American Melody, pg 784
Applebox Studio, pg 788
Folk-Legacy, pg 871
Ironik Design & Post, pg 902
Music 2 Hues, pg 951

DELAWARE

Ken-Del Productions Inc, pg 909

FLORIDA

Alliance Entertainment Corp (AEC) LLC, pg 781
Kat Epple Music Productions, pg 862
Gulf Coast Audio Visual Producers Inc, pg 883
Home Shopping Network (HSN), pg 890
LHV Audio Services, pg 919
Promidi Music, pg 986
Top Hat Productions, pg 1042
Universal Studios Florida® Production Group, pg 1049

GEORGIA

Beachwood Productions, pg 804
Doppler Studios, pg 851

ILLINOIS

Analog Free Media, pg 786
Folk Era Productions Inc, pg 870
Rediscover Music, pg 993
Video Impressions, pg 1055
WEEK TV, pg 1063
Woodside Avenue Music Productions Inc, pg 1069

INDIANA

Folkcraft Instruments, pg 871

MAINE

Serendipity Recordings, pg 1007

MARYLAND

Adelphi Records Inc, pg 776
CSPMedia.com, pg 840

MASSACHUSETTS

Labrecque Creative Sound, pg 915
Revels Records, pg 995
Ben Rudnick & Friends, pg 1000
Soundtrack Recording Studios, pg 1018
The Well-Tempered Music Library, pg 1063

MICHIGAN

GMP Music, pg 879
HighScope Press, pg 889

MISSOURI

Production Consultants, pg 984
Show-Me Audio-Visual, pg 1009

MONTANA

Jereco Studios Inc, pg 905

NEBRASKA

JoeAudio, pg 905

NEVADA

JCS Video Productions, pg 904
Tanglewood Productions, pg 1031

NEW HAMPSHIRE

French American Music Enterprises, pg 873

NEW JERSEY

Milgrom Productions, pg 943
Oasis CD Manufacturing, pg 960
TRF Production Music Libraries, pg 1044
VCSvideo, pg 1052

NEW MEXICO

Production Outfitters, pg 984

NEW YORK

Audio Network US Inc, pg 794
Beekman Books Inc, pg 804
Dyer-Bennet Records, pg 854
Greyfalcon House, pg 882
Heavy Melody, pg 887
Irish Music Corp, pg 902
Kamen Entertainment Group Inc, pg 908
Loftin Productions, pg 924
Manhattan Production Music Inc, pg 930
Mother West, pg 947
Now Hear This, pg 960
Omnimusic, pg 962
Patco Resources Inc, pg 970
Sony Music Entertainment, pg 1016
TBA Global Events, pg 1032
TecNec Distributing, pg 1035

NORTH CAROLINA

Pat Appleson Studios Inc, pg 788
Baker & Taylor Inc, pg 801
Duke Media Services, pg 853
Ladyslipper Inc, pg 915
Take One Productions Ltd, pg 1031

NORTH DAKOTA

Media Productions, pg 937

OHIO

Aztec Video Productions, pg 801
EDR Media LLC, pg 857
Mills James Productions, pg 943
R&B Communications Inc, pg 991
Take 1 Media Services, pg 1031

OKLAHOMA

PDC Productions, pg 970

PENNSYLVANIA

Monster Tracks, pg 945
The Videohouse Inc, pg 1057

RHODE ISLAND

Sound-FX-Design, pg 1017

SOUTH CAROLINA

Genesis Creative, pg 877
Stages Video Productions, pg 1023

TENNESSEE

Anode Inc, pg 787
Center for Southern Folklore Inc, pg 822
Film House Inc, pg 867
Fricon Entertainment Co Inc, pg 873

TEXAS

The Editing Co, pg 857
FirstCom Music, pg 869
The Music Bakery, pg 950
Julye Newlin Productions Inc, pg 956
Production Garden Music, pg 984
The Sound Lab Inc, pg 1017
South Coast Film & Video, pg 1019

VERMONT

Multicultural Media, pg 950

VIRGINIA

Allied Media Corp, pg 781
CALIBRE, pg 816

WASHINGTON

Avast! Recording Co, pg 798

WISCONSIN

Alliance Publications Inc (API)/ Sinsinawa Studios Productions, pg 781
5th Floor Recording Co, pg 867
USAV Group Inc, pg 1050

ONTARIO

Canamedia Inc, pg 818
DebsVoice, pg 844
Entertainment One Distribution, pg 861
MCS Recording Studios, pg 936
Metalworks Recording Studios Inc, pg 939
Morning Music Ltd, pg 946
Nightingale Music Productions Inc, pg 957
Sound Ideas, pg 1017
StockMusic.com, pg 1025
VO2 Mix Studios, pg 1060
Wanted! Sound + Picture, pg 1062
Westar Music, pg 1064

Music Libraries—Holiday

ALABAMA

Sound of Birmingham Productions, pg 1017

ARIZONA

Direct Current Video Productions, pg 848
Film Creations Ltd, pg 867
Fire Power Music Inc, pg 868
Merestone, pg 938
Productiontrax.com, pg 985

ARKANSAS

Shadowbox Video Productions, pg 1007
White Diamond Productions, pg 1065

CALIFORNIA

Aaron & Le Duc, pg 772
Aliso Creek Productions Inc, pg 780
Associated Production Music LLC, pg 792
Berke Creative Inc, pg 805
Creative Support Services/CSS Music, pg 838
Dogma Studios, pg 850
5 Alarm Music, pg 869
Bruce Goldberg Inc, pg 880
Kaleidosound, pg 907
Killer Tracks, pg 910
Lynch Communications, pg 926
Megatrax, pg 938
The Music Kitchen Inc, pg 950
Joseph Nicoletti Consulting-Promotion/California International Records/Global Village Records, pg 957
OGM Production Music, pg 961
Steve Shapiro Music, pg 1008
Sonoton Music Library, pg 1016
Still N'Motion, pg 1025
Welk Music Group, pg 1063

COLORADO

Tim Cissell Music, pg 828
Daylight Productions & Rentals, pg 844
Flashback Media Productions, pg 869
Los Angeles Post Music Inc, pg 924
Transtar Entertainment Co Inc, pg 1043

CONNECTICUT

Applebox Studio, pg 788
Fox Connecticut, pg 872
Music 2 Hues, pg 951

DELAWARE

Ken-Del Productions Inc, pg 909

FLORIDA

Alliance Entertainment Corp (AEC) LLC, pg 781
Catholic Books & Tapes, pg 821
Cinema East, pg 827
Kat Epple Music Productions, pg 862
Gulf Coast Audio Visual Producers Inc, pg 883
Home Shopping Network (HSN), pg 890
LHV Audio Services, pg 919
Promidi Music, pg 986
Top Hat Productions, pg 1042
Universal Studios Florida® Production Group, pg 1049

GEORGIA

Beachwood Productions, pg 804
Doppler Studios, pg 851
ECG Productions, pg 856
Guerrilla Productions LLC, pg 883

ILLINOIS

Analog Free Media, pg 786
Video Impressions, pg 1055
WEEK TV, pg 1063

INDIANA

Folkcraft Instruments, pg 871

KANSAS

Chapman Recording & Mastering, pg 824

MAINE

Serendipity Recordings, pg 1007

MARYLAND

Adelphi Records Inc, pg 776
CSPMedia.com, pg 840

MASSACHUSETTS

Labrecque Creative Sound, pg 915
Revels Records, pg 995
Soundtrack Recording Studios, pg 1018

MICHIGAN

GMP Music, pg 879

MISSOURI

Production Consultants, pg 984
Show-Me Audio-Visual, pg 1009

NEBRASKA

JoeAudio, pg 905

NEVADA

JCS Video Productions, pg 904
Tanglewood Productions, pg 1031

NEW HAMPSHIRE

French American Music Enterprises, pg 873

NEW JERSEY

CFP Video Productions Inc, pg 823
Milgrom Productions, pg 943
Oasis CD Manufacturing, pg 960
TRF Production Music Libraries, pg 1044
VCSvideo, pg 1052

NEW MEXICO

Production Outfitters, pg 984

NEW YORK

Audio Network US Inc, pg 794
Beekman Books Inc, pg 804
Irish Music Corp, pg 902
Kamen Entertainment Group Inc, pg 908
Loftin Productions, pg 924
Manhattan Production Music Inc, pg 930
Mark Custom Recording Service Inc, pg 931
Mother West, pg 947
Now Hear This, pg 960
Omnimusic, pg 962
Patco Resources Inc, pg 970
Sony Music Entertainment, pg 1016
TBA Global Events, pg 1032
TecNec Distributing, pg 1035

NORTH CAROLINA

Pat Appleson Studios Inc, pg 788
Baker & Taylor Inc, pg 801
Duke Media Services, pg 853
Franklin Video Inc, pg 872
Ladyslipper Inc, pg 915

AUDIO

Music Libraries—Holiday (continued)

NORTH CAROLINA (continued)

NASCAR Media Group LLC, pg 952
Take One Productions Ltd, pg 1031

NORTH DAKOTA

Media Productions, pg 937

OHIO

Aztec Video Productions, pg 801
EDR Media LLC, pg 857
Mills James Productions, pg 943
R&B Communications Inc, pg 991
Take 1 Media Services, pg 1031

OKLAHOMA

PDC Productions, pg 970

OREGON

"PBTM" Music, pg 970

PENNSYLVANIA

Craig Recording Studios, pg 837
The Videohouse Inc, pg 1057

RHODE ISLAND

Sound-FX-Design, pg 1017

SOUTH CAROLINA

Genesis Creative, pg 877
Stages Video Productions, pg 1023

TENNESSEE

Anode Inc, pg 787
Film House Inc, pg 867
Fricon Entertainment Co Inc, pg 873
Word Label Group, pg 1069

TEXAS

The Editing Co, pg 857
FirstCom Music, pg 869
Mediaforce Productions, pg 937
The Music Bakery, pg 950
Julye Newlin Productions Inc, pg 956
Production Garden Music, pg 984
Real to Reel Studios Inc, pg 992
The Sound Lab Inc, pg 1017
Sound Works, pg 1018
South Coast Film & Video, pg 1019
TM Studios Inc, pg 1041

VERMONT

Multicultural Media, pg 950

VIRGINIA

Allied Media Corp, pg 781
CALIBRE, pg 816

WEST VIRGINIA

Sweetsong Productions, pg 1029

WISCONSIN

Alliance Publications Inc (API)/ Sinsinawa Studios Productions, pg 781
5th Floor Recording Co, pg 867
USAV Group Inc, pg 1050

ONTARIO

Canamedia Inc, pg 818
DebsVoice, pg 844
Entertainment One Distribution, pg 861
MCS Recording Studios, pg 936
Metalworks Recording Studios Inc, pg 939
Morning Music Ltd, pg 946
Nightingale Music Productions Inc, pg 957
Sound Ideas, pg 1017
StockMusic.com, pg 1025
VO2 Mix Studios, pg 1060
Wanted! Sound + Picture, pg 1062
Westar Music, pg 1064

Music Libraries—Instrumental

ALABAMA

Sound of Birmingham Productions, pg 1017

ARIZONA

BeachWare Inc, pg 804
Direct Current Video Productions, pg 848
Film Creations Ltd, pg 867
Fire Power Music Inc, pg 868
Merestone, pg 938
Phoenix VideoFilms®, pg 974
Productiontrax.com, pg 985
SPEAK HOUSE Audio™, pg 1019

ARKANSAS

Shadowbox Video Productions, pg 1007
White Diamond Productions, pg 1065

CALIFORNIA

Aaron & Le Duc, pg 772
Aliso Creek Productions Inc, pg 780
Ancient Future, pg 786
Associated Production Music LLC, pg 792
Berke Creative Inc, pg 805
Berkeley Sound Artists Inc, pg 805
Bruce Chianese, pg 824
Creative Support Services/CSS Music, pg 838
Diamond Dreams Music Productions, pg 846
Dogma Studios, pg 850
Eye & I Productions, pg 864
5 Alarm Music, pg 869
Bruce Goldberg Inc, pg 880
Increase Video/Silver Mine Video, pg 897
K2B2 Records, pg 907
Kaleidosound, pg 907
Killer Tracks, pg 910
Lynch Communications, pg 926
Megatrax, pg 938
Mind Over Eye Inc, pg 943
The Music Kitchen Inc, pg 950
Joseph Nicoletti Consulting-Promotion/California International Records/Global Village Records, pg 957
OGM Production Music, pg 961
Osho Viha Information Center & Book Distributors, pg 965
OTR Studios, pg 966
Polarity Post Production, pg 978
Pyramind Studios, pg 988
Reality Check Systems, pg 992
Regent Press Publishers & Printers, pg 994
Ron Roy Productions/Moodtapes, pg 1000
Saturn Studios, pg 1003
Steve Shapiro Music, pg 1008
Sonoton Music Library, pg 1016
Still N'Motion, pg 1025
Timeless Productions, pg 1040
Total Media Group, pg 1042
Visions Plus, pg 1058
WalkerVision Interarts, pg 1061

COLORADO

Tim Cissell Music, pg 828
Conly Productions, pg 835
Daylight Productions & Rentals, pg 844
Flashback Media Productions, pg 869
Los Angeles Post Music Inc, pg 924
Transtar Entertainment Co Inc, pg 1043

CONNECTICUT

Applebox Studio, pg 788
Fox Connecticut, pg 872
Ironik Design & Post, pg 902
Music 2 Hues, pg 951

DELAWARE

Ken-Del Productions Inc, pg 909

FLORIDA

Alliance Entertainment Corp (AEC) LLC, pg 781
Cinema East, pg 827
Kat Epple Music Productions, pg 862
Gulf Coast Audio Visual Producers Inc, pg 883
Hard Hat Radio Music Service, pg 884
Home Shopping Network (HSN), pg 890
LHV Audio Services, pg 919
Promidi Music, pg 986
Top Hat Productions, pg 1042
Universal Studios Florida® Production Group, pg 1049

GEORGIA

Beachwood Productions, pg 804
Doppler Studios, pg 851
ECG Productions, pg 856
Guerrilla Productions LLC, pg 883
Hottrax Records, pg 891

ILLINOIS

Analog Free Media, pg 786
Convenience, pg 835
Creative Technology, pg 838
Twisted Media Inc, pg 1047
Video Impressions, pg 1055
WEEK TV, pg 1063
Woodside Avenue Music Productions Inc, pg 1069

INDIANA

Folkcraft Instruments, pg 871
Indiana University Press, pg 897

KANSAS

Chapman Recording & Mastering, pg 824
KAKE-TV, pg 907

MAINE

Serendipity Recordings, pg 1007

MARYLAND

Adelphi Records Inc, pg 776
CPR MultiMedia Solutions, pg 837
CSPMedia.com, pg 840

MASSACHUSETTS

Labrecque Creative Sound, pg 915
Manchester Music Library Inc, pg 929
Soundtrack Recording Studios, pg 1018

MICHIGAN

GMP Music, pg 879

MINNESOTA

MultiMedia, pg 950

MISSOURI

Production Consultants, pg 984
Show-Me Audio-Visual, pg 1009

MONTANA

Jereco Studios Inc, pg 905

NEBRASKA

JoeAudio, pg 905

NEVADA

JCS Video Productions, pg 904
Tanglewood Productions, pg 1031

NEW HAMPSHIRE

Channell One Video, pg 824

NEW JERSEY

CFP Video Productions Inc, pg 823
Milgrom Productions, pg 943
Oasis CD Manufacturing, pg 960
Bill Quinn Productions, pg 989
Richard Reiter Productions Inc, pg 994
Shanachie Entertainment Corp, pg 1008
TRF Production Music Libraries, pg 1044
VCSvideo, pg 1052

NEW MEXICO

Production Outfitters, pg 984
Uncharted Country Publishing, pg 1048

NEW YORK

Beekman Books Inc, pg 804
Big Fish Productions Inc, pg 807
Heavy Melody, pg 887
IAI Video, pg 893
Kamen Entertainment Group Inc, pg 908
Loftin Productions, pg 924
Manhattan Production Music Inc, pg 930
Mark Custom Recording Service Inc, pg 931
Mother West, pg 947
Now Hear This, pg 960
Omnimusic, pg 962
Patco Resources Inc, pg 970
Sony Music Entertainment, pg 1016
TBA Global Events, pg 1032
TecNec Distributing, pg 1035

NORTH CAROLINA

Pat Appleson Studios Inc, pg 788
Baker & Taylor Inc, pg 801
Duke Media Services, pg 853
Franklin Video Inc, pg 872
Ladyslipper Inc, pg 915
NASCAR Media Group LLC, pg 952
Take One Productions Ltd, pg 1031

NORTH DAKOTA

Media Productions, pg 937

OHIO

Aztec Video Productions, pg 801
Creative Technology, pg 838
EDR Media LLC, pg 857
Mills James Productions, pg 943
R&B Communications Inc, pg 991
Take 1 Media Services, pg 1031
Twin Sisters Productions LLC, pg 1047
Vista Color Imaging Inc, pg 1059

OKLAHOMA

PDC Productions, pg 970
University of Oklahoma Academic Media & Digital Services, pg 1050

OREGON

"PBTM" Music, pg 970

PENNSYLVANIA

Craig Recording Studios, pg 837
Fusion Brand Experiences, pg 874
Monster Tracks, pg 945
The Videohouse Inc, pg 1057

RHODE ISLAND

Sound-FX-Design, pg 1017

SOUTH CAROLINA

DaviSound, pg 843
Genesis Creative, pg 877
Stages Video Productions, pg 1023

TENNESSEE

Anode Inc, pg 787
Film House Inc, pg 867
Fricon Entertainment Co Inc, pg 873
Word Label Group, pg 1069

TEXAS

Audiomoxie®, pg 796
The Editing Co, pg 857
FirstCom Music, pg 869
The Music Bakery, pg 950
Julye Newlin Productions Inc, pg 956
Production Garden Music, pg 984
Real to Reel Studios Inc, pg 992
The Samuels Co, pg 1002
The Sound Lab Inc, pg 1017
Sound Works, pg 1018
South Coast Film & Video, pg 1019
Stage Directions, pg 1022
TM Studios Inc, pg 1041
Tropikal Productions, pg 1045

VIRGINIA

Allied Media Corp, pg 781
CALIBRE, pg 816
Creative Video of Washington Inc, pg 839

WASHINGTON

Avast! Recording Co, pg 798

WEST VIRGINIA

Sweetsong Productions, pg 1029

WISCONSIN

Alliance Publications Inc (API)/ Sinsinawa Studios Productions, pg 781
5th Floor Recording Co, pg 867
ProVideo, pg 986
USAV Group Inc, pg 1050

ONTARIO

Broughton's Church Supplies, Religious Books & Gifts, pg 814
Canamedia Inc, pg 818
DebsVoice, pg 844
Entertainment One Distribution, pg 861
MCS Recording Studios, pg 936
Metalworks Recording Studios Inc, pg 939
Morning Music Ltd, pg 946
Nightingale Music Productions Inc, pg 957
Sound Ideas, pg 1017
StockMusic.com, pg 1025
Video Excellence Productions, pg 1055
VO2 Mix Studios, pg 1060
Wanted! Sound + Picture, pg 1062
Westar Music, pg 1064

QUEBEC

Muse Entertainment Enterprises, pg 950

Music Libraries—Jazz

ALABAMA

Sound of Birmingham Productions, pg 1017

ARIZONA

BeachWare Inc, pg 804
Direct Current Video Productions, pg 848
Film Creations Ltd, pg 867
Fire Power Music Inc, pg 868
Merestone, pg 938
Phoenix VideoFilms®, pg 974
Productiontrax.com, pg 985

ARKANSAS

Shadowbox Video Productions, pg 1007
White Diamond Productions, pg 1065

CALIFORNIA

Aaron & Le Duc, pg 772
Aliso Creek Productions Inc, pg 780
Ancient Future, pg 786
Associated Production Music LLC, pg 792
Berke Creative Inc, pg 805
CCI Digital, pg 821
Bruce Chianese, pg 824
Concord Records Inc, pg 835
Creative Support Services/CSS Music, pg 838
Diamond Dreams Music Productions, pg 846
Dogma Studios, pg 850
Eye & I Productions, pg 864
5 Alarm Music, pg 869
Bruce Goldberg Inc, pg 880
The Hollywood Edge, pg 890
Increase Video/Silver Mine Video, pg 897
K2B2 Records, pg 907
Kaleidosound, pg 907
Killer Tracks, pg 910
Lynch Communications, pg 926
Megatrax, pg 938
The Music Kitchen Inc, pg 950
Joseph Nicoletti Consulting-Promotion/California International Records/Global Village Records, pg 957
OGM Production Music, pg 961
OTR Studios, pg 966
Polarity Post Production, pg 978
Saturn Studios, pg 1003
Steve Shapiro Music, pg 1008
Sonoton Music Library, pg 1016
Still N'Motion, pg 1025
Total Media Group, pg 1042
Visions Plus, pg 1058
WalkerVision Interarts, pg 1061

COLORADO

Tim Cissell Music, pg 828
Flashback Media Productions, pg 869
Los Angeles Post Music Inc, pg 924
Transtar Entertainment Co Inc, pg 1043

CONNECTICUT

Applebox Studio, pg 788
EagleVision Inc, pg 855
Ironik Design & Post, pg 902
Music 2 Hues, pg 951
P&P Studios Inc, pg 968

DELAWARE

Ken-Del Productions Inc, pg 909

DISTRICT OF COLUMBIA

Library of Congress, Motion Picture, Broadcasting & Recorded Sound Division, pg 919
Smithsonian Folkways Recordings, pg 1014

FLORIDA

Alliance Entertainment Corp (AEC) LLC, pg 781
Kat Epple Music Productions, pg 862
Gulf Coast Audio Visual Producers Inc, pg 883
Home Shopping Network (HSN), pg 890
LHV Audio Services, pg 919
Promidi Music, pg 986
SOS Worldwide Productions Inc, pg 1016
Top Hat Productions, pg 1042
Universal Studios Florida® Production Group, pg 1049

GEORGIA

Beachwood Productions, pg 804
Doppler Studios, pg 851
ECG Productions, pg 856
Guerrilla Productions LLC, pg 883
Hottrax Records, pg 891

ILLINOIS

Analog Free Media, pg 786
Convenience, pg 835
Delmark Records, pg 845
Jim Passin Productions, pg 970
Video Impressions, pg 1055
WEEK TV, pg 1063
Woodside Avenue Music Productions Inc, pg 1069

INDIANA

Indiana University Press, pg 897

KANSAS

Chapman Recording & Mastering, pg 824

LOUISIANA

Centaur Records Inc, pg 822
Great Chefs/Leisure Jazz Video, pg 881
Leisure Video, pg 918

MAINE

Serendipity Recordings, pg 1007

MARYLAND

Adelphi Records Inc, pg 776
CPR MultiMedia Solutions, pg 837
CSPMedia.com, pg 840
The Cutting Corp, pg 841

MASSACHUSETTS

CommCreative, pg 832
Labrecque Creative Sound, pg 915
Manchester Music Library Inc, pg 929
Soundtrack Recording Studios, pg 1018
TR Productions, pg 1043
The Well-Tempered Music Library, pg 1063

MICHIGAN

AirBrands Event & Marketing Group, pg 779
GMP Music, pg 879
Rebirth/Wenha Records, pg 993

MINNESOTA

MultiMedia, pg 950

MISSOURI

Production Consultants, pg 984
Show-Me Audio-Visual, pg 1009

MONTANA

Jereco Studios Inc, pg 905

NEBRASKA

JoeAudio, pg 905

NEVADA

Tanglewood Productions, pg 1031

NEW JERSEY

Milgrom Productions, pg 943
Oasis CD Manufacturing, pg 960
Bill Quinn Productions, pg 989
Richard Reiter Productions Inc, pg 994
Shanachie Entertainment Corp, pg 1008
TRF Production Music Libraries, pg 1044

NEW MEXICO

Production Outfitters, pg 984

AUDIO

Music Libraries—Jazz (continued)

Music Libraries—New Age

PENNSYLVANIA

Monster Tracks, pg 945
The Videohouse Inc, pg 1057

RHODE ISLAND

Sound-FX-Design, pg 1017

SOUTH CAROLINA

Genesis Creative, pg 877
Stages Video Productions, pg 1023

TENNESSEE

Anode Inc, pg 787
Film House Inc, pg 867
Fricon Entertainment Co Inc, pg 873

TEXAS

Audiomoxie®, pg 796
The Editing Co, pg 857
FirstCom Music, pg 869
Horizon Film + Video Productions, pg 891
The Music Bakery, pg 950
Julye Newlin Productions Inc, pg 956
Production Garden Music, pg 984
Real to Reel Studios Inc, pg 992
The Sound Lab Inc, pg 1017
South Coast Film & Video, pg 1019
Tropikal Productions, pg 1045

VIRGINIA

Allied Media Corp, pg 781
CALIBRE, pg 816

WISCONSIN

5th Floor Recording Co, pg 867

ONTARIO

Canamedia Inc, pg 818
DebsVoice, pg 844
Entertainment One Distribution, pg 861
GAPC (General Assembly Production Centre), pg 875
MCS Recording Studios, pg 936
Metalworks Recording Studios Inc, pg 939
Nightingale Music Productions Inc, pg 957
Sound Ideas, pg 1017
StockMusic.com, pg 1025
Video Excellence Productions, pg 1055
VO2 Mix Studios, pg 1060
Wanted! Sound + Picture, pg 1062
Westar Music, pg 1064

Music Libraries—Popular

ALABAMA

Sound of Birmingham Productions, pg 1017

ARIZONA

Direct Current Video Productions, pg 848
Film Creations Ltd, pg 867
Fire Power Music Inc, pg 868
Merestone, pg 938
Productiontrax.com, pg 985

ARKANSAS

Shadowbox Video Productions, pg 1007
White Diamond Productions, pg 1065

CALIFORNIA

Aaron & Le Duc, pg 772
Aliso Creek Productions Inc, pg 780
Associated Production Music LLC, pg 792
Berke Creative Inc, pg 805
Berkeley Sound Artists Inc, pg 805
CCI Digital, pg 821
Bruce Chianese, pg 824
Creative Support Services/CSS Music, pg 838
Diamond Dreams Music Productions, pg 846
Dogma Studios, pg 850
5 Alarm Music, pg 869
Bruce Goldberg Inc, pg 880
Increase Video/Silver Mine Video, pg 897
Kaleidosound, pg 907
Killer Tracks, pg 910
Lynch Communications, pg 926
Megatrax, pg 938
The Music Kitchen Inc, pg 950
Joseph Nicoletti Consulting-Promotion/California International Records/Global Village Records, pg 957
OGM Production Music, pg 961
OTR Studios, pg 966
Polarity Post Production, pg 978
Pyramind Studios, pg 988
Reality Check Systems, pg 992
Reprise Records Burbank, pg 995
Saturn Studios, pg 1003
Steve Shapiro Music, pg 1008
Sonoton Music Library, pg 1016
Still N'Motion, pg 1025
Total Media Group, pg 1042
Visions Plus, pg 1058
WalkerVision Interarts, pg 1061
Welk Music Group, pg 1063

COLORADO

Tim Cissell Music, pg 828
Flashback Media Productions, pg 869
Los Angeles Post Music Inc, pg 924
Transtar Entertainment Co Inc, pg 1043

CONNECTICUT

Applebox Studio, pg 788
EagleVision Inc, pg 855
Fox Connecticut, pg 872
Music 2 Hues, pg 951
P&P Studios Inc, pg 968

DELAWARE

Ken-Del Productions Inc, pg 909

FLORIDA

Alliance Entertainment Corp (AEC) LLC, pg 781
Gulf Coast Audio Visual Producers Inc, pg 883
Hard Hat Radio Music Service, pg 884
Home Shopping Network (HSN), pg 890
LHV Audio Services, pg 919
Promidi Music, pg 986
Times-Square Fantasy Theatre, pg 1041
Top Hat Productions, pg 1042
Universal Studios Florida® Production Group, pg 1049

GEORGIA

Beachwood Productions, pg 804
Doppler Studios, pg 851
ECG Productions, pg 856
Guerrilla Productions LLC, pg 883

ILLINOIS

Analog Free Media, pg 786
Jay Jay Record & Tape Co, pg 904
Twisted Media Inc, pg 1047
Video Impressions, pg 1055
WEEK TV, pg 1063
Woodside Avenue Music Productions Inc, pg 1069

KANSAS

Chapman Recording & Mastering, pg 824

MAINE

Serendipity Recordings, pg 1007
WGME-TV, pg 1065

MARYLAND

CPR MultiMedia Solutions, pg 837
CSPMedia.com, pg 840
The Cutting Corp, pg 841

MASSACHUSETTS

CommCreative, pg 832
Labrecque Creative Sound, pg 915
Manchester Music Library Inc, pg 929
Soundtrack Recording Studios, pg 1018
TR Productions, pg 1043

MICHIGAN

AirBrands Event & Marketing Group, pg 779
GMP Music, pg 879

MINNESOTA

MultiMedia, pg 950

MISSOURI

Production Consultants, pg 984
Show-Me Audio-Visual, pg 1009
Swank Audio Visuals, pg 1029

MONTANA

Jereco Studios Inc, pg 905
North Country Media Group, pg 959

NEBRASKA

JoeAudio, pg 905

NEVADA

DVDs4Less, pg 854
Tanglewood Productions, pg 1031

NEW JERSEY

CFP Video Productions Inc, pg 823
Milbrodt/Music & Sound Design, pg 943
Milgrom Productions, pg 943
NFL Films Music Library, pg 957
Oasis CD Manufacturing, pg 960
Bill Quinn Productions, pg 989
Richard Reiter Productions Inc, pg 994
TRF Production Music Libraries, pg 1044
VCSvideo, pg 1052

NEW MEXICO

Production Outfitters, pg 984

NEW YORK

Audio Network US Inc, pg 794
Beekman Books Inc, pg 804
De Wolfe Music USA, pg 844
Heavy Melody, pg 887
Historic Films, pg 889
HOThead, pg 891
Kamen Entertainment Group Inc, pg 908
Loftin Productions, pg 924
Manhattan Center Studios Inc, pg 930
Manhattan Production Music Inc, pg 930
Mother West, pg 947
Now Hear This, pg 960
Nutmeg Post, pg 960
Shelly Palmer Production, pg 968
Pennebaker Hegedus Films Inc, pg 972
Sony Music Custom Marketing, pg 1016
Sony Music Entertainment, pg 1016
TBA Global Events, pg 1032
TecNec Distributing, pg 1035

NORTH CAROLINA

Pat Appleson Studios Inc, pg 788
Baker & Taylor Inc, pg 801
Duke Media Services, pg 853
Ladyslipper Inc, pg 915
NASCAR Media Group LLC, pg 952
Take One Productions Ltd, pg 1031

NORTH DAKOTA

Media Productions, pg 937

OHIO

Aztec Video Productions, pg 801
Creative Technology, pg 838
EDR Media LLC, pg 857
Mills James Productions, pg 943
R&B Communications Inc, pg 991
Take 1 Media Services, pg 1031
VGI Productions, pg 1053

OKLAHOMA

PDC Productions, pg 970

PENNSYLVANIA

BRg Music Works, pg 812
Brown Bag Imaging, pg 814
Craig Recording Studios, pg 837
Fusion Brand Experiences, pg 874
Monster Tracks, pg 945
The Videohouse Inc, pg 1057

RHODE ISLAND

Sound-FX-Design, pg 1017

SOUTH CAROLINA

Genesis Creative, pg 877
Stages Video Productions, pg 1023

TENNESSEE

Anode Inc, pg 787
Emerald Records, pg 860

AUDIO

Music Libraries—Popular (continued)

TENNESSEE (continued)

Film House Inc, pg 867
Fricon Entertainment Co Inc, pg 873
Memphis Communications Corp, pg 938
WKPT-TV, pg 1068
Word Label Group, pg 1069

TEXAS

Audiomoxie®, pg 796
The Editing Co, pg 857
FirstCom Music, pg 869
Horizon Film + Video Productions, pg 891
Mediaforce Productions, pg 937
The Music Bakery, pg 950
Julye Newlin Productions Inc, pg 956
Production Garden Music, pg 984
Real to Reel Studios Inc, pg 992
The Samuels Co, pg 1002
The Sound Lab Inc, pg 1017
Sound Works, pg 1018
South Coast Film & Video, pg 1019
Stage Directions, pg 1022
TM Studios Inc, pg 1041

VIRGINIA

CALIBRE, pg 816

WASHINGTON

Avast! Recording Co, pg 798

WEST VIRGINIA

Sweetsong Productions, pg 1029

WISCONSIN

5th Floor Recording Co, pg 867
ProVideo, pg 986
USAV Group Inc, pg 1050

ONTARIO

Canamedia Inc, pg 818
DebsVoice, pg 844
Entertainment One Distribution, pg 861
GAPC (General Assembly Production Centre), pg 875
MCS Recording Studios, pg 936
Metalworks Recording Studios Inc, pg 939
Morning Music Ltd, pg 946
Nightingale Music Productions Inc, pg 957
Sound Ideas, pg 1017
StockMusic.com, pg 1025
VO2 Mix Studios, pg 1060
Wanted! Sound + Picture, pg 1062
Westar Music, pg 1064

Music Libraries—Rap

ALABAMA

Sound of Birmingham Productions, pg 1017

ARIZONA

Direct Current Video Productions, pg 848
Film Creations Ltd, pg 867
Merestone, pg 938
Productiontrax.com, pg 985

ARKANSAS

Shadowbox Video Productions, pg 1007
White Diamond Productions, pg 1065

CALIFORNIA

Aaron & Le Duc, pg 772
Aliso Creek Productions Inc, pg 780
Berke Creative Inc, pg 805
Creative Support Services/CSS Music, pg 838
Diamond Dreams Music Productions, pg 846
Dogma Studios, pg 850
Eye & I Productions, pg 864
5 Alarm Music, pg 869
Kaleidosound, pg 907
Killer Tracks, pg 910
Lynch Communications, pg 926
Megatrax, pg 938
The Music Kitchen Inc, pg 950
OGM Production Music, pg 961
Reality Check Systems, pg 992
Steve Shapiro Music, pg 1008
Sonoton Music Library, pg 1016
Still N'Motion, pg 1025
Total Media Group, pg 1042

COLORADO

Tim Cissell Music, pg 828
Flashback Media Productions, pg 869
Los Angeles Post Music Inc, pg 924

CONNECTICUT

Applebox Studio, pg 788

DELAWARE

Ken-Del Productions Inc, pg 909

FLORIDA

LHV Audio Services, pg 919
Promidi Music, pg 986
SOS Worldwide Productions Inc, pg 1016
Top Hat Productions, pg 1042
Universal Studios Florida® Production Group, pg 1049

GEORGIA

Doppler Studios, pg 851
ECG Productions, pg 856

ILLINOIS

Twisted Media Inc, pg 1047
Video Impressions, pg 1055

MASSACHUSETTS

Labrecque Creative Sound, pg 915
Soundtrack Recording Studios, pg 1018

MICHIGAN

GMP Music, pg 879

MISSOURI

Production Consultants, pg 984
Show-Me Audio-Visual, pg 1009

MONTANA

Jereco Studios Inc, pg 905

NEBRASKA

JoeAudio, pg 905

NEVADA

Tanglewood Productions, pg 1031

NEW JERSEY

Milgrom Productions, pg 943
Oasis CD Manufacturing, pg 960
VCSvideo, pg 1052

NEW MEXICO

Production Outfitters, pg 984

NEW YORK

Audio Network US Inc, pg 794
Beekman Books Inc, pg 804
Big Fish Productions Inc, pg 807
Heavy Melody, pg 887
Loftin Productions, pg 924
Mother West, pg 947
Now Hear This, pg 960
TecNec Distributing, pg 1035

NORTH CAROLINA

Take One Productions Ltd, pg 1031

NORTH DAKOTA

Media Productions, pg 937

OHIO

Aztec Video Productions, pg 801
EDR Media LLC, pg 857
Mills James Productions, pg 943
R&B Communications Inc, pg 991
Take 1 Media Services, pg 1031

OKLAHOMA

PDC Productions, pg 970

PENNSYLVANIA

The Videohouse Inc, pg 1057

RHODE ISLAND

Sound-FX-Design, pg 1017

SOUTH CAROLINA

Stages Video Productions, pg 1023

TENNESSEE

Anode Inc, pg 787
Film House Inc, pg 867
Fricon Entertainment Co Inc, pg 873

TEXAS

The Editing Co, pg 857
FirstCom Music, pg 869
Horizon Film + Video Productions, pg 891
Mediaforce Productions, pg 937
The Music Bakery, pg 950
Julye Newlin Productions Inc, pg 956
Production Garden Music, pg 984
The Sound Lab Inc, pg 1017
South Coast Film & Video, pg 1019
TM Studios Inc, pg 1041
Tropikal Productions, pg 1045

VIRGINIA

CALIBRE, pg 816

WISCONSIN

5th Floor Recording Co, pg 867

ONTARIO

Canamedia Inc, pg 818
DebsVoice, pg 844
Entertainment One Distribution, pg 861
MCS Recording Studios, pg 936
Metalworks Recording Studios Inc, pg 939
Nightingale Music Productions Inc, pg 957
Sound Ideas, pg 1017
StockMusic.com, pg 1025
VO2 Mix Studios, pg 1060
Wanted! Sound + Picture, pg 1062
Westar Music, pg 1064

Music Libraries—Rhythm & Blues

ALABAMA

Sound of Birmingham Productions, pg 1017

ARIZONA

Direct Current Video Productions, pg 848
Film Creations Ltd, pg 867
Merestone, pg 938
Productiontrax.com, pg 985

ARKANSAS

Shadowbox Video Productions, pg 1007
White Diamond Productions, pg 1065

CALIFORNIA

Aaron & Le Duc, pg 772
Aliso Creek Productions Inc, pg 780
Berke Creative Inc, pg 805
Creative Support Services/CSS Music, pg 838
Diamond Dreams Music Productions, pg 846
Dogma Studios, pg 850
5 Alarm Music, pg 869
Kaleidosound, pg 907
Killer Tracks, pg 910
Lynch Communications, pg 926
Megatrax, pg 938
The Music Kitchen Inc, pg 950
OGM Production Music, pg 961
Reality Check Systems, pg 992
Steve Shapiro Music, pg 1008
Sonoton Music Library, pg 1016
Still N'Motion, pg 1025
Total Media Group, pg 1042
Visions Plus, pg 1058

COLORADO

Tim Cissell Music, pg 828
Flashback Media Productions, pg 869
Los Angeles Post Music Inc, pg 924

CONNECTICUT

Applebox Studio, pg 788
Ironik Design & Post, pg 902
Music 2 Hues, pg 951

DELAWARE

Ken-Del Productions Inc, pg 909

Music Libraries—Rock

AUDIO

Music Libraries—Rock (continued)

NEBRASKA

JoeAudio, pg 905

NEVADA

JCS Video Productions, pg 904
Tanglewood Productions, pg 1031

NEW HAMPSHIRE

Channell One Video, pg 824

NEW JERSEY

CFP Video Productions Inc, pg 823
Milbrodt/Music & Sound Design, pg 943
Milgrom Productions, pg 943
Oasis CD Manufacturing, pg 960
Richard Reiter Productions Inc, pg 994
TRF Production Music Libraries, pg 1044
VCSvideo, pg 1052

NEW MEXICO

Production Outfitters, pg 984

NEW YORK

Beekman Books Inc, pg 804
Big Fish Productions Inc, pg 807
De Wolfe Music USA, pg 844
Heavy Melody, pg 887
Historic Films, pg 889
HOThead, pg 891
Kamen Entertainment Group Inc, pg 908
Loftin Productions, pg 924
Manhattan Center Studios Inc, pg 930
Manhattan Production Music Inc, pg 930
Mother West, pg 947
New York Sound Inc, pg 956
Now Hear This, pg 960
Nutmeg Post, pg 960
Omnimusic, pg 962
Shelly Palmer Production, pg 968
Pennebaker Hegedus Films Inc, pg 972
David Rapkin Audio Production, pg 991
Sony Music Custom Marketing, pg 1016
Sony Music Entertainment, pg 1016
TecNec Distributing, pg 1035

NORTH CAROLINA

Pat Appleson Studios Inc, pg 788
Baker & Taylor Inc, pg 801
Duke Media Services, pg 853
Ladyslipper Inc, pg 915
NASCAR Media Group LLC, pg 952
Take One Productions Ltd, pg 1031

NORTH DAKOTA

Media Productions, pg 937

OHIO

Aztec Video Productions, pg 801
Creative Technology, pg 838
EDR Media LLC, pg 857
Mills James Productions, pg 943
R&B Communications Inc, pg 991
Take 1 Media Services, pg 1031
VGI Productions, pg 1053

OKLAHOMA

PDC Productions, pg 970

OREGON

"PBTM" Music, pg 970

PENNSYLVANIA

Brown Bag Imaging, pg 814
Craig Recording Studios, pg 837
Monster Tracks, pg 945
The Videohouse Inc, pg 1057

RHODE ISLAND

Sound-FX-Design, pg 1017

SOUTH CAROLINA

Genesis Creative, pg 877
Stages Video Productions, pg 1023

TENNESSEE

Anode Inc, pg 787
Emerald Records, pg 860
Film House Inc, pg 867
Fricon Entertainment Co Inc, pg 873
Sun Entertainment Corp, pg 1028
WKPT-TV, pg 1068
Word Label Group, pg 1069

TEXAS

The Editing Co, pg 857
FirstCom Music, pg 869
Horizon Film + Video Productions, pg 891
Mediaforce Productions, pg 937
The Music Bakery, pg 950
Julye Newlin Productions Inc, pg 956
Production Garden Music, pg 984
Real to Reel Studios Inc, pg 992
The Samuels Co, pg 1002
The Sound Lab Inc, pg 1017
Sound Works, pg 1018
South Coast Film & Video, pg 1019
TM Studios Inc, pg 1041
Tropikal Productions, pg 1045

VIRGINIA

Allied Media Corp, pg 781
CALIBRE, pg 816

WASHINGTON

Avast! Recording Co, pg 798

WISCONSIN

5th Floor Recording Co, pg 867
ProVideo, pg 986
USAV Group Inc, pg 1050

ONTARIO

Canamedia Inc, pg 818
DebsVoice, pg 844
Entertainment One Distribution, pg 861
MCS Recording Studios, pg 936
Metalworks Recording Studios Inc, pg 939
Nightingale Music Productions Inc, pg 957
Sound Ideas, pg 1017
StockMusic.com, pg 1025
VO2 Mix Studios, pg 1060
Wanted! Sound + Picture, pg 1062
Westar Music, pg 1064

Music Libraries—Spiritual

ALABAMA

Sound of Birmingham Productions, pg 1017

ARIZONA

Direct Current Video Productions, pg 848
Film Creations Ltd, pg 867
Fire Power Music Inc, pg 868
Merestone, pg 938
Productiontrax.com, pg 985
Valley of the Sun Publishing Co, pg 1051

ARKANSAS

Shadowbox Video Productions, pg 1007
White Diamond Productions, pg 1065

CALIFORNIA

Aaron & Le Duc, pg 772
Aliso Creek Productions Inc, pg 780
Associated Production Music LLC, pg 792
Berke Creative Inc, pg 805
Christian Media Network, pg 825
Creative Support Services/CSS Music, pg 838
Diamond Dreams Music Productions, pg 846
Dogma Studios, pg 850
Eye & I Productions, pg 864
5 Alarm Music, pg 869
Kaleidosound, pg 907
Killer Tracks, pg 910
Lynch Communications, pg 926
Megatrax, pg 938
The Music Kitchen Inc, pg 950
Joseph Nicoletti Consulting-Promotion/California International Records/Global Village Records, pg 957
OGM Production Music, pg 961
Osho Viha Information Center & Book Distributors, pg 965
Steve Shapiro Music, pg 1008
Sonoton Music Library, pg 1016
Still N'Motion, pg 1025
Timeless Productions, pg 1040
Total Media Group, pg 1042
Welk Music Group, pg 1063

COLORADO

Tim Cissell Music, pg 828
Flashback Media Productions, pg 869
Los Angeles Post Music Inc, pg 924

CONNECTICUT

Applebox Studio, pg 788
EagleVision Inc, pg 855

DELAWARE

Ken-Del Productions Inc, pg 909

DISTRICT OF COLUMBIA

Library of Congress, Motion Picture, Broadcasting & Recorded Sound Division, pg 919

FLORIDA

Alliance Entertainment Corp (AEC) LLC, pg 781
Children of Mary, pg 825
Gulf Coast Audio Visual Producers Inc, pg 883
Home Shopping Network (HSN), pg 890
Jordan Klein Film & Video (JKFV), pg 906
LHV Audio Services, pg 919
Promidi Music, pg 986
SOS Worldwide Productions Inc, pg 1016
Sound*Light, pg 1017
Top Hat Productions, pg 1042
Universal Studios Florida® Production Group, pg 1049

GEORGIA

Beachwood Productions, pg 804
Doppler Studios, pg 851
Guerrilla Productions LLC, pg 883

ILLINOIS

Analog Free Media, pg 786
Video Impressions, pg 1055
WEEK TV, pg 1063
Woodside Avenue Music Productions Inc, pg 1069

KENTUCKY

Trusty Tuneshop Recording Studios, pg 1045

MARYLAND

Adelphi Records Inc, pg 776
The Cutting Corp, pg 841

MASSACHUSETTS

Labrecque Creative Sound, pg 915
Soundtrack Recording Studios, pg 1018

MICHIGAN

AirBrands Event & Marketing Group, pg 779
GMP Music, pg 879

MISSOURI

Production Consultants, pg 984
Show-Me Audio-Visual, pg 1009

MONTANA

Jereco Studios Inc, pg 905

NEBRASKA

JoeAudio, pg 905

NEVADA

JCS Video Productions, pg 904
Tanglewood Productions, pg 1031

NEW JERSEY

CFP Video Productions Inc, pg 823
Milgrom Productions, pg 943
Oasis CD Manufacturing, pg 960
TRF Production Music Libraries, pg 1044
VCSvideo, pg 1052

NEW MEXICO

Production Outfitters, pg 984

NEW YORK

Audio Network US Inc, pg 794
Beekman Books Inc, pg 804
Big Fish Productions Inc, pg 807
De Wolfe Music USA, pg 844

Music—Original

AUDIO

Music—Original (continued)

MASSACHUSETTS

ARF!ARF!, pg 789
Continental Recordings Inc, pg 835
Green Mountain Post Films (GMP), pg 882
Labrecque Creative Sound, pg 915
Manchester Music Library Inc, pg 929
Professional Audio Design Inc, pg 985
Ben Rudnick & Friends, pg 1000
Shambhala Publications, pg 1008
Sounds Interesting Studios, pg 1018
Soundtrack Recording Studios, pg 1018
Rik Tinory Productions, pg 1041
TR Productions, pg 1043
Veritech Corp, pg 1053

MICHIGAN

Audio Graphic Services, pg 794
Digi Sign Design LLC, pg 847
Digital Image Studios LLC, pg 847
GMP Music, pg 879
K&R's Recording Studios Inc, pg 908
MessageMakers, pg 939
Michigan Recording Arts Institute & Technologies, pg 941
Rebirth/Wenha Records, pg 993
RingSide Creative, pg 997
Studio A Recording Inc, pg 1026

MINNESOTA

The ADS Group, pg 777
Aggressive Records Audio Duplication LLC, pg 778
Beyers Sound & Essay Audio, pg 806
Media Loft Inc, pg 937
MultiMedia, pg 950
Winterland Studios, pg 1068

MISSOURI

Avatar Studios, pg 798

MONTANA

Jereco Studios Inc, pg 905
KCFW Television, pg 908
North Country Media Group, pg 959

NEVADA

Tanglewood Productions, pg 1031

NEW HAMPSHIRE

Apertura, pg 788
Captain Fiddle Music & Publications, pg 820
Chip Taylor Communications LLC, pg 1032

NEW JERSEY

CFP Video Productions Inc, pg 823
Jeep Jazz Media Solutions, pg 905
Mia Mind Music, pg 941
Milbrodt/Music & Sound Design, pg 943
Milgrom Productions, pg 943
NFL Films Inc, pg 957
Oasis CD Manufacturing, pg 960
Presence Records, pg 981
Propeller Music Group, pg 986
Richard Reiter Productions Inc, pg 994
Starlite Productions, pg 1024
Suede Interactive, pg 1027
TRF Production Music Libraries, pg 1044
VCSvideo, pg 1052

NEW MEXICO

Uncharted Country Publishing, pg 1048

NEW YORK

Aural Gratification Inc, pg 796
aurora productions, pg 797
Big Fish Productions Inc, pg 807
The Big House Group, pg 807
Chromavision Corp, pg 826
Fingerpaint, pg 868
A Gentle Wind, pg 877
Bob Gerardi Music Productions, pg 877
HB-Content, pg 886
Headroom Digital Audio, pg 887
Heavy Melody, pg 887
IAI Video, pg 893
Icontent, pg 893
Jupiter Moon Productions, pg 907
KAS Music & Sound, pg 908
L&P Media, pg 915
Lylofilm Productions, pg 926
Magnetic Music Publishing Co, pg 928
Manhattan Center Studios Inc, pg 930
Manhattan Production Music Inc, pg 930
Mark Custom Recording Service Inc, pg 931
Jack Morton Worldwide, pg 946
Mother West, pg 947
MRG Productions Inc, pg 948
No Soap Productions, pg 957
Now Hear This, pg 960
Nutmeg Post, pg 960
Omnimusic, pg 962
Shelly Palmer Production, pg 968
Patco Resources Inc, pg 970
Elliot Sokolov Music, pg 1015
Sony Music Entertainment, pg 1016
TBA Global Events, pg 1032
TeleTime Productions, pg 1036
Tiki Recording Studios Inc, pg 1040

NORTH CAROLINA

Pat Appleson Studios Inc, pg 788
Audio Art, pg 794
Davenport Music Library, pg 843
Franklin Video Inc, pg 872
Howard Hanger, pg 884
Horizon Video Productions Inc, pg 891
Trailblazer Studios®, pg 1043
2BruceStudio, pg 1047

NORTH DAKOTA

Media Productions, pg 937

OHIO

Bartha, pg 803
Challenge Productions, pg 823
Creative Technology, pg 838
EDR Media LLC, pg 857
Mills James Productions, pg 943
SoundSpace Inc, pg 1018
Twin Sisters Productions LLC, pg 1047

OKLAHOMA

PDC Productions, pg 970

OREGON

Intersect Video, pg 901
Rex, pg 995

PENNSYLVANIA

American Artist Studio, pg 783
Brown Bag Imaging, pg 814
Dreambox Media Inc, pg 852
Innovision Media Group, pg 899
Ivory Productions, pg 903
Javboy Records, pg 904
JPL, pg 906
Kloss Studios Co, pg 912
Robin Miller, Filmaker Inc, pg 943
Monster Tracks, pg 945
Production Masters Inc (PMI), pg 984
Right Coast Recording Inc, pg 997
The Videohouse Inc, pg 1057

RHODE ISLAND

Sound-FX-Design, pg 1017
StarTrak Studios Inc, pg 1024

TENNESSEE

American Blackguard Inc, pg 784
Analog Man Recording Studio, pg 786
Ardent Music LLC, pg 789
Cupit Music Group, pg 841
Fricon Entertainment Co Inc, pg 873
Green Linnet Records, pg 882
JamSync, pg 904
Mr Mark's Used Musical, Stereo & Studio Equipment Store, pg 944
Motion Picture Services, pg 947
Scripps Networks, pg 1005
Stage Post, pg 1022
Zion Music Group, pg 1074

TEXAS

AMS Pictures, pg 786
Audiomoxie®, pg 796
Biway Media, pg 808
Communication Arts Multimedia Inc, pg 832
The Editing Co, pg 857
FirstCom Music, pg 869
Mediaforce Productions, pg 937
The Music Bakery, pg 950
Out of the BLUE Media, pg 966
Planet Dallas Recording Studios, pg 976
The Samuels Co, pg 1002
Sound Arts Recording Studio, pg 1017
The Sound Lab Inc, pg 1017
Stage Directions, pg 1022
TM Studios Inc, pg 1041
TopCat Records LLC, pg 1042
Tropikal Productions, pg 1045
World Beat Studio, pg 1069

UTAH

Soularium Recording Studios, pg 1016

VERMONT

University of Vermont, Instructional Television Dept, pg 1050

VIRGINIA

AudioImage Recording, pg 796
BES Studios, pg 805
Wally Cleaver's Recording Service, pg 830
Henninger Media Services, pg 888
Lion Recording Services Inc, pg 922
Mark Sonder Productions Inc, pg 931
Metro Productions, pg 939
Studio Center Corp, pg 1026

WASHINGTON

Jake Barner Studio, pg 803
D A Sound, pg 842
Hamilton Studio, pg 884
Inland Audio Visual Co, pg 898
Kostov Productions, pg 913
North-by-Northwest Productions, pg 958
Sound Sound/Savage Fruitarian Productions, pg 1017
Victory Studios, pg 1054

WEST VIRGINIA

Sweetsong Productions, pg 1029

WISCONSIN

Concept Productions Inc, pg 834
5th Floor Recording Co, pg 867
USAV Group Inc, pg 1050
Wisconsin Public Television, pg 1068

WYOMING

Bridger Productions Inc, pg 812

BRITISH COLUMBIA

Pinewood Sound, pg 975

MANITOBA

daCapo Productions, pg 842

ONTARIO

ADS Media, pg 777
AMPLUS Productions, pg 786
GAPC (General Assembly Production Centre), pg 875
JL Recording Studios, pg 905
Morning Music Ltd, pg 946
Nightingale Music Productions Inc, pg 957
Purefire Communications Inc, pg 987
Sound Ideas, pg 1017
StockMusic.com, pg 1025
VO2 Mix Studios, pg 1060
Wanted! Sound + Picture, pg 1062
Westbury National Show Systems Ltd, pg 1064

Music Scoring

ALABAMA

Dogwood Recording Studios, pg 850
Sound of Birmingham Productions, pg 1017

ARIZONA

Creative Backstage, pg 838
Merestone, pg 938
Phoenix VideoFilms®, pg 974
Productiontrax.com, pg 985

CALIFORNIA

AB Audio Visual Entertainment Inc, pg 772
Aliso Creek Productions Inc, pg 780

AUDIO

Music Scoring (continued)

TENNESSEE (continued)

Marine Geographic, pg 931
Motion Picture Services, pg 947
Stage Post, pg 1022
Zion Music Group, pg 1074

TEXAS

AMS Pictures, pg 786
Audiomoxie®, pg 796
Biway Media, pg 808
Communication Arts Multimedia Inc, pg 832
Harbor House Studios, pg 884
Mediaforce Productions, pg 937
The Music Bakery, pg 950
Reelsound Recording Co, pg 994
The Samuels Co, pg 1002
The Sound Lab Inc, pg 1017
Stage Directions, pg 1022
TM Studios Inc, pg 1041
Tropikal Productions, pg 1045

UTAH

Soularium Recording Studios, pg 1016

VERMONT

University of Vermont, Instructional Television Dept, pg 1050

VIRGINIA

AudioImage Recording, pg 796
BES Studios, pg 805
Wally Cleaver's Recording Service, pg 830
Lion Recording Services Inc, pg 922
Studio Center Corp, pg 1026

WASHINGTON

Hamilton Studio, pg 884
Inland Audio Visual Co, pg 898
Kostov Productions, pg 913
North-by-Northwest Productions, pg 958
Sound Sound/Savage Fruitarian Productions, pg 1017
Victory Studios, pg 1054

WISCONSIN

5th Floor Recording Co, pg 867
USAV Group Inc, pg 1050

WYOMING

Bridger Productions Inc, pg 812

BRITISH COLUMBIA

Pinewood Sound, pg 975

MANITOBA

daCapo Productions, pg 842

ONTARIO

ADS Media, pg 777
GAPC (General Assembly Production Centre), pg 875
Nightingale Music Productions Inc, pg 957
VO2 Mix Studios, pg 1060

New Age Music, *see* Music Libraries—New Age

Noise Reducer Distributors

ARIZONA

EAR Professional Audio/Video, pg 855
Troxell Communications Inc, pg 1045
David Wexler & Co, pg 1064

CALIFORNIA

Ametron Audio/Video, pg 785
ARS Electronics, pg 791
Associated Sound, pg 792
Audio Images Corp, pg 794
Be Media, pg 804
Design FX Audio, pg 845
Location Sound Corp, pg 924
MediaPOINTE, pg 938
Sound Service Co, pg 1017
Towards 2000 Inc, pg 1043
VMI Inc, pg 1060

COLORADO

Audio Consultant Services Inc, pg 794

DELAWARE

Actors Attic, pg 775

FLORIDA

Access Media Group, pg 773
Allstar Audio Systems Inc, pg 782
BAI Distributors Inc, pg 801
Broadcasters General Store Inc, pg 813
Digital Video Systems Inc, pg 848
Hi-Tech Enterprises Inc, pg 888
Lighting Sales Connections, pg 920
Photomart Cine-Video Inc, pg 975
Pro Stage Inc, pg 983
Recording Media & Equipment Inc (RM&E), pg 993
Stereo Sales Inc, pg 1024
TAI Audio, pg 1031
Technomedia Solutions, pg 1035

GEORGIA

Clark, pg 829
Lighting & Production Equipment Inc, pg 920
Stage Front Presentation Systems, pg 1022

HAWAII

The Audio Visual Co (AVCO), pg 795

ILLINOIS

Allen Visual Systems Inc, pg 781
Quintessence Audio Ltd, pg 989
Woodside Avenue Music Productions Inc, pg 1069

INDIANA

Sensory Technologies LLC, pg 1006
SHP Electronics, pg 1010
Sweetwater Sound Inc, pg 1029

IOWA

ECS Inc, pg 856

KENTUCKY

Audio Visual Techniques Inc, pg 796
Axxis Inc, pg 800
NOR-COM Inc, pg 958

MAINE

Headlight Audio Visual Inc, pg 887
Independent Audio Inc, pg 897

MARYLAND

Bradley Broadcast & Pro Audio, pg 811

MASSACHUSETTS

Professional Audio Design Inc, pg 985
Rule Broadcast Systems, pg 1000
Silent Source, pg 1011

MICHIGAN

Olson Anderson Co, pg 786
Digi Sign Design LLC, pg 847
TeL Systems, pg 1035

MINNESOTA

NetWell Noise Control, pg 954

NEW HAMPSHIRE

Technet® Systems Group, pg 1033

NEW JERSEY

Alltec Stores, a Vcom IMC Company, pg 782
Starlite Productions, pg 1024
Wired 4 Sound Inc, pg 1068
York Telecom, pg 1072

NEW YORK

ALTEL Systems Inc, pg 783
Audio-Video Corp, pg 795
BTX Technologies, pg 814
Colortone Audio Visual, pg 832
Custom Media Environments, pg 841
Design Audio Visual Inc, pg 845
DSan Corp, pg 852
HAVE Inc, pg 886
Toys From The Attic, pg 1043

OHIO

ITA Audio Visual Solutions, pg 902
Jimmy Rea Electronics Inc, pg 992

OREGON

ASC-Tube Trap, pg 791
TARA Labs, pg 1032

PENNSYLVANIA

Advanced AV, pg 777
Grise Audio Visual Center Inc, pg 882
Vistacom Inc, pg 1059

TENNESSEE

Durrell LLC, pg 854
Lowrance Sound Co Inc, pg 925
Mr Mark's Used Musical, Stereo & Studio Equipment Store, pg 944
Spectrum Sound Inc, pg 1021
Technical Support Systems LLC, pg 1034

TEXAS

AVES Audio Visual Systems Inc, pg 798
Lubbock Audio Visual Inc, pg 925
Pro Video & Film Equipment Co Inc, pg 983
RF Specialties of Texas LLC, pg 996
Southwest Sound & Electronics Inc, pg 1019
Tarpley Media Systems, pg 1032

UTAH

Performance Audio, pg 973

VIRGINIA

Avitecture Inc, pg 799
Intellidyne LLC, pg 899
Rocktown Media, pg 998

WASHINGTON

CCI Solutions, pg 821
Northern Lights & Pro Audio, pg 959
Pacific Northwest Theatre Associates Inc (PNTA), pg 967

WISCONSIN

Audio Visual of Milwaukee Inc, pg 795
Full Compass Systems, pg 874

PUERTO RICO

Audio Visual Concepts Inc, pg 795
Bonnin Electronics Inc, pg 810

ALBERTA

Infosat Communications Inc, pg 898
Matrix Video Communications Corp (MVCC), pg 934

BRITISH COLUMBIA

Commercial Electronics Ltd, pg 832

MANITOBA

Advance Pro, pg 777
Inland Audio Visual Ltd, pg 898

ONTARIO

Cinema Stage Inc, pg 827
Westbury National Show Systems Ltd, pg 1064

QUEBEC

SC Media Canada, pg 1003

Noise Reducer Manufacturers

CALIFORNIA

FM Systems Inc, pg 870
Furman, pg 874
Mackenzie Laboratories Inc, pg 927

FLORIDA

Compuvideo Sales USA Ltd, pg 834

ILLINOIS

Esoteric Sound, pg 862
J K Audio Inc, pg 903
SoundTech, pg 1018

MINNESOTA

NetWell Noise Control, pg 954

NEW JERSEY

Prism Media Products Inc, pg 982

NEW YORK

Allen Avionics Inc, pg 781
Broadcast Devices Inc, pg 813
DSan Corp, pg 852

NORTH CAROLINA

Micro Technology Unlimited, pg 941

OREGON

ASC-Tube Trap, pg 791
TARA Labs, pg 1032

TEXAS

ETA Systems, pg 862
International Cellulose Corp, pg 900

VIRGINIA

Acoustical Solutions Inc, pg 774

BRITISH COLUMBIA

Primacoustic, pg 982

Noise Reducer Rentals

ALABAMA

Audio-Video Resources Inc, pg 795

ARIZONA

Merestone, pg 938
Video West Inc, pg 1056

CALIFORNIA

Absolute Rentals, pg 772
Alliant Event Services, pg 781
Ametron Audio/Video, pg 785
Associated Sound, pg 792
Audio Rents, pg 794
Big Time Picture Company Inc, pg 807
Design FX Audio, pg 845
Express Media Inc, pg 864
McCune Audio-Video-Lighting, pg 935
Munday & Collins AV, pg 950
On-Trax Inc, pg 963
Towards 2000 Inc, pg 1043
VER-Video Equipment Rentals, pg 1053

COLORADO

Audio Consultant Services Inc, pg 794

CONNECTICUT

A/V Davey, pg 797

DELAWARE

Actors Attic, pg 775

FLORIDA

Allstar Audio Systems Inc, pg 782
Image Technical Services, pg 895
Lighting Sales Connections, pg 920
Pro Stage Inc, pg 983
TAI Audio, pg 1031

GEORGIA

Lighting & Production Equipment Inc, pg 920
Stage Front Presentation Systems, pg 1022

HAWAII

Sight & Sound Studios, pg 1010

ILLINOIS

On Stage Audio, pg 963
Show Department Inc, pg 1009
Woodside Avenue Music Productions Inc, pg 1069

IOWA

ECS Inc, pg 856

KENTUCKY

Audio Visual Techniques Inc, pg 796

MARYLAND

CPR MultiMedia Solutions, pg 837
Maryland Sound International Holding Co LLC, pg 933

MASSACHUSETTS

AVFX Inc, pg 798
Preston Productions Inc, pg 981

MICHIGAN

Digi Sign Design LLC, pg 847
K&R All Media Productions Inc, pg 908
K&R's Recording Studios Inc, pg 908

MINNESOTA

Big Event Productions LLC, pg 807

MISSOURI

Show-Me Audio-Visual, pg 1009

NEVADA

GES Audio Visual, pg 877

NEW JERSEY

Audio Visual Dynamics®, pg 795
CFP Video Productions Inc, pg 823
PLS Staging, pg 977
Starlite Productions, pg 1024
Wired 4 Sound Inc, pg 1068

NEW YORK

Colortone Audio Visual, pg 832
CP Communications, pg 837
Design Audio Visual Inc, pg 845
Manhattan Center Studios Inc, pg 930
TBA Global Events, pg 1032

PENNSYLVANIA

Advanced AV, pg 777
Grise Audio Visual Center Inc, pg 882
Production Solutions Inc, pg 985

TENNESSEE

Mr Mark's Used Musical, Stereo & Studio Equipment Store, pg 944
Technical Support Systems LLC, pg 1034

TEXAS

Lubbock Audio Visual Inc, pg 925
Onstage Systems, pg 963
The Samuels Co, pg 1002
Stage Directions, pg 1022

UTAH

Performance Audio, pg 973

VERMONT

Parlato Productions, pg 969

VIRGINIA

American AV, pg 783

WASHINGTON

Pacific Northwest Theatre Associates Inc (PNTA), pg 967
Victory Studios, pg 1054

WISCONSIN

Full Compass Systems, pg 874

PUERTO RICO

Stage Crew Audiovisual Inc, pg 1022

BRITISH COLUMBIA

Commercial Electronics Ltd, pg 832

MANITOBA

Inland Audio Visual Ltd, pg 898

ONTARIO

RB Productions, pg 992
Westbury National Show Systems Ltd, pg 1064

Noise Reducer Repairs

CALIFORNIA

Ametron Audio/Video, pg 785
Audio Images Corp, pg 794
McAlister Electronics, pg 935
Towards 2000 Inc, pg 1043

CONNECTICUT

HB Communications Inc, pg 886

FLORIDA

Hi-Tech Enterprises Inc, pg 888
Phat Planet Recording Studios, pg 973
Stereo Sales Inc, pg 1024
TAI Audio, pg 1031

GEORGIA

Lighting & Production Equipment Inc, pg 920
Stage Front Presentation Systems, pg 1022

INDIANA

Sweetwater Sound Inc, pg 1029

IOWA

ECS Inc, pg 856

KENTUCKY

Axxis Inc, pg 800
NOR-COM Inc, pg 958

MASSACHUSETTS

Professional Audio Design Inc, pg 985

MICHIGAN

K&R's Recording Studios Inc, pg 908
TeL Systems, pg 1035

NEW JERSEY

Starlite Productions, pg 1024

NEW YORK

Toys From The Attic, pg 1043

NORTH CAROLINA

Micro Technology Unlimited, pg 941

OREGON

All Service Musical Electronics Repair, pg 780

TENNESSEE

Technical Support Systems LLC, pg 1034

TEXAS

Southwest Sound & Electronics Inc, pg 1019
Tarpley Media Systems, pg 1032

VIRGINIA

Avitecture Inc, pg 799

WASHINGTON

Pacific Northwest Theatre Associates Inc (PNTA), pg 967

WISCONSIN

Full Compass Systems, pg 874

PUERTO RICO

Bonnin Electronics Inc, pg 810

ALBERTA

Infosat Communications Inc, pg 898

BRITISH COLUMBIA

Commercial Electronics Ltd, pg 832

MANITOBA

Inland Audio Visual Ltd, pg 898

ONTARIO

Westbury National Show Systems Ltd, pg 1064

QUEBEC

SC Media Canada, pg 1003

Optical Sound Recording, *see* Sound Recording—Optical

Original Music, *see* Music—Original

Part & Accessory Distributors

ALABAMA

Media Visions Inc, pg 937

AUDIO

Part & Accessory Distributors (continued)

ARIZONA

Arizona Cine Equipment, pg 789
Audio Video Resources, pg 795
Troxell Communications Inc, pg 1045
WindTech™ Microphone Windscreens & Accessories, pg 1067

ARKANSAS

Jay S Stanley & Associates Inc, pg 1023

CALIFORNIA

Addlogix, pg 776
Adolph Gasser Inc, pg 776
Advanced Systems Group LLC, pg 778
Ametron Audio/Video, pg 785
Apex Jr, pg 788
ARS Electronics, pg 791
Associated Sound, pg 792
Audio Images Corp, pg 794
Be Media, pg 804
BroadcastStore.com, pg 813
California Tape Products Inc, pg 817
Carvin Corp, pg 820
Christy's Editorial, pg 826
Delicate Electronics Sales Inc, pg 845
El Mar Plastics Inc, pg 858
Empire Wholesale Inc, pg 860
FXC Communications, pg 874
Get Organized, pg 877
GMF Sound Inc, pg 879
Hosa Technology Inc, pg 891
IAMP Professional Audio, pg 893
Instructional Materials & Equipment Distributors (I-Med), pg 899
Jameco Electronics, pg 903
JD Audio Visual Inc, pg 904
The LAST Factory, pg 916
Location Sound Corp, pg 924
Magnet Sales & Manufacturing Co Inc, pg 928
Lloyd F McKinney Associates Inc, pg 935
Media Fabricators Inc, pg 936
MediaPOINTE, pg 938
Orevox USA Corp, pg 965
POP TV, pg 978
Professional Sound Corp, pg 985
Randall Schiller Productions, pg 1004
Signal Transport, pg 1011
Sound Service Co, pg 1017
Southern California Sound Image Inc, pg 1019
SSL Industries Inc, pg 1022
TOA Electronics Inc, pg 1041
Towards 2000 Inc, pg 1043
Yamaha Electronics Corp, pg 1071
Zack Electronics Inc, pg 1073

COLORADO

Audio Consultant Services Inc, pg 794
Case Logic Inc, pg 820
Ceavco Audio/Visual Co, pg 822

CONNECTICUT

Concord Communications, pg 835
Connecticut Audio & Theatrical Supply, pg 835
HB Communications Inc, pg 886
MAVCO, pg 934
The Music People Inc, pg 951
Rockwell Communications Inc, pg 998
Sennheiser Electronic Corp, pg 1006

DELAWARE

Actors Attic, pg 775

FLORIDA

Allstar Audio Systems Inc, pg 782
AMP Services Inc, pg 785
Broadcasters General Store Inc, pg 813
Digital Video Systems Inc, pg 848
Gulf Coast Audio Visual Producers Inc, pg 883
Hi-Tech Import Export Corp, pg 888
Hunter Electronics LLC, pg 892
Intermark Industries Inc, pg 900
Midtown Video Inc, pg 942
Photomart Cine-Video Inc, pg 975
Pro Stage Inc, pg 983
Recording Media & Equipment Inc (RM&E), pg 993
Sight & Sound Productions, pg 1010
Stereo Sales Inc, pg 1024
Straight Wire Inc, pg 1025
TAI Audio, pg 1031
Tallahassee Audio Visual, pg 1031
Technomedia Solutions, pg 1035

GEORGIA

Audio Visual Resources Inc, pg 795
Baker Audio Inc, pg 801
Convergent Media Systems, pg 836
Lighting & Production Equipment Inc, pg 920
Stage Front Presentation Systems, pg 1022
Technical Innovation, pg 1033
Visioneering International Inc, pg 1058

HAWAII

The Audio Visual Co (AVCO), pg 795

ILLINOIS

Allen Visual Systems Inc, pg 781
Clark Wire & Cable, pg 829
Gepco®, a General Cable brand, pg 877
Joseph Electronics, pg 906
C V Lloyde, pg 923
On Site Video, pg 963
Quintessence Audio Ltd, pg 989
Rauland-Borg Corp, pg 991
Sound Vision Inc, pg 1018
Woodside Avenue Music Productions Inc, pg 1069

INDIANA

Sensory Technologies LLC, pg 1006
SHP Electronics, pg 1010
Sweetwater Sound Inc, pg 1029

IOWA

ECS Inc, pg 856

KANSAS

Smith Audio-Visual Inc, pg 1014

KENTUCKY

Audio Visual Techniques Inc, pg 796
Axxis Inc, pg 800
Barney Miller's Inc, pg 943
NOR-COM Inc, pg 958

LOUISIANA

Intermedia Technologies, pg 900

MAINE

Independent Audio Inc, pg 897

MARYLAND

Bradley Broadcast & Pro Audio, pg 811
Cardinal Sound & Video, pg 820
Noventri, pg 960
Nicholas P Pipino Associates Inc, pg 976
RTZ Audio Visual, pg 1000
Visual Aids Electronics Corp, pg 1059

MASSACHUSETTS

Professional Audio Design Inc, pg 985

MICHIGAN

Olson Anderson Co, pg 786
Ascom Communications Contractors, pg 791
City Events Group, pg 828
Digi Sign Design LLC, pg 847
Lowing Light & Grip Inc, pg 925
On Stage Visuals, pg 963
Stedman Corp, pg 1024
TeL Systems, pg 1035

MINNESOTA

Advanced Audio-Visual Inc, pg 777
Alpha Video & Audio Inc, pg 782
AVI Systems, pg 799
Cinequipt Inc, pg 828
New Life Communications Inc, pg 956

MISSISSIPPI

Jasper Ewing & Sons Inc, pg 864

MISSOURI

Communitronics Corp, pg 833
Modern Communications Inc, pg 944
The RapcoHorizon Co, pg 991

NEVADA

Selco Products Co, pg 1006

NEW HAMPSHIRE

Audio Accessories Inc, pg 794

NEW JERSEY

Alltec Stores, a Vcom IMC Company, pg 782
AV Bluebook, pg 797
Canare Corporation of America, pg 819
Earl Girls Inc, pg 855
FlagHouse, pg 869
Hamilton Buhl, pg 884
Interstate Connecting Components, pg 901
JRF Magnetic Sciences Inc, pg 906
National Audio-Visual Supply, pg 952
Outwater Plastics Industries Inc, pg 966
PatchAmp, pg 970
Starlite Productions, pg 1024
Tele-Measurements Inc, pg 1035
Turner Engineering Inc, pg 1046
VCom International Multimedia Corp, pg 1052
Video Corporation of America (VCA), pg 1055
York Telecom, pg 1072

NEW MEXICO

Quickbeam Systems Inc (QSI), pg 989

NEW YORK

Audio-Video Corp, pg 795
Aura Sonic Ltd, pg 796
AV Workshop, pg 797
beyerdynamic Inc, pg 806
BTX Technologies, pg 814
Cine 60 Inc, pg 826
Colortone Audio Visual, pg 832
Communication Corner Inc, pg 832
Custom Media Environments, pg 841
Gaylord Brothers, pg 876
HAVE Inc, pg 886
Indigo Productions, pg 897
Langie Audio Visual Systems, pg 915
Long Island Video Enterprises Live Inc, pg 924
Saul Mineroff Electronics Inc, pg 943
Posthorn Recordings, pg 979
Ray Supply Inc, pg 992
RNJ Electronics, pg 997
Russell Industries Inc, pg 1001
Sentry Industries Inc, pg 1007
Technisphere Corp, pg 1034
Visual Technologies Corp, pg 1060
Whirlwind Music Distributors Inc, pg 1065
Willoughby's Imaging Center, pg 1067
Yorkville Sound Inc, pg 1072

NORTH CAROLINA

Camcor Inc, pg 818
Strategic Connections, pg 1026

OHIO

Copp Integrated Systems, pg 836
ITA Audio Visual Solutions, pg 902
Parts Express, pg 969

OREGON

ASC-Tube Trap, pg 791
TARA Labs, pg 1032

PENNSYLVANIA

Advanced AV, pg 777
Audio Visions Inc, pg 795
Brodart Co, pg 813
Clair Brothers Audio Systems Inc, pg 829
J E Foss Co, pg 871
Grise Audio Visual Center Inc, pg 882
Har-Ken Specialties, pg 884
The Lerro Corp, pg 919
Morefield Communications Inc, pg 946

RHODE ISLAND

Custom Computer Specialists Inc, pg 841

Part & Accessory Manufacturers

AUDIO

Part & Accessory Manufacturers (continued)

VIRGINIA

Acoustics First Corp, pg 775

WASHINGTON

Tecplot Inc, pg 1035

WISCONSIN

Brady Corp, pg 811
Koss Corp, pg 913

ONTARIO

DW Electrochemicals Ltd, pg 854
McCurdy Radio Ltd, pg 935
Ward-Beck Systems Ltd, pg 1062

Part & Accessory Rentals

ARIZONA

Arizona Cine Equipment, pg 789
Merestone, pg 938

CALIFORNIA

Absolute Rentals, pg 772
Ametron Audio/Video, pg 785
Associated Sound, pg 792
Express Media Inc, pg 864
Gold Standard Productions, pg 880
Alan Gordon Enterprises Inc, pg 880
IAMP Professional Audio, pg 893
Location Sound Corp, pg 924
McCune Audio-Video-Lighting, pg 935
Media Fabricators Inc, pg 936
PSAV® Presentation Services, pg 986
Sound Service Co, pg 1017
Total Media Group, pg 1042
Towards 2000 Inc, pg 1043

COLORADO

Audio Consultant Services Inc, pg 794

CONNECTICUT

A/V Davey, pg 797
Rockwell Communications Inc, pg 998
Videofilm Systems Inc, pg 1057

FLORIDA

Allstar Audio Systems Inc, pg 782
Steven Cohen Motion Picture Production, pg 831
Gulf Coast Audio Visual Producers Inc, pg 883
Image Technical Services, pg 895
Paradise Show & Design Inc, pg 969
Pro Stage Inc, pg 983
Technomedia Solutions, pg 1035

GEORGIA

Convergent Media Systems, pg 836
First Cut Communications LLC, pg 868
Lighting & Production Equipment Inc, pg 920
MAGNUM Companies Ltd, pg 929
Stage Front Presentation Systems, pg 1022
Staging Directions Inc, pg 1023

ILLINOIS

Allen Visual Systems Inc, pg 781
Helix Camera & Video, pg 887
On Stage Audio, pg 963
Show Department Inc, pg 1009
Woodside Avenue Music Productions Inc, pg 1069

IOWA

ECS Inc, pg 856

KENTUCKY

Audio Visual Techniques Inc, pg 796

MARYLAND

CPR MultiMedia Solutions, pg 837
Event Tech, pg 863
Maryland Sound International Holding Co LLC, pg 933
RTZ Audio Visual, pg 1000

MASSACHUSETTS

Capron Lighting & Sound Co Inc, pg 819
massAV, pg 933
Preston Productions Inc, pg 981

MICHIGAN

City Events Group, pg 828
Digi Sign Design LLC, pg 847
K&R All Media Productions Inc, pg 908
K&R's Recording Studios Inc, pg 908
Lowing Light & Grip Inc, pg 925
On Stage Visuals, pg 963
Stedman Corp, pg 1024
TeL Systems, pg 1035

MINNESOTA

Advanced Audio-Visual Inc, pg 777
Alpha Video & Audio Inc, pg 782

MISSOURI

Image Technologies Corp, pg 895
Show-Me Audio-Visual, pg 1009
Swank Audio Visuals, pg 1029

NEW HAMPSHIRE

Apertura, pg 788

NEW JERSEY

Audio Visual Dynamics®, pg 795
Earl Girls Inc, pg 855
JRF Magnetic Sciences Inc, pg 906
PLS Staging, pg 977
Starlite Productions, pg 1024
Video Corporation of America (VCA), pg 1055

NEW MEXICO

Production Outfitters, pg 984

NEW YORK

AV Workshop, pg 797
CP Communications, pg 837
Langie Audio Visual Systems, pg 915
Long Island Video Enterprises Live Inc, pg 924
Posthorn Recordings, pg 979
Specialized Audio-Visual Inc, pg 1020
TBA Global Events, pg 1032
Technisphere Corp, pg 1034
Visual Technologies Corp, pg 1060
WorldStage, pg 1070

NORTH CAROLINA

AV Metro Inc, pg 797
Camcor Inc, pg 818
Special Event Services, pg 1020
Strategic Connections, pg 1026
Take One Productions Ltd, pg 1031

OREGON

Rose City Sound, pg 999

PENNSYLVANIA

Advanced AV, pg 777
Audio Visual Communications Inc, pg 795
Grise Audio Visual Center Inc, pg 882
Production Solutions Inc, pg 985
Visual Sound Inc, pg 1059

TENNESSEE

Brantley Sound Associates Inc, pg 812
Mr Mark's Used Musical, Stereo & Studio Equipment Store, pg 944
Technical Support Systems LLC, pg 1034

TEXAS

FitzCo Sound Inc, pg 869
J&S Audio Visual Inc, pg 904
Music Lab Inc, pg 950

UTAH

Performance Audio, pg 973

VERMONT

Parlato Productions, pg 969

VIRGINIA

American AV, pg 783
Boitnott Visual Communications Corp (BVC), pg 810
Lee Hartman & Sons Inc, pg 918
Projection Presentation Technology, pg 985

WASHINGTON

D A Sound, pg 842
Inland Audio Visual Co, pg 898
Pacific Northwest Theatre Associates Inc (PNTA), pg 967

WEST VIRGINIA

United Sound & Electronics, pg 1048

WISCONSIN

Event Essentials, pg 863
Full Compass Systems, pg 874
Wisconsin Public Television, pg 1068

WYOMING

Bridger Productions Inc, pg 812

PUERTO RICO

Stage Crew Audiovisual Inc, pg 1022

BRITISH COLUMBIA

Clark's Audio Visual Services Ltd, pg 829
Commercial Electronics Ltd, pg 832
DL Sound & Lighting Productions Ltd, pg 849

MANITOBA

Inland Audio Visual Ltd, pg 898

ONTARIO

Edcom Multimedia Products, pg 856
Westbury National Show Systems Ltd, pg 1064

QUEBEC

Concept Audio-Visual, pg 834
Panavideo Inc, pg 968

Part & Accessory Repairs

CALIFORNIA

Ametron Audio/Video, pg 785
Audio Images Corp, pg 794
Alan Gordon Enterprises Inc, pg 880
McAlister Electronics, pg 935
Sound Service Co, pg 1017
TOA Electronics Inc, pg 1041
Towards 2000 Inc, pg 1043

CONNECTICUT

HB Communications Inc, pg 886
Rockwell Communications Inc, pg 998
Sennheiser Electronic Corp, pg 1006

FLORIDA

AMP Services Inc, pg 785
JT Communications, pg 906
Stereo Sales Inc, pg 1024

GEORGIA

Audio Visual Resources Inc, pg 795
Lighting & Production Equipment Inc, pg 920
Stage Front Presentation Systems, pg 1022
Technical Innovation, pg 1033

ILLINOIS

Allen Visual Systems Inc, pg 781
Midwest Digital Corp, pg 942

IOWA

ECS Inc, pg 856

KENTUCKY

NOR-COM Inc, pg 958

MAINE

Headlight Audio Visual Inc, pg 887

MARYLAND

RTZ Audio Visual, pg 1000

MICHIGAN

K&R's Recording Studios Inc, pg 908
Stedman Corp, pg 1024
TeL Systems, pg 1035

Phonograph Equipment & Supply Distributors

AUDIO

Phonograph Equipment & Supply Distributors (continued)

ONTARIO (continued)

Premier A/V Sales Ltd, pg 980
Westbury National Show Systems Ltd, pg 1064

QUEBEC

Concept Audio-Visual, pg 834
JAM Industries Ltd, pg 903

Phonograph Equipment & Supply Manufacturers

ARIZONA

Radio Design Labs (RDL), pg 990

CALIFORNIA

Califone International Inc, pg 817
The LAST Factory, pg 916
Nady Systems Inc, pg 952
Parasound Products Inc, pg 969
Sumiko Inc, pg 1028

IDAHO

Transtector Systems Inc, pg 1043

ILLINOIS

Esoteric Sound, pg 862
LKG Industries Inc, pg 923
Shure Inc, pg 1010
SOTA Sales & Service Center, pg 1016

INDIANA

Klipsch Audio Technologies, pg 912

NEW JERSEY

National Audio-Visual Supply, pg 952
Pro-Tape & Specialities Inc, pg 983
Technics, pg 1034

NEW YORK

GLI Sound Systems, pg 878
Harbro Corp, pg 884
Music Hall LLC, pg 950
Russell Industries Inc, pg 1001

OHIO

Audio-Technica US Inc, pg 794

TENNESSEE

Stanton Magnetics, pg 1023

UTAH

Rolls Corp, pg 999

Phonograph Equipment & Supply Rentals

ARIZONA

Merestone, pg 938

CALIFORNIA

Ametron Audio/Video, pg 785
Audio Rents, pg 794
Instructional Materials & Equipment Distributors (I-Med), pg 899
McCune Audio-Video-Lighting, pg 935
Media Fabricators Inc, pg 936
Muse Presentation Technologies, pg 950
Randall Schiller Productions, pg 1004
Sound Service Co, pg 1017
Synthesizer Systems Technologies (SST), pg 1030
Towards 2000 Inc, pg 1043

COLORADO

Audio Consultant Services Inc, pg 794

CONNECTICUT

A/V Davey, pg 797
Videofilm Systems Inc, pg 1057

DELAWARE

Actors Attic, pg 775

FLORIDA

Pro Stage Inc, pg 983

GEORGIA

Audio Visual Resources Inc, pg 795
Lighting & Production Equipment Inc, pg 920
Staging Directions Inc, pg 1023

ILLINOIS

AV Chicago Inc, pg 797
Central Audio-Visual Equipment Inc, pg 823
On Stage Audio, pg 963

IOWA

ECS Inc, pg 856

KENTUCKY

Audio Visual Techniques Inc, pg 796

LOUISIANA

Pace Systems, pg 966

MARYLAND

Event Tech, pg 863
Nicholas P Pipino Associates Inc, pg 976
RTZ Audio Visual, pg 1000

MASSACHUSETTS

AVFX Inc, pg 798
massAV, pg 933
Preston Productions Inc, pg 981

MICHIGAN

City Events Group, pg 828
K&R All Media Productions Inc, pg 908
K&R's Recording Studios Inc, pg 908

MISSISSIPPI

Bowie Audio Visual Enterprises Inc, pg 811

MISSOURI

Image Technologies Corp, pg 895
Show-Me Audio-Visual, pg 1009
Swank Audio Visuals, pg 1029

NEW JERSEY

Starlite Productions, pg 1024
Video Corporation of America (VCA), pg 1055

NEW YORK

AV Workshop, pg 797
Dreamhire LLC, pg 852
Langie Audio Visual Systems, pg 915
Long Island Video Enterprises Live Inc, pg 924
Visual Technologies Corp, pg 1060

NORTH CAROLINA

Camcor Inc, pg 818
Special Event Services, pg 1020

OHIO

Audio Visual Media, pg 795

PENNSYLVANIA

Audio Visions Inc, pg 795
Grise Audio Visual Center Inc, pg 882
Production Solutions Inc, pg 985

TENNESSEE

Mr Mark's Used Musical, Stereo & Studio Equipment Store, pg 944
Technical Support Systems LLC, pg 1034
Tennessee Visual Service Co, pg 1037

TEXAS

Audio Visual Technologies Group, pg 796
Crossroads Audio Inc, pg 840
J&S Audio Visual Inc, pg 904
Lubbock Audio Visual Inc, pg 925
The Samuels Co, pg 1002
Stage Directions, pg 1022

UTAH

Performance Audio, pg 973
Webb Audio Visual Communication, pg 1063

VIRGINIA

American AV, pg 783
Lee Hartman & Sons Inc, pg 918
Rainbow Rentals, pg 991

WASHINGTON

Inland Audio Visual Co, pg 898

WEST VIRGINIA

United Sound & Electronics, pg 1048

WISCONSIN

Event Essentials, pg 863
Full Compass Systems, pg 874

BRITISH COLUMBIA

Commercial Electronics Ltd, pg 832

MANITOBA

Inland Audio Visual Ltd, pg 898

ONTARIO

Westbury National Show Systems Ltd, pg 1064

QUEBEC

Concept Audio-Visual, pg 834

Phonograph Equipment & Supply Repairs

CALIFORNIA

Ametron Audio/Video, pg 785
Audio Images Corp, pg 794
Instructional Materials & Equipment Distributors (I-Med), pg 899
McAlister Electronics, pg 935
Randall Schiller Productions, pg 1004
Sound Service Co, pg 1017
Towards 2000 Inc, pg 1043
Yamaha Electronics Corp, pg 1071

CONNECTICUT

HB Communications Inc, pg 886

FLORIDA

JT Communications, pg 906
Stereo Sales Inc, pg 1024

GEORGIA

Audio Visual Resources Inc, pg 795
Lighting & Production Equipment Inc, pg 920
Technical Innovation, pg 1033

IOWA

ECS Inc, pg 856

KANSAS

KK Office Solutions Inc, pg 911

KENTUCKY

Barney Miller's Inc, pg 943
NOR-COM Inc, pg 958

MARYLAND

Nicholas P Pipino Associates Inc, pg 976
RTZ Audio Visual, pg 1000
Strauss Photo Technical Service Inc, pg 1026

MICHIGAN

City Events Group, pg 828
K&R's Recording Studios Inc, pg 908
TeL Systems, pg 1035

MISSISSIPPI

Bowie Audio Visual Enterprises Inc, pg 811

NEW JERSEY

Starlite Productions, pg 1024

NEW YORK

Colortone Audio Visual, pg 832
Langie Audio Visual Systems, pg 915

Player & Recorder Distributors

AUDIO

Player & Recorder Distributors (continued)

NEW YORK (continued)

Visual Technologies Corp, pg 1060
Willoughby's Imaging Center, pg 1067

NORTH CAROLINA

Camcor Inc, pg 818
Strategic Connections, pg 1026

OHIO

Audio Visual Media, pg 795
Copp Integrated Systems, pg 836
Icom Multimedia, pg 893
ITA Audio Visual Solutions, pg 902
Twin Sisters Productions LLC, pg 1047

OREGON

Spectrum Systems Design, pg 1021

PENNSYLVANIA

Advanced AV, pg 777
Brodart Co, pg 813
Clair Brothers Audio Systems Inc, pg 829
J E Foss Co, pg 871
Garcia Marketing Inc, pg 875
Grise Audio Visual Center Inc, pg 882
The Lerro Corp, pg 919
Morefield Communications Inc, pg 946
Visual Sound Inc, pg 1059
Wespen Audio Visual Co, pg 1063

RHODE ISLAND

Custom Computer Specialists Inc, pg 841

TENNESSEE

Continental Film, pg 835
Lowrance Sound Co Inc, pg 925
Memphis Communications Corp, pg 938
Mr Mark's Used Musical, Stereo & Studio Equipment Store, pg 944
Technical Support Systems LLC, pg 1034
Tennessee Visual Service Co, pg 1037
Zion Music Group, pg 1074

TEXAS

Audio Visual Technologies Group, pg 796
AVES Audio Visual Systems Inc, pg 798
CAM Audio Inc, pg 817
Crossroads Audio Inc, pg 840
Data Projections Inc, pg 843
Heffernan Audio Visual, pg 887
J&S Audio Visual Inc, pg 904
Lex Lawson Associates, pg 917
Lubbock Audio Visual Inc, pg 925
Pro Video & Film Equipment Co Inc, pg 983
RadioShack Corp, pg 990
Schoolhouse Audio Visual, pg 1004
Stage Directions, pg 1022
Tarpley Media Systems, pg 1032

UTAH

Performance Audio, pg 973
RIA Corp, pg 996
Webb Audio Visual Communication, pg 1063

VIRGINIA

Boitnott Visual Communications Corp (BVC), pg 810
Intellidyne LLC, pg 899
Lee Hartman & Sons Inc, pg 918
The Whitlock Group, pg 1065

WASHINGTON

CCI Solutions, pg 821
Inland Audio Visual Co, pg 898

WEST VIRGINIA

United Sound & Electronics, pg 1048

WISCONSIN

Audio Visual of Milwaukee Inc, pg 795
Camera Corner Connecting Point, pg 818
Demco Inc, pg 845
Full Compass Systems, pg 874
School Specialty Inc, pg 1004

PUERTO RICO

Bonnin Electronics Inc, pg 810

ALBERTA

McBain Audio Visual Ltd, pg 935
Unique Communications Ltd, pg 1048

MANITOBA

Advance Pro, pg 777
Evolution Presentation Technologies, pg 863
Inland Audio Visual Ltd, pg 898

ONTARIO

Edcom Multimedia Products, pg 856
HD Source, pg 886
Nationwide Audio Visual Co, pg 953
Premier A/V Sales Ltd, pg 980
Technovision® Interactive Inc, pg 1035
Westbury National Show Systems Ltd, pg 1064

QUEBEC

AVS Technologies Inc, pg 800
Concept Audio-Visual, pg 834
JAM Industries Ltd, pg 903

Player & Recorder Manufacturers

CALIFORNIA

Califone International Inc, pg 817
Eiki International, pg 858
Gilderfluke & Co Inc, pg 878
Mackenzie Laboratories Inc, pg 927
Panasonic Broadcast & Digital Systems Co, pg 968
Panasonic Professional Audio Systems, pg 968
Roland Corp US, pg 998
360 Systems, pg 1039
Yamaha Electronics Corp, pg 1071
Young Chang America, pg 1072

COLORADO

Arrakis Systems, pg 790

CONNECTICUT

Alarmco Intelligent Message Repeaters, pg 779
Vista Group International Inc, pg 1059

FLORIDA

Magna-Tech Electronic Co Inc, pg 928

ILLINOIS

AmpliVox Portable Sound Systems, pg 785

MICHIGAN

TeL Systems, pg 1035

MISSISSIPPI

Peavey Electronics Corp, pg 970

NEW JERSEY

Emerson Radio Corp, pg 860
National Audio-Visual Supply, pg 952
Panasonic Consumer Electronics Co, pg 968
Panasonic Corp, pg 968

NEW YORK

RCS Enterprises, pg 992
Recordex USA Inc, pg 993

SOUTH CAROLINA

Paso Sound Products Inc, pg 969

TENNESSEE

Adtec Digital Inc, pg 777

Player & Recorder Rentals

ALABAMA

Audio-Video Resources Inc, pg 795

ARIZONA

Arizona Cine Equipment, pg 789
Audio Video Resources, pg 795
Merestone, pg 938
Metropolitan Audio-Visual Inc, pg 940
Video Media Productions (VMP), pg 1055
Video West Inc, pg 1056

ARKANSAS

White Diamond Productions, pg 1065

CALIFORNIA

Absolute Rentals, pg 772
Alliant Event Services, pg 781
Ametron Audio/Video, pg 785
Artichoke Productions, pg 791
Associated Sound, pg 792
Audio Rents, pg 794
Big Time Picture Company Inc, pg 807
Cherry Multimedia, pg 824
Express Media Inc, pg 864
GMF Sound Inc, pg 879
Gold Standard Productions, pg 880
Golden Gate Studios, pg 880
Hollywood Sound Systems, pg 890
Instructional Materials & Equipment Distributors (I-Med), pg 899
LA Sound Co, pg 915
Location Sound Corp, pg 924
McCune Audio-Video-Lighting, pg 935
Media Fabricators Inc, pg 936
Mobilized Tech Systems, pg 944
Munday & Collins AV, pg 950
PSAV® Presentation Services, pg 986
Pyxis Industries Inc, pg 988
Alwin Sauers Audio Productions (ASAP), pg 1003
Randall Schiller Productions, pg 1004
Sound Service Co, pg 1017
Synthesizer Systems Technologies (SST), pg 1030
Towards 2000 Inc, pg 1043
University of Southern California, pg 1050
VER-Video Equipment Rentals, pg 1053
Warner Bros Production Sound & Video Services, pg 1062

COLORADO

Audio Consultant Services Inc, pg 794
Ceavco Audio/Visual Co, pg 822
Daylight Productions & Rentals, pg 844
Multimedia Audio Visual Inc, pg 950
Open Media Foundation, pg 964
Spectrum Audio Visual Services, pg 1020

CONNECTICUT

A/V Davey, pg 797
Concord Communications, pg 835
Rockwell Communications Inc, pg 998
Videofilm Systems Inc, pg 1057

DELAWARE

Showorks Audio Visual Inc, pg 1010
Side Door Studio Inc, pg 1010

FLORIDA

Access Media Group, pg 773
Accord Productions, pg 773
Allstar Audio Systems Inc, pg 782
Steven Cohen Motion Picture Production, pg 831
Gulf Coast Audio Visual Producers Inc, pg 883
Image Technical Services, pg 895
Media Concepts Inc, pg 936
Miami Daylight Studios, pg 941
Photosound of Orlando Inc, pg 975
Pro Stage Inc, pg 983
Sight & Sound Productions, pg 1010
TAI Audio, pg 1031
Tallahassee Audio Visual, pg 1031
Universal Studios Florida® Production Group, pg 1049

GEORGIA

Audio Visual Resources Inc, pg 795
Convergent Media Systems, pg 836
ECG Productions, pg 856
First Cut Communications LLC, pg 868

Lighting & Production Equipment Inc, pg 920
Stage Front Presentation Systems, pg 1022
Staging Directions Inc, pg 1023

HAWAII

Hawaii Sound & Vision, pg 886

ILLINOIS

Allen Visual Systems Inc, pg 781
Audio Visual Services Corp, pg 796
AV Chicago Inc, pg 797
Central Audio-Visual Equipment Inc, pg 823
Creative Technology, pg 838
Helix Camera & Video, pg 887
On Site Video, pg 963
On Stage Audio, pg 963
PSAV® Presentation Services (Hotel Services Division), pg 987
QuickSet International Inc, pg 989
RC Communications, pg 992
SCI Television Productions LLC, pg 1004
Woodside Avenue Music Productions Inc, pg 1069

INDIANA

Advanced Media Integration, pg 777
Gaither Studios LLC, pg 875
OMNI Productions, pg 962

IOWA

ECS Inc, pg 856

KENTUCKY

Audio Visual Techniques Inc, pg 796

MAINE

Headlight Audio Visual Inc, pg 887

MARYLAND

Cardinal Sound & Video, pg 820
CPR MultiMedia Solutions, pg 837
Event Tech, pg 863
Hargrove Inc, pg 885
Maryland Sound International Holding Co LLC, pg 933

MASSACHUSETTS

AVFX Inc, pg 798
Camera Co Inc/Broadcast Divison, pg 818
Capron Lighting & Sound Co Inc, pg 819
massAV, pg 933
Preston Productions Inc, pg 981
TR Productions, pg 1043

MICHIGAN

City Events Group, pg 828
K&R All Media Productions Inc, pg 908
K&R's Recording Studios Inc, pg 908
On Stage Visuals, pg 963
Technology Learning Services, pg 1035

MINNESOTA

Advanced Audio-Visual Inc, pg 777
Alpha Video & Audio Inc, pg 782
AVI Systems, pg 799

MISSISSIPPI

Bowie Audio Visual Enterprises Inc, pg 811

MISSOURI

Production Support Services Inc, pg 985
Show-Me Audio-Visual, pg 1009
Swank Audio Visuals, pg 1029

MONTANA

Jereco Studios Inc, pg 905

NEBRASKA

Dog & Pony Productions Inc, pg 850

NEVADA

GES Audio Visual, pg 877
Lefco Video Services Inc, pg 918
MG Studio, pg 940

NEW HAMPSHIRE

Academic & Campus Technology Services, pg 773
APS Lighting-Sound-AV, pg 789

NEW JERSEY

Audio Visual Associates, pg 795
Audio Visual Dynamics®, pg 795
Giant Audio Visual Inc, pg 878
International Audio Visual Inc, pg 900
PLS Staging, pg 977
Starlite Productions, pg 1024
Turner Engineering Inc, pg 1046

NEW YORK

Adwar Video, pg 778
American Video Inc, pg 785
Aura Sonic Ltd, pg 796
AV Workshop, pg 797
Bond Street Studio, pg 810
CMI Communications, pg 830
Colortone Audio Visual, pg 832
Communication Corner Inc, pg 832
CP Communications, pg 837
Dreamhire LLC, pg 852
Hello World Communications, pg 888
KVL Audio Visual Services Inc, pg 914
Langie Audio Visual Systems, pg 915
Long Island Video Enterprises Live Inc, pg 924
Manhattan Center Studios Inc, pg 930
Ray Supply Inc, pg 992
See Factor Industry Inc, pg 1006
SmartSource Computer & AV Rentals, pg 1014
Specialized Audio-Visual Inc, pg 1020
TBA Global Events, pg 1032
Technisphere Corp, pg 1034
Visual Technologies Corp, pg 1060
WorldStage, pg 1070

NORTH CAROLINA

A&V Company, pg 772
AV Metro Inc, pg 797
Camcor Inc, pg 818
Special Event Services, pg 1020
Strategic Connections, pg 1026
Take One Productions Ltd, pg 1031

NORTH DAKOTA

Media Productions, pg 937

OHIO

Audio Visual Media, pg 795
Icom Multimedia, pg 893
Vista Color Imaging Inc, pg 1059

OREGON

Picture This Production Services, pg 975

PENNSYLVANIA

Advanced AV, pg 777
Audio Visions Inc, pg 795
Audio Visual Communications Inc, pg 795
FMP Media Solutions Inc, pg 870
Grise Audio Visual Center Inc, pg 882
Production Solutions Inc, pg 985
Visual Sound Inc, pg 1059

TENNESSEE

Memphis Communications Corp, pg 938
Mr Mark's Used Musical, Stereo & Studio Equipment Store, pg 944
Technical Support Systems LLC, pg 1034
Tennessee Visual Service Co, pg 1037

TEXAS

Alford Media Services, pg 780
Astro Audio Visual, pg 792
Audio Visual Technologies Group, pg 796
Bright Giant Creative Group, pg 812
Crossroads Audio Inc, pg 840
Heffernan Audio Visual, pg 887
J&S Audio Visual Inc, pg 904
Lubbock Audio Visual Inc, pg 925
Omega Productions, pg 962
The Samuels Co, pg 1002
Stage Directions, pg 1022

UTAH

Performance Audio, pg 973
Webb Audio Visual Communication, pg 1063

VERMONT

Parlato Productions, pg 969

VIRGINIA

American AV, pg 783
Boitnott Visual Communications Corp (BVC), pg 810
D&B Television & Video Productions Inc, pg 842
Lee Hartman & Sons Inc, pg 918
Projection Presentation Technology, pg 985
Rainbow Rentals, pg 991
The Whitlock Group, pg 1065

WASHINGTON

Inland Audio Visual Co, pg 898
Pacific Northwest Theatre Associates Inc (PNTA), pg 967
Victory Studios, pg 1054

WEST VIRGINIA

United Sound & Electronics, pg 1048

WISCONSIN

Camera Corner Connecting Point, pg 818
Event Essentials, pg 863
Full Compass Systems, pg 874
School Specialty Inc, pg 1004
University of Wisconsin-Oshkosh Radio-TV-Film Dept, pg 1050
USAV Group Inc, pg 1050
Wisconsin Public Television, pg 1068

WYOMING

Bridger Productions Inc, pg 812

PUERTO RICO

Stage Crew Audiovisual Inc, pg 1022

ALBERTA

McBain Audio Visual Ltd, pg 935
Unique Communications Ltd, pg 1048

BRITISH COLUMBIA

Clark's Audio Visual Services Ltd, pg 829
Commercial Electronics Ltd, pg 832
DL Sound & Lighting Productions Ltd, pg 849
Finale Editworks, pg 868
MicrophoneRentals.com, pg 941
Video In Studios/Video Out Distribution, pg 1055

MANITOBA

Evolution Presentation Technologies, pg 863
Inland Audio Visual Ltd, pg 898

ONTARIO

Edcom Multimedia Products, pg 856
HD Source, pg 886
Premier A/V Sales Ltd, pg 980
SIM Digital, pg 1011
Westbury National Show Systems Ltd, pg 1064

QUEBEC

Audio Visual Dynamics Ltd, pg 795
AVW-TELAV Audio Visual Solutions, a Freeman Company, pg 800
Concept Audio-Visual, pg 834
Group PVP, pg 882

Player & Recorder Repairs

ARKANSAS

Jay S Stanley & Associates Inc, pg 1023

CALIFORNIA

ALC (Auernheimer Labs & Co), pg 780
Ametron Audio/Video, pg 785
Audio Images Corp, pg 794
Audio Upgrades, pg 795
Instructional Materials & Equipment Distributors (I-Med), pg 899
Location Sound Corp, pg 924
Martel Electronics Sales Inc, pg 932
McAlister Electronics, pg 935
Lloyd F McKinney Associates Inc, pg 935

AUDIO

Player & Recorder Repairs (continued)

CALIFORNIA (continued)

Randall Schiller Productions, pg 1004
Sound Service Co, pg 1017
SSL Industries Inc, pg 1022
Towards 2000 Inc, pg 1043
Yamaha Electronics Corp, pg 1071

COLORADO

Ceavco Audio/Visual Co, pg 822

CONNECTICUT

HB Communications Inc, pg 886
Rockwell Communications Inc, pg 998
Sennheiser Electronic Corp, pg 1006

FLORIDA

AMP Services Inc, pg 785
Hi-Tech Enterprises Inc, pg 888
JT Communications, pg 906
Phat Planet Recording Studios, pg 973
Stereo Sales Inc, pg 1024
TAI Audio, pg 1031
Tallahassee Audio Visual, pg 1031

GEORGIA

Audio Visual Resources Inc, pg 795
Lighting & Production Equipment Inc, pg 920
Stage Front Presentation Systems, pg 1022
Technical Innovation, pg 1033

ILLINOIS

Allen Visual Systems Inc, pg 781
Central Audio-Visual Equipment Inc, pg 823
Midwest Digital Corp, pg 942

INDIANA

Sweetwater Sound Inc, pg 1029

IOWA

ECS Inc, pg 856

KANSAS

KK Office Solutions Inc, pg 911

KENTUCKY

NOR-COM Inc, pg 958

MAINE

Headlight Audio Visual Inc, pg 887

MARYLAND

Cardinal Sound & Video, pg 820
RTZ Audio Visual, pg 1000
Strauss Photo Technical Service Inc, pg 1026

MASSACHUSETTS

Camera Co Inc/Broadcast Divison, pg 818
Capron Lighting & Sound Co Inc, pg 819
Professional Audio Design Inc, pg 985

MICHIGAN

City Events Group, pg 828
K&R's Recording Studios Inc, pg 908
TeL Systems, pg 1035

MINNESOTA

AVI Systems, pg 799

MISSISSIPPI

Bowie Audio Visual Enterprises Inc, pg 811

MISSOURI

Communitronics Corp, pg 833

NEW JERSEY

Starlite Productions, pg 1024
Turner Engineering Inc, pg 1046

NEW YORK

Adwar Video, pg 778
American Video Inc, pg 785
Colortone Audio Visual, pg 832
Langie Audio Visual Systems, pg 915
Ray Supply Inc, pg 992
Technisphere Corp, pg 1034
Visual Technologies Corp, pg 1060

NORTH CAROLINA

Camcor Inc, pg 818
Strategic Connections, pg 1026

OHIO

Audio Visual Media, pg 795
Copp Integrated Systems, pg 836
Icom Multimedia, pg 893

OREGON

All Service Musical Electronics Repair, pg 780

PENNSYLVANIA

J E Foss Co, pg 871
Visual Sound Inc, pg 1059
Wespen Audio Visual Co, pg 1063

RHODE ISLAND

Custom Computer Specialists Inc, pg 841

TENNESSEE

Memphis Communications Corp, pg 938
Technical Support Systems LLC, pg 1034
Tennessee Visual Service Co, pg 1037

TEXAS

Astro Audio Visual, pg 792
Audio Visual Technologies Group, pg 796
Heffernan Audio Visual, pg 887
Lubbock Audio Visual Inc, pg 925

VIRGINIA

Avitecture Inc, pg 799
Boitnott Visual Communications Corp (BVC), pg 810
Lee Hartman & Sons Inc, pg 918
The Whitlock Group, pg 1065

WASHINGTON

Inland Audio Visual Co, pg 898

WEST VIRGINIA

United Sound & Electronics, pg 1048

WISCONSIN

Camera Corner Connecting Point, pg 818
Full Compass Systems, pg 874
School Specialty Inc, pg 1004

PUERTO RICO

Bonnin Electronics Inc, pg 810

ALBERTA

Unique Communications Ltd, pg 1048

BRITISH COLUMBIA

Commercial Electronics Ltd, pg 832

MANITOBA

Evolution Presentation Technologies, pg 863
Inland Audio Visual Ltd, pg 898

ONTARIO

Edcom Multimedia Products, pg 856
Premier A/V Sales Ltd, pg 980
Technovision® Interactive Inc, pg 1035
Westbury National Show Systems Ltd, pg 1064

Popular Music, *see* Music Libraries—Popular

Portable Sound System, *see* Sound System—Portable

Public Address System Distributors

ALABAMA

Curtis Company, pg 841

ARIZONA

Arizona Cine Equipment, pg 789
EAR Professional Audio/Video, pg 855
Metropolitan Audio-Visual Inc, pg 940
Projector SuperStore LLC, pg 986
Troxell Communications Inc, pg 1045
Ultimate Presentation Systems Inc, pg 1047

ARKANSAS

Jay S Stanley & Associates Inc, pg 1023

CALIFORNIA

Ametron Audio/Video, pg 785
Associated Sound, pg 792
ATV Video Center Inc, pg 793
Audio Images Corp, pg 794
Be Media, pg 804
California Tape Products Inc, pg 817
Delicate Electronics Sales Inc, pg 845
Empire Wholesale Inc, pg 860
FXC Communications, pg 874
Hosa Technology Inc, pg 891
IAMP Professional Audio, pg 893
Instructional Materials & Equipment Distributors (I-Med), pg 899
Jaguar Distribution Corp, pg 903
JD Audio Visual Inc, pg 904
L Acoustics US, pg 914
Location Sound Corp, pg 924
Lloyd F McKinney Associates Inc, pg 935
MediaPOINTE, pg 938
Phonic Ear Inc (FrontRow), pg 974
QSC Audio Products LLC, pg 988
Related Visual Inc, pg 994
Randall Schiller Productions, pg 1004
Sonance, pg 1015
Sound Service Co, pg 1017
Sounds Unique, pg 1018
SSL Industries Inc, pg 1022
Stanislaus Audio Video Inc, pg 1023
TOA Electronics Inc, pg 1041
Towards 2000 Inc, pg 1043
VMI Inc, pg 1060

COLORADO

Audio Consultant Services Inc, pg 794
Spectrum Audio Visual Services, pg 1020

CONNECTICUT

Connecticut Audio & Theatrical Supply, pg 835
Everett Hall Associates Inc, pg 863
HB Communications Inc, pg 886

DELAWARE

Actors Attic, pg 775

FLORIDA

Allstar Audio Systems Inc, pg 782
BAI Distributors Inc, pg 801
Broadcasters General Store Inc, pg 813
Digital Video Systems Inc, pg 848
General Projection Systems Inc, pg 877
Gulf Coast Audio Visual Producers Inc, pg 883
Harmon's Audio-Visual Services, pg 885
Harris Corp, pg 885
Hi-Tech Import Export Corp, pg 888
Lighting Sales Connections, pg 920
Photomart Cine-Video Inc, pg 975
Pro Stage Inc, pg 983
Recording Media & Equipment Inc (RM&E), pg 993
Stereo Sales Inc, pg 1024
TAI Audio, pg 1031
Technomedia Solutions, pg 1035

GEORGIA

Baker Audio Inc, pg 801
Lighting & Production Equipment Inc, pg 920
Omnimedia Inc, pg 962
Stage Front Presentation Systems, pg 1022

Public Address System Manufacturers

AUDIO

Public Address System Manufacturers (continued)

ILLINOIS (continued)

Precision Electronics Inc, pg 980
Shure Inc, pg 1010
SoundTech, pg 1018

KANSAS

Galaxy Audio, pg 875
Speco/Systems & Products Engineering Co, pg 1020

MASSACHUSETTS

Bose Corp, pg 811
Technomad™ Inc, pg 1035

MINNESOTA

Digital Audio Labs, pg 847
Telex Communications Inc, pg 1037
Telex EVI, pg 1037

MISSISSIPPI

Peavey Electronics Corp, pg 970

NEBRASKA

REI - Radio Engineering Industries, pg 994

NEVADA

Pignose-Gorilla, pg 975

NEW JERSEY

Apogee Sound International LLC, pg 788
AV Bluebook, pg 797
Bogen Communications Inc, pg 810
Oklahoma Sound Corp, pg 961
Starlite Productions, pg 1024

NEW MEXICO

Lectrosonics Inc, pg 918

NEW YORK

Protech Audio Corp, pg 986

OREGON

BIAMP Systems, pg 806

PENNSYLVANIA

Community Professional Loudspeakers, pg 833

SOUTH CAROLINA

Paso Sound Products Inc, pg 969

TENNESSEE

Brantley Sound Associates Inc, pg 812
Cerwin-Vega! Inc, pg 823

UTAH

Aphex LLC, pg 788

VIRGINIA

Acoustics First Corp, pg 775

WASHINGTON

Aiphone Corp, pg 779
McCauley Sound Inc, pg 935

ONTARIO

KDM Electronics Inc, pg 908
Tannoy North America Inc, pg 1031

Public Address System Rentals

ALABAMA

Audio-Video Resources Inc, pg 795

ARIZONA

Arizona Cine Equipment, pg 789
Merestone, pg 938
Metropolitan Audio-Visual Inc, pg 940
Ultimate Presentation Systems Inc, pg 1047
Video West Inc, pg 1056

CALIFORNIA

Alliant Event Services, pg 781
Ametron Audio/Video, pg 785
Associated Sound, pg 792
ATV Video Center Inc, pg 793
Audio Rents, pg 794
AV Guys, pg 797
Dan Dugan Sound Design Inc, pg 853
Express Media Inc, pg 864
Fuller Street Productions, pg 874
IAMP Professional Audio, pg 893
Impact Group, pg 897
Instructional Materials & Equipment Distributors (I-Med), pg 899
JD Audio Visual Inc, pg 904
Location Sound Corp, pg 924
Lynch Communications, pg 926
Maximus Media Inc, pg 934
McCune Audio-Video-Lighting, pg 935
Munday & Collins AV, pg 950
Muse Presentation Technologies, pg 950
On-Trax Inc, pg 963
PSAV® Presentation Services, pg 986
Related Visual Inc, pg 994
Alwin Sauers Audio Productions (ASAP), pg 1003
Randall Schiller Productions, pg 1004
Slate Media Group, pg 1013
Sound Service Co, pg 1017
Stanislaus Audio Video Inc, pg 1023
The Studios at Paramount, pg 1027
Synthesizer Rental Service, pg 1030
Third Ear Sound Co, pg 1038
Towards 2000 Inc, pg 1043
Video Resources Inc, pg 1056
VMI Inc, pg 1060
Voice & Video Rentals, pg 1060
Westcoast Video Productions Inc, pg 1064

COLORADO

Audio Consultant Services Inc, pg 794
Daylight Productions & Rentals, pg 844
Multimedia Audio Visual Inc, pg 950
Spectrum Audio Visual Services, pg 1020

CONNECTICUT

A/V Davey, pg 797
Connecticut Audio & Theatrical Supply, pg 835
Everett Hall Associates Inc, pg 863

DELAWARE

Actors Attic, pg 775
Showorks Audio Visual Inc, pg 1010
Side Door Studio Inc, pg 1010

FLORIDA

Allstar Audio Systems Inc, pg 782
AVI-SPL, pg 798
Gulf Coast Audio Visual Producers Inc, pg 883
Harmon's Audio-Visual Services, pg 885
Image Technical Services, pg 895
Industrial Strength Inc, pg 897
Lighting Sales Connections, pg 920
Paradise Show & Design Inc, pg 969
Pro Stage Inc, pg 983
TAI Audio, pg 1031
Technomedia Solutions, pg 1035
Universal Studios Florida® Production Group, pg 1049

GEORGIA

Lighting & Production Equipment Inc, pg 920
MAGNUM Companies Ltd, pg 929
Stage Front Presentation Systems, pg 1022
Staging Directions Inc, pg 1023

HAWAII

Hawaii Sound & Vision, pg 886

ILLINOIS

Allen Visual Systems Inc, pg 781
AV Chicago Inc, pg 797
Beatty TeleVisual Productions, pg 804
Central Audio-Visual Equipment Inc, pg 823
Creative Technology, pg 838
C V Lloyde, pg 923
On Stage Audio, pg 963
QuickSet International Inc, pg 989
RC Communications, pg 992
SCI Television Productions LLC, pg 1004
Show Department Inc, pg 1009

IOWA

ECS Inc, pg 856

KENTUCKY

Audio Visual Techniques Inc, pg 796
Barney Miller's Inc, pg 943

LOUISIANA

Clark Services Audio Visual & Exhibit Inc, pg 829
Pace Systems, pg 966

MARYLAND

Advance Audiovisual Presentation Ltd, pg 777
Cardinal Sound & Video, pg 820
CPR MultiMedia Solutions, pg 837
CSPMedia.com, pg 840
Event Tech, pg 863
Hargrove Inc, pg 885
Shadowstone R & R™, pg 1008
Visual Aids Electronics Corp, pg 1059

MASSACHUSETTS

AVFX Inc, pg 798
Terry Hanley Audio Systems Inc, pg 884
massAV, pg 933
Preston Productions Inc, pg 981

MICHIGAN

Olson Anderson Co, pg 786
City Events Group, pg 828
Digi Sign Design LLC, pg 847
K&R All Media Productions Inc, pg 908
K&R's Recording Studios Inc, pg 908
On Stage Visuals, pg 963
TeL Systems, pg 1035

MINNESOTA

Advanced Audio-Visual Inc, pg 777
Big Event Productions LLC, pg 807
New Life Communications Inc, pg 956

MISSISSIPPI

Bowie Audio Visual Enterprises Inc, pg 811

MISSOURI

Communitronics Corp, pg 833
Production Support Services Inc, pg 985
Schiller's Audio-Visual, pg 1004
Show-Me Audio-Visual, pg 1009
Switch, pg 1030

NEW HAMPSHIRE

APS Lighting-Sound-AV, pg 789

NEW JERSEY

Audio Visual Associates, pg 795
Audio Visual Dynamics®, pg 795
Earl Girls Inc, pg 855
Giant Audio Visual Inc, pg 878
International Audio Visual Inc, pg 900
Moe AV LLC, pg 945
Nelson Enterprises Theatrical Supply Co, pg 954
PLS Staging, pg 977
SLD Lighting, pg 1013
Starlite Productions, pg 1024
Video Corporation of America (VCA), pg 1055
Wired 4 Sound Inc, pg 1068

NEW MEXICO

Quickbeam Systems Inc (QSI), pg 989

NEW YORK

Ace Video, pg 774
Audio Visual Resources LLC, pg 795
AV Workshop, pg 797
Colortone Audio Visual, pg 832
Communication Corner Inc, pg 832
CP Communications, pg 837
Design Audio Visual Inc, pg 845
Hello World Communications, pg 888
KVL Audio Visual Services Inc, pg 914

Public Address System Repairs

AUDIO

Public Address System Repairs (continued)

ALBERTA

Allstar Show Industries Inc, pg 782
Infosat Communications Inc, pg 898
Sharp's Audio-Visual Ltd, pg 1008
Unique Communications Ltd, pg 1048

BRITISH COLUMBIA

Commercial Electronics Ltd, pg 832

MANITOBA

Inland Audio Visual Ltd, pg 898

ONTARIO

Premier A/V Sales Ltd, pg 980
Westbury National Show Systems Ltd, pg 1064

Radio & Accessory Equipment Distributors

ALABAMA

Media Visions Inc, pg 937

ARIZONA

Coustic Car Audio, pg 837
Troxell Communications Inc, pg 1045
WindTech™ Microphone Windscreens & Accessories, pg 1067

ARKANSAS

White Diamond Productions, pg 1065

CALIFORNIA

Ametron Audio/Video, pg 785
Audio Images Corp, pg 794
Educational Technology Services (ETS), pg 857
FXC Communications, pg 874
Jaguar Distribution Corp, pg 903
MediaPOINTE, pg 938
PROTOCOL, pg 986
Sound Service Co, pg 1017
Southern California Sound Image Inc, pg 1019
Towards 2000 Inc, pg 1043

COLORADO

Audio Consultant Services Inc, pg 794
Stanco Sales LLC, pg 1023

CONNECTICUT

Sennheiser Electronic Corp, pg 1006

DELAWARE

Actors Attic, pg 775
HiFi House, pg 888

FLORIDA

Allstar Audio Systems Inc, pg 782
Broadcasters General Store Inc, pg 813
Harris Corp, pg 885
Hi-Tech Import Export Corp, pg 888
Photomart Cine-Video Inc, pg 975
Recording Media & Equipment Inc (RM&E), pg 993
Stereo Sales Inc, pg 1024
TAI Audio, pg 1031

GEORGIA

Lighting & Production Equipment Inc, pg 920
Stage Front Presentation Systems, pg 1022
Technical Innovation, pg 1033

ILLINOIS

Joseph Electronics, pg 906
Production Intercom Inc, pg 984
RC Communications, pg 992

INDIANA

Sensory Technologies LLC, pg 1006

IOWA

ECS Inc, pg 856

KANSAS

Smith Audio-Visual Inc, pg 1014

KENTUCKY

Axxis Inc, pg 800
Barney Miller's Inc, pg 943
NOR-COM Inc, pg 958

MAINE

Independent Audio Inc, pg 897

MARYLAND

Bradley Broadcast & Pro Audio, pg 811
Cardinal Sound & Video, pg 820
RTZ Audio Visual, pg 1000

MINNESOTA

Advanced Audio-Visual Inc, pg 777

MISSOURI

Image Technologies Corp, pg 895

NEW HAMPSHIRE

Technet® Systems Group, pg 1033

NEW JERSEY

Alltec Stores, a Vcom IMC Company, pg 782
AV Bluebook, pg 797
FlagHouse, pg 869
National Audio-Visual Supply, pg 952
Starlite Productions, pg 1024
Tele-Measurements Inc, pg 1035
Turner Engineering Inc, pg 1046
Video Corporation of America (VCA), pg 1055
Wired 4 Sound Inc, pg 1068

NEW YORK

Audiovox, pg 796
Centennial Electric Sound Co Ltd, pg 822
Custom Media Environments, pg 841
Indigo Productions, pg 897
Langie Audio Visual Systems, pg 915
NorthCountry Distributors, pg 959
Production Radio Rentals Inc, pg 984
Ray Supply Inc, pg 992
RNJ Electronics, pg 997
SmartSource Computer & AV Rentals, pg 1014
Technisphere Corp, pg 1034
Visual Technologies Corp, pg 1060

NORTH CAROLINA

Camcor Inc, pg 818
Strategic Connections, pg 1026

OHIO

Universal Radio Inc, pg 1049

OREGON

Frontier Communications Corp, pg 873

PENNSYLVANIA

Advanced AV, pg 777
The Lerro Corp, pg 919
Morefield Communications Inc, pg 946

TENNESSEE

Lowrance Sound Co Inc, pg 925
Technical Support Systems LLC, pg 1034

TEXAS

Crossroads Audio Inc, pg 840
Lubbock Audio Visual Inc, pg 925
RadioShack Corp, pg 990
RF Specialties of Texas LLC, pg 996
Schoolhouse Audio Visual, pg 1004
Sundance Systems, Fibox Products Division, pg 1028

UTAH

Performance Audio, pg 973
Webb Audio Visual Communication, pg 1063

VIRGINIA

Lee Hartman & Sons Inc, pg 918
Old Dominion Broadcasting, pg 961
Schafer World Communications Corp, pg 1004

WEST VIRGINIA

United Sound & Electronics, pg 1048

WISCONSIN

Audio Visual of Milwaukee Inc, pg 795
Camera Corner Connecting Point, pg 818
Full Compass Systems, pg 874

PUERTO RICO

Bonnin Electronics Inc, pg 810

ALBERTA

Infosat Communications Inc, pg 898

MANITOBA

Advance Pro, pg 777
Inland Audio Visual Ltd, pg 898

ONTARIO

Applied Electronics Ltd, pg 788
Nationwide Audio Visual Co, pg 953
Premier A/V Sales Ltd, pg 980
Westbury National Show Systems Ltd, pg 1064

QUEBEC

Concept Audio-Visual, pg 834

Radio & Accessory Equipment Manufacturers

ARIZONA

Eagle Inc, pg 855
WindTech™ Microphone Windscreens & Accessories, pg 1067

ARKANSAS

Autogram/Crl, pg 797

CALIFORNIA

Fanon Courier, pg 865
Magnum Towers Inc, pg 929
Nady Systems Inc, pg 952
Panasonic Professional Audio Systems, pg 968
TeachLogic Inc, pg 1033
TFT Inc, pg 1038

CONNECTICUT

Earmark LLC, pg 855
Harman International Industries Inc, pg 885
Sennheiser Electronic Corp, pg 1006

FLORIDA

CircuitWerkes Inc, pg 828
JT Communications, pg 906
Sonar Radio Corp, pg 1015

IDAHO

Marketron Broadcast Solutions, pg 931
Transtector Systems Inc, pg 1043

ILLINOIS

Broadcast Electronics, pg 813
J K Audio Inc, pg 903
Kart-A-Bag Manufacturing Inc, pg 908
Marti Electronics Inc, pg 932
Production Intercom Inc, pg 984
Switchcraft® Inc, pg 1030

INDIANA

Auralex Acoustics Inc, pg 796
Star Case Manufacturing Co Inc, pg 1023

MAINE

Dielectric Communications, pg 846

MASSACHUSETTS

David Clark Co Inc, pg 843

NEBRASKA

REI - Radio Engineering Industries, pg 994

NEW JERSEY

ATI Audio, pg 793
Modulation Sciences Inc, pg 945
Panasonic Consumer Electronics Co, pg 968
Pioneer Research Inc, pg 976
Techflex Inc, pg 1033
Technics, pg 1034
Turner Engineering Inc, pg 1046

NEW YORK

Production Radio Rentals Inc, pg 984
RCS Enterprises, pg 992

NORTH CAROLINA

LBA Technology Inc, pg 917

PENNSYLVANIA

Belar Electronics Laboratory Inc, pg 804
Wireless Xcessories Group Inc, pg 1068

TEXAS

Setcom Corp™, pg 1007
Sundance Systems, Fibox Products Division, pg 1028

UTAH

Aphex LLC, pg 788
Rolls Corp, pg 999

ONTARIO

DW Electrochemicals Ltd, pg 854
McCurdy Radio Ltd, pg 935

Radio & Accessory Equipment Rentals

ARIZONA

Arizona Cine Equipment, pg 789
Merestone, pg 938
Metropolitan Audio-Visual Inc, pg 940

ARKANSAS

White Diamond Productions, pg 1065

CALIFORNIA

Alliant Event Services, pg 781
Ametron Audio/Video, pg 785
Audio Rents, pg 794
AV Guys, pg 797
Golden Gate Studios, pg 880
Munday & Collins AV, pg 950
PROTOCOL, pg 986
PSAV® Presentation Services, pg 986
Sound Service Co, pg 1017
Towards 2000 Inc, pg 1043
Videorama Industries LLC, pg 1057

COLORADO

Audio Consultant Services Inc, pg 794

CONNECTICUT

A/V Davey, pg 797
Videofilm Systems Inc, pg 1057

FLORIDA

Allstar Audio Systems Inc, pg 782
Image Technical Services, pg 895
TAI Audio, pg 1031

GEORGIA

Lighting & Production Equipment Inc, pg 920
Stage Front Presentation Systems, pg 1022
Staging Directions Inc, pg 1023

ILLINOIS

AV Chicago Inc, pg 797
On Stage Audio, pg 963
RC Communications, pg 992
Show Department Inc, pg 1009

IOWA

ECS Inc, pg 856

KENTUCKY

Audio Visual Techniques Inc, pg 796

MARYLAND

Event Tech, pg 863
RTZ Audio Visual, pg 1000
Shadowstone R & R™, pg 1008
Visual Aids Electronics Corp, pg 1059

MASSACHUSETTS

Capron Lighting & Sound Co Inc, pg 819
massAV, pg 933
Preston Productions Inc, pg 981

MICHIGAN

K&R All Media Productions Inc, pg 908
K&R's Recording Studios Inc, pg 908
Lowing Light & Grip Inc, pg 925

MINNESOTA

Advanced Audio-Visual Inc, pg 777

MISSOURI

Image Technologies Corp, pg 895
Show-Me Audio-Visual, pg 1009
Swank Audio Visuals, pg 1029

NEW JERSEY

Audio Visual Dynamics®, pg 795
PLS Staging, pg 977
Starlite Productions, pg 1024

NEW YORK

Ace Video, pg 774
Big Foot Productions Inc, pg 807
CP Communications, pg 837
Hello World Communications, pg 888
Production Radio Rentals Inc, pg 984
SmartSource Computer & AV Rentals, pg 1014
Specialized Audio-Visual Inc, pg 1020
TBA Global Events, pg 1032
Technisphere Corp, pg 1034
Visual Technologies Corp, pg 1060
Xtech Inc, pg 1071

NORTH CAROLINA

A&V Company, pg 772
Camcor Inc, pg 818
Special Event Services, pg 1020
Strategic Connections, pg 1026

NORTH DAKOTA

Media Productions, pg 937

PENNSYLVANIA

Advanced AV, pg 777
Production Solutions Inc, pg 985

TENNESSEE

Technical Support Systems LLC, pg 1034

TEXAS

Crossroads Audio Inc, pg 840
GEAR Cameras & Lighting, pg 876
Lubbock Audio Visual Inc, pg 925
The Samuels Co, pg 1002

UTAH

Performance Audio, pg 973

VERMONT

Parlato Productions, pg 969

VIRGINIA

American AV, pg 783
Lee Hartman & Sons Inc, pg 918
Projection Presentation Technology, pg 985
Rainbow Rentals, pg 991
Schafer World Communications Corp, pg 1004

WEST VIRGINIA

United Sound & Electronics, pg 1048

WISCONSIN

Event Essentials, pg 863

BRITISH COLUMBIA

Clark's Audio Visual Services Ltd, pg 829
MicrophoneRentals.com, pg 941

MANITOBA

Inland Audio Visual Ltd, pg 898

ONTARIO

Westbury National Show Systems Ltd, pg 1064

QUEBEC

Concept Audio-Visual, pg 834

Radio & Accessory Equipment Repairs

ALABAMA

Media Visions Inc, pg 937

CALIFORNIA

Ametron Audio/Video, pg 785
Audio Images Corp, pg 794
McAlister Electronics, pg 935
PROTOCOL, pg 986
Sound Service Co, pg 1017
Towards 2000 Inc, pg 1043

CONNECTICUT

Earmark LLC, pg 855
HB Communications Inc, pg 886
Videofilm Systems Inc, pg 1057

FLORIDA

JT Communications, pg 906
Stereo Sales Inc, pg 1024
TAI Audio, pg 1031

GEORGIA

Audio Visual Resources Inc, pg 795
Lighting & Production Equipment Inc, pg 920
Stage Front Presentation Systems, pg 1022
Technical Innovation, pg 1033

ILLINOIS

Midwest Digital Corp, pg 942

IOWA

ECS Inc, pg 856

KENTUCKY

Axxis Inc, pg 800
Barney Miller's Inc, pg 943
NOR-COM Inc, pg 958

MARYLAND

RTZ Audio Visual, pg 1000
Visual Aids Electronics Corp, pg 1059

MICHIGAN

K&R's Recording Studios Inc, pg 908
TeL Systems, pg 1035

NEW JERSEY

Starlite Productions, pg 1024

NEW YORK

Langie Audio Visual Systems, pg 915
Visual Technologies Corp, pg 1060
Xtech Inc, pg 1071

NORTH CAROLINA

Camcor Inc, pg 818
Strategic Connections, pg 1026

OREGON

All Service Musical Electronics Repair, pg 780
Frontier Communications Corp, pg 873

TENNESSEE

Technical Support Systems LLC, pg 1034

TEXAS

Audio Visual Technologies Group, pg 796
Lubbock Audio Visual Inc, pg 925

VIRGINIA

Lee Hartman & Sons Inc, pg 918
Old Dominion Broadcasting, pg 961
Schafer World Communications Corp, pg 1004

AUDIO

Radio & Accessory Equipment Repairs (continued)

WEST VIRGINIA

United Sound & Electronics, pg 1048

WISCONSIN

Full Compass Systems, pg 874

PUERTO RICO

Bonnin Electronics Inc, pg 810

ALBERTA

Infosat Communications Inc, pg 898

MANITOBA

Inland Audio Visual Ltd, pg 898

ONTARIO

Westbury National Show Systems Ltd, pg 1064

Rap Music, *see* Music Libraries—Rap

Record Mastering

ARIZONA

Allusion Studios & Pure Wave Audio, pg 782
Fire Power Music Inc, pg 868
Merestone, pg 938

CALIFORNIA

AB Audio Visual Entertainment Inc, pg 772
ACDC Audio CD & Cassette, pg 774
AM Productions, pg 783
The Annex, pg 787
Audio Mechanics, pg 794
Audio Upgrades, pg 795
Berkeley Sound Artists Inc, pg 805
Christian Media Network, pg 825
Custom Video Productions Inc, pg 841
Different Fur Recording Ltd, pg 846
Digital Jungle, pg 847
5 Alarm Music, pg 869
JDS Video & Media Productions Inc, pg 904
K2B2 Records, pg 907
KVIE-Channel 6, pg 914
Lynch Communications, pg 926
On-Trax Inc, pg 963
Private Island Trax, pg 982
Pyramind Studios, pg 988
QRS Software Services, pg 988
Saturn Studios, pg 1003
SonicPool, pg 1016
Studio 132, pg 1027
Timeless Productions, pg 1040
Todd-AO Studios, pg 1041
Total Media Group, pg 1042
Trac Record Co & Recording Studio, pg 1043
WalkerVision Interarts, pg 1061

COLORADO

Airshow Mastering, pg 779
Tim Cissell Music, pg 828
Clear Gravy Productions, pg 829
Daylight Productions & Rentals, pg 844
Rocky Mountain Audio/Video Productions Inc, pg 998
Side 3 Studios, pg 1010

CONNECTICUT

American Melody, pg 784
BRB Audiovisual Productions, pg 812
Ironik Design & Post, pg 902

FLORIDA

Global Video Distributors Inc, pg 879
Morrisound Recording, pg 946
Phat Planet Recording Studios, pg 973
Progressive Media & Music, pg 985
Sunfire Communications Inc, pg 1028

GEORGIA

Hottrax Records, pg 891
Stage Front Presentation Systems, pg 1022

HAWAII

KHNL/KGMB, pg 910
Media Bridge Gamekids, pg 936

ILLINOIS

RBR Productions, pg 992
Sound/Video Impressions Inc, pg 1018
Southern Illinois University, pg 1019
Woodside Avenue Music Productions Inc, pg 1069

INDIANA

AVA Productions, pg 798
Bright Ideas Creative Services, pg 812
Alan Johnson Recording, pg 905
Optical Disc Solutions Inc, pg 964
Sweetwater Sound Inc, pg 1029

MARYLAND

The Cutting Corp, pg 841
dbF a Media Company, pg 844
Omega Recording Studios, pg 962
Pro Cuts Editing Services, pg 982
Smolian Sound Studios, pg 1014

MASSACHUSETTS

M Works Mastering Studios, pg 927
Northeastern Digital Recording Inc, pg 959
Soundtrack Recording Studios, pg 1018
TR Productions, pg 1043

MICHIGAN

Brilliance Audio, pg 812
The Brookwood Studio Inc, pg 814
Digi Sign Design LLC, pg 847
K&R's Recording Studios Inc, pg 908
Studio A Recording Inc, pg 1026

MINNESOTA

The ADS Group, pg 777
Aggressive Records Audio Duplication LLC, pg 778
Beyers Sound & Essay Audio, pg 806
Winterland Studios, pg 1068

MISSOURI

Show-Me Audio-Visual, pg 1009
Studio Worx Inc, pg 1027

MONTANA

Jereco Studios Inc, pg 905

NEW JERSEY

CFP Video Productions Inc, pg 823
Milgrom Productions, pg 943
Oasis CD Manufacturing, pg 960
Suede Interactive, pg 1027

NEW YORK

Aura Sonic Ltd, pg 796
Big Fish Productions Inc, pg 807
The Big House Group, pg 807
Communication Corner Inc, pg 832
Digital Force, pg 847
Eastco Multimedia Solutions Inc, pg 856
Fingerpaint, pg 868
Foothill Digital Inc, pg 871
HB-Content, pg 886
Masterdisk Corp, pg 933
Mother West, pg 947
Now Hear This, pg 960
Posthorn Recordings, pg 979
Sony Music Entertainment, pg 1016
TBA Global Events, pg 1032

NORTH CAROLINA

Pat Appleson Studios Inc, pg 788
Duke Media Services, pg 853
Studio B Mastering, pg 1026

NORTH DAKOTA

Media Productions, pg 937

OHIO

Lyon Video Inc, pg 927
Mills James Productions, pg 943
Musicol Recording, pg 951

PENNSYLVANIA

American Artist Studio, pg 783
Audio Visual Communications Inc, pg 795
Ivory Productions, pg 903
Javboy Records, pg 904
JPL, pg 906
Right Coast Recording Inc, pg 997

RHODE ISLAND

Sound-FX-Design, pg 1017

TENNESSEE

American Blackguard Inc, pg 784
Analog Man Recording Studio, pg 786
Ardent Music LLC, pg 789
Ardent Studios Inc, pg 789
Cupit Music Group, pg 841
Durrell LLC, pg 854
Green Dot Audio Electronics, pg 882
JamSync, pg 904
Love Shack Recording Studios, pg 925
Motion Picture Services, pg 947
Stage Post, pg 1022
Zion Music Group, pg 1074

TEXAS

Audiomoxie®, pg 796
Digital Services Recording Studios, pg 848
Fire Station Studios, pg 868
Harbor House Studios, pg 884
Phillips MediaSource, pg 974
Planet Dallas Recording Studios, pg 976
The Samuels Co, pg 1002
The Sound Lab Inc, pg 1017
Stage Directions, pg 1022
TopCat Records LLC, pg 1042
World Beat Studio, pg 1069

VIRGINIA

Furnace MFG, pg 874
Lion Recording Services Inc, pg 922
Metro Productions, pg 939

WASHINGTON

Jake Barner Studio, pg 803
Sound Sound/Savage Fruitarian Productions, pg 1017

WISCONSIN

Concept Productions Inc, pg 834
5th Floor Recording Co, pg 867
Sound Strations Audio Productions Inc, pg 1017
Video Wisconsin Inc, pg 1056

BRITISH COLUMBIA

Triad Communications Ltd, pg 1044

MANITOBA

daCapo Productions, pg 842

ONTARIO

ADS Media, pg 777
GAPC (General Assembly Production Centre), pg 875
JL Recording Studios, pg 905
Legendary Entertainment, pg 918
MCS Recording Studios, pg 936
Metalworks Recording Studios Inc, pg 939
Phase One Studios, pg 973
The Pocket Studios, pg 977
VO2 Mix Studios, pg 1060
Westbury National Show Systems Ltd, pg 1064

Record Pressing

ARIZONA

Merestone, pg 938

CALIFORNIA

Audio Upgrades, pg 795
Christian Media Network, pg 825
Lynch Communications, pg 926
QRS Software Services, pg 988
Saturn Studios, pg 1003

FLORIDA

Global Video Distributors Inc, pg 879
Sunfire Communications Inc, pg 1028

HAWAII

Media Bridge Gamekids, pg 936

INDIANA

Sweetwater Sound Inc, pg 1029
World Media Group Inc, pg 1069

MASSACHUSETTS

M Works Mastering Studios, pg 927

MICHIGAN

Brilliance Audio, pg 812
Digi Sign Design LLC, pg 847
GMP Music, pg 879
K&R's Recording Studios Inc, pg 908

MINNESOTA

The ADS Group, pg 777

NEW JERSEY

Suede Interactive, pg 1027

NEW YORK

Now Hear This, pg 960
Sony Music Entertainment, pg 1016
TBA Global Events, pg 1032

OHIO

Musicol Recording, pg 951

PENNSYLVANIA

American Artist Studio, pg 783

TENNESSEE

Stage Post, pg 1022

TEXAS

The Samuels Co, pg 1002
TopCat Records LLC, pg 1042

VIRGINIA

Lion Recording Services Inc, pg 922

ONTARIO

Music Manufacturing Services, pg 950
The Pocket Studios, pg 977

Recorder & Player, *see* Player & Recorder

Recording, *see* Sound Recording

Recording Equipment Distributors

ARIZONA

Allusion Studios & Pure Wave Audio, pg 782
Arizona Cine Equipment, pg 789
ATCi (Antenna Technology Communication Solutions Inc), pg 793
Audio Video Resources, pg 795
EAR Professional Audio/Video, pg 855
Metropolitan Audio-Visual Inc, pg 940
Troxell Communications Inc, pg 1045

ARKANSAS

White Diamond Productions, pg 1065

CALIFORNIA

Advanced Systems Group LLC, pg 778
American Music & Sound (AM&S), pg 785
Ametron Audio/Video, pg 785
Audio Images Corp, pg 794
Empire Wholesale Inc, pg 860
FXC Communications, pg 874
GigaSonic, pg 878
Instructional Materials & Equipment Distributors (I-Med), pg 899
JD Audio Visual Inc, pg 904
Location Sound Corp, pg 924
Media Fabricators Inc, pg 936
MediaPOINTE, pg 938
Professional Sound Corp, pg 985
RF Specialties of California Inc, pg 995
Randall Schiller Productions, pg 1004
SNAP, pg 1014
Sound Service Co, pg 1017
Soundcraft USA, pg 1018
Southern California Sound Image Inc, pg 1019
SSL Industries Inc, pg 1022
TASCAM, pg 1032
Towards 2000 Inc, pg 1043
Tri-Ed, pg 1044
VTP Inc, pg 1061

COLORADO

Audio Consultant Services Inc, pg 794
Spectrum Audio Visual Services, pg 1020
Stanco Sales LLC, pg 1023

CONNECTICUT

Connecticut Audio & Theatrical Supply, pg 835
HB Communications Inc, pg 886
MAVCO, pg 934
The Music People Inc, pg 951
Sennheiser Electronic Corp, pg 1006

FLORIDA

Allstar Audio Systems Inc, pg 782
A2D Solutions Inc, pg 793
BAI Distributors Inc, pg 801
Broadcasters General Store Inc, pg 813
Digital Video Systems Inc, pg 848
Gulf Coast Audio Visual Producers Inc, pg 883
Harris Corp, pg 885
Hi-Tech Enterprises Inc, pg 888
Hi-Tech Import Export Corp, pg 888
Industrial Strength Inc, pg 897
Media Concepts Inc, pg 936
Midtown Video Inc, pg 942
Photomart Cine-Video Inc, pg 975
Photosound of Orlando Inc, pg 975
Pro Stage Inc, pg 983
Recording Media & Equipment Inc (RM&E), pg 993
Sight & Sound Productions, pg 1010
Stereo Sales Inc, pg 1024
TAI Audio, pg 1031
Tallahassee Audio Visual, pg 1031
Technomedia Solutions, pg 1035

GEORGIA

Baker Audio Inc, pg 801
Convergent Media Systems, pg 836
Lighting & Production Equipment Inc, pg 920
LT Sound Inc, pg 925
Stage Front Presentation Systems, pg 1022

HAWAII

The Audio Visual Co (AVCO), pg 795

ILLINOIS

Allen Visual Systems Inc, pg 781
Central Audio-Visual Equipment Inc, pg 823
Jay Jay Record & Tape Co, pg 904
C V Lloyde, pg 923
RAM Systems LLC, pg 991
Sound Vision Inc, pg 1018
Woodside Avenue Music Productions Inc, pg 1069

INDIANA

Sensory Technologies LLC, pg 1006
SHP Electronics, pg 1010
Sweetwater Sound Inc, pg 1029

IOWA

ECS Inc, pg 856

KANSAS

Smith Audio-Visual Inc, pg 1014

KENTUCKY

Axxis Inc, pg 800
Barney Miller's Inc, pg 943
NOR-COM Inc, pg 958
Northern Kentucky University, pg 959

MAINE

Independent Audio Inc, pg 897

MARYLAND

Bradley Broadcast & Pro Audio, pg 811
RTZ Audio Visual, pg 1000

MASSACHUSETTS

Avid Technology Inc, pg 799
Terry Hanley Audio Systems Inc, pg 884
Professional Audio Design Inc, pg 985

MICHIGAN

Ascom Communications Contractors, pg 791
City Events Group, pg 828
Digi Sign Design LLC, pg 847
On Stage Visuals, pg 963
TeL Systems, pg 1035

MINNESOTA

Advanced Audio-Visual Inc, pg 777
Alpha Video & Audio Inc, pg 782
AVI Systems, pg 799
Digital Audio Labs, pg 847

MISSISSIPPI

Bowie Audio Visual Enterprises Inc, pg 811

MISSOURI

Conference Technologies Inc, pg 835

NEBRASKA

Dog & Pony Productions Inc, pg 850

NEVADA

Midas Consoles North America, pg 942

NEW HAMPSHIRE

APS Lighting-Sound-AV, pg 789
Technet® Systems Group, pg 1033

NEW JERSEY

Alltec Stores, a Vcom IMC Company, pg 782
Audio Visual Associates, pg 795
Audio Visual Dynamics®, pg 795
AV Bluebook, pg 797
Comprehensive Cable & Connectivity Co, pg 833
Diversified Systems Inc, pg 849
Entel Systems Inc, pg 861
FlagHouse, pg 869
G&G Technologies Inc, pg 875
Hamilton Buhl, pg 884
The Music Place, pg 951
National Audio-Visual Supply, pg 952
PatchAmp, pg 970
Starlite Productions, pg 1024
Wired 4 Sound Inc, pg 1068
York Telecom, pg 1072

NEW YORK

Aura Sonic Ltd, pg 796
AV Workshop, pg 797
B&H Photo & Video Pro Audio, pg 802
Colortone Audio Visual, pg 832
Communication Corner Inc, pg 832
Design Audio Visual Inc, pg 845
Flash Electronics Inc, pg 869
Hot House Professional Audio, pg 891
Indigo Productions, pg 897
Korg USA Inc, pg 913
Long Island Video Enterprises Live Inc, pg 924
Mark Custom Recording Service Inc, pg 931
Markertek Video Supply, pg 931
Saul Mineroff Electronics Inc, pg 943
NorthCountry Distributors, pg 959
Posthorn Recordings, pg 979
RNJ Electronics, pg 997
Sanako Inc, pg 1002
Technisphere Corp, pg 1034
Visual Technologies Corp, pg 1060
Visual Word Systems Inc, pg 1060
Voyetra Turtle Beach, pg 1061
Willoughby's Imaging Center, pg 1067

NORTH CAROLINA

Camcor Inc, pg 818
Strategic Connections, pg 1026

OHIO

Copp Integrated Systems, pg 836
ITA Audio Visual Solutions, pg 902
The Little Warehouse Inc, pg 923
Jimmy Rea Electronics Inc, pg 992
Tri-State Audio Visual Co, pg 1044

AUDIO

Recording Equipment Distributors (continued)

OREGON

ASC-Tube Trap, pg 791
SuperDigital Ltd, pg 1029

PENNSYLVANIA

Advanced AV, pg 777
Audio Visions Inc, pg 795
Innovision Media Group, pg 899
Morefield Communications Inc, pg 946
Vistacom Inc, pg 1059
Visual Sound Inc, pg 1059

RHODE ISLAND

Akai Professional, pg 779
Custom Computer Specialists Inc, pg 841
M-Audio, pg 927

SOUTH CAROLINA

DaviSound, pg 843

TENNESSEE

Durrell LLC, pg 854
Lowrance Sound Co Inc, pg 925
Mr Mark's Used Musical, Stereo & Studio Equipment Store, pg 944
Technical Support Systems LLC, pg 1034
Trew Audio Inc, pg 1044
Zion Music Group, pg 1074

TEXAS

Audio Visual Technologies Group, pg 796
AVES Audio Visual Systems Inc, pg 798
CAM Audio Inc, pg 817
Crossroads Audio Inc, pg 840
FitzCo Sound Inc, pg 869
Heffernan Audio Visual, pg 887
J&S Audio Visual Inc, pg 904
Lubbock Audio Visual Inc, pg 925
Precision Camera & Video, pg 980
Pro Video & Film Equipment Co Inc, pg 983
RadioShack Corp, pg 990
Schoolhouse Audio Visual, pg 1004
Stage Directions, pg 1022
Sundance Systems, Fibox Products Division, pg 1028
TapeWorks Texas Inc, pg 1032
Tarpley Media Systems, pg 1032

UTAH

DigiTech, pg 848
Performance Audio, pg 973
RIA Corp, pg 996
Webb Audio Visual Communication, pg 1063

VIRGINIA

Avitecture Inc, pg 799
Boitnott Visual Communications Corp (BVC), pg 810
Communications Specialists Inc, pg 833
Hoppmann Audio Visual, pg 891
Intellidyne LLC, pg 899
Lee Hartman & Sons Inc, pg 918
Old Dominion Broadcasting, pg 961
Schafer World Communications Corp, pg 1004
The Whitlock Group, pg 1065

WASHINGTON

Broadcast Supply World Wide, pg 813
CCI Solutions, pg 821
Northern Lights & Pro Audio, pg 959

WEST VIRGINIA

United Sound & Electronics, pg 1048

WISCONSIN

Audio Visual of Milwaukee Inc, pg 795
Camera Corner Connecting Point, pg 818
Full Compass Systems, pg 874
Safe Harbor Computers, pg 1001

PUERTO RICO

Bonnin Electronics Inc, pg 810

ALBERTA

Infosat Communications Inc, pg 898
McBain Audio Visual Ltd, pg 935
Sharp's Audio-Visual Ltd, pg 1008
Unique Communications Ltd, pg 1048

BRITISH COLUMBIA

ADI Systems Inc, pg 776
Commercial Electronics Ltd, pg 832
ProVision Video Sales & Rentals Inc, pg 986
Radial Engineering Ltd, pg 990

MANITOBA

Advance Pro, pg 777
Inland Audio Visual Ltd, pg 898

ONTARIO

Edcom Multimedia Products, pg 856
HD Source, pg 886
Henry's Camera, pg 888
Nationwide Audio Visual Co, pg 953
Sascom Marketing Group Inc, pg 1003
SVAT Electronics, pg 1029
Westbury National Show Systems Ltd, pg 1064

QUEBEC

Concept Audio-Visual, pg 834
JAM Industries Ltd, pg 903

Recording Equipment Manufacturers

ARIZONA

Orban, pg 965

CALIFORNIA

American Music & Sound (AM&S), pg 785
Antex Electronics Corp, pg 787
Audio Upgrades, pg 795
Dolby Labs Inc, pg 850
Dorrough Electronics Inc, pg 851
Furman, pg 874
Henry Engineering, pg 888
Jensen Transformers Inc, pg 905
Lynx Studio Technology Inc, pg 927
Mackenzie Laboratories Inc, pg 927
Manley Laboratories Inc, pg 930
Martinsound Inc, pg 932
Newdoll Enterprises LLC, pg 956
ODC Nimbus Inc, pg 961
Opamp Labs Inc, pg 964
Panasonic Broadcast & Digital Systems Co, pg 968
Roland Corp US, pg 998
Simon - Kaloi Engineering, pg 1011
Sony Electronics Inc, pg 1016
Soundcraft USA, pg 1018
TASCAM, pg 1032
360 Systems, pg 1039

COLORADO

Arrakis Systems, pg 790

CONNECTICUT

Sennheiser Electronic Corp, pg 1006

FLORIDA

Magna-Tech Electronic Co Inc, pg 928

GEORGIA

LT Sound Inc, pg 925
Register Data Systems, pg 994

ILLINOIS

Bag End Loudspeakers, pg 801
Superscope Technologies Inc, pg 1029

INDIANA

Auralex Acoustics Inc, pg 796

MASSACHUSETTS

Avid Technology Inc, pg 799

MINNESOTA

Digital Audio Labs, pg 847
Great River Electronics, pg 881
Telex Communications Inc, pg 1037

MISSISSIPPI

Peavey Electronics Corp, pg 970

NEW JERSEY

National Audio-Visual Supply, pg 952
Wireworks Corp, pg 1068

NEW YORK

ART (Applied Research & Technology Inc), pg 791
Ashly Audio Inc, pg 792
MultiDyne Video & Fiber Optics Systems, pg 950
Posthorn Recordings, pg 979
RCS Enterprises, pg 992
Voyetra Turtle Beach, pg 1061

OREGON

ASC-Tube Trap, pg 791

PENNSYLVANIA

D W Fearn, pg 866
Right Coast Recording Inc, pg 997

RHODE ISLAND

Akai Professional, pg 779
M-Audio, pg 927

SOUTH CAROLINA

DaviSound, pg 843

TENNESSEE

Audio Media Productions, pg 794

TEXAS

Sundance Systems, Fibox Products Division, pg 1028

UTAH

Aphex LLC, pg 788
dbx Professional Products, pg 844
DigiTech, pg 848
Spectra Sonics Applied Technology Inc, pg 1020

WASHINGTON

Conex Electro-Systems Inc, pg 835

BRITISH COLUMBIA

Creation Technologies Inc, pg 838
Radial Engineering Ltd, pg 990

ONTARIO

SVAT Electronics, pg 1029

Recording Equipment Rentals

ALABAMA

Airwave Recording Studio, pg 779
Audio-Video Resources Inc, pg 795
Media Visions Inc, pg 937

ARIZONA

Arizona Cine Equipment, pg 789
Audio Video Resources, pg 795
Broadcast Rentals, pg 813
Merestone, pg 938
Metropolitan Audio-Visual Inc, pg 940
Video Media Productions (VMP), pg 1055

ARKANSAS

White Diamond Productions, pg 1065

CALIFORNIA

Absolute Rentals, pg 772
Advanced Media LLC, pg 778
AGF Media Services, pg 778
Ametron Audio/Video, pg 785
The Annex, pg 787
Artichoke Productions, pg 791
ATV Video Center Inc, pg 793
Audio Rents, pg 794
Balboa Capital Corp, pg 802
Chater Camera Inc, pg 824
Design FX Audio, pg 845
Express Media Inc, pg 864
FJ Productions Inc, pg 869
FXC Communications, pg 874
Gold Standard Productions, pg 880
Golden Gate Studios, pg 880
Imagecraft Productions, pg 896
JD Audio Visual Inc, pg 904
Location Sound Corp, pg 924
Maximus Media Inc, pg 934

AUDIO

Recording Equipment Rentals (continued)

TEXAS (continued)

Stage Directions, pg 1022
Tropikal Productions, pg 1045

UTAH

Ron Hill Imagery, pg 889
Performance Audio, pg 973
Webb Audio Visual Communication, pg 1063

VERMONT

Edgewood Studios, pg 857
Parlato Productions, pg 969

VIRGINIA

American AV, pg 783
Audio Visual Actions Inc (AVA), pg 795
Boitnott Visual Communications Corp (BVC), pg 810
D&B Television & Video Productions Inc, pg 842
Projection Presentation Technology, pg 985
Schafer World Communications Corp, pg 1004
The Whitlock Group, pg 1065

WASHINGTON

Northern Lights & Pro Audio, pg 959
Victory Studios, pg 1054

WEST VIRGINIA

United Sound & Electronics, pg 1048

WISCONSIN

Audio Visual of Milwaukee Inc, pg 795
Event Essentials, pg 863
Full Compass Systems, pg 874
University of Wisconsin-Oshkosh Radio-TV-Film Dept, pg 1050
USAV Group Inc, pg 1050
Wisconsin Public Television, pg 1068

WYOMING

Bridger Productions Inc, pg 812

PUERTO RICO

Stage Crew Audiovisual Inc, pg 1022

ALBERTA

Allstar Show Industries Inc, pg 782
McBain Audio Visual Ltd, pg 935
Sharp's Audio-Visual Ltd, pg 1008
Unique Communications Ltd, pg 1048

BRITISH COLUMBIA

Clark's Audio Visual Services Ltd, pg 829
Commercial Electronics Ltd, pg 832
Finale Editworks, pg 868
Image Media Farm, pg 895
MicrophoneRentals.com, pg 941
ProVision Video Sales & Rentals Inc, pg 986

MANITOBA

Inland Audio Visual Ltd, pg 898

ONTARIO

Boxcar Studio, pg 811
Edcom Multimedia Products, pg 856
GAPC (General Assembly Production Centre), pg 875
HD Source, pg 886
Phase One Studios, pg 973
RB Productions, pg 992
VO2 Mix Studios, pg 1060
Westbury National Show Systems Ltd, pg 1064

QUEBEC

Audio Visual Dynamics Ltd, pg 795
AVW-TELAV Audio Visual Solutions, a Freeman Company, pg 800
Group PVP, pg 882

Recording Equipment Repairs

ALABAMA

Media Visions Inc, pg 937

CALIFORNIA

Advanced Media LLC, pg 778
Audio Images Corp, pg 794
Audio Upgrades, pg 795
Diemer Amp & Keyboard Repair, pg 846
FXC Communications, pg 874
Location Sound Corp, pg 924
McAlister Electronics, pg 935
Randall Schiller Productions, pg 1004
Sound Service Co, pg 1017
SSL Industries Inc, pg 1022
Towards 2000 Inc, pg 1043

CONNECTICUT

HB Communications Inc, pg 886
Sennheiser Electronic Corp, pg 1006

FLORIDA

AMP Services Inc, pg 785
Digital Video Systems Inc, pg 848
Hi-Tech Enterprises Inc, pg 888
JT Communications, pg 906
Midtown Video Inc, pg 942
Phat Planet Recording Studios, pg 973
Stereo Sales Inc, pg 1024
TAI Audio, pg 1031
Tallahassee Audio Visual, pg 1031

GEORGIA

Lighting & Production Equipment Inc, pg 920
Stage Front Presentation Systems, pg 1022

ILLINOIS

Allen Visual Systems Inc, pg 781
Beatty TeleVisual Productions, pg 804
C V Lloyde, pg 923
Midwest Digital Corp, pg 942
On Site Video, pg 963

INDIANA

SHP Electronics, pg 1010

IOWA

ECS Inc, pg 856

KENTUCKY

Axxis Inc, pg 800
Barney Miller's Inc, pg 943
NOR-COM Inc, pg 958

MARYLAND

RTZ Audio Visual, pg 1000
Visual Aids Electronics Corp, pg 1059

MASSACHUSETTS

Capron Lighting & Sound Co Inc, pg 819
Professional Audio Design Inc, pg 985

MICHIGAN

City Events Group, pg 828
K&R's Recording Studios Inc, pg 908
On Stage Visuals, pg 963
TeL Systems, pg 1035

MINNESOTA

AVI Systems, pg 799

NEW JERSEY

JRF Magnetic Sciences Inc, pg 906
The Music Place, pg 951
Starlite Productions, pg 1024

NEW YORK

Design Audio Visual Inc, pg 845
Visual Technologies Corp, pg 1060

NORTH CAROLINA

Camcor Inc, pg 818

OHIO

Copp Integrated Systems, pg 836
Tri-State Audio Visual Co, pg 1044

OREGON

All Service Musical Electronics Repair, pg 780

PENNSYLVANIA

Right Coast Recording Inc, pg 997
Vistacom Inc, pg 1059

RHODE ISLAND

Custom Computer Specialists Inc, pg 841

SOUTH CAROLINA

DaviSound, pg 843

TENNESSEE

Durrell LLC, pg 854
Technical Support Systems LLC, pg 1034
Trew Audio Inc, pg 1044

TEXAS

Astro Audio Visual, pg 792
Lubbock Audio Visual Inc, pg 925
Pro Video & Film Equipment Co Inc, pg 983
Tarpley Media Systems, pg 1032

UTAH

Spectra Sonics Applied Technology Inc, pg 1020

VIRGINIA

Boitnott Visual Communications Corp (BVC), pg 810
Hoppmann Audio Visual, pg 891
Intellidyne LLC, pg 899
Old Dominion Broadcasting, pg 961
Schafer World Communications Corp, pg 1004
The Whitlock Group, pg 1065

WASHINGTON

Northern Lights & Pro Audio, pg 959

WEST VIRGINIA

United Sound & Electronics, pg 1048

WISCONSIN

Audio Visual of Milwaukee Inc, pg 795
Camera Corner Connecting Point, pg 818
Full Compass Systems, pg 874

PUERTO RICO

Bonnin Electronics Inc, pg 810

ALBERTA

Allstar Show Industries Inc, pg 782
Infosat Communications Inc, pg 898
Sharp's Audio-Visual Ltd, pg 1008
Unique Communications Ltd, pg 1048

BRITISH COLUMBIA

Commercial Electronics Ltd, pg 832

MANITOBA

Inland Audio Visual Ltd, pg 898

ONTARIO

Edcom Multimedia Products, pg 856
Westbury National Show Systems Ltd, pg 1064

Recording Equipment—Magnetic, *see* Magnetic Recording Equipment

Recording Facility Manufacturers

CALIFORNIA

Ametron Audio/Video, pg 785
The Banquet Sound Studios, pg 802
Martinsound Inc, pg 932
QRS Software Services, pg 988
Westlake Recording Studios, pg 1064
Yanchar Design & Consulting Group, pg 1072

COLORADO

Arrakis Systems, pg 790

AUDIO

Recording Facility Rentals (continued)

NORTH CAROLINA

Duke Media Services, pg 853
Evolve Inc, pg 863
Media-Comm, pg 936
Take One Productions Ltd, pg 1031

NORTH DAKOTA

Media Productions, pg 937

OHIO

EDR Media LLC, pg 857
Icom Multimedia, pg 893
Lyon Video Inc, pg 927
Mills James Productions, pg 943
OSV Studios, pg 966
Vista Color Imaging Inc, pg 1059

OKLAHOMA

PDC Productions, pg 970

OREGON

BingoLewis, pg 807
Intersect Video, pg 901

PENNSYLVANIA

American Artist Studio, pg 783
Audio Visual Communications Inc, pg 795
Canadian American Records, pg 818
Dreambox Media Inc, pg 852
Innovision Media Group, pg 899
Ivory Productions, pg 903
Javboy Records, pg 904
JPL, pg 906
Robin Miller, Filmaker Inc, pg 943
Right Coast Recording Inc, pg 997
Visual Sound Inc, pg 1059
WHYY Inc, pg 1066
WQED-Multimedia, pg 1070

SOUTH CAROLINA

DaviSound, pg 843

TENNESSEE

Ardent Music LLC, pg 789
Brantley Sound Associates Inc, pg 812
Continental Film, pg 835
Cupit Music Group, pg 841
Durrell LLC, pg 854
Love Shack Recording Studios, pg 925
Mellow Hollow Studio, pg 938
Mr Mark's Used Musical, Stereo & Studio Equipment Store, pg 944
OMNISound Recording Studio, pg 963
Technical Support Systems LLC, pg 1034
University of Memphis, Music Industry Division, pg 1050
Zion Music Group, pg 1074

TEXAS

Digital Services Recording Studios, pg 848
Fire Station Studios, pg 868
Music Lab Inc, pg 950
Omega Productions, pg 962
Out of the BLUE Media, pg 966
Phillips MediaSource, pg 974
Real to Reel Studios Inc, pg 992
Reelsound Recording Co, pg 994
Replicopy Digital Media Center, pg 995
The Sound Lab Inc, pg 1017
Stage Directions, pg 1022
TM Studios Inc, pg 1041
Tropikal Productions, pg 1045

UTAH

Ron Hill Imagery, pg 889
Performance Audio, pg 973

VERMONT

Edgewood Studios, pg 857

VIRGINIA

Advance Concepts Inc, pg 777
Video Solutions, pg 1056

WASHINGTON

Avast! Recording Co, pg 798
Inland Audio Visual Co, pg 898
Victory Studios, pg 1054

WISCONSIN

Audio Visual of Milwaukee Inc, pg 795
5th Floor Recording Co, pg 867
Sound Strations Audio Productions Inc, pg 1017
TBC Studios, pg 1033
University of Wisconsin-Oshkosh Radio-TV-Film Dept, pg 1050
USAV Group Inc, pg 1050
Wisconsin Public Television, pg 1068

WYOMING

Bridger Productions Inc, pg 812

ALBERTA

Black Media Works, pg 808
Global Television Station, pg 879

BRITISH COLUMBIA

Finale Editworks, pg 868
Image Media Farm, pg 895
The Vocal Point/Profile Communications Ltd, pg 1060

ONTARIO

ADS Media, pg 777
GAPC (General Assembly Production Centre), pg 875
Phase One Studios, pg 973
The Pocket Studios, pg 977
Purefire Communications Inc, pg 987
VO2 Mix Studios, pg 1060

Recording Facility Repairs

ALABAMA

Media Visions Inc, pg 937

CALIFORNIA

Audio Images Corp, pg 794
Audio Upgrades, pg 795
McAlister Electronics, pg 935
SSL Industries Inc, pg 1022

CONNECTICUT

HB Communications Inc, pg 886

FLORIDA

Phat Planet Recording Studios, pg 973
Stereo Sales Inc, pg 1024

GEORGIA

Stage Front Presentation Systems, pg 1022

ILLINOIS

Midwest Digital Corp, pg 942

IOWA

ECS Inc, pg 856

KENTUCKY

NOR-COM Inc, pg 958

MASSACHUSETTS

Professional Audio Design Inc, pg 985

MICHIGAN

City Events Group, pg 828
K&R's Recording Studios Inc, pg 908
Studio Consulting & Construction Inc, pg 1026
TeL Systems, pg 1035

NEW JERSEY

Radio Visions, pg 990
Starlite Productions, pg 1024

PENNSYLVANIA

Audio Visual Communications Inc, pg 795
Right Coast Recording Inc, pg 997

TENNESSEE

Durrell LLC, pg 854

TEXAS

Pro Video & Film Equipment Co Inc, pg 983
The Sound Lab Inc, pg 1017

WISCONSIN

Audio Visual of Milwaukee Inc, pg 795
Full Compass Systems, pg 874

Rehearsal Studio Distributors

CALIFORNIA

Kris Stevens Enterprises, pg 1024

Rehearsal Studio Manufacturers

Ametron Audio/Video, pg 785
Yanchar Design & Consulting Group, pg 1072

MARYLAND

RPG Diffusor Systems Inc, pg 1000

NEW YORK

CP Communications, pg 837
IAC Acoustics, pg 893

OHIO

Soundfold International, pg 1018

TEXAS

L'AIR International, pg 914

VIRGINIA

Acoustics First Corp, pg 775

Rehearsal Studio Rentals

ALABAMA

Airwave Recording Studio, pg 779

ARIZONA

Merestone, pg 938

CALIFORNIA

Adolph Gasser Inc, pg 776
Ametron Audio/Video, pg 785
Chapman/Leonard Studios & Production Center, pg 824
Full Moon & High Tide Productions & Studios, pg 874
Golden Gate Studios, pg 880
Lynch Communications, pg 926
Still N'Motion, pg 1025
Studio 637, pg 1027
Total Media Group, pg 1042
Towards 2000 Inc, pg 1043

COLORADO

Clear Gravy Productions, pg 829
Daylight Productions & Rentals, pg 844

CONNECTICUT

Trod Nossel Productions & Recording Studios, pg 1045

DELAWARE

Side Door Studio Inc, pg 1010

FLORIDA

CopShopMiami.com, pg 836
Jordan Klein Film & Video (JKFV), pg 906
National Teleproductions Inc, pg 953
Phat Planet Recording Studios, pg 973
South Florida Rehearsal Studios, pg 1019
Style-City Music Inc, pg 1027
Mike Vasilinda Productions Inc, pg 1052

GEORGIA

Convergent Media Systems, pg 836
Lighting & Production Equipment Inc, pg 920
Stage Front Presentation Systems, pg 1022
Staging Directions Inc, pg 1023

ILLINOIS

On Stage Audio, pg 963
QuickSet International Inc, pg 989
Roadworthy Image Magnification, pg 998
Show Department Inc, pg 1009
Woodside Avenue Music Productions Inc, pg 1069

INDIANA

Sweetwater Sound Inc, pg 1029

IOWA

ECS Inc, pg 856

LOUISIANA

Independent Studios, pg 897

MARYLAND

CPR MultiMedia Solutions, pg 837
Sheffield Audio/Video Productions, pg 1008

MASSACHUSETTS

Preston Productions Inc, pg 981

MICHIGAN

Brilliance Audio, pg 812
City Events Group, pg 828
Digi Sign Design LLC, pg 847
K&R All Media Productions Inc, pg 908
K&R's Recording Studios Inc, pg 908

MINNESOTA

Aggressive Records Audio Duplication LLC, pg 778

MISSOURI

Show-Me Audio-Visual, pg 1009
Swank Audio Visuals, pg 1029

NEW JERSEY

Audio Visual Dynamics®, pg 795
Color Leasing Studios, pg 831
MIB Mediaworks, pg 941

NEW YORK

Big Foot Productions Inc, pg 807
Manhattan Center Studios Inc, pg 930
Shelly Palmer Production, pg 968
Sony Music Entertainment, pg 1016
Studio Instrument Rentals (SIR), pg 1027
TBA Global Events, pg 1032
Universal Rehearsal, pg 1049
Videograf, pg 1057

NORTH CAROLINA

Duke Media Services, pg 853
Take One Productions Ltd, pg 1031

NORTH DAKOTA

Media Productions, pg 937

OHIO

Bartha, pg 803
EDR Media LLC, pg 857
Vista Color Imaging Inc, pg 1059

PENNSYLVANIA

Innovision Media Group, pg 899
WHYY Inc, pg 1066

SOUTH CAROLINA

DaviSound, pg 843

TENNESSEE

Ardent Music LLC, pg 789
Durrell LLC, pg 854

Mr Mark's Used Musical, Stereo & Studio Equipment Store, pg 944
Technical Support Systems LLC, pg 1034

TEXAS

Fire Station Studios, pg 868
Music Lab Inc, pg 950
South Coast Film & Video, pg 1019
Stage Directions, pg 1022

UTAH

Performance Audio, pg 973

VERMONT

Edgewood Studios, pg 857

WASHINGTON

Victory Studios, pg 1054

WISCONSIN

TBC Studios, pg 1033
USAV Group Inc, pg 1050
Wisconsin Public Television, pg 1068

WYOMING

Bridger Productions Inc, pg 812

ALBERTA

Global Television Station, pg 879

BRITISH COLUMBIA

Video In Studios/Video Out Distribution, pg 1055

ONTARIO

Purefire Communications Inc, pg 987

Rehearsal Studio Repairs

CALIFORNIA

Audio Images Corp, pg 794
McAlister Electronics, pg 935

CONNECTICUT

HB Communications Inc, pg 886

FLORIDA

Stereo Sales Inc, pg 1024

GEORGIA

Stage Front Presentation Systems, pg 1022

ILLINOIS

Midwest Digital Corp, pg 942

IOWA

ECS Inc, pg 856

KENTUCKY

NOR-COM Inc, pg 958

MICHIGAN

K&R's Recording Studios Inc, pg 908
TeL Systems, pg 1035

NEW JERSEY

Starlite Productions, pg 1024

TENNESSEE

Durrell LLC, pg 854

TEXAS

Pro Video & Film Equipment Co Inc, pg 983

Repetitive Tape Equipment Distributors

ARIZONA

Arizona Cine Equipment, pg 789

ARKANSAS

Jay S Stanley & Associates Inc, pg 1023

CALIFORNIA

Ametron Audio/Video, pg 785
Media Fabricators Inc, pg 936
MediaPOINTE, pg 938
Kris Stevens Enterprises, pg 1024

CONNECTICUT

Concord Communications, pg 835
MAVCO, pg 934

DELAWARE

Actors Attic, pg 775

FLORIDA

Hi-Tech Import Export Corp, pg 888
Recording Media & Equipment Inc (RM&E), pg 993
Stereo Sales Inc, pg 1024
TAI Audio, pg 1031

GEORGIA

Baker Audio Inc, pg 801
Stage Front Presentation Systems, pg 1022
Visioneering International Inc, pg 1058

ILLINOIS

Major Reproductions Equipment Co, pg 929

INDIANA

Sensory Technologies LLC, pg 1006

IOWA

ECS Inc, pg 856

KANSAS

Smith Audio-Visual Inc, pg 1014

KENTUCKY

NOR-COM Inc, pg 958

MARYLAND

Bradley Broadcast & Pro Audio, pg 811
Visual Aids Electronics Corp, pg 1059

MICHIGAN

City Events Group, pg 828
TeL Systems, pg 1035

MISSISSIPPI

Jasper Ewing & Sons Inc, pg 864

MISSOURI

Swank Audio Visuals, pg 1029

NEW JERSEY

Audio Visual Dynamics®, pg 795
G&G Technologies Inc, pg 875
Hamilton Buhl, pg 884
Starlite Productions, pg 1024

NEW YORK

Design Audio Visual Inc, pg 845
Indigo Productions, pg 897
MRG Productions Inc, pg 948
Visual Technologies Corp, pg 1060
Willoughby's Imaging Center, pg 1067

NORTH CAROLINA

Strategic Connections, pg 1026

PENNSYLVANIA

Advanced AV, pg 777
Morefield Communications Inc, pg 946

TENNESSEE

Continental Film, pg 835
Lowrance Sound Co Inc, pg 925
Tennessee Visual Service Co, pg 1037

TEXAS

Audio Visual Technologies Group, pg 796
Heffernan Audio Visual, pg 887
J&S Audio Visual Inc, pg 904
Lubbock Audio Visual Inc, pg 925
Schoolhouse Audio Visual, pg 1004

UTAH

Performance Audio, pg 973

WISCONSIN

Audio Visual of Milwaukee Inc, pg 795
Demco Inc, pg 845
Full Compass Systems, pg 874

PUERTO RICO

Bonnin Electronics Inc, pg 810

MANITOBA

Advance Pro, pg 777
Inland Audio Visual Ltd, pg 898

ONTARIO

Nationwide Audio Visual Co, pg 953

QUEBEC

Concept Audio-Visual, pg 834

Repetitive Tape Equipment Manufacturers

CALIFORNIA

Mackenzie Laboratories Inc, pg 927

AUDIO

Repetitive Tape Equipment Manufacturers (continued)

NEW YORK

Clever Devices Ltd, pg 830
MultiDyne Video & Fiber Optics Systems, pg 950

Repetitive Tape Equipment Rentals

ARIZONA

Arizona Cine Equipment, pg 789
Metropolitan Audio-Visual Inc, pg 940

CALIFORNIA

Ametron Audio/Video, pg 785
Lynch Communications, pg 926
Media Fabricators Inc, pg 936

CONNECTICUT

Concord Communications, pg 835

GEORGIA

Stage Front Presentation Systems, pg 1022
Staging Directions Inc, pg 1023

ILLINOIS

On Stage Audio, pg 963

IOWA

ECS Inc, pg 856

KENTUCKY

Audio Visual Techniques Inc, pg 796

MASSACHUSETTS

massAV, pg 933
Preston Productions Inc, pg 981

MICHIGAN

City Events Group, pg 828
K&R All Media Productions Inc, pg 908
K&R's Recording Studios Inc, pg 908

MISSOURI

Swank Audio Visuals, pg 1029

NEW JERSEY

Audio Visual Dynamics®, pg 795
Starlite Productions, pg 1024

NEW YORK

Design Audio Visual Inc, pg 845
Dreamhire LLC, pg 852
TBA Global Events, pg 1032
Visual Technologies Corp, pg 1060

NORTH CAROLINA

Strategic Connections, pg 1026

TEXAS

J&S Audio Visual Inc, pg 904
Lubbock Audio Visual Inc, pg 925

UTAH

Performance Audio, pg 973

VIRGINIA

American AV, pg 783
Projection Presentation Technology, pg 985

WISCONSIN

Audio Visual of Milwaukee Inc, pg 795

BRITISH COLUMBIA

Clark's Audio Visual Services Ltd, pg 829

MANITOBA

Inland Audio Visual Ltd, pg 898

ONTARIO

Edcom Multimedia Products, pg 856
VO2 Mix Studios, pg 1060

QUEBEC

Concept Audio-Visual, pg 834

Repetitive Tape Equipment Repairs

CALIFORNIA

Ametron Audio/Video, pg 785
Audio Images Corp, pg 794
Audio Upgrades, pg 795
McAlister Electronics, pg 935

CONNECTICUT

HB Communications Inc, pg 886

FLORIDA

Stereo Sales Inc, pg 1024

GEORGIA

Stage Front Presentation Systems, pg 1022

IOWA

ECS Inc, pg 856

KENTUCKY

NOR-COM Inc, pg 958

MICHIGAN

City Events Group, pg 828
K&R's Recording Studios Inc, pg 908
TeL Systems, pg 1035

NEW JERSEY

Starlite Productions, pg 1024

NEW YORK

Visual Technologies Corp, pg 1060

OREGON

All Service Musical Electronics Repair, pg 780

TEXAS

Audio Visual Technologies Group, pg 796
Lubbock Audio Visual Inc, pg 925

WISCONSIN

Audio Visual of Milwaukee Inc, pg 795
Full Compass Systems, pg 874

MANITOBA

Inland Audio Visual Ltd, pg 898

Rhythm & Blues Music, *see* Music Libraries—Rhythm & Blues

Rock Music, *see* Music Libraries—Rock

Sampling

ALABAMA

Dogwood Recording Studios, pg 850

ARIZONA

Merestone, pg 938

CALIFORNIA

Aliso Creek Productions Inc, pg 780
Artichoke Productions, pg 791
Bruce Chianese, pg 824
Diamond Dreams Music Productions, pg 846
Earwax Productions Inc, pg 855
Eye & I Productions, pg 864
Ilio Enterprises LLC, pg 894
Lynch Communications, pg 926
Maximus Media Inc, pg 934
Pyramind Studios, pg 988
QRS Software Services, pg 988
Reality Check Systems, pg 992
Saturn Studios, pg 1003
Steve Shapiro Music, pg 1008
Studio 132, pg 1027
Timeless Productions, pg 1040
Total Media Group, pg 1042

COLORADO

Tim Cissell Music, pg 828
Colorado Sound Recording Studios, pg 831
Conly Productions, pg 835

CONNECTICUT

Broadcast Video Productions LLC, pg 813

DELAWARE

Side Door Studio Inc, pg 1010

FLORIDA

Ed Ethridge Productions Inc, pg 863
LHV Audio Services, pg 919
Phat Planet Recording Studios, pg 973
Promidi Music, pg 986
Sunfire Communications Inc, pg 1028

GEORGIA

NorthTown Sounds Inc, pg 959

HAWAII

Hyperspective Studios Inc, pg 893
Media Bridge Gamekids, pg 936
TV Juice Productions Inc, pg 1046

ILLINOIS

Solid Sound Recording Studio, pg 1015
Woodside Avenue Music Productions Inc, pg 1069

INDIANA

Sweetwater Sound Inc, pg 1029

MARYLAND

CPR MultiMedia Solutions, pg 837
CSPMedia.com, pg 840
dbF a Media Company, pg 844
Omega Recording Studios, pg 962

MASSACHUSETTS

Cramer Productions, pg 837
Professional Audio Design Inc, pg 985
Soundtrack Recording Studios, pg 1018
Rik Tinory Productions, pg 1041

MICHIGAN

Digi Sign Design LLC, pg 847
GMP Music, pg 879
K&R's Recording Studios Inc, pg 908

MINNESOTA

The ADS Group, pg 777

MISSOURI

Avatar Studios, pg 798

MONTANA

Jereco Studios Inc, pg 905

NEW JERSEY

Jeep Jazz Media Solutions, pg 905
Suede Interactive, pg 1027

NEW YORK

Aural Gratification Inc, pg 796
The Big House Group, pg 807
Manhattan Center Studios Inc, pg 930
Now Hear This, pg 960
TBA Global Events, pg 1032

NORTH CAROLINA

Pat Appleson Studios Inc, pg 788
2BruceStudio, pg 1047

OHIO

Creative Technology, pg 838
EDR Media LLC, pg 857
Mills James Productions, pg 943
SoundSpace Inc, pg 1018

PENNSYLVANIA

AiH Group Inc, pg 779
Brown Bag Imaging, pg 814
Forge Recording LLC, pg 871
Ivory Productions, pg 903
Kloss Studios Co, pg 912
Right Coast Recording Inc, pg 997

RHODE ISLAND

Sound-FX-Design, pg 1017

Script Writing

AUDIO

Script Writing (continued)

NEVADA

DVDs4Less, pg 854
JCS Video Productions, pg 904
Tanglewood Productions, pg 1031

NEW HAMPSHIRE

Apertura, pg 788
Chip Taylor Communications LLC, pg 1032
The Troupe, pg 1045

NEW JERSEY

All Jersey Studios, pg 780
Audio Vistas LLC, pg 795
CFP Video Productions Inc, pg 823
Color Leasing Studios, pg 831
Euro-Pacific Film & Video Productions Inc, pg 863
Laurel Video Productions, pg 916
MediaNow, pg 938
MIB Mediaworks, pg 941
Milgrom Productions, pg 943
Newark Beth Israel Medical Center, pg 956
Optisonics Productions, pg 965
Reed Presentations Inc (RPI), pg 993
Suede Interactive, pg 1027
VCSvideo, pg 1052

NEW MEXICO

Production Outfitters, pg 984

NEW YORK

aurora productions, pg 797
Big Fish Productions Inc, pg 807
The Big House Group, pg 807
Broad Street Inc, pg 812
Chromavision Corp, pg 826
Cohn Creative Group LLC, pg 831
Conversation Arts Media, pg 836
Thomas Craven Film Corp, pg 837
De Nonno Productions Inc (DPI), pg 844
dM works, pg 849
Eastco Multimedia Solutions Inc, pg 856
Edgeware Associates/Travel Arts Syndicate, pg 856
Educational Images Ltd, pg 857
The Food & Beverage Institute, pg 871
4-D Creative Media, pg 871
Karen Frankel Productions, pg 872
Greyfalcon House, pg 882
Gurrilla Video Solutions, pg 883
HB-Content, pg 886
Icontent, pg 893
KickedUp Media Group Inc, pg 910
La Paloma Films, pg 915
L&P Media, pg 915
Lylofilm Productions, pg 926
Manhattan Center Studios Inc, pg 930
Neal Marshad Productions, pg 931
Mood Creations Ltd, pg 946
Jack Morton Worldwide, pg 946
MRM Worldwide, pg 948
MRY, pg 949
News Broadcast Network, pg 956
No Soap Productions, pg 957
Northeast Video Productions Inc, pg 959
Now Hear This, pg 960
Shelly Palmer Production, pg 968
Peckham Productions Inc, pg 970
Peter Schleger Co, pg 1004
Split Image Productions, pg 1021
Synaptic Digital, pg 1030
TBA Global Events, pg 1032
Zelman Studios Ltd, pg 1073

NORTH CAROLINA

Pat Appleson Studios Inc, pg 788
The Communications Group Inc, pg 833
Duke Media Services, pg 853
Unifour Productions Inc, pg 1048

NORTH DAKOTA

Media Productions, pg 937

OHIO

Challenge Productions, pg 823
Creative Technology, pg 838
Curtis Inc, pg 841
Cuyahoga Community College Media Center, pg 841
Icom Multimedia, pg 893
MainSail Production Services Inc, pg 929
Mills James Productions, pg 943
R&B Communications Inc, pg 991
Treehaus Communications Inc, pg 1044
Vista Color Imaging Inc, pg 1059

OKLAHOMA

Garman Productions LLC, pg 875
PDC Productions, pg 970
University of Oklahoma Academic Media & Digital Services, pg 1050

OREGON

A KTVA Production LLC, pg 771
Odyssey Productions Inc, pg 961
Producers Studio, pg 984

PENNSYLVANIA

AiH Group Inc, pg 779
Audio Visual Communications Inc, pg 795
Goodman Associates Inc, pg 880
Innovision Media Group, pg 899
JPL, pg 906
Robin Miller, Filmaker Inc, pg 943
Panta Rhei Media Inc, pg 968
Production Masters Inc (PMI), pg 984
The Videohouse Inc, pg 1057
WPHL-TV, pg 1070
WQED-Multimedia, pg 1070

RHODE ISLAND

A&M Productions, pg 771
Sound-FX-Design, pg 1017
StarTrak Studios Inc, pg 1024

SOUTH CAROLINA

DaviSound, pg 843
Genesis Creative, pg 877
Venture Media, pg 1052

TENNESSEE

American Blackguard Inc, pg 784
Continental Film, pg 835
Marine Geographic, pg 931
Memphis Communications Corp, pg 938
Motion Picture Services, pg 947
Scripps Networks, pg 1005
Stage Post, pg 1022
WKPT-TV, pg 1068

TEXAS

Best Film & Video, pg 805
Biway Media, pg 808
The Black Academy of Arts & Letters Inc, pg 808
Castleview Productions, pg 821
Cerutti Productions Inc, pg 823
Communication Arts Multimedia Inc, pg 832
Dykeman Associates Inc, pg 854
The Editing Co, pg 857
Epic Software Group Inc, pg 862
Phillips MediaSource, pg 974
Romar Learning, pg 999
The Samuels Co, pg 1002
Stage Directions, pg 1022
Tecfilms Inc, pg 1033
Texas Heart Institute Visual Communication Services, pg 1037
The Yesterday USA Radio Networks, pg 1072

UTAH

ImageWorks Communications, pg 896

VERMONT

University of Vermont, Instructional Television Dept, pg 1050
Wilson McLeran Inc, pg 1067

VIRGINIA

Advance Concepts Inc, pg 777
Blair Inc, pg 809
CACI Productions Group, pg 816
CALIBRE, pg 816
CDR Communications Inc, pg 822
Wally Cleaver's Recording Service, pg 830
Studio Center Corp, pg 1026

WASHINGTON

Adams Creative & Production Services, pg 775
Global Net Productions Inc, pg 879
Inland Audio Visual Co, pg 898
Kostov Productions, pg 913
Laser Fantasy/HECK Industries/ Photon Manufacturing, pg 916
North-by-Northwest Productions, pg 958
Sound Sound/Savage Fruitarian Productions, pg 1017
Victory Studios, pg 1054

WISCONSIN

Audio Visual of Milwaukee Inc, pg 795
Learning Technology Services, pg 917
Meridian Studios, pg 939
Sound Strations Audio Productions Inc, pg 1017
USAV Group Inc, pg 1050
Video Wisconsin Inc, pg 1056
Watts Communications Inc, pg 1062
Wisconsin Public Television, pg 1068

WYOMING

Bridger Productions Inc, pg 812

ALBERTA

Global Television, pg 879
Global Television Station, pg 879

BRITISH COLUMBIA

Triad Communications Ltd, pg 1044

ONTARIO

DebsVoice, pg 844
GAPC (General Assembly Production Centre), pg 875
JFB Communications, pg 905
Purefire Communications Inc, pg 987
Wanted! Sound + Picture, pg 1062

Signal Compression Equipment, *see* Compression & Decompression Equipment

Signal Processing Equipment Distributors

ALABAMA

PESA, pg 973

ARIZONA

Allusion Studios & Pure Wave Audio, pg 782
EAR Professional Audio/Video, pg 855
Troxell Communications Inc, pg 1045

CALIFORNIA

Ametron Audio/Video, pg 785
Associated Sound, pg 792
Audio Images Corp, pg 794
Be Media, pg 804
Delicate Electronics Sales Inc, pg 845
Empire Wholesale Inc, pg 860
FXC Communications, pg 874
GigaSonic, pg 878
Harman Pro North America, pg 885
Hi-Tech Audio Systems Inc, pg 888
JD Audio Visual Inc, pg 904
Linear LLC, pg 922
Location Sound Corp, pg 924
Media Control Systems LLC, pg 936
MediaMation Inc, pg 937
MediaPOINTE, pg 938
Parasound Products Inc, pg 969
POP TV, pg 978
QSC Audio Products LLC, pg 988
Signal Transport, pg 1011
Sound Service Co, pg 1017
Southern California Sound Image Inc, pg 1019
Synthesizer Systems Technologies (SST), pg 1030
TOA Electronics Inc, pg 1041
Towards 2000 Inc, pg 1043

COLORADO

Audio Consultant Services Inc, pg 794

CONNECTICUT

Everett Hall Associates Inc, pg 863
Gold Line/TEF, pg 880
HB Communications Inc, pg 886
The Music People Inc, pg 951
Sennheiser Electronic Corp, pg 1006

DELAWARE

Actors Attic, pg 775

FLORIDA

Access Media Group, pg 773
Allstar Audio Systems Inc, pg 782
BAI Distributors Inc, pg 801
Broadcasters General Store Inc, pg 813
Digital Video Systems Inc, pg 848
Griffiths Broadcast Co Inc, pg 882
Harris Corp, pg 885
Hi-Tech Enterprises Inc, pg 888
Intermark Industries Inc, pg 900
Media Concepts Inc, pg 936
Midtown Video Inc, pg 942
Recording Media & Equipment Inc (RM&E), pg 993
Sight & Sound Productions, pg 1010
Stereo Sales Inc, pg 1024
TAI Audio, pg 1031
Technomedia Solutions, pg 1035

GEORGIA

Lighting & Production Equipment Inc, pg 920
Omnimedia Inc, pg 962
Stage Front Presentation Systems, pg 1022

INDIANA

Sensory Technologies LLC, pg 1006
SHP Electronics, pg 1010
Sweetwater Sound Inc, pg 1029

IOWA

ECS Inc, pg 856

KENTUCKY

NOR-COM Inc, pg 958

MAINE

Independent Audio Inc, pg 897

MARYLAND

Bradley Broadcast & Pro Audio, pg 811
Cardinal Sound & Video, pg 820
Human Circuit, pg 892

MASSACHUSETTS

Terry Hanley Audio Systems Inc, pg 884
Professional Audio Design Inc, pg 985

MICHIGAN

Ascom Communications Contractors, pg 791
On Stage Visuals, pg 963
TeL Systems, pg 1035

NEVADA

Midas Consoles North America, pg 942

NEW HAMPSHIRE

APS Lighting-Sound-AV, pg 789
Technet® Systems Group, pg 1033

NEW JERSEY

Alltec Stores, a Vcom IMC Company, pg 782
Diversified Systems Inc, pg 849
Earl Girls Inc, pg 855
JRF Magnetic Sciences Inc, pg 906
Onkyo USA Corp, pg 963
PatchAmp, pg 970
Starlite Productions, pg 1024
Wired 4 Sound Inc, pg 1068
York Telecom, pg 1072

NEW YORK

ALTEL Systems Inc, pg 783
Aura Sonic Ltd, pg 796
BTX Technologies, pg 814
Communications Specialties Inc, pg 833
Design Audio Visual Inc, pg 845
Group One Ltd, pg 882
Hot House Professional Audio, pg 891
Korg USA Inc, pg 913
L-3 GCS, pg 915
Mark Custom Recording Service Inc, pg 931
Markertek Video Supply, pg 931
Posthorn Recordings, pg 979
Video International Development Inc, pg 1055
XTA Electronics Ltd, pg 1071
Yorkville Sound Inc, pg 1072

NORTH CAROLINA

Moog Music Inc, pg 946

OHIO

GatesAir, pg 875
ITA Audio Visual Solutions, pg 902
Omnia Audio, pg 962
Jimmy Rea Electronics Inc, pg 992

OREGON

SuperDigital Ltd, pg 1029

PENNSYLVANIA

Advanced AV, pg 777
Clair Brothers Audio Systems Inc, pg 829
Vistacom Inc, pg 1059

SOUTH CAROLINA

DaviSound, pg 843

SOUTH DAKOTA

Sencore Inc, pg 1006

TENNESSEE

Durrell LLC, pg 854
Lowrance Sound Co Inc, pg 925
Spectrum Sound Inc, pg 1021
Technical Support Systems LLC, pg 1034
Zion Music Group, pg 1074

TEXAS

Crossroads Audio Inc, pg 840
Data Projections Inc, pg 843
Lubbock Audio Visual Inc, pg 925
Pro Video & Film Equipment Co Inc, pg 983
RF Specialties of Texas LLC, pg 996
Southwest Sound & Electronics Inc, pg 1019
Tarpley Media Systems, pg 1032

UTAH

Performance Audio, pg 973

VERMONT

Production Advantage Inc, pg 984

VIRGINIA

Avitecture Inc, pg 799
Intellidyne LLC, pg 899
Schafer World Communications Corp, pg 1004

WASHINGTON

CCI Solutions, pg 821
D A Sound, pg 842
Northern Lights & Pro Audio, pg 959

WISCONSIN

Audio Visual of Milwaukee Inc, pg 795
Camera Corner Connecting Point, pg 818
Full Compass Systems, pg 874

ALBERTA

Infosat Communications Inc, pg 898
Matrix Video Communications Corp (MVCC), pg 934
Unique Communications Ltd, pg 1048

BRITISH COLUMBIA

ADI Systems Inc, pg 776
Radial Engineering Ltd, pg 990

MANITOBA

Advance Pro, pg 777
Inland Audio Visual Ltd, pg 898

ONTARIO

Cinema Stage Inc, pg 827
Sascom Marketing Group Inc, pg 1003
Westbury National Show Systems Ltd, pg 1064

QUEBEC

JAM Industries Ltd, pg 903
SC Media Canada, pg 1003

Signal Processing Equipment Manufacturers

ALABAMA

PESA, pg 973

ARIZONA

MTX Audio, pg 949
Radio Design Labs (RDL), pg 990

ARKANSAS

Autogram/Crl, pg 797

CALIFORNIA

AB Systems Amplifiers, pg 772
ALTINEX Inc, pg 783
Antex Electronics Corp, pg 787
BBE Sound Inc, pg 803
Digital Music Corp, pg 847
Dorrough Electronics Inc, pg 851
Dan Dugan Sound Design Inc, pg 853
Ensemble Designs Inc, pg 861
ESE, pg 862
FM Systems Inc, pg 870
Furman, pg 874
Graham-Patten, pg 881
Linear LLC, pg 922
Linkabit, pg 922
Lynx Studio Technology Inc, pg 927
Manley Laboratories Inc, pg 930
Martinsound Inc, pg 932
Media Control Systems LLC, pg 936
Millennia Media FPC, pg 943
Nady Systems Inc, pg 952
Panasonic Broadcast & Digital Systems Co, pg 968
Parasound Products Inc, pg 969
Physical Optics Corp, pg 975
PowerPhysics Inc, pg 979
Renkus-Heinz Inc, pg 994
Signal Transport, pg 1011
Simon - Kaloi Engineering, pg 1011
Soundcraft USA, pg 1018
Summit Audio Inc, pg 1028
TFT Inc, pg 1038
TOA Electronics Inc, pg 1041
Xantech LLC, pg 1071

CONNECTICUT

Gold Line/TEF, pg 880
Sound Control Technologies Inc, pg 1017
Titus Technological Laboratories (TTL), pg 1041

FLORIDA

Compuvideo Sales USA Ltd, pg 834
JT Communications, pg 906
Sabine® Inc, pg 1001
Tel-Test, pg 1035
Z-Systems Audio Engineering, pg 1073

ILLINOIS

Bag End Loudspeakers, pg 801
Esoteric Sound, pg 862
SoundTech, pg 1018
Studio Technologies Inc, pg 1027
Symbolic Sound Corp, pg 1030

KENTUCKY

Innovative Electronic Designs LLC, pg 898
TV One Multimedia Solutions, pg 1046

MAINE

Dielectric Communications, pg 846

MARYLAND

API, pg 788
RCI Custom Products, pg 992

MASSACHUSETTS

Eastern Acoustic Works Inc (EAW), pg 856

MICHIGAN

ASC Systems, pg 791

MINNESOTA

Digital Audio Labs, pg 847
Great River Electronics, pg 881
Telex Communications Inc, pg 1037
Telex EVI, pg 1037

MISSISSIPPI

Peavey Electronics Corp, pg 970

AUDIO

Signal Processing Equipment Manufacturers (continued)

NEW JERSEY

ATI Audio, pg 793
Bogen Communications Inc, pg 810
Crestron Electronics Inc, pg 839
Eventide Inc, pg 863
FSR Inc, pg 873
Kramer Electronics USA Inc, pg 913
Modulation Sciences Inc, pg 945
Onkyo USA Corp, pg 963
Prism Media Products Inc, pg 982
Tech 21 USA Inc, pg 1033

NEW MEXICO

Lectrosonics Inc, pg 918

NEW YORK

Ashly Audio Inc, pg 792
Broadcast Devices Inc, pg 813
ChyronHego Corp, pg 826
Communications Specialties Inc, pg 833
GLI Sound Systems, pg 878
Hot House Professional Audio, pg 891
Image Labs Corp, pg 895
Key Digital Systems, pg 910
Laird Digital Cinema, pg 915
MultiDyne Video & Fiber Optics Systems, pg 950
Sescom Inc, pg 1007
Solid State Logic Inc, pg 1015
Video International Development Inc, pg 1055
Yorkville Sound Inc, pg 1072

NORTH CAROLINA

Moog Music Inc, pg 946
Wheatstone Corp, pg 1065

OHIO

GatesAir, pg 875
Omnia Audio, pg 962
Telos Systems, pg 1037

OREGON

BIAMP Systems, pg 806

PENNSYLVANIA

D W Fearn, pg 866

SOUTH CAROLINA

DaviSound, pg 843

SOUTH DAKOTA

Sencore Inc, pg 1006
Tepco Corp, pg 1037

TENNESSEE

Auratron Systems, pg 796
Durrell LLC, pg 854

UTAH

Aphex LLC, pg 788
ClearOne Inc, pg 830
dbx Professional Products, pg 844
DigiTech, pg 848
Ivie Technologies Inc, pg 903
Rolls Corp, pg 999

WASHINGTON

AudioControl®, pg 796
Rane, pg 991

WISCONSIN

Intelix LLC, pg 899

ALBERTA

QSound Labs Inc, pg 988

BRITISH COLUMBIA

Radial Engineering Ltd, pg 990

ONTARIO

Artaflex Inc, pg 791
Ward-Beck Systems Ltd, pg 1062

QUEBEC

Miranda Technologies, pg 944

Signal Processing Equipment Rentals

ARIZONA

Video West Inc, pg 1056

ARKANSAS

White Diamond Productions, pg 1065

CALIFORNIA

Absolute Rentals, pg 772
Action Audio & Visual, pg 775
Ametron Audio/Video, pg 785
Artichoke Productions, pg 791
Associated Sound, pg 792
Audio Rents, pg 794
Dan Dugan Sound Design Inc, pg 853
Express Media Inc, pg 864
Golden Gate Studios, pg 880
JD Audio Visual Inc, pg 904
Location Sound Corp, pg 924
Maximus Media Inc, pg 934
Munday & Collins AV, pg 950
Muse Presentation Technologies, pg 950
Pacific Audio-Visual Enterprises, pg 967
PSAV® Presentation Services, pg 986
Alwin Sauers Audio Productions (ASAP), pg 1003
Sound Service Co, pg 1017
VER-Video Equipment Rentals, pg 1053
Video Resources Inc, pg 1056

COLORADO

Audio Consultant Services Inc, pg 794

CONNECTICUT

Everett Hall Associates Inc, pg 863

DELAWARE

Side Door Studio Inc, pg 1010

FLORIDA

Access Media Group, pg 773
Allstar Audio Systems Inc, pg 782
Hi-Tech Enterprises Inc, pg 888
Sight & Sound Productions, pg 1010
Universal Studios Florida® Production Group, pg 1049

GEORGIA

Stage Front Presentation Systems, pg 1022

ILLINOIS

AV Chicago Inc, pg 797
The Meetinghouse Companies Inc, pg 938
Show Department Inc, pg 1009

KENTUCKY

Audio Visual Techniques Inc, pg 796

MARYLAND

CPR MultiMedia Solutions, pg 837
Event Tech, pg 863

MASSACHUSETTS

Terry Hanley Audio Systems Inc, pg 884
Preston Productions Inc, pg 981

MICHIGAN

K&R All Media Productions Inc, pg 908
On Stage Visuals, pg 963

MISSOURI

Show-Me Audio-Visual, pg 1009

NEW HAMPSHIRE

APS Lighting-Sound-AV, pg 789

NEW JERSEY

Audio Visual Dynamics®, pg 795
Earl Girls Inc, pg 855
Soundtracks Production Services LLC, pg 1018
Starlite Productions, pg 1024
Wired 4 Sound Inc, pg 1068

NEW YORK

Audio Visual Resources LLC, pg 795
Aura Sonic Ltd, pg 796
CP Communications, pg 837
Design Audio Visual Inc, pg 845

NORTH CAROLINA

A&V Company, pg 772
Take One Productions Ltd, pg 1031

NORTH DAKOTA

Media Productions, pg 937

OHIO

Production Solutions Inc, pg 984

PENNSYLVANIA

Right Coast Recording Inc, pg 997

TENNESSEE

Durrell LLC, pg 854
Love Shack Recording Studios, pg 925
Mr Mark's Used Musical, Stereo & Studio Equipment Store, pg 944
Technical Support Systems LLC, pg 1034

TEXAS

Alford Media Services, pg 780
Bright Star Productions Inc, pg 812
Crossroads Audio Inc, pg 840
Music Lab Inc, pg 950
Tropikal Productions, pg 1045

VIRGINIA

Audio Visual Actions Inc (AVA), pg 795

WASHINGTON

D A Sound, pg 842

PUERTO RICO

Stage Crew Audiovisual Inc, pg 1022

MANITOBA

Inland Audio Visual Ltd, pg 898

ONTARIO

Westbury National Show Systems Ltd, pg 1064

Signal Processing Equipment Repairs

CALIFORNIA

AB Systems Amplifiers, pg 772
Ametron Audio/Video, pg 785
Audio Images Corp, pg 794
Audio Upgrades, pg 795
Diemer Amp & Keyboard Repair, pg 846
McAlister Electronics, pg 935
QSC Audio Products LLC, pg 988
Sound Service Co, pg 1017
TOA Electronics Inc, pg 1041
Towards 2000 Inc, pg 1043

CONNECTICUT

HB Communications Inc, pg 886
Sennheiser Electronic Corp, pg 1006

FLORIDA

Hi-Tech Enterprises Inc, pg 888
JT Communications, pg 906
Phat Planet Recording Studios, pg 973
Stereo Sales Inc, pg 1024
TAI Audio, pg 1031
Tel-Test, pg 1035

GEORGIA

Lighting & Production Equipment Inc, pg 920
Stage Front Presentation Systems, pg 1022

INDIANA

SHP Electronics, pg 1010
Sweetwater Sound Inc, pg 1029

IOWA

ECS Inc, pg 856

KENTUCKY

NOR-COM Inc, pg 958

Sound Booths

AUDIO

Sound Booths (continued)

NEW JERSEY (continued)

Optisonics Productions, pg 965
Shamrock Communications, pg 1008
Suede Interactive, pg 1027
VCSvideo, pg 1052

NEW MEXICO

Production Outfitters, pg 984

NEW YORK

The Big House Group, pg 807
Chromavision Corp, pg 826
Cornell Laboratory of Ornithology, pg 836
CP Communications, pg 837
De Wolfe Music USA, pg 844
dM works, pg 849
DuArt, pg 853
HB-Content, pg 886
Headroom Digital Audio, pg 887
Heavy Melody, pg 887
Mood Creations Ltd, pg 946
MRG Productions Inc, pg 948
MRM Worldwide, pg 948
The Napoleon Group, pg 952
No Soap Productions, pg 957
Now Hear This, pg 960
Nutmeg Post, pg 960
Shelly Palmer Production, pg 968
RadioArt/Bob & Ray CDs & MP3 Files, pg 990
Sony Music Entertainment, pg 1016
TBA Global Events, pg 1032
TeleTime Productions, pg 1036
WNET/NET TELECON, pg 1069
Zelman Studios Ltd, pg 1073

NORTH CAROLINA

Pat Appleson Studios Inc, pg 788
The Communications Group Inc, pg 833
Duke Media Services, pg 853
Franklin Video Inc, pg 872
Horizon Video Productions Inc, pg 891
Take One Productions Ltd, pg 1031
Trailblazer Studios®, pg 1043

NORTH DAKOTA

Media Productions, pg 937

OHIO

Creative Technology, pg 838
Curtis Inc, pg 841
Cuyahoga Community College Media Center, pg 841
EDR Media LLC, pg 857
Lyon Video Inc, pg 927
Mills James Productions, pg 943
Vista Color Imaging Inc, pg 1059

OKLAHOMA

Garman Productions LLC, pg 875
PDC Productions, pg 970
University of Oklahoma Academic Media & Digital Services, pg 1050

OREGON

A KTVA Production LLC, pg 771
Rex, pg 995

PENNSYLVANIA

Audio Visual Communications Inc, pg 795
FMP Media Solutions Inc, pg 870
Forge Recording LLC, pg 871
Innovision Media Group, pg 899
JPL, pg 906
Panta Rhei Media Inc, pg 968
Production Masters Inc (PMI), pg 984
The Videohouse Inc, pg 1057
Visual Sound Inc, pg 1059
WHYY Inc, pg 1066
WPHL-TV, pg 1070

RHODE ISLAND

Sound-FX-Design, pg 1017

SOUTH CAROLINA

DaviSound, pg 843
Genesis Creative, pg 877
Venture Media, pg 1052

TENNESSEE

Anode Inc, pg 787
Continental Film, pg 835
Cupit Music Group, pg 841
Love Shack Recording Studios, pg 925
Memphis Communications Corp, pg 938
Scripps Networks, pg 1005
Stage Post, pg 1022
Technical Support Systems LLC, pg 1034
UMCom Productions, pg 1048
WKPT-TV, pg 1068
Zion Music Group, pg 1074

TEXAS

Acoustic Systems, pg 774
Audiomoxie®, pg 796
The Editing Co, pg 857
Fire Station Studios, pg 868
Marx InDigital, pg 933
Matson Multi-Media, pg 934
Maverick Video Productions, pg 934
Out of the BLUE Media, pg 966
Phillips MediaSource, pg 974
Romar Learning, pg 999
The Samuels Co, pg 1002
The Sound Lab Inc, pg 1017
Sound Works, pg 1018
South Coast Film & Video, pg 1019
Stage Directions, pg 1022
Texas Heart Institute Visual Communication Services, pg 1037
TM Studios Inc, pg 1041
The Yesterday USA Radio Networks, pg 1072

UTAH

K-SAR Video & DVD Productions, pg 907
Performance Audio, pg 973
Soularium Recording Studios, pg 1016

VERMONT

University of Vermont, Instructional Television Dept, pg 1050

VIRGINIA

Acoustical Solutions Inc, pg 774
AudioImage Recording, pg 796
BES Studios, pg 805
CACI Productions Group, pg 816
CDR Communications Inc, pg 822
Wally Cleaver's Recording Service, pg 830
Creative Video of Washington Inc, pg 839
Lion Recording Services Inc, pg 922
Metro Productions, pg 939
Studio Center Corp, pg 1026
Video Solutions, pg 1056

WASHINGTON

Avast! Recording Co, pg 798
Global Net Productions Inc, pg 879
Hamilton Studio, pg 884
Inland Audio Visual Co, pg 898
North-by-Northwest Productions, pg 958
Sound Sound/Savage Fruitarian Productions, pg 1017
Victory Studios, pg 1054

WISCONSIN

Audio Visual of Milwaukee Inc, pg 795
Concept Productions Inc, pg 834
5th Floor Recording Co, pg 867
Logan Productions Inc, pg 924
USAV Group Inc, pg 1050
Video Wisconsin Inc, pg 1056
Wisconsin Public Television, pg 1068

BRITISH COLUMBIA

Finale Editworks, pg 868
Pinewood Sound, pg 975
Triad Communications Ltd, pg 1044

MANITOBA

daCapo Productions, pg 842

ONTARIO

ADS Media, pg 777
AMPLUS Productions, pg 786
DebsVoice, pg 844
GAPC (General Assembly Production Centre), pg 875
JL Recording Studios, pg 905
MCS Recording Studios, pg 936
Metalworks Recording Studios Inc, pg 939
Purefire Communications Inc, pg 987
Spence-Thomas Audio Post, pg 1021
VO2 Mix Studios, pg 1060
Wanted! Sound + Picture, pg 1062

Sound Effect Libraries

ALABAMA

Airwave Recording Studio, pg 779
Dogwood Recording Studios, pg 850

ARIZONA

BeachWare Inc, pg 804
Direct Current Video Productions, pg 848
Film Creations Ltd, pg 867
Merestone, pg 938
Productiontrax.com, pg 985
SPEAK HOUSE Audio™, pg 1019

ARKANSAS

Shadowbox Video Productions, pg 1007
White Diamond Productions, pg 1065

CALIFORNIA

Aaron & Le Duc, pg 772
Artichoke Productions, pg 791
Associated Production Music LLC, pg 792
The Banquet Sound Studios, pg 802
Berke Creative Inc, pg 805
Berkeley Sound Artists Inc, pg 805
Blaise Media, pg 809
CCI Digital, pg 821
Bruce Chianese, pg 824
Creative Media Recording, pg 838
Creative Support Services/CSS Music, pg 838
Dogma Studios, pg 850
Earwax Productions Inc, pg 855
Eye & I Productions, pg 864
Gilderfluke & Co Inc, pg 878
The Hollywood Edge, pg 890
Ilio Enterprises LLC, pg 894
ITV Productions, pg 903
Jaguar Distribution Corp, pg 903
JDS Video & Media Productions Inc, pg 904
Juice, pg 906
Kaleidosound, pg 907
Killer Tracks, pg 910
Leonardo Software, pg 919
Maximus Media Inc, pg 934
Megatrax, pg 938
Pacific Audio-Visual Enterprises, pg 967
Polarity Post Production, pg 978
Pyramind Studios, pg 988
Reality Check Systems, pg 992
Saturn Studios, pg 1003
Steve Shapiro Music, pg 1008
SonicPool, pg 1016
Sonoton Music Library, pg 1016
Still N'Motion, pg 1025
Synthesizer Systems Technologies (SST), pg 1030
Total Media Group, pg 1042
Tranquil Technology Music, pg 1043
Universal Studios, pg 1049
Visions Plus, pg 1058

COLORADO

Conly Productions, pg 835
Daylight Productions & Rentals, pg 844
Flashback Media Productions, pg 869

CONNECTICUT

Broadcast Video Productions LLC, pg 813
Fox Connecticut, pg 872
Music 2 Hues, pg 951
P&P Studios Inc, pg 968
Trod Nossel Productions & Recording Studios, pg 1045

DELAWARE

Ken-Del Productions Inc, pg 909
Ken-Del Studios, pg 909

DISTRICT OF COLUMBIA

Interface Media Group, pg 900
Smithsonian Folkways Recordings, pg 1014

FLORIDA

Gulf Coast Audio Visual Producers Inc, pg 883
Jordan Klein Film & Video (JKFV), pg 906
LHV Audio Services, pg 919
Motion Image Group LLC, pg 947
Paradise Show & Design Inc, pg 969
Top Hat Productions, pg 1042
Universal Studios Florida® Production Group, pg 1049

GEORGIA

Beachwood Productions, pg 804
Doppler Studios, pg 851
ECG Productions, pg 856
Guerrilla Productions LLC, pg 883
NorthTown Sounds Inc, pg 959

HAWAII

Audio Resource Honolulu, pg 794
KHNL/KGMB, pg 910

IDAHO

Brad Shaw Productions Inc, pg 1008

ILLINOIS

AnswersMedia, pg 787
Creative Technology, pg 838
Esoteric Sound, pg 862
Jim Passin Productions, pg 970
The Pepper Group, pg 972
RBR Productions, pg 992
WEEK TV, pg 1063
Woodside Avenue Music Productions Inc, pg 1069

INDIANA

AVA Productions, pg 798
OMNI Productions, pg 962

KANSAS

Chapman Recording & Mastering, pg 824
KAKE-TV, pg 907
Walterscheid Productions, pg 1062

KENTUCKY

Hammond Communications Group, pg 884
Prosper Media Group Inc, pg 986

MARYLAND

Adventure Productions LLC, pg 778
Bethesda Softworks LLC, pg 806
CAS Video Productions, pg 820
CPR MultiMedia Solutions, pg 837
The Cutting Corp, pg 841
Pro Cuts Editing Services, pg 982
Satellite Media Production, pg 1003

MASSACHUSETTS

CommCreative, pg 832
Labrecque Creative Sound, pg 915
Soundtrack Recording Studios, pg 1018
TR Productions, pg 1043

MICHIGAN

Audio Graphic Services, pg 794
The Brookwood Studio Inc, pg 814
GMP Music, pg 879
K&R's Recording Studios Inc, pg 908
MessageMakers, pg 939

MINNESOTA

The ADS Group, pg 777
Aggressive Records Audio Duplication LLC, pg 778
Media Loft Inc, pg 937
MultiMedia, pg 950

MISSISSIPPI

Dollarhide Film Inc, pg 850

MISSOURI

Production Consultants, pg 984
Show-Me Audio-Visual, pg 1009

MONTANA

Jereco Studios Inc, pg 905
North Country Media Group, pg 959

NEBRASKA

JoeAudio, pg 905

NEVADA

JCS Video Productions, pg 904
Tanglewood Productions, pg 1031

NEW HAMPSHIRE

Apertura, pg 788
The Troupe, pg 1045

NEW JERSEY

Megavideo Productions, pg 938
Midnight Media Group Inc, pg 942
Milbrodt/Music & Sound Design, pg 943
Milgrom Productions, pg 943
Oasis CD Manufacturing, pg 960
Bill Quinn Productions, pg 989
Richard Reiter Productions Inc, pg 994
TRF Production Music Libraries, pg 1044
VCSvideo, pg 1052

NEW MEXICO

Production Outfitters, pg 984

NEW YORK

The Audio Department Inc, pg 794
Cornell Laboratory of Ornithology, pg 836
De Wolfe Music USA, pg 844
Dreamhire LLC, pg 852
Fingerpaint, pg 868
Heavy Melody, pg 887
HOThead, pg 891
Korg USA Inc, pg 913
Loftin Productions, pg 924
Madison Square Garden, pg 927
Manhattan Production Music Inc, pg 930
New York Sound Inc, pg 956
Nutmeg Post, pg 960
Omnimusic, pg 962
Shelly Palmer Production, pg 968
David Rapkin Audio Production, pg 991
Robbins Media Inc, pg 998
Sear Sound, pg 1005
Sony Music Custom Marketing, pg 1016
Sony Music Entertainment, pg 1016
TBA Global Events, pg 1032
TecNec Distributing, pg 1035
Tiki Recording Studios Inc, pg 1040
Zelman Studios Ltd, pg 1073

NORTH CAROLINA

Pat Appleson Studios Inc, pg 788
Franklin Video Inc, pg 872
NASCAR Media Group LLC, pg 952
2BruceStudio, pg 1047

OHIO

Bartha, pg 803
Lyon Video Inc, pg 927
Mills James Productions, pg 943
Take 1 Media Services, pg 1031
VGI Productions, pg 1053
Vista Color Imaging Inc, pg 1059

OKLAHOMA

PDC Productions, pg 970

PENNSYLVANIA

John E Allen Inc, pg 781
Audio Visual Communications Inc, pg 795
Brown Bag Imaging, pg 814
Craig Recording Studios, pg 837
FMP Media Solutions Inc, pg 870
JPL, pg 906
Panta Rhei Media Inc, pg 968

SOUTH CAROLINA

Genesis Creative, pg 877

TENNESSEE

Film House Inc, pg 867
Memphis Communications Corp, pg 938
WKPT-TV, pg 1068

TEXAS

The Editing Co, pg 857
FirstCom Music, pg 869
Mediaforce Productions, pg 937
The Music Bakery, pg 950
Julye Newlin Productions Inc, pg 956
Planet Dallas Recording Studios, pg 976
Pro Video & Film Equipment Co Inc, pg 983
Real to Reel Studios Inc, pg 992
South Coast Film & Video, pg 1019
Stage Directions, pg 1022
Texas Heart Institute Visual Communication Services, pg 1037
TM Studios Inc, pg 1041
The Yesterday USA Radio Networks, pg 1072

UTAH

Soularium Recording Studios, pg 1016

VERMONT

Production Advantage Inc, pg 984

VIRGINIA

AudioImage Recording, pg 796
CALIBRE, pg 816
Wally Cleaver's Recording Service, pg 830
Henninger Media Services, pg 888
Lion Recording Services Inc, pg 922
National Media Services Inc, pg 953
Rocktown Media, pg 998

WASHINGTON

Avast! Recording Co, pg 798
Kostov Productions, pg 913
Laser Fantasy/HECK Industries/ Photon Manufacturing, pg 916
Quiet Planet LLC, pg 989
Victory Studios, pg 1054

WISCONSIN

5th Floor Recording Co, pg 867
ProVideo, pg 986
USAV Group Inc, pg 1050
Video Wisconsin Inc, pg 1056
Wisconsin Public Television, pg 1068

WYOMING

Bridger Productions Inc, pg 812

MANITOBA

daCapo Productions, pg 842

ONTARIO

JL Recording Studios, pg 905
MCS Recording Studios, pg 936
Metalworks Recording Studios Inc, pg 939
Nightingale Music Productions Inc, pg 957
Sonic Science Inc, pg 1016
Sound Ideas, pg 1017
StockMusic.com, pg 1025
Video Excellence Productions, pg 1055
VO2 Mix Studios, pg 1060

QUEBEC

Group PVP, pg 882

Sound Effect Production Services

ALABAMA

Sound of Birmingham Productions, pg 1017

ARIZONA

Fire Power Music Inc, pg 868
Merestone, pg 938
Phoenix VideoFilms®, pg 974

ARKANSAS

Live'N'Loud, pg 923

CALIFORNIA

Aaron & Le Duc, pg 772
AB Audio Visual Entertainment Inc, pg 772
AlphaDogs Inc, pg 782
The Annex, pg 787
Argyle Post, pg 789
Artichoke Productions, pg 791
Barbosa Video Services, pg 802
Berke Creative Inc, pg 805
Berkeley Sound Artists Inc, pg 805
Blaise Media, pg 809
CCI Digital, pg 821
Chace Audio by Deluxe, pg 823
Creative Media Recording, pg 838
Creative Support Services/CSS Music, pg 838
Crystal Pyramid Productions™, pg 840
Custom Video Productions Inc, pg 841

AUDIO

Sound Effect Production Services (continued)

CALIFORNIA (continued)

Diamond Dreams Music Productions, pg 846
Digital Jungle, pg 847
Dogma Studios, pg 850
DreamWorks Animation SKG Inc, pg 852
Earwax Productions Inc, pg 855
Eye & I Productions, pg 864
48 Windows, pg 871
The Hollywood Edge, pg 890
iCorpTv, pg 893
ITV Productions, pg 903
Kaleidosound, pg 907
The Kitchen, pg 911
KTVU-Retail Services, pg 914
KVIE-Channel 6, pg 914
Maximus Media Inc, pg 934
McCune Audio-Video-Lighting, pg 935
The Media Staff Inc, pg 937
MediaMation Inc, pg 937
Mind Over Eye Inc, pg 943
On-Trax Inc, pg 963
Palardo Productions, pg 968
piXvfm, pg 976
Polarity Post Production, pg 978
Private Island Trax, pg 982
PSI Inc, pg 987
Pyramind Studios, pg 988
QRS Software Services, pg 988
Reality Check Systems, pg 992
Roundabout Entertainment Inc, pg 1000
Sahara Records & Filmworks Entertainment Co, pg 1001
Saturn Studios, pg 1003
SBS Productions, pg 1003
Steve Shapiro Music, pg 1008
SonicPool, pg 1016
Kris Stevens Enterprises, pg 1024
Still N'Motion, pg 1025
Studio 132, pg 1027
Synthesizer Systems Technologies (SST), pg 1030
Total Media Group, pg 1042
Tranquil Technology Music, pg 1043
Universal Studios, pg 1049
West Coast Projections Inc, pg 1063
Wildfire Post Production Studios, pg 1066

COLORADO

Tim Cissell Music, pg 828
Conly Productions, pg 835
Daylight Productions & Rentals, pg 844
Flashback Media Productions, pg 869
Open Media Foundation, pg 964
Starwest Productions, pg 1024

CONNECTICUT

Antenna International, pg 787
BRB Audiovisual Productions, pg 812
Broadcast Video Productions LLC, pg 813
The Gary-Paul Agency, pg 875
Guymark Studios LLC, pg 883
Ironik Design & Post, pg 902
Music 2 Hues, pg 951
Palace Digital Studios, pg 967
P&P Studios Inc, pg 968
Sonalysts Media, pg 1015

DISTRICT OF COLUMBIA

Interface Media Group, pg 900

FLORIDA

Access Media Group, pg 773
Allegro Productions Inc, pg 781
Audacity Creative, pg 793
Audio Visual Imagineering Inc, pg 795
Cinema East, pg 827
Communications Concepts Inc (CCI), pg 833
Eastern Video, pg 856
Gulf Coast Audio Visual Producers Inc, pg 883
Home Shopping Network (HSN), pg 890
LHV Audio Services, pg 919
Mach 1 Productions, pg 927
Media Entertainment Inc, pg 936
Morrisound Recording, pg 946
Phat Planet Recording Studios, pg 973
Promidi Music, pg 986
Sunfire Communications Inc, pg 1028
Top Hat Productions, pg 1042
Universal Studios Florida® Production Group, pg 1049

GEORGIA

COMPRO Productions Inc, pg 834
Crawford Media Services, pg 838
Doppler Studios, pg 851
Guerrilla Productions LLC, pg 883
Magick Lantern, pg 928
NorthTown Sounds Inc, pg 959
White Dog Studios, pg 1065

HAWAII

Audio Resource Honolulu, pg 794
Hyperspective Studios Inc, pg 893
KHNL/KGMB, pg 910
Media Bridge Gamekids, pg 936
TV Juice Productions Inc, pg 1046

ILLINOIS

ABS Enterprises, pg 772
Beatty TeleVisual Productions, pg 804
CCore Media Inc, pg 821
Esoteric Sound, pg 862
Major Media Inc, pg 929
MIGHTYbYTES Inc, pg 942
Paragon Studios Inc, pg 969
Jim Passin Productions, pg 970
RBR Productions, pg 992
Steven Samler Music & Sound, pg 1002
Sound/Video Impressions Inc, pg 1018
Sparkfactor, pg 1019
WEEK TV, pg 1063
Woodside Avenue Music Productions Inc, pg 1069

INDIANA

AVA Productions, pg 798
Alan Johnson Recording, pg 905
OMNI Productions, pg 962
Sweetwater Sound Inc, pg 1029

IOWA

Hedquist Productions Inc, pg 887

KANSAS

Chapman Recording & Mastering, pg 824

LOUISIANA

Disk Productions, pg 849
Vidox Motion Imagery, pg 1057

MARYLAND

Bethesda Softworks LLC, pg 806
CPR MultiMedia Solutions, pg 837
CSPMedia.com, pg 840
The Cutting Corp, pg 841
dbF a Media Company, pg 844
Kramer Communications Video Production, pg 913
Lion & Fox Recording Studios, pg 922
Omega Recording Studios, pg 962

MASSACHUSETTS

CommCreative, pg 832
Continental Recordings Inc, pg 835
Cramer Productions, pg 837
Green Mountain Post Films (GMP), pg 882
Penfield Productions Ltd, pg 971
Soundtrack Recording Studios, pg 1018
TR Productions, pg 1043

MICHIGAN

Audio Graphic Services, pg 794
The Brookwood Studio Inc, pg 814
Digi Sign Design LLC, pg 847
Digital Image Studios LLC, pg 847
GMP Music, pg 879
K&R's Recording Studios Inc, pg 908

MINNESOTA

The ADS Group, pg 777
Aggressive Records Audio Duplication LLC, pg 778
Badiyan Inc, pg 801
Media Loft Inc, pg 937
MultiMedia, pg 950

MISSOURI

Avatar Studios, pg 798
Ozam Production, pg 966
Production Consultants, pg 984
Show-Me Audio-Visual, pg 1009

MONTANA

Jereco Studios Inc, pg 905
North Country Media Group, pg 959

NEBRASKA

JoeAudio, pg 905

NEVADA

DVDs4Less, pg 854
Tanglewood Productions, pg 1031
VirtualMix, pg 1058

NEW HAMPSHIRE

Apertura, pg 788

NEW JERSEY

Jeep Jazz Media Solutions, pg 905
Laurel Video Productions, pg 916
Megavideo Productions, pg 938
Midnight Media Group Inc, pg 942
Milgrom Productions, pg 943
NFL Films Inc, pg 957
NFL Films Music Library, pg 957
Oasis CD Manufacturing, pg 960
Optisonics Productions, pg 965
Suede Interactive, pg 1027
TRF Production Music Libraries, pg 1044
VCSvideo, pg 1052

NEW MEXICO

Production Outfitters, pg 984

NEW YORK

Aural Gratification Inc, pg 796
Big Fish Productions Inc, pg 807
The Big House Group, pg 807
Chromavision Corp, pg 826
De Wolfe Music USA, pg 844
Headroom Digital Audio, pg 887
Heavy Melody, pg 887
Kamen Entertainment Group Inc, pg 908
KAS Music & Sound, pg 908
Magno Sound & Video, pg 929
Mood Creations Ltd, pg 946
MRM Worldwide, pg 948
Mutual Hardware, pg 951
The Napoleon Group, pg 952
New York Audio Productions, pg 956
No Soap Productions, pg 957
Now Hear This, pg 960
Nutmeg Post, pg 960
Shelly Palmer Production, pg 968
David Rapkin Audio Production, pg 991
Elliot Sokolov Music, pg 1015
TBA Global Events, pg 1032
TeleTime Productions, pg 1036
Tiki Recording Studios Inc, pg 1040
Visual Technologies Corp, pg 1060
Zelman Studios Ltd, pg 1073

NORTH CAROLINA

Pat Appleson Studios Inc, pg 788
Audio Art, pg 794
Franklin Video Inc, pg 872
Horizon Video Productions Inc, pg 891
Take One Productions Ltd, pg 1031
Trailblazer Studios®, pg 1043
2BruceStudio, pg 1047

NORTH DAKOTA

Media Productions, pg 937

OHIO

Creative Technology, pg 838
Curtis Inc, pg 841
EDR Media LLC, pg 857
Lyon Video Inc, pg 927
Mills James Productions, pg 943
R&B Communications Inc, pg 991
Smithall Electronics Inc, pg 1014
Vista Color Imaging Inc, pg 1059

OKLAHOMA

Garman Productions LLC, pg 875
PDC Productions, pg 970
University of Oklahoma Academic Media & Digital Services, pg 1050

OREGON

KPDX-TV Production Center, pg 913
Rex, pg 995

PENNSYLVANIA

American Artist Studio, pg 783
Audio Visual Communications Inc, pg 795
Dreambox Media Inc, pg 852

RHODE ISLAND

SOUTH CAROLINA

TENNESSEE

TEXAS

UTAH

VERMONT

VIRGINIA

WASHINGTON

WISCONSIN

WYOMING

BRITISH COLUMBIA

MANITOBA

ONTARIO

Sound Recording

ALABAMA

ARIZONA

ARKANSAS

CALIFORNIA

COLORADO

CONNECTICUT

DELAWARE

DISTRICT OF COLUMBIA

FLORIDA

AUDIO

Sound Recording (continued)

FLORIDA (continued)

Home Shopping Network (HSN), pg 890
Jordan Klein Film & Video (JKFV), pg 906
LHV Audio Services, pg 919
Mach 1 Productions, pg 927
Media Entertainment Inc, pg 936
Morrisound Recording, pg 946
Phat Planet Recording Studios, pg 973
Progressive Media & Music, pg 985
Promidi Music, pg 986
Shooting Stars Post Inc, pg 1009
Stereo Sales Inc, pg 1024
Style-City Music Inc, pg 1027
Sunfire Communications Inc, pg 1028
Sunrise Studios, pg 1028
Tel-Air Interests Inc, pg 1035
Times-Square Fantasy Theatre, pg 1041
Top Hat Productions, pg 1042
Universal Studios Florida® Production Group, pg 1049

GEORGIA

Beachwood Productions, pg 804
Beast Atlanta, pg 804
COMPRO Productions Inc, pg 834
Crawford Media Services, pg 838
Doppler Studios, pg 851
ECG Productions, pg 856
Guerrilla Productions LLC, pg 883
Hottrax Records, pg 891
Lighting & Production Equipment Inc, pg 920
NorthTown Sounds Inc, pg 959
Omega Media Group Inc, pg 962
White Dog Studios, pg 1065

HAWAII

Audio Resource Honolulu, pg 794
KHNL/KGMB, pg 910
Media Bridge Gamekids, pg 936
TV Juice Productions Inc, pg 1046

IDAHO

Channel Productions, pg 823
Rex Morris Productions, pg 946

ILLINOIS

ABS Enterprises, pg 772
Analog Free Media, pg 786
AnswersMedia, pg 787
Assignment Desk, pg 792
Audio Visual Services Corp, pg 796
AudioTransitions, pg 796
Beatty TeleVisual Productions, pg 804
CCore Media Inc, pg 821
Comtech Multimedia Marketing, pg 834
Major Media Inc, pg 929
MIGHTYbYTES Inc, pg 942
Paragon Studios Inc, pg 969
Jim Passin Productions, pg 970
The Prairie Production Group, pg 980
PSAV® Presentation Services (Hotel Services Division), pg 987
RBR Productions, pg 992
Solid Sound Recording Studio, pg 1015
Sound/Video Impressions Inc, pg 1018
WEEK TV, pg 1063
Woodside Avenue Music Productions Inc, pg 1069

INDIANA

Advanced Media Integration, pg 777
AVA Productions, pg 798
Bright Ideas Creative Services, pg 812
Covenant Productions®, pg 837
Gaither Studios LLC, pg 875
Alan Johnson Recording, pg 905
OMNI Productions, pg 962
Sweetwater Sound Inc, pg 1029

IOWA

Hedquist Productions Inc, pg 887
The Production House, pg 984

KANSAS

Chapman Recording & Mastering, pg 824

KENTUCKY

Broadway Digital, pg 813
Hammond Communications Group, pg 884
Northern Kentucky University, pg 959
The PPS Group, pg 980
Trusty Tuneshop Recording Studios, pg 1045

LOUISIANA

Bay Records, pg 803
Disk Productions, pg 849
Moxie Media, pg 948
Vidox Motion Imagery, pg 1057

MAINE

Headlight Audio Visual Inc, pg 887

MARYLAND

The Ahern Group, pg 779
Bethesda Softworks LLC, pg 806
CPR MultiMedia Solutions, pg 837
CSPMedia.com, pg 840
The Cutting Corp, pg 841
dbF a Media Company, pg 844
The Image Generators, pg 895
Lion & Fox Recording Studios, pg 922
Milner-Fenwick Inc, pg 943
Omega Recording Studios, pg 962
Pro Cuts Editing Services, pg 982
Satellite Media Production, pg 1003
Sheffield Audio/Video Productions, pg 1008
Soundtrax Optical Sound Recording, pg 1018
Speakeasy Productions, pg 1020

MASSACHUSETTS

Continental Recordings Inc, pg 835
Cramer Productions, pg 837
Emergency Film Group, pg 860
Goin' Mobile, pg 880
Green Mountain Post Films (GMP), pg 882
Labrecque Creative Sound, pg 915
M Works Mastering Studios, pg 927
Newbury Media, pg 956
Northeastern Digital Recording Inc, pg 959
Penfield Productions Ltd, pg 971
Preston Productions Inc, pg 981
Professional Audio Design Inc, pg 985
Revels Records, pg 995
Ben Rudnick & Friends, pg 1000
Sound & Vision Media, pg 1017
Sounds Interesting Studios, pg 1018
Soundtrack Recording Studios, pg 1018
Rik Tinory Productions, pg 1041

MICHIGAN

Audio Graphic Services, pg 794
Brilliance Audio, pg 812
The Brookwood Studio Inc, pg 814
Digi Sign Design LLC, pg 847
GMP Music, pg 879
K&R's Recording Studios Inc, pg 908
MessageMakers, pg 939
Michigan Recording Arts Institute & Technologies, pg 941
Rebirth/Wenha Records, pg 993
TGA Recording Co, pg 1038

MINNESOTA

The ADS Group, pg 777
Aggressive Records Audio Duplication LLC, pg 778
Badiyan Inc, pg 801
Beyers Sound & Essay Audio, pg 806
GMI Productions, pg 879
Jamieson & Associates Inc, pg 904
Media Loft Inc, pg 937
MultiMedia, pg 950
Rum Jungle Media, pg 1000
Winterland Studios, pg 1068

MISSOURI

Avatar Studios, pg 798
Hardcastle Films & Video, pg 885
Ozam Production, pg 966
Production Consultants, pg 984
Show-Me Audio-Visual, pg 1009
Studio Worx Inc, pg 1027

MONTANA

Jereco Studios Inc, pg 905
KCFW Television, pg 908
KUSM TV, pg 914
North Country Media Group, pg 959
ooLite Media, pg 964

NEBRASKA

JoeAudio, pg 905
Three Pillars Media, pg 1040

NEVADA

DVDs4Less, pg 854
HDTV Productions Inc, pg 886
JCS Video Productions, pg 904
Tanglewood Productions, pg 1031
VirtualMix, pg 1058

NEW HAMPSHIRE

Apertura, pg 788
Captain Fiddle Music & Publications, pg 820

NEW JERSEY

All Jersey Studios, pg 780
Audio Visual Dynamics®, pg 795
Color Leasing Studios, pg 831
Euro-Pacific Film & Video Productions Inc, pg 863
Image Up, pg 895
Jeep Jazz Media Solutions, pg 905
Kimbo Educational, pg 910
Laurel Video Productions, pg 916
Mia Mind Music, pg 941
MIB Mediaworks, pg 941
Midnight Media Group Inc, pg 942
Milbrodt/Music & Sound Design, pg 943
Milgrom Productions, pg 943
Moe AV LLC, pg 945
NFL Films Inc, pg 957
NFL Films Music Library, pg 957
Oasis CD Manufacturing, pg 960
Optisonics Productions, pg 965
Shanachie Entertainment Corp, pg 1008
Starlite Productions, pg 1024
Suede Interactive, pg 1027
VCSvideo, pg 1052
Video Ideas Productions, pg 1055

NEW MEXICO

Production Outfitters, pg 984

NEW YORK

Acme Recording Studios Inc, pg 774
The Audio Department Inc, pg 794
Aura Sonic Ltd, pg 796
Aural Gratification Inc, pg 796
aurora productions, pg 797
Big Fish Productions Inc, pg 807
The Big House Group, pg 807
Bridge Records Inc, pg 812
Chromavision Corp, pg 826
dM works, pg 849
Eastco Multimedia Solutions Inc, pg 856
Electric Lady Studios, pg 858
Fingerpaint, pg 868
HB-Content, pg 886
Headroom Digital Audio, pg 887
Heavy Melody, pg 887
Hello World Communications, pg 888
InterNation Inc, pg 900
Kamen Entertainment Group Inc, pg 908
KAS Music & Sound, pg 908
L A Bruell Inc, pg 914
Magno Sound & Video, pg 929
Manhattan Center Studios Inc, pg 930
Mark Custom Recording Service Inc, pg 931
Jack Morton Worldwide, pg 946
Mother West, pg 947
MRG Productions Inc, pg 948
MRM Worldwide, pg 948
The Napoleon Group, pg 952
New York Audio Productions, pg 956
No Soap Productions, pg 957
Now Hear This, pg 960
Nutmeg Post, pg 960
Shelly Palmer Production, pg 968
Posthorn Recordings, pg 979
Quad Recording Studios, pg 988
RadioArt/Bob & Ray CDs & MP3 Files, pg 990
David Rapkin Audio Production, pg 991
Sear Sound, pg 1005
Elliot Sokolov Music, pg 1015
Sony Music Entertainment, pg 1016
TBA Global Events, pg 1032
Tiki Recording Studios Inc, pg 1040
Visual Technologies Corp, pg 1060
Zelman Studios Ltd, pg 1073

NORTH CAROLINA

Pat Appleson Studios Inc, pg 788
J Arnold Productions Inc, pg 790

Sound Recording—Magnetic

AUDIO

Sound Recording—Magnetic (continued)

FLORIDA

Allegro Productions Inc, pg 781
Cinema East, pg 827
Communications Concepts Inc (CCI), pg 833
Eastern Video, pg 856
Gulf Coast Audio Visual Producers Inc, pg 883
Home Shopping Network (HSN), pg 890
LHV Audio Services, pg 919
Mach 1 Productions, pg 927
Morrisound Recording, pg 946
Phat Planet Recording Studios, pg 973
Progressive Media & Music, pg 985
Style-City Music Inc, pg 1027
Universal Studios Florida® Production Group, pg 1049
Mike Vasilinda Productions Inc, pg 1052

GEORGIA

Beachwood Productions, pg 804
Doppler Studios, pg 851
Hottrax Records, pg 891
Stage Front Presentation Systems, pg 1022

HAWAII

Audio Resource Honolulu, pg 794
Media Bridge Gamekids, pg 936
TV Juice Productions Inc, pg 1046

ILLINOIS

CCore Media Inc, pg 821
Comtech Multimedia Marketing, pg 834
Delmark Records, pg 845
On Site Video, pg 963
Paragon Studios Inc, pg 969
RBR Productions, pg 992
WEEK TV, pg 1063
Woodside Avenue Music Productions Inc, pg 1069

INDIANA

AVA Productions, pg 798
Communication Ministries, pg 833
OMNI Productions, pg 962

IOWA

The Production House, pg 984

KANSAS

Chapman Recording & Mastering, pg 824

LOUISIANA

Moxie Media, pg 948

MARYLAND

Bethesda Softworks LLC, pg 806
CPR MultiMedia Solutions, pg 837
The Cutting Corp, pg 841
dbF a Media Company, pg 844
Omega Recording Studios, pg 962
Satellite Media Production, pg 1003
Sheffield Audio/Video Productions, pg 1008

MASSACHUSETTS

CommCreative, pg 832
Continental Recordings Inc, pg 835
Green Mountain Post Films (GMP), pg 882
Labrecque Creative Sound, pg 915
Monadnock Media Inc, pg 945
Penfield Productions Ltd, pg 971
Professional Audio Design Inc, pg 985
Soundtrack Recording Studios, pg 1018

MICHIGAN

Audio Graphic Services, pg 794
Brilliance Audio, pg 812
The Brookwood Studio Inc, pg 814
Digi Sign Design LLC, pg 847
GMP Music, pg 879
K&R's Recording Studios Inc, pg 908
MessageMakers, pg 939
Michigan Recording Arts Institute & Technologies, pg 941

MINNESOTA

The ADS Group, pg 777
Aggressive Records Audio Duplication LLC, pg 778
Badiyan Inc, pg 801
GMI Productions, pg 879
MultiMedia, pg 950

MISSOURI

Avatar Studios, pg 798
Production Consultants, pg 984
Show-Me Audio-Visual, pg 1009

MONTANA

Jereco Studios Inc, pg 905
KCFW Television, pg 908
KUSM TV, pg 914
North Country Media Group, pg 959

NEVADA

DVDs4Less, pg 854

NEW HAMPSHIRE

Apertura, pg 788
Captain Fiddle Music & Publications, pg 820

NEW JERSEY

All Jersey Studios, pg 780
Audio Visual Dynamics®, pg 795
Midnight Media Group Inc, pg 942
NFL Films Music Library, pg 957
Optisonics Productions, pg 965
Prism Media Products Inc, pg 982
Shanachie Entertainment Corp, pg 1008
Suede Interactive, pg 1027
VCSvideo, pg 1052

NEW MEXICO

Production Outfitters, pg 984

NEW YORK

aurora productions, pg 797
The Big House Group, pg 807
Chromavision Corp, pg 826
DuArt, pg 853
Heavy Melody, pg 887
Kamen Entertainment Group Inc, pg 908
KAS Music & Sound, pg 908
Magno Sound & Video, pg 929
Mother West, pg 947
MRG Productions Inc, pg 948
MRM Worldwide, pg 948
New York Audio Productions, pg 956
Now Hear This, pg 960
Shelly Palmer Production, pg 968
Posthorn Recordings, pg 979
David Rapkin Audio Production, pg 991
Sony Music Entertainment, pg 1016
TBA Global Events, pg 1032
Zelman Studios Ltd, pg 1073

NORTH CAROLINA

Pat Appleson Studios Inc, pg 788
Duke Media Services, pg 853
Franklin Video Inc, pg 872
Horizon Video Productions Inc, pg 891
Special Event Services, pg 1020
Trailblazer Studios®, pg 1043
2BruceStudio, pg 1047

OHIO

Russ Beckner Pictures, pg 804
Creative Technology, pg 838
Cuyahoga Community College Media Center, pg 841
Lyon Video Inc, pg 927
Mills James Productions, pg 943
Musicol Recording, pg 951
SoundSpace Inc, pg 1018
Vista Color Imaging Inc, pg 1059

PENNSYLVANIA

Audio Visual Communications Inc, pg 795
Craig Recording Studios, pg 837
FMP Media Solutions Inc, pg 870
Forge Recording LLC, pg 871
Goodman Associates Inc, pg 880
Ivory Productions, pg 903
Kloss Studios Co, pg 912
Production Masters Inc (PMI), pg 984
Right Coast Recording Inc, pg 997
Ted The Fiddler Music, pg 1035

RHODE ISLAND

Sound-FX-Design, pg 1017

SOUTH CAROLINA

DaviSound, pg 843
Venture Media, pg 1052

TENNESSEE

Analog Man Recording Studio, pg 786
Ardent Studios Inc, pg 789
Continental Film, pg 835
Love Shack Recording Studios, pg 925
Memphis Communications Corp, pg 938
Mr Mark's Used Musical, Stereo & Studio Equipment Store, pg 944
Motion Picture Services, pg 947
Scripps Networks, pg 1005
Stage Post, pg 1022
Technical Support Systems LLC, pg 1034
Zion Music Group, pg 1074

TEXAS

Audiomoxie®, pg 796
Fire Station Studios, pg 868
Marx InDigital, pg 933
The Samuels Co, pg 1002
Sound Works, pg 1018
South Coast Film & Video, pg 1019
Texas Heart Institute Visual Communication Services, pg 1037
Tropikal Productions, pg 1045

VIRGINIA

American AV, pg 783
AudioImage Recording, pg 796
BES Studios, pg 805
Bias Studios, pg 806
CACI Productions Group, pg 816
Wally Cleaver's Recording Service, pg 830
Lion Recording Services Inc, pg 922

WASHINGTON

Inland Audio Visual Co, pg 898
Pacific Multimedia Inc, pg 967
Victory Studios, pg 1054

WISCONSIN

Audio Visual of Milwaukee Inc, pg 795
USAV Group Inc, pg 1050
Wisconsin Public Television, pg 1068

WYOMING

Bridger Productions Inc, pg 812

BRITISH COLUMBIA

Finale Editworks, pg 868
Pinewood Sound, pg 975

ONTARIO

MCS Recording Studios, pg 936
Metalworks Recording Studios Inc, pg 939
Spence-Thomas Audio Post, pg 1021
VO2 Mix Studios, pg 1060
Westbury National Show Systems Ltd, pg 1064

Sound Recording—Optical

ARIZONA

Allusion Studios & Pure Wave Audio, pg 782
Merestone, pg 938

CALIFORNIA

AB Audio Visual Entertainment Inc, pg 772
Chace Audio by Deluxe, pg 823
Diamond Dreams Music Productions, pg 846
Earwax Productions Inc, pg 855
Film Technology Co Inc, pg 867
Lynch Communications, pg 926
Main Street Media Inc, pg 929
OTR Studios, pg 966
QRS Software Services, pg 988
Saturn Studios, pg 1003
SonicPool, pg 1016
Todd-AO Studios, pg 1041
Total Media Group, pg 1042
Tranquil Technology Music, pg 1043
Wildfire Post Production Studios, pg 1066

COLORADO

The Cinema Lab, pg 827

FLORIDA

Allegro Productions Inc, pg 781
CD ROM™ Inc, pg 822
Gulf Coast Audio Visual Producers Inc, pg 883
LHV Audio Services, pg 919
Phat Planet Recording Studios, pg 973
Progressive Media & Music, pg 985
Style-City Music Inc, pg 1027

GEORGIA

Hottrax Records, pg 891
NorthTown Sounds Inc, pg 959
Stage Front Presentation Systems, pg 1022

HAWAII

Media Bridge Gamekids, pg 936
TV Juice Productions Inc, pg 1046

ILLINOIS

RBR Productions, pg 992
Sparrow Sound Design, pg 1019
Woodside Avenue Music Productions Inc, pg 1069

INDIANA

Covenant Productions®, pg 837
Alan Johnson Recording, pg 905

LOUISIANA

Disk Productions, pg 849

MARYLAND

Bethesda Softworks LLC, pg 806
Omega Recording Studios, pg 962
Sheffield Audio/Video Productions, pg 1008
Soundtrax Optical Sound Recording, pg 1018

MASSACHUSETTS

CommCreative, pg 832
Professional Audio Design Inc, pg 985
Soundtrack Recording Studios, pg 1018
WVP Boston, pg 1071

MICHIGAN

Brilliance Audio, pg 812
Digi Sign Design LLC, pg 847
GMP Music, pg 879
K&R's Recording Studios Inc, pg 908
Michigan Recording Arts Institute & Technologies, pg 941

MINNESOTA

Aggressive Records Audio Duplication LLC, pg 778

MISSOURI

Avatar Studios, pg 798
Show-Me Audio-Visual, pg 1009

MONTANA

Jereco Studios Inc, pg 905

NEW HAMPSHIRE

Apertura, pg 788

NEW JERSEY

CFP Video Productions Inc, pg 823
Midnight Media Group Inc, pg 942
Milgrom Productions, pg 943
NFL Films Music Library, pg 957
Prism Media Products Inc, pg 982
Suede Interactive, pg 1027

NEW YORK

DuArt, pg 853
Heavy Melody, pg 887
Magno Sound & Video, pg 929
Mother West, pg 947
MRG Productions Inc, pg 948
Now Hear This, pg 960
Shelly Palmer Production, pg 968
TBA Global Events, pg 1032

NORTH CAROLINA

Pat Appleson Studios Inc, pg 788

PENNSYLVANIA

Craig Recording Studios, pg 837
Javboy Records, pg 904

RHODE ISLAND

Sound-FX-Design, pg 1017

TENNESSEE

American Blackguard Inc, pg 784
Analog Man Recording Studio, pg 786
Ardent Studios Inc, pg 789
Memphis Communications Corp, pg 938
Motion Picture Services, pg 947
Stage Post, pg 1022

TEXAS

The Sound Lab Inc, pg 1017
Tropikal Productions, pg 1045

VIRGINIA

AudioImage Recording, pg 796
Lion Recording Services Inc, pg 922

WASHINGTON

Quiet Planet LLC, pg 989
Victory Studios, pg 1054

WISCONSIN

Audio Visual of Milwaukee Inc, pg 795

ONTARIO

Metalworks Recording Studios Inc, pg 939
VO2 Mix Studios, pg 1060

Sound Stripping

ARIZONA

Merestone, pg 938

CALIFORNIA

Lynch Communications, pg 926
PM Productions, pg 977
Polarity Post Production, pg 978
QRS Software Services, pg 988

FLORIDA

Phat Planet Recording Studios, pg 973

ILLINOIS

Woodside Avenue Music Productions Inc, pg 1069

MARYLAND

Bethesda Softworks LLC, pg 806
CPR MultiMedia Solutions, pg 837

MASSACHUSETTS

Soundtrack Recording Studios, pg 1018

MICHIGAN

Digi Sign Design LLC, pg 847
K&R's Recording Studios Inc, pg 908
Michigan Recording Arts Institute & Technologies, pg 941

MINNESOTA

Aggressive Records Audio Duplication LLC, pg 778

NEW JERSEY

CFP Video Productions Inc, pg 823
Suede Interactive, pg 1027

NEW YORK

The Big House Group, pg 807
Heavy Melody, pg 887
Hello World Communications, pg 888
Kamen Entertainment Group Inc, pg 908
KAS Music & Sound, pg 908
MRG Productions Inc, pg 948
Now Hear This, pg 960
Nutmeg Post, pg 960
Shelly Palmer Production, pg 968
TBA Global Events, pg 1032

NORTH CAROLINA

Pat Appleson Studios Inc, pg 788

TENNESSEE

Love Shack Recording Studios, pg 925
Motion Picture Services, pg 947
Stage Post, pg 1022

TEXAS

Sound Works, pg 1018

VIRGINIA

Lion Recording Services Inc, pg 922

WASHINGTON

Hamilton Studio, pg 884

WISCONSIN

Audio Visual of Milwaukee Inc, pg 795
Wisconsin Public Television, pg 1068

MANITOBA

daCapo Productions, pg 842

ONTARIO

Spence-Thomas Audio Post, pg 1021
VO2 Mix Studios, pg 1060

Sound System—Portable Distributors

ALABAMA

Curtis Company, pg 841

ARIZONA

Arizona Cine Equipment, pg 789
EAR Professional Audio/Video, pg 855
Metropolitan Audio-Visual Inc, pg 940
Projector SuperStore LLC, pg 986
Troxell Communications Inc, pg 1045
Ultimate Presentation Systems Inc, pg 1047

ARKANSAS

White Diamond Productions, pg 1065

CALIFORNIA

Adolph Gasser Inc, pg 776
Ametron Audio/Video, pg 785
Associated Sound, pg 792
ATV Video Center Inc, pg 793
Audio Images Corp, pg 794
Be Media, pg 804
California Tape Products Inc, pg 817
Carvin Corp, pg 820
Delicate Electronics Sales Inc, pg 845
Empire Wholesale Inc, pg 860
FXC Communications, pg 874
Gallien/Krueger, pg 875
Hosa Technology Inc, pg 891
IAMP Professional Audio, pg 893
Instructional Materials & Equipment Distributors (I-Med), pg 899
JD Audio Visual Inc, pg 904
L Acoustics US, pg 914
Location Sound Corp, pg 924
Lloyd F McKinney Associates Inc, pg 935
MediaPOINTE, pg 938
Phonic Ear Inc (FrontRow), pg 974
POP TV, pg 978
Professional Sound Corp, pg 985
QSC Audio Products LLC, pg 988
Radian Audio Engineering Inc, pg 990
Related Visual Inc, pg 994
Randall Schiller Productions, pg 1004
Sonance, pg 1015
Sound Service Co, pg 1017
Southern California Sound Image Inc, pg 1019
SSL Industries Inc, pg 1022
Stanislaus Audio Video Inc, pg 1023
Synthesizer Systems Technologies (SST), pg 1030
Technical Audio Devices (TAD)™, pg 1033
TOA Electronics Inc, pg 1041
Towards 2000 Inc, pg 1043
VMI Inc, pg 1060

COLORADO

Audio Consultant Services Inc, pg 794
Daylight Productions & Rentals, pg 844
Spectrum Audio Visual Services, pg 1020

AUDIO

Sound System—Portable Distributors (continued)

CONNECTICUT

Connecticut Audio & Theatrical Supply, pg 835
Everett Hall Associates Inc, pg 863
HB Communications Inc, pg 886
Sennheiser Electronic Corp, pg 1006

DELAWARE

Actors Attic, pg 775

FLORIDA

Allstar Audio Systems Inc, pg 782
AVI-SPL, pg 798
BAI Distributors Inc, pg 801
Broadcasters General Store Inc, pg 813
Digital Video Systems Inc, pg 848
General Projection Systems Inc, pg 877
Gulf Coast Audio Visual Producers Inc, pg 883
Harmon's Audio-Visual Services, pg 885
Harris Corp, pg 885
Hi-Tech Import Export Corp, pg 888
Hunter Electronics LLC, pg 892
Industrial Strength Inc, pg 897
Lighting Sales Connections, pg 920
Midtown Video Inc, pg 942
Photomart Cine-Video Inc, pg 975
Pro Stage Inc, pg 983
Recording Media & Equipment Inc (RM&E), pg 993
Sight & Sound Productions, pg 1010
Stereo Sales Inc, pg 1024
TAI Audio, pg 1031
Technomedia Solutions, pg 1035

GEORGIA

Lighting & Production Equipment Inc, pg 920
LT Sound Inc, pg 925
Omnimedia Inc, pg 962
Stage Front Presentation Systems, pg 1022

HAWAII

The Audio Visual Co (AVCO), pg 795

ILLINOIS

Allen Visual Systems Inc, pg 781
Central Audio-Visual Equipment Inc, pg 823
Joseph Electronics, pg 906
G T Luscombe Co Inc, pg 926
Sound Vision Inc, pg 1018

INDIANA

Heart Breaker Entertainment LLC, pg 887
Sensory Technologies LLC, pg 1006
SHP Electronics, pg 1010
Sweetwater Sound Inc, pg 1029

IOWA

ECS Inc, pg 856

KANSAS

Smith Audio-Visual Inc, pg 1014

KENTUCKY

Audio Visual Techniques Inc, pg 796
Axxis Inc, pg 800
Barney Miller's Inc, pg 943
NOR-COM Inc, pg 958
Northern Kentucky University, pg 959

LOUISIANA

Intermedia Technologies, pg 900
Pace Systems, pg 966

MAINE

Headlight Audio Visual Inc, pg 887

MARYLAND

Advance Audiovisual Presentation Ltd, pg 777
Bradley Broadcast & Pro Audio, pg 811
Cardinal Sound & Video, pg 820
Kipp Visual Systems Inc, pg 911

MASSACHUSETTS

Terry Hanley Audio Systems Inc, pg 884
Rule Broadcast Systems, pg 1000

MICHIGAN

Olson Anderson Co, pg 786
Ascom Communications Contractors, pg 791
City Events Group, pg 828
Digi Sign Design LLC, pg 847
On Stage Visuals, pg 963
TeL Systems, pg 1035

MINNESOTA

Advanced Audio-Visual Inc, pg 777
Alpha Video & Audio Inc, pg 782
Harris Communications Inc, pg 885
New Life Communications Inc, pg 956

MISSISSIPPI

Bowie Audio Visual Enterprises Inc, pg 811

MISSOURI

Communitronics Corp, pg 833
Conference Technologies Inc, pg 835
MIS Technologies, pg 944
Schiller's Audio-Visual, pg 1004

NEVADA

Pignose-Gorilla, pg 975

NEW HAMPSHIRE

APS Lighting-Sound-AV, pg 789

NEW JERSEY

Alltec Stores, a Vcom IMC Company, pg 782
Audio Visual Associates, pg 795
AV Bluebook, pg 797
Comprehensive Cable & Connectivity Co, pg 833
Earl Girls Inc, pg 855
G&G Technologies Inc, pg 875
Hamilton Buhl, pg 884

The Music Place, pg 951
National Audio-Visual Supply, pg 952
Nelson Enterprises Theatrical Supply Co, pg 954
Onkyo USA Corp, pg 963
SLD Lighting, pg 1013
Starlite Productions, pg 1024
Total Video Products Inc, pg 1042
Video Corporation of America (VCA), pg 1055
Wilray Audio Visual Corp, pg 1067
Wired 4 Sound Inc, pg 1068
York Telecom, pg 1072

NEW MEXICO

Quickbeam Systems Inc (QSI), pg 989

NEW YORK

Ace Video, pg 774
Albany Theatre Supply Co Inc, pg 780
ALTEL Systems Inc, pg 783
Audio-Video Corp, pg 795
Aura Sonic Ltd, pg 796
AV Workshop, pg 797
Colortone Audio Visual, pg 832
Communication Corner Inc, pg 832
Custom Media Environments, pg 841
Design Audio Visual Inc, pg 845
Gaylord Brothers, pg 876
Hot House Professional Audio, pg 891
Indigo Productions, pg 897
KVL Audio Visual Services Inc, pg 914
Lee Dan® Communications Inc, pg 918
Long Island Video Enterprises Live Inc, pg 924
Magnaplan Corp, pg 928
Markertek Video Supply, pg 931
NorthCountry Distributors, pg 959
RNJ Electronics, pg 997
SmartSource Computer & AV Rentals, pg 1014
Technisphere Corp, pg 1034
Theatrical Services & Supplies Inc, pg 1038
Visual Word Systems Inc, pg 1060
Yorkville Sound Inc, pg 1072

OHIO

Copp Integrated Systems, pg 836
ITA Audio Visual Solutions, pg 902
Lubell Labs Inc, pg 925
Luminaud Inc, pg 926
Parts Express, pg 969
Jimmy Rea Electronics Inc, pg 992
Smithall Electronics, pg 1014
Tri-State Audio Visual Co, pg 1044

OREGON

Lightspeed Technologies Inc, pg 921
Spectrum Systems Design, pg 1021
SuperDigital Ltd, pg 1029

PENNSYLVANIA

Advanced AV, pg 777
Audio Visions Inc, pg 795
Audio Visual Communications Inc, pg 795
Bernie's Photo Center, pg 805
Clair Brothers Audio Systems Inc, pg 829
J E Foss Co, pg 871
Garcia Marketing Inc, pg 875

Grise Audio Visual Center Inc, pg 882
Morefield Communications Inc, pg 946
RSS Distributors, pg 1000
Sound by Fitch, pg 1017
Vistacom Inc, pg 1059
Visual Sound Inc, pg 1059

SOUTH CAROLINA

DaviSound, pg 843

TENNESSEE

Belew Enterprises, pg 804
Durrell LLC, pg 854
Lowrance Sound Co Inc, pg 925
Mr Mark's Used Musical, Stereo & Studio Equipment Store, pg 944
Spectrum Sound Inc, pg 1021
Technical Support Systems LLC, pg 1034
Trew Audio Inc, pg 1044
Zion Music Group, pg 1074

TEXAS

AVES Audio Visual Systems Inc, pg 798
CAM Audio Inc, pg 817
Crossroads Audio Inc, pg 840
Data Projections Inc, pg 843
Digital Display Solutions Inc, pg 847
FitzCo Sound Inc, pg 869
Heffernan Audio Visual, pg 887
Lubbock Audio Visual Inc, pg 925
Pro Video & Film Equipment Co Inc, pg 983
Quality Audio Visual Service Inc, pg 988
Schoolhouse Audio Visual, pg 1004
Southwest Sound & Electronics Inc, pg 1019
Stage Directions, pg 1022
Tarpley Media Systems, pg 1032

UTAH

Performance Audio, pg 973

VIRGINIA

Acoustics First Corp, pg 775
Avitecture Inc, pg 799
Boitnott Visual Communications Corp (BVC), pg 810
Communications Specialists Inc, pg 833
Lee Hartman & Sons Inc, pg 918
Rocktown Media, pg 998
The Whitlock Group, pg 1065

WASHINGTON

CCI Solutions, pg 821
D A Sound, pg 842
Northern Lights & Pro Audio, pg 959
Pacific Northwest Theatre Associates Inc (PNTA), pg 967

WEST VIRGINIA

United Sound & Electronics, pg 1048

WISCONSIN

Audio Visual of Milwaukee Inc, pg 795
Camera Corner Connecting Point, pg 818
Full Compass Systems, pg 874

PUERTO RICO

Audio Visual Concepts Inc, pg 795
Bonnin Electronics Inc, pg 810

ALBERTA

Infosat Communications Inc, pg 898
Matrix Video Communications Corp (MVCC), pg 934
McBain Audio Visual Ltd, pg 935
Sharp's Audio-Visual Ltd, pg 1008
Unique Communications Ltd, pg 1048

BRITISH COLUMBIA

ADI Systems Inc, pg 776
Commercial Electronics Ltd, pg 832

MANITOBA

Advance Pro, pg 777
Inland Audio Visual Ltd, pg 898

ONTARIO

Cinema Stage Inc, pg 827
HD Source, pg 886
Nationwide Audio Visual Co, pg 953
Premier A/V Sales Ltd, pg 980
Westbury National Show Systems Ltd, pg 1064

QUEBEC

AVS Technologies Inc, pg 800
Concept Audio-Visual, pg 834
JAM Industries Ltd, pg 903
SC Media Canada, pg 1003

Sound System—Portable Manufacturers

ARIZONA

Fender Musical Instruments Corp, pg 866
MTX Audio, pg 949

ARKANSAS

Sound-Craft Systems Inc, pg 1017

CALIFORNIA

Anchor Audio Inc, pg 786
Califone International Inc, pg 817
Carvin Corp, pg 820
Directed Electronics, pg 848
Gallien/Krueger, pg 875
Hosa Technology Inc, pg 891
L Acoustics US, pg 914
Orevox USA Corp, pg 965
Panasonic Broadcast & Digital Systems Co, pg 968
Panasonic Professional Audio Systems, pg 968
Professional Sound Corp, pg 985
Radian Audio Engineering Inc, pg 990
Renkus-Heinz Inc, pg 994
Sonance, pg 1015
TeachLogic Inc, pg 1033
Technical Audio Devices (TAD)™, pg 1033
TOA Electronics Inc, pg 1041

FLORIDA

Magna-Tech Electronic Co Inc, pg 928

ILLINOIS

ACCO Brands Corp, pg 773
AmpliVox Portable Sound Systems, pg 785
Bag End Loudspeakers, pg 801
Sound Physics Labs Inc, pg 1017
SoundTech, pg 1018

KANSAS

Galaxy Audio, pg 875

MARYLAND

RCI Custom Products, pg 992

MASSACHUSETTS

Bose Corp, pg 811
Eastern Acoustic Works Inc (EAW), pg 856
Technomad™ Inc, pg 1035

MINNESOTA

Telex Communications Inc, pg 1037
Telex EVI, pg 1037

MISSISSIPPI

Peavey Electronics Corp, pg 970

NEVADA

Pignose-Gorilla, pg 975

NEW JERSEY

AV Bluebook, pg 797
National Audio-Visual Supply, pg 952
Oklahoma Sound Corp, pg 961
Onkyo USA Corp, pg 963
Panasonic Corp, pg 968

NEW MEXICO

Lectrosonics Inc, pg 918

NEW YORK

Ashly Audio Inc, pg 792
MG Electronics, pg 940
Yorkville Sound Inc, pg 1072

OHIO

Luminaud Inc, pg 926

OKLAHOMA

Digital Designs, pg 847

OREGON

BIAMP Systems, pg 806
Lightspeed Technologies Inc, pg 921

PENNSYLVANIA

Clair Brothers Audio Systems Inc, pg 829
Community Professional Loudspeakers, pg 833

RHODE ISLAND

Numark Industries Inc, pg 960

SOUTH CAROLINA

DaviSound, pg 843
Paso Sound Products Inc, pg 969

TENNESSEE

Auratron Systems, pg 796
Brantley Sound Associates Inc, pg 812
Cerwin-Vega! Inc, pg 823
Durrell LLC, pg 854

UTAH

Listen Technologies Corp, pg 923
Spectra Sonics Applied Technology Inc, pg 1020

VIRGINIA

Acoustics First Corp, pg 775

WASHINGTON

McCauley Sound Inc, pg 935

WEST VIRGINIA

United Sound & Electronics, pg 1048

ONTARIO

Tannoy North America Inc, pg 1031

Sound System—Portable Rentals

ALABAMA

Audio-Video Resources Inc, pg 795

ARIZONA

Arizona Cine Equipment, pg 789
AV Concepts, pg 797
Merestone, pg 938
Metropolitan Audio-Visual Inc, pg 940
Ultimate Presentation Systems Inc, pg 1047
Video West Inc, pg 1056

ARKANSAS

White Diamond Productions, pg 1065

CALIFORNIA

Absolute Rentals, pg 772
Adolph Gasser Inc, pg 776
AGF Media Services, pg 778
Alliant Event Services, pg 781
Ametron Audio/Video, pg 785
Associated Sound, pg 792
ATV Video Center Inc, pg 793
Audio Rents, pg 794
AV Guys, pg 797
Express Media Inc, pg 864
FXC Communications, pg 874
IAMP Professional Audio, pg 893
Instructional Materials & Equipment Distributors (I-Med), pg 899
JD Audio Visual Inc, pg 904
Location Sound Corp, pg 924
Lynch Communications, pg 926
Maximus Media Inc, pg 934
McCune Audio-Video-Lighting, pg 935
Munday & Collins AV, pg 950
Muse Presentation Technologies, pg 950
On-Trax Inc, pg 963
PSAV® Presentation Services, pg 986
Related Visual Inc, pg 994
Alwin Sauers Audio Productions (ASAP), pg 1003
Randall Schiller Productions, pg 1004
Slate Media Group, pg 1013
Sonance, pg 1015
Sound Service Co, pg 1017
Stanislaus Audio Video Inc, pg 1023
Towards 2000 Inc, pg 1043
VER-Video Equipment Rentals, pg 1053
Video Resources Inc, pg 1056
Videorama Industries LLC, pg 1057
VMI Inc, pg 1060
Voice & Video Rentals, pg 1060

COLORADO

Audio Consultant Services Inc, pg 794
Daylight Productions & Rentals, pg 844
Maniac Productions, pg 930
Multimedia Audio Visual Inc, pg 950
Spectrum Audio Visual Services, pg 1020

CONNECTICUT

A/V Davey, pg 797
Connecticut Audio & Theatrical Supply, pg 835
Everett Hall Associates Inc, pg 863
Videofilm Systems Inc, pg 1057

DELAWARE

Actors Attic, pg 775
Showorks Audio Visual Inc, pg 1010
Side Door Studio Inc, pg 1010

FLORIDA

Allstar Audio Systems Inc, pg 782
AVI-SPL, pg 798
Gulf Coast Audio Visual Producers Inc, pg 883
Harmon's Audio-Visual Services, pg 885
Hi-Tech Enterprises Inc, pg 888
Image Technical Services, pg 895
Industrial Strength Inc, pg 897
Lighting Sales Connections, pg 920
Paradise Show & Design Inc, pg 969
Pro Stage Inc, pg 983
Sight & Sound Productions, pg 1010
TAI Audio, pg 1031
Technomedia Solutions, pg 1035
Universal Studios Florida® Production Group, pg 1049

GEORGIA

Lighting & Production Equipment Inc, pg 920
MAGNUM Companies Ltd, pg 929
Stage Front Presentation Systems, pg 1022
Staging Directions Inc, pg 1023

HAWAII

Sight & Sound Studios, pg 1010

ILLINOIS

Allen Visual Systems Inc, pg 781
AV Chicago Inc, pg 797
Backstar Creative Media Inc, pg 801
Beatty TeleVisual Productions, pg 804

AUDIO

Sound System—Portable Rentals (continued)

ILLINOIS (continued)

Central Audio-Visual Equipment Inc, pg 823
Creative Technology, pg 838
The Meetinghouse Companies Inc, pg 938
On Stage Audio, pg 963
RC Communications, pg 992
Show Department Inc, pg 1009
Sound Physics Labs Inc, pg 1017

INDIANA

Heart Breaker Entertainment LLC, pg 887

IOWA

Central Lighting & Equipment Inc (CLE), pg 823
ECS Inc, pg 856

KENTUCKY

Audio Visual Techniques Inc, pg 796
Barney Miller's Inc, pg 943

LOUISIANA

Clark Services Audio Visual & Exhibit Inc, pg 829
Pace Systems, pg 966

MAINE

Headlight Audio Visual Inc, pg 887

MARYLAND

Advance Audiovisual Presentation Ltd, pg 777
Cardinal Sound & Video, pg 820
CPR MultiMedia Solutions, pg 837
CSPMedia.com, pg 840
Event Tech, pg 863
Hargrove Inc, pg 885
Shadowstone R & R™, pg 1008
Visual Aids Electronics Corp, pg 1059

MASSACHUSETTS

AVFX Inc, pg 798
Terry Hanley Audio Systems Inc, pg 884
massAV, pg 933
Preston Productions Inc, pg 981

MICHIGAN

City Events Group, pg 828
Digi Sign Design LLC, pg 847
K&R All Media Productions Inc, pg 908
K&R's Recording Studios Inc, pg 908
On Stage Visuals, pg 963
TeL Systems, pg 1035

MINNESOTA

Advanced Audio-Visual Inc, pg 777
Aggressive Records Audio Duplication LLC, pg 778
Alpha Video & Audio Inc, pg 782
Big Event Productions LLC, pg 807
New Life Communications Inc, pg 956

MISSISSIPPI

Bowie Audio Visual Enterprises Inc, pg 811

MISSOURI

Show-Me Audio-Visual, pg 1009
Switch, pg 1030

MONTANA

Jereco Studios Inc, pg 905

NEVADA

GES Audio Visual, pg 877
Lefco Video Services Inc, pg 918

NEW HAMPSHIRE

APS Lighting-Sound-AV, pg 789

NEW JERSEY

Audio Visual Associates, pg 795
Audio Visual Dynamics®, pg 795
Earl Girls Inc, pg 855
Giant Audio Visual Inc, pg 878
International Audio Visual Inc, pg 900
MIB Mediaworks, pg 941
Moe AV LLC, pg 945
The Music Place, pg 951
Nelson Enterprises Theatrical Supply Co, pg 954
PLS Staging, pg 977
SLD Lighting, pg 1013
Starlite Productions, pg 1024
Wired 4 Sound Inc, pg 1068

NEW MEXICO

Production Outfitters, pg 984
Quickbeam Systems Inc (QSI), pg 989

NEW YORK

Ace Video, pg 774
Albany Theatre Supply Co Inc, pg 780
Audio Visual Resources LLC, pg 795
Aura Sonic Ltd, pg 796
AV Workshop, pg 797
Colortone Audio Visual, pg 832
Communication Corner Inc, pg 832
CP Communications, pg 837
Custom Media Environments, pg 841
Design Audio Visual Inc, pg 845
Dreamhire LLC, pg 852
Hello World Communications, pg 888
KVL Audio Visual Services Inc, pg 914
Long Island Video Enterprises Live Inc, pg 924
Posthorn Recordings, pg 979
See Factor Industry Inc, pg 1006
SmartSource Computer & AV Rentals, pg 1014
Specialized Audio-Visual Inc, pg 1020
Studio Instrument Rentals (SIR), pg 1027
TBA Global Events, pg 1032
Technisphere Corp, pg 1034
Theatrical Services & Supplies Inc, pg 1038
Visual Word Systems Inc, pg 1060
WorldStage, pg 1070

NORTH CAROLINA

A&V Company, pg 772
Audio & Light, pg 794
AV Metro Inc, pg 797
Special Event Services, pg 1020
Visual Aids Electronics of North Carolina Inc, pg 1059

NORTH DAKOTA

Media Productions, pg 937

OHIO

Hughie's Event Production Services, pg 892
ITA Audio Visual Solutions, pg 902
Mills James Productions, pg 943
Production Solutions Inc, pg 984
R&B Communications Inc, pg 991
Smithall Electronics Inc, pg 1014

OKLAHOMA

PDC Productions, pg 970

OREGON

Rose City Sound, pg 999

PENNSYLVANIA

Advanced AV, pg 777
Audio Visions Inc, pg 795
Audio Visual Communications Inc, pg 795
Clair Brothers Audio Systems Inc, pg 829
FMP Media Solutions Inc, pg 870
Grise Audio Visual Center Inc, pg 882
North Star Satellite Communications Inc, pg 959
Production Solutions Inc, pg 985
Sound by Fitch, pg 1017
Vistacom Inc, pg 1059
Visual Sound Inc, pg 1059

SOUTH CAROLINA

DaviSound, pg 843

TENNESSEE

Belew Enterprises, pg 804
Brantley Sound Associates Inc, pg 812
Durrell LLC, pg 854
Love Shack Recording Studios, pg 925
Mr Mark's Used Musical, Stereo & Studio Equipment Store, pg 944
Technical Support Systems LLC, pg 1034
Trew Audio Inc, pg 1044

TEXAS

Alford Media Services, pg 780
Bright Star Productions Inc, pg 812
Crossroads Audio Inc, pg 840
Data Projections Inc, pg 843
Digital Display Solutions Inc, pg 847
FitzCo Sound Inc, pg 869
Lubbock Audio Visual Inc, pg 925
Music Lab Inc, pg 950
Onstage Systems, pg 963
Padgitt's, pg 967
Power Factory Productions, pg 979
Quality Audio Visual Service Inc, pg 988
Tropikal Productions, pg 1045

UTAH

Listen Technologies Corp, pg 923
Performance Audio, pg 973

VERMONT

Parlato Productions, pg 969

VIRGINIA

Advance Concepts Inc, pg 777
American AV, pg 783
Avitecture Inc, pg 799
Boitnott Visual Communications Corp (BVC), pg 810
Lee Hartman & Sons Inc, pg 918
The Whitlock Group, pg 1065

WASHINGTON

D A Sound, pg 842
Northern Lights & Pro Audio, pg 959
Pacific Northwest Theatre Associates Inc (PNTA), pg 967

WEST VIRGINIA

Blackwater Video Productions, pg 808
United Sound & Electronics, pg 1048

WISCONSIN

Camera Corner Connecting Point, pg 818
Event Essentials, pg 863
Full Compass Systems, pg 874

WYOMING

Bridger Productions Inc, pg 812

PUERTO RICO

Stage Crew Audiovisual Inc, pg 1022

ALBERTA

Allstar Show Industries Inc, pg 782
Cine Audio Visual Sales & Service Ltd, pg 826
Evolution Presentation Technologies, pg 863
L R Light & Sound, pg 915
McBain Audio Visual Ltd, pg 935
Sharp's Audio-Visual Ltd, pg 1008
Unique Communications Ltd, pg 1048

BRITISH COLUMBIA

Clark's Audio Visual Services Ltd, pg 829
DL Sound & Lighting Productions Ltd, pg 849

MANITOBA

Inland Audio Visual Ltd, pg 898

ONTARIO

HD Source, pg 886
Premier A/V Sales Ltd, pg 980
Westbury National Show Systems Ltd, pg 1064

QUEBEC

Audio Visual Dynamics Ltd, pg 795
Concept Audio-Visual, pg 834

AUDIO

Sound Transfer (continued)

MICHIGAN (continued)

K&R's Recording Studios Inc, pg 908
Michigan Recording Arts Institute & Technologies, pg 941
RingSide Creative, pg 997

MINNESOTA

The ADS Group, pg 777
Aggressive Records Audio Duplication LLC, pg 778
MultiMedia, pg 950
Winterland Studios, pg 1068

MISSOURI

Production Consultants, pg 984
Show-Me Audio-Visual, pg 1009

MONTANA

Jereco Studios Inc, pg 905

NEBRASKA

Three Pillars Media, pg 1040

NEW HAMPSHIRE

Apertura, pg 788

NEW JERSEY

All Jersey Studios, pg 780
CFP Video Productions Inc, pg 823
Image Up, pg 895
Midnight Media Group Inc, pg 942
NFL Films Inc, pg 957
NFL Films Music Library, pg 957
Oasis CD Manufacturing, pg 960
SADiE Inc, pg 1001
Suede Interactive, pg 1027
TRF Production Music Libraries, pg 1044

NEW YORK

Ace Video, pg 774
aurora productions, pg 797
The Big House Group, pg 807
Chromavision Corp, pg 826
De Wolfe Music USA, pg 844
Digital Force, pg 847
Heavy Melody, pg 887
KAS Music & Sound, pg 908
Magno Sound & Video, pg 929
Masterdisk Corp, pg 933
Mother West, pg 947
MRG Productions Inc, pg 948
Now Hear This, pg 960
Shelly Palmer Production, pg 968
Peckham Productions Inc, pg 970
Posthorn Recordings, pg 979
Sear Sound, pg 1005
Elliot Sokolov Music, pg 1015
TBA Global Events, pg 1032
Zelman Studios Ltd, pg 1073

NORTH CAROLINA

Pat Appleson Studios Inc, pg 788
Duke Media Services, pg 853
Trailblazer Studios®, pg 1043

OHIO

Cuyahoga Community College Media Center, pg 841
Lyon Video Inc, pg 927
Musicol Recording, pg 951
Vista Color Imaging Inc, pg 1059

OREGON

Lightspeed Technologies Inc, pg 921

PENNSYLVANIA

American Artist Studio, pg 783

RHODE ISLAND

Sound-FX-Design, pg 1017

TENNESSEE

Continental Film, pg 835
Love Shack Recording Studios, pg 925
Mr Mark's Used Musical, Stereo & Studio Equipment Store, pg 944
Motion Picture Services, pg 947
Stage Post, pg 1022
UMCom Productions, pg 1048

TEXAS

Audiomoxie®, pg 796
The Editing Co, pg 857
Out of the BLUE Media, pg 966
The Samuels Co, pg 1002
Texas Heart Institute Visual Communication Services, pg 1037
Tropikal Productions, pg 1045

VERMONT

University of Vermont, Instructional Television Dept, pg 1050

VIRGINIA

Lion Recording Services Inc, pg 922

WASHINGTON

Hamilton Studio, pg 884

WISCONSIN

Audio Visual of Milwaukee Inc, pg 795
Concept Productions Inc, pg 834
5th Floor Recording Co, pg 867
USAV Group Inc, pg 1050
Wisconsin Public Television, pg 1068

WYOMING

Bridger Productions Inc, pg 812

PUERTO RICO

Stage Crew Audiovisual Inc, pg 1022

BRITISH COLUMBIA

Finale Editworks, pg 868
Pinewood Sound, pg 975

MANITOBA

daCapo Productions, pg 842

ONTARIO

GAPC (General Assembly Production Centre), pg 875
JL Recording Studios, pg 905
Spence-Thomas Audio Post, pg 1021
VO2 Mix Studios, pg 1060
Wanted! Sound + Picture, pg 1062

Speaker Distributors

ALABAMA

Media Visions Inc, pg 937

ARIZONA

Allusion Studios & Pure Wave Audio, pg 782
Arizona Cine Equipment, pg 789
EAR Professional Audio/Video, pg 855
Metropolitan Audio-Visual Inc, pg 940
Projector SuperStore LLC, pg 986
Troxell Communications Inc, pg 1045

ARKANSAS

White Diamond Productions, pg 1065

CALIFORNIA

Ametron Audio/Video, pg 785
Apex Jr, pg 788
ARS Electronics, pg 791
Associated Sound, pg 792
ATV Video Center Inc, pg 793
Audio Images Corp, pg 794
AV Conferencing, pg 797
Be Media, pg 804
Christy's Editorial, pg 826
Cibola Systems, pg 826
Cinema Equipment Sales of California Inc, pg 827
Delicate Electronics Sales Inc, pg 845
Directed Electronics, pg 848
Educational Technology Services (ETS), pg 857
Empire Wholesale Inc, pg 860
FXC Communications, pg 874
Gallien/Krueger, pg 875
Gluskin's Custom Audio Video, pg 879
Hosa Technology Inc, pg 891
IAMP Professional Audio, pg 893
Instructional Materials & Equipment Distributors (I-Med), pg 899
Jameco Electronics, pg 903
JD Audio Visual Inc, pg 904
L Acoustics US, pg 914
Location Sound Corp, pg 924
Media Fabricators Inc, pg 936
MediaMation Inc, pg 937
MediaPOINTE, pg 938
Mitsubishi Electric Visual Solutions America Inc (MEVSA), pg 944
Orvac Electronics, pg 965
OWI Inc, pg 966
Parasound Products Inc, pg 969
POP TV, pg 978
Promax Systems, pg 986
QSC Audio Products LLC, pg 988
Radian Audio Engineering Inc, pg 990
Related Visual Inc, pg 994
RF Specialties of California Inc, pg 995
Randall Schiller Productions, pg 1004
SNAP, pg 1014
Sonance, pg 1015
Sound Service Co, pg 1017
Sounds Unique, pg 1018
Southern California Sound Image Inc, pg 1019
SSL Industries Inc, pg 1022
Stanislaus Audio Video Inc, pg 1023
SuperVision, pg 1029
Synthesizer Systems Technologies (SST), pg 1030
TOA Electronics Inc, pg 1041
Towards 2000 Inc, pg 1043
Tri-Ed, pg 1044
VMI Inc, pg 1060
VTP Inc, pg 1061
Waterworks Acoustics, pg 1062
Yamaha Electronics Corp, pg 1071
Yanchar Design & Consulting Group, pg 1072

COLORADO

Audio Consultant Services Inc, pg 794
Daylight Productions & Rentals, pg 844

CONNECTICUT

Connecticut Audio & Theatrical Supply, pg 835
Everett Hall Associates Inc, pg 863
HB Communications Inc, pg 886
MAVCO, pg 934
The Music People Inc, pg 951
Sennheiser Electronic Corp, pg 1006

DELAWARE

Actors Attic, pg 775

FLORIDA

Access Media Group, pg 773
Allstar Audio Systems Inc, pg 782
A2D Solutions Inc, pg 793
AVI-SPL, pg 798
BAI Distributors Inc, pg 801
Broadcasters General Store Inc, pg 813
Cinema Equipment & Supplies Inc, pg 827
D A S Audio of America Inc, pg 842
Digital Video Systems Inc, pg 848
Harmon's Audio-Visual Services, pg 885
Harris Corp, pg 885
Herman Pro AV, pg 888
Hi-Tech Enterprises Inc, pg 888
Hi-Tech Import Export Corp, pg 888
Industrial Strength Inc, pg 897
Intermark Industries Inc, pg 900
Midtown Video Inc, pg 942
Photomart Cine-Video Inc, pg 975
Pro Stage Inc, pg 983
Recording Media & Equipment Inc (RM&E), pg 993
Sight & Sound Productions, pg 1010
Skyline Broadcast, pg 1013
Stereo Sales Inc, pg 1024
TAI Audio, pg 1031
Technomedia Solutions, pg 1035

GEORGIA

AVForSale, pg 798
Baker Audio Inc, pg 801
Lighting & Production Equipment Inc, pg 920
Omnimedia Inc, pg 962
Stage Front Presentation Systems, pg 1022
Visioneering International Inc, pg 1058

HAWAII

The Audio Visual Co (AVCO), pg 795

ILLINOIS

Allen Visual Systems Inc, pg 781
Joseph Electronics, pg 906
C V Lloyde, pg 923
Quintessence Audio Ltd, pg 989
Sound Vision Inc, pg 1018
Waldom Electronics Corp, pg 1061
Woodside Avenue Music Productions Inc, pg 1069

INDIANA

Heart Breaker Entertainment LLC, pg 887
Sensory Technologies LLC, pg 1006
SHP Electronics, pg 1010
Sweetwater Sound Inc, pg 1029

IOWA

ECS Inc, pg 856

KANSAS

Smith Audio-Visual Inc, pg 1014

KENTUCKY

Audio Visual Techniques Inc, pg 796
Axxis Inc, pg 800
Barney Miller's Inc, pg 943
NOR-COM Inc, pg 958
Northern Kentucky University, pg 959

LOUISIANA

Intermedia Technologies, pg 900
Pace Systems, pg 966

MAINE

Headlight Audio Visual Inc, pg 887

MARYLAND

Bradley Broadcast & Pro Audio, pg 811
Cardinal Sound & Video, pg 820
Human Circuit, pg 892
Kipp Visual Systems Inc, pg 911

MASSACHUSETTS

Terry Hanley Audio Systems Inc, pg 884
Professional Audio Design Inc, pg 985
Rule Broadcast Systems, pg 1000
Technomad™ Inc, pg 1035

MICHIGAN

Olson Anderson Co, pg 786
Ascom Communications Contractors, pg 791
City Events Group, pg 828
On Stage Visuals, pg 963
TeL Systems, pg 1035

MINNESOTA

Advanced Audio-Visual Inc, pg 777
Alpha Video & Audio Inc, pg 782
New Life Communications Inc, pg 956

MISSISSIPPI

Bowie Audio Visual Enterprises Inc, pg 811

MISSOURI

Communitronics Corp, pg 833
Conference Technologies Inc, pg 835
Image Technologies Corp, pg 895
MIS Technologies, pg 944
Production Support Services Inc, pg 985
Schiller's Audio-Visual, pg 1004
VMI (Video Masters Inc), pg 1060

NEVADA

Pignose-Gorilla, pg 975

NEW HAMPSHIRE

APS Lighting-Sound-AV, pg 789
Technet® Systems Group, pg 1033

NEW JERSEY

Alltec Stores, a Vcom IMC Company, pg 782
Audio Visual Associates, pg 795
Audio Visual Dynamics®, pg 795
Comprehensive Cable & Connectivity Co, pg 833
Diversified Systems Inc, pg 849
Earl Girls Inc, pg 855
Entel Systems Inc, pg 861
G&G Technologies Inc, pg 875
Hamilton Buhl, pg 884
The Music Place, pg 951
National Audio-Visual Supply, pg 952
Nelson Enterprises Theatrical Supply Co, pg 954
Onkyo USA Corp, pg 963
SLD Lighting, pg 1013
Starlite Productions, pg 1024
SYMCO Inc, pg 1030
Total Video Products Inc, pg 1042
Video Corporation of America (VCA), pg 1055
Wilray Audio Visual Corp, pg 1067
Wired 4 Sound Inc, pg 1068
York Telecom, pg 1072

NEW MEXICO

Quickbeam Systems Inc (QSI), pg 989

NEW YORK

Albany Theatre Supply Co Inc, pg 780
ALTEL Systems Inc, pg 783
American Video Inc, pg 785
Audio-Video Corp, pg 795
Audiovox, pg 796
Aura Sonic Ltd, pg 796
AV Workshop, pg 797
Colortone Audio Visual, pg 832
Communication Corner Inc, pg 832
Custom Media Environments, pg 841
Design Audio Visual Inc, pg 845
Gaylord Brothers, pg 876
General Audio-Visual Inc (GAVI), pg 876
Gotham Sound & Communications Inc, pg 881
Group One Ltd, pg 882
Hot House Professional Audio, pg 891
Indigo Productions, pg 897
KVL Audio Visual Services Inc, pg 914
Lee Dan® Communications Inc, pg 918
Long Island Video Enterprises Live Inc, pg 924
Magnaplan Corp, pg 928
Markertek Video Supply, pg 931
NorthCountry Distributors, pg 959
Posthorn Recordings, pg 979
Presentation Products Inc, pg 981
RNJ Electronics, pg 997
SmartSource Computer & AV Rentals, pg 1014
Technisphere Corp, pg 1034
Theatrical Services & Supplies Inc, pg 1038
Toys From The Attic, pg 1043
Visual Word Systems Inc, pg 1060
Yorkville Sound Inc, pg 1072

NORTH CAROLINA

Strategic Connections, pg 1026

OHIO

Aztec Video Productions, pg 801
Copp Integrated Systems, pg 836
ITA Audio Visual Solutions, pg 902
Lubell Labs Inc, pg 925
Parts Express, pg 969
Jimmy Rea Electronics Inc, pg 992
Smithall Electronics Inc, pg 1014
Tri-State Audio Visual Co, pg 1044

OKLAHOMA

Digital Designs, pg 847

OREGON

Audix Corp, pg 796
Spectrum Systems Design, pg 1021
SuperDigital Ltd, pg 1029

PENNSYLVANIA

Advanced AV, pg 777
Audio Visions Inc, pg 795
J E Foss Co, pg 871
Grise Audio Visual Center Inc, pg 882
Innovision Media Group, pg 899
The Lerro Corp, pg 919
Morefield Communications Inc, pg 946
Sound by Fitch, pg 1017
Tri-State Loudspeaker, pg 1044
Vistacom Inc, pg 1059
Visual Sound Inc, pg 1059
Wespen Audio Visual Co, pg 1063

RHODE ISLAND

M-Audio, pg 927
Shanix Inc, pg 1008

SOUTH CAROLINA

DaviSound, pg 843

TENNESSEE

Advanced Sound, pg 778
Belew Enterprises, pg 804
Durrell LLC, pg 854
Lowrance Sound Co Inc, pg 925
Mr Mark's Used Musical, Stereo & Studio Equipment Store, pg 944
Spectrum Sound Inc, pg 1021
Technical Support Systems LLC, pg 1034
Trew Audio Inc, pg 1044
Zion Music Group, pg 1074

TEXAS

Audio Visual Technologies Group, pg 796
AVES Audio Visual Systems Inc, pg 798
CAM Audio Inc, pg 817
Crossroads Audio Inc, pg 840
Data Projections Inc, pg 843
Digital Display Solutions Inc, pg 847
FitzCo Sound Inc, pg 869
Heffernan Audio Visual, pg 887
Industrial Audio/Video Inc, pg 897
Lubbock Audio Visual Inc, pg 925
Media Management LLC, pg 937
Pro Video & Film Equipment Co Inc, pg 983
Quality Audio Visual Service Inc, pg 988
RadioShack Corp, pg 990
RF Specialties of Texas LLC, pg 996
Schoolhouse Audio Visual, pg 1004
Southwest Sound & Electronics Inc, pg 1019
Stage Directions, pg 1022
Tarpley Media Systems, pg 1032

UTAH

ClearOne Inc, pg 830
Performance Audio, pg 973

VERMONT

Artech Electronics Ltd, pg 791
Production Advantage Inc, pg 984

VIRGINIA

Avitecture Inc, pg 799
Boitnott Visual Communications Corp (BVC), pg 810
Hoppmann Audio Visual, pg 891
Intellidyne LLC, pg 899
Lee Hartman & Sons Inc, pg 918
Old Dominion Broadcasting, pg 961
StageSound, pg 1023
The Whitlock Group, pg 1065

WASHINGTON

CCI Solutions, pg 821
D A Sound, pg 842
Northern Lights & Pro Audio, pg 959
Pacific Northwest Theatre Associates Inc (PNTA), pg 967

WEST VIRGINIA

United Sound & Electronics, pg 1048

WISCONSIN

Audio Visual of Milwaukee Inc, pg 795
Camera Corner Connecting Point, pg 818
Full Compass Systems, pg 874
Madisound Speaker Components Inc, pg 928
Safe Harbor Computers, pg 1001

PUERTO RICO

Audio Visual Concepts Inc, pg 795
Bonnin Electronics Inc, pg 810

ALBERTA

Infosat Communications Inc, pg 898
Matrix Video Communications Corp (MVCC), pg 934
Sharp's Audio-Visual Ltd, pg 1008
Unique Communications Ltd, pg 1048

BRITISH COLUMBIA

ADI Systems Inc, pg 776
Commercial Electronics Ltd, pg 832

MANITOBA

Advance Pro, pg 777
Inland Audio Visual Ltd, pg 898

AUDIO

Speaker Distributors (continued)

ONTARIO

Cinema Stage Inc, pg 827
Edcom Multimedia Products, pg 856
HD Source, pg 886
KDM Electronics Inc, pg 908
Nationwide Audio Visual Co, pg 953
Premier A/V Sales Ltd, pg 980
PSB Speakers International, pg 987
Tannoy North America Inc, pg 1031
Westbury National Show Systems Ltd, pg 1064

QUEBEC

AVS Technologies Inc, pg 800
Concept Audio-Visual, pg 834
JAM Industries Ltd, pg 903
Panavideo Inc, pg 968
SC Media Canada, pg 1003

Speaker Manufacturers

ARIZONA

Atlas Sound, pg 793
Fender Musical Instruments Corp, pg 866
David Wexler & Co, pg 1064

CALIFORNIA

ALC (Auernheimer Labs & Co), pg 780
B&K Components Ltd, pg 802
Califone International Inc, pg 817
Calrad Electronics, pg 817
Clear-Com®, pg 829
Directed Electronics, pg 848
Extron Electronics, pg 864
Gallien/Krueger, pg 875
Hosa Technology Inc, pg 891
JBL Professional, pg 904
L Acoustics US, pg 914
Meyer Sound Laboratories Inc, pg 940
Mitsubishi Electric Visual Solutions America Inc (MEVSA), pg 944
Nady Systems Inc, pg 952
Orevox USA Corp, pg 965
OWI Inc, pg 966
Panasonic Broadcast & Digital Systems Co, pg 968
Panasonic Professional Audio Systems, pg 968
Parasound Products Inc, pg 969
Penn Elcom Inc, pg 971
Radian Audio Engineering Inc, pg 990
Renkus-Heinz Inc, pg 994
Roland Corp US, pg 998
Sherwood America Inc, pg 1009
Sonance, pg 1015
Sony Electronics Inc, pg 1016
TeachLogic Inc, pg 1033
TOA Electronics Inc, pg 1041
Velodyne Acoustics Inc, pg 1052
Waterworks Acoustics, pg 1062
Wohler Technologies Inc, pg 1069
Xantech LLC, pg 1071
Yamaha Electronics Corp, pg 1071
Yanchar Design & Consulting Group, pg 1072

COLORADO

Avalon Acoustics, pg 798
Green Mountain Audio Inc, pg 882

CONNECTICUT

Soundsphere, pg 1018

FLORIDA

BAI Distributors Inc, pg 801
CTG Audio, pg 840
Intermark Industries Inc, pg 900
Phase Technology, pg 973

GEORGIA

OAP Audio Products, pg 960

ILLINOIS

AmpliVox Portable Sound Systems, pg 785
Bag End Loudspeakers, pg 801
Dukane Corp, Audio Visual Products Division, pg 853
Sound Physics Labs Inc, pg 1017
SoundTech, pg 1018

INDIANA

Auralex Acoustics Inc, pg 796

KANSAS

Galaxy Audio, pg 875

MARYLAND

Definitive Technology LLP, pg 845

MASSACHUSETTS

Bose Corp, pg 811
Boston Acoustics, pg 811
Eastern Acoustic Works Inc (EAW), pg 856
Technomad™ Inc, pg 1035

MINNESOTA

Magnepan Inc, pg 928
MISCO, pg 944
Telex Communications Inc, pg 1037
Telex EVI, pg 1037

MISSISSIPPI

Peavey Electronics Corp, pg 970

MISSOURI

Lowell Manufacturing, pg 925

NEBRASKA

REI - Radio Engineering Industries, pg 994

NEVADA

Pignose-Gorilla, pg 975

NEW HAMPSHIRE

Russound, pg 1001

NEW JERSEY

Apogee Sound International LLC, pg 788
Bogen Communications Inc, pg 810
Crestron Electronics Inc, pg 839
Gemini Sound, pg 876
Onkyo USA Corp, pg 963
Panasonic Consumer Electronics Co, pg 968
Panasonic Corp, pg 968
Technics, pg 1034

NEW YORK

Custom Media Environments, pg 841
GLI Sound Systems, pg 878
Harbro Corp, pg 884
Hot House Professional Audio, pg 891
MG Electronics, pg 940
Sentry Industries Inc, pg 1007
Yorkville Sound Inc, pg 1072

OHIO

Lubell Labs Inc, pg 925

OKLAHOMA

Digital Designs, pg 847

OREGON

Audix Corp, pg 796

PENNSYLVANIA

Community Professional Loudspeakers, pg 833
Right Coast Recording Inc, pg 997
Tri-State Loudspeaker, pg 1044

RHODE ISLAND

M-Audio, pg 927
Numark Industries Inc, pg 960

SOUTH CAROLINA

DaviSound, pg 843

TENNESSEE

Advanced Sound, pg 778
Auratron Systems, pg 796
Cerwin-Vega! Inc, pg 823
Durrell LLC, pg 854
KRK Systems, pg 914
Remote Audio Products, pg 994

TEXAS

Mitchell Acoustics Research, pg 944

UTAH

SoundTube Entertainment, pg 1018
Spectra Sonics Applied Technology Inc, pg 1020

WASHINGTON

D A Sound, pg 842
McCauley Sound Inc, pg 935

WISCONSIN

Madisound Speaker Components Inc, pg 928

ONTARIO

KDM Electronics Inc, pg 908
PSB Speakers International, pg 987
Tannoy North America Inc, pg 1031

Speaker Rentals

ALABAMA

Audio-Video Resources Inc, pg 795

ARIZONA

Arizona Cine Equipment, pg 789
AV Concepts, pg 797
Merestone, pg 938
Metropolitan Audio-Visual Inc, pg 940
Reel Men Rentals Inc, pg 994
Video West Inc, pg 1056

ARKANSAS

White Diamond Productions, pg 1065

CALIFORNIA

Absolute Rentals, pg 772
Action Audio & Visual, pg 775
AGF Media Services, pg 778
Alliant Event Services, pg 781
Ametron Audio/Video, pg 785
Associated Sound, pg 792
ATV Video Center Inc, pg 793
Audio Rents, pg 794
AV Guys, pg 797
Design FX Audio, pg 845
Dan Dugan Sound Design Inc, pg 853
Express Media Inc, pg 864
FXC Communications, pg 874
Hollywood Sound Systems, pg 890
IAMP Professional Audio, pg 893
Imagecraft Productions, pg 896
Impact Group, pg 897
JD Audio Visual Inc, pg 904
LA Sound Co, pg 915
Location Sound Corp, pg 924
Lynch Communications, pg 926
Maximus Media Inc, pg 934
McCune Audio-Video-Lighting, pg 935
Media Fabricators Inc, pg 936
Munday & Collins AV, pg 950
Muse Presentation Technologies, pg 950
Next Arts, pg 957
Old School Cameras, pg 961
On-Trax Inc, pg 963
PSAV® Presentation Services, pg 986
Pyxis Industries Inc, pg 988
Alwin Sauers Audio Productions (ASAP), pg 1003
Randall Schiller Productions, pg 1004
Slate Media Group, pg 1013
Sound Service Co, pg 1017
Stanislaus Audio Video Inc, pg 1023
The Studios at Paramount, pg 1027
Synthesizer Rental Service, pg 1030
Third Ear Sound Co, pg 1038
Towards 2000 Inc, pg 1043
VER-Video Equipment Rentals, pg 1053
Video Resources Inc, pg 1056
Videorama Industries LLC, pg 1057
VMI Inc, pg 1060
Voice & Video Rentals, pg 1060
Warner Bros Production Sound & Video Services, pg 1062
Westcoast Video Productions Inc, pg 1064

COLORADO

Audio Consultant Services Inc, pg 794
Daylight Productions & Rentals, pg 844
Multimedia Audio Visual Inc, pg 950
Spectrum Audio Visual Services, pg 1020

CONNECTICUT

A/V Davey, pg 797
Connecticut Audio & Theatrical Supply, pg 835

AUDIO

Speaker Rentals (continued)

ALBERTA

Allstar Show Industries Inc, pg 782
Evolution Presentation Technologies, pg 863
L R Light & Sound, pg 915
McBain Audio Visual Ltd, pg 935
Unique Communications Ltd, pg 1048

BRITISH COLUMBIA

Clark's Audio Visual Services Ltd, pg 829
Commercial Electronics Ltd, pg 832
DL Sound & Lighting Productions Ltd, pg 849
MicrophoneRentals.com, pg 941

MANITOBA

Inland Audio Visual Ltd, pg 898

ONTARIO

Edcom Multimedia Products, pg 856
HD Source, pg 886
RB Productions, pg 992
Westbury National Show Systems Ltd, pg 1064
ZTV Broadcast Services Inc, pg 1074

QUEBEC

Audio Visual Dynamics Ltd, pg 795
Concept Audio-Visual, pg 834
Panavideo Inc, pg 968

Speaker Repairs

ALABAMA

Media Visions Inc, pg 937

ARIZONA

Metropolitan Audio-Visual Inc, pg 940

CALIFORNIA

ALC (Auernheimer Labs & Co), pg 780
Ametron Audio/Video, pg 785
Audio Images Corp, pg 794
Digitron Electronics, pg 848
Gluskin's Custom Audio Video, pg 879
IAMP Professional Audio, pg 893
Instructional Materials & Equipment Distributors (I-Med), pg 899
McAlister Electronics, pg 935
Parasound Products Inc, pg 969
QSC Audio Products LLC, pg 988
Radian Audio Engineering Inc, pg 990
Randall Schiller Productions, pg 1004
Sonance, pg 1015
Sound Service Co, pg 1017
SSL Industries Inc, pg 1022
Third Ear Sound Co, pg 1038
TOA Electronics Inc, pg 1041
Towards 2000 Inc, pg 1043
Yamaha Electronics Corp, pg 1071

CONNECTICUT

HB Communications Inc, pg 886
Sennheiser Electronic Corp, pg 1006
Soundsphere, pg 1018

DELAWARE

Actors Attic, pg 775

FLORIDA

Hi-Tech Enterprises Inc, pg 888
TAI Audio, pg 1031

GEORGIA

Lighting & Production Equipment Inc, pg 920
Stage Front Presentation Systems, pg 1022

ILLINOIS

Allen Visual Systems Inc, pg 781
Beatty TeleVisual Productions, pg 804
C V Lloyde, pg 923
On Site Video, pg 963
Sound Physics Labs Inc, pg 1017

INDIANA

SHP Electronics, pg 1010
Sweetwater Sound Inc, pg 1029

IOWA

ECS Inc, pg 856

KENTUCKY

Axxis Inc, pg 800
Barney Miller's Inc, pg 943
NOR-COM Inc, pg 958

MARYLAND

Cardinal Sound & Video, pg 820
Strauss Photo Technical Service Inc, pg 1026

MASSACHUSETTS

Capron Lighting & Sound Co Inc, pg 819
Professional Audio Design Inc, pg 985

MICHIGAN

City Events Group, pg 828
K&R's Recording Studios Inc, pg 908
On Stage Visuals, pg 963
TeL Systems, pg 1035

MISSOURI

Communitronics Corp, pg 833

NEW JERSEY

Audio Visual Associates, pg 795
Earl Girls Inc, pg 855
The Music Place, pg 951
Nelson Enterprises Theatrical Supply Co, pg 954
Starlite Productions, pg 1024

NEW MEXICO

Quickbeam Systems Inc (QSI), pg 989

NEW YORK

Custom Media Environments, pg 841
Hot House Professional Audio, pg 891
Toys From The Attic, pg 1043

OHIO

Copp Integrated Systems, pg 836
ITA Audio Visual Solutions, pg 902
Smithall Electronics Inc, pg 1014

OREGON

All Service Musical Electronics Repair, pg 780

PENNSYLVANIA

Right Coast Recording Inc, pg 997
Tri-State Loudspeaker, pg 1044

SOUTH CAROLINA

DaviSound, pg 843

TENNESSEE

Belew Enterprises, pg 804
Durrell LLC, pg 854
Technical Support Systems LLC, pg 1034

TEXAS

Audio Visual Technologies Group, pg 796
Music Lab Inc, pg 950
Quality Audio Visual Service Inc, pg 988

VIRGINIA

Boitnott Visual Communications Corp (BVC), pg 810
Hoppmann Audio Visual, pg 891
Intellidyne LLC, pg 899
Old Dominion Broadcasting, pg 961

WASHINGTON

D A Sound, pg 842
Northern Lights & Pro Audio, pg 959
Pacific Northwest Theatre Associates Inc (PNTA), pg 967

WEST VIRGINIA

United Sound & Electronics, pg 1048

WISCONSIN

Full Compass Systems, pg 874
Madisound Speaker Components Inc, pg 928

PUERTO RICO

Bonnin Electronics Inc, pg 810

ALBERTA

Allstar Show Industries Inc, pg 782
Infosat Communications Inc, pg 898
Sharp's Audio-Visual Ltd, pg 1008
Unique Communications Ltd, pg 1048

MANITOBA

Inland Audio Visual Ltd, pg 898

ONTARIO

Edcom Multimedia Products, pg 856
HD Source, pg 886
Westbury National Show Systems Ltd, pg 1064

QUEBEC

Panavideo Inc, pg 968
SC Media Canada, pg 1003

Spiritual, *see* Music Libraries—Spiritual

Surround Sound Device Distributors

ARIZONA

EAR Professional Audio/Video, pg 855
Troxell Communications Inc, pg 1045

CALIFORNIA

Ametron Audio/Video, pg 785
Associated Sound, pg 792
Audio Images Corp, pg 794
Be Media, pg 804
Cinema Equipment Sales of California Inc, pg 827
Delicate Electronics Sales Inc, pg 845
FXC Communications, pg 874
Linear LLC, pg 922
MediaPOINTE, pg 938
Parasound Products Inc, pg 969
POP TV, pg 978
Sound Service Co, pg 1017
Southern California Sound Image Inc, pg 1019
Kris Stevens Enterprises, pg 1024
SuperVision, pg 1029
Towards 2000 Inc, pg 1043
Universal Audio Inc, pg 1049

COLORADO

Audio Consultant Services Inc, pg 794

DELAWARE

Actors Attic, pg 775

FLORIDA

Allstar Audio Systems Inc, pg 782
BAI Distributors Inc, pg 801
Broadcasters General Store Inc, pg 813
Digital Video Systems Inc, pg 848
Photomart Cine-Video Inc, pg 975
Pro Stage Inc, pg 983
Recording Media & Equipment Inc (RM&E), pg 993
Sight & Sound Productions, pg 1010
Stereo Sales Inc, pg 1024
TAI Audio, pg 1031
Technomedia Solutions, pg 1035

GEORGIA

Lighting & Production Equipment Inc, pg 920
Stage Front Presentation Systems, pg 1022

HAWAII

The Audio Visual Co (AVCO), pg 795

ILLINOIS

Allen Visual Systems Inc, pg 781
Quintessence Audio Ltd, pg 989
Sound Vision Inc, pg 1018

INDIANA

Sensory Technologies LLC, pg 1006
SHP Electronics, pg 1010
Sweetwater Sound Inc, pg 1029

IOWA

ECS Inc, pg 856

KENTUCKY

Axxis Inc, pg 800
Barney Miller's Inc, pg 943
NOR-COM Inc, pg 958

MAINE

Independent Audio Inc, pg 897

MARYLAND

Bradley Broadcast & Pro Audio, pg 811
Kipp Visual Systems Inc, pg 911

MICHIGAN

Olson Anderson Co, pg 786
Ascom Communications Contractors, pg 791
On Stage Visuals, pg 963
TeL Systems, pg 1035

NEW JERSEY

Diversified Systems Inc, pg 849
National Audio-Visual Supply, pg 952
Onkyo USA Corp, pg 963
Starlite Productions, pg 1024
SYMCO Inc, pg 1030
Wilray Audio Visual Corp, pg 1067
Wired 4 Sound Inc, pg 1068
York Telecom, pg 1072

NEW YORK

ALTEL Systems Inc, pg 783
Audio-Video Corp, pg 795
Aura Sonic Ltd, pg 796
beyerdynamic Inc, pg 806
Custom Media Environments, pg 841
Design Audio Visual Inc, pg 845
General Audio-Visual Inc (GAVI), pg 876
Group One Ltd, pg 882
NorthCountry Distributors, pg 959
Posthorn Recordings, pg 979
Presentation Products Inc, pg 981
RNJ Electronics, pg 997
Toys From The Attic, pg 1043

OHIO

ITA Audio Visual Solutions, pg 902
Parts Express, pg 969

OREGON

Lightspeed Technologies Inc, pg 921

PENNSYLVANIA

Advanced AV, pg 777
J E Foss Co, pg 871

RHODE ISLAND

Shanix Inc, pg 1008

TENNESSEE

Advanced Sound, pg 778
Durrell LLC, pg 854
Lowrance Sound Co Inc, pg 925
Technical Support Systems LLC, pg 1034
Zion Music Group, pg 1074

TEXAS

Audio Visual Technologies Group, pg 796
Crossroads Audio Inc, pg 840
Data Projections Inc, pg 843
Industrial Audio/Video Inc, pg 897
Lubbock Audio Visual Inc, pg 925
RadioShack Corp, pg 990
Tarpley Media Systems, pg 1032

UTAH

Performance Audio, pg 973

VIRGINIA

Avitecture Inc, pg 799
Communications Specialists Inc, pg 833
Intellidyne LLC, pg 899
Lee Hartman & Sons Inc, pg 918
The Whitlock Group, pg 1065

WASHINGTON

Northern Lights & Pro Audio, pg 959

WISCONSIN

Audio Visual of Milwaukee Inc, pg 795
Full Compass Systems, pg 874

PUERTO RICO

Bonnin Electronics Inc, pg 810

ALBERTA

Infosat Communications Inc, pg 898

BRITISH COLUMBIA

Commercial Electronics Ltd, pg 832

MANITOBA

Advance Pro, pg 777
Inland Audio Visual Ltd, pg 898

ONTARIO

Cinema Stage Inc, pg 827
Westbury National Show Systems Ltd, pg 1064

QUEBEC

AVS Technologies Inc, pg 800

Surround Sound Device Manufacturers

ARIZONA

Adcom LLC, pg 776
MTX Audio, pg 949
OmniMount Systems, pg 962

CALIFORNIA

AB Systems Amplifiers, pg 772
B&K Components Ltd, pg 802
Dorrough Electronics Inc, pg 851
Linear LLC, pg 922
Lynx Studio Technology Inc, pg 927
Martinsound Inc, pg 932
Orevox USA Corp, pg 965
OWI Inc, pg 966
Parasound Products Inc, pg 969
Sherwood America Inc, pg 1009
TeachLogic Inc, pg 1033
Wohler Technologies Inc, pg 1069

ILLINOIS

AmpliVox Portable Sound Systems, pg 785
Bag End Loudspeakers, pg 801

MINNESOTA

Digital Audio Labs, pg 847

NEW JERSEY

Crestron Electronics Inc, pg 839
Modulation Sciences Inc, pg 945
Onkyo USA Corp, pg 963

NEW YORK

beyerdynamic Inc, pg 806
Posthorn Recordings, pg 979

NORTH CAROLINA

Audioarts Engineering, pg 796

PENNSYLVANIA

Community Professional Loudspeakers, pg 833

TENNESSEE

Advanced Sound, pg 778
Harrison Consoles, pg 885

WASHINGTON

AudioControl®, pg 796
Rane, pg 991

BRITISH COLUMBIA

Richmond Sound Design Ltd, pg 996

ONTARIO

Tannoy North America Inc, pg 1031
Ward-Beck Systems Ltd, pg 1062

Surround Sound Device Rentals

ARIZONA

Merestone, pg 938
Video West Inc, pg 1056

CALIFORNIA

Absolute Rentals, pg 772
Alliant Event Services, pg 781
Ametron Audio/Video, pg 785
Associated Sound, pg 792
Audio Rents, pg 794
AV Guys, pg 797
Hollywood Sound Systems, pg 890
Lynch Communications, pg 926
McCune Audio-Video-Lighting, pg 935
Muse Presentation Technologies, pg 950
Sound Service Co, pg 1017
Total Media Group, pg 1042
Towards 2000 Inc, pg 1043
VER-Video Equipment Rentals, pg 1053
Videorama Industries LLC, pg 1057

COLORADO

Audio Consultant Services Inc, pg 794

FLORIDA

Allstar Audio Systems Inc, pg 782
Phat Planet Recording Studios, pg 973
Pro Stage Inc, pg 983
Sight & Sound Productions, pg 1010

GEORGIA

Lighting & Production Equipment Inc, pg 920
Stage Front Presentation Systems, pg 1022

ILLINOIS

Allen Visual Systems Inc, pg 781
On Stage Audio, pg 963
RC Communications, pg 992

IOWA

ECS Inc, pg 856

KENTUCKY

Audio Visual Techniques Inc, pg 796

MARYLAND

CPR MultiMedia Solutions, pg 837
Event Tech, pg 863

MASSACHUSETTS

AVFX Inc, pg 798
massAV, pg 933
Preston Productions Inc, pg 981

MICHIGAN

K&R All Media Productions Inc, pg 908
On Stage Visuals, pg 963

MISSOURI

Show-Me Audio-Visual, pg 1009

MONTANA

Jereco Studios Inc, pg 905

NEW JERSEY

PLS Staging, pg 977
Bill Quinn Productions, pg 989
Starlite Productions, pg 1024
Wired 4 Sound Inc, pg 1068

NEW YORK

Aura Sonic Ltd, pg 796
CP Communications, pg 837
Custom Media Environments, pg 841
Dreamhire LLC, pg 852
Posthorn Recordings, pg 979

NORTH CAROLINA

A&V Company, pg 772

OKLAHOMA

PDC Productions, pg 970

AUDIO

Surround Sound Device Rentals (continued)

PENNSYLVANIA

Advanced AV, pg 777
Production Solutions Inc, pg 985

TENNESSEE

Durrell LLC, pg 854
Love Shack Recording Studios, pg 925
Technical Support Systems LLC, pg 1034

TEXAS

Alford Media Services, pg 780
The Samuels Co, pg 1002

UTAH

Performance Audio, pg 973

VERMONT

Parlato Productions, pg 969

VIRGINIA

Lee Hartman & Sons Inc, pg 918

WASHINGTON

Northern Lights & Pro Audio, pg 959
Victory Studios, pg 1054

MANITOBA

Inland Audio Visual Ltd, pg 898

Surround Sound Device Repairs

CALIFORNIA

AB Systems Amplifiers, pg 772
Ametron Audio/Video, pg 785
Audio Images Corp, pg 794
McAlister Electronics, pg 935
Sound Service Co, pg 1017
Towards 2000 Inc, pg 1043

CONNECTICUT

HB Communications Inc, pg 886

FLORIDA

JT Communications, pg 906
Phat Planet Recording Studios, pg 973
Stereo Sales Inc, pg 1024
TAI Audio, pg 1031

GEORGIA

Lighting & Production Equipment Inc, pg 920
Stage Front Presentation Systems, pg 1022

ILLINOIS

Allen Visual Systems Inc, pg 781

INDIANA

Sweetwater Sound Inc, pg 1029

IOWA

ECS Inc, pg 856

KENTUCKY

Axxis Inc, pg 800
Barney Miller's Inc, pg 943
NOR-COM Inc, pg 958

MICHIGAN

K&R's Recording Studios Inc, pg 908
TeL Systems, pg 1035

NEW JERSEY

Starlite Productions, pg 1024

NEW YORK

Custom Media Environments, pg 841
Toys From The Attic, pg 1043

OREGON

All Service Musical Electronics Repair, pg 780

TENNESSEE

Technical Support Systems LLC, pg 1034

WASHINGTON

Northern Lights & Pro Audio, pg 959

WISCONSIN

Full Compass Systems, pg 874

PUERTO RICO

Bonnin Electronics Inc, pg 810

ALBERTA

Infosat Communications Inc, pg 898

MANITOBA

Inland Audio Visual Ltd, pg 898

ONTARIO

Westbury National Show Systems Ltd, pg 1064

Switcher & Matrix—Analog & Digital Distributors

ALABAMA

PESA, pg 973

ARIZONA

EAR Professional Audio/Video, pg 855
Troxell Communications Inc, pg 1045

ARKANSAS

White Diamond Productions, pg 1065

CALIFORNIA

Ametron Audio/Video, pg 785
Associated Sound, pg 792
ATV Video Center Inc, pg 793
Audio Images Corp, pg 794
Be Media, pg 804
Cibola Systems, pg 826
Delicate Electronics Sales Inc, pg 845
Empire Wholesale Inc, pg 860
FXC Communications, pg 874
JD Audio Visual Inc, pg 904
MediaPOINTE, pg 938
POP TV, pg 978
Southern California Sound Image Inc, pg 1019
Stanislaus Audio Video Inc, pg 1023
TOA Electronics Inc, pg 1041
Towards 2000 Inc, pg 1043
Videobotics, pg 1056
VMI Inc, pg 1060
VTP Inc, pg 1061
Zack Electronics Inc, pg 1073

COLORADO

Audio Consultant Services Inc, pg 794

CONNECTICUT

Everett Hall Associates Inc, pg 863
HB Communications Inc, pg 886

DELAWARE

Actors Attic, pg 775

FLORIDA

Access Media Group, pg 773
Allstar Audio Systems Inc, pg 782
BAI Distributors Inc, pg 801
Digital Video Systems Inc, pg 848
Griffiths Broadcast Co Inc, pg 882
Harris Corp, pg 885
Hi-Tech Enterprises Inc, pg 888
Media Concepts Inc, pg 936
Midtown Video Inc, pg 942
Photomart Cine-Video Inc, pg 975
Recording Media & Equipment Inc (RM&E), pg 993
Sight & Sound Productions, pg 1010
Stereo Sales Inc, pg 1024
Technomedia Solutions, pg 1035

GEORGIA

Omnimedia Inc, pg 962
Stage Front Presentation Systems, pg 1022

HAWAII

The Audio Visual Co (AVCO), pg 795

ILLINOIS

Allen Visual Systems Inc, pg 781
Joseph Electronics, pg 906
Quintessence Audio Ltd, pg 989
Sound Vision Inc, pg 1018

INDIANA

Sensory Technologies LLC, pg 1006
SHP Electronics, pg 1010

IOWA

ECS Inc, pg 856

KENTUCKY

Audio Visual Techniques Inc, pg 796
Axxis Inc, pg 800
NOR-COM Inc, pg 958

LOUISIANA

Intermedia Technologies, pg 900

MAINE

Headlight Audio Visual Inc, pg 887
Independent Audio Inc, pg 897

MARYLAND

Bradley Broadcast & Pro Audio, pg 811
Cardinal Sound & Video, pg 820
Human Circuit, pg 892
Kipp Visual Systems Inc, pg 911

MASSACHUSETTS

Professional Audio Design Inc, pg 985

MICHIGAN

Ascom Communications Contractors, pg 791
On Stage Visuals, pg 963
TeL Systems, pg 1035

MINNESOTA

Alpha Video & Audio Inc, pg 782

MISSISSIPPI

Bowie Audio Visual Enterprises Inc, pg 811

MISSOURI

MIS Technologies, pg 944

NEW JERSEY

Alltec Stores, a Vcom IMC Company, pg 782
Audio Visual Associates, pg 795
AV Bluebook, pg 797
Diversified Systems Inc, pg 849
National Audio-Visual Supply, pg 952
PatchAmp, pg 970
Starlite Productions, pg 1024
SYMCO Inc, pg 1030
Total Video Products Inc, pg 1042
Wired 4 Sound Inc, pg 1068
York Telecom, pg 1072

NEW YORK

ALTEL Systems Inc, pg 783
Audio-Video Corp, pg 795
Custom Media Environments, pg 841
Design Audio Visual Inc, pg 845
Image Labs Corp, pg 895
Markertek Video Supply, pg 931
NorthCountry Distributors, pg 959
Presentation Products Inc, pg 981
Toys From The Attic, pg 1043
Visual Word Systems Inc, pg 1060

OHIO

ITA Audio Visual Solutions, pg 902
Jimmy Rea Electronics Inc, pg 992
Tri-State Audio Visual Co, pg 1044

PENNSYLVANIA

Advanced AV, pg 777
Innovision Media Group, pg 899
The Lerro Corp, pg 919
Vistacom Inc, pg 1059

RHODE ISLAND

Shanix Inc, pg 1008

TENNESSEE

Durrell LLC, pg 854
Lowrance Sound Co Inc, pg 925

Spectrum Sound Inc, pg 1021
Technical Support Systems LLC, pg 1034

TEXAS

Audio Visual Technologies Group, pg 796
Data Projections Inc, pg 843
Digital Display Solutions Inc, pg 847
First Group Communications Inc, pg 868
Industrial Audio/Video Inc, pg 897
Lubbock Audio Visual Inc, pg 925
Media Management LLC, pg 937
Pro Video & Film Equipment Co Inc, pg 983
Southwest Sound & Electronics Inc, pg 1019
Stage Directions, pg 1022
Sundance Systems, Fibox Products Division, pg 1028
Tarpley Media Systems, pg 1032

UTAH

Performance Audio, pg 973

VIRGINIA

Avitecture Inc, pg 799
Communications Specialists Inc, pg 833
Hoppmann Audio Visual, pg 891
Intellidyne LLC, pg 899
Lee Hartman & Sons Inc, pg 918

WASHINGTON

CCI Solutions, pg 821
Telect Inc, pg 1036

WISCONSIN

Audio Visual of Milwaukee Inc, pg 795
Full Compass Systems, pg 874
Safe Harbor Computers, pg 1001

PUERTO RICO

Bonnin Electronics Inc, pg 810

ALBERTA

Infosat Communications Inc, pg 898

BRITISH COLUMBIA

Commercial Electronics Ltd, pg 832
Dav Tronics Ltd, pg 843
ProVision Video Sales & Rentals Inc, pg 986

MANITOBA

Advance Pro, pg 777
Inland Audio Visual Ltd, pg 898

ONTARIO

Cinema Stage Inc, pg 827
Westbury National Show Systems Ltd, pg 1064

Switcher & Matrix—Analog & Digital Manufacturers

ALABAMA

PESA, pg 973

ARIZONA

Adcom LLC, pg 776
Radio Design Labs (RDL), pg 990

CALIFORNIA

ALTINEX Inc, pg 783
Digital Music Corp, pg 847
Extron Electronics, pg 864
Gefen, pg 876
Henry Engineering, pg 888
Opamp Labs Inc, pg 964
Opticomm-EMCORE, pg 964
Penny + Giles, pg 972
Sierra Automated Systems, pg 1010
Sprocket Digital, pg 1022
TOA Electronics Inc, pg 1041

COLORADO

Clear Blue Audio Video, pg 829

CONNECTICUT

Sound Control Technologies Inc, pg 1017

FLORIDA

Compuvideo Sales USA Ltd, pg 834
Tel-Test, pg 1035
Z-Systems Audio Engineering, pg 1073

INDIANA

JFW Industries Inc, pg 905

KENTUCKY

TV One Multimedia Solutions, pg 1046

MARYLAND

Knox Video Technologies, pg 912

MISSOURI

Link Electronics Inc, pg 922

NEW JERSEY

Crestron Electronics Inc, pg 839
FSR Inc, pg 873
Kramer Electronics USA Inc, pg 913

NEW MEXICO

Burst Electronics Inc, pg 815

NEW YORK

Analog Way Inc, pg 786
Benchmark Media Systems Inc, pg 805
Broadcast Devices Inc, pg 813
Custom Media Environments, pg 841
Image Labs Corp, pg 895
Key Digital Systems, pg 910
Laird Digital Cinema, pg 915
MultiDyne Video & Fiber Optics Systems, pg 950
Protech Audio Corp, pg 986
Sescom Inc, pg 1007

NORTH CAROLINA

Audioarts Engineering, pg 796
Wheatstone Corp, pg 1065

OREGON

BIAMP Systems, pg 806

PENNSYLVANIA

Aviom Inc, pg 799
Rossman Audio LLC, pg 1000

TENNESSEE

Durrell LLC, pg 854

TEXAS

Logitek Electronic Systems Inc, pg 924
Sundance Systems, Fibox Products Division, pg 1028

UTAH

Ivie Technologies Inc, pg 903
SoundTube Entertainment, pg 1018
Utah Scientific Inc, pg 1051

WASHINGTON

AudioControl®, pg 796
Conex Electro-Systems Inc, pg 835
Telect Inc, pg 1036

WISCONSIN

Intelix LLC, pg 899

BRITISH COLUMBIA

Dav Tronics Ltd, pg 843
Richmond Sound Design Ltd, pg 996

ONTARIO

McCurdy Radio Ltd, pg 935

QUEBEC

Miranda Technologies, pg 944

Switcher & Matrix—Analog & Digital Rentals

ALABAMA

Audio-Video Resources Inc, pg 795

ARIZONA

AV Concepts, pg 797
Merestone, pg 938
Video West Inc, pg 1056

ARKANSAS

White Diamond Productions, pg 1065

CALIFORNIA

AGF Media Services, pg 778
Ametron Audio/Video, pg 785
Associated Sound, pg 792
ATV Video Center Inc, pg 793
Audio Rents, pg 794
Express Media Inc, pg 864
FXC Communications, pg 874
Golden Gate Studios, pg 880
JD Audio Visual Inc, pg 904
Muse Presentation Technologies, pg 950
PSAV® Presentation Services, pg 986
VER-Video Equipment Rentals, pg 1053
Videorama Industries LLC, pg 1057
Voice & Video Rentals, pg 1060

COLORADO

Audio Consultant Services Inc, pg 794

CONNECTICUT

Everett Hall Associates Inc, pg 863
Videofilm Systems Inc, pg 1057

FLORIDA

Access Media Group, pg 773
Allstar Audio Systems Inc, pg 782
Sight & Sound Productions, pg 1010
Universal Studios Florida® Production Group, pg 1049

GEORGIA

Stage Front Presentation Systems, pg 1022

ILLINOIS

RC Communications, pg 992
Show Department Inc, pg 1009

KENTUCKY

Audio Visual Techniques Inc, pg 796

MAINE

Headlight Audio Visual Inc, pg 887

MARYLAND

CPR MultiMedia Solutions, pg 837
Event Tech, pg 863
Kramer Communications Video Production, pg 913

MASSACHUSETTS

Preston Productions Inc, pg 981

MICHIGAN

K&R All Media Productions Inc, pg 908
On Stage Visuals, pg 963

MISSISSIPPI

Bowie Audio Visual Enterprises Inc, pg 811

MISSOURI

Show-Me Audio-Visual, pg 1009

NEW JERSEY

Audio Visual Associates, pg 795
MIB Mediaworks, pg 941
Starlite Productions, pg 1024
Wired 4 Sound Inc, pg 1068

NEW YORK

CP Communications, pg 837
Design Audio Visual Inc, pg 845
Visual Word Systems Inc, pg 1060

NORTH CAROLINA

A&V Company, pg 772
Take One Productions Ltd, pg 1031

PENNSYLVANIA

Innovision Media Group, pg 899

TENNESSEE

Durrell LLC, pg 854
Technical Support Systems LLC, pg 1034

AUDIO

Switcher & Matrix—Analog & Digital Rentals (continued)

TEXAS

Alford Media Services, pg 780
Data Display Audio Visual Co LP, pg 843
Digital Display Solutions Inc, pg 847
Stage Directions, pg 1022

VERMONT

Parlato Productions, pg 969

VIRGINIA

Lee Hartman & Sons Inc, pg 918

BRITISH COLUMBIA

DL Sound & Lighting Productions Ltd, pg 849
Finale Editworks, pg 868
Image Media Farm, pg 895
ProVision Video Sales & Rentals Inc, pg 986

MANITOBA

Inland Audio Visual Ltd, pg 898

Switcher & Matrix—Analog & Digital Repairs

CALIFORNIA

Ametron Audio/Video, pg 785
TOA Electronics Inc, pg 1041

FLORIDA

Hi-Tech Enterprises Inc, pg 888

GEORGIA

Stage Front Presentation Systems, pg 1022

KENTUCKY

NOR-COM Inc, pg 958

MASSACHUSETTS

Professional Audio Design Inc, pg 985

MICHIGAN

TeL Systems, pg 1035

NEW JERSEY

Audio Visual Associates, pg 795
Starlite Productions, pg 1024

NEW YORK

Analog Way Inc, pg 786
Toys From The Attic, pg 1043

OHIO

Tri-State Audio Visual Co, pg 1044

OREGON

All Service Musical Electronics Repair, pg 780

TENNESSEE

Durrell LLC, pg 854
Technical Support Systems LLC, pg 1034

ALBERTA

Infosat Communications Inc, pg 898

MANITOBA

Inland Audio Visual Ltd, pg 898

ONTARIO

Westbury National Show Systems Ltd, pg 1064

Switcher & Matrix—Mechanical & Electronic Distributors

ARIZONA

EAR Professional Audio/Video, pg 855
Troxell Communications Inc, pg 1045

CALIFORNIA

Ametron Audio/Video, pg 785
Audio Images Corp, pg 794
Be Media, pg 804
Cibola Systems, pg 826
Delicate Electronics Sales Inc, pg 845
FXC Communications, pg 874
Media Control Systems LLC, pg 936
MediaPOINTE, pg 938
POP TV, pg 978
Southern California Sound Image Inc, pg 1019
Stanislaus Audio Video Inc, pg 1023
Towards 2000 Inc, pg 1043
Videobotics, pg 1056
VMI Inc, pg 1060

CONNECTICUT

HB Communications Inc, pg 886

DELAWARE

Actors Attic, pg 775

FLORIDA

Access Media Group, pg 773
Allstar Audio Systems Inc, pg 782
BAI Distributors Inc, pg 801
Griffiths Broadcast Co Inc, pg 882
Harris Corp, pg 885
Hi-Tech Enterprises Inc, pg 888
Media Concepts Inc, pg 936
Midtown Video Inc, pg 942
Photomart Cine-Video Inc, pg 975
Recording Media & Equipment Inc (RM&E), pg 993
Stereo Sales Inc, pg 1024
Technomedia Solutions, pg 1035

GEORGIA

Omnimedia Inc, pg 962
Stage Front Presentation Systems, pg 1022

HAWAII

The Audio Visual Co (AVCO), pg 795

ILLINOIS

Allen Visual Systems Inc, pg 781
Joseph Electronics, pg 906
Quintessence Audio Ltd, pg 989
Sound Vision Inc, pg 1018

INDIANA

Sensory Technologies LLC, pg 1006
SHP Electronics, pg 1010

IOWA

ECS Inc, pg 856

KENTUCKY

Audio Visual Techniques Inc, pg 796
Axxis Inc, pg 800
NOR-COM Inc, pg 958

LOUISIANA

Intermedia Technologies, pg 900

MAINE

Headlight Audio Visual Inc, pg 887

MARYLAND

Bradley Broadcast & Pro Audio, pg 811
Kipp Visual Systems Inc, pg 911

MICHIGAN

Ascom Communications Contractors, pg 791
On Stage Visuals, pg 963
TeL Systems, pg 1035

NEW HAMPSHIRE

Technet® Systems Group, pg 1033

NEW JERSEY

Audio Visual Associates, pg 795
Diversified Systems Inc, pg 849
National Audio-Visual Supply, pg 952
PatchAmp, pg 970
Starlite Productions, pg 1024
SYMCO Inc, pg 1030
Total Video Products Inc, pg 1042
Wired 4 Sound Inc, pg 1068
York Telecom, pg 1072

NEW YORK

ALTEL Systems Inc, pg 783
Audio-Video Corp, pg 795
Custom Media Environments, pg 841
Design Audio Visual Inc, pg 845
Markertek Video Supply, pg 931
NorthCountry Distributors, pg 959
Presentation Products Inc, pg 981
TecNec Distributing, pg 1035
Toys From The Attic, pg 1043

OHIO

ITA Audio Visual Solutions, pg 902
Jimmy Rea Electronics Inc, pg 992
Tri-State Audio Visual Co, pg 1044

PENNSYLVANIA

Advanced AV, pg 777
Vistacom Inc, pg 1059

TENNESSEE

Durrell LLC, pg 854
Lowrance Sound Co Inc, pg 925
Technical Support Systems LLC, pg 1034

TEXAS

Data Projections Inc, pg 843
Digital Display Solutions Inc, pg 847
Industrial Audio/Video Inc, pg 897
Lubbock Audio Visual Inc, pg 925
Media Management LLC, pg 937
Pro Video & Film Equipment Co Inc, pg 983
Tarpley Media Systems, pg 1032

UTAH

Performance Audio, pg 973

VIRGINIA

Avitecture Inc, pg 799
Communications Specialists Inc, pg 833
Hoppmann Audio Visual, pg 891
Lee Hartman & Sons Inc, pg 918

WASHINGTON

Telect Inc, pg 1036

WISCONSIN

Audio Visual of Milwaukee Inc, pg 795
Full Compass Systems, pg 874
Safe Harbor Computers, pg 1001

PUERTO RICO

Bonnin Electronics Inc, pg 810

ALBERTA

Infosat Communications Inc, pg 898

BRITISH COLUMBIA

Commercial Electronics Ltd, pg 832
Dav Tronics Ltd, pg 843
ProVision Video Sales & Rentals Inc, pg 986

MANITOBA

Advance Pro, pg 777
Inland Audio Visual Ltd, pg 898

ONTARIO

Cinema Stage Inc, pg 827

Switcher & Matrix—Mechanical & Electronic Manufacturers

ARIZONA

Adcom LLC, pg 776

CALIFORNIA

ALTINEX Inc, pg 783
Henry Engineering, pg 888
Opticomm-EMCORE, pg 964
Wohler Technologies Inc, pg 1069

COLORADO

Clear Blue Audio Video, pg 829

FLORIDA

Compuvideo Sales USA Ltd, pg 834
Tel-Test, pg 1035

ILLINOIS

Esoteric Sound, pg 862

INDIANA

JFW Industries Inc, pg 905

MARYLAND

Knox Video Technologies, pg 912

NEW JERSEY

FSR Inc, pg 873
Kramer Electronics USA Inc, pg 913

NEW YORK

Analog Way Inc, pg 786
Custom Media Environments, pg 841
Image Labs Corp, pg 895
MultiDyne Video & Fiber Optics Systems, pg 950
Protech Audio Corp, pg 986
Sescom Inc, pg 1007
TecNec Distributing, pg 1035

OREGON

BIAMP Systems, pg 806

PENNSYLVANIA

Rossman Audio LLC, pg 1000

TENNESSEE

Durrell LLC, pg 854

TEXAS

Logitek Electronic Systems Inc, pg 924

UTAH

ClearOne Inc, pg 830

WASHINGTON

Conex Electro-Systems Inc, pg 835
Telect Inc, pg 1036

BRITISH COLUMBIA

Dav Tronics Ltd, pg 843

Switcher & Matrix—Mechanical & Electronic Rentals

ARIZONA

Merestone, pg 938

CALIFORNIA

Ametron Audio/Video, pg 785
FXC Communications, pg 874
Golden Gate Studios, pg 880
VER-Video Equipment Rentals, pg 1053
Videorama Industries LLC, pg 1057

FLORIDA

Access Media Group, pg 773
Allstar Audio Systems Inc, pg 782
Universal Studios Florida® Production Group, pg 1049

GEORGIA

Stage Front Presentation Systems, pg 1022

ILLINOIS

RC Communications, pg 992

KENTUCKY

Audio Visual Techniques Inc, pg 796

MARYLAND

CPR MultiMedia Solutions, pg 837
Event Tech, pg 863

MASSACHUSETTS

Preston Productions Inc, pg 981

MICHIGAN

K&R All Media Productions Inc, pg 908
On Stage Visuals, pg 963

MISSOURI

Show-Me Audio-Visual, pg 1009

NEW JERSEY

Audio Visual Associates, pg 795
Starlite Productions, pg 1024
Wired 4 Sound Inc, pg 1068

NEW YORK

CP Communications, pg 837
Design Audio Visual Inc, pg 845

NORTH CAROLINA

A&V Company, pg 772
Take One Productions Ltd, pg 1031

TENNESSEE

Durrell LLC, pg 854
Technical Support Systems LLC, pg 1034

TEXAS

Digital Display Solutions Inc, pg 847

VIRGINIA

Lee Hartman & Sons Inc, pg 918

BRITISH COLUMBIA

DL Sound & Lighting Productions Ltd, pg 849
ProVision Video Sales & Rentals Inc, pg 986

MANITOBA

Inland Audio Visual Ltd, pg 898

Switcher & Matrix—Mechanical & Electronic Repairs

CALIFORNIA

Ametron Audio/Video, pg 785

FLORIDA

Hi-Tech Enterprises Inc, pg 888

GEORGIA

Stage Front Presentation Systems, pg 1022

ILLINOIS

Midwest Digital Corp, pg 942

KENTUCKY

NOR-COM Inc, pg 958

MICHIGAN

TeL Systems, pg 1035

NEW JERSEY

Audio Visual Associates, pg 795
Starlite Productions, pg 1024

NEW YORK

Analog Way Inc, pg 786
Toys From The Attic, pg 1043

OHIO

Tri-State Audio Visual Co, pg 1044

OREGON

All Service Musical Electronics Repair, pg 780

TENNESSEE

Durrell LLC, pg 854
Technical Support Systems LLC, pg 1034

ALBERTA

Infosat Communications Inc, pg 898

MANITOBA

Inland Audio Visual Ltd, pg 898

Synchronizer Distributors

ARIZONA

Arizona Cine Equipment, pg 789
EAR Professional Audio/Video, pg 855

CALIFORNIA

Ametron Audio/Video, pg 785
Audio Images Corp, pg 794
Be Media, pg 804
BroadcastStore.com, pg 813
Christy's Editorial, pg 826
Delicate Electronics Sales Inc, pg 845
FXC Communications, pg 874
Location Sound Corp, pg 924
MediaPOINTE, pg 938
TASCAM, pg 1032
Tri-Ed, pg 1044
VTP Inc, pg 1061

COLORADO

Audio Consultant Services Inc, pg 794
Spectrum Audio Visual Services, pg 1020

CONNECTICUT

HB Communications Inc, pg 886
Sennheiser Electronic Corp, pg 1006

FLORIDA

Access Media Group, pg 773
Allstar Audio Systems Inc, pg 782
Digital Video Systems Inc, pg 848
Hi-Tech Enterprises Inc, pg 888
Hi-Tech Import Export Corp, pg 888
Photomart Cine-Video Inc, pg 975
Recording Media & Equipment Inc (RM&E), pg 993
Sight & Sound Productions, pg 1010
Stereo Sales Inc, pg 1024
TAI Audio, pg 1031

GEORGIA

Stage Front Presentation Systems, pg 1022

ILLINOIS

Allen Visual Systems Inc, pg 781
Joseph Electronics, pg 906
Woodside Avenue Music Productions Inc, pg 1069

INDIANA

Sensory Technologies LLC, pg 1006
Sweetwater Sound Inc, pg 1029

IOWA

ECS Inc, pg 856

KANSAS

Smith Audio-Visual Inc, pg 1014

KENTUCKY

Axxis Inc, pg 800
NOR-COM Inc, pg 958

MAINE

Independent Audio Inc, pg 897

MARYLAND

Bradley Broadcast & Pro Audio, pg 811
Kipp Visual Systems Inc, pg 911

MASSACHUSETTS

Professional Audio Design Inc, pg 985

MICHIGAN

Olson Anderson Co, pg 786
City Events Group, pg 828
TeL Systems, pg 1035

NEW JERSEY

Diversified Systems Inc, pg 849
Hamilton Buhl, pg 884
JRF Magnetic Sciences Inc, pg 906
National Audio-Visual Supply, pg 952
PatchAmp, pg 970
Starlite Productions, pg 1024
Wired 4 Sound Inc, pg 1068
York Telecom, pg 1072

NEW YORK

Audio-Video Corp, pg 795
AV Workshop, pg 797

AUDIO

Synchronizer Distributors (continued)

NEW YORK (continued)

Custom Media Environments, pg 841
Design Audio Visual Inc, pg 845
Technisphere Corp, pg 1034

OHIO

Aztec Video Productions, pg 801
ITA Audio Visual Solutions, pg 902
Jimmy Rea Electronics Inc, pg 992

PENNSYLVANIA

Advanced AV, pg 777
The Lerro Corp, pg 919
Morefield Communications Inc, pg 946

TENNESSEE

Lowrance Sound Co Inc, pg 925
Technical Support Systems LLC, pg 1034

TEXAS

Lubbock Audio Visual Inc, pg 925
Pro Video & Film Equipment Co Inc, pg 983
Schoolhouse Audio Visual, pg 1004
Stage Directions, pg 1022
Tarpley Media Systems, pg 1032

UTAH

Performance Audio, pg 973

VIRGINIA

Avitecture Inc, pg 799
Boitnott Visual Communications Corp (BVC), pg 810
Communications Specialists Inc, pg 833
Intellidyne LLC, pg 899

WISCONSIN

Audio Visual of Milwaukee Inc, pg 795
Full Compass Systems, pg 874

PUERTO RICO

Bonnin Electronics Inc, pg 810

BRITISH COLUMBIA

Commercial Electronics Ltd, pg 832

MANITOBA

Advance Pro, pg 777
Inland Audio Visual Ltd, pg 898

ONTARIO

Nationwide Audio Visual Co, pg 953
Soundmaster Group, pg 1018

QUEBEC

Concept Audio-Visual, pg 834

Synchronizer Manufacturers

CALIFORNIA

ESE, pg 862
FutureVideo, pg 874
Roland Corp US, pg 998
TASCAM, pg 1032

RHODE ISLAND

M-Audio, pg 927

TENNESSEE

Adtec Digital Inc, pg 777

ONTARIO

Soundmaster Group, pg 1018

Synchronizer Rentals

ALABAMA

Audio-Video Resources Inc, pg 795

ARIZONA

Arizona Cine Equipment, pg 789
Merestone, pg 938

CALIFORNIA

Absolute Rentals, pg 772
Ametron Audio/Video, pg 785
Audio Rents, pg 794
Bexel Corp, pg 806
Big Time Picture Company Inc, pg 807
Christy's Editorial, pg 826
Lynch Communications, pg 926
McCune Audio-Video-Lighting, pg 935
Munday & Collins AV, pg 950
PSAV® Presentation Services, pg 986
Synthesizer Rental Service, pg 1030
Synthesizer Systems Technologies (SST), pg 1030
VER-Video Equipment Rentals, pg 1053

COLORADO

Audio Consultant Services Inc, pg 794
Daylight Productions & Rentals, pg 844
Spectrum Audio Visual Services, pg 1020

FLORIDA

Access Media Group, pg 773
Allstar Audio Systems Inc, pg 782
Sight & Sound Productions, pg 1010
TAI Audio, pg 1031

GEORGIA

Stage Front Presentation Systems, pg 1022
Staging Directions Inc, pg 1023

HAWAII

Audio Resource Honolulu, pg 794

ILLINOIS

Allen Visual Systems Inc, pg 781
On Stage Audio, pg 963
Show Department Inc, pg 1009
Woodside Avenue Music Productions Inc, pg 1069

IOWA

ECS Inc, pg 856

MARYLAND

Maryland Sound International Holding Co LLC, pg 933
Shadowstone R & R™, pg 1008

MASSACHUSETTS

Preston Productions Inc, pg 981

MICHIGAN

City Events Group, pg 828
K&R All Media Productions Inc, pg 908

MISSOURI

Show-Me Audio-Visual, pg 1009

NEW HAMPSHIRE

Apertura, pg 788

NEW JERSEY

Starlite Productions, pg 1024
Video Corporation of America (VCA), pg 1055

NEW YORK

AV Workshop, pg 797
Design Audio Visual Inc, pg 845
Dreamhire LLC, pg 852
Manhattan Center Studios Inc, pg 930
TBA Global Events, pg 1032
Technisphere Corp, pg 1034
WorldStage, pg 1070

OREGON

Northwest Film Center, pg 959

PENNSYLVANIA

Advanced AV, pg 777

TENNESSEE

Technical Support Systems LLC, pg 1034

TEXAS

Lubbock Audio Visual Inc, pg 925
The Samuels Co, pg 1002
Stage Directions, pg 1022

UTAH

Performance Audio, pg 973

VIRGINIA

American AV, pg 783
Boitnott Visual Communications Corp (BVC), pg 810

WISCONSIN

Event Essentials, pg 863

BRITISH COLUMBIA

Commercial Electronics Ltd, pg 832

MANITOBA

Inland Audio Visual Ltd, pg 898

QUEBEC

Audio Visual Dynamics Ltd, pg 795
Concept Audio-Visual, pg 834

Synchronizer Repairs

CALIFORNIA

Ametron Audio/Video, pg 785
Audio Images Corp, pg 794
Big Time Picture Company Inc, pg 807
Christy's Editorial, pg 826
McAlister Electronics, pg 935

CONNECTICUT

Sennheiser Electronic Corp, pg 1006

FLORIDA

Hi-Tech Enterprises Inc, pg 888
Stereo Sales Inc, pg 1024
TAI Audio, pg 1031

GEORGIA

Stage Front Presentation Systems, pg 1022

ILLINOIS

Allen Visual Systems Inc, pg 781

IOWA

ECS Inc, pg 856

KENTUCKY

NOR-COM Inc, pg 958

MICHIGAN

City Events Group, pg 828
K&R's Recording Studios Inc, pg 908
TeL Systems, pg 1035

NEW JERSEY

Starlite Productions, pg 1024

OREGON

All Service Musical Electronics Repair, pg 780

TENNESSEE

Technical Support Systems LLC, pg 1034

VIRGINIA

Boitnott Visual Communications Corp (BVC), pg 810

WISCONSIN

Full Compass Systems, pg 874

MANITOBA

Inland Audio Visual Ltd, pg 898

Synthesizer—Bass, *see* Bass Synthesizer

Tape Duplicator Distributors

ALABAMA

Dogwood Recording Studios, pg 850

ARIZONA

Arizona Cine Equipment, pg 789
Metropolitan Audio-Visual Inc, pg 940
Troxell Communications Inc, pg 1045

ARKANSAS

Jay S Stanley & Associates Inc, pg 1023
White Diamond Productions, pg 1065

CALIFORNIA

Ametron Audio/Video, pg 785
Audio Images Corp, pg 794
Audio/Video Supply Inc, pg 795
BroadcastStore.com, pg 813
California Tape Products Inc, pg 817
Delicate Electronics Sales Inc, pg 845
FXC Communications, pg 874
Instructional Materials & Equipment Distributors (I-Med), pg 899
JD Audio Visual Inc, pg 904
KABA Audio Productions, pg 907
Media Fabricators Inc, pg 936
MediaPOINTE, pg 938
Related Visual Inc, pg 994
SSL Industries Inc, pg 1022

COLORADO

Audio Consultant Services Inc, pg 794
Ceavco Audio/Visual Co, pg 822
Spectrum Audio Visual Services, pg 1020

CONNECTICUT

Concord Communications, pg 835
HB Communications Inc, pg 886
MAVCO, pg 934
Rockwell Communications Inc, pg 998

DELAWARE

Actors Attic, pg 775

FLORIDA

Access Media Group, pg 773
Allstar Audio Systems Inc, pg 782
BAI Distributors Inc, pg 801
Digital Video Systems Inc, pg 848
Gulf Coast Audio Visual Producers Inc, pg 883
Harris Corp, pg 885
Hi-Tech Import Export Corp, pg 888
Intermark Industries Inc, pg 900
Media Concepts Inc, pg 936
Photomart Cine-Video Inc, pg 975
Photosound of Orlando Inc, pg 975
Recording Media & Equipment Inc (RM&E), pg 993
Sight & Sound Productions, pg 1010
Stereo Sales Inc, pg 1024
TAI Audio, pg 1031
Tallahassee Audio Visual, pg 1031

GEORGIA

Audio Visual Resources Inc, pg 795
Stage Front Presentation Systems, pg 1022
Technical Innovation, pg 1033
Visioneering International Inc, pg 1058

HAWAII

The Audio Visual Co (AVCO), pg 795

ILLINOIS

RAM Systems LLC, pg 991

INDIANA

Sensory Technologies LLC, pg 1006
SHP Electronics, pg 1010

IOWA

ECS Inc, pg 856

KANSAS

KK Office Solutions Inc, pg 911
Smith Audio-Visual Inc, pg 1014

KENTUCKY

Axxis Inc, pg 800
Barney Miller's Inc, pg 943
NOR-COM Inc, pg 958

MAINE

Headlight Audio Visual Inc, pg 887
Independent Audio Inc, pg 897

MARYLAND

Bradley Broadcast & Pro Audio, pg 811
Cardinal Sound & Video, pg 820
Kipp Visual Systems Inc, pg 911
Nicholas P Pipino Associates Inc, pg 976
RTZ Audio Visual, pg 1000
Visual Aids Electronics Corp, pg 1059

MICHIGAN

Olson Anderson Co, pg 786
Ascom Communications Contractors, pg 791
City Events Group, pg 828
Digi Sign Design LLC, pg 847
TeL Systems, pg 1035

MINNESOTA

Advanced Audio-Visual Inc, pg 777
Aggressive Records Audio Duplication LLC, pg 778
New Life Communications Inc, pg 956

MISSISSIPPI

Bowie Audio Visual Enterprises Inc, pg 811
Jasper Ewing & Sons Inc, pg 864

MISSOURI

Communitronics Corp, pg 833
Conference Technologies Inc, pg 835
Image Technologies Corp, pg 895
Modern Communications Inc, pg 944
Schiller's Audio-Visual, pg 1004
Swank Audio Visuals, pg 1029

NEW JERSEY

Alltec Stores, a Vcom IMC Company, pg 782
Audio Visual Associates, pg 795
Audio Visual Dynamics®, pg 795
AV Bluebook, pg 797
Diversified Systems Inc, pg 849
G&G Technologies Inc, pg 875
Hamilton Buhl, pg 884
National Audio-Visual Supply, pg 952
PatchAmp, pg 970
Starlite Productions, pg 1024
Turner Engineering Inc, pg 1046
VCom International Multimedia Corp, pg 1052
Wilray Audio Visual Corp, pg 1067
Wired 4 Sound Inc, pg 1068
York Telecom, pg 1072

NEW YORK

AV Workshop, pg 797
Burlington A/V Recording Media, pg 815
Communication Corner Inc, pg 832
Custom Media Environments, pg 841
Design Audio Visual Inc, pg 845
Eastco Multimedia Solutions Inc, pg 856
Gaylord Brothers, pg 876
Indigo Productions, pg 897
Long Island Video Enterprises Live Inc, pg 924
Saul Mineroff Electronics Inc, pg 943
Neptune Photo Inc, pg 954
Ray Supply Inc, pg 992
RNJ Electronics, pg 997
Technisphere Corp, pg 1034
Visual Technologies Corp, pg 1060
Willoughby's Imaging Center, pg 1067

NORTH CAROLINA

Camcor Inc, pg 818
Strategic Connections, pg 1026

OHIO

Audio Visual Media, pg 795
Copp Integrated Systems, pg 836
ITA Audio Visual Solutions, pg 902
Jimmy Rea Electronics Inc, pg 992
Tri-State Audio Visual Co, pg 1044

OKLAHOMA

Piper Media Services Inc, pg 976

PENNSYLVANIA

Advanced AV, pg 777
Audio Visual Communications Inc, pg 795
Brodart Co, pg 813
FMP Media Solutions Inc, pg 870
J E Foss Co, pg 871
Garcia Marketing Inc, pg 875
Grise Audio Visual Center Inc, pg 882
The Lerro Corp, pg 919
Morefield Communications Inc, pg 946
Visual Sound Inc, pg 1059
Wespen Audio Visual Co, pg 1063

RHODE ISLAND

Custom Computer Specialists Inc, pg 841

TENNESSEE

Continental Film, pg 835
Lowrance Sound Co Inc, pg 925
Memphis Communications Corp, pg 938
Mr Mark's Used Musical, Stereo & Studio Equipment Store, pg 944
Technical Support Systems LLC, pg 1034
Tennessee Visual Service Co, pg 1037
Zion Music Group, pg 1074

TEXAS

Audio Visual Technologies Group, pg 796
Crossroads Audio Inc, pg 840
Heffernan Audio Visual, pg 887
Industrial Audio/Video Inc, pg 897
J&S Audio Visual Inc, pg 904
Lubbock Audio Visual Inc, pg 925
Pro Video & Film Equipment Co Inc, pg 983
RadioShack Corp, pg 990
RF Specialties of Texas LLC, pg 996
Schoolhouse Audio Visual, pg 1004
Tarpley Media Systems, pg 1032

UTAH

Performance Audio, pg 973
RIA Corp, pg 996

VIRGINIA

Boitnott Visual Communications Corp (BVC), pg 810
Communications Specialists Inc, pg 833
Lee Hartman & Sons Inc, pg 918
The Whitlock Group, pg 1065

WASHINGTON

CCI Solutions, pg 821
Inland Audio Visual Co, pg 898

WEST VIRGINIA

United Sound & Electronics, pg 1048

WISCONSIN

Audio Visual of Milwaukee Inc, pg 795
Camera Corner Connecting Point, pg 818
Full Compass Systems, pg 874
School Specialty Inc, pg 1004

PUERTO RICO

Bonnin Electronics Inc, pg 810

ALBERTA

Matrix Video Communications Corp (MVCC), pg 934
McBain Audio Visual Ltd, pg 935
Sharp's Audio-Visual Ltd, pg 1008
Unique Communications Ltd, pg 1048

BRITISH COLUMBIA

Commercial Electronics Ltd, pg 832

MANITOBA

Advance Pro, pg 777
Inland Audio Visual Ltd, pg 898

AUDIO

Tape Duplicator Distributors (continued)

ONTARIO

Edcom Multimedia Products, pg 856
Nationwide Audio Visual Co, pg 953
Premier A/V Sales Ltd, pg 980
Westbury National Show Systems Ltd, pg 1064

Tape Duplicator Manufacturers

CALIFORNIA

Bridge Publications Inc, pg 812
KABA Audio Productions, pg 907
Newdoll Enterprises LLC, pg 956
Recortec Inc, pg 993
SF Global Sourcing, pg 1007
Sony Electronics Inc, pg 1016

INDIANA

Crystal Clear Media Group, pg 840
Infonics Inc, pg 898

MINNESOTA

Telex Communications Inc, pg 1037

NEW YORK

FSL Media Inc, pg 873
Recordex USA Inc, pg 993

PENNSYLVANIA

FMP Media Solutions Inc, pg 870

ONTARIO

Cinram Inc, pg 828

Tape Duplicator Rentals

ALABAMA

Audio-Video Resources Inc, pg 795
Media Visions Inc, pg 937

ARIZONA

Arizona Cine Equipment, pg 789
Merestone, pg 938
Metropolitan Audio-Visual Inc, pg 940

ARKANSAS

White Diamond Productions, pg 1065

CALIFORNIA

Alliant Event Services, pg 781
Ametron Audio/Video, pg 785
Express Media Inc, pg 864
Golden Gate Studios, pg 880
Instructional Materials & Equipment Distributors (I-Med), pg 899
JD Audio Visual Inc, pg 904
Lynch Communications, pg 926
Munday & Collins AV, pg 950
Roundabout Entertainment Inc, pg 1000

COLORADO

Audio Consultant Services Inc, pg 794
Daylight Productions & Rentals, pg 844
Spectrum Audio Visual Services, pg 1020

CONNECTICUT

A/V Davey, pg 797
Concord Communications, pg 835
Rockwell Communications Inc, pg 998
Trod Nossel Productions & Recording Studios, pg 1045

DELAWARE

Side Door Studio Inc, pg 1010

FLORIDA

Access Media Group, pg 773
Allstar Audio Systems Inc, pg 782
Gulf Coast Audio Visual Producers Inc, pg 883
Media Concepts Inc, pg 936
Photosound of Orlando Inc, pg 975
Pro Stage Inc, pg 983
Sight & Sound Productions, pg 1010

GEORGIA

Stage Front Presentation Systems, pg 1022
Staging Directions Inc, pg 1023

ILLINOIS

Central Audio-Visual Equipment Inc, pg 823
Communications Corporation of America, pg 833
Helix Camera & Video, pg 887
On Stage Audio, pg 963
The Pepper Group, pg 972

INDIANA

Advanced Media Integration, pg 777

IOWA

ECS Inc, pg 856

MAINE

Headlight Audio Visual Inc, pg 887

MARYLAND

Advance Audiovisual Presentation Ltd, pg 777
RTZ Audio Visual, pg 1000
Shadowstone R & R™, pg 1008

MASSACHUSETTS

massAV, pg 933
Preston Productions Inc, pg 981

MICHIGAN

Olson Anderson Co, pg 786
City Events Group, pg 828
Digi Sign Design LLC, pg 847
K&R All Media Productions Inc, pg 908
K&R's Recording Studios Inc, pg 908

MINNESOTA

Advanced Audio-Visual Inc, pg 777
AVI Systems, pg 799

MISSISSIPPI

Bowie Audio Visual Enterprises Inc, pg 811

MISSOURI

Schiller's Audio-Visual, pg 1004
Show-Me Audio-Visual, pg 1009
Swank Audio Visuals, pg 1029

NEW JERSEY

Audio Visual Dynamics®, pg 795
Bill Quinn Productions, pg 989
Starlite Productions, pg 1024
Wired 4 Sound Inc, pg 1068

NEW YORK

AV Workshop, pg 797
CMI Communications, pg 830
Communication Corner Inc, pg 832
Design Audio Visual Inc, pg 845
Langie Audio Visual Systems, pg 915
Long Island Video Enterprises Live Inc, pg 924
Manhattan Center Studios Inc, pg 930
Specialized Audio-Visual Inc, pg 1020
Technisphere Corp, pg 1034
Visual Technologies Corp, pg 1060
Visual Word Systems Inc, pg 1060

NORTH CAROLINA

Camcor Inc, pg 818
Special Event Services, pg 1020
Strategic Connections, pg 1026
Visual Aids Electronics of North Carolina Inc, pg 1059

OHIO

Audio Visual Media, pg 795
Hughie's Event Production Services, pg 892

PENNSYLVANIA

American Artist Studio, pg 783
Audio Visual Communications Inc, pg 795
Forge Recording LLC, pg 871
Grise Audio Visual Center Inc, pg 882
Visual Sound Inc, pg 1059

TENNESSEE

Brantley Sound Associates Inc, pg 812
Memphis Communications Corp, pg 938
Mr Mark's Used Musical, Stereo & Studio Equipment Store, pg 944
Technical Support Systems LLC, pg 1034
Tennessee Visual Service Co, pg 1037

TEXAS

Audio Visual Technologies Group, pg 796
J&S Audio Visual Inc, pg 904
Lubbock Audio Visual Inc, pg 925
Omega Productions, pg 962

VIRGINIA

Boitnott Visual Communications Corp (BVC), pg 810
Lee Hartman & Sons Inc, pg 918
Projection Presentation Technology, pg 985

WASHINGTON

Inland Audio Visual Co, pg 898
Victory Studios, pg 1054

WISCONSIN

Event Essentials, pg 863
School Specialty Inc, pg 1004

WYOMING

Bridger Productions Inc, pg 812

ALBERTA

McBain Audio Visual Ltd, pg 935
Unique Communications Ltd, pg 1048

BRITISH COLUMBIA

Clark's Audio Visual Services Ltd, pg 829
Commercial Electronics Ltd, pg 832
Finale Editworks, pg 868
Image Media Farm, pg 895

MANITOBA

Inland Audio Visual Ltd, pg 898

ONTARIO

Edcom Multimedia Products, pg 856

QUEBEC

Audio Visual Dynamics Ltd, pg 795
AVW-TELAV Audio Visual Solutions, a Freeman Company, pg 800
Concept Audio-Visual, pg 834

Tape Duplicator Repairs

CALIFORNIA

Ametron Audio/Video, pg 785
Audio Images Corp, pg 794
Instructional Materials & Equipment Distributors (I-Med), pg 899
McAlister Electronics, pg 935
Lloyd F McKinney Associates Inc, pg 935
SSL Industries Inc, pg 1022

CONNECTICUT

HB Communications Inc, pg 886
Rockwell Communications Inc, pg 998

FLORIDA

AMP Services Inc, pg 785
Gulf Coast Audio Visual Producers Inc, pg 883
Hi-Tech Enterprises Inc, pg 888
JT Communications, pg 906
Stereo Sales Inc, pg 1024
Tallahassee Audio Visual, pg 1031

GEORGIA

Audio Visual Resources Inc, pg 795
Stage Front Presentation Systems, pg 1022
Technical Innovation, pg 1033

ILLINOIS

Central Audio-Visual Equipment Inc, pg 823
Midwest Digital Corp, pg 942

IOWA

ECS Inc, pg 856

KANSAS

KK Office Solutions Inc, pg 911

KENTUCKY

Barney Miller's Inc, pg 943
NOR-COM Inc, pg 958

MAINE

Headlight Audio Visual Inc, pg 887

MARYLAND

Cardinal Sound & Video, pg 820
RTZ Audio Visual, pg 1000

MICHIGAN

Olson Anderson Co, pg 786
City Events Group, pg 828
K&R's Recording Studios Inc, pg 908
TeL Systems, pg 1035

MINNESOTA

AVI Systems, pg 799

MISSISSIPPI

Bowie Audio Visual Enterprises Inc, pg 811

NEW JERSEY

Starlite Productions, pg 1024
Turner Engineering Inc, pg 1046

NEW YORK

Colortone Audio Visual, pg 832
Langie Audio Visual Systems, pg 915
Visual Technologies Corp, pg 1060

NORTH CAROLINA

Camcor Inc, pg 818
Strategic Connections, pg 1026

OHIO

Audio Visual Media, pg 795
Copp Integrated Systems, pg 836
Tri-State Audio Visual Co, pg 1044

OREGON

All Service Musical Electronics Repair, pg 780

PENNSYLVANIA

Audio Visions Inc, pg 795
J E Foss Co, pg 871
Visual Sound Inc, pg 1059
Wespen Audio Visual Co, pg 1063

RHODE ISLAND

Custom Computer Specialists Inc, pg 841

TENNESSEE

Memphis Communications Corp, pg 938
Technical Support Systems LLC, pg 1034
Tennessee Visual Service Co, pg 1037

TEXAS

Audio Visual Technologies Group, pg 796
Lubbock Audio Visual Inc, pg 925
Padgitt's, pg 967

VIRGINIA

Boitnott Visual Communications Corp (BVC), pg 810
Lee Hartman & Sons Inc, pg 918
The Whitlock Group, pg 1065

WASHINGTON

Inland Audio Visual Co, pg 898

WEST VIRGINIA

United Sound & Electronics, pg 1048

WISCONSIN

Camera Corner Connecting Point, pg 818
Full Compass Systems, pg 874
School Specialty Inc, pg 1004

ALBERTA

Sharp's Audio-Visual Ltd, pg 1008
Unique Communications Ltd, pg 1048

BRITISH COLUMBIA

Commercial Electronics Ltd, pg 832

MANITOBA

Evolution Presentation Technologies, pg 863
Inland Audio Visual Ltd, pg 898

ONTARIO

Edcom Multimedia Products, pg 856
Premier A/V Sales Ltd, pg 980

Tape Equipment, *see* Repetitive Tape Equipment

Tape Eraser Distributors

ARIZONA

Troxell Communications Inc, pg 1045

ARKANSAS

White Diamond Productions, pg 1065

CALIFORNIA

Adolph Gasser Inc, pg 776
Ametron Audio/Video, pg 785
Audio Images Corp, pg 794
California Tape Products Inc, pg 817
Christy's Editorial, pg 826
FXC Communications, pg 874
Instructional Materials & Equipment Distributors (I-Med), pg 899
JD Audio Visual Inc, pg 904
MediaPOINTE, pg 938
Newdoll Enterprises LLC, pg 956
SNAP, pg 1014
Kris Stevens Enterprises, pg 1024

CONNECTICUT

HB Communications Inc, pg 886

FLORIDA

Access Media Group, pg 773
Broadcasters General Store Inc, pg 813
Digital Video Systems Inc, pg 848
Harris Corp, pg 885
Hunter Electronics LLC, pg 892
Midtown Video Inc, pg 942
Photomart Cine-Video Inc, pg 975
Recording Media & Equipment Inc (RM&E), pg 993
Stereo Sales Inc, pg 1024

GEORGIA

Stage Front Presentation Systems, pg 1022

HAWAII

The Audio Visual Co (AVCO), pg 795

INDIANA

R B Annis Instruments Inc, pg 787
Sensory Technologies LLC, pg 1006

IOWA

ECS Inc, pg 856

KENTUCKY

Barney Miller's Inc, pg 943
NOR-COM Inc, pg 958

MAINE

Headlight Audio Visual Inc, pg 887

MARYLAND

Bradley Broadcast & Pro Audio, pg 811
Kipp Visual Systems Inc, pg 911

MASSACHUSETTS

Rule Broadcast Systems, pg 1000

MICHIGAN

TeL Systems, pg 1035

MISSOURI

Schiller's Audio-Visual, pg 1004

NEW HAMPSHIRE

Technet® Systems Group, pg 1033

NEW JERSEY

AV Bluebook, pg 797
Hamilton Buhl, pg 884
National Audio-Visual Supply, pg 952
Starlite Productions, pg 1024
VCom International Multimedia Corp, pg 1052
York Telecom, pg 1072

NEW YORK

B&H Photo & Video Pro Audio, pg 802
Design Audio Visual Inc, pg 845
Eastco Multimedia Solutions Inc, pg 856

OHIO

Jimmy Rea Electronics Inc, pg 992
Tri-State Audio Visual Co, pg 1044

PENNSYLVANIA

Advanced AV, pg 777
Brodart Co, pg 813
J E Foss Co, pg 871
The Lerro Corp, pg 919
Wespen Audio Visual Co, pg 1063

TENNESSEE

Lowrance Sound Co Inc, pg 925

TEXAS

Lubbock Audio Visual Inc, pg 925
Pro Video & Film Equipment Co Inc, pg 983
RadioShack Corp, pg 990
RF Specialties of Texas LLC, pg 996
Tarpley Media Systems, pg 1032

UTAH

Performance Audio, pg 973

VIRGINIA

Lee Hartman & Sons Inc, pg 918
Old Dominion Broadcasting, pg 961

WASHINGTON

CCI Solutions, pg 821
Northern Lights & Pro Audio, pg 959

WISCONSIN

Audio Visual of Milwaukee Inc, pg 795
Full Compass Systems, pg 874

PUERTO RICO

Bonnin Electronics Inc, pg 810

ALBERTA

Matrix Video Communications Corp (MVCC), pg 934

BRITISH COLUMBIA

Commercial Electronics Ltd, pg 832

MANITOBA

Advance Pro, pg 777
Inland Audio Visual Ltd, pg 898

ONTARIO

Premier A/V Sales Ltd, pg 980

Tape Eraser Manufacturers

CALIFORNIA

Garner Products Inc, pg 875

FLORIDA

Sonar Radio Corp, pg 1015

INDIANA

R B Annis Instruments Inc, pg 787

NEBRASKA

Data Security Inc, pg 843

AUDIO

Tape Eraser Rentals

ARIZONA

Merestone, pg 938

ARKANSAS

White Diamond Productions, pg 1065

CALIFORNIA

Ametron Audio/Video, pg 785
Artichoke Productions, pg 791
Garner Products Inc, pg 875
Golden Gate Studios, pg 880

CONNECTICUT

A/V Davey, pg 797

GEORGIA

Stage Front Presentation Systems, pg 1022

MASSACHUSETTS

Preston Productions Inc, pg 981

MICHIGAN

Digi Sign Design LLC, pg 847
K&R All Media Productions Inc, pg 908

NEW JERSEY

Bill Quinn Productions, pg 989
Starlite Productions, pg 1024

BRITISH COLUMBIA

Finale Editworks, pg 868

MANITOBA

Inland Audio Visual Ltd, pg 898

Tape Eraser Repairs

CALIFORNIA

Ametron Audio/Video, pg 785
Garner Products Inc, pg 875

GEORGIA

Stage Front Presentation Systems, pg 1022

KENTUCKY

NOR-COM Inc, pg 958

MICHIGAN

TeL Systems, pg 1035

NEW JERSEY

Starlite Productions, pg 1024

OREGON

All Service Musical Electronics Repair, pg 780

MANITOBA

Inland Audio Visual Ltd, pg 898

Tape Loading Equipment Distributors

ARIZONA

Troxell Communications Inc, pg 1045

CALIFORNIA

Ametron Audio/Video, pg 785
FXC Communications, pg 874
KABA Audio Productions, pg 907
Newdoll Enterprises LLC, pg 956
Kris Stevens Enterprises, pg 1024
VTP Inc, pg 1061

FLORIDA

Digital Video Systems Inc, pg 848
Recording Media & Equipment Inc (RM&E), pg 993

INDIANA

Sensory Technologies LLC, pg 1006

KENTUCKY

NOR-COM Inc, pg 958

MARYLAND

Bradley Broadcast & Pro Audio, pg 811

NEW JERSEY

Hamilton Buhl, pg 884
Starlite Productions, pg 1024
York Telecom, pg 1072

PENNSYLVANIA

Advanced AV, pg 777
The Lerro Corp, pg 919

TEXAS

Tarpley Media Systems, pg 1032

VIRGINIA

Old Dominion Broadcasting, pg 961

WISCONSIN

Audio Visual of Milwaukee Inc, pg 795

PUERTO RICO

Bonnin Electronics Inc, pg 810

MANITOBA

Advance Pro, pg 777
Inland Audio Visual Ltd, pg 898

Tape Loading Equipment Manufacturers

CALIFORNIA

Opticomm-EMCORE, pg 964

Tape Loading Equipment Rentals

ARIZONA

Merestone, pg 938

CALIFORNIA

Ametron Audio/Video, pg 785
Roundabout Entertainment Inc, pg 1000

ILLINOIS

On Stage Audio, pg 963

MASSACHUSETTS

Preston Productions Inc, pg 981

MICHIGAN

K&R All Media Productions Inc, pg 908

MANITOBA

Inland Audio Visual Ltd, pg 898

Tape Loading Equipment Repairs

CALIFORNIA

Ametron Audio/Video, pg 785
McAlister Electronics, pg 935

ILLINOIS

Midwest Digital Corp, pg 942

KENTUCKY

NOR-COM Inc, pg 958

MICHIGAN

TeL Systems, pg 1035

NEW JERSEY

Starlite Productions, pg 1024

VIRGINIA

Old Dominion Broadcasting, pg 961

WISCONSIN

Full Compass Systems, pg 874

MANITOBA

Inland Audio Visual Ltd, pg 898

Teleconferencing

ALABAMA

Media Visions Inc, pg 937

ARIZONA

Merestone, pg 938
Metropolitan Audio-Visual Inc, pg 940

ARKANSAS

White Diamond Productions, pg 1065

CALIFORNIA

AGF Media Services, pg 778
Associated Sound, pg 792
AV Conferencing, pg 797
Cibola Systems, pg 826
Earwax Productions Inc, pg 855
FXC Communications, pg 874
Havas Edge, pg 885
JDS Video & Media Productions Inc, pg 904
Lynch Communications, pg 926
McCune Audio-Video-Lighting, pg 935
Opticomm-EMCORE, pg 964
Palardo Productions, pg 968
Producers Group Ltd, pg 983
PSSI, pg 987
QRS Software Services, pg 988
Tele-Video Production Services (TVPS), pg 1036
Thorburn Associates, Acoustic, Technology, Lighting Design, pg 1039
Total Media Group, pg 1042
University of Southern California, pg 1050

COLORADO

Ceavco Audio/Visual Co, pg 822
Level 3 Communications Inc, pg 919
Spectrum Audio Visual Services, pg 1020

CONNECTICUT

A/V Davey, pg 797
Broadcast Video Productions LLC, pg 813
Guymark Studios LLC, pg 883

DISTRICT OF COLUMBIA

Educational Film Center, pg 857
Interface Media Group, pg 900

FLORIDA

Communications Concepts Inc (CCI), pg 833
Comtel Inc, pg 834
Home Shopping Network (HSN), pg 890
Universal Studios Florida® Production Group, pg 1049

GEORGIA

Convergent Media Systems, pg 836
Lighting & Production Equipment Inc, pg 920
Stage Front Presentation Systems, pg 1022
Staging Directions Inc, pg 1023

ILLINOIS

ABS Enterprises, pg 772
Audio Visual Services Corp, pg 796
Cresta Creative, pg 839
On Stage Audio, pg 963
PSAV® Presentation Services (Hotel Services Division), pg 987
Universal Training, pg 1049

INDIANA

OMNI Productions, pg 962

IOWA

Iowa State University-Information Technology Services, pg 902
The Production House, pg 984

KENTUCKY

Audio Visual Techniques Inc, pg 796
Axxis Inc, pg 800
Broadway Digital, pg 813
Hammond Communications Group, pg 884
The Learning House Inc, pg 917
NOR-COM Inc, pg 958

Teleconferencing Equipment Distributors

AUDIO

Teleconferencing Equipment Distributors (continued)

NEW YORK

ALTEL Systems Inc, pg 783
Audio-Video Corp, pg 795
Colortone Audio Visual, pg 832
Custom Media Environments, pg 841
Design Audio Visual Inc, pg 845
Image Management Systems Inc, pg 895
KVL Audio Visual Services Inc, pg 914
L-3 GCS, pg 915
Magnaplan Corp, pg 928
SmartSource Computer & AV Rentals, pg 1014
Theatrical Services & Supplies Inc, pg 1038
Toys From The Attic, pg 1043
Visual Technologies Corp, pg 1060

OHIO

ITA Audio Visual Solutions, pg 902
Tri-State Audio Visual Co, pg 1044

PENNSYLVANIA

Advanced AV, pg 777
Grise Audio Visual Center Inc, pg 882
The Lerro Corp, pg 919

RHODE ISLAND

Shanix Inc, pg 1008

TENNESSEE

Continental Film, pg 835
Lowrance Sound Co Inc, pg 925
Technical Support Systems LLC, pg 1034

TEXAS

Audio Visual Technologies Group, pg 796
Data Projections Inc, pg 843
Industrial Audio/Video Inc, pg 897
Media Management LLC, pg 937
Schoolhouse Audio Visual, pg 1004
Tarpley Media Systems, pg 1032

UTAH

Listen Technologies Corp, pg 923

VIRGINIA

Avitecture Inc, pg 799
Intellidyne LLC, pg 899
Lee Hartman & Sons Inc, pg 918
Old Dominion Broadcasting, pg 961

WASHINGTON

Pacific Northwest Theatre Associates Inc (PNTA), pg 967

WISCONSIN

Audio Visual of Milwaukee Inc, pg 795
Full Compass Systems, pg 874

PUERTO RICO

Audio Visual Concepts Inc, pg 795
Bonnin Electronics Inc, pg 810

ALBERTA

Infosat Communications Inc, pg 898
Matrix Video Communications Corp (MVCC), pg 934

BRITISH COLUMBIA

Commercial Electronics Ltd, pg 832

MANITOBA

Advance Pro, pg 777
Inland Audio Visual Ltd, pg 898

ONTARIO

Cinema Stage Inc, pg 827
Edcom Multimedia Products, pg 856
Westbury National Show Systems Ltd, pg 1064

QUEBEC

Sennheiser (Canada) Inc, pg 1006

Teleconferencing Equipment Manufacturers

ARIZONA

Covid Inc, pg 837

CALIFORNIA

ALTINEX Inc, pg 783
Computer Modules Inc, pg 834

COLORADO

Display Devices, pg 849
Image Audiovisuals, pg 894

CONNECTICUT

Sound Control Technologies Inc, pg 1017

FLORIDA

CircuitWerkes Inc, pg 828

ILLINOIS

A T Products Inc, pg 771
J K Audio Inc, pg 903
Marshall Furniture Inc, pg 932

KENTUCKY

Innovative Electronic Designs LLC, pg 898

MASSACHUSETTS

Avidex Inc, pg 799
Comrex Corp, pg 834

MICHIGAN

ASC Systems, pg 791

MINNESOTA

Telex EVI, pg 1037
Winsted Corp, pg 1068

NEW JERSEY

Avaya Inc, pg 798
Bogen Communications Inc, pg 810
Crestron Electronics Inc, pg 839

NEW MEXICO

Lectrosonics Inc, pg 918

NEW YORK

Harry Joseph & Associates Inc, pg 906
MultiDyne Video & Fiber Optics Systems, pg 950

OHIO

Telos Systems, pg 1037

OREGON

BIAMP Systems, pg 806

TENNESSEE

Adtec Digital Inc, pg 777

UTAH

ClearOne Inc, pg 830

Teleconferencing Equipment Rentals

ARIZONA

Merestone, pg 938
Video West Inc, pg 1056

ARKANSAS

White Diamond Productions, pg 1065

CALIFORNIA

AGF Media Services, pg 778
Ametron Audio/Video, pg 785
Associated Sound, pg 792
AV Conferencing, pg 797
AV Guys, pg 797
Lynch Communications, pg 926
McCune Audio-Video-Lighting, pg 935
Stanislaus Audio Video Inc, pg 1023
VER-Video Equipment Rentals, pg 1053
VMI Inc, pg 1060

COLORADO

Spectrum Audio Visual Services, pg 1020

CONNECTICUT

A/V Davey, pg 797
Everett Hall Associates Inc, pg 863
Videofilm Systems Inc, pg 1057

DELAWARE

Actors Attic, pg 775

FLORIDA

Digital Video Systems Inc, pg 848
Harmon's Audio-Visual Services, pg 885
Pro Stage Inc, pg 983
Sight & Sound Productions, pg 1010

GEORGIA

Stage Front Presentation Systems, pg 1022

ILLINOIS

A T Products Inc, pg 771
Allen Visual Systems Inc, pg 781
On Stage Audio, pg 963
RC Communications, pg 992

KENTUCKY

Audio Visual Techniques Inc, pg 796

MARYLAND

Advance Audiovisual Presentation Ltd, pg 777
CPR MultiMedia Solutions, pg 837

MASSACHUSETTS

Terry Hanley Audio Systems Inc, pg 884
Preston Productions Inc, pg 981

MICHIGAN

K&R All Media Productions Inc, pg 908

MINNESOTA

Alpha Video & Audio Inc, pg 782

MISSOURI

Show-Me Audio-Visual, pg 1009

NEW JERSEY

Audio Visual Associates, pg 795
MIB Mediaworks, pg 941
Starlite Productions, pg 1024
Wired 4 Sound Inc, pg 1068

NEW YORK

Colortone Audio Visual, pg 832
Design Audio Visual Inc, pg 845
Dreamhire LLC, pg 852
KVL Audio Visual Services Inc, pg 914
Magnaplan Corp, pg 928
SmartSource Computer & AV Rentals, pg 1014
Visual Technologies Corp, pg 1060

NORTH CAROLINA

A&V Company, pg 772

OHIO

ITA Audio Visual Solutions, pg 902
Mills James Productions, pg 943

PENNSYLVANIA

Grise Audio Visual Center Inc, pg 882

TENNESSEE

Love Shack Recording Studios, pg 925
Technical Support Systems LLC, pg 1034

TEXAS

Audio Visual Technologies Group, pg 796
Data Display Audio Visual Co LP, pg 843

VIRGINIA

American AV, pg 783
Audio Visual Actions Inc (AVA), pg 795
Intellidyne LLC, pg 899
Lee Hartman & Sons Inc, pg 918

PUERTO RICO

Stage Crew Audiovisual Inc, pg 1022

BRITISH COLUMBIA

Commercial Electronics Ltd, pg 832

MANITOBA

Inland Audio Visual Ltd, pg 898

ONTARIO

Edcom Multimedia Products, pg 856
Westbury National Show Systems Ltd, pg 1064

Teleconferencing Equipment Repairs

CALIFORNIA

Ametron Audio/Video, pg 785
McAlister Electronics, pg 935

CONNECTICUT

HB Communications Inc, pg 886

DELAWARE

Actors Attic, pg 775

FLORIDA

Hi-Tech Enterprises Inc, pg 888

GEORGIA

Lighting & Production Equipment Inc, pg 920
Stage Front Presentation Systems, pg 1022

ILLINOIS

A T Products Inc, pg 771
Allen Visual Systems Inc, pg 781

KENTUCKY

NOR-COM Inc, pg 958

MICHIGAN

TeL Systems, pg 1035

NEW JERSEY

Audio Visual Associates, pg 795
Starlite Productions, pg 1024

NEW YORK

Toys From The Attic, pg 1043
Visual Technologies Corp, pg 1060

OHIO

ITA Audio Visual Solutions, pg 902
Tri-State Audio Visual Co, pg 1044

TENNESSEE

Technical Support Systems LLC, pg 1034

VIRGINIA

Avitecture Inc, pg 799
Intellidyne LLC, pg 899
Old Dominion Broadcasting, pg 961

WASHINGTON

Pacific Northwest Theatre Associates Inc (PNTA), pg 967

WISCONSIN

Full Compass Systems, pg 874

ALBERTA

Infosat Communications Inc, pg 898

BRITISH COLUMBIA

Commercial Electronics Ltd, pg 832

MANITOBA

Inland Audio Visual Ltd, pg 898

ONTARIO

Edcom Multimedia Products, pg 856
Westbury National Show Systems Ltd, pg 1064

Test Equipment Distributors

ARIZONA

Arizona Cine Equipment, pg 789
ATCi (Antenna Technology Communication Solutions Inc), pg 793
Troxell Communications Inc, pg 1045

ARKANSAS

White Diamond Productions, pg 1065

CALIFORNIA

Ametron Audio/Video, pg 785
Apex Jr, pg 788
Audio Images Corp, pg 794
BroadcastStore.com, pg 813
Delicate Electronics Sales Inc, pg 845
FXC Communications, pg 874
Gearhouse Broadcast LLC, pg 876
The Hollywood Edge, pg 890
Jameco Electronics, pg 903
Leader Instruments Corp, pg 917
Location Sound Corp, pg 924
Magnetic Reference Laboratory Inc, pg 928
MediaPOINTE, pg 938
Mobilized Tech Systems, pg 944
Newdoll Enterprises LLC, pg 956
Related Visual Inc, pg 994
Southern California Sound Image Inc, pg 1019
SSL Industries Inc, pg 1022
Stanford Research Systems Inc, pg 1023
Tri-Ed, pg 1044
VMI Inc, pg 1060
VTP Inc, pg 1061
Zack Electronics Inc, pg 1073

COLORADO

Spectrum Audio Visual Services, pg 1020

CONNECTICUT

Gold Line/TEF, pg 880
HB Communications Inc, pg 886

FLORIDA

Access Media Group, pg 773
Allstar Audio Systems Inc, pg 782
Broadcasters General Store Inc, pg 813
Digital Video Systems Inc, pg 848
General Projection Systems Inc, pg 877
Griffiths Broadcast Co Inc, pg 882
Harris Corp, pg 885
Hi-Tech Enterprises Inc, pg 888
Hi-Tech Import Export Corp, pg 888
Hunter Electronics LLC, pg 892
Intermark Industries Inc, pg 900
Midtown Video Inc, pg 942
Pro Stage Inc, pg 983
PTL Test Equipment Inc, pg 987
Recording Media & Equipment Inc (RM&E), pg 993
Stereo Sales Inc, pg 1024
Technomedia Solutions, pg 1035

GEORGIA

Convergent Media Systems, pg 836

HAWAII

The Audio Visual Co (AVCO), pg 795

ILLINOIS

Allen Visual Systems Inc, pg 781
Joseph Electronics, pg 906
RAM Systems LLC, pg 991
Research Technology International (RTI), pg 995

INDIANA

Sensory Technologies LLC, pg 1006

IOWA

ECS Inc, pg 856

KANSAS

Smith Audio-Visual Inc, pg 1014

KENTUCKY

Axxis Inc, pg 800
NOR-COM Inc, pg 958

MARYLAND

Bradley Broadcast & Pro Audio, pg 811
Human Circuit, pg 892
Kipp Visual Systems Inc, pg 911
Rohde & Schwarz Inc, pg 998
Visual Aids Electronics Corp, pg 1059

MASSACHUSETTS

ASACA/ShibaSoku Corp of America, pg 791
Capron Lighting & Sound Co Inc, pg 819
HMC Electronics, pg 889
Stanley Supply & Services Inc, pg 1023

MICHIGAN

TeL Systems, pg 1035

MINNESOTA

AVI Systems, pg 799
Digital Audio Labs, pg 847

MISSOURI

Modern Communications Inc, pg 944

NEW JERSEY

Alltec Stores, a Vcom IMC Company, pg 782
Comprehensive Cable & Connectivity Co, pg 833
Diversified Systems Inc, pg 849
Electro Impulse Laboratory Inc, pg 858
JRF Magnetic Sciences Inc, pg 906
National Audio-Visual Supply, pg 952
PatchAmp, pg 970
Starlite Productions, pg 1024
SYMCO Inc, pg 1030
Turner Engineering Inc, pg 1046
Wired 4 Sound Inc, pg 1068
York Telecom, pg 1072

NEW YORK

Audio-Video Corp, pg 795
AV Workshop, pg 797
BTX Technologies, pg 814
Design Audio Visual Inc, pg 845
Group One Ltd, pg 882
Hot House Professional Audio, pg 891
Indigo Productions, pg 897
Long Island Video Enterprises Live Inc, pg 924
Posthorn Recordings, pg 979
Ray Supply Inc, pg 992
RNJ Electronics, pg 997
Russell Industries Inc, pg 1001
Technisphere Corp, pg 1034
Unitron Ltd, pg 1048

NORTH CAROLINA

Camcor Inc, pg 818

OHIO

Parts Express, pg 969

OREGON

Audio Precision, pg 794
NTI Americas Inc, pg 960

PENNSYLVANIA

Advanced AV, pg 777
The Lerro Corp, pg 919
Techni-Tool Inc, pg 1033

SOUTH DAKOTA

Sencore Inc, pg 1006

TENNESSEE

Green Dot Audio Electronics, pg 882
Lowrance Sound Co Inc, pg 925
Memphis Communications Corp, pg 938
True Audio, pg 1045

TEXAS

Industrial Audio/Video Inc, pg 897
Lubbock Audio Visual Inc, pg 925
Pro Video & Film Equipment Co Inc, pg 983
RadioShack Corp, pg 990
Specialized Products Co, pg 1020
Tarpley Media Systems, pg 1032

UTAH

DigiTech, pg 848
Performance Audio, pg 973
RIA Corp, pg 996

VIRGINIA

Intellidyne LLC, pg 899
Lee Hartman & Sons Inc, pg 918

AUDIO

Test Equipment Distributors (continued)

WASHINGTON

CCI Solutions, pg 821
Northern Lights & Pro Audio, pg 959

WEST VIRGINIA

United Sound & Electronics, pg 1048

WISCONSIN

Audio Visual of Milwaukee Inc, pg 795
Full Compass Systems, pg 874

PUERTO RICO

Bonnin Electronics Inc, pg 810

ALBERTA

Matrix Video Communications Corp (MVCC), pg 934

MANITOBA

Advance Pro, pg 777

ONTARIO

Edcom Multimedia Products, pg 856
Nationwide Audio Visual Co, pg 953

QUEBEC

Concept Audio-Visual, pg 834
Panavideo Inc, pg 968

Test Equipment Manufacturers

CALIFORNIA

ACO Pacific Inc, pg 774
Ametek Programmable Power, pg 785
Calrad Electronics, pg 817
Dorrough Electronics Inc, pg 851
Ensemble Designs Inc, pg 861
ESE, pg 862
FM Systems Inc, pg 870
Graham-Patten, pg 881
The Hollywood Edge, pg 890
Horita Co Inc, pg 891
Leader Instruments Corp, pg 917
Magnetic Reference Laboratory Inc, pg 928
Stanford Research Systems Inc, pg 1023

CONNECTICUT

Gold Line/TEF, pg 880
Titus Technological Laboratories (TTL), pg 1041

FLORIDA

Compuvideo Sales USA Ltd, pg 834
Imtronics Industries Inc, pg 897
JT Communications, pg 906

ILLINOIS

Quantum Data Inc, pg 989
Research Technology International (RTI), pg 995

INDIANA

R B Annis Instruments Inc, pg 787

KANSAS

Galaxy Audio, pg 875

MARYLAND

Potomac Instruments Inc, pg 979

MASSACHUSETTS

AEMC Instruments, pg 778
ASACA/ShibaSoku Corp of America, pg 791
Capron Lighting & Sound Co Inc, pg 819
Eastern Acoustic Works Inc (EAW), pg 856
Prior Scientific Inc, pg 982

MINNESOTA

Digital Audio Labs, pg 847
Tremetrics Inc Industrial Instruments Division, pg 1044

NEW HAMPSHIRE

Earthworks Inc, pg 855

NEW JERSEY

ATI Audio, pg 793
Boonton Electronics, pg 811
Modulation Sciences Inc, pg 945
Wireworks Corp, pg 1068

NEW YORK

Entertainment One Distribution, pg 861
Laird Digital Cinema, pg 915
MultiDyne Video & Fiber Optics Systems, pg 950
Sescom Inc, pg 1007

OREGON

Audio Precision, pg 794
NTI Americas Inc, pg 960

PENNSYLVANIA

Belar Electronics Laboratory Inc, pg 804

SOUTH DAKOTA

Sencore Inc, pg 1006

TENNESSEE

Remote Audio Products, pg 994
True Audio, pg 1045

TEXAS

Logitek Electronic Systems Inc, pg 924
National Instruments Corp, pg 953

UTAH

DigiTech, pg 848
Ivie Technologies Inc, pg 903
Rolls Corp, pg 999

VIRGINIA

Delta Electronics Inc, pg 845

WASHINGTON

AudioControl®, pg 796
Conex Electro-Systems Inc, pg 835
Fluke Corp, pg 870

WISCONSIN

Magnetek Inc, pg 928
Simpson Electric Co, pg 1011

ONTARIO

McCurdy Radio Ltd, pg 935
Ward-Beck Systems Ltd, pg 1062

Test Equipment Rentals

ARIZONA

Arizona Cine Equipment, pg 789
Merestone, pg 938

ARKANSAS

White Diamond Productions, pg 1065

CALIFORNIA

Audio Rents, pg 794
Bexel Corp, pg 806
Express Media Inc, pg 864
Golden Gate Studios, pg 880
McCune Audio-Video-Lighting, pg 935
Stanford Research Systems Inc, pg 1023
VER-Video Equipment Rentals, pg 1053

COLORADO

Spectrum Audio Visual Services, pg 1020

CONNECTICUT

Videofilm Systems Inc, pg 1057

FLORIDA

Access Media Group, pg 773
Allstar Audio Systems Inc, pg 782
Phat Planet Recording Studios, pg 973
Pro Stage Inc, pg 983

GEORGIA

Convergent Media Systems, pg 836
Staging Directions Inc, pg 1023

ILLINOIS

Allen Visual Systems Inc, pg 781
On Stage Audio, pg 963
RC Communications, pg 992

IOWA

ECS Inc, pg 856

MASSACHUSETTS

Capron Lighting & Sound Co Inc, pg 819
Preston Productions Inc, pg 981

MICHIGAN

K&R All Media Productions Inc, pg 908
K&R's Recording Studios Inc, pg 908

MINNESOTA

AVI Systems, pg 799

NEVADA

GES Audio Visual, pg 877

NEW HAMPSHIRE

Apertura, pg 788

NEW JERSEY

Moe AV LLC, pg 945
Starlite Productions, pg 1024
Video Corporation of America (VCA), pg 1055
Wired 4 Sound Inc, pg 1068

NEW YORK

AV Workshop, pg 797
Design Audio Visual Inc, pg 845
Long Island Video Enterprises Live Inc, pg 924
Manhattan Center Studios Inc, pg 930
Posthorn Recordings, pg 979
Specialized Audio-Visual Inc, pg 1020
Technisphere Corp, pg 1034

NORTH CAROLINA

Camcor Inc, pg 818
Take One Productions Ltd, pg 1031

OREGON

NTI Americas Inc, pg 960

PENNSYLVANIA

Audio Visions Inc, pg 795
Production Solutions Inc, pg 985
Right Coast Recording Inc, pg 997

TENNESSEE

Brantley Sound Associates Inc, pg 812
Durrell LLC, pg 854

TEXAS

Lubbock Audio Visual Inc, pg 925

WASHINGTON

D A Sound, pg 842
Northern Lights & Pro Audio, pg 959

WISCONSIN

Full Compass Systems, pg 874

ALBERTA

L R Light & Sound, pg 915

QUEBEC

Concept Audio-Visual, pg 834

Test Equipment Repairs

CALIFORNIA

Ametron Audio/Video, pg 785
Audio Images Corp, pg 794
McAlister Electronics, pg 935
SSL Industries Inc, pg 1022

CONNECTICUT

HB Communications Inc, pg 886

Wireless Microphone, *see* Microphone—Wireless

AUDIO/VISUAL

Animation System Distributors

ARIZONA

Audio Video Resources, pg 795
Troxell Communications Inc, pg 1045

CALIFORNIA

Adolph Gasser Inc, pg 776
Audio Images Corp, pg 794
Audio/Video Supply Inc, pg 795
California Tape Products Inc, pg 817
Diaquest, pg 846
Educational Technology Services (ETS), pg 857
FXC Communications, pg 874
MAXON Computer Inc, pg 934
SBS Productions, pg 1003
Kris Stevens Enterprises, pg 1024
Tri-Ed, pg 1044
Videobotics, pg 1056
VMI Inc, pg 1060

COLORADO

Spectrum Audio Visual Services, pg 1020

CONNECTICUT

HB Communications Inc, pg 886

FLORIDA

Digital Video Systems Inc, pg 848
Hi-Tech Enterprises Inc, pg 888

GEORGIA

Stage Front Presentation Systems, pg 1022

ILLINOIS

Lyn Norstad & Associates Inc, pg 926

IOWA

ECS Inc, pg 856

LOUISIANA

Digital FX Inc, pg 847

MASSACHUSETTS

Camera Co Inc/Broadcast Divison, pg 818
Psych Soft Inc, pg 987
WSI, pg 1070

MICHIGAN

ASC Systems, pg 791
Ascom Communications Contractors, pg 791
TeL Systems, pg 1035

MISSOURI

Conference Technologies Inc, pg 835

NEW JERSEY

York Telecom, pg 1072

NEW YORK

Audio-Video Corp, pg 795
B&H Photo & Video Pro Audio, pg 802
Custom Media Environments, pg 841
Indigo Productions, pg 897

OHIO

Audio Visual Media, pg 795
Copp Integrated Systems, pg 836

PENNSYLVANIA

AccuWeather Inc, pg 774
Advanced AV, pg 777
The Lerro Corp, pg 919

TEXAS

Lubbock Audio Visual Inc, pg 925
Pro Video & Film Equipment Co Inc, pg 983
Videotex Systems Inc, pg 1057

UTAH

RIA Corp, pg 996

WISCONSIN

Audio Visual of Milwaukee Inc, pg 795
Camera Corner Connecting Point, pg 818
Full Compass Systems, pg 874
Safe Harbor Computers, pg 1001

PUERTO RICO

Bonnin Electronics Inc, pg 810

MANITOBA

Inland Audio Visual Ltd, pg 898

ONTARIO

HD Source, pg 886
Nationwide Audio Visual Co, pg 953

Animation System Manufacturers

CALIFORNIA

Apple Inc, pg 788
Diaquest, pg 846
Fax Animation Co, pg 866
Gilderfluke & Co Inc, pg 878
Alan Gordon Enterprises Inc, pg 880
Linker Systems Inc, pg 922
MAXON Computer Inc, pg 934
Pinnacle Systems Inc, pg 975

ILLINOIS

EPIX Inc, pg 862

MASSACHUSETTS

Psych Soft Inc, pg 987
WSI, pg 1070

NEW JERSEY

Fiber Optic Systems Inc (FOSI), pg 866
PeopleVisionFX, pg 972

NEW YORK

Custom Media Environments, pg 841
Gagne Inc, pg 875
Quantel Inc, pg 989

PENNSYLVANIA

AccuWeather Inc, pg 774

WASHINGTON

Laser Fantasy/HECK Industries/Photon Manufacturing, pg 916

WISCONSIN

Safe Harbor Computers, pg 1001

BRITISH COLUMBIA

Triad Communications Ltd, pg 1044

Animation System Rentals

ARIZONA

Merestone, pg 938

CALIFORNIA

Artichoke Productions, pg 791
Fax Animation Co, pg 866
Alan Gordon Enterprises Inc, pg 880
McCune Audio-Video-Lighting, pg 935
Total Media Group, pg 1042

COLORADO

Daylight Productions & Rentals, pg 844

GEORGIA

Stage Front Presentation Systems, pg 1022
Staging Directions Inc, pg 1023

LOUISIANA

Digital FX Inc, pg 847

MARYLAND

CSPMedia.com, pg 840

MASSACHUSETTS

Preston Productions Inc, pg 981

MICHIGAN

K&R All Media Productions Inc, pg 908

NEW JERSEY

MediaMix Inc, pg 937
PLS Staging, pg 977

NEW YORK

AV Workshop, pg 797
Custom Media Environments, pg 841
HB-Content, pg 886
Manhattan Center Studios Inc, pg 930

NORTH CAROLINA

Take One Productions Ltd, pg 1031

OREGON

Northwest Film Center, pg 959

PENNSYLVANIA

FMP Media Solutions Inc, pg 870
Production Solutions Inc, pg 985

TEXAS

Phillips MediaSource, pg 974
Stage Directions, pg 1022

WASHINGTON

Laser Fantasy/HECK Industries/Photon Manufacturing, pg 916

WYOMING

Bridger Productions Inc, pg 812

MANITOBA

Inland Audio Visual Ltd, pg 898

Animation System Repairs

CALIFORNIA

Fax Animation Co, pg 866
Alan Gordon Enterprises Inc, pg 880
McAlister Electronics, pg 935
Technical Services, pg 1034

FLORIDA

Hi-Tech Enterprises Inc, pg 888
Spire Audio Visual Co Inc, pg 1021

GEORGIA

Stage Front Presentation Systems, pg 1022

MICHIGAN

TeL Systems, pg 1035

NEW YORK

Custom Media Environments, pg 841

OHIO

Copp Integrated Systems, pg 836

WASHINGTON

Laser Fantasy/HECK Industries/Photon Manufacturing, pg 916

WISCONSIN

Full Compass Systems, pg 874

MANITOBA

Inland Audio Visual Ltd, pg 898

Artwork & Titling Services

ALABAMA

Media Visions Inc, pg 937

ALASKA

Alaska Film Services Inc, pg 779

ARIZONA

Merestone, pg 938

ARKANSAS

Live'N'Loud, pg 923
Shadowbox Video Productions, pg 1007
White Diamond Productions, pg 1065

CALIFORNIA

Action Video, pg 775
AM Productions, pg 783
Blind, pg 809
Christopher Gray Post Production, pg 826
Coloredge, pg 832
Custom Video Productions Inc, pg 841
Diamond Dreams Music Productions, pg 846
Digital Jungle, pg 847
Digital Media West, pg 847
Dogma Studios, pg 850
Express Media Inc, pg 864
First Person™, pg 868
FXF Productions Inc, pg 874
Gold Standard Productions, pg 880
Gordon Productions Inc, pg 880
Havas Edge, pg 885
iCorpTv, pg 893
JDS Video & Media Productions Inc, pg 904
K2B2 Records, pg 907
The Kitchen, pg 911
Lumeni Productions Inc, pg 926
Maximus Media Inc, pg 934
The Media Staff Inc, pg 937
Medical Visual Creations (MVC), pg 938
Mind Over Eye Inc, pg 943
Moving Art by Louie Schwartzberg, pg 947
Pantomime Pictures Inc, pg 968
Penrose Productions, pg 972
piXvfm, pg 976
Planet Blue, pg 976
PM Productions, pg 977
PSI Inc, pg 987
QRS Software Services, pg 988
Reality Check Systems, pg 992
SBS Productions, pg 1003
Shapeshifter, pg 1008
SonicPool, pg 1016
StereoScope International, pg 1024
Still N'Motion, pg 1025
Timecode Multimedia, pg 1040
Toon Makers, pg 1042
Total Media Group, pg 1042
Universal Studios, pg 1049
West Coast Projections Inc, pg 1063

COLORADO

The Cinema Lab, pg 827
CSI Films, pg 840
Flashback Media Productions, pg 869
Full Spectrum Arts & Services, pg 874
Starwest Productions, pg 1024

CONNECTICUT

Broadcast Video Productions LLC, pg 813
EagleVision Inc, pg 855
Guymark Studios LLC, pg 883
Ironik Design & Post, pg 902
New London Media, pg 956

DISTRICT OF COLUMBIA

O'Keefe Communications Inc, pg 961

FLORIDA

Allegro Productions Inc, pg 781
Big Byte Video Productions, pg 806
Civins Productions Inc, pg 828
Communications Concepts Inc (CCI), pg 833
Ed Ethridge Productions Inc, pg 863
Gulf Coast Audio Visual Producers Inc, pg 883
Home Shopping Network (HSN), pg 890
Jordan Klein Film & Video (JKFV), pg 906
Photosound of Orlando Inc, pg 975
Progressive Media & Music, pg 985
Sunrise Studios, pg 1028
Video Techniques Inc, pg 1056
Vistamax Productions, pg 1059

GEORGIA

Beachwood Productions, pg 804
Beast Atlanta, pg 804
Continental Film & Video, pg 835
ECG Productions, pg 856
Guerrilla Productions LLC, pg 883
Imagers, pg 896
Symmes Systems, pg 1030

HAWAII

Hyperspective Studios Inc, pg 893

ILLINOIS

ABS Enterprises, pg 772
ABSA Productions Inc, pg 772
Airways Digital Media, pg 779
Analog Free Media, pg 786
Backstar Creative Media Inc, pg 801
Breeze Productions Inc, pg 812
CCore Media Inc, pg 821
Comtech Multimedia Marketing, pg 834
IV Media Resources, pg 903
LightCraft Graphics Inc, pg 920
MIGHTYbYTES Inc, pg 942
Jim Passin Productions, pg 970
The Pepper Group, pg 972
Southern Illinois University, pg 1019
Sparkfactor, pg 1019
20/20 Communications Inc, pg 1047
WEEK TV, pg 1063

INDIANA

AVA Productions, pg 798
Bright Ideas Creative Services, pg 812
OMNI Productions, pg 962

IOWA

The Production House, pg 984

LOUISIANA

Digital FX Inc, pg 847
Louisiana State University Health Sciences Center - Shreveport, pg 925
Vidox Motion Imagery, pg 1057

MARYLAND

Adventure Productions LLC, pg 778
CPR MultiMedia Solutions, pg 837
dbF a Media Company, pg 844
Kramer Communications Video Production, pg 913
Pro Cuts Editing Services, pg 982

MASSACHUSETTS

CommCreative, pg 832
MotionArt Studios, pg 947
Northern Light Productions, pg 959
Penfield Productions Ltd, pg 971
Gabriel Polonsky Studio, pg 978
Preston Productions Inc, pg 981
TR Productions, pg 1043

MICHIGAN

Audio Graphic Services, pg 794
Blue Mouse Studio, pg 809
Digi Sign Design LLC, pg 847
Digital Image Studios LLC, pg 847
K&R's Recording Studios Inc, pg 908
Progressive AE, pg 985
RingSide Creative, pg 997
Tectonics Industries Inc, pg 1035
Tri-Color, pg 1044

MINNESOTA

Aggressive Records Audio Duplication LLC, pg 778
Beyers Sound & Essay Audio, pg 806
Media Loft Inc, pg 937
MultiMedia, pg 950

MISSOURI

Allied Photo Color Co, pg 781
Visionworks Design Services Inc, pg 1059

NEBRASKA

Three Pillars Media, pg 1040

NEVADA

Aardvark Video & Media Productions, pg 772
Encore Productions Inc, pg 861
JCS Video Productions, pg 904
Tanglewood Productions, pg 1031

NEW HAMPSHIRE

Apertura, pg 788
Chip Taylor Communications LLC, pg 1032

NEW JERSEY

CELCO-Constantine Engineering Labs Co, pg 822
CFP Video Productions Inc, pg 823
Laurel Video Productions, pg 916
NFL Films Music Library, pg 957
Optisonics Productions, pg 965
Outside The Box Interactive LLC, pg 966
Video Ideas Productions, pg 1055

NEW YORK

Animotion Inc, pg 787
Big Film Design, pg 807
The Big House Group, pg 807
Digital Art Video Inc, pg 847
dM works, pg 849
Duggal Visual Solutions, pg 853
Eastco Multimedia Solutions Inc, pg 856
4-D Creative Media, pg 871
Gurrilla Video Solutions, pg 883
HB-Content, pg 886
Icontent, pg 893
InterNation Inc, pg 900
L&P Media, pg 915
Lylofilm Productions, pg 926
Magnaplan Corp, pg 928
Manhattan Center Studios Inc, pg 930
Neal Marshad Productions, pg 931
Jack Morton Worldwide, pg 946
MRG Productions Inc, pg 948
Polestar Films & Associated Arts Ltd, pg 978
Joseph Struhl Co Inc, pg 1026
TBA Global Events, pg 1032
Tiki Recording Studios Inc, pg 1040
Zelman Studios Ltd, pg 1073

NORTH CAROLINA

Pat Appleson Studios Inc, pg 788
Image Associates Inc, pg 894
LCW Productions LLC, pg 917
Moving Pictures, pg 948
Studio South, pg 1027
Take One Productions Ltd, pg 1031

NORTH DAKOTA

Media Productions, pg 937

OHIO

Advent Media Inc, pg 778
Aztec Video Productions, pg 801
Creative Technology, pg 838
Cuyahoga Community College Media Center, pg 841
Mills James Productions, pg 943
Take 1 Media Services, pg 1031
Vista Color Imaging Inc, pg 1059

OKLAHOMA

Comm-Arts, pg 832
Garman Productions LLC, pg 875
PDC Productions, pg 970

OREGON

Rex, pg 995

PENNSYLVANIA

AiH Group Inc, pg 779
Bang Pictures, pg 802
Innovision Media Group, pg 899
JPL, pg 906
Main Point Productions, pg 929
Pemcor LLC, pg 971
The Videohouse Inc, pg 1057
WPHL-TV, pg 1070

RHODE ISLAND

Sound-FX-Design, pg 1017

SOUTH CAROLINA

Genesis Creative, pg 877

TENNESSEE

American Blackguard Inc, pg 784
Continental Film, pg 835
Paradigm Marketing & Creative, pg 969
Scripps Networks, pg 1005
Stage Post, pg 1022

TEXAS

Biway Media, pg 808
Digi-matics, pg 847
Romar Learning, pg 999
The Samuels Co, pg 1002
South Coast Film & Video, pg 1019
Stage Directions, pg 1022
Superior Graphics, pg 1029
Tecfilms Inc, pg 1033
Texas Heart Institute Visual Communication Services, pg 1037

AUDIO/VISUAL

Artwork & Titling Services (continued)

VERMONT

University of Vermont, Instructional Television Dept, pg 1050

VIRGINIA

Allied Media Corp, pg 781
Blair Inc, pg 809
Rocktown Media, pg 998

WASHINGTON

Adams Creative & Production Services, pg 775
Inland Audio Visual Co, pg 898
Victory Studios, pg 1054

WISCONSIN

Audio Visual of Milwaukee Inc, pg 795
Meridian Studios, pg 939
Midland Video Productions Inc, pg 942
USAV Group Inc, pg 1050
Video Wisconsin Inc, pg 1056
Watts Communications Inc, pg 1062

WYOMING

Bridger Productions Inc, pg 812

ONTARIO

ADS Media, pg 777
Image Video Services & Productions, pg 895
Music Manufacturing Services, pg 950
Purefire Communications Inc, pg 987
Video Excellence Productions, pg 1055
Westbury National Show Systems Ltd, pg 1064

AV Pulsing, *see* Pulsing—AV

AV System Design & Installation, *see* System Design & Installation

Color Correction Services

ARIZONA

Film Creations Ltd, pg 867
Merestone, pg 938

ARKANSAS

White Diamond Productions, pg 1065

CALIFORNIA

Aaron & Le Duc, pg 772
Action Video, pg 775
Angstrom Lighting, pg 786
Christopher Gray Post Production, pg 826
Coloredge, pg 832
Custom Video Productions Inc, pg 841
Digital Jungle, pg 847
Dogma Studios, pg 850
First Person™, pg 868
FXF Productions Inc, pg 874
Havas Edge, pg 885
iCorpTv, pg 893
JDS Video & Media Productions Inc, pg 904
Main Street Media Inc, pg 929
McCune Audio-Video-Lighting, pg 935
Mind Over Eye Inc, pg 943
Planet Blue, pg 976
PM Productions, pg 977
Pro8mm, pg 983
QRS Software Services, pg 988
Reality Check Systems, pg 992
Shapeshifter, pg 1008
SonicPool, pg 1016
StereoScope International, pg 1024
Still N'Motion, pg 1025
Timecode Multimedia, pg 1040
Total Media Group, pg 1042
Twin Peaks Creative, pg 1047
Two Door Productions, pg 1047
Universal Studios, pg 1049

COLORADO

The Cinema Lab, pg 827

CONNECTICUT

Broadcast Video Productions LLC, pg 813
Digital Video Productions, pg 848
Guymark Studios LLC, pg 883
Ironik Design & Post, pg 902
MAVCO, pg 934

DISTRICT OF COLUMBIA

Interface Media Group, pg 900

FLORIDA

Access Media Group, pg 773
Big Byte Video Productions, pg 806
Civins Productions Inc, pg 828
Communications Concepts Inc (CCI), pg 833
Ed Ethridge Productions Inc, pg 863
Gulf Coast Audio Visual Producers Inc, pg 883
Home Shopping Network (HSN), pg 890
Progressive Media & Music, pg 985
Sunrise Studios, pg 1028
Video Techniques Inc, pg 1056
Vistamax Productions, pg 1059

GEORGIA

Continental Film & Video, pg 835
ECG Productions, pg 856
Guerrilla Productions LLC, pg 883
Imagers, pg 896
Stage Front Presentation Systems, pg 1022
Staging Directions Inc, pg 1023
Visioneering International Inc, pg 1058

HAWAII

Hyperspective Studios Inc, pg 893

ILLINOIS

Analog Free Media, pg 786
Breeze Productions Inc, pg 812
CCore Media Inc, pg 821
Chicago Spotlight Inc, pg 825
LightCraft Graphics Inc, pg 920
MIGHTYbYTES Inc, pg 942
Sparkfactor, pg 1019
20/20 Communications Inc, pg 1047
Wells-Gardner Electronics Corp, pg 1063

INDIANA

OMNI Productions, pg 962

KANSAS

Custom Color Corp, pg 841

LOUISIANA

Primary Color Laboratory Inc, pg 982

MARYLAND

CPR MultiMedia Solutions, pg 837
dbF a Media Company, pg 844
Kramer Communications Video Production, pg 913
Pro Cuts Editing Services, pg 982

MASSACHUSETTS

Monotype Inc, pg 945
Northern Light Productions, pg 959
TR Productions, pg 1043

MICHIGAN

Audio Graphic Services, pg 794
Digi Sign Design LLC, pg 847
K&R's Recording Studios Inc, pg 908
Tectonics Industries Inc, pg 1035
Tri-Color, pg 1044

MINNESOTA

AVI Systems, pg 799
Thomas Reprographics, pg 1039

MISSOURI

Allied Photo Color Co, pg 781

NEBRASKA

Three Pillars Media, pg 1040

NEVADA

Aardvark Video & Media Productions, pg 772
Encore Productions Inc, pg 861
JCS Video Productions, pg 904
Lefco Video Services Inc, pg 918

NEW JERSEY

CELCO-Constantine Engineering Labs Co, pg 822
CFP Video Productions Inc, pg 823
NFL Films Music Library, pg 957
Reider Photography & Video Productions, pg 994

NEW YORK

Air Sea Land Productions Inc (ASL), pg 779
Albany Theatre Supply Co Inc, pg 780
aurora productions, pg 797
The Big House Group, pg 807
BMI Supply, pg 810
Digital Art Video Inc, pg 847
Duggal Visual Solutions, pg 853
Eastco Multimedia Solutions Inc, pg 856
4-D Creative Media, pg 871
FSL Media Inc, pg 873
HB-Content, pg 886
Hello World Communications, pg 888
International Digital Centre, pg 901
Modernage Photographic Services Inc, pg 944
Jack Morton Worldwide, pg 946
MRG Productions Inc, pg 948
Mutual Hardware, pg 951
Sima Products Corp, pg 1011
Tobin Productions Inc, pg 1041
USA Studios, pg 1050

NORTH CAROLINA

Pat Appleson Studios Inc, pg 788
Take One Productions Ltd, pg 1031

OHIO

Aztec Video Productions, pg 801
Creative Technology, pg 838
Mills James Productions, pg 943

OKLAHOMA

Garman Productions LLC, pg 875
PDC Productions, pg 970

OREGON

Rex, pg 995

PENNSYLVANIA

AiH Group Inc, pg 779
Berry & Homer, pg 805
FMP Media Solutions Inc, pg 870
Panta Rhei Media Inc, pg 968
Pemcor LLC, pg 971
The Videohouse Inc, pg 1057
WPHL-TV, pg 1070

RHODE ISLAND

Sound-FX-Design, pg 1017

SOUTH CAROLINA

Genesis Creative, pg 877

TENNESSEE

Stage Post, pg 1022

TEXAS

Biway Media, pg 808
Digi-matics, pg 847
Epic Software Group Inc, pg 862
Freeman, pg 872
Julye Newlin Productions Inc, pg 956
South Coast Film & Video, pg 1019
Superior Graphics, pg 1029

UTAH

K-SAR Video & DVD Productions, pg 907

VERMONT

University of Vermont, Instructional Television Dept, pg 1050

VIRGINIA

Allied Media Corp, pg 781
The Whitlock Group, pg 1065

WASHINGTON

Bennett-Watt HD Productions Inc, pg 805
Victory Studios, pg 1054

WISCONSIN

Audio Visual of Milwaukee Inc, pg 795
Meridian Studios, pg 939

Color Media Distributors

Color Media Manufacturers

Color Media Rentals

Color Media Repairs

Color Photostats

AUDIO/VISUAL

Computer Graphics

ALABAMA

Media Visions Inc, pg 937

ARIZONA

Merestone, pg 938
On-Site Video, pg 963
Phoenix VideoFilms®, pg 974
Professional Marketing Services Inc, pg 985

ARKANSAS

Shadowbox Video Productions, pg 1007
White Diamond Productions, pg 1065

CALIFORNIA

Aaron & Le Duc, pg 772
Action Video, pg 775
Aztek Inc, pg 801
Buttercup Pictures, pg 816
Classic Images, pg 829
Coloredge, pg 832
Crystal Pyramid Productions™, pg 840
Custom Video Productions Inc, pg 841
Diamond Dreams Music Productions, pg 846
Diaquest, pg 846
Digital Jungle, pg 847
Dogma Studios, pg 850
Dolphin MultiMedia Inc, pg 850
Dynamic Digital Depth Inc (DDD), pg 854
Express Media Inc, pg 864
First Person™, pg 868
FXF Productions Inc, pg 874
Gold Standard Productions, pg 880
Havas Edge, pg 885
iCorpTv, pg 893
JDS Video & Media Productions Inc, pg 904
K2B2 Records, pg 907
The Kitchen, pg 911
KO Creative, pg 912
Lumeni Productions Inc, pg 926
Maximus Media Inc, pg 934
McCune Audio-Video-Lighting, pg 935
Media Fabricators Inc, pg 936
Media Magic, pg 937
The Media Staff Inc, pg 937
Medical Visual Creations (MVC), pg 938
Mind Over Eye Inc, pg 943
New Wave Entertainment, pg 956
On-Trax Inc, pg 963
Panorama Productions, pg 968
piXvfm, pg 976
Planet Blue, pg 976
PM Productions, pg 977
PSI Inc, pg 987
QRS Software Services, pg 988
Reality Check Systems, pg 992
RetinaVision Productions, pg 995
Shapeshifter, pg 1008
SonicPool, pg 1016
Staylor-Made Communications Inc, pg 1024
StereoScope International, pg 1024
Still N'Motion, pg 1025
Tam Communications Inc, pg 1031
Timecode Multimedia, pg 1040
Toon Makers, pg 1042
Total Media Group, pg 1042
Towards 2000 Inc, pg 1043
Twin Peaks Creative, pg 1047
Two Door Productions, pg 1047
Universal Studios, pg 1049
Videografix LLC, pg 1057
Wavemaker Media Design, pg 1062
West Coast Projections Inc, pg 1063

COLORADO

CSI Films, pg 840
Daylight Productions & Rentals, pg 844
Flashback Media Productions, pg 869
Full Spectrum Arts & Services, pg 874
Rocky Mountain Audio/Video Productions Inc, pg 998

CONNECTICUT

Broadcast Video Productions LLC, pg 813
Cine-Med Inc, pg 826
The Gary-Paul Agency, pg 875
Guymark Studios LLC, pg 883
Musivision Inc, pg 951
New London Media, pg 956

DELAWARE

Side Door Studio Inc, pg 1010

DISTRICT OF COLUMBIA

Interface Media Group, pg 900
O'Keefe Communications Inc, pg 961

FLORIDA

Access Media Group, pg 773
Allegro Productions Inc, pg 781
AVI-SPL, pg 798
Big Byte Video Productions, pg 806
CD ROM™ Inc, pg 822
Civins Productions Inc, pg 828
Communications Concepts Inc (CCI), pg 833
Digimation, pg 847
Eastern Video, pg 856
Ed Ethridge Productions Inc, pg 863
Gulf Coast Audio Visual Producers Inc, pg 883
Home Shopping Network (HSN), pg 890
Image Technical Services, pg 895
Media Concepts Inc, pg 936
Progressive Media & Music, pg 985
Sunfire Communications Inc, pg 1028
Sunrise Studios, pg 1028
Teach America Corp, pg 1033
Universal Studios Florida® Production Group, pg 1049
Vistamax Productions, pg 1059

GEORGIA

Beachwood Productions, pg 804
Beast Atlanta, pg 804
Continental Film & Video, pg 835
ECG Productions, pg 856
Guerrilla Productions LLC, pg 883
Imagers, pg 896
Stage Front Presentation Systems, pg 1022
Staging Directions Inc, pg 1023
Visioneering International Inc, pg 1058

HAWAII

Hyperspective Studios Inc, pg 893

ILLINOIS

ABSA Productions Inc, pg 772
Airways Digital Media, pg 779
Audio Visual Services Corp, pg 796
Breeze Productions Inc, pg 812
CCore Media Inc, pg 821
Comtech Multimedia Marketing, pg 834
Cresta Creative, pg 839
Extraordinary Demos, pg 864
Gamma Imaging, pg 875
IV Media Resources, pg 903
LightCraft Graphics Inc, pg 920
Manning Productions, pg 930
MIGHTYbYTES Inc, pg 942
Jim Passin Productions, pg 970
The Pepper Group, pg 972
PSAV® Presentation Services (Hotel Services Division), pg 987
Sound/Video Impressions Inc, pg 1018
Southern Illinois University, pg 1019
Sparkfactor, pg 1019
20/20 Communications Inc, pg 1047
Waveland Software Inc, pg 1062
WEEK TV, pg 1063

INDIANA

Advanced Designs Corp, pg 777
AVA Productions, pg 798
Bright Ideas Creative Services, pg 812
OMNI Productions, pg 962

IOWA

The Production House, pg 984

KENTUCKY

Broadway Digital, pg 813

LOUISIANA

Louisiana State University Health Sciences Center - Shreveport, pg 925
Moxie Media, pg 948
Vidox Motion Imagery, pg 1057

MAINE

Headlight Audio Visual Inc, pg 887

MARYLAND

Adventure Productions LLC, pg 778
CAS Video Productions, pg 820
CPR MultiMedia Solutions, pg 837
dbF a Media Company, pg 844
Kramer Communications Video Production, pg 913
Media Dimensions Inc, pg 936
Sheffield Audio/Video Productions, pg 1008
Sign Media Inc, pg 1011
Welocalize, pg 1063

MASSACHUSETTS

Colortek of Boston, pg 832
CommCreative, pg 832
Graphx Inc, pg 881
Northern Light Productions, pg 959
Preston Productions Inc, pg 981
TR Productions, pg 1043
TVN-The Video Network, pg 1046
WSI, pg 1070

MICHIGAN

ASC Systems, pg 791
Audio Graphic Services, pg 794
Digi Sign Design LLC, pg 847
Digital Image Studios LLC, pg 847
GMP Music, pg 879
K&R's Recording Studios Inc, pg 908
Michigan Office Solutions, pg 941
Michigan Recording Arts Institute & Technologies, pg 941
On Stage Visuals, pg 963
Progressive AE, pg 985
Tri-Color, pg 1044

MINNESOTA

Aggressive Records Audio Duplication LLC, pg 778
The Richard Diercks Co Inc, pg 846
Sight Creative, pg 1010
Thomas Reprographics, pg 1039

MISSOURI

Avatar Studios, pg 798
Communitronics Corp, pg 833
Show-Me Audio-Visual, pg 1009
Switch, pg 1030
Visionworks Design Services Inc, pg 1059

MONTANA

North Country Media Group, pg 959

NEBRASKA

Dog & Pony Productions Inc, pg 850
Three Pillars Media, pg 1040

NEVADA

Aardvark Video & Media Productions, pg 772
Encore Productions Inc, pg 861
JCS Video Productions, pg 904
Tanglewood Productions, pg 1031
21st Century Video Productions, pg 1047

NEW JERSEY

Audio Visual Dynamics®, pg 795
Broadcast Center Studios, pg 813
CD Meyer Inc, pg 822
CELCO-Constantine Engineering Labs Co, pg 822
CFP Video Productions Inc, pg 823
DWJ Television, pg 854
Early Films, pg 855
Laurel Video Productions, pg 916
MediaMix Inc, pg 937
MIB Mediaworks, pg 941
Midnight Media Group Inc, pg 942
NFL Films Inc, pg 957
Optisonics Productions, pg 965
Outside The Box Interactive LLC, pg 966
Peppers Ghost HD®, pg 973
Suede Interactive, pg 1027
VCSvideo, pg 1052

NEW YORK

Air Sea Land Productions Inc (ASL), pg 779
Animotion Inc, pg 787
Big Film Design, pg 807
The Big House Group, pg 807
Chromavision Corp, pg 826
Digital Art Video Inc, pg 847
dM works, pg 849
Duggal Visual Solutions, pg 853
Eastco Multimedia Solutions Inc, pg 856
4-D Creative Media, pg 871
Greyfalcon House, pg 882

Computer Three-D Effects on Slide

AUDIO/VISUAL

Computer Three-D Effects on Slide (continued)

SOUTH CAROLINA

Genesis Creative, pg 877

TENNESSEE

Stage Post, pg 1022

TEXAS

Digi-matics, pg 847
Epic Software Group Inc, pg 862
South Coast Film & Video, pg 1019
Stage Directions, pg 1022
Texas Heart Institute Visual Communication Services, pg 1037

UTAH

Ferrari Color®, pg 866

VIRGINIA

Advance Concepts Inc, pg 777
Allied Media Corp, pg 781

WISCONSIN

Audio Visual of Milwaukee Inc, pg 795
AVS Group, pg 800
USAV Group Inc, pg 1050
Watts Communications Inc, pg 1062

Computerized Animation Production Services, *see* Animation System

Consulting

ALABAMA

CMEInfo, pg 830
Media Visions Inc, pg 937

ALASKA

Aurora Films, pg 797

ARIZONA

Covid Inc, pg 837
Creative Backstage, pg 838
MediaWorks, pg 938
Merestone, pg 938
Metropolitan Audio-Visual Inc, pg 940
Tellens Inc, pg 1037

ARKANSAS

Shadowbox Video Productions, pg 1007

CALIFORNIA

Aaron & Le Duc, pg 772
AGF Media Services, pg 778
Associated Sound, pg 792
AV Conferencing, pg 797
Cibola Systems, pg 826
Coloredge, pg 832
Crystal Pyramid Productions™, pg 840
Custom Video Productions Inc, pg 841
Design Media, pg 845
Dogma Studios, pg 850
Dolphin MultiMedia Inc, pg 850
Tom Donald Films, pg 850
Electrosonic Inc, pg 859
Em Gee Film Library, pg 860
Express Media Inc, pg 864
First Person™, pg 868
FXC Communications, pg 874
Goal Productions, pg 879
Gold Standard Productions, pg 880
Havas Edge, pg 885
Jaguar Distribution Corp, pg 903
JDS Video & Media Productions Inc, pg 904
The Kitchen, pg 911
KVIE-Channel 6, pg 914
Lumeni Productions Inc, pg 926
Lynch Communications, pg 926
Maximus Media Inc, pg 934
McCune Audio-Video-Lighting, pg 935
McKay Conant Hoover Inc, pg 935
Media Fabricators Inc, pg 936
Media Systems Design Group, pg 937
New & Unique Videos™, pg 955
New Wave Entertainment, pg 956
Joseph Nicoletti Consulting-Promotion/California International Records/Global Village Records, pg 957
Panorama Productions, pg 968
piXvfm, pg 976
Players Press, pg 977
PM Productions, pg 977
Melvin Powers Television Marketing, pg 979
Prime Cut Productions, pg 982
PSI Inc, pg 987
Pyro Spectaculars, pg 988
QRS Software Services, pg 988
Regent Press Publishers & Printers, pg 994
RetinaVision Productions, pg 995
Ron Roy Productions/Moodtapes, pg 1000
Russ InVision Co/AbridgeClub.com, pg 1001
Sahara Records & Filmworks Entertainment Co, pg 1001
Charles M Salter Associates Inc, pg 1001
Randall Schiller Productions, pg 1004
SNAP, pg 1014
SonicPool, pg 1016
StereoScope International, pg 1024
Still N'Motion, pg 1025
Tam Communications Inc, pg 1031
Thorburn Associates, Acoustic, Technology, Lighting Design, pg 1039
Toon Makers, pg 1042
Total Media Group, pg 1042
University of Southern California, pg 1050
WARPed Pictures, pg 1062
Wavemaker Media Design, pg 1062
West Coast Projections Inc, pg 1063

COLORADO

D L Adams Associates Inc, pg 775
Paul L Anderson Productions Inc, pg 786
Audio Consultant Services Inc, pg 794
The Cinema Lab, pg 827
CSI Films, pg 840
Daylight Productions & Rentals, pg 844
Flashback Media Productions, pg 869
Maniac Productions, pg 930
Spectrum Audio Visual Services, pg 1020

CONNECTICUT

Boyce Nemec Designs, pg 811
Broadcast Video Productions LLC, pg 813
Crossroads Video, pg 840
Guymark Studios LLC, pg 883
MAVCO, pg 934
MCC Films, pg 935
New London Media, pg 956
P&P Studios Inc, pg 968
Skyviews Survey Inc, pg 1013

DELAWARE

So Smart Productions, pg 1015

DISTRICT OF COLUMBIA

Hillmann & Carr Inc, pg 889
Susan Hormuth, Visual Resource Consultant, pg 891
O'Keefe Communications Inc, pg 961

FLORIDA

Access Media Group, pg 773
AVI-SPL, pg 798
CD ROM™ Inc, pg 822
Communications Concepts Inc (CCI), pg 833
Digital Video Systems Inc, pg 848
Eastern Video, pg 856
Ed Ethridge Productions Inc, pg 863
Gulf Coast Audio Visual Producers Inc, pg 883
National Teleproductions Inc, pg 953
Pro Stage Inc, pg 983
Sight & Sound Productions, pg 1010
Stereo Sales Inc, pg 1024
Sunfire Communications Inc, pg 1028
Teach America Corp, pg 1033
Tricycle Studios, pg 1044
Universal Studios Florida® Production Group, pg 1049
Vistamax Productions, pg 1059

GEORGIA

CDAI Innovative Design Solutions, pg 822
Continental Film & Video, pg 835
Guerrilla Productions LLC, pg 883
Lighting & Production Equipment Inc, pg 920
Merck & Hill Consultants Inc, pg 938
Stage Front Presentation Systems, pg 1022
Staging Directions Inc, pg 1023
USMotivation, pg 1051
Visioneering International Inc, pg 1058

HAWAII

DL Adams Associates Ltd, pg 775
Ken Herkes Productions & Entertainment (KHPE), pg 888
Hyperspective Studios Inc, pg 893
Media Bridge Gamekids, pg 936

IDAHO

KTVB-TV, pg 914

ILLINOIS

ABSA Productions Inc, pg 772
Accenture, pg 773
Airways Digital Media, pg 779
Analog Free Media, pg 786
Audio Visual Services Corp, pg 796
Beatty TeleVisual Productions, pg 804
CCore Media Inc, pg 821
Communications Corporation of America, pg 833
Comtech Multimedia Marketing, pg 834
Cresta Creative, pg 839
Extraordinary Demos, pg 864
Film Police, pg 867
LightCraft Graphics Inc, pg 920
Jim Passin Productions, pg 970
The Pepper Group, pg 972
PSAV® Presentation Services (Hotel Services Division), pg 987
Southern Illinois University, pg 1019
Sparkfactor, pg 1019
20/20 Communications Inc, pg 1047
Woodside Avenue Music Productions Inc, pg 1069

INDIANA

Bright Ideas Creative Services, pg 812
Digital Rain LLC, pg 847

IOWA

The Production House, pg 984

KENTUCKY

Axxis Inc, pg 800
Broadway Digital, pg 813
NOR-COM Inc, pg 958
Prosper Media Group Inc, pg 986

LOUISIANA

Louisiana State University Health Sciences Center - Shreveport, pg 925
Moxie Media, pg 948

MAINE

Headlight Audio Visual Inc, pg 887

MARYLAND

CPR MultiMedia Solutions, pg 837
The Cutting Corp, pg 841
dbF a Media Company, pg 844
Kramer Communications Video Production, pg 913
Media Dimensions Inc, pg 936
Welocalize, pg 1063

MASSACHUSETTS

Capron Lighting & Sound Co Inc, pg 819
Cavanaugh Tocci Associates Inc, pg 821
CommCreative, pg 832
Communications Design Associates, pg 833
Continental Recordings Inc, pg 835
High Output Inc, pg 888
Monadnock Media Inc, pg 945
MotionArt Studios, pg 947
Northern Light Productions, pg 959
Preston Productions Inc, pg 981
TR Productions, pg 1043
TVN-The Video Network, pg 1046

Co-Production Services

AUDIO/VISUAL

Co-Production Services (continued)

ARIZONA

Aardvark Productions LLC, pg 772
MediaWorks, pg 938
Merestone, pg 938
Tellens Inc, pg 1037
Video Media Productions (VMP), pg 1055

ARKANSAS

Shadowbox Video Productions, pg 1007

CALIFORNIA

Aaron & Le Duc, pg 772
Blaise Media, pg 809
Bridge Publications Inc, pg 812
Concrete Images, pg 835
Crystal Pyramid Productions™, pg 840
Custom Video Productions Inc, pg 841
Deja View Video, pg 845
Design Media, pg 845
Dogma Studios, pg 850
Dolphin MultiMedia Inc, pg 850
Tom Donald Films, pg 850
ECONEWS (Environmental Television Series) & (Environmental Directions Radio Series), pg 856
Express Media Inc, pg 864
First Person™, pg 868
FXF Productions Inc, pg 874
Havas Edge, pg 885
iCorpTv, pg 893
Impact Group, pg 897
Jaguar Distribution Corp, pg 903
JDS Video & Media Productions Inc, pg 904
The Kitchen, pg 911
KVIE-Channel 6, pg 914
Lynch Communications, pg 926
Maximus Media Inc, pg 934
McCune Audio-Video-Lighting, pg 935
New & Unique Videos™, pg 955
Panorama Productions, pg 968
piXvfm, pg 976
Planet Blue, pg 976
PM Productions, pg 977
Melvin Powers Television Marketing, pg 979
PSI Inc, pg 987
Pyramind Studios, pg 988
QRS Software Services, pg 988
Regent Press Publishers & Printers, pg 994
Ron Roy Productions/Moodtapes, pg 1000
Russ InVision Co/AbridgeClub.com, pg 1001
Sahara Records & Filmworks Entertainment Co, pg 1001
Sports Cinematography Group, pg 1021
StereoScope International, pg 1024
Still N'Motion, pg 1025
Tam Communications Inc, pg 1031
Toon Makers, pg 1042
Total Media Group, pg 1042
WARPed Pictures, pg 1062
Wavemaker Media Design, pg 1062
Z-Ville Productions, pg 1073

COLORADO

Paul L Anderson Productions Inc, pg 786
Daylight Productions & Rentals, pg 844
Flashback Media Productions, pg 869
Spectrum Audio Visual Services, pg 1020

CONNECTICUT

Broadcast Video Productions LLC, pg 813
Crossroads Video, pg 840
Guymark Studios LLC, pg 883
Ironik Design & Post, pg 902
MAVCO, pg 934
New London Media, pg 956
Skyviews Survey Inc, pg 1013

DELAWARE

So Smart Productions, pg 1015

DISTRICT OF COLUMBIA

Hillmann & Carr Inc, pg 889
O'Keefe Communications Inc, pg 961

FLORIDA

Audio Visual Imagineering Inc, pg 795
Communications Concepts Inc (CCI), pg 833
Eastern Video, pg 856
Ed Ethridge Productions Inc, pg 863
National Teleproductions Inc, pg 953
SOS Worldwide Productions Inc, pg 1016
Sunfire Communications Inc, pg 1028
Teach America Corp, pg 1033
Tricycle Studios, pg 1044

GEORGIA

Beast Atlanta, pg 804
Continental Film & Video, pg 835
Guerrilla Productions LLC, pg 883
Myriad Productions, pg 951
Stage Front Presentation Systems, pg 1022
Staging Directions Inc, pg 1023
Visioneering International Inc, pg 1058

HAWAII

Ken Herkes Productions & Entertainment (KHPE), pg 888
Hyperspective Studios Inc, pg 893
Media Bridge Gamekids, pg 936

IDAHO

KTVB-TV, pg 914

ILLINOIS

ABSA Productions Inc, pg 772
Airways Digital Media, pg 779
Analog Free Media, pg 786
Audio Visual Services Corp, pg 796
CCore Media Inc, pg 821
Communications Corporation of America, pg 833
Comtech Multimedia Marketing, pg 834
Cresta Creative, pg 839
Extraordinary Demos, pg 864
Film Police, pg 867
LightCraft Graphics Inc, pg 920
The Pepper Group, pg 972
Perspectives Media, pg 973
PSAV® Presentation Services (Hotel Services Division), pg 987
Steven Samler Music & Sound, pg 1002
Sound/Video Impressions Inc, pg 1018
20/20 Communications Inc, pg 1047
Woodside Avenue Music Productions Inc, pg 1069

INDIANA

Bright Ideas Creative Services, pg 812
Digital Rain LLC, pg 847
Explore Media LLC, pg 864
PentaVision Communications Inc, pg 972

IOWA

The Production House, pg 984

KENTUCKY

Broadway Digital, pg 813
Prosper Media Group Inc, pg 986

LOUISIANA

Louisiana State University Health Sciences Center - Shreveport, pg 925

MAINE

Headlight Audio Visual Inc, pg 887

MARYLAND

CPR MultiMedia Solutions, pg 837
The Cutting Corp, pg 841
dbF a Media Company, pg 844
Kramer Communications Video Production, pg 913

MASSACHUSETTS

Capron Lighting & Sound Co Inc, pg 819
Monadnock Media Inc, pg 945
MotionArt Studios, pg 947
Preston Productions Inc, pg 981
TR Productions, pg 1043

MICHIGAN

ASC Systems, pg 791
Digi Sign Design LLC, pg 847
K&R's Recording Studios Inc, pg 908
On Stage Visuals, pg 963

MINNESOTA

Jamieson & Associates Inc, pg 904

MISSOURI

Production Consultants, pg 984
Visionworks Design Services Inc, pg 1059

MONTANA

KCFW Television, pg 908
North Country Media Group, pg 959

NEVADA

Aardvark Video & Media Productions, pg 772
Encore Productions Inc, pg 861
JCS Video Productions, pg 904
Lefco Video Services Inc, pg 918

NEW HAMPSHIRE

Apertura, pg 788
Chip Taylor Communications LLC, pg 1032

NEW JERSEY

CELCO-Constantine Engineering Labs Co, pg 822
CFP Video Productions Inc, pg 823
Euro-Pacific Film & Video Productions Inc, pg 863
Laurel Video Productions, pg 916
MIB Mediaworks, pg 941
Optisonics Productions, pg 965
Outside The Box Interactive LLC, pg 966
Producer East Productions, pg 983

NEW YORK

A&E Home Video, pg 771
aurora productions, pg 797
BC Video Inc, pg 803
The Big House Group, pg 807
Chromavision Corp, pg 826
Duggal Visual Solutions, pg 853
Eastco Multimedia Solutions Inc, pg 856
4-D Creative Media, pg 871
Greyfalcon House, pg 882
HAVE Inc, pg 886
HB-Content, pg 886
Hello World Communications, pg 888
Icontent, pg 893
L&P Media, pg 915
Long Island Video Enterprises Live Inc, pg 924
Lylofilm Productions, pg 926
Jack Morton Worldwide, pg 946
MRG Productions Inc, pg 948
TBA Global Events, pg 1032
VIEW Inc (Video International Entertainment World Inc), pg 1058
Zelman Studios Ltd, pg 1073

NORTH CAROLINA

Pat Appleson Studios Inc, pg 788
The Communications Group Inc, pg 833
LCW Productions LLC, pg 917
Special Event Services, pg 1020
Take One Productions Ltd, pg 1031

NORTH DAKOTA

Media Productions, pg 937

OHIO

Aztec Video Productions, pg 801
Cuyahoga Community College Media Center, pg 841
Take 1 Media Services, pg 1031
Treehaus Communications Inc, pg 1044
Vista Color Imaging Inc, pg 1059

OKLAHOMA

PDC Productions, pg 970
University of Oklahoma Academic Media & Digital Services, pg 1050

OREGON

Rex, pg 995

PENNSYLVANIA

AiH Group Inc, pg 779
Audio Visions Inc, pg 795

Display Equipment, Easel & Accessory Distributors

AUDIO/VISUAL

Display Equipment, Easel & Accessory Distributors (continued)

NEW YORK (continued)

Light Impressions, pg 920
Long Island Video Enterprises Live Inc, pg 924
Magnaplan Corp, pg 928
PASCO, pg 969
Presentation Products Inc, pg 981
Ray Supply Inc, pg 992
RNJ Electronics, pg 997
SmartSource Computer & AV Rentals, pg 1014
Joseph Struhl Co Inc, pg 1026
Technisphere Corp, pg 1034
Visual Technologies Corp, pg 1060

NORTH CAROLINA

Camcor Inc, pg 818
Harrison Brothers, pg 885
Strategic Connections, pg 1026

OHIO

Audio Visual Media, pg 795
Copp Integrated Systems, pg 836
Hughie's Event Production Services, pg 892
ITA Audio Visual Solutions, pg 902
Tri-State Audio Visual Co, pg 1044
Tri-State Visual Products, pg 1044

OREGON

Anthro Corp, pg 787

PENNSYLVANIA

Advanced AV, pg 777
Audio Visions Inc, pg 795
Aydin Displays Inc, pg 800
Bernie's Photo Center, pg 805
Brodart Co, pg 813
Clair Brothers Audio Systems Inc, pg 829
J E Foss Co, pg 871
The Lerro Corp, pg 919
RSS Distributors, pg 1000
Visual Sound Inc, pg 1059
Wespen Audio Visual Co, pg 1063

TENNESSEE

Continental Film, pg 835
Durrell LLC, pg 854
Memphis Communications Corp, pg 938
Spring Arbor Distributors, pg 1022
Technical Support Systems LLC, pg 1034
Tennessee Visual Service Co, pg 1037
Zion Music Group, pg 1074

TEXAS

Audio Visual Technologies Group, pg 796
AVES Audio Visual Systems Inc, pg 798
Data Display Audio Visual Co LP, pg 843
Heffernan Audio Visual, pg 887
Lubbock Audio Visual Inc, pg 925
Media Management LLC, pg 937
RadioShack Corp, pg 990
Radius® Display Products Inc, pg 990
Videotex Systems Inc, pg 1057

UTAH

KAE Corp, pg 907
Webb Audio Visual Communication, pg 1063

VIRGINIA

Avitecture Inc, pg 799
Boitnott Visual Communications Corp (BVC), pg 810
Communications Specialists Inc, pg 833
Hoppmann Audio Visual, pg 891
Intellidyne LLC, pg 899
Lee Hartman & Sons Inc, pg 918
Metropolitan Audio Visual Co LLC, pg 940
Quince Imaging Inc, pg 989
The Whitlock Group, pg 1065

WASHINGTON

eMagin Corp, pg 860
Inland Audio Visual Co, pg 898

WISCONSIN

Audio Visual of Milwaukee Inc, pg 795
Camera Corner Connecting Point, pg 818
Demco Inc, pg 845
Full Compass Systems, pg 874
Safe Harbor Computers, pg 1001
School Specialty Inc, pg 1004

ALBERTA

Infosat Communications Inc, pg 898
McBain Audio Visual Ltd, pg 935
Sharp's Audio-Visual Ltd, pg 1008
SMART Technologies Inc, pg 1013
Unique Communications Ltd, pg 1048

BRITISH COLUMBIA

Commercial Electronics Ltd, pg 832

MANITOBA

Inland Audio Visual Ltd, pg 898

ONTARIO

Carr McLean Ltd, pg 820
CBM Metal, pg 821
Edcom Multimedia Products, pg 856
MVI Multivision Inc, pg 951
Premier A/V Sales Ltd, pg 980
Westbury National Show Systems Ltd, pg 1064

QUEBEC

Concept Audio-Visual, pg 834

Display Equipment, Easel & Accessory Manufacturers

ARIZONA

OmniMount Systems, pg 962

CALIFORNIA

ALTINEX Inc, pg 783
Auton Motorized Systems, pg 797
Boland Communications, pg 810
Ellison Educational Equipment Inc, pg 859
Extron Electronics, pg 864
Hoodman Corp, pg 891
Omnirax, pg 963
Penn Elcom Inc, pg 971
Silvestri California, pg 1011
Tasman Group Pacific Rim, pg 1032
Wohler Technologies Inc, pg 1069

COLORADO

Colorado Display Systems, pg 831
Display Devices, pg 849
National Teaching Aids Inc, pg 953

CONNECTICUT

KOH Design Inc, pg 913

FLORIDA

The Great Southern Studios, pg 882
Vutec Corp, Video Products Division, pg 1061

GEORGIA

PolyVision Corporation, pg 978

ILLINOIS

Bretford Manufacturing Inc, pg 812
Kart-A-Bag Manufacturing Inc, pg 908
Luxor, pg 926
Peerless Industries, pg 971
Quartet Manufacturing Co, pg 989
H Wilson Co, pg 1067
Windel International/Weyel, pg 1067

INDIANA

Da-Lite, pg 842
Draper Inc, pg 852
Porter Case Inc, pg 978

MARYLAND

Absolute Hollywood, pg 772
Video Mount Products (VMP), pg 1055

MASSACHUSETTS

International Display & Exhibit Corp, pg 901
Lineco, pg 922
University Products Inc, pg 1050

MINNESOTA

Chief, pg 825

MISSOURI

Magna Visual Inc, pg 928

NEW JERSEY

Hannecke Display Systems Inc, pg 884
National Audio-Visual Supply, pg 952
PeopleVisionFX, pg 972
Pro-Tape & Specialities Inc, pg 983
Sharp Electronics Corp, Professional Display Division, pg 1008
Tally Display Corp, pg 1031
Techflex Inc, pg 1033

NEW YORK

Canon USA Inc, pg 819
Century Business Solutions, pg 823
ELMO USA Corp, pg 859
General Audio-Visual Inc (GAVI), pg 876
Hybrid Cases, pg 892
Light Impressions, pg 920
Magnaplan Corp, pg 928
Swivelier, pg 1030
TecNec Distributing, pg 1035

OHIO

Electronic Vision Inc (EV), pg 859
Ghent Manufacturing, pg 878
Hilferty & Associates Inc, pg 889

OREGON

Anthro Corp, pg 787

PENNSYLVANIA

Automatic Devices Co, pg 797
Aydin Displays Inc, pg 800

TEXAS

MooreCo Inc, pg 946
RadioShack Corp, pg 990
Radius® Display Products Inc, pg 990
Smith System Inc, pg 1014

UTAH

KAE Corp, pg 907

VIRGINIA

Avitecture Inc, pg 799
Drytac Corp, pg 852
Optikinetics Ltd - The Americas, pg 964

WASHINGTON

eMagin Corp, pg 860

ALBERTA

SMART Technologies Inc, pg 1013

ONTARIO

CBM Metal, pg 821
Egan Visual Inc/Egan TeamBoard Inc, pg 858

Display Equipment, Easel & Accessory Rentals

ALABAMA

Audio-Video Resources Inc, pg 795
Media Visions Inc, pg 937

ARIZONA

Arizona Cine Equipment, pg 789
Merestone, pg 938
Metropolitan Audio-Visual Inc, pg 940

ARKANSAS

White Diamond Productions, pg 1065

CALIFORNIA

Ametron Audio/Video, pg 785
Associated Sound, pg 792
ATV Video Center Inc, pg 793
AV Guys, pg 797
Instructional Materials & Equipment Distributors (I-Med), pg 899
JD Audio Visual Inc, pg 904
Lynch Communications, pg 926
McCune Audio-Video-Lighting, pg 935
Media Fabricators Inc, pg 936
MSI Productions, pg 949
Munday & Collins AV, pg 950

PSAV® Presentation Services, pg 986
Slate Media Group, pg 1013
Stanislaus Audio Video Inc, pg 1023
Total Media Group, pg 1042
VER-Video Equipment Rentals, pg 1053

COLORADO

Daylight Productions & Rentals, pg 844

CONNECTICUT

A/V Davey, pg 797
Concord Communications, pg 835
Everett Hall Associates Inc, pg 863

FLORIDA

AVI-SPL, pg 798
The Great Southern Studios, pg 882
Gulf Coast Audio Visual Producers Inc, pg 883
Harmon's Audio-Visual Services, pg 885
Image Technical Services, pg 895
Industrial Strength Inc, pg 897
Jordan Klein Film & Video (JKFV), pg 906
Lighting Sales Connections, pg 920
Media Concepts Inc, pg 936
Photosound of Orlando Inc, pg 975
Pro Stage Inc, pg 983
Sight & Sound Productions, pg 1010
Spire Audio Visual Co Inc, pg 1021

GEORGIA

Convergent Media Systems, pg 836
Dixie Theatre Service & Supply Co Inc, pg 849
Lighting & Production Equipment Inc, pg 920
ON Event Services, pg 963
Stage Front Presentation Systems, pg 1022
Staging Directions Inc, pg 1023

HAWAII

ATTCO Inc, pg 793

ILLINOIS

Allen Visual Systems Inc, pg 781
Audio Visual Services Corp, pg 796
Backstar Creative Media Inc, pg 801
Beatty TeleVisual Productions, pg 804
Central Audio-Visual Equipment Inc, pg 823
Helix Camera & Video, pg 887
PSAV® Presentation Services (Hotel Services Division), pg 987
Show Department Inc, pg 1009

INDIANA

OMNI Productions, pg 962

KENTUCKY

Audio Visual Techniques Inc, pg 796

LOUISIANA

Clark Services Audio Visual & Exhibit Inc, pg 829

MARYLAND

Absolute Hollywood, pg 772
Advance Audiovisual Presentation Ltd, pg 777
CSPMedia.com, pg 840

MASSACHUSETTS

Capron Lighting & Sound Co Inc, pg 819
massAV, pg 933
Preston Productions Inc, pg 981

MICHIGAN

Olson Anderson Co, pg 786
City Events Group, pg 828
K&R All Media Productions Inc, pg 908
TeL Systems, pg 1035

MINNESOTA

Advanced Audio-Visual Inc, pg 777
AVI Systems, pg 799

MISSISSIPPI

Bowie Audio Visual Enterprises Inc, pg 811

MISSOURI

Communitronics Corp, pg 833
Schiller's Audio-Visual, pg 1004
Show-Me Audio-Visual, pg 1009
Swank Audio Visuals, pg 1029

NEBRASKA

Dog & Pony Productions Inc, pg 850

NEW HAMPSHIRE

Academic & Campus Technology Services, pg 773

NEW JERSEY

Audio Visual Associates, pg 795
Audio Visual Dynamics®, pg 795
Audio Visual Systems Rental Centres, pg 796
Earl Girls Inc, pg 855
International Audio Visual Inc, pg 900
PLS Staging, pg 977
Starlite Productions, pg 1024
Wilray Audio Visual Corp, pg 1067

NEW YORK

AV Workshop, pg 797
Colortone Audio Visual, pg 832
Communication Corner Inc, pg 832
Design Audio Visual Inc, pg 845
KVL Audio Visual Services Inc, pg 914
Langie Audio Visual Systems, pg 915
Long Island Video Enterprises Live Inc, pg 924
Magnaplan Corp, pg 928
Manhattan Center Studios Inc, pg 930
SmartSource Computer & AV Rentals, pg 1014
Specialized Audio-Visual Inc, pg 1020
Visual Technologies Corp, pg 1060
Visual Word Systems Inc, pg 1060
Zelman Studios Ltd, pg 1073

NORTH CAROLINA

A&V Company, pg 772
AV Metro Inc, pg 797
Camcor Inc, pg 818

OHIO

Audio Visual Media, pg 795
Aztec Video Productions, pg 801
Hughie's Event Production Services, pg 892
ITA Audio Visual Solutions, pg 902
Mills James Productions, pg 943

PENNSYLVANIA

Advanced AV, pg 777
Audio Visions Inc, pg 795
FirstGeneration Audio/Visual Services, pg 869
FMP Media Solutions Inc, pg 870
Ott Film Rentals, pg 966
Production Solutions Inc, pg 985
Visual Sound Inc, pg 1059

SOUTH CAROLINA

Sound & Images Inc, pg 1016

TENNESSEE

Memphis Communications Corp, pg 938
Technical Support Systems LLC, pg 1034

TEXAS

Audio Visual Technologies Group, pg 796
Industrial Audio/Video Inc, pg 897
Lubbock Audio Visual Inc, pg 925
Stage Directions, pg 1022

UTAH

Webb Audio Visual Communication, pg 1063

VERMONT

Parlato Productions, pg 969

VIRGINIA

American AV, pg 783
Boitnott Visual Communications Corp (BVC), pg 810
Lee Hartman & Sons Inc, pg 918
Projection Presentation Technology, pg 985
Quince Imaging Inc, pg 989
Rainbow Rentals, pg 991

WASHINGTON

Inland Audio Visual Co, pg 898

WISCONSIN

Event Essentials, pg 863
Full Compass Systems, pg 874

PUERTO RICO

Bonnin Electronics Inc, pg 810
Stage Crew Audiovisual Inc, pg 1022

ALBERTA

Allstar Show Industries Inc, pg 782
Cine Audio Visual Sales & Service Ltd, pg 826
Evolution Presentation Technologies, pg 863
McBain Audio Visual Ltd, pg 935
Sharp's Audio-Visual Ltd, pg 1008
Unique Communications Ltd, pg 1048

BRITISH COLUMBIA

Triad Communications Ltd, pg 1044
Video In Studios/Video Out Distribution, pg 1055

MANITOBA

Inland Audio Visual Ltd, pg 898

ONTARIO

Edcom Multimedia Products, pg 856
HD Source, pg 886
MVI Multivision Inc, pg 951
Westbury National Show Systems Ltd, pg 1064

Display Equipment, Easel & Accessory Repairs

CALIFORNIA

Ametron Audio/Video, pg 785
McAlister Electronics, pg 935
Lloyd F McKinney Associates Inc, pg 935

COLORADO

Colorado Display Systems, pg 831

FLORIDA

AVI-SPL, pg 798
Spire Audio Visual Co Inc, pg 1021

GEORGIA

Lighting & Production Equipment Inc, pg 920
Stage Front Presentation Systems, pg 1022

ILLINOIS

Allen Visual Systems Inc, pg 781

KENTUCKY

Axxis Inc, pg 800
NOR-COM Inc, pg 958

MARYLAND

Absolute Hollywood, pg 772

MICHIGAN

City Events Group, pg 828
TeL Systems, pg 1035

MINNESOTA

AVI Systems, pg 799

NEW JERSEY

Audio Visual Associates, pg 795
Turner Engineering Inc, pg 1046

NEW YORK

Colortone Audio Visual, pg 832
Magnaplan Corp, pg 928
Visual Technologies Corp, pg 1060

NORTH CAROLINA

Camcor Inc, pg 818

AUDIO/VISUAL

Display Equipment, Easel & Accessory Repairs (continued)

OHIO

Audio Visual Media, pg 795
Aztec Video Productions, pg 801
ITA Audio Visual Solutions, pg 902

PENNSYLVANIA

Advanced AV, pg 777
Audio Visions Inc, pg 795

TENNESSEE

Memphis Communications Corp, pg 938
Technical Support Systems LLC, pg 1034

TEXAS

Audio Visual Technologies Group, pg 796
Industrial Audio/Video Inc, pg 897
Lubbock Audio Visual Inc, pg 925
Padgitt's, pg 967

VIRGINIA

Avitecture Inc, pg 799
Hoppmann Audio Visual, pg 891

WASHINGTON

Inland Audio Visual Co, pg 898

WISCONSIN

Full Compass Systems, pg 874

ALBERTA

Infosat Communications Inc, pg 898
Sharp's Audio-Visual Ltd, pg 1008

MANITOBA

Inland Audio Visual Ltd, pg 898

ONTARIO

Edcom Multimedia Products, pg 856
MVI Multivision Inc, pg 951

Dry Mounting & Laminating Equipment & Supply Distributors

ALABAMA

Curtis Company, pg 841
Media Visions Inc, pg 937

ARIZONA

Professional Marketing Services Inc, pg 985
Troxell Communications Inc, pg 1045

CALIFORNIA

Educational Technology Services (ETS), pg 857
Gluskin's Custom Audio Video, pg 879
Hooper Camera & Imaging, pg 891
Instructional Materials & Equipment Distributors (I-Med), pg 899
Media Fabricators Inc, pg 936
Related Visual Inc, pg 994

COLORADO

Ceavco Audio/Visual Co, pg 822

CONNECTICUT

HB Communications Inc, pg 886
MAVCO, pg 934
Rockwell Communications Inc, pg 998
USI Inc, pg 1051

FLORIDA

Gulf Coast Audio Visual Producers Inc, pg 883
Hi-Tech Import Export Corp, pg 888
Photomart Cine-Video Inc, pg 975
Spire Audio Visual Co Inc, pg 1021
Tallahassee Audio Visual, pg 1031

GEORGIA

Audio Visual Resources Inc, pg 795
Technical Innovation, pg 1033

ILLINOIS

Central Audio-Visual Equipment Inc, pg 823
Pres-On Merchandising Corp, pg 981
Sound Vision Inc, pg 1018

IOWA

Sitler's Supplies Inc, pg 1012

KANSAS

KK Office Solutions Inc, pg 911
Nazdar®, pg 953

LOUISIANA

Intermedia Technologies, pg 900

MAINE

Headlight Audio Visual Inc, pg 887

MARYLAND

Nelson White Systems Inc, pg 954
Nicholas P Pipino Associates Inc, pg 976
RTZ Audio Visual, pg 1000

MASSACHUSETTS

Hunt's Photo, Video & Digital, pg 892
Lineco, pg 922
University Products Inc, pg 1050

MICHIGAN

Olson Anderson Co, pg 786
City Events Group, pg 828
Michigan Office Solutions, pg 941

MINNESOTA

Rayven Inc, pg 992
Tierney Brothers Inc, pg 1040

MISSISSIPPI

Bowie Audio Visual Enterprises Inc, pg 811
Jasper Ewing & Sons Inc, pg 864

MISSOURI

Conference Technologies Inc, pg 835
Image Technologies Corp, pg 895
Swank Audio Visuals, pg 1029

NEW JERSEY

Argraph Corp, pg 789
AV Bluebook, pg 797
Falcon Safety Products Inc, pg 865
Graphics Depot Inc, pg 881
Hamilton Buhl, pg 884
National Audio-Visual Supply, pg 952
VCom International Multimedia Corp, pg 1052

NEW YORK

A M Graphics Products, dba Affton Graphics Inc, pg 771
Communication Corner Inc, pg 832
Custom Media Environments, pg 841
Gaylord Brothers, pg 876
Indigo Productions, pg 897
Langie Audio Visual Systems, pg 915
Light Impressions, pg 920
Magnaplan Corp, pg 928
Markertek Video Supply, pg 931
Neptune Photo Inc, pg 954
PASCO, pg 969
Ray Supply Inc, pg 992
Willoughby's Imaging Center, pg 1067

NORTH CAROLINA

Camcor Inc, pg 818

OHIO

Audio Visual Media, pg 795
Graphic Laminating LLC, pg 881
Tri-State Audio Visual Co, pg 1044
Tri-State Visual Products, pg 1044

PENNSYLVANIA

Advanced AV, pg 777
Bernie's Photo Center, pg 805
Brodart Co, pg 813
J E Foss Co, pg 871
Garcia Marketing Inc, pg 875
Grise Audio Visual Center Inc, pg 882
IDenticard Systems Inc, pg 894
Visual Sound Inc, pg 1059
Wespen Audio Visual Co, pg 1063

RHODE ISLAND

Custom Computer Specialists Inc, pg 841

TENNESSEE

Bryce Corp, pg 814
Tennessee Visual Service Co, pg 1037

TEXAS

AVES Audio Visual Systems Inc, pg 798
Heffernan Audio Visual, pg 887
J&S Audio Visual Inc, pg 904
Lubbock Audio Visual Inc, pg 925
Schoolhouse Audio Visual, pg 1004

VIRGINIA

Communications Specialists Inc, pg 833
Drytac Corp, pg 852
Lee Hartman & Sons Inc, pg 918
Metropolitan Audio Visual Co LLC, pg 940
The Whitlock Group, pg 1065

WASHINGTON

Inland Audio Visual Co, pg 898

WISCONSIN

Audio Visual of Milwaukee Inc, pg 795
Camera Corner Connecting Point, pg 818
Demco Inc, pg 845
Pro Studio Supply, pg 983
School Specialty Inc, pg 1004

PUERTO RICO

Audio Visual Concepts Inc, pg 795
Bonnin Electronics Inc, pg 810

ALBERTA

McBain Audio Visual Ltd, pg 935

ONTARIO

Edcom Multimedia Products, pg 856
Premier A/V Sales Ltd, pg 980

QUEBEC

Concept Audio-Visual, pg 834

Dry Mounting & Laminating Equipment & Supply Manufacturers

ARIZONA

Savage Universal Corp, pg 1003

CONNECTICUT

USI Inc, pg 1051

FLORIDA

Kinetronics Corp, pg 911

ILLINOIS

ACCO Brands Corp, pg 773
GBC Document Finishing, pg 876
Graphic Products Corp, pg 881
Pres-On Merchandising Corp, pg 981
Quartet Manufacturing Co, pg 989
Sprayway Inc, pg 1022

MASSACHUSETTS

University Products Inc, pg 1050

MINNESOTA

Rayven Inc, pg 992

MISSOURI

Southwest Binding & Laminating, pg 1019

NEW JERSEY

Falcon Safety Products Inc, pg 865

NEW YORK

TecNec Distributing, pg 1035

OKLAHOMA

Marvel Photo Inc, pg 932

PENNSYLVANIA

IDenticard Systems Inc, pg 894

TENNESSEE

Bryce Corp, pg 814

TEXAS

Image Innovations Inc, pg 895
MooreCo Inc, pg 946

VIRGINIA

Drytac Corp, pg 852

Dry Mounting & Laminating Equipment & Supply Rentals

ALABAMA

Media Visions Inc, pg 937

ARIZONA

Merestone, pg 938

CALIFORNIA

Media Fabricators Inc, pg 936
VER-Video Equipment Rentals, pg 1053

FLORIDA

Spire Audio Visual Co Inc, pg 1021

GEORGIA

Staging Directions Inc, pg 1023

ILLINOIS

Central Audio-Visual Equipment Inc, pg 823
Helix Camera & Video, pg 887

MINNESOTA

AVI Systems, pg 799

MISSISSIPPI

Bowie Audio Visual Enterprises Inc, pg 811
Jasper Ewing & Sons Inc, pg 864

MISSOURI

Image Technologies Corp, pg 895

NEW HAMPSHIRE

Apertura, pg 788

NEW JERSEY

Video Corporation of America (VCA), pg 1055

NEW YORK

Magnaplan Corp, pg 928
Ray Supply Inc, pg 992

OHIO

Audio Visual Media, pg 795
Vista Color Imaging Inc, pg 1059

PENNSYLVANIA

Grise Audio Visual Center Inc, pg 882
Production Solutions Inc, pg 985

VIRGINIA

Lee Hartman & Sons Inc, pg 918
Projection Presentation Technology, pg 985

WASHINGTON

Inland Audio Visual Co, pg 898

QUEBEC

Concept Audio-Visual, pg 834

Dry Mounting & Laminating Equipment & Supply Repairs

CALIFORNIA

McAlister Electronics, pg 935

CONNECTICUT

HB Communications Inc, pg 886

FLORIDA

Spire Audio Visual Co Inc, pg 1021

KANSAS

KK Office Solutions Inc, pg 911

MAINE

Headlight Audio Visual Inc, pg 887

MARYLAND

Nelson White Systems Inc, pg 954

MICHIGAN

City Events Group, pg 828
TeL Systems, pg 1035

MINNESOTA

AVI Systems, pg 799

MISSISSIPPI

Bowie Audio Visual Enterprises Inc, pg 811

NEW YORK

Colortone Audio Visual, pg 832
Langie Audio Visual Systems, pg 915
Magnaplan Corp, pg 928
Ray Supply Inc, pg 992

OHIO

Audio Visual Media, pg 795
Aztec Video Productions, pg 801
Tri-State Audio Visual Co, pg 1044

PENNSYLVANIA

J E Foss Co, pg 871
IDenticard Systems Inc, pg 894

RHODE ISLAND

Custom Computer Specialists Inc, pg 841

TEXAS

Audio Visual Technologies Group, pg 796
Lubbock Audio Visual Inc, pg 925
Padgitt's, pg 967
Schoolhouse Audio Visual, pg 1004

VIRGINIA

Boitnott Visual Communications Corp (BVC), pg 810
Drytac Corp, pg 852
Metropolitan Audio Visual Co LLC, pg 940
The Whitlock Group, pg 1065

WASHINGTON

Inland Audio Visual Co, pg 898

WISCONSIN

School Specialty Inc, pg 1004

ONTARIO

Premier A/V Sales Ltd, pg 980

Duplication—Filmstrips

ALABAMA

Media Visions Inc, pg 937

CALIFORNIA

Allied Artists International Inc, pg 781
Coloredge, pg 832
Digital Media West, pg 847
Lynch Communications, pg 926
QRS Software Services, pg 988

COLORADO

The Cinema Lab, pg 827
Maniac Productions, pg 930

CONNECTICUT

Broadcast Video Productions LLC, pg 813

FLORIDA

Gulf Coast Audio Visual Producers Inc, pg 883
Jordan Klein Film & Video (JKFV), pg 906
Tallahassee Audio Visual, pg 1031

GEORGIA

Imagers, pg 896
Visioneering International Inc, pg 1058

MASSACHUSETTS

Colortek of Boston, pg 832
CommCreative, pg 832
TR Productions, pg 1043

MINNESOTA

Aggressive Records Audio Duplication LLC, pg 778

MISSOURI

Show-Me Audio-Visual, pg 1009

NEW HAMPSHIRE

Apertura, pg 788

NEW JERSEY

Broadcast Center Studios, pg 813
CELCO-Constantine Engineering Labs Co, pg 822
Reed Presentations Inc (RPI), pg 993

NEW YORK

Duggal Visual Solutions, pg 853
Duplication Specialists Inc, pg 853
Educational Images Ltd, pg 857
Ketchum Pleon Change, pg 910
Modernage Photographic Services Inc, pg 944
MRG Productions Inc, pg 948
Visual Technologies Corp, pg 1060
Visual Word Systems Inc, pg 1060
Zelman Studios Ltd, pg 1073

OHIO

Aztec Video Productions, pg 801

PENNSYLVANIA

Audio Visual Communications Inc, pg 795
Berry & Homer, pg 805

TENNESSEE

Memphis Communications Corp, pg 938
Stage Post, pg 1022

TEXAS

Digi-matics, pg 847
Stage Directions, pg 1022

VIRGINIA

Blair Inc, pg 809

WISCONSIN

Audio Visual of Milwaukee Inc, pg 795
USAV Group Inc, pg 1050

ONTARIO

McNabb & Connolly, pg 935

Duplication—Slides

ALABAMA

Media Visions Inc, pg 937

ARIZONA

Image Craft LLC, pg 894

CALIFORNIA

Action Photo Service Inc, pg 775
Adolph Gasser Inc, pg 776
CCI Digital, pg 821
Coloredge, pg 832
Gluskin's Custom Audio Video, pg 879
Joan Kramer & Associates Inc, pg 913
Lynch Communications, pg 926
PSI Inc, pg 987
QRS Software Services, pg 988
Shokus Video, pg 1009

CONNECTICUT

Broadcast Video Productions LLC, pg 813

FLORIDA

Cheuvront Studios, pg 824
Communications Concepts Inc (CCI), pg 833
Gulf Coast Audio Visual Producers Inc, pg 883
Tallahassee Audio Visual, pg 1031

AUDIO/VISUAL

Duplication—Slides (continued)

GEORGIA

Imagers, pg 896
Visioneering International Inc, pg 1058

ILLINOIS

CCore Media Inc, pg 821
Gamma Imaging, pg 875
Helix Camera & Video, pg 887
JMC Photo & Digital Services Inc, pg 905
Major Media Inc, pg 929
Southern Illinois University, pg 1019

INDIANA

OMNI Productions, pg 962

IOWA

The Production House, pg 984

KANSAS

Genigraphics®, pg 877

LOUISIANA

Louisiana State University Health Sciences Center - Shreveport, pg 925
Primary Color Laboratory Inc, pg 982

MARYLAND

Optic Bindery & Packaging, pg 964

MASSACHUSETTS

Camera Co Inc/Broadcast Divison, pg 818
Colortek of Boston, pg 832
CommCreative, pg 832
DGI-Invisuals LLC, pg 846
TR Productions, pg 1043

MICHIGAN

K&R's Recording Studios Inc, pg 908
Michigan Office Solutions, pg 941
Tri-Color, pg 1044

MINNESOTA

Aggressive Records Audio Duplication LLC, pg 778
Linhoff Photo & Digital Imaging, pg 922
Sight Creative, pg 1010
Thomas Reprographics, pg 1039

MISSISSIPPI

Jasper Ewing & Sons Inc, pg 864

MISSOURI

Allied Photo Color Co, pg 781
Show-Me Audio-Visual, pg 1009
Visionworks Design Services Inc, pg 1059

MONTANA

KUSM TV, pg 914

NEVADA

Aardvark Video & Media Productions, pg 772

NEW HAMPSHIRE

Apertura, pg 788

NEW JERSEY

Broadcast Center Studios, pg 813
CELCO-Constantine Engineering Labs Co, pg 822
Laurel Video Productions, pg 916
Reed Presentations Inc (RPI), pg 993
Suede Interactive, pg 1027
Video Corporation of America (VCA), pg 1055

NEW YORK

Duggal Visual Solutions, pg 853
Duplication Specialists Inc, pg 853
Eastco Multimedia Solutions Inc, pg 856
Educational Images Ltd, pg 857
Ken Lieberman Labs Inc, pg 920
Magnaplan Corp, pg 928
Modernage Photographic Services Inc, pg 944
Jack Morton Worldwide, pg 946
MRG Productions Inc, pg 948
SMP Digital Graphics, pg 1014
TBA Global Events, pg 1032
Visual Technologies Corp, pg 1060
Visual Word Systems Inc, pg 1060
Zelman Studios Ltd, pg 1073

NORTH CAROLINA

Camcor Inc, pg 818
Image Associates Inc, pg 894

OHIO

Aztec Video Productions, pg 801
Cuyahoga Community College Media Center, pg 841
Thread Marketing Group, pg 1039
Vista Color Imaging Inc, pg 1059

PENNSYLVANIA

Audio Visual Communications Inc, pg 795
Bernie's Photo Center, pg 805
Berry & Homer, pg 805
FMP Media Solutions Inc, pg 870
Main Point Productions, pg 929
Ott Film Rentals, pg 966

TENNESSEE

Memphis Communications Corp, pg 938
Stage Post, pg 1022
WKPT-TV, pg 1068

TEXAS

City Color, pg 828
Digi-matics, pg 847
IntegraColor, pg 899
Stage Directions, pg 1022
Texas Heart Institute Visual Communication Services, pg 1037

UTAH

Ferrari Color®, pg 866

VERMONT

University of Vermont, Instructional Television Dept, pg 1050

VIRGINIA

Blair Inc, pg 809

WASHINGTON

Kostov Productions, pg 913

WISCONSIN

Audio Visual of Milwaukee Inc, pg 795
USAV Group Inc, pg 1050

ALBERTA

Cine Audio Visual Sales & Service Ltd, pg 826

ONTARIO

Purefire Communications Inc, pg 987

Duplication—Transparencies

ALABAMA

Media Visions Inc, pg 937

ARIZONA

Image Craft LLC, pg 894
Video Media Productions (VMP), pg 1055

CALIFORNIA

Action Photo Service Inc, pg 775
Coloredge, pg 832
FXC Communications, pg 874
Gluskin's Custom Audio Video, pg 879
Lynch Communications, pg 926
McCune Audio-Video-Lighting, pg 935
QRS Software Services, pg 988
Total Media Group, pg 1042

CONNECTICUT

Broadcast Video Productions LLC, pg 813
MAVCO, pg 934
USI Inc, pg 1051

FLORIDA

Cheuvront Studios, pg 824
Gulf Coast Audio Visual Producers Inc, pg 883
Jordan Klein Film & Video (JKFV), pg 906
Tallahassee Audio Visual, pg 1031

GEORGIA

Imagers, pg 896
Visioneering International Inc, pg 1058

ILLINOIS

Gamma Imaging, pg 875
JMC Photo & Digital Services Inc, pg 905
Southern Illinois University, pg 1019

INDIANA

OMNI Productions, pg 962

IOWA

The Production House, pg 984

LOUISIANA

Primary Color Laboratory Inc, pg 982

MARYLAND

Optic Bindery & Packaging, pg 964
Satellite Media Production, pg 1003

MASSACHUSETTS

Capron Lighting & Sound Co Inc, pg 819
Colortek of Boston, pg 832
CommCreative, pg 832
DGI-Invisuals LLC, pg 846
TR Productions, pg 1043

MICHIGAN

K&R's Recording Studios Inc, pg 908
Michigan Office Solutions, pg 941

MINNESOTA

Aggressive Records Audio Duplication LLC, pg 778
Thomas Reprographics, pg 1039

MISSISSIPPI

Jasper Ewing & Sons Inc, pg 864

MISSOURI

Allied Photo Color Co, pg 781
Visionworks Design Services Inc, pg 1059
VSG Digital Media Solutions, pg 1061

NEW HAMPSHIRE

Apertura, pg 788
Chip Taylor Communications LLC, pg 1032

NEW JERSEY

Broadcast Center Studios, pg 813
CELCO-Constantine Engineering Labs Co, pg 822
NFL Films Music Library, pg 957
Reed Presentations Inc (RPI), pg 993
Video Corporation of America (VCA), pg 1055

NEW YORK

C2 Imaging LLC, pg 841
Duggal Visual Solutions, pg 853
Eastco Multimedia Solutions Inc, pg 856
FSL Media Inc, pg 873
Ken Lieberman Labs Inc, pg 920
Long Island Video Enterprises Live Inc, pg 924
Magnaplan Corp, pg 928
Modernage Photographic Services Inc, pg 944
Jack Morton Worldwide, pg 946
MRG Productions Inc, pg 948
Neptune Photo Inc, pg 954
SMP Digital Graphics, pg 1014
TBA Global Events, pg 1032
Visual Technologies Corp, pg 1060
Zelman Studios Ltd, pg 1073

NORTH CAROLINA

Image Associates Inc, pg 894

OHIO

Aztec Video Productions, pg 801
Thread Marketing Group, pg 1039
Vista Color Imaging Inc, pg 1059

PENNSYLVANIA

Audio Visual Communications Inc, pg 795
Berry & Homer, pg 805

TENNESSEE

Memphis Communications Corp, pg 938
Stage Post, pg 1022

TEXAS

City Color, pg 828
Digi-matics, pg 847
Stage Directions, pg 1022

UTAH

Ferrari Color®, pg 866

VIRGINIA

Blair Inc, pg 809
The Whitlock Group, pg 1065

WISCONSIN

Audio Visual of Milwaukee Inc, pg 795
USAV Group Inc, pg 1050

Easels, *see* Display Equipment, Easel & Accessory

Electronic Chalkboard Distributors

ARIZONA

Troxell Communications Inc, pg 1045
Ultimate Presentation Systems Inc, pg 1047

ARKANSAS

Jay S Stanley & Associates Inc, pg 1023
White Diamond Productions, pg 1065

CALIFORNIA

Ametron Audio/Video, pg 785
Beta Electronics Inc, pg 806
Christy's Editorial, pg 826
Cibola Systems, pg 826
Delicate Electronics Sales Inc, pg 845
MediaPOINTE, pg 938
Stanislaus Audio Video Inc, pg 1023

COLORADO

Daylight Productions & Rentals, pg 844

CONNECTICUT

HB Communications Inc, pg 886

FLORIDA

AVI-SPL, pg 798
Harris Corp, pg 885
Pro Stage Inc, pg 983

GEORGIA

Omnimedia Inc, pg 962
PolyVision Corporation, pg 978
Stage Front Presentation Systems, pg 1022

HAWAII

The Audio Visual Co (AVCO), pg 795

ILLINOIS

Allen Visual Systems Inc, pg 781
Quintessence Audio Ltd, pg 989
The Screen Works®, pg 1005

INDIANA

Sensory Technologies LLC, pg 1006

IOWA

ECS Inc, pg 856

KENTUCKY

NOR-COM Inc, pg 958

LOUISIANA

Intermedia Technologies, pg 900

MAINE

Headlight Audio Visual Inc, pg 887

MARYLAND

Cardinal Sound & Video, pg 820

MASSACHUSETTS

Rule Broadcast Systems, pg 1000

MICHIGAN

Ascom Communications Contractors, pg 791
Michigan Office Solutions, pg 941
TeL Systems, pg 1035

MINNESOTA

Tierney Brothers Inc, pg 1040

MISSOURI

Schiller's Audio-Visual, pg 1004

NEW JERSEY

Audio Visual Associates, pg 795
AV Bluebook, pg 797
Hamilton Buhl, pg 884
National Audio-Visual Supply, pg 952
Total Video Products Inc, pg 1042
Wired 4 Sound Inc, pg 1068
York Telecom, pg 1072

NEW YORK

ALTEL Systems Inc, pg 783
Audio-Video Corp, pg 795
Colortone Audio Visual, pg 832
Custom Media Environments, pg 841
Design Audio Visual Inc, pg 845
General Audio-Visual Inc (GAVI), pg 876
Magnaplan Corp, pg 928
Markertek Video Supply, pg 931
Presentation Products Inc, pg 981
Stampede Presentation Products Inc, pg 1023

OHIO

Tri-State Audio Visual Co, pg 1044
Tri-State Visual Products, pg 1044

PENNSYLVANIA

Advanced AV, pg 777
J E Foss Co, pg 871
Grise Audio Visual Center Inc, pg 882
Wespen Audio Visual Co, pg 1063

RHODE ISLAND

Shanix Inc, pg 1008

TENNESSEE

Durrell LLC, pg 854
Spring Arbor Distributors, pg 1022
Technical Support Systems LLC, pg 1034

TEXAS

Audio Visual Technologies Group, pg 796
AVES Audio Visual Systems Inc, pg 798
Data Display Audio Visual Co LP, pg 843
Data Projections Inc, pg 843
Lubbock Audio Visual Inc, pg 925
Media Management LLC, pg 937
Tarpley Media Systems, pg 1032

VIRGINIA

Avitecture Inc, pg 799
Communications Specialists Inc, pg 833
Design & Production Inc, pg 845
Intellidyne LLC, pg 899
Lee Hartman & Sons Inc, pg 918

WISCONSIN

Audio Visual of Milwaukee Inc, pg 795
Full Compass Systems, pg 874
Safe Harbor Computers, pg 1001

PUERTO RICO

Audio Visual Concepts Inc, pg 795

ALBERTA

Infosat Communications Inc, pg 898
Matrix Video Communications Corp (MVCC), pg 934
SMART Technologies Inc, pg 1013

BRITISH COLUMBIA

Commercial Electronics Ltd, pg 832

MANITOBA

Inland Audio Visual Ltd, pg 898

ONTARIO

Cinema Stage Inc, pg 827
Westbury National Show Systems Ltd, pg 1064

Electronic Chalkboard Manufacturers

ARIZONA

eInstruction Corp, pg 858

CALIFORNIA

Beta Electronics Inc, pg 806

GEORGIA

PolyVision Corporation, pg 978

ILLINOIS

Quartet Manufacturing Co, pg 989

NEW JERSEY

Tally Display Corp, pg 1031

NEW YORK

TecNec Distributing, pg 1035

OREGON

PLUS Corp of America, pg 977

ALBERTA

SMART Technologies Inc, pg 1013

Electronic Chalkboard Rentals

ARIZONA

Merestone, pg 938
Ultimate Presentation Systems Inc, pg 1047

ARKANSAS

White Diamond Productions, pg 1065

CALIFORNIA

Adolph Gasser Inc, pg 776
Alliant Event Services, pg 781
Ametron Audio/Video, pg 785
Lynch Communications, pg 926
VER-Video Equipment Rentals, pg 1053
Video Resources Inc, pg 1056

CONNECTICUT

A/V Davey, pg 797

FLORIDA

AVI-SPL, pg 798
Pro Stage Inc, pg 983

GEORGIA

ON Event Services, pg 963
Stage Front Presentation Systems, pg 1022

ILLINOIS

Allen Visual Systems Inc, pg 781

MASSACHUSETTS

Preston Productions Inc, pg 981

NEW JERSEY

Wired 4 Sound Inc, pg 1068

NEW YORK

Colortone Audio Visual, pg 832
Magnaplan Corp, pg 928

NORTH CAROLINA

A&V Company, pg 772

PENNSYLVANIA

Production Solutions Inc, pg 985

AUDIO/VISUAL

Electronic Chalkboard Rentals (continued)

TENNESSEE

Technical Support Systems LLC, pg 1034

VIRGINIA

Lee Hartman & Sons Inc, pg 918

WISCONSIN

Full Compass Systems, pg 874

MANITOBA

Inland Audio Visual Ltd, pg 898

ONTARIO

Westbury National Show Systems Ltd, pg 1064

Electronic Chalkboard Repairs

CALIFORNIA

Ametron Audio/Video, pg 785
McAlister Electronics, pg 935

GEORGIA

Stage Front Presentation Systems, pg 1022

ILLINOIS

Allen Visual Systems Inc, pg 781

KENTUCKY

NOR-COM Inc, pg 958

MAINE

Headlight Audio Visual Inc, pg 887

MICHIGAN

TeL Systems, pg 1035

MISSOURI

Schiller's Audio-Visual, pg 1004

OHIO

Aztec Video Productions, pg 801
ITA Audio Visual Solutions, pg 902

TENNESSEE

Technical Support Systems LLC, pg 1034

TEXAS

Audio Visual Technologies Group, pg 796
Tarpley Media Systems, pg 1032

VIRGINIA

Avitecture Inc, pg 799

WISCONSIN

Full Compass Systems, pg 874

ALBERTA

Infosat Communications Inc, pg 898

MANITOBA

Inland Audio Visual Ltd, pg 898

Enlargement—Transparencies

ALABAMA

Media Visions Inc, pg 937

ARIZONA

Image Craft LLC, pg 894
Merestone, pg 938

CALIFORNIA

Action Photo Service Inc, pg 775
Bay Photo Lab, pg 803
Coloredge, pg 832
Lynch Communications, pg 926
QRS Software Services, pg 988

COLORADO

Stanco Sales LLC, pg 1023

CONNECTICUT

Broadcast Video Productions LLC, pg 813
New London Media, pg 956

GEORGIA

Imagers, pg 896
Staging Directions Inc, pg 1023

ILLINOIS

Gamma Imaging, pg 875
Helix Camera & Video, pg 887
JMC Photo & Digital Services Inc, pg 905
Southern Illinois University, pg 1019

IOWA

American Color Imaging (ACI), pg 784
The Production House, pg 984

KENTUCKY

Kinetic Corp, pg 911

LOUISIANA

Louisiana State University Health Sciences Center - Shreveport, pg 925
Primary Color Laboratory Inc, pg 982

MASSACHUSETTS

Colortek of Boston, pg 832
DGI-Invisuals LLC, pg 846

MICHIGAN

K&R's Recording Studios Inc, pg 908
Michigan Office Solutions, pg 941
Tectonics Industries Inc, pg 1035
Tri-Color, pg 1044

MINNESOTA

Jamieson & Associates Inc, pg 904
Thomas Reprographics, pg 1039

MISSISSIPPI

Jasper Ewing & Sons Inc, pg 864

MISSOURI

Allied Photo Color Co, pg 781
Visionworks Design Services Inc, pg 1059

NEW YORK

C2 Imaging LLC, pg 841
Duggal Visual Solutions, pg 853
Eastco Multimedia Solutions Inc, pg 856
Greyfalcon House, pg 882
Ken Lieberman Labs Inc, pg 920
Modernage Photographic Services Inc, pg 944
MRG Productions Inc, pg 948
Neptune Photo Inc, pg 954
Zelman Studios Ltd, pg 1073

NORTH CAROLINA

Image Associates Inc, pg 894

OHIO

Aztec Video Productions, pg 801
Thread Marketing Group, pg 1039
Vista Color Imaging Inc, pg 1059

PENNSYLVANIA

Berry & Homer, pg 805
Fusion Brand Experiences, pg 874

RHODE ISLAND

A&M Productions, pg 771

TENNESSEE

Stage Post, pg 1022
WKPT-TV, pg 1068

TEXAS

City Color, pg 828
IntegraColor, pg 899

UTAH

Ferrari Color®, pg 866

VIRGINIA

Blair Inc, pg 809

WISCONSIN

USAV Group Inc, pg 1050

BRITISH COLUMBIA

Triad Communications Ltd, pg 1044

Filmstrip Duplication, *see* Duplication—Filmstrips

Filmstrip Printing, *see* Processing & Printing—Filmstrips

Filmstrip Printing, *see* Volume Printing—Filmstrips

Filmstrip Processing & Printing, *see* Processing & Printing—Filmstrips

Filmstrip Projector, Viewer & Equipment Distributors

ALABAMA

Curtis Company, pg 841
Media Visions Inc, pg 937

ARIZONA

Arizona Cine Equipment, pg 789
Professional Marketing Services Inc, pg 985
Troxell Communications Inc, pg 1045

ARKANSAS

White Diamond Productions, pg 1065

CALIFORNIA

Ametron Audio/Video, pg 785
California Tape Products Inc, pg 817
Christy's Editorial, pg 826
Gluskin's Custom Audio Video, pg 879
Instructional Materials & Equipment Distributors (I-Med), pg 899
Media Fabricators Inc, pg 936
Related Visual Inc, pg 994

COLORADO

National Teaching Aids Inc, pg 953
Stanco Sales LLC, pg 1023

CONNECTICUT

Concord Communications, pg 835
HB Communications Inc, pg 886
MAVCO, pg 934
Rockwell Communications Inc, pg 998
USI Inc, pg 1051

FLORIDA

Gulf Coast Audio Visual Producers Inc, pg 883
Hi-Tech Import Export Corp, pg 888
Photomart Cine-Video Inc, pg 975
Pro Stage Inc, pg 983
Sight & Sound Productions, pg 1010
Spire Audio Visual Co Inc, pg 1021
Tallahassee Audio Visual, pg 1031

GEORGIA

Audio Visual Resources Inc, pg 795
Stage Front Presentation Systems, pg 1022
Technical Innovation, pg 1033
Visioneering International Inc, pg 1058

HAWAII

The Audio Visual Co (AVCO), pg 795

ILLINOIS

Allen Visual Systems Inc, pg 781
Central Audio-Visual Equipment Inc, pg 823
Major Reproductions Equipment Co, pg 929

INDIANA

Victoria Supply Inc/Topbulb.com, pg 1054

IOWA

ECS Inc, pg 856

KENTUCKY

NOR-COM Inc, pg 958

LOUISIANA

Intermedia Technologies, pg 900

MARYLAND

Cardinal Sound & Video, pg 820
Visual Aids Electronics Corp, pg 1059

MASSACHUSETTS

Lineco, pg 922
University Products Inc, pg 1050

MICHIGAN

City Events Group, pg 828
Michigan Office Solutions, pg 941

MISSISSIPPI

Bowie Audio Visual Enterprises Inc, pg 811

MISSOURI

Communitronics Corp, pg 833
Conference Technologies Inc, pg 835
Image Technologies Corp, pg 895
Schiller's Audio-Visual, pg 1004
Swank Audio Visuals, pg 1029

NEW JERSEY

Audio Visual Associates, pg 795
Audio Visual Dynamics®, pg 795
AV Bluebook, pg 797
Hamilton Buhl, pg 884
National Audio-Visual Supply, pg 952
SYMCO Inc, pg 1030
Turner Engineering Inc, pg 1046
VCom International Multimedia Corp, pg 1052
Video Corporation of America (VCA), pg 1055
Wired 4 Sound Inc, pg 1068
York Telecom, pg 1072

NEW YORK

Audio-Video Corp, pg 795
AV Workshop, pg 797
Communication Corner Inc, pg 832
Gaylord Brothers, pg 876
Indigo Productions, pg 897
Langie Audio Visual Systems, pg 915
Long Island Video Enterprises Live Inc, pg 924
Magnaplan Corp, pg 928
Markertek Video Supply, pg 931
Neptune Photo Inc, pg 954
Ray Supply Inc, pg 992
Visual Technologies Corp, pg 1060
Willoughby's Imaging Center, pg 1067

NORTH CAROLINA

Camcor Inc, pg 818

OHIO

Audio Visual Media, pg 795
ITA Audio Visual Solutions, pg 902
Smithall Electronics Inc, pg 1014
Tri-State Visual Products, pg 1044

PENNSYLVANIA

Advanced AV, pg 777
Audio Visions Inc, pg 795
Audio Visual Communications Inc, pg 795
Bernie's Photo Center, pg 805
Brodart Co, pg 813
J E Foss Co, pg 871
Grise Audio Visual Center Inc, pg 882
Visual Sound Inc, pg 1059
Wespen Audio Visual Co, pg 1063

RHODE ISLAND

Custom Computer Specialists Inc, pg 841

TENNESSEE

Memphis Communications Corp, pg 938
Tennessee Visual Service Co, pg 1037

TEXAS

Astro Audio Visual, pg 792
Audio Visual Technologies Group, pg 796
J&S Audio Visual Inc, pg 904
Lubbock Audio Visual Inc, pg 925
Quality Audio Visual Service Inc, pg 988

VIRGINIA

Communications Specialists Inc, pg 833
Filmdex Inc, pg 867
Lee Hartman & Sons Inc, pg 918
Metropolitan Audio Visual Co LLC, pg 940
The Whitlock Group, pg 1065

WASHINGTON

Inland Audio Visual Co, pg 898

WISCONSIN

Audio Visual of Milwaukee Inc, pg 795
Camera Corner Connecting Point, pg 818
Demco Inc, pg 845
School Specialty Inc, pg 1004

ALBERTA

McBain Audio Visual Ltd, pg 935
Sharp's Audio-Visual Ltd, pg 1008

MANITOBA

Evolution Presentation Technologies, pg 863
Inland Audio Visual Ltd, pg 898

ONTARIO

Carr McLean Ltd, pg 820
Edcom Multimedia Products, pg 856
Nationwide Audio Visual Co, pg 953
Premier A/V Sales Ltd, pg 980

QUEBEC

Concept Audio-Visual, pg 834

Filmstrip Projector, Viewer & Equipment Manufacturers

CALIFORNIA

Auton Motorized Systems, pg 797

COLORADO

National Teaching Aids Inc, pg 953

INDIANA

Star Case Manufacturing Co Inc, pg 1023

NEW YORK

General Audio-Visual Inc (GAVI), pg 876
TecNec Distributing, pg 1035

Filmstrip Projector, Viewer & Equipment Rentals

ALABAMA

Media Visions Inc, pg 937

ARIZONA

Arizona Cine Equipment, pg 789
Merestone, pg 938
Metropolitan Audio-Visual Inc, pg 940
Video Media Productions (VMP), pg 1055

ARKANSAS

White Diamond Productions, pg 1065

CALIFORNIA

Ametron Audio/Video, pg 785
Artichoke Productions, pg 791
Gluskin's Custom Audio Video, pg 879
Instructional Materials & Equipment Distributors (I-Med), pg 899
Lynch Communications, pg 926
McCune Audio-Video-Lighting, pg 935
Media Fabricators Inc, pg 936
Munday & Collins AV, pg 950
University of Southern California, pg 1050
VER-Video Equipment Rentals, pg 1053

COLORADO

The Cinema Lab, pg 827
Multimedia Audio Visual Inc, pg 950

CONNECTICUT

A/V Davey, pg 797
Rockwell Communications Inc, pg 998

FLORIDA

Gulf Coast Audio Visual Producers Inc, pg 883
Image Technical Services, pg 895
Jordan Klein Film & Video (JKFV), pg 906
Pro Stage Inc, pg 983
Sight & Sound Productions, pg 1010
Spire Audio Visual Co Inc, pg 1021
Tallahassee Audio Visual, pg 1031

GEORGIA

Audio Visual Resources Inc, pg 795
Dixie Theatre Service & Supply Co Inc, pg 849
ON Event Services, pg 963
Stage Front Presentation Systems, pg 1022
Staging Directions Inc, pg 1023

ILLINOIS

Allen Visual Systems Inc, pg 781
Audio Visual Services Corp, pg 796
Central Audio-Visual Equipment Inc, pg 823
Helix Camera & Video, pg 887
The Pepper Group, pg 972
PSAV® Presentation Services (Hotel Services Division), pg 987
RC Communications, pg 992

INDIANA

Advanced Media Integration, pg 777
Gary Camera & Digital, pg 875
OMNI Productions, pg 962

KENTUCKY

Audio Visual Techniques Inc, pg 796

MARYLAND

dbF a Media Company, pg 844
Nelson White Systems Inc, pg 954

MASSACHUSETTS

massAV, pg 933

MICHIGAN

City Events Group, pg 828

MINNESOTA

AVI Systems, pg 799

MISSISSIPPI

Bowie Audio Visual Enterprises Inc, pg 811
Jasper Ewing & Sons Inc, pg 864

MISSOURI

Communitronics Corp, pg 833
Show-Me Audio-Visual, pg 1009
Swank Audio Visuals, pg 1029

NEW JERSEY

Audio Visual Dynamics®, pg 795
International Audio Visual Inc, pg 900

NEW YORK

Ace Video, pg 774
AV Workshop, pg 797
CMI Communications, pg 830
Communication Corner Inc, pg 832
Langie Audio Visual Systems, pg 915
Long Island Video Enterprises Live Inc, pg 924
Magnaplan Corp, pg 928
Neptune Photo Inc, pg 954
Ray Supply Inc, pg 992
Technisphere Corp, pg 1034
Visual Technologies Corp, pg 1060

AUDIO/VISUAL

Filmstrip Projector, Viewer & Equipment Rentals (continued)

NORTH CAROLINA

Camcor Inc, pg 818

OHIO

Audio Visual Media, pg 795
Aztec Video Productions, pg 801

PENNSYLVANIA

Advanced AV, pg 777
Audio Visions Inc, pg 795
Audio Visual Communications Inc, pg 795
Grise Audio Visual Center Inc, pg 882
Ott Film Rentals, pg 966
Production Solutions Inc, pg 985
Visual Sound Inc, pg 1059

TENNESSEE

Memphis Communications Corp, pg 938
Tennessee Visual Service Co, pg 1037

TEXAS

Astro Audio Visual, pg 792
Audio Visual Technologies Group, pg 796
J&S Audio Visual Inc, pg 904
Lubbock Audio Visual Inc, pg 925
Schoolhouse Audio Visual, pg 1004

VIRGINIA

Lee Hartman & Sons Inc, pg 918
Metropolitan Audio Visual Co LLC, pg 940
Projection Presentation Technology, pg 985
Rainbow Rentals, pg 991
The Whitlock Group, pg 1065

WASHINGTON

Inland Audio Visual Co, pg 898

WISCONSIN

Camera Corner Connecting Point, pg 818
Event Essentials, pg 863
School Specialty Inc, pg 1004

PUERTO RICO

Stage Crew Audiovisual Inc, pg 1022

ALBERTA

Global Television Station, pg 879
Sharp's Audio-Visual Ltd, pg 1008
Unique Communications Ltd, pg 1048

BRITISH COLUMBIA

Clark's Audio Visual Services Ltd, pg 829
Triad Communications Ltd, pg 1044

MANITOBA

Evolution Presentation Technologies, pg 863
Inland Audio Visual Ltd, pg 898

ONTARIO

Edcom Multimedia Products, pg 856

QUEBEC

Concept Audio-Visual, pg 834
Group PVP, pg 882

Filmstrip Projector, Viewer & Equipment Repairs

CALIFORNIA

Ametron Audio/Video, pg 785
Instructional Materials & Equipment Distributors (I-Med), pg 899
McAlister Electronics, pg 935
Lloyd F McKinney Associates Inc, pg 935
Pro Camera Repair, pg 982

CONNECTICUT

HB Communications Inc, pg 886
Rockwell Communications Inc, pg 998

FLORIDA

Spire Audio Visual Co Inc, pg 1021
Tallahassee Audio Visual, pg 1031

GEORGIA

Audio Visual Resources Inc, pg 795
Stage Front Presentation Systems, pg 1022
Technical Innovation, pg 1033

ILLINOIS

Allen Visual Systems Inc, pg 781
Central Audio-Visual Equipment Inc, pg 823

INDIANA

Gary Camera & Digital, pg 875

KENTUCKY

NOR-COM Inc, pg 958

MARYLAND

Strauss Photo Technical Service Inc, pg 1026

MICHIGAN

City Events Group, pg 828
TeL Systems, pg 1035

MINNESOTA

AVI Systems, pg 799

MISSISSIPPI

Bowie Audio Visual Enterprises Inc, pg 811

MISSOURI

Cintrex Audio Visual, pg 828
Communitronics Corp, pg 833
Schiller's Audio-Visual, pg 1004

NEW JERSEY

Audio Visual Associates, pg 795

NEW YORK

Colortone Audio Visual, pg 832
Langie Audio Visual Systems, pg 915
Magnaplan Corp, pg 928
Ray Supply Inc, pg 992
Visual Technologies Corp, pg 1060

NORTH CAROLINA

Camcor Inc, pg 818

OHIO

Audio Visual Media, pg 795
Aztec Video Productions, pg 801
Tri-State Audio Visual Co, pg 1044
Tri-State Visual Products, pg 1044

PENNSYLVANIA

Audio Visions Inc, pg 795
J E Foss Co, pg 871
Ott Film Rentals, pg 966
Wespen Audio Visual Co, pg 1063

RHODE ISLAND

Custom Computer Specialists Inc, pg 841

TENNESSEE

Memphis Communications Corp, pg 938
Tennessee Visual Service Co, pg 1037

TEXAS

Astro Audio Visual, pg 792
Audio Visual Technologies Group, pg 796
Lubbock Audio Visual Inc, pg 925
Padgitt's, pg 967
Quality Audio Visual Service Inc, pg 988
Schoolhouse Audio Visual, pg 1004

VIRGINIA

Boitnott Visual Communications Corp (BVC), pg 810
Lee Hartman & Sons Inc, pg 918
Metropolitan Audio Visual Co LLC, pg 940
The Whitlock Group, pg 1065

WASHINGTON

Inland Audio Visual Co, pg 898

WISCONSIN

Camera Corner Connecting Point, pg 818
School Specialty Inc, pg 1004

ALBERTA

Infosat Communications Inc, pg 898
Sharp's Audio-Visual Ltd, pg 1008

MANITOBA

Evolution Presentation Technologies, pg 863
Inland Audio Visual Ltd, pg 898

ONTARIO

Edcom Multimedia Products, pg 856
Premier A/V Sales Ltd, pg 980

Filmstrip Pulsing, *see* Pulsing—Filmstrip

Filmstrip Retouching, *see* Retouching—Filmstrips

Filmstrip to Slide Transfers, *see* Transfers—Filmstrip to Slide

Filmstrip Viewer, *see* Filmstrip Projector, Viewer & Equipment

Intercom System Distributors

ALABAMA

Curtis Company, pg 841
Media Visions Inc, pg 937

ARIZONA

Arizona Cine Equipment, pg 789
EAR Professional Audio/Video, pg 855
Metropolitan Audio-Visual Inc, pg 940
Projector SuperStore LLC, pg 986
Troxell Communications Inc, pg 1045

ARKANSAS

White Diamond Productions, pg 1065

CALIFORNIA

Advanced Systems Group LLC, pg 778
Ametron Audio/Video, pg 785
Associated Sound, pg 792
Audio Images Corp, pg 794
Clear-Com®, pg 829
Delicate Electronics Sales Inc, pg 845
Empire Wholesale Inc, pg 860
FXC Communications, pg 874
GMF Sound Inc, pg 879
JD Audio Visual Inc, pg 904
Location Sound Corp, pg 924
Lloyd F McKinney Associates Inc, pg 935
Media Fabricators Inc, pg 936
MediaPOINTE, pg 938
Orvac Electronics, pg 965
Southern California Sound Image Inc, pg 1019
SSL Industries Inc, pg 1022
TOA Electronics Inc, pg 1041
Tri-Ed, pg 1044
VMI Inc, pg 1060

COLORADO

Ceavco Audio/Visual Co, pg 822

CONNECTICUT

Concord Communications, pg 835
Connecticut Audio & Theatrical Supply, pg 835
HB Communications Inc, pg 886
Sennheiser Electronic Corp, pg 1006

FLORIDA

Access Media Group, pg 773
Allstar Audio Systems Inc, pg 782
BAI Distributors Inc, pg 801

Intercom System Manufacturers

AUDIO/VISUAL

Intercom System Manufacturers (continued)

NEW YORK

Goddard Design Co, pg 880
Lee Dan® Communications Inc, pg 918
Protech Audio Corp, pg 986
TecNec Distributing, pg 1035
Television Equipment Associates Inc (TEA), pg 1036

NORTH CAROLINA

Strategic Connections, pg 1026

OHIO

Telos Systems, pg 1037

SOUTH CAROLINA

DaviSound, pg 843
Paso Sound Products Inc, pg 969

TEXAS

Setcom Corp™, pg 1007

VIRGINIA

Old Dominion Broadcasting, pg 961

WASHINGTON

Aiphone Corp, pg 779

WEST VIRGINIA

United Sound & Electronics, pg 1048

Intercom System Rentals

ALABAMA

Media Visions Inc, pg 937

ARIZONA

Arizona Cine Equipment, pg 789
Glendale Media Center, pg 878
Merestone, pg 938
Metropolitan Audio-Visual Inc, pg 940
Video Media Productions (VMP), pg 1055

ARKANSAS

White Diamond Productions, pg 1065

CALIFORNIA

AGF Media Services, pg 778
Alliant Event Services, pg 781
Ametron Audio/Video, pg 785
Associated Sound, pg 792
AV Guys, pg 797
Express Media Inc, pg 864
GMF Sound Inc, pg 879
Golden Gate Studios, pg 880
JD Audio Visual Inc, pg 904
Location Sound Corp, pg 924
Lynch Communications, pg 926
McCune Audio-Video-Lighting, pg 935
Media Fabricators Inc, pg 936
MSI Productions, pg 949
Munday & Collins AV, pg 950
PSAV® Presentation Services, pg 986
Randall Schiller Productions, pg 1004
Slate Media Group, pg 1013
Video Resources Inc, pg 1056
Videorama Industries LLC, pg 1057
VMI Inc, pg 1060
Voice & Video Rentals, pg 1060
Warner Bros Entertainment Inc, pg 1062
Warner Bros Production Sound & Video Services, pg 1062

COLORADO

Ceavco Audio/Visual Co, pg 822
Daylight Productions & Rentals, pg 844
Multimedia Audio Visual Inc, pg 950

CONNECTICUT

Connecticut Audio & Theatrical Supply, pg 835

DELAWARE

Ken-Del Productions Inc, pg 909
Showorks Audio Visual Inc, pg 1010

FLORIDA

Access Media Group, pg 773
Allstar Audio Systems Inc, pg 782
Jordan Klein Film & Video (JKFV), pg 906
Lighting Sales Connections, pg 920
Paradise Show & Design Inc, pg 969
Pro Stage Inc, pg 983
TAI Audio, pg 1031
Universal Studios Florida® Production Group, pg 1049

GEORGIA

Lighting & Production Equipment Inc, pg 920
Stage Front Presentation Systems, pg 1022
Staging Directions Inc, pg 1023

HAWAII

ATTCO Inc, pg 793
Sight & Sound Studios, pg 1010

ILLINOIS

Allen Visual Systems Inc, pg 781
Audio Visual Services Corp, pg 796
AV Chicago Inc, pg 797
Backstar Creative Media Inc, pg 801
Beatty TeleVisual Productions, pg 804
Chicago Spotlight Inc, pg 825
Creative Technology, pg 838
Helix Camera & Video, pg 887
PSAV® Presentation Services (Hotel Services Division), pg 987
RC Communications, pg 992
Show Department Inc, pg 1009

INDIANA

Gary Camera & Digital, pg 875

IOWA

Central Lighting & Equipment Inc (CLE), pg 823
ECS Inc, pg 856

LOUISIANA

Pace Systems, pg 966

MARYLAND

CPR MultiMedia Solutions, pg 837
Event Tech, pg 863
Hargrove Inc, pg 885

MASSACHUSETTS

Advanced Lighting & Production Services Inc (ALPS), pg 777
AVFX Inc, pg 798
Capron Lighting & Sound Co Inc, pg 819
massAV, pg 933
Preston Productions Inc, pg 981

MICHIGAN

Olson Anderson Co, pg 786
City Events Group, pg 828
On Stage Visuals, pg 963

MINNESOTA

Advanced Audio-Visual Inc, pg 777
AVI Systems, pg 799

MISSOURI

A to Z Theatrical Supply & Service, pg 771
Production Support Services Inc, pg 985
Show-Me Audio-Visual, pg 1009
Southwest Audio-Visual Inc, pg 1019
Swank Audio Visuals, pg 1029
Switch, pg 1030

NEBRASKA

Dog & Pony Productions Inc, pg 850

NEW HAMPSHIRE

APS Lighting-Sound-AV, pg 789

NEW JERSEY

Audio Visual Dynamics®, pg 795
Earl Girls Inc, pg 855
Giant Audio Visual Inc, pg 878
Moe AV LLC, pg 945
PLS Staging, pg 977
Starlite Productions, pg 1024
Video Corporation of America (VCA), pg 1055
Wired 4 Sound Inc, pg 1068

NEW YORK

AV Workshop, pg 797
Big Foot Productions Inc, pg 807
CMI Communications, pg 830
Communication Corner Inc, pg 832
CP Communications, pg 837
Creative Stage Lighting Co Inc, pg 838
Custom Media Environments, pg 841
Langie Audio Visual Systems, pg 915
Long Island Video Enterprises Live Inc, pg 924
Northern Lights, pg 959
Production Radio Rentals Inc, pg 984
Specialized Audio-Visual Inc, pg 1020
Syracuse Scenery & Stage Lighting Co Inc, pg 1031
Technisphere Corp, pg 1034
Theatrical Services & Supplies Inc, pg 1038
WorldStage, pg 1070

NORTH CAROLINA

A&V Company, pg 772
Camcor Inc, pg 818
Special Event Services, pg 1020
Strategic Connections, pg 1026
Visual Aids Electronics of North Carolina Inc, pg 1059

NORTH DAKOTA

Media Productions, pg 937

OHIO

Aztec Video Productions, pg 801
Bartha, pg 803
Hughie's Event Production Services, pg 892
Lyon Video Inc, pg 927
Mills James Productions, pg 943
Smithall Electronics Inc, pg 1014

OKLAHOMA

PDC Productions, pg 970

OREGON

Picture This Production Services, pg 975

PENNSYLVANIA

JPL, pg 906
Production Solutions Inc, pg 985
Visual Sound Inc, pg 1059

SOUTH CAROLINA

Sound & Images Inc, pg 1016

TENNESSEE

Memphis Communications Corp, pg 938
Technical Support Systems LLC, pg 1034

TEXAS

Alford Media Services, pg 780
GEAR Cameras & Lighting, pg 876
J&S Audio Visual Inc, pg 904
Lubbock Audio Visual Inc, pg 925

VERMONT

Parlato Productions, pg 969

VIRGINIA

American AV, pg 783
Boitnott Visual Communications Corp (BVC), pg 810
Lee Hartman & Sons Inc, pg 918

WASHINGTON

D A Sound, pg 842
Northern Lights & Pro Audio, pg 959
Pacific Northwest Theatre Associates Inc (PNTA), pg 967

WEST VIRGINIA

United Sound & Electronics, pg 1048

WISCONSIN

Event Essentials, pg 863

PUERTO RICO

Stage Crew Audiovisual Inc, pg 1022

ALBERTA

Allstar Show Industries Inc, pg 782
Global Television Station, pg 879
Unique Communications Ltd, pg 1048

BRITISH COLUMBIA

ProVision Video Sales & Rentals Inc, pg 986

ONTARIO

Edcom Multimedia Products, pg 856
HD Source, pg 886
JIB Shots Equipment Inc, pg 905
SIM Digital, pg 1011
Westbury National Show Systems Ltd, pg 1064

QUEBEC

Audio Visual Dynamics Ltd, pg 795
Concept Audio-Visual, pg 834

Intercom System Repairs

CALIFORNIA

Ametron Audio/Video, pg 785
GMF Sound Inc, pg 879
HM Electronics Inc (HME), pg 889
McAlister Electronics, pg 935
Lloyd F McKinney Associates Inc, pg 935
SSL Industries Inc, pg 1022
Technical Services, pg 1034
TOA Electronics Inc, pg 1041

COLORADO

Ceavco Audio/Visual Co, pg 822

CONNECTICUT

HB Communications Inc, pg 886
Sennheiser Electronic Corp, pg 1006

FLORIDA

Stereo Sales Inc, pg 1024
TAI Audio, pg 1031

GEORGIA

Lighting & Production Equipment Inc, pg 920
Stage Front Presentation Systems, pg 1022
Technical Innovation, pg 1033

ILLINOIS

Allen Visual Systems Inc, pg 781
Beatty TeleVisual Productions, pg 804
Chicago Spotlight Inc, pg 825

INDIANA

Gary Camera & Digital, pg 875

IOWA

ECS Inc, pg 856

KENTUCKY

Axxis Inc, pg 800
NOR-COM Inc, pg 958

MARYLAND

Cardinal Sound & Video, pg 820

MASSACHUSETTS

Capron Lighting & Sound Co Inc, pg 819

MICHIGAN

Olson Anderson Co, pg 786
City Events Group, pg 828
On Stage Visuals, pg 963
TeL Systems, pg 1035

MINNESOTA

AVI Systems, pg 799

MISSOURI

A to Z Theatrical Supply & Service, pg 771
Cintrex Audio Visual, pg 828

NEW JERSEY

Earl Girls Inc, pg 855
Starlite Productions, pg 1024

NEW YORK

Custom Media Environments, pg 841
Langie Audio Visual Systems, pg 915
Northern Lights, pg 959

NORTH CAROLINA

Camcor Inc, pg 818
Strategic Connections, pg 1026

OHIO

Aztec Video Productions, pg 801
Copp Integrated Systems, pg 836
ITA Audio Visual Solutions, pg 902
Smithall Electronics Inc, pg 1014
Tri-State Audio Visual Co, pg 1044

PENNSYLVANIA

Audio Visions Inc, pg 795
Vistacom Inc, pg 1059

SOUTH CAROLINA

DaviSound, pg 843

TENNESSEE

Belew Enterprises, pg 804
Memphis Communications Corp, pg 938
Technical Support Systems LLC, pg 1034

TEXAS

Crossroads Audio Inc, pg 840
Lubbock Audio Visual Inc, pg 925
Padgitt's, pg 967
Schoolhouse Audio Visual, pg 1004
Southwest Sound & Electronics Inc, pg 1019

VIRGINIA

Avitecture Inc, pg 799
Boitnott Visual Communications Corp (BVC), pg 810
Hoppmann Audio Visual, pg 891
Lee Hartman & Sons Inc, pg 918
The Whitlock Group, pg 1065

WASHINGTON

Aiphone Corp, pg 779
Northern Lights & Pro Audio, pg 959
Pacific Northwest Theatre Associates Inc (PNTA), pg 967

WEST VIRGINIA

United Sound & Electronics, pg 1048

WISCONSIN

Full Compass Systems, pg 874

ALBERTA

Infosat Communications Inc, pg 898
Unique Communications Ltd, pg 1048

MANITOBA

Inland Audio Visual Ltd, pg 898

ONTARIO

Edcom Multimedia Products, pg 856
Westbury National Show Systems Ltd, pg 1064

Laminating Equipment, *see* Dry Mounting & Laminating Equipment & Supply

Laser Pointer & Laser Projection Equipment Distributors

ALABAMA

Curtis Company, pg 841
Media Visions Inc, pg 937

ARIZONA

Arizona Cine Equipment, pg 789
Metropolitan Audio-Visual Inc, pg 940
Professional Marketing Services Inc, pg 985
Troxell Communications Inc, pg 1045

ARKANSAS

Jay S Stanley & Associates Inc, pg 1023
White Diamond Productions, pg 1065

CALIFORNIA

Adolph Gasser Inc, pg 776
Ametron Audio/Video, pg 785
Audio/Video Supply Inc, pg 795
Beta Electronics Inc, pg 806
California Tape Products Inc, pg 817
Christy's Editorial, pg 826
Cibola Systems, pg 826
Educational Technology Services (ETS), pg 857
FXC Communications, pg 874
Gluskin's Custom Audio Video, pg 879
Hooper Camera & Imaging, pg 891
Impact Group, pg 897
Instructional Materials & Equipment Distributors (I-Med), pg 899
Jaguar Distribution Corp, pg 903
Jameco Electronics, pg 903
JD Audio Visual Inc, pg 904
Laser Magic Productions, pg 916
Laserium, pg 916
Lloyd F McKinney Associates Inc, pg 935
Media Fabricators Inc, pg 936
MediaPOINTE, pg 938
POP TV, pg 978
Precision Projection Systems Inc, pg 980
Related Visual Inc, pg 994
Sound Service Co, pg 1017
Stanislaus Audio Video Inc, pg 1023
Towards 2000 Inc, pg 1043
Tri-Ed, pg 1044
VMI Inc, pg 1060

COLORADO

Daylight Productions & Rentals, pg 844
Spectrum Audio Visual Services, pg 1020

CONNECTICUT

Everett Hall Associates Inc, pg 863
HB Communications Inc, pg 886
MAVCO, pg 934
USI Inc, pg 1051

FLORIDA

Audio Visual Imagineering Inc, pg 795
AVI-SPL, pg 798
Digital Video Systems Inc, pg 848
General Projection Systems Inc, pg 877
Gulf Coast Audio Visual Producers Inc, pg 883
Hi-Tech Import Export Corp, pg 888
Industrial Strength Inc, pg 897
Photomart Cine-Video Inc, pg 975
Photosound of Orlando Inc, pg 975
Pro Stage Inc, pg 983
Recording Media & Equipment Inc (RM&E), pg 993
Sight & Sound Productions, pg 1010
Spire Audio Visual Co Inc, pg 1021
Tallahassee Audio Visual, pg 1031
Techni-Lux Inc, pg 1033

GEORGIA

Convergent Media Systems, pg 836
Stage Front Presentation Systems, pg 1022
Visioneering International Inc, pg 1058

HAWAII

The Audio Visual Co (AVCO), pg 795

ILLINOIS

Allen Visual Systems Inc, pg 781
Central Audio-Visual Equipment Inc, pg 823
RC Communications, pg 992
Sound Vision Inc, pg 1018

INDIANA

Da-Lite, pg 842
Sensory Technologies LLC, pg 1006

IOWA

ECS Inc, pg 856

AUDIO/VISUAL

Laser Pointer & Laser Projection Equipment Distributors (continued)

KANSAS

Smith Audio-Visual Inc, pg 1014

KENTUCKY

Audio Visual Techniques Inc, pg 796
Axxis Inc, pg 800
Barney Miller's Inc, pg 943
NOR-COM Inc, pg 958
Theatre Effects, pg 1038

LOUISIANA

Intermedia Technologies, pg 900

MAINE

Headlight Audio Visual Inc, pg 887

MARYLAND

Advance Audiovisual Presentation Ltd, pg 777
Cardinal Sound & Video, pg 820
Nelson White Systems Inc, pg 954
RTZ Audio Visual, pg 1000
Visual Aids Electronics Corp, pg 1059

MASSACHUSETTS

Limelight Productions Inc, pg 921
Lineco, pg 922

MICHIGAN

Olson Anderson Co, pg 786
City Events Group, pg 828
Michigan Office Solutions, pg 941
TeL Systems, pg 1035

MINNESOTA

Advanced Audio-Visual Inc, pg 777
AVI Systems, pg 799
Tierney Brothers Inc, pg 1040

MISSISSIPPI

Bowie Audio Visual Enterprises Inc, pg 811
Jasper Ewing & Sons Inc, pg 864

MISSOURI

Communitronics Corp, pg 833
Conference Technologies Inc, pg 835
Image Technologies Corp, pg 895
Modern Communications Inc, pg 944
Schiller's Audio-Visual, pg 1004
Swank Audio Visuals, pg 1029

NEVADA

MeshTel-Intelite, pg 939

NEW JERSEY

A-V Services Inc, pg 771
Audio Visual Associates, pg 795
Audio Visual Dynamics®, pg 795
AV Bluebook, pg 797
Earl Girls Inc, pg 855
Hamilton Buhl, pg 884
National Audio-Visual Supply, pg 952
Starlite Productions, pg 1024
Total Video Products Inc, pg 1042
VCom International Multimedia Corp, pg 1052
Video Corporation of America (VCA), pg 1055
Wired 4 Sound Inc, pg 1068
York Telecom, pg 1072

NEW YORK

American Video Inc, pg 785
Audio-Video Corp, pg 795
AV Workshop, pg 797
Bulbtronics Inc, pg 815
Communication Corner Inc, pg 832
Custom Media Environments, pg 841
Design Audio Visual Inc, pg 845
DSan Corp, pg 852
Edmund Scientific, pg 857
Gaylord Brothers, pg 876
Indigo Productions, pg 897
KVL Audio Visual Services Inc, pg 914
Long Island Video Enterprises Live Inc, pg 924
Magnaplan Corp, pg 928
Markertek Video Supply, pg 931
Neptune Photo Inc, pg 954
Northern Lights, pg 959
Presentation Products Inc, pg 981
SmartSource Computer & AV Rentals, pg 1014
Technisphere Corp, pg 1034
Theatrical Services & Supplies Inc, pg 1038
Willoughby's Imaging Center, pg 1067

NORTH CAROLINA

Camcor Inc, pg 818
Strategic Connections, pg 1026

OHIO

Copp Integrated Systems, pg 836
ITA Audio Visual Solutions, pg 902
Jimmy Rea Electronics Inc, pg 992
Tri-State Audio Visual Co, pg 1044
Tri-State Visual Products, pg 1044

PENNSYLVANIA

Advanced AV, pg 777
Audio Visions Inc, pg 795
Audio Visual Communications Inc, pg 795
Bernie's Photo Center, pg 805
J E Foss Co, pg 871
Garcia Marketing Inc, pg 875
Grise Audio Visual Center Inc, pg 882
The Lerro Corp, pg 919
Vistacom Inc, pg 1059
Visual Sound Inc, pg 1059

RHODE ISLAND

Custom Computer Specialists Inc, pg 841

TENNESSEE

Durrell LLC, pg 854
Lowrance Sound Co Inc, pg 925
Tennessee Visual Service Co, pg 1037

TEXAS

Astro Audio Visual, pg 792
Audio Visual Technologies Group, pg 796
AVES Audio Visual Systems Inc, pg 798
Data Display Audio Visual Co LP, pg 843
Data Projections Inc, pg 843
FitzCo Sound Inc, pg 869
Heffernan Audio Visual, pg 887
J&S Audio Visual Inc, pg 904
Laser Spectacles Inc, pg 916
Lubbock Audio Visual Inc, pg 925
Quality Audio Visual Service Inc, pg 988
Schoolhouse Audio Visual, pg 1004
Southwest Sound & Electronics Inc, pg 1019
Stage Directions, pg 1022

UTAH

Webb Audio Visual Communication, pg 1063

VIRGINIA

Boitnott Visual Communications Corp (BVC), pg 810
Communications Specialists Inc, pg 833
Hoppmann Audio Visual, pg 891
Intellidyne LLC, pg 899
Lee Hartman & Sons Inc, pg 918
Metropolitan Audio Visual Co LLC, pg 940
The Whitlock Group, pg 1065

WISCONSIN

Audio Visual of Milwaukee Inc, pg 795
Camera Corner Connecting Point, pg 818
Full Compass Systems, pg 874
Pro Studio Supply, pg 983

PUERTO RICO

Bonnin Electronics Inc, pg 810

ALBERTA

Infosat Communications Inc, pg 898
McBain Audio Visual Ltd, pg 935
Sharp's Audio-Visual Ltd, pg 1008
Unique Communications Ltd, pg 1048

BRITISH COLUMBIA

Commercial Electronics Ltd, pg 832

MANITOBA

Inland Audio Visual Ltd, pg 898

ONTARIO

Edcom Multimedia Products, pg 856
Nationwide Audio Visual Co, pg 953
Premier A/V Sales Ltd, pg 980

QUEBEC

Concept Audio-Visual, pg 834
Panavideo Inc, pg 968

Laser Pointer & Laser Projection Equipment Manufacturers

CALIFORNIA

Alpec®, pg 782
Beta Electronics Inc, pg 806
Laser Magic Productions, pg 916
Laserium, pg 916
Precision Projection Systems Inc, pg 980

FLORIDA

Audio Visual Imagineering Inc, pg 795
Pangolin Laser Systems Inc, pg 968
Vutec Corp, Video Products Division, pg 1061

ILLINOIS

ACCO Brands Corp, pg 773

INDIANA

Da-Lite, pg 842

NEVADA

MeshTel-Intelite, pg 939

NEW HAMPSHIRE

ProPhotonix Ltd, pg 986

NEW JERSEY

National Audio-Visual Supply, pg 952

NEW YORK

DSan Corp, pg 852
TecNec Distributing, pg 1035

OREGON

Lumalaser, pg 926
PLUS Corp of America, pg 977

TEXAS

Laser Spectacles Inc, pg 916

WASHINGTON

Laser Fantasy/HECK Industries/Photon Manufacturing, pg 916

Laser Pointer & Laser Projection Equipment Rentals

ALABAMA

Audio-Video Resources Inc, pg 795
Media Visions Inc, pg 937

ARIZONA

Arizona Cine Equipment, pg 789
Merestone, pg 938
Metropolitan Audio-Visual Inc, pg 940
Video Media Productions (VMP), pg 1055
Video West Inc, pg 1056

ARKANSAS

White Diamond Productions, pg 1065

CALIFORNIA

Adolph Gasser Inc, pg 776
AGF Media Services, pg 778
Alliant Event Services, pg 781
Ametron Audio/Video, pg 785
Automated Entertainment, pg 797
AV Guys, pg 797
Gluskin's Custom Audio Video, pg 879

Gold Standard Productions, pg 880
Impact Group, pg 897
JD Audio Visual Inc, pg 904
Laser Magic Productions, pg 916
Laserium, pg 916
Lynch Communications, pg 926
McCune Audio-Video-Lighting, pg 935
Media Fabricators Inc, pg 936
Munday & Collins AV, pg 950
Precision Projection Systems Inc, pg 980
PSAV® Presentation Services, pg 986
Sound Service Co, pg 1017
Stanislaus Audio Video Inc, pg 1023
VER-Video Equipment Rentals, pg 1053
Video Resources Inc, pg 1056
Voice & Video Rentals, pg 1060

COLORADO

Daylight Productions & Rentals, pg 844
Spectrum Audio Visual Services, pg 1020

CONNECTICUT

A/V Davey, pg 797
Everett Hall Associates Inc, pg 863

DELAWARE

Ken-Del Productions Inc, pg 909
Showorks Audio Visual Inc, pg 1010

FLORIDA

Audio Visual Imagineering Inc, pg 795
AVI-SPL, pg 798
Gulf Coast Audio Visual Producers Inc, pg 883
Image Technical Services, pg 895
Industrial Strength Inc, pg 897
Pro Stage Inc, pg 983
Sight & Sound Productions, pg 1010
Spire Audio Visual Co Inc, pg 1021

GEORGIA

Convergent Media Systems, pg 836
ON Event Services, pg 963
Stage Front Presentation Systems, pg 1022
Staging Directions Inc, pg 1023

HAWAII

ATTCO Inc, pg 793

ILLINOIS

Allen Visual Systems Inc, pg 781
AV Chicago Inc, pg 797
Backstar Creative Media Inc, pg 801
Beatty TeleVisual Productions, pg 804
Central Audio-Visual Equipment Inc, pg 823
The Pepper Group, pg 972

IOWA

ECS Inc, pg 856

KANSAS

Smith Audio-Visual Inc, pg 1014

KENTUCKY

Audio Visual Techniques Inc, pg 796

LOUISIANA

Pace Systems, pg 966

MAINE

Headlight Audio Visual Inc, pg 887

MARYLAND

Absolute Hollywood, pg 772
Advance Audiovisual Presentation Ltd, pg 777
Nelson White Systems Inc, pg 954
RTZ Audio Visual, pg 1000
Visual Aids Electronics Corp, pg 1059

MASSACHUSETTS

Capron Lighting & Sound Co Inc, pg 819
Limelight Productions Inc, pg 921
massAV, pg 933
Preston Productions Inc, pg 981

MICHIGAN

Olson Anderson Co, pg 786
City Events Group, pg 828

MINNESOTA

Advanced Audio-Visual Inc, pg 777
AVI Systems, pg 799

MISSISSIPPI

Bowie Audio Visual Enterprises Inc, pg 811

MISSOURI

Communitronics Corp, pg 833
Schiller's Audio-Visual, pg 1004
Show-Me Audio-Visual, pg 1009
Swank Audio Visuals, pg 1029

NEVADA

GES Audio Visual, pg 877

NEW JERSEY

Audio Visual Associates, pg 795
Audio Visual Dynamics®, pg 795
Earl Girls Inc, pg 855
Giant Audio Visual Inc, pg 878
Moe AV LLC, pg 945
PLS Staging, pg 977
Starlite Productions, pg 1024
Video Corporation of America (VCA), pg 1055
Wired 4 Sound Inc, pg 1068

NEW YORK

Ace Video, pg 774
American Video Inc, pg 785
AV Workshop, pg 797
CMI Communications, pg 830
Communication Corner Inc, pg 832
Custom Media Environments, pg 841
KVL Audio Visual Services Inc, pg 914
Long Island Video Enterprises Live Inc, pg 924
SmartSource Computer & AV Rentals, pg 1014
Technisphere Corp, pg 1034
Visual Word Systems Inc, pg 1060
WorldStage, pg 1070

NORTH CAROLINA

A&V Company, pg 772
AV Metro Inc, pg 797
Camcor Inc, pg 818
Special Event Services, pg 1020
Visual Aids Electronics of North Carolina Inc, pg 1059

NORTH DAKOTA

Media Productions, pg 937

OHIO

Aztec Video Productions, pg 801
Mills James Productions, pg 943

PENNSYLVANIA

Advanced AV, pg 777
Audio Visions Inc, pg 795
Audio Visual Communications Inc, pg 795
FirstGeneration Audio/Visual Services, pg 869
Grise Audio Visual Center Inc, pg 882
Production Solutions Inc, pg 985
Visual Sound Inc, pg 1059

SOUTH CAROLINA

Sound & Images Inc, pg 1016

TENNESSEE

Memphis Communications Corp, pg 938
Tennessee Visual Service Co, pg 1037

TEXAS

Alford Media Services, pg 780
Astro Audio Visual, pg 792
Audio Visual Technologies Group, pg 796
Data Display Audio Visual Co LP, pg 843
FitzCo Sound Inc, pg 869
J&S Audio Visual Inc, pg 904
Laser Spectacles Inc, pg 916
Lubbock Audio Visual Inc, pg 925
Padgitt's, pg 967
Quality Audio Visual Service Inc, pg 988
Schoolhouse Audio Visual, pg 1004
Stage Directions, pg 1022

UTAH

Webb Audio Visual Communication, pg 1063

VIRGINIA

American AV, pg 783
Boitnott Visual Communications Corp (BVC), pg 810
Lee Hartman & Sons Inc, pg 918
The Whitlock Group, pg 1065

WASHINGTON

Laser Fantasy/HECK Industries/Photon Manufacturing, pg 916

WISCONSIN

Audio Visual of Milwaukee Inc, pg 795
Camera Corner Connecting Point, pg 818
Event Essentials, pg 863

PUERTO RICO

Stage Crew Audiovisual Inc, pg 1022

ALBERTA

Evolution Presentation Technologies, pg 863
McBain Audio Visual Ltd, pg 935
Sharp's Audio-Visual Ltd, pg 1008
Unique Communications Ltd, pg 1048

BRITISH COLUMBIA

Clark's Audio Visual Services Ltd, pg 829
Commercial Electronics Ltd, pg 832

MANITOBA

Inland Audio Visual Ltd, pg 898

ONTARIO

Edcom Multimedia Products, pg 856
HD Source, pg 886

QUEBEC

Audio Visual Dynamics Ltd, pg 795
Concept Audio-Visual, pg 834
Panavideo Inc, pg 968

Laser Pointer & Laser Projection Equipment Repairs

CALIFORNIA

Ametron Audio/Video, pg 785
Beta Electronics Inc, pg 806
McAlister Electronics, pg 935
Lloyd F McKinney Associates Inc, pg 935
Towards 2000 Inc, pg 1043

CONNECTICUT

HB Communications Inc, pg 886

FLORIDA

Spire Audio Visual Co Inc, pg 1021

GEORGIA

Stage Front Presentation Systems, pg 1022

ILLINOIS

Allen Visual Systems Inc, pg 781
RC Communications, pg 992

IOWA

ECS Inc, pg 856

KENTUCKY

Axxis Inc, pg 800
NOR-COM Inc, pg 958

MARYLAND

RTZ Audio Visual, pg 1000
Visual Aids Electronics Corp, pg 1059

MICHIGAN

City Events Group, pg 828
TeL Systems, pg 1035

AUDIO/VISUAL

Laser Pointer & Laser Projection Equipment Repairs (continued)

MINNESOTA

AVI Systems, pg 799

MISSISSIPPI

Bowie Audio Visual Enterprises Inc, pg 811

MISSOURI

Communitronics Corp, pg 833

NEW JERSEY

Earl Girls Inc, pg 855

NEW YORK

Custom Media Environments, pg 841

NORTH CAROLINA

Camcor Inc, pg 818

OHIO

Aztec Video Productions, pg 801
ITA Audio Visual Solutions, pg 902

PENNSYLVANIA

Audio Visions Inc, pg 795

TENNESSEE

Memphis Communications Corp, pg 938

TEXAS

Audio Visual Technologies Group, pg 796
Lubbock Audio Visual Inc, pg 925
Schoolhouse Audio Visual, pg 1004

VIRGINIA

Boitnott Visual Communications Corp (BVC), pg 810
Hoppmann Audio Visual, pg 891
The Whitlock Group, pg 1065

WASHINGTON

Laser Fantasy/HECK Industries/Photon Manufacturing, pg 916

ALBERTA

Infosat Communications Inc, pg 898
Sharp's Audio-Visual Ltd, pg 1008

MANITOBA

Inland Audio Visual Ltd, pg 898

ONTARIO

Edcom Multimedia Products, pg 856

Lectern Distributors

ALABAMA

Curtis Company, pg 841
Media Visions Inc, pg 937

ARIZONA

Arizona Cine Equipment, pg 789
Metropolitan Audio-Visual Inc, pg 940
Troxell Communications Inc, pg 1045

ARKANSAS

Jay S Stanley & Associates Inc, pg 1023
White Diamond Productions, pg 1065

CALIFORNIA

Ametron Audio/Video, pg 785
Associated Sound, pg 792
Audio Images Corp, pg 794
Auton Motorized Systems, pg 797
AV Conferencing, pg 797
California Tape Products Inc, pg 817
Christy's Editorial, pg 826
Delicate Electronics Sales Inc, pg 845
FXC Communications, pg 874
Gluskin's Custom Audio Video, pg 879
GMF Sound Inc, pg 879
Impact Group, pg 897
Instructional Materials & Equipment Distributors (I-Med), pg 899
JD Audio Visual Inc, pg 904
Lloyd F McKinney Associates Inc, pg 935
Media Fabricators Inc, pg 936
MediaPOINTE, pg 938
Mobilized Tech Systems, pg 944
Related Visual Inc, pg 994
Sound Service Co, pg 1017
Southern California Sound Image Inc, pg 1019
SSL Industries Inc, pg 1022
Stanislaus Audio Video Inc, pg 1023
Towards 2000 Inc, pg 1043
Tri-Ed, pg 1044

COLORADO

Ceavco Audio/Visual Co, pg 822
Spectrum Audio Visual Services, pg 1020

CONNECTICUT

Concord Communications, pg 835
Connecticut Audio & Theatrical Supply, pg 835
Everett Hall Associates Inc, pg 863
HB Communications Inc, pg 886
MAVCO, pg 934
Rockwell Communications Inc, pg 998

FLORIDA

Allstar Audio Systems Inc, pg 782
AVI-SPL, pg 798
Broadcasters General Store Inc, pg 813
Digital Video Systems Inc, pg 848
General Projection Systems Inc, pg 877
Gulf Coast Audio Visual Producers Inc, pg 883
Harmon's Audio-Visual Services, pg 885
Hi-Tech Import Export Corp, pg 888
Hollywood Theatre Equipment Inc, pg 890
Industrial Strength Inc, pg 897
Photomart Cine-Video Inc, pg 975
Photosound of Orlando Inc, pg 975
Pro Stage Inc, pg 983
Recording Media & Equipment Inc (RM&E), pg 993
Sight & Sound Productions, pg 1010
Spire Audio Visual Co Inc, pg 1021
Stereo Sales Inc, pg 1024
TAI Audio, pg 1031
Tallahassee Audio Visual, pg 1031

GEORGIA

Audio Visual Resources Inc, pg 795
Baker Audio Inc, pg 801
Convergent Media Systems, pg 836
Omnimedia Inc, pg 962
PolyVision Corporation, pg 978
Stage Front Presentation Systems, pg 1022
Technical Innovation, pg 1033
Visioneering International Inc, pg 1058

HAWAII

ATTCO Inc, pg 793
The Audio Visual Co (AVCO), pg 795

ILLINOIS

Allen Visual Systems Inc, pg 781
AmpliVox Portable Sound Systems, pg 785
Central Audio-Visual Equipment Inc, pg 823
Joseph Electronics, pg 906
G T Luscombe Co Inc, pg 926
Quintessence Audio Ltd, pg 989
Sound Vision Inc, pg 1018

INDIANA

Heart Breaker Entertainment LLC, pg 887
Sensory Technologies LLC, pg 1006
SHP Electronics, pg 1010

IOWA

ECS Inc, pg 856

KANSAS

KK Office Solutions Inc, pg 911
Smith Audio-Visual Inc, pg 1014

KENTUCKY

Audio Visual Techniques Inc, pg 796
Axxis Inc, pg 800
Barney Miller's Inc, pg 943
NOR-COM Inc, pg 958

LOUISIANA

Intermedia Technologies, pg 900

MAINE

Headlight Audio Visual Inc, pg 887

MARYLAND

Advance Audiovisual Presentation Ltd, pg 777
Cardinal Sound & Video, pg 820
Nelson White Systems Inc, pg 954
Nicholas P Pipino Associates Inc, pg 976
RTZ Audio Visual, pg 1000
Visual Aids Electronics Corp, pg 1059

MASSACHUSETTS

Antronics Inc, pg 787
International Display & Exhibit Corp, pg 901
Lineco, pg 922
Rule Broadcast Systems, pg 1000
University Products Inc, pg 1050

MICHIGAN

Olson Anderson Co, pg 786
Ascom Communications Contractors, pg 791
City Events Group, pg 828
Michigan Office Solutions, pg 941
On Stage Visuals, pg 963
TeL Systems, pg 1035

MINNESOTA

Advanced Audio-Visual Inc, pg 777
AVI Systems, pg 799

MISSISSIPPI

Bowie Audio Visual Enterprises Inc, pg 811
Jasper Ewing & Sons Inc, pg 864

MISSOURI

Communitronics Corp, pg 833
Conference Technologies Inc, pg 835
Image Technologies Corp, pg 895
Schiller's Audio-Visual, pg 1004
Southwest Audio-Visual Inc, pg 1019
Swank Audio Visuals, pg 1029

NEBRASKA

Dog & Pony Productions Inc, pg 850

NEVADA

Flex-A-Lite West, pg 870

NEW HAMPSHIRE

APS Lighting-Sound-AV, pg 789

NEW JERSEY

A-V Services Inc, pg 771
Alltec Stores, a Vcom IMC Company, pg 782
Audio Visual Associates, pg 795
Audio Visual Dynamics®, pg 795
AV Bluebook, pg 797
Comprehensive Cable & Connectivity Co, pg 833
Earl Girls Inc, pg 855
FlagHouse, pg 869
Hamilton Buhl, pg 884
National Audio-Visual Supply, pg 952
SLD Lighting, pg 1013
Starlite Productions, pg 1024
Tele-Measurements Inc, pg 1035
Total Video Products Inc, pg 1042
Turner Engineering Inc, pg 1046
VCom International Multimedia Corp, pg 1052
Video Corporation of America (VCA), pg 1055
Wilray Audio Visual Corp, pg 1067
Wired 4 Sound Inc, pg 1068
York Telecom, pg 1072

NEW YORK

Albany Theatre Supply Co Inc, pg 780
ALTEL Systems Inc, pg 783

Lectern Manufacturers

Lectern Rentals

AUDIO/VISUAL

Lectern Rentals (continued)

DELAWARE

Actors Attic, pg 775
Ken-Del Productions Inc, pg 909
Showorks Audio Visual Inc, pg 1010

FLORIDA

Allstar Audio Systems Inc, pg 782
AVI-SPL, pg 798
Gulf Coast Audio Visual Producers Inc, pg 883
Harmon's Audio-Visual Services, pg 885
Image Technical Services, pg 895
Industrial Strength Inc, pg 897
National Teleproductions Inc, pg 953
Paradise Show & Design Inc, pg 969
Photosound of Orlando Inc, pg 975
Pro Stage Inc, pg 983
Sight & Sound Productions, pg 1010
Spire Audio Visual Co Inc, pg 1021
TAI Audio, pg 1031
Tallahassee Audio Visual, pg 1031

GEORGIA

Audio Visual Resources Inc, pg 795
Convergent Media Systems, pg 836
Lighting & Production Equipment Inc, pg 920
ON Event Services, pg 963
Stage Front Presentation Systems, pg 1022
Staging Directions Inc, pg 1023

HAWAII

ATTCO Inc, pg 793

ILLINOIS

Allen Visual Systems Inc, pg 781
AV Chicago Inc, pg 797
Backstar Creative Media Inc, pg 801
Beatty TeleVisual Productions, pg 804
Central Audio-Visual Equipment Inc, pg 823
Creative Technology, pg 838
Helix Camera & Video, pg 887
QuickSet International Inc, pg 989
RC Communications, pg 992
Show Department Inc, pg 1009

INDIANA

Heart Breaker Entertainment LLC, pg 887

IOWA

Central Lighting & Equipment Inc (CLE), pg 823
ECS Inc, pg 856

KANSAS

Smith Audio-Visual Inc, pg 1014

KENTUCKY

Audio Visual Techniques Inc, pg 796

LOUISIANA

Clark Services Audio Visual & Exhibit Inc, pg 829
Pace Systems, pg 966

MAINE

Headlight Audio Visual Inc, pg 887

MARYLAND

Absolute Hollywood, pg 772
Advance Audiovisual Presentation Ltd, pg 777
Cardinal Sound & Video, pg 820
CPR MultiMedia Solutions, pg 837
Hargrove Inc, pg 885
Nelson White Systems Inc, pg 954
RTZ Audio Visual, pg 1000

MASSACHUSETTS

massAV, pg 933
Preston Productions Inc, pg 981

MICHIGAN

Olson Anderson Co, pg 786
City Events Group, pg 828
K&R All Media Productions Inc, pg 908
K&R's Recording Studios Inc, pg 908
On Stage Visuals, pg 963

MINNESOTA

Advanced Audio-Visual Inc, pg 777
AVI Systems, pg 799

MISSISSIPPI

Bowie Audio Visual Enterprises Inc, pg 811
Jasper Ewing & Sons Inc, pg 864

MISSOURI

Cashmark Media Inc, pg 820
Communitronics Corp, pg 833
Schiller's Audio-Visual, pg 1004
Show-Me Audio-Visual, pg 1009
Southwest Audio-Visual Inc, pg 1019
Swank Audio Visuals, pg 1029
Switch, pg 1030

NEBRASKA

Dog & Pony Productions Inc, pg 850

NEVADA

GES Audio Visual, pg 877

NEW HAMPSHIRE

APS Lighting-Sound-AV, pg 789

NEW JERSEY

Audio Visual Associates, pg 795
Audio Visual Dynamics®, pg 795
Earl Girls Inc, pg 855
Giant Audio Visual Inc, pg 878
International Audio Visual Inc, pg 900
SLD Lighting, pg 1013
Starlite Productions, pg 1024
Video Corporation of America (VCA), pg 1055
Wired 4 Sound Inc, pg 1068

NEW YORK

Ace Video, pg 774
AV Workshop, pg 797
Colortone Audio Visual, pg 832
Communication Corner Inc, pg 832
Design Audio Visual Inc, pg 845
KVL Audio Visual Services Inc, pg 914
Langie Audio Visual Systems, pg 915
Long Island Video Enterprises Live Inc, pg 924
Magnaplan Corp, pg 928
Ray Supply Inc, pg 992
SmartSource Computer & AV Rentals, pg 1014
Technisphere Corp, pg 1034
Visual Technologies Corp, pg 1060
Visual Word Systems Inc, pg 1060

NORTH CAROLINA

A&V Company, pg 772
AV Metro Inc, pg 797
Camcor Inc, pg 818
Special Event Services, pg 1020
Strategic Connections, pg 1026
Visual Aids Electronics of North Carolina Inc, pg 1059

NORTH DAKOTA

Media Productions, pg 937

OHIO

Audio Visual Media, pg 795
Aztec Video Productions, pg 801
Hughie's Event Production Services, pg 892
ITA Audio Visual Solutions, pg 902

OKLAHOMA

PDC Productions, pg 970

OREGON

Rose City Sound, pg 999

PENNSYLVANIA

Advanced AV, pg 777
Audio Visions Inc, pg 795
Audio Visual Communications Inc, pg 795
Production Solutions Inc, pg 985
Visual Sound Inc, pg 1059

SOUTH CAROLINA

Sound & Images Inc, pg 1016

TENNESSEE

Brantley Sound Associates Inc, pg 812
Memphis Communications Corp, pg 938
Technical Support Systems LLC, pg 1034
Tennessee Visual Service Co, pg 1037

TEXAS

Alford Media Services, pg 780
Astro Audio Visual, pg 792
Audio Visual Technologies Group, pg 796
Heffernan Audio Visual, pg 887
J&S Audio Visual Inc, pg 904
Lubbock Audio Visual Inc, pg 925
Padgitt's, pg 967
Schoolhouse Audio Visual, pg 1004

UTAH

Performance Audio, pg 973
Webb Audio Visual Communication, pg 1063

VIRGINIA

American AV, pg 783
Audio Visual Actions Inc (AVA), pg 795
Boitnott Visual Communications Corp (BVC), pg 810
Lee Hartman & Sons Inc, pg 918
Metropolitan Audio Visual Co LLC, pg 940
Projection Presentation Technology, pg 985
Rainbow Rentals, pg 991

WASHINGTON

D A Sound, pg 842
Inland Audio Visual Co, pg 898
Pacific Northwest Theatre Associates Inc (PNTA), pg 967

WISCONSIN

Audio Visual of Milwaukee Inc, pg 795
Camera Corner Connecting Point, pg 818
Event Essentials, pg 863
Full Compass Systems, pg 874

PUERTO RICO

Stage Crew Audiovisual Inc, pg 1022

ALBERTA

Evolution Presentation Technologies, pg 863
McBain Audio Visual Ltd, pg 935
Unique Communications Ltd, pg 1048

BRITISH COLUMBIA

Clark's Audio Visual Services Ltd, pg 829

MANITOBA

Inland Audio Visual Ltd, pg 898

ONTARIO

Edcom Multimedia Products, pg 856
HD Source, pg 886
Premier A/V Sales Ltd, pg 980
Westbury National Show Systems Ltd, pg 1064

QUEBEC

Audio Visual Dynamics Ltd, pg 795
Concept Audio-Visual, pg 834

Lectern Repairs

ARKANSAS

Jay S Stanley & Associates Inc, pg 1023

CALIFORNIA

Ametron Audio/Video, pg 785
Instructional Materials & Equipment Distributors (I-Med), pg 899
McAlister Electronics, pg 935
Lloyd F McKinney Associates Inc, pg 935
SSL Industries Inc, pg 1022
Towards 2000 Inc, pg 1043

COLORADO

Ceavco Audio/Visual Co, pg 822

CONNECTICUT

HB Communications Inc, pg 886
Rockwell Communications Inc, pg 998

FLORIDA

Spire Audio Visual Co Inc, pg 1021
Stereo Sales Inc, pg 1024
TAI Audio, pg 1031

GEORGIA

Audio Visual Resources Inc, pg 795
Lighting & Production Equipment Inc, pg 920
Stage Front Presentation Systems, pg 1022
Technical Innovation, pg 1033

ILLINOIS

Allen Visual Systems Inc, pg 781

KENTUCKY

Axxis Inc, pg 800
NOR-COM Inc, pg 958

MAINE

Headlight Audio Visual Inc, pg 887

MARYLAND

Cardinal Sound & Video, pg 820
RTZ Audio Visual, pg 1000

MICHIGAN

Olson Anderson Co, pg 786
City Events Group, pg 828
TeL Systems, pg 1035

MINNESOTA

AVI Systems, pg 799

MISSISSIPPI

Bowie Audio Visual Enterprises Inc, pg 811

MISSOURI

Schiller's Audio-Visual, pg 1004

NEW JERSEY

Earl Girls Inc, pg 855

NEW YORK

Langie Audio Visual Systems, pg 915
Magnaplan Corp, pg 928
Ray Supply Inc, pg 992
Visual Technologies Corp, pg 1060

NORTH CAROLINA

Camcor Inc, pg 818

OHIO

Audio Visual Media, pg 795
Aztec Video Productions, pg 801
ITA Audio Visual Solutions, pg 902
Smithall Electronics Inc, pg 1014

OREGON

All Service Musical Electronics Repair, pg 780

PENNSYLVANIA

Audio Visions Inc, pg 795

TENNESSEE

Memphis Communications Corp, pg 938
Technical Support Systems LLC, pg 1034
Tennessee Visual Service Co, pg 1037

TEXAS

Audio Visual Technologies Group, pg 796
Heffernan Audio Visual, pg 887
Lubbock Audio Visual Inc, pg 925
Quality Audio Visual Service Inc, pg 988
Southwest Sound & Electronics Inc, pg 1019
Tarpley Media Systems, pg 1032

VIRGINIA

Avitecture Inc, pg 799
Boitnott Visual Communications Corp (BVC), pg 810
Hoppmann Audio Visual, pg 891
Lee Hartman & Sons Inc, pg 918
Metropolitan Audio Visual Co LLC, pg 940
The Whitlock Group, pg 1065

WASHINGTON

D A Sound, pg 842
Inland Audio Visual Co, pg 898

WISCONSIN

Full Compass Systems, pg 874

ALBERTA

Infosat Communications Inc, pg 898

MANITOBA

Inland Audio Visual Ltd, pg 898

ONTARIO

Edcom Multimedia Products, pg 856
Premier A/V Sales Ltd, pg 980

Manual Slide Presentation System, *see* Slide Presentation System—Programmable & Manual

Megaphone—Power Distributors

ALABAMA

Media Visions Inc, pg 937

ARIZONA

Arizona Cine Equipment, pg 789
Troxell Communications Inc, pg 1045

ARKANSAS

Sound-Craft Systems Inc, pg 1017

CALIFORNIA

Adolph Gasser Inc, pg 776
Ametron Audio/Video, pg 785
Associated Sound, pg 792
California Tape Products Inc, pg 817
Delicate Electronics Sales Inc, pg 845
FXC Communications, pg 874
GMF Sound Inc, pg 879
Instructional Materials & Equipment Distributors (I-Med), pg 899
JD Audio Visual Inc, pg 904
Location Sound Corp, pg 924
Lloyd F McKinney Associates Inc, pg 935
Media Fabricators Inc, pg 936
Related Visual Inc, pg 994
SSL Industries Inc, pg 1022
Stanislaus Audio Video Inc, pg 1023
TOA Electronics Inc, pg 1041
Towards 2000 Inc, pg 1043

COLORADO

Ceavco Audio/Visual Co, pg 822
Daylight Productions & Rentals, pg 844

CONNECTICUT

Concord Communications, pg 835
HB Communications Inc, pg 886
MAVCO, pg 934

DELAWARE

Actors Attic, pg 775

FLORIDA

Allstar Audio Systems Inc, pg 782
BAI Distributors Inc, pg 801
Broadcasters General Store Inc, pg 813
Hi-Tech Import Export Corp, pg 888
Hollywood Theatre Equipment Inc, pg 890
Photomart Cine-Video Inc, pg 975
Photosound of Orlando Inc, pg 975
Pro Stage Inc, pg 983
Sight & Sound Productions, pg 1010
Spire Audio Visual Co Inc, pg 1021
Stereo Sales Inc, pg 1024
TAI Audio, pg 1031

GEORGIA

Stage Front Presentation Systems, pg 1022
Technical Innovation, pg 1033
Visioneering International Inc, pg 1058

HAWAII

The Audio Visual Co (AVCO), pg 795

ILLINOIS

Allen Visual Systems Inc, pg 781
Joseph Electronics, pg 906

INDIANA

SHP Electronics, pg 1010

IOWA

ECS Inc, pg 856

KANSAS

KK Office Solutions Inc, pg 911

KENTUCKY

Audio Visual Techniques Inc, pg 796
NOR-COM Inc, pg 958

MAINE

Headlight Audio Visual Inc, pg 887

MARYLAND

Cardinal Sound & Video, pg 820
RTZ Audio Visual, pg 1000

MASSACHUSETTS

Rule Broadcast Systems, pg 1000

MICHIGAN

Olson Anderson Co, pg 786
Ascom Communications Contractors, pg 791
City Events Group, pg 828
TeL Systems, pg 1035

MINNESOTA

AVI Systems, pg 799
New Life Communications Inc, pg 956

MISSISSIPPI

Jasper Ewing & Sons Inc, pg 864

MISSOURI

Communitronics Corp, pg 833
Image Technologies Corp, pg 895
Schiller's Audio-Visual, pg 1004
Swank Audio Visuals, pg 1029

NEW HAMPSHIRE

APS Lighting-Sound-AV, pg 789

NEW JERSEY

Alltec Stores, a Vcom IMC Company, pg 782
Audio Visual Associates, pg 795
Audio Visual Dynamics®, pg 795
AV Bluebook, pg 797
Earl Girls Inc, pg 855
FlagHouse, pg 869
Hamilton Buhl, pg 884
National Audio-Visual Supply, pg 952
Starlite Productions, pg 1024
Total Video Products Inc, pg 1042
VCom International Multimedia Corp, pg 1052
Wilray Audio Visual Corp, pg 1067
Wired 4 Sound Inc, pg 1068

NEW YORK

Audio-Video Corp, pg 795
AV Workshop, pg 797
Centennial Electric Sound Co Ltd, pg 822
Communication Corner Inc, pg 832
Custom Media Environments, pg 841
Design Audio Visual Inc, pg 845
Indigo Productions, pg 897
Langie Audio Visual Systems, pg 915
Lee Dan® Communications Inc, pg 918
Long Island Video Enterprises Live Inc, pg 924
Markertek Video Supply, pg 931
Neptune Photo Inc, pg 954
Presentation Products Inc, pg 981
Ray Supply Inc, pg 992
RNJ Electronics, pg 997
Technisphere Corp, pg 1034
Visual Technologies Corp, pg 1060
Willoughby's Imaging Center, pg 1067

AUDIO/VISUAL

Megaphone—Power Distributors (continued)

NORTH CAROLINA

Camcor Inc, pg 818
Strategic Connections, pg 1026

OHIO

Copp Integrated Systems, pg 836
ITA Audio Visual Solutions, pg 902
Jimmy Rea Electronics Inc, pg 992
Smithall Electronics Inc, pg 1014
Tri-State Audio Visual Co, pg 1044
Tri-State Visual Products, pg 1044

PENNSYLVANIA

Advanced AV, pg 777
Audio Visions Inc, pg 795
Brodart Co, pg 813
J E Foss Co, pg 871
Garcia Marketing Inc, pg 875
Grise Audio Visual Center Inc, pg 882
Morefield Communications Inc, pg 946
RSS Distributors, pg 1000
Vistacom Inc, pg 1059
Visual Sound Inc, pg 1059
Wespen Audio Visual Co, pg 1063

RHODE ISLAND

Custom Computer Specialists Inc, pg 841

TENNESSEE

Durrell LLC, pg 854
Lowrance Sound Co Inc, pg 925
Memphis Communications Corp, pg 938
Technical Support Systems LLC, pg 1034
Tennessee Visual Service Co, pg 1037

TEXAS

Astro Audio Visual, pg 792
Audio Visual Technologies Group, pg 796
AVES Audio Visual Systems Inc, pg 798
Crossroads Audio Inc, pg 840
Data Display Audio Visual Co LP, pg 843
Heffernan Audio Visual, pg 887
J&S Audio Visual Inc, pg 904
Lubbock Audio Visual Inc, pg 925
Quality Audio Visual Service Inc, pg 988
Schoolhouse Audio Visual, pg 1004
Southwest Sound & Electronics Inc, pg 1019
Tarpley Media Systems, pg 1032

UTAH

Performance Audio, pg 973
Webb Audio Visual Communication, pg 1063

VIRGINIA

Avitecture Inc, pg 799
Boitnott Visual Communications Corp (BVC), pg 810
Communications Specialists Inc, pg 833
Lee Hartman & Sons Inc, pg 918
The Whitlock Group, pg 1065

WASHINGTON

CCI Solutions, pg 821
Inland Audio Visual Co, pg 898
Pacific Northwest Theatre Associates Inc (PNTA), pg 967

WEST VIRGINIA

United Sound & Electronics, pg 1048

WISCONSIN

Audio Visual of Milwaukee Inc, pg 795
Camera Corner Connecting Point, pg 818
Full Compass Systems, pg 874

PUERTO RICO

Audio Visual Concepts Inc, pg 795
Bonnin Electronics Inc, pg 810

ALBERTA

Infosat Communications Inc, pg 898
McBain Audio Visual Ltd, pg 935
Sharp's Audio-Visual Ltd, pg 1008

BRITISH COLUMBIA

Commercial Electronics Ltd, pg 832
ProVision Video Sales & Rentals Inc, pg 986

MANITOBA

Inland Audio Visual Ltd, pg 898

ONTARIO

Cinema Stage Inc, pg 827
Edcom Multimedia Products, pg 856
Nationwide Audio Visual Co, pg 953
Premier A/V Sales Ltd, pg 980
Westbury National Show Systems Ltd, pg 1064

QUEBEC

Concept Audio-Visual, pg 834

Megaphone—Power Manufacturers

ARIZONA

David Wexler & Co, pg 1064

CALIFORNIA

Anchor Audio Inc, pg 786
Califone International Inc, pg 817
Fanon Courier, pg 865
TOA Electronics Inc, pg 1041

ILLINOIS

AmpliVox Portable Sound Systems, pg 785

NEVADA

Pignose-Gorilla, pg 975

NEW JERSEY

National Audio-Visual Supply, pg 952

NEW YORK

Centennial Electric Sound Co Ltd, pg 822
MG Electronics, pg 940
TecNec Distributing, pg 1035

SOUTH CAROLINA

Paso Sound Products Inc, pg 969

Megaphone—Power Rentals

ALABAMA

Audio-Video Resources Inc, pg 795
Media Visions Inc, pg 937

ARIZONA

Arizona Cine Equipment, pg 789
Merestone, pg 938
Metropolitan Audio-Visual Inc, pg 940

CALIFORNIA

Adolph Gasser Inc, pg 776
AGF Media Services, pg 778
Alliant Event Services, pg 781
Ametron Audio/Video, pg 785
Artichoke Productions, pg 791
Associated Sound, pg 792
Audio Rents, pg 794
GMF Sound Inc, pg 879
Instructional Materials & Equipment Distributors (I-Med), pg 899
JD Audio Visual Inc, pg 904
Location Sound Corp, pg 924
Lynch Communications, pg 926
McCune Audio-Video-Lighting, pg 935
Media Fabricators Inc, pg 936
Munday & Collins AV, pg 950
Related Visual Inc, pg 994
Slate Media Group, pg 1013
Stanislaus Audio Video Inc, pg 1023
Towards 2000 Inc, pg 1043
Voice & Video Rentals, pg 1060

COLORADO

Multimedia Audio Visual Inc, pg 950

CONNECTICUT

A/V Davey, pg 797
Concord Communications, pg 835

DELAWARE

Actors Attic, pg 775

FLORIDA

Allstar Audio Systems Inc, pg 782
AVI-SPL, pg 798
Paradise Show & Design Inc, pg 969
Photosound of Orlando Inc, pg 975
Pro Stage Inc, pg 983
Sight & Sound Productions, pg 1010
TAI Audio, pg 1031

GEORGIA

Stage Front Presentation Systems, pg 1022
Staging Directions Inc, pg 1023

ILLINOIS

Allen Visual Systems Inc, pg 781
AV Chicago Inc, pg 797
Central Audio-Visual Equipment Inc, pg 823
Helix Camera & Video, pg 887
QuickSet International Inc, pg 989
RC Communications, pg 992

INDIANA

OMNI Productions, pg 962

KENTUCKY

Audio Visual Techniques Inc, pg 796

MARYLAND

Advance Audiovisual Presentation Ltd, pg 777
Cardinal Sound & Video, pg 820
Event Tech, pg 863
RTZ Audio Visual, pg 1000
Shadowstone R & R™, pg 1008

MASSACHUSETTS

Preston Productions Inc, pg 981

MICHIGAN

Olson Anderson Co, pg 786
City Events Group, pg 828
K&R All Media Productions Inc, pg 908

MINNESOTA

AVI Systems, pg 799

MISSOURI

Communitronics Corp, pg 833
Show-Me Audio-Visual, pg 1009
Swank Audio Visuals, pg 1029

NEVADA

GES Audio Visual, pg 877
PRG Lighting, pg 981

NEW HAMPSHIRE

APS Lighting-Sound-AV, pg 789

NEW JERSEY

Audio Visual Associates, pg 795
Earl Girls Inc, pg 855
Video Corporation of America (VCA), pg 1055

NEW YORK

Ace Video, pg 774
AV Workshop, pg 797
Communication Corner Inc, pg 832
Design Audio Visual Inc, pg 845
Hello World Communications, pg 888
Langie Audio Visual Systems, pg 915
Visual Technologies Corp, pg 1060

NORTH CAROLINA

A&V Company, pg 772
Special Event Services, pg 1020
Strategic Connections, pg 1026

OHIO

Aztec Video Productions, pg 801
ITA Audio Visual Solutions, pg 902
Smithall Electronics Inc, pg 1014

OREGON

Rose City Sound, pg 999

PENNSYLVANIA

Advanced AV, pg 777
Audio Visions Inc, pg 795
Grise Audio Visual Center Inc, pg 882
Production Solutions Inc, pg 985

TENNESSEE

Brantley Sound Associates Inc, pg 812
Memphis Communications Corp, pg 938
Technical Support Systems LLC, pg 1034
Tennessee Visual Service Co, pg 1037

TEXAS

Astro Audio Visual, pg 792
Audio Visual Technologies Group, pg 796
GEAR Cameras & Lighting, pg 876
J&S Audio Visual Inc, pg 904
Lubbock Audio Visual Inc, pg 925
Quality Audio Visual Service Inc, pg 988
Schoolhouse Audio Visual, pg 1004

UTAH

Performance Audio, pg 973
Redman Movies & Stories, pg 993
Webb Audio Visual Communication, pg 1063

VIRGINIA

American AV, pg 783
Boitnott Visual Communications Corp (BVC), pg 810
Lee Hartman & Sons Inc, pg 918
Projection Presentation Technology, pg 985
Rainbow Rentals, pg 991

WASHINGTON

Inland Audio Visual Co, pg 898
Oppenheimer Camera Products, pg 964
Pacific Northwest Theatre Associates Inc (PNTA), pg 967

WEST VIRGINIA

United Sound & Electronics, pg 1048

WISCONSIN

Audio Visual of Milwaukee Inc, pg 795
Event Essentials, pg 863

ALBERTA

Evolution Presentation Technologies, pg 863
McBain Audio Visual Ltd, pg 935
Sharp's Audio-Visual Ltd, pg 1008
Unique Communications Ltd, pg 1048

BRITISH COLUMBIA

Clark's Audio Visual Services Ltd, pg 829
Commercial Electronics Ltd, pg 832
ProVision Video Sales & Rentals Inc, pg 986

MANITOBA

Inland Audio Visual Ltd, pg 898

ONTARIO

Edcom Multimedia Products, pg 856
Premier A/V Sales Ltd, pg 980
Westbury National Show Systems Ltd, pg 1064

QUEBEC

Audio Visual Dynamics Ltd, pg 795
Concept Audio-Visual, pg 834

Megaphone—Power Repairs

CALIFORNIA

Ametron Audio/Video, pg 785
Instructional Materials & Equipment Distributors (I-Med), pg 899
McAlister Electronics, pg 935
Lloyd F McKinney Associates Inc, pg 935
SSL Industries Inc, pg 1022
TOA Electronics Inc, pg 1041
Towards 2000 Inc, pg 1043

CONNECTICUT

HB Communications Inc, pg 886

FLORIDA

Spire Audio Visual Co Inc, pg 1021
Stereo Sales Inc, pg 1024
TAI Audio, pg 1031

GEORGIA

Stage Front Presentation Systems, pg 1022

ILLINOIS

Allen Visual Systems Inc, pg 781
Central Audio-Visual Equipment Inc, pg 823

KENTUCKY

NOR-COM Inc, pg 958

MARYLAND

Cardinal Sound & Video, pg 820
RTZ Audio Visual, pg 1000

MICHIGAN

Olson Anderson Co, pg 786
City Events Group, pg 828
TeL Systems, pg 1035

MINNESOTA

AVI Systems, pg 799

NEW JERSEY

Earl Girls Inc, pg 855

NEW YORK

Colortone Audio Visual, pg 832
Langie Audio Visual Systems, pg 915

OHIO

Aztec Video Productions, pg 801
ITA Audio Visual Solutions, pg 902
Smithall Electronics Inc, pg 1014
Tri-State Audio Visual Co, pg 1044

OREGON

All Service Musical Electronics Repair, pg 780

PENNSYLVANIA

Audio Visions Inc, pg 795
J E Foss Co, pg 871

RHODE ISLAND

Custom Computer Specialists Inc, pg 841

TENNESSEE

Memphis Communications Corp, pg 938
Technical Support Systems LLC, pg 1034
Tennessee Visual Service Co, pg 1037

TEXAS

Audio Visual Technologies Group, pg 796
Lubbock Audio Visual Inc, pg 925
Quality Audio Visual Service Inc, pg 988
Schoolhouse Audio Visual, pg 1004
Southwest Sound & Electronics Inc, pg 1019
Tarpley Media Systems, pg 1032

VIRGINIA

Boitnott Visual Communications Corp (BVC), pg 810

WASHINGTON

Inland Audio Visual Co, pg 898
Pacific Northwest Theatre Associates Inc (PNTA), pg 967

WEST VIRGINIA

United Sound & Electronics, pg 1048

WISCONSIN

Full Compass Systems, pg 874

ALBERTA

Infosat Communications Inc, pg 898
Sharp's Audio-Visual Ltd, pg 1008

BRITISH COLUMBIA

Commercial Electronics Ltd, pg 832

MANITOBA

Inland Audio Visual Ltd, pg 898

ONTARIO

Edcom Multimedia Products, pg 856
Premier A/V Sales Ltd, pg 980

Microcomputer Distributors

ARIZONA

Arizona Cine Equipment, pg 789
CADint, pg 816
Troxell Communications Inc, pg 1045

CALIFORNIA

Ametron Audio/Video, pg 785
Audio Images Corp, pg 794
California Tape Products Inc, pg 817
FXC Communications, pg 874
Instructional Materials & Equipment Distributors (I-Med), pg 899
Kontron America, pg 913
Media Fabricators Inc, pg 936
Photodyne Technologies, pg 974
Promax Systems, pg 986
VMI Inc, pg 1060

FLORIDA

Hi-Tech Import Export Corp, pg 888
Pro Stage Inc, pg 983
Sight & Sound Productions, pg 1010

GEORGIA

Lighting & Production Equipment Inc, pg 920
Stage Front Presentation Systems, pg 1022
Visioneering International Inc, pg 1058

ILLINOIS

Creative Technology, pg 838
Major Reproductions Equipment Co, pg 929
Woodside Avenue Music Productions Inc, pg 1069

IOWA

ECS Inc, pg 856

KENTUCKY

NOR-COM Inc, pg 958

MAINE

Headlight Audio Visual Inc, pg 887

MARYLAND

Kipp Visual Systems Inc, pg 911
Visual Aids Electronics Corp, pg 1059

MASSACHUSETTS

Lineco, pg 922
Professional Audio Design Inc, pg 985
Psych Soft Inc, pg 987

MICHIGAN

Digi Sign Design LLC, pg 847
TeL Systems, pg 1035

MINNESOTA

AVI Systems, pg 799

MISSISSIPPI

Jasper Ewing & Sons Inc, pg 864

MISSOURI

Schiller's Audio-Visual, pg 1004
Swank Audio Visuals, pg 1029

NEW JERSEY

Audio Visual Dynamics®, pg 795
AV Bluebook, pg 797
Hamilton Buhl, pg 884
Starlite Productions, pg 1024

AUDIO/VISUAL

Microcomputer Distributors (continued)

NEW JERSEY (continued)

Turner Engineering Inc, pg 1046
York Telecom, pg 1072

NEW YORK

Langie Audio Visual Systems, pg 915
Presentation Products Inc, pg 981
SmartSource Computer & AV Rentals, pg 1014
Technisphere Corp, pg 1034

NORTH CAROLINA

Camcor Inc, pg 818

OHIO

Tri-State Audio Visual Co, pg 1044

PENNSYLVANIA

Advanced AV, pg 777
Garcia Marketing Inc, pg 875
Visual Sound Inc, pg 1059

RHODE ISLAND

Custom Computer Specialists Inc, pg 841

TENNESSEE

Memphis Communications Corp, pg 938
Spring Arbor Distributors, pg 1022
Tennessee Visual Service Co, pg 1037

TEXAS

Data Display Audio Visual Co LP, pg 843
Lubbock Audio Visual Inc, pg 925
RadioShack Corp, pg 990
Schoolhouse Audio Visual, pg 1004
Tarpley Media Systems, pg 1032
Videotex Systems Inc, pg 1057

VIRGINIA

The Whitlock Group, pg 1065

WISCONSIN

Audio Visual of Milwaukee Inc, pg 795
Camera Corner Connecting Point, pg 818
Comprompter Inc, pg 834
Full Compass Systems, pg 874

QUEBEC

Concept Audio-Visual, pg 834

Microcomputer Manufacturers

ARIZONA

CADint, pg 816

CALIFORNIA

Kontron America, pg 913
Micro Express, pg 941
Recortec Inc, pg 993

CONNECTICUT

Titus Technological Laboratories (TTL), pg 1041

GEORGIA

Outsource Engineering & Manufacturing Inc dba Texscan MSI, pg 966

MASSACHUSETTS

Psych Soft Inc, pg 987

MICHIGAN

ASC Systems, pg 791

TEXAS

RadioShack Corp, pg 990

ONTARIO

Technovision® Interactive Inc, pg 1035

Microcomputer Rentals

ALABAMA

Media Visions Inc, pg 937

ARIZONA

Arizona Cine Equipment, pg 789
CADint, pg 816
Merestone, pg 938

CALIFORNIA

Ametron Audio/Video, pg 785
AV Guys, pg 797
McCune Audio-Video-Lighting, pg 935
Media Fabricators Inc, pg 936
Munday & Collins AV, pg 950
Muse Presentation Technologies, pg 950
PSAV® Presentation Services, pg 986

CONNECTICUT

A/V Davey, pg 797
Trod Nossel Productions & Recording Studios, pg 1045

FLORIDA

Industrial Strength Inc, pg 897
Paradise Show & Design Inc, pg 969
Pro Stage Inc, pg 983

GEORGIA

Lighting & Production Equipment Inc, pg 920
Stage Front Presentation Systems, pg 1022
Staging Directions Inc, pg 1023

ILLINOIS

Creative Technology, pg 838
Show Department Inc, pg 1009
Woodside Avenue Music Productions Inc, pg 1069

LOUISIANA

Pace Systems, pg 966

MARYLAND

CSPMedia.com, pg 840

MASSACHUSETTS

Preston Productions Inc, pg 981

MICHIGAN

Digi Sign Design LLC, pg 847
K&R All Media Productions Inc, pg 908
K&R's Recording Studios Inc, pg 908

MINNESOTA

AVI Systems, pg 799

MISSISSIPPI

Bowie Audio Visual Enterprises Inc, pg 811

MISSOURI

Show-Me Audio-Visual, pg 1009
Swank Audio Visuals, pg 1029

NEW HAMPSHIRE

Academic & Campus Technology Services, pg 773

NEW JERSEY

Audio Visual Dynamics®, pg 795
PLS Staging, pg 977
Starlite Productions, pg 1024

NEW YORK

Ace Video, pg 774
Design Audio Visual Inc, pg 845
Interactive International Inc, pg 899
Langie Audio Visual Systems, pg 915
Long Island Video Enterprises Live Inc, pg 924
SmartSource Computer & AV Rentals, pg 1014

NORTH CAROLINA

Camcor Inc, pg 818
Special Event Services, pg 1020
Strategic Connections, pg 1026
Visual Aids Electronics of North Carolina Inc, pg 1059

OHIO

Icom Multimedia, pg 893
Mills James Productions, pg 943

OKLAHOMA

PDC Productions, pg 970

PENNSYLVANIA

Production Solutions Inc, pg 985
Visual Sound Inc, pg 1059

TENNESSEE

Memphis Communications Corp, pg 938
Tennessee Visual Service Co, pg 1037

TEXAS

Lubbock Audio Visual Inc, pg 925
Schoolhouse Audio Visual, pg 1004

VERMONT

Parlato Productions, pg 969

VIRGINIA

American AV, pg 783
Projection Presentation Technology, pg 985
Quince Imaging Inc, pg 989

WEST VIRGINIA

United Sound & Electronics, pg 1048

WISCONSIN

Audio Visual of Milwaukee Inc, pg 795
Camera Corner Connecting Point, pg 818

BRITISH COLUMBIA

Clark's Audio Visual Services Ltd, pg 829

ONTARIO

Edcom Multimedia Products, pg 856

QUEBEC

Concept Audio-Visual, pg 834

Microcomputer Repairs

CALIFORNIA

Ametron Audio/Video, pg 785
McAlister Electronics, pg 935

FLORIDA

Hi-Tech Enterprises Inc, pg 888
Tel-Test, pg 1035

GEORGIA

Lighting & Production Equipment Inc, pg 920

KENTUCKY

NOR-COM Inc, pg 958

MARYLAND

RTZ Audio Visual, pg 1000

MICHIGAN

TeL Systems, pg 1035

MINNESOTA

AVI Systems, pg 799

NEW YORK

Interactive International Inc, pg 899
Langie Audio Visual Systems, pg 915

NORTH CAROLINA

Camcor Inc, pg 818

OHIO

Aztec Video Productions, pg 801
Tri-State Audio Visual Co, pg 1044

PENNSYLVANIA

Visual Sound Inc, pg 1059

RHODE ISLAND

Custom Computer Specialists Inc, pg 841

TENNESSEE

Memphis Communications Corp, pg 938
Tennessee Visual Service Co, pg 1037

TEXAS

Lubbock Audio Visual Inc, pg 925
Schoolhouse Audio Visual, pg 1004

VIRGINIA

Quince Imaging Inc, pg 989
The Whitlock Group, pg 1065

WEST VIRGINIA

United Sound & Electronics, pg 1048

WISCONSIN

Camera Corner Connecting Point, pg 818
Full Compass Systems, pg 874

Multi-Image Device & Presentation Accessory Distributors

ALABAMA

Media Visions Inc, pg 937

ARIZONA

Arizona Cine Equipment, pg 789
Metropolitan Audio-Visual Inc, pg 940
Troxell Communications Inc, pg 1045
Ultimate Presentation Systems Inc, pg 1047

ARKANSAS

Jay S Stanley & Associates Inc, pg 1023
White Diamond Productions, pg 1065

CALIFORNIA

Ametron Audio/Video, pg 785
Associated Sound, pg 792
AVerMedia Technologies Inc, pg 798
California Tape Products Inc, pg 817
Christy's Editorial, pg 826
Cibola Systems, pg 826
Electrosonic Inc, pg 859
FXC Communications, pg 874
Gluskin's Custom Audio Video, pg 879
JD Audio Visual Inc, pg 904
Laser Magic Productions, pg 916
Lloyd F McKinney Associates Inc, pg 935
Media Fabricators Inc, pg 936
MediaPOINTE, pg 938
Mobilized Tech Systems, pg 944
PMP Marketing Inc, pg 977
POP TV, pg 978
Related Visual Inc, pg 994
Southern California Sound Image Inc, pg 1019
Stanislaus Audio Video Inc, pg 1023
Tri-Ed, pg 1044

COLORADO

Ceavco Audio/Visual Co, pg 822
Daylight Productions & Rentals, pg 844
National Teaching Aids Inc, pg 953

CONNECTICUT

HB Communications Inc, pg 886
MAVCO, pg 934
Rockwell Communications Inc, pg 998
USI Inc, pg 1051
The Video Messenger Co, pg 1055

FLORIDA

AVI-SPL, pg 798
Digital Video Systems Inc, pg 848
General Projection Systems Inc, pg 877
Gulf Coast Audio Visual Producers Inc, pg 883
Harmon's Audio-Visual Services, pg 885
Harris Corp, pg 885
Industrial Strength Inc, pg 897
Photosound of Orlando Inc, pg 975
Pro Stage Inc, pg 983
Sight & Sound Productions, pg 1010
Spire Audio Visual Co Inc, pg 1021
Tallahassee Audio Visual, pg 1031

GEORGIA

Audio Visual Resources Inc, pg 795
Baker Audio Inc, pg 801
Convergent Media Systems, pg 836
Omnimedia Inc, pg 962
PolyVision Corporation, pg 978
Stage Front Presentation Systems, pg 1022
Technical Innovation, pg 1033
Visioneering International Inc, pg 1058

HAWAII

The Audio Visual Co (AVCO), pg 795

ILLINOIS

Creative Technology, pg 838
Dukane Corp, Audio Visual Products Division, pg 853
Lyn Norstad & Associates Inc, pg 926
Quintessence Audio Ltd, pg 989
RC Communications, pg 992

INDIANA

Porter Case Inc, pg 978
Sensory Technologies LLC, pg 1006
SHP Electronics, pg 1010

IOWA

ECS Inc, pg 856

KENTUCKY

Audio Visual Techniques Inc, pg 796
Axxis Inc, pg 800
NOR-COM Inc, pg 958

LOUISIANA

Intermedia Technologies, pg 900

MAINE

Headlight Audio Visual Inc, pg 887

MARYLAND

Absolute Hollywood, pg 772
Hargrove Inc, pg 885
Image Logic Corp, pg 895
Kipp Visual Systems Inc, pg 911
Nelson White Systems Inc, pg 954
Nicholas P Pipino Associates Inc, pg 976
RTZ Audio Visual, pg 1000
Visual Aids Electronics Corp, pg 1059

MASSACHUSETTS

Lineco, pg 922

MICHIGAN

ASC Systems, pg 791
Ascom Communications Contractors, pg 791
City Events Group, pg 828
Digi Sign Design LLC, pg 847
Michigan Office Solutions, pg 941
TeL Systems, pg 1035

MINNESOTA

Advanced Audio-Visual Inc, pg 777
AVI Systems, pg 799
Media Loft Inc, pg 937

MISSISSIPPI

Bowie Audio Visual Enterprises Inc, pg 811
Jasper Ewing & Sons Inc, pg 864

MISSOURI

Communitronics Corp, pg 833
Conference Technologies Inc, pg 835
Image Technologies Corp, pg 895
MIS Technologies, pg 944
Schiller's Audio-Visual, pg 1004
Swank Audio Visuals, pg 1029

NEW JERSEY

A-V Services Inc, pg 771
Audio Visual Associates, pg 795
Audio Visual Dynamics®, pg 795
AV Bluebook, pg 797
Color Leasing Studios, pg 831
Earl Girls Inc, pg 855
Hamilton Buhl, pg 884
National Audio-Visual Supply, pg 952
Reed Presentations Inc (RPI), pg 993
Starlite Productions, pg 1024
SYMCO Inc, pg 1030
Video Corporation of America (VCA), pg 1055
Wired 4 Sound Inc, pg 1068
York Telecom, pg 1072

NEW YORK

AV Workshop, pg 797
Communication Corner Inc, pg 832
Custom Media Environments, pg 841
Design Audio Visual Inc, pg 845
DSan Corp, pg 852
General Audio-Visual Inc (GAVI), pg 876
Gordon Visual Solutions, pg 880
Indigo Productions, pg 897
Langie Audio Visual Systems, pg 915
Long Island Video Enterprises Live Inc, pg 924
Magnaplan Corp, pg 928
Markertek Video Supply, pg 931
Neptune Photo Inc, pg 954
Presentation Products Inc, pg 981
Ray Supply Inc, pg 992
RNJ Electronics, pg 997
Visual Technologies Corp, pg 1060
Willoughby's Imaging Center, pg 1067

NORTH CAROLINA

Camcor Inc, pg 818
Strategic Connections, pg 1026

OHIO

Audio Visual Media, pg 795
Copp Integrated Systems, pg 836
Icom Multimedia, pg 893
Tri-State Audio Visual Co, pg 1044
Tri-State Visual Products, pg 1044

PENNSYLVANIA

Advanced AV, pg 777
Audio Visions Inc, pg 795
Audio Visual Communications Inc, pg 795
Bernie's Photo Center, pg 805
Brodart Co, pg 813
J E Foss Co, pg 871
Vistacom Inc, pg 1059
Visual Sound Inc, pg 1059
Wespen Audio Visual Co, pg 1063

RHODE ISLAND

Custom Computer Specialists Inc, pg 841
Shanix Inc, pg 1008

TENNESSEE

Continental Film, pg 835
Durrell LLC, pg 854
Lowrance Sound Co Inc, pg 925
Memphis Communications Corp, pg 938
Technical Support Systems LLC, pg 1034
Tennessee Visual Service Co, pg 1037

TEXAS

Audio Visual Technologies Group, pg 796
Heffernan Audio Visual, pg 887
High End Systems Inc, pg 888
J&S Audio Visual Inc, pg 904
Lubbock Audio Visual Inc, pg 925
Quality Audio Visual Service Inc, pg 988
Schoolhouse Audio Visual, pg 1004
Stage Directions, pg 1022
Tarpley Media Systems, pg 1032
Videotex Systems Inc, pg 1057

UTAH

Webb Audio Visual Communication, pg 1063

VIRGINIA

Boitnott Visual Communications Corp (BVC), pg 810
Communications Specialists Inc, pg 833
Design & Production Inc, pg 845
Hoppmann Audio Visual, pg 891
Intellidyne LLC, pg 899
Quince Imaging Inc, pg 989
The Whitlock Group, pg 1065

AUDIO/VISUAL

Multi-Image Device & Presentation Accessory Distributors (continued)

WASHINGTON

Inland Audio Visual Co, pg 898

WISCONSIN

Audio Visual of Milwaukee Inc, pg 795
Camera Corner Connecting Point, pg 818
Full Compass Systems, pg 874
School Specialty Inc, pg 1004
USAV Group Inc, pg 1050

PUERTO RICO

Audio Visual Concepts Inc, pg 795

ALBERTA

Infosat Communications Inc, pg 898
McBain Audio Visual Ltd, pg 935
Sharp's Audio-Visual Ltd, pg 1008
SMART Technologies Inc, pg 1013
Unique Communications Ltd, pg 1048

BRITISH COLUMBIA

Commercial Electronics Ltd, pg 832

MANITOBA

Evolution Presentation Technologies, pg 863
Inland Audio Visual Ltd, pg 898

ONTARIO

Edcom Multimedia Products, pg 856
Gesturetek, pg 877
Image Video, pg 895
Premier A/V Sales Ltd, pg 980
Westbury National Show Systems Ltd, pg 1064

QUEBEC

Concept Audio-Visual, pg 834

Multi-Image Device & Presentation Accessory Manufacturers

ARIZONA

Boeckeler Instruments Inc, pg 810
eInstruction Corp, pg 858

CALIFORNIA

AITech International, pg 779
AVerMedia Technologies Inc, pg 798
Extron Electronics, pg 864
Laser Magic Productions, pg 916
MediaPOINTE, pg 938
RGB Spectrum, pg 996
Xantech LLC, pg 1071

COLORADO

National Teaching Aids Inc, pg 953

CONNECTICUT

The Video Messenger Co, pg 1055

FLORIDA

Vutec Corp, Video Products Division, pg 1061

GEORGIA

PolyVision Corporation, pg 978

ILLINOIS

Bretford Manufacturing Inc, pg 812
Dukane Corp, Audio Visual Products Division, pg 853

INDIANA

Da-Lite, pg 842
Draper Inc, pg 852
Porter Case Inc, pg 978
Star Case Manufacturing Co Inc, pg 1023

KENTUCKY

TV One Multimedia Solutions, pg 1046

MARYLAND

Absolute Hollywood, pg 772
Image Logic Corp, pg 895

MICHIGAN

Leightronix Inc, pg 918

MINNESOTA

Chief, pg 825

NEW JERSEY

Crestron Electronics Inc, pg 839
FSR Inc, pg 873
Reed Presentations Inc (RPI), pg 993

NEW YORK

Analog Way Inc, pg 786
DSan Corp, pg 852
Eastman Kodak Professional, pg 856
ELMO USA Corp, pg 859
General Audio-Visual Inc (GAVI), pg 876
Gordon Visual Solutions, pg 880
Judson Rosebush Co Inc, pg 999

OHIO

Kroy LLC, pg 914

PENNSYLVANIA

Scala Inc, pg 1003

TEXAS

AMX, pg 786
High End Systems Inc, pg 888

VIRGINIA

Quince Imaging Inc, pg 989

ALBERTA

SMART Technologies Inc, pg 1013

ONTARIO

Gesturetek, pg 877
Image Video, pg 895
Technovision® Interactive Inc, pg 1035

QUEBEC

Matrox Video Products Group, pg 934
Miranda Technologies, pg 944

Multi-Image Device & Presentation Accessory Rentals

ALABAMA

Media Visions Inc, pg 937

ARIZONA

Arizona Cine Equipment, pg 789
Merestone, pg 938
Metropolitan Audio-Visual Inc, pg 940
Ultimate Presentation Systems Inc, pg 1047
Video Media Productions (VMP), pg 1055

ARKANSAS

White Diamond Productions, pg 1065

CALIFORNIA

Ametron Audio/Video, pg 785
Associated Sound, pg 792
AV Guys, pg 797
California Teleprompter, pg 817
Gold Standard Productions, pg 880
JD Audio Visual Inc, pg 904
Lynch Communications, pg 926
McCune Audio-Video-Lighting, pg 935
Media Fabricators Inc, pg 936
Munday & Collins AV, pg 950
Muse Presentation Technologies, pg 950
PSAV® Presentation Services, pg 986
Related Visual Inc, pg 994
Slate Media Group, pg 1013
Stanislaus Audio Video Inc, pg 1023
Towards 2000 Inc, pg 1043
Tri-Ed, pg 1044
VER-Video Equipment Rentals, pg 1053
Video Resources Inc, pg 1056

COLORADO

Ceavco Audio/Visual Co, pg 822
Daylight Productions & Rentals, pg 844
Multimedia Audio Visual Inc, pg 950
Spectrum Audio Visual Services, pg 1020

CONNECTICUT

A/V Davey, pg 797
Videofilm Systems Inc, pg 1057

DELAWARE

Showorks Audio Visual Inc, pg 1010

FLORIDA

AVI-SPL, pg 798
Gulf Coast Audio Visual Producers Inc, pg 883
Harmon's Audio-Visual Services, pg 885
Image Technical Services, pg 895
Industrial Strength Inc, pg 897
Jordan Klein Film & Video (JKFV), pg 906
Media Concepts Inc, pg 936
Photosound of Orlando Inc, pg 975
Pro Stage Inc, pg 983
Spire Audio Visual Co Inc, pg 1021

GEORGIA

Convergent Media Systems, pg 836
Stage Front Presentation Systems, pg 1022
Staging Directions Inc, pg 1023

ILLINOIS

Airways Digital Media, pg 779
Audio Visual Services Corp, pg 796
Beatty TeleVisual Productions, pg 804
Creative Technology, pg 838
Helix Camera & Video, pg 887
The Pepper Group, pg 972
PSAV® Presentation Services (Hotel Services Division), pg 987
RC Communications, pg 992
SCI Television Productions LLC, pg 1004
Show Department Inc, pg 1009

INDIANA

Advanced Media Integration, pg 777
OMNI Productions, pg 962

KENTUCKY

Audio Visual Techniques Inc, pg 796

LOUISIANA

Clark Services Audio Visual & Exhibit Inc, pg 829
Pace Systems, pg 966

MARYLAND

Absolute Hollywood, pg 772
Advance Audiovisual Presentation Ltd, pg 777
CSPMedia.com, pg 840
dbF a Media Company, pg 844
Hargrove Inc, pg 885
Nelson White Systems Inc, pg 954
RTZ Audio Visual, pg 1000
Visual Aids Electronics Corp, pg 1059

MASSACHUSETTS

AVFX Inc, pg 798
Capron Lighting & Sound Co Inc, pg 819
massAV, pg 933
Preston Productions Inc, pg 981
TR Productions, pg 1043

MICHIGAN

City Events Group, pg 828
Digi Sign Design LLC, pg 847
K&R All Media Productions Inc, pg 908
K&R's Recording Studios Inc, pg 908

MINNESOTA

Advanced Audio-Visual Inc, pg 777
AVI Systems, pg 799
Media Loft Inc, pg 937

MISSISSIPPI

Bowie Audio Visual Enterprises Inc, pg 811
Jasper Ewing & Sons Inc, pg 864

MISSOURI

Communitronics Corp, pg 833
Show-Me Audio-Visual, pg 1009
Swank Audio Visuals, pg 1029
Switch, pg 1030

NEVADA

GES Audio Visual, pg 877

NEW HAMPSHIRE

Academic & Campus Technology Services, pg 773
Apertura, pg 788

NEW JERSEY

Audio Visual Associates, pg 795
Audio Visual Dynamics®, pg 795
Color Leasing Studios, pg 831
Earl Girls Inc, pg 855
International Audio Visual Inc, pg 900
Moe AV LLC, pg 945
PLS Staging, pg 977
Starlite Productions, pg 1024
Wired 4 Sound Inc, pg 1068

NEW YORK

AV Workshop, pg 797
CMI Communications, pg 830
Communication Corner Inc, pg 832
CP Communications, pg 837
Design Audio Visual Inc, pg 845
General Audio-Visual Inc (GAVI), pg 876
Langie Audio Visual Systems, pg 915
Long Island Video Enterprises Live Inc, pg 924
Visual Technologies Corp, pg 1060
Visual Word Systems Inc, pg 1060
WorldStage, pg 1070

NORTH CAROLINA

A&V Company, pg 772
AV Metro Inc, pg 797
Camcor Inc, pg 818
Special Event Services, pg 1020
Strategic Connections, pg 1026
Visual Aids Electronics of North Carolina Inc, pg 1059

NORTH DAKOTA

Media Productions, pg 937

OHIO

Audio Visual Media, pg 795
Icom Multimedia, pg 893
Thread Marketing Group, pg 1039
Vista Color Imaging Inc, pg 1059

PENNSYLVANIA

Advanced AV, pg 777
Audio Visions Inc, pg 795
Audio Visual Communications Inc, pg 795
FMP Media Solutions Inc, pg 870
Grise Audio Visual Center Inc, pg 882
Production Solutions Inc, pg 985
Visual Sound Inc, pg 1059

SOUTH CAROLINA

Sound & Images Inc, pg 1016

TENNESSEE

Memphis Communications Corp, pg 938
Russ Sturgeon Productions/RSVP, pg 1027
Technical Support Systems LLC, pg 1034
Tennessee Visual Service Co, pg 1037

TEXAS

Audio Visual Technologies Group, pg 796
Freeman, pg 872
J&S Audio Visual Inc, pg 904
Lubbock Audio Visual Inc, pg 925
Schoolhouse Audio Visual, pg 1004
Stage Directions, pg 1022

UTAH

Webb Audio Visual Communication, pg 1063

VERMONT

Parlato Productions, pg 969

VIRGINIA

American AV, pg 783
Boitnott Visual Communications Corp (BVC), pg 810
Projection Presentation Technology, pg 985
Quince Imaging Inc, pg 989

WASHINGTON

D A Sound, pg 842
Inland Audio Visual Co, pg 898
Kostov Productions, pg 913

WISCONSIN

Audio Visual of Milwaukee Inc, pg 795
Camera Corner Connecting Point, pg 818
Event Essentials, pg 863
Full Compass Systems, pg 874

WYOMING

Bridger Productions Inc, pg 812

PUERTO RICO

Stage Crew Audiovisual Inc, pg 1022

ALBERTA

Cine Audio Visual Sales & Service Ltd, pg 826
Evolution Presentation Technologies, pg 863
McBain Audio Visual Ltd, pg 935
Sharp's Audio-Visual Ltd, pg 1008
Unique Communications Ltd, pg 1048

BRITISH COLUMBIA

Clark's Audio Visual Services Ltd, pg 829
Commercial Electronics Ltd, pg 832

MANITOBA

Evolution Presentation Technologies, pg 863
Inland Audio Visual Ltd, pg 898

ONTARIO

Edcom Multimedia Products, pg 856
Gesturetek, pg 877
HD Source, pg 886
MVI Multivision Inc, pg 951
Westbury National Show Systems Ltd, pg 1064

QUEBEC

Audio Visual Dynamics Ltd, pg 795
AVW-TELAV Audio Visual Solutions, a Freeman Company, pg 800
Concept Audio-Visual, pg 834

Multi-Image Device & Presentation Accessory Repairs

ARKANSAS

Jay S Stanley & Associates Inc, pg 1023

CALIFORNIA

Ametron Audio/Video, pg 785
AVerMedia Technologies Inc, pg 798
Electrosonic Inc, pg 859
Instructional Materials & Equipment Distributors (I-Med), pg 899
McAlister Electronics, pg 935
Lloyd F McKinney Associates Inc, pg 935
Pro Camera Repair, pg 982
Towards 2000 Inc, pg 1043

COLORADO

Ceavco Audio/Visual Co, pg 822

CONNECTICUT

HB Communications Inc, pg 886

FLORIDA

Spire Audio Visual Co Inc, pg 1021
Tallahassee Audio Visual, pg 1031

GEORGIA

Audio Visual Resources Inc, pg 795
Stage Front Presentation Systems, pg 1022

ILLINOIS

RC Communications, pg 992

KENTUCKY

Axxis Inc, pg 800
NOR-COM Inc, pg 958

MARYLAND

Nelson White Systems Inc, pg 954
RTZ Audio Visual, pg 1000
Visual Aids Electronics Corp, pg 1059

MICHIGAN

City Events Group, pg 828
TeL Systems, pg 1035

MINNESOTA

AVI Systems, pg 799

MISSISSIPPI

Bowie Audio Visual Enterprises Inc, pg 811

MISSOURI

Communitronics Corp, pg 833

NEW JERSEY

Earl Girls Inc, pg 855
Starlite Productions, pg 1024

NEW YORK

Analog Way Inc, pg 786
Colortone Audio Visual, pg 832
ELMO USA Corp, pg 859
Langie Audio Visual Systems, pg 915
Visual Technologies Corp, pg 1060

NORTH CAROLINA

Camcor Inc, pg 818
Strategic Connections, pg 1026

OHIO

Audio Visual Media, pg 795
Aztec Video Productions, pg 801
Icom Multimedia, pg 893
Tri-State Audio Visual Co, pg 1044

PENNSYLVANIA

Audio Visions Inc, pg 795

RHODE ISLAND

Custom Computer Specialists Inc, pg 841

TENNESSEE

Memphis Communications Corp, pg 938
Technical Support Systems LLC, pg 1034
Tennessee Visual Service Co, pg 1037

TEXAS

Audio Visual Technologies Group, pg 796
Heffernan Audio Visual, pg 887
Lubbock Audio Visual Inc, pg 925

VIRGINIA

Boitnott Visual Communications Corp (BVC), pg 810
Hoppmann Audio Visual, pg 891
Lee Hartman & Sons Inc, pg 918
Quince Imaging Inc, pg 989
The Whitlock Group, pg 1065

WASHINGTON

Inland Audio Visual Co, pg 898

WISCONSIN

Full Compass Systems, pg 874

ALBERTA

Infosat Communications Inc, pg 898
Sharp's Audio-Visual Ltd, pg 1008
Unique Communications Ltd, pg 1048

MANITOBA

Evolution Presentation Technologies, pg 863
Inland Audio Visual Ltd, pg 898

AUDIO/VISUAL

Multi-Image Device & Presentation Accessory Repairs (continued)

ONTARIO

Edcom Multimedia Products, pg 856
MVI Multivision Inc, pg 951
Technovision® Interactive Inc, pg 1035
Westbury National Show Systems Ltd, pg 1064

Music Scoring

ALABAMA

Media Visions Inc, pg 937
Sound of Birmingham Productions, pg 1017

ARIZONA

Creative Backstage, pg 838
Merestone, pg 938
Productiontrax.com, pg 985

ARKANSAS

Live'N'Loud, pg 923
Shadowbox Video Productions, pg 1007

CALIFORNIA

AB Audio Visual Entertainment Inc, pg 772
Aliso Creek Productions Inc, pg 780
Ancient Future, pg 786
Argyle Post, pg 789
Berkeley Sound Artists Inc, pg 805
CCI Digital, pg 821
Creative Media Recording, pg 838
Creative Support Services/CSS Music, pg 838
Crystal Pyramid Productions™, pg 840
Diamond Dreams Music Productions, pg 846
Dogma Studios, pg 850
Earwax Productions Inc, pg 855
GrooveWorx, pg 882
iCorpTv, pg 893
JDS Video & Media Productions Inc, pg 904
K2B2 Records, pg 907
Kaleidosound, pg 907
The Kitchen, pg 911
Lynch Communications, pg 926
Maximus Media Inc, pg 934
The Media Staff Inc, pg 937
Mind Over Eye Inc, pg 943
Joseph Nicoletti Consulting-Promotion/California International Records/Global Village Records, pg 957
OTR Studios, pg 966
piXvfm, pg 976
PM Productions, pg 977
Polarity Post Production, pg 978
Pyramind Studios, pg 988
QRS Software Services, pg 988
Reality Check Systems, pg 992
Rhythms Productions (Tom Thumb Music), pg 996
Russ InVision Co/AbridgeClub.com, pg 1001
Sahara Records & Filmworks Entertainment Co, pg 1001
SBS Productions, pg 1003
Sonic Gravy, pg 1015
SonicPool, pg 1016
Still N'Motion, pg 1025
Studio 132, pg 1027
Total Media Group, pg 1042
West Coast Projections Inc, pg 1063

COLORADO

Tim Cissell Music, pg 828
Conly Productions, pg 835
Flashback Media Productions, pg 869
Los Angeles Post Music Inc, pg 924

CONNECTICUT

Broadcast Video Productions LLC, pg 813
EagleVision Inc, pg 855
Guymark Studios LLC, pg 883
MAVCO, pg 934
Music 2 Hues, pg 951
P&P Studios Inc, pg 968

DELAWARE

Side Door Studio Inc, pg 1010

DISTRICT OF COLUMBIA

Interface Media Group, pg 900

FLORIDA

Allegro Productions Inc, pg 781
Audacity Creative, pg 793
Digital Video Arts, pg 848
Kat Epple Music Productions, pg 862
Gulf Coast Audio Visual Producers Inc, pg 883
Mach 1 Productions, pg 927
Progressive Media & Music, pg 985
Promidi Music, pg 986
Sunfire Communications Inc, pg 1028

GEORGIA

Crawford Media Services, pg 838
NorthTown Sounds Inc, pg 959
Symmes Systems, pg 1030
USMotivation, pg 1051
Visioneering International Inc, pg 1058
White Dog Studios, pg 1065

HAWAII

Ken Herkes Productions & Entertainment (KHPE), pg 888
Media Bridge Gamekids, pg 936

ILLINOIS

ABS Enterprises, pg 772
MIGHTYbYTES Inc, pg 942
Paragon Studios Inc, pg 969
Jim Passin Productions, pg 970
The Pepper Group, pg 972
Steven Samler Music & Sound, pg 1002
Solid Sound Recording Studio, pg 1015
Twisted Media Inc, pg 1047
Woodside Avenue Music Productions Inc, pg 1069

INDIANA

OMNI Productions, pg 962

KANSAS

Chapman Recording & Mastering, pg 824

KENTUCKY

Broadway Digital, pg 813
The Media Collaboratory, pg 936

LOUISIANA

Disk Productions, pg 849

MARYLAND

CSPMedia.com, pg 840
dbF a Media Company, pg 844

MASSACHUSETTS

Continental Recordings Inc, pg 835
Labrecque Creative Sound, pg 915
Northern Light Productions, pg 959
Penfield Productions Ltd, pg 971
Preston Productions Inc, pg 981
Soundtrack Recording Studios, pg 1018
TR Productions, pg 1043

MICHIGAN

Audio Graphic Services, pg 794
Digi Sign Design LLC, pg 847
GMP Music, pg 879
K&R's Recording Studios Inc, pg 908
Michigan Recording Arts Institute & Technologies, pg 941
Studio A Recording Inc, pg 1026

MINNESOTA

The ADS Group, pg 777
Beyers Sound & Essay Audio, pg 806
Media Loft Inc, pg 937
MultiMedia, pg 950

MISSOURI

Production Consultants, pg 984

MONTANA

North Country Media Group, pg 959

NEVADA

Tanglewood Productions, pg 1031

NEW HAMPSHIRE

Chip Taylor Communications LLC, pg 1032

NEW JERSEY

CFP Video Productions Inc, pg 823
Color Leasing Studios, pg 831
Milbrodt/Music & Sound Design, pg 943
Milgrom Productions, pg 943
NFL Films Music Library, pg 957
Richard Reiter Productions Inc, pg 994
Suede Interactive, pg 1027
TRF Production Music Libraries, pg 1044
VCSvideo, pg 1052

NEW YORK

Air Sea Land Productions Inc (ASL), pg 779
Big Fish Productions Inc, pg 807
The Big House Group, pg 807
Duggal Visual Solutions, pg 853
Fingerpaint, pg 868
Bob Gerardi Music Productions, pg 877
HB-Content, pg 886
Headroom Digital Audio, pg 887
Heavy Melody, pg 887
Icontent, pg 893
KAS Music & Sound, pg 908
L&P Media, pg 915
Lylofilm Productions, pg 926
Manhattan Production Music Inc, pg 930
Jack Morton Worldwide, pg 946
MRG Productions Inc, pg 948
New York Audio Productions, pg 956
Nutmeg Post, pg 960
Omnimusic, pg 962
Shelly Palmer Production, pg 968
Patco Resources Inc, pg 970
David Rapkin Audio Production, pg 991
Score Productions Inc, pg 1005
Elliot Sokolov Music, pg 1015
Sony Music Entertainment, pg 1016
TBA Global Events, pg 1032
Tiki Recording Studios Inc, pg 1040
USA Studios, pg 1050
Zelman Studios Ltd, pg 1073

NORTH CAROLINA

Audio Art, pg 794
Davenport Music Library, pg 843
Trailblazer Studios®, pg 1043
2BruceStudio, pg 1047

NORTH DAKOTA

Media Productions, pg 937

OHIO

Aztec Video Productions, pg 801
EDR Media LLC, pg 857
Mills James Productions, pg 943

OKLAHOMA

Garman Productions LLC, pg 875

OREGON

Rex, pg 995

PENNSYLVANIA

Audio Visual Communications Inc, pg 795
Dreambox Media Inc, pg 852
Monster Tracks, pg 945
Panta Rhei Media Inc, pg 968
Production Masters Inc (PMI), pg 984

RHODE ISLAND

Sound-FX-Design, pg 1017
StarTrak Studios Inc, pg 1024

TENNESSEE

American Blackguard Inc, pg 784
Continental Film, pg 835
Fricon Entertainment Co Inc, pg 873
Motion Picture Services, pg 947
Scripps Networks, pg 1005
Stage Post, pg 1022
Zion Music Group, pg 1074

TEXAS

Audio Visual Technologies Group, pg 796
Audiomoxie®, pg 796
Communication Arts Multimedia Inc, pg 832
Harbor House Studios, pg 884
Mediaforce Productions, pg 937
The Sound Lab Inc, pg 1017

Sound Works, pg 1018
Stage Directions, pg 1022
TM Studios Inc, pg 1041
Tropikal Productions, pg 1045

VERMONT

University of Vermont, Instructional Television Dept, pg 1050

VIRGINIA

Studio Center Corp, pg 1026

WASHINGTON

Hamilton Studio, pg 884
Inland Audio Visual Co, pg 898
Kostov Productions, pg 913
North-by-Northwest Productions, pg 958
Sound Sound/Savage Fruitarian Productions, pg 1017
Victory Studios, pg 1054

WISCONSIN

5th Floor Recording Co, pg 867
USAV Group Inc, pg 1050

WYOMING

Bridger Productions Inc, pg 812

BRITISH COLUMBIA

Pinewood Sound, pg 975

ONTARIO

ADS Media, pg 777
GAPC (General Assembly Production Centre), pg 875
Metalworks Recording Studios Inc, pg 939
Nightingale Music Productions Inc, pg 957
VO2 Mix Studios, pg 1060

Opaque & Overhead Projector Distributors

ALABAMA

Curtis Company, pg 841
Media Visions Inc, pg 937

ARIZONA

Arizona Cine Equipment, pg 789
Metropolitan Audio-Visual Inc, pg 940
Professional Marketing Services Inc, pg 985
Troxell Communications Inc, pg 1045

ARKANSAS

Carlton-Bates Co, pg 820
Jay S Stanley & Associates Inc, pg 1023
White Diamond Productions, pg 1065

CALIFORNIA

Ametron Audio/Video, pg 785
Associated Sound, pg 792
Audio/Video Supply Inc, pg 795
California Tape Products Inc, pg 817
Christy's Editorial, pg 826
Eiki International, pg 858
FXC Communications, pg 874
Gluskin's Custom Audio Video, pg 879
Hooper Camera & Imaging, pg 891
Instructional Materials & Equipment Distributors (I-Med), pg 899
JD Audio Visual Inc, pg 904
Media Fabricators Inc, pg 936
MediaMation Inc, pg 937
MediaPOINTE, pg 938
PMP Marketing Inc, pg 977
POP TV, pg 978
Related Visual Inc, pg 994
Southern California Sound Image Inc, pg 1019
Towards 2000 Inc, pg 1043
Tri-Ed, pg 1044

COLORADO

Ceavco Audio/Visual Co, pg 822
Daylight Productions & Rentals, pg 844
Spectrum Audio Visual Services, pg 1020
Stanco Sales LLC, pg 1023

CONNECTICUT

Concord Communications, pg 835
HB Communications Inc, pg 886
MAVCO, pg 934
Rockwell Communications Inc, pg 998
USI Inc, pg 1051

FLORIDA

AVI-SPL, pg 798
Digital Video Systems Inc, pg 848
Gulf Coast Audio Visual Producers Inc, pg 883
Harmon's Audio-Visual Services, pg 885
Hi-Tech Import Export Corp, pg 888
Industrial Strength Inc, pg 897
Photomart Cine-Video Inc, pg 975
Photosound of Orlando Inc, pg 975
Pro Stage Inc, pg 983
Sight & Sound Productions, pg 1010
Spire Audio Visual Co Inc, pg 1021
Tallahassee Audio Visual, pg 1031

GEORGIA

Audio Visual Resources Inc, pg 795
Baker Audio Inc, pg 801
Stage Front Presentation Systems, pg 1022
Technical Innovation, pg 1033
Visioneering International Inc, pg 1058

HAWAII

The Audio Visual Co (AVCO), pg 795

ILLINOIS

Allen Visual Systems Inc, pg 781
Central Audio-Visual Equipment Inc, pg 823
RC Communications, pg 992
Sound Vision Inc, pg 1018

INDIANA

SHP Electronics, pg 1010
Victoria Supply Inc/Topbulb.com, pg 1054

IOWA

ECS Inc, pg 856

KANSAS

KK Office Solutions Inc, pg 911

KENTUCKY

Audio Visual Techniques Inc, pg 796
Axxis Inc, pg 800
NOR-COM Inc, pg 958
Northern Kentucky University, pg 959

LOUISIANA

Intermedia Technologies, pg 900

MAINE

Headlight Audio Visual Inc, pg 887

MARYLAND

Cardinal Sound & Video, pg 820
Kipp Visual Systems Inc, pg 911
Nelson White Systems Inc, pg 954
Nicholas P Pipino Associates Inc, pg 976
Ritz Camera & Image, pg 997
RTZ Audio Visual, pg 1000
Visual Aids Electronics Corp, pg 1059

MASSACHUSETTS

Camera Co Inc/Broadcast Divison, pg 818
Hunt's Photo, Video & Digital, pg 892
Lineco, pg 922
Rule Broadcast Systems, pg 1000
University Products Inc, pg 1050

MICHIGAN

Olson Anderson Co, pg 786
City Events Group, pg 828
Digi Sign Design LLC, pg 847
Michigan Office Solutions, pg 941
TeL Systems, pg 1035

MINNESOTA

Advanced Audio-Visual Inc, pg 777
AVI Systems, pg 799
Tierney Brothers Inc, pg 1040

MISSISSIPPI

Bowie Audio Visual Enterprises Inc, pg 811
Jasper Ewing & Sons Inc, pg 864

MISSOURI

Communitronics Corp, pg 833
Conference Technologies Inc, pg 835
Image Technologies Corp, pg 895
MIS Technologies, pg 944
Schiller's Audio-Visual, pg 1004
Swank Audio Visuals, pg 1029

NEW JERSEY

A-V Services Inc, pg 771
Argraph Corp, pg 789
Audio Visual Associates, pg 795
Audio Visual Dynamics®, pg 795
AV Bluebook, pg 797
Hamilton Buhl, pg 884
National Audio-Visual Supply, pg 952
Starlite Productions, pg 1024
SYMCO Inc, pg 1030
Total Video Products Inc, pg 1042
VCom International Multimedia Corp, pg 1052
Video Corporation of America (VCA), pg 1055
Wilray Audio Visual Corp, pg 1067
Wired 4 Sound Inc, pg 1068
York Telecom, pg 1072

NEW YORK

ALTEL Systems Inc, pg 783
AV Workshop, pg 797
Colortone Audio Visual, pg 832
Communication Corner Inc, pg 832
Custom Media Environments, pg 841
Design Audio Visual Inc, pg 845
Gaylord Brothers, pg 876
Gordon Visual Solutions, pg 880
Indigo Productions, pg 897
Langie Audio Visual Systems, pg 915
Long Island Video Enterprises Live Inc, pg 924
Magnaplan Corp, pg 928
Markertek Video Supply, pg 931
Neptune Photo Inc, pg 954
Ray Supply Inc, pg 992
RNJ Electronics, pg 997
Technisphere Corp, pg 1034
Visual Technologies Corp, pg 1060
Willoughby's Imaging Center, pg 1067

NORTH CAROLINA

Camcor Inc, pg 818
Strategic Connections, pg 1026

OHIO

Audio Visual Media, pg 795
Copp Integrated Systems, pg 836
Smithall Electronics Inc, pg 1014
Tri-State Audio Visual Co, pg 1044
Tri-State Visual Products, pg 1044
Xetron, pg 1071

OREGON

PLUS Corp of America, pg 977

PENNSYLVANIA

Advanced AV, pg 777
Audio Visions Inc, pg 795
Audio Visual Communications Inc, pg 795
Bernie's Photo Center, pg 805
Brodart Co, pg 813
J E Foss Co, pg 871
Garcia Marketing Inc, pg 875
Grise Audio Visual Center Inc, pg 882
TRC Interactive Inc, pg 1044
Vistacom Inc, pg 1059
Visual Sound Inc, pg 1059
Wespen Audio Visual Co, pg 1063

RHODE ISLAND

Custom Computer Specialists Inc, pg 841

TENNESSEE

Durrell LLC, pg 854
Lowrance Sound Co Inc, pg 925
Memphis Communications Corp, pg 938
Spring Arbor Distributors, pg 1022
Tennessee Visual Service Co, pg 1037

TEXAS

Astro Audio Visual, pg 792
Audio Visual Technologies Group, pg 796

AUDIO/VISUAL

Opaque & Overhead Projector Distributors (continued)

TEXAS (continued)

AVES Audio Visual Systems Inc, pg 798
Data Projections Inc, pg 843
FitzCo Sound Inc, pg 869
Heffernan Audio Visual, pg 887
J&S Audio Visual Inc, pg 904
Lubbock Audio Visual Inc, pg 925
Media Management LLC, pg 937
Quality Audio Visual Service Inc, pg 988
Schoolhouse Audio Visual, pg 1004
Videotex Systems Inc, pg 1057

UTAH

Webb Audio Visual Communication, pg 1063

VIRGINIA

Boitnott Visual Communications Corp (BVC), pg 810
Communications Specialists Inc, pg 833
Filmdex Inc, pg 867
Hoppmann Audio Visual, pg 891
Intellidyne LLC, pg 899
Lee Hartman & Sons Inc, pg 918
Metropolitan Audio Visual Co LLC, pg 940
The Whitlock Group, pg 1065

WASHINGTON

CCI Solutions, pg 821
Inland Audio Visual Co, pg 898
Pacific Northwest Theatre Associates Inc (PNTA), pg 967

WISCONSIN

Camera Corner Connecting Point, pg 818
Demco Inc, pg 845
Full Compass Systems, pg 874
Pro Studio Supply, pg 983
School Specialty Inc, pg 1004

PUERTO RICO

Bonnin Electronics Inc, pg 810

ALBERTA

Infosat Communications Inc, pg 898
McBain Audio Visual Ltd, pg 935
Sharp's Audio-Visual Ltd, pg 1008
Unique Communications Ltd, pg 1048

BRITISH COLUMBIA

Commercial Electronics Ltd, pg 832

MANITOBA

Evolution Presentation Technologies, pg 863
Inland Audio Visual Ltd, pg 898

ONTARIO

Carr McLean Ltd, pg 820
Edcom Multimedia Products, pg 856
Nationwide Audio Visual Co, pg 953
Premier A/V Sales Ltd, pg 980
Westbury National Show Systems Ltd, pg 1064

QUEBEC

Concept Audio-Visual, pg 834
Panavideo Inc, pg 968

Opaque & Overhead Projector Manufacturers

ILLINOIS

ACCO Brands Corp, pg 773
Dukane Corp, Audio Visual Products Division, pg 853

MINNESOTA

Artograph Inc, pg 791

NEW JERSEY

National Audio-Visual Supply, pg 952

NEW YORK

ELMO USA Corp, pg 859
Gagne Inc, pg 875
Gordon Visual Solutions, pg 880
TecNec Distributing, pg 1035

OHIO

Xetron, pg 1071

VIRGINIA

Hoppmann Audio Visual, pg 891

Opaque & Overhead Projector Rentals

ALABAMA

Audio-Video Resources Inc, pg 795
Media Visions Inc, pg 937

ARIZONA

Arizona Cine Equipment, pg 789
Merestone, pg 938
Metropolitan Audio-Visual Inc, pg 940
Video Media Productions (VMP), pg 1055

ARKANSAS

Carlton-Bates Co, pg 820
White Diamond Productions, pg 1065

CALIFORNIA

AGF Media Services, pg 778
Alliant Event Services, pg 781
Ametron Audio/Video, pg 785
Associated Sound, pg 792
AV Guys, pg 797
Hooper Camera & Imaging, pg 891
Impact Group, pg 897
Instructional Materials & Equipment Distributors (I-Med), pg 899
JD Audio Visual Inc, pg 904
Lynch Communications, pg 926
Media Fabricators Inc, pg 936
Munday & Collins AV, pg 950
PSAV® Presentation Services, pg 986
Related Visual Inc, pg 994
Slate Media Group, pg 1013
Stanislaus Audio Video Inc, pg 1023
Towards 2000 Inc, pg 1043
University of Southern California, pg 1050
VER-Video Equipment Rentals, pg 1053
Voice & Video Rentals, pg 1060

COLORADO

Ceavco Audio/Visual Co, pg 822
Daylight Productions & Rentals, pg 844
Multimedia Audio Visual Inc, pg 950
Spectrum Audio Visual Services, pg 1020

CONNECTICUT

A/V Davey, pg 797
Rockwell Communications Inc, pg 998
Videofilm Systems Inc, pg 1057

FLORIDA

AVI-SPL, pg 798
Gulf Coast Audio Visual Producers Inc, pg 883
Harmon's Audio-Visual Services, pg 885
Image Technical Services, pg 895
Industrial Strength Inc, pg 897
Photosound of Orlando Inc, pg 975
Pro Stage Inc, pg 983
Sight & Sound Productions, pg 1010
Spire Audio Visual Co Inc, pg 1021
Tallahassee Audio Visual, pg 1031
Universal Studios Florida® Production Group, pg 1049

GEORGIA

Audio Visual Resources Inc, pg 795
Dixie Theatre Service & Supply Co Inc, pg 849
MAGNUM Companies Ltd, pg 929
ON Event Services, pg 963
Stage Front Presentation Systems, pg 1022
Staging Directions Inc, pg 1023

HAWAII

ATTCO Inc, pg 793

ILLINOIS

Allen Visual Systems Inc, pg 781
Audio Visual Services Corp, pg 796
AV Chicago Inc, pg 797
Backstar Creative Media Inc, pg 801
Beatty TeleVisual Productions, pg 804
Central Audio-Visual Equipment Inc, pg 823
Helix Camera & Video, pg 887
PSAV® Presentation Services (Hotel Services Division), pg 987
RC Communications, pg 992

INDIANA

Gary Camera & Digital, pg 875

IOWA

ECS Inc, pg 856

KENTUCKY

Audio Visual Techniques Inc, pg 796

LOUISIANA

Clark Services Audio Visual & Exhibit Inc, pg 829

MAINE

Headlight Audio Visual Inc, pg 887

MARYLAND

Advance Audiovisual Presentation Ltd, pg 777
CPR MultiMedia Solutions, pg 837
dbF a Media Company, pg 844
Nelson White Systems Inc, pg 954
Nicholas P Pipino Associates Inc, pg 976
RTZ Audio Visual, pg 1000
Visual Aids Electronics Corp, pg 1059

MASSACHUSETTS

Camera Co Inc/Broadcast Divison, pg 818
Capron Lighting & Sound Co Inc, pg 819
massAV, pg 933
Preston Productions Inc, pg 981

MICHIGAN

Olson Anderson Co, pg 786
City Events Group, pg 828
Digi Sign Design LLC, pg 847
K&R All Media Productions Inc, pg 908

MINNESOTA

Advanced Audio-Visual Inc, pg 777
AVI Systems, pg 799

MISSISSIPPI

Bowie Audio Visual Enterprises Inc, pg 811
Jasper Ewing & Sons Inc, pg 864

MISSOURI

Communitronics Corp, pg 833
Schiller's Audio-Visual, pg 1004
Show-Me Audio-Visual, pg 1009
Swank Audio Visuals, pg 1029

NEVADA

GES Audio Visual, pg 877

NEW HAMPSHIRE

Academic & Campus Technology Services, pg 773

NEW JERSEY

Audio Visual Associates, pg 795
Audio Visual Dynamics®, pg 795
International Audio Visual Inc, pg 900
Moe AV LLC, pg 945
Starlite Productions, pg 1024
Video Corporation of America (VCA), pg 1055
Wired 4 Sound Inc, pg 1068

NEW YORK

Ace Video, pg 774
AV Workshop, pg 797
Colortone Audio Visual, pg 832
Communication Corner Inc, pg 832
Design Audio Visual Inc, pg 845
Langie Audio Visual Systems, pg 915

Long Island Video Enterprises Live Inc, pg 924
Magnaplan Corp, pg 928
Neptune Photo Inc, pg 954
Specialized Audio-Visual Inc, pg 1020
Technisphere Corp, pg 1034
Visual Technologies Corp, pg 1060
Visual Word Systems Inc, pg 1060
WorldStage, pg 1070

NORTH CAROLINA

A&V Company, pg 772
Camcor Inc, pg 818
Special Event Services, pg 1020
Visual Aids Electronics of North Carolina Inc, pg 1059

OHIO

Audio Visual Media, pg 795
Aztec Video Productions, pg 801
Hughie's Event Production Services, pg 892

PENNSYLVANIA

Advanced AV, pg 777
Audio Visions Inc, pg 795
Audio Visual Communications Inc, pg 795
Grise Audio Visual Center Inc, pg 882
Ott Film Rentals, pg 966
Production Solutions Inc, pg 985
Visual Sound Inc, pg 1059

SOUTH CAROLINA

Sound & Images Inc, pg 1016

TENNESSEE

Memphis Communications Corp, pg 938
Tennessee Visual Service Co, pg 1037

TEXAS

Astro Audio Visual, pg 792
Audio Visual Technologies Group, pg 796
FitzCo Sound Inc, pg 869
Heffernan Audio Visual, pg 887
J&S Audio Visual Inc, pg 904
Lubbock Audio Visual Inc, pg 925
Quality Audio Visual Service Inc, pg 988
Schoolhouse Audio Visual, pg 1004

UTAH

Webb Audio Visual Communication, pg 1063

VERMONT

Parlato Productions, pg 969

VIRGINIA

American AV, pg 783
Boitnott Visual Communications Corp (BVC), pg 810
Lee Hartman & Sons Inc, pg 918
Metropolitan Audio Visual Co LLC, pg 940
Projection Presentation Technology, pg 985
Rainbow Rentals, pg 991
The Whitlock Group, pg 1065

WASHINGTON

D A Sound, pg 842
Inland Audio Visual Co, pg 898
Pacific Northwest Theatre Associates Inc (PNTA), pg 967

WISCONSIN

Camera Corner Connecting Point, pg 818
Event Essentials, pg 863
Full Compass Systems, pg 874
School Specialty Inc, pg 1004

PUERTO RICO

Stage Crew Audiovisual Inc, pg 1022

ALBERTA

Allstar Show Industries Inc, pg 782
Evolution Presentation Technologies, pg 863
McBain Audio Visual Ltd, pg 935
Sharp's Audio-Visual Ltd, pg 1008
Unique Communications Ltd, pg 1048

BRITISH COLUMBIA

Clark's Audio Visual Services Ltd, pg 829
Commercial Electronics Ltd, pg 832
Triad Communications Ltd, pg 1044

MANITOBA

Inland Audio Visual Ltd, pg 898

ONTARIO

Edcom Multimedia Products, pg 856
HD Source, pg 886
Westbury National Show Systems Ltd, pg 1064

QUEBEC

Audio Visual Dynamics Ltd, pg 795
AVW-TELAV Audio Visual Solutions, a Freeman Company, pg 800
Concept Audio-Visual, pg 834
Panavideo Inc, pg 968

Opaque & Overhead Projector Repairs

ARKANSAS

Carlton-Bates Co, pg 820
Jay S Stanley & Associates Inc, pg 1023

CALIFORNIA

Ametron Audio/Video, pg 785
Gluskin's Custom Audio Video, pg 879
Hooper Camera & Imaging, pg 891
Instructional Materials & Equipment Distributors (I-Med), pg 899
McAlister Electronics, pg 935
Lloyd F McKinney Associates Inc, pg 935
Pro Camera Repair, pg 982
Towards 2000 Inc, pg 1043

COLORADO

Ceavco Audio/Visual Co, pg 822

CONNECTICUT

HB Communications Inc, pg 886
Rockwell Communications Inc, pg 998

FLORIDA

Spire Audio Visual Co Inc, pg 1021
Tallahassee Audio Visual, pg 1031

GEORGIA

Audio Visual Resources Inc, pg 795
Stage Front Presentation Systems, pg 1022

ILLINOIS

Allen Visual Systems Inc, pg 781
RC Communications, pg 992

INDIANA

Gary Camera & Digital, pg 875

IOWA

ECS Inc, pg 856

KANSAS

KK Office Solutions Inc, pg 911

KENTUCKY

Axxis Inc, pg 800
NOR-COM Inc, pg 958

MAINE

Headlight Audio Visual Inc, pg 887

MARYLAND

Nelson White Systems Inc, pg 954
Nicholas P Pipino Associates Inc, pg 976
RTZ Audio Visual, pg 1000
Strauss Photo Technical Service Inc, pg 1026
Visual Aids Electronics Corp, pg 1059

MASSACHUSETTS

Camera Co Inc/Broadcast Divison, pg 818

MICHIGAN

City Events Group, pg 828
TeL Systems, pg 1035

MINNESOTA

AVI Systems, pg 799

MISSISSIPPI

Bowie Audio Visual Enterprises Inc, pg 811

MISSOURI

Cintrex Audio Visual, pg 828
Communitronics Corp, pg 833
Schiller's Audio-Visual, pg 1004

NEW JERSEY

Audio Visual Associates, pg 795

NEW YORK

Colortone Audio Visual, pg 832
ELMO USA Corp, pg 859
Langie Audio Visual Systems, pg 915
Magnaplan Corp, pg 928
Ray Supply Inc, pg 992
Visual Technologies Corp, pg 1060

NORTH CAROLINA

Camcor Inc, pg 818

OHIO

Audio Visual Media, pg 795
Aztec Video Productions, pg 801
Copp Integrated Systems, pg 836
Tri-State Audio Visual Co, pg 1044

PENNSYLVANIA

Audio Visions Inc, pg 795
J E Foss Co, pg 871
Ott Film Rentals, pg 966
Wespen Audio Visual Co, pg 1063

RHODE ISLAND

Custom Computer Specialists Inc, pg 841

TENNESSEE

Memphis Communications Corp, pg 938
Tennessee Visual Service Co, pg 1037

TEXAS

Astro Audio Visual, pg 792
Audio Visual Technologies Group, pg 796
Heffernan Audio Visual, pg 887
Lubbock Audio Visual Inc, pg 925
Quality Audio Visual Service Inc, pg 988
Schoolhouse Audio Visual, pg 1004

VIRGINIA

Boitnott Visual Communications Corp (BVC), pg 810
Hoppmann Audio Visual, pg 891
Lee Hartman & Sons Inc, pg 918
Metropolitan Audio Visual Co LLC, pg 940
The Whitlock Group, pg 1065

WASHINGTON

Inland Audio Visual Co, pg 898
Pacific Northwest Theatre Associates Inc (PNTA), pg 967

WISCONSIN

Full Compass Systems, pg 874
School Specialty Inc, pg 1004

ALBERTA

Infosat Communications Inc, pg 898
Sharp's Audio-Visual Ltd, pg 1008

MANITOBA

Evolution Presentation Technologies, pg 863
Inland Audio Visual Ltd, pg 898

ONTARIO

Edcom Multimedia Products, pg 856
Premier A/V Sales Ltd, pg 980
Westbury National Show Systems Ltd, pg 1064

QUEBEC

Panavideo Inc, pg 968

AUDIO/VISUAL

Opaque & Overhead Supply & Accessory Distributors

ALABAMA

Curtis Company, pg 841
Media Visions Inc, pg 937

ARIZONA

Arizona Cine Equipment, pg 789
Docter Optics Inc, pg 849
Metropolitan Audio-Visual Inc, pg 940
Troxell Communications Inc, pg 1045

ARKANSAS

Carlton-Bates Co, pg 820
Jay S Stanley & Associates Inc, pg 1023
White Diamond Productions, pg 1065

CALIFORNIA

Ametron Audio/Video, pg 785
California Tape Products Inc, pg 817
Christy's Editorial, pg 826
Educational Technology Services (ETS), pg 857
FXC Communications, pg 874
Hooper Camera & Imaging, pg 891
Instructional Materials & Equipment Distributors (I-Med), pg 899
JD Audio Visual Inc, pg 904
Media Fabricators Inc, pg 936
MediaPOINTE, pg 938
PMP Marketing Inc, pg 977
Related Visual Inc, pg 994
Southern California Sound Image Inc, pg 1019
Tri-Ed, pg 1044

COLORADO

Ceavco Audio/Visual Co, pg 822
Daylight Productions & Rentals, pg 844
Spectrum Audio Visual Services, pg 1020

CONNECTICUT

Concord Communications, pg 835
HB Communications Inc, pg 886
MAVCO, pg 934
Rockwell Communications Inc, pg 998
USI Inc, pg 1051

FLORIDA

AVI-SPL, pg 798
Digital Video Systems Inc, pg 848
Gulf Coast Audio Visual Producers Inc, pg 883
Hi-Tech Import Export Corp, pg 888
Industrial Strength Inc, pg 897
Photomart Cine-Video Inc, pg 975
Photosound of Orlando Inc, pg 975
Pro Stage Inc, pg 983
Spire Audio Visual Co Inc, pg 1021
Tallahassee Audio Visual, pg 1031

GEORGIA

Audio Visual Resources Inc, pg 795
Convergent Media Systems, pg 836
Stage Front Presentation Systems, pg 1022
Technical Innovation, pg 1033
Visioneering International Inc, pg 1058

HAWAII

The Audio Visual Co (AVCO), pg 795

ILLINOIS

Allen Visual Systems Inc, pg 781
Central Audio-Visual Equipment Inc, pg 823
G T Luscombe Co Inc, pg 926
Sound Vision Inc, pg 1018
H Wilson Co, pg 1067

INDIANA

Victoria Supply Inc/Topbulb.com, pg 1054

IOWA

ECS Inc, pg 856

KANSAS

KK Office Solutions Inc, pg 911
Smith Audio-Visual Inc, pg 1014

KENTUCKY

Audio Visual Techniques Inc, pg 796
NOR-COM Inc, pg 958

LOUISIANA

Intermedia Technologies, pg 900

MAINE

Headlight Audio Visual Inc, pg 887

MARYLAND

Nelson White Systems Inc, pg 954
Nicholas P Pipino Associates Inc, pg 976
RTZ Audio Visual, pg 1000
Visual Aids Electronics Corp, pg 1059

MASSACHUSETTS

Camera Co Inc/Broadcast Divison, pg 818
Lineco, pg 922
University Products Inc, pg 1050

MICHIGAN

City Events Group, pg 828
Digi Sign Design LLC, pg 847
Michigan Office Solutions, pg 941
TeL Systems, pg 1035

MINNESOTA

AVI Systems, pg 799
Tierney Brothers Inc, pg 1040

MISSISSIPPI

Bowie Audio Visual Enterprises Inc, pg 811
Jasper Ewing & Sons Inc, pg 864

MISSOURI

Communitronics Corp, pg 833
Conference Technologies Inc, pg 835
Image Technologies Corp, pg 895
MIS Technologies, pg 944
Schiller's Audio-Visual, pg 1004
Swank Audio Visuals, pg 1029

NEVADA

Bulbman Inc, pg 815

NEW JERSEY

Argraph Corp, pg 789
Audio Visual Associates, pg 795
Audio Visual Dynamics®, pg 795
AV Bluebook, pg 797
Graphics Depot Inc, pg 881
Hamilton Buhl, pg 884
National Audio-Visual Supply, pg 952
Starlite Productions, pg 1024
SYMCO Inc, pg 1030
Tele-Measurements Inc, pg 1035
Total Video Products Inc, pg 1042
VCom International Multimedia Corp, pg 1052
Video Corporation of America (VCA), pg 1055
Wilray Audio Visual Corp, pg 1067
Wired 4 Sound Inc, pg 1068
York Telecom, pg 1072

NEW YORK

AV Workshop, pg 797
Bulb Direct, pg 815
Bulbtronics Inc, pg 815
Colortone Audio Visual, pg 832
Communication Corner Inc, pg 832
Custom Media Environments, pg 841
Edmund Scientific, pg 857
Gaylord Brothers, pg 876
Indigo Productions, pg 897
Langie Audio Visual Systems, pg 915
Long Island Video Enterprises Live Inc, pg 924
Magnaplan Corp, pg 928
Markertek Video Supply, pg 931
Neptune Photo Inc, pg 954
Ray Supply Inc, pg 992
Technisphere Corp, pg 1034
Visual Technologies Corp, pg 1060
Willoughby's Imaging Center, pg 1067

NORTH CAROLINA

Camcor Inc, pg 818
Strategic Connections, pg 1026

OHIO

Audio Visual Media, pg 795
Copp Integrated Systems, pg 836
Hughie's Event Production Services, pg 892
Tri-State Audio Visual Co, pg 1044
Tri-State Visual Products, pg 1044
Xetron, pg 1071

PENNSYLVANIA

Advanced AV, pg 777
Audio Visions Inc, pg 795
Audio Visual Communications Inc, pg 795
Bernie's Photo Center, pg 805
Brodart Co, pg 813
J E Foss Co, pg 871
Grise Audio Visual Center Inc, pg 882
Visual Sound Inc, pg 1059
Wespen Audio Visual Co, pg 1063

RHODE ISLAND

Custom Computer Specialists Inc, pg 841

TENNESSEE

Durrell LLC, pg 854
Lowrance Sound Co Inc, pg 925
Memphis Communications Corp, pg 938
Spring Arbor Distributors, pg 1022
Tennessee Visual Service Co, pg 1037

TEXAS

Astro Audio Visual, pg 792
Audio Visual Technologies Group, pg 796
AVES Audio Visual Systems Inc, pg 798
Data Projections Inc, pg 843
Heffernan Audio Visual, pg 887
J&S Audio Visual Inc, pg 904
Lubbock Audio Visual Inc, pg 925
Quality Audio Visual Service Inc, pg 988
Schoolhouse Audio Visual, pg 1004
Stage Directions, pg 1022

VIRGINIA

Boitnott Visual Communications Corp (BVC), pg 810
Communications Specialists Inc, pg 833
Filmdex Inc, pg 867
Hoppmann Audio Visual, pg 891
Intellidyne LLC, pg 899
Lee Hartman & Sons Inc, pg 918
Metropolitan Audio Visual Co LLC, pg 940
The Whitlock Group, pg 1065

WASHINGTON

Inland Audio Visual Co, pg 898

WISCONSIN

Camera Corner Connecting Point, pg 818
Demco Inc, pg 845
Full Compass Systems, pg 874
Pro Studio Supply, pg 983
School Specialty Inc, pg 1004

PUERTO RICO

Bonnin Electronics Inc, pg 810

ALBERTA

Infosat Communications Inc, pg 898
McBain Audio Visual Ltd, pg 935
Sharp's Audio-Visual Ltd, pg 1008
Unique Communications Ltd, pg 1048

BRITISH COLUMBIA

Commercial Electronics Ltd, pg 832
Speciality Bulb Products Inc, pg 1020

MANITOBA

Evolution Presentation Technologies, pg 863
Inland Audio Visual Ltd, pg 898

ONTARIO

Carr McLean Ltd, pg 820
Edcom Multimedia Products, pg 856

Nationwide Audio Visual Co, pg 953
Premier A/V Sales Ltd, pg 980
Westbury National Show Systems Ltd, pg 1064

QUEBEC

Concept Audio-Visual, pg 834
Panavideo Inc, pg 968

Opaque & Overhead Supply & Accessory Manufacturers

CALIFORNIA

Ushio America Inc, pg 1051

ILLINOIS

ACCO Brands Corp, pg 773
Dukane Corp, Audio Visual Products Division, pg 853
Kart-A-Bag Manufacturing Inc, pg 908

MASSACHUSETTS

Lineco, pg 922
Technologies at Excelitas, pg 1034
University Products Inc, pg 1050

MINNESOTA

Artograph Inc, pg 791

NEW JERSEY

National Audio-Visual Supply, pg 952
Pro-Tape & Specialities Inc, pg 983

NEW YORK

Eastman Kodak Professional, pg 856
ELMO USA Corp, pg 859
Gagne Inc, pg 875
TecNec Distributing, pg 1035

OHIO

Kroy LLC, pg 914
Xetron, pg 1071

VIRGINIA

Hoppmann Audio Visual, pg 891

ONTARIO

Staedtler-Mars Ltd, pg 1022

Opaque & Overhead Supply & Accessory Rentals

ALABAMA

Media Visions Inc, pg 937

ARIZONA

Arizona Cine Equipment, pg 789
Merestone, pg 938
Video Media Productions (VMP), pg 1055

ARKANSAS

Carlton-Bates Co, pg 820
White Diamond Productions, pg 1065

CALIFORNIA

Ametron Audio/Video, pg 785
AV Guys, pg 797
Hooper Camera & Imaging, pg 891
Impact Group, pg 897
JD Audio Visual Inc, pg 904
Lynch Communications, pg 926
Media Fabricators Inc, pg 936
Munday & Collins AV, pg 950
PSAV® Presentation Services, pg 986
Towards 2000 Inc, pg 1043
University of Southern California, pg 1050
VER-Video Equipment Rentals, pg 1053
Voice & Video Rentals, pg 1060

COLORADO

Ceavco Audio/Visual Co, pg 822
Daylight Productions & Rentals, pg 844

CONNECTICUT

A/V Davey, pg 797
Concord Communications, pg 835
Rockwell Communications Inc, pg 998

FLORIDA

Image Technical Services, pg 895
Industrial Strength Inc, pg 897
Photosound of Orlando Inc, pg 975
Pro Stage Inc, pg 983
Spire Audio Visual Co Inc, pg 1021
Tallahassee Audio Visual, pg 1031

GEORGIA

Audio Visual Resources Inc, pg 795
Convergent Media Systems, pg 836
Dixie Theatre Service & Supply Co Inc, pg 849
MAGNUM Companies Ltd, pg 929
ON Event Services, pg 963
Stage Front Presentation Systems, pg 1022
Staging Directions Inc, pg 1023

HAWAII

ATTCO Inc, pg 793

ILLINOIS

Allen Visual Systems Inc, pg 781
Audio Visual Services Corp, pg 796
Beatty TeleVisual Productions, pg 804
Creative Technology, pg 838
Helix Camera & Video, pg 887
Jim Passin Productions, pg 970
PSAV® Presentation Services (Hotel Services Division), pg 987

INDIANA

Gary Camera & Digital, pg 875

KENTUCKY

Audio Visual Techniques Inc, pg 796

LOUISIANA

Clark Services Audio Visual & Exhibit Inc, pg 829

MAINE

Headlight Audio Visual Inc, pg 887

MARYLAND

Nelson White Systems Inc, pg 954
Nicholas P Pipino Associates Inc, pg 976
RTZ Audio Visual, pg 1000

MASSACHUSETTS

Capron Lighting & Sound Co Inc, pg 819
massAV, pg 933
Preston Productions Inc, pg 981

MICHIGAN

Digi Sign Design LLC, pg 847
K&R All Media Productions Inc, pg 908

MINNESOTA

AVI Systems, pg 799

MISSISSIPPI

Bowie Audio Visual Enterprises Inc, pg 811
Jasper Ewing & Sons Inc, pg 864

MISSOURI

Show-Me Audio-Visual, pg 1009
Swank Audio Visuals, pg 1029

NEVADA

GES Audio Visual, pg 877

NEW HAMPSHIRE

Academic & Campus Technology Services, pg 773

NEW JERSEY

Audio Visual Associates, pg 795
Audio Visual Dynamics®, pg 795
Moe AV LLC, pg 945

NEW YORK

Ace Video, pg 774
AV Workshop, pg 797
CMI Communications, pg 830
Langie Audio Visual Systems, pg 915
Long Island Video Enterprises Live Inc, pg 924
Magnaplan Corp, pg 928
Ray Supply Inc, pg 992
Specialized Audio-Visual Inc, pg 1020
Technisphere Corp, pg 1034
Visual Technologies Corp, pg 1060

NORTH CAROLINA

A&V Company, pg 772
Camcor Inc, pg 818
Special Event Services, pg 1020
Strategic Connections, pg 1026

OHIO

Audio Visual Media, pg 795
Aztec Video Productions, pg 801
Hughie's Event Production Services, pg 892

PENNSYLVANIA

Advanced AV, pg 777
Audio Visions Inc, pg 795
Audio Visual Communications Inc, pg 795
Grise Audio Visual Center Inc, pg 882
Production Solutions Inc, pg 985
Visual Sound Inc, pg 1059

TENNESSEE

Memphis Communications Corp, pg 938
Tennessee Visual Service Co, pg 1037

TEXAS

Audio Visual Technologies Group, pg 796
J&S Audio Visual Inc, pg 904
Lubbock Audio Visual Inc, pg 925
Schoolhouse Audio Visual, pg 1004

UTAH

Webb Audio Visual Communication, pg 1063

VIRGINIA

American AV, pg 783
Lee Hartman & Sons Inc, pg 918
Projection Presentation Technology, pg 985
Rainbow Rentals, pg 991

WASHINGTON

Inland Audio Visual Co, pg 898

WISCONSIN

Camera Corner Connecting Point, pg 818
Event Essentials, pg 863
Full Compass Systems, pg 874
School Specialty Inc, pg 1004

PUERTO RICO

Stage Crew Audiovisual Inc, pg 1022

ALBERTA

Cine Audio Visual Sales & Service Ltd, pg 826
Unique Communications Ltd, pg 1048

BRITISH COLUMBIA

Clark's Audio Visual Services Ltd, pg 829

MANITOBA

Evolution Presentation Technologies, pg 863

ONTARIO

Edcom Multimedia Products, pg 856
Westbury National Show Systems Ltd, pg 1064

QUEBEC

AVW-TELAV Audio Visual Solutions, a Freeman Company, pg 800
Concept Audio-Visual, pg 834
Panavideo Inc, pg 968

Opaque & Overhead Supply & Accessory Repairs

ARKANSAS

Carlton-Bates Co, pg 820

AUDIO/VISUAL

Opaque & Overhead Supply & Accessory Repairs (continued)

CALIFORNIA

Ametron Audio/Video, pg 785
Hooper Camera & Imaging, pg 891
Instructional Materials & Equipment Distributors (I-Med), pg 899
McAlister Electronics, pg 935
Lloyd F McKinney Associates Inc, pg 935
Pro Camera Repair, pg 982
Towards 2000 Inc, pg 1043

COLORADO

Ceavco Audio/Visual Co, pg 822

CONNECTICUT

HB Communications Inc, pg 886
Rockwell Communications Inc, pg 998

FLORIDA

Spire Audio Visual Co Inc, pg 1021
Tallahassee Audio Visual, pg 1031

GEORGIA

Audio Visual Resources Inc, pg 795
Dixie Theatre Service & Supply Co Inc, pg 849
Stage Front Presentation Systems, pg 1022
Technical Innovation, pg 1033

ILLINOIS

Allen Visual Systems Inc, pg 781

INDIANA

Gary Camera & Digital, pg 875

KANSAS

KK Office Solutions Inc, pg 911

KENTUCKY

Axxis Inc, pg 800
NOR-COM Inc, pg 958

MAINE

Headlight Audio Visual Inc, pg 887

MARYLAND

Nicholas P Pipino Associates Inc, pg 976
RTZ Audio Visual, pg 1000

MICHIGAN

City Events Group, pg 828
TeL Systems, pg 1035

MINNESOTA

AVI Systems, pg 799

MISSISSIPPI

Bowie Audio Visual Enterprises Inc, pg 811

MISSOURI

Schiller's Audio-Visual, pg 1004

NEW JERSEY

Audio Visual Associates, pg 795

NEW YORK

Colortone Audio Visual, pg 832
ELMO USA Corp, pg 859
Langie Audio Visual Systems, pg 915
Magnaplan Corp, pg 928
Ray Supply Inc, pg 992
Visual Technologies Corp, pg 1060

NORTH CAROLINA

Camcor Inc, pg 818
Strategic Connections, pg 1026

OHIO

Audio Visual Media, pg 795
Aztec Video Productions, pg 801
Tri-State Audio Visual Co, pg 1044

PENNSYLVANIA

Audio Visions Inc, pg 795
Wespen Audio Visual Co, pg 1063

RHODE ISLAND

Custom Computer Specialists Inc, pg 841

TENNESSEE

Memphis Communications Corp, pg 938
Tennessee Visual Service Co, pg 1037

TEXAS

Audio Visual Technologies Group, pg 796
Heffernan Audio Visual, pg 887
Lubbock Audio Visual Inc, pg 925
Schoolhouse Audio Visual, pg 1004

VIRGINIA

Hoppmann Audio Visual, pg 891
Lee Hartman & Sons Inc, pg 918
The Whitlock Group, pg 1065

WASHINGTON

Inland Audio Visual Co, pg 898

WISCONSIN

Camera Corner Connecting Point, pg 818
Full Compass Systems, pg 874
School Specialty Inc, pg 1004

ALBERTA

Infosat Communications Inc, pg 898

BRITISH COLUMBIA

Commercial Electronics Ltd, pg 832

MANITOBA

Evolution Presentation Technologies, pg 863
Inland Audio Visual Ltd, pg 898

ONTARIO

Premier A/V Sales Ltd, pg 980
Westbury National Show Systems Ltd, pg 1064

QUEBEC

Panavideo Inc, pg 968

Overhead Projector, *see* Opaque & Overhead Projector

Overhead Supply and Accessory, *see* Opaque & Overhead Supply & Accessory

Overhead Transparency Printing, *see* Volume Printing—Overhead Transparencies

Phonograph Distributors

ALABAMA

Curtis Company, pg 841
Media Visions Inc, pg 937

ARIZONA

Arizona Cine Equipment, pg 789
Troxell Communications Inc, pg 1045

CALIFORNIA

Ametron Audio/Video, pg 785
Empire Wholesale Inc, pg 860
FXC Communications, pg 874
Instructional Materials & Equipment Distributors (I-Med), pg 899
Media Fabricators Inc, pg 936
Related Visual Inc, pg 994
Sounds Unique, pg 1018
Towards 2000 Inc, pg 1043

CONNECTICUT

Concord Communications, pg 835
MAVCO, pg 934
Rockwell Communications Inc, pg 998

FLORIDA

BAI Distributors Inc, pg 801
Hi-Tech Import Export Corp, pg 888
Pro Stage Inc, pg 983
Sight & Sound Productions, pg 1010
Spire Audio Visual Co Inc, pg 1021
Stereo Sales Inc, pg 1024
Tallahassee Audio Visual, pg 1031

GEORGIA

Audio Visual Resources Inc, pg 795
Dixie Theatre Service & Supply Co Inc, pg 849
Technical Innovation, pg 1033

HAWAII

The Audio Visual Co (AVCO), pg 795

ILLINOIS

Central Audio-Visual Equipment Inc, pg 823
Esoteric Sound, pg 862
LKG Industries Inc, pg 923
Quintessence Audio Ltd, pg 989

IOWA

ECS Inc, pg 856

KANSAS

KK Office Solutions Inc, pg 911

KENTUCKY

Barney Miller's Inc, pg 943
NOR-COM Inc, pg 958

MAINE

Headlight Audio Visual Inc, pg 887

MARYLAND

Nicholas P Pipino Associates Inc, pg 976
Visual Aids Electronics Corp, pg 1059

MICHIGAN

City Events Group, pg 828

MISSOURI

Conference Technologies Inc, pg 835
Schiller's Audio-Visual, pg 1004

NEW JERSEY

Alltec Stores, a Vcom IMC Company, pg 782
AV Bluebook, pg 797
FlagHouse, pg 869
Hamilton Buhl, pg 884
National Audio-Visual Supply, pg 952
Onkyo USA Corp, pg 963
Starlite Productions, pg 1024
VCom International Multimedia Corp, pg 1052
Video Corporation of America (VCA), pg 1055
Wired 4 Sound Inc, pg 1068

NEW YORK

AV Workshop, pg 797
Cadence Jazz Records, pg 816
Communication Corner Inc, pg 832
Gaylord Brothers, pg 876
Indigo Productions, pg 897
Langie Audio Visual Systems, pg 915
NorthCountry Distributors, pg 959
RNJ Electronics, pg 997
Toys From The Attic, pg 1043
Willoughby's Imaging Center, pg 1067

NORTH CAROLINA

Camcor Inc, pg 818

OHIO

Audio Visual Media, pg 795

PENNSYLVANIA

Advanced AV, pg 777
Brodart Co, pg 813
J E Foss Co, pg 871
Grise Audio Visual Center Inc, pg 882
Visual Sound Inc, pg 1059
Wespen Audio Visual Co, pg 1063

RHODE ISLAND

Custom Computer Specialists Inc, pg 841

TENNESSEE

Lowrance Sound Co Inc, pg 925
Technical Support Systems LLC, pg 1034
Tennessee Visual Service Co, pg 1037

TEXAS

Audio Visual Technologies Group, pg 796
Crossroads Audio Inc, pg 840
J&S Audio Visual Inc, pg 904
Lubbock Audio Visual Inc, pg 925
Quality Audio Visual Service Inc, pg 988
RadioShack Corp, pg 990
Schoolhouse Audio Visual, pg 1004

UTAH

Webb Audio Visual Communication, pg 1063

VIRGINIA

Boitnott Visual Communications Corp (BVC), pg 810
Communications Specialists Inc, pg 833
Lee Hartman & Sons Inc, pg 918
Metropolitan Audio Visual Co LLC, pg 940
The Whitlock Group, pg 1065

WASHINGTON

D A Sound, pg 842
Inland Audio Visual Co, pg 898

WISCONSIN

Camera Corner Connecting Point, pg 818
Demco Inc, pg 845
Full Compass Systems, pg 874
School Specialty Inc, pg 1004

ALBERTA

Sharp's Audio-Visual Ltd, pg 1008

BRITISH COLUMBIA

Commercial Electronics Ltd, pg 832

MANITOBA

Evolution Presentation Technologies, pg 863
Inland Audio Visual Ltd, pg 898

ONTARIO

Edcom Multimedia Products, pg 856
Nationwide Audio Visual Co, pg 953
Premier A/V Sales Ltd, pg 980
Westbury National Show Systems Ltd, pg 1064

Phonograph Manufacturers

CALIFORNIA

Califone International Inc, pg 817

ILLINOIS

Esoteric Sound, pg 862
SoundTech, pg 1018

NEW JERSEY

Hamilton Buhl, pg 884
Onkyo USA Corp, pg 963
Panasonic Corp, pg 968

SOUTH CAROLINA

Paso Sound Products Inc, pg 969

TEXAS

RadioShack Corp, pg 990

Phonograph Rentals

ALABAMA

Media Visions Inc, pg 937

ARIZONA

Arizona Cine Equipment, pg 789
Merestone, pg 938
Video Media Productions (VMP), pg 1055

CALIFORNIA

Ametron Audio/Video, pg 785
Audio Rents, pg 794
Instructional Materials & Equipment Distributors (I-Med), pg 899
JD Audio Visual Inc, pg 904
Lynch Communications, pg 926
McCune Audio-Video-Lighting, pg 935
Media Fabricators Inc, pg 936
Munday & Collins AV, pg 950
Towards 2000 Inc, pg 1043

CONNECTICUT

A/V Davey, pg 797
Rockwell Communications Inc, pg 998

FLORIDA

Pro Stage Inc, pg 983
Spire Audio Visual Co Inc, pg 1021

GEORGIA

Audio Visual Resources Inc, pg 795
Dixie Theatre Service & Supply Co Inc, pg 849
Staging Directions Inc, pg 1023

ILLINOIS

Audio Visual Services Corp, pg 796
AV Chicago Inc, pg 797
Central Audio-Visual Equipment Inc, pg 823

INDIANA

OMNI Productions, pg 962

MARYLAND

Event Tech, pg 863

MASSACHUSETTS

Preston Productions Inc, pg 981

MICHIGAN

City Events Group, pg 828
K&R All Media Productions Inc, pg 908
K&R's Recording Studios Inc, pg 908
On Stage Visuals, pg 963

MISSISSIPPI

Bowie Audio Visual Enterprises Inc, pg 811
Jasper Ewing & Sons Inc, pg 864

MISSOURI

Show-Me Audio-Visual, pg 1009
Southwest Audio-Visual Inc, pg 1019
Swank Audio Visuals, pg 1029

NEW HAMPSHIRE

Academic & Campus Technology Services, pg 773

NEW JERSEY

Starlite Productions, pg 1024

NEW YORK

AV Workshop, pg 797
Langie Audio Visual Systems, pg 915
Long Island Video Enterprises Live Inc, pg 924

NORTH CAROLINA

Special Event Services, pg 1020
Strategic Connections, pg 1026

OHIO

Audio Visual Media, pg 795

PENNSYLVANIA

Grise Audio Visual Center Inc, pg 882
Production Solutions Inc, pg 985

TENNESSEE

Technical Support Systems LLC, pg 1034
Tennessee Visual Service Co, pg 1037

TEXAS

Audio Visual Technologies Group, pg 796
Lubbock Audio Visual Inc, pg 925
Schoolhouse Audio Visual, pg 1004
Stage Directions, pg 1022
The Yesterday USA Radio Networks, pg 1072

UTAH

Webb Audio Visual Communication, pg 1063

VIRGINIA

American AV, pg 783
Lee Hartman & Sons Inc, pg 918
Rainbow Rentals, pg 991
The Whitlock Group, pg 1065

WASHINGTON

D A Sound, pg 842
Inland Audio Visual Co, pg 898

WISCONSIN

Event Essentials, pg 863
Full Compass Systems, pg 874
School Specialty Inc, pg 1004

WYOMING

Bridger Productions Inc, pg 812

BRITISH COLUMBIA

Commercial Electronics Ltd, pg 832
MicrophoneRentals.com, pg 941

MANITOBA

Evolution Presentation Technologies, pg 863
Inland Audio Visual Ltd, pg 898

ONTARIO

Westbury National Show Systems Ltd, pg 1064

Phonograph Repairs

CALIFORNIA

ALC (Auernheimer Labs & Co), pg 780
Ametron Audio/Video, pg 785
Instructional Materials & Equipment Distributors (I-Med), pg 899
McAlister Electronics, pg 935
Towards 2000 Inc, pg 1043

CONNECTICUT

HB Communications Inc, pg 886
Rockwell Communications Inc, pg 998

FLORIDA

JT Communications, pg 906
Spire Audio Visual Co Inc, pg 1021
Stereo Sales Inc, pg 1024
Tallahassee Audio Visual, pg 1031

GEORGIA

Audio Visual Resources Inc, pg 795

ILLINOIS

Central Audio-Visual Equipment Inc, pg 823

KANSAS

KK Office Solutions Inc, pg 911

KENTUCKY

Barney Miller's Inc, pg 943
NOR-COM Inc, pg 958

MARYLAND

Strauss Photo Technical Service Inc, pg 1026

MICHIGAN

City Events Group, pg 828
TeL Systems, pg 1035

MISSISSIPPI

Bowie Audio Visual Enterprises Inc, pg 811

MISSOURI

Schiller's Audio-Visual, pg 1004

NEW JERSEY

Starlite Productions, pg 1024

NEW YORK

Colortone Audio Visual, pg 832
Langie Audio Visual Systems, pg 915
Toys From The Attic, pg 1043

AUDIO/VISUAL

Phonograph Repairs (continued)

OHIO

Audio Visual Media, pg 795
Aztec Video Productions, pg 801
Tri-State Audio Visual Co, pg 1044

OREGON

All Service Musical Electronics Repair, pg 780

PENNSYLVANIA

J E Foss Co, pg 871
Wespen Audio Visual Co, pg 1063

RHODE ISLAND

Custom Computer Specialists Inc, pg 841

TENNESSEE

Technical Support Systems LLC, pg 1034
Tennessee Visual Service Co, pg 1037

TEXAS

Audio Visual Technologies Group, pg 796
Crossroads Audio Inc, pg 840
Lubbock Audio Visual Inc, pg 925
Padgitt's, pg 967
Quality Audio Visual Service Inc, pg 988
Schoolhouse Audio Visual, pg 1004
The Yesterday USA Radio Networks, pg 1072

VIRGINIA

Lee Hartman & Sons Inc, pg 918
Metropolitan Audio Visual Co LLC, pg 940
The Whitlock Group, pg 1065

WASHINGTON

Inland Audio Visual Co, pg 898

WISCONSIN

Audio Visual of Milwaukee Inc, pg 795
Full Compass Systems, pg 874
School Specialty Inc, pg 1004

ALBERTA

Sharp's Audio-Visual Ltd, pg 1008

BRITISH COLUMBIA

Commercial Electronics Ltd, pg 832

MANITOBA

Evolution Presentation Technologies, pg 863
Inland Audio Visual Ltd, pg 898

ONTARIO

Edcom Multimedia Products, pg 856
Premier A/V Sales Ltd, pg 980
Westbury National Show Systems Ltd, pg 1064

Photograph Printing, *see* Processing & Printing—Photographs

Photograph Processing, *see* Processing & Printing—Photographs

Photographs from Slides, *see* Prints from Slides

Photostats, *see* Color Photostats

Planetarium Distributors

ALABAMA

Media Visions Inc, pg 937

ARIZONA

Arizona Cine Equipment, pg 789

CALIFORNIA

Cinema Xenon International Inc, pg 827

FLORIDA

Audio Visual Imagineering Inc, pg 795
Hi-Tech Import Export Corp, pg 888
Science First/STARLAB™, pg 1005

GEORGIA

Visioneering International Inc, pg 1058

MARYLAND

Nicholas P Pipino Associates Inc, pg 976

NEW JERSEY

Starlite Productions, pg 1024

NEW YORK

Edmund Scientific, pg 857
Langie Audio Visual Systems, pg 915
MRG Productions Inc, pg 948

PENNSYLVANIA

Advanced AV, pg 777

TEXAS

Lubbock Audio Visual Inc, pg 925
Schoolhouse Audio Visual, pg 1004

WASHINGTON

Laser Fantasy/HECK Industries/Photon Manufacturing, pg 916

WISCONSIN

Audio Visual of Milwaukee Inc, pg 795
Demco Inc, pg 845

MANITOBA

Inland Audio Visual Ltd, pg 898

Planetarium Manufacturers

CALIFORNIA

Cinema Xenon International Inc, pg 827

FLORIDA

Audio Visual Imagineering Inc, pg 795
Science First/STARLAB™, pg 1005

MARYLAND

Absolute Hollywood, pg 772
MMI Corp, pg 944

NEW JERSEY

Konica Minolta Business Solutions, pg 913
Starlite Productions, pg 1024

Planetarium Rentals

ALABAMA

Media Visions Inc, pg 937

ARIZONA

Arizona Cine Equipment, pg 789

FLORIDA

Audio Visual Imagineering Inc, pg 795

GEORGIA

Staging Directions Inc, pg 1023

MARYLAND

Absolute Hollywood, pg 772

TEXAS

Schoolhouse Audio Visual, pg 1004

WASHINGTON

Laser Fantasy/HECK Industries/Photon Manufacturing, pg 916

ALBERTA

McBain Audio Visual Ltd, pg 935

MANITOBA

Inland Audio Visual Ltd, pg 898

Planetarium Repairs

CALIFORNIA

McAlister Electronics, pg 935

MICHIGAN

TeL Systems, pg 1035

NEW JERSEY

Konica Minolta Business Solutions, pg 913
Starlite Productions, pg 1024

NEW YORK

MRG Productions Inc, pg 948

OHIO

Aztec Video Productions, pg 801

TENNESSEE

Memphis Communications Corp, pg 938

TEXAS

Lubbock Audio Visual Inc, pg 925
Schoolhouse Audio Visual, pg 1004

MANITOBA

Inland Audio Visual Ltd, pg 898

Power Megaphone, *see* Megaphone—Power

Presentation Board & Supply Distributors

ALABAMA

Curtis Company, pg 841
Media Visions Inc, pg 937

ARIZONA

Arizona Cine Equipment, pg 789
Metropolitan Audio-Visual Inc, pg 940
Troxell Communications Inc, pg 1045
Ultimate Presentation Systems Inc, pg 1047

ARKANSAS

Jay S Stanley & Associates Inc, pg 1023
White Diamond Productions, pg 1065

CALIFORNIA

Advanced Systems Group LLC, pg 778
Ametron Audio/Video, pg 785
California Tape Products Inc, pg 817
Christy's Editorial, pg 826
Delicate Electronics Sales Inc, pg 845
Educational Technology Services (ETS), pg 857
Ellison Educational Equipment Inc, pg 859
FXC Communications, pg 874
Instructional Materials & Equipment Distributors (I-Med), pg 899
JD Audio Visual Inc, pg 904
Media Fabricators Inc, pg 936
MediaPOINTE, pg 938
Related Visual Inc, pg 994
Stanislaus Audio Video Inc, pg 1023

COLORADO

Ceavco Audio/Visual Co, pg 822
Daylight Productions & Rentals, pg 844
National Teaching Aids Inc, pg 953
Spectrum Audio Visual Services, pg 1020
Stanco Sales LLC, pg 1023

Presentation Board & Supply Manufacturers

AUDIO/VISUAL

Presentation Board & Supply Manufacturers (continued)

NEW JERSEY

National Audio-Visual Supply, pg 952

NEW YORK

Light Impressions, pg 920
Magnaplan Corp, pg 928
TecNec Distributing, pg 1035

OHIO

Ghent Manufacturing, pg 878
Walltalkers, pg 1061

PENNSYLVANIA

Interactive Products, pg 899

TEXAS

MooreCo Inc, pg 946

VIRGINIA

Drytac Corp, pg 852

WISCONSIN

Bardes Products Inc, pg 803
USAV Group Inc, pg 1050

ALBERTA

SMART Technologies Inc, pg 1013

ONTARIO

Egan Visual Inc/Egan TeamBoard Inc, pg 858

Presentation Board & Supply Rentals

ALABAMA

Media Visions Inc, pg 937

ARIZONA

Arizona Cine Equipment, pg 789
Merestone, pg 938
Metropolitan Audio-Visual Inc, pg 940
Ultimate Presentation Systems Inc, pg 1047
Video Media Productions (VMP), pg 1055

ARKANSAS

White Diamond Productions, pg 1065

CALIFORNIA

Alliant Event Services, pg 781
Ametron Audio/Video, pg 785
AV Guys, pg 797
Bexel Corp, pg 806
Golden Gate Studios, pg 880
Lynch Communications, pg 926
McCune Audio-Video-Lighting, pg 935
Media Fabricators Inc, pg 936
Munday & Collins AV, pg 950
PSAV® Presentation Services, pg 986
Related Visual Inc, pg 994
Stanislaus Audio Video Inc, pg 1023
VER-Video Equipment Rentals, pg 1053
Video Resources Inc, pg 1056
Voice & Video Rentals, pg 1060

COLORADO

Ceavco Audio/Visual Co, pg 822
Spectrum Audio Visual Services, pg 1020

CONNECTICUT

A/V Davey, pg 797

DELAWARE

Ken-Del Productions Inc, pg 909

FLORIDA

Gulf Coast Audio Visual Producers Inc, pg 883
Image Technical Services, pg 895
Industrial Strength Inc, pg 897
Photosound of Orlando Inc, pg 975
Pro Stage Inc, pg 983

GEORGIA

Stage Front Presentation Systems, pg 1022
Staging Directions Inc, pg 1023

HAWAII

ATTCO Inc, pg 793

ILLINOIS

Allen Visual Systems Inc, pg 781
Audio Visual Services Corp, pg 796
AV Chicago Inc, pg 797
PSAV® Presentation Services (Hotel Services Division), pg 987
QuickSet International Inc, pg 989

INDIANA

Heart Breaker Entertainment LLC, pg 887

KANSAS

Smith Audio-Visual Inc, pg 1014

MARYLAND

Advance Audiovisual Presentation Ltd, pg 777
RTZ Audio Visual, pg 1000

MASSACHUSETTS

massAV, pg 933
Preston Productions Inc, pg 981

MICHIGAN

City Events Group, pg 828
Digi Sign Design LLC, pg 847
K&R All Media Productions Inc, pg 908

MINNESOTA

Advanced Audio-Visual Inc, pg 777
AVI Systems, pg 799

MISSISSIPPI

Bowie Audio Visual Enterprises Inc, pg 811
Jasper Ewing & Sons Inc, pg 864

MISSOURI

Show-Me Audio-Visual, pg 1009
Swank Audio Visuals, pg 1029

NEBRASKA

Dog & Pony Productions Inc, pg 850

NEVADA

GES Audio Visual, pg 877

NEW JERSEY

Audio Visual Associates, pg 795
Giant Audio Visual Inc, pg 878
Tele-Measurements Inc, pg 1035
Wired 4 Sound Inc, pg 1068

NEW YORK

AV Workshop, pg 797
Communication Corner Inc, pg 832
KVL Audio Visual Services Inc, pg 914
Langie Audio Visual Systems, pg 915
Long Island Video Enterprises Live Inc, pg 924
Magnaplan Corp, pg 928
Visual Technologies Corp, pg 1060
Visual Word Systems Inc, pg 1060

NORTH CAROLINA

A&V Company, pg 772
Camcor Inc, pg 818
Strategic Connections, pg 1026
Visual Aids Electronics of North Carolina Inc, pg 1059

OHIO

Audio Visual Media, pg 795
Aztec Video Productions, pg 801
Mills James Productions, pg 943
Vista Color Imaging Inc, pg 1059

PENNSYLVANIA

Audio Visions Inc, pg 795
FirstGeneration Audio/Visual Services, pg 869
FMP Media Solutions Inc, pg 870
Production Solutions Inc, pg 985
Visual Sound Inc, pg 1059

TENNESSEE

Memphis Communications Corp, pg 938
Technical Support Systems LLC, pg 1034
Tennessee Visual Service Co, pg 1037

TEXAS

Audio Visual Technologies Group, pg 796
Lubbock Audio Visual Inc, pg 925
Schoolhouse Audio Visual, pg 1004

VIRGINIA

American AV, pg 783
Lee Hartman & Sons Inc, pg 918
Projection Presentation Technology, pg 985
Rainbow Rentals, pg 991
The Whitlock Group, pg 1065

WASHINGTON

Inland Audio Visual Co, pg 898

WISCONSIN

Audio Visual of Milwaukee Inc, pg 795
Camera Corner Connecting Point, pg 818
USAV Group Inc, pg 1050

PUERTO RICO

Stage Crew Audiovisual Inc, pg 1022

ALBERTA

Evolution Presentation Technologies, pg 863
McBain Audio Visual Ltd, pg 935

BRITISH COLUMBIA

Clark's Audio Visual Services Ltd, pg 829

MANITOBA

Evolution Presentation Technologies, pg 863
Inland Audio Visual Ltd, pg 898

ONTARIO

HD Source, pg 886
Westbury National Show Systems Ltd, pg 1064

QUEBEC

Concept Audio-Visual, pg 834

Presentation Board & Supply Repairs

CALIFORNIA

Ametron Audio/Video, pg 785
McAlister Electronics, pg 935
Lloyd F McKinney Associates Inc, pg 935

COLORADO

Ceavco Audio/Visual Co, pg 822

GEORGIA

Stage Front Presentation Systems, pg 1022

ILLINOIS

Allen Visual Systems Inc, pg 781

KENTUCKY

Axxis Inc, pg 800
NOR-COM Inc, pg 958

MARYLAND

RTZ Audio Visual, pg 1000

MICHIGAN

City Events Group, pg 828
TeL Systems, pg 1035

MINNESOTA

AVI Systems, pg 799

NEW YORK

Colortone Audio Visual, pg 832
Langie Audio Visual Systems, pg 915
Magnaplan Corp, pg 928
Visual Technologies Corp, pg 1060

Prints from Slides

Processing & Printing—Filmstrips

Processing & Printing—Photographs

AUDIO/VISUAL

Processing & Printing—Photographs (continued)

CALIFORNIA (continued)

Lynch Communications, pg 926
Monaco Digital Films Labs, pg 945
QRS Software Services, pg 988

CONNECTICUT

Broadcast Video Productions LLC, pg 813
New London Media, pg 956
Skyviews Survey Inc, pg 1013

FLORIDA

Cheuvront Studios, pg 824
Gulf Coast Audio Visual Producers Inc, pg 883

GEORGIA

Imagers, pg 896

ILLINOIS

Beatty TeleVisual Productions, pg 804

IOWA

American Color Imaging (ACI), pg 784
The Production House, pg 984

LOUISIANA

Louisiana State University Health Sciences Center - Shreveport, pg 925

MARYLAND

Fugro EarthData, pg 873
Ritz Camera & Image, pg 997

MASSACHUSETTS

Dorian Color, pg 851

MICHIGAN

K&R's Recording Studios Inc, pg 908
Tri-Color, pg 1044

NEW JERSEY

All Jersey Studios, pg 780

NEW YORK

Eastco Multimedia Solutions Inc, pg 856
Greyfalcon House, pg 882
Ken Lieberman Labs Inc, pg 920
Modernage Photographic Services Inc, pg 944
Neptune Photo Inc, pg 954
TBA Global Events, pg 1032

NORTH CAROLINA

Image Associates Inc, pg 894

OHIO

Aztec Video Productions, pg 801
Thread Marketing Group, pg 1039
Vista Color Imaging Inc, pg 1059

PENNSYLVANIA

Bernie's Photo Center, pg 805
Main Point Productions, pg 929
Visual Sound Inc, pg 1059

RHODE ISLAND

A&M Productions, pg 771

TENNESSEE

Mid-South Color Labs Inc, pg 942
Stage Post, pg 1022

TEXAS

City Color, pg 828
The Color Lab Inc, pg 831
Institute of Texan Cultures, pg 899
Pounds Photographic Labs Inc, pg 979
The Samuels Co, pg 1002
Texas Heart Institute Visual Communication Services, pg 1037

UTAH

Ferrari Color®, pg 866

WISCONSIN

USAV Group Inc, pg 1050

Processing & Printing—Slides

ARIZONA

Image Craft LLC, pg 894
Professional Marketing Services Inc, pg 985

CALIFORNIA

Action Photo Service Inc, pg 775
Adolph Gasser Inc, pg 776
Coloredge, pg 832
The Kenwood Group, pg 909
Lynch Communications, pg 926
QRS Software Services, pg 988

CONNECTICUT

Broadcast Video Productions LLC, pg 813

DISTRICT OF COLUMBIA

O'Keefe Communications Inc, pg 961

FLORIDA

Cheuvront Studios, pg 824
Communications Concepts Inc (CCI), pg 833
Gulf Coast Audio Visual Producers Inc, pg 883
Tallahassee Audio Visual, pg 1031

GEORGIA

Imagers, pg 896

ILLINOIS

CCore Media Inc, pg 821
Filmworkers, pg 868
Gamma Imaging, pg 875
Helix Camera & Video, pg 887
JMC Photo & Digital Services Inc, pg 905
The Pepper Group, pg 972

INDIANA

OMNI Productions, pg 962

IOWA

American Color Imaging (ACI), pg 784
The Production House, pg 984

KANSAS

Genigraphics®, pg 877

LOUISIANA

Louisiana State University Health Sciences Center - Shreveport, pg 925
Primary Color Laboratory Inc, pg 982

MASSACHUSETTS

Camera Co Inc/Broadcast Divison, pg 818
Colortek of Boston, pg 832
CommCreative, pg 832
DGI-Invisuals LLC, pg 846
Graphx Inc, pg 881
ICL Imaging Inc, pg 893
TR Productions, pg 1043

MICHIGAN

K&R's Recording Studios Inc, pg 908
Tectonics Industries Inc, pg 1035
Tri-Color, pg 1044

MINNESOTA

Linhoff Photo & Digital Imaging, pg 922
Sight Creative, pg 1010

MISSISSIPPI

Jasper Ewing & Sons Inc, pg 864

MISSOURI

Allied Photo Color Co, pg 781

NEW HAMPSHIRE

Academic & Campus Technology Services, pg 773

NEW JERSEY

All Jersey Studios, pg 780
Newark Beth Israel Medical Center, pg 956

NEW YORK

C2 Imaging LLC, pg 841
Duggal Visual Solutions, pg 853
Eastco Multimedia Solutions Inc, pg 856
FSL Media Inc, pg 873
Ken Lieberman Labs Inc, pg 920
Modernage Photographic Services Inc, pg 944
Jack Morton Worldwide, pg 946
Neptune Photo Inc, pg 954
SMP Digital Graphics, pg 1014
TBA Global Events, pg 1032

NORTH CAROLINA

Image Associates Inc, pg 894

OHIO

Aztec Video Productions, pg 801
Cuyahoga Community College Media Center, pg 841
Thread Marketing Group, pg 1039
Vista Color Imaging Inc, pg 1059

PENNSYLVANIA

Audio Visual Communications Inc, pg 795
Bernie's Photo Center, pg 805
Berry & Homer, pg 805
FMP Media Solutions Inc, pg 870
Main Point Productions, pg 929
Visual Sound Inc, pg 1059

TENNESSEE

Memphis Communications Corp, pg 938
Stage Post, pg 1022

TEXAS

City Color, pg 828
IntegraColor, pg 899
The Samuels Co, pg 1002
Texas Heart Institute Visual Communication Services, pg 1037

UTAH

Ferrari Color®, pg 866

VERMONT

University of Vermont, Instructional Television Dept, pg 1050

VIRGINIA

Advance Concepts Inc, pg 777
Blair Inc, pg 809

WISCONSIN

Audio Visual of Milwaukee Inc, pg 795
Frank D Hurst Corp dba Pechman Imaging, pg 892
USAV Group Inc, pg 1050

ONTARIO

Purefire Communications Inc, pg 987

Production Workshops

ALABAMA

Media Visions Inc, pg 937

ARIZONA

Creative Backstage, pg 838
Tellens Inc, pg 1037

CALIFORNIA

Crystal Pyramid Productions™, pg 840
Film TV Sound, pg 867
JDS Video & Media Productions Inc, pg 904
Panorama Productions, pg 968
QRS Software Services, pg 988
Russ InVision Co/AbridgeClub.com, pg 1001
StereoScope International, pg 1024

CONNECTICUT

Broadcast Video Productions LLC, pg 813

DISTRICT OF COLUMBIA

Theatrical Technicians Inc (TTI), pg 1038

AUDIO/VISUAL

Projection Equipment & Accessory Distributors (continued)

INDIANA (continued)

Sensory Technologies LLC, pg 1006
SHP Electronics, pg 1010
Victoria Supply Inc/Topbulb.com, pg 1054

IOWA

ECS Inc, pg 856
Sitler's Supplies Inc, pg 1012

KANSAS

KK Office Solutions Inc, pg 911
SKC Communication Products Inc, pg 1012

KENTUCKY

Audio Visual Techniques Inc, pg 796
Axxis Inc, pg 800
Barney Miller's Inc, pg 943
NOR-COM Inc, pg 958
Northern Kentucky University, pg 959

LOUISIANA

Intermedia Technologies, pg 900

MAINE

Headlight Audio Visual Inc, pg 887

MARYLAND

Absolute Hollywood, pg 772
Advance Audiovisual Presentation Ltd, pg 777
Baron Stage Curtain & Equipment Co Inc, pg 803
Cardinal Sound & Video, pg 820
CPR MultiMedia Solutions, pg 837
DSR Computer Technology Specialists Inc, pg 853
Kipp Visual Systems Inc, pg 911
Nelson White Systems Inc, pg 954
Nicholas P Pipino Associates Inc, pg 976
RTZ Audio Visual, pg 1000
Theatre Service & Supply Corp, pg 1038
Visual Aids Electronics Corp, pg 1059

MASSACHUSETTS

Antronics Inc, pg 787
Camera Co Inc/Broadcast Divison, pg 818
Elite Video, pg 859
Hunt's Photo, Video & Digital, pg 892
Limelight Productions Inc, pg 921
Lineco, pg 922
Rule Broadcast Systems, pg 1000
University Products Inc, pg 1050

MICHIGAN

Olson Anderson Co, pg 786
ASC Systems, pg 791
Ascom Communications Contractors, pg 791
City Events Group, pg 828
Digi Sign Design LLC, pg 847
Michigan Office Solutions, pg 941
On Stage Visuals, pg 963
TeL Systems, pg 1035

MINNESOTA

Advanced Audio-Visual Inc, pg 777
Alpha Video & Audio Inc, pg 782
AVI Systems, pg 799
Media Loft Inc, pg 937
Tierney Brothers Inc, pg 1040

MISSISSIPPI

Bowie Audio Visual Enterprises Inc, pg 811
Jasper Ewing & Sons Inc, pg 864

MISSOURI

A to Z Theatrical Supply & Service, pg 771
Communitronics Corp, pg 833
Conference Technologies Inc, pg 835
Image Technologies Corp, pg 895
MIS Technologies, pg 944
Modern Communications Inc, pg 944
Schiller's Audio-Visual, pg 1004
Southwest Audio-Visual Inc, pg 1019
Swank Audio Visuals, pg 1029

NEBRASKA

ATV Research Inc, pg 793
Ballantyne Strong Inc, pg 802
Dog & Pony Productions Inc, pg 850

NEVADA

Bulbman Inc, pg 815
Flex-A-Lite West, pg 870

NEW JERSEY

A-V Services Inc, pg 771
Argraph Corp, pg 789
Audio Visual Dynamics®, pg 795
AV Bluebook, pg 797
Color Leasing Studios, pg 831
Diversified Systems Inc, pg 849
Earl Girls Inc, pg 855
G&G Technologies Inc, pg 875
Hamilton Buhl, pg 884
JVC Professional Products Co, pg 907
Leica Camera Inc, pg 918
National Audio-Visual Supply, pg 952
Sharp Electronics Corp, Professional Display Division, pg 1008
SLD Lighting, pg 1013
Starlite Productions, pg 1024
SYMCO Inc, pg 1030
Tele-Measurements Inc, pg 1035
Total Video Products Inc, pg 1042
Turner Engineering Inc, pg 1046
VCom International Multimedia Corp, pg 1052
Video Corporation of America (VCA), pg 1055
Wilray Audio Visual Corp, pg 1067
Wired 4 Sound Inc, pg 1068
York Telecom, pg 1072

NEW MEXICO

Quickbeam Systems Inc (QSI), pg 989

NEW YORK

Ace Video, pg 774
ALTEL Systems Inc, pg 783
American Video Inc, pg 785
Audio-Video Corp, pg 795
AV Workshop, pg 797
BTX Technologies, pg 814
Bulb Direct, pg 815
Bulbtronics Inc, pg 815
Colortone Audio Visual, pg 832
Communication Corner Inc, pg 832
Creative Stage Lighting Co Inc, pg 838
Custom Media Environments, pg 841
Design Audio Visual Inc, pg 845
DSan Corp, pg 852
Gaylord Brothers, pg 876
Indigo Productions, pg 897
Just Bulbs - The Light Bulb Store, pg 907
KVL Audio Visual Services Inc, pg 914
Langie Audio Visual Systems, pg 915
Long Island Video Enterprises Live Inc, pg 924
Magnaplan Corp, pg 928
Markertek Video Supply, pg 931
Motion Picture Enterprises Inc, pg 947
Neptune Photo Inc, pg 954
Presentation Products Inc, pg 981
Raven Screen Corp, pg 992
Ray Supply Inc, pg 992
RNJ Electronics, pg 997
SmartSource Computer & AV Rentals, pg 1014
Stampede Presentation Products Inc, pg 1023
Technisphere Corp, pg 1034
Theatrical Services & Supplies Inc, pg 1038
Toys From The Attic, pg 1043
Video Technology Services Inc, pg 1056
Visual Technologies Corp, pg 1060
Willoughby's Imaging Center, pg 1067

NORTH CAROLINA

Camcor Inc, pg 818
Strategic Connections, pg 1026

OHIO

Advent Media Inc, pg 778
Audio Visual Media, pg 795
Copp Integrated Systems, pg 836
Hughie's Event Production Services, pg 892
Icom Multimedia, pg 893
ITA Audio Visual Solutions, pg 902
Jimmy Rea Electronics Inc, pg 992
Smithall Electronics Inc, pg 1014
Tri-State Audio Visual Co, pg 1044
Tri-State Visual Products, pg 1044
Xetron, pg 1071

OREGON

PLUS Corp of America, pg 977
Spectrum Systems Design, pg 1021

PENNSYLVANIA

Advanced AV, pg 777
Audio Visions Inc, pg 795
Audio Visual Communications Inc, pg 795
Bernie's Photo Center, pg 805
Brodart Co, pg 813
Clair Brothers Audio Systems Inc, pg 829
J E Foss Co, pg 871
Garcia Marketing Inc, pg 875
Grise Audio Visual Center Inc, pg 882
Innovision Media Group, pg 899
The Lerro Corp, pg 919
RSS Distributors, pg 1000
Vistacom Inc, pg 1059
Visual Sound Inc, pg 1059
Wespen Audio Visual Co, pg 1063

RHODE ISLAND

Custom Computer Specialists Inc, pg 841
Shanix Inc, pg 1008

TENNESSEE

Continental Film, pg 835
Durrell LLC, pg 854
Lowrance Sound Co Inc, pg 925
Memphis Communications Corp, pg 938
Technical Support Systems LLC, pg 1034
Tennessee Visual Service Co, pg 1037
Zion Music Group, pg 1074

TEXAS

Astro Audio Visual, pg 792
Audio Visual Technologies Group, pg 796
AVES Audio Visual Systems Inc, pg 798
CAM Audio Inc, pg 817
Crossroads Audio Inc, pg 840
Data Display Audio Visual Co LP, pg 843
Data Projections Inc, pg 843
Digital Display Solutions Inc, pg 847
FitzCo Sound Inc, pg 869
Heffernan Audio Visual, pg 887
Industrial Audio/Video Inc, pg 897
J&S Audio Visual Inc, pg 904
Lubbock Audio Visual Inc, pg 925
Media Management LLC, pg 937
Quality Audio Visual Service Inc, pg 988
Schoolhouse Audio Visual, pg 1004
Southwest Sound & Electronics Inc, pg 1019
Stage Directions, pg 1022
Tarpley Media Systems, pg 1032

UTAH

Webb Audio Visual Communication, pg 1063

VIRGINIA

Avitecture Inc, pg 799
Boitnott Visual Communications Corp (BVC), pg 810
Communications Specialists Inc, pg 833
Design & Production Inc, pg 845
Filmdex Inc, pg 867
Hoppmann Audio Visual, pg 891
Intellidyne LLC, pg 899
Lee Hartman & Sons Inc, pg 918
Metropolitan Audio Visual Co LLC, pg 940
Quince Imaging Inc, pg 989
Rocktown Media, pg 998
The Whitlock Group, pg 1065

WASHINGTON

Boxlight Inc, pg 811
CCI Solutions, pg 821
Inland Audio Visual Co, pg 898

AUDIO/VISUAL

Projection Equipment & Accessory Rentals (continued)

DELAWARE

Showorks Audio Visual Inc, pg 1010

FLORIDA

All Communications Rentals Inc (ALLCOMM), pg 780
AVI-SPL, pg 798
Gulf Coast Audio Visual Producers Inc, pg 883
Harmon's Audio-Visual Services, pg 885
Image Technical Services, pg 895
Industrial Strength Inc, pg 897
Jordan Klein Film & Video (JKFV), pg 906
Lighting Sales Connections, pg 920
Media Concepts Inc, pg 936
Multivision Video & Film, pg 950
Paradise Show & Design Inc, pg 969
Photosound of Orlando Inc, pg 975
Pro Stage Inc, pg 983
Sight & Sound Productions, pg 1010
Sound*Light, pg 1017
Tallahassee Audio Visual, pg 1031
Universal Studios Florida® Production Group, pg 1049

GEORGIA

Audio Visual Resources Inc, pg 795
Cinevision Corp, pg 828
Convergent Media Systems, pg 836
Dixie Theatre Service & Supply Co Inc, pg 849
Lighting & Production Equipment Inc, pg 920
MAGNUM Companies Ltd, pg 929
ON Event Services, pg 963
Stage Front Presentation Systems, pg 1022
Staging Directions Inc, pg 1023

HAWAII

ATTCO Inc, pg 793
Ken Herkes Productions & Entertainment (KHPE), pg 888

ILLINOIS

Allen Visual Systems Inc, pg 781
Audio Visual Services Corp, pg 796
AV Chicago Inc, pg 797
Backstar Creative Media Inc, pg 801
Beatty TeleVisual Productions, pg 804
Central Audio-Visual Equipment Inc, pg 823
Chicago Spotlight Inc, pg 825
Creative Technology, pg 838
Helix Camera & Video, pg 887
The Meetinghouse Companies Inc, pg 938
The Pepper Group, pg 972
PSAV® Presentation Services (Hotel Services Division), pg 987
QuickSet International Inc, pg 989
RC Communications, pg 992
SCI Television Productions LLC, pg 1004
The Screen Works®, pg 1005
Show Department Inc, pg 1009

INDIANA

Advanced Media Integration, pg 777
Gary Camera & Digital, pg 875
Heart Breaker Entertainment LLC, pg 887
OMNI Productions, pg 962

IOWA

Central Lighting & Equipment Inc (CLE), pg 823
ECS Inc, pg 856

KANSAS

Genigraphics®, pg 877
Smith Audio-Visual Inc, pg 1014

KENTUCKY

Audio Visual Techniques Inc, pg 796
Barney Miller's Inc, pg 943
Northern Kentucky University, pg 959

LOUISIANA

Clark Services Audio Visual & Exhibit Inc, pg 829
Intermedia Technologies, pg 900
Pace Systems, pg 966

MARYLAND

Absolute Hollywood, pg 772
Advance Audiovisual Presentation Ltd, pg 777
CPR MultiMedia Solutions, pg 837
Event Tech, pg 863
Hargrove Inc, pg 885
Nelson White Systems Inc, pg 954
RTZ Audio Visual, pg 1000
Visual Aids Electronics Corp, pg 1059

MASSACHUSETTS

A/V Presentations Inc, pg 797
AVFX Inc, pg 798
Camera Co Inc/Broadcast Divison, pg 818
Capron Lighting & Sound Co Inc, pg 819
Cramer Productions, pg 837
Elite Video, pg 859
massAV, pg 933
Preston Productions Inc, pg 981
TR Productions, pg 1043

MICHIGAN

Olson Anderson Co, pg 786
City Events Group, pg 828
Digi Sign Design LLC, pg 847
K&R All Media Productions Inc, pg 908
On Stage Visuals, pg 963
TeL Systems, pg 1035

MINNESOTA

Advanced Audio-Visual Inc, pg 777
Alpha Video & Audio Inc, pg 782
AVI Systems, pg 799
Big Event Productions LLC, pg 807
Media Loft Inc, pg 937

MISSISSIPPI

Bowie Audio Visual Enterprises Inc, pg 811
Jasper Ewing & Sons Inc, pg 864

MISSOURI

Communitronics Corp, pg 833
Show-Me Audio-Visual, pg 1009
Southwest Audio-Visual Inc, pg 1019
Swank Audio Visuals, pg 1029

NEBRASKA

Dog & Pony Productions Inc, pg 850

NEVADA

GES Audio Visual, pg 877
Lefco Video Services Inc, pg 918

NEW HAMPSHIRE

Academic & Campus Technology Services, pg 773
Apertura, pg 788

NEW JERSEY

Audio Visual Dynamics®, pg 795
Audio Visual Systems Rental Centres, pg 796
Color Leasing Studios, pg 831
Earl Girls Inc, pg 855
Gerriets International, pg 877
Giant Audio Visual Inc, pg 878
International Audio Visual Inc, pg 900
MIB Mediaworks, pg 941
Bill Quinn Productions, pg 989
SLD Lighting, pg 1013
Starlite Productions, pg 1024
Tele-Measurements Inc, pg 1035
Video Corporation of America (VCA), pg 1055
Wired 4 Sound Inc, pg 1068

NEW MEXICO

Quickbeam Systems Inc (QSI), pg 989

NEW YORK

Ace Video, pg 774
American Video Inc, pg 785
Audio Visual Resources LLC, pg 795
AV Workshop, pg 797
CMI Communications, pg 830
Colortone Audio Visual, pg 832
Communication Corner Inc, pg 832
Creative Stage Lighting Co Inc, pg 838
Custom Media Environments, pg 841
Design Audio Visual Inc, pg 845
Hello World Communications, pg 888
KVL Audio Visual Services Inc, pg 914
Langie Audio Visual Systems, pg 915
Long Island Video Enterprises Live Inc, pg 924
Magnaplan Corp, pg 928
Manhattan Center Studios Inc, pg 930
Motion Picture Enterprises Inc, pg 947
See Factor Industry Inc, pg 1006
SmartSource Computer & AV Rentals, pg 1014
Specialized Audio-Visual Inc, pg 1020
TBA Global Events, pg 1032
Technisphere Corp, pg 1034
Theatrical Services & Supplies Inc, pg 1038
Visual Technologies Corp, pg 1060
WorldStage, pg 1070

NORTH CAROLINA

A&V Company, pg 772
Audio & Light, pg 794
AV Metro Inc, pg 797
Camcor Inc, pg 818
Special Event Services, pg 1020
Strategic Connections, pg 1026
Visual Aids Electronics of North Carolina Inc, pg 1059

NORTH DAKOTA

Media Productions, pg 937

OHIO

Advent Media Inc, pg 778
Audio Visual Media, pg 795
Aztec Video Productions, pg 801
Bartha, pg 803
Hughie's Event Production Services, pg 892
Icom Multimedia, pg 893
ITA Audio Visual Solutions, pg 902
Lyon Video Inc, pg 927
Mills James Productions, pg 943
Thread Marketing Group, pg 1039
Tri-State Visual Products, pg 1044
Vista Color Imaging Inc, pg 1059

OKLAHOMA

PDC Productions, pg 970

OREGON

Northwest Film Center, pg 959
Rose City Sound, pg 999

PENNSYLVANIA

Advanced AV, pg 777
Audio Visions Inc, pg 795
Audio Visual Communications Inc, pg 795
Bernie's Photo Center, pg 805
FMP Media Solutions Inc, pg 870
Grise Audio Visual Center Inc, pg 882
Innovision Media Group, pg 899
Ott Film Rentals, pg 966
Production Solutions Inc, pg 985
Vistacom Inc, pg 1059
Visual Sound Inc, pg 1059

SOUTH CAROLINA

Encore Video Productions, pg 861
Sound & Images Inc, pg 1016

TENNESSEE

Memphis Communications Corp, pg 938
Russ Sturgeon Productions/RSVP, pg 1027
Technical Support Systems LLC, pg 1034
Tennessee Visual Service Co, pg 1037

TEXAS

Alford Media Services, pg 780
Astro Audio Visual, pg 792
Audio Visual Technologies Group, pg 796
AVES Audio Visual Systems Inc, pg 798
Bright Star Productions Inc, pg 812
Data Display Audio Visual Co LP, pg 843
Data Projections Inc, pg 843

Projection Equipment & Accessory Repairs

AUDIO/VISUAL

Projection Equipment & Accessory Repairs (continued)

WISCONSIN

Audio Visual of Milwaukee Inc, pg 795
Full Compass Systems, pg 874

ALBERTA

Infosat Communications Inc, pg 898
Sharp's Audio-Visual Ltd, pg 1008
Unique Communications Ltd, pg 1048

BRITISH COLUMBIA

Commercial Electronics Ltd, pg 832

MANITOBA

Evolution Presentation Technologies, pg 863
Inland Audio Visual Ltd, pg 898

ONTARIO

Edcom Multimedia Products, pg 856
MVI Multivision Inc, pg 951
Premier A/V Sales Ltd, pg 980
Technovision® Interactive Inc, pg 1035
Westbury National Show Systems Ltd, pg 1064

QUEBEC

Panavideo Inc, pg 968

Projection Panel Distributors

ARIZONA

EAR Professional Audio/Video, pg 855
Professional Marketing Services Inc, pg 985
Troxell Communications Inc, pg 1045

ARKANSAS

White Diamond Productions, pg 1065

CALIFORNIA

Ametron Audio/Video, pg 785
Associated Sound, pg 792
California Tape Products Inc, pg 817
Cibola Systems, pg 826
Computer Modules Inc, pg 834
Delicate Electronics Sales Inc, pg 845
Electrosonic Inc, pg 859
MediaPOINTE, pg 938
Mitsubishi Electric Visual Solutions America Inc (MEVSA), pg 944
Sound Service Co, pg 1017
Southern California Sound Image Inc, pg 1019
Towards 2000 Inc, pg 1043
VTP Inc, pg 1061

COLORADO

Daylight Productions & Rentals, pg 844

CONNECTICUT

Everett Hall Associates Inc, pg 863
HB Communications Inc, pg 886

FLORIDA

Digital Video Systems Inc, pg 848
Hi-Tech Import Export Corp, pg 888
Industrial Strength Inc, pg 897
Lighting Sales Connections, pg 920
Photomart Cine-Video Inc, pg 975
Pro Stage Inc, pg 983
Sight & Sound Productions, pg 1010
Techni-Lux Inc, pg 1033

GEORGIA

Stage Front Presentation Systems, pg 1022

HAWAII

The Audio Visual Co (AVCO), pg 795

ILLINOIS

Allen Visual Systems Inc, pg 781
Dukane Corp, Audio Visual Products Division, pg 853
Joseph Electronics, pg 906
Quintessence Audio Ltd, pg 989

INDIANA

Sensory Technologies LLC, pg 1006
SHP Electronics, pg 1010

IOWA

ECS Inc, pg 856

KENTUCKY

NOR-COM Inc, pg 958

LOUISIANA

Intermedia Technologies, pg 900

MARYLAND

Absolute Hollywood, pg 772
DSR Computer Technology Specialists Inc, pg 853
Kipp Visual Systems Inc, pg 911

MASSACHUSETTS

Lineco, pg 922

MICHIGAN

Ascom Communications Contractors, pg 791
Digi Sign Design LLC, pg 847
Michigan Office Solutions, pg 941
TeL Systems, pg 1035

MINNESOTA

Alpha Video & Audio Inc, pg 782
Tierney Brothers Inc, pg 1040

MISSOURI

Modern Communications Inc, pg 944
Schiller's Audio-Visual, pg 1004

NEBRASKA

Strong Cinema Products, pg 1026

NEW JERSEY

AV Bluebook, pg 797
Diversified Systems Inc, pg 849
Earl Girls Inc, pg 855
Hamilton Buhl, pg 884
Starlite Productions, pg 1024
Total Video Products Inc, pg 1042
Wilray Audio Visual Corp, pg 1067
Wired 4 Sound Inc, pg 1068
York Telecom, pg 1072

NEW YORK

Audio-Video Corp, pg 795
Colortone Audio Visual, pg 832
Custom Media Environments, pg 841
Gaylord Brothers, pg 876
KVL Audio Visual Services Inc, pg 914
Magnaplan Corp, pg 928
Markertek Video Supply, pg 931
Neptune Photo Inc, pg 954
Presentation Products Inc, pg 981
Video Technology Services Inc, pg 1056
Visual Technologies Corp, pg 1060

OHIO

Electronic Vision Inc (EV), pg 859
Tri-State Audio Visual Co, pg 1044
Walltalkers, pg 1061

PENNSYLVANIA

Advanced AV, pg 777
Bernie's Photo Center, pg 805
Clair Brothers Audio Systems Inc, pg 829
J E Foss Co, pg 871
Grise Audio Visual Center Inc, pg 882
The Lerro Corp, pg 919
Vistacom Inc, pg 1059
Visual Sound Inc, pg 1059

TENNESSEE

Durrell LLC, pg 854
Lowrance Sound Co Inc, pg 925
Spring Arbor Distributors, pg 1022
Technical Support Systems LLC, pg 1034
Tennessee Visual Service Co, pg 1037
Zion Music Group, pg 1074

TEXAS

Lubbock Audio Visual Inc, pg 925
Media Management LLC, pg 937
Quality Audio Visual Service Inc, pg 988
Schoolhouse Audio Visual, pg 1004
Tarpley Media Systems, pg 1032
Videotex Systems Inc, pg 1057

VIRGINIA

Avitecture Inc, pg 799
Communications Specialists Inc, pg 833
Intellidyne LLC, pg 899
Lee Hartman & Sons Inc, pg 918
Quince Imaging Inc, pg 989

WASHINGTON

Boxlight Inc, pg 811
CCI Solutions, pg 821

WISCONSIN

Audio Visual of Milwaukee Inc, pg 795
Full Compass Systems, pg 874

PUERTO RICO

Audio Visual Concepts Inc, pg 795

ALBERTA

Sharp's Audio-Visual Ltd, pg 1008

BRITISH COLUMBIA

Commercial Electronics Ltd, pg 832

MANITOBA

Inland Audio Visual Ltd, pg 898

ONTARIO

MVI Multivision Inc, pg 951
Westbury National Show Systems Ltd, pg 1064

Projection Panel Manufacturers

CALIFORNIA

Mitsubishi Electric Visual Solutions America Inc (MEVSA), pg 944

FLORIDA

Vutec Corp, Video Products Division, pg 1061

ILLINOIS

ACCO Brands Corp, pg 773
GBC Document Finishing, pg 876

INDIANA

Da-Lite, pg 842

MARYLAND

Absolute Hollywood, pg 772

NEW JERSEY

Sharp Electronics Corp, Professional Display Division, pg 1008

NEW YORK

TecNec Distributing, pg 1035
Video Technology Services Inc, pg 1056

OHIO

Walltalkers, pg 1061
Xetron, pg 1071

TEXAS

MooreCo Inc, pg 946

VIRGINIA

Optikinetics Ltd - The Americas, pg 964
Quince Imaging Inc, pg 989

ONTARIO

Evertz Microsystems Ltd, pg 863

Projection Panel Rentals

ARIZONA

Broadcast Rentals, pg 813
Merestone, pg 938

CALIFORNIA

Alliant Event Services, pg 781
Ametron Audio/Video, pg 785
Associated Sound, pg 792
Lynch Communications, pg 926
McCune Audio-Video-Lighting, pg 935
Munday & Collins AV, pg 950
Muse Presentation Technologies, pg 950
Slate Media Group, pg 1013
Sound Service Co, pg 1017
Towards 2000 Inc, pg 1043
VER-Video Equipment Rentals, pg 1053
Video Resources Inc, pg 1056

COLORADO

Multimedia Audio Visual Inc, pg 950

CONNECTICUT

Everett Hall Associates Inc, pg 863

FLORIDA

AVI-SPL, pg 798
Image Technical Services, pg 895
Industrial Strength Inc, pg 897
Lighting Sales Connections, pg 920
Pro Stage Inc, pg 983

GEORGIA

ON Event Services, pg 963
Stage Front Presentation Systems, pg 1022

ILLINOIS

Allen Visual Systems Inc, pg 781
Backstar Creative Media Inc, pg 801
RC Communications, pg 992
SCI Television Productions LLC, pg 1004

KENTUCKY

Audio Visual Techniques Inc, pg 796

MARYLAND

Absolute Hollywood, pg 772
CPR MultiMedia Solutions, pg 837
Event Tech, pg 863
Visual Aids Electronics Corp, pg 1059

MASSACHUSETTS

massAV, pg 933
Preston Productions Inc, pg 981

MICHIGAN

Digi Sign Design LLC, pg 847
K&R All Media Productions Inc, pg 908

MINNESOTA

Alpha Video & Audio Inc, pg 782

MISSOURI

Schiller's Audio-Visual, pg 1004
Show-Me Audio-Visual, pg 1009

NEVADA

GES Audio Visual, pg 877

NEW JERSEY

Earl Girls Inc, pg 855
Moe AV LLC, pg 945
PLS Staging, pg 977
Starlite Productions, pg 1024
Wired 4 Sound Inc, pg 1068

NEW YORK

Audio Visual Resources LLC, pg 795
Colortone Audio Visual, pg 832
Custom Media Environments, pg 841
KVL Audio Visual Services Inc, pg 914
Magnaplan Corp, pg 928
Visual Technologies Corp, pg 1060

NORTH CAROLINA

A&V Company, pg 772
Audio & Light, pg 794
Special Event Services, pg 1020
Visual Aids Electronics of North Carolina Inc, pg 1059

OHIO

Aztec Video Productions, pg 801
Hughie's Event Production Services, pg 892
Mills James Productions, pg 943

PENNSYLVANIA

Advanced AV, pg 777
FirstGeneration Audio/Visual Services, pg 869
Grise Audio Visual Center Inc, pg 882
Production Solutions Inc, pg 985
Visual Sound Inc, pg 1059

TENNESSEE

Technical Support Systems LLC, pg 1034
Tennessee Visual Service Co, pg 1037

TEXAS

Alford Media Services, pg 780
Lubbock Audio Visual Inc, pg 925
Quality Audio Visual Service Inc, pg 988

VERMONT

Parlato Productions, pg 969

VIRGINIA

American AV, pg 783
Audio Visual Actions Inc (AVA), pg 795
Quince Imaging Inc, pg 989

WASHINGTON

Boxlight Inc, pg 811

WISCONSIN

Audio Visual of Milwaukee Inc, pg 795
Full Compass Systems, pg 874

ALBERTA

L R Light & Sound, pg 915
Sharp's Audio-Visual Ltd, pg 1008

BRITISH COLUMBIA

Commercial Electronics Ltd, pg 832
DL Sound & Lighting Productions Ltd, pg 849

MANITOBA

Inland Audio Visual Ltd, pg 898

ONTARIO

Metalworks Recording Studios Inc, pg 939
MVI Multivision Inc, pg 951
Westbury National Show Systems Ltd, pg 1064

Projection Panel Repairs

CALIFORNIA

Ametron Audio/Video, pg 785
Electrosonic Inc, pg 859
McAlister Electronics, pg 935
Towards 2000 Inc, pg 1043

CONNECTICUT

HB Communications Inc, pg 886

FLORIDA

AVI-SPL, pg 798
ELC Sales & Service Inc, pg 858

GEORGIA

Stage Front Presentation Systems, pg 1022

ILLINOIS

Allen Visual Systems Inc, pg 781

KENTUCKY

Axxis Inc, pg 800
NOR-COM Inc, pg 958

MARYLAND

Visual Aids Electronics Corp, pg 1059

MICHIGAN

TeL Systems, pg 1035

MINNESOTA

Alpha Video & Audio Inc, pg 782

NEW JERSEY

Earl Girls Inc, pg 855
Starlite Productions, pg 1024

NEW YORK

Custom Media Environments, pg 841
Visual Technologies Corp, pg 1060

OHIO

Aztec Video Productions, pg 801
Tri-State Audio Visual Co, pg 1044

PENNSYLVANIA

J E Foss Co, pg 871

TENNESSEE

Technical Support Systems LLC, pg 1034

TEXAS

Lubbock Audio Visual Inc, pg 925
Quality Audio Visual Service Inc, pg 988
Tarpley Media Systems, pg 1032

VIRGINIA

Avitecture Inc, pg 799
Quince Imaging Inc, pg 989

WASHINGTON

Boxlight Inc, pg 811

WISCONSIN

Audio Visual of Milwaukee Inc, pg 795
Full Compass Systems, pg 874

ALBERTA

Sharp's Audio-Visual Ltd, pg 1008

MANITOBA

Inland Audio Visual Ltd, pg 898

ONTARIO

MVI Multivision Inc, pg 951
Westbury National Show Systems Ltd, pg 1064

Projection Part Distributors

ALABAMA

Media Visions Inc, pg 937

ARIZONA

Metropolitan Audio-Visual Inc, pg 940
Troxell Communications Inc, pg 1045

ARKANSAS

White Diamond Productions, pg 1065

CALIFORNIA

Ametron Audio/Video, pg 785
Barber Tech Video Products, pg 802
California Tape Products Inc, pg 817
Cinema Equipment Sales of California Inc, pg 827
Delicate Electronics Sales Inc, pg 845
Educational Technology Services (ETS), pg 857
Alan Gordon Enterprises Inc, pg 880
Instructional Materials & Equipment Distributors (I-Med), pg 899
J & R Film Co, pg 903
Media Fabricators Inc, pg 936
MediaPOINTE, pg 938
PMP Marketing Inc, pg 977
Sound Service Co, pg 1017
Southern California Sound Image Inc, pg 1019
VTP Inc, pg 1061

AUDIO/VISUAL

Projection Part Distributors (continued)

COLORADO

Ceavco Audio/Visual Co, pg 822
Goldberg Brothers Inc, pg 880
Stanco Sales LLC, pg 1023

CONNECTICUT

HB Communications Inc, pg 886
MAVCO, pg 934
Rockwell Communications Inc, pg 998

FLORIDA

AVI-SPL, pg 798
Cinema Equipment & Supplies Inc, pg 827
Digital Video Systems Inc, pg 848
Gulf Coast Audio Visual Producers Inc, pg 883
Hi-Tech Import Export Corp, pg 888
Photomart Cine-Video Inc, pg 975
Pro Stage Inc, pg 983
Tallahassee Audio Visual, pg 1031
Techni-Lux Inc, pg 1033
Technomedia Solutions, pg 1035

GEORGIA

Audio Visual Resources Inc, pg 795
Convergent Media Systems, pg 836
Stage Front Presentation Systems, pg 1022
Technical Innovation, pg 1033
Visioneering International Inc, pg 1058

HAWAII

The Audio Visual Co (AVCO), pg 795

ILLINOIS

Joseph Electronics, pg 906

INDIANA

Sensory Technologies LLC, pg 1006
SHP Electronics, pg 1010
Victoria Supply Inc/Topbulb.com, pg 1054

IOWA

ECS Inc, pg 856

KENTUCKY

Audio Visual Techniques Inc, pg 796
Axxis Inc, pg 800
NOR-COM Inc, pg 958

LOUISIANA

Intermedia Technologies, pg 900

MARYLAND

Nicholas P Pipino Associates Inc, pg 976
Visual Aids Electronics Corp, pg 1059

MASSACHUSETTS

Elite Video, pg 859

MICHIGAN

Ascom Communications Contractors, pg 791
City Events Group, pg 828
Digi Sign Design LLC, pg 847

MINNESOTA

Alpha Video & Audio Inc, pg 782
AVI Systems, pg 799
Tierney Brothers Inc, pg 1040

MISSISSIPPI

Bowie Audio Visual Enterprises Inc, pg 811
Jasper Ewing & Sons Inc, pg 864

MISSOURI

Communitronics Corp, pg 833
Conference Technologies Inc, pg 835
MIS Technologies, pg 944
Modern Communications Inc, pg 944
Schiller's Audio-Visual, pg 1004
Southwest Audio-Visual Inc, pg 1019

NEBRASKA

Ballantyne Strong Inc, pg 802

NEW JERSEY

Earl Girls Inc, pg 855
Hamilton Buhl, pg 884
Starlite Productions, pg 1024
Total Video Products Inc, pg 1042
VCom International Multimedia Corp, pg 1052
Video Corporation of America (VCA), pg 1055
Wired 4 Sound Inc, pg 1068
York Telecom, pg 1072

NEW YORK

American Video Inc, pg 785
Audio-Video Corp, pg 795
AV Workshop, pg 797
Bulbtronics Inc, pg 815
Communication Corner Inc, pg 832
Custom Media Environments, pg 841
General Audio-Visual Inc (GAVI), pg 876
Indigo Productions, pg 897
Langie Audio Visual Systems, pg 915
Long Island Video Enterprises Live Inc, pg 924
Magnaplan Corp, pg 928
Ray Supply Inc, pg 992
Russell Industries Inc, pg 1001
Theatrical Services & Supplies Inc, pg 1038
Video Technology Services Inc, pg 1056
Visual Technologies Corp, pg 1060

NORTH CAROLINA

Camcor Inc, pg 818
Strategic Connections, pg 1026

OHIO

Audio Visual Media, pg 795
Hughie's Event Production Services, pg 892
ITA Audio Visual Solutions, pg 902
Tri-State Visual Products, pg 1044
Xetron, pg 1071

PENNSYLVANIA

Advanced AV, pg 777
Audio Visions Inc, pg 795
Clair Brothers Audio Systems Inc, pg 829
J E Foss Co, pg 871
Grise Audio Visual Center Inc, pg 882
The Lerro Corp, pg 919
Wespen Audio Visual Co, pg 1063

RHODE ISLAND

Custom Computer Specialists Inc, pg 841

TENNESSEE

Durrell LLC, pg 854
Lowrance Sound Co Inc, pg 925
Memphis Communications Corp, pg 938
Technical Support Systems LLC, pg 1034
Tennessee Visual Service Co, pg 1037

TEXAS

Audio Visual Technologies Group, pg 796
AVES Audio Visual Systems Inc, pg 798
Lubbock Audio Visual Inc, pg 925
Media Management LLC, pg 937
Schoolhouse Audio Visual, pg 1004
Tarpley Media Systems, pg 1032

VIRGINIA

Avitecture Inc, pg 799
Boitnott Visual Communications Corp (BVC), pg 810
Hoppmann Audio Visual, pg 891
Intellidyne LLC, pg 899
Lee Hartman & Sons Inc, pg 918
Metropolitan Audio Visual Co LLC, pg 940
Quince Imaging Inc, pg 989
The Whitlock Group, pg 1065

WASHINGTON

CCI Solutions, pg 821
Inland Audio Visual Co, pg 898

WISCONSIN

Alpha Source Inc, pg 782
Audio Visual of Milwaukee Inc, pg 795
Camera Corner Connecting Point, pg 818
Full Compass Systems, pg 874

ALBERTA

McBain Audio Visual Ltd, pg 935
Sharp's Audio-Visual Ltd, pg 1008

BRITISH COLUMBIA

Speciality Bulb Products Inc, pg 1020

MANITOBA

Evolution Presentation Technologies, pg 863
Inland Audio Visual Ltd, pg 898

ONTARIO

Edcom Multimedia Products, pg 856
Nationwide Audio Visual Co, pg 953
Premier A/V Sales Ltd, pg 980
Westbury National Show Systems Ltd, pg 1064

QUEBEC

Concept Audio-Visual, pg 834
Panavideo Inc, pg 968
Strong Screen Systems, pg 1026

Projection Part Manufacturers

ARIZONA

NKK Switches, pg 957

CALIFORNIA

Alan Gordon Enterprises Inc, pg 880
J & R Film Co, pg 903
JDSU, pg 905
Ushio America Inc, pg 1051

CONNECTICUT

General Electric Co, pg 876

FLORIDA

Vutec Corp, Video Products Division, pg 1061

ILLINOIS

Dukane Corp, Audio Visual Products Division, pg 853
La Vezzi Precision Inc, pg 1053

INDIANA

Da-Lite, pg 842

KANSAS

Speco/Systems & Products Engineering Co, pg 1020

MASSACHUSETTS

Elite Video, pg 859

NEBRASKA

Ballantyne Strong Inc, pg 802
Strong Cinema Products, pg 1026

NEW YORK

American Video Inc, pg 785
General Audio-Visual Inc (GAVI), pg 876
Russell Industries Inc, pg 1001

TENNESSEE

Durrell LLC, pg 854

VIRGINIA

Optikinetics Ltd - The Americas, pg 964
Quince Imaging Inc, pg 989

ONTARIO

Evertz Microsystems Ltd, pg 863

QUEBEC

Strong Screen Systems, pg 1026

Projection Part Rentals

ALABAMA

Media Visions Inc, pg 937

ARIZONA

Merestone, pg 938
Metropolitan Audio-Visual Inc, pg 940

CALIFORNIA

Ametron Audio/Video, pg 785
Lynch Communications, pg 926
McCune Audio-Video-Lighting, pg 935
Media Fabricators Inc, pg 936
Sound Service Co, pg 1017

COLORADO

Ceavco Audio/Visual Co, pg 822

FLORIDA

Image Technical Services, pg 895
Pro Stage Inc, pg 983

GEORGIA

Stage Front Presentation Systems, pg 1022
Staging Directions Inc, pg 1023

ILLINOIS

SCI Television Productions LLC, pg 1004

KENTUCKY

Audio Visual Techniques Inc, pg 796

LOUISIANA

Pace Systems, pg 966

MARYLAND

CPR MultiMedia Solutions, pg 837
RTZ Audio Visual, pg 1000

MICHIGAN

Digi Sign Design LLC, pg 847
K&R All Media Productions Inc, pg 908

MINNESOTA

AVI Systems, pg 799

MISSOURI

Schiller's Audio-Visual, pg 1004
Show-Me Audio-Visual, pg 1009
Southwest Audio-Visual Inc, pg 1019
Swank Audio Visuals, pg 1029

NEW HAMPSHIRE

Apertura, pg 788

NEW JERSEY

Earl Girls Inc, pg 855
Moe AV LLC, pg 945
Video Corporation of America (VCA), pg 1055

NEW YORK

American Video Inc, pg 785
AV Workshop, pg 797
Langie Audio Visual Systems, pg 915
Long Island Video Enterprises Live Inc, pg 924
Specialized Audio-Visual Inc, pg 1020

NORTH CAROLINA

AV Metro Inc, pg 797
Special Event Services, pg 1020

OHIO

Audio Visual Media, pg 795
Aztec Video Productions, pg 801
Icom Multimedia, pg 893

PENNSYLVANIA

Advanced AV, pg 777
Grise Audio Visual Center Inc, pg 882
Production Solutions Inc, pg 985

TENNESSEE

Durrell LLC, pg 854
Memphis Communications Corp, pg 938
Technical Support Systems LLC, pg 1034

TEXAS

Schoolhouse Audio Visual, pg 1004

VIRGINIA

American AV, pg 783
Quince Imaging Inc, pg 989

WISCONSIN

Audio Visual of Milwaukee Inc, pg 795

PUERTO RICO

Stage Crew Audiovisual Inc, pg 1022

ALBERTA

McBain Audio Visual Ltd, pg 935
Unique Communications Ltd, pg 1048

BRITISH COLUMBIA

DL Sound & Lighting Productions Ltd, pg 849

ONTARIO

Metalworks Recording Studios Inc, pg 939
Westbury National Show Systems Ltd, pg 1064

QUEBEC

Audio Visual Dynamics Ltd, pg 795
Concept Audio-Visual, pg 834

Projection Part Repairs

CALIFORNIA

Ametron Audio/Video, pg 785
McAlister Electronics, pg 935
Lloyd F McKinney Associates Inc, pg 935
Pro Camera Repair, pg 982

COLORADO

Ceavco Audio/Visual Co, pg 822

CONNECTICUT

HB Communications Inc, pg 886
Rockwell Communications Inc, pg 998

DISTRICT OF COLUMBIA

Future View Inc, pg 874

FLORIDA

ELC Sales & Service Inc, pg 858

GEORGIA

Audio Visual Resources Inc, pg 795
Stage Front Presentation Systems, pg 1022

KENTUCKY

Axxis Inc, pg 800
NOR-COM Inc, pg 958

MARYLAND

RTZ Audio Visual, pg 1000

MASSACHUSETTS

Elite Video, pg 859

MICHIGAN

TeL Systems, pg 1035

MINNESOTA

AVI Systems, pg 799

NEW JERSEY

Earl Girls Inc, pg 855

NEW YORK

American Video Inc, pg 785
Colortone Audio Visual, pg 832
Langie Audio Visual Systems, pg 915
Visual Technologies Corp, pg 1060

NORTH CAROLINA

Camcor Inc, pg 818

OHIO

Audio Visual Media, pg 795
Aztec Video Productions, pg 801
Icom Multimedia, pg 893

TENNESSEE

Durrell LLC, pg 854
Memphis Communications Corp, pg 938
Technical Support Systems LLC, pg 1034
Tennessee Visual Service Co, pg 1037

TEXAS

Audio Visual Technologies Group, pg 796
Padgitt's, pg 967
Schoolhouse Audio Visual, pg 1004
Tarpley Media Systems, pg 1032

VIRGINIA

Avitecture Inc, pg 799
Hoppmann Audio Visual, pg 891
Quince Imaging Inc, pg 989

WISCONSIN

Audio Visual of Milwaukee Inc, pg 795
Full Compass Systems, pg 874

ONTARIO

Edcom Multimedia Products, pg 856
HD Source, pg 886
Westbury National Show Systems Ltd, pg 1064

Public Address System Distributors

ALABAMA

Curtis Company, pg 841
Media Visions Inc, pg 937

ARIZONA

Arizona Cine Equipment, pg 789
EAR Professional Audio/Video, pg 855
Metropolitan Audio-Visual Inc, pg 940
Troxell Communications Inc, pg 1045

ARKANSAS

Carlton-Bates Co, pg 820

CALIFORNIA

Ametron Audio/Video, pg 785
Associated Sound, pg 792
ATV Video Center Inc, pg 793
Audio Images Corp, pg 794
AV Conferencing, pg 797
Be Media, pg 804
California Tape Products Inc, pg 817
Delicate Electronics Sales Inc, pg 845
Empire Wholesale Inc, pg 860
FXC Communications, pg 874
GMF Sound Inc, pg 879
Instructional Materials & Equipment Distributors (I-Med), pg 899
JD Audio Visual Inc, pg 904
L Acoustics US, pg 914
Location Sound Corp, pg 924
Marshall Electronics Inc, pg 932
Lloyd F McKinney Associates Inc, pg 935
Media Fabricators Inc, pg 936
MediaMation Inc, pg 937
MediaPOINTE, pg 938
POP TV, pg 978
Related Visual Inc, pg 994
Sound Service Co, pg 1017
SSL Industries Inc, pg 1022
Stanislaus Audio Video Inc, pg 1023
Third Ear Sound Co, pg 1038
TOA Electronics Inc, pg 1041
Towards 2000 Inc, pg 1043
VMI Inc, pg 1060
VTP Inc, pg 1061

COLORADO

Audio Consultant Services Inc, pg 794
Ceavco Audio/Visual Co, pg 822

CONNECTICUT

Concord Communications, pg 835
Connecticut Audio & Theatrical Supply, pg 835
Everett Hall Associates Inc, pg 863
MAVCO, pg 934
Sennheiser Electronic Corp, pg 1006

AUDIO/VISUAL

Public Address System Distributors (continued)

DELAWARE

Actors Attic, pg 775

FLORIDA

Allstar Audio Systems Inc, pg 782
BAI Distributors Inc, pg 801
Broadcasters General Store Inc, pg 813
Digital Video Systems Inc, pg 848
General Projection Systems Inc, pg 877
Gulf Coast Audio Visual Producers Inc, pg 883
Harmon's Audio-Visual Services, pg 885
Harris Corp, pg 885
Hi-Tech Import Export Corp, pg 888
Hollywood Theatre Equipment Inc, pg 890
Lighting Sales Connections, pg 920
Photomart Cine-Video Inc, pg 975
Photosound of Orlando Inc, pg 975
Pro Stage Inc, pg 983
Stereo Sales Inc, pg 1024
TAI Audio, pg 1031

GEORGIA

Baker Audio Inc, pg 801
Lighting & Production Equipment Inc, pg 920
Omnimedia Inc, pg 962
Stage Front Presentation Systems, pg 1022
Technical Innovation, pg 1033
Visioneering International Inc, pg 1058

HAWAII

The Audio Visual Co (AVCO), pg 795

ILLINOIS

Allen Visual Systems Inc, pg 781
Central Audio-Visual Equipment Inc, pg 823
Creative Technology, pg 838
Joseph Electronics, pg 906
G T Luscombe Co Inc, pg 926
Quintessence Audio Ltd, pg 989

INDIANA

Sensory Technologies LLC, pg 1006
SHP Electronics, pg 1010

IOWA

ECS Inc, pg 856

KANSAS

Smith Audio-Visual Inc, pg 1014

KENTUCKY

Audio Visual Techniques Inc, pg 796
Barney Miller's Inc, pg 943
NOR-COM Inc, pg 958
Northern Kentucky University, pg 959

MAINE

Headlight Audio Visual Inc, pg 887

MARYLAND

Cardinal Sound & Video, pg 820
Nicholas P Pipino Associates Inc, pg 976
RTZ Audio Visual, pg 1000
Visual Aids Electronics Corp, pg 1059

MASSACHUSETTS

Antronics Inc, pg 787
Terry Hanley Audio Systems Inc, pg 884
Professional Audio Design Inc, pg 985

MICHIGAN

Olson Anderson Co, pg 786
Ascom Communications Contractors, pg 791
City Events Group, pg 828
Digi Sign Design LLC, pg 847
On Stage Visuals, pg 963
TeL Systems, pg 1035

MINNESOTA

Advanced Audio-Visual Inc, pg 777
AVI Systems, pg 799
New Life Communications Inc, pg 956

MISSISSIPPI

Bowie Audio Visual Enterprises Inc, pg 811
Jasper Ewing & Sons Inc, pg 864

MISSOURI

Communitronics Corp, pg 833
Conference Technologies Inc, pg 835
Image Technologies Corp, pg 895
Modern Communications Inc, pg 944
Schiller's Audio-Visual, pg 1004
Southwest Audio-Visual Inc, pg 1019

NEBRASKA

Dog & Pony Productions Inc, pg 850

NEW HAMPSHIRE

APS Lighting-Sound-AV, pg 789

NEW JERSEY

A-V Services Inc, pg 771
Alltec Stores, a Vcom IMC Company, pg 782
Audio Visual Associates, pg 795
Audio Visual Dynamics®, pg 795
AV Bluebook, pg 797
Comprehensive Cable & Connectivity Co, pg 833
Earl Girls Inc, pg 855
FlagHouse, pg 869
Hamilton Buhl, pg 884
National Audio-Visual Supply, pg 952
Starlite Productions, pg 1024
Total Video Products Inc, pg 1042
Turner Engineering Inc, pg 1046
Wired 4 Sound Inc, pg 1068
York Telecom, pg 1072

NEW MEXICO

Quickbeam Systems Inc (QSI), pg 989

NEW YORK

Albany Theatre Supply Co Inc, pg 780
ALTEL Systems Inc, pg 783
Audio-Video Corp, pg 795
AV Workshop, pg 797
Colortone Audio Visual, pg 832
Communication Corner Inc, pg 832
Custom Media Environments, pg 841
Design Audio Visual Inc, pg 845
Gaylord Brothers, pg 876
Indigo Productions, pg 897
Langie Audio Visual Systems, pg 915
Lee Dan® Communications Inc, pg 918
Long Island Video Enterprises Live Inc, pg 924
Magnaplan Corp, pg 928
Markertek Video Supply, pg 931
Neptune Photo Inc, pg 954
Ray Supply Inc, pg 992
RNJ Electronics, pg 997
SmartSource Computer & AV Rentals, pg 1014
Technisphere Corp, pg 1034
Theatrical Services & Supplies Inc, pg 1038
Visual Technologies Corp, pg 1060
Whirlwind Music Distributors Inc, pg 1065
Willoughby's Imaging Center, pg 1067

NORTH CAROLINA

Camcor Inc, pg 818
Strategic Connections, pg 1026

OHIO

Audio Visual Media, pg 795
Copp Integrated Systems, pg 836
ITA Audio Visual Solutions, pg 902
Luminaud Inc, pg 926
Jimmy Rea Electronics Inc, pg 992
Tri-State Audio Visual Co, pg 1044
Tri-State Visual Products, pg 1044

OREGON

Lightspeed Technologies Inc, pg 921
PLUS Corp of America, pg 977

PENNSYLVANIA

Advanced AV, pg 777
Audio Visions Inc, pg 795
Bernie's Photo Center, pg 805
Brodart Co, pg 813
Clair Brothers Audio Systems Inc, pg 829
J E Foss Co, pg 871
Garcia Marketing Inc, pg 875
Grise Audio Visual Center Inc, pg 882
Hite Co, pg 889
The Lerro Corp, pg 919
Morefield Communications Inc, pg 946
RSS Distributors, pg 1000
Vistacom Inc, pg 1059
Visual Sound Inc, pg 1059
Wespen Audio Visual Co, pg 1063

SOUTH CAROLINA

DaviSound, pg 843

TENNESSEE

Belew Enterprises, pg 804
Continental Film, pg 835
Durrell LLC, pg 854
Lowrance Sound Co Inc, pg 925
Memphis Communications Corp, pg 938
Technical Support Systems LLC, pg 1034
Tennessee Visual Service Co, pg 1037
Zion Music Group, pg 1074

TEXAS

Astro Audio Visual, pg 792
Audio Visual Technologies Group, pg 796
AVES Audio Visual Systems Inc, pg 798
CAM Audio Inc, pg 817
Crossroads Audio Inc, pg 840
Data Display Audio Visual Co LP, pg 843
Digital Display Solutions Inc, pg 847
FitzCo Sound Inc, pg 869
Heffernan Audio Visual, pg 887
J&S Audio Visual Inc, pg 904
Lubbock Audio Visual Inc, pg 925
Media Management LLC, pg 937
Quality Audio Visual Service Inc, pg 988
RadioShack Corp, pg 990
Schoolhouse Audio Visual, pg 1004
Southwest Sound & Electronics Inc, pg 1019
Tarpley Media Systems, pg 1032

UTAH

Performance Audio, pg 973
Webb Audio Visual Communication, pg 1063

VERMONT

Production Advantage Inc, pg 984

VIRGINIA

Acoustics First Corp, pg 775
Avitecture Inc, pg 799
Boitnott Visual Communications Corp (BVC), pg 810
Communications Specialists Inc, pg 833
Hoppmann Audio Visual, pg 891
Lee Hartman & Sons Inc, pg 918
Rocktown Media, pg 998
The Whitlock Group, pg 1065

WASHINGTON

CCI Solutions, pg 821
D A Sound, pg 842
Inland Audio Visual Co, pg 898
Northern Lights & Pro Audio, pg 959
Pacific Northwest Theatre Associates Inc (PNTA), pg 967

WEST VIRGINIA

United Sound & Electronics, pg 1048

WISCONSIN

Audio Visual of Milwaukee Inc, pg 795
Camera Corner Connecting Point, pg 818
Demco Inc, pg 845
Full Compass Systems, pg 874

PUERTO RICO

Bonnin Electronics Inc, pg 810

Public Address System Manufacturers

Public Address System Rentals

AUDIO/VISUAL

Public Address System Rentals (continued)

MICHIGAN

Olson Anderson Co, pg 786
City Events Group, pg 828
Digi Sign Design LLC, pg 847
K&R All Media Productions Inc, pg 908
On Stage Visuals, pg 963
TeL Systems, pg 1035

MINNESOTA

Advanced Audio-Visual Inc, pg 777
AVI Systems, pg 799
New Life Communications Inc, pg 956

MISSISSIPPI

Bowie Audio Visual Enterprises Inc, pg 811
Jasper Ewing & Sons Inc, pg 864

MISSOURI

Communitronics Corp, pg 833
Schiller's Audio-Visual, pg 1004
Show-Me Audio-Visual, pg 1009
Southwest Audio-Visual Inc, pg 1019
Swank Audio Visuals, pg 1029

NEBRASKA

Dog & Pony Productions Inc, pg 850

NEVADA

GES Audio Visual, pg 877

NEW HAMPSHIRE

Academic & Campus Technology Services, pg 773
APS Lighting-Sound-AV, pg 789

NEW JERSEY

Audio Visual Associates, pg 795
Audio Visual Dynamics®, pg 795
Earl Girls Inc, pg 855
Giant Audio Visual Inc, pg 878
International Audio Visual Inc, pg 900
MIB Mediaworks, pg 941
Moe AV LLC, pg 945
Starlite Productions, pg 1024
Wired 4 Sound Inc, pg 1068

NEW MEXICO

Quickbeam Systems Inc (QSI), pg 989

NEW YORK

Ace Video, pg 774
AV Workshop, pg 797
CMI Communications, pg 830
Colortone Audio Visual, pg 832
Communication Corner Inc, pg 832
CP Communications, pg 837
Custom Media Environments, pg 841
Design Audio Visual Inc, pg 845
Hello World Communications, pg 888
Langie Audio Visual Systems, pg 915
Long Island Video Enterprises Live Inc, pg 924
Manhattan Center Studios Inc, pg 930
Ray Supply Inc, pg 992
SmartSource Computer & AV Rentals, pg 1014
Specialized Audio-Visual Inc, pg 1020
Technisphere Corp, pg 1034
Visual Technologies Corp, pg 1060
Visual Word Systems Inc, pg 1060
WorldStage, pg 1070

NORTH CAROLINA

A&V Company, pg 772
AV Metro Inc, pg 797
Camcor Inc, pg 818
Special Event Services, pg 1020
Strategic Connections, pg 1026
Visual Aids Electronics of North Carolina Inc, pg 1059

NORTH DAKOTA

Media Productions, pg 937

OHIO

Audio Visual Media, pg 795
Aztec Video Productions, pg 801
Bartha, pg 803
Hughie's Event Production Services, pg 892
ITA Audio Visual Solutions, pg 902
Mills James Productions, pg 943
OSV Studios, pg 966

OKLAHOMA

PDC Productions, pg 970

OREGON

Rose City Sound, pg 999

PENNSYLVANIA

Advanced AV, pg 777
Audio Visions Inc, pg 795
Audio Visual Communications Inc, pg 795
Grise Audio Visual Center Inc, pg 882
Production Solutions Inc, pg 985
Vistacom Inc, pg 1059
Visual Sound Inc, pg 1059

SOUTH CAROLINA

Sound & Images Inc, pg 1016

TENNESSEE

Brantley Sound Associates Inc, pg 812
Memphis Communications Corp, pg 938
Russ Sturgeon Productions/RSVP, pg 1027
Technical Support Systems LLC, pg 1034
Tennessee Visual Service Co, pg 1037

TEXAS

Astro Audio Visual, pg 792
Audio Visual Technologies Group, pg 796
Digital Display Solutions Inc, pg 847
FitzCo Sound Inc, pg 869
J&S Audio Visual Inc, pg 904
Lubbock Audio Visual Inc, pg 925
Music Lab Inc, pg 950
Padgitt's, pg 967
Quality Audio Visual Service Inc, pg 988
Schoolhouse Audio Visual, pg 1004
Southwest Sound & Electronics Inc, pg 1019
Stage Directions, pg 1022

UTAH

Performance Audio, pg 973
Webb Audio Visual Communication, pg 1063

VERMONT

Parlato Productions, pg 969

VIRGINIA

American AV, pg 783
Avitecture Inc, pg 799
Boitnott Visual Communications Corp (BVC), pg 810
Lee Hartman & Sons Inc, pg 918
Projection Presentation Technology, pg 985
Rainbow Rentals, pg 991
The Whitlock Group, pg 1065

WASHINGTON

CCI Solutions, pg 821
D A Sound, pg 842
Inland Audio Visual Co, pg 898
Northern Lights & Pro Audio, pg 959
Pacific Northwest Theatre Associates Inc (PNTA), pg 967

WEST VIRGINIA

Blackwater Video Productions, pg 808
United Sound & Electronics, pg 1048

WISCONSIN

Audio Visual of Milwaukee Inc, pg 795
Camera Corner Connecting Point, pg 818
Event Essentials, pg 863
Full Compass Systems, pg 874
USAV Group Inc, pg 1050

PUERTO RICO

Stage Crew Audiovisual Inc, pg 1022

ALBERTA

Allstar Show Industries Inc, pg 782
Cine Audio Visual Sales & Service Ltd, pg 826
Evolution Presentation Technologies, pg 863
L R Light & Sound, pg 915
McBain Audio Visual Ltd, pg 935
Sharp's Audio-Visual Ltd, pg 1008
Unique Communications Ltd, pg 1048

BRITISH COLUMBIA

Clark's Audio Visual Services Ltd, pg 829
Commercial Electronics Ltd, pg 832
DL Sound & Lighting Productions Ltd, pg 849

MANITOBA

Advance Pro, pg 777
Evolution Presentation Technologies, pg 863
Inland Audio Visual Ltd, pg 898

ONTARIO

Edcom Multimedia Products, pg 856
HD Source, pg 886
Metalworks Recording Studios Inc, pg 939
Premier A/V Sales Ltd, pg 980
Westbury National Show Systems Ltd, pg 1064

QUEBEC

Audio Visual Dynamics Ltd, pg 795
Concept Audio-Visual, pg 834

Public Address System Repairs

ARKANSAS

Carlton-Bates Co, pg 820

CALIFORNIA

ALC (Auernheimer Labs & Co), pg 780
Ametron Audio/Video, pg 785
Diemer Amp & Keyboard Repair, pg 846
GMF Sound Inc, pg 879
Instructional Materials & Equipment Distributors (I-Med), pg 899
McAlister Electronics, pg 935
Lloyd F McKinney Associates Inc, pg 935
Sound Service Co, pg 1017
SSL Industries Inc, pg 1022
Third Ear Sound Co, pg 1038
TOA Electronics Inc, pg 1041
Towards 2000 Inc, pg 1043

COLORADO

Ceavco Audio/Visual Co, pg 822

CONNECTICUT

A/V Davey, pg 797
HB Communications Inc, pg 886
Rockwell Communications Inc, pg 998
Sennheiser Electronic Corp, pg 1006

DELAWARE

Actors Attic, pg 775

FLORIDA

JT Communications, pg 906
Spire Audio Visual Co Inc, pg 1021
Stereo Sales Inc, pg 1024
TAI Audio, pg 1031

GEORGIA

Audio Visual Resources Inc, pg 795
Lighting & Production Equipment Inc, pg 920
Stage Front Presentation Systems, pg 1022
Technical Innovation, pg 1033

ILLINOIS

Allen Visual Systems Inc, pg 781
Central Audio-Visual Equipment Inc, pg 823

INDIANA

SHP Electronics, pg 1010

Pulsing—AV

AUDIO/VISUAL

Pulsing—AV (continued)

WASHINGTON

Inland Audio Visual Co, pg 898
Kostov Productions, pg 913

WISCONSIN

AVS Group, pg 800
Concept Productions Inc, pg 834
USAV Group Inc, pg 1050

ALBERTA

Unique Communications Ltd, pg 1048

Pulsing—Filmstrip

ALABAMA

Media Visions Inc, pg 937

ARIZONA

Audio Video Resources, pg 795

CALIFORNIA

Creative Media Recording, pg 838
Lynch Communications, pg 926
QRS Software Services, pg 988
SBS Productions, pg 1003

CONNECTICUT

Broadcast Video Productions LLC, pg 813

GEORGIA

Staging Directions Inc, pg 1023

ILLINOIS

Audio Visual Services Corp, pg 796
CCore Media Inc, pg 821
The Pepper Group, pg 972
PSAV® Presentation Services (Hotel Services Division), pg 987

INDIANA

OMNI Productions, pg 962

MASSACHUSETTS

CommCreative, pg 832
TR Productions, pg 1043

MONTANA

KUSM TV, pg 914

NEVADA

Encore Productions Inc, pg 861

NEW JERSEY

Optisonics Productions, pg 965

NEW YORK

De Nonno Productions Inc (DPI), pg 844
FSL Media Inc, pg 873
Shelly Palmer Production, pg 968
David Rapkin Audio Production, pg 991
Visual Technologies Corp, pg 1060
Zelman Studios Ltd, pg 1073

NORTH CAROLINA

Camcor Inc, pg 818

NORTH DAKOTA

Media Productions, pg 937

OHIO

Aztec Video Productions, pg 801

OREGON

Rex, pg 995

PENNSYLVANIA

Visual Sound Inc, pg 1059

TENNESSEE

Memphis Communications Corp, pg 938
Stage Post, pg 1022

TEXAS

Matson Multi-Media, pg 934

VIRGINIA

Lion Recording Services Inc, pg 922

WASHINGTON

Inland Audio Visual Co, pg 898

WISCONSIN

USAV Group Inc, pg 1050

Record Player, *see* Phonograph

Retouching—Filmstrips

ALABAMA

Media Visions Inc, pg 937

ARKANSAS

White Diamond Productions, pg 1065

CALIFORNIA

FXC Communications, pg 874
Pro8mm, pg 983
QRS Software Services, pg 988

CONNECTICUT

Broadcast Video Productions LLC, pg 813

MASSACHUSETTS

TR Productions, pg 1043

NEW JERSEY

All Jersey Studios, pg 780

NEW YORK

Duggal Visual Solutions, pg 853
Modernage Photographic Services Inc, pg 944
MRG Productions Inc, pg 948

OHIO

Aztec Video Productions, pg 801

PENNSYLVANIA

Berry & Homer, pg 805

TENNESSEE

Stage Post, pg 1022

VIRGINIA

Blair Inc, pg 809

Retouching—Slides

ALABAMA

Media Visions Inc, pg 937

ARIZONA

Professional Marketing Services Inc, pg 985

ARKANSAS

White Diamond Productions, pg 1065

CALIFORNIA

Action Photo Service Inc, pg 775
FXC Communications, pg 874
QRS Software Services, pg 988

CONNECTICUT

Broadcast Video Productions LLC, pg 813

FLORIDA

Gulf Coast Audio Visual Producers Inc, pg 883

ILLINOIS

Gamma Imaging, pg 875
The Pepper Group, pg 972

INDIANA

OMNI Productions, pg 962

KENTUCKY

Kinetic Corp, pg 911

MASSACHUSETTS

TR Productions, pg 1043

MICHIGAN

Tectonics Industries Inc, pg 1035

MINNESOTA

Thomas Reprographics, pg 1039

NEW JERSEY

All Jersey Studios, pg 780

NEW YORK

C2 Imaging LLC, pg 841
Duggal Visual Solutions, pg 853
Modernage Photographic Services Inc, pg 944
MRG Productions Inc, pg 948
TBA Global Events, pg 1032

NORTH CAROLINA

Image Associates Inc, pg 894

OHIO

Aztec Video Productions, pg 801
Thread Marketing Group, pg 1039
Vista Color Imaging Inc, pg 1059

PENNSYLVANIA

Bernie's Photo Center, pg 805
Berry & Homer, pg 805

TENNESSEE

Stage Post, pg 1022

TEXAS

City Color, pg 828
Texas Heart Institute Visual Communication Services, pg 1037

UTAH

Ferrari Color®, pg 866

VIRGINIA

Advance Concepts Inc, pg 777
Blair Inc, pg 809

WISCONSIN

USAV Group Inc, pg 1050

Script Writing

ALABAMA

CMEInfo, pg 830
Media Visions Inc, pg 937

ALASKA

Aurora Films, pg 797

ARIZONA

MediaWorks, pg 938
Merestone, pg 938
Metropolitan Audio-Visual Inc, pg 940
On-Site Video, pg 963
Tellens Inc, pg 1037

ARKANSAS

Live'N'Loud, pg 923
Shadowbox Video Productions, pg 1007
White Diamond Productions, pg 1065

CALIFORNIA

Aaron & Le Duc, pg 772
Action Video, pg 775
Animax, pg 787
Barbosa Video Services, pg 802
Coastline Productions, pg 831
Crystal Pyramid Productions™, pg 840
Custom Video Productions Inc, pg 841
Deja View Video, pg 845
Design Media, pg 845
Dogma Studios, pg 850
Dolphin MultiMedia Inc, pg 850
Tom Donald Films, pg 850
Final Draft Inc, pg 868
Gold Standard Productions, pg 880
iCorpTv, pg 893
Increase Video/Silver Mine Video, pg 897
KVIE-Channel 6, pg 914
Lynch Communications, pg 926
Main Street Media Inc, pg 929
Maximus Media Inc, pg 934
Media Magic, pg 937
The Media Staff Inc, pg 937

AUDIO/VISUAL

Script Writing (continued)

VIRGINIA

Advance Concepts Inc, pg 777
American AV, pg 783
CACI Productions Group, pg 816
CALIBRE, pg 816
CDR Communications Inc, pg 822
D&B Television & Video Productions Inc, pg 842
Metro Productions, pg 939
Rocktown Media, pg 998

WASHINGTON

Adams Creative & Production Services, pg 775
Kostov Productions, pg 913
Laser Fantasy/HECK Industries/ Photon Manufacturing, pg 916
Medical Media Systems, pg 938
Victory Studios, pg 1054

WEST VIRGINIA

Altruist Media LLC, pg 783

WISCONSIN

Meridian Studios, pg 939
USAV Group Inc, pg 1050
Video Wisconsin Inc, pg 1056
Watts Communications Inc, pg 1062
Wisconsin Public Television, pg 1068

WYOMING

Bridger Productions Inc, pg 812

PUERTO RICO

Stage Crew Audiovisual Inc, pg 1022

ALBERTA

Global Television, pg 879

BRITISH COLUMBIA

Triad Communications Ltd, pg 1044

NORTHWEST TERRITORIES

Yellowknife Films Inc, pg 1072

ONTARIO

ADS Media, pg 777
DebsVoice, pg 844
Image Video Services & Productions, pg 895
Purefire Communications Inc, pg 987

Slide & Transparency Equipment & Supply Distributors

ALABAMA

Curtis Company, pg 841
Media Visions Inc, pg 937

ARIZONA

Arizona Cine Equipment, pg 789
Docter Optics Inc, pg 849
Metropolitan Audio-Visual Inc, pg 940
Professional Marketing Services Inc, pg 985
Troxell Communications Inc, pg 1045

ARKANSAS

Jay S Stanley & Associates Inc, pg 1023

CALIFORNIA

Adolph Gasser Inc, pg 776
Ametron Audio/Video, pg 785
California Tape Products Inc, pg 817
Diversified Imaging Supply, pg 849
FXC Communications, pg 874
Gluskin's Custom Audio Video, pg 879
GMF Sound Inc, pg 879
Hooper Camera & Imaging, pg 891
Instructional Materials & Equipment Distributors (I-Med), pg 899
Media Fabricators Inc, pg 936
Related Visual Inc, pg 994

COLORADO

Ceavco Audio/Visual Co, pg 822
National Teaching Aids Inc, pg 953

CONNECTICUT

Concord Communications, pg 835
HB Communications Inc, pg 886
MAVCO, pg 934
Rockwell Communications Inc, pg 998
USI Inc, pg 1051

FLORIDA

AVI-SPL, pg 798
Cinema Equipment & Supplies Inc, pg 827
Digital Video Systems Inc, pg 848
Gulf Coast Audio Visual Producers Inc, pg 883
Hi-Tech Import Export Corp, pg 888
Photomart Cine-Video Inc, pg 975
Photosound of Orlando Inc, pg 975
Pro Stage Inc, pg 983
Spire Audio Visual Co Inc, pg 1021
Tallahassee Audio Visual, pg 1031
Techni-Lux Inc, pg 1033

GEORGIA

Audio Visual Resources Inc, pg 795
Technical Innovation, pg 1033
Visioneering International Inc, pg 1058

HAWAII

The Audio Visual Co (AVCO), pg 795

ILLINOIS

Allen Visual Systems Inc, pg 781
Central Audio-Visual Equipment Inc, pg 823
FUJIFILM Graphic Systems Division, pg 873
G T Luscombe Co Inc, pg 926
Sound Vision Inc, pg 1018

INDIANA

OMNI Productions, pg 962

IOWA

ECS Inc, pg 856

KENTUCKY

Audio Visual Techniques Inc, pg 796
Axxis Inc, pg 800
NOR-COM Inc, pg 958

LOUISIANA

Intermedia Technologies, pg 900

MAINE

Headlight Audio Visual Inc, pg 887

MARYLAND

RTZ Audio Visual, pg 1000
Visual Aids Electronics Corp, pg 1059

MASSACHUSETTS

Hunt's Photo, Video & Digital, pg 892
Lineco, pg 922
University Products Inc, pg 1050

MICHIGAN

City Events Group, pg 828
Michigan Office Solutions, pg 941

MINNESOTA

Rayven Inc, pg 992

MISSISSIPPI

Bowie Audio Visual Enterprises Inc, pg 811
Jasper Ewing & Sons Inc, pg 864

MISSOURI

Conference Technologies Inc, pg 835
Image Technologies Corp, pg 895
Modern Communications Inc, pg 944
Schiller's Audio-Visual, pg 1004

NEBRASKA

Images II Inc, pg 896

NEVADA

Bulbman Inc, pg 815

NEW JERSEY

Argraph Corp, pg 789
AV Bluebook, pg 797
Hamilton Buhl, pg 884
HP Marketing Corp, pg 892
Leica Camera Inc, pg 918
National Audio-Visual Supply, pg 952
Starlite Productions, pg 1024
SYMCO Inc, pg 1030
Total Video Products Inc, pg 1042
Transparent Office Products LLC, pg 1043
Wired 4 Sound Inc, pg 1068
York Telecom, pg 1072

NEW YORK

AV Workshop, pg 797
Bulbtronics Inc, pg 815
Communication Corner Inc, pg 832
Gaylord Brothers, pg 876
Get Smart Products, pg 877
Gordon Visual Solutions, pg 880
Langie Audio Visual Systems, pg 915
Light Impressions, pg 920
Long Island Video Enterprises Live Inc, pg 924
Magnaplan Corp, pg 928
Markertek Video Supply, pg 931
Motion Picture Enterprises Inc, pg 947
Neptune Photo Inc, pg 954
Olden Camera & Lens Co Inc, pg 962
Ray Supply Inc, pg 992
Visual Technologies Corp, pg 1060
Willoughby's Imaging Center, pg 1067

NORTH CAROLINA

Camcor Inc, pg 818

OHIO

Audio Visual Media, pg 795
Copp Integrated Systems, pg 836
Icom Multimedia, pg 893
Tri-State Visual Products, pg 1044

PENNSYLVANIA

Advanced AV, pg 777
Audio Visions Inc, pg 795
Audio Visual Communications Inc, pg 795
Bernie's Photo Center, pg 805
Brodart Co, pg 813
Charles Beseler Co, pg 824
Electron Microscopy Sciences (EMS), pg 859
J E Foss Co, pg 871
Grise Audio Visual Center Inc, pg 882
Vistacom Inc, pg 1059

RHODE ISLAND

Custom Computer Specialists Inc, pg 841

TENNESSEE

Continental Film, pg 835
Durrell LLC, pg 854
Lowrance Sound Co Inc, pg 925
Memphis Communications Corp, pg 938
Tennessee Visual Service Co, pg 1037

TEXAS

Audio Visual Technologies Group, pg 796
J&S Audio Visual Inc, pg 904
Lubbock Audio Visual Inc, pg 925
Quality Audio Visual Service Inc, pg 988
Schoolhouse Audio Visual, pg 1004
Stage Directions, pg 1022
Videotex Systems Inc, pg 1057

VIRGINIA

Boitnott Visual Communications Corp (BVC), pg 810
Communications Specialists Inc, pg 833
Filmdex Inc, pg 867
Intellidyne LLC, pg 899
Lee Hartman & Sons Inc, pg 918
Metropolitan Audio Visual Co LLC, pg 940
The Whitlock Group, pg 1065

WASHINGTON

Inland Audio Visual Co, pg 898

Slide & Transparency Equipment & Supply Manufacturers

Slide & Transparency Equipment & Supply Rentals

AUDIO/VISUAL

Slide & Transparency Equipment & Supply Rentals (continued)

QUEBEC

AVW-TELAV Audio Visual Solutions, a Freeman Company, pg 800
Concept Audio-Visual, pg 834
Panavideo Inc, pg 968

Slide & Transparency Equipment & Supply Repairs

CALIFORNIA

Ametron Audio/Video, pg 785
Gluskin's Custom Audio Video, pg 879
Hooper Camera & Imaging, pg 891
Instructional Materials & Equipment Distributors (I-Med), pg 899
McAlister Electronics, pg 935
Lloyd F McKinney Associates Inc, pg 935
Pro Camera Repair, pg 982

COLORADO

Ceavco Audio/Visual Co, pg 822

CONNECTICUT

A/V Davey, pg 797
HB Communications Inc, pg 886

FLORIDA

Spire Audio Visual Co Inc, pg 1021

ILLINOIS

Allen Visual Systems Inc, pg 781

INDIANA

Gary Camera & Digital, pg 875

IOWA

ECS Inc, pg 856

KENTUCKY

Axxis Inc, pg 800
NOR-COM Inc, pg 958

MAINE

Headlight Audio Visual Inc, pg 887

MARYLAND

RTZ Audio Visual, pg 1000
Strauss Photo Technical Service Inc, pg 1026

MICHIGAN

City Events Group, pg 828
TeL Systems, pg 1035

MINNESOTA

AVI Systems, pg 799

MISSISSIPPI

Bowie Audio Visual Enterprises Inc, pg 811

MISSOURI

Cintrex Audio Visual, pg 828
Communitronics Corp, pg 833
Schiller's Audio-Visual, pg 1004

NEW JERSEY

Leica Camera Inc, pg 918

NEW YORK

Langie Audio Visual Systems, pg 915
Ray Supply Inc, pg 992
Visual Technologies Corp, pg 1060

OHIO

Audio Visual Media, pg 795
Aztec Video Productions, pg 801
Icom Multimedia, pg 893
Tri-State Audio Visual Co, pg 1044

PENNSYLVANIA

Audio Visions Inc, pg 795
Bernie's Photo Center, pg 805

RHODE ISLAND

Custom Computer Specialists Inc, pg 841

TENNESSEE

Memphis Communications Corp, pg 938

TEXAS

Audio Visual Technologies Group, pg 796
Lubbock Audio Visual Inc, pg 925
Quality Audio Visual Service Inc, pg 988
Schoolhouse Audio Visual, pg 1004

VIRGINIA

Hoppmann Audio Visual, pg 891
Metropolitan Audio Visual Co LLC, pg 940
The Whitlock Group, pg 1065

WISCONSIN

Audio Visual of Milwaukee Inc, pg 795
Full Compass Systems, pg 874

ALBERTA

Sharp's Audio-Visual Ltd, pg 1008

ONTARIO

Edcom Multimedia Products, pg 856
Premier A/V Sales Ltd, pg 980

QUEBEC

Panavideo Inc, pg 968

Slide Binding & Mounting Equipment & Supply Distributors

ALABAMA

Media Visions Inc, pg 937

ARIZONA

Troxell Communications Inc, pg 1045

CALIFORNIA

Adolph Gasser Inc, pg 776
Ametron Audio/Video, pg 785
California Tape Products Inc, pg 817
Diversified Imaging Supply, pg 849
Media Fabricators Inc, pg 936

CONNECTICUT

MAVCO, pg 934
USI Inc, pg 1051

FLORIDA

AVI-SPL, pg 798
Photomart Cine-Video Inc, pg 975
Pro Stage Inc, pg 983
Tallahassee Audio Visual, pg 1031

GEORGIA

Visioneering International Inc, pg 1058

IOWA

ECS Inc, pg 856

KENTUCKY

K&R Photo Digital, pg 908
NOR-COM Inc, pg 958

MASSACHUSETTS

Lineco, pg 922
University Products Inc, pg 1050

MICHIGAN

Michigan Office Solutions, pg 941

MISSISSIPPI

Jasper Ewing & Sons Inc, pg 864

MISSOURI

Schiller's Audio-Visual, pg 1004

NEW JERSEY

Argraph Corp, pg 789
AV Bluebook, pg 797
Callen Photo Mount, pg 817
Hamilton Buhl, pg 884
HP Marketing Corp, pg 892
National Audio-Visual Supply, pg 952
VCom International Multimedia Corp, pg 1052
Wired 4 Sound Inc, pg 1068
York Telecom, pg 1072

NEW YORK

AV Workshop, pg 797
Gaylord Brothers, pg 876
Get Smart Products, pg 877
Langie Audio Visual Systems, pg 915
Light Impressions, pg 920
Magnaplan Corp, pg 928
Markertek Video Supply, pg 931
Ray Supply Inc, pg 992
Visual Technologies Corp, pg 1060
Willoughby's Imaging Center, pg 1067

NORTH CAROLINA

Camcor Inc, pg 818

OHIO

Icom Multimedia, pg 893

PENNSYLVANIA

Advanced AV, pg 777
Audio Visions Inc, pg 795
Bernie's Photo Center, pg 805
J E Foss Co, pg 871
Wespen Audio Visual Co, pg 1063

RHODE ISLAND

Custom Computer Specialists Inc, pg 841

TENNESSEE

Durrell LLC, pg 854
Memphis Communications Corp, pg 938

TEXAS

Image Innovations Inc, pg 895
Lubbock Audio Visual Inc, pg 925
Schoolhouse Audio Visual, pg 1004

VIRGINIA

Intellidyne LLC, pg 899
Lee Hartman & Sons Inc, pg 918

WISCONSIN

Audio Visual of Milwaukee Inc, pg 795
Pro Studio Supply, pg 983

ALBERTA

McBain Audio Visual Ltd, pg 935

QUEBEC

Concept Audio-Visual, pg 834

Slide Binding & Mounting Equipment & Supply Manufacturers

ARIZONA

Savage Universal Corp, pg 1003

MASSACHUSETTS

Lineco, pg 922

NEW JERSEY

Leica Camera Inc, pg 918
Pro-Tape & Specialities Inc, pg 983

NEW YORK

Light Impressions, pg 920

TEXAS

Image Innovations Inc, pg 895

WISCONSIN

Bardes Products Inc, pg 803

Slide Binding & Mounting Equipment & Supply Rentals

ALABAMA

Media Visions Inc, pg 937

ARIZONA

Arizona Cine Equipment, pg 789

CALIFORNIA

Adolph Gasser Inc, pg 776
Ametron Audio/Video, pg 785
Media Fabricators Inc, pg 936
Samy's Camera, pg 1002

FLORIDA

Pro Stage Inc, pg 983
Spire Audio Visual Co Inc, pg 1021

GEORGIA

Staging Directions Inc, pg 1023

MICHIGAN

Digi Sign Design LLC, pg 847
K&R All Media Productions Inc, pg 908

MINNESOTA

AVI Systems, pg 799

NEW HAMPSHIRE

Apertura, pg 788

NEW YORK

AV Workshop, pg 797

OHIO

Icom Multimedia, pg 893
Vista Color Imaging Inc, pg 1059

PENNSYLVANIA

Ott Film Rentals, pg 966
Production Solutions Inc, pg 985

TENNESSEE

Memphis Communications Corp, pg 938

TEXAS

Schoolhouse Audio Visual, pg 1004

WISCONSIN

Audio Visual of Milwaukee Inc, pg 795

ALBERTA

McBain Audio Visual Ltd, pg 935

QUEBEC

Concept Audio-Visual, pg 834

Slide Binding & Mounting Equipment & Supply Repairs

CALIFORNIA

Ametron Audio/Video, pg 785
McAlister Electronics, pg 935

CONNECTICUT

HB Communications Inc, pg 886

FLORIDA

Spire Audio Visual Co Inc, pg 1021

KENTUCKY

NOR-COM Inc, pg 958

MICHIGAN

TeL Systems, pg 1035

MINNESOTA

AVI Systems, pg 799

MISSOURI

Schiller's Audio-Visual, pg 1004

OHIO

Aztec Video Productions, pg 801
Icom Multimedia, pg 893

PENNSYLVANIA

Ott Film Rentals, pg 966

TENNESSEE

Memphis Communications Corp, pg 938

TEXAS

Schoolhouse Audio Visual, pg 1004

WISCONSIN

Audio Visual of Milwaukee Inc, pg 795

Slide Duplication, *see* Duplication—Slides

Slide Mounting Equipment & Supply, *see* Slide Binding & Mounting Equipment & Supply

Slide Presentation System—Programmable & Manual Distributors

ALABAMA

Media Visions Inc, pg 937

ARIZONA

Arizona Cine Equipment, pg 789
Metropolitan Audio-Visual Inc, pg 940
Professional Marketing Services Inc, pg 985
Troxell Communications Inc, pg 1045

ARKANSAS

Jay S Stanley & Associates Inc, pg 1023

CALIFORNIA

Adolph Gasser Inc, pg 776
Ametron Audio/Video, pg 785
California Tape Products Inc, pg 817
Educational Technology Services (ETS), pg 857
Lloyd F McKinney Associates Inc, pg 935
Media Fabricators Inc, pg 936
MediaPOINTE, pg 938
PMP Marketing Inc, pg 977
Related Visual Inc, pg 994
Southern California Sound Image Inc, pg 1019

COLORADO

Spectrum Audio Visual Services, pg 1020

CONNECTICUT

Concord Communications, pg 835
HB Communications Inc, pg 886
MAVCO, pg 934
Rockwell Communications Inc, pg 998

FLORIDA

AVI-SPL, pg 798
Cinema Equipment & Supplies Inc, pg 827
Gulf Coast Audio Visual Producers Inc, pg 883
Lighting Sales Connections, pg 920
Pro Stage Inc, pg 983
Spire Audio Visual Co Inc, pg 1021
Techni-Lux Inc, pg 1033

GEORGIA

Audio Visual Resources Inc, pg 795
Baker Audio Inc, pg 801
Convergent Media Systems, pg 836
Imagers, pg 896
Stage Front Presentation Systems, pg 1022
Visioneering International Inc, pg 1058

HAWAII

The Audio Visual Co (AVCO), pg 795

IOWA

ECS Inc, pg 856

KENTUCKY

Audio Visual Techniques Inc, pg 796
Axxis Inc, pg 800
NOR-COM Inc, pg 958

MARYLAND

RTZ Audio Visual, pg 1000
Visual Aids Electronics Corp, pg 1059

MASSACHUSETTS

Graphx Inc, pg 881
Lineco, pg 922
University Products Inc, pg 1050

MICHIGAN

City Events Group, pg 828
Michigan Office Solutions, pg 941

MINNESOTA

Advanced Audio-Visual Inc, pg 777
AVI Systems, pg 799

MISSISSIPPI

Bowie Audio Visual Enterprises Inc, pg 811
Jasper Ewing & Sons Inc, pg 864

MISSOURI

Communitronics Corp, pg 833
Conference Technologies Inc, pg 835
Image Technologies Corp, pg 895
Modern Communications Inc, pg 944
Schiller's Audio-Visual, pg 1004

NEW JERSEY

Argraph Corp, pg 789
AV Bluebook, pg 797
Hamilton Buhl, pg 884
Leica Camera Inc, pg 918
National Audio-Visual Supply, pg 952
Reed Presentations Inc (RPI), pg 993
Starlite Productions, pg 1024
Total Video Products Inc, pg 1042
Transparent Office Products LLC, pg 1043
Video Corporation of America (VCA), pg 1055
Wired 4 Sound Inc, pg 1068
York Telecom, pg 1072

NEW YORK

AV Workshop, pg 797
Communication Corner Inc, pg 832
Custom Media Environments, pg 841
Design Audio Visual Inc, pg 845
DSan Corp, pg 852
Gaylord Brothers, pg 876
Indigo Productions, pg 897
Long Island Video Enterprises Live Inc, pg 924
Magnaplan Corp, pg 928
Neptune Photo Inc, pg 954
Ray Supply Inc, pg 992
Visual Technologies Corp, pg 1060
Willoughby's Imaging Center, pg 1067

NORTH CAROLINA

Camcor Inc, pg 818

OHIO

Audio Visual Media, pg 795
Icom Multimedia, pg 893
Smithall Electronics Inc, pg 1014

PENNSYLVANIA

Advanced AV, pg 777
Audio Visions Inc, pg 795
Audio Visual Communications Inc, pg 795
Bernie's Photo Center, pg 805
J E Foss Co, pg 871
Grise Audio Visual Center Inc, pg 882
The Lerro Corp, pg 919

RHODE ISLAND

Custom Computer Specialists Inc, pg 841

TENNESSEE

Durrell LLC, pg 854
Memphis Communications Corp, pg 938
Technical Support Systems LLC, pg 1034

TEXAS

Audio Visual Technologies Group, pg 796
Image Innovations Inc, pg 895
J&S Audio Visual Inc, pg 904
Lubbock Audio Visual Inc, pg 925
Schoolhouse Audio Visual, pg 1004
Videotex Systems Inc, pg 1057

AUDIO/VISUAL

Slide Presentation System—Programmable & Manual Distributors (continued)

VIRGINIA

Boitnott Visual Communications Corp (BVC), pg 810
Communications Specialists Inc, pg 833
Hoppmann Audio Visual, pg 891
Intellidyne LLC, pg 899
Lee Hartman & Sons Inc, pg 918
Quince Imaging Inc, pg 989

WASHINGTON

Inland Audio Visual Co, pg 898
Pacific Northwest Theatre Associates Inc (PNTA), pg 967

WISCONSIN

Audio Visual of Milwaukee Inc, pg 795
Camera Corner Connecting Point, pg 818
Full Compass Systems, pg 874
School Specialty Inc, pg 1004

ALBERTA

McBain Audio Visual Ltd, pg 935
SMART Technologies Inc, pg 1013
Unique Communications Ltd, pg 1048

BRITISH COLUMBIA

Commercial Electronics Ltd, pg 832

MANITOBA

Inland Audio Visual Ltd, pg 898

ONTARIO

Nationwide Audio Visual Co, pg 953

QUEBEC

Concept Audio-Visual, pg 834
Panavideo Inc, pg 968

Slide Presentation System—Programmable & Manual Manufacturers

MASSACHUSETTS

Graphx Inc, pg 881

NEW JERSEY

Crestron Electronics Inc, pg 839
Leica Camera Inc, pg 918
Transparent Office Products LLC, pg 1043

NEW YORK

DSan Corp, pg 852
ELMO USA Corp, pg 859

PENNSYLVANIA

Scala Inc, pg 1003

TEXAS

AMX, pg 786

VIRGINIA

Quince Imaging Inc, pg 989

WISCONSIN

Bardes Products Inc, pg 803

ALBERTA

SMART Technologies Inc, pg 1013

Slide Presentation System—Programmable & Manual Rentals

ALABAMA

Media Visions Inc, pg 937

ARIZONA

Arizona Cine Equipment, pg 789
Metropolitan Audio-Visual Inc, pg 940

CALIFORNIA

Alliant Event Services, pg 781
Ametron Audio/Video, pg 785
Gold Standard Productions, pg 880
Media Fabricators Inc, pg 936
Related Visual Inc, pg 994
Samy's Camera, pg 1002

COLORADO

Daylight Productions & Rentals, pg 844
Spectrum Audio Visual Services, pg 1020

CONNECTICUT

A/V Davey, pg 797

DELAWARE

Ken-Del Productions Inc, pg 909
Showorks Audio Visual Inc, pg 1010

FLORIDA

Gulf Coast Audio Visual Producers Inc, pg 883
Image Technical Services, pg 895
Lighting Sales Connections, pg 920
Photosound of Orlando Inc, pg 975
Pro Stage Inc, pg 983
Spire Audio Visual Co Inc, pg 1021
Universal Studios Florida® Production Group, pg 1049

GEORGIA

Convergent Media Systems, pg 836
MAGNUM Companies Ltd, pg 929
ON Event Services, pg 963
Stage Front Presentation Systems, pg 1022
Staging Directions Inc, pg 1023

ILLINOIS

Audio Visual Services Corp, pg 796
Backstar Creative Media Inc, pg 801
PSAV® Presentation Services (Hotel Services Division), pg 987
QuickSet International Inc, pg 989
Show Department Inc, pg 1009

KENTUCKY

Audio Visual Techniques Inc, pg 796

LOUISIANA

Pace Systems, pg 966

MARYLAND

dbF a Media Company, pg 844
RTZ Audio Visual, pg 1000

MASSACHUSETTS

AVFX Inc, pg 798
massAV, pg 933
Preston Productions Inc, pg 981

MICHIGAN

City Events Group, pg 828
Digi Sign Design LLC, pg 847
K&R All Media Productions Inc, pg 908
K&R's Recording Studios Inc, pg 908

MINNESOTA

Advanced Audio-Visual Inc, pg 777
AVI Systems, pg 799

MISSISSIPPI

Bowie Audio Visual Enterprises Inc, pg 811

MISSOURI

Communitronics Corp, pg 833
Schiller's Audio-Visual, pg 1004
Southwest Audio-Visual Inc, pg 1019
Swank Audio Visuals, pg 1029

NEVADA

GES Audio Visual, pg 877

NEW HAMPSHIRE

Academic & Campus Technology Services, pg 773
Apertura, pg 788

NEW JERSEY

PLS Staging, pg 977

NEW YORK

AV Workshop, pg 797
Communication Corner Inc, pg 832
Custom Media Environments, pg 841
Design Audio Visual Inc, pg 845
Langie Audio Visual Systems, pg 915
Long Island Video Enterprises Live Inc, pg 924
Manhattan Center Studios Inc, pg 930
Specialized Audio-Visual Inc, pg 1020
TBA Global Events, pg 1032
Visual Technologies Corp, pg 1060
Visual Word Systems Inc, pg 1060

NORTH CAROLINA

A&V Company, pg 772
Special Event Services, pg 1020
Visual Aids Electronics of North Carolina Inc, pg 1059

NORTH DAKOTA

Media Productions, pg 937

OHIO

Audio Visual Media, pg 795
Aztec Video Productions, pg 801
Hughie's Event Production Services, pg 892
Icom Multimedia, pg 893
Mills James Productions, pg 943
Vista Color Imaging Inc, pg 1059

PENNSYLVANIA

Advanced AV, pg 777
Audio Visions Inc, pg 795
Audio Visual Communications Inc, pg 795
Bernie's Photo Center, pg 805
Grise Audio Visual Center Inc, pg 882
Ott Film Rentals, pg 966
Production Solutions Inc, pg 985

TENNESSEE

Memphis Communications Corp, pg 938
Russ Sturgeon Productions/RSVP, pg 1027
Technical Support Systems LLC, pg 1034

TEXAS

Audio Visual Technologies Group, pg 796
J&S Audio Visual Inc, pg 904
Lubbock Audio Visual Inc, pg 925
Schoolhouse Audio Visual, pg 1004
Stage Directions, pg 1022

VIRGINIA

American AV, pg 783
Boitnott Visual Communications Corp (BVC), pg 810
Lee Hartman & Sons Inc, pg 918
Projection Presentation Technology, pg 985
Quince Imaging Inc, pg 989
Rainbow Rentals, pg 991

WASHINGTON

Inland Audio Visual Co, pg 898
Pacific Northwest Theatre Associates Inc (PNTA), pg 967

WISCONSIN

Audio Visual of Milwaukee Inc, pg 795
Camera Corner Connecting Point, pg 818
Event Essentials, pg 863
Full Compass Systems, pg 874

PUERTO RICO

Stage Crew Audiovisual Inc, pg 1022

ALBERTA

Allstar Show Industries Inc, pg 782
Evolution Presentation Technologies, pg 863
McBain Audio Visual Ltd, pg 935
Unique Communications Ltd, pg 1048

BRITISH COLUMBIA

Triad Communications Ltd, pg 1044

MANITOBA

Inland Audio Visual Ltd, pg 898

ONTARIO

Edcom Multimedia Products, pg 856

QUEBEC

AVW-TELAV Audio Visual Solutions, a Freeman Company, pg 800
Concept Audio-Visual, pg 834
Panavideo Inc, pg 968

Slide Presentation System—Programmable & Manual Repairs

CALIFORNIA

Ametron Audio/Video, pg 785
McAlister Electronics, pg 935
Lloyd F McKinney Associates Inc, pg 935
Pro Camera Repair, pg 982

CONNECTICUT

A/V Davey, pg 797
HB Communications Inc, pg 886
Precision Camera & Video Repair Inc, pg 980

FLORIDA

Spire Audio Visual Co Inc, pg 1021

GEORGIA

Stage Front Presentation Systems, pg 1022

KENTUCKY

Axxis Inc, pg 800
NOR-COM Inc, pg 958

MAINE

Headlight Audio Visual Inc, pg 887

MARYLAND

RTZ Audio Visual, pg 1000
Strauss Photo Technical Service Inc, pg 1026

MICHIGAN

City Events Group, pg 828
TeL Systems, pg 1035

MINNESOTA

AVI Systems, pg 799

MISSISSIPPI

Bowie Audio Visual Enterprises Inc, pg 811

MISSOURI

Schiller's Audio-Visual, pg 1004

NEW JERSEY

Leica Camera Inc, pg 918

NEW YORK

Custom Media Environments, pg 841
ELMO USA Corp, pg 859
Langie Audio Visual Systems, pg 915
Visual Technologies Corp, pg 1060

OHIO

Audio Visual Media, pg 795
Aztec Video Productions, pg 801
Icom Multimedia, pg 893

PENNSYLVANIA

Audio Visions Inc, pg 795
Bernie's Photo Center, pg 805
Ott Film Rentals, pg 966

RHODE ISLAND

Custom Computer Specialists Inc, pg 841

TENNESSEE

Memphis Communications Corp, pg 938
Technical Support Systems LLC, pg 1034

TEXAS

Audio Visual Technologies Group, pg 796
Lubbock Audio Visual Inc, pg 925
Schoolhouse Audio Visual, pg 1004

VIRGINIA

Boitnott Visual Communications Corp (BVC), pg 810
Hoppmann Audio Visual, pg 891
Quince Imaging Inc, pg 989

WASHINGTON

Inland Audio Visual Co, pg 898
Pacific Northwest Theatre Associates Inc (PNTA), pg 967

WISCONSIN

Audio Visual of Milwaukee Inc, pg 795
Full Compass Systems, pg 874

ALBERTA

Infosat Communications Inc, pg 898
Unique Communications Ltd, pg 1048

MANITOBA

Inland Audio Visual Ltd, pg 898

QUEBEC

Panavideo Inc, pg 968

Slide Printing, *see* Processing & Printing—Slides

Slide Printing, *see* Volume Printing—Slides

Slide Processing, *see* Processing & Printing—Slides

Slide Projector Distributors

ALABAMA

Curtis Company, pg 841
Media Visions Inc, pg 937

ARIZONA

Arizona Cine Equipment, pg 789
Troxell Communications Inc, pg 1045
Ultimate Presentation Systems Inc, pg 1047

ARKANSAS

Carlton-Bates Co, pg 820
Jay S Stanley & Associates Inc, pg 1023
White Diamond Productions, pg 1065

CALIFORNIA

Adolph Gasser Inc, pg 776
Ametron Audio/Video, pg 785
Audio/Video Supply Inc, pg 795
California Tape Products Inc, pg 817
Diversified Imaging Supply, pg 849
Gluskin's Custom Audio Video, pg 879
Hooper Camera & Imaging, pg 891
Instructional Materials & Equipment Distributors (I-Med), pg 899
Lloyd F McKinney Associates Inc, pg 935
Media Fabricators Inc, pg 936
MediaMation Inc, pg 937
MediaPOINTE, pg 938
PMP Marketing Inc, pg 977
POP TV, pg 978
Southern California Sound Image Inc, pg 1019
Stanislaus Audio Video Inc, pg 1023

COLORADO

Ceavco Audio/Visual Co, pg 822
Spectrum Audio Visual Services, pg 1020

CONNECTICUT

HB Communications Inc, pg 886
MAVCO, pg 934
Rockwell Communications Inc, pg 998

FLORIDA

AVI-SPL, pg 798
Cinema Equipment & Supplies Inc, pg 827
Digital Video Systems Inc, pg 848
Gulf Coast Audio Visual Producers Inc, pg 883
Harmon's Audio-Visual Services, pg 885
Hi-Tech Import Export Corp, pg 888
Industrial Strength Inc, pg 897
Intermark Industries Inc, pg 900
Lighting Sales Connections, pg 920
Pro Stage Inc, pg 983
Sight & Sound Productions, pg 1010
Spire Audio Visual Co Inc, pg 1021
Tallahassee Audio Visual, pg 1031
Techni-Lux Inc, pg 1033

GEORGIA

Audio Visual Resources Inc, pg 795
Baker Audio Inc, pg 801
Convergent Media Systems, pg 836
Imagers, pg 896
Lighting & Production Equipment Inc, pg 920
Stage Front Presentation Systems, pg 1022
Technical Innovation, pg 1033
Visioneering International Inc, pg 1058

HAWAII

The Audio Visual Co (AVCO), pg 795

ILLINOIS

Allen Visual Systems Inc, pg 781
Central Audio-Visual Equipment Inc, pg 823
Creative Technology, pg 838
FUJIFILM Graphic Systems Division, pg 873
RC Communications, pg 992
Sound Vision Inc, pg 1018

INDIANA

Victoria Supply Inc/Topbulb.com, pg 1054

IOWA

ECS Inc, pg 856

KENTUCKY

Axxis Inc, pg 800
NOR-COM Inc, pg 958
Northern Kentucky University, pg 959

LOUISIANA

Intermedia Technologies, pg 900

MAINE

Headlight Audio Visual Inc, pg 887

MARYLAND

Cardinal Sound & Video, pg 820
Nelson White Systems Inc, pg 954
Ritz Camera & Image, pg 997
RTZ Audio Visual, pg 1000
Visual Aids Electronics Corp, pg 1059

MASSACHUSETTS

Camera Co Inc/Broadcast Divison, pg 818
Rule Broadcast Systems, pg 1000
University Products Inc, pg 1050

MICHIGAN

Olson Anderson Co, pg 786
City Events Group, pg 828
Michigan Office Solutions, pg 941
TeL Systems, pg 1035

MINNESOTA

Advanced Audio-Visual Inc, pg 777
AVI Systems, pg 799
Media Loft Inc, pg 937

MISSISSIPPI

Bowie Audio Visual Enterprises Inc, pg 811
Jasper Ewing & Sons Inc, pg 864

AUDIO/VISUAL

Slide Projector Distributors (continued)

MISSOURI

Communitronics Corp, pg 833
Conference Technologies Inc, pg 835
Image Technologies Corp, pg 895
Modern Communications Inc, pg 944
Schiller's Audio-Visual, pg 1004
Southwest Audio-Visual Inc, pg 1019
Swank Audio Visuals, pg 1029

NEW JERSEY

A-V Services Inc, pg 771
Argraph Corp, pg 789
Audio Visual Dynamics®, pg 795
AV Bluebook, pg 797
Hamilton Buhl, pg 884
Hasselblad Bron Inc, pg 885
HP Marketing Corp, pg 892
Leica Camera Inc, pg 918
National Audio-Visual Supply, pg 952
Starlite Productions, pg 1024
SYMCO Inc, pg 1030
Total Video Products Inc, pg 1042
VCom International Multimedia Corp, pg 1052
Video Corporation of America (VCA), pg 1055
Wilray Audio Visual Corp, pg 1067
Wired 4 Sound Inc, pg 1068
York Telecom, pg 1072

NEW YORK

Audio Visual Sales & Service Inc, pg 796
AV Workshop, pg 797
Communication Corner Inc, pg 832
Custom Media Environments, pg 841
Design Audio Visual Inc, pg 845
Eastman Kodak Professional, pg 856
Gaylord Brothers, pg 876
General Audio-Visual Inc (GAVI), pg 876
Indigo Productions, pg 897
Long Island Video Enterprises Live Inc, pg 924
Magnaplan Corp, pg 928
Markertek Video Supply, pg 931
Motion Picture Enterprises Inc, pg 947
Neptune Photo Inc, pg 954
Presentation Products Inc, pg 981
SmartSource Computer & AV Rentals, pg 1014
Technisphere Corp, pg 1034
Visual Technologies Corp, pg 1060
Willoughby's Imaging Center, pg 1067

NORTH CAROLINA

Camcor Inc, pg 818
Strategic Connections, pg 1026

OHIO

Audio Visual Media, pg 795
Copp Integrated Systems, pg 836
Icom Multimedia, pg 893
Smithall Electronics Inc, pg 1014
Tri-State Visual Products, pg 1044

OREGON

Spectrum Systems Design, pg 1021

PENNSYLVANIA

Advanced AV, pg 777
Audio Visions Inc, pg 795
Audio Visual Communications Inc, pg 795
Bernie's Photo Center, pg 805
Brodart Co, pg 813
J E Foss Co, pg 871
Garcia Marketing Inc, pg 875
Grise Audio Visual Center Inc, pg 882
Vistacom Inc, pg 1059
Wespen Audio Visual Co, pg 1063

RHODE ISLAND

Custom Computer Specialists Inc, pg 841

TENNESSEE

Continental Film, pg 835
Lowrance Sound Co Inc, pg 925
Memphis Communications Corp, pg 938
Technical Support Systems LLC, pg 1034
Tennessee Visual Service Co, pg 1037

TEXAS

Astro Audio Visual, pg 792
Audio Visual Technologies Group, pg 796
Digital Display Solutions Inc, pg 847
FitzCo Sound Inc, pg 869
J&S Audio Visual Inc, pg 904
Lubbock Audio Visual Inc, pg 925
Quality Audio Visual Service Inc, pg 988

VIRGINIA

Boitnott Visual Communications Corp (BVC), pg 810
Communications Specialists Inc, pg 833
Filmdex Inc, pg 867
Hoppmann Audio Visual, pg 891
Intellidyne LLC, pg 899
Lee Hartman & Sons Inc, pg 918
Metropolitan Audio Visual Co LLC, pg 940
The Whitlock Group, pg 1065

WASHINGTON

Inland Audio Visual Co, pg 898
Northern Lights & Pro Audio, pg 959
Pacific Northwest Theatre Associates Inc (PNTA), pg 967

WISCONSIN

Audio Visual of Milwaukee Inc, pg 795
Demco Inc, pg 845
Full Compass Systems, pg 874
Pro Studio Supply, pg 983
School Specialty Inc, pg 1004

PUERTO RICO

Bonnin Electronics Inc, pg 810

ALBERTA

Infosat Communications Inc, pg 898
Sharp's Audio-Visual Ltd, pg 1008
Unique Communications Ltd, pg 1048

BRITISH COLUMBIA

Commercial Electronics Ltd, pg 832

MANITOBA

Evolution Presentation Technologies, pg 863
Inland Audio Visual Ltd, pg 898

ONTARIO

Carr McLean Ltd, pg 820
Edcom Multimedia Products, pg 856
Nationwide Audio Visual Co, pg 953
Premier A/V Sales Ltd, pg 980

QUEBEC

Concept Audio-Visual, pg 834
Panavideo Inc, pg 968

Slide Projector Manufacturers

ALABAMA

Media Visions Inc, pg 937

CALIFORNIA

Lasergraphics Inc, pg 916

ILLINOIS

ACCO Brands Corp, pg 773

NEVADA

Keystone View, pg 910

NEW JERSEY

Crestron Electronics Inc, pg 839
Leica Camera Inc, pg 918

NEW YORK

American Video Inc, pg 785
Eastman Kodak Professional, pg 856
ELMO USA Corp, pg 859
General Audio-Visual Inc (GAVI), pg 876
Navitar Inc, pg 953
TecNec Distributing, pg 1035

Slide Projector Rentals

ALABAMA

Audio-Video Resources Inc, pg 795
Media Visions Inc, pg 937

ARIZONA

Arizona Cine Equipment, pg 789
Merestone, pg 938
Metropolitan Audio-Visual Inc, pg 940
Ultimate Presentation Systems Inc, pg 1047
Video Media Productions (VMP), pg 1055

ARKANSAS

Carlton-Bates Co, pg 820
White Diamond Productions, pg 1065

CALIFORNIA

Adolph Gasser Inc, pg 776
AGF Media Services, pg 778
Alliant Event Services, pg 781
Ametron Audio/Video, pg 785
Artichoke Productions, pg 791
AV Guys, pg 797
Gluskin's Custom Audio Video, pg 879
Gold Standard Productions, pg 880
Hooper Camera & Imaging, pg 891
Impact Group, pg 897
Instructional Materials & Equipment Distributors (I-Med), pg 899
JD Audio Visual Inc, pg 904
McCune Audio-Video-Lighting, pg 935
Media Fabricators Inc, pg 936
Munday & Collins AV, pg 950
On-Trax Inc, pg 963
PSAV® Presentation Services, pg 986
Related Visual Inc, pg 994
Samy's Camera, pg 1002
Slate Media Group, pg 1013
Sound Service Co, pg 1017
Stanislaus Audio Video Inc, pg 1023
University of Southern California, pg 1050
VER-Video Equipment Rentals, pg 1053
Voice & Video Rentals, pg 1060

COLORADO

Ceavco Audio/Visual Co, pg 822
Daylight Productions & Rentals, pg 844
Multimedia Audio Visual Inc, pg 950
Spectrum Audio Visual Services, pg 1020

CONNECTICUT

A/V Davey, pg 797
Concord Communications, pg 835
Rockwell Communications Inc, pg 998

DELAWARE

Ken-Del Productions Inc, pg 909

FLORIDA

AVI-SPL, pg 798
Gulf Coast Audio Visual Producers Inc, pg 883
Harmon's Audio-Visual Services, pg 885
Image Technical Services, pg 895
Industrial Strength Inc, pg 897
Lighting Sales Connections, pg 920
Media Concepts Inc, pg 936
Photosound of Orlando Inc, pg 975
Pro Stage Inc, pg 983
Sight & Sound Productions, pg 1010
Spire Audio Visual Co Inc, pg 1021
Tallahassee Audio Visual, pg 1031
Universal Studios Florida® Production Group, pg 1049

GEORGIA

Audio Visual Resources Inc, pg 795
Convergent Media Systems, pg 836

Dixie Theatre Service & Supply Co Inc, pg 849
Lighting & Production Equipment Inc, pg 920
MAGNUM Companies Ltd, pg 929
ON Event Services, pg 963
Stage Front Presentation Systems, pg 1022
Staging Directions Inc, pg 1023

HAWAII

ATTCO Inc, pg 793

ILLINOIS

Allen Visual Systems Inc, pg 781
Audio Visual Services Corp, pg 796
AV Chicago Inc, pg 797
Backstar Creative Media Inc, pg 801
Beatty TeleVisual Productions, pg 804
Central Audio-Visual Equipment Inc, pg 823
Communications Corporation of America, pg 833
Creative Technology, pg 838
Helix Camera & Video, pg 887
The Pepper Group, pg 972
PSAV® Presentation Services (Hotel Services Division), pg 987
QuickSet International Inc, pg 989
RC Communications, pg 992
Show Department Inc, pg 1009

INDIANA

Advanced Media Integration, pg 777
Gary Camera & Digital, pg 875

KANSAS

Genigraphics®, pg 877
Smith Audio-Visual Inc, pg 1014

KENTUCKY

Audio Visual Techniques Inc, pg 796
Barney Miller's Inc, pg 943

LOUISIANA

Clark Services Audio Visual & Exhibit Inc, pg 829
Pace Systems, pg 966

MAINE

Headlight Audio Visual Inc, pg 887

MARYLAND

Advance Audiovisual Presentation Ltd, pg 777
CSPMedia.com, pg 840
dbF a Media Company, pg 844
Hargrove Inc, pg 885
Nelson White Systems Inc, pg 954
RTZ Audio Visual, pg 1000
Visual Aids Electronics Corp, pg 1059

MASSACHUSETTS

AVFX Inc, pg 798
Camera Co Inc/Broadcast Divison, pg 818
Capron Lighting & Sound Co Inc, pg 819
massAV, pg 933
Preston Productions Inc, pg 981
TR Productions, pg 1043

MICHIGAN

Olson Anderson Co, pg 786
Digi Sign Design LLC, pg 847
K&R All Media Productions Inc, pg 908
K&R's Recording Studios Inc, pg 908
TeL Systems, pg 1035

MINNESOTA

Advanced Audio-Visual Inc, pg 777
AVI Systems, pg 799
Media Loft Inc, pg 937

MISSISSIPPI

Bowie Audio Visual Enterprises Inc, pg 811
Jasper Ewing & Sons Inc, pg 864

MISSOURI

Communitronics Corp, pg 833
Schiller's Audio-Visual, pg 1004
Show-Me Audio-Visual, pg 1009
Southwest Audio-Visual Inc, pg 1019
Swank Audio Visuals, pg 1029

NEVADA

GES Audio Visual, pg 877

NEW HAMPSHIRE

Apertura, pg 788

NEW JERSEY

Audio Visual Dynamics®, pg 795
Giant Audio Visual Inc, pg 878
International Audio Visual Inc, pg 900
Moe AV LLC, pg 945
PLS Staging, pg 977
Starlite Productions, pg 1024
Wired 4 Sound Inc, pg 1068

NEW YORK

Ace Video, pg 774
Adwar Video, pg 778
American Video Inc, pg 785
Audio Visual Resources LLC, pg 795
AV Workshop, pg 797
CMI Communications, pg 830
Communication Corner Inc, pg 832
Design Audio Visual Inc, pg 845
Langie Audio Visual Systems, pg 915
Long Island Video Enterprises Live Inc, pg 924
Magnaplan Corp, pg 928
Manhattan Center Studios Inc, pg 930
Neptune Photo Inc, pg 954
SmartSource Computer & AV Rentals, pg 1014
Specialized Audio-Visual Inc, pg 1020
TBA Global Events, pg 1032
Technisphere Corp, pg 1034
Visual Technologies Corp, pg 1060
Visual Word Systems Inc, pg 1060
WorldStage, pg 1070

NORTH CAROLINA

A&V Company, pg 772
Camcor Inc, pg 818
Special Event Services, pg 1020
Strategic Connections, pg 1026
Visual Aids Electronics of North Carolina Inc, pg 1059

NORTH DAKOTA

Media Productions, pg 937

OHIO

Audio Visual Media, pg 795
Aztec Video Productions, pg 801
Hughie's Event Production Services, pg 892
Icom Multimedia, pg 893
ITA Audio Visual Solutions, pg 902
Mills James Productions, pg 943
Thread Marketing Group, pg 1039
Vista Color Imaging Inc, pg 1059

OREGON

Rose City Sound, pg 999

PENNSYLVANIA

Advanced AV, pg 777
Audio Visions Inc, pg 795
Audio Visual Communications Inc, pg 795
Grise Audio Visual Center Inc, pg 882
Ott Film Rentals, pg 966
Production Solutions Inc, pg 985
Visual Sound Inc, pg 1059

SOUTH CAROLINA

Sound & Images Inc, pg 1016

TENNESSEE

Memphis Communications Corp, pg 938
Russ Sturgeon Productions/RSVP, pg 1027
Technical Support Systems LLC, pg 1034
Tennessee Visual Service Co, pg 1037

TEXAS

Astro Audio Visual, pg 792
Audio Visual Technologies Group, pg 796
Bright Star Productions Inc, pg 812
Digital Display Solutions Inc, pg 847
FitzCo Sound Inc, pg 869
J&S Audio Visual Inc, pg 904
Lubbock Audio Visual Inc, pg 925
Padgitt's, pg 967
Quality Audio Visual Service Inc, pg 988
Stage Directions, pg 1022

VERMONT

Parlato Productions, pg 969

VIRGINIA

American AV, pg 783
Boitnott Visual Communications Corp (BVC), pg 810
Lee Hartman & Sons Inc, pg 918
Metropolitan Audio Visual Co LLC, pg 940
Projection Presentation Technology, pg 985
Rainbow Rentals, pg 991
The Whitlock Group, pg 1065

WASHINGTON

Inland Audio Visual Co, pg 898
Kostov Productions, pg 913
Pacific Northwest Theatre Associates Inc (PNTA), pg 967

WISCONSIN

Audio Visual of Milwaukee Inc, pg 795
Camera Corner Connecting Point, pg 818
Event Essentials, pg 863
Full Compass Systems, pg 874
School Specialty Inc, pg 1004

PUERTO RICO

Stage Crew Audiovisual Inc, pg 1022

ALBERTA

Allstar Show Industries Inc, pg 782
Cine Audio Visual Sales & Service Ltd, pg 826
Evolution Presentation Technologies, pg 863
McBain Audio Visual Ltd, pg 935
Sharp's Audio-Visual Ltd, pg 1008
Unique Communications Ltd, pg 1048

BRITISH COLUMBIA

Clark's Audio Visual Services Ltd, pg 829
Commercial Electronics Ltd, pg 832
Triad Communications Ltd, pg 1044

MANITOBA

Evolution Presentation Technologies, pg 863
Inland Audio Visual Ltd, pg 898

ONTARIO

Edcom Multimedia Products, pg 856
HD Source, pg 886

QUEBEC

Audio Visual Dynamics Ltd, pg 795
AVW-TELAV Audio Visual Solutions, a Freeman Company, pg 800
Concept Audio-Visual, pg 834
Panavideo Inc, pg 968

Slide Projector Repairs

ALABAMA

Media Visions Inc, pg 937

ARKANSAS

Carlton-Bates Co, pg 820

CALIFORNIA

Ametron Audio/Video, pg 785
Gluskin's Custom Audio Video, pg 879
Hooper Camera & Imaging, pg 891
Instructional Materials & Equipment Distributors (I-Med), pg 899
McAlister Electronics, pg 935
Lloyd F McKinney Associates Inc, pg 935
Pro Camera Repair, pg 982

COLORADO

Ceavco Audio/Visual Co, pg 822

CONNECTICUT

A/V Davey, pg 797
HB Communications Inc, pg 886

AUDIO/VISUAL

Slide Projector Repairs (continued)

CONNECTICUT (continued)

Precision Camera & Video Repair Inc, pg 980
Rockwell Communications Inc, pg 998

FLORIDA

Spire Audio Visual Co Inc, pg 1021
Tallahassee Audio Visual, pg 1031

GEORGIA

Audio Visual Resources Inc, pg 795
Lighting & Production Equipment Inc, pg 920
Stage Front Presentation Systems, pg 1022
Technical Innovation, pg 1033

ILLINOIS

Allen Visual Systems Inc, pg 781
Beatty TeleVisual Productions, pg 804
Central Audio-Visual Equipment Inc, pg 823
RC Communications, pg 992

INDIANA

Gary Camera & Digital, pg 875

KENTUCKY

Axxis Inc, pg 800
NOR-COM Inc, pg 958

MAINE

Headlight Audio Visual Inc, pg 887

MARYLAND

Nelson White Systems Inc, pg 954
RTZ Audio Visual, pg 1000
Strauss Photo Technical Service Inc, pg 1026
Visual Aids Electronics Corp, pg 1059

MASSACHUSETTS

Camera Co Inc/Broadcast Divison, pg 818
Capron Lighting & Sound Co Inc, pg 819

MICHIGAN

Olson Anderson Co, pg 786
City Events Group, pg 828
TeL Systems, pg 1035

MINNESOTA

AVI Systems, pg 799

MISSISSIPPI

Bowie Audio Visual Enterprises Inc, pg 811

MISSOURI

Cintrex Audio Visual, pg 828
Communitronics Corp, pg 833
Schiller's Audio-Visual, pg 1004

NEW JERSEY

Hasselblad Bron Inc, pg 885
Leica Camera Inc, pg 918

NEW YORK

Colortone Audio Visual, pg 832
ELMO USA Corp, pg 859
Langie Audio Visual Systems, pg 915
Magnaplan Corp, pg 928
Visual Technologies Corp, pg 1060

NORTH CAROLINA

Camcor Inc, pg 818
Strategic Connections, pg 1026

OHIO

Audio Visual Media, pg 795
Aztec Video Productions, pg 801
Copp Integrated Systems, pg 836
Icom Multimedia, pg 893
Tri-State Audio Visual Co, pg 1044

PENNSYLVANIA

Audio Visions Inc, pg 795
J E Foss Co, pg 871
Ott Film Rentals, pg 966
Wespen Audio Visual Co, pg 1063

RHODE ISLAND

Custom Computer Specialists Inc, pg 841

TENNESSEE

Memphis Communications Corp, pg 938
Technical Support Systems LLC, pg 1034
Tennessee Visual Service Co, pg 1037

TEXAS

Astro Audio Visual, pg 792
Audio Visual Technologies Group, pg 796
Lubbock Audio Visual Inc, pg 925
Padgitt's, pg 967
Quality Audio Visual Service Inc, pg 988

VIRGINIA

Avitecture Inc, pg 799
Boitnott Visual Communications Corp (BVC), pg 810
Hoppmann Audio Visual, pg 891
Lee Hartman & Sons Inc, pg 918
Metropolitan Audio Visual Co LLC, pg 940
The Whitlock Group, pg 1065

WASHINGTON

Inland Audio Visual Co, pg 898
Pacific Northwest Theatre Associates Inc (PNTA), pg 967

WISCONSIN

Audio Visual of Milwaukee Inc, pg 795
Camera Corner Connecting Point, pg 818
Full Compass Systems, pg 874
School Specialty Inc, pg 1004

ALBERTA

Infosat Communications Inc, pg 898
Sharp's Audio-Visual Ltd, pg 1008
Unique Communications Ltd, pg 1048

BRITISH COLUMBIA

Commercial Electronics Ltd, pg 832

MANITOBA

Evolution Presentation Technologies, pg 863
Inland Audio Visual Ltd, pg 898

ONTARIO

Edcom Multimedia Products, pg 856
Premier A/V Sales Ltd, pg 980

QUEBEC

Panavideo Inc, pg 968

Slide Retouching, *see* Retouching—Slides

Slide to Film Transfers, *see* Transfers—Slide to Film

Slide to Filmstrip Transfers, *see* Transfers—Slide to Filmstrip

Slide to Video Transfers, *see* Transfers—Slide to Video

Slides from Artwork

ALABAMA

Media Visions Inc, pg 937

ARIZONA

Image Craft LLC, pg 894
Merestone, pg 938
Professional Marketing Services Inc, pg 985

ARKANSAS

White Diamond Productions, pg 1065

CALIFORNIA

Action Photo Service Inc, pg 775
Adolph Gasser Inc, pg 776
Coloredge, pg 832
Lynch Communications, pg 926
The Media Staff Inc, pg 937
Point of View Productions, pg 977
PSI Inc, pg 987
QRS Software Services, pg 988
Regent Press Publishers & Printers, pg 994
Dick Reizner Film & Video, pg 994
SBS Productions, pg 1003
StereoScope International, pg 1024
The Studio Center, pg 1026

CONNECTICUT

Broadcast Video Productions LLC, pg 813

DISTRICT OF COLUMBIA

O'Keefe Communications Inc, pg 961

FLORIDA

Communications Concepts Inc (CCI), pg 833
Gulf Coast Audio Visual Producers Inc, pg 883
Jordan Klein Film & Video (JKFV), pg 906

GEORGIA

Imagers, pg 896
USMotivation, pg 1051
Visioneering International Inc, pg 1058

ILLINOIS

Audio Visual Services Corp, pg 796
CCore Media Inc, pg 821
Gamma Imaging, pg 875
Helix Camera & Video, pg 887
JMC Photo & Digital Services Inc, pg 905
Lyn Norstad & Associates Inc, pg 926
Major Media Inc, pg 929
The Pepper Group, pg 972
PSAV® Presentation Services (Hotel Services Division), pg 987
Southern Illinois University, pg 1019

INDIANA

Communication Ministries, pg 833
OMNI Productions, pg 962

IOWA

The Production House, pg 984

KANSAS

Genigraphics®, pg 877

LOUISIANA

Louisiana State University Health Sciences Center - Shreveport, pg 925
Primary Color Laboratory Inc, pg 982

MASSACHUSETTS

Colortek of Boston, pg 832
CommCreative, pg 832
DGI-Invisuals LLC, pg 846
Emergency Film Group, pg 860
Preston Productions Inc, pg 981
TR Productions, pg 1043

MICHIGAN

Blue Mouse Studio, pg 809
Digi Sign Design LLC, pg 847
K&R's Recording Studios Inc, pg 908
MessageMakers, pg 939
Michigan Office Solutions, pg 941
On Stage Visuals, pg 963
Tectonics Industries Inc, pg 1035
Tri-Color, pg 1044

Slides from Color Negatives

Slides from Other Media

AUDIO/VISUAL

Slides from Other Media (continued)

FLORIDA

Communications Concepts Inc (CCI), pg 833
Gulf Coast Audio Visual Producers Inc, pg 883

GEORGIA

Imagers, pg 896
Visioneering International Inc, pg 1058

ILLINOIS

CCore Media Inc, pg 821
Gamma Imaging, pg 875
Lyn Norstad & Associates Inc, pg 926
The Pepper Group, pg 972
WEEK TV, pg 1063

INDIANA

OMNI Productions, pg 962

IOWA

The Production House, pg 984

KANSAS

Genigraphics®, pg 877

LOUISIANA

Louisiana State University Health Sciences Center - Shreveport, pg 925

MARYLAND

Spectrum Productions, pg 1021

MASSACHUSETTS

Colortek of Boston, pg 832
CommCreative, pg 832
Preston Productions Inc, pg 981
TR Productions, pg 1043

MICHIGAN

K&R's Recording Studios Inc, pg 908
Michigan Office Solutions, pg 941
The Transfer Zone®, pg 1043
Tri-Color, pg 1044

MINNESOTA

Media Loft Inc, pg 937
Thomas Reprographics, pg 1039

MISSISSIPPI

Jasper Ewing & Sons Inc, pg 864

MISSOURI

Communitronics Corp, pg 833
Visionworks Design Services Inc, pg 1059

NEBRASKA

Dog & Pony Productions Inc, pg 850

NEVADA

Encore Productions Inc, pg 861

NEW HAMPSHIRE

Apertura, pg 788

NEW JERSEY

All Jersey Studios, pg 780
CELCO-Constantine Engineering Labs Co, pg 822
Laurel Video Productions, pg 916
Reed Presentations Inc (RPI), pg 993

NEW YORK

Broad Street Inc, pg 812
Duggal Visual Solutions, pg 853
Eastco Multimedia Solutions Inc, pg 856
Greyfalcon House, pg 882
Ketchum Pleon Change, pg 910
L&P Media, pg 915
Modernage Photographic Services Inc, pg 944
Jack Morton Worldwide, pg 946
MRG Productions Inc, pg 948
SMP Digital Graphics, pg 1014
Zelman Studios Ltd, pg 1073

NORTH CAROLINA

Image Associates Inc, pg 894

NORTH DAKOTA

Media Productions, pg 937

OHIO

Aztec Video Productions, pg 801
Thread Marketing Group, pg 1039
Vista Color Imaging Inc, pg 1059

PENNSYLVANIA

Audio Visual Communications Inc, pg 795
Berry & Homer, pg 805
Main Point Productions, pg 929
Visual Sound Inc, pg 1059

TENNESSEE

Marine Geographic, pg 931
Memphis Communications Corp, pg 938
Stage Post, pg 1022

TEXAS

Audio Visual Technologies Group, pg 796
City Color, pg 828
Stage Directions, pg 1022
Texas Heart Institute Visual Communication Services, pg 1037

UTAH

Ferrari Color®, pg 866

WISCONSIN

USAV Group Inc, pg 1050

WYOMING

Bridger Productions Inc, pg 812

System Design & Installation

ALABAMA

Media Visions Inc, pg 937

ARIZONA

Covid Inc, pg 837
Metropolitan Audio-Visual Inc, pg 940
Ultimate Presentation Systems Inc, pg 1047

CALIFORNIA

Automated Entertainment, pg 797
BroadcastStore.com, pg 813
Cibola Systems, pg 826
Electrosonic Inc, pg 859
Gold Standard Productions, pg 880
McKay Conant Hoover Inc, pg 935
Lloyd F McKinney Associates Inc, pg 935
Media Systems Design Group, pg 937
Pro Media/Ultra Sound, pg 983
QRS Software Services, pg 988
RetinaVision Productions, pg 995
Randall Schiller Productions, pg 1004
StereoScope International, pg 1024
Technical Services, pg 1034
Thorburn Associates, Acoustic, Technology, Lighting Design, pg 1039
VMI Inc, pg 1060

COLORADO

Ceavco Audio/Visual Co, pg 822
Daylight Productions & Rentals, pg 844
Maniac Productions, pg 930
Spectrum Audio Visual Services, pg 1020
Starwest Productions, pg 1024

CONNECTICUT

Boyce Nemec Designs, pg 811
Everett Hall Associates Inc, pg 863
Guymark Studios LLC, pg 883
MAVCO, pg 934
Rockwell Communications Inc, pg 998

DISTRICT OF COLUMBIA

Hillmann & Carr Inc, pg 889

FLORIDA

Allegro Productions Inc, pg 781
Audio Visual Imagineering Inc, pg 795
AVI-SPL, pg 798
Communications Concepts Inc (CCI), pg 833
Ed Ethridge Productions Inc, pg 863
Gulf Coast Audio Visual Producers Inc, pg 883
Multicom Inc, pg 949
Multivision Video & Film, pg 950

GEORGIA

Audio Visual Resources Inc, pg 795
CDAI Innovative Design Solutions, pg 822
Lighting & Production Equipment Inc, pg 920
Merck & Hill Consultants Inc, pg 938
Omnimedia Inc, pg 962
Visioneering International Inc, pg 1058

ILLINOIS

ABS Enterprises, pg 772
Audio Visual Services Corp, pg 796
Beatty TeleVisual Productions, pg 804
C V Lloyde, pg 923
Paragon Studios Inc, pg 969
PSAV® Presentation Services (Hotel Services Division), pg 987

INDIANA

Advanced Media Integration, pg 777
OMNI Productions, pg 962

IOWA

The Production House, pg 984

KENTUCKY

Axxis Inc, pg 800
NOR-COM Inc, pg 958

LOUISIANA

Digital FX Inc, pg 847
Louisiana State University Health Sciences Center - Shreveport, pg 925

MARYLAND

dbF a Media Company, pg 844

MASSACHUSETTS

Capron Lighting & Sound Co Inc, pg 819
CommCreative, pg 832
Monadnock Media Inc, pg 945
TR Productions, pg 1043

MICHIGAN

Audio Graphic Services, pg 794
K&R's Recording Studios Inc, pg 908
Teletech Inc, pg 1036

MINNESOTA

AVI Systems, pg 799
GMI Productions, pg 879
Jamieson & Associates Inc, pg 904
Media Loft Inc, pg 937

MISSISSIPPI

Jasper Ewing & Sons Inc, pg 864

MISSOURI

Communitronics Corp, pg 833
Swank Audio Visuals, pg 1029

MONTANA

KUSM TV, pg 914

NEBRASKA

Dog & Pony Productions Inc, pg 850
Rainbow Video Productions Inc, pg 991

NEVADA

Encore Productions Inc, pg 861
Stage America LLC, pg 1022

NEW HAMPSHIRE

Apertura, pg 788
Chip Taylor Communications LLC, pg 1032

NEW JERSEY

A-V Services Inc, pg 771
Activu Corp, pg 775

Audio Visual Associates, pg 795
Audio Visual Dynamics®, pg 795
CELCO-Constantine Engineering Labs Co, pg 822
Diversified Systems Inc, pg 849
Emanuel Audiovisual Consultants, pg 860
Euro-Pacific Film & Video Productions Inc, pg 863
Laurel Video Productions, pg 916
PatchAmp, pg 970
Princeton Acoustics Corp, pg 982
Starlite Productions, pg 1024
Suede Interactive, pg 1027
Total Video Products Inc, pg 1042
Wired 4 Sound Inc, pg 1068

NEW MEXICO

Quickbeam Systems Inc (QSI), pg 989

NEW YORK

Communication Corner Inc, pg 832
Duggal Visual Solutions, pg 853
Long Island Video Enterprises Live Inc, pg 924
Jack Morton Worldwide, pg 946
MRG Productions Inc, pg 948
Judson Rosebush Co Inc, pg 999
Specialized Audio-Visual Inc, pg 1020
TBA Global Events, pg 1032
Theatrical Services & Supplies Inc, pg 1038
Tritech Communications, pg 1045
Visual Technologies Corp, pg 1060
Visual Word Systems Inc, pg 1060
Zelman Studios Ltd, pg 1073

NORTH CAROLINA

A&V Company, pg 772
Pat Appleson Studios Inc, pg 788
Lawrence Behr Associates Inc, pg 804
Camcor Inc, pg 818
Moving Pictures, pg 948

OHIO

Aztec Video Productions, pg 801
Copp Integrated Systems, pg 836
Mills James Productions, pg 943

OKLAHOMA

Digital Designs, pg 847

OREGON

Spectrum Systems Design, pg 1021

PENNSYLVANIA

Clair Brothers Audio Systems Inc, pg 829
Production Solutions Inc, pg 985
Visual Sound Inc, pg 1059

RHODE ISLAND

Sound-FX-Design, pg 1017

TENNESSEE

Continental Film, pg 835
Memphis Communications Corp, pg 938
Stage Post, pg 1022
Technical Support Systems LLC, pg 1034

TEXAS

Audio Visual Technologies Group, pg 796
AVES Audio Visual Systems Inc, pg 798
Lubbock Audio Visual Inc, pg 925
Stage Directions, pg 1022
Tarpley Media Systems, pg 1032

VERMONT

University of Vermont, Instructional Television Dept, pg 1050

VIRGINIA

Acoustics First Corp, pg 775
American AV, pg 783
Design & Production Inc, pg 845
Old Dominion Broadcasting, pg 961
Opterna AM, pg 964

WASHINGTON

Inland Audio Visual Co, pg 898
Kostov Productions, pg 913
Laser Fantasy/HECK Industries/Photon Manufacturing, pg 916

WEST VIRGINIA

United Sound & Electronics, pg 1048

WISCONSIN

Full Compass Systems, pg 874
USAV Group Inc, pg 1050
Video Wisconsin Inc, pg 1056
Wisconsin Public Television, pg 1068

WYOMING

Bridger Productions Inc, pg 812

ALBERTA

Sharp's Audio-Visual Ltd, pg 1008
Unique Communications Ltd, pg 1048

BRITISH COLUMBIA

DL Sound & Lighting Productions Ltd, pg 849

ONTARIO

Cinema Stage Inc, pg 827
MVI Multivision Inc, pg 951
State of the Art Acoustik Inc, pg 1024
Technovision® Interactive Inc, pg 1035
Westbury National Show Systems Ltd, pg 1064

QUEBEC

Sceno Plus, pg 1004
Trebas Institute, pg 1044

Tape Recorder & Player Distributors

ALABAMA

Curtis Company, pg 841
Media Visions Inc, pg 937

ARIZONA

Arizona Cine Equipment, pg 789
EAR Professional Audio/Video, pg 855
Troxell Communications Inc, pg 1045

ARKANSAS

White Diamond Productions, pg 1065

CALIFORNIA

Adolph Gasser Inc, pg 776
Ametron Audio/Video, pg 785
Associated Sound, pg 792
ATV Video Center Inc, pg 793
Audio Images Corp, pg 794
Birns & Sawyer Inc, pg 808
California Tape Products Inc, pg 817
Delicate Electronics Sales Inc, pg 845
Empire Wholesale Inc, pg 860
FXC Communications, pg 874
Gluskin's Custom Audio Video, pg 879
GMF Sound Inc, pg 879
Instructional Materials & Equipment Distributors (I-Med), pg 899
Jaguar Distribution Corp, pg 903
Location Sound Corp, pg 924
Martel Electronics Sales Inc, pg 932
Media Fabricators Inc, pg 936
MediaPOINTE, pg 938
Mobilized Tech Systems, pg 944
POP TV, pg 978
Related Visual Inc, pg 994
SNAP, pg 1014
Southern California Sound Image Inc, pg 1019
SSL Industries Inc, pg 1022
SuperVision, pg 1029
Towards 2000 Inc, pg 1043
Tri-Ed, pg 1044
VMI Inc, pg 1060

COLORADO

Spectrum Audio Visual Services, pg 1020
Stanco Sales LLC, pg 1023

CONNECTICUT

Connecticut Audio & Theatrical Supply, pg 835
HB Communications Inc, pg 886
MAVCO, pg 934

DELAWARE

Actors Attic, pg 775

FLORIDA

Allstar Audio Systems Inc, pg 782
AVI-SPL, pg 798
BAI Distributors Inc, pg 801
Broadcasters General Store Inc, pg 813
Digital Video Systems Inc, pg 848
Gulf Coast Audio Visual Producers Inc, pg 883
Harmon's Audio-Visual Services, pg 885
Harris Corp, pg 885
Hi-Tech Enterprises Inc, pg 888
Hi-Tech Import Export Corp, pg 888
Industrial Strength Inc, pg 897
Intermark Industries Inc, pg 900
Photomart Cine-Video Inc, pg 975
Photosound of Orlando Inc, pg 975
Pro Stage Inc, pg 983
Recording Media & Equipment Inc (RM&E), pg 993
Sight & Sound Productions, pg 1010
Stereo Sales Inc, pg 1024
TAI Audio, pg 1031
Tallahassee Audio Visual, pg 1031

GEORGIA

Baker Audio Inc, pg 801
Convergent Media Systems, pg 836
Lighting & Production Equipment Inc, pg 920
Stage Front Presentation Systems, pg 1022
Visioneering International Inc, pg 1058

HAWAII

The Audio Visual Co (AVCO), pg 795

ILLINOIS

Allen Visual Systems Inc, pg 781
Central Audio-Visual Equipment Inc, pg 823
Joseph Electronics, pg 906
Quintessence Audio Ltd, pg 989
RAM Systems LLC, pg 991
RC Communications, pg 992

INDIANA

Sensory Technologies LLC, pg 1006
SHP Electronics, pg 1010

IOWA

ECS Inc, pg 856

KANSAS

KK Office Solutions Inc, pg 911
Smith Audio-Visual Inc, pg 1014

KENTUCKY

Axxis Inc, pg 800
Barney Miller's Inc, pg 943
NOR-COM Inc, pg 958
Northern Kentucky University, pg 959

MAINE

Headlight Audio Visual Inc, pg 887

MARYLAND

Cardinal Sound & Video, pg 820
RTZ Audio Visual, pg 1000
Visual Aids Electronics Corp, pg 1059

MASSACHUSETTS

Professional Audio Design Inc, pg 985
University Products Inc, pg 1050

MICHIGAN

Ascom Communications Contractors, pg 791
City Events Group, pg 828
On Stage Visuals, pg 963

MINNESOTA

Advanced Audio-Visual Inc, pg 777
Aggressive Records Audio Duplication LLC, pg 778
Alpha Video & Audio Inc, pg 782
AVI Systems, pg 799

AUDIO/VISUAL

Tape Recorder & Player Distributors (continued)

MISSISSIPPI

Bowie Audio Visual Enterprises Inc, pg 811

MISSOURI

Communitronics Corp, pg 833
Conference Technologies Inc, pg 835
Image Technologies Corp, pg 895
Modern Communications Inc, pg 944
Schiller's Audio-Visual, pg 1004
Swank Audio Visuals, pg 1029

NEW HAMPSHIRE

APS Lighting-Sound-AV, pg 789

NEW JERSEY

A-V Services Inc, pg 771
Alltec Stores, a Vcom IMC Company, pg 782
Audio Visual Dynamics®, pg 795
AV Bluebook, pg 797
Earl Girls Inc, pg 855
FlagHouse, pg 869
G&G Technologies Inc, pg 875
Hamilton Buhl, pg 884
National Audio-Visual Supply, pg 952
Starlite Productions, pg 1024
SYMCO Inc, pg 1030
Total Video Products Inc, pg 1042
Turner Engineering Inc, pg 1046
Video Corporation of America (VCA), pg 1055
Wilray Audio Visual Corp, pg 1067
Wired 4 Sound Inc, pg 1068
York Telecom, pg 1072

NEW YORK

ALTEL Systems Inc, pg 783
American Video Inc, pg 785
AV Workshop, pg 797
Communication Corner Inc, pg 832
Custom Media Environments, pg 841
Design Audio Visual Inc, pg 845
Flash Electronics Inc, pg 869
Gaylord Brothers, pg 876
Indigo Productions, pg 897
Long Island Video Enterprises Live Inc, pg 924
Magnaplan Corp, pg 928
Markertek Video Supply, pg 931
MRG Productions Inc, pg 948
Neptune Photo Inc, pg 954
NorthCountry Distributors, pg 959
Ray Supply Inc, pg 992
RNJ Electronics, pg 997
Sanako Inc, pg 1002
Technisphere Corp, pg 1034
Video Technology Services Inc, pg 1056
Willoughby's Imaging Center, pg 1067

NORTH CAROLINA

Camcor Inc, pg 818
Strategic Connections, pg 1026

OHIO

Copp Integrated Systems, pg 836
The Little Warehouse Inc, pg 923
Jimmy Rea Electronics Inc, pg 992
Smithall Electronics Inc, pg 1014

OREGON

Spectrum Systems Design, pg 1021

PENNSYLVANIA

Advanced AV, pg 777
Audio Visions Inc, pg 795
Audio Visual Communications Inc, pg 795
Bernie's Photo Center, pg 805
Brodart Co, pg 813
J E Foss Co, pg 871
Grise Audio Visual Center Inc, pg 882
The Lerro Corp, pg 919
Morefield Communications Inc, pg 946
Vistacom Inc, pg 1059
Wespen Audio Visual Co, pg 1063

RHODE ISLAND

Custom Computer Specialists Inc, pg 841

TENNESSEE

Durrell LLC, pg 854
Lowrance Sound Co Inc, pg 925
Spring Arbor Distributors, pg 1022
Technical Support Systems LLC, pg 1034
Tennessee Visual Service Co, pg 1037
Zion Music Group, pg 1074

TEXAS

Astro Audio Visual, pg 792
Audio Visual Technologies Group, pg 796
AVES Audio Visual Systems Inc, pg 798
Crossroads Audio Inc, pg 840
Heffernan Audio Visual, pg 887
J&S Audio Visual Inc, pg 904
Lubbock Audio Visual Inc, pg 925
Pro Video & Film Equipment Co Inc, pg 983
Quality Audio Visual Service Inc, pg 988
RadioShack Corp, pg 990
Schoolhouse Audio Visual, pg 1004
Tarpley Media Systems, pg 1032

UTAH

Performance Audio, pg 973
RIA Corp, pg 996

VIRGINIA

Boitnott Visual Communications Corp (BVC), pg 810
Communications Specialists Inc, pg 833
Cybernetics, pg 841
Hoppmann Audio Visual, pg 891
Intellidyne LLC, pg 899
Lee Hartman & Sons Inc, pg 918
Metropolitan Audio Visual Co LLC, pg 940
Schafer World Communications Corp, pg 1004
The Whitlock Group, pg 1065

WASHINGTON

CCI Solutions, pg 821
Northern Lights & Pro Audio, pg 959
Pacific Northwest Theatre Associates Inc (PNTA), pg 967

WEST VIRGINIA

United Sound & Electronics, pg 1048

WISCONSIN

Audio Visual of Milwaukee Inc, pg 795
Demco Inc, pg 845
Full Compass Systems, pg 874

PUERTO RICO

Bonnin Electronics Inc, pg 810

ALBERTA

McBain Audio Visual Ltd, pg 935
Sharp's Audio-Visual Ltd, pg 1008
Unique Communications Ltd, pg 1048

BRITISH COLUMBIA

Commercial Electronics Ltd, pg 832

MANITOBA

Evolution Presentation Technologies, pg 863
Inland Audio Visual Ltd, pg 898

ONTARIO

Edcom Multimedia Products, pg 856
HD Source, pg 886
Nationwide Audio Visual Co, pg 953
Premier A/V Sales Ltd, pg 980
Westbury National Show Systems Ltd, pg 1064

QUEBEC

Concept Audio-Visual, pg 834
Panavideo Inc, pg 968

Tape Recorder & Player Manufacturers

ALABAMA

Media Visions Inc, pg 937

CALIFORNIA

Califone International Inc, pg 817
Eiki International, pg 858
Panasonic Professional Audio Systems, pg 968
TEAC America Inc, pg 1033

ILLINOIS

SoundTech, pg 1018

NEW JERSEY

Hamilton Buhl, pg 884
National Audio-Visual Supply, pg 952
Panasonic Corp, pg 968

NEW YORK

TecNec Distributing, pg 1035
Video Technology Services Inc, pg 1056

TEXAS

RadioShack Corp, pg 990

Tape Recorder & Player Rentals

ALABAMA

Audio-Video Resources Inc, pg 795
Media Visions Inc, pg 937

ARIZONA

Arizona Cine Equipment, pg 789
Merestone, pg 938
Metropolitan Audio-Visual Inc, pg 940
Video West Inc, pg 1056

ARKANSAS

White Diamond Productions, pg 1065

CALIFORNIA

Advanced Media LLC, pg 778
AGF Media Services, pg 778
Ametron Audio/Video, pg 785
Artichoke Productions, pg 791
Associated Sound, pg 792
ATV Video Center Inc, pg 793
Audio Rents, pg 794
AV Guys, pg 797
Deck Hand Inc, pg 844
Express Media Inc, pg 864
GMF Sound Inc, pg 879
Gold Standard Productions, pg 880
Golden Gate Studios, pg 880
Instructional Materials & Equipment Distributors (I-Med), pg 899
JD Audio Visual Inc, pg 904
Location Sound Corp, pg 924
Lynch Communications, pg 926
Maximus Media Inc, pg 934
Media Fabricators Inc, pg 936
Mobilized Tech Systems, pg 944
Munday & Collins AV, pg 950
On-Trax Inc, pg 963
PSAV® Presentation Services, pg 986
QRS Software Services, pg 988
Related Visual Inc, pg 994
Slate Media Group, pg 1013
SNAP, pg 1014
Technical Services, pg 1034
Third Ear Sound Co, pg 1038
Towards 2000 Inc, pg 1043
University of Southern California, pg 1050
VER-Video Equipment Rentals, pg 1053
Video Resources Inc, pg 1056
Videorama Industries LLC, pg 1057
VMI Inc, pg 1060
Voice & Video Rentals, pg 1060

COLORADO

Daylight Productions & Rentals, pg 844
Spectrum Audio Visual Services, pg 1020

CONNECTICUT

A/V Davey, pg 797
Connecticut Audio & Theatrical Supply, pg 835

DELAWARE

Actors Attic, pg 775
Ken-Del Productions Inc, pg 909

FLORIDA

Accord Productions, pg 773
Allstar Audio Systems Inc, pg 782

AUDIO/VISUAL

Tape Recorder & Player Repairs

ALABAMA

Media Visions Inc, pg 937

CALIFORNIA

Advanced Media LLC, pg 778
ALC (Auernheimer Labs & Co), pg 780
Ametron Audio/Video, pg 785
Gluskin's Custom Audio Video, pg 879
Instructional Materials & Equipment Distributors (I-Med), pg 899
Location Sound Corp, pg 924
McAlister Electronics, pg 935
Lloyd F McKinney Associates Inc, pg 935
Mobilized Tech Systems, pg 944
SSL Industries Inc, pg 1022
Technical Services, pg 1034
Towards 2000 Inc, pg 1043
VMI Inc, pg 1060

CONNECTICUT

A/V Davey, pg 797
HB Communications Inc, pg 886

FLORIDA

Hi-Tech Enterprises Inc, pg 888
JT Communications, pg 906
Spire Audio Visual Co Inc, pg 1021
Stereo Sales Inc, pg 1024
TAI Audio, pg 1031
Tallahassee Audio Visual, pg 1031

GEORGIA

Lighting & Production Equipment Inc, pg 920
Stage Front Presentation Systems, pg 1022

ILLINOIS

Allen Visual Systems Inc, pg 781
Beatty TeleVisual Productions, pg 804
Central Audio-Visual Equipment Inc, pg 823
Midwest Digital Corp, pg 942
On Site Video, pg 963

IOWA

ECS Inc, pg 856

KANSAS

KK Office Solutions Inc, pg 911

KENTUCKY

Axxis Inc, pg 800
Barney Miller's Inc, pg 943
NOR-COM Inc, pg 958

MARYLAND

Nelson White Systems Inc, pg 954
RTZ Audio Visual, pg 1000
Strauss Photo Technical Service Inc, pg 1026
Visual Aids Electronics Corp, pg 1059

MASSACHUSETTS

Capron Lighting & Sound Co Inc, pg 819
Professional Audio Design Inc, pg 985

MICHIGAN

City Events Group, pg 828
TeL Systems, pg 1035

MINNESOTA

Alpha Video & Audio Inc, pg 782
AVI Systems, pg 799

MISSISSIPPI

Bowie Audio Visual Enterprises Inc, pg 811

MISSOURI

Cintrex Audio Visual, pg 828
Communitronics Corp, pg 833
Schiller's Audio-Visual, pg 1004

NEW JERSEY

Earl Girls Inc, pg 855
Starlite Productions, pg 1024
Turner Engineering Inc, pg 1046

NEW YORK

Adwar Video, pg 778
American Video Inc, pg 785
MRG Productions Inc, pg 948
Ray Supply Inc, pg 992
Video Technology Services Inc, pg 1056

NORTH CAROLINA

Camcor Inc, pg 818
Strategic Connections, pg 1026

OHIO

Aztec Video Productions, pg 801
Copp Integrated Systems, pg 836
Smithall Electronics Inc, pg 1014
Tri-State Audio Visual Co, pg 1044

PENNSYLVANIA

Audio Visions Inc, pg 795
Bernie's Photo Center, pg 805
J E Foss Co, pg 871
Ott Film Rentals, pg 966
Vistacom Inc, pg 1059

RHODE ISLAND

Custom Computer Specialists Inc, pg 841

TENNESSEE

Memphis Communications Corp, pg 938
Technical Support Systems LLC, pg 1034
Tennessee Visual Service Co, pg 1037

TEXAS

Astro Audio Visual, pg 792
Audio Visual Technologies Group, pg 796
Crossroads Audio Inc, pg 840
Lubbock Audio Visual Inc, pg 925
Music Lab Inc, pg 950
Padgitt's, pg 967
Quality Audio Visual Service Inc, pg 988
Schoolhouse Audio Visual, pg 1004
Tarpley Media Systems, pg 1032

VIRGINIA

Boitnott Visual Communications Corp (BVC), pg 810
Hoppmann Audio Visual, pg 891
Metropolitan Audio Visual Co LLC, pg 940
Schafer World Communications Corp, pg 1004
The Whitlock Group, pg 1065

WASHINGTON

Northern Lights & Pro Audio, pg 959
Pacific Northwest Theatre Associates Inc (PNTA), pg 967

WEST VIRGINIA

United Sound & Electronics, pg 1048

WISCONSIN

Audio Visual of Milwaukee Inc, pg 795
Full Compass Systems, pg 874

ALBERTA

Sharp's Audio-Visual Ltd, pg 1008
Unique Communications Ltd, pg 1048

MANITOBA

Evolution Presentation Technologies, pg 863
Inland Audio Visual Ltd, pg 898

ONTARIO

Edcom Multimedia Products, pg 856
HD Source, pg 886
Premier A/V Sales Ltd, pg 980
Westbury National Show Systems Ltd, pg 1064

QUEBEC

Panavideo Inc, pg 968

Three-D Effects, *see* Computer Three-D Effects on Slide

Titling & Artwork Services, *see* Artwork & Titling Services

Transfers—Filmstrip to Slide

ALABAMA

Media Visions Inc, pg 937

ARIZONA

Phoenix VideoFilms®, pg 974
Professional Marketing Services Inc, pg 985

CALIFORNIA

Action Photo Service Inc, pg 775
Coloredge, pg 832
iCorpTv, pg 893
Lynch Communications, pg 926
QRS Software Services, pg 988

CONNECTICUT

Broadcast Video Productions LLC, pg 813

FLORIDA

Gulf Coast Audio Visual Producers Inc, pg 883
Tallahassee Audio Visual, pg 1031

GEORGIA

Staging Directions Inc, pg 1023

ILLINOIS

Gamma Imaging, pg 875

MASSACHUSETTS

CommCreative, pg 832
TR Productions, pg 1043

MICHIGAN

K&R's Recording Studios Inc, pg 908

MISSOURI

Allied Photo Color Co, pg 781

NEVADA

JCS Video Productions, pg 904

NEW JERSEY

All Jersey Studios, pg 780
CELCO-Constantine Engineering Labs Co, pg 822
Reed Presentations Inc (RPI), pg 993

NEW YORK

Duggal Visual Solutions, pg 853
FSL Media Inc, pg 873
Greyfalcon House, pg 882
Jack Morton Worldwide, pg 946
MRG Productions Inc, pg 948
Shelly Palmer Production, pg 968
TBA Global Events, pg 1032
Zelman Studios Ltd, pg 1073

OHIO

Aztec Video Productions, pg 801
Vista Color Imaging Inc, pg 1059

PENNSYLVANIA

Audio Visual Communications Inc, pg 795
Berry & Homer, pg 805
FMP Media Solutions Inc, pg 870

TENNESSEE

Memphis Communications Corp, pg 938
Stage Post, pg 1022

TEXAS

Stage Directions, pg 1022

VIRGINIA

Blair Inc, pg 809

WISCONSIN

USAV Group Inc, pg 1050

Transfers—Slide to Film

ALABAMA

Media Visions Inc, pg 937

ARIZONA

Phoenix VideoFilms®, pg 974
Professional Marketing Services Inc, pg 985
Star Video Duplicating, pg 1024

CALIFORNIA

Adolph Gasser Inc, pg 776
iCorpTv, pg 893
Lynch Communications, pg 926
QRS Software Services, pg 988
SBS Productions, pg 1003

COLORADO

The Cinema Lab, pg 827

CONNECTICUT

Broadcast Video Productions LLC, pg 813
EagleVision Inc, pg 855

FLORIDA

Communications Concepts Inc (CCI), pg 833
Gulf Coast Audio Visual Producers Inc, pg 883

GEORGIA

Staging Directions Inc, pg 1023
Visioneering International Inc, pg 1058

MAINE

Headlight Audio Visual Inc, pg 887

MASSACHUSETTS

Camera Co Inc/Broadcast Divison, pg 818
CommCreative, pg 832
TR Productions, pg 1043

MICHIGAN

K&R's Recording Studios Inc, pg 908

MISSOURI

Allied Photo Color Co, pg 781

NEVADA

JCS Video Productions, pg 904

NEW HAMPSHIRE

Apertura, pg 788

NEW JERSEY

All Jersey Studios, pg 780
CELCO-Constantine Engineering Labs Co, pg 822

NEW YORK

Thomas Craven Film Corp, pg 837
FSL Media Inc, pg 873
Gordon Visual Solutions, pg 880
Greyfalcon House, pg 882
Modernage Photographic Services Inc, pg 944
Jack Morton Worldwide, pg 946
MRG Productions Inc, pg 948
Shelly Palmer Production, pg 968
Zelman Studios Ltd, pg 1073

OHIO

Aztec Video Productions, pg 801

PENNSYLVANIA

John E Allen Inc, pg 781
Audio Visual Communications Inc, pg 795
FMP Media Solutions Inc, pg 870

TENNESSEE

Memphis Communications Corp, pg 938
Stage Post, pg 1022

TEXAS

Digi-matics, pg 847
The Samuels Co, pg 1002
Stage Directions, pg 1022

VIRGINIA

Blair Inc, pg 809

WISCONSIN

Audio Visual of Milwaukee Inc, pg 795
USAV Group Inc, pg 1050

Transfers—Slide to Filmstrip

ALABAMA

Media Visions Inc, pg 937

ARIZONA

Phoenix VideoFilms®, pg 974
Professional Marketing Services Inc, pg 985

CALIFORNIA

Coloredge, pg 832
iCorpTv, pg 893
Lynch Communications, pg 926
QRS Software Services, pg 988
SBS Productions, pg 1003

CONNECTICUT

Broadcast Video Productions LLC, pg 813

GEORGIA

Staging Directions Inc, pg 1023
Visioneering International Inc, pg 1058

ILLINOIS

Southern Illinois University, pg 1019

MASSACHUSETTS

CommCreative, pg 832
TR Productions, pg 1043

MICHIGAN

K&R's Recording Studios Inc, pg 908

MISSOURI

Allied Photo Color Co, pg 781

NEVADA

JCS Video Productions, pg 904

NEW JERSEY

All Jersey Studios, pg 780
CELCO-Constantine Engineering Labs Co, pg 822

NEW YORK

Duggal Visual Solutions, pg 853
FSL Media Inc, pg 873
L&P Media, pg 915
Jack Morton Worldwide, pg 946
MRG Productions Inc, pg 948
Shelly Palmer Production, pg 968
Zelman Studios Ltd, pg 1073

OHIO

Aztec Video Productions, pg 801

PENNSYLVANIA

Audio Visual Communications Inc, pg 795
FMP Media Solutions Inc, pg 870
Innovision Media Group, pg 899

TENNESSEE

Memphis Communications Corp, pg 938
Stage Post, pg 1022

TEXAS

Digi-matics, pg 847
McNee Productions Inc, pg 935
Stage Directions, pg 1022

VIRGINIA

Blair Inc, pg 809

WISCONSIN

Audio Visual of Milwaukee Inc, pg 795
USAV Group Inc, pg 1050

Transfers—Slide to Video

ALABAMA

CMEInfo, pg 830
Media Visions Inc, pg 937

ARIZONA

Metropolitan Audio-Visual Inc, pg 940
On-Site Video, pg 963
Phoenix VideoFilms®, pg 974
Star Video Duplicating, pg 1024

ARKANSAS

Cedar Crest Studio, pg 822
White Diamond Productions, pg 1065

CALIFORNIA

Aaron & Le Duc, pg 772
Access Video in Berkeley, pg 773
Action Photo Service Inc, pg 775
Adolph Gasser Inc, pg 776
Barbosa Video Services, pg 802
CCI Digital, pg 821
Custom Video Productions Inc, pg 841
Digital Media West, pg 847
FXC Communications, pg 874
Gold Standard Productions, pg 880
iCorpTv, pg 893
Lynch Communications, pg 926
Penrose Productions, pg 972
Peterson's Video Transfer Services, pg 973
PM Productions, pg 977
PSI Inc, pg 987
QRS Software Services, pg 988
RJ Video Productions, pg 997
SBS Productions, pg 1003
Shokus Video, pg 1009
SonicPool, pg 1016
Tele-Video Production Services (TVPS), pg 1036
Videolady, pg 1057
Wavemaker Media Design, pg 1062
WMS Media Inc, pg 1069

COLORADO

Alpine Media, pg 782
Ceavco Audio/Visual Co, pg 822
The Cinema Lab, pg 827
CSI Films, pg 840
Daylight Productions & Rentals, pg 844
Spectrum Audio Visual Services, pg 1020

CONNECTICUT

Broadcast Video Productions LLC, pg 813
Concord Communications, pg 835
Digital Video Productions, pg 848
EagleVision Inc, pg 855
Guymark Studios LLC, pg 883
MCC Films, pg 935
Rockwell Communications Inc, pg 998

DISTRICT OF COLUMBIA

Interface Media Group, pg 900
O'Keefe Communications Inc, pg 961

FLORIDA

Access Media Group, pg 773
Communications Concepts Inc (CCI), pg 833
Gulf Coast Audio Visual Producers Inc, pg 883
Home Shopping Network (HSN), pg 890
Media Concepts Inc, pg 936
Sunrise Studios, pg 1028
Tallahassee Audio Visual, pg 1031
Video Techniques Inc, pg 1056

GEORGIA

Beachwood Productions, pg 804
Memory Lane Productions, pg 938
Staging Directions Inc, pg 1023
USMotivation, pg 1051
Visioneering International Inc, pg 1058

ILLINOIS

Analog Free Media, pg 786
Audio Visual Services Corp, pg 796
Beatty TeleVisual Productions, pg 804
CCore Media Inc, pg 821
Major Media Inc, pg 929
Major Media Productions Inc, pg 929
PSAV® Presentation Services (Hotel Services Division), pg 987
20/20 Communications Inc, pg 1047
WEEK TV, pg 1063

AUDIO/VISUAL

Transfers—Slide to Video (continued)

INDIANA

OMNI Productions, pg 962

IOWA

The Production House, pg 984

KENTUCKY

Audio Visual Techniques Inc, pg 796
Barney Miller's Inc, pg 943

LOUISIANA

Louisiana State University Health Sciences Center - Shreveport, pg 925
Moxie Media, pg 948
Vidox Motion Imagery, pg 1057

MAINE

Headlight Audio Visual Inc, pg 887

MARYLAND

Pro Cuts Editing Services, pg 982
Satellite Media Production, pg 1003
Spectrum Productions, pg 1021
Video Labs, pg 1055

MASSACHUSETTS

Camera Co Inc/Broadcast Divison, pg 818
Capron Lighting & Sound Co Inc, pg 819
CommCreative, pg 832
Inter-Media Electronics, pg 899
TR Productions, pg 1043

MICHIGAN

K&R's Recording Studios Inc, pg 908
MessageMakers, pg 939
The Program Source International, pg 985
RingSide Creative, pg 997
The Transfer Zone®, pg 1043

MINNESOTA

Badiyan Inc, pg 801
Media Loft Inc, pg 937
Rum Jungle Media, pg 1000

MISSISSIPPI

Jasper Ewing & Sons Inc, pg 864

MISSOURI

Communitronics Corp, pg 833
Show-Me Audio-Visual, pg 1009

NEVADA

JCS Video Productions, pg 904

NEW HAMPSHIRE

Academic & Campus Technology Services, pg 773
Apertura, pg 788

NEW JERSEY

All Jersey Studios, pg 780
CELCO-Constantine Engineering Labs Co, pg 822
Deluxe Media Services, pg 845
Laurel Video Productions, pg 916
VCSvideo, pg 1052
Video Corporation of America (VCA), pg 1055

NEW YORK

aurora productions, pg 797
Colortone Audio Visual, pg 832
Thomas Craven Film Corp, pg 837
Duggal Visual Solutions, pg 853
Duplication Depot Inc, pg 853
Duplication Specialists Inc, pg 853
Gurrilla Video Solutions, pg 883
Long Island Video Enterprises Live Inc, pg 924
Jack Morton Worldwide, pg 946
MRG Productions Inc, pg 948
Neptune Photo Inc, pg 954
Shelly Palmer Production, pg 968
TBA Global Events, pg 1032
Teatown Communications Group, pg 1033
TeleTime Productions, pg 1036
Tobin Productions Inc, pg 1041
Visual Technologies Corp, pg 1060
Zelman Studios Ltd, pg 1073

NORTH CAROLINA

A&V Company, pg 772
Camcor Inc, pg 818
Duke Media Services, pg 853
Image Associates Inc, pg 894

NORTH DAKOTA

Media Productions, pg 937

OHIO

Advent Media Inc, pg 778
Aztec Video Productions, pg 801
Curtis Inc, pg 841
Take 1 Media Services, pg 1031
Ungar Video & Film, pg 1048
VGI Productions, pg 1053
Vista Color Imaging Inc, pg 1059

OKLAHOMA

Garman Productions LLC, pg 875

OREGON

A KTVA Production LLC, pg 771
Rex, pg 995

PENNSYLVANIA

John E Allen Inc, pg 781
Audio Visions Inc, pg 795
Audio Visual Communications Inc, pg 795
Bernie's Photo Center, pg 805
Center City Film & Video Inc, pg 822
FMP Media Solutions Inc, pg 870
Innovision Media Group, pg 899
Panta Rhei Media Inc, pg 968
Pemcor LLC, pg 971
Production Masters Inc (PMI), pg 984
The Videohouse Inc, pg 1057
Visual Sound Inc, pg 1059
WPHL-TV, pg 1070

TENNESSEE

Memphis Communications Corp, pg 938
Stage Post, pg 1022
WKPT-TV, pg 1068

TEXAS

Digi-matics, pg 847
Dub King, pg 853
Julye Newlin Productions Inc, pg 956
Replicopy Digital Media Center, pg 995
Romar Learning, pg 999
South Coast Film & Video, pg 1019
Stage Directions, pg 1022
Texas Heart Institute Visual Communication Services, pg 1037

VERMONT

University of Vermont, Instructional Television Dept, pg 1050

VIRGINIA

Advance Concepts Inc, pg 777

WASHINGTON

Inland Audio Visual Co, pg 898
Pro Image, pg 983
Victory Studios, pg 1054

WISCONSIN

Audio Visual of Milwaukee Inc, pg 795
AVS Group, pg 800
University of Wisconsin-Oshkosh Radio-TV-Film Dept, pg 1050
USAV Group Inc, pg 1050
Video Wisconsin Inc, pg 1056
Wisconsin Public Television, pg 1068

PUERTO RICO

Stage Crew Audiovisual Inc, pg 1022

BRITISH COLUMBIA

Commercial Electronics Ltd, pg 832
Triad Communications Ltd, pg 1044
24 Frames Film & Video, pg 1047

ONTARIO

Purefire Communications Inc, pg 987
Video Excellence Productions, pg 1055

Transparency & Slide Equipment & Supply, *see* Slide & Transparency Equipment & Supply

Transparency Duplication, *see* Duplication—Transparencies

Transparency Enlargement, *see* Enlargement—Transparencies

Transparency Printing, *see* Volume Printing—Overhead Transparencies

Volume Printing—Filmstrips

CALIFORNIA

Coloredge, pg 832
QRS Software Services, pg 988

COLORADO

The Cinema Lab, pg 827

GEORGIA

Staging Directions Inc, pg 1023

ILLINOIS

Filmworkers, pg 868
Gamma Imaging, pg 875

MICHIGAN

K&R's Recording Studios Inc, pg 908

NEW YORK

Duggal Visual Solutions, pg 853
FSL Media Inc, pg 873
Zelman Studios Ltd, pg 1073

OHIO

Aztec Video Productions, pg 801

PENNSYLVANIA

Audio Visual Communications Inc, pg 795
Berry & Homer, pg 805

TENNESSEE

Stage Post, pg 1022

TEXAS

Digi-matics, pg 847

VIRGINIA

Blair Inc, pg 809

WISCONSIN

Audio Visual of Milwaukee Inc, pg 795

Volume Printing—Overhead Transparencies

ARIZONA

Professional Marketing Services Inc, pg 985

CALIFORNIA

Action Photo Service Inc, pg 775
Lynch Communications, pg 926
QRS Software Services, pg 988

GEORGIA

Staging Directions Inc, pg 1023

ILLINOIS

Gamma Imaging, pg 875

KENTUCKY

NIMCO Inc, pg 957

Volume Printing—Slides

Workshops, *see* Production Workshops

COMPUTER SYSTEMS

Animation System Distributors

CALIFORNIA

Audio Images Corp, pg 794
California Tape Products Inc, pg 817
Computer Modules Inc, pg 834
Diaquest, pg 846
MediaPOINTE, pg 938
Promax Systems, pg 986
Videobotics, pg 1056
VMI Inc, pg 1060

COLORADO

Aspen Systems Inc, pg 792
Dot Hill Systems Corp, pg 851
G W Hannaway & Associates, pg 884

CONNECTICUT

HB Communications Inc, pg 886

FLORIDA

Access Media Group, pg 773
Digital Video Systems Inc, pg 848
Hi-Tech Enterprises Inc, pg 888

ILLINOIS

Lyn Norstad & Associates Inc, pg 926

IOWA

ECS Inc, pg 856

MARYLAND

Kipp Visual Systems Inc, pg 911

MASSACHUSETTS

Avid Technology Inc, pg 799
Psych Soft Inc, pg 987
Rule Broadcast Systems, pg 1000
WSI, pg 1070

MICHIGAN

ASC Systems, pg 791
Ascom Communications Contractors, pg 791
Digi Sign Design LLC, pg 847
On Stage Visuals, pg 963
TeL Systems, pg 1035

MISSOURI

Conference Technologies Inc, pg 835
Modern Communications Inc, pg 944

NEW JERSEY

York Telecom, pg 1072

NEW YORK

Custom Media Environments, pg 841

OHIO

AutoDesSys Inc, pg 797
Electronic Vision Inc (EV), pg 859

PENNSYLVANIA

AccuWeather Inc, pg 774
Advanced AV, pg 777
The Lerro Corp, pg 919

TEXAS

Biway Media, pg 808
Epic Software Group Inc, pg 862
Videotex Systems Inc, pg 1057

VIRGINIA

The Whitlock Group, pg 1065

WISCONSIN

Audio Visual of Milwaukee Inc, pg 795
Full Compass Systems, pg 874
Safe Harbor Computers, pg 1001

BRITISH COLUMBIA

Credo Interactive Inc, pg 839

MANITOBA

Advance Pro, pg 777

ONTARIO

Edcom Multimedia Products, pg 856
Gesturetek, pg 877

Animation System Manufacturers

CALIFORNIA

Diaquest, pg 846
Gilderfluke & Co Inc, pg 878
Grande Vitesse Systems Inc (GVS), pg 881
Linker Systems Inc, pg 922

COLORADO

Aspen Systems Inc, pg 792

FLORIDA

Midtown Video Inc, pg 942

MASSACHUSETTS

Avid Technology Inc, pg 799
Psych Soft Inc, pg 987
WSI, pg 1070

NEW JERSEY

CELCO-Constantine Engineering Labs Co, pg 822

OHIO

AutoDesSys Inc, pg 797

PENNSYLVANIA

AccuWeather Inc, pg 774

TEXAS

Biway Media, pg 808

VERMONT

Polhemus, pg 978

WISCONSIN

Safe Harbor Computers, pg 1001

BRITISH COLUMBIA

Credo Interactive Inc, pg 839
Richmond Sound Design Ltd, pg 996
Triad Communications Ltd, pg 1044

ONTARIO

Edcom Multimedia Products, pg 856
Gesturetek, pg 877

Animation System Rentals

ARIZONA

Merestone, pg 938

CALIFORNIA

Artichoke Productions, pg 791
Muse Presentation Technologies, pg 950

FLORIDA

Access Media Group, pg 773

MARYLAND

Kramer Communications Video Production, pg 913

MASSACHUSETTS

Preston Productions Inc, pg 981

MICHIGAN

Digi Sign Design LLC, pg 847
K&R All Media Productions Inc, pg 908
On Stage Visuals, pg 963

NEW MEXICO

Production Outfitters, pg 984

NEW YORK

HB-Content, pg 886

NORTH CAROLINA

Take One Productions Ltd, pg 1031

PENNSYLVANIA

The Videohouse Inc, pg 1057

TEXAS

Stage Directions, pg 1022

ONTARIO

RB Productions, pg 992

Animation System Repairs

FLORIDA

Hi-Tech Enterprises Inc, pg 888

IOWA

ECS Inc, pg 856

TEXAS

Biway Media, pg 808

WISCONSIN

Full Compass Systems, pg 874

Audience Response System Distributors

ARIZONA

Troxell Communications Inc, pg 1045

ARKANSAS

Jay S Stanley & Associates Inc, pg 1023

CALIFORNIA

Ametron Audio/Video, pg 785
California Tape Products Inc, pg 817
FXC Communications, pg 874
Media Fabricators Inc, pg 936
MediaPOINTE, pg 938
One Touch Systems Inc, pg 963

CONNECTICUT

HB Communications Inc, pg 886

FLORIDA

Access Media Group, pg 773
Alcorn McBride Inc, pg 780
AVI-SPL, pg 798

INDIANA

Audience Response Systems Inc, pg 794

KENTUCKY

NOR-COM Inc, pg 958

MICHIGAN

Ascom Communications Contractors, pg 791
TeL Systems, pg 1035

NEW JERSEY

Audio Visual Associates, pg 795

NEW YORK

General Audio-Visual Inc (GAVI), pg 876

PENNSYLVANIA

Advanced AV, pg 777
Meridia Audience Response, pg 939

TENNESSEE

Durrell LLC, pg 854

WISCONSIN

Audio Visual of Milwaukee Inc, pg 795

MANITOBA

Advance Pro, pg 777
Inland Audio Visual Ltd, pg 898

Audience Response System Manufacturers

ARIZONA

eInstruction Corp, pg 858

CALIFORNIA

One Touch Systems Inc, pg 963

FLORIDA

Alcorn McBride Inc, pg 780

MICHIGAN

ENCO Systems Inc, pg 860
Fleetwood Group Inc, pg 870

PENNSYLVANIA

Meridia Audience Response, pg 939

BRITISH COLUMBIA

Commercial Electronics Ltd, pg 832

Audience Response System Rentals

ARIZONA

Merestone, pg 938

CALIFORNIA

Ametron Audio/Video, pg 785
AV Guys, pg 797
Lynch Communications, pg 926
Muse Presentation Technologies, pg 950
Video Resources Inc, pg 1056

COLORADO

Multimedia Audio Visual Inc, pg 950
Spectrum Audio Visual Services, pg 1020

FLORIDA

Access Media Group, pg 773
Pro Stage Inc, pg 983

GEORGIA

Stage Front Presentation Systems, pg 1022

ILLINOIS

The Meetinghouse Companies Inc, pg 938

INDIANA

Audience Response Systems Inc, pg 794

KENTUCKY

Audio Visual Techniques Inc, pg 796

MARYLAND

CSPMedia.com, pg 840

MASSACHUSETTS

Preston Productions Inc, pg 981

MICHIGAN

K&R All Media Productions Inc, pg 908
TeL Systems, pg 1035

NEW JERSEY

Audio Visual Associates, pg 795

NEW YORK

Design Audio Visual Inc, pg 845
Visual Word Systems Inc, pg 1060

NORTH CAROLINA

A&V Company, pg 772

OKLAHOMA

PDC Productions, pg 970

PENNSYLVANIA

Meridia Audience Response, pg 939

TEXAS

Stage Directions, pg 1022

PUERTO RICO

Stage Crew Audiovisual Inc, pg 1022

MANITOBA

Inland Audio Visual Ltd, pg 898

QUEBEC

Audio Visual Dynamics Ltd, pg 795
AVW-TELAV Audio Visual Solutions, a Freeman Company, pg 800

Audience Response System Repairs

CALIFORNIA

Ametron Audio/Video, pg 785

INDIANA

Audience Response Systems Inc, pg 794

IOWA

ECS Inc, pg 856

KENTUCKY

NOR-COM Inc, pg 958

MANITOBA

Inland Audio Visual Ltd, pg 898

CD-ROM Equipment Distributors

ARIZONA

CADint, pg 816
EAR Professional Audio/Video, pg 855
Professional Marketing Services Inc, pg 985
Troxell Communications Inc, pg 1045

ARKANSAS

White Diamond Productions, pg 1065

CALIFORNIA

Ametron Audio/Video, pg 785
Audio Images Corp, pg 794
California Tape Products Inc, pg 817
Computer Modules Inc, pg 834
Ingram Micro, pg 898
Jameco Electronics, pg 903
Kontron America, pg 913
Media Fabricators Inc, pg 936
MediaPOINTE, pg 938
New Cyberian Systems Inc, pg 955
Photodyne Technologies, pg 974
Shimad Corp, pg 1009
Videobotics, pg 1056
VMI Inc, pg 1060

COLORADO

Dot Hill Systems Corp, pg 851
G W Hannaway & Associates, pg 884

CONNECTICUT

HB Communications Inc, pg 886

FLORIDA

Access Media Group, pg 773
CD ROM™ Inc, pg 822
Communications Concepts Inc (CCI), pg 833
Hi-Tech Import Export Corp, pg 888
Hunter Electronics LLC, pg 892
Recording Media & Equipment Inc (RM&E), pg 993
Sight & Sound Productions, pg 1010

GEORGIA

Stage Front Presentation Systems, pg 1022
TAPPI, pg 1032

HAWAII

The Audio Visual Co (AVCO), pg 795

ILLINOIS

Lyn Norstad & Associates Inc, pg 926
Woodside Avenue Music Productions Inc, pg 1069

IOWA

ECS Inc, pg 856

MARYLAND

Kipp Visual Systems Inc, pg 911
NewWave Technologies Inc, pg 957

MASSACHUSETTS

PrimeArray Systems Inc, pg 982
Professional Audio Design Inc, pg 985

MICHIGAN

ASC Systems, pg 791
TeL Systems, pg 1035

MINNESOTA

Aggressive Records Audio Duplication LLC, pg 778
Microboards Technology LLC, pg 941

MISSOURI

Conference Technologies Inc, pg 835
Modern Communications Inc, pg 944
Schiller's Audio-Visual, pg 1004

NEW JERSEY

Starlite Productions, pg 1024
SYMCO Inc, pg 1030
Total Video Products Inc, pg 1042
VCom International Multimedia Corp, pg 1052
York Telecom, pg 1072

NEW YORK

Custom Media Environments, pg 841
Design Audio Visual Inc, pg 845
Duplication Depot Inc, pg 853
Gaylord Brothers, pg 876
Guidance Associates Inc Center for Humanities, pg 883
Image Management Systems Inc, pg 895
Neptune Photo Inc, pg 954
Princeton Architectural Press, pg 982
SmartSource Computer & AV Rentals, pg 1014

OHIO

Electronic Vision Inc (EV), pg 859

PENNSYLVANIA

Advanced AV, pg 777
Brodart Co, pg 813
IMR Limited, pg 897
The Lerro Corp, pg 919

SOUTH CAROLINA

Professional Management Services Inc, pg 985

TENNESSEE

Spring Arbor Distributors, pg 1022

TEXAS

Audio Visual Technologies Group, pg 796
Biway Media, pg 808
Data Display Audio Visual Co LP, pg 843
Replicopy Digital Media Center, pg 995
Tarpley Media Systems, pg 1032
Videotex Systems Inc, pg 1057

UTAH

Performance Audio, pg 973

VIRGINIA

Filmdex Inc, pg 867
Lee Hartman & Sons Inc, pg 918
Schafer World Communications Corp, pg 1004
The Whitlock Group, pg 1065

WISCONSIN

Audio Visual of Milwaukee Inc, pg 795
Full Compass Systems, pg 874
Indus International Inc, pg 897

WYOMING

Bridger Productions Inc, pg 812

BRITISH COLUMBIA

Richmond Sound Design Ltd, pg 996

MANITOBA

Advance Pro, pg 777
Inland Audio Visual Ltd, pg 898

ONTARIO

HD Source, pg 886

COMPUTER SYSTEMS

CD-ROM Equipment Manufacturers

CALIFORNIA

ADS Technologies, pg 777
Colby Systems Corp, pg 831
New Cyberian Systems Inc, pg 955
Pioneer Electronics (USA) Inc, pg 976
QRS Software Services, pg 988
Tasman Group Pacific Rim, pg 1032
Young Minds Inc, pg 1072

COLORADO

ProLine Digital, pg 986

FLORIDA

CD ROM™ Inc, pg 822
Midtown Video Inc, pg 942

ILLINOIS

Woodside Avenue Music Productions Inc, pg 1069

MASSACHUSETTS

PrimeArray Systems Inc, pg 982

MINNESOTA

Telex Communications Inc, pg 1037

NEW YORK

Princeton Architectural Press, pg 982

NORTH CAROLINA

Micro Technology Unlimited, pg 941

TEXAS

Biway Media, pg 808

WISCONSIN

Bardes Products Inc, pg 803

BRITISH COLUMBIA

Triad Communications Ltd, pg 1044

CD-ROM Equipment Repairs

CALIFORNIA

Ametron Audio/Video, pg 785

CONNECTICUT

HB Communications Inc, pg 886

GEORGIA

Stage Front Presentation Systems, pg 1022

IOWA

ECS Inc, pg 856

MASSACHUSETTS

PrimeArray Systems Inc, pg 982

MINNESOTA

Microboards Technology LLC, pg 941

NEW JERSEY

Starlite Productions, pg 1024

OHIO

Tri-State Audio Visual Co, pg 1044

TEXAS

Biway Media, pg 808

WISCONSIN

Full Compass Systems, pg 874

MANITOBA

Inland Audio Visual Ltd, pg 898

Character Generator Distributors

ARIZONA

EAR Professional Audio/Video, pg 855
Media Computing Inc, pg 936
Troxell Communications Inc, pg 1045

ARKANSAS

Jay S Stanley & Associates Inc, pg 1023
White Diamond Productions, pg 1065

CALIFORNIA

Ametron Audio/Video, pg 785
California Tape Products Inc, pg 817
Diaquest, pg 846
FXC Communications, pg 874
Media Control Systems LLC, pg 936
MediaPOINTE, pg 938
SNAP, pg 1014
VMI Inc, pg 1060

COLORADO

Spectrum Audio Visual Services, pg 1020

CONNECTICUT

HB Communications Inc, pg 886

FLORIDA

Access Media Group, pg 773
Communications Concepts Inc (CCI), pg 833
Digital Video Systems Inc, pg 848
Griffiths Broadcast Co Inc, pg 882
Hi-Tech Enterprises Inc, pg 888
Hi-Tech Import Export Corp, pg 888
Midtown Video Inc, pg 942

GEORGIA

Lighting & Production Equipment Inc, pg 920
Stage Front Presentation Systems, pg 1022

HAWAII

The Audio Visual Co (AVCO), pg 795

ILLINOIS

Lyn Norstad & Associates Inc, pg 926

INDIANA

Sensory Technologies LLC, pg 1006

IOWA

ECS Inc, pg 856

KENTUCKY

NOR-COM Inc, pg 958

MARYLAND

Human Circuit, pg 892
Image Logic Corp, pg 895
Kipp Visual Systems Inc, pg 911

MASSACHUSETTS

Duxbury Systems Inc, pg 854
Rule Broadcast Systems, pg 1000

MICHIGAN

Ascom Communications Contractors, pg 791
DAWNco, pg 843
On Stage Visuals, pg 963
TeL Systems, pg 1035

MISSOURI

Conference Technologies Inc, pg 835
Modern Communications Inc, pg 944
Schiller's Audio-Visual, pg 1004

NEBRASKA

Dog & Pony Productions Inc, pg 850

NEW JERSEY

Diversified Systems Inc, pg 849
National Audio-Visual Supply, pg 952
Starlite Productions, pg 1024
SYMCO Inc, pg 1030
Total Video Products Inc, pg 1042
Wilray Audio Visual Corp, pg 1067
Wired 4 Sound Inc, pg 1068
York Telecom, pg 1072

NEW YORK

Audio-Video Corp, pg 795
Custom Media Environments, pg 841
Design Audio Visual Inc, pg 845

NORTH CAROLINA

Crispin Corp, pg 839

OREGON

ClearOne MagicBox Inc, pg 830

PENNSYLVANIA

Advanced AV, pg 777
The Lerro Corp, pg 919

TENNESSEE

Lowrance Sound Co Inc, pg 925
Zion Music Group, pg 1074

TEXAS

Media Management LLC, pg 937
Videotex Systems Inc, pg 1057

VIRGINIA

Quince Imaging Inc, pg 989
Schafer World Communications Corp, pg 1004
The Whitlock Group, pg 1065

WASHINGTON

Linguist's Software Inc, pg 922

WISCONSIN

Audio Visual of Milwaukee Inc, pg 795
Camera Corner Connecting Point, pg 818
Full Compass Systems, pg 874

ALBERTA

Infosat Communications Inc, pg 898
Matrix Video Communications Corp (MVCC), pg 934

BRITISH COLUMBIA

Commercial Electronics Ltd, pg 832
Credo Interactive Inc, pg 839
ProVision Video Sales & Rentals Inc, pg 986

MANITOBA

Advance Pro, pg 777
Inland Audio Visual Ltd, pg 898

ONTARIO

Harris Canada Systems, pg 885
HD Source, pg 886

QUEBEC

Teledac Inc, pg 1036

SASKATCHEWAN

Display Systems International, pg 849

Character Generator Manufacturers

CALIFORNIA

AJA Video Systems Inc, pg 779
Enright Co, pg 861

CONNECTICUT

The Video Messenger Co, pg 1055

GEORGIA

Outsource Engineering & Manufacturing Inc dba Texscan MSI, pg 966
Visix™ Inc, pg 1059

KANSAS

Keywest Technology Inc, pg 910

LOUISIANA

Outland Technology Inc, pg 966

MASSACHUSETTS

Duxbury Systems Inc, pg 854

NEW JERSEY

CELCO-Constantine Engineering Labs Co, pg 822

NEW MEXICO

Burst Electronics Inc, pg 815

NEW YORK

ChyronHego Corp, pg 826
MultiDyne Video & Fiber Optics Systems, pg 950

NORTH CAROLINA

Micro Technology Unlimited, pg 941

OREGON

ClearOne MagicBox Inc, pg 830

PENNSYLVANIA

Scala Inc, pg 1003

TENNESSEE

Adtec Digital Inc, pg 777

WASHINGTON

Linguist's Software Inc, pg 922

BRITISH COLUMBIA

Credo Interactive Inc, pg 839
Triad Communications Ltd, pg 1044

ONTARIO

Harris Canada Systems, pg 885

QUEBEC

Teledac Inc, pg 1036

SASKATCHEWAN

Display Systems International, pg 849

Character Generator Rentals

ARIZONA

Merestone, pg 938
Video West Inc, pg 1056

CALIFORNIA

Artichoke Productions, pg 791
Express Media Inc, pg 864
Golden Gate Studios, pg 880
VER-Video Equipment Rentals, pg 1053
Video Resources Inc, pg 1056

CONNECTICUT

Videofilm Systems Inc, pg 1057

FLORIDA

Access Media Group, pg 773

GEORGIA

Stage Front Presentation Systems, pg 1022

ILLINOIS

Show Department Inc, pg 1009

KANSAS

KAKE-TV, pg 907

KENTUCKY

Audio Visual Techniques Inc, pg 796

MARYLAND

CPR MultiMedia Solutions, pg 837

MASSACHUSETTS

Preston Productions Inc, pg 981

MICHIGAN

K&R All Media Productions Inc, pg 908
On Stage Visuals, pg 963

MISSOURI

Show-Me Audio-Visual, pg 1009

NEBRASKA

Dog & Pony Productions Inc, pg 850

NEW JERSEY

Wired 4 Sound Inc, pg 1068

NEW MEXICO

Production Outfitters, pg 984

NEW YORK

Design Audio Visual Inc, pg 845
HB-Content, pg 886

OKLAHOMA

PDC Productions, pg 970

PENNSYLVANIA

The Videohouse Inc, pg 1057

TEXAS

Stage Directions, pg 1022

VIRGINIA

Quince Imaging Inc, pg 989

MANITOBA

Inland Audio Visual Ltd, pg 898

QUEBEC

Group PVP, pg 882

Character Generator Repairs

CALIFORNIA

Ametron Audio/Video, pg 785
VMI Inc, pg 1060

FLORIDA

Hi-Tech Enterprises Inc, pg 888

GEORGIA

Stage Front Presentation Systems, pg 1022

IOWA

ECS Inc, pg 856

KENTUCKY

NOR-COM Inc, pg 958

WISCONSIN

Camera Corner Connecting Point, pg 818
Full Compass Systems, pg 874

ALBERTA

Infosat Communications Inc, pg 898

MANITOBA

Inland Audio Visual Ltd, pg 898

Computer Interfacing Device Distributors

ARIZONA

Arizona Cine Equipment, pg 789
CADint, pg 816
Media Computing Inc, pg 936
Troxell Communications Inc, pg 1045
Ultimate Presentation Systems Inc, pg 1047

ARKANSAS

Jay S Stanley & Associates Inc, pg 1023

CALIFORNIA

Advanced Systems Group LLC, pg 778
Ametron Audio/Video, pg 785
Audio/Video Supply Inc, pg 795
AV Conferencing, pg 797
California Tape Products Inc, pg 817
Educational Technology Services (ETS), pg 857
Electrosonic Inc, pg 859
Elo TouchSystems, pg 859
FXC Communications, pg 874
Impact Group, pg 897
Ingram Micro, pg 898
Jaguar Distribution Corp, pg 903
JD Audio Visual Inc, pg 904
Kontron America, pg 913
Lloyd F McKinney Associates Inc, pg 935
MediaPOINTE, pg 938
NSM Surveillance, pg 960
Orevox USA Corp, pg 965
Photodyne Technologies, pg 974
PMP Marketing Inc, pg 977
Promax Systems, pg 986
Skjonberg Controls Inc, pg 1012
Tri-Ed, pg 1044
Videobotics, pg 1056
VMI Inc, pg 1060

COLORADO

Daylight Productions & Rentals, pg 844
Dot Hill Systems Corp, pg 851

CONNECTICUT

Everett Hall Associates Inc, pg 863
HB Communications Inc, pg 886

FLORIDA

Access Media Group, pg 773
General Projection Systems Inc, pg 877
Hi-Tech Enterprises Inc, pg 888
Hunter Electronics LLC, pg 892
Industrial Strength Inc, pg 897
ITEC Entertainment Corp, pg 903
Midtown Video Inc, pg 942
Pro Stage Inc, pg 983

GEORGIA

PolyVision Corporation, pg 978
Stage Front Presentation Systems, pg 1022

HAWAII

The Audio Visual Co (AVCO), pg 795

ILLINOIS

RC Communications, pg 992
Sound Vision Inc, pg 1018
Woodside Avenue Music Productions Inc, pg 1069

INDIANA

Sensory Technologies LLC, pg 1006

IOWA

ECS Inc, pg 856

KENTUCKY

NOR-COM Inc, pg 958

MARYLAND

Image Logic Corp, pg 895
Kipp Visual Systems Inc, pg 911
OmegaBrandess Distribution, pg 962

MASSACHUSETTS

Data Translation Inc, pg 843
Graphx Inc, pg 881
Professional Audio Design Inc, pg 985
3M Touch Systems, pg 1039

MICHIGAN

ASC Systems, pg 791
Ascom Communications Contractors, pg 791
City Events Group, pg 828
Digi Sign Design LLC, pg 847
On Stage Visuals, pg 963

MISSOURI

Communitronics Corp, pg 833
Conference Technologies Inc, pg 835
Modern Communications Inc, pg 944
Schiller's Audio-Visual, pg 1004

NEBRASKA

Dog & Pony Productions Inc, pg 850

NEW JERSEY

A-V Services Inc, pg 771
Audio Visual Associates, pg 795
Earl Girls Inc, pg 855
Starlite Productions, pg 1024
SYMCO Inc, pg 1030
Total Video Products Inc, pg 1042
Video Corporation of America (VCA), pg 1055
York Telecom, pg 1072

NEW YORK

American Video Inc, pg 785
Communications Specialties Inc, pg 833
Custom Media Environments, pg 841
Design Audio Visual Inc, pg 845

COMPUTER SYSTEMS

Computer Interfacing Device Distributors (continued)

NEW YORK (continued)

General Audio-Visual Inc (GAVI), pg 876
KVL Audio Visual Services Inc, pg 914
L-3 GCS, pg 915
Long Island Video Enterprises Live Inc, pg 924
SmartSource Computer & AV Rentals, pg 1014
Visual Technologies Corp, pg 1060
Visual Word Systems Inc, pg 1060

NORTH CAROLINA

Crispin Corp, pg 839

OHIO

Copp Integrated Systems, pg 836
Electronic Vision Inc (EV), pg 859
ITA Audio Visual Solutions, pg 902
iVideo Technologies, pg 903

PENNSYLVANIA

Advanced AV, pg 777
Garcia Marketing Inc, pg 875
The Lerro Corp, pg 919
Visual Sound Inc, pg 1059

TENNESSEE

Lowrance Sound Co Inc, pg 925
Technical Support Systems LLC, pg 1034
Zion Music Group, pg 1074

TEXAS

AVES Audio Visual Systems Inc, pg 798
Biway Media, pg 808
Heffernan Audio Visual, pg 887
Industrial Audio/Video Inc, pg 897
J&S Audio Visual Inc, pg 904
Media Management LLC, pg 937
Quality Audio Visual Service Inc, pg 988
Schoolhouse Audio Visual, pg 1004
Stage Directions, pg 1022
Tarpley Media Systems, pg 1032
Videotex Systems Inc, pg 1057

UTAH

NVerzion, pg 960
Performance Audio, pg 973
RIA Corp, pg 996

VIRGINIA

Avitecture Inc, pg 799
Cybernetics, pg 841
Filmdex Inc, pg 867
Hoppmann Audio Visual, pg 891
Quince Imaging Inc, pg 989
Schafer World Communications Corp, pg 1004
The Whitlock Group, pg 1065

WISCONSIN

Audio Visual of Milwaukee Inc, pg 795
Camera Corner Connecting Point, pg 818
DNASTAR Inc, pg 849
Full Compass Systems, pg 874

ALBERTA

McBain Audio Visual Ltd, pg 935
Sharp's Audio-Visual Ltd, pg 1008

MANITOBA

Advance Pro, pg 777
Inland Audio Visual Ltd, pg 898

ONTARIO

Gesturetek, pg 877
HD Source, pg 886
Technovision® Interactive Inc, pg 1035

QUEBEC

AVW-TELAV Audio Visual Solutions, a Freeman Company, pg 800
Concept Audio-Visual, pg 834

Computer Interfacing Device Manufacturers

ARIZONA

Covid Inc, pg 837
eInstruction Corp, pg 858

CALIFORNIA

Advanced Systems Group LLC, pg 778
AITech International, pg 779
ALTINEX Inc, pg 783
Antex Electronics Corp, pg 787
Diaquest, pg 846
Extron Electronics, pg 864
FutureVideo, pg 874
Gefen, pg 876
Hewlett-Packard Co, pg 888
Kontron America, pg 913
MRV Communications Inc, pg 948
NSM Surveillance, pg 960
Opticomm-EMCORE, pg 964
Photodyne Technologies, pg 974
Point Source Audio, pg 977
RetinaVision Productions, pg 995
RGB Spectrum, pg 996
Roland Corp US, pg 998
RPM-PSI, pg 1000
Skjonberg Controls Inc, pg 1012
Videobotics, pg 1056
VITEC Multimedia, pg 1060
Western Digital Corp, pg 1064
Zhone Technologies Inc, pg 1073

COLORADO

Arrakis Systems, pg 790

FLORIDA

Tel-Test, pg 1035

GEORGIA

PolyVision Corporation, pg 978

ILLINOIS

B&B Electronics Manufacturing Co, pg 802
NEC Display Solutions of America, pg 954
SoundTech, pg 1018
Woodside Avenue Music Productions Inc, pg 1069

INDIANA

General Devices Co Inc, pg 876

MARYLAND

Image Logic Corp, pg 895

MASSACHUSETTS

Data Translation Inc, pg 843
Graphx Inc, pg 881
Monotype Inc, pg 945
New England Keyboard Inc, pg 955
3M Touch Systems, pg 1039

MICHIGAN

ASC Systems, pg 791
Leightronix Inc, pg 918

MINNESOTA

Digital Audio Labs, pg 847

MISSOURI

Link Electronics Inc, pg 922

NEVADA

Adrienne Electronics Corp (AEC), pg 777

NEW JERSEY

CELCO-Constantine Engineering Labs Co, pg 822
FSR Inc, pg 873

NEW YORK

American Video Inc, pg 785
ATTO Technology Inc, pg 793
Communications Specialties Inc, pg 833
Judson Rosebush Co Inc, pg 999

NORTH CAROLINA

Eaton Corp, pg 856
Micro Technology Unlimited, pg 941

OHIO

Network Technologies Inc, pg 955

OKLAHOMA

BCD Associates Inc, pg 803
Versatech Industries Inc, pg 1053

PENNSYLVANIA

DecisionOne, pg 844
Scala Inc, pg 1003

RHODE ISLAND

M-Audio, pg 927

TEXAS

National Instruments Corp, pg 953

UTAH

Ivie Technologies Inc, pg 903
NVerzion, pg 960

VIRGINIA

Opterna AM, pg 964
Quince Imaging Inc, pg 989

WISCONSIN

Comprompter Inc, pg 834
maney-logic, pg 929

BRITISH COLUMBIA

Triad Communications Ltd, pg 1044

ONTARIO

Gesturetek, pg 877
McCurdy Radio Ltd, pg 935
Technovision® Interactive Inc, pg 1035

QUEBEC

Matrox Video Products Group, pg 934

Computer Interfacing Device Rentals

ALABAMA

Audio-Video Resources Inc, pg 795

ARIZONA

Merestone, pg 938
Ultimate Presentation Systems Inc, pg 1047

CALIFORNIA

AV Guys, pg 797
Express Media Inc, pg 864
JD Audio Visual Inc, pg 904
Muse Presentation Technologies, pg 950
RetinaVision Productions, pg 995
Synthesizer Systems Technologies (SST), pg 1030
VER-Video Equipment Rentals, pg 1053
VMI Inc, pg 1060

CONNECTICUT

Everett Hall Associates Inc, pg 863

FLORIDA

Universal Studios Florida® Production Group, pg 1049

GEORGIA

Stage Front Presentation Systems, pg 1022

KENTUCKY

Audio Visual Techniques Inc, pg 796

MARYLAND

CPR MultiMedia Solutions, pg 837

MASSACHUSETTS

Preston Productions Inc, pg 981

MICHIGAN

Digi Sign Design LLC, pg 847
K&R All Media Productions Inc, pg 908
On Stage Visuals, pg 963

MISSOURI

Show-Me Audio-Visual, pg 1009

NEBRASKA

Dog & Pony Productions Inc, pg 850

Computer Interfacing Device Repairs

Control System & Equipment Distributors

Control System & Equipment Manufacturers

COMPUTER SYSTEMS

Control System & Equipment Manufacturers (continued)

CALIFORNIA

ALTINEX Inc, pg 783
Diaquest, pg 846
Extron Electronics, pg 864
FM Systems Inc, pg 870
FutureVideo, pg 874
JLCooper Electronics, pg 905
Kontron America, pg 913
Media Control Systems LLC, pg 936
Photodyne Technologies, pg 974
Point Source Audio, pg 977
POP TV, pg 978
PsiTech Inc, pg 987
QSC Audio Products LLC, pg 988
RetinaVision Productions, pg 995
RGB Spectrum, pg 996
Skjonberg Controls Inc, pg 1012
Unique Business Systems, pg 1048

FLORIDA

Alcorn McBride Inc, pg 780
Harris Corp, pg 885

GEORGIA

Register Data Systems, pg 994
Simtrol Inc, pg 1011
Visix™ Inc, pg 1059

ILLINOIS

B&B Electronics Manufacturing Co, pg 802
Dukane Corp, Audio Visual Products Division, pg 853

INDIANA

General Devices Co Inc, pg 876

KENTUCKY

Innovative Electronic Designs LLC, pg 898

LOUISIANA

Outland Technology Inc, pg 966

MARYLAND

Image Logic Corp, pg 895

MASSACHUSETTS

AVFX Inc, pg 798

MICHIGAN

ASC Systems, pg 791

NEVADA

Adrienne Electronics Corp (AEC), pg 777

NEW JERSEY

Crestron Electronics Inc, pg 839
FSR Inc, pg 873
Starlite Productions, pg 1024

NEW YORK

ATTO Technology Inc, pg 793
Norman N Axelrod Associates, pg 800
beyerdynamic Inc, pg 806
ChyronHego Corp, pg 826
DSan Corp, pg 852
Monroe Electronics Inc, pg 945

NORTH CAROLINA

Eaton Corp, pg 856
Micro Technology Unlimited, pg 941

OKLAHOMA

BCD Associates Inc, pg 803

PENNSYLVANIA

Rossman Audio LLC, pg 1000
Scala Inc, pg 1003
Sensaphone, pg 1006

RHODE ISLAND

APC by Schneider Electric, pg 788

TEXAS

Contemporary Research, pg 835
Graftek Imaging Inc, pg 881
National Instruments Corp, pg 953

UTAH

NVerzion, pg 960
SirsiDynix, pg 1012

VIRGINIA

Schafer World Communications Corp, pg 1004

WISCONSIN

maney-logic, pg 929

ALBERTA

Johnson Systems Inc (JSI), pg 906

BRITISH COLUMBIA

Commercial Electronics Ltd, pg 832
Richmond Sound Design Ltd, pg 996

ONTARIO

Broadview Software Inc, pg 813
McCurdy Radio Ltd, pg 935
Soundmaster Group, pg 1018
Technovision® Interactive Inc, pg 1035

Control System & Equipment Rentals

ARIZONA

Merestone, pg 938

CALIFORNIA

Ametron Audio/Video, pg 785
Express Media Inc, pg 864
JD Audio Visual Inc, pg 904
Lynch Communications, pg 926
Muse Presentation Technologies, pg 950
RetinaVision Productions, pg 995
Skjonberg Controls Inc, pg 1012
VER-Video Equipment Rentals, pg 1053
Video Resources Inc, pg 1056

CONNECTICUT

A/V Davey, pg 797
Everett Hall Associates Inc, pg 863

FLORIDA

Image Technical Services, pg 895
Pro Stage Inc, pg 983
Universal Studios Florida® Production Group, pg 1049

GEORGIA

Stage Front Presentation Systems, pg 1022

IOWA

ECS Inc, pg 856

KENTUCKY

Audio Visual Techniques Inc, pg 796

MARYLAND

CPR MultiMedia Solutions, pg 837

MASSACHUSETTS

AVFX Inc, pg 798
Preston Productions Inc, pg 981

MICHIGAN

K&R All Media Productions Inc, pg 908

MISSOURI

Schiller's Audio-Visual, pg 1004
Show-Me Audio-Visual, pg 1009

NEBRASKA

Dog & Pony Productions Inc, pg 850

NEW JERSEY

Earl Girls Inc, pg 855
PLS Staging, pg 977
Starlite Productions, pg 1024
Wired 4 Sound Inc, pg 1068

NEW YORK

Visual Word Systems Inc, pg 1060

NORTH CAROLINA

A&V Company, pg 772

OHIO

ITA Audio Visual Solutions, pg 902

SOUTH CAROLINA

Encore Video Productions, pg 861

TENNESSEE

Technical Support Systems LLC, pg 1034

UTAH

Performance Audio, pg 973

VIRGINIA

American AV, pg 783
Quince Imaging Inc, pg 989
Schafer World Communications Corp, pg 1004

WISCONSIN

Full Compass Systems, pg 874

MANITOBA

Inland Audio Visual Ltd, pg 898

ONTARIO

HD Source, pg 886
MVI Multivision Inc, pg 951
Westbury National Show Systems Ltd, pg 1064

Control System & Equipment Repairs

CALIFORNIA

Ametron Audio/Video, pg 785
Electrosonic Inc, pg 859
HM Electronics Inc (HME), pg 889
Skjonberg Controls Inc, pg 1012

CONNECTICUT

A/V Davey, pg 797
HB Communications Inc, pg 886

IOWA

ECS Inc, pg 856

KENTUCKY

NOR-COM Inc, pg 958

NEW JERSEY

Earl Girls Inc, pg 855
Starlite Productions, pg 1024

OHIO

ITA Audio Visual Solutions, pg 902
Tri-State Audio Visual Co, pg 1044

TENNESSEE

Technical Support Systems LLC, pg 1034

TEXAS

Data Display Audio Visual Co LP, pg 843
Tarpley Media Systems, pg 1032

VIRGINIA

Intellidyne LLC, pg 899
Schafer World Communications Corp, pg 1004

WISCONSIN

Camera Corner Connecting Point, pg 818
Full Compass Systems, pg 874

ALBERTA

Infosat Communications Inc, pg 898

MANITOBA

Inland Audio Visual Ltd, pg 898

ONTARIO

HD Source, pg 886
MVI Multivision Inc, pg 951
Westbury National Show Systems Ltd, pg 1064

Digital Multimedia Distributors

ARIZONA

CADint, pg 816
EAR Professional Audio/Video, pg 855
Professional Marketing Services Inc, pg 985
Troxell Communications Inc, pg 1045

CALIFORNIA

Adolph Gasser Inc, pg 776
ADS Technologies, pg 777
Ametron Audio/Video, pg 785
Audio Images Corp, pg 794
California Tape Products Inc, pg 817
Computer Modules Inc, pg 834
Diaquest, pg 846
FXC Communications, pg 874
HM Electronics Inc (HME), pg 889
Ingram Micro, pg 898
Kontron America, pg 913
Media Fabricators Inc, pg 936
Mitsubishi Electric Visual Solutions America Inc (MEVSA), pg 944
Mobilized Tech Systems, pg 944
Optibase Inc, pg 964
Photodyne Technologies, pg 974
POP TV, pg 978
Promax Systems, pg 986
QRS Software Services, pg 988
Total Media Group, pg 1042
Videobotics, pg 1056
VMI Inc, pg 1060

COLORADO

Dot Hill Systems Corp, pg 851
G W Hannaway & Associates, pg 884
National Teaching Aids Inc, pg 953

CONNECTICUT

HB Communications Inc, pg 886
The Video Messenger Co, pg 1055

FLORIDA

Access Media Group, pg 773
Accusoft, pg 774
CD ROM™ Inc, pg 822
Communications Concepts Inc (CCI), pg 833
Digital Video Systems Inc, pg 848
Harris Corp, pg 885
Hunter Electronics LLC, pg 892
Midtown Video Inc, pg 942
Pro Stage Inc, pg 983
Sight & Sound Productions, pg 1010
Thayer Birding Software, pg 1038

GEORGIA

Ligos Corporation, pg 921
PolyVision Corporation, pg 978
Stage Front Presentation Systems, pg 1022

HAWAII

The Audio Visual Co (AVCO), pg 795

ILLINOIS

Lyn Norstad & Associates Inc, pg 926
Tape Resources, pg 1031

INDIANA

Sensory Technologies LLC, pg 1006

IOWA

ECS Inc, pg 856

KENTUCKY

NOR-COM Inc, pg 958

LOUISIANA

Intermedia Technologies, pg 900

MARYLAND

dbF a Media Company, pg 844
Human Circuit, pg 892

MASSACHUSETTS

Avid Technology Inc, pg 799
Psych Soft Inc, pg 987
Rule Broadcast Systems, pg 1000
SeaChange International Inc, pg 1005

MICHIGAN

ASC Systems, pg 791
Ascom Communications Contractors, pg 791
Digi Sign Design LLC, pg 847
On Stage Visuals, pg 963

MINNESOTA

Beyers Sound & Essay Audio, pg 806
Microboards Technology LLC, pg 941

MISSOURI

Schiller's Audio-Visual, pg 1004

NEBRASKA

Dog & Pony Productions Inc, pg 850

NEW JERSEY

Diversified Systems Inc, pg 849
Lucerne Media, pg 925
MIB Mediaworks, pg 941
National Audio-Visual Supply, pg 952
Starlite Productions, pg 1024
Total Media, pg 1042
Total Video Products Inc, pg 1042
York Telecom, pg 1072

NEW YORK

Audio-Video Corp, pg 795
Custom Media Environments, pg 841
Image Management Systems Inc, pg 895
Sanako Inc, pg 1002
Videoguys, pg 1057

NORTH CAROLINA

Alien Skin Software LLC, pg 780

PENNSYLVANIA

AccuWeather Inc, pg 774
Advanced AV, pg 777
Bernie's Photo Center, pg 805
Brodart Co, pg 813
The Lerro Corp, pg 919
Vistacom Inc, pg 1059
Visual Sound Inc, pg 1059
Wespen Audio Visual Co, pg 1063

RHODE ISLAND

M-Audio, pg 927

SOUTH CAROLINA

Professional Management Services Inc, pg 985

TENNESSEE

Lowrance Sound Co Inc, pg 925
Technical Support Systems LLC, pg 1034

TEXAS

Audio Visual Technologies Group, pg 796
Biway Media, pg 808
Epic Software Group Inc, pg 862
Media Management LLC, pg 937
Videotex Systems Inc, pg 1057

UTAH

HEC Reading Horizons, pg 887
Performance Audio, pg 973

VIRGINIA

Avitecture Inc, pg 799
Design & Production Inc, pg 845
Filmdex Inc, pg 867
Rocktown Media, pg 998
Schafer World Communications Corp, pg 1004
The Whitlock Group, pg 1065

WISCONSIN

Audio Visual of Milwaukee Inc, pg 795
Full Compass Systems, pg 874
Safe Harbor Computers, pg 1001

ALBERTA

Matrix Video Communications Corp (MVCC), pg 934

BRITISH COLUMBIA

Kodak Canada Inc, pg 912

MANITOBA

Advance Pro, pg 777
Inland Audio Visual Ltd, pg 898
Tek Gear, pg 1035

ONTARIO

Cinema Stage Inc, pg 827
Gesturetek, pg 877
HD Source, pg 886
Premier A/V Sales Ltd, pg 980

QUEBEC

Teledac Inc, pg 1036

SASKATCHEWAN

Display Systems International, pg 849

Digital Multimedia Manufacturers

ARIZONA

Applied Integration Corp, pg 789

CALIFORNIA

ADS Technologies, pg 777
AITech International, pg 779
The Banquet Sound Studios, pg 802
Diaquest, pg 846
Gefen, pg 876
Mitsubishi Electric Visual Solutions America Inc (MEVSA), pg 944
Optibase Inc, pg 964
Photodyne Technologies, pg 974
Point Source Audio, pg 977
POP TV, pg 978
QRS Software Services, pg 988
RGB Spectrum, pg 996
VITEC Multimedia, pg 1060

COLORADO

National Teaching Aids Inc, pg 953

CONNECTICUT

The Video Messenger Co, pg 1055

FLORIDA

CD ROM™ Inc, pg 822
Thayer Birding Software, pg 1038

GEORGIA

Ligos Corporation, pg 921
PolyVision Corporation, pg 978

ILLINOIS

Symbolic Sound Corp, pg 1030
Wells-Gardner Electronics Corp, pg 1063

MARYLAND

dbF a Media Company, pg 844
Media Cybernetics Inc, pg 936

MASSACHUSETTS

Avid Technology Inc, pg 799
Psych Soft Inc, pg 987
SeaChange International Inc, pg 1005
Small Planet Communications Inc, pg 1013

MICHIGAN

ENCO Systems Inc, pg 860

NEW JERSEY

CELCO-Constantine Engineering Labs Co, pg 822
Map Resources, pg 930

NEW YORK

RCS Enterprises, pg 992

NORTH CAROLINA

Alien Skin Software LLC, pg 780
Computer Dynamics, pg 834
SAS Institute Inc, pg 1002

OHIO

Electronic Vision Inc (EV), pg 859
Tosoh USA Inc, pg 1042

OREGON

NeoSoft Corp, pg 954

PENNSYLVANIA

AccuWeather Inc, pg 774
Prime Image Inc, pg 982
Scala Inc, pg 1003

RHODE ISLAND

M-Audio, pg 927

COMPUTER SYSTEMS

Digital Multimedia Manufacturers (continued)

UTAH

HEC Reading Horizons, pg 887

WASHINGTON

Victory Studios, pg 1054

BRITISH COLUMBIA

Kodak Canada Inc, pg 912
Richmond Sound Design Ltd, pg 996
Triad Communications Ltd, pg 1044

ONTARIO

Gesturetek, pg 877
PixeLINK, pg 976

QUEBEC

Teledac Inc, pg 1036

SASKATCHEWAN

Display Systems International, pg 849

Digital Multimedia Rentals

ARIZONA

Merestone, pg 938

CALIFORNIA

Adolph Gasser Inc, pg 776
Advanced Media LLC, pg 778
Big Time Picture Company Inc, pg 807
Express Media Inc, pg 864
Golden Gate Studios, pg 880
Muse Presentation Technologies, pg 950
PSAV® Presentation Services, pg 986
RetinaVision Productions, pg 995

FLORIDA

Access Media Group, pg 773
Universal Studios Florida® Production Group, pg 1049

GEORGIA

Stage Front Presentation Systems, pg 1022

ILLINOIS

Show Department Inc, pg 1009

MARYLAND

dbF a Media Company, pg 844
Kramer Communications Video Production, pg 913

MASSACHUSETTS

Preston Productions Inc, pg 981

MICHIGAN

Digi Sign Design LLC, pg 847
K&R All Media Productions Inc, pg 908
On Stage Visuals, pg 963

MISSOURI

Show-Me Audio-Visual, pg 1009

NEBRASKA

Dog & Pony Productions Inc, pg 850

NEW JERSEY

Audio Visual Dynamics®, pg 795
MIB Mediaworks, pg 941
Milgrom Productions, pg 943
Starlite Productions, pg 1024

NEW MEXICO

Production Outfitters, pg 984

NEW YORK

Interactive International Inc, pg 899

NORTH CAROLINA

A&V Company, pg 772

OHIO

Bartha, pg 803

OKLAHOMA

PDC Productions, pg 970

OREGON

Hollywood Lights Inc, pg 890

PENNSYLVANIA

Argentine Productions Inc, pg 789
FMP Media Solutions Inc, pg 870

SOUTH CAROLINA

Encore Video Productions, pg 861

TENNESSEE

Love Shack Recording Studios, pg 925
Technical Support Systems LLC, pg 1034

TEXAS

Stage Directions, pg 1022

VIRGINIA

Advance Concepts Inc, pg 777
Quince Imaging Inc, pg 989

MANITOBA

Inland Audio Visual Ltd, pg 898

ONTARIO

Premier A/V Sales Ltd, pg 980

QUEBEC

Group PVP, pg 882

SASKATCHEWAN

plan9films, pg 976

Digital Multimedia Repairs

CALIFORNIA

Advanced Media LLC, pg 778
Ametron Audio/Video, pg 785
HM Electronics Inc (HME), pg 889
Technical Services, pg 1034

CONNECTICUT

HB Communications Inc, pg 886

GEORGIA

Stage Front Presentation Systems, pg 1022

IOWA

ECS Inc, pg 856

KENTUCKY

NOR-COM Inc, pg 958

MINNESOTA

Microboards Technology LLC, pg 941

NEW YORK

Custom Media Environments, pg 841

TENNESSEE

Technical Support Systems LLC, pg 1034

VIRGINIA

Schafer World Communications Corp, pg 1004

WISCONSIN

Full Compass Systems, pg 874

MANITOBA

Inland Audio Visual Ltd, pg 898

Digitizing Input System Distributors

ARIZONA

Arizona Cine Equipment, pg 789
EAR Professional Audio/Video, pg 855

ARKANSAS

Jay S Stanley & Associates Inc, pg 1023

CALIFORNIA

ADS Technologies, pg 777
Ametron Audio/Video, pg 785
Audio Images Corp, pg 794
Audio/Video Supply Inc, pg 795
California Tape Products Inc, pg 817
Diaquest, pg 846
Ingram Micro, pg 898
Jaguar Distribution Corp, pg 903
Media Control Systems LLC, pg 936
Media Fabricators Inc, pg 936
MediaPOINTE, pg 938
Photodyne Technologies, pg 974
POP TV, pg 978
Promax Systems, pg 986
Total Media Group, pg 1042

COLORADO

Macrosystem US Inc, pg 927

CONNECTICUT

HB Communications Inc, pg 886

FLORIDA

Access Media Group, pg 773
Accusoft, pg 774
General Projection Systems Inc, pg 877
Midtown Video Inc, pg 942
Pro Stage Inc, pg 983
Sight & Sound Productions, pg 1010

GEORGIA

PolyVision Corporation, pg 978
Stage Front Presentation Systems, pg 1022

HAWAII

The Audio Visual Co (AVCO), pg 795

ILLINOIS

Lyn Norstad & Associates Inc, pg 926
Manning Productions, pg 930
Woodside Avenue Music Productions Inc, pg 1069

IOWA

ECS Inc, pg 856

KENTUCKY

NOR-COM Inc, pg 958

MARYLAND

Kipp Visual Systems Inc, pg 911
Wiltronix, pg 1067

MASSACHUSETTS

Avid Technology Inc, pg 799
Data Translation Inc, pg 843
Monotype Inc, pg 945
Psych Soft Inc, pg 987
Rule Broadcast Systems, pg 1000
SeaChange International Inc, pg 1005
3M Touch Systems, pg 1039

MICHIGAN

ASC Systems, pg 791

MISSOURI

Communitronics Corp, pg 833
Modern Communications Inc, pg 944
Schiller's Audio-Visual, pg 1004

NEBRASKA

Dog & Pony Productions Inc, pg 850

NEW JERSEY

Advanced Imaging Concepts Inc, pg 777
MIB Mediaworks, pg 941
Starlite Productions, pg 1024
SYMCO Inc, pg 1030
Video Corporation of America (VCA), pg 1055

NEW YORK

Audio-Video Corp, pg 795
Custom Media Environments, pg 841
Neptune Photo Inc, pg 954

OHIO

iVideo Technologies, pg 903

PENNSYLVANIA

Advanced AV, pg 777
IMR Limited, pg 897
Visual Sound Inc, pg 1059

TEXAS

Audio Visual Technologies Group, pg 796
Biway Media, pg 808
DNP Photo Imaging America Corp, pg 849
Stage Directions, pg 1022
Videotex Systems Inc, pg 1057

UTAH

NVerzion, pg 960

VIRGINIA

Filmdex Inc, pg 867
Schafer World Communications Corp, pg 1004
The Whitlock Group, pg 1065

WASHINGTON

Linguist's Software Inc, pg 922
Wacom Technology Corp, pg 1061

WISCONSIN

Audio Visual of Milwaukee Inc, pg 795
Camera Corner Connecting Point, pg 818
DNASTAR Inc, pg 849
Full Compass Systems, pg 874
Indus International Inc, pg 897

MANITOBA

Advance Pro, pg 777
Inland Audio Visual Ltd, pg 898

QUEBEC

Concept Audio-Visual, pg 834

Digitizing Input System Manufacturers

ARIZONA

eInstruction Corp, pg 858
Mutoh America Inc, pg 951

CALIFORNIA

ADS Technologies, pg 777
AJA Video Systems Inc, pg 779
Antex Electronics Corp, pg 787
Aztek Inc, pg 801
Diaquest, pg 846
Opticomm-EMCORE, pg 964
Photodyne Technologies, pg 974
POP TV, pg 978

COLORADO

Macrosystem US Inc, pg 927
Vexcel Corp, pg 1053

CONNECTICUT

Video Automation Systems Inc, pg 1054

GEORGIA

PolyVision Corporation, pg 978

ILLINOIS

EPIX Inc, pg 862
Woodside Avenue Music Productions Inc, pg 1069

MASSACHUSETTS

Avid Technology Inc, pg 799
Data Translation Inc, pg 843
Monotype Inc, pg 945
Psych Soft Inc, pg 987
SeaChange International Inc, pg 1005
3M Touch Systems, pg 1039

MICHIGAN

ASC Systems, pg 791

NEW JERSEY

CELCO-Constantine Engineering Labs Co, pg 822

NEW YORK

Laird Digital Cinema, pg 915
Judson Rosebush Co Inc, pg 999

PENNSYLVANIA

Interactive Products, pg 899

TENNESSEE

Adtec Digital Inc, pg 777

TEXAS

Biway Media, pg 808
DNP Photo Imaging America Corp, pg 849

UTAH

NVerzion, pg 960

VERMONT

Polhemus, pg 978

WASHINGTON

Linguist's Software Inc, pg 922

WISCONSIN

DNASTAR Inc, pg 849

BRITISH COLUMBIA

Kodak Canada Inc, pg 912
Triad Communications Ltd, pg 1044

ONTARIO

PixeLINK, pg 976

QUEBEC

Matrox Video Products Group, pg 934
Miranda Technologies, pg 944

Digitizing Input System Rentals

ARIZONA

Arizona Cine Equipment, pg 789
Merestone, pg 938

CALIFORNIA

Ametron Audio/Video, pg 785
Artichoke Productions, pg 791
Aztek Inc, pg 801
Big Time Picture Company Inc, pg 807
Deck Hand Inc, pg 844
Express Media Inc, pg 864
Golden Gate Studios, pg 880
Lynch Communications, pg 926
Media Fabricators Inc, pg 936
PSAV® Presentation Services, pg 986
RetinaVision Productions, pg 995
Total Media Group, pg 1042

COLORADO

Open Media Foundation, pg 964

CONNECTICUT

A/V Davey, pg 797
Broadcast Video Productions LLC, pg 813

FLORIDA

Image Technical Services, pg 895
Pro Stage Inc, pg 983
Universal Studios Florida® Production Group, pg 1049

GEORGIA

Stage Front Presentation Systems, pg 1022
Staging Directions Inc, pg 1023

ILLINOIS

Show Department Inc, pg 1009

IOWA

ECS Inc, pg 856

LOUISIANA

Pace Systems, pg 966

MASSACHUSETTS

massAV, pg 933
Preston Productions Inc, pg 981

MICHIGAN

K&R All Media Productions Inc, pg 908

MISSOURI

Show-Me Audio-Visual, pg 1009

MONTANA

High Plains Films, pg 889

NEBRASKA

Dog & Pony Productions Inc, pg 850

NEW JERSEY

MIB Mediaworks, pg 941
PLS Staging, pg 977

NEW MEXICO

Production Outfitters, pg 984

NEW YORK

HB-Content, pg 886
Manhattan Center Studios Inc, pg 930

NORTH CAROLINA

Take One Productions Ltd, pg 1031

OREGON

Northwest Film Center, pg 959

PENNSYLVANIA

FMP Media Solutions Inc, pg 870
Rahlic Publishing Co, pg 990

TEXAS

J&S Audio Visual Inc, pg 904

VIRGINIA

Quince Imaging Inc, pg 989

WISCONSIN

Full Compass Systems, pg 874

WYOMING

Bridger Productions Inc, pg 812

BRITISH COLUMBIA

Image Media Farm, pg 895
Video In Studios/Video Out Distribution, pg 1055

MANITOBA

Inland Audio Visual Ltd, pg 898

QUEBEC

Concept Audio-Visual, pg 834
Group PVP, pg 882

SASKATCHEWAN

plan9films, pg 976

Digitizing Input System Repairs

CALIFORNIA

Ametron Audio/Video, pg 785
Technical Services, pg 1034

COLORADO

Macrosystem US Inc, pg 927

CONNECTICUT

HB Communications Inc, pg 886

GEORGIA

Stage Front Presentation Systems, pg 1022

IOWA

ECS Inc, pg 856

KENTUCKY

NOR-COM Inc, pg 958

MASSACHUSETTS

BitFlow Inc, pg 808
Monotype Inc, pg 945

TEXAS

Biway Media, pg 808

WISCONSIN

Camera Corner Connecting Point, pg 818
Full Compass Systems, pg 874

COMPUTER SYSTEMS

Digitizing Input System Repairs (continued)

MANITOBA

Inland Audio Visual Ltd, pg 898

DVD Equipment Distributors

ARIZONA

EAR Professional Audio/Video, pg 855
Troxell Communications Inc, pg 1045

ARKANSAS

White Diamond Productions, pg 1065

CALIFORNIA

Adolph Gasser Inc, pg 776
Be Media, pg 804
Computer Modules Inc, pg 834
Educational Technology Services (ETS), pg 857
JD Audio Visual Inc, pg 904
MSE Media Solutions, pg 949
New Cyberian Systems Inc, pg 955
POP TV, pg 978
Promax Systems, pg 986
Sound Service Co, pg 1017
Stanislaus Audio Video Inc, pg 1023

COLORADO

Macrosystem US Inc, pg 927

CONNECTICUT

Everett Hall Associates Inc, pg 863

FLORIDA

Access Media Group, pg 773
Communications Concepts Inc (CCI), pg 833
Digital Video Systems Inc, pg 848
Hunter Electronics LLC, pg 892
Recording Media & Equipment Inc (RM&E), pg 993
Sight & Sound Productions, pg 1010

GEORGIA

Outsource Engineering & Manufacturing Inc dba Texscan MSI, pg 966
Stage Front Presentation Systems, pg 1022

ILLINOIS

Dukane Corp, Audio Visual Products Division, pg 853
Quintessence Audio Ltd, pg 989
Sound Vision Inc, pg 1018

INDIANA

Sensory Technologies LLC, pg 1006

KENTUCKY

NOR-COM Inc, pg 958

LOUISIANA

Intermedia Technologies, pg 900

MARYLAND

Human Circuit, pg 892

MASSACHUSETTS

Rule Broadcast Systems, pg 1000

MICHIGAN

Ascom Communications Contractors, pg 791
Digi Sign Design LLC, pg 847
On Stage Visuals, pg 963

MINNESOTA

Aggressive Records Audio Duplication LLC, pg 778
Alpha Video & Audio Inc, pg 782

MISSISSIPPI

Bowie Audio Visual Enterprises Inc, pg 811

NEBRASKA

Dog & Pony Productions Inc, pg 850
Strong Cinema Products, pg 1026

NEW HAMPSHIRE

APS Lighting-Sound-AV, pg 789

NEW JERSEY

Audio Visual Associates, pg 795
Earl Girls Inc, pg 855
MIB Mediaworks, pg 941
Starlite Productions, pg 1024
Total Video Products Inc, pg 1042
Wilray Audio Visual Corp, pg 1067
Wired 4 Sound Inc, pg 1068

NEW YORK

Colortone Audio Visual, pg 832
Custom Media Environments, pg 841
Design Audio Visual Inc, pg 845
Duplication Depot Inc, pg 853
Image Management Systems Inc, pg 895
KVL Audio Visual Services Inc, pg 914

OHIO

Jimmy Rea Electronics Inc, pg 992
Tri-State Audio Visual Co, pg 1044

PENNSYLVANIA

Advanced AV, pg 777
Audio Visions Inc, pg 795
Brodart Co, pg 813
J E Foss Co, pg 871
Innovision Media Group, pg 899
Vistacom Inc, pg 1059
Wespen Audio Visual Co, pg 1063

TENNESSEE

Lowrance Sound Co Inc, pg 925
Technical Support Systems LLC, pg 1034
Zion Music Group, pg 1074

TEXAS

AVES Audio Visual Systems Inc, pg 798
Biway Media, pg 808
Data Display Audio Visual Co LP, pg 843
Data Projections Inc, pg 843
Digital Display Solutions Inc, pg 847
DNP Photo Imaging America Corp, pg 849
Replicopy Digital Media Center, pg 995

VIRGINIA

Avitecture Inc, pg 799
Design & Production Inc, pg 845
Intellidyne LLC, pg 899
Lee Hartman & Sons Inc, pg 918

WISCONSIN

Audio Visual of Milwaukee Inc, pg 795
Camera Corner Connecting Point, pg 818
Safe Harbor Computers, pg 1001

WYOMING

Bridger Productions Inc, pg 812

ALBERTA

Infosat Communications Inc, pg 898
Matrix Video Communications Corp (MVCC), pg 934

MANITOBA

Advance Pro, pg 777
Inland Audio Visual Ltd, pg 898

ONTARIO

Westbury National Show Systems Ltd, pg 1064

DVD Equipment Manufacturers

CALIFORNIA

Grande Vitesse Systems Inc (GVS), pg 881
New Cyberian Systems Inc, pg 955

COLORADO

Macrosystem US Inc, pg 927

FLORIDA

CD ROM™ Inc, pg 822

GEORGIA

Outsource Engineering & Manufacturing Inc dba Texscan MSI, pg 966

MINNESOTA

Telex Communications Inc, pg 1037

OKLAHOMA

BCD Associates Inc, pg 803

TENNESSEE

Adtec Digital Inc, pg 777

TEXAS

Adams Evidence Grade Technology Inc, pg 775
Biway Media, pg 808
DNP Photo Imaging America Corp, pg 849

BRITISH COLUMBIA

Triad Communications Ltd, pg 1044

DVD Equipment Rentals

ARIZONA

Merestone, pg 938
Video West Inc, pg 1056

ARKANSAS

White Diamond Productions, pg 1065

CALIFORNIA

Absolute Rentals, pg 772
Adolph Gasser Inc, pg 776
Advanced Media LLC, pg 778
AGF Media Services, pg 778
Artichoke Productions, pg 791
Audio Rents, pg 794
AV Guys, pg 797
Express Media Inc, pg 864
JD Audio Visual Inc, pg 904
Maximus Media Inc, pg 934
Muse Presentation Technologies, pg 950
PSAV® Presentation Services, pg 986
RetinaVision Productions, pg 995
Sound Service Co, pg 1017
Stanislaus Audio Video Inc, pg 1023
Synthesizer Systems Technologies (SST), pg 1030
Total Media Group, pg 1042
VER-Video Equipment Rentals, pg 1053
Video Resources Inc, pg 1056
VMI Inc, pg 1060
Voice & Video Rentals, pg 1060

COLORADO

Open Media Foundation, pg 964

CONNECTICUT

A/V Davey, pg 797
Everett Hall Associates Inc, pg 863

FLORIDA

Accord Productions, pg 773
Sight & Sound Productions, pg 1010

GEORGIA

Stage Front Presentation Systems, pg 1022

ILLINOIS

RC Communications, pg 992
Show Department Inc, pg 1009

IOWA

Central Lighting & Equipment Inc (CLE), pg 823

KENTUCKY

Audio Visual Techniques Inc, pg 796

MARYLAND

CPR MultiMedia Solutions, pg 837
dbF a Media Company, pg 844
Event Tech, pg 863

MASSACHUSETTS

Preston Productions Inc, pg 981

MICHIGAN

Digi Sign Design LLC, pg 847
K&R All Media Productions Inc, pg 908
On Stage Visuals, pg 963

MINNESOTA

Aggressive Records Audio Duplication LLC, pg 778
Alpha Video & Audio Inc, pg 782

MISSISSIPPI

Bowie Audio Visual Enterprises Inc, pg 811

MISSOURI

Show-Me Audio-Visual, pg 1009

NEBRASKA

Dog & Pony Productions Inc, pg 850

NEW HAMPSHIRE

APS Lighting-Sound-AV, pg 789

NEW JERSEY

Audio Visual Associates, pg 795
Audio Visual Dynamics®, pg 795
Earl Girls Inc, pg 855
MIB Mediaworks, pg 941
Starlite Productions, pg 1024
Wired 4 Sound Inc, pg 1068

NEW MEXICO

Production Outfitters, pg 984

NEW YORK

Colortone Audio Visual, pg 832
Design Audio Visual Inc, pg 845
HB-Content, pg 886
KVL Audio Visual Services Inc, pg 914

NORTH CAROLINA

A&V Company, pg 772
Take One Productions Ltd, pg 1031

OKLAHOMA

PDC Productions, pg 970

PENNSYLVANIA

Audio Visual Communications Inc, pg 795
FMP Media Solutions Inc, pg 870
Innovision Media Group, pg 899

SOUTH CAROLINA

Encore Video Productions, pg 861

TENNESSEE

Love Shack Recording Studios, pg 925
Technical Support Systems LLC, pg 1034

TEXAS

Digital Display Solutions Inc, pg 847
Stage Directions, pg 1022

VERMONT

Parlato Productions, pg 969

VIRGINIA

Advance Concepts Inc, pg 777
Lee Hartman & Sons Inc, pg 918
Quince Imaging Inc, pg 989

PUERTO RICO

Stage Crew Audiovisual Inc, pg 1022

BRITISH COLUMBIA

Image Media Farm, pg 895

MANITOBA

Inland Audio Visual Ltd, pg 898

ONTARIO

RB Productions, pg 992
Westbury National Show Systems Ltd, pg 1064

QUEBEC

Group PVP, pg 882

SASKATCHEWAN

plan9films, pg 976

DVD Equipment Repairs

CALIFORNIA

Advanced Media LLC, pg 778
Sound Service Co, pg 1017

COLORADO

Macrosystem US Inc, pg 927

CONNECTICUT

A/V Davey, pg 797

FLORIDA

Hi-Tech Enterprises Inc, pg 888

GEORGIA

Stage Front Presentation Systems, pg 1022

ILLINOIS

Midwest Digital Corp, pg 942

KENTUCKY

NOR-COM Inc, pg 958

NEW JERSEY

Earl Girls Inc, pg 855
Starlite Productions, pg 1024

OHIO

Tri-State Audio Visual Co, pg 1044

TENNESSEE

Technical Support Systems LLC, pg 1034

TEXAS

Biway Media, pg 808
Data Display Audio Visual Co LP, pg 843

WISCONSIN

Camera Corner Connecting Point, pg 818

ALBERTA

Infosat Communications Inc, pg 898

MANITOBA

Inland Audio Visual Ltd, pg 898

ONTARIO

Westbury National Show Systems Ltd, pg 1064

Frame Grabber Distributors

ARIZONA

EAR Professional Audio/Video, pg 855
Troxell Communications Inc, pg 1045

CALIFORNIA

ADS Technologies, pg 777
Audio Images Corp, pg 794
California Tape Products Inc, pg 817
Computer Modules Inc, pg 834
Diaquest, pg 846
Ingram Micro, pg 898
Kappa optronics Inc, pg 908
Kontron America, pg 913
MediaPOINTE, pg 938
NSM Surveillance, pg 960
PsiTech Inc, pg 987
VMI Inc, pg 1060

COLORADO

Aspen Systems Inc, pg 792

CONNECTICUT

HB Communications Inc, pg 886
Video Automation Systems Inc, pg 1054

FLORIDA

Access Media Group, pg 773
Accusoft, pg 774
Digital Video Systems Inc, pg 848
Hi-Tech Enterprises Inc, pg 888
Midtown Video Inc, pg 942
Pro Stage Inc, pg 983

GEORGIA

Stage Front Presentation Systems, pg 1022

HAWAII

The Audio Visual Co (AVCO), pg 795

ILLINOIS

Lyn Norstad & Associates Inc, pg 926

IOWA

ECS Inc, pg 856

MARYLAND

Kipp Visual Systems Inc, pg 911
Wiltronix, pg 1067

MICHIGAN

TeL Systems, pg 1035

MISSOURI

Modern Communications Inc, pg 944
Schiller's Audio-Visual, pg 1004

NEW JERSEY

Advanced Imaging Concepts Inc, pg 777
SYMCO Inc, pg 1030

NEW YORK

Audio-Video Corp, pg 795
Design Audio Visual Inc, pg 845
Image Management Systems Inc, pg 895
Langie Audio Visual Systems, pg 915
Neptune Photo Inc, pg 954
Vision Identics Systems Inc, pg 1058

PENNSYLVANIA

Advanced AV, pg 777
Innovision Media Group, pg 899

TEXAS

Graftek Imaging Inc, pg 881
Industrial Audio/Video Inc, pg 897
Videotex Systems Inc, pg 1057

VIRGINIA

Filmdex Inc, pg 867
The Whitlock Group, pg 1065

WISCONSIN

Audio Visual of Milwaukee Inc, pg 795
Camera Corner Connecting Point, pg 818
Full Compass Systems, pg 874

ALBERTA

Infosat Communications Inc, pg 898

BRITISH COLUMBIA

Commercial Electronics Ltd, pg 832

MANITOBA

Advance Pro, pg 777

ONTARIO

HD Source, pg 886

Frame Grabber Manufacturers

ARIZONA

Applied Integration Corp, pg 789

CALIFORNIA

ADS Technologies, pg 777
Linkabit, pg 922
NSM Surveillance, pg 960
PsiTech Inc, pg 987

COLORADO

Colorado Video Inc, pg 832

ILLINOIS

EPIX Inc, pg 862

COMPUTER SYSTEMS

Frame Grabber Manufacturers (continued)

KANSAS

GlobalStreams™ Corp, pg 879

MARYLAND

Media Cybernetics Inc, pg 936

MASSACHUSETTS

BitFlow Inc, pg 808
Foresight Imaging, pg 871

MINNESOTA

CyberOptics, pg 841

MISSOURI

Ken-A-Vision Manufacturing Co Inc, pg 909

TEXAS

National Instruments Corp, pg 953

VIRGINIA

Quince Imaging Inc, pg 989

BRITISH COLUMBIA

Image Media Farm, pg 895

SASKATCHEWAN

plan9films, pg 976

Frame Grabber Rentals

ARIZONA

Merestone, pg 938

CALIFORNIA

Aaron & Le Duc, pg 772
AV Guys, pg 797
Express Media Inc, pg 864
RetinaVision Productions, pg 995

GEORGIA

Stage Front Presentation Systems, pg 1022

ILLINOIS

Show Department Inc, pg 1009

MARYLAND

CPR MultiMedia Solutions, pg 837

MASSACHUSETTS

Preston Productions Inc, pg 981

MICHIGAN

K&R All Media Productions Inc, pg 908

NEW MEXICO

Production Outfitters, pg 984

NEW YORK

Design Audio Visual Inc, pg 845

NORTH DAKOTA

Media Productions, pg 937

PENNSYLVANIA

Innovision Media Group, pg 899

TEXAS

Stage Directions, pg 1022

Frame Grabber Repairs

CONNECTICUT

HB Communications Inc, pg 886

FLORIDA

Hi-Tech Enterprises Inc, pg 888

GEORGIA

Stage Front Presentation Systems, pg 1022

IOWA

ECS Inc, pg 856

MASSACHUSETTS

BitFlow Inc, pg 808

WISCONSIN

Camera Corner Connecting Point, pg 818
Full Compass Systems, pg 874

Graphic Card Distributors

ARIZONA

CADint, pg 816
EAR Professional Audio/Video, pg 855
Troxell Communications Inc, pg 1045

CALIFORNIA

Audio Images Corp, pg 794
Audio/Video Supply Inc, pg 795
Be Media, pg 804
California Tape Products Inc, pg 817
Diaquest, pg 846
Ingram Micro, pg 898
Jameco Electronics, pg 903
Kontron America, pg 913
Media Fabricators Inc, pg 936
MediaPOINTE, pg 938
Promax Systems, pg 986
Total Media Group, pg 1042
VMI Inc, pg 1060

COLORADO

Aspen Systems Inc, pg 792
Dot Hill Systems Corp, pg 851
Stanco Sales LLC, pg 1023

CONNECTICUT

HB Communications Inc, pg 886

FLORIDA

Access Media Group, pg 773
Digital Video Systems Inc, pg 848
General Projection Systems Inc, pg 877
Hi-Tech Enterprises Inc, pg 888
Hi-Tech Import Export Corp, pg 888

GEORGIA

Outsource Engineering & Manufacturing Inc dba Texscan MSI, pg 966
Stage Front Presentation Systems, pg 1022

ILLINOIS

Lyn Norstad & Associates Inc, pg 926

IOWA

ECS Inc, pg 856

MARYLAND

Human Circuit, pg 892

MASSACHUSETTS

Psych Soft Inc, pg 987
Seaport Graphics, pg 1005

MICHIGAN

TeL Systems, pg 1035

MISSOURI

Communitronics Corp, pg 833
Schiller's Audio-Visual, pg 1004

NEW JERSEY

Argraph Corp, pg 789
SYMCO Inc, pg 1030
Video Corporation of America (VCA), pg 1055

NEW YORK

Audio-Video Corp, pg 795

OHIO

Electronic Vision Inc (EV), pg 859
iVideo Technologies, pg 903

PENNSYLVANIA

Advanced AV, pg 777
The Lerro Corp, pg 919
Visual Sound Inc, pg 1059

TENNESSEE

Lowrance Sound Co Inc, pg 925
Spring Arbor Distributors, pg 1022

TEXAS

Biway Media, pg 808
Videotex Systems Inc, pg 1057

VIRGINIA

Filmdex Inc, pg 867
Lee Hartman & Sons Inc, pg 918
The Whitlock Group, pg 1065

WISCONSIN

Audio Visual of Milwaukee Inc, pg 795
Camera Corner Connecting Point, pg 818
Full Compass Systems, pg 874
Safe Harbor Computers, pg 1001

ALBERTA

Infosat Communications Inc, pg 898

BRITISH COLUMBIA

Commercial Electronics Ltd, pg 832

MANITOBA

Advance Pro, pg 777

QUEBEC

Concept Audio-Visual, pg 834

Graphic Card Manufacturers

CALIFORNIA

AJA Video Systems Inc, pg 779
Apple Inc, pg 788
Diaquest, pg 846
Enright Co, pg 861
Hewlett-Packard Co, pg 888
iQstor Networks Inc, pg 902
Linkabit, pg 922

MASSACHUSETTS

Foresight Imaging, pg 871
Seaport Graphics, pg 1005

BRITISH COLUMBIA

Triad Communications Ltd, pg 1044

Graphic System Distributors

ARIZONA

EAR Professional Audio/Video, pg 855
Professional Marketing Services Inc, pg 985

ARKANSAS

White Diamond Productions, pg 1065

CALIFORNIA

Audio Images Corp, pg 794
Be Media, pg 804
California Tape Products Inc, pg 817
Diaquest, pg 846
Media Fabricators Inc, pg 936
MediaPOINTE, pg 938
Promax Systems, pg 986
Total Media Group, pg 1042
VMI Inc, pg 1060

COLORADO

Aspen Systems Inc, pg 792

CONNECTICUT

HB Communications Inc, pg 886

FLORIDA

Access Media Group, pg 773
Digital Video Systems Inc, pg 848
Hi-Tech Enterprises Inc, pg 888
ITEC Entertainment Corp, pg 903
Pro Stage Inc, pg 983

GEORGIA

Outsource Engineering & Manufacturing Inc dba Texscan MSI, pg 966
Stage Front Presentation Systems, pg 1022

ILLINOIS

Lyn Norstad & Associates Inc, pg 926

INDIANA

Advanced Designs Corp, pg 777

IOWA

ECS Inc, pg 856

MASSACHUSETTS

Psych Soft Inc, pg 987
WSI, pg 1070

MICHIGAN

Michigan Office Solutions, pg 941

MINNESOTA

Varitronics LLC, pg 1052

MISSOURI

Schiller's Audio-Visual, pg 1004

NEW JERSEY

Argraph Corp, pg 789

NEW YORK

A M Graphics Products, dba Affton Graphics Inc, pg 771
Audio-Video Corp, pg 795

OHIO

AutoDesSys Inc, pg 797

PENNSYLVANIA

AccuWeather Inc, pg 774
Advanced AV, pg 777
The Lerro Corp, pg 919

TENNESSEE

Lowrance Sound Co Inc, pg 925

TEXAS

Biway Media, pg 808
Videotex Systems Inc, pg 1057

VIRGINIA

Rocktown Media, pg 998

WISCONSIN

Audio Visual of Milwaukee Inc, pg 795
Camera Corner Connecting Point, pg 818
Full Compass Systems, pg 874

MANITOBA

Advance Pro, pg 777

Graphic System Manufacturers

CALIFORNIA

Aztek Inc, pg 801
Diaquest, pg 846
Grande Vitesse Systems Inc (GVS), pg 881
Pinnacle Systems Inc, pg 975

COLORADO

Aspen Systems Inc, pg 792
Vexcel Corp, pg 1053

GEORGIA

Outsource Engineering & Manufacturing Inc dba Texscan MSI, pg 966

ILLINOIS

IBM SPSS, pg 893

KANSAS

Keywest Technology Inc, pg 910

MASSACHUSETTS

Psych Soft Inc, pg 987
WSI, pg 1070

NEW JERSEY

CELCO-Constantine Engineering Labs Co, pg 822

NEW YORK

ChyronHego Corp, pg 826

NORTH CAROLINA

Computer Dynamics, pg 834

OHIO

AutoDesSys Inc, pg 797

OREGON

Grass Valley, pg 881

PENNSYLVANIA

AccuWeather Inc, pg 774

TEXAS

Biway Media, pg 808

WISCONSIN

Safe Harbor Computers, pg 1001

BRITISH COLUMBIA

Triad Communications Ltd, pg 1044

Graphic System Rentals

ARIZONA

Merestone, pg 938
Video West Inc, pg 1056

ARKANSAS

White Diamond Productions, pg 1065

CALIFORNIA

Artichoke Productions, pg 791
Bexel Corp, pg 806
Express Media Inc, pg 864
Golden Gate Studios, pg 880
Lynch Communications, pg 926
Media Fabricators Inc, pg 936
Total Media Group, pg 1042

CONNECTICUT

Videofilm Systems Inc, pg 1057

FLORIDA

Accord Productions, pg 773
Pro Stage Inc, pg 983
Universal Studios Florida® Production Group, pg 1049

GEORGIA

Stage Front Presentation Systems, pg 1022

ILLINOIS

Airways Digital Media, pg 779
Show Department Inc, pg 1009

IOWA

ECS Inc, pg 856

KANSAS

KAKE-TV, pg 907

MARYLAND

CPR MultiMedia Solutions, pg 837
Shadowstone R & R™, pg 1008

MASSACHUSETTS

Preston Productions Inc, pg 981

MISSOURI

Show-Me Audio-Visual, pg 1009

NEW MEXICO

Production Outfitters, pg 984

NEW YORK

HB-Content, pg 886
Manhattan Center Studios Inc, pg 930

NORTH CAROLINA

AV Metro Inc, pg 797
Take One Productions Ltd, pg 1031

OHIO

Lyon Video Inc, pg 927

OKLAHOMA

PDC Productions, pg 970

PENNSYLVANIA

FMP Media Solutions Inc, pg 870
The Videohouse Inc, pg 1057

TEXAS

Phillips MediaSource, pg 974

VIRGINIA

Quince Imaging Inc, pg 989

ONTARIO

RB Productions, pg 992
Westbury National Show Systems Ltd, pg 1064

QUEBEC

Group PVP, pg 882

SASKATCHEWAN

plan9films, pg 976

Graphic System Repairs

FLORIDA

Hi-Tech Enterprises Inc, pg 888

GEORGIA

Stage Front Presentation Systems, pg 1022

IOWA

ECS Inc, pg 856

TEXAS

Biway Media, pg 808

WISCONSIN

Camera Corner Connecting Point, pg 818
Full Compass Systems, pg 874

ONTARIO

Westbury National Show Systems Ltd, pg 1064

Graphic Tablet Distributors

ARIZONA

CADint, pg 816
EAR Professional Audio/Video, pg 855
Troxell Communications Inc, pg 1045

ARKANSAS

Jay S Stanley & Associates Inc, pg 1023

CALIFORNIA

Advanced Systems Group LLC, pg 778
Diaquest, pg 846
Ingram Micro, pg 898
Media Fabricators Inc, pg 936
MediaPOINTE, pg 938
Promax Systems, pg 986
VMI Inc, pg 1060

COLORADO

Stanco Sales LLC, pg 1023

CONNECTICUT

HB Communications Inc, pg 886

FLORIDA

Digital Video Systems Inc, pg 848
Hi-Tech Import Export Corp, pg 888

GEORGIA

PolyVision Corporation, pg 978
Stage Front Presentation Systems, pg 1022

ILLINOIS

Lyn Norstad & Associates Inc, pg 926

IOWA

ECS Inc, pg 856

MASSACHUSETTS

Psych Soft Inc, pg 987
Seaport Graphics, pg 1005
3M Touch Systems, pg 1039

MISSOURI

Communitronics Corp, pg 833
Schiller's Audio-Visual, pg 1004

COMPUTER SYSTEMS

Graphic Tablet Distributors (continued)

NEW JERSEY

Argraph Corp, pg 789
Video Corporation of America (VCA), pg 1055

NEW YORK

Audio-Video Corp, pg 795
Design Audio Visual Inc, pg 845

OHIO

iVideo Technologies, pg 903

PENNSYLVANIA

Advanced AV, pg 777
Visual Sound Inc, pg 1059

TENNESSEE

Lowrance Sound Co Inc, pg 925

TEXAS

Videotex Systems Inc, pg 1057

VIRGINIA

Lee Hartman & Sons Inc, pg 918
The Whitlock Group, pg 1065

WISCONSIN

Audio Visual of Milwaukee Inc, pg 795
Camera Corner Connecting Point, pg 818
Safe Harbor Computers, pg 1001

ALBERTA

Infosat Communications Inc, pg 898

MANITOBA

Advance Pro, pg 777

ONTARIO

Westbury National Show Systems Ltd, pg 1064

QUEBEC

Concept Audio-Visual, pg 834

Graphic Tablet Manufacturers

ARIZONA

eInstruction Corp, pg 858

CALIFORNIA

Apple Inc, pg 788
Hewlett-Packard Co, pg 888

GEORGIA

PolyVision Corporation, pg 978

MASSACHUSETTS

3M Touch Systems, pg 1039

PENNSYLVANIA

Interactive Products, pg 899

Image Capture Equipment Distributors

ARIZONA

Troxell Communications Inc, pg 1045

ARKANSAS

Jay S Stanley & Associates Inc, pg 1023
White Diamond Productions, pg 1065

CALIFORNIA

ADS Technologies, pg 777
Audio Images Corp, pg 794
California Tape Products Inc, pg 817
Computer Modules Inc, pg 834
Diaquest, pg 846
Educational Technology Services (ETS), pg 857
Electrosonic Inc, pg 859
Hooper Camera & Imaging, pg 891
Ingram Micro, pg 898
Kappa optronics Inc, pg 908
Media Fabricators Inc, pg 936
MediaPOINTE, pg 938
NSM Surveillance, pg 960
POP TV, pg 978
PsiTech Inc, pg 987
Videobotics, pg 1056
VMI Inc, pg 1060

COLORADO

G W Hannaway & Associates, pg 884

CONNECTICUT

HB Communications Inc, pg 886
Westbrook Technologies Inc, pg 1064

FLORIDA

Access Media Group, pg 773
Digital Video Systems Inc, pg 848
Hi-Tech Enterprises Inc, pg 888

GEORGIA

Outsource Engineering & Manufacturing Inc dba Texscan MSI, pg 966
PolyVision Corporation, pg 978
Stage Front Presentation Systems, pg 1022

ILLINOIS

Lyn Norstad & Associates Inc, pg 926

IOWA

ECS Inc, pg 856

KENTUCKY

NOR-COM Inc, pg 958

MARYLAND

NewWave Technologies Inc, pg 957
Wiltronix, pg 1067

MASSACHUSETTS

Rule Broadcast Systems, pg 1000
SeaChange International Inc, pg 1005
3M Touch Systems, pg 1039

MICHIGAN

ASC Systems, pg 791
Ascom Communications Contractors, pg 791
On Stage Visuals, pg 963
TeL Systems, pg 1035

MISSOURI

Ken-A-Vision Manufacturing Co Inc, pg 909
Schiller's Audio-Visual, pg 1004

NEW JERSEY

Advanced Imaging Concepts Inc, pg 777
Alltec Stores, a Vcom IMC Company, pg 782
Argraph Corp, pg 789
Hasselblad Bron Inc, pg 885
Starlite Productions, pg 1024
SYMCO Inc, pg 1030

NEW YORK

Audio-Video Corp, pg 795
Design Audio Visual Inc, pg 845
Image Management Systems Inc, pg 895
Neptune Photo Inc, pg 954
Vision Identics Systems Inc, pg 1058

OHIO

Electronic Vision Inc (EV), pg 859

PENNSYLVANIA

Advanced AV, pg 777
Bernie's Photo Center, pg 805
IMR Limited, pg 897

TENNESSEE

Lowrance Sound Co Inc, pg 925
Zion Music Group, pg 1074

TEXAS

Biway Media, pg 808
Graftek Imaging Inc, pg 881
Tarpley Media Systems, pg 1032
Videotex Systems Inc, pg 1057

VIRGINIA

Avitecture Inc, pg 799
Filmdex Inc, pg 867
The Whitlock Group, pg 1065

WISCONSIN

Audio Visual of Milwaukee Inc, pg 795
Camera Corner Connecting Point, pg 818
Full Compass Systems, pg 874
Indus International Inc, pg 897
Safe Harbor Computers, pg 1001

ALBERTA

Infosat Communications Inc, pg 898

BRITISH COLUMBIA

Commercial Electronics Ltd, pg 832

MANITOBA

Advance Pro, pg 777
Inland Audio Visual Ltd, pg 898

Image Capture Equipment Manufacturers

ARIZONA

Applied Integration Corp, pg 789

CALIFORNIA

ADS Technologies, pg 777
Aztek Inc, pg 801
Diaquest, pg 846
Grande Vitesse Systems Inc (GVS), pg 881
Hoodman Corp, pg 891
Kappa optronics Inc, pg 908
Kofax Image Products, pg 912
Linkabit, pg 922
NSM Surveillance, pg 960
PsiTech Inc, pg 987

COLORADO

Vexcel Corp, pg 1053

CONNECTICUT

Westbrook Technologies Inc, pg 1064

GEORGIA

PolyVision Corporation, pg 978

ILLINOIS

EPIX Inc, pg 862

MARYLAND

Media Cybernetics Inc, pg 936

MASSACHUSETTS

BitFlow Inc, pg 808
Foresight Imaging, pg 871
MorphoTrust USA, pg 946
SeaChange International Inc, pg 1005

MICHIGAN

ASC Systems, pg 791

MISSOURI

Ken-A-Vision Manufacturing Co Inc, pg 909

NEW JERSEY

CELCO-Constantine Engineering Labs Co, pg 822

NEW YORK

Judson Rosebush Co Inc, pg 999

TEXAS

Biway Media, pg 808
Graftek Imaging Inc, pg 881
National Instruments Corp, pg 953
Ron Scott Inc, pg 1005

BRITISH COLUMBIA

Kodak Canada Inc, pg 912
Triad Communications Ltd, pg 1044

ONTARIO

PixeLINK, pg 976

QUEBEC

Matrox Video Products Group, pg 934
Miranda Technologies, pg 944

Image Capture Equipment Rentals

ARIZONA

Merestone, pg 938

ARKANSAS

White Diamond Productions, pg 1065

CALIFORNIA

Artichoke Productions, pg 791
Express Media Inc, pg 864
Golden Gate Studios, pg 880
Muse Presentation Technologies, pg 950
RetinaVision Productions, pg 995

CONNECTICUT

Videofilm Systems Inc, pg 1057

GEORGIA

Stage Front Presentation Systems, pg 1022

KENTUCKY

Audio Visual Techniques Inc, pg 796

MARYLAND

CPR MultiMedia Solutions, pg 837
Kramer Communications Video Production, pg 913

MASSACHUSETTS

Preston Productions Inc, pg 981

MICHIGAN

K&R All Media Productions Inc, pg 908
On Stage Visuals, pg 963

NEW JERSEY

Starlite Productions, pg 1024

NEW YORK

Design Audio Visual Inc, pg 845
HB-Content, pg 886

NORTH DAKOTA

Media Productions, pg 937

OKLAHOMA

PDC Productions, pg 970

TEXAS

Stage Directions, pg 1022

PUERTO RICO

Stage Crew Audiovisual Inc, pg 1022

MANITOBA

Inland Audio Visual Ltd, pg 898

ONTARIO

RB Productions, pg 992

QUEBEC

Group PVP, pg 882

SASKATCHEWAN

plan9films, pg 976

Image Capture Equipment Repairs

CALIFORNIA

Electrosonic Inc, pg 859

FLORIDA

Hi-Tech Enterprises Inc, pg 888

GEORGIA

Stage Front Presentation Systems, pg 1022

IOWA

ECS Inc, pg 856

KENTUCKY

NOR-COM Inc, pg 958

MASSACHUSETTS

BitFlow Inc, pg 808

TEXAS

Biway Media, pg 808
Tarpley Media Systems, pg 1032

WISCONSIN

Camera Corner Connecting Point, pg 818
Full Compass Systems, pg 874

MANITOBA

Inland Audio Visual Ltd, pg 898

Interactive System Distributors

ARKANSAS

Jay S Stanley & Associates Inc, pg 1023

CALIFORNIA

Audio Images Corp, pg 794
Beta Electronics Inc, pg 806
California Tape Products Inc, pg 817
JD Audio Visual Inc, pg 904
MediaPOINTE, pg 938
NSM Surveillance, pg 960
Promax Systems, pg 986
VMI Inc, pg 1060

FLORIDA

Access Media Group, pg 773
Alcorn McBride Inc, pg 780
Digital Video Systems Inc, pg 848
Hi-Tech Enterprises Inc, pg 888
Technomedia Solutions, pg 1035

GEORGIA

PolyVision Corporation, pg 978
Stage Front Presentation Systems, pg 1022

INDIANA

Sensory Technologies LLC, pg 1006

IOWA

ECS Inc, pg 856

KENTUCKY

Axxis Inc, pg 800
NOR-COM Inc, pg 958

MASSACHUSETTS

Psych Soft Inc, pg 987

MICHIGAN

Ascom Communications Contractors, pg 791
Mastery Technologies Inc, pg 933
TeL Systems, pg 1035

NEW JERSEY

MIB Mediaworks, pg 941
Starlite Productions, pg 1024

NEW YORK

Interactive International Inc, pg 899
Neptune Photo Inc, pg 954
Sanako Inc, pg 1002

OHIO

ITA Audio Visual Solutions, pg 902
Tri-State Audio Visual Co, pg 1044

OREGON

NeoSoft Corp, pg 954

PENNSYLVANIA

Advanced AV, pg 777
Innovision Media Group, pg 899
Meridia Audience Response, pg 939

TEXAS

Epic Software Group Inc, pg 862
Tarpley Media Systems, pg 1032
Videotex Systems Inc, pg 1057

VIRGINIA

Avitecture Inc, pg 799
Design & Production Inc, pg 845
Lee Hartman & Sons Inc, pg 918

WISCONSIN

Audio Visual of Milwaukee Inc, pg 795
Full Compass Systems, pg 874

ALBERTA

SMART Technologies Inc, pg 1013

MANITOBA

Advance Pro, pg 777
Inland Audio Visual Ltd, pg 898
Tek Gear, pg 1035

ONTARIO

Cinema Stage Inc, pg 827
Gesturetek, pg 877
Technovision® Interactive Inc, pg 1035
Westbury National Show Systems Ltd, pg 1064

QUEBEC

Presagis, pg 981

Interactive System Manufacturers

ARIZONA

eInstruction Corp, pg 858

CALIFORNIA

Beta Electronics Inc, pg 806
NSM Surveillance, pg 960
One Touch Systems Inc, pg 963
POP TV, pg 978

CONNECTICUT

Vista Group International Inc, pg 1059

FLORIDA

Alcorn McBride Inc, pg 780
Pangolin Laser Systems Inc, pg 968

GEORGIA

PolyVision Corporation, pg 978

KANSAS

Keywest Technology Inc, pg 910

MASSACHUSETTS

MorphoTrust USA, pg 946
Psych Soft Inc, pg 987

MICHIGAN

ASC Systems, pg 791
Mastery Technologies Inc, pg 933

NEW YORK

Interactive International Inc, pg 899

NORTH CAROLINA

Computer Dynamics, pg 834

OHIO

Electronic Vision Inc (EV), pg 859

OKLAHOMA

BCD Associates Inc, pg 803

OREGON

NeoSoft Corp, pg 954

PENNSYLVANIA

Meridia Audience Response, pg 939

BRITISH COLUMBIA

Commercial Electronics Ltd, pg 832
Richmond Sound Design Ltd, pg 996
Triad Communications Ltd, pg 1044

MANITOBA

Tek Gear, pg 1035

ONTARIO

Gesturetek, pg 877
Technovision® Interactive Inc, pg 1035

QUEBEC

AVW-TELAV Audio Visual Solutions, a Freeman Company, pg 800
Presagis, pg 981

Interactive System Rentals

ARIZONA

Merestone, pg 938

COMPUTER SYSTEMS

Interactive System Rentals (continued)

CALIFORNIA

Express Media Inc, pg 864
JD Audio Visual Inc, pg 904
Lynch Communications, pg 926
Muse Presentation Technologies, pg 950
RetinaVision Productions, pg 995
Total Media Group, pg 1042

GEORGIA

Stage Front Presentation Systems, pg 1022

ILLINOIS

Airways Digital Media, pg 779
Show Department Inc, pg 1009

IOWA

ECS Inc, pg 856

MASSACHUSETTS

Preston Productions Inc, pg 981

MICHIGAN

K&R All Media Productions Inc, pg 908

NEW JERSEY

PLS Staging, pg 977
Starlite Productions, pg 1024

NEW YORK

Interactive International Inc, pg 899

PENNSYLVANIA

FMP Media Solutions Inc, pg 870
Innovision Media Group, pg 899
Meridia Audience Response, pg 939

TEXAS

Stage Directions, pg 1022

VIRGINIA

American AV, pg 783

MANITOBA

Inland Audio Visual Ltd, pg 898
Tek Gear, pg 1035

ONTARIO

Gesturetek, pg 877
RB Productions, pg 992
Westbury National Show Systems Ltd, pg 1064

QUEBEC

AVW-TELAV Audio Visual Solutions, a Freeman Company, pg 800

Interactive System Repairs

FLORIDA

Hi-Tech Enterprises Inc, pg 888

GEORGIA

Stage Front Presentation Systems, pg 1022

IOWA

ECS Inc, pg 856

KENTUCKY

Axxis Inc, pg 800
NOR-COM Inc, pg 958

NEW JERSEY

Starlite Productions, pg 1024

NEW YORK

Interactive International Inc, pg 899

OHIO

Tri-State Audio Visual Co, pg 1044

TEXAS

Tarpley Media Systems, pg 1032

WISCONSIN

Full Compass Systems, pg 874

MANITOBA

Inland Audio Visual Ltd, pg 898

ONTARIO

Westbury National Show Systems Ltd, pg 1064

LCD Panel Distributors

ARIZONA

CADint, pg 816
EAR Professional Audio/Video, pg 855
Professional Marketing Services Inc, pg 985
Troxell Communications Inc, pg 1045
Ultimate Presentation Systems Inc, pg 1047

ARKANSAS

Jay S Stanley & Associates Inc, pg 1023
White Diamond Productions, pg 1065

CALIFORNIA

Adolph Gasser Inc, pg 776
Ametron Audio/Video, pg 785
Associated Sound, pg 792
Be Media, pg 804
Boland Communications, pg 810
California Tape Products Inc, pg 817
Delicate Electronics Sales Inc, pg 845
Dynamic Digital Depth Inc (DDD), pg 854
FXC Communications, pg 874
Hooper Camera & Imaging, pg 891
Kappa optronics Inc, pg 908
Marshall Electronics Inc, pg 932
Media Fabricators Inc, pg 936
MediaPOINTE, pg 938
Mobilized Tech Systems, pg 944
NSM Surveillance, pg 960
POP TV, pg 978
Promax Systems, pg 986
TEK Media Group, pg 1035
Transvideo International, pg 1044
VMI Inc, pg 1060
Zack Electronics Inc, pg 1073

COLORADO

Aspen Systems Inc, pg 792
Daylight Productions & Rentals, pg 844
Dot Hill Systems Corp, pg 851
ProLine Digital, pg 986
Spectrum Audio Visual Services, pg 1020

CONNECTICUT

Everett Hall Associates Inc, pg 863
The Video Messenger Co, pg 1055

FLORIDA

Access Media Group, pg 773
AVI-SPL, pg 798
Digital Video Systems Inc, pg 848
Hi-Tech Enterprises Inc, pg 888
Hi-Tech Import Export Corp, pg 888
Hunter Electronics LLC, pg 892
Industrial Strength Inc, pg 897
Pro Stage Inc, pg 983
Sight & Sound Productions, pg 1010
Technomedia Solutions, pg 1035

GEORGIA

AVForSale, pg 798
Clark, pg 829
Stage Front Presentation Systems, pg 1022

HAWAII

The Audio Visual Co (AVCO), pg 795

ILLINOIS

Allen Visual Systems Inc, pg 781
Canvys™, pg 819
Dukane Corp, Audio Visual Products Division, pg 853
Educational Insights, pg 857
Joseph Electronics, pg 906
Quintessence Audio Ltd, pg 989

INDIANA

Sensory Technologies LLC, pg 1006

IOWA

ECS Inc, pg 856

KENTUCKY

NOR-COM Inc, pg 958

LOUISIANA

Intermedia Technologies, pg 900

MARYLAND

Cardinal Sound & Video, pg 820
DSR Computer Technology Specialists Inc, pg 853
Human Circuit, pg 892
Nelson White Systems Inc, pg 954
Noventri, pg 960

MASSACHUSETTS

Professional Audio Design Inc, pg 985
Psych Soft Inc, pg 987
Rule Broadcast Systems, pg 1000

MICHIGAN

Olson Anderson Co, pg 786
ASC Systems, pg 791
Ascom Communications Contractors, pg 791
Michigan Office Solutions, pg 941

MINNESOTA

Alpha Video & Audio Inc, pg 782

MISSISSIPPI

Bowie Audio Visual Enterprises Inc, pg 811

MISSOURI

Modern Communications Inc, pg 944
Schiller's Audio-Visual, pg 1004

NEW JERSEY

Argraph Corp, pg 789
Audio Visual Associates, pg 795
AV Bluebook, pg 797
Diversified Systems Inc, pg 849
MIB Mediaworks, pg 941
Starlite Productions, pg 1024
Total Video Products Inc, pg 1042
Wilray Audio Visual Corp, pg 1067
Wired 4 Sound Inc, pg 1068

NEW YORK

ALTEL Systems Inc, pg 783
Audio-Video Corp, pg 795
BTX Technologies, pg 814
Colortone Audio Visual, pg 832
Custom Media Environments, pg 841
Gaylord Brothers, pg 876
Image Management Systems Inc, pg 895
KVL Audio Visual Services Inc, pg 914
Langie Audio Visual Systems, pg 915
Magnaplan Corp, pg 928
Neptune Photo Inc, pg 954
SmartSource Computer & AV Rentals, pg 1014
Stampede Presentation Products Inc, pg 1023
Technisphere Corp, pg 1034
Video Technology Services Inc, pg 1056
Vision Identics Systems Inc, pg 1058
Visual Technologies Corp, pg 1060
Visual Word Systems Inc, pg 1060

NORTH CAROLINA

Crest Electronics Inc, pg 839
Crispin Corp, pg 839

OHIO

Electronic Vision Inc (EV), pg 859
ITA Audio Visual Solutions, pg 902
Jimmy Rea Electronics Inc, pg 992
Tri-State Audio Visual Co, pg 1044

PENNSYLVANIA

Advanced AV, pg 777
Aydin Displays Inc, pg 800
Bernie's Photo Center, pg 805
Brodart Co, pg 813
J E Foss Co, pg 871
Interactive Products, pg 899
The Lerro Corp, pg 919

LCD Panel Manufacturers

LCD Panel Rentals

COMPUTER SYSTEMS

LCD Panel Rentals (continued)

WISCONSIN

Audio Visual of Milwaukee Inc, pg 795
Full Compass Systems, pg 874

PUERTO RICO

Stage Crew Audiovisual Inc, pg 1022

ALBERTA

Sharp's Audio-Visual Ltd, pg 1008

BRITISH COLUMBIA

Commercial Electronics Ltd, pg 832

MANITOBA

Inland Audio Visual Ltd, pg 898

ONTARIO

MVI Multivision Inc, pg 951
RB Productions, pg 992
Westbury National Show Systems Ltd, pg 1064

LCD Panel Repairs

CALIFORNIA

Advanced Media LLC, pg 778
Ametron Audio/Video, pg 785
McAlister Electronics, pg 935
Transvideo International, pg 1044

CONNECTICUT

HB Communications Inc, pg 886

FLORIDA

Hi-Tech Enterprises Inc, pg 888

GEORGIA

Stage Front Presentation Systems, pg 1022

ILLINOIS

Allen Visual Systems Inc, pg 781

IOWA

ECS Inc, pg 856

KENTUCKY

NOR-COM Inc, pg 958

MAINE

Headlight Audio Visual Inc, pg 887

MARYLAND

Nelson White Systems Inc, pg 954
Visual Aids Electronics Corp, pg 1059

MICHIGAN

TeL Systems, pg 1035

NEW YORK

Custom Media Environments, pg 841
Langie Audio Visual Systems, pg 915
Technisphere Corp, pg 1034
Video Technology Services Inc, pg 1056
Visual Technologies Corp, pg 1060

OHIO

ITA Audio Visual Solutions, pg 902
Tri-State Audio Visual Co, pg 1044

PENNSYLVANIA

J E Foss Co, pg 871

TENNESSEE

Technical Support Systems LLC, pg 1034

TEXAS

Tarpley Media Systems, pg 1032

VIRGINIA

Avitecture Inc, pg 799

WISCONSIN

Camera Corner Connecting Point, pg 818
Full Compass Systems, pg 874

ALBERTA

Sharp's Audio-Visual Ltd, pg 1008

MANITOBA

Inland Audio Visual Ltd, pg 898

ONTARIO

Westbury National Show Systems Ltd, pg 1064

Monitor Distributors

ARIZONA

CADint, pg 816
EAR Professional Audio/Video, pg 855
Troxell Communications Inc, pg 1045

ARKANSAS

White Diamond Productions, pg 1065

CALIFORNIA

Adolph Gasser Inc, pg 776
Ametron Audio/Video, pg 785
Associated Sound, pg 792
Audio Images Corp, pg 794
Be Media, pg 804
Boland Communications, pg 810
California Tape Products Inc, pg 817
Delicate Electronics Sales Inc, pg 845
FXC Communications, pg 874
Jameco Electronics, pg 903
Kappa optronics Inc, pg 908
Kontron America, pg 913
Media Fabricators Inc, pg 936
MediaPOINTE, pg 938
Mobilized Tech Systems, pg 944
Photodyne Technologies, pg 974
POP TV, pg 978
Promax Systems, pg 986
SNAP, pg 1014
Stanislaus Audio Video Inc, pg 1023
Transvideo International, pg 1044
VMI Inc, pg 1060

COLORADO

Aspen Systems Inc, pg 792
Daylight Productions & Rentals, pg 844
Dot Hill Systems Corp, pg 851
Spectrum Audio Visual Services, pg 1020

CONNECTICUT

Concord Communications, pg 835

FLORIDA

Access Media Group, pg 773
AVI-SPL, pg 798
Digital Video Systems Inc, pg 848
Harris Corp, pg 885
Hi-Tech Enterprises Inc, pg 888
Hi-Tech Import Export Corp, pg 888
Hunter Electronics LLC, pg 892
Midtown Video Inc, pg 942
Pro Stage Inc, pg 983
Sight & Sound Productions, pg 1010

GEORGIA

Clark, pg 829
Outsource Engineering & Manufacturing Inc dba Texscan MSI, pg 966
Stage Front Presentation Systems, pg 1022
TAPPI, pg 1032

HAWAII

The Audio Visual Co (AVCO), pg 795

ILLINOIS

Allen Visual Systems Inc, pg 781
Dukane Corp, Audio Visual Products Division, pg 853
Joseph Electronics, pg 906
Lyn Norstad & Associates Inc, pg 926
Quintessence Audio Ltd, pg 989
Woodside Avenue Music Productions Inc, pg 1069

INDIANA

Sensory Technologies LLC, pg 1006

IOWA

ECS Inc, pg 856

KENTUCKY

NOR-COM Inc, pg 958

LOUISIANA

Intermedia Technologies, pg 900

MAINE

Headlight Audio Visual Inc, pg 887

MARYLAND

DSR Computer Technology Specialists Inc, pg 853
Human Circuit, pg 892
NewWave Technologies Inc, pg 957
Noventri, pg 960

MASSACHUSETTS

Professional Audio Design Inc, pg 985
Psych Soft Inc, pg 987
Rule Broadcast Systems, pg 1000

MICHIGAN

Olson Anderson Co, pg 786
Ascom Communications Contractors, pg 791
Digi Sign Design LLC, pg 847
Michigan Office Solutions, pg 941
On Stage Visuals, pg 963

MINNESOTA

Alpha Video & Audio Inc, pg 782

MISSOURI

Modern Communications Inc, pg 944
Schiller's Audio-Visual, pg 1004

NEBRASKA

Dog & Pony Productions Inc, pg 850

NEW JERSEY

Argraph Corp, pg 789
Audio Visual Associates, pg 795
Diversified Systems Inc, pg 849
Earl Girls Inc, pg 855
Starlite Productions, pg 1024
Total Video Products Inc, pg 1042
Wilray Audio Visual Corp, pg 1067
Wired 4 Sound Inc, pg 1068

NEW YORK

ALTEL Systems Inc, pg 783
Audio-Video Corp, pg 795
Colortone Audio Visual, pg 832
Custom Media Environments, pg 841
Design Audio Visual Inc, pg 845
Guidance Associates Inc Center for Humanities, pg 883
Image Management Systems Inc, pg 895
KVL Audio Visual Services Inc, pg 914
Langie Audio Visual Systems, pg 915
Magnaplan Corp, pg 928
SmartSource Computer & AV Rentals, pg 1014
Technisphere Corp, pg 1034
Video Technology Services Inc, pg 1056
Videoguys, pg 1057
Vision Identics Systems Inc, pg 1058
Visual Word Systems Inc, pg 1060

NORTH CAROLINA

Crest Electronics Inc, pg 839
Crispin Corp, pg 839

OHIO

Electronic Vision Inc (EV), pg 859
ITA Audio Visual Solutions, pg 902
Midwest Photo Exchange, pg 942
Jimmy Rea Electronics Inc, pg 992
Tri-State Audio Visual Co, pg 1044

PENNSYLVANIA

Advanced AV, pg 777
Aydin Displays Inc, pg 800
J E Foss Co, pg 871
Innovision Media Group, pg 899
The Lerro Corp, pg 919

SOUTH CAROLINA

Professional Management Services Inc, pg 985

TENNESSEE

Lowrance Sound Co Inc, pg 925
Spring Arbor Distributors, pg 1022
Technical Support Systems LLC, pg 1034
Zion Music Group, pg 1074

TEXAS

Astro Audio Visual, pg 792
AVES Audio Visual Systems Inc, pg 798
Biway Media, pg 808
CAM Audio Inc, pg 817
Data Display Audio Visual Co LP, pg 843
Data Projections Inc, pg 843
Digital Display Solutions Inc, pg 847
Industrial Audio/Video Inc, pg 897
Media Management LLC, pg 937
RadioShack Corp, pg 990
Schoolhouse Audio Visual, pg 1004
Supercircuits, pg 1029
Tarpley Media Systems, pg 1032
Videotex Systems Inc, pg 1057

VIRGINIA

Avitecture Inc, pg 799
Design & Production Inc, pg 845
Filmdex Inc, pg 867
Intellidyne LLC, pg 899
Lee Hartman & Sons Inc, pg 918
Quince Imaging Inc, pg 989
Rocktown Media, pg 998

WASHINGTON

eMagin Corp, pg 860
ToteVision, pg 1042

WISCONSIN

Audio Visual of Milwaukee Inc, pg 795
Camera Corner Connecting Point, pg 818
Full Compass Systems, pg 874
Safe Harbor Computers, pg 1001

ALBERTA

Allstar Show Industries Inc, pg 782
Infosat Communications Inc, pg 898
Matrix Video Communications Corp (MVCC), pg 934

BRITISH COLUMBIA

Commercial Electronics Ltd, pg 832

MANITOBA

Advance Pro, pg 777
Inland Audio Visual Ltd, pg 898

ONTARIO

Cinema Stage Inc, pg 827

Monitor Manufacturers

CALIFORNIA

Aztek Inc, pg 801
Boland Communications, pg 810
Enright Co, pg 861
GVISION USA Inc, pg 883
Hoodman Corp, pg 891
Panasonic Broadcast & Digital Systems Co, pg 968
Transvideo International, pg 1044
ViewSonic, pg 1058

CONNECTICUT

Intermed Video Technologies Inc, pg 900

ILLINOIS

Canvys™, pg 819

NEW JERSEY

Sharp Electronics Corp, Professional Display Division, pg 1008

NEW YORK

Video Technology Services Inc, pg 1056

NORTH CAROLINA

Computer Dynamics, pg 834

PENNSYLVANIA

Aydin Displays Inc, pg 800

VIRGINIA

Quince Imaging Inc, pg 989

WASHINGTON

eMagin Corp, pg 860
ToteVision, pg 1042

BRITISH COLUMBIA

Triad Communications Ltd, pg 1044

Monitor Rentals

ALABAMA

Audio-Video Resources Inc, pg 795

ARIZONA

Merestone, pg 938
Video West Inc, pg 1056

ARKANSAS

White Diamond Productions, pg 1065

CALIFORNIA

Absolute Rentals, pg 772
Adolph Gasser Inc, pg 776
Advanced Media LLC, pg 778
AGF Media Services, pg 778
Alliant Event Services, pg 781
Ametron Audio/Video, pg 785
Artichoke Productions, pg 791
Associated Sound, pg 792
Audio Rents, pg 794
AV Guys, pg 797
Bexel Corp, pg 806
Big Time Picture Company Inc, pg 807
Cherry Multimedia, pg 824
Deck Hand Inc, pg 844
Express Media Inc, pg 864
Golden Gate Studios, pg 880
Lynch Communications, pg 926
McCune Audio-Video-Lighting, pg 935
Media Fabricators Inc, pg 936
Munday & Collins AV, pg 950
Muse Presentation Technologies, pg 950
PIX, pg 976
Production Gear Rentals (PGR), pg 984
PSAV® Presentation Services, pg 986
Radiant Images, pg 990
RetinaVision Productions, pg 995
Revolution Cinema Rentals, pg 995
Slate Media Group, pg 1013
Sound Service Co, pg 1017
Stanislaus Audio Video Inc, pg 1023
Synthesizer Rental Service, pg 1030
Synthesizer Systems Technologies (SST), pg 1030
Total Media Group, pg 1042
VER-Video Equipment Rentals, pg 1053
VMI Inc, pg 1060
Voice & Video Rentals, pg 1060
Warner Bros Production Sound & Video Services, pg 1062

COLORADO

Multimedia Audio Visual Inc, pg 950
Open Media Foundation, pg 964
Spectrum Audio Visual Services, pg 1020

CONNECTICUT

A/V Davey, pg 797
Videofilm Systems Inc, pg 1057

FLORIDA

Access Media Group, pg 773
Accord Productions, pg 773
AVI-SPL, pg 798
Hi-Tech Enterprises Inc, pg 888
Industrial Strength Inc, pg 897
MAPS Production House, pg 930
Pro Stage Inc, pg 983
Sight & Sound Productions, pg 1010

GEORGIA

Lighting & Production Equipment Inc, pg 920
Stage Front Presentation Systems, pg 1022

HAWAII

FOTON Hawaii, pg 871

ILLINOIS

Allen Visual Systems Inc, pg 781
AV Chicago Inc, pg 797
Backstar Creative Media Inc, pg 801
Product Productions, pg 984
RC Communications, pg 992
Show Department Inc, pg 1009
Woodside Avenue Music Productions Inc, pg 1069

IOWA

ECS Inc, pg 856

KENTUCKY

Audio Visual Techniques Inc, pg 796

MAINE

Headlight Audio Visual Inc, pg 887

MARYLAND

Advance Audiovisual Presentation Ltd, pg 777
CPR MultiMedia Solutions, pg 837
CSPMedia.com, pg 840
Event Tech, pg 863
Visual Aids Electronics Corp, pg 1059

MASSACHUSETTS

AVFX Inc, pg 798
Cramer Productions, pg 837
massAV, pg 933
Preston Productions Inc, pg 981

MICHIGAN

Digi Sign Design LLC, pg 847
K&R All Media Productions Inc, pg 908
On Stage Visuals, pg 963

MINNESOTA

Alpha Video & Audio Inc, pg 782

MISSOURI

Schiller's Audio-Visual, pg 1004
Show-Me Audio-Visual, pg 1009

NEBRASKA

Dog & Pony Productions Inc, pg 850

NEVADA

GES Audio Visual, pg 877

NEW JERSEY

Audio Visual Dynamics®, pg 795
Earl Girls Inc, pg 855
Giant Audio Visual Inc, pg 878
PLS Staging, pg 977
Starlite Productions, pg 1024
Wired 4 Sound Inc, pg 1068

NEW MEXICO

Production Outfitters, pg 984

NEW YORK

Colortone Audio Visual, pg 832
Design Audio Visual Inc, pg 845
Dreamhire LLC, pg 852
Hello World Communications, pg 888
Interactive International Inc, pg 899
KVL Audio Visual Services Inc, pg 914
Langie Audio Visual Systems, pg 915
Magnaplan Corp, pg 928
Manhattan Center Studios Inc, pg 930
SmartSource Computer & AV Rentals, pg 1014
Technisphere Corp, pg 1034
Visual Word Systems Inc, pg 1060

NORTH CAROLINA

A&V Company, pg 772
AV Metro Inc, pg 797
Visual Aids Electronics of North Carolina Inc, pg 1059

NORTH DAKOTA

Media Productions, pg 937

COMPUTER SYSTEMS

Monitor Rentals (continued)

OHIO

Hughie's Event Production Services, pg 892

OKLAHOMA

PDC Productions, pg 970

PENNSYLVANIA

Advanced AV, pg 777
Argentine Productions Inc, pg 789
FMP Media Solutions Inc, pg 870
Innovision Media Group, pg 899
The Videohouse Inc, pg 1057

TENNESSEE

RentACamera.com, pg 995
Technical Support Systems LLC, pg 1034

TEXAS

Alford Media Services, pg 780
Data Display Audio Visual Co LP, pg 843
Digital Display Solutions Inc, pg 847
Stage Directions, pg 1022

VERMONT

Parlato Productions, pg 969

VIRGINIA

American AV, pg 783
Quince Imaging Inc, pg 989

WASHINGTON

The House Studios, pg 891

WISCONSIN

Audio Visual of Milwaukee Inc, pg 795
Full Compass Systems, pg 874

PUERTO RICO

Stage Crew Audiovisual Inc, pg 1022

ALBERTA

Evolution Presentation Technologies, pg 863

BRITISH COLUMBIA

Commercial Electronics Ltd, pg 832

MANITOBA

Inland Audio Visual Ltd, pg 898

ONTARIO

RB Productions, pg 992

QUEBEC

Audio Visual Dynamics Ltd, pg 795

Monitor Repairs

CALIFORNIA

Advanced Media LLC, pg 778
Ametron Audio/Video, pg 785
McAlister Electronics, pg 935
Transvideo International, pg 1044
TV Pro Gear, pg 1046
VMI Inc, pg 1060

CONNECTICUT

HB Communications Inc, pg 886

FLORIDA

Digital Video Systems Inc, pg 848
Hi-Tech Enterprises Inc, pg 888

GEORGIA

Stage Front Presentation Systems, pg 1022

ILLINOIS

Allen Visual Systems Inc, pg 781
Midwest Digital Corp, pg 942

IOWA

ECS Inc, pg 856

KENTUCKY

NOR-COM Inc, pg 958

MAINE

Headlight Audio Visual Inc, pg 887

MARYLAND

Visual Aids Electronics Corp, pg 1059

MICHIGAN

TeL Systems, pg 1035

NEW JERSEY

Earl Girls Inc, pg 855

NEW YORK

Interactive International Inc, pg 899
Langie Audio Visual Systems, pg 915
Technisphere Corp, pg 1034
Video Technology Services Inc, pg 1056

OHIO

ITA Audio Visual Solutions, pg 902
Tri-State Audio Visual Co, pg 1044

PENNSYLVANIA

J E Foss Co, pg 871

TENNESSEE

Technical Support Systems LLC, pg 1034

TEXAS

Data Display Audio Visual Co LP, pg 843

VIRGINIA

Avitecture Inc, pg 799

WASHINGTON

ToteVision, pg 1042

WISCONSIN

Camera Corner Connecting Point, pg 818
Full Compass Systems, pg 874

ALBERTA

Infosat Communications Inc, pg 898

BRITISH COLUMBIA

Commercial Electronics Ltd, pg 832

MANITOBA

Inland Audio Visual Ltd, pg 898

Mouse System Distributors

CALIFORNIA

Ametron Audio/Video, pg 785
Audio Images Corp, pg 794
California Tape Products Inc, pg 817
Gyration, pg 883
Jameco Electronics, pg 903
Kontron America, pg 913
MediaPOINTE, pg 938
Photodyne Technologies, pg 974
Promax Systems, pg 986
Related Visual Inc, pg 994

COLORADO

Spectrum Audio Visual Services, pg 1020

FLORIDA

Access Media Group, pg 773
Hi-Tech Import Export Corp, pg 888
Pro Stage Inc, pg 983
Sight & Sound Productions, pg 1010

GEORGIA

Stage Front Presentation Systems, pg 1022

ILLINOIS

Lyn Norstad & Associates Inc, pg 926
Manning Productions, pg 930
Woodside Avenue Music Productions Inc, pg 1069

IOWA

ECS Inc, pg 856

KENTUCKY

NOR-COM Inc, pg 958

MARYLAND

DSR Computer Technology Specialists Inc, pg 853

MASSACHUSETTS

Psych Soft Inc, pg 987

MICHIGAN

Olson Anderson Co, pg 786

MISSOURI

Schiller's Audio-Visual, pg 1004

NEBRASKA

Dog & Pony Productions Inc, pg 850

NEW JERSEY

Argraph Corp, pg 789
Starlite Productions, pg 1024

NEW YORK

ALTEL Systems Inc, pg 783
Audio-Video Corp, pg 795
Custom Media Environments, pg 841
Design Audio Visual Inc, pg 845
Guidance Associates Inc Center for Humanities, pg 883
Magnaplan Corp, pg 928

NORTH CAROLINA

Crispin Corp, pg 839

PENNSYLVANIA

Advanced AV, pg 777
The Lerro Corp, pg 919

SOUTH CAROLINA

Professional Management Services Inc, pg 985

TENNESSEE

Lowrance Sound Co Inc, pg 925
Technical Support Systems LLC, pg 1034

TEXAS

Data Display Audio Visual Co LP, pg 843
RadioShack Corp, pg 990
Videotex Systems Inc, pg 1057

VIRGINIA

Intellidyne LLC, pg 899
Lee Hartman & Sons Inc, pg 918

WISCONSIN

Audio Visual of Milwaukee Inc, pg 795
Camera Corner Connecting Point, pg 818
Full Compass Systems, pg 874

ALBERTA

Infosat Communications Inc, pg 898

MANITOBA

Advance Pro, pg 777
Inland Audio Visual Ltd, pg 898

Mouse System Manufacturers

ARIZONA

Covid Inc, pg 837

CALIFORNIA

Gyration, pg 883
Kensington Technology Group, pg 909
Kontron America, pg 913

TEXAS

Origin Instruments Corp, pg 965

Multimedia System Distributors

ARIZONA

EAR Professional Audio/Video, pg 855

ARKANSAS

Jay S Stanley & Associates Inc, pg 1023
White Diamond Productions, pg 1065

CALIFORNIA

Ametron Audio/Video, pg 785
Associated Sound, pg 792
Audio Images Corp, pg 794
Be Media, pg 804
California Tape Products Inc, pg 817
Computer Modules Inc, pg 834
Diaquest, pg 846
Electrosonic Inc, pg 859
Jameco Electronics, pg 903
JD Audio Visual Inc, pg 904
Kontron America, pg 913
Media Fabricators Inc, pg 936
MediaMation Inc, pg 937
MediaPOINTE, pg 938
Mobilized Tech Systems, pg 944
Optibase Inc, pg 964
Photodyne Technologies, pg 974
POP TV, pg 978
Promax Systems, pg 986
Stanislaus Audio Video Inc, pg 1023
Total Media Group, pg 1042
Videobotics, pg 1056
VMI Inc, pg 1060

COLORADO

Aspen Systems Inc, pg 792
G W Hannaway & Associates, pg 884

FLORIDA

Access Media Group, pg 773
Digital Video Systems Inc, pg 848
Harmon's Audio-Visual Services, pg 885
Harris Corp, pg 885
Hi-Tech Enterprises Inc, pg 888
Hi-Tech Import Export Corp, pg 888
Hunter Electronics LLC, pg 892
ITEC Entertainment Corp, pg 903
Sight & Sound Productions, pg 1010
Technomedia Solutions, pg 1035

GEORGIA

Clark, pg 829
PolyVision Corporation, pg 978
Stage Front Presentation Systems, pg 1022
TAPPI, pg 1032

HAWAII

The Audio Visual Co (AVCO), pg 795

ILLINOIS

Lyn Norstad & Associates Inc, pg 926

INDIANA

Sensory Technologies LLC, pg 1006

IOWA

ECS Inc, pg 856

KENTUCKY

NOR-COM Inc, pg 958

LOUISIANA

Intermedia Technologies, pg 900

MARYLAND

DSR Computer Technology Specialists Inc, pg 853
Human Circuit, pg 892
Image Logic Corp, pg 895
Nelson White Systems Inc, pg 954

MASSACHUSETTS

Avid Technology Inc, pg 799
Professional Audio Design Inc, pg 985
Psych Soft Inc, pg 987
Rule Broadcast Systems, pg 1000

MICHIGAN

Olson Anderson Co, pg 786
Ascom Communications Contractors, pg 791
Digi Sign Design LLC, pg 847
Michigan Office Solutions, pg 941

MINNESOTA

Alpha Video & Audio Inc, pg 782
Beyers Sound & Essay Audio, pg 806

MISSISSIPPI

Bowie Audio Visual Enterprises Inc, pg 811

MISSOURI

Schiller's Audio-Visual, pg 1004

NEBRASKA

Strong Cinema Products, pg 1026

NEW JERSEY

Diversified Systems Inc, pg 849
Earl Girls Inc, pg 855
Entel Systems Inc, pg 861
MIB Mediaworks, pg 941
National Audio-Visual Supply, pg 952
Starlite Productions, pg 1024
Total Video Products Inc, pg 1042
Wilray Audio Visual Corp, pg 1067

NEW YORK

Audio-Video Corp, pg 795
Colortone Audio Visual, pg 832
Communication Corner Inc, pg 832
Custom Media Environments, pg 841
Guidance Associates Inc Center for Humanities, pg 883
Image Management Systems Inc, pg 895
Interactive International Inc, pg 899
Magnaplan Corp, pg 928
Sanako Inc, pg 1002
SmartSource Computer & AV Rentals, pg 1014
Visual Technologies Corp, pg 1060

OHIO

Tri-State Audio Visual Co, pg 1044

OREGON

ClearOne MagicBox Inc, pg 830
NeoSoft Corp, pg 954

PENNSYLVANIA

AccuWeather Inc, pg 774
Advanced AV, pg 777
J E Foss Co, pg 871
Innovision Media Group, pg 899
The Lerro Corp, pg 919
Wespen Audio Visual Co, pg 1063

SOUTH CAROLINA

Professional Management Services Inc, pg 985

TENNESSEE

Lowrance Sound Co Inc, pg 925
Spring Arbor Distributors, pg 1022
Technical Support Systems LLC, pg 1034
Zion Music Group, pg 1074

TEXAS

Audio Visual Technologies Group, pg 796
Biway Media, pg 808
Data Projections Inc, pg 843
Epic Software Group Inc, pg 862
Media Management LLC, pg 937
RadioShack Corp, pg 990
Tarpley Media Systems, pg 1032
Videotex Systems Inc, pg 1057

VIRGINIA

Design & Production Inc, pg 845
Intellidyne LLC, pg 899
Lee Hartman & Sons Inc, pg 918
RGB Technology Inc, pg 996
Rocktown Media, pg 998

WISCONSIN

Audio Visual of Milwaukee Inc, pg 795
Camera Corner Connecting Point, pg 818
Full Compass Systems, pg 874
Safe Harbor Computers, pg 1001

WYOMING

Bridger Productions Inc, pg 812

ALBERTA

Infosat Communications Inc, pg 898
Matrix Video Communications Corp (MVCC), pg 934
SMART Technologies Inc, pg 1013

MANITOBA

Advance Pro, pg 777
Inland Audio Visual Ltd, pg 898
Tek Gear, pg 1035

ONTARIO

Cinema Stage Inc, pg 827
Edcom Multimedia Products, pg 856
Gesturetek, pg 877
Premier A/V Sales Ltd, pg 980
Westbury National Show Systems Ltd, pg 1064

QUEBEC

Teledac Inc, pg 1036

Multimedia System Manufacturers

ARIZONA

Applied Integration Corp, pg 789

CALIFORNIA

AITech International, pg 779
Computer Modules Inc, pg 834
Diaquest, pg 846
FutureVideo, pg 874
Grande Vitesse Systems Inc (GVS), pg 881
Micro Express, pg 941
Optibase Inc, pg 964
POP TV, pg 978
QRS Software Services, pg 988
Toshiba America Information Systems Inc, pg 1042
VITEC Multimedia, pg 1060

COLORADO

Aspen Systems Inc, pg 792

FLORIDA

CD ROM™ Inc, pg 822

GEORGIA

Outsource Engineering & Manufacturing Inc dba Texscan MSI, pg 966
PolyVision Corporation, pg 978

ILLINOIS

AmpliVox Portable Sound Systems, pg 785

KANSAS

Keywest Technology Inc, pg 910

MARYLAND

Image Logic Corp, pg 895

MASSACHUSETTS

Avid Technology Inc, pg 799
MorphoTrust USA, pg 946
Psych Soft Inc, pg 987

MICHIGAN

ASC Systems, pg 791

NEW JERSEY

CELCO-Constantine Engineering Labs Co, pg 822
Crestron Electronics Inc, pg 839
FSR Inc, pg 873
PeopleVisionFX, pg 972

NEW YORK

Interactive International Inc, pg 899
Laird Digital Cinema, pg 915
RCS Enterprises, pg 992

NORTH CAROLINA

Micro Technology Unlimited, pg 941

OHIO

Electronic Vision Inc (EV), pg 859

OREGON

ClearOne MagicBox Inc, pg 830
NeoSoft Corp, pg 954

COMPUTER SYSTEMS

Multimedia System Manufacturers (continued)

PENNSYLVANIA

AccuWeather Inc, pg 774
Scala Inc, pg 1003

TENNESSEE

Adtec Digital Inc, pg 777

TEXAS

Biway Media, pg 808

VIRGINIA

Intellidyne LLC, pg 899
RGB Technology Inc, pg 996

ALBERTA

SMART Technologies Inc, pg 1013

BRITISH COLUMBIA

Triad Communications Ltd, pg 1044

MANITOBA

Tek Gear, pg 1035

ONTARIO

Gesturetek, pg 877

QUEBEC

Teledac Inc, pg 1036

Multimedia System Rentals

ALABAMA

Audio-Video Resources Inc, pg 795

ARIZONA

Merestone, pg 938

ARKANSAS

White Diamond Productions, pg 1065

CALIFORNIA

Ametron Audio/Video, pg 785
Associated Sound, pg 792
Big Time Picture Company Inc, pg 807
Express Media Inc, pg 864
Golden Gate Studios, pg 880
Hooper Camera & Imaging, pg 891
JD Audio Visual Inc, pg 904
Lynch Communications, pg 926
Muse Presentation Technologies, pg 950
RetinaVision Productions, pg 995
Total Media Group, pg 1042

CONNECTICUT

A/V Davey, pg 797
Videofilm Systems Inc, pg 1057

FLORIDA

Access Media Group, pg 773
Harmon's Audio-Visual Services, pg 885
Industrial Strength Inc, pg 897
Universal Studios Florida® Production Group, pg 1049

GEORGIA

Stage Front Presentation Systems, pg 1022

HAWAII

Ken Herkes Productions & Entertainment (KHPE), pg 888

ILLINOIS

Airways Digital Media, pg 779
Creative Technology, pg 838
QuickSet International Inc, pg 989
RC Communications, pg 992
Show Department Inc, pg 1009

IOWA

ECS Inc, pg 856

KENTUCKY

Audio Visual Techniques Inc, pg 796

MARYLAND

Advance Audiovisual Presentation Ltd, pg 777
CSPMedia.com, pg 840
Kramer Communications Video Production, pg 913
Nelson White Systems Inc, pg 954

MASSACHUSETTS

Preston Productions Inc, pg 981

MICHIGAN

Digi Sign Design LLC, pg 847
K&R All Media Productions Inc, pg 908

MISSISSIPPI

Bowie Audio Visual Enterprises Inc, pg 811

MISSOURI

Show-Me Audio-Visual, pg 1009

NEW JERSEY

Earl Girls Inc, pg 855
PLS Staging, pg 977

NEW YORK

Communication Corner Inc, pg 832
Custom Media Environments, pg 841
Interactive International Inc, pg 899
Manhattan Center Studios Inc, pg 930
SmartSource Computer & AV Rentals, pg 1014
Visual Technologies Corp, pg 1060

NORTH CAROLINA

A&V Company, pg 772

NORTH DAKOTA

Media Productions, pg 937

OHIO

Bartha, pg 803

OKLAHOMA

PDC Productions, pg 970

PENNSYLVANIA

FMP Media Solutions Inc, pg 870
Innovision Media Group, pg 899

TENNESSEE

Love Shack Recording Studios, pg 925
Technical Support Systems LLC, pg 1034

TEXAS

Stage Directions, pg 1022

VIRGINIA

Advance Concepts Inc, pg 777
American AV, pg 783

WISCONSIN

Full Compass Systems, pg 874

PUERTO RICO

Stage Crew Audiovisual Inc, pg 1022

BRITISH COLUMBIA

Image Media Farm, pg 895

MANITOBA

Inland Audio Visual Ltd, pg 898
Tek Gear, pg 1035

ONTARIO

Edcom Multimedia Products, pg 856
RB Productions, pg 992
Westbury National Show Systems Ltd, pg 1064

QUEBEC

Group PVP, pg 882

Multimedia System Repairs

CALIFORNIA

Ametron Audio/Video, pg 785
Technical Services, pg 1034

COLORADO

Aspen Systems Inc, pg 792

CONNECTICUT

HB Communications Inc, pg 886

FLORIDA

Hi-Tech Enterprises Inc, pg 888

GEORGIA

Stage Front Presentation Systems, pg 1022

IOWA

ECS Inc, pg 856

KENTUCKY

NOR-COM Inc, pg 958

MARYLAND

DSR Computer Technology Specialists Inc, pg 853
Nelson White Systems Inc, pg 954

NEW JERSEY

Earl Girls Inc, pg 855

NEW YORK

Custom Media Environments, pg 841
Interactive International Inc, pg 899
Visual Technologies Corp, pg 1060

OHIO

Advent Media Inc, pg 778
Tri-State Audio Visual Co, pg 1044

TENNESSEE

Technical Support Systems LLC, pg 1034

TEXAS

Biway Media, pg 808

VIRGINIA

Intellidyne LLC, pg 899

WISCONSIN

Camera Corner Connecting Point, pg 818
Full Compass Systems, pg 874

ALBERTA

Infosat Communications Inc, pg 898

MANITOBA

Inland Audio Visual Ltd, pg 898

ONTARIO

Westbury National Show Systems Ltd, pg 1064

Multimedia Workstation Distributors

ARIZONA

CADint, pg 816
EAR Professional Audio/Video, pg 855

CALIFORNIA

Ametron Audio/Video, pg 785
Audio Images Corp, pg 794
Be Media, pg 804
California Tape Products Inc, pg 817
Computer Modules Inc, pg 834
Diaquest, pg 846
DiskFaktory Direct, pg 849
Electrosonic Inc, pg 859
Media Fabricators Inc, pg 936
MediaPOINTE, pg 938
Mobilized Tech Systems, pg 944
Photodyne Technologies, pg 974
POP TV, pg 978
Promax Systems, pg 986
Total Media Group, pg 1042
Videobotics, pg 1056
VMI Inc, pg 1060
Zack Electronics Inc, pg 1073

COLORADO

Aspen Systems Inc, pg 792
Dot Hill Systems Corp, pg 851
G W Hannaway & Associates, pg 884

FLORIDA

Access Media Group, pg 773
CD ROM™ Inc, pg 822
Digital Video Systems Inc, pg 848
Harris Corp, pg 885
Hi-Tech Enterprises Inc, pg 888
Hi-Tech Import Export Corp, pg 888
Hunter Electronics LLC, pg 892
Sight & Sound Productions, pg 1010

GEORGIA

Stage Front Presentation Systems, pg 1022

HAWAII

The Audio Visual Co (AVCO), pg 795

ILLINOIS

Lyn Norstad & Associates Inc, pg 926
Manning Productions, pg 930

IOWA

ECS Inc, pg 856

KENTUCKY

NOR-COM Inc, pg 958

LOUISIANA

Intermedia Technologies, pg 900

MARYLAND

Bradley Broadcast & Pro Audio, pg 811
DSR Computer Technology Specialists Inc, pg 853
Human Circuit, pg 892
Image Logic Corp, pg 895
NewWave Technologies Inc, pg 957

MASSACHUSETTS

Avid Technology Inc, pg 799
Psych Soft Inc, pg 987
Rule Broadcast Systems, pg 1000

MICHIGAN

Olson Anderson Co, pg 786
Digi Sign Design LLC, pg 847

MISSOURI

Schiller's Audio-Visual, pg 1004

NEW JERSEY

Diversified Systems Inc, pg 849
MIB Mediaworks, pg 941
Wilray Audio Visual Corp, pg 1067

NEW YORK

Audio-Video Corp, pg 795
Custom Media Environments, pg 841
Image Management Systems Inc, pg 895
Interactive International Inc, pg 899
Korg USA Inc, pg 913
KVL Audio Visual Services Inc, pg 914
Sanako Inc, pg 1002
SmartSource Computer & AV Rentals, pg 1014
Videoguys, pg 1057

OHIO

Tri-State Audio Visual Co, pg 1044

PENNSYLVANIA

AccuWeather Inc, pg 774
Advanced AV, pg 777
J E Foss Co, pg 871
The Lerro Corp, pg 919

SOUTH CAROLINA

Professional Management Services Inc, pg 985

TENNESSEE

Technical Support Systems LLC, pg 1034

TEXAS

Biway Media, pg 808
Tarpley Media Systems, pg 1032
Videotex Systems Inc, pg 1057

VIRGINIA

Lee Hartman & Sons Inc, pg 918
RGB Technology Inc, pg 996

WISCONSIN

Audio Visual of Milwaukee Inc, pg 795
Camera Corner Connecting Point, pg 818
Full Compass Systems, pg 874
Safe Harbor Computers, pg 1001
Spectrum Industries Inc, pg 1021

ALBERTA

Matrix Video Communications Corp (MVCC), pg 934

MANITOBA

Advance Pro, pg 777
Inland Audio Visual Ltd, pg 898

ONTARIO

Edcom Multimedia Products, pg 856
Premier A/V Sales Ltd, pg 980

Multimedia Workstation Manufacturers

ALABAMA

Marco Inc, pg 930

ARKANSAS

Sound-Craft Systems Inc, pg 1017

CALIFORNIA

Diaquest, pg 846
DiskFaktory Direct, pg 849
Grande Vitesse Systems Inc (GVS), pg 881
iQstor Networks Inc, pg 902
Kontron America, pg 913
Micro Express, pg 941
Pinnacle Systems Inc, pg 975
VITEC Multimedia, pg 1060

COLORADO

Aspen Systems Inc, pg 792

FLORIDA

CD ROM™ Inc, pg 822
Hi-Tech Enterprises Inc, pg 888

ILLINOIS

Bretford Manufacturing Inc, pg 812
Dukane Corp, Audio Visual Products Division, pg 853
Luxor, pg 926
Marshall Furniture Inc, pg 932

INDIANA

Da-Lite, pg 842

MARYLAND

Image Logic Corp, pg 895

MASSACHUSETTS

Avid Technology Inc, pg 799
Psych Soft Inc, pg 987

MICHIGAN

ASC Systems, pg 791

MINNESOTA

Emcor Enclosures-Crenlo, pg 860
Winsted Corp, pg 1068

NEW YORK

Interactive International Inc, pg 899
Laird Digital Cinema, pg 915

NORTH CAROLINA

Computer Dynamics, pg 834
Micro Technology Unlimited, pg 941

OHIO

Electronic Vision Inc (EV), pg 859
Interlink Technologies, pg 900

TENNESSEE

Adtec Digital Inc, pg 777

TEXAS

Biway Media, pg 808
MooreCo Inc, pg 946

VIRGINIA

RGB Technology Inc, pg 996

WASHINGTON

Synsor Corp, pg 1030
Watson Desking, pg 1062

WISCONSIN

Safe Harbor Computers, pg 1001
Spectrum Industries Inc, pg 1021

BRITISH COLUMBIA

Richmond Sound Design Ltd, pg 996

Multimedia Workstation Rentals

ARIZONA

Merestone, pg 938

CALIFORNIA

Absolute Rentals, pg 772
Big Time Picture Company Inc, pg 807
Express Media Inc, pg 864
Golden Gate Studios, pg 880
Lynch Communications, pg 926
Maximus Media Inc, pg 934
Media Fabricators Inc, pg 936
Muse Presentation Technologies, pg 950
Total Media Group, pg 1042
VER-Video Equipment Rentals, pg 1053
Warner Bros Production Sound & Video Services, pg 1062

DELAWARE

Side Door Studio Inc, pg 1010

FLORIDA

Access Media Group, pg 773
Universal Studios Florida® Production Group, pg 1049

GEORGIA

Stage Front Presentation Systems, pg 1022

ILLINOIS

Airways Digital Media, pg 779
RC Communications, pg 992

IOWA

ECS Inc, pg 856

MARYLAND

CSPMedia.com, pg 840
Kramer Communications Video Production, pg 913

MASSACHUSETTS

Preston Productions Inc, pg 981

MICHIGAN

Digi Sign Design LLC, pg 847
K&R All Media Productions Inc, pg 908

MISSOURI

Schiller's Audio-Visual, pg 1004

NEW JERSEY

PLS Staging, pg 977

NEW YORK

Interactive International Inc, pg 899
KVL Audio Visual Services Inc, pg 914
SmartSource Computer & AV Rentals, pg 1014

NORTH CAROLINA

A&V Company, pg 772

OHIO

Hughie's Event Production Services, pg 892

OKLAHOMA

PDC Productions, pg 970

PENNSYLVANIA

FMP Media Solutions Inc, pg 870

COMPUTER SYSTEMS

Multimedia Workstation Rentals (continued)

TENNESSEE

Love Shack Recording Studios, pg 925
Technical Support Systems LLC, pg 1034

VIRGINIA

Advance Concepts Inc, pg 777

PUERTO RICO

Stage Crew Audiovisual Inc, pg 1022

MANITOBA

Inland Audio Visual Ltd, pg 898

ONTARIO

Edcom Multimedia Products, pg 856
RB Productions, pg 992

QUEBEC

Group PVP, pg 882

Multimedia Workstation Repairs

CALIFORNIA

Ametron Audio/Video, pg 785

CONNECTICUT

HB Communications Inc, pg 886

FLORIDA

Hi-Tech Enterprises Inc, pg 888

GEORGIA

Stage Front Presentation Systems, pg 1022

IOWA

ECS Inc, pg 856

KENTUCKY

NOR-COM Inc, pg 958

MARYLAND

DSR Computer Technology Specialists Inc, pg 853

NEW YORK

Interactive International Inc, pg 899

OHIO

Advent Media Inc, pg 778
Tri-State Audio Visual Co, pg 1044

TENNESSEE

Technical Support Systems LLC, pg 1034

TEXAS

Biway Media, pg 808

WISCONSIN

Camera Corner Connecting Point, pg 818
Full Compass Systems, pg 874

MANITOBA

Inland Audio Visual Ltd, pg 898

Networking System Distributors

ARIZONA

CADint, pg 816
EAR Professional Audio/Video, pg 855
Media Computing Inc, pg 936

CALIFORNIA

Advanced Systems Group LLC, pg 778
Audio Images Corp, pg 794
California Tape Products Inc, pg 817
DataDirect Networks, pg 843
Electrosonic Inc, pg 859
Ingram Micro, pg 898
Jameco Electronics, pg 903
Kontron America, pg 913
Media Fabricators Inc, pg 936
MediaPOINTE, pg 938
Joseph Nicoletti Consulting-Promotion/California International Records/Global Village Records, pg 957
Photodyne Technologies, pg 974
Promax Systems, pg 986
TOA Electronics Inc, pg 1041

COLORADO

Aspen Systems Inc, pg 792
Dot Hill Systems Corp, pg 851

CONNECTICUT

The Video Messenger Co, pg 1055

FLORIDA

Access Media Group, pg 773
Digital Video Systems Inc, pg 848
Harris Corp, pg 885
Hi-Tech Import Export Corp, pg 888
Sight & Sound Productions, pg 1010

GEORGIA

Accu-Tech, pg 773
Stage Front Presentation Systems, pg 1022

ILLINOIS

Anixter Inc, pg 787
Lyn Norstad & Associates Inc, pg 926

IOWA

ECS Inc, pg 856

KENTUCKY

NOR-COM Inc, pg 958

MARYLAND

DSR Computer Technology Specialists Inc, pg 853
Human Circuit, pg 892

MASSACHUSETTS

Artel Video Systems, pg 791
Avid Technology Inc, pg 799
Psych Soft Inc, pg 987

MICHIGAN

ASC Systems, pg 791
Ascom Communications Contractors, pg 791
Digi Sign Design LLC, pg 847

MINNESOTA

Alpha Video & Audio Inc, pg 782

NEW JERSEY

Diversified Systems Inc, pg 849
Nesbit Systems Inc, pg 954
Starlite Productions, pg 1024

NEW YORK

Custom Media Environments, pg 841
Production Radio Rentals Inc, pg 984
Sanako Inc, pg 1002
SmartSource Computer & AV Rentals, pg 1014

NORTH CAROLINA

Crispin Corp, pg 839

OHIO

iVideo Technologies, pg 903
Tri-State Audio Visual Co, pg 1044

PENNSYLVANIA

Advanced AV, pg 777
IMR Limited, pg 897
The Lerro Corp, pg 919
Visual Sound Inc, pg 1059

SOUTH CAROLINA

Professional Management Services Inc, pg 985

TEXAS

Biway Media, pg 808
Industrial Audio/Video Inc, pg 897

UTAH

SirsiDynix, pg 1012

VIRGINIA

Filmdex Inc, pg 867
Intellidyne LLC, pg 899
Lee Hartman & Sons Inc, pg 918
The Whitlock Group, pg 1065

WISCONSIN

Audio Visual of Milwaukee Inc, pg 795
Camera Corner Connecting Point, pg 818
Comprompter Inc, pg 834
Full Compass Systems, pg 874

ALBERTA

Infosat Communications Inc, pg 898

MANITOBA

Advance Pro, pg 777
Inland Audio Visual Ltd, pg 898

ONTARIO

Technovision® Interactive Inc, pg 1035
Westbury National Show Systems Ltd, pg 1064

QUEBEC

Presagis, pg 981

Networking System Manufacturers

CALIFORNIA

DataDirect Networks, pg 843
Get Organized, pg 877
Grande Vitesse Systems Inc (GVS), pg 881
Hewlett-Packard Co, pg 888
iQstor Networks Inc, pg 902
Kontron America, pg 913
Opticomm-EMCORE, pg 964
QSC Audio Products LLC, pg 988
RF Industries, pg 995
TOA Electronics Inc, pg 1041
VITEC Multimedia, pg 1060
Western Digital Corp, pg 1064

COLORADO

Aspen Systems Inc, pg 792

CONNECTICUT

The Video Messenger Co, pg 1055

GEORGIA

Visix™ Inc, pg 1059

ILLINOIS

Broadcast Electronics, pg 813

MASSACHUSETTS

Artel Video Systems, pg 791
Avid Technology Inc, pg 799
CSPI, pg 840
Psych Soft Inc, pg 987

MICHIGAN

ASC Systems, pg 791

NEW JERSEY

Nesbit Systems Inc, pg 954
Starlite Productions, pg 1024

NEW YORK

ATTO Technology Inc, pg 793
MultiDyne Video & Fiber Optics Systems, pg 950

OHIO

Electronic Vision Inc (EV), pg 859
Network Technologies Inc, pg 955

PENNSYLVANIA

Mastech, pg 933
Scala Inc, pg 1003

TEXAS

Biway Media, pg 808

BRITISH COLUMBIA

Richmond Sound Design Ltd, pg 996

ONTARIO

Technovision® Interactive Inc, pg 1035

QUEBEC

Presagis, pg 981

Networking System Rentals

ARIZONA

Merestone, pg 938

CALIFORNIA

Muse Presentation Technologies, pg 950
PSAV® Presentation Services, pg 986

GEORGIA

Stage Front Presentation Systems, pg 1022

KENTUCKY

Audio Visual Techniques Inc, pg 796

MASSACHUSETTS

Preston Productions Inc, pg 981

MICHIGAN

Digi Sign Design LLC, pg 847
K&R All Media Productions Inc, pg 908

MISSOURI

Show-Me Audio-Visual, pg 1009

NEW JERSEY

Audio Visual Dynamics®, pg 795

NORTH CAROLINA

A&V Company, pg 772

OHIO

Hughie's Event Production Services, pg 892

MANITOBA

Inland Audio Visual Ltd, pg 898

Networking System Repairs

CALIFORNIA

Aztek Inc, pg 801
TOA Electronics Inc, pg 1041

COLORADO

Aspen Systems Inc, pg 792

CONNECTICUT

HB Communications Inc, pg 886

IOWA

ECS Inc, pg 856

KENTUCKY

NOR-COM Inc, pg 958

MARYLAND

DSR Computer Technology Specialists Inc, pg 853

OHIO

Tri-State Audio Visual Co, pg 1044

TEXAS

Biway Media, pg 808

VIRGINIA

The Whitlock Group, pg 1065

WISCONSIN

Camera Corner Connecting Point, pg 818
Full Compass Systems, pg 874

ALBERTA

Infosat Communications Inc, pg 898

MANITOBA

Inland Audio Visual Ltd, pg 898

Optical Disc Recorder Distributors

ARIZONA

EAR Professional Audio/Video, pg 855

CALIFORNIA

Ametron Audio/Video, pg 785
California Tape Products Inc, pg 817
Computer Modules Inc, pg 834
DiskFaktory Direct, pg 849
Media Fabricators Inc, pg 936
MediaPOINTE, pg 938
Shimad Corp, pg 1009
VMI Inc, pg 1060

COLORADO

Aspen Systems Inc, pg 792
Dot Hill Systems Corp, pg 851

FLORIDA

Access Media Group, pg 773
CD ROM™ Inc, pg 822
Digital Video Systems Inc, pg 848
Fidelity Information Services (FIS), pg 866
Harris Corp, pg 885
Hi-Tech Import Export Corp, pg 888
Pro Stage Inc, pg 983
Recording Media & Equipment Inc (RM&E), pg 993
Sight & Sound Productions, pg 1010
TAI Audio, pg 1031

GEORGIA

Stage Front Presentation Systems, pg 1022

IOWA

ECS Inc, pg 856

KENTUCKY

NOR-COM Inc, pg 958

MARYLAND

DSR Computer Technology Specialists Inc, pg 853
NewWave Technologies Inc, pg 957

MASSACHUSETTS

Psych Soft Inc, pg 987

MICHIGAN

Ascom Communications Contractors, pg 791
Digi Sign Design LLC, pg 847
Michigan Office Solutions, pg 941

MINNESOTA

Microboards Technology LLC, pg 941

MISSOURI

Modern Communications Inc, pg 944
Schiller's Audio-Visual, pg 1004

NEW JERSEY

Starlite Productions, pg 1024
Total Video Products Inc, pg 1042

NEW YORK

Audio-Video Corp, pg 795
Custom Media Environments, pg 841
Image Management Systems Inc, pg 895

NORTH CAROLINA

Crispin Corp, pg 839

OHIO

Electronic Vision Inc (EV), pg 859

PENNSYLVANIA

Advanced AV, pg 777

TEXAS

Astro Audio Visual, pg 792
Biway Media, pg 808
Replicopy Digital Media Center, pg 995
Tarpley Media Systems, pg 1032
Videotex Systems Inc, pg 1057

UTAH

Performance Audio, pg 973

VIRGINIA

Avitecture Inc, pg 799
Cybernetics, pg 841
Filmdex Inc, pg 867

WISCONSIN

Audio Visual of Milwaukee Inc, pg 795
Full Compass Systems, pg 874
Indus International Inc, pg 897

ALBERTA

Matrix Video Communications Corp (MVCC), pg 934

BRITISH COLUMBIA

ProVision Video Sales & Rentals Inc, pg 986

MANITOBA

Advance Pro, pg 777
Inland Audio Visual Ltd, pg 898

Optical Disc Recorder Manufacturers

CALIFORNIA

DiskFaktory Direct, pg 849
Grande Vitesse Systems Inc (GVS), pg 881
Panasonic Broadcast & Digital Systems Co, pg 968

COLORADO

MAM-A Inc, pg 929

FLORIDA

CD ROM™ Inc, pg 822

OHIO

Tosoh USA Inc, pg 1042

Optical Disc Recorder Rentals

ARIZONA

Merestone, pg 938

CALIFORNIA

Ametron Audio/Video, pg 785
Muse Presentation Technologies, pg 950
VER-Video Equipment Rentals, pg 1053

FLORIDA

Fidelity Information Services (FIS), pg 866
Pro Stage Inc, pg 983

GEORGIA

Stage Front Presentation Systems, pg 1022

IOWA

ECS Inc, pg 856

MARYLAND

CSPMedia.com, pg 840

MASSACHUSETTS

Preston Productions Inc, pg 981

MICHIGAN

Digi Sign Design LLC, pg 847
K&R All Media Productions Inc, pg 908
K&R's Recording Studios Inc, pg 908
TeL Systems, pg 1035

NEW YORK

Dreamhire LLC, pg 852

WISCONSIN

Full Compass Systems, pg 874

PUERTO RICO

Stage Crew Audiovisual Inc, pg 1022

COMPUTER SYSTEMS

Optical Disc Recorder Rentals (continued)

MANITOBA

Inland Audio Visual Ltd, pg 898

ONTARIO

Technovision® Interactive Inc, pg 1035

QUEBEC

Group PVP, pg 882

Optical Disc Recorder Repairs

CALIFORNIA

Ametron Audio/Video, pg 785
McAlister Electronics, pg 935

CONNECTICUT

HB Communications Inc, pg 886

FLORIDA

Fidelity Information Services (FIS), pg 866

IOWA

ECS Inc, pg 856

KENTUCKY

NOR-COM Inc, pg 958

MINNESOTA

Microboards Technology LLC, pg 941

WISCONSIN

Full Compass Systems, pg 874

MANITOBA

Inland Audio Visual Ltd, pg 898

Plotter Distributors

ARIZONA

CADint, pg 816
Mutoh America Inc, pg 951
Professional Marketing Services Inc, pg 985

CALIFORNIA

Aztek Inc, pg 801
Ingram Micro, pg 898
MediaPOINTE, pg 938

COLORADO

Aspen Systems Inc, pg 792
Stanco Sales LLC, pg 1023

FLORIDA

Hi-Tech Import Export Corp, pg 888

GEORGIA

Stage Front Presentation Systems, pg 1022

IOWA

ECS Inc, pg 856

KENTUCKY

NOR-COM Inc, pg 958

MARYLAND

DSR Computer Technology Specialists Inc, pg 853

MASSACHUSETTS

Psych Soft Inc, pg 987

MICHIGAN

ASC Systems, pg 791
Michigan Office Solutions, pg 941

MINNESOTA

Tierney Brothers Inc, pg 1040

MISSOURI

Communitronics Corp, pg 833

NEW JERSEY

Argraph Corp, pg 789
Starlite Productions, pg 1024
Video Corporation of America (VCA), pg 1055

NEW YORK

Image Management Systems Inc, pg 895
Max USA, pg 934
SmartSource Computer & AV Rentals, pg 1014

OHIO

iVideo Technologies, pg 903

PENNSYLVANIA

Advanced AV, pg 777
Visual Sound Inc, pg 1059

VIRGINIA

Lee Hartman & Sons Inc, pg 918
The Whitlock Group, pg 1065

WISCONSIN

Audio Visual of Milwaukee Inc, pg 795
Camera Corner Connecting Point, pg 818

MANITOBA

Advance Pro, pg 777

Plotter Manufacturers

ARIZONA

Mutoh America Inc, pg 951

CALIFORNIA

Hewlett-Packard Co, pg 888

NEW YORK

Max USA, pg 934

Plotter Rentals

ARIZONA

Merestone, pg 938

CALIFORNIA

Artichoke Productions, pg 791
Express Media Inc, pg 864

MISSOURI

Show-Me Audio-Visual, pg 1009

NEW YORK

SmartSource Computer & AV Rentals, pg 1014

Plotter Repairs

CONNECTICUT

HB Communications Inc, pg 886

GEORGIA

Stage Front Presentation Systems, pg 1022

IOWA

ECS Inc, pg 856

KENTUCKY

NOR-COM Inc, pg 958

WISCONSIN

Camera Corner Connecting Point, pg 818

Presentation System Distributors

ARIZONA

EAR Professional Audio/Video, pg 855

ARKANSAS

White Diamond Productions, pg 1065

CALIFORNIA

ADS Technologies, pg 777
AITech International, pg 779
Ametron Audio/Video, pg 785
Associated Sound, pg 792
ATV Video Center Inc, pg 793
Be Media, pg 804
California Tape Products Inc, pg 817
Computer Modules Inc, pg 834
Dynamic Digital Depth Inc (DDD), pg 854
Electrosonic Inc, pg 859
FXC Communications, pg 874
Hooper Camera & Imaging, pg 891
JD Audio Visual Inc, pg 904
Laser Magic Productions, pg 916
Media Fabricators Inc, pg 936
MediaPOINTE, pg 938
Mobilized Tech Systems, pg 944
POP TV, pg 978
Promax Systems, pg 986
Stanislaus Audio Video Inc, pg 1023
Total Media Group, pg 1042

COLORADO

Aspen Systems Inc, pg 792
Daylight Productions & Rentals, pg 844
ProLine Digital, pg 986

CONNECTICUT

Everett Hall Associates Inc, pg 863
The Video Messenger Co, pg 1055

FLORIDA

AVI-SPL, pg 798
Digital Video Systems Inc, pg 848
Pro Stage Inc, pg 983
Sight & Sound Productions, pg 1010

GEORGIA

PolyVision Corporation, pg 978
Stage Front Presentation Systems, pg 1022

HAWAII

The Audio Visual Co (AVCO), pg 795

ILLINOIS

Dukane Corp, Audio Visual Products Division, pg 853
G T Luscombe Co Inc, pg 926
H Wilson Co, pg 1067

IOWA

ECS Inc, pg 856

KENTUCKY

NOR-COM Inc, pg 958

LOUISIANA

Intermedia Technologies, pg 900

MARYLAND

DSR Computer Technology Specialists Inc, pg 853
Human Circuit, pg 892
Image Logic Corp, pg 895
Nelson White Systems Inc, pg 954

MASSACHUSETTS

Graphx Inc, pg 881
Monotype Inc, pg 945
Psych Soft Inc, pg 987
Rule Broadcast Systems, pg 1000
WSI, pg 1070

MICHIGAN

ASC Systems, pg 791
Ascom Communications Contractors, pg 791
Digi Sign Design LLC, pg 847
Michigan Office Solutions, pg 941
On Stage Visuals, pg 963

MINNESOTA

Alpha Video & Audio Inc, pg 782
Tierney Brothers Inc, pg 1040
Varitronics LLC, pg 1052

MISSOURI

Modern Communications Inc, pg 944
Schiller's Audio-Visual, pg 1004

NEBRASKA

Dog & Pony Productions Inc, pg 850

NEW HAMPSHIRE

Optics 1 Inc, pg 964

NEW JERSEY

Audio Visual Associates, pg 795
Diversified Systems Inc, pg 849
Starlite Productions, pg 1024
Total Video Products Inc, pg 1042
Wilray Audio Visual Corp, pg 1067
Wired 4 Sound Inc, pg 1068

NEW YORK

Audio-Video Corp, pg 795
Design Audio Visual Inc, pg 845
DSan Corp, pg 852
Image Management Systems Inc, pg 895
KVL Audio Visual Services Inc, pg 914
SmartSource Computer & AV Rentals, pg 1014
Visual Technologies Corp, pg 1060

OHIO

Electronic Vision Inc (EV), pg 859
ITA Audio Visual Solutions, pg 902
Midwest Photo Exchange, pg 942
Tri-State Audio Visual Co, pg 1044

OREGON

NeoSoft Corp, pg 954

PENNSYLVANIA

AccuWeather Inc, pg 774
Advanced AV, pg 777
Bernie's Photo Center, pg 805
Grise Audio Visual Center Inc, pg 882
Innovision Media Group, pg 899
The Lerro Corp, pg 919
Meridia Audience Response, pg 939
Wespen Audio Visual Co, pg 1063

TENNESSEE

Lowrance Sound Co Inc, pg 925
Technical Support Systems LLC, pg 1034
Tennessee Visual Service Co, pg 1037
Zion Music Group, pg 1074

TEXAS

Audio Visual Technologies Group, pg 796
AVES Audio Visual Systems Inc, pg 798
Data Display Audio Visual Co LP, pg 843
Data Projections Inc, pg 843
Epic Software Group Inc, pg 862
Media Management LLC, pg 937
Schoolhouse Audio Visual, pg 1004
Stage Directions, pg 1022
Videotex Systems Inc, pg 1057

VIRGINIA

Avitecture Inc, pg 799
Intellidyne LLC, pg 899
Lee Hartman & Sons Inc, pg 918
Quince Imaging Inc, pg 989

WASHINGTON

eMagin Corp, pg 860

WISCONSIN

Audio Visual of Milwaukee Inc, pg 795
Camera Corner Connecting Point, pg 818
Full Compass Systems, pg 874
Safe Harbor Computers, pg 1001

ALBERTA

Infosat Communications Inc, pg 898
Matrix Video Communications Corp (MVCC), pg 934
SMART Technologies Inc, pg 1013

BRITISH COLUMBIA

Commercial Electronics Ltd, pg 832

MANITOBA

Advance Pro, pg 777
Inland Audio Visual Ltd, pg 898

ONTARIO

Cinema Stage Inc, pg 827
Gesturetek, pg 877
Image Video, pg 895
Premier A/V Sales Ltd, pg 980
Westbury National Show Systems Ltd, pg 1064

Presentation System Manufacturers

ARIZONA

Boeckeler Instruments Inc, pg 810
Covid Inc, pg 837
eInstruction Corp, pg 858

CALIFORNIA

ADS Technologies, pg 777
AITech International, pg 779
Enright Co, pg 861
Extron Electronics, pg 864
Gefen, pg 876
Grande Vitesse Systems Inc (GVS), pg 881
Laser Magic Productions, pg 916
Micro Express, pg 941
Panasonic Broadcast & Digital Systems Co, pg 968
VITEC Multimedia, pg 1060

CONNECTICUT

The Video Messenger Co, pg 1055

GEORGIA

PolyVision Corporation, pg 978
Visix™ Inc, pg 1059

ILLINOIS

Bretford Manufacturing Inc, pg 812
Dukane Corp, Audio Visual Products Division, pg 853
Kart-A-Bag Manufacturing Inc, pg 908

MARYLAND

Image Logic Corp, pg 895

MASSACHUSETTS

Graphx Inc, pg 881
Monotype Inc, pg 945
Psych Soft Inc, pg 987
WSI, pg 1070

MISSOURI

Ken-A-Vision Manufacturing Co Inc, pg 909
Magna Visual Inc, pg 928

NEW HAMPSHIRE

Optics 1 Inc, pg 964

NEW JERSEY

Crestron Electronics Inc, pg 839
FSR Inc, pg 873

NEW YORK

DSan Corp, pg 852

OREGON

NeoSoft Corp, pg 954

PENNSYLVANIA

AccuWeather Inc, pg 774
Interactive Products, pg 899
Meridia Audience Response, pg 939
Scala Inc, pg 1003

TENNESSEE

Adtec Digital Inc, pg 777

TEXAS

MooreCo Inc, pg 946

VIRGINIA

Avitecture Inc, pg 799
Quince Imaging Inc, pg 989

WASHINGTON

eMagin Corp, pg 860

WISCONSIN

Bardes Products Inc, pg 803

ALBERTA

SMART Technologies Inc, pg 1013

BRITISH COLUMBIA

Richmond Sound Design Ltd, pg 996

ONTARIO

Gesturetek, pg 877
Image Video, pg 895

Presentation System Rentals

ALABAMA

Audio-Video Resources Inc, pg 795

ARIZONA

Merestone, pg 938
Video West Inc, pg 1056

ARKANSAS

White Diamond Productions, pg 1065

CALIFORNIA

Alliant Event Services, pg 781
Ametron Audio/Video, pg 785
Associated Sound, pg 792
ATV Video Center Inc, pg 793
Dynamic Digital Depth Inc (DDD), pg 854
Express Media Inc, pg 864
Hooper Camera & Imaging, pg 891
JD Audio Visual Inc, pg 904
Lynch Communications, pg 926
Media Fabricators Inc, pg 936
Muse Presentation Technologies, pg 950
Slate Media Group, pg 1013
VER-Video Equipment Rentals, pg 1053

COLORADO

Multimedia Audio Visual Inc, pg 950

CONNECTICUT

A/V Davey, pg 797
Everett Hall Associates Inc, pg 863

FLORIDA

Industrial Strength Inc, pg 897
Pro Stage Inc, pg 983

GEORGIA

Stage Front Presentation Systems, pg 1022

ILLINOIS

Airways Digital Media, pg 779
Backstar Creative Media Inc, pg 801
QuickSet International Inc, pg 989
RC Communications, pg 992
Show Department Inc, pg 1009

IOWA

ECS Inc, pg 856

KENTUCKY

Audio Visual Techniques Inc, pg 796

MARYLAND

Advance Audiovisual Presentation Ltd, pg 777
CPR MultiMedia Solutions, pg 837
Nelson White Systems Inc, pg 954

MASSACHUSETTS

AVFX Inc, pg 798
massAV, pg 933

MICHIGAN

Digi Sign Design LLC, pg 847
K&R All Media Productions Inc, pg 908
On Stage Visuals, pg 963

MINNESOTA

Alpha Video & Audio Inc, pg 782

MISSOURI

Schiller's Audio-Visual, pg 1004
Show-Me Audio-Visual, pg 1009

NEBRASKA

Dog & Pony Productions Inc, pg 850

NEW JERSEY

Audio Visual Dynamics®, pg 795
PLS Staging, pg 977
Starlite Productions, pg 1024
Wired 4 Sound Inc, pg 1068

NEW YORK

Design Audio Visual Inc, pg 845
KVL Audio Visual Services Inc, pg 914

COMPUTER SYSTEMS

Presentation System Rentals (continued)

NEW YORK (continued)

SmartSource Computer & AV Rentals, pg 1014
Visual Technologies Corp, pg 1060

NORTH CAROLINA

A&V Company, pg 772
AV Metro Inc, pg 797

NORTH DAKOTA

Media Productions, pg 937

OHIO

Bartha, pg 803

OKLAHOMA

PDC Productions, pg 970

PENNSYLVANIA

Advanced AV, pg 777
Grise Audio Visual Center Inc, pg 882
Innovision Media Group, pg 899
Meridia Audience Response, pg 939

TENNESSEE

Technical Support Systems LLC, pg 1034
Tennessee Visual Service Co, pg 1037

TEXAS

Freeman, pg 872
Stage Directions, pg 1022

VIRGINIA

Advance Concepts Inc, pg 777
Quince Imaging Inc, pg 989

WISCONSIN

Audio Visual of Milwaukee Inc, pg 795
Full Compass Systems, pg 874

PUERTO RICO

Stage Crew Audiovisual Inc, pg 1022

BRITISH COLUMBIA

Commercial Electronics Ltd, pg 832

MANITOBA

Inland Audio Visual Ltd, pg 898

ONTARIO

Metalworks Recording Studios Inc, pg 939
Westbury National Show Systems Ltd, pg 1064

QUEBEC

Audio Visual Dynamics Ltd, pg 795

Presentation System Repairs

CONNECTICUT

HB Communications Inc, pg 886

GEORGIA

Stage Front Presentation Systems, pg 1022

IOWA

ECS Inc, pg 856

KENTUCKY

NOR-COM Inc, pg 958

MARYLAND

Nelson White Systems Inc, pg 954

MASSACHUSETTS

Monotype Inc, pg 945

NEW JERSEY

Starlite Productions, pg 1024

NEW YORK

Visual Technologies Corp, pg 1060

OHIO

Advent Media Inc, pg 778
ITA Audio Visual Solutions, pg 902
Tri-State Audio Visual Co, pg 1044

TENNESSEE

Technical Support Systems LLC, pg 1034

TEXAS

Data Display Audio Visual Co LP, pg 843
Industrial Audio/Video Inc, pg 897

VIRGINIA

Avitecture Inc, pg 799

WISCONSIN

Camera Corner Connecting Point, pg 818
Full Compass Systems, pg 874

ALBERTA

Infosat Communications Inc, pg 898

MANITOBA

Inland Audio Visual Ltd, pg 898

ONTARIO

Westbury National Show Systems Ltd, pg 1064

Projection Panel Distributors

ARIZONA

EAR Professional Audio/Video, pg 855
Professional Marketing Services Inc, pg 985
Troxell Communications Inc, pg 1045
Ultimate Presentation Systems Inc, pg 1047

CALIFORNIA

Ametron Audio/Video, pg 785
Barber Tech Video Products, pg 802
Be Media, pg 804
California Tape Products Inc, pg 817
Cibola Systems, pg 826
Electrosonic Inc, pg 859
FXC Communications, pg 874
Media Fabricators Inc, pg 936
MediaPOINTE, pg 938
VMI Inc, pg 1060

COLORADO

Daylight Productions & Rentals, pg 844

CONNECTICUT

Everett Hall Associates Inc, pg 863

FLORIDA

AVI-SPL, pg 798
Digital Video Systems Inc, pg 848
Harmon's Audio-Visual Services, pg 885
Industrial Strength Inc, pg 897
Pro Stage Inc, pg 983

GEORGIA

Clark, pg 829
Stage Front Presentation Systems, pg 1022

HAWAII

The Audio Visual Co (AVCO), pg 795

ILLINOIS

Joseph Electronics, pg 906

INDIANA

Lee Co Inc, pg 918
Sensory Technologies LLC, pg 1006

IOWA

ECS Inc, pg 856

KENTUCKY

Axxis Inc, pg 800
NOR-COM Inc, pg 958

LOUISIANA

Intermedia Technologies, pg 900

MARYLAND

Cardinal Sound & Video, pg 820
dbF a Media Company, pg 844
DSR Computer Technology Specialists Inc, pg 853

MASSACHUSETTS

Camera Co Inc/Broadcast Divison, pg 818

MICHIGAN

Ascom Communications Contractors, pg 791
Digi Sign Design LLC, pg 847
Michigan Office Solutions, pg 941

MINNESOTA

Alpha Video & Audio Inc, pg 782

MISSOURI

Modern Communications Inc, pg 944
Schiller's Audio-Visual, pg 1004

NEBRASKA

Strong Cinema Products, pg 1026

NEVADA

Aardvark Video & Media Productions, pg 772

NEW JERSEY

AV Bluebook, pg 797
Diversified Systems Inc, pg 849
Earl Girls Inc, pg 855
Starlite Productions, pg 1024
Total Video Products Inc, pg 1042
Wilray Audio Visual Corp, pg 1067
Wired 4 Sound Inc, pg 1068

NEW YORK

ALTEL Systems Inc, pg 783
Audio-Video Corp, pg 795
Custom Media Environments, pg 841
Gaylord Brothers, pg 876
Langie Audio Visual Systems, pg 915
Magnaplan Corp, pg 928
Neptune Photo Inc, pg 954
SmartSource Computer & AV Rentals, pg 1014
TecNec Distributing, pg 1035
Video Technology Services Inc, pg 1056
Visual Technologies Corp, pg 1060

OHIO

ITA Audio Visual Solutions, pg 902
Midwest Photo Exchange, pg 942
Tri-State Audio Visual Co, pg 1044

PENNSYLVANIA

Advanced AV, pg 777
Bernie's Photo Center, pg 805
Clair Brothers Audio Systems Inc, pg 829
J E Foss Co, pg 871
The Lerro Corp, pg 919
Vistacom Inc, pg 1059

TENNESSEE

Lowrance Sound Co Inc, pg 925
Technical Support Systems LLC, pg 1034
Tennessee Visual Service Co, pg 1037

TEXAS

Audio Visual Technologies Group, pg 796
Media Management LLC, pg 937
Schoolhouse Audio Visual, pg 1004
Tarpley Media Systems, pg 1032
Videotex Systems Inc, pg 1057

VIRGINIA

Communications Specialists Inc, pg 833
Lee Hartman & Sons Inc, pg 918

WASHINGTON

Boxlight Inc, pg 811
CCI Solutions, pg 821

WISCONSIN

Camera Corner Connecting Point, pg 818
Full Compass Systems, pg 874

ALBERTA

Sharp's Audio-Visual Ltd, pg 1008
SMART Technologies Inc, pg 1013

BRITISH COLUMBIA

Commercial Electronics Ltd, pg 832

MANITOBA

Inland Audio Visual Ltd, pg 898

ONTARIO

Premier A/V Sales Ltd, pg 980
Westbury National Show Systems Ltd, pg 1064

Projection Panel Manufacturers

FLORIDA

Vutec Corp, Video Products Division, pg 1061

ILLINOIS

ACCO Brands Corp, pg 773

NEW JERSEY

Sharp Electronics Corp, Professional Display Division, pg 1008

TEXAS

MooreCo Inc, pg 946

VIRGINIA

Optikinetics Ltd - The Americas, pg 964
Quince Imaging Inc, pg 989

ALBERTA

SMART Technologies Inc, pg 1013

ONTARIO

Evertz Microsystems Ltd, pg 863

Projection Panel Rentals

ARIZONA

Merestone, pg 938
Ultimate Presentation Systems Inc, pg 1047

CALIFORNIA

Alliant Event Services, pg 781
Ametron Audio/Video, pg 785
Barber Tech Video Products, pg 802
Media Fabricators Inc, pg 936
Munday & Collins AV, pg 950
Muse Presentation Technologies, pg 950
PSAV® Presentation Services, pg 986
Voice & Video Rentals, pg 1060

COLORADO

Daylight Productions & Rentals, pg 844
Multimedia Audio Visual Inc, pg 950

CONNECTICUT

Everett Hall Associates Inc, pg 863

FLORIDA

AVI-SPL, pg 798
Harmon's Audio-Visual Services, pg 885
Industrial Strength Inc, pg 897
Pro Stage Inc, pg 983

GEORGIA

Stage Front Presentation Systems, pg 1022

ILLINOIS

Backstar Creative Media Inc, pg 801
RC Communications, pg 992

IOWA

ECS Inc, pg 856

KENTUCKY

Audio Visual Techniques Inc, pg 796

MARYLAND

CPR MultiMedia Solutions, pg 837
dbF a Media Company, pg 844
Event Tech, pg 863

MASSACHUSETTS

Cramer Productions, pg 837
massAV, pg 933
Preston Productions Inc, pg 981

MICHIGAN

Digi Sign Design LLC, pg 847
K&R All Media Productions Inc, pg 908
TeL Systems, pg 1035

MINNESOTA

Alpha Video & Audio Inc, pg 782

MISSOURI

Schiller's Audio-Visual, pg 1004
Show-Me Audio-Visual, pg 1009

NEVADA

GES Audio Visual, pg 877

NEW JERSEY

Audio Visual Dynamics®, pg 795
Earl Girls Inc, pg 855
Starlite Productions, pg 1024
Wired 4 Sound Inc, pg 1068

NEW YORK

Langie Audio Visual Systems, pg 915
Magnaplan Corp, pg 928
SmartSource Computer & AV Rentals, pg 1014
Visual Technologies Corp, pg 1060

NORTH CAROLINA

A&V Company, pg 772
AV Metro Inc, pg 797

PENNSYLVANIA

Advanced AV, pg 777
FMP Media Solutions Inc, pg 870

TENNESSEE

Technical Support Systems LLC, pg 1034
Tennessee Visual Service Co, pg 1037

TEXAS

Industrial Audio/Video Inc, pg 897
Stage Directions, pg 1022

WASHINGTON

Boxlight Inc, pg 811

ALBERTA

L R Light & Sound, pg 915
Sharp's Audio-Visual Ltd, pg 1008

BRITISH COLUMBIA

Commercial Electronics Ltd, pg 832

MANITOBA

Inland Audio Visual Ltd, pg 898

ONTARIO

Metalworks Recording Studios Inc, pg 939
Premier A/V Sales Ltd, pg 980
Westbury National Show Systems Ltd, pg 1064

Projection Panel Repairs

CALIFORNIA

Ametron Audio/Video, pg 785
Electrosonic Inc, pg 859
VMI Inc, pg 1060

CONNECTICUT

HB Communications Inc, pg 886

GEORGIA

Stage Front Presentation Systems, pg 1022

IOWA

ECS Inc, pg 856

KENTUCKY

Axxis Inc, pg 800
NOR-COM Inc, pg 958

MARYLAND

Visual Aids Electronics Corp, pg 1059

MISSOURI

Schiller's Audio-Visual, pg 1004

NEW JERSEY

Earl Girls Inc, pg 855
Starlite Productions, pg 1024

NEW YORK

Langie Audio Visual Systems, pg 915
Visual Technologies Corp, pg 1060

OHIO

ITA Audio Visual Solutions, pg 902
Tri-State Audio Visual Co, pg 1044

PENNSYLVANIA

J E Foss Co, pg 871

TENNESSEE

Technical Support Systems LLC, pg 1034

TEXAS

Industrial Audio/Video Inc, pg 897

WISCONSIN

Camera Corner Connecting Point, pg 818
Full Compass Systems, pg 874

ALBERTA

Sharp's Audio-Visual Ltd, pg 1008

MANITOBA

Inland Audio Visual Ltd, pg 898

ONTARIO

Westbury National Show Systems Ltd, pg 1064

RGB/NTSC Converter Distributors

ALABAMA

PESA, pg 973

ARIZONA

EAR Professional Audio/Video, pg 855
Troxell Communications Inc, pg 1045
Ultimate Presentation Systems Inc, pg 1047

ARKANSAS

Jay S Stanley & Associates Inc, pg 1023
White Diamond Productions, pg 1065

CALIFORNIA

Addlogix, pg 776
Advanced Systems Group LLC, pg 778
AITech International, pg 779
Ametron Audio/Video, pg 785
Audio Images Corp, pg 794
Audio/Video Supply Inc, pg 795
Be Media, pg 804
California Tape Products Inc, pg 817
FXC Communications, pg 874
Ingram Micro, pg 898
MediaPOINTE, pg 938
POP TV, pg 978
Total Media Group, pg 1042
Tri-Ed, pg 1044
Videobotics, pg 1056
VMI Inc, pg 1060
Zack Electronics Inc, pg 1073

COMPUTER SYSTEMS

RGB/NTSC Converter Distributors (continued)

CONNECTICUT

Video Automation Systems Inc, pg 1054

FLORIDA

Access Media Group, pg 773
Digital Video Systems Inc, pg 848
General Projection Systems Inc, pg 877
Hi-Tech Enterprises Inc, pg 888
Hi-Tech Import Export Corp, pg 888
Industrial Strength Inc, pg 897
Midtown Video Inc, pg 942
Pro Stage Inc, pg 983
Sight & Sound Productions, pg 1010

GEORGIA

Baker Audio Inc, pg 801
Barco Inc, pg 803
Omnimedia Inc, pg 962
Stage Front Presentation Systems, pg 1022

HAWAII

The Audio Visual Co (AVCO), pg 795

ILLINOIS

Allen Visual Systems Inc, pg 781
Joseph Electronics, pg 906

INDIANA

Sensory Technologies LLC, pg 1006

IOWA

ECS Inc, pg 856

KANSAS

Smith Audio-Visual Inc, pg 1014

KENTUCKY

Audio Visual Techniques Inc, pg 796
NOR-COM Inc, pg 958

MAINE

Headlight Audio Visual Inc, pg 887

MARYLAND

Cardinal Sound & Video, pg 820

MASSACHUSETTS

Camera Co Inc/Broadcast Divison, pg 818
Data Translation Inc, pg 843

MICHIGAN

ASC Systems, pg 791
Ascom Communications Contractors, pg 791
City Events Group, pg 828
Digi Sign Design LLC, pg 847
On Stage Visuals, pg 963

MISSOURI

Communitronics Corp, pg 833
MIS Technologies, pg 944
Modern Communications Inc, pg 944
Schiller's Audio-Visual, pg 1004

NEBRASKA

Dog & Pony Productions Inc, pg 850

NEVADA

Aardvark Video & Media Productions, pg 772

NEW JERSEY

A-V Services Inc, pg 771
Audio Visual Associates, pg 795
Comprehensive Cable & Connectivity Co, pg 833
Diversified Systems Inc, pg 849
Earl Girls Inc, pg 855
PatchAmp, pg 970
PLS Staging, pg 977
Starlite Productions, pg 1024
SYMCO Inc, pg 1030
Total Video Products Inc, pg 1042
Video Corporation of America (VCA), pg 1055
Wired 4 Sound Inc, pg 1068

NEW YORK

ALTEL Systems Inc, pg 783
Audio-Video Corp, pg 795
AV Workshop, pg 797
BTX Technologies, pg 814
Communication Corner Inc, pg 832
Communications Specialties Inc, pg 833
General Audio-Visual Inc (GAVI), pg 876
Indigo Productions, pg 897
Langie Audio Visual Systems, pg 915
Technisphere Corp, pg 1034
TecNec Distributing, pg 1035
Visual Technologies Corp, pg 1060
Visual Word Systems Inc, pg 1060

NORTH CAROLINA

Crest Electronics Inc, pg 839

OHIO

Copp Integrated Systems, pg 836
ITA Audio Visual Solutions, pg 902
iVideo Technologies, pg 903
Jimmy Rea Electronics Inc, pg 992
Tri-State Audio Visual Co, pg 1044
Tri-State Visual Products, pg 1044

PENNSYLVANIA

Advanced AV, pg 777
Aydin Displays Inc, pg 800
Clair Brothers Audio Systems Inc, pg 829
The Lerro Corp, pg 919
Vistacom Inc, pg 1059
Visual Sound Inc, pg 1059

TENNESSEE

Lowrance Sound Co Inc, pg 925
Technical Support Systems LLC, pg 1034
Tennessee Visual Service Co, pg 1037

TEXAS

Audio Visual Technologies Group, pg 796
AVES Audio Visual Systems Inc, pg 798
Biway Media, pg 808
Industrial Audio/Video Inc, pg 897
Media Management LLC, pg 937
Stage Directions, pg 1022
Tarpley Media Systems, pg 1032
Videotex Systems Inc, pg 1057

UTAH

RIA Corp, pg 996

VIRGINIA

Communications Specialists Inc, pg 833
Hoppmann Audio Visual, pg 891
Quince Imaging Inc, pg 989
The Whitlock Group, pg 1065

WISCONSIN

Audio Visual of Milwaukee Inc, pg 795
Camera Corner Connecting Point, pg 818
Full Compass Systems, pg 874
Safe Harbor Computers, pg 1001

ALBERTA

Infosat Communications Inc, pg 898
Matrix Video Communications Corp (MVCC), pg 934
Sharp's Audio-Visual Ltd, pg 1008

BRITISH COLUMBIA

Commercial Electronics Ltd, pg 832

MANITOBA

Tek Gear, pg 1035

ONTARIO

Premier A/V Sales Ltd, pg 980
Westbury National Show Systems Ltd, pg 1064

QUEBEC

Concept Audio-Visual, pg 834

RGB/NTSC Converter Manufacturers

ALABAMA

PESA, pg 973

ARIZONA

Covid Inc, pg 837

CALIFORNIA

AITech International, pg 779
ALTINEX Inc, pg 783
Extron Electronics, pg 864
For-A Corp of America, pg 871
Grande Vitesse Systems Inc (GVS), pg 881
Opticomm-EMCORE, pg 964
QRS Software Services, pg 988
RGB Spectrum, pg 996

CONNECTICUT

Video Automation Systems Inc, pg 1054

GEORGIA

Barco Inc, pg 803

ILLINOIS

NEC Display Solutions of America, pg 954

MASSACHUSETTS

Data Translation Inc, pg 843

MISSOURI

Link Electronics Inc, pg 922

NEW JERSEY

FSR Inc, pg 873

NEW YORK

Communications Specialties Inc, pg 833
MultiDyne Video & Fiber Optics Systems, pg 950
Judson Rosebush Co Inc, pg 999

VIRGINIA

Quince Imaging Inc, pg 989

BRITISH COLUMBIA

Triad Communications Ltd, pg 1044

QUEBEC

Matrox Video Products Group, pg 934

RGB/NTSC Converter Rentals

ARIZONA

Video West Inc, pg 1056

ARKANSAS

White Diamond Productions, pg 1065

CALIFORNIA

Ametron Audio/Video, pg 785
AV Guys, pg 797
Express Media Inc, pg 864
Munday & Collins AV, pg 950
Muse Presentation Technologies, pg 950
RetinaVision Productions, pg 995
VMI Inc, pg 1060
Voice & Video Rentals, pg 1060

FLORIDA

Access Media Group, pg 773
Accord Productions, pg 773
Sight & Sound Productions, pg 1010
Universal Studios Florida® Production Group, pg 1049

GEORGIA

Stage Front Presentation Systems, pg 1022

ILLINOIS

Show Department Inc, pg 1009

KENTUCKY

Audio Visual Techniques Inc, pg 796

MAINE

Headlight Audio Visual Inc, pg 887

MARYLAND

CPR MultiMedia Solutions, pg 837
Event Tech, pg 863

MASSACHUSETTS

Preston Productions Inc, pg 981

MICHIGAN

Digi Sign Design LLC, pg 847
K&R All Media Productions Inc, pg 908
On Stage Visuals, pg 963

MISSOURI

Show-Me Audio-Visual, pg 1009

NEBRASKA

Dog & Pony Productions Inc, pg 850

NEW JERSEY

Audio Visual Associates, pg 795
Audio Visual Dynamics®, pg 795
Earl Girls Inc, pg 855
Giant Audio Visual Inc, pg 878
Starlite Productions, pg 1024
Wired 4 Sound Inc, pg 1068

NEW YORK

Visual Word Systems Inc, pg 1060

NORTH CAROLINA

A&V Company, pg 772
Take One Productions Ltd, pg 1031

NORTH DAKOTA

Media Productions, pg 937

OKLAHOMA

PDC Productions, pg 970

PENNSYLVANIA

FMP Media Solutions Inc, pg 870
Visual Sound Inc, pg 1059

TENNESSEE

Technical Support Systems LLC, pg 1034

TEXAS

Digital Display Solutions Inc, pg 847
Stage Directions, pg 1022

VIRGINIA

Quince Imaging Inc, pg 989

WISCONSIN

Audio Visual of Milwaukee Inc, pg 795

PUERTO RICO

Stage Crew Audiovisual Inc, pg 1022

ONTARIO

Westbury National Show Systems Ltd, pg 1064

RGB/NTSC Converter Repairs

CALIFORNIA

Ametron Audio/Video, pg 785

FLORIDA

Hi-Tech Enterprises Inc, pg 888
JT Communications, pg 906

GEORGIA

Stage Front Presentation Systems, pg 1022

ILLINOIS

Allen Visual Systems Inc, pg 781
Midwest Digital Corp, pg 942

IOWA

ECS Inc, pg 856

KENTUCKY

NOR-COM Inc, pg 958

NEW JERSEY

Audio Visual Associates, pg 795

NEW YORK

Technisphere Corp, pg 1034
Visual Technologies Corp, pg 1060

OHIO

Tri-State Audio Visual Co, pg 1044

TENNESSEE

Technical Support Systems LLC, pg 1034

TEXAS

Tarpley Media Systems, pg 1032

VIRGINIA

Hoppmann Audio Visual, pg 891
Quince Imaging Inc, pg 989

WISCONSIN

Audio Visual of Milwaukee Inc, pg 795
Camera Corner Connecting Point, pg 818
Full Compass Systems, pg 874

ALBERTA

Infosat Communications Inc, pg 898
Sharp's Audio-Visual Ltd, pg 1008

ONTARIO

Westbury National Show Systems Ltd, pg 1064

Sound Card Distributors

ARIZONA

Allusion Studios & Pure Wave Audio, pg 782
EAR Professional Audio/Video, pg 855
Troxell Communications Inc, pg 1045

CALIFORNIA

Ametron Audio/Video, pg 785
Audio Images Corp, pg 794
Be Media, pg 804
California Tape Products Inc, pg 817
Empire Wholesale Inc, pg 860
Eye & I Productions, pg 864
Media Fabricators Inc, pg 936
MediaPOINTE, pg 938
Plus 24, pg 977
POP TV, pg 978
Promax Systems, pg 986
Total Media Group, pg 1042
VMI Inc, pg 1060

FLORIDA

Access Media Group, pg 773
Digital Video Systems Inc, pg 848
Harris Corp, pg 885
Hi-Tech Enterprises Inc, pg 888
TAI Audio, pg 1031

GEORGIA

Stage Front Presentation Systems, pg 1022

HAWAII

The Audio Visual Co (AVCO), pg 795

INDIANA

Lee Co Inc, pg 918

IOWA

ECS Inc, pg 856

KENTUCKY

NOR-COM Inc, pg 958

MARYLAND

DSR Computer Technology Specialists Inc, pg 853

MASSACHUSETTS

Camera Co Inc/Broadcast Divison, pg 818
Professional Audio Design Inc, pg 985

MICHIGAN

Digi Sign Design LLC, pg 847

MINNESOTA

Digital Audio Labs, pg 847

MISSOURI

Modern Communications Inc, pg 944
Schiller's Audio-Visual, pg 1004

NEVADA

Aardvark Video & Media Productions, pg 772

NEW JERSEY

Argraph Corp, pg 789

NEW YORK

Audio-Video Corp, pg 795
SmartSource Computer & AV Rentals, pg 1014

PENNSYLVANIA

Advanced AV, pg 777
Clair Brothers Audio Systems Inc, pg 829
The Lerro Corp, pg 919

RHODE ISLAND

M-Audio, pg 927

SOUTH CAROLINA

Professional Management Services Inc, pg 985

TENNESSEE

Lowrance Sound Co Inc, pg 925

TEXAS

Biway Media, pg 808
RadioShack Corp, pg 990
Tarpley Media Systems, pg 1032
Videotex Systems Inc, pg 1057

VIRGINIA

Lee Hartman & Sons Inc, pg 918

WASHINGTON

CCI Solutions, pg 821

WISCONSIN

Audio Visual of Milwaukee Inc, pg 795
Camera Corner Connecting Point, pg 818
Full Compass Systems, pg 874
Safe Harbor Computers, pg 1001

BRITISH COLUMBIA

Richmond Sound Design Ltd, pg 996

MANITOBA

Inland Audio Visual Ltd, pg 898

ONTARIO

Westbury National Show Systems Ltd, pg 1064

Sound Card Manufacturers

CALIFORNIA

Antex Electronics Corp, pg 787
Eye & I Productions, pg 864
Lynx Studio Technology Inc, pg 927
Point Source Audio, pg 977
QRS Software Services, pg 988
SEK'D™ America, pg 1006

ILLINOIS

Symbolic Sound Corp, pg 1030

MINNESOTA

Digital Audio Labs, pg 847
Telex Communications Inc, pg 1037

RHODE ISLAND

M-Audio, pg 927

ALBERTA

QSound Labs Inc, pg 988

BRITISH COLUMBIA

Triad Communications Ltd, pg 1044

COMPUTER SYSTEMS

Sound Card Rentals

CALIFORNIA

Ametron Audio/Video, pg 785
Synthesizer Rental Service, pg 1030
Total Media Group, pg 1042

IOWA

ECS Inc, pg 856

NEW YORK

SmartSource Computer & AV Rentals, pg 1014

PENNSYLVANIA

Advanced AV, pg 777
FMP Media Solutions Inc, pg 870

Sound Card Repairs

CALIFORNIA

Ametron Audio/Video, pg 785

CONNECTICUT

HB Communications Inc, pg 886

IOWA

ECS Inc, pg 856

WISCONSIN

Full Compass Systems, pg 874

Touch Panel Distributors

ARIZONA

Troxell Communications Inc, pg 1045

ARKANSAS

Jay S Stanley & Associates Inc, pg 1023

CALIFORNIA

Ametron Audio/Video, pg 785
Associated Sound, pg 792
AV Conferencing, pg 797
Be Media, pg 804
Boland Communications, pg 810
California Tape Products Inc, pg 817
Electrosonic Inc, pg 859
Elo TouchSystems, pg 859
JD Audio Visual Inc, pg 904
MediaMation Inc, pg 937
MediaPOINTE, pg 938
POP TV, pg 978
Sound Service Co, pg 1017
Stanislaus Audio Video Inc, pg 1023

COLORADO

Daylight Productions & Rentals, pg 844

CONNECTICUT

Everett Hall Associates Inc, pg 863

FLORIDA

AVI-SPL, pg 798
Digital Video Systems Inc, pg 848
Hi-Tech Enterprises Inc, pg 888
Pro Stage Inc, pg 983

GEORGIA

Lighting & Production Equipment Inc, pg 920
Simtrol Inc, pg 1011
Stage Front Presentation Systems, pg 1022

HAWAII

The Audio Visual Co (AVCO), pg 795

ILLINOIS

Allen Visual Systems Inc, pg 781
Quintessence Audio Ltd, pg 989
Sound Vision Inc, pg 1018
Wells-Gardner Electronics Corp, pg 1063

INDIANA

Lee Co Inc, pg 918
Sensory Technologies LLC, pg 1006

IOWA

ECS Inc, pg 856

KENTUCKY

Axxis Inc, pg 800
NOR-COM Inc, pg 958

LOUISIANA

Intermedia Technologies, pg 900

MAINE

Headlight Audio Visual Inc, pg 887

MARYLAND

Human Circuit, pg 892
Nelson White Systems Inc, pg 954

MICHIGAN

Ascom Communications Contractors, pg 791
Digi Sign Design LLC, pg 847

MINNESOTA

Tierney Brothers Inc, pg 1040

NEW JERSEY

Argraph Corp, pg 789
Audio Visual Associates, pg 795
Starlite Productions, pg 1024
Total Video Products Inc, pg 1042

NEW YORK

ALTEL Systems Inc, pg 783
Audio-Video Corp, pg 795
General Audio-Visual Inc (GAVI), pg 876
Langie Audio Visual Systems, pg 915
SmartSource Computer & AV Rentals, pg 1014

OHIO

ITA Audio Visual Solutions, pg 902
Tri-State Audio Visual Co, pg 1044

PENNSYLVANIA

Advanced AV, pg 777
Aydin Displays Inc, pg 800
Clair Brothers Audio Systems Inc, pg 829
The Lerro Corp, pg 919
Vistacom Inc, pg 1059
Wespen Audio Visual Co, pg 1063

TENNESSEE

Lowrance Sound Co Inc, pg 925
Spring Arbor Distributors, pg 1022
Technical Support Systems LLC, pg 1034

TEXAS

Data Projections Inc, pg 843
Media Management LLC, pg 937
Schoolhouse Audio Visual, pg 1004
Tarpley Media Systems, pg 1032
Videotex Systems Inc, pg 1057

VIRGINIA

Intellidyne LLC, pg 899
Lee Hartman & Sons Inc, pg 918

WISCONSIN

Audio Visual of Milwaukee Inc, pg 795
Camera Corner Connecting Point, pg 818
Full Compass Systems, pg 874

PUERTO RICO

Audio Visual Concepts Inc, pg 795

ALBERTA

Sharp's Audio-Visual Ltd, pg 1008
SMART Technologies Inc, pg 1013

BRITISH COLUMBIA

Richmond Sound Design Ltd, pg 996

MANITOBA

Inland Audio Visual Ltd, pg 898

ONTARIO

Cinema Stage Inc, pg 827
Gesturetek, pg 877
Westbury National Show Systems Ltd, pg 1064

Touch Panel Manufacturers

ARIZONA

eInstruction Corp, pg 858

CALIFORNIA

Boland Communications, pg 810

ILLINOIS

Windel International/Weyel, pg 1067

MICHIGAN

ASC Systems, pg 791

NEW JERSEY

Crestron Electronics Inc, pg 839
FSR Inc, pg 873

PENNSYLVANIA

Aydin Displays Inc, pg 800

TENNESSEE

Spring Arbor Distributors, pg 1022

UTAH

Vantage/Legrand, pg 1051

ALBERTA

SMART Technologies Inc, pg 1013

ONTARIO

Gesturetek, pg 877

Touch Panel Rentals

ARIZONA

Merestone, pg 938

CALIFORNIA

Alliant Event Services, pg 781
Ametron Audio/Video, pg 785
Associated Sound, pg 792
Bexel Corp, pg 806
McCune Audio-Video-Lighting, pg 935
Muse Presentation Technologies, pg 950
VER-Video Equipment Rentals, pg 1053

CONNECTICUT

Everett Hall Associates Inc, pg 863

FLORIDA

Pro Stage Inc, pg 983

GEORGIA

Stage Front Presentation Systems, pg 1022

ILLINOIS

Allen Visual Systems Inc, pg 781

IOWA

ECS Inc, pg 856

MARYLAND

CPR MultiMedia Solutions, pg 837

MICHIGAN

Digi Sign Design LLC, pg 847

MISSOURI

Show-Me Audio-Visual, pg 1009

NEW YORK

SmartSource Computer & AV Rentals, pg 1014

NORTH CAROLINA

A&V Company, pg 772

PENNSYLVANIA

FMP Media Solutions Inc, pg 870

TENNESSEE

Technical Support Systems LLC, pg 1034

TEXAS

Digital Display Solutions Inc, pg 847

MANITOBA

Inland Audio Visual Ltd, pg 898

ONTARIO

Westbury National Show Systems Ltd, pg 1064

Touch Panel Repairs

CALIFORNIA

Ametron Audio/Video, pg 785

GEORGIA

Lighting & Production Equipment Inc, pg 920
Stage Front Presentation Systems, pg 1022

ILLINOIS

Allen Visual Systems Inc, pg 781

IOWA

ECS Inc, pg 856

KENTUCKY

Axxis Inc, pg 800
NOR-COM Inc, pg 958

MAINE

Headlight Audio Visual Inc, pg 887

OHIO

ITA Audio Visual Solutions, pg 902
Tri-State Audio Visual Co, pg 1044

TENNESSEE

Technical Support Systems LLC, pg 1034

TEXAS

Tarpley Media Systems, pg 1032

VIRGINIA

Avitecture Inc, pg 799

WISCONSIN

Camera Corner Connecting Point, pg 818
Full Compass Systems, pg 874

ALBERTA

Sharp's Audio-Visual Ltd, pg 1008

MANITOBA

Inland Audio Visual Ltd, pg 898

ONTARIO

Westbury National Show Systems Ltd, pg 1064

Touch Screen Monitor Distributors

ARIZONA

Troxell Communications Inc, pg 1045

ARKANSAS

Jay S Stanley & Associates Inc, pg 1023

CALIFORNIA

Ametron Audio/Video, pg 785
Associated Sound, pg 792
Be Media, pg 804
California Tape Products Inc, pg 817
Elo TouchSystems, pg 859
MediaMation Inc, pg 937
MediaPOINTE, pg 938
NSM Surveillance, pg 960
POP TV, pg 978
Sound Service Co, pg 1017
Stanislaus Audio Video Inc, pg 1023
Total Media Group, pg 1042
Troll Touch, pg 1045

CONNECTICUT

Everett Hall Associates Inc, pg 863

FLORIDA

AVI-SPL, pg 798
Digital Video Systems Inc, pg 848
Harris Corp, pg 885
Hi-Tech Enterprises Inc, pg 888
Pro Stage Inc, pg 983
Sight & Sound Productions, pg 1010

GEORGIA

PolyVision Corporation, pg 978
Stage Front Presentation Systems, pg 1022

HAWAII

The Audio Visual Co (AVCO), pg 795

ILLINOIS

Allen Visual Systems Inc, pg 781
Quintessence Audio Ltd, pg 989
Sound Vision Inc, pg 1018

INDIANA

Lee Co Inc, pg 918
Sensory Technologies LLC, pg 1006

IOWA

ECS Inc, pg 856

KANSAS

Keywest Technology Inc, pg 910

KENTUCKY

NOR-COM Inc, pg 958

LOUISIANA

Intermedia Technologies, pg 900

MAINE

Headlight Audio Visual Inc, pg 887

MARYLAND

DSR Computer Technology Specialists Inc, pg 853
Human Circuit, pg 892
Nelson White Systems Inc, pg 954

MASSACHUSETTS

Graphx Inc, pg 881

MICHIGAN

ASC Systems, pg 791
Ascom Communications Contractors, pg 791
Digi Sign Design LLC, pg 847

MINNESOTA

Tierney Brothers Inc, pg 1040

NEW JERSEY

Argraph Corp, pg 789
Diversified Systems Inc, pg 849
Starlite Productions, pg 1024
SYMCO Inc, pg 1030
Total Video Products Inc, pg 1042

NEW YORK

ALTEL Systems Inc, pg 783
General Audio-Visual Inc (GAVI), pg 876
Langie Audio Visual Systems, pg 915
SmartSource Computer & AV Rentals, pg 1014

OHIO

ITA Audio Visual Solutions, pg 902
Tri-State Audio Visual Co, pg 1044

PENNSYLVANIA

Advanced AV, pg 777
Clair Brothers Audio Systems Inc, pg 829
Innovision Media Group, pg 899
The Lerro Corp, pg 919
Vistacom Inc, pg 1059

TENNESSEE

Lowrance Sound Co Inc, pg 925
Spring Arbor Distributors, pg 1022
Technical Support Systems LLC, pg 1034

TEXAS

Audio Visual Technologies Group, pg 796
Data Display Audio Visual Co LP, pg 843
Data Projections Inc, pg 843
Media Management LLC, pg 937
Schoolhouse Audio Visual, pg 1004
Tarpley Media Systems, pg 1032

VIRGINIA

Avitecture Inc, pg 799
Design & Production Inc, pg 845
Intellidyne LLC, pg 899
Lee Hartman & Sons Inc, pg 918

WASHINGTON

ToteVision, pg 1042

WISCONSIN

Audio Visual of Milwaukee Inc, pg 795
Camera Corner Connecting Point, pg 818
Full Compass Systems, pg 874

ALBERTA

Infosat Communications Inc, pg 898

MANITOBA

Inland Audio Visual Ltd, pg 898

ONTARIO

Cinema Stage Inc, pg 827
Egan Visual Inc/Egan TeamBoard Inc, pg 858
Gesturetek, pg 877
Westbury National Show Systems Ltd, pg 1064

Touch Screen Monitor Manufacturers

CALIFORNIA

Boland Communications, pg 810
GVISION USA Inc, pg 883

GEORGIA

PolyVision Corporation, pg 978

ILLINOIS

Wells-Gardner Electronics Corp, pg 1063

MASSACHUSETTS

3M Touch Systems, pg 1039

MICHIGAN

ASC Systems, pg 791

NEW JERSEY

Crestron Electronics Inc, pg 839

NORTH CAROLINA

Computer Dynamics, pg 834

WASHINGTON

ToteVision, pg 1042

ONTARIO

Gesturetek, pg 877

Touch Screen Monitor Rentals

ARIZONA

Merestone, pg 938

CALIFORNIA

Ametron Audio/Video, pg 785
Munday & Collins AV, pg 950
Muse Presentation Technologies, pg 950
VER-Video Equipment Rentals, pg 1053
Video Resources Inc, pg 1056

CONNECTICUT

Everett Hall Associates Inc, pg 863

GEORGIA

Stage Front Presentation Systems, pg 1022

ILLINOIS

RC Communications, pg 992

MARYLAND

CPR MultiMedia Solutions, pg 837

MICHIGAN

Digi Sign Design LLC, pg 847

COMPUTER SYSTEMS

Touch Screen Monitor Rentals (continued)

MISSOURI

Show-Me Audio-Visual, pg 1009

NEW YORK

Interactive International Inc, pg 899
SmartSource Computer & AV Rentals, pg 1014

NORTH CAROLINA

A&V Company, pg 772

PENNSYLVANIA

Innovision Media Group, pg 899

TENNESSEE

Technical Support Systems LLC, pg 1034

TEXAS

Bright Star Productions Inc, pg 812
Digital Display Solutions Inc, pg 847

UTAH

Redman Movies & Stories, pg 993

MANITOBA

Inland Audio Visual Ltd, pg 898

ONTARIO

Westbury National Show Systems Ltd, pg 1064

Touch Screen Monitor Repairs

CALIFORNIA

Ametron Audio/Video, pg 785
Troll Touch, pg 1045

FLORIDA

Hi-Tech Enterprises Inc, pg 888

GEORGIA

Stage Front Presentation Systems, pg 1022

ILLINOIS

Allen Visual Systems Inc, pg 781

IOWA

ECS Inc, pg 856

KENTUCKY

Axxis Inc, pg 800
NOR-COM Inc, pg 958

MASSACHUSETTS

3M Touch Systems, pg 1039

NEW YORK

Interactive International Inc, pg 899

OHIO

ITA Audio Visual Solutions, pg 902
Tri-State Audio Visual Co, pg 1044

TENNESSEE

Technical Support Systems LLC, pg 1034

TEXAS

Data Display Audio Visual Co LP, pg 843
Tarpley Media Systems, pg 1032

VIRGINIA

Avitecture Inc, pg 799

WASHINGTON

ToteVision, pg 1042

WISCONSIN

Camera Corner Connecting Point, pg 818
Full Compass Systems, pg 874

ALBERTA

Infosat Communications Inc, pg 898

MANITOBA

Inland Audio Visual Ltd, pg 898

ONTARIO

Westbury National Show Systems Ltd, pg 1064

Virtual Reality Force Feedback Device Distributors

GEORGIA

Stage Front Presentation Systems, pg 1022

INDIANA

Sensory Technologies LLC, pg 1006

KENTUCKY

NOR-COM Inc, pg 958

PENNSYLVANIA

AccuWeather Inc, pg 774
Advanced AV, pg 777

VIRGINIA

Avitecture Inc, pg 799

WISCONSIN

Audio Visual of Milwaukee Inc, pg 795

Virtual Reality Force Feedback Device Manufacturers

CALIFORNIA

Immersion Corp, pg 896

Virtual Reality Force Feedback Device Repairs

KENTUCKY

NOR-COM Inc, pg 958

Virtual Reality Imaging Device Distributors

CALIFORNIA

Ametron Audio/Video, pg 785
California Tape Products Inc, pg 817
Dynamic Digital Depth Inc (DDD), pg 854
Laser Magic Productions, pg 916
Total Media Group, pg 1042
Videobotics, pg 1056
Virtual Research Systems Inc, pg 1058

GEORGIA

Stage Front Presentation Systems, pg 1022

INDIANA

Sensory Technologies LLC, pg 1006

KENTUCKY

NOR-COM Inc, pg 958

LOUISIANA

Intermedia Technologies, pg 900

NEW HAMPSHIRE

Optics 1 Inc, pg 964

PENNSYLVANIA

AccuWeather Inc, pg 774
Advanced AV, pg 777

TEXAS

Supercircuits, pg 1029

VIRGINIA

Avitecture Inc, pg 799
Quince Imaging Inc, pg 989

WASHINGTON

eMagin Corp, pg 860

WISCONSIN

Audio Visual of Milwaukee Inc, pg 795

MANITOBA

Inland Audio Visual Ltd, pg 898
Tek Gear, pg 1035

ONTARIO

Gesturetek, pg 877

QUEBEC

Presagis, pg 981

Virtual Reality Imaging Device Manufacturers

CALIFORNIA

Dynamic Digital Depth Inc (DDD), pg 854
For-A Corp of America, pg 871
Immersion Corp, pg 896
Laser Magic Productions, pg 916
Virtual Research Systems Inc, pg 1058

MARYLAND

Absolute Hollywood, pg 772

NEW HAMPSHIRE

Optics 1 Inc, pg 964

NEW JERSEY

CELCO-Constantine Engineering Labs Co, pg 822

VIRGINIA

Quince Imaging Inc, pg 989

WASHINGTON

eMagin Corp, pg 860

MANITOBA

Tek Gear, pg 1035

ONTARIO

Gesturetek, pg 877

QUEBEC

Presagis, pg 981

Virtual Reality Imaging Device Rentals

CALIFORNIA

Ametron Audio/Video, pg 785
Dynamic Digital Depth Inc (DDD), pg 854
Virtual Research Systems Inc, pg 1058

GEORGIA

Stage Front Presentation Systems, pg 1022

MARYLAND

Absolute Hollywood, pg 772

VIRGINIA

Quince Imaging Inc, pg 989

MANITOBA

Inland Audio Visual Ltd, pg 898
Tek Gear, pg 1035

Virtual Reality Imaging Device Repairs

CALIFORNIA

Ametron Audio/Video, pg 785
Virtual Research Systems Inc, pg 1058

KENTUCKY

NOR-COM Inc, pg 958

VIRGINIA

Quince Imaging Inc, pg 989

MANITOBA

Inland Audio Visual Ltd, pg 898
Tek Gear, pg 1035

Virtual Reality Position & Motion Sensor Distributors

CALIFORNIA

For-A Corp of America, pg 871

GEORGIA

Stage Front Presentation Systems, pg 1022

INDIANA

Sensory Technologies LLC, pg 1006

KENTUCKY

NOR-COM Inc, pg 958

PENNSYLVANIA

AccuWeather Inc, pg 774
Advanced AV, pg 777

VERMONT

Polhemus, pg 978

VIRGINIA

Avitecture Inc, pg 799
Quince Imaging Inc, pg 989

WISCONSIN

Audio Visual of Milwaukee Inc, pg 795

MANITOBA

Tek Gear, pg 1035

ONTARIO

Gesturetek, pg 877

Virtual Reality Position & Motion Sensor Manufacturers

CALIFORNIA

For-A Corp of America, pg 871
Immersion Corp, pg 896

MARYLAND

Absolute Hollywood, pg 772

MASSACHUSETTS

ISCAN Inc, pg 902

TEXAS

Origin Instruments Corp, pg 965

VIRGINIA

Quince Imaging Inc, pg 989

ONTARIO

Gesturetek, pg 877

Virtual Reality Position & Motion Sensor Rentals

GEORGIA

Stage Front Presentation Systems, pg 1022

MARYLAND

Absolute Hollywood, pg 772

VIRGINIA

Quince Imaging Inc, pg 989

MANITOBA

Tek Gear, pg 1035

Virtual Reality Position & Motion Sensor Repairs

KENTUCKY

NOR-COM Inc, pg 958

VIRGINIA

Quince Imaging Inc, pg 989

MANITOBA

Tek Gear, pg 1035

Virtual Reality Sound System Distributors

CALIFORNIA

Ametron Audio/Video, pg 785
California Tape Products Inc, pg 817

GEORGIA

Stage Front Presentation Systems, pg 1022

ILLINOIS

Quintessence Audio Ltd, pg 989

INDIANA

Sensory Technologies LLC, pg 1006

KENTUCKY

NOR-COM Inc, pg 958

LOUISIANA

Intermedia Technologies, pg 900

NEW YORK

Custom Media Environments, pg 841

PENNSYLVANIA

AccuWeather Inc, pg 774
Advanced AV, pg 777

VIRGINIA

Avitecture Inc, pg 799

WISCONSIN

Audio Visual of Milwaukee Inc, pg 795

BRITISH COLUMBIA

Richmond Sound Design Ltd, pg 996

MANITOBA

Tek Gear, pg 1035

ONTARIO

Cinema Stage Inc, pg 827

QUEBEC

Presagis, pg 981

Virtual Reality Sound System Manufacturers

ILLINOIS

Symbolic Sound Corp, pg 1030

MINNESOTA

Digital Audio Labs, pg 847

QUEBEC

Presagis, pg 981

Virtual Reality Sound System Rentals

CALIFORNIA

Ametron Audio/Video, pg 785

GEORGIA

Stage Front Presentation Systems, pg 1022

MANITOBA

Tek Gear, pg 1035

Virtual Reality Sound System Repairs

CALIFORNIA

Ametron Audio/Video, pg 785

GEORGIA

Stage Front Presentation Systems, pg 1022

KENTUCKY

NOR-COM Inc, pg 958

Voice Automation System Distributors

FLORIDA

Harris Corp, pg 885
JT Communications, pg 906

GEORGIA

Stage Front Presentation Systems, pg 1022

INDIANA

Sensory Technologies LLC, pg 1006

KENTUCKY

NOR-COM Inc, pg 958

MICHIGAN

Ascom Communications Contractors, pg 791
Digi Sign Design LLC, pg 847

PENNSYLVANIA

AccuWeather Inc, pg 774
Advanced AV, pg 777

SOUTH CAROLINA

Professional Management Services Inc, pg 985

TEXAS

Tarpley Media Systems, pg 1032

VIRGINIA

Lee Hartman & Sons Inc, pg 918

WISCONSIN

Audio Visual of Milwaukee Inc, pg 795
Full Compass Systems, pg 874

Voice Automation System Manufacturers

CALIFORNIA

Point Source Audio, pg 977

CONNECTICUT

Alarmco Intelligent Message Repeaters, pg 779

FLORIDA

JT Communications, pg 906

NEW JERSEY

Crestron Electronics Inc, pg 839

Voice Automation System Rentals

CALIFORNIA

VER-Video Equipment Rentals, pg 1053

GEORGIA

Stage Front Presentation Systems, pg 1022

ILLINOIS

RC Communications, pg 992

MICHIGAN

Digi Sign Design LLC, pg 847

Voice Automation System Repairs

GEORGIA

Stage Front Presentation Systems, pg 1022

KENTUCKY

NOR-COM Inc, pg 958

TEXAS

Tarpley Media Systems, pg 1032

WISCONSIN

Full Compass Systems, pg 874

FILM

Accessory, *see* Equipment & Accessory

Aerial Photography, *see* Photography—Aerial

Animation Production Services

ARIZONA

Merestone, pg 938
Phoenix VideoFilms®, pg 974

ARKANSAS

Shadowbox Video Productions, pg 1007

CALIFORNIA

Animax, pg 787
Artichoke Productions, pg 791
Classic Images, pg 829
Crystal Pyramid Productions™, pg 840
Diaquest, pg 846
Digital Media West, pg 847
Duck Studios, pg 853
First Person™, pg 868
Goal Productions, pg 879
Hydrogen Whiskey Studios, pg 893
iCorpTv, pg 893
Industrial Light & Magic (ILM), pg 897
JDS Video & Media Productions Inc, pg 904
Laser Magic Productions, pg 916
Lumeni Productions Inc, pg 926
Mind Over Eye Inc, pg 943
Moving Art by Louie Schwartzberg, pg 947
New & Unique Videos™, pg 955
Palardo Productions, pg 968
Pantomime Pictures Inc, pg 968
piXvfm, pg 976
QRS Software Services, pg 988
SBS Productions, pg 1003
StereoScope International, pg 1024
Tigar Hare Studios, pg 1040
Timestream Video, pg 1041
Toon Makers, pg 1042
Two Door Productions, pg 1047
Warner Bros Animation, pg 1062
Warner Bros Entertainment Inc, pg 1062
Wavemaker Media Design, pg 1062

COLORADO

CSI Films, pg 840
Flashback Media Productions, pg 869
Full Spectrum Arts & Services, pg 874

CONNECTICUT

New London Media, pg 956

DISTRICT OF COLUMBIA

Hillmann & Carr Inc, pg 889

FLORIDA

Communications Concepts Inc (CCI), pg 833
Little Big Bang Design Inc, pg 923
Universal Studios Florida® Production Group, pg 1049

GEORGIA

Crawford Media Services, pg 838
First Cut Communications LLC, pg 868
Guerrilla Productions LLC, pg 883

HAWAII

Hyperspective Studios Inc, pg 893

ILLINOIS

ABS Enterprises, pg 772
Richter Studios, pg 996

INDIANA

OMNI Productions, pg 962
Perennial Pictures Film Corp, pg 973

IOWA

Hellman Associates Inc, pg 887
The Production House, pg 984

KENTUCKY

Hammond Communications Group, pg 884

LOUISIANA

Digital FX Inc, pg 847

MARYLAND

Kramer Communications Video Production, pg 913
Milner-Fenwick Inc, pg 943

MASSACHUSETTS

CommCreative, pg 832
Extreme Reach Inc, pg 864
MotionArt Studios, pg 947
Northern Light Productions, pg 959
Gabriel Polonsky Studio, pg 978
Preston Productions Inc, pg 981
TR Productions, pg 1043
WSI, pg 1070

MICHIGAN

Blue Mouse Studio, pg 809
Digi Sign Design LLC, pg 847

MINNESOTA

MultiMedia, pg 950

MISSOURI

Celebrities Productions, pg 822

NEW HAMPSHIRE

Apertura, pg 788
Chip Taylor Communications LLC, pg 1032

NEW JERSEY

MediaNow, pg 938
NFL Films Music Library, pg 957
PeopleVisionFX, pg 972
Telequest Inc, pg 1036
Two Animators LLP, pg 1047

NEW MEXICO

Stevens Design & Animation LLC, pg 1024

NEW YORK

American Artists Representatives Inc, pg 783
Animotion Inc, pg 787
Big Fish Productions Inc, pg 807
Buzzco Associates Inc, pg 816
Curious Pictures, pg 841
Digital Art Video Inc, pg 847
DuArt, pg 853
FSL Media Inc, pg 873
Lylofilm Productions, pg 926
Neal Marshad Productions, pg 931
Polestar Films & Associated Arts Ltd, pg 978
R/GA, pg 990

NORTH CAROLINA

NASCAR Media Group LLC, pg 952
Trailblazer Studios®, pg 1043

OHIO

Creative Technology, pg 838
EDR Media LLC, pg 857
VGI Productions, pg 1053

OREGON

Artbeats, pg 791
Wallace Creative Inc, pg 1061

PENNSYLVANIA

Innovision Media Group, pg 899
JPL, pg 906
Kensington Falls Animation, pg 909
WPHL-TV, pg 1070

RHODE ISLAND

Sound-FX-Design, pg 1017

TENNESSEE

Motion Picture Services, pg 947
Paradigm Marketing & Creative, pg 969
Stage Post, pg 1022

TEXAS

Alexander Media Productions, pg 780
Digi-matics, pg 847
Epic Software Group Inc, pg 862
Horizon Film + Video Productions, pg 891
Stage Directions, pg 1022
Texas Heart Institute Visual Communication Services, pg 1037

VERMONT

University of Vermont, Instructional Television Dept, pg 1050

VIRGINIA

Blair Inc, pg 809
Eagle Films, pg 855
Metro Productions, pg 939

WISCONSIN

USAV Group Inc, pg 1050

WYOMING

Bridger Productions Inc, pg 812

BRITISH COLUMBIA

Credo Interactive Inc, pg 839

ONTARIO

Loopmedia Inc, pg 924
Purefire Communications Inc, pg 987

QUEBEC

National Film Board of Canada/Office National du Film du Canada, pg 952

Animation Production Services—Computerized

ARIZONA

Merestone, pg 938

ARKANSAS

Shadowbox Video Productions, pg 1007

CALIFORNIA

Animax, pg 787
Artichoke Productions, pg 791
Blind, pg 809
Classic Images, pg 829
Crystal Pyramid Productions™, pg 840
Diaquest, pg 846
Dolphin MultiMedia Inc, pg 850
DreamWorks Animation SKG Inc, pg 852
Duck Studios, pg 853
Durrenberger Engineering Inc, pg 854
Elektrashock, pg 859
First Person™, pg 868
Havas Edge, pg 885
Hydrogen Whiskey Studios, pg 893
iCorpTv, pg 893
Industrial Light & Magic (ILM), pg 897
JDS Video & Media Productions Inc, pg 904
The Kenwood Group, pg 909
Laser Magic Productions, pg 916
Lumeni Productions Inc, pg 926
Mind Over Eye Inc, pg 943
Moving Art by Louie Schwartzberg, pg 947
New & Unique Videos™, pg 955
Pixar Animation Studios, pg 976
Planet Blue, pg 976
QRS Software Services, pg 988
Reality Check Systems, pg 992
Rhythm & Hues, pg 996
StereoScope International, pg 1024
Tigar Hare Studios, pg 1040
Toon Makers, pg 1042
Two Door Productions, pg 1047
Universal Studios, pg 1049
Wavemaker Media Design, pg 1062

COLORADO

CSI Films, pg 840
Flashback Media Productions, pg 869
Full Spectrum Arts & Services, pg 874

CONNECTICUT

New London Media, pg 956

DISTRICT OF COLUMBIA

Hillmann & Carr Inc, pg 889

FLORIDA

Audio Visual Imagineering Inc, pg 795
CD ROM™ Inc, pg 822
Communications Concepts Inc (CCI), pg 833
Comtel Inc, pg 834
Digimation, pg 847
Ed Ethridge Productions Inc, pg 863
Universal Studios Florida® Production Group, pg 1049

GEORGIA

Cinema Concepts, pg 827
Guerrilla Productions LLC, pg 883

HAWAII

Hyperspective Studios Inc, pg 893

ILLINOIS

ABS Enterprises, pg 772
Lyn Norstad & Associates Inc, pg 926
MIGHTYbYTES Inc, pg 942
Richter Studios, pg 996

INDIANA

AVA Productions, pg 798
Bright Ideas Creative Services, pg 812
OMNI Productions, pg 962

LOUISIANA

Digital FX Inc, pg 847

MASSACHUSETTS

CommCreative, pg 832
Northern Light Productions, pg 959
WSI, pg 1070

MICHIGAN

ASC Systems, pg 791
Digi Sign Design LLC, pg 847
Digital Image Studios LLC, pg 847

MINNESOTA

Aggressive Records Audio Duplication LLC, pg 778
Beyers Sound & Essay Audio, pg 806
The Richard Diercks Co Inc, pg 846
MultiMedia, pg 950

MISSOURI

Avatar Studios, pg 798

NEW HAMPSHIRE

Chip Taylor Communications LLC, pg 1032

NEW JERSEY

CELCO-Constantine Engineering Labs Co, pg 822
Early Films, pg 855
NFL Films Inc, pg 957
NFL Films Music Library, pg 957
Outside The Box Interactive LLC, pg 966
Suede Interactive, pg 1027
Two Animators LLP, pg 1047

NEW MEXICO

Stevens Design & Animation LLC, pg 1024

NEW YORK

American Artists Representatives Inc, pg 783
Animotion Inc, pg 787
Big Film Design, pg 807
Buzzco Associates Inc, pg 816
Curious Pictures, pg 841
Digital Art Video Inc, pg 847
DuArt, pg 853
Eastco Multimedia Solutions Inc, pg 856
4-D Creative Media, pg 871
HB-Content, pg 886
Lylofilm Productions, pg 926
Neal Marshad Productions, pg 931
R/GA, pg 990
Judson Rosebush Co Inc, pg 999

NORTH CAROLINA

The Communications Group Inc, pg 833
Image Associates Inc, pg 894
NASCAR Media Group LLC, pg 952
Unifour Productions Inc, pg 1048

OHIO

Creative Technology, pg 838
Lyon Video Inc, pg 927
Mills James Productions, pg 943

OREGON

Artbeats, pg 791
Wallace Creative Inc, pg 1061

PENNSYLVANIA

AccuWeather Inc, pg 774
Bang Pictures, pg 802
Innovision Media Group, pg 899
JPL, pg 906
The Videohouse Inc, pg 1057
WPHL-TV, pg 1070

RHODE ISLAND

Sound-FX-Design, pg 1017

SOUTH CAROLINA

Genesis Creative, pg 877

TENNESSEE

Motion Picture Services, pg 947
Paradigm Marketing & Creative, pg 969
Stage Post, pg 1022

TEXAS

Castleview Productions, pg 821
Digi-matics, pg 847
Epic Software Group Inc, pg 862
Horizon Film + Video Productions, pg 891
Maverick Video Productions, pg 934

UTAH

Strata™, pg 1025

VIRGINIA

Eagle Films, pg 855
Metro Productions, pg 939

WASHINGTON

North-by-Northwest Productions, pg 958

WISCONSIN

USAV Group Inc, pg 1050
Watts Communications Inc, pg 1062

BRITISH COLUMBIA

Credo Interactive Inc, pg 839

ONTARIO

GAPC (General Assembly Production Centre), pg 875

Artwork & Titling Services

ARIZONA

Merestone, pg 938

ARKANSAS

Shadowbox Video Productions, pg 1007

CALIFORNIA

Animax, pg 787
Blind, pg 809
Duck Studios, pg 853
First Person™, pg 868
FXF Productions Inc, pg 874
Goal Productions, pg 879
Havas Edge, pg 885
Hydrogen Whiskey Studios, pg 893
iCorpTv, pg 893
JDS Video & Media Productions Inc, pg 904
Laser Magic Productions, pg 916
Lumeni Productions Inc, pg 926
Mind Over Eye Inc, pg 943
Moving Art by Louie Schwartzberg, pg 947
New & Unique Videos™, pg 955
Palardo Productions, pg 968
Pantomime Pictures Inc, pg 968
QRS Software Services, pg 988
Reality Check Systems, pg 992
SBS Productions, pg 1003
Shapeshifter, pg 1008
SonicPool, pg 1016
StereoScope International, pg 1024
Timecode Multimedia, pg 1040
Toon Makers, pg 1042
Total Media Group, pg 1042
Universal Studios, pg 1049
WalkerVision Interarts, pg 1061
Wavemaker Media Design, pg 1062

COLORADO

The Cinema Lab, pg 827
CSI Films, pg 840
Flashback Media Productions, pg 869
Full Spectrum Arts & Services, pg 874

CONNECTICUT

Cine-Med Inc, pg 826
New London Media, pg 956

FLORIDA

Communications Concepts Inc (CCI), pg 833
Gulf Coast Audio Visual Producers Inc, pg 883
Jordan Klein Film & Video (JKFV), pg 906
Tom Stack & Associates Inc, pg 1022

GEORGIA

Guerrilla Productions LLC, pg 883

HAWAII

Hyperspective Studios Inc, pg 893

ILLINOIS

ABSA Productions Inc, pg 772
MIGHTYbYTES Inc, pg 942
RADMAR Inc, pg 990

INDIANA

AVA Productions, pg 798
Bright Ideas Creative Services, pg 812

IOWA

The Production House, pg 984

LOUISIANA

Digital FX Inc, pg 847

MASSACHUSETTS

CommCreative, pg 832
MotionArt Studios, pg 947
Northern Light Productions, pg 959
Gabriel Polonsky Studio, pg 978

MICHIGAN

Blue Mouse Studio, pg 809
Digi Sign Design LLC, pg 847
Michigan Recording Arts Institute & Technologies, pg 941
Progressive AE, pg 985

MINNESOTA

Aggressive Records Audio Duplication LLC, pg 778
MultiMedia, pg 950

NEW HAMPSHIRE

Apertura, pg 788
Chip Taylor Communications LLC, pg 1032

NEW JERSEY

CELCO-Constantine Engineering Labs Co, pg 822
Early Films, pg 855
Outside The Box Interactive LLC, pg 966
Two Animators LLP, pg 1047

NEW YORK

Animotion Inc, pg 787
aurora productions, pg 797
Big Film Design, pg 807
Digital Art Video Inc, pg 847
4-D Creative Media, pg 871
Gage-Line Technology Inc, pg 874
Greyfalcon House, pg 882
HB-Content, pg 886
Lylofilm Productions, pg 926
MRG Productions Inc, pg 948
Polestar Films & Associated Arts Ltd, pg 978
R/GA, pg 990
VDO Lab Inc, pg 1052

OHIO

Creative Technology, pg 838
Lyon Video Inc, pg 927

PENNSYLVANIA

Bang Pictures, pg 802
JPL, pg 906
Kensington Falls Animation, pg 909
Pemcor LLC, pg 971
The Videohouse Inc, pg 1057

FILM

Artwork & Titling Services (continued)

RHODE ISLAND

Sound-FX-Design, pg 1017

TENNESSEE

Motion Picture Services, pg 947
Paradigm Marketing & Creative, pg 969
Stage Post, pg 1022

TEXAS

Digi-matics, pg 847
Epic Software Group Inc, pg 862

UTAH

Ferrari Color®, pg 866

VIRGINIA

Eagle Films, pg 855

WISCONSIN

USAV Group Inc, pg 1050
Watts Communications Inc, pg 1062

ALBERTA

Global Television Station, pg 879

ONTARIO

ADS Media, pg 777

Audio Editing, *see* Dubbing

Camera, *see* Movie & Still Camera

Can, *see* Reel & Can

Chain & Multiplexer Equipment Distributors

ALABAMA

Media Visions Inc, pg 937

CALIFORNIA

Media Fabricators Inc, pg 936
MediaPOINTE, pg 938
Peterson's Video Transfer Services, pg 973

COLORADO

Ceavco Audio/Visual Co, pg 822
Spectrum Audio Visual Services, pg 1020

CONNECTICUT

Rockwell Communications Inc, pg 998

FLORIDA

Media Concepts Inc, pg 936

GEORGIA

Technical Innovation, pg 1033
Visioneering International Inc, pg 1058

ILLINOIS

Urbanski Film, pg 1050

INDIANA

Lee Co Inc, pg 918

KENTUCKY

NOR-COM Inc, pg 958

MICHIGAN

City Events Group, pg 828
TeL Systems, pg 1035

MINNESOTA

AVI Systems, pg 799

MISSISSIPPI

Jasper Ewing & Sons Inc, pg 864

MISSOURI

Communitronics Corp, pg 833

NEW JERSEY

Audio Visual Dynamics®, pg 795
Tele-Measurements Inc, pg 1035
Video Corporation of America (VCA), pg 1055

NEW YORK

Colortone Audio Visual, pg 832
Langie Audio Visual Systems, pg 915
Visual Technologies Corp, pg 1060
Willoughby's Imaging Center, pg 1067

NORTH CAROLINA

Camcor Inc, pg 818
Strategic Connections, pg 1026

OHIO

Copp Integrated Systems, pg 836

PENNSYLVANIA

J E Foss Co, pg 871
Hite Co, pg 889
Visual Sound Inc, pg 1059

TENNESSEE

Memphis Communications Corp, pg 938

TEXAS

Pro Video & Film Equipment Co Inc, pg 983

UTAH

RIA Corp, pg 996

VIRGINIA

Communications Specialists Inc, pg 833
Lee Hartman & Sons Inc, pg 918

ALBERTA

McBain Audio Visual Ltd, pg 935

ONTARIO

Edcom Multimedia Products, pg 856

Chain & Multiplexer Equipment Manufacturers

CALIFORNIA

FM Systems Inc, pg 870

FLORIDA

Magna-Tech Electronic Co Inc, pg 928

WASHINGTON

Tobin Cinema Systems Inc, pg 1041

Chain & Multiplexer Equipment Rentals

ALABAMA

Media Visions Inc, pg 937

ARIZONA

Arizona Cine Equipment, pg 789

CALIFORNIA

Artichoke Productions, pg 791

COLORADO

The Cinema Lab, pg 827

CONNECTICUT

Rockwell Communications Inc, pg 998

MICHIGAN

TeL Systems, pg 1035

MINNESOTA

AVI Systems, pg 799

NEW JERSEY

Video Corporation of America (VCA), pg 1055

NEW YORK

Adwar Video, pg 778
CMI Communications, pg 830

NORTH CAROLINA

Duke Media Services, pg 853

OHIO

Vista Color Imaging Inc, pg 1059

PENNSYLVANIA

Fusion Brand Experiences, pg 874

TENNESSEE

Russ Sturgeon Productions/RSVP, pg 1027

VIRGINIA

Projection Presentation Technology, pg 985

WISCONSIN

University of Wisconsin-Oshkosh Radio-TV-Film Dept, pg 1050

Chain & Multiplexer Equipment Repairs

ALABAMA

Media Visions Inc, pg 937

KENTUCKY

NOR-COM Inc, pg 958

MINNESOTA

AVI Systems, pg 799

NEW YORK

Langie Audio Visual Systems, pg 915
Visual Technologies Corp, pg 1060

VIRGINIA

Lee Hartman & Sons Inc, pg 918

ONTARIO

Edcom Multimedia Products, pg 856

Cleaning Equipment, *see* Film Cleaning & Inspection Equipment

Computerized Animation Production Services, *see* Animation Production Services—Computerized

Computerized Editing, *see* Editing—Computerized

Consulting

ALABAMA

Diamond Studios, pg 846
Media Visions Inc, pg 937

ALASKA

Alaska Film Services Inc, pg 779
Aurora Films, pg 797

ARIZONA

MediaWorks, pg 938
Merestone, pg 938
Metropolitan Audio-Visual Inc, pg 940
Phoenix VideoFilms®, pg 974
Tellens Inc, pg 1037

ARKANSAS

Shadowbox Video Productions, pg 1007

CALIFORNIA

Artichoke Productions, pg 791
Automated Entertainment, pg 797
Blind, pg 809
Larry Burr, pg 815
Cinema Engineering Co, pg 827
Crystal Pyramid Productions™, pg 840
Design Media, pg 845
Dolphin MultiMedia Inc, pg 850
Tom Donald Films, pg 850

FILM

Consulting (continued)

TEXAS (continued)

Julye Newlin Productions Inc, pg 956
Texas Heart Institute Visual Communication Services, pg 1037

VIRGINIA

CACI Productions Group, pg 816
CALIBRE, pg 816
CDR Communications Inc, pg 822
Eagle Films, pg 855
SNL Kagan Media & Communications, pg 1014

WASHINGTON

Adams Creative & Production Services, pg 775
Media Elite Productions, pg 936
North-by-Northwest Productions, pg 958
Pal Productions Inc, pg 967

WEST VIRGINIA

Altruist Media LLC, pg 783

WISCONSIN

University of Wisconsin-Oshkosh Radio-TV-Film Dept, pg 1050
USAV Group Inc, pg 1050
Wisconsin Public Television, pg 1068

WYOMING

Bridger Productions Inc, pg 812

ALBERTA

Black Media Works, pg 808
Global Television Station, pg 879

BRITISH COLUMBIA

MicrophoneRentals.com, pg 941
Network Entertainment Inc, pg 954
West Eagle Films Inc, pg 1064

NORTHWEST TERRITORIES

Yellowknife Films Inc, pg 1072

ONTARIO

ADS Media, pg 777
Artaflex Inc, pg 791

QUEBEC

Sceno Plus, pg 1004

SASKATCHEWAN

Thomega Entertainment Inc, pg 1039

Continuous Still Projector Distributors

ALABAMA

Media Visions Inc, pg 937

ARIZONA

Troxell Communications Inc, pg 1045

ARKANSAS

Jay S Stanley & Associates Inc, pg 1023

CALIFORNIA

Jaguar Distribution Corp, pg 903
Media Fabricators Inc, pg 936
MediaPOINTE, pg 938

COLORADO

Ceavco Audio/Visual Co, pg 822
National Teaching Aids Inc, pg 953

CONNECTICUT

Concord Communications, pg 835

FLORIDA

Tallahassee Audio Visual, pg 1031

GEORGIA

Visioneering International Inc, pg 1058

ILLINOIS

Major Reproductions Equipment Co, pg 929

INDIANA

Lee Co Inc, pg 918

KENTUCKY

NOR-COM Inc, pg 958

MARYLAND

RTZ Audio Visual, pg 1000

MICHIGAN

City Events Group, pg 828

MINNESOTA

AVI Systems, pg 799

MISSISSIPPI

Jasper Ewing & Sons Inc, pg 864

MISSOURI

Communitronics Corp, pg 833
Schiller's Audio-Visual, pg 1004

NEW JERSEY

Audio Visual Dynamics®, pg 795
Leica Camera Inc, pg 918

NEW YORK

AV Workshop, pg 797
Colortone Audio Visual, pg 832
Langie Audio Visual Systems, pg 915
Visual Technologies Corp, pg 1060
Willoughby's Imaging Center, pg 1067

NORTH CAROLINA

Strategic Connections, pg 1026

OHIO

Audio Visual Media, pg 795
Copp Integrated Systems, pg 836
Icom Multimedia, pg 893

TENNESSEE

Memphis Communications Corp, pg 938

TEXAS

Audio Visual Technologies Group, pg 796

VIRGINIA

Filmdex Inc, pg 867
Lee Hartman & Sons Inc, pg 918
The Whitlock Group, pg 1065

WASHINGTON

Inland Audio Visual Co, pg 898

ALBERTA

McBain Audio Visual Ltd, pg 935

ONTARIO

Edcom Multimedia Products, pg 856

Continuous Still Projector Manufacturers

COLORADO

National Teaching Aids Inc, pg 953

MISSOURI

Schiller's Audio-Visual, pg 1004

NEW JERSEY

Leica Camera Inc, pg 918

NEW YORK

ELMO USA Corp, pg 859

Continuous Still Projector Rentals

ALABAMA

Audio-Video Resources Inc, pg 795

ARIZONA

Merestone, pg 938

CALIFORNIA

JD Audio Visual Inc, pg 904
McCune Audio-Video-Lighting, pg 935
Media Fabricators Inc, pg 936

COLORADO

Ceavco Audio/Visual Co, pg 822

CONNECTICUT

Concord Communications, pg 835

GEORGIA

Dixie Theatre Service & Supply Co Inc, pg 849

ILLINOIS

Helix Camera & Video, pg 887
RC Communications, pg 992

MARYLAND

RTZ Audio Visual, pg 1000

MICHIGAN

City Events Group, pg 828

MINNESOTA

AVI Systems, pg 799

MISSISSIPPI

Jasper Ewing & Sons Inc, pg 864

MISSOURI

Swank Audio Visuals, pg 1029

NEW JERSEY

Audio Visual Dynamics®, pg 795
PLS Staging, pg 977

NEW YORK

AV Workshop, pg 797
Colortone Audio Visual, pg 832
Langie Audio Visual Systems, pg 915
Visual Technologies Corp, pg 1060

NORTH CAROLINA

Strategic Connections, pg 1026

OHIO

Audio Visual Media, pg 795
Icom Multimedia, pg 893

TENNESSEE

Memphis Communications Corp, pg 938

VIRGINIA

Lee Hartman & Sons Inc, pg 918
Projection Presentation Technology, pg 985

WASHINGTON

Inland Audio Visual Co, pg 898

Continuous Still Projector Repairs

ARKANSAS

Jay S Stanley & Associates Inc, pg 1023

CALIFORNIA

Pro Camera Repair, pg 982

COLORADO

Ceavco Audio/Visual Co, pg 822

CONNECTICUT

Precision Camera & Video Repair Inc, pg 980

FLORIDA

Hi-Tech Enterprises Inc, pg 888

KENTUCKY

NOR-COM Inc, pg 958

MARYLAND

RTZ Audio Visual, pg 1000

MINNESOTA

AVI Systems, pg 799

MISSOURI

Schiller's Audio-Visual, pg 1004

NEW YORK

Colortone Audio Visual, pg 832
ELMO USA Corp, pg 859
Langie Audio Visual Systems, pg 915
Visual Technologies Corp, pg 1060

NORTH CAROLINA

Strategic Connections, pg 1026

OHIO

Audio Visual Media, pg 795
Icom Multimedia, pg 893

TENNESSEE

Memphis Communications Corp, pg 938

VIRGINIA

Lee Hartman & Sons Inc, pg 918
The Whitlock Group, pg 1065

WASHINGTON

Inland Audio Visual Co, pg 898

ONTARIO

Edcom Multimedia Products, pg 856

Co-Production Services

ALABAMA

Diamond Studios, pg 846
Media Visions Inc, pg 937

ALASKA

Alaska Film Services Inc, pg 779
Aurora Films, pg 797

ARIZONA

Creative Backstage, pg 838
MediaWorks, pg 938
Merestone, pg 938
Metropolitan Audio-Visual Inc, pg 940
Phoenix VideoFilms®, pg 974
Tellens Inc, pg 1037

ARKANSAS

Shadowbox Video Productions, pg 1007

CALIFORNIA

Artichoke Productions, pg 791
Automated Entertainment, pg 797
Backstage Pass Entertainment Inc, pg 801
Bridge Publications Inc, pg 812
Concrete Images, pg 835
Crystal Pyramid Productions™, pg 840
Custom Video Productions Inc, pg 841
deKramer Productions Inc, pg 845
Design Media, pg 845
Tom Donald Films, pg 850
First Person™, pg 868
FXF Productions Inc, pg 874
Havas Edge, pg 885
iCorpTv, pg 893
Image G, pg 895
Ishtar Films, pg 902
Jaguar Distribution Corp, pg 903
JDS Video & Media Productions Inc, pg 904
The Kitchen, pg 911
Main Street Media Inc, pg 929
New & Unique Videos™, pg 955
New Circuit Films LLC, pg 955
Joseph Nicoletti Consulting-Promotion/California International Records/Global Village Records, pg 957
Panorama Productions, pg 968
Pantomime Pictures Inc, pg 968
Planet Blue, pg 976
Point of View Productions, pg 977
QRS Software Services, pg 988
Raymond Entertainment Direct (RED), pg 992
Ron Roy Productions/Moodtapes, pg 1000
Russ InVision Co/AbridgeClub.com, pg 1001
Sahara Records & Filmworks Entertainment Co, pg 1001
Sea Studios Foundation, pg 1005
Signature Entertainment, pg 1011
Sports Cinematography Group, pg 1021
StereoScope International, pg 1024
Tam Communications Inc, pg 1031
Tigar Hare Studios, pg 1040
Toon Makers, pg 1042
Total Media Group, pg 1042
Via Verde Productions, pg 1053
Vineyard Productions, pg 1058
Visual Communications - Southern California Asian American Studies Central Inc, pg 1059
WARPed Pictures, pg 1062
Wavemaker Media Design, pg 1062
Z-Ville Productions, pg 1073

COLORADO

Conly Productions, pg 835
Flashback Media Productions, pg 869
Tatum Video, pg 1032
Transtar Entertainment Co Inc, pg 1043

CONNECTICUT

The Gary-Paul Agency, pg 875
MCC Films, pg 935
New London Media, pg 956

DISTRICT OF COLUMBIA

Durrin Productions Inc, pg 854
Hillmann & Carr Inc, pg 889

FLORIDA

C&I Studios, pg 819
Chatterbox Productions Inc, pg 824
Cinema East, pg 827
Civins Productions Inc, pg 828
Communications Concepts Inc (CCI), pg 833
Eastern Video, pg 856
Ed Ethridge Productions Inc, pg 863
Home Shopping Network (HSN), pg 890
Media Entertainment Inc, pg 936
Universal Studios Florida® Production Group, pg 1049

GEORGIA

Guerrilla Productions LLC, pg 883
MAGNUM Companies Ltd, pg 929
Myriad Productions, pg 951
Malcolm Neal Productions, pg 954

HAWAII

FilmWorks Pacific, pg 868
Hyperspective Studios Inc, pg 893
Media Bridge Gamekids, pg 936
1013 Integrated, pg 1037

ILLINOIS

Communications Corporation of America, pg 833
Cresta Creative, pg 839
Film Police, pg 867
Mimi Productions, pg 943
The Pepper Group, pg 972
Perspectives Media, pg 973
SCI Television Productions LLC, pg 1004
WEEK TV, pg 1063

INDIANA

AVA Productions, pg 798
Bright Ideas Creative Services, pg 812
Perennial Pictures Film Corp, pg 973

IOWA

The Production House, pg 984

KENTUCKY

Idle Minds Productions Inc, pg 894

LOUISIANA

Digital FX Inc, pg 847
Louisiana State University Health Sciences Center - Shreveport, pg 925
Moxie Media, pg 948

MAINE

Portland Models & Talent LLC, pg 979

MARYLAND

Butler Films Inc, pg 815
DBM Communications Inc, pg 844
DSR Computer Technology Specialists Inc, pg 853
James Agee Film Project, pg 904

MASSACHUSETTS

Documentary Educational Resources Inc, pg 850
Emergency Film Group, pg 860
Green Mountain Post Films (GMP), pg 882
Heliotrope Studios, pg 887
Monadnock Media Inc, pg 945
MotionArt Studios, pg 947
Northern Light Productions, pg 959
Gabriel Polonsky Studio, pg 978

MICHIGAN

Digi Sign Design LLC, pg 847

MINNESOTA

House of Cinemagraphics, pg 891
Jamieson & Associates Inc, pg 904

MISSOURI

Visionworks Design Services Inc, pg 1059

MONTANA

KCFW Television, pg 908

NEVADA

DVDs4Less, pg 854
Encore Productions Inc, pg 861
Lefco Video Services Inc, pg 918

NEW HAMPSHIRE

Apertura, pg 788
Chip Taylor Communications LLC, pg 1032

NEW JERSEY

CELCO-Constantine Engineering Labs Co, pg 822
Euro-Pacific Film & Video Productions Inc, pg 863
Half Moon Video Productions, pg 883
Outside The Box Interactive LLC, pg 966
Bill Quinn Productions, pg 989
VCSvideo, pg 1052

NEW YORK

American Artists Representatives Inc, pg 783
aurora productions, pg 797
De Nonno Productions Inc (DPI), pg 844
4-D Creative Media, pg 871
Greyfalcon House, pg 882
HB-Content, pg 886
Icontent, pg 893
Richard Kaplan Productions, pg 908
Kinetic Arts, pg 911
L&P Media, pg 915
Lylofilm Productions, pg 926
Neal Marshad Productions, pg 931
Mastervision Inc, pg 933
Jack Morton Worldwide, pg 946
MRG Productions Inc, pg 948
NSR Productions Inc & Capricorn Five Films, pg 960
Shadow Pictures Inc, pg 1007
Sunrise Media LLC, pg 1028
TBA Global Events, pg 1032
Timed Exposures Films, pg 1040
VIEW Inc (Video International Entertainment World Inc), pg 1058
Zelman Studios Ltd, pg 1073

NORTH CAROLINA

The Communications Group Inc, pg 833
Moving Pictures, pg 948

NORTH DAKOTA

Media Productions, pg 937

OHIO

Challenge Productions, pg 823
Creative Technology, pg 838
Take 1 Media Services, pg 1031
Vista Color Imaging Inc, pg 1059

PENNSYLVANIA

Innovision Media Group, pg 899
JPL, pg 906
Kensington Falls Animation, pg 909
Main Point Productions, pg 929

RHODE ISLAND

Sound-FX-Design, pg 1017

TENNESSEE

American Blackguard Inc, pg 784
Fricon Entertainment Co Inc, pg 873

FILM

Co-Production Services (continued)

Dubbing

Edge Numbering

Editing

Editing—Computerized

FILM

Editing—Computerized (continued)

CALIFORNIA (continued)

Goal Productions, pg 879
Havas Edge, pg 885
iCorpTv, pg 893
imageReal Pictures LLC, pg 896
JDS Video & Media Productions Inc, pg 904
JR Media Services, pg 906
KO Creative, pg 912
Main Street Media Inc, pg 929
Maximus Media Inc, pg 934
Mind Over Eye Inc, pg 943
New & Unique Videos™, pg 955
Palardo Productions, pg 968
Planet Blue, pg 976
QRS Software Services, pg 988
Reality Check Systems, pg 992
RetinaVision Productions, pg 995
Shapeshifter, pg 1008
Shoulder High Productions, pg 1009
SonicPool, pg 1016
Stray Angel Films, pg 1026
30 Second Films, pg 1039
Tigar Hare Studios, pg 1040
Timecode Multimedia, pg 1040
Toon Makers, pg 1042
Total Media Group, pg 1042
Universal Studios, pg 1049
Video Symphony TV & Film School, pg 1056
Vineyard Productions, pg 1058
WalkerVision Interarts, pg 1061

COLORADO

Alpine Media, pg 782
blue onion, pg 810
Flashback Media Productions, pg 869

CONNECTICUT

Essex Television Group Inc, pg 862
The Gary-Paul Agency, pg 875

DISTRICT OF COLUMBIA

Hillmann & Carr Inc, pg 889
Interface Media Group, pg 900

FLORIDA

ACT Productions, pg 775
Allegro Productions Inc, pg 781
CD ROM™ Inc, pg 822
Communications Concepts Inc (CCI), pg 833
Ed Ethridge Productions Inc, pg 863
New Art Miami, pg 955

GEORGIA

First Cut Communications LLC, pg 868
Guerrilla Productions LLC, pg 883
TV Crews, pg 1046

HAWAII

Hyperspective Studios Inc, pg 893

IDAHO

Brad Shaw Productions Inc, pg 1008

ILLINOIS

ABS Enterprises, pg 772
ABSA Productions Inc, pg 772
Optimus, pg 964
Richter Studios, pg 996
WEEK TV, pg 1063

INDIANA

Bright Ideas Creative Services, pg 812

IOWA

The Production House, pg 984

KENTUCKY

Horizon Films & Media LLC, pg 891

LOUISIANA

Digital FX Inc, pg 847

MARYLAND

Butler Films Inc, pg 815
DBM Communications Inc, pg 844
Pro Cuts Editing Services, pg 982

MASSACHUSETTS

Northern Light Productions, pg 959
WGBH Production Group, pg 1065

MICHIGAN

Digital Image Studios LLC, pg 847
TeL Systems, pg 1035

MINNESOTA

Badiyan Inc, pg 801
House of Cinemagraphics, pg 891

NEW HAMPSHIRE

Chip Taylor Communications LLC, pg 1032

NEW JERSEY

CELCO-Constantine Engineering Labs Co, pg 822
CFP Video Productions Inc, pg 823
Early Films, pg 855
Euro-Pacific Film & Video Productions Inc, pg 863
Producer East Productions, pg 983

NEW YORK

American Montage Inc, pg 784
Big Film Design, pg 807
Devlin Video International, pg 846
DuArt, pg 853
Eastco Multimedia Solutions Inc, pg 856
William Greaves Productions Inc, pg 882
Greyfalcon House, pg 882
HB-Content, pg 886
Heavy Melody, pg 887
La Paloma Films, pg 915
Lylofilm Productions, pg 926
Magno Sound & Video, pg 929
Neal Marshad Productions, pg 931
NBC Production Facilities, pg 953
Shelly Palmer Production, pg 968
Shadow Pictures Inc, pg 1007
Technisphere Corp, pg 1034
TeleTime Productions, pg 1036
Videography Productions, pg 1057
Zelman Studios Ltd, pg 1073

NORTH CAROLINA

The Communications Group Inc, pg 833
NASCAR Media Group LLC, pg 952
Trailblazer Studios®, pg 1043
2BruceStudio, pg 1047
Unifour Productions Inc, pg 1048

OHIO

Creative Technology, pg 838
Maslowski Productions, pg 933
Mills James Productions, pg 943
VGI Productions, pg 1053

PENNSYLVANIA

Argentine Productions Inc, pg 789
Center City Film & Video Inc, pg 822
Innovision Media Group, pg 899
WPHL-TV, pg 1070

SOUTH CAROLINA

Genesis Creative, pg 877

TENNESSEE

American Blackguard Inc, pg 784
Motion Picture Services, pg 947
Paradigm Marketing & Creative, pg 969
Stage Post, pg 1022

TEXAS

Best Film & Video, pg 805
Castleview Productions, pg 821
Digi-matics, pg 847
Horizon Film + Video Productions, pg 891
Julye Newlin Productions Inc, pg 956
Phil Lights, pg 973
Stage Directions, pg 1022

UTAH

Strata™, pg 1025

VERMONT

University of Vermont, Instructional Television Dept, pg 1050

VIRGINIA

Eagle Films, pg 855
Studio Center Corp, pg 1026

WASHINGTON

Hamilton Studio, pg 884
Robert McConnell Productions, pg 935
North-by-Northwest Productions, pg 958

WISCONSIN

Meridian Studios, pg 939

WYOMING

Bridger Productions Inc, pg 812

ALBERTA

Global Television Station, pg 879

BRITISH COLUMBIA

Finale Editworks, pg 868

MANITOBA

Lank/Beach Productions Inc, pg 916

NORTHWEST TERRITORIES

Yellowknife Films Inc, pg 1072

SASKATCHEWAN

Thomega Entertainment Inc, pg 1039

Editing Equipment Distributors

ALABAMA

Media Visions Inc, pg 937

ARIZONA

Arizona Cine Equipment, pg 789
EAR Professional Audio/Video, pg 855
Troxell Communications Inc, pg 1045

ARKANSAS

Carlton-Bates Co, pg 820

CALIFORNIA

Adolph Gasser Inc, pg 776
Birns & Sawyer Inc, pg 808
Christy's Editorial, pg 826
FXC Communications, pg 874
Alan Gordon Enterprises Inc, pg 880
J & R Film Co, pg 903
Jaguar Distribution Corp, pg 903
MediaPOINTE, pg 938
Metric Splicer Inc, pg 939
Moviola, pg 948
Plus 24, pg 977
Yale Film & Video, pg 1071

COLORADO

Ceavco Audio/Visual Co, pg 822
Stanco Sales LLC, pg 1023

CONNECTICUT

Concord Communications, pg 835

FLORIDA

AVI-SPL, pg 798
Gulf Coast Audio Visual Producers Inc, pg 883
Media Concepts Inc, pg 936
Photomart Cine-Video Inc, pg 975

GEORGIA

Visioneering International Inc, pg 1058

ILLINOIS

Joseph Electronics, pg 906
Research Technology International (RTI), pg 995
Urbanski Film, pg 1050

INDIANA

Lee Co Inc, pg 918

KENTUCKY

NOR-COM Inc, pg 958

MARYLAND

RTZ Audio Visual, pg 1000

MASSACHUSETTS

Avid Technology Inc, pg 799
The Boston Connection Inc, pg 811

MICHIGAN

City Events Group, pg 828
TeL Systems, pg 1035

MINNESOTA

Alpha Video & Audio Inc, pg 782
AVI Systems, pg 799
Cinequipt Inc, pg 828

MISSISSIPPI

Jasper Ewing & Sons Inc, pg 864

MISSOURI

Communitronics Corp, pg 833

NEVADA

Aardvark Video & Media Productions, pg 772

NEW JERSEY

Audio Visual Dynamics®, pg 795
AV Bluebook, pg 797
Comprehensive Cable & Connectivity Co, pg 833
National Audio-Visual Supply, pg 952
SYMCO Inc, pg 1030
Wilray Audio Visual Corp, pg 1067

NEW YORK

Cine 60 Inc, pg 826
Colortone Audio Visual, pg 832
Langie Audio Visual Systems, pg 915
Motion Picture Enterprises Inc, pg 947
Visual Technologies Corp, pg 1060
Willoughby's Imaging Center, pg 1067

NORTH CAROLINA

Camcor Inc, pg 818
Strategic Connections, pg 1026

OHIO

Visual Products Inc, pg 1059
Xetron, pg 1071

OREGON

Anthro Corp, pg 787

PENNSYLVANIA

Hite Co, pg 889
IMR Limited, pg 897
The Lerro Corp, pg 919
Wespen Audio Visual Co, pg 1063

TENNESSEE

Memphis Communications Corp, pg 938

TEXAS

Pro Video & Film Equipment Co Inc, pg 983

UTAH

Webb Audio Visual Communication, pg 1063

VIRGINIA

Communications Specialists Inc, pg 833
Cybernetics, pg 841
Filmdex Inc, pg 867
Lee Hartman & Sons Inc, pg 918
The Whitlock Group, pg 1065

WISCONSIN

Full Compass Systems, pg 874
Safe Harbor Computers, pg 1001

ONTARIO

Premier A/V Sales Ltd, pg 980

QUEBEC

Concept Audio-Visual, pg 834

Editing Equipment Manufacturers

CALIFORNIA

Christy's Editorial, pg 826
J & R Film Co, pg 903
Metric Splicer Inc, pg 939
Moviola, pg 948
Sprocket Digital, pg 1022
TV Pro Gear, pg 1046

FLORIDA

Tel-Test, pg 1035

GEORGIA

Outsource Engineering & Manufacturing Inc dba Texscan MSI, pg 966

ILLINOIS

Lipsner-Smith Co, pg 922
Research Technology International (RTI), pg 995

MASSACHUSETTS

Avid Technology Inc, pg 799
The Boston Connection Inc, pg 811

NEW JERSEY

CELCO-Constantine Engineering Labs Co, pg 822

NEW YORK

GTI (Graphic Technology Inc), pg 883
Quantel Inc, pg 989

OHIO

Xetron, pg 1071

OREGON

Anthro Corp, pg 787

PENNSYLVANIA

IMR Limited, pg 897

Editing Equipment Rentals

ARIZONA

Arizona Cine Equipment, pg 789
Merestone, pg 938

ARKANSAS

White Diamond Productions, pg 1065

CALIFORNIA

Adolph Gasser Inc, pg 776
Artichoke Productions, pg 791
Balboa Capital Corp, pg 802
Big Door, pg 807
Big Time Picture Company Inc, pg 807
Birns & Sawyer Inc, pg 808
Christy's Editorial, pg 826
Direct Cinema Ltd Inc, pg 848
Film Converter Co of America Inc, pg 867
Alan Gordon Enterprises Inc, pg 880
J & R Film Co, pg 903
Main Street Media Inc, pg 929
Moviola, pg 948
Reality Check Systems, pg 992
The Studios at Paramount, pg 1027
Synthesizer Systems Technologies (SST), pg 1030
Total Media Group, pg 1042
Universal Studios, pg 1049

COLORADO

Centre Communications Inc, pg 823
The Cinema Lab, pg 827

DISTRICT OF COLUMBIA

Educational Film Center, pg 857

FLORIDA

Cinema East, pg 827
Jordan Klein Film & Video (JKFV), pg 906
Media Concepts Inc, pg 936

GEORGIA

COMPRO Productions Inc, pg 834

ILLINOIS

Helix Camera & Video, pg 887

LOUISIANA

Digital FX Inc, pg 847

MARYLAND

Kramer Communications Video Production, pg 913
RTZ Audio Visual, pg 1000

MASSACHUSETTS

The Boston Connection Inc, pg 811
Capron Lighting & Sound Co Inc, pg 819
Green Mountain Post Films (GMP), pg 882

MICHIGAN

City Events Group, pg 828
TeL Systems, pg 1035

MINNESOTA

AVI Systems, pg 799
Cinequipt Inc, pg 828
House of Cinemagraphics, pg 891

MISSOURI

Show-Me Audio-Visual, pg 1009
Swank Audio Visuals, pg 1029

NEW HAMPSHIRE

Apertura, pg 788

NEW JERSEY

Audio Visual Dynamics®, pg 795

NEW YORK

Adwar Video, pg 778
CMI Communications, pg 830
Colortone Audio Visual, pg 832
Gurrilla Video Solutions, pg 883
HB-Content, pg 886
Langie Audio Visual Systems, pg 915
Motion Picture Enterprises Inc, pg 947
Richter Productions Inc, pg 996
The Visual Studies Workshop (VSW), pg 1059

PENNSYLVANIA

FMP Media Solutions Inc, pg 870
IMR Limited, pg 897
Videosmith Inc, pg 1057

TEXAS

Phil Lights, pg 973

UTAH

Webb Audio Visual Communication, pg 1063

VERMONT

Marlboro Film & Video Productions, pg 931

WASHINGTON

Inland Audio Visual Co, pg 898

WISCONSIN

University of Wisconsin-Oshkosh Radio-TV-Film Dept, pg 1050
Wisconsin Public Television, pg 1068

ALBERTA

Global Television Station, pg 879

BRITISH COLUMBIA

Finale Editworks, pg 868
24 Frames Film & Video, pg 1047
Video In Studios/Video Out Distribution, pg 1055

Editing Equipment Repairs

ARKANSAS

Carlton-Bates Co, pg 820

CALIFORNIA

Adolph Gasser Inc, pg 776
Big Time Picture Company Inc, pg 807
Birns & Sawyer Inc, pg 808
Christy's Editorial, pg 826
Alan Gordon Enterprises Inc, pg 880
J & R Film Co, pg 903
Metric Splicer Inc, pg 939
Moviola, pg 948
Pro Camera Repair, pg 982

CONNECTICUT

HB Communications Inc, pg 886

FILM

Editing Equipment Repairs (continued)

FLORIDA

Hi-Tech Enterprises Inc, pg 888
Media Concepts Inc, pg 936
Tel-Test, pg 1035

KENTUCKY

NOR-COM Inc, pg 958

MARYLAND

RTZ Audio Visual, pg 1000

MASSACHUSETTS

The Boston Connection Inc, pg 811

MICHIGAN

City Events Group, pg 828

MINNESOTA

AVI Systems, pg 799

MISSOURI

Communitronics Corp, pg 833

NEW YORK

Adwar Video, pg 778
Langie Audio Visual Systems, pg 915
Motion Picture Enterprises Inc, pg 947

PENNSYLVANIA

IMR Limited, pg 897

VIRGINIA

The Whitlock Group, pg 1065

WISCONSIN

Full Compass Systems, pg 874

Eight mm Projector & Equipment, *see* Projector & Equipment—8mm

Equipment & Accessory Distributors

ALABAMA

Media Visions Inc, pg 937

ARIZONA

Arizona Cine Equipment, pg 789
Troxell Communications Inc, pg 1045

ARKANSAS

Jay S Stanley & Associates Inc, pg 1023

CALIFORNIA

Ametron Audio/Video, pg 785
ARRI Inc, pg 790
Band Pro Film & Digital Inc, pg 802
Birns & Sawyer Inc, pg 808
Camera Essentials, pg 818
Christy's Editorial, pg 826
Cinema Equipment Sales of California Inc, pg 827
Cinematography Electronics Inc, pg 828
Diversified Imaging Supply, pg 849
FXC Communications, pg 874
Alan Gordon Enterprises Inc, pg 880
IDX System Technology Inc, pg 894
Intel-A-Jib™, pg 899
J & R Film Co, pg 903
Manios Digital & Film, pg 930
MediaPOINTE, pg 938
Mole-Richardson Co, pg 945
Moviola, pg 948
Nalpak Inc, pg 952
Slow Motion Film & Digital Inc, pg 1013
Steeldeck® Inc, pg 1024
Thermodyne Cases, pg 1038
Transvideo International, pg 1044
Visual Systems, pg 1060

COLORADO

Ceavco Audio/Visual Co, pg 822
Goldberg Brothers Inc, pg 880
Stanco Sales LLC, pg 1023

CONNECTICUT

Concord Communications, pg 835
Rockwell Communications Inc, pg 998

FLORIDA

AVI-SPL, pg 798
Cinema Equipment & Supplies Inc, pg 827
Gulf Coast Audio Visual Producers Inc, pg 883
Hunter Electronics LLC, pg 892
Photomart Cine-Video Inc, pg 975

GEORGIA

Audio Visual Resources Inc, pg 795
PC&E, pg 970
Technical Innovation, pg 1033
Visioneering International Inc, pg 1058

ILLINOIS

Creative Technology, pg 838
Joseph Electronics, pg 906
QuickSet International Inc, pg 989
Research Technology International (RTI), pg 995
Urbanski Film, pg 1050
Zacuto, pg 1073

INDIANA

Lee Co Inc, pg 918

KENTUCKY

NOR-COM Inc, pg 958

MARYLAND

RTZ Audio Visual, pg 1000

MASSACHUSETTS

The Boston Connection Inc, pg 811
High Output Inc, pg 888
Hunt's Photo, Video & Digital, pg 892
University Products Inc, pg 1050

MINNESOTA

Alpha Video & Audio Inc, pg 782
AVI Systems, pg 799
Cinequipt Inc, pg 828

MISSISSIPPI

Jasper Ewing & Sons Inc, pg 864

MISSOURI

Communitronics Corp, pg 833
Image Technologies Corp, pg 895

NEVADA

Aardvark Video & Media Productions, pg 772

NEW HAMPSHIRE

APS Lighting-Sound-AV, pg 789

NEW JERSEY

Agfa Graphics, pg 778
Argraph Corp, pg 789
AV Bluebook, pg 797
Caprock Developments Inc, pg 819
Comprehensive Cable & Connectivity Co, pg 833
National Audio-Visual Supply, pg 952
Bill Quinn Productions, pg 989
Rose Brand, pg 999
Transparent Office Products LLC, pg 1043
VCom International Multimedia Corp, pg 1052

NEW YORK

AZ Spectrum, pg 801
Bulbtronics Inc, pg 815
Cine 60 Inc, pg 826
Colortone Audio Visual, pg 832
Gaylord Brothers, pg 876
Get Smart Products, pg 877
Just Bulbs - The Light Bulb Store, pg 907
Langie Audio Visual Systems, pg 915
Magnaplan Corp, pg 928
Motion Picture Enterprises Inc, pg 947
Rafik, pg 990
Sargent-Welch, pg 1002
Visual Technologies Corp, pg 1060
Vitec Videocom Inc, pg 1060
Willoughby's Imaging Center, pg 1067

NORTH CAROLINA

Strategic Connections, pg 1026

OHIO

Graphic Laminating LLC, pg 881
Visual Products Inc, pg 1059
Xetron, pg 1071

PENNSYLVANIA

Charles Beseler Co, pg 824
Garcia Marketing Inc, pg 875
Hite Co, pg 889

TENNESSEE

Memphis Communications Corp, pg 938

TEXAS

Audio Visual Technologies Group, pg 796
Pro Video & Film Equipment Co Inc, pg 983
Stage Directions, pg 1022

UTAH

Redman Movies & Stories, pg 993

VIRGINIA

Communications Specialists Inc, pg 833
Design & Production Inc, pg 845
Filmdex Inc, pg 867
Lee Hartman & Sons Inc, pg 918
The Whitlock Group, pg 1065

WASHINGTON

Inland Audio Visual Co, pg 898
Oppenheimer Camera Products, pg 964

WISCONSIN

Demco Inc, pg 845
ETC, pg 862
Full Compass Systems, pg 874
Safe Harbor Computers, pg 1001

BRITISH COLUMBIA

Speciality Bulb Products Inc, pg 1020

NEW BRUNSWICK

Kabuki, pg 907

ONTARIO

Premier A/V Sales Ltd, pg 980
VFGadgets Inc, pg 1053

Equipment & Accessory Manufacturers

CALIFORNIA

ARRI Inc, pg 790
Backstage Equipment Inc, pg 801
Birns & Sawyer Inc, pg 808
Camera Essentials, pg 818
CineBags Inc, pg 826
Cinematography Electronics Inc, pg 828
DataDirect Networks, pg 843
General Production Services, pg 877
Alan Gordon Enterprises Inc, pg 880
IDX System Technology Inc, pg 894
Intel-A-Jib™, pg 899
J & R Film Co, pg 903
Lasergraphics Inc, pg 916
Liberty Photo Products, pg 919
Mole-Richardson Co, pg 945
Moviola, pg 948
O'Connor Engineering Labs, pg 961
Penny + Giles, pg 972
The Rip-Tie Co, pg 997
Sprocket Digital, pg 1022
Steeldeck® Inc, pg 1024
Thermodyne Cases, pg 1038
Transvideo International, pg 1044
TV Pro Gear, pg 1046

COLORADO

Goldberg Brothers Inc, pg 880

FLORIDA

JBK Cinequipt LLC, pg 904
Magna-Tech Electronic Co Inc, pg 928
Techni-Lux Inc, pg 1033
Tel-Test, pg 1035

GEORGIA

Lighting & Production Equipment Inc, pg 920

ILLINOIS

Kart-A-Bag Manufacturing Inc, pg 908
Lipsner-Smith Co, pg 922
March Manufacturing Inc, pg 930
PolyScience, pg 978
Research Technology International (RTI), pg 995
Sprayway Inc, pg 1022
La Vezzi Precision Inc, pg 1053
H Wilson Co, pg 1067

INDIANA

General Devices Co Inc, pg 876
Premier™, pg 980
Star Case Manufacturing Co Inc, pg 1023
Stouffer Graphic Arts, pg 1025

MASSACHUSETTS

The Boston Connection Inc, pg 811
Glidecam Industries Inc, pg 878
Technologies at Excelitas, pg 1034

NEVADA

Calculated Industries Inc, pg 816

NEW JERSEY

CELCO-Constantine Engineering Labs Co, pg 822
Falcon Safety Products Inc, pg 865
National Audio-Visual Supply, pg 952
Pro-Tape & Specialities Inc, pg 983

NEW YORK

MultiDyne Video & Fiber Optics Systems, pg 950
Precision Microproducts of America, pg 980
Joseph Struhl Co Inc, pg 1026
Tapemaker, pg 1032
Vitec Videocom Inc, pg 1060

OHIO

Xetron, pg 1071

PENNSYLVANIA

Charles Beseler Co, pg 824

WASHINGTON

Oppenheimer Camera Products, pg 964
Tobin Cinema Systems Inc, pg 1041

WISCONSIN

ETC, pg 862

NEW BRUNSWICK

Kabuki, pg 907

ONTARIO

DW Electrochemicals Ltd, pg 854

Equipment & Accessory Rentals

ARIZONA

Arizona Cine Equipment, pg 789
Creative Backstage, pg 838
Merestone, pg 938
Reel Men Rentals Inc, pg 994

ARKANSAS

Jones Film Video, pg 906

CALIFORNIA

Alternative Rentals, pg 783
Ametron Audio/Video, pg 785
Best Bet Camera Rentals, pg 805
Big Door, pg 807
Big Time Picture Company Inc, pg 807
Birns & Sawyer Inc, pg 808
CamTec Motion Picture Cameras, pg 818
Chapman/Leonard Studios & Production Center, pg 824
Christy's Editorial, pg 826
Cinema Camera Rentals, pg 827
Cinema Rentals Inc, pg 827
Clairmont Camera Inc, pg 829
DTC Lighting & Grip, pg 853
Film Converter Co of America Inc, pg 867
Alan Gordon Enterprises Inc, pg 880
Greenery Studios, pg 882
Imagecraft Productions, pg 896
Intel-A-Jib™, pg 899
J & R Film Co, pg 903
The Lot (Skye Partners), pg 925
Main Street Media Inc, pg 929
Mole-Richardson Co, pg 945
Motion Picture Marine, pg 947
Moviola, pg 948
Otto Nemenz International Inc, pg 954
North County Media Center, pg 959
Pro HD Rentals, pg 983
Radiant Images, pg 990
RED Studios Hollywood, pg 993
Revolution Cinema Rentals, pg 995
Slow Motion Film & Digital Inc, pg 1013
SpaceCam, pg 1019
Steeldeck® Inc, pg 1024
Stray Angel Films, pg 1026
The Studios at Paramount, pg 1027
Synthesizer Systems Technologies (SST), pg 1030
T-stop Inc, pg 1031
Total Media Group, pg 1042
Tyler Camera Systems, pg 1047
VER-Video Equipment Rentals, pg 1053
Videofax, pg 1056
Z-Ville Productions, pg 1073

COLORADO

Ceavco Audio/Visual Co, pg 822
The Cinema Lab, pg 827
Tatum Video, pg 1032

CONNECTICUT

Rockwell Communications Inc, pg 998

DISTRICT OF COLUMBIA

Educational Film Center, pg 857

FLORIDA

Jordan Klein Film & Video (JKFV), pg 906
MAPS Production House, pg 930
Moving Picture, pg 947
Photosound of Orlando Inc, pg 975

GEORGIA

Audio Visual Resources Inc, pg 795
PC&E, pg 970
Studio Space Atlanta, pg 1027

ILLINOIS

Audio Visual Services Corp, pg 796
Creative Technology, pg 838
Helix Camera & Video, pg 887
LITE-IT Grip Truck Rentals, pg 923
Magnanimous Media, pg 928
Product Productions, pg 984
PSAV® Presentation Services (Hotel Services Division), pg 987
Zacuto, pg 1073

MARYLAND

Kramer Communications Video Production, pg 913
RTZ Audio Visual, pg 1000

MASSACHUSETTS

The Boston Connection Inc, pg 811
Green Mountain Post Films (GMP), pg 882
High Output Inc, pg 888

MINNESOTA

AVI Systems, pg 799
Cinequipt Inc, pg 828
House of Cinemagraphics, pg 891

MISSISSIPPI

Jasper Ewing & Sons Inc, pg 864

MISSOURI

Show-Me Audio-Visual, pg 1009
Swank Audio Visuals, pg 1029

MONTANA

Filmlites Montana, pg 867

NEVADA

MG Studio, pg 940

NEW HAMPSHIRE

Apertura, pg 788
APS Lighting-Sound-AV, pg 789

NEW JERSEY

Butter Tree Studio, pg 816
Ironbound Film & Television Studios LLC, pg 902
PLS Staging, pg 977
Bill Quinn Productions, pg 989

NEW YORK

Adorama Rental Co, pg 776
Adwar Video, pg 778
Available Light, pg 798
Big Apple Films, pg 806
Bond Street Studio, pg 810
Bravo Studios, pg 812
Brooklyn Studios, pg 814
Thomas Cestare Inc, pg 823
Cine 60 Inc, pg 826
City Stage, pg 828
Colortone Audio Visual, pg 832
Hand Held Films, pg 884
Langie Audio Visual Systems, pg 915
LightHouse Films, pg 920
LightSpace Studios, pg 921
Magnaplan Corp, pg 928
Motion Picture Enterprises Inc, pg 947
RGH Lighting LLC, pg 996
Scheimpflug Digital, pg 1004
See Factor Industry Inc, pg 1006
The Visual Studies Workshop (VSW), pg 1059
Visual Technologies Corp, pg 1060

NORTH CAROLINA

K2 Productions, pg 914
Strategic Connections, pg 1026

OHIO

Production Partners Media, pg 984

OREGON

Koerner Camera Systems, pg 912
Northwest Film Center, pg 959
Pacific Grip & Lighting Inc, pg 967
Picture This Production Services, pg 975

PENNSYLVANIA

Videosmith Inc, pg 1057

SOUTH CAROLINA

Studio Charleston, pg 1026

TENNESSEE

Memphis Communications Corp, pg 938

TEXAS

Earl Miller Productions Inc, pg 943
Muller Entertainment, pg 949
Panavision Dallas, pg 968
Phil Lights, pg 973

UTAH

Ron Hill Imagery, pg 889
Redman Movies & Stories, pg 993

VIRGINIA

Projection Presentation Technology, pg 985

WASHINGTON

Inland Audio Visual Co, pg 898
Oppenheimer Camera Products, pg 964

WISCONSIN

University of Wisconsin-Oshkosh Radio-TV-Film Dept, pg 1050
Wisconsin Public Television, pg 1068

WYOMING

Bridger Productions Inc, pg 812

ALBERTA

Global Television Station, pg 879

BRITISH COLUMBIA

North West Digital Ltd, pg 959

FILM

Equipment & Accessory Rentals (continued)

MANITOBA

MidCanada Production Services Inc (MidCan), pg 942

NEW BRUNSWICK

Kabuki, pg 907

ONTARIO

JIB Shots Equipment Inc, pg 905
SIM Digital, pg 1011
Wallace Film Studios, pg 1061

Equipment & Accessory Repairs

ARIZONA

PROCAM, pg 983

ARKANSAS

Jay S Stanley & Associates Inc, pg 1023

CALIFORNIA

ARRI Inc, pg 790
Big Time Picture Company Inc, pg 807
Birns & Sawyer Inc, pg 808
Christy's Editorial, pg 826
Alan Gordon Enterprises Inc, pg 880
J & R Film Co, pg 903
Moviola, pg 948
Pro Camera Repair, pg 982
Transvideo International, pg 1044

COLORADO

Ceavco Audio/Visual Co, pg 822

CONNECTICUT

Precision Camera & Video Repair Inc, pg 980
Rockwell Communications Inc, pg 998

FLORIDA

Hi-Tech Enterprises Inc, pg 888
JBK Cinequipt LLC, pg 904
Tel-Test, pg 1035

GEORGIA

Audio Visual Resources Inc, pg 795
Technical Innovation, pg 1033

KENTUCKY

NOR-COM Inc, pg 958

MARYLAND

RTZ Audio Visual, pg 1000
Strauss Photo Technical Service Inc, pg 1026

MASSACHUSETTS

The Boston Connection Inc, pg 811
High Output Inc, pg 888

MINNESOTA

AVI Systems, pg 799

NEW YORK

AZ Spectrum, pg 801
Colortone Audio Visual, pg 832
Langie Audio Visual Systems, pg 915
Magnaplan Corp, pg 928
Motion Picture Enterprises Inc, pg 947
Precision Microproducts of America, pg 980
Visual Technologies Corp, pg 1060
Vitec Videocom Inc, pg 1060

TENNESSEE

Memphis Communications Corp, pg 938

UTAH

Redman Movies & Stories, pg 993

VIRGINIA

The Whitlock Group, pg 1065

WASHINGTON

Oppenheimer Camera Products, pg 964

WISCONSIN

Full Compass Systems, pg 874

Film Cleaning & Inspection Equipment Distributors

ARIZONA

Arizona Cine Equipment, pg 789

CALIFORNIA

Adolph Gasser Inc, pg 776
Christy's Editorial, pg 826
Diversified Imaging Supply, pg 849
FXC Communications, pg 874
Peterson's Video Transfer Services, pg 973
Samy's Camera, pg 1002

COLORADO

Stanco Sales LLC, pg 1023

FLORIDA

Cinema Equipment & Supplies Inc, pg 827
Photographic Solutions Inc, pg 975
Photomart Cine-Video Inc, pg 975

ILLINOIS

Facets Multi-Media Inc, pg 865
Lipsner-Smith Co, pg 922
Research Technology International (RTI), pg 995
Urbanski Film, pg 1050

KENTUCKY

K&R Photo Digital, pg 908

MISSOURI

Communitronics Corp, pg 833

NEVADA

Aardvark Video & Media Productions, pg 772

NEW JERSEY

Argraph Corp, pg 789

NEW YORK

Barbizon Electric Co Inc, pg 802
Get Smart Products, pg 877
NRD LLC, A Mark IV Industries Co, pg 960

PENNSYLVANIA

Bernie's Photo Center, pg 805
IMR Limited, pg 897

TEXAS

Pro Video & Film Equipment Co Inc, pg 983

VIRGINIA

Filmdex Inc, pg 867
The Whitlock Group, pg 1065

ALBERTA

McBain Audio Visual Ltd, pg 935

ONTARIO

Edcom Multimedia Products, pg 856
Premier A/V Sales Ltd, pg 980

Film Cleaning & Inspection Equipment Manufacturers

FLORIDA

Kinetronics Corp, pg 911
Photographic Solutions Inc, pg 975

ILLINOIS

Lipsner-Smith Co, pg 922
Research Technology International (RTI), pg 995
Sprayway Inc, pg 1022
Urbanski Film, pg 1050

NEW JERSEY

Falcon Safety Products Inc, pg 865

NEW YORK

NRD LLC, A Mark IV Industries Co, pg 960
Precision Microproducts of America, pg 980

OHIO

Xetron, pg 1071

Film Cleaning & Inspection Equipment Rentals

ARIZONA

Arizona Cine Equipment, pg 789

CALIFORNIA

Big Time Picture Company Inc, pg 807
Christy's Editorial, pg 826

COLORADO

The Cinema Lab, pg 827

FLORIDA

Jordan Klein Film & Video (JKFV), pg 906

MISSOURI

Show-Me Audio-Visual, pg 1009

PENNSYLVANIA

Fusion Brand Experiences, pg 874

Film Cleaning & Inspection Equipment Repairs

CALIFORNIA

Christy's Editorial, pg 826
Mole-Richardson Co, pg 945

NEW YORK

Precision Microproducts of America, pg 980

PENNSYLVANIA

IMR Limited, pg 897

ONTARIO

Edcom Multimedia Products, pg 856

Film Libraries, *see* Libraries—Film or Stock-Shot

Film to Videotape Transfers, *see* Transfers—Film to Videotape

Grip Equipment Distributors

ARIZONA

Arizona Cine Equipment, pg 789
CamMate Systems, pg 818
Troxell Communications Inc, pg 1045

CALIFORNIA

Adolph Gasser Inc, pg 776
Birns & Sawyer Inc, pg 808
Christy's Editorial, pg 826
Cinemills Corp, pg 828
DTC Lighting & Grip, pg 853
Filmtools®, pg 868
Alan Gordon Enterprises Inc, pg 880
Innovision Optics, pg 899
Intel-A-Jib™, pg 899
Lee Filters, pg 918
Manios Digital & Film, pg 930
Matthews Studio Equipment Inc, pg 934
Mole-Richardson Co, pg 945
Nalpak Inc, pg 952
Photoflex Inc, pg 974
The Rosenthal Group, pg 999
Sacramento Theatrical Lighting Ltd (STL), pg 1001
San Diego Stage & Lighting Supply Inc, pg 1002
Shotmaker Co, pg 1009

Grip Equipment Manufacturers

Grip Equipment Rentals

FILM

Grip Equipment Rentals (continued)

LOUISIANA (continued)
Moxie Media, pg 948
Second Line Stages, pg 1006

MARYLAND
The Ahern Group, pg 779
Event Tech, pg 863
Kramer Communications Video Production, pg 913
Shadowstone R & R™, pg 1008

MASSACHUSETTS
Capron Lighting & Sound Co Inc, pg 819
Green Mountain Post Films (GMP), pg 882
High Output Inc, pg 888
Limelight Productions Inc, pg 921

MICHIGAN
Lowing Light & Grip Inc, pg 925

MINNESOTA
AVI Systems, pg 799
Cinequipt Inc, pg 828
House of Cinemagraphics, pg 891

MISSOURI
Show-Me Audio-Visual, pg 1009
Sight & Sound Production Services Inc, pg 1010

MONTANA
Filmlites Montana, pg 867

NEVADA
MG Studio, pg 940
PRG Lighting, pg 981

NEW HAMPSHIRE
Apertura, pg 788
APS Lighting-Sound-AV, pg 789

NEW JERSEY
Ironbound Film & Television Studios LLC, pg 902
Bill Quinn Productions, pg 989
Unilux Inc, pg 1048

NEW MEXICO
Quickbeam Systems Inc (QSI), pg 989

NEW YORK
Available Light, pg 798
BC Video Inc, pg 803
Bond Street Studio, pg 810
Bravo Studios, pg 812
Brooklyn Fire Proof, pg 814
Brooklyn Studios, pg 814
Thomas Cestare Inc, pg 823
Cine 60 Inc, pg 826
City Stage, pg 828
Eastern Effects Inc, pg 856
LightSpace Studios, pg 921
RGH Lighting LLC, pg 996
Scheimpflug Digital, pg 1004
See Factor Industry Inc, pg 1006
Steiner Studios, pg 1024
Umbra of Newburgh LLC, pg 1048

NORTH CAROLINA
The Communications Group Inc, pg 833
Duke Media Services, pg 853
Take One Productions Ltd, pg 1031

NORTH DAKOTA
Media Productions, pg 937

OHIO
Lyon Video Inc, pg 927
Vincent Lighting Systems, pg 1058

OREGON
Pacific Grip & Lighting Inc, pg 967
Picture This Production Services, pg 975

PENNSYLVANIA
Fusion Brand Experiences, pg 874
Innovision Media Group, pg 899
The Videohouse Inc, pg 1057
Videosmith Inc, pg 1057

TENNESSEE
DR&A Inc, pg 852
RentACamera.com, pg 995

TEXAS
GEAR Cameras & Lighting, pg 876
Earl Miller Productions Inc, pg 943
Muller Entertainment, pg 949
Olden Lighting, pg 962
Panavision Dallas, pg 968
Phil Lights, pg 973
Phillips MediaSource, pg 974
Stage Directions, pg 1022
Texcam Inc, pg 1038

UTAH
Redman Movies & Stories, pg 993

WASHINGTON
Oppenheimer Camera Products, pg 964
Victory Studios, pg 1054

WEST VIRGINIA
Blackwater Video Productions, pg 808

WYOMING
Bridger Productions Inc, pg 812

ALBERTA
Global Television Station, pg 879

ONTARIO
JIB Shots Equipment Inc, pg 905
SIM Digital, pg 1011
Wallace Film Studios, pg 1061

Grip Equipment Repairs

CALIFORNIA
Cinemills Corp, pg 828
DTC Lighting & Grip, pg 853
Matthews Studio Equipment Inc, pg 934
Mole-Richardson Co, pg 945
Shotmaker Co, pg 1009
Spectra Cine Inc, pg 1020

COLORADO
Ceavco Audio/Visual Co, pg 822

FLORIDA
Hi-Tech Enterprises Inc, pg 888

GEORGIA
Lighting & Production Equipment Inc, pg 920
MAGNUM Companies Ltd, pg 929

HAWAII
ATTCO Inc, pg 793

MARYLAND
RTZ Audio Visual, pg 1000
Shadowstone R & R™, pg 1008

MASSACHUSETTS
Capron Lighting & Sound Co Inc, pg 819
High Output Inc, pg 888
Limelight Productions Inc, pg 921

MICHIGAN
Lowing Light & Grip Inc, pg 925

MINNESOTA
AVI Systems, pg 799

NEVADA
PRG Lighting, pg 981

NEW MEXICO
Quickbeam Systems Inc (QSI), pg 989

NEW YORK
Flash Clinic Inc, pg 869
Lowel-Light Manufacturing Inc, pg 925
Vitec Videocom Inc, pg 1060

OHIO
Future Light Inc, pg 874
Vincent Lighting Systems, pg 1058

TEXAS
GEAR Cameras & Lighting, pg 876
Olden Lighting, pg 962

UTAH
Redman Movies & Stories, pg 993

WISCONSIN
Full Compass Systems, pg 874

Inspection Equipment, *see* Film Cleaning & Inspection Equipment

Lens Distributors

ARIZONA
Arizona Cine Equipment, pg 789
Docter Optics Inc, pg 849
EAR Professional Audio/Video, pg 855
PROCAM, pg 983
Troxell Communications Inc, pg 1045

ARKANSAS
Carlton-Bates Co, pg 820
Jay S Stanley & Associates Inc, pg 1023

CALIFORNIA
Adolph Gasser Inc, pg 776
ARRI Inc, pg 790
Birns & Sawyer Inc, pg 808
Cibola Systems, pg 826
Cinema Engineering Co, pg 827
Cinema Equipment Sales of California Inc, pg 827
Cinemills Corp, pg 828
Diversified Imaging Supply, pg 849
DTC Lighting & Grip, pg 853
FXC Communications, pg 874
Gluskin's Custom Audio Video, pg 879
Alan Gordon Enterprises Inc, pg 880
Hooper Camera & Imaging, pg 891
Innovision Optics, pg 899
Instructional Materials & Equipment Distributors (I-Med), pg 899
Jaguar Distribution Corp, pg 903
Lloyd F McKinney Associates Inc, pg 935
Media Fabricators Inc, pg 936
MediaPOINTE, pg 938
Otto Nemenz International Inc, pg 954
Promax Systems, pg 986
Related Visual Inc, pg 994
Slow Motion Film & Digital Inc, pg 1013
THK Photo Products Inc, pg 1039
Video Gear Rentals Inc, pg 1055
Visual Instrumentation Corp, pg 1059

COLORADO
Ceavco Audio/Visual Co, pg 822

CONNECTICUT
Concord Communications, pg 835
Rockwell Communications Inc, pg 998

FLORIDA
Access Media Group, pg 773
AVI-SPL, pg 798
Cinema Equipment & Supplies Inc, pg 827
Gulf Coast Audio Visual Producers Inc, pg 883
Hollywood Theatre Equipment Inc, pg 890
Media Concepts Inc, pg 936
Photomart Cine-Video Inc, pg 975
Sight & Sound Productions, pg 1010
Tallahassee Audio Visual, pg 1031

GEORGIA
Audio Visual Resources Inc, pg 795
Technical Innovation, pg 1033
Visioneering International Inc, pg 1058

ILLINOIS
Creative Technology, pg 838
Facets Multi-Media Inc, pg 865
Major Reproductions Equipment Co, pg 929
Urbanski Film, pg 1050

KENTUCKY
NOR-COM Inc, pg 958

Lens Manufacturers

Lens Rentals

FILM

Lens Rentals (continued)

MICHIGAN

Olson Anderson Co, pg 786
City Events Group, pg 828

MINNESOTA

AVI Systems, pg 799
House of Cinemagraphics, pg 891

MISSISSIPPI

Bowie Audio Visual Enterprises Inc, pg 811

MISSOURI

Show-Me Audio-Visual, pg 1009
Swank Audio Visuals, pg 1029

NEVADA

MG Studio, pg 940

NEW HAMPSHIRE

Apertura, pg 788

NEW JERSEY

Audio Visual Dynamics®, pg 795
PLS Staging, pg 977
Bill Quinn Productions, pg 989

NEW YORK

Adorama Rental Co, pg 776
AV Workshop, pg 797
Big Apple Films, pg 806
Bond Street Studio, pg 810
Cine 60 Inc, pg 826
Cinema-Vision, pg 827
CMI Communications, pg 830
Colortone Audio Visual, pg 832
CPT Rental Inc, pg 837
Hand Held Films, pg 884
Langie Audio Visual Systems, pg 915
LightHouse Films, pg 920
LightSpace Studios, pg 921
Olden Camera & Lens Co Inc, pg 962
Scheimpflug Digital, pg 1004
Visual Technologies Corp, pg 1060

NORTH CAROLINA

Strategic Connections, pg 1026
Take One Productions Ltd, pg 1031

NORTH DAKOTA

Media Productions, pg 937

OHIO

Audio Visual Media, pg 795
Icom Multimedia, pg 893
Thread Marketing Group, pg 1039

OREGON

Koerner Camera Systems, pg 912
Picture This Production Services, pg 975

PENNSYLVANIA

Audio Visions Inc, pg 795
Bernie's Photo Center, pg 805
Grise Audio Visual Center Inc, pg 882
Innovision Media Group, pg 899
Location Camera Ltd, pg 923
Videosmith Inc, pg 1057
Visual Sound Inc, pg 1059

TENNESSEE

RentACamera.com, pg 995
Russ Sturgeon Productions/RSVP, pg 1027

TEXAS

Audio Visual Technologies Group, pg 796
Bright Star Productions Inc, pg 812
GEAR Cameras & Lighting, pg 876
Phil Lights, pg 973
Stage Directions, pg 1022
Texcam Inc, pg 1038

UTAH

Ron Hill Imagery, pg 889
Redman Movies & Stories, pg 993

VIRGINIA

Lee Hartman & Sons Inc, pg 918
Projection Presentation Technology, pg 985

WASHINGTON

Inland Audio Visual Co, pg 898
Oppenheimer Camera Products, pg 964

WISCONSIN

Camera Corner Connecting Point, pg 818
Event Essentials, pg 863
Wisconsin Public Television, pg 1068

ALBERTA

Global Television Station, pg 879
McBain Audio Visual Ltd, pg 935

ONTARIO

JIB Shots Equipment Inc, pg 905
Kingsway Motion Picture Ltd, pg 911
SIM Digital, pg 1011

Lens Repairs

ARIZONA

PROCAM, pg 983

CALIFORNIA

ARRI Inc, pg 790
Birns & Sawyer Inc, pg 808
Cinema Engineering Co, pg 827
Alan Gordon Enterprises Inc, pg 880
Pro Camera Repair, pg 982
Visual Instrumentation Corp, pg 1059

COLORADO

Ceavco Audio/Visual Co, pg 822

CONNECTICUT

Precision Camera & Video Repair Inc, pg 980

FLORIDA

Hi-Tech Enterprises Inc, pg 888

GEORGIA

Dixie Theatre Service & Supply Co Inc, pg 849

INDIANA

Gary Camera & Digital, pg 875

KENTUCKY

NOR-COM Inc, pg 958

MARYLAND

RTZ Audio Visual, pg 1000
Strauss Photo Technical Service Inc, pg 1026

MINNESOTA

AVI Systems, pg 799

NEW JERSEY

Angenieux, pg 786
FUJIFILM Optical Devices Division, pg 873
Konica Minolta Business Solutions, pg 913
Leica Camera Inc, pg 918
ZGC Inc, pg 1073

NEW YORK

Canon Broadcast & Communications Division, pg 819
Colortone Audio Visual, pg 832
CPT Rental Inc, pg 837
Langie Audio Visual Systems, pg 915
Mamiya, pg 929
Schneider Optics Inc, pg 1004
Sigma Corp of America, pg 1010
Visual Technologies Corp, pg 1060

OHIO

Audio Visual Media, pg 795

PENNSYLVANIA

Audio Visions Inc, pg 795
Bernie's Photo Center, pg 805

WASHINGTON

Oppenheimer Camera Products, pg 964

ONTARIO

Kingsway Motion Picture Ltd, pg 911

Libraries—Film or Stock-Shot

ALASKA

Alaska Film Services Inc, pg 779

ARIZONA

Productiontrax.com, pg 985
The Source Stock Footage Library Inc, pg 1019

ARKANSAS

Shadowbox Video Productions, pg 1007

CALIFORNIA

Aaron & Le Duc, pg 772
Action Sports/All Stock, pg 775
AM Stock-Cameo Film Library, pg 783
American Playback Images, pg 785
Carl Barth Images, pg 803
Birds & Animals Unlimited, pg 808
Budget Films Stock Footage Inc, pg 814
Larry Burr, pg 815
Burrud Productions Inc, pg 815
Classic Images, pg 829
Crystal Pyramid Productions™, pg 840
eFootage LLC, pg 858
Em Gee Film Library, pg 860
Envirovision, pg 861
Fish Films Footage World, pg 869
FootageBank HD, pg 871
FXF Productions Inc, pg 874
Global Village Stock Footage Library, pg 879
Gold Standard Productions, pg 880
Havas Edge, pg 885
iCorpTv, pg 893
JDS Video & Media Productions Inc, pg 904
The Kenwood Group, pg 909
Fred Lyon Pictures, pg 927
MacGillivray Freeman Films Inc, pg 927
Moving Art by Louie Schwartzberg, pg 947
Oddball Film + Video, pg 961
Palardo Productions, pg 968
piXvfm, pg 976
Point Lobos Productions, pg 977
Prelinger Archives, pg 980
Producers Library, pg 983
Pyramid Media, pg 987
QRS Software Services, pg 988
SBS Productions, pg 1003
Sports Cinematography Group, pg 1021
The Studios at Paramount, pg 1027
Total Media Group, pg 1042

COLORADO

Paul L Anderson Productions Inc, pg 786
CSI Films, pg 840
Flashback Media Productions, pg 869
Freewheelin' Films, pg 872
Greg Hensley Productions, pg 888
Mammoth HD, pg 929
Tatum Video, pg 1032
T3Media, pg 1046

CONNECTICUT

Cine-Med Inc, pg 826
Skyviews Survey Inc, pg 1013

DISTRICT OF COLUMBIA

Susan Hormuth, Visual Resource Consultant, pg 891

FLORIDA

Best Shot, pg 806
Bill Bachmann Studios, pg 807
Eastern Video, pg 856
Framepool, pg 872
Gulf Coast Audio Visual Producers Inc, pg 883
Media Entertainment Inc, pg 936
Tom Stack & Associates Inc, pg 1022
SuperStock Inc, pg 1029

GEORGIA

Guerrilla Productions LLC, pg 883
Symmes Systems, pg 1030

Location Equipment & Facility Distributors

Location Equipment & Facility Manufacturers

FILM

Location Equipment & Facility Manufacturers (continued)

OHIO

Future Light Inc, pg 874

PENNSYLVANIA

Aztech Productions LLC, pg 801

Location Equipment & Facility Rentals

ALABAMA

Media Visions Inc, pg 937

ARIZONA

Arizona Cine Equipment, pg 789

ARKANSAS

Jones Film Video, pg 906
White Diamond Productions, pg 1065

CALIFORNIA

Antelope Valley Locations & Production Services, pg 787
Big Door, pg 807
Chapman/Leonard Studios & Production Center, pg 824
Cineworks Inc, pg 828
Colby Systems Corp, pg 831
DTC Lighting & Grip, pg 853
Golden Gate Studios, pg 880
Image G, pg 895
Innovision Optics, pg 899
KTVU-Retail Services, pg 914
The Location Connection Inc, pg 924
Mole-Richardson Co, pg 945
Phoebus Lighting, pg 974
Samy's Camera, pg 1002
Santa Clarita Studios, pg 1002
SOS Film Works (Space Ordnance Systems), pg 1016
The Studios at Paramount, pg 1027
Sunset Bronson Studios, pg 1028
Total Media Group, pg 1042
Warner Bros Entertainment Inc, pg 1062
Z-Ville Productions, pg 1073

COLORADO

Apogee Communications Group, pg 788
Ceavco Audio/Visual Co, pg 822
Chimera®, pg 825
Tatum Video, pg 1032

FLORIDA

Cinema East, pg 827
Steven Cohen Motion Picture Production, pg 831
CopShopMiami.com, pg 836
Jordan Klein Film & Video (JKFV), pg 906
Universal Studios Florida® Production Group, pg 1049

GEORGIA

COMPRO Productions Inc, pg 834
Lighting & Production Equipment Inc, pg 920

HAWAII

ATTCO Inc, pg 793

ILLINOIS

Audio Visual Services Corp, pg 796
Beatty TeleVisual Productions, pg 804
LITE-IT Grip Truck Rentals, pg 923
On Site Video, pg 963
Product Productions, pg 984
PSAV® Presentation Services (Hotel Services Division), pg 987

INDIANA

OMNI Productions, pg 962

IOWA

Musco Lighting, pg 950

KENTUCKY

Idle Minds Productions Inc, pg 894

LOUISIANA

Digital FX Inc, pg 847
Moxie Media, pg 948

MARYLAND

Producers Video, pg 984

MASSACHUSETTS

The Boston Connection Inc, pg 811
Goin' Mobile, pg 880
Green Mountain Post Films (GMP), pg 882
High Output Inc, pg 888

MICHIGAN

City Events Group, pg 828

MINNESOTA

AVI Systems, pg 799
Cinequipt Inc, pg 828

MISSOURI

Show-Me Audio-Visual, pg 1009

MONTANA

Jereco Studios Inc, pg 905

NEVADA

PRG Lighting, pg 981

NEW HAMPSHIRE

Apertura, pg 788

NEW JERSEY

Audio Visual Dynamics®, pg 795
Bill Quinn Productions, pg 989

NEW YORK

Available Light, pg 798
Thomas Cestare Inc, pg 823
Cine 60 Inc, pg 826
CMI Communications, pg 830
Manhattan Center Studios Inc, pg 930
MRG Productions Inc, pg 948
RGH Lighting LLC, pg 996

NORTH CAROLINA

The Communications Group Inc, pg 833
Take One Productions Ltd, pg 1031

NORTH DAKOTA

Media Productions, pg 937

OHIO

Lyon Video Inc, pg 927
Mills James Productions, pg 943
Thread Marketing Group, pg 1039

OREGON

Pacific Grip & Lighting Inc, pg 967

PENNSYLVANIA

Fusion Brand Experiences, pg 874
Innovision Media Group, pg 899
Videosmith Inc, pg 1057

TENNESSEE

Russ Sturgeon Productions/RSVP, pg 1027
UMCom Productions, pg 1048

TEXAS

Earl Miller Productions Inc, pg 943
Muller Entertainment, pg 949
Omega Productions, pg 962
Panavision Dallas, pg 968
Phil Lights, pg 973
Phillips MediaSource, pg 974
Stage Directions, pg 1022
Texcam Inc, pg 1038

UTAH

Redman Movies & Stories, pg 993
Webb Audio Visual Communication, pg 1063

VERMONT

Marlboro Film & Video Productions, pg 931

WISCONSIN

Logan Productions Inc, pg 924
University of Wisconsin-Oshkosh Radio-TV-Film Dept, pg 1050
Wisconsin Public Television, pg 1068

WYOMING

Bridger Productions Inc, pg 812

ALBERTA

Global Television Station, pg 879

BRITISH COLUMBIA

Finale Editworks, pg 868
Video In Studios/Video Out Distribution, pg 1055

ONTARIO

JIB Shots Equipment Inc, pg 905

Location Equipment & Facility Repairs

ALABAMA

Media Visions Inc, pg 937

CALIFORNIA

Mole-Richardson Co, pg 945

COLORADO

Ceavco Audio/Visual Co, pg 822

GEORGIA

Lighting & Production Equipment Inc, pg 920

ILLINOIS

On Site Video, pg 963

MASSACHUSETTS

The Boston Connection Inc, pg 811

MICHIGAN

Studio Consulting & Construction Inc, pg 1026

MINNESOTA

AVI Systems, pg 799

NEVADA

PRG Lighting, pg 981

NEW YORK

Lowel-Light Manufacturing Inc, pg 925
MRG Productions Inc, pg 948

Location Photography, *see* Photography—Location

Magnetic Recording Equipment Distributors

ALABAMA

Media Visions Inc, pg 937

ARIZONA

Troxell Communications Inc, pg 1045

CALIFORNIA

Audio Images Corp, pg 794
Birns & Sawyer Inc, pg 808
Christy's Editorial, pg 826
FXC Communications, pg 874
Media Fabricators Inc, pg 936
MediaPOINTE, pg 938
Related Visual Inc, pg 994
Tri-Ed, pg 1044

FLORIDA

Tallahassee Audio Visual, pg 1031

GEORGIA

Lighting & Production Equipment Inc, pg 920

KENTUCKY

NOR-COM Inc, pg 958

MARYLAND

Visual Aids Electronics Corp, pg 1059

MINNESOTA

AVI Systems, pg 799
Cinequipt Inc, pg 828

Magnetic Recording Equipment Manufacturers

Magnetic Recording Equipment Rentals

Magnetic Recording Equipment Repairs

Mixing

FILM

Mixing (continued)

MONTANA

Jereco Studios Inc, pg 905
KUSM TV, pg 914

NEW HAMPSHIRE

Apertura, pg 788

NEW JERSEY

Milgrom Productions, pg 943
NFL Films Music Library, pg 957

NEW YORK

Aura Sonic Ltd, pg 796
DuArt, pg 853
Greyfalcon House, pg 882
HB-Content, pg 886
KAS Music & Sound, pg 908
Magno Sound & Video, pg 929
Mother West, pg 947
MRG Productions Inc, pg 948
Now Hear This, pg 960
Shelly Palmer Production, pg 968
Peckham Productions Inc, pg 970

NORTH CAROLINA

Horizon Video Productions Inc, pg 891
2BruceStudio, pg 1047

PENNSYLVANIA

Right Coast Recording Inc, pg 997

RHODE ISLAND

Sound-FX-Design, pg 1017

SOUTH CAROLINA

Venture Media, pg 1052

TENNESSEE

JamSync, pg 904
Love Shack Recording Studios, pg 925
Motion Picture Services, pg 947
Stage Post, pg 1022

TEXAS

The Sound Lab Inc, pg 1017
Sound Works, pg 1018

UTAH

Soularium Recording Studios, pg 1016

VERMONT

Edgewood Studios, pg 857

VIRGINIA

AudioImage Recording, pg 796

WASHINGTON

Hamilton Studio, pg 884
North-by-Northwest Productions, pg 958
Sound Sound/Savage Fruitarian Productions, pg 1017
Victory Studios, pg 1054

WISCONSIN

5th Floor Recording Co, pg 867
Wisconsin Public Television, pg 1068

ALBERTA

Global Television Station, pg 879

BRITISH COLUMBIA

Pinewood Sound, pg 975

ONTARIO

ADS Media, pg 777
Metalworks Recording Studios Inc, pg 939
Phase One Studios, pg 973
Wanted! Sound + Picture, pg 1062

QUEBEC

Muse Entertainment Enterprises, pg 950

Mixing—Stereo or Dolby Stereo

ALABAMA

Dogwood Recording Studios, pg 850

ARIZONA

Merestone, pg 938

CALIFORNIA

AB Audio Visual Entertainment Inc, pg 772
Aliso Creek Productions Inc, pg 780
Chace Audio by Deluxe, pg 823
Different Fur Recording Ltd, pg 846
Earwax Productions Inc, pg 855
iCorpTv, pg 893
Lynch Communications, pg 926
Maximus Media Inc, pg 934
Mind Over Eye Inc, pg 943
OTR Studios, pg 966
Palardo Productions, pg 968
piXvfm, pg 976
Polarity Post Production, pg 978
Private Island Trax, pg 982
QRS Software Services, pg 988
Roundabout Entertainment Inc, pg 1000
Shapeshifter, pg 1008
SonicPool, pg 1016
Total Media Group, pg 1042
Universal Studios, pg 1049
Wildfire Post Production Studios, pg 1066

COLORADO

Tim Cissell Music, pg 828
Open Media Foundation, pg 964

DELAWARE

Side Door Studio Inc, pg 1010

DISTRICT OF COLUMBIA

Interface Media Group, pg 900

FLORIDA

Audio Visual Imagineering Inc, pg 795
Communications Concepts Inc (CCI), pg 833
Morrisound Recording, pg 946

GEORGIA

Crawford Media Services, pg 838
First Cut Communications LLC, pg 868
Guerrilla Productions LLC, pg 883

HAWAII

Media Bridge Gamekids, pg 936

ILLINOIS

ABSA Productions Inc, pg 772
Steven Samler Music & Sound, pg 1002

INDIANA

AVA Productions, pg 798
InterComm, pg 900

KENTUCKY

Horizon Films & Media LLC, pg 891

MARYLAND

Bethesda Softworks LLC, pg 806
dbF a Media Company, pg 844
Pro Cuts Editing Services, pg 982

MASSACHUSETTS

CommCreative, pg 832
Labrecque Creative Sound, pg 915
Northern Light Productions, pg 959
Preston Productions Inc, pg 981
WGBH Production Group, pg 1065

MICHIGAN

Digi Sign Design LLC, pg 847
Digital Image Studios LLC, pg 847
GMP Music, pg 879
Michigan Recording Arts Institute & Technologies, pg 941

MINNESOTA

Aggressive Records Audio Duplication LLC, pg 778
The Richard Diercks Co Inc, pg 846

MONTANA

Jereco Studios Inc, pg 905

NEW JERSEY

Deluxe Media Services, pg 845
Milgrom Productions, pg 943
NFL Films Inc, pg 957

NEW YORK

Aura Sonic Ltd, pg 796
DuArt, pg 853
Fingerpaint, pg 868
Greyfalcon House, pg 882
HB-Content, pg 886
KAS Music & Sound, pg 908
Magno Sound & Video, pg 929
Mother West, pg 947
MRG Productions Inc, pg 948
Now Hear This, pg 960
Shelly Palmer Production, pg 968

NORTH CAROLINA

Horizon Video Productions Inc, pg 891
2BruceStudio, pg 1047

OHIO

Creative Technology, pg 838

PENNSYLVANIA

Javboy Records, pg 904
Right Coast Recording Inc, pg 997

RHODE ISLAND

Sound-FX-Design, pg 1017

SOUTH CAROLINA

Venture Media, pg 1052

TENNESSEE

American Blackguard Inc, pg 784
JamSync, pg 904
Love Shack Recording Studios, pg 925
Motion Picture Services, pg 947
Stage Post, pg 1022
Zion Music Group, pg 1074

TEXAS

Harbor House Studios, pg 884
Julye Newlin Productions Inc, pg 956
The Samuels Co, pg 1002
The Sound Lab Inc, pg 1017
Sound Works, pg 1018

UTAH

Soularium Recording Studios, pg 1016

WASHINGTON

North-by-Northwest Productions, pg 958
Sound Sound/Savage Fruitarian Productions, pg 1017
Victory Studios, pg 1054

WISCONSIN

5th Floor Recording Co, pg 867
USAV Group Inc, pg 1050

ALBERTA

Global Television Station, pg 879

BRITISH COLUMBIA

Pinewood Sound, pg 975

MANITOBA

daCapo Productions, pg 842

ONTARIO

ADS Media, pg 777
Metalworks Recording Studios Inc, pg 939
Phase One Studios, pg 973
Wanted! Sound + Picture, pg 1062

QUEBEC

Muse Entertainment Enterprises, pg 950

Mixing—Stereo Surround or Dolby Surround

CALIFORNIA

Berkeley Sound Artists Inc, pg 805
Chace Audio by Deluxe, pg 823
Earwax Productions Inc, pg 855
iCorpTv, pg 893
Maximus Media Inc, pg 934
Mind Over Eye Inc, pg 943
OTR Studios, pg 966
Palardo Productions, pg 968

piXvfm, pg 976
Polarity Post Production, pg 978
Private Island Trax, pg 982
QRS Software Services, pg 988
Roundabout Entertainment Inc, pg 1000
Shapeshifter, pg 1008
SonicPool, pg 1016
Total Media Group, pg 1042
Universal Studios, pg 1049
WalkerVision Interarts, pg 1061
Wildfire Post Production Studios, pg 1066

COLORADO

Tim Cissell Music, pg 828

DISTRICT OF COLUMBIA

Interface Media Group, pg 900

FLORIDA

Communications Concepts Inc (CCI), pg 833
Morrisound Recording, pg 946
WKMG-TV Channel 6, pg 1068

GEORGIA

Crawford Media Services, pg 838
Guerrilla Productions LLC, pg 883

HAWAII

Media Bridge Gamekids, pg 936

INDIANA

OMNI Productions, pg 962

MARYLAND

dbF a Media Company, pg 844

MASSACHUSETTS

Northern Light Productions, pg 959
Preston Productions Inc, pg 981
WGBH Production Group, pg 1065

MICHIGAN

Digi Sign Design LLC, pg 847
Digital Image Studios LLC, pg 847
GMP Music, pg 879
Michigan Recording Arts Institute & Technologies, pg 941

MINNESOTA

Aggressive Records Audio Duplication LLC, pg 778
The Richard Diercks Co Inc, pg 846

MONTANA

Jereco Studios Inc, pg 905

NEW JERSEY

Milgrom Productions, pg 943
NFL Films Inc, pg 957

NEW YORK

Aura Sonic Ltd, pg 796
Big Fish Productions Inc, pg 807
Greyfalcon House, pg 882
Magno Sound & Video, pg 929
MRG Productions Inc, pg 948
Now Hear This, pg 960
Shelly Palmer Production, pg 968
Zelman Studios Ltd, pg 1073

NORTH CAROLINA

Horizon Video Productions Inc, pg 891

OHIO

Creative Technology, pg 838

OREGON

Rex, pg 995

PENNSYLVANIA

Right Coast Recording Inc, pg 997

RHODE ISLAND

Sound-FX-Design, pg 1017

TENNESSEE

American Blackguard Inc, pg 784
JamSync, pg 904
Love Shack Recording Studios, pg 925
Motion Picture Services, pg 947
Stage Post, pg 1022

TEXAS

Harbor House Studios, pg 884
Media Event Concepts Inc, pg 936
The Samuels Co, pg 1002

UTAH

Soularium Recording Studios, pg 1016

WASHINGTON

North-by-Northwest Productions, pg 958
Victory Studios, pg 1054

WISCONSIN

5th Floor Recording Co, pg 867

ALBERTA

Global Television Station, pg 879

BRITISH COLUMBIA

Pinewood Sound, pg 975

MANITOBA

daCapo Productions, pg 842

ONTARIO

ADS Media, pg 777
Metalworks Recording Studios Inc, pg 939
Phase One Studios, pg 973
Wanted! Sound + Picture, pg 1062

QUEBEC

Muse Entertainment Enterprises, pg 950

Mobile Production Vehicle Distributors

MICHIGAN

TeL Systems, pg 1035

NEW JERSEY

Tele-Measurements Inc, pg 1035

NEW YORK

MRG Productions Inc, pg 948

PENNSYLVANIA

Innovision Media Group, pg 899
The Lerro Corp, pg 919

TEXAS

Pro Video & Film Equipment Co Inc, pg 983
Shook Mobile Technology LP, pg 1009

UTAH

RIA Corp, pg 996

VIRGINIA

Acoustics First Corp, pg 775

Mobile Production Vehicle Manufacturers

CALIFORNIA

Technical Services, pg 1034

MASSACHUSETTS

L-3 ESSCO, pg 915

TEXAS

Shook Mobile Technology LP, pg 1009

VIRGINIA

Acoustics First Corp, pg 775

Mobile Production Vehicle Rentals

CALIFORNIA

DTC Lighting & Grip, pg 853
Phoebus Lighting, pg 974
The Rosenthal Group, pg 999
Santa Clarita Studios, pg 1002
SNAP, pg 1014
Stray Angel Films, pg 1026
Total Media Group, pg 1042
Z-Ville Productions, pg 1073

FLORIDA

ACT Productions, pg 775
Cinema East, pg 827
CopShopMiami.com, pg 836
Jordan Klein Film & Video (JKFV), pg 906

ILLINOIS

Audio Visual Services Corp, pg 796
Product Productions, pg 984
PSAV® Presentation Services (Hotel Services Division), pg 987

LOUISIANA

Digital FX Inc, pg 847
Moxie Media, pg 948

MARYLAND

Producers Video, pg 984

MASSACHUSETTS

Goin' Mobile, pg 880
Green Mountain Post Films (GMP), pg 882

MISSOURI

Show-Me Audio-Visual, pg 1009

NEW HAMPSHIRE

Apertura, pg 788

NEW JERSEY

Bill Quinn Productions, pg 989

NEW YORK

Thomas Cestare Inc, pg 823
CP Communications, pg 837
MRG Productions Inc, pg 948
RGH Lighting LLC, pg 996

OHIO

Lyon Video Inc, pg 927

OREGON

Pacific Grip & Lighting Inc, pg 967

PENNSYLVANIA

Fusion Brand Experiences, pg 874
Innovision Media Group, pg 899
Location Lighting Ltd, pg 924
WPHL-TV, pg 1070

TENNESSEE

DR&A Inc, pg 852

TEXAS

Muller Entertainment, pg 949
Omega Productions, pg 962
Phillips MediaSource, pg 974
Reelsound Recording Co, pg 994
Texcam Inc, pg 1038

WISCONSIN

Logan Productions Inc, pg 924
Wisconsin Public Television, pg 1068

ALBERTA

Global Television Station, pg 879

ONTARIO

JIB Shots Equipment Inc, pg 905

Mobile Production Vehicle Repairs

CALIFORNIA

Technical Services, pg 1034

NEW YORK

MRG Productions Inc, pg 948

TEXAS

Shook Mobile Technology LP, pg 1009

Mobile Unit Distributors

COLORADO

Ceavco Audio/Visual Co, pg 822

MARYLAND

Nicholas P Pipino Associates Inc, pg 976

FILM

Mobile Unit Distributors (continued)

MINNESOTA

Alpha Video & Audio Inc, pg 782

MISSOURI

Conference Technologies Inc, pg 835

NEW YORK

MRG Productions Inc, pg 948
Ray Supply Inc, pg 992
Visual Technologies Corp, pg 1060

PENNSYLVANIA

Innovision Media Group, pg 899
The Lerro Corp, pg 919

TEXAS

Pro Video & Film Equipment Co Inc, pg 983
Shook Mobile Technology LP, pg 1009

Mobile Unit Manufacturers

CALIFORNIA

Technical Services, pg 1034
TV Pro Gear, pg 1046

COLORADO

Display Devices, pg 849

MARYLAND

Absolute Hollywood, pg 772

MASSACHUSETTS

L-3 ESSCO, pg 915

TEXAS

Shook Mobile Technology LP, pg 1009

Mobile Unit Rentals

CALIFORNIA

RetinaVision Productions, pg 995
SNAP, pg 1014
Z-Ville Productions, pg 1073

COLORADO

Ceavco Audio/Visual Co, pg 822
Maniac Productions, pg 930

FLORIDA

CineVideotech Inc, pg 828
Jordan Klein Film & Video (JKFV), pg 906

GEORGIA

Studio Space Atlanta, pg 1027

ILLINOIS

Audio Visual Services Corp, pg 796
On Site Video, pg 963
PSAV® Presentation Services (Hotel Services Division), pg 987

LOUISIANA

Digital FX Inc, pg 847

MARYLAND

Absolute Hollywood, pg 772
Shadowstone R & R™, pg 1008

MASSACHUSETTS

Goin' Mobile, pg 880

MICHIGAN

Lowing Light & Grip Inc, pg 925

NEW HAMPSHIRE

Apertura, pg 788

NEW JERSEY

Ironbound Film & Television Studios LLC, pg 902
Bill Quinn Productions, pg 989

NEW YORK

Thomas Cestare Inc, pg 823
MRG Productions Inc, pg 948
Scheimpflug Digital, pg 1004
Visual Technologies Corp, pg 1060

OHIO

Lyon Video Inc, pg 927

OREGON

Pacific Grip & Lighting Inc, pg 967

PENNSYLVANIA

Innovision Media Group, pg 899

TEXAS

Muller Entertainment, pg 949
Omega Productions, pg 962

WISCONSIN

Logan Productions Inc, pg 924
Wisconsin Public Television, pg 1068

ALBERTA

Global Television Station, pg 879

MANITOBA

MidCanada Production Services Inc (MidCan), pg 942

Mobile Unit Repairs

CALIFORNIA

Technical Services, pg 1034

COLORADO

Ceavco Audio/Visual Co, pg 822

NEW YORK

MRG Productions Inc, pg 948
Visual Technologies Corp, pg 1060

Movie & Still Camera Distributors

ARIZONA

EAR Professional Audio/Video, pg 855
Troxell Communications Inc, pg 1045

CALIFORNIA

Adolph Gasser Inc, pg 776
ARRI Inc, pg 790
Birns & Sawyer Inc, pg 808
Diversified Imaging Supply, pg 849
FXC Communications, pg 874
Alan Gordon Enterprises Inc, pg 880
Hooper Camera & Imaging, pg 891
MediaPOINTE, pg 938
Otto Nemenz International Inc, pg 954
Point of View Productions, pg 977
Pro8mm, pg 983
Yale Film & Video, pg 1071

FLORIDA

AVI-SPL, pg 798
Gulf Coast Audio Visual Producers Inc, pg 883
Hi-Tech Enterprises Inc, pg 888
Photomart Cine-Video Inc, pg 975
Tallahassee Audio Visual, pg 1031

ILLINOIS

Urbanski Film, pg 1050

MARYLAND

RTZ Audio Visual, pg 1000

MASSACHUSETTS

Hunt's Photo, Video & Digital, pg 892

MINNESOTA

AVI Systems, pg 799
Cinequipt Inc, pg 828

MISSISSIPPI

Jasper Ewing & Sons Inc, pg 864

NEW JERSEY

Leica Camera Inc, pg 918
National Audio-Visual Supply, pg 952
Wilray Audio Visual Corp, pg 1067

NEW YORK

AZ Spectrum, pg 801
Canon USA Inc, pg 819
Colortone Audio Visual, pg 832
Langie Audio Visual Systems, pg 915
Mamiya, pg 929
Motion Picture Enterprises Inc, pg 947
Neptune Photo Inc, pg 954
Olden Camera & Lens Co Inc, pg 962
Ray Supply Inc, pg 992
Sigma Corp of America, pg 1010
Visual Technologies Corp, pg 1060
Willoughby's Imaging Center, pg 1067

NORTH CAROLINA

Camcor Inc, pg 818

OHIO

Midwest Photo Exchange, pg 942

PENNSYLVANIA

Audio Visions Inc, pg 795
Bernie's Photo Center, pg 805
Brodart Co, pg 813
The Lerro Corp, pg 919

RHODE ISLAND

Custom Computer Specialists Inc, pg 841

TENNESSEE

Memphis Communications Corp, pg 938

TEXAS

AVES Audio Visual Systems Inc, pg 798
Pro Video & Film Equipment Co Inc, pg 983

VIRGINIA

Lee Hartman & Sons Inc, pg 918

WASHINGTON

Inland Audio Visual Co, pg 898
Oppenheimer Camera Products, pg 964

WISCONSIN

Camera Corner Connecting Point, pg 818

Movie & Still Camera Manufacturers

CALIFORNIA

ARRI Inc, pg 790
Birns & Sawyer Inc, pg 808
Alan Gordon Enterprises Inc, pg 880
Preston Cinema Systems, pg 981
Pro8mm, pg 983

FLORIDA

JBK Cinequipt LLC, pg 904

NEW JERSEY

CELCO-Constantine Engineering Labs Co, pg 822
Leica Camera Inc, pg 918

NEW YORK

Canon USA Inc, pg 819
ELMO USA Corp, pg 859
Sigma Corp of America, pg 1010

PENNSYLVANIA

Olympus America Inc, pg 962

ONTARIO

IMAX Corp, pg 896

Movie & Still Camera Rentals

ALABAMA

Media Visions Inc, pg 937

Movie & Still Camera Repairs

Multiplexer Equipment, *see* Chain & Multiplexer Equipment

Music Scoring

FILM

Music Scoring (continued)

CALIFORNIA (continued)
Berke Creative Inc, pg 805
Berkeley Sound Artists Inc, pg 805
Creative Media Recording, pg 838
Creative Support Services/CSS Music, pg 838
Crystal Pyramid Productions™, pg 840
Diamond Dreams Music Productions, pg 846
Dogma Studios, pg 850
DreamWorks Animation SKG Inc, pg 852
Earwax Productions Inc, pg 855
4th Street Recording, pg 872
GrooveWorx, pg 882
Havas Edge, pg 885
iCorpTv, pg 893
Kaleidosound, pg 907
Lynch Communications, pg 926
Maximus Media Inc, pg 934
The Media Staff Inc, pg 937
Megatrax, pg 938
Mind Over Eye Inc, pg 943
New & Unique Videos™, pg 955
OTR Studios, pg 966
Palardo Productions, pg 968
Polarity Post Production, pg 978
Private Island Trax, pg 982
Pyramind Studios, pg 988
QRS Software Services, pg 988
Regent Press Publishers & Printers, pg 994
Rhythms Productions (Tom Thumb Music), pg 996
Russ InVision Co/AbridgeClub.com, pg 1001
Sahara Records & Filmworks Entertainment Co, pg 1001
SBS Productions, pg 1003
Sonic Gravy, pg 1015
SonicPool, pg 1016
Studio 132, pg 1027
Timeless Productions, pg 1040
Total Media Group, pg 1042
West Coast Projections Inc, pg 1063

COLORADO
Tim Cissell Music, pg 828
Conly Productions, pg 835
Flashback Media Productions, pg 869

CONNECTICUT
EagleVision Inc, pg 855
Music 2 Hues, pg 951

DELAWARE
Side Door Studio Inc, pg 1010

DISTRICT OF COLUMBIA
Interface Media Group, pg 900

FLORIDA
Digital Video Arts, pg 848
Kat Epple Music Productions, pg 862
Gulf Coast Audio Visual Producers Inc, pg 883
Mach 1 Productions, pg 927
Media Entertainment Inc, pg 936
Sunfire Communications Inc, pg 1028

GEORGIA
First Cut Communications LLC, pg 868
White Dog Studios, pg 1065

HAWAII
Media Bridge Gamekids, pg 936

ILLINOIS
ABS Enterprises, pg 772
MIGHTYbYTES Inc, pg 942
Jim Passin Productions, pg 970
The Pepper Group, pg 972
Steven Samler Music & Sound, pg 1002

INDIANA
AVA Productions, pg 798
OMNI Productions, pg 962

KANSAS
Chapman Recording & Mastering, pg 824

KENTUCKY
Horizon Films & Media LLC, pg 891
The Media Collaboratory, pg 936

LOUISIANA
Disk Productions, pg 849

MARYLAND
CSPMedia.com, pg 840
dbF a Media Company, pg 844
Kramer Communications Video Production, pg 913
Satellite Media Production, pg 1003

MASSACHUSETTS
Green Mountain Post Films (GMP), pg 882
Labrecque Creative Sound, pg 915
Northern Light Productions, pg 959
Penfield Productions Ltd, pg 971
Soundtrack Recording Studios, pg 1018
TR Productions, pg 1043

MICHIGAN
Digi Sign Design LLC, pg 847
GMP Music, pg 879
K&R's Recording Studios Inc, pg 908
Michigan Recording Arts Institute & Technologies, pg 941

MINNESOTA
Aggressive Records Audio Duplication LLC, pg 778
MultiMedia, pg 950

MONTANA
Jereco Studios Inc, pg 905
North Country Media Group, pg 959

NEVADA
Tanglewood Productions, pg 1031

NEW JERSEY
Milbrodt/Music & Sound Design, pg 943
Milgrom Productions, pg 943
NFL Films Music Library, pg 957
Richard Reiter Productions Inc, pg 994
Suede Interactive, pg 1027
TRF Production Music Libraries, pg 1044

NEW YORK
Air Sea Land Productions Inc (ASL), pg 779
aurora productions, pg 797
Big Fish Productions Inc, pg 807
Fingerpaint, pg 868
Bob Gerardi Music Productions, pg 877
HB-Content, pg 886
Headroom Digital Audio, pg 887
Heavy Melody, pg 887
Icontent, pg 893
Kamen Entertainment Group Inc, pg 908
KAS Music & Sound, pg 908
L&P Media, pg 915
Lylofilm Productions, pg 926
Manhattan Production Music Inc, pg 930
Jack Morton Worldwide, pg 946
Mother West, pg 947
MRG Productions Inc, pg 948
New York Audio Productions, pg 956
Now Hear This, pg 960
Nutmeg Post, pg 960
Omnimusic, pg 962
Shelly Palmer Production, pg 968
Patco Resources Inc, pg 970
Peckham Productions Inc, pg 970
David Rapkin Audio Production, pg 991
Elliot Sokolov Music, pg 1015
Sony Music Entertainment, pg 1016
Tiki Recording Studios Inc, pg 1040
Zelman Studios Ltd, pg 1073

NORTH CAROLINA
Audio Art, pg 794
Horizon Video Productions Inc, pg 891
Trailblazer Studios®, pg 1043
2BruceStudio, pg 1047

OHIO
Challenge Productions, pg 823
Creative Technology, pg 838
Mills James Productions, pg 943

OREGON
Odyssey Productions Inc, pg 961

PENNSYLVANIA
Dreambox Media Inc, pg 852
Monster Tracks, pg 945
WPHL-TV, pg 1070

RHODE ISLAND
Sound-FX-Design, pg 1017

TENNESSEE
American Blackguard Inc, pg 784
Continental Film, pg 835
Fricon Entertainment Co Inc, pg 873
Motion Picture Services, pg 947
Stage Post, pg 1022
Zion Music Group, pg 1074

TEXAS
Audiomoxie®, pg 796
Communication Arts Multimedia Inc, pg 832
Harbor House Studios, pg 884
The Sound Lab Inc, pg 1017
Sound Works, pg 1018
Stage Directions, pg 1022
TM Studios Inc, pg 1041
Tropikal Productions, pg 1045

UTAH
Soularium Recording Studios, pg 1016

VERMONT
University of Vermont, Instructional Television Dept, pg 1050

VIRGINIA
BES Studios, pg 805
Mark Sonder Productions Inc, pg 931

WASHINGTON
Hamilton Studio, pg 884
Inland Audio Visual Co, pg 898
Kostov Productions, pg 913
North-by-Northwest Productions, pg 958
Sound Sound/Savage Fruitarian Productions, pg 1017
Victory Studios, pg 1054

WEST VIRGINIA
Sweetsong Productions, pg 1029

WISCONSIN
5th Floor Recording Co, pg 867
USAV Group Inc, pg 1050

WYOMING
Bridger Productions Inc, pg 812

BRITISH COLUMBIA
Pinewood Sound, pg 975

MANITOBA
daCapo Productions, pg 842

ONTARIO
ADS Media, pg 777
Metalworks Recording Studios Inc, pg 939

QUEBEC
Muse Entertainment Enterprises, pg 950

Optical Effects, *see* Special Effects

Optical Printing

CALIFORNIA
Crystal Pyramid Productions™, pg 840
Film Technology Co Inc, pg 867
Goal Productions, pg 879
iCorpTv, pg 893
Palardo Productions, pg 968
piXvfm, pg 976
QRS Software Services, pg 988
SonicPool, pg 1016

COLORADO
The Cinema Lab, pg 827

INDIANA

Optical Disc Solutions Inc, pg 964

MINNESOTA

Aggressive Records Audio Duplication LLC, pg 778

NEW HAMPSHIRE

Apertura, pg 788

NEW JERSEY

CELCO-Constantine Engineering Labs Co, pg 822
Newark Beth Israel Medical Center, pg 956

NEW YORK

Black Star Publishing Co Inc, pg 808
Gage-Line Technology Inc, pg 874
Ketchum Pleon Change, pg 910
R/GA, pg 990

OHIO

Vista Color Imaging Inc, pg 1059

PENNSYLVANIA

John E Allen Inc, pg 781

TENNESSEE

Motion Picture Services, pg 947
Stage Post, pg 1022

TEXAS

The Color Lab Inc, pg 831
Stage Directions, pg 1022

WASHINGTON

Inland Audio Visual Co, pg 898

WISCONSIN

USAV Group Inc, pg 1050

BRITISH COLUMBIA

Pinewood Sound, pg 975

Photographic Equipment & Supply Distributors

ARIZONA

Docter Optics Inc, pg 849
Professional Marketing Services Inc, pg 985
Troxell Communications Inc, pg 1045

ARKANSAS

Carlton-Bates Co, pg 820

CALIFORNIA

A&I, pg 771
Adolph Gasser Inc, pg 776
Backdrop Outlet, pg 801
Birns & Sawyer Inc, pg 808
Camera Essentials, pg 818
Cinema Engineering Co, pg 827
Diversified Imaging Supply, pg 849
DTC Lighting & Grip, pg 853
Freestyle Photographic Supplies, pg 872
FXC Communications, pg 874
Gluskin's Custom Audio Video, pg 879
Alan Gordon Enterprises Inc, pg 880
Harrah's Theatre Equipment Co, pg 885
Hooper Camera & Imaging, pg 891
Intel-A-Jib™, pg 899
J & R Film Co, pg 903
Lee Filters, pg 918
Matthews Studio Equipment Inc, pg 934
Mole-Richardson Co, pg 945
Nalpak Inc, pg 952
Noritsu America Corp, pg 958
Photoflex Inc, pg 974
Promax Systems, pg 986
The Rip-Tie Co, pg 997
Thermodyne Cases, pg 1038
THK Photo Products Inc, pg 1039
Tri-Ed, pg 1044
Video Gear Rentals Inc, pg 1055

COLORADO

Goldberg Brothers Inc, pg 880
Stanco Sales LLC, pg 1023

CONNECTICUT

Connecticut Audio & Theatrical Supply, pg 835
Kenyon Laboratories LLC, pg 909

FLORIDA

Gulf Coast Audio Visual Producers Inc, pg 883
Harmon's Audio-Visual Services, pg 885
Lumedyne Inc, pg 926
Photographic Solutions Inc, pg 975
Sight & Sound Productions, pg 1010
Tallahassee Audio Visual, pg 1031
Techni-Lux Inc, pg 1033

GEORGIA

Audio Visual Resources Inc, pg 795

IDAHO

Idaho Camera Inc, pg 893

ILLINOIS

Facets Multi-Media Inc, pg 865
FUJIFILM Graphic Systems Division, pg 873
Leedal Inc, pg 918
Lipsner-Smith Co, pg 922
Smith-Victor Corp, pg 1014
Speedotron Corp, pg 1021
Urbanski Film, pg 1050

INDIANA

Porter Case Inc, pg 978

LOUISIANA

Available Lighting & Motion Picture Services Inc, pg 798

MARYLAND

OmegaBrandess Distribution, pg 962
Ritz Camera & Image, pg 997
RTZ Audio Visual, pg 1000

MASSACHUSETTS

Hunt's Photo, Video & Digital, pg 892
Lineco, pg 922
Visual Departures Ltd, pg 1059

MICHIGAN

Lacquer-Mat Inc, pg 915
Lowing Light & Grip Inc, pg 925

MINNESOTA

Alpha Video & Audio Inc, pg 782
AVI Systems, pg 799
Cinequipt Inc, pg 828

MISSISSIPPI

Jasper Ewing & Sons Inc, pg 864

MISSOURI

Schiller's Audio-Visual, pg 1004

NEBRASKA

Images II Inc, pg 896

NEVADA

Aardvark Video & Media Productions, pg 772
Bulbman Inc, pg 815
PRG Lighting, pg 981

NEW JERSEY

Agfa Graphics, pg 778
Argraph Corp, pg 789
AV Bluebook, pg 797
Caprock Developments Inc, pg 819
Hakuba Sunpak Velbon, pg 883
Hasselblad Bron Inc, pg 885
HP Marketing Corp, pg 892
Leica Camera Inc, pg 918
Manfrotto Distribution Inc, pg 930
National Audio-Visual Supply, pg 952
Pioneer Research Inc, pg 976

NEW YORK

Barbizon Electric Co Inc, pg 802
Bulbtronics Inc, pg 815
Century Business Solutions, pg 823
Colortone Audio Visual, pg 832
Eastman Kodak Professional, pg 856
Edmund Scientific, pg 857
Flash Clinic Inc, pg 869
Gage-Line Technology Inc, pg 874
Get Smart Products, pg 877
Gordon Visual Solutions, pg 880
Just Bulbs - The Light Bulb Store, pg 907
Langie Audio Visual Systems, pg 915
Light Impressions, pg 920
Motion Picture Enterprises Inc, pg 947
Neptune Photo Inc, pg 954
Olden Camera & Lens Co Inc, pg 962
PASCO, pg 969
Precision Microproducts of America, pg 980
Qioptiq, pg 988
Ray Supply Inc, pg 992
RTS Inc, pg 1000
Schneider Optics Inc, pg 1004
Sigma Corp of America, pg 1010
The Tiffen Co LLC, pg 1040
Vincent Associates, pg 1058
Visual Technologies Corp, pg 1060
Willoughby's Imaging Center, pg 1067

NORTH CAROLINA

Camcor Inc, pg 818

OREGON

Pacific Grip & Lighting Inc, pg 967

PENNSYLVANIA

Audio Visions Inc, pg 795
Bernie's Photo Center, pg 805
Bromwell Marketing, pg 813
Charles Beseler Co, pg 824
Electron Microscopy Sciences (EMS), pg 859
Garcia Marketing Inc, pg 875
Innovision Media Group, pg 899
The Lerro Corp, pg 919
Visual Sound Inc, pg 1059
VWR International LLC, pg 1061

RHODE ISLAND

Custom Computer Specialists Inc, pg 841

TENNESSEE

Memphis Communications Corp, pg 938

TEXAS

Audio Visual Technologies Group, pg 796
Olden Lighting, pg 962

UTAH

Redman Movies & Stories, pg 993
Webb Audio Visual Communication, pg 1063

VIRGINIA

Filmdex Inc, pg 867
Lee Hartman & Sons Inc, pg 918

WASHINGTON

Inland Audio Visual Co, pg 898
Oppenheimer Camera Products, pg 964

WISCONSIN

Alpha Source Inc, pg 782
Camera Corner Connecting Point, pg 818
Indus International Inc, pg 897
Pro Studio Supply, pg 983
Regal Photo Products Inc/Arkay Corp, pg 994
Safe Harbor Computers, pg 1001

BRITISH COLUMBIA

Speciality Bulb Products Inc, pg 1020

ONTARIO

Henry's Camera, pg 888

Photographic Equipment & Supply Manufacturers

CALIFORNIA

Backdrop Outlet, pg 801
California Stainless Manufacturing Inc, pg 817
Camera Essentials, pg 818
Cinema Engineering Co, pg 827
Cinema Xenon International Inc, pg 827
Alan Gordon Enterprises Inc, pg 880
Hooper Camera & Imaging, pg 891
Intel-A-Jib™, pg 899

FILM

Photographic Equipment & Supply Manufacturers (continued)

CALIFORNIA (continued)

Lee Filters, pg 918
Matthews Studio Equipment Inc, pg 934
Mole-Richardson Co, pg 945
Noritsu America Corp, pg 958
O'Connor Engineering Labs, pg 961
Photoflex Inc, pg 974
The Rip-Tie Co, pg 997
Stewart Filmscreen Corp, pg 1025
Thermodyne Cases, pg 1038
Ushio America Inc, pg 1051

COLORADO

Goldberg Brothers Inc, pg 880

CONNECTICUT

ILFORD America Inc, pg 894
Kenyon Laboratories LLC, pg 909

FLORIDA

Kinetronics Corp, pg 911
Lumedyne Inc, pg 926
Magna-Tech Electronic Co Inc, pg 928
Photographic Solutions Inc, pg 975
Photoquip Inc, pg 975
Print File Inc, pg 982

GEORGIA

Lighting & Production Equipment Inc, pg 920

ILLINOIS

Kart-A-Bag Manufacturing Inc, pg 908
Leedal Inc, pg 918
Quantum Instruments Inc, pg 989
QuickSet International Inc, pg 989
Smith-Victor Corp, pg 1014
Speedotron Corp, pg 1021

INDIANA

Porter Case Inc, pg 978
Star Case Manufacturing Co Inc, pg 1023
Stouffer Graphic Arts, pg 1025

MARYLAND

OmegaBrandess Distribution, pg 962

MASSACHUSETTS

Lineco, pg 922
Solutek Corp, pg 1015
Visual Departures Ltd, pg 1059

MICHIGAN

Photo Technicians Inc, pg 974
X-Rite, pg 1071

MINNESOTA

Photo Tech Inc, pg 974

NEVADA

Lensless Camera Manufacturing Co, pg 919

NEW JERSEY

Hakuba Sunpak Velbon, pg 883
Konica Minolta Business Solutions, pg 913
Leica Camera Inc, pg 918
Pioneer Research Inc, pg 976
Pro-Tape & Specialities Inc, pg 983
Sofradir EC, pg 1015
Unilux Inc, pg 1048

NEW YORK

Century Business Solutions, pg 823
Flash Clinic Inc, pg 869
Gage-Line Technology Inc, pg 874
Gagne Inc, pg 875
Gordon Visual Solutions, pg 880
Precision Microproducts of America, pg 980
Qioptiq, pg 988
Schneider Optics Inc, pg 1004
Sigma Corp of America, pg 1010
Sima Products Corp, pg 1011
Tamron USA Inc, pg 1031
The Tiffen Co LLC, pg 1040
Vincent Associates, pg 1058

OHIO

Roconex Corp, pg 998

OKLAHOMA

Dunning Photo Equipment Inc, pg 853
ESECO Speedmaster, pg 862

OREGON

Rockland Colloid LLC, pg 998

PENNSYLVANIA

Charles Beseler Co, pg 824
Electron Microscopy Sciences (EMS), pg 859
IDenticard Systems Inc, pg 894
Olympus America Inc, pg 962
Tobias Associates Inc, pg 1041

VIRGINIA

Filmdex Inc, pg 867

WISCONSIN

Bardes Products Inc, pg 803
Indus International Inc, pg 897
Regal Photo Products Inc/Arkay Corp, pg 994

ONTARIO

DW Electrochemicals Ltd, pg 854
FUJIFILM Canada Inc, pg 873
Osram Sylvania Ltd/LTEE, pg 966

Photographic Equipment & Supply Rentals

ARIZONA

Reel Men Rentals Inc, pg 994

CALIFORNIA

Adolph Gasser Inc, pg 776
Artichoke Productions, pg 791
Backdrop Outlet, pg 801
Birns & Sawyer Inc, pg 808
Gluskin's Custom Audio Video, pg 879
Hooper Camera & Imaging, pg 891
Intel-A-Jib™, pg 899
Main Street Media Inc, pg 929
Mole-Richardson Co, pg 945
Samy's Camera, pg 1002
Straight Shoot'r Cranes Inc, pg 1025
Total Media Group, pg 1042
Video Gear Rentals Inc, pg 1055

CONNECTICUT

Kenyon Laboratories LLC, pg 909

FLORIDA

Gulf Coast Audio Visual Producers Inc, pg 883
Jordan Klein Film & Video (JKFV), pg 906
Tallahassee Audio Visual, pg 1031

ILLINOIS

Communications Corporation of America, pg 833
Helix Camera & Video, pg 887

INDIANA

Gary Camera & Digital, pg 875
Jack's Camera Shop, pg 903
OMNI Productions, pg 962

KENTUCKY

Idle Minds Productions Inc, pg 894

LOUISIANA

Available Lighting & Motion Picture Services Inc, pg 798

MARYLAND

RTZ Audio Visual, pg 1000
Shadowstone R & R™, pg 1008

MASSACHUSETTS

The Boston Connection Inc, pg 811

MICHIGAN

Lowing Light & Grip Inc, pg 925

MINNESOTA

AVI Systems, pg 799

MISSISSIPPI

Jasper Ewing & Sons Inc, pg 864

MISSOURI

Schiller's Audio-Visual, pg 1004
Show-Me Audio-Visual, pg 1009

NEVADA

PRG Lighting, pg 981

NEW HAMPSHIRE

Apertura, pg 788

NEW JERSEY

Bill Quinn Productions, pg 989
Unilux Inc, pg 1048

NEW YORK

Available Light, pg 798
Colortone Audio Visual, pg 832
Flash Clinic Inc, pg 869
Langie Audio Visual Systems, pg 915
Manhattan Center Studios Inc, pg 930
Motion Picture Enterprises Inc, pg 947

NORTH CAROLINA

Camcor Inc, pg 818

NORTH DAKOTA

Media Productions, pg 937

OHIO

Vista Color Imaging Inc, pg 1059

OREGON

Pacific Grip & Lighting Inc, pg 967

PENNSYLVANIA

Audio Visions Inc, pg 795
Bernie's Photo Center, pg 805
Innovision Media Group, pg 899
Ott Film Rentals, pg 966

TENNESSEE

Memphis Communications Corp, pg 938

TEXAS

Olden Lighting, pg 962
Texcam Inc, pg 1038

UTAH

Redman Movies & Stories, pg 993
Webb Audio Visual Communication, pg 1063

VIRGINIA

Lee Hartman & Sons Inc, pg 918

WASHINGTON

Inland Audio Visual Co, pg 898
Oppenheimer Camera Products, pg 964

ALBERTA

Global Television Station, pg 879
McBain Audio Visual Ltd, pg 935

Photographic Equipment & Supply Repairs

ARIZONA

PROCAM, pg 983

CALIFORNIA

Adolph Gasser Inc, pg 776
FXC Communications, pg 874
Gluskin's Custom Audio Video, pg 879
Hooper Camera & Imaging, pg 891
Matthews Studio Equipment Inc, pg 934
Mole-Richardson Co, pg 945
Nikon Inc, pg 957
Pro Camera Repair, pg 982

CONNECTICUT

Precision Camera & Video Repair Inc, pg 980

FLORIDA

Tallahassee Audio Visual, pg 1031

GEORGIA

Dixie Theatre Service & Supply Co Inc, pg 849

Photography—Aerial

FILM

Photography—Aerial (continued)

SOUTH CAROLINA

Genesis Creative, pg 877
Venture Media, pg 1052

TENNESSEE

Continental Film, pg 835
Motion Picture Services, pg 947
Phoenix Aerial Photography Inc, pg 974
Scripps Networks, pg 1005
Stage Post, pg 1022

TEXAS

Alexander Media Productions, pg 780
AMS Pictures, pg 786
Castleview Productions, pg 821
Communication Arts Multimedia Inc, pg 832
Horizon Film + Video Productions, pg 891
Inferno Films, pg 898
McNee Productions Inc, pg 935
Earl Miller Productions Inc, pg 943
Julye Newlin Productions Inc, pg 956
Phillips MediaSource, pg 974
The Samuels Co, pg 1002
South Coast Film & Video, pg 1019
Stage Directions, pg 1022
Stockyard Photos/Jim Olive Photography, pg 1025

VERMONT

University of Vermont, Instructional Television Dept, pg 1050

VIRGINIA

Advance Concepts Inc, pg 777
CACI Productions Group, pg 816
HeloAir Inc, pg 888
Metro Productions, pg 939
Lynda Richardson Photography, pg 996

WASHINGTON

North-by-Northwest Productions, pg 958
Oppenheimer Camera Products, pg 964
Pro Image, pg 983
Stuart Westmorland Photography, pg 1064
White Rain Films Ltd, pg 1065

WISCONSIN

Audio Visual of Milwaukee Inc, pg 795
USAV Group Inc, pg 1050
Wisconsin Public Television, pg 1068

WYOMING

Bridger Productions Inc, pg 812

ALBERTA

Black Media Works, pg 808

BRITISH COLUMBIA

Image Media Farm, pg 895

NORTHWEST TERRITORIES

Yellowknife Films Inc, pg 1072

ONTARIO

GAPC (General Assembly Production Centre), pg 875
WESCAM Inc, pg 1063

Photography—Location

ALABAMA

Diamond Studios, pg 846

ALASKA

Alaska Film Services Inc, pg 779
Aurora Films, pg 797

ARIZONA

Aardvark Productions LLC, pg 772
Metropolitan Audio-Visual Inc, pg 940
Phoenix VideoFilms®, pg 974
Productiontrax.com, pg 985
Stevenson Photography, pg 1024

ARKANSAS

Live'N'Loud, pg 923
Shadowbox Video Productions, pg 1007

CALIFORNIA

A Go Go Films, pg 771
Action Sports/All Stock, pg 775
Artichoke Productions, pg 791
Auslender Productions/Celestial Images, pg 797
Carl Barth Images, pg 803
Larry Burr, pg 815
Cinema Engineering Co, pg 827
Classic Images, pg 829
Concrete Images, pg 835
Crystal Pyramid Productions™, pg 840
deKramer Productions Inc, pg 845
Design Media, pg 845
eFootage LLC, pg 858
Envirovision, pg 861
Robert Fried Photography, pg 873
FXC Communications, pg 874
FXF Productions Inc, pg 874
Goal Productions, pg 879
Havas Edge, pg 885
iCorpTv, pg 893
Jaguar Distribution Corp, pg 903
Kavich Reynolds Productions Inc, pg 908
KTVU-Retail Services, pg 914
MacGillivray Freeman Films Inc, pg 927
Main Street Media Inc, pg 929
The Media Staff Inc, pg 937
Motion Picture Marine, pg 947
Moving Art by Louie Schwartzberg, pg 947
New Circuit Films LLC, pg 955
Palardo Productions, pg 968
Panorama Productions, pg 968
Point of View Productions, pg 977
James Porter Photography, pg 979
PSI Inc, pg 987
QRS Software Services, pg 988
Dick Reizner Film & Video, pg 994
RetinaVision Productions, pg 995
Santa Barbara Location Services, pg 1002
SBS Productions, pg 1003
Sea Studios Foundation, pg 1005
SNAP, pg 1014
StereoScope International, pg 1024
Still N'Motion, pg 1025
Stray Angel Films, pg 1026
The Studio Center, pg 1026
The Studio of David Inocencio/ Minette Siegel, pg 1027
Tam Communications Inc, pg 1031
30 Second Films, pg 1039
Total Media Group, pg 1042
Utopia Films, pg 1051
Via Verde Productions, pg 1053
Vineyard Productions, pg 1058
WARPed Pictures, pg 1062
Wavemaker Media Design, pg 1062

COLORADO

Paul L Anderson Productions Inc, pg 786
Apogee Communications Group, pg 788
Blue River Productions, pg 810
CSI Films, pg 840
Flashback Media Productions, pg 869
Greg Hensley Productions, pg 888
Open Media Foundation, pg 964
Tatum Video, pg 1032
Transtar Entertainment Co Inc, pg 1043

CONNECTICUT

Broadcast Video Productions LLC, pg 813
The Gary-Paul Agency, pg 875
MAVCO, pg 934
New London Media, pg 956
Skyviews Survey Inc, pg 1013

FLORIDA

America By Air Stock Footage Library, pg 783
Bill Bachmann Studios, pg 807
Cinema East, pg 827
Civins Productions Inc, pg 828
Steven Cohen Motion Picture Production, pg 831
Communications Concepts Inc (CCI), pg 833
CopShopMiami.com, pg 836
Eastern Video, pg 856
Gulf Coast Audio Visual Producers Inc, pg 883
Home Shopping Network (HSN), pg 890
Jordan Klein Film & Video (JKFV), pg 906
Media Entertainment Inc, pg 936
Paradise Video & Film, pg 969
Roger Scruggs Films, pg 1005
Shooting Stars Post Inc, pg 1009
Sound*Light, pg 1017
Tom Stack & Associates Inc, pg 1022
SuperStock Inc, pg 1029
Mike Vasilinda Productions Inc, pg 1052

GEORGIA

COMPRO Productions Inc, pg 834
Continental Film & Video, pg 835
Guerrilla Productions LLC, pg 883
Malcolm Neal Productions, pg 954
USMotivation, pg 1051
Visioneering International Inc, pg 1058

HAWAII

1013 Integrated, pg 1037

IDAHO

Rex Morris Productions, pg 946

ILLINOIS

Communications Corporation of America, pg 833
Custom Medical Stock Photo Inc, pg 841
Film Police, pg 867
MIGHTYbYTES Inc, pg 942
SCI Television Productions LLC, pg 1004
WEEK TV, pg 1063

INDIANA

AVA Productions, pg 798

IOWA

The Production House, pg 984

KENTUCKY

Broadway Digital, pg 813
Horizon Films & Media LLC, pg 891
Idle Minds Productions Inc, pg 894

LOUISIANA

Digital FX Inc, pg 847
Moxie Media, pg 948
Vidox Motion Imagery, pg 1057

MAINE

Portland Models & Talent LLC, pg 979

MARYLAND

Richard Chisolm Cinematography, pg 825
DBM Communications Inc, pg 844
Kramer Communications Video Production, pg 913

MASSACHUSETTS

CommCreative, pg 832
Cramer Productions, pg 837
Emergency Film Group, pg 860
Green Mountain Post Films (GMP), pg 882
Heliotrope Studios, pg 887
In the Wild Productions, pg 897
Northern Light Productions, pg 959
Tom Pantages, pg 968

MICHIGAN

Digi Sign Design LLC, pg 847
K&R's Recording Studios Inc, pg 908
Maritz Performance Improvement Co, pg 931

MINNESOTA

Aggressive Records Audio Duplication LLC, pg 778
Badiyan Inc, pg 801
House of Cinemagraphics, pg 891
Media Loft Inc, pg 937
MultiMedia, pg 950

MISSOURI

Avatar Studios, pg 798
Visionworks Design Services Inc, pg 1059

Photography—Slow Motion

FILM

Photography—Slow Motion (continued)

Photography—Studio

MONTANA

Clarkson Studio, pg 829
KCFW Television, pg 908
North Country Media Group, pg 959

NEVADA

DVDs4Less, pg 854

NEW HAMPSHIRE

Apertura, pg 788
Chip Taylor Communications LLC, pg 1032

NEW JERSEY

18 Label Studios, pg 858
Euro-Pacific Film & Video Productions Inc, pg 863
NFL Films Inc, pg 957
Bill Quinn Productions, pg 989
Set To Go Studios, pg 1007

NEW YORK

Bevilacqua Studios, pg 806
Big Film Design, pg 807
Black Star Publishing Co Inc, pg 808
Brian Film Productions LLC, pg 812
Broad Street Inc, pg 812
C2 Imaging LLC, pg 841
Elite Video & Photography Services Inc, pg 859
Gurrilla Video Solutions, pg 883
HB-Content, pg 886
Image Makers of Pittsford/Image Maker Productions, pg 895
La Paloma Films, pg 915
L&P Media, pg 915
Neal Marshad Productions, pg 931
MHS-TV, pg 941
Jack Morton Worldwide, pg 946
MRG Productions Inc, pg 948
Museum of the City of New York, pg 950
New Horizon Studios, pg 955
Peckham Productions Inc, pg 970
R/GA, pg 990
RGH Lighting LLC, pg 996
Zelman Studios Ltd, pg 1073

NORTH CAROLINA

The Communications Group Inc, pg 833
Horizon Video Productions Inc, pg 891
Image Associates Inc, pg 894
On Location North Carolina, pg 963
Take One Productions Ltd, pg 1031
Trailblazer Studios®, pg 1043
Unifour Productions Inc, pg 1048

NORTH DAKOTA

Media Productions, pg 937

OHIO

Challenge Productions, pg 823
Creative Technology, pg 838
Lyon Video Inc, pg 927
Mills James Productions, pg 943
Thread Marketing Group, pg 1039
Treehaus Communications Inc, pg 1044
Vista Color Imaging Inc, pg 1059

OKLAHOMA

University of Oklahoma Academic Media & Digital Services, pg 1050

OREGON

A KTVA Production LLC, pg 771
Odyssey Productions Inc, pg 961

PENNSYLVANIA

Argentine Productions Inc, pg 789
Berry & Homer, pg 805
Center City Film & Video Inc, pg 822
Fusion Brand Experiences, pg 874
Innovision Media Group, pg 899
JPL, pg 906
Production Masters Inc (PMI), pg 984

RHODE ISLAND

A&M Productions, pg 771

SOUTH CAROLINA

Genesis Creative, pg 877
Venture Media, pg 1052

TENNESSEE

Motion Picture Services, pg 947
Scripps Networks, pg 1005
Stage Post, pg 1022
UMCom Productions, pg 1048
WKPT-TV, pg 1068

TEXAS

AMS Pictures, pg 786
Best Film & Video, pg 805
Castleview Productions, pg 821
Cerutti Productions Inc, pg 823
Communication Arts Multimedia Inc, pg 832
Horizon Film + Video Productions, pg 891
Inferno Films, pg 898
Maverick Video Productions, pg 934
Phil Lights, pg 973
Prairie Pictures Film & Video, pg 980
The Samuels Co, pg 1002
South Coast Film & Video, pg 1019
South Trunk Studios, pg 1019
Stage Directions, pg 1022
Stockyard Photos/Jim Olive Photography, pg 1025
Texcam Inc, pg 1038

UTAH

Ferrari Color®, pg 866

VIRGINIA

Advance Concepts Inc, pg 777
BES Studios, pg 805
CACI Productions Group, pg 816
Maniglia Media, pg 930
Lynda Richardson Photography, pg 996

WASHINGTON

Hamilton Studio, pg 884
North-by-Northwest Productions, pg 958
Oppenheimer Camera Products, pg 964
White Rain Films Ltd, pg 1065

WEST VIRGINIA

MotionMasters, pg 947

WISCONSIN

Logan Productions Inc, pg 924
Meridian Studios, pg 939
University of Wisconsin-Oshkosh Radio-TV-Film Dept, pg 1050
USAV Group Inc, pg 1050
Video Wisconsin Inc, pg 1056
Watts Communications Inc, pg 1062
Wisconsin Public Television, pg 1068

WYOMING

Bridger Productions Inc, pg 812

ALBERTA

Global Television, pg 879
Global Television Station, pg 879

BRITISH COLUMBIA

Image Media Farm, pg 895

ONTARIO

ADS Media, pg 777
GAPC (General Assembly Production Centre), pg 875
Purefire Communications Inc, pg 987

QUEBEC

Muse Entertainment Enterprises, pg 950

Photography—Underwater

ARIZONA

Phoenix VideoFilms®, pg 974
Productiontrax.com, pg 985

CALIFORNIA

Action Sports/All Stock, pg 775
Classic Images, pg 829
Concrete Images, pg 835
Envirovision, pg 861
FXF Productions Inc, pg 874
Goal Productions, pg 879
iCorpTv, pg 893
MacGillivray Freeman Films Inc, pg 927
Motion Picture Marine, pg 947
Moving Art by Louie Schwartzberg, pg 947
New Circuit Films LLC, pg 955
QRS Software Services, pg 988
Dick Reizner Film & Video, pg 994
SBS Productions, pg 1003
Sea Studios Foundation, pg 1005
StereoScope International, pg 1024
30 Second Films, pg 1039
Utopia Films, pg 1051
WARPed Pictures, pg 1062

COLORADO

CSI Films, pg 840
Flashback Media Productions, pg 869
Greg Hensley Productions, pg 888

CONNECTICUT

Broadcast Video Productions LLC, pg 813
Skyviews Survey Inc, pg 1013

FLORIDA

Allegro Productions Inc, pg 781
Steven Cohen Motion Picture Production, pg 831
Communications Concepts Inc (CCI), pg 833
Courter Films LLC, pg 837
Eastern Video, pg 856
Gulf Coast Audio Visual Producers Inc, pg 883
Home Shopping Network (HSN), pg 890
Jordan Klein Film & Video (JKFV), pg 906
Tom Stack & Associates Inc, pg 1022
SuperStock Inc, pg 1029

GEORGIA

COMPRO Productions Inc, pg 834
Continental Film & Video, pg 835
Guerrilla Productions LLC, pg 883
USMotivation, pg 1051

ILLINOIS

ABS Enterprises, pg 772
Film Police, pg 867
Helix Camera & Video, pg 887
Major Media Productions Inc, pg 929

LOUISIANA

Digital FX Inc, pg 847

MARYLAND

Kramer Communications Video Production, pg 913

MASSACHUSETTS

CommCreative, pg 832
In the Wild Productions, pg 897
Northern Light Productions, pg 959

MINNESOTA

Aggressive Records Audio Duplication LLC, pg 778
House of Cinemagraphics, pg 891
Media Loft Inc, pg 937
MultiMedia, pg 950

MONTANA

Clarkson Studio, pg 829

NEW JERSEY

Pioneer Research Inc, pg 976

NEW YORK

Black Star Publishing Co Inc, pg 808
Broad Street Inc, pg 812
Gurrilla Video Solutions, pg 883
Ketchum Pleon Change, pg 910
La Paloma Films, pg 915
L&P Media, pg 915
Neal Marshad Productions, pg 931
Jack Morton Worldwide, pg 946
MRG Productions Inc, pg 948
R/GA, pg 990
Split Image Productions, pg 1021

NORTH DAKOTA

Media Productions, pg 937

OHIO

Challenge Productions, pg 823

OREGON

Odyssey Productions Inc, pg 961

FILM

Photography—Underwater (continued)

Post-Production Services

Preservation & Rejuvenation

FILM

Preservation & Rejuvenation (continued)

PENNSYLVANIA

John E Allen Inc, pg 781
Innovision Media Group, pg 899

TENNESSEE

Continental Film, pg 835
Stage Post, pg 1022

TEXAS

The Color Lab Inc, pg 831
Matson Multi-Media, pg 934

Printing, *see* Processing & Printing

Printing, *see* Release Printing

Processing & Printing

CALIFORNIA

A&I, pg 771
Action Photo Service Inc, pg 775
Deluxe Laboratories Inc, pg 845
Film Technology Co Inc, pg 867
Hooper Camera & Imaging, pg 891
Monaco Digital Films Labs, pg 945
Pro8mm, pg 983
QRS Software Services, pg 988
SonicPool, pg 1016
StereoScope International, pg 1024

COLORADO

The Cinema Lab, pg 827

CONNECTICUT

New London Media, pg 956
Skyviews Survey Inc, pg 1013

FLORIDA

Gulf Coast Audio Visual Producers Inc, pg 883
Tom Stack & Associates Inc, pg 1022
Tallahassee Audio Visual, pg 1031

GEORGIA

CineFilm Lab, pg 827
Guerrilla Productions LLC, pg 883

ILLINOIS

Filmworkers, pg 868

INDIANA

OMNI Productions, pg 962

IOWA

American Color Imaging (ACI), pg 784

KENTUCKY

Kinetic Corp, pg 911

LOUISIANA

Primary Color Laboratory Inc, pg 982

MARYLAND

Fugro EarthData, pg 873

MASSACHUSETTS

Camera Co Inc/Broadcast Divison, pg 818
Colortek of Boston, pg 832
DGI-Invisuals LLC, pg 846
ICL Imaging Inc, pg 893

MICHIGAN

Tri-Color, pg 1044

MINNESOTA

Aggressive Records Audio Duplication LLC, pg 778

MISSISSIPPI

Jasper Ewing & Sons Inc, pg 864

MISSOURI

Allied Photo Color Co, pg 781
Schiller's Audio-Visual, pg 1004

NEW JERSEY

NFL Films Inc, pg 957

NEW YORK

DuArt, pg 853
Duggal Visual Solutions, pg 853
FSL Media Inc, pg 873
Gage-Line Technology Inc, pg 874
Ken Lieberman Labs Inc, pg 920
PASCO, pg 969

NORTH CAROLINA

Camcor Inc, pg 818
Image Associates Inc, pg 894

OHIO

Vista Color Imaging Inc, pg 1059

PENNSYLVANIA

John E Allen Inc, pg 781
Audio Visual Communications Inc, pg 795
Bernie's Photo Center, pg 805
Berry & Homer, pg 805
Visual Sound Inc, pg 1059

TENNESSEE

Continental Film, pg 835
Motion Picture Services, pg 947
Phoenix Aerial Photography Inc, pg 974
Stage Post, pg 1022

TEXAS

The Color Lab Inc, pg 831
IntegraColor, pg 899

UTAH

Ferrari Color®, pg 866

VERMONT

University of Vermont, Instructional Television Dept, pg 1050

VIRGINIA

Blair Inc, pg 809

WISCONSIN

Frank D Hurst Corp dba Pechman Imaging, pg 892
USAV Group Inc, pg 1050

Production Workshops

ARIZONA

Tellens Inc, pg 1037

CALIFORNIA

Opticomm-EMCORE, pg 964
Palardo Productions, pg 968
Pro8mm, pg 983
QRS Software Services, pg 988
Dick Reizner Film & Video, pg 994
Russ InVision Co/AbridgeClub.com, pg 1001
StereoScope International, pg 1024
Vineyard Productions, pg 1058

COLORADO

Open Media Foundation, pg 964

CONNECTICUT

The Gary-Paul Agency, pg 875

FLORIDA

Audacity Creative, pg 793
Communications Concepts Inc (CCI), pg 833
Glanz Technologies Inc, pg 878

GEORGIA

Guerrilla Productions LLC, pg 883
Lighting & Production Equipment Inc, pg 920
On-Line Productions, pg 963

IOWA

The Production House, pg 984

LOUISIANA

Moxie Media, pg 948

MASSACHUSETTS

DGI-Invisuals LLC, pg 846
MotionArt Studios, pg 947

MICHIGAN

Digi Sign Design LLC, pg 847
Michigan Recording Arts Institute & Technologies, pg 941

MINNESOTA

House of Cinemagraphics, pg 891

NEW YORK

De Nonno Productions Inc (DPI), pg 844
Richard Kaplan Productions, pg 908
Third World Newsreel/Camera News Inc, pg 1039
Zelman Studios Ltd, pg 1073

OHIO

Challenge Productions, pg 823
Thread Marketing Group, pg 1039

PENNSYLVANIA

Kensington Falls Animation, pg 909
Video/Film Associates, pg 1055

TENNESSEE

Stage Post, pg 1022

TEXAS

Julye Newlin Productions Inc, pg 956

WISCONSIN

Wisconsin Public Television, pg 1068

ONTARIO

GAPC (General Assembly Production Centre), pg 875

QUEBEC

Trebas Institute, pg 1044

Projection Equipment & Accessory Distributors

ARIZONA

Docter Optics Inc, pg 849
EAR Professional Audio/Video, pg 855
Troxell Communications Inc, pg 1045

ARKANSAS

White Diamond Productions, pg 1065

CALIFORNIA

Adolph Gasser Inc, pg 776
Ametron Audio/Video, pg 785
Be Media, pg 804
Christie Digital Systems USA Inc, pg 825
Christy's Editorial, pg 826
Cibola Systems, pg 826
Cinema Equipment Sales of California Inc, pg 827
Cinema Xenon International Inc, pg 827
Derksen (USA) Inc, pg 845
Diversified Imaging Supply, pg 849
FXC Communications, pg 874
Hi-Tech Lamps Inc, pg 888
Hooper Camera & Imaging, pg 891
Instructional Materials & Equipment Distributors (I-Med), pg 899
JD Audio Visual Inc, pg 904
Lloyd F McKinney Associates Inc, pg 935
Media Fabricators Inc, pg 936
MediaPOINTE, pg 938
PMP Marketing Inc, pg 977
Stanislaus Audio Video Inc, pg 1023
SuperVision, pg 1029
Tri-Ed, pg 1044

COLORADO

Goldberg Brothers Inc, pg 880
Stanco Sales LLC, pg 1023

CONNECTICUT

MAVCO, pg 934
USI Inc, pg 1051

FLORIDA

AVI-SPL, pg 798
Cinema Equipment & Supplies Inc, pg 827
Gulf Coast Audio Visual Producers Inc, pg 883

Projection Equipment & Accessory Manufacturers

Projection Equipment & Accessory Rentals

FILM

Projection Equipment & Accessory Rentals (continued)

INDIANA

Advanced Media Integration, pg 777
Jack's Camera Shop, pg 903

MARYLAND

Absolute Hollywood, pg 772
Advance Audiovisual Presentation Ltd, pg 777
Nelson White Systems Inc, pg 954
RTZ Audio Visual, pg 1000

MASSACHUSETTS

The Boston Connection Inc, pg 811
Capron Lighting & Sound Co Inc, pg 819
massAV, pg 933

MICHIGAN

City Events Group, pg 828

MINNESOTA

AVI Systems, pg 799

MISSISSIPPI

Bowie Audio Visual Enterprises Inc, pg 811
Jasper Ewing & Sons Inc, pg 864

MISSOURI

Schiller's Audio-Visual, pg 1004
Show-Me Audio-Visual, pg 1009
Swank Audio Visuals, pg 1029

NEW HAMPSHIRE

Apertura, pg 788
APS Lighting-Sound-AV, pg 789

NEW JERSEY

Audio Visual Associates, pg 795
Gerriets International, pg 877
Bill Quinn Productions, pg 989

NEW YORK

Albany Theatre Supply Co Inc, pg 780
AV Workshop, pg 797
CMI Communications, pg 830
Magnaplan Corp, pg 928
Motion Picture Enterprises Inc, pg 947
Specialized Audio-Visual Inc, pg 1020

NORTH CAROLINA

Camcor Inc, pg 818

NORTH DAKOTA

Media Productions, pg 937

OHIO

Mills James Productions, pg 943
Thread Marketing Group, pg 1039

OREGON

Northwest Film Center, pg 959

PENNSYLVANIA

Audio Visions Inc, pg 795
Bernie's Photo Center, pg 805
Grise Audio Visual Center Inc, pg 882
Ott Film Rentals, pg 966
Vistacom Inc, pg 1059
Visual Sound Inc, pg 1059

TENNESSEE

Memphis Communications Corp, pg 938
Tennessee Visual Service Co, pg 1037

TEXAS

Padgitt's, pg 967

UTAH

Webb Audio Visual Communication, pg 1063

VERMONT

Marlboro Film & Video Productions, pg 931

VIRGINIA

Boitnott Visual Communications Corp (BVC), pg 810
Projection Presentation Technology, pg 985
Quince Imaging Inc, pg 989
The Whitlock Group, pg 1065

WASHINGTON

Kostov Productions, pg 913

ALBERTA

Global Television Station, pg 879
McBain Audio Visual Ltd, pg 935
Unique Communications Ltd, pg 1048

BRITISH COLUMBIA

Clark's Audio Visual Services Ltd, pg 829

ONTARIO

SIM Digital, pg 1011
Westbury National Show Systems Ltd, pg 1064

QUEBEC

Audio Visual Dynamics Ltd, pg 795

Projection Equipment & Accessory Repairs

CALIFORNIA

Adolph Gasser Inc, pg 776
Christie Digital Systems USA Inc, pg 825
FXC Communications, pg 874
Hooper Camera & Imaging, pg 891
Instructional Materials & Equipment Distributors (I-Med), pg 899
Lloyd F McKinney Associates Inc, pg 935

CONNECTICUT

Precision Camera & Video Repair Inc, pg 980

FLORIDA

Hi-Tech Enterprises Inc, pg 888
Hollywood Theatre Equipment Inc, pg 890
Tallahassee Audio Visual, pg 1031

GEORGIA

Lighting & Production Equipment Inc, pg 920

ILLINOIS

Beatty TeleVisual Productions, pg 804
Chicago Spotlight Inc, pg 825

KENTUCKY

NOR-COM Inc, pg 958

MARYLAND

RTZ Audio Visual, pg 1000
Strauss Photo Technical Service Inc, pg 1026

MASSACHUSETTS

The Boston Connection Inc, pg 811
Capron Lighting & Sound Co Inc, pg 819

MINNESOTA

AVI Systems, pg 799

MISSISSIPPI

Bowie Audio Visual Enterprises Inc, pg 811

MISSOURI

Cintrex Audio Visual, pg 828
Schiller's Audio-Visual, pg 1004

NEW JERSEY

Audio Visual Associates, pg 795

NEW YORK

ELMO USA Corp, pg 859
Motion Picture Enterprises Inc, pg 947

NORTH CAROLINA

Camcor Inc, pg 818

PENNSYLVANIA

Audio Visions Inc, pg 795
Bernie's Photo Center, pg 805
Ott Film Rentals, pg 966
Vistacom Inc, pg 1059

RHODE ISLAND

Custom Computer Specialists Inc, pg 841

TENNESSEE

Tennessee Visual Service Co, pg 1037

TEXAS

Padgitt's, pg 967

VIRGINIA

Boitnott Visual Communications Corp (BVC), pg 810
Hoppmann Audio Visual, pg 891
Quince Imaging Inc, pg 989

WISCONSIN

Camera Corner Connecting Point, pg 818

ONTARIO

Edcom Multimedia Products, pg 856
Premier A/V Sales Ltd, pg 980
Westbury National Show Systems Ltd, pg 1064

Projection Part Distributors

ARIZONA

Troxell Communications Inc, pg 1045

CALIFORNIA

Be Media, pg 804
Christy's Editorial, pg 826
Cinema Equipment Sales of California Inc, pg 827
FXC Communications, pg 874
Hooper Camera & Imaging, pg 891
JD Audio Visual Inc, pg 904
Media Fabricators Inc, pg 936

COLORADO

Stanco Sales LLC, pg 1023

FLORIDA

AVI-SPL, pg 798
Cinema Equipment & Supplies Inc, pg 827
Gulf Coast Audio Visual Producers Inc, pg 883
Hollywood Theatre Equipment Inc, pg 890
Hunter Electronics LLC, pg 892

ILLINOIS

Joseph Electronics, pg 906
Urbanski Film, pg 1050

KANSAS

EiKO Ltd, pg 858

KENTUCKY

NOR-COM Inc, pg 958

LOUISIANA

Intermedia Technologies, pg 900

MINNESOTA

AVI Systems, pg 799

MISSISSIPPI

Bowie Audio Visual Enterprises Inc, pg 811

MISSOURI

Schiller's Audio-Visual, pg 1004
Swank Audio Visuals, pg 1029

NEBRASKA

Ballantyne Strong Inc, pg 802

NEW JERSEY

Audio Visual Associates, pg 795
National Audio-Visual Supply, pg 952

Video Corporation of America (VCA), pg 1055
Wilray Audio Visual Corp, pg 1067

NEW YORK

AV Workshop, pg 797
Bulbtronics Inc, pg 815
DSan Corp, pg 852
Ray Supply Inc, pg 992
Russell Industries Inc, pg 1001

NORTH CAROLINA

Camcor Inc, pg 818

OHIO

Tri-State Audio Visual Co, pg 1044

PENNSYLVANIA

Audio Visions Inc, pg 795
J E Foss Co, pg 871
Grise Audio Visual Center Inc, pg 882
The Lerro Corp, pg 919

RHODE ISLAND

Custom Computer Specialists Inc, pg 841

TENNESSEE

Memphis Communications Corp, pg 938

TEXAS

Audio Visual Technologies Group, pg 796

VIRGINIA

Boitnott Visual Communications Corp (BVC), pg 810
Hoppmann Audio Visual, pg 891
Lee Hartman & Sons Inc, pg 918
The Whitlock Group, pg 1065

WISCONSIN

Alpha Source Inc, pg 782

ONTARIO

Edcom Multimedia Products, pg 856
Nationwide Audio Visual Co, pg 953
Premier A/V Sales Ltd, pg 980
Westbury National Show Systems Ltd, pg 1064

QUEBEC

Strong Screen Systems, pg 1026

Projection Part Manufacturers

ILLINOIS

Dukane Corp, Audio Visual Products Division, pg 853
La Vezzi Precision Inc, pg 1053

INDIANA

Crystal Clear Media Group, pg 840

KANSAS

EiKO Ltd, pg 858
Speco/Systems & Products Engineering Co, pg 1020

NEBRASKA

Strong Cinema Products, pg 1026

NEW YORK

Russell Industries Inc, pg 1001

VIRGINIA

Optikinetics Ltd - The Americas, pg 964

Projection Part Rentals

CALIFORNIA

Hooper Camera & Imaging, pg 891
JD Audio Visual Inc, pg 904
Media Fabricators Inc, pg 936

DELAWARE

Ken-Del Productions Inc, pg 909

FLORIDA

Gulf Coast Audio Visual Producers Inc, pg 883
Jordan Klein Film & Video (JKFV), pg 906

MARYLAND

RTZ Audio Visual, pg 1000

MINNESOTA

AVI Systems, pg 799

MISSISSIPPI

Bowie Audio Visual Enterprises Inc, pg 811

MISSOURI

Show-Me Audio-Visual, pg 1009

NEW HAMPSHIRE

Apertura, pg 788

NEW YORK

AV Workshop, pg 797

PENNSYLVANIA

Audio Visions Inc, pg 795
Grise Audio Visual Center Inc, pg 882
Ott Film Rentals, pg 966

BRITISH COLUMBIA

Clark's Audio Visual Services Ltd, pg 829

Projection Part Repairs

CALIFORNIA

FXC Communications, pg 874
Hooper Camera & Imaging, pg 891
Lloyd F McKinney Associates Inc, pg 935

CONNECTICUT

MAVCO, pg 934

KENTUCKY

NOR-COM Inc, pg 958

MARYLAND

RTZ Audio Visual, pg 1000

MINNESOTA

AVI Systems, pg 799

MISSOURI

Cintrex Audio Visual, pg 828

NORTH CAROLINA

Camcor Inc, pg 818

PENNSYLVANIA

Audio Visions Inc, pg 795
Ott Film Rentals, pg 966

TEXAS

Padgitt's, pg 967

VIRGINIA

Hoppmann Audio Visual, pg 891

ONTARIO

Edcom Multimedia Products, pg 856

Projector & Equipment—8mm Distributors

ARIZONA

Troxell Communications Inc, pg 1045

CALIFORNIA

Adolph Gasser Inc, pg 776
Ametron Audio/Video, pg 785
Be Media, pg 804
Jaguar Distribution Corp, pg 903
Pro8mm, pg 983

COLORADO

Ceavco Audio/Visual Co, pg 822
Stanco Sales LLC, pg 1023

CONNECTICUT

MAVCO, pg 934
Rockwell Communications Inc, pg 998

FLORIDA

AVI-SPL, pg 798
Gulf Coast Audio Visual Producers Inc, pg 883
Media Concepts Inc, pg 936
Tallahassee Audio Visual, pg 1031

GEORGIA

Visioneering International Inc, pg 1058

ILLINOIS

Urbanski Film, pg 1050

LOUISIANA

Intermedia Technologies, pg 900

MARYLAND

Visual Aids Electronics Corp, pg 1059

MINNESOTA

AVI Systems, pg 799

MISSISSIPPI

Jasper Ewing & Sons Inc, pg 864

MISSOURI

Image Technologies Corp, pg 895

NEW JERSEY

Audio Visual Associates, pg 795
Audio Visual Dynamics®, pg 795
Video Corporation of America (VCA), pg 1055

NEW YORK

AV Workshop, pg 797
Colortone Audio Visual, pg 832
Langie Audio Visual Systems, pg 915
Magnaplan Corp, pg 928
Motion Picture Enterprises Inc, pg 947
Willoughby's Imaging Center, pg 1067

NORTH CAROLINA

Camcor Inc, pg 818
Strategic Connections, pg 1026

OHIO

Audio Visual Media, pg 795

PENNSYLVANIA

Audio Visions Inc, pg 795
Bernie's Photo Center, pg 805
The Lerro Corp, pg 919

RHODE ISLAND

Custom Computer Specialists Inc, pg 841

TEXAS

Astro Audio Visual, pg 792
Pro Video & Film Equipment Co Inc, pg 983

UTAH

Webb Audio Visual Communication, pg 1063

VIRGINIA

Filmdex Inc, pg 867
Hoppmann Audio Visual, pg 891

ONTARIO

Edcom Multimedia Products, pg 856

Projector & Equipment—8mm Manufacturers

CALIFORNIA

Pro8mm, pg 983

NEW YORK

General Audio-Visual Inc (GAVI), pg 876

WASHINGTON

Tobin Cinema Systems Inc, pg 1041

BRITISH COLUMBIA

Triad Communications Ltd, pg 1044

FILM

Projector & Equipment—8mm Rentals

ARIZONA

Arizona Cine Equipment, pg 789
Video Media Productions (VMP), pg 1055

ARKANSAS

White Diamond Productions, pg 1065

CALIFORNIA

Adolph Gasser Inc, pg 776
Ametron Audio/Video, pg 785
Gold Standard Productions, pg 880
Pro8mm, pg 983
PSAV® Presentation Services, pg 986

COLORADO

Ceavco Audio/Visual Co, pg 822
The Cinema Lab, pg 827

CONNECTICUT

A/V Davey, pg 797
Rockwell Communications Inc, pg 998

DELAWARE

Ken-Del Productions Inc, pg 909

FLORIDA

Gulf Coast Audio Visual Producers Inc, pg 883
Jordan Klein Film & Video (JKFV), pg 906
Tallahassee Audio Visual, pg 1031

ILLINOIS

Audio Visual Services Corp, pg 796
Beatty TeleVisual Productions, pg 804
Helix Camera & Video, pg 887
PSAV® Presentation Services (Hotel Services Division), pg 987

INDIANA

Gary Camera & Digital, pg 875
OMNI Productions, pg 962

KENTUCKY

Audio Visual Techniques Inc, pg 796

LOUISIANA

Pace Systems, pg 966

MARYLAND

Advance Audiovisual Presentation Ltd, pg 777
RTZ Audio Visual, pg 1000

MINNESOTA

AVI Systems, pg 799
House of Cinemagraphics, pg 891

MISSISSIPPI

Jasper Ewing & Sons Inc, pg 864

MISSOURI

Image Technologies Corp, pg 895
Show-Me Audio-Visual, pg 1009
Swank Audio Visuals, pg 1029

NEW HAMPSHIRE

Academic & Campus Technology Services, pg 773
Apertura, pg 788

NEW JERSEY

Audio Visual Dynamics®, pg 795

NEW YORK

AV Workshop, pg 797
CMI Communications, pg 830
Colortone Audio Visual, pg 832
Langie Audio Visual Systems, pg 915
Magnaplan Corp, pg 928
Motion Picture Enterprises Inc, pg 947

NORTH CAROLINA

Camcor Inc, pg 818
Strategic Connections, pg 1026

OHIO

Audio Visual Media, pg 795
Hughie's Event Production Services, pg 892

OREGON

Northwest Film Center, pg 959

PENNSYLVANIA

Audio Visions Inc, pg 795
Bernie's Photo Center, pg 805
Grise Audio Visual Center Inc, pg 882
Ott Film Rentals, pg 966
Visual Sound Inc, pg 1059

TENNESSEE

Belew Enterprises, pg 804
Memphis Communications Corp, pg 938
Russ Sturgeon Productions/RSVP, pg 1027

TEXAS

Astro Audio Visual, pg 792

UTAH

Webb Audio Visual Communication, pg 1063

VIRGINIA

Boitnott Visual Communications Corp (BVC), pg 810
Projection Presentation Technology, pg 985
Rainbow Rentals, pg 991

WASHINGTON

Inland Audio Visual Co, pg 898

WISCONSIN

Event Essentials, pg 863
USAV Group Inc, pg 1050

WYOMING

Bridger Productions Inc, pg 812

ALBERTA

Unique Communications Ltd, pg 1048

BRITISH COLUMBIA

MicrophoneRentals.com, pg 941

ONTARIO

Edcom Multimedia Products, pg 856

Projector & Equipment—8mm Repairs

CALIFORNIA

Adolph Gasser Inc, pg 776
ALC (Auernheimer Labs & Co), pg 780
Pro Camera Repair, pg 982
Pro8mm, pg 983

COLORADO

Ceavco Audio/Visual Co, pg 822

CONNECTICUT

A/V Davey, pg 797
Precision Camera & Video Repair Inc, pg 980
Rockwell Communications Inc, pg 998

FLORIDA

Tallahassee Audio Visual, pg 1031

GEORGIA

Audio Visual Resources Inc, pg 795
Dixie Theatre Service & Supply Co Inc, pg 849

INDIANA

Gary Camera & Digital, pg 875

MARYLAND

RTZ Audio Visual, pg 1000
Strauss Photo Technical Service Inc, pg 1026

MINNESOTA

AVI Systems, pg 799

NEW JERSEY

Konica Minolta Business Solutions, pg 913

NEW YORK

Colortone Audio Visual, pg 832
Langie Audio Visual Systems, pg 915
Magnaplan Corp, pg 928
Motion Picture Enterprises Inc, pg 947

NORTH CAROLINA

Camcor Inc, pg 818
Strategic Connections, pg 1026

OHIO

Audio Visual Media, pg 795

PENNSYLVANIA

Audio Visions Inc, pg 795
Bernie's Photo Center, pg 805
Ott Film Rentals, pg 966

RHODE ISLAND

Custom Computer Specialists Inc, pg 841

TENNESSEE

Memphis Communications Corp, pg 938

TEXAS

Astro Audio Visual, pg 792
Audio Visual Technologies Group, pg 796

VIRGINIA

Hoppmann Audio Visual, pg 891

WASHINGTON

Inland Audio Visual Co, pg 898

WISCONSIN

Audio Visual of Milwaukee Inc, pg 795

ONTARIO

Edcom Multimedia Products, pg 856
Premier A/V Sales Ltd, pg 980

Projector & Equipment—16mm Distributors

ALABAMA

Curtis Company, pg 841
Media Visions Inc, pg 937

ARIZONA

Troxell Communications Inc, pg 1045

ARKANSAS

Carlton-Bates Co, pg 820
Jay S Stanley & Associates Inc, pg 1023

CALIFORNIA

Adolph Gasser Inc, pg 776
Ametron Audio/Video, pg 785
Be Media, pg 804
Birns & Sawyer Inc, pg 808
Christy's Editorial, pg 826
Cinema Equipment Sales of California Inc, pg 827
FXC Communications, pg 874
Glenn Photo Supply, pg 878
Alan Gordon Enterprises Inc, pg 880
Instructional Materials & Equipment Distributors (I-Med), pg 899
Instrumentation Marketing Corp, pg 899
Jaguar Distribution Corp, pg 903
JD Audio Visual Inc, pg 904
Lloyd F McKinney Associates Inc, pg 935
Media Fabricators Inc, pg 936
MediaPOINTE, pg 938
PMP Marketing Inc, pg 977
Pro8mm, pg 983
Related Visual Inc, pg 994

COLORADO

Ceavco Audio/Visual Co, pg 822
Stanco Sales LLC, pg 1023

CONNECTICUT

Concord Communications, pg 835
MAVCO, pg 934
Rockwell Communications Inc, pg 998

FLORIDA

AVI-SPL, pg 798
Cinema Equipment & Supplies Inc, pg 827
Gulf Coast Audio Visual Producers Inc, pg 883
Hi-Tech Enterprises Inc, pg 888
Media Concepts Inc, pg 936
Tallahassee Audio Visual, pg 1031

GEORGIA

Audio Visual Resources Inc, pg 795
Baker Audio Inc, pg 801
Technical Innovation, pg 1033

HAWAII

The Audio Visual Co (AVCO), pg 795

ILLINOIS

Creative Technology, pg 838
Urbanski Film, pg 1050

INDIANA

Lee Co Inc, pg 918

LOUISIANA

Intermedia Technologies, pg 900

MARYLAND

Cardinal Sound & Video, pg 820
Nelson White Systems Inc, pg 954
Nicholas P Pipino Associates Inc, pg 976
RTZ Audio Visual, pg 1000
Visual Aids Electronics Corp, pg 1059

MICHIGAN

Michigan Office Solutions, pg 941

MINNESOTA

AVI Systems, pg 799

MISSISSIPPI

Bowie Audio Visual Enterprises Inc, pg 811
Jasper Ewing & Sons Inc, pg 864

MISSOURI

Conference Technologies Inc, pg 835
Image Technologies Corp, pg 895
Swank Audio Visuals, pg 1029

NEW JERSEY

Audio Visual Associates, pg 795
Audio Visual Dynamics®, pg 795
AV Bluebook, pg 797
Leica Camera Inc, pg 918
National Audio-Visual Supply, pg 952
Total Video Products Inc, pg 1042
Video Corporation of America (VCA), pg 1055

NEW YORK

AV Workshop, pg 797
Colortone Audio Visual, pg 832
Eastman Kodak Professional, pg 856
Gaylord Brothers, pg 876
Indigo Productions, pg 897
Langie Audio Visual Systems, pg 915
Long Island Video Enterprises Live Inc, pg 924
Magnaplan Corp, pg 928
Motion Picture Enterprises Inc, pg 947
Neptune Photo Inc, pg 954
Willoughby's Imaging Center, pg 1067

NORTH CAROLINA

Camcor Inc, pg 818
Strategic Connections, pg 1026

OHIO

Audio Visual Media, pg 795
Copp Integrated Systems, pg 836
Tri-State Audio Visual Co, pg 1044
Visual Products Inc, pg 1059

PENNSYLVANIA

Audio Visions Inc, pg 795
Bernie's Photo Center, pg 805
J E Foss Co, pg 871
Grise Audio Visual Center Inc, pg 882
The Lerro Corp, pg 919
Vistacom Inc, pg 1059
Visual Sound Inc, pg 1059

TENNESSEE

Memphis Communications Corp, pg 938
Tennessee Visual Service Co, pg 1037

TEXAS

Astro Audio Visual, pg 792
Audio Visual Technologies Group, pg 796
Pro Video & Film Equipment Co Inc, pg 983
Schoolhouse Audio Visual, pg 1004

UTAH

Webb Audio Visual Communication, pg 1063

VIRGINIA

Communications Specialists Inc, pg 833
Filmdex Inc, pg 867
Hoppmann Audio Visual, pg 891
Lee Hartman & Sons Inc, pg 918
The Whitlock Group, pg 1065

WASHINGTON

Inland Audio Visual Co, pg 898

WISCONSIN

Demco Inc, pg 845
School Specialty Inc, pg 1004

ALBERTA

Unique Communications Ltd, pg 1048

MANITOBA

Inland Audio Visual Ltd, pg 898
Lank/Beach Productions Inc, pg 916

ONTARIO

Edcom Multimedia Products, pg 856
Nationwide Audio Visual Co, pg 953
Premier A/V Sales Ltd, pg 980

Projector & Equipment—16mm Manufacturers

CALIFORNIA

Alan Gordon Enterprises Inc, pg 880
Pro8mm, pg 983
Visual Instrumentation Corp, pg 1059

FLORIDA

Magna-Tech Electronic Co Inc, pg 928

ILLINOIS

Lipsner-Smith Co, pg 922

NEW YORK

Eastman Kodak Professional, pg 856
ELMO USA Corp, pg 859

WASHINGTON

Tobin Cinema Systems Inc, pg 1041

WISCONSIN

Indus International Inc, pg 897

BRITISH COLUMBIA

Triad Communications Ltd, pg 1044

Projector & Equipment—16mm Rentals

ALABAMA

Audio-Video Resources Inc, pg 795
Media Visions Inc, pg 937

ARIZONA

Video Media Productions (VMP), pg 1055

ARKANSAS

White Diamond Productions, pg 1065

CALIFORNIA

Ametron Audio/Video, pg 785
Artichoke Productions, pg 791
Birns & Sawyer Inc, pg 808
Alan Gordon Enterprises Inc, pg 880
Instructional Materials & Equipment Distributors (I-Med), pg 899
JD Audio Visual Inc, pg 904
Media Fabricators Inc, pg 936
Munday & Collins AV, pg 950
Pro8mm, pg 983
PSAV® Presentation Services, pg 986
University of Southern California, pg 1050

COLORADO

Ceavco Audio/Visual Co, pg 822
The Cinema Lab, pg 827
Daylight Productions & Rentals, pg 844

CONNECTICUT

A/V Davey, pg 797
Concord Communications, pg 835
Rockwell Communications Inc, pg 998

DELAWARE

Ken-Del Productions Inc, pg 909

FLORIDA

Gulf Coast Audio Visual Producers Inc, pg 883
Jordan Klein Film & Video (JKFV), pg 906
Photosound of Orlando Inc, pg 975
Tallahassee Audio Visual, pg 1031

GEORGIA

Audio Visual Resources Inc, pg 795
Dixie Theatre Service & Supply Co Inc, pg 849

ILLINOIS

Audio Visual Services Corp, pg 796
Beatty TeleVisual Productions, pg 804
Creative Technology, pg 838
Helix Camera & Video, pg 887
PSAV® Presentation Services (Hotel Services Division), pg 987
Show Department Inc, pg 1009

INDIANA

Advanced Media Integration, pg 777
Gary Camera & Digital, pg 875
OMNI Productions, pg 962

KENTUCKY

Audio Visual Techniques Inc, pg 796

MARYLAND

Advance Audiovisual Presentation Ltd, pg 777
Nelson White Systems Inc, pg 954
RTZ Audio Visual, pg 1000

MASSACHUSETTS

Capron Lighting & Sound Co Inc, pg 819
massAV, pg 933
Preston Productions Inc, pg 981

MICHIGAN

City Events Group, pg 828

MINNESOTA

AVI Systems, pg 799
House of Cinemagraphics, pg 891

MISSISSIPPI

Bowie Audio Visual Enterprises Inc, pg 811
Jasper Ewing & Sons Inc, pg 864

MISSOURI

Show-Me Audio-Visual, pg 1009
Swank Audio Visuals, pg 1029

FILM

Projector & Equipment—16mm Rentals (continued)

NEVADA

GES Audio Visual, pg 877

NEW HAMPSHIRE

Academic & Campus Technology Services, pg 773
Apertura, pg 788

NEW JERSEY

Audio Visual Associates, pg 795
Audio Visual Dynamics®, pg 795
PLS Staging, pg 977
Bill Quinn Productions, pg 989

NEW YORK

AV Workshop, pg 797
CMI Communications, pg 830
Colortone Audio Visual, pg 832
Langie Audio Visual Systems, pg 915
Long Island Video Enterprises Live Inc, pg 924
Magnaplan Corp, pg 928
Motion Picture Enterprises Inc, pg 947

NORTH CAROLINA

Camcor Inc, pg 818
Strategic Connections, pg 1026
Visual Aids Electronics of North Carolina Inc, pg 1059

OHIO

Audio Visual Media, pg 795
Hughie's Event Production Services, pg 892

OREGON

Northwest Film Center, pg 959

PENNSYLVANIA

Audio Visions Inc, pg 795
Bernie's Photo Center, pg 805
Grise Audio Visual Center Inc, pg 882
Ott Film Rentals, pg 966
Production Solutions Inc, pg 985
Visual Sound Inc, pg 1059

TENNESSEE

Belew Enterprises, pg 804
Memphis Communications Corp, pg 938
Russ Sturgeon Productions/RSVP, pg 1027
Tennessee Visual Service Co, pg 1037

TEXAS

Astro Audio Visual, pg 792
Audio Visual Technologies Group, pg 796
Padgitt's, pg 967

UTAH

Webb Audio Visual Communication, pg 1063

VERMONT

Marlboro Film & Video Productions, pg 931

VIRGINIA

Boitnott Visual Communications Corp (BVC), pg 810
Lee Hartman & Sons Inc, pg 918
Projection Presentation Technology, pg 985
Rainbow Rentals, pg 991
The Whitlock Group, pg 1065

WASHINGTON

Inland Audio Visual Co, pg 898

WISCONSIN

Event Essentials, pg 863
School Specialty Inc, pg 1004
USAV Group Inc, pg 1050

ALBERTA

Global Television Station, pg 879
Unique Communications Ltd, pg 1048

BRITISH COLUMBIA

Clark's Audio Visual Services Ltd, pg 829

MANITOBA

Inland Audio Visual Ltd, pg 898

ONTARIO

Edcom Multimedia Products, pg 856

QUEBEC

Audio Visual Dynamics Ltd, pg 795
AVW-TELAV Audio Visual Solutions, a Freeman Company, pg 800

Projector & Equipment—16mm Repairs

ARKANSAS

Carlton-Bates Co, pg 820

CALIFORNIA

Adolph Gasser Inc, pg 776
ALC (Auernheimer Labs & Co), pg 780
FXC Communications, pg 874
Alan Gordon Enterprises Inc, pg 880
Instructional Materials & Equipment Distributors (I-Med), pg 899
Lloyd F McKinney Associates Inc, pg 935
Pro Camera Repair, pg 982
Pro8mm, pg 983
Visual Instrumentation Corp, pg 1059

COLORADO

Ceavco Audio/Visual Co, pg 822

CONNECTICUT

A/V Davey, pg 797
Precision Camera & Video Repair Inc, pg 980
Rockwell Communications Inc, pg 998

FLORIDA

Tallahassee Audio Visual, pg 1031

GEORGIA

Audio Visual Resources Inc, pg 795
Dixie Theatre Service & Supply Co Inc, pg 849
Technical Innovation, pg 1033

ILLINOIS

Beatty TeleVisual Productions, pg 804

INDIANA

Gary Camera & Digital, pg 875

MARYLAND

Nelson White Systems Inc, pg 954
RTZ Audio Visual, pg 1000
Strauss Photo Technical Service Inc, pg 1026

MASSACHUSETTS

Capron Lighting & Sound Co Inc, pg 819

MINNESOTA

AVI Systems, pg 799

MISSISSIPPI

Bowie Audio Visual Enterprises Inc, pg 811

MISSOURI

Cintrex Audio Visual, pg 828

NEW JERSEY

Audio Visual Associates, pg 795

NEW YORK

Colortone Audio Visual, pg 832
ELMO USA Corp, pg 859
Langie Audio Visual Systems, pg 915
Magnaplan Corp, pg 928
Motion Picture Enterprises Inc, pg 947

NORTH CAROLINA

Camcor Inc, pg 818
Strategic Connections, pg 1026

OHIO

Audio Visual Media, pg 795
Tri-State Audio Visual Co, pg 1044

PENNSYLVANIA

Audio Visions Inc, pg 795
Bernie's Photo Center, pg 805
J E Foss Co, pg 871
Ott Film Rentals, pg 966
Visual Sound Inc, pg 1059
Wespen Audio Visual Co, pg 1063

RHODE ISLAND

Custom Computer Specialists Inc, pg 841

TENNESSEE

Memphis Communications Corp, pg 938
Tennessee Visual Service Co, pg 1037

TEXAS

Astro Audio Visual, pg 792
Audio Visual Technologies Group, pg 796
Padgitt's, pg 967

VIRGINIA

Boitnott Visual Communications Corp (BVC), pg 810
Hoppmann Audio Visual, pg 891
Lee Hartman & Sons Inc, pg 918
The Whitlock Group, pg 1065

WASHINGTON

Inland Audio Visual Co, pg 898

WISCONSIN

Audio Visual of Milwaukee Inc, pg 795
Camera Corner Connecting Point, pg 818
School Specialty Inc, pg 1004

MANITOBA

Inland Audio Visual Ltd, pg 898

ONTARIO

Edcom Multimedia Products, pg 856
Premier A/V Sales Ltd, pg 980

Projector & Equipment—35mm Distributors

ALABAMA

Curtis Company, pg 841
Media Visions Inc, pg 937

ARIZONA

Troxell Communications Inc, pg 1045

ARKANSAS

Carlton-Bates Co, pg 820

CALIFORNIA

Adolph Gasser Inc, pg 776
Ametron Audio/Video, pg 785
Be Media, pg 804
Christie Digital Systems USA Inc, pg 825
Cinema Equipment Sales of California Inc, pg 827
FXC Communications, pg 874
Alan Gordon Enterprises Inc, pg 880
Instructional Materials & Equipment Distributors (I-Med), pg 899
Jaguar Distribution Corp, pg 903
Lloyd F McKinney Associates Inc, pg 935
Media Fabricators Inc, pg 936

COLORADO

National Teaching Aids Inc, pg 953
Stanco Sales LLC, pg 1023

FLORIDA

AVI-SPL, pg 798
Cinema Equipment & Supplies Inc, pg 827
Gulf Coast Audio Visual Producers Inc, pg 883

Hollywood Theatre Equipment Inc, pg 890
Tallahassee Audio Visual, pg 1031

GEORGIA

Cinevision Corp, pg 828
Technical Innovation, pg 1033

ILLINOIS

Creative Technology, pg 838
Urbanski Film, pg 1050

INDIANA

Lee Co Inc, pg 918

LOUISIANA

Intermedia Technologies, pg 900

MARYLAND

Nicholas P Pipino Associates Inc, pg 976

MASSACHUSETTS

Boston Light & Sound Inc, pg 811

MINNESOTA

Cinequipt Inc, pg 828

MISSISSIPPI

Jasper Ewing & Sons Inc, pg 864

NEBRASKA

Ballantyne Strong Inc, pg 802

NEW JERSEY

Argraph Corp, pg 789
Audio Visual Associates, pg 795

NEW YORK

ALTEL Systems Inc, pg 783
Colortone Audio Visual, pg 832
Magnaplan Corp, pg 928
Motion Picture Enterprises Inc, pg 947
Neptune Photo Inc, pg 954
Rafik, pg 990
Willoughby's Imaging Center, pg 1067

OHIO

Audio Visual Media, pg 795
Visual Products Inc, pg 1059

PENNSYLVANIA

Audio Visions Inc, pg 795
Bernie's Photo Center, pg 805
J E Foss Co, pg 871
The Lerro Corp, pg 919
Wespen Audio Visual Co, pg 1063

TENNESSEE

Memphis Communications Corp, pg 938

TEXAS

Audio Visual Technologies Group, pg 796
Pro Video & Film Equipment Co Inc, pg 983

VIRGINIA

Communications Specialists Inc, pg 833
Filmdex Inc, pg 867
Hoppmann Audio Visual, pg 891
The Whitlock Group, pg 1065

WISCONSIN

School Specialty Inc, pg 1004

MANITOBA

Inland Audio Visual Ltd, pg 898
Lank/Beach Productions Inc, pg 916

ONTARIO

Cinema Stage Inc, pg 827
Edcom Multimedia Products, pg 856
Premier A/V Sales Ltd, pg 980

QUEBEC

Strong Screen Systems, pg 1026

Projector & Equipment—35mm Manufacturers

CALIFORNIA

Christie Digital Systems USA Inc, pg 825
Alan Gordon Enterprises Inc, pg 880
Lasergraphics Inc, pg 916

COLORADO

National Teaching Aids Inc, pg 953

FLORIDA

Magna-Tech Electronic Co Inc, pg 928

ILLINOIS

Lipsner-Smith Co, pg 922

KANSAS

Speco/Systems & Products Engineering Co, pg 1020

NEBRASKA

Ballantyne Strong Inc, pg 802
Strong Cinema Products, pg 1026

OHIO

Xetron, pg 1071

WISCONSIN

Indus International Inc, pg 897

QUEBEC

Strong Screen Systems, pg 1026

Projector & Equipment—35mm Rentals

ARIZONA

Arizona Cine Equipment, pg 789

ARKANSAS

Carlton-Bates Co, pg 820

CALIFORNIA

Ametron Audio/Video, pg 785
Artichoke Productions, pg 791
Alan Gordon Enterprises Inc, pg 880
Instructional Materials & Equipment Distributors (I-Med), pg 899
Media Fabricators Inc, pg 936
PSAV® Presentation Services, pg 986

COLORADO

The Cinema Lab, pg 827

DELAWARE

Ken-Del Productions Inc, pg 909

FLORIDA

Gulf Coast Audio Visual Producers Inc, pg 883
Jordan Klein Film & Video (JKFV), pg 906
Tallahassee Audio Visual, pg 1031

ILLINOIS

Creative Technology, pg 838

MASSACHUSETTS

Boston Light & Sound Inc, pg 811

MICHIGAN

City Events Group, pg 828
K&R All Media Productions Inc, pg 908

MINNESOTA

House of Cinemagraphics, pg 891

MISSISSIPPI

Jasper Ewing & Sons Inc, pg 864

MISSOURI

Swank Audio Visuals, pg 1029

NEW HAMPSHIRE

Academic & Campus Technology Services, pg 773

NEW JERSEY

Audio Visual Associates, pg 795
Bill Quinn Productions, pg 989

NEW YORK

Colortone Audio Visual, pg 832
Magnaplan Corp, pg 928
Motion Picture Enterprises Inc, pg 947

NORTH DAKOTA

Media Productions, pg 937

OHIO

Audio Visual Media, pg 795
Aztec Video Productions, pg 801
Thread Marketing Group, pg 1039

PENNSYLVANIA

Audio Visions Inc, pg 795
Bernie's Photo Center, pg 805
Ott Film Rentals, pg 966

TENNESSEE

Memphis Communications Corp, pg 938
Russ Sturgeon Productions/RSVP, pg 1027

TEXAS

Audio Visual Technologies Group, pg 796
Bright Star Productions Inc, pg 812

VIRGINIA

Projection Presentation Technology, pg 985
Rainbow Rentals, pg 991
The Whitlock Group, pg 1065

WISCONSIN

School Specialty Inc, pg 1004

ALBERTA

Global Television Station, pg 879

MANITOBA

Inland Audio Visual Ltd, pg 898

Projector & Equipment—35mm Repairs

ARKANSAS

Carlton-Bates Co, pg 820

CALIFORNIA

FXC Communications, pg 874
Alan Gordon Enterprises Inc, pg 880
Instructional Materials & Equipment Distributors (I-Med), pg 899
Pro Camera Repair, pg 982

FLORIDA

Hollywood Theatre Equipment Inc, pg 890
Tallahassee Audio Visual, pg 1031

GEORGIA

Dixie Theatre Service & Supply Co Inc, pg 849
Technical Innovation, pg 1033

MASSACHUSETTS

Boston Light & Sound Inc, pg 811

NEW JERSEY

Audio Visual Associates, pg 795

NEW YORK

Colortone Audio Visual, pg 832
Magnaplan Corp, pg 928
Motion Picture Enterprises Inc, pg 947

NORTH CAROLINA

Strategic Connections, pg 1026

OHIO

Audio Visual Media, pg 795

PENNSYLVANIA

Audio Visions Inc, pg 795
Bernie's Photo Center, pg 805
Ott Film Rentals, pg 966
Wespen Audio Visual Co, pg 1063

TENNESSEE

Memphis Communications Corp, pg 938

FILM

Projector & Equipment—35mm Repairs (continued)

TEXAS

Audio Visual Technologies Group, pg 796

VIRGINIA

Hoppmann Audio Visual, pg 891
The Whitlock Group, pg 1065

WISCONSIN

School Specialty Inc, pg 1004

MANITOBA

Inland Audio Visual Ltd, pg 898

ONTARIO

Edcom Multimedia Products, pg 856

Property Agencies, *see* Talent & Property Agencies

Raw Stock Distributors

ALABAMA

Media Visions Inc, pg 937

CALIFORNIA

Christy's Editorial, pg 826
Edgewise Media Inc, pg 856
Express Video Supply Inc, pg 864
Liberty Photo Products, pg 919
Media Distributors, pg 936
Total Media Group, pg 1042
Yale Film & Video, pg 1071

FLORIDA

CineVideotech Inc, pg 828
Jordan Klein Film & Video (JKFV), pg 906

ILLINOIS

Creative Technology, pg 838

NEW JERSEY

Tele-Measurements Inc, pg 1035

NEW YORK

Film Emporium, pg 867

OREGON

Wilderness Video, pg 1066

PENNSYLVANIA

FMP Media Solutions Inc, pg 870

TEXAS

Texcam Inc, pg 1038

VIRGINIA

Filmdex Inc, pg 867

WASHINGTON

Inland Audio Visual Co, pg 898

WISCONSIN

USAV Group Inc, pg 1050

BRITISH COLUMBIA

Finale Editworks, pg 868

Raw Stock Manufacturers

CALIFORNIA

Media Distributors, pg 936

NEW YORK

Eastman Kodak Professional, pg 856

OREGON

Wilderness Video, pg 1066

BRITISH COLUMBIA

Kodak Canada Inc, pg 912

ONTARIO

FUJIFILM Canada Inc, pg 873

Recording Equipment—Magnetic, *see* Magnetic Recording Equipment

Recording Facility Manufacturers

CALIFORNIA

Yanchar Design & Consulting Group, pg 1072

NEW YORK

IAC Acoustics, pg 893

TEXAS

Stage Directions, pg 1022

Recording Facility Rentals

ARIZONA

Arizona Virtual Studios, pg 790
Glendale Media Center, pg 878
Loft 19, pg 924

CALIFORNIA

Adolph Gasser Inc, pg 776
Ametron Audio/Video, pg 785
AMG Studios-Los Angeles, pg 785
Blue Lotus Temple Studio, pg 809
Cutting Edge Productions, pg 841
Different Fur Recording Ltd, pg 846
Golden Gate Studios, pg 880
Greenery Studios, pg 882
Groovy Like a Movie, pg 882
Hollywood Center Studios, pg 890
Hollywood Loft, pg 890
KESSPRO Studios, pg 910
LA Castle Studios, pg 915
Los Angeles Center Studios, pg 924
LW Media Group, pg 926
Maximus Media Inc, pg 934
North County Media Center, pg 959
Opulen Studios, pg 965
Polarity Post Production, pg 978
Pro HD Rentals, pg 983
The Producer's Loft, pg 983
RED Studios Hollywood, pg 993
Roundabout Entertainment Inc, pg 1000
Santa Clarita Studios, pg 1002
ShowBiz Studios, pg 1009
Sonora Recorders, pg 1016
Stray Angel Films, pg 1026
Studio 1444, pg 1026
The Studios at Paramount, pg 1027
Sunset Bronson Studios, pg 1028
Synthesizer Systems Technologies (SST), pg 1030
Total Media Group, pg 1042
Valencia Studios, pg 1051

COLORADO

Colorado Studios, pg 832

FLORIDA

C&I Studios, pg 819
Cinema Entertainment Inc, pg 827
Eastern Video, pg 856
Jordan Klein Film & Video (JKFV), pg 906
LHV Audio Services, pg 919
MAPS Production House, pg 930
Phat Planet Recording Studios, pg 973
South Florida Rehearsal Studios, pg 1019
Universal Studios Florida® Production Group, pg 1049

GEORGIA

Atlanta Filmworks, pg 793
Mailing Avenue Stageworks, pg 929
Studio Space Atlanta, pg 1027

ILLINOIS

Audio Visual Services Corp, pg 796
Beatty TeleVisual Productions, pg 804
Magnanimous Media, pg 928
PSAV® Presentation Services (Hotel Services Division), pg 987
RBR Productions, pg 992

INDIANA

InterComm, pg 900

LOUISIANA

Second Line Stages, pg 1006
WVLA-TV, pg 1071

MARYLAND

Cre-a-tv Studios, pg 839
The Cutting Corp, pg 841
Soundtrax Optical Sound Recording, pg 1018

MICHIGAN

City Events Group, pg 828
K&R All Media Productions Inc, pg 908

MISSOURI

Show-Me Audio-Visual, pg 1009

MONTANA

Jereco Studios Inc, pg 905

NEW HAMPSHIRE

Apertura, pg 788

NEW JERSEY

Butter Tree Studio, pg 816
18 Label Studios, pg 858
Ironbound Film & Television Studios LLC, pg 902

NEW MEXICO

I-25 Studios, pg 893

NEW YORK

BC Video Inc, pg 803
Bond Street Studio, pg 810
Bravo Studios, pg 812
Brooklyn Fire Proof, pg 814
Brooklyn Studios, pg 814
City Stage, pg 828
KAS Music & Sound, pg 908
LightBox-NY, pg 920
LightSpace Studios, pg 921
Location 05 Studios, pg 924
Manhattan Center Studios Inc, pg 930
Shelly Palmer Production, pg 968
Steiner Studios, pg 1024
Umbra of Newburgh LLC, pg 1048

NORTH CAROLINA

Duke Media Services, pg 853
K2 Productions, pg 914

NORTH DAKOTA

Media Productions, pg 937

OHIO

Vista Color Imaging Inc, pg 1059

PENNSYLVANIA

Fusion Brand Experiences, pg 874
31st Street Studios, pg 1039

SOUTH CAROLINA

Studio Charleston, pg 1026

TENNESSEE

Cupit Music Group, pg 841
DR&A Inc, pg 852
Memphis Communications Corp, pg 938

TEXAS

Maverick Video Productions, pg 934
Omega Productions, pg 962
Phillips MediaSource, pg 974
Real to Reel Studios Inc, pg 992
Reelsound Recording Co, pg 994
Saint Elmo Soundstage, pg 1001
Stage Directions, pg 1022
Texcam Inc, pg 1038

WASHINGTON

Kostov Productions, pg 913

WISCONSIN

University of Wisconsin-Oshkosh Radio-TV-Film Dept, pg 1050
Wisconsin Public Television, pg 1068

WYOMING

Bridger Productions Inc, pg 812

ALBERTA

Global Television Station, pg 879

BRITISH COLUMBIA

Finale Editworks, pg 868
Vancouver Film Studios Ltd, pg 1051

MANITOBA

MidCanada Production Services Inc (MidCan), pg 942

ONTARIO

Optimum Production Services Inc, pg 964
The Pocket Studios, pg 977
Wallace Film Studios, pg 1061

Recording Facility Repairs

CALIFORNIA

Technical Services, pg 1034

Reel & Can Distributors

ALABAMA

Curtis Company, pg 841
Media Visions Inc, pg 937

ARIZONA

Troxell Communications Inc, pg 1045

ARKANSAS

Carlton-Bates Co, pg 820

CALIFORNIA

Adolph Gasser Inc, pg 776
Birns & Sawyer Inc, pg 808
Christy's Editorial, pg 826
Cinema Equipment Sales of California Inc, pg 827
Edgewise Media Inc, pg 856
El Mar Plastics Inc, pg 858
Alan Gordon Enterprises Inc, pg 880
Instructional Materials & Equipment Distributors (I-Med), pg 899
J & R Film Co, pg 903
Jaguar Distribution Corp, pg 903
Media Fabricators Inc, pg 936
Pro8mm, pg 983
Yale Film & Video, pg 1071

COLORADO

The Cinema Lab, pg 827
Goldberg Brothers Inc, pg 880
Stanco Sales LLC, pg 1023

CONNECTICUT

MAVCO, pg 934
Rockwell Communications Inc, pg 998

FLORIDA

Cinema Equipment & Supplies Inc, pg 827
Hollywood Theatre Equipment Inc, pg 890
Photomart Cine-Video Inc, pg 975
Tallahassee Audio Visual, pg 1031

GEORGIA

Audio Visual Resources Inc, pg 795
Cinevision Corp, pg 828
Technical Innovation, pg 1033

ILLINOIS

Research Technology International (RTI), pg 995
Urbanski Film, pg 1050

INDIANA

Lee Co Inc, pg 918

KENTUCKY

Audio Visual Techniques Inc, pg 796

MARYLAND

Nicholas P Pipino Associates Inc, pg 976

MASSACHUSETTS

Hunt's Photo, Video & Digital, pg 892
University Products Inc, pg 1050

MINNESOTA

AVI Systems, pg 799

MISSISSIPPI

Bowie Audio Visual Enterprises Inc, pg 811
Jasper Ewing & Sons Inc, pg 864

NEW JERSEY

HP Marketing Corp, pg 892

NEW YORK

Colortone Audio Visual, pg 832
Film Emporium, pg 867
Magnaplan Corp, pg 928
Motion Picture Enterprises Inc, pg 947
Neptune Photo Inc, pg 954
Rafik, pg 990

NORTH CAROLINA

Camcor Inc, pg 818

OHIO

Tri-State Audio Visual Co, pg 1044

PENNSYLVANIA

Audio Visions Inc, pg 795
Brodart Co, pg 813
Visual Sound Inc, pg 1059
Wespen Audio Visual Co, pg 1063

TENNESSEE

Memphis Communications Corp, pg 938
Tennessee Visual Service Co, pg 1037

TEXAS

Audio Visual Technologies Group, pg 796
Pro Video & Film Equipment Co Inc, pg 983

UTAH

Redman Movies & Stories, pg 993

VIRGINIA

Filmdex Inc, pg 867
Lee Hartman & Sons Inc, pg 918
The Whitlock Group, pg 1065

WASHINGTON

Inland Audio Visual Co, pg 898

MANITOBA

Inland Audio Visual Ltd, pg 898

ONTARIO

Carr McLean Ltd, pg 820
Edcom Multimedia Products, pg 856
Premier A/V Sales Ltd, pg 980

Reel & Can Manufacturers

CALIFORNIA

J & R Film Co, pg 903

COLORADO

Goldberg Brothers Inc, pg 880

ILLINOIS

Research Technology International (RTI), pg 995
Urbanski Film, pg 1050

NEBRASKA

Strong Cinema Products, pg 1026

NEW YORK

Motion Picture Enterprises Inc, pg 947

OHIO

Xetron, pg 1071

WISCONSIN

Regal Photo Products Inc/Arkay Corp, pg 994

Reel & Can Rentals

ARIZONA

Arizona Cine Equipment, pg 789

CALIFORNIA

Ametron Audio/Video, pg 785
Big Time Picture Company Inc, pg 807
Christy's Editorial, pg 826
Film Converter Co of America Inc, pg 867

FLORIDA

Jordan Klein Film & Video (JKFV), pg 906

ILLINOIS

Communications Corporation of America, pg 833
Helix Camera & Video, pg 887

MISSISSIPPI

Bowie Audio Visual Enterprises Inc, pg 811
Jasper Ewing & Sons Inc, pg 864

NEW HAMPSHIRE

Apertura, pg 788

NEW YORK

Motion Picture Enterprises Inc, pg 947

PENNSYLVANIA

Audio Visions Inc, pg 795

TENNESSEE

Memphis Communications Corp, pg 938

UTAH

Redman Movies & Stories, pg 993

ALBERTA

Global Television Station, pg 879

Rehearsal Studio Manufacturers

CALIFORNIA

Yanchar Design & Consulting Group, pg 1072

GEORGIA

Lighting & Production Equipment Inc, pg 920

MICHIGAN

Studio Consulting & Construction Inc, pg 1026

Rehearsal Studio Rentals

ARIZONA

Arizona Cine Equipment, pg 789

CALIFORNIA

Big Door, pg 807
Chapman/Leonard Studios & Production Center, pg 824
Golden Gate Studios, pg 880
ShowBiz Studios, pg 1009

FLORIDA

CopShopMiami.com, pg 836
Jordan Klein Film & Video (JKFV), pg 906
Phat Planet Recording Studios, pg 973
South Florida Rehearsal Studios, pg 1019

GEORGIA

Lighting & Production Equipment Inc, pg 920

LOUISIANA

WVLA-TV, pg 1071

MARYLAND

Shadowstone R & R™, pg 1008

MASSACHUSETTS

National Boston, pg 952

MICHIGAN

City Events Group, pg 828
K&R All Media Productions Inc, pg 908

MISSOURI

Show-Me Audio-Visual, pg 1009

NEW JERSEY

Audio Visual Dynamics®, pg 795

FILM

Rehearsal Studio Rentals (continued)

NEW YORK

Manhattan Center Studios Inc, pg 930
Studio Instrument Rentals (SIR), pg 1027

NORTH CAROLINA

Take One Productions Ltd, pg 1031

OHIO

Mills James Productions, pg 943
Vista Color Imaging Inc, pg 1059

OREGON

Pacific Grip & Lighting Inc, pg 967

PENNSYLVANIA

Fusion Brand Experiences, pg 874
WHYY Inc, pg 1066

TEXAS

Maverick Video Productions, pg 934
Muller Entertainment, pg 949
Stage Directions, pg 1022

WASHINGTON

Victory Studios, pg 1054

WISCONSIN

Wisconsin Public Television, pg 1068

WYOMING

Bridger Productions Inc, pg 812

ALBERTA

Global Television Station, pg 879

ONTARIO

JIB Shots Equipment Inc, pg 905

Rehearsal Studio Repairs

MICHIGAN

Studio Consulting & Construction Inc, pg 1026

Rejuvenation, *see* Preservation & Rejuvenation

Release Printing

CALIFORNIA

Deluxe Laboratories Inc, pg 845
Film Technology Co Inc, pg 867
Monaco Digital Films Labs, pg 945
Point of View Productions, pg 977
QRS Software Services, pg 988

COLORADO

The Cinema Lab, pg 827

CONNECTICUT

Century Color Labs Inc, pg 823

FLORIDA

Roger Scruggs Films, pg 1005

ILLINOIS

Filmworkers, pg 868

MASSACHUSETTS

Extreme Reach Inc, pg 864

MINNESOTA

Aggressive Records Audio Duplication LLC, pg 778
Badiyan Inc, pg 801

NEW HAMPSHIRE

Apertura, pg 788
Chip Taylor Communications LLC, pg 1032

NEW YORK

De Nonno Productions Inc (DPI), pg 844
MRG Productions Inc, pg 948

PENNSYLVANIA

John E Allen Inc, pg 781

TENNESSEE

Motion Picture Services, pg 947
Stage Post, pg 1022

WISCONSIN

USAV Group Inc, pg 1050

Script Writing

ALABAMA

Diamond Studios, pg 846

ALASKA

Alaska Film Services Inc, pg 779
Aurora Films, pg 797

ARIZONA

MediaWorks, pg 938
Merestone, pg 938
Metropolitan Audio-Visual Inc, pg 940
Phoenix VideoFilms®, pg 974
Tellens Inc, pg 1037

ARKANSAS

Live'N'Loud, pg 923
Shadowbox Video Productions, pg 1007

CALIFORNIA

Aaron & Le Duc, pg 772
Animax, pg 787
Concrete Images, pg 835
Crystal Pyramid Productions™, pg 840
Custom Video Productions Inc, pg 841
Design Media, pg 845
Tom Donald Films, pg 850
DreamWorks Animation SKG Inc, pg 852
Goal Productions, pg 879
Gold Standard Productions, pg 880
Havas Edge, pg 885
iCorpTv, pg 893
Increase Video/Silver Mine Video, pg 897
ITV Productions, pg 903
Joyce Media Inc, pg 906
KION-TV, pg 911
KO Creative, pg 912
KTVU-Retail Services, pg 914
The Media Staff Inc, pg 937
Nandar Entertainment Pictures, pg 952
New & Unique Videos™, pg 955
Palardo Productions, pg 968
Panorama Productions, pg 968
Players Press, pg 977
PSI Inc, pg 987
QRS Software Services, pg 988
Regent Press Publishers & Printers, pg 994
SBS Productions, pg 1003
Signature Entertainment, pg 1011
The Studio Center, pg 1026
Tam Communications Inc, pg 1031
Tigar Hare Studios, pg 1040
Toon Makers, pg 1042
Total Media Group, pg 1042
Vineyard Productions, pg 1058
WMS Media Inc, pg 1069

COLORADO

Flashback Media Productions, pg 869
Open Media Foundation, pg 964
Scriptware, pg 1005
Tatum Video, pg 1032
Transtar Entertainment Co Inc, pg 1043

CONNECTICUT

ACM Productions Ltd, pg 774
Broadcast Video Productions LLC, pg 813
Essex Television Group Inc, pg 862
MCC Films, pg 935
New London Media, pg 956

DISTRICT OF COLUMBIA

Hillmann & Carr Inc, pg 889
O'Keefe Communications Inc, pg 961

FLORIDA

ACT Productions, pg 775
Chatterbox Productions Inc, pg 824
Civins Productions Inc, pg 828
Communications Concepts Inc (CCI), pg 833
CopShopMiami.com, pg 836
Courter Films LLC, pg 837
Eastern Video, pg 856
Ed Ethridge Productions Inc, pg 863
Gulf Coast Audio Visual Producers Inc, pg 883
Jordan Klein Film & Video (JKFV), pg 906
Media Entertainment Inc, pg 936
Multivision Video & Film, pg 950
Universal Studios Florida® Production Group, pg 1049

GEORGIA

Burst Video/Film Inc, pg 815
COMPRO Productions Inc, pg 834
Guerrilla Productions LLC, pg 883
The Intellications Co, pg 899
Memory Lane Productions, pg 938
Myriad Productions, pg 951
Malcolm Neal Productions, pg 954
On-Line Productions, pg 963
Visioneering International Inc, pg 1058

HAWAII

Media Bridge Gamekids, pg 936
1013 Integrated, pg 1037

IDAHO

Brad Shaw Productions Inc, pg 1008

ILLINOIS

ABSA Productions Inc, pg 772
Audio Visual Services Corp, pg 796
Communications Corporation of America, pg 833
Film Police, pg 867
Major Media Productions Inc, pg 929
MIGHTYbYTES Inc, pg 942
Perspectives Media, pg 973
PSAV® Presentation Services (Hotel Services Division), pg 987
SCI Television Productions LLC, pg 1004
WEEK TV, pg 1063

INDIANA

AVA Productions, pg 798
Perennial Pictures Film Corp, pg 973

IOWA

The Production House, pg 984

KENTUCKY

Hammond Communications Group, pg 884
Horizon Films & Media LLC, pg 891

LOUISIANA

Digital FX Inc, pg 847
Louisiana State University Health Sciences Center - Shreveport, pg 925
Moxie Media, pg 948
Vidox Motion Imagery, pg 1057

MAINE

Slim Goodbody Corp, pg 1013

MARYLAND

Adventure Productions LLC, pg 778
The Ahern Group, pg 779
dbF a Media Company, pg 844
James Agee Film Project, pg 904
Kramer Communications Video Production, pg 913

MASSACHUSETTS

CommCreative, pg 832
Cramer Productions, pg 837
Emergency Film Group, pg 860
Green Mountain Post Films (GMP), pg 882
Monadnock Media Inc, pg 945
Northern Light Productions, pg 959
Preston Productions Inc, pg 981

MICHIGAN

Digi Sign Design LLC, pg 847
Maritz Performance Improvement Co, pg 931
Michigan Recording Arts Institute & Technologies, pg 941

Sixteen mm Projector and Equipment, *see* Projector & Equipment—16mm

Slide to Film Transfers, *see* Transfers—Slide to Film

Slow Motion Photography, *see* Photography—Slow Motion

Special Effects

FILM

Special Effects (continued)

ILLINOIS

ABSA Productions Inc, pg 772
Chicago Spotlight Inc, pg 825
Comtech Multimedia Marketing, pg 834
Consolidated Display Co Inc, pg 835
MIGHTYbYTES Inc, pg 942
The Pepper Group, pg 972

INDIANA

AVA Productions, pg 798

KENTUCKY

Theatre Effects, pg 1038

LOUISIANA

Vidox Motion Imagery, pg 1057

MARYLAND

Kramer Communications Video Production, pg 913

MASSACHUSETTS

CommCreative, pg 832
MotionArt Studios, pg 947
Northern Light Productions, pg 959
Preston Productions Inc, pg 981
TR Productions, pg 1043

MICHIGAN

Digi Sign Design LLC, pg 847
Tectonics Industries Inc, pg 1035

MINNESOTA

Aggressive Records Audio Duplication LLC, pg 778
House of Cinemagraphics, pg 891
Media Loft Inc, pg 937
MultiMedia, pg 950
Sight Creative, pg 1010

MISSOURI

Fantasy Creations FX, pg 865

MONTANA

Filmlites Montana, pg 867

NEVADA

DVDs4Less, pg 854
GES Audio Visual, pg 877

NEW HAMPSHIRE

Apertura, pg 788

NEW JERSEY

CELCO-Constantine Engineering Labs Co, pg 822
Early Films, pg 855
NFL Films Inc, pg 957
NFL Films Music Library, pg 957
Starlite Productions, pg 1024

NEW YORK

Norman N Axelrod Associates, pg 800
Big Film Design, pg 807
Big Fish Productions Inc, pg 807
Broad Street Inc, pg 812
Chromavision Corp, pg 826
La Paloma Films, pg 915
Lylofilm Productions, pg 926
Neal Marshad Productions, pg 931
MRG Productions Inc, pg 948
Shelly Palmer Production, pg 968
R/GA, pg 990
Judson Rosebush Co Inc, pg 999

NORTH CAROLINA

The Communications Group Inc, pg 833
Image Associates Inc, pg 894

OHIO

Creative Technology, pg 838
Mills James Productions, pg 943
Thread Marketing Group, pg 1039

OREGON

Artbeats, pg 791

PENNSYLVANIA

Innovision Media Group, pg 899
Shore Manufacturing Co, pg 1009
31st Street Studios, pg 1039

RHODE ISLAND

Sound-FX-Design, pg 1017

SOUTH CAROLINA

Genesis Creative, pg 877

TENNESSEE

High-Tech Special Effects Inc, pg 889
Marine Geographic, pg 931
Motion Picture Services, pg 947
Paradigm Marketing & Creative, pg 969
Stage Post, pg 1022

TEXAS

Biway Media, pg 808
Magic By Bruce Chadwick, pg 928
The Samuels Co, pg 1002
Stage Directions, pg 1022
Superior Graphics, pg 1029

UTAH

Strata™, pg 1025

VIRGINIA

Blair Inc, pg 809

WASHINGTON

Inland Audio Visual Co, pg 898
Laser Fantasy/HECK Industries/ Photon Manufacturing, pg 916
Riggs Production Associates Inc, pg 996

WISCONSIN

5th Floor Recording Co, pg 867
USAV Group Inc, pg 1050

WYOMING

Bridger Productions Inc, pg 812

ALBERTA

Global Television Station, pg 879

ONTARIO

ADS Media, pg 777
The Fluorescent Co Inc, pg 870
Gesturetek, pg 877
Pyrotek Special Effects Inc, pg 988

Still Camera, *see* Movie & Still Camera

Still Projector, *see* Continuous Still Projector

Stock-Shot Libraries, *see* Libraries—Film or Stock-Shot

Stock Transfer

CALIFORNIA

Chace Audio by Deluxe, pg 823
Goal Productions, pg 879
iCorpTv, pg 893
Polarity Post Production, pg 978
QRS Software Services, pg 988
SonicPool, pg 1016

COLORADO

The Cinema Lab, pg 827

FLORIDA

Cinema East, pg 827
Eastern Video, pg 856

GEORGIA

CineFilm Lab, pg 827

KENTUCKY

Broadway Digital, pg 813

MARYLAND

Bethesda Softworks LLC, pg 806
dbF a Media Company, pg 844
Soundtrax Optical Sound Recording, pg 1018

MASSACHUSETTS

Green Mountain Post Films (GMP), pg 882
Soundtrack Recording Studios, pg 1018

MICHIGAN

Digi Sign Design LLC, pg 847

MINNESOTA

Aggressive Records Audio Duplication LLC, pg 778

NEW HAMPSHIRE

Apertura, pg 788

NEW JERSEY

CELCO-Constantine Engineering Labs Co, pg 822
NFL Films Music Library, pg 957

NEW YORK

KAS Music & Sound, pg 908
MRG Productions Inc, pg 948
Shelly Palmer Production, pg 968
TBA Global Events, pg 1032

RHODE ISLAND

A&M Productions, pg 771

TENNESSEE

Motion Picture Services, pg 947
Stage Post, pg 1022

WISCONSIN

Video Wisconsin Inc, pg 1056

QUEBEC

Muse Entertainment Enterprises, pg 950

Storage Vault Distributors

ONTARIO

DG Mijo, pg 846

Storage Vault Manufacturers

OHIO

Xetron, pg 1071

Storage Vault Rentals

CALIFORNIA

Total Media Group, pg 1042

COLORADO

The Cinema Lab, pg 827

NORTH CAROLINA

Take One Productions Ltd, pg 1031

ONTARIO

DG Mijo, pg 846

Studio Photography, *see* Photography—Studio

Synchronizer Distributors

ARIZONA

Audio Video Resources, pg 795
EAR Professional Audio/Video, pg 855

CALIFORNIA

Christy's Editorial, pg 826
Cinema Equipment Sales of California Inc, pg 827
Alan Gordon Enterprises Inc, pg 880
J & R Film Co, pg 903
JLCooper Electronics, pg 905
Plus 24, pg 977
Tri-Ed, pg 1044

COLORADO

Ceavco Audio/Visual Co, pg 822
Stanco Sales LLC, pg 1023

CONNECTICUT

Concord Communications, pg 835
Rockwell Communications Inc, pg 998

FLORIDA

Photomart Cine-Video Inc, pg 975
Recording Media & Equipment Inc (RM&E), pg 993

GEORGIA

Technical Innovation, pg 1033

KENTUCKY

NOR-COM Inc, pg 958

MARYLAND

RTZ Audio Visual, pg 1000
Visual Aids Electronics Corp, pg 1059

MICHIGAN

TeL Systems, pg 1035

MINNESOTA

AVI Systems, pg 799

MISSISSIPPI

Jasper Ewing & Sons Inc, pg 864

NEW JERSEY

Audio Visual Dynamics®, pg 795
JRF Magnetic Sciences Inc, pg 906
SYMCO Inc, pg 1030

NEW YORK

Colortone Audio Visual, pg 832
Motion Picture Enterprises Inc, pg 947

OHIO

Audio Visual Media, pg 795
Icom Multimedia, pg 893

PENNSYLVANIA

J E Foss Co, pg 871
Hite Co, pg 889
Wespen Audio Visual Co, pg 1063

TENNESSEE

Memphis Communications Corp, pg 938

TEXAS

Audio Visual Technologies Group, pg 796
Pro Video & Film Equipment Co Inc, pg 983

UTAH

Performance Audio, pg 973
RIA Corp, pg 996

VIRGINIA

Lee Hartman & Sons Inc, pg 918

WASHINGTON

Inland Audio Visual Co, pg 898

ONTARIO

Nationwide Audio Visual Co, pg 953

Synchronizer Manufacturers

CALIFORNIA

J & R Film Co, pg 903
JLCooper Electronics, pg 905

FLORIDA

Magna-Tech Electronic Co Inc, pg 928

RHODE ISLAND

M-Audio, pg 927

Synchronizer Rentals

ARIZONA

Audio Video Resources, pg 795

CALIFORNIA

Artichoke Productions, pg 791
Christy's Editorial, pg 826
Alan Gordon Enterprises Inc, pg 880
J & R Film Co, pg 903
Synthesizer Rental Service, pg 1030
Synthesizer Systems Technologies (SST), pg 1030
University of Southern California, pg 1050

COLORADO

Ceavco Audio/Visual Co, pg 822
The Cinema Lab, pg 827

CONNECTICUT

Rockwell Communications Inc, pg 998

ILLINOIS

Helix Camera & Video, pg 887

INDIANA

OMNI Productions, pg 962

MARYLAND

RTZ Audio Visual, pg 1000

MASSACHUSETTS

Green Mountain Post Films (GMP), pg 882

MICHIGAN

City Events Group, pg 828
K&R All Media Productions Inc, pg 908

MINNESOTA

AVI Systems, pg 799

MISSISSIPPI

Jasper Ewing & Sons Inc, pg 864

NEW HAMPSHIRE

Apertura, pg 788

NEW JERSEY

Audio Visual Dynamics®, pg 795

NEW YORK

Langie Audio Visual Systems, pg 915
Motion Picture Enterprises Inc, pg 947

OHIO

Audio Visual Media, pg 795
Icom Multimedia, pg 893

OREGON

Northwest Film Center, pg 959

TENNESSEE

Memphis Communications Corp, pg 938

TEXAS

Omega Productions, pg 962

VIRGINIA

Projection Presentation Technology, pg 985

WASHINGTON

Inland Audio Visual Co, pg 898

ALBERTA

Global Television Station, pg 879

Synchronizer Repairs

CALIFORNIA

Christy's Editorial, pg 826
Alan Gordon Enterprises Inc, pg 880
J & R Film Co, pg 903

COLORADO

Ceavco Audio/Visual Co, pg 822

CONNECTICUT

Rockwell Communications Inc, pg 998

FLORIDA

Hi-Tech Enterprises Inc, pg 888

GEORGIA

Technical Innovation, pg 1033

KENTUCKY

NOR-COM Inc, pg 958

MARYLAND

RTZ Audio Visual, pg 1000

MINNESOTA

AVI Systems, pg 799

NEW YORK

Langie Audio Visual Systems, pg 915
Motion Picture Enterprises Inc, pg 947
MRG Productions Inc, pg 948

OHIO

Audio Visual Media, pg 795
Icom Multimedia, pg 893

PENNSYLVANIA

Wespen Audio Visual Co, pg 1063

TENNESSEE

Memphis Communications Corp, pg 938

VIRGINIA

Lee Hartman & Sons Inc, pg 918

WASHINGTON

Inland Audio Visual Co, pg 898

Syndication

CALIFORNIA

Custom Video Productions Inc, pg 841
Point of View Productions, pg 977
QRS Software Services, pg 988

FLORIDA

Media Entertainment Inc, pg 936
Multivision Video & Film, pg 950

GEORGIA

COMPRO Productions Inc, pg 834
Guerrilla Productions LLC, pg 883

ILLINOIS

Chicago Satellite & Video, pg 825
Communications Corporation of America, pg 833
Moviecraft Inc, pg 947

INDIANA

Perennial Pictures Film Corp, pg 973

MASSACHUSETTS

Extreme Reach Inc, pg 864

MISSOURI

Cable Films & Video, pg 816

NEW YORK

Jalbert Productions International, pg 903
MRG Productions Inc, pg 948
Shelly Palmer Production, pg 968
VIEW Inc (Video International Entertainment World Inc), pg 1058

NORTH CAROLINA

Crystal Pictures Inc, pg 840

TENNESSEE

Continental Film, pg 835
Motion Picture Services, pg 947
Stage Post, pg 1022

VIRGINIA

CACI Productions Group, pg 816

WISCONSIN

Wisconsin Public Television, pg 1068

WYOMING

Bridger Productions Inc, pg 812

FILM

Syndication (continued)

ALBERTA

Global Television Station, pg 879

Talent & Property Agencies

ALABAMA

Sound of Birmingham Productions, pg 1017

ALASKA

Alaska Film Services Inc, pg 779

CALIFORNIA

Havas Edge, pg 885
International Contact Inc, pg 900
The Location Connection Inc, pg 924
Palardo Productions, pg 968
QRS Software Services, pg 988
Sahara Records & Filmworks Entertainment Co, pg 1001
Santa Barbara Location Services, pg 1002
Signature Entertainment, pg 1011
SonicPool, pg 1016
WARPed Pictures, pg 1062

FLORIDA

CopShopMiami.com, pg 836

HAWAII

Media Bridge Gamekids, pg 936

ILLINOIS

Communications Corporation of America, pg 833

MARYLAND

The Image Generators, pg 895

MASSACHUSETTS

Preston Productions Inc, pg 981

MICHIGAN

Digi Sign Design LLC, pg 847

MINNESOTA

Moore Creative Talent Inc, pg 946

NEW HAMPSHIRE

Chip Taylor Communications LLC, pg 1032

NEW JERSEY

Suede Interactive, pg 1027

NEW YORK

InterNation Inc, pg 900
MRG Productions Inc, pg 948

RHODE ISLAND

Sound-FX-Design, pg 1017

TENNESSEE

Colonel Buster Doss Music Group, pg 831
Motion Picture Services, pg 947
Stage Post, pg 1022

TEXAS

Magic By Bruce Chadwick, pg 928

VIRGINIA

CACI Productions Group, pg 816

WYOMING

Bridger Productions Inc, pg 812

BRITISH COLUMBIA

MicrophoneRentals.com, pg 941

MANITOBA

2BK9 Acting Animals, pg 1047

Thirty-Five mm Projector & Equipment, *see* Projector & Equipment—35mm

Titling & Artwork Services, *see* Artwork & Titling Services

Transfer & Conversion Equipment Distributors

ARIZONA

Professional Marketing Services Inc, pg 985
Troxell Communications Inc, pg 1045

ARKANSAS

White Diamond Productions, pg 1065

CALIFORNIA

MediaPOINTE, pg 938
Snell, pg 1014
Yale Film & Video, pg 1071

FLORIDA

Pro Stage Inc, pg 983

ILLINOIS

Lipsner-Smith Co, pg 922
Urbanski Film, pg 1050

INDIANA

Lee Co Inc, pg 918

KENTUCKY

Barney Miller's Inc, pg 943
NOR-COM Inc, pg 958

MISSOURI

Cintrex Audio Visual, pg 828
Schiller's Audio-Visual, pg 1004

NEW JERSEY

SADiE Inc, pg 1001

NEW YORK

Neptune Photo Inc, pg 954
Video International Development Inc, pg 1055

PENNSYLVANIA

J E Foss Co, pg 871

TEXAS

Pro Video & Film Equipment Co Inc, pg 983

WISCONSIN

Safe Harbor Computers, pg 1001

BRITISH COLUMBIA

Commercial Electronics Ltd, pg 832

Transfer & Conversion Equipment Manufacturers

CALIFORNIA

Snell, pg 1014

NEW JERSEY

CELCO-Constantine Engineering Labs Co, pg 822
SADiE Inc, pg 1001

NEW YORK

ELMO USA Corp, pg 859
Video International Development Inc, pg 1055

WASHINGTON

Tobin Cinema Systems Inc, pg 1041

BRITISH COLUMBIA

Triad Communications Ltd, pg 1044

Transfer & Conversion Equipment Rentals

ARKANSAS

White Diamond Productions, pg 1065

CALIFORNIA

Roundabout Entertainment Inc, pg 1000

COLORADO

The Cinema Lab, pg 827

FLORIDA

Pro Stage Inc, pg 983

MISSOURI

Schiller's Audio-Visual, pg 1004
Show-Me Audio-Visual, pg 1009

NEW YORK

Posthorn Recordings, pg 979

NORTH CAROLINA

Duke Media Services, pg 853

PENNSYLVANIA

FMP Media Solutions Inc, pg 870

TEXAS

Astro Audio Visual, pg 792

BRITISH COLUMBIA

Finale Editworks, pg 868

Transfer & Conversion Equipment Repairs

KENTUCKY

NOR-COM Inc, pg 958

MISSOURI

Cintrex Audio Visual, pg 828

NEW YORK

ELMO USA Corp, pg 859

TEXAS

Astro Audio Visual, pg 792

Transfers—Film to Videotape

ALABAMA

Media Visions Inc, pg 937

ARIZONA

On-Site Video, pg 963
Phoenix VideoFilms®, pg 974

ARKANSAS

Cedar Crest Studio, pg 822

CALIFORNIA

Access Video in Berkeley, pg 773
Action Photo Service Inc, pg 775
Action Video, pg 775
Adolph Gasser Inc, pg 776
Artichoke Productions, pg 791
Barbosa Video Services, pg 802
Custom Video Productions Inc, pg 841
Deluxe Laboratories Inc, pg 845
Digital Jungle, pg 847
Em Gee Film Library, pg 860
Film Technology Co Inc, pg 867
FXC Communications, pg 874
Havas Edge, pg 885
Hooper Camera & Imaging, pg 891
iCorpTv, pg 893
Method Studios, pg 939
Monaco Digital Films Labs, pg 945
Pacific Video Products Inc, pg 967
Peterson's Video Transfer Services, pg 973
Point 360, pg 978
Pro8mm, pg 983
QRS Software Services, pg 988
RetinaVision Productions, pg 995
SBS Productions, pg 1003
SonicPool, pg 1016
Tele-Video Production Services (TVPS), pg 1036
Wavemaker Media Design, pg 1062
Yale Film & Video, pg 1071

COLORADO

Ceavco Audio/Visual Co, pg 822
The Cinema Lab, pg 827
Rocky Mountain Audio/Video Productions Inc, pg 998

CONNECTICUT

Concord Communications, pg 835
Digital Video Productions, pg 848
EagleVision Inc, pg 855
The Gary-Paul Agency, pg 875
Rockwell Communications Inc, pg 998

DELAWARE

Ken-Del Productions Inc, pg 909
Ken-Del Studios, pg 909

DISTRICT OF COLUMBIA

Interface Media Group, pg 900
Library of Congress, Motion Picture, Broadcasting & Recorded Sound Division, pg 919

FLORIDA

Accord Productions, pg 773
Civins Productions Inc, pg 828
Communications Concepts Inc (CCI), pg 833
Gulf Coast Audio Visual Producers Inc, pg 883
Multivision Video & Film, pg 950
Photosound of Orlando Inc, pg 975
Sunrise Studios, pg 1028
Tallahassee Audio Visual, pg 1031

GEORGIA

Audio Visual Resources Inc, pg 795
CineFilm Lab, pg 827
Crawford Media Services, pg 838
Memory Lane Productions, pg 938

ILLINOIS

Beatty TeleVisual Productions, pg 804
Filmworkers, pg 868
IV Media Resources, pg 903
Major Media Inc, pg 929
Major Media Productions Inc, pg 929
Midwest Digital Corp, pg 942
Moviecraft Inc, pg 947
Optimus, pg 964
The Pepper Group, pg 972
Sound/Video Impressions Inc, pg 1018
WEEK TV, pg 1063

INDIANA

OMNI Productions, pg 962

IOWA

Duplication Media, pg 853
The Production House, pg 984

KENTUCKY

Audio Visual Techniques Inc, pg 796
Barney Miller's Inc, pg 943
The PPS Group, pg 980

LOUISIANA

Moxie Media, pg 948

MARYLAND

Kramer Communications Video Production, pg 913
Milner-Fenwick Inc, pg 943

MASSACHUSETTS

Brodsky & Treadway, pg 813
Camera Co Inc/Broadcast Divison, pg 818
Capron Lighting & Sound Co Inc, pg 819
CommCreative, pg 832
National Boston, pg 952

MICHIGAN

Encore Home Video, pg 861
K&R's Recording Studios Inc, pg 908
RingSide Creative, pg 997
The Transfer Zone®, pg 1043

MINNESOTA

Aggressive Records Audio Duplication LLC, pg 778
Badiyan Inc, pg 801
MultiMedia, pg 950
Rum Jungle Media, pg 1000

MISSISSIPPI

Jasper Ewing & Sons Inc, pg 864

MISSOURI

Schiller's Audio-Visual, pg 1004

MONTANA

KUSM TV, pg 914

NEW HAMPSHIRE

Academic & Campus Technology Services, pg 773
Apertura, pg 788

NEW JERSEY

CELCO-Constantine Engineering Labs Co, pg 822
Deluxe Media Services, pg 845
NFL Films Inc, pg 957
NFL Films Music Library, pg 957
Video Corporation of America (VCA), pg 1055

NEW YORK

aurora productions, pg 797
Colortone Audio Visual, pg 832
Thomas Craven Film Corp, pg 837
DuArt, pg 853
Duplication Specialists Inc, pg 853
International Digital Centre, pg 901
Magno Sound & Video, pg 929
Neal Marshad Productions, pg 931
MRG Productions Inc, pg 948
Shelly Palmer Production, pg 968
PostWorks, pg 979
TeleTime Productions, pg 1036
USA Studios, pg 1050
Zelman Studios Ltd, pg 1073

NORTH CAROLINA

A&V Company, pg 772
Camcor Inc, pg 818
Duke Media Services, pg 853

OHIO

Russ Beckner Pictures, pg 804
Creative Technology, pg 838
VGI Productions, pg 1053
Vista Color Imaging Inc, pg 1059

PENNSYLVANIA

John E Allen Inc, pg 781
Audio Visions Inc, pg 795
Audio Visual Communications Inc, pg 795
Bernie's Photo Center, pg 805
Center City Film & Video Inc, pg 822
Fusion Brand Experiences, pg 874
Muderick Media, pg 949
Visual Sound Inc, pg 1059
WPHL-TV, pg 1070

RHODE ISLAND

A&M Productions, pg 771

TENNESSEE

Motion Picture Services, pg 947
Stage Post, pg 1022
WKPT-TV, pg 1068

TEXAS

Astro Audio Visual, pg 792
Dub King, pg 853
Matson Multi-Media, pg 934
McNee Productions Inc, pg 935
Julye Newlin Productions Inc, pg 956
Replicopy Digital Media Center, pg 995
Texas Heart Institute Visual Communication Services, pg 1037

VERMONT

University of Vermont, Instructional Television Dept, pg 1050

VIRGINIA

BES Studios, pg 805
CDR Communications Inc, pg 822
Henninger Media Services, pg 888

WASHINGTON

Pro Image, pg 983
Tobin Cinema Systems Inc, pg 1041
Victory Studios, pg 1054

WISCONSIN

Audio Visual of Milwaukee Inc, pg 795
University of Wisconsin-Oshkosh Radio-TV-Film Dept, pg 1050
Wisconsin Public Television, pg 1068

WYOMING

Bridger Productions Inc, pg 812

BRITISH COLUMBIA

Commercial Electronics Ltd, pg 832
Finale Editworks, pg 868
Triad Communications Ltd, pg 1044

ONTARIO

Cinram Inc, pg 828
DG Mijo, pg 846

QUEBEC

Muse Entertainment Enterprises, pg 950

Transfers—Slide to Film

ARIZONA

Phoenix VideoFilms®, pg 974
Professional Marketing Services Inc, pg 985

CALIFORNIA

Artichoke Productions, pg 791
iCorpTv, pg 893
QRS Software Services, pg 988
RetinaVision Productions, pg 995

FLORIDA

Gulf Coast Audio Visual Producers Inc, pg 883
Sunrise Studios, pg 1028
Tallahassee Audio Visual, pg 1031

GEORGIA

Visioneering International Inc, pg 1058

LOUISIANA

Moxie Media, pg 948

MICHIGAN

Encore Home Video, pg 861
K&R's Recording Studios Inc, pg 908

MINNESOTA

Aggressive Records Audio Duplication LLC, pg 778

MISSOURI

Schiller's Audio-Visual, pg 1004

NEW HAMPSHIRE

Apertura, pg 788

NEW JERSEY

CELCO-Constantine Engineering Labs Co, pg 822

NEW YORK

Gurrilla Video Solutions, pg 883
Neal Marshad Productions, pg 931
Jack Morton Worldwide, pg 946
MRG Productions Inc, pg 948
Shelly Palmer Production, pg 968
Zelman Studios Ltd, pg 1073

PENNSYLVANIA

John E Allen Inc, pg 781
Audio Visual Communications Inc, pg 795
Bernie's Photo Center, pg 805

RHODE ISLAND

A&M Productions, pg 771

TENNESSEE

Motion Picture Services, pg 947
Stage Post, pg 1022

TEXAS

Stage Directions, pg 1022

WISCONSIN

Audio Visual of Milwaukee Inc, pg 795

ALBERTA

Global Television Station, pg 879

FILM

Transfers—Videotape to Film

Underwater Photography, *see* Photography—Underwater

Videotape to Film Transfers, *see* Transfers—Videotape to Film

Workshops, *see* Production Workshops

VIDEO

Accessory, *see* Equipment & Accessory

Aerial Photography, *see* Photography—Aerial

Animation Production Services

ALABAMA

Diamond Studios, pg 846

ARIZONA

Merestone, pg 938
Phoenix VideoFilms®, pg 974

ARKANSAS

Cedar Crest Studio, pg 822
Jones Film Video, pg 906
Shadowbox Video Productions, pg 1007
White Diamond Productions, pg 1065

CALIFORNIA

Aaron & Le Duc, pg 772
Access Video in Berkeley, pg 773
Advanced Systems Group LLC, pg 778
Animax, pg 787
Artichoke Productions, pg 791
Blind, pg 809
Buttercup Pictures, pg 816
CCI Digital, pg 821
Classic Images, pg 829
Crystal Pyramid Productions™, pg 840
Custom Video Productions Inc, pg 841
Diaquest, pg 846
Digital Outpost, pg 847
Direct Images Interactive Inc, pg 848
Duck Studios, pg 853
First Person™, pg 868
Goal Productions, pg 879
Havas Edge, pg 885
Hydrogen Whiskey Studios, pg 893
iCorpTv, pg 893
Images in Motion Media Inc, pg 896
Imageworks, pg 896
JDS Video & Media Productions Inc, pg 904
KION-TV, pg 911
Laser Magic Productions, pg 916
Lumeni Productions Inc, pg 926
Lynch Communications, pg 926
Maximus Media Inc, pg 934
The Media Staff Inc, pg 937
Medical Visual Creations (MVC), pg 938
Mind Over Eye Inc, pg 943
New & Unique Videos™, pg 955
Nolte Media, pg 958
Panorama Productions, pg 968
QRS Software Services, pg 988
Regent Press Publishers & Printers, pg 994
Saturn Studios, pg 1003
Staylor-Made Communications Inc, pg 1024
Still N'Motion, pg 1025
Tam Communications Inc, pg 1031
Tigar Hare Studios, pg 1040
Timestream Video, pg 1041
Toon Makers, pg 1042
Total Media Group, pg 1042
Twin Peaks Creative, pg 1047
Two Door Productions, pg 1047
Uniconn Productions, pg 1048
Universal Studios, pg 1049
VidCan Media Solutions, pg 1054
Videobotics, pg 1056
Warner Bros Entertainment Inc, pg 1062
Wavemaker Media Design, pg 1062
WMS Media Inc, pg 1069

COLORADO

CSI Films, pg 840
Flashback Media Productions, pg 869
Full Spectrum Arts & Services, pg 874
Rocky Mountain Audio/Video Productions Inc, pg 998
Spectrum Audio Visual Services, pg 1020

CONNECTICUT

Applebox Studio, pg 788
BRB Audiovisual Productions, pg 812
Geomatrix Productions, pg 877
Musivision Inc, pg 951
New London Media, pg 956
Palace Digital Studios, pg 967

DELAWARE

So Smart Productions, pg 1015

DISTRICT OF COLUMBIA

Hillmann & Carr Inc, pg 889
Interface Media Group, pg 900
O'Keefe Communications Inc, pg 961

FLORIDA

Access Media Group, pg 773
Accord Productions, pg 773
Allegro Productions Inc, pg 781
Audio Visual Imagineering Inc, pg 795
Civins Productions Inc, pg 828
Communications Concepts Inc (CCI), pg 833
Ed Ethridge Productions Inc, pg 863
Hi-Tech Enterprises Inc, pg 888
Home Shopping Network (HSN), pg 890
Little Big Bang Design Inc, pg 923
Progressive Media & Music, pg 985
Sunfire Communications Inc, pg 1028
Tricycle Studios, pg 1044
Mike Vasilinda Productions Inc, pg 1052
Video Techniques Inc, pg 1056
Vistamax Productions, pg 1059

GEORGIA

Beachwood Productions, pg 804
Beast Atlanta, pg 804
Crawford Media Services, pg 838
The DVI Group, pg 854
ECG Productions, pg 856
First Cut Communications LLC, pg 868
Guerrilla Productions LLC, pg 883
Staging Directions Inc, pg 1023

HAWAII

Hyperspective Studios Inc, pg 893
Media Bridge Gamekids, pg 936

ILLINOIS

Airways Digital Media, pg 779
Analog Free Media, pg 786
Audio Producers Group, pg 794
Chicago Satellite & Video, pg 825
Manning Productions, pg 930
Mimi Productions, pg 943
Optimus, pg 964
The Pepper Group, pg 972
Richter Studios, pg 996
SCI Television Productions LLC, pg 1004
Sparkfactor, pg 1019
Tele-Time Systems, pg 1036
Video Impressions, pg 1055
WEEK TV, pg 1063

INDIANA

AVA Productions, pg 798
OMNI Productions, pg 962

KENTUCKY

Broadway Digital, pg 813
Hammond Communications Group, pg 884
The PPS Group, pg 980

LOUISIANA

Digital FX Inc, pg 847
Louisiana State University Health Sciences Center - Shreveport, pg 925
Vidox Motion Imagery, pg 1057
WVLA-TV, pg 1071

MARYLAND

Adventure Productions LLC, pg 778
CPR MultiMedia Solutions, pg 837
dbF a Media Company, pg 844
Kramer Communications Video Production, pg 913
Library Video Network (LVN), pg 920
Media Dimensions Inc, pg 936
Pro Cuts Editing Services, pg 982
Producers Video, pg 984
Shadowstone R & R™, pg 1008

MASSACHUSETTS

CommCreative, pg 832
Cramer Productions, pg 837
Extreme Reach Inc, pg 864
MotionArt Studios, pg 947
Northern Light Productions, pg 959
Penfield Productions Ltd, pg 971
Gabriel Polonsky Studio, pg 978
Preston Productions Inc, pg 981
Real Cool TV Productions, pg 992
Veritech Corp, pg 1053
WSI, pg 1070

MICHIGAN

Blue Mouse Studio, pg 809
Digi Sign Design LLC, pg 847
Digital Image Studios LLC, pg 847
K&R's Recording Studios Inc, pg 908
Michigan Recording Arts Institute & Technologies, pg 941
Universal Images, pg 1049

MINNESOTA

The ADS Group, pg 777
MultiMedia, pg 950

MISSOURI

Avatar Studios, pg 798
Conference Technologies Inc, pg 835
Show-Me Audio-Visual, pg 1009
StoryTrack, pg 1025

MONTANA

North Country Media Group, pg 959

NEVADA

Aardvark Video & Media Productions, pg 772
Encore Productions Inc, pg 861
JCS Video Productions, pg 904
21st Century Video Productions, pg 1047

NEW HAMPSHIRE

Apertura, pg 788
Chip Taylor Communications LLC, pg 1032

NEW JERSEY

A-V Services Inc, pg 771
Broadcast Center Studios, pg 813
CD Meyer Inc, pg 822
Diversified Systems Inc, pg 849
DWJ Television, pg 854
MediaMix Inc, pg 937
MediaNow, pg 938
MIB Mediaworks, pg 941
NFL Films Inc, pg 957
PeopleVisionFX, pg 972
PLS Staging, pg 977
Two Animators LLP, pg 1047
VCSvideo, pg 1052

NEW MEXICO

Production Outfitters, pg 984

NEW YORK

American Artists Representatives Inc, pg 783
Animotion Inc, pg 787
The Big House Group, pg 807
BioMedia Inc, pg 807
Buzzco Associates Inc, pg 816
Chromavision Corp, pg 826
Cohn Creative Group LLC, pg 831
CPdigital, pg 837
Curious Pictures, pg 841
Digital Art Video Inc, pg 847
dM works, pg 849
DuArt, pg 853
Eastco Multimedia Solutions Inc, pg 856
4-D Creative Media, pg 871
Giant Interactive, pg 878
IAI Video, pg 893
Lylofilm Productions, pg 926
Manhattan Center Studios Inc, pg 930
Neal Marshad Productions, pg 931
Mood Creations Ltd, pg 946
MRG Productions Inc, pg 948
MRY, pg 949
Polestar Films & Associated Arts Ltd, pg 978
PostWorks, pg 979
PrimeLight Productions Inc, pg 982
Reinhardt Productions Inc, pg 994
Synaptic Digital, pg 1030
TBA Global Events, pg 1032
Teatown Communications Group, pg 1033
Alan Weiss Productions, pg 1063

VIDEO

Animation Production Services (continued)

NORTH CAROLINA

The Communications Group Inc, pg 833
Franklin Video Inc, pg 872
Gotham City Studios, pg 880
Horizon Video Productions Inc, pg 891
L A Management Co LLC, pg 914
Moving Pictures, pg 948
On Location North Carolina, pg 963
Take One Productions Ltd, pg 1031

OHIO

Aztec Video Productions, pg 801
Bartha, pg 803
Creative Technology, pg 838
Lyon Video Inc, pg 927
Mills James Productions, pg 943
VGI Productions, pg 1053
Vista Color Imaging Inc, pg 1059

OKLAHOMA

PDC Productions, pg 970
Smart Concepts Ltd, pg 1013

OREGON

Artbeats, pg 791
InterVision Media, pg 902
Wallace Creative Inc, pg 1061

PENNSYLVANIA

AccuWeather Inc, pg 774
AiH Group Inc, pg 779
FMP Media Solutions Inc, pg 870
Fusion Brand Experiences, pg 874
Innovision Media Group, pg 899
JPL, pg 906
Main Point Productions, pg 929
Muderick Media, pg 949
Production Masters Inc (PMI), pg 984
Scala Inc, pg 1003
WPHL-TV, pg 1070

RHODE ISLAND

Sound-FX-Design, pg 1017

SOUTH CAROLINA

American Production Services LLC, pg 785
Genesis Creative, pg 877

TENNESSEE

Motion Picture Services, pg 947
Paradigm Marketing & Creative, pg 969
Running Pony Productions LLC, pg 1000
Scripps Networks, pg 1005
Stage Post, pg 1022
Russ Sturgeon Productions/RSVP, pg 1027

TEXAS

AMS Pictures, pg 786
Biway Media, pg 808
Chalk Dust Co, pg 823
Digi-matics, pg 847
Epic Software Group Inc, pg 862
First Group Communications Inc, pg 868
Horizon Film + Video Productions, pg 891
McNee Productions Inc, pg 935
Julye Newlin Productions Inc, pg 956
Phillips MediaSource, pg 974
South Coast Film & Video, pg 1019
Texas Heart Institute Visual Communication Services, pg 1037

UTAH

ImageWorks Communications, pg 896

VIRGINIA

Allied Media Corp, pg 781
BES Studios, pg 805
CACI Productions Group, pg 816
Eagle Films, pg 855
EFX Media, pg 858
Gingerbread Productions, pg 878
Henninger Media Services, pg 888
Metro Productions, pg 939

WASHINGTON

North-by-Northwest Productions, pg 958
Sparkworks Media, pg 1019
Victory Studios, pg 1054

WEST VIRGINIA

Altruist Media LLC, pg 783

WISCONSIN

Learning Technology Services, pg 917
Logan Productions Inc, pg 924
Media Communications Association-International (MCA-I), pg 936
Meridian Studios, pg 939
ProVideo, pg 986
USAV Group Inc, pg 1050
Video Wisconsin Inc, pg 1056

WYOMING

Bridger Productions Inc, pg 812

ALBERTA

Black Media Works, pg 808
Global Television, pg 879
Global Television Station, pg 879

BRITISH COLUMBIA

Credo Interactive Inc, pg 839
Triad Communications Ltd, pg 1044
24 Frames Film & Video, pg 1047

NEWFOUNDLAND AND LABRADOR

Vidcraft Productions Ltd, pg 1054

ONTARIO

ADS Media, pg 777
Purefire Communications Inc, pg 987
RB Productions, pg 992
Shaw Street Productions, pg 1008
Video Excellence Productions, pg 1055

QUEBEC

Group PVP, pg 882
National Film Board of Canada/Office National du Film du Canada, pg 952

Animation Production Services—Computerized

ALABAMA

Diamond Studios, pg 846
Motion & Graphic Image Corp Inc (MAGIC), pg 947

ARIZONA

Arizona Virtual Studios, pg 790
Fox 10 Productions (KSAZ-TV), pg 872
MediaWorks, pg 938
Merestone, pg 938

ARKANSAS

Cedar Crest Studio, pg 822
Jones Film Video, pg 906
Live'N'Loud, pg 923
Shadowbox Video Productions, pg 1007
White Diamond Productions, pg 1065

CALIFORNIA

Aaron & Le Duc, pg 772
Access Video in Berkeley, pg 773
Advanced Systems Group LLC, pg 778
AlphaDogs Inc, pg 782
Animax, pg 787
Artichoke Productions, pg 791
Audio Visual Consultants, pg 795
Blind, pg 809
Buttercup Pictures, pg 816
Classic Images, pg 829
Crystal Pyramid Productions™, pg 840
Custom Video Productions Inc, pg 841
Diaquest, pg 846
Digital Outpost, pg 847
Direct Images Interactive Inc, pg 848
Dolphin MultiMedia Inc, pg 850
DreamWorks Animation SKG Inc, pg 852
Duck Studios, pg 853
Dynamic Digital Depth Inc (DDD), pg 854
Elektrashock, pg 859
First Person™, pg 868
Havas Edge, pg 885
Hydrogen Whiskey Studios, pg 893
iCorpTv, pg 893
Imageworks, pg 896
Joyce Media Inc, pg 906
KION-TV, pg 911
KTVU-Retail Services, pg 914
Ludlow Media Solutions, pg 926
Lumeni Productions Inc, pg 926
Lynch Communications, pg 926
Maximus Media Inc, pg 934
The Media Staff Inc, pg 937
Medical Visual Creations (MVC), pg 938
Mind Over Eye Inc, pg 943
New & Unique Videos™, pg 955
Nolte Media, pg 958
On-Trax Inc, pg 963
Palardo Productions, pg 968
Panorama Productions, pg 968
Penrose Productions, pg 972
Pixar Animation Studios, pg 976
Planet Blue, pg 976
QRS Software Services, pg 988
Reality Check Systems, pg 992
Saturn Studios, pg 1003
SBS Productions, pg 1003
Starburns Industries, pg 1024
Staylor-Made Communications Inc, pg 1024
Still N'Motion, pg 1025
Tam Communications Inc, pg 1031
30 Second Films, pg 1039
Tigar Hare Studios, pg 1040
Toon Makers, pg 1042
Total Media Group, pg 1042
Towards 2000 Inc, pg 1043
Two Door Productions, pg 1047
Uniconn Productions, pg 1048
Universal Studios, pg 1049
VidCan Media Solutions, pg 1054
Videobotics, pg 1056
Videografix LLC, pg 1057
Videolady, pg 1057
Wavemaker Media Design, pg 1062
WMS Media Inc, pg 1069

COLORADO

Colorado Studios, pg 832
CSI Films, pg 840
Daylight Productions & Rentals, pg 844
Flashback Media Productions, pg 869
Full Spectrum Arts & Services, pg 874
Rocky Mountain Audio/Video Productions Inc, pg 998
Side 3 Studios, pg 1010
Z-Axis Corp, pg 1073

CONNECTICUT

BRB Audiovisual Productions, pg 812
Guymark Studios LLC, pg 883
Musivision Inc, pg 951
New London Media, pg 956
Palace Digital Studios, pg 967
Sonalysts Media, pg 1015

DELAWARE

So Smart Productions, pg 1015

DISTRICT OF COLUMBIA

Hillmann & Carr Inc, pg 889
Interface Media Group, pg 900

FLORIDA

Accel Video Productions, pg 773
Access Media Group, pg 773
Accord Productions, pg 773
Allegro Productions Inc, pg 781
Audio Visual Imagineering Inc, pg 795
Civins Productions Inc, pg 828
Communications Concepts Inc (CCI), pg 833
Comtel Inc, pg 834
Digimation, pg 847
Ed Ethridge Productions Inc, pg 863
Gulf Coast Audio Visual Producers Inc, pg 883
Hi-Tech Enterprises Inc, pg 888
Home Shopping Network (HSN), pg 890
Image Technical Services, pg 895
JungleTV, pg 906
New Art Miami, pg 955
Progressive Media & Music, pg 985
Shooting Stars Post Inc, pg 1009
Sound & Vision Communications Inc, pg 1016
Sunfire Communications Inc, pg 1028
Tricycle Studios, pg 1044
Mike Vasilinda Productions Inc, pg 1052

VIDEO

Animation Production Services—Computerized (continued)

TEXAS (continued)

Communication Arts Multimedia Inc, pg 832
Data Display Audio Visual Co LP, pg 843
Digi-matics, pg 847
The Editing Co, pg 857
Epic Software Group Inc, pg 862
First Group Communications Inc, pg 868
Horizon Film + Video Productions, pg 891
Maverick Video Productions, pg 934
McNee Productions Inc, pg 935
Julye Newlin Productions Inc, pg 956
Phillips MediaSource, pg 974
R&O Studios, pg 991
South Coast Film & Video, pg 1019
Stage Directions, pg 1022
Texas Heart Institute Visual Communication Services, pg 1037

UTAH

ImageWorks Communications, pg 896
Strata™, pg 1025

VIRGINIA

Advance Concepts Inc, pg 777
Allied Media Corp, pg 781
BES Studios, pg 805
CACI Productions Group, pg 816
Creative Video of Washington Inc, pg 839
Eagle Films, pg 855
EFX Media, pg 858
Gingerbread Productions, pg 878
Henninger Media Services, pg 888
Metro Productions, pg 939

WASHINGTON

Global Net Productions Inc, pg 879
Hamilton Studio, pg 884
Medical Media Systems, pg 938
North-by-Northwest Productions, pg 958
Victory Studios, pg 1054

WEST VIRGINIA

Altruist Media LLC, pg 783

WISCONSIN

Audio Visual of Milwaukee Inc, pg 795
Logan Productions Inc, pg 924
Media Communications Association-International (MCA-I), pg 936
Meridian Studios, pg 939
Midland Video Productions Inc, pg 942
ProVideo, pg 986
Video Wisconsin Inc, pg 1056
Watts Communications Inc, pg 1062
Win Media Inc, pg 1067

WYOMING

Bridger Productions Inc, pg 812

ALBERTA

Black Media Works, pg 808
Global Television, pg 879
Global Television Station, pg 879

BRITISH COLUMBIA

Credo Interactive Inc, pg 839
Finale Editworks, pg 868
Triad Communications Ltd, pg 1044

MANITOBA

Spectra Video Productions Ltd, pg 1020

NEWFOUNDLAND AND LABRADOR

Vidcraft Productions Ltd, pg 1054

ONTARIO

ADS Media, pg 777
GAPC (General Assembly Production Centre), pg 875
Gesturetek, pg 877
JFB Communications, pg 905
Optix Digital Pictures & Sound, pg 965
RB Productions, pg 992
Shaw Street Productions, pg 1008
Video Excellence Productions, pg 1055

QUEBEC

Group PVP, pg 882
Sceno Plus, pg 1004

Animation System Distributors

ARIZONA

Troxell Communications Inc, pg 1045

CALIFORNIA

Advanced Systems Group LLC, pg 778
Ametron Audio/Video, pg 785
Audio Images Corp, pg 794
Audio/Video Supply Inc, pg 795
California Tape Products Inc, pg 817
Computer Modules Inc, pg 834
Diaquest, pg 846
Jaguar Distribution Corp, pg 903
MediaPOINTE, pg 938
PMP Marketing Inc, pg 977
Tri-Ed, pg 1044
Videobotics, pg 1056
VMI Inc, pg 1060

COLORADO

Dot Hill Systems Corp, pg 851

FLORIDA

Access Media Group, pg 773
Digital Video Systems Inc, pg 848
Hi-Tech Enterprises Inc, pg 888
Pro Stage Inc, pg 983

GEORGIA

Outsource Engineering & Manufacturing Inc dba Texscan MSI, pg 966
Stage Front Presentation Systems, pg 1022

ILLINOIS

Lyn Norstad & Associates Inc, pg 926

IOWA

ECS Inc, pg 856

MAINE

Headlight Audio Visual Inc, pg 887

MARYLAND

Kipp Visual Systems Inc, pg 911

MASSACHUSETTS

Camera Co Inc/Broadcast Divison, pg 818
Psych Soft Inc, pg 987

MICHIGAN

ASC Systems, pg 791
Ascom Communications Contractors, pg 791
Digi Sign Design LLC, pg 847
On Stage Visuals, pg 963

MINNESOTA

Alpha Video & Audio Inc, pg 782

MISSOURI

Communitronics Corp, pg 833
Modern Communications Inc, pg 944
Southwest Audio-Visual Inc, pg 1019

NEVADA

Aardvark Video & Media Productions, pg 772

NEW JERSEY

Color Leasing Studios, pg 831
PatchAmp, pg 970
PLS Staging, pg 977
Total Video Products Inc, pg 1042

NEW YORK

Audio-Video Corp, pg 795
Creative Stage Lighting Co Inc, pg 838
Indigo Productions, pg 897
Technisphere Corp, pg 1034

PENNSYLVANIA

AccuWeather Inc, pg 774
Advanced AV, pg 777
The Lerro Corp, pg 919
Morefield Communications Inc, pg 946
Visual Sound Inc, pg 1059

TEXAS

Biway Media, pg 808
Epic Software Group Inc, pg 862
Pro Video & Film Equipment Co Inc, pg 983

UTAH

RIA Corp, pg 996

VIRGINIA

Lee Hartman & Sons Inc, pg 918
The Whitlock Group, pg 1065

WISCONSIN

Camera Corner Connecting Point, pg 818
Full Compass Systems, pg 874
Safe Harbor Computers, pg 1001

ALBERTA

Matrix Video Communications Corp (MVCC), pg 934

QUEBEC

Panavideo Inc, pg 968

SASKATCHEWAN

Display Systems International, pg 849

Animation System Manufacturers

CALIFORNIA

Advanced Systems Group LLC, pg 778
Diaquest, pg 846
Grande Vitesse Systems Inc (GVS), pg 881
Linker Systems Inc, pg 922
Rough House, pg 1000
Simon - Kaloi Engineering, pg 1011

ILLINOIS

EPIX Inc, pg 862

KANSAS

GlobalStreams™ Corp, pg 879

MASSACHUSETTS

Psych Soft Inc, pg 987

MICHIGAN

ASC Systems, pg 791

NEW JERSEY

CELCO-Constantine Engineering Labs Co, pg 822
PeopleVisionFX, pg 972

NEW YORK

Quantel Inc, pg 989

PENNSYLVANIA

AccuWeather Inc, pg 774

TEXAS

Biway Media, pg 808

VERMONT

Polhemus, pg 978

WISCONSIN

Safe Harbor Computers, pg 1001

BRITISH COLUMBIA

Triad Communications Ltd, pg 1044

SASKATCHEWAN

Display Systems International, pg 849

Animation System Rentals

ARIZONA

Merestone, pg 938

CALIFORNIA

Artichoke Productions, pg 791

CONNECTICUT

Videofilm Systems Inc, pg 1057

FLORIDA

Access Media Group, pg 773
Accord Productions, pg 773

GEORGIA

Stage Front Presentation Systems, pg 1022

ILLINOIS

Chicago Satellite & Video, pg 825

MARYLAND

Kramer Communications Video Production, pg 913

MASSACHUSETTS

Preston Productions Inc, pg 981

MICHIGAN

Digi Sign Design LLC, pg 847
K&R All Media Productions Inc, pg 908
On Stage Visuals, pg 963

NEW YORK

Creative Stage Lighting Co Inc, pg 838
HB-Content, pg 886

NORTH CAROLINA

Take One Productions Ltd, pg 1031

OKLAHOMA

PDC Productions, pg 970

PENNSYLVANIA

JPL, pg 906
The Videohouse Inc, pg 1057

VIRGINIA

Quince Imaging Inc, pg 989

Animation System Repairs

CALIFORNIA

Ametron Audio/Video, pg 785

FLORIDA

Hi-Tech Enterprises Inc, pg 888

GEORGIA

Stage Front Presentation Systems, pg 1022

IOWA

ECS Inc, pg 856

MICHIGAN

TeL Systems, pg 1035

MINNESOTA

Alpha Video & Audio Inc, pg 782

TEXAS

Biway Media, pg 808

UTAH

RIA Corp, pg 996

WISCONSIN

Full Compass Systems, pg 874

Artwork & Titling Services

ALABAMA

Media Visions Inc, pg 937

ALASKA

Alaska Film Services Inc, pg 779

ARIZONA

Fox 10 Productions (KSAZ-TV), pg 872
MediaWorks, pg 938
Merestone, pg 938

ARKANSAS

Jones Film Video, pg 906
Live'N'Loud, pg 923
Shadowbox Video Productions, pg 1007
White Diamond Productions, pg 1065

CALIFORNIA

Aaron & Le Duc, pg 772
Aberdeen Broadcast Services, pg 772
Access Video in Berkeley, pg 773
All Video Productions, pg 781
AlphaDogs Inc, pg 782
Animax, pg 787
Artichoke Productions, pg 791
Barbosa Video Services, pg 802
Crystal Pyramid Productions™, pg 840
Custom Video Productions Inc, pg 841
Digital Jungle, pg 847
Digital Outpost, pg 847
Direct Images Interactive Inc, pg 848
Dogma Studios, pg 850
Duck Studios, pg 853
Face Digital Post, pg 865
First Person™, pg 868
Global Village Productions, pg 879
Goal Productions, pg 879
Gold Standard Productions, pg 880
Havas Edge, pg 885
Hydrogen Whiskey Studios, pg 893
iCorpTv, pg 893
ITV Productions, pg 903
JDS Video & Media Productions Inc, pg 904
KION-TV, pg 911
KPBS TV FM-San Diego, pg 913
KTVU-Retail Services, pg 914
Laser Magic Productions, pg 916
Ludlow Media Solutions, pg 926
Lumeni Productions Inc, pg 926
Maximus Media Inc, pg 934
Media Magic, pg 937
The Media Staff Inc, pg 937
Medical Visual Creations (MVC), pg 938
Mind Over Eye Inc, pg 943
Mist Media Inc, pg 944
Moving Art by Louie Schwartzberg, pg 947
New & Unique Videos™, pg 955
Nolte Media, pg 958
Palardo Productions, pg 968
Panorama Productions, pg 968
Penrose Productions, pg 972
Planet Blue, pg 976
PM Productions, pg 977
Point 360, pg 978
PSI Inc, pg 987
QRS Software Services, pg 988
Reality Check Systems, pg 992
Saturn Studios, pg 1003
SBS Productions, pg 1003
Shapeshifter, pg 1008
Shokus Video, pg 1009
SonicPool, pg 1016
Staylor-Made Communications Inc, pg 1024
StereoScope International, pg 1024
Still N'Motion, pg 1025
Tam Communications Inc, pg 1031
Timecode Multimedia, pg 1040
Toon Makers, pg 1042
Total Media Group, pg 1042
Universal Studios, pg 1049
Via Verde Productions, pg 1053
Videografix LLC, pg 1057
Videolady, pg 1057
Visions Plus, pg 1058
WalkerVision Interarts, pg 1061
Wavemaker Media Design, pg 1062
West Coast Projections Inc, pg 1063

COLORADO

CSI Films, pg 840
Daylight Productions & Rentals, pg 844
Flashback Media Productions, pg 869
Full Spectrum Arts & Services, pg 874
Rocky Mountain Audio/Video Productions Inc, pg 998

CONNECTICUT

Applebox Studio, pg 788
BRB Audiovisual Productions, pg 812
Broadcast Video Productions LLC, pg 813
Cine-Med Inc, pg 826
Fox Connecticut, pg 872
Guymark Studios LLC, pg 883
Ironik Design & Post, pg 902
Musivision Inc, pg 951
New London Media, pg 956
Palace Digital Studios, pg 967
Powerstation Events, pg 979
Video Production Associates Inc, pg 1056

DISTRICT OF COLUMBIA

Interface Media Group, pg 900

FLORIDA

Access Media Group, pg 773
Allegro Productions Inc, pg 781
Civins Productions Inc, pg 828
Communications Concepts Inc (CCI), pg 833
Comtel Inc, pg 834
Courter Films LLC, pg 837
Ed Ethridge Productions Inc, pg 863
Gulf Coast Audio Visual Producers Inc, pg 883
Hi-Tech Enterprises Inc, pg 888
Home Shopping Network (HSN), pg 890
Jordan Klein Film & Video (JKFV), pg 906
Photosound of Orlando Inc, pg 975
Shooting Stars Post Inc, pg 1009
Sound & Vision Communications Inc, pg 1016
Sunfire Communications Inc, pg 1028
Sunrise Studios, pg 1028
Tricycle Studios, pg 1044
Universal Studios Florida® Production Group, pg 1049
Mike Vasilinda Productions Inc, pg 1052
Video Techniques Inc, pg 1056
Vistamax Productions, pg 1059

GEORGIA

Beachwood Productions, pg 804
Beast Atlanta, pg 804
Continental Film & Video, pg 835
Crawford Media Services, pg 838
The DVI Group, pg 854
ECG Productions, pg 856
Guerrilla Productions LLC, pg 883
Imagers, pg 896
Staging Directions Inc, pg 1023

HAWAII

Hyperspective Studios Inc, pg 893
KHNL/KGMB, pg 910
Media Bridge Gamekids, pg 936
1013 Integrated, pg 1037

ILLINOIS

ABSA Productions Inc, pg 772
Airways Digital Media, pg 779
Analog Free Media, pg 786
Audio Producers Group, pg 794
Beatty TeleVisual Productions, pg 804
Breeze Productions Inc, pg 812
CCore Media Inc, pg 821
Centrax Corp, pg 823
Chicago Satellite & Video, pg 825
IV Media Resources, pg 903
Manning Productions, pg 930
MIGHTYbYTES Inc, pg 942
Optimus, pg 964
Jim Passin Productions, pg 970
The Pepper Group, pg 972
Richter Studios, pg 996
SCI Television Productions LLC, pg 1004
Sound/Video Impressions Inc, pg 1018
Southern Illinois University, pg 1019
Sparkfactor, pg 1019
Tele-Time Systems, pg 1036
20/20 Communications Inc, pg 1047
Video Impressions, pg 1055
WEEK TV, pg 1063

INDIANA

AVA Productions, pg 798
Bright Ideas Creative Services, pg 812

IOWA

The Production House, pg 984

KANSAS

KAKE-TV, pg 907

KENTUCKY

WKYT Productions, pg 1068

VIDEO

Artwork & Titling Services (continued)

Audio Editing, *see* Dubbing

Blank DVD, *see* DVD—Blank

Blank Videocassette, *see* Videocassette—Blank

Blank Videodisc, *see* Videodisc—Blank

Blank Videotape, *see* Videotape—Blank

Cable Distributors

ARIZONA

EAR Professional Audio/Video, pg 855

CALIFORNIA

Adolph Gasser Inc, pg 776
Ametron Audio/Video, pg 785
ARS Electronics, pg 791
Associated Sound, pg 792
Audio Images Corp, pg 794
AV Conferencing, pg 797
California Tape Products Inc, pg 817
Christy's Editorial, pg 826
Cibola Systems, pg 826
Delicate Electronics Sales Inc, pg 845
Diaquest, pg 846
FXC Communications, pg 874
Hosa Technology Inc, pg 891
Jameco Electronics, pg 903
JD Audio Visual Inc, pg 904
Kappa optronics Inc, pg 908
Marshall Electronics Inc, pg 932
Orvac Electronics, pg 965
Photodyne Technologies, pg 974
POP TV, pg 978
Sound Service Co, pg 1017
Southern California Sound Image Inc, pg 1019
Stanislaus Audio Video Inc, pg 1023
Video Gear Rentals Inc, pg 1055
VMI Inc, pg 1060
Zack Electronics Inc, pg 1073

COLORADO

Daylight Productions & Rentals, pg 844

FLORIDA

Access Media Group, pg 773
A2D Solutions Inc, pg 793
Digital Video Systems Inc, pg 848
Harris Corp, pg 885
Herman Pro AV, pg 888
Hi-Tech Enterprises Inc, pg 888
Hunter Electronics LLC, pg 892
Media Concepts Inc, pg 936
Midtown Video Inc, pg 942
Multicom Inc, pg 949
Photomart Cine-Video Inc, pg 975
Sight & Sound Productions, pg 1010
TAI Audio, pg 1031

GEORGIA

Accu-Tech, pg 773
Omnimedia Inc, pg 962
Stage Front Presentation Systems, pg 1022

HAWAII

The Audio Visual Co (AVCO), pg 795

ILLINOIS

Arcor Electronics Co, pg 789
Clark Wire & Cable, pg 829
Cole Wire & Cable Co Inc, pg 831
Gepco®, a General Cable brand, pg 877
Joseph Electronics, pg 906
LKG Industries Inc, pg 923
Quintessence Audio Ltd, pg 989
Sound Vision Inc, pg 1018
Waldom Electronics Corp, pg 1061

INDIANA

Sensory Technologies LLC, pg 1006
SHP Electronics, pg 1010

KENTUCKY

Axxis Inc, pg 800
NOR-COM Inc, pg 958

LOUISIANA

Intermedia Technologies, pg 900

MAINE

Headlight Audio Visual Inc, pg 887

MARYLAND

Noventri, pg 960

MASSACHUSETTS

Antronics Inc, pg 787
Camera Co Inc/Broadcast Divison, pg 818
Rule Broadcast Systems, pg 1000
SLR Enterprises LLC, pg 1013

MICHIGAN

Ascom Communications Contractors, pg 791
DAWNco, pg 843
On Stage Visuals, pg 963

MINNESOTA

Alpha Video & Audio Inc, pg 782

MISSOURI

MIS Technologies, pg 944
Modern Communications Inc, pg 944
The RapcoHorizon Co, pg 991
Southwest Audio-Visual Inc, pg 1019

NEBRASKA

Dog & Pony Productions Inc, pg 850

NEW JERSEY

Alltec Stores, a Vcom IMC Company, pg 782
Argraph Corp, pg 789
AV Bluebook, pg 797
Avtech Systems Inc, pg 800
Diversified Systems Inc, pg 849
Earl Girls Inc, pg 855
MCCOM Inc, pg 935
MIB Mediaworks, pg 941
National Audio-Visual Supply, pg 952
Starlite Productions, pg 1024
Tele-Measurements Inc, pg 1035
Total Video Products Inc, pg 1042
Wired 4 Sound Inc, pg 1068

NEW YORK

ALTEL Systems Inc, pg 783
Audio-Video Corp, pg 795
BMI Supply, pg 810
BTX Technologies, pg 814
Custom Media Environments, pg 841
Design Audio Visual Inc, pg 845
Gaylord Brothers, pg 876
Gotham Sound & Communications Inc, pg 881
HAVE Inc, pg 886
KVL Audio Visual Services Inc, pg 914
Markertek Video Supply, pg 931
Neptune Photo Inc, pg 954
RNJ Electronics, pg 997
Russell Industries Inc, pg 1001
TecNec Distributing, pg 1035
Whirlwind Music Distributors Inc, pg 1065

OHIO

ITA Audio Visual Solutions, pg 902
Parts Express, pg 969
Jimmy Rea Electronics Inc, pg 992
Tri-State Audio Visual Co, pg 1044

OREGON

TARA Labs, pg 1032

PENNSYLVANIA

Advanced AV, pg 777
The Lerro Corp, pg 919
West Penn Wire, pg 1064

TENNESSEE

Lowrance Sound Co Inc, pg 925
Technical Support Systems LLC, pg 1034

TEXAS

Data Projections Inc, pg 843
Digital Display Solutions Inc, pg 847
Precision Camera & Video, pg 980
Pro Video & Film Equipment Co Inc, pg 983
RadioShack Corp, pg 990

UTAH

Performance Audio, pg 973

VERMONT

Power & Telephone Supply Co, pg 979

VIRGINIA

Avitecture Inc, pg 799
Communications Specialists Inc, pg 833
Lee Hartman & Sons Inc, pg 918

WASHINGTON

CCI Solutions, pg 821
Telect Inc, pg 1036

WISCONSIN

Full Compass Systems, pg 874
Safe Harbor Computers, pg 1001

ALBERTA

Matrix Video Communications Corp (MVCC), pg 934

BRITISH COLUMBIA

Commercial Electronics Ltd, pg 832
Noramco Wire & Cable, pg 958
ProVision Video Sales & Rentals Inc, pg 986

ONTARIO

Cinema Stage Inc, pg 827
Premier A/V Sales Ltd, pg 980
Westbury National Show Systems Ltd, pg 1064

Cable Manufacturers

ARIZONA

Covid Inc, pg 837

CALIFORNIA

Addlogix, pg 776
AITech International, pg 779
ALTINEX Inc, pg 783
Calrad Electronics, pg 817
Enright Co, pg 861
Extron Electronics, pg 864
Fiber Optic Cable Shop, pg 866
Get Organized, pg 877
Hosa Technology Inc, pg 891
Marshall Electronics Inc, pg 932
Monster Cable Products Inc, pg 945
Taperwire, pg 1032

FLORIDA

Multicom Inc, pg 949
Nemal Electronics International Inc, pg 954

GEORGIA

Outsource Engineering & Manufacturing Inc dba Texscan MSI, pg 966

ILLINOIS

Arcor Electronics Co, pg 789
Clark Wire & Cable, pg 829
Gepco®, a General Cable brand, pg 877
Joseph Electronics, pg 906
Tripp Lite, pg 1045

INDIANA

Belden, pg 804

MARYLAND

RCI Custom Products, pg 992

MASSACHUSETTS

Miranda Telecast Fiber Systems Inc, pg 944
Mohawk, pg 945

MINNESOTA

Intercon 1, pg 900
Trompeter Electronics Inc, pg 1045
Vaddio, pg 1051

VIDEO

Cable Manufacturers (continued)

MISSOURI

The RapcoHorizon Co, pg 991

NEW JERSEY

Alltec Stores, a Vcom IMC Company, pg 782
Alpha Wire Co, pg 782
AV Bluebook, pg 797
Brim Electronics, pg 812
Comprehensive Cable & Connectivity Co, pg 833
Crestron Electronics Inc, pg 839
Daburn Electronics & Cable Corp, pg 842
FSR Inc, pg 873
JSC Wire & Cable, pg 906
Kramer Electronics USA Inc, pg 913
National Audio-Visual Supply, pg 952

NEW YORK

Hannay Reels Inc, pg 884
HAVE Inc, pg 886
Laird Digital Cinema, pg 915
Markertek Video Supply, pg 931
MultiDyne Video & Fiber Optics Systems, pg 950

NORTH CAROLINA

CommScope Inc, pg 832

OHIO

Network Technologies Inc, pg 955

OREGON

TARA Labs, pg 1032

PENNSYLVANIA

MicroImage Video Systems, pg 941
West Penn Wire, pg 1064
World Video Sales Co Inc, pg 1070

WASHINGTON

Telect Inc, pg 1036

WISCONSIN

Intelix LLC, pg 899

BRITISH COLUMBIA

Triad Communications Ltd, pg 1044

ONTARIO

Westbury National Show Systems Ltd, pg 1064

Cable Repairs

FLORIDA

ELC Sales & Service Inc, pg 858
Hi-Tech Enterprises Inc, pg 888

GEORGIA

Stage Front Presentation Systems, pg 1022

ILLINOIS

Joseph Electronics, pg 906

KENTUCKY

NOR-COM Inc, pg 958

MICHIGAN

TeL Systems, pg 1035

NEW JERSEY

Starlite Productions, pg 1024

OHIO

Tri-State Audio Visual Co, pg 1044

OREGON

All Service Musical Electronics Repair, pg 780

TENNESSEE

Technical Support Systems LLC, pg 1034

Camcorder Distributors

ALABAMA

Curtis Company, pg 841

ARIZONA

EAR Professional Audio/Video, pg 855
Troxell Communications Inc, pg 1045

ARKANSAS

White Diamond Productions, pg 1065

CALIFORNIA

Adolph Gasser Inc, pg 776
Advanced Systems Group LLC, pg 778
Ametron Audio/Video, pg 785
Audio/Video Supply Inc, pg 795
Band Pro Film & Digital Inc, pg 802
Barber Tech Video Products, pg 802
Be Media, pg 804
BroadcastStore.com, pg 813
Christy's Editorial, pg 826
Computer Modules Inc, pg 834
Delicate Electronics Sales Inc, pg 845
Diaquest, pg 846
Diversified Imaging Supply, pg 849
Gearhouse Broadcast LLC, pg 876
Gluskin's Custom Audio Video, pg 879
Alan Gordon Enterprises Inc, pg 880
Hooper Camera & Imaging, pg 891
JD Audio Visual Inc, pg 904
MediaPOINTE, pg 938
Mobilized Tech Systems, pg 944
Photodyne Technologies, pg 974
Point of View Productions, pg 977
POP TV, pg 978
Promax Systems, pg 986
Related Visual Inc, pg 994
SANYO Fisher Co, pg 1002
SNAP, pg 1014
Southern California Sound Image Inc, pg 1019
SSL Industries Inc, pg 1022
Tri-Ed, pg 1044
VMI Inc, pg 1060
VTP Inc, pg 1061

COLORADO

Daylight Productions & Rentals, pg 844
Spectrum Audio Visual Services, pg 1020
Stanco Sales LLC, pg 1023

CONNECTICUT

Everett Hall Associates Inc, pg 863

FLORIDA

Access Media Group, pg 773
A2D Solutions Inc, pg 793
AVI-SPL, pg 798
Digital Video Systems Inc, pg 848
Encore Broadcast Solutions, pg 860
Enhanced View Services Inc, pg 861
Gulf Coast Audio Visual Producers Inc, pg 883
Harmon's Audio-Visual Services, pg 885
Harris Corp, pg 885
Hi-Tech Enterprises Inc, pg 888
Hi-Tech Import Export Corp, pg 888
Hunter Electronics LLC, pg 892
Media Concepts Inc, pg 936
Midtown Video Inc, pg 942
Pro Stage Inc, pg 983
Recording Media & Equipment Inc (RM&E), pg 993
Reef Photo & Video, pg 993
Sight & Sound Productions, pg 1010
Skyline Broadcast, pg 1013
Videoscope, pg 1057

GEORGIA

Baker Audio Inc, pg 801
Stage Front Presentation Systems, pg 1022

HAWAII

The Audio Visual Co (AVCO), pg 795

ILLINOIS

Allen Visual Systems Inc, pg 781
RAM Systems LLC, pg 991
RC Communications, pg 992

INDIANA

Jack's Camera Shop, pg 903
Lee Co Inc, pg 918
Sensory Technologies LLC, pg 1006
SHP Electronics, pg 1010

KANSAS

Smith Audio-Visual Inc, pg 1014

KENTUCKY

Audio Visual Techniques Inc, pg 796
Axxis Inc, pg 800
Barney Miller's Inc, pg 943
NOR-COM Inc, pg 958
Northern Kentucky University, pg 959

MAINE

Headlight Audio Visual Inc, pg 887

MARYLAND

Noventri, pg 960
Ritz Camera & Image, pg 997

MASSACHUSETTS

Camera Co Inc/Broadcast Divison, pg 818
Hunt's Photo, Video & Digital, pg 892
Rule Broadcast Systems, pg 1000

MICHIGAN

Ascom Communications Contractors, pg 791
TeL Systems, pg 1035

MINNESOTA

Alpha Video & Audio Inc, pg 782
Vaddio, pg 1051

MISSISSIPPI

Bowie Audio Visual Enterprises Inc, pg 811

MISSOURI

Communitronics Corp, pg 833
Conference Technologies Inc, pg 835
MIS Technologies, pg 944
Modern Communications Inc, pg 944
Schiller's Audio-Visual, pg 1004
Southwest Audio-Visual Inc, pg 1019

NEBRASKA

Dog & Pony Productions Inc, pg 850
Video Service of America Inc (VSA), pg 1056

NEVADA

Aardvark Video & Media Productions, pg 772

NEW JERSEY

A-V Services Inc, pg 771
Alltec Stores, a Vcom IMC Company, pg 782
AV Bluebook, pg 797
Diversified Systems Inc, pg 849
Earl Girls Inc, pg 855
Euro-Pacific Film & Video Productions Inc, pg 863
G&G Technologies Inc, pg 875
Hamilton Buhl, pg 884
MCCOM Inc, pg 935
MIB Mediaworks, pg 941
National Audio-Visual Supply, pg 952
PatchAmp, pg 970
Starlite Productions, pg 1024
SYMCO Inc, pg 1030
Tele-Measurements Inc, pg 1035
Total Video Products Inc, pg 1042
Video Corporation of America (VCA), pg 1055
Wilray Audio Visual Corp, pg 1067

NEW YORK

ALTEL Systems Inc, pg 783
Audio-Video Corp, pg 795
AV Workshop, pg 797
Canon USA Inc, pg 819
Colortone Audio Visual, pg 832
Communication Corner Inc, pg 832
Custom Media Environments, pg 841
Design Audio Visual Inc, pg 845
Indigo Productions, pg 897
KVL Audio Visual Services Inc, pg 914

Camcorder Manufacturers

Camcorder Rentals

VIDEO

Camcorder Rentals (continued)

QUEBEC

Audio Visual Dynamics Ltd, pg 795
Group PVP, pg 882
Kerrigan Productions Inc, pg 910
Panavideo Inc, pg 968

Camcorder Repairs

CALIFORNIA

Adolph Gasser Inc, pg 776
Advanced Media LLC, pg 778
Ametron Audio/Video, pg 785
Band Pro Film & Digital Inc, pg 802
BroadcastStore.com, pg 813
Digitron Electronics, pg 848
Gluskin's Custom Audio Video, pg 879
McAlister Electronics, pg 935
Nikon Inc, pg 957
Pro Camera Repair, pg 982
SSL Industries Inc, pg 1022
Technical Services, pg 1034
TEK Media Group, pg 1035
Tri-Ed, pg 1044
TV Pro Gear, pg 1046
VMI Inc, pg 1060

CONNECTICUT

A/V Davey, pg 797
Precision Camera & Video Repair Inc, pg 980

FLORIDA

Access Media Group, pg 773
Digital Video Systems Inc, pg 848
ELC Sales & Service Inc, pg 858
Hi-Tech Enterprises Inc, pg 888
Media Concepts Inc, pg 936
Midtown Video Inc, pg 942

GEORGIA

Stage Front Presentation Systems, pg 1022

ILLINOIS

Allen Visual Systems Inc, pg 781
Beatty TeleVisual Productions, pg 804
Midwest Digital Corp, pg 942

IOWA

ECS Inc, pg 856

KENTUCKY

Axxis Inc, pg 800
Barney Miller's Inc, pg 943
NOR-COM Inc, pg 958

MAINE

Headlight Audio Visual Inc, pg 887

MARYLAND

Strauss Photo Technical Service Inc, pg 1026

MICHIGAN

TeL Systems, pg 1035

MINNESOTA

Alpha Video & Audio Inc, pg 782

MISSISSIPPI

Bowie Audio Visual Enterprises Inc, pg 811

MISSOURI

Schiller's Audio-Visual, pg 1004
Southwest Audio-Visual Inc, pg 1019

NEW JERSEY

G&G Technologies Inc, pg 875
Starlite Productions, pg 1024

NEW YORK

Ray Supply Inc, pg 992
Technisphere Corp, pg 1034
Visual Technologies Corp, pg 1060

OHIO

Copp Integrated Systems, pg 836
ITA Audio Visual Solutions, pg 902
Tri-State Audio Visual Co, pg 1044
Tri-State Visual Products, pg 1044

PENNSYLVANIA

Audio Visions Inc, pg 795
Bernie's Photo Center, pg 805
J E Foss Co, pg 871
Ott Film Rentals, pg 966
Visual Sound Inc, pg 1059

TENNESSEE

Technical Support Systems LLC, pg 1034

TEXAS

Data Display Audio Visual Co LP, pg 843
Industrial Audio/Video Inc, pg 897
Quality Audio Visual Service Inc, pg 988
Tarpley Media Systems, pg 1032

UTAH

RIA Corp, pg 996
TV Specialists Inc, pg 1046

VIRGINIA

Boitnott Visual Communications Corp (BVC), pg 810
Hoppmann Audio Visual, pg 891
Lee Hartman & Sons Inc, pg 918
The Whitlock Group, pg 1065

WISCONSIN

Camera Corner Connecting Point, pg 818
Full Compass Systems, pg 874

ALBERTA

Infosat Communications Inc, pg 898
Matrix Video Communications Corp (MVCC), pg 934
Sharp's Audio-Visual Ltd, pg 1008

BRITISH COLUMBIA

Commercial Electronics Ltd, pg 832

ONTARIO

HD Source, pg 886

QUEBEC

Panavideo Inc, pg 968

Camera, *see* Video Camera

Camera Tripod Distributors

ALABAMA

Curtis Company, pg 841

ARIZONA

EAR Professional Audio/Video, pg 855
Troxell Communications Inc, pg 1045

ARKANSAS

White Diamond Productions, pg 1065

CALIFORNIA

Abel Cine Tech Los Angeles, pg 772
Adolph Gasser Inc, pg 776
Advanced Systems Group LLC, pg 778
Ametron Audio/Video, pg 785
Audio/Video Supply Inc, pg 795
Band Pro Film & Digital Inc, pg 802
Barber Tech Video Products, pg 802
BroadcastStore.com, pg 813
Christy's Editorial, pg 826
Cibola Systems, pg 826
Delicate Electronics Sales Inc, pg 845
Diaquest, pg 846
Diversified Imaging Supply, pg 849
Gearhouse Broadcast LLC, pg 876
Gluskin's Custom Audio Video, pg 879
Alan Gordon Enterprises Inc, pg 880
Hooper Camera & Imaging, pg 891
JD Audio Visual Inc, pg 904
Manios Digital & Film, pg 930
Media Fabricators Inc, pg 936
MediaPOINTE, pg 938
Mobilized Tech Systems, pg 944
Photodyne Technologies, pg 974
Related Visual Inc, pg 994
Slow Motion Film & Digital Inc, pg 1013
SNAP, pg 1014
Southern California Sound Image Inc, pg 1019
SSL Industries Inc, pg 1022
Tri-Ed, pg 1044
Video Gear Rentals Inc, pg 1055
VMI Inc, pg 1060
VTP Inc, pg 1061

COLORADO

Daylight Productions & Rentals, pg 844
Spectrum Audio Visual Services, pg 1020
Stanco Sales LLC, pg 1023

CONNECTICUT

Connecticut Audio & Theatrical Supply, pg 835
Everett Hall Associates Inc, pg 863

FLORIDA

Access Media Group, pg 773
Allstar Audio Systems Inc, pg 782
A2D Solutions Inc, pg 793
AVI-SPL, pg 798
Digital Video Systems Inc, pg 848
Enhanced View Services Inc, pg 861
EZ FX Inc, pg 865
Gulf Coast Audio Visual Producers Inc, pg 883
Harris Corp, pg 885
Hi-Tech Enterprises Inc, pg 888
Hi-Tech Import Export Corp, pg 888
Hunter Electronics LLC, pg 892
Media Concepts Inc, pg 936
Midtown Video Inc, pg 942
Photomart Cine-Video Inc, pg 975
Pro Stage Inc, pg 983
Sight & Sound Productions, pg 1010
Videoscope, pg 1057

GEORGIA

Baker Audio Inc, pg 801
Stage Front Presentation Systems, pg 1022

HAWAII

The Audio Visual Co (AVCO), pg 795

ILLINOIS

Allen Visual Systems Inc, pg 781
QuickSet International Inc, pg 989
RC Communications, pg 992
Smith-Victor Corp, pg 1014
H Wilson Co, pg 1067

INDIANA

Lee Co Inc, pg 918
Sensory Technologies LLC, pg 1006
SHP Electronics, pg 1010

IOWA

ECS Inc, pg 856

KANSAS

Smith Audio-Visual Inc, pg 1014

KENTUCKY

Audio Visual Techniques Inc, pg 796
Axxis Inc, pg 800
Barney Miller's Inc, pg 943
NOR-COM Inc, pg 958
Northern Kentucky University, pg 959

MAINE

Headlight Audio Visual Inc, pg 887

MARYLAND

Noventri, pg 960
Ritz Camera & Image, pg 997

MASSACHUSETTS

Camera Co Inc/Broadcast Divison, pg 818
Hunt's Photo, Video & Digital, pg 892
Rule Broadcast Systems, pg 1000

MICHIGAN

Ascom Communications Contractors, pg 791
Digi Sign Design LLC, pg 847
Lowing Light & Grip Inc, pg 925
On Stage Visuals, pg 963
TeL Systems, pg 1035

VIDEO

Camera Tripod Distributors (continued)

MINNESOTA

Alpha Video & Audio Inc, pg 782
Vaddio, pg 1051

MISSISSIPPI

Bowie Audio Visual Enterprises Inc, pg 811

MISSOURI

Communitronics Corp, pg 833
Conference Technologies Inc, pg 835
MIS Technologies, pg 944
Modern Communications Inc, pg 944
Schiller's Audio-Visual, pg 1004
Southwest Audio-Visual Inc, pg 1019

NEBRASKA

Dog & Pony Productions Inc, pg 850
Video Service of America Inc (VSA), pg 1056

NEVADA

Aardvark Video & Media Productions, pg 772

NEW JERSEY

A-V Services Inc, pg 771
Alltec Stores, a Vcom IMC Company, pg 782
Argraph Corp, pg 789
AV Bluebook, pg 797
Comprehensive Cable & Connectivity Co, pg 833
Diversified Systems Inc, pg 849
Earl Girls Inc, pg 855
Euro-Pacific Film & Video Productions Inc, pg 863
G&G Technologies Inc, pg 875
Hakuba Sunpak Velbon, pg 883
Hamilton Buhl, pg 884
HP Marketing Corp, pg 892
Manfrotto Distribution Inc, pg 930
MCCOM Inc, pg 935
MIB Mediaworks, pg 941
Miller Camera Support LLC, pg 943
National Audio-Visual Supply, pg 952
PatchAmp, pg 970
Starlite Productions, pg 1024
SYMCO Inc, pg 1030
Tele-Measurements Inc, pg 1035
Total Video Products Inc, pg 1042
Video Corporation of America (VCA), pg 1055
Wilray Audio Visual Corp, pg 1067

NEW YORK

ALTEL Systems Inc, pg 783
Audio-Video Corp, pg 795
AV Workshop, pg 797
Benro, pg 805
Colortone Audio Visual, pg 832
Communication Corner Inc, pg 832
Custom Media Environments, pg 841
Design Audio Visual Inc, pg 845
Edmund Scientific, pg 857
HAVE Inc, pg 886
Indigo Productions, pg 897
Induro, pg 897
KVL Audio Visual Services Inc, pg 914
Long Island Video Enterprises Live Inc, pg 924
Markertek Video Supply, pg 931
Neptune Photo Inc, pg 954
RNJ Electronics, pg 997
Technisphere Corp, pg 1034
TecNec Distributing, pg 1035
Visual Technologies Corp, pg 1060
Visual Word Systems Inc, pg 1060
Vitec Videocom Inc, pg 1060

NORTH CAROLINA

Innocinema, pg 898

OHIO

Copp Integrated Systems, pg 836
ITA Audio Visual Solutions, pg 902
Midwest Photo Exchange, pg 942
Parts Express, pg 969
Jimmy Rea Electronics Inc, pg 992
Smithall Electronics Inc, pg 1014
Tri-State Audio Visual Co, pg 1044
Tri-State Visual Products, pg 1044
Visual Products Inc, pg 1059

PENNSYLVANIA

Advanced AV, pg 777
Audio Visions Inc, pg 795
Bernie's Photo Center, pg 805
Brodart Co, pg 813
Clair Brothers Audio Systems Inc, pg 829
J E Foss Co, pg 871
Garcia Marketing Inc, pg 875
Grise Audio Visual Center Inc, pg 882
The Lerro Corp, pg 919
Morefield Communications Inc, pg 946
New York Camera & Video, pg 956
Visual Sound Inc, pg 1059

TENNESSEE

Lowrance Sound Co Inc, pg 925
Technical Support Systems LLC, pg 1034
Zion Music Group, pg 1074

TEXAS

Astro Audio Visual, pg 792
Audio Visual Technologies Group, pg 796
AVES Audio Visual Systems Inc, pg 798
Biway Media, pg 808
CAM Audio Inc, pg 817
Data Display Audio Visual Co LP, pg 843
Data Projections Inc, pg 843
Heffernan Audio Visual, pg 887
Industrial Audio/Video Inc, pg 897
Omega Broadcast Group, pg 962
Precision Camera & Video, pg 980
Pro Video & Film Equipment Co Inc, pg 983
Quality Audio Visual Service Inc, pg 988
RadioShack Corp, pg 990
Schoolhouse Audio Visual, pg 1004
Stage Directions, pg 1022
Tarpley Media Systems, pg 1032

UTAH

Redman Movies & Stories, pg 993
RIA Corp, pg 996

VIRGINIA

Avitecture Inc, pg 799
Boitnott Visual Communications Corp (BVC), pg 810
Communications Specialists Inc, pg 833
Filmdex Inc, pg 867
Lee Hartman & Sons Inc, pg 918
The Whitlock Group, pg 1065

WASHINGTON

CCI Solutions, pg 821
Global Net Productions Inc, pg 879
Oppenheimer Camera Products, pg 964

WISCONSIN

Camera Corner Connecting Point, pg 818
Demco Inc, pg 845
Full Compass Systems, pg 874
Pro Studio Supply, pg 983
Safe Harbor Computers, pg 1001

ALBERTA

Infosat Communications Inc, pg 898
Matrix Video Communications Corp (MVCC), pg 934
Sharp's Audio-Visual Ltd, pg 1008

BRITISH COLUMBIA

Commercial Electronics Ltd, pg 832
ProVision Video Sales & Rentals Inc, pg 986

ONTARIO

FUJIFILM Canada Inc, pg 873
HD Source, pg 886
Henry's Camera, pg 888
Nationwide Audio Visual Co, pg 953
Premier A/V Sales Ltd, pg 980
Westbury National Show Systems Ltd, pg 1064

QUEBEC

Panavideo Inc, pg 968

Camera Tripod Manufacturers

CALIFORNIA

Microdolly Hollywood, pg 941
O'Connor Engineering Labs, pg 961
RPM-PSI, pg 1000

CONNECTICUT

Skyviews Survey Inc, pg 1013

ILLINOIS

ACCO Brands Corp, pg 773
QuickSet International Inc, pg 989
Smith-Victor Corp, pg 1014

NEW JERSEY

National Audio-Visual Supply, pg 952

NEW YORK

Induro, pg 897
Sima Products Corp, pg 1011

VIRGINIA

Spider Support Systems, pg 1021

WASHINGTON

KB Systems, pg 908

WISCONSIN

Regal Photo Products Inc/Arkay Corp, pg 994

BRITISH COLUMBIA

Triad Communications Ltd, pg 1044

Camera Tripod Rentals

ARIZONA

AV Concepts, pg 797
Broadcast Rentals, pg 813
Merestone, pg 938
Metropolitan Audio-Visual Inc, pg 940
Video West Inc, pg 1056

ARKANSAS

White Diamond Productions, pg 1065

CALIFORNIA

Aaron & Le Duc, pg 772
Abel Cine Tech Los Angeles, pg 772
Absolute Rentals, pg 772
Action Video, pg 775
Adolph Gasser Inc, pg 776
Advanced Media LLC, pg 778
Alliant Event Services, pg 781
Alternative Rentals, pg 783
Ametron Audio/Video, pg 785
Artichoke Productions, pg 791
AV Guys, pg 797
Barber Tech Video Products, pg 802
Bexel Corp, pg 806
Big Door, pg 807
Chater Camera Inc, pg 824
Cherry Multimedia, pg 824
Clean Slate Video, pg 829
Crystal Pyramid Productions™, pg 840
Deck Hand Inc, pg 844
The Dreaming Tree, pg 852
Dystopian Studios, pg 854
Express Media Inc, pg 864
First Camera, pg 868
Full Moon & High Tide Productions & Studios, pg 874
Gear Monkey, pg 876
Gearhouse Broadcast LLC, pg 876
Gluskin's Custom Audio Video, pg 879
Gold Standard Productions, pg 880
Golden Gate Studios, pg 880
Alan Gordon Enterprises Inc, pg 880
HD Cinema, pg 886
HDrental.com, pg 886
Hollywood Sound Systems, pg 890
iCorpTv, pg 893
Image Integration, pg 895
Imagecraft Productions, pg 896
Images in Motion Media Inc, pg 896
Impact Group, pg 897
JD Audio Visual Inc, pg 904
JFA Studio, pg 905
Loyal Studios, pg 925
Lynch Communications, pg 926
Main Street Media Inc, pg 929
Maximus Media Inc, pg 934
McCune Audio-Video-Lighting, pg 935
Media Fabricators Inc, pg 936
Motion Picture Marine, pg 947

VIDEO

Camera Tripod Rentals (continued)

PENNSYLVANIA

Argentine Productions Inc, pg 789
Audio Visions Inc, pg 795
Bernie's Photo Center, pg 805
FirstGeneration Audio/Visual Services, pg 869
FMP Media Solutions Inc, pg 870
Fusion Brand Experiences, pg 874
Goodman Associates Inc, pg 880
Grise Audio Visual Center Inc, pg 882
Innovision Media Group, pg 899
JPL, pg 906
Muderick Media, pg 949
New York Camera & Video, pg 956
Ott Film Rentals, pg 966
Philadelphia Soundstages, pg 974
The Videohouse Inc, pg 1057
Visual Sound Inc, pg 1059

SOUTH CAROLINA

Genesis Creative, pg 877

TENNESSEE

Nashville Production Rentals (NPR), pg 952
RentACamera.com, pg 995
Russ Sturgeon Productions/RSVP, pg 1027
Technical Support Systems LLC, pg 1034

TEXAS

Audio Visual Technologies Group, pg 796
Bright Giant Creative Group, pg 812
FitzCo Sound Inc, pg 869
GEAR Cameras & Lighting, pg 876
Industrial Audio/Video Inc, pg 897
Light Tec, pg 920
Media Event Concepts Inc, pg 936
Mediaforce Productions, pg 937
Muller Entertainment, pg 949
Omega Broadcast Group, pg 962
Phil Lights, pg 973
Precision Camera & Video, pg 980
Quality Audio Visual Service Inc, pg 988
The Samuels Co, pg 1002
South Coast Film & Video, pg 1019
Stage Directions, pg 1022
Texcam Inc, pg 1038
Video Perspective, pg 1056

UTAH

Ron Hill Imagery, pg 889
Redman Movies & Stories, pg 993

VIRGINIA

Audio Visual Actions Inc (AVA), pg 795
Boitnott Visual Communications Corp (BVC), pg 810
Creative Video of Washington Inc, pg 839
D&B Television & Video Productions Inc, pg 842
Lee Hartman & Sons Inc, pg 918
Quince Imaging Inc, pg 989
StageSound, pg 1023
The Whitlock Group, pg 1065

WASHINGTON

D A Sound, pg 842
The House Studios, pg 891
Kostov Productions, pg 913
Oppenheimer Camera Products, pg 964
Victory Studios, pg 1054

WEST VIRGINIA

Blackwater Video Productions, pg 808

WISCONSIN

Camera Corner Connecting Point, pg 818
Event Essentials, pg 863
Full Compass Systems, pg 874
MKE Production Rental, pg 944

WYOMING

Bridger Productions Inc, pg 812

PUERTO RICO

Stage Crew Audiovisual Inc, pg 1022

ALBERTA

Evolution Presentation Technologies, pg 863
Matrix Video Communications Corp (MVCC), pg 934
Sharp's Audio-Visual Ltd, pg 1008
Unique Communications Ltd, pg 1048

BRITISH COLUMBIA

Commercial Electronics Ltd, pg 832
ProVision Video Sales & Rentals Inc, pg 986
Video In Studios/Video Out Distribution, pg 1055

MANITOBA

MidCanada Production Services Inc (MidCan), pg 942

ONTARIO

Boxcar Studio, pg 811
GAPC (General Assembly Production Centre), pg 875
HD Source, pg 886
JIB Shots Equipment Inc, pg 905
RB Productions, pg 992
SIM Digital, pg 1011
Westbury National Show Systems Ltd, pg 1064
ZTV Broadcast Services Inc, pg 1074

QUEBEC

Audio Visual Dynamics Ltd, pg 795
Group PVP, pg 882
Kerrigan Productions Inc, pg 910
Panavideo Inc, pg 968

Camera Tripod Repairs

CALIFORNIA

Adolph Gasser Inc, pg 776
Ametron Audio/Video, pg 785
BroadcastStore.com, pg 813
Gluskin's Custom Audio Video, pg 879
Alan Gordon Enterprises Inc, pg 880
Matthews Studio Equipment Inc, pg 934
Slow Motion Film & Digital Inc, pg 1013
VMI Inc, pg 1060

CONNECTICUT

Precision Camera & Video Repair Inc, pg 980

FLORIDA

Hi-Tech Enterprises Inc, pg 888
Midtown Video Inc, pg 942

GEORGIA

Stage Front Presentation Systems, pg 1022

ILLINOIS

Allen Visual Systems Inc, pg 781
Beatty TeleVisual Productions, pg 804

IOWA

ECS Inc, pg 856

KENTUCKY

Axxis Inc, pg 800
NOR-COM Inc, pg 958

MICHIGAN

Lowing Light & Grip Inc, pg 925
TeL Systems, pg 1035

MINNESOTA

Alpha Video & Audio Inc, pg 782

MISSISSIPPI

Bowie Audio Visual Enterprises Inc, pg 811

MISSOURI

Schiller's Audio-Visual, pg 1004
Southwest Audio-Visual Inc, pg 1019

NEW JERSEY

Hakuba Sunpak Velbon, pg 883
Miller Camera Support LLC, pg 943

NEW YORK

Benro, pg 805
Induro, pg 897
Technisphere Corp, pg 1034
The Tiffen Co LLC, pg 1040
Visual Technologies Corp, pg 1060

OHIO

ITA Audio Visual Solutions, pg 902

PENNSYLVANIA

Audio Visions Inc, pg 795
Bernie's Photo Center, pg 805

TENNESSEE

Technical Support Systems LLC, pg 1034

TEXAS

Industrial Audio/Video Inc, pg 897
Quality Audio Visual Service Inc, pg 988
Tarpley Media Systems, pg 1032

UTAH

RIA Corp, pg 996

VIRGINIA

Boitnott Visual Communications Corp (BVC), pg 810
Lee Hartman & Sons Inc, pg 918
The Whitlock Group, pg 1065

WASHINGTON

Oppenheimer Camera Products, pg 964

WISCONSIN

Camera Corner Connecting Point, pg 818
Full Compass Systems, pg 874

ALBERTA

Infosat Communications Inc, pg 898
Sharp's Audio-Visual Ltd, pg 1008

BRITISH COLUMBIA

Commercial Electronics Ltd, pg 832

ONTARIO

HD Source, pg 886

QUEBEC

Panavideo Inc, pg 968

Can, *see* Reel & Can

CD-ROM Interactive Production Services

ARIZONA

MediaWorks, pg 938
Merestone, pg 938
Tellens Inc, pg 1037

ARKANSAS

Shadowbox Video Productions, pg 1007

CALIFORNIA

All Video Productions, pg 781
Animax, pg 787
Christian Media Network, pg 825
Coloredge, pg 832
Custom Video Productions Inc, pg 841
Digital Outpost, pg 847
Direct Images Interactive Inc, pg 848
Dogma Studios, pg 850
Duck Studios, pg 853
DV Post, pg 854
Dynamic Digital Depth Inc (DDD), pg 854
First Person™, pg 868
FXF Productions Inc, pg 874
Havas Edge, pg 885
iCorpTv, pg 893
Imageworks, pg 896
JDS Video & Media Productions Inc, pg 904
Ludlow Media Solutions, pg 926
Lumeni Productions Inc, pg 926
Lynch Communications, pg 926
Maximus Media Inc, pg 934
Media Magic, pg 937
Medical Visual Creations (MVC), pg 938

Mist Media Inc, pg 944
New Cyberian Systems Inc, pg 955
Nolte Media, pg 958
Panorama Productions, pg 968
QRS Software Services, pg 988
RetinaVision Productions, pg 995
Rovi Corp, pg 1000
SonicPool, pg 1016
Staylor-Made Communications Inc, pg 1024
Still N'Motion, pg 1025
Tam Communications Inc, pg 1031
Timecode Multimedia, pg 1040
Toon Makers, pg 1042
Total Media Group, pg 1042
Towards 2000 Inc, pg 1043
Twin Peaks Creative, pg 1047
Via Verde Productions, pg 1053
Video Movie Magic, pg 1056
Videolady, pg 1057
Wavemaker Media Design, pg 1062
WMS Media Inc, pg 1069

COLORADO

Paul L Anderson Productions Inc, pg 786
Daylight Productions & Rentals, pg 844
Flashback Media Productions, pg 869
Rocky Mountain Audio/Video Productions Inc, pg 998

CONNECTICUT

Applebox Studio, pg 788
BRB Audiovisual Productions, pg 812
Geomatrix Productions, pg 877
Ironik Design & Post, pg 902
New London Media, pg 956
Palace Digital Studios, pg 967
P&P Studios Inc, pg 968
T & M Digital Services, pg 1031
Video Production Associates Inc, pg 1056

DELAWARE

So Smart Productions, pg 1015

DISTRICT OF COLUMBIA

Interface Media Group, pg 900
O'Keefe Communications Inc, pg 961

FLORIDA

Access Media Group, pg 773
Allegro Productions Inc, pg 781
Civins Productions Inc, pg 828
Florida Digital Studios, pg 870
Hi-Tech Enterprises Inc, pg 888
Image Technical Services, pg 895
Progressive Media & Music, pg 985
Shooting Stars Post Inc, pg 1009
Sound & Vision Communications Inc, pg 1016
Sunfire Communications Inc, pg 1028
Sunrise Studios, pg 1028
Tricycle Studios, pg 1044
Video Techniques Inc, pg 1056

GEORGIA

Continental Film & Video, pg 835
The DVI Group, pg 854
ECG Productions, pg 856
Guerrilla Productions LLC, pg 883
Imagers, pg 896
Omega Media Group Inc, pg 962
Outsource Engineering & Manufacturing Inc dba Texscan MSI, pg 966

HAWAII

Hyperspective Studios Inc, pg 893
1013 Integrated, pg 1037

ILLINOIS

ABSA Productions Inc, pg 772
Advanced Audio Technology, pg 777
Airways Digital Media, pg 779
Analog Free Media, pg 786
CCore Media Inc, pg 821
Chicago Satellite & Video, pg 825
Extraordinary Demos, pg 864
IV Media Resources, pg 903
Kelmscott Communications, pg 909
Major Media Inc, pg 929
Manning Productions, pg 930
MIGHTYbYTES Inc, pg 942
The Pepper Group, pg 972
RADMAR Inc, pg 990
Richter Studios, pg 996
Sparkfactor, pg 1019
20/20 Communications Inc, pg 1047
Video I-D Teleproductions Inc, pg 1055
Video Impressions, pg 1055

INDIANA

AVA Productions, pg 798
Bright Ideas Creative Services, pg 812
Optical Disc Solutions Inc, pg 964
PentaVision Communications Inc, pg 972

IOWA

Iowa State University-Information Technology Services, pg 902

KENTUCKY

Prosper Media Group Inc, pg 986

LOUISIANA

Louisiana State University Health Sciences Center - Shreveport, pg 925
Vidox Motion Imagery, pg 1057

MARYLAND

The Ahern Group, pg 779
CPR MultiMedia Solutions, pg 837
dbF a Media Company, pg 844
DBM Communications Inc, pg 844
Kramer Communications Video Production, pg 913
Media Dimensions Inc, pg 936
Saah Video, pg 1001
Video Labs, pg 1055

MASSACHUSETTS

Boston Productions Inc, pg 811
Cramer Productions, pg 837
Northern Light Productions, pg 959
Penfield Productions Ltd, pg 971
TR Productions, pg 1043
Veritech Corp, pg 1053

MICHIGAN

ASC Systems, pg 791
Digi Sign Design LLC, pg 847
Digital Image Studios LLC, pg 847
K&R's Recording Studios Inc, pg 908
TGA Recording Co, pg 1038

MINNESOTA

The ADS Group, pg 777
Aggressive Records Audio Duplication LLC, pg 778
Beyers Sound & Essay Audio, pg 806
The Richard Diercks Co Inc, pg 846
Master Communications Group, pg 933
Worthwhile Films, pg 1070

MISSOURI

Avatar Studios, pg 798
Show-Me Audio-Visual, pg 1009

MONTANA

ooLite Media, pg 964

NEBRASKA

B & B Video Productions Inc, pg 801
Rainbow Video Productions Inc, pg 991
Three Pillars Media, pg 1040

NEVADA

Aardvark Video & Media Productions, pg 772
JCS Video Productions, pg 904

NEW HAMPSHIRE

Heinemann, pg 887
Chip Taylor Communications LLC, pg 1032

NEW JERSEY

All Jersey Studios, pg 780
CD Meyer Inc, pg 822
CFP Video Productions Inc, pg 823
Diversified Systems Inc, pg 849
Megavideo Productions, pg 938
MIB Mediaworks, pg 941
Midnight Media Group Inc, pg 942
Outside The Box Interactive LLC, pg 966
Producer East Productions, pg 983
Public Eye Productions, pg 987
Reed Presentations Inc (RPI), pg 993
Suede Interactive, pg 1027
Two Animators LLP, pg 1047
VCSvideo, pg 1052

NEW YORK

American Artists Representatives Inc, pg 783
Animotion Inc, pg 787
Bellin Productions, pg 805
The Big House Group, pg 807
Chromavision Corp, pg 826
Thomas Craven Film Corp, pg 837
Digital Force, pg 847
dM works, pg 849
Duplication Depot Inc, pg 853
Duplication Specialists Inc, pg 853
Eastco Multimedia Solutions Inc, pg 856
Educational Images Ltd, pg 857
4-D Creative Media, pg 871
FSL Media Inc, pg 873
Greyfalcon House, pg 882
Guidance Associates Inc Center for Humanities, pg 883
HAVE Inc, pg 886
HB-Content, pg 886
International Digital Centre, pg 901
L A Bruell Inc, pg 914
Neal Marshad Productions, pg 931
New York Audio Productions, pg 956
Princeton Architectural Press, pg 982
TBA Global Events, pg 1032
Teatown Communications Group, pg 1033

NORTH CAROLINA

All Pro Media Inc, pg 780
Pat Appleson Studios Inc, pg 788
The Communications Group Inc, pg 833
Horizon Video Productions Inc, pg 891
Moving Pictures, pg 948
NASCAR Media Group LLC, pg 952
On Location North Carolina, pg 963
Take One Productions Ltd, pg 1031
2BruceStudio, pg 1047
Unifour Productions Inc, pg 1048

OHIO

Advent Media Inc, pg 778
Aztec Video Productions, pg 801
Cinecraft Productions Inc, pg 827
Commercial Video, pg 832
Creative Technology, pg 838
Curtis Inc, pg 841
EDR Media LLC, pg 857
Electronic Vision Inc (EV), pg 859
Lyon Video Inc, pg 927
Mills James Productions, pg 943
Take 1 Media Services, pg 1031

OREGON

InterVision Media, pg 902
Odyssey Productions Inc, pg 961
Production West, pg 985
Rex, pg 995
Wallace Creative Inc, pg 1061
Wilderness Video, pg 1066

PENNSYLVANIA

AiH Group Inc, pg 779
Beholder Productions Inc, pg 804
FMP Media Solutions Inc, pg 870
Innovision Media Group, pg 899
JPL, pg 906
Panta Rhei Media Inc, pg 968
Production Masters Inc (PMI), pg 984
Science for Kids, pg 1005

RHODE ISLAND

Sound-FX-Design, pg 1017

SOUTH CAROLINA

Genesis Creative, pg 877

TENNESSEE

Motion Picture Services, pg 947
Paradigm Marketing & Creative, pg 969
Running Pony Productions LLC, pg 1000
Stage Post, pg 1022

TEXAS

Biway Media, pg 808
Communication Arts Multimedia Inc, pg 832
Digi-matics, pg 847

VIDEO

CD-ROM Interactive Production Services (continued)

TEXAS (continued)

The Editing Co, pg 857
Epic Software Group Inc, pg 862
Fire Station Studios, pg 868
First Group Communications Inc, pg 868
Horizon Film + Video Productions, pg 891
Mediaforce Productions, pg 937
Julye Newlin Productions Inc, pg 956
Out of the BLUE Media, pg 966
Phil Lights, pg 973
Replicopy Digital Media Center, pg 995
South Coast Film & Video, pg 1019
Stage Directions, pg 1022
Texas Heart Institute Visual Communication Services, pg 1037
TopCat Records LLC, pg 1042

UTAH

ImageWorks Communications, pg 896

VERMONT

Ashgate Publishing Co, pg 792

VIRGINIA

Advance Concepts Inc, pg 777
Allied Media Corp, pg 781
CALIBRE, pg 816
D&B Television & Video Productions Inc, pg 842
Metro Productions, pg 939

WASHINGTON

North-by-Northwest Productions, pg 958
Tri-Digital Software Inc, pg 1044
Victory Studios, pg 1054

WEST VIRGINIA

Altruist Media LLC, pg 783

WISCONSIN

Logan Productions Inc, pg 924
Video Wisconsin Inc, pg 1056
Watts Communications Inc, pg 1062
Win Media Inc, pg 1067

PUERTO RICO

Stage Crew Audiovisual Inc, pg 1022

BRITISH COLUMBIA

Credo Interactive Inc, pg 839
Finale Editworks, pg 868
Triad Communications Ltd, pg 1044
24 Frames Film & Video, pg 1047

NEWFOUNDLAND AND LABRADOR

Vidcraft Productions Ltd, pg 1054

ONTARIO

ADS Media, pg 777
Cinram Inc, pg 828
Gesturetek, pg 877
Image Video Services & Productions, pg 895
JFB Communications, pg 905
Marblemedia, pg 930
Music Manufacturing Services, pg 950
Purefire Communications Inc, pg 987
RB Productions, pg 992
Shaw Street Productions, pg 1008
SLI Manufacturing Inc, pg 1013
Video Excellence Productions, pg 1055

QUEBEC

Group PVP, pg 882

Character Generator Distributors

ALABAMA

Media Visions Inc, pg 937

ARIZONA

ATCi (Antenna Technology Communication Solutions Inc), pg 793
Audio Video Resources, pg 795
EAR Professional Audio/Video, pg 855
Media Computing Inc, pg 936
Troxell Communications Inc, pg 1045

ARKANSAS

Jay S Stanley & Associates Inc, pg 1023
White Diamond Productions, pg 1065

CALIFORNIA

Advanced Systems Group LLC, pg 778
Ametron Audio/Video, pg 785
Audio/Video Supply Inc, pg 795
BroadcastStore.com, pg 813
Cibola Systems, pg 826
Diaquest, pg 846
FXC Communications, pg 874
Gluskin's Custom Audio Video, pg 879
Linear LLC, pg 922
Media Control Systems LLC, pg 936
Media Fabricators Inc, pg 936
MediaPOINTE, pg 938
Metro Video Systems Inc, pg 940
SNAP, pg 1014
Tri-Ed, pg 1044
VMI Inc, pg 1060
VTP Inc, pg 1061

COLORADO

Spectrum Audio Visual Services, pg 1020

CONNECTICUT

MAVCO, pg 934
Video Automation Systems Inc, pg 1054
The Video Messenger Co, pg 1055

FLORIDA

Access Media Group, pg 773
AVI-SPL, pg 798
Digital Video Systems Inc, pg 848
Griffiths Broadcast Co Inc, pg 882
Gulf Coast Audio Visual Producers Inc, pg 883
Harris Corp, pg 885
Hi-Tech Enterprises Inc, pg 888
Hi-Tech Import Export Corp, pg 888
Hunter Electronics LLC, pg 892
Industrial Strength Inc, pg 897
Media Concepts Inc, pg 936
Midtown Video Inc, pg 942
Multicom Inc, pg 949
Pro Stage Inc, pg 983
Tallahassee Audio Visual, pg 1031

GEORGIA

Convergent Media Systems, pg 836
Outsource Engineering & Manufacturing Inc dba Texscan MSI, pg 966
Stage Front Presentation Systems, pg 1022

HAWAII

The Audio Visual Co (AVCO), pg 795

ILLINOIS

Allen Visual Systems Inc, pg 781
Joseph Electronics, pg 906
Lyn Norstad & Associates Inc, pg 926
RAM Systems LLC, pg 991
Tele-Time Systems, pg 1036

INDIANA

Sensory Technologies LLC, pg 1006

IOWA

ECS Inc, pg 856

KANSAS

Smith Audio-Visual Inc, pg 1014

KENTUCKY

Barney Miller's Inc, pg 943
NOR-COM Inc, pg 958

LOUISIANA

Digital FX Inc, pg 847

MAINE

Headlight Audio Visual Inc, pg 887

MARYLAND

Image Logic Corp, pg 895
RTZ Audio Visual, pg 1000

MASSACHUSETTS

Camera Co Inc/Broadcast Divison, pg 818
Rule Broadcast Systems, pg 1000

MICHIGAN

ASC Systems, pg 791
Ascom Communications Contractors, pg 791
City Events Group, pg 828
DAWNco, pg 843
Digi Sign Design LLC, pg 847
Michigan Office Solutions, pg 941
On Stage Visuals, pg 963
TeL Systems, pg 1035

MINNESOTA

Alpha Video & Audio Inc, pg 782
AVI Systems, pg 799

MISSISSIPPI

MFJ Enterprises Inc, pg 940

MISSOURI

Communitronics Corp, pg 833
Conference Technologies Inc, pg 835
Modern Communications Inc, pg 944
Schiller's Audio-Visual, pg 1004
Southwest Audio-Visual Inc, pg 1019
Swank Audio Visuals, pg 1029

NEBRASKA

Dog & Pony Productions Inc, pg 850

NEVADA

Aardvark Video & Media Productions, pg 772

NEW JERSEY

A-V Services Inc, pg 771
Alltec Stores, a Vcom IMC Company, pg 782
Audio Visual Dynamics®, pg 795
AV Bluebook, pg 797
Comprehensive Cable & Connectivity Co, pg 833
Diversified Systems Inc, pg 849
G&G Technologies Inc, pg 875
Hamilton Buhl, pg 884
MCCOM Inc, pg 935
National Audio-Visual Supply, pg 952
Starlite Productions, pg 1024
SYMCO Inc, pg 1030
Tele-Measurements Inc, pg 1035
Turner Engineering Inc, pg 1046
Video Corporation of America (VCA), pg 1055
Wilray Audio Visual Corp, pg 1067
Wired 4 Sound Inc, pg 1068

NEW YORK

ALTEL Systems Inc, pg 783
Audio-Video Corp, pg 795
AV Workshop, pg 797
ChyronHego Corp, pg 826
Creative Stage Lighting Co Inc, pg 838
Custom Media Environments, pg 841
Design Audio Visual Inc, pg 845
Gaylord Brothers, pg 876
Indigo Productions, pg 897
Long Island Video Enterprises Live Inc, pg 924
Markertek Video Supply, pg 931
Neptune Photo Inc, pg 954
NorthCountry Distributors, pg 959
RNJ Electronics, pg 997
Technisphere Corp, pg 1034
TecNec Distributing, pg 1035
Visual Word Systems Inc, pg 1060
Willoughby's Imaging Center, pg 1067

NORTH CAROLINA

Camcor Inc, pg 818
Crispin Corp, pg 839
Strategic Connections, pg 1026

OHIO

Copp Integrated Systems, pg 836
ITA Audio Visual Solutions, pg 902
Jimmy Rea Electronics Inc, pg 992
Smithall Electronics Inc, pg 1014
Tri-State Audio Visual Co, pg 1044

OREGON

ClearOne MagicBox Inc, pg 830

PENNSYLVANIA

Clair Brothers Audio Systems Inc, pg 829
J E Foss Co, pg 871
Grise Audio Visual Center Inc, pg 882
The Lerro Corp, pg 919
Morefield Communications Inc, pg 946
Visual Sound Inc, pg 1059

TENNESSEE

Lowrance Sound Co Inc, pg 925
Memphis Communications Corp, pg 938
Technical Support Systems LLC, pg 1034
Zion Music Group, pg 1074

TEXAS

AVES Audio Visual Systems Inc, pg 798
Data Display Audio Visual Co LP, pg 843
Media Management LLC, pg 937
Pro Video & Film Equipment Co Inc, pg 983
RadioShack Corp, pg 990
Stage Directions, pg 1022
Tarpley Media Systems, pg 1032
Videotex Systems Inc, pg 1057

VIRGINIA

Boitnott Visual Communications Corp (BVC), pg 810
Communications Specialists Inc, pg 833
Lee Hartman & Sons Inc, pg 918
RGB Technology Inc, pg 996
The Whitlock Group, pg 1065

WISCONSIN

Camera Corner Connecting Point, pg 818
Full Compass Systems, pg 874

ALBERTA

Infosat Communications Inc, pg 898
Matrix Video Communications Corp (MVCC), pg 934
McBain Audio Visual Ltd, pg 935

BRITISH COLUMBIA

Commercial Electronics Ltd, pg 832
ProVision Video Sales & Rentals Inc, pg 986

ONTARIO

Edcom Multimedia Products, pg 856
Harris Canada Systems, pg 885
HD Source, pg 886
Nationwide Audio Visual Co, pg 953

QUEBEC

Teledac Inc, pg 1036

SASKATCHEWAN

Display Systems International, pg 849

Character Generator Manufacturers

CALIFORNIA

AJA Video Systems Inc, pg 779
Effective Engineering, pg 858
Horita Co Inc, pg 891
Linear LLC, pg 922
Panasonic Broadcast & Digital Systems Co, pg 968
TV Pro Gear, pg 1046

CONNECTICUT

Video Automation Systems Inc, pg 1054
The Video Messenger Co, pg 1055

FLORIDA

Compuvideo Sales USA Ltd, pg 834

GEORGIA

Outsource Engineering & Manufacturing Inc dba Texscan MSI, pg 966

KANSAS

GlobalStreams™ Corp, pg 879
Keywest Technology Inc, pg 910

MARYLAND

Image Logic Corp, pg 895

MISSISSIPPI

MFJ Enterprises Inc, pg 940

NEW JERSEY

CELCO-Constantine Engineering Labs Co, pg 822

NEW MEXICO

Burst Electronics Inc, pg 815

NEW YORK

ChyronHego Corp, pg 826
EEG Enterprises Inc, pg 858
Markertek Video Supply, pg 931
MultiDyne Video & Fiber Optics Systems, pg 950

OREGON

ClearOne MagicBox Inc, pg 830

PENNSYLVANIA

MicroImage Video Systems, pg 941
Scala Inc, pg 1003

RHODE ISLAND

M-Audio, pg 927

TENNESSEE

Adtec Digital Inc, pg 777

VIRGINIA

RGB Technology Inc, pg 996

BRITISH COLUMBIA

Triad Communications Ltd, pg 1044

ONTARIO

Harris Canada Systems, pg 885

QUEBEC

Teledac Inc, pg 1036

SASKATCHEWAN

Display Systems International, pg 849

Character Generator Rentals

ARIZONA

Merestone, pg 938
Metropolitan Audio-Visual Inc, pg 940

ARKANSAS

White Diamond Productions, pg 1065

CALIFORNIA

Aaron & Le Duc, pg 772
Ametron Audio/Video, pg 785
Artichoke Productions, pg 791
Bexel Corp, pg 806
Express Media Inc, pg 864
Full Moon & High Tide Productions & Studios, pg 874
Golden Gate Studios, pg 880
Lynch Communications, pg 926
McCune Audio-Video-Lighting, pg 935
Media Fabricators Inc, pg 936
Munday & Collins AV, pg 950
On-Trax Inc, pg 963
PSAV® Presentation Services, pg 986
PSSI, pg 987
Slate Media Group, pg 1013
Technical Services, pg 1034
Total Media Group, pg 1042
Twin Peaks Creative, pg 1047
VER-Video Equipment Rentals, pg 1053
VMI Inc, pg 1060
Voice & Video Rentals, pg 1060
Westcoast Video Productions Inc, pg 1064

COLORADO

Daylight Productions & Rentals, pg 844
Multimedia Audio Visual Inc, pg 950
Spectrum Audio Visual Services, pg 1020

CONNECTICUT

Fox Connecticut, pg 872
Videofilm Systems Inc, pg 1057

FLORIDA

Access Media Group, pg 773
Budget Video Rentals, pg 815
Industrial Strength Inc, pg 897
Jordan Klein Film & Video (JKFV), pg 906
Media Concepts Inc, pg 936
Midtown Video Inc, pg 942
Paradise Show & Design Inc, pg 969
Pro Stage Inc, pg 983

GEORGIA

Convergent Media Systems, pg 836
ON Event Services, pg 963
Stage Front Presentation Systems, pg 1022
Staging Directions Inc, pg 1023

ILLINOIS

Allen Visual Systems Inc, pg 781
Backstar Creative Media Inc, pg 801
Chicago Satellite & Video, pg 825
On Site Video, pg 963
QuickSet International Inc, pg 989
Show Department Inc, pg 1009
Tele-Time Systems, pg 1036

IOWA

ECS Inc, pg 856

KANSAS

Smith Audio-Visual Inc, pg 1014

KENTUCKY

Audio Visual Techniques Inc, pg 796

LOUISIANA

Digital FX Inc, pg 847
Pace Systems, pg 966

MARYLAND

CPR MultiMedia Solutions, pg 837
Shadowstone R & R™, pg 1008

MASSACHUSETTS

Camera Co Inc/Broadcast Divison, pg 818
Preston Productions Inc, pg 981

MICHIGAN

Digi Sign Design LLC, pg 847
K&R All Media Productions Inc, pg 908
K&R's Recording Studios Inc, pg 908
On Stage Visuals, pg 963
TeL Systems, pg 1035

MINNESOTA

Alpha Video & Audio Inc, pg 782
AVI Systems, pg 799
Cinequipt Inc, pg 828

MISSOURI

Schiller's Audio-Visual, pg 1004
Show-Me Audio-Visual, pg 1009
Southwest Audio-Visual Inc, pg 1019
Swank Audio Visuals, pg 1029

NEBRASKA

Dog & Pony Productions Inc, pg 850

NEVADA

GES Audio Visual, pg 877
Lefco Video Services Inc, pg 918

NEW HAMPSHIRE

Academic & Campus Technology Services, pg 773

VIDEO

Character Generator Rentals (continued)

NEW JERSEY

MediaMix Inc, pg 937
PLS Staging, pg 977
Bill Quinn Productions, pg 989
Starlite Productions, pg 1024
Wired 4 Sound Inc, pg 1068

NEW MEXICO

Production Outfitters, pg 984

NEW YORK

Adwar Video, pg 778
AV Workshop, pg 797
CMI Communications, pg 830
Creative Stage Lighting Co Inc, pg 838
Design Audio Visual Inc, pg 845
Long Island Video Enterprises Live Inc, pg 924
Manhattan Center Studios Inc, pg 930
PrimaLux Video Inc, pg 982
TBA Global Events, pg 1032
Technisphere Corp, pg 1034
Visual Word Systems Inc, pg 1060

NORTH CAROLINA

Camcor Inc, pg 818
The Communications Group Inc, pg 833
Duke Media Services, pg 853
Visual Aids Electronics of North Carolina Inc, pg 1059

OHIO

Lyon Video Inc, pg 927
R&B Communications Inc, pg 991
Vista Color Imaging Inc, pg 1059

OKLAHOMA

PDC Productions, pg 970

OREGON

BingoLewis, pg 807

PENNSYLVANIA

FMP Media Solutions Inc, pg 870
Grise Audio Visual Center Inc, pg 882
Innovision Media Group, pg 899
Muderick Media, pg 949
Producers Management Television (PMTV), pg 983
The Videohouse Inc, pg 1057

TENNESSEE

Memphis Communications Corp, pg 938
Russ Sturgeon Productions/RSVP, pg 1027
Technical Support Systems LLC, pg 1034

TEXAS

J&S Audio Visual Inc, pg 904
Media Event Concepts Inc, pg 936
Phillips MediaSource, pg 974
The Samuels Co, pg 1002
Stage Directions, pg 1022

VIRGINIA

Boitnott Visual Communications Corp (BVC), pg 810
Creative Video of Washington Inc, pg 839
Lee Hartman & Sons Inc, pg 918
Quince Imaging Inc, pg 989

WASHINGTON

Victory Studios, pg 1054

WISCONSIN

Camera Corner Connecting Point, pg 818
Full Compass Systems, pg 874
University of Wisconsin-Oshkosh Radio-TV-Film Dept, pg 1050
Wisconsin Public Television, pg 1068

PUERTO RICO

Stage Crew Audiovisual Inc, pg 1022

ALBERTA

Global Television Station, pg 879
Matrix Video Communications Corp (MVCC), pg 934

BRITISH COLUMBIA

Commercial Electronics Ltd, pg 832
Finale Editworks, pg 868
Image Media Farm, pg 895
Video In Studios/Video Out Distribution, pg 1055

ONTARIO

Edcom Multimedia Products, pg 856
HD Source, pg 886
RB Productions, pg 992

Character Generator Repairs

CALIFORNIA

Ametron Audio/Video, pg 785
Metro Video Systems Inc, pg 940
Technical Services, pg 1034
VMI Inc, pg 1060

FLORIDA

ELC Sales & Service Inc, pg 858
Hi-Tech Enterprises Inc, pg 888
Midtown Video Inc, pg 942

GEORGIA

Outsource Engineering & Manufacturing Inc dba Texscan MSI, pg 966
Stage Front Presentation Systems, pg 1022

ILLINOIS

Allen Visual Systems Inc, pg 781
On Site Video, pg 963

IOWA

ECS Inc, pg 856

KENTUCKY

Barney Miller's Inc, pg 943
NOR-COM Inc, pg 958

MICHIGAN

City Events Group, pg 828
TeL Systems, pg 1035

MINNESOTA

Alpha Video & Audio Inc, pg 782
AVI Systems, pg 799

MISSOURI

Southwest Audio-Visual Inc, pg 1019

NEW JERSEY

Turner Engineering Inc, pg 1046

NEW YORK

Ace Video, pg 774
Technisphere Corp, pg 1034

NORTH CAROLINA

Camcor Inc, pg 818

OHIO

Copp Integrated Systems, pg 836
ITA Audio Visual Solutions, pg 902

TENNESSEE

Memphis Communications Corp, pg 938
Technical Support Systems LLC, pg 1034

TEXAS

Tarpley Media Systems, pg 1032

VIRGINIA

Boitnott Visual Communications Corp (BVC), pg 810
The Whitlock Group, pg 1065

WISCONSIN

Full Compass Systems, pg 874

ALBERTA

Infosat Communications Inc, pg 898

BRITISH COLUMBIA

Commercial Electronics Ltd, pg 832

ONTARIO

Edcom Multimedia Products, pg 856

QUEBEC

Teledac Inc, pg 1036

Character Generator Production Services

ALABAMA

Diamond Studios, pg 846
Media Visions Inc, pg 937

ARIZONA

Direct Current Video Productions, pg 848
Fox 10 Productions (KSAZ-TV), pg 872
Merestone, pg 938
Metropolitan Audio-Visual Inc, pg 940
On-Site Video, pg 963
Phoenix VideoFilms®, pg 974
Star Video Duplicating, pg 1024

ARKANSAS

Shadowbox Video Productions, pg 1007
White Diamond Productions, pg 1065

CALIFORNIA

Aaron & Le Duc, pg 772
Access Video in Berkeley, pg 773
Action Video, pg 775
AlphaDogs Inc, pg 782
Artichoke Productions, pg 791
Barbosa Video Services, pg 802
Crystal Pyramid Productions™, pg 840
Custom Video Productions Inc, pg 841
Digital Jungle, pg 847
Dogma Studios, pg 850
DV Post, pg 854
Express Media Inc, pg 864
First Person™, pg 868
Full Moon & High Tide Productions & Studios, pg 874
Golden Gate Studios, pg 880
Hydrogen Whiskey Studios, pg 893
iCorpTv, pg 893
JDS Video & Media Productions Inc, pg 904
Lumeni Productions Inc, pg 926
Lynch Communications, pg 926
Maximus Media Inc, pg 934
McCune Audio-Video-Lighting, pg 935
Medical Visual Creations (MVC), pg 938
Mind Over Eye Inc, pg 943
Mist Media Inc, pg 944
Nolte Media, pg 958
Penrose Productions, pg 972
Peterson's Video Transfer Services, pg 973
PM Productions, pg 977
Point 360, pg 978
QRS Software Services, pg 988
Reality Check Systems, pg 992
Saturn Studios, pg 1003
Shapeshifter, pg 1008
SonicPool, pg 1016
Tam Communications Inc, pg 1031
Toon Makers, pg 1042
Total Media Group, pg 1042
Twin Peaks Creative, pg 1047
Universal Studios, pg 1049
Videografix LLC, pg 1057
Videolady, pg 1057
Visions Plus, pg 1058
Wavemaker Media Design, pg 1062

COLORADO

CSI Films, pg 840
Daylight Productions & Rentals, pg 844
Flashback Media Productions, pg 869
Rocky Mountain Audio/Video Productions Inc, pg 998
Spectrum Audio Visual Services, pg 1020

CONNECTICUT

Applebox Studio, pg 788
BRB Audiovisual Productions, pg 812
Guymark Studios LLC, pg 883
Ironik Design & Post, pg 902
MAVCO, pg 934
New London Media, pg 956

VIDEO

Character Generator Production Services (continued)

TEXAS (continued)

The Samuels Co, pg 1002
South Coast Film & Video, pg 1019
Stage Directions, pg 1022

UTAH

ImageWorks Communications, pg 896

VIRGINIA

American AV, pg 783
CDR Communications Inc, pg 822
Creative Video of Washington Inc, pg 839
Eagle Films, pg 855
Henninger Media Services, pg 888
Maniglia Media, pg 930
Metro Productions, pg 939
Rocktown Media, pg 998
The Whitlock Group, pg 1065

WASHINGTON

Bennett-Watt HD Productions Inc, pg 805
Linguist's Software Inc, pg 922
North-by-Northwest Productions, pg 958
Victory Studios, pg 1054

WISCONSIN

Audio Visual of Milwaukee Inc, pg 795
Meridian Studios, pg 939
ProVideo, pg 986
University of Wisconsin-Oshkosh Radio-TV-Film Dept, pg 1050
Video Wisconsin Inc, pg 1056
Watts Communications Inc, pg 1062
Wisconsin Public Television, pg 1068

WYOMING

Bridger Productions Inc, pg 812

PUERTO RICO

Stage Crew Audiovisual Inc, pg 1022

BRITISH COLUMBIA

Finale Editworks, pg 868
Image Media Farm, pg 895
Triad Communications Ltd, pg 1044

NEWFOUNDLAND AND LABRADOR

Vidcraft Productions Ltd, pg 1054

ONTARIO

ADS Media, pg 777
Edcom Multimedia Products, pg 856
Harris Canada Systems, pg 885
Image Video Services & Productions, pg 895
JFB Communications, pg 905
Video Excellence Productions, pg 1055

QUEBEC

Group PVP, pg 882

Closed Captioning Production Services

ARIZONA

Merestone, pg 938
Star Video Duplicating, pg 1024

ARKANSAS

Shadowbox Video Productions, pg 1007

CALIFORNIA

Aberdeen Broadcast Services, pg 772
Express Media Inc, pg 864
Full Moon & High Tide Productions & Studios, pg 874
Havas Edge, pg 885
iCorpTv, pg 893
JDS Video & Media Productions Inc, pg 904
The Kitchen, pg 911
Lightning Media, pg 921
Ludlow Media Solutions, pg 926
Lumeni Productions Inc, pg 926
Lynch Communications, pg 926
Point 360, pg 978
QRS Software Services, pg 988
Roundabout Entertainment Inc, pg 1000
Shapeshifter, pg 1008
SonicPool, pg 1016
Staylor-Made Communications Inc, pg 1024
Studio 637, pg 1027
Total Media Group, pg 1042

COLORADO

Caption Colorado LLC, pg 820
Flashback Media Productions, pg 869

CONNECTICUT

Ironik Design & Post, pg 902

DISTRICT OF COLUMBIA

Interface Media Group, pg 900

FLORIDA

Access Media Group, pg 773
Accord Productions, pg 773
Allegro Productions Inc, pg 781
Easy Edit Video Inc, pg 856
Florida Digital Studios, pg 870
Sunfire Communications Inc, pg 1028
Tricycle Studios, pg 1044
Video Techniques Inc, pg 1056

GEORGIA

Crawford Media Services, pg 838
Guerrilla Productions LLC, pg 883

ILLINOIS

Analog Free Media, pg 786
Captions & Subtitle Services Ltd, pg 820
Joseph Electronics, pg 906
Richter Studios, pg 996
SCI Television Productions LLC, pg 1004
Televersions, pg 1036
Video Impressions, pg 1055

INDIANA

AVA Productions, pg 798

KANSAS

KAKE-TV, pg 907

KENTUCKY

Broadway Digital, pg 813
Prosper Media Group Inc, pg 986

MAINE

WGME-TV, pg 1065

MARYLAND

Adventure Productions LLC, pg 778
CPR MultiMedia Solutions, pg 837
Image Logic Corp, pg 895
Kramer Communications Video Production, pg 913
Pro Cuts Editing Services, pg 982
Video Labs, pg 1055

MASSACHUSETTS

Award Productions, pg 800
Extreme Reach Inc, pg 864
Video Express, pg 1055
WGBH Production Group, pg 1065

MICHIGAN

Digi Sign Design LLC, pg 847
K&R's Recording Studios Inc, pg 908

MINNESOTA

The ADS Group, pg 777
Aggressive Records Audio Duplication LLC, pg 778
CaptionMax, pg 820

MISSOURI

Show-Me Audio-Visual, pg 1009
Substation K, pg 1027

MONTANA

ooLite Media, pg 964

NEW HAMPSHIRE

Chip Taylor Communications LLC, pg 1032

NEW JERSEY

Color Leasing Studios, pg 831
Diversified Systems Inc, pg 849
Laurel Video Productions, pg 916
MIB Mediaworks, pg 941
Suede Interactive, pg 1027

NEW MEXICO

Production Outfitters, pg 984

NEW YORK

Chromavision Corp, pg 826
Devlin Video International, pg 846
Eastco Multimedia Solutions Inc, pg 856
HAVE Inc, pg 886
International Digital Centre, pg 901
iProbe Multilingual Solutions Inc, pg 902
Mood Creations Ltd, pg 946
PostWorks, pg 979
Teatown Communications Group, pg 1033
Tobin Productions Inc, pg 1041
Video Caption Corp, pg 1054
Visual Technologies Corp, pg 1060

NORTH CAROLINA

Pat Appleson Studios Inc, pg 788

OHIO

Aztec Video Productions, pg 801
Bartha, pg 803
Curtis Inc, pg 841
Mills James Productions, pg 943
Production Partners Media, pg 984
Take 1 Media Services, pg 1031

OKLAHOMA

Garman Productions LLC, pg 875
Producers Playhouse, pg 983

OREGON

Odyssey Productions Inc, pg 961
Production West, pg 985

PENNSYLVANIA

FMP Media Solutions Inc, pg 870
Innovision Media Group, pg 899
JPL, pg 906
Panta Rhei Media Inc, pg 968
Production Masters Inc (PMI), pg 984

SOUTH CAROLINA

American Production Services LLC, pg 785

TENNESSEE

Motion Picture Services, pg 947
Running Pony Productions LLC, pg 1000
Stage Post, pg 1022

TEXAS

Contemporary Research, pg 835
Digi-matics, pg 847
The Editing Co, pg 857
Horizon Film + Video Productions, pg 891
Mediaforce Productions, pg 937
Replicopy Digital Media Center, pg 995

UTAH

ImageWorks Communications, pg 896
K-SAR Video & DVD Productions, pg 907

VIRGINIA

Henninger Media Services, pg 888
Metro Productions, pg 939

WASHINGTON

Victory Studios, pg 1054

BRITISH COLUMBIA

Finale Editworks, pg 868
24 Frames Film & Video, pg 1047

ONTARIO

GAPC (General Assembly Production Centre), pg 875

Color Correction Services

VIDEO

Color Correction Services (continued)

Compact Disc Recorder & Player Distributors

MANITOBA

Inland Audio Visual Ltd, pg 898

ONTARIO

Premier A/V Sales Ltd, pg 980
Westbury National Show Systems Ltd, pg 1064

Compact Disc Recorder & Player Manufacturers

CALIFORNIA

DiskFaktory Direct, pg 849

FLORIDA

Alcorn McBride Inc, pg 780

TENNESSEE

Adtec Digital Inc, pg 777

Compact Disc Recorder & Player Rentals

ARIZONA

Merestone, pg 938
Video West Inc, pg 1056

ARKANSAS

White Diamond Productions, pg 1065

CALIFORNIA

Aaron & Le Duc, pg 772
Absolute Rentals, pg 772
Adolph Gasser Inc, pg 776
Advanced Media LLC, pg 778
AGF Media Services, pg 778
Ametron Audio/Video, pg 785
Artichoke Productions, pg 791
Audio Rents, pg 794
AV Guys, pg 797
Big Time Picture Company Inc, pg 807
Express Media Inc, pg 864
JD Audio Visual Inc, pg 904
Lynch Communications, pg 926
Maximus Media Inc, pg 934
McCune Audio-Video-Lighting, pg 935
Munday & Collins AV, pg 950
Muse Presentation Technologies, pg 950
PSAV® Presentation Services, pg 986
RetinaVision Productions, pg 995
Roundabout Entertainment Inc, pg 1000
Slate Media Group, pg 1013
SNAP, pg 1014
Sound Service Co, pg 1017
Total Media Group, pg 1042
Twin Peaks Creative, pg 1047
VER-Video Equipment Rentals, pg 1053
Videorama Industries LLC, pg 1057
VMI Inc, pg 1060
Voice & Video Rentals, pg 1060

COLORADO

Spectrum Audio Visual Services, pg 1020

CONNECTICUT

A/V Davey, pg 797
Everett Hall Associates Inc, pg 863

FLORIDA

Accord Productions, pg 773
Media Concepts Inc, pg 936
Paradise Show & Design Inc, pg 969
Pro Stage Inc, pg 983
Sight & Sound Productions, pg 1010
Universal Studios Florida® Production Group, pg 1049

GEORGIA

Stage Front Presentation Systems, pg 1022

ILLINOIS

Allen Visual Systems Inc, pg 781
AV Chicago Inc, pg 797
Backstar Creative Media Inc, pg 801
Chicago Satellite & Video, pg 825
QuickSet International Inc, pg 989
RC Communications, pg 992
Show Department Inc, pg 1009

INDIANA

Digital Rain LLC, pg 847

KANSAS

KAKE-TV, pg 907

KENTUCKY

Audio Visual Techniques Inc, pg 796

MARYLAND

CPR MultiMedia Solutions, pg 837
Event Tech, pg 863

MASSACHUSETTS

massAV, pg 933
Preston Productions Inc, pg 981

MICHIGAN

Digi Sign Design LLC, pg 847
K&R All Media Productions Inc, pg 908
K&R's Recording Studios Inc, pg 908
On Stage Visuals, pg 963

MISSISSIPPI

Bowie Audio Visual Enterprises Inc, pg 811

MISSOURI

Show-Me Audio-Visual, pg 1009

NEBRASKA

Dog & Pony Productions Inc, pg 850

NEVADA

GES Audio Visual, pg 877
JCS Video Productions, pg 904

NEW JERSEY

Audio Visual Associates, pg 795
Audio Visual Dynamics®, pg 795
CFP Video Productions Inc, pg 823
Earl Girls Inc, pg 855
Giant Audio Visual Inc, pg 878
Starlite Productions, pg 1024
Wired 4 Sound Inc, pg 1068

NEW MEXICO

Production Outfitters, pg 984

NEW YORK

Audio Visual Resources LLC, pg 795
CP Communications, pg 837
Design Audio Visual Inc, pg 845
Hello World Communications, pg 888
KVL Audio Visual Services Inc, pg 914

NORTH CAROLINA

A&V Company, pg 772
The Communications Group Inc, pg 833
Take One Productions Ltd, pg 1031

OHIO

Hughie's Event Production Services, pg 892
Lyon Video Inc, pg 927
Mills James Productions, pg 943

OREGON

Northwest Film Center, pg 959
Rose City Sound, pg 999

PENNSYLVANIA

Advanced AV, pg 777
Audio Visual Communications Inc, pg 795
FMP Media Solutions Inc, pg 870
Grise Audio Visual Center Inc, pg 882

TENNESSEE

Love Shack Recording Studios, pg 925
Technical Support Systems LLC, pg 1034
Tennessee Visual Service Co, pg 1037

TEXAS

Alford Media Services, pg 780
Astro Audio Visual, pg 792
Industrial Audio/Video Inc, pg 897
The Samuels Co, pg 1002
Stage Directions, pg 1022

VIRGINIA

Lee Hartman & Sons Inc, pg 918
Quince Imaging Inc, pg 989

WASHINGTON

Victory Studios, pg 1054

WISCONSIN

Full Compass Systems, pg 874

PUERTO RICO

Stage Crew Audiovisual Inc, pg 1022

BRITISH COLUMBIA

Finale Editworks, pg 868

MANITOBA

Inland Audio Visual Ltd, pg 898

ONTARIO

Wanted! Sound + Picture, pg 1062
Westbury National Show Systems Ltd, pg 1064

QUEBEC

Group PVP, pg 882

Compact Disc Recorder & Player Repairs

CALIFORNIA

Advanced Media LLC, pg 778
Ametron Audio/Video, pg 785
McAlister Electronics, pg 935
Pro Camera Repair, pg 982
Towards 2000 Inc, pg 1043
VMI Inc, pg 1060

FLORIDA

Digital Video Systems Inc, pg 848
ELC Sales & Service Inc, pg 858
Hi-Tech Enterprises Inc, pg 888

GEORGIA

Stage Front Presentation Systems, pg 1022

ILLINOIS

Allen Visual Systems Inc, pg 781
Midwest Digital Corp, pg 942

KENTUCKY

Axxis Inc, pg 800
NOR-COM Inc, pg 958

MICHIGAN

TeL Systems, pg 1035

NEW JERSEY

Audio Visual Associates, pg 795
Earl Girls Inc, pg 855
Starlite Productions, pg 1024

OHIO

Tri-State Audio Visual Co, pg 1044

OREGON

All Service Musical Electronics Repair, pg 780

PENNSYLVANIA

J E Foss Co, pg 871

TENNESSEE

Technical Support Systems LLC, pg 1034

TEXAS

Astro Audio Visual, pg 792
Pro Video & Film Equipment Co Inc, pg 983
Tarpley Media Systems, pg 1032

WISCONSIN

Full Compass Systems, pg 874

ALBERTA

Infosat Communications Inc, pg 898

MANITOBA

Inland Audio Visual Ltd, pg 898

VIDEO

Compact Disc Recorder & Player Repairs (continued)

ONTARIO

Premier A/V Sales Ltd, pg 980
Westbury National Show Systems Ltd, pg 1064

Compression & Decompression Equipment Distributors

ARIZONA

EAR Professional Audio/Video, pg 855

ARKANSAS

Jay S Stanley & Associates Inc, pg 1023

CALIFORNIA

Ametron Audio/Video, pg 785
Computer Modules Inc, pg 834
Diaquest, pg 846
DiskFaktory Direct, pg 849
Electrosonic Inc, pg 859
Media Control Systems LLC, pg 936
MediaPOINTE, pg 938
Optibase Inc, pg 964
Pico Digital, pg 975
Promax Systems, pg 986
Snell, pg 1014
Videobotics, pg 1056
VMI Inc, pg 1060
VTP Inc, pg 1061

FLORIDA

Access Media Group, pg 773
Digital Video Systems Inc, pg 848
Harris Corp, pg 885
Pro Stage Inc, pg 983
Recording Media & Equipment Inc (RM&E), pg 993
Vela Research, pg 1052

GEORGIA

Ligos Corporation, pg 921
Simtrol Inc, pg 1011
Stage Front Presentation Systems, pg 1022

HAWAII

The Audio Visual Co (AVCO), pg 795

ILLINOIS

Joseph Electronics, pg 906
Toko America Inc, pg 1041

INDIANA

Sensory Technologies LLC, pg 1006
SHP Electronics, pg 1010

IOWA

ECS Inc, pg 856

KENTUCKY

NOR-COM Inc, pg 958

MAINE

Headlight Audio Visual Inc, pg 887

MARYLAND

TKH Security Solutions USA Inc, pg 1041

MASSACHUSETTS

Rule Broadcast Systems, pg 1000
SeaChange International Inc, pg 1005

MICHIGAN

ASC Systems, pg 791
Digi Sign Design LLC, pg 847

MINNESOTA

Alpha Video & Audio Inc, pg 782

MISSOURI

Modern Communications Inc, pg 944
Schiller's Audio-Visual, pg 1004
Southwest Audio-Visual Inc, pg 1019

NEW JERSEY

Diversified Systems Inc, pg 849
Starlite Productions, pg 1024
SYMCO Inc, pg 1030
Tele-Measurements Inc, pg 1035
Total Video Products Inc, pg 1042
Wired 4 Sound Inc, pg 1068

NEW YORK

Audio-Video Corp, pg 795
Custom Media Environments, pg 841
TecNec Distributing, pg 1035

OHIO

Tri-State Audio Visual Co, pg 1044

PENNSYLVANIA

AccuWeather Inc, pg 774
Advanced AV, pg 777
Innovision Media Group, pg 899
The Lerro Corp, pg 919

SOUTH DAKOTA

Sencore Inc, pg 1006

TENNESSEE

Lowrance Sound Co Inc, pg 925
Technical Support Systems LLC, pg 1034
Zion Music Group, pg 1074

TEXAS

Biway Media, pg 808
Media Management LLC, pg 937
Pro Video & Film Equipment Co Inc, pg 983
Tarpley Media Systems, pg 1032
Videotex Systems Inc, pg 1057

VIRGINIA

Filmdex Inc, pg 867

WISCONSIN

Audio Visual of Milwaukee Inc, pg 795
Full Compass Systems, pg 874
Safe Harbor Computers, pg 1001

MANITOBA

Inland Audio Visual Ltd, pg 898

Compression & Decompression Equipment Manufacturers

ARIZONA

Applied Integration Corp, pg 789

CALIFORNIA

Computer Modules Inc, pg 834
DiskFaktory Direct, pg 849
Doremi Labs, pg 851
Linkabit, pg 922
Optibase Inc, pg 964
Opticomm-EMCORE, pg 964
Snell, pg 1014
Telestream Inc, pg 1036
VITEC Multimedia, pg 1060

FLORIDA

CD ROM™ Inc, pg 822
Compuvideo Sales USA Ltd, pg 834
Vela Research, pg 1052

GEORGIA

Ligos Corporation, pg 921
Wegener Communications, pg 1063

ILLINOIS

Toko America Inc, pg 1041

MASSACHUSETTS

SeaChange International Inc, pg 1005

MINNESOTA

Vaddio, pg 1051

NEW JERSEY

Ikegami Electronics (USA) Inc, pg 894

NEW YORK

Laird Digital Cinema, pg 915
Judson Rosebush Co Inc, pg 999

OREGON

Grass Valley, pg 881

SOUTH DAKOTA

Sencore Inc, pg 1006

TENNESSEE

Adtec Digital Inc, pg 777

QUEBEC

Matrox Video Products Group, pg 934

Compression & Decompression Equipment Rentals

ARIZONA

Merestone, pg 938
Video West Inc, pg 1056

CALIFORNIA

Aaron & Le Duc, pg 772
Ametron Audio/Video, pg 785
Audio Rents, pg 794
Express Media Inc, pg 864
Golden Gate Studios, pg 880
Image Integration, pg 895
Lynch Communications, pg 926
Main Street Media Inc, pg 929
McCune Audio-Video-Lighting, pg 935
Muse Presentation Technologies, pg 950
PSSI, pg 987
Total Media Group, pg 1042
Twin Peaks Creative, pg 1047

COLORADO

Spectrum Audio Visual Services, pg 1020

FLORIDA

Access Media Group, pg 773
Pro Stage Inc, pg 983
Universal Studios Florida® Production Group, pg 1049

GEORGIA

Stage Front Presentation Systems, pg 1022

ILLINOIS

Chicago Satellite & Video, pg 825
QuickSet International Inc, pg 989
Show Department Inc, pg 1009

IOWA

ECS Inc, pg 856

KANSAS

KAKE-TV, pg 907

MARYLAND

CPR MultiMedia Solutions, pg 837
Event Tech, pg 863

MASSACHUSETTS

Preston Productions Inc, pg 981

MICHIGAN

Digi Sign Design LLC, pg 847
K&R All Media Productions Inc, pg 908

MINNESOTA

Alpha Video & Audio Inc, pg 782

MISSOURI

Show-Me Audio-Visual, pg 1009
Southwest Audio-Visual Inc, pg 1019

NEVADA

JCS Video Productions, pg 904

NEW JERSEY

Audio Visual Dynamics®, pg 795
Starlite Productions, pg 1024
Tele-Measurements Inc, pg 1035
Wired 4 Sound Inc, pg 1068

Compression & Decompression Equipment Repairs

Computer Graphics

VIDEO

Computer Graphics (continued)

FLORIDA (continued)

Sound & Vision Communications Inc, pg 1016
Sunfire Communications Inc, pg 1028
Sunrise Studios, pg 1028
Tricycle Studios, pg 1044
Universal Studios Florida® Production Group, pg 1049
Mike Vasilinda Productions Inc, pg 1052
Video Techniques Inc, pg 1056
Vistamax Productions, pg 1059

GEORGIA

Beachwood Productions, pg 804
Beast Atlanta, pg 804
Continental Film & Video, pg 835
Crawford Media Services, pg 838
The DVI Group, pg 854
ECG Productions, pg 856
Guerrilla Productions LLC, pg 883
Imagers, pg 896
Myriad Productions, pg 951
Outsource Engineering & Manufacturing Inc dba Texscan MSI, pg 966
Showcase Photo & Video, pg 1009
Staging Directions Inc, pg 1023

HAWAII

Hyperspective Studios Inc, pg 893
1013 Integrated, pg 1037
TV Juice Productions Inc, pg 1046

ILLINOIS

ABSA Productions Inc, pg 772
Airways Digital Media, pg 779
Analog Free Media, pg 786
AnswersMedia, pg 787
Beatty TeleVisual Productions, pg 804
Breeze Productions Inc, pg 812
CCore Media Inc, pg 821
Centrax Corp, pg 823
Chicago Satellite & Video, pg 825
Cresta Creative, pg 839
IV Media Resources, pg 903
Optimus, pg 964
Jim Passin Productions, pg 970
The Pepper Group, pg 972
The Prairie Production Group, pg 980
Richter Studios, pg 996
Roadworthy Image Magnification, pg 998
SCI Television Productions LLC, pg 1004
Sound/Video Impressions Inc, pg 1018
Southern Illinois University, pg 1019
Sparkfactor, pg 1019
Tele-Time Systems, pg 1036
20/20 Communications Inc, pg 1047
Video I-D Teleproductions Inc, pg 1055
Video Impressions, pg 1055
Waveland Software Inc, pg 1062

INDIANA

AVA Productions, pg 798
Bright Ideas Creative Services, pg 812
Covenant Productions®, pg 837
Explore Media LLC, pg 864
OMNI Productions, pg 962

IOWA

Iowa State University-Information Technology Services, pg 902

KANSAS

KAKE-TV, pg 907

KENTUCKY

Hammond Communications Group, pg 884
The PPS Group, pg 980

LOUISIANA

Digital FX Inc, pg 847
Launch Media, pg 916
Louisiana State University Health Sciences Center - Shreveport, pg 925
Moxie Media, pg 948
Vidox Motion Imagery, pg 1057
WVLA-TV, pg 1071
YES Productions, pg 1072

MARYLAND

Adventure Productions LLC, pg 778
CAS Video Productions, pg 820
CPR MultiMedia Solutions, pg 837
dbF a Media Company, pg 844
DBM Communications Inc, pg 844
Kramer Communications Video Production, pg 913
Library Video Network (LVN), pg 920
Media Dimensions Inc, pg 936
Mobile-Video Productions Inc, pg 944
Pro Cuts Editing Services, pg 982
Producers Video, pg 984
Quality Film & Video, pg 988
Shadowstone R & R™, pg 1008
Sheffield Audio/Video Productions, pg 1008
Sign Media Inc, pg 1011
Welocalize, pg 1063

MASSACHUSETTS

Award Productions, pg 800
Boston Productions Inc, pg 811
CommCreative, pg 832
Cramer Productions, pg 837
Home Inc, pg 890
Penfield Productions Ltd, pg 971
Preston Productions Inc, pg 981
TR Productions, pg 1043
TVN-The Video Network, pg 1046
Veritech Corp, pg 1053
WSI, pg 1070

MICHIGAN

ASC Systems, pg 791
Blue Mouse Studio, pg 809
Digi Sign Design LLC, pg 847
Digital Image Studios LLC, pg 847
K&R's Recording Studios Inc, pg 908
On Stage Visuals, pg 963
Progressive AE, pg 985
RingSide Creative, pg 997
Universal Images, pg 1049

MINNESOTA

The ADS Group, pg 777
Aggressive Records Audio Duplication LLC, pg 778
The Richard Diercks Co Inc, pg 846
Master Communications Group, pg 933
Worthwhile Films, pg 1070

MISSOURI

Avatar Studios, pg 798
Communitronics Corp, pg 833
Show-Me Audio-Visual, pg 1009
Substation K, pg 1027
Switch, pg 1030

MONTANA

North Country Media Group, pg 959
ooLite Media, pg 964

NEBRASKA

B & B Video Productions Inc, pg 801
Dog & Pony Productions Inc, pg 850
Rainbow Video Productions Inc, pg 991
Three Pillars Media, pg 1040

NEVADA

Aardvark Video & Media Productions, pg 772
Encore Productions Inc, pg 861
HDTV Productions Inc, pg 886
JCS Video Productions, pg 904

NEW HAMPSHIRE

Academic & Campus Technology Services, pg 773
Channell One Video, pg 824
NH Movies Inc, pg 957
Chip Taylor Communications LLC, pg 1032
The Troupe, pg 1045

NEW JERSEY

A-V Services Inc, pg 771
All Jersey Studios, pg 780
Audio Visual Dynamics®, pg 795
CD Meyer Inc, pg 822
CFP Video Productions Inc, pg 823
Deluxe Media Services, pg 845
Diversified Systems Inc, pg 849
DWJ Television, pg 854
Early Films, pg 855
Euro-Pacific Film & Video Productions Inc, pg 863
Laurel Video Productions, pg 916
MediaMix Inc, pg 937
MediaNow, pg 938
Megavideo Productions, pg 938
MIB Mediaworks, pg 941
Midnight Media Group Inc, pg 942
NFL Films Inc, pg 957
NFL Films Music Library, pg 957
Outside The Box Interactive LLC, pg 966
PLS Staging, pg 977
Shamrock Communications, pg 1008
Suede Interactive, pg 1027
VCSvideo, pg 1052
Video Ideas Productions, pg 1055
VTS Video & Media, pg 1061

NEW MEXICO

Production Outfitters, pg 984

NEW YORK

Air Sea Land Productions Inc (ASL), pg 779
American Artists Representatives Inc, pg 783
Animotion Inc, pg 787
aurora productions, pg 797
Big Film Design, pg 807
The Big House Group, pg 807
Chromavision Corp, pg 826
Cohn Creative Group LLC, pg 831
CPdigital, pg 837
Designomotion, pg 846
Digital Art Video Inc, pg 847
dM works, pg 849
Downtown Community Television Center (DCTV), pg 851
Eastco Multimedia Solutions Inc, pg 856
4-D Creative Media, pg 871
Giant Interactive, pg 878
Greyfalcon House, pg 882
Gurrilla Video Solutions, pg 883
Hallel Communications, pg 884
HAVE Inc, pg 886
HB-Content, pg 886
Heavy Melody, pg 887
Hello World Communications, pg 888
IAI Video, pg 893
L A Bruell Inc, pg 914
Lylofilm Productions, pg 926
Magnetic Post Production, pg 928
Manhattan Center Studios Inc, pg 930
Neal Marshad Productions, pg 931
Mood Creations Ltd, pg 946
Jack Morton Worldwide, pg 946
MRG Productions Inc, pg 948
MRY, pg 949
The Napoleon Group, pg 952
PostWorks, pg 979
PrimeLight Productions Inc, pg 982
R/GA, pg 990
Refinery, pg 994
Judson Rosebush Co Inc, pg 999
SmartPros Ltd, pg 1014
TBA Global Events, pg 1032
Teatown Communications Group, pg 1033
Technisphere Corp, pg 1034
TeleTime Productions, pg 1036
Visual Technologies Corp, pg 1060
WNET/NET TELECON, pg 1069

NORTH CAROLINA

All Pro Media Inc, pg 780
Pat Appleson Studios Inc, pg 788
The Communications Group Inc, pg 833
Horizon Video Productions Inc, pg 891
L A Management Co LLC, pg 914
LCW Productions LLC, pg 917
Moving Pictures, pg 948
NASCAR Media Group LLC, pg 952
On Location North Carolina, pg 963
Take One Productions Ltd, pg 1031
Unifour Productions Inc, pg 1048

NORTH DAKOTA

Media Productions, pg 937

OHIO

Advent Media Inc, pg 778
Aztec Video Productions, pg 801
Bartha, pg 803
Russ Beckner Pictures, pg 804
Cinecraft Productions Inc, pg 827
Clear Choice Creative Corp, pg 829
Commercial Video, pg 832
Creative Technology, pg 838
Cuyahoga Community College Media Center, pg 841
EDR Media LLC, pg 857

Computerized Animation Production Services, *see* Animation Production Services—Computerized

Computerized Editing, *see* Editing—Computerized

Consulting

VIDEO

Consulting (continued)

CALIFORNIA (continued)

Jaguar Distribution Corp, pg 903
JDS Video & Media Productions Inc, pg 904
KION-TV, pg 911
The Kitchen, pg 911
KPBS TV FM-San Diego, pg 913
KVIE-Channel 6, pg 914
Ludlow Media Solutions, pg 926
Lumeni Productions Inc, pg 926
Main Street Media Inc, pg 929
Maximus Media Inc, pg 934
McKay Conant Hoover Inc, pg 935
Media Magic, pg 937
Media Systems Design Group, pg 937
Mist Media Inc, pg 944
Moving Art by Louie Schwartzberg, pg 947
New & Unique Videos™, pg 955
Nolte Media, pg 958
ODC Publishing, pg 961
Panorama Productions, pg 968
Penrose Productions, pg 972
piXvfm, pg 976
Players Press, pg 977
PM Productions, pg 977
Point of View Productions, pg 977
POP TV, pg 978
Prime Cut Productions, pg 982
Promax Systems, pg 986
PSI Inc, pg 987
PSSI, pg 987
QRS Software Services, pg 988
Regent Press Publishers & Printers, pg 994
RetinaVision Productions, pg 995
Rough House, pg 1000
Ron Roy Productions/Moodtapes, pg 1000
Russ InVision Co/AbridgeClub.com, pg 1001
Sahara Records & Filmworks Entertainment Co, pg 1001
Randall Schiller Productions, pg 1004
Screen Door Entertainment Inc, pg 1005
Sea Studios Foundation, pg 1005
Semiconductor Services, pg 1006
SNAP, pg 1014
SonicPool, pg 1016
Staylor-Made Communications Inc, pg 1024
StereoScope International, pg 1024
Still N'Motion, pg 1025
Stunt Wings Adventure Sports Talent & Equipment, pg 1027
Tam Communications Inc, pg 1031
Technical Services, pg 1034
30 Second Films, pg 1039
Thorburn Associates, Acoustic, Technology, Lighting Design, pg 1039
Toon Makers, pg 1042
Total Media Group, pg 1042
Twin Peaks Creative, pg 1047
University of Southern California, pg 1050
Via Verde Productions, pg 1053
Videobotics, pg 1056
Videolady, pg 1057
Videowerks, pg 1057
Visions Plus, pg 1058
VMI Inc, pg 1060
WARPed Pictures, pg 1062
Wavemaker Media Design, pg 1062
West Coast Projections Inc, pg 1063
Z-Ville Productions, pg 1073

COLORADO

D L Adams Associates Inc, pg 775
Paul L Anderson Productions Inc, pg 786
Blue River Productions, pg 810
Conly Productions, pg 835
Daylight Productions & Rentals, pg 844
Flashback Media Productions, pg 869
G W Hannaway & Associates, pg 884
Maniac Productions, pg 930
Old Army Press (OAP), pg 961
Rocky Mountain Audio/Video Productions Inc, pg 998
Spectrum Audio Visual Services, pg 1020
Transtar Entertainment Co Inc, pg 1043
Z-Axis Corp, pg 1073

CONNECTICUT

ACM Productions Ltd, pg 774
Antenna International, pg 787
Applebox Studio, pg 788
Boyce Nemec Designs, pg 811
BRB Audiovisual Productions, pg 812
Broadcast Video Productions LLC, pg 813
Crossroads Video, pg 840
Fox Connecticut, pg 872
The Gary-Paul Agency, pg 875
Geomatrix Productions, pg 877
Guymark Studios LLC, pg 883
Ironik Design & Post, pg 902
MAVCO, pg 934
MCC Films, pg 935
Moving Pictures, pg 947
New London Media, pg 956
Palace Digital Studios, pg 967
P&P Studios Inc, pg 968
Video Automation Systems Inc, pg 1054
Video Production Associates Inc, pg 1056

DELAWARE

So Smart Productions, pg 1015

DISTRICT OF COLUMBIA

Durrin Productions Inc, pg 854
Hillmann & Carr Inc, pg 889
Susan Hormuth, Visual Resource Consultant, pg 891
Interface Media Group, pg 900
Metro Teleproductions Inc (MTI), pg 939
O'Keefe Communications Inc, pg 961
Yellow Cat Productions Inc, pg 1072

FLORIDA

Access Media Group, pg 773
Allegro Productions Inc, pg 781
America By Air Stock Footage Library, pg 783
Civins Productions Inc, pg 828
Communications Concepts Inc (CCI), pg 833
Courter Films LLC, pg 837
Digital Video Systems Inc, pg 848
Eastern Video, pg 856
Ed Ethridge Productions Inc, pg 863
Florida Digital Studios, pg 870
Griffiths Broadcast Co Inc, pg 882
Gulf Coast Audio Visual Producers Inc, pg 883
Hi-Tech Enterprises Inc, pg 888
Home Shopping Network (HSN), pg 890
Media Entertainment Inc, pg 936
National Teleproductions Inc, pg 953
Pro Stage Inc, pg 983
Progressive Media & Music, pg 985
Roger Scruggs Films, pg 1005
Shooting Stars Post Inc, pg 1009
Sight & Sound Productions, pg 1010
Sound & Vision Communications Inc, pg 1016
Sunfire Communications Inc, pg 1028
Sunrise Studios, pg 1028
Tricycle Studios, pg 1044
Universal Studios Florida® Production Group, pg 1049
Mike Vasilinda Productions Inc, pg 1052
Video Techniques Inc, pg 1056
Vistamax Productions, pg 1059

GEORGIA

Beast Atlanta, pg 804
Burst Video/Film Inc, pg 815
COMPRO Productions Inc, pg 834
Continental Film & Video, pg 835
ECG Productions, pg 856
Guerrilla Productions LLC, pg 883
Lighting & Production Equipment Inc, pg 920
Myriad Productions, pg 951
Malcolm Neal Productions, pg 954
On-Line Productions, pg 963
Showcase Photo & Video, pg 1009
Staging Directions Inc, pg 1023

HAWAII

DL Adams Associates Ltd, pg 775
Ken Herkes Productions & Entertainment (KHPE), pg 888
Hyperspective Studios Inc, pg 893
KHNL/KGMB, pg 910
Media Bridge Gamekids, pg 936
1013 Integrated, pg 1037
TV Juice Productions Inc, pg 1046

IDAHO

KTVB-TV, pg 914
Brad Shaw Productions Inc, pg 1008
Wide Eye Productions, pg 1066

ILLINOIS

ABSA Productions Inc, pg 772
Accenture, pg 773
Airways Digital Media, pg 779
Analog Free Media, pg 786
AnswersMedia, pg 787
Audio Visual Services Corp, pg 796
Beatty TeleVisual Productions, pg 804
Breeze Productions Inc, pg 812
CCore Media Inc, pg 821
Chicago Satellite & Video, pg 825
Communications Corporation of America, pg 833
Comtech Multimedia Marketing, pg 834
Creative Technology, pg 838
Cresta Creative, pg 839
Extraordinary Demos, pg 864
Film Police, pg 867
IV Media Resources, pg 903
The Market Place, pg 931
Mimi Productions, pg 943
On Site Video, pg 963
Jim Passin Productions, pg 970
The Pepper Group, pg 972
Perspectives Media, pg 973
PSAV® Presentation Services (Hotel Services Division), pg 987
Richter Studios, pg 996
SCI Television Productions LLC, pg 1004
Sound/Video Impressions Inc, pg 1018
Southern Illinois University, pg 1019
Sparkfactor, pg 1019
Terra Nova Films Inc, pg 1037
20/20 Communications Inc, pg 1047
Video I-D Teleproductions Inc, pg 1055
Video Impressions, pg 1055
WEEK TV, pg 1063

INDIANA

AVA Productions, pg 798
Bright Ideas Creative Services, pg 812
Digital Rain LLC, pg 847
Explore Media LLC, pg 864
PentaVision Communications Inc, pg 972

IOWA

Iowa State University-Information Technology Services, pg 902
The Production House, pg 984

KANSAS

KAKE-TV, pg 907

KENTUCKY

Axxis Inc, pg 800
Broadway Digital, pg 813
Hammond Communications Group, pg 884
Idle Minds Productions Inc, pg 894
NOR-COM Inc, pg 958
Prosper Media Group Inc, pg 986
WKYT Productions, pg 1068

LOUISIANA

Digital FX Inc, pg 847
Louisiana State University Health Sciences Center - Shreveport, pg 925
Moxie Media, pg 948
Vidox Motion Imagery, pg 1057
WVLA-TV, pg 1071

MAINE

Slim Goodbody Corp, pg 1013

MARYLAND

The Ahern Group, pg 779
CPR MultiMedia Solutions, pg 837
dbF a Media Company, pg 844
DBM Communications Inc, pg 844
The Image Generators, pg 895
James Agee Film Project, pg 904
Kramer Communications Video Production, pg 913
Library Video Network (LVN), pg 920
Media Dimensions Inc, pg 936
Mobile-Video Productions Inc, pg 944
Producers Video, pg 984
Spectrum Productions, pg 1021
Welocalize, pg 1063

MASSACHUSETTS

Award Productions, pg 800
Capron Lighting & Sound Co Inc, pg 819
Cavanaugh Tocci Associates Inc, pg 821
CommCreative, pg 832
Communications Design Associates, pg 833
Cramer Productions, pg 837
Documentary Educational Resources Inc, pg 850
Green Mountain Post Films (GMP), pg 882
Home Inc, pg 890
Monadnock Media Inc, pg 945
MotionArt Studios, pg 947
Northern Light Productions, pg 959
Penfield Productions Ltd, pg 971
PixMix Video Services, pg 976
Gabriel Polonsky Studio, pg 978
Preston Productions Inc, pg 981
TVN-The Video Network, pg 1046
Veritech Corp, pg 1053
WVP Boston, pg 1071

MICHIGAN

ASC Systems, pg 791
Benjamin Creative Productions, pg 805
Digi Sign Design LLC, pg 847
K&R's Recording Studios Inc, pg 908
Michigan Recording Arts Institute & Technologies, pg 941
On Stage Visuals, pg 963
The Program Source International, pg 985
Technology Learning Services, pg 1035

MINNESOTA

The ADS Group, pg 777
Aggressive Records Audio Duplication LLC, pg 778
Beyers Sound & Essay Audio, pg 806
Big Event Productions LLC, pg 807
The Richard Diercks Co Inc, pg 846
House of Cinemagraphics, pg 891
Jamieson & Associates Inc, pg 904
Master Communications Group, pg 933
Media Loft Inc, pg 937
MultiMedia, pg 950
Phil Sykes & Associates Inc, pg 974
Worthwhile Films, pg 1070

MISSOURI

Avatar Studios, pg 798
Communitronics Corp, pg 833
Production Consultants, pg 984
Schiller's Audio-Visual, pg 1004
Show-Me Audio-Visual, pg 1009
Switch, pg 1030
Visionworks Design Services Inc, pg 1059

MONTANA

KCFW Television, pg 908
North Country Media Group, pg 959

NEBRASKA

Dog & Pony Productions Inc, pg 850
Rainbow Video Productions Inc, pg 991
Three Pillars Media, pg 1040

NEVADA

Aardvark Video & Media Productions, pg 772
DVDs4Less, pg 854
Encore Productions Inc, pg 861
HDTV Productions Inc, pg 886
JCS Video Productions, pg 904
Lefco Video Services Inc, pg 918

NEW HAMPSHIRE

Academic & Campus Technology Services, pg 773
Apertura, pg 788
Channell One Video, pg 824
Chip Taylor Communications LLC, pg 1032
The Troupe, pg 1045

NEW JERSEY

A-V Services Inc, pg 771
All Jersey Studios, pg 780
Audio Visual Dynamics®, pg 795
Broadcast Center Studios, pg 813
CD Meyer Inc, pg 822
CFP Video Productions Inc, pg 823
Diversified Systems Inc, pg 849
Emanuel Audiovisual Consultants, pg 860
Euro-Pacific Film & Video Productions Inc, pg 863
Laurel Video Productions, pg 916
MediaNow, pg 938
Megavideo Productions, pg 938
MIB Mediaworks, pg 941
Midnight Media Group Inc, pg 942
Ray Mueller Productions, pg 949
NFL Films Inc, pg 957
Outside The Box Interactive LLC, pg 966
PatchAmp, pg 970
PLS Staging, pg 977
Producer East Productions, pg 983
Public Eye Productions, pg 987
Reed Presentations Inc (RPI), pg 993
Starlite Productions, pg 1024
Suede Interactive, pg 1027
Telemanagement Resources International Inc (TRI), pg 1036
Varto Technologies, pg 1052
VCSvideo, pg 1052
Video Ideas Productions, pg 1055
Wired 4 Sound Inc, pg 1068
York Telecom, pg 1072

NEW MEXICO

Mountainair Films, pg 947
Production Outfitters, pg 984

NEW YORK

Air Sea Land Productions Inc (ASL), pg 779
Animotion Inc, pg 787
aurora productions, pg 797
Norman N Axelrod Associates, pg 800
Bellin Productions, pg 805
Bevilacqua Studios, pg 806
The Big House Group, pg 807
BZ/Rights & Permissions Inc, pg 816
Christian TV Services of Ellicottville, NY, pg 825
Chromavision Corp, pg 826
Cohn Creative Group LLC, pg 831
Designomotion, pg 846
Digital Art Video Inc, pg 847
dM works, pg 849
Downtown Community Television Center (DCTV), pg 851
Eastco Multimedia Solutions Inc, pg 856
Edgeware Associates/Travel Arts Syndicate, pg 856
Four Corners Productions, pg 871
4-D Creative Media, pg 871
GHO Group LLC, pg 878
Giant Interactive, pg 878
Greyfalcon House, pg 882
Gurrilla Video Solutions, pg 883
Hallel Communications, pg 884
HAVE Inc, pg 886
HB-Content, pg 886
Hello World Communications, pg 888
IAI Video, pg 893
Icontent, pg 893
Richard Kaplan Productions, pg 908
Kinetic Arts, pg 911
L A Bruell Inc, pg 914
L&P Media, pg 915
Lylofilm Productions, pg 926
Neal Marshad Productions, pg 931
Mood Creations Ltd, pg 946
Jack Morton Worldwide, pg 946
MRG Productions Inc, pg 948
MRY, pg 949
News Broadcast Network, pg 956
NSR Productions Inc & Capricorn Five Films, pg 960
Pat Kogan Productions Inc, pg 970
PostWorks, pg 979
PrimaLux Video Inc, pg 982
Refinery, pg 994
Judson Rosebush Co Inc, pg 999
Shadow Pictures Inc, pg 1007
Shen Milsom & Wilke LLC, pg 1008
D S Simon Productions, pg 1011
SmartPros Ltd, pg 1014
Synaptic Digital, pg 1030
TBA Global Events, pg 1032
Teatown Communications Group, pg 1033
Technisphere Corp, pg 1034
Third World Newsreel/Camera News Inc, pg 1039
Tobin Productions Inc, pg 1041
VIEW Inc (Video International Entertainment World Inc), pg 1058
Visual Technologies Corp, pg 1060
Visual Word Systems Inc, pg 1060
White Buffalo Multimedia, pg 1065
Willow Mixed Media Inc, pg 1067
WNET/NET TELECON, pg 1069
Zelman Studios Ltd, pg 1073

NORTH CAROLINA

All Pro Media Inc, pg 780
Pat Appleson Studios Inc, pg 788
Bill Barnes Video Productions LLC, pg 803
Lawrence Behr Associates Inc, pg 804
Camcor Inc, pg 818
The Communications Group Inc, pg 833
Duke Media Services, pg 853
Franklin Video Inc, pg 872
Horizon Video Productions Inc, pg 891
LCW Productions LLC, pg 917
Moving Pictures, pg 948
NASCAR Media Group LLC, pg 952
On Location North Carolina, pg 963
Sinclair Institute, pg 1012
Special Event Services, pg 1020
Take One Productions Ltd, pg 1031
Unifour Productions Inc, pg 1048

NORTH DAKOTA

UND Television Center, pg 1048

OHIO

Advent Media Inc, pg 778
Aztec Video Productions, pg 801
Bartha, pg 803
Russ Beckner Pictures, pg 804
CET, pg 823
Challenge Productions, pg 823
Commercial Video, pg 832
Copp Integrated Systems, pg 836
Creative Technology, pg 838
EDR Media LLC, pg 857
Griesinger Films LLC, pg 882
iVideo Technologies, pg 903
Lyon Video Inc, pg 927
MainSail Production Services Inc, pg 929
Mills James Productions, pg 943
Production Partners Media, pg 984
R&B Communications Inc, pg 991
Take 1 Media Services, pg 1031
Treehaus Communications Inc, pg 1044
VGI Productions, pg 1053
Vista Color Imaging Inc, pg 1059

OKLAHOMA

Garman Productions LLC, pg 875
PDC Productions, pg 970
Smart Concepts Ltd, pg 1013
University of Oklahoma Academic Media & Digital Services, pg 1050

OREGON

A KTVA Production LLC, pg 771
InterVision Media, pg 902
MediaFX, pg 937
Producers Studio, pg 984
Production West, pg 985
Spectrum Systems Design, pg 1021
Spirit Media, pg 1021
Sugar Mountain PR, pg 1028

PENNSYLVANIA

Argentine Productions Inc, pg 789
Bang Pictures, pg 802
Beholder Productions Inc, pg 804
FMP Media Solutions Inc, pg 870
Fusion Brand Experiences, pg 874
Goodman Associates Inc, pg 880
Innovision Media Group, pg 899
JPL, pg 906
Main Point Productions, pg 929
Panta Rhei Media Inc, pg 968
Pemcor LLC, pg 971
Producers Management Television (PMTV), pg 983
Production Masters Inc (PMI), pg 984
Scala Inc, pg 1003
The Videohouse Inc, pg 1057
The Whale Video Co, pg 1065
WPHL-TV, pg 1070

RHODE ISLAND

Sound-FX-Design, pg 1017

SOUTH CAROLINA

American Production Services LLC, pg 785
Genesis Creative, pg 877
Stages Video Productions, pg 1023

VIDEO

Consulting (continued)

TENNESSEE

American Blackguard Inc, pg 784
Fricon Entertainment Co Inc,
 pg 873
Marine Geographic, pg 931
Memphis Communications Corp,
 pg 938
Motion Picture Services, pg 947
Paradigm Marketing & Creative,
 pg 969
Running Pony Productions LLC,
 pg 1000
Scripps Networks, pg 1005
Stage Post, pg 1022
Russ Sturgeon Productions/RSVP,
 pg 1027
UMCom Productions, pg 1048
WKPT-TV, pg 1068
Zion Music Group, pg 1074

TEXAS

AMS Pictures, pg 786
AVES Audio Visual Systems Inc,
 pg 798
Biway Media, pg 808
Castleview Productions, pg 821
Cerutti Productions Inc, pg 823
Communication Arts Multimedia
 Inc, pg 832
Digi-matics, pg 847
Dykeman Associates Inc, pg 854
The Editing Co, pg 857
Epic Software Group Inc, pg 862
First Group Communications Inc,
 pg 868
Horizon Film + Video Productions,
 pg 891
Imagine Communications Corp,
 pg 896
Matson Multi-Media, pg 934
Mediaforce Productions, pg 937
Earl Miller Productions Inc, pg 943
Julye Newlin Productions Inc,
 pg 956
Out of the BLUE Media, pg 966
Phillips MediaSource, pg 974
R&O Studios, pg 991
Romar Learning, pg 999
The Samuels Co, pg 1002
South Coast Film & Video, pg 1019
Texas Heart Institute Visual
 Communication Services,
 pg 1037

UTAH

ImageWorks Communications,
 pg 896
Redman Movies & Stories, pg 993
Spectrum Engineers, pg 1021

VIRGINIA

Advance Concepts Inc, pg 777
Allied Media Corp, pg 781
BES Studios, pg 805
CACI Productions Group, pg 816
CALIBRE, pg 816
CDR Communications Inc, pg 822
Computer Sciences Corp, pg 834
Eagle Films, pg 855
EFX Media, pg 858
Gingerbread Productions, pg 878
Limelight Communications Inc,
 pg 921
Metro Productions, pg 939
Quince Imaging Inc, pg 989
Rocktown Media, pg 998
Video Solutions, pg 1056

WASHINGTON

Adams Creative & Production
 Services, pg 775
Bennett-Watt HD Productions Inc,
 pg 805
Global Net Productions Inc, pg 879
Kostov Productions, pg 913
Laser Fantasy/HECK Industries/
 Photon Manufacturing, pg 916
Media Elite Productions, pg 936
Medical Media Systems, pg 938
North-by-Northwest Productions,
 pg 958
Pal Productions Inc, pg 967
Pro Image, pg 983
Ritchie's Perfect Press, pg 997
Victory Studios, pg 1054

WEST VIRGINIA

Focus on Animals, pg 870

WISCONSIN

Audio Visual of Milwaukee Inc,
 pg 795
Full Compass Systems, pg 874
Grassland Media Inc, pg 881
Learning Technology Services,
 pg 917
Media Communications
 Association-International (MCA-
 I), pg 936
Meridian Studios, pg 939
ProVideo, pg 986
University of Wisconsin-Oshkosh
 Radio-TV-Film Dept, pg 1050
USAV Group Inc, pg 1050
Video Wisconsin Inc, pg 1056
Watts Communications Inc, pg 1062
Wisconsin Public Television,
 pg 1068

WYOMING

Bridger Productions Inc, pg 812

PUERTO RICO

Stage Crew Audiovisual Inc,
 pg 1022

ALBERTA

Black Media Works, pg 808
Global Television Station, pg 879

BRITISH COLUMBIA

DWD Theatre Design & Consulting,
 pg 854
Finale Editworks, pg 868
Triad Communications Ltd, pg 1044

MANITOBA

Spectra Video Productions Ltd,
 pg 1020
Tek Gear, pg 1035

NEWFOUNDLAND AND LABRADOR

Vidcraft Productions Ltd, pg 1054

ONTARIO

ADS Media, pg 777
Artaflex Inc, pg 791
Cinema Stage Inc, pg 827
Edcom Multimedia Products,
 pg 856
GAPC (General Assembly
 Production Centre), pg 875
Gesturetek, pg 877
JFB Communications, pg 905

Kimono Surf Studios, pg 911
Marblemedia, pg 930
Purefire Communications Inc,
 pg 987
State of the Art Acoustik Inc,
 pg 1024
Technovision® Interactive Inc,
 pg 1035
Video Excellence Productions,
 pg 1055

QUEBEC

Group PVP, pg 882
Sceno Plus, pg 1004
20k, pg 1047

Control System & Equipment Distributors

ALABAMA

PESA, pg 973

ARIZONA

EAR Professional Audio/Video,
 pg 855

ARKANSAS

Jay S Stanley & Associates Inc,
 pg 1023

CALIFORNIA

Ametron Audio/Video, pg 785
Be Media, pg 804
Cibola Systems, pg 826
Delicate Electronics Sales Inc,
 pg 845
Diaquest, pg 846
Electrosonic Inc, pg 859
FXC Communications, pg 874
Innovision Optics, pg 899
JD Audio Visual Inc, pg 904
Media Control Systems LLC,
 pg 936
MediaPOINTE, pg 938
Photodyne Technologies, pg 974
POP TV, pg 978
Southern California Sound Image
 Inc, pg 1019
Videobotics, pg 1056
VTP Inc, pg 1061

CONNECTICUT

Everett Hall Associates Inc, pg 863

FLORIDA

Access Media Group, pg 773
Alcorn McBride Inc, pg 780
AVI-SPL, pg 798
Digital Video Systems Inc, pg 848
Harris Corp, pg 885
Hi-Tech Enterprises Inc, pg 888
Midtown Video Inc, pg 942
Pro Stage Inc, pg 983
Sight & Sound Productions,
 pg 1010

GEORGIA

Clark, pg 829
Stage Front Presentation Systems,
 pg 1022

HAWAII

The Audio Visual Co (AVCO),
 pg 795

ILLINOIS

Allen Visual Systems Inc, pg 781
Joseph Electronics, pg 906
Quintessence Audio Ltd, pg 989
Sound Vision Inc, pg 1018

INDIANA

Lee Co Inc, pg 918
Sensory Technologies LLC, pg 1006
SHP Electronics, pg 1010

IOWA

ECS Inc, pg 856

KENTUCKY

Axxis Inc, pg 800
NOR-COM Inc, pg 958

MARYLAND

Image Logic Corp, pg 895
Noventri, pg 960

MASSACHUSETTS

Antronics Inc, pg 787
Rule Broadcast Systems, pg 1000

MICHIGAN

Ascom Communications
 Contractors, pg 791
On Stage Visuals, pg 963

MINNESOTA

Alpha Video & Audio Inc, pg 782

MISSOURI

MIS Technologies, pg 944
Modern Communications Inc,
 pg 944
Schiller's Audio-Visual, pg 1004
Southwest Audio-Visual Inc,
 pg 1019

NEW JERSEY

Alltec Stores, a Vcom IMC
 Company, pg 782
Audio Visual Associates, pg 795
AV Bluebook, pg 797
Diversified Systems Inc, pg 849
Earl Girls Inc, pg 855
Hamilton Buhl, pg 884
MCCOM Inc, pg 935
National Audio-Visual Supply,
 pg 952
Starlite Productions, pg 1024
Tele-Measurements Inc, pg 1035
Total Video Products Inc, pg 1042
Wired 4 Sound Inc, pg 1068

NEW YORK

Audio-Video Corp, pg 795
Creative Stage Lighting Co Inc,
 pg 838
Custom Media Environments,
 pg 841
Design Audio Visual Inc, pg 845
General Audio-Visual Inc (GAVI),
 pg 876
Presentation Products Inc, pg 981

NORTH CAROLINA

Crispin Corp, pg 839

OHIO

Jimmy Rea Electronics Inc, pg 992
Smithall Electronics Inc, pg 1014

Tri-State Audio Visual Co, pg 1044
Vincent Lighting Systems, pg 1058

PENNSYLVANIA

Advanced AV, pg 777
Clair Brothers Audio Systems Inc, pg 829
The Lerro Corp, pg 919
Rossman Audio LLC, pg 1000
Vistacom Inc, pg 1059

RHODE ISLAND

Shanix Inc, pg 1008

TENNESSEE

Lowrance Sound Co Inc, pg 925
Technical Support Systems LLC, pg 1034

TEXAS

Audio Visual Technologies Group, pg 796
Biway Media, pg 808
Data Display Audio Visual Co LP, pg 843
Data Projections Inc, pg 843
Digital Display Solutions Inc, pg 847
Graftek Imaging Inc, pg 881
Industrial Audio/Video Inc, pg 897
Omega Broadcast Group, pg 962
Pro Video & Film Equipment Co Inc, pg 983
Tarpley Media Systems, pg 1032

UTAH

SirsiDynix, pg 1012

VIRGINIA

Avitecture Inc, pg 799
Intellidyne LLC, pg 899

WISCONSIN

Audio Visual of Milwaukee Inc, pg 795
Full Compass Systems, pg 874
Safe Harbor Computers, pg 1001

ALBERTA

Infosat Communications Inc, pg 898

BRITISH COLUMBIA

Norsat International Inc, pg 958

MANITOBA

Inland Audio Visual Ltd, pg 898

ONTARIO

Cinema Stage Inc, pg 827
Soundmaster Group, pg 1018
Technovision® Interactive Inc, pg 1035
Westbury National Show Systems Ltd, pg 1064

Control System & Equipment Manufacturers

ALABAMA

PESA, pg 973

ARIZONA

Media Computing Inc, pg 936

CALIFORNIA

ALTINEX Inc, pg 783
CohuHD, pg 831
Diaquest, pg 846
FM Systems Inc, pg 870
FutureVideo, pg 874
Innovision Optics, pg 899
Jupiter Systems, pg 907
Media Control Systems LLC, pg 936
Photodyne Technologies, pg 974
POP TV, pg 978
RetinaVision Productions, pg 995
Simon - Kaloi Engineering, pg 1011
TV Pro Gear, pg 1046
Videobotics, pg 1056
Xantech LLC, pg 1071

COLORADO

Clear Blue Audio Video, pg 829

FLORIDA

Alcorn McBride Inc, pg 780
Compuvideo Sales USA Ltd, pg 834
Harris Corp, pg 885

GEORGIA

Barco Inc, pg 803
Outsource Engineering & Manufacturing Inc dba Texscan MSI, pg 966
Simtrol Inc, pg 1011
Wegener Communications, pg 1063

MARYLAND

Image Logic Corp, pg 895

MICHIGAN

Leightronix Inc, pg 918

MINNESOTA

Vaddio, pg 1051

NEW JERSEY

Crestron Electronics Inc, pg 839
FSR Inc, pg 873
Starlite Productions, pg 1024
Telemetrics Inc, pg 1036

NEW YORK

Norman N Axelrod Associates, pg 800
Monroe Electronics Inc, pg 945
Vicon Industries Inc, pg 1053

PENNSYLVANIA

Rossman Audio LLC, pg 1000
Scala Inc, pg 1003

TENNESSEE

Adtec Digital Inc, pg 777

TEXAS

Contemporary Research, pg 835

UTAH

SirsiDynix, pg 1012

BRITISH COLUMBIA

Norsat International Inc, pg 958
Richmond Sound Design Ltd, pg 996

ONTARIO

McCurdy Radio Ltd, pg 935
Soundmaster Group, pg 1018
Technovision® Interactive Inc, pg 1035

Control System & Equipment Rentals

ARIZONA

Merestone, pg 938
Video West Inc, pg 1056

CALIFORNIA

Aaron & Le Duc, pg 772
Ametron Audio/Video, pg 785
Bexel Corp, pg 806
Express Media Inc, pg 864
Innovision Optics, pg 899
JD Audio Visual Inc, pg 904
Lynch Communications, pg 926
McCune Audio-Video-Lighting, pg 935
Munday & Collins AV, pg 950
Muse Presentation Technologies, pg 950
RetinaVision Productions, pg 995
Slate Media Group, pg 1013
Total Media Group, pg 1042
Twin Peaks Creative, pg 1047

COLORADO

Spectrum Audio Visual Services, pg 1020

CONNECTICUT

Everett Hall Associates Inc, pg 863
Videofilm Systems Inc, pg 1057

FLORIDA

Midtown Video Inc, pg 942
Paradise Show & Design Inc, pg 969
Pro Stage Inc, pg 983
Sight & Sound Productions, pg 1010

GEORGIA

Stage Front Presentation Systems, pg 1022

ILLINOIS

Allen Visual Systems Inc, pg 781
Backstar Creative Media Inc, pg 801
Creative Technology, pg 838
QuickSet International Inc, pg 989
RC Communications, pg 992
Show Department Inc, pg 1009

IOWA

ECS Inc, pg 856

KANSAS

KAKE-TV, pg 907

KENTUCKY

Audio Visual Techniques Inc, pg 796

MARYLAND

CPR MultiMedia Solutions, pg 837

MASSACHUSETTS

AVFX Inc, pg 798
Preston Productions Inc, pg 981

MICHIGAN

K&R's Recording Studios Inc, pg 908
On Stage Visuals, pg 963

MINNESOTA

Alpha Video & Audio Inc, pg 782

MISSOURI

Show-Me Audio-Visual, pg 1009
Southwest Audio-Visual Inc, pg 1019

NEW JERSEY

Earl Girls Inc, pg 855
PLS Staging, pg 977
Starlite Productions, pg 1024
Tele-Measurements Inc, pg 1035
Wired 4 Sound Inc, pg 1068

NEW MEXICO

Production Outfitters, pg 984

NEW YORK

CP Communications, pg 837
Creative Stage Lighting Co Inc, pg 838
Manhattan Center Studios Inc, pg 930
TBA Global Events, pg 1032

NORTH CAROLINA

A&V Company, pg 772

OHIO

Lyon Video Inc, pg 927
Vincent Lighting Systems, pg 1058

PENNSYLVANIA

Advanced AV, pg 777
FMP Media Solutions Inc, pg 870

TENNESSEE

Technical Support Systems LLC, pg 1034

TEXAS

Alford Media Services, pg 780
Omega Broadcast Group, pg 962
The Samuels Co, pg 1002

VIRGINIA

Quince Imaging Inc, pg 989

WASHINGTON

Victory Studios, pg 1054

WISCONSIN

Full Compass Systems, pg 874

MANITOBA

Inland Audio Visual Ltd, pg 898

ONTARIO

Wanted! Sound + Picture, pg 1062
Westbury National Show Systems Ltd, pg 1064

VIDEO

Control System & Equipment Repairs

CALIFORNIA

Ametron Audio/Video, pg 785
Electrosonic Inc, pg 859
Media Control Systems LLC, pg 936

FLORIDA

ELC Sales & Service Inc, pg 858
Hi-Tech Enterprises Inc, pg 888
Midtown Video Inc, pg 942

GEORGIA

Stage Front Presentation Systems, pg 1022

ILLINOIS

Allen Visual Systems Inc, pg 781

IOWA

ECS Inc, pg 856

KENTUCKY

Axxis Inc, pg 800
NOR-COM Inc, pg 958

MICHIGAN

TeL Systems, pg 1035

MINNESOTA

Alpha Video & Audio Inc, pg 782

MISSOURI

Southwest Audio-Visual Inc, pg 1019

NEW JERSEY

Audio Visual Associates, pg 795
Earl Girls Inc, pg 855
Starlite Productions, pg 1024

OHIO

Vincent Lighting Systems, pg 1058

OREGON

All Service Musical Electronics Repair, pg 780

TENNESSEE

Technical Support Systems LLC, pg 1034

TEXAS

Pro Video & Film Equipment Co Inc, pg 983
Tarpley Media Systems, pg 1032

VIRGINIA

Intellidyne LLC, pg 899

WISCONSIN

Full Compass Systems, pg 874

ALBERTA

Infosat Communications Inc, pg 898

MANITOBA

Inland Audio Visual Ltd, pg 898

ONTARIO

Westbury National Show Systems Ltd, pg 1064

Co-Production Services

ALABAMA

CMEInfo, pg 830
Diamond Studios, pg 846
Dogwood Recording Studios, pg 850
Media Visions Inc, pg 937

ALASKA

Alaska Film Services Inc, pg 779
Aurora Films, pg 797

ARIZONA

Creative Backstage, pg 838
Direct Current Video Productions, pg 848
Film Creations Ltd, pg 867
Fox 10 Productions (KSAZ-TV), pg 872
MediaWorks, pg 938
Merestone, pg 938
On-Site Video, pg 963
Phoenix VideoFilms®, pg 974
Rodeo Video Inc, pg 998
Tellens Inc, pg 1037
Video Media Productions (VMP), pg 1055

ARKANSAS

Live'N'Loud, pg 923
Shadowbox Video Productions, pg 1007

CALIFORNIA

A&I, pg 771
Aaron & Le Duc, pg 772
Access Video in Berkeley, pg 773
All Video Productions, pg 781
Artichoke Productions, pg 791
Automated Entertainment, pg 797
Backstage Pass Entertainment Inc, pg 801
Barbosa Video Services, pg 802
Bennett Media Corp, pg 805
Blind, pg 809
Bridge Publications Inc, pg 812
Coastline Productions, pg 831
Concrete Images, pg 835
Crystal Pyramid Productions™, pg 840
Custom Video Productions Inc, pg 841
deKramer Productions Inc, pg 845
Design Media, pg 845
Direct Images Interactive Inc, pg 848
Dogma Studios, pg 850
Dolphin MultiMedia Inc, pg 850
Tom Donald Films, pg 850
ECONEWS (Environmental Television Series) & (Environmental Directions Radio Series), pg 856
Express Media Inc, pg 864
Face Digital Post, pg 865
First Camera, pg 868
First Person™, pg 868
FJ Productions Inc, pg 869
Full Moon & High Tide Productions & Studios, pg 874

FXF Productions Inc, pg 874
Geddes Productions LLC, pg 876
Glenray Productions Inc, pg 878
Global Village Productions, pg 879
Goal Productions, pg 879
Havas Edge, pg 885
iCorpTv, pg 893
imageReal Pictures LLC, pg 896
Imageworks, pg 896
InVision Productions, pg 902
Ishtar Films, pg 902
ITV Productions, pg 903
Jaguar Distribution Corp, pg 903
JDS Video & Media Productions Inc, pg 904
JFA Studio, pg 905
K2B2 Records, pg 907
Kantola Productions LLC, pg 908
Kavich Reynolds Productions Inc, pg 908
KION-TV, pg 911
The Kitchen, pg 911
KPBS TV FM-San Diego, pg 913
KVIE-Channel 6, pg 914
Ludlow Media Solutions, pg 926
Main Street Media Inc, pg 929
Maximus Media Inc, pg 934
McCune Audio-Video-Lighting, pg 935
Media Magic, pg 937
Mist Media Inc, pg 944
New & Unique Videos™, pg 955
New Circuit Films LLC, pg 955
Nolte Media, pg 958
ODC Publishing, pg 961
Panorama Productions, pg 968
Penrose Productions, pg 972
piXvfm, pg 976
Players Press, pg 977
PM Productions, pg 977
Point of View Productions, pg 977
Point 360, pg 978
Prime Cut Productions, pg 982
PSI Inc, pg 987
PSSI, pg 987
QRS Software Services, pg 988
Raymond Entertainment Direct (RED), pg 992
Regent Press Publishers & Printers, pg 994
Rough House, pg 1000
Ron Roy Productions/Moodtapes, pg 1000
Russ InVision Co/AbridgeClub.com, pg 1001
Sahara Records & Filmworks Entertainment Co, pg 1001
Screen Door Entertainment Inc, pg 1005
Sea Studios Foundation, pg 1005
SNAP, pg 1014
Staylor-Made Communications Inc, pg 1024
StereoScope International, pg 1024
Still N'Motion, pg 1025
The Studio Center, pg 1026
Tam Communications Inc, pg 1031
Tigar Hare Studios, pg 1040
Toon Makers, pg 1042
Total Media Group, pg 1042
Twin Peaks Creative, pg 1047
Via Verde Productions, pg 1053
Videowerks, pg 1057
Vineyard Productions, pg 1058
Visions Plus, pg 1058
Visual Communications - Southern California Asian American Studies Central Inc, pg 1059
WARPed Pictures, pg 1062
Wavemaker Media Design, pg 1062
West Coast Projections Inc, pg 1063
Z-Ville Productions, pg 1073

COLORADO

Paul L Anderson Productions Inc, pg 786
Centre Communications Inc, pg 823
Conly Productions, pg 835
Daylight Productions & Rentals, pg 844
Flashback Media Productions, pg 869
Maniac Productions, pg 930
Old Army Press (OAP), pg 961
Rocky Mountain Audio/Video Productions Inc, pg 998
Spectrum Audio Visual Services, pg 1020
Tatum Video, pg 1032
Transtar Entertainment Co Inc, pg 1043

CONNECTICUT

Antenna International, pg 787
Applebox Studio, pg 788
BRB Audiovisual Productions, pg 812
Broadcast Video Productions LLC, pg 813
Crossroads Video, pg 840
Fox Connecticut, pg 872
The Gary-Paul Agency, pg 875
Guymark Studios LLC, pg 883
Ironik Design & Post, pg 902
MAVCO, pg 934
MCC Films, pg 935
Moving Pictures, pg 947
New London Media, pg 956
Video Production Associates Inc, pg 1056

DELAWARE

So Smart Productions, pg 1015

DISTRICT OF COLUMBIA

Durrin Productions Inc, pg 854
Hillmann & Carr Inc, pg 889
Interface Media Group, pg 900
Metro Teleproductions Inc (MTI), pg 939
O'Keefe Communications Inc, pg 961
Yellow Cat Productions Inc, pg 1072

FLORIDA

Access Media Group, pg 773
Allegro Productions Inc, pg 781
Big Byte Video Productions, pg 806
C&I Studios, pg 819
Chatterbox Productions Inc, pg 824
Cinema East, pg 827
Cinema Entertainment Inc, pg 827
Civins Productions Inc, pg 828
Communications Concepts Inc (CCI), pg 833
Eastern Video, pg 856
Ed Ethridge Productions Inc, pg 863
Florida Digital Studios, pg 870
Florida Film & Tape, pg 870
Hi-Tech Enterprises Inc, pg 888
Home Shopping Network (HSN), pg 890
JungleTV, pg 906
Knowles Video Inc (KVI), pg 912
Media Entertainment Inc, pg 936
National Teleproductions Inc, pg 953
Paradise Video & Film, pg 969
Progressive Media & Music, pg 985
Roger Scruggs Films, pg 1005
Sight & Sound Productions, pg 1010

VIDEO

Co-Production Services (continued)

NORTH CAROLINA (continued)
LCW Productions LLC, pg 917
Moving Pictures, pg 948
NASCAR Media Group LLC, pg 952
On Location North Carolina, pg 963
Special Event Services, pg 1020
Take One Productions Ltd, pg 1031

NORTH DAKOTA
UND Television Center, pg 1048

OHIO
Advent Media Inc, pg 778
Aztec Video Productions, pg 801
Bartha, pg 803
Russ Beckner Pictures, pg 804
CET, pg 823
Challenge Productions, pg 823
Creative Technology, pg 838
Cuyahoga Community College Media Center, pg 841
iVideo Technologies, pg 903
Lyon Video Inc, pg 927
MainSail Production Services Inc, pg 929
Maslowski Productions, pg 933
Mills James Productions, pg 943
R&B Communications Inc, pg 991
Take 1 Media Services, pg 1031
Treehaus Communications Inc, pg 1044
VGI Productions, pg 1053
Vista Color Imaging Inc, pg 1059

OKLAHOMA
Garman Productions LLC, pg 875
PDC Productions, pg 970
University of Oklahoma Academic Media & Digital Services, pg 1050

OREGON
A KTVA Production LLC, pg 771
KPDX-TV Production Center, pg 913
Production West, pg 985
Rex, pg 995
Spirit Media, pg 1021

PENNSYLVANIA
AiH Group Inc, pg 779
Audio Visions Inc, pg 795
Bang Pictures, pg 802
Beholder Productions Inc, pg 804
FMP Media Solutions Inc, pg 870
Fusion Brand Experiences, pg 874
Innovision Media Group, pg 899
JPL, pg 906
Main Point Productions, pg 929
Muderick Media, pg 949
Pemcor LLC, pg 971
Production Masters Inc (PMI), pg 984
Production Solutions Inc, pg 985
The Videohouse Inc, pg 1057
Visual Sound Inc, pg 1059

RHODE ISLAND
Sound-FX-Design, pg 1017

SOUTH CAROLINA
American Production Services LLC, pg 785
Stages Video Productions, pg 1023
Venture Media, pg 1052

TENNESSEE
American Blackguard Inc, pg 784
Fricon Entertainment Co Inc, pg 873
Marine Geographic, pg 931
Memphis Communications Corp, pg 938
Motion Picture Services, pg 947
Paradigm Marketing & Creative, pg 969
Running Pony Productions LLC, pg 1000
Scripps Networks, pg 1005
ST Productions, pg 1022
Stage Post, pg 1022
WKPT-TV, pg 1068
Zion Music Group, pg 1074

TEXAS
AMS Pictures, pg 786
Biway Media, pg 808
Castleview Productions, pg 821
Cerutti Productions Inc, pg 823
Countdown Productions Inc, pg 837
Dallas Learning Solutions, pg 842
Digi-matics, pg 847
Eyecon Video Productions, pg 865
Paul Flanagan Productions, pg 869
Mediaforce Productions, pg 937
Earl Miller Productions Inc, pg 943
Julye Newlin Productions Inc, pg 956
Out of the BLUE Media, pg 966
Phillips MediaSource, pg 974
Romar Learning, pg 999
RuffHouse LLC, pg 1000
The Samuels Co, pg 1002
South Coast Film & Video, pg 1019
Stage Directions, pg 1022
Texas Heart Institute Visual Communication Services, pg 1037

UTAH
ImageWorks Communications, pg 896

VERMONT
Dorothy Tod Films, pg 1041

VIRGINIA
Advance Concepts Inc, pg 777
BES Studios, pg 805
CACI Productions Group, pg 816
CALIBRE, pg 816
CDR Communications Inc, pg 822
Computer Sciences Corp, pg 834
D&B Television & Video Productions Inc, pg 842
Eagle Films, pg 855
EFX Media, pg 858
Gingerbread Productions, pg 878
Henninger Media Services, pg 888
Metro Productions, pg 939
Quince Imaging Inc, pg 989
Video Solutions, pg 1056

WASHINGTON
Adams Creative & Production Services, pg 775
Bennett-Watt HD Productions Inc, pg 805
Global Net Productions Inc, pg 879

Hamilton Studio, pg 884
The House Studios, pg 891
North-by-Northwest Productions, pg 958
Pal Productions Inc, pg 967
Ritchie's Perfect Press, pg 997
Small World Productions Inc, pg 1013
Victory Studios, pg 1054

WEST VIRGINIA
Altruist Media LLC, pg 783
Sweetsong Productions, pg 1029
WSAZ-TV 3/WSAZ Productions, pg 1070

WISCONSIN
Audio Visual of Milwaukee Inc, pg 795
Learning Technology Services, pg 917
Media Communications Association-International (MCA-I), pg 936
Meridian Studios, pg 939
Midland Video Productions Inc, pg 942
Rucinski & Reetz Communications LLC, pg 1000
University of Wisconsin-Oshkosh Radio-TV-Film Dept, pg 1050
USAV Group Inc, pg 1050
Video Wisconsin Inc, pg 1056
Watts Communications Inc, pg 1062
Wisconsin Public Television, pg 1068

WYOMING
Bridger Productions Inc, pg 812

PUERTO RICO
Stage Crew Audiovisual Inc, pg 1022

ALBERTA
Black Media Works, pg 808
Global Television Station, pg 879

BRITISH COLUMBIA
Finale Editworks, pg 868
Image Media Farm, pg 895
Video In Studios/Video Out Distribution, pg 1055

MANITOBA
Spectra Video Productions Ltd, pg 1020

NEWFOUNDLAND AND LABRADOR
Vidcraft Productions Ltd, pg 1054

NORTHWEST TERRITORIES
Yellowknife Films Inc, pg 1072

ONTARIO
ADS Media, pg 777
DebsVoice, pg 844
GAPC (General Assembly Production Centre), pg 875
Image Video Services & Productions, pg 895
JFB Communications, pg 905
Marblemedia, pg 930

Purefire Communications Inc, pg 987
Video Excellence Productions, pg 1055

QUEBEC
Group PVP, pg 882

SASKATCHEWAN
Thomega Entertainment Inc, pg 1039

Cueing System, *see* **Teleprompting & Cueing System**

Digital Special Effect Generator Distributors

ARIZONA
EAR Professional Audio/Video, pg 855

CALIFORNIA
ADS Technologies, pg 777
Ametron Audio/Video, pg 785
BroadcastStore.com, pg 813
Delicate Electronics Sales Inc, pg 845
Diaquest, pg 846
FXC Communications, pg 874
MediaPOINTE, pg 938
Photodyne Technologies, pg 974
Pinnacle Systems Inc, pg 975
SNAP, pg 1014
Videobotics, pg 1056
VMI Inc, pg 1060
VTP Inc, pg 1061

COLORADO
Dot Hill Systems Corp, pg 851
Spectrum Audio Visual Services, pg 1020

FLORIDA
Access Media Group, pg 773
Digital Video Systems Inc, pg 848
Harris Corp, pg 885
Hi-Tech Enterprises Inc, pg 888
Media Concepts Inc, pg 936
Midtown Video Inc, pg 942
Pro Stage Inc, pg 983

GEORGIA
Stage Front Presentation Systems, pg 1022

HAWAII
The Audio Visual Co (AVCO), pg 795

ILLINOIS
Joseph Electronics, pg 906
Lyn Norstad & Associates Inc, pg 926

INDIANA
Sensory Technologies LLC, pg 1006

IOWA
ECS Inc, pg 856

KENTUCKY

Barney Miller's Inc, pg 943
NOR-COM Inc, pg 958

MASSACHUSETTS

Rule Broadcast Systems, pg 1000

MICHIGAN

ASC Systems, pg 791
Ascom Communications Contractors, pg 791
Digi Sign Design LLC, pg 847

MINNESOTA

Alpha Video & Audio Inc, pg 782

MISSOURI

Conference Technologies Inc, pg 835
Modern Communications Inc, pg 944
Schiller's Audio-Visual, pg 1004
Southwest Audio-Visual Inc, pg 1019

NEVADA

Aardvark Video & Media Productions, pg 772

NEW JERSEY

Alltec Stores, a Vcom IMC Company, pg 782
Diversified Systems Inc, pg 849
Hamilton Buhl, pg 884
MCCOM Inc, pg 935
PatchAmp, pg 970
SYMCO Inc, pg 1030
Tele-Measurements Inc, pg 1035
Total Video Products Inc, pg 1042

NEW YORK

Audio-Video Corp, pg 795
BMI Supply, pg 810
Creative Stage Lighting Co Inc, pg 838
Custom Media Environments, pg 841
Indigo Productions, pg 897
Technisphere Corp, pg 1034

NORTH CAROLINA

Alien Skin Software LLC, pg 780

OHIO

Jimmy Rea Electronics Inc, pg 992

PENNSYLVANIA

AccuWeather Inc, pg 774
Advanced AV, pg 777
Clair Brothers Audio Systems Inc, pg 829
J E Foss Co, pg 871
Innovision Media Group, pg 899
The Lerro Corp, pg 919

TENNESSEE

Lowrance Sound Co Inc, pg 925
Technical Support Systems LLC, pg 1034
Zion Music Group, pg 1074

TEXAS

AVES Audio Visual Systems Inc, pg 798
Biway Media, pg 808
High End Systems Inc, pg 888
Pro Video & Film Equipment Co Inc, pg 983
Videotex Systems Inc, pg 1057

UTAH

Strata™, pg 1025

VIRGINIA

Communications Specialists Inc, pg 833
Lee Hartman & Sons Inc, pg 918
The Whitlock Group, pg 1065

WASHINGTON

CCI Solutions, pg 821

WISCONSIN

Audio Visual of Milwaukee Inc, pg 795
Camera Corner Connecting Point, pg 818
Full Compass Systems, pg 874

ALBERTA

Matrix Video Communications Corp (MVCC), pg 934

MANITOBA

Inland Audio Visual Ltd, pg 898

Digital Special Effect Generator Manufacturers

CALIFORNIA

ADS Technologies, pg 777
Diaquest, pg 846
For-A Corp of America, pg 871
Grande Vitesse Systems Inc (GVS), pg 881
Linker Systems Inc, pg 922
Pinnacle Systems Inc, pg 975
Ultimatte Corp, pg 1047

FLORIDA

Compuvideo Sales USA Ltd, pg 834

KANSAS

GlobalStreams™ Corp, pg 879

NEW JERSEY

CELCO-Constantine Engineering Labs Co, pg 822

NORTH CAROLINA

Alien Skin Software LLC, pg 780

PENNSYLVANIA

AccuWeather Inc, pg 774

TEXAS

High End Systems Inc, pg 888

UTAH

Strata™, pg 1025

BRITISH COLUMBIA

Triad Communications Ltd, pg 1044

Digital Special Effect Generator Rentals

ARIZONA

Merestone, pg 938
Video West Inc, pg 1056

CALIFORNIA

Artichoke Productions, pg 791
Express Media Inc, pg 864
Maximus Media Inc, pg 934
McCune Audio-Video-Lighting, pg 935
Reality Check Systems, pg 992
RetinaVision Productions, pg 995
Twin Peaks Creative, pg 1047

CONNECTICUT

Videofilm Systems Inc, pg 1057

FLORIDA

Access Media Group, pg 773
Media Concepts Inc, pg 936
Paradise Show & Design Inc, pg 969
Pro Stage Inc, pg 983

GEORGIA

Stage Front Presentation Systems, pg 1022

ILLINOIS

Chicago Satellite & Video, pg 825
RC Communications, pg 992
Show Department Inc, pg 1009

KANSAS

KAKE-TV, pg 907

MARYLAND

CPR MultiMedia Solutions, pg 837

MASSACHUSETTS

massAV, pg 933
Preston Productions Inc, pg 981

MICHIGAN

Digi Sign Design LLC, pg 847
K&R All Media Productions Inc, pg 908

MISSOURI

Show-Me Audio-Visual, pg 1009

NEW JERSEY

CFP Video Productions Inc, pg 823
Tele-Measurements Inc, pg 1035

NEW YORK

Creative Stage Lighting Co Inc, pg 838

NORTH DAKOTA

Media Productions, pg 937

OHIO

Lyon Video Inc, pg 927
Mills James Productions, pg 943

PENNSYLVANIA

Advanced AV, pg 777
Innovision Media Group, pg 899
Producers Management Television (PMTV), pg 983
The Videohouse Inc, pg 1057

TENNESSEE

Technical Support Systems LLC, pg 1034

TEXAS

Alford Media Services, pg 780
Stage Directions, pg 1022

VIRGINIA

Quince Imaging Inc, pg 989

BRITISH COLUMBIA

Finale Editworks, pg 868
Image Media Farm, pg 895

MANITOBA

Inland Audio Visual Ltd, pg 898

SASKATCHEWAN

plan9films, pg 976

Digital Special Effect Generator Repairs

CALIFORNIA

Ametron Audio/Video, pg 785
VMI Inc, pg 1060

FLORIDA

ELC Sales & Service Inc, pg 858
Hi-Tech Enterprises Inc, pg 888
Midtown Video Inc, pg 942

GEORGIA

Stage Front Presentation Systems, pg 1022

IOWA

ECS Inc, pg 856

KENTUCKY

Barney Miller's Inc, pg 943
NOR-COM Inc, pg 958

MICHIGAN

TeL Systems, pg 1035

MINNESOTA

Alpha Video & Audio Inc, pg 782

MISSOURI

Southwest Audio-Visual Inc, pg 1019

NEW YORK

Technisphere Corp, pg 1034

TENNESSEE

Technical Support Systems LLC, pg 1034

TEXAS

Pro Video & Film Equipment Co Inc, pg 983

WISCONSIN

Full Compass Systems, pg 874

VIDEO

Digital Special Effect Generator Repairs (continued)

MANITOBA

Inland Audio Visual Ltd, pg 898

Digital Video Workstation Distributors

ARIZONA

EAR Professional Audio/Video, pg 855

ARKANSAS

White Diamond Productions, pg 1065

CALIFORNIA

Ametron Audio/Video, pg 785
Audio Images Corp, pg 794
California Tape Products Inc, pg 817
Computer Modules Inc, pg 834
Diaquest, pg 846
DiskFaktory Direct, pg 849
MediaPOINTE, pg 938
Optibase Inc, pg 964
Photodyne Technologies, pg 974
Point of View Productions, pg 977
Promax Systems, pg 986
SNAP, pg 1014
Southern California Sound Image Inc, pg 1019
Videobotics, pg 1056
VMI Inc, pg 1060
VTP Inc, pg 1061

COLORADO

Dot Hill Systems Corp, pg 851
Macrosystem US Inc, pg 927

FLORIDA

Access Media Group, pg 773
Digital Video Systems Inc, pg 848
Harris Corp, pg 885
Hi-Tech Enterprises Inc, pg 888
Midtown Video Inc, pg 942
Pro Stage Inc, pg 983
Recording Media & Equipment Inc (RM&E), pg 993

GEORGIA

Stage Front Presentation Systems, pg 1022

HAWAII

The Audio Visual Co (AVCO), pg 795

ILLINOIS

Lyn Norstad & Associates Inc, pg 926

INDIANA

Lee Co Inc, pg 918
Sensory Technologies LLC, pg 1006

IOWA

ECS Inc, pg 856

KENTUCKY

Barney Miller's Inc, pg 943
NOR-COM Inc, pg 958

MARYLAND

Image Logic Corp, pg 895
Kipp Visual Systems Inc, pg 911
Wiltronix, pg 1067

MASSACHUSETTS

Avid Technology Inc, pg 799
Psych Soft Inc, pg 987
Rule Broadcast Systems, pg 1000

MICHIGAN

Ascom Communications Contractors, pg 791
Digi Sign Design LLC, pg 847
TeL Systems, pg 1035

MINNESOTA

Alpha Video & Audio Inc, pg 782

MISSOURI

Modern Communications Inc, pg 944
Schiller's Audio-Visual, pg 1004
Southwest Audio-Visual Inc, pg 1019

NEVADA

Aardvark Video & Media Productions, pg 772

NEW JERSEY

Diversified Systems Inc, pg 849
Hamilton Buhl, pg 884
MCCOM Inc, pg 935
Total Video Products Inc, pg 1042

NEW YORK

Audio-Video Corp, pg 795
Image Management Systems Inc, pg 895
Technisphere Corp, pg 1034

OHIO

Jimmy Rea Electronics Inc, pg 992

OREGON

Anthro Corp, pg 787

PENNSYLVANIA

AccuWeather Inc, pg 774
Advanced AV, pg 777
The Lerro Corp, pg 919

TENNESSEE

Lowrance Sound Co Inc, pg 925
Technical Support Systems LLC, pg 1034
Zion Music Group, pg 1074

TEXAS

Biway Media, pg 808
Digital Display Solutions Inc, pg 847
Media Management LLC, pg 937
Pro Video & Film Equipment Co Inc, pg 983
Videotex Systems Inc, pg 1057

VIRGINIA

Filmdex Inc, pg 867

WASHINGTON

CCI Solutions, pg 821
Global Net Productions Inc, pg 879

WISCONSIN

Audio Visual of Milwaukee Inc, pg 795
Full Compass Systems, pg 874
Safe Harbor Computers, pg 1001
Spectrum Industries Inc, pg 1021

ALBERTA

Matrix Video Communications Corp (MVCC), pg 934

MANITOBA

Inland Audio Visual Ltd, pg 898

ONTARIO

Drastic Technologies Ltd, pg 852
HD Source, pg 886

Digital Video Workstation Manufacturers

ARIZONA

Applied Integration Corp, pg 789

CALIFORNIA

Computer Modules Inc, pg 834
Diaquest, pg 846
DiskFaktory Direct, pg 849
FutureVideo, pg 874
Grande Vitesse Systems Inc (GVS), pg 881
Ipitek, pg 902
Optibase Inc, pg 964
Opticomm-EMCORE, pg 964
Panasonic Broadcast & Digital Systems Co, pg 968
Photodyne Technologies, pg 974
Pinnacle Systems Inc, pg 975
VITEC Multimedia, pg 1060

COLORADO

Macrosystem US Inc, pg 927

FLORIDA

Hi-Tech Enterprises Inc, pg 888

MARYLAND

Image Logic Corp, pg 895

MASSACHUSETTS

Avid Technology Inc, pg 799
Psych Soft Inc, pg 987

NEW YORK

Laird Digital Cinema, pg 915
Quantel Inc, pg 989
Sima Products Corp, pg 1011
Vicon Industries Inc, pg 1053

OREGON

Anthro Corp, pg 787

PENNSYLVANIA

AccuWeather Inc, pg 774
Aztech Productions LLC, pg 801

TENNESSEE

Adtec Digital Inc, pg 777

TEXAS

Biway Media, pg 808

WASHINGTON

Watson Desking, pg 1062

WISCONSIN

Safe Harbor Computers, pg 1001
Spectrum Industries Inc, pg 1021

ONTARIO

Drastic Technologies Ltd, pg 852
Evertz Microsystems Ltd, pg 863

Digital Video Workstation Rentals

ARIZONA

Merestone, pg 938

ARKANSAS

White Diamond Productions, pg 1065

CALIFORNIA

Aaron & Le Duc, pg 772
Absolute Rentals, pg 772
Advanced Media LLC, pg 778
Ametron Audio/Video, pg 785
Artichoke Productions, pg 791
Express Media Inc, pg 864
Image Integration, pg 895
Lynch Communications, pg 926
Main Street Media Inc, pg 929
McCune Audio-Video-Lighting, pg 935
RetinaVision Productions, pg 995
Roundabout Entertainment Inc, pg 1000
Slate Media Group, pg 1013
Total Media Group, pg 1042
Twin Peaks Creative, pg 1047
Universal Studios, pg 1049

COLORADO

Open Media Foundation, pg 964

CONNECTICUT

Fox Connecticut, pg 872

FLORIDA

Access Media Group, pg 773
Accord Productions, pg 773
Pro Stage Inc, pg 983
Universal Studios Florida® Production Group, pg 1049

GEORGIA

ECG Productions, pg 856
Stage Front Presentation Systems, pg 1022

HAWAII

Ken Herkes Productions & Entertainment (KHPE), pg 888

ILLINOIS

Airways Digital Media, pg 779
Chicago Satellite & Video, pg 825
QuickSet International Inc, pg 989
Show Department Inc, pg 1009

IOWA

ECS Inc, pg 856

KANSAS

KAKE-TV, pg 907

MARYLAND

CPR MultiMedia Solutions, pg 837

MASSACHUSETTS

massAV, pg 933
Preston Productions Inc, pg 981

MICHIGAN

Digi Sign Design LLC, pg 847
K&R All Media Productions Inc, pg 908
TeL Systems, pg 1035

MINNESOTA

Alpha Video & Audio Inc, pg 782

MISSOURI

Schiller's Audio-Visual, pg 1004
Show-Me Audio-Visual, pg 1009
Southwest Audio-Visual Inc, pg 1019

NEVADA

JCS Video Productions, pg 904

NEW JERSEY

CFP Video Productions Inc, pg 823
MIB Mediaworks, pg 941
PLS Staging, pg 977

NEW MEXICO

Production Outfitters, pg 984

NEW YORK

Gurrilla Video Solutions, pg 883
HB-Content, pg 886
Manhattan Center Studios Inc, pg 930
Shadow Pictures Inc, pg 1007
TBA Global Events, pg 1032

NORTH CAROLINA

The Communications Group Inc, pg 833
Duke Media Services, pg 853
Moving Pictures, pg 948
On Location North Carolina, pg 963
Take One Productions Ltd, pg 1031

OHIO

Aztec Video Productions, pg 801
Lyon Video Inc, pg 927
Mills James Productions, pg 943

OKLAHOMA

PDC Productions, pg 970

OREGON

Northwest Film Center, pg 959

PENNSYLVANIA

Argentine Productions Inc, pg 789
FMP Media Solutions Inc, pg 870
Innovision Media Group, pg 899
Rahlic Publishing Co, pg 990
The Videohouse Inc, pg 1057

SOUTH CAROLINA

Genesis Creative, pg 877

TENNESSEE

Technical Support Systems LLC, pg 1034

TEXAS

Countdown Productions Inc, pg 837
The Samuels Co, pg 1002
South Coast Film & Video, pg 1019
Stage Directions, pg 1022
Video Perspective, pg 1056

VIRGINIA

Creative Video of Washington Inc, pg 839

WASHINGTON

911 Media Arts Center, pg 957

WISCONSIN

Full Compass Systems, pg 874

PUERTO RICO

Stage Crew Audiovisual Inc, pg 1022

BRITISH COLUMBIA

Finale Editworks, pg 868
Image Media Farm, pg 895
Video In Studios/Video Out Distribution, pg 1055

MANITOBA

Inland Audio Visual Ltd, pg 898

QUEBEC

Group PVP, pg 882
Whalley-Abbey Media Holdings Inc, pg 1065

SASKATCHEWAN

plan9films, pg 976

Digital Video Workstation Repairs

CALIFORNIA

Advanced Media LLC, pg 778
Ametron Audio/Video, pg 785
VMI Inc, pg 1060

COLORADO

Macrosystem US Inc, pg 927

FLORIDA

ELC Sales & Service Inc, pg 858
Hi-Tech Enterprises Inc, pg 888

GEORGIA

Stage Front Presentation Systems, pg 1022

IOWA

ECS Inc, pg 856

KENTUCKY

Barney Miller's Inc, pg 943
NOR-COM Inc, pg 958

MICHIGAN

TeL Systems, pg 1035

MINNESOTA

Alpha Video & Audio Inc, pg 782

MISSOURI

Schiller's Audio-Visual, pg 1004
Southwest Audio-Visual Inc, pg 1019

TENNESSEE

Technical Support Systems LLC, pg 1034

TEXAS

Biway Media, pg 808
Industrial Audio/Video Inc, pg 897
Pro Video & Film Equipment Co Inc, pg 983

WISCONSIN

Full Compass Systems, pg 874

MANITOBA

Inland Audio Visual Ltd, pg 898

Digitizer Distributors

ARIZONA

EAR Professional Audio/Video, pg 855

CALIFORNIA

Ametron Audio/Video, pg 785
FXC Communications, pg 874
Media Control Systems LLC, pg 936
POP TV, pg 978
QRS Software Services, pg 988
VMI Inc, pg 1060
VTP Inc, pg 1061

FLORIDA

Access Media Group, pg 773
Digital Video Systems Inc, pg 848
Hi-Tech Enterprises Inc, pg 888
Sight & Sound Productions, pg 1010

GEORGIA

Stage Front Presentation Systems, pg 1022

HAWAII

The Audio Visual Co (AVCO), pg 795

ILLINOIS

Joseph Electronics, pg 906
Lyn Norstad & Associates Inc, pg 926

INDIANA

Sensory Technologies LLC, pg 1006

KENTUCKY

NOR-COM Inc, pg 958

MASSACHUSETTS

Avid Technology Inc, pg 799
Rule Broadcast Systems, pg 1000

MICHIGAN

Digi Sign Design LLC, pg 847

MISSOURI

Ken-A-Vision Manufacturing Co Inc, pg 909
Schiller's Audio-Visual, pg 1004

NEVADA

Aardvark Video & Media Productions, pg 772

NEW JERSEY

Diversified Systems Inc, pg 849

NEW YORK

ALTEL Systems Inc, pg 783
Audio-Video Corp, pg 795
B&H Photo & Video Pro Audio, pg 802
Gaylord Brothers, pg 876
Vision Identics Systems Inc, pg 1058

PENNSYLVANIA

Advanced AV, pg 777

TENNESSEE

Lowrance Sound Co Inc, pg 925

TEXAS

AVES Audio Visual Systems Inc, pg 798
Digital Display Solutions Inc, pg 847
Pro Video & Film Equipment Co Inc, pg 983

VIRGINIA

Filmdex Inc, pg 867
The Whitlock Group, pg 1065

WISCONSIN

Audio Visual of Milwaukee Inc, pg 795
Full Compass Systems, pg 874

MANITOBA

Inland Audio Visual Ltd, pg 898

Digitizer Manufacturers

ARIZONA

eInstruction Corp, pg 858

CALIFORNIA

AJA Video Systems Inc, pg 779
Grande Vitesse Systems Inc (GVS), pg 881
QRS Software Services, pg 988

CONNECTICUT

Xintekvideo Inc, pg 1071

MASSACHUSETTS

Avid Technology Inc, pg 799

MICHIGAN

Leightronix Inc, pg 918

MISSOURI

Ken-A-Vision Manufacturing Co Inc, pg 909

VIDEO

Digitizer Manufacturers (continued)

NEW JERSEY

CELCO-Constantine Engineering Labs Co, pg 822

TENNESSEE

Adtec Digital Inc, pg 777

ONTARIO

PixeLINK, pg 976

Digitizer Rentals

ARIZONA

Merestone, pg 938

CALIFORNIA

Absolute Rentals, pg 772
Artichoke Productions, pg 791
Express Media Inc, pg 864
RetinaVision Productions, pg 995
Twin Peaks Creative, pg 1047

FLORIDA

Access Media Group, pg 773
Universal Studios Florida® Production Group, pg 1049

GEORGIA

Stage Front Presentation Systems, pg 1022

ILLINOIS

Chicago Satellite & Video, pg 825
RC Communications, pg 992
Show Department Inc, pg 1009

KANSAS

KAKE-TV, pg 907

MARYLAND

CPR MultiMedia Solutions, pg 837

MASSACHUSETTS

Preston Productions Inc, pg 981

MICHIGAN

Digi Sign Design LLC, pg 847
K&R All Media Productions Inc, pg 908

MISSOURI

Show-Me Audio-Visual, pg 1009

NEW YORK

HB-Content, pg 886

NORTH CAROLINA

On Location North Carolina, pg 963
Take One Productions Ltd, pg 1031

PENNSYLVANIA

Argentine Productions Inc, pg 789
Innovision Media Group, pg 899
The Videohouse Inc, pg 1057

TEXAS

Stage Directions, pg 1022

VIRGINIA

Quince Imaging Inc, pg 989

PUERTO RICO

Stage Crew Audiovisual Inc, pg 1022

BRITISH COLUMBIA

Finale Editworks, pg 868
Image Media Farm, pg 895

MANITOBA

Inland Audio Visual Ltd, pg 898

SASKATCHEWAN

plan9films, pg 976

Digitizer Repairs

CALIFORNIA

Ametron Audio/Video, pg 785

FLORIDA

ELC Sales & Service Inc, pg 858
Hi-Tech Enterprises Inc, pg 888

GEORGIA

Stage Front Presentation Systems, pg 1022

IOWA

ECS Inc, pg 856

KENTUCKY

NOR-COM Inc, pg 958

MICHIGAN

TeL Systems, pg 1035

MINNESOTA

Alpha Video & Audio Inc, pg 782

MISSOURI

Southwest Audio-Visual Inc, pg 1019

TEXAS

Pro Video & Film Equipment Co Inc, pg 983

WISCONSIN

Full Compass Systems, pg 874

MANITOBA

Inland Audio Visual Ltd, pg 898

Dubbing

ALABAMA

CMEInfo, pg 830
Diamond Studios, pg 846

ARIZONA

Audio Video Resources, pg 795
Film Creations Ltd, pg 867
Merestone, pg 938
Metropolitan Audio-Visual Inc, pg 940
On-Site Video, pg 963
Rodeo Video Inc, pg 998
Star Video Duplicating, pg 1024
Video Media Productions (VMP), pg 1055

ARKANSAS

Live'N'Loud, pg 923
Shadowbox Video Productions, pg 1007
White Diamond Productions, pg 1065

CALIFORNIA

Aaron & Le Duc, pg 772
AB Audio Visual Entertainment Inc, pg 772
Aberdeen Broadcast Services, pg 772
Access Video in Berkeley, pg 773
ACDC Audio CD & Cassette, pg 774
Action Video, pg 775
Advanced Media LLC, pg 778
All Video Productions, pg 781
AlphaDogs Inc, pg 782
AM Productions, pg 783
Artichoke Productions, pg 791
Barbosa Video Services, pg 802
CCI Digital, pg 821
Christopher Gray Post Production, pg 826
Crystal Pyramid Productions™, pg 840
Custom Video Productions Inc, pg 841
Digital Jungle, pg 847
Digital Media West, pg 847
Digital Outpost, pg 847
Dogma Studios, pg 850
Express Media Inc, pg 864
Face Digital Post, pg 865
Far West Media Services Inc, pg 865
First Camera, pg 868
Full Moon & High Tide Productions & Studios, pg 874
Global Village Productions, pg 879
Gold Standard Productions, pg 880
Golden Gate Studios, pg 880
Havas Edge, pg 885
iCorpTv, pg 893
International Contact Inc, pg 900
InVision Productions, pg 902
ITV Productions, pg 903
JDS Video & Media Productions Inc, pg 904
KION-TV, pg 911
The Kitchen, pg 911
KPBS TV FM-San Diego, pg 913
KTVU-Retail Services, pg 914
KVIE-Channel 6, pg 914
Ludlow Media Solutions, pg 926
Lynch Communications, pg 926
Maximus Media Inc, pg 934
McCune Audio-Video-Lighting, pg 935
Mind Over Eye Inc, pg 943
Monaco Digital Films Labs, pg 945
New & Unique Videos™, pg 955
Nolte Media, pg 958
Penrose Productions, pg 972
Peterson's Video Transfer Services, pg 973
piXvfm, pg 976
Planet Blue, pg 976
PM Productions, pg 977
Point 360, pg 978
Prime Cut Productions, pg 982
QRS Software Services, pg 988
Reel Picture, pg 994
RJ Video Productions, pg 997
Rough House, pg 1000
Roundabout Entertainment Inc, pg 1000
Rovi Corp, pg 1000
Saturn Studios, pg 1003
Screen Door Entertainment Inc, pg 1005
Shapeshifter, pg 1008
SonicPool, pg 1016
Still N'Motion, pg 1025
Technicolor, pg 1034
Tele-Video Production Services (TVPS), pg 1036
Toon Makers, pg 1042
Total Media Group, pg 1042
TVA Productions, pg 1046
Twin Peaks Creative, pg 1047
Universal Studios, pg 1049
VidCan Media Solutions, pg 1054
Videolady, pg 1057
Visions Plus, pg 1058
VMI Inc, pg 1060
WMS Media Inc, pg 1069

COLORADO

Alpine Media, pg 782
blue onion, pg 810
Ceavco Audio/Visual Co, pg 822
The Cinema Lab, pg 827
Daylight Productions & Rentals, pg 844
Flashback Media Productions, pg 869
Rocky Mountain Audio/Video Productions Inc, pg 998

CONNECTICUT

Applebox Studio, pg 788
A/V Davey, pg 797
BRB Audiovisual Productions, pg 812
Broadcast Video Productions LLC, pg 813
Cine-Med Inc, pg 826
Concord Communications, pg 835
EagleVision Inc, pg 855
Fox Connecticut, pg 872
Geomatrix Productions, pg 877
Guymark Studios LLC, pg 883
Ironik Design & Post, pg 902
MCC Films, pg 935
Rockwell Communications Inc, pg 998

DISTRICT OF COLUMBIA

Interface Media Group, pg 900
Library of Congress, Motion Picture, Broadcasting & Recorded Sound Division, pg 919

FLORIDA

Access Media Group, pg 773
Allegro Productions Inc, pg 781
Cinema East, pg 827
Communications Concepts Inc (CCI), pg 833
Eastern Video, pg 856
Florida Digital Studios, pg 870
Gulf Coast Audio Visual Producers Inc, pg 883
Harmon's Audio-Visual Services, pg 885
Home Shopping Network (HSN), pg 890
Mach 1 Productions, pg 927
Media Concepts Inc, pg 936
Progressive Media & Music, pg 985
RLX Media LLC, pg 997
Shooting Stars Post Inc, pg 1009
Sight & Sound Productions, pg 1010

Sunfire Communications Inc, pg 1028
Tricycle Studios, pg 1044
Mike Vasilinda Productions Inc, pg 1052
Video Techniques Inc, pg 1056

GEORGIA

Associated Video, pg 792
Audio Visual Resources Inc, pg 795
Beachwood Productions, pg 804
COMPRO Productions Inc, pg 834
Continental Film & Video, pg 835
Crawford Media Services, pg 838
First Cut Communications LLC, pg 868
Guerrilla Productions LLC, pg 883
Omega Media Group Inc, pg 962
On-Line Productions, pg 963
Showcase Photo & Video, pg 1009
Staging Directions Inc, pg 1023

HAWAII

KHNL/KGMB, pg 910
1013 Integrated, pg 1037
Tropical Visions Video Inc, pg 1045

IDAHO

KTVB-TV, pg 914

ILLINOIS

ABS Enterprises, pg 772
ABSA Productions Inc, pg 772
Analog Free Media, pg 786
AnswersMedia, pg 787
Backstar Creative Media Inc, pg 801
Beatty TeleVisual Productions, pg 804
Chicago Satellite & Video, pg 825
IV Media Resources, pg 903
Major Media Inc, pg 929
Moviecraft Inc, pg 947
On Site Video, pg 963
The Prairie Production Group, pg 980
SCI Television Productions LLC, pg 1004
Southern Illinois University, pg 1019
Sparkfactor, pg 1019
Tele-Time Systems, pg 1036
20/20 Communications Inc, pg 1047
Video I-D Teleproductions Inc, pg 1055
Video Impressions, pg 1055
WEEK TV, pg 1063

INDIANA

Advanced Media Integration, pg 777
Covenant Productions®, pg 837
PentaVision Communications Inc, pg 972

IOWA

Duplication Media, pg 853
Iowa State University-Information Technology Services, pg 902
The Production House, pg 984

KANSAS

KAKE-TV, pg 907

KENTUCKY

Media Resources, pg 937
Barney Miller's Inc, pg 943
The PPS Group, pg 980
WKYT Productions, pg 1068

LOUISIANA

Digital FX Inc, pg 847
Louisiana State University Health Sciences Center - Shreveport, pg 925
Moxie Media, pg 948
Vidox Motion Imagery, pg 1057
WVLA-TV, pg 1071

MAINE

Headlight Audio Visual Inc, pg 887

MARYLAND

Adventure Productions LLC, pg 778
CPR MultiMedia Solutions, pg 837
dbF a Media Company, pg 844
DBM Communications Inc, pg 844
DSR Computer Technology Specialists Inc, pg 853
Media Dimensions Inc, pg 936
Milner-Fenwick Inc, pg 943
Producers Video, pg 984
Saah Video, pg 1001
Shadowstone R & R™, pg 1008
Sheffield Audio/Video Productions, pg 1008
Spectrum Productions, pg 1021
Video Labs, pg 1055
Welocalize, pg 1063

MASSACHUSETTS

Award Productions, pg 800
Capron Lighting & Sound Co Inc, pg 819
Cramer Productions, pg 837
Documentary Educational Resources Inc, pg 850
Extreme Reach Inc, pg 864
Home Inc, pg 890
In the Wild Productions, pg 897
Inter-Media Electronics, pg 899
Linguistic Systems Inc, pg 922
Penfield Productions Ltd, pg 971
TR Productions, pg 1043
Veritech Corp, pg 1053
WGBH Production Group, pg 1065

MICHIGAN

Digi Sign Design LLC, pg 847
Encore Home Video, pg 861
K&R's Recording Studios Inc, pg 908
MessageMakers, pg 939
The Program Source International, pg 985
RingSide Creative, pg 997
TeL Systems, pg 1035
The Transfer Zone®, pg 1043

MINNESOTA

The ADS Group, pg 777
Aggressive Records Audio Duplication LLC, pg 778
GMI Productions, pg 879
Jamieson & Associates Inc, pg 904
MultiMedia, pg 950
Rum Jungle Media, pg 1000
Worthwhile Films, pg 1070

MISSOURI

Avatar Studios, pg 798
Communitronics Corp, pg 833
Conference Technologies Inc, pg 835
Show-Me Audio-Visual, pg 1009
Visionworks Design Services Inc, pg 1059

MONTANA

KUSM TV, pg 914
North Country Media Group, pg 959

NEVADA

Aardvark Video & Media Productions, pg 772
DVDs4Less, pg 854
Encore Productions Inc, pg 861
HDTV Productions Inc, pg 886
Lefco Video Services Inc, pg 918

NEW HAMPSHIRE

Academic & Campus Technology Services, pg 773
Apertura, pg 788
Channell One Video, pg 824
Chip Taylor Communications LLC, pg 1032

NEW JERSEY

All Jersey Studios, pg 780
Audio Visual Associates, pg 795
CFP Video Productions Inc, pg 823
Deluxe Media Services, pg 845
Diversified Systems Inc, pg 849
DWJ Television, pg 854
Laurel Video Productions, pg 916
MediaMix Inc, pg 937
Megavideo Productions, pg 938
MIB Mediaworks, pg 941
Midnight Media Group Inc, pg 942
NFL Films Music Library, pg 957
Optisonics Productions, pg 965
Bill Quinn Productions, pg 989
Starlite Productions, pg 1024
Tele-Measurements Inc, pg 1035
VCSvideo, pg 1052
Video Corporation of America (VCA), pg 1055

NEW MEXICO

Production Outfitters, pg 984
30 Second Street Ltd, pg 1039

NEW YORK

aurora productions, pg 797
The Big House Group, pg 807
BioMedia Inc, pg 807
CMI Media Management, pg 830
Digital Art Video Inc, pg 847
Downtown Community Television Center (DCTV), pg 851
DuArt, pg 853
Duplication Depot Inc, pg 853
Duplication Specialists Inc, pg 853
Eastco Multimedia Solutions Inc, pg 856
4-D Creative Media, pg 871
Hallel Communications, pg 884
HAVE Inc, pg 886
HB-Content, pg 886
Heavy Melody, pg 887
InterNation Inc, pg 900
International Digital Centre, pg 901
J & D Laboratories Inc, pg 903
L&P Media, pg 915
Long Island Video Enterprises Live Inc, pg 924
Lylofilm Productions, pg 926
Magno Sound & Video, pg 929
Neal Marshad Productions, pg 931
Mood Creations Ltd, pg 946
MRG Productions Inc, pg 948
Shelly Palmer Production, pg 968
Post Josh Productions, pg 979
PostWorks, pg 979
PrimaLux Video Inc, pg 982
Rafik, pg 990
Refinery, pg 994
Synaptic Digital, pg 1030
TBA Global Events, pg 1032
Teatown Communications Group, pg 1033
Technisphere Corp, pg 1034
TeleTime Productions, pg 1036
Tobin Productions Inc, pg 1041
USA Studios, pg 1050
Visual Technologies Corp, pg 1060
Zelman Studios Ltd, pg 1073

NORTH CAROLINA

All Pro Media Inc, pg 780
Pat Appleson Studios Inc, pg 788
Camcor Inc, pg 818
Duke Media Services, pg 853
Franklin Video Inc, pg 872
Horizon Video Productions Inc, pg 891
LCW Productions LLC, pg 917
Moving Pictures, pg 948
Take One Productions Ltd, pg 1031
Unifour Productions Inc, pg 1048

OHIO

Advent Media Inc, pg 778
Aztec Video Productions, pg 801
Russ Beckner Pictures, pg 804
CET, pg 823
Cinecraft Productions Inc, pg 827
Creative Technology, pg 838
Curtis Inc, pg 841
Cuyahoga Community College Media Center, pg 841
EDR Media LLC, pg 857
Image Video Teleproductions Inc, pg 895
iVideo Technologies, pg 903
Lyon Video Inc, pg 927
MainSail Production Services Inc, pg 929
Mills James Productions, pg 943
Musicol Recording, pg 951
Promedia Digital, pg 986
R&B Communications Inc, pg 991
Take 1 Media Services, pg 1031
VGI Productions, pg 1053
Vista Color Imaging Inc, pg 1059

OKLAHOMA

Garman Productions LLC, pg 875
Piper Media Services Inc, pg 976
University of Oklahoma Academic Media & Digital Services, pg 1050

OREGON

A KTVA Production LLC, pg 771
KPDX-TV Production Center, pg 913
Production West, pg 985
Rex, pg 995

PENNSYLVANIA

Argentine Productions Inc, pg 789
Audio Visions Inc, pg 795
Audio Visual Communications Inc, pg 795
Center City Film & Video Inc, pg 822
FMP Media Solutions Inc, pg 870
Fusion Brand Experiences, pg 874
Innovision Media Group, pg 899
JPL, pg 906
Kloss Studios Co, pg 912
Laser Video Corp, pg 916
Production Masters Inc (PMI), pg 984
The Videohouse Inc, pg 1057
WPHL-TV, pg 1070

VIDEO

Dubbing (continued)

RHODE ISLAND

A&M Productions, pg 771

SOUTH CAROLINA

American Production Services LLC, pg 785
Genesis Creative, pg 877
Sound & Images Inc, pg 1016
Stages Video Productions, pg 1023
Venture Media, pg 1052

TENNESSEE

Continental Film, pg 835
Motion Picture Services, pg 947
Running Pony Productions LLC, pg 1000
Scripps Networks, pg 1005
Stage Post, pg 1022
Russ Sturgeon Productions/RSVP, pg 1027
UMCom Productions, pg 1048
WKPT-TV, pg 1068

TEXAS

Astro Audio Visual, pg 792
Biway Media, pg 808
Castleview Productions, pg 821
Dub King, pg 853
The Editing Co, pg 857
Horizon Film + Video Productions, pg 891
Matson Multi-Media, pg 934
Maverick Video Productions, pg 934
McNee Productions Inc, pg 935
Mediaforce Productions, pg 937
Earl Miller Productions Inc, pg 943
Julye Newlin Productions Inc, pg 956
Replicopy Digital Media Center, pg 995
Romar Learning, pg 999
The Samuels Co, pg 1002
South Coast Film & Video, pg 1019
Texas Heart Institute Visual Communication Services, pg 1037

UTAH

ImageWorks Communications, pg 896

VERMONT

University of Vermont, Instructional Television Dept, pg 1050

VIRGINIA

American AV, pg 783
BES Studios, pg 805
CACI Productions Group, pg 816
CDR Communications Inc, pg 822
Creative Video of Washington Inc, pg 839
Gingerbread Productions, pg 878
Henninger Media Services, pg 888
Limelight Communications Inc, pg 921
Video Solutions, pg 1056

WASHINGTON

Bennett-Watt HD Productions Inc, pg 805
Global Net Productions Inc, pg 879
Inland Audio Visual Co, pg 898
North-by-Northwest Productions, pg 958
Victory Studios, pg 1054

WISCONSIN

Audio Visual of Milwaukee Inc, pg 795
Learning Technology Services, pg 917
Meridian Studios, pg 939
ProVideo, pg 986
USAV Group Inc, pg 1050
Video Wisconsin Inc, pg 1056
Watts Communications Inc, pg 1062
Wisconsin Public Television, pg 1068

WYOMING

Bridger Productions Inc, pg 812

PUERTO RICO

Stage Crew Audiovisual Inc, pg 1022

ALBERTA

Cine Audio Visual Sales & Service Ltd, pg 826
Global Television Station, pg 879

BRITISH COLUMBIA

Finale Editworks, pg 868
Image Media Farm, pg 895
Triad Communications Ltd, pg 1044
24 Frames Film & Video, pg 1047
Video In Studios/Video Out Distribution, pg 1055

NEWFOUNDLAND AND LABRADOR

Vidcraft Productions Ltd, pg 1054

ONTARIO

DG Mijo, pg 846
Edcom Multimedia Products, pg 856
GAPC (General Assembly Production Centre), pg 875
Image Video Services & Productions, pg 895
Optimum Production Services Inc, pg 964
Purefire Communications Inc, pg 987
Video Excellence Productions, pg 1055

QUEBEC

Group PVP, pg 882

SASKATCHEWAN

Thomega Entertainment Inc, pg 1039

Duplication—DVDs

ALABAMA

AVS Media Group, pg 800
Sound of Birmingham Productions, pg 1017

ARIZONA

Creative Backstage, pg 838
Film Creations Ltd, pg 867
Forensic Video Deposition Service, pg 871
Merestone, pg 938
Metropolitan Audio-Visual Inc, pg 940
On-Site Video, pg 963
Star Video Duplicating, pg 1024
Video Media Productions (VMP), pg 1055

ARKANSAS

Shadowbox Video Productions, pg 1007
White Diamond Productions, pg 1065

CALIFORNIA

Aaron & Le Duc, pg 772
AB Audio Visual Entertainment Inc, pg 772
ACDC Audio CD & Cassette, pg 774
Action Video, pg 775
Adolph Gasser Inc, pg 776
Advanced Media LLC, pg 778
AGF Media Services, pg 778
All Video Productions, pg 781
AM Productions, pg 783
Audio Rents, pg 794
Audio Visual Consultants, pg 795
AVerMedia Technologies Inc, pg 798
Barbosa Video Services, pg 802
California Tape Products Inc, pg 817
Christopher Gray Post Production, pg 826
Coloredge, pg 832
Crystal Pyramid Productions™, pg 840
Custom Video Productions Inc, pg 841
Digital Jungle, pg 847
Digital Outpost, pg 847
Dogma Studios, pg 850
Express Media Inc, pg 864
Face Digital Post, pg 865
FJ Productions Inc, pg 869
FXC Communications, pg 874
Gluskin's Custom Audio Video, pg 879
Havas Edge, pg 885
iCorpTv, pg 893
Imageworks, pg 896
InVision Productions, pg 902
JD Audio Visual Inc, pg 904
JDS Video & Media Productions Inc, pg 904
Lightning Media, pg 921
Ludlow Media Solutions, pg 926
Maximus Media Inc, pg 934
Media Magic, pg 937
New & Unique Videos™, pg 955
New Cyberian Systems Inc, pg 955
On-Trax Inc, pg 963
Pacific Video Image, pg 967
Penrose Productions, pg 972
Peterson's Video Transfer Services, pg 973
Planet Blue, pg 976
PM Productions, pg 977
PME Audio/Video, pg 977
Pro8mm, pg 983
QRS Software Services, pg 988
Reel Picture, pg 994
Related Visual Inc, pg 994
RJ Video Productions, pg 997
Rough House, pg 1000
Roundabout Entertainment Inc, pg 1000
Saturn Studios, pg 1003
SF Global Sourcing, pg 1007
Shapeshifter, pg 1008
Shokus Video, pg 1009
SonicPool, pg 1016
Staylor-Made Communications Inc, pg 1024
Still N'Motion, pg 1025
Studio 637, pg 1027
Timecode Multimedia, pg 1040
Toon Makers, pg 1042
Total Media Group, pg 1042
Twin Peaks Creative, pg 1047
Universal Studios, pg 1049
VidCan Media Solutions, pg 1054
Video Movie Magic, pg 1056
Videolady, pg 1057
Visions Plus, pg 1058
VMI Inc, pg 1060
WalkerVision Interarts, pg 1061

COLORADO

The Cinema Lab, pg 827
Flashback Media Productions, pg 869
Jeppesen, pg 905
Rocky Mountain Audio/Video Productions Inc, pg 998
Side 3 Studios, pg 1010

CONNECTICUT

Applebox Studio, pg 788
A/V Davey, pg 797
BRB Audiovisual Productions, pg 812
Cine-Med Inc, pg 826
Digital Video Productions, pg 848
Guymark Studios LLC, pg 883
Ironik Design & Post, pg 902
MCC Films, pg 935
New London Media, pg 956
Rockwell Communications Inc, pg 998
T & M Digital Services, pg 1031
Video Design Group, pg 1055
Video Production Associates Inc, pg 1056

DELAWARE

Ken-Del Productions Inc, pg 909
Ken-Del Studios, pg 909

DISTRICT OF COLUMBIA

Interface Media Group, pg 900

FLORIDA

Access Media Group, pg 773
Accord Productions, pg 773
Allegro Productions Inc, pg 781
CD ROM™ Inc, pg 822
Cinema East, pg 827
Civins Productions Inc, pg 828
Comtel Inc, pg 834
Easy Edit Video Inc, pg 856
Florida Digital Studios, pg 870
Global Video Distributors Inc, pg 879
Harmon's Audio-Visual Services, pg 885
Hi-Tech Enterprises Inc, pg 888
MAC Production Group, pg 927
Mach 1 Productions, pg 927
Media Concepts Inc, pg 936
The Newhouse Media Group, pg 956
Photosound of Orlando Inc, pg 975
Progressive Media & Music, pg 985
Sight & Sound Productions, pg 1010
Sound & Vision Communications Inc, pg 1016
Sunrise Studios, pg 1028
Tricycle Studios, pg 1044
Mike Vasilinda Productions Inc, pg 1052

Venice Media Group, pg 1052
Video Techniques Inc, pg 1056

GEORGIA

Beast Atlanta, pg 804
Cinema Concepts, pg 827
Crawford Media Services, pg 838
ECG Productions, pg 856
Guerrilla Productions LLC, pg 883
Omega Media Group Inc, pg 962
On-Line Productions, pg 963

ILLINOIS

ABSA Productions Inc, pg 772
Advanced Audio Technology, pg 777
Airways Digital Media, pg 779
Analog Free Media, pg 786
AnswersMedia, pg 787
Backstar Creative Media Inc, pg 801
Big Shoulders Digital Video Productions, pg 807
Chicago Satellite & Video, pg 825
International Historic Films Inc, pg 901
Intervideo Duplication Services, pg 902
IV Media Resources, pg 903
Kelmscott Communications, pg 909
Major Media Inc, pg 929
Midwest Digital Corp, pg 942
RADMAR Inc, pg 990
RBR Productions, pg 992
SCI Television Productions LLC, pg 1004
Sound/Video Impressions Inc, pg 1018
Televersions, pg 1036
20/20 Communications Inc, pg 1047
Video I-D Teleproductions Inc, pg 1055
Video Impressions, pg 1055

INDIANA

Advanced Media Integration, pg 777
AVA Productions, pg 798
Covenant Productions®, pg 837
Crystal Clear Media Group, pg 840
Educational Video Group Inc, pg 857
Optical Disc Solutions Inc, pg 964

IOWA

Duplication Media, pg 853
Pro Video, pg 983

KANSAS

Genigraphics®, pg 877

KENTUCKY

Audio Visual Techniques Inc, pg 796
The PPS Group, pg 980
Prosper Media Group Inc, pg 986

LOUISIANA

Louisiana State University Health Sciences Center - Shreveport, pg 925
Moxie Media, pg 948
Vidox Motion Imagery, pg 1057

MAINE

Headlight Audio Visual Inc, pg 887

MARYLAND

Adventure Productions LLC, pg 778
Carpel Video Inc, pg 820
CPR MultiMedia Solutions, pg 837
dbF a Media Company, pg 844
DBM Communications Inc, pg 844
Kramer Communications Video Production, pg 913
Lion & Fox Recording Studios, pg 922
Media Dimensions Inc, pg 936
Milner-Fenwick Inc, pg 943
Optic Bindery & Packaging, pg 964
Pro Cuts Editing Services, pg 982
Quality Film & Video, pg 988
RTZ Audio Visual, pg 1000
Saah Video, pg 1001
Satellite Media Production, pg 1003
Video Labs, pg 1055

MASSACHUSETTS

Continental Recordings Inc, pg 835
Documentary Educational Resources Inc, pg 850
In the Wild Productions, pg 897
Inter-Media Electronics, pg 899
MALCO Electronics, pg 929
Video Express, pg 1055

MICHIGAN

Digi Sign Design LLC, pg 847
The Program Source International, pg 985
TGA Recording Co, pg 1038
The Transfer Zone®, pg 1043

MINNESOTA

The ADS Group, pg 777
Aggressive Records Audio Duplication LLC, pg 778
C Vision Productions, pg 816
MultiMedia, pg 950
Pro Media Productions, pg 983
Rum Jungle Media, pg 1000

MISSISSIPPI

Bowie Audio Visual Enterprises Inc, pg 811

MISSOURI

Allied Photo Color Co, pg 781
Show-Me Audio-Visual, pg 1009
Studio Worx Inc, pg 1027

MONTANA

Jereco Studios Inc, pg 905

NEBRASKA

Dog & Pony Productions Inc, pg 850
Three Pillars Media, pg 1040

NEVADA

Aardvark Video & Media Productions, pg 772
HDTV Productions Inc, pg 886
JCS Video Productions, pg 904

NEW HAMPSHIRE

Channell One Video, pg 824
Chip Taylor Communications LLC, pg 1032

NEW JERSEY

All Jersey Studios, pg 780
Audio Visual Associates, pg 795
Color Leasing Studios, pg 831
Creative Video, pg 838
Diversified Systems Inc, pg 849
Euro-Pacific Film & Video Productions Inc, pg 863
International Audio Visual Inc, pg 900
Megavideo Productions, pg 938
MIB Mediaworks, pg 941
Midnight Media Group Inc, pg 942
Starlite Productions, pg 1024
Synergem, pg 1030
VCSvideo, pg 1052
Video Ideas Productions, pg 1055
VTS Video & Media, pg 1061

NEW MEXICO

Production Outfitters, pg 984

NEW YORK

Adwar Video, pg 778
Bellin Productions, pg 805
Big Foot Productions Inc, pg 807
The Big House Group, pg 807
Chromavision Corp, pg 826
CMI Media Management, pg 830
Design Audio Visual Inc, pg 845
Digital Art Video Inc, pg 847
Downtown Community Television Center (DCTV), pg 851
DuArt, pg 853
Duplication Depot Inc, pg 853
Eastco Multimedia Solutions Inc, pg 856
Foothill Digital Inc, pg 871
4-D Creative Media, pg 871
FSL Media Inc, pg 873
HB-Content, pg 886
Heavy Melody, pg 887
Hello World Communications, pg 888
Image Makers of Pittsford/Image Maker Productions, pg 895
International Digital Centre, pg 901
iProbe Multilingual Solutions Inc, pg 902
J & D Laboratories Inc, pg 903
Mark Custom Recording Service Inc, pg 931
Neal Marshad Productions, pg 931
Mood Creations Ltd, pg 946
Mother West, pg 947
Motion Picture Enterprises Inc, pg 947
MRG Productions Inc, pg 948
Production Central, pg 984
Teatown Communications Group, pg 1033
Tobin Productions Inc, pg 1041
Video Caption Corp, pg 1054
Video Concepts Unlimited, pg 1055
Visual Technologies Corp, pg 1060
Visual Word Systems Inc, pg 1060
WTL Productions, pg 1071

NORTH CAROLINA

A&V Company, pg 772
All Pro Media Inc, pg 780
Pat Appleson Studios Inc, pg 788
Franklin Video Inc, pg 872
Horizon Video Productions Inc, pg 891
Ladyslipper Inc, pg 915
LCW Productions LLC, pg 917
Moving Pictures, pg 948
Take One Productions Ltd, pg 1031
Unifour Productions Inc, pg 1048
Visual Aids Electronics of North Carolina Inc, pg 1059

OHIO

Curtis Inc, pg 841
ITA Audio Visual Solutions, pg 902
The Little Warehouse Inc, pg 923
Musicol Recording, pg 951
Production Partners Media, pg 984
Promedia Digital, pg 986
QCA, pg 988
R&B Communications Inc, pg 991
Ungar Video & Film, pg 1048
Vista Color Imaging Inc, pg 1059

OKLAHOMA

Garman Productions LLC, pg 875
Piper Media Services Inc, pg 976

OREGON

A KTVA Production LLC, pg 771
MediaFX, pg 937
Phylco Audio Duplication, pg 975
Rex, pg 995

PENNSYLVANIA

John E Allen Inc, pg 781
Argentine Productions Inc, pg 789
Audio Visions Inc, pg 795
Audio Visual Communications Inc, pg 795
Beholder Productions Inc, pg 804
Bernie's Photo Center, pg 805
FMP Media Solutions Inc, pg 870
Innovision Media Group, pg 899
Laser Video Corp, pg 916
New York Camera & Video, pg 956
Panta Rhei Media Inc, pg 968
The Videohouse Inc, pg 1057

RHODE ISLAND

A&M Productions, pg 771

SOUTH CAROLINA

American Production Services LLC, pg 785
Genesis Creative, pg 877
Stages Video Productions, pg 1023
Venture Media, pg 1052

TENNESSEE

Anode Inc, pg 787
CRT Custom Products Inc, pg 840
JamSync, pg 904
Kingswood Productions, pg 911
Motion Picture Services, pg 947
NTS ProMedia, pg 960
Running Pony Productions LLC, pg 1000
Stage Post, pg 1022

TEXAS

Arcube Multimedia Inc, pg 789
Biway Media, pg 808
CEV Multimedia Ltd, pg 823
Chalk Dust Co, pg 823
Communication Arts Multimedia Inc, pg 832
The Editing Co, pg 857
First Group Communications Inc, pg 868
Paul Flanagan Productions, pg 869
Harbor House Studios, pg 884
Horizon Film + Video Productions, pg 891
Matson Multi-Media, pg 934
Mediaforce Productions, pg 937
Julye Newlin Productions Inc, pg 956
Omega Broadcast Group, pg 962
Replicopy Digital Media Center, pg 995

VIDEO

Duplication—DVDs (continued)

TEXAS (continued)

Stage Directions, pg 1022
U-Edit Video, pg 1047

UTAH

ELS Productions Inc, pg 860
ImageWorks Communications, pg 896
One Stop CD Shop LLC, pg 963

VIRGINIA

American AV, pg 783
CALIBRE, pg 816
CDR Communications Inc, pg 822
Furnace MFG, pg 874
Gingerbread Productions, pg 878
Lee Hartman & Sons Inc, pg 918
Limelight Communications Inc, pg 921
Rocktown Media, pg 998
SoundView Services Inc, pg 1018

WASHINGTON

Bennett-Watt HD Productions Inc, pg 805
CCI Solutions, pg 821
911 Media Arts Center, pg 957
Pacific Multimedia Inc, pg 967
Pro Image, pg 983
Proforma GW Marketing, pg 985
Victory Studios, pg 1054

WEST VIRGINIA

Blackwater Video Productions, pg 808
MotionMasters, pg 947

WISCONSIN

Audio Visual of Milwaukee Inc, pg 795
AVS Group, pg 800
Concept Productions Inc, pg 834
Excel Duplication Services, pg 864
NEWIST/CESA 7, pg 956
Sound Strations Audio Productions Inc, pg 1017
USAV Group Inc, pg 1050
Watts Communications Inc, pg 1062
Win Media Inc, pg 1067

WYOMING

Bridger Productions Inc, pg 812

PUERTO RICO

Stage Crew Audiovisual Inc, pg 1022

BRITISH COLUMBIA

Finale Editworks, pg 868
Image Media Farm, pg 895
Norlynn Audio Visual Services, pg 958
ProVision Video Sales & Rentals Inc, pg 986
Triad Communications Ltd, pg 1044
24 Frames Film & Video, pg 1047

MANITOBA

Ironstone Technologies, pg 902

NEWFOUNDLAND AND LABRADOR

Vidcraft Productions Ltd, pg 1054

ONTARIO

ADS Media, pg 777
GAPC (General Assembly Production Centre), pg 875
Image Video Services & Productions, pg 895
Music Manufacturing Services, pg 950
Purefire Communications Inc, pg 987
SLI Manufacturing Inc, pg 1013
Video Excellence Productions, pg 1055

QUEBEC

Group PVP, pg 882
Muse Entertainment Enterprises, pg 950

SASKATCHEWAN

Thomega Entertainment Inc, pg 1039

Duplication—Videocassettes

ALABAMA

AVS Media Group, pg 800
CMEInfo, pg 830
Media Visions Inc, pg 937

ARIZONA

Allusion Studios & Pure Wave Audio, pg 782
Film Creations Ltd, pg 867
Merestone, pg 938
Metropolitan Audio-Visual Inc, pg 940
On-Site Video, pg 963
Phoenix VideoFilms®, pg 974
Star Video Duplicating, pg 1024
Video Media Productions (VMP), pg 1055

ARKANSAS

Shadowbox Video Productions, pg 1007
White Diamond Productions, pg 1065

CALIFORNIA

Aaron & Le Duc, pg 772
Aberdeen Broadcast Services, pg 772
ACDC Audio CD & Cassette, pg 774
Action Video, pg 775
Adolph Gasser Inc, pg 776
Advanced Media LLC, pg 778
AGF Media Services, pg 778
All Video Productions, pg 781
ALOM Technologies Corp, pg 782
AlphaDogs Inc, pg 782
AM Productions, pg 783
Audio Visual Consultants, pg 795
Bridge Publications Inc, pg 812
California Tape Products Inc, pg 817
CCI Digital, pg 821
Christopher Gray Post Production, pg 826
Creative Media Recording, pg 838
Crystal Pyramid Productions™, pg 840
Custom Video Productions Inc, pg 841
Digital Jungle, pg 847
Digital Outpost, pg 847
Dogma Studios, pg 850
DVS InteleStream, pg 854
Express Media Inc, pg 864
Far West Media Services Inc, pg 865
Global Village Productions, pg 879
Gluskin's Custom Audio Video, pg 879
Gold Standard Productions, pg 880
Golden Gate Studios, pg 880
Gordon Productions Inc, pg 880
Havas Edge, pg 885
iCorpTv, pg 893
Imageworks, pg 896
InVision Productions, pg 902
JD Audio Visual Inc, pg 904
KTVU-Retail Services, pg 914
Ludlow Media Solutions, pg 926
Lynch Communications, pg 926
Maximus Media Inc, pg 934
Media Magic, pg 937
Method Studios, pg 939
New & Unique Videos™, pg 955
Joseph Nicoletti Consulting-Promotion/California International Records/Global Village Records, pg 957
Nolte Media, pg 958
On-Trax Inc, pg 963
Penrose Productions, pg 972
Peterson's Video Transfer Services, pg 973
piXvfm, pg 976
PM Productions, pg 977
PME Audio/Video, pg 977
Point 360, pg 978
Pro8mm, pg 983
PSI Inc, pg 987
QRS Software Services, pg 988
Reel Picture, pg 994
RJ Video Productions, pg 997
Rough House, pg 1000
Roundabout Entertainment Inc, pg 1000
Rovi Corp, pg 1000
Saturn Studios, pg 1003
Shapeshifter, pg 1008
Shokus Video, pg 1009
SonicPool, pg 1016
Staylor-Made Communications Inc, pg 1024
Still N'Motion, pg 1025
Technicolor, pg 1034
Tele-Video Production Services (TVPS), pg 1036
Toon Makers, pg 1042
Total Media Group, pg 1042
TVA Productions, pg 1046
Twin Peaks Creative, pg 1047
Universal Studios, pg 1049
University of Southern California, pg 1050
VidCan Media Solutions, pg 1054
Video Movie Magic, pg 1056
VMI Inc, pg 1060

COLORADO

The Cinema Lab, pg 827
Daylight Productions & Rentals, pg 844
Flashback Media Productions, pg 869
Rocky Mountain Audio/Video Productions Inc, pg 998
Spectrum Audio Visual Services, pg 1020

CONNECTICUT

A/V Davey, pg 797
Biomedical Media Communications Dept, pg 807
BRB Audiovisual Productions, pg 812
Cine-Med Inc, pg 826
Concord Communications, pg 835
Digital Video Productions, pg 848
EagleVision Inc, pg 855
Guymark Studios LLC, pg 883
Ironik Design & Post, pg 902
MAVCO, pg 934
MCC Films, pg 935
Rockwell Communications Inc, pg 998
T & M Digital Services, pg 1031
Video Design Group, pg 1055
Video Production Associates Inc, pg 1056

DELAWARE

Ken-Del Productions Inc, pg 909

DISTRICT OF COLUMBIA

Educational Film Center, pg 857
Interface Media Group, pg 900
Library of Congress, Motion Picture, Broadcasting & Recorded Sound Division, pg 919

FLORIDA

Accel Video Productions, pg 773
Access Media Group, pg 773
Accord Productions, pg 773
Cinema East, pg 827
Civins Productions Inc, pg 828
Communications Concepts Inc (CCI), pg 833
Eastern Video, pg 856
Easy Edit Video Inc, pg 856
Florida Digital Studios, pg 870
Gulf Coast Audio Visual Producers Inc, pg 883
Hi-Tech Enterprises Inc, pg 888
Home Shopping Network (HSN), pg 890
Mach 1 Productions, pg 927
Media Concepts Inc, pg 936
Photosound of Orlando Inc, pg 975
Progressive Media & Music, pg 985
Sight & Sound Productions, pg 1010
Tallahassee Audio Visual, pg 1031
Mike Vasilinda Productions Inc, pg 1052
Video Techniques Inc, pg 1056

GEORGIA

Audio Visual Resources Inc, pg 795
Beachwood Productions, pg 804
Beast Atlanta, pg 804
Crawford Media Services, pg 838
Guerrilla Productions LLC, pg 883
Omega Media Group Inc, pg 962
Showcase Photo & Video, pg 1009
Sirius Images Corp dba WaveGuide Studios, pg 1012
Staging Directions Inc, pg 1023
USMotivation, pg 1051
Video Copy Services Inc, pg 1055

HAWAII

1013 Integrated, pg 1037

IDAHO

KTVB-TV, pg 914

VIDEO

Duplication—Videocassettes (continued)

PENNSYLVANIA (continued)

JPL, pg 906
Karol Media Inc, pg 908
Ott Film Rentals, pg 966
Panta Rhei Media Inc, pg 968
Production Masters Inc (PMI), pg 984
The Videohouse Inc, pg 1057
Visual Sound Inc, pg 1059
WPHL-TV, pg 1070

SOUTH CAROLINA

American Production Services LLC, pg 785
Genesis Creative, pg 877
Stages Video Productions, pg 1023
Venture Media, pg 1052

TENNESSEE

Memphis Communications Corp, pg 938
Motion Picture Services, pg 947
Running Pony Productions LLC, pg 1000
ST Productions, pg 1022
Stage Post, pg 1022
Russ Sturgeon Productions/RSVP, pg 1027
WKPT-TV, pg 1068

TEXAS

Astro Audio Visual, pg 792
Biway Media, pg 808
Cerutti Productions Inc, pg 823
CEV Multimedia Ltd, pg 823
Communication Arts Multimedia Inc, pg 832
Dub King, pg 853
The Editing Co, pg 857
First Group Communications Inc, pg 868
Paul Flanagan Productions, pg 869
Harbor House Studios, pg 884
Horizon Film + Video Productions, pg 891
J&S Audio Visual Inc, pg 904
McNee Productions Inc, pg 935
Mediaforce Productions, pg 937
Earl Miller Productions Inc, pg 943
Julye Newlin Productions Inc, pg 956
Replicopy Digital Media Center, pg 995
Romar Learning, pg 999
South Coast Film & Video, pg 1019
Stage Directions, pg 1022
Texas Heart Institute Visual Communication Services, pg 1037
U-Edit Video, pg 1047

UTAH

One Stop CD Shop LLC, pg 963

VERMONT

University of Vermont, Instructional Television Dept, pg 1050

VIRGINIA

American AV, pg 783
BES Studios, pg 805
CACI Productions Group, pg 816
CALIBRE, pg 816
CDR Communications Inc, pg 822
Creative Video of Washington Inc, pg 839
Gingerbread Productions, pg 878
Henninger Media Services, pg 888
Lee Hartman & Sons Inc, pg 918
Limelight Communications Inc, pg 921
Lion Recording Services Inc, pg 922
National Media Services Inc, pg 953
The Whitlock Group, pg 1065

WASHINGTON

Global Net Productions Inc, pg 879
Inland Audio Visual Co, pg 898
Robert McConnell Productions, pg 935
Proforma GW Marketing, pg 985
Victory Studios, pg 1054

WEST VIRGINIA

MotionMasters, pg 947

WISCONSIN

Audio Visual of Milwaukee Inc, pg 795
Excel Duplication Services, pg 864
Learning Technology Services, pg 917
Media Communications Association-International (MCA-I), pg 936
NEWIST/CESA 7, pg 956
USAV Group Inc, pg 1050
Video Wisconsin Inc, pg 1056
Watts Communications Inc, pg 1062
Wisconsin Public Television, pg 1068

WYOMING

Bridger Productions Inc, pg 812

PUERTO RICO

Stage Crew Audiovisual Inc, pg 1022

BRITISH COLUMBIA

Commercial Electronics Ltd, pg 832
Finale Editworks, pg 868
Triad Communications Ltd, pg 1044
24 Frames Film & Video, pg 1047

NEWFOUNDLAND AND LABRADOR

Vidcraft Productions Ltd, pg 1054

ONTARIO

ADS Media, pg 777
Cinram Inc, pg 828
DG Mijo, pg 846
Edcom Multimedia Products, pg 856
Purefire Communications Inc, pg 987
Video Excellence Productions, pg 1055

QUEBEC

Group PVP, pg 882

SASKATCHEWAN

Thomega Entertainment Inc, pg 1039

Duplication—Videodiscs

ARIZONA

Film Creations Ltd, pg 867
Merestone, pg 938

ARKANSAS

Shadowbox Video Productions, pg 1007

CALIFORNIA

Advanced Media LLC, pg 778
All Video Productions, pg 781
Custom Video Productions Inc, pg 841
Dogma Studios, pg 850
Express Media Inc, pg 864
FXC Communications, pg 874
iCorpTv, pg 893
ITV Productions, pg 903
Lynch Communications, pg 926
Maximus Media Inc, pg 934
Pioneer Electronics (USA) Inc, pg 976
Planet Blue, pg 976
PM Productions, pg 977
QRS Software Services, pg 988
Quality Clones, pg 988
Roundabout Entertainment Inc, pg 1000
Shapeshifter, pg 1008
SNAP, pg 1014
SonicPool, pg 1016
Still N'Motion, pg 1025
Universal Studios, pg 1049

COLORADO

Flashback Media Productions, pg 869
Rocky Mountain Audio/Video Productions Inc, pg 998
Spectrum Audio Visual Services, pg 1020

CONNECTICUT

Cine-Med Inc, pg 826
Ironik Design & Post, pg 902

DELAWARE

Ken-Del Productions Inc, pg 909

FLORIDA

Cinema East, pg 827
Civins Productions Inc, pg 828
Progressive Media & Music, pg 985

GEORGIA

Crawford Media Services, pg 838
Guerrilla Productions LLC, pg 883
KEF Media, pg 908
Omega Media Group Inc, pg 962
Staging Directions Inc, pg 1023

ILLINOIS

Analog Free Media, pg 786
Big Shoulders Digital Video Productions, pg 807
Major Media Inc, pg 929
SCI Television Productions LLC, pg 1004
Tele-Time Systems, pg 1036

INDIANA

Optical Disc Solutions Inc, pg 964

LOUISIANA

Digital FX Inc, pg 847
Louisiana State University Health Sciences Center - Shreveport, pg 925

MAINE

Headlight Audio Visual Inc, pg 887

MARYLAND

dbF a Media Company, pg 844
Optic Bindery & Packaging, pg 964
Pro Cuts Editing Services, pg 982
Saah Video, pg 1001

MICHIGAN

Digi Sign Design LLC, pg 847
K&R's Recording Studios Inc, pg 908

MINNESOTA

Aggressive Records Audio Duplication LLC, pg 778

NEVADA

Encore Productions Inc, pg 861

NEW HAMPSHIRE

Apertura, pg 788

NEW JERSEY

Broadcast Center Studios, pg 813
Diversified Systems Inc, pg 849
DWJ Television, pg 854
MIB Mediaworks, pg 941
Reed Presentations Inc (RPI), pg 993
SES World Skies, pg 1007
Suede Interactive, pg 1027

NEW YORK

Burlington A/V Recording Media, pg 815
Design Audio Visual Inc, pg 845
Duplication Specialists Inc, pg 853
Eastco Multimedia Solutions Inc, pg 856
General Audio-Visual Inc (GAVI), pg 876
HAVE Inc, pg 886
International Digital Centre, pg 901
Mood Creations Ltd, pg 946
PostWorks, pg 979
PrimaLux Video Inc, pg 982
TBA Global Events, pg 1032
Teatown Communications Group, pg 1033
Visual Technologies Corp, pg 1060

NORTH CAROLINA

Pat Appleson Studios Inc, pg 788
LCW Productions LLC, pg 917

OHIO

Aztec Video Productions, pg 801

OKLAHOMA

Smart Concepts Ltd, pg 1013

PENNSYLVANIA

Innovision Media Group, pg 899
Laser Video Corp, pg 916

SOUTH CAROLINA

American Production Services LLC, pg 785

TENNESSEE

Stage Post, pg 1022

TEXAS

The Editing Co, pg 857
Horizon Film + Video Productions, pg 891
Mediaforce Productions, pg 937
Stage Directions, pg 1022

VIRGINIA

Lee Hartman & Sons Inc, pg 918
Lion Recording Services Inc, pg 922

WASHINGTON

Victory Studios, pg 1054

WISCONSIN

Audio Visual of Milwaukee Inc, pg 795
NEWIST/CESA 7, pg 956

BRITISH COLUMBIA

Finale Editworks, pg 868
Triad Communications Ltd, pg 1044
24 Frames Film & Video, pg 1047

ONTARIO

Purefire Communications Inc, pg 987

Duplication—Videotapes

ALABAMA

Media Visions Inc, pg 937

ARIZONA

Film Creations Ltd, pg 867
Merestone, pg 938
Metropolitan Audio-Visual Inc, pg 940
On-Site Video, pg 963
Star Video Duplicating, pg 1024
Video Media Productions (VMP), pg 1055

ARKANSAS

KTHV Television, a Gannett Company, pg 914
Shadowbox Video Productions, pg 1007
White Diamond Productions, pg 1065

CALIFORNIA

Aaron & Le Duc, pg 772
Action Video, pg 775
Adolph Gasser Inc, pg 776
Advanced Media LLC, pg 778
AGF Media Services, pg 778
All Video Productions, pg 781
ALOM Technologies Corp, pg 782
AlphaDogs Inc, pg 782
AM Productions, pg 783
California Tape Products Inc, pg 817
CCI Digital, pg 821
Chesney Communications, pg 824
Christopher Gray Post Production, pg 826
Creative Media Recording, pg 838
Crystal Pyramid Productions™, pg 840
Custom Video Productions Inc, pg 841
Digital Jungle, pg 847
Digital Media West, pg 847
Digital Outpost, pg 847
Dogma Studios, pg 850
DVS InteleStream, pg 854
Express Media Inc, pg 864
First Person™, pg 868
Fox Television Center, pg 872
Global Village Productions, pg 879
Gluskin's Custom Audio Video, pg 879
Golden Gate Studios, pg 880
Gordon Productions Inc, pg 880
Havas Edge, pg 885
iCorpTv, pg 893
InVision Productions, pg 902
JD Audio Visual Inc, pg 904
KTVU-Retail Services, pg 914
KVIE-Channel 6, pg 914
Ludlow Media Solutions, pg 926
Lynch Communications, pg 926
Maximus Media Inc, pg 934
Media Magic, pg 937
Method Studios, pg 939
Joseph Nicoletti Consulting-Promotion/California International Records/Global Village Records, pg 957
Nolte Media, pg 958
On-Trax Inc, pg 963
Pacific Video Image, pg 967
Penrose Productions, pg 972
Peterson's Video Transfer Services, pg 973
piXvfm, pg 976
PM Productions, pg 977
Point 360, pg 978
Prime Cut Productions, pg 982
Pro8mm, pg 983
PSI Inc, pg 987
QRS Software Services, pg 988
Reel Picture, pg 994
Rough House, pg 1000
Roundabout Entertainment Inc, pg 1000
Rovi Corp, pg 1000
Shapeshifter, pg 1008
SonicPool, pg 1016
Still N'Motion, pg 1025
Technicolor, pg 1034
Tele-Video Production Services (TVPS), pg 1036
Toon Makers, pg 1042
Total Media Group, pg 1042
TVA Productions, pg 1046
Twin Peaks Creative, pg 1047
Universal Studios, pg 1049
VidCan Media Solutions, pg 1054
Video Movie Magic, pg 1056
Videolady, pg 1057
VMI Inc, pg 1060
WMS Media Inc, pg 1069

COLORADO

Daylight Productions & Rentals, pg 844
Flashback Media Productions, pg 869
Rocky Mountain Audio/Video Productions Inc, pg 998

CONNECTICUT

Applebox Studio, pg 788
A/V Davey, pg 797
BRB Audiovisual Productions, pg 812
Cine-Med Inc, pg 826
Digital Video Productions, pg 848
EagleVision Inc, pg 855
Fox Connecticut, pg 872
Ironik Design & Post, pg 902
MAVCO, pg 934
MCC Films, pg 935
Palace Digital Studios, pg 967
Rockwell Communications Inc, pg 998
Video Design Group, pg 1055

DELAWARE

Ken-Del Productions Inc, pg 909
Ken-Del Studios, pg 909

DISTRICT OF COLUMBIA

Interface Media Group, pg 900
Library of Congress, Motion Picture, Broadcasting & Recorded Sound Division, pg 919

FLORIDA

Accel Video Productions, pg 773
Access Media Group, pg 773
Accord Productions, pg 773
Cinema East, pg 827
Civins Productions Inc, pg 828
Steven Cohen Motion Picture Production, pg 831
Communications Concepts Inc (CCI), pg 833
Comtel Inc, pg 834
Eastern Video, pg 856
Easy Edit Video Inc, pg 856
Florida Digital Studios, pg 870
Gulf Coast Audio Visual Producers Inc, pg 883
Hi-Tech Enterprises Inc, pg 888
Home Shopping Network (HSN), pg 890
Jordan Klein Film & Video (JKFV), pg 906
Knowles Video Inc (KVI), pg 912
Media Concepts Inc, pg 936
Paradise Video & Film, pg 969
Progressive Media & Music, pg 985
RLX Media LLC, pg 997
Sight & Sound Productions, pg 1010
Tallahassee Audio Visual, pg 1031
Mike Vasilinda Productions Inc, pg 1052
Video Techniques Inc, pg 1056

GEORGIA

Audio Visual Resources Inc, pg 795
Beachwood Productions, pg 804
Beast Atlanta, pg 804
Crawford Media Services, pg 838
ECG Productions, pg 856
First Cut Communications LLC, pg 868
Guerrilla Productions LLC, pg 883
Omega Media Group Inc, pg 962
Showcase Photo & Video, pg 1009
Sirius Images Corp dba WaveGuide Studios, pg 1012
Staging Directions Inc, pg 1023
Video Copy Services Inc, pg 1055

HAWAII

1013 Integrated, pg 1037

ILLINOIS

Analog Free Media, pg 786
Backstar Creative Media Inc, pg 801
Beatty TeleVisual Productions, pg 804
Big Shoulders Digital Video Productions, pg 807
CCore Media Inc, pg 821
Chicago Satellite & Video, pg 825
Filmworkers, pg 868
IV Media Resources, pg 903
Major Media Inc, pg 929
Moviecraft Inc, pg 947
The Pepper Group, pg 972
RBR Productions, pg 992
SCI Television Productions LLC, pg 1004
Southern Illinois University, pg 1019
Tele-Time Systems, pg 1036
Televersions, pg 1036
Video I-D Teleproductions Inc, pg 1055
Video Impressions, pg 1055
WEEK TV, pg 1063

INDIANA

Advanced Media Integration, pg 777
Educational Video Group Inc, pg 857
PentaVision Communications Inc, pg 972

IOWA

Duplication Media, pg 853
The Production House, pg 984

KENTUCKY

Hammond Communications Group, pg 884
Media Resources, pg 937
Barney Miller's Inc, pg 943
The PPS Group, pg 980

LOUISIANA

Digital FX Inc, pg 847
Louisiana State University Health Sciences Center - Shreveport, pg 925
Moxie Media, pg 948
Vidox Motion Imagery, pg 1057
WVLA-TV, pg 1071

MAINE

WGME-TV, pg 1065

MARYLAND

The Ahern Group, pg 779
CPR MultiMedia Solutions, pg 837
The Cutting Corp, pg 841
dbF a Media Company, pg 844
DBM Communications Inc, pg 844
Media Dimensions Inc, pg 936
Optic Bindery & Packaging, pg 964
Pro Cuts Editing Services, pg 982
Producers Video, pg 984
Professional Label Inc, pg 985
Saah Video, pg 1001
Shadowstone R & R™, pg 1008
Sheffield Audio/Video Productions, pg 1008
Sign Media Inc, pg 1011
Strauss Photo Technical Service Inc, pg 1026
Video Labs, pg 1055

MASSACHUSETTS

Award Productions, pg 800
CommCreative, pg 832
Cramer Productions, pg 837
In the Wild Productions, pg 897
MALCO Electronics, pg 929
Penfield Productions Ltd, pg 971

VIDEO

Duplication—Videotapes (continued)

MASSACHUSETTS (continued)

Small Planet Communications Inc, pg 1013
Video Express, pg 1055

MICHIGAN

Digi Sign Design LLC, pg 847
K&R's Recording Studios Inc, pg 908
RingSide Creative, pg 997
TeL Systems, pg 1035
The Transfer Zone®, pg 1043

MINNESOTA

Aggressive Records Audio Duplication LLC, pg 778
Cinequipt Inc, pg 828
GMI Productions, pg 879
Pro Media Productions, pg 983
Rum Jungle Media, pg 1000

MISSISSIPPI

Jasper Ewing & Sons Inc, pg 864

MISSOURI

Allied Photo Color Co, pg 781
Audio-VideoGraphics Inc, pg 795
Avatar Studios, pg 798
Cable Films & Video, pg 816
Communitronics Corp, pg 833
Conference Technologies Inc, pg 835
Show-Me Audio-Visual, pg 1009
Visionworks Design Services Inc, pg 1059
VSG Digital Media Solutions, pg 1061

MONTANA

KUSM TV, pg 914
North Country Media Group, pg 959

NEBRASKA

Dog & Pony Productions Inc, pg 850

NEVADA

Aardvark Video & Media Productions, pg 772
DVDs4Less, pg 854
Encore Productions Inc, pg 861
HDTV Productions Inc, pg 886
21st Century Video Productions, pg 1047

NEW HAMPSHIRE

Apertura, pg 788
Channell One Video, pg 824
Chip Taylor Communications LLC, pg 1032
The Troupe, pg 1045

NEW JERSEY

All Jersey Studios, pg 780
Broadcast Center Studios, pg 813
Deluxe Media Services, pg 845
Diversified Systems Inc, pg 849
DWJ Television, pg 854
Hogpenny Studios, pg 890
Laurel Video Productions, pg 916
MediaMix Inc, pg 937
Megavideo Productions, pg 938
Midnight Media Group Inc, pg 942
NFL Films Inc, pg 957
NFL Films Music Library, pg 957
Producer East Productions, pg 983
Reed Presentations Inc (RPI), pg 993
Suede Interactive, pg 1027
Tele-Measurements Inc, pg 1035
VCSvideo, pg 1052
Video Corporation of America (VCA), pg 1055
Video Ideas Productions, pg 1055
VTS Video & Media, pg 1061

NEW MEXICO

Production Outfitters, pg 984

NEW YORK

Adwar Video, pg 778
aurora productions, pg 797
The Big House Group, pg 807
Burlington A/V Recording Media, pg 815
Chromavision Corp, pg 826
CMI Media Management, pg 830
Colortone Audio Visual, pg 832
Communication Corner Inc, pg 832
Thomas Craven Film Corp, pg 837
Design Audio Visual Inc, pg 845
Digital Art Video Inc, pg 847
Downtown Community Television Center (DCTV), pg 851
DuArt, pg 853
Duplication Depot Inc, pg 853
Duplication Specialists Inc, pg 853
Eastco Multimedia Solutions Inc, pg 856
Elite Video & Photography Services Inc, pg 859
4-D Creative Media, pg 871
General Audio-Visual Inc (GAVI), pg 876
Hallel Communications, pg 884
HAVE Inc, pg 886
HB-Content, pg 886
Hello World Communications, pg 888
Icontent, pg 893
International Digital Centre, pg 901
J & D Laboratories Inc, pg 903
Long Island Video Enterprises Live Inc, pg 924
Magno Sound & Video, pg 929
Jack Morton Worldwide, pg 946
MRG Productions Inc, pg 948
Shelly Palmer Production, pg 968
PostWorks, pg 979
Refinery, pg 994
TBA Global Events, pg 1032
Teatown Communications Group, pg 1033
Technisphere Corp, pg 1034
TeleTime Productions, pg 1036
Tobin Productions Inc, pg 1041
USA Studios, pg 1050
VDO Lab Inc, pg 1052
Video Caption Corp, pg 1054
Video Concepts Unlimited, pg 1055
Visual Technologies Corp, pg 1060
Visual Word Systems Inc, pg 1060
WTL Productions, pg 1071
Zelman Studios Ltd, pg 1073

NORTH CAROLINA

A&V Company, pg 772
All Pro Media Inc, pg 780
Pat Appleson Studios Inc, pg 788
Camcor Inc, pg 818
Duke Media Services, pg 853
LCW Productions LLC, pg 917
Moving Pictures, pg 948
Take One Productions Ltd, pg 1031
Trailblazer Studios®, pg 1043

OHIO

Aztec Video Productions, pg 801
EDR Media LLC, pg 857
Image Video Teleproductions Inc, pg 895
iVideo Technologies, pg 903
The Little Warehouse Inc, pg 923
Lyon Video Inc, pg 927
MainSail Production Services Inc, pg 929
Mills James Productions, pg 943
Promedia Digital, pg 986
R&B Communications Inc, pg 991
Take 1 Media Services, pg 1031
Ungar Video & Film, pg 1048
VGI Productions, pg 1053
Vista Color Imaging Inc, pg 1059

OKLAHOMA

Garman Productions LLC, pg 875
Piper Media Services Inc, pg 976
University of Oklahoma Academic Media & Digital Services, pg 1050

OREGON

BingoLewis, pg 807
KPDX-TV Production Center, pg 913
Production West, pg 985

PENNSYLVANIA

John E Allen Inc, pg 781
Audio Visual Communications Inc, pg 795
Bernie's Photo Center, pg 805
Center City Film & Video Inc, pg 822
FMP Media Solutions Inc, pg 870
Fusion Brand Experiences, pg 874
JPL, pg 906
Laser Video Corp, pg 916
Ott Film Rentals, pg 966
Production Masters Inc (PMI), pg 984
The Videohouse Inc, pg 1057
WPHL-TV, pg 1070

SOUTH CAROLINA

American Production Services LLC, pg 785
Genesis Creative, pg 877
Sound & Images Inc, pg 1016
Stages Video Productions, pg 1023
Venture Media, pg 1052

TENNESSEE

Memphis Communications Corp, pg 938
Motion Picture Services, pg 947
Running Pony Productions LLC, pg 1000
Stage Post, pg 1022
Russ Sturgeon Productions/RSVP, pg 1027
WKPT-TV, pg 1068

TEXAS

Astro Audio Visual, pg 792
Biway Media, pg 808
CEV Multimedia Ltd, pg 823
Dub King, pg 853
The Editing Co, pg 857
First Group Communications Inc, pg 868
Paul Flanagan Productions, pg 869
Harbor House Studios, pg 884
Horizon Film + Video Productions, pg 891
Maverick Video Productions, pg 934
McNee Productions Inc, pg 935
Mediaforce Productions, pg 937
Earl Miller Productions Inc, pg 943
Julye Newlin Productions Inc, pg 956
Replicopy Digital Media Center, pg 995
The Samuels Co, pg 1002
South Coast Film & Video, pg 1019
Stage Directions, pg 1022
Texas Heart Institute Visual Communication Services, pg 1037

UTAH

One Stop CD Shop LLC, pg 963

VERMONT

University of Vermont, Instructional Television Dept, pg 1050

VIRGINIA

BES Studios, pg 805
CACI Productions Group, pg 816
Creative Video of Washington Inc, pg 839
Gingerbread Productions, pg 878
Henninger Media Services, pg 888
Lee Hartman & Sons Inc, pg 918
Limelight Communications Inc, pg 921
Lion Recording Services Inc, pg 922
The Whitlock Group, pg 1065

WASHINGTON

Global Net Productions Inc, pg 879
Inland Audio Visual Co, pg 898
Kostov Productions, pg 913
911 Media Arts Center, pg 957
Pacific Multimedia Inc, pg 967
Pro Image, pg 983
Proforma GW Marketing, pg 985
Victory Studios, pg 1054

WEST VIRGINIA

MotionMasters, pg 947

WISCONSIN

Audio Visual of Milwaukee Inc, pg 795
Excel Duplication Services, pg 864
Learning Technology Services, pg 917
Media Communications Association-International (MCA-I), pg 936
NEWIST/CESA 7, pg 956
USAV Group Inc, pg 1050
Video Wisconsin Inc, pg 1056
Watts Communications Inc, pg 1062
Wisconsin Public Television, pg 1068

WYOMING

Bridger Productions Inc, pg 812

PUERTO RICO

Stage Crew Audiovisual Inc, pg 1022

Duplicator, *see* Tape Duplicator

DVD Authoring

VIDEO

DVD Authoring (continued)

MINNESOTA (continued)

Master Communications Group, pg 933
Pro Media Productions, pg 983
Rum Jungle Media, pg 1000
Worthwhile Films, pg 1070

MISSOURI

Avatar Studios, pg 798
Production Consultants, pg 984
Show-Me Audio-Visual, pg 1009
Studio Worx Inc, pg 1027

MONTANA

ooLite Media, pg 964

NEBRASKA

Rainbow Video Productions Inc, pg 991
Three Pillars Media, pg 1040

NEVADA

Aardvark Video & Media Productions, pg 772
JCS Video Productions, pg 904

NEW HAMPSHIRE

Captain Fiddle Music & Publications, pg 820
Chip Taylor Communications LLC, pg 1032

NEW JERSEY

All Jersey Studios, pg 780
CD Meyer Inc, pg 822
Color Leasing Studios, pg 831
Creative Video, pg 838
Diversified Systems Inc, pg 849
Early Films, pg 855
Euro-Pacific Film & Video Productions Inc, pg 863
MIB Mediaworks, pg 941
Midnight Media Group Inc, pg 942
Ray Mueller Productions, pg 949
Outside The Box Interactive LLC, pg 966
Public Eye Productions, pg 987
Shamrock Communications, pg 1008
VCSvideo, pg 1052
Video Ideas Productions, pg 1055
VTS Video & Media, pg 1061

NEW MEXICO

Production Outfitters, pg 984

NEW YORK

Big Foot Productions Inc, pg 807
The Big House Group, pg 807
BioMedia Inc, pg 807
Brooklyn Films, pg 814
Chromavision Corp, pg 826
CMI Media Management, pg 830
Design Audio Visual Inc, pg 845
Digital Art Video Inc, pg 847
Digital Force, pg 847
dM works, pg 849
Downtown Community Television Center (DCTV), pg 851
DuArt, pg 853
Duplication Depot Inc, pg 853
Eastco Multimedia Solutions Inc, pg 856
Foothill Digital Inc, pg 871
4-D Creative Media, pg 871
General Audio-Visual Inc (GAVI), pg 876
Giant Interactive, pg 878
HAVE Inc, pg 886
HB-Content, pg 886
Heavy Melody, pg 887
Hello World Communications, pg 888
InterNation Inc, pg 900
International Digital Centre, pg 901
iProbe Multilingual Solutions Inc, pg 902
J & D Laboratories Inc, pg 903
L A Bruell Inc, pg 914
La Paloma Films, pg 915
Lylofilm Productions, pg 926
Neal Marshad Productions, pg 931
The Napoleon Group, pg 952
Post Josh Productions, pg 979
Production Central, pg 984
Teatown Communications Group, pg 1033
Tobin Productions Inc, pg 1041
Video Caption Corp, pg 1054
Visual Technologies Corp, pg 1060

NORTH CAROLINA

Pat Appleson Studios Inc, pg 788
The Communications Group Inc, pg 833
Ladyslipper Inc, pg 915
LCW Productions LLC, pg 917
Moving Pictures, pg 948
On Location North Carolina, pg 963
Take One Productions Ltd, pg 1031
2BruceStudio, pg 1047
Unifour Productions Inc, pg 1048

NORTH DAKOTA

Media Productions, pg 937

OHIO

Advent Media Inc, pg 778
Commercial Video, pg 832
EDR Media LLC, pg 857
Maslowski Productions, pg 933
Musicol Recording, pg 951
R&B Communications Inc, pg 991
Vista Color Imaging Inc, pg 1059

OKLAHOMA

Garman Productions LLC, pg 875
Producers Playhouse, pg 983
Smart Concepts Ltd, pg 1013

OREGON

A KTVA Production LLC, pg 771
BingoLewis, pg 807
Future Disc LLC, pg 874
Intersect Video, pg 901
InterVision Media, pg 902
MediaFX, pg 937
Odyssey Productions Inc, pg 961
Rex, pg 995

PENNSYLVANIA

Argentine Productions Inc, pg 789
Audio Visions Inc, pg 795
Aztech Productions LLC, pg 801
Beholder Productions Inc, pg 804
FMP Media Solutions Inc, pg 870
Innovision Media Group, pg 899
JPL, pg 906
Laser Video Corp, pg 916
Panta Rhei Media Inc, pg 968
The Videohouse Inc, pg 1057

SOUTH CAROLINA

Genesis Creative, pg 877

TENNESSEE

American Blackguard Inc, pg 784
Anode Inc, pg 787
JamSync, pg 904
Kingswood Productions, pg 911
Motion Picture Services, pg 947
Paradigm Marketing & Creative, pg 969
Running Pony Productions LLC, pg 1000
Stage Post, pg 1022
Technical Support Systems LLC, pg 1034

TEXAS

Biway Media, pg 808
Communication Arts Multimedia Inc, pg 832
The Editing Co, pg 857
Epic Software Group Inc, pg 862
Fire Station Studios, pg 868
First Group Communications Inc, pg 868
Harbor House Studios, pg 884
Horizon Film + Video Productions, pg 891
McNee Productions Inc, pg 935
Mediaforce Productions, pg 937
Julye Newlin Productions Inc, pg 956
Phil Lights, pg 973
Replicopy Digital Media Center, pg 995
Stage Directions, pg 1022

UTAH

Ron Hill Imagery, pg 889
ImageWorks Communications, pg 896
K-SAR Video & DVD Productions, pg 907

VIRGINIA

CALIBRE, pg 816
D&B Television & Video Productions Inc, pg 842
Furnace MFG, pg 874
Gingerbread Productions, pg 878
Limelight Communications Inc, pg 921
Metro Productions, pg 939
Rocktown Media, pg 998
Video Solutions, pg 1056

WASHINGTON

Bennett-Watt HD Productions Inc, pg 805
Hamilton Studio, pg 884
Sparkworks Media, pg 1019
Victory Studios, pg 1054

WEST VIRGINIA

Blackwater Video Productions, pg 808

WISCONSIN

Audio Visual of Milwaukee Inc, pg 795
USAV Group Inc, pg 1050
Watts Communications Inc, pg 1062
Win Media Inc, pg 1067

WYOMING

Bridger Productions Inc, pg 812

PUERTO RICO

Stage Crew Audiovisual Inc, pg 1022

BRITISH COLUMBIA

Finale Editworks, pg 868
Norlynn Audio Visual Services, pg 958
North West Digital Ltd, pg 959
Triad Communications Ltd, pg 1044
24 Frames Film & Video, pg 1047

MANITOBA

Ironstone Technologies, pg 902

NEWFOUNDLAND AND LABRADOR

Vidcraft Productions Ltd, pg 1054

ONTARIO

ADS Media, pg 777
GAPC (General Assembly Production Centre), pg 875
Image Video Services & Productions, pg 895
JFB Communications, pg 905
Marblemedia, pg 930
Metalworks Recording Studios Inc, pg 939
Music Manufacturing Services, pg 950
Pendulum Entertainment, pg 971
Purefire Communications Inc, pg 987
RB Productions, pg 992
Shaw Street Productions, pg 1008
Video Excellence Productions, pg 1055
Westbury National Show Systems Ltd, pg 1064

QUEBEC

Group PVP, pg 882

SASKATCHEWAN

Thomega Entertainment Inc, pg 1039

DVD—Blank Distributors

ARIZONA

EAR Professional Audio/Video, pg 855

ARKANSAS

White Diamond Productions, pg 1065

CALIFORNIA

Adolph Gasser Inc, pg 776
Ametron Audio/Video, pg 785
Delicate Electronics Sales Inc, pg 845
Edgewise Media Inc, pg 856
Hooper Camera & Imaging, pg 891
JD Audio Visual Inc, pg 904
MSE Media Solutions, pg 949
New Cyberian Systems Inc, pg 955
Promax Systems, pg 986
Reel Picture, pg 994
Revolt Pro Media Inc, pg 995
TapeStockOnline.com, pg 1032

COLORADO

Alpine Media, pg 782

CONNECTICUT

Sennheiser Electronic Corp, pg 1006
T & M Digital Services, pg 1031

FLORIDA

Access Media Group, pg 773
BAI Distributors Inc, pg 801
CD ROM™ Inc, pg 822
Digital Video Systems Inc, pg 848
Global Video Distributors Inc, pg 879
Hunter Electronics LLC, pg 892
Media Concepts Inc, pg 936
Recording Media & Equipment Inc (RM&E), pg 993
Sight & Sound Productions, pg 1010
Universal Studios Florida® Production Group, pg 1049

GEORGIA

Stage Front Presentation Systems, pg 1022

ILLINOIS

Analog Free Media, pg 786
Joseph Electronics, pg 906
Polyline LLC, pg 978
Tape Resources, pg 1031

INDIANA

Advanced Media Integration, pg 777
Lee Co Inc, pg 918
Optical Disc Solutions Inc, pg 964
Sensory Technologies LLC, pg 1006
SHP Electronics, pg 1010

KENTUCKY

NOR-COM Inc, pg 958
Northern Kentucky University, pg 959

MAINE

Headlight Audio Visual Inc, pg 887

MASSACHUSETTS

Hunt's Photo, Video & Digital, pg 892
Rule Broadcast Systems, pg 1000

MICHIGAN

K&R All Media Productions Inc, pg 908

MISSISSIPPI

Bowie Audio Visual Enterprises Inc, pg 811

NEBRASKA

Dog & Pony Productions Inc, pg 850

NEW HAMPSHIRE

Channell One Video, pg 824

NEW JERSEY

Argraph Corp, pg 789
Audio Visual Dynamics®, pg 795
MIB Mediaworks, pg 941
Starlite Productions, pg 1024
Tele-Measurements Inc, pg 1035
Total Media, pg 1042
Total Video Products Inc, pg 1042
Wired 4 Sound Inc, pg 1068

NEW YORK

Design Audio Visual Inc, pg 845
Digital Force, pg 847
Duplication Depot Inc, pg 853
Eastco Multimedia Solutions Inc, pg 856
Mark Custom Recording Service Inc, pg 931
Women Make Movies Inc, pg 1069

OHIO

The Little Warehouse Inc, pg 923
Midwest Photo Exchange, pg 942
Promedia Digital, pg 986
Tri-State Audio Visual Co, pg 1044

PENNSYLVANIA

Advanced AV, pg 777
Bernie's Photo Center, pg 805
J E Foss Co, pg 871
Innovision Media Group, pg 899

TENNESSEE

Lowrance Sound Co Inc, pg 925
NTS ProMedia, pg 960

TEXAS

Biway Media, pg 808
CAM Audio Inc, pg 817
Data Display Audio Visual Co LP, pg 843
Harbor House Studios, pg 884
Replicopy Digital Media Center, pg 995
TapeWorks Texas Inc, pg 1032

VIRGINIA

Furnace MFG, pg 874
Lee Hartman & Sons Inc, pg 918

WASHINGTON

CCI Solutions, pg 821

WISCONSIN

Audio Visual of Milwaukee Inc, pg 795

ALBERTA

Matrix Video Communications Corp (MVCC), pg 934

BRITISH COLUMBIA

Finale Editworks, pg 868
ProVision Video Sales & Rentals Inc, pg 986

MANITOBA

Inland Audio Visual Ltd, pg 898

DVD—Blank Manufacturers

INDIANA

Optical Disc Solutions Inc, pg 964

NEW JERSEY

Disc Makers, pg 848
Synergem, pg 1030

NEW YORK

Digital Force, pg 847

OREGON

Phylco Audio Duplication, pg 975

TEXAS

Adams Evidence Grade Technology Inc, pg 775

DVD Duplication, *see* Duplication—DVDs

DVD Recorder & Player Distributors

ARIZONA

EAR Professional Audio/Video, pg 855

ARKANSAS

White Diamond Productions, pg 1065

CALIFORNIA

Adolph Gasser Inc, pg 776
Ametron Audio/Video, pg 785
Associated Sound, pg 792
Be Media, pg 804
Delicate Electronics Sales Inc, pg 845
Empire Wholesale Inc, pg 860
Gluskin's Custom Audio Video, pg 879
Instructional Materials & Equipment Distributors (I-Med), pg 899
JD Audio Visual Inc, pg 904
Photodyne Technologies, pg 974
POP TV, pg 978
SNAP, pg 1014
Southern California Sound Image Inc, pg 1019
Stanislaus Audio Video Inc, pg 1023
VMI Inc, pg 1060

CONNECTICUT

Concord Communications, pg 835
Everett Hall Associates Inc, pg 863
Rockwell Communications Inc, pg 998
Video Automation Systems Inc, pg 1054

FLORIDA

Access Media Group, pg 773
BAI Distributors Inc, pg 801
CD ROM™ Inc, pg 822
Digital Video Systems Inc, pg 848
General Projection Systems Inc, pg 877
Hunter Electronics LLC, pg 892
Media Concepts Inc, pg 936
Photomart Cine-Video Inc, pg 975
Recording Media & Equipment Inc (RM&E), pg 993
Sight & Sound Productions, pg 1010
Skyline Broadcast, pg 1013

GEORGIA

Clark, pg 829
Outsource Engineering & Manufacturing Inc dba Texscan MSI, pg 966
Stage Front Presentation Systems, pg 1022

ILLINOIS

Dukane Corp, Audio Visual Products Division, pg 853
Quintessence Audio Ltd, pg 989
Sound Vision Inc, pg 1018
Zenith Electronics LLC, pg 1073

INDIANA

Lee Co Inc, pg 918
Sensory Technologies LLC, pg 1006
SHP Electronics, pg 1010

KENTUCKY

NOR-COM Inc, pg 958

LOUISIANA

Intermedia Technologies, pg 900

MAINE

Headlight Audio Visual Inc, pg 887

MARYLAND

DSR Computer Technology Specialists Inc, pg 853
RTZ Audio Visual, pg 1000
Visual Aids Electronics Corp, pg 1059

MASSACHUSETTS

Hunt's Photo, Video & Digital, pg 892
Rule Broadcast Systems, pg 1000

MICHIGAN

Ascom Communications Contractors, pg 791
Digi Sign Design LLC, pg 847
On Stage Visuals, pg 963

MINNESOTA

Alpha Video & Audio Inc, pg 782

MISSISSIPPI

Bowie Audio Visual Enterprises Inc, pg 811

MISSOURI

MIS Technologies, pg 944
Modern Communications Inc, pg 944
Schiller's Audio-Visual, pg 1004

NEBRASKA

ATV Research Inc, pg 793
Dog & Pony Productions Inc, pg 850
Strong Cinema Products, pg 1026

NEVADA

Aardvark Video & Media Productions, pg 772

NEW JERSEY

Alltec Stores, a Vcom IMC Company, pg 782
Samsung Electronics America, pg 1002
Starlite Productions, pg 1024
Total Video Products Inc, pg 1042
Wired 4 Sound Inc, pg 1068

NEW YORK

ALTEL Systems Inc, pg 783
Audiovox, pg 796

VIDEO

DVD Recorder & Player Distributors (continued)

NEW YORK (continued)

Colortone Audio Visual, pg 832
Design Audio Visual Inc, pg 845
Duplication Depot Inc, pg 853
Eastco Multimedia Solutions Inc, pg 856
Gaylord Brothers, pg 876
General Audio-Visual Inc (GAVI), pg 876
Image Management Systems Inc, pg 895
KVL Audio Visual Services Inc, pg 914
Presentation Products Inc, pg 981
Visual Technologies Corp, pg 1060
Visual Word Systems Inc, pg 1060

OHIO

ITA Audio Visual Solutions, pg 902
The Little Warehouse Inc, pg 923
Jimmy Rea Electronics Inc, pg 992
Tri-State Audio Visual Co, pg 1044
Tri-State Visual Products, pg 1044

PENNSYLVANIA

Advanced AV, pg 777
Bernie's Photo Center, pg 805
J E Foss Co, pg 871
Vistacom Inc, pg 1059

RHODE ISLAND

Shanix Inc, pg 1008

TENNESSEE

Lowrance Sound Co Inc, pg 925
Technical Support Systems LLC, pg 1034
Zion Music Group, pg 1074

TEXAS

Astro Audio Visual, pg 792
AVES Audio Visual Systems Inc, pg 798
Biway Media, pg 808
CAM Audio Inc, pg 817
Data Display Audio Visual Co LP, pg 843
Data Projections Inc, pg 843
Digital Display Solutions Inc, pg 847
Heffernan Audio Visual, pg 887
Media Management LLC, pg 937
Replicopy Digital Media Center, pg 995
Schoolhouse Audio Visual, pg 1004
Tarpley Media Systems, pg 1032

VIRGINIA

Lee Hartman & Sons Inc, pg 918

WASHINGTON

CCI Solutions, pg 821
Global Net Productions Inc, pg 879
ToteVision, pg 1042

WISCONSIN

Audio Visual of Milwaukee Inc, pg 795
Safe Harbor Computers, pg 1001

ALBERTA

Infosat Communications Inc, pg 898
Matrix Video Communications Corp (MVCC), pg 934
Unique Communications Ltd, pg 1048

BRITISH COLUMBIA

DL Sound & Lighting Productions Ltd, pg 849
ProVision Video Sales & Rentals Inc, pg 986

MANITOBA

Advance Pro, pg 777
Inland Audio Visual Ltd, pg 898

ONTARIO

HD Source, pg 886
Premier A/V Sales Ltd, pg 980
SVAT Electronics, pg 1029
Westbury National Show Systems Ltd, pg 1064

DVD Recorder & Player Manufacturers

ARIZONA

Applied Integration Corp, pg 789

CALIFORNIA

Grande Vitesse Systems Inc (GVS), pg 881
SANYO Fisher Co, pg 1002
TEAC America Inc, pg 1033

GEORGIA

Outsource Engineering & Manufacturing Inc dba Texscan MSI, pg 966

NEW JERSEY

Emerson Radio Corp, pg 860
Samsung Electronics America, pg 1002

NEW YORK

Video Technology Services Inc, pg 1056

OKLAHOMA

BCD Associates Inc, pg 803

TENNESSEE

Adtec Digital Inc, pg 777

BRITISH COLUMBIA

Triad Communications Ltd, pg 1044

ONTARIO

SVAT Electronics, pg 1029

DVD Recorder & Player Rentals

ARIZONA

Merestone, pg 938
Video West Inc, pg 1056

ARKANSAS

White Diamond Productions, pg 1065

CALIFORNIA

Aaron & Le Duc, pg 772
Absolute Rentals, pg 772
Adolph Gasser Inc, pg 776
AGF Media Services, pg 778
Ametron Audio/Video, pg 785
Artichoke Productions, pg 791
Associated Sound, pg 792
Audio Rents, pg 794
AV Guys, pg 797
Big Time Picture Company Inc, pg 807
Express Media Inc, pg 864
Gluskin's Custom Audio Video, pg 879
Gold Standard Productions, pg 880
Hollywood Sound Systems, pg 890
Image Integration, pg 895
Instructional Materials & Equipment Distributors (I-Med), pg 899
JD Audio Visual Inc, pg 904
Maximus Media Inc, pg 934
Media Fabricators Inc, pg 936
Munday & Collins AV, pg 950
PSAV® Presentation Services, pg 986
Pyxis Industries Inc, pg 988
RetinaVision Productions, pg 995
Stanislaus Audio Video Inc, pg 1023
Synthesizer Systems Technologies (SST), pg 1030
Total Media Group, pg 1042
Twin Peaks Creative, pg 1047
Videorama Industries LLC, pg 1057
VMI Inc, pg 1060
Voice & Video Rentals, pg 1060
Warner Bros Production Sound & Video Services, pg 1062

COLORADO

Multimedia Audio Visual Inc, pg 950
Open Media Foundation, pg 964

CONNECTICUT

A/V Davey, pg 797
Everett Hall Associates Inc, pg 863
Videofilm Systems Inc, pg 1057

FLORIDA

Accord Productions, pg 773
Cinema East, pg 827
Media Concepts Inc, pg 936
Paradise Show & Design Inc, pg 969
Photosound of Orlando Inc, pg 975
Sight & Sound Productions, pg 1010
Universal Studios Florida® Production Group, pg 1049

GEORGIA

Continental Film & Video, pg 835
Stage Front Presentation Systems, pg 1022

HAWAII

Hawaii Sound & Vision, pg 886
Ken Herkes Productions & Entertainment (KHPE), pg 888

ILLINOIS

AV Chicago Inc, pg 797
Backstar Creative Media Inc, pg 801
Chicago Satellite & Video, pg 825
The Meetinghouse Companies Inc, pg 938
RC Communications, pg 992
Show Department Inc, pg 1009

INDIANA

Digital Rain LLC, pg 847

IOWA

Central Lighting & Equipment Inc (CLE), pg 823
Pro Video, pg 983

KANSAS

KAKE-TV, pg 907

KENTUCKY

Audio Visual Techniques Inc, pg 796

MARYLAND

Advance Audiovisual Presentation Ltd, pg 777
CPR MultiMedia Solutions, pg 837
Event Tech, pg 863
RTZ Audio Visual, pg 1000

MASSACHUSETTS

Preston Productions Inc, pg 981

MICHIGAN

Digi Sign Design LLC, pg 847
K&R All Media Productions Inc, pg 908
On Stage Visuals, pg 963

MINNESOTA

Alpha Video & Audio Inc, pg 782

MISSISSIPPI

Bowie Audio Visual Enterprises Inc, pg 811

MISSOURI

Schiller's Audio-Visual, pg 1004
Show-Me Audio-Visual, pg 1009

NEBRASKA

Dog & Pony Productions Inc, pg 850

NEVADA

JCS Video Productions, pg 904

NEW JERSEY

Audio Visual Dynamics®, pg 795
Color Leasing Studios, pg 831
Euro-Pacific Film & Video Productions Inc, pg 863
International Audio Visual Inc, pg 900
Starlite Productions, pg 1024
Tele-Measurements Inc, pg 1035
Wired 4 Sound Inc, pg 1068

NEW MEXICO

Production Outfitters, pg 984

NEW YORK

Colortone Audio Visual, pg 832
Design Audio Visual Inc, pg 845
HB-Content, pg 886
Hello World Communications, pg 888
KVL Audio Visual Services Inc, pg 914

DVD Recorder & Player Repairs

Edit Controller Distributors

VIDEO

Edit Controller Distributors (continued)

TENNESSEE

Lowrance Sound Co Inc, pg 925
Technical Support Systems LLC, pg 1034
Zion Music Group, pg 1074

TEXAS

AVES Audio Visual Systems Inc, pg 798
Biway Media, pg 808
Pro Video & Film Equipment Co Inc, pg 983
Videotex Systems Inc, pg 1057

VIRGINIA

Lee Hartman & Sons Inc, pg 918

WISCONSIN

Audio Visual of Milwaukee Inc, pg 795
Full Compass Systems, pg 874
Safe Harbor Computers, pg 1001

ALBERTA

Infosat Communications Inc, pg 898
Matrix Video Communications Corp (MVCC), pg 934

BRITISH COLUMBIA

Commercial Electronics Ltd, pg 832

ONTARIO

Soundmaster Group, pg 1018

Edit Controller Manufacturers

CALIFORNIA

ADS Technologies, pg 777
BUF Technology, pg 815
Diaquest, pg 846
Enright Co, pg 861
FutureVideo, pg 874
JLCooper Electronics, pg 905
Panasonic Broadcast & Digital Systems Co, pg 968
QRS Software Services, pg 988
TV Pro Gear, pg 1046

FLORIDA

Florical Systems Inc, pg 870

KANSAS

GlobalStreams™ Corp, pg 879

MINNESOTA

Vaddio, pg 1051

BRITISH COLUMBIA

Triad Communications Ltd, pg 1044

ONTARIO

Soundmaster Group, pg 1018

Edit Controller Rentals

ARIZONA

Merestone, pg 938
Video West Inc, pg 1056

CALIFORNIA

Aaron & Le Duc, pg 772
Ametron Audio/Video, pg 785
Artichoke Productions, pg 791
Bexel Corp, pg 806
BUF Technology, pg 815
Express Media Inc, pg 864
Lynch Communications, pg 926
McCune Audio-Video-Lighting, pg 935
Munday & Collins AV, pg 950
RetinaVision Productions, pg 995
Slate Media Group, pg 1013
SNAP, pg 1014
Total Media Group, pg 1042
Twin Peaks Creative, pg 1047
VMI Inc, pg 1060

COLORADO

Spectrum Audio Visual Services, pg 1020

CONNECTICUT

Fox Connecticut, pg 872

FLORIDA

Access Media Group, pg 773
Budget Video Rentals, pg 815
Media Concepts Inc, pg 936
Midtown Video Inc, pg 942
Pro Stage Inc, pg 983

GEORGIA

Continental Film & Video, pg 835
ON Event Services, pg 963
Stage Front Presentation Systems, pg 1022

ILLINOIS

Airways Digital Media, pg 779
Allen Visual Systems Inc, pg 781
Backstar Creative Media Inc, pg 801
Chicago Satellite & Video, pg 825
QuickSet International Inc, pg 989
Show Department Inc, pg 1009

IOWA

ECS Inc, pg 856

KANSAS

KAKE-TV, pg 907

KENTUCKY

Audio Visual Techniques Inc, pg 796

MARYLAND

CPR MultiMedia Solutions, pg 837

MASSACHUSETTS

Preston Productions Inc, pg 981
Small Planet Communications Inc, pg 1013

MICHIGAN

Digi Sign Design LLC, pg 847
K&R All Media Productions Inc, pg 908
TeL Systems, pg 1035

MINNESOTA

Alpha Video & Audio Inc, pg 782

MISSOURI

Show-Me Audio-Visual, pg 1009
Southwest Audio-Visual Inc, pg 1019

NEVADA

JCS Video Productions, pg 904

NEW JERSEY

PLS Staging, pg 977
Starlite Productions, pg 1024
Tele-Measurements Inc, pg 1035
Wired 4 Sound Inc, pg 1068

NEW YORK

Ace Video, pg 774
HB-Content, pg 886
Manhattan Center Studios Inc, pg 930
PrimaLux Video Inc, pg 982
TBA Global Events, pg 1032
Visual Technologies Corp, pg 1060
Visual Word Systems Inc, pg 1060

NORTH CAROLINA

The Communications Group Inc, pg 833
Duke Media Services, pg 853
Moving Pictures, pg 948
On Location North Carolina, pg 963
Special Event Services, pg 1020
Take One Productions Ltd, pg 1031

NORTH DAKOTA

Media Productions, pg 937

OHIO

Aztec Video Productions, pg 801
ITA Audio Visual Solutions, pg 902
Lyon Video Inc, pg 927
Mills James Productions, pg 943

PENNSYLVANIA

FMP Media Solutions Inc, pg 870
Innovision Media Group, pg 899
The Videohouse Inc, pg 1057

TENNESSEE

Technical Support Systems LLC, pg 1034

TEXAS

Media Event Concepts Inc, pg 936
Phillips MediaSource, pg 974
The Samuels Co, pg 1002
Stage Directions, pg 1022

VIRGINIA

Creative Video of Washington Inc, pg 839
Lee Hartman & Sons Inc, pg 918

WASHINGTON

Victory Studios, pg 1054

WISCONSIN

Full Compass Systems, pg 874

PUERTO RICO

Stage Crew Audiovisual Inc, pg 1022

ALBERTA

Matrix Video Communications Corp (MVCC), pg 934

BRITISH COLUMBIA

Commercial Electronics Ltd, pg 832
Finale Editworks, pg 868

QUEBEC

Group PVP, pg 882

SASKATCHEWAN

plan9films, pg 976

Edit Controller Repairs

CALIFORNIA

Ametron Audio/Video, pg 785
VMI Inc, pg 1060

FLORIDA

ELC Sales & Service Inc, pg 858
Hi-Tech Enterprises Inc, pg 888
Midtown Video Inc, pg 942

GEORGIA

Stage Front Presentation Systems, pg 1022

ILLINOIS

Allen Visual Systems Inc, pg 781

IOWA

ECS Inc, pg 856

KENTUCKY

NOR-COM Inc, pg 958

MARYLAND

Noventri, pg 960

MICHIGAN

TeL Systems, pg 1035

MINNESOTA

Alpha Video & Audio Inc, pg 782

MISSOURI

Southwest Audio-Visual Inc, pg 1019

NEW YORK

Visual Technologies Corp, pg 1060

OHIO

ITA Audio Visual Solutions, pg 902

TENNESSEE

Technical Support Systems LLC, pg 1034

TEXAS

Pro Video & Film Equipment Co Inc, pg 983

Editing—Computerized

VIDEO

Editing—Computerized (continued)

IDAHO

KTVB-TV, pg 914
Brad Shaw Productions Inc, pg 1008
Wide Eye Productions, pg 1066

ILLINOIS

Abacus Group of Saint Louis LLC, pg 772
ABSA Productions Inc, pg 772
Airways Digital Media, pg 779
Analog Free Media, pg 786
AnswersMedia, pg 787
Audio Visual Services Corp, pg 796
Backstar Creative Media Inc, pg 801
Beatty TeleVisual Productions, pg 804
Big Shoulders Digital Video Productions, pg 807
Breeze Productions Inc, pg 812
Chicago Satellite & Video, pg 825
Edit House Chicago, pg 857
Filmworkers, pg 868
IV Media Resources, pg 903
Lyn Norstad & Associates Inc, pg 926
Manning Productions, pg 930
MIGHTYbYTES Inc, pg 942
Mimi Productions, pg 943
Optimus, pg 964
Rob Orr Productions Ltd, pg 965
The Pepper Group, pg 972
PSAV® Presentation Services (Hotel Services Division), pg 987
RADMAR Inc, pg 990
Richter Studios, pg 996
Roadworthy Image Magnification, pg 998
SCI Television Productions LLC, pg 1004
Sound/Video Impressions Inc, pg 1018
Sparkfactor, pg 1019
Tele-Time Systems, pg 1036
Televersions, pg 1036
20/20 Communications Inc, pg 1047
Video I-D Teleproductions Inc, pg 1055
Video Impressions, pg 1055
WEEK TV, pg 1063
WIFR-TV, pg 1066

INDIANA

Advanced Media Integration, pg 777
AVA Productions, pg 798
Bright Ideas Creative Services, pg 812
Covenant Productions®, pg 837
Digital Rain LLC, pg 847
Educational Video Group Inc, pg 857
Explore Media LLC, pg 864
Lakeshore Productions, pg 915
Lighthouse Photo & Video Productions, pg 920
PentaVision Communications Inc, pg 972

IOWA

Iowa State University-Information Technology Services, pg 902
Kuhn Productions LLC, pg 914
The Production House, pg 984

KANSAS

KAKE-TV, pg 907

KENTUCKY

Audio Visual Techniques Inc, pg 796
Horizon Films & Media LLC, pg 891
Idle Minds Productions Inc, pg 894
The Media Collaboratory, pg 936
Northern Kentucky University, pg 959
The PPS Group, pg 980
Prosper Media Group Inc, pg 986
WKYT Productions, pg 1068

LOUISIANA

Digital FX Inc, pg 847
Independent Studios, pg 897
Launch Media, pg 916
Louisiana State University Health Sciences Center - Shreveport, pg 925
Moxie Media, pg 948
Vidox Motion Imagery, pg 1057
WVLA-TV, pg 1071
YES Productions, pg 1072

MAINE

Headlight Audio Visual Inc, pg 887
WGME-TV, pg 1065

MARYLAND

Adventure Productions LLC, pg 778
The Ahern Group, pg 779
Butler Films Inc, pg 815
Carpel Video Inc, pg 820
CAS Video Productions, pg 820
CPR MultiMedia Solutions, pg 837
CSPMedia.com, pg 840
dbF a Media Company, pg 844
DBM Communications Inc, pg 844
Kramer Communications Video Production, pg 913
Library Video Network (LVN), pg 920
Media Dimensions Inc, pg 936
Mobile-Video Productions Inc, pg 944
Pro Cuts Editing Services, pg 982
Producers Video, pg 984
Quality Film & Video, pg 988
Shadowstone R & R™, pg 1008
Sheffield Audio/Video Productions, pg 1008
Sign Media Inc, pg 1011

MASSACHUSETTS

Award Productions, pg 800
Boston Productions Inc, pg 811
Capron Lighting & Sound Co Inc, pg 819
CommCreative, pg 832
Cramer Productions, pg 837
Documentary Educational Resources Inc, pg 850
Extreme Reach Inc, pg 864
Home Inc, pg 890
In the Wild Productions, pg 897
Inter-Media Electronics, pg 899
Monadnock Media Inc, pg 945
Northern Light Productions, pg 959
Penfield Productions Ltd, pg 971
Preston Productions Inc, pg 981
Real Cool TV Productions, pg 992
Small Planet Communications Inc, pg 1013
TR Productions, pg 1043
Veritech Corp, pg 1053
VideoLink Inc, pg 1057

MICHIGAN

Digi Sign Design LLC, pg 847
Digital Image Studios LLC, pg 847
K&R's Recording Studios Inc, pg 908
Lawrence Productions Inc, pg 917
Maritz Performance Improvement Co, pg 931
Michigan Recording Arts Institute & Technologies, pg 941
On Stage Visuals, pg 963
The Program Source International, pg 985
RingSide Creative, pg 997
TGA Recording Co, pg 1038
The Transfer Zone®, pg 1043
Universal Images, pg 1049
WGVU TV, pg 1065

MINNESOTA

The ADS Group, pg 777
Aggressive Records Audio Duplication LLC, pg 778
Badiyan Inc, pg 801
Beyers Sound & Essay Audio, pg 806
Big Event Productions LLC, pg 807
The Richard Diercks Co Inc, pg 846
GMI Productions, pg 879
House of Cinemagraphics, pg 891
Master Communications Group, pg 933
Media Loft Inc, pg 937
MultiMedia, pg 950
Rum Jungle Media, pg 1000
Worthwhile Films, pg 1070

MISSOURI

Avatar Studios, pg 798
Communitronics Corp, pg 833
Conference Technologies Inc, pg 835
KPLR-TV, pg 913
Production Consultants, pg 984
Show-Me Audio-Visual, pg 1009
StoryTrack, pg 1025
Studio Worx Inc, pg 1027
Substation K, pg 1027
Swank Audio Visuals, pg 1029

MONTANA

High Plains Films, pg 889
North Country Media Group, pg 959
ooLite Media, pg 964

NEBRASKA

B & B Video Productions Inc, pg 801
Dog & Pony Productions Inc, pg 850
Rainbow Video Productions Inc, pg 991
Three Pillars Media, pg 1040

NEVADA

Aardvark Video & Media Productions, pg 772
DVDs4Less, pg 854
Encore Productions Inc, pg 861
HDTV Productions Inc, pg 886
JCS Video Productions, pg 904
Lefco Video Services Inc, pg 918

NEW HAMPSHIRE

Apertura, pg 788
NH Movies Inc, pg 957
Chip Taylor Communications LLC, pg 1032
The Troupe, pg 1045

NEW JERSEY

All Jersey Studios, pg 780
Audio Visual Associates, pg 795
Broadcast Center Studios, pg 813
CD Meyer Inc, pg 822
CFP Video Productions Inc, pg 823
Color Leasing Studios, pg 831
Diversified Systems Inc, pg 849
DWJ Television, pg 854
Early Films, pg 855
Euro-Pacific Film & Video Productions Inc, pg 863
Half Moon Video Productions, pg 883
Laurel Video Productions, pg 916
MediaMix Inc, pg 937
Megavideo Productions, pg 938
MIB Mediaworks, pg 941
Midnight Media Group Inc, pg 942
Ray Mueller Productions, pg 949
Optisonics Productions, pg 965
Producer East Productions, pg 983
Public Eye Productions, pg 987
Bill Quinn Productions, pg 989
Reider Photography & Video Productions, pg 994
Suede Interactive, pg 1027
Tele-Measurements Inc, pg 1035
VCSvideo, pg 1052
Video Corporation of America (VCA), pg 1055
Video Ideas Productions, pg 1055
VTS Video & Media, pg 1061

NEW MEXICO

Production Outfitters, pg 984
30 Second Street Ltd, pg 1039

NEW YORK

Air Sea Land Productions Inc (ASL), pg 779
American Montage Inc, pg 784
Animotion Inc, pg 787
aurora productions, pg 797
Bellin Productions, pg 805
Big Apple Films, pg 806
Big Film Design, pg 807
Big Foot Productions Inc, pg 807
The Big House Group, pg 807
Broad Street Inc, pg 812
Brooklyn Films, pg 814
Chromavision Corp, pg 826
Cohn Creative Group LLC, pg 831
CPdigital, pg 837
Design Audio Visual Inc, pg 845
Designomotion, pg 846
Devlin Video International, pg 846
Digital Art Video Inc, pg 847
dM works, pg 849
Downtown Community Television Center (DCTV), pg 851
DuArt, pg 853
Duplication Depot Inc, pg 853
Duplication Specialists Inc, pg 853
Eastco Multimedia Solutions Inc, pg 856
Fingerpaint, pg 868
4-D Creative Media, pg 871
General Audio-Visual Inc (GAVI), pg 876
Giant Interactive, pg 878
Golden Lamb Productions, pg 880
William Greaves Productions Inc, pg 882
Gurrilla Video Solutions, pg 883
Hallel Communications, pg 884
HAVE Inc, pg 886

VIDEO

Editing—Computerized (continued)

MANITOBA

Lank/Beach Productions Inc, pg 916
Spectra Video Productions Ltd, pg 1020

NEWFOUNDLAND AND LABRADOR

Vidcraft Productions Ltd, pg 1054

NORTHWEST TERRITORIES

Yellowknife Films Inc, pg 1072

ONTARIO

ADS Media, pg 777
Canamedia Inc, pg 818
GAPC (General Assembly Production Centre), pg 875
Image Video Services & Productions, pg 895
JFB Communications, pg 905
Marblemedia, pg 930
Metalworks Recording Studios Inc, pg 939
Music Manufacturing Services, pg 950
Purefire Communications Inc, pg 987
RB Productions, pg 992
Shaw Street Productions, pg 1008
Video Excellence Productions, pg 1055
Westbury National Show Systems Ltd, pg 1064

QUEBEC

Group PVP, pg 882

Editing Equipment Distributors

ALABAMA

Media Visions Inc, pg 937

ARIZONA

Audio Video Resources, pg 795
EAR Professional Audio/Video, pg 855
Troxell Communications Inc, pg 1045

ARKANSAS

White Diamond Productions, pg 1065

CALIFORNIA

Adolph Gasser Inc, pg 776
ADS Technologies, pg 777
Advanced Systems Group LLC, pg 778
Ametron Audio/Video, pg 785
Audio/Video Supply Inc, pg 795
Band Pro Film & Digital Inc, pg 802
BroadcastStore.com, pg 813
Christy's Editorial, pg 826
Diaquest, pg 846
DiskFaktory Direct, pg 849
FXC Communications, pg 874
Gluskin's Custom Audio Video, pg 879
Media Fabricators Inc, pg 936
MediaPOINTE, pg 938
Mobilized Tech Systems, pg 944
Photoflex Inc, pg 974
Point of View Productions, pg 977
Promax Systems, pg 986
SNAP, pg 1014
SSL Industries Inc, pg 1022
Stanislaus Audio Video Inc, pg 1023
Tri-Ed, pg 1044
VMI Inc, pg 1060
VTP Inc, pg 1061

COLORADO

G W Hannaway & Associates, pg 884
Macrosystem US Inc, pg 927
Spectrum Audio Visual Services, pg 1020
Stanco Sales LLC, pg 1023

CONNECTICUT

MAVCO, pg 934

FLORIDA

Access Media Group, pg 773
AVI-SPL, pg 798
Digital Video Systems Inc, pg 848
Enhanced View Services Inc, pg 861
Gulf Coast Audio Visual Producers Inc, pg 883
Harris Corp, pg 885
Hi-Tech Enterprises Inc, pg 888
Media Concepts Inc, pg 936
Midtown Video Inc, pg 942
Pro Stage Inc, pg 983
Recording Media & Equipment Inc (RM&E), pg 993
Tallahassee Audio Visual, pg 1031

GEORGIA

Convergent Media Systems, pg 836
Stage Front Presentation Systems, pg 1022

HAWAII

The Audio Visual Co (AVCO), pg 795

ILLINOIS

Allen Visual Systems Inc, pg 781
Joseph Electronics, pg 906
Lyn Norstad & Associates Inc, pg 926
Quintessence Audio Ltd, pg 989
RAM Systems LLC, pg 991
RC Communications, pg 992
Research Technology International (RTI), pg 995
Tele-Time Systems, pg 1036

INDIANA

Lee Co Inc, pg 918
Sensory Technologies LLC, pg 1006

IOWA

ECS Inc, pg 856

KANSAS

Smith Audio-Visual Inc, pg 1014

KENTUCKY

Axxis Inc, pg 800
Barney Miller's Inc, pg 943
NOR-COM Inc, pg 958

MAINE

Headlight Audio Visual Inc, pg 887

MARYLAND

Noventri, pg 960
RTZ Audio Visual, pg 1000
Visual Aids Electronics Corp, pg 1059

MASSACHUSETTS

Avid Technology Inc, pg 799
Camera Co Inc/Broadcast Divison, pg 818
Psych Soft Inc, pg 987
Rule Broadcast Systems, pg 1000

MICHIGAN

ASC Systems, pg 791
Ascom Communications Contractors, pg 791
Digi Sign Design LLC, pg 847
TeL Systems, pg 1035

MINNESOTA

Alpha Video & Audio Inc, pg 782
AVI Systems, pg 799
Cinequipt Inc, pg 828

MISSISSIPPI

Bowie Audio Visual Enterprises Inc, pg 811
Jasper Ewing & Sons Inc, pg 864
MFJ Enterprises Inc, pg 940

MISSOURI

Communitronics Corp, pg 833
Conference Technologies Inc, pg 835
Image Technologies Corp, pg 895
MIS Technologies, pg 944
Modern Communications Inc, pg 944
Schiller's Audio-Visual, pg 1004
Southwest Audio-Visual Inc, pg 1019
Swank Audio Visuals, pg 1029

NEBRASKA

Dog & Pony Productions Inc, pg 850
Video Service of America Inc (VSA), pg 1056

NEVADA

Aardvark Video & Media Productions, pg 772

NEW JERSEY

Audio Visual Dynamics®, pg 795
AV Bluebook, pg 797
Comprehensive Cable & Connectivity Co, pg 833
Diversified Systems Inc, pg 849
Euro-Pacific Film & Video Productions Inc, pg 863
G&G Technologies Inc, pg 875
Hamilton Buhl, pg 884
MCCOM Inc, pg 935
MIB Mediaworks, pg 941
National Audio-Visual Supply, pg 952
PatchAmp, pg 970
Starlite Productions, pg 1024
SYMCO Inc, pg 1030
Tele-Measurements Inc, pg 1035
Total Video Products Inc, pg 1042
Turner Engineering Inc, pg 1046
Video Corporation of America (VCA), pg 1055
Wired 4 Sound Inc, pg 1068

NEW YORK

Adwar Video, pg 778
Audio-Video Corp, pg 795
AV Workshop, pg 797
B&H Photo & Video Pro Audio, pg 802
Custom Media Environments, pg 841
Gaylord Brothers, pg 876
Indigo Productions, pg 897
Long Island Video Enterprises Live Inc, pg 924
Markertek Video Supply, pg 931
Neptune Photo Inc, pg 954
Technisphere Corp, pg 1034
TecNec Distributing, pg 1035
Visual Technologies Corp, pg 1060
Willoughby's Imaging Center, pg 1067

NORTH CAROLINA

Camcor Inc, pg 818
Crispin Corp, pg 839
Strategic Connections, pg 1026

OHIO

ITA Audio Visual Solutions, pg 902
iVideo Technologies, pg 903
Jimmy Rea Electronics Inc, pg 992
Smithall Electronics Inc, pg 1014
Tri-State Audio Visual Co, pg 1044
Visual Products Inc, pg 1059

PENNSYLVANIA

Advanced AV, pg 777
Audio Visions Inc, pg 795
Bernie's Photo Center, pg 805
Clair Brothers Audio Systems Inc, pg 829
J E Foss Co, pg 871
Innovision Media Group, pg 899
The Lerro Corp, pg 919
Morefield Communications Inc, pg 946
Olympus America Inc, pg 962
Vistacom Inc, pg 1059
Visual Sound Inc, pg 1059

RHODE ISLAND

Custom Computer Specialists Inc, pg 841

TENNESSEE

Lowrance Sound Co Inc, pg 925
Technical Support Systems LLC, pg 1034
Zion Music Group, pg 1074

TEXAS

Audio Visual Technologies Group, pg 796
AVES Audio Visual Systems Inc, pg 798
Biway Media, pg 808
Industrial Audio/Video Inc, pg 897
Media Management LLC, pg 937
Pro Video & Film Equipment Co Inc, pg 983
RadioShack Corp, pg 990
Videotex Systems Inc, pg 1057

UTAH

RIA Corp, pg 996
TV Specialists Inc, pg 1046
Webb Audio Visual Communication, pg 1063

VIRGINIA

Boitnott Visual Communications Corp (BVC), pg 810
Communications Specialists Inc, pg 833
Cybernetics, pg 841
Lee Hartman & Sons Inc, pg 918
The Whitlock Group, pg 1065

WISCONSIN

Audio Visual of Milwaukee Inc, pg 795
Camera Corner Connecting Point, pg 818
Demco Inc, pg 845
Full Compass Systems, pg 874
Safe Harbor Computers, pg 1001

ALBERTA

Matrix Video Communications Corp (MVCC), pg 934

BRITISH COLUMBIA

Commercial Electronics Ltd, pg 832

ONTARIO

Edcom Multimedia Products, pg 856
HD Source, pg 886
Majortech Inc, pg 929
Nationwide Audio Visual Co, pg 953
Premier A/V Sales Ltd, pg 980
Soundmaster Group, pg 1018

QUEBEC

Panavideo Inc, pg 968

Editing Equipment Manufacturers

CALIFORNIA

ADS Technologies, pg 777
BUF Technology, pg 815
Diaquest, pg 846
DiskFaktory Direct, pg 849
FutureVideo, pg 874
Horita Co Inc, pg 891
Hotronic Inc, pg 891
Panasonic Broadcast & Digital Systems Co, pg 968
Pinnacle Systems Inc, pg 975
Sony Electronics Inc, pg 1016
TimeLogic Corp, pg 1040
TV Pro Gear, pg 1046
VITEC Multimedia, pg 1060

COLORADO

Macrosystem US Inc, pg 927

FLORIDA

Hi-Tech Enterprises Inc, pg 888

GEORGIA

Outsource Engineering & Manufacturing Inc dba Texscan MSI, pg 966

KANSAS

GlobalStreams™ Corp, pg 879

MASSACHUSETTS

Avid Technology Inc, pg 799
Psych Soft Inc, pg 987

MISSISSIPPI

MFJ Enterprises Inc, pg 940

NEW JERSEY

CELCO-Constantine Engineering Labs Co, pg 822
Pro-Tape & Specialities Inc, pg 983
Turner Engineering Inc, pg 1046

NEW MEXICO

Burst Electronics Inc, pg 815

NEW YORK

Laird Digital Cinema, pg 915
Quantel Inc, pg 989
Judson Rosebush Co Inc, pg 999
Sima Products Corp, pg 1011
TBC Consoles Inc, pg 1033

PENNSYLVANIA

Prime Image Inc, pg 982

TEXAS

Biway Media, pg 808

BRITISH COLUMBIA

Triad Communications Ltd, pg 1044

ONTARIO

Soundmaster Group, pg 1018

QUEBEC

Matrox Video Products Group, pg 934
Skotel Corp, pg 1012

Editing Equipment Rentals

ALABAMA

Media Visions Inc, pg 937

ARIZONA

Arizona Cine Equipment, pg 789
Audio Video Resources, pg 795
Merestone, pg 938
Metropolitan Audio-Visual Inc, pg 940
Rodeo Video Inc, pg 998
Video Media Productions (VMP), pg 1055

ARKANSAS

Jones Film Video, pg 906
White Diamond Productions, pg 1065

CALIFORNIA

Aaron & Le Duc, pg 772
Absolute Rentals, pg 772
Access Video in Berkeley, pg 773
Advanced Media LLC, pg 778
Alliant Event Services, pg 781
AlphaDogs Inc, pg 782
Ametron Audio/Video, pg 785
Artichoke Productions, pg 791
Balboa Capital Corp, pg 802
Barbosa Video Services, pg 802
Bexel Corp, pg 806
Big Door, pg 807
Big Time Picture Company Inc, pg 807
Blue Lotus Temple Studio, pg 809
BUF Technology, pg 815
Christy's Editorial, pg 826
Deck Hand Inc, pg 844
The Dreaming Tree, pg 852
Express Media Inc, pg 864
Film Converter Co of America Inc, pg 867
First Camera, pg 868
FJ Productions Inc, pg 869
Flip 2 Media Inc, pg 870
Goal Productions, pg 879
Lynch Communications, pg 926
Main Street Media Inc, pg 929
Maximus Media Inc, pg 934
McCune Audio-Video-Lighting, pg 935
Media Fabricators Inc, pg 936
Munday & Collins AV, pg 950
New Circuit Films LLC, pg 955
Panorama Productions, pg 968
Prime Cut Productions, pg 982
Reality Check Systems, pg 992
RetinaVision Productions, pg 995
Screen Door Entertainment Inc, pg 1005
Slate Media Group, pg 1013
SNAP, pg 1014
Synthesizer Rental Service, pg 1030
30 Second Films, pg 1039
Timestream Video, pg 1041
Total Media Group, pg 1042
Tri-Ed, pg 1044
Twin Peaks Creative, pg 1047
Universal Studios, pg 1049
Video Symphony TV & Film School, pg 1056
VMI Inc, pg 1060
Voice & Video Rentals, pg 1060

COLORADO

Daylight Productions & Rentals, pg 844
Multimedia Audio Visual Inc, pg 950
Open Media Foundation, pg 964
Spectrum Audio Visual Services, pg 1020

CONNECTICUT

Fox Connecticut, pg 872
Videofilm Systems Inc, pg 1057

FLORIDA

Access Media Group, pg 773
Cinema East, pg 827
Eastern Video, pg 856
Glanz Technologies Inc, pg 878
Industrial Strength Inc, pg 897
Interscreen America Inc, pg 901
Jordan Klein Film & Video (JKFV), pg 906
Media Concepts Inc, pg 936
Midtown Video Inc, pg 942
National Teleproductions Inc, pg 953
Paradise Show & Design Inc, pg 969
Photosound of Orlando Inc, pg 975
Pro Stage Inc, pg 983

GEORGIA

Continental Film & Video, pg 835
Convergent Media Systems, pg 836
ECG Productions, pg 856
ON Event Services, pg 963
Stage Front Presentation Systems, pg 1022

HAWAII

Sight & Sound Studios, pg 1010

ILLINOIS

Airways Digital Media, pg 779
Allen Visual Systems Inc, pg 781
Analog Free Media, pg 786
Audio Visual Services Corp, pg 796
Backstar Creative Media Inc, pg 801
Beatty TeleVisual Productions, pg 804
Chicago Satellite & Video, pg 825
PSAV® Presentation Services (Hotel Services Division), pg 987
QuickSet International Inc, pg 989
Roadworthy Image Magnification, pg 998
SCI Television Productions LLC, pg 1004
Show Department Inc, pg 1009
Tele-Time Systems, pg 1036

INDIANA

Advanced Media Integration, pg 777

IOWA

ECS Inc, pg 856

KANSAS

KAKE-TV, pg 907
Smith Audio-Visual Inc, pg 1014

KENTUCKY

Audio Visual Techniques Inc, pg 796
The PPS Group, pg 980

LOUISIANA

Digital FX Inc, pg 847
Moxie Media, pg 948
Pace Systems, pg 966

MARYLAND

CPR MultiMedia Solutions, pg 837
Kramer Communications Video Production, pg 913
Producers Video, pg 984
Quality Film & Video, pg 988
RTZ Audio Visual, pg 1000

MASSACHUSETTS

Capron Lighting & Sound Co Inc, pg 819
Green Mountain Post Films (GMP), pg 882
Home Inc, pg 890
massAV, pg 933
Preston Productions Inc, pg 981
Small Planet Communications Inc, pg 1013

MICHIGAN

City Events Group, pg 828
Digi Sign Design LLC, pg 847
K&R All Media Productions Inc, pg 908
K&R's Recording Studios Inc, pg 908
Technology Learning Services, pg 1035
TeL Systems, pg 1035

VIDEO

Editing Equipment Rentals (continued)

Editing Equipment Repairs

OHIO

ITA Audio Visual Solutions, pg 902
iVideo Technologies, pg 903

PENNSYLVANIA

Audio Visions Inc, pg 795

RHODE ISLAND

Custom Computer Specialists Inc, pg 841

TENNESSEE

Memphis Communications Corp, pg 938
Technical Support Systems LLC, pg 1034

TEXAS

Biway Media, pg 808
Pro Video & Film Equipment Co Inc, pg 983

UTAH

RIA Corp, pg 996
TV Specialists Inc, pg 1046

VIRGINIA

Boitnott Visual Communications Corp (BVC), pg 810
The Whitlock Group, pg 1065

WISCONSIN

Camera Corner Connecting Point, pg 818
Full Compass Systems, pg 874

ALBERTA

Matrix Video Communications Corp (MVCC), pg 934

BRITISH COLUMBIA

Commercial Electronics Ltd, pg 832

ONTARIO

Edcom Multimedia Products, pg 856
HD Source, pg 886

QUEBEC

Panavideo Inc, pg 968

Editing—Videocassettes

ALABAMA

CMEInfo, pg 830

ALASKA

Alaska Film Services Inc, pg 779
Aurora Films, pg 797

ARIZONA

Film Creations Ltd, pg 867
Merestone, pg 938
Metropolitan Audio-Visual Inc, pg 940
On-Site Video, pg 963
Phoenix VideoFilms®, pg 974
Rodeo Video Inc, pg 998
Star Video Duplicating, pg 1024
Video Media Productions (VMP), pg 1055

ARKANSAS

Cedar Crest Studio, pg 822
Live'N'Loud, pg 923
Shadowbox Video Productions, pg 1007
White Diamond Productions, pg 1065

CALIFORNIA

Aaron & Le Duc, pg 772
Action Video, pg 775
Adolph Gasser Inc, pg 776
Advanced Media LLC, pg 778
All Video Productions, pg 781
AlphaDogs Inc, pg 782
AM Productions, pg 783
Artichoke Productions, pg 791
Audio Visual Consultants, pg 795
CCI Digital, pg 821
Crystal Pyramid Productions™, pg 840
Custom Video Productions Inc, pg 841
Deja View Video, pg 845
Digital Outpost, pg 847
Dogma Studios, pg 850
The Dreaming Tree, pg 852
DVS InteleStream, pg 854
ECONEWS (Environmental Television Series) & (Environmental Directions Radio Series), pg 856
Express Media Inc, pg 864
Face Digital Post, pg 865
First Camera, pg 868
First Person™, pg 868
Full Moon & High Tide Productions & Studios, pg 874
FXF Productions Inc, pg 874
Global Village Productions, pg 879
Goal Productions, pg 879
Gold Standard Productions, pg 880
Gordon Productions Inc, pg 880
Havas Edge, pg 885
iCorpTv, pg 893
Imageworks, pg 896
InVision Productions, pg 902
ITV Productions, pg 903
JDS Video & Media Productions Inc, pg 904
Joyce Media Inc, pg 906
JR Media Services, pg 906
K2B2 Records, pg 907
The Kenwood Group, pg 909
KION-TV, pg 911
KPBS TV FM-San Diego, pg 913
KVIE-Channel 6, pg 914
Ludlow Media Solutions, pg 926
Lynch Communications, pg 926
Main Street Media Inc, pg 929
Maximus Media Inc, pg 934
McCune Audio-Video-Lighting, pg 935
Media Magic, pg 937
Mind Over Eye Inc, pg 943
Mist Media Inc, pg 944
New & Unique Videos™, pg 955
Nolte Media, pg 958
On-Trax Inc, pg 963
Palardo Productions, pg 968
Panorama Productions, pg 968
Penrose Productions, pg 972
Peterson's Video Transfer Services, pg 973
piXvfm, pg 976
PM Productions, pg 977
Point of View Productions, pg 977
Point 360, pg 978
Prime Cut Productions, pg 982
PSI Inc, pg 987
QRS Software Services, pg 988
Dick Reizner Film & Video, pg 994
RetinaVision Productions, pg 995
Rough House, pg 1000
Roundabout Entertainment Inc, pg 1000
Saturn Studios, pg 1003
SBS Productions, pg 1003
Shapeshifter, pg 1008
Shokus Video, pg 1009
SNAP, pg 1014
SonicPool, pg 1016
Still N'Motion, pg 1025
Tam Communications Inc, pg 1031
Tele-Video Production Services (TVPS), pg 1036
Toon Makers, pg 1042
Total Media Group, pg 1042
Tubeworks Video Productions, pg 1046
Twin Peaks Creative, pg 1047
Universal Studios, pg 1049
Via Verde Productions, pg 1053
VidCan Media Solutions, pg 1054
Video Movie Magic, pg 1056
Videolady, pg 1057
Visions Plus, pg 1058
Wavemaker Media Design, pg 1062
West Coast Projections Inc, pg 1063
WMS Media Inc, pg 1069

COLORADO

Daylight Productions & Rentals, pg 844
Flashback Media Productions, pg 869
Rocky Mountain Audio/Video Productions Inc, pg 998
Spectrum Audio Visual Services, pg 1020
Transtar Entertainment Co Inc, pg 1043
Z-Axis Corp, pg 1073

CONNECTICUT

A/V Davey, pg 797
BRB Audiovisual Productions, pg 812
Cine-Med Inc, pg 826
EagleVision Inc, pg 855
Guymark Studios LLC, pg 883
Ironik Design & Post, pg 902
MAVCO, pg 934
Palace Digital Studios, pg 967
Rockwell Communications Inc, pg 998
Video Production Associates Inc, pg 1056

DISTRICT OF COLUMBIA

Educational Film Center, pg 857
Hillmann & Carr Inc, pg 889
Interface Media Group, pg 900
Yellow Cat Productions Inc, pg 1072

FLORIDA

Access Media Group, pg 773
Accord Productions, pg 773
AVI-SPL, pg 798
Cinema East, pg 827
Civins Productions Inc, pg 828
Communications Concepts Inc (CCI), pg 833
Courter Films LLC, pg 837
Eastern Video, pg 856
Easy Edit Video Inc, pg 856
Ed Ethridge Productions Inc, pg 863
Gulf Coast Audio Visual Producers Inc, pg 883
Hi-Tech Enterprises Inc, pg 888
Home Shopping Network (HSN), pg 890
Jordan Klein Film & Video (JKFV), pg 906
Knowles Video Inc (KVI), pg 912
Media Concepts Inc, pg 936
National Teleproductions Inc, pg 953
Parallax Productions Inc, pg 969
Progressive Media & Music, pg 985
Shooting Stars Post Inc, pg 1009
Sight & Sound Productions, pg 1010
Sound & Vision Communications Inc, pg 1016
Sunfire Communications Inc, pg 1028
Universal Studios Florida® Production Group, pg 1049
Video Techniques Inc, pg 1056
Vistamax Productions, pg 1059

GEORGIA

Associated Video, pg 792
Beachwood Productions, pg 804
COMPRO Productions Inc, pg 834
Crawford Media Services, pg 838
ECG Productions, pg 856
First Cut Communications LLC, pg 868
Guerrilla Productions LLC, pg 883
Omega Media Group Inc, pg 962
Sirius Images Corp dba WaveGuide Studios, pg 1012
Staging Directions Inc, pg 1023
TV Crews, pg 1046
Video Copy Services Inc, pg 1055

HAWAII

Hyperspective Studios Inc, pg 893
KHNL/KGMB, pg 910
Sight & Sound Studios, pg 1010
1013 Integrated, pg 1037

IDAHO

KTVB-TV, pg 914
Brad Shaw Productions Inc, pg 1008
Wide Eye Productions, pg 1066

ILLINOIS

Analog Free Media, pg 786
AnswersMedia, pg 787
Audio Visual Services Corp, pg 796
Backstar Creative Media Inc, pg 801
Beatty TeleVisual Productions, pg 804
Breeze Productions Inc, pg 812
Chicago Satellite & Video, pg 825
Filmworkers, pg 868
IV Media Resources, pg 903
Major Media Inc, pg 929
Manning Productions, pg 930
Optimus, pg 964
The Pepper Group, pg 972
PSAV® Presentation Services (Hotel Services Division), pg 987
RBR Productions, pg 992
SCI Television Productions LLC, pg 1004
Southern Illinois University, pg 1019
20/20 Communications Inc, pg 1047
Video I-D Teleproductions Inc, pg 1055
Video Impressions, pg 1055
WEEK TV, pg 1063

INDIANA

AVA Productions, pg 798
Communication Ministries, pg 833

VIDEO

Editing—Videocassettes (continued)

INDIANA (continued)

Digital Rain LLC, pg 847
OMNI Productions, pg 962

IOWA

The Production House, pg 984

KENTUCKY

Idle Minds Productions Inc, pg 894
The Media Collaboratory, pg 936
Barney Miller's Inc, pg 943
Northern Kentucky University, pg 959

LOUISIANA

Digital FX Inc, pg 847
Louisiana State University Health Sciences Center - Shreveport, pg 925
Moxie Media, pg 948
Pace Systems, pg 966
Vidox Motion Imagery, pg 1057

MAINE

Headlight Audio Visual Inc, pg 887
WGME-TV, pg 1065

MARYLAND

The Ahern Group, pg 779
Carpel Video Inc, pg 820
CPR MultiMedia Solutions, pg 837
dbF a Media Company, pg 844
Media Dimensions Inc, pg 936
Milner-Fenwick Inc, pg 943
Mobile-Video Productions Inc, pg 944
Pro Cuts Editing Services, pg 982
Quality Film & Video, pg 988
Sheffield Audio/Video Productions, pg 1008
Sign Media Inc, pg 1011
Spectrum Productions, pg 1021

MASSACHUSETTS

Award Productions, pg 800
Boston Productions Inc, pg 811
Camera Co Inc/Broadcast Divison, pg 818
Emergency Film Group, pg 860
Green Mountain Post Films (GMP), pg 882
Home Inc, pg 890
In the Wild Productions, pg 897
Penfield Productions Ltd, pg 971
Preston Productions Inc, pg 981
Small Planet Communications Inc, pg 1013
TVN-The Video Network, pg 1046

MICHIGAN

Digi Sign Design LLC, pg 847
K&R's Recording Studios Inc, pg 908
Maritz Performance Improvement Co, pg 931
MessageMakers, pg 939
RingSide Creative, pg 997
The Transfer Zone®, pg 1043
Universal Images, pg 1049

MINNESOTA

Aggressive Records Audio Duplication LLC, pg 778
GMI Productions, pg 879
House of Cinemagraphics, pg 891
Master Communications Group, pg 933
Media Loft Inc, pg 937
MultiMedia, pg 950
Worthwhile Films, pg 1070

MISSOURI

Avatar Studios, pg 798
Communitronics Corp, pg 833
Conference Technologies Inc, pg 835
KPLR-TV, pg 913
Production Consultants, pg 984
Show-Me Audio-Visual, pg 1009
Visionworks Design Services Inc, pg 1059

MONTANA

KCFW Television, pg 908
KUSM TV, pg 914
North Country Media Group, pg 959

NEBRASKA

Dog & Pony Productions Inc, pg 850
Rainbow Video Productions Inc, pg 991

NEVADA

Aardvark Video & Media Productions, pg 772
DVDs4Less, pg 854
Encore Productions Inc, pg 861
JCS Video Productions, pg 904
Lefco Video Services Inc, pg 918
Stage America LLC, pg 1022

NEW HAMPSHIRE

Academic & Campus Technology Services, pg 773
Apertura, pg 788
Channell One Video, pg 824
Chip Taylor Communications LLC, pg 1032

NEW JERSEY

All Jersey Studios, pg 780
Audio Visual Associates, pg 795
Broadcast Center Studios, pg 813
CFP Video Productions Inc, pg 823
Color Leasing Studios, pg 831
Deluxe Media Services, pg 845
Diversified Systems Inc, pg 849
Half Moon Video Productions, pg 883
Hogpenny Studios, pg 890
Laurel Video Productions, pg 916
MediaMix Inc, pg 937
Megavideo Productions, pg 938
MIB Mediaworks, pg 941
Midnight Media Group Inc, pg 942
NFL Films Music Library, pg 957
Optisonics Productions, pg 965
Producer East Productions, pg 983
Bill Quinn Productions, pg 989
Suede Interactive, pg 1027
Tele-Measurements Inc, pg 1035
Telequest Inc, pg 1036
VCSvideo, pg 1052
Video Corporation of America (VCA), pg 1055
Video Ideas Productions, pg 1055
VTS Video & Media, pg 1061

NEW MEXICO

30 Second Street Ltd, pg 1039

NEW YORK

Adwar Video, pg 778
The Big House Group, pg 807
BioMedia Inc, pg 807
Broad Street Inc, pg 812
Chromavision Corp, pg 826
CMI Communications, pg 830
Thomas Craven Film Corp, pg 837
Design Audio Visual Inc, pg 845
Downtown Community Television Center (DCTV), pg 851
DuArt, pg 853
Duplication Depot Inc, pg 853
Eastco Multimedia Solutions Inc, pg 856
Elite Video & Photography Services Inc, pg 859
General Audio-Visual Inc (GAVI), pg 876
William Greaves Productions Inc, pg 882
Gurrilla Video Solutions, pg 883
Hallel Communications, pg 884
HAVE Inc, pg 886
Image Makers of Pittsford/Image Maker Productions, pg 895
International Digital Centre, pg 901
J & D Laboratories Inc, pg 903
Ketchum Pleon Change, pg 910
L&P Media, pg 915
Magno Sound & Video, pg 929
Neal Marshad Productions, pg 931
Mood Creations Ltd, pg 946
Jack Morton Worldwide, pg 946
MRG Productions Inc, pg 948
NBC Production Facilities, pg 953
Post Josh Productions, pg 979
PostWorks, pg 979
PrimaLux Video Inc, pg 982
Rafik, pg 990
Refinery, pg 994
Richter Productions Inc, pg 996
SmartPros Ltd, pg 1014
Split Image Productions, pg 1021
Synaptic Digital, pg 1030
TBA Global Events, pg 1032
Teatown Communications Group, pg 1033
Technisphere Corp, pg 1034
TeleTime Productions, pg 1036
Third World Newsreel/Camera News Inc, pg 1039
Tobin Productions Inc, pg 1041
USA Studios, pg 1050
VDO Lab Inc, pg 1052
Visual Technologies Corp, pg 1060
Alan Weiss Productions, pg 1063
WNET/NET TELECON, pg 1069
Zelman Studios Ltd, pg 1073

NORTH CAROLINA

Pat Appleson Studios Inc, pg 788
Bill Barnes Video Productions LLC, pg 803
Camcor Inc, pg 818
The Communications Group Inc, pg 833
Duke Media Services, pg 853
Horizon Video Productions Inc, pg 891
LCW Productions LLC, pg 917
Moving Pictures, pg 948
NASCAR Media Group LLC, pg 952
On Location North Carolina, pg 963
Take One Productions Ltd, pg 1031
Trailblazer Studios®, pg 1043

NORTH DAKOTA

Media Productions, pg 937
UND Television Center, pg 1048

OHIO

Aztec Video Productions, pg 801
Russ Beckner Pictures, pg 804
Commercial Video, pg 832
Curtis Inc, pg 841
Cuyahoga Community College Media Center, pg 841
Image Video Teleproductions Inc, pg 895
iVideo Technologies, pg 903
Lyon Video Inc, pg 927
MainSail Production Services Inc, pg 929
Maslowski Productions, pg 933
Mills James Productions, pg 943
Musicol Recording, pg 951
R&B Communications Inc, pg 991
Shelburne Films, pg 1008
Take 1 Media Services, pg 1031
VGI Productions, pg 1053
Vista Color Imaging Inc, pg 1059

OKLAHOMA

Institute for Teaching & Learning Excellence (ITLE), pg 899
Smart Concepts Ltd, pg 1013
University of Oklahoma Academic Media & Digital Services, pg 1050

OREGON

A KTVA Production LLC, pg 771
BingoLewis, pg 807
InterVision Media, pg 902
KPDX-TV Production Center, pg 913
Odyssey Productions Inc, pg 961
Production West, pg 985
Rex, pg 995

PENNSYLVANIA

Audio Visions Inc, pg 795
Audio Visual Communications Inc, pg 795
Center City Film & Video Inc, pg 822
FMP Media Solutions Inc, pg 870
Fusion Brand Experiences, pg 874
Innovision Media Group, pg 899
JPL, pg 906
Muderick Media, pg 949
Production Masters Inc (PMI), pg 984
Rahlic Publishing Co, pg 990
The Videohouse Inc, pg 1057
Visual Sound Inc, pg 1059
WPHL-TV, pg 1070

SOUTH CAROLINA

American Production Services LLC, pg 785
Genesis Creative, pg 877
Venture Media, pg 1052

TENNESSEE

Memphis Communications Corp, pg 938
Motion Picture Services, pg 947
Running Pony Productions LLC, pg 1000
Scripps Networks, pg 1005
ST Productions, pg 1022
Stage Post, pg 1022
Russ Sturgeon Productions/RSVP, pg 1027

Editing—Videotapes

VIDEO

Editing—Videotapes (continued)

GEORGIA

Associated Video, pg 792
Beachwood Productions, pg 804
COMPRO Productions Inc, pg 834
Crawford Media Services, pg 838
ECG Productions, pg 856
First Cut Communications LLC, pg 868
Guerrilla Productions LLC, pg 883
Omega Media Group Inc, pg 962
Showcase Photo & Video, pg 1009
Sirius Images Corp dba WaveGuide Studios, pg 1012
Staging Directions Inc, pg 1023
TV Crews, pg 1046
Video Copy Services Inc, pg 1055

HAWAII

FilmWorks Pacific, pg 868
Hyperspective Studios Inc, pg 893
KHNL/KGMB, pg 910
Sight & Sound Studios, pg 1010
1013 Integrated, pg 1037

IDAHO

KTVB-TV, pg 914
Brad Shaw Productions Inc, pg 1008
Wide Eye Productions, pg 1066

ILLINOIS

Airways Digital Media, pg 779
Analog Free Media, pg 786
AnswersMedia, pg 787
Audio Visual Services Corp, pg 796
Backstar Creative Media Inc, pg 801
Beatty TeleVisual Productions, pg 804
Chicago Satellite & Video, pg 825
Comtech Multimedia Marketing, pg 834
Extraordinary Demos, pg 864
Filmworkers, pg 868
IV Media Resources, pg 903
Major Media Inc, pg 929
Manning Productions, pg 930
Optimus, pg 964
Rob Orr Productions Ltd, pg 965
The Pepper Group, pg 972
The Prairie Production Group, pg 980
PSAV® Presentation Services (Hotel Services Division), pg 987
RBR Productions, pg 992
SCI Television Productions LLC, pg 1004
Sound/Video Impressions Inc, pg 1018
Southern Illinois University, pg 1019
Sparkfactor, pg 1019
Tele-Time Systems, pg 1036
Televersions, pg 1036
20/20 Communications Inc, pg 1047
Video I-D Teleproductions Inc, pg 1055
Video Impressions, pg 1055
WEEK TV, pg 1063

INDIANA

AVA Productions, pg 798
Calumet College of Saint Joseph, pg 817
Communication Ministries, pg 833
PentaVision Communications Inc, pg 972

IOWA

The Production House, pg 984

KENTUCKY

Audio Visual Techniques Inc, pg 796
Hammond Communications Group, pg 884
Idle Minds Productions Inc, pg 894
The Media Collaboratory, pg 936
Media Resources, pg 937
Barney Miller's Inc, pg 943
The PPS Group, pg 980
WKYT Productions, pg 1068

LOUISIANA

Digital FX Inc, pg 847
Louisiana State University Health Sciences Center - Shreveport, pg 925
Moxie Media, pg 948
Pace Systems, pg 966
Vidox Motion Imagery, pg 1057
YES Productions, pg 1072

MAINE

Headlight Audio Visual Inc, pg 887
WGME-TV, pg 1065

MARYLAND

Adventure Productions LLC, pg 778
The Ahern Group, pg 779
Carpel Video Inc, pg 820
CPR MultiMedia Solutions, pg 837
dbF a Media Company, pg 844
Library Video Network (LVN), pg 920
Media Dimensions Inc, pg 936
Milner-Fenwick Inc, pg 943
Mobile-Video Productions Inc, pg 944
Pro Cuts Editing Services, pg 982
Producers Video, pg 984
Satellite Media Production, pg 1003
Shadowstone R & R™, pg 1008
Sheffield Audio/Video Productions, pg 1008
Sign Media Inc, pg 1011
Welocalize, pg 1063

MASSACHUSETTS

Award Productions, pg 800
Boston Productions Inc, pg 811
Capron Lighting & Sound Co Inc, pg 819
CommCreative, pg 832
Documentary Educational Resources Inc, pg 850
Emergency Film Group, pg 860
Home Inc, pg 890
In the Wild Productions, pg 897
Penfield Productions Ltd, pg 971
Preston Productions Inc, pg 981
Small Planet Communications Inc, pg 1013
TR Productions, pg 1043
Veritech Corp, pg 1053

MICHIGAN

Digi Sign Design LLC, pg 847
K&R's Recording Studios Inc, pg 908
Maritz Performance Improvement Co, pg 931
MessageMakers, pg 939
Michigan Recording Arts Institute & Technologies, pg 941
RingSide Creative, pg 997
The Transfer Zone®, pg 1043
Universal Images, pg 1049
WGVU TV, pg 1065
WTVS-Station Enterprises, pg 1071

MINNESOTA

The ADS Group, pg 777
Aggressive Records Audio Duplication LLC, pg 778
Badiyan Inc, pg 801
The Richard Dierks Co Inc, pg 846
GMI Productions, pg 879
House of Cinemagraphics, pg 891
Master Communications Group, pg 933
Media Loft Inc, pg 937
Rum Jungle Media, pg 1000
Stoney-Wolf Productions Inc, pg 1025
Worthwhile Films, pg 1070

MISSOURI

Avatar Studios, pg 798
Conference Technologies Inc, pg 835
Hardcastle Films & Video, pg 885
KPLR-TV, pg 913
Show-Me Audio-Visual, pg 1009
Switch, pg 1030
Visionworks Design Services Inc, pg 1059

MONTANA

KCFW Television, pg 908
KUSM TV, pg 914
North Country Media Group, pg 959

NEBRASKA

Dog & Pony Productions Inc, pg 850
Rainbow Video Productions Inc, pg 991

NEVADA

Aardvark Video & Media Productions, pg 772
Encore Productions Inc, pg 861
HDTV Productions Inc, pg 886
JCS Video Productions, pg 904
Lefco Video Services Inc, pg 918
Stage America LLC, pg 1022
21st Century Video Productions, pg 1047

NEW HAMPSHIRE

Apertura, pg 788
Channell One Video, pg 824
Chip Taylor Communications LLC, pg 1032
The Troupe, pg 1045

NEW JERSEY

All Jersey Studios, pg 780
Broadcast Center Studios, pg 813
CFP Video Productions Inc, pg 823
Color Leasing Studios, pg 831
Deluxe Media Services, pg 845
Diversified Systems Inc, pg 849
DWJ Television, pg 854
Hogpenny Studios, pg 890
Laurel Video Productions, pg 916
MediaMix Inc, pg 937
MIB Mediaworks, pg 941
Midnight Media Group Inc, pg 942
Newark Beth Israel Medical Center, pg 956
NFL Films Inc, pg 957
NFL Films Music Library, pg 957
Optisonics Productions, pg 965
Producer East Productions, pg 983
Reed Presentations Inc (RPI), pg 993
Suede Interactive, pg 1027
Tele-Measurements Inc, pg 1035
Telequest Inc, pg 1036
VCSvideo, pg 1052
Video Corporation of America (VCA), pg 1055
VTS Video & Media, pg 1061

NEW MEXICO

Production Outfitters, pg 984
30 Second Street Ltd, pg 1039

NEW YORK

Ace Video, pg 774
Adwar Video, pg 778
aurora productions, pg 797
BC Video Inc, pg 803
Bevilacqua Studios, pg 806
The Big House Group, pg 807
Broad Street Inc, pg 812
Chromavision Corp, pg 826
Thomas Craven Film Corp, pg 837
Design Audio Visual Inc, pg 845
Downtown Community Television Center (DCTV), pg 851
DuArt, pg 853
Duplication Depot Inc, pg 853
Eastco Multimedia Solutions Inc, pg 856
Fingerpaint, pg 868
General Audio-Visual Inc (GAVI), pg 876
William Greaves Productions Inc, pg 882
Hallel Communications, pg 884
HAVE Inc, pg 886
HB-Content, pg 886
Hello World Communications, pg 888
International Digital Centre, pg 901
J & D Laboratories Inc, pg 903
Ketchum Pleon Change, pg 910
L&P Media, pg 915
Loftin Productions, pg 924
Magnetic Post Production, pg 928
Magno Sound & Video, pg 929
Manhattan Center Studios Inc, pg 930
Neal Marshad Productions, pg 931
Mood Creations Ltd, pg 946
MRG Productions Inc, pg 948
MRM Worldwide, pg 948
NBC Production Facilities, pg 953
New Horizon Studios, pg 955
New York Audio Productions, pg 956
News Broadcast Network, pg 956
Post Josh Productions, pg 979
PostWorks, pg 979
PrimaLux Video Inc, pg 982
Refinery, pg 994
Richter Productions Inc, pg 996
SmartPros Ltd, pg 1014
SoundByte Productions Inc, pg 1018
Split Image Productions, pg 1021
Synaptic Digital, pg 1030
TBA Global Events, pg 1032
Teatown Communications Group, pg 1033
Technisphere Corp, pg 1034
TeleTime Productions, pg 1036
Tobin Productions Inc, pg 1041
USA Studios, pg 1050

VDO Lab Inc, pg 1052
Videograf, pg 1057
Visual Technologies Corp, pg 1060
White Buffalo Multimedia, pg 1065
Willow Mixed Media Inc, pg 1067
WNET/NET TELECON, pg 1069
Zelman Studios Ltd, pg 1073

NORTH CAROLINA

Pat Appleson Studios Inc, pg 788
Camcor Inc, pg 818
The Communications Group Inc, pg 833
Duke Media Services, pg 853
Franklin Video Inc, pg 872
Horizon Video Productions Inc, pg 891
LCW Productions LLC, pg 917
Moving Pictures, pg 948
NASCAR Media Group LLC, pg 952
On Location North Carolina, pg 963
PACE Worldwide, pg 966
Take One Productions Ltd, pg 1031
Trailblazer Studios®, pg 1043
Unifour Productions Inc, pg 1048
Visual Aids Electronics of North Carolina Inc, pg 1059

NORTH DAKOTA

Media Productions, pg 937

OHIO

Alegra House Publishers, pg 780
Aztec Video Productions, pg 801
Russ Beckner Pictures, pg 804
Commercial Video, pg 832
Creative Technology, pg 838
Curtis Inc, pg 841
Cuyahoga Community College Media Center, pg 841
EDR Media LLC, pg 857
Image Video Teleproductions Inc, pg 895
iVideo Technologies, pg 903
Lyon Video Inc, pg 927
MainSail Production Services Inc, pg 929
Maslowski Productions, pg 933
Mills James Productions, pg 943
R&B Communications Inc, pg 991
Shelburne Films, pg 1008
Take 1 Media Services, pg 1031
Treehaus Communications Inc, pg 1044
VGI Productions, pg 1053
Vista Color Imaging Inc, pg 1059

OKLAHOMA

Smart Concepts Ltd, pg 1013
University of Oklahoma Academic Media & Digital Services, pg 1050

OREGON

A KTVA Production LLC, pg 771
BingoLewis, pg 807
InterVision Media, pg 902
KPDX-TV Production Center, pg 913
Odyssey Productions Inc, pg 961
Production West, pg 985
Rex, pg 995

PENNSYLVANIA

Audio Visual Communications Inc, pg 795
Beholder Productions Inc, pg 804
Center City Film & Video Inc, pg 822
FMP Media Solutions Inc, pg 870
Fusion Brand Experiences, pg 874
Innovision Media Group, pg 899
JPL, pg 906
Laser Video Corp, pg 916
Muderick Media, pg 949
Production Masters Inc (PMI), pg 984
Rahlic Publishing Co, pg 990
The Videohouse Inc, pg 1057
Visual Sound Inc, pg 1059
WHYY Inc, pg 1066
WPHL-TV, pg 1070

SOUTH CAROLINA

American Production Services LLC, pg 785
Genesis Creative, pg 877
Sound & Images Inc, pg 1016
Stages Video Productions, pg 1023
Venture Media, pg 1052

TENNESSEE

Marine Geographic, pg 931
Memphis Communications Corp, pg 938
Motion Picture Services, pg 947
Running Pony Productions LLC, pg 1000
Scripps Networks, pg 1005
ST Productions, pg 1022
Stage Post, pg 1022
Russ Sturgeon Productions/RSVP, pg 1027
Technical Support Systems LLC, pg 1034
WKPT-TV, pg 1068

TEXAS

Castleview Productions, pg 821
Cerutti Productions Inc, pg 823
Communication Arts Multimedia Inc, pg 832
Dub King, pg 853
The Editing Co, pg 857
First Group Communications Inc, pg 868
Paul Flanagan Productions, pg 869
Harbor House Studios, pg 884
Horizon Film + Video Productions, pg 891
Marx InDigital, pg 933
McNee Productions Inc, pg 935
Media Event Concepts Inc, pg 936
Mediaforce Productions, pg 937
Earl Miller Productions Inc, pg 943
Julye Newlin Productions Inc, pg 956
Phillips MediaSource, pg 974
The Samuels Co, pg 1002
South Coast Film & Video, pg 1019
Texas Heart Institute Visual Communication Services, pg 1037

UTAH

ImageWorks Communications, pg 896

VERMONT

Marlboro Film & Video Productions, pg 931
Perceptions Inc, pg 973
University of Vermont, Instructional Television Dept, pg 1050

VIRGINIA

Allied Media Corp, pg 781
BES Studios, pg 805
CACI Productions Group, pg 816
CALIBRE, pg 816
Creative Video of Washington Inc, pg 839
D&B Television & Video Productions Inc, pg 842
EFX Media, pg 858
Gingerbread Productions, pg 878
The Whitlock Group, pg 1065

WASHINGTON

Bennett-Watt HD Productions Inc, pg 805
Pal Productions Inc, pg 967
Victory Studios, pg 1054

WEST VIRGINIA

Blackwater Video Productions, pg 808
WSAZ-TV 3/WSAZ Productions, pg 1070

WISCONSIN

Audio Visual of Milwaukee Inc, pg 795
Learning Technology Services, pg 917
Logan Productions Inc, pg 924
Meridian Studios, pg 939
ProVideo, pg 986
University of Wisconsin-Oshkosh Radio-TV-Film Dept, pg 1050
USAV Group Inc, pg 1050
Video Wisconsin Inc, pg 1056
Watts Communications Inc, pg 1062
Wisconsin Public Television, pg 1068

WYOMING

Bridger Productions Inc, pg 812

PUERTO RICO

Stage Crew Audiovisual Inc, pg 1022

ALBERTA

Black Media Works, pg 808
Cine Audio Visual Sales & Service Ltd, pg 826
Global Television, pg 879
Global Television Station, pg 879

BRITISH COLUMBIA

Finale Editworks, pg 868
Triad Communications Ltd, pg 1044
Video In Studios/Video Out Distribution, pg 1055

MANITOBA

Spectra Video Productions Ltd, pg 1020

ONTARIO

Edcom Multimedia Products, pg 856
Purefire Communications Inc, pg 987
RB Productions, pg 992
Video Excellence Productions, pg 1055

QUEBEC

Group PVP, pg 882
Muse Entertainment Enterprises, pg 950

Equipment & Accessory Distributors

ALABAMA

CMEInfo, pg 830
Media Visions Inc, pg 937

ARIZONA

Audio Video Resources, pg 795
EAR Professional Audio/Video, pg 855
On-Site Video, pg 963
Troxell Communications Inc, pg 1045

ARKANSAS

Carlton-Bates Co, pg 820
Jay S Stanley & Associates Inc, pg 1023
White Diamond Productions, pg 1065

CALIFORNIA

Addlogix, pg 776
Adolph Gasser Inc, pg 776
Advanced Systems Group LLC, pg 778
Ametron Audio/Video, pg 785
Audio/Video Supply Inc, pg 795
AVerMedia Technologies Inc, pg 798
Band Pro Film & Digital Inc, pg 802
Be Media, pg 804
Big Time Picture Company Inc, pg 807
Birns & Sawyer Inc, pg 808
Boland Communications, pg 810
BroadcastStore.com, pg 813
Christy's Editorial, pg 826
Cibola Systems, pg 826
Cinema Xenon International Inc, pg 827
DTC Lighting & Grip, pg 853
FXC Communications, pg 874
GMF Sound Inc, pg 879
IDX System Technology Inc, pg 894
Innovision Optics, pg 899
Intel-A-Jib™, pg 899
Jameco Electronics, pg 903
JD Audio Visual Inc, pg 904
Leader Instruments Corp, pg 917
Marshall Electronics Inc, pg 932
Matthews Studio Equipment Inc, pg 934
Media Control Systems LLC, pg 936
Media Fabricators Inc, pg 936
MediaPOINTE, pg 938
Metro Video Systems Inc, pg 940
Mobilized Tech Systems, pg 944
Nalpak Inc, pg 952
POP TV, pg 978
Promax Systems, pg 986
The Rip-Tie Co, pg 997
16 x 9 Inc, pg 1012
Slow Motion Film & Digital Inc, pg 1013
Southern California Sound Image Inc, pg 1019
SSL Industries Inc, pg 1022
Stanislaus Audio Video Inc, pg 1023
Steeldeck® Inc, pg 1024
Thermodyne Cases, pg 1038
Transvideo International, pg 1044
Tri-Ed, pg 1044
Video Gear Rentals Inc, pg 1055
The Video Store Shopper, pg 1056

VIDEO

Equipment & Accessory Distributors (continued)

CALIFORNIA (continued)

Visual Systems, pg 1060
VMI Inc, pg 1060
VTP Inc, pg 1061
Xantech LLC, pg 1071
Zack Electronics Inc, pg 1073

COLORADO

Ceavco Audio/Visual Co, pg 822
Goldberg Brothers Inc, pg 880
ProLine Digital, pg 986
Spectrum Audio Visual Services, pg 1020
Stanco Sales LLC, pg 1023

CONNECTICUT

Concord Communications, pg 835
MAVCO, pg 934
Rockwell Communications Inc, pg 998

FLORIDA

Access Media Group, pg 773
A2D Solutions Inc, pg 793
Digital Video Systems Inc, pg 848
Encore Broadcast Solutions, pg 860
Enhanced View Services Inc, pg 861
EZ FX Inc, pg 865
Glanz Technologies Inc, pg 878
Gulf Coast Audio Visual Producers Inc, pg 883
Harris Corp, pg 885
Hi-Tech Enterprises Inc, pg 888
Hi-Tech Import Export Corp, pg 888
Hollywood Theatre Equipment Inc, pg 890
Hunter Electronics LLC, pg 892
Midtown Video Inc, pg 942
Multicom Inc, pg 949
Nemal Electronics International Inc, pg 954
Photosound of Orlando Inc, pg 975
Pro Stage Inc, pg 983
Projector Protector Inc, pg 986
Recording Media & Equipment Inc (RM&E), pg 993
Reef Photo & Video, pg 993
Sight & Sound Productions, pg 1010
Summit Electronics Corp, pg 1028
Tallahassee Audio Visual, pg 1031

GEORGIA

Audio Visual Resources Inc, pg 795
Convergent Media Systems, pg 836
Stage Front Presentation Systems, pg 1022
Technical Innovation, pg 1033

HAWAII

The Audio Visual Co (AVCO), pg 795

ILLINOIS

Gepco®, a General Cable brand, pg 877
Joseph Electronics, pg 906
LKG Industries Inc, pg 923
Quintessence Audio Ltd, pg 989
RAM Systems LLC, pg 991
Research Technology International (RTI), pg 995
Tele-Time Systems, pg 1036
Toko America Inc, pg 1041
Zacuto, pg 1073

INDIANA

Jack's Camera Shop, pg 903
Lee Co Inc, pg 918
Porter Case Inc, pg 978
Sensory Technologies LLC, pg 1006
SHP Electronics, pg 1010
Victoria Supply Inc/Topbulb.com, pg 1054

IOWA

ECS Inc, pg 856

KANSAS

Smith Audio-Visual Inc, pg 1014

KENTUCKY

Barney Miller's Inc, pg 943
NOR-COM Inc, pg 958

LOUISIANA

Intermedia Technologies, pg 900

MARYLAND

Image Logic Corp, pg 895
Noventri, pg 960
Nicholas P Pipino Associates Inc, pg 976
Rohde & Schwarz Inc, pg 998
RTZ Audio Visual, pg 1000
Visual Aids Electronics Corp, pg 1059
Wiltronix, pg 1067

MASSACHUSETTS

Gyrus ACMI, pg 883
Hunt's Photo, Video & Digital, pg 892
Rule Broadcast Systems, pg 1000
Visual Departures Ltd, pg 1059

MICHIGAN

Olson Anderson Co, pg 786
Ascom Communications Contractors, pg 791
Lowing Light & Grip Inc, pg 925
On Stage Visuals, pg 963
TeL Systems, pg 1035

MINNESOTA

Advanced Audio-Visual Inc, pg 777
Alpha Video & Audio Inc, pg 782
AVI Systems, pg 799
Cinequipt Inc, pg 828

MISSISSIPPI

Jasper Ewing & Sons Inc, pg 864
MFJ Enterprises Inc, pg 940

MISSOURI

Communitronics Corp, pg 833
Conference Technologies Inc, pg 835
Image Technologies Corp, pg 895
Modern Communications Inc, pg 944
Production Support Services Inc, pg 985
Schiller's Audio-Visual, pg 1004
Southwest Audio-Visual Inc, pg 1019
Swank Audio Visuals, pg 1029

NEBRASKA

Video Service of America Inc (VSA), pg 1056

NEVADA

Bulbman Inc, pg 815
DVDs4Less, pg 854

NEW HAMPSHIRE

APS Lighting-Sound-AV, pg 789

NEW JERSEY

Audio Visual Dynamics®, pg 795
AV Bluebook, pg 797
Avtech Systems Inc, pg 800
Canare Corporation of America, pg 819
Color Leasing Studios, pg 831
Diversified Systems Inc, pg 849
Earl Girls Inc, pg 855
Euro-Pacific Film & Video Productions Inc, pg 863
G&G Technologies Inc, pg 875
Hakuba Sunpak Velbon, pg 883
Hamilton Buhl, pg 884
Hannecke Display Systems Inc, pg 884
Herbach & Rademan Co Inc, pg 888
MCCOM Inc, pg 935
National Audio-Visual Supply, pg 952
PatchAmp, pg 970
Radio Visions, pg 990
Starlite Productions, pg 1024
SYMCO Inc, pg 1030
Tele-Measurements Inc, pg 1035
Total Video Products Inc, pg 1042
Turner Engineering Inc, pg 1046
VCom International Multimedia Corp, pg 1052

NEW YORK

Adwar Video, pg 778
Allen Avionics Inc, pg 781
Audio-Video Corp, pg 795
Audio Visual Sales & Service Inc, pg 796
Audiovox, pg 796
AV Workshop, pg 797
B&H Photo & Video Pro Audio, pg 802
Bosch Security Systems North America, pg 811
BTX Technologies, pg 814
Bulb Direct, pg 815
Bulbtronics Inc, pg 815
Campus Film Distributors Corp, pg 818
Canon USA Inc, pg 819
Communication Corner Inc, pg 832
Design Audio Visual Inc, pg 845
Flash Electronics Inc, pg 869
General Audio-Visual Inc (GAVI), pg 876
HAVE Inc, pg 886
Image Labs Corp, pg 895
Indigo Productions, pg 897
KVL Audio Visual Services Inc, pg 914
Langie Audio Visual Systems, pg 915
Long Island Video Enterprises Live Inc, pg 924
Markertek Video Supply, pg 931
Russell Industries Inc, pg 1001
Technisphere Corp, pg 1034
TecNec Distributing, pg 1035
The Tiffen Co LLC, pg 1040
Visual Technologies Corp, pg 1060
Visual Word Systems Inc, pg 1060
Vitec Videocom Inc, pg 1060
Willoughby's Imaging Center, pg 1067

NORTH CAROLINA

Camcor Inc, pg 818
Carolina Biological Supply Co, pg 820
Strategic Connections, pg 1026

OHIO

Audio Visual Media, pg 795
ITA Audio Visual Solutions, pg 902
iVideo Technologies, pg 903
Midwest Photo Exchange, pg 942
Parts Express, pg 969
Smithall Electronics Inc, pg 1014
Tri-State Audio Visual Co, pg 1044
Visual Products Inc, pg 1059

PENNSYLVANIA

Advanced AV, pg 777
Bernie's Photo Center, pg 805
Clair Brothers Audio Systems Inc, pg 829
J E Foss Co, pg 871
Garcia Marketing Inc, pg 875
Hite Co, pg 889
Innovision Media Group, pg 899
The Lerro Corp, pg 919
Morefield Communications Inc, pg 946
Visual Sound Inc, pg 1059
Wespen Audio Visual Co, pg 1063

RHODE ISLAND

Custom Computer Specialists Inc, pg 841

TENNESSEE

Continental Film, pg 835
Lowrance Sound Co Inc, pg 925
Memphis Communications Corp, pg 938
Technical Support Systems LLC, pg 1034

TEXAS

Audio Visual Technologies Group, pg 796
AVES Audio Visual Systems Inc, pg 798
Biway Media, pg 808
Digital Display Solutions Inc, pg 847
Heffernan Audio Visual, pg 887
J&S Audio Visual Inc, pg 904
Media Management LLC, pg 937
Pro Video & Film Equipment Co Inc, pg 983
RadioShack Corp, pg 990
Specialized Products Co, pg 1020
TapeWorks Texas Inc, pg 1032

UTAH

RIA Corp, pg 996
TV Specialists Inc, pg 1046

VIRGINIA

Boitnott Visual Communications Corp (BVC), pg 810
Communications Specialists Inc, pg 833
Design & Production Inc, pg 845
Hoppmann Audio Visual, pg 891
Lee Hartman & Sons Inc, pg 918
Quince Imaging Inc, pg 989

StageSound, pg 1023
The Whitlock Group, pg 1065

WASHINGTON

Global Net Productions Inc, pg 879
Inland Audio Visual Co, pg 898
Oppenheimer Camera Products, pg 964

WISCONSIN

Audio Visual of Milwaukee Inc, pg 795
Brady Corp, pg 811
Camera Corner Connecting Point, pg 818
Demco Inc, pg 845
Full Compass Systems, pg 874
Safe Harbor Computers, pg 1001

PUERTO RICO

Bonnin Electronics Inc, pg 810

ALBERTA

Matrix Video Communications Corp (MVCC), pg 934

BRITISH COLUMBIA

Commercial Electronics Ltd, pg 832
DL Sound & Lighting Productions Ltd, pg 849
Speciality Bulb Products Inc, pg 1020

NEW BRUNSWICK

Kabuki, pg 907

ONTARIO

Applied Electronics Ltd, pg 788
CBM Metal, pg 821
Cinema Stage Inc, pg 827
Edcom Multimedia Products, pg 856
HD Source, pg 886
Premier A/V Sales Ltd, pg 980
Teledyne DALSA Inc, pg 1036
VFGadgets Inc, pg 1053

Equipment & Accessory Manufacturers

ALABAMA

Marco Inc, pg 930

ARIZONA

Covid Inc, pg 837
OmniMount Systems, pg 962

CALIFORNIA

AheadTeK, pg 778
ALTINEX Inc, pg 783
Ampex Data Systems Corp, pg 785
Auton Motorized Systems, pg 797
AVerMedia Technologies Inc, pg 798
Boland Communications, pg 810
California Stainless Manufacturing Inc, pg 817
Calrad Electronics, pg 817
CineBags Inc, pg 826
CohuHD, pg 831
DataDirect Networks, pg 843
Deerfield Laboratory Inc, pg 844
Dow-Key Microwave Corp, pg 851
Electrorack Legrand Division, pg 859
Enright Co, pg 861
ESE, pg 862
Extron Electronics, pg 864
FM Systems Inc, pg 870
For-A Corp of America, pg 871
Hoodman Corp, pg 891
Horita Co Inc, pg 891
IDX System Technology Inc, pg 894
Innovision Optics, pg 899
Intel-A-Jib™, pg 899
Jensen Transformers Inc, pg 905
LEMO USA Inc, pg 918
Marshall Electronics Inc, pg 932
Matthews Studio Equipment Inc, pg 934
Media Control Systems LLC, pg 936
MRV Communications Inc, pg 948
Nalpak Inc, pg 952
Nevion, pg 955
O'Connor Engineering Labs, pg 961
Opticomm-EMCORE, pg 964
Photoflex Inc, pg 974
RPM-PSI, pg 1000
Sony Electronics Inc, pg 1016
Sprocket Digital, pg 1022
Steeldeck® Inc, pg 1024
Tamrac® Inc, pg 1031
Tasman Group Pacific Rim, pg 1032
Thermodyne Cases, pg 1038
Transvideo International, pg 1044
TV Pro Gear, pg 1046
Ultimatte Corp, pg 1047
VITEC Multimedia, pg 1060
Xantech LLC, pg 1071

COLORADO

Colorado Video Inc, pg 832
Goldberg Brothers Inc, pg 880
ProLine Digital, pg 986
Rose Packaging & Design Inc, pg 999
Video Accessory Corp, pg 1054
Videomagnetics, pg 1057

CONNECTICUT

Anton/Bauer Inc, pg 787
Sound Control Technologies Inc, pg 1017
Video Automation Systems Inc, pg 1054
Xintekvideo Inc, pg 1071

FLORIDA

Compuvideo Sales USA Ltd, pg 834
Electriduct Inc, pg 858
JBK Cinequipt LLC, pg 904
Projector Protector Inc, pg 986
Straight Wire Inc, pg 1025
Techni-Lux Inc, pg 1033
Union Connector Co Inc, pg 1048
Vutec Corp, Video Products Division, pg 1061

GEORGIA

ARRIS Group Inc, pg 790
Lighting & Production Equipment Inc, pg 920

ILLINOIS

Bretford Manufacturing Inc, pg 812
Cool-Lux, pg 836
FJW Optical Systems Inc, pg 869
Kart-A-Bag Manufacturing Inc, pg 908
Luxor, pg 926
Peerless Industries, pg 971
Quantum Instruments Inc, pg 989
Research Technology International (RTI), pg 995
Switchcraft® Inc, pg 1030
Toko America Inc, pg 1041
Waldom Electronics Corp, pg 1061

INDIANA

R B Annis Instruments Inc, pg 787
Auralex Acoustics Inc, pg 796
Dage-MTI, pg 842
General Devices Co Inc, pg 876
Porter Case Inc, pg 978
Star Case Manufacturing Co Inc, pg 1023
Technicolor SA, pg 1034

IOWA

Winegard Co, pg 1067

KANSAS

Desktop Video Systems, pg 846

MARYLAND

Image Logic Corp, pg 895
Video Mount Products (VMP), pg 1055

MASSACHUSETTS

David Clark Co Inc, pg 843
Dedotec USA Inc, pg 844
Glidecam Industries Inc, pg 878
Miranda Telecast Fiber Systems Inc, pg 944
Visual Departures Ltd, pg 1059

MICHIGAN

Leightronix Inc, pg 918
TeL Systems, pg 1035

MINNESOTA

Trompeter Electronics Inc, pg 1045
Vaddio, pg 1051
Winsted Corp, pg 1068

MISSISSIPPI

MFJ Enterprises Inc, pg 940

MISSOURI

Link Electronics Inc, pg 922

NEBRASKA

Data Security Inc, pg 843

NEVADA

Calculated Industries Inc, pg 816

NEW HAMPSHIRE

ProPhotonix Ltd, pg 986

NEW JERSEY

Alpha Wire Co, pg 782
ATI Audio, pg 793
Canare Corporation of America, pg 819
Daburn Electronics & Cable Corp, pg 842
Hannecke Display Systems Inc, pg 884
Konica Minolta Business Solutions, pg 913
Kramer Electronics USA Inc, pg 913
Middle Atlantic Products Inc, pg 942
Pioneer Research Inc, pg 976
Pro-Tape & Specialities Inc, pg 983
Radio Visions, pg 990
Sofradir EC, pg 1015
Techflex Inc, pg 1033
Telemetrics Inc, pg 1036
Turner Engineering Inc, pg 1046
Wireworks Corp, pg 1068

NEW MEXICO

Burst Electronics Inc, pg 815

NEW YORK

Allen Avionics Inc, pg 781
Bosch Security Systems North America, pg 811
BTX Technologies, pg 814
Campus Film Distributors Corp, pg 818
Canon USA Inc, pg 819
ChyronHego Corp, pg 826
GKM Broadcast Racks, pg 878
Image Labs Corp, pg 895
Key Digital Systems, pg 910
Lowel-Light Manufacturing Inc, pg 925
Microwave Filter Co Inc, pg 942
Sima Products Corp, pg 1011
Joseph Struhl Co Inc, pg 1026
Tapemaker, pg 1032
TBC Consoles Inc, pg 1033
Television Equipment Associates Inc (TEA), pg 1036
The Tiffen Co LLC, pg 1040

NORTH CAROLINA

Newton Instrument Co Inc, pg 957

OREGON

Anthro Corp, pg 787

PENNSYLVANIA

Ac-cetera Inc, pg 772
AVA Electronics Corp, pg 798
MicroImage Video Systems, pg 941
Olympus America Inc, pg 962
Prime Image Inc, pg 982
Sandusky Lee Corp, pg 1002
World Video Sales Co Inc, pg 1070

TEXAS

Biway Media, pg 808

VIRGINIA

Quince Imaging Inc, pg 989

WASHINGTON

Oppenheimer Camera Products, pg 964
Tobin Cinema Systems Inc, pg 1041

WISCONSIN

Brady Corp, pg 811
DH Satellite, pg 846

BRITISH COLUMBIA

Cavision Enterprises Ltd, pg 821
Triad Communications Ltd, pg 1044

NEW BRUNSWICK

Kabuki, pg 907

ONTARIO

Broadcast Video Systems Corp, pg 813
CBM Metal, pg 821
DW Electrochemicals Ltd, pg 854

VIDEO

Equipment & Accessory Manufacturers (continued)

ONTARIO (continued)

Ross Video Ltd, pg 999
Ward-Beck Systems Ltd, pg 1062

QUEBEC

Skotel Corp, pg 1012

Equipment & Accessory Rentals

ARIZONA

Arizona Cine Equipment, pg 789
Audio Video Resources, pg 795
Broadcast Rentals, pg 813
Cox Creative Studios, pg 837
Creative Backstage, pg 838
Crew West Inc, pg 839
Merestone, pg 938
Metropolitan Audio-Visual Inc, pg 940
Reel Men Rentals Inc, pg 994
Rodeo Video Inc, pg 998
Video Media Productions (VMP), pg 1055
Video West Inc, pg 1056

ARKANSAS

Jones Film Video, pg 906
White Diamond Productions, pg 1065

CALIFORNIA

Action Audio & Visual, pg 775
Adolph Gasser Inc, pg 776
Advanced Media LLC, pg 778
Ametron Audio/Video, pg 785
Artichoke Productions, pg 791
Best Bet Camera Rentals, pg 805
Bexel Corp, pg 806
Big Door, pg 807
Big Time Picture Company Inc, pg 807
Birns & Sawyer Inc, pg 808
CenterStaging LLC, pg 822
Chapman/Leonard Studios & Production Center, pg 824
Chater Camera Inc, pg 824
Cherry Multimedia, pg 824
Christy's Editorial, pg 826
Cinema Camera Rentals, pg 827
Cinema Rentals Inc, pg 827
Crystal Pyramid Productions™, pg 840
Dadco, pg 842
Division Camera, pg 849
DTC Lighting & Grip, pg 853
Express Media Inc, pg 864
First Camera, pg 868
Gear Monkey, pg 876
Goal Productions, pg 879
Gold Standard Productions, pg 880
Golden Gate Studios, pg 880
Alan Gordon Enterprises Inc, pg 880
Greenery Studios, pg 882
Hollywood Center Studios, pg 890
Hollywood Loft, pg 890
Illuminate Studios, pg 894
Imagecraft Productions, pg 896
Images in Motion Media Inc, pg 896
Innovision Optics, pg 899

Intel-A-Jib™, pg 899
JD Audio Visual Inc, pg 904
JFA Studio, pg 905
Laurel Canyon Stages, pg 916
Lynch Communications, pg 926
Main Street Media Inc, pg 929
Maximus Media Inc, pg 934
McCune Audio-Video-Lighting, pg 935
Media Fabricators Inc, pg 936
Motion Picture Marine, pg 947
Munday & Collins AV, pg 950
New Circuit Films LLC, pg 955
North County Media Center, pg 959
Old School Cameras, pg 961
Pro HD Rentals, pg 983
Production Gear Rentals (PGR), pg 984
RetinaVision Productions, pg 995
Shooting Star Video, pg 1009
Shoulder High Productions, pg 1009
Slate Media Group, pg 1013
Slow Motion Film & Digital Inc, pg 1013
SNAP, pg 1014
Source Film Studio, pg 1018
Steeldeck® Inc, pg 1024
Straight Shoot'r Cranes Inc, pg 1025
Stray Angel Films, pg 1026
Synthesizer Rental Service, pg 1030
T-stop Inc, pg 1031
Timestream Video, pg 1041
Total Media Group, pg 1042
Tri-Ed, pg 1044
Twin Peaks Creative, pg 1047
VER-Video Equipment Rentals, pg 1053
Video Gear Rentals Inc, pg 1055
Videofax, pg 1056
Vitruvian Entertainment, pg 1060
VMI Inc, pg 1060
Voice & Video Rentals, pg 1060
Warner Bros Entertainment Inc, pg 1062
Z-Ville Productions, pg 1073

COLORADO

Apogee Communications Group, pg 788
Ceavco Audio/Visual Co, pg 822
Daylight Productions & Rentals, pg 844
Spectrum Audio Visual Services, pg 1020
Tatum Video, pg 1032

CONNECTICUT

Concord Communications, pg 835
EagleVision Inc, pg 855
Fox Connecticut, pg 872
Rockwell Communications Inc, pg 998
Videofilm Systems Inc, pg 1057

DISTRICT OF COLUMBIA

Future View Inc, pg 874

FLORIDA

Access Media Group, pg 773
Budget Video Rentals, pg 815
C&I Studios, pg 819
Cinema East, pg 827
Cinema Entertainment Inc, pg 827
Eastern Video, pg 856
Facet Media, pg 865
F&F Productions, pg 865
Glanz Technologies Inc, pg 878
The Great Southern Studios, pg 882
Jordan Klein Film & Video (JKFV), pg 906

JungleTV, pg 906
MAPS Production House, pg 930
Midtown Video Inc, pg 942
Moving Picture, pg 947
National Teleproductions Inc, pg 953
Photosound of Orlando Inc, pg 975
Pro Stage Inc, pg 983
Sight & Sound Productions, pg 1010
Tallahassee Audio Visual, pg 1031
10-20 Productions, pg 1037
Trendy Studio LLC, pg 1044
Universal Studios Florida® Production Group, pg 1049

GEORGIA

Audio Visual Resources Inc, pg 795
Continental Film & Video, pg 835
Convergent Media Systems, pg 836
First Cut Communications LLC, pg 868
Stage Front Presentation Systems, pg 1022
Studio Space Atlanta, pg 1027

HAWAII

Sight & Sound Studios, pg 1010

ILLINOIS

Analog Free Media, pg 786
Audio Visual Services Corp, pg 796
AV Chicago Inc, pg 797
Backstar Creative Media Inc, pg 801
Chicago Satellite & Video, pg 825
Communications Corporation of America, pg 833
Helix Camera & Video, pg 887
Magnanimous Media, pg 928
On Site Video, pg 963
Product Productions, pg 984
PSAV® Presentation Services (Hotel Services Division), pg 987
QuickSet International Inc, pg 989
2nd Cine, pg 1006
Show Department Inc, pg 1009
Tele-Time Systems, pg 1036
Zacuto, pg 1073

INDIANA

Digital Rain LLC, pg 847
Gary Camera & Digital, pg 875
OMNI Productions, pg 962

IOWA

Central Lighting & Equipment Inc (CLE), pg 823
ECS Inc, pg 856
Pro Video, pg 983

KANSAS

KAKE-TV, pg 907
Smith Audio-Visual Inc, pg 1014

KENTUCKY

Audio Visual Techniques Inc, pg 796

LOUISIANA

Digital FX Inc, pg 847
Moxie Media, pg 948
Pace Systems, pg 966

MARYLAND

Archai Media, pg 789
Kramer Communications Video Production, pg 913

Milner-Fenwick Inc, pg 943
Quality Film & Video, pg 988
RTZ Audio Visual, pg 1000

MASSACHUSETTS

Capron Lighting & Sound Co Inc, pg 819
Green Mountain Post Films (GMP), pg 882
High Output Inc, pg 888
Home Inc, pg 890
massAV, pg 933
Preston Productions Inc, pg 981
Small Planet Communications Inc, pg 1013

MICHIGAN

Olson Anderson Co, pg 786
City Events Group, pg 828
K&R All Media Productions Inc, pg 908
Lowing Light & Grip Inc, pg 925
On Stage Visuals, pg 963
Technology Learning Services, pg 1035
TeL Systems, pg 1035

MINNESOTA

Alpha Video & Audio Inc, pg 782
AVI Systems, pg 799
Cinequipt Inc, pg 828
House of Cinemagraphics, pg 891

MISSISSIPPI

Jasper Ewing & Sons Inc, pg 864

MISSOURI

Production Support Services Inc, pg 985
Schiller's Audio-Visual, pg 1004
Show-Me Audio-Visual, pg 1009
Southwest Audio-Visual Inc, pg 1019
Swank Audio Visuals, pg 1029
Switch, pg 1030

NEBRASKA

Dog & Pony Productions Inc, pg 850

NEVADA

MG Studio, pg 940

NEW HAMPSHIRE

Apertura, pg 788
APS Lighting-Sound-AV, pg 789

NEW JERSEY

Audio Visual Dynamics®, pg 795
The Brick Studio, pg 812
Butter Tree Studio, pg 816
CFP Video Productions Inc, pg 823
Color Leasing Studios, pg 831
Creative Video, pg 838
Earl Girls Inc, pg 855
Euro-Pacific Film & Video Productions Inc, pg 863
Ironbound Film & Television Studios LLC, pg 902
MediaMix Inc, pg 937
PLS Staging, pg 977
Reider Photography & Video Productions, pg 994
Starlite Productions, pg 1024
Telemetrics Inc, pg 1036
Video Corporation of America (VCA), pg 1055

NEW MEXICO

Production Outfitters, pg 984

NEW YORK

Ace Video, pg 774
Adorama Rental Co, pg 776
Adwar Video, pg 778
Air Sea Land Productions Inc (ASL), pg 779
AV Workshop, pg 797
Big Apple Films, pg 806
Big Foot Productions Inc, pg 807
Bond Street Studio, pg 810
Bravo Studios, pg 812
Brooklyn Studios, pg 814
C&C Studios Corp, pg 819
Cine 60 Inc, pg 826
Cinema-Vision, pg 827
City Stage, pg 828
Communication Corner Inc, pg 832
CP Communications, pg 837
CPT Rental Inc, pg 837
Design Audio Visual Inc, pg 845
Gearhead Rentals, pg 876
Hand Held Films, pg 884
HB-Content, pg 886
KVL Audio Visual Services Inc, pg 914
Langie Audio Visual Systems, pg 915
LightHouse Films, pg 920
LightSpace Studios, pg 921
Long Island Video Enterprises Live Inc, pg 924
Manhattan Center Studios Inc, pg 930
MRG Productions Inc, pg 948
PrimaLux Video Inc, pg 982
Rollin Studios, pg 998
Scheimpflug Digital, pg 1004
Specialized Audio-Visual Inc, pg 1020
TBA Global Events, pg 1032
Technisphere Corp, pg 1034
Visual Technologies Corp, pg 1060
Visual Word Systems Inc, pg 1060

NORTH CAROLINA

A&V Company, pg 772
Camcor Inc, pg 818
The Communications Group Inc, pg 833
K2 Productions, pg 914
Moving Pictures, pg 948
On Location North Carolina, pg 963
Special Event Services, pg 1020
Strategic Connections, pg 1026
Take One Productions Ltd, pg 1031
Trailblazer Studios®, pg 1043

NORTH DAKOTA

Media Productions, pg 937

OHIO

Audio Visual Media, pg 795
Aztec Video Productions, pg 801
ITA Audio Visual Solutions, pg 902
iVideo Technologies, pg 903
Lyon Video Inc, pg 927
Mills James Productions, pg 943
Production Partners Media, pg 984
R&B Communications Inc, pg 991
Jimmy Rea Electronics Inc, pg 992
Vista Color Imaging Inc, pg 1059

OKLAHOMA

PDC Productions, pg 970

OREGON

BingoLewis, pg 807
Koerner Camera Systems, pg 912
Northwest Film Center, pg 959
Pacific Grip & Lighting Inc, pg 967
Picture This Production Services, pg 975

PENNSYLVANIA

Argentine Productions Inc, pg 789
Bernie's Photo Center, pg 805
FirstGeneration Audio/Visual Services, pg 869
FMP Media Solutions Inc, pg 870
Fusion Brand Experiences, pg 874
Goodman Associates Inc, pg 880
Innovision Media Group, pg 899
Muderick Media, pg 949
New York Camera & Video, pg 956
Philadelphia Soundstages, pg 974
Videosmith Inc, pg 1057
Viewpoint Production Services Inc, pg 1058
Visual Sound Inc, pg 1059

SOUTH CAROLINA

Studio Charleston, pg 1026

TENNESSEE

Memphis Communications Corp, pg 938
RentACamera.com, pg 995
Russ Sturgeon Productions/RSVP, pg 1027
Technical Support Systems LLC, pg 1034

TEXAS

Audio Visual Technologies Group, pg 796
GEAR Cameras & Lighting, pg 876
J&S Audio Visual Inc, pg 904
Earl Miller Productions Inc, pg 943
Muller Entertainment, pg 949
Phil Lights, pg 973
Phillips MediaSource, pg 974
The Samuels Co, pg 1002
South Coast Film & Video, pg 1019
Stage Directions, pg 1022
Texcam Inc, pg 1038

UTAH

8K Productions, pg 858
Ron Hill Imagery, pg 889
TV Specialists Inc, pg 1046

VERMONT

Dark Star Lighting & Production, pg 842
Marlboro Film & Video Productions, pg 931

VIRGINIA

Audio Visual Actions Inc (AVA), pg 795
Boitnott Visual Communications Corp (BVC), pg 810
Creative Video of Washington Inc, pg 839
Lee Hartman & Sons Inc, pg 918
Projection Presentation Technology, pg 985
Quince Imaging Inc, pg 989
Rainbow Rentals, pg 991
StageSound, pg 1023

WASHINGTON

The House Studios, pg 891
Inland Audio Visual Co, pg 898
Kostov Productions, pg 913
Oppenheimer Camera Products, pg 964
Victory Studios, pg 1054

WISCONSIN

Audio Visual of Milwaukee Inc, pg 795
Camera Corner Connecting Point, pg 818
Event Essentials, pg 863
Full Compass Systems, pg 874
USAV Group Inc, pg 1050
Wisconsin Public Television, pg 1068

WYOMING

Bridger Productions Inc, pg 812

PUERTO RICO

Stage Crew Audiovisual Inc, pg 1022

ALBERTA

Global Television Station, pg 879

BRITISH COLUMBIA

Commercial Electronics Ltd, pg 832
DL Sound & Lighting Productions Ltd, pg 849
Finale Editworks, pg 868
Video In Studios/Video Out Distribution, pg 1055

MANITOBA

Evolution Presentation Technologies, pg 863
MidCanada Production Services Inc (MidCan), pg 942

NEW BRUNSWICK

Kabuki, pg 907

ONTARIO

Edcom Multimedia Products, pg 856
GAPC (General Assembly Production Centre), pg 875
HD Source, pg 886
Kimono Surf Studios, pg 911
RB Productions, pg 992
SIM Digital, pg 1011
ZTV Broadcast Services Inc, pg 1074

QUEBEC

AVW-TELAV Audio Visual Solutions, a Freeman Company, pg 800
Group PVP, pg 882
Kerrigan Productions Inc, pg 910

Equipment & Accessory Repairs

CALIFORNIA

Advanced Media LLC, pg 778
Advanced Systems Group LLC, pg 778
Ametron Audio/Video, pg 785
AVerMedia Technologies Inc, pg 798
Christy's Editorial, pg 826
Matthews Studio Equipment Inc, pg 934
Metro Video Systems Inc, pg 940
Pro Camera Repair, pg 982
Slow Motion Film & Digital Inc, pg 1013
SSL Industries Inc, pg 1022
Steeldeck® Inc, pg 1024
Technical Services, pg 1034
Transvideo International, pg 1044
Tri-Ed, pg 1044
VMI Inc, pg 1060

COLORADO

Ceavco Audio/Visual Co, pg 822
Videomagnetics, pg 1057

CONNECTICUT

Precision Camera & Video Repair Inc, pg 980
Rockwell Communications Inc, pg 998
Video Automation Systems Inc, pg 1054

FLORIDA

ELC Sales & Service Inc, pg 858
Encore Broadcast Solutions, pg 860
Glanz Technologies Inc, pg 878
Media Concepts Inc, pg 936
Midtown Video Inc, pg 942
Tallahassee Audio Visual, pg 1031

GEORGIA

Audio Visual Resources Inc, pg 795
Stage Front Presentation Systems, pg 1022
Technical Innovation, pg 1033

ILLINOIS

Beatty TeleVisual Productions, pg 804
On Site Video, pg 963
Tele-Time Systems, pg 1036

INDIANA

Gary Camera & Digital, pg 875

KENTUCKY

NOR-COM Inc, pg 958

MARYLAND

RTZ Audio Visual, pg 1000

MICHIGAN

Olson Anderson Co, pg 786
Lowing Light & Grip Inc, pg 925
TeL Systems, pg 1035

MINNESOTA

Alpha Video & Audio Inc, pg 782
AVI Systems, pg 799

MISSOURI

Southwest Audio-Visual Inc, pg 1019

NEW JERSEY

Earl Girls Inc, pg 855
Konica Minolta Business Solutions, pg 913
Starlite Productions, pg 1024
Turner Engineering Inc, pg 1046

VIDEO

Equipment & Accessory Repairs (continued)

NEW YORK

Adwar Video, pg 778
Campus Film Distributors Corp, pg 818
Colortone Audio Visual, pg 832
Langie Audio Visual Systems, pg 915
MRG Productions Inc, pg 948
Technisphere Corp, pg 1034
Visual Technologies Corp, pg 1060
Vitec Videocom Inc, pg 1060

NORTH CAROLINA

Camcor Inc, pg 818
Strategic Connections, pg 1026

OHIO

Audio Visual Media, pg 795
ITA Audio Visual Solutions, pg 902
iVideo Technologies, pg 903

PENNSYLVANIA

Bernie's Photo Center, pg 805
Wespen Audio Visual Co, pg 1063

RHODE ISLAND

Custom Computer Specialists Inc, pg 841

TENNESSEE

Memphis Communications Corp, pg 938
Technical Support Systems LLC, pg 1034

TEXAS

Audio Visual Technologies Group, pg 796
Pro Video & Film Equipment Co Inc, pg 983

UTAH

RIA Corp, pg 996
TV Specialists Inc, pg 1046

VIRGINIA

Avitecture Inc, pg 799
Hoppmann Audio Visual, pg 891
Lee Hartman & Sons Inc, pg 918

WASHINGTON

Inland Audio Visual Co, pg 898
Oppenheimer Camera Products, pg 964

WISCONSIN

Camera Corner Connecting Point, pg 818
Full Compass Systems, pg 874

PUERTO RICO

Bonnin Electronics Inc, pg 810

BRITISH COLUMBIA

Commercial Electronics Ltd, pg 832

MANITOBA

Evolution Presentation Technologies, pg 863

ONTARIO

Edcom Multimedia Products, pg 856
HD Source, pg 886

Fiber Optic Cable Distributors

ARIZONA

EAR Professional Audio/Video, pg 855

ARKANSAS

Jay S Stanley & Associates Inc, pg 1023

CALIFORNIA

Adolph Gasser Inc, pg 776
Ametron Audio/Video, pg 785
Delicate Electronics Sales Inc, pg 845
FXC Communications, pg 874
Hosa Technology Inc, pg 891
MediaPOINTE, pg 938
Orvac Electronics, pg 965
Southern California Sound Image Inc, pg 1019
SSL Industries Inc, pg 1022
VMI Inc, pg 1060
VTP Inc, pg 1061
Westlake Recording Studios, pg 1064
Zack Electronics Inc, pg 1073

COLORADO

Dot Hill Systems Corp, pg 851

FLORIDA

Digital Video Systems Inc, pg 848
Griffiths Broadcast Co Inc, pg 882
Herman Pro AV, pg 888
Hunter Electronics LLC, pg 892
Multicom Inc, pg 949
Sight & Sound Productions, pg 1010

GEORGIA

Accu-Tech, pg 773
Stage Front Presentation Systems, pg 1022

HAWAII

The Audio Visual Co (AVCO), pg 795

ILLINOIS

Arcor Electronics Co, pg 789
Clark Wire & Cable, pg 829
Cole Wire & Cable Co Inc, pg 831
Gepco®, a General Cable brand, pg 877
Joseph Electronics, pg 906
Quintessence Audio Ltd, pg 989

INDIANA

Sensory Technologies LLC, pg 1006
SHP Electronics, pg 1010

KENTUCKY

Axxis Inc, pg 800
NOR-COM Inc, pg 958

MARYLAND

TKH Security Solutions USA Inc, pg 1041

MASSACHUSETTS

Antronics Inc, pg 787
Rule Broadcast Systems, pg 1000
SLR Enterprises LLC, pg 1013

MICHIGAN

DAWNco, pg 843

MINNESOTA

Alpha Video & Audio Inc, pg 782

MISSOURI

Modern Communications Inc, pg 944
The RapcoHorizon Co, pg 991
Southwest Audio-Visual Inc, pg 1019

NEVADA

MeshTel-Intelite, pg 939

NEW JERSEY

Alltec Stores, a Vcom IMC Company, pg 782
American Fibertek Inc, pg 784
Avtech Systems Inc, pg 800
Canare Corporation of America, pg 819
Diversified Systems Inc, pg 849
Fiber Optic Systems Inc (FOSI), pg 866
Tele-Measurements Inc, pg 1035

NEW YORK

BTX Technologies, pg 814
CP Communications, pg 837
HAVE Inc, pg 886
Markertek Video Supply, pg 931
MultiDyne Video & Fiber Optics Systems, pg 950
TecNec Distributing, pg 1035

PENNSYLVANIA

Advanced AV, pg 777
Clair Brothers Audio Systems Inc, pg 829
West Penn Wire, pg 1064

TENNESSEE

Lowrance Sound Co Inc, pg 925

TEXAS

AVES Audio Visual Systems Inc, pg 798
Digital Display Solutions Inc, pg 847
Industrial Audio/Video Inc, pg 897
Sundance Systems, Fibox Products Division, pg 1028

VIRGINIA

Avitecture Inc, pg 799
Communications Specialists Inc, pg 833
The Whitlock Group, pg 1065

WASHINGTON

Telect Inc, pg 1036

WISCONSIN

Audio Visual of Milwaukee Inc, pg 795
Full Compass Systems, pg 874

ALBERTA

Infosat Communications Inc, pg 898

ONTARIO

Westbury National Show Systems Ltd, pg 1064

Fiber Optic Cable Manufacturers

ARIZONA

Covid Inc, pg 837

CALIFORNIA

Fiber Optic Cable Shop, pg 866
Gefen, pg 876
Hosa Technology Inc, pg 891
Monster Cable Products Inc, pg 945
Physical Optics Corp, pg 975

FLORIDA

Nemal Electronics International Inc, pg 954

ILLINOIS

Gepco®, a General Cable brand, pg 877
Joseph Electronics, pg 906

INDIANA

Belden, pg 804

MARYLAND

RCI Custom Products, pg 992

MASSACHUSETTS

Miranda Telecast Fiber Systems Inc, pg 944
Mohawk, pg 945

MISSOURI

The RapcoHorizon Co, pg 991

NEVADA

MeshTel-Intelite, pg 939

NEW JERSEY

Canare Corporation of America, pg 819
Crestron Electronics Inc, pg 839

NEW YORK

CP Communications, pg 837
MultiDyne Video & Fiber Optics Systems, pg 950

PENNSYLVANIA

West Penn Wire, pg 1064

WASHINGTON

Telect Inc, pg 1036

BRITISH COLUMBIA

Triad Communications Ltd, pg 1044

Fiber Optic Cable Repairs

CALIFORNIA

Ametron Audio/Video, pg 785

Film Libraries, *see* Libraries—Film or Stock-Shot

Film to Videotape Transfers, *see* Transfers—Film to Videotape

Filter Distributors

Filter Manufacturers

Filter Rentals

VIDEO

Filter Rentals (continued)

MINNESOTA

Alpha Video & Audio Inc, pg 782

MISSOURI

Southwest Audio-Visual Inc, pg 1019

NEBRASKA

Lights On Nebraska, pg 921

NEW MEXICO

Production Outfitters, pg 984

NEW YORK

Adorama Rental Co, pg 776
Bond Street Studio, pg 810
Cinema-Vision, pg 827
LightHouse Films, pg 920
TBA Global Events, pg 1032

NORTH CAROLINA

Moving Pictures, pg 948
On Location North Carolina, pg 963

NORTH DAKOTA

Media Productions, pg 937

OHIO

Aztec Video Productions, pg 801
Lyon Video Inc, pg 927
Mills James Productions, pg 943
R&B Communications Inc, pg 991

OREGON

Koerner Camera Systems, pg 912
Picture This Production Services, pg 975

PENNSYLVANIA

Argentine Productions Inc, pg 789
FMP Media Solutions Inc, pg 870
Goodman Associates Inc, pg 880
Location Camera Ltd, pg 923
New York Camera & Video, pg 956
The Videohouse Inc, pg 1057
Viewpoint Production Services Inc, pg 1058

TEXAS

GEAR Cameras & Lighting, pg 876
Phil Lights, pg 973
The Samuels Co, pg 1002
Texcam Inc, pg 1038

WASHINGTON

Oppenheimer Camera Products, pg 964

WISCONSIN

MKE Production Rental, pg 944

BRITISH COLUMBIA

ProVision Video Sales & Rentals Inc, pg 986

MANITOBA

MidCanada Production Services Inc (MidCan), pg 942

ONTARIO

JIB Shots Equipment Inc, pg 905
RB Productions, pg 992

Filter Repairs

GEORGIA

Stage Front Presentation Systems, pg 1022

KENTUCKY

NOR-COM Inc, pg 958

MICHIGAN

TeL Systems, pg 1035

Frame Storage Device, *see* Still Frame Storage Device

Grip Equipment Distributors

ALABAMA

Media Visions Inc, pg 937

ARIZONA

CamMate Systems, pg 818
Troxell Communications Inc, pg 1045

ARKANSAS

White Diamond Productions, pg 1065

CALIFORNIA

Adolph Gasser Inc, pg 776
Ametron Audio/Video, pg 785
BroadcastStore.com, pg 813
Christy's Editorial, pg 826
Filmtools®, pg 868
FXC Communications, pg 874
Alan Gordon Enterprises Inc, pg 880
Intel-A-Jib™, pg 899
Lee Filters, pg 918
Manios Digital & Film, pg 930
Matthews Studio Equipment Inc, pg 934
Mole-Richardson Co, pg 945
Nalpak Inc, pg 952
Photoflex Inc, pg 974
Premier Lighting & Production Co, pg 980
The Rosenthal Group, pg 999
Sacramento Theatrical Lighting Ltd (STL), pg 1001
San Diego Stage & Lighting Supply Inc, pg 1002
Shotmaker Co, pg 1009
Slow Motion Film & Digital Inc, pg 1013
SNAP, pg 1014
Steeldeck® Inc, pg 1024
Tri-Ed, pg 1044
Video Gear Rentals Inc, pg 1055
VMI Inc, pg 1060

CONNECTICUT

Connecticut Audio & Theatrical Supply, pg 835

FLORIDA

Access Media Group, pg 773
Digital Video Systems Inc, pg 848
EZ FX Inc, pg 865
Hi-Tech Enterprises Inc, pg 888
Hi-Tech Import Export Corp, pg 888
Hunter Electronics LLC, pg 892
Media Concepts Inc, pg 936
Pro Stage Inc, pg 983
Techni-Lux Inc, pg 1033

GEORGIA

Lighting & Production Equipment Inc, pg 920
MAGNUM Companies Ltd, pg 929
Stage Front Presentation Systems, pg 1022

HAWAII

ATTCO Inc, pg 793
The Audio Visual Co (AVCO), pg 795

ILLINOIS

Grand Stage Co Inc, pg 881

INDIANA

Sensory Technologies LLC, pg 1006

IOWA

ECS Inc, pg 856

KANSAS

Smith Audio-Visual Inc, pg 1014

LOUISIANA

Available Lighting & Motion Picture Services Inc, pg 798

MARYLAND

Noventri, pg 960
Theatre Service & Supply Corp, pg 1038

MASSACHUSETTS

Hunt's Photo, Video & Digital, pg 892
Limelight Productions Inc, pg 921
Rule Broadcast Systems, pg 1000
Visual Departures Ltd, pg 1059

MICHIGAN

Lowing Light & Grip Inc, pg 925

MINNESOTA

Alpha Video & Audio Inc, pg 782
Cinequipt Inc, pg 828
Lights On, pg 921

MISSOURI

Modern Communications Inc, pg 944
Schiller's Audio-Visual, pg 1004
Southwest Audio-Visual Inc, pg 1019

NEVADA

Aardvark Video & Media Productions, pg 772
PRG Lighting, pg 981

NEW HAMPSHIRE

APS Lighting-Sound-AV, pg 789

NEW JERSEY

AV Bluebook, pg 797
Comprehensive Cable & Connectivity Co, pg 833
Earl Girls Inc, pg 855
Euro-Pacific Film & Video Productions Inc, pg 863
Manfrotto Distribution Inc, pg 930
Bill Quinn Productions, pg 989
Rose Brand, pg 999
Video Corporation of America (VCA), pg 1055

NEW MEXICO

Quickbeam Systems Inc (QSI), pg 989

NEW YORK

Audio-Video Corp, pg 795
AV Workshop, pg 797
B&H Photo & Video Pro Audio, pg 802
Barbizon Electric Co Inc, pg 802
BMI Supply, pg 810
Creative Stage Lighting Co Inc, pg 838
Flash Clinic Inc, pg 869
Gotham Sound & Communications Inc, pg 881
HAVE Inc, pg 886
Long Island Video Enterprises Live Inc, pg 924
Markertek Video Supply, pg 931
RGH Lighting LLC, pg 996
Technisphere Corp, pg 1034
TecNec Distributing, pg 1035
Vitec Videocom Inc, pg 1060

NORTH CAROLINA

Camcor Inc, pg 818
Harrison Brothers, pg 885
Innocinema, pg 898
Strategic Connections, pg 1026

OHIO

Future Light Inc, pg 874
Jimmy Rea Electronics Inc, pg 992
Vincent Lighting Systems, pg 1058
Visual Products Inc, pg 1059

OREGON

Pacific Grip & Lighting Inc, pg 967

PENNSYLVANIA

Advanced AV, pg 777
Innovision Media Group, pg 899
The Lerro Corp, pg 919
Morefield Communications Inc, pg 946

TENNESSEE

Egripment USA Inc, pg 858
Lowrance Sound Co Inc, pg 925

TEXAS

GEAR Cameras & Lighting, pg 876
Olden Lighting, pg 962
Omega Broadcast Group, pg 962
Precision Camera & Video, pg 980
Pro Video & Film Equipment Co Inc, pg 983

UTAH

Redman Movies & Stories, pg 993
RIA Corp, pg 996

Grip Equipment Manufacturers

Grip Equipment Rentals

VIDEO

Grip Equipment Rentals (continued)

MARYLAND

Archai Media, pg 789
CPR MultiMedia Solutions, pg 837
Event Tech, pg 863
Kramer Communications Video Production, pg 913
RTZ Audio Visual, pg 1000

MASSACHUSETTS

Capron Lighting & Sound Co Inc, pg 819
Green Mountain Post Films (GMP), pg 882
High Output Inc, pg 888
Limelight Productions Inc, pg 921
Red Sky Studios, pg 993

MICHIGAN

City Events Group, pg 828
K&R All Media Productions Inc, pg 908
K&R's Recording Studios Inc, pg 908
Lowing Light & Grip Inc, pg 925

MINNESOTA

Alpha Video & Audio Inc, pg 782
Cinequipt Inc, pg 828
House of Cinemagraphics, pg 891
Lights On, pg 921

MISSOURI

Schiller's Audio-Visual, pg 1004
Show-Me Audio-Visual, pg 1009
Sight & Sound Production Services Inc, pg 1010
Southwest Audio-Visual Inc, pg 1019

MONTANA

Filmlites Montana, pg 867

NEBRASKA

Dog & Pony Productions Inc, pg 850
Lights On Nebraska, pg 921

NEVADA

JCS Video Productions, pg 904
MG Studio, pg 940
PRG Lighting, pg 981

NEW HAMPSHIRE

Apertura, pg 788
APS Lighting-Sound-AV, pg 789

NEW JERSEY

Butter Tree Studio, pg 816
CFP Video Productions Inc, pg 823
Earl Girls Inc, pg 855
Euro-Pacific Film & Video Productions Inc, pg 863
Ironbound Film & Television Studios LLC, pg 902
MediaMix Inc, pg 937
MIB Mediaworks, pg 941
Bill Quinn Productions, pg 989
Unilux Inc, pg 1048
Video Corporation of America (VCA), pg 1055

NEW MEXICO

Production Outfitters, pg 984
Quickbeam Systems Inc (QSI), pg 989

NEW YORK

Ace Video, pg 774
Adorama Rental Co, pg 776
AV Workshop, pg 797
Available Light, pg 798
BC Video Inc, pg 803
Big Foot Productions Inc, pg 807
Bond Street Studio, pg 810
Bravo Studios, pg 812
Brooklyn Fire Proof, pg 814
Brooklyn Studios, pg 814
City Stage, pg 828
Creative Stage Lighting Co Inc, pg 838
CSI Rentals, pg 840
Flash Clinic Inc, pg 869
Gearhead Rentals, pg 876
Gotham Sound & Communications Inc, pg 881
Hand Held Films, pg 884
Hello World Communications, pg 888
LightHouse Films, pg 920
LightSpace Studios, pg 921
Long Island Video Enterprises Live Inc, pg 924
Manhattan Center Studios Inc, pg 930
MRG Productions Inc, pg 948
Neo Studios, pg 954
PrimaLux Video Inc, pg 982
Production Central, pg 984
RGH Lighting LLC, pg 996
Rollin Studios, pg 998
Scheimpflug Digital, pg 1004
Steiner Studios, pg 1024
TBA Global Events, pg 1032
Technisphere Corp, pg 1034
Vitec Videocom Inc, pg 1060

NORTH CAROLINA

Camcor Inc, pg 818
The Communications Group Inc, pg 833
Duke Media Services, pg 853
Moving Pictures, pg 948
On Location North Carolina, pg 963
Special Event Services, pg 1020
Take One Productions Ltd, pg 1031

NORTH DAKOTA

Media Productions, pg 937

OHIO

Aztec Video Productions, pg 801
Lyon Video Inc, pg 927
Mills James Productions, pg 943
Ohio HD Video, pg 961
OSV Studios, pg 966
R&B Communications Inc, pg 991
Vincent Lighting Systems, pg 1058
Vista Color Imaging Inc, pg 1059

OREGON

Pacific Grip & Lighting Inc, pg 967
Picture This Production Services, pg 975

PENNSYLVANIA

FMP Media Solutions Inc, pg 870
Fusion Brand Experiences, pg 874
Innovision Media Group, pg 899
JPL, pg 906
Location Camera Ltd, pg 923
Location Lighting Ltd, pg 924
New York Camera & Video, pg 956
Philadelphia Soundstages, pg 974
The Videohouse Inc, pg 1057
Viewpoint Production Services Inc, pg 1058

SOUTH CAROLINA

Studio Charleston, pg 1026

TENNESSEE

DR&A Inc, pg 852
NuMynd Studios, pg 960
Russ Sturgeon Productions/RSVP, pg 1027

TEXAS

Bright Giant Creative Group, pg 812
GEAR Cameras & Lighting, pg 876
Light Tec, pg 920
Earl Miller Productions Inc, pg 943
Muller Entertainment, pg 949
Olden Lighting, pg 962
Omega Broadcast Group, pg 962
Phil Lights, pg 973
Phillips MediaSource, pg 974
Photogroup Studios, pg 975
The Samuels Co, pg 1002
South Coast Film & Video, pg 1019
Stage Directions, pg 1022
Texcam Inc, pg 1038
Video Perspective, pg 1056

UTAH

Ron Hill Imagery, pg 889
Redman Movies & Stories, pg 993

VIRGINIA

D&B Television & Video Productions Inc, pg 842

WASHINGTON

The House Studios, pg 891
Intermedia Inc, pg 900
Oppenheimer Camera Products, pg 964
Victory Studios, pg 1054

WEST VIRGINIA

Blackwater Video Productions, pg 808

WISCONSIN

Audio Visual of Milwaukee Inc, pg 795
MKE Production Rental, pg 944

WYOMING

Bridger Productions Inc, pg 812

ALBERTA

Global Television Station, pg 879
Matrix Video Communications Corp (MVCC), pg 934
MTM Equipment Rentals Ltd, pg 949

BRITISH COLUMBIA

ProVision Video Sales & Rentals Inc, pg 986

MANITOBA

MidCanada Production Services Inc (MidCan), pg 942

ONTARIO

Boxcar Studio, pg 811
GAPC (General Assembly Production Centre), pg 875
HD Source, pg 886
JIB Shots Equipment Inc, pg 905
RB Productions, pg 992
SIM Digital, pg 1011
ZTV Broadcast Services Inc, pg 1074

QUEBEC

Group PVP, pg 882
Kerrigan Productions Inc, pg 910

Grip Equipment Repairs

CALIFORNIA

Ametron Audio/Video, pg 785
Chapman/Leonard Studios & Production Center, pg 824
Matthews Studio Equipment Inc, pg 934
Mole-Richardson Co, pg 945
Shotmaker Co, pg 1009
Steeldeck® Inc, pg 1024

FLORIDA

Hi-Tech Enterprises Inc, pg 888

GEORGIA

Lighting & Production Equipment Inc, pg 920
MAGNUM Companies Ltd, pg 929
Stage Front Presentation Systems, pg 1022

IOWA

ECS Inc, pg 856

MICHIGAN

Lowing Light & Grip Inc, pg 925
TeL Systems, pg 1035

MINNESOTA

Alpha Video & Audio Inc, pg 782

MISSOURI

Schiller's Audio-Visual, pg 1004
Southwest Audio-Visual Inc, pg 1019

NEVADA

PRG Lighting, pg 981

NEW JERSEY

Earl Girls Inc, pg 855

NEW MEXICO

Quickbeam Systems Inc (QSI), pg 989

NEW YORK

Lowel-Light Manufacturing Inc, pg 925
MRG Productions Inc, pg 948
Vitec Videocom Inc, pg 1060

NORTH CAROLINA

Camcor Inc, pg 818

TEXAS

GEAR Cameras & Lighting, pg 876
Olden Lighting, pg 962

UTAH

Redman Movies & Stories, pg 993
RIA Corp, pg 996

WISCONSIN

Full Compass Systems, pg 874

Head Distributors

ARIZONA

EAR Professional Audio/Video, pg 855

CALIFORNIA

Ametron Audio/Video, pg 785
Christy's Editorial, pg 826
Cibola Systems, pg 826
Manios Digital & Film, pg 930
Mobilized Tech Systems, pg 944
SNAP, pg 1014

CONNECTICUT

Connecticut Audio & Theatrical Supply, pg 835

FLORIDA

Digital Video Systems Inc, pg 848
Enhanced View Services Inc, pg 861
Hunter Electronics LLC, pg 892
Media Concepts Inc, pg 936

HAWAII

The Audio Visual Co (AVCO), pg 795

ILLINOIS

International Electro-Magnetics Inc, pg 901
Joseph Electronics, pg 906

INDIANA

Sensory Technologies LLC, pg 1006

MARYLAND

Noventri, pg 960

MASSACHUSETTS

Hunt's Photo, Video & Digital, pg 892
Rule Broadcast Systems, pg 1000

MINNESOTA

Alpha Video & Audio Inc, pg 782

MISSOURI

Modern Communications Inc, pg 944
Schiller's Audio-Visual, pg 1004
Southwest Audio-Visual Inc, pg 1019

NEW JERSEY

AV Bluebook, pg 797
HP Marketing Corp, pg 892
JRF Magnetic Sciences Inc, pg 906
Manfrotto Distribution Inc, pg 930
MCCOM Inc, pg 935
Total Video Products Inc, pg 1042

NEW YORK

Audio-Video Corp, pg 795
Benro, pg 805
Induro, pg 897
RNJ Electronics, pg 997
Russell Industries Inc, pg 1001

PENNSYLVANIA

Advanced AV, pg 777
The Lerro Corp, pg 919

TENNESSEE

Egripment USA Inc, pg 858
Lowrance Sound Co Inc, pg 925

TEXAS

Pro Video & Film Equipment Co Inc, pg 983

WASHINGTON

Oppenheimer Camera Products, pg 964

WISCONSIN

Audio Visual of Milwaukee Inc, pg 795
Full Compass Systems, pg 874

BRITISH COLUMBIA

Commercial Electronics Ltd, pg 832

MANITOBA

Lank/Beach Productions Inc, pg 916

Head Manufacturers

CALIFORNIA

Microdolly Hollywood, pg 941

COLORADO

Videomagnetics, pg 1057

MASSACHUSETTS

Glidecam Industries Inc, pg 878

NEW YORK

Induro, pg 897

TENNESSEE

Egripment USA Inc, pg 858

Interactive TV Hardware Distributors

ARKANSAS

Jay S Stanley & Associates Inc, pg 1023

CALIFORNIA

ADS Technologies, pg 777
POP TV, pg 978
VMI Inc, pg 1060

FLORIDA

Access Media Group, pg 773
Digital Video Systems Inc, pg 848
Hi-Tech Enterprises Inc, pg 888
Pro Stage Inc, pg 983

GEORGIA

PolyVision Corporation, pg 978
Stage Front Presentation Systems, pg 1022

HAWAII

The Audio Visual Co (AVCO), pg 795

INDIANA

Sensory Technologies LLC, pg 1006

KENTUCKY

Axxis Inc, pg 800
NOR-COM Inc, pg 958

NEVADA

Aardvark Video & Media Productions, pg 772

NEW JERSEY

Alltec Stores, a Vcom IMC Company, pg 782
Tele-Measurements Inc, pg 1035

NEW YORK

Audio-Video Corp, pg 795

PENNSYLVANIA

Advanced AV, pg 777

TENNESSEE

Lowrance Sound Co Inc, pg 925

VIRGINIA

Lee Hartman & Sons Inc, pg 918

WISCONSIN

Full Compass Systems, pg 874

ALBERTA

SMART Technologies Inc, pg 1013

MANITOBA

Inland Audio Visual Ltd, pg 898
Tek Gear, pg 1035

ONTARIO

Gesturetek, pg 877
Westbury National Show Systems Ltd, pg 1064

Interactive TV Hardware Manufacturers

ARIZONA

Boeckeler Instruments Inc, pg 810

CALIFORNIA

ADS Technologies, pg 777
POP TV, pg 978

FLORIDA

Vutec Corp, Video Products Division, pg 1061

GEORGIA

Outsource Engineering & Manufacturing Inc dba Texscan MSI, pg 966
PolyVision Corporation, pg 978

MICHIGAN

ASC Systems, pg 791

NEVADA

MeshTel-Intelite, pg 939

NEW YORK

ChyronHego Corp, pg 826
Key Digital Systems, pg 910

TENNESSEE

Adtec Digital Inc, pg 777

ALBERTA

SMART Technologies Inc, pg 1013

MANITOBA

Tek Gear, pg 1035

ONTARIO

Gesturetek, pg 877

Interactive TV Hardware Rentals

ARIZONA

Merestone, pg 938

CALIFORNIA

Big Door, pg 807
Munday & Collins AV, pg 950
RetinaVision Productions, pg 995

FLORIDA

Access Media Group, pg 773
Pro Stage Inc, pg 983

GEORGIA

Stage Front Presentation Systems, pg 1022

ILLINOIS

QuickSet International Inc, pg 989

OHIO

Aztec Video Productions, pg 801

PENNSYLVANIA

FMP Media Solutions Inc, pg 870
Innovision Media Group, pg 899

TEXAS

GEAR Cameras & Lighting, pg 876
The Samuels Co, pg 1002

WASHINGTON

Victory Studios, pg 1054

MANITOBA

Inland Audio Visual Ltd, pg 898

ONTARIO

Westbury National Show Systems Ltd, pg 1064

Interactive TV Hardware Repairs

FLORIDA

ELC Sales & Service Inc, pg 858
Hi-Tech Enterprises Inc, pg 888

VIDEO

Interactive TV Hardware Repairs (continued)

GEORGIA

Stage Front Presentation Systems, pg 1022

KENTUCKY

Axxis Inc, pg 800
NOR-COM Inc, pg 958

MICHIGAN

TeL Systems, pg 1035

WISCONSIN

Full Compass Systems, pg 874

MANITOBA

Inland Audio Visual Ltd, pg 898
Tek Gear, pg 1035

ONTARIO

Westbury National Show Systems Ltd, pg 1064

Lens Distributors

ALABAMA

Media Visions Inc, pg 937

ARIZONA

EAR Professional Audio/Video, pg 855
Projector SuperStore LLC, pg 986
Tempe Camera, pg 1037
Troxell Communications Inc, pg 1045

ARKANSAS

Jay S Stanley & Associates Inc, pg 1023

CALIFORNIA

Abel Cine Tech Los Angeles, pg 772
Adolph Gasser Inc, pg 776
Advanced Systems Group LLC, pg 778
Ametron Audio/Video, pg 785
Audio/Video Supply Inc, pg 795
Band Pro Film & Digital Inc, pg 802
Birns & Sawyer Inc, pg 808
BroadcastStore.com, pg 813
Cibola Systems, pg 826
CohuHD, pg 831
Delicate Electronics Sales Inc, pg 845
DTC Lighting & Grip, pg 853
FXC Communications, pg 874
Gearhouse Broadcast LLC, pg 876
Hooper Camera & Imaging, pg 891
Innovision Optics, pg 899
Kappa optronics Inc, pg 908
L-3 Integrated Optical Systems, pg 915
Marshall Electronics Inc, pg 932
MediaPOINTE, pg 938
PMP Marketing Inc, pg 977
POP TV, pg 978
Promax Systems, pg 986
Jai Pulnix, pg 987
16 x 9 Inc, pg 1012
Slow Motion Film & Digital Inc, pg 1013
SNAP, pg 1014
Southern California Sound Image Inc, pg 1019
SSL Industries Inc, pg 1022
THK Photo Products Inc, pg 1039
Tri-Ed, pg 1044
Video Gear Rentals Inc, pg 1055
Visual Instrumentation Corp, pg 1059
VMI Inc, pg 1060
VTP Inc, pg 1061

CONNECTICUT

MAVCO, pg 934

FLORIDA

Access Media Group, pg 773
Cinema Equipment & Supplies Inc, pg 827
Digital Video Systems Inc, pg 848
Glanz Technologies Inc, pg 878
Gulf Coast Audio Visual Producers Inc, pg 883
Media Concepts Inc, pg 936
Midtown Video Inc, pg 942
Pro Stage Inc, pg 983
Reef Photo & Video, pg 993
Sight & Sound Productions, pg 1010
Skyline Broadcast, pg 1013
Tallahassee Audio Visual, pg 1031

GEORGIA

Convergent Media Systems, pg 836
Stage Front Presentation Systems, pg 1022

HAWAII

The Audio Visual Co (AVCO), pg 795

ILLINOIS

Sound Vision Inc, pg 1018
Tele-Time Systems, pg 1036

INDIANA

Sensory Technologies LLC, pg 1006

IOWA

ECS Inc, pg 856

KANSAS

Smith Audio-Visual Inc, pg 1014

KENTUCKY

Barney Miller's Inc, pg 943
NOR-COM Inc, pg 958

LOUISIANA

Intermedia Technologies, pg 900

MARYLAND

Noventri, pg 960
RTZ Audio Visual, pg 1000
Visual Aids Electronics Corp, pg 1059

MASSACHUSETTS

Antronics Inc, pg 787
Camera Co Inc/Broadcast Divison, pg 818
Rule Broadcast Systems, pg 1000

MICHIGAN

Ascom Communications Contractors, pg 791

MINNESOTA

Alpha Video & Audio Inc, pg 782
AVI Systems, pg 799
Cinequipt Inc, pg 828

MISSISSIPPI

Bowie Audio Visual Enterprises Inc, pg 811
Jasper Ewing & Sons Inc, pg 864

MISSOURI

Communitronics Corp, pg 833
Conference Technologies Inc, pg 835
Modern Communications Inc, pg 944
Schiller's Audio-Visual, pg 1004
Southwest Audio-Visual Inc, pg 1019
Swank Audio Visuals, pg 1029

NEBRASKA

ATV Research Inc, pg 793
Dog & Pony Productions Inc, pg 850
Strong Entertainment Lighting, pg 1026
Video Service of America Inc (VSA), pg 1056

NEVADA

Aardvark Video & Media Productions, pg 772
MeshTel-Intelite, pg 939

NEW JERSEY

Alltec Stores, a Vcom IMC Company, pg 782
Angenieux, pg 786
Audio Visual Dynamics®, pg 795
Avtech Systems Inc, pg 800
Comprehensive Cable & Connectivity Co, pg 833
Diversified Systems Inc, pg 849
DSI RF Systems Inc, pg 853
FUJIFILM Optical Devices Division, pg 873
G&G Technologies Inc, pg 875
Hakuba Sunpak Velbon, pg 883
Hamilton Buhl, pg 884
Herbach & Rademan Co Inc, pg 888
MCCOM Inc, pg 935
PatchAmp, pg 970
Starlite Productions, pg 1024
SYMCO Inc, pg 1030
Total Video Products Inc, pg 1042
Turner Engineering Inc, pg 1046
Video Corporation of America (VCA), pg 1055

NEW YORK

Audio-Video Corp, pg 795
AV Workshop, pg 797
B&H Photo & Video Pro Audio, pg 802
Barbizon Electric Co Inc, pg 802
Bosch Security Systems North America, pg 811
BTX Technologies, pg 814
Gage-Line Technology Inc, pg 874
Indigo Productions, pg 897
KVL Audio Visual Services Inc, pg 914
Long Island Video Enterprises Live Inc, pg 924
Mamiya, pg 929
Markertek Video Supply, pg 931
Qioptiq, pg 988
RNJ Electronics, pg 997
Schneider Optics Inc, pg 1004
Technisphere Corp, pg 1034
Universe Kogaku America Inc, pg 1049
Vision Identics Systems Inc, pg 1058
Willoughby's Imaging Center, pg 1067

NORTH CAROLINA

Alpine Optics Inc, pg 783
Camcor Inc, pg 818
Innocinema, pg 898

OHIO

Copp Integrated Systems, pg 836
iVideo Technologies, pg 903
Visual Products Inc, pg 1059

OREGON

PLUS Corp of America, pg 977

PENNSYLVANIA

Advanced AV, pg 777
Audio Visions Inc, pg 795
Bernie's Photo Center, pg 805
J E Foss Co, pg 871
Grise Audio Visual Center Inc, pg 882
The Lerro Corp, pg 919
Morefield Communications Inc, pg 946
New York Camera & Video, pg 956
Questar Corp, pg 989
Visual Sound Inc, pg 1059

RHODE ISLAND

Custom Computer Specialists Inc, pg 841

TENNESSEE

Lowrance Sound Co Inc, pg 925
Memphis Communications Corp, pg 938
Technical Support Systems LLC, pg 1034

TEXAS

Audio Visual Technologies Group, pg 796
AVES Audio Visual Systems Inc, pg 798
Biway Media, pg 808
Heffernan Audio Visual, pg 887
Industrial Audio/Video Inc, pg 897
IVS Imaging, pg 903
Omega Broadcast Group, pg 962
Precision Camera & Video, pg 980
Pro Video & Film Equipment Co Inc, pg 983
Supercircuits, pg 1029

UTAH

RIA Corp, pg 996
Webb Audio Visual Communication, pg 1063

VIRGINIA

Avitecture Inc, pg 799
Boitnott Visual Communications Corp (BVC), pg 810

Lens Manufacturers

Lens Rentals

VIDEO

Lens Rentals (continued)

NEW YORK (continued)

Cinema-Vision, pg 827
CMI Communications, pg 830
CP Communications, pg 837
CSI Rentals, pg 840
Gearhead Rentals, pg 876
Hand Held Films, pg 884
KVL Audio Visual Services Inc, pg 914
LightHouse Films, pg 920
LightSpace Studios, pg 921
Long Island Video Enterprises Live Inc, pg 924
Manhattan Center Studios Inc, pg 930
MRG Productions Inc, pg 948
Scheimpflug Digital, pg 1004
TBA Global Events, pg 1032

NORTH CAROLINA

A&V Company, pg 772
Camcor Inc, pg 818
The Communications Group Inc, pg 833
Moving Pictures, pg 948
On Location North Carolina, pg 963
Strategic Connections, pg 1026
Take One Productions Ltd, pg 1031

OHIO

Lyon Video Inc, pg 927
Mills James Productions, pg 943
Ohio HD Video, pg 961
R&B Communications Inc, pg 991
Vista Color Imaging Inc, pg 1059

OKLAHOMA

PDC Productions, pg 970

OREGON

Koerner Camera Systems, pg 912
Picture This Production Services, pg 975

PENNSYLVANIA

Argentine Productions Inc, pg 789
Audio Visions Inc, pg 795
Bernie's Photo Center, pg 805
FMP Media Solutions Inc, pg 870
Fusion Brand Experiences, pg 874
Grise Audio Visual Center Inc, pg 882
Innovision Media Group, pg 899
JPL, pg 906
Location Camera Ltd, pg 923
Muderick Media, pg 949
New York Camera & Video, pg 956
Philadelphia Soundstages, pg 974
Producers Management Television (PMTV), pg 983
The Videohouse Inc, pg 1057
Videosmith Inc, pg 1057
Viewpoint Production Services Inc, pg 1058

TENNESSEE

Memphis Communications Corp, pg 938
Nashville Production Rentals (NPR), pg 952
RentACamera.com, pg 995
Russ Sturgeon Productions/RSVP, pg 1027
Technical Support Systems LLC, pg 1034

TEXAS

Alford Media Services, pg 780
Bright Giant Creative Group, pg 812
Light Tec, pg 920
Omega Broadcast Group, pg 962
Precision Camera & Video, pg 980
The Samuels Co, pg 1002
Stage Directions, pg 1022
Texcam Inc, pg 1038

UTAH

8K Productions, pg 858
Ron Hill Imagery, pg 889
Webb Audio Visual Communication, pg 1063

VIRGINIA

Boitnott Visual Communications Corp (BVC), pg 810
Quince Imaging Inc, pg 989
StageSound, pg 1023

WASHINGTON

The House Studios, pg 891
Oppenheimer Camera Products, pg 964
Victory Studios, pg 1054

WISCONSIN

Audio Visual of Milwaukee Inc, pg 795
Full Compass Systems, pg 874
Logan Productions Inc, pg 924
MKE Production Rental, pg 944

WYOMING

Bridger Productions Inc, pg 812

ALBERTA

Global Television Station, pg 879
Matrix Video Communications Corp (MVCC), pg 934

BRITISH COLUMBIA

Image Media Farm, pg 895
ProVision Video Sales & Rentals Inc, pg 986

MANITOBA

Inland Audio Visual Ltd, pg 898
MidCanada Production Services Inc (MidCan), pg 942

ONTARIO

HD Source, pg 886
JIB Shots Equipment Inc, pg 905
RB Productions, pg 992
SIM Digital, pg 1011
ZTV Broadcast Services Inc, pg 1074

QUEBEC

AVW-TELAV Audio Visual Solutions, a Freeman Company, pg 800
Group PVP, pg 882
Kerrigan Productions Inc, pg 910

Lens Repairs

CALIFORNIA

Ametron Audio/Video, pg 785
L-3 Integrated Optical Systems, pg 915
Lloyd F McKinney Associates Inc, pg 935
Pro Camera Repair, pg 982
Slow Motion Film & Digital Inc, pg 1013
TEK Media Group, pg 1035
VMI Inc, pg 1060

CONNECTICUT

Precision Camera & Video Repair Inc, pg 980

FLORIDA

Midtown Video Inc, pg 942

IOWA

ECS Inc, pg 856

KENTUCKY

NOR-COM Inc, pg 958

MARYLAND

Noventri, pg 960
RTZ Audio Visual, pg 1000
Strauss Photo Technical Service Inc, pg 1026

MICHIGAN

TeL Systems, pg 1035

MINNESOTA

Alpha Video & Audio Inc, pg 782
AVI Systems, pg 799

MISSOURI

Southwest Audio-Visual Inc, pg 1019

NEW JERSEY

Angenieux, pg 786
FUJIFILM Optical Devices Division, pg 873

NEW YORK

Canon Broadcast & Communications Division, pg 819
Mamiya, pg 929
MRG Productions Inc, pg 948
Technisphere Corp, pg 1034

NORTH CAROLINA

Alpine Optics Inc, pg 783
Camcor Inc, pg 818

PENNSYLVANIA

Bernie's Photo Center, pg 805
Questar Corp, pg 989

TENNESSEE

Memphis Communications Corp, pg 938
Technical Support Systems LLC, pg 1034

TEXAS

Pro Video & Film Equipment Co Inc, pg 983

UTAH

RIA Corp, pg 996

WISCONSIN

Full Compass Systems, pg 874

ALBERTA

Infosat Communications Inc, pg 898
Matrix Video Communications Corp (MVCC), pg 934

MANITOBA

Inland Audio Visual Ltd, pg 898

ONTARIO

Edcom Multimedia Products, pg 856
HD Source, pg 886

Libraries—Film or Stock-Shot

ALASKA

Alaska Film Services Inc, pg 779

ARIZONA

Fox 10 Productions (KSAZ-TV), pg 872
Merestone, pg 938
Productiontrax.com, pg 985
The Source Stock Footage Library Inc, pg 1019
Wild Visions Inc, pg 1066

ARKANSAS

Cedar Crest Studio, pg 822
Shadowbox Video Productions, pg 1007
White Diamond Productions, pg 1065

CALIFORNIA

Aaron & Le Duc, pg 772
Action Sports/All Stock, pg 775
American Playback Images, pg 785
Artichoke Productions, pg 791
Carl Barth Images, pg 803
Birds & Animals Unlimited, pg 808
Budget Films Stock Footage Inc, pg 814
Classic Images, pg 829
Crystal Pyramid Productions™, pg 840
Dogma Studios, pg 850
ECONEWS (Environmental Television Series) & (Environmental Directions Radio Series), pg 856
Em Gee Film Library, pg 860
Envirovision, pg 861
First Camera, pg 868
Fish Films Footage World, pg 869
FJ Productions Inc, pg 869
FXF Productions Inc, pg 874
Geddes Productions LLC, pg 876
Global Village Stock Footage Library, pg 879
Gold Standard Productions, pg 880
Howard Hall Productions, pg 883
iCorpTv, pg 893
JDS Video & Media Productions Inc, pg 904
KTVU-Retail Services, pg 914
Lieberman Productions, pg 920
Media Magic, pg 937
Mind Over Eye Inc, pg 943
Moving Art by Louie Schwartzberg, pg 947
New & Unique Videos™, pg 955
Palardo Productions, pg 968
PM Productions, pg 977
Point Lobos Productions, pg 977
Prelinger Archives, pg 980
Producers Library, pg 983

VIDEO

Libraries—Film or Stock-Shot (continued)

BRITISH COLUMBIA

Finale Editworks, pg 868

MANITOBA

Spectra Video Productions Ltd, pg 1020

NEWFOUNDLAND AND LABRADOR

Vidcraft Productions Ltd, pg 1054

NORTHWEST TERRITORIES

Yellowknife Films Inc, pg 1072

ONTARIO

Canamedia Inc, pg 818
GAPC (General Assembly Production Centre), pg 875
Purefire Communications Inc, pg 987

QUEBEC

Les Productions Via Le Monde (Daniel Bertolino) Inc, pg 985

SASKATCHEWAN

Thomega Entertainment Inc, pg 1039

Location Equipment & Facility Distributors

ALABAMA

Media Visions Inc, pg 937

ARIZONA

Audio Video Resources, pg 795

ARKANSAS

White Diamond Productions, pg 1065

CALIFORNIA

Advanced Systems Group LLC, pg 778
Ametron Audio/Video, pg 785
DTC Lighting & Grip, pg 853
Mole-Richardson Co, pg 945
Photoflex Inc, pg 974
Satellite Digital Teleproductions (SDTV), pg 1003
VMI Inc, pg 1060

COLORADO

Chimera®, pg 825

FLORIDA

Access Media Group, pg 773
Midtown Video Inc, pg 942
Pro Stage Inc, pg 983

GEORGIA

Convergent Media Systems, pg 836
Lighting & Production Equipment Inc, pg 920
Stage Front Presentation Systems, pg 1022

HAWAII

The Audio Visual Co (AVCO), pg 795

ILLINOIS

Cool-Lux, pg 836
Corplex, pg 836

INDIANA

Sensory Technologies LLC, pg 1006

IOWA

ECS Inc, pg 856

MARYLAND

Theatre Service & Supply Corp, pg 1038

MASSACHUSETTS

Rule Broadcast Systems, pg 1000

MINNESOTA

Alpha Video & Audio Inc, pg 782
AVI Systems, pg 799

MISSOURI

Communitronics Corp, pg 833
Conference Technologies Inc, pg 835
Modern Communications Inc, pg 944
Southwest Audio-Visual Inc, pg 1019

NEBRASKA

Dog & Pony Productions Inc, pg 850

NEW JERSEY

Comprehensive Cable & Connectivity Co, pg 833
Earl Girls Inc, pg 855

NEW YORK

Audio-Video Corp, pg 795
Barbizon Electric Co Inc, pg 802
Long Island Video Enterprises Live Inc, pg 924
RGH Lighting LLC, pg 996
Technisphere Corp, pg 1034
Xtech Inc, pg 1071

NORTH CAROLINA

Camcor Inc, pg 818
Strategic Connections, pg 1026

PENNSYLVANIA

Advanced AV, pg 777
Morefield Communications Inc, pg 946

TENNESSEE

Memphis Communications Corp, pg 938
Technical Support Systems LLC, pg 1034
TOMCAT USA Inc, pg 1041

TEXAS

Pro Video & Film Equipment Co Inc, pg 983
Shook Mobile Technology LP, pg 1009

UTAH

RIA Corp, pg 996

VERMONT

Production Advantage Inc, pg 984

VIRGINIA

Avitecture Inc, pg 799
Communications Specialists Inc, pg 833

WISCONSIN

Audio Visual of Milwaukee Inc, pg 795
Full Compass Systems, pg 874

ONTARIO

HD Source, pg 886

Location Equipment & Facility Manufacturers

ALABAMA

Marco Inc, pg 930

CALIFORNIA

ALTINEX Inc, pg 783
Clear-Com®, pg 829
Electrorack Legrand Division, pg 859
Microdolly Hollywood, pg 941
Mole-Richardson Co, pg 945
Photoflex Inc, pg 974
Synergy Group Inc, pg 1030

COLORADO

Chimera®, pg 825

FLORIDA

Union Connector Co Inc, pg 1048

ILLINOIS

Kart-A-Bag Manufacturing Inc, pg 908

INDIANA

Star Case Manufacturing Co Inc, pg 1023

MARYLAND

Theatre Service & Supply Corp, pg 1038

MASSACHUSETTS

Dedotec USA Inc, pg 844

MICHIGAN

Studio Consulting & Construction Inc, pg 1026

NEW YORK

Lowel-Light Manufacturing Inc, pg 925

PENNSYLVANIA

Aztech Productions LLC, pg 801

TENNESSEE

TOMCAT USA Inc, pg 1041

TEXAS

Shook Mobile Technology LP, pg 1009

Location Equipment & Facility Rentals

ALABAMA

AVS Media Group, pg 800

ARIZONA

Arizona Cine Equipment, pg 789
Merestone, pg 938
Rodeo Video Inc, pg 998
Video Media Productions (VMP), pg 1055

ARKANSAS

Jones Film Video, pg 906
White Diamond Productions, pg 1065

CALIFORNIA

Ametron Audio/Video, pg 785
Antelope Valley Locations & Production Services, pg 787
Bexel Corp, pg 806
Big Door, pg 807
Chapman/Leonard Studios & Production Center, pg 824
Cineworks Inc, pg 828
Crystal Pyramid Productions™, pg 840
DTC Lighting & Grip, pg 853
Express Media Inc, pg 864
First Camera, pg 868
FJ Productions Inc, pg 869
Gold Standard Productions, pg 880
Golden Gate Studios, pg 880
KTVU-Retail Services, pg 914
The Location Connection Inc, pg 924
Lynch Communications, pg 926
Maximus Media Inc, pg 934
McCune Audio-Video-Lighting, pg 935
Mole-Richardson Co, pg 945
New Circuit Films LLC, pg 955
Panorama Productions, pg 968
Samy's Camera, pg 1002
Santa Clarita Studios, pg 1002
Sunset Bronson Studios, pg 1028
Sunset Gower Studios, pg 1028
Timestream Video, pg 1041
Total Media Group, pg 1042
Twin Peaks Creative, pg 1047
Videowerks, pg 1057
VMI Inc, pg 1060
Warner Bros Entertainment Inc, pg 1062
Westcoast Video Productions Inc, pg 1064
Z-Ville Productions, pg 1073

COLORADO

Chimera®, pg 825

CONNECTICUT

Broadcast Video Productions LLC, pg 813
Fox Connecticut, pg 872
Videofilm Systems Inc, pg 1057

DELAWARE

Ken-Del Productions Inc, pg 909

Location Equipment & Facility Repairs

VIDEO

Location Equipment & Facility Repairs (continued)

WISCONSIN

Full Compass Systems, pg 874

Mastering, *see* Videodisc Mastering

Mixer Distributors

ARIZONA

EAR Professional Audio/Video, pg 855

ARKANSAS

White Diamond Productions, pg 1065

CALIFORNIA

Adolph Gasser Inc, pg 776
Ametron Audio/Video, pg 785
Delicate Electronics Sales Inc, pg 845
Empire Wholesale Inc, pg 860
FXC Communications, pg 874
Gearhouse Broadcast LLC, pg 876
JD Audio Visual Inc, pg 904
Location Sound Corp, pg 924
MediaPOINTE, pg 938
POP TV, pg 978
Promax Systems, pg 986
SNAP, pg 1014
Southern California Sound Image Inc, pg 1019
Video Gear Rentals Inc, pg 1055
VMI Inc, pg 1060
VTP Inc, pg 1061
Westlake Recording Studios, pg 1064

CONNECTICUT

Connecticut Audio & Theatrical Supply, pg 835

FLORIDA

Access Media Group, pg 773
A2D Solutions Inc, pg 793
AVI-SPL, pg 798
Digital Video Systems Inc, pg 848
Harris Corp, pg 885
Hi-Tech Enterprises Inc, pg 888
Hunter Electronics LLC, pg 892
Media Concepts Inc, pg 936
Midtown Video Inc, pg 942
Recording Media & Equipment Inc (RM&E), pg 993
Sight & Sound Productions, pg 1010
Videoscope, pg 1057

GEORGIA

Clark, pg 829
Lighting & Production Equipment Inc, pg 920
Stage Front Presentation Systems, pg 1022

HAWAII

The Audio Visual Co (AVCO), pg 795

ILLINOIS

Quintessence Audio Ltd, pg 989
Sound Vision Inc, pg 1018

INDIANA

Porter Case Inc, pg 978
Sensory Technologies LLC, pg 1006
SHP Electronics, pg 1010

KENTUCKY

Barney Miller's Inc, pg 943
NOR-COM Inc, pg 958

LOUISIANA

Intermedia Technologies, pg 900

MARYLAND

Noventri, pg 960
Wiltronix, pg 1067

MASSACHUSETTS

Rule Broadcast Systems, pg 1000

MICHIGAN

Olson Anderson Co, pg 786
Ascom Communications Contractors, pg 791
On Stage Visuals, pg 963

MINNESOTA

Alpha Video & Audio Inc, pg 782

MISSOURI

Conference Technologies Inc, pg 835
MIS Technologies, pg 944
Modern Communications Inc, pg 944
Schiller's Audio-Visual, pg 1004
Southwest Audio-Visual Inc, pg 1019

NEBRASKA

ATV Research Inc, pg 793
Dog & Pony Productions Inc, pg 850
Video Service of America Inc (VSA), pg 1056

NEVADA

Aardvark Video & Media Productions, pg 772

NEW JERSEY

Audio Visual Associates, pg 795
Hamilton Buhl, pg 884
MCCOM Inc, pg 935
National Audio-Visual Supply, pg 952
PatchAmp, pg 970
Starlite Productions, pg 1024
SYMCO Inc, pg 1030
Total Video Products Inc, pg 1042

NEW YORK

Audio-Video Corp, pg 795
B&H Photo & Video Pro Audio, pg 802
Custom Media Environments, pg 841
Design Audio Visual Inc, pg 845
HAVE Inc, pg 886
Image Labs Corp, pg 895
Indigo Productions, pg 897
KVL Audio Visual Services Inc, pg 914
Markertek Video Supply, pg 931
TecNec Distributing, pg 1035
Videoguys, pg 1057
Visual Technologies Corp, pg 1060

OHIO

Smithall Electronics Inc, pg 1014
Tri-State Audio Visual Co, pg 1044

PENNSYLVANIA

Advanced AV, pg 777
Clair Brothers Audio Systems Inc, pg 829
The Lerro Corp, pg 919

RHODE ISLAND

Shanix Inc, pg 1008

TENNESSEE

Lowrance Sound Co Inc, pg 925
Zion Music Group, pg 1074

TEXAS

AVES Audio Visual Systems Inc, pg 798
Data Display Audio Visual Co LP, pg 843
Industrial Audio/Video Inc, pg 897
Pro Video & Film Equipment Co Inc, pg 983
Tarpley Media Systems, pg 1032

VIRGINIA

Avitecture Inc, pg 799
Communications Specialists Inc, pg 833
Lee Hartman & Sons Inc, pg 918
StageSound, pg 1023
The Whitlock Group, pg 1065

WISCONSIN

Audio Visual of Milwaukee Inc, pg 795
Camera Corner Connecting Point, pg 818
Full Compass Systems, pg 874
Safe Harbor Computers, pg 1001

ALBERTA

Infosat Communications Inc, pg 898

BRITISH COLUMBIA

Commercial Electronics Ltd, pg 832
ProVision Video Sales & Rentals Inc, pg 986

MANITOBA

Inland Audio Visual Ltd, pg 898

ONTARIO

Cinema Stage Inc, pg 827
Westbury National Show Systems Ltd, pg 1064

Mixer Manufacturers

CALIFORNIA

ALTINEX Inc, pg 783
Enright Co, pg 861
Opticomm-EMCORE, pg 964
Panasonic Broadcast & Digital Systems Co, pg 968

FLORIDA

Tel-Test, pg 1035

ILLINOIS

SoundTech, pg 1018

INDIANA

Porter Case Inc, pg 978

KANSAS

GlobalStreams™ Corp, pg 879

MINNESOTA

Vaddio, pg 1051

NEW MEXICO

Burst Electronics Inc, pg 815

NEW YORK

Image Labs Corp, pg 895
Sima Products Corp, pg 1011

OREGON

Grass Valley, pg 881

PENNSYLVANIA

MicroImage Video Systems, pg 941
World Video Sales Co Inc, pg 1070

WASHINGTON

Rane, pg 991

WISCONSIN

Intelix LLC, pg 899

BRITISH COLUMBIA

Triad Communications Ltd, pg 1044

ONTARIO

McCurdy Radio Ltd, pg 935

Mixer Rentals

ALABAMA

Audio-Video Resources Inc, pg 795

ARIZONA

Creative Backstage, pg 838
Merestone, pg 938
Video West Inc, pg 1056

ARKANSAS

White Diamond Productions, pg 1065

CALIFORNIA

Absolute Rentals, pg 772
AGF Media Services, pg 778
Alternative Rentals, pg 783
Ametron Audio/Video, pg 785
Artichoke Productions, pg 791
Audio Rents, pg 794
AV Guys, pg 797
Big Door, pg 807
Big Time Picture Company Inc, pg 807
Express Media Inc, pg 864
Full Moon & High Tide Productions & Studios, pg 874
Gearhouse Broadcast LLC, pg 876
Golden Gate Studios, pg 880
Image Integration, pg 895

JD Audio Visual Inc, pg 904
Maximus Media Inc, pg 934
Munday & Collins AV, pg 950
Muse Presentation Technologies, pg 950
New Circuit Films LLC, pg 955
Pro HD Rentals, pg 983
Production Gear Rentals (PGR), pg 984
Radiant Images, pg 990
RetinaVision Productions, pg 995
Shooting Star Video, pg 1009
SNAP, pg 1014
Studio 637, pg 1027
The Studios at Paramount, pg 1027
Synthesizer Systems Technologies (SST), pg 1030
Twin Peaks Creative, pg 1047
VER-Video Equipment Rentals, pg 1053
Video Gear Rentals Inc, pg 1055
Voice & Video Rentals, pg 1060
Warner Bros Production Sound & Video Services, pg 1062
Westcoast Video Productions Inc, pg 1064

CONNECTICUT

A/V Davey, pg 797
Videofilm Systems Inc, pg 1057

DISTRICT OF COLUMBIA

Metro Teleproductions Inc (MTI), pg 939

FLORIDA

Access Media Group, pg 773
AVI-SPL, pg 798
Cinema East, pg 827
Hi-Tech Enterprises Inc, pg 888
Phat Planet Recording Studios, pg 973
Sight & Sound Productions, pg 1010
Universal Studios Florida® Production Group, pg 1049

GEORGIA

See Production Services, pg 1006
Stage Front Presentation Systems, pg 1022

HAWAII

Sight & Sound Studios, pg 1010

ILLINOIS

Chicago Satellite & Video, pg 825
RC Communications, pg 992
SCI Television Productions LLC, pg 1004
Show Department Inc, pg 1009

IOWA

Pro Video, pg 983

KANSAS

KAKE-TV, pg 907

KENTUCKY

Audio Visual Techniques Inc, pg 796

MARYLAND

CPR MultiMedia Solutions, pg 837
Event Tech, pg 863

MASSACHUSETTS

Preston Productions Inc, pg 981

MICHIGAN

Olson Anderson Co, pg 786
K&R All Media Productions Inc, pg 908
On Stage Visuals, pg 963

MINNESOTA

Alpha Video & Audio Inc, pg 782

MISSOURI

Show-Me Audio-Visual, pg 1009

NEBRASKA

Dog & Pony Productions Inc, pg 850

NEW JERSEY

Audio Visual Associates, pg 795
Audio Visual Dynamics®, pg 795
MIB Mediaworks, pg 941
Soundtracks Production Services LLC, pg 1018
Starlite Productions, pg 1024

NEW MEXICO

Production Outfitters, pg 984

NEW YORK

Adorama Rental Co, pg 776
Big Foot Productions Inc, pg 807
CP Communications, pg 837
Design Audio Visual Inc, pg 845
KVL Audio Visual Services Inc, pg 914
PrimaLux Video Inc, pg 982
Production Central, pg 984

NORTH CAROLINA

A&V Company, pg 772
The Communications Group Inc, pg 833
Microspace Communications Corp, pg 942
On Location North Carolina, pg 963
Take One Productions Ltd, pg 1031

NORTH DAKOTA

Media Productions, pg 937

OHIO

R&B Communications Inc, pg 991

OKLAHOMA

PDC Productions, pg 970

PENNSYLVANIA

Innovision Media Group, pg 899
Producers Management Television (PMTV), pg 983
The Videohouse Inc, pg 1057
Viewpoint Production Services Inc, pg 1058

TENNESSEE

Love Shack Recording Studios, pg 925

TEXAS

Bright Giant Creative Group, pg 812
GEAR Cameras & Lighting, pg 876
Stage Directions, pg 1022

UTAH

Ron Hill Imagery, pg 889

VERMONT

Dark Star Lighting & Production, pg 842

VIRGINIA

D&B Television & Video Productions Inc, pg 842
Quince Imaging Inc, pg 989

PUERTO RICO

Stage Crew Audiovisual Inc, pg 1022

ALBERTA

L R Light & Sound, pg 915

BRITISH COLUMBIA

Finale Editworks, pg 868
Image Media Farm, pg 895
ProVision Video Sales & Rentals Inc, pg 986

MANITOBA

Inland Audio Visual Ltd, pg 898

ONTARIO

Wanted! Sound + Picture, pg 1062
Westbury National Show Systems Ltd, pg 1064
ZTV Broadcast Services Inc, pg 1074

QUEBEC

Group PVP, pg 882

Mixer Repairs

CALIFORNIA

Ametron Audio/Video, pg 785
Location Sound Corp, pg 924
TV Pro Gear, pg 1046
VMI Inc, pg 1060

CONNECTICUT

A/V Davey, pg 797

FLORIDA

Digital Video Systems Inc, pg 848
ELC Sales & Service Inc, pg 858
Hi-Tech Enterprises Inc, pg 888
Midtown Video Inc, pg 942
Phat Planet Recording Studios, pg 973
Tel-Test, pg 1035

GEORGIA

Stage Front Presentation Systems, pg 1022

ILLINOIS

Midwest Digital Corp, pg 942

KENTUCKY

NOR-COM Inc, pg 958

MARYLAND

Noventri, pg 960

MICHIGAN

TeL Systems, pg 1035

MINNESOTA

Alpha Video & Audio Inc, pg 782

MISSOURI

Southwest Audio-Visual Inc, pg 1019

NEW JERSEY

Audio Visual Associates, pg 795
Starlite Productions, pg 1024

NEW YORK

Visual Technologies Corp, pg 1060

OHIO

Tri-State Audio Visual Co, pg 1044

OREGON

All Service Musical Electronics Repair, pg 780

TEXAS

Pro Video & Film Equipment Co Inc, pg 983
Tarpley Media Systems, pg 1032

WISCONSIN

Full Compass Systems, pg 874

ALBERTA

Infosat Communications Inc, pg 898

BRITISH COLUMBIA

Commercial Electronics Ltd, pg 832

MANITOBA

Inland Audio Visual Ltd, pg 898

ONTARIO

Westbury National Show Systems Ltd, pg 1064

Mixing—Stereo or Dolby Stereo

ALABAMA

Dogwood Recording Studios, pg 850

ARIZONA

Aardvark Productions LLC, pg 772
Allusion Studios & Pure Wave Audio, pg 782
Merestone, pg 938
Metropolitan Audio-Visual Inc, pg 940
Video West Inc, pg 1056

ARKANSAS

White Diamond Productions, pg 1065

CALIFORNIA

AB Audio Visual Entertainment Inc, pg 772
Aliso Creek Productions Inc, pg 780

VIDEO

Mixing—Stereo or Dolby Stereo (continued)

CALIFORNIA (continued)

AlphaDogs Inc, pg 782
Argyle Post, pg 789
Artichoke Productions, pg 791
Berke Creative Inc, pg 805
Chace Audio by Deluxe, pg 823
Creative Media Recording, pg 838
Crystal Pyramid Productions™, pg 840
Custom Video Productions Inc, pg 841
Diamond Dreams Music Productions, pg 846
Digital Jungle, pg 847
Digital Outpost, pg 847
Dogma Studios, pg 850
Earwax Productions Inc, pg 855
Express Media Inc, pg 864
Film Technology Co Inc, pg 867
48 Windows, pg 871
Full Moon & High Tide Productions & Studios, pg 874
FXF Productions Inc, pg 874
Golden Gate Studios, pg 880
iCorpTv, pg 893
The Kitchen, pg 911
KPBS TV FM-San Diego, pg 913
Ludlow Media Solutions, pg 926
Lynch Communications, pg 926
Maximus Media Inc, pg 934
McCune Audio-Video-Lighting, pg 935
Mind Over Eye Inc, pg 943
Mist Media Inc, pg 944
New & Unique Videos™, pg 955
Nolte Media, pg 958
OTR Studios, pg 966
Palardo Productions, pg 968
PM Productions, pg 977
Polarity Post Production, pg 978
Private Island Trax, pg 982
Pyramind Studios, pg 988
QRS Software Services, pg 988
Roundabout Entertainment Inc, pg 1000
Shapeshifter, pg 1008
SonicPool, pg 1016
Sonora Recorders, pg 1016
Staylor-Made Communications Inc, pg 1024
Still N'Motion, pg 1025
Studio 132, pg 1027
Total Media Group, pg 1042
Twin Peaks Creative, pg 1047
Universal Studios, pg 1049
Wildfire Post Production Studios, pg 1066

COLORADO

Paul L Anderson Productions Inc, pg 786
Tim Cissell Music, pg 828
Conly Productions, pg 835
Flashback Media Productions, pg 869
Rocky Mountain Audio/Video Productions Inc, pg 998

CONNECTICUT

Antenna International, pg 787
Applebox Studio, pg 788
BRB Audiovisual Productions, pg 812
Fox Connecticut, pg 872
Ironik Design & Post, pg 902
Palace Digital Studios, pg 967
P&P Studios Inc, pg 968
T & M Digital Services, pg 1031

DELAWARE

Side Door Studio Inc, pg 1010

DISTRICT OF COLUMBIA

Interface Media Group, pg 900

FLORIDA

Access Media Group, pg 773
Allegro Productions Inc, pg 781
Big Byte Video Productions, pg 806
Civins Productions Inc, pg 828
Communications Concepts Inc (CCI), pg 833
Courter Films LLC, pg 837
Eastern Video, pg 856
Ed Ethridge Productions Inc, pg 863
Global Video Distributors Inc, pg 879
Home Shopping Network (HSN), pg 890
Media Entertainment Inc, pg 936
Morrisound Recording, pg 946
Progressive Media & Music, pg 985
Sight & Sound Productions, pg 1010
Sound & Vision Communications Inc, pg 1016
Sunfire Communications Inc, pg 1028
Universal Studios Florida® Production Group, pg 1049
Vistamax Productions, pg 1059

GEORGIA

Beachwood Productions, pg 804
Beast Atlanta, pg 804
Continental Film & Video, pg 835
Crawford Media Services, pg 838
Doppler Studios, pg 851
The DVI Group, pg 854
First Cut Communications LLC, pg 868
Guerrilla Productions LLC, pg 883
Staging Directions Inc, pg 1023

HAWAII

Audio Resource Honolulu, pg 794
TV Juice Productions Inc, pg 1046

ILLINOIS

ABSA Productions Inc, pg 772
CCore Media Inc, pg 821
Chicago Satellite & Video, pg 825
Comtech Multimedia Marketing, pg 834
IV Media Resources, pg 903
Steven Samler Music & Sound, pg 1002
SCI Television Productions LLC, pg 1004
Southern Illinois University, pg 1019
Sparkfactor, pg 1019
20/20 Communications Inc, pg 1047
Video Impressions, pg 1055

INDIANA

Advanced Media Integration, pg 777
Bright Ideas Creative Services, pg 812
Covenant Productions®, pg 837

LOUISIANA

Digital FX Inc, pg 847
Vidox Motion Imagery, pg 1057
WVLA-TV, pg 1071

MAINE

WGME-TV, pg 1065

MARYLAND

CPR MultiMedia Solutions, pg 837
dbF a Media Company, pg 844
DBM Communications Inc, pg 844
Media Dimensions Inc, pg 936
Pro Cuts Editing Services, pg 982
Sheffield Audio/Video Productions, pg 1008
Soundtrax Optical Sound Recording, pg 1018

MASSACHUSETTS

Capron Lighting & Sound Co Inc, pg 819
Continental Recordings Inc, pg 835
Documentary Educational Resources Inc, pg 850
Labrecque Creative Sound, pg 915
Northern Light Productions, pg 959
Soundtrack Recording Studios, pg 1018

MICHIGAN

Digi Sign Design LLC, pg 847
Digital Image Studios LLC, pg 847
GMP Music, pg 879
K&R's Recording Studios Inc, pg 908
Universal Images, pg 1049

MINNESOTA

The ADS Group, pg 777
Aggressive Records Audio Duplication LLC, pg 778
Beyers Sound & Essay Audio, pg 806
The Richard Diercks Co Inc, pg 846
Worthwhile Films, pg 1070

MISSOURI

Avatar Studios, pg 798
Production Consultants, pg 984
Show-Me Audio-Visual, pg 1009

MONTANA

Jereco Studios Inc, pg 905

NEVADA

DVDs4Less, pg 854
Encore Productions Inc, pg 861
JCS Video Productions, pg 904
Tanglewood Productions, pg 1031

NEW HAMPSHIRE

Channell One Video, pg 824
Chip Taylor Communications LLC, pg 1032

NEW JERSEY

All Jersey Studios, pg 780
Broadcast Center Studios, pg 813
CFP Video Productions Inc, pg 823
Diversified Systems Inc, pg 849
Laurel Video Productions, pg 916
Mia Mind Music, pg 941
MIB Mediaworks, pg 941
Midnight Media Group Inc, pg 942
Milgrom Productions, pg 943
Ray Mueller Productions, pg 949
NFL Films Inc, pg 957
NFL Films Music Library, pg 957
Starlite Productions, pg 1024
Suede Interactive, pg 1027
VCSvideo, pg 1052

NEW MEXICO

Production Outfitters, pg 984

NEW YORK

Aural Gratification Inc, pg 796
The Big House Group, pg 807
CP Communications, pg 837
Design Audio Visual Inc, pg 845
Digital Art Video Inc, pg 847
Downtown Community Television Center (DCTV), pg 851
Eastco Multimedia Solutions Inc, pg 856
Fingerpaint, pg 868
4-D Creative Media, pg 871
Gurrilla Video Solutions, pg 883
Hallel Communications, pg 884
HAVE Inc, pg 886
HB-Content, pg 886
KAS Music & Sound, pg 908
Magno Sound & Video, pg 929
Mood Creations Ltd, pg 946
The Napoleon Group, pg 952
Now Hear This, pg 960
Shelly Palmer Production, pg 968
PostWorks, pg 979
TBA Global Events, pg 1032
Teatown Communications Group, pg 1033
Tiki Recording Studios Inc, pg 1040
Tobin Productions Inc, pg 1041
Visual Technologies Corp, pg 1060

NORTH CAROLINA

Pat Appleson Studios Inc, pg 788
The Communications Group Inc, pg 833
Duke Media Services, pg 853
Franklin Video Inc, pg 872
Horizon Video Productions Inc, pg 891
LCW Productions LLC, pg 917
Take One Productions Ltd, pg 1031
2BruceStudio, pg 1047
Unifour Productions Inc, pg 1048

NORTH DAKOTA

Media Productions, pg 937

OHIO

Advent Media Inc, pg 778
Aztec Video Productions, pg 801
Creative Technology, pg 838
EDR Media LLC, pg 857
Lyon Video Inc, pg 927
Mills James Productions, pg 943
R&B Communications Inc, pg 991

OKLAHOMA

PDC Productions, pg 970

OREGON

A KTVA Production LLC, pg 771
Production West, pg 985

PENNSYLVANIA

Audio Visual Communications Inc, pg 795
Beholder Productions Inc, pg 804
FMP Media Solutions Inc, pg 870
Innovision Media Group, pg 899
Javboy Records, pg 904
Laser Video Corp, pg 916
Panta Rhei Media Inc, pg 968
Production Masters Inc (PMI), pg 984

Mixing—Stereo Surround or Dolby Surround

VIDEO

Mixing—Stereo Surround or Dolby Surround (continued)

OHIO

Aztec Video Productions, pg 801
Creative Technology, pg 838
EDR Media LLC, pg 857
Mills James Productions, pg 943

OKLAHOMA

PDC Productions, pg 970

OREGON

Rex, pg 995

PENNSYLVANIA

Audio Visual Communications Inc, pg 795
FMP Media Solutions Inc, pg 870
Production Masters Inc (PMI), pg 984
Right Coast Recording Inc, pg 997

SOUTH CAROLINA

Genesis Creative, pg 877

TENNESSEE

American Blackguard Inc, pg 784
JamSync, pg 904
Love Shack Recording Studios, pg 925
Memphis Communications Corp, pg 938
Motion Picture Services, pg 947
Scripps Networks, pg 1005
Stage Post, pg 1022
Technical Support Systems LLC, pg 1034

TEXAS

Harbor House Studios, pg 884
Mediaforce Productions, pg 937
The Samuels Co, pg 1002
South Coast Film & Video, pg 1019
Stage Directions, pg 1022

UTAH

One Stop CD Shop LLC, pg 963
Soularium Recording Studios, pg 1016

VIRGINIA

Metro Productions, pg 939

WASHINGTON

North-by-Northwest Productions, pg 958
Victory Studios, pg 1054

WISCONSIN

Audio Visual of Milwaukee Inc, pg 795
5th Floor Recording Co, pg 867
Media Communications Association-International (MCA-I), pg 936

ALBERTA

Global Television Station, pg 879

BRITISH COLUMBIA

Finale Editworks, pg 868
Pinewood Sound, pg 975

MANITOBA

daCapo Productions, pg 842

ONTARIO

ADS Media, pg 777
GAPC (General Assembly Production Centre), pg 875
Metalworks Recording Studios Inc, pg 939
Phase One Studios, pg 973
Purefire Communications Inc, pg 987
Westbury National Show Systems Ltd, pg 1064

QUEBEC

Muse Entertainment Enterprises, pg 950

Mixing—Videotapes

ALABAMA

CMEInfo, pg 830

ARIZONA

Fox 10 Productions (KSAZ-TV), pg 872
Merestone, pg 938
Metropolitan Audio-Visual Inc, pg 940
Phoenix VideoFilms®, pg 974
Video Media Productions (VMP), pg 1055

ARKANSAS

Live'N'Loud, pg 923
White Diamond Productions, pg 1065

CALIFORNIA

Action Video, pg 775
All Video Productions, pg 781
AlphaDogs Inc, pg 782
Artichoke Productions, pg 791
Berke Creative Inc, pg 805
Berkeley Sound Artists Inc, pg 805
CCI Digital, pg 821
Chace Audio by Deluxe, pg 823
Creative Media Recording, pg 838
Crystal Pyramid Productions™, pg 840
Custom Video Productions Inc, pg 841
Diamond Dreams Music Productions, pg 846
Digital Media West, pg 847
Dogma Studios, pg 850
Earwax Productions Inc, pg 855
Express Media Inc, pg 864
Film Technology Co Inc, pg 867
First Person™, pg 868
Global Village Stock Footage Library, pg 879
Gordon Productions Inc, pg 880
iCorpTv, pg 893
KION-TV, pg 911
The Kitchen, pg 911
KPBS TV FM-San Diego, pg 913
KTVU-Retail Services, pg 914
KVIE-Channel 6, pg 914
Ludlow Media Solutions, pg 926
Maximus Media Inc, pg 934
McCune Audio-Video-Lighting, pg 935
The Media Staff Inc, pg 937
Mind Over Eye Inc, pg 943
Mist Media Inc, pg 944
Nolte Media, pg 958
On-Trax Inc, pg 963
Palardo Productions, pg 968
Penrose Productions, pg 972
piXvfm, pg 976
PM Productions, pg 977
Polarity Post Production, pg 978
PSI Inc, pg 987
QRS Software Services, pg 988
RetinaVision Productions, pg 995
Roundabout Entertainment Inc, pg 1000
SBS Productions, pg 1003
Shapeshifter, pg 1008
SonicPool, pg 1016
Tele-Video Production Services (TVPS), pg 1036
Total Media Group, pg 1042
Twin Peaks Creative, pg 1047
Universal Studios, pg 1049
Videolady, pg 1057
Visions Plus, pg 1058
West Coast Projections Inc, pg 1063
Wildfire Post Production Studios, pg 1066

COLORADO

Tim Cissell Music, pg 828
CSI Films, pg 840
Daylight Productions & Rentals, pg 844
Flashback Media Productions, pg 869
Open Media Foundation, pg 964
Rocky Mountain Audio/Video Productions Inc, pg 998
Transtar Entertainment Co Inc, pg 1043

CONNECTICUT

BRB Audiovisual Productions, pg 812
Fox Connecticut, pg 872
Geomatrix Productions, pg 877
Guymark Studios LLC, pg 883
Ironik Design & Post, pg 902
MAVCO, pg 934

DELAWARE

Side Door Studio Inc, pg 1010

DISTRICT OF COLUMBIA

Interface Media Group, pg 900

FLORIDA

Access Media Group, pg 773
Accord Productions, pg 773
Allegro Productions Inc, pg 781
Big Byte Video Productions, pg 806
Cinema East, pg 827
Communications Concepts Inc (CCI), pg 833
Courter Films LLC, pg 837
Eastern Video, pg 856
Easy Edit Video Inc, pg 856
Ed Ethridge Productions Inc, pg 863
Gulf Coast Audio Visual Producers Inc, pg 883
Home Shopping Network (HSN), pg 890
Jordan Klein Film & Video (JKFV), pg 906
Mach 1 Productions, pg 927
Media Concepts Inc, pg 936
Media Entertainment Inc, pg 936
National Teleproductions Inc, pg 953
Progressive Media & Music, pg 985
Sound & Vision Communications Inc, pg 1016
Sunfire Communications Inc, pg 1028
Universal Studios Florida® Production Group, pg 1049
Mike Vasilinda Productions Inc, pg 1052
Video Techniques Inc, pg 1056
Vistamax Productions, pg 1059

GEORGIA

Beachwood Productions, pg 804
COMPRO Productions Inc, pg 834
Crawford Media Services, pg 838
First Cut Communications LLC, pg 868
Guerrilla Productions LLC, pg 883
Staging Directions Inc, pg 1023

HAWAII

1013 Integrated, pg 1037
TV Juice Productions Inc, pg 1046

IDAHO

KTVB-TV, pg 914
Wide Eye Productions, pg 1066

ILLINOIS

Audio Visual Services Corp, pg 796
Beatty TeleVisual Productions, pg 804
Chicago Satellite & Video, pg 825
Extraordinary Demos, pg 864
IV Media Resources, pg 903
The Pepper Group, pg 972
PSAV® Presentation Services (Hotel Services Division), pg 987
Steven Samler Music & Sound, pg 1002
SCI Television Productions LLC, pg 1004
Tele-Time Systems, pg 1036
20/20 Communications Inc, pg 1047
Video I-D Teleproductions Inc, pg 1055
Video Impressions, pg 1055
WEEK TV, pg 1063

INDIANA

Advanced Media Integration, pg 777
AVA Productions, pg 798
Communication Ministries, pg 833

IOWA

The Production House, pg 984

KANSAS

Chapman Recording & Mastering, pg 824
KAKE-TV, pg 907

KENTUCKY

Barney Miller's Inc, pg 943
The PPS Group, pg 980

LOUISIANA

Digital FX Inc, pg 847
Louisiana State University Health Sciences Center - Shreveport, pg 925
Moxie Media, pg 948
Vidox Motion Imagery, pg 1057
YES Productions, pg 1072

MAINE

Headlight Audio Visual Inc, pg 887
WGME-TV, pg 1065

MARYLAND

Adventure Productions LLC, pg 778
The Ahern Group, pg 779
Bethesda Softworks LLC, pg 806
CAS Video Productions, pg 820
CPR MultiMedia Solutions, pg 837
dbF a Media Company, pg 844
Library Video Network (LVN), pg 920
Media Dimensions Inc, pg 936
Milner-Fenwick Inc, pg 943
Shadowstone R & R™, pg 1008
Sheffield Audio/Video Productions, pg 1008
Welocalize, pg 1063

MASSACHUSETTS

CommCreative, pg 832
Documentary Educational Resources Inc, pg 850
Home Inc, pg 890
Inter-Media Electronics, pg 899
Penfield Productions Ltd, pg 971
Small Planet Communications Inc, pg 1013

MICHIGAN

Digi Sign Design LLC, pg 847
K&R's Recording Studios Inc, pg 908
Michigan Recording Arts Institute & Technologies, pg 941

MINNESOTA

The ADS Group, pg 777
Aggressive Records Audio Duplication LLC, pg 778
The Richard Diercks Co Inc, pg 846
GMI Productions, pg 879
Master Communications Group, pg 933
Worthwhile Films, pg 1070

MISSOURI

Avatar Studios, pg 798
Conference Technologies Inc, pg 835
KPLR-TV, pg 913
Production Consultants, pg 984
Show-Me Audio-Visual, pg 1009

MONTANA

Jereco Studios Inc, pg 905
KCFW Television, pg 908
KUSM TV, pg 914

NEVADA

Aardvark Video & Media Productions, pg 772
DVDs4Less, pg 854
Encore Productions Inc, pg 861
JCS Video Productions, pg 904
Lefco Video Services Inc, pg 918

NEW HAMPSHIRE

Academic & Campus Technology Services, pg 773
Apertura, pg 788
Channell One Video, pg 824
Chip Taylor Communications LLC, pg 1032
The Troupe, pg 1045

NEW JERSEY

All Jersey Studios, pg 780
Broadcast Center Studios, pg 813
CFP Video Productions Inc, pg 823
Deluxe Media Services, pg 845
Diversified Systems Inc, pg 849
DWJ Television, pg 854
Laurel Video Productions, pg 916
MediaMix Inc, pg 937
Megavideo Productions, pg 938
MIB Mediaworks, pg 941
Midnight Media Group Inc, pg 942
NFL Films Music Library, pg 957
Optisonics Productions, pg 965
Starlite Productions, pg 1024
Suede Interactive, pg 1027
VCSvideo, pg 1052
Video Corporation of America (VCA), pg 1055

NEW MEXICO

Production Outfitters, pg 984
30 Second Street Ltd, pg 1039

NEW YORK

Adwar Video, pg 778
aurora productions, pg 797
The Big House Group, pg 807
Broad Street Inc, pg 812
Chromavision Corp, pg 826
Design Audio Visual Inc, pg 845
Downtown Community Television Center (DCTV), pg 851
Eastco Multimedia Solutions Inc, pg 856
4-D Creative Media, pg 871
Hallel Communications, pg 884
HAVE Inc, pg 886
HB-Content, pg 886
KAS Music & Sound, pg 908
Ketchum Pleon Change, pg 910
Long Island Video Enterprises Live Inc, pg 924
Magno Sound & Video, pg 929
MRM Worldwide, pg 948
Nutmeg Post, pg 960
Shelly Palmer Production, pg 968
Post Josh Productions, pg 979
PostWorks, pg 979
TBA Global Events, pg 1032
Teatown Communications Group, pg 1033
Technisphere Corp, pg 1034
Tobin Productions Inc, pg 1041
Visual Technologies Corp, pg 1060
Zelman Studios Ltd, pg 1073

NORTH CAROLINA

Pat Appleson Studios Inc, pg 788
The Communications Group Inc, pg 833
Duke Media Services, pg 853
Horizon Video Productions Inc, pg 891
LCW Productions LLC, pg 917
Moving Pictures, pg 948
NASCAR Media Group LLC, pg 952
On Location North Carolina, pg 963
Take One Productions Ltd, pg 1031
Trailblazer Studios®, pg 1043
Unifour Productions Inc, pg 1048

NORTH DAKOTA

Media Productions, pg 937

OHIO

Aztec Video Productions, pg 801
Cuyahoga Community College Media Center, pg 841
EDR Media LLC, pg 857
iVideo Technologies, pg 903
Lyon Video Inc, pg 927
MainSail Production Services Inc, pg 929
Mills James Productions, pg 943
Musicol Recording, pg 951
Take 1 Media Services, pg 1031
VGI Productions, pg 1053
Vista Color Imaging Inc, pg 1059

OREGON

A KTVA Production LLC, pg 771
KPDX-TV Production Center, pg 913
Production West, pg 985
Rex, pg 995

PENNSYLVANIA

Center City Film & Video Inc, pg 822
FMP Media Solutions Inc, pg 870
Fusion Brand Experiences, pg 874
Innovision Media Group, pg 899
Laser Video Corp, pg 916
Production Masters Inc (PMI), pg 984
The Videohouse Inc, pg 1057
Visual Sound Inc, pg 1059
WHYY Inc, pg 1066
WPHL-TV, pg 1070

SOUTH CAROLINA

Genesis Creative, pg 877
Stages Video Productions, pg 1023
Venture Media, pg 1052

TENNESSEE

JamSync, pg 904
Love Shack Recording Studios, pg 925
Memphis Communications Corp, pg 938
Motion Picture Services, pg 947
Scripps Networks, pg 1005
ST Productions, pg 1022
Stage Post, pg 1022

TEXAS

Cerutti Productions Inc, pg 823
Communication Arts Multimedia Inc, pg 832
The Editing Co, pg 857
Harbor House Studios, pg 884
Horizon Film + Video Productions, pg 891
McNee Productions Inc, pg 935
Mediaforce Productions, pg 937
Julye Newlin Productions Inc, pg 956
Phillips MediaSource, pg 974
The Samuels Co, pg 1002
South Coast Film & Video, pg 1019
Texas Heart Institute Visual Communication Services, pg 1037

VERMONT

University of Vermont, Instructional Television Dept, pg 1050

VIRGINIA

BES Studios, pg 805
CACI Productions Group, pg 816
Creative Video of Washington Inc, pg 839
D&B Television & Video Productions Inc, pg 842
Maniglia Media, pg 930

WASHINGTON

Robert McConnell Productions, pg 935
North-by-Northwest Productions, pg 958
Victory Studios, pg 1054

WEST VIRGINIA

WSAZ-TV 3/WSAZ Productions, pg 1070

WISCONSIN

Audio Visual of Milwaukee Inc, pg 795
Grassland Media Inc, pg 881
Learning Technology Services, pg 917
Logan Productions Inc, pg 924
Media Communications Association-International (MCA-I), pg 936
USAV Group Inc, pg 1050
Video Wisconsin Inc, pg 1056
Wisconsin Public Television, pg 1068

WYOMING

Bridger Productions Inc, pg 812

PUERTO RICO

Stage Crew Audiovisual Inc, pg 1022

BRITISH COLUMBIA

Finale Editworks, pg 868
Image Media Farm, pg 895
Pinewood Sound, pg 975
Triad Communications Ltd, pg 1044
Video In Studios/Video Out Distribution, pg 1055

MANITOBA

Spectra Video Productions Ltd, pg 1020

NEWFOUNDLAND AND LABRADOR

Vidcraft Productions Ltd, pg 1054

ONTARIO

Edcom Multimedia Products, pg 856
GAPC (General Assembly Production Centre), pg 875
JFB Communications, pg 905
Metalworks Recording Studios Inc, pg 939
Purefire Communications Inc, pg 987
Spence-Thomas Audio Post, pg 1021
Video Excellence Productions, pg 1055

QUEBEC

Muse Entertainment Enterprises, pg 950

Mobile Production Vehicle Distributors

ALABAMA

Media Visions Inc, pg 937

VIDEO

Mobile Production Vehicle Distributors (continued)

CALIFORNIA

Ametron Audio/Video, pg 785
Satellite Digital Teleproductions (SDTV), pg 1003
SNAP, pg 1014

FLORIDA

Digital Video Systems Inc, pg 848
Pro Stage Inc, pg 983

HAWAII

The Audio Visual Co (AVCO), pg 795

ILLINOIS

Corplex, pg 836

INDIANA

Sensory Technologies LLC, pg 1006

IOWA

ECS Inc, pg 856

MARYLAND

Absolute Hollywood, pg 772

MINNESOTA

Alpha Video & Audio Inc, pg 782

MISSOURI

Communitronics Corp, pg 833
Modern Communications Inc, pg 944
Southwest Audio-Visual Inc, pg 1019

NEW JERSEY

Diversified Systems Inc, pg 849
Tele-Measurements Inc, pg 1035
Turner Engineering Inc, pg 1046

NEW YORK

Audio-Video Corp, pg 795

NORTH CAROLINA

Strategic Connections, pg 1026

OHIO

iVideo Technologies, pg 903

PENNSYLVANIA

Advanced AV, pg 777
The Lerro Corp, pg 919
Morefield Communications Inc, pg 946

TENNESSEE

Zion Music Group, pg 1074

TEXAS

Pro Video & Film Equipment Co Inc, pg 983
Shook Mobile Technology LP, pg 1009

UTAH

RIA Corp, pg 996

VIRGINIA

Quince Imaging Inc, pg 989

WISCONSIN

Demco Inc, pg 845
Safe Harbor Computers, pg 1001

Mobile Production Vehicle Manufacturers

CALIFORNIA

Broadcast Microwave Services (BMS), pg 813
Technical Services, pg 1034

FLORIDA

Frontline Communications, pg 873

ILLINOIS

Corplex, pg 836

MARYLAND

Absolute Hollywood, pg 772

MASSACHUSETTS

L-3 ESSCO, pg 915

MISSOURI

VMI (Video Masters Inc), pg 1060

NEW YORK

CP Communications, pg 837

TEXAS

Exeltech Inc, pg 864
Shook Mobile Technology LP, pg 1009

VIRGINIA

Quince Imaging Inc, pg 989

Mobile Production Vehicle Rentals

ALABAMA

Crosscreek Television Productions Inc, pg 839

ARIZONA

Arizona Cine Equipment, pg 789
Cox Creative Studios, pg 837
Merestone, pg 938
Rodeo Video Inc, pg 998

CALIFORNIA

Aerial Video Systems, pg 778
Ametron Audio/Video, pg 785
CineVantage LLC, pg 828
Crystal Pyramid Productions™, pg 840
DTC Lighting & Grip, pg 853
Express Media Inc, pg 864
First Camera, pg 868
Golden Gate Studios, pg 880
Lynch Communications, pg 926
PSSI, pg 987
RetinaVision Productions, pg 995
Santa Clarita Studios, pg 1002
SNAP, pg 1014
Stray Angel Films, pg 1026
Total Media Group, pg 1042
Universal Satellite Communications Inc, pg 1049
Videowerks, pg 1057
Z-Ville Productions, pg 1073

DISTRICT OF COLUMBIA

Interface Media Group, pg 900

FLORIDA

ACT Productions, pg 775
CopShopMiami.com, pg 836
Jordan Klein Film & Video (JKFV), pg 906
National Teleproductions Inc, pg 953
Pro Stage Inc, pg 983
Skystorm Productions, pg 1013
Trendy Studio LLC, pg 1044

GEORGIA

Continental Film & Video, pg 835
ON Event Services, pg 963
Stage Front Presentation Systems, pg 1022

HAWAII

FOTON Hawaii, pg 871
Sight & Sound Studios, pg 1010

ILLINOIS

Assignment Desk, pg 792
Audio Visual Services Corp, pg 796
Big Shoulders Digital Video Productions, pg 807
Chicago Satellite & Video, pg 825
Corplex, pg 836
Product Productions, pg 984
PSAV® Presentation Services (Hotel Services Division), pg 987
QuickSet International Inc, pg 989
Roadworthy Image Magnification, pg 998
Satellite Technology Systems Inc, pg 1003
Trio Video, pg 1045

INDIANA

Lakeshore Productions, pg 915

IOWA

ECS Inc, pg 856

KENTUCKY

WKYT Productions, pg 1068

LOUISIANA

Digital FX Inc, pg 847
Moxie Media, pg 948
Satellite Center, pg 1003
YES Productions, pg 1072

MARYLAND

Absolute Hollywood, pg 772
CPR MultiMedia Solutions, pg 837
Producers Video, pg 984
Sheffield Audio/Video Productions, pg 1008

MASSACHUSETTS

A/V Presentations Inc, pg 797
Goin' Mobile, pg 880

MICHIGAN

K&R All Media Productions Inc, pg 908
K&R's Recording Studios Inc, pg 908
WTVS-Station Enterprises, pg 1071

MISSOURI

Southwest Audio-Visual Inc, pg 1019

NEVADA

Lefco Video Services Inc, pg 918

NEW HAMPSHIRE

Channell One Video, pg 824

NEW JERSEY

E Video Productions, pg 855
MediaMix Inc, pg 937
MIB Mediaworks, pg 941
Bill Quinn Productions, pg 989
Vision Quest Productions Inc, pg 1058

NEW MEXICO

Production Outfitters, pg 984

NEW YORK

C&C Studios Corp, pg 819
CP Communications, pg 837
Direct Broadcast Services Inc (DBS), pg 848
Manhattan Center Studios Inc, pg 930
MRG Productions Inc, pg 948
RGH Lighting LLC, pg 996
Sony Music Entertainment, pg 1016
Visual Word Systems Inc, pg 1060

NORTH CAROLINA

J Arnold Productions Inc, pg 790
The Communications Group Inc, pg 833
On Location North Carolina, pg 963
Take One Productions Ltd, pg 1031

OHIO

Aztec Video Productions, pg 801
Image Video Teleproductions Inc, pg 895
Lyon Video Inc, pg 927
Mills James Productions, pg 943

OKLAHOMA

Institute for Teaching & Learning Excellence (ITLE), pg 899

OREGON

Pacific Grip & Lighting Inc, pg 967

PENNSYLVANIA

FMP Media Solutions Inc, pg 870
Fusion Brand Experiences, pg 874
Innovision Media Group, pg 899
Location Lighting Ltd, pg 924
Producers Management Television (PMTV), pg 983
Upstage Video, pg 1050

TENNESSEE

DR&A Inc, pg 852
Russ Sturgeon Productions/RSVP, pg 1027
Technical Support Systems LLC, pg 1034

TEXAS

AMS Pictures, pg 786
Imagine Communications Corp, pg 896
JWP Inc, pg 907

Earl Miller Productions Inc, pg 943
Muller Entertainment, pg 949
Omega Productions, pg 962
Phillips MediaSource, pg 974
Reelsound Recording Co, pg 994
The Samuels Co, pg 1002
Texcam Inc, pg 1038

VIRGINIA

Quince Imaging Inc, pg 989

WASHINGTON

Victory Studios, pg 1054

WISCONSIN

Logan Productions Inc, pg 924
Wisconsin Public Television, pg 1068

ALBERTA

Global Television Station, pg 879

BRITISH COLUMBIA

Image Media Farm, pg 895

ONTARIO

JIB Shots Equipment Inc, pg 905

QUEBEC

Group PVP, pg 882

Mobile Production Vehicle Repairs

CALIFORNIA

Ametron Audio/Video, pg 785
Technical Services, pg 1034

FLORIDA

ELC Sales & Service Inc, pg 858
JT Communications, pg 906

IOWA

ECS Inc, pg 856

MICHIGAN

TeL Systems, pg 1035

MINNESOTA

Alpha Video & Audio Inc, pg 782

MISSOURI

Southwest Audio-Visual Inc, pg 1019

NEW JERSEY

Turner Engineering Inc, pg 1046

NEW YORK

MRG Productions Inc, pg 948

TENNESSEE

Technical Support Systems LLC, pg 1034

TEXAS

Pro Video & Film Equipment Co Inc, pg 983
Shook Mobile Technology LP, pg 1009

UTAH

RIA Corp, pg 996

VIRGINIA

Quince Imaging Inc, pg 989

Mobile Unit Distributors

ALABAMA

Media Visions Inc, pg 937

CALIFORNIA

Ametron Audio/Video, pg 785
Mobilized Tech Systems, pg 944
NSM Surveillance, pg 960
Satellite Digital Teleproductions (SDTV), pg 1003

CONNECTICUT

Rockwell Communications Inc, pg 998

FLORIDA

Communications Concepts Inc (CCI), pg 833
Digital Video Systems Inc, pg 848

GEORGIA

Convergent Media Systems, pg 836
Stage Front Presentation Systems, pg 1022
Technical Innovation, pg 1033

ILLINOIS

Corplex, pg 836
Toko America Inc, pg 1041

INDIANA

Porter Case Inc, pg 978
Sensory Technologies LLC, pg 1006

IOWA

ECS Inc, pg 856

MARYLAND

Nicholas P Pipino Associates Inc, pg 976

MINNESOTA

Alpha Video & Audio Inc, pg 782

MISSOURI

Communitronics Corp, pg 833
Modern Communications Inc, pg 944
Southwest Audio-Visual Inc, pg 1019

NEW JERSEY

Diversified Systems Inc, pg 849
Turner Engineering Inc, pg 1046

NEW YORK

Audio-Video Corp, pg 795
L-3 GCS, pg 915
Visual Technologies Corp, pg 1060

NORTH CAROLINA

Strategic Connections, pg 1026

PENNSYLVANIA

Advanced AV, pg 777
The Lerro Corp, pg 919
Morefield Communications Inc, pg 946
Wespen Audio Visual Co, pg 1063

TENNESSEE

Lowrance Sound Co Inc, pg 925
Zion Music Group, pg 1074

TEXAS

Heffernan Audio Visual, pg 887
Pro Video & Film Equipment Co Inc, pg 983
Shook Mobile Technology LP, pg 1009

UTAH

RIA Corp, pg 996

VIRGINIA

Quince Imaging Inc, pg 989

WISCONSIN

Spectrum Industries Inc, pg 1021

ONTARIO

Majortech Inc, pg 929

Mobile Unit Manufacturers

ARIZONA

Applied Integration Corp, pg 789

CALIFORNIA

Broadcast Microwave Services (BMS), pg 813
NSM Surveillance, pg 960
Technical Services, pg 1034
TV Pro Gear, pg 1046

COLORADO

Display Devices, pg 849

FLORIDA

Frontline Communications, pg 873

ILLINOIS

Corplex, pg 836
Dukane Corp, Audio Visual Products Division, pg 853
Toko America Inc, pg 1041

INDIANA

Porter Case Inc, pg 978

IOWA

Winegard Co, pg 1067

MASSACHUSETTS

L-3 ESSCO, pg 915

MISSOURI

VMI (Video Masters Inc), pg 1060

NEW YORK

Judson Rosebush Co Inc, pg 999

TEXAS

Exeltech Inc, pg 864
Shook Mobile Technology LP, pg 1009
The Yesterday USA Radio Networks, pg 1072

VIRGINIA

Quince Imaging Inc, pg 989

WISCONSIN

Spectrum Industries Inc, pg 1021

QUEBEC

Matrox Video Products Group, pg 934

Mobile Unit Rentals

ALABAMA

AVS Media Group, pg 800

ARIZONA

Arizona Cine Equipment, pg 789
Crew West Inc, pg 839
Merestone, pg 938
Rodeo Video Inc, pg 998

CALIFORNIA

Aaron & Le Duc, pg 772
Aerial Video Systems, pg 778
Ametron Audio/Video, pg 785
Crash Video Productions, pg 837
Crystal Pyramid Productions™, pg 840
Digital Film Studios, pg 847
DTC Lighting & Grip, pg 853
Express Media Inc, pg 864
Gear Monkey, pg 876
Golden Gate Studios, pg 880
Illuminate Studios, pg 894
KTVU-Retail Services, pg 914
Lynch Communications, pg 926
Maximus Media Inc, pg 934
McCune Audio-Video-Lighting, pg 935
PSSI, pg 987
RetinaVision Productions, pg 995
Shoulder High Productions, pg 1009
SNAP, pg 1014
Twin Peaks Creative, pg 1047

COLORADO

Maniac Productions, pg 930
Open Media Foundation, pg 964

CONNECTICUT

Rockwell Communications Inc, pg 998

FLORIDA

Astoria Communications Inc, pg 792
Communications Concepts Inc (CCI), pg 833
Digital Comm Link Inc, pg 847
F&F Productions, pg 865
Jordan Klein Film & Video (JKFV), pg 906
National Teleproductions Inc, pg 953
Phat Planet Recording Studios, pg 973

GEORGIA

Convergent Media Systems, pg 836
Stage Front Presentation Systems, pg 1022
Studio Space Atlanta, pg 1027

VIDEO

Mobile Unit Rentals (continued)

ILLINOIS

Audio Visual Services Corp, pg 796
Big Shoulders Digital Video Productions, pg 807
Chicago Satellite & Video, pg 825
Corplex, pg 836
On Site Video, pg 963
PSAV® Presentation Services (Hotel Services Division), pg 987
QuickSet International Inc, pg 989
Trio Video, pg 1045

INDIANA

Midwest Uplink Inc, pg 942

IOWA

ECS Inc, pg 856

KENTUCKY

WKYT Productions, pg 1068

LOUISIANA

Digital FX Inc, pg 847
Moxie Media, pg 948
Pace Systems, pg 966
YES Productions, pg 1072

MARYLAND

CPR MultiMedia Solutions, pg 837
Sheffield Audio/Video Productions, pg 1008

MASSACHUSETTS

Goin' Mobile, pg 880
Red Sky Studios, pg 993

MICHIGAN

K&R All Media Productions Inc, pg 908
Lowing Light & Grip Inc, pg 925

MISSOURI

Southwest Audio-Visual Inc, pg 1019
Swank Audio Visuals, pg 1029

NEVADA

Lefco Video Services Inc, pg 918

NEW JERSEY

Ironbound Film & Television Studios LLC, pg 902
MediaMix Inc, pg 937
Vision Quest Productions Inc, pg 1058

NEW MEXICO

Production Outfitters, pg 984

NEW YORK

CP Communications, pg 837
Gearhead Rentals, pg 876
Manhattan Center Studios Inc, pg 930
MRG Productions Inc, pg 948
NBC Production Facilities, pg 953
PrimaLux Video Inc, pg 982
Scheimpflug Digital, pg 1004
Visual Technologies Corp, pg 1060
Visual Word Systems Inc, pg 1060
WNET/NET TELECON, pg 1069

NORTH CAROLINA

Bill Barnes Video Productions LLC, pg 803
On Location North Carolina, pg 963
Take One Productions Ltd, pg 1031

NORTH DAKOTA

Media Productions, pg 937

OHIO

Aztec Video Productions, pg 801
Image Video Teleproductions Inc, pg 895
Lyon Video Inc, pg 927
Mills James Productions, pg 943
OSV Studios, pg 966
Vista Color Imaging Inc, pg 1059

OREGON

Pacific Grip & Lighting Inc, pg 967
Picture This Production Services, pg 975

PENNSYLVANIA

Fusion Brand Experiences, pg 874
Innovision Media Group, pg 899
Liberty Uplink, pg 919
Upstage Video, pg 1050
Videosmith Inc, pg 1057
Viewpoint Production Services Inc, pg 1058
WPHL-TV, pg 1070

TENNESSEE

Russ Sturgeon Productions/RSVP, pg 1027

TEXAS

Countdown Productions Inc, pg 837
Earl Miller Productions Inc, pg 943
Muller Entertainment, pg 949
Omega Productions, pg 962
The Samuels Co, pg 1002
Stage Directions, pg 1022

VIRGINIA

Quince Imaging Inc, pg 989

WASHINGTON

Victory Studios, pg 1054

WISCONSIN

Logan Productions Inc, pg 924
Wisconsin Public Television, pg 1068

ALBERTA

Global Television, pg 879
Global Television Station, pg 879

BRITISH COLUMBIA

Image Media Farm, pg 895
Video In Studios/Video Out Distribution, pg 1055

Mobile Unit Repairs

CALIFORNIA

Ametron Audio/Video, pg 785
Mobilized Tech Systems, pg 944
Technical Services, pg 1034

FLORIDA

ELC Sales & Service Inc, pg 858

GEORGIA

Stage Front Presentation Systems, pg 1022

ILLINOIS

On Site Video, pg 963

IOWA

ECS Inc, pg 856

MICHIGAN

TeL Systems, pg 1035

MINNESOTA

Alpha Video & Audio Inc, pg 782

MISSOURI

Southwest Audio-Visual Inc, pg 1019

NEW YORK

MRG Productions Inc, pg 948
Visual Technologies Corp, pg 1060

TEXAS

Shook Mobile Technology LP, pg 1009
The Yesterday USA Radio Networks, pg 1072

UTAH

RIA Corp, pg 996

VIRGINIA

Quince Imaging Inc, pg 989

Monitor, *see* Video Receiver & Monitor

Music Scoring

ALABAMA

Airwave Recording Studio, pg 779
Sound of Birmingham Productions, pg 1017

ARIZONA

Creative Backstage, pg 838
Merestone, pg 938
Phoenix VideoFilms®, pg 974

ARKANSAS

Live'N'Loud, pg 923
White Diamond Productions, pg 1065

CALIFORNIA

AB Audio Visual Entertainment Inc, pg 772
Aliso Creek Productions Inc, pg 780
Ancient Future, pg 786
Argyle Post, pg 789
Berke Creative Inc, pg 805
Berkeley Sound Artists Inc, pg 805
CCI Digital, pg 821
Creative Media Recording, pg 838
Creative Support Services/CSS Music, pg 838
Crystal Pyramid Productions™, pg 840
Diamond Dreams Music Productions, pg 846
Digital Outpost, pg 847
Dogma Studios, pg 850
DreamWorks Animation SKG Inc, pg 852
Earwax Productions Inc, pg 855
4th Street Recording, pg 872
GrooveWorx, pg 882
Steven Halpern's Inner Peace Music, pg 884
iCorpTv, pg 893
JDS Video & Media Productions Inc, pg 904
Kaleidosound, pg 907
The Kitchen, pg 911
Lynch Communications, pg 926
Maximus Media Inc, pg 934
The Media Staff Inc, pg 937
Megatrax, pg 938
Mind Over Eye Inc, pg 943
The Music Kitchen Inc, pg 950
Joseph Nicoletti Consulting-Promotion/California International Records/Global Village Records, pg 957
OTR Studios, pg 966
Palardo Productions, pg 968
PM Productions, pg 977
Polarity Post Production, pg 978
Private Island Trax, pg 982
Pyramind Studios, pg 988
QRS Software Services, pg 988
Reality Check Systems, pg 992
Rhythms Productions (Tom Thumb Music), pg 996
Russ InVision Co/AbridgeClub.com, pg 1001
Sahara Records & Filmworks Entertainment Co, pg 1001
Saturn Studios, pg 1003
SBS Productions, pg 1003
Sonic Gravy, pg 1015
SonicPool, pg 1016
Sonora Recorders, pg 1016
Staylor-Made Communications Inc, pg 1024
Still N'Motion, pg 1025
Studio 132, pg 1027
Timeless Productions, pg 1040
Total Media Group, pg 1042
Videolady, pg 1057
West Coast Projections Inc, pg 1063

COLORADO

Tim Cissell Music, pg 828
Conly Productions, pg 835
Flashback Media Productions, pg 869
Los Angeles Post Music Inc, pg 924

CONNECTICUT

Applebox Studio, pg 788
Broadcast Video Productions LLC, pg 813
EagleVision Inc, pg 855
Fox Connecticut, pg 872
Guymark Studios LLC, pg 883
Music 2 Hues, pg 951
Palace Digital Studios, pg 967
P&P Studios Inc, pg 968

DELAWARE

Side Door Studio Inc, pg 1010

DISTRICT OF COLUMBIA

Interface Media Group, pg 900
Yellow Cat Productions Inc, pg 1072

FLORIDA

Allegro Productions Inc, pg 781
Audacity Creative, pg 793
Digital Video Arts, pg 848
Kat Epple Music Productions, pg 862
Ed Ethridge Productions Inc, pg 863
Gulf Coast Audio Visual Producers Inc, pg 883
Home Shopping Network (HSN), pg 890
Jordan Klein Film & Video (JKFV), pg 906
Mach 1 Productions, pg 927
Phat Planet Recording Studios, pg 973
Progressive Media & Music, pg 985
Promidi Music, pg 986
Sunfire Communications Inc, pg 1028
Mike Vasilinda Productions Inc, pg 1052

GEORGIA

Crawford Media Services, pg 838
First Cut Communications LLC, pg 868
Staging Directions Inc, pg 1023
White Dog Studios, pg 1065

HAWAII

Ken Herkes Productions & Entertainment (KHPE), pg 888
Media Bridge Gamekids, pg 936
TV Juice Productions Inc, pg 1046

ILLINOIS

ABS Enterprises, pg 772
CCore Media Inc, pg 821
Jim Passin Productions, pg 970
The Pepper Group, pg 972
Steven Samler Music & Sound, pg 1002
WEEK TV, pg 1063
Woodside Avenue Music Productions Inc, pg 1069

KANSAS

Chapman Recording & Mastering, pg 824

KENTUCKY

Broadway Digital, pg 813
Horizon Films & Media LLC, pg 891
The Media Collaboratory, pg 936

LOUISIANA

Digital FX Inc, pg 847
Vidox Motion Imagery, pg 1057

MARYLAND

CPR MultiMedia Solutions, pg 837
CSPMedia.com, pg 840
dbF a Media Company, pg 844
Kramer Communications Video Production, pg 913
Satellite Media Production, pg 1003

MASSACHUSETTS

CommCreative, pg 832
Continental Recordings Inc, pg 835
Cramer Productions, pg 837
Green Mountain Post Films (GMP), pg 882
Labrecque Creative Sound, pg 915
Northern Light Productions, pg 959
Penfield Productions Ltd, pg 971
Soundtrack Recording Studios, pg 1018
TR Productions, pg 1043
Veritech Corp, pg 1053

MICHIGAN

Digi Sign Design LLC, pg 847
GMP Music, pg 879
K&R's Recording Studios Inc, pg 908
Michigan Recording Arts Institute & Technologies, pg 941
RingSide Creative, pg 997
Studio A Recording Inc, pg 1026

MINNESOTA

The ADS Group, pg 777
Aggressive Records Audio Duplication LLC, pg 778
Beyers Sound & Essay Audio, pg 806
Media Loft Inc, pg 937
MultiMedia, pg 950

MISSOURI

Production Consultants, pg 984

MONTANA

Jereco Studios Inc, pg 905
North Country Media Group, pg 959

NEVADA

Aardvark Video & Media Productions, pg 772
Tanglewood Productions, pg 1031

NEW HAMPSHIRE

Channell One Video, pg 824
Chip Taylor Communications LLC, pg 1032

NEW JERSEY

Broadcast Center Studios, pg 813
CFP Video Productions Inc, pg 823
Color Leasing Studios, pg 831
Milgrom Productions, pg 943
NFL Films Inc, pg 957
NFL Films Music Library, pg 957
Bill Quinn Productions, pg 989
Richard Reiter Productions Inc, pg 994
Suede Interactive, pg 1027
TRF Production Music Libraries, pg 1044
VCSvideo, pg 1052
Video Corporation of America (VCA), pg 1055

NEW MEXICO

Production Outfitters, pg 984

NEW YORK

Air Sea Land Productions Inc (ASL), pg 779
Aural Gratification Inc, pg 796
aurora productions, pg 797
The Big House Group, pg 807
Chromavision Corp, pg 826
Fingerpaint, pg 868
Bob Gerardi Music Productions, pg 877
Hallel Communications, pg 884
Headroom Digital Audio, pg 887
Heavy Melody, pg 887
IAI Video, pg 893
Icontent, pg 893
Kamen Entertainment Group Inc, pg 908
KAS Music & Sound, pg 908
L&P Media, pg 915
Lylofilm Productions, pg 926
Manhattan Center Studios Inc, pg 930
Manhattan Production Music Inc, pg 930
Neal Marshad Productions, pg 931
Jack Morton Worldwide, pg 946
Mother West, pg 947
MRG Productions Inc, pg 948
New York Audio Productions, pg 956
Nutmeg Post, pg 960
Omnimusic, pg 962
Shelly Palmer Production, pg 968
Patco Resources Inc, pg 970
PostWorks, pg 979
PrimeLight Productions Inc, pg 982
Elliot Sokolov Music, pg 1015
Sony Music Entertainment, pg 1016
TBA Global Events, pg 1032
Teatown Communications Group, pg 1033
Tiki Recording Studios Inc, pg 1040
Zelman Studios Ltd, pg 1073

NORTH CAROLINA

Audio Art, pg 794
The Communications Group Inc, pg 833
Horizon Video Productions Inc, pg 891
Trailblazer Studios®, pg 1043
2BruceStudio, pg 1047

NORTH DAKOTA

Media Productions, pg 937

OHIO

Aztec Video Productions, pg 801
Challenge Productions, pg 823
Creative Technology, pg 838
EDR Media LLC, pg 857
MainSail Production Services Inc, pg 929
Mills James Productions, pg 943
Take 1 Media Services, pg 1031

OREGON

Odyssey Productions Inc, pg 961
Rex, pg 995

PENNSYLVANIA

BRg Music Works, pg 812
Dreambox Media Inc, pg 852
Robin Miller, Filmaker Inc, pg 943
Monster Tracks, pg 945
Production Masters Inc (PMI), pg 984
WPHL-TV, pg 1070

RHODE ISLAND

M-Audio, pg 927
Sound-FX-Design, pg 1017

TENNESSEE

American Blackguard Inc, pg 784
Fricon Entertainment Co Inc, pg 873
JamSync, pg 904
Motion Picture Services, pg 947
Scripps Networks, pg 1005
Stage Post, pg 1022

TEXAS

Audiomoxie®, pg 796
Communication Arts Multimedia Inc, pg 832
The Editing Co, pg 857
Harbor House Studios, pg 884
Horizon Film + Video Productions, pg 891
McNee Productions Inc, pg 935
Mediaforce Productions, pg 937
Phillips MediaSource, pg 974
Reelsound Recording Co, pg 994
The Samuels Co, pg 1002
The Sound Lab Inc, pg 1017
Stage Directions, pg 1022
TM Studios Inc, pg 1041
Tropikal Productions, pg 1045

UTAH

Soularium Recording Studios, pg 1016

VERMONT

University of Vermont, Instructional Television Dept, pg 1050

VIRGINIA

BES Studios, pg 805
Studio Center Corp, pg 1026

WASHINGTON

Inland Audio Visual Co, pg 898
Kostov Productions, pg 913
North-by-Northwest Productions, pg 958
Sound Sound/Savage Fruitarian Productions, pg 1017
Victory Studios, pg 1054

WISCONSIN

Audio Visual of Milwaukee Inc, pg 795
5th Floor Recording Co, pg 867
Media Communications Association-International (MCA-I), pg 936
USAV Group Inc, pg 1050

WYOMING

Bridger Productions Inc, pg 812

BRITISH COLUMBIA

Pinewood Sound, pg 975

MANITOBA

daCapo Productions, pg 842
Spectra Video Productions Ltd, pg 1020

NEWFOUNDLAND AND LABRADOR

Vidcraft Productions Ltd, pg 1054

ONTARIO

ADS Media, pg 777
GAPC (General Assembly Production Centre), pg 875
Metalworks Recording Studios Inc, pg 939
Nightingale Music Productions Inc, pg 957
Purefire Communications Inc, pg 987

VIDEO

Music Videos

ALABAMA

Diamond Studios, pg 846

ARIZONA

Arizona Virtual Studios, pg 790
Creative Backstage, pg 838
Film Creations Ltd, pg 867
Illuma Studios, pg 894
Merestone, pg 938
Phoenix VideoFilms®, pg 974

ARKANSAS

Cedar Crest Studio, pg 822
Live'N'Loud, pg 923
Shadowbox Video Productions, pg 1007
White Diamond Productions, pg 1065

CALIFORNIA

A Go Go Films, pg 771
AB Audio Visual Entertainment Inc, pg 772
Access Video in Berkeley, pg 773
All Video Productions, pg 781
Artichoke Productions, pg 791
Automated Entertainment, pg 797
Backstage Pass Entertainment Inc, pg 801
Barber Tech Video Products, pg 802
Barbosa Video Services, pg 802
Big Door, pg 807
Blueyed Pictures Inc, pg 810
Cherry Multimedia, pg 824
Concrete Images, pg 835
Crystal Pyramid Productions™, pg 840
Custom Video Productions Inc, pg 841
deKramer Productions Inc, pg 845
Diamond Dreams Music Productions, pg 846
Direct Images Interactive Inc, pg 848
Earwax Productions Inc, pg 855
First Camera, pg 868
First Person™, pg 868
Full Moon & High Tide Productions & Studios, pg 874
FXF Productions Inc, pg 874
Gold Standard Productions, pg 880
Bruce Goldberg Inc, pg 880
GrooveWorx, pg 882
Steven Halpern's Inner Peace Music, pg 884
iCorpTv, pg 893
JDS Video & Media Productions Inc, pg 904
KION-TV, pg 911
KVIE-Channel 6, pg 914
Laser Magic Productions, pg 916
Ludlow Media Solutions, pg 926
Lynch Communications, pg 926
Maximus Media Inc, pg 934
Media Magic, pg 937
Method Studios, pg 939
Mind Over Eye Inc, pg 943
New & Unique Videos™, pg 955
Joseph Nicoletti Consulting-Promotion/California International Records/Global Village Records, pg 957
On-Trax Inc, pg 963
OTR Studios, pg 966
Palardo Productions, pg 968
Playback Recording Studio, pg 977
PM Productions, pg 977
QRS Software Services, pg 988
Regent Press Publishers & Printers, pg 994
RetinaVision Productions, pg 995
Sahara Records & Filmworks Entertainment Co, pg 1001
Saturn Studios, pg 1003
Shapeshifter, pg 1008
SNAP, pg 1014
SonicPool, pg 1016
Sonora Recorders, pg 1016
Staylor-Made Communications Inc, pg 1024
Still N'Motion, pg 1025
Tam Communications Inc, pg 1031
Tigar Hare Studios, pg 1040
Toon Makers, pg 1042
Total Media Group, pg 1042
Tranquil Technology Music, pg 1043
Twin Peaks Creative, pg 1047
Two Door Productions, pg 1047
Universal Studios, pg 1049
Videolady, pg 1057
WARPed Pictures, pg 1062
Wavemaker Media Design, pg 1062
Z-Ville Productions, pg 1073

COLORADO

Conly Productions, pg 835
Denver Media Center, pg 845
Flashback Media Productions, pg 869
Full Spectrum Arts & Services, pg 874
Open Media Foundation, pg 964
Rocky Mountain Audio/Video Productions Inc, pg 998
Side 3 Studios, pg 1010

CONNECTICUT

Applebox Studio, pg 788
Broadcast Video Productions LLC, pg 813
Digital Video Productions, pg 848
Fox Connecticut, pg 872
The Gary-Paul Agency, pg 875
Ironik Design & Post, pg 902
MAVCO, pg 934
MCC Films, pg 935
New London Media, pg 956
P&P Studios Inc, pg 968

DISTRICT OF COLUMBIA

Interface Media Group, pg 900
Metro Teleproductions Inc (MTI), pg 939

FLORIDA

Allegro Productions Inc, pg 781
Audio Visual Imagineering Inc, pg 795
Big Byte Video Productions, pg 806
Chatterbox Productions Inc, pg 824
Cinema East, pg 827
Cinema Entertainment Inc, pg 827
Civins Productions Inc, pg 828
Steven Cohen Motion Picture Production, pg 831
Communications Concepts Inc (CCI), pg 833
Courter Films LLC, pg 837
Kat Epple Music Productions, pg 862
Ed Ethridge Productions Inc, pg 863
Harmon's Audio-Visual Services, pg 885
Home Shopping Network (HSN), pg 890
Media Concepts Inc, pg 936
Olympusat Entertainment, pg 962
Parallax Productions Inc, pg 969
Progressive Media & Music, pg 985
SOS Worldwide Productions Inc, pg 1016
Sunfire Communications Inc, pg 1028
Tricycle Studios, pg 1044
Universal Studios Florida® Production Group, pg 1049
Mike Vasilinda Productions Inc, pg 1052
Venice Media Group, pg 1052
Vistamax Productions, pg 1059

GEORGIA

Beachwood Productions, pg 804
Beast Atlanta, pg 804
COMPRO Productions Inc, pg 834
Continental Film & Video, pg 835
The DVI Group, pg 854
ECG Productions, pg 856
Guerrilla Productions LLC, pg 883
Myriad Productions, pg 951
On-Line Productions, pg 963

HAWAII

Ken Herkes Productions & Entertainment (KHPE), pg 888
Hyperspective Studios Inc, pg 893
Media Bridge Gamekids, pg 936
Sight & Sound Studios, pg 1010
1013 Integrated, pg 1037
TV Juice Productions Inc, pg 1046

IDAHO

Wide Eye Productions, pg 1066

ILLINOIS

ABSA Productions Inc, pg 772
AnswersMedia, pg 787
CCore Media Inc, pg 821
The Chicago Production Center, pg 825
IV Media Resources, pg 903
Optimus, pg 964
Paragon Studios Inc, pg 969
The Pepper Group, pg 972
Richter Studios, pg 996
Steven Samler Music & Sound, pg 1002
SCI Television Productions LLC, pg 1004
20/20 Communications Inc, pg 1047
Video Impressions, pg 1055
Winter Productions, pg 1068
Woodside Avenue Music Productions Inc, pg 1069

INDIANA

AVA Productions, pg 798
Covenant Productions®, pg 837
Digital Rain LLC, pg 847
Explore Media LLC, pg 864
PentaVision Communications Inc, pg 972

KANSAS

Chapman Recording & Mastering, pg 824

KENTUCKY

Hammond Communications Group, pg 884
Idle Minds Productions Inc, pg 894
The Media Collaboratory, pg 936
The PPS Group, pg 980
Prosper Media Group Inc, pg 986

LOUISIANA

Digital FX Inc, pg 847
Moxie Media, pg 948
Vidox Motion Imagery, pg 1057
YES Productions, pg 1072

MARYLAND

Adventure Productions LLC, pg 778
CPR MultiMedia Solutions, pg 837
dbF a Media Company, pg 844
Kramer Communications Video Production, pg 913
Shadowstone R & R™, pg 1008

MASSACHUSETTS

Extreme Reach Inc, pg 864
Green Mountain Post Films (GMP), pg 882
Home Inc, pg 890
Penfield Productions Ltd, pg 971
Sound & Vision Media, pg 1017
Soundtrack Recording Studios, pg 1018
TVN-The Video Network, pg 1046
Veritech Corp, pg 1053

MICHIGAN

Digi Sign Design LLC, pg 847
Digital Image Studios LLC, pg 847
K&R's Recording Studios Inc, pg 908
Michigan Recording Arts Institute & Technologies, pg 941
On Stage Visuals, pg 963

MINNESOTA

Aggressive Records Audio Duplication LLC, pg 778
Big Event Productions LLC, pg 807
Jamieson & Associates Inc, pg 904
Master Communications Group, pg 933

MISSOURI

Avatar Studios, pg 798
Production Consultants, pg 984
Studio Worx Inc, pg 1027

MONTANA

Jereco Studios Inc, pg 905
KCFW Television, pg 908
North Country Media Group, pg 959
ooLite Media, pg 964

NEVADA

Aardvark Video & Media Productions, pg 772
DVDs4Less, pg 854
HDTV Productions Inc, pg 886
JCS Video Productions, pg 904
Lefco Video Services Inc, pg 918
Tanglewood Productions, pg 1031

NEW HAMPSHIRE

Channell One Video, pg 824
Chip Taylor Communications LLC, pg 1032

NEW JERSEY

All Jersey Studios, pg 780
Broadcast Center Studios, pg 813
CFP Video Productions Inc, pg 823
MediaMix Inc, pg 937
MediaNow, pg 938
Megavideo Productions, pg 938
NFL Films Inc, pg 957
Optisonics Productions, pg 965

Public Eye Productions, pg 987
Bill Quinn Productions, pg 989
Richard Reiter Productions Inc, pg 994
Suede Interactive, pg 1027
VCSvideo, pg 1052
Video Corporation of America (VCA), pg 1055

NEW MEXICO

Production Outfitters, pg 984

NEW YORK

Air Sea Land Productions Inc (ASL), pg 779
aurora productions, pg 797
Bevilacqua Studios, pg 806
Big Foot Productions Inc, pg 807
The Big House Group, pg 807
Brooklyn Films, pg 814
Chromavision Corp, pg 826
CPdigital, pg 837
Design Audio Visual Inc, pg 845
Designomotion, pg 846
Devlin Video International, pg 846
Digital Art Video Inc, pg 847
dM works, pg 849
East of Hollywood NY, pg 855
Eastco Multimedia Solutions Inc, pg 856
Hello World Communications, pg 888
IAI Video, pg 893
Icontent, pg 893
Kamen Entertainment Group Inc, pg 908
Long Island Video Enterprises Live Inc, pg 924
Lylofilm Productions, pg 926
Magnetic Music Publishing Co, pg 928
Manhattan Center Studios Inc, pg 930
Neal Marshad Productions, pg 931
Mood Creations Ltd, pg 946
New Horizon Studios, pg 955
Nutmeg Post, pg 960
Shelly Palmer Production, pg 968
Peckham Productions Inc, pg 970
Pennebaker Hegedus Films Inc, pg 972
Shadow Pictures Inc, pg 1007
Elliot Sokolov Music, pg 1015
Sony Music Entertainment, pg 1016
Teatown Communications Group, pg 1033
Tiki Recording Studios Inc, pg 1040
Tobin Productions Inc, pg 1041
USA Studios, pg 1050
VIEW Inc (Video International Entertainment World Inc), pg 1058
Zelman Studios Ltd, pg 1073

NORTH CAROLINA

All Pro Media Inc, pg 780
Pat Appleson Studios Inc, pg 788
Bill Barnes Video Productions LLC, pg 803
The Communications Group Inc, pg 833
Crystal Pictures Inc, pg 840
Duke Media Services, pg 853
LCW Productions LLC, pg 917
Moving Pictures, pg 948
NASCAR Media Group LLC, pg 952
On Location North Carolina, pg 963
Take One Productions Ltd, pg 1031

NORTH DAKOTA

Media Productions, pg 937

OHIO

Advent Media Inc, pg 778
Aztec Video Productions, pg 801
Challenge Productions, pg 823
Creative Technology, pg 838
Lyon Video Inc, pg 927
Mills James Productions, pg 943
R&B Communications Inc, pg 991
Take 1 Media Services, pg 1031
VGI Productions, pg 1053
Vista Color Imaging Inc, pg 1059

OREGON

KPDX-TV Production Center, pg 913
Rex, pg 995
Wilderness Video, pg 1066

PENNSYLVANIA

Bang Pictures, pg 802
Center City Film & Video Inc, pg 822
Dreambox Media Inc, pg 852
FMP Media Solutions Inc, pg 870
Fusion Brand Experiences, pg 874
Kensington Falls Animation, pg 909
Visual Sound Inc, pg 1059
WHYY Inc, pg 1066

RHODE ISLAND

Sound-FX-Design, pg 1017

SOUTH CAROLINA

Genesis Creative, pg 877
Stages Video Productions, pg 1023
Venture Media, pg 1052

TENNESSEE

Fricon Entertainment Co Inc, pg 873
Griffith Productions, pg 882
Love Shack Recording Studios, pg 925
Motion Picture Services, pg 947
SmackDab Media, pg 1013
Stage Post, pg 1022
WKPT-TV, pg 1068
Zion Music Group, pg 1074

TEXAS

Astro Audio Visual, pg 792
Biway Media, pg 808
Cerutti Productions Inc, pg 823
Communication Arts Multimedia Inc, pg 832
The Editing Co, pg 857
Epic Software Group Inc, pg 862
Eyecon Video Productions, pg 865
Harbor House Studios, pg 884
Horizon Film + Video Productions, pg 891
Maverick Video Productions, pg 934
McNee Productions Inc, pg 935
Mediaforce Productions, pg 937
Earl Miller Productions Inc, pg 943
Muller Entertainment, pg 949
Out of the BLUE Media, pg 966
Phil Lights, pg 973
Phillips MediaSource, pg 974
R&O Studios, pg 991
RuffHouse LLC, pg 1000
The Samuels Co, pg 1002
Sound Works, pg 1018
South Coast Film & Video, pg 1019
TopCat Records LLC, pg 1042

UTAH

ImageWorks Communications, pg 896

VIRGINIA

BES Studios, pg 805
CACI Productions Group, pg 816
Creative Video of Washington Inc, pg 839
Goose Creek Music & Entertainment, pg 880
Henninger Media Services, pg 888
Limelight Communications Inc, pg 921
Rocktown Media, pg 998

WASHINGTON

Bennett-Watt HD Productions Inc, pg 805
North-by-Northwest Productions, pg 958
Victory Studios, pg 1054

WEST VIRGINIA

Blackwater Video Productions, pg 808
Sweetsong Productions, pg 1029

WISCONSIN

Audio Visual of Milwaukee Inc, pg 795
Concept Productions Inc, pg 834
Meridian Studios, pg 939
Midland Video Productions Inc, pg 942
TBC Studios, pg 1033
USAV Group Inc, pg 1050
Video Wisconsin Inc, pg 1056
Wisconsin Public Television, pg 1068

WYOMING

Bridger Productions Inc, pg 812

ALBERTA

Black Media Works, pg 808
Global Television Station, pg 879

BRITISH COLUMBIA

Finale Editworks, pg 868
Pinewood Sound, pg 975
Triad Communications Ltd, pg 1044
24 Frames Film & Video, pg 1047

MANITOBA

Spectra Video Productions Ltd, pg 1020

ONTARIO

ADS Media, pg 777
GAPC (General Assembly Production Centre), pg 875
Image Video Services & Productions, pg 895
JFB Communications, pg 905
Legendary Entertainment, pg 918
Marblemedia, pg 930
Metalworks Recording Studios Inc, pg 939
Purefire Communications Inc, pg 987
Spence-Thomas Audio Post, pg 1021
Video Excellence Productions, pg 1055

QUEBEC

Trebas Institute, pg 1044

Optical Effects, *see* Special Effects

Packaging & Storage—Cassette & Disc Distributors

ARIZONA

Troxell Communications Inc, pg 1045

ARKANSAS

White Diamond Productions, pg 1065

CALIFORNIA

Adolph Gasser Inc, pg 776
Ametron Audio/Video, pg 785
Audio/Video Supply Inc, pg 795
Christy's Editorial, pg 826
VMI Inc, pg 1060

COLORADO

Case Logic Inc, pg 820
ProLine Digital, pg 986
Rose Packaging & Design Inc, pg 999
Stanco Sales LLC, pg 1023

FLORIDA

Digital Video Systems Inc, pg 848
Gulf Coast Audio Visual Producers Inc, pg 883
Media Concepts Inc, pg 936
Midtown Video Inc, pg 942
Photomart Cine-Video Inc, pg 975
Recording Media & Equipment Inc (RM&E), pg 993

GEORGIA

Blue Media Supply Inc, pg 809
Stage Front Presentation Systems, pg 1022

ILLINOIS

LKG Industries Inc, pg 923
Magnetic Shield Corp, pg 928
Polyline LLC, pg 978

INDIANA

Crystal Clear Media Group, pg 840
Lee Co Inc, pg 918
Sensory Technologies LLC, pg 1006

KANSAS

Smith Audio-Visual Inc, pg 1014

KENTUCKY

American Recordable Media, pg 785
NOR-COM Inc, pg 958

MARYLAND

Ever-Ready Media Packaging, pg 863
Kipp Visual Systems Inc, pg 911
Professional Label Inc, pg 985

MASSACHUSETTS

Rule Broadcast Systems, pg 1000

VIDEO

Packaging & Storage—Cassette & Disc Distributors (continued)

MINNESOTA

Alpha Video & Audio Inc, pg 782

MISSOURI

Audio-VideoGraphics Inc, pg 795
Conference Technologies Inc, pg 835
Modern Communications Inc, pg 944
Southwest Audio-Visual Inc, pg 1019

NEW JERSEY

AV Bluebook, pg 797
Hannecke Display Systems Inc, pg 884
National Audio-Visual Supply, pg 952

NEW YORK

Century Business Solutions, pg 823
Eastco Multimedia Solutions Inc, pg 856
Gaylord Brothers, pg 876
HAVE Inc, pg 886
A Liss & Co, pg 922
Long Island Video Enterprises Live Inc, pg 924
Magnaplan Corp, pg 928
Markertek Video Supply, pg 931
Sentry Industries Inc, pg 1007
Technisphere Corp, pg 1034
TecNec Distributing, pg 1035

OHIO

Promedia Digital, pg 986
Univenture Inc, pg 1049

OKLAHOMA

Piper Media Services Inc, pg 976

PENNSYLVANIA

Advanced AV, pg 777
Bernie's Photo Center, pg 805
Brodart Co, pg 813
Electron Microscopy Sciences (EMS), pg 859
Morefield Communications Inc, pg 946
Visual Sound Inc, pg 1059

TENNESSEE

Lowrance Sound Co Inc, pg 925

TEXAS

Heffernan Audio Visual, pg 887

UTAH

RIA Corp, pg 996

VIRGINIA

Cybernetics, pg 841
Filmdex Inc, pg 867
Furnace MFG, pg 874
Lee Hartman & Sons Inc, pg 918

WISCONSIN

Camera Corner Connecting Point, pg 818
Full Compass Systems, pg 874

BRITISH COLUMBIA

Finale Editworks, pg 868
Triad Communications Ltd, pg 1044

ONTARIO

HD Source, pg 886
Premier A/V Sales Ltd, pg 980

Packaging & Storage—Cassette & Disc Manufacturers

CALIFORNIA

El Mar Plastics Inc, pg 858
iQstor Networks Inc, pg 902
SF Global Sourcing, pg 1007
Tasman Group Pacific Rim, pg 1032

COLORADO

ProLine Digital, pg 986
Rose Packaging & Design Inc, pg 999

FLORIDA

Viking Cases, pg 1058
VIP Presentation Products, pg 1058

ILLINOIS

Flight Form Cases Inc, pg 870
Magnetic Shield Corp, pg 928

INDIANA

Star Case Manufacturing Co Inc, pg 1023

MARYLAND

Ever-Ready Media Packaging, pg 863
Professional Label Inc, pg 985

MICHIGAN

Brilliance Audio, pg 812

MINNESOTA

Sunrise Packaging Inc, pg 1028
Winsted Corp, pg 1068

NEW JERSEY

Hannecke Display Systems Inc, pg 884
Reed Presentations Inc (RPI), pg 993

NEW YORK

Century Business Solutions, pg 823

OHIO

Univenture Inc, pg 1049

PENNSYLVANIA

American Thermoplastic Co, pg 785
Electron Microscopy Sciences (EMS), pg 859
Sandusky Lee Corp, pg 1002

WISCONSIN

Bardes Products Inc, pg 803
Full Compass Systems, pg 874

ONTARIO

Can-Am Merchandising Systems, pg 818

Packaging & Storage—Cassette & Disc Rentals

CALIFORNIA

Express Media Inc, pg 864

NORTH CAROLINA

Take One Productions Ltd, pg 1031

Packaging & Storage—Cassette & Disc Repairs

MICHIGAN

TeL Systems, pg 1035

Photography—Aerial

ALABAMA

Diamond Studios, pg 846

ARIZONA

Direct Current Video Productions, pg 848
Fox 10 Productions (KSAZ-TV), pg 872
Merestone, pg 938
Phoenix VideoFilms®, pg 974
Video Media Productions (VMP), pg 1055

ARKANSAS

Live'N'Loud, pg 923
Shadowbox Video Productions, pg 1007
White Diamond Productions, pg 1065

CALIFORNIA

Aaron & Le Duc, pg 772
Action Sports/All Stock, pg 775
Aerial Video Systems, pg 778
All Video Productions, pg 781
Celebrity Helicopters Inc, pg 822
Classic Images, pg 829
Concrete Images, pg 835
Crystal Pyramid Productions™, pg 840
Custom Video Productions Inc, pg 841
Dolphin MultiMedia Inc, pg 850
First Camera, pg 868
FXF Productions Inc, pg 874
Global Village Productions, pg 879
Global Village Stock Footage Library, pg 879
Goal Productions, pg 879
Gold Standard Productions, pg 880
iCorpTv, pg 893
Image Integration, pg 895
Indie Aerials, pg 897
JDS Video & Media Productions Inc, pg 904
KION-TV, pg 911
KTVU-Retail Services, pg 914
Maximus Media Inc, pg 934
Media Magic, pg 937
New & Unique Videos™, pg 955
Panorama Productions, pg 968
Point of View Productions, pg 977
PSI Inc, pg 987
QRS Software Services, pg 988
Dick Reizner Film & Video, pg 994
RetinaVision Productions, pg 995
SpaceCam, pg 1019
StereoScope International, pg 1024
Stunt Wings Adventure Sports Talent & Equipment, pg 1027
30 Second Films, pg 1039
Total Media Group, pg 1042
Towards 2000 Inc, pg 1043
Twin Peaks Creative, pg 1047
Two Door Productions, pg 1047
Tyler Camera Systems, pg 1047
Vineyard Productions, pg 1058
WARPed Pictures, pg 1062
West Coast Projections Inc, pg 1063

COLORADO

Aerial Imaging Productions, pg 778
Flashback Media Productions, pg 869
Greg Hensley Productions, pg 888
Rocky Mountain Audio/Video Productions Inc, pg 998
Tatum Video, pg 1032
Transtar Entertainment Co Inc, pg 1043

CONNECTICUT

Applebox Studio, pg 788
BRB Audiovisual Productions, pg 812
Broadcast Video Productions LLC, pg 813
MAVCO, pg 934

FLORIDA

America By Air Stock Footage Library, pg 783
Cinema East, pg 827
Civins Productions Inc, pg 828
Steven Cohen Motion Picture Production, pg 831
Communications Concepts Inc (CCI), pg 833
Courter Films LLC, pg 837
Eastern Video, pg 856
Fiddler Films, pg 866
Glanz Technologies Inc, pg 878
Home Shopping Network (HSN), pg 890
Jordan Klein Film & Video (JKFV), pg 906
Norman Kent Productions, pg 909
Knowles Video Inc (KVI), pg 912
Midtown Video Inc, pg 942
National Teleproductions Inc, pg 953
Paradise Video & Film, pg 969
Parallax Productions Inc, pg 969
Roger Scruggs Films, pg 1005
Shooting Stars Post Inc, pg 1009
Sunfire Communications Inc, pg 1028
Sunrise Studios, pg 1028
Universal Studios Florida® Production Group, pg 1049
Mike Vasilinda Productions Inc, pg 1052
Venice Media Group, pg 1052
Video Techniques Inc, pg 1056

GEORGIA

Beachwood Productions, pg 804
COMPRO Productions Inc, pg 834
Continental Film & Video, pg 835
ECG Productions, pg 856
Guerrilla Productions LLC, pg 883

VIDEO

Photography—Location

ALABAMA

ALASKA

ARIZONA

ARKANSAS

CALIFORNIA

COLORADO

CONNECTICUT

DISTRICT OF COLUMBIA

FLORIDA

GEORGIA

HAWAII

IDAHO

ILLINOIS

INDIANA

IOWA

KANSAS

KENTUCKY

LOUISIANA

MAINE

Maine Imaging, pg 929
WGME-TV, pg 1065

MARYLAND

Absolute Hollywood, pg 772
Adventure Productions LLC, pg 778
The Ahern Group, pg 779
CAS Video Productions, pg 820
Richard Chisolm Cinematography, pg 825
CPR MultiMedia Solutions, pg 837
dbF a Media Company, pg 844
DBM Communications Inc, pg 844
Kramer Communications Video Production, pg 913
Library Video Network (LVN), pg 920
Media Dimensions Inc, pg 936
Producers Video, pg 984
Quality Film & Video, pg 988
Sheffield Audio/Video Productions, pg 1008
Spectrum Productions, pg 1021

MASSACHUSETTS

Award Productions, pg 800
Capron Lighting & Sound Co Inc, pg 819
CommCreative, pg 832
Documentary Educational Resources Inc, pg 850
Emergency Film Group, pg 860
Green Mountain Post Films (GMP), pg 882
Heliotrope Studios, pg 887
In the Wild Productions, pg 897
Monadnock Media Inc, pg 945
Northern Light Productions, pg 959
Small Planet Communications Inc, pg 1013
TR Productions, pg 1043
TVN-The Video Network, pg 1046
VideoLink Inc, pg 1057

MICHIGAN

Digi Sign Design LLC, pg 847
K&R's Recording Studios Inc, pg 908
Maritz Performance Improvement Co, pg 931
The Program Source International, pg 985

MINNESOTA

Aggressive Records Audio Duplication LLC, pg 778
Badiyan Inc, pg 801
Big Event Productions LLC, pg 807
The Richard Diercks Co Inc, pg 846
House of Cinemagraphics, pg 891
Master Communications Group, pg 933
Media Loft Inc, pg 937
MultiMedia, pg 950
Rum Jungle Media, pg 1000
Worthwhile Films, pg 1070

MISSOURI

Avatar Studios, pg 798
Hardcastle Films & Video, pg 885
Visionworks Design Services Inc, pg 1059

MONTANA

KCFW Television, pg 908
North Country Media Group, pg 959

NEBRASKA

B & B Video Productions Inc, pg 801
Rainbow Video Productions Inc, pg 991
Three Pillars Media, pg 1040

NEVADA

Aardvark Video & Media Productions, pg 772
DVDs4Less, pg 854
HDTV Productions Inc, pg 886
JCS Video Productions, pg 904

NEW HAMPSHIRE

Apertura, pg 788
NH Movies Inc, pg 957
Chip Taylor Communications LLC, pg 1032

NEW JERSEY

All Jersey Studios, pg 780
Broadcast Center Studios, pg 813
CFP Video Productions Inc, pg 823
Color Leasing Studios, pg 831
DWJ Television, pg 854
Early Films, pg 855
Euro-Pacific Film & Video Productions Inc, pg 863
Laurel Video Productions, pg 916
MediaMix Inc, pg 937
MIB Mediaworks, pg 941
Midnight Media Group Inc, pg 942
NFL Films Inc, pg 957
Producer East Productions, pg 983
Public Eye Productions, pg 987
Bill Quinn Productions, pg 989
Suede Interactive, pg 1027
Telequest Inc, pg 1036
VCSvideo, pg 1052

NEW MEXICO

Production Outfitters, pg 984

NEW YORK

aurora productions, pg 797
BC Video Inc, pg 803
Big Film Design, pg 807
The Big House Group, pg 807
Brian Film Productions LLC, pg 812
Broad Street Inc, pg 812
Chromavision Corp, pg 826
Cohn Creative Group LLC, pg 831
Debbie Regan Locations Ltd, pg 844
Digital Art Video Inc, pg 847
dM works, pg 849
Douglas House Inc, pg 851
4-D Creative Media, pg 871
Golden Lamb Productions, pg 880
Greyfalcon House, pg 882
Gurrilla Video Solutions, pg 883
Hallel Communications, pg 884
HB-Content, pg 886
Icontent, pg 893
Image Makers of Pittsford/Image Maker Productions, pg 895
Ketchum Pleon Change, pg 910
L A Bruell Inc, pg 914
La Paloma Films, pg 915
L&P Media, pg 915
Long Island Video Enterprises Live Inc, pg 924
Neal Marshad Productions, pg 931
Mood Creations Ltd, pg 946
Jack Morton Worldwide, pg 946
The Napoleon Group, pg 952
New Horizon Studios, pg 955
News Broadcast Network, pg 956
Peckham Productions Inc, pg 970
PrimaLux Video Inc, pg 982
PrimeLight Productions Inc, pg 982
SmartPros Ltd, pg 1014
Synaptic Digital, pg 1030
TBA Global Events, pg 1032
TeleTime Productions, pg 1036
Videograf, pg 1057
Visual Technologies Corp, pg 1060
Zelman Studios Ltd, pg 1073

NORTH CAROLINA

All Pro Media Inc, pg 780
Pat Appleson Studios Inc, pg 788
J Arnold Productions Inc, pg 790
Bill Barnes Video Productions LLC, pg 803
The Communications Group Inc, pg 833
Duke Media Services, pg 853
Franklin Video Inc, pg 872
Horizon Video Productions Inc, pg 891
Image Associates Inc, pg 894
Kino Mountain Productions LLC, pg 911
LCW Productions LLC, pg 917
Moving Pictures, pg 948
NASCAR Media Group LLC, pg 952
On Location North Carolina, pg 963
Take One Productions Ltd, pg 1031
Trailblazer Studios®, pg 1043
Unifour Productions Inc, pg 1048

NORTH DAKOTA

Media Productions, pg 937

OHIO

Advent Media Inc, pg 778
Aztec Video Productions, pg 801
Russ Beckner Pictures, pg 804
Challenge Productions, pg 823
Cinecraft Productions Inc, pg 827
Commercial Video, pg 832
Creative Technology, pg 838
Cuyahoga Community College Media Center, pg 841
Lyon Video Inc, pg 927
Maslowski Productions, pg 933
Mills James Productions, pg 943
Take 1 Media Services, pg 1031
Treehaus Communications Inc, pg 1044
Ungar Video & Film, pg 1048
VGI Productions, pg 1053

OKLAHOMA

Garman Productions LLC, pg 875
Institute for Teaching & Learning Excellence (ITLE), pg 899
PDC Productions, pg 970
Smart Concepts Ltd, pg 1013
University of Oklahoma Academic Media & Digital Services, pg 1050

OREGON

A KTVA Production LLC, pg 771
Creative Media Development, pg 838
KVAL, pg 914
MediaFX, pg 937
Odyssey Productions Inc, pg 961
Wilderness Video, pg 1066

PENNSYLVANIA

Argentine Productions Inc, pg 789
Audio Visions Inc, pg 795
Bang Pictures, pg 802
Beholder Productions Inc, pg 804
Center City Film & Video Inc, pg 822
FMP Media Solutions Inc, pg 870
Goodman Associates Inc, pg 880
Innovision Media Group, pg 899
JPL, pg 906
Main Point Productions, pg 929
Panta Rhei Media Inc, pg 968
Pemcor LLC, pg 971
Production Masters Inc (PMI), pg 984
Video Communication Productions Inc, pg 1054
The Videohouse Inc, pg 1057

SOUTH CAROLINA

Genesis Creative, pg 877
Venture Media, pg 1052

TENNESSEE

Jaguar Productions, pg 903
Marine Geographic, pg 931
Motion Picture Services, pg 947
Paradigm Marketing & Creative, pg 969
Phoenix Aerial Photography Inc, pg 974
Running Pony Productions LLC, pg 1000
Scripps Networks, pg 1005
Stage Post, pg 1022
UMCom Productions, pg 1048
WKPT-TV, pg 1068

TEXAS

Alpha Video Productions, pg 782
AMS Pictures, pg 786
Best Film & Video, pg 805
Castleview Productions, pg 821
Cerutti Productions Inc, pg 823
Communication Arts Multimedia Inc, pg 832
Countdown Productions Inc, pg 837
Epic Software Group Inc, pg 862
First Group Communications Inc, pg 868
Paul Flanagan Productions, pg 869
Horizon Film + Video Productions, pg 891
Inferno Films, pg 898
Marx InDigital, pg 933
Maverick Video Productions, pg 934
McNee Productions Inc, pg 935
Mediaforce Productions, pg 937
Earl Miller Productions Inc, pg 943
Julye Newlin Productions Inc, pg 956
Out of the BLUE Media, pg 966
Phil Lights, pg 973
Phillips MediaSource, pg 974
Prairie Pictures Film & Video, pg 980
The Samuels Co, pg 1002
South Coast Film & Video, pg 1019
South Trunk Studios, pg 1019
Stage Directions, pg 1022
Tecfilms Inc, pg 1033
Texas Heart Institute Visual Communication Services, pg 1037
Video Perspective, pg 1056

UTAH

ImageWorks Communications, pg 896

VERMONT

Marlboro Film & Video Productions, pg 931
Wilson McLeran Inc, pg 1067

VIDEO

Photography—Location (continued)

VIRGINIA

Advance Concepts Inc, pg 777
BES Studios, pg 805
CACI Productions Group, pg 816
CALIBRE, pg 816
D&B Television & Video Productions Inc, pg 842
Limelight Communications Inc, pg 921
Metro Productions, pg 939
Rocktown Media, pg 998

WASHINGTON

Bennett-Watt HD Productions Inc, pg 805
Global Net Productions Inc, pg 879
Hamilton Studio, pg 884
Kostov Productions, pg 913
North-by-Northwest Productions, pg 958
Oppenheimer Camera Products, pg 964
Pal Productions Inc, pg 967
Victory Studios, pg 1054
White Rain Films Ltd, pg 1065

WEST VIRGINIA

Blackwater Video Productions, pg 808
MotionMasters, pg 947
WSAZ-TV 3/WSAZ Productions, pg 1070

WISCONSIN

AVS Group, pg 800
Logan Productions Inc, pg 924
Media Communications Association-International (MCA-I), pg 936
Meridian Studios, pg 939
Midland Video Productions Inc, pg 942
University of Wisconsin-Oshkosh Radio-TV-Film Dept, pg 1050
USAV Group Inc, pg 1050
Video Wisconsin Inc, pg 1056
Watts Communications Inc, pg 1062
Wisconsin Public Television, pg 1068

WYOMING

Bridger Productions Inc, pg 812

PUERTO RICO

Stage Crew Audiovisual Inc, pg 1022

ALBERTA

Black Media Works, pg 808
Global Television, pg 879
Global Television Station, pg 879

BRITISH COLUMBIA

Image Media Farm, pg 895
Triad Communications Ltd, pg 1044

MANITOBA

Spectra Video Productions Ltd, pg 1020

NEWFOUNDLAND AND LABRADOR

Vidcraft Productions Ltd, pg 1054

NORTHWEST TERRITORIES

Yellowknife Films Inc, pg 1072

ONTARIO

ADS Media, pg 777
GAPC (General Assembly Production Centre), pg 875
Image Video Services & Productions, pg 895
Purefire Communications Inc, pg 987

QUEBEC

Kerrigan Productions Inc, pg 910
Muse Entertainment Enterprises, pg 950

Photography—Slow Motion

ALABAMA

Diamond Studios, pg 846

ARIZONA

Direct Current Video Productions, pg 848
Merestone, pg 938
Phoenix VideoFilms®, pg 974
Rodeo Video Inc, pg 998
Video Media Productions (VMP), pg 1055

ARKANSAS

Shadowbox Video Productions, pg 1007
White Diamond Productions, pg 1065

CALIFORNIA

A Go Go Films, pg 771
Aaron & Le Duc, pg 772
Action Sports/All Stock, pg 775
All Video Productions, pg 781
Classic Images, pg 829
Concrete Images, pg 835
Crystal Pyramid Productions™, pg 840
FXF Productions Inc, pg 874
Goal Productions, pg 879
Havas Edge, pg 885
iCorpTv, pg 893
Instrumentation Marketing Corp, pg 899
Maximus Media Inc, pg 934
New & Unique Videos™, pg 955
New Circuit Films LLC, pg 955
Panorama Productions, pg 968
PM Productions, pg 977
QRS Software Services, pg 988
RetinaVision Productions, pg 995
Staylor-Made Communications Inc, pg 1024
StereoScope International, pg 1024
Still N'Motion, pg 1025
Tam Communications Inc, pg 1031
30 Second Films, pg 1039
Total Media Group, pg 1042
Twin Peaks Creative, pg 1047
WARPed Pictures, pg 1062

COLORADO

Flashback Media Productions, pg 869
Greg Hensley Productions, pg 888
Rocky Mountain Audio/Video Productions Inc, pg 998
Tatum Video, pg 1032

CONNECTICUT

BRB Audiovisual Productions, pg 812
Broadcast Video Productions LLC, pg 813
Fox Connecticut, pg 872
Guymark Studios LLC, pg 883

FLORIDA

Cinema East, pg 827
Civins Productions Inc, pg 828
Steven Cohen Motion Picture Production, pg 831
Communications Concepts Inc (CCI), pg 833
Courter Films LLC, pg 837
Eastern Video, pg 856
Home Shopping Network (HSN), pg 890
Jordan Klein Film & Video (JKFV), pg 906
Midtown Video Inc, pg 942
Paradise Video & Film, pg 969
Sunfire Communications Inc, pg 1028
Sunrise Studios, pg 1028
Universal Studios Florida® Production Group, pg 1049
Mike Vasilinda Productions Inc, pg 1052

GEORGIA

Beachwood Productions, pg 804
COMPRO Productions Inc, pg 834
Guerrilla Productions LLC, pg 883
USMotivation, pg 1051

HAWAII

Hyperspective Studios Inc, pg 893
Sight & Sound Studios, pg 1010
TV Juice Productions Inc, pg 1046

IDAHO

KTVB-TV, pg 914
Wide Eye Productions, pg 1066

ILLINOIS

Audio Visual Services Corp, pg 796
Film Police, pg 867
PSAV® Presentation Services (Hotel Services Division), pg 987
SCI Television Productions LLC, pg 1004
WEEK TV, pg 1063
Winter Productions, pg 1068

INDIANA

AVA Productions, pg 798

KENTUCKY

Idle Minds Productions Inc, pg 894
Kentucky Grip & Lighting, pg 909
The Media Collaboratory, pg 936

LOUISIANA

Digital FX Inc, pg 847
Moxie Media, pg 948
Vidox Motion Imagery, pg 1057

MAINE

WGME-TV, pg 1065

MARYLAND

Adventure Productions LLC, pg 778
CPR MultiMedia Solutions, pg 837
Kramer Communications Video Production, pg 913
Library Video Network (LVN), pg 920
Producers Video, pg 984

MASSACHUSETTS

Award Productions, pg 800
Green Mountain Post Films (GMP), pg 882
Heliotrope Studios, pg 887
Northern Light Productions, pg 959

MICHIGAN

Digi Sign Design LLC, pg 847
K&R's Recording Studios Inc, pg 908

MINNESOTA

Aggressive Records Audio Duplication LLC, pg 778
Badiyan Inc, pg 801
House of Cinemagraphics, pg 891
Master Communications Group, pg 933

MISSOURI

Avatar Studios, pg 798

MONTANA

North Country Media Group, pg 959

NEVADA

Aardvark Video & Media Productions, pg 772
DVDs4Less, pg 854
HDTV Productions Inc, pg 886
JCS Video Productions, pg 904

NEW HAMPSHIRE

Apertura, pg 788

NEW JERSEY

All Jersey Studios, pg 780
Broadcast Center Studios, pg 813
CFP Video Productions Inc, pg 823
Color Leasing Studios, pg 831
DWJ Television, pg 854
MIB Mediaworks, pg 941
Bill Quinn Productions, pg 989
Suede Interactive, pg 1027

NEW MEXICO

Production Outfitters, pg 984

NEW YORK

Broad Street Inc, pg 812
Gurrilla Video Solutions, pg 883
Icontent, pg 893
La Paloma Films, pg 915
L&P Media, pg 915
Long Island Video Enterprises Live Inc, pg 924
Neal Marshad Productions, pg 931
Mood Creations Ltd, pg 946
Jack Morton Worldwide, pg 946
TBA Global Events, pg 1032

NORTH CAROLINA

Pat Appleson Studios Inc, pg 788
Duke Media Services, pg 853

Horizon Video Productions Inc, pg 891
LCW Productions LLC, pg 917
NASCAR Media Group LLC, pg 952
Take One Productions Ltd, pg 1031
Trailblazer Studios®, pg 1043

NORTH DAKOTA

Media Productions, pg 937

OHIO

Aztec Video Productions, pg 801
Challenge Productions, pg 823
Creative Technology, pg 838
Lyon Video Inc, pg 927
VGI Productions, pg 1053

OKLAHOMA

Institute for Teaching & Learning Excellence (ITLE), pg 899

OREGON

Odyssey Productions Inc, pg 961

PENNSYLVANIA

Argentine Productions Inc, pg 789
Center City Film & Video Inc, pg 822
Goodman Associates Inc, pg 880
Innovision Media Group, pg 899
JPL, pg 906
Production Masters Inc (PMI), pg 984
The Videohouse Inc, pg 1057

SOUTH CAROLINA

Genesis Creative, pg 877
Venture Media, pg 1052

TENNESSEE

Motion Picture Services, pg 947
Stage Post, pg 1022
WKPT-TV, pg 1068

TEXAS

Castleview Productions, pg 821
Horizon Film + Video Productions, pg 891
Inferno Films, pg 898
Julye Newlin Productions Inc, pg 956
Phillips MediaSource, pg 974
The Samuels Co, pg 1002
Stage Directions, pg 1022

UTAH

ImageWorks Communications, pg 896

VERMONT

Perceptions Inc, pg 973

VIRGINIA

BES Studios, pg 805
CACI Productions Group, pg 816
Metro Productions, pg 939

WASHINGTON

Bennett-Watt HD Productions Inc, pg 805
Hamilton Studio, pg 884
North-by-Northwest Productions, pg 958
Victory Studios, pg 1054
White Rain Films Ltd, pg 1065

WEST VIRGINIA

WSAZ-TV 3/WSAZ Productions, pg 1070

WISCONSIN

AVS Group, pg 800
Midland Video Productions Inc, pg 942
USAV Group Inc, pg 1050
Video Wisconsin Inc, pg 1056
Wisconsin Public Television, pg 1068

WYOMING

Bridger Productions Inc, pg 812

ALBERTA

Black Media Works, pg 808
Global Television Station, pg 879

BRITISH COLUMBIA

Image Media Farm, pg 895
Triad Communications Ltd, pg 1044

MANITOBA

Spectra Video Productions Ltd, pg 1020

NEWFOUNDLAND AND LABRADOR

Vidcraft Productions Ltd, pg 1054

ONTARIO

GAPC (General Assembly Production Centre), pg 875
Video Excellence Productions, pg 1055

Photography—Studio

ALABAMA

CMEInfo, pg 830
Diamond Studios, pg 846

ALASKA

Alaska Film Services Inc, pg 779

ARIZONA

Arizona Virtual Studios, pg 790
Direct Current Video Productions, pg 848
MediaWorks, pg 938
Merestone, pg 938
Metropolitan Audio-Visual Inc, pg 940
On-Site Video, pg 963
Rodeo Video Inc, pg 998
Video Media Productions (VMP), pg 1055

ARKANSAS

Live'N'Loud, pg 923
Shadowbox Video Productions, pg 1007
White Diamond Productions, pg 1065

CALIFORNIA

Aaron & Le Duc, pg 772
All Video Productions, pg 781
Artichoke Productions, pg 791
Auslender Productions/Celestial Images, pg 797
Big Door, pg 807
Cherry Multimedia, pg 824
Concrete Images, pg 835
Crystal Pyramid Productions™, pg 840
deKramer Productions Inc, pg 845
Design Media, pg 845
Direct Images Interactive Inc, pg 848
First Camera, pg 868
FXF Productions Inc, pg 874
Global Village Productions, pg 879
Goal Productions, pg 879
Golden Gate Studios, pg 880
Havas Edge, pg 885
iCorpTv, pg 893
Imageworks, pg 896
JDS Video & Media Productions Inc, pg 904
KESSPRO Studios, pg 910
KTVU-Retail Services, pg 914
KVIE-Channel 6, pg 914
Main Street Media Inc, pg 929
Maximus Media Inc, pg 934
Media Magic, pg 937
The Media Staff Inc, pg 937
New & Unique Videos™, pg 955
New Circuit Films LLC, pg 955
Pacific Light Studios, pg 967
Panorama Productions, pg 968
PM Productions, pg 977
James Porter Photography, pg 979
PSI Inc, pg 987
QRS Software Services, pg 988
Raymond Entertainment Direct (RED), pg 992
Dick Reizner Film & Video, pg 994
RetinaVision Productions, pg 995
Saturn Studios, pg 1003
SBS Productions, pg 1003
Screen Door Entertainment Inc, pg 1005
Sea Studios Foundation, pg 1005
The Mack Sennett Studios, pg 1006
Staylor-Made Communications Inc, pg 1024
StereoScope International, pg 1024
Still N'Motion, pg 1025
Stray Angel Films, pg 1026
The Studio of David Inocencio/ Minette Siegel, pg 1027
30 Second Films, pg 1039
Total Media Group, pg 1042
Twin Peaks Creative, pg 1047
Videowerks, pg 1057
Warner Bros Entertainment Inc, pg 1062
WARPed Pictures, pg 1062
Wavemaker Media Design, pg 1062

COLORADO

Paul L Anderson Productions Inc, pg 786
CSI Films, pg 840
Daylight Productions & Rentals, pg 844
Flashback Media Productions, pg 869
Greg Hensley Productions, pg 888
Lightware Inc, pg 921
Rocky Mountain Audio/Video Productions Inc, pg 998
Tatum Video, pg 1032

CONNECTICUT

Applebox Studio, pg 788
BRB Audiovisual Productions, pg 812
Broadcast Video Productions LLC, pg 813
Fox Connecticut, pg 872
Guymark Studios LLC, pg 883
MAVCO, pg 934
New London Media, pg 956

DISTRICT OF COLUMBIA

Metro Teleproductions Inc (MTI), pg 939

FLORIDA

A Cut Above Video Productions Inc, pg 771
Allegro Productions Inc, pg 781
Bill Bachmann Studios, pg 807
C&I Studios, pg 819
Cinema East, pg 827
Civins Productions Inc, pg 828
Steven Cohen Motion Picture Production, pg 831
Communications Concepts Inc (CCI), pg 833
Courter Films LLC, pg 837
Eastern Video, pg 856
Ed Ethridge Productions Inc, pg 863
The Great Southern Studios, pg 882
Gulf Coast Audio Visual Producers Inc, pg 883
Home Shopping Network (HSN), pg 890
Jordan Klein Film & Video (JKFV), pg 906
JungleTV, pg 906
Midtown Video Inc, pg 942
Paradise Video & Film, pg 969
Parallax Productions Inc, pg 969
Shooting Stars Post Inc, pg 1009
Sound*Light, pg 1017
Sunfire Communications Inc, pg 1028
Sunrise Studios, pg 1028
Tricycle Studios, pg 1044
Universal Studios Florida® Production Group, pg 1049
Mike Vasilinda Productions Inc, pg 1052
Venice Media Group, pg 1052

GEORGIA

Beachwood Productions, pg 804
COMPRO Productions Inc, pg 834
Continental Film & Video, pg 835
ECG Productions, pg 856
Guerrilla Productions LLC, pg 883
Malcolm Neal Productions, pg 954
Showcase Photo & Video, pg 1009
USMotivation, pg 1051

HAWAII

Hyperspective Studios Inc, pg 893
KHNL/KGMB, pg 910
Sight & Sound Studios, pg 1010
1013 Integrated, pg 1037
TV Juice Productions Inc, pg 1046

IDAHO

KTVB-TV, pg 914
Brad Shaw Productions Inc, pg 1008
Wide Eye Productions, pg 1066

ILLINOIS

Assignment Desk, pg 792
Audio Visual Services Corp, pg 796
Beatty TeleVisual Productions, pg 804
Breeze Productions Inc, pg 812
CCore Media Inc, pg 821
Chicago Satellite & Video, pg 825
Communications Corporation of America, pg 833
Custom Medical Stock Photo Inc, pg 841
Film Police, pg 867

VIDEO

Photography—Studio (continued)

WASHINGTON

Global Net Productions Inc, pg 879
Hamilton Studio, pg 884
North-by-Northwest Productions, pg 958
Oppenheimer Camera Products, pg 964
Victory Studios, pg 1054
White Rain Films Ltd, pg 1065

WEST VIRGINIA

MotionMasters, pg 947
WSAZ-TV 3/WSAZ Productions, pg 1070

WISCONSIN

AVS Group, pg 800
Logan Productions Inc, pg 924
Media Communications Association-International (MCA-I), pg 936
Meridian Studios, pg 939
Midland Video Productions Inc, pg 942
University of Wisconsin-Oshkosh Radio-TV-Film Dept, pg 1050
USAV Group Inc, pg 1050
Video Wisconsin Inc, pg 1056
Watts Communications Inc, pg 1062
Wisconsin Public Television, pg 1068

WYOMING

Bridger Productions Inc, pg 812

ALBERTA

Black Media Works, pg 808
Global Television, pg 879
Global Television Station, pg 879

BRITISH COLUMBIA

Image Media Farm, pg 895
Triad Communications Ltd, pg 1044

MANITOBA

Spectra Video Productions Ltd, pg 1020

NEWFOUNDLAND AND LABRADOR

Vidcraft Productions Ltd, pg 1054

ONTARIO

ADS Media, pg 777
GAPC (General Assembly Production Centre), pg 875
Image Video Services & Productions, pg 895
Purefire Communications Inc, pg 987

QUEBEC

Group PVP, pg 882
Kerrigan Productions Inc, pg 910
Muse Entertainment Enterprises, pg 950

Photography—Underwater

ALASKA

Alaska Film Services Inc, pg 779

ARIZONA

Direct Current Video Productions, pg 848
Merestone, pg 938

CALIFORNIA

Aaron & Le Duc, pg 772
Action Sports/All Stock, pg 775
Big Door, pg 807
Concrete Images, pg 835
Envirovision, pg 861
FXF Productions Inc, pg 874
Global Village Productions, pg 879
Global Village Stock Footage Library, pg 879
Howard Hall Productions, pg 883
iCorpTv, pg 893
Maximus Media Inc, pg 934
Motion Picture Marine, pg 947
New Circuit Films LLC, pg 955
Penrose Productions, pg 972
QRS Software Services, pg 988
Dick Reizner Film & Video, pg 994
RetinaVision Productions, pg 995
Screen Door Entertainment Inc, pg 1005
Sea Studios Foundation, pg 1005
StereoScope International, pg 1024
Tam Communications Inc, pg 1031
30 Second Films, pg 1039
Twin Peaks Creative, pg 1047
WARPed Pictures, pg 1062

COLORADO

CSI Films, pg 840
Flashback Media Productions, pg 869
Greg Hensley Productions, pg 888
Tatum Video, pg 1032

CONNECTICUT

Broadcast Video Productions LLC, pg 813
Fox Connecticut, pg 872

DISTRICT OF COLUMBIA

Yellow Cat Productions Inc, pg 1072

FLORIDA

Cinema East, pg 827
Civins Productions Inc, pg 828
Steven Cohen Motion Picture Production, pg 831
Communications Concepts Inc (CCI), pg 833
Courter Films LLC, pg 837
Eastern Video, pg 856
Fiddler Films, pg 866
Home Shopping Network (HSN), pg 890
Jordan Klein Film & Video (JKFV), pg 906
Midtown Video Inc, pg 942
National Teleproductions Inc, pg 953
Paradise Video & Film, pg 969
Shooting Stars Post Inc, pg 1009
Sunfire Communications Inc, pg 1028
Sunrise Studios, pg 1028

GEORGIA

Beachwood Productions, pg 804
COMPRO Productions Inc, pg 834
Continental Film & Video, pg 835
Guerrilla Productions LLC, pg 883
USMotivation, pg 1051

HAWAII

Hyperspective Studios Inc, pg 893
TV Juice Productions Inc, pg 1046

IDAHO

Wide Eye Productions, pg 1066

ILLINOIS

Airways Digital Media, pg 779
Assignment Desk, pg 792
Film Police, pg 867
Major Media Inc, pg 929

LOUISIANA

Digital FX Inc, pg 847
Louisiana State University Health Sciences Center - Shreveport, pg 925

MARYLAND

Adventure Productions LLC, pg 778
CAS Video Productions, pg 820
CPR MultiMedia Solutions, pg 837
Kramer Communications Video Production, pg 913
Pro Cuts Editing Services, pg 982

MASSACHUSETTS

Capron Lighting & Sound Co Inc, pg 819
CommCreative, pg 832
Northern Light Productions, pg 959

MICHIGAN

The Program Source International, pg 985

MINNESOTA

Aggressive Records Audio Duplication LLC, pg 778
Badiyan Inc, pg 801
House of Cinemagraphics, pg 891
MultiMedia, pg 950

NEVADA

JCS Video Productions, pg 904

NEW HAMPSHIRE

Chip Taylor Communications LLC, pg 1032

NEW JERSEY

Broadcast Center Studios, pg 813
MIB Mediaworks, pg 941
Suede Interactive, pg 1027

NEW MEXICO

Production Outfitters, pg 984

NEW YORK

Air Sea Land Productions Inc (ASL), pg 779
Broad Street Inc, pg 812
Chromavision Corp, pg 826
Digital Art Video Inc, pg 847
Gurrilla Video Solutions, pg 883
Ketchum Pleon Change, pg 910
La Paloma Films, pg 915
L&P Media, pg 915
Neal Marshad Productions, pg 931
Jack Morton Worldwide, pg 946
SmartPros Ltd, pg 1014
Videograf, pg 1057

NORTH CAROLINA

Pat Appleson Studios Inc, pg 788
J Arnold Productions Inc, pg 790
The Communications Group Inc, pg 833
Take One Productions Ltd, pg 1031

NORTH DAKOTA

Media Productions, pg 937

OHIO

Aztec Video Productions, pg 801
Challenge Productions, pg 823

OKLAHOMA

Smart Concepts Ltd, pg 1013

OREGON

Odyssey Productions Inc, pg 961

PENNSYLVANIA

Argentine Productions Inc, pg 789
Audio Visions Inc, pg 795
Innovision Media Group, pg 899
The Videohouse Inc, pg 1057
WPHL-TV, pg 1070

TENNESSEE

Marine Geographic, pg 931
Motion Picture Services, pg 947
Scripps Networks, pg 1005
Stage Post, pg 1022

TEXAS

Horizon Film + Video Productions, pg 891
Julye Newlin Productions Inc, pg 956
Phillips MediaSource, pg 974
Prairie Pictures Film & Video, pg 980
South Coast Film & Video, pg 1019

VIRGINIA

CACI Productions Group, pg 816

WASHINGTON

Bennett-Watt HD Productions Inc, pg 805
Global Net Productions Inc, pg 879
Victory Studios, pg 1054

WISCONSIN

Media Communications Association-International (MCA-I), pg 936
ProVideo, pg 986
Video Wisconsin Inc, pg 1056
Wisconsin Public Television, pg 1068

ALBERTA

Global Television Station, pg 879

NEWFOUNDLAND AND LABRADOR

Vidcraft Productions Ltd, pg 1054

QUEBEC

Group PVP, pg 882
Kerrigan Productions Inc, pg 910

Post-Production Services

ALABAMA

AVS Media Group, pg 800
CMEInfo, pg 830
Diamond Studios, pg 846
Motion & Graphic Image Corp Inc (MAGIC), pg 947

VIDEO

Post-Production Services (continued)

ALASKA

Alaska Film Services Inc, pg 779

ARIZONA

Candee Productions Inc, pg 819
Cox Creative Studios, pg 837
Direct Current Video Productions, pg 848
Film Creations Ltd, pg 867
Fox 10 Productions (KSAZ-TV), pg 872
Illuma Studios, pg 894
MediaWorks, pg 938
Merestone, pg 938
Metropolitan Audio-Visual Inc, pg 940
On-Site Video, pg 963
Phoenix VideoFilms®, pg 974
Rodeo Video Inc, pg 998
Star Video Duplicating, pg 1024
Video Media Productions (VMP), pg 1055
Wild Visions Inc, pg 1066

ARKANSAS

Cedar Crest Studio, pg 822
Live'N'Loud, pg 923
Shadowbox Video Productions, pg 1007
White Diamond Productions, pg 1065

CALIFORNIA

A Go Go Films, pg 771
Aaron & Le Duc, pg 772
AB Audio Visual Entertainment Inc, pg 772
Aberdeen Broadcast Services, pg 772
Access Video in Berkeley, pg 773
Action Video, pg 775
Advanced Media LLC, pg 778
All Video Productions, pg 781
AlphaDogs Inc, pg 782
AM Productions, pg 783
Argyle Post, pg 789
Artichoke Productions, pg 791
Baldwin Productions, pg 802
Berkeley Sound Artists Inc, pg 805
Big Door, pg 807
Blind, pg 809
CCI Digital, pg 821
Cherry Multimedia, pg 824
Christopher Gray Post Production, pg 826
Coastline Productions, pg 831
Crystal Pyramid Productions™, pg 840
Custom Video Productions Inc, pg 841
Deja View Video, pg 845
deKramer Productions Inc, pg 845
Digital Jungle, pg 847
Digital Outpost, pg 847
Direct Images Interactive Inc, pg 848
Dogma Studios, pg 850
The Dreaming Tree, pg 852
DV Post, pg 854
eMotion Studios, pg 860
Express Media Inc, pg 864
Face Digital Post, pg 865
First Camera, pg 868
First Person™, pg 868
FJ Productions Inc, pg 869
48 Windows, pg 871
4th Street Recording, pg 872
Fox Television Center, pg 872
Full Moon & High Tide Productions & Studios, pg 874
FXC Communications, pg 874
FXF Productions Inc, pg 874
Glix Studios, pg 879
Global Village Productions, pg 879
Goal Productions, pg 879
Gold Standard Productions, pg 880
Golden Gate Studios, pg 880
Groovy Like a Movie, pg 882
Havas Edge, pg 885
Hollywood Vaults Inc, pg 890
Hybrid Studios, pg 892
iCorpTv, pg 893
Illuminate Post/Digital Finishing, pg 894
imageReal Pictures LLC, pg 896
Imageworks, pg 896
JDS Video & Media Productions Inc, pg 904
JFA Studio, pg 905
JR Media Services, pg 906
K2B2 Records, pg 907
Kavich Reynolds Productions Inc, pg 908
KION-TV, pg 911
KO Creative, pg 912
KPBS TV FM-San Diego, pg 913
KTVU-Retail Services, pg 914
KVIE-Channel 6, pg 914
Lightning Media, pg 921
Los Feliz Post, pg 924
Ludlow Media Solutions, pg 926
Main Street Media Inc, pg 929
Maximus Media Inc, pg 934
McCune Audio-Video-Lighting, pg 935
Media Magic, pg 937
The Media Staff Inc, pg 937
Medical Visual Creations (MVC), pg 938
Method Studios, pg 939
Mind Over Eye Inc, pg 943
Mist Media Inc, pg 944
Mobilized Tech Systems, pg 944
Nandar Entertainment Pictures, pg 952
New & Unique Videos™, pg 955
New Deal Studios, pg 955
Nolte Media, pg 958
On-Trax Inc, pg 963
Opticomm-EMCORE, pg 964
Pacific Light Studios, pg 967
Pacific Video Image, pg 967
Palardo Productions, pg 968
Panorama Productions, pg 968
Penrose Productions, pg 972
Peterson's Video Transfer Services, pg 973
Planet Blue, pg 976
PM Productions, pg 977
Point 360, pg 978
PSI Inc, pg 987
Pyramind Studios, pg 988
QRS Software Services, pg 988
Reality Check Systems, pg 992
RetinaVision Productions, pg 995
Rough House, pg 1000
Roundabout Entertainment Inc, pg 1000
Sahara Records & Filmworks Entertainment Co, pg 1001
Sand Box Studio, pg 1002
SBS Productions, pg 1003
Screen Door Entertainment Inc, pg 1005
Shapeshifter, pg 1008
Shoulder High Productions, pg 1009
SonicPool, pg 1016
Starburns Industries, pg 1024
Staylor-Made Communications Inc, pg 1024
StereoScope International, pg 1024
Still N'Motion, pg 1025
Studio 637, pg 1027
The Studios at Paramount, pg 1027
Tam Communications Inc, pg 1031
30 Second Films, pg 1039
Tigar Hare Studios, pg 1040
Timecode Multimedia, pg 1040
Toon Makers, pg 1042
Total Media Group, pg 1042
Tubeworks Video Productions, pg 1046
TVA Productions, pg 1046
Twin Peaks Creative, pg 1047
Two Door Productions, pg 1047
Universal Satellite Communications Inc, pg 1049
Universal Studios, pg 1049
Via Verde Productions, pg 1053
VidCan Media Solutions, pg 1054
Video Movie Magic, pg 1056
Video Symphony TV & Film School, pg 1056
Videografix LLC, pg 1057
Videolady, pg 1057
Visions Plus, pg 1058
Vitruvian Entertainment, pg 1060
Warner Bros Entertainment Inc, pg 1062
WARPed Pictures, pg 1062
Wavemaker Media Design, pg 1062
West Coast Projections Inc, pg 1063

COLORADO

Aerial Imaging Productions, pg 778
Paul L Anderson Productions Inc, pg 786
blue onion, pg 810
The Cinema Lab, pg 827
Colorado Studios, pg 832
CSI Films, pg 840
Daylight Productions & Rentals, pg 844
Flashback Media Productions, pg 869
Old Army Press (OAP), pg 961
Open Media Foundation, pg 964
Rocky Mountain Audio/Video Productions Inc, pg 998
Spectrum Audio Visual Services, pg 1020
Tatum Video, pg 1032
Transtar Entertainment Co Inc, pg 1043
Westworks Studios, pg 1064
Z-Axis Corp, pg 1073

CONNECTICUT

ACM Productions Ltd, pg 774
Antenna International, pg 787
Applebox Studio, pg 788
Biomedical Media Communications Dept, pg 807
BRB Audiovisual Productions, pg 812
Broadcast Video Productions LLC, pg 813
Cine-Med Inc, pg 826
Essex Television Group Inc, pg 862
Fox Connecticut, pg 872
Geomatrix Productions, pg 877
Guymark Studios LLC, pg 883
Ironik Design & Post, pg 902
MAVCO, pg 934
Moving Pictures, pg 947
Musivision Inc, pg 951
New London Media, pg 956
Palace Digital Studios, pg 967
P&P Studios Inc, pg 968
Powerstation Events, pg 979
Sonalysts Media, pg 1015
Video Production Associates Inc, pg 1056

DELAWARE

Cornerstone Media Productions Inc, pg 836

DISTRICT OF COLUMBIA

Hillmann & Carr Inc, pg 889
Interface Media Group, pg 900
Metro Teleproductions Inc (MTI), pg 939
Yellow Cat Productions Inc, pg 1072

FLORIDA

A Cut Above Video Productions Inc, pg 771
Accel Video Productions, pg 773
Access Media Group, pg 773
Accord Productions, pg 773
ACT Productions, pg 775
Allegro Productions Inc, pg 781
Audacity Creative, pg 793
AVI-SPL, pg 798
Big Byte Video Productions, pg 806
Bill Bachmann Studios, pg 807
Cinema East, pg 827
Cinema Entertainment Inc, pg 827
Civins Productions Inc, pg 828
Communications Concepts Inc (CCI), pg 833
Comtel Inc, pg 834
Courter Films LLC, pg 837
Digital Zoetrope Productions, pg 848
DME Studios, pg 849
Eastern Video, pg 856
Easy Edit Video Inc, pg 856
Kat Epple Music Productions, pg 862
Ed Ethridge Productions Inc, pg 863
Florida Digital Studios, pg 870
Glanz Technologies Inc, pg 878
Gulf Coast Audio Visual Producers Inc, pg 883
Harmon's Audio-Visual Services, pg 885
Hi-Tech Enterprises Inc, pg 888
Home Shopping Network (HSN), pg 890
Image Technical Services, pg 895
Jordan Klein Film & Video (JKFV), pg 906
Norman Kent Productions, pg 909
Knowles Video Inc (KVI), pg 912
Little Big Bang Design Inc, pg 923
MAC Production Group, pg 927
Media Concepts Inc, pg 936
Media Entertainment Inc, pg 936
Moxie Video Productions Inc, pg 948
National Teleproductions Inc, pg 953
New Art Miami, pg 955
The Newhouse Media Group, pg 956
Parallax Productions Inc, pg 969
Phat Planet Recording Studios, pg 973
Progressive Media & Music, pg 985
Shooting Stars Post Inc, pg 1009
Sound & Vision Communications Inc, pg 1016
Sunfire Communications Inc, pg 1028
Sunrise Studios, pg 1028
Tricycle Studios, pg 1044
Universal Studios Florida® Production Group, pg 1049

Mike Vasilinda Productions Inc, pg 1052
Video Techniques Inc, pg 1056
Vistamax Productions, pg 1059

GEORGIA

Beachwood Productions, pg 804
Beast Atlanta, pg 804
COMPRO Productions Inc, pg 834
Continental Film & Video, pg 835
Crawford Media Services, pg 838
The DVI Group, pg 854
ECG Productions, pg 856
Guerrilla Productions LLC, pg 883
Imagers, pg 896
Magick Lantern, pg 928
Omega Media Group Inc, pg 962
On-Line Productions, pg 963
Showcase Photo & Video, pg 1009
TV Crews, pg 1046
USMotivation, pg 1051
Video Copy Services Inc, pg 1055
WATL-TV Inc, pg 1062

HAWAII

Dot C Software Inc, pg 851
Hyperspective Studios Inc, pg 893
KHNL/KGMB, pg 910
Media Bridge Gamekids, pg 936
Sight & Sound Studios, pg 1010
1013 Integrated, pg 1037
Tropical Visions Video Inc, pg 1045
TV Juice Productions Inc, pg 1046

IDAHO

KTVB-TV, pg 914
Brad Shaw Productions Inc, pg 1008
Wide Eye Productions, pg 1066

ILLINOIS

ABSA Productions Inc, pg 772
Airways Digital Media, pg 779
Analog Free Media, pg 786
AnswersMedia, pg 787
Assignment Desk, pg 792
Audio Visual Services Corp, pg 796
Backstar Creative Media Inc, pg 801
Beatty TeleVisual Productions, pg 804
Big Shoulders Digital Video Productions, pg 807
Breeze Productions Inc, pg 812
CCore Media Inc, pg 821
The Chicago Production Center, pg 825
Chicago Satellite & Video, pg 825
Comtech Multimedia Marketing, pg 834
Edit House Chicago, pg 857
Filmworkers, pg 868
IV Media Resources, pg 903
Manning Productions, pg 930
The Market Place, pg 931
MIGHTYbYTES Inc, pg 942
Mimi Productions, pg 943
Optimus, pg 964
Rob Orr Productions Ltd, pg 965
The Pepper Group, pg 972
The Prairie Production Group, pg 980
PSAV® Presentation Services (Hotel Services Division), pg 987
RADMAR Inc, pg 990
Richter Studios, pg 996
SCI Television Productions LLC, pg 1004
Sound/Video Impressions Inc, pg 1018
Sparkfactor, pg 1019
Tele-Time Systems, pg 1036
20/20 Communications Inc, pg 1047
Video I-D Teleproductions Inc, pg 1055
Video Impressions, pg 1055
WIFR-TV, pg 1066

INDIANA

Advanced Media Integration, pg 777
AVA Productions, pg 798
Bright Ideas Creative Services, pg 812
Covenant Productions®, pg 837
Digital Rain LLC, pg 847
Educational Video Group Inc, pg 857
Explore Media LLC, pg 864
Lakeshore Productions, pg 915
PentaVision Communications Inc, pg 972

IOWA

Iowa State University-Information Technology Services, pg 902
The Production House, pg 984

KANSAS

KAKE-TV, pg 907

KENTUCKY

Broadway Digital, pg 813
Hammond Communications Group, pg 884
Horizon Films & Media LLC, pg 891
Idle Minds Productions Inc, pg 894
The Media Collaboratory, pg 936
Northern Kentucky University, pg 959
The PPS Group, pg 980
Prosper Media Group Inc, pg 986

LOUISIANA

Digital FX Inc, pg 847
Louisiana State University Health Sciences Center - Shreveport, pg 925
Moxie Media, pg 948
Pace Systems, pg 966
Vidox Motion Imagery, pg 1057
WVLA-TV, pg 1071
YES Productions, pg 1072

MAINE

WGME-TV, pg 1065

MARYLAND

Adventure Productions LLC, pg 778
The Ahern Group, pg 779
CAS Video Productions, pg 820
CPR MultiMedia Solutions, pg 837
dbF a Media Company, pg 844
DBM Communications Inc, pg 844
James Agee Film Project, pg 904
Kramer Communications Video Production, pg 913
Library Video Network (LVN), pg 920
Media Dimensions Inc, pg 936
Mobile-Video Productions Inc, pg 944
Pro Cuts Editing Services, pg 982
Producers Video, pg 984
Quality Film & Video, pg 988
Shadowstone R & R™, pg 1008
Sheffield Audio/Video Productions, pg 1008
Sign Media Inc, pg 1011
Spectrum Productions, pg 1021

MASSACHUSETTS

Award Productions, pg 800
Boston Productions Inc, pg 811
Continental Recordings Inc, pg 835
Documentary Educational Resources Inc, pg 850
Emergency Film Group, pg 860
Extreme Reach Inc, pg 864
Green Mountain Post Films (GMP), pg 882
Heliotrope Studios, pg 887
Home Inc, pg 890
Inter-Media Electronics, pg 899
Monadnock Media Inc, pg 945
MotionArt Studios, pg 947
Northern Light Productions, pg 959
Penfield Productions Ltd, pg 971
Small Planet Communications Inc, pg 1013
Sound & Vision Media, pg 1017
Soundtrack Recording Studios, pg 1018
TR Productions, pg 1043
TVN-The Video Network, pg 1046
Veritech Corp, pg 1053
VideoLink Inc, pg 1057
WGBH Production Group, pg 1065
WVP Boston, pg 1071

MICHIGAN

Digi Sign Design LLC, pg 847
Digital Image Studios LLC, pg 847
K&R's Recording Studios Inc, pg 908
Lawrence Productions Inc, pg 917
Maritz Performance Improvement Co, pg 931
Michigan Recording Arts Institute & Technologies, pg 941
The Program Source International, pg 985
RingSide Creative, pg 997
TGA Recording Co, pg 1038
The Transfer Zone®, pg 1043
Universal Images, pg 1049
WTVS-Station Enterprises, pg 1071

MINNESOTA

The ADS Group, pg 777
Aggressive Records Audio Duplication LLC, pg 778
Big Event Productions LLC, pg 807
The Richard Diercks Co Inc, pg 846
GMI Productions, pg 879
House of Cinemagraphics, pg 891
Jamieson & Associates Inc, pg 904
Master Communications Group, pg 933
MultiMedia, pg 950
Pro Media Productions, pg 983
Rum Jungle Media, pg 1000
Stoney-Wolf Productions Inc, pg 1025
Worthwhile Films, pg 1070

MISSOURI

Avatar Studios, pg 798
Communitronics Corp, pg 833
Conference Technologies Inc, pg 835
Hardcastle Films & Video, pg 885
KPLR-TV, pg 913
Production Consultants, pg 984
Spot Media Production Group, pg 1022
Studio Worx Inc, pg 1027
Substation K, pg 1027
Visionworks Design Services Inc, pg 1059

MONTANA

Jereco Studios Inc, pg 905
KCFW Television, pg 908
North Country Media Group, pg 959
ooLite Media, pg 964

NEBRASKA

B & B Video Productions Inc, pg 801
Dog & Pony Productions Inc, pg 850
Rainbow Video Productions Inc, pg 991
Three Pillars Media, pg 1040

NEVADA

Aardvark Video & Media Productions, pg 772
DVDs4Less, pg 854
Encore Productions Inc, pg 861
HDTV Productions Inc, pg 886
JCS Video Productions, pg 904
Lefco Video Services Inc, pg 918
21st Century Video Productions, pg 1047
VirtualMix, pg 1058

NEW HAMPSHIRE

Academic & Campus Technology Services, pg 773
Apertura, pg 788
Channell One Video, pg 824
NH Movies Inc, pg 957
Chip Taylor Communications LLC, pg 1032
The Troupe, pg 1045

NEW JERSEY

All Jersey Studios, pg 780
The Brick Studio, pg 812
Broadcast Center Studios, pg 813
CD Meyer Inc, pg 822
CELCO-Constantine Engineering Labs Co, pg 822
CFP Video Productions Inc, pg 823
Color Leasing Studios, pg 831
Concepts TV Production, pg 834
Creative Video, pg 838
Deluxe Media Services, pg 845
Diversified Systems Inc, pg 849
DWJ Television, pg 854
Early Films, pg 855
Euro-Pacific Film & Video Productions Inc, pg 863
Hogpenny Studios, pg 890
IMP Digital Studios, pg 896
Laurel Video Productions, pg 916
MediaMix Inc, pg 937
MediaNow, pg 938
MIB Mediaworks, pg 941
Milbrodt/Music & Sound Design, pg 943
Ray Mueller Productions, pg 949
NFL Films Inc, pg 957
NFL Films Music Library, pg 957
PeopleVisionFX, pg 972
Public Eye Productions, pg 987
Bill Quinn Productions, pg 989
Set To Go Studios, pg 1007
Suede Interactive, pg 1027
Telequest Inc, pg 1036
VCSvideo, pg 1052
Video Corporation of America (VCA), pg 1055
Video Ideas Productions, pg 1055
VTS Video & Media, pg 1061

VIDEO

Post-Production Services (continued)

NEW MEXICO

I-25 Studios, pg 893
Mountainair Films, pg 947
Production Outfitters, pg 984
30 Second Street Ltd, pg 1039

NEW YORK

Ace Video, pg 774
Adwar Video, pg 778
Air Sea Land Productions Inc (ASL), pg 779
American Montage Inc, pg 784
American Video Inc, pg 785
aurora productions, pg 797
BC Video Inc, pg 803
Bellin Productions, pg 805
Bevilacqua Studios, pg 806
Big Film Design, pg 807
Big Foot Productions Inc, pg 807
The Big House Group, pg 807
Bravo Studios, pg 812
Broad Street Inc, pg 812
Brooklyn Films, pg 814
C&C Studios Corp, pg 819
Chromavision Corp, pg 826
CMI Media Management, pg 830
Cohn Creative Group LLC, pg 831
Communication Corner Inc, pg 832
CPdigital, pg 837
Design Audio Visual Inc, pg 845
Devlin Video International, pg 846
Digital Art Video Inc, pg 847
dM works, pg 849
Downtown Community Television Center (DCTV), pg 851
DuArt, pg 853
East of Hollywood NY, pg 855
Eastco Multimedia Solutions Inc, pg 856
4-D Creative Media, pg 871
Golden Lamb Productions, pg 880
Greyfalcon House, pg 882
Gurrilla Video Solutions, pg 883
Hallel Communications, pg 884
HAVE Inc, pg 886
Hayden 5 Media LLC, pg 886
HB-Content, pg 886
Heavy Melody, pg 887
Hello World Communications, pg 888
Image Makers of Pittsford/Image Maker Productions, pg 895
InterNation Inc, pg 900
International Digital Centre, pg 901
iProbe Multilingual Solutions Inc, pg 902
J & D Laboratories Inc, pg 903
Jupiter Moon Productions, pg 907
KAS Music & Sound, pg 908
Kavanagh Productions Inc, pg 908
KickedUp Media Group Inc, pg 910
La Paloma Films, pg 915
L&P Media, pg 915
Loftin Productions, pg 924
Long Island Video Enterprises Live Inc, pg 924
Lylofilm Productions, pg 926
Magnetic Post Production, pg 928
Manhattan Center Studios Inc, pg 930
Neal Marshad Productions, pg 931
Mood Creations Ltd, pg 946
Jack Morton Worldwide, pg 946
MRM Worldwide, pg 948
MRY, pg 949
The Napoleon Group, pg 952
NSR Productions Inc & Capricorn Five Films, pg 960
Nutmeg Post, pg 960
Post Josh Productions, pg 979
PostWorks, pg 979
PrimaLux Video Inc, pg 982
Production Central, pg 984
R/GA, pg 990
Rafik, pg 990
RAVA Films, pg 991
Refinery, pg 994
Rollin Studios, pg 998
Shadow Pictures Inc, pg 1007
D S Simon Productions, pg 1011
SmartPros Ltd, pg 1014
Synaptic Digital, pg 1030
TBA Global Events, pg 1032
Teatown Communications Group, pg 1033
Technisphere Corp, pg 1034
TeleTime Productions, pg 1036
Third World Newsreel/Camera News Inc, pg 1039
Tobin Productions Inc, pg 1041
USA Studios, pg 1050
Visual Technologies Corp, pg 1060
White Buffalo Multimedia, pg 1065
Willow Mixed Media Inc, pg 1067
WNET/NET TELECON, pg 1069
Zelman Studios Ltd, pg 1073

NORTH CAROLINA

All Pro Media Inc, pg 780
Pat Appleson Studios Inc, pg 788
Bill Barnes Video Productions LLC, pg 803
The Communications Group Inc, pg 833
Duke Media Services, pg 853
Franklin Video Inc, pg 872
Gotham City Studios, pg 880
Horizon Video Productions Inc, pg 891
Kino Mountain Productions LLC, pg 911
K2 Productions, pg 914
LCW Productions LLC, pg 917
Media-Comm, pg 936
Moving Pictures, pg 948
On Location North Carolina, pg 963
Take One Productions Ltd, pg 1031
Trailblazer Studios®, pg 1043
2BruceStudio, pg 1047
Unifour Productions Inc, pg 1048

NORTH DAKOTA

Media Productions, pg 937

OHIO

Advent Media Inc, pg 778
Aztec Video Productions, pg 801
Bartha, pg 803
Russ Beckner Pictures, pg 804
CET, pg 823
Challenge Productions, pg 823
Commercial Video, pg 832
Creative Technology, pg 838
Curtis Inc, pg 841
Cuyahoga Community College Media Center, pg 841
EDR Media LLC, pg 857
Image Video Teleproductions Inc, pg 895
Lyon Video Inc, pg 927
MainSail Production Services Inc, pg 929
Maslowski Productions, pg 933
Mills James Productions, pg 943
R&B Communications Inc, pg 991
Take 1 Media Services, pg 1031
Treehaus Communications Inc, pg 1044
VGI Productions, pg 1053
Vista Color Imaging Inc, pg 1059

OKLAHOMA

Garman Productions LLC, pg 875
Institute for Teaching & Learning Excellence (ITLE), pg 899
PDC Productions, pg 970
Producers Playhouse, pg 983
Smart Concepts Ltd, pg 1013
University of Oklahoma Academic Media & Digital Services, pg 1050

OREGON

A KTVA Production LLC, pg 771
Artbeats, pg 791
BingoLewis, pg 807
Creative Media Development, pg 838
Intersect Video, pg 901
InterVision Media, pg 902
KVAL, pg 914
MediaFX, pg 937
Odyssey Productions Inc, pg 961
Picture This Production Services, pg 975
Production West, pg 985
Rex, pg 995

PENNSYLVANIA

AiH Group Inc, pg 779
Argentine Productions Inc, pg 789
Audio Visions Inc, pg 795
Bang Pictures, pg 802
Beholder Productions Inc, pg 804
Center City Film & Video Inc, pg 822
FMP Media Solutions Inc, pg 870
Fusion Brand Experiences, pg 874
Goodman Associates Inc, pg 880
Innovision Media Group, pg 899
JPL, pg 906
Panta Rhei Media Inc, pg 968
Pemcor LLC, pg 971
Production Masters Inc (PMI), pg 984
Rahlic Publishing Co, pg 990
The Videohouse Inc, pg 1057
Visual Sound Inc, pg 1059
WHYY Inc, pg 1066
WPHL-TV, pg 1070

RHODE ISLAND

Sound-FX-Design, pg 1017

SOUTH CAROLINA

American Production Services LLC, pg 785
Genesis Creative, pg 877
Stages Video Productions, pg 1023
Venture Media, pg 1052

TENNESSEE

Anode Inc, pg 787
Love Shack Recording Studios, pg 925
Marine Geographic, pg 931
Motion Picture Services, pg 947
Running Pony Productions LLC, pg 1000
Scripps Networks, pg 1005
ST Productions, pg 1022
Stage Post, pg 1022
Russ Sturgeon Productions/RSVP, pg 1027
UMCom Productions, pg 1048
WKPT-TV, pg 1068

TEXAS

Alpha Video Productions, pg 782
AMS Pictures, pg 786
Aries Productions, pg 789
Best Film & Video, pg 805
Biway Media, pg 808
Castleview Productions, pg 821
Cerutti Productions Inc, pg 823
Communication Arts Multimedia Inc, pg 832
Countdown Productions Inc, pg 837
Dallas Learning Solutions, pg 842
Dub King, pg 853
The Editing Co, pg 857
Eyecon Video Productions, pg 865
First Group Communications Inc, pg 868
Paul Flanagan Productions, pg 869
Freeman, pg 872
Horizon Film + Video Productions, pg 891
Inferno Films, pg 898
J&S Audio Visual Inc, pg 904
Marx InDigital, pg 933
Matson Multi-Media, pg 934
Maverick Video Productions, pg 934
McNee Productions Inc, pg 935
Media Event Concepts Inc, pg 936
Mediaforce Productions, pg 937
Julye Newlin Productions Inc, pg 956
Out of the BLUE Media, pg 966
Phillips MediaSource, pg 974
Romar Learning, pg 999
RuffHouse LLC, pg 1000
The Samuels Co, pg 1002
Sound Works, pg 1018
South Coast Film & Video, pg 1019
Tecfilms Inc, pg 1033
Texas Heart Institute Visual Communication Services, pg 1037
Video Perspective, pg 1056

UTAH

Ron Hill Imagery, pg 889
ImageWorks Communications, pg 896
K-SAR Video & DVD Productions, pg 907
Soularium Recording Studios, pg 1016

VERMONT

Marlboro Film & Video Productions, pg 931
Perceptions Inc, pg 973

VIRGINIA

Advance Concepts Inc, pg 777
Allied Media Corp, pg 781
BES Studios, pg 805
CACI Productions Group, pg 816
CALIBRE, pg 816
CDR Communications Inc, pg 822
Creative Video of Washington Inc, pg 839
D&B Television & Video Productions Inc, pg 842
EFX Media, pg 858
Gingerbread Productions, pg 878
Goose Creek Music & Entertainment, pg 880
Henninger Media Services, pg 888
Limelight Communications Inc, pg 921
Maniglia Media, pg 930
Metro Productions, pg 939
Rocktown Media, pg 998
Studio Center Corp, pg 1026
Video Solutions, pg 1056

Premastering, *see* Videodisc Premastering

Presentation System Distributors

VIDEO

Presentation System Distributors (continued)

WASHINGTON

eMagin Corp, pg 860

WISCONSIN

Audio Visual of Milwaukee Inc, pg 795
Camera Corner Connecting Point, pg 818
Full Compass Systems, pg 874

PUERTO RICO

Audio Visual Concepts Inc, pg 795

MANITOBA

Inland Audio Visual Ltd, pg 898

ONTARIO

Cinema Stage Inc, pg 827
HD Source, pg 886
Image Video, pg 895
Premier A/V Sales Ltd, pg 980
Technovision® Interactive Inc, pg 1035
Westbury National Show Systems Ltd, pg 1064

Presentation System Manufacturers

CALIFORNIA

Auton Motorized Systems, pg 797
Boland Communications, pg 810
Enright Co, pg 861
Extron Electronics, pg 864
Gefen, pg 876
Gyration, pg 883
Lasergraphics Inc, pg 916
Lucasey Manufacturing Corp, pg 925
Pinnacle Systems Inc, pg 975
Pioneer Electronics (USA) Inc, pg 976
POP TV, pg 978
RGB Spectrum, pg 996
Sonance, pg 1015
WolfVision Inc, pg 1069

CONNECTICUT

KOH Design Inc, pg 913
The Video Messenger Co, pg 1055

FLORIDA

Florical Systems Inc, pg 870

GEORGIA

Barco Inc, pg 803
Comprehensive Technical Group, pg 833
PolyVision Corporation, pg 978

ILLINOIS

Dukane Corp, Audio Visual Products Division, pg 853
GBC Document Finishing, pg 876
NEC Display Solutions of America, pg 954

INDIANA

Da-Lite, pg 842

KANSAS

Keywest Technology Inc, pg 910

KENTUCKY

TV One Multimedia Solutions, pg 1046

MARYLAND

Absolute Hollywood, pg 772

MASSACHUSETTS

ASACA/ShibaSoku Corp of America, pg 791
Avidex Inc, pg 799
Elite Video, pg 859

MINNESOTA

Vaddio, pg 1051

NEW JERSEY

Crestron Electronics Inc, pg 839
FSR Inc, pg 873

NEW YORK

Gordon Visual Solutions, pg 880
Uniset Co LLC, pg 1048

OHIO

Network Technologies Inc, pg 955

PENNSYLVANIA

AccuWeather Inc, pg 774
Interactive Products, pg 899
Scala Inc, pg 1003

TENNESSEE

Adtec Digital Inc, pg 777

VIRGINIA

Quince Imaging Inc, pg 989

WASHINGTON

eMagin Corp, pg 860

ONTARIO

Image Video, pg 895
McCurdy Radio Ltd, pg 935

Presentation System Rentals

ALABAMA

Audio-Video Resources Inc, pg 795

ARIZONA

Merestone, pg 938

ARKANSAS

White Diamond Productions, pg 1065

CALIFORNIA

Associated Sound, pg 792
Express Media Inc, pg 864
JD Audio Visual Inc, pg 904
Munday & Collins AV, pg 950
Muse Presentation Technologies, pg 950
VER-Video Equipment Rentals, pg 1053
VMI Inc, pg 1060

CONNECTICUT

A/V Davey, pg 797
Videofilm Systems Inc, pg 1057

FLORIDA

Allstar Audio Systems Inc, pg 782
Astoria Communications Inc, pg 792
Media Concepts Inc, pg 936
Paradise Show & Design Inc, pg 969

GEORGIA

Stage Front Presentation Systems, pg 1022

HAWAII

Hawaii Sound & Vision, pg 886

ILLINOIS

AV Chicago Inc, pg 797
Chicago Satellite & Video, pg 825
RC Communications, pg 992
Show Department Inc, pg 1009

KENTUCKY

Audio Visual Techniques Inc, pg 796

MARYLAND

CPR MultiMedia Solutions, pg 837
Event Tech, pg 863

MASSACHUSETTS

Preston Productions Inc, pg 981

MICHIGAN

K&R All Media Productions Inc, pg 908

MINNESOTA

Alpha Video & Audio Inc, pg 782

MISSOURI

Show-Me Audio-Visual, pg 1009

NEW JERSEY

Earl Girls Inc, pg 855
Starlite Productions, pg 1024

NEW YORK

Design Audio Visual Inc, pg 845
KVL Audio Visual Services Inc, pg 914
SmartSource Computer & AV Rentals, pg 1014
Visual Word Systems Inc, pg 1060

NORTH CAROLINA

A&V Company, pg 772

NORTH DAKOTA

Media Productions, pg 937

OHIO

Bartha, pg 803

OKLAHOMA

PDC Productions, pg 970

PENNSYLVANIA

Bernie's Photo Center, pg 805
Innovision Media Group, pg 899

TENNESSEE

Technical Support Systems LLC, pg 1034

TEXAS

Bright Star Productions Inc, pg 812
Data Display Audio Visual Co LP, pg 843
Stage Directions, pg 1022

VIRGINIA

Advance Concepts Inc, pg 777
Quince Imaging Inc, pg 989

WISCONSIN

Audio Visual of Milwaukee Inc, pg 795

PUERTO RICO

Stage Crew Audiovisual Inc, pg 1022

MANITOBA

Inland Audio Visual Ltd, pg 898

ONTARIO

HD Source, pg 886
Metalworks Recording Studios Inc, pg 939
RB Productions, pg 992
Westbury National Show Systems Ltd, pg 1064

Presentation System Repairs

CALIFORNIA

Electrosonic Inc, pg 859
Sonance, pg 1015
VMI Inc, pg 1060

FLORIDA

ELC Sales & Service Inc, pg 858

GEORGIA

Stage Front Presentation Systems, pg 1022

ILLINOIS

GBC Document Finishing, pg 876

KENTUCKY

Axxis Inc, pg 800
NOR-COM Inc, pg 958

MICHIGAN

TeL Systems, pg 1035

MINNESOTA

Alpha Video & Audio Inc, pg 782

MISSOURI

Schiller's Audio-Visual, pg 1004
Southwest Audio-Visual Inc, pg 1019

NEW JERSEY

Earl Girls Inc, pg 855
Starlite Productions, pg 1024

NEW YORK

Visual Technologies Corp, pg 1060

OHIO

Network Technologies Inc, pg 955
Tri-State Audio Visual Co, pg 1044

PENNSYLVANIA

Bernie's Photo Center, pg 805
J E Foss Co, pg 871

TENNESSEE

Technical Support Systems LLC, pg 1034

VIRGINIA

Avitecture Inc, pg 799
Hoppmann Audio Visual, pg 891
Quince Imaging Inc, pg 989
The Whitlock Group, pg 1065

WISCONSIN

Full Compass Systems, pg 874

MANITOBA

Inland Audio Visual Ltd, pg 898

ONTARIO

HD Source, pg 886
Westbury National Show Systems Ltd, pg 1064

Printing Videos, *see* Volume Printing—Videos

Production Workshops

ALASKA

Alaska Film Services Inc, pg 779

ARIZONA

Direct Current Video Productions, pg 848
Film Creations Ltd, pg 867
Merestone, pg 938
Tellens Inc, pg 1037

CALIFORNIA

Audio Visual Consultants, pg 795
Barbosa Video Services, pg 802
Crystal Pyramid Productions™, pg 840
Film TV Sound, pg 867
JDS Video & Media Productions Inc, pg 904
Maximus Media Inc, pg 934
Palardo Productions, pg 968
QCI International, pg 988
QRS Software Services, pg 988
Dick Reizner Film & Video, pg 994
Russ InVision Co/AbridgeClub.com, pg 1001
Staylor-Made Communications Inc, pg 1024
Vineyard Productions, pg 1058
Visual Communications - Southern California Asian American Studies Central Inc, pg 1059

CONNECTICUT

BRB Audiovisual Productions, pg 812
The Gary-Paul Agency, pg 875

DISTRICT OF COLUMBIA

Interface Media Group, pg 900

FLORIDA

Access Media Group, pg 773
Communications Concepts Inc (CCI), pg 833
Home Shopping Network (HSN), pg 890
Media Concepts Inc, pg 936
Progressive Media & Music, pg 985

GEORGIA

Guerrilla Productions LLC, pg 883
Lighting & Production Equipment Inc, pg 920
On-Line Productions, pg 963

HAWAII

Media Bridge Gamekids, pg 936

IDAHO

Wide Eye Productions, pg 1066

ILLINOIS

Audio Visual Services Corp, pg 796
Beatty TeleVisual Productions, pg 804
CCore Media Inc, pg 821
PSAV® Presentation Services (Hotel Services Division), pg 987

IOWA

The Production House, pg 984

LOUISIANA

Moxie Media, pg 948

MARYLAND

dbF a Media Company, pg 844

MASSACHUSETTS

Award Productions, pg 800
Home Inc, pg 890
MotionArt Studios, pg 947

MICHIGAN

Digi Sign Design LLC, pg 847
K&R's Recording Studios Inc, pg 908
Michigan Recording Arts Institute & Technologies, pg 941

MINNESOTA

Aggressive Records Audio Duplication LLC, pg 778
House of Cinemagraphics, pg 891
MultiMedia, pg 950
Worthwhile Films, pg 1070

NEVADA

HDTV Productions Inc, pg 886
Lefco Video Services Inc, pg 918

NEW HAMPSHIRE

Channell One Video, pg 824

NEW JERSEY

Diversified Systems Inc, pg 849
Euro-Pacific Film & Video Productions Inc, pg 863
MIB Mediaworks, pg 941
Suede Interactive, pg 1027
York Telecom, pg 1072

NEW MEXICO

Blue Sky Stock Footage, pg 810

NEW YORK

Digital Art Video Inc, pg 847
Downtown Community Television Center (DCTV), pg 851
HB-Content, pg 886
Richard Kaplan Productions, pg 908
La Paloma Films, pg 915
Neal Marshad Productions, pg 931
TBA Global Events, pg 1032
Teatown Communications Group, pg 1033
Third World Newsreel/Camera News Inc, pg 1039
Zelman Studios Ltd, pg 1073

NORTH CAROLINA

Duke Media Services, pg 853

OHIO

Advent Media Inc, pg 778
Aztec Video Productions, pg 801
Cuyahoga Community College Media Center, pg 841
Vista Color Imaging Inc, pg 1059

OREGON

Odyssey Productions Inc, pg 961

PENNSYLVANIA

Video/Film Associates, pg 1055
The Videohouse Inc, pg 1057
Visual Sound Inc, pg 1059

RHODE ISLAND

Sound-FX-Design, pg 1017

TENNESSEE

Stage Post, pg 1022
Zion Music Group, pg 1074

TEXAS

McNee Productions Inc, pg 935
Julye Newlin Productions Inc, pg 956
Richie Media Productions LLC, pg 996
Romar Learning, pg 999

VIRGINIA

Gingerbread Productions, pg 878
Rocktown Media, pg 998

WASHINGTON

911 Media Arts Center, pg 957
Pro Image, pg 983
Ritchie's Perfect Press, pg 997
Victory Studios, pg 1054

WISCONSIN

Audio Visual of Milwaukee Inc, pg 795
AVS Group, pg 800
USAV Group Inc, pg 1050
Wisconsin Public Television, pg 1068

BRITISH COLUMBIA

Finale Editworks, pg 868
Video In Studios/Video Out Distribution, pg 1055

ONTARIO

GAPC (General Assembly Production Centre), pg 875
Image Video Services & Productions, pg 895

QUEBEC

Trebas Institute, pg 1044

Projector & Projection System Distributors

ALABAMA

Curtis Company, pg 841
Media Visions Inc, pg 937

ARIZONA

Audio Video Resources, pg 795
EAR Professional Audio/Video, pg 855
Metropolitan Audio-Visual Inc, pg 940
Projector SuperStore LLC, pg 986
Troxell Communications Inc, pg 1045
Ultimate Presentation Systems Inc, pg 1047

ARKANSAS

Carlton-Bates Co, pg 820
Jay S Stanley & Associates Inc, pg 1023
White Diamond Productions, pg 1065

CALIFORNIA

Advanced Systems Group LLC, pg 778
Ametron Audio/Video, pg 785
Associated Sound, pg 792
Audio/Video Supply Inc, pg 795
AV Conferencing, pg 797
Barber Tech Video Products, pg 802
Be Media, pg 804
BroadcastStore.com, pg 813
California Tape Products Inc, pg 817
Christie Digital Systems USA Inc, pg 825
Christy's Editorial, pg 826
Cinema Equipment Sales of California Inc, pg 827
Cinema Xenon International Inc, pg 827
Delicate Electronics Sales Inc, pg 845
Eiki International, pg 858
Electrosonic Inc, pg 859
Gluskin's Custom Audio Video, pg 879
Instructional Materials & Equipment Distributors (I-Med), pg 899
Inter Video, pg 899
JD Audio Visual Inc, pg 904
Lloyd F McKinney Associates Inc, pg 935
Media Fabricators Inc, pg 936
MediaPOINTE, pg 938
Mitsubishi Electric Visual Solutions America Inc (MEVSA), pg 944
Mobilized Tech Systems, pg 944
Muse Presentation Technologies, pg 950
PMP Marketing Inc, pg 977
POP TV, pg 978
Premier Lighting & Production Co, pg 980
Related Visual Inc, pg 994
SNAP, pg 1014
Sound Service Co, pg 1017
Southern California Sound Image Inc, pg 1019
Stanislaus Audio Video Inc, pg 1023

VIDEO

Projector & Projection System Distributors (continued)

CALIFORNIA (continued)

SuperVision, pg 1029
Tri-Ed, pg 1044
VMI Inc, pg 1060

COLORADO

Ceavco Audio/Visual Co, pg 822
Daylight Productions & Rentals, pg 844
Spectrum Audio Visual Services, pg 1020

CONNECTICUT

Concord Communications, pg 835
General Electric Co, pg 876
MAVCO, pg 934
Rockwell Communications Inc, pg 998

DISTRICT OF COLUMBIA

Future View Inc, pg 874

FLORIDA

Access Media Group, pg 773
A2D Solutions Inc, pg 793
AVI-SPL, pg 798
BAI Distributors Inc, pg 801
Cinema Equipment & Supplies Inc, pg 827
Digital Video Systems Inc, pg 848
General Projection Systems Inc, pg 877
Glanz Technologies Inc, pg 878
Harmon's Audio-Visual Services, pg 885
Hollywood Theatre Equipment Inc, pg 890
Industrial Strength Inc, pg 897
Media Concepts Inc, pg 936
Photomart Cine-Video Inc, pg 975
Photosound of Orlando Inc, pg 975
Pro Stage Inc, pg 983
Sight & Sound Productions, pg 1010
Skyline Broadcast, pg 1013
Tallahassee Audio Visual, pg 1031
Techni-Lux Inc, pg 1033

GEORGIA

Audio Visual Resources Inc, pg 795
AVForSale, pg 798
Baker Audio Inc, pg 801
Cinevision Corp, pg 828
Convergent Media Systems, pg 836
Digital Projection, pg 847
Lighting & Production Equipment Inc, pg 920
Omnimedia Inc, pg 962
Stage Front Presentation Systems, pg 1022
Technical Innovation, pg 1033

ILLINOIS

Allen Visual Systems Inc, pg 781
Chicago Spotlight Inc, pg 825
G T Luscombe Co Inc, pg 926
Quintessence Audio Ltd, pg 989
RC Communications, pg 992
The Screen Works®, pg 1005
Tele-Time Systems, pg 1036

INDIANA

Heart Breaker Entertainment LLC, pg 887
Lee Co Inc, pg 918
Sensory Technologies LLC, pg 1006
SHP Electronics, pg 1010
Victoria Supply Inc/Topbulb.com, pg 1054

IOWA

ECS Inc, pg 856

KANSAS

SKC Communication Products Inc, pg 1012
Smith Audio-Visual Inc, pg 1014

KENTUCKY

Axxis Inc, pg 800
Barney Miller's Inc, pg 943
NOR-COM Inc, pg 958

LOUISIANA

Intermedia Technologies, pg 900

MAINE

Headlight Audio Visual Inc, pg 887

MARYLAND

Absolute Hollywood, pg 772
Cardinal Sound & Video, pg 820
Nelson White Systems Inc, pg 954
Nicholas P Pipino Associates Inc, pg 976
RTZ Audio Visual, pg 1000
Visual Aids Electronics Corp, pg 1059

MASSACHUSETTS

Elite Video, pg 859
Rule Broadcast Systems, pg 1000

MICHIGAN

Olson Anderson Co, pg 786
ASC Systems, pg 791
Ascom Communications Contractors, pg 791
Michigan Office Solutions, pg 941
TeL Systems, pg 1035

MINNESOTA

Advanced Audio-Visual Inc, pg 777
Alpha Video & Audio Inc, pg 782
AVI Systems, pg 799
New Life Communications Inc, pg 956

MISSISSIPPI

Bowie Audio Visual Enterprises Inc, pg 811
Jasper Ewing & Sons Inc, pg 864

MISSOURI

Communitronics Corp, pg 833
Conference Technologies Inc, pg 835
Image Technologies Corp, pg 895
MIS Technologies, pg 944
Modern Communications Inc, pg 944
Production Support Services Inc, pg 985
Southwest Audio-Visual Inc, pg 1019
Swank Audio Visuals, pg 1029

NEBRASKA

ATV Research Inc, pg 793
Dog & Pony Productions Inc, pg 850
Video Service of America Inc (VSA), pg 1056

NEVADA

Aardvark Video & Media Productions, pg 772
MeshTel-Intelite, pg 939

NEW JERSEY

A-V Services Inc, pg 771
Alltec Stores, a Vcom IMC Company, pg 782
Argraph Corp, pg 789
Audio Visual Associates, pg 795
Audio Visual Dynamics®, pg 795
AV Bluebook, pg 797
Diversified Systems Inc, pg 849
Earl Girls Inc, pg 855
G&G Technologies Inc, pg 875
Hamilton Buhl, pg 884
SLD Lighting, pg 1013
Starlite Productions, pg 1024
SYMCO Inc, pg 1030
Tele-Measurements Inc, pg 1035
Total Video Products Inc, pg 1042
Turner Engineering Inc, pg 1046
Video Corporation of America (VCA), pg 1055
Wired 4 Sound Inc, pg 1068

NEW YORK

Adwar Video, pg 778
ALTEL Systems Inc, pg 783
American Video Inc, pg 785
AV Workshop, pg 797
Canon USA Inc, pg 819
Communication Corner Inc, pg 832
Custom Media Environments, pg 841
Design Audio Visual Inc, pg 845
Gaylord Brothers, pg 876
General Audio-Visual Inc (GAVI), pg 876
Gordon Visual Solutions, pg 880
Indigo Productions, pg 897
Langie Audio Visual Systems, pg 915
A Liss & Co, pg 922
Long Island Video Enterprises Live Inc, pg 924
Magnaplan Corp, pg 928
Markertek Video Supply, pg 931
Neptune Photo Inc, pg 954
Presentation Products Inc, pg 981
Ray Supply Inc, pg 992
RNJ Electronics, pg 997
RTS Inc, pg 1000
SmartSource Computer & AV Rentals, pg 1014
Stampede Presentation Products Inc, pg 1023
Technisphere Corp, pg 1034
Visual Technologies Corp, pg 1060
Visual Word Systems Inc, pg 1060
Willoughby's Imaging Center, pg 1067

NORTH CAROLINA

Camcor Inc, pg 818
Carolina Biological Supply Co, pg 820
Strategic Connections, pg 1026

OHIO

Audio Visual Media, pg 795
Copp Integrated Systems, pg 836
ITA Audio Visual Solutions, pg 902
Jimmy Rea Electronics Inc, pg 992
Smithall Electronics Inc, pg 1014
Tri-State Audio Visual Co, pg 1044
Tri-State Visual Products, pg 1044

OREGON

PLUS Corp of America, pg 977
Spectrum Systems Design, pg 1021

PENNSYLVANIA

Advanced AV, pg 777
Audio Visions Inc, pg 795
Bernie's Photo Center, pg 805
Brodart Co, pg 813
Clair Brothers Audio Systems Inc, pg 829
J E Foss Co, pg 871
Garcia Marketing Inc, pg 875
Hite Co, pg 889
The Lerro Corp, pg 919
Morefield Communications Inc, pg 946
RSS Distributors, pg 1000
Vistacom Inc, pg 1059
Visual Sound Inc, pg 1059
Wespen Audio Visual Co, pg 1063

RHODE ISLAND

Custom Computer Specialists Inc, pg 841
Shanix Inc, pg 1008

TENNESSEE

Auratron Systems, pg 796
Continental Film, pg 835
Lowrance Sound Co Inc, pg 925
Memphis Communications Corp, pg 938
Technical Support Systems LLC, pg 1034
Tennessee Visual Service Co, pg 1037

TEXAS

Audio Visual Technologies Group, pg 796
AVES Audio Visual Systems Inc, pg 798
Data Projections Inc, pg 843
Digital Display Solutions Inc, pg 847
Heffernan Audio Visual, pg 887
J&S Audio Visual Inc, pg 904
Media Management LLC, pg 937
Schoolhouse Audio Visual, pg 1004
Tarpley Media Systems, pg 1032

UTAH

RIA Corp, pg 996
TV Specialists Inc, pg 1046
Webb Audio Visual Communication, pg 1063

VIRGINIA

Avitecture Inc, pg 799
Boitnott Visual Communications Corp (BVC), pg 810
Communications Specialists Inc, pg 833
Hoppmann Audio Visual, pg 891
Intellidyne LLC, pg 899
Lee Hartman & Sons Inc, pg 918
Quince Imaging Inc, pg 989
StageSound, pg 1023
The Whitlock Group, pg 1065

WASHINGTON

Boxlight Inc, pg 811
Inland Audio Visual Co, pg 898
Laser Fantasy/HECK Industries/ Photon Manufacturing, pg 916
Osum Event Rentals, pg 966

WISCONSIN

Audio Visual of Milwaukee Inc, pg 795
Camera Corner Connecting Point, pg 818
Demco Inc, pg 845
Full Compass Systems, pg 874
Safe Harbor Computers, pg 1001

PUERTO RICO

Audio Visual Concepts Inc, pg 795

ALBERTA

Matrix Video Communications Corp (MVCC), pg 934
Sharp's Audio-Visual Ltd, pg 1008
SMART Technologies Inc, pg 1013

BRITISH COLUMBIA

DL Sound & Lighting Productions Ltd, pg 849
ProVision Video Sales & Rentals Inc, pg 986

MANITOBA

Inland Audio Visual Ltd, pg 898

ONTARIO

Cinema Stage Inc, pg 827
Edcom Multimedia Products, pg 856
HD Source, pg 886
Nationwide Audio Visual Co, pg 953
Premier A/V Sales Ltd, pg 980
Westbury National Show Systems Ltd, pg 1064

QUEBEC

AVW-TELAV Audio Visual Solutions, a Freeman Company, pg 800
Panavideo Inc, pg 968

Projector & Projection System Manufacturers

CALIFORNIA

Christie Digital Systems USA Inc, pg 825
Cinema Xenon International Inc, pg 827
Enright Co, pg 861
JDSU, pg 905
Laser Magic Productions, pg 916
Mitsubishi Electric Visual Solutions America Inc (MEVSA), pg 944
Panasonic Broadcast & Digital Systems Co, pg 968
Panasonic Professional Audio Systems, pg 968
POP TV, pg 978
Stewart Filmscreen Corp, pg 1025

CONNECTICUT

General Electric Co, pg 876
KOH Design Inc, pg 913

FLORIDA

SVS Inc, pg 1029
Vutec Corp, Video Products Division, pg 1061

GEORGIA

Digital Projection, pg 847

ILLINOIS

ACCO Brands Corp, pg 773
Dukane Corp, Audio Visual Products Division, pg 853
NEC Display Solutions of America, pg 954

MARYLAND

Absolute Hollywood, pg 772

MASSACHUSETTS

Elite Video, pg 859

NEBRASKA

Strong Cinema Products, pg 1026

NEVADA

MeshTel-Intelite, pg 939

NEW JERSEY

CELCO-Constantine Engineering Labs Co, pg 822
Gerriets International, pg 877
Sharp Electronics Corp, Professional Display Division, pg 1008

NEW YORK

American Video Inc, pg 785
Canon USA Inc, pg 819
Gordon Visual Solutions, pg 880
Hitachi Kokusai Electric America Ltd, pg 889

OHIO

Xetron, pg 1071

PENNSYLVANIA

Questar Corp, pg 989

VIRGINIA

Optikinetics Ltd - The Americas, pg 964
Quince Imaging Inc, pg 989

ALBERTA

SMART Technologies Inc, pg 1013

BRITISH COLUMBIA

Triad Communications Ltd, pg 1044

Projector & Projection System Rentals

ALABAMA

Audio-Video Resources Inc, pg 795

ARIZONA

Audio Video Resources, pg 795
AV Concepts, pg 797
Creative Backstage, pg 838
Merestone, pg 938
Metropolitan Audio-Visual Inc, pg 940
Ultimate Presentation Systems Inc, pg 1047
Video Media Productions (VMP), pg 1055
Video West Inc, pg 1056

ARKANSAS

White Diamond Productions, pg 1065

CALIFORNIA

Absolute Rentals, pg 772
Action Audio & Visual, pg 775
Action Video, pg 775
Adolph Gasser Inc, pg 776
Advanced Media LLC, pg 778
AGF Media Services, pg 778
Alliant Event Services, pg 781
Alternative Rentals, pg 783
Ametron Audio/Video, pg 785
Associated Sound, pg 792
ATV Video Center Inc, pg 793
Audio/Video Supply Inc, pg 795
AV Conferencing, pg 797
AV Guys, pg 797
Barber Tech Video Products, pg 802
Cherry Multimedia, pg 824
Express Media Inc, pg 864
Fuller Street Productions, pg 874
Gluskin's Custom Audio Video, pg 879
Gold Standard Productions, pg 880
Alan Gordon Enterprises Inc, pg 880
Impact Group, pg 897
Instructional Materials & Equipment Distributors (I-Med), pg 899
Inter Video, pg 899
JD Audio Visual Inc, pg 904
Lynch Communications, pg 926
McCune Audio-Video-Lighting, pg 935
Media Fabricators Inc, pg 936
Munday & Collins AV, pg 950
Muse Presentation Technologies, pg 950
Next Arts, pg 957
On-Trax Inc, pg 963
Panorama Productions, pg 968
Premier Lighting & Production Co, pg 980
PSAV® Presentation Services, pg 986
Pyxis Industries Inc, pg 988
Related Visual Inc, pg 994
Slate Media Group, pg 1013
Sound Service Co, pg 1017
Stanislaus Audio Video Inc, pg 1023
Tri-Ed, pg 1044
University of Southern California, pg 1050
VER-Video Equipment Rentals, pg 1053
VMI Inc, pg 1060

COLORADO

Ceavco Audio/Visual Co, pg 822
Daylight Productions & Rentals, pg 844
Multimedia Audio Visual Inc, pg 950
Open Media Foundation, pg 964
Spectrum Audio Visual Services, pg 1020

CONNECTICUT

A/V Davey, pg 797
Concord Communications, pg 835
EagleVision Inc, pg 855
General Electric Co, pg 876
Rockwell Communications Inc, pg 998
Videofilm Systems Inc, pg 1057

DELAWARE

Ken-Del Productions Inc, pg 909
Showorks Audio Visual Inc, pg 1010

DISTRICT OF COLUMBIA

Future View Inc, pg 874

FLORIDA

Access Media Group, pg 773
Astoria Communications Inc, pg 792
AVI-SPL, pg 798
Eastern Video, pg 856
Glanz Technologies Inc, pg 878
Harmon's Audio-Visual Services, pg 885
Industrial Strength Inc, pg 897
Jordan Klein Film & Video (JKFV), pg 906
Media Concepts Inc, pg 936
Midtown Video Inc, pg 942
Paradise Show & Design Inc, pg 969
Photosound of Orlando Inc, pg 975
Pro Stage Inc, pg 983
Sight & Sound Productions, pg 1010
Sound*Light, pg 1017
Tallahassee Audio Visual, pg 1031

GEORGIA

Audio Visual Resources Inc, pg 795
Cinevision Corp, pg 828
Convergent Media Systems, pg 836
Lighting & Production Equipment Inc, pg 920
ON Event Services, pg 963
Stage Front Presentation Systems, pg 1022

HAWAII

Hawaii Sound & Vision, pg 886
Ken Herkes Productions & Entertainment (KHPE), pg 888

ILLINOIS

Allen Visual Systems Inc, pg 781
Audio Visual Services Corp, pg 796
AV Chicago Inc, pg 797
Backstar Creative Media Inc, pg 801
Beatty TeleVisual Productions, pg 804
Chicago Spotlight Inc, pg 825
Creative Technology, pg 838
The Meetinghouse Companies Inc, pg 938
The Pepper Group, pg 972
PSAV® Presentation Services (Hotel Services Division), pg 987
QuickSet International Inc, pg 989
RC Communications, pg 992
Roadworthy Image Magnification, pg 998
SCI Television Productions LLC, pg 1004
The Screen Works®, pg 1005
2nd Cine, pg 1006
Show Department Inc, pg 1009
Staging Resources Inc, pg 1023
Tele-Time Systems, pg 1036

VIDEO

Projector & Projection System Rentals (continued)

INDIANA

Advanced Media Integration, pg 777
Heart Breaker Entertainment LLC, pg 887
OMNI Productions, pg 962

IOWA

Central Lighting & Equipment Inc (CLE), pg 823
ECS Inc, pg 856
Pro Video, pg 983

KENTUCKY

Audio Visual Techniques Inc, pg 796
Barney Miller's Inc, pg 943

LOUISIANA

Clark Services Audio Visual & Exhibit Inc, pg 829
Digital FX Inc, pg 847
Pace Systems, pg 966

MAINE

Via-Vision Film & Video Productions, pg 1053

MARYLAND

Absolute Hollywood, pg 772
Advance Audiovisual Presentation Ltd, pg 777
CPR MultiMedia Solutions, pg 837
Event Tech, pg 863
Hargrove Inc, pg 885
Nelson White Systems Inc, pg 954
RTZ Audio Visual, pg 1000
Visual Aids Electronics Corp, pg 1059

MASSACHUSETTS

AVFX Inc, pg 798
Capron Lighting & Sound Co Inc, pg 819
Elite Video, pg 859
massAV, pg 933
Preston Productions Inc, pg 981

MICHIGAN

Olson Anderson Co, pg 786
City Events Group, pg 828
K&R All Media Productions Inc, pg 908
K&R's Recording Studios Inc, pg 908
TeL Systems, pg 1035

MINNESOTA

Alpha Video & Audio Inc, pg 782
AVI Systems, pg 799

MISSISSIPPI

Bowie Audio Visual Enterprises Inc, pg 811

MISSOURI

Cashmark Media Inc, pg 820
Production Support Services Inc, pg 985
Schiller's Audio-Visual, pg 1004
Show-Me Audio-Visual, pg 1009
Southwest Audio-Visual Inc, pg 1019
Swank Audio Visuals, pg 1029
Switch, pg 1030
Wise Audio Video, pg 1068

NEBRASKA

Dog & Pony Productions Inc, pg 850

NEVADA

GES Audio Visual, pg 877
JCS Video Productions, pg 904
Lefco Video Services Inc, pg 918

NEW JERSEY

Audio Visual Associates, pg 795
Audio Visual Dynamics®, pg 795
Earl Girls Inc, pg 855
Gerriets International, pg 877
International Audio Visual Inc, pg 900
MB Productions, pg 934
PLS Staging, pg 977
SLD Lighting, pg 1013
Soundtracks Production Services LLC, pg 1018
Starlite Productions, pg 1024
Video Corporation of America (VCA), pg 1055
Wired 4 Sound Inc, pg 1068

NEW YORK

Adwar Video, pg 778
American Video Inc, pg 785
Audio Visual Resources LLC, pg 795
AV Workshop, pg 797
CMI Communications, pg 830
Communication Corner Inc, pg 832
Design Audio Visual Inc, pg 845
General Audio-Visual Inc (GAVI), pg 876
Hello World Communications, pg 888
Langie Audio Visual Systems, pg 915
Long Island Video Enterprises Live Inc, pg 924
Magnaplan Corp, pg 928
Manhattan Center Studios Inc, pg 930
MRG Productions Inc, pg 948
Production Central, pg 984
SmartSource Computer & AV Rentals, pg 1014
Specialized Audio-Visual Inc, pg 1020
Technisphere Corp, pg 1034
Visual Technologies Corp, pg 1060
Visual Word Systems Inc, pg 1060
WorldStage, pg 1070

NORTH CAROLINA

A&V Company, pg 772
AV Metro Inc, pg 797
Camcor Inc, pg 818
Special Event Services, pg 1020
Strategic Connections, pg 1026
Visual Aids Electronics of North Carolina Inc, pg 1059

NORTH DAKOTA

Media Productions, pg 937

OHIO

Audio Visual Media, pg 795
Hughie's Event Production Services, pg 892
ITA Audio Visual Solutions, pg 902
Mills James Productions, pg 943
OSV Studios, pg 966

OKLAHOMA

PDC Productions, pg 970

OREGON

Northwest Film Center, pg 959
Picture This Production Services, pg 975

PENNSYLVANIA

Advanced AV, pg 777
Audio Visions Inc, pg 795
Audio Visual Communications Inc, pg 795
New York Camera & Video, pg 956
North Star Satellite Communications Inc, pg 959
Producers Management Television (PMTV), pg 983
Vistacom Inc, pg 1059
Visual Sound Inc, pg 1059

SOUTH CAROLINA

Sound & Images Inc, pg 1016

TENNESSEE

Memphis Communications Corp, pg 938
NuMynd Studios, pg 960
Russ Sturgeon Productions/RSVP, pg 1027
Technical Support Systems LLC, pg 1034
Tennessee Visual Service Co, pg 1037

TEXAS

Alford Media Services, pg 780
Audio Visual Technologies Group, pg 796
AVES Audio Visual Systems Inc, pg 798
Big House Sound Inc, pg 807
Bright Giant Creative Group, pg 812
Bright Star Productions Inc, pg 812
FitzCo Sound Inc, pg 869
GEAR Cameras & Lighting, pg 876
Industrial Audio/Video Inc, pg 897
J&S Audio Visual Inc, pg 904
Media Event Concepts Inc, pg 936
Padgitt's, pg 967

UTAH

TV Specialists Inc, pg 1046
Webb Audio Visual Communication, pg 1063

VERMONT

Dark Star Lighting & Production, pg 842

VIRGINIA

Advance Concepts Inc, pg 777
Audio Visual Actions Inc (AVA), pg 795
Boitnott Visual Communications Corp (BVC), pg 810
Creative Video of Washington Inc, pg 839
Lee Hartman & Sons Inc, pg 918
Projection Presentation Technology, pg 985
Quince Imaging Inc, pg 989
StageSound, pg 1023
The Whitlock Group, pg 1065

WASHINGTON

Boxlight Inc, pg 811
Inland Audio Visual Co, pg 898
Kostov Productions, pg 913
911 Media Arts Center, pg 957
Osum Event Rentals, pg 966

WISCONSIN

Audio Visual of Milwaukee Inc, pg 795
Event Essentials, pg 863
Full Compass Systems, pg 874
Logan Productions Inc, pg 924

PUERTO RICO

Stage Crew Audiovisual Inc, pg 1022

ALBERTA

Cine Audio Visual Sales & Service Ltd, pg 826
Global Television Station, pg 879
L R Light & Sound, pg 915
Matrix Video Communications Corp (MVCC), pg 934
Sharp's Audio-Visual Ltd, pg 1008
Unique Communications Ltd, pg 1048

BRITISH COLUMBIA

Clark's Audio Visual Services Ltd, pg 829
Commercial Electronics Ltd, pg 832
DL Sound & Lighting Productions Ltd, pg 849
ProVision Video Sales & Rentals Inc, pg 986
Triad Communications Ltd, pg 1044
24 Frames Film & Video, pg 1047
Video In Studios/Video Out Distribution, pg 1055

MANITOBA

Evolution Presentation Technologies, pg 863
Inland Audio Visual Ltd, pg 898

ONTARIO

Edcom Multimedia Products, pg 856
HD Source, pg 886
Metalworks Recording Studios Inc, pg 939
MVI Multivision Inc, pg 951
Premier A/V Sales Ltd, pg 980
RB Productions, pg 992
SIM Digital, pg 1011
Westbury National Show Systems Ltd, pg 1064

QUEBEC

Audio Visual Dynamics Ltd, pg 795
AVW-TELAV Audio Visual Solutions, a Freeman Company, pg 800
Panavideo Inc, pg 968

Projector & Projection System Repairs

CALIFORNIA

Advanced Media LLC, pg 778
Advanced Systems Group LLC, pg 778

Ametron Audio/Video, pg 785
Christie Digital Systems USA Inc, pg 825
Digitron Electronics, pg 848
Electrosonic Inc, pg 859
Instructional Materials & Equipment Distributors (I-Med), pg 899
Lloyd F McKinney Associates Inc, pg 935
Tri-Ed, pg 1044
VMI Inc, pg 1060

COLORADO

Ceavco Audio/Visual Co, pg 822

CONNECTICUT

A/V Davey, pg 797
General Electric Co, pg 876
Rockwell Communications Inc, pg 998

FLORIDA

Digital Video Systems Inc, pg 848
ELC Sales & Service Inc, pg 858
Glanz Technologies Inc, pg 878
Hi-Tech Enterprises Inc, pg 888
Media Concepts Inc, pg 936
Tallahassee Audio Visual, pg 1031

GEORGIA

Audio Visual Resources Inc, pg 795
Lighting & Production Equipment Inc, pg 920
Stage Front Presentation Systems, pg 1022
Technical Innovation, pg 1033

ILLINOIS

Allen Visual Systems Inc, pg 781
Beatty TeleVisual Productions, pg 804
Chicago Spotlight Inc, pg 825
Midwest Digital Corp, pg 942
RC Communications, pg 992
Tele-Time Systems, pg 1036

IOWA

ECS Inc, pg 856

KENTUCKY

Axxis Inc, pg 800
Barney Miller's Inc, pg 943
NOR-COM Inc, pg 958

MARYLAND

Nelson White Systems Inc, pg 954
RTZ Audio Visual, pg 1000
Strauss Photo Technical Service Inc, pg 1026
Visual Aids Electronics Corp, pg 1059

MASSACHUSETTS

Camera Co Inc/Broadcast Divison, pg 818
Elite Video, pg 859

MICHIGAN

Olson Anderson Co, pg 786
TeL Systems, pg 1035

MINNESOTA

Alpha Video & Audio Inc, pg 782
AVI Systems, pg 799

MISSISSIPPI

Bowie Audio Visual Enterprises Inc, pg 811

MISSOURI

Schiller's Audio-Visual, pg 1004
Southwest Audio-Visual Inc, pg 1019

NEW JERSEY

Audio Visual Associates, pg 795
Earl Girls Inc, pg 855
Starlite Productions, pg 1024
Turner Engineering Inc, pg 1046

NEW YORK

Adwar Video, pg 778
American Video Inc, pg 785
Colortone Audio Visual, pg 832
General Audio-Visual Inc (GAVI), pg 876
Langie Audio Visual Systems, pg 915
MRG Productions Inc, pg 948
Ray Supply Inc, pg 992
Technisphere Corp, pg 1034
Visual Technologies Corp, pg 1060

NORTH CAROLINA

Camcor Inc, pg 818
Strategic Connections, pg 1026

OHIO

Audio Visual Media, pg 795
Copp Integrated Systems, pg 836
ITA Audio Visual Solutions, pg 902
Tri-State Audio Visual Co, pg 1044
Tri-State Visual Products, pg 1044

PENNSYLVANIA

J E Foss Co, pg 871
Vistacom Inc, pg 1059
Visual Sound Inc, pg 1059

TENNESSEE

Memphis Communications Corp, pg 938
Technical Support Systems LLC, pg 1034
Tennessee Visual Service Co, pg 1037

TEXAS

Audio Visual Technologies Group, pg 796
Digital Display Solutions Inc, pg 847
Industrial Audio/Video Inc, pg 897
Padgitt's, pg 967
Tarpley Media Systems, pg 1032

UTAH

TV Specialists Inc, pg 1046

VIRGINIA

Avitecture Inc, pg 799
Boitnott Visual Communications Corp (BVC), pg 810
Hoppmann Audio Visual, pg 891
Lee Hartman & Sons Inc, pg 918
Metropolitan Audio Visual Co LLC, pg 940
Quince Imaging Inc, pg 989
The Whitlock Group, pg 1065

WASHINGTON

Boxlight Inc, pg 811
Inland Audio Visual Co, pg 898

WISCONSIN

Full Compass Systems, pg 874

ALBERTA

Matrix Video Communications Corp (MVCC), pg 934
Sharp's Audio-Visual Ltd, pg 1008

BRITISH COLUMBIA

Commercial Electronics Ltd, pg 832

MANITOBA

Inland Audio Visual Ltd, pg 898

ONTARIO

Edcom Multimedia Products, pg 856
HD Source, pg 886
MVI Multivision Inc, pg 951
Premier A/V Sales Ltd, pg 980
Westbury National Show Systems Ltd, pg 1064

QUEBEC

Panavideo Inc, pg 968

Property Agencies—Television, *see* Talent & Property Agencies—Television

Raw Stock Distributors

ALABAMA

Media Visions Inc, pg 937

ARIZONA

Metropolitan Audio-Visual Inc, pg 940
Video Media Productions (VMP), pg 1055

CALIFORNIA

Adolph Gasser Inc, pg 776
Advanced Media LLC, pg 778
Advanced Systems Group LLC, pg 778
Ametron Audio/Video, pg 785
Audio/Video Supply Inc, pg 795
California Tape Products Inc, pg 817
Edgewise Media Inc, pg 856
Alan Gordon Enterprises Inc, pg 880
Media Fabricators Inc, pg 936
Tri-Ed, pg 1044

COLORADO

The Cinema Lab, pg 827
Stanco Sales LLC, pg 1023

CONNECTICUT

Concord Communications, pg 835
Rockwell Communications Inc, pg 998

FLORIDA

Jordan Klein Film & Video (JKFV), pg 906
Pro Stage Inc, pg 983
Summit Electronics Corp, pg 1028

GEORGIA

Video Copy Services Inc, pg 1055

HAWAII

Sight & Sound Studios, pg 1010

ILLINOIS

Creative Technology, pg 838

INDIANA

Sensory Technologies LLC, pg 1006

KENTUCKY

American Recordable Media, pg 785

MARYLAND

Nicholas P Pipino Associates Inc, pg 976

MICHIGAN

TeL Systems, pg 1035

MINNESOTA

Cinequipt Inc, pg 828
Stoney-Wolf Productions Inc, pg 1025

MISSOURI

Southwest Audio-Visual Inc, pg 1019

NEVADA

Aardvark Video & Media Productions, pg 772

NEW JERSEY

MIB Mediaworks, pg 941
Starlite Productions, pg 1024
Video Corporation of America (VCA), pg 1055

NEW YORK

Aura Sonic Ltd, pg 796
Burlington A/V Recording Media, pg 815
Communication Corner Inc, pg 832
Film Emporium, pg 867
HAVE Inc, pg 886
Long Island Video Enterprises Live Inc, pg 924
Moviola, pg 948
Rafik, pg 990
Technisphere Corp, pg 1034

OHIO

iVideo Technologies, pg 903

OKLAHOMA

Piper Media Services Inc, pg 976

OREGON

Wilderness Video, pg 1066

VIDEO

Raw Stock Distributors (continued)

PENNSYLVANIA

Advanced AV, pg 777
Morefield Communications Inc, pg 946
The Whale Video Co, pg 1065

TENNESSEE

Memphis Communications Corp, pg 938
Phoenix Aerial Photography Inc, pg 974

TEXAS

Texcam Inc, pg 1038

VIRGINIA

Creative Video of Washington Inc, pg 839
Filmdex Inc, pg 867

WISCONSIN

Audio Visual of Milwaukee Inc, pg 795
Camera Corner Connecting Point, pg 818
Full Compass Systems, pg 874

ONTARIO

FUJIFILM Canada Inc, pg 873
HD Source, pg 886

Raw Stock Manufacturers

COLORADO

InJoy Birth & Parenting Education, pg 898

FLORIDA

Vutec Corp, Video Products Division, pg 1061

OREGON

Wilderness Video, pg 1066

PENNSYLVANIA

FMP Media Solutions Inc, pg 870

WISCONSIN

Full Compass Systems, pg 874

ONTARIO

FUJIFILM Canada Inc, pg 873

Receiver, *see* Video Receiver & Monitor

Recorder, *see* Video Recorder & Player

Recording Facility Distributors

ILLINOIS

Major Media Inc, pg 929

Recording Facility Manufacturers

CALIFORNIA

Westlake Recording Studios, pg 1064
Yanchar Design & Consulting Group, pg 1072

MARYLAND

RPG Diffusor Systems Inc, pg 1000

MICHIGAN

Studio Consulting & Construction Inc, pg 1026

NEW JERSEY

Radio Visions, pg 990
Turner Engineering Inc, pg 1046

NEW YORK

CP Communications, pg 837
IAC Acoustics, pg 893

PENNSYLVANIA

Kloss Studios Co, pg 912

TEXAS

Acoustic Systems, pg 774

VIRGINIA

Acoustics First Corp, pg 775

BRITISH COLUMBIA

Triad Communications Ltd, pg 1044

Recording Facility Rentals

ALABAMA

AVS Media Group, pg 800

ARIZONA

Arizona Virtual Studios, pg 790
Cox Creative Studios, pg 837
Crew West Inc, pg 839
Glendale Media Center, pg 878
Illuma Studios, pg 894
Loft 19, pg 924
Merestone, pg 938
Rodeo Video Inc, pg 998
Video Media Productions (VMP), pg 1055

ARKANSAS

Jones Film Video, pg 906
White Diamond Productions, pg 1065

CALIFORNIA

Absolute Rentals, pg 772
Adolph Gasser Inc, pg 776
Ametron Audio/Video, pg 785
AMG Studios-Los Angeles, pg 785
Arctek Studios, pg 789
Artichoke Productions, pg 791
Big Time Picture Company Inc, pg 807
Blue Lotus Temple Studio, pg 809
CenterStaging LLC, pg 822
Cherry Multimedia, pg 824
Crystal Pyramid Productions™, pg 840
Cutting Edge Productions, pg 841
Dystopian Studios, pg 854
5 Alarm Music, pg 869
Flip 2 Media Inc, pg 870
Full Moon & High Tide Productions & Studios, pg 874
Glendale Production Centre, pg 878
Golden Gate Studios, pg 880
Greenery Studios, pg 882
Groovy Like a Movie, pg 882
Hampshire Street Studios, pg 884
Hollywood Center Studios, pg 890
Hollywood Loft, pg 890
Hybrid Studios, pg 892
Illuminate Studios, pg 894
Images in Motion Media Inc, pg 896
JFA Studio, pg 905
KESSPRO Studios, pg 910
KTVU-Retail Services, pg 914
LA Castle Studios, pg 915
Laurel Canyon Stages, pg 916
Los Angeles Center Studios, pg 924
Loyal Studios, pg 925
LW Media Group, pg 926
Lynch Communications, pg 926
Maximus Media Inc, pg 934
McCune Audio-Video-Lighting, pg 935
McCune Design, pg 935
MediaOne Services, pg 938
New Deal Studios, pg 955
North County Media Center, pg 959
On-Trax Inc, pg 963
Opulen Studios, pg 965
Orange County Sound Stage, pg 965
Pacific Light Studios, pg 967
Photo Film Stage, pg 974
Playback Recording Studio, pg 977
Pollution Studios, pg 978
Pro HD Rentals, pg 983
The Producer's Loft, pg 983
RED Studios Hollywood, pg 993
Roundabout Entertainment Inc, pg 1000
Sand Box Studio, pg 1002
Santa Clarita Studios, pg 1002
ShowBiz Studios, pg 1009
Slow Motion Film & Digital Inc, pg 1013
Solar Studios, pg 1015
Source Film Studio, pg 1018
Still N'Motion, pg 1025
Stray Angel Films, pg 1026
Studio 1444, pg 1026
Studio 6429, pg 1027
Studio 637, pg 1027
Sunset Bronson Studios, pg 1028
Sunset Gower Studios, pg 1028
Total Media Group, pg 1042
Valencia Studios, pg 1051
Westlake Recording Studios, pg 1064

COLORADO

Colorado Studios, pg 832
Daylight Productions & Rentals, pg 844
Denver Media Center, pg 845
Platypi Studios, pg 977
Side 3 Studios, pg 1010
Westworks Studios, pg 1064

CONNECTICUT

Broadcast Video Productions LLC, pg 813
Fox Connecticut, pg 872
Sonalysts Media, pg 1015
SoNo Studios, pg 1016

DELAWARE

Cornerstone Media Productions Inc, pg 836
Ken-Del Productions Inc, pg 909

DISTRICT OF COLUMBIA

Bella Faccia Inc, pg 804
Flying Colors Broadcasts, pg 870
Interface Media Group, pg 900
Studio14DC, pg 1027

FLORIDA

Accord Productions, pg 773
Adrenaline Films, pg 777
Aperture Studios Miami, pg 788
C&I Studios, pg 819
Cheuvront Studios, pg 824
Cinema Entertainment Inc, pg 827
Digital Comm Link Inc, pg 847
Eastern Video, pg 856
Facet Media, pg 865
Fiddler Films, pg 866
The Great Southern Studios, pg 882
HD House, pg 886
Jordan Klein Film & Video (JKFV), pg 906
LHV Audio Services, pg 919
MAPS Production House, pg 930
Media Concepts Inc, pg 936
Miami Daylight Studios, pg 941
National Teleproductions Inc, pg 953
New Art Miami, pg 955
Phat Planet Recording Studios, pg 973
South Florida Rehearsal Studios, pg 1019
Trendy Studio LLC, pg 1044
Universal Studios Florida® Production Group, pg 1049

GEORGIA

Atlanta Filmworks, pg 793
ECG Productions, pg 856
Encyclomedia, pg 861
HallBrook Productions, pg 884
Lighting & Production Equipment Inc, pg 920
Magick Lantern, pg 928
Mailing Avenue Stageworks, pg 929
Stage Front Presentation Systems, pg 1022
Studio Space Atlanta, pg 1027
WATL-TV Inc, pg 1062

HAWAII

FOTON Hawaii, pg 871

ILLINOIS

Audio Visual Services Corp, pg 796
Beatty TeleVisual Productions, pg 804
Big Shoulders Digital Video Productions, pg 807
Delmark Records, pg 845
Firehouse Studios, pg 868
Harvest Studios, pg 885
Magnanimous Media, pg 928
PSAV® Presentation Services (Hotel Services Division), pg 987
QuickSet International Inc, pg 989
ShiftFocus Productions, pg 1009
Show Department Inc, pg 1009
Tele-Time Systems, pg 1036

INDIANA

Lakeshore Productions, pg 915
Midwest Uplink Inc, pg 942

KANSAS

KAKE-TV, pg 907

LOUISIANA

Digital FX Inc, pg 847
Launch Media, pg 916
Second Line Stages, pg 1006

MARYLAND

CPR MultiMedia Solutions, pg 837
Cre-a-tv Studios, pg 839
The Cutting Corp, pg 841
Quality Film & Video, pg 988
Sheffield Audio/Video Productions, pg 1008

MASSACHUSETTS

Home Inc, pg 890
Penfield Productions Ltd, pg 971
Preston Productions Inc, pg 981
Red Sky Studios, pg 993

MICHIGAN

Brilliance Audio, pg 812
City Events Group, pg 828
K&R's Recording Studios Inc, pg 908
Stage 3 Productions, pg 1022
Technology Learning Services, pg 1035
WTVS-Station Enterprises, pg 1071

MINNESOTA

Alpha Video & Audio Inc, pg 782
Area 19, pg 789
Broadview Media, pg 813

MISSOURI

Show-Me Audio-Visual, pg 1009
Southwest Audio-Visual Inc, pg 1019
Studio Worx Inc, pg 1027
Swank Audio Visuals, pg 1029

NEBRASKA

Lights On Nebraska, pg 921

NEVADA

DVDs4Less, pg 854
JCS Video Productions, pg 904
Lefco Video Services Inc, pg 918
MG Studio, pg 940

NEW JERSEY

The Brick Studio, pg 812
Butter Tree Studio, pg 816
Color Leasing Studios, pg 831
Creative Video, pg 838
E Video Productions, pg 855
18 Label Studios, pg 858
Euro-Pacific Film & Video Productions Inc, pg 863
Ironbound Film & Television Studios LLC, pg 902
Laurel Video Productions, pg 916
MediaMix Inc, pg 937
Milgrom Productions, pg 943
Optisonics Productions, pg 965
Public Eye Productions, pg 987
Shamrock Communications, pg 1008

NEW MEXICO

I-25 Studios, pg 893

NEW YORK

BC Video Inc, pg 803
Big Foot Productions Inc, pg 807
Bond Street Studio, pg 810
Bravo Studios, pg 812
Brooklyn Fire Proof, pg 814
Brooklyn Studios, pg 814
Camart, pg 817
C&C Studios Corp, pg 819
City Stage, pg 828
Communication Corner Inc, pg 832
CP Communications, pg 837
East of Hollywood NY, pg 855
Hayden 5 Media LLC, pg 886
LightBox-NY, pg 920
LightSpace Studios, pg 921
Location 05 Studios, pg 924
Long Island Video Enterprises Live Inc, pg 924
Manhattan Center Studios Inc, pg 930
Mark Custom Recording Service Inc, pg 931
Media 3 Ltd, pg 937
MRG Productions Inc, pg 948
Neo Studios, pg 954
Shelly Palmer Production, pg 968
Production Central, pg 984
Rollin Studios, pg 998
D S Simon Productions, pg 1011
Sony Music Entertainment, pg 1016
Steiner Studios, pg 1024
TBA Global Events, pg 1032
Technisphere Corp, pg 1034
Tobin Productions Inc, pg 1041
WNET/NET TELECON, pg 1069

NORTH CAROLINA

Duke Media Services, pg 853
Evolve Inc, pg 863
Gotham City Studios, pg 880
K2 Productions, pg 914
Media-Comm, pg 936
Moving Pictures, pg 948
Take One Productions Ltd, pg 1031

NORTH DAKOTA

Media Productions, pg 937

OHIO

Mills James Productions, pg 943
OSV Studios, pg 966
Vista Color Imaging Inc, pg 1059

OKLAHOMA

Institute for Teaching & Learning Excellence (ITLE), pg 899
Producers Playhouse, pg 983

OREGON

BingoLewis, pg 807
Intersect Video, pg 901

PENNSYLVANIA

Fusion Brand Experiences, pg 874
JPL, pg 906
Philadelphia Soundstages, pg 974
31st Street Studios, pg 1039
The Videohouse Inc, pg 1057
Visual Sound Inc, pg 1059
WHYY Inc, pg 1066

SOUTH CAROLINA

Genesis Creative, pg 877
Studio Charleston, pg 1026

TENNESSEE

Cupit Music Group, pg 841
DR&A Inc, pg 852
Love Shack Recording Studios, pg 925
Memphis Communications Corp, pg 938
NuMynd Studios, pg 960
SmackDab Media, pg 1013
Technical Support Systems LLC, pg 1034
UMCom Productions, pg 1048

TEXAS

AMS Pictures, pg 786
Digital Services Recording Studios, pg 848
Maverick Video Productions, pg 934
Earl Miller Productions Inc, pg 943
Omega Productions, pg 962
Photogroup Studios, pg 975
Reelsound Recording Co, pg 994
Saint Elmo Soundstage, pg 1001
The Sound Lab Inc, pg 1017
South Coast Film & Video, pg 1019

VIRGINIA

Allied Media Corp, pg 781
Bias Studios, pg 806
WETA Production Center, pg 1064

WASHINGTON

Avast! Recording Co, pg 798
The House Studios, pg 891
Kostov Productions, pg 913
Victory Studios, pg 1054

WISCONSIN

Sound Strations Audio Productions Inc, pg 1017
TBC Studios, pg 1033
University of Wisconsin-Oshkosh Radio-TV-Film Dept, pg 1050
Wisconsin Public Television, pg 1068

WYOMING

Bridger Productions Inc, pg 812

ALBERTA

Global Television Station, pg 879
MTM Equipment Rentals Ltd, pg 949

BRITISH COLUMBIA

Finale Editworks, pg 868
Vancouver Film Studios Ltd, pg 1051
Video In Studios/Video Out Distribution, pg 1055

ONTARIO

Boxcar Studio, pg 811
Edcom Multimedia Products, pg 856
Kimono Surf Studios, pg 911
Optimum Production Services Inc, pg 964
The Pocket Studios, pg 977
RB Productions, pg 992
Wanted! Sound + Picture, pg 1062

Recording Facility Repairs

CALIFORNIA

Advanced Systems Group LLC, pg 778
Ametron Audio/Video, pg 785

ILLINOIS

Tele-Time Systems, pg 1036

MICHIGAN

Studio Consulting & Construction Inc, pg 1026
TeL Systems, pg 1035

MINNESOTA

Alpha Video & Audio Inc, pg 782

MISSOURI

Southwest Audio-Visual Inc, pg 1019

NEW JERSEY

Turner Engineering Inc, pg 1046

NEW YORK

Manhattan Center Studios Inc, pg 930
MRG Productions Inc, pg 948

TENNESSEE

Technical Support Systems LLC, pg 1034

WISCONSIN

Full Compass Systems, pg 874

Recording—Videotapes

ALABAMA

CMEInfo, pg 830

ARIZONA

Aardvark Productions LLC, pg 772
Film Creations Ltd, pg 867
Merestone, pg 938
Metropolitan Audio-Visual Inc, pg 940
On-Site Video, pg 963
Rodeo Video Inc, pg 998
Video Media Productions (VMP), pg 1055
Video West Inc, pg 1056

ARKANSAS

Cedar Crest Studio, pg 822
Shadowbox Video Productions, pg 1007
White Diamond Productions, pg 1065

CALIFORNIA

Action Video, pg 775
Adolph Gasser Inc, pg 776
All Video Productions, pg 781
Artichoke Productions, pg 791
Audio Visual Consultants, pg 795
CCI Digital, pg 821
Crystal Pyramid Productions™, pg 840
Custom Video Productions Inc, pg 841
Digital Media West, pg 847
Express Media Inc, pg 864

VIDEO

Recording—Videotapes (continued)

CALIFORNIA (continued)

COLORADO

CONNECTICUT

DISTRICT OF COLUMBIA

FLORIDA

GEORGIA

HAWAII

IDAHO

ILLINOIS

INDIANA

IOWA

KANSAS

KENTUCKY

LOUISIANA

MAINE

MARYLAND

MASSACHUSETTS

MICHIGAN

MINNESOTA

MISSOURI

MONTANA

NEBRASKA

NEVADA

NEW HAMPSHIRE

Apertura, pg 788
Channell One Video, pg 824
Chip Taylor Communications LLC, pg 1032

NEW JERSEY

All Jersey Studios, pg 780
CFP Video Productions Inc, pg 823
Deluxe Media Services, pg 845
Diversified Systems Inc, pg 849
DWJ Television, pg 854
Laurel Video Productions, pg 916
MediaMix Inc, pg 937
Megavideo Productions, pg 938
MIB Mediaworks, pg 941
Midnight Media Group Inc, pg 942
NFL Films Inc, pg 957
Optisonics Productions, pg 965
Producer East Productions, pg 983
Public Eye Productions, pg 987
SES World Skies, pg 1007
Suede Interactive, pg 1027
Synergem, pg 1030
VCSvideo, pg 1052
Video Corporation of America (VCA), pg 1055
Video Ideas Productions, pg 1055
VTS Video & Media, pg 1061

NEW MEXICO

Production Outfitters, pg 984

NEW YORK

Adwar Video, pg 778
Associated Press Television News, pg 792
aurora productions, pg 797
BC Video Inc, pg 803
Bellin Productions, pg 805
Bevilacqua Studios, pg 806
The Big House Group, pg 807
Broad Street Inc, pg 812
Communication Corner Inc, pg 832
CPdigital, pg 837
Thomas Craven Film Corp, pg 837
Design Audio Visual Inc, pg 845
Downtown Community Television Center (DCTV), pg 851
Duplication Depot Inc, pg 853
Eastco Multimedia Solutions Inc, pg 856
4-D Creative Media, pg 871
Greyfalcon House, pg 882
HAVE Inc, pg 886
Image Makers of Pittsford/Image Maker Productions, pg 895
International Digital Centre, pg 901
La Paloma Films, pg 915
Magno Sound & Video, pg 929
Neal Marshad Productions, pg 931
NBC Production Facilities, pg 953
Shelly Palmer Production, pg 968
PrimaLux Video Inc, pg 982
Rafik, pg 990
Refinery, pg 994
SmartPros Ltd, pg 1014
Synaptic Digital, pg 1030
TBA Global Events, pg 1032
Teatown Communications Group, pg 1033
Technisphere Corp, pg 1034
USA Studios, pg 1050
Visual Technologies Corp, pg 1060
Willow Mixed Media Inc, pg 1067
WTL Productions, pg 1071
Zelman Studios Ltd, pg 1073

NORTH CAROLINA

Pat Appleson Studios Inc, pg 788
The Communications Group Inc, pg 833
Duke Media Services, pg 853
Horizon Video Productions Inc, pg 891
LCW Productions LLC, pg 917
Microspace Communications Corp, pg 942
Moving Pictures, pg 948
NASCAR Media Group LLC, pg 952
On Location North Carolina, pg 963
Take One Productions Ltd, pg 1031
Trailblazer Studios®, pg 1043
Unifour Productions Inc, pg 1048
Visual Aids Electronics of North Carolina Inc, pg 1059

OHIO

Advent Media Inc, pg 778
Aztec Video Productions, pg 801
Russ Beckner Pictures, pg 804
Curtis Inc, pg 841
Cuyahoga Community College Media Center, pg 841
EDR Media LLC, pg 857
Lyon Video Inc, pg 927
MainSail Production Services Inc, pg 929
Mills James Productions, pg 943
Musicol Recording, pg 951
R&B Communications Inc, pg 991
Take 1 Media Services, pg 1031
VGI Productions, pg 1053
Vista Color Imaging Inc, pg 1059

OKLAHOMA

Garman Productions LLC, pg 875
Institute for Teaching & Learning Excellence (ITLE), pg 899
University of Oklahoma Academic Media & Digital Services, pg 1050

OREGON

A KTVA Production LLC, pg 771
KPDX-TV Production Center, pg 913
Odyssey Productions Inc, pg 961
Production West, pg 985
Rex, pg 995

PENNSYLVANIA

Audio Visual Communications Inc, pg 795
Center City Film & Video Inc, pg 822
FMP Media Solutions Inc, pg 870
Innovision Media Group, pg 899
JPL, pg 906
Laser Video Corp, pg 916
Muderick Media, pg 949
Production Masters Inc (PMI), pg 984
The Videohouse Inc, pg 1057
Visual Sound Inc, pg 1059
WHYY Inc, pg 1066
WPHL-TV, pg 1070

SOUTH CAROLINA

Encore Video Productions, pg 861
Genesis Creative, pg 877
Venture Media, pg 1052

TENNESSEE

Marine Geographic, pg 931
Motion Picture Services, pg 947
Running Pony Productions LLC, pg 1000
Scripps Networks, pg 1005
ST Productions, pg 1022
Stage Post, pg 1022
Russ Sturgeon Productions/RSVP, pg 1027
Zion Music Group, pg 1074

TEXAS

Castleview Productions, pg 821
CEV Multimedia Ltd, pg 823
Communication Arts Multimedia Inc, pg 832
The Editing Co, pg 857
Eyecon Video Productions, pg 865
Horizon Film + Video Productions, pg 891
Marx InDigital, pg 933
Maverick Video Productions, pg 934
Media Event Concepts Inc, pg 936
Mediaforce Productions, pg 937
Earl Miller Productions Inc, pg 943
Julye Newlin Productions Inc, pg 956
Replicopy Digital Media Center, pg 995
Romar Learning, pg 999
South Coast Film & Video, pg 1019
Texas Heart Institute Visual Communication Services, pg 1037

UTAH

ImageWorks Communications, pg 896

VERMONT

University of Vermont, Instructional Television Dept, pg 1050

VIRGINIA

American AV, pg 783
BES Studios, pg 805
CACI Productions Group, pg 816
Creative Video of Washington Inc, pg 839
D&B Television & Video Productions Inc, pg 842
Gingerbread Productions, pg 878
Quince Imaging Inc, pg 989
WETA Production Center, pg 1064

WASHINGTON

Global Net Productions Inc, pg 879
Hamilton Studio, pg 884
Small World Productions Inc, pg 1013
Victory Studios, pg 1054

WEST VIRGINIA

Blackwater Video Productions, pg 808

WISCONSIN

Audio Visual of Milwaukee Inc, pg 795
Grassland Media Inc, pg 881
Learning Technology Services, pg 917
Meridian Studios, pg 939
University of Wisconsin-Oshkosh Radio-TV-Film Dept, pg 1050
USAV Group Inc, pg 1050
Video Wisconsin Inc, pg 1056
Wisconsin Public Television, pg 1068

WYOMING

Bridger Productions Inc, pg 812

PUERTO RICO

Stage Crew Audiovisual Inc, pg 1022

ALBERTA

Black Media Works, pg 808
Global Television Station, pg 879

BRITISH COLUMBIA

Finale Editworks, pg 868
ProVision Video Sales & Rentals Inc, pg 986
Triad Communications Ltd, pg 1044
Video In Studios/Video Out Distribution, pg 1055

MANITOBA

Spectra Video Productions Ltd, pg 1020

NEWFOUNDLAND AND LABRADOR

Vidcraft Productions Ltd, pg 1054

ONTARIO

Edcom Multimedia Products, pg 856
Purefire Communications Inc, pg 987
Video Excellence Productions, pg 1055

QUEBEC

Muse Entertainment Enterprises, pg 950

Reel & Can Distributors

ALABAMA

Media Visions Inc, pg 937

ARIZONA

Troxell Communications Inc, pg 1045

CALIFORNIA

Adolph Gasser Inc, pg 776
Christy's Editorial, pg 826
Cinema Equipment Sales of California Inc, pg 827
Edgewise Media Inc, pg 856
Hooper Camera & Imaging, pg 891
Zack Electronics Inc, pg 1073

COLORADO

The Cinema Lab, pg 827
Goldberg Brothers Inc, pg 880
Stanco Sales LLC, pg 1023

FLORIDA

Photomart Cine-Video Inc, pg 975
Tallahassee Audio Visual, pg 1031

ILLINOIS

Clark Wire & Cable, pg 829
Research Technology International (RTI), pg 995

MARYLAND

Professional Label Inc, pg 985

VIDEO

Reel & Can Distributors (continued)

MASSACHUSETTS

Hunt's Photo, Video & Digital, pg 892
University Products Inc, pg 1050

MINNESOTA

Alpha Video & Audio Inc, pg 782

MISSISSIPPI

Jasper Ewing & Sons Inc, pg 864

MISSOURI

Image Technologies Corp, pg 895
Modern Communications Inc, pg 944
Southwest Audio-Visual Inc, pg 1019

NEW JERSEY

AV Bluebook, pg 797
Hamilton Buhl, pg 884
HP Marketing Corp, pg 892
Video Corporation of America (VCA), pg 1055

NEW YORK

Burlington A/V Recording Media, pg 815
Film Emporium, pg 867
Gaylord Brothers, pg 876
Markertek Video Supply, pg 931
Motion Picture Enterprises Inc, pg 947
Rafik, pg 990

NORTH CAROLINA

Camcor Inc, pg 818

PENNSYLVANIA

Advanced AV, pg 777
Morefield Communications Inc, pg 946
Visual Sound Inc, pg 1059

TENNESSEE

Memphis Communications Corp, pg 938

UTAH

Redman Movies & Stories, pg 993

VIRGINIA

Filmdex Inc, pg 867
Lee Hartman & Sons Inc, pg 918
The Whitlock Group, pg 1065

WISCONSIN

Camera Corner Connecting Point, pg 818
Full Compass Systems, pg 874

PUERTO RICO

Bonnin Electronics Inc, pg 810

ONTARIO

Carr McLean Ltd, pg 820
Premier A/V Sales Ltd, pg 980

QUEBEC

STIL Casing Solution, pg 1025

Reel & Can Manufacturers

COLORADO

Goldberg Brothers Inc, pg 880

MARYLAND

Professional Label Inc, pg 985

OHIO

Xetron, pg 1071

WISCONSIN

Regal Photo Products Inc/Arkay Corp, pg 994

QUEBEC

STIL Casing Solution, pg 1025

Reel & Can Rentals

ARIZONA

Merestone, pg 938

CALIFORNIA

Big Time Picture Company Inc, pg 807

FLORIDA

Jordan Klein Film & Video (JKFV), pg 906

ILLINOIS

QuickSet International Inc, pg 989

LOUISIANA

Digital FX Inc, pg 847

MISSOURI

Image Technologies Corp, pg 895
Southwest Audio-Visual Inc, pg 1019

NEW YORK

Long Island Video Enterprises Live Inc, pg 924
MRG Productions Inc, pg 948

TEXAS

Stage Directions, pg 1022

UTAH

Redman Movies & Stories, pg 993

ALBERTA

Global Television Station, pg 879

Rehearsal Studio Manufacturers

CALIFORNIA

Ametron Audio/Video, pg 785
Yanchar Design & Consulting Group, pg 1072

GEORGIA

Lighting & Production Equipment Inc, pg 920

MICHIGAN

Studio Consulting & Construction Inc, pg 1026

NEW YORK

CP Communications, pg 837
IAC Acoustics, pg 893

TEXAS

The Yesterday USA Radio Networks, pg 1072

Rehearsal Studio Rentals

ARIZONA

Merestone, pg 938
Video Media Productions (VMP), pg 1055

CALIFORNIA

Adolph Gasser Inc, pg 776
CenterStaging LLC, pg 822
Chapman/Leonard Studios & Production Center, pg 824
DTC Lighting & Grip, pg 853
Golden Gate Studios, pg 880
ShowBiz Studios, pg 1009
Still N'Motion, pg 1025
Studio 637, pg 1027

CONNECTICUT

Fox Connecticut, pg 872
Videofilm Systems Inc, pg 1057

DELAWARE

Ken-Del Productions Inc, pg 909

FLORIDA

Comtel Inc, pg 834
CopShopMiami.com, pg 836
Jordan Klein Film & Video (JKFV), pg 906
National Teleproductions Inc, pg 953
South Florida Rehearsal Studios, pg 1019

GEORGIA

ECG Productions, pg 856
Lighting & Production Equipment Inc, pg 920
Stage Front Presentation Systems, pg 1022
WATL-TV Inc, pg 1062

ILLINOIS

Chicago Satellite & Video, pg 825
QuickSet International Inc, pg 989
Show Department Inc, pg 1009

KANSAS

KAKE-TV, pg 907

LOUISIANA

Digital FX Inc, pg 847

MARYLAND

CPR MultiMedia Solutions, pg 837

MASSACHUSETTS

National Boston, pg 952
Penfield Productions Ltd, pg 971

MICHIGAN

City Events Group, pg 828
K&R All Media Productions Inc, pg 908
WTVS-Station Enterprises, pg 1071

MISSOURI

Show-Me Audio-Visual, pg 1009
Southwest Audio-Visual Inc, pg 1019

NEVADA

DVDs4Less, pg 854

NEW JERSEY

Audio Visual Dynamics®, pg 795

NEW MEXICO

Production Outfitters, pg 984

NEW YORK

Big Foot Productions Inc, pg 807
Long Island Video Enterprises Live Inc, pg 924
Manhattan Center Studios Inc, pg 930
MRG Productions Inc, pg 948
Sony Music Entertainment, pg 1016
Studio Instrument Rentals (SIR), pg 1027
TBA Global Events, pg 1032

NORTH CAROLINA

Duke Media Services, pg 853
Microspace Communications Corp, pg 942
Moving Pictures, pg 948
On Location North Carolina, pg 963
Take One Productions Ltd, pg 1031

NORTH DAKOTA

Media Productions, pg 937

OHIO

CET, pg 823
Mills James Productions, pg 943
Vista Color Imaging Inc, pg 1059

OREGON

Pacific Grip & Lighting Inc, pg 967

PENNSYLVANIA

Fusion Brand Experiences, pg 874
JPL, pg 906

TENNESSEE

Memphis Communications Corp, pg 938
SmackDab Media, pg 1013
Technical Support Systems LLC, pg 1034

TEXAS

Biway Media, pg 808
Maverick Video Productions, pg 934
Muller Entertainment, pg 949
Stage Directions, pg 1022

VIRGINIA

Allied Media Corp, pg 781

WASHINGTON

Victory Studios, pg 1054

WISCONSIN

TBC Studios, pg 1033
USAV Group Inc, pg 1050
Wisconsin Public Television, pg 1068

WYOMING

Bridger Productions Inc, pg 812

ALBERTA

Global Television Station, pg 879

BRITISH COLUMBIA

Video In Studios/Video Out Distribution, pg 1055

ONTARIO

JIB Shots Equipment Inc, pg 905

Rehearsal Studio Repairs

CALIFORNIA

Ametron Audio/Video, pg 785

FLORIDA

JT Communications, pg 906

MICHIGAN

Studio Consulting & Construction Inc, pg 1026
TeL Systems, pg 1035

MINNESOTA

Alpha Video & Audio Inc, pg 782

MISSOURI

Southwest Audio-Visual Inc, pg 1019

NEW YORK

MRG Productions Inc, pg 948

TENNESSEE

Technical Support Systems LLC, pg 1034

Rewinder Distributors

CALIFORNIA

Adolph Gasser Inc, pg 776
Ametron Audio/Video, pg 785
Garner Products Inc, pg 875
Alan Gordon Enterprises Inc, pg 880

FLORIDA

Access Media Group, pg 773
Digital Video Systems Inc, pg 848
Media Concepts Inc, pg 936
Photomart Cine-Video Inc, pg 975

GEORGIA

Stage Front Presentation Systems, pg 1022

ILLINOIS

Research Technology International (RTI), pg 995

INDIANA

Lee Co Inc, pg 918
Sensory Technologies LLC, pg 1006

KENTUCKY

Barney Miller's Inc, pg 943

MASSACHUSETTS

Rule Broadcast Systems, pg 1000

MINNESOTA

Alpha Video & Audio Inc, pg 782

MISSOURI

Modern Communications Inc, pg 944
Southwest Audio-Visual Inc, pg 1019

NEW JERSEY

Hamilton Buhl, pg 884
MCCOM Inc, pg 935
VCom International Multimedia Corp, pg 1052

NEW YORK

B&H Photo & Video Pro Audio, pg 802
Gaylord Brothers, pg 876
HAVE Inc, pg 886
Markertek Video Supply, pg 931
RNJ Electronics, pg 997
TecNec Distributing, pg 1035

PENNSYLVANIA

Advanced AV, pg 777
Brodart Co, pg 813
J E Foss Co, pg 871

TENNESSEE

Lowrance Sound Co Inc, pg 925
Spring Arbor Distributors, pg 1022

TEXAS

Quality Audio Visual Service Inc, pg 988
RadioShack Corp, pg 990

VIRGINIA

Filmdex Inc, pg 867

WISCONSIN

Audio Visual of Milwaukee Inc, pg 795

ONTARIO

Premier A/V Sales Ltd, pg 980

Rewinder Manufacturers

CALIFORNIA

Ametron Audio/Video, pg 785

ILLINOIS

ACCO Brands Corp, pg 773
Research Technology International (RTI), pg 995

INDIANA

Infonics Inc, pg 898

NEW YORK

Sima Products Corp, pg 1011

OHIO

Xetron, pg 1071

Rewinder Rentals

ARIZONA

Merestone, pg 938

ARKANSAS

White Diamond Productions, pg 1065

CALIFORNIA

JD Audio Visual Inc, pg 904

GEORGIA

Stage Front Presentation Systems, pg 1022

MINNESOTA

House of Cinemagraphics, pg 891

MISSOURI

Show-Me Audio-Visual, pg 1009

NORTH CAROLINA

Take One Productions Ltd, pg 1031

Rewinder Repairs

GEORGIA

Stage Front Presentation Systems, pg 1022

KENTUCKY

NOR-COM Inc, pg 958

MICHIGAN

TeL Systems, pg 1035

Script Writing

ALABAMA

CMEInfo, pg 830
Diamond Studios, pg 846

ALASKA

Alaska Film Services Inc, pg 779
Aurora Films, pg 797

ARIZONA

Candee Productions Inc, pg 819
Direct Current Video Productions, pg 848
Film Creations Ltd, pg 867
Fox 10 Productions (KSAZ-TV), pg 872
MediaWorks, pg 938
Merestone, pg 938
Metropolitan Audio-Visual Inc, pg 940
On-Site Video, pg 963
Phoenix VideoFilms®, pg 974
Tellens Inc, pg 1037
Wild Visions Inc, pg 1066

ARKANSAS

Cedar Crest Studio, pg 822
Live'N'Loud, pg 923
Shadowbox Video Productions, pg 1007
White Diamond Productions, pg 1065

CALIFORNIA

A&I, pg 771
Aaron & Le Duc, pg 772
Action Video, pg 775
Animax, pg 787
Barbosa Video Services, pg 802
Concrete Images, pg 835
Creativity Unlimited Press®, pg 839
Crystal Pyramid Productions™, pg 840
Custom Video Productions Inc, pg 841
Deja View Video, pg 845
deKramer Productions Inc, pg 845
Design Media, pg 845
Digital Outpost, pg 847
Dogma Studios, pg 850
Dolphin MultiMedia Inc, pg 850
Tom Donald Films, pg 850
DreamWorks Animation SKG Inc, pg 852
Far West Media Services Inc, pg 865
Final Draft Inc, pg 868
FJ Productions Inc, pg 869
Full Moon & High Tide Productions & Studios, pg 874
Global Village Productions, pg 879
Goal Productions, pg 879
Havas Edge, pg 885
iCorpTv, pg 893
Imageworks, pg 896
Increase Video/Silver Mine Video, pg 897
ITV Productions, pg 903
JDS Video & Media Productions Inc, pg 904
Joyce Media Inc, pg 906
KION-TV, pg 911
KO Creative, pg 912
KPBS TV FM-San Diego, pg 913
KTVU-Retail Services, pg 914
KVIE-Channel 6, pg 914
Maximus Media Inc, pg 934
Media Magic, pg 937
The Media Staff Inc, pg 937
Nandar Entertainment Pictures, pg 952
New & Unique Videos™, pg 955
Nolte Media, pg 958
On-Trax Inc, pg 963
Pacific Light Studios, pg 967
Palardo Productions, pg 968
Panorama Productions, pg 968
Penrose Productions, pg 972
piXvfm, pg 976
Players Press, pg 977
PM Productions, pg 977
PSI Inc, pg 987
QRS Software Services, pg 988
Regent Press Publishers & Printers, pg 994
Sahara Records & Filmworks Entertainment Co, pg 1001
Saturn Studios, pg 1003
SBS Productions, pg 1003
Staylor-Made Communications Inc, pg 1024
Still N'Motion, pg 1025
The Studio Center, pg 1026
Tam Communications Inc, pg 1031
Tigar Hare Studios, pg 1040
Toon Makers, pg 1042
Total Media Group, pg 1042
Twin Peaks Creative, pg 1047
University of Southern California, pg 1050
Via Verde Productions, pg 1053
Videografix LLC, pg 1057
Videolady, pg 1057
Vineyard Productions, pg 1058
Visions Plus, pg 1058

VIDEO

Script Writing (continued)

CALIFORNIA (continued)

West Coast Projections Inc, pg 1063
WMS Media Inc, pg 1069

COLORADO

Paul L Anderson Productions Inc, pg 786
blue onion, pg 810
Centre Communications Inc, pg 823
Daylight Productions & Rentals, pg 844
Flashback Media Productions, pg 869
Old Army Press (OAP), pg 961
Open Media Foundation, pg 964
Rocky Mountain Audio/Video Productions Inc, pg 998
Scriptware, pg 1005
Tatum Video, pg 1032
Transtar Entertainment Co Inc, pg 1043
Z-Axis Corp, pg 1073

CONNECTICUT

ACM Productions Ltd, pg 774
Antenna International, pg 787
Applebox Studio, pg 788
BRB Audiovisual Productions, pg 812
Broadcast Video Productions LLC, pg 813
Cine-Med Inc, pg 826
Essex Television Group Inc, pg 862
Fox Connecticut, pg 872
The Gary-Paul Agency, pg 875
Geomatrix Productions, pg 877
Guymark Studios LLC, pg 883
Ironik Design & Post, pg 902
MCC Films, pg 935
P&P Studios Inc, pg 968
Pictures of Record Inc, pg 975
Powerstation Events, pg 979
Video Production Associates Inc, pg 1056

DELAWARE

So Smart Productions, pg 1015

DISTRICT OF COLUMBIA

Hillmann & Carr Inc, pg 889
Interface Media Group, pg 900
O'Keefe Communications Inc, pg 961
Yellow Cat Productions Inc, pg 1072

FLORIDA

Accel Video Productions, pg 773
Accord Productions, pg 773
ACT Productions, pg 775
Allegro Productions Inc, pg 781
Big Byte Video Productions, pg 806
Chatterbox Productions Inc, pg 824
Civins Productions Inc, pg 828
Communications Concepts Inc (CCI), pg 833
Courter Films LLC, pg 837
DME Studios, pg 849
Eastern Video, pg 856
Ed Ethridge Productions Inc, pg 863
Florida Digital Studios, pg 870
Gulf Coast Audio Visual Producers Inc, pg 883
Home Shopping Network (HSN), pg 890

Image Technical Services, pg 895
Jordan Klein Film & Video (JKFV), pg 906
Media Concepts Inc, pg 936
Media Entertainment Inc, pg 936
National Teleproductions Inc, pg 953
The Newhouse Media Group, pg 956
Progressive Media & Music, pg 985
Sound & Vision Communications Inc, pg 1016
Sunfire Communications Inc, pg 1028
Sunrise Studios, pg 1028
Tricycle Studios, pg 1044
Universal Studios Florida® Production Group, pg 1049
Mike Vasilinda Productions Inc, pg 1052
Video Techniques Inc, pg 1056
Vistamax Productions, pg 1059

GEORGIA

Beachwood Productions, pg 804
Burst Video/Film Inc, pg 815
COMPRO Productions Inc, pg 834
The DVI Group, pg 854
ECG Productions, pg 856
Guerrilla Productions LLC, pg 883
The Intellications Co, pg 899
Memory Lane Productions, pg 938
Myriad Productions, pg 951
Malcolm Neal Productions, pg 954
On-Line Productions, pg 963
Showcase Photo & Video, pg 1009
USMotivation, pg 1051
Visioneering International Inc, pg 1058

HAWAII

FilmWorks Pacific, pg 868
Hyperspective Studios Inc, pg 893
KHNL/KGMB, pg 910
Sight & Sound Studios, pg 1010
1013 Integrated, pg 1037
Tropical Visions Video Inc, pg 1045
TV Juice Productions Inc, pg 1046

IDAHO

KTVB-TV, pg 914
Brad Shaw Productions Inc, pg 1008
Wide Eye Productions, pg 1066

ILLINOIS

ABSA Productions Inc, pg 772
Airways Digital Media, pg 779
Audio Visual Services Corp, pg 796
Big Shoulders Digital Video Productions, pg 807
Breeze Productions Inc, pg 812
CCore Media Inc, pg 821
Centrax Corp, pg 823
Chicago Satellite & Video, pg 825
Communications Corporation of America, pg 833
Edit House Chicago, pg 857
Extraordinary Demos, pg 864
Film Police, pg 867
1st Financial Training Services Inc, pg 868
IV Media Resources, pg 903
Major Media Productions Inc, pg 929
Manning Productions, pg 930
The Market Place, pg 931
MIGHTYbYTES Inc, pg 942
Mimi Productions, pg 943
Rob Orr Productions Ltd, pg 965
Perspectives Media, pg 973

Production Craft Inc, pg 984
PSAV® Presentation Services (Hotel Services Division), pg 987
Richter Studios, pg 996
SCI Television Productions LLC, pg 1004
Sound/Video Impressions Inc, pg 1018
Southern Illinois University, pg 1019
Sparkfactor, pg 1019
20/20 Communications Inc, pg 1047
Video I-D Teleproductions Inc, pg 1055
Video Impressions, pg 1055
WEEK TV, pg 1063
WIFR-TV, pg 1066

INDIANA

AVA Productions, pg 798
Bright Ideas Creative Services, pg 812
Digital Rain LLC, pg 847
Educational Video Group Inc, pg 857
Explore Media LLC, pg 864
PentaVision Communications Inc, pg 972

IOWA

The Production House, pg 984

KANSAS

KAKE-TV, pg 907

KENTUCKY

Hammond Communications Group, pg 884
Horizon Films & Media LLC, pg 891
Idle Minds Productions Inc, pg 894
Prosper Media Group Inc, pg 986

LOUISIANA

Digital FX Inc, pg 847
Launch Media, pg 916
Louisiana State University Health Sciences Center - Shreveport, pg 925
Moxie Media, pg 948
Vidox Motion Imagery, pg 1057
WVLA-TV, pg 1071

MAINE

Slim Goodbody Corp, pg 1013
WGME-TV, pg 1065

MARYLAND

Adventure Productions LLC, pg 778
The Ahern Group, pg 779
CAS Video Productions, pg 820
CPR MultiMedia Solutions, pg 837
dbF a Media Company, pg 844
The Image Generators, pg 895
Kramer Communications Video Production, pg 913
Library Video Network (LVN), pg 920
Media Dimensions Inc, pg 936
Mobile-Video Productions Inc, pg 944
Pro Cuts Editing Services, pg 982
Quality Film & Video, pg 988
Sign Media Inc, pg 1011
Spectrum Productions, pg 1021

MASSACHUSETTS

Award Productions, pg 800
CommCreative, pg 832

Emergency Film Group, pg 860
Green Mountain Post Films (GMP), pg 882
Home Inc, pg 890
Monadnock Media Inc, pg 945
Northern Light Productions, pg 959
Preston Productions Inc, pg 981
Small Planet Communications Inc, pg 1013
Sound & Vision Media, pg 1017
TR Productions, pg 1043
Veritech Corp, pg 1053
VideoLink Inc, pg 1057

MICHIGAN

Benjamin Creative Productions, pg 805
Digi Sign Design LLC, pg 847
K&R's Recording Studios Inc, pg 908
Maritz Performance Improvement Co, pg 931
Michigan Recording Arts Institute & Technologies, pg 941
The Program Source International, pg 985
Technology Learning Services, pg 1035

MINNESOTA

Aggressive Records Audio Duplication LLC, pg 778
Badiyan Inc, pg 801
C Vision Productions, pg 816
The Richard Diercks Co Inc, pg 846
Jamieson & Associates Inc, pg 904
Master Communications Group, pg 933
Media Loft Inc, pg 937
MultiMedia, pg 950
Stoney-Wolf Productions Inc, pg 1025
Worthwhile Films, pg 1070

MISSOURI

Communitronics Corp, pg 833
Studio Worx Inc, pg 1027
Switch, pg 1030

MONTANA

KCFW Television, pg 908
North Country Media Group, pg 959

NEBRASKA

B & B Video Productions Inc, pg 801

NEVADA

Aardvark Video & Media Productions, pg 772
Encore Productions Inc, pg 861
HDTV Productions Inc, pg 886

NEW HAMPSHIRE

Apertura, pg 788
Channell One Video, pg 824
NH Movies Inc, pg 957
Chip Taylor Communications LLC, pg 1032

NEW JERSEY

All Jersey Studios, pg 780
CFP Video Productions Inc, pg 823
Color Leasing Studios, pg 831
Creative Video, pg 838
DWJ Television, pg 854
Euro-Pacific Film & Video Productions Inc, pg 863

VIDEO

Script Writing (continued)

PUERTO RICO

Stage Crew Audiovisual Inc, pg 1022

ALBERTA

Global Television, pg 879
Global Television Station, pg 879

BRITISH COLUMBIA

Triad Communications Ltd, pg 1044

MANITOBA

Spectra Video Productions Ltd, pg 1020

NEWFOUNDLAND AND LABRADOR

Vidcraft Productions Ltd, pg 1054

NORTHWEST TERRITORIES

Yellowknife Films Inc, pg 1072

ONTARIO

ADS Media, pg 777
DebsVoice, pg 844
GAPC (General Assembly Production Centre), pg 875
Image Video Services & Productions, pg 895
JFB Communications, pg 905
Purefire Communications Inc, pg 987
RB Productions, pg 992
Video Excellence Productions, pg 1055

QUEBEC

Muse Entertainment Enterprises, pg 950

Signal Processing Equipment Distributors

ALABAMA

PESA, pg 973

ARIZONA

EAR Professional Audio/Video, pg 855
Troxell Communications Inc, pg 1045

CALIFORNIA

Ametron Audio/Video, pg 785
Audio/Video Supply Inc, pg 795
Computer Modules Inc, pg 834
Delicate Electronics Sales Inc, pg 845
Empire Wholesale Inc, pg 860
Location Sound Corp, pg 924
Media Control Systems LLC, pg 936
Mobilized Tech Systems, pg 944
POP TV, pg 978
Snell, pg 1014
Southern California Sound Image Inc, pg 1019
SSL Industries Inc, pg 1022
Stanislaus Audio Video Inc, pg 1023
Tri-Ed, pg 1044
VMI Inc, pg 1060
Westlake Recording Studios, pg 1064

CONNECTICUT

Everett Hall Associates Inc, pg 863
Video Automation Systems Inc, pg 1054

FLORIDA

Access Media Group, pg 773
Digital Video Systems Inc, pg 848
General Projection Systems Inc, pg 877
Harris Corp, pg 885
Hi-Tech Enterprises Inc, pg 888
Media Concepts Inc, pg 936
Midtown Video Inc, pg 942
Multicom Inc, pg 949
Pro Stage Inc, pg 983
Recording Media & Equipment Inc (RM&E), pg 993
Videoscope, pg 1057

GEORGIA

Baker Audio Inc, pg 801
Barco Inc, pg 803
Clark, pg 829
Omnimedia Inc, pg 962
Stage Front Presentation Systems, pg 1022

INDIANA

Sensory Technologies LLC, pg 1006
SHP Electronics, pg 1010

KANSAS

Smith Audio-Visual Inc, pg 1014

KENTUCKY

NOR-COM Inc, pg 958

MARYLAND

Wiltronix, pg 1067

MASSACHUSETTS

Rule Broadcast Systems, pg 1000

MICHIGAN

Ascom Communications Contractors, pg 791
DAWNco, pg 843
Digi Sign Design LLC, pg 847
On Stage Visuals, pg 963

MINNESOTA

Alpha Video & Audio Inc, pg 782

MISSOURI

Communitronics Corp, pg 833
Modern Communications Inc, pg 944
Southwest Audio-Visual Inc, pg 1019

NEBRASKA

ATV Research Inc, pg 793

NEVADA

Aardvark Video & Media Productions, pg 772

NEW JERSEY

A-V Services Inc, pg 771
American Fibertek Inc, pg 784
Comprehensive Cable & Connectivity Co, pg 833
Diversified Systems Inc, pg 849
FSR Inc, pg 873
MCCOM Inc, pg 935
PatchAmp, pg 970
Starlite Productions, pg 1024
SYMCO Inc, pg 1030
Total Video Products Inc, pg 1042
Video Corporation of America (VCA), pg 1055
Wired 4 Sound Inc, pg 1068

NEW YORK

AV Workshop, pg 797
Communications Specialties Inc, pg 833
HAVE Inc, pg 886
Long Island Video Enterprises Live Inc, pg 924
Markertek Video Supply, pg 931
Technisphere Corp, pg 1034
Video International Development Inc, pg 1055

OHIO

Copp Integrated Systems, pg 836
Smithall Electronics Inc, pg 1014
Tri-State Audio Visual Co, pg 1044

PENNSYLVANIA

Advanced AV, pg 777
Morefield Communications Inc, pg 946
Vistacom Inc, pg 1059
Visual Sound Inc, pg 1059

RHODE ISLAND

Shanix Inc, pg 1008

SOUTH DAKOTA

Sencore Inc, pg 1006

TENNESSEE

Lowrance Sound Co Inc, pg 925
Technical Support Systems LLC, pg 1034

TEXAS

Audio Visual Technologies Group, pg 796
Data Projections Inc, pg 843
FitzCo Sound Inc, pg 869
FWT LLC, pg 874
Pro Video & Film Equipment Co Inc, pg 983
Tarpley Media Systems, pg 1032

UTAH

RIA Corp, pg 996

VIRGINIA

Hoppmann Audio Visual, pg 891
Quince Imaging Inc, pg 989

WISCONSIN

Audio Visual of Milwaukee Inc, pg 795
Camera Corner Connecting Point, pg 818
Full Compass Systems, pg 874

ALBERTA

McBain Audio Visual Ltd, pg 935

BRITISH COLUMBIA

DL Sound & Lighting Productions Ltd, pg 849

ONTARIO

HD Source, pg 886
Westbury National Show Systems Ltd, pg 1064

Signal Processing Equipment Manufacturers

ALABAMA

PESA, pg 973

ARIZONA

Covid Inc, pg 837

CALIFORNIA

ALTINEX Inc, pg 783
Computer Modules Inc, pg 834
Doremi Labs, pg 851
Ensemble Designs Inc, pg 861
ESE, pg 862
Extron Electronics, pg 864
FM Systems Inc, pg 870
For-A Corp of America, pg 871
Graham-Patten, pg 881
Hotronic Inc, pg 891
JBL Professional, pg 904
Linkabit, pg 922
Loma Scientific International (LSI), pg 924
MRV Communications Inc, pg 948
RF Industries, pg 995
Snell, pg 1014
Telestream Inc, pg 1036
VITEC Multimedia, pg 1060
Wohler Technologies Inc, pg 1069
Xantech LLC, pg 1071
Zhone Technologies Inc, pg 1073

COLORADO

Colorado Video Inc, pg 832
Vexcel Corp, pg 1053
Video Accessory Corp, pg 1054

CONNECTICUT

Video Automation Systems Inc, pg 1054
Xintekvideo Inc, pg 1071

FLORIDA

Compuvideo Sales USA Ltd, pg 834
Sensormatic®, pg 1006
Tel-Test, pg 1035

GEORGIA

Barco Inc, pg 803

IOWA

Winegard Co, pg 1067

KENTUCKY

AV Toolbox, pg 797

MAINE

Dielectric Communications, pg 846

MICHIGAN

ASC Systems, pg 791

MINNESOTA

Lynx Broadband, pg 926

MISSOURI

Link Electronics Inc, pg 922

NEW JERSEY

American Fibertek Inc, pg 784
Blonder Tongue Laboratories Inc, pg 809
CELCO-Constantine Engineering Labs Co, pg 822
Crestron Electronics Inc, pg 839
FSR Inc, pg 873
Kramer Electronics USA Inc, pg 913

NEW MEXICO

Burst Electronics Inc, pg 815

NEW YORK

Communications Specialties Inc, pg 833
Image Labs Corp, pg 895
Key Digital Systems, pg 910
Laird Digital Cinema, pg 915
MultiDyne Video & Fiber Optics Systems, pg 950
Judson Rosebush Co Inc, pg 999
Video International Development Inc, pg 1055

PENNSYLVANIA

MicroImage Video Systems, pg 941
Prime Image Inc, pg 982
World Video Sales Co Inc, pg 1070

SOUTH DAKOTA

Sencore Inc, pg 1006

TEXAS

Contemporary Research, pg 835
National Instruments Corp, pg 953

UTAH

DigiTech, pg 848

WISCONSIN

Intelix LLC, pg 899

ALBERTA

QSound Labs Inc, pg 988

ONTARIO

Artaflex Inc, pg 791
Broadcast Video Systems Corp, pg 813
Ward-Beck Systems Ltd, pg 1062

QUEBEC

Matrox Video Products Group, pg 934

Signal Processing Equipment Rentals

ARIZONA

Merestone, pg 938
Metropolitan Audio-Visual Inc, pg 940
Video West Inc, pg 1056

CALIFORNIA

Advanced Media LLC, pg 778
Ametron Audio/Video, pg 785
Artichoke Productions, pg 791
Bexel Corp, pg 806
Express Media Inc, pg 864
Golden Gate Studios, pg 880
Imagecraft Productions, pg 896
Lynch Communications, pg 926
Maximus Media Inc, pg 934
McCune Audio-Video-Lighting, pg 935
Munday & Collins AV, pg 950
Muse Presentation Technologies, pg 950
On-Trax Inc, pg 963
RetinaVision Productions, pg 995
Stanislaus Audio Video Inc, pg 1023
Synthesizer Systems Technologies (SST), pg 1030
VMI Inc, pg 1060

COLORADO

Daylight Productions & Rentals, pg 844
Spectrum Audio Visual Services, pg 1020

CONNECTICUT

Everett Hall Associates Inc, pg 863

FLORIDA

Access Media Group, pg 773
All Communications Rentals Inc (ALLCOMM), pg 780
Eastern Video, pg 856
Midtown Video Inc, pg 942
Paradise Show & Design Inc, pg 969
Phat Planet Recording Studios, pg 973
Pro Stage Inc, pg 983
Universal Studios Florida® Production Group, pg 1049

GEORGIA

Stage Front Presentation Systems, pg 1022

ILLINOIS

Backstar Creative Media Inc, pg 801
Chicago Satellite & Video, pg 825
QuickSet International Inc, pg 989
Show Department Inc, pg 1009

KANSAS

KAKE-TV, pg 907

LOUISIANA

Digital FX Inc, pg 847
Pace Systems, pg 966

MARYLAND

CPR MultiMedia Solutions, pg 837

MICHIGAN

Digi Sign Design LLC, pg 847
K&R All Media Productions Inc, pg 908
On Stage Visuals, pg 963

MINNESOTA

Alpha Video & Audio Inc, pg 782

MISSOURI

Show-Me Audio-Visual, pg 1009
Southwest Audio-Visual Inc, pg 1019

NEVADA

GES Audio Visual, pg 877
Lefco Video Services Inc, pg 918

NEW HAMPSHIRE

Apertura, pg 788

NEW JERSEY

MB Productions, pg 934
MediaMix Inc, pg 937
PLS Staging, pg 977
Starlite Productions, pg 1024
Video Corporation of America (VCA), pg 1055
Wired 4 Sound Inc, pg 1068

NEW YORK

AV Workshop, pg 797
Long Island Video Enterprises Live Inc, pg 924
Specialized Audio-Visual Inc, pg 1020

NORTH CAROLINA

Special Event Services, pg 1020
Take One Productions Ltd, pg 1031

OHIO

Lyon Video Inc, pg 927

TENNESSEE

Mr Mark's Used Musical, Stereo & Studio Equipment Store, pg 944
Technical Support Systems LLC, pg 1034

TEXAS

Alford Media Services, pg 780
FitzCo Sound Inc, pg 869

VIRGINIA

Quince Imaging Inc, pg 989

WASHINGTON

Victory Studios, pg 1054

WISCONSIN

Camera Corner Connecting Point, pg 818
Full Compass Systems, pg 874

WYOMING

Bridger Productions Inc, pg 812

PUERTO RICO

Stage Crew Audiovisual Inc, pg 1022

ALBERTA

QSound Labs Inc, pg 988

BRITISH COLUMBIA

DL Sound & Lighting Productions Ltd, pg 849
Finale Editworks, pg 868

ONTARIO

HD Source, pg 886
Westbury National Show Systems Ltd, pg 1064

Signal Processing Equipment Repairs

CALIFORNIA

Advanced Media LLC, pg 778
Ametron Audio/Video, pg 785
SSL Industries Inc, pg 1022
VMI Inc, pg 1060

FLORIDA

Hi-Tech Enterprises Inc, pg 888
Midtown Video Inc, pg 942
Phat Planet Recording Studios, pg 973
Tel-Test, pg 1035

GEORGIA

Stage Front Presentation Systems, pg 1022

ILLINOIS

Beatty TeleVisual Productions, pg 804
Midwest Digital Corp, pg 942

KENTUCKY

NOR-COM Inc, pg 958

MICHIGAN

TeL Systems, pg 1035

MINNESOTA

Alpha Video & Audio Inc, pg 782

MISSOURI

Southwest Audio-Visual Inc, pg 1019

NEW JERSEY

Starlite Productions, pg 1024

OREGON

All Service Musical Electronics Repair, pg 780

TENNESSEE

Technical Support Systems LLC, pg 1034

TEXAS

Industrial Audio/Video Inc, pg 897
Tarpley Media Systems, pg 1032

UTAH

RIA Corp, pg 996

VIRGINIA

Hoppmann Audio Visual, pg 891

WISCONSIN

Camera Corner Connecting Point, pg 818
Full Compass Systems, pg 874

ONTARIO

Westbury National Show Systems Ltd, pg 1064

VIDEO

Slide to Video Transfers, *see* Transfers—Slide to Video

Slow Motion Photography, *see* Photography—Slow Motion

Special Effects

ALABAMA

Diamond Studios, pg 846

ARIZONA

Arizona Virtual Studios, pg 790
Creative Backstage, pg 838
Merestone, pg 938
Metropolitan Audio-Visual Inc, pg 940

ARKANSAS

Live'N'Loud, pg 923
Shadowbox Video Productions, pg 1007
White Diamond Productions, pg 1065

CALIFORNIA

Aaron & Le Duc, pg 772
Access Video in Berkeley, pg 773
Action Video, pg 775
Artichoke Productions, pg 791
Auslender Productions/Celestial Images, pg 797
Automated Entertainment, pg 797
Blind, pg 809
Branam Enterprises Inc, pg 811
Buttercup Pictures, pg 816
Calbor Enterprises Two Inc, pg 816
Cherry Multimedia, pg 824
Crystal Pyramid Productions™, pg 840
Custom Video Productions Inc, pg 841
deKramer Productions Inc, pg 845
Direct Images Interactive Inc, pg 848
DreamWorks Animation SKG Inc, pg 852
Duck Studios, pg 853
Elektrashock, pg 859
First Person™, pg 868
Full Scale Effects, pg 874
Global Village Productions, pg 879
iCorpTv, pg 893
JDS Video & Media Productions Inc, pg 904
Laser Magic Productions, pg 916
Lumeni Productions Inc, pg 926
Maximus Media Inc, pg 934
McCune Audio-Video-Lighting, pg 935
The Media Staff Inc, pg 937
Method Studios, pg 939
Mind Over Eye Inc, pg 943
Moving Art by Louie Schwartzberg, pg 947
New & Unique Videos™, pg 955
New Deal Studios, pg 955
New Wave Entertainment, pg 956
Palardo Productions, pg 968
Planet Blue, pg 976
PSI Inc, pg 987
Pyro Spectaculars, pg 988
QRS Software Services, pg 988
Reality Check Systems, pg 992
RetinaVision Productions, pg 995
Ron Roy Productions/Moodtapes, pg 1000
Saturn Studios, pg 1003
SBS Productions, pg 1003
Shapeshifter, pg 1008
SonicPool, pg 1016
Special Effects Unlimited Inc, pg 1020
Staylor-Made Communications Inc, pg 1024
StereoScope International, pg 1024
Still N'Motion, pg 1025
Studio 637, pg 1027
Tam Communications Inc, pg 1031
Tigar Hare Studios, pg 1040
Toon Makers, pg 1042
Total Media Group, pg 1042
Twin Peaks Creative, pg 1047
Two Door Productions, pg 1047
VidCan Media Solutions, pg 1054
Videografix LLC, pg 1057
Videolady, pg 1057
Visions Plus, pg 1058
Vitruvian Entertainment, pg 1060
Wavemaker Media Design, pg 1062
Mark Woollen & Associates, pg 1069

COLORADO

Flashback Media Productions, pg 869
Full Spectrum Arts & Services, pg 874
Maniac Productions, pg 930
Rocky Mountain Audio/Video Productions Inc, pg 998
Z-Axis Corp, pg 1073

CONNECTICUT

Applebox Studio, pg 788
BRB Audiovisual Productions, pg 812
Fox Connecticut, pg 872
Guymark Studios LLC, pg 883
Ironik Design & Post, pg 902
MAVCO, pg 934
Musivision Inc, pg 951
Palace Digital Studios, pg 967
Think 3-D.com, pg 1038

DISTRICT OF COLUMBIA

Interface Media Group, pg 900
Yellow Cat Productions Inc, pg 1072

FLORIDA

Access Media Group, pg 773
Allegro Productions Inc, pg 781
Audio Visual Imagineering Inc, pg 795
Big Byte Video Productions, pg 806
Cinema East, pg 827
Civins Productions Inc, pg 828
Communications Concepts Inc (CCI), pg 833
Courter Films LLC, pg 837
Eastern Video, pg 856
Ed Ethridge Productions Inc, pg 863
Everlast Productions, pg 863
Hi-Tech Enterprises Inc, pg 888
Home Shopping Network (HSN), pg 890
Media Concepts Inc, pg 936
Orlando Special Effects, pg 965
Progressive Media & Music, pg 985
Sound & Vision Communications Inc, pg 1016
Sunfire Communications Inc, pg 1028
Sunrise Studios, pg 1028
Tricycle Studios, pg 1044
Vistamax Productions, pg 1059

GEORGIA

Crawford Media Services, pg 838
The DVI Group, pg 854
First Cut Communications LLC, pg 868
Guerrilla Productions LLC, pg 883

HAWAII

Dot C Software Inc, pg 851
Hyperspective Studios Inc, pg 893
1013 Integrated, pg 1037

ILLINOIS

ABSA Productions Inc, pg 772
Airways Digital Media, pg 779
Analog Free Media, pg 786
AnswersMedia, pg 787
Audio Visual Services Corp, pg 796
Backstar Creative Media Inc, pg 801
Chicago Satellite & Video, pg 825
Chicago Spotlight Inc, pg 825
Comtech Multimedia Marketing, pg 834
Consolidated Display Co Inc, pg 835
IV Media Resources, pg 903
MIGHTYbYTES Inc, pg 942
Optimus, pg 964
The Pepper Group, pg 972
PSAV® Presentation Services (Hotel Services Division), pg 987
Richter Studios, pg 996
20/20 Communications Inc, pg 1047
Video Impressions, pg 1055

INDIANA

AVA Productions, pg 798
Covenant Productions®, pg 837

KENTUCKY

The Media Collaboratory, pg 936
The PPS Group, pg 980
Theatre Effects, pg 1038

LOUISIANA

Digital FX Inc, pg 847
Vidox Motion Imagery, pg 1057

MAINE

WGME-TV, pg 1065

MARYLAND

Adventure Productions LLC, pg 778
CPR MultiMedia Solutions, pg 837
dbF a Media Company, pg 844
Kramer Communications Video Production, pg 913
Mobile-Video Productions Inc, pg 944
Producers Video, pg 984
Shadowstone R & R™, pg 1008

MASSACHUSETTS

Award Productions, pg 800
Northern Light Productions, pg 959
Penfield Productions Ltd, pg 971
Veritech Corp, pg 1053

MICHIGAN

Digi Sign Design LLC, pg 847
Digital Image Studios LLC, pg 847
K&R's Recording Studios Inc, pg 908
Michigan Recording Arts Institute & Technologies, pg 941
The Program Source International, pg 985
RingSide Creative, pg 997
Universal Images, pg 1049

MINNESOTA

Aggressive Records Audio Duplication LLC, pg 778
House of Cinemagraphics, pg 891
Master Communications Group, pg 933

MISSOURI

Conference Technologies Inc, pg 835
Fantasy Creations FX, pg 865
Laser Rentals Inc, pg 916

MONTANA

Filmlites Montana, pg 867
North Country Media Group, pg 959

NEVADA

Aardvark Video & Media Productions, pg 772
DVDs4Less, pg 854
Encore Productions Inc, pg 861
GES Audio Visual, pg 877
MeshTel-Intelite, pg 939

NEW HAMPSHIRE

Apertura, pg 788
Channell One Video, pg 824

NEW JERSEY

All Jersey Studios, pg 780
Broadcast Center Studios, pg 813
CD Meyer Inc, pg 822
CELCO-Constantine Engineering Labs Co, pg 822
CFP Video Productions Inc, pg 823
Color Leasing Studios, pg 831
Deluxe Media Services, pg 845
Early Films, pg 855
Euro-Pacific Film & Video Productions Inc, pg 863
Laurel Video Productions, pg 916
Megavideo Productions, pg 938
MIB Mediaworks, pg 941
Midnight Media Group Inc, pg 942
NFL Films Inc, pg 957
PeopleVisionFX, pg 972
Starlite Productions, pg 1024
Suede Interactive, pg 1027
VCSvideo, pg 1052

NEW MEXICO

Production Outfitters, pg 984

NEW YORK

Animotion Inc, pg 787
Norman N Axelrod Associates, pg 800
Big Film Design, pg 807
The Big House Group, pg 807
Broad Street Inc, pg 812
Chromavision Corp, pg 826
Design Audio Visual Inc, pg 845
Designomotion, pg 846
Digital Art Video Inc, pg 847
Eastco Multimedia Solutions Inc, pg 856
4-D Creative Media, pg 871

Special Effects Generator Distributors

VIDEO

Special Effects Generator Distributors (continued)

PENNSYLVANIA

Advanced AV, pg 777
The Lerro Corp, pg 919
Morefield Communications Inc, pg 946
Shore Manufacturing Co, pg 1009
Visual Sound Inc, pg 1059

TENNESSEE

Lowrance Sound Co Inc, pg 925

TEXAS

AVES Audio Visual Systems Inc, pg 798
Biway Media, pg 808
Pro Video & Film Equipment Co Inc, pg 983
Videotex Systems Inc, pg 1057

UTAH

RIA Corp, pg 996
TV Specialists Inc, pg 1046

VIRGINIA

Avitecture Inc, pg 799
Hoppmann Audio Visual, pg 891
The Whitlock Group, pg 1065

WASHINGTON

Laser Fantasy/HECK Industries/Photon Manufacturing, pg 916

WISCONSIN

Audio Visual of Milwaukee Inc, pg 795
Camera Corner Connecting Point, pg 818
Full Compass Systems, pg 874

ALBERTA

McBain Audio Visual Ltd, pg 935

NEW BRUNSWICK

Rockeffects Canada Inc/KABUKI, pg 998

ONTARIO

HD Source, pg 886
Majortech Inc, pg 929
Nationwide Audio Visual Co, pg 953

QUEBEC

Panavideo Inc, pg 968

Special Effects Generator Manufacturers

CALIFORNIA

Diaquest, pg 846
Enright Co, pg 861
For-A Corp of America, pg 871
Grande Vitesse Systems Inc (GVS), pg 881
Panasonic Broadcast & Digital Systems Co, pg 968
Pinnacle Systems Inc, pg 975
Ultimatte Corp, pg 1047

COLORADO

Colorado Video Inc, pg 832

FLORIDA

Compuvideo Sales USA Ltd, pg 834
Florical Systems Inc, pg 870
JEM Smoke Machine Co Ltd, pg 905
Tel-Test, pg 1035

KANSAS

GlobalStreams™ Corp, pg 879

MARYLAND

Image Logic Corp, pg 895

NEW JERSEY

CELCO-Constantine Engineering Labs Co, pg 822

NEW YORK

Image Labs Corp, pg 895
Quantel Inc, pg 989

PENNSYLVANIA

Shore Manufacturing Co, pg 1009

TEXAS

Biway Media, pg 808

VERMONT

Polhemus, pg 978

WASHINGTON

Laser Fantasy/HECK Industries/Photon Manufacturing, pg 916

BRITISH COLUMBIA

Triad Communications Ltd, pg 1044

NEW BRUNSWICK

Rockeffects Canada Inc/KABUKI, pg 998

Special Effects Generator Rentals

ARIZONA

Merestone, pg 938

CALIFORNIA

Ametron Audio/Video, pg 785
Artichoke Productions, pg 791
Express Media Inc, pg 864
Reality Check Systems, pg 992
RetinaVision Productions, pg 995

CONNECTICUT

Videofilm Systems Inc, pg 1057

FLORIDA

Access Media Group, pg 773
Media Concepts Inc, pg 936
Paradise Show & Design Inc, pg 969

GEORGIA

Stage Front Presentation Systems, pg 1022

ILLINOIS

Chicago Satellite & Video, pg 825
Show Department Inc, pg 1009

KANSAS

KAKE-TV, pg 907

KENTUCKY

Audio Visual Techniques Inc, pg 796

MARYLAND

CPR MultiMedia Solutions, pg 837

MICHIGAN

Digi Sign Design LLC, pg 847
On Stage Visuals, pg 963

MISSOURI

Production Support Services Inc, pg 985
Show-Me Audio-Visual, pg 1009

NEVADA

Lefco Video Services Inc, pg 918

NEW JERSEY

Soundtracks Production Services LLC, pg 1018
Starlite Productions, pg 1024
Wired 4 Sound Inc, pg 1068

NEW YORK

Design Audio Visual Inc, pg 845
LightSpace Studios, pg 921

OKLAHOMA

PDC Productions, pg 970

PENNSYLVANIA

Producers Management Television (PMTV), pg 983

UTAH

TV Specialists Inc, pg 1046

BRITISH COLUMBIA

Finale Editworks, pg 868

ONTARIO

JIB Shots Equipment Inc, pg 905

SASKATCHEWAN

plan9films, pg 976

Special Effects Generator Repairs

CALIFORNIA

BroadcastStore.com, pg 813
VMI Inc, pg 1060

FLORIDA

ELC Sales & Service Inc, pg 858
Glanz Technologies Inc, pg 878
Hi-Tech Enterprises Inc, pg 888
Midtown Video Inc, pg 942

GEORGIA

Stage Front Presentation Systems, pg 1022

ILLINOIS

Allen Visual Systems Inc, pg 781
Beatty TeleVisual Productions, pg 804

KENTUCKY

Barney Miller's Inc, pg 943
NOR-COM Inc, pg 958

MICHIGAN

TeL Systems, pg 1035

MINNESOTA

Alpha Video & Audio Inc, pg 782

MISSOURI

Southwest Audio-Visual Inc, pg 1019

NEW JERSEY

Starlite Productions, pg 1024

NEW YORK

Technisphere Corp, pg 1034
Visual Technologies Corp, pg 1060

TEXAS

Biway Media, pg 808

UTAH

RIA Corp, pg 996
TV Specialists Inc, pg 1046

WISCONSIN

Camera Corner Connecting Point, pg 818
Full Compass Systems, pg 874

BRITISH COLUMBIA

Commercial Electronics Ltd, pg 832

Standards Conversion, *see* Video Standards Conversion

Still Frame Storage Device Distributors

ALABAMA

Media Visions Inc, pg 937

ARIZONA

Audio Video Resources, pg 795
Troxell Communications Inc, pg 1045

CALIFORNIA

Advanced Systems Group LLC, pg 778
Ametron Audio/Video, pg 785
Audio/Video Supply Inc, pg 795
FXC Communications, pg 874
Tri-Ed, pg 1044

FLORIDA

Access Media Group, pg 773
Digital Video Systems Inc, pg 848
Media Concepts Inc, pg 936
Midtown Video Inc, pg 942
Pro Stage Inc, pg 983

GEORGIA

Baker Audio Inc, pg 801
Stage Front Presentation Systems, pg 1022

ILLINOIS

RAM Systems LLC, pg 991
Tele-Time Systems, pg 1036

INDIANA

Sensory Technologies LLC, pg 1006

MARYLAND

Visual Aids Electronics Corp, pg 1059
Wiltronix, pg 1067

MASSACHUSETTS

ASACA/ShibaSoku Corp of America, pg 791

MINNESOTA

Alpha Video & Audio Inc, pg 782
AVI Systems, pg 799

MISSOURI

Communitronics Corp, pg 833
Modern Communications Inc, pg 944
Southwest Audio-Visual Inc, pg 1019

NEBRASKA

Dog & Pony Productions Inc, pg 850

NEW JERSEY

Advanced Imaging Concepts Inc, pg 777
G&G Technologies Inc, pg 875
MCCOM Inc, pg 935
PatchAmp, pg 970
SYMCO Inc, pg 1030
Total Video Products Inc, pg 1042
Video Corporation of America (VCA), pg 1055

NEW YORK

Audio-Video Corp, pg 795
AV Workshop, pg 797
Long Island Video Enterprises Live Inc, pg 924
Technisphere Corp, pg 1034
Vision Identics Systems Inc, pg 1058

NORTH CAROLINA

Camcor Inc, pg 818

PENNSYLVANIA

Advanced AV, pg 777
The Lerro Corp, pg 919
Morefield Communications Inc, pg 946
Visual Sound Inc, pg 1059

TENNESSEE

Memphis Communications Corp, pg 938

TEXAS

Pro Video & Film Equipment Co Inc, pg 983
Videotex Systems Inc, pg 1057

UTAH

RIA Corp, pg 996

VIRGINIA

Avitecture Inc, pg 799
Hoppmann Audio Visual, pg 891
Quince Imaging Inc, pg 989
The Whitlock Group, pg 1065

WISCONSIN

Audio Visual of Milwaukee Inc, pg 795
Camera Corner Connecting Point, pg 818
Full Compass Systems, pg 874

ALBERTA

McBain Audio Visual Ltd, pg 935

ONTARIO

Edcom Multimedia Products, pg 856
HD Source, pg 886
Majortech Inc, pg 929

Still Frame Storage Device Manufacturers

CALIFORNIA

Grande Vitesse Systems Inc (GVS), pg 881
Hotronic Inc, pg 891
Pinnacle Systems Inc, pg 975
Sony Electronics Inc, pg 1016

COLORADO

Colorado Video Inc, pg 832

ILLINOIS

EPIX Inc, pg 862

KANSAS

GlobalStreams™ Corp, pg 879

MASSACHUSETTS

ASACA/ShibaSoku Corp of America, pg 791

NEW JERSEY

Advanced Imaging Concepts Inc, pg 777
Transparent Office Products LLC, pg 1043

NEW YORK

Eastman Kodak Professional, pg 856
Quantel Inc, pg 989

OREGON

Grass Valley, pg 881

PENNSYLVANIA

MicroImage Video Systems, pg 941
World Video Sales Co Inc, pg 1070

BRITISH COLUMBIA

Triad Communications Ltd, pg 1044

Still Frame Storage Device Rentals

ARIZONA

Audio Video Resources, pg 795
Merestone, pg 938

CALIFORNIA

Artichoke Productions, pg 791
Bexel Corp, pg 806
Express Media Inc, pg 864
Golden Gate Studios, pg 880
Lynch Communications, pg 926
Main Street Media Inc, pg 929
McCune Audio-Video-Lighting, pg 935
RetinaVision Productions, pg 995
Twin Peaks Creative, pg 1047

COLORADO

Daylight Productions & Rentals, pg 844
Multimedia Audio Visual Inc, pg 950

CONNECTICUT

Fox Connecticut, pg 872

FLORIDA

Access Media Group, pg 773
Jordan Klein Film & Video (JKFV), pg 906
Media Concepts Inc, pg 936
Pro Stage Inc, pg 983

GEORGIA

Stage Front Presentation Systems, pg 1022

ILLINOIS

Backstar Creative Media Inc, pg 801
Beatty TeleVisual Productions, pg 804
Chicago Satellite & Video, pg 825
On Site Video, pg 963
QuickSet International Inc, pg 989
Show Department Inc, pg 1009
Tele-Time Systems, pg 1036

KENTUCKY

Audio Visual Techniques Inc, pg 796

LOUISIANA

Digital FX Inc, pg 847
Pace Systems, pg 966

MARYLAND

CPR MultiMedia Solutions, pg 837

MASSACHUSETTS

Home Inc, pg 890
massAV, pg 933
Preston Productions Inc, pg 981

MINNESOTA

Alpha Video & Audio Inc, pg 782
AVI Systems, pg 799

MISSOURI

Southwest Audio-Visual Inc, pg 1019

NEVADA

GES Audio Visual, pg 877
Lefco Video Services Inc, pg 918

NEW JERSEY

MediaMix Inc, pg 937
PLS Staging, pg 977

NEW YORK

Ace Video, pg 774
AV Workshop, pg 797
Long Island Video Enterprises Live Inc, pg 924
Manhattan Center Studios Inc, pg 930
MRG Productions Inc, pg 948
TBA Global Events, pg 1032
Technisphere Corp, pg 1034
WNET/NET TELECON, pg 1069

NORTH CAROLINA

A&V Company, pg 772
Camcor Inc, pg 818

OHIO

Lyon Video Inc, pg 927
Vista Color Imaging Inc, pg 1059

OKLAHOMA

PDC Productions, pg 970

PENNSYLVANIA

FMP Media Solutions Inc, pg 870
Fusion Brand Experiences, pg 874

TENNESSEE

Russ Sturgeon Productions/RSVP, pg 1027

TEXAS

Alford Media Services, pg 780
Earl Miller Productions Inc, pg 943
Stage Directions, pg 1022

VIRGINIA

Creative Video of Washington Inc, pg 839
Quince Imaging Inc, pg 989

WYOMING

Bridger Productions Inc, pg 812

ALBERTA

Global Television Station, pg 879

BRITISH COLUMBIA

Finale Editworks, pg 868

ONTARIO

HD Source, pg 886

SASKATCHEWAN

plan9films, pg 976

Still Frame Storage Device Repairs

CALIFORNIA

VMI Inc, pg 1060

FLORIDA

Midtown Video Inc, pg 942

VIDEO

Still Frame Storage Device Repairs (continued)

GEORGIA

Stage Front Presentation Systems, pg 1022

ILLINOIS

Beatty TeleVisual Productions, pg 804
On Site Video, pg 963

MARYLAND

RTZ Audio Visual, pg 1000

MICHIGAN

TeL Systems, pg 1035

MINNESOTA

Alpha Video & Audio Inc, pg 782
AVI Systems, pg 799

MISSOURI

Southwest Audio-Visual Inc, pg 1019

NEW YORK

Ace Video, pg 774
MRG Productions Inc, pg 948

NORTH CAROLINA

Camcor Inc, pg 818

UTAH

RIA Corp, pg 996

VIRGINIA

Hoppmann Audio Visual, pg 891
The Whitlock Group, pg 1065

WISCONSIN

Full Compass Systems, pg 874

ONTARIO

Edcom Multimedia Products, pg 856

Still Printer Distributors

ARKANSAS

Jay S Stanley & Associates Inc, pg 1023

CALIFORNIA

Ametron Audio/Video, pg 785
FXC Communications, pg 874

FLORIDA

Access Media Group, pg 773
Digital Video Systems Inc, pg 848
Midtown Video Inc, pg 942

GEORGIA

Stage Front Presentation Systems, pg 1022

ILLINOIS

Allen Visual Systems Inc, pg 781

INDIANA

Sensory Technologies LLC, pg 1006

MASSACHUSETTS

Hunt's Photo, Video & Digital, pg 892

MINNESOTA

Alpha Video & Audio Inc, pg 782

MISSOURI

Modern Communications Inc, pg 944
Southwest Audio-Visual Inc, pg 1019

NEBRASKA

Video Service of America Inc (VSA), pg 1056

NEVADA

Aardvark Video & Media Productions, pg 772

NEW JERSEY

Advanced Imaging Concepts Inc, pg 777
SYMCO Inc, pg 1030
Total Video Products Inc, pg 1042

NEW YORK

B&H Photo & Video Pro Audio, pg 802
TecNec Distributing, pg 1035
Vision Identics Systems Inc, pg 1058

OHIO

Jimmy Rea Electronics Inc, pg 992

PENNSYLVANIA

Advanced AV, pg 777
The Lerro Corp, pg 919

VIRGINIA

Filmdex Inc, pg 867

WISCONSIN

Camera Corner Connecting Point, pg 818
Full Compass Systems, pg 874

ALBERTA

Matrix Video Communications Corp (MVCC), pg 934

Still Printer Manufacturers

CALIFORNIA

Panasonic Broadcast & Digital Systems Co, pg 968

BRITISH COLUMBIA

Triad Communications Ltd, pg 1044

Still Printer Rentals

ARIZONA

Merestone, pg 938

CALIFORNIA

Express Media Inc, pg 864
RetinaVision Productions, pg 995
VMI Inc, pg 1060

FLORIDA

Cinema East, pg 827

GEORGIA

Stage Front Presentation Systems, pg 1022

KENTUCKY

Audio Visual Techniques Inc, pg 796

MARYLAND

CPR MultiMedia Solutions, pg 837

MISSOURI

Show-Me Audio-Visual, pg 1009

Still Printer Repairs

CALIFORNIA

Ametron Audio/Video, pg 785
VMI Inc, pg 1060

FLORIDA

ELC Sales & Service Inc, pg 858

GEORGIA

Stage Front Presentation Systems, pg 1022

ILLINOIS

Allen Visual Systems Inc, pg 781

MICHIGAN

TeL Systems, pg 1035

MINNESOTA

Alpha Video & Audio Inc, pg 782

MISSOURI

Southwest Audio-Visual Inc, pg 1019

VIRGINIA

Avitecture Inc, pg 799

WISCONSIN

Camera Corner Connecting Point, pg 818
Full Compass Systems, pg 874

Stock-Shot Libraries, *see* Libraries—Film or Stock-Shot

Storage Vault Distributors

FLORIDA

Midtown Video Inc, pg 942

INDIANA

Sensory Technologies LLC, pg 1006

KANSAS

Desktop Video Systems, pg 846

MASSACHUSETTS

University Products Inc, pg 1050

MINNESOTA

Alpha Video & Audio Inc, pg 782

MISSOURI

Southwest Audio-Visual Inc, pg 1019

PENNSYLVANIA

Advanced AV, pg 777
The Lerro Corp, pg 919

WISCONSIN

Audio Visual of Milwaukee Inc, pg 795

Storage Vault Manufacturers

KANSAS

Desktop Video Systems, pg 846
GlobalStreams™ Corp, pg 879

MINNESOTA

Telex Communications Inc, pg 1037

Storage Vault Rentals

CALIFORNIA

Roundabout Entertainment Inc, pg 1000

ILLINOIS

Chicago Satellite & Video, pg 825

NORTH CAROLINA

Take One Productions Ltd, pg 1031

BRITISH COLUMBIA

Finale Editworks, pg 868

Storage Vault Repairs

MICHIGAN

TeL Systems, pg 1035

Studio Photography, *see* Photography—Studio

Switcher & Matrix—Analog & Digital Distributors

ALABAMA

PESA, pg 973

ARIZONA

EAR Professional Audio/Video, pg 855

ARKANSAS

Jay S Stanley & Associates Inc, pg 1023

CALIFORNIA

Addlogix, pg 776
Ametron Audio/Video, pg 785
BroadcastStore.com, pg 813
California Tape Products Inc, pg 817
Cibola Systems, pg 826
Delicate Electronics Sales Inc, pg 845
FXC Communications, pg 874
JD Audio Visual Inc, pg 904
Marshall Electronics Inc, pg 932
Media Control Systems LLC, pg 936
Mobilized Tech Systems, pg 944
POP TV, pg 978
SNAP, pg 1014
Southern California Sound Image Inc, pg 1019
Stanislaus Audio Video Inc, pg 1023
Videobotics, pg 1056
VMI Inc, pg 1060

COLORADO

Daylight Productions & Rentals, pg 844
Spectrum Audio Visual Services, pg 1020

CONNECTICUT

Everett Hall Associates Inc, pg 863

FLORIDA

Access Media Group, pg 773
Allstar Audio Systems Inc, pg 782
Digital Video Systems Inc, pg 848
Griffiths Broadcast Co Inc, pg 882
Harris Corp, pg 885
Hi-Tech Enterprises Inc, pg 888
Media Concepts Inc, pg 936
Midtown Video Inc, pg 942
Multicom Inc, pg 949
Sight & Sound Productions, pg 1010

GEORGIA

Clark, pg 829
Omnimedia Inc, pg 962
Stage Front Presentation Systems, pg 1022

ILLINOIS

Allen Visual Systems Inc, pg 781
Joseph Electronics, pg 906
Quintessence Audio Ltd, pg 989
Sound Vision Inc, pg 1018

INDIANA

Sensory Technologies LLC, pg 1006
SHP Electronics, pg 1010

KENTUCKY

NOR-COM Inc, pg 958

LOUISIANA

Intermedia Technologies, pg 900

MAINE

Independent Audio Inc, pg 897

MARYLAND

Human Circuit, pg 892
Wiltronix, pg 1067

MASSACHUSETTS

Antronics Inc, pg 787
Rule Broadcast Systems, pg 1000

MICHIGAN

ASC Systems, pg 791
Ascom Communications Contractors, pg 791
On Stage Visuals, pg 963

MINNESOTA

Alpha Video & Audio Inc, pg 782

MISSOURI

MIS Technologies, pg 944
Modern Communications Inc, pg 944
Southwest Audio-Visual Inc, pg 1019

NEBRASKA

ATV Research Inc, pg 793

NEW JERSEY

Alltec Stores, a Vcom IMC Company, pg 782
Diversified Systems Inc, pg 849
Earl Girls Inc, pg 855
Hamilton Buhl, pg 884
MCCOM Inc, pg 935
PatchAmp, pg 970
Starlite Productions, pg 1024
SYMCO Inc, pg 1030
Total Video Products Inc, pg 1042
Wired 4 Sound Inc, pg 1068

NEW YORK

ALTEL Systems Inc, pg 783
BTX Technologies, pg 814
Custom Media Environments, pg 841
Design Audio Visual Inc, pg 845
General Audio-Visual Inc (GAVI), pg 876
HAVE Inc, pg 886
Image Labs Corp, pg 895
Markertek Video Supply, pg 931
Stampede Presentation Products Inc, pg 1023
Technisphere Corp, pg 1034
TecNec Distributing, pg 1035
Visual Word Systems Inc, pg 1060

OHIO

ITA Audio Visual Solutions, pg 902
Jimmy Rea Electronics Inc, pg 992

PENNSYLVANIA

AccuWeather Inc, pg 774
Advanced AV, pg 777
The Lerro Corp, pg 919
Rossman Audio LLC, pg 1000
Vistacom Inc, pg 1059

RHODE ISLAND

Shanix Inc, pg 1008

TENNESSEE

Lowrance Sound Co Inc, pg 925
Technical Support Systems LLC, pg 1034
Zion Music Group, pg 1074

TEXAS

Audio Visual Technologies Group, pg 796
AVES Audio Visual Systems Inc, pg 798
Data Projections Inc, pg 843
Digital Display Solutions Inc, pg 847
Pro Video & Film Equipment Co Inc, pg 983
Sundance Systems, Fibox Products Division, pg 1028
Tarpley Media Systems, pg 1032
Videotex Systems Inc, pg 1057

VIRGINIA

Quince Imaging Inc, pg 989

WASHINGTON

Telect Inc, pg 1036

WISCONSIN

Audio Visual of Milwaukee Inc, pg 795
Camera Corner Connecting Point, pg 818
Full Compass Systems, pg 874
Safe Harbor Computers, pg 1001

BRITISH COLUMBIA

ProVision Video Sales & Rentals Inc, pg 986

MANITOBA

Advance Pro, pg 777

ONTARIO

Cinema Stage Inc, pg 827
McCurdy Radio Ltd, pg 935
Westbury National Show Systems Ltd, pg 1064

Switcher & Matrix—Analog & Digital Manufacturers

ALABAMA

PESA, pg 973

ARIZONA

Applied Integration Corp, pg 789
Covid Inc, pg 837

CALIFORNIA

ALTINEX Inc, pg 783
Extron Electronics, pg 864
For-A Corp of America, pg 871
Gefen, pg 876
Graham-Patten, pg 881
Hosa Technology Inc, pg 891
Marshall Electronics Inc, pg 932
Media Control Systems LLC, pg 936
RGB Spectrum, pg 996
Wohler Technologies Inc, pg 1069

COLORADO

Clear Blue Audio Video, pg 829

FLORIDA

Compuvideo Sales USA Ltd, pg 834
Tel-Test, pg 1035

GEORGIA

Outsource Engineering & Manufacturing Inc dba Texscan MSI, pg 966

KANSAS

GlobalStreams™ Corp, pg 879

KENTUCKY

TV One Multimedia Solutions, pg 1046

MARYLAND

Knox Video Technologies, pg 912

MICHIGAN

Leightronix Inc, pg 918

MINNESOTA

Vaddio, pg 1051

MISSOURI

Link Electronics Inc, pg 922

NEVADA

Adrienne Electronics Corp (AEC), pg 777

NEW JERSEY

Crestron Electronics Inc, pg 839
FSR Inc, pg 873
Kramer Electronics USA Inc, pg 913

NEW MEXICO

Burst Electronics Inc, pg 815

NEW YORK

Analog Way Inc, pg 786
Image Labs Corp, pg 895
Key Digital Systems, pg 910
Laird Digital Cinema, pg 915
Markertek Video Supply, pg 931
MultiDyne Video & Fiber Optics Systems, pg 950
Vicon Industries Inc, pg 1053

NORTH CAROLINA

Crest Electronics Inc, pg 839

PENNSYLVANIA

MicroImage Video Systems, pg 941
Rossman Audio LLC, pg 1000
World Video Sales Co Inc, pg 1070

TENNESSEE

Adtec Digital Inc, pg 777

TEXAS

Sundance Systems, Fibox Products Division, pg 1028

UTAH

Utah Scientific Inc, pg 1051

VIRGINIA

Quince Imaging Inc, pg 989

WASHINGTON

Telect Inc, pg 1036

VIDEO

Switcher & Matrix—Analog & Digital Manufacturers (continued)

WISCONSIN

Intelix LLC, pg 899

BRITISH COLUMBIA

Richmond Sound Design Ltd, pg 996

Switcher & Matrix—Analog & Digital Rentals

ALABAMA

Audio-Video Resources Inc, pg 795

ARIZONA

Merestone, pg 938
Video West Inc, pg 1056

CALIFORNIA

Ametron Audio/Video, pg 785
Artichoke Productions, pg 791
AV Guys, pg 797
Express Media Inc, pg 864
Full Moon & High Tide Productions & Studios, pg 874
Golden Gate Studios, pg 880
JD Audio Visual Inc, pg 904
Muse Presentation Technologies, pg 950
RetinaVision Productions, pg 995
Voice & Video Rentals, pg 1060
Westcoast Video Productions Inc, pg 1064

CONNECTICUT

Everett Hall Associates Inc, pg 863
Videofilm Systems Inc, pg 1057

FLORIDA

Access Media Group, pg 773
Allstar Audio Systems Inc, pg 782
Paradise Show & Design Inc, pg 969
Sight & Sound Productions, pg 1010

GEORGIA

Stage Front Presentation Systems, pg 1022

ILLINOIS

Chicago Satellite & Video, pg 825
The Meetinghouse Companies Inc, pg 938
Show Department Inc, pg 1009
Staging Resources Inc, pg 1023

KANSAS

KAKE-TV, pg 907

KENTUCKY

Audio Visual Techniques Inc, pg 796

MARYLAND

CPR MultiMedia Solutions, pg 837
Event Tech, pg 863
Kramer Communications Video Production, pg 913

MASSACHUSETTS

Preston Productions Inc, pg 981

MICHIGAN

On Stage Visuals, pg 963

MISSOURI

Show-Me Audio-Visual, pg 1009

NEW JERSEY

Earl Girls Inc, pg 855
Starlite Productions, pg 1024
Wired 4 Sound Inc, pg 1068

NEW YORK

Analog Way Inc, pg 786
Big Foot Productions Inc, pg 807
CP Communications, pg 837
Design Audio Visual Inc, pg 845
Visual Word Systems Inc, pg 1060

NORTH CAROLINA

A&V Company, pg 772

NORTH DAKOTA

Media Productions, pg 937

OKLAHOMA

PDC Productions, pg 970

OREGON

Picture This Production Services, pg 975

PENNSYLVANIA

FMP Media Solutions Inc, pg 870
Innovision Media Group, pg 899

TENNESSEE

Technical Support Systems LLC, pg 1034

TEXAS

Alford Media Services, pg 780
Bright Star Productions Inc, pg 812
Stage Directions, pg 1022

VIRGINIA

Advance Concepts Inc, pg 777
Quince Imaging Inc, pg 989

PUERTO RICO

Stage Crew Audiovisual Inc, pg 1022

BRITISH COLUMBIA

Finale Editworks, pg 868
Image Media Farm, pg 895
ProVision Video Sales & Rentals Inc, pg 986

ONTARIO

JIB Shots Equipment Inc, pg 905
Westbury National Show Systems Ltd, pg 1064

Switcher & Matrix—Analog & Digital Repairs

FLORIDA

ELC Sales & Service Inc, pg 858
Hi-Tech Enterprises Inc, pg 888

GEORGIA

Stage Front Presentation Systems, pg 1022

ILLINOIS

Midwest Digital Corp, pg 942

KENTUCKY

NOR-COM Inc, pg 958

MICHIGAN

TeL Systems, pg 1035

NEW JERSEY

Starlite Productions, pg 1024

OREGON

All Service Musical Electronics Repair, pg 780

TENNESSEE

Technical Support Systems LLC, pg 1034

TEXAS

Tarpley Media Systems, pg 1032

ONTARIO

Westbury National Show Systems Ltd, pg 1064

Switcher & Matrix—Mechanical & Electronic Distributors

ARIZONA

EAR Professional Audio/Video, pg 855

CALIFORNIA

Ametron Audio/Video, pg 785
BroadcastStore.com, pg 813
ChronTrol Corp, pg 826
Delicate Electronics Sales Inc, pg 845
FXC Communications, pg 874
JD Audio Visual Inc, pg 904
Media Control Systems LLC, pg 936
Mobilized Tech Systems, pg 944
POP TV, pg 978
SNAP, pg 1014
Stanislaus Audio Video Inc, pg 1023
VMI Inc, pg 1060

COLORADO

Daylight Productions & Rentals, pg 844

FLORIDA

Access Media Group, pg 773
Allstar Audio Systems Inc, pg 782
Digital Video Systems Inc, pg 848
Hi-Tech Enterprises Inc, pg 888
Media Concepts Inc, pg 936
Midtown Video Inc, pg 942

GEORGIA

Omnimedia Inc, pg 962
Stage Front Presentation Systems, pg 1022

ILLINOIS

Allen Visual Systems Inc, pg 781
Joseph Electronics, pg 906
Sound Vision Inc, pg 1018

INDIANA

Sensory Technologies LLC, pg 1006
SHP Electronics, pg 1010

KENTUCKY

NOR-COM Inc, pg 958

LOUISIANA

Intermedia Technologies, pg 900

MAINE

Independent Audio Inc, pg 897

MARYLAND

Human Circuit, pg 892

MASSACHUSETTS

Antronics Inc, pg 787
Rule Broadcast Systems, pg 1000

MICHIGAN

ASC Systems, pg 791
Ascom Communications Contractors, pg 791
On Stage Visuals, pg 963

MINNESOTA

Alpha Video & Audio Inc, pg 782

MISSOURI

Conference Technologies Inc, pg 835
Modern Communications Inc, pg 944
Southwest Audio-Visual Inc, pg 1019

NEBRASKA

ATV Research Inc, pg 793

NEW JERSEY

Diversified Systems Inc, pg 849
FSR Inc, pg 873
Hamilton Buhl, pg 884
MCCOM Inc, pg 935
PatchAmp, pg 970
Starlite Productions, pg 1024
SYMCO Inc, pg 1030
Total Video Products Inc, pg 1042
Wired 4 Sound Inc, pg 1068

NEW YORK

ALTEL Systems Inc, pg 783
Custom Media Environments, pg 841
Design Audio Visual Inc, pg 845
General Audio-Visual Inc (GAVI), pg 876
HAVE Inc, pg 886
Markertek Video Supply, pg 931
Technisphere Corp, pg 1034

TecNec Distributing, pg 1035
Visual Word Systems Inc, pg 1060

OHIO

Jimmy Rea Electronics Inc, pg 992

PENNSYLVANIA

Advanced AV, pg 777
Bernie's Photo Center, pg 805
The Lerro Corp, pg 919
Rossman Audio LLC, pg 1000
Vistacom Inc, pg 1059

TENNESSEE

Lowrance Sound Co Inc, pg 925
Technical Support Systems LLC, pg 1034

TEXAS

Audio Visual Technologies Group, pg 796
Data Projections Inc, pg 843
Digital Display Solutions Inc, pg 847
Pro Video & Film Equipment Co Inc, pg 983
Sundance Systems, Fibox Products Division, pg 1028
Tarpley Media Systems, pg 1032

VIRGINIA

Communications Specialists Inc, pg 833
Quince Imaging Inc, pg 989

WASHINGTON

Telect Inc, pg 1036

WISCONSIN

Audio Visual of Milwaukee Inc, pg 795
Camera Corner Connecting Point, pg 818
Full Compass Systems, pg 874

BRITISH COLUMBIA

ProVision Video Sales & Rentals Inc, pg 986

MANITOBA

Advance Pro, pg 777

ONTARIO

Cinema Stage Inc, pg 827

Switcher & Matrix—Mechanical & Electronic Manufacturers

ARIZONA

NKK Switches, pg 957

CALIFORNIA

ALTINEX Inc, pg 783
ChronTrol Corp, pg 826
DiCon Fiberoptics Inc, pg 846
For-A Corp of America, pg 871
Hosa Technology Inc, pg 891
Media Control Systems LLC, pg 936
Wohler Technologies Inc, pg 1069

COLORADO

Clear Blue Audio Video, pg 829

FLORIDA

Compuvideo Sales USA Ltd, pg 834
Tel-Test, pg 1035

MARYLAND

Knox Video Technologies, pg 912

MINNESOTA

Vaddio, pg 1051

NEBRASKA

Veetronix Inc, pg 1052

NEVADA

Adrienne Electronics Corp (AEC), pg 777

NEW JERSEY

FSR Inc, pg 873
Kramer Electronics USA Inc, pg 913

NEW MEXICO

Burst Electronics Inc, pg 815

NEW YORK

Analog Way Inc, pg 786
Image Labs Corp, pg 895
Markertek Video Supply, pg 931
MultiDyne Video & Fiber Optics Systems, pg 950

NORTH CAROLINA

Crest Electronics Inc, pg 839

OHIO

Network Technologies Inc, pg 955

PENNSYLVANIA

MicroImage Video Systems, pg 941
Rossman Audio LLC, pg 1000
World Video Sales Co Inc, pg 1070

TEXAS

Sundance Systems, Fibox Products Division, pg 1028

VIRGINIA

Quince Imaging Inc, pg 989

WASHINGTON

Telect Inc, pg 1036

Switcher & Matrix—Mechanical & Electronic Rentals

ARIZONA

Merestone, pg 938

CALIFORNIA

Ametron Audio/Video, pg 785
Express Media Inc, pg 864
Golden Gate Studios, pg 880
JD Audio Visual Inc, pg 904
Muse Presentation Technologies, pg 950
RetinaVision Productions, pg 995

FLORIDA

Access Media Group, pg 773
Allstar Audio Systems Inc, pg 782
Paradise Show & Design Inc, pg 969

GEORGIA

Stage Front Presentation Systems, pg 1022

ILLINOIS

Chicago Satellite & Video, pg 825

KENTUCKY

Audio Visual Techniques Inc, pg 796

MARYLAND

CPR MultiMedia Solutions, pg 837
Event Tech, pg 863

MASSACHUSETTS

Preston Productions Inc, pg 981

MICHIGAN

On Stage Visuals, pg 963

MISSOURI

Show-Me Audio-Visual, pg 1009

NEW JERSEY

Starlite Productions, pg 1024
Wired 4 Sound Inc, pg 1068

NEW YORK

Analog Way Inc, pg 786
CP Communications, pg 837
Design Audio Visual Inc, pg 845
Visual Word Systems Inc, pg 1060

NORTH CAROLINA

A&V Company, pg 772

NORTH DAKOTA

Media Productions, pg 937

OKLAHOMA

PDC Productions, pg 970

PENNSYLVANIA

Innovision Media Group, pg 899

TENNESSEE

Technical Support Systems LLC, pg 1034

VIRGINIA

Quince Imaging Inc, pg 989

PUERTO RICO

Stage Crew Audiovisual Inc, pg 1022

BRITISH COLUMBIA

Image Media Farm, pg 895
ProVision Video Sales & Rentals Inc, pg 986

ONTARIO

JIB Shots Equipment Inc, pg 905

Switcher & Matrix—Mechanical & Electronic Repairs

FLORIDA

ELC Sales & Service Inc, pg 858

GEORGIA

Stage Front Presentation Systems, pg 1022

ILLINOIS

Midwest Digital Corp, pg 942

KENTUCKY

NOR-COM Inc, pg 958

MICHIGAN

TeL Systems, pg 1035

NEW JERSEY

Starlite Productions, pg 1024

OREGON

All Service Musical Electronics Repair, pg 780

TENNESSEE

Technical Support Systems LLC, pg 1034

TEXAS

Tarpley Media Systems, pg 1032

Syndication

ARIZONA

Merestone, pg 938
Phoenix VideoFilms®, pg 974

CALIFORNIA

Custom Video Productions Inc, pg 841
Dogma Studios, pg 850
Full Moon & High Tide Productions & Studios, pg 874
JDS Video & Media Productions Inc, pg 904
New & Unique Videos™, pg 955
Point 360, pg 978
QRS Software Services, pg 988
Visions Plus, pg 1058
The Wyland Group, pg 1071

COLORADO

Flashback Media Productions, pg 869

FLORIDA

National Teleproductions Inc, pg 953

GEORGIA

Guerrilla Productions LLC, pg 883
On-Line Productions, pg 963

ILLINOIS

Chicago Satellite & Video, pg 825
Communications Corporation of America, pg 833
Moviecraft Inc, pg 947

VIDEO

Syndication (continued)

LOUISIANA

Great Chefs/Leisure Jazz Video, pg 881
Leisure Video, pg 918

MASSACHUSETTS

Extreme Reach Inc, pg 864

MICHIGAN

K&R's Recording Studios Inc, pg 908

MINNESOTA

Aggressive Records Audio Duplication LLC, pg 778

MISSOURI

Cable Films & Video, pg 816

NEW HAMPSHIRE

Channell One Video, pg 824

NEW JERSEY

Broadcast Center Studios, pg 813
MIB Mediaworks, pg 941
Suede Interactive, pg 1027

NEW YORK

Adwar Video, pg 778
Animotion Inc, pg 787
The Big House Group, pg 807
Jalbert Productions International, pg 903
TBA Global Events, pg 1032
Teatown Communications Group, pg 1033
VIEW Inc (Video International Entertainment World Inc), pg 1058

NORTH CAROLINA

Pat Appleson Studios Inc, pg 788
Crystal Pictures Inc, pg 840
NASCAR Media Group LLC, pg 952

OHIO

Aztec Video Productions, pg 801

TENNESSEE

Motion Picture Services, pg 947
Scripps Networks, pg 1005
Stage Post, pg 1022

TEXAS

Phillips MediaSource, pg 974
The Samuels Co, pg 1002

VIRGINIA

CACI Productions Group, pg 816

WASHINGTON

Victory Studios, pg 1054

WISCONSIN

Wisconsin Public Television, pg 1068

WYOMING

Bridger Productions Inc, pg 812

ALBERTA

Global Television Station, pg 879

ONTARIO

Canamedia Inc, pg 818
GAPC (General Assembly Production Centre), pg 875

Talent & Property Agencies—Television

ALASKA

Alaska Film Services Inc, pg 779

ARIZONA

Film Creations Ltd, pg 867
Merestone, pg 938

ARKANSAS

Shadowbox Video Productions, pg 1007
White Diamond Productions, pg 1065

CALIFORNIA

Havas Edge, pg 885
International Contact Inc, pg 900
JDS Video & Media Productions Inc, pg 904
KTVU-Retail Services, pg 914
The Location Connection Inc, pg 924
Joseph Nicoletti Consulting-Promotion/California International Records/Global Village Records, pg 957
Palardo Productions, pg 968
QRS Software Services, pg 988
Sahara Records & Filmworks Entertainment Co, pg 1001
Santa Barbara Location Services, pg 1002
SonicPool, pg 1016

COLORADO

Flashback Media Productions, pg 869

CONNECTICUT

Ironik Design & Post, pg 902

HAWAII

Media Bridge Gamekids, pg 936

ILLINOIS

Communications Corporation of America, pg 833

LOUISIANA

Digital FX Inc, pg 847
Great Chefs/Leisure Jazz Video, pg 881
Leisure Video, pg 918

MASSACHUSETTS

Preston Productions Inc, pg 981

MICHIGAN

K&R's Recording Studios Inc, pg 908

MINNESOTA

Moore Creative Talent Inc, pg 946

NEW HAMPSHIRE

Channell One Video, pg 824
Chip Taylor Communications LLC, pg 1032

NEW JERSEY

Broadcast Center Studios, pg 813
Bill Quinn Productions, pg 989
Suede Interactive, pg 1027

NEW YORK

InterNation Inc, pg 900
SmartPros Ltd, pg 1014
TBA Global Events, pg 1032
WNET/NET TELECON, pg 1069

OHIO

Aztec Video Productions, pg 801
R&B Communications Inc, pg 991

RHODE ISLAND

A&M Productions, pg 771
Sound-FX-Design, pg 1017

TENNESSEE

Anode Inc, pg 787
Colonel Buster Doss Music Group, pg 831
Motion Picture Services, pg 947
Stage Post, pg 1022

TEXAS

Magic By Bruce Chadwick, pg 928

VIRGINIA

CACI Productions Group, pg 816
Studio Center Corp, pg 1026

WISCONSIN

Media Communications Association-International (MCA-I), pg 936
Video Wisconsin Inc, pg 1056

WYOMING

Bridger Productions Inc, pg 812

MANITOBA

2BK9 Acting Animals, pg 1047

Tape Duplicator Distributors

ARIZONA

Audio Video Resources, pg 795

ARKANSAS

White Diamond Productions, pg 1065

CALIFORNIA

Adolph Gasser Inc, pg 776
Advanced Systems Group LLC, pg 778
Ametron Audio/Video, pg 785
Audio/Video Supply Inc, pg 795
BroadcastStore.com, pg 813
Christy's Editorial, pg 826
FXC Communications, pg 874
Mobilized Tech Systems, pg 944
QRS Software Services, pg 988
SNAP, pg 1014
Westlake Recording Studios, pg 1064

COLORADO

Spectrum Audio Visual Services, pg 1020

FLORIDA

Access Media Group, pg 773
BAI Distributors Inc, pg 801
Digital Video Systems Inc, pg 848
Gulf Coast Audio Visual Producers Inc, pg 883
Harris Corp, pg 885
Hi-Tech Import Export Corp, pg 888
Media Concepts Inc, pg 936
Midtown Video Inc, pg 942
Pro Stage Inc, pg 983
Recording Media & Equipment Inc (RM&E), pg 993

GEORGIA

Stage Front Presentation Systems, pg 1022

ILLINOIS

Tele-Time Systems, pg 1036

INDIANA

Lee Co Inc, pg 918
Sensory Technologies LLC, pg 1006
SHP Electronics, pg 1010

KANSAS

Smith Audio-Visual Inc, pg 1014

KENTUCKY

Barney Miller's Inc, pg 943
NOR-COM Inc, pg 958

MAINE

Headlight Audio Visual Inc, pg 887

MARYLAND

RTZ Audio Visual, pg 1000
Visual Aids Electronics Corp, pg 1059

MASSACHUSETTS

Rule Broadcast Systems, pg 1000

MICHIGAN

Ascom Communications Contractors, pg 791

MINNESOTA

Alpha Video & Audio Inc, pg 782
Cinequipt Inc, pg 828

MISSISSIPPI

Bowie Audio Visual Enterprises Inc, pg 811
Jasper Ewing & Sons Inc, pg 864

MISSOURI

Conference Technologies Inc, pg 835
Modern Communications Inc, pg 944
Southwest Audio-Visual Inc, pg 1019

Swank Audio Visuals, pg 1029
VSG Digital Media Solutions, pg 1061

NEVADA

Aardvark Video & Media Productions, pg 772

NEW JERSEY

Audio Visual Associates, pg 795
Audio Visual Dynamics®, pg 795
Diversified Systems Inc, pg 849
G&G Technologies Inc, pg 875
Hamilton Buhl, pg 884
MCCOM Inc, pg 935
PatchAmp, pg 970
Reed Presentations Inc (RPI), pg 993
Starlite Productions, pg 1024
Total Video Products Inc, pg 1042
Video Corporation of America (VCA), pg 1055

NEW YORK

AV Workshop, pg 797
B&H Photo & Video Pro Audio, pg 802
Burlington A/V Recording Media, pg 815
Communication Corner Inc, pg 832
Eastco Multimedia Solutions Inc, pg 856
Gaylord Brothers, pg 876
HAVE Inc, pg 886
Saul Mineroff Electronics Inc, pg 943
Technisphere Corp, pg 1034
TecNec Distributing, pg 1035
Willoughby's Imaging Center, pg 1067

NORTH CAROLINA

Camcor Inc, pg 818
Strategic Connections, pg 1026

OHIO

iVideo Technologies, pg 903
Jimmy Rea Electronics Inc, pg 992
Smithall Electronics Inc, pg 1014

PENNSYLVANIA

Advanced AV, pg 777
Audio Visions Inc, pg 795
Audio Visual Communications Inc, pg 795
J E Foss Co, pg 871
Grise Audio Visual Center Inc, pg 882
The Lerro Corp, pg 919
Morefield Communications Inc, pg 946

TENNESSEE

Lowrance Sound Co Inc, pg 925
Memphis Communications Corp, pg 938
Technical Support Systems LLC, pg 1034
Zion Music Group, pg 1074

TEXAS

Heffernan Audio Visual, pg 887
Pro Video & Film Equipment Co Inc, pg 983
Tarpley Media Systems, pg 1032

UTAH

RIA Corp, pg 996

VIRGINIA

Lee Hartman & Sons Inc, pg 918
The Whitlock Group, pg 1065

WASHINGTON

Global Net Productions Inc, pg 879

WISCONSIN

Audio Visual of Milwaukee Inc, pg 795
Full Compass Systems, pg 874

PUERTO RICO

Bonnin Electronics Inc, pg 810

ALBERTA

McBain Audio Visual Ltd, pg 935
Sharp's Audio-Visual Ltd, pg 1008

BRITISH COLUMBIA

ProVision Video Sales & Rentals Inc, pg 986

MANITOBA

Inland Audio Visual Ltd, pg 898

ONTARIO

Edcom Multimedia Products, pg 856
Nationwide Audio Visual Co, pg 953
Premier A/V Sales Ltd, pg 980
Westbury National Show Systems Ltd, pg 1064

Tape Duplicator Manufacturers

CALIFORNIA

Panasonic Broadcast & Digital Systems Co, pg 968
QRS Software Services, pg 988
Recortec Inc, pg 993
Rovi Corp, pg 1000
Sony Electronics Inc, pg 1016

GEORGIA

Visix™ Inc, pg 1059

INDIANA

World Media Group Inc, pg 1069

MICHIGAN

Leightronix Inc, pg 918

MINNESOTA

Telex Communications Inc, pg 1037

NEW JERSEY

CELCO-Constantine Engineering Labs Co, pg 822

NEW YORK

TecNec Distributing, pg 1035

BRITISH COLUMBIA

Triad Communications Ltd, pg 1044

Tape Duplicator Rentals

ARIZONA

Merestone, pg 938
Metropolitan Audio-Visual Inc, pg 940

ARKANSAS

White Diamond Productions, pg 1065

CALIFORNIA

Advanced Media LLC, pg 778
AlphaDogs Inc, pg 782
Ametron Audio/Video, pg 785
Balboa Capital Corp, pg 802
Bexel Corp, pg 806
Crystal Pyramid Productions™, pg 840
Express Media Inc, pg 864
Golden Gate Studios, pg 880
Maximus Media Inc, pg 934
Munday & Collins AV, pg 950
RetinaVision Productions, pg 995
Total Media Group, pg 1042
Twin Peaks Creative, pg 1047
Voice & Video Rentals, pg 1060

COLORADO

Daylight Productions & Rentals, pg 844
Spectrum Audio Visual Services, pg 1020

CONNECTICUT

A/V Davey, pg 797
Fox Connecticut, pg 872
Videofilm Systems Inc, pg 1057

DELAWARE

Ken-Del Productions Inc, pg 909

FLORIDA

Cinema East, pg 827
Eastern Video, pg 856
Gulf Coast Audio Visual Producers Inc, pg 883
Jordan Klein Film & Video (JKFV), pg 906
Pro Stage Inc, pg 983

GEORGIA

ON Event Services, pg 963
Stage Front Presentation Systems, pg 1022

ILLINOIS

Chicago Satellite & Video, pg 825
QuickSet International Inc, pg 989

KANSAS

Smith Audio-Visual Inc, pg 1014

KENTUCKY

The PPS Group, pg 980

LOUISIANA

Digital FX Inc, pg 847

MARYLAND

CPR MultiMedia Solutions, pg 837
RTZ Audio Visual, pg 1000
Shadowstone R & R™, pg 1008

MASSACHUSETTS

Capron Lighting & Sound Co Inc, pg 819
massAV, pg 933

MICHIGAN

Digi Sign Design LLC, pg 847
K&R All Media Productions Inc, pg 908

MINNESOTA

Alpha Video & Audio Inc, pg 782
AVI Systems, pg 799

MISSISSIPPI

Bowie Audio Visual Enterprises Inc, pg 811

MISSOURI

Image Technologies Corp, pg 895
Show-Me Audio-Visual, pg 1009
Southwest Audio-Visual Inc, pg 1019
Swank Audio Visuals, pg 1029

NEVADA

JCS Video Productions, pg 904

NEW JERSEY

Audio Visual Associates, pg 795
Audio Visual Dynamics®, pg 795
MediaMix Inc, pg 937
Starlite Productions, pg 1024
Video Corporation of America (VCA), pg 1055

NEW MEXICO

Production Outfitters, pg 984

NEW YORK

AV Workshop, pg 797
CMI Communications, pg 830
MRG Productions Inc, pg 948
TBA Global Events, pg 1032
Technisphere Corp, pg 1034
WNET/NET TELECON, pg 1069

NORTH CAROLINA

Camcor Inc, pg 818
Duke Media Services, pg 853
Special Event Services, pg 1020
Strategic Connections, pg 1026
Take One Productions Ltd, pg 1031

OHIO

Hughie's Event Production Services, pg 892
Mills James Productions, pg 943
Vista Color Imaging Inc, pg 1059

PENNSYLVANIA

Audio Visions Inc, pg 795
Audio Visual Communications Inc, pg 795
FMP Media Solutions Inc, pg 870
Fusion Brand Experiences, pg 874
Grise Audio Visual Center Inc, pg 882
Innovision Media Group, pg 899

SOUTH CAROLINA

Sound & Images Inc, pg 1016

VIDEO

Tape Duplicator Rentals (continued)

TENNESSEE

Memphis Communications Corp, pg 938
Technical Support Systems LLC, pg 1034

TEXAS

J&S Audio Visual Inc, pg 904
Earl Miller Productions Inc, pg 943
Stage Directions, pg 1022

WASHINGTON

Kostov Productions, pg 913

WISCONSIN

Full Compass Systems, pg 874

WYOMING

Bridger Productions Inc, pg 812

ALBERTA

Global Television Station, pg 879

BRITISH COLUMBIA

Commercial Electronics Ltd, pg 832
Finale Editworks, pg 868

MANITOBA

Inland Audio Visual Ltd, pg 898

ONTARIO

Wanted! Sound + Picture, pg 1062
Westbury National Show Systems Ltd, pg 1064

Tape Duplicator Repairs

CALIFORNIA

Advanced Media LLC, pg 778
Ametron Audio/Video, pg 785
BroadcastStore.com, pg 813
Mobilized Tech Systems, pg 944
VMI Inc, pg 1060

FLORIDA

ELC Sales & Service Inc, pg 858
JT Communications, pg 906

GEORGIA

Stage Front Presentation Systems, pg 1022

ILLINOIS

Beatty TeleVisual Productions, pg 804

KENTUCKY

Barney Miller's Inc, pg 943
NOR-COM Inc, pg 958

MARYLAND

RTZ Audio Visual, pg 1000

MICHIGAN

TeL Systems, pg 1035

MINNESOTA

Alpha Video & Audio Inc, pg 782
AVI Systems, pg 799

MISSOURI

Southwest Audio-Visual Inc, pg 1019

NEW JERSEY

Starlite Productions, pg 1024

NEW YORK

MRG Productions Inc, pg 948
Technisphere Corp, pg 1034

NORTH CAROLINA

Camcor Inc, pg 818

OHIO

Tri-State Audio Visual Co, pg 1044

OREGON

All Service Musical Electronics Repair, pg 780

PENNSYLVANIA

Audio Visions Inc, pg 795
J E Foss Co, pg 871
Visual Sound Inc, pg 1059

TENNESSEE

Memphis Communications Corp, pg 938
Technical Support Systems LLC, pg 1034

TEXAS

Audio Visual Technologies Group, pg 796
Tarpley Media Systems, pg 1032

UTAH

RIA Corp, pg 996

VIRGINIA

The Whitlock Group, pg 1065

WISCONSIN

Full Compass Systems, pg 874

ALBERTA

Sharp's Audio-Visual Ltd, pg 1008

MANITOBA

Inland Audio Visual Ltd, pg 898

ONTARIO

Edcom Multimedia Products, pg 856
Westbury National Show Systems Ltd, pg 1064

Tape Eraser Distributors

ARKANSAS

White Diamond Productions, pg 1065

CALIFORNIA

Adolph Gasser Inc, pg 776
Ametron Audio/Video, pg 785
California Tape Products Inc, pg 817
Christy's Editorial, pg 826
FXC Communications, pg 874
QRS Software Services, pg 988
SNAP, pg 1014
Westlake Recording Studios, pg 1064

FLORIDA

Digital Video Systems Inc, pg 848
Harris Corp, pg 885
Hi-Tech Import Export Corp, pg 888
Hunter Electronics LLC, pg 892
Media Concepts Inc, pg 936
Midtown Video Inc, pg 942
Photomart Cine-Video Inc, pg 975
Recording Media & Equipment Inc (RM&E), pg 993
Sonar Radio Corp, pg 1015

GEORGIA

Stage Front Presentation Systems, pg 1022

INDIANA

Lee Co Inc, pg 918
Sensory Technologies LLC, pg 1006

KENTUCKY

NOR-COM Inc, pg 958

MASSACHUSETTS

Rule Broadcast Systems, pg 1000

MINNESOTA

Alpha Video & Audio Inc, pg 782

MISSOURI

Modern Communications Inc, pg 944
Southwest Audio-Visual Inc, pg 1019

NEW JERSEY

AV Bluebook, pg 797
Hamilton Buhl, pg 884
National Audio-Visual Supply, pg 952
Starlite Productions, pg 1024
VCom International Multimedia Corp, pg 1052

NEW YORK

B&H Photo & Video Pro Audio, pg 802
Eastco Multimedia Solutions Inc, pg 856
HAVE Inc, pg 886
Markertek Video Supply, pg 931
TecNec Distributing, pg 1035

OHIO

Jimmy Rea Electronics Inc, pg 992
Smithall Electronics Inc, pg 1014

PENNSYLVANIA

Advanced AV, pg 777
Brodart Co, pg 813
J E Foss Co, pg 871
The Lerro Corp, pg 919

TENNESSEE

Lowrance Sound Co Inc, pg 925

TEXAS

Pro Video & Film Equipment Co Inc, pg 983
RadioShack Corp, pg 990

VIRGINIA

Lee Hartman & Sons Inc, pg 918

WISCONSIN

Audio Visual of Milwaukee Inc, pg 795
Full Compass Systems, pg 874

BRITISH COLUMBIA

ProVision Video Sales & Rentals Inc, pg 986

ONTARIO

Premier A/V Sales Ltd, pg 980

Tape Eraser Manufacturers

CALIFORNIA

Garner Products Inc, pg 875
QRS Software Services, pg 988

FLORIDA

Sonar Radio Corp, pg 1015

ILLINOIS

Research Technology International (RTI), pg 995

INDIANA

R B Annis Instruments Inc, pg 787

NEBRASKA

Data Security Inc, pg 843

Tape Eraser Rentals

ARKANSAS

White Diamond Productions, pg 1065

CALIFORNIA

Ametron Audio/Video, pg 785
Artichoke Productions, pg 791
Garner Products Inc, pg 875
Golden Gate Studios, pg 880
Maximus Media Inc, pg 934
Twin Peaks Creative, pg 1047

COLORADO

The Cinema Lab, pg 827

CONNECTICUT

A/V Davey, pg 797
Videofilm Systems Inc, pg 1057

GEORGIA

Stage Front Presentation Systems, pg 1022

MARYLAND

CPR MultiMedia Solutions, pg 837

MICHIGAN

Digi Sign Design LLC, pg 847
K&R All Media Productions Inc, pg 908

VIDEO

Teleconferencing Equipment Distributors (continued)

TEXAS (continued)

Heffernan Audio Visual, pg 887
Media Management LLC, pg 937
Tarpley Media Systems, pg 1032

UTAH

RIA Corp, pg 996

VIRGINIA

Avitecture Inc, pg 799
Boitnott Visual Communications Corp (BVC), pg 810
Communications Specialists Inc, pg 833
Hoppmann Audio Visual, pg 891
Intellidyne LLC, pg 899
Lee Hartman & Sons Inc, pg 918
RGB Technology Inc, pg 996

WISCONSIN

Audio Visual of Milwaukee Inc, pg 795
Full Compass Systems, pg 874
Spectrum Industries Inc, pg 1021

PUERTO RICO

Audio Visual Concepts Inc, pg 795

ALBERTA

Infosat Communications Inc, pg 898
Matrix Video Communications Corp (MVCC), pg 934
Sharp's Audio-Visual Ltd, pg 1008
SMART Technologies Inc, pg 1013

BRITISH COLUMBIA

Commercial Electronics Ltd, pg 832

MANITOBA

Inland Audio Visual Ltd, pg 898

ONTARIO

Gesturetek, pg 877
Westbury National Show Systems Ltd, pg 1064

Teleconferencing Equipment Manufacturers

ARIZONA

Boeckeler Instruments Inc, pg 810
Covid Inc, pg 837

CALIFORNIA

ADS Technologies, pg 777
ALTINEX Inc, pg 783
Colby Systems Corp, pg 831
Computer Modules Inc, pg 834
ESE, pg 862
Hotronic Inc, pg 891
Opticomm-EMCORE, pg 964
RGB Spectrum, pg 996
WolfVision Inc, pg 1069
Zhone Technologies Inc, pg 1073

COLORADO

Display Devices, pg 849
Image Audiovisuals, pg 894

CONNECTICUT

Sound Control Technologies Inc, pg 1017

GEORGIA

PolyVision Corporation, pg 978

ILLINOIS

A T Products Inc, pg 771
Bretford Manufacturing Inc, pg 812
NEC Display Solutions of America, pg 954
Tellabs Inc, pg 1037
Toko America Inc, pg 1041
Windel International/Weyel, pg 1067

INDIANA

Draper Inc, pg 852

MARYLAND

RPG Diffusor Systems Inc, pg 1000

MASSACHUSETTS

Avidex Inc, pg 799
Miranda Telecast Fiber Systems Inc, pg 944

MICHIGAN

ASC Systems, pg 791

MINNESOTA

Vaddio, pg 1051
Winsted Corp, pg 1068

MISSOURI

Ken-A-Vision Manufacturing Co Inc, pg 909

NEW JERSEY

Crestron Electronics Inc, pg 839
FSR Inc, pg 873
Radio Visions, pg 990
Telemetrics Inc, pg 1036
Turner Engineering Inc, pg 1046

NEW YORK

ELMO USA Corp, pg 859
MultiDyne Video & Fiber Optics Systems, pg 950
Servoreeler Systems, pg 1007

PENNSYLVANIA

North Star Satellite Communications Inc, pg 959

TENNESSEE

Adtec Digital Inc, pg 777

TEXAS

AMX, pg 786

UTAH

ClearOne Inc, pg 830

VIRGINIA

Avitecture Inc, pg 799
RGB Technology Inc, pg 996

WISCONSIN

Spectrum Industries Inc, pg 1021

ALBERTA

SMART Technologies Inc, pg 1013

ONTARIO

Gesturetek, pg 877

Teleconferencing Equipment Rentals

ARIZONA

Merestone, pg 938
Metropolitan Audio-Visual Inc, pg 940
Ultimate Presentation Systems Inc, pg 1047

ARKANSAS

White Diamond Productions, pg 1065

CALIFORNIA

AGF Media Services, pg 778
Ametron Audio/Video, pg 785
AV Conferencing, pg 797
AV Guys, pg 797
Balboa Capital Corp, pg 802
Cosumnes River College, pg 836
KTVU-Retail Services, pg 914
Lynch Communications, pg 926
McCune Audio-Video-Lighting, pg 935
Stanislaus Audio Video Inc, pg 1023
Twin Peaks Creative, pg 1047
University of Southern California, pg 1050
VER-Video Equipment Rentals, pg 1053
VMI Inc, pg 1060
Voice & Video Rentals, pg 1060

COLORADO

Spectrum Audio Visual Services, pg 1020

CONNECTICUT

A/V Davey, pg 797
Everett Hall Associates Inc, pg 863
Fox Connecticut, pg 872
Videofilm Systems Inc, pg 1057

FLORIDA

Allstar Audio Systems Inc, pg 782
Digital Video Systems Inc, pg 848
Pro Stage Inc, pg 983
Sight & Sound Productions, pg 1010
TAI Audio, pg 1031

GEORGIA

Convergent Media Systems, pg 836
Lighting & Production Equipment Inc, pg 920
Stage Front Presentation Systems, pg 1022
WATL-TV Inc, pg 1062

ILLINOIS

A T Products Inc, pg 771
Allen Visual Systems Inc, pg 781
Chicago Satellite & Video, pg 825
QuickSet International Inc, pg 989
RC Communications, pg 992

KENTUCKY

Audio Visual Techniques Inc, pg 796

LOUISIANA

Pace Systems, pg 966

MARYLAND

CPR MultiMedia Solutions, pg 837

MASSACHUSETTS

Capron Lighting & Sound Co Inc, pg 819
High Output Inc, pg 888
Preston Productions Inc, pg 981

MICHIGAN

Digi Sign Design LLC, pg 847
K&R All Media Productions Inc, pg 908

MINNESOTA

Alpha Video & Audio Inc, pg 782

MISSOURI

Show-Me Audio-Visual, pg 1009
Swank Audio Visuals, pg 1029
Wise Audio Video, pg 1068

NEVADA

Lefco Video Services Inc, pg 918

NEW JERSEY

Audio Visual Associates, pg 795
Starlite Productions, pg 1024
Wired 4 Sound Inc, pg 1068

NEW YORK

American Video Inc, pg 785
Big Foot Productions Inc, pg 807
Colortone Audio Visual, pg 832
CP Communications, pg 837
Design Audio Visual Inc, pg 845
KVL Audio Visual Services Inc, pg 914
Manhattan Center Studios Inc, pg 930
MRG Productions Inc, pg 948
Shelly Palmer Production, pg 968
PrimaLux Video Inc, pg 982
Visual Technologies Corp, pg 1060

NORTH CAROLINA

A&V Company, pg 772
Visual Aids Electronics of North Carolina Inc, pg 1059

OHIO

ITA Audio Visual Solutions, pg 902
Mills James Productions, pg 943

OKLAHOMA

Institute for Teaching & Learning Excellence (ITLE), pg 899

PENNSYLVANIA

Advanced AV, pg 777
FMP Media Solutions Inc, pg 870
Fusion Brand Experiences, pg 874
Grise Audio Visual Center Inc, pg 882
North Star Satellite Communications Inc, pg 959
Visual Sound Inc, pg 1059
WHYY Inc, pg 1066

SOUTH CAROLINA

Sound & Images Inc, pg 1016

TENNESSEE

Technical Support Systems LLC, pg 1034
UMCom Productions, pg 1048

TEXAS

Audio Visual Technologies Group, pg 796
Crossroads Audio Inc, pg 840
Digital Display Solutions Inc, pg 847
Industrial Audio/Video Inc, pg 897
J&S Audio Visual Inc, pg 904
Earl Miller Productions Inc, pg 943
Omega Productions, pg 962

VIRGINIA

Boitnott Visual Communications Corp (BVC), pg 810
Projection Presentation Technology, pg 985
WETA Production Center, pg 1064

WASHINGTON

Victory Studios, pg 1054

WISCONSIN

Event Essentials, pg 863
Full Compass Systems, pg 874
University of Wisconsin-Oshkosh Radio-TV-Film Dept, pg 1050
Wisconsin Public Television, pg 1068

PUERTO RICO

Stage Crew Audiovisual Inc, pg 1022

ALBERTA

Cine Audio Visual Sales & Service Ltd, pg 826
Matrix Video Communications Corp (MVCC), pg 934

BRITISH COLUMBIA

Commercial Electronics Ltd, pg 832

MANITOBA

Inland Audio Visual Ltd, pg 898

ONTARIO

Westbury National Show Systems Ltd, pg 1064

QUEBEC

AVW-TELAV Audio Visual Solutions, a Freeman Company, pg 800

Teleconferencing Equipment Repairs

CALIFORNIA

Ametron Audio/Video, pg 785
SSL Industries Inc, pg 1022
VMI Inc, pg 1060

CONNECTICUT

A/V Davey, pg 797

FLORIDA

ELC Sales & Service Inc, pg 858
Hi-Tech Enterprises Inc, pg 888
JT Communications, pg 906

GEORGIA

Lighting & Production Equipment Inc, pg 920
Stage Front Presentation Systems, pg 1022

ILLINOIS

A T Products Inc, pg 771
Allen Visual Systems Inc, pg 781

KENTUCKY

Axxis Inc, pg 800
NOR-COM Inc, pg 958

MICHIGAN

TeL Systems, pg 1035

NEW JERSEY

Audio Visual Associates, pg 795
Radio Visions, pg 990
Turner Engineering Inc, pg 1046

NEW YORK

ELMO USA Corp, pg 859
MRG Productions Inc, pg 948
Visual Technologies Corp, pg 1060

OHIO

ITA Audio Visual Solutions, pg 902
Tri-State Audio Visual Co, pg 1044

OREGON

All Service Musical Electronics Repair, pg 780

TENNESSEE

Technical Support Systems LLC, pg 1034

TEXAS

Industrial Audio/Video Inc, pg 897
Tarpley Media Systems, pg 1032

VIRGINIA

Avitecture Inc, pg 799
Boitnott Visual Communications Corp (BVC), pg 810
Hoppmann Audio Visual, pg 891
Intellidyne LLC, pg 899

WISCONSIN

Full Compass Systems, pg 874

ALBERTA

Infosat Communications Inc, pg 898
Matrix Video Communications Corp (MVCC), pg 934
Sharp's Audio-Visual Ltd, pg 1008

BRITISH COLUMBIA

Commercial Electronics Ltd, pg 832

MANITOBA

Inland Audio Visual Ltd, pg 898

ONTARIO

Westbury National Show Systems Ltd, pg 1064

Teleprompting & Cueing System Distributors

ALABAMA

Media Visions Inc, pg 937

ARIZONA

EAR Professional Audio/Video, pg 855

ARKANSAS

Jay S Stanley & Associates Inc, pg 1023
White Diamond Productions, pg 1065

CALIFORNIA

Ametron Audio/Video, pg 785
Audio/Video Supply Inc, pg 795
Barber Tech Video Products, pg 802
Alan Gordon Enterprises Inc, pg 880
Jaguar Distribution Corp, pg 903
SSL Industries Inc, pg 1022
Transvideo International, pg 1044
Tri-Ed, pg 1044
VMI Inc, pg 1060

CONNECTICUT

Everett Hall Associates Inc, pg 863

FLORIDA

Access Media Group, pg 773
Allstar Audio Systems Inc, pg 782
A2D Solutions Inc, pg 793
Digital Video Systems Inc, pg 848
Enhanced View Services Inc, pg 861
Hi-Tech Enterprises Inc, pg 888
Hunter Electronics LLC, pg 892
Media Concepts Inc, pg 936
Midtown Video Inc, pg 942
Photomart Cine-Video Inc, pg 975
Pro Stage Inc, pg 983
Sight & Sound Productions, pg 1010

GEORGIA

Lighting & Production Equipment Inc, pg 920
Stage Front Presentation Systems, pg 1022
Visioneering International Inc, pg 1058

ILLINOIS

Tele-Time Systems, pg 1036

INDIANA

Sensory Technologies LLC, pg 1006

KANSAS

Smith Audio-Visual Inc, pg 1014

KENTUCKY

Axxis Inc, pg 800
NOR-COM Inc, pg 958

MARYLAND

Human Circuit, pg 892
Kipp Visual Systems Inc, pg 911

MASSACHUSETTS

Rule Broadcast Systems, pg 1000

MICHIGAN

On Stage Visuals, pg 963

MINNESOTA

Alpha Video & Audio Inc, pg 782

MISSOURI

Conference Technologies Inc, pg 835
Southwest Audio-Visual Inc, pg 1019

NEBRASKA

Dog & Pony Productions Inc, pg 850

NEVADA

Aardvark Video & Media Productions, pg 772

NEW JERSEY

Audio Visual Associates, pg 795
Audio Visual Dynamics®, pg 795
Diversified Systems Inc, pg 849
MIB Mediaworks, pg 941
PatchAmp, pg 970
Starlite Productions, pg 1024
SYMCO Inc, pg 1030
Tele-Measurements Inc, pg 1035
Wired 4 Sound Inc, pg 1068

NEW YORK

Ace Video, pg 774
Audio-Video Corp, pg 795
AV Workshop, pg 797
Communication Corner Inc, pg 832
Foxtrot Teleprompt, pg 872
Image Makers of Pittsford/Image Maker Productions, pg 895
Long Island Video Enterprises Live Inc, pg 924
Markertek Video Supply, pg 931
Technisphere Corp, pg 1034

NORTH CAROLINA

Strategic Connections, pg 1026

OHIO

ITA Audio Visual Solutions, pg 902
Jimmy Rea Electronics Inc, pg 992

PENNSYLVANIA

Advanced AV, pg 777
The Lerro Corp, pg 919
Morefield Communications Inc, pg 946
Visual Sound Inc, pg 1059

TENNESSEE

Lowrance Sound Co Inc, pg 925

TEXAS

AVES Audio Visual Systems Inc, pg 798
Digital Display Solutions Inc, pg 847
Pro Video & Film Equipment Co Inc, pg 983

UTAH

Comtek Communications Technology Inc, pg 834
RIA Corp, pg 996

VIDEO

Teleprompting & Cueing System Distributors (continued)

VIRGINIA

Lee Hartman & Sons Inc, pg 918

WEST VIRGINIA

Blackwater Video Productions, pg 808

WISCONSIN

Audio Visual of Milwaukee Inc, pg 795
Camera Corner Connecting Point, pg 818
Full Compass Systems, pg 874

ALBERTA

Matrix Video Communications Corp (MVCC), pg 934

BRITISH COLUMBIA

ProVision Video Sales & Rentals Inc, pg 986

MANITOBA

Inland Audio Visual Ltd, pg 898

ONTARIO

Edcom Multimedia Products, pg 856

QUEBEC

Panavideo Inc, pg 968

Teleprompting & Cueing System Manufacturers

CALIFORNIA

Barber Tech Video Products, pg 802
Boland Communications, pg 810
Magic Teleprompting Inc, pg 928
Transvideo International, pg 1044

NEW JERSEY

Telescript International, pg 1036

NEW YORK

QTV, pg 988

UTAH

Comtek Communications Technology Inc, pg 834

VIRGINIA

Quince Imaging Inc, pg 989

WISCONSIN

Comprompter Inc, pg 834

BRITISH COLUMBIA

Tekskil Industries Inc, pg 1035

Teleprompting & Cueing System Rentals

ARIZONA

Broadcast Rentals, pg 813
Glendale Media Center, pg 878
Merestone, pg 938
Metropolitan Audio-Visual Inc, pg 940

ARKANSAS

White Diamond Productions, pg 1065

CALIFORNIA

Ametron Audio/Video, pg 785
Artichoke Productions, pg 791
AV Guys, pg 797
Barber Tech Video Products, pg 802
Bexel Corp, pg 806
California Teleprompter, pg 817
Cherry Multimedia, pg 824
Crash Video Productions, pg 837
Crystal Pyramid Productions™, pg 840
Cue Tech Teleprompting, pg 841
Golden Gate Studios, pg 880
Alan Gordon Enterprises Inc, pg 880
JFA Studio, pg 905
Lynch Communications, pg 926
McCune Audio-Video-Lighting, pg 935
Pro HD Rentals, pg 983
PSAV® Presentation Services, pg 986
Slate Media Group, pg 1013
Studio 637, pg 1027
The Studios at Paramount, pg 1027
Total Media Group, pg 1042
VER-Video Equipment Rentals, pg 1053
Video Gear Rentals Inc, pg 1055
VMI Inc, pg 1060
Voice & Video Rentals, pg 1060

COLORADO

Daylight Productions & Rentals, pg 844
Spectrum Audio Visual Services, pg 1020

CONNECTICUT

Everett Hall Associates Inc, pg 863
Fox Connecticut, pg 872
Videofilm Systems Inc, pg 1057

FLORIDA

Accord Productions, pg 773
Allstar Audio Systems Inc, pg 782
Budget Video Rentals, pg 815
Digital Zoetrope Productions, pg 848
Eastern Video, pg 856
Hi-Tech Enterprises Inc, pg 888
Industrial Strength Inc, pg 897
Jordan Klein Film & Video (JKFV), pg 906
JungleTV, pg 906
Media Concepts Inc, pg 936
Midtown Video Inc, pg 942
Paradise Show & Design Inc, pg 969
Parallax Productions Inc, pg 969
Pro Stage Inc, pg 983
Sight & Sound Productions, pg 1010
10-20 Productions, pg 1037
Mike Vasilinda Productions Inc, pg 1052

GEORGIA

Continental Film & Video, pg 835
Lighting & Production Equipment Inc, pg 920
ON Event Services, pg 963
See Production Services, pg 1006
Stage Front Presentation Systems, pg 1022

ILLINOIS

Backstar Creative Media Inc, pg 801
Beatty TeleVisual Productions, pg 804
Chicago Satellite & Video, pg 825
Creative Technology, pg 838
Firehouse Studios, pg 868
QuickSet International Inc, pg 989
SGW Teleprompter Solutions Inc, pg 1007
Show Department Inc, pg 1009

KANSAS

KAKE-TV, pg 907
Smith Audio-Visual Inc, pg 1014

KENTUCKY

Audio Visual Techniques Inc, pg 796

LOUISIANA

Digital FX Inc, pg 847
Moxie Media, pg 948
Pace Systems, pg 966

MARYLAND

CPR MultiMedia Solutions, pg 837
Kramer Communications Video Production, pg 913

MASSACHUSETTS

Capron Lighting & Sound Co Inc, pg 819

MICHIGAN

Digi Sign Design LLC, pg 847
K&R All Media Productions Inc, pg 908

MINNESOTA

Alpha Video & Audio Inc, pg 782
Big Event Productions LLC, pg 807
Lights On, pg 921

MISSOURI

Cashmark Media Inc, pg 820
Show-Me Audio-Visual, pg 1009
Southwest Audio-Visual Inc, pg 1019
Switch, pg 1030

NEBRASKA

Dog & Pony Productions Inc, pg 850

NEVADA

GES Audio Visual, pg 877
JCS Video Productions, pg 904

NEW JERSEY

Audio Visual Associates, pg 795
Audio Visual Dynamics®, pg 795
MediaMix Inc, pg 937
MIB Mediaworks, pg 941
Starlite Productions, pg 1024
VCSvideo, pg 1052
Video Corporation of America (VCA), pg 1055
Wired 4 Sound Inc, pg 1068

NEW MEXICO

Production Outfitters, pg 984

NEW YORK

Ace Video, pg 774
Ansonia Prompting Inc, pg 787
AV Workshop, pg 797
BC Video Inc, pg 803
Big Foot Productions Inc, pg 807
CSI Rentals, pg 840
Design Audio Visual Inc, pg 845
Foxtrot Teleprompt, pg 872
Gearhead Rentals, pg 876
Image Makers of Pittsford/Image Maker Productions, pg 895
Long Island Video Enterprises Live Inc, pg 924
Manhattan Center Studios Inc, pg 930
Media 3 Ltd, pg 937
MRG Productions Inc, pg 948
PrimaLux Video Inc, pg 982
QTV, pg 988
TBA Global Events, pg 1032
Technisphere Corp, pg 1034
Visual Word Systems Inc, pg 1060

NORTH CAROLINA

A&V Company, pg 772
The Communications Group Inc, pg 833
Moving Pictures, pg 948
On Location North Carolina, pg 963

OHIO

Bartha, pg 803
ITA Audio Visual Solutions, pg 902
Mills James Productions, pg 943
Ohio HD Video, pg 961
OSV Studios, pg 966
Vista Color Imaging Inc, pg 1059

OREGON

Picture This Production Services, pg 975

PENNSYLVANIA

FMP Media Solutions Inc, pg 870
Fusion Brand Experiences, pg 874
Innovision Media Group, pg 899
JPL, pg 906
Muderick Media, pg 949
New York Camera & Video, pg 956
Producers Management Television (PMTV), pg 983

SOUTH CAROLINA

Genesis Creative, pg 877
Sound & Images Inc, pg 1016

TENNESSEE

NuMynd Studios, pg 960
Tennessee Prompters, pg 1037

TEXAS

Dallas Prompter, pg 842
Maverick Video Productions, pg 934
Media Event Concepts Inc, pg 936
Phil Lights, pg 973

South Coast Film & Video, pg 1019
Stage Directions, pg 1022

UTAH

Ron Hill Imagery, pg 889

VIRGINIA

Allied Media Corp, pg 781
D&B Television & Video Productions Inc, pg 842
Quince Imaging Inc, pg 989

WASHINGTON

Victory Studios, pg 1054

WEST VIRGINIA

Blackwater Video Productions, pg 808

WISCONSIN

Logan Productions Inc, pg 924

WYOMING

Bridger Productions Inc, pg 812

PUERTO RICO

Stage Crew Audiovisual Inc, pg 1022

ALBERTA

Global Television Station, pg 879

BRITISH COLUMBIA

Image Media Farm, pg 895
ProVision Video Sales & Rentals Inc, pg 986
24 Frames Film & Video, pg 1047

MANITOBA

Inland Audio Visual Ltd, pg 898
MidCanada Production Services Inc (MidCan), pg 942

ONTARIO

Edcom Multimedia Products, pg 856
Q-Prompt Inc, pg 988
RB Productions, pg 992

QUEBEC

Audio Visual Dynamics Ltd, pg 795
AVW-TELAV Audio Visual Solutions, a Freeman Company, pg 800

Teleprompting & Cueing System Repairs

CALIFORNIA

Ametron Audio/Video, pg 785
Barber Tech Video Products, pg 802
SSL Industries Inc, pg 1022
Transvideo International, pg 1044
VMI Inc, pg 1060

FLORIDA

Hi-Tech Enterprises Inc, pg 888
Midtown Video Inc, pg 942

GEORGIA

Lighting & Production Equipment Inc, pg 920
Stage Front Presentation Systems, pg 1022

ILLINOIS

Beatty TeleVisual Productions, pg 804

KENTUCKY

Axxis Inc, pg 800
NOR-COM Inc, pg 958

MICHIGAN

TeL Systems, pg 1035

MINNESOTA

Alpha Video & Audio Inc, pg 782

MISSOURI

Southwest Audio-Visual Inc, pg 1019

NEW YORK

Ace Video, pg 774
Foxtrot Teleprompt, pg 872
MRG Productions Inc, pg 948
QTV, pg 988

OHIO

ITA Audio Visual Solutions, pg 902

UTAH

RIA Corp, pg 996

VIRGINIA

Avitecture Inc, pg 799

MANITOBA

Inland Audio Visual Ltd, pg 898

ONTARIO

Edcom Multimedia Products, pg 856

Time Base Corrector Distributors

ARIZONA

EAR Professional Audio/Video, pg 855

ARKANSAS

Jay S Stanley & Associates Inc, pg 1023

CALIFORNIA

Advanced Systems Group LLC, pg 778
Ametron Audio/Video, pg 785
Audio/Video Supply Inc, pg 795
BroadcastStore.com, pg 813
California Tape Products Inc, pg 817
Cibola Systems, pg 826
Computer Modules Inc, pg 834
FXC Communications, pg 874
Media Control Systems LLC, pg 936
Mobilized Tech Systems, pg 944
POP TV, pg 978
SNAP, pg 1014
Snell, pg 1014
SSL Industries Inc, pg 1022
Stanislaus Audio Video Inc, pg 1023
Tri-Ed, pg 1044
VMI Inc, pg 1060
Westlake Recording Studios, pg 1064

FLORIDA

Access Media Group, pg 773
Digital Video Systems Inc, pg 848
Griffiths Broadcast Co Inc, pg 882
Harris Corp, pg 885
Hi-Tech Enterprises Inc, pg 888
Hi-Tech Import Export Corp, pg 888
Media Concepts Inc, pg 936
Midtown Video Inc, pg 942
Pro Stage Inc, pg 983

GEORGIA

Baker Audio Inc, pg 801
Simtrol Inc, pg 1011
Stage Front Presentation Systems, pg 1022

ILLINOIS

Allen Visual Systems Inc, pg 781
RAM Systems LLC, pg 991

INDIANA

Sensory Technologies LLC, pg 1006

KANSAS

Smith Audio-Visual Inc, pg 1014

KENTUCKY

NOR-COM Inc, pg 958

MARYLAND

Wiltronix, pg 1067

MASSACHUSETTS

Rule Broadcast Systems, pg 1000

MICHIGAN

Ascom Communications Contractors, pg 791
TeL Systems, pg 1035

MINNESOTA

Alpha Video & Audio Inc, pg 782

MISSOURI

Communitronics Corp, pg 833
Conference Technologies Inc, pg 835
Southwest Audio-Visual Inc, pg 1019

NEBRASKA

Dog & Pony Productions Inc, pg 850

NEVADA

Aardvark Video & Media Productions, pg 772

NEW JERSEY

A-V Services Inc, pg 771
Audio Visual Associates, pg 795
Diversified Systems Inc, pg 849
Earl Girls Inc, pg 855
G&G Technologies Inc, pg 875
MCCOM Inc, pg 935
PatchAmp, pg 970
SYMCO Inc, pg 1030
Total Video Products Inc, pg 1042
Wired 4 Sound Inc, pg 1068

NEW YORK

Ace Video, pg 774
Audio-Video Corp, pg 795
AV Workshop, pg 797
B&H Photo & Video Pro Audio, pg 802
Communication Corner Inc, pg 832
Custom Media Environments, pg 841
Design Audio Visual Inc, pg 845
General Audio-Visual Inc (GAVI), pg 876
Long Island Video Enterprises Live Inc, pg 924
Markertek Video Supply, pg 931
Technisphere Corp, pg 1034
TecNec Distributing, pg 1035
Video International Development Inc, pg 1055
Visual Technologies Corp, pg 1060

OHIO

ITA Audio Visual Solutions, pg 902
Jimmy Rea Electronics Inc, pg 992

PENNSYLVANIA

Advanced AV, pg 777
The Lerro Corp, pg 919
Morefield Communications Inc, pg 946
Visual Sound Inc, pg 1059

TENNESSEE

Lowrance Sound Co Inc, pg 925
Zion Music Group, pg 1074

TEXAS

AVES Audio Visual Systems Inc, pg 798
Media Management LLC, pg 937
Pro Video & Film Equipment Co Inc, pg 983
Videotex Systems Inc, pg 1057

UTAH

RIA Corp, pg 996

VIRGINIA

Avitecture Inc, pg 799
Boitnott Visual Communications Corp (BVC), pg 810
Hoppmann Audio Visual, pg 891
The Whitlock Group, pg 1065

WISCONSIN

Audio Visual of Milwaukee Inc, pg 795
Camera Corner Connecting Point, pg 818
Full Compass Systems, pg 874

ALBERTA

Infosat Communications Inc, pg 898
Matrix Video Communications Corp (MVCC), pg 934

MANITOBA

Inland Audio Visual Ltd, pg 898

VIDEO

Time Base Corrector Distributors (continued)

ONTARIO

Cinema Stage Inc, pg 827
HD Source, pg 886
Majortech Inc, pg 929

QUEBEC

Panavideo Inc, pg 968

Time Base Corrector Manufacturers

ARIZONA

Applied Integration Corp, pg 789

CALIFORNIA

Enright Co, pg 861
Ensemble Designs Inc, pg 861
Extron Electronics, pg 864
For-A Corp of America, pg 871
Hotronic Inc, pg 891
Snell, pg 1014

KANSAS

GlobalStreams™ Corp, pg 879

KENTUCKY

TV One Multimedia Solutions, pg 1046

NEW JERSEY

Kramer Electronics USA Inc, pg 913

NEW MEXICO

Burst Electronics Inc, pg 815

NEW YORK

Video International Development Inc, pg 1055

PENNSYLVANIA

Prime Image Inc, pg 982

BRITISH COLUMBIA

Triad Communications Ltd, pg 1044

Time Base Corrector Rentals

ARIZONA

Merestone, pg 938
Metropolitan Audio-Visual Inc, pg 940

ARKANSAS

White Diamond Productions, pg 1065

CALIFORNIA

Aaron & Le Duc, pg 772
Alliant Event Services, pg 781
Ametron Audio/Video, pg 785
AV Guys, pg 797
Bexel Corp, pg 806
BroadcastStore.com, pg 813
Crystal Pyramid Productions™, pg 840
Express Media Inc, pg 864
Full Moon & High Tide Productions & Studios, pg 874
Golden Gate Studios, pg 880
Lynch Communications, pg 926
McCune Audio-Video-Lighting, pg 935
Munday & Collins AV, pg 950
On-Trax Inc, pg 963
RetinaVision Productions, pg 995
Slate Media Group, pg 1013
Total Media Group, pg 1042
Twin Peaks Creative, pg 1047
VER-Video Equipment Rentals, pg 1053
VMI Inc, pg 1060
Voice & Video Rentals, pg 1060

COLORADO

Daylight Productions & Rentals, pg 844
Multimedia Audio Visual Inc, pg 950

CONNECTICUT

Fox Connecticut, pg 872
Videofilm Systems Inc, pg 1057

DELAWARE

Showorks Audio Visual Inc, pg 1010

FLORIDA

Eastern Video, pg 856
Knowles Video Inc (KVI), pg 912
Media Concepts Inc, pg 936
Midtown Video Inc, pg 942
Paradise Show & Design Inc, pg 969
Pro Stage Inc, pg 983

GEORGIA

ON Event Services, pg 963
Stage Front Presentation Systems, pg 1022

ILLINOIS

Airways Digital Media, pg 779
Backstar Creative Media Inc, pg 801
Beatty TeleVisual Productions, pg 804
Chicago Satellite & Video, pg 825
QuickSet International Inc, pg 989
Show Department Inc, pg 1009
Tele-Time Systems, pg 1036

KANSAS

KAKE-TV, pg 907
Smith Audio-Visual Inc, pg 1014

KENTUCKY

Audio Visual Techniques Inc, pg 796

LOUISIANA

Digital FX Inc, pg 847
Pace Systems, pg 966

MARYLAND

CPR MultiMedia Solutions, pg 837

MASSACHUSETTS

massAV, pg 933
Preston Productions Inc, pg 981

MICHIGAN

Digi Sign Design LLC, pg 847
K&R All Media Productions Inc, pg 908
K&R's Recording Studios Inc, pg 908
TeL Systems, pg 1035

MINNESOTA

Alpha Video & Audio Inc, pg 782

MISSOURI

Communitronics Corp, pg 833
Show-Me Audio-Visual, pg 1009
Southwest Audio-Visual Inc, pg 1019
Switch, pg 1030

NEBRASKA

Dog & Pony Productions Inc, pg 850

NEVADA

GES Audio Visual, pg 877

NEW JERSEY

Audio Visual Associates, pg 795
Earl Girls Inc, pg 855
MB Productions, pg 934
MediaMix Inc, pg 937
PLS Staging, pg 977
Video Corporation of America (VCA), pg 1055
Wired 4 Sound Inc, pg 1068

NEW MEXICO

Production Outfitters, pg 984

NEW YORK

Ace Video, pg 774
AV Workshop, pg 797
CP Communications, pg 837
Long Island Video Enterprises Live Inc, pg 924
Manhattan Center Studios Inc, pg 930
TBA Global Events, pg 1032
Technisphere Corp, pg 1034
Visual Technologies Corp, pg 1060
Visual Word Systems Inc, pg 1060

NORTH CAROLINA

A&V Company, pg 772
Moving Pictures, pg 948
Special Event Services, pg 1020

NORTH DAKOTA

Media Productions, pg 937

OHIO

ITA Audio Visual Solutions, pg 902
Lyon Video Inc, pg 927

PENNSYLVANIA

FMP Media Solutions Inc, pg 870
Fusion Brand Experiences, pg 874
Innovision Media Group, pg 899
JPL, pg 906

TENNESSEE

Russ Sturgeon Productions/RSVP, pg 1027

TEXAS

FitzCo Sound Inc, pg 869
Media Event Concepts Inc, pg 936
The Samuels Co, pg 1002
Stage Directions, pg 1022

VIRGINIA

Boitnott Visual Communications Corp (BVC), pg 810
Creative Video of Washington Inc, pg 839

WISCONSIN

Camera Corner Connecting Point, pg 818
Full Compass Systems, pg 874

WYOMING

Bridger Productions Inc, pg 812

PUERTO RICO

Stage Crew Audiovisual Inc, pg 1022

ALBERTA

Cine Audio Visual Sales & Service Ltd, pg 826
Matrix Video Communications Corp (MVCC), pg 934

BRITISH COLUMBIA

Commercial Electronics Ltd, pg 832
Finale Editworks, pg 868
Image Media Farm, pg 895
Video In Studios/Video Out Distribution, pg 1055

MANITOBA

Inland Audio Visual Ltd, pg 898

ONTARIO

HD Source, pg 886
RB Productions, pg 992

QUEBEC

Panavideo Inc, pg 968

Time Base Corrector Repairs

CALIFORNIA

Ametron Audio/Video, pg 785
BroadcastStore.com, pg 813
Mobilized Tech Systems, pg 944
SSL Industries Inc, pg 1022
VMI Inc, pg 1060

FLORIDA

ELC Sales & Service Inc, pg 858
Hi-Tech Enterprises Inc, pg 888

GEORGIA

Stage Front Presentation Systems, pg 1022

ILLINOIS

Beatty TeleVisual Productions, pg 804
Midwest Digital Corp, pg 942

KENTUCKY

NOR-COM Inc, pg 958

Titling & Artwork Services, *see* Artwork & Titling Services

Transfer & Conversion Equipment Distributors

Transfer & Conversion Equipment Manufacturers

Transfer & Conversion Equipment Rentals

VIDEO

Transfer & Conversion Equipment Rentals (continued)

MICHIGAN

Digi Sign Design LLC, pg 847
K&R All Media Productions Inc, pg 908

MINNESOTA

Alpha Video & Audio Inc, pg 782

MISSOURI

Show-Me Audio-Visual, pg 1009
Southwest Audio-Visual Inc, pg 1019

NEVADA

JCS Video Productions, pg 904

NEW JERSEY

Euro-Pacific Film & Video Productions Inc, pg 863
Starlite Productions, pg 1024
Tele-Measurements Inc, pg 1035

NEW YORK

Ace Video, pg 774
Colortone Audio Visual, pg 832
Design Audio Visual Inc, pg 845
Hello World Communications, pg 888
PrimaLux Video Inc, pg 982
TBA Global Events, pg 1032
Technisphere Corp, pg 1034
Visual Technologies Corp, pg 1060
Visual Word Systems Inc, pg 1060

NORTH CAROLINA

Take One Productions Ltd, pg 1031

OHIO

Mills James Productions, pg 943

PENNSYLVANIA

FMP Media Solutions Inc, pg 870
JPL, pg 906
The Videohouse Inc, pg 1057

TENNESSEE

Technical Support Systems LLC, pg 1034

TEXAS

Astro Audio Visual, pg 792
The Samuels Co, pg 1002
Stage Directions, pg 1022

VIRGINIA

Quince Imaging Inc, pg 989

WASHINGTON

Victory Studios, pg 1054

WISCONSIN

Audio Visual of Milwaukee Inc, pg 795

PUERTO RICO

Stage Crew Audiovisual Inc, pg 1022

BRITISH COLUMBIA

Commercial Electronics Ltd, pg 832
Finale Editworks, pg 868

MANITOBA

Inland Audio Visual Ltd, pg 898

ONTARIO

RB Productions, pg 992

Transfer & Conversion Equipment Repairs

CALIFORNIA

Ametron Audio/Video, pg 785
VMI Inc, pg 1060

COLORADO

Macrosystem US Inc, pg 927

FLORIDA

ELC Sales & Service Inc, pg 858

GEORGIA

Stage Front Presentation Systems, pg 1022

KENTUCKY

NOR-COM Inc, pg 958

MICHIGAN

TeL Systems, pg 1035

MINNESOTA

Alpha Video & Audio Inc, pg 782

MISSOURI

Southwest Audio-Visual Inc, pg 1019

NEW YORK

Technisphere Corp, pg 1034
Visual Technologies Corp, pg 1060

TENNESSEE

Technical Support Systems LLC, pg 1034

TEXAS

Astro Audio Visual, pg 792
Pro Video & Film Equipment Co Inc, pg 983

WISCONSIN

Full Compass Systems, pg 874

BRITISH COLUMBIA

Commercial Electronics Ltd, pg 832

MANITOBA

Inland Audio Visual Ltd, pg 898

Transfers—Film to Videotape

ALABAMA

Media Visions Inc, pg 937

ARIZONA

Merestone, pg 938
Metropolitan Audio-Visual Inc, pg 940
On-Site Video, pg 963
Phoenix VideoFilms®, pg 974
Star Video Duplicating, pg 1024

ARKANSAS

Cedar Crest Studio, pg 822

CALIFORNIA

Access Video in Berkeley, pg 773
Action Photo Service Inc, pg 775
Action Video, pg 775
Adolph Gasser Inc, pg 776
Advanced Media LLC, pg 778
All Video Productions, pg 781
ALOM Technologies Corp, pg 782
AM Productions, pg 783
Artichoke Productions, pg 791
Barbosa Video Services, pg 802
Custom Video Productions Inc, pg 841
Dogma Studios, pg 850
Film Technology Co Inc, pg 867
FXC Communications, pg 874
Havas Edge, pg 885
Hooper Camera & Imaging, pg 891
iCorpTv, pg 893
K2B2 Records, pg 907
Ludlow Media Solutions, pg 926
Method Studios, pg 939
Oddball Film + Video, pg 961
Peterson's Video Transfer Services, pg 973
PM Productions, pg 977
Point 360, pg 978
Pro8mm, pg 983
QRS Software Services, pg 988
RetinaVision Productions, pg 995
RJ Video Productions, pg 997
SonicPool, pg 1016
Universal Studios, pg 1049
Wavemaker Media Design, pg 1062
Yale Film & Video, pg 1071

COLORADO

The Cinema Lab, pg 827
Rocky Mountain Audio/Video Productions Inc, pg 998

CONNECTICUT

Applebox Studio, pg 788
A/V Davey, pg 797
Digital Video Productions, pg 848
The Gary-Paul Agency, pg 875
Guymark Studios LLC, pg 883
MAVCO, pg 934

DISTRICT OF COLUMBIA

Interface Media Group, pg 900
Library of Congress, Motion Picture, Broadcasting & Recorded Sound Division, pg 919

FLORIDA

Access Media Group, pg 773
Civins Productions Inc, pg 828
Communications Concepts Inc (CCI), pg 833
Easy Edit Video Inc, pg 856
Gulf Coast Audio Visual Producers Inc, pg 883
Hi-Tech Enterprises Inc, pg 888
Knowles Video Inc (KVI), pg 912
Media Concepts Inc, pg 936
Photosound of Orlando Inc, pg 975
Sunrise Studios, pg 1028
Video Techniques Inc, pg 1056

GEORGIA

Crawford Media Services, pg 838
Memory Lane Productions, pg 938

IDAHO

KTVB-TV, pg 914

ILLINOIS

Analog Free Media, pg 786
Filmworkers, pg 868
Intervideo Duplication Services, pg 902
Major Media Inc, pg 929
Moviecraft Inc, pg 947
Optimus, pg 964
The Pepper Group, pg 972
Sound/Video Impressions Inc, pg 1018
Southern Illinois University, pg 1019
Video Impressions, pg 1055
WEEK TV, pg 1063

INDIANA

Advanced Media Integration, pg 777
Educational Video Group Inc, pg 857
Lighthouse Photo & Video Productions, pg 920

IOWA

Duplication Media, pg 853
The Production House, pg 984

KENTUCKY

Audio Visual Techniques Inc, pg 796
Barney Miller's Inc, pg 943
The PPS Group, pg 980

LOUISIANA

Digital FX Inc, pg 847
Moxie Media, pg 948

MARYLAND

Carpel Video Inc, pg 820
CSPMedia.com, pg 840
Kramer Communications Video Production, pg 913
Pro Cuts Editing Services, pg 982
Quality Film & Video, pg 988
Saah Video, pg 1001
Strauss Photo Technical Service Inc, pg 1026

MASSACHUSETTS

Brodsky & Treadway, pg 813
Capron Lighting & Sound Co Inc, pg 819
Inter-Media Electronics, pg 899

MICHIGAN

Encore Home Video, pg 861
K&R's Recording Studios Inc, pg 908
The Transfer Zone®, pg 1043

MINNESOTA

MultiMedia, pg 950

MISSISSIPPI

Jasper Ewing & Sons Inc, pg 864

MISSOURI

Communitronics Corp, pg 833
Conference Technologies Inc, pg 835
Schiller's Audio-Visual, pg 1004
Show-Me Audio-Visual, pg 1009

NEVADA

Aardvark Video & Media Productions, pg 772
JCS Video Productions, pg 904
21st Century Video Productions, pg 1047

NEW HAMPSHIRE

Apertura, pg 788
Channell One Video, pg 824

NEW JERSEY

All Jersey Studios, pg 780
Broadcast Center Studios, pg 813
CFP Video Productions Inc, pg 823
Deluxe Media Services, pg 845
Hogpenny Studios, pg 890
NFL Films Inc, pg 957
NFL Films Music Library, pg 957
Reed Presentations Inc (RPI), pg 993
Suede Interactive, pg 1027
Video Corporation of America (VCA), pg 1055

NEW YORK

Adwar Video, pg 778
aurora productions, pg 797
CMI Communications, pg 830
Colortone Audio Visual, pg 832
Communication Corner Inc, pg 832
Digital Art Video Inc, pg 847
DuArt, pg 853
Duplication Depot Inc, pg 853
Duplication Specialists Inc, pg 853
Elite Video & Photography Services Inc, pg 859
Greyfalcon House, pg 882
Gurrilla Video Solutions, pg 883
Hallel Communications, pg 884
HAVE Inc, pg 886
International Digital Centre, pg 901
J & D Laboratories Inc, pg 903
Long Island Video Enterprises Live Inc, pg 924
Magno Sound & Video, pg 929
Shelly Palmer Production, pg 968
PostWorks, pg 979
Rafik, pg 990
Technisphere Corp, pg 1034
USA Studios, pg 1050
White Buffalo Multimedia, pg 1065

NORTH CAROLINA

A&V Company, pg 772
Camcor Inc, pg 818
Duke Media Services, pg 853

OHIO

Advent Media Inc, pg 778
Audio Visual Media, pg 795
Aztec Video Productions, pg 801
Russ Beckner Pictures, pg 804
Commercial Video, pg 832
Creative Technology, pg 838
MainSail Production Services Inc, pg 929
Take 1 Media Services, pg 1031
Vista Color Imaging Inc, pg 1059

OKLAHOMA

University of Oklahoma Academic Media & Digital Services, pg 1050

OREGON

Nostalgia Family Video Inc, pg 959

PENNSYLVANIA

John E Allen Inc, pg 781
Audio Visions Inc, pg 795
Audio Visual Communications Inc, pg 795
Bernie's Photo Center, pg 805
Center City Film & Video Inc, pg 822
FMP Media Solutions Inc, pg 870
Fusion Brand Experiences, pg 874
Visual Sound Inc, pg 1059
WPHL-TV, pg 1070

RHODE ISLAND

A&M Productions, pg 771

TENNESSEE

Motion Picture Services, pg 947
Stage Post, pg 1022
Russ Sturgeon Productions/RSVP, pg 1027
WKPT-TV, pg 1068

TEXAS

Astro Audio Visual, pg 792
Dub King, pg 853
McNee Productions Inc, pg 935
Julye Newlin Productions Inc, pg 956
Phillips MediaSource, pg 974
Replicopy Digital Media Center, pg 995
The Samuels Co, pg 1002
Texas Heart Institute Visual Communication Services, pg 1037

VIRGINIA

BES Studios, pg 805
CDR Communications Inc, pg 822
Gingerbread Productions, pg 878
Henninger Media Services, pg 888

WASHINGTON

Kostov Productions, pg 913
Pro Image, pg 983
Tobin Cinema Systems Inc, pg 1041
Victory Studios, pg 1054

WISCONSIN

Audio Visual of Milwaukee Inc, pg 795
University of Wisconsin-Oshkosh Radio-TV-Film Dept, pg 1050
USAV Group Inc, pg 1050
Video Wisconsin Inc, pg 1056
Wisconsin Public Television, pg 1068

WYOMING

Bridger Productions Inc, pg 812

ALBERTA

Cine Audio Visual Sales & Service Ltd, pg 826

BRITISH COLUMBIA

Commercial Electronics Ltd, pg 832
Finale Editworks, pg 868
Triad Communications Ltd, pg 1044
24 Frames Film & Video, pg 1047

ONTARIO

Edcom Multimedia Products, pg 856
Purefire Communications Inc, pg 987

QUEBEC

Group PVP, pg 882

Transfers—Slide to Video

ALABAMA

CMEInfo, pg 830

ARIZONA

Merestone, pg 938
Metropolitan Audio-Visual Inc, pg 940
On-Site Video, pg 963
Phoenix VideoFilms®, pg 974
Star Video Duplicating, pg 1024

ARKANSAS

White Diamond Productions, pg 1065

CALIFORNIA

Aaron & Le Duc, pg 772
Access Video in Berkeley, pg 773
Adolph Gasser Inc, pg 776
All Video Productions, pg 781
AM Productions, pg 783
Ametron Audio/Video, pg 785
Artichoke Productions, pg 791
Barbosa Video Services, pg 802
CCI Digital, pg 821
Custom Video Productions Inc, pg 841
First Camera, pg 868
Gold Standard Productions, pg 880
Hooper Camera & Imaging, pg 891
iCorpTv, pg 893
ITV Productions, pg 903
KION-TV, pg 911
KTVU-Retail Services, pg 914
McCune Audio-Video-Lighting, pg 935
Media Magic, pg 937
Method Studios, pg 939
On-Trax Inc, pg 963
Penrose Productions, pg 972
Peterson's Video Transfer Services, pg 973
PM Productions, pg 977
PSI Inc, pg 987
QRS Software Services, pg 988
Dick Reizner Film & Video, pg 994
RetinaVision Productions, pg 995
RJ Video Productions, pg 997
Staylor-Made Communications Inc, pg 1024
StereoScope International, pg 1024
Tam Communications Inc, pg 1031
Twin Peaks Creative, pg 1047
Videolady, pg 1057
West Coast Projections Inc, pg 1063
WMS Media Inc, pg 1069

COLORADO

The Cinema Lab, pg 827
Daylight Productions & Rentals, pg 844
Rocky Mountain Audio/Video Productions Inc, pg 998
Spectrum Audio Visual Services, pg 1020
Tatum Video, pg 1032

CONNECTICUT

Applebox Studio, pg 788
Digital Video Productions, pg 848
Fox Connecticut, pg 872
The Gary-Paul Agency, pg 875
Guymark Studios LLC, pg 883
MAVCO, pg 934
MCC Films, pg 935
Palace Digital Studios, pg 967
Video Design Group, pg 1055

DISTRICT OF COLUMBIA

Interface Media Group, pg 900

FLORIDA

Access Media Group, pg 773
Communications Concepts Inc (CCI), pg 833
Easy Edit Video Inc, pg 856
Gulf Coast Audio Visual Producers Inc, pg 883
Hi-Tech Enterprises Inc, pg 888
Home Shopping Network (HSN), pg 890
Knowles Video Inc (KVI), pg 912
Media Concepts Inc, pg 936
Parallax Productions Inc, pg 969
Pro Stage Inc, pg 983
Sunrise Studios, pg 1028
Tallahassee Audio Visual, pg 1031
Venice Media Group, pg 1052
Video Techniques Inc, pg 1056
Vistamax Productions, pg 1059

GEORGIA

Beachwood Productions, pg 804
Crawford Media Services, pg 838
Memory Lane Productions, pg 938
USMotivation, pg 1051
Visioneering International Inc, pg 1058

IDAHO

KTVB-TV, pg 914

ILLINOIS

Analog Free Media, pg 786
Audio Visual Services Corp, pg 796
Backstar Creative Media Inc, pg 801
IV Media Resources, pg 903
Major Media Inc, pg 929
The Pepper Group, pg 972
PSAV® Presentation Services (Hotel Services Division), pg 987
Tele-Time Systems, pg 1036
20/20 Communications Inc, pg 1047
Video Impressions, pg 1055
WEEK TV, pg 1063

INDIANA

Advanced Media Integration, pg 777

IOWA

Duplication Media, pg 853
The Production House, pg 984

KENTUCKY

Audio Visual Techniques Inc, pg 796
Barney Miller's Inc, pg 943
WKYT Productions, pg 1068

VIDEO

Transfers—Slide to Video (continued)

Transfers—Videotape to Film

NEW HAMPSHIRE

Apertura, pg 788

NEW JERSEY

All Jersey Studios, pg 780
Broadcast Center Studios, pg 813
MediaMix Inc, pg 937
Suede Interactive, pg 1027
Video Corporation of America (VCA), pg 1055

NEW YORK

Adwar Video, pg 778
aurora productions, pg 797
DuArt, pg 853
Greyfalcon House, pg 882
HAVE Inc, pg 886
Jack Morton Worldwide, pg 946
Shelly Palmer Production, pg 968
PostWorks, pg 979
Zelman Studios Ltd, pg 1073

OHIO

Aztec Video Productions, pg 801

PENNSYLVANIA

Audio Visual Communications Inc, pg 795
Bernie's Photo Center, pg 805
FMP Media Solutions Inc, pg 870
Muderick Media, pg 949

RHODE ISLAND

A&M Productions, pg 771

TENNESSEE

Motion Picture Services, pg 947
Stage Post, pg 1022

WISCONSIN

Audio Visual of Milwaukee Inc, pg 795
Media Communications Association-International (MCA-I), pg 936
Video Wisconsin Inc, pg 1056

ALBERTA

Cine Audio Visual Sales & Service Ltd, pg 826
Global Television Station, pg 879

BRITISH COLUMBIA

Finale Editworks, pg 868

ONTARIO

Purefire Communications Inc, pg 987

Underwater Photography, *see* Photography—Underwater

VCR, *see* Videocassette Recorder & Player

Video Camera Distributors

ALABAMA

Curtis Company, pg 841

ARIZONA

EAR Professional Audio/Video, pg 855
Projector SuperStore LLC, pg 986
Tempe Camera, pg 1037

CALIFORNIA

Abel Cine Tech Los Angeles, pg 772
Adolph Gasser Inc, pg 776
Advanced Systems Group LLC, pg 778
Ametron Audio/Video, pg 785
Audio/Video Supply Inc, pg 795
AV Conferencing, pg 797
Band Pro Film & Digital Inc, pg 802
Barber Tech Video Products, pg 802
Be Media, pg 804
BroadcastStore.com, pg 813
Christy's Editorial, pg 826
Cibola Systems, pg 826
Computer Modules Inc, pg 834
Delicate Electronics Sales Inc, pg 845
Diaquest, pg 846
Diversified Imaging Supply, pg 849
Educational Technology Services (ETS), pg 857
FXC Communications, pg 874
Gearhouse Broadcast LLC, pg 876
Gluskin's Custom Audio Video, pg 879
Alan Gordon Enterprises Inc, pg 880
Hooper Camera & Imaging, pg 891
Innovision Optics, pg 899
Inter Video, pg 899
Jameco Electronics, pg 903
JD Audio Visual Inc, pg 904
Kappa optronics Inc, pg 908
Linear LLC, pg 922
Marshall Electronics Inc, pg 932
MediaPOINTE, pg 938
Mobilized Tech Systems, pg 944
Optronics®, pg 965
Photodyne Technologies, pg 974
PMP Marketing Inc, pg 977
POP TV, pg 978
Promax Systems, pg 986
Related Visual Inc, pg 994
SNAP, pg 1014
Sound Service Co, pg 1017
Southern California Sound Image Inc, pg 1019
SSL Industries Inc, pg 1022
Tri-Ed, pg 1044
Videobotics, pg 1056
VMI Inc, pg 1060
WolfVision Inc, pg 1069

COLORADO

Daylight Productions & Rentals, pg 844
G W Hannaway & Associates, pg 884
Spectrum Audio Visual Services, pg 1020

CONNECTICUT

Everett Hall Associates Inc, pg 863
Video Automation Systems Inc, pg 1054

FLORIDA

Access Media Group, pg 773
A2D Solutions Inc, pg 793
AVI-SPL, pg 798
Digital Video Systems Inc, pg 848
Encore Broadcast Solutions, pg 860
Enhanced View Services Inc, pg 861
General Projection Systems Inc, pg 877
Glanz Technologies Inc, pg 878
Griffiths Broadcast Co Inc, pg 882
Gulf Coast Audio Visual Producers Inc, pg 883
Harmon's Audio-Visual Services, pg 885
Harris Corp, pg 885
Hi-Tech Enterprises Inc, pg 888
Hi-Tech Import Export Corp, pg 888
Hunter Electronics LLC, pg 892
Media Concepts Inc, pg 936
Midtown Video Inc, pg 942
Pro Stage Inc, pg 983
Recording Media & Equipment Inc (RM&E), pg 993
Reef Photo & Video, pg 993
Sight & Sound Productions, pg 1010
Skyline Broadcast, pg 1013

GEORGIA

Baker Audio Inc, pg 801
Stage Front Presentation Systems, pg 1022

HAWAII

The Audio Visual Co (AVCO), pg 795

ILLINOIS

Allen Visual Systems Inc, pg 781
Cool-Lux, pg 836
RC Communications, pg 992

INDIANA

Lee Co Inc, pg 918
Sensory Technologies LLC, pg 1006
SHP Electronics, pg 1010

IOWA

ECS Inc, pg 856

KANSAS

Smith Audio-Visual Inc, pg 1014

KENTUCKY

Axxis Inc, pg 800
Barney Miller's Inc, pg 943
NOR-COM Inc, pg 958

MARYLAND

Noventri, pg 960

MASSACHUSETTS

Antronics Inc, pg 787
Camera Co Inc/Broadcast Divison, pg 818
Hunt's Photo, Video & Digital, pg 892
Rule Broadcast Systems, pg 1000

MICHIGAN

ASC Systems, pg 791
Ascom Communications Contractors, pg 791
On Stage Visuals, pg 963
TeL Systems, pg 1035

MINNESOTA

Alpha Video & Audio Inc, pg 782
Vaddio, pg 1051

MISSISSIPPI

Bowie Audio Visual Enterprises Inc, pg 811

MISSOURI

Communitronics Corp, pg 833
Conference Technologies Inc, pg 835
MIS Technologies, pg 944
Modern Communications Inc, pg 944
Schiller's Audio-Visual, pg 1004
Southwest Audio-Visual Inc, pg 1019

NEBRASKA

ATV Research Inc, pg 793
Dog & Pony Productions Inc, pg 850
Video Service of America Inc (VSA), pg 1056

NEVADA

Aardvark Video & Media Productions, pg 772

NEW JERSEY

A-V Services Inc, pg 771
Advanced Imaging Concepts Inc, pg 777
Alltec Stores, a Vcom IMC Company, pg 782
AV Bluebook, pg 797
Avtech Systems Inc, pg 800
Diversified Systems Inc, pg 849
Earl Girls Inc, pg 855
Entel Systems Inc, pg 861
Euro-Pacific Film & Video Productions Inc, pg 863
G&G Technologies Inc, pg 875
Hamilton Buhl, pg 884
Herbach & Rademan Co Inc, pg 888
MCCOM Inc, pg 935
National Audio-Visual Supply, pg 952
PatchAmp, pg 970
Starlite Productions, pg 1024
SYMCO Inc, pg 1030
Tele-Measurements Inc, pg 1035
Total Video Products Inc, pg 1042
Varto Technologies, pg 1052
York Telecom, pg 1072
ZGC Inc, pg 1073

NEW YORK

ALTEL Systems Inc, pg 783
American Video Inc, pg 785
Audio-Video Corp, pg 795
AV Workshop, pg 797
B&H Photo & Video Pro Audio, pg 802
Bosch Security Systems North America, pg 811
Colortone Audio Visual, pg 832
Communication Corner Inc, pg 832
Design Audio Visual Inc, pg 845
Edmund Scientific, pg 857
Image Management Systems Inc, pg 895
KVL Audio Visual Services Inc, pg 914
Long Island Video Enterprises Live Inc, pg 924
Markertek Video Supply, pg 931
Neptune Photo Inc, pg 954
RNJ Electronics, pg 997
Technisphere Corp, pg 1034
TecNec Distributing, pg 1035
Unitron Ltd, pg 1048

VIDEO

Video Camera Distributors (continued)

NEW YORK (continued)

Videoguys, pg 1057
Vision Identics Systems Inc, pg 1058
Visual Word Systems Inc, pg 1060

NORTH CAROLINA

Innocinema, pg 898

OHIO

Copp Integrated Systems, pg 836
ITA Audio Visual Solutions, pg 902
Midwest Photo Exchange, pg 942
Jimmy Rea Electronics Inc, pg 992
Tri-State Audio Visual Co, pg 1044
Visual Products Inc, pg 1059

OREGON

FLIR Systems Inc, pg 870

PENNSYLVANIA

Advanced AV, pg 777
Audio Visions Inc, pg 795
Bernie's Photo Center, pg 805
Brodart Co, pg 813
Clair Brothers Audio Systems Inc, pg 829
J E Foss Co, pg 871
Grise Audio Visual Center Inc, pg 882
Innovision Media Group, pg 899
The Lerro Corp, pg 919
Morefield Communications Inc, pg 946
New York Camera & Video, pg 956
Questar Corp, pg 989
Visual Sound Inc, pg 1059
Wespen Audio Visual Co, pg 1063

TENNESSEE

Lowrance Sound Co Inc, pg 925
Technical Support Systems LLC, pg 1034

TEXAS

Astro Audio Visual, pg 792
AVES Audio Visual Systems Inc, pg 798
Biway Media, pg 808
CAM Audio Inc, pg 817
Data Display Audio Visual Co LP, pg 843
Data Projections Inc, pg 843
Digital Display Solutions Inc, pg 847
Graftek Imaging Inc, pg 881
Heffernan Audio Visual, pg 887
Industrial Audio/Video Inc, pg 897
IVS Imaging, pg 903
Media Management LLC, pg 937
Omega Broadcast Group, pg 962
Precision Camera & Video, pg 980
Pro Video & Film Equipment Co Inc, pg 983
Quality Audio Visual Service Inc, pg 988
RadioShack Corp, pg 990
Supercircuits, pg 1029
Tarpley Media Systems, pg 1032
Videotex Systems Inc, pg 1057

UTAH

RIA Corp, pg 996

VIRGINIA

Avitecture Inc, pg 799
Boitnott Visual Communications Corp (BVC), pg 810
Communications Specialists Inc, pg 833
Filmdex Inc, pg 867
Hoppmann Audio Visual, pg 891
Intellidyne LLC, pg 899
Lee Hartman & Sons Inc, pg 918
Quince Imaging Inc, pg 989
The Whitlock Group, pg 1065

WASHINGTON

CCI Solutions, pg 821
Global Net Productions Inc, pg 879
Oppenheimer Camera Products, pg 964
ToteVision, pg 1042

WISCONSIN

Audio Visual of Milwaukee Inc, pg 795
Camera Corner Connecting Point, pg 818
Full Compass Systems, pg 874
Safe Harbor Computers, pg 1001

ALBERTA

Matrix Video Communications Corp (MVCC), pg 934
McBain Audio Visual Ltd, pg 935
Sharp's Audio-Visual Ltd, pg 1008

BRITISH COLUMBIA

Commercial Electronics Ltd, pg 832
ProVision Video Sales & Rentals Inc, pg 986

MANITOBA

Advance Pro, pg 777
Inland Audio Visual Ltd, pg 898

ONTARIO

Cinema Stage Inc, pg 827
HD Source, pg 886
Henry's Camera, pg 888
Majortech Inc, pg 929
Nationwide Audio Visual Co, pg 953
Premier A/V Sales Ltd, pg 980
WESCAM Inc, pg 1063

QUEBEC

Panavideo Inc, pg 968

Video Camera Manufacturers

CALIFORNIA

CohuHD, pg 831
Enright Co, pg 861
Innovision Optics, pg 899
Kappa optronics Inc, pg 908
Linear LLC, pg 922
Marshall Electronics Inc, pg 932
Optronics®, pg 965
Panasonic Broadcast & Digital Systems Co, pg 968
Jai Pulnix, pg 987
Sony Electronics Inc, pg 1016
Visionary Solutions Inc, pg 1058
WolfVision Inc, pg 1069

CONNECTICUT

Video Automation Systems Inc, pg 1054

FLORIDA

JBK Cinequipt LLC, pg 904

ILLINOIS

FJW Optical Systems Inc, pg 869

MASSACHUSETTS

Gyrus ACMI, pg 883

MINNESOTA

Vaddio, pg 1051

MISSOURI

Ken-A-Vision Manufacturing Co Inc, pg 909

NEW JERSEY

Ikegami Electronics (USA) Inc, pg 894
JVC Professional Products Co, pg 907

NEW YORK

Bosch Security Systems North America, pg 811
Hitachi Kokusai Electric America Ltd, pg 889
Vicon Industries Inc, pg 1053

NORTH CAROLINA

Crest Electronics Inc, pg 839

OREGON

FLIR Systems Inc, pg 870
Grass Valley, pg 881

PENNSYLVANIA

MicroImage Video Systems, pg 941
World Video Sales Co Inc, pg 1070

TEXAS

IVS Imaging, pg 903

VIRGINIA

Quince Imaging Inc, pg 989

WASHINGTON

Aiphone Corp, pg 779
ToteVision, pg 1042

BRITISH COLUMBIA

Triad Communications Ltd, pg 1044

ONTARIO

PixeLINK, pg 976
Teledyne DALSA Inc, pg 1036

Video Camera Rentals

ARIZONA

AV Concepts, pg 797
Broadcast Rentals, pg 813
Creative Backstage, pg 838
Crew West Inc, pg 839
Loft 19, pg 924
Merestone, pg 938
Metropolitan Audio-Visual Inc, pg 940
Tempe Camera, pg 1037
Ultimate Presentation Systems Inc, pg 1047
Video West Inc, pg 1056

ARKANSAS

White Diamond Productions, pg 1065

CALIFORNIA

Aaron & Le Duc, pg 772
Abel Cine Tech Los Angeles, pg 772
Absolute Rentals, pg 772
Action Audio & Visual, pg 775
Advanced Media LLC, pg 778
AGF Media Services, pg 778
Alliant Event Services, pg 781
Alternative Rentals, pg 783
Ametron Audio/Video, pg 785
Artichoke Productions, pg 791
AV Conferencing, pg 797
AV Guys, pg 797
Balboa Capital Corp, pg 802
Barber Tech Video Products, pg 802
Best Bet Camera Rentals, pg 805
Bexel Corp, pg 806
Big Door, pg 807
Blue Lotus Temple Studio, pg 809
BroadcastStore.com, pg 813
Chater Camera Inc, pg 824
Cherry Multimedia, pg 824
Cinema Camera Rentals, pg 827
Clean Slate Video, pg 829
Crash Video Productions, pg 837
Crystal Pyramid Productions™, pg 840
Deck Hand Inc, pg 844
Digital Film Studios, pg 847
Division Camera, pg 849
The Dreaming Tree, pg 852
Dystopian Studios, pg 854
Express Media Inc, pg 864
First Camera, pg 868
FJ Productions Inc, pg 869
Flip 2 Media Inc, pg 870
Full Moon & High Tide Productions & Studios, pg 874
Gear Monkey, pg 876
Gearhouse Broadcast LLC, pg 876
Glendale Production Centre, pg 878
Gluskin's Custom Audio Video, pg 879
Goal Productions, pg 879
Gold Standard Productions, pg 880
Golden Gate Studios, pg 880
Alan Gordon Enterprises Inc, pg 880
Greenery Studios, pg 882
HD Cinema, pg 886
HDrental.com, pg 886
iCorpTv, pg 893
Illuminate Studios, pg 894
Image Integration, pg 895
Imagecraft Productions, pg 896
Images in Motion Media Inc, pg 896
Impact Group, pg 897
Innovision Optics, pg 899
Inter Video, pg 899
InVision Productions, pg 902
JD Audio Visual Inc, pg 904
JFA Studio, pg 905
Loyal Studios, pg 925
Lynch Communications, pg 926
Main Street Media Inc, pg 929
Maximus Media Inc, pg 934
McCune Audio-Video-Lighting, pg 935
Mobilized Tech Systems, pg 944
Munday & Collins AV, pg 950
New Circuit Films LLC, pg 955
Next Arts, pg 957
North County Media Center, pg 959
Old School Cameras, pg 961

PACSAT, pg 967
Panorama Productions, pg 968
Photo Film Stage, pg 974
Pollution Studios, pg 978
Prime Cut Productions, pg 982
Pro HD Rentals, pg 983
Production Gear Rentals (PGR), pg 984
PSAV® Presentation Services, pg 986
Radiant Images, pg 990
Related Visual Inc, pg 994
RetinaVision Productions, pg 995
Revolution Cinema Rentals, pg 995
Shooting Star Video, pg 1009
Shoulder High Productions, pg 1009
Slate Media Group, pg 1013
SNAP, pg 1014
Sound Service Co, pg 1017
Stray Angel Films, pg 1026
Studio 637, pg 1027
The Studios at Paramount, pg 1027
T-stop Inc, pg 1031
Total Media Group, pg 1042
Twin Peaks Creative, pg 1047
VER-Video Equipment Rentals, pg 1053
Video Gear Rentals Inc, pg 1055
Videofax, pg 1056
Videorama Industries LLC, pg 1057
Videowerks, pg 1057
VMI Inc, pg 1060
Voice & Video Rentals, pg 1060
Warner Bros Entertainment Inc, pg 1062
Warner Bros Production Sound & Video Services, pg 1062
Westcoast Video Productions Inc, pg 1064
Z-Ville Productions, pg 1073

COLORADO

Daylight Productions & Rentals, pg 844
Denver Media Center, pg 845
Multimedia Audio Visual Inc, pg 950
Open Media Foundation, pg 964
Spectrum Audio Visual Services, pg 1020
Tatum Video, pg 1032
Zelo Productions Inc, pg 1073

CONNECTICUT

A/V Davey, pg 797
Broadcast Video Productions LLC, pg 813
Everett Hall Associates Inc, pg 863
Fox Connecticut, pg 872
Videofilm Systems Inc, pg 1057

DELAWARE

Cornerstone Media Productions Inc, pg 836
Ken-Del Productions Inc, pg 909
Showorks Audio Visual Inc, pg 1010

DISTRICT OF COLUMBIA

Future View Inc, pg 874
Metro Teleproductions Inc (MTI), pg 939

FLORIDA

Access Media Group, pg 773
Accord Productions, pg 773
All Communications Rentals Inc (ALLCOMM), pg 780
Astoria Communications Inc, pg 792
AVI-SPL, pg 798
Budget Video Rentals, pg 815
C&I Studios, pg 819
Cinema East, pg 827
Cinema Entertainment Inc, pg 827
CopShopMiami.com, pg 836
Digital Zoetrope Productions, pg 848
Eastern Video, pg 856
Facet Media, pg 865
Glanz Technologies Inc, pg 878
Gulf Coast Audio Visual Producers Inc, pg 883
Harmon's Audio-Visual Services, pg 885
HD House, pg 886
Hi-Tech Enterprises Inc, pg 888
Industrial Strength Inc, pg 897
Interscreen America Inc, pg 901
Knowles Video Inc (KVI), pg 912
Media Concepts Inc, pg 936
Midtown Video Inc, pg 942
Moving Picture, pg 947
Paradise Show & Design Inc, pg 969
Pro Stage Inc, pg 983
Sight & Sound Productions, pg 1010
Skyline Broadcast, pg 1013
10-20 Productions, pg 1037
Universal Studios Florida® Production Group, pg 1049
Mike Vasilinda Productions Inc, pg 1052

GEORGIA

Cine Photo Tech, pg 826
Continental Film & Video, pg 835
ECG Productions, pg 856
Lighting & Production Equipment Inc, pg 920
MAGNUM Companies Ltd, pg 929
ON Event Services, pg 963
See Production Services, pg 1006
Stage Front Presentation Systems, pg 1022
TV Crews, pg 1046

HAWAII

Sight & Sound Studios, pg 1010

ILLINOIS

Allen Visual Systems Inc, pg 781
Analog Free Media, pg 786
AV Chicago Inc, pg 797
Backstar Creative Media Inc, pg 801
Beatty TeleVisual Productions, pg 804
Creative Technology, pg 838
Firehouse Studios, pg 868
LITE-IT Grip Truck Rentals, pg 923
Magnanimous Media, pg 928
QuickSet International Inc, pg 989
RC Communications, pg 992
Roadworthy Image Magnification, pg 998
SCI Television Productions LLC, pg 1004
2nd Cine, pg 1006
Show Department Inc, pg 1009
Staging Resources Inc, pg 1023
Tele-Time Systems, pg 1036
Zacuto, pg 1073

INDIANA

Digital Rain LLC, pg 847

IOWA

ECS Inc, pg 856
Pro Video, pg 983

KANSAS

KAKE-TV, pg 907
Smith Audio-Visual Inc, pg 1014

KENTUCKY

Audio Visual Techniques Inc, pg 796
Idle Minds Productions Inc, pg 894
Kentucky Grip & Lighting, pg 909

LOUISIANA

Clark Services Audio Visual & Exhibit Inc, pg 829
Digital FX Inc, pg 847
Moxie Media, pg 948
Pace Systems, pg 966

MARYLAND

Advance Audiovisual Presentation Ltd, pg 777
The Ahern Group, pg 779
Archai Media, pg 789
CPR MultiMedia Solutions, pg 837
Event Tech, pg 863
Kramer Communications Video Production, pg 913
Visual Aids Electronics Corp, pg 1059

MASSACHUSETTS

AVFX Inc, pg 798
Camera Co Inc/Broadcast Divison, pg 818
Green Mountain Post Films (GMP), pg 882
massAV, pg 933
Preston Productions Inc, pg 981
Small Planet Communications Inc, pg 1013

MICHIGAN

Digi Sign Design LLC, pg 847
K&R All Media Productions Inc, pg 908
K&R's Recording Studios Inc, pg 908
On Stage Visuals, pg 963
TeL Systems, pg 1035

MINNESOTA

Alpha Video & Audio Inc, pg 782
Big Event Productions LLC, pg 807
House of Cinemagraphics, pg 891
Lights On, pg 921
Pro Media Productions, pg 983

MISSISSIPPI

Bowie Audio Visual Enterprises Inc, pg 811

MISSOURI

Cashmark Media Inc, pg 820
Communitronics Corp, pg 833
Schiller's Audio-Visual, pg 1004
Show-Me Audio-Visual, pg 1009
Southwest Audio-Visual Inc, pg 1019
Switch, pg 1030

MONTANA

Filmlites Montana, pg 867

NEBRASKA

Dog & Pony Productions Inc, pg 850
Lights On Nebraska, pg 921

NEVADA

GES Audio Visual, pg 877
JCS Video Productions, pg 904
Lefco Video Services Inc, pg 918
MG Studio, pg 940

NEW JERSEY

Audio Visual Dynamics®, pg 795
CFP Video Productions Inc, pg 823
Earl Girls Inc, pg 855
Euro-Pacific Film & Video Productions Inc, pg 863
G&G Technologies Inc, pg 875
International Audio Visual Inc, pg 900
MB Productions, pg 934
MediaMix Inc, pg 937
PLS Staging, pg 977
Bill Quinn Productions, pg 989
Reider Photography & Video Productions, pg 994
Starlite Productions, pg 1024
Tele-Measurements Inc, pg 1035
Video Corporation of America (VCA), pg 1055

NEW MEXICO

Production Outfitters, pg 984

NEW YORK

Adorama Rental Co, pg 776
Air Sea Land Productions Inc (ASL), pg 779
American Video Inc, pg 785
AV Workshop, pg 797
Big Apple Films, pg 806
Big Foot Productions Inc, pg 807
Bond Street Studio, pg 810
Cinema-Vision, pg 827
Colortone Audio Visual, pg 832
Communication Corner Inc, pg 832
CP Communications, pg 837
CSI Rentals, pg 840
Design Audio Visual Inc, pg 845
Gearhead Rentals, pg 876
Hand Held Films, pg 884
HB-Content, pg 886
Hello World Communications, pg 888
KVL Audio Visual Services Inc, pg 914
LightHouse Films, pg 920
LightSpace Studios, pg 921
Long Island Video Enterprises Live Inc, pg 924
Manhattan Center Studios Inc, pg 930
Production Central, pg 984
Scheimpflug Digital, pg 1004
TBA Global Events, pg 1032
Technisphere Corp, pg 1034
The Visual Studies Workshop (VSW), pg 1059
Visual Word Systems Inc, pg 1060
WNET/NET TELECON, pg 1069

NORTH CAROLINA

A&V Company, pg 772
All Pro Media Inc, pg 780
AV Metro Inc, pg 797
The Communications Group Inc, pg 833
Duke Media Services, pg 853
Moving Pictures, pg 948
On Location North Carolina, pg 963
Special Event Services, pg 1020
Take One Productions Ltd, pg 1031
Visual Aids Electronics of North Carolina Inc, pg 1059

VIDEO

Video Camera Rentals (continued)

NORTH DAKOTA

Media Productions, pg 937

OHIO

Aztec Video Productions, pg 801
Hughie's Event Production Services, pg 892
ITA Audio Visual Solutions, pg 902
Lyon Video Inc, pg 927
Mills James Productions, pg 943
Ohio HD Video, pg 961
OSV Studios, pg 966
R&B Communications Inc, pg 991

OKLAHOMA

PDC Productions, pg 970

OREGON

Koerner Camera Systems, pg 912
Northwest Film Center, pg 959
Picture This Production Services, pg 975

PENNSYLVANIA

Advanced AV, pg 777
Argentine Productions Inc, pg 789
Audio Visions Inc, pg 795
Audio Visual Communications Inc, pg 795
Bang Pictures, pg 802
FirstGeneration Audio/Visual Services, pg 869
FMP Media Solutions Inc, pg 870
Fusion Brand Experiences, pg 874
Goodman Associates Inc, pg 880
Grise Audio Visual Center Inc, pg 882
Innovision Media Group, pg 899
JPL, pg 906
Muderick Media, pg 949
New York Camera & Video, pg 956
Philadelphia Soundstages, pg 974
Producers Management Television (PMTV), pg 983
Upstage Video, pg 1050
Video Communication Productions Inc, pg 1054
The Videohouse Inc, pg 1057
Viewpoint Production Services Inc, pg 1058
Visual Sound Inc, pg 1059

TENNESSEE

Nashville Production Rentals (NPR), pg 952
NuMynd Studios, pg 960
RentACamera.com, pg 995
Russ Sturgeon Productions/RSVP, pg 1027
Technical Support Systems LLC, pg 1034

TEXAS

Alford Media Services, pg 780
Astro Audio Visual, pg 792
Big House Sound Inc, pg 807
Bright Giant Creative Group, pg 812
Countdown Productions Inc, pg 837
Data Display Audio Visual Co LP, pg 843
Digital Display Solutions Inc, pg 847
GEAR Cameras & Lighting, pg 876
Industrial Audio/Video Inc, pg 897
Light Tec, pg 920
Media Event Concepts Inc, pg 936
Mediaforce Productions, pg 937
Earl Miller Productions Inc, pg 943
Omega Broadcast Group, pg 962
Phil Lights, pg 973
Phillips MediaSource, pg 974
Precision Camera & Video, pg 980
The Samuels Co, pg 1002
South Coast Film & Video, pg 1019
Stage Directions, pg 1022
Texcam Inc, pg 1038
Video Perspective, pg 1056

UTAH

8K Productions, pg 858
Ron Hill Imagery, pg 889

VERMONT

Dark Star Lighting & Production, pg 842

VIRGINIA

Advance Concepts Inc, pg 777
Audio Visual Actions Inc (AVA), pg 795
Boitnott Visual Communications Corp (BVC), pg 810
Creative Video of Washington Inc, pg 839
D&B Television & Video Productions Inc, pg 842
Lee Hartman & Sons Inc, pg 918
Quince Imaging Inc, pg 989
StageSound, pg 1023
The Whitlock Group, pg 1065

WASHINGTON

The House Studios, pg 891
Kostov Productions, pg 913
911 Media Arts Center, pg 957
Oppenheimer Camera Products, pg 964
Victory Studios, pg 1054

WEST VIRGINIA

Blackwater Video Productions, pg 808

WISCONSIN

Audio Visual of Milwaukee Inc, pg 795
Camera Corner Connecting Point, pg 818
Event Essentials, pg 863
Full Compass Systems, pg 874
Logan Productions Inc, pg 924
MKE Production Rental, pg 944

WYOMING

Bridger Productions Inc, pg 812

PUERTO RICO

Stage Crew Audiovisual Inc, pg 1022

ALBERTA

Evolution Presentation Technologies, pg 863
Matrix Video Communications Corp (MVCC), pg 934
Unique Communications Ltd, pg 1048

BRITISH COLUMBIA

Clark's Audio Visual Services Ltd, pg 829
Commercial Electronics Ltd, pg 832
Finale Editworks, pg 868
Image Media Farm, pg 895
ProVision Video Sales & Rentals Inc, pg 986
Video In Studios/Video Out Distribution, pg 1055

MANITOBA

Inland Audio Visual Ltd, pg 898
MidCanada Production Services Inc (MidCan), pg 942

ONTARIO

GAPC (General Assembly Production Centre), pg 875
HD Source, pg 886
JIB Shots Equipment Inc, pg 905
Metalworks Recording Studios Inc, pg 939
RB Productions, pg 992
SIM Digital, pg 1011
WESCAM Inc, pg 1063

QUEBEC

Audio Visual Dynamics Ltd, pg 795
AVW-TELAV Audio Visual Solutions, a Freeman Company, pg 800
Group PVP, pg 882
Panavideo Inc, pg 968

Video Camera Repairs

ARIZONA

Tempe Camera, pg 1037

CALIFORNIA

Advanced Media LLC, pg 778
Ametron Audio/Video, pg 785
Band Pro Film & Digital Inc, pg 802
BroadcastStore.com, pg 813
Gluskin's Custom Audio Video, pg 879
Kappa optronics Inc, pg 908
McAlister Electronics, pg 935
Mobilized Tech Systems, pg 944
Pro Camera Repair, pg 982
SSL Industries Inc, pg 1022
Technical Services, pg 1034
TEK Media Group, pg 1035
VMI Inc, pg 1060

CONNECTICUT

A/V Davey, pg 797
Precision Camera & Video Repair Inc, pg 980
Video Automation Systems Inc, pg 1054

FLORIDA

Digital Video Systems Inc, pg 848
ELC Sales & Service Inc, pg 858
Glanz Technologies Inc, pg 878
Hi-Tech Enterprises Inc, pg 888
Media Concepts Inc, pg 936
Midtown Video Inc, pg 942

GEORGIA

Stage Front Presentation Systems, pg 1022

ILLINOIS

Allen Visual Systems Inc, pg 781
Beatty TeleVisual Productions, pg 804
Midwest Digital Corp, pg 942
RC Communications, pg 992

IOWA

ECS Inc, pg 856

KENTUCKY

Axxis Inc, pg 800
Barney Miller's Inc, pg 943
NOR-COM Inc, pg 958

MARYLAND

Noventri, pg 960
Strauss Photo Technical Service Inc, pg 1026

MASSACHUSETTS

Antronics Inc, pg 787
Camera Co Inc/Broadcast Divison, pg 818

MICHIGAN

TeL Systems, pg 1035

MINNESOTA

Alpha Video & Audio Inc, pg 782

MISSOURI

Communitronics Corp, pg 833
Schiller's Audio-Visual, pg 1004
Southwest Audio-Visual Inc, pg 1019

NEW JERSEY

Entel Systems Inc, pg 861
G&G Technologies Inc, pg 875

NEW YORK

Technisphere Corp, pg 1034

OHIO

Copp Integrated Systems, pg 836
ITA Audio Visual Solutions, pg 902
Tri-State Audio Visual Co, pg 1044

OREGON

FLIR Systems Inc, pg 870

PENNSYLVANIA

Audio Visions Inc, pg 795
Bernie's Photo Center, pg 805
Visual Sound Inc, pg 1059

TENNESSEE

Technical Support Systems LLC, pg 1034

TEXAS

Astro Audio Visual, pg 792
Data Display Audio Visual Co LP, pg 843
Industrial Audio/Video Inc, pg 897
Pro Video & Film Equipment Co Inc, pg 983
Quality Audio Visual Service Inc, pg 988
Tarpley Media Systems, pg 1032

UTAH

RIA Corp, pg 996

VIRGINIA

Hoppmann Audio Visual, pg 891
Lee Hartman & Sons Inc, pg 918
Quince Imaging Inc, pg 989
The Whitlock Group, pg 1065

WASHINGTON

Aiphone Corp, pg 779

WISCONSIN

Camera Corner Connecting Point, pg 818
Full Compass Systems, pg 874

ALBERTA

Matrix Video Communications Corp (MVCC), pg 934
Sharp's Audio-Visual Ltd, pg 1008

BRITISH COLUMBIA

Commercial Electronics Ltd, pg 832

MANITOBA

Inland Audio Visual Ltd, pg 898

ONTARIO

HD Source, pg 886

QUEBEC

Panavideo Inc, pg 968

Video Presentation System Distributors

ALABAMA

CMEInfo, pg 830
Curtis Company, pg 841
Media Visions Inc, pg 937

ARIZONA

EAR Professional Audio/Video, pg 855

ARKANSAS

Jay S Stanley & Associates Inc, pg 1023

CALIFORNIA

Adolph Gasser Inc, pg 776
Advanced Systems Group LLC, pg 778
AITech International, pg 779
Ametron Audio/Video, pg 785
Audio/Video Supply Inc, pg 795
AV Conferencing, pg 797
Band Pro Film & Digital Inc, pg 802
Be Media, pg 804
Christy's Editorial, pg 826
Delicate Electronics Sales Inc, pg 845
Diversified Imaging Supply, pg 849
Educational Technology Services (ETS), pg 857
Electrosonic Inc, pg 859
FXC Communications, pg 874
JD Audio Visual Inc, pg 904
Media Fabricators Inc, pg 936
Muse Presentation Technologies, pg 950
PMP Marketing Inc, pg 977
POP TV, pg 978
Promax Systems, pg 986
Sonance, pg 1015
Southern California Sound Image Inc, pg 1019
SSL Industries Inc, pg 1022
Stanislaus Audio Video Inc, pg 1023
SuperVision, pg 1029
Tri-Ed, pg 1044
VMI Inc, pg 1060
WolfVision Inc, pg 1069

COLORADO

Daylight Productions & Rentals, pg 844
Macrosystem US Inc, pg 927
Spectrum Audio Visual Services, pg 1020

CONNECTICUT

Everett Hall Associates Inc, pg 863
General Electric Co, pg 876
MAVCO, pg 934
The Video Messenger Co, pg 1055

FLORIDA

Access Media Group, pg 773
Allstar Audio Systems Inc, pg 782
AVI-SPL, pg 798
Digital Video Systems Inc, pg 848
General Projection Systems Inc, pg 877
Gulf Coast Audio Visual Producers Inc, pg 883
Harmon's Audio-Visual Services, pg 885
Hi-Tech Import Export Corp, pg 888
Industrial Strength Inc, pg 897
Media Concepts Inc, pg 936
Midtown Video Inc, pg 942
Pro Stage Inc, pg 983
Sight & Sound Productions, pg 1010
Vela Research, pg 1052

GEORGIA

Baker Audio Inc, pg 801
Barco Inc, pg 803
Omnimedia Inc, pg 962
Stage Front Presentation Systems, pg 1022

ILLINOIS

Allen Visual Systems Inc, pg 781
Tele-Time Systems, pg 1036
Zenith Electronics LLC, pg 1073

INDIANA

Lee Co Inc, pg 918
Sensory Technologies LLC, pg 1006
SHP Electronics, pg 1010

KANSAS

Smith Audio-Visual Inc, pg 1014

KENTUCKY

Axxis Inc, pg 800
Barney Miller's Inc, pg 943
NOR-COM Inc, pg 958

LOUISIANA

Intermedia Technologies, pg 900

MAINE

Headlight Audio Visual Inc, pg 887

MARYLAND

Human Circuit, pg 892

MASSACHUSETTS

ASACA/ShibaSoku Corp of America, pg 791
Camera Co Inc/Broadcast Divison, pg 818
Rule Broadcast Systems, pg 1000

MICHIGAN

ASC Systems, pg 791
Ascom Communications Contractors, pg 791
Digi Sign Design LLC, pg 847
Michigan Office Solutions, pg 941
TeL Systems, pg 1035

MINNESOTA

Alpha Video & Audio Inc, pg 782

MISSISSIPPI

Bowie Audio Visual Enterprises Inc, pg 811

MISSOURI

Communitronics Corp, pg 833
Conference Technologies Inc, pg 835
MIS Technologies, pg 944
Southwest Audio-Visual Inc, pg 1019

NEVADA

Aardvark Video & Media Productions, pg 772

NEW HAMPSHIRE

Optics 1 Inc, pg 964

NEW JERSEY

A-V Services Inc, pg 771
Advanced Imaging Concepts Inc, pg 777
AV Bluebook, pg 797
Avtech Systems Inc, pg 800
Color Leasing Studios, pg 831
Diversified Systems Inc, pg 849
Earl Girls Inc, pg 855
Hamilton Buhl, pg 884
MCCOM Inc, pg 935
MIB Mediaworks, pg 941
National Audio-Visual Supply, pg 952
Starlite Productions, pg 1024
SYMCO Inc, pg 1030
Tele-Measurements Inc, pg 1035
Total Video Products Inc, pg 1042
York Telecom, pg 1072

NEW YORK

Ace Video, pg 774
ALTEL Systems Inc, pg 783
Audio-Video Corp, pg 795
AV Workshop, pg 797
Colortone Audio Visual, pg 832
Design Audio Visual Inc, pg 845
Image Management Systems Inc, pg 895
KVL Audio Visual Services Inc, pg 914
Long Island Video Enterprises Live Inc, pg 924
Markertek Video Supply, pg 931
Neptune Photo Inc, pg 954
Presentation Products Inc, pg 981
SmartSource Computer & AV Rentals, pg 1014
Technisphere Corp, pg 1034
Visual Word Systems Inc, pg 1060

NORTH CAROLINA

Strategic Connections, pg 1026

OHIO

Copp Integrated Systems, pg 836
ITA Audio Visual Solutions, pg 902
Jimmy Rea Electronics Inc, pg 992
Smithall Electronics Inc, pg 1014
Tri-State Audio Visual Co, pg 1044

OREGON

ClearOne MagicBox Inc, pg 830

PENNSYLVANIA

AccuWeather Inc, pg 774
Advanced AV, pg 777
Audio Visions Inc, pg 795
Grise Audio Visual Center Inc, pg 882
The Lerro Corp, pg 919
Morefield Communications Inc, pg 946
Vistacom Inc, pg 1059
Visual Sound Inc, pg 1059
Wespen Audio Visual Co, pg 1063

RHODE ISLAND

Shanix Inc, pg 1008

TENNESSEE

Lowrance Sound Co Inc, pg 925
Technical Support Systems LLC, pg 1034

TEXAS

Audio Visual Technologies Group, pg 796
AVES Audio Visual Systems Inc, pg 798
Biway Media, pg 808
Data Display Audio Visual Co LP, pg 843
Digital Display Solutions Inc, pg 847
Heffernan Audio Visual, pg 887
Lex Lawson Associates, pg 917
Media Management LLC, pg 937
Schoolhouse Audio Visual, pg 1004
Tarpley Media Systems, pg 1032

UTAH

RIA Corp, pg 996

VIRGINIA

Avitecture Inc, pg 799
Boitnott Visual Communications Corp (BVC), pg 810
Communications Specialists Inc, pg 833
Hoppmann Audio Visual, pg 891
Intellidyne LLC, pg 899
Lee Hartman & Sons Inc, pg 918
Quince Imaging Inc, pg 989
The Whitlock Group, pg 1065

WASHINGTON

eMagin Corp, pg 860
ToteVision, pg 1042

WISCONSIN

Audio Visual of Milwaukee Inc, pg 795
Camera Corner Connecting Point, pg 818
Full Compass Systems, pg 874

VIDEO

Video Presentation System Distributors (continued)

ALBERTA

Infosat Communications Inc, pg 898
Matrix Video Communications Corp (MVCC), pg 934

BRITISH COLUMBIA

ProVision Video Sales & Rentals Inc, pg 986

MANITOBA

Advance Pro, pg 777
Inland Audio Visual Ltd, pg 898

ONTARIO

Cinema Stage Inc, pg 827
Edcom Multimedia Products, pg 856
HD Source, pg 886
Nationwide Audio Visual Co, pg 953
Premier A/V Sales Ltd, pg 980
Technovision® Interactive Inc, pg 1035
Westbury National Show Systems Ltd, pg 1064

QUEBEC

Panavideo Inc, pg 968

Video Presentation System Manufacturers

ARIZONA

Boeckeler Instruments Inc, pg 810

CALIFORNIA

AITech International, pg 779
Doremi Labs, pg 851
Enright Co, pg 861
Extron Electronics, pg 864
Jupiter Systems, pg 907
Lucasey Manufacturing Corp, pg 925
Panasonic Broadcast & Digital Systems Co, pg 968
Pioneer Electronics (USA) Inc, pg 976
POP TV, pg 978
RGB Spectrum, pg 996
Sonance, pg 1015
Sony Electronics Inc, pg 1016
WolfVision Inc, pg 1069

COLORADO

Macrosystem US Inc, pg 927

CONNECTICUT

General Electric Co, pg 876
The Video Messenger Co, pg 1055

FLORIDA

Pangolin Laser Systems Inc, pg 968
Vela Research, pg 1052
Vutec Corp, Video Products Division, pg 1061

GEORGIA

Barco Inc, pg 803
Visix™ Inc, pg 1059

ILLINOIS

Dukane Corp, Audio Visual Products Division, pg 853
NEC Display Solutions of America, pg 954

INDIANA

Da-Lite, pg 842
Draper Inc, pg 852

KANSAS

Keywest Technology Inc, pg 910

KENTUCKY

TV One Multimedia Solutions, pg 1046

MARYLAND

Absolute Hollywood, pg 772

MASSACHUSETTS

ASACA/ShibaSoku Corp of America, pg 791
Elite Video, pg 859

MICHIGAN

ASC Systems, pg 791

MINNESOTA

Dotronix Technology Inc, pg 851
Vaddio, pg 1051

MISSOURI

Ken-A-Vision Manufacturing Co Inc, pg 909

NEVADA

Keystone View, pg 910

NEW HAMPSHIRE

Optics 1 Inc, pg 964

NEW JERSEY

FSR Inc, pg 873
Sharp Electronics Corp, Professional Display Division, pg 1008

NEW YORK

Gordon Visual Solutions, pg 880
Navitar Inc, pg 953
Quantel Inc, pg 989

OREGON

ClearOne MagicBox Inc, pg 830

PENNSYLVANIA

AccuWeather Inc, pg 774

TENNESSEE

Adtec Digital Inc, pg 777

TEXAS

Contemporary Research, pg 835

VIRGINIA

Quince Imaging Inc, pg 989

WASHINGTON

eMagin Corp, pg 860
ToteVision, pg 1042

BRITISH COLUMBIA

Triad Communications Ltd, pg 1044

ONTARIO

Evertz Microsystems Ltd, pg 863
McCurdy Radio Ltd, pg 935

Video Presentation System Rentals

ALABAMA

Audio-Video Resources Inc, pg 795

ARIZONA

American Audio Visual Center, pg 783
Creative Backstage, pg 838
Merestone, pg 938
Metropolitan Audio-Visual Inc, pg 940

ARKANSAS

White Diamond Productions, pg 1065

CALIFORNIA

Aaron & Le Duc, pg 772
Adolph Gasser Inc, pg 776
Alliant Event Services, pg 781
Ametron Audio/Video, pg 785
AV Guys, pg 797
Christy's Editorial, pg 826
Crystal Pyramid Productions™, pg 840
Express Media Inc, pg 864
First Camera, pg 868
Golden Gate Studios, pg 880
Impact Group, pg 897
JD Audio Visual Inc, pg 904
Lynch Communications, pg 926
McCune Audio-Video-Lighting, pg 935
Media Fabricators Inc, pg 936
Munday & Collins AV, pg 950
Muse Presentation Technologies, pg 950
On-Trax Inc, pg 963
Panorama Productions, pg 968
Pioneer Electronics (USA) Inc, pg 976
PSAV® Presentation Services, pg 986
RetinaVision Productions, pg 995
Slate Media Group, pg 1013
SNAP, pg 1014
Total Media Group, pg 1042
Tri-Ed, pg 1044
VER-Video Equipment Rentals, pg 1053
VMI Inc, pg 1060
Voice & Video Rentals, pg 1060

COLORADO

Daylight Productions & Rentals, pg 844
Multimedia Audio Visual Inc, pg 950
Spectrum Audio Visual Services, pg 1020

CONNECTICUT

A/V Davey, pg 797
Everett Hall Associates Inc, pg 863
Fox Connecticut, pg 872
General Electric Co, pg 876
Videofilm Systems Inc, pg 1057

DELAWARE

Ken-Del Productions Inc, pg 909

DISTRICT OF COLUMBIA

Future View Inc, pg 874
Metro Teleproductions Inc (MTI), pg 939

FLORIDA

Allstar Audio Systems Inc, pg 782
AVI-SPL, pg 798
Budget Video Rentals, pg 815
Gulf Coast Audio Visual Producers Inc, pg 883
Harmon's Audio-Visual Services, pg 885
Industrial Strength Inc, pg 897
Jordan Klein Film & Video (JKFV), pg 906
Media Concepts Inc, pg 936
Paradise Show & Design Inc, pg 969
Pro Stage Inc, pg 983
Sight & Sound Productions, pg 1010

GEORGIA

MAGNUM Companies Ltd, pg 929
ON Event Services, pg 963
Stage Front Presentation Systems, pg 1022

ILLINOIS

Airways Digital Media, pg 779
Allen Visual Systems Inc, pg 781
AV Chicago Inc, pg 797
Backstar Creative Media Inc, pg 801
Beatty TeleVisual Productions, pg 804
Creative Technology, pg 838
QuickSet International Inc, pg 989
RC Communications, pg 992
Roadworthy Image Magnification, pg 998
SCI Television Productions LLC, pg 1004
Show Department Inc, pg 1009
Tele-Time Systems, pg 1036

INDIANA

Advanced Media Integration, pg 777

KANSAS

Smith Audio-Visual Inc, pg 1014

KENTUCKY

Audio Visual Techniques Inc, pg 796
Idle Minds Productions Inc, pg 894

LOUISIANA

Clark Services Audio Visual & Exhibit Inc, pg 829
Digital FX Inc, pg 847
Pace Systems, pg 966

MAINE

Headlight Audio Visual Inc, pg 887

MARYLAND

Absolute Hollywood, pg 772
Advance Audiovisual Presentation Ltd, pg 777
CPR MultiMedia Solutions, pg 837
Event Tech, pg 863

MASSACHUSETTS

AVFX Inc, pg 798
Capron Lighting & Sound Co Inc, pg 819
Elite Video, pg 859
massAV, pg 933
Preston Productions Inc, pg 981

MICHIGAN

Digi Sign Design LLC, pg 847
K&R All Media Productions Inc, pg 908
TeL Systems, pg 1035

MINNESOTA

Alpha Video & Audio Inc, pg 782
Big Event Productions LLC, pg 807

MISSISSIPPI

Bowie Audio Visual Enterprises Inc, pg 811

MISSOURI

Communitronics Corp, pg 833
Schiller's Audio-Visual, pg 1004
Show-Me Audio-Visual, pg 1009
Southwest Audio-Visual Inc, pg 1019
Switch, pg 1030

NEVADA

GES Audio Visual, pg 877
Lefco Video Services Inc, pg 918

NEW JERSEY

Audio Visual Dynamics®, pg 795
Color Leasing Studios, pg 831
Earl Girls Inc, pg 855
MB Productions, pg 934
MIB Mediaworks, pg 941
PLS Staging, pg 977
Reider Photography & Video Productions, pg 994
Starlite Productions, pg 1024
Tele-Measurements Inc, pg 1035
Video Corporation of America (VCA), pg 1055

NEW YORK

Ace Video, pg 774
AV Workshop, pg 797
Colortone Audio Visual, pg 832
Design Audio Visual Inc, pg 845
General Audio-Visual Inc (GAVI), pg 876
KVL Audio Visual Services Inc, pg 914
Long Island Video Enterprises Live Inc, pg 924
Manhattan Center Studios Inc, pg 930
MRG Productions Inc, pg 948
SmartSource Computer & AV Rentals, pg 1014
TBA Global Events, pg 1032
Technisphere Corp, pg 1034
Visual Word Systems Inc, pg 1060
WorldStage, pg 1070

NORTH CAROLINA

A&V Company, pg 772
AV Metro Inc, pg 797
Special Event Services, pg 1020

NORTH DAKOTA

Media Productions, pg 937

OHIO

Bartha, pg 803
Hughie's Event Production Services, pg 892
ITA Audio Visual Solutions, pg 902
Mills James Productions, pg 943
R&B Communications Inc, pg 991
Vista Color Imaging Inc, pg 1059

OKLAHOMA

PDC Productions, pg 970

PENNSYLVANIA

Advanced AV, pg 777
Audio Visions Inc, pg 795
FMP Media Solutions Inc, pg 870
Upstage Video, pg 1050
Visual Sound Inc, pg 1059

TENNESSEE

Russ Sturgeon Productions/RSVP, pg 1027
Technical Support Systems LLC, pg 1034

TEXAS

Astro Audio Visual, pg 792
Bright Star Productions Inc, pg 812
Data Display Audio Visual Co LP, pg 843
Digital Display Solutions Inc, pg 847
Media Event Concepts Inc, pg 936
The Samuels Co, pg 1002
Stage Directions, pg 1022

VIRGINIA

Advance Concepts Inc, pg 777
Boitnott Visual Communications Corp (BVC), pg 810
Quince Imaging Inc, pg 989
The Whitlock Group, pg 1065

WASHINGTON

Victory Studios, pg 1054

WISCONSIN

Audio Visual of Milwaukee Inc, pg 795
Camera Corner Connecting Point, pg 818
Event Essentials, pg 863
Full Compass Systems, pg 874

WYOMING

Bridger Productions Inc, pg 812

PUERTO RICO

Stage Crew Audiovisual Inc, pg 1022

ALBERTA

Cine Audio Visual Sales & Service Ltd, pg 826
Global Television Station, pg 879
Matrix Video Communications Corp (MVCC), pg 934
Unique Communications Ltd, pg 1048

BRITISH COLUMBIA

Clark's Audio Visual Services Ltd, pg 829
Video In Studios/Video Out Distribution, pg 1055

MANITOBA

Inland Audio Visual Ltd, pg 898

ONTARIO

HD Source, pg 886
Metalworks Recording Studios Inc, pg 939
RB Productions, pg 992
Westbury National Show Systems Ltd, pg 1064

QUEBEC

Audio Visual Dynamics Ltd, pg 795
Panavideo Inc, pg 968

Video Presentation System Repairs

CALIFORNIA

Ametron Audio/Video, pg 785
Band Pro Film & Digital Inc, pg 802
Christy's Editorial, pg 826
Sonance, pg 1015
SSL Industries Inc, pg 1022
Tri-Ed, pg 1044
VMI Inc, pg 1060

COLORADO

Macrosystem US Inc, pg 927

CONNECTICUT

A/V Davey, pg 797
General Electric Co, pg 876

DISTRICT OF COLUMBIA

Future View Inc, pg 874

FLORIDA

ELC Sales & Service Inc, pg 858
Midtown Video Inc, pg 942
Vela Research, pg 1052

GEORGIA

Stage Front Presentation Systems, pg 1022

ILLINOIS

Allen Visual Systems Inc, pg 781
Beatty TeleVisual Productions, pg 804
Midwest Digital Corp, pg 942

KENTUCKY

Axxis Inc, pg 800
Barney Miller's Inc, pg 943
NOR-COM Inc, pg 958

MARYLAND

Strauss Photo Technical Service Inc, pg 1026

MASSACHUSETTS

Elite Video, pg 859

MICHIGAN

TeL Systems, pg 1035

MINNESOTA

Alpha Video & Audio Inc, pg 782

MISSOURI

Communitronics Corp, pg 833
Schiller's Audio-Visual, pg 1004
Southwest Audio-Visual Inc, pg 1019

NEW YORK

Ace Video, pg 774
MRG Productions Inc, pg 948

OHIO

Copp Integrated Systems, pg 836
ITA Audio Visual Solutions, pg 902
Tri-State Audio Visual Co, pg 1044

PENNSYLVANIA

Audio Visions Inc, pg 795
Visual Sound Inc, pg 1059

TENNESSEE

Technical Support Systems LLC, pg 1034

TEXAS

Astro Audio Visual, pg 792
Data Display Audio Visual Co LP, pg 843
Tarpley Media Systems, pg 1032

UTAH

RIA Corp, pg 996

VIRGINIA

Avitecture Inc, pg 799
Boitnott Visual Communications Corp (BVC), pg 810
Hoppmann Audio Visual, pg 891
The Whitlock Group, pg 1065

WISCONSIN

Camera Corner Connecting Point, pg 818
Full Compass Systems, pg 874

ALBERTA

Infosat Communications Inc, pg 898
Matrix Video Communications Corp (MVCC), pg 934

MANITOBA

Inland Audio Visual Ltd, pg 898

ONTARIO

Edcom Multimedia Products, pg 856
Westbury National Show Systems Ltd, pg 1064

QUEBEC

Panavideo Inc, pg 968

Video Receiver & Monitor Distributors

ALABAMA

Curtis Company, pg 841
Media Visions Inc, pg 937

VIDEO

Video Receiver & Monitor Distributors (continued)

ARIZONA

ATCi (Antenna Technology Communication Solutions Inc), pg 793
EAR Professional Audio/Video, pg 855

ARKANSAS

Jay S Stanley & Associates Inc, pg 1023

CALIFORNIA

Adolph Gasser Inc, pg 776
Advanced Systems Group LLC, pg 778
Ametron Audio/Video, pg 785
Audio/Video Supply Inc, pg 795
Band Pro Film & Digital Inc, pg 802
Be Media, pg 804
BroadcastStore.com, pg 813
Christy's Editorial, pg 826
Computer Modules Inc, pg 834
Delicate Electronics Sales Inc, pg 845
Diaquest, pg 846
FXC Communications, pg 874
Gluskin's Custom Audio Video, pg 879
HM Electronics Inc (HME), pg 889
Instructional Materials & Equipment Distributors (I-Med), pg 899
JD Audio Visual Inc, pg 904
Kappa optronics Inc, pg 908
Leader Instruments Corp, pg 917
Media Control Systems LLC, pg 936
Media Fabricators Inc, pg 936
Metro Video Systems Inc, pg 940
Photodyne Technologies, pg 974
PMP Marketing Inc, pg 977
POP TV, pg 978
Promax Systems, pg 986
SNAP, pg 1014
Southern California Sound Image Inc, pg 1019
SSL Industries Inc, pg 1022
Stanislaus Audio Video Inc, pg 1023
SuperVision, pg 1029
Transvideo International, pg 1044
Tri-Ed, pg 1044
VMI Inc, pg 1060

COLORADO

Daylight Productions & Rentals, pg 844
Spectrum Audio Visual Services, pg 1020

CONNECTICUT

MAVCO, pg 934
Video Automation Systems Inc, pg 1054

DISTRICT OF COLUMBIA

Future View Inc, pg 874

FLORIDA

Access Media Group, pg 773
Allstar Audio Systems Inc, pg 782
A2D Solutions Inc, pg 793
AVI-SPL, pg 798
Digital Video Systems Inc, pg 848
General Projection Systems Inc, pg 877
Glanz Technologies Inc, pg 878
Griffiths Broadcast Co Inc, pg 882
Gulf Coast Audio Visual Producers Inc, pg 883
Hi-Tech Enterprises Inc, pg 888
Hi-Tech Import Export Corp, pg 888
Industrial Strength Inc, pg 897
Media Concepts Inc, pg 936
Midtown Video Inc, pg 942
Pro Stage Inc, pg 983
Reef Photo & Video, pg 993
Sight & Sound Productions, pg 1010
Skyline Broadcast, pg 1013
Vela Research, pg 1052
Videoscope, pg 1057

GEORGIA

Baker Audio Inc, pg 801
Clark, pg 829
Stage Front Presentation Systems, pg 1022

ILLINOIS

Allen Visual Systems Inc, pg 781
RAM Systems LLC, pg 991
RC Communications, pg 992
Tele-Time Systems, pg 1036
Woodside Avenue Music Productions Inc, pg 1069

INDIANA

Lee Co Inc, pg 918
Sensory Technologies LLC, pg 1006
SHP Electronics, pg 1010

KANSAS

Smith Audio-Visual Inc, pg 1014

KENTUCKY

Axxis Inc, pg 800
Barney Miller's Inc, pg 943
NOR-COM Inc, pg 958

MAINE

Headlight Audio Visual Inc, pg 887
Independent Audio Inc, pg 897

MARYLAND

Advance Audiovisual Presentation Ltd, pg 777
Human Circuit, pg 892
Wiltronix, pg 1067

MASSACHUSETTS

Antronics Inc, pg 787
Rule Broadcast Systems, pg 1000

MICHIGAN

ASC Systems, pg 791
Ascom Communications Contractors, pg 791
Digi Sign Design LLC, pg 847
On Stage Visuals, pg 963
TeL Systems, pg 1035

MINNESOTA

Alpha Video & Audio Inc, pg 782

MISSISSIPPI

Bowie Audio Visual Enterprises Inc, pg 811

MISSOURI

Communitronics Corp, pg 833
Conference Technologies Inc, pg 835
MIS Technologies, pg 944
Production Support Services Inc, pg 985
Southwest Audio-Visual Inc, pg 1019

NEBRASKA

ATV Research Inc, pg 793
Dog & Pony Productions Inc, pg 850
Video Service of America Inc (VSA), pg 1056

NEVADA

Aardvark Video & Media Productions, pg 772

NEW HAMPSHIRE

Optics 1 Inc, pg 964

NEW JERSEY

A-V Services Inc, pg 771
Audio Visual Dynamics®, pg 795
AV Bluebook, pg 797
Avtech Systems Inc, pg 800
Diversified Systems Inc, pg 849
Earl Girls Inc, pg 855
Euro-Pacific Film & Video Productions Inc, pg 863
G&G Technologies Inc, pg 875
Hamilton Buhl, pg 884
Herbach & Rademan Co Inc, pg 888
MCCOM Inc, pg 935
National Audio-Visual Supply, pg 952
PatchAmp, pg 970
Starlite Productions, pg 1024
Tele-Measurements Inc, pg 1035
Total Video Products Inc, pg 1042
VCom International Multimedia Corp, pg 1052
York Telecom, pg 1072

NEW YORK

Ace Video, pg 774
Adwar Video, pg 778
ALTEL Systems Inc, pg 783
American Video Inc, pg 785
Audio-Video Corp, pg 795
Audiovox, pg 796
AV Workshop, pg 797
B&H Photo & Video Pro Audio, pg 802
Bosch Security Systems North America, pg 811
Colortone Audio Visual, pg 832
Communication Corner Inc, pg 832
Design Audio Visual Inc, pg 845
General Audio-Visual Inc (GAVI), pg 876
Image Management Systems Inc, pg 895
KVL Audio Visual Services Inc, pg 914
Long Island Video Enterprises Live Inc, pg 924
Magnaplan Corp, pg 928
Markertek Video Supply, pg 931
Neptune Photo Inc, pg 954
Presentation Products Inc, pg 981
RNJ Electronics, pg 997
SmartSource Computer & AV Rentals, pg 1014
Technisphere Corp, pg 1034
TecNec Distributing, pg 1035
Videoguys, pg 1057
Visual Word Systems Inc, pg 1060

NORTH CAROLINA

Innocinema, pg 898
Strategic Connections, pg 1026

OHIO

Copp Integrated Systems, pg 836
ITA Audio Visual Solutions, pg 902
Jimmy Rea Electronics Inc, pg 992
Smithall Electronics Inc, pg 1014
Tri-State Audio Visual Co, pg 1044
Visual Products Inc, pg 1059

PENNSYLVANIA

Advanced AV, pg 777
Audio Visions Inc, pg 795
Audio Visual Communications Inc, pg 795
Brodart Co, pg 813
J E Foss Co, pg 871
Grise Audio Visual Center Inc, pg 882
The Lerro Corp, pg 919
Morefield Communications Inc, pg 946
Questar Corp, pg 989
Vistacom Inc, pg 1059
Visual Sound Inc, pg 1059

TENNESSEE

Lowrance Sound Co Inc, pg 925
Technical Support Systems LLC, pg 1034

TEXAS

Astro Audio Visual, pg 792
Audio Visual Technologies Group, pg 796
AVES Audio Visual Systems Inc, pg 798
CAM Audio Inc, pg 817
Data Display Audio Visual Co LP, pg 843
Data Projections Inc, pg 843
Digital Display Solutions Inc, pg 847
Heffernan Audio Visual, pg 887
Industrial Audio/Video Inc, pg 897
IVS Imaging, pg 903
Media Management LLC, pg 937
Precision Camera & Video, pg 980
Pro Video & Film Equipment Co Inc, pg 983
RadioShack Corp, pg 990
Replicopy Digital Media Center, pg 995
Schoolhouse Audio Visual, pg 1004
Tarpley Media Systems, pg 1032
Videotex Systems Inc, pg 1057

UTAH

RIA Corp, pg 996

VIRGINIA

Avitecture Inc, pg 799
Boitnott Visual Communications Corp (BVC), pg 810
Communications Specialists Inc, pg 833
Filmdex Inc, pg 867
Hoppmann Audio Visual, pg 891
Intellidyne LLC, pg 899
Quince Imaging Inc, pg 989
The Whitlock Group, pg 1065

WASHINGTON

Global Net Productions Inc, pg 879
Oppenheimer Camera Products, pg 964
ToteVision, pg 1042

WISCONSIN

Audio Visual of Milwaukee Inc, pg 795
Camera Corner Connecting Point, pg 818
Demco Inc, pg 845
Full Compass Systems, pg 874
Safe Harbor Computers, pg 1001

ALBERTA

Infosat Communications Inc, pg 898
Matrix Video Communications Corp (MVCC), pg 934
McBain Audio Visual Ltd, pg 935
Sharp's Audio-Visual Ltd, pg 1008

BRITISH COLUMBIA

ProVision Video Sales & Rentals Inc, pg 986

MANITOBA

Advance Pro, pg 777
Inland Audio Visual Ltd, pg 898

ONTARIO

Edcom Multimedia Products, pg 856
HD Source, pg 886
Henry's Camera, pg 888
Majortech Inc, pg 929
Nationwide Audio Visual Co, pg 953
Premier A/V Sales Ltd, pg 980
Westbury National Show Systems Ltd, pg 1064

QUEBEC

Panavideo Inc, pg 968

Video Receiver & Monitor Manufacturers

ARIZONA

Applied Integration Corp, pg 789

CALIFORNIA

Boland Communications, pg 810
Citizens Systems America Corp, pg 828
Hewlett-Packard Co, pg 888
Leader Instruments Corp, pg 917
Panasonic Broadcast & Digital Systems Co, pg 968
Physical Optics Corp, pg 975
SANYO Fisher Co, pg 1002
Sony Electronics Inc, pg 1016
Transvideo International, pg 1044
Zhone Technologies Inc, pg 1073

CONNECTICUT

Harman International Industries Inc, pg 885

FLORIDA

Compuvideo Sales USA Ltd, pg 834
Vela Research, pg 1052

ILLINOIS

Canvys™, pg 819
NEC Display Solutions of America, pg 954

MASSACHUSETTS

Elite Video, pg 859

MINNESOTA

Dotronix Technology Inc, pg 851

NEW HAMPSHIRE

Optics 1 Inc, pg 964

NEW JERSEY

Ikegami Electronics (USA) Inc, pg 894
JVC Professional Products Co, pg 907
Panasonic Consumer Electronics Co, pg 968
Sharp Electronics Corp, Professional Display Division, pg 1008

NEW YORK

Bosch Security Systems North America, pg 811
Hitachi Kokusai Electric America Ltd, pg 889
Vicon Industries Inc, pg 1053

NORTH CAROLINA

Crest Electronics Inc, pg 839

TENNESSEE

Adtec Digital Inc, pg 777

TEXAS

Contemporary Research, pg 835

VIRGINIA

Quince Imaging Inc, pg 989

WASHINGTON

Aiphone Corp, pg 779
ToteVision, pg 1042

BRITISH COLUMBIA

Triad Communications Ltd, pg 1044

ONTARIO

Evertz Microsystems Ltd, pg 863

Video Receiver & Monitor Rentals

ALABAMA

Audio-Video Resources Inc, pg 795

ARIZONA

Broadcast Rentals, pg 813
Creative Backstage, pg 838
Merestone, pg 938
Metropolitan Audio-Visual Inc, pg 940
Video West Inc, pg 1056

ARKANSAS

White Diamond Productions, pg 1065

CALIFORNIA

Aaron & Le Duc, pg 772
Action Audio & Visual, pg 775
Adolph Gasser Inc, pg 776
Advanced Media LLC, pg 778
Alliant Event Services, pg 781
Alternative Rentals, pg 783
Ametron Audio/Video, pg 785
Artichoke Productions, pg 791
AV Guys, pg 797
Best Bet Camera Rentals, pg 805
Bexel Corp, pg 806
Chater Camera Inc, pg 824
Cherry Multimedia, pg 824
Christy's Editorial, pg 826
Clean Slate Video, pg 829
Crystal Pyramid Productions™, pg 840
Deck Hand Inc, pg 844
Express Media Inc, pg 864
First Camera, pg 868
Flip 2 Media Inc, pg 870
Gear Monkey, pg 876
Gluskin's Custom Audio Video, pg 879
Gold Standard Productions, pg 880
Golden Gate Studios, pg 880
HD Cinema, pg 886
HDrental.com, pg 886
Image Integration, pg 895
Imagecraft Productions, pg 896
Impact Group, pg 897
JD Audio Visual Inc, pg 904
Lynch Communications, pg 926
Main Street Media Inc, pg 929
McCune Audio-Video-Lighting, pg 935
Media Fabricators Inc, pg 936
Munday & Collins AV, pg 950
Muse Presentation Technologies, pg 950
Otto Nemenz International Inc, pg 954
On-Trax Inc, pg 963
Pro HD Rentals, pg 983
The Producer's Loft, pg 983
Production Gear Rentals (PGR), pg 984
PSAV® Presentation Services, pg 986
Radiant Images, pg 990
RetinaVision Productions, pg 995
Shooting Star Video, pg 1009
Shoulder High Productions, pg 1009
Slate Media Group, pg 1013
SNAP, pg 1014
Stanislaus Audio Video Inc, pg 1023
Stray Angel Films, pg 1026
The Studios at Paramount, pg 1027
Synthesizer Rental Service, pg 1030
T-stop Inc, pg 1031
Total Media Group, pg 1042
Tri-Ed, pg 1044
Twin Peaks Creative, pg 1047
VER-Video Equipment Rentals, pg 1053
Video Gear Rentals Inc, pg 1055
Videofax, pg 1056
VMI Inc, pg 1060
Voice & Video Rentals, pg 1060
Westcoast Video Productions Inc, pg 1064

COLORADO

Daylight Productions & Rentals, pg 844
Multimedia Audio Visual Inc, pg 950
Spectrum Audio Visual Services, pg 1020
Tatum Video, pg 1032

CONNECTICUT

Fox Connecticut, pg 872
Videofilm Systems Inc, pg 1057

DELAWARE

Ken-Del Productions Inc, pg 909
Showorks Audio Visual Inc, pg 1010

DISTRICT OF COLUMBIA

Future View Inc, pg 874

FLORIDA

Access Media Group, pg 773
Allstar Audio Systems Inc, pg 782
AVI-SPL, pg 798
Budget Video Rentals, pg 815
Cinema East, pg 827
CopShopMiami.com, pg 836
Eastern Video, pg 856
Glanz Technologies Inc, pg 878
Gulf Coast Audio Visual Producers Inc, pg 883
Industrial Strength Inc, pg 897
Jordan Klein Film & Video (JKFV), pg 906
Knowles Video Inc (KVI), pg 912
Media Concepts Inc, pg 936
Midtown Video Inc, pg 942
Moving Picture, pg 947
Paradise Show & Design Inc, pg 969
Pro Stage Inc, pg 983
Sight & Sound Productions, pg 1010
Universal Studios Florida® Production Group, pg 1049

GEORGIA

Cine Photo Tech, pg 826
ECG Productions, pg 856
Lighting & Production Equipment Inc, pg 920
MAGNUM Companies Ltd, pg 929
ON Event Services, pg 963
See Production Services, pg 1006
Stage Front Presentation Systems, pg 1022

ILLINOIS

Allen Visual Systems Inc, pg 781
AV Chicago Inc, pg 797
Backstar Creative Media Inc, pg 801
Beatty TeleVisual Productions, pg 804
Chicago Satellite & Video, pg 825
Creative Technology, pg 838
Firehouse Studios, pg 868
LITE-IT Grip Truck Rentals, pg 923
Magnanimous Media, pg 928
On Site Video, pg 963
Product Productions, pg 984
QuickSet International Inc, pg 989
RC Communications, pg 992
2nd Cine, pg 1006
Show Department Inc, pg 1009
Staging Resources Inc, pg 1023
Tele-Time Systems, pg 1036
Woodside Avenue Music Productions Inc, pg 1069
Zacuto, pg 1073

INDIANA

Advanced Media Integration, pg 777

IOWA

Pro Video, pg 983

VIDEO

Video Receiver & Monitor Rentals (continued)

KANSAS

KAKE-TV, pg 907
Smith Audio-Visual Inc, pg 1014

KENTUCKY

Audio Visual Techniques Inc, pg 796
Idle Minds Productions Inc, pg 894

LOUISIANA

Clark Services Audio Visual & Exhibit Inc, pg 829
Digital FX Inc, pg 847
Pace Systems, pg 966

MAINE

Headlight Audio Visual Inc, pg 887

MARYLAND

Advance Audiovisual Presentation Ltd, pg 777
CPR MultiMedia Solutions, pg 837
Event Tech, pg 863
Hargrove Inc, pg 885

MASSACHUSETTS

AVFX Inc, pg 798
Camera Co Inc/Broadcast Divison, pg 818
Capron Lighting & Sound Co Inc, pg 819
Elite Video, pg 859
massAV, pg 933
Preston Productions Inc, pg 981

MICHIGAN

Digi Sign Design LLC, pg 847
K&R All Media Productions Inc, pg 908
On Stage Visuals, pg 963
TeL Systems, pg 1035

MINNESOTA

Alpha Video & Audio Inc, pg 782
Lights On, pg 921

MISSISSIPPI

Bowie Audio Visual Enterprises Inc, pg 811

MISSOURI

Communitronics Corp, pg 833
Production Support Services Inc, pg 985
Schiller's Audio-Visual, pg 1004
Show-Me Audio-Visual, pg 1009
Southwest Audio-Visual Inc, pg 1019
Switch, pg 1030

NEBRASKA

Dog & Pony Productions Inc, pg 850
Lights On Nebraska, pg 921

NEVADA

GES Audio Visual, pg 877
Lefco Video Services Inc, pg 918
MG Studio, pg 940

NEW HAMPSHIRE

Apertura, pg 788

NEW JERSEY

Audio Visual Dynamics®, pg 795
Earl Girls Inc, pg 855
Euro-Pacific Film & Video Productions Inc, pg 863
G&G Technologies Inc, pg 875
MB Productions, pg 934
PLS Staging, pg 977
Bill Quinn Productions, pg 989
Reider Photography & Video Productions, pg 994
Soundtracks Production Services LLC, pg 1018
Starlite Productions, pg 1024
Tele-Measurements Inc, pg 1035
Video Corporation of America (VCA), pg 1055

NEW YORK

Ace Video, pg 774
Adorama Rental Co, pg 776
Adwar Video, pg 778
American Video Inc, pg 785
AV Workshop, pg 797
Big Apple Films, pg 806
Bond Street Studio, pg 810
Cinema-Vision, pg 827
Colortone Audio Visual, pg 832
Communication Corner Inc, pg 832
CP Communications, pg 837
CPT Rental Inc, pg 837
Design Audio Visual Inc, pg 845
Gearhead Rentals, pg 876
Hand Held Films, pg 884
KVL Audio Visual Services Inc, pg 914
LightHouse Films, pg 920
Long Island Video Enterprises Live Inc, pg 924
Magnaplan Corp, pg 928
Manhattan Center Studios Inc, pg 930
MRG Productions Inc, pg 948
PrimaLux Video Inc, pg 982
SmartSource Computer & AV Rentals, pg 1014
Specialized Audio-Visual Inc, pg 1020
TBA Global Events, pg 1032
Technisphere Corp, pg 1034
Visual Word Systems Inc, pg 1060

NORTH CAROLINA

A&V Company, pg 772
All Pro Media Inc, pg 780
AV Metro Inc, pg 797
Duke Media Services, pg 853
Moving Pictures, pg 948
On Location North Carolina, pg 963
Special Event Services, pg 1020
Strategic Connections, pg 1026
Visual Aids Electronics of North Carolina Inc, pg 1059

NORTH DAKOTA

Media Productions, pg 937

OHIO

Hughie's Event Production Services, pg 892
ITA Audio Visual Solutions, pg 902
Lyon Video Inc, pg 927
Mills James Productions, pg 943
Ohio HD Video, pg 961
OSV Studios, pg 966
R&B Communications Inc, pg 991
Vista Color Imaging Inc, pg 1059

OKLAHOMA

PDC Productions, pg 970

OREGON

Koerner Camera Systems, pg 912

PENNSYLVANIA

Advanced AV, pg 777
Audio Visions Inc, pg 795
Audio Visual Communications Inc, pg 795
FMP Media Solutions Inc, pg 870
Fusion Brand Experiences, pg 874
Grise Audio Visual Center Inc, pg 882
New York Camera & Video, pg 956
Upstage Video, pg 1050
The Videohouse Inc, pg 1057
Viewpoint Production Services Inc, pg 1058
Visual Sound Inc, pg 1059

SOUTH CAROLINA

Sound & Images Inc, pg 1016

TENNESSEE

Nashville Production Rentals (NPR), pg 952
RentACamera.com, pg 995
Technical Support Systems LLC, pg 1034

TEXAS

Alford Media Services, pg 780
Astro Audio Visual, pg 792
Audio Visual Technologies Group, pg 796
Big House Sound Inc, pg 807
Bright Star Productions Inc, pg 812
Data Display Audio Visual Co LP, pg 843
Digital Display Solutions Inc, pg 847
FitzCo Sound Inc, pg 869
Heffernan Audio Visual, pg 887
Industrial Audio/Video Inc, pg 897
Media Event Concepts Inc, pg 936
The Samuels Co, pg 1002
Stage Directions, pg 1022
Texcam Inc, pg 1038

UTAH

Ron Hill Imagery, pg 889

VERMONT

Dark Star Lighting & Production, pg 842

VIRGINIA

Boitnott Visual Communications Corp (BVC), pg 810
Creative Video of Washington Inc, pg 839
Quince Imaging Inc, pg 989

WASHINGTON

Kostov Productions, pg 913
Oppenheimer Camera Products, pg 964
Victory Studios, pg 1054

WISCONSIN

Audio Visual of Milwaukee Inc, pg 795
Camera Corner Connecting Point, pg 818
Event Essentials, pg 863
Full Compass Systems, pg 874

WYOMING

Bridger Productions Inc, pg 812

PUERTO RICO

Stage Crew Audiovisual Inc, pg 1022

ALBERTA

Cine Audio Visual Sales & Service Ltd, pg 826
Global Television Station, pg 879
Matrix Video Communications Corp (MVCC), pg 934
Sharp's Audio-Visual Ltd, pg 1008
Unique Communications Ltd, pg 1048

BRITISH COLUMBIA

Clark's Audio Visual Services Ltd, pg 829
Commercial Electronics Ltd, pg 832
Finale Editworks, pg 868
Video In Studios/Video Out Distribution, pg 1055

MANITOBA

Inland Audio Visual Ltd, pg 898

ONTARIO

Edcom Multimedia Products, pg 856
HD Source, pg 886
JIB Shots Equipment Inc, pg 905
Metalworks Recording Studios Inc, pg 939
MVI Multivision Inc, pg 951
RB Productions, pg 992
SIM Digital, pg 1011
Westbury National Show Systems Ltd, pg 1064
ZTV Broadcast Services Inc, pg 1074

QUEBEC

Audio Visual Dynamics Ltd, pg 795
Panavideo Inc, pg 968

Video Receiver & Monitor Repairs

CALIFORNIA

Advanced Media LLC, pg 778
Ametron Audio/Video, pg 785
Band Pro Film & Digital Inc, pg 802
BroadcastStore.com, pg 813
Christy's Editorial, pg 826
Gluskin's Custom Audio Video, pg 879
HM Electronics Inc (HME), pg 889
McAlister Electronics, pg 935
Metro Video Systems Inc, pg 940
SSL Industries Inc, pg 1022
Technical Services, pg 1034
TEK Media Group, pg 1035
Transvideo International, pg 1044
Tri-Ed, pg 1044
VMI Inc, pg 1060

FLORIDA

Digital Video Systems Inc, pg 848
ELC Sales & Service Inc, pg 858
Glanz Technologies Inc, pg 878

Video Recorder & Player Distributors

VIDEO

Video Recorder & Player Distributors (continued)

MISSOURI (continued)

Production Support Services Inc, pg 985
Southwest Audio-Visual Inc, pg 1019

NEBRASKA

ATV Research Inc, pg 793
Video Service of America Inc (VSA), pg 1056

NEVADA

Aardvark Video & Media Productions, pg 772

NEW JERSEY

A-V Services Inc, pg 771
Alltec Stores, a Vcom IMC Company, pg 782
Audio Visual Dynamics®, pg 795
AV Bluebook, pg 797
Diversified Systems Inc, pg 849
Earl Girls Inc, pg 855
Euro-Pacific Film & Video Productions Inc, pg 863
G&G Technologies Inc, pg 875
Hamilton Buhl, pg 884
Herbach & Rademan Co Inc, pg 888
MCCOM Inc, pg 935
PatchAmp, pg 970
Starlite Productions, pg 1024
SYMCO Inc, pg 1030
Tele-Measurements Inc, pg 1035
Total Video Products Inc, pg 1042
Turner Engineering Inc, pg 1046
VCom International Multimedia Corp, pg 1052
Video Corporation of America (VCA), pg 1055
York Telecom, pg 1072

NEW YORK

Adwar Video, pg 778
ALTEL Systems Inc, pg 783
American Video Inc, pg 785
Audio-Video Corp, pg 795
Audiovox, pg 796
AV Workshop, pg 797
B&H Photo & Video Pro Audio, pg 802
Bosch Security Systems North America, pg 811
Colortone Audio Visual, pg 832
Communication Corner Inc, pg 832
Design Audio Visual Inc, pg 845
Flash Electronics Inc, pg 869
General Audio-Visual Inc (GAVI), pg 876
HAVE Inc, pg 886
Image Management Systems Inc, pg 895
Langie Audio Visual Systems, pg 915
Long Island Video Enterprises Live Inc, pg 924
Magnaplan Corp, pg 928
Markertek Video Supply, pg 931
Saul Mineroff Electronics Inc, pg 943
Neptune Photo Inc, pg 954
Presentation Products Inc, pg 981
Ray Supply Inc, pg 992
RNJ Electronics, pg 997
Technisphere Corp, pg 1034
TecNec Distributing, pg 1035
Videoguys, pg 1057
Visual Technologies Corp, pg 1060
Visual Word Systems Inc, pg 1060
Willoughby's Imaging Center, pg 1067

NORTH CAROLINA

Camcor Inc, pg 818
Carolina Biological Supply Co, pg 820
Strategic Connections, pg 1026

OHIO

Audio Visual Media, pg 795
Copp Integrated Systems, pg 836
ITA Audio Visual Solutions, pg 902
iVideo Technologies, pg 903
Jimmy Rea Electronics Inc, pg 992
Smithall Electronics Inc, pg 1014
Tri-State Audio Visual Co, pg 1044

OREGON

ClearOne MagicBox Inc, pg 830
Spectrum Systems Design, pg 1021

PENNSYLVANIA

Advanced AV, pg 777
Audio Visual Communications Inc, pg 795
Bernie's Photo Center, pg 805
J E Foss Co, pg 871
Grise Audio Visual Center Inc, pg 882
Hite Co, pg 889
The Lerro Corp, pg 919
Morefield Communications Inc, pg 946
Questar Corp, pg 989
Vistacom Inc, pg 1059
Visual Sound Inc, pg 1059
Wespen Audio Visual Co, pg 1063

RHODE ISLAND

Custom Computer Specialists Inc, pg 841
Shanix Inc, pg 1008

TENNESSEE

Continental Film, pg 835
Lowrance Sound Co Inc, pg 925
Memphis Communications Corp, pg 938
Technical Support Systems LLC, pg 1034

TEXAS

Astro Audio Visual, pg 792
Audio Visual Technologies Group, pg 796
AVES Audio Visual Systems Inc, pg 798
Biway Media, pg 808
CAM Audio Inc, pg 817
Data Display Audio Visual Co LP, pg 843
Data Projections Inc, pg 843
Digital Display Solutions Inc, pg 847
Heffernan Audio Visual, pg 887
IVS Imaging, pg 903
J&S Audio Visual Inc, pg 904
Media Management LLC, pg 937
Pro Video & Film Equipment Co Inc, pg 983
RadioShack Corp, pg 990
Replicopy Digital Media Center, pg 995
Schoolhouse Audio Visual, pg 1004
TapeWorks Texas Inc, pg 1032
Tarpley Media Systems, pg 1032
Videotex Systems Inc, pg 1057

UTAH

RIA Corp, pg 996
TV Specialists Inc, pg 1046
Webb Audio Visual Communication, pg 1063

VIRGINIA

Avitecture Inc, pg 799
Boitnott Visual Communications Corp (BVC), pg 810
Communications Specialists Inc, pg 833
Filmdex Inc, pg 867
Hoppmann Audio Visual, pg 891
Intellidyne LLC, pg 899
Metropolitan Audio Visual Co LLC, pg 940
Quince Imaging Inc, pg 989
StageSound, pg 1023
The Whitlock Group, pg 1065

WASHINGTON

Global Net Productions Inc, pg 879
Inland Audio Visual Co, pg 898
Oppenheimer Camera Products, pg 964

WISCONSIN

Audio Visual of Milwaukee Inc, pg 795
Camera Corner Connecting Point, pg 818
Demco Inc, pg 845
Full Compass Systems, pg 874
Safe Harbor Computers, pg 1001

PUERTO RICO

Bonnin Electronics Inc, pg 810

ALBERTA

Matrix Video Communications Corp (MVCC), pg 934
McBain Audio Visual Ltd, pg 935
Sharp's Audio-Visual Ltd, pg 1008

BRITISH COLUMBIA

ProVision Video Sales & Rentals Inc, pg 986
Triad Communications Ltd, pg 1044

MANITOBA

Advance Pro, pg 777
Inland Audio Visual Ltd, pg 898

ONTARIO

Cinema Stage Inc, pg 827
Drastic Technologies Ltd, pg 852
Edcom Multimedia Products, pg 856
HD Source, pg 886
Majortech Inc, pg 929
Nationwide Audio Visual Co, pg 953
Premier A/V Sales Ltd, pg 980
Westbury National Show Systems Ltd, pg 1064

QUEBEC

AVS Technologies Inc, pg 800
Panavideo Inc, pg 968

Video Recorder & Player Manufacturers

ARIZONA

Applied Integration Corp, pg 789

CALIFORNIA

Ampex Data Systems Corp, pg 785
Doremi Labs, pg 851
FutureVideo, pg 874
ODC Nimbus Inc, pg 961
Panasonic Broadcast & Digital Systems Co, pg 968
Panasonic Professional Audio Systems, pg 968
Simon - Kaloi Engineering, pg 1011
Sony Electronics Inc, pg 1016
VITEC Multimedia, pg 1060

CONNECTICUT

Video Automation Systems Inc, pg 1054

FLORIDA

Cobham Tactical Communications & Surveillance, pg 831

MICHIGAN

Leightronix Inc, pg 918

NEW JERSEY

Emerson Radio Corp, pg 860
JVC Professional Products Co, pg 907
Konica Minolta Business Solutions, pg 913
Panasonic Consumer Electronics Co, pg 968
Starlite Productions, pg 1024

NEW YORK

Bosch Security Systems North America, pg 811
Hitachi Kokusai Electric America Ltd, pg 889

NORTH CAROLINA

Crest Electronics Inc, pg 839

OREGON

ClearOne MagicBox Inc, pg 830

TENNESSEE

Adtec Digital Inc, pg 777

VIRGINIA

Quince Imaging Inc, pg 989

BRITISH COLUMBIA

Triad Communications Ltd, pg 1044

ONTARIO

Drastic Technologies Ltd, pg 852

Video Recorder & Player Rentals

ALABAMA

Audio-Video Resources Inc, pg 795

ARIZONA

Audio Video Resources, pg 795
Broadcast Rentals, pg 813

VIDEO

Video Recorder & Player Rentals (continued)

NEW YORK (continued)

Visual Word Systems Inc, pg 1060
WNET/NET TELECON, pg 1069
WorldStage, pg 1070

NORTH CAROLINA

A&V Company, pg 772
All Pro Media Inc, pg 780
AV Metro Inc, pg 797
Camcor Inc, pg 818
The Communications Group Inc, pg 833
Duke Media Services, pg 853
Moving Pictures, pg 948
On Location North Carolina, pg 963
Special Event Services, pg 1020
Strategic Connections, pg 1026
Take One Productions Ltd, pg 1031
Trailblazer Studios®, pg 1043
Visual Aids Electronics of North Carolina Inc, pg 1059

NORTH DAKOTA

Media Productions, pg 937

OHIO

Audio Visual Media, pg 795
CET, pg 823
Hughie's Event Production Services, pg 892
ITA Audio Visual Solutions, pg 902
iVideo Technologies, pg 903
Lyon Video Inc, pg 927
Mills James Productions, pg 943
Ohio HD Video, pg 961
R&B Communications Inc, pg 991
Vista Color Imaging Inc, pg 1059

OKLAHOMA

PDC Productions, pg 970

OREGON

BingoLewis, pg 807
Northwest Film Center, pg 959
Picture This Production Services, pg 975

PENNSYLVANIA

Advanced AV, pg 777
Audio Visions Inc, pg 795
Audio Visual Communications Inc, pg 795
FMP Media Solutions Inc, pg 870
Fusion Brand Experiences, pg 874
Grise Audio Visual Center Inc, pg 882
JPL, pg 906
Muderick Media, pg 949
New York Camera & Video, pg 956
North Star Satellite Communications Inc, pg 959
Producers Management Television (PMTV), pg 983
Upstage Video, pg 1050
The Videohouse Inc, pg 1057
Videosmith Inc, pg 1057
Visual Sound Inc, pg 1059

TENNESSEE

Memphis Communications Corp, pg 938
Russ Sturgeon Productions/RSVP, pg 1027
Technical Support Systems LLC, pg 1034
Tennessee Visual Service Co, pg 1037

TEXAS

Alford Media Services, pg 780
Astro Audio Visual, pg 792
Audio Visual Technologies Group, pg 796
Bright Star Productions Inc, pg 812
Data Display Audio Visual Co LP, pg 843
Digital Display Solutions Inc, pg 847
FitzCo Sound Inc, pg 869
Heffernan Audio Visual, pg 887
J&S Audio Visual Inc, pg 904
Media Event Concepts Inc, pg 936
Earl Miller Productions Inc, pg 943
The Samuels Co, pg 1002
South Coast Film & Video, pg 1019
Stage Directions, pg 1022
Texcam Inc, pg 1038

UTAH

TV Specialists Inc, pg 1046
Webb Audio Visual Communication, pg 1063

VERMONT

Marlboro Film & Video Productions, pg 931

VIRGINIA

Advance Concepts Inc, pg 777
Audio Visual Actions Inc (AVA), pg 795
Boitnott Visual Communications Corp (BVC), pg 810
Creative Video of Washington Inc, pg 839
D&B Television & Video Productions Inc, pg 842
Lee Hartman & Sons Inc, pg 918
Metropolitan Audio Visual Co LLC, pg 940
Projection Presentation Technology, pg 985
Quince Imaging Inc, pg 989
Rainbow Rentals, pg 991
The Whitlock Group, pg 1065

WASHINGTON

Inland Audio Visual Co, pg 898
Intermedia Inc, pg 900
Kostov Productions, pg 913
Oppenheimer Camera Products, pg 964
Victory Studios, pg 1054

WISCONSIN

Audio Visual of Milwaukee Inc, pg 795
Camera Corner Connecting Point, pg 818
Event Essentials, pg 863
Full Compass Systems, pg 874
University of Wisconsin-Oshkosh Radio-TV-Film Dept, pg 1050
USAV Group Inc, pg 1050
Wisconsin Public Television, pg 1068

WYOMING

Bridger Productions Inc, pg 812

PUERTO RICO

Stage Crew Audiovisual Inc, pg 1022

ALBERTA

Cine Audio Visual Sales & Service Ltd, pg 826
Global Television Station, pg 879
Matrix Video Communications Corp (MVCC), pg 934
Sharp's Audio-Visual Ltd, pg 1008
Unique Communications Ltd, pg 1048

BRITISH COLUMBIA

Clark's Audio Visual Services Ltd, pg 829
Commercial Electronics Ltd, pg 832
Finale Editworks, pg 868
ProVision Video Sales & Rentals Inc, pg 986
Video In Studios/Video Out Distribution, pg 1055

MANITOBA

Inland Audio Visual Ltd, pg 898

ONTARIO

Edcom Multimedia Products, pg 856
HD Source, pg 886
JIB Shots Equipment Inc, pg 905
MVI Multivision Inc, pg 951
Wanted! Sound + Picture, pg 1062
Westbury National Show Systems Ltd, pg 1064

QUEBEC

Audio Visual Dynamics Ltd, pg 795
AVW-TELAV Audio Visual Solutions, a Freeman Company, pg 800
Group PVP, pg 882
Kerrigan Productions Inc, pg 910
Panavideo Inc, pg 968

Video Recorder & Player Repairs

CALIFORNIA

Advanced Media LLC, pg 778
Advanced Systems Group LLC, pg 778
Ametron Audio/Video, pg 785
Band Pro Film & Digital Inc, pg 802
BroadcastStore.com, pg 813
Gluskin's Custom Audio Video, pg 879
Instructional Materials & Equipment Distributors (I-Med), pg 899
McAlister Electronics, pg 935
Metro Video Systems Inc, pg 940
Mobilized Tech Systems, pg 944
Pro Camera Repair, pg 982
SSL Industries Inc, pg 1022
Technical Services, pg 1034
Tri-Ed, pg 1044
VMI Inc, pg 1060

COLORADO

Ceavco Audio/Visual Co, pg 822

CONNECTICUT

A/V Davey, pg 797
Rockwell Communications Inc, pg 998
Video Automation Systems Inc, pg 1054

FLORIDA

Access Media Group, pg 773
Digital Video Systems Inc, pg 848
ELC Sales & Service Inc, pg 858
Glanz Technologies Inc, pg 878
Hi-Tech Enterprises Inc, pg 888
Media Concepts Inc, pg 936
Midtown Video Inc, pg 942
TAI Audio, pg 1031
Tallahassee Audio Visual, pg 1031

GEORGIA

Audio Visual Resources Inc, pg 795
Stage Front Presentation Systems, pg 1022
Technical Innovation, pg 1033

ILLINOIS

Allen Visual Systems Inc, pg 781
Beatty TeleVisual Productions, pg 804
Central Audio-Visual Equipment Inc, pg 823
Midwest Digital Corp, pg 942
On Site Video, pg 963
Tele-Time Systems, pg 1036

KENTUCKY

Axxis Inc, pg 800
Barney Miller's Inc, pg 943
NOR-COM Inc, pg 958

MARYLAND

RTZ Audio Visual, pg 1000
Strauss Photo Technical Service Inc, pg 1026

MASSACHUSETTS

Antronics Inc, pg 787
Camera Co Inc/Broadcast Divison, pg 818

MICHIGAN

Olson Anderson Co, pg 786
TeL Systems, pg 1035

MINNESOTA

Alpha Video & Audio Inc, pg 782
AVI Systems, pg 799

MISSOURI

Schiller's Audio-Visual, pg 1004
Southwest Audio-Visual Inc, pg 1019

NEW JERSEY

G&G Technologies Inc, pg 875
Konica Minolta Business Solutions, pg 913

NEW YORK

Adwar Video, pg 778
American Video Inc, pg 785
Colortone Audio Visual, pg 832
Langie Audio Visual Systems, pg 915
MRG Productions Inc, pg 948
Ray Supply Inc, pg 992
Technisphere Corp, pg 1034

NORTH CAROLINA

Camcor Inc, pg 818
Strategic Connections, pg 1026

OHIO

Audio Visual Media, pg 795
Copp Integrated Systems, pg 836
ITA Audio Visual Solutions, pg 902
iVideo Technologies, pg 903
Tri-State Audio Visual Co, pg 1044

PENNSYLVANIA

Bernie's Photo Center, pg 805
J E Foss Co, pg 871
Visual Sound Inc, pg 1059
Wespen Audio Visual Co, pg 1063

RHODE ISLAND

Custom Computer Specialists Inc, pg 841

TENNESSEE

Memphis Communications Corp, pg 938
Technical Support Systems LLC, pg 1034
Tennessee Visual Service Co, pg 1037

TEXAS

Astro Audio Visual, pg 792
Audio Visual Technologies Group, pg 796
Data Display Audio Visual Co LP, pg 843
Heffernan Audio Visual, pg 887
Industrial Audio/Video Inc, pg 897
Pro Video & Film Equipment Co Inc, pg 983
Tarpley Media Systems, pg 1032

UTAH

RIA Corp, pg 996
TV Specialists Inc, pg 1046

VIRGINIA

Avitecture Inc, pg 799
Boitnott Visual Communications Corp (BVC), pg 810
Hoppmann Audio Visual, pg 891
Lee Hartman & Sons Inc, pg 918
Metropolitan Audio Visual Co LLC, pg 940
The Whitlock Group, pg 1065

WASHINGTON

Inland Audio Visual Co, pg 898

WISCONSIN

Camera Corner Connecting Point, pg 818
Full Compass Systems, pg 874

PUERTO RICO

Bonnin Electronics Inc, pg 810

ALBERTA

Matrix Video Communications Corp (MVCC), pg 934
Sharp's Audio-Visual Ltd, pg 1008

BRITISH COLUMBIA

Commercial Electronics Ltd, pg 832

MANITOBA

Inland Audio Visual Ltd, pg 898

ONTARIO

Edcom Multimedia Products, pg 856
HD Source, pg 886
MVI Multivision Inc, pg 951
Westbury National Show Systems Ltd, pg 1064

QUEBEC

Panavideo Inc, pg 968

Video Standards Conversion

ARIZONA

Merestone, pg 938
Metropolitan Audio-Visual Inc, pg 940
On-Site Video, pg 963
Star Video Duplicating, pg 1024
Video Media Productions (VMP), pg 1055
Video West Inc, pg 1056

ARKANSAS

Shadowbox Video Productions, pg 1007
White Diamond Productions, pg 1065

CALIFORNIA

Access Video in Berkeley, pg 773
Action Video, pg 775
Adolph Gasser Inc, pg 776
Advanced Media LLC, pg 778
AGF Media Services, pg 778
All Video Productions, pg 781
ALOM Technologies Corp, pg 782
Artichoke Productions, pg 791
Custom Video Productions Inc, pg 841
Digital Jungle, pg 847
Digital Media West, pg 847
Dogma Studios, pg 850
Express Media Inc, pg 864
Film Technology Co Inc, pg 867
Full Moon & High Tide Productions & Studios, pg 874
FXF Productions Inc, pg 874
iCorpTv, pg 893
ITV Productions, pg 903
JDS Video & Media Productions Inc, pg 904
The Kitchen, pg 911
McCune Audio-Video-Lighting, pg 935
Method Studios, pg 939
Mind Over Eye Inc, pg 943
Penrose Productions, pg 972
Peterson's Video Transfer Services, pg 973
Point 360, pg 978
QRS Software Services, pg 988
Reel Picture, pg 994
RetinaVision Productions, pg 995
Roundabout Entertainment Inc, pg 1000
Rovi Corp, pg 1000
SF Global Sourcing, pg 1007
Shapeshifter, pg 1008
SNAP, pg 1014
SonicPool, pg 1016
Total Media Group, pg 1042
Video Movie Magic, pg 1056
VMI Inc, pg 1060

COLORADO

Daylight Productions & Rentals, pg 844
Flashback Media Productions, pg 869
Old Army Press (OAP), pg 961
Rocky Mountain Audio/Video Productions Inc, pg 998

CONNECTICUT

Concord Communications, pg 835
Digital Video Productions, pg 848
Guymark Studios LLC, pg 883
Ironik Design & Post, pg 902
Video Design Group, pg 1055
Video Production Associates Inc, pg 1056

DISTRICT OF COLUMBIA

Interface Media Group, pg 900

FLORIDA

Access Media Group, pg 773
Accord Productions, pg 773
Allegro Productions Inc, pg 781
Cinema East, pg 827
Communications Concepts Inc (CCI), pg 833
Easy Edit Video Inc, pg 856
Ed Ethridge Productions Inc, pg 863
Florida Digital Studios, pg 870
Gulf Coast Audio Visual Producers Inc, pg 883
Hi-Tech Enterprises Inc, pg 888
Media Concepts Inc, pg 936
RLX Media LLC, pg 997
Sunrise Studios, pg 1028
Video Techniques Inc, pg 1056

GEORGIA

Crawford Media Services, pg 838
Guerrilla Productions LLC, pg 883
ON Event Services, pg 963
Video Copy Services Inc, pg 1055
Visioneering International Inc, pg 1058

ILLINOIS

ABSA Productions Inc, pg 772
Analog Free Media, pg 786
Backstar Creative Media Inc, pg 801
Chicago Satellite & Video, pg 825
International Historic Films Inc, pg 901
Major Media Inc, pg 929
The Pepper Group, pg 972
RADMAR Inc, pg 990
Televersions, pg 1036
20/20 Communications Inc, pg 1047
Video Impressions, pg 1055

INDIANA

Advanced Media Integration, pg 777

IOWA

Duplication Media, pg 853

KENTUCKY

Audio Visual Techniques Inc, pg 796

LOUISIANA

Digital FX Inc, pg 847

MARYLAND

CPR MultiMedia Solutions, pg 837
Pro Cuts Editing Services, pg 982
Quality Film & Video, pg 988
Saah Video, pg 1001
Strauss Photo Technical Service Inc, pg 1026
Video Labs, pg 1055

MASSACHUSETTS

Cramer Productions, pg 837
Extreme Reach Inc, pg 864
Inter-Media Electronics, pg 899
Veritech Corp, pg 1053
Video Express, pg 1055

MICHIGAN

Digi Sign Design LLC, pg 847
Encore Home Video, pg 861
K&R's Recording Studios Inc, pg 908
TGA Recording Co, pg 1038
The Transfer Zone®, pg 1043

MINNESOTA

The ADS Group, pg 777
Aggressive Records Audio Duplication LLC, pg 778
Rum Jungle Media, pg 1000

MISSOURI

Audio-VideoGraphics Inc, pg 795
Schiller's Audio-Visual, pg 1004
VSG Digital Media Solutions, pg 1061

NEVADA

Aardvark Video & Media Productions, pg 772
Encore Productions Inc, pg 861
JCS Video Productions, pg 904
21st Century Video Productions, pg 1047

NEW HAMPSHIRE

Channell One Video, pg 824
Chip Taylor Communications LLC, pg 1032

NEW JERSEY

Broadcast Center Studios, pg 813
CFP Video Productions Inc, pg 823
Deluxe Media Services, pg 845
Euro-Pacific Film & Video Productions Inc, pg 863
Hogpenny Studios, pg 890
Laurel Video Productions, pg 916
Midnight Media Group Inc, pg 942
NFL Films Music Library, pg 957
Reider Photography & Video Productions, pg 994
Starlite Productions, pg 1024
Suede Interactive, pg 1027
VCSvideo, pg 1052
VTS Video & Media, pg 1061

NEW YORK

Ace Video, pg 774
Adwar Video, pg 778
Associated Press Television News, pg 792
aurora productions, pg 797
Chromavision Corp, pg 826
CMI Media Management, pg 830
Communication Corner Inc, pg 832
Design Audio Visual Inc, pg 845
DuArt, pg 853
Duplication Depot Inc, pg 853

VIDEO

Video Standards Conversion (continued)

NEW YORK (continued)

Duplication Specialists Inc, pg 853
Eastco Multimedia Solutions Inc, pg 856
Elite Video & Photography Services Inc, pg 859
HAVE Inc, pg 886
Hello World Communications, pg 888
International Digital Centre, pg 901
J & D Laboratories Inc, pg 903
Long Island Video Enterprises Live Inc, pg 924
Magno Sound & Video, pg 929
Neal Marshad Productions, pg 931
Mood Creations Ltd, pg 946
Shelly Palmer Production, pg 968
PostWorks, pg 979
Rafik, pg 990
Teatown Communications Group, pg 1033
Technisphere Corp, pg 1034
TeleTime Productions, pg 1036
Tobin Productions Inc, pg 1041
USA Studios, pg 1050
VIEW Inc (Video International Entertainment World Inc), pg 1058
Visual Technologies Corp, pg 1060
Visual Word Systems Inc, pg 1060
WTL Productions, pg 1071
Zelman Studios Ltd, pg 1073

NORTH CAROLINA

A&V Company, pg 772
Camcor Inc, pg 818
Duke Media Services, pg 853
Franklin Video Inc, pg 872
Moving Pictures, pg 948
Take One Productions Ltd, pg 1031

NORTH DAKOTA

Media Productions, pg 937

OHIO

Aztec Video Productions, pg 801
Curtis Inc, pg 841
EDR Media LLC, pg 857
Lyon Video Inc, pg 927
Mills James Productions, pg 943
Promedia Digital, pg 986
Take 1 Media Services, pg 1031

OKLAHOMA

Garman Productions LLC, pg 875

OREGON

BingoLewis, pg 807

PENNSYLVANIA

Audio Visions Inc, pg 795
Audio Visual Communications Inc, pg 795
Bernie's Photo Center, pg 805
FMP Media Solutions Inc, pg 870
Innovision Media Group, pg 899
JPL, pg 906
Laser Video Corp, pg 916
Panta Rhei Media Inc, pg 968
The Videohouse Inc, pg 1057
Visual Sound Inc, pg 1059

RHODE ISLAND

A&M Productions, pg 771

SOUTH CAROLINA

American Production Services LLC, pg 785

TENNESSEE

Continental Film, pg 835
Motion Picture Services, pg 947
Stage Post, pg 1022

TEXAS

Astro Audio Visual, pg 792
CEV Multimedia Ltd, pg 823
Dub King, pg 853
The Editing Co, pg 857
Horizon Film + Video Productions, pg 891
McNee Productions Inc, pg 935
Mediaforce Productions, pg 937
Julye Newlin Productions Inc, pg 956
Replicopy Digital Media Center, pg 995
The Samuels Co, pg 1002

UTAH

ImageWorks Communications, pg 896

VIRGINIA

Gingerbread Productions, pg 878
Shakticom, pg 1008

WASHINGTON

Bennett-Watt HD Productions Inc, pg 805
Pro Image, pg 983
Victory Studios, pg 1054

WEST VIRGINIA

Blackwater Video Productions, pg 808

WISCONSIN

Audio Visual of Milwaukee Inc, pg 795
AVS Group, pg 800
Media Communications Association-International (MCA-I), pg 936

WYOMING

Bridger Productions Inc, pg 812

ALBERTA

Cine Audio Visual Sales & Service Ltd, pg 826

BRITISH COLUMBIA

Commercial Electronics Ltd, pg 832
Finale Editworks, pg 868
Triad Communications Ltd, pg 1044
24 Frames Film & Video, pg 1047

NEWFOUNDLAND AND LABRADOR

Vidcraft Productions Ltd, pg 1054

ONTARIO

Edcom Multimedia Products, pg 856
Image Video Services & Productions, pg 895
Purefire Communications Inc, pg 987

QUEBEC

Group PVP, pg 882

SASKATCHEWAN

Thomega Entertainment Inc, pg 1039

Video Switcher Distributors

ALABAMA

PESA, pg 973

ARIZONA

ATCi (Antenna Technology Communication Solutions Inc), pg 793
EAR Professional Audio/Video, pg 855

ARKANSAS

Jay S Stanley & Associates Inc, pg 1023

CALIFORNIA

Addlogix, pg 776
Adolph Gasser Inc, pg 776
Advanced Systems Group LLC, pg 778
Ametron Audio/Video, pg 785
Audio/Video Supply Inc, pg 795
AV Conferencing, pg 797
Be Media, pg 804
BroadcastStore.com, pg 813
Cibola Systems, pg 826
Delicate Electronics Sales Inc, pg 845
FXC Communications, pg 874
Gearhouse Broadcast LLC, pg 876
Instructional Materials & Equipment Distributors (I-Med), pg 899
JD Audio Visual Inc, pg 904
Linear LLC, pg 922
Media Control Systems LLC, pg 936
Mobilized Tech Systems, pg 944
POP TV, pg 978
Promax Systems, pg 986
SNAP, pg 1014
Snell, pg 1014
Southern California Sound Image Inc, pg 1019
SSL Industries Inc, pg 1022
Stanislaus Audio Video Inc, pg 1023
Tri-Ed, pg 1044
Videobotics, pg 1056
VMI Inc, pg 1060

COLORADO

Spectrum Audio Visual Services, pg 1020

CONNECTICUT

Everett Hall Associates Inc, pg 863
Video Automation Systems Inc, pg 1054

FLORIDA

Access Media Group, pg 773
Allstar Audio Systems Inc, pg 782
A2D Solutions Inc, pg 793
AVI-SPL, pg 798
BAI Distributors Inc, pg 801
Digital Video Systems Inc, pg 848
Encore Broadcast Solutions, pg 860
General Projection Systems Inc, pg 877
Glanz Technologies Inc, pg 878
Griffiths Broadcast Co Inc, pg 882
Gulf Coast Audio Visual Producers Inc, pg 883
Hi-Tech Enterprises Inc, pg 888
Hunter Electronics LLC, pg 892
Media Concepts Inc, pg 936
Midtown Video Inc, pg 942
Multicom Inc, pg 949
Pro Stage Inc, pg 983
Sight & Sound Productions, pg 1010
Videoscope, pg 1057

GEORGIA

Baker Audio Inc, pg 801
Barco Inc, pg 803
Clark, pg 829
Outsource Engineering & Manufacturing Inc dba Texscan MSI, pg 966
Simtrol Inc, pg 1011
Stage Front Presentation Systems, pg 1022

ILLINOIS

Allen Visual Systems Inc, pg 781
Dukane Corp, Audio Visual Products Division, pg 853
Joseph Electronics, pg 906
Quintessence Audio Ltd, pg 989
RAM Systems LLC, pg 991

INDIANA

Lee Co Inc, pg 918
Sensory Technologies LLC, pg 1006
SHP Electronics, pg 1010

KANSAS

Smith Audio-Visual Inc, pg 1014

KENTUCKY

Axxis Inc, pg 800
Barney Miller's Inc, pg 943
NOR-COM Inc, pg 958

LOUISIANA

Intermedia Technologies, pg 900

MARYLAND

Human Circuit, pg 892
Noventri, pg 960
Wiltronix, pg 1067

MASSACHUSETTS

Rule Broadcast Systems, pg 1000

MICHIGAN

Ascom Communications Contractors, pg 791
On Stage Visuals, pg 963

MINNESOTA

Alpha Video & Audio Inc, pg 782

MISSISSIPPI

Bowie Audio Visual Enterprises Inc, pg 811

MISSOURI

Communitronics Corp, pg 833
Conference Technologies Inc, pg 835
MIS Technologies, pg 944
Southwest Audio-Visual Inc, pg 1019

NEBRASKA

ATV Research Inc, pg 793
Video Service of America Inc (VSA), pg 1056

NEVADA

Aardvark Video & Media Productions, pg 772

NEW JERSEY

A-V Services Inc, pg 771
Alltec Stores, a Vcom IMC Company, pg 782
Avtech Systems Inc, pg 800
Diversified Systems Inc, pg 849
Earl Girls Inc, pg 855
Euro-Pacific Film & Video Productions Inc, pg 863
G&G Technologies Inc, pg 875
Hamilton Buhl, pg 884
Herbach & Rademan Co Inc, pg 888
MCCOM Inc, pg 935
MIB Mediaworks, pg 941
National Audio-Visual Supply, pg 952
PatchAmp, pg 970
Starlite Productions, pg 1024
SYMCO Inc, pg 1030
Tele-Measurements Inc, pg 1035
Total Video Products Inc, pg 1042
Varto Technologies, pg 1052
York Telecom, pg 1072

NEW YORK

ALTEL Systems Inc, pg 783
Audio-Video Corp, pg 795
AV Workshop, pg 797
B&H Photo & Video Pro Audio, pg 802
Bosch Security Systems North America, pg 811
BTX Technologies, pg 814
Communication Corner Inc, pg 832
Communications Specialties Inc, pg 833
Custom Media Environments, pg 841
Design Audio Visual Inc, pg 845
General Audio-Visual Inc (GAVI), pg 876
Image Labs Corp, pg 895
Image Management Systems Inc, pg 895
KVL Audio Visual Services Inc, pg 914
Long Island Video Enterprises Live Inc, pg 924
Markertek Video Supply, pg 931
Presentation Products Inc, pg 981
RNJ Electronics, pg 997
SmartSource Computer & AV Rentals, pg 1014
Technisphere Corp, pg 1034
TecNec Distributing, pg 1035
Videoguys, pg 1057
Visual Word Systems Inc, pg 1060

NORTH CAROLINA

Crispin Corp, pg 839
Innocinema, pg 898

OHIO

Copp Integrated Systems, pg 836
ITA Audio Visual Solutions, pg 902
Parts Express, pg 969
Jimmy Rea Electronics Inc, pg 992
Smithall Electronics Inc, pg 1014
Tri-State Audio Visual Co, pg 1044

PENNSYLVANIA

AccuWeather Inc, pg 774
Advanced AV, pg 777
Audio Visions Inc, pg 795
Innovision Media Group, pg 899
The Lerro Corp, pg 919
Morefield Communications Inc, pg 946
Rossman Audio LLC, pg 1000
Vistacom Inc, pg 1059
Visual Sound Inc, pg 1059

RHODE ISLAND

Shanix Inc, pg 1008

TENNESSEE

Lowrance Sound Co Inc, pg 925
Technical Support Systems LLC, pg 1034
Zion Music Group, pg 1074

TEXAS

Audio Visual Technologies Group, pg 796
AVES Audio Visual Systems Inc, pg 798
Biway Media, pg 808
Data Display Audio Visual Co LP, pg 843
Data Projections Inc, pg 843
Digital Display Solutions Inc, pg 847
Media Management LLC, pg 937
Pro Video & Film Equipment Co Inc, pg 983
TapeWorks Texas Inc, pg 1032
Tarpley Media Systems, pg 1032
Videotex Systems Inc, pg 1057

UTAH

RIA Corp, pg 996

VIRGINIA

Avitecture Inc, pg 799
Boitnott Visual Communications Corp (BVC), pg 810
Communications Specialists Inc, pg 833
Filmdex Inc, pg 867
Hoppmann Audio Visual, pg 891
Intellidyne LLC, pg 899
Quince Imaging Inc, pg 989
StageSound, pg 1023
The Whitlock Group, pg 1065

WASHINGTON

CCI Solutions, pg 821
Global Net Productions Inc, pg 879
Telect Inc, pg 1036

WISCONSIN

Audio Visual of Milwaukee Inc, pg 795
Camera Corner Connecting Point, pg 818
Full Compass Systems, pg 874
Safe Harbor Computers, pg 1001

ALBERTA

Matrix Video Communications Corp (MVCC), pg 934
McBain Audio Visual Ltd, pg 935
Sharp's Audio-Visual Ltd, pg 1008

BRITISH COLUMBIA

DL Sound & Lighting Productions Ltd, pg 849

MANITOBA

Advance Pro, pg 777
Inland Audio Visual Ltd, pg 898

ONTARIO

Cinema Stage Inc, pg 827
HD Source, pg 886
Majortech Inc, pg 929
Nationwide Audio Visual Co, pg 953
Technovision® Interactive Inc, pg 1035
Westbury National Show Systems Ltd, pg 1064

QUEBEC

Panavideo Inc, pg 968

Video Switcher Manufacturers

ALABAMA

PESA, pg 973

ARIZONA

Applied Integration Corp, pg 789
ATCi (Antenna Technology Communication Solutions Inc), pg 793
Covid Inc, pg 837

CALIFORNIA

ALTINEX Inc, pg 783
Ampex Data Systems Corp, pg 785
Extron Electronics, pg 864
FM Systems Inc, pg 870
For-A Corp of America, pg 871
Gefen, pg 876
Graham-Patten, pg 881
Hosa Technology Inc, pg 891
Hotronic Inc, pg 891
Linear LLC, pg 922
Panasonic Broadcast & Digital Systems Co, pg 968
Physical Optics Corp, pg 975
RGB Spectrum, pg 996
Snell, pg 1014
Sony Electronics Inc, pg 1016
Zhone Technologies Inc, pg 1073

COLORADO

Clear Blue Audio Video, pg 829
Video Accessory Corp, pg 1054

FLORIDA

Hi-Tech Enterprises Inc, pg 888
Sensormatic®, pg 1006
Tel-Test, pg 1035

GEORGIA

Barco Inc, pg 803
Visix™ Inc, pg 1059

ILLINOIS

NEC Display Solutions of America, pg 954

KANSAS

GlobalStreams™ Corp, pg 879

KENTUCKY

AV Toolbox, pg 797
TV One Multimedia Solutions, pg 1046

MICHIGAN

Leightronix Inc, pg 918

MINNESOTA

CyberOptics, pg 841
Vaddio, pg 1051

MISSOURI

Link Electronics Inc, pg 922

NEVADA

Adrienne Electronics Corp (AEC), pg 777

NEW JERSEY

Comprehensive Cable & Connectivity Co, pg 833
FSR Inc, pg 873
Kramer Electronics USA Inc, pg 913

NEW MEXICO

Burst Electronics Inc, pg 815

NEW YORK

Analog Way Inc, pg 786
Bosch Security Systems North America, pg 811
Image Labs Corp, pg 895
Key Digital Systems, pg 910
Monroe Electronics Inc, pg 945
MultiDyne Video & Fiber Optics Systems, pg 950
Judson Rosebush Co Inc, pg 999
TecNec Distributing, pg 1035
Vicon Industries Inc, pg 1053

NORTH CAROLINA

Crest Electronics Inc, pg 839

OHIO

Network Technologies Inc, pg 955

OKLAHOMA

Versatech Industries Inc, pg 1053

OREGON

Grass Valley, pg 881

PENNSYLVANIA

MicroImage Video Systems, pg 941
Rossman Audio LLC, pg 1000

VIRGINIA

Quince Imaging Inc, pg 989

WASHINGTON

Telect Inc, pg 1036

WISCONSIN

Intelix LLC, pg 899

VIDEO

Video Switcher Manufacturers (continued)

BRITISH COLUMBIA

Triad Communications Ltd, pg 1044

ONTARIO

Broadcast Video Systems Corp, pg 813
Semtech, pg 1006
Technovision® Interactive Inc, pg 1035

QUEBEC

Matrox Video Products Group, pg 934

Video Switcher Rentals

ARIZONA

AV Concepts, pg 797
Creative Backstage, pg 838
Glendale Media Center, pg 878
Merestone, pg 938
Video West Inc, pg 1056

ARKANSAS

White Diamond Productions, pg 1065

CALIFORNIA

Alliant Event Services, pg 781
Ametron Audio/Video, pg 785
Artichoke Productions, pg 791
AV Conferencing, pg 797
AV Guys, pg 797
Big Time Picture Company Inc, pg 807
Express Media Inc, pg 864
First Camera, pg 868
Full Moon & High Tide Productions & Studios, pg 874
Golden Gate Studios, pg 880
Impact Group, pg 897
JD Audio Visual Inc, pg 904
Maximus Media Inc, pg 934
McCune Audio-Video-Lighting, pg 935
Munday & Collins AV, pg 950
Muse Presentation Technologies, pg 950
Production Gear Rentals (PGR), pg 984
PSAV® Presentation Services, pg 986
Pyxis Industries Inc, pg 988
RetinaVision Productions, pg 995
Shooting Star Video, pg 1009
Shoulder High Productions, pg 1009
SNAP, pg 1014
The Studios at Paramount, pg 1027
VER-Video Equipment Rentals, pg 1053
VMI Inc, pg 1060
Voice & Video Rentals, pg 1060
Warner Bros Production Sound & Video Services, pg 1062
Westcoast Video Productions Inc, pg 1064

COLORADO

Denver Media Center, pg 845

CONNECTICUT

A/V Davey, pg 797
Everett Hall Associates Inc, pg 863
Videofilm Systems Inc, pg 1057

DISTRICT OF COLUMBIA

Metro Teleproductions Inc (MTI), pg 939

FLORIDA

Access Media Group, pg 773
Accord Productions, pg 773
Allstar Audio Systems Inc, pg 782
Budget Video Rentals, pg 815
Hi-Tech Enterprises Inc, pg 888
Media Concepts Inc, pg 936
Paradise Show & Design Inc, pg 969
Pro Stage Inc, pg 983
Sight & Sound Productions, pg 1010

GEORGIA

Continental Film & Video, pg 835
See Production Services, pg 1006
Stage Front Presentation Systems, pg 1022

ILLINOIS

Allen Visual Systems Inc, pg 781
AV Chicago Inc, pg 797
Beatty TeleVisual Productions, pg 804
Chicago Satellite & Video, pg 825
The Meetinghouse Companies Inc, pg 938
RC Communications, pg 992
Show Department Inc, pg 1009

IOWA

Pro Video, pg 983

KANSAS

KAKE-TV, pg 907

KENTUCKY

Audio Visual Techniques Inc, pg 796

MARYLAND

CPR MultiMedia Solutions, pg 837
Event Tech, pg 863
Kramer Communications Video Production, pg 913

MASSACHUSETTS

massAV, pg 933
Preston Productions Inc, pg 981

MICHIGAN

K&R All Media Productions Inc, pg 908
K&R's Recording Studios Inc, pg 908
On Stage Visuals, pg 963

MINNESOTA

Alpha Video & Audio Inc, pg 782

MISSISSIPPI

Bowie Audio Visual Enterprises Inc, pg 811

MISSOURI

Show-Me Audio-Visual, pg 1009

NEW JERSEY

Audio Visual Dynamics®, pg 795
Earl Girls Inc, pg 855
Euro-Pacific Film & Video Productions Inc, pg 863
Starlite Productions, pg 1024
Tele-Measurements Inc, pg 1035

NEW MEXICO

Production Outfitters, pg 984

NEW YORK

Analog Way Inc, pg 786
Big Foot Productions Inc, pg 807
CP Communications, pg 837
Design Audio Visual Inc, pg 845
KVL Audio Visual Services Inc, pg 914
SmartSource Computer & AV Rentals, pg 1014
Visual Word Systems Inc, pg 1060

NORTH CAROLINA

A&V Company, pg 772
The Communications Group Inc, pg 833
On Location North Carolina, pg 963
Take One Productions Ltd, pg 1031
Visual Aids Electronics of North Carolina Inc, pg 1059

NORTH DAKOTA

Media Productions, pg 937

OHIO

Lyon Video Inc, pg 927
Mills James Productions, pg 943

OKLAHOMA

PDC Productions, pg 970

OREGON

Picture This Production Services, pg 975

PENNSYLVANIA

Advanced AV, pg 777
FirstGeneration Audio/Visual Services, pg 869
FMP Media Solutions Inc, pg 870
Grise Audio Visual Center Inc, pg 882
Innovision Media Group, pg 899
JPL, pg 906
New York Camera & Video, pg 956
Producers Management Television (PMTV), pg 983
Upstage Video, pg 1050
The Videohouse Inc, pg 1057
Viewpoint Production Services Inc, pg 1058

TENNESSEE

Technical Support Systems LLC, pg 1034

TEXAS

Alford Media Services, pg 780
Bright Star Productions Inc, pg 812
Data Display Audio Visual Co LP, pg 843
GEAR Cameras & Lighting, pg 876
The Samuels Co, pg 1002
Stage Directions, pg 1022

VIRGINIA

Advance Concepts Inc, pg 777
Audio Visual Actions Inc (AVA), pg 795
D&B Television & Video Productions Inc, pg 842
Quince Imaging Inc, pg 989
StageSound, pg 1023

WISCONSIN

Audio Visual of Milwaukee Inc, pg 795

PUERTO RICO

Stage Crew Audiovisual Inc, pg 1022

ALBERTA

L R Light & Sound, pg 915
Matrix Video Communications Corp (MVCC), pg 934

BRITISH COLUMBIA

DL Sound & Lighting Productions Ltd, pg 849
Finale Editworks, pg 868

MANITOBA

Inland Audio Visual Ltd, pg 898

ONTARIO

HD Source, pg 886
JIB Shots Equipment Inc, pg 905
SIM Digital, pg 1011
Westbury National Show Systems Ltd, pg 1064
ZTV Broadcast Services Inc, pg 1074

Video Switcher Repairs

CALIFORNIA

Ametron Audio/Video, pg 785
BroadcastStore.com, pg 813
SSL Industries Inc, pg 1022
Technical Services, pg 1034
VMI Inc, pg 1060

CONNECTICUT

A/V Davey, pg 797

FLORIDA

Access Media Group, pg 773
ELC Sales & Service Inc, pg 858
Glanz Technologies Inc, pg 878
Hi-Tech Enterprises Inc, pg 888
Midtown Video Inc, pg 942
Tel-Test, pg 1035

GEORGIA

Stage Front Presentation Systems, pg 1022

ILLINOIS

Beatty TeleVisual Productions, pg 804
Midwest Digital Corp, pg 942

KENTUCKY

Axxis Inc, pg 800
Barney Miller's Inc, pg 943
NOR-COM Inc, pg 958

Video Wall & Control System Distributors

Video Wall & Control System Manufacturers

VIDEO

Video Wall & Control System Manufacturers (continued)

INDIANA

Draper Inc, pg 852

MINNESOTA

Dotronix Technology Inc, pg 851
Winsted Corp, pg 1068

NEW JERSEY

Activu Corp, pg 775
FSR Inc, pg 873

NEW YORK

Vicon Industries Inc, pg 1053

PENNSYLVANIA

Video Visions Inc, pg 1056

TENNESSEE

Adtec Digital Inc, pg 777

ONTARIO

Image Video, pg 895
Technovision® Interactive Inc, pg 1035

Video Wall & Control System Rentals

ARIZONA

American Audio Visual Center, pg 783
AV Concepts, pg 797
Merestone, pg 938

ARKANSAS

White Diamond Productions, pg 1065

CALIFORNIA

Alliant Event Services, pg 781
Ametron Audio/Video, pg 785
Express Media Inc, pg 864
Lynch Communications, pg 926
Multimedia LED, pg 950
Muse Presentation Technologies, pg 950
Panorama Productions, pg 968
Pioneer Electronics (USA) Inc, pg 976
PSAV® Presentation Services, pg 986
Slate Media Group, pg 1013
SNAP, pg 1014
VER-Video Equipment Rentals, pg 1053
VMI Inc, pg 1060

COLORADO

Spectrum Audio Visual Services, pg 1020

CONNECTICUT

Everett Hall Associates Inc, pg 863

DISTRICT OF COLUMBIA

Future View Inc, pg 874

FLORIDA

Allstar Audio Systems Inc, pg 782
Industrial Strength Inc, pg 897
Jordan Klein Film & Video (JKFV), pg 906
Midtown Video Inc, pg 942
Multivision Video & Film, pg 950
Pro Stage Inc, pg 983

GEORGIA

Continental Film & Video, pg 835
MAGNUM Companies Ltd, pg 929
ON Event Services, pg 963
Stage Front Presentation Systems, pg 1022

ILLINOIS

Backstar Creative Media Inc, pg 801
QuickSet International Inc, pg 989
RC Communications, pg 992
Roadworthy Image Magnification, pg 998
SCI Television Productions LLC, pg 1004

LOUISIANA

Digital FX Inc, pg 847
Pace Systems, pg 966

MAINE

Headlight Audio Visual Inc, pg 887

MARYLAND

CPR MultiMedia Solutions, pg 837

MASSACHUSETTS

AVFX Inc, pg 798
Preston Productions Inc, pg 981

MICHIGAN

Digi Sign Design LLC, pg 847
K&R All Media Productions Inc, pg 908
K&R's Recording Studios Inc, pg 908

MISSOURI

Communitronics Corp, pg 833
Southwest Audio-Visual Inc, pg 1019

NEVADA

GES Audio Visual, pg 877

NEW JERSEY

Audio Visual Dynamics®, pg 795
Earl Girls Inc, pg 855
Euro-Pacific Film & Video Productions Inc, pg 863
PLS Staging, pg 977
Starlite Productions, pg 1024
Tele-Measurements Inc, pg 1035

NEW YORK

Ace Video, pg 774
American Video Inc, pg 785
AV Workshop, pg 797
CP Communications, pg 837
Design Audio Visual Inc, pg 845
KVL Audio Visual Services Inc, pg 914
Long Island Video Enterprises Live Inc, pg 924
PrimaLux Video Inc, pg 982
SmartSource Computer & AV Rentals, pg 1014
Technisphere Corp, pg 1034
Visual Word Systems Inc, pg 1060
WorldStage, pg 1070

NORTH CAROLINA

A&V Company, pg 772
Special Event Services, pg 1020

OHIO

Hughie's Event Production Services, pg 892
ITA Audio Visual Solutions, pg 902

PENNSYLVANIA

Advanced AV, pg 777
FMP Media Solutions Inc, pg 870
Innovision Media Group, pg 899
Producers Management Television (PMTV), pg 983
Upstage Video, pg 1050

TENNESSEE

Technical Support Systems LLC, pg 1034

TEXAS

Data Display Audio Visual Co LP, pg 843
The Samuels Co, pg 1002
Stage Directions, pg 1022

VIRGINIA

Quince Imaging Inc, pg 989

WISCONSIN

Audio Visual of Milwaukee Inc, pg 795

ALBERTA

Unique Communications Ltd, pg 1048

BRITISH COLUMBIA

Clark's Audio Visual Services Ltd, pg 829

MANITOBA

Inland Audio Visual Ltd, pg 898

ONTARIO

HD Source, pg 886
MVI Multivision Inc, pg 951
Westbury National Show Systems Ltd, pg 1064

QUEBEC

Audio Visual Dynamics Ltd, pg 795
AVW-TELAV Audio Visual Solutions, a Freeman Company, pg 800

Video Wall & Control System Repairs

CALIFORNIA

Ametron Audio/Video, pg 785
Sonance, pg 1015

FLORIDA

ELC Sales & Service Inc, pg 858
Multivision Video & Film, pg 950
Vela Research, pg 1052

GEORGIA

Stage Front Presentation Systems, pg 1022

ILLINOIS

RC Communications, pg 992

KENTUCKY

Axxis Inc, pg 800
NOR-COM Inc, pg 958

MICHIGAN

TeL Systems, pg 1035

MINNESOTA

Alpha Video & Audio Inc, pg 782
Dotronix Technology Inc, pg 851

NEW YORK

MRG Productions Inc, pg 948

OHIO

ITA Audio Visual Solutions, pg 902
Tri-State Audio Visual Co, pg 1044

TENNESSEE

Technical Support Systems LLC, pg 1034

TEXAS

Data Display Audio Visual Co LP, pg 843
Tarpley Media Systems, pg 1032

UTAH

RIA Corp, pg 996

VIRGINIA

Avitecture Inc, pg 799
Hoppmann Audio Visual, pg 891
Quince Imaging Inc, pg 989

WISCONSIN

Full Compass Systems, pg 874

ALBERTA

Infosat Communications Inc, pg 898
Sharp's Audio-Visual Ltd, pg 1008
Unique Communications Ltd, pg 1048

MANITOBA

Inland Audio Visual Ltd, pg 898

ONTARIO

MVI Multivision Inc, pg 951
Westbury National Show Systems Ltd, pg 1064

Videocassette—Blank Distributors

ALABAMA

Curtis Company, pg 841
Media Visions Inc, pg 937

ARIZONA

Metropolitan Audio-Visual Inc, pg 940
On-Site Video, pg 963

Rodeo Video Inc, pg 998
Video Media Productions (VMP), pg 1055

ARKANSAS

Carlton-Bates Co, pg 820

CALIFORNIA

Adolph Gasser Inc, pg 776
Ametron Audio/Video, pg 785
Audio/Video Supply Inc, pg 795
California Tape Products Inc, pg 817
Delicate Electronics Sales Inc, pg 845
Diversified Imaging Supply, pg 849
Educational Technology Services (ETS), pg 857
FXC Communications, pg 874
Gluskin's Custom Audio Video, pg 879
Alan Gordon Enterprises Inc, pg 880
Instructional Materials & Equipment Distributors (I-Med), pg 899
JD Audio Visual Inc, pg 904
Lynch Communications, pg 926
Media Fabricators Inc, pg 936
MSE Media Solutions, pg 949
On-Trax Inc, pg 963
QRS Software Services, pg 988
Reel Picture, pg 994
Related Visual Inc, pg 994
Revolt Pro Media Inc, pg 995
RJ Video Productions, pg 997
SSL Industries Inc, pg 1022
TapeStockOnline.com, pg 1032
Tri-Ed, pg 1044
VMI Inc, pg 1060

COLORADO

The Cinema Lab, pg 827
Daylight Productions & Rentals, pg 844
Spectrum Audio Visual Services, pg 1020

CONNECTICUT

Concord Communications, pg 835
MAVCO, pg 934
Rockwell Communications Inc, pg 998
Trod Nossel Productions & Recording Studios, pg 1045

FLORIDA

Access Media Group, pg 773
AVI-SPL, pg 798
Digital Video Systems Inc, pg 848
Gulf Coast Audio Visual Producers Inc, pg 883
Hi-Tech Import Export Corp, pg 888
Industrial Strength Inc, pg 897
Jordan Klein Film & Video (JKFV), pg 906
Media Concepts Inc, pg 936
Midtown Video Inc, pg 942
Photosound of Orlando Inc, pg 975
Pro Stage Inc, pg 983
Recording Media & Equipment Inc (RM&E), pg 993
Tallahassee Audio Visual, pg 1031

GEORGIA

Audio Visual Resources Inc, pg 795
Convergent Media Systems, pg 836
Lighting & Production Equipment Inc, pg 920
Stage Front Presentation Systems, pg 1022
Technical Innovation, pg 1033
Video Copy Services Inc, pg 1055

ILLINOIS

Allen Visual Systems Inc, pg 781
Creative Technology, pg 838
FUJIFILM Graphic Systems Division, pg 873
Joseph Electronics, pg 906
Major Reproductions Equipment Co, pg 929
Polyline LLC, pg 978
Research Technology International (RTI), pg 995
Tape Resources, pg 1031
Tele-Time Systems, pg 1036

INDIANA

Lee Co Inc, pg 918
Sensory Technologies LLC, pg 1006
SHP Electronics, pg 1010

KANSAS

Smith Audio-Visual Inc, pg 1014

KENTUCKY

American Recordable Media, pg 785
Audio Visual Techniques Inc, pg 796
Axxis Inc, pg 800
Barney Miller's Inc, pg 943
NOR-COM Inc, pg 958
Northern Kentucky University, pg 959
WaxWorks VideoWorks, pg 1063

LOUISIANA

Digital FX Inc, pg 847

MAINE

Headlight Audio Visual Inc, pg 887

MARYLAND

Nicholas P Pipino Associates Inc, pg 976
RTZ Audio Visual, pg 1000
Video Labs, pg 1055
Visual Aids Electronics Corp, pg 1059

MASSACHUSETTS

Antronics Inc, pg 787
Camera Co Inc/Broadcast Divison, pg 818
Gyrus ACMI, pg 883
Hunt's Photo, Video & Digital, pg 892
Rule Broadcast Systems, pg 1000

MICHIGAN

TeL Systems, pg 1035

MINNESOTA

Cinequipt Inc, pg 828
Lights On, pg 921

MISSISSIPPI

Bowie Audio Visual Enterprises Inc, pg 811
Jasper Ewing & Sons Inc, pg 864

MISSOURI

Audio-VideoGraphics Inc, pg 795
Communitronics Corp, pg 833
Conference Technologies Inc, pg 835
Image Technologies Corp, pg 895
Southwest Audio-Visual Inc, pg 1019
Swank Audio Visuals, pg 1029

NEBRASKA

Dog & Pony Productions Inc, pg 850
Video Service of America Inc (VSA), pg 1056

NEW HAMPSHIRE

Channell One Video, pg 824

NEW JERSEY

Agfa Graphics, pg 778
Audio Visual Dynamics®, pg 795
AV Bluebook, pg 797
Comprehensive Cable & Connectivity Co, pg 833
G&G Technologies Inc, pg 875
Hamilton Buhl, pg 884
Maxell Corp of America, pg 934
National Audio-Visual Supply, pg 952
PatchAmp, pg 970
SDI Technologies Inc, pg 1005
Starlite Productions, pg 1024
SYMCO Inc, pg 1030
Tele-Measurements Inc, pg 1035
Total Media, pg 1042
Total Video Products Inc, pg 1042
Turner Engineering Inc, pg 1046
VCom International Multimedia Corp, pg 1052

NEW YORK

Adwar Video, pg 778
ALTEL Systems Inc, pg 783
AV Workshop, pg 797
Barbizon Electric Co Inc, pg 802
Burlington A/V Recording Media, pg 815
Colortone Audio Visual, pg 832
Communication Corner Inc, pg 832
Design Audio Visual Inc, pg 845
Eastco Multimedia Solutions Inc, pg 856
Film Emporium, pg 867
Flash Electronics Inc, pg 869
Gaylord Brothers, pg 876
HAVE Inc, pg 886
Langie Audio Visual Systems, pg 915
Long Island Video Enterprises Live Inc, pg 924
Markertek Video Supply, pg 931
Saul Mineroff Electronics Inc, pg 943
Moviola, pg 948
Neptune Photo Inc, pg 954
Presentation Products Inc, pg 981
Rafik, pg 990
Ray Supply Inc, pg 992
Russell Industries Inc, pg 1001
Sentry Industries Inc, pg 1007
Technisphere Corp, pg 1034
TecNec Distributing, pg 1035
Visual Technologies Corp, pg 1060
Willoughby's Imaging Center, pg 1067

NORTH CAROLINA

Camcor Inc, pg 818
Duke Media Services, pg 853
Strategic Connections, pg 1026

OHIO

Audio Visual Media, pg 795
Copp Integrated Systems, pg 836
Hughie's Event Production Services, pg 892
ITA Audio Visual Solutions, pg 902
iVideo Technologies, pg 903
The Little Warehouse Inc, pg 923
Promedia Digital, pg 986
Tri-State Audio Visual Co, pg 1044

OKLAHOMA

Piper Media Services Inc, pg 976

PENNSYLVANIA

Advanced AV, pg 777
Audio Visual Communications Inc, pg 795
Bernie's Photo Center, pg 805
FMP Media Solutions Inc, pg 870
J E Foss Co, pg 871
Grise Audio Visual Center Inc, pg 882
Hite Co, pg 889
The Lerro Corp, pg 919
Morefield Communications Inc, pg 946
Wespen Audio Visual Co, pg 1063

RHODE ISLAND

Custom Computer Specialists Inc, pg 841

TENNESSEE

Lowrance Sound Co Inc, pg 925
Memphis Communications Corp, pg 938
Spring Arbor Distributors, pg 1022
Tennessee Visual Service Co, pg 1037

TEXAS

Astro Audio Visual, pg 792
Data Display Audio Visual Co LP, pg 843
Harbor House Studios, pg 884
Heffernan Audio Visual, pg 887
J&S Audio Visual Inc, pg 904
RadioShack Corp, pg 990
Stage Directions, pg 1022

UTAH

RIA Corp, pg 996
TV Specialists Inc, pg 1046
Webb Audio Visual Communication, pg 1063

VIRGINIA

Boitnott Visual Communications Corp (BVC), pg 810
Filmdex Inc, pg 867
Hoppmann Audio Visual, pg 891
Lee Hartman & Sons Inc, pg 918
Metropolitan Audio Visual Co LLC, pg 940
The Whitlock Group, pg 1065

WASHINGTON

Inland Audio Visual Co, pg 898
Oppenheimer Camera Products, pg 964

VIDEO

Videocassette—Blank Distributors (continued)

WISCONSIN

Demco Inc, pg 845
Full Compass Systems, pg 874
School Specialty Inc, pg 1004

PUERTO RICO

Bonnin Electronics Inc, pg 810

ALBERTA

Infosat Communications Inc, pg 898
Matrix Video Communications Corp (MVCC), pg 934
McBain Audio Visual Ltd, pg 935
Sharp's Audio-Visual Ltd, pg 1008

BRITISH COLUMBIA

Finale Editworks, pg 868
Triad Communications Ltd, pg 1044

MANITOBA

Advance Pro, pg 777
Evolution Presentation Technologies, pg 863
Inland Audio Visual Ltd, pg 898

ONTARIO

Edcom Multimedia Products, pg 856
FUJIFILM Canada Inc, pg 873
HD Source, pg 886
Nationwide Audio Visual Co, pg 953
Premier A/V Sales Ltd, pg 980

QUEBEC

AVS Technologies Inc, pg 800
Panavideo Inc, pg 968

Videocassette—Blank Manufacturers

CALIFORNIA

Panasonic Broadcast & Digital Systems Co, pg 968
QRS Software Services, pg 988
Reel Picture, pg 994
Sony Electronics Inc, pg 1016
Technicolor, pg 1034

MARYLAND

Saah Video, pg 1001

NEW JERSEY

Konica Minolta Business Solutions, pg 913
Maxell Corp of America, pg 934
National Audio-Visual Supply, pg 952
Reed Presentations Inc (RPI), pg 993
SDI Technologies Inc, pg 1005
Synergem, pg 1030

NEW YORK

FUJIFILM North America Corp, pg 873
Tapemaker, pg 1032

TEXAS

Adams Evidence Grade Technology Inc, pg 775
RadioShack Corp, pg 990

UTAH

One Stop CD Shop LLC, pg 963

WISCONSIN

Full Compass Systems, pg 874

ONTARIO

FUJIFILM Canada Inc, pg 873

Videocassette Duplication, *see* Duplication—Videocassettes

Videocassette Editing, *see* Editing—Videocassettes

Videocassette Recorder & Player Distributors

ARIZONA

EAR Professional Audio/Video, pg 855

CALIFORNIA

Adolph Gasser Inc, pg 776
Ametron Audio/Video, pg 785
Band Pro Film & Digital Inc, pg 802
Be Media, pg 804
Christy's Editorial, pg 826
Cibola Systems, pg 826
Delicate Electronics Sales Inc, pg 845
Diaquest, pg 846
FXC Communications, pg 874
Alan Gordon Enterprises Inc, pg 880
Instructional Materials & Equipment Distributors (I-Med), pg 899
Jameco Electronics, pg 903
JD Audio Visual Inc, pg 904
Mitsubishi Electric Visual Solutions America Inc (MEVSA), pg 944
Mobilized Tech Systems, pg 944
POP TV, pg 978
Southern California Sound Image Inc, pg 1019
VMI Inc, pg 1060

COLORADO

Spectrum Audio Visual Services, pg 1020

CONNECTICUT

Video Automation Systems Inc, pg 1054

FLORIDA

Access Media Group, pg 773
AVI-SPL, pg 798
Digital Video Systems Inc, pg 848
Hi-Tech Import Export Corp, pg 888
Media Concepts Inc, pg 936
Midtown Video Inc, pg 942
Pro Stage Inc, pg 983
Recording Media & Equipment Inc (RM&E), pg 993
Sight & Sound Productions, pg 1010
Skyline Broadcast, pg 1013

GEORGIA

Outsource Engineering & Manufacturing Inc dba Texscan MSI, pg 966
Stage Front Presentation Systems, pg 1022

ILLINOIS

Joseph Electronics, pg 906
Woodside Avenue Music Productions Inc, pg 1069

INDIANA

Lee Co Inc, pg 918
Sensory Technologies LLC, pg 1006
SHP Electronics, pg 1010

KENTUCKY

Axxis Inc, pg 800
Barney Miller's Inc, pg 943
NOR-COM Inc, pg 958

MASSACHUSETTS

Rule Broadcast Systems, pg 1000

MICHIGAN

Digi Sign Design LLC, pg 847
TeL Systems, pg 1035

MISSOURI

Southwest Audio-Visual Inc, pg 1019

NEBRASKA

ATV Research Inc, pg 793
Dog & Pony Productions Inc, pg 850
Video Service of America Inc (VSA), pg 1056

NEW JERSEY

Alltec Stores, a Vcom IMC Company, pg 782
AV Bluebook, pg 797
Color Leasing Studios, pg 831
Diversified Systems Inc, pg 849
Hamilton Buhl, pg 884
MCCOM Inc, pg 935
National Audio-Visual Supply, pg 952
Starlite Productions, pg 1024
Tele-Measurements Inc, pg 1035
Total Video Products Inc, pg 1042

NEW YORK

B&H Photo & Video Pro Audio, pg 802
Colortone Audio Visual, pg 832
Custom Media Environments, pg 841
Design Audio Visual Inc, pg 845
Eastco Multimedia Solutions Inc, pg 856
Gaylord Brothers, pg 876
Image Management Systems Inc, pg 895
Magnaplan Corp, pg 928
Markertek Video Supply, pg 931
Presentation Products Inc, pg 981
RNJ Electronics, pg 997
TecNec Distributing, pg 1035
Visual Word Systems Inc, pg 1060

OHIO

ITA Audio Visual Solutions, pg 902
Jimmy Rea Electronics Inc, pg 992
Tri-State Audio Visual Co, pg 1044

PENNSYLVANIA

Advanced AV, pg 777
Bernie's Photo Center, pg 805
Brodart Co, pg 813
J E Foss Co, pg 871
Grise Audio Visual Center Inc, pg 882
The Lerro Corp, pg 919

TENNESSEE

Lowrance Sound Co Inc, pg 925
Technical Support Systems LLC, pg 1034

TEXAS

Astro Audio Visual, pg 792
AVES Audio Visual Systems Inc, pg 798
Data Display Audio Visual Co LP, pg 843
Digital Display Solutions Inc, pg 847
Industrial Audio/Video Inc, pg 897
Media Management LLC, pg 937
Pro Video & Film Equipment Co Inc, pg 983
Quality Audio Visual Service Inc, pg 988
RadioShack Corp, pg 990
Videotex Systems Inc, pg 1057

VIRGINIA

Lee Hartman & Sons Inc, pg 918

WASHINGTON

Global Net Productions Inc, pg 879
ToteVision, pg 1042

WISCONSIN

Full Compass Systems, pg 874

ALBERTA

Matrix Video Communications Corp (MVCC), pg 934

MANITOBA

Advance Pro, pg 777
Inland Audio Visual Ltd, pg 898

ONTARIO

Westbury National Show Systems Ltd, pg 1064

QUEBEC

AVS Technologies Inc, pg 800

Videocassette Recorder & Player Manufacturers

CALIFORNIA

Mitsubishi Electric Visual Solutions America Inc (MEVSA), pg 944
Panasonic Broadcast & Digital Systems Co, pg 968

GEORGIA

Outsource Engineering & Manufacturing Inc dba Texscan MSI, pg 966

Videocassette Recorder & Player Rentals

Videocassette Recorder & Player Repairs

VIDEO

Videocassette Recorder & Player Repairs (continued)

Videodisc—Blank Distributors

Videodisc—Blank Manufacturers

Videodisc Duplication, *see* Duplication—Videodiscs

Videodisc Mastering

Videodisc Premastering

Custom Video Productions Inc, pg 841
Dogma Studios, pg 850
Express Media Inc, pg 864
First Person™, pg 868
iCorpTv, pg 893
JDS Video & Media Productions Inc, pg 904
QRS Software Services, pg 988
RetinaVision Productions, pg 995
Roundabout Entertainment Inc, pg 1000
Total Media Group, pg 1042

COLORADO

Rocky Mountain Audio/Video Productions Inc, pg 998
Z-Axis Corp, pg 1073

CONNECTICUT

Palace Digital Studios, pg 967

DISTRICT OF COLUMBIA

Interface Media Group, pg 900

FLORIDA

Allegro Productions Inc, pg 781
Communications Concepts Inc (CCI), pg 833
Global Video Distributors Inc, pg 879
Knowles Video Inc (KVI), pg 912
Sunfire Communications Inc, pg 1028

GEORGIA

Beachwood Productions, pg 804
Crawford Media Services, pg 838

HAWAII

1013 Integrated, pg 1037

ILLINOIS

Analog Free Media, pg 786
Optimus, pg 964
Southern Illinois University, pg 1019

LOUISIANA

Digital FX Inc, pg 847
Louisiana State University Health Sciences Center - Shreveport, pg 925

MARYLAND

Sign Media Inc, pg 1011

MASSACHUSETTS

Veritech Corp, pg 1053

MICHIGAN

Digi Sign Design LLC, pg 847
K&R's Recording Studios Inc, pg 908
Maritz Performance Improvement Co, pg 931
RingSide Creative, pg 997
Universal Images, pg 1049

MINNESOTA

The Richard Diercks Co Inc, pg 846

NEVADA

Encore Productions Inc, pg 861
Lefco Video Services Inc, pg 918
21st Century Video Productions, pg 1047

NEW HAMPSHIRE

Academic & Campus Technology Services, pg 773
The Troupe, pg 1045

NEW JERSEY

Broadcast Center Studios, pg 813
MIB Mediaworks, pg 941
Midnight Media Group Inc, pg 942
Suede Interactive, pg 1027
VCSvideo, pg 1052

NEW YORK

Chromavision Corp, pg 826
Duplication Specialists Inc, pg 853
HAVE Inc, pg 886
Shelly Palmer Production, pg 968
PostWorks, pg 979
TBA Global Events, pg 1032
Teatown Communications Group, pg 1033

NORTH CAROLINA

Duke Media Services, pg 853
LCW Productions LLC, pg 917
Trailblazer Studios®, pg 1043

OHIO

Aztec Video Productions, pg 801
Cuyahoga Community College Media Center, pg 841
Electronic Vision Inc (EV), pg 859

OREGON

BingoLewis, pg 807

PENNSYLVANIA

Audio Visual Communications Inc, pg 795
Center City Film & Video Inc, pg 822
Innovision Media Group, pg 899
Production Masters Inc (PMI), pg 984

TENNESSEE

Continental Film, pg 835
Stage Post, pg 1022

TEXAS

The Editing Co, pg 857
Stage Directions, pg 1022

VIRGINIA

BES Studios, pg 805
Henninger Media Services, pg 888

WASHINGTON

Bennett-Watt HD Productions Inc, pg 805

WISCONSIN

Audio Visual of Milwaukee Inc, pg 795
Media Communications Association-International (MCA-I), pg 936
USAV Group Inc, pg 1050
Video Wisconsin Inc, pg 1056

WYOMING

Bridger Productions Inc, pg 812

ONTARIO

Technovision® Interactive Inc, pg 1035

Videodisc Recorder & Player Distributors

ARIZONA

EAR Professional Audio/Video, pg 855

CALIFORNIA

Advanced Systems Group LLC, pg 778
Ametron Audio/Video, pg 785
Audio/Video Supply Inc, pg 795
Be Media, pg 804
Delicate Electronics Sales Inc, pg 845
Diaquest, pg 846
FXC Communications, pg 874
Gluskin's Custom Audio Video, pg 879
Instructional Materials & Equipment Distributors (I-Med), pg 899
Jaguar Distribution Corp, pg 903
Media Fabricators Inc, pg 936
Pioneer Electronics (USA) Inc, pg 976
SNAP, pg 1014
Southern California Sound Image Inc, pg 1019
SSL Industries Inc, pg 1022
Tri-Ed, pg 1044

COLORADO

Spectrum Audio Visual Services, pg 1020

FLORIDA

AVI-SPL, pg 798
Digital Video Systems Inc, pg 848
Hi-Tech Import Export Corp, pg 888
Media Concepts Inc, pg 936
Midtown Video Inc, pg 942
Pro Stage Inc, pg 983
Recording Media & Equipment Inc (RM&E), pg 993
Sight & Sound Productions, pg 1010

GEORGIA

Clark, pg 829
Stage Front Presentation Systems, pg 1022

ILLINOIS

Joseph Electronics, pg 906

INDIANA

Lee Co Inc, pg 918
Sensory Technologies LLC, pg 1006
SHP Electronics, pg 1010

KANSAS

Smith Audio-Visual Inc, pg 1014

KENTUCKY

Axxis Inc, pg 800
NOR-COM Inc, pg 958

MICHIGAN

ASC Systems, pg 791
Digi Sign Design LLC, pg 847

MISSOURI

Communitronics Corp, pg 833
Southwest Audio-Visual Inc, pg 1019

NEBRASKA

Dog & Pony Productions Inc, pg 850
Video Service of America Inc (VSA), pg 1056

NEVADA

Aardvark Video & Media Productions, pg 772

NEW JERSEY

A-V Services Inc, pg 771
Hamilton Buhl, pg 884
MCCOM Inc, pg 935
National Audio-Visual Supply, pg 952
Starlite Productions, pg 1024
Total Video Products Inc, pg 1042

NEW YORK

American Video Inc, pg 785
AV Workshop, pg 797
B&H Photo & Video Pro Audio, pg 802
Design Audio Visual Inc, pg 845
Gaylord Brothers, pg 876
Gotham Sound & Communications Inc, pg 881
Image Management Systems Inc, pg 895
KVL Audio Visual Services Inc, pg 914
Neptune Photo Inc, pg 954
Technisphere Corp, pg 1034
TecNec Distributing, pg 1035
Visual Word Systems Inc, pg 1060

OHIO

Tri-State Audio Visual Co, pg 1044

PENNSYLVANIA

Advanced AV, pg 777
The Lerro Corp, pg 919
Morefield Communications Inc, pg 946

TENNESSEE

Lowrance Sound Co Inc, pg 925
Technical Support Systems LLC, pg 1034

TEXAS

Audio Visual Technologies Group, pg 796
Data Display Audio Visual Co LP, pg 843
Digital Display Solutions Inc, pg 847
Stage Directions, pg 1022
Videotex Systems Inc, pg 1057

UTAH

RIA Corp, pg 996

VIDEO

Videodisc Recorder & Player Distributors (continued)

VIRGINIA

Avitecture Inc, pg 799
Hoppmann Audio Visual, pg 891
Lee Hartman & Sons Inc, pg 918

WISCONSIN

Camera Corner Connecting Point, pg 818
Full Compass Systems, pg 874

MANITOBA

Advance Pro, pg 777
Inland Audio Visual Ltd, pg 898

ONTARIO

HD Source, pg 886
Technovision® Interactive Inc, pg 1035

QUEBEC

Panavideo Inc, pg 968

Videodisc Recorder & Player Manufacturers

CALIFORNIA

Colby Systems Corp, pg 831
Doremi Labs, pg 851
Grande Vitesse Systems Inc (GVS), pg 881
Panasonic Broadcast & Digital Systems Co, pg 968
Pioneer Electronics (USA) Inc, pg 976

MICHIGAN

Leightronix Inc, pg 918

NEW JERSEY

Panasonic Corp, pg 968

NEW YORK

Laird Digital Cinema, pg 915

TENNESSEE

Adtec Digital Inc, pg 777

ONTARIO

McCurdy Radio Ltd, pg 935

Videodisc Recorder & Player Rentals

ARIZONA

Merestone, pg 938

ARKANSAS

White Diamond Productions, pg 1065

CALIFORNIA

Aaron & Le Duc, pg 772
Advanced Media LLC, pg 778
Alliant Event Services, pg 781
Ametron Audio/Video, pg 785
AV Guys, pg 797
Bexel Corp, pg 806
BroadcastStore.com, pg 813
Golden Gate Studios, pg 880
Instructional Materials & Equipment Distributors (I-Med), pg 899
JD Audio Visual Inc, pg 904
Lynch Communications, pg 926
Main Street Media Inc, pg 929
McCune Audio-Video-Lighting, pg 935
Media Fabricators Inc, pg 936
Munday & Collins AV, pg 950
PSAV® Presentation Services, pg 986
RetinaVision Productions, pg 995
Slate Media Group, pg 1013
SNAP, pg 1014
VER-Video Equipment Rentals, pg 1053
VMI Inc, pg 1060
Voice & Video Rentals, pg 1060

COLORADO

Spectrum Audio Visual Services, pg 1020

DELAWARE

Showorks Audio Visual Inc, pg 1010

FLORIDA

AVI-SPL, pg 798
Eastern Video, pg 856
Industrial Strength Inc, pg 897
Paradise Show & Design Inc, pg 969
Pro Stage Inc, pg 983
Sight & Sound Productions, pg 1010

GEORGIA

Lighting & Production Equipment Inc, pg 920
ON Event Services, pg 963
Stage Front Presentation Systems, pg 1022

ILLINOIS

AV Chicago Inc, pg 797
Backstar Creative Media Inc, pg 801
Creative Technology, pg 838
QuickSet International Inc, pg 989
RC Communications, pg 992

LOUISIANA

Digital FX Inc, pg 847
Pace Systems, pg 966

MARYLAND

CPR MultiMedia Solutions, pg 837

MASSACHUSETTS

AVFX Inc, pg 798
Preston Productions Inc, pg 981

MICHIGAN

Digi Sign Design LLC, pg 847
K&R's Recording Studios Inc, pg 908
TeL Systems, pg 1035

MISSOURI

Schiller's Audio-Visual, pg 1004
Southwest Audio-Visual Inc, pg 1019

NEBRASKA

Dog & Pony Productions Inc, pg 850

NEVADA

GES Audio Visual, pg 877

NEW JERSEY

PLS Staging, pg 977
Starlite Productions, pg 1024

NEW YORK

American Video Inc, pg 785
AV Workshop, pg 797
Design Audio Visual Inc, pg 845
KVL Audio Visual Services Inc, pg 914
TBA Global Events, pg 1032
Technisphere Corp, pg 1034
Visual Word Systems Inc, pg 1060

NORTH CAROLINA

A&V Company, pg 772
On Location North Carolina, pg 963
Take One Productions Ltd, pg 1031
Visual Aids Electronics of North Carolina Inc, pg 1059

OHIO

R&B Communications Inc, pg 991

PENNSYLVANIA

Advanced AV, pg 777
FMP Media Solutions Inc, pg 870

TENNESSEE

Technical Support Systems LLC, pg 1034

TEXAS

Alford Media Services, pg 780
Astro Audio Visual, pg 792
Digital Display Solutions Inc, pg 847
Stage Directions, pg 1022

WASHINGTON

Victory Studios, pg 1054

WISCONSIN

Audio Visual of Milwaukee Inc, pg 795
Full Compass Systems, pg 874

PUERTO RICO

Stage Crew Audiovisual Inc, pg 1022

BRITISH COLUMBIA

Finale Editworks, pg 868

MANITOBA

Inland Audio Visual Ltd, pg 898

ONTARIO

HD Source, pg 886
Technovision® Interactive Inc, pg 1035
Wanted! Sound + Picture, pg 1062

QUEBEC

Panavideo Inc, pg 968

Videodisc Recorder & Player Repairs

CALIFORNIA

Advanced Media LLC, pg 778
Ametron Audio/Video, pg 785
McAlister Electronics, pg 935
SSL Industries Inc, pg 1022
VMI Inc, pg 1060

FLORIDA

ELC Sales & Service Inc, pg 858

GEORGIA

Stage Front Presentation Systems, pg 1022

ILLINOIS

Beatty TeleVisual Productions, pg 804

KENTUCKY

Axxis Inc, pg 800
Barney Miller's Inc, pg 943
NOR-COM Inc, pg 958

MARYLAND

Strauss Photo Technical Service Inc, pg 1026

MICHIGAN

TeL Systems, pg 1035

MINNESOTA

Alpha Video & Audio Inc, pg 782

MISSOURI

Schiller's Audio-Visual, pg 1004
Southwest Audio-Visual Inc, pg 1019

TENNESSEE

Technical Support Systems LLC, pg 1034

TEXAS

Astro Audio Visual, pg 792
Data Display Audio Visual Co LP, pg 843

UTAH

RIA Corp, pg 996

VIRGINIA

Hoppmann Audio Visual, pg 891

WISCONSIN

Audio Visual of Milwaukee Inc, pg 795
Full Compass Systems, pg 874

MANITOBA

Inland Audio Visual Ltd, pg 898

ONTARIO

HD Source, pg 886
Technovision® Interactive Inc, pg 1035

QUEBEC

Panavideo Inc, pg 968

Videodisc System—Hardware Distributors

ALABAMA

Curtis Company, pg 841

ARIZONA

Audio Video Resources, pg 795
EAR Professional Audio/Video, pg 855

CALIFORNIA

Advanced Systems Group LLC, pg 778
Ametron Audio/Video, pg 785
Audio/Video Supply Inc, pg 795
Be Media, pg 804
Diaquest, pg 846
Jaguar Distribution Corp, pg 903
Media Fabricators Inc, pg 936
Tri-Ed, pg 1044

COLORADO

Spectrum Audio Visual Services, pg 1020

CONNECTICUT

MAVCO, pg 934

FLORIDA

Alcorn McBride Inc, pg 780
Digital Video Systems Inc, pg 848
General Projection Systems Inc, pg 877
Media Concepts Inc, pg 936
Midtown Video Inc, pg 942
Pro Stage Inc, pg 983
Tallahassee Audio Visual, pg 1031

GEORGIA

Convergent Media Systems, pg 836
Stage Front Presentation Systems, pg 1022
Visioneering International Inc, pg 1058

ILLINOIS

Allen Visual Systems Inc, pg 781
RC Communications, pg 992
Tele-Time Systems, pg 1036

INDIANA

Lee Co Inc, pg 918
Sensory Technologies LLC, pg 1006
SHP Electronics, pg 1010

KANSAS

Smith Audio-Visual Inc, pg 1014

KENTUCKY

Barney Miller's Inc, pg 943
NOR-COM Inc, pg 958

LOUISIANA

Digital FX Inc, pg 847

MARYLAND

RTZ Audio Visual, pg 1000
Visual Aids Electronics Corp, pg 1059

MICHIGAN

ASC Systems, pg 791
Digi Sign Design LLC, pg 847
TeL Systems, pg 1035

MINNESOTA

Alpha Video & Audio Inc, pg 782
AVI Systems, pg 799

MISSOURI

Communitronics Corp, pg 833
Southwest Audio-Visual Inc, pg 1019
Swank Audio Visuals, pg 1029

NEW JERSEY

A-V Services Inc, pg 771
AV Bluebook, pg 797
G&G Technologies Inc, pg 875
Hamilton Buhl, pg 884
Maxell Corp of America, pg 934
National Audio-Visual Supply, pg 952
Starlite Productions, pg 1024
SYMCO Inc, pg 1030
Total Video Products Inc, pg 1042
Turner Engineering Inc, pg 1046

NEW YORK

AV Workshop, pg 797
Design Audio Visual Inc, pg 845
Flash Electronics Inc, pg 869
Image Management Systems Inc, pg 895
Technisphere Corp, pg 1034
Willoughby's Imaging Center, pg 1067

NORTH CAROLINA

Camcor Inc, pg 818

OHIO

iVideo Technologies, pg 903

PENNSYLVANIA

Advanced AV, pg 777
The Lerro Corp, pg 919
Morefield Communications Inc, pg 946

RHODE ISLAND

Custom Computer Specialists Inc, pg 841

TENNESSEE

Lowrance Sound Co Inc, pg 925
Memphis Communications Corp, pg 938
Technical Support Systems LLC, pg 1034

TEXAS

Digital Display Solutions Inc, pg 847
J&S Audio Visual Inc, pg 904
Schoolhouse Audio Visual, pg 1004
Stage Directions, pg 1022
Videotex Systems Inc, pg 1057

UTAH

RIA Corp, pg 996
Webb Audio Visual Communication, pg 1063

VIRGINIA

Avitecture Inc, pg 799
Lee Hartman & Sons Inc, pg 918
The Whitlock Group, pg 1065

WISCONSIN

Camera Corner Connecting Point, pg 818
Full Compass Systems, pg 874

ALBERTA

Sharp's Audio-Visual Ltd, pg 1008

MANITOBA

Advance Pro, pg 777
Inland Audio Visual Ltd, pg 898

ONTARIO

HD Source, pg 886
Nationwide Audio Visual Co, pg 953
Technovision® Interactive Inc, pg 1035

QUEBEC

Panavideo Inc, pg 968

Videodisc System—Hardware Manufacturers

CALIFORNIA

Doremi Labs, pg 851
Grande Vitesse Systems Inc (GVS), pg 881
Panasonic Broadcast & Digital Systems Co, pg 968
Pioneer Electronics (USA) Inc, pg 976
Sony Electronics Inc, pg 1016

FLORIDA

Alcorn McBride Inc, pg 780

GEORGIA

Visix™ Inc, pg 1059

MICHIGAN

ASC Systems, pg 791
Leightronix Inc, pg 918

NEW JERSEY

Maxell Corp of America, pg 934

NEW YORK

Quantel Inc, pg 989

TENNESSEE

Adtec Digital Inc, pg 777

ONTARIO

McCurdy Radio Ltd, pg 935
Technovision® Interactive Inc, pg 1035

Videodisc System—Hardware Rentals

ARIZONA

Audio Video Resources, pg 795
Merestone, pg 938
Metropolitan Audio-Visual Inc, pg 940

CALIFORNIA

Alliant Event Services, pg 781
Ametron Audio/Video, pg 785
Lynch Communications, pg 926
Main Street Media Inc, pg 929
Media Fabricators Inc, pg 936
Munday & Collins AV, pg 950
PSAV® Presentation Services, pg 986
RetinaVision Productions, pg 995
Slate Media Group, pg 1013

COLORADO

Spectrum Audio Visual Services, pg 1020

CONNECTICUT

A/V Davey, pg 797

FLORIDA

Eastern Video, pg 856
Pro Stage Inc, pg 983
Universal Studios Florida® Production Group, pg 1049

GEORGIA

Convergent Media Systems, pg 836
Lighting & Production Equipment Inc, pg 920
Stage Front Presentation Systems, pg 1022

ILLINOIS

Allen Visual Systems Inc, pg 781
Backstar Creative Media Inc, pg 801
QuickSet International Inc, pg 989
RC Communications, pg 992
Tele-Time Systems, pg 1036

KENTUCKY

Audio Visual Techniques Inc, pg 796

LOUISIANA

Digital FX Inc, pg 847

MARYLAND

CPR MultiMedia Solutions, pg 837
RTZ Audio Visual, pg 1000

MASSACHUSETTS

AVFX Inc, pg 798
Preston Productions Inc, pg 981

MICHIGAN

Digi Sign Design LLC, pg 847
TeL Systems, pg 1035

MISSOURI

Schiller's Audio-Visual, pg 1004
Southwest Audio-Visual Inc, pg 1019
Switch, pg 1030

VIDEO

Videodisc System—Hardware Rentals (continued)

NEW JERSEY

PLS Staging, pg 977
Starlite Productions, pg 1024
Turner Engineering Inc, pg 1046

NEW YORK

Adwar Video, pg 778
AV Workshop, pg 797
Interactive International Inc, pg 899
TBA Global Events, pg 1032
Technisphere Corp, pg 1034

OHIO

ITA Audio Visual Solutions, pg 902

PENNSYLVANIA

FMP Media Solutions Inc, pg 870
Visual Sound Inc, pg 1059

TENNESSEE

Technical Support Systems LLC, pg 1034

TEXAS

Stage Directions, pg 1022

UTAH

Webb Audio Visual Communication, pg 1063

WASHINGTON

Victory Studios, pg 1054

WISCONSIN

Full Compass Systems, pg 874

MANITOBA

Inland Audio Visual Ltd, pg 898

ONTARIO

HD Source, pg 886
Technovision® Interactive Inc, pg 1035

QUEBEC

Panavideo Inc, pg 968

Videodisc System—Hardware Repairs

CALIFORNIA

Advanced Systems Group LLC, pg 778
Ametron Audio/Video, pg 785
McAlister Electronics, pg 935

FLORIDA

ELC Sales & Service Inc, pg 858

GEORGIA

Stage Front Presentation Systems, pg 1022

KENTUCKY

Barney Miller's Inc, pg 943
NOR-COM Inc, pg 958

MARYLAND

RTZ Audio Visual, pg 1000

MICHIGAN

TeL Systems, pg 1035

MINNESOTA

Alpha Video & Audio Inc, pg 782

MISSOURI

Schiller's Audio-Visual, pg 1004
Southwest Audio-Visual Inc, pg 1019

NEW JERSEY

Turner Engineering Inc, pg 1046

NEW YORK

Adwar Video, pg 778
Interactive International Inc, pg 899

PENNSYLVANIA

Visual Sound Inc, pg 1059

TENNESSEE

Technical Support Systems LLC, pg 1034

UTAH

RIA Corp, pg 996

WISCONSIN

Full Compass Systems, pg 874

ALBERTA

Sharp's Audio-Visual Ltd, pg 1008

MANITOBA

Inland Audio Visual Ltd, pg 898

ONTARIO

Technovision® Interactive Inc, pg 1035

QUEBEC

Panavideo Inc, pg 968

Videodisc System—Software Distributors

ARIZONA

EAR Professional Audio/Video, pg 855

CALIFORNIA

Advanced Systems Group LLC, pg 778
Ametron Audio/Video, pg 785
Audio/Video Supply Inc, pg 795
Be Media, pg 804
Diaquest, pg 846
Jaguar Distribution Corp, pg 903
Sony Pictures Home Entertainment, pg 1016

COLORADO

Spectrum Audio Visual Services, pg 1020

CONNECTICUT

MAVCO, pg 934

FLORIDA

Digital Video Systems Inc, pg 848
Media Concepts Inc, pg 936
Pro Stage Inc, pg 983
Thayer Birding Software, pg 1038

GEORGIA

Stage Front Presentation Systems, pg 1022
Visioneering International Inc, pg 1058

ILLINOIS

Rand McNally Education, pg 991

INDIANA

Sensory Technologies LLC, pg 1006

KANSAS

Smith Audio-Visual Inc, pg 1014

KENTUCKY

NOR-COM Inc, pg 958
WaxWorks VideoWorks, pg 1063

LOUISIANA

Digital FX Inc, pg 847

MICHIGAN

Digi Sign Design LLC, pg 847

MINNESOTA

Alpha Video & Audio Inc, pg 782

MISSOURI

Communitronics Corp, pg 833
Southwest Audio-Visual Inc, pg 1019

NEW JERSEY

AV Bluebook, pg 797
National Audio-Visual Supply, pg 952

NEW YORK

AV Workshop, pg 797
Flash Electronics Inc, pg 869
Image Management Systems Inc, pg 895
Technisphere Corp, pg 1034

PENNSYLVANIA

Advanced AV, pg 777
The Lerro Corp, pg 919
Morefield Communications Inc, pg 946

TENNESSEE

Lowrance Sound Co Inc, pg 925
Technical Support Systems LLC, pg 1034

TEXAS

Digital Display Solutions Inc, pg 847
Videotex Systems Inc, pg 1057

UTAH

RIA Corp, pg 996

VIRGINIA

Avitecture Inc, pg 799
Lee Hartman & Sons Inc, pg 918

WISCONSIN

Full Compass Systems, pg 874

MANITOBA

Advance Pro, pg 777

ONTARIO

Technovision® Interactive Inc, pg 1035

Videodisc System—Software Manufacturers

CALIFORNIA

Grande Vitesse Systems Inc (GVS), pg 881
Pioneer Electronics (USA) Inc, pg 976
Sony Pictures Home Entertainment, pg 1016

FLORIDA

Thayer Birding Software, pg 1038

ILLINOIS

Rand McNally Education, pg 991

MICHIGAN

Leightronix Inc, pg 918

NEW YORK

Lenel Systems International Inc, pg 919

TENNESSEE

Adtec Digital Inc, pg 777

ONTARIO

McCurdy Radio Ltd, pg 935
Technovision® Interactive Inc, pg 1035

Videotape—Blank Distributors

ALABAMA

Curtis Company, pg 841
Media Visions Inc, pg 937

ARIZONA

Metropolitan Audio-Visual Inc, pg 940
On-Site Video, pg 963
Video Media Productions (VMP), pg 1055

CALIFORNIA

Adolph Gasser Inc, pg 776
Advanced Systems Group LLC, pg 778
Ametron Audio/Video, pg 785
Audio/Video Supply Inc, pg 795
California Tape Products Inc, pg 817
Diaquest, pg 846
Edgewise Media Inc, pg 856
Express Video Supply Inc, pg 864
First Camera, pg 868
Gluskin's Custom Audio Video, pg 879
Alan Gordon Enterprises Inc, pg 880

Hooper Camera & Imaging, pg 891
Instructional Materials & Equipment Distributors (I-Med), pg 899
Jaguar Distribution Corp, pg 903
JD Audio Visual Inc, pg 904
Media Distributors, pg 936
Media Fabricators Inc, pg 936
MSE Media Solutions, pg 949
On-Trax Inc, pg 963
QRS Software Services, pg 988
Reel Picture, pg 994
Related Visual Inc, pg 994
Revolt Pro Media Inc, pg 995
SSL Industries Inc, pg 1022
TapeStockOnline.com, pg 1032
Tri-Ed, pg 1044
VMI Inc, pg 1060
Westcoast Video Productions Inc, pg 1064

COLORADO

The Cinema Lab, pg 827
Daylight Productions & Rentals, pg 844
Spectrum Audio Visual Services, pg 1020
Stanco Sales LLC, pg 1023

CONNECTICUT

MAVCO, pg 934
Rockwell Communications Inc, pg 998
Trod Nossel Productions & Recording Studios, pg 1045

FLORIDA

Access Media Group, pg 773
Digital Video Systems Inc, pg 848
Gulf Coast Audio Visual Producers Inc, pg 883
Hi-Tech Import Export Corp, pg 888
Jordan Klein Film & Video (JKFV), pg 906
Media Concepts Inc, pg 936
Midtown Video Inc, pg 942
Photosound of Orlando Inc, pg 975
Pro Stage Inc, pg 983
Recording Media & Equipment Inc (RM&E), pg 993
RLX Media LLC, pg 997
Tallahassee Audio Visual, pg 1031

GEORGIA

Audio Visual Resources Inc, pg 795
Convergent Media Systems, pg 836
Lighting & Production Equipment Inc, pg 920
ON Event Services, pg 963
Stage Front Presentation Systems, pg 1022
Technical Innovation, pg 1033
Video Copy Services Inc, pg 1055

ILLINOIS

Allen Visual Systems Inc, pg 781
Creative Technology, pg 838
FUJIFILM Graphic Systems Division, pg 873
Joseph Electronics, pg 906
Major Reproductions Equipment Co, pg 929
Polyline LLC, pg 978
Tape Resources, pg 1031
Tele-Time Systems, pg 1036

INDIANA

Lee Co Inc, pg 918
Sensory Technologies LLC, pg 1006
SHP Electronics, pg 1010

KANSAS

Smith Audio-Visual Inc, pg 1014

KENTUCKY

American Recordable Media, pg 785
Barney Miller's Inc, pg 943
NOR-COM Inc, pg 958
WaxWorks VideoWorks, pg 1063

LOUISIANA

Digital FX Inc, pg 847

MARYLAND

Nicholas P Pipino Associates Inc, pg 976
RTZ Audio Visual, pg 1000
Visual Aids Electronics Corp, pg 1059

MASSACHUSETTS

Antronics Inc, pg 787
Camera Co Inc/Broadcast Divison, pg 818
Home Inc, pg 890
MALCO Electronics, pg 929
Rule Broadcast Systems, pg 1000

MICHIGAN

TeL Systems, pg 1035

MINNESOTA

Aggressive Records Audio Duplication LLC, pg 778
Alpha Video & Audio Inc, pg 782
Cinequipt Inc, pg 828

MISSISSIPPI

Bowie Audio Visual Enterprises Inc, pg 811
Jasper Ewing & Sons Inc, pg 864

MISSOURI

Audio-VideoGraphics Inc, pg 795
Communitronics Corp, pg 833
Southwest Audio-Visual Inc, pg 1019
Swank Audio Visuals, pg 1029

NEBRASKA

Dog & Pony Productions Inc, pg 850
Video Service of America Inc (VSA), pg 1056

NEW JERSEY

Agfa Graphics, pg 778
Audio Visual Dynamics®, pg 795
AV Bluebook, pg 797
Comprehensive Cable & Connectivity Co, pg 833
G&G Technologies Inc, pg 875
Hamilton Buhl, pg 884
Maxell Corp of America, pg 934
National Audio-Visual Supply, pg 952
PatchAmp, pg 970
Tele-Measurements Inc, pg 1035
Total Media, pg 1042
Total Video Products Inc, pg 1042
Turner Engineering Inc, pg 1046
VCom International Multimedia Corp, pg 1052
Video Corporation of America (VCA), pg 1055

NEW YORK

Adwar Video, pg 778
Aura Sonic Ltd, pg 796
AV Workshop, pg 797
Burlington A/V Recording Media, pg 815
Canon USA Inc, pg 819
Colortone Audio Visual, pg 832
Communication Corner Inc, pg 832
Design Audio Visual Inc, pg 845
Eastco Multimedia Solutions Inc, pg 856
Film Emporium, pg 867
Flash Electronics Inc, pg 869
Gaylord Brothers, pg 876
HAVE Inc, pg 886
Langie Audio Visual Systems, pg 915
Long Island Video Enterprises Live Inc, pg 924
Markertek Video Supply, pg 931
Saul Mineroff Electronics Inc, pg 943
Moviola, pg 948
Neptune Photo Inc, pg 954
Rafik, pg 990
Ray Supply Inc, pg 992
RNJ Electronics, pg 997
Russell Industries Inc, pg 1001
Technisphere Corp, pg 1034
TecNec Distributing, pg 1035
Visual Technologies Corp, pg 1060
Visual Word Systems Inc, pg 1060

NORTH CAROLINA

Camcor Inc, pg 818
Duke Media Services, pg 853
Strategic Connections, pg 1026

OHIO

Copp Integrated Systems, pg 836
Hughie's Event Production Services, pg 892
iVideo Technologies, pg 903
The Little Warehouse Inc, pg 923
Jimmy Rea Electronics Inc, pg 992
Tri-State Audio Visual Co, pg 1044

OKLAHOMA

Piper Media Services Inc, pg 976

PENNSYLVANIA

Advanced AV, pg 777
Audio Visual Communications Inc, pg 795
Bernie's Photo Center, pg 805
FMP Media Solutions Inc, pg 870
J E Foss Co, pg 871
Morefield Communications Inc, pg 946
Wespen Audio Visual Co, pg 1063

RHODE ISLAND

Custom Computer Specialists Inc, pg 841

TENNESSEE

Lowrance Sound Co Inc, pg 925
Memphis Communications Corp, pg 938
Spring Arbor Distributors, pg 1022

TEXAS

Astro Audio Visual, pg 792
Harbor House Studios, pg 884
Quality Audio Visual Service Inc, pg 988
RadioShack Corp, pg 990
Replicopy Digital Media Center, pg 995
Texcam Inc, pg 1038

UTAH

RIA Corp, pg 996
TV Specialists Inc, pg 1046
Webb Audio Visual Communication, pg 1063

VIRGINIA

Filmdex Inc, pg 867
Lee Hartman & Sons Inc, pg 918
The Whitlock Group, pg 1065

WASHINGTON

Global Net Productions Inc, pg 879
Inland Audio Visual Co, pg 898

WISCONSIN

Demco Inc, pg 845
Full Compass Systems, pg 874

PUERTO RICO

Bonnin Electronics Inc, pg 810

ALBERTA

Matrix Video Communications Corp (MVCC), pg 934
McBain Audio Visual Ltd, pg 935
Sharp's Audio-Visual Ltd, pg 1008
Unique Communications Ltd, pg 1048

BRITISH COLUMBIA

Finale Editworks, pg 868
Triad Communications Ltd, pg 1044

MANITOBA

Advance Pro, pg 777
Inland Audio Visual Ltd, pg 898

ONTARIO

Edcom Multimedia Products, pg 856
FUJIFILM Canada Inc, pg 873
HD Source, pg 886
Majortech Inc, pg 929
Nationwide Audio Visual Co, pg 953

QUEBEC

AVS Technologies Inc, pg 800
Panavideo Inc, pg 968

Videotape—Blank Manufacturers

CALIFORNIA

Media Distributors, pg 936
MSE Media Solutions, pg 949
Panasonic Broadcast & Digital Systems Co, pg 968
QRS Software Services, pg 988
Reel Picture, pg 994
Sony Electronics Inc, pg 1016
Technicolor, pg 1034

FLORIDA

RLX Media LLC, pg 997

VIDEO

Videotape—Blank Manufacturers (continued)

NEW JERSEY

Maxell Corp of America, pg 934
National Audio-Visual Supply, pg 952
Synergem, pg 1030

NEW YORK

FUJIFILM North America Corp, pg 873
Tapemaker, pg 1032

TEXAS

RadioShack Corp, pg 990

UTAH

One Stop CD Shop LLC, pg 963

WISCONSIN

Full Compass Systems, pg 874

ONTARIO

FUJIFILM Canada Inc, pg 873

Videotape Duplication, *see* Duplication—Videotapes

Videotape Editing, *see* Editing—Videotapes

Videotape Recording, *see* Recording—Videotapes

Videotape to Film Transfers, *see* Transfers—Videotape to Film

Virtual Conferencing

ARIZONA

Merestone, pg 938
Metropolitan Audio-Visual Inc, pg 940
Video Media Productions (VMP), pg 1055

ARKANSAS

White Diamond Productions, pg 1065

CALIFORNIA

All Video Productions, pg 781
AV Conferencing, pg 797
Cibola Systems, pg 826
ITV Productions, pg 903
JDS Video & Media Productions Inc, pg 904
KION-TV, pg 911
KPBS TV FM-San Diego, pg 913
KTVU-Retail Services, pg 914
KVIE-Channel 6, pg 914
Laser Magic Productions, pg 916
Ludlow Media Solutions, pg 926
Lynch Communications, pg 926
McCune Audio-Video-Lighting, pg 935
Opticomm-EMCORE, pg 964
Palardo Productions, pg 968
PSSI, pg 987
QRS Software Services, pg 988
Still N'Motion, pg 1025
Thorburn Associates, Acoustic, Technology, Lighting Design, pg 1039
University of Southern California, pg 1050
VMI Inc, pg 1060

COLORADO

Level 3 Communications Inc, pg 919
Spectrum Audio Visual Services, pg 1020

CONNECTICUT

Biomedical Media Communications Dept, pg 807
Broadcast Video Productions LLC, pg 813
Fox Connecticut, pg 872
Guymark Studios LLC, pg 883
Media Vision Productions Inc, pg 937

DISTRICT OF COLUMBIA

Interface Media Group, pg 900
O'Keefe Communications Inc, pg 961

FLORIDA

All Communications Rentals Inc (ALLCOMM), pg 780
AVI-SPL, pg 798
Civins Productions Inc, pg 828
Communications Concepts Inc (CCI), pg 833
Home Shopping Network (HSN), pg 890
Pro Stage Inc, pg 983
Sensormatic®, pg 1006
Universal Studios Florida® Production Group, pg 1049

GEORGIA

CDAI Innovative Design Solutions, pg 822
Digital Projection, pg 847
Myriad Productions, pg 951
Omega Media Group Inc, pg 962
On-Line Productions, pg 963

ILLINOIS

Audio Visual Services Corp, pg 796
Chicago Satellite & Video, pg 825
Production Craft Inc, pg 984
PSAV® Presentation Services (Hotel Services Division), pg 987
Roadworthy Image Magnification, pg 998
Satellite Technology Systems Inc, pg 1003
Video I-D Teleproductions Inc, pg 1055

IOWA

Iowa State University-Information Technology Services, pg 902
The Production House, pg 984

KENTUCKY

Axxis Inc, pg 800
Hammond Communications Group, pg 884
Idle Minds Productions Inc, pg 894
Northern Kentucky University, pg 959
WKYT Productions, pg 1068

LOUISIANA

Digital FX Inc, pg 847
Louisiana State University Health Sciences Center - Shreveport, pg 925
Pace Systems, pg 966

MARYLAND

Absolute Hollywood, pg 772
CPR MultiMedia Solutions, pg 837

MASSACHUSETTS

High Output Inc, pg 888
Preston Productions Inc, pg 981
TVN-The Video Network, pg 1046
Veritech Corp, pg 1053
VideoLink Inc, pg 1057
WVP Boston, pg 1071

MICHIGAN

ASC Systems, pg 791
Digi Sign Design LLC, pg 847
K&R's Recording Studios Inc, pg 908
Maritz Performance Improvement Co, pg 931
RingSide Creative, pg 997

MINNESOTA

Alpha Video & Audio Inc, pg 782
Jamieson & Associates Inc, pg 904
Vaddio, pg 1051

MISSOURI

Communitronics Corp, pg 833
Conference Technologies Inc, pg 835

NEVADA

Encore Productions Inc, pg 861
Lefco Video Services Inc, pg 918

NEW HAMPSHIRE

Academic & Campus Technology Services, pg 773

NEW JERSEY

Broadcast Center Studios, pg 813
DWJ Television, pg 854
Laurel Video Productions, pg 916
MIB Mediaworks, pg 941
NFL Films Inc, pg 957
Suede Interactive, pg 1027
Tele-Measurements Inc, pg 1035
Telemanagement Resources International Inc (TRI), pg 1036
Total Video Products Inc, pg 1042
Turner Engineering Inc, pg 1046
Vision Quest Productions Inc, pg 1058

NEW YORK

Adwar Video, pg 778
Associated Press Television News, pg 792
Broad Street Inc, pg 812
Colortone Audio Visual, pg 832
HBO Studio Productions, pg 886
Long Island Video Enterprises Live Inc, pg 924
Neal Marshad Productions, pg 931
Jack Morton Worldwide, pg 946
Shelly Palmer Production, pg 968
Servoreeler Systems, pg 1007
Synaptic Digital, pg 1030
TBA Global Events, pg 1032
Visual Technologies Corp, pg 1060

NORTH CAROLINA

Bill Barnes Video Productions LLC, pg 803
Lawrence Behr Associates Inc, pg 804
NASCAR Media Group LLC, pg 952

OHIO

Aztec Video Productions, pg 801
CET, pg 823
Copp Integrated Systems, pg 836
Cuyahoga Community College Media Center, pg 841
Mills James Productions, pg 943
WOUB Public Media, pg 1070

OKLAHOMA

Institute for Teaching & Learning Excellence (ITLE), pg 899
Smart Concepts Ltd, pg 1013
University of Oklahoma Academic Media & Digital Services, pg 1050

OREGON

A KTVA Production LLC, pg 771
Creative Media Development, pg 838

PENNSYLVANIA

FMP Media Solutions Inc, pg 870
Fusion Brand Experiences, pg 874
Innovision Media Group, pg 899
Luzerne County Community College, pg 926
Muderick Media, pg 949
Production Masters Inc (PMI), pg 984
Visual Sound Inc, pg 1059
WHYY Inc, pg 1066
WPHL-TV, pg 1070
WQED-Multimedia, pg 1070

SOUTH CAROLINA

Sound & Images Inc, pg 1016
Venture Media, pg 1052

TENNESSEE

Continental Film, pg 835
Stage Post, pg 1022
UMCom Productions, pg 1048

TEXAS

AMS Pictures, pg 786
Dallas Learning Solutions, pg 842
First Group Communications Inc, pg 868
J&S Audio Visual Inc, pg 904
Earl Miller Productions Inc, pg 943
Romar Learning, pg 999
Texas Heart Institute Visual Communication Services, pg 1037

Volume Printing—Videos

Workshops, *see* Production Workshops

PROGRAMMING — AUDIO

Audiobook Distributors

ARIZONA

Valley of the Sun Publishing Co, pg 1051

ARKANSAS

Master Books, pg 933

CALIFORNIA

Audio Editions Books-On-Cassette & CD, pg 794
Blue Dolphin Multimedia, pg 809
Bridge Publications Inc, pg 812
Hay House Inc, pg 886
Krishnamurti Foundation of America, pg 913
Maximus Media Inc, pg 934
monterey video, pg 946
M2 Communications, pg 949
Multi-Media Mathematics, pg 949
Music World/Vocal Power School, pg 951
National Lampoon, pg 953
ODC Publishing, pg 961
Osho Viha Information Center & Book Distributors, pg 965
People Skills International, pg 972
QRS Software Services, pg 988
Redwood Audiobooks, pg 993
Regent Press Publishers & Printers, pg 994
SevenStar Communications, pg 1007
The Wine Appreciation Guild Ltd, pg 1067

CONNECTICUT

Tantor Media Inc, pg 1031

FLORIDA

Distribution Video & Audio (DVA), pg 849
Health Communications Inc, pg 887
Times-Square Fantasy Theatre, pg 1041

GEORGIA

August House Audio, pg 796
New Leaf Distributing Co, pg 955

HAWAII

Media Bridge Gamekids, pg 936

ILLINOIS

African American Images, pg 778
CCore Media Inc, pg 821
Encyclopaedia Britannica Inc, pg 861

INDIANA

Herff Jones | Nystrom, pg 888

KANSAS

Chapman Recording & Mastering, pg 824

LOUISIANA

Pelican Publishing Co, pg 971

MAINE

WoodenBoat Publications, pg 1069

MARYLAND

Audio Book Contractors LLC, pg 794
Discovery Education - Silver Spring, pg 848
Recorded Books LLC, pg 993
RLJ Entertainment Inc, pg 997

MASSACHUSETTS

Penfield Productions Ltd, pg 971

MICHIGAN

Brilliance Audio, pg 812
Digi Sign Design LLC, pg 847
Emery-Pratt Co, pg 860
University of Michigan, Center for Middle Eastern & North African Studies, pg 1050

MINNESOTA

Effective Learning Systems Inc, pg 858
Hazelden Publishing & Educational Services, pg 886
HighBridge Audio, pg 889

MISSOURI

American Audio Prose Library Inc (AAPL), pg 783
SOM Publishing Co, pg 1015

NEW HAMPSHIRE

Captain Fiddle Music & Publications, pg 820
Chip Taylor Communications LLC, pg 1032

NEW JERSEY

Alden Films, pg 780
Learning Ally, pg 917
Listen & Live Audio Inc, pg 923
Paulist Press, pg 970

NEW MEXICO

National Information Center for Educational Media (NICEM)/MediaSleuth, pg 952

NEW YORK

Bantam Doubleday Dell Audio Publishing, pg 802
Beekman Books Inc, pg 804
Conversation Arts Media, pg 836
Cross-Cultural Communications, pg 839
Digital Force, pg 847
Listening Library, pg 923
MRG Productions Inc, pg 948
Penguin Audiobooks, pg 971
Posthorn Recordings, pg 979
RadioArt/Bob & Ray CDs & MP3 Files, pg 990
Random House Children's Books, pg 991
ZBS Foundation, pg 1073

NORTH CAROLINA

Baker & Taylor Inc, pg 801
Ladyslipper Inc, pg 915
Vide-O-Go/That's Infotainment!, pg 1054

OHIO

Curtis Inc, pg 841

OREGON

Blackstone Audio Inc, pg 808
Downpour.com, pg 851
The Keyboard Workshop, pg 910
Sugar Mountain PR, pg 1028

PENNSYLVANIA

Himalayan Institute Audio/Video, pg 889
The Fred Rogers Co, pg 998

SOUTH CAROLINA

BJU Press, pg 808
DaviSound, pg 843
University of South Carolina Press, pg 1050

TENNESSEE

American Blackguard Inc, pg 784
Cokesbury, pg 831
Ingram Book Group, pg 898
Spring Arbor Distributors, pg 1022

TEXAS

Big Kids Productions Inc, pg 807
Milky Way Press, pg 943

VERMONT

Chelsea Green Publishing Co, pg 824
Dialect Accent Specialists Inc, pg 846
Trafalgar Square Books, pg 1043

VIRGINIA

National Media Services Inc, pg 953

WASHINGTON

Books In Motion, pg 811

BRITISH COLUMBIA

Raincoast Books, pg 991
Timeless Books, pg 1040

ONTARIO

Gospel Folio Press, pg 880

Audiobook Producers

ARIZONA

Allusion Studios & Pure Wave Audio, pg 782
SPEAK HOUSE Audio™, pg 1019
Tellens Inc, pg 1037
Valley of the Sun Publishing Co, pg 1051
Walt Disney Records Consumer Products Division, pg 1061

ARKANSAS

Live'N'Loud, pg 923

CALIFORNIA

The Banquet Sound Studios, pg 802
Blue Dolphin Multimedia, pg 809
Creative Media Recording, pg 838
Creativity Unlimited Press®, pg 839
Dogma Studios, pg 850
4th Street Recording, pg 872
Hay House Inc, pg 886
International Contact Inc, pg 900
KABA Audio Productions, pg 907
Krishnamurti Foundation of America, pg 913
Lynch Communications, pg 926
monterey video, pg 946
M2 Communications, pg 949
Multi-Media Mathematics, pg 949
Music World/Vocal Power School, pg 951
National Lampoon, pg 953
ODC Publishing, pg 961
OTR Studios, pg 966
QRS Software Services, pg 988
Redwood Audiobooks, pg 993
Regent Press Publishers & Printers, pg 994
SevenStar Communications, pg 1007
Steve Shapiro Music, pg 1008
Studio 132, pg 1027
WalkerVision Interarts, pg 1061
Webster Communications, pg 1063

CONNECTICUT

P&P Studios Inc, pg 968
Tantor Media Inc, pg 1031

DISTRICT OF COLUMBIA

Biblical Archaeology Society (BAS), pg 806

FLORIDA

Blackburst Entertainment, pg 808
Courter Films LLC, pg 837
Health Communications Inc, pg 887
LHV Audio Services, pg 919
Sunfire Communications Inc, pg 1028
Sunrise Studios, pg 1028
Times-Square Fantasy Theatre, pg 1041
Top Hat Productions, pg 1042

GEORGIA

August House Audio, pg 796
Guerrilla Productions LLC, pg 883

HAWAII

Media Bridge Gamekids, pg 936

ILLINOIS

African American Images, pg 778
AudioTransitions, pg 796
CCore Media Inc, pg 821
Steven Samler Music & Sound, pg 1002

INDIANA

AVA Productions, pg 798
Herff Jones | Nystrom, pg 888

IOWA

Hedquist Productions Inc, pg 887

KANSAS

Chapman Recording & Mastering, pg 824

LOUISIANA

Pelican Publishing Co, pg 971

MARYLAND

Books on Tape®, pg 811
CSPMedia.com, pg 840
dbF a Media Company, pg 844

Audiobook Rentals

Audiocassette Distributors

PROGRAMMING — AUDIO

Audiocassette Distributors (continued)

INDIANA

Lee Co Inc, pg 918
Optical Disc Solutions Inc, pg 964

IOWA

Perfection Learning Corp, pg 973

KANSAS

Chapman Recording & Mastering, pg 824
Day Star Productions, pg 844

KENTUCKY

The Learning House Inc, pg 917

LOUISIANA

Great Chefs/Leisure Jazz Video, pg 881
Leisure Video, pg 918
Pelican Publishing Co, pg 971

MARYLAND

Audio Book Contractors LLC, pg 794
Bradley Broadcast & Pro Audio, pg 811
dbF a Media Company, pg 844
Department of Education Resources, pg 845
MMI Corp, pg 944
Nicholas P Pipino Associates Inc, pg 976
Recorded Books LLC, pg 993

MASSACHUSETTS

Cheng & Tsui Co, pg 824
Pauline Books & Media, pg 970
Penfield Productions Ltd, pg 971
St Bede's Publications, pg 1001
Triumph Learning LLC, pg 1045
Yellow Moon Press, pg 1072

MICHIGAN

Brilliance Audio, pg 812
Digi Sign Design LLC, pg 847
Master Mind Publishing Co, pg 933
Phoenix Society for Burn Survivors Inc, pg 974
Wayne State University Media Services, pg 1063
Zondervan, A HarperCollins Company, pg 1074

MINNESOTA

American Choral Catalog Ltd, pg 784
Effective Learning Systems Inc, pg 858
GMI Productions, pg 879
Hazelden Publishing & Educational Services, pg 886
HighBridge Audio, pg 889
Llewellyn Publications, pg 923
Science Museum of Minnesota, pg 1005
Whole Person Associates Inc, pg 1066

MISSOURI

American Audio Prose Library Inc (AAPL), pg 783
Grace Church - St Louis, pg 881
Impact Christian Books Inc, pg 897
Mosby Inc, pg 947
Vedanta Society of St Louis, pg 1052

NEBRASKA

AdventSource, pg 778
The Recruiters Library, pg 993

NEW HAMPSHIRE

Captain Fiddle Music & Publications, pg 820
Frey Scientific, pg 873
Chip Taylor Communications LLC, pg 1032

NEW JERSEY

Dance Horizons Video, pg 842
Educational Impressions, pg 857
Faith Fellowship Ministries World Outreach Center, pg 865
Hamilton Buhl, pg 884
Learning Ally, pg 917
Milestone Film & Video Inc, pg 943
A W Peller & Associates Inc, pg 971
Shanachie Entertainment Corp, pg 1008
Tele-Measurements Inc, pg 1035

NEW MEXICO

Indian House, pg 897
National Information Center for Educational Media (NICEM)/MediaSleuth, pg 952

NEW YORK

Bantam Doubleday Dell Audio Publishing, pg 802
Digital Force, pg 847
Dover Publications Inc, pg 851
DRG Records Inc, pg 852
Educational Activities Inc, pg 857
Film Emporium, pg 867
Flash Electronics Inc, pg 869
Guilford Publications, pg 883
HB-Content, pg 886
Homespun Video, pg 890
Janus Films Inc, pg 904
Live Oak Media, pg 923
Manhattan Center Studios Inc, pg 930
Maryknoll Productions, pg 933
Saul Mineroff Electronics Inc, pg 943
Motown Record Co, pg 947
MRG Productions Inc, pg 948
Neptune Photo Inc, pg 954
New World Records, pg 956
Penguin Audiobooks, pg 971
Qualiton Imports Ltd, pg 988
The Fulton J Sheen Co Inc, pg 1008
Simon & Schuster, Inc, pg 1011
SISU Home Entertainment Inc, pg 1012
Sony Music Entertainment, pg 1016
Spoken Arts Inc, pg 1021
Synaptic Digital, pg 1030
United Nations Department of Public Information-News & Media Division, pg 1048
The Verve Music Group, pg 1053
Visual Technologies Corp, pg 1060
Zim Records, pg 1074

NORTH CAROLINA

Carolina Biological Supply Co, pg 820
Eli Research Group, pg 859
Howard Hanger, pg 884
Ladyslipper Inc, pg 915
Vide-O-Go/That's Infotainment!, pg 1054

OHIO

Curtis Inc, pg 841
Cuyahoga Community College Media Center, pg 841
Franciscan Media, pg 872
McGraw-Hill School Education Group, pg 935
Ohio State University Foreign Language Publications, pg 961
South-Western Publishing Co, pg 1019
Telarc International Corp, pg 1035
Visual Education, pg 1059

OKLAHOMA

Piper Media Services Inc, pg 976

OREGON

The Keyboard Workshop, pg 910

PENNSYLVANIA

Discovery Education - South Burlington, pg 848
Dreambox Media Inc, pg 852
Forge Recording LLC, pg 871
Himalayan Institute Audio/Video, pg 889
Library Video Company, pg 920
Lippincott Williams & Wilkins, pg 922
Newtown Psychological Center, pg 957
TRC Interactive Inc, pg 1044

SOUTH CAROLINA

DaviSound, pg 843

TENNESSEE

American Blackguard Inc, pg 784
EMI CMG Distribution, pg 860
Green Linnet Records, pg 882
Ingram Book Group, pg 898
Provident-Integrity Distribution, pg 986
Randall House Publications, pg 991
Spring Arbor Distributors, pg 1022
Word Label Group, pg 1069

TEXAS

Astro Audio Visual, pg 792
Endtime Inc, pg 861
Executive Development Systems, pg 864
Lamb & Lion Ministries, pg 915
Milky Way Press, pg 943
Sound Works, pg 1018
Stage Directions, pg 1022
Texas Heart Institute Visual Communication Services, pg 1037

VIRGINIA

Colonial Williamsburg Foundation, pg 831
County Sales, pg 837
Filmdex Inc, pg 867
National Media Services Inc, pg 953
Rebel Records, pg 993

WISCONSIN

Aylmer Press, pg 801
Demco Inc, pg 845
School Specialty Inc, pg 1004
Wisconsin Technical College System Foundation Inc, pg 1068

PUERTO RICO

Bonnin Electronics Inc, pg 810

BRITISH COLUMBIA

Thompson Rivers University Open Learning, pg 1039

ONTARIO

CBC/Radio-Canada, pg 821
Mind Resources Inc, pg 943
Novalis, pg 959
The Resource Centre, pg 995
Scholastic Canada Ltd, pg 1004

Audiocassette Producers

ALABAMA

CMEInfo, pg 830
Media Visions Inc, pg 937

ARIZONA

Merestone, pg 938
Perception Publications, pg 973
Personal Achievement Institute, pg 973
SPEAK HOUSE Audio™, pg 1019
Tellens Inc, pg 1037
Truth Consciousness Publications, pg 1045

ARKANSAS

Live'N'Loud, pg 923
White Diamond Productions, pg 1065

CALIFORNIA

ACDC Audio CD & Cassette, pg 774
Artichoke Productions, pg 791
California Language Laboratories, pg 817
Concord Jazz Inc, pg 835
Concord Records Inc, pg 835
Custom Video Productions Inc, pg 841
Design Media, pg 845
Discovery Education - Los Angeles, pg 848
4th Street Recording, pg 872
Gateways, pg 876
Gateways Books & Tapes, pg 876
Gold Standard Productions, pg 880
Bruce Goldberg Inc, pg 880
Steven Halpern's Inner Peace Music, pg 884
Hay House Inc, pg 886
KABA Audio Productions, pg 907
Krishnamurti Foundation of America, pg 913
Lynch Communications, pg 926
Maximus Media Inc, pg 934
monterey media inc, pg 945
monterey video, pg 946
M2 Communications, pg 949
Music World/Vocal Power School, pg 951
Nilgiri Press, pg 957
ODC Publishing, pg 961
On-Trax Inc, pg 963
Pacific Audio-Visual Enterprises, pg 967

PROGRAMMING — AUDIO

Audiocassette Producers (continued)

OHIO (continued)

McGraw-Hill School Education Group, pg 935
Musicol Recording, pg 951
Ohio State University Foreign Language Publications, pg 961
R&B Communications Inc, pg 991
South-Western Publishing Co, pg 1019
Vista Color Imaging Inc, pg 1059

OKLAHOMA

Piper Media Services Inc, pg 976
University of Oklahoma Academic Media & Digital Services, pg 1050

OREGON

A KTVA Production LLC, pg 771
Ideascape Inc, pg 894
The Keyboard Workshop, pg 910
Rex, pg 995

PENNSYLVANIA

American Artist Studio, pg 783
Audio Visual Communications Inc, pg 795
Discovery Education - South Burlington, pg 848
Dreambox Media Inc, pg 852
FMP Media Solutions Inc, pg 870
Forge Recording LLC, pg 871
Goodman Associates Inc, pg 880
Himalayan Institute Audio/Video, pg 889
Innovision Media Group, pg 899
JPL, pg 906
Key of David Publications, pg 910
Lippincott Williams & Wilkins, pg 922
Muderick Media, pg 949
Newtown Psychological Center, pg 957
Production Masters Inc (PMI), pg 984
Ted The Fiddler Music, pg 1035
The Videohouse Inc, pg 1057

SOUTH CAROLINA

DaviSound, pg 843

TENNESSEE

Green Linnet Records, pg 882
Memphis Communications Corp, pg 938
Provident-Integrity Distribution, pg 986
Word Label Group, pg 1069

TEXAS

Endtime Inc, pg 861
Lamb & Lion Ministries, pg 915
Milky Way Press, pg 943
Music Lab Inc, pg 950
Romar Learning, pg 999
The Samuels Co, pg 1002
Sound Works, pg 1018
Stage Directions, pg 1022
Texas Heart Institute Visual Communication Services, pg 1037
Tropikal Productions, pg 1045
The Yesterday USA Radio Networks, pg 1072

UTAH

One Stop CD Shop LLC, pg 963

VERMONT

Inner Traditions International, pg 898

VIRGINIA

AudioImage Recording, pg 796
BES Studios, pg 805
CACI Productions Group, pg 816
County Sales, pg 837
Lion Recording Services Inc, pg 922
Metro Productions, pg 939
National Media Services Inc, pg 953
Rebel Records, pg 993
Studio Center Corp, pg 1026

WASHINGTON

Kostov Productions, pg 913
Pacific Multimedia Inc, pg 967

WISCONSIN

5th Floor Recording Co, pg 867
Meridian Studios, pg 939
USAV Group Inc, pg 1050
Video Wisconsin Inc, pg 1056

WYOMING

Bridger Productions Inc, pg 812

BRITISH COLUMBIA

Thompson Rivers University Open Learning, pg 1039

ONTARIO

CBC/Radio-Canada, pg 821
Novalis, pg 959
Purefire Communications Inc, pg 987

Audiocassette Rentals

CALIFORNIA

Ametron Audio/Video, pg 785
Steven Halpern's Inner Peace Music, pg 884
Medcom Inc, pg 936

DELAWARE

Side Door Studio Inc, pg 1010

FLORIDA

Times-Square Fantasy Theatre, pg 1041

GEORGIA

Symmes Systems, pg 1030

ILLINOIS

RBR Productions, pg 992
Woodside Avenue Music Productions Inc, pg 1069

MICHIGAN

Digi Sign Design LLC, pg 847
Wayne State University Media Services, pg 1063

NEW HAMPSHIRE

Chip Taylor Communications LLC, pg 1032

NEW YORK

MRG Productions Inc, pg 948
United Nations Multimedia Resources Unit, pg 1048

OREGON

The Keyboard Workshop, pg 910

WISCONSIN

Wisconsin Technical College System Foundation Inc, pg 1068

Audiotape Distributors

ARIZONA

Arizona Cine Equipment, pg 789
Drumbeat Indian Arts Inc, pg 852

CALIFORNIA

Ametron Audio/Video, pg 785
Audio Editions Books-On-Cassette & CD, pg 794
Educational Technology Services (ETS), pg 857
Gateways, pg 876
Golden State Dance Teachers Association (GSDTA), pg 880
Steven Halpern's Inner Peace Music, pg 884
Hay House Inc, pg 886
Medcom Inc, pg 936
monterey video, pg 946
Music World/Vocal Power School, pg 951
Joseph Nicoletti Consulting-Promotion/California International Records/Global Village Records, pg 957
ODC Publishing, pg 961
Players Press, pg 977
QRS Software Services, pg 988
Regent Press Publishers & Printers, pg 994
Sahara Records & Filmworks Entertainment Co, pg 1001
Sodanceabit, pg 1015
Valley Media, pg 1051
Welk Music Group, pg 1063

COLORADO

Gaiam Inc, pg 875

CONNECTICUT

Connecticut Audio & Theatrical Supply, pg 835
Crossroads Video, pg 840
EagleVision Inc, pg 855

DELAWARE

So Smart Productions, pg 1015

DISTRICT OF COLUMBIA

Library of Congress, Motion Picture, Broadcasting & Recorded Sound Division, pg 919

FLORIDA

Gulf Coast Audio Visual Producers Inc, pg 883
I M P A C T Publishing Inc, pg 893
Photomart Cine-Video Inc, pg 975
Psychological Assessment Resources Inc (PAR), pg 987
Tallahassee Audio Visual, pg 1031

GEORGIA

Audio Visual Resources Inc, pg 795

ILLINOIS

Educational Insights, pg 857
Woodside Avenue Music Productions Inc, pg 1069

INDIANA

Lee Co Inc, pg 918
Optical Disc Solutions Inc, pg 964

KENTUCKY

The Learning House Inc, pg 917

LOUISIANA

Pelican Publishing Co, pg 971

MARYLAND

Bradley Broadcast & Pro Audio, pg 811
Nicholas P Pipino Associates Inc, pg 976
Recorded Books LLC, pg 993

MICHIGAN

Brilliance Audio, pg 812
Digi Sign Design LLC, pg 847
Master Mind Publishing Co, pg 933
MSU Technologies, pg 949
University of Michigan, Center for Middle Eastern & North African Studies, pg 1050
Wayne State University Media Services, pg 1063

MINNESOTA

American Choral Catalog Ltd, pg 784
Effective Learning Systems Inc, pg 858
HighBridge Audio, pg 889
Learning Strategies Corp, pg 917

NEW HAMPSHIRE

Chip Taylor Communications LLC, pg 1032

NEW JERSEY

Hamilton Buhl, pg 884

NEW MEXICO

National Information Center for Educational Media (NICEM)/MediaSleuth, pg 952

NEW YORK

Digital Force, pg 847
DRG Records Inc, pg 852
Film Emporium, pg 867
Flash Electronics Inc, pg 869
HB-Content, pg 886
Janus Films Inc, pg 904
Listening Library, pg 923
Madison Square Garden, pg 927
Manhattan Center Studios Inc, pg 930
Maryknoll Productions, pg 933
Saul Mineroff Electronics Inc, pg 943
MRG Productions Inc, pg 948
Neptune Photo Inc, pg 954

SISU Home Entertainment Inc, pg 1012
Sony Music Entertainment, pg 1016
Synaptic Digital, pg 1030
Touchstone Center Publications, pg 1043
The Verve Music Group, pg 1053
Visual Technologies Corp, pg 1060

NORTH CAROLINA

Ladyslipper Inc, pg 915

OHIO

Curtis Inc, pg 841
Cuyahoga Community College Media Center, pg 841
Ohio State University Foreign Language Publications, pg 961

OKLAHOMA

Piper Media Services Inc, pg 976

PENNSYLVANIA

Forge Recording LLC, pg 871
Himalayan Institute Audio/Video, pg 889

TENNESSEE

American Blackguard Inc, pg 784
Center for Southern Folklore Inc, pg 822
Green Linnet Records, pg 882
Spring Arbor Distributors, pg 1022

TEXAS

Astro Audio Visual, pg 792
Milky Way Press, pg 943
Sound Works, pg 1018
Stage Directions, pg 1022

VIRGINIA

County Sales, pg 837
Filmdex Inc, pg 867

WISCONSIN

Demco Inc, pg 845

PUERTO RICO

Bonnin Electronics Inc, pg 810

BRITISH COLUMBIA

Timeless Books, pg 1040

ONTARIO

CBC/Radio-Canada, pg 821
Entertainment One Distribution, pg 861

Audiotape Producers

ALABAMA

CMEInfo, pg 830

ARIZONA

Merestone, pg 938
SPEAK HOUSE Audio™, pg 1019
Tellens Inc, pg 1037

ARKANSAS

Live'N'Loud, pg 923

CALIFORNIA

ACDC Audio CD & Cassette, pg 774
Artichoke Productions, pg 791
The Banquet Sound Studios, pg 802
Custom Video Productions Inc, pg 841
Design Media, pg 845
Dogma Studios, pg 850
Educational Technology Services (ETS), pg 857
4th Street Recording, pg 872
Gateways, pg 876
Gold Standard Productions, pg 880
Steven Halpern's Inner Peace Music, pg 884
Hay House Inc, pg 886
International Contact Inc, pg 900
Lynch Communications, pg 926
Maximus Media Inc, pg 934
monterey video, pg 946
M2 Communications, pg 949
Music World/Vocal Power School, pg 951
New Harbinger Publications, pg 955
Joseph Nicoletti Consulting-Promotion/California International Records/Global Village Records, pg 957
ODC Publishing, pg 961
On-Trax Inc, pg 963
Pacific Audio-Visual Enterprises, pg 967
Panorama Productions, pg 968
Players Press, pg 977
QRS Software Services, pg 988
Regent Press Publishers & Printers, pg 994
Rhythms Productions (Tom Thumb Music), pg 996
Sahara Records & Filmworks Entertainment Co, pg 1001
Saturn Studios, pg 1003
SBS Productions, pg 1003
Steve Shapiro Music, pg 1008
Sodanceabit, pg 1015
Studio 132, pg 1027
Total Media Group, pg 1042
Tranquil Technology Music, pg 1043
Twin Peaks Creative, pg 1047
Vedanta Press & Catalog, pg 1052
Video Resources Inc, pg 1056
Webster Communications, pg 1063

COLORADO

Tim Cissell Music, pg 828
Daylight Productions & Rentals, pg 844
Flashback Media Productions, pg 869
Gaiam Inc, pg 875
Rocky Mountain Audio/Video Productions Inc, pg 998

CONNECTICUT

Biomedical Media Communications Dept, pg 807
Broadcast Video Productions LLC, pg 813
Crossroads Video, pg 840
EagleVision Inc, pg 855

DELAWARE

Ken-Del Productions Inc, pg 909
So Smart Productions, pg 1015

DISTRICT OF COLUMBIA

Hillmann & Carr Inc, pg 889
Interface Media Group, pg 900

FLORIDA

Audio Visual Imagineering Inc, pg 795
Courter Films LLC, pg 837
Gulf Coast Audio Visual Producers Inc, pg 883
Home Shopping Network (HSN), pg 890
LHV Audio Services, pg 919
Psychological Assessment Resources Inc (PAR), pg 987
Sunfire Communications Inc, pg 1028
Tel-Air Interests Inc, pg 1035

GEORGIA

First Cut Communications LLC, pg 868
Guerrilla Productions LLC, pg 883

ILLINOIS

Audio Visual Services Corp, pg 796
Cresta Creative, pg 839
Major Media Inc, pg 929
Paragon Studios Inc, pg 969
Jim Passin Productions, pg 970
PSAV® Presentation Services (Hotel Services Division), pg 987
Universal Training, pg 1049
Woodside Avenue Music Productions Inc, pg 1069

INDIANA

AVA Productions, pg 798
Bright Ideas Creative Services, pg 812
OMNI Productions, pg 962
Optical Disc Solutions Inc, pg 964

IOWA

The Production House, pg 984

KANSAS

Chapman Recording & Mastering, pg 824

KENTUCKY

Donna Lawrence Productions, pg 917
The Learning House Inc, pg 917
Trusty Tuneshop Recording Studios, pg 1045

LOUISIANA

Leisure Video, pg 918

MAINE

Serendipity Recordings, pg 1007

MARYLAND

The Ahern Group, pg 779
Books on Tape®, pg 811
CSPMedia.com, pg 840
The Cutting Corp, pg 841
The Image Generators, pg 895
Lion & Fox Recording Studios, pg 922
Recorded Books LLC, pg 993

MASSACHUSETTS

CommCreative, pg 832
Emergency Film Group, pg 860
Labrecque Creative Sound, pg 915
Monadnock Media Inc, pg 945
Penfield Productions Ltd, pg 971
Shambhala Publications, pg 1008
Soundtrack Recording Studios, pg 1018
TR Productions, pg 1043

MICHIGAN

Brilliance Audio, pg 812
Digi Sign Design LLC, pg 847
K&R All Media Productions Inc, pg 908
K&R's Recording Studios Inc, pg 908
Master Mind Publishing Co, pg 933
MessageMakers, pg 939
MSU Technologies, pg 949
University of Michigan, Center for Middle Eastern & North African Studies, pg 1050
Wayne State University Media Services, pg 1063

MINNESOTA

American Choral Catalog Ltd, pg 784
Effective Learning Systems Inc, pg 858
GMI Productions, pg 879
HighBridge Audio, pg 889
Learning Strategies Corp, pg 917

MISSOURI

Audio-VideoGraphics Inc, pg 795
Celebrities Productions, pg 822
Fambrough & Associates Inc, pg 865

NEW HAMPSHIRE

Chip Taylor Communications LLC, pg 1032

NEW JERSEY

Broadcast Center Studios, pg 813
CFP Video Productions Inc, pg 823
Optisonics Productions, pg 965
Suede Interactive, pg 1027

NEW MEXICO

Michael Dunn Productions, pg 853

NEW YORK

Applause Learning Resources, pg 788
Aural Gratification Inc, pg 796
Broad Street Inc, pg 812
Thomas Craven Film Corp, pg 837
Digital Force, pg 847
Eastco Multimedia Solutions Inc, pg 856
Edgeware Associates/Travel Arts Syndicate, pg 856
HB-Content, pg 886
International Digital Centre, pg 901
Juston Records, pg 907
Kamen Entertainment Group Inc, pg 908
Listening Library, pg 923
Madison Square Garden, pg 927
Manhattan Center Studios Inc, pg 930
Maryknoll Productions, pg 933
MRG Productions Inc, pg 948
MRM Worldwide, pg 948
New York Audio Productions, pg 956
Shelly Palmer Production, pg 968
RCA Records, pg 992
Peter Schleger Co, pg 1004
Sear Sound, pg 1005
SISU Home Entertainment Inc, pg 1012

PROGRAMMING — AUDIO

Audiotape Producers (continued)

NEW YORK (continued)

Elliot Sokolov Music, pg 1015
Sony Music Custom Marketing, pg 1016
Sony Music Entertainment, pg 1016
Split Image Productions, pg 1021
Synaptic Digital, pg 1030
TBA Global Events, pg 1032
Touchstone Center Publications, pg 1043
Zelman Studios Ltd, pg 1073

NORTH CAROLINA

Pat Appleson Studios Inc, pg 788
The Communications Group Inc, pg 833

OHIO

Curtis Inc, pg 841
Cuyahoga Community College Media Center, pg 841
EDR Media LLC, pg 857
Lyon Video Inc, pg 927
Musicol Recording, pg 951
Ohio State University Foreign Language Publications, pg 961
R&B Communications Inc, pg 991
Vista Color Imaging Inc, pg 1059

OKLAHOMA

Piper Media Services Inc, pg 976
University of Oklahoma Academic Media & Digital Services, pg 1050

OREGON

A KTVA Production LLC, pg 771
Rex, pg 995

PENNSYLVANIA

Audio Visual Communications Inc, pg 795
Canadian American Records, pg 818
FMP Media Solutions Inc, pg 870
Forge Recording LLC, pg 871
Goodman Associates Inc, pg 880
Himalayan Institute Audio/Video, pg 889
Innovision Media Group, pg 899
JPL, pg 906
Muderick Media, pg 949
Primary Press, pg 982
Production Masters Inc (PMI), pg 984
The Videohouse Inc, pg 1057

TENNESSEE

Center for Southern Folklore Inc, pg 822
Green Linnet Records, pg 882
Memphis Communications Corp, pg 938

TEXAS

The Editing Co, pg 857
Milky Way Press, pg 943
Romar Learning, pg 999
The Samuels Co, pg 1002
Sound Works, pg 1018
Stage Directions, pg 1022
Texas Heart Institute Visual Communication Services, pg 1037
Tropikal Productions, pg 1045
The Yesterday USA Radio Networks, pg 1072

UTAH

One Stop CD Shop LLC, pg 963

VIRGINIA

AudioImage Recording, pg 796
BES Studios, pg 805
CACI Productions Group, pg 816
County Sales, pg 837
Lion Recording Services Inc, pg 922
National Media Services Inc, pg 953
Studio Center Corp, pg 1026

WASHINGTON

Kostov Productions, pg 913

WISCONSIN

5th Floor Recording Co, pg 867
Meridian Studios, pg 939
USAV Group Inc, pg 1050
Video Wisconsin Inc, pg 1056

WYOMING

Bridger Productions Inc, pg 812

BRITISH COLUMBIA

Timeless Books, pg 1040

ONTARIO

CBC/Radio-Canada, pg 821
JFB Communications, pg 905
Purefire Communications Inc, pg 987

Audiotape Rentals

CALIFORNIA

Ametron Audio/Video, pg 785
Educational Technology Services (ETS), pg 857
Steven Halpern's Inner Peace Music, pg 884
Medcom Inc, pg 936

CONNECTICUT

Crossroads Video, pg 840

ILLINOIS

RBR Productions, pg 992
Woodside Avenue Music Productions Inc, pg 1069

MICHIGAN

Digi Sign Design LLC, pg 847
Wayne State University Media Services, pg 1063

NEW HAMPSHIRE

Chip Taylor Communications LLC, pg 1032

NEW YORK

MRG Productions Inc, pg 948

Business Program Distributors

ARIZONA

Personal Achievement Institute, pg 973

CALIFORNIA

Direct Cinema Ltd Inc, pg 848
Bruce Goldberg Inc, pg 880
Jossey-Bass, pg 906
Learning Communications LLC, pg 917
Maximus Media Inc, pg 934
ODC Publishing, pg 961
Publishers Group West Inc, pg 987
QRS Software Services, pg 988
University of Southern California, pg 1050

COLORADO

National Teaching Aids Inc, pg 953

CONNECTICUT

Tantor Media Inc, pg 1031

FLORIDA

Capital Communications Inc, pg 819

GEORGIA

Convergent Media Systems, pg 836
Playback Now, pg 977
School Media Associates LLC, pg 1004
Symmes Systems, pg 1030

HAWAII

Media Bridge Gamekids, pg 936

ILLINOIS

CCH Continuing Education, pg 821
CCore Media Inc, pg 821
Nightingale-Conant Corp, pg 957
Oasis Audio, pg 960

IOWA

Long-Term Success Publishing, pg 924

LOUISIANA

Pelican Publishing Co, pg 971

MAINE

Slim Goodbody Corp, pg 1013

MARYLAND

Recorded Books LLC, pg 993

MASSACHUSETTS

Emergency Film Group, pg 860
Penfield Productions Ltd, pg 971

MICHIGAN

Digi Sign Design LLC, pg 847
Emery-Pratt Co, pg 860

MINNESOTA

Effective Learning Systems Inc, pg 858
HighBridge Audio, pg 889
Learning Strategies Corp, pg 917

MISSOURI

Phoenix/BFA/Coronet, pg 974

NEVADA

DVDs4Less, pg 854

NEW HAMPSHIRE

Chip Taylor Communications LLC, pg 1032

NEW JERSEY

Listen & Live Audio Inc, pg 923

NEW MEXICO

National Information Center for Educational Media (NICEM)/MediaSleuth, pg 952

NEW YORK

American Management Association International, pg 784
The Cinema Guild Inc, pg 827
Educational Images Ltd, pg 857
Films Media Group, pg 868
HarperAudio, pg 885
HB-Content, pg 886
MRG Productions Inc, pg 948
Penguin Audiobooks, pg 971
Practising Law Institute, pg 980
Random House Audio Publishing Group, pg 991
Synaptic Digital, pg 1030
TeleTime Productions, pg 1036
Visual Technologies Corp, pg 1060

NORTH CAROLINA

Baker & Taylor Inc, pg 801
Eli Research Group, pg 859
Vide-O-Go/That's Infotainment!, pg 1054

OHIO

Curtis Inc, pg 841
South-Western Publishing Co, pg 1019
Speakers Unlimited, pg 1020

OREGON

InterVision Media, pg 902

PENNSYLVANIA

FMP Media Solutions Inc, pg 870
Newtown Psychological Center, pg 957

SOUTH CAROLINA

DaviSound, pg 843

TENNESSEE

Continental Film, pg 835
Ingram Book Group, pg 898
Zion Music Group, pg 1074

VERMONT

Taylor Associates, pg 1032

VIRGINIA

CACI Productions Group, pg 816

WASHINGTON

AEON Communications Inc, pg 778

BRITISH COLUMBIA

Thompson Rivers University Open Learning, pg 1039

ONTARIO

Canadian Learning Co Inc, pg 818

Business Program Producers

ALABAMA

Leo Ticheli Productions, pg 1040

ARIZONA

Allusion Studios & Pure Wave Audio, pg 782
Candee Productions Inc, pg 819
Personal Achievement Institute, pg 973
SPEAK HOUSE Audio™, pg 1019

CALIFORNIA

The Banquet Sound Studios, pg 802
Big Door, pg 807
Concrete Images, pg 835
Creative Media Recording, pg 838
Custom Video Productions Inc, pg 841
Design Media, pg 845
Direct Cinema Ltd Inc, pg 848
Dogma Studios, pg 850
Goal Productions, pg 879
Gold Standard Productions, pg 880
Bruce Goldberg Inc, pg 880
Havas Edge, pg 885
Jossey-Bass, pg 906
KABA Audio Productions, pg 907
The Kenwood Group, pg 909
Lynch Communications, pg 926
Maximus Media Inc, pg 934
Media Magic, pg 937
The Media Staff Inc, pg 937
ODC Publishing, pg 961
OTR Studios, pg 966
piXvfm, pg 976
PM Productions, pg 977
Point of View Productions, pg 977
Producers Group Ltd, pg 983
QRS Software Services, pg 988
SBS Productions, pg 1003
Steve Shapiro Music, pg 1008
Still N'Motion, pg 1025
Studio 132, pg 1027
Tam Communications Inc, pg 1031
Tele-Video Production Services (TVPS), pg 1036
Total Media Group, pg 1042
University of Southern California, pg 1050
WalkerVision Interarts, pg 1061
Webster Communications, pg 1063

COLORADO

Daylight Productions & Rentals, pg 844
Flashback Media Productions, pg 869
National Teaching Aids Inc, pg 953
Starwest Productions, pg 1024

CONNECTICUT

EagleVision Inc, pg 855
P&P Studios Inc, pg 968
Tantor Media Inc, pg 1031

DISTRICT OF COLUMBIA

Educational Film Center, pg 857
Hillmann & Carr Inc, pg 889

FLORIDA

Audio Visual Imagineering Inc, pg 795
Blackburst Entertainment, pg 808
Capital Communications Inc, pg 819
Eastern Video, pg 856
LHV Audio Services, pg 919
Sunfire Communications Inc, pg 1028
Sunrise Studios, pg 1028
Top Hat Productions, pg 1042
Tricycle Studios, pg 1044
Universal Studios Florida® Production Group, pg 1049

GEORGIA

Guerrilla Productions LLC, pg 883
Playback Now, pg 977
Symmes Systems, pg 1030

HAWAII

Media Bridge Gamekids, pg 936

IDAHO

Wide Eye Productions, pg 1066

ILLINOIS

ABS Enterprises, pg 772
Accenture, pg 773
Audio Visual Services Corp, pg 796
AudioTransitions, pg 796
CCH Continuing Education, pg 821
CCore Media Inc, pg 821
Centrax Corp, pg 823
Communications Corporation of America, pg 833
Cresta Creative, pg 839
Major Media Productions Inc, pg 929
Nightingale-Conant Corp, pg 957
Oasis Audio, pg 960
The Pepper Group, pg 972
PSAV® Presentation Services (Hotel Services Division), pg 987
Steven Samler Music & Sound, pg 1002
Sparkfactor, pg 1019
Video Impressions, pg 1055

INDIANA

Advanced Media Integration, pg 777
AVA Productions, pg 798
Bright Ideas Creative Services, pg 812
OMNI Productions, pg 962
PentaVision Communications Inc, pg 972

IOWA

Hedquist Productions Inc, pg 887
Long-Term Success Publishing, pg 924

KANSAS

Chapman Recording & Mastering, pg 824

LOUISIANA

Disk Productions, pg 849

MARYLAND

CPR MultiMedia Solutions, pg 837
CSPMedia.com, pg 840
The Cutting Corp, pg 841
dbF a Media Company, pg 844
The Image Generators, pg 895
Kramer Communications Video Production, pg 913
Recorded Books LLC, pg 993

MASSACHUSETTS

CommCreative, pg 832
Emergency Film Group, pg 860
Heliotrope Studios, pg 887
Labrecque Creative Sound, pg 915
Northern Light Productions, pg 959
Penfield Productions Ltd, pg 971
Preston Productions Inc, pg 981
Shambhala Publications, pg 1008
Soundtrack Recording Studios, pg 1018
TR Productions, pg 1043
TVN-The Video Network, pg 1046

MICHIGAN

The Brookwood Studio Inc, pg 814
Digi Sign Design LLC, pg 847
K&R All Media Productions Inc, pg 908
K&R's Recording Studios Inc, pg 908
Maritz Performance Improvement Co, pg 931
MessageMakers, pg 939
TGA Recording Co, pg 1038

MINNESOTA

Aggressive Records Audio Duplication LLC, pg 778
Effective Learning Systems Inc, pg 858
HighBridge Audio, pg 889
Jamieson & Associates Inc, pg 904
Learning Strategies Corp, pg 917
Master Communications Group, pg 933
Media Loft Inc, pg 937
MultiMedia, pg 950

MISSOURI

Audio-VideoGraphics Inc, pg 795
Celebrities Productions, pg 822
Fambrough & Associates Inc, pg 865

MONTANA

Jereco Studios Inc, pg 905
North Country Media Group, pg 959

NEBRASKA

Dog & Pony Productions Inc, pg 850

NEVADA

DVDs4Less, pg 854
JCS Video Productions, pg 904
Tanglewood Productions, pg 1031

NEW HAMPSHIRE

Apertura, pg 788
Chip Taylor Communications LLC, pg 1032

NEW JERSEY

Audio Vistas LLC, pg 795
CFP Video Productions Inc, pg 823
Half Moon Video Productions, pg 883
Laurel Video Productions, pg 916
Listen & Live Audio Inc, pg 923
MIB Mediaworks, pg 941
Milgrom Productions, pg 943
Optisonics Productions, pg 965
Producer East Productions, pg 983
Bill Quinn Productions, pg 989
Suede Interactive, pg 1027

NEW YORK

American Management Association International, pg 784
Avekta Productions Inc, pg 798
BioMedia Inc, pg 807
Blue Barn Pictures Inc, pg 809
Broad Street Inc, pg 812
Cohn Creative Group LLC, pg 831
Thomas Craven Film Corp, pg 837
C2 Imaging LLC, pg 841
Digital Force, pg 847
dM works, pg 849
Fingerpaint, pg 868
Karen Frankel Productions, pg 872
HarperAudio, pg 885
HB-Content, pg 886
Hello World Communications, pg 888
Icontent, pg 893
Kamen Entertainment Group Inc, pg 908
Ketchum Pleon Change, pg 910
L A Bruell Inc, pg 914
Jack Morton Worldwide, pg 946
MRG Productions Inc, pg 948
MRM Worldwide, pg 948
MRY, pg 949
New York Audio Productions, pg 956
News Broadcast Network, pg 956
NSR Productions Inc & Capricorn Five Films, pg 960
Shelly Palmer Production, pg 968
Pat Kogan Productions Inc, pg 970
Penguin Audiobooks, pg 971
Practising Law Institute, pg 980
Random House Audio Publishing Group, pg 991
David Rapkin Audio Production, pg 991
Elliot Sokolov Music, pg 1015
Split Image Productions, pg 1021
Suggs Media Productions Inc, pg 1028
Synaptic Digital, pg 1030
TBA Global Events, pg 1032
Tiki Recording Studios Inc, pg 1040
Zelman Studios Ltd, pg 1073

NORTH CAROLINA

Pat Appleson Studios Inc, pg 788
The Communications Group Inc, pg 833
Eli Research Group, pg 859
LCW Productions LLC, pg 917
Sinclair Institute, pg 1012
2BruceStudio, pg 1047

OHIO

Advent Media Inc, pg 778
Creative Technology, pg 838
Curtis Inc, pg 841
EDR Media LLC, pg 857
Musicol Recording, pg 951
R&B Communications Inc, pg 991
South-Western Publishing Co, pg 1019
Take 1 Media Services, pg 1031
VGI Productions, pg 1053
Vista Color Imaging Inc, pg 1059

OKLAHOMA

Piper Media Services Inc, pg 976

PROGRAMMING — AUDIO

Business Program Producers (continued)

OREGON

A KTVA Production LLC, pg 771
ERA Learning, pg 862
Ideascape Inc, pg 894
InterVision Media, pg 902
The Keyboard Workshop, pg 910
Rex, pg 995

PENNSYLVANIA

American Artist Studio, pg 783
FMP Media Solutions Inc, pg 870
Forge Recording LLC, pg 871
JPL, pg 906
Muderick Media, pg 949
Newtown Psychological Center, pg 957
Panta Rhei Media Inc, pg 968
Production Masters Inc (PMI), pg 984

RHODE ISLAND

Sound Advantage, pg 1016
Sound-FX-Design, pg 1017

SOUTH CAROLINA

DaviSound, pg 843
Venture Media, pg 1052

TENNESSEE

Continental Film, pg 835
Memphis Communications Corp, pg 938

TEXAS

AMA Nystrom Printing/Finishing, pg 783
Biway Media, pg 808
The Editing Co, pg 857
Epic Software Group Inc, pg 862
Matson Multi-Media, pg 934
Omega Productions, pg 962
Romar Learning, pg 999
The Sound Lab Inc, pg 1017
Sound Works, pg 1018
South Coast Film & Video, pg 1019
Stage Directions, pg 1022
Tropikal Productions, pg 1045
Writer's AudioShop/Davenport Productions, pg 1070

VIRGINIA

BES Studios, pg 805
CACI Productions Group, pg 816
Limelight Communications Inc, pg 921
Lion Recording Services Inc, pg 922
Metro Productions, pg 939
National Media Services Inc, pg 953
Rocktown Media, pg 998
SNL Kagan Media & Communications, pg 1014
Video Solutions, pg 1056

WASHINGTON

Getty Images, pg 877
Pacific Multimedia Inc, pg 967

WEST VIRGINIA

Blackwater Video Productions, pg 808

WISCONSIN

5th Floor Recording Co, pg 867
Meridian Studios, pg 939
USAV Group Inc, pg 1050
Video Wisconsin Inc, pg 1056
Watts Communications Inc, pg 1062
Wisconsin Public Television, pg 1068

WYOMING

Bridger Productions Inc, pg 812

ALBERTA

HBW Entertainment Inc, pg 886

BRITISH COLUMBIA

Thompson Rivers University Open Learning, pg 1039

ONTARIO

ADS Media, pg 777
DebsVoice, pg 844
GAPC (General Assembly Production Centre), pg 875
Shaw Street Productions, pg 1008

QUEBEC

Kerrigan Productions Inc, pg 910

Business Program Rentals

CALIFORNIA

Direct Cinema Ltd Inc, pg 848
University of Southern California, pg 1050

GEORGIA

Convergent Media Systems, pg 836
Symmes Systems, pg 1030

MASSACHUSETTS

Emergency Film Group, pg 860
Preston Productions Inc, pg 981

MICHIGAN

Digi Sign Design LLC, pg 847

NEW HAMPSHIRE

Chip Taylor Communications LLC, pg 1032

NEW JERSEY

Alden Films, pg 780
Listen & Live Audio Inc, pg 923

PENNSYLVANIA

Karol Media Inc, pg 908
Penn State University MediaTech, pg 972

UTAH

Webb Audio Visual Communication, pg 1063

ONTARIO

Simply Audiobooks, pg 1011

Children's Program Distributors

ARIZONA

Drumbeat Indian Arts Inc, pg 852
Earth Mother Productions Inc™, pg 855

CALIFORNIA

Astronomical Society of the Pacific, pg 792
California Language Laboratories, pg 817
Clarity Sound & Light, pg 829
Digital Media West, pg 847
Direct Cinema Ltd Inc, pg 848
Discovery Toys, pg 848
Gateways, pg 876
Steven Halpern's Inner Peace Music, pg 884
Klutz, pg 912
Madera Video, pg 927
Maximus Media Inc, pg 934
monterey media inc, pg 945
monterey video, pg 946
Moose School Productions, pg 946
ODC Publishing, pg 961
People Skills International, pg 972
Publishers Group West Inc, pg 987
QRS Software Services, pg 988
Rhythms Productions (Tom Thumb Music), pg 996
Sound Feelings Records, pg 1017
Warner Home Video Inc, pg 1062
Western Instructional Television Inc, pg 1064

CONNECTICUT

American Melody, pg 784
EagleVision Inc, pg 855
Scholastic Library Publishing, pg 1004
Tantor Media Inc, pg 1031
Weston Woods Studios Inc, pg 1064

DELAWARE

So Smart Productions, pg 1015

FLORIDA

ACE Video Resources Software, pg 774
Allegro Productions Inc, pg 781
Capital Communications Inc, pg 819
Media Concepts Inc, pg 936
Potentials Unlimited, pg 979
SOS Worldwide Productions Inc, pg 1016

GEORGIA

August House Audio, pg 796
New Leaf Distributing Co, pg 955
School Media Associates LLC, pg 1004

HAWAII

Media Bridge Gamekids, pg 936

ILLINOIS

Communications Corporation of America, pg 833
Educational Insights, pg 857
Jim Gill Music Inc, pg 878
Liturgy Training Publications, pg 923
Nightingale-Conant Corp, pg 957
Oasis Audio, pg 960

INDIANA

Herff Jones | Nystrom, pg 888
InterComm, pg 900

KANSAS

Chapman Recording & Mastering, pg 824

LOUISIANA

Pelican Publishing Co, pg 971

MAINE

Slim Goodbody Corp, pg 1013

MARYLAND

Kids on the Block Inc, pg 910
Recorded Books LLC, pg 993
RLJ Entertainment Inc, pg 997

MASSACHUSETTS

Cheng & Tsui Co, pg 824
Documentary Educational Resources Inc, pg 850
Pauline Books & Media, pg 970
Penfield Productions Ltd, pg 971
Revels Records, pg 995
Ben Rudnick & Friends, pg 1000
Yellow Moon Press, pg 1072

MICHIGAN

Digi Sign Design LLC, pg 847
Emery-Pratt Co, pg 860
Gemini, pg 876
Meuninck's Media Methods Inc, pg 940

MINNESOTA

Effective Learning Systems Inc, pg 858
HighBridge Audio, pg 889

MISSOURI

Marsh Media, pg 931
SOM Publishing Co, pg 1015

NEBRASKA

Vision Maker Media, pg 1058

NEW HAMPSHIRE

Chip Taylor Communications LLC, pg 1032

NEW JERSEY

Kimbo Educational, pg 910
Listen & Live Audio Inc, pg 923
A W Peller & Associates Inc, pg 971

NEW MEXICO

National Information Center for Educational Media (NICEM)/MediaSleuth, pg 952

NEW YORK

Brooklyn Botanic Garden, pg 814
The Christophers, pg 826
De Nonno Productions Inc (DPI), pg 844
Educational Activities Inc, pg 857
Educational Images Ltd, pg 857
A Gentle Wind, pg 877
Granny Press LLC, pg 881
Hallel Communications, pg 884
HarperAudio, pg 885
Homespun Video, pg 890

Children's Program Producers

PROGRAMMING — AUDIO

Children's Program Producers (continued)

NEW JERSEY

CFP Video Productions Inc, pg 823
Kimbo Educational, pg 910
Listen & Live Audio Inc, pg 923
Milgrom Productions, pg 943
Optisonics Productions, pg 965
Bill Quinn Productions, pg 989
Suede Interactive, pg 1027

NEW MEXICO

Production Outfitters, pg 984
Rainbow International Inc/Rainbow Productions Inc, pg 990

NEW YORK

Air Sea Land Productions Inc (ASL), pg 779
American History Workshop (NY) Inc, pg 784
Avekta Productions Inc, pg 798
Brooklyn Botanic Garden, pg 814
Thomas Craven Film Corp, pg 837
C2 Imaging LLC, pg 841
De Nonno Productions Inc (DPI), pg 844
Digital Force, pg 847
Dyer-Bennet Records, pg 854
Educational Activities Inc, pg 857
Fingerpaint, pg 868
Karen Frankel Productions, pg 872
A Gentle Wind, pg 877
Granny Press LLC, pg 881
Greyfalcon House, pg 882
Hallel Communications, pg 884
HarperAudio, pg 885
Hello World Communications, pg 888
Irish Music Corp, pg 902
Kamen Entertainment Group Inc, pg 908
Listening Library, pg 923
Live Oak Media, pg 923
Jack Morton Worldwide, pg 946
MRG Productions Inc, pg 948
MRY, pg 949
New York Audio Productions, pg 956
Shelly Palmer Production, pg 968
Parabola Audio/Video, pg 968
Penguin Audiobooks, pg 971
Price Stern Sloan, pg 981
Random House Children's Books, pg 991
David Rapkin Audio Production, pg 991
Elliot Sokolov Music, pg 1015
Split Image Productions, pg 1021
Spoken Arts Inc, pg 1021
Synaptic Digital, pg 1030
Tiki Recording Studios Inc, pg 1040
Zelman Studios Ltd, pg 1073

NORTH CAROLINA

Pat Appleson Studios Inc, pg 788
Howard Hanger, pg 884
High Windy Audio/Banjoman Inc, pg 889
LCW Productions LLC, pg 917
World Class Learning Materials Inc, pg 1069

OHIO

Advent Media Inc, pg 778
Alegra House Publishers, pg 780
Creative Technology, pg 838
EDR Media LLC, pg 857
Franciscan Media, pg 872
Twin Sisters Productions LLC, pg 1047
VGI Productions, pg 1053
Vista Color Imaging Inc, pg 1059

OKLAHOMA

Piper Media Services Inc, pg 976

OREGON

Downpour.com, pg 851
Ideascape Inc, pg 894
InterVision Media, pg 902
Norman Beerger Productions, pg 958
Odyssey Productions Inc, pg 961

PENNSYLVANIA

Discovery Education - South Burlington, pg 848
Forge Recording LLC, pg 871
Innovision Media Group, pg 899
Kensington Falls Animation, pg 909
The Fred Rogers Co, pg 998
WQED-Multimedia, pg 1070

RHODE ISLAND

Sound-FX-Design, pg 1017

SOUTH CAROLINA

BJU Press, pg 808

TENNESSEE

Abingdon Press, pg 772
American Blackguard Inc, pg 784
Cokesbury, pg 831
EMI CMG Distribution, pg 860
Provident-Integrity Distribution, pg 986
Word Label Group, pg 1069

TEXAS

AMA Nystrom Printing/Finishing, pg 783
Biway Media, pg 808
Communication Arts Multimedia Inc, pg 832
Epic Software Group Inc, pg 862
Institute of Texan Cultures, pg 899
Omega Productions, pg 962
Shadow Play Records & Video, pg 1007
The Sound Lab Inc, pg 1017
Sound Works, pg 1018
South Coast Film & Video, pg 1019
Tropikal Productions, pg 1045

VIRGINIA

BES Studios, pg 805
Lion Recording Services Inc, pg 922
Metro Productions, pg 939
National Media Services Inc, pg 953
Rocktown Media, pg 998

WASHINGTON

Pacific Multimedia Inc, pg 967

WISCONSIN

5th Floor Recording Co, pg 867
Plank Road Publishing Inc, pg 976
Tomorrow River Music, pg 1042
Watts Communications Inc, pg 1062
Wisconsin Public Television, pg 1068

WYOMING

Bridger Productions Inc, pg 812

ALBERTA

Global Television Station, pg 879
HBW Entertainment Inc, pg 886

ONTARIO

DebsVoice, pg 844
GAPC (General Assembly Production Centre), pg 875
VO2 Mix Studios, pg 1060

QUEBEC

Kerrigan Productions Inc, pg 910

Children's Program Rentals

CALIFORNIA

Direct Cinema Ltd Inc, pg 848
Paulist Productions, pg 970
Western Instructional Television Inc, pg 1064

INDIANA

InterComm, pg 900

MARYLAND

Kids on the Block Inc, pg 910

MASSACHUSETTS

Documentary Educational Resources Inc, pg 850

MICHIGAN

Digi Sign Design LLC, pg 847

NEBRASKA

Vision Maker Media, pg 1058

NEW HAMPSHIRE

Chip Taylor Communications LLC, pg 1032

NEW JERSEY

Listen & Live Audio Inc, pg 923

NEW YORK

Adwar Video, pg 778
Brooklyn Botanic Garden, pg 814
Hallel Communications, pg 884

UTAH

Webb Audio Visual Communication, pg 1063

ONTARIO

Simply Audiobooks, pg 1011

Classic Radio Program, *see* Radio Program—Classic

Commercial, *see* Test Commercial

Compact Disc Distributors

ALABAMA

Eternal Word Television Network (EWTN), pg 862

ARIZONA

Celestial Harmonies/Fortuna Records/Kuckuck Schallplatten/Black Sun Music/MonteVideo, pg 822
Coyote Cowboy Co, pg 837
Drumbeat Indian Arts Inc, pg 852
Earth Mother Productions Inc™, pg 855
Tom Hopkins International Inc, pg 891
Personal Achievement Institute, pg 973
TSG Publishing Foundation Inc USA, pg 1046
Valley of the Sun Publishing Co, pg 1051

CALIFORNIA

Ametron Audio/Video, pg 785
Audio Editions Books-On-Cassette & CD, pg 794
Blind Pig Records, pg 809
California Language Laboratories, pg 817
Capitol Records, pg 819
Cibola Systems, pg 826
Clarity Sound & Light, pg 829
Concord Records Inc, pg 835
Discovery Toys, pg 848
ECONEWS (Environmental Television Series) & (Environmental Directions Radio Series), pg 856
Eye & I Productions, pg 864
Fantasy Studios, pg 865
Gateways, pg 876
GNP Crescendo Records, pg 879
Bruce Goldberg Inc, pg 880
Golden State Dance Teachers Association (GSDTA), pg 880
Steven Halpern's Inner Peace Music, pg 884
Harmonia Mundi USA, pg 885
Hay House Inc, pg 886
Interscope, Geffen, A&M Records, pg 901
KABA Audio Productions, pg 907
LANGUAGE/30™, pg 916
Lightworks Audio & Video Inc, pg 921
monterey video, pg 946
Multi-Media Mathematics, pg 949
Music World/Vocal Power School, pg 951
Nilgiri Press, pg 957
ODC Publishing, pg 961
Osho Viha Information Center & Book Distributors, pg 965
Players Press, pg 977
Prime Cut Productions, pg 982
QRS Software Services, pg 988
Randolf Productions Inc, pg 991
Ron Roy Productions/Moodtapes, pg 1000
Sahara Records & Filmworks Entertainment Co, pg 1001
Saturn Studios, pg 1003
Sisters' Choice Press, pg 1012
Sound Feelings Records, pg 1017
Timeless Productions, pg 1040
Universal Music Group, pg 1049
Valley Media, pg 1051
Varese Sarabande Records Inc, pg 1052

PROGRAMMING — AUDIO

Compact Disc Distributors (continued)

WASHINGTON

Books In Motion, pg 811
College of Nursing, Washington State University, pg 831
Voyager Recordings & Publications, pg 1060

WISCONSIN

Plank Road Publishing Inc, pg 976
School Specialty Inc, pg 1004
Tomorrow River Music, pg 1042

PUERTO RICO

Bonnin Electronics Inc, pg 810

BRITISH COLUMBIA

Timeless Books, pg 1040

ONTARIO

CBC/Radio-Canada, pg 821
The Children's Book Store Distribution (CBSD), pg 825
Entertainment One Distribution, pg 861
GAPC (General Assembly Production Centre), pg 875
Mind Resources Inc, pg 943
Nelson Education Ltd, pg 954
Random House of Canada Limited, pg 991
The Resource Centre, pg 995
Scholastic Canada Ltd, pg 1004

Compact Disc Producers

ALABAMA

Eternal Word Television Network (EWTN), pg 862

ARIZONA

Celestial Harmonies/Fortuna Records/Kuckuck Schallplatten/ Black Sun Music/MonteVideo, pg 822
Drumbeat Indian Arts Inc, pg 852
Merestone, pg 938
Personal Achievement Institute, pg 973
SPEAK HOUSE Audio™, pg 1019
Truth Consciousness Publications, pg 1045
TSG Publishing Foundation Inc USA, pg 1046
Valley of the Sun Publishing Co, pg 1051

ARKANSAS

Live'N'Loud, pg 923

CALIFORNIA

ACDC Audio CD & Cassette, pg 774
Ancient Future, pg 786
Arhoolie Productions Inc (aka Arhoolie Records), pg 789
Artichoke Productions, pg 791
The Banquet Sound Studios, pg 802
Blind Pig Records, pg 809
California Language Laboratories, pg 817
Clarity Sound & Light, pg 829
Concord Jazz Inc, pg 835
Concord Records Inc, pg 835
Creative Media Recording, pg 838
Creativity Unlimited Press®, pg 839
Custom Video Productions Inc, pg 841
Dogma Studios, pg 850
e-MEDIAtely, pg 855
ECONEWS (Environmental Television Series) & (Environmental Directions Radio Series), pg 856
Eye & I Productions, pg 864
Face Digital Post, pg 865
4th Street Recording, pg 872
Gateways, pg 876
Gold Standard Productions, pg 880
Bruce Goldberg Inc, pg 880
Steven Halpern's Inner Peace Music, pg 884
Harmonia Mundi USA, pg 885
Hay House Inc, pg 886
Interscope, Geffen, A&M Records, pg 901
K2B2 Records, pg 907
KABA Audio Productions, pg 907
LANGUAGE/30™, pg 916
Lynch Communications, pg 926
Maximus Media Inc, pg 934
Media Magic, pg 937
monterey video, pg 946
M2 Communications, pg 949
Multi-Media Mathematics, pg 949
Music World/Vocal Power School, pg 951
Nilgiri Press, pg 957
ODC Publishing, pg 961
On-Trax Inc, pg 963
Pacific Audio-Visual Enterprises, pg 967
Penrose Productions, pg 972
Players Press, pg 977
Prime Cut Productions, pg 982
QRS Software Services, pg 988
Randolf Productions Inc, pg 991
Reference Recordings, pg 994
Rhythms Productions (Tom Thumb Music), pg 996
Ron Roy Productions/Moodtapes, pg 1000
Sahara Records & Filmworks Entertainment Co, pg 1001
Saturn Studios, pg 1003
Alwin Sauers Audio Productions (ASAP), pg 1003
Schroder Music Co, pg 1004
Steve Shapiro Music, pg 1008
Sisters' Choice Press, pg 1012
Sound Feelings Records, pg 1017
Studio 132, pg 1027
Tam Communications Inc, pg 1031
Timeless Productions, pg 1040
Total Media Group, pg 1042
Twin Peaks Creative, pg 1047
Universal Music Group, pg 1049
Varese Sarabande Records Inc, pg 1052
Vedanta Press & Catalog, pg 1052
Video Resources Inc, pg 1056
WalkerVision Interarts, pg 1061
Webster Communications, pg 1063
The Wyland Group, pg 1071

COLORADO

Alpine Media, pg 782
Paul L Anderson Productions Inc, pg 786
Tim Cissell Music, pg 828
Crown Ministries International, pg 840
Flashback Media Productions, pg 869
Los Angeles Post Music Inc, pg 924
Meriwether Publishing Ltd, pg 939
National Institute for Trial Advocacy (NITA), pg 953
Rocky Mountain Audio/Video Productions Inc, pg 998

CONNECTICUT

Broadcast Video Productions LLC, pg 813
Crossroads Video, pg 840
Folk-Legacy, pg 871
T & M Digital Services, pg 1031
Tantor Media Inc, pg 1031
Weston Woods Studios Inc, pg 1064

DELAWARE

Ken-Del Productions Inc, pg 909
So Smart Productions, pg 1015

DISTRICT OF COLUMBIA

American Chemical Society (ACS), pg 784
Hillmann & Carr Inc, pg 889
Interface Media Group, pg 900
Smithsonian Folkways Recordings, pg 1014

FLORIDA

Bartok Records & Publications, pg 803
Blackburst Entertainment, pg 808
Courter Films LLC, pg 837
Kat Epple Music Productions, pg 862
Hard Hat Radio Music Service, pg 884
LHV Audio Services, pg 919
Motion Image Group LLC, pg 947
Sunfire Communications Inc, pg 1028
Sunrise Studios, pg 1028
Tight Line Productions, pg 1040
Times-Square Fantasy Theatre, pg 1041
Top Hat Productions, pg 1042

GEORGIA

August House Audio, pg 796
Guerrilla Productions LLC, pg 883
Hottrax Records, pg 891

IDAHO

Channel Productions, pg 823

ILLINOIS

Analog Free Media, pg 786
AudioTransitions, pg 796
Britannica Film & Video, pg 812
CCore Media Inc, pg 821
Convenience, pg 835
Cresta Creative, pg 839
Delmark Records, pg 845
Earwig Music Co Inc, pg 855
Film Ideas, pg 867
Folk Era Productions Inc, pg 870
Major Media Inc, pg 929
Oasis Audio, pg 960
The Pepper Group, pg 972
RADMAR Inc, pg 990
Sparkfactor, pg 1019
Video Impressions, pg 1055
Woodside Avenue Music Productions Inc, pg 1069

INDIANA

AVA Productions, pg 798
Bright Ideas Creative Services, pg 812
Optical Disc Solutions Inc, pg 964

IOWA

Hedquist Productions Inc, pg 887
Long-Term Success Publishing, pg 924

KANSAS

Chapman Recording & Mastering, pg 824
Rhythmic Medicine, pg 996

KENTUCKY

Horizon Films & Media LLC, pg 891
Donna Lawrence Productions, pg 917
Northern Kentucky University, pg 959
Prosper Media Group Inc, pg 986
Trusty Tuneshop Recording Studios, pg 1045

LOUISIANA

Centaur Records Inc, pg 822
Flat Town Music Co, pg 869
Great Chefs/Leisure Jazz Video, pg 881
Jazzology, pg 904
Jin, pg 905
Leisure Video, pg 918
Louisiana State University Health Sciences Center - Shreveport, pg 925
Maison de Soul Records, pg 929
Swallow, pg 1029

MAINE

Serendipity Recordings, pg 1007

MARYLAND

Adelphi Records Inc, pg 776
The Ahern Group, pg 779
Books on Tape®, pg 811
CSPMedia.com, pg 840
dbF a Media Company, pg 844
The Image Generators, pg 895
Kids on the Block Inc, pg 910
Lion & Fox Recording Studios, pg 922
Recorded Books LLC, pg 993

MASSACHUSETTS

Cheng & Tsui Co, pg 824
Inter-Media Electronics, pg 899
Labrecque Creative Sound, pg 915
Pauline Books & Media, pg 970
Penfield Productions Ltd, pg 971
Revels Records, pg 995
Ben Rudnick & Friends, pg 1000
Soundtrack Recording Studios, pg 1018
Rik Tinory Productions, pg 1041
Yellow Moon Press, pg 1072

MICHIGAN

Brilliance Audio, pg 812
The Brookwood Studio Inc, pg 814
Digi Sign Design LLC, pg 847
International Tae Kwon Do Association (ITA Institute), pg 901
K&R All Media Productions Inc, pg 908

Compact Disc Rentals

PROGRAMMING — AUDIO

Compact Disc Rentals (continued)

ONTARIO

Simply Audiobooks, pg 1011

Current Event Program Distributors

ARKANSAS

Master Books, pg 933

CALIFORNIA

Digital Media West, pg 847
Direct Cinema Ltd Inc, pg 848
Maximus Media Inc, pg 934
Pacifica Radio Archives, pg 967
Publishers Group West Inc, pg 987
QRS Software Services, pg 988
Social Studies School Service, pg 1015

CONNECTICUT

Tantor Media Inc, pg 1031

DISTRICT OF COLUMBIA

National Council of Churches, pg 952

FLORIDA

Capital Communications Inc, pg 819

GEORGIA

School Media Associates LLC, pg 1004

HAWAII

Media Bridge Gamekids, pg 936

MARYLAND

Recorded Books LLC, pg 993

MASSACHUSETTS

Emergency Film Group, pg 860

MICHIGAN

Digi Sign Design LLC, pg 847

MINNESOTA

HighBridge Audio, pg 889

NEW HAMPSHIRE

Chip Taylor Communications LLC, pg 1032

NEW JERSEY

Listen & Live Audio Inc, pg 923

NEW YORK

The Cinema Guild Inc, pg 827
HarperAudio, pg 885
HB-Content, pg 886
Janus Films Inc, pg 904
KickedUp Media Group Inc, pg 910
MRG Productions Inc, pg 948
News Broadcast Network, pg 956
Penguin Audiobooks, pg 971
Practising Law Institute, pg 980
Timed Exposures Films, pg 1040
United Nations Department of Public Information-News & Media Division, pg 1048
United Nations Multimedia Resources Unit, pg 1048

NORTH CAROLINA

Baker & Taylor Inc, pg 801
Vide-O-Go/That's Infotainment!, pg 1054

OREGON

InterVision Media, pg 902

TENNESSEE

Ingram Book Group, pg 898
Spring Arbor Distributors, pg 1022

VIRGINIA

CACI Productions Group, pg 816
CDR Communications Inc, pg 822

ALBERTA

Global Television Station, pg 879

BRITISH COLUMBIA

Video In Studios/Video Out Distribution, pg 1055

ONTARIO

Canadian Learning Co Inc, pg 818
Life Cycle Books Ltd, pg 920

Current Event Program Producers

CALIFORNIA

Big Door, pg 807
Direct Cinema Ltd Inc, pg 848
Dogma Studios, pg 850
Lynch Communications, pg 926
PM Productions, pg 977
Producers Group Ltd, pg 983
QRS Software Services, pg 988
Still N'Motion, pg 1025
Studio 132, pg 1027
Tele-Video Production Services (TVPS), pg 1036
Total Media Group, pg 1042
Video Resources Inc, pg 1056
Wavemaker Media Design, pg 1062
Webster Communications, pg 1063

COLORADO

Apogee Communications Group, pg 788
Flashback Media Productions, pg 869

CONNECTICUT

EagleVision Inc, pg 855
Essex Television Group Inc, pg 862
Tantor Media Inc, pg 1031

FLORIDA

Blackburst Entertainment, pg 808
Capital Communications Inc, pg 819
Courter Films LLC, pg 837
LHV Audio Services, pg 919
Sunfire Communications Inc, pg 1028
Sunrise Studios, pg 1028
Top Hat Productions, pg 1042

GEORGIA

Guerrilla Productions LLC, pg 883

IDAHO

Wide Eye Productions, pg 1066

ILLINOIS

ABS Enterprises, pg 772
Communications Corporation of America, pg 833
The Pepper Group, pg 972

INDIANA

AVA Productions, pg 798

KENTUCKY

National Geographic Learning, pg 952

MARYLAND

CPR MultiMedia Solutions, pg 837
CSPMedia.com, pg 840
The Cutting Corp, pg 841
dbF a Media Company, pg 844
The Image Generators, pg 895
Kramer Communications Video Production, pg 913
Recorded Books LLC, pg 993

MASSACHUSETTS

Emergency Film Group, pg 860
Heliotrope Studios, pg 887
Labrecque Creative Sound, pg 915
Northern Light Productions, pg 959
Soundtrack Recording Studios, pg 1018

MICHIGAN

The Brookwood Studio Inc, pg 814
Digi Sign Design LLC, pg 847
K&R All Media Productions Inc, pg 908
K&R's Recording Studios Inc, pg 908

MINNESOTA

Aggressive Records Audio Duplication LLC, pg 778
HighBridge Audio, pg 889
Jamieson & Associates Inc, pg 904

MISSOURI

Celebrities Productions, pg 822
Fambrough & Associates Inc, pg 865
Hardcastle Films & Video, pg 885

MONTANA

North Country Media Group, pg 959

NEVADA

JCS Video Productions, pg 904

NEW HAMPSHIRE

Apertura, pg 788
Chip Taylor Communications LLC, pg 1032

NEW JERSEY

CFP Video Productions Inc, pg 823
Half Moon Video Productions, pg 883
Listen & Live Audio Inc, pg 923
MIB Mediaworks, pg 941
Optisonics Productions, pg 965
Bill Quinn Productions, pg 989
Suede Interactive, pg 1027

NEW MEXICO

Production Outfitters, pg 984

NEW YORK

Avekta Productions Inc, pg 798
Blue Barn Pictures Inc, pg 809
Broad Street Inc, pg 812
Digital Force, pg 847
Karen Frankel Productions, pg 872
HarperAudio, pg 885
HB-Content, pg 886
Kamen Entertainment Group Inc, pg 908
KickedUp Media Group Inc, pg 910
Jack Morton Worldwide, pg 946
MRG Productions Inc, pg 948
New York Audio Productions, pg 956
News Broadcast Network, pg 956
Shelly Palmer Production, pg 968
Penguin Audiobooks, pg 971
Practising Law Institute, pg 980
David Rapkin Audio Production, pg 991
Split Image Productions, pg 1021
Timed Exposures Films, pg 1040
United Nations Multimedia Resources Unit, pg 1048
Zelman Studios Ltd, pg 1073

NORTH CAROLINA

Pat Appleson Studios Inc, pg 788

OHIO

Advent Media Inc, pg 778
Creative Technology, pg 838
EDR Media LLC, pg 857
R&B Communications Inc, pg 991
VGI Productions, pg 1053
Vista Color Imaging Inc, pg 1059

OKLAHOMA

Piper Media Services Inc, pg 976

OREGON

InterVision Media, pg 902

PENNSYLVANIA

Forge Recording LLC, pg 871
Innovision Media Group, pg 899
Production Masters Inc (PMI), pg 984

RHODE ISLAND

Sound-FX-Design, pg 1017

TEXAS

Omega Productions, pg 962
The Sound Lab Inc, pg 1017
Sound Works, pg 1018
South Coast Film & Video, pg 1019
Stage Directions, pg 1022

VIRGINIA

BES Studios, pg 805
CACI Productions Group, pg 816
CDR Communications Inc, pg 822
Limelight Communications Inc, pg 921
Lion Recording Services Inc, pg 922
Metro Productions, pg 939
Rocktown Media, pg 998

WISCONSIN

5th Floor Recording Co, pg 867
Knowledge Unlimited Inc, pg 912
Video Wisconsin Inc, pg 1056
Wisconsin Public Television, pg 1068

WYOMING

Bridger Productions Inc, pg 812

ALBERTA

Global Television Station, pg 879

ONTARIO

DebsVoice, pg 844

QUEBEC

Kerrigan Productions Inc, pg 910

Current Event Program Rentals

CALIFORNIA

Direct Cinema Ltd Inc, pg 848

MICHIGAN

Digi Sign Design LLC, pg 847

NEW HAMPSHIRE

Chip Taylor Communications LLC, pg 1032

NEW JERSEY

Listen & Live Audio Inc, pg 923

NEW YORK

Timed Exposures Films, pg 1040

BRITISH COLUMBIA

Video In Studios/Video Out Distribution, pg 1055

Digital Audiotape Distributors

CALIFORNIA

Ametron Audio/Video, pg 785
Players Press, pg 977
QRS Software Services, pg 988

CONNECTICUT

Connecticut Audio & Theatrical Supply, pg 835
Crossroads Video, pg 840

FLORIDA

Photomart Cine-Video Inc, pg 975
Times-Square Fantasy Theatre, pg 1041

ILLINOIS

CCore Media Inc, pg 821

INDIANA

Optical Disc Solutions Inc, pg 964

MARYLAND

Bradley Broadcast & Pro Audio, pg 811
Recorded Books LLC, pg 993

MICHIGAN

Brilliance Audio, pg 812
Digi Sign Design LLC, pg 847

NEW MEXICO

National Information Center for Educational Media (NICEM)/MediaSleuth, pg 952

NEW YORK

Bantam Doubleday Dell Audio Publishing, pg 802
Digital Force, pg 847
DRG Records Inc, pg 852
Film Emporium, pg 867
Synaptic Digital, pg 1030

TENNESSEE

American Blackguard Inc, pg 784

PUERTO RICO

Bonnin Electronics Inc, pg 810

ONTARIO

Entertainment One Distribution, pg 861

Digital Audiotape Producers

ARIZONA

Merestone, pg 938

CALIFORNIA

ACDC Audio CD & Cassette, pg 774
Artichoke Productions, pg 791
Custom Video Productions Inc, pg 841
Dogma Studios, pg 850
K2B2 Records, pg 907
Lynch Communications, pg 926
Maximus Media Inc, pg 934
Media Magic, pg 937
On-Trax Inc, pg 963
Pacific Audio-Visual Enterprises, pg 967
Players Press, pg 977
QRS Software Services, pg 988
Saturn Studios, pg 1003
Steve Shapiro Music, pg 1008
Total Media Group, pg 1042
Twin Peaks Creative, pg 1047
Video Resources Inc, pg 1056

COLORADO

Tim Cissell Music, pg 828
Daylight Productions & Rentals, pg 844

CONNECTICUT

Broadcast Video Productions LLC, pg 813
Crossroads Video, pg 840

DISTRICT OF COLUMBIA

Interface Media Group, pg 900

FLORIDA

LHV Audio Services, pg 919
Sunfire Communications Inc, pg 1028

GEORGIA

Guerrilla Productions LLC, pg 883

ILLINOIS

CCore Media Inc, pg 821
Cresta Creative, pg 839
Major Media Inc, pg 929

INDIANA

AVA Productions, pg 798
Bright Ideas Creative Services, pg 812
Optical Disc Solutions Inc, pg 964

MARYLAND

The Ahern Group, pg 779
Books on Tape®, pg 811
The Image Generators, pg 895
Lion & Fox Recording Studios, pg 922
Recorded Books LLC, pg 993

MASSACHUSETTS

Labrecque Creative Sound, pg 915

MICHIGAN

Brilliance Audio, pg 812
Digi Sign Design LLC, pg 847
K&R All Media Productions Inc, pg 908
K&R's Recording Studios Inc, pg 908

MINNESOTA

Aggressive Records Audio Duplication LLC, pg 778

MISSOURI

Fambrough & Associates Inc, pg 865

NEW JERSEY

Jeep Jazz Media Solutions, pg 905
Laurel Video Productions, pg 916
Suede Interactive, pg 1027

NEW YORK

Aural Gratification Inc, pg 796
Bantam Doubleday Dell Audio Publishing, pg 802
Bridge Records Inc, pg 812
Digital Force, pg 847
Eastco Multimedia Solutions Inc, pg 856
Fingerpaint, pg 868
International Digital Centre, pg 901
Sear Sound, pg 1005
Synaptic Digital, pg 1030

NORTH CAROLINA

Pat Appleson Studios Inc, pg 788

OHIO

EDR Media LLC, pg 857
Lyon Video Inc, pg 927
Musicol Recording, pg 951
R&B Communications Inc, pg 991

OREGON

Rex, pg 995

PENNSYLVANIA

Canadian American Records, pg 818
Forge Recording LLC, pg 871
Innovision Media Group, pg 899
JPL, pg 906
Production Masters Inc (PMI), pg 984

TEXAS

Biway Media, pg 808
Romar Learning, pg 999
The Samuels Co, pg 1002
Stage Directions, pg 1022
Tropikal Productions, pg 1045

VIRGINIA

Advance Concepts Inc, pg 777
AudioImage Recording, pg 796
CALIBRE, pg 816
Lion Recording Services Inc, pg 922
Studio Center Corp, pg 1026

WISCONSIN

5th Floor Recording Co, pg 867
Meridian Studios, pg 939

Digital Audiotape Rentals

CONNECTICUT

Crossroads Video, pg 840

DELAWARE

Side Door Studio Inc, pg 1010

MICHIGAN

Digi Sign Design LLC, pg 847

Documentary Distributors

ARKANSAS

Master Books, pg 933

CALIFORNIA

Astronomical Society of the Pacific, pg 792
Blue Dolphin Multimedia, pg 809
Digital Media West, pg 847
Direct Cinema Ltd Inc, pg 848
Eagle Multimedia, pg 855
ECONEWS (Environmental Television Series) & (Environmental Directions Radio Series), pg 856
Maximus Media Inc, pg 934
Multi-Media Mathematics, pg 949
New Line Cinema, pg 956
Oral Tradition Sound & Music, pg 965
Pacific Media, pg 967
Pacifica Radio Archives, pg 967
QRS Software Services, pg 988
Regent Press Publishers & Printers, pg 994
Sea Studios Foundation, pg 1005
Social Studies School Service, pg 1015
Warner Home Video Inc, pg 1062
The Wine Appreciation Guild Ltd, pg 1067

CONNECTICUT

EagleVision Inc, pg 855
Save the Children Federation Inc, pg 1003

DISTRICT OF COLUMBIA

National Council of Churches, pg 952

PROGRAMMING — AUDIO

Documentary Distributors (continued)

FLORIDA

Allegro Productions Inc, pg 781
Capital Communications Inc, pg 819
Media Concepts Inc, pg 936

GEORGIA

School Media Associates LLC, pg 1004
Symmes Systems, pg 1030

HAWAII

Media Bridge Gamekids, pg 936

ILLINOIS

CCore Media Inc, pg 821
Communications Corporation of America, pg 833
Theosophical Publishing House, pg 1038

INDIANA

Communication Ministries, pg 833
InterComm, pg 900

KENTUCKY

Horizon Films & Media LLC, pg 891

MARYLAND

MMI Corp, pg 944
Recorded Books LLC, pg 993
RLJ Entertainment Inc, pg 997
Special Archives Division, Motion Picture Branch, pg 1020

MASSACHUSETTS

Documentary Educational Resources Inc, pg 850
Emergency Film Group, pg 860
Penfield Productions Ltd, pg 971

MICHIGAN

Digi Sign Design LLC, pg 847

MINNESOTA

HighBridge Audio, pg 889

MISSOURI

SOM Publishing Co, pg 1015

MONTANA

High Plains Films, pg 889

NEBRASKA

Vision Maker Media, pg 1058

NEVADA

DVDs4Less, pg 854

NEW HAMPSHIRE

Captain Fiddle Music & Publications, pg 820
Chip Taylor Communications LLC, pg 1032

NEW JERSEY

Shanachie Entertainment Corp, pg 1008

NEW MEXICO

National Information Center for Educational Media (NICEM)/MediaSleuth, pg 952

NEW YORK

The Cinema Guild Inc, pg 827
De Nonno Productions Inc (DPI), pg 844
Films Media Group, pg 868
Hallel Communications, pg 884
HB-Content, pg 886
Irish Music Corp, pg 902
Janus Films Inc, pg 904
KickedUp Media Group Inc, pg 910
MRG Productions Inc, pg 948
Timed Exposures Films, pg 1040
United Nations Department of Public Information-News & Media Division, pg 1048
United Nations Multimedia Resources Unit, pg 1048

NORTH CAROLINA

Baker & Taylor Inc, pg 801
Ladyslipper Inc, pg 915
Vide-O-Go/That's Infotainment!, pg 1054

OREGON

InterVision Media, pg 902
Norman Beerger Productions, pg 958

PENNSYLVANIA

FMP Media Solutions Inc, pg 870
S I Video Sales Group, pg 1001

RHODE ISLAND

Sound Advantage, pg 1016

TENNESSEE

American Blackguard Inc, pg 784
Center for Southern Folklore Inc, pg 822
EMI CMG Distribution, pg 860
Ingram Book Group, pg 898
Marine Geographic, pg 931
Spring Arbor Distributors, pg 1022

VIRGINIA

CACI Productions Group, pg 816

WISCONSIN

Her Own Words LLC, pg 888

ALBERTA

Global Television Station, pg 879

BRITISH COLUMBIA

Timeless Books, pg 1040
Video In Studios/Video Out Distribution, pg 1055

ONTARIO

Canadian Learning Co Inc, pg 818
CBC/Radio-Canada, pg 821
Life Cycle Books Ltd, pg 920

Documentary Producers

ALABAMA

Dogwood Recording Studios, pg 850
Leo Ticheli Productions, pg 1040

ARIZONA

Candee Productions Inc, pg 819
Tellens Inc, pg 1037

ARKANSAS

Live'N'Loud, pg 923

CALIFORNIA

AM Productions, pg 783
The Banquet Sound Studios, pg 802
Big Door, pg 807
Blue Dolphin Multimedia, pg 809
Custom Video Productions Inc, pg 841
Design Media, pg 845
Direct Cinema Ltd Inc, pg 848
Dogma Studios, pg 850
ECONEWS (Environmental Television Series) & (Environmental Directions Radio Series), pg 856
Goal Productions, pg 879
Gold Standard Productions, pg 880
imageReal Pictures LLC, pg 896
Lynch Communications, pg 926
Maximus Media Inc, pg 934
The Media Staff Inc, pg 937
Multi-Media Mathematics, pg 949
New Circuit Films LLC, pg 955
On-Trax Inc, pg 963
Pacific Audio-Visual Enterprises, pg 967
Pacific Media, pg 967
PM Productions, pg 977
Point of View Productions, pg 977
Prime Cut Productions, pg 982
Producers Group Ltd, pg 983
QRS Software Services, pg 988
Regent Press Publishers & Printers, pg 994
SBS Productions, pg 1003
Sea Studios Foundation, pg 1005
Steve Shapiro Music, pg 1008
Still N'Motion, pg 1025
Studio 132, pg 1027
Timestream Video, pg 1041
Total Media Group, pg 1042
WalkerVision Interarts, pg 1061
Wavemaker Media Design, pg 1062
Webster Communications, pg 1063
Zamacona Productions, pg 1073

COLORADO

Apogee Communications Group, pg 788
Tim Cissell Music, pg 828
Daylight Productions & Rentals, pg 844
Flashback Media Productions, pg 869
Rocky Mountain Audio/Video Productions Inc, pg 998
Starwest Productions, pg 1024
Tatum Video, pg 1032

CONNECTICUT

ACM Productions Ltd, pg 774
Biomedical Media Communications Dept, pg 807
EagleVision Inc, pg 855
Essex Television Group Inc, pg 862
The Gary-Paul Agency, pg 875
P&P Studios Inc, pg 968
Save the Children Federation Inc, pg 1003

DISTRICT OF COLUMBIA

Educational Film Center, pg 857
Hillmann & Carr Inc, pg 889

FLORIDA

Allegro Productions Inc, pg 781
Blackburst Entertainment, pg 808
Capital Communications Inc, pg 819
Communications Concepts Inc (CCI), pg 833
Courter Films LLC, pg 837
Eastern Video, pg 856
LHV Audio Services, pg 919
Motion Image Group LLC, pg 947
Roger Scruggs Films, pg 1005
Sunfire Communications Inc, pg 1028
Sunrise Studios, pg 1028
Top Hat Productions, pg 1042

GEORGIA

COMPRO Productions Inc, pg 834
Guerrilla Productions LLC, pg 883
Symmes Systems, pg 1030

HAWAII

Media Bridge Gamekids, pg 936

IDAHO

Wide Eye Productions, pg 1066

ILLINOIS

ABS Enterprises, pg 772
Communications Corporation of America, pg 833
Jim Passin Productions, pg 970
The Pepper Group, pg 972
Perspectives Media, pg 973
QuickSet International Inc, pg 989
Steven Samler Music & Sound, pg 1002
Theosophical Publishing House, pg 1038
20/20 Communications Inc, pg 1047

INDIANA

AVA Productions, pg 798
Bright Ideas Creative Services, pg 812
Communication Ministries, pg 833
Digital Rain LLC, pg 847
InterComm, pg 900
PentaVision Communications Inc, pg 972

IOWA

Iowa State University-Information Technology Services, pg 902
The Production House, pg 984

KANSAS

Chapman Recording & Mastering, pg 824

KENTUCKY

Horizon Films & Media LLC, pg 891
Donna Lawrence Productions, pg 917

LOUISIANA

Digital FX Inc, pg 847
Moxie Media, pg 948

MARYLAND

CPR MultiMedia Solutions, pg 837
CSPMedia.com, pg 840
The Cutting Corp, pg 841
dbF a Media Company, pg 844
The Image Generators, pg 895
Kramer Communications Video Production, pg 913
Recorded Books LLC, pg 993
RLJ Entertainment Inc, pg 997

MASSACHUSETTS

CommCreative, pg 832
Documentary Educational Resources Inc, pg 850
Emergency Film Group, pg 860
Heliotrope Studios, pg 887
Home Inc, pg 890
Labrecque Creative Sound, pg 915
Monadnock Media Inc, pg 945
Northern Light Productions, pg 959
Penfield Productions Ltd, pg 971
Shambhala Publications, pg 1008
Soundtrack Recording Studios, pg 1018
TR Productions, pg 1043

MICHIGAN

Digi Sign Design LLC, pg 847
K&R All Media Productions Inc, pg 908
K&R's Recording Studios Inc, pg 908
MessageMakers, pg 939

MINNESOTA

Aggressive Records Audio Duplication LLC, pg 778
HighBridge Audio, pg 889
Jamieson & Associates Inc, pg 904
Llewellyn Publications, pg 923
Master Communications Group, pg 933
Media Loft Inc, pg 937
MultiMedia, pg 950

MISSOURI

Celebrities Productions, pg 822
Fambrough & Associates Inc, pg 865
Hardcastle Films & Video, pg 885
SOM Publishing Co, pg 1015

MONTANA

High Plains Films, pg 889
North Country Media Group, pg 959

NEBRASKA

Dog & Pony Productions Inc, pg 850
Vision Maker Media, pg 1058

NEVADA

DVDs4Less, pg 854
JCS Video Productions, pg 904

NEW HAMPSHIRE

Apertura, pg 788
Captain Fiddle Music & Publications, pg 820
Chip Taylor Communications LLC, pg 1032

NEW JERSEY

CFP Video Productions Inc, pg 823
Half Moon Video Productions, pg 883
MIB Mediaworks, pg 941
Optisonics Productions, pg 965
Bill Quinn Productions, pg 989
Shanachie Entertainment Corp, pg 1008
Suede Interactive, pg 1027

NEW MEXICO

Michael Dunn Productions, pg 853
Production Outfitters, pg 984

NEW YORK

American History Workshop (NY) Inc, pg 784
Avekta Productions Inc, pg 798
BioMedia Inc, pg 807
Blue Barn Pictures Inc, pg 809
Broad Street Inc, pg 812
Clarity Media Group, pg 829
Thomas Craven Film Corp, pg 837
De Nonno Productions Inc (DPI), pg 844
Digital Force, pg 847
Downtown Community Television Center (DCTV), pg 851
Dyer-Bennet Records, pg 854
Fingerpaint, pg 868
Karen Frankel Productions, pg 872
Hallel Communications, pg 884
HB-Content, pg 886
Hello World Communications, pg 888
Kamen Entertainment Group Inc, pg 908
Ketchum Pleon Change, pg 910
KickedUp Media Group Inc, pg 910
L A Bruell Inc, pg 914
Lavine Production Group, pg 917
Mood Creations Ltd, pg 946
Jack Morton Worldwide, pg 946
MRG Productions Inc, pg 948
MRY, pg 949
New York Audio Productions, pg 956
Shelly Palmer Production, pg 968
Pat Kogan Productions Inc, pg 970
David Rapkin Audio Production, pg 991
Shadow Pictures Inc, pg 1007
Elliot Sokolov Music, pg 1015
Split Image Productions, pg 1021
Spoken Arts Inc, pg 1021
Suggs Media Productions Inc, pg 1028
Third World Newsreel/Camera News Inc, pg 1039
Timed Exposures Films, pg 1040
United Nations Multimedia Resources Unit, pg 1048
Videograf, pg 1057
Zelman Studios Ltd, pg 1073

NORTH CAROLINA

Pat Appleson Studios Inc, pg 788
LCW Productions LLC, pg 917
Trailblazer Studios®, pg 1043
2BruceStudio, pg 1047

OHIO

Advent Media Inc, pg 778
Creative Technology, pg 838
EDR Media LLC, pg 857
Maslowski Productions, pg 933
R&B Communications Inc, pg 991
Take 1 Media Services, pg 1031
VGI Productions, pg 1053
Vista Color Imaging Inc, pg 1059

OKLAHOMA

Piper Media Services Inc, pg 976

OREGON

Ideascape Inc, pg 894
Inner Explorations, pg 898
InterVision Media, pg 902
Norman Beerger Productions, pg 958
Odyssey Productions Inc, pg 961

PENNSYLVANIA

Bang Pictures, pg 802
FMP Media Solutions Inc, pg 870
Innovision Media Group, pg 899
Muderick Media, pg 949
Panta Rhei Media Inc, pg 968
Production Masters Inc (PMI), pg 984
S I Video Sales Group, pg 1001
Videosmith Inc, pg 1057
WQED-Multimedia, pg 1070

RHODE ISLAND

Sound-FX-Design, pg 1017

SOUTH CAROLINA

Stages Video Productions, pg 1023

TENNESSEE

American Blackguard Inc, pg 784
Continental Film, pg 835
Marine Geographic, pg 931

TEXAS

The Editing Co, pg 857
Omega Productions, pg 962
The Sound Lab Inc, pg 1017
Sound Works, pg 1018
South Coast Film & Video, pg 1019
Tropikal Productions, pg 1045

VIRGINIA

BES Studios, pg 805
CACI Productions Group, pg 816
Limelight Communications Inc, pg 921
Lion Recording Services Inc, pg 922
Metro Productions, pg 939
Rocktown Media, pg 998

WASHINGTON

Getty Images, pg 877

WEST VIRGINIA

Blackwater Video Productions, pg 808

WISCONSIN

5th Floor Recording Co, pg 867
USAV Group Inc, pg 1050
Watts Communications Inc, pg 1062
Wisconsin Public Television, pg 1068

WYOMING

Bridger Productions Inc, pg 812

ALBERTA

Black Media Works, pg 808
Global Television Station, pg 879

BRITISH COLUMBIA

Timeless Books, pg 1040

ONTARIO

ADS Media, pg 777
Art Gallery of Ontario, pg 791
CBC/Radio-Canada, pg 821
DebsVoice, pg 844
GAPC (General Assembly Production Centre), pg 875
VO2 Mix Studios, pg 1060

QUEBEC

Kerrigan Productions Inc, pg 910

Documentary Rentals

CALIFORNIA

Direct Cinema Ltd Inc, pg 848
New Line Cinema, pg 956
Point of View Productions, pg 977

GEORGIA

Symmes Systems, pg 1030

ILLINOIS

Perspectives Media, pg 973

INDIANA

InterComm, pg 900

MAINE

University of Maine Audio Visual Services, pg 1049

MASSACHUSETTS

Documentary Educational Resources Inc, pg 850
Emergency Film Group, pg 860

MICHIGAN

Digi Sign Design LLC, pg 847

NEBRASKA

Vision Maker Media, pg 1058

NEW HAMPSHIRE

Chip Taylor Communications LLC, pg 1032

NEW JERSEY

Alden Films, pg 780

NEW YORK

Adwar Video, pg 778
Downtown Community Television Center (DCTV), pg 851
Hallel Communications, pg 884
Timed Exposures Films, pg 1040

PENNSYLVANIA

Penn State University MediaTech, pg 972

WISCONSIN

Her Own Words LLC, pg 888

BRITISH COLUMBIA

Video In Studios/Video Out Distribution, pg 1055

ONTARIO

Simply Audiobooks, pg 1011

PROGRAMMING — AUDIO

Educational Program Distributors

ARIZONA

Arizona Public Media, pg 790
CyberIconics International, pg 841
Drumbeat Indian Arts Inc, pg 852
Tom Hopkins International Inc, pg 891
Personal Achievement Institute, pg 973
TSG Publishing Foundation Inc USA, pg 1046

ARKANSAS

Master Books, pg 933

CALIFORNIA

Academy Savant, pg 773
Astronomical Society of the Pacific, pg 792
Blue Dolphin Multimedia, pg 809
California Language Laboratories, pg 817
Clarity Sound & Light, pg 829
Crystal Pyramid Productions™, pg 840
Deja View Video, pg 845
Digital Media West, pg 847
Direct Cinema Ltd Inc, pg 848
ECONEWS (Environmental Television Series) & (Environmental Directions Radio Series), pg 856
Educational Technology Services (ETS), pg 857
Feldenkrais® Movement Institute, pg 866
Gateways, pg 876
Bruce Goldberg Inc, pg 880
Golden State Dance Teachers Association (GSDTA), pg 880
Health Education Services, pg 887
Joyce Media Inc, pg 906
Klutz, pg 912
Krishnamurti Foundation of America, pg 913
LANGUAGE/30™, pg 916
Lightyear Entertainment, pg 921
Madera Video, pg 927
Maximus Media Inc, pg 934
Medcom Inc, pg 936
monterey media inc, pg 945
Moose School Productions, pg 946
Music World/Vocal Power School, pg 951
ODC Publishing, pg 961
Oral Tradition Sound & Music, pg 965
Pacific Media, pg 967
Pacifica Radio Archives, pg 967
Panorama Publishing Co, pg 968
Paulist Productions, pg 970
QRS Software Services, pg 988
Redwood Audiobooks, pg 993
Regent Press Publishers & Printers, pg 994
Rhythms Productions (Tom Thumb Music), pg 996
Sea Studios Foundation, pg 1005
SevenStar Communications, pg 1007
Social Studies School Service, pg 1015
Sodanceabit, pg 1015
Sound Feelings Records, pg 1017
University of Southern California, pg 1050
Western Instructional Television Inc, pg 1064
The Wine Appreciation Guild Ltd, pg 1067
The Writing Co, pg 1070

COLORADO

Crown Ministries International, pg 840
Gaiam Inc, pg 875
Meriwether Publishing Ltd, pg 939
National Institute for Trial Advocacy (NITA), pg 953
National Teaching Aids Inc, pg 953

CONNECTICUT

Crossroads Video, pg 840
Scholastic Library Publishing, pg 1004
Weston Woods Studios Inc, pg 1064

DELAWARE

Intercollegiate Studies Institute Inc (ISI), pg 900
So Smart Productions, pg 1015

DISTRICT OF COLUMBIA

American Chemical Society (ACS), pg 784
Biblical Archaeology Society (BAS), pg 806
Educational Film Center, pg 857
National Council of Churches, pg 952

FLORIDA

ACE Video Resources Software, pg 774
Allegro Productions Inc, pg 781
Bisk Education, pg 808
Capital Communications Inc, pg 819
I M P A C T Publishing Inc, pg 893
Media Concepts Inc, pg 936
Potentials Unlimited, pg 979
Psychological Assessment Resources Inc (PAR), pg 987
SOS Worldwide Productions Inc, pg 1016

GEORGIA

August House Audio, pg 796
New Leaf Distributing Co, pg 955
Playback Now, pg 977
School Media Associates LLC, pg 1004
Symmes Systems, pg 1030

HAWAII

Media Bridge Gamekids, pg 936
Source School of Tantra Yoga Inc, pg 1019

ILLINOIS

CCH Continuing Education, pg 821
Educational Insights, pg 857
Liturgy Training Publications, pg 923
National Safety Council (NSC), pg 953
Nightingale-Conant Corp, pg 957
Oasis Audio, pg 960
Pieces of Learning, pg 975
Research Press Co, pg 995
Spoken Language Services Inc, pg 1021
Theosophical Publishing House, pg 1038

INDIANA

Career & Self Directed Extended Programs at Purdue University, pg 820
Herff Jones | Nystrom, pg 888
Indiana University Press, pg 897

IOWA

Accelerated Learning Foundation, pg 773
Long-Term Success Publishing, pg 924
Perfection Learning Corp, pg 973

KENTUCKY

The Learning House Inc, pg 917

MAINE

Slim Goodbody Corp, pg 1013

MARYLAND

Department of Education Resources, pg 845
Hearing Loss Association of America (HLAA), pg 887
James Agee Film Project, pg 904
Kids on the Block Inc, pg 910
Milner-Fenwick Inc, pg 943
MMI Corp, pg 944
Nicholas P Pipino Associates Inc, pg 976
Recorded Books LLC, pg 993

MASSACHUSETTS

Brookline Books, pg 814
Cheng & Tsui Co, pg 824
Documentary Educational Resources Inc, pg 850
Emergency Film Group, pg 860
Pauline Books & Media, pg 970
Penfield Productions Ltd, pg 971
Ben Rudnick & Friends, pg 1000
Triumph Learning LLC, pg 1045
Yellow Moon Press, pg 1072

MICHIGAN

Digi Sign Design LLC, pg 847
Emery-Pratt Co, pg 860
HighScope Press, pg 889
Meuninck's Media Methods Inc, pg 940
Technology Learning Services, pg 1035
Zondervan, A HarperCollins Company, pg 1074

MINNESOTA

Effective Learning Systems Inc, pg 858
EMC/Paradigm Publishing, pg 860
HighBridge Audio, pg 889
Learning Strategies Corp, pg 917
Llewellyn Publications, pg 923
MakeMusic® Inc, pg 929
Science Museum of Minnesota, pg 1005

MISSOURI

American Audio Prose Library Inc (AAPL), pg 783
Marsh Media, pg 931
Mosby Inc, pg 947
New Letters on the Air, pg 956
SOM Publishing Co, pg 1015
Vedanta Society of St Louis, pg 1052

MONTANA

High Plains Films, pg 889

NEBRASKA

Vision Maker Media, pg 1058

NEVADA

DVDs4Less, pg 854

NEW HAMPSHIRE

Captain Fiddle Music & Publications, pg 820
French American Music Enterprises, pg 873
Chip Taylor Communications LLC, pg 1032

NEW JERSEY

Educational Impressions, pg 857
Jointure for Community Adult Education Inc, pg 906
Learning Ally, pg 917
Listen & Live Audio Inc, pg 923
A W Peller & Associates Inc, pg 971
Shanachie Entertainment Corp, pg 1008

NEW MEXICO

National Information Center for Educational Media (NICEM)/ MediaSleuth, pg 952
Uncharted Country Publishing, pg 1048

NEW YORK

American Management Association International, pg 784
Asia Society, pg 792
Beekman Books Inc, pg 804
Brooklyn Botanic Garden, pg 814
Cambridge University Press, pg 818
The Cinema Guild Inc, pg 827
Conversation Arts Media, pg 836
Cross-Cultural Communications, pg 839
Dover Publications Inc, pg 851
Educational Activities Inc, pg 857
Educational Images Ltd, pg 857
Albert Ellis Institute (AEI), pg 859
Films Media Group, pg 868
Granny Press LLC, pg 881
Guilford Publications, pg 883
Hallel Communications, pg 884
Homespun Video, pg 890
Irish Music Corp, pg 902
Janus Films Inc, pg 904
Listening Library, pg 923
March of Dimes Foundation, pg 930
Maryknoll Productions, pg 933
MRG Productions Inc, pg 948
NSR Productions Inc & Capricorn Five Films, pg 960
Penguin Audiobooks, pg 971
Practising Law Institute, pg 980
Price Stern Sloan, pg 981
Random House Children's Books, pg 991
Scholastic Media, pg 1004
TeleTime Productions, pg 1036
Timed Exposures Films, pg 1040
United Nations Multimedia Resources Unit, pg 1048
Visual Technologies Corp, pg 1060
Weigl Publishers Inc, pg 1063

Educational Program Producers

PROGRAMMING — AUDIO

Educational Program Producers (continued)

GEORGIA (continued)

Playback Now, pg 977
Sirius Images Corp dba WaveGuide Studios, pg 1012
Symmes Systems, pg 1030

HAWAII

Media Bridge Gamekids, pg 936
Source School of Tantra Yoga Inc, pg 1019

IDAHO

Wide Eye Productions, pg 1066

ILLINOIS

ABS Enterprises, pg 772
Accenture, pg 773
Audio Visual Services Corp, pg 796
AudioTransitions, pg 796
CCH Continuing Education, pg 821
CCore Media Inc, pg 821
Centrax Corp, pg 823
Communications Corporation of America, pg 833
Comtech Multimedia Marketing, pg 834
Esoteric Sound, pg 862
Liturgy Training Publications, pg 923
Major Media Productions Inc, pg 929
Manning Productions, pg 930
Nightingale-Conant Corp, pg 957
Oasis Audio, pg 960
Jim Passin Productions, pg 970
The Pepper Group, pg 972
Perspectives Media, pg 973
Pieces of Learning, pg 975
PSAV® Presentation Services (Hotel Services Division), pg 987
QuickSet International Inc, pg 989
Rand McNally Education, pg 991
Research Press Co, pg 995
Spoken Language Services Inc, pg 1021
Theosophical Publishing House, pg 1038
Video Impressions, pg 1055

INDIANA

AVA Productions, pg 798
Bright Ideas Creative Services, pg 812
Covenant Productions®, pg 837
Digital Rain LLC, pg 847
Herff Jones | Nystrom, pg 888
OMNI Productions, pg 962
PentaVision Communications Inc, pg 972

IOWA

Accelerated Learning Foundation, pg 773
Hedquist Productions Inc, pg 887
Iowa State University-Information Technology Services, pg 902
Long-Term Success Publishing, pg 924
The Production House, pg 984

KENTUCKY

Donna Lawrence Productions, pg 917
The Learning House Inc, pg 917
National Geographic Learning, pg 952
Northern Kentucky University, pg 959

LOUISIANA

Digital FX Inc, pg 847

MAINE

Slim Goodbody Corp, pg 1013

MARYLAND

CPR MultiMedia Solutions, pg 837
CSPMedia.com, pg 840
The Cutting Corp, pg 841
dbF a Media Company, pg 844
Department of Education Resources, pg 845
The Image Generators, pg 895
James Agee Film Project, pg 904
Kids on the Block Inc, pg 910
Kramer Communications Video Production, pg 913
Milner-Fenwick Inc, pg 943
MMI Corp, pg 944
Recorded Books LLC, pg 993

MASSACHUSETTS

Cheng & Tsui Co, pg 824
CommCreative, pg 832
Documentary Educational Resources Inc, pg 850
Emergency Film Group, pg 860
Heliotrope Studios, pg 887
Home Inc, pg 890
Labrecque Creative Sound, pg 915
Monadnock Media Inc, pg 945
Pauline Books & Media, pg 970
Penfield Productions Ltd, pg 971
Shambhala Publications, pg 1008
Soundtrack Recording Studios, pg 1018
TR Productions, pg 1043
Triumph Learning LLC, pg 1045

MICHIGAN

Digi Sign Design LLC, pg 847
HighScope Press, pg 889
International Tae Kwon Do Association (ITA Institute), pg 901
K&R All Media Productions Inc, pg 908
K&R's Recording Studios Inc, pg 908
MessageMakers, pg 939
Technology Learning Services, pg 1035
TGA Recording Co, pg 1038
University of Michigan, Center for Middle Eastern & North African Studies, pg 1050
Zondervan, A HarperCollins Company, pg 1074

MINNESOTA

Aggressive Records Audio Duplication LLC, pg 778
Effective Learning Systems Inc, pg 858
EMC/Paradigm Publishing, pg 860
HighBridge Audio, pg 889
Jamieson & Associates Inc, pg 904
Learning Strategies Corp, pg 917
Master Communications Group, pg 933
MultiMedia, pg 950
Science Museum of Minnesota, pg 1005

MISSOURI

Audio-VideoGraphics Inc, pg 795
Celebrities Productions, pg 822
Fambrough & Associates Inc, pg 865
Hardcastle Films & Video, pg 885
Marsh Media, pg 931
Mosby Inc, pg 947
New Letters on the Air, pg 956
SOM Publishing Co, pg 1015
Vedanta Society of St Louis, pg 1052

MONTANA

High Plains Films, pg 889
North Country Media Group, pg 959

NEBRASKA

AdventSource, pg 778
Dog & Pony Productions Inc, pg 850
Vision Maker Media, pg 1058

NEVADA

DVDs4Less, pg 854
JCS Video Productions, pg 904
Tetrahedron LLC, pg 1037

NEW HAMPSHIRE

Academic & Campus Technology Services, pg 773
Apertura, pg 788
Captain Fiddle Music & Publications, pg 820
Chip Taylor Communications LLC, pg 1032

NEW JERSEY

Audio Vistas LLC, pg 795
Broadcast Center Studios, pg 813
CFP Video Productions Inc, pg 823
Educational Impressions, pg 857
Half Moon Video Productions, pg 883
Laurel Video Productions, pg 916
Learning Ally, pg 917
Listen & Live Audio Inc, pg 923
MIB Mediaworks, pg 941
Optisonics Productions, pg 965
Bill Quinn Productions, pg 989
Shanachie Entertainment Corp, pg 1008
Suede Interactive, pg 1027

NEW MEXICO

Michael Dunn Productions, pg 853
Production Outfitters, pg 984
Rainbow International Inc/Rainbow Productions Inc, pg 990
Uncharted Country Publishing, pg 1048

NEW YORK

American History Workshop (NY) Inc, pg 784
American Management Association International, pg 784
Asia Society, pg 792
Avekta Productions Inc, pg 798
Barron's Educational Series Inc, pg 803
Blue Barn Pictures Inc, pg 809
Broad Street Inc, pg 812
Brooklyn Botanic Garden, pg 814
Conversation Arts Media, pg 836
Thomas Craven Film Corp, pg 837
Cross-Cultural Communications, pg 839
C2 Imaging LLC, pg 841
Digital Force, pg 847
dM works, pg 849
Downtown Community Television Center (DCTV), pg 851
Dyer-Bennet Records, pg 854
Educational Activities Inc, pg 857
Educational Images Ltd, pg 857
Albert Ellis Institute (AEI), pg 859
Eye on Dance, pg 865
Films Media Group, pg 868
Fingerpaint, pg 868
Karen Frankel Productions, pg 872
Granny Press LLC, pg 881
Greyfalcon House, pg 882
Guilford Publications, pg 883
Hallel Communications, pg 884
Hello World Communications, pg 888
Homespun Video, pg 890
Human Relations Media, pg 892
Icontent, pg 893
Kamen Entertainment Group Inc, pg 908
Ketchum Pleon Change, pg 910
L A Bruell Inc, pg 914
Lavine Production Group, pg 917
Listening Library, pg 923
March of Dimes Foundation, pg 930
Mark Custom Recording Service Inc, pg 931
Maryknoll Productions, pg 933
Jack Morton Worldwide, pg 946
MRG Productions Inc, pg 948
MRY, pg 949
New York Audio Productions, pg 956
NSR Productions Inc & Capricorn Five Films, pg 960
Shelly Palmer Production, pg 968
Pat Kogan Productions Inc, pg 970
Penguin Audiobooks, pg 971
Practising Law Institute, pg 980
Price Stern Sloan, pg 981
Random House Children's Books, pg 991
David Rapkin Audio Production, pg 991
Elliot Sokolov Music, pg 1015
Split Image Productions, pg 1021
Spoken Arts Inc, pg 1021
Suggs Media Productions Inc, pg 1028
Tiki Recording Studios Inc, pg 1040
Timed Exposures Films, pg 1040
United Nations Multimedia Resources Unit, pg 1048
Videograf, pg 1057
Weigl Publishers Inc, pg 1063
WorldView Software, pg 1070
Zelman Studios Ltd, pg 1073

NORTH CAROLINA

Pat Appleson Studios Inc, pg 788
The Communications Group Inc, pg 833
Creative Services Inc, pg 838
Eli Research Group, pg 859
The International Society of Automation (ISA), pg 901
LCW Productions LLC, pg 917
Sinclair Institute, pg 1012
World Class Learning Materials Inc, pg 1069

OHIO

Advent Media Inc, pg 778
Alegra House Publishers, pg 780
Creative Technology, pg 838
Cuyahoga Community College Media Center, pg 841
EDR Media LLC, pg 857
Maslowski Productions, pg 933
McGraw-Hill School Education Group, pg 935
Musicol Recording, pg 951
Ohio State University Foreign Language Publications, pg 961
South-Western Publishing Co, pg 1019
Take 1 Media Services, pg 1031
Twin Sisters Productions LLC, pg 1047
VGI Productions, pg 1053
Vista Color Imaging Inc, pg 1059
Visual Education, pg 1059

OKLAHOMA

Piper Media Services Inc, pg 976
University of Oklahoma Academic Media & Digital Services, pg 1050

OREGON

A KTVA Production LLC, pg 771
ADD Plus, pg 776
ERA Learning, pg 862
Ideascape Inc, pg 894
Inner Explorations, pg 898
InterVision Media, pg 902
The Keyboard Workshop, pg 910
Norman Beerger Productions, pg 958
Odyssey Productions Inc, pg 961

PENNSYLVANIA

American Artist Studio, pg 783
Discovery Education - South Burlington, pg 848
FMP Media Solutions Inc, pg 870
Forge Recording LLC, pg 871
Innovision Media Group, pg 899
JPL, pg 906
Kensington Falls Animation, pg 909
Newtown Psychological Center, pg 957
Panta Rhei Media Inc, pg 968
Production Masters Inc (PMI), pg 984
The Fred Rogers Co, pg 998
S I Video Sales Group, pg 1001
The Videohouse Inc, pg 1057
Videosmith Inc, pg 1057
WQED-Multimedia, pg 1070

RHODE ISLAND

Sound Advantage, pg 1016
Sound-FX-Design, pg 1017

SOUTH CAROLINA

BJU Press, pg 808
Venture Media, pg 1052

TENNESSEE

Abingdon Press, pg 772
American Blackguard Inc, pg 784
Continental Film, pg 835
Marine Geographic, pg 931
Memphis Communications Corp, pg 938

TEXAS

AMA Nystrom Printing/Finishing, pg 783
The Editing Co, pg 857
Educational Video Network, pg 857
Epic Software Group Inc, pg 862
First Group Communications Inc, pg 868
Institute of Texan Cultures, pg 899
Lamb & Lion Ministries, pg 915
Matson Multi-Media, pg 934
Milky Way Press, pg 943
Omega Productions, pg 962
Romar Learning, pg 999
Shadow Play Records & Video, pg 1007
SMI Inc, pg 1014
The Sound Lab Inc, pg 1017
Sound Works, pg 1018
South Coast Film & Video, pg 1019
Stage Directions, pg 1022
Texas Heart Institute Visual Communication Services, pg 1037
Tropikal Productions, pg 1045
Writer's AudioShop/Davenport Productions, pg 1070

UTAH

K-SAR Video & DVD Productions, pg 907
San Juan School District Heritage Language Resource Center, pg 1002

VERMONT

Dialect Accent Specialists Inc, pg 846

VIRGINIA

BES Studios, pg 805
CACI Productions Group, pg 816
Limelight Communications Inc, pg 921
Lion Recording Services Inc, pg 922
Metro Productions, pg 939
National Media Services Inc, pg 953
Rocktown Media, pg 998

WASHINGTON

Center for Touch Drawing, pg 822

WEST VIRGINIA

Blackwater Video Productions, pg 808

WISCONSIN

Alliance Publications Inc (API)/ Sinsinawa Studios Productions, pg 781
5th Floor Recording Co, pg 867
Knowledge Unlimited Inc, pg 912
Meridian Studios, pg 939
Plank Road Publishing Inc, pg 976
Tomorrow River Music, pg 1042
USAV Group Inc, pg 1050
Watts Communications Inc, pg 1062
Wisconsin Public Television, pg 1068

WYOMING

Bridger Productions Inc, pg 812

ALBERTA

Black Media Works, pg 808

BRITISH COLUMBIA

Thompson Rivers University Open Learning, pg 1039
Video In Studios/Video Out Distribution, pg 1055

ONTARIO

ADS Media, pg 777
Art Gallery of Ontario, pg 791
CBC/Radio-Canada, pg 821
DebsVoice, pg 844
Nelson Education Ltd, pg 954
Novalis, pg 959
Pearson Education Canada, pg 970
VO2 Mix Studios, pg 1060

QUEBEC

Les Editions CEC Inc, pg 857
Kerrigan Productions Inc, pg 910

Educational Program Rentals

ARIZONA

Arizona Public Media, pg 790

CALIFORNIA

Auslender Productions/Celestial Images, pg 797
Direct Cinema Ltd Inc, pg 848
ECONEWS (Environmental Television Series) & (Environmental Directions Radio Series), pg 856
Educational Technology Services (ETS), pg 857
Medcom Inc, pg 936
Paulist Productions, pg 970
Point of View Productions, pg 977
Western Instructional Television Inc, pg 1064

CONNECTICUT

Crossroads Video, pg 840
EagleVision Inc, pg 855

GEORGIA

Symmes Systems, pg 1030

MAINE

University of Maine Audio Visual Services, pg 1049

MARYLAND

James Agee Film Project, pg 904
Kids on the Block Inc, pg 910

MASSACHUSETTS

Documentary Educational Resources Inc, pg 850
Emergency Film Group, pg 860

MICHIGAN

Digi Sign Design LLC, pg 847

NEBRASKA

Vision Maker Media, pg 1058

NEW HAMPSHIRE

Chip Taylor Communications LLC, pg 1032

NEW JERSEY

Alden Films, pg 780
Listen & Live Audio Inc, pg 923

NEW YORK

Brooklyn Botanic Garden, pg 814
Downtown Community Television Center (DCTV), pg 851
Hallel Communications, pg 884
Timed Exposures Films, pg 1040

PENNSYLVANIA

Karol Media Inc, pg 908
Penn State University MediaTech, pg 972

WISCONSIN

Her Own Words LLC, pg 888

ONTARIO

Simply Audiobooks, pg 1011

Feature Program Distributors

CALIFORNIA

Digital Media West, pg 847
Direct Cinema Ltd Inc, pg 848
Bruce Goldberg Inc, pg 880
Hope Productions, pg 891
Jaguar Distribution Corp, pg 903
Madera Video, pg 927
Maximus Media Inc, pg 934
Moose School Productions, pg 946
New Line Cinema, pg 956
Pacific Media, pg 967
Pacifica Radio Archives, pg 967
Palardo Productions, pg 968
Publishers Group West Inc, pg 987
QRS Software Services, pg 988
Varese Sarabande Records Inc, pg 1052
Warner Home Video Inc, pg 1062

DELAWARE

Intercollegiate Studies Institute Inc (ISI), pg 900

FLORIDA

Capital Communications Inc, pg 819

ILLINOIS

CCore Media Inc, pg 821
Communications Corporation of America, pg 833

IOWA

American Visions, pg 785
Right Stuf Inc, pg 997

MARYLAND

Recorded Books LLC, pg 993

MINNESOTA

HighBridge Audio, pg 889

MISSOURI

SOM Publishing Co, pg 1015

MONTANA

High Plains Films, pg 889

PROGRAMMING — AUDIO

Feature Program Distributors (continued)

NEBRASKA

Vision Maker Media, pg 1058

NEVADA

DVDs4Less, pg 854

NEW HAMPSHIRE

Chip Taylor Communications LLC, pg 1032

NEW YORK

The Cinema Guild Inc, pg 827
Albert Ellis Institute (AEI), pg 859
HarperAudio, pg 885
HB-Content, pg 886
Janus Films Inc, pg 904
Maryknoll Productions, pg 933
MRG Productions Inc, pg 948
RadioArt/Bob & Ray CDs & MP3 Files, pg 990
Random House Audio Publishing Group, pg 991
Simon & Schuster, Inc, pg 1011
Synaptic Digital, pg 1030

NORTH CAROLINA

Baker & Taylor Inc, pg 801
Vide-O-Go/That's Infotainment!, pg 1054

OREGON

InterVision Media, pg 902

TENNESSEE

American Blackguard Inc, pg 784
Ingram Book Group, pg 898
Spring Arbor Distributors, pg 1022

VIRGINIA

CACI Productions Group, pg 816

ALBERTA

Global Television Station, pg 879

ONTARIO

CBC/Radio-Canada, pg 821
Life Cycle Books Ltd, pg 920

Feature Program Producers

ARIZONA

Walt Disney Records Consumer Products Division, pg 1061

ARKANSAS

Live'N'Loud, pg 923

CALIFORNIA

Auslender Productions/Celestial Images, pg 797
The Banquet Sound Studios, pg 802
Big Door, pg 807
Catapult Films Inc, pg 821
Custom Video Productions Inc, pg 841
Direct Cinema Ltd Inc, pg 848
Dogma Studios, pg 850
Bruce Goldberg Inc, pg 880
Hope Productions, pg 891
imageReal Pictures LLC, pg 896
Jaguar Distribution Corp, pg 903
Lynch Communications, pg 926
Maximus Media Inc, pg 934
Moose School Productions, pg 946
New Line Cinema, pg 956
Pacific Audio-Visual Enterprises, pg 967
Pacific Media, pg 967
Palardo Productions, pg 968
PM Productions, pg 977
Producers Group Ltd, pg 983
QRS Software Services, pg 988
Studio 132, pg 1027
Total Media Group, pg 1042
Video Resources Inc, pg 1056
WalkerVision Interarts, pg 1061
Webster Communications, pg 1063

COLORADO

Tim Cissell Music, pg 828
Starwest Productions, pg 1024
Tatum Video, pg 1032

CONNECTICUT

EagleVision Inc, pg 855
Essex Television Group Inc, pg 862
The Gary-Paul Agency, pg 875

FLORIDA

Blackburst Entertainment, pg 808
Capital Communications Inc, pg 819
Chatterbox Productions Inc, pg 824
Communications Concepts Inc (CCI), pg 833
Courter Films LLC, pg 837
LHV Audio Services, pg 919
Sunfire Communications Inc, pg 1028
Top Hat Productions, pg 1042

GEORGIA

Guerrilla Productions LLC, pg 883

IDAHO

Wide Eye Productions, pg 1066

ILLINOIS

CCore Media Inc, pg 821
Communications Corporation of America, pg 833
The Pepper Group, pg 972

INDIANA

AVA Productions, pg 798
Digital Rain LLC, pg 847

IOWA

American Visions, pg 785
Right Stuf Inc, pg 997

MARYLAND

The Cutting Corp, pg 841
dbF a Media Company, pg 844
Kramer Communications Video Production, pg 913
Recorded Books LLC, pg 993

MASSACHUSETTS

Emergency Film Group, pg 860
Heliotrope Studios, pg 887
Labrecque Creative Sound, pg 915
Monadnock Media Inc, pg 945
Penfield Productions Ltd, pg 971
Shambhala Publications, pg 1008
Soundtrack Recording Studios, pg 1018

MICHIGAN

The Brookwood Studio Inc, pg 814
K&R All Media Productions Inc, pg 908
K&R's Recording Studios Inc, pg 908

MINNESOTA

Aggressive Records Audio Duplication LLC, pg 778
HighBridge Audio, pg 889

MISSOURI

Celebrities Productions, pg 822
Fambrough & Associates Inc, pg 865
SOM Publishing Co, pg 1015

MONTANA

High Plains Films, pg 889

NEBRASKA

AdventSource, pg 778

NEVADA

DVDs4Less, pg 854

NEW HAMPSHIRE

Chip Taylor Communications LLC, pg 1032

NEW JERSEY

CFP Video Productions Inc, pg 823
MIB Mediaworks, pg 941
Optisonics Productions, pg 965
Bill Quinn Productions, pg 989
Suede Interactive, pg 1027

NEW MEXICO

Production Outfitters, pg 984

NEW YORK

Big Fish Productions Inc, pg 807
Broad Street Inc, pg 812
CompuWeather Inc, pg 834
Digital Force, pg 847
Albert Ellis Institute (AEI), pg 859
Femme Productions Inc, pg 866
Greyfalcon House, pg 882
HarperAudio, pg 885
HB-Content, pg 886
Kamen Entertainment Group Inc, pg 908
Maryknoll Productions, pg 933
Jack Morton Worldwide, pg 946
MRG Productions Inc, pg 948
Shelly Palmer Production, pg 968
Random House Audio Publishing Group, pg 991
David Rapkin Audio Production, pg 991
Shadow Pictures Inc, pg 1007
Simon & Schuster, Inc, pg 1011
Elliot Sokolov Music, pg 1015
Split Image Productions, pg 1021
Suggs Media Productions Inc, pg 1028
Synaptic Digital, pg 1030
Zelman Studios Ltd, pg 1073

NORTH CAROLINA

LCW Productions LLC, pg 917
Trailblazer Studios®, pg 1043
2BruceStudio, pg 1047

OHIO

Advent Media Inc, pg 778
Creative Technology, pg 838
EDR Media LLC, pg 857
R&B Communications Inc, pg 991
Vista Color Imaging Inc, pg 1059

OKLAHOMA

Piper Media Services Inc, pg 976

OREGON

Ideascape Inc, pg 894
InterVision Media, pg 902

PENNSYLVANIA

Innovision Media Group, pg 899
WQED-Multimedia, pg 1070

RHODE ISLAND

Sound-FX-Design, pg 1017

TENNESSEE

American Blackguard Inc, pg 784

TEXAS

Educational Video Network, pg 857
Omega Productions, pg 962
The Sound Lab Inc, pg 1017
Sound Works, pg 1018

VIRGINIA

BES Studios, pg 805
CACI Productions Group, pg 816
Lion Recording Services Inc, pg 922
Metro Productions, pg 939

WISCONSIN

5th Floor Recording Co, pg 867
Knowledge Unlimited Inc, pg 912
Wisconsin Public Television, pg 1068

WYOMING

Bridger Productions Inc, pg 812

ALBERTA

Global Television Station, pg 879

ONTARIO

ADS Media, pg 777
CBC/Radio-Canada, pg 821
VO2 Mix Studios, pg 1060

QUEBEC

Kerrigan Productions Inc, pg 910

Feature Program Rentals

CALIFORNIA

Direct Cinema Ltd Inc, pg 848
New Line Cinema, pg 956
Palardo Productions, pg 968

NEBRASKA

Vision Maker Media, pg 1058

NEW HAMPSHIRE

Chip Taylor Communications LLC, pg 1032

NEW YORK

Adwar Video, pg 778

PENNSYLVANIA

Penn State University MediaTech, pg 972

Foreign Program Distributors

ARIZONA

Drumbeat Indian Arts Inc, pg 852

CALIFORNIA

Digital Media West, pg 847
Jaguar Distribution Corp, pg 903
LANGUAGE/30™, pg 916
Maximus Media Inc, pg 934
Pacifica Radio Archives, pg 967
QRS Software Services, pg 988
Warner Home Video Inc, pg 1062

DISTRICT OF COLUMBIA

Biblical Archaeology Society (BAS), pg 806

FLORIDA

Capital Communications Inc, pg 819

ILLINOIS

Oasis Audio, pg 960
Spoken Language Services Inc, pg 1021

MARYLAND

Recorded Books LLC, pg 993

MASSACHUSETTS

Documentary Educational Resources Inc, pg 850

MICHIGAN

Digi Sign Design LLC, pg 847

NEW HAMPSHIRE

Chip Taylor Communications LLC, pg 1032

NEW YORK

Applause Learning Resources, pg 788
Beekman Books Inc, pg 804
The Cinema Guild Inc, pg 827
Cross-Cultural Communications, pg 839
Dover Publications Inc, pg 851
Hallel Communications, pg 884
Irish Music Corp, pg 902
Janus Films Inc, pg 904
Live Oak Media, pg 923
MRG Productions Inc, pg 948
SISU Home Entertainment Inc, pg 1012

NORTH CAROLINA

Baker & Taylor Inc, pg 801
Ladyslipper Inc, pg 915
Vide-O-Go/That's Infotainment!, pg 1054

OHIO

Ohio State University Foreign Language Publications, pg 961

PENNSYLVANIA

FMP Media Solutions Inc, pg 870
S I Video Sales Group, pg 1001

TENNESSEE

Ingram Book Group, pg 898
Spring Arbor Distributors, pg 1022

TEXAS

Educational Video Network, pg 857

VERMONT

Trafalgar Square Books, pg 1043

WISCONSIN

Plank Road Publishing Inc, pg 976

ALBERTA

Global Television Station, pg 879

BRITISH COLUMBIA

Video In Studios/Video Out Distribution, pg 1055

Foreign Program Producers

CALIFORNIA

Custom Video Productions Inc, pg 841
Dogma Studios, pg 850
Hope Productions, pg 891
Jaguar Distribution Corp, pg 903
LANGUAGE/30™, pg 916
Lynch Communications, pg 926
Prime Cut Productions, pg 982
Producers Group Ltd, pg 983
QRS Software Services, pg 988
Studio 132, pg 1027
Total Media Group, pg 1042

COLORADO

Tim Cissell Music, pg 828

CONNECTICUT

EagleVision Inc, pg 855

DISTRICT OF COLUMBIA

Biblical Archaeology Society (BAS), pg 806
Hillmann & Carr Inc, pg 889

FLORIDA

Blackburst Entertainment, pg 808
Capital Communications Inc, pg 819
Courter Films LLC, pg 837
LHV Audio Services, pg 919
Sunfire Communications Inc, pg 1028

GEORGIA

Guerrilla Productions LLC, pg 883

IDAHO

Wide Eye Productions, pg 1066

ILLINOIS

ABS Enterprises, pg 772
The Pepper Group, pg 972
Spoken Language Services Inc, pg 1021

INDIANA

AVA Productions, pg 798

IOWA

Right Stuf Inc, pg 997

KANSAS

Chapman Recording & Mastering, pg 824

MARYLAND

CSPMedia.com, pg 840
The Cutting Corp, pg 841
Recorded Books LLC, pg 993

MASSACHUSETTS

Documentary Educational Resources Inc, pg 850
Heliotrope Studios, pg 887
Labrecque Creative Sound, pg 915
Penfield Productions Ltd, pg 971
Soundtrack Recording Studios, pg 1018

MICHIGAN

Digi Sign Design LLC, pg 847
K&R All Media Productions Inc, pg 908
K&R's Recording Studios Inc, pg 908

MINNESOTA

Aggressive Records Audio Duplication LLC, pg 778
Jamieson & Associates Inc, pg 904
Master Communications Group, pg 933

MISSOURI

Celebrities Productions, pg 822
Fambrough & Associates Inc, pg 865

NEW HAMPSHIRE

Apertura, pg 788
Chip Taylor Communications LLC, pg 1032

NEW JERSEY

CFP Video Productions Inc, pg 823
MIB Mediaworks, pg 941
Suede Interactive, pg 1027

NEW YORK

Applause Learning Resources, pg 788
Avekta Productions Inc, pg 798
Cross-Cultural Communications, pg 839
Digital Force, pg 847
Downtown Community Television Center (DCTV), pg 851
Fingerpaint, pg 868
Hallel Communications, pg 884
Kamen Entertainment Group Inc, pg 908
Live Oak Media, pg 923
Maryknoll Productions, pg 933
Jack Morton Worldwide, pg 946
MRG Productions Inc, pg 948
New York Audio Productions, pg 956
Shelly Palmer Production, pg 968
Shadow Pictures Inc, pg 1007
SISU Home Entertainment Inc, pg 1012
Split Image Productions, pg 1021
Spoken Arts Inc, pg 1021
Zelman Studios Ltd, pg 1073

NORTH CAROLINA

Pat Appleson Studios Inc, pg 788

OHIO

Creative Technology, pg 838
EDR Media LLC, pg 857
Ohio State University Foreign Language Publications, pg 961
Vista Color Imaging Inc, pg 1059

OKLAHOMA

Piper Media Services Inc, pg 976

PENNSYLVANIA

FMP Media Solutions Inc, pg 870

RHODE ISLAND

Sound-FX-Design, pg 1017

TEXAS

Omega Productions, pg 962
Omni Intercommunications Inc, pg 962
Romar Learning, pg 999
The Sound Lab Inc, pg 1017
Tropikal Productions, pg 1045

VERMONT

Inner Traditions International, pg 898

VIRGINIA

Lion Recording Services Inc, pg 922

WASHINGTON

Kostov Productions, pg 913

WISCONSIN

5th Floor Recording Co, pg 867
Wisconsin Public Television, pg 1068

WYOMING

Bridger Productions Inc, pg 812

ONTARIO

VO2 Mix Studios, pg 1060

QUEBEC

Kerrigan Productions Inc, pg 910

Foreign Program Rentals

CALIFORNIA

New Line Cinema, pg 956

MASSACHUSETTS

Documentary Educational Resources Inc, pg 850

MICHIGAN

Digi Sign Design LLC, pg 847

PROGRAMMING — AUDIO

Foreign Program Rentals (continued)

NEW HAMPSHIRE

Chip Taylor Communications LLC, pg 1032

NEW JERSEY

Alden Films, pg 780

NEW YORK

Downtown Community Television Center (DCTV), pg 851
Hallel Communications, pg 884

PENNSYLVANIA

Penn State University MediaTech, pg 972

BRITISH COLUMBIA

Video In Studios/Video Out Distribution, pg 1055

ONTARIO

Simply Audiobooks, pg 1011

Government Program Distributors

CALIFORNIA

Digital Media West, pg 847
Direct Cinema Ltd Inc, pg 848
Maximus Media Inc, pg 934
QRS Software Services, pg 988

FLORIDA

Allegro Productions Inc, pg 781
Bisk Education, pg 808
Capital Communications Inc, pg 819
Gulf Coast Audio Visual Producers Inc, pg 883

ILLINOIS

CCH Inc, A Wolters Kluwer business, pg 821
CCore Media Inc, pg 821
Cool-Lux, pg 836

MARYLAND

Recorded Books LLC, pg 993
Special Archives Division, Motion Picture Branch, pg 1020

MICHIGAN

Digi Sign Design LLC, pg 847

MONTANA

Jereco Studios Inc, pg 905

NEVADA

DVDs4Less, pg 854

NEW HAMPSHIRE

Chip Taylor Communications LLC, pg 1032

NEW MEXICO

National Information Center for Educational Media (NICEM)/MediaSleuth, pg 952

NEW YORK

Films Media Group, pg 868
Janus Films Inc, pg 904
MRG Productions Inc, pg 948
Synaptic Digital, pg 1030
Visual Technologies Corp, pg 1060

NORTH CAROLINA

Baker & Taylor Inc, pg 801
Vide-O-Go/That's Infotainment!, pg 1054

OHIO

Curtis Inc, pg 841

OREGON

InterVision Media, pg 902

PENNSYLVANIA

FMP Media Solutions Inc, pg 870

VIRGINIA

CACI Productions Group, pg 816
CDR Communications Inc, pg 822

Government Program Producers

CALIFORNIA

Creative Media Recording, pg 838
Custom Video Productions Inc, pg 841
Design Media, pg 845
Direct Cinema Ltd Inc, pg 848
Dogma Studios, pg 850
Havas Edge, pg 885
Jaguar Distribution Corp, pg 903
The Kenwood Group, pg 909
Lynch Communications, pg 926
Maximus Media Inc, pg 934
The Media Staff Inc, pg 937
On-Trax Inc, pg 963
piXvfm, pg 976
PM Productions, pg 977
QRS Software Services, pg 988
Steve Shapiro Music, pg 1008
Still N'Motion, pg 1025
Studio 132, pg 1027
Tele-Video Production Services (TVPS), pg 1036
Total Media Group, pg 1042

COLORADO

Daylight Productions & Rentals, pg 844
Flashback Media Productions, pg 869
Rocky Mountain Audio/Video Productions Inc, pg 998
Tatum Video, pg 1032

CONNECTICUT

Biomedical Media Communications Dept, pg 807
EagleVision Inc, pg 855

DISTRICT OF COLUMBIA

Educational Film Center, pg 857
Hillmann & Carr Inc, pg 889

FLORIDA

Allegro Productions Inc, pg 781
Audio Visual Imagineering Inc, pg 795
Bisk Education, pg 808
Blackburst Entertainment, pg 808
Capital Communications Inc, pg 819
Communications Concepts Inc (CCI), pg 833
Courter Films LLC, pg 837
Eastern Video, pg 856
Gulf Coast Audio Visual Producers Inc, pg 883
LHV Audio Services, pg 919
Sunfire Communications Inc, pg 1028
Sunrise Studios, pg 1028
Top Hat Productions, pg 1042

GEORGIA

COMPRO Productions Inc, pg 834
Guerrilla Productions LLC, pg 883

IDAHO

Wide Eye Productions, pg 1066

ILLINOIS

ABS Enterprises, pg 772
Accenture, pg 773
CCH Inc, A Wolters Kluwer business, pg 821
CCore Media Inc, pg 821
The Pepper Group, pg 972
Video Impressions, pg 1055

INDIANA

AVA Productions, pg 798
Digital Rain LLC, pg 847
OMNI Productions, pg 962

IOWA

The Production House, pg 984

KANSAS

Chapman Recording & Mastering, pg 824

LOUISIANA

Moxie Media, pg 948

MARYLAND

CPR MultiMedia Solutions, pg 837
CSPMedia.com, pg 840
The Cutting Corp, pg 841
dbF a Media Company, pg 844
The Image Generators, pg 895
Kramer Communications Video Production, pg 913
Milner-Fenwick Inc, pg 943
Recorded Books LLC, pg 993

MASSACHUSETTS

Emergency Film Group, pg 860
Labrecque Creative Sound, pg 915
Monadnock Media Inc, pg 945
Penfield Productions Ltd, pg 971
Soundtrack Recording Studios, pg 1018
TR Productions, pg 1043

MICHIGAN

Digi Sign Design LLC, pg 847
K&R All Media Productions Inc, pg 908
K&R's Recording Studios Inc, pg 908
MessageMakers, pg 939

MINNESOTA

Aggressive Records Audio Duplication LLC, pg 778
Jamieson & Associates Inc, pg 904
Master Communications Group, pg 933

MISSOURI

Audio-VideoGraphics Inc, pg 795
Celebrities Productions, pg 822
Fambrough & Associates Inc, pg 865
Hardcastle Films & Video, pg 885

MONTANA

Jereco Studios Inc, pg 905
North Country Media Group, pg 959

NEBRASKA

Dog & Pony Productions Inc, pg 850

NEVADA

DVDs4Less, pg 854
JCS Video Productions, pg 904

NEW HAMPSHIRE

Apertura, pg 788
Chip Taylor Communications LLC, pg 1032

NEW JERSEY

CFP Video Productions Inc, pg 823
MIB Mediaworks, pg 941
Optisonics Productions, pg 965
Bill Quinn Productions, pg 989
Suede Interactive, pg 1027

NEW YORK

Avekta Productions Inc, pg 798
BioMedia Inc, pg 807
Thomas Craven Film Corp, pg 837
C2 Imaging LLC, pg 841
Digital Force, pg 847
Kamen Entertainment Group Inc, pg 908
Ketchum Pleon Change, pg 910
Mood Creations Ltd, pg 946
Jack Morton Worldwide, pg 946
MRG Productions Inc, pg 948
MRY, pg 949
New York Audio Productions, pg 956
Shelly Palmer Production, pg 968
Split Image Productions, pg 1021
Suggs Media Productions Inc, pg 1028
Synaptic Digital, pg 1030
Zelman Studios Ltd, pg 1073

NORTH CAROLINA

Pat Appleson Studios Inc, pg 788
LCW Productions LLC, pg 917
2BruceStudio, pg 1047

OHIO

Advent Media Inc, pg 778
Creative Technology, pg 838
Curtis Inc, pg 841
EDR Media LLC, pg 857
R&B Communications Inc, pg 991
Take 1 Media Services, pg 1031

Government Program Rentals

Industrial Program Distributors

Industrial Program Producers

PROGRAMMING — AUDIO

Industrial Program Producers (continued)

FLORIDA (continued)

Blackburst Entertainment, pg 808
Capital Communications Inc, pg 819
Courter Films LLC, pg 837
Eastern Video, pg 856
LHV Audio Services, pg 919
Motion Image Group LLC, pg 947
Sunfire Communications Inc, pg 1028
Sunrise Studios, pg 1028
Top Hat Productions, pg 1042
Tricycle Studios, pg 1044
Mike Vasilinda Productions Inc, pg 1052

GEORGIA

COMPRO Productions Inc, pg 834
Guerrilla Productions LLC, pg 883
Sirius Images Corp dba WaveGuide Studios, pg 1012
Symmes Systems, pg 1030

IDAHO

Wide Eye Productions, pg 1066

ILLINOIS

ABS Enterprises, pg 772
Audio Visual Services Corp, pg 796
CCore Media Inc, pg 821
Comtech Multimedia Marketing, pg 834
Cresta Creative, pg 839
Lyon Workspace Products LLC, pg 927
Major Media Productions Inc, pg 929
Jim Passin Productions, pg 970
The Pepper Group, pg 972
PSAV® Presentation Services (Hotel Services Division), pg 987
Sparkfactor, pg 1019
20/20 Communications Inc, pg 1047
Video Impressions, pg 1055

INDIANA

Advanced Media Integration, pg 777
AVA Productions, pg 798
Bright Ideas Creative Services, pg 812
Covenant Productions®, pg 837
Digital Rain LLC, pg 847
OMNI Productions, pg 962
PentaVision Communications Inc, pg 972

IOWA

Hedquist Productions Inc, pg 887
The Production House, pg 984

KANSAS

Chapman Recording & Mastering, pg 824
KAKE-TV, pg 907

KENTUCKY

NIMCO Inc, pg 957

LOUISIANA

Digital FX Inc, pg 847
Disk Productions, pg 849
Moxie Media, pg 948

MARYLAND

CPR MultiMedia Solutions, pg 837
CSPMedia.com, pg 840
The Cutting Corp, pg 841
dbF a Media Company, pg 844
The Image Generators, pg 895
Kramer Communications Video Production, pg 913
Milner-Fenwick Inc, pg 943

MASSACHUSETTS

CommCreative, pg 832
Emergency Film Group, pg 860
Heliotrope Studios, pg 887
Labrecque Creative Sound, pg 915
Northern Light Productions, pg 959
Penfield Productions Ltd, pg 971
Preston Productions Inc, pg 981
Soundtrack Recording Studios, pg 1018
TR Productions, pg 1043
TVN-The Video Network, pg 1046

MICHIGAN

The Brookwood Studio Inc, pg 814
Digi Sign Design LLC, pg 847
K&R All Media Productions Inc, pg 908
K&R's Recording Studios Inc, pg 908
Maritz Performance Improvement Co, pg 931
MessageMakers, pg 939
TGA Recording Co, pg 1038

MINNESOTA

Aggressive Records Audio Duplication LLC, pg 778
Jamieson & Associates Inc, pg 904
Master Communications Group, pg 933
Media Loft Inc, pg 937
MultiMedia, pg 950

MISSOURI

Audio-VideoGraphics Inc, pg 795
Celebrities Productions, pg 822
Fambrough & Associates Inc, pg 865
Hardcastle Films & Video, pg 885

MONTANA

Jereco Studios Inc, pg 905
North Country Media Group, pg 959

NEBRASKA

Dog & Pony Productions Inc, pg 850

NEVADA

DVDs4Less, pg 854
JCS Video Productions, pg 904
Tanglewood Productions, pg 1031

NEW HAMPSHIRE

Apertura, pg 788
Chip Taylor Communications LLC, pg 1032

NEW JERSEY

Audio Vistas LLC, pg 795
CFP Video Productions Inc, pg 823
Laurel Video Productions, pg 916
MIB Mediaworks, pg 941
Optisonics Productions, pg 965
Bill Quinn Productions, pg 989
Suede Interactive, pg 1027

NEW MEXICO

Michael Dunn Productions, pg 853
Production Outfitters, pg 984
Rainbow International Inc/Rainbow Productions Inc, pg 990

NEW YORK

American Management Association International, pg 784
Aural Gratification Inc, pg 796
Avekta Productions Inc, pg 798
BioMedia Inc, pg 807
Blue Barn Pictures Inc, pg 809
Broad Street Inc, pg 812
Cohn Creative Group LLC, pg 831
Thomas Craven Film Corp, pg 837
C2 Imaging LLC, pg 841
Digital Force, pg 847
dM works, pg 849
Fingerpaint, pg 868
Karen Frankel Productions, pg 872
HB-Content, pg 886
Hello World Communications, pg 888
Icontent, pg 893
Kamen Entertainment Group Inc, pg 908
Ketchum Pleon Change, pg 910
KickedUp Media Group Inc, pg 910
L A Bruell Inc, pg 914
Mood Creations Ltd, pg 946
Jack Morton Worldwide, pg 946
MRG Productions Inc, pg 948
MRM Worldwide, pg 948
MRY, pg 949
New York Audio Productions, pg 956
Shelly Palmer Production, pg 968
Pat Kogan Productions Inc, pg 970
David Rapkin Audio Production, pg 991
Elliot Sokolov Music, pg 1015
Split Image Productions, pg 1021
Suggs Media Productions Inc, pg 1028
Synaptic Digital, pg 1030
TBA Global Events, pg 1032
Tiki Recording Studios Inc, pg 1040
Videograf, pg 1057
Zelman Studios Ltd, pg 1073

NORTH CAROLINA

Pat Appleson Studios Inc, pg 788
LCW Productions LLC, pg 917
PACE Worldwide, pg 966
Sinclair Institute, pg 1012
Trailblazer Studios®, pg 1043
2BruceStudio, pg 1047

OHIO

Advent Media Inc, pg 778
Creative Technology, pg 838
Curtis Inc, pg 841
Cuyahoga Community College Media Center, pg 841
EDR Media LLC, pg 857
R&B Communications Inc, pg 991
South-Western Publishing Co, pg 1019
Take 1 Media Services, pg 1031
VGI Productions, pg 1053
Vista Color Imaging Inc, pg 1059

OKLAHOMA

Piper Media Services Inc, pg 976

OREGON

A KTVA Production LLC, pg 771
Ideascape Inc, pg 894
InterVision Media, pg 902
Odyssey Productions Inc, pg 961

PENNSYLVANIA

Audio Visual Communications Inc, pg 795
FMP Media Solutions Inc, pg 870
Forge Recording LLC, pg 871
JPL, pg 906
Kensington Falls Animation, pg 909
Muderick Media, pg 949
Newtown Psychological Center, pg 957
Panta Rhei Media Inc, pg 968
Production Masters Inc (PMI), pg 984
Videosmith Inc, pg 1057
Visual Sound Inc, pg 1059
WQED-Multimedia, pg 1070

RHODE ISLAND

Sound-FX-Design, pg 1017

SOUTH CAROLINA

DaviSound, pg 843
Stages Video Productions, pg 1023
Venture Media, pg 1052

TENNESSEE

Continental Film, pg 835
Marine Geographic, pg 931
Memphis Communications Corp, pg 938

TEXAS

AMA Nystrom Printing/Finishing, pg 783
Dykeman Associates Inc, pg 854
The Editing Co, pg 857
Epic Software Group Inc, pg 862
First Group Communications Inc, pg 868
Omega Productions, pg 962
Romar Learning, pg 999
The Sound Lab Inc, pg 1017
Sound Works, pg 1018
South Coast Film & Video, pg 1019
Stage Directions, pg 1022
Tropikal Productions, pg 1045

VIRGINIA

Advance Concepts Inc, pg 777
BES Studios, pg 805
CACI Productions Group, pg 816
Limelight Communications Inc, pg 921
Lion Recording Services Inc, pg 922
Metro Productions, pg 939
National Media Services Inc, pg 953
Rocktown Media, pg 998
Studio Center Corp, pg 1026

WASHINGTON

Getty Images, pg 877
Hamilton Studio, pg 884
Kostov Productions, pg 913

WEST VIRGINIA

Blackwater Video Productions, pg 808

Industrial Program Rentals

Literature, *see* Feature Program

Medical Program Distributors

Medical Program Producers

PROGRAMMING — AUDIO

Medical Program Producers (continued)

ILLINOIS (continued)

Major Media Productions Inc, pg 929
Oasis Audio, pg 960
The Pepper Group, pg 972
20/20 Communications Inc, pg 1047
Video Impressions, pg 1055

INDIANA

AVA Productions, pg 798
Bright Ideas Creative Services, pg 812
Digital Rain LLC, pg 847
OMNI Productions, pg 962
PentaVision Communications Inc, pg 972

IOWA

Hedquist Productions Inc, pg 887
Long-Term Success Publishing, pg 924

KANSAS

Chapman Recording & Mastering, pg 824

LOUISIANA

Louisiana State University Health Sciences Center - Shreveport, pg 925

MARYLAND

CSPMedia.com, pg 840
The Cutting Corp, pg 841
dbF a Media Company, pg 844
The Image Generators, pg 895
Kramer Communications Video Production, pg 913
Milner-Fenwick Inc, pg 943

MASSACHUSETTS

Emergency Film Group, pg 860
Gyrus ACMI, pg 883
Heliotrope Studios, pg 887
Labrecque Creative Sound, pg 915
Penfield Productions Ltd, pg 971
Preston Productions Inc, pg 981
Soundtrack Recording Studios, pg 1018
TR Productions, pg 1043
TVN-The Video Network, pg 1046

MICHIGAN

Digi Sign Design LLC, pg 847
K&R All Media Productions Inc, pg 908
K&R's Recording Studios Inc, pg 908
Phoenix Society for Burn Survivors Inc, pg 974

MINNESOTA

Aggressive Records Audio Duplication LLC, pg 778
Jamieson & Associates Inc, pg 904
Media Loft Inc, pg 937
MultiMedia, pg 950

MISSOURI

Audio-VideoGraphics Inc, pg 795
Celebrities Productions, pg 822
Fambrough & Associates Inc, pg 865
Marsh Media, pg 931
Mosby Inc, pg 947
University of Missouri-Kansas City School of Dentistry, pg 1050

MONTANA

North Country Media Group, pg 959

NEBRASKA

Dog & Pony Productions Inc, pg 850

NEVADA

JCS Video Productions, pg 904
Tetrahedron LLC, pg 1037

NEW HAMPSHIRE

Apertura, pg 788
Chip Taylor Communications LLC, pg 1032

NEW JERSEY

CFP Video Productions Inc, pg 823
Laurel Video Productions, pg 916
MIB Mediaworks, pg 941
Optisonics Productions, pg 965
Projects in Knowledge Inc, pg 986
Bill Quinn Productions, pg 989
Suede Interactive, pg 1027

NEW MEXICO

Michael Dunn Productions, pg 853
Production Outfitters, pg 984
Uncharted Country Publishing, pg 1048

NEW YORK

Aural Gratification Inc, pg 796
Avekta Productions Inc, pg 798
BioMedia Inc, pg 807
Broad Street Inc, pg 812
Billy Budd Films Inc, pg 814
Cohn Creative Group LLC, pg 831
C2 Imaging LLC, pg 841
Digital Force, pg 847
dM works, pg 849
Downtown Community Television Center (DCTV), pg 851
Fingerpaint, pg 868
Guilford Publications, pg 883
HB-Content, pg 886
Hello World Communications, pg 888
Icontent, pg 893
Kamen Entertainment Group Inc, pg 908
Ketchum Pleon Change, pg 910
KickedUp Media Group Inc, pg 910
L A Bruell Inc, pg 914
Mood Creations Ltd, pg 946
Jack Morton Worldwide, pg 946
MRG Productions Inc, pg 948
MRY, pg 949
News Broadcast Network, pg 956
NSR Productions Inc & Capricorn Five Films, pg 960
Shelly Palmer Production, pg 968
Pat Kogan Productions Inc, pg 970
Random House Audio Publishing Group, pg 991
Elliot Sokolov Music, pg 1015
Split Image Productions, pg 1021
Synaptic Digital, pg 1030
Tiki Recording Studios Inc, pg 1040
Videograf, pg 1057
Zelman Studios Ltd, pg 1073

NORTH CAROLINA

Pat Appleson Studios Inc, pg 788
Sinclair Institute, pg 1012
Trailblazer Studios®, pg 1043
2BruceStudio, pg 1047

OHIO

Advent Media Inc, pg 778
Creative Technology, pg 838
Curtis Inc, pg 841
Cuyahoga Community College Media Center, pg 841
EDR Media LLC, pg 857
R&B Communications Inc, pg 991
South-Western Publishing Co, pg 1019
Take 1 Media Services, pg 1031
VGI Productions, pg 1053
Vista Color Imaging Inc, pg 1059

OKLAHOMA

Piper Media Services Inc, pg 976
University of Oklahoma Academic Media & Digital Services, pg 1050

OREGON

ERA Learning, pg 862
Ideascape Inc, pg 894
InterVision Media, pg 902

PENNSYLVANIA

Audio Visual Communications Inc, pg 795
FMP Media Solutions Inc, pg 870
Forge Recording LLC, pg 871
Innovision Media Group, pg 899
JPL, pg 906
Kensington Falls Animation, pg 909
Lippincott Williams & Wilkins, pg 922
Panta Rhei Media Inc, pg 968
S I Video Sales Group, pg 1001
TouchStar Productions Inc, pg 1042
WQED-Multimedia, pg 1070

RHODE ISLAND

Sound Advantage, pg 1016
Sound-FX-Design, pg 1017

SOUTH CAROLINA

Venture Media, pg 1052

TENNESSEE

Continental Film, pg 835
Memphis Communications Corp, pg 938

TEXAS

The Editing Co, pg 857
Epic Software Group Inc, pg 862
Omega Productions, pg 962
Romar Learning, pg 999
The Sound Lab Inc, pg 1017
South Coast Film & Video, pg 1019
Stage Directions, pg 1022
Texas Heart Institute Visual Communication Services, pg 1037

VIRGINIA

BES Studios, pg 805
CACI Productions Group, pg 816
Limelight Communications Inc, pg 921
Lion Recording Services Inc, pg 922
Metro Productions, pg 939
National Media Services Inc, pg 953
Rocktown Media, pg 998
Studio Center Corp, pg 1026

WASHINGTON

Kostov Productions, pg 913
Medical Media Systems, pg 938

WEST VIRGINIA

Blackwater Video Productions, pg 808

WISCONSIN

5th Floor Recording Co, pg 867
Meridian Studios, pg 939
USAV Group Inc, pg 1050
Video Wisconsin Inc, pg 1056
Watts Communications Inc, pg 1062
Wisconsin Public Television, pg 1068

WYOMING

Bridger Productions Inc, pg 812

ONTARIO

ADS Media, pg 777
DebsVoice, pg 844
GAPC (General Assembly Production Centre), pg 875
Shaw Street Productions, pg 1008
VO2 Mix Studios, pg 1060

QUEBEC

Kerrigan Productions Inc, pg 910

Medical Program Rentals

CALIFORNIA

Direct Cinema Ltd Inc, pg 848
Educational Technology Services (ETS), pg 857
Point of View Productions, pg 977

MAINE

University of Maine Audio Visual Services, pg 1049

MASSACHUSETTS

Emergency Film Group, pg 860
Preston Productions Inc, pg 981

MICHIGAN

Digi Sign Design LLC, pg 847

MISSOURI

University of Missouri-Kansas City School of Dentistry, pg 1050

NEW HAMPSHIRE

Chip Taylor Communications LLC, pg 1032

NEW JERSEY

Alden Films, pg 780

NEW YORK

Downtown Community Television Center (DCTV), pg 851

PENNSYLVANIA

Penn State University MediaTech, pg 972

TEXAS

Romar Learning, pg 999

Multimedia, CD-ROM & DVD Interactive Program Distributors

ARKANSAS

Mullikin Agency, pg 949

CALIFORNIA

Astronomical Society of the Pacific, pg 792
Blue Dolphin Multimedia, pg 809
Digital Media West, pg 847
Eye & I Productions, pg 864
Maximus Media Inc, pg 934
QRS Software Services, pg 988
Rovi Corp, pg 1000

COLORADO

Gaiam Inc, pg 875
Meriwether Publishing Ltd, pg 939
National Teaching Aids Inc, pg 953

FLORIDA

ACE Video Resources Software, pg 774
Allegro Productions Inc, pg 781

GEORGIA

Convergent Media Systems, pg 836
School Media Associates LLC, pg 1004

HAWAII

Media Bridge Gamekids, pg 936

ILLINOIS

Britannica Film & Video, pg 812
CCore Media Inc, pg 821

INDIANA

Herff Jones | Nystrom, pg 888

IOWA

Right Stuf Inc, pg 997

MARYLAND

Department of Education Resources, pg 845

MASSACHUSETTS

Cheng & Tsui Co, pg 824
Documentary Educational Resources Inc, pg 850
Emergency Film Group, pg 860
Penfield Productions Ltd, pg 971

MICHIGAN

Digi Sign Design LLC, pg 847

MINNESOTA

Beyers Sound & Essay Audio, pg 806

MISSOURI

Mosby Inc, pg 947

NEW HAMPSHIRE

Chip Taylor Communications LLC, pg 1032

NEW MEXICO

National Information Center for Educational Media (NICEM)/MediaSleuth, pg 952

NEW YORK

Films Media Group, pg 868
HB-Content, pg 886
MRG Productions Inc, pg 948
Penguin Audiobooks, pg 971

NORTH CAROLINA

Vide-O-Go/That's Infotainment!, pg 1054

OREGON

InterVision Media, pg 902

PENNSYLVANIA

Anchor Distributors, pg 786
Discovery Education - South Burlington, pg 848
FMP Media Solutions Inc, pg 870

TENNESSEE

Center for Southern Folklore Inc, pg 822
Marine Geographic, pg 931
Spring Arbor Distributors, pg 1022

TEXAS

Replicopy Digital Media Center, pg 995

UTAH

Strata™, pg 1025
Webb Audio Visual Communication, pg 1063

VERMONT

Multicultural Media, pg 950

BRITISH COLUMBIA

Video In Studios/Video Out Distribution, pg 1055

ONTARIO

Canadian Learning Co Inc, pg 818

Multimedia, CD-ROM & DVD Interactive Program Producers

ARIZONA

Merestone, pg 938

ARKANSAS

Live'N'Loud, pg 923
Mullikin Agency, pg 949

CALIFORNIA

Ancient Future, pg 786
Berkeley Sound Artists Inc, pg 805
Big Door, pg 807
Blue Dolphin Multimedia, pg 809
Concrete Images, pg 835
Creative Media Recording, pg 838
Custom Video Productions Inc, pg 841
Design Media, pg 845
Dogma Studios, pg 850
Eye & I Productions, pg 864
Gold Standard Productions, pg 880
Havas Edge, pg 885
International Contact Inc, pg 900
KABA Audio Productions, pg 907
The Kenwood Group, pg 909
Lynch Communications, pg 926
Maximus Media Inc, pg 934
Media Magic, pg 937
New Circuit Films LLC, pg 955
OTR Studios, pg 966
Palardo Productions, pg 968
Panorama Productions, pg 968
piXvfm, pg 976
Producers Group Ltd, pg 983
QRS Software Services, pg 988
SBS Productions, pg 1003
Steve Shapiro Music, pg 1008
Still N'Motion, pg 1025
The Studio of David Inocencio/ Minette Siegel, pg 1027
Studio 132, pg 1027
Tam Communications Inc, pg 1031
Total Media Group, pg 1042
Video Movie Magic, pg 1056
Video Resources Inc, pg 1056
WalkerVision Interarts, pg 1061
Wavemaker Media Design, pg 1062
Webster Communications, pg 1063
The Wine Appreciation Guild Ltd, pg 1067

COLORADO

Flashback Media Productions, pg 869
Gaiam Inc, pg 875
Meriwether Publishing Ltd, pg 939
National Teaching Aids Inc, pg 953
Starwest Productions, pg 1024

CONNECTICUT

EagleVision Inc, pg 855
Moving Pictures, pg 947
P&P Studios Inc, pg 968

DISTRICT OF COLUMBIA

Hillmann & Carr Inc, pg 889

FLORIDA

ACE Video Resources Software, pg 774
Allegro Productions Inc, pg 781
Audacity Creative, pg 793
Audio Visual Imagineering Inc, pg 795
Blackburst Entertainment, pg 808
CD ROM™ Inc, pg 822
Communications Concepts Inc (CCI), pg 833
Courter Films LLC, pg 837
Image Technical Services, pg 895
LHV Audio Services, pg 919
Motion Image Group LLC, pg 947
Sunfire Communications Inc, pg 1028
Sunrise Studios, pg 1028
Top Hat Productions, pg 1042
Tricycle Studios, pg 1044
Z-Systems Audio Engineering, pg 1073

GEORGIA

Guerrilla Productions LLC, pg 883
Myriad Productions, pg 951
Sirius Images Corp dba WaveGuide Studios, pg 1012
Symmes Systems, pg 1030

HAWAII

Media Bridge Gamekids, pg 936

IDAHO

Wide Eye Productions, pg 1066

ILLINOIS

ABS Enterprises, pg 772
Advanced Audio Technology, pg 777
Airways Digital Media, pg 779
Analog Free Media, pg 786
Audio Visual Services Corp, pg 796
Britannica Film & Video, pg 812
CCore Media Inc, pg 821
Centrax Corp, pg 823
Cresta Creative, pg 839
Major Media Inc, pg 929
Major Media Productions Inc, pg 929
The Pepper Group, pg 972
The Prairie Production Group, pg 980
PSAV® Presentation Services (Hotel Services Division), pg 987
QuickSet International Inc, pg 989
Sparkfactor, pg 1019
20/20 Communications Inc, pg 1047
Video Impressions, pg 1055

INDIANA

Advanced Media Integration, pg 777
AVA Productions, pg 798
Bright Ideas Creative Services, pg 812
Communication Ministries, pg 833
Herff Jones | Nystrom, pg 888
OMNI Productions, pg 962
PentaVision Communications Inc, pg 972

IOWA

The Production House, pg 984
Right Stuf Inc, pg 997

KENTUCKY

Hammond Communications Group, pg 884
Donna Lawrence Productions, pg 917
Northern Kentucky University, pg 959

LOUISIANA

Digital FX Inc, pg 847
Louisiana State University Health Sciences Center - Shreveport, pg 925

MARYLAND

The Ahern Group, pg 779
CPR MultiMedia Solutions, pg 837
CSPMedia.com, pg 840
The Cutting Corp, pg 841
dbF a Media Company, pg 844
Department of Education Resources, pg 845
The Image Generators, pg 895
Kramer Communications Video Production, pg 913
Media Dimensions Inc, pg 936

MASSACHUSETTS

Cheng & Tsui Co, pg 824
CommCreative, pg 832
Documentary Educational Resources Inc, pg 850
Emergency Film Group, pg 860

PROGRAMMING — AUDIO

Multimedia, CD-ROM & DVD Interactive Program Producers (continued)

MASSACHUSETTS (continued)

Home Inc, pg 890
Labrecque Creative Sound, pg 915
Northern Light Productions, pg 959
Penfield Productions Ltd, pg 971
Preston Productions Inc, pg 981
Soundtrack Recording Studios, pg 1018
TR Productions, pg 1043
TVN-The Video Network, pg 1046
Veritech Corp, pg 1053

MICHIGAN

Digi Sign Design LLC, pg 847
K&R All Media Productions Inc, pg 908
K&R's Recording Studios Inc, pg 908
MessageMakers, pg 939
TGA Recording Co, pg 1038

MINNESOTA

Aggressive Records Audio Duplication LLC, pg 778
Beyers Sound & Essay Audio, pg 806
Jamieson & Associates Inc, pg 904
Media Loft Inc, pg 937
MultiMedia, pg 950

MISSOURI

Celebrities Productions, pg 822
Mosby Inc, pg 947

NEBRASKA

Dog & Pony Productions Inc, pg 850
Rainbow Video Productions Inc, pg 991

NEVADA

JCS Video Productions, pg 904

NEW HAMPSHIRE

Apertura, pg 788
Chip Taylor Communications LLC, pg 1032

NEW JERSEY

Audio Vistas LLC, pg 795
Broadcast Center Studios, pg 813
MIB Mediaworks, pg 941
Midnight Media Group Inc, pg 942
Optisonics Productions, pg 965
Outside The Box Interactive LLC, pg 966
Suede Interactive, pg 1027
VCSvideo, pg 1052

NEW MEXICO

Production Outfitters, pg 984

NEW YORK

Aural Gratification Inc, pg 796
Avekta Productions Inc, pg 798
Blue Barn Pictures Inc, pg 809
Broad Street Inc, pg 812
Cohn Creative Group LLC, pg 831
Conversation Arts Media, pg 836
C2 Imaging LLC, pg 841
Digital Force, pg 847
dM works, pg 849
Duplication Depot Inc, pg 853
Films Media Group, pg 868
Fingerpaint, pg 868
Greyfalcon House, pg 882
HB-Content, pg 886
Icontent, pg 893
Image Zone Inc, pg 896
Kamen Entertainment Group Inc, pg 908
L A Bruell Inc, pg 914
Jack Morton Worldwide, pg 946
MRG Productions Inc, pg 948
MRY, pg 949
New York Audio Productions, pg 956
Penguin Audiobooks, pg 971
David Rapkin Audio Production, pg 991
Judson Rosebush Co Inc, pg 999
Elliot Sokolov Music, pg 1015
Split Image Productions, pg 1021
Spoken Arts Inc, pg 1021
Tiki Recording Studios Inc, pg 1040
Zelman Studios Ltd, pg 1073

NORTH CAROLINA

Pat Appleson Studios Inc, pg 788
Creative Services Inc, pg 838
Image Associates Inc, pg 894
NASCAR Media Group LLC, pg 952
2BruceStudio, pg 1047
Unifour Productions Inc, pg 1048
World Class Learning Materials Inc, pg 1069

OHIO

Advent Media Inc, pg 778
Creative Technology, pg 838
EDR Media LLC, pg 857
R&B Communications Inc, pg 991
Take 1 Media Services, pg 1031
Vista Color Imaging Inc, pg 1059

OKLAHOMA

Piper Media Services Inc, pg 976

OREGON

ERA Learning, pg 862
Ideascape Inc, pg 894
InterVision Media, pg 902
NeoSoft Corp, pg 954
Odyssey Productions Inc, pg 961
Rex, pg 995

PENNSYLVANIA

AiH Group Inc, pg 779
Audio Visual Communications Inc, pg 795
Discovery Education - South Burlington, pg 848
FMP Media Solutions Inc, pg 870
Innovision Media Group, pg 899
JPL, pg 906
Kenexa, pg 909
New Horizons Computer Learning Centers Inc, pg 955
Panta Rhei Media Inc, pg 968
Production Masters Inc (PMI), pg 984
Scala Inc, pg 1003
Visual Sound Inc, pg 1059

RHODE ISLAND

Sound-FX-Design, pg 1017

SOUTH CAROLINA

Venture Media, pg 1052

TENNESSEE

Anode Inc, pg 787
Continental Film, pg 835
Love Shack Recording Studios, pg 925
Marine Geographic, pg 931
Memphis Communications Corp, pg 938
Russ Sturgeon Productions/RSVP, pg 1027

TEXAS

Biway Media, pg 808
Epic Software Group Inc, pg 862
InterCom, pg 900
Matson Multi-Media, pg 934
Omega Productions, pg 962
Romar Learning, pg 999
The Sound Lab Inc, pg 1017
Sound Works, pg 1018
Stage Directions, pg 1022

UTAH

Webb Audio Visual Communication, pg 1063

VIRGINIA

Advance Concepts Inc, pg 777
Lion Recording Services Inc, pg 922
Metro Productions, pg 939
Studio Center Corp, pg 1026

WASHINGTON

Inland Audio Visual Co, pg 898
Kostov Productions, pg 913

WISCONSIN

AVS Group, pg 800
5th Floor Recording Co, pg 867
USAV Group Inc, pg 1050
Video Wisconsin Inc, pg 1056
Watts Communications Inc, pg 1062
Wisconsin Public Television, pg 1068

WYOMING

Bridger Productions Inc, pg 812

NEWFOUNDLAND AND LABRADOR

Vidcraft Productions Ltd, pg 1054

ONTARIO

ADS Media, pg 777
Art Gallery of Ontario, pg 791
DebsVoice, pg 844
GAPC (General Assembly Production Centre), pg 875
JFB Communications, pg 905
Marblemedia, pg 930
Shaw Street Productions, pg 1008
SLI Manufacturing Inc, pg 1013
VO2 Mix Studios, pg 1060

QUEBEC

Kerrigan Productions Inc, pg 910

Multimedia, CD-ROM & DVD Interactive Program Rentals

DELAWARE

Side Door Studio Inc, pg 1010

GEORGIA

Convergent Media Systems, pg 836

MASSACHUSETTS

Documentary Educational Resources Inc, pg 850
Preston Productions Inc, pg 981

MICHIGAN

Digi Sign Design LLC, pg 847

NEW HAMPSHIRE

Chip Taylor Communications LLC, pg 1032

UTAH

Webb Audio Visual Communication, pg 1063

News Program Distributors

CALIFORNIA

Digital Media West, pg 847
Maximus Media Inc, pg 934
Pacifica Radio Archives, pg 967

GEORGIA

School Media Associates LLC, pg 1004

INDIANA

Communication Ministries, pg 833

MICHIGAN

Digi Sign Design LLC, pg 847

NEBRASKA

Vision Maker Media, pg 1058

NEW YORK

De Nonno Productions Inc (DPI), pg 844
HB-Content, pg 886
MRG Productions Inc, pg 948
News Broadcast Network, pg 956
United Nations Multimedia Resources Unit, pg 1048

NORTH CAROLINA

Baker & Taylor Inc, pg 801
Vide-O-Go/That's Infotainment!, pg 1054

PENNSYLVANIA

AccuWeather Inc, pg 774

VIRGINIA

CACI Productions Group, pg 816

ALBERTA

Global Television Station, pg 879

News Program Producers

CALIFORNIA

Big Door, pg 807
Direct Cinema Ltd Inc, pg 848
Gold Standard Productions, pg 880
Jaguar Distribution Corp, pg 903
Lynch Communications, pg 926
PM Productions, pg 977
Steve Shapiro Music, pg 1008
Studio 132, pg 1027
Total Media Group, pg 1042
Webster Communications, pg 1063

COLORADO

Apogee Communications Group, pg 788

CONNECTICUT

EagleVision Inc, pg 855
Essex Television Group Inc, pg 862
P&P Studios Inc, pg 968

FLORIDA

Blackburst Entertainment, pg 808
Communications Concepts Inc (CCI), pg 833
Eastern Video, pg 856
LHV Audio Services, pg 919
Roger Scruggs Films, pg 1005
Sunfire Communications Inc, pg 1028
Top Hat Productions, pg 1042

GEORGIA

Guerrilla Productions LLC, pg 883

IDAHO

Wide Eye Productions, pg 1066

ILLINOIS

ABS Enterprises, pg 772
The Pepper Group, pg 972

INDIANA

AVA Productions, pg 798
Communication Ministries, pg 833
Digital Rain LLC, pg 847

KANSAS

KAKE-TV, pg 907

LOUISIANA

Digital FX Inc, pg 847

MARYLAND

CPR MultiMedia Solutions, pg 837
CSPMedia.com, pg 840
The Cutting Corp, pg 841
dbF a Media Company, pg 844
The Image Generators, pg 895
Kramer Communications Video Production, pg 913

MASSACHUSETTS

Emergency Film Group, pg 860
Labrecque Creative Sound, pg 915
Soundtrack Recording Studios, pg 1018
TVN-The Video Network, pg 1046

MICHIGAN

Digi Sign Design LLC, pg 847
K&R All Media Productions Inc, pg 908
K&R's Recording Studios Inc, pg 908

MINNESOTA

Aggressive Records Audio Duplication LLC, pg 778
MultiMedia, pg 950

MISSOURI

Celebrities Productions, pg 822
Fambrough & Associates Inc, pg 865

NEBRASKA

Dog & Pony Productions Inc, pg 850

NEVADA

JCS Video Productions, pg 904

NEW JERSEY

CFP Video Productions Inc, pg 823
Laurel Video Productions, pg 916
MIB Mediaworks, pg 941
Optisonics Productions, pg 965
Bill Quinn Productions, pg 989

NEW MEXICO

Michael Dunn Productions, pg 853
Production Outfitters, pg 984

NEW YORK

CompuWeather Inc, pg 834
De Nonno Productions Inc (DPI), pg 844
Digital Force, pg 847
Downtown Community Television Center (DCTV), pg 851
HB-Content, pg 886
Hello World Communications, pg 888
Kamen Entertainment Group Inc, pg 908
Jack Morton Worldwide, pg 946
MRG Productions Inc, pg 948
New York Audio Productions, pg 956
News Broadcast Network, pg 956
Shelly Palmer Production, pg 968
David Rapkin Audio Production, pg 991
Split Image Productions, pg 1021
Suggs Media Productions Inc, pg 1028
United Nations Multimedia Resources Unit, pg 1048
Zelman Studios Ltd, pg 1073

NORTH CAROLINA

Pat Appleson Studios Inc, pg 788
LCW Productions LLC, pg 917

OHIO

Creative Technology, pg 838
EDR Media LLC, pg 857
R&B Communications Inc, pg 991
VGI Productions, pg 1053
Vista Color Imaging Inc, pg 1059

OKLAHOMA

Piper Media Services Inc, pg 976

OREGON

InterVision Media, pg 902

PENNSYLVANIA

AccuWeather Inc, pg 774
Scala Inc, pg 1003
The Videohouse Inc, pg 1057

RHODE ISLAND

Sound-FX-Design, pg 1017

SOUTH CAROLINA

Stages Video Productions, pg 1023

TEXAS

Dykeman Associates Inc, pg 854
Epic Software Group Inc, pg 862
Omega Productions, pg 962
Romar Learning, pg 999
The Sound Lab Inc, pg 1017
Sound Works, pg 1018
Stage Directions, pg 1022
Texas Heart Institute Visual Communication Services, pg 1037

VIRGINIA

CACI Productions Group, pg 816
Limelight Communications Inc, pg 921
Lion Recording Services Inc, pg 922
National Media Services Inc, pg 953
Rocktown Media, pg 998

WEST VIRGINIA

Blackwater Video Productions, pg 808

WISCONSIN

5th Floor Recording Co, pg 867
University of Wisconsin-Oshkosh Radio-TV-Film Dept, pg 1050
Video Wisconsin Inc, pg 1056
Watts Communications Inc, pg 1062
Wisconsin Public Television, pg 1068

WYOMING

Bridger Productions Inc, pg 812

ALBERTA

Global Television Station, pg 879

ONTARIO

DebsVoice, pg 844
VO2 Mix Studios, pg 1060

QUEBEC

Kerrigan Productions Inc, pg 910

News Program Rentals

CALIFORNIA

Direct Cinema Ltd Inc, pg 848

MICHIGAN

Digi Sign Design LLC, pg 847

NEBRASKA

Vision Maker Media, pg 1058

NEW JERSEY

Alden Films, pg 780

NEW YORK

Downtown Community Television Center (DCTV), pg 851

UTAH

Webb Audio Visual Communication, pg 1063

Phonograph Record Distributors

CALIFORNIA

Ametron Audio/Video, pg 785
Fantasy Studios, pg 865
GNP Crescendo Records, pg 879
Harmonia Mundi USA, pg 885
Sahara Records & Filmworks Entertainment Co, pg 1001
Universal Music Group, pg 1049
Welk Music Group, pg 1063

CONNECTICUT

Folk-Legacy, pg 871
Original Cast Records, pg 965

DISTRICT OF COLUMBIA

Library of Congress, Motion Picture, Broadcasting & Recorded Sound Division, pg 919

FLORIDA

Bartok Records & Publications, pg 803
Kat Epple Music Productions, pg 862
Times-Square Fantasy Theatre, pg 1041

ILLINOIS

Earwig Music Co Inc, pg 855

KANSAS

Chapman Recording & Mastering, pg 824

MARYLAND

Adelphi Records Inc, pg 776
Bradley Broadcast & Pro Audio, pg 811

NEW JERSEY

Hamilton Buhl, pg 884
A W Peller & Associates Inc, pg 971

NEW MEXICO

National Information Center for Educational Media (NICEM)/MediaSleuth, pg 952

NEW YORK

Amherst Records Inc, pg 785
Cadence Jazz Records, pg 816
Digital Force, pg 847
DRG Records Inc, pg 852
Dyer-Bennet Records, pg 854
MRG Productions Inc, pg 948
Sony Music Entertainment, pg 1016
Tommy Boy Entertainment LLC, pg 1042
The Verve Music Group, pg 1053
Zim Records, pg 1074

PROGRAMMING — AUDIO

Phonograph Record Distributors (continued)

NORTH CAROLINA

Howard Hanger, pg 884

PENNSYLVANIA

Dreambox Media Inc, pg 852

TENNESSEE

Center for Southern Folklore Inc, pg 822
Rounder Records, pg 1000
Spring Arbor Distributors, pg 1022

VIRGINIA

County Sales, pg 837
Rebel Records, pg 993

WISCONSIN

School Specialty Inc, pg 1004

ONTARIO

CBC/Radio-Canada, pg 821
Entertainment One Distribution, pg 861

Phonograph Record Producers

ALABAMA

Media Visions Inc, pg 937

CALIFORNIA

Arhoolie Productions Inc (aka Arhoolie Records), pg 789
Concord Records Inc, pg 835
4th Street Recording, pg 872
Lynch Communications, pg 926
Maximus Media Inc, pg 934
OTR Studios, pg 966
Reference Recordings, pg 994
Sahara Records & Filmworks Entertainment Co, pg 1001
Schroder Music Co, pg 1004
Universal Music Group, pg 1049
Webster Communications, pg 1063

COLORADO

Tim Cissell Music, pg 828

CONNECTICUT

Folk-Legacy, pg 871

DELAWARE

Ken-Del Productions Inc, pg 909

FLORIDA

Bartok Records & Publications, pg 803
Kat Epple Music Productions, pg 862
Times-Square Fantasy Theatre, pg 1041

GEORGIA

Hottrax Records, pg 891

ILLINOIS

Delmark Records, pg 845
Earwig Music Co Inc, pg 855
Major Media Inc, pg 929

KANSAS

Chapman Recording & Mastering, pg 824

LOUISIANA

Jazzology, pg 904

MAINE

Serendipity Recordings, pg 1007

MARYLAND

Adelphi Records Inc, pg 776
CSPMedia.com, pg 840

MICHIGAN

K&R All Media Productions Inc, pg 908
K&R's Recording Studios Inc, pg 908

MINNESOTA

Aggressive Records Audio Duplication LLC, pg 778

MISSOURI

Celebrities Productions, pg 822

NEW JERSEY

Presence Records, pg 981
Suede Interactive, pg 1027

NEW YORK

Amherst Records Inc, pg 785
Digital Force, pg 847
Dyer-Bennet Records, pg 854
Fingerpaint, pg 868
Juston Records, pg 907
MRG Productions Inc, pg 948
Oriental Records Inc, pg 965
Shelly Palmer Production, pg 968
RCA Records, pg 992
Elliot Sokolov Music, pg 1015
Sony Music Custom Marketing, pg 1016
Sony Music Entertainment, pg 1016
Tommy Boy Entertainment LLC, pg 1042

NORTH CAROLINA

Howard Hanger, pg 884

OHIO

Musicol Recording, pg 951

PENNSYLVANIA

Dreambox Media Inc, pg 852
Innovision Media Group, pg 899

TENNESSEE

Center for Southern Folklore Inc, pg 822

TEXAS

The Samuels Co, pg 1002

VIRGINIA

County Sales, pg 837
Rebel Records, pg 993

ONTARIO

CBC/Radio-Canada, pg 821

Phonograph Record Rentals

CALIFORNIA

Ametron Audio/Video, pg 785

FLORIDA

Times-Square Fantasy Theatre, pg 1041

MISSOURI

Show-Me Audio-Visual, pg 1009

NEW YORK

MRG Productions Inc, pg 948

Public Relations Program Distributors

ARKANSAS

Mullikin Agency, pg 949

CALIFORNIA

Digital Media West, pg 847
Direct Cinema Ltd Inc, pg 848
Maximus Media Inc, pg 934
Joseph Nicoletti Consulting-Promotion/California International Records/Global Village Records, pg 957
QRS Software Services, pg 988

FLORIDA

Allegro Productions Inc, pg 781
Capital Communications Inc, pg 819

GEORGIA

Convergent Media Systems, pg 836

ILLINOIS

CCore Media Inc, pg 821

MASSACHUSETTS

Emergency Film Group, pg 860
Penfield Productions Ltd, pg 971

MICHIGAN

Digi Sign Design LLC, pg 847

NEVADA

DVDs4Less, pg 854

NEW HAMPSHIRE

Chip Taylor Communications LLC, pg 1032

NEW YORK

HB-Content, pg 886
Janus Films Inc, pg 904
KickedUp Media Group Inc, pg 910
MRG Productions Inc, pg 948
News Broadcast Network, pg 956
Synaptic Digital, pg 1030

NORTH CAROLINA

Vide-O-Go/That's Infotainment!, pg 1054

OREGON

InterVision Media, pg 902

PENNSYLVANIA

FMP Media Solutions Inc, pg 870
Karol Media Inc, pg 908

SOUTH CAROLINA

DaviSound, pg 843

TENNESSEE

American Blackguard Inc, pg 784

VIRGINIA

CACI Productions Group, pg 816

WISCONSIN

Wisconsin Public Television, pg 1068

ALBERTA

Global Television Station, pg 879

Public Relations Program Producers

ALABAMA

Leo Ticheli Productions, pg 1040

ARIZONA

Candee Productions Inc, pg 819
Metropolitan Audio-Visual Inc, pg 940
SPEAK HOUSE Audio™, pg 1019

ARKANSAS

Live'N'Loud, pg 923
Mullikin Agency, pg 949

CALIFORNIA

Big Door, pg 807
Creative Media Recording, pg 838
Custom Video Productions Inc, pg 841
Design Media, pg 845
Direct Cinema Ltd Inc, pg 848
Dogma Studios, pg 850
Goal Productions, pg 879
Gold Standard Productions, pg 880
International Contact Inc, pg 900
The Kenwood Group, pg 909
Lynch Communications, pg 926
The Media Staff Inc, pg 937
Joseph Nicoletti Consulting-Promotion/California International Records/Global Village Records, pg 957
On-Trax Inc, pg 963
piXvfm, pg 976
Point of View Productions, pg 977
Prime Cut Productions, pg 982
Producers Group Ltd, pg 983
QRS Software Services, pg 988
SBS Productions, pg 1003
Steve Shapiro Music, pg 1008
Still N'Motion, pg 1025
Studio 132, pg 1027
Tele-Video Production Services (TVPS), pg 1036
Total Media Group, pg 1042
Video Resources Inc, pg 1056
WalkerVision Interarts, pg 1061
Wavemaker Media Design, pg 1062
Webster Communications, pg 1063
Zamacona Productions, pg 1073

PROGRAMMING — AUDIO

Public Relations Program Rentals

CALIFORNIA

Direct Cinema Ltd Inc, pg 848

GEORGIA

Convergent Media Systems, pg 836

MASSACHUSETTS

Preston Productions Inc, pg 981

MICHIGAN

Digi Sign Design LLC, pg 847

NEW HAMPSHIRE

Chip Taylor Communications LLC, pg 1032

UTAH

Webb Audio Visual Communication, pg 1063

Public Service Announcement Distributors

CALIFORNIA

Digital Media West, pg 847
ECONEWS (Environmental Television Series) & (Environmental Directions Radio Series), pg 856
Maximus Media Inc, pg 934
QRS Software Services, pg 988
The Wyland Group, pg 1071

CONNECTICUT

Save the Children Federation Inc, pg 1003

FLORIDA

Mike Vasilinda Productions Inc, pg 1052

ILLINOIS

Communications Corporation of America, pg 833

INDIANA

Communication Ministries, pg 833

MASSACHUSETTS

Penfield Productions Ltd, pg 971

MICHIGAN

Digi Sign Design LLC, pg 847
Zondervan, A HarperCollins Company, pg 1074

NEVADA

DVDs4Less, pg 854

NEW HAMPSHIRE

Chip Taylor Communications LLC, pg 1032

NEW YORK

The Christophers, pg 826
De Nonno Productions Inc (DPI), pg 844
HB-Content, pg 886
KickedUp Media Group Inc, pg 910
March of Dimes Foundation, pg 930
MRG Productions Inc, pg 948
News Broadcast Network, pg 956
Synaptic Digital, pg 1030
United Nations Multimedia Resources Unit, pg 1048
Visual Technologies Corp, pg 1060

NORTH CAROLINA

Baker & Taylor Inc, pg 801

OHIO

Franciscan Media, pg 872

PENNSYLVANIA

Karol Media Inc, pg 908

SOUTH CAROLINA

DaviSound, pg 843

TENNESSEE

American Blackguard Inc, pg 784

TEXAS

Institute of Texan Cultures, pg 899
TM Studios Inc, pg 1041

VIRGINIA

CACI Productions Group, pg 816
CDR Communications Inc, pg 822

WISCONSIN

Wisconsin Public Television, pg 1068

Public Service Announcement Producers

ALABAMA

CMEInfo, pg 830

ARIZONA

Candee Productions Inc, pg 819
Metropolitan Audio-Visual Inc, pg 940

ARKANSAS

Live'N'Loud, pg 923

CALIFORNIA

Big Door, pg 807
Concrete Images, pg 835
Creative Media Recording, pg 838
Custom Video Productions Inc, pg 841
Direct Cinema Ltd Inc, pg 848
Dogma Studios, pg 850
ECONEWS (Environmental Television Series) & (Environmental Directions Radio Series), pg 856
4th Street Recording, pg 872
imageReal Pictures LLC, pg 896
KABA Audio Productions, pg 907
KTVU-Retail Services, pg 914
Lynch Communications, pg 926
Maximus Media Inc, pg 934
Media Magic, pg 937
The Media Staff Inc, pg 937
On-Trax Inc, pg 963
OTR Studios, pg 966
PM Productions, pg 977
Point of View Productions, pg 977
Producers Group Ltd, pg 983
QRS Software Services, pg 988
Steve Shapiro Music, pg 1008
Still N'Motion, pg 1025
Studio 132, pg 1027
Tam Communications Inc, pg 1031
Tele-Video Production Services (TVPS), pg 1036
Total Media Group, pg 1042
Wavemaker Media Design, pg 1062
Webster Communications, pg 1063
The Wyland Group, pg 1071

COLORADO

Apogee Communications Group, pg 788
Rocky Mountain Audio/Video Productions Inc, pg 998

CONNECTICUT

Biomedical Media Communications Dept, pg 807
EagleVision Inc, pg 855
The Gary-Paul Agency, pg 875
Moving Pictures, pg 947
P&P Studios Inc, pg 968
Save the Children Federation Inc, pg 1003

DISTRICT OF COLUMBIA

Hillmann & Carr Inc, pg 889

FLORIDA

Blackburst Entertainment, pg 808
Communications Concepts Inc (CCI), pg 833
Eastern Video, pg 856
LHV Audio Services, pg 919
Sunfire Communications Inc, pg 1028
Sunrise Studios, pg 1028
Top Hat Productions, pg 1042
Tricycle Studios, pg 1044
Mike Vasilinda Productions Inc, pg 1052

GEORGIA

COMPRO Productions Inc, pg 834
Guerrilla Productions LLC, pg 883
Symmes Systems, pg 1030

IDAHO

Wide Eye Productions, pg 1066

ILLINOIS

ABS Enterprises, pg 772
Audio Visual Services Corp, pg 796
Communications Corporation of America, pg 833
Comtech Multimedia Marketing, pg 834
Cresta Creative, pg 839
Major Media Productions Inc, pg 929
Jim Passin Productions, pg 970
The Pepper Group, pg 972
PSAV® Presentation Services (Hotel Services Division), pg 987
Steven Samler Music & Sound, pg 1002
Sparkfactor, pg 1019
20/20 Communications Inc, pg 1047

INDIANA

AVA Productions, pg 798
Communication Ministries, pg 833
Covenant Productions®, pg 837
Digital Rain LLC, pg 847
OMNI Productions, pg 962

IOWA

Hedquist Productions Inc, pg 887

LOUISIANA

Disk Productions, pg 849
Louisiana State University Health Sciences Center - Shreveport, pg 925

MARYLAND

CPR MultiMedia Solutions, pg 837
CSPMedia.com, pg 840
The Cutting Corp, pg 841
dbF a Media Company, pg 844
The Image Generators, pg 895
Kramer Communications Video Production, pg 913

MASSACHUSETTS

Documentary Educational Resources Inc, pg 850
Emergency Film Group, pg 860
Heliotrope Studios, pg 887
Home Inc, pg 890
Labrecque Creative Sound, pg 915
Penfield Productions Ltd, pg 971
Soundtrack Recording Studios, pg 1018
TR Productions, pg 1043
TVN-The Video Network, pg 1046

MICHIGAN

The Brookwood Studio Inc, pg 814
Digi Sign Design LLC, pg 847
K&R All Media Productions Inc, pg 908
K&R's Recording Studios Inc, pg 908
MessageMakers, pg 939
Zondervan, A HarperCollins Company, pg 1074

MINNESOTA

Aggressive Records Audio Duplication LLC, pg 778
Jamieson & Associates Inc, pg 904
Master Communications Group, pg 933
MultiMedia, pg 950

MISSOURI

Audio-VideoGraphics Inc, pg 795
Celebrities Productions, pg 822
Fambrough & Associates Inc, pg 865

MONTANA

North Country Media Group, pg 959

NEBRASKA

Dog & Pony Productions Inc, pg 850

NEVADA

DVDs4Less, pg 854
JCS Video Productions, pg 904

NEW HAMPSHIRE

Apertura, pg 788
Chip Taylor Communications LLC, pg 1032

NEW JERSEY

Audio Vistas LLC, pg 795
Broadcast Center Studios, pg 813
CFP Video Productions Inc, pg 823
MIB Mediaworks, pg 941
Midnight Media Group Inc, pg 942
Optisonics Productions, pg 965
Presence Records, pg 981
Bill Quinn Productions, pg 989
Suede Interactive, pg 1027

NEW MEXICO

Michael Dunn Productions, pg 853
Production Outfitters, pg 984

NEW YORK

Aural Gratification Inc, pg 796
Avekta Productions Inc, pg 798
BioMedia Inc, pg 807
Blue Barn Pictures Inc, pg 809
Broad Street Inc, pg 812
The Christophers, pg 826
Clarity Media Group, pg 829
Thomas Craven Film Corp, pg 837
De Nonno Productions Inc (DPI), pg 844
Digital Force, pg 847
Downtown Community Television Center (DCTV), pg 851
Fingerpaint, pg 868
HB-Content, pg 886
Kamen Entertainment Group Inc, pg 908
KickedUp Media Group Inc, pg 910
L A Bruell Inc, pg 914
March of Dimes Foundation, pg 930
Jack Morton Worldwide, pg 946
MRG Productions Inc, pg 948
MRM Worldwide, pg 948
New York Audio Productions, pg 956
News Broadcast Network, pg 956
No Soap Productions, pg 957
Shelly Palmer Production, pg 968
Pat Kogan Productions Inc, pg 970
David Rapkin Audio Production, pg 991
Shadow Pictures Inc, pg 1007
Elliot Sokolov Music, pg 1015
Split Image Productions, pg 1021
Suggs Media Productions Inc, pg 1028
Synaptic Digital, pg 1030
Tiki Recording Studios Inc, pg 1040
United Nations Multimedia Resources Unit, pg 1048
Zelman Studios Ltd, pg 1073

NORTH CAROLINA

Pat Appleson Studios Inc, pg 788
The Communications Group Inc, pg 833
LCW Productions LLC, pg 917
Trailblazer Studios®, pg 1043
2BruceStudio, pg 1047

OHIO

Advent Media Inc, pg 778
Creative Technology, pg 838
Cuyahoga Community College Media Center, pg 841
EDR Media LLC, pg 857
Franciscan Media, pg 872
MainSail Production Services Inc, pg 929
R&B Communications Inc, pg 991
Take 1 Media Services, pg 1031
VGI Productions, pg 1053
Vista Color Imaging Inc, pg 1059

OKLAHOMA

Piper Media Services Inc, pg 976
University of Oklahoma Academic Media & Digital Services, pg 1050

OREGON

Ideascape Inc, pg 894
InterVision Media, pg 902
Odyssey Productions Inc, pg 961
Producers Studio, pg 984

PENNSYLVANIA

Audio Visual Communications Inc, pg 795
Forge Recording LLC, pg 871
Innovision Media Group, pg 899
JPL, pg 906
Kensington Falls Animation, pg 909
Muderick Media, pg 949
Panta Rhei Media Inc, pg 968
Production Masters Inc (PMI), pg 984
The Videohouse Inc, pg 1057
WQED-Multimedia, pg 1070

RHODE ISLAND

Sound-FX-Design, pg 1017

SOUTH CAROLINA

DaviSound, pg 843
Stages Video Productions, pg 1023
Venture Media, pg 1052

TENNESSEE

American Blackguard Inc, pg 784
Continental Film, pg 835

TEXAS

Biway Media, pg 808
Communication Arts Multimedia Inc, pg 832
Dykeman Associates Inc, pg 854
The Editing Co, pg 857
Epic Software Group Inc, pg 862
Institute of Texan Cultures, pg 899
Omega Productions, pg 962
The Sound Lab Inc, pg 1017
Sound Works, pg 1018
Stage Directions, pg 1022
TM Studios Inc, pg 1041
Tropikal Productions, pg 1045

UTAH

K-SAR Video & DVD Productions, pg 907

VIRGINIA

CACI Productions Group, pg 816
CDR Communications Inc, pg 822
Limelight Communications Inc, pg 921
Lion Recording Services Inc, pg 922
Metro Productions, pg 939
National Media Services Inc, pg 953
Rocktown Media, pg 998
Studio Center Corp, pg 1026

WASHINGTON

Hamilton Studio, pg 884
Kostov Productions, pg 913
Pacific Multimedia Inc, pg 967

WEST VIRGINIA

Blackwater Video Productions, pg 808

WISCONSIN

5th Floor Recording Co, pg 867
Meridian Studios, pg 939
University of Wisconsin-Oshkosh Radio-TV-Film Dept, pg 1050
USAV Group Inc, pg 1050
Video Wisconsin Inc, pg 1056
Watts Communications Inc, pg 1062
Wisconsin Public Television, pg 1068

WYOMING

Bridger Productions Inc, pg 812

ALBERTA

Black Media Works, pg 808
Global Television Station, pg 879
HBW Entertainment Inc, pg 886

NEWFOUNDLAND AND LABRADOR

Vidcraft Productions Ltd, pg 1054

ONTARIO

ADS Media, pg 777
DebsVoice, pg 844
GAPC (General Assembly Production Centre), pg 875
Shaw Street Productions, pg 1008

QUEBEC

Kerrigan Productions Inc, pg 910

Public Service Announcement Rentals

CALIFORNIA

Direct Cinema Ltd Inc, pg 848
ECONEWS (Environmental Television Series) & (Environmental Directions Radio Series), pg 856

MICHIGAN

Digi Sign Design LLC, pg 847

NEW HAMPSHIRE

Chip Taylor Communications LLC, pg 1032

Radio Commercial Distributors

CALIFORNIA

Digital Media West, pg 847
Far West Media Services Inc, pg 865
Maximus Media Inc, pg 934
QRS Software Services, pg 988

CONNECTICUT

EagleVision Inc, pg 855

ILLINOIS

Communications Corporation of America, pg 833
Woodside Avenue Music Productions Inc, pg 1069

KANSAS

Chapman Recording & Mastering, pg 824

MASSACHUSETTS

Penfield Productions Ltd, pg 971

MICHIGAN

Digi Sign Design LLC, pg 847

NEVADA

DVDs4Less, pg 854

NEW HAMPSHIRE

Chip Taylor Communications LLC, pg 1032

NEW YORK

HB-Content, pg 886
MRG Productions Inc, pg 948

NORTH CAROLINA

Baker & Taylor Inc, pg 801

SOUTH CAROLINA

DaviSound, pg 843

TENNESSEE

American Blackguard Inc, pg 784
Zion Music Group, pg 1074

TEXAS

TM Studios Inc, pg 1041

Radio Commercial Producers

ALABAMA

Dogwood Recording Studios, pg 850
Leo Ticheli Productions, pg 1040

ARIZONA

KOOL FM Radio, pg 913
SPEAK HOUSE Audio™, pg 1019

ARKANSAS

Live'N'Loud, pg 923
White Diamond Productions, pg 1065

CALIFORNIA

AM Productions, pg 783
The Banquet Sound Studios, pg 802
Creative Media Recording, pg 838
Custom Video Productions Inc, pg 841
Dogma Studios, pg 850
Far West Media Services Inc, pg 865
4th Street Recording, pg 872
Havas Edge, pg 885
International Contact Inc, pg 900
KTVU-Retail Services, pg 914
Lynch Communications, pg 926
Maximus Media Inc, pg 934
Media Magic, pg 937

PROGRAMMING — AUDIO

Radio Commercial Producers (continued)

CALIFORNIA (continued)

The Media Staff Inc, pg 937
On-Trax Inc, pg 963
OTR Studios, pg 966
piXvfm, pg 976
PM Productions, pg 977
QRS Software Services, pg 988
Steve Shapiro Music, pg 1008
Kris Stevens Enterprises, pg 1024
Still N'Motion, pg 1025
Studio 132, pg 1027
Tam Communications Inc, pg 1031
Total Media Group, pg 1042
WalkerVision Interarts, pg 1061
Webster Communications, pg 1063

COLORADO

Tim Cissell Music, pg 828
Clear Gravy Productions, pg 829
Daylight Productions & Rentals, pg 844
Rocky Mountain Audio/Video Productions Inc, pg 998

CONNECTICUT

EagleVision Inc, pg 855
Moving Pictures, pg 947
P&P Studios Inc, pg 968
Powerstation Events, pg 979

FLORIDA

Blackburst Entertainment, pg 808
Communications Concepts Inc (CCI), pg 833
Digital Zoetrope Productions, pg 848
Eastern Video, pg 856
Home Shopping Network (HSN), pg 890
LHV Audio Services, pg 919
Motion Image Group LLC, pg 947
Promidi Music, pg 986
Sunfire Communications Inc, pg 1028
Sunrise Studios, pg 1028
Top Hat Productions, pg 1042
Tricycle Studios, pg 1044
Universal Studios Florida® Production Group, pg 1049

GEORGIA

Guerrilla Productions LLC, pg 883
Symmes Systems, pg 1030
White Dog Studios, pg 1065

ILLINOIS

ABS Enterprises, pg 772
CCore Media Inc, pg 821
Communications Corporation of America, pg 833
Comtech Multimedia Marketing, pg 834
Cresta Creative, pg 839
Major Media Productions Inc, pg 929
Jim Passin Productions, pg 970
The Pepper Group, pg 972
The Prairie Production Group, pg 980
Steven Samler Music & Sound, pg 1002
Video Impressions, pg 1055
Woodside Avenue Music Productions Inc, pg 1069

INDIANA

Advanced Media Integration, pg 777
AVA Productions, pg 798

IOWA

Hedquist Productions Inc, pg 887

KANSAS

Chapman Recording & Mastering, pg 824

KENTUCKY

Trusty Tuneshop Recording Studios, pg 1045

LOUISIANA

Digital FX Inc, pg 847
Disk Productions, pg 849

MAINE

Serendipity Recordings, pg 1007

MARYLAND

The Ahern Group, pg 779
CPR MultiMedia Solutions, pg 837
CSPMedia.com, pg 840
The Cutting Corp, pg 841
dbF a Media Company, pg 844
The Image Generators, pg 895

MASSACHUSETTS

Labrecque Creative Sound, pg 915
Penfield Productions Ltd, pg 971
Soundtrack Recording Studios, pg 1018
Rik Tinory Productions, pg 1041
TR Productions, pg 1043
TVN-The Video Network, pg 1046

MICHIGAN

Digi Sign Design LLC, pg 847
K&R All Media Productions Inc, pg 908
K&R's Recording Studios Inc, pg 908
MessageMakers, pg 939

MINNESOTA

Aggressive Records Audio Duplication LLC, pg 778
Jamieson & Associates Inc, pg 904

MISSOURI

Audio-VideoGraphics Inc, pg 795
Celebrities Productions, pg 822
Fambrough & Associates Inc, pg 865

MONTANA

North Country Media Group, pg 959

NEVADA

DVDs4Less, pg 854
JCS Video Productions, pg 904

NEW HAMPSHIRE

Apertura, pg 788
Chip Taylor Communications LLC, pg 1032

NEW JERSEY

CFP Video Productions Inc, pg 823
Euro-Pacific Film & Video Productions Inc, pg 863
Laurel Video Productions, pg 916
Midnight Media Group Inc, pg 942
Optisonics Productions, pg 965
Presence Records, pg 981
Bill Quinn Productions, pg 989
Suede Interactive, pg 1027
VCSvideo, pg 1052

NEW MEXICO

Production Outfitters, pg 984

NEW YORK

Big Fish Productions Inc, pg 807
Blue Barn Pictures Inc, pg 809
Thomas Craven Film Corp, pg 837
Digital Force, pg 847
dM works, pg 849
Fingerpaint, pg 868
HB-Content, pg 886
Irish Music Corp, pg 902
Kamen Entertainment Group Inc, pg 908
Mood Creations Ltd, pg 946
Jack Morton Worldwide, pg 946
MRG Productions Inc, pg 948
The Napoleon Group, pg 952
New York Audio Productions, pg 956
No Soap Productions, pg 957
NSR Productions Inc & Capricorn Five Films, pg 960
Shelly Palmer Production, pg 968
RadioArt/Bob & Ray CDs & MP3 Files, pg 990
David Rapkin Audio Production, pg 991
Elliot Sokolov Music, pg 1015
Split Image Productions, pg 1021
Suggs Media Productions Inc, pg 1028
Tiki Recording Studios Inc, pg 1040
Zelman Studios Ltd, pg 1073

NORTH CAROLINA

Pat Appleson Studios Inc, pg 788
The Communications Group Inc, pg 833
Trailblazer Studios®, pg 1043
2BruceStudio, pg 1047

OHIO

Advent Media Inc, pg 778
EDR Media LLC, pg 857
Musicol Recording, pg 951
Take 1 Media Services, pg 1031
Vista Color Imaging Inc, pg 1059

OKLAHOMA

Piper Media Services Inc, pg 976

OREGON

A KTVA Production LLC, pg 771
Ideascape Inc, pg 894
Odyssey Productions Inc, pg 961
Producers Studio, pg 984
Rex, pg 995

PENNSYLVANIA

AiH Group Inc, pg 779
Audio Visual Communications Inc, pg 795
Forge Recording LLC, pg 871
Innovision Media Group, pg 899
JPL, pg 906
Production Masters Inc (PMI), pg 984
The Videohouse Inc, pg 1057

RHODE ISLAND

Sound-FX-Design, pg 1017

SOUTH CAROLINA

DaviSound, pg 843
Venture Media, pg 1052

TENNESSEE

American Blackguard Inc, pg 784
Continental Film, pg 835
Love Shack Recording Studios, pg 925

TEXAS

Audiomoxie®, pg 796
Communication Arts Multimedia Inc, pg 832
Dykeman Associates Inc, pg 854
The Editing Co, pg 857
James Loupas Associates Inc, pg 925
Music Lab Inc, pg 950
Omega Productions, pg 962
Radio Vision Inc, pg 990
The Sound Lab Inc, pg 1017
Sound Works, pg 1018
Stage Directions, pg 1022
TM Studios Inc, pg 1041
Tropikal Productions, pg 1045
The Yesterday USA Radio Networks, pg 1072

UTAH

K-SAR Video & DVD Productions, pg 907

VIRGINIA

Limelight Communications Inc, pg 921
Lion Recording Services Inc, pg 922
Metro Productions, pg 939
National Media Services Inc, pg 953
Rocktown Media, pg 998
Studio Center Corp, pg 1026

WASHINGTON

Hamilton Studio, pg 884
Kostov Productions, pg 913
Pacific Multimedia Inc, pg 967

WISCONSIN

5th Floor Recording Co, pg 867
Meridian Studios, pg 939
University of Wisconsin-Oshkosh Radio-TV-Film Dept, pg 1050
USAV Group Inc, pg 1050
Video Wisconsin Inc, pg 1056
Watts Communications Inc, pg 1062

WYOMING

Bridger Productions Inc, pg 812

NEWFOUNDLAND AND LABRADOR

Vidcraft Productions Ltd, pg 1054

ONTARIO

ADS Media, pg 777
DebsVoice, pg 844

GAPC (General Assembly Production Centre), pg 875
VO2 Mix Studios, pg 1060

Radio Commercial Rentals

ILLINOIS

Woodside Avenue Music Productions Inc, pg 1069

MICHIGAN

Digi Sign Design LLC, pg 847

NEW HAMPSHIRE

Chip Taylor Communications LLC, pg 1032

UTAH

Webb Audio Visual Communication, pg 1063

Radio Program—Classic Distributors

ARIZONA

Valley of the Sun Publishing Co, pg 1051

CALIFORNIA

National Lampoon, pg 953
Pacifica Radio Archives, pg 967
QRS Software Services, pg 988

ILLINOIS

Major Media Inc, pg 929

MASSACHUSETTS

Penfield Productions Ltd, pg 971

MICHIGAN

Digi Sign Design LLC, pg 847

MINNESOTA

HighBridge Audio, pg 889

NEW YORK

RadioArt/Bob & Ray CDs & MP3 Files, pg 990

SOUTH CAROLINA

DaviSound, pg 843

TEXAS

Endtime Inc, pg 861
Lamb & Lion Ministries, pg 915
Marengo Films, pg 931
TM Studios Inc, pg 1041

Radio Program—Classic Producers

CALIFORNIA

Creative Media Recording, pg 838
Lynch Communications, pg 926
Maximus Media Inc, pg 934
National Lampoon, pg 953
Pacific Audio-Visual Enterprises, pg 967
QRS Software Services, pg 988
Steve Shapiro Music, pg 1008
Kris Stevens Enterprises, pg 1024
Total Media Group, pg 1042

FLORIDA

LHV Audio Services, pg 919
Sunfire Communications Inc, pg 1028

GEORGIA

Guerrilla Productions LLC, pg 883

ILLINOIS

Major Media Inc, pg 929

INDIANA

AVA Productions, pg 798

MARYLAND

dbF a Media Company, pg 844

MASSACHUSETTS

Labrecque Creative Sound, pg 915
Penfield Productions Ltd, pg 971
Soundtrack Recording Studios, pg 1018

MICHIGAN

Digi Sign Design LLC, pg 847
K&R All Media Productions Inc, pg 908
K&R's Recording Studios Inc, pg 908

MINNESOTA

Aggressive Records Audio Duplication LLC, pg 778
HighBridge Audio, pg 889

NEVADA

JCS Video Productions, pg 904

NEW JERSEY

Suede Interactive, pg 1027

NEW YORK

Digital Force, pg 847
Lavine Production Group, pg 917
RadioArt/Bob & Ray CDs & MP3 Files, pg 990

NORTH CAROLINA

Pat Appleson Studios Inc, pg 788

OHIO

EDR Media LLC, pg 857
Musicol Recording, pg 951
Take 1 Media Services, pg 1031

PENNSYLVANIA

Forge Recording LLC, pg 871

RHODE ISLAND

Sound-FX-Design, pg 1017

SOUTH CAROLINA

DaviSound, pg 843

TENNESSEE

Love Shack Recording Studios, pg 925

TEXAS

Endtime Inc, pg 861
Lamb & Lion Ministries, pg 915
The Sound Lab Inc, pg 1017
TM Studios Inc, pg 1041
The Yesterday USA Radio Networks, pg 1072

VIRGINIA

Lion Recording Services Inc, pg 922
National Media Services Inc, pg 953
Rocktown Media, pg 998

WISCONSIN

5th Floor Recording Co, pg 867

ONTARIO

DebsVoice, pg 844
GAPC (General Assembly Production Centre), pg 875

Radio Program—Classic Rentals

MICHIGAN

Digi Sign Design LLC, pg 847

Religious Program Distributors

ALABAMA

Eternal Word Television Network (EWTN), pg 862

ARIZONA

Drumbeat Indian Arts Inc, pg 852
TSG Publishing Foundation Inc USA, pg 1046

CALIFORNIA

Blue Dolphin Multimedia, pg 809
Christian Media Network, pg 825
Clarity Sound & Light, pg 829
Digital Media West, pg 847
Direct Cinema Ltd Inc, pg 848
Hay House Inc, pg 886
Maximus Media Inc, pg 934
Nilgiri Press, pg 957
Osho Viha Information Center & Book Distributors, pg 965
Pacifica Radio Archives, pg 967
Paulist Productions, pg 970
QRS Software Services, pg 988
Vedanta Press & Catalog, pg 1052
The Wyland Group, pg 1071

COLORADO

Crown Ministries International, pg 840
Meriwether Publishing Ltd, pg 939

CONNECTICUT

EagleVision Inc, pg 855

DISTRICT OF COLUMBIA

Biblical Archaeology Society (BAS), pg 806
National Council of Churches, pg 952
USCCB Publishing, pg 1051

FLORIDA

Capital Communications Inc, pg 819
Children of Mary, pg 825

GEORGIA

Dake Publishing Inc, pg 842
New Leaf Distributing Co, pg 955

HAWAII

Media Bridge Gamekids, pg 936

ILLINOIS

ACTA Publications, pg 775
Baha'i Distribution Service (BDS), pg 801
CCore Media Inc, pg 821
Film Ideas, pg 867
Liturgy Training Publications, pg 923
Theosophical Publishing House, pg 1038

INDIANA

Communication Ministries, pg 833

MASSACHUSETTS

Pauline Books & Media, pg 970

MICHIGAN

Digi Sign Design LLC, pg 847
Emery-Pratt Co, pg 860
Gemini, pg 876
Master Mind Publishing Co, pg 933
Jack Van Impe Ministries International, pg 1051
Zondervan, A HarperCollins Company, pg 1074

MINNESOTA

Augsburg Fortress Publishers, pg 796
HighBridge Audio, pg 889

MISSOURI

Grace Church - St Louis, pg 881
Impact Christian Books Inc, pg 897
SOM Publishing Co, pg 1015
Vedanta Society of St Louis, pg 1052

NEBRASKA

Back to the Bible, pg 801

NEW HAMPSHIRE

Chip Taylor Communications LLC, pg 1032

NEW JERSEY

Listen & Live Audio Inc, pg 923
Paulist Press, pg 970

NEW YORK

Billy Budd Films Inc, pg 814
Hallel Communications, pg 884
HarperAudio, pg 885
Irish Music Corp, pg 902
Janus Films Inc, pg 904
Maryknoll Productions, pg 933
MRG Productions Inc, pg 948
Random House Audio Publishing Group, pg 991
The Fulton J Sheen Co Inc, pg 1008
SISU Home Entertainment Inc, pg 1012

NORTH CAROLINA

Baker & Taylor Inc, pg 801
Howard Hanger, pg 884

PROGRAMMING — AUDIO

Religious Program Distributors (continued)

Religious Program Producers

Religious Program Rentals

Research—Technical Program, *see* Technical Research Program

Sales Promotion & Training Program Distributors

Sales Promotion & Training Program Producers

PROGRAMMING — AUDIO

Sales Promotion & Training Program Producers (continued)

FLORIDA (continued)

Home Shopping Network (HSN), pg 890
I M P A C T Publishing Inc, pg 893
LHV Audio Services, pg 919
Roger Scruggs Films, pg 1005
Sunfire Communications Inc, pg 1028
Sunrise Studios, pg 1028
Top Hat Productions, pg 1042
Tricycle Studios, pg 1044
Universal Studios Florida® Production Group, pg 1049
Mike Vasilinda Productions Inc, pg 1052

GEORGIA

COMPRO Productions Inc, pg 834
Guerrilla Productions LLC, pg 883
Playback Now, pg 977
Sirius Images Corp dba WaveGuide Studios, pg 1012
Symmes Systems, pg 1030

IDAHO

Wide Eye Productions, pg 1066

ILLINOIS

ABS Enterprises, pg 772
Accenture, pg 773
Audio Visual Services Corp, pg 796
CCore Media Inc, pg 821
Chicago Satellite & Video, pg 825
Comtech Multimedia Marketing, pg 834
Cresta Creative, pg 839
Major Media Productions Inc, pg 929
Nightingale-Conant Corp, pg 957
Oasis Audio, pg 960
The Pepper Group, pg 972
PSAV® Presentation Services (Hotel Services Division), pg 987
Steven Samler Music & Sound, pg 1002
Sparkfactor, pg 1019
20/20 Communications Inc, pg 1047
Video Impressions, pg 1055

INDIANA

Advanced Media Integration, pg 777
AVA Productions, pg 798
Bright Ideas Creative Services, pg 812
Covenant Productions®, pg 837
OMNI Productions, pg 962
PentaVision Communications Inc, pg 972

IOWA

Hedquist Productions Inc, pg 887

KANSAS

Chapman Recording & Mastering, pg 824

LOUISIANA

Digital FX Inc, pg 847

MARYLAND

CPR MultiMedia Solutions, pg 837
CSPMedia.com, pg 840
The Cutting Corp, pg 841
dbF a Media Company, pg 844
The Image Generators, pg 895
Kramer Communications Video Production, pg 913
Milner-Fenwick Inc, pg 943
Mobile-Video Productions Inc, pg 944

MASSACHUSETTS

CommCreative, pg 832
Emergency Film Group, pg 860
Labrecque Creative Sound, pg 915
Penfield Productions Ltd, pg 971
Preston Productions Inc, pg 981
Soundtrack Recording Studios, pg 1018
TR Productions, pg 1043
TVN-The Video Network, pg 1046

MICHIGAN

Digi Sign Design LLC, pg 847
K&R All Media Productions Inc, pg 908
K&R's Recording Studios Inc, pg 908
Maritz Performance Improvement Co, pg 931
MessageMakers, pg 939
TGA Recording Co, pg 1038

MINNESOTA

Aggressive Records Audio Duplication LLC, pg 778
Effective Learning Systems Inc, pg 858
GMI Productions, pg 879
Jamieson & Associates Inc, pg 904
Learning Strategies Corp, pg 917
Media Loft Inc, pg 937
MultiMedia, pg 950

MISSOURI

Audio-VideoGraphics Inc, pg 795
Celebrities Productions, pg 822
Fambrough & Associates Inc, pg 865
Hardcastle Films & Video, pg 885
SOM Publishing Co, pg 1015

MONTANA

Jereco Studios Inc, pg 905
North Country Media Group, pg 959

NEBRASKA

Dog & Pony Productions Inc, pg 850

NEVADA

DVDs4Less, pg 854
JCS Video Productions, pg 904

NEW HAMPSHIRE

Apertura, pg 788
Chip Taylor Communications LLC, pg 1032

NEW JERSEY

Audio Vistas LLC, pg 795
CFP Video Productions Inc, pg 823
Laurel Video Productions, pg 916
Listen & Live Audio Inc, pg 923
MIB Mediaworks, pg 941
Optisonics Productions, pg 965
Producer East Productions, pg 983
Projects in Knowledge Inc, pg 986
Suede Interactive, pg 1027

NEW MEXICO

Michael Dunn Productions, pg 853

NEW YORK

American Management Association International, pg 784
Avekta Productions Inc, pg 798
BioMedia Inc, pg 807
Broad Street Inc, pg 812
Cohn Creative Group LLC, pg 831
Conversation Arts Media, pg 836
C2 Imaging LLC, pg 841
Digital Force, pg 847
dM works, pg 849
Albert Ellis Institute (AEI), pg 859
Fingerpaint, pg 868
HarperAudio, pg 885
HB-Content, pg 886
Hello World Communications, pg 888
Icontent, pg 893
Kamen Entertainment Group Inc, pg 908
Ketchum Pleon Change, pg 910
KickedUp Media Group Inc, pg 910
Jack Morton Worldwide, pg 946
MRG Productions Inc, pg 948
MRM Worldwide, pg 948
MRY, pg 949
The Napoleon Group, pg 952
New York Audio Productions, pg 956
News Broadcast Network, pg 956
Shelly Palmer Production, pg 968
Pat Kogan Productions Inc, pg 970
David Rapkin Audio Production, pg 991
Split Image Productions, pg 1021
Suggs Media Productions Inc, pg 1028
Synaptic Digital, pg 1030
Tiki Recording Studios Inc, pg 1040
Zelman Studios Ltd, pg 1073

NORTH CAROLINA

Pat Appleson Studios Inc, pg 788
The Communications Group Inc, pg 833
Eli Research Group, pg 859
LCW Productions LLC, pg 917
Sinclair Institute, pg 1012
Trailblazer Studios®, pg 1043
2BruceStudio, pg 1047

OHIO

Advent Media Inc, pg 778
Creative Technology, pg 838
EDR Media LLC, pg 857
MainSail Production Services Inc, pg 929
Musicol Recording, pg 951
R&B Communications Inc, pg 991
South-Western Publishing Co, pg 1019
Take 1 Media Services, pg 1031
VGI Productions, pg 1053
Vista Color Imaging Inc, pg 1059

OKLAHOMA

Piper Media Services Inc, pg 976

OREGON

A KTVA Production LLC, pg 771
Ideascape Inc, pg 894
InterVision Media, pg 902
Odyssey Productions Inc, pg 961
Rex, pg 995

PENNSYLVANIA

AiH Group Inc, pg 779
American Artist Studio, pg 783
Audio Visual Communications Inc, pg 795
Bang Pictures, pg 802
FMP Media Solutions Inc, pg 870
Forge Recording LLC, pg 871
Innovision Media Group, pg 899
JPL, pg 906
Kensington Falls Animation, pg 909
Muderick Media, pg 949
Panta Rhei Media Inc, pg 968
Production Masters Inc (PMI), pg 984
The Videohouse Inc, pg 1057
Visual Sound Inc, pg 1059

RHODE ISLAND

Sound-FX-Design, pg 1017

SOUTH CAROLINA

Stages Video Productions, pg 1023
Venture Media, pg 1052

TENNESSEE

American Blackguard Inc, pg 784
Continental Film, pg 835
Marine Geographic, pg 931
Memphis Communications Corp, pg 938
Stage Post, pg 1022
Russ Sturgeon Productions/RSVP, pg 1027

TEXAS

AMA Nystrom Printing/Finishing, pg 783
Biway Media, pg 808
Dykeman Associates Inc, pg 854
The Editing Co, pg 857
Epic Software Group Inc, pg 862
Omega Productions, pg 962
Romar Learning, pg 999
The Sound Lab Inc, pg 1017
Sound Works, pg 1018
Stage Directions, pg 1022

VIRGINIA

Advance Concepts Inc, pg 777
CACI Productions Group, pg 816
Limelight Communications Inc, pg 921
Lion Recording Services Inc, pg 922
Metro Productions, pg 939
National Media Services Inc, pg 953
Rocktown Media, pg 998

WASHINGTON

Kostov Productions, pg 913
Pacific Multimedia Inc, pg 967

WISCONSIN

Audio Visual of Milwaukee Inc, pg 795
5th Floor Recording Co, pg 867
Meridian Studios, pg 939
USAV Group Inc, pg 1050
Video Wisconsin Inc, pg 1056
Watts Communications Inc, pg 1062
Wisconsin Public Television, pg 1068

PROGRAMMING — AUDIO

Scientific Program Producers (continued)

MONTANA

High Plains Films, pg 889
North Country Media Group, pg 959

NEVADA

JCS Video Productions, pg 904
Tetrahedron LLC, pg 1037

NEW HAMPSHIRE

Apertura, pg 788
Chip Taylor Communications LLC, pg 1032

NEW JERSEY

Audio Vistas LLC, pg 795
CFP Video Productions Inc, pg 823
Laurel Video Productions, pg 916
MIB Mediaworks, pg 941
Optisonics Productions, pg 965
Suede Interactive, pg 1027

NEW MEXICO

Uncharted Country Publishing, pg 1048

NEW YORK

Avekta Productions Inc, pg 798
BioMedia Inc, pg 807
Broad Street Inc, pg 812
CompuWeather Inc, pg 834
C2 Imaging LLC, pg 841
Digital Force, pg 847
Fingerpaint, pg 868
Guilford Publications, pg 883
Icontent, pg 893
Kamen Entertainment Group Inc, pg 908
March of Dimes Foundation, pg 930
Jack Morton Worldwide, pg 946
MRG Productions Inc, pg 948
MRY, pg 949
New York Audio Productions, pg 956
News Broadcast Network, pg 956
Shelly Palmer Production, pg 968
Pat Kogan Productions Inc, pg 970
David Rapkin Audio Production, pg 991
Split Image Productions, pg 1021
Tiki Recording Studios Inc, pg 1040
Videograf, pg 1057
Zelman Studios Ltd, pg 1073

NORTH CAROLINA

Pat Appleson Studios Inc, pg 788
Trailblazer Studios®, pg 1043
2BruceStudio, pg 1047

OHIO

Advent Media Inc, pg 778
EDR Media LLC, pg 857
Maslowski Productions, pg 933
R&B Communications Inc, pg 991
Take 1 Media Services, pg 1031
VGI Productions, pg 1053
Vista Color Imaging Inc, pg 1059

OKLAHOMA

Piper Media Services Inc, pg 976

OREGON

ERA Learning, pg 862
Ideascape Inc, pg 894
Norman Beerger Productions, pg 958
Odyssey Productions Inc, pg 961

PENNSYLVANIA

Audio Visual Communications Inc, pg 795
FMP Media Solutions Inc, pg 870
Forge Recording LLC, pg 871
JPL, pg 906
Production Masters Inc (PMI), pg 984

RHODE ISLAND

Sound-FX-Design, pg 1017

SOUTH CAROLINA

Venture Media, pg 1052

TENNESSEE

Continental Film, pg 835
Memphis Communications Corp, pg 938

TEXAS

Educational Video Network, pg 857
Omega Productions, pg 962
Romar Learning, pg 999
The Sound Lab Inc, pg 1017
Sound Works, pg 1018
Texas Heart Institute Visual Communication Services, pg 1037

VIRGINIA

CACI Productions Group, pg 816
Limelight Communications Inc, pg 921
Lion Recording Services Inc, pg 922
Metro Productions, pg 939
National Media Services Inc, pg 953
Rocktown Media, pg 998

WASHINGTON

Pacific Multimedia Inc, pg 967

WISCONSIN

5th Floor Recording Co, pg 867
USAV Group Inc, pg 1050
Wisconsin Public Television, pg 1068

WYOMING

Bridger Productions Inc, pg 812

ONTARIO

ADS Media, pg 777
JFB Communications, pg 905

QUEBEC

Kerrigan Productions Inc, pg 910

Scientific Program Rentals

CALIFORNIA

Direct Cinema Ltd Inc, pg 848

MAINE

University of Maine Audio Visual Services, pg 1049

MASSACHUSETTS

Emergency Film Group, pg 860

MICHIGAN

Digi Sign Design LLC, pg 847

NEW HAMPSHIRE

Chip Taylor Communications LLC, pg 1032

PENNSYLVANIA

Penn State University MediaTech, pg 972

UTAH

Webb Audio Visual Communication, pg 1063

Sponsored Program Distributors

CALIFORNIA

Digital Media West, pg 847
Direct Cinema Ltd Inc, pg 848
Maximus Media Inc, pg 934
Medcom Inc, pg 936
QRS Software Services, pg 988

FLORIDA

Allegro Productions Inc, pg 781
Capital Communications Inc, pg 819

GEORGIA

Symmes Systems, pg 1030

ILLINOIS

CCore Media Inc, pg 821
Nightingale-Conant Corp, pg 957

MASSACHUSETTS

Penfield Productions Ltd, pg 971

MICHIGAN

Digi Sign Design LLC, pg 847

NEW HAMPSHIRE

Chip Taylor Communications LLC, pg 1032

NEW YORK

Hallel Communications, pg 884
HB-Content, pg 886
KickedUp Media Group Inc, pg 910
MRG Productions Inc, pg 948
NSR Productions Inc & Capricorn Five Films, pg 960
Synaptic Digital, pg 1030

NORTH CAROLINA

Baker & Taylor Inc, pg 801

OREGON

InterVision Media, pg 902

PENNSYLVANIA

FMP Media Solutions Inc, pg 870
Karol Media Inc, pg 908

SOUTH CAROLINA

DaviSound, pg 843

TENNESSEE

American Blackguard Inc, pg 784
Continental Film, pg 835

ALBERTA

Global Television Station, pg 879

Sponsored Program Producers

ALABAMA

Leo Ticheli Productions, pg 1040

CALIFORNIA

Big Door, pg 807
Creative Media Recording, pg 838
Custom Video Productions Inc, pg 841
Direct Cinema Ltd Inc, pg 848
Dogma Studios, pg 850
imageReal Pictures LLC, pg 896
KTVU-Retail Services, pg 914
Lynch Communications, pg 926
Maximus Media Inc, pg 934
Medcom Inc, pg 936
The Media Staff Inc, pg 937
Producers Group Ltd, pg 983
QRS Software Services, pg 988
Still N'Motion, pg 1025
Studio 132, pg 1027
Total Media Group, pg 1042
Video Resources Inc, pg 1056
Webster Communications, pg 1063
Zamacona Productions, pg 1073

COLORADO

Apogee Communications Group, pg 788
Tatum Video, pg 1032

CONNECTICUT

ACM Productions Ltd, pg 774
EagleVision Inc, pg 855
Moving Pictures, pg 947

DISTRICT OF COLUMBIA

Hillmann & Carr Inc, pg 889

FLORIDA

Allegro Productions Inc, pg 781
Audio Visual Imagineering Inc, pg 795
Blackburst Entertainment, pg 808
Capital Communications Inc, pg 819
Communications Concepts Inc (CCI), pg 833
Eastern Video, pg 856
LHV Audio Services, pg 919
Roger Scruggs Films, pg 1005
Sunfire Communications Inc, pg 1028
Sunrise Studios, pg 1028
Top Hat Productions, pg 1042
Tricycle Studios, pg-1044

GEORGIA

Guerrilla Productions LLC, pg 883
Symmes Systems, pg 1030

IDAHO

Wide Eye Productions, pg 1066

ILLINOIS

Audio Visual Services Corp, pg 796
CCore Media Inc, pg 821
Chicago Satellite & Video, pg 825
Communications Corporation of America, pg 833
Nightingale-Conant Corp, pg 957
Jim Passin Productions, pg 970
The Pepper Group, pg 972
PSAV® Presentation Services (Hotel Services Division), pg 987
Video Impressions, pg 1055

INDIANA

AVA Productions, pg 798

IOWA

The Production House, pg 984

MARYLAND

CPR MultiMedia Solutions, pg 837
CSPMedia.com, pg 840
The Cutting Corp, pg 841
dbF a Media Company, pg 844
The Image Generators, pg 895

MASSACHUSETTS

Emergency Film Group, pg 860
Labrecque Creative Sound, pg 915
Penfield Productions Ltd, pg 971
Preston Productions Inc, pg 981
Soundtrack Recording Studios, pg 1018
TR Productions, pg 1043

MICHIGAN

Digi Sign Design LLC, pg 847
K&R All Media Productions Inc, pg 908
K&R's Recording Studios Inc, pg 908

MINNESOTA

Aggressive Records Audio Duplication LLC, pg 778
Jamieson & Associates Inc, pg 904
MultiMedia, pg 950

MISSOURI

Celebrities Productions, pg 822
Fambrough & Associates Inc, pg 865

MONTANA

North Country Media Group, pg 959

NEVADA

JCS Video Productions, pg 904

NEW HAMPSHIRE

Apertura, pg 788
Chip Taylor Communications LLC, pg 1032

NEW JERSEY

CFP Video Productions Inc, pg 823
Laurel Video Productions, pg 916
Optisonics Productions, pg 965
Suede Interactive, pg 1027

NEW MEXICO

Michael Dunn Productions, pg 853

NEW YORK

Avekta Productions Inc, pg 798
BioMedia Inc, pg 807
Blue Barn Pictures Inc, pg 809
Broad Street Inc, pg 812
Cohn Creative Group LLC, pg 831
Digital Force, pg 847
Hallel Communications, pg 884
HB-Content, pg 886
Kamen Entertainment Group Inc, pg 908
Ketchum Pleon Change, pg 910
KickedUp Media Group Inc, pg 910
Jack Morton Worldwide, pg 946
MRG Productions Inc, pg 948
New York Audio Productions, pg 956
News Broadcast Network, pg 956
NSR Productions Inc & Capricorn Five Films, pg 960
Shelly Palmer Production, pg 968
Pat Kogan Productions Inc, pg 970
David Rapkin Audio Production, pg 991
Elliot Sokolov Music, pg 1015
Split Image Productions, pg 1021
Suggs Media Productions Inc, pg 1028
Synaptic Digital, pg 1030
Videograf, pg 1057
Zelman Studios Ltd, pg 1073

NORTH CAROLINA

Pat Appleson Studios Inc, pg 788

OHIO

Advent Media Inc, pg 778
Creative Technology, pg 838
EDR Media LLC, pg 857
R&B Communications Inc, pg 991
Take 1 Media Services, pg 1031
Vista Color Imaging Inc, pg 1059

OKLAHOMA

Piper Media Services Inc, pg 976

OREGON

Ideascape Inc, pg 894
InterVision Media, pg 902
Odyssey Productions Inc, pg 961

PENNSYLVANIA

FMP Media Solutions Inc, pg 870
Forge Recording LLC, pg 871
JPL, pg 906
Production Masters Inc (PMI), pg 984

RHODE ISLAND

Sound-FX-Design, pg 1017

SOUTH CAROLINA

DaviSound, pg 843

TENNESSEE

American Blackguard Inc, pg 784

TEXAS

Omega Productions, pg 962
Romar Learning, pg 999
The Sound Lab Inc, pg 1017
Sound Works, pg 1018
South Coast Film & Video, pg 1019
Texas Heart Institute Visual Communication Services, pg 1037

VIRGINIA

Lion Recording Services Inc, pg 922
Metro Productions, pg 939
National Media Services Inc, pg 953
Rocktown Media, pg 998

WISCONSIN

5th Floor Recording Co, pg 867
Video Wisconsin Inc, pg 1056
Watts Communications Inc, pg 1062

WYOMING

Bridger Productions Inc, pg 812

ALBERTA

Global Television Station, pg 879

ONTARIO

GAPC (General Assembly Production Centre), pg 875
JFB Communications, pg 905

QUEBEC

Kerrigan Productions Inc, pg 910

Sponsored Program Rentals

CALIFORNIA

Direct Cinema Ltd Inc, pg 848
Medcom Inc, pg 936

GEORGIA

Symmes Systems, pg 1030

ILLINOIS

Nightingale-Conant Corp, pg 957

MASSACHUSETTS

Preston Productions Inc, pg 981

MICHIGAN

Digi Sign Design LLC, pg 847

NEW HAMPSHIRE

Chip Taylor Communications LLC, pg 1032

NEW YORK

Hallel Communications, pg 884

UTAH

Webb Audio Visual Communication, pg 1063

Sports Program Distributors

CALIFORNIA

Crystal Pyramid Productions™, pg 840
Deja View Video, pg 845
Digital Media West, pg 847
Maximus Media Inc, pg 934
QRS Software Services, pg 988
Sodanceabit, pg 1015

COLORADO

Gaiam Inc, pg 875

FLORIDA

Capital Communications Inc, pg 819
I M P A C T Publishing Inc, pg 893
Peak Performance Sports LLC, pg 970
Lee Pitts Enterprises, pg 976
Potentials Unlimited, pg 979
SOS Worldwide Productions Inc, pg 1016

ILLINOIS

Nightingale-Conant Corp, pg 957

IOWA

Championship Productions Inc, pg 823

MASSACHUSETTS

Penfield Productions Ltd, pg 971

MICHIGAN

Digi Sign Design LLC, pg 847

MINNESOTA

Effective Learning Systems Inc, pg 858
HighBridge Audio, pg 889

NEW HAMPSHIRE

Chip Taylor Communications LLC, pg 1032

NEW JERSEY

Listen & Live Audio Inc, pg 923

NEW MEXICO

Uncharted Country Publishing, pg 1048

NEW YORK

HarperAudio, pg 885
HB-Content, pg 886
Irish Music Corp, pg 902
Madison Square Garden, pg 927
MRG Productions Inc, pg 948
Penguin Audiobooks, pg 971
Synaptic Digital, pg 1030

NORTH CAROLINA

Baker & Taylor Inc, pg 801
MRN Radio, pg 948

OREGON

InterVision Media, pg 902

PENNSYLVANIA

FMP Media Solutions Inc, pg 870
Karol Media Inc, pg 908

TENNESSEE

Marine Geographic, pg 931
Spring Arbor Distributors, pg 1022

VIRGINIA

CACI Productions Group, pg 816

ALBERTA

Global Television Station, pg 879

ONTARIO

Canadian Learning Co Inc, pg 818

PROGRAMMING — AUDIO

Sports Program Producers

ARKANSAS

White Diamond Productions, pg 1065

CALIFORNIA

A Go Go Films, pg 771
Big Door, pg 807
Crystal Pyramid Productions™, pg 840
Custom Video Productions Inc, pg 841
Deja View Video, pg 845
Direct Cinema Ltd Inc, pg 848
Dogma Studios, pg 850
Havas Edge, pg 885
Lynch Communications, pg 926
On-Trax Inc, pg 963
Producers Group Ltd, pg 983
QRS Software Services, pg 988
Reality Check Systems, pg 992
Steve Shapiro Music, pg 1008
Sodanceabit, pg 1015
Studio 132, pg 1027
Total Media Group, pg 1042
Video Resources Inc, pg 1056
Webster Communications, pg 1063

COLORADO

Gaiam Inc, pg 875
Tatum Video, pg 1032

CONNECTICUT

ACM Productions Ltd, pg 774
EagleVision Inc, pg 855
The Gary-Paul Agency, pg 875
Golf Digest, pg 880

FLORIDA

Blackburst Entertainment, pg 808
Capital Communications Inc, pg 819
Communications Concepts Inc (CCI), pg 833
Eastern Video, pg 856
I M P A C T Publishing Inc, pg 893
LHV Audio Services, pg 919
Peak Performance Sports LLC, pg 970
Roger Scruggs Films, pg 1005
Sunfire Communications Inc, pg 1028
Sunrise Studios, pg 1028
Top Hat Productions, pg 1042

GEORGIA

Guerrilla Productions LLC, pg 883
Myriad Productions, pg 951

IDAHO

Wide Eye Productions, pg 1066

ILLINOIS

ABS Enterprises, pg 772
Chicago Satellite & Video, pg 825
Nightingale-Conant Corp, pg 957
The Pepper Group, pg 972
20/20 Communications Inc, pg 1047

INDIANA

AVA Productions, pg 798
Digital Rain LLC, pg 847
PentaVision Communications Inc, pg 972

IOWA

Championship Productions Inc, pg 823

LOUISIANA

Disk Productions, pg 849

MARYLAND

CPR MultiMedia Solutions, pg 837
CSPMedia.com, pg 840
The Cutting Corp, pg 841
dbF a Media Company, pg 844
Kramer Communications Video Production, pg 913

MASSACHUSETTS

Emergency Film Group, pg 860
Labrecque Creative Sound, pg 915
Penfield Productions Ltd, pg 971
Soundtrack Recording Studios, pg 1018

MICHIGAN

Digi Sign Design LLC, pg 847
K&R All Media Productions Inc, pg 908
K&R's Recording Studios Inc, pg 908

MINNESOTA

Aggressive Records Audio Duplication LLC, pg 778
Effective Learning Systems Inc, pg 858
HighBridge Audio, pg 889

MISSOURI

Celebrities Productions, pg 822
Fambrough & Associates Inc, pg 865

MONTANA

North Country Media Group, pg 959

NEVADA

JCS Video Productions, pg 904

NEW HAMPSHIRE

Apertura, pg 788
Chip Taylor Communications LLC, pg 1032

NEW JERSEY

CFP Video Productions Inc, pg 823
Listen & Live Audio Inc, pg 923
Optisonics Productions, pg 965
Bill Quinn Productions, pg 989
Suede Interactive, pg 1027

NEW MEXICO

Michael Dunn Productions, pg 853
Uncharted Country Publishing, pg 1048

NEW YORK

Avekta Productions Inc, pg 798
Broad Street Inc, pg 812
C2 Imaging LLC, pg 841
Digital Force, pg 847
HarperAudio, pg 885
HB-Content, pg 886
Hello World Communications, pg 888
Kamen Entertainment Group Inc, pg 908
Madison Square Garden, pg 927
Jack Morton Worldwide, pg 946
MRG Productions Inc, pg 948
MRY, pg 949
New York Audio Productions, pg 956
Shelly Palmer Production, pg 968
Penguin Audiobooks, pg 971
Synaptic Digital, pg 1030
Zelman Studios Ltd, pg 1073

NORTH CAROLINA

Pat Appleson Studios Inc, pg 788
MRN Radio, pg 948

OHIO

Creative Technology, pg 838
EDR Media LLC, pg 857
R&B Communications Inc, pg 991
VGI Productions, pg 1053

OKLAHOMA

Piper Media Services Inc, pg 976

OREGON

InterVision Media, pg 902
Odyssey Productions Inc, pg 961

PENNSYLVANIA

FMP Media Solutions Inc, pg 870
Innovision Media Group, pg 899
Production Masters Inc (PMI), pg 984

RHODE ISLAND

Sound-FX-Design, pg 1017

TENNESSEE

Continental Film, pg 835
Marine Geographic, pg 931
Russ Sturgeon Productions/RSVP, pg 1027

TEXAS

Epic Software Group Inc, pg 862
The Music Bakery, pg 950
Omega Productions, pg 962
Oncourt Offcourt Ltd, pg 963
The Sound Lab Inc, pg 1017
Sound Works, pg 1018
Tropikal Productions, pg 1045

VERMONT

Trafalgar Square Books, pg 1043

VIRGINIA

CACI Productions Group, pg 816
Lion Recording Services Inc, pg 922
Metro Productions, pg 939

WEST VIRGINIA

Blackwater Video Productions, pg 808

WISCONSIN

5th Floor Recording Co, pg 867
Watts Communications Inc, pg 1062
Wisconsin Public Television, pg 1068

WYOMING

Bridger Productions Inc, pg 812

ALBERTA

Black Media Works, pg 808
Global Television Station, pg 879

ONTARIO

ADS Media, pg 777

QUEBEC

Kerrigan Productions Inc, pg 910

Sports Program Rentals

CALIFORNIA

Direct Cinema Ltd Inc, pg 848

MICHIGAN

Digi Sign Design LLC, pg 847

NEW HAMPSHIRE

Chip Taylor Communications LLC, pg 1032

NEW JERSEY

Listen & Live Audio Inc, pg 923

PENNSYLVANIA

Penn State University MediaTech, pg 972

UTAH

Webb Audio Visual Communication, pg 1063

ONTARIO

Simply Audiobooks, pg 1011

Technical Research Program Distributors

CALIFORNIA

Digital Media West, pg 847
Maximus Media Inc, pg 934
QRS Software Services, pg 988

DISTRICT OF COLUMBIA

American Chemical Society (ACS), pg 784

FLORIDA

Capital Communications Inc, pg 819

ILLINOIS

CCH Continuing Education, pg 821

MASSACHUSETTS

Emergency Film Group, pg 860
Penfield Productions Ltd, pg 971

MICHIGAN

Digi Sign Design LLC, pg 847

NEW HAMPSHIRE

Chip Taylor Communications LLC, pg 1032

NEW YORK

MRG Productions Inc, pg 948
Synaptic Digital, pg 1030

OREGON

Norman Beerger Productions, pg 958

Technical Research Program Producers

CALIFORNIA

Big Door, pg 807
Creative Media Recording, pg 838
Custom Video Productions Inc, pg 841
Design Media, pg 845
Havas Edge, pg 885
Lynch Communications, pg 926
QRS Software Services, pg 988
Still N'Motion, pg 1025
Studio 132, pg 1027
Tele-Video Production Services (TVPS), pg 1036
Timestream Video, pg 1041
Total Media Group, pg 1042
WalkerVision Interarts, pg 1061

COLORADO

Daylight Productions & Rentals, pg 844
Flashback Media Productions, pg 869

CONNECTICUT

EagleVision Inc, pg 855

DISTRICT OF COLUMBIA

American Chemical Society (ACS), pg 784

FLORIDA

Capital Communications Inc, pg 819
LHV Audio Services, pg 919
Sunfire Communications Inc, pg 1028
Sunrise Studios, pg 1028
Top Hat Productions, pg 1042

GEORGIA

Guerrilla Productions LLC, pg 883

ILLINOIS

ABS Enterprises, pg 772
CCH Continuing Education, pg 821
Major Media Productions Inc, pg 929
The Pepper Group, pg 972
20/20 Communications Inc, pg 1047
Video Impressions, pg 1055

INDIANA

AVA Productions, pg 798

LOUISIANA

Louisiana State University Health Sciences Center - Shreveport, pg 925

MARYLAND

CPR MultiMedia Solutions, pg 837
CSPMedia.com, pg 840
The Cutting Corp, pg 841
dbF a Media Company, pg 844
Kramer Communications Video Production, pg 913

MASSACHUSETTS

Emergency Film Group, pg 860
Heliotrope Studios, pg 887
Labrecque Creative Sound, pg 915
Penfield Productions Ltd, pg 971
Soundtrack Recording Studios, pg 1018

MICHIGAN

Digi Sign Design LLC, pg 847
K&R All Media Productions Inc, pg 908
K&R's Recording Studios Inc, pg 908

MINNESOTA

Aggressive Records Audio Duplication LLC, pg 778
GMI Productions, pg 879

MISSOURI

Celebrities Productions, pg 822

MONTANA

North Country Media Group, pg 959

NEW HAMPSHIRE

Apertura, pg 788
Chip Taylor Communications LLC, pg 1032

NEW JERSEY

CFP Video Productions Inc, pg 823
Optisonics Productions, pg 965
Suede Interactive, pg 1027

NEW MEXICO

Michael Dunn Productions, pg 853

NEW YORK

Avekta Productions Inc, pg 798
Digital Force, pg 847
dM works, pg 849
Fingerpaint, pg 868
Kamen Entertainment Group Inc, pg 908
Jack Morton Worldwide, pg 946
MRG Productions Inc, pg 948
Shelly Palmer Production, pg 968
Split Image Productions, pg 1021
Synaptic Digital, pg 1030
Tiki Recording Studios Inc, pg 1040
Videograf, pg 1057
Zelman Studios Ltd, pg 1073

NORTH CAROLINA

Pat Appleson Studios Inc, pg 788
Trailblazer Studios®, pg 1043

OHIO

Creative Technology, pg 838
EDR Media LLC, pg 857
R&B Communications Inc, pg 991
Vista Color Imaging Inc, pg 1059

OKLAHOMA

Piper Media Services Inc, pg 976

OREGON

Ideascape Inc, pg 894
InterVision Media, pg 902
Norman Beerger Productions, pg 958

PENNSYLVANIA

Muderick Media, pg 949
Panta Rhei Media Inc, pg 968

RHODE ISLAND

Sound-FX-Design, pg 1017

TEXAS

James Loupas Associates Inc, pg 925
The Music Bakery, pg 950
Omega Productions, pg 962
Romar Learning, pg 999
The Sound Lab Inc, pg 1017
Texas Heart Institute Visual Communication Services, pg 1037

VIRGINIA

Lion Recording Services Inc, pg 922

WISCONSIN

5th Floor Recording Co, pg 867
USAV Group Inc, pg 1050
Wisconsin Public Television, pg 1068

WYOMING

Bridger Productions Inc, pg 812

ALBERTA

Global Television Station, pg 879

QUEBEC

Kerrigan Productions Inc, pg 910

Technical Research Program Rentals

MASSACHUSETTS

Emergency Film Group, pg 860

MICHIGAN

Digi Sign Design LLC, pg 847

NEW HAMPSHIRE

Chip Taylor Communications LLC, pg 1032

UTAH

Webb Audio Visual Communication, pg 1063

Test Commercial Distributors

CALIFORNIA

Digital Media West, pg 847
Maximus Media Inc, pg 934
QRS Software Services, pg 988

MASSACHUSETTS

Penfield Productions Ltd, pg 971

MICHIGAN

Digi Sign Design LLC, pg 847

NEVADA

DVDs4Less, pg 854

NEW YORK

HB-Content, pg 886
Janus Films Inc, pg 904
MRG Productions Inc, pg 948

NORTH CAROLINA

Baker & Taylor Inc, pg 801

TEXAS

TM Studios Inc, pg 1041

Test Commercial Producers

ARIZONA

Candee Productions Inc, pg 819

ARKANSAS

Live'N'Loud, pg 923

CALIFORNIA

A Go Go Films, pg 771
Big Door, pg 807
Concrete Images, pg 835
Creative Media Recording, pg 838
Custom Video Productions Inc, pg 841
Design Media, pg 845
Tom Donald Films, pg 850
Havas Edge, pg 885
KTVU-Retail Services, pg 914
Lynch Communications, pg 926
Maximus Media Inc, pg 934
Media Magic, pg 937
QRS Software Services, pg 988
Steve Shapiro Music, pg 1008
Still N'Motion, pg 1025
Studio 132, pg 1027
Tele-Video Production Services (TVPS), pg 1036
Total Media Group, pg 1042
Video Resources Inc, pg 1056
Webster Communications, pg 1063
Zamacona Productions, pg 1073

COLORADO

Tim Cissell Music, pg 828
Flashback Media Productions, pg 869

CONNECTICUT

EagleVision Inc, pg 855
P&P Studios Inc, pg 968

FLORIDA

Blackburst Entertainment, pg 808
Eastern Video, pg 856
Home Shopping Network (HSN), pg 890
LHV Audio Services, pg 919
Sunfire Communications Inc, pg 1028
Sunrise Studios, pg 1028
Top Hat Productions, pg 1042
Tricycle Studios, pg 1044

GEORGIA

Guerrilla Productions LLC, pg 883
Sirius Images Corp dba WaveGuide Studios, pg 1012

PROGRAMMING — AUDIO

Test Commercial Producers (continued)

IDAHO

Wide Eye Productions, pg 1066

ILLINOIS

ABS Enterprises, pg 772
Chicago Satellite & Video, pg 825
The Pepper Group, pg 972
Steven Samler Music & Sound, pg 1002
Video Impressions, pg 1055

INDIANA

AVA Productions, pg 798

KANSAS

KAKE-TV, pg 907

MAINE

Serendipity Recordings, pg 1007

MARYLAND

CPR MultiMedia Solutions, pg 837
CSPMedia.com, pg 840
The Cutting Corp, pg 841
dbF a Media Company, pg 844
The Image Generators, pg 895

MASSACHUSETTS

Emergency Film Group, pg 860
Labrecque Creative Sound, pg 915
Penfield Productions Ltd, pg 971
Soundtrack Recording Studios, pg 1018

MICHIGAN

The Brookwood Studio Inc, pg 814
Digi Sign Design LLC, pg 847
K&R All Media Productions Inc, pg 908
K&R's Recording Studios Inc, pg 908

MINNESOTA

Aggressive Records Audio Duplication LLC, pg 778
GMI Productions, pg 879
Jamieson & Associates Inc, pg 904

MISSOURI

Celebrities Productions, pg 822
Fambrough & Associates Inc, pg 865
Hardcastle Films & Video, pg 885

MONTANA

North Country Media Group, pg 959

NEVADA

DVDs4Less, pg 854

NEW JERSEY

CFP Video Productions Inc, pg 823
Euro-Pacific Film & Video Productions Inc, pg 863
Optisonics Productions, pg 965
Bill Quinn Productions, pg 989
Suede Interactive, pg 1027

NEW YORK

Avekta Productions Inc, pg 798
BioMedia Inc, pg 807
Thomas Craven Film Corp, pg 837
Digital Force, pg 847
dM works, pg 849
HB-Content, pg 886
Hello World Communications, pg 888
Icontent, pg 893
Kamen Entertainment Group Inc, pg 908
Mood Creations Ltd, pg 946
Jack Morton Worldwide, pg 946
MRG Productions Inc, pg 948
MRY, pg 949
The Napoleon Group, pg 952
No Soap Productions, pg 957
Shelly Palmer Production, pg 968
Pat Kogan Productions Inc, pg 970
David Rapkin Audio Production, pg 991
Shadow Pictures Inc, pg 1007
Elliot Sokolov Music, pg 1015
Split Image Productions, pg 1021
Suggs Media Productions Inc, pg 1028
Zelman Studios Ltd, pg 1073

NORTH CAROLINA

2BruceStudio, pg 1047

OHIO

Advent Media Inc, pg 778
Creative Technology, pg 838
EDR Media LLC, pg 857
Musicol Recording, pg 951
Take 1 Media Services, pg 1031
Vista Color Imaging Inc, pg 1059

OKLAHOMA

Piper Media Services Inc, pg 976

PENNSYLVANIA

Forge Recording LLC, pg 871
Innovision Media Group, pg 899
JPL, pg 906
The Videohouse Inc, pg 1057

RHODE ISLAND

Sound-FX-Design, pg 1017

SOUTH CAROLINA

Stages Video Productions, pg 1023

TEXAS

Audiomoxie®, pg 796
Communication Arts Multimedia Inc, pg 832
The Music Bakery, pg 950
Omega Productions, pg 962
The Sound Lab Inc, pg 1017
South Coast Film & Video, pg 1019
Stage Directions, pg 1022
TM Studios Inc, pg 1041

VIRGINIA

Limelight Communications Inc, pg 921
Lion Recording Services Inc, pg 922
Metro Productions, pg 939
Rocktown Media, pg 998
Studio Center Corp, pg 1026

WISCONSIN

5th Floor Recording Co, pg 867
Video Wisconsin Inc, pg 1056

WYOMING

Bridger Productions Inc, pg 812

ALBERTA

Global Television Station, pg 879

ONTARIO

DebsVoice, pg 844
VO2 Mix Studios, pg 1060

QUEBEC

Kerrigan Productions Inc, pg 910

Test Commercial Rentals

MICHIGAN

Digi Sign Design LLC, pg 847

UTAH

Webb Audio Visual Communication, pg 1063

Training Program Distributors

ARIZONA

Tom Hopkins International Inc, pg 891
Video Learning Library, pg 1055

CALIFORNIA

California Language Laboratories, pg 817
Golden State Dance Teachers Association (GSDTA), pg 880
Jossey-Bass, pg 906
Learning Communications LLC, pg 917
Maximus Media Inc, pg 934
Medcom Inc, pg 936
ODC Publishing, pg 961
People Skills International, pg 972
Captain J Charles Plumb, pg 977
QRS Software Services, pg 988
SevenStar Communications, pg 1007
University of Southern California, pg 1050
The Wine Appreciation Guild Ltd, pg 1067

COLORADO

National Institute for Trial Advocacy (NITA), pg 953

CONNECTICUT

Crossroads Video, pg 840
Gold Line/TEF, pg 880

FLORIDA

Bisk Education, pg 808
Capital Communications Inc, pg 819
Psychological Assessment Resources Inc (PAR), pg 987

HAWAII

Source School of Tantra Yoga Inc, pg 1019

ILLINOIS

CCH Continuing Education, pg 821
CCore Media Inc, pg 821
Film Ideas, pg 867
Liturgy Training Publications, pg 923
National Safety Council (NSC), pg 953
Nightingale-Conant Corp, pg 957

MARYLAND

MMI Corp, pg 944

MASSACHUSETTS

Emergency Film Group, pg 860
Penfield Productions Ltd, pg 971

MICHIGAN

Digi Sign Design LLC, pg 847

MINNESOTA

Whole Person Associates Inc, pg 1066

NEVADA

DVDs4Less, pg 854

NEW HAMPSHIRE

Chip Taylor Communications LLC, pg 1032

NEW MEXICO

National Information Center for Educational Media (NICEM)/ MediaSleuth, pg 952
Uncharted Country Publishing, pg 1048

NEW YORK

Albert Ellis Institute (AEI), pg 859
Guidance Associates Inc Center for Humanities, pg 883
Guilford Publications, pg 883
HB-Content, pg 886
Homespun Video, pg 890
MRG Productions Inc, pg 948
TeleTime Productions, pg 1036

NORTH CAROLINA

Baker & Taylor Inc, pg 801
Eli Research Group, pg 859
Vide-O-Go/That's Infotainment!, pg 1054

OHIO

Speakers Unlimited, pg 1020

OREGON

InterVision Media, pg 902
The Keyboard Workshop, pg 910

PENNSYLVANIA

American Law Institute Continuing Legal Education (ALICLE), pg 784
FMP Media Solutions Inc, pg 870
TRC Interactive Inc, pg 1044

SOUTH CAROLINA

DaviSound, pg 843

TENNESSEE

American Blackguard Inc, pg 784
Randall House Publications, pg 991
Spring Arbor Distributors, pg 1022

Training Program Producers

PROGRAMMING — AUDIO

Training Program Producers (continued)

OKLAHOMA

Piper Media Services Inc, pg 976

OREGON

A KTVA Production LLC, pg 771
ERA Learning, pg 862
Ideascape Inc, pg 894
InterVision Media, pg 902
The Keyboard Workshop, pg 910

PENNSYLVANIA

American Law Institute Continuing Legal Education (ALICLE), pg 784
Audio Visual Communications Inc, pg 795
FMP Media Solutions Inc, pg 870
Innovision Media Group, pg 899
JPL, pg 906
Muderick Media, pg 949
Newtown Psychological Center, pg 957
Panta Rhei Media Inc, pg 968
Production Masters Inc (PMI), pg 984
Scala Inc, pg 1003
The Videohouse Inc, pg 1057

RHODE ISLAND

Sound-FX-Design, pg 1017

SOUTH CAROLINA

DaviSound, pg 843
Stages Video Productions, pg 1023
Venture Media, pg 1052

TENNESSEE

American Blackguard Inc, pg 784
Continental Film, pg 835
Memphis Communications Corp, pg 938
Spring Arbor Distributors, pg 1022
Stage Post, pg 1022

TEXAS

AMA Nystrom Printing/Finishing, pg 783
Audiomoxie®, pg 796
Biway Media, pg 808
Dykeman Associates Inc, pg 854
The Editing Co, pg 857
First Group Communications Inc, pg 868
InterCom, pg 900
The Music Bakery, pg 950
Omega Productions, pg 962
Romar Learning, pg 999
The Sound Lab Inc, pg 1017
Sound Works, pg 1018
South Coast Film & Video, pg 1019
Stage Directions, pg 1022
Telemetrics International, pg 1036
Writer's AudioShop/Davenport Productions, pg 1070
The Yesterday USA Radio Networks, pg 1072

VERMONT

Dialect Accent Specialists Inc, pg 846

VIRGINIA

CACI Productions Group, pg 816
Limelight Communications Inc, pg 921
Lion Recording Services Inc, pg 922
Metro Productions, pg 939
National Media Services Inc, pg 953
Rocktown Media, pg 998
Studio Center Corp, pg 1026

WASHINGTON

Kostov Productions, pg 913
Pacific Multimedia Inc, pg 967

WISCONSIN

5th Floor Recording Co, pg 867
Meridian Studios, pg 939
USAV Group Inc, pg 1050
Video Wisconsin Inc, pg 1056
Watts Communications Inc, pg 1062
Wisconsin Public Television, pg 1068

WYOMING

Bridger Productions Inc, pg 812

ALBERTA

Black Media Works, pg 808
Global Television Station, pg 879

BRITISH COLUMBIA

Thompson Rivers University Open Learning, pg 1039

ONTARIO

ADS Media, pg 777
DebsVoice, pg 844
GAPC (General Assembly Production Centre), pg 875
JFB Communications, pg 905
Purefire Communications Inc, pg 987
VO2 Mix Studios, pg 1060

QUEBEC

Kerrigan Productions Inc, pg 910

Training Program Rentals

CALIFORNIA

Jossey-Bass, pg 906
Medcom Inc, pg 936
University of Southern California, pg 1050

MASSACHUSETTS

Emergency Film Group, pg 860

MICHIGAN

Digi Sign Design LLC, pg 847

NEW HAMPSHIRE

Chip Taylor Communications LLC, pg 1032

OREGON

The Keyboard Workshop, pg 910

TEXAS

InterCom, pg 900

UTAH

Webb Audio Visual Communication, pg 1063

Travelog Distributors

ARIZONA

Video Learning Library, pg 1055

CALIFORNIA

Digital Media West, pg 847
Jaguar Distribution Corp, pg 903
Maximus Media Inc, pg 934
QRS Software Services, pg 988

CONNECTICUT

EagleVision Inc, pg 855

FLORIDA

Capital Communications Inc, pg 819

MASSACHUSETTS

Penfield Productions Ltd, pg 971

MICHIGAN

Digi Sign Design LLC, pg 847

NEW HAMPSHIRE

Chip Taylor Communications LLC, pg 1032

NEW YORK

Irish Music Corp, pg 902
MRG Productions Inc, pg 948

NORTH CAROLINA

Vide-O-Go/That's Infotainment!, pg 1054

OREGON

Norman Beerger Productions, pg 958

PENNSYLVANIA

FMP Media Solutions Inc, pg 870

SOUTH CAROLINA

DaviSound, pg 843

TENNESSEE

American Blackguard Inc, pg 784
Marine Geographic, pg 931
Spring Arbor Distributors, pg 1022

TEXAS

Educational Video Network, pg 857

VIRGINIA

CACI Productions Group, pg 816

ONTARIO

Canadian Learning Co Inc, pg 818

Travelog Producers

ARIZONA

Video Learning Library, pg 1055

CALIFORNIA

The Banquet Sound Studios, pg 802
Big Door, pg 807
Dogma Studios, pg 850
Gold Standard Productions, pg 880
Jaguar Distribution Corp, pg 903
KABA Audio Productions, pg 907
Lynch Communications, pg 926
On-Trax Inc, pg 963
PM Productions, pg 977
Producers Group Ltd, pg 983
QRS Software Services, pg 988
SBS Productions, pg 1003
Studio 132, pg 1027
Total Media Group, pg 1042
WalkerVision Interarts, pg 1061
Wavemaker Media Design, pg 1062
Webster Communications, pg 1063

COLORADO

Apogee Communications Group, pg 788
Rocky Mountain Audio/Video Productions Inc, pg 998
Tatum Video, pg 1032

CONNECTICUT

EagleVision Inc, pg 855
The Gary-Paul Agency, pg 875

FLORIDA

Blackburst Entertainment, pg 808
Eastern Video, pg 856
LHV Audio Services, pg 919
Sunfire Communications Inc, pg 1028
Top Hat Productions, pg 1042

GEORGIA

COMPRO Productions Inc, pg 834
Guerrilla Productions LLC, pg 883
Symmes Systems, pg 1030

HAWAII

Source School of Tantra Yoga Inc, pg 1019

IDAHO

Wide Eye Productions, pg 1066

ILLINOIS

Audio Visual Services Corp, pg 796
The Pepper Group, pg 972
PSAV® Presentation Services (Hotel Services Division), pg 987
Steven Samler Music & Sound, pg 1002
Video Impressions, pg 1055

INDIANA

AVA Productions, pg 798
Digital Rain LLC, pg 847

KANSAS

Chapman Recording & Mastering, pg 824

MARYLAND

CPR MultiMedia Solutions, pg 837
CSPMedia.com, pg 840
The Cutting Corp, pg 841
dbF a Media Company, pg 844
The Image Generators, pg 895

Travelog Rentals

Vocational Program Distributors

Vocational Program Producers

PROGRAMMING — AUDIO

Vocational Program Producers (continued)

Vocational Program Rentals

PROGRAMMING — AUDIO/VISUAL

Business Program Distributors

ARIZONA

Video Learning Library, pg 1055

CALIFORNIA

Crystal Pyramid Productions™, pg 840
Deja View Video, pg 845
Discovery Education - Los Angeles, pg 848
Bruce Goldberg Inc, pg 880
Griggs Productions Inc, pg 882
Kantola Productions LLC, pg 908
New & Unique Videos™, pg 955
Melvin Powers Television Marketing, pg 979
TMW Media Group, pg 1041
Westlake Recording Studios, pg 1064

COLORADO

Vital Learning LLC, pg 1060

CONNECTICUT

Book Marketing Works LLC, pg 810

FLORIDA

ACE Video Resources Software, pg 774
Allegro Productions Inc, pg 781
Capital Communications Inc, pg 819

GEORGIA

Convergent Media Systems, pg 836
School Media Associates LLC, pg 1004
Thompson-Mitchell & Associates Inc, pg 1039

HAWAII

Media Bridge Gamekids, pg 936

ILLINOIS

CCH Continuing Education, pg 821
CCH Inc, A Wolters Kluwer business, pg 821
CCore Media Inc, pg 821
Cool-Lux, pg 836
Film Ideas, pg 867
1st Financial Training Services Inc, pg 868

KENTUCKY

KET The Kentucky Network, pg 910

MASSACHUSETTS

Preston Productions Inc, pg 981

MICHIGAN

Digi Sign Design LLC, pg 847
Emery-Pratt Co, pg 860
MSU Technologies, pg 949

MISSOURI

The Phoenix Learning Group Inc, pg 974

NEW HAMPSHIRE

Frey Scientific, pg 873
Chip Taylor Communications LLC, pg 1032

NEW JERSEY

Euro-Pacific Film & Video Productions Inc, pg 863

NEW MEXICO

National Information Center for Educational Media (NICEM)/MediaSleuth, pg 952

NEW YORK

Fanlight Productions, pg 865
Films for the Humanities & Sciences, pg 868
Films Media Group, pg 868
Guidance Associates Inc Center for Humanities, pg 883
HB-Content, pg 886
Meridian Education Corp, pg 939
MRG Productions Inc, pg 948
Practising Law Institute, pg 980
Shopware, pg 1009
TeleTime Productions, pg 1036

NORTH CAROLINA

Vide-O-Go/That's Infotainment!, pg 1054

OHIO

South-Western Publishing Co, pg 1019

PENNSYLVANIA

FMP Media Solutions Inc, pg 870

SOUTH CAROLINA

DaviSound, pg 843

TENNESSEE

Zion Music Group, pg 1074

TEXAS

Educational Video Network, pg 857
The Samuels Co, pg 1002
Stage Directions, pg 1022

VERMONT

Wilson McLeran Inc, pg 1067

VIRGINIA

Design & Production Inc, pg 845
PBS Video, pg 970

ONTARIO

BBC Worldwide Canada Ltd, pg 803
Canadian Learning Co Inc, pg 818
Kineticvideo.com, pg 911

Business Program Producers

ALABAMA

AVS Media Group, pg 800
Media Visions Inc, pg 937

ARIZONA

Aardvark Productions LLC, pg 772
Candee Productions Inc, pg 819
Creative Backstage, pg 838
Video Learning Library, pg 1055

ARKANSAS

White Diamond Productions, pg 1065

CALIFORNIA

Animax, pg 787
Crystal Pyramid Productions™, pg 840
Design Media, pg 845
Direct Images Interactive Inc, pg 848
Discovery Education - Los Angeles, pg 848
Dolphin MultiMedia Inc, pg 850
imageReal Pictures LLC, pg 896
KABA Audio Productions, pg 907
Kantola Productions LLC, pg 908
Lynch Communications, pg 926
Main Street Media Inc, pg 929
Media Magic, pg 937
The Media Staff Inc, pg 937
New Circuit Films LLC, pg 955
Panorama Productions, pg 968
PM Productions, pg 977
SBS Productions, pg 1003
SNAP, pg 1014
Tam Communications Inc, pg 1031
TMW Media Group, pg 1041
Total Media Group, pg 1042
Vineyard Video & Photography, pg 1058
Wavemaker Media Design, pg 1062
Webster Communications, pg 1063
West Coast Projections Inc, pg 1063

COLORADO

Paul L Anderson Productions Inc, pg 786
Daylight Productions & Rentals, pg 844
Flashback Media Productions, pg 869
Vital Learning LLC, pg 1060

CONNECTICUT

Applebox Studio, pg 788
Broadcast Video Productions LLC, pg 813
MCC Films, pg 935
New London Media, pg 956

DISTRICT OF COLUMBIA

O'Keefe Communications Inc, pg 961

FLORIDA

Accel Video Productions, pg 773
ACE Video Resources Software, pg 774
Allegro Productions Inc, pg 781
Capital Communications Inc, pg 819
Communications Concepts Inc (CCI), pg 833
Gulf Coast Audio Visual Producers Inc, pg 883
Sunfire Communications Inc, pg 1028
Tricycle Studios, pg 1044
Universal Studios Florida® Production Group, pg 1049

GEORGIA

Beachwood Productions, pg 804
Continental Film & Video, pg 835
Guerrilla Productions LLC, pg 883
Myriad Productions, pg 951

HAWAII

Hyperspective Studios Inc, pg 893
Media Bridge Gamekids, pg 936

ILLINOIS

Airways Digital Media, pg 779
Audio Visual Services Corp, pg 796
CCH Continuing Education, pg 821
CCH Inc, A Wolters Kluwer business, pg 821
CCore Media Inc, pg 821
Chicago Satellite & Video, pg 825
Comtech Multimedia Marketing, pg 834
Cresta Creative, pg 839
1st Financial Training Services Inc, pg 868
Major Media Productions Inc, pg 929
Manning Productions, pg 930
The Pepper Group, pg 972
PSAV® Presentation Services (Hotel Services Division), pg 987
Roadworthy Image Magnification, pg 998
SCI Television Productions LLC, pg 1004
Sparkfactor, pg 1019
20/20 Communications Inc, pg 1047
Video Impressions, pg 1055

INDIANA

AVA Productions, pg 798
Digital Rain LLC, pg 847

KANSAS

Chapman Recording & Mastering, pg 824

KENTUCKY

KET The Kentucky Network, pg 910

LOUISIANA

Digital FX Inc, pg 847
Disk Productions, pg 849

MARYLAND

The Cutting Corp, pg 841
dbF a Media Company, pg 844
The Image Generators, pg 895
Lehigh Phoenix™, pg 918
Mobile-Video Productions Inc, pg 944

MASSACHUSETTS

CommCreative, pg 832
Cramer Productions, pg 837
Soundtrack Recording Studios, pg 1018
TVN-The Video Network, pg 1046
WGBH Production Group, pg 1065

MICHIGAN

Benjamin Creative Productions, pg 805
Digi Sign Design LLC, pg 847
K&R All Media Productions Inc, pg 908
K&R's Recording Studios Inc, pg 908
Universal Images, pg 1049

PROGRAMMING — AUDIO/VISUAL

Business Program Producers (continued)

MINNESOTA

Live Spark Inc, pg 923
Master Communications Group, pg 933
Media Loft Inc, pg 937
MultiMedia, pg 950

MONTANA

North Country Media Group, pg 959

NEBRASKA

Dog & Pony Productions Inc, pg 850

NEVADA

HDTV Productions Inc, pg 886
JCS Video Productions, pg 904

NEW HAMPSHIRE

Apertura, pg 788
Chip Taylor Communications LLC, pg 1032

NEW JERSEY

Broadcast Center Studios, pg 813
Laurel Video Productions, pg 916
Milgrom Productions, pg 943
Optisonics Productions, pg 965
Outside The Box Interactive LLC, pg 966
TimeSteps Productions Inc, pg 1041

NEW MEXICO

Michael Dunn Productions, pg 853

NEW YORK

Blue Barn Pictures Inc, pg 809
Broad Street Inc, pg 812
De Nonno Productions Inc (DPI), pg 844
dM works, pg 849
Duggal Visual Solutions, pg 853
Fanlight Productions, pg 865
Films Media Group, pg 868
Karen Frankel Productions, pg 872
Guidance Associates Inc Center for Humanities, pg 883
Havas Worldwide, pg 886
HB-Content, pg 886
Hello World Communications, pg 888
Image Zone Inc, pg 896
Ketchum Pleon Change, pg 910
Long Island Video Enterprises Live Inc, pg 924
Neal Marshad Productions, pg 931
Jack Morton Worldwide, pg 946
MRG Productions Inc, pg 948
MRY, pg 949
News Broadcast Network, pg 956
Northeast Video Productions Inc, pg 959
Shelly Palmer Production, pg 968
Practising Law Institute, pg 980
Suggs Media Productions Inc, pg 1028
TBA Global Events, pg 1032
Total Impact Multimedia Group Ltd, pg 1042
Zelman Studios Ltd, pg 1073

NORTH CAROLINA

Pat Appleson Studios Inc, pg 788
The Communications Group Inc, pg 833
Image Associates Inc, pg 894
Kino Mountain Productions LLC, pg 911
LCW Productions LLC, pg 917
Moving Pictures, pg 948
Sinclair Institute, pg 1012

OHIO

Advent Media Inc, pg 778
Creative Technology, pg 838
MainSail Production Services Inc, pg 929
R&B Communications Inc, pg 991
South-Western Publishing Co, pg 1019
Take 1 Media Services, pg 1031
Vista Color Imaging Inc, pg 1059

OREGON

A KTVA Production LLC, pg 771
ERA Learning, pg 862
Ideascape Inc, pg 894
Odyssey Productions Inc, pg 961
Rex, pg 995

PENNSYLVANIA

AccuWeather Inc, pg 774
AiH Group Inc, pg 779
Audio Visual Communications Inc, pg 795
Bang Pictures, pg 802
FMP Media Solutions Inc, pg 870
JPL, pg 906
Main Point Productions, pg 929
Muderick Media, pg 949
New Horizons Computer Learning Centers Inc, pg 955
Panta Rhei Media Inc, pg 968
Pemcor LLC, pg 971
Production Masters Inc (PMI), pg 984

RHODE ISLAND

Sound-FX-Design, pg 1017

SOUTH CAROLINA

DaviSound, pg 843

TENNESSEE

Continental Film, pg 835
Running Pony Productions LLC, pg 1000
Russ Sturgeon Productions/RSVP, pg 1027
WKPT-TV, pg 1068

TEXAS

Biway Media, pg 808
Educational Video Network, pg 857
Epic Software Group Inc, pg 862
Mediaforce Productions, pg 937
The Samuels Co, pg 1002
South Coast Film & Video, pg 1019
Stage Directions, pg 1022
Stockyard Photos/Jim Olive Photography, pg 1025
Tropikal Productions, pg 1045

VERMONT

Wilson McLeran Inc, pg 1067

VIRGINIA

CALIBRE, pg 816
D&B Television & Video Productions Inc, pg 842
Lion Recording Services Inc, pg 922
Metro Productions, pg 939

WASHINGTON

Adams Creative & Production Services, pg 775
Kostov Productions, pg 913
Laser Fantasy/HECK Industries/Photon Manufacturing, pg 916

WEST VIRGINIA

Altruist Media LLC, pg 783

WISCONSIN

Audio Visual of Milwaukee Inc, pg 795
AVS Group, pg 800
Rucinski & Reetz Communications LLC, pg 1000
USAV Group Inc, pg 1050
Video Wisconsin Inc, pg 1056
Watts Communications Inc, pg 1062
Wisconsin Public Television, pg 1068

WYOMING

Bridger Productions Inc, pg 812

ALBERTA

Black Media Works, pg 808

BRITISH COLUMBIA

West Eagle Films Inc, pg 1064

NEWFOUNDLAND AND LABRADOR

Vidcraft Productions Ltd, pg 1054

ONTARIO

BBC Worldwide Canada Ltd, pg 803
DebsVoice, pg 844
JFB Communications, pg 905
Mediaimage Communications Group, pg 937

QUEBEC

Kerrigan Productions Inc, pg 910

Business Program Rentals

GEORGIA

Convergent Media Systems, pg 836
ON Event Services, pg 963

ILLINOIS

1st Financial Training Services Inc, pg 868

MASSACHUSETTS

Preston Productions Inc, pg 981

MICHIGAN

Digi Sign Design LLC, pg 847

NEW HAMPSHIRE

Chip Taylor Communications LLC, pg 1032

NEW JERSEY

Euro-Pacific Film & Video Productions Inc, pg 863

NEW YORK

Historic Films, pg 889
TBA Global Events, pg 1032

TEXAS

Stage Directions, pg 1022

UTAH

Webb Audio Visual Communication, pg 1063

Chart Distributors

CALIFORNIA

Ametron Audio/Video, pg 785
Astronomical Society of the Pacific, pg 792
Health Education Services, pg 887
Medcom Inc, pg 936
QRS Software Services, pg 988
Social Studies School Service, pg 1015
The Writing Co, pg 1070

COLORADO

National Teaching Aids Inc, pg 953

FLORIDA

Gulf Coast Audio Visual Producers Inc, pg 883
Photomart Cine-Video Inc, pg 975
Psychological Assessment Resources Inc (PAR), pg 987

GEORGIA

School Media Associates LLC, pg 1004

ILLINOIS

CCore Media Inc, pg 821

INDIANA

Herff Jones | Nystrom, pg 888

MAINE

Headlight Audio Visual Inc, pg 887

MARYLAND

MMI Corp, pg 944
Nicholas P Pipino Associates Inc, pg 976

NEW HAMPSHIRE

Frey Scientific, pg 873

NEW JERSEY

A W Peller & Associates Inc, pg 971

NORTH CAROLINA

Carolina Biological Supply Co, pg 820

OHIO

South-Western Publishing Co, pg 1019

OREGON

The Keyboard Workshop, pg 910

PENNSYLVANIA

AccuWeather Inc, pg 774

SOUTH CAROLINA

BJU Press, pg 808

TENNESSEE

Randall House Publications, pg 991

TEXAS

Audio Visual Technologies Group, pg 796
Endtime Inc, pg 861

WISCONSIN

Knowledge Unlimited Inc, pg 912
School Specialty Inc, pg 1004

Chart Producers

CALIFORNIA

Dolphin MultiMedia Inc, pg 850
Geddes Productions LLC, pg 876
Lynch Communications, pg 926
Panorama Productions, pg 968
QRS Software Services, pg 988
Total Media Group, pg 1042
The Wine Appreciation Guild Ltd, pg 1067

COLORADO

National Teaching Aids Inc, pg 953
Starwest Productions, pg 1024
Stretching Inc, pg 1026

CONNECTICUT

Broadcast Video Productions LLC, pg 813

FLORIDA

Gulf Coast Audio Visual Producers Inc, pg 883
Tricycle Studios, pg 1044

GEORGIA

Guerrilla Productions LLC, pg 883
Imagers, pg 896
Symmes Systems, pg 1030

ILLINOIS

Cresta Creative, pg 839
LightCraft Graphics Inc, pg 920
Rand McNally Education, pg 991

INDIANA

Bright Ideas Creative Services, pg 812
Herff Jones | Nystrom, pg 888
OMNI Productions, pg 962

IOWA

The Production House, pg 984

KENTUCKY

National Geographic Learning, pg 952

LOUISIANA

Digital FX Inc, pg 847

MASSACHUSETTS

CommCreative, pg 832
TR Productions, pg 1043

MICHIGAN

K&R All Media Productions Inc, pg 908
K&R's Recording Studios Inc, pg 908

MINNESOTA

Aggressive Records Audio Duplication LLC, pg 778

MISSOURI

Celebrities Productions, pg 822
Switch, pg 1030

NEW HAMPSHIRE

Frey Scientific, pg 873

NEW JERSEY

Optisonics Productions, pg 965
Outside The Box Interactive LLC, pg 966

NEW YORK

Applause Learning Resources, pg 788
Blue Barn Pictures Inc, pg 809
Broad Street Inc, pg 812
SMP Digital Graphics, pg 1014

NORTH CAROLINA

Carolina Biological Supply Co, pg 820
World Class Learning Materials Inc, pg 1069

OHIO

Cuyahoga Community College Media Center, pg 841
South-Western Publishing Co, pg 1019
Take 1 Media Services, pg 1031
Vista Color Imaging Inc, pg 1059

OREGON

The Keyboard Workshop, pg 910

PENNSYLVANIA

AccuWeather Inc, pg 774
Kensington Falls Animation, pg 909

SOUTH CAROLINA

BJU Press, pg 808

TENNESSEE

WKPT-TV, pg 1068

TEXAS

Endtime Inc, pg 861
Romar Learning, pg 999

VIRGINIA

Advance Concepts Inc, pg 777
Blair Inc, pg 809
CALIBRE, pg 816

WASHINGTON

Kostov Productions, pg 913

WISCONSIN

USAV Group Inc, pg 1050

Chart Rentals

CALIFORNIA

Ametron Audio/Video, pg 785

COLORADO

Spectrum Audio Visual Services, pg 1020

MAINE

Headlight Audio Visual Inc, pg 887

MISSOURI

Show-Me Audio-Visual, pg 1009

NEW JERSEY

PLS Staging, pg 977
Video Corporation of America (VCA), pg 1055

NORTH CAROLINA

Special Event Services, pg 1020

Children's Program Distributors

ARIZONA

Video Learning Library, pg 1055

CALIFORNIA

Astronomical Society of the Pacific, pg 792
California Language Laboratories, pg 817
Crystal Productions, pg 840
Crystal Pyramid Productions™, pg 840
Discovery Education - Los Angeles, pg 848
Glenn Photo Supply, pg 878
Madera Video, pg 927
Main Street Media Inc, pg 929
MarVista Entertainment Inc, pg 933
monterey video, pg 946
Moose School Productions, pg 946
Music Rhapsody, pg 951
Music World/Vocal Power School, pg 951
New & Unique Videos™, pg 955
Rhythms Productions (Tom Thumb Music), pg 996
Sea Studios Foundation, pg 1005
TMW Media Group, pg 1041

COLORADO

Gaiam Inc, pg 875

CONNECTICUT

Weston Woods Studios Inc, pg 1064

FLORIDA

ACE Video Resources Software, pg 774
Allegro Productions Inc, pg 781
Capital Communications Inc, pg 819
Cifex Corp, pg 826

GEORGIA

School Media Associates LLC, pg 1004

HAWAII

Media Bridge Gamekids, pg 936

ILLINOIS

Discovery Education - Chicago, pg 848
Educational Insights, pg 857
Film Ideas, pg 867

INDIANA

Agency for Instructional Technology (AIT), pg 778
Herff Jones | Nystrom, pg 888
InterComm, pg 900

KENTUCKY

Horizon Films & Media LLC, pg 891
KET The Kentucky Network, pg 910
National Geographic Learning, pg 952

MAINE

Slim Goodbody Corp, pg 1013

MASSACHUSETTS

Cheng & Tsui Co, pg 824
Documentary Educational Resources Inc, pg 850
Pauline Books & Media, pg 970

MICHIGAN

Digi Sign Design LLC, pg 847
Emery-Pratt Co, pg 860
Meuninck's Media Methods Inc, pg 940

MISSOURI

Marsh Media, pg 931
Phoenix/BFA/Coronet, pg 974

NEW HAMPSHIRE

Chip Taylor Communications LLC, pg 1032

NEW JERSEY

Educational Impressions, pg 857
Lucerne Media, pg 925
A W Peller & Associates Inc, pg 971

NEW MEXICO

National Information Center for Educational Media (NICEM)/MediaSleuth, pg 952

NEW YORK

Brooklyn Botanic Garden, pg 814
The Bureau for At-Risk Youth, pg 815
De Nonno Productions Inc (DPI), pg 844
Educational Activities Inc, pg 857
Guidance Associates Inc Center for Humanities, pg 883
Hallel Communications, pg 884
Human Relations Media, pg 892
Janson Media, pg 904
Listening Library, pg 923
Live Oak Media, pg 923
MRG Productions Inc, pg 948
Random House Children's Books, pg 991
Select Media Inc, pg 1006
VIEW Inc (Video International Entertainment World Inc), pg 1058

PROGRAMMING — AUDIO/VISUAL

Children's Program Distributors (continued)

NORTH CAROLINA

Humanities Extension Publications, pg 892
Vide-O-Go/That's Infotainment!, pg 1054

OHIO

Alegra House Publishers, pg 780
Franciscan Media, pg 872
Treehaus Communications Inc, pg 1044

PENNSYLVANIA

Discovery Education - South Burlington, pg 848
Media Inc, pg 936

TENNESSEE

American Blackguard Inc, pg 784
National School Products, pg 953
Randall House Publications, pg 991
Spring Arbor Distributors, pg 1022

TEXAS

Educational Video Network, pg 857
Horizon Film + Video Productions, pg 891
Institute of Texan Cultures, pg 899
Marengo Films, pg 931

VIRGINIA

Design & Production Inc, pg 845
PBS Video, pg 970

WISCONSIN

Aylmer Press, pg 801

ONTARIO

BBC Worldwide Canada Ltd, pg 803
Broughton's Church Supplies, Religious Books & Gifts, pg 814
Canadian Learning Co Inc, pg 818
Canamedia Inc, pg 818
The Children's Book Store Distribution (CBSD), pg 825
Kineticvideo.com, pg 911
McIntyre Media Inc, pg 935

Children's Program Producers

ARIZONA

Aardvark Productions LLC, pg 772
Candee Productions Inc, pg 819

CALIFORNIA

Animax, pg 787
Crystal Productions, pg 840
Crystal Pyramid Productions™, pg 840
Discovery Education - Los Angeles, pg 848
Lynch Communications, pg 926
Main Street Media Inc, pg 929
Media Magic, pg 937
The Media Staff Inc, pg 937
Music Rhapsody, pg 951
Music World/Vocal Power School, pg 951
PM Productions, pg 977
Rhythms Productions (Tom Thumb Music), pg 996
Screen Door Entertainment Inc, pg 1005
Sea Studios Foundation, pg 1005
Tigar Hare Studios, pg 1040
TMW Media Group, pg 1041
Total Media Group, pg 1042
Vineyard Video & Photography, pg 1058
Wavemaker Media Design, pg 1062
Webster Communications, pg 1063

COLORADO

Flashback Media Productions, pg 869
Gaiam Inc, pg 875

CONNECTICUT

Applebox Studio, pg 788
Broadcast Video Productions LLC, pg 813
MCC Films, pg 935
Weston Woods Studios Inc, pg 1064

DISTRICT OF COLUMBIA

Hillmann & Carr Inc, pg 889

FLORIDA

Accel Video Productions, pg 773
ACE Video Resources Software, pg 774
Allegro Productions Inc, pg 781
Capital Communications Inc, pg 819
Sunfire Communications Inc, pg 1028
Tricycle Studios, pg 1044

GEORGIA

Beachwood Productions, pg 804
Guerrilla Productions LLC, pg 883

HAWAII

Hyperspective Studios Inc, pg 893
Media Bridge Gamekids, pg 936

ILLINOIS

Chicago Satellite & Video, pg 825
Discovery Education - Chicago, pg 848
Manning Productions, pg 930
The Pepper Group, pg 972
Roadworthy Image Magnification, pg 998
20/20 Communications Inc, pg 1047

INDIANA

Agency for Instructional Technology (AIT), pg 778
Digital Rain LLC, pg 847
Herff Jones | Nystrom, pg 888
InterComm, pg 900

KANSAS

Sagebrush Video Productions, pg 1001

KENTUCKY

Horizon Films & Media LLC, pg 891
KET The Kentucky Network, pg 910
National Geographic Learning, pg 952

LOUISIANA

Disk Productions, pg 849

MAINE

Slim Goodbody Corp, pg 1013

MARYLAND

The Cutting Corp, pg 841

MASSACHUSETTS

Documentary Educational Resources Inc, pg 850
MotionArt Studios, pg 947
Pauline Books & Media, pg 970
Soundtrack Recording Studios, pg 1018
WGBH Production Group, pg 1065

MICHIGAN

Blue Mouse Studio, pg 809
Digi Sign Design LLC, pg 847
K&R All Media Productions Inc, pg 908
K&R's Recording Studios Inc, pg 908

MISSOURI

Marsh Media, pg 931
Phoenix/BFA/Coronet, pg 974

MONTANA

North Country Media Group, pg 959

NEVADA

JCS Video Productions, pg 904

NEW HAMPSHIRE

Apertura, pg 788
Chip Taylor Communications LLC, pg 1032

NEW JERSEY

Educational Impressions, pg 857
Milgrom Productions, pg 943
Optisonics Productions, pg 965
Outside The Box Interactive LLC, pg 966

NEW YORK

Air Sea Land Productions Inc (ASL), pg 779
American History Workshop (NY) Inc, pg 784
Brooklyn Botanic Garden, pg 814
The Bureau for At-Risk Youth, pg 815
De Nonno Productions Inc (DPI), pg 844
Duggal Visual Solutions, pg 853
Educational Activities Inc, pg 857
Fanlight Productions, pg 865
Karen Frankel Productions, pg 872
Greyfalcon House, pg 882
Guidance Associates Inc Center for Humanities, pg 883
Hallel Communications, pg 884
Havas Worldwide, pg 886
Hello World Communications, pg 888
Human Relations Media, pg 892
Listening Library, pg 923
Live Oak Media, pg 923
Manhattan Center Studios Inc, pg 930
Neal Marshad Productions, pg 931
Jack Morton Worldwide, pg 946
MRG Productions Inc, pg 948
MRY, pg 949
Shelly Palmer Production, pg 968
Polestar Films & Associated Arts Ltd, pg 978
Random House Children's Books, pg 991
Spoken Arts Inc, pg 1021
VIEW Inc (Video International Entertainment World Inc), pg 1058
Zelman Studios Ltd, pg 1073

NORTH CAROLINA

Pat Appleson Studios Inc, pg 788
Humanities Extension Publications, pg 892
Kino Mountain Productions LLC, pg 911
LCW Productions LLC, pg 917
Moving Pictures, pg 948

OHIO

Advent Media Inc, pg 778
Alegra House Publishers, pg 780
Creative Technology, pg 838
Franciscan Media, pg 872
Lyon Video Inc, pg 927
MainSail Production Services Inc, pg 929
R&B Communications Inc, pg 991
Take 1 Media Services, pg 1031
Treehaus Communications Inc, pg 1044
Vista Color Imaging Inc, pg 1059

OREGON

Ideascape Inc, pg 894
Odyssey Productions Inc, pg 961

PENNSYLVANIA

AiH Group Inc, pg 779
Discovery Education - South Burlington, pg 848
Media Inc, pg 936
Production Masters Inc (PMI), pg 984

RHODE ISLAND

Sound-FX-Design, pg 1017

SOUTH CAROLINA

BJU Press, pg 808

TENNESSEE

American Blackguard Inc, pg 784
WKPT-TV, pg 1068

TEXAS

Biway Media, pg 808
Communication Arts Multimedia Inc, pg 832
Educational Video Network, pg 857
Epic Software Group Inc, pg 862
Horizon Film + Video Productions, pg 891
Institute of Texan Cultures, pg 899
Mediaforce Productions, pg 937
Tropikal Productions, pg 1045

VIRGINIA

D&B Television & Video Productions Inc, pg 842
Lion Recording Services Inc, pg 922
Metro Productions, pg 939

Children's Program Rentals

Current Event Program Distributors

Current Event Program Producers

PROGRAMMING — AUDIO/VISUAL

Current Event Program Producers (continued)

VIRGINIA

D&B Television & Video Productions Inc, pg 842
Lion Recording Services Inc, pg 922
Metro Productions, pg 939

WISCONSIN

Knowledge Unlimited Inc, pg 912
Rucinski & Reetz Communications LLC, pg 1000
USAV Group Inc, pg 1050
Wisconsin Public Television, pg 1068

WYOMING

Bridger Productions Inc, pg 812

ALBERTA

Black Media Works, pg 808

BRITISH COLUMBIA

West Eagle Films Inc, pg 1064

ONTARIO

BBC Worldwide Canada Ltd, pg 803
Canamedia Inc, pg 818

QUEBEC

Kerrigan Productions Inc, pg 910

Current Event Program Rentals

ILLINOIS

Discovery Education - Chicago, pg 848

MICHIGAN

Digi Sign Design LLC, pg 847

NEW HAMPSHIRE

Chip Taylor Communications LLC, pg 1032

NEW YORK

Historic Films, pg 889
Select Media Inc, pg 1006

Documentary Distributors

ARIZONA

Video Learning Library, pg 1055

CALIFORNIA

Astronomical Society of the Pacific, pg 792
Les Blank Films Inc, pg 809
California/International Arts Foundation, pg 817
California Newsreel, pg 817
Crystal Pyramid Productions™, pg 840
Discovery Education - Los Angeles, pg 848
Glenn Photo Supply, pg 878
Madera Video, pg 927
MarVista Entertainment Inc, pg 933
monterey video, pg 946
New & Unique Videos™, pg 955
Point Lobos Productions, pg 977
Regent Press Publishers & Printers, pg 994
Sea Studios Foundation, pg 1005
TMW Media Group, pg 1041
The Wine Appreciation Guild Ltd, pg 1067

CONNECTICUT

Hartley Film Foundation, pg 885
Pictures of Record Inc, pg 975

DISTRICT OF COLUMBIA

Art Museum of the Americas, pg 791
Biblical Archaeology Society (BAS), pg 806
USCCB Publishing, pg 1051

FLORIDA

Allegro Productions Inc, pg 781
Capital Communications Inc, pg 819

GEORGIA

School Media Associates LLC, pg 1004

HAWAII

Media Bridge Gamekids, pg 936

ILLINOIS

Discovery Education - Chicago, pg 848
Film Ideas, pg 867
International Historic Films Inc, pg 901
Questar Inc, pg 989
Terra Nova Films Inc, pg 1037

KANSAS

Sagebrush Video Productions, pg 1001

KENTUCKY

Horizon Films & Media LLC, pg 891
KET The Kentucky Network, pg 910
National Geographic Learning, pg 952

MARYLAND

James Agee Film Project, pg 904
MMI Corp, pg 944
Special Archives Division, Motion Picture Branch, pg 1020

MASSACHUSETTS

Documentary Educational Resources Inc, pg 850
The New Film Company Inc, pg 955
WGBH Production Group, pg 1065

MICHIGAN

Digi Sign Design LLC, pg 847
Meuninck's Media Methods Inc, pg 940

MISSOURI

The Phoenix Learning Group Inc, pg 974

MONTANA

High Plains Films, pg 889

NEW HAMPSHIRE

Captain Fiddle Music & Publications, pg 820
Chip Taylor Communications LLC, pg 1032

NEW JERSEY

Euro-Pacific Film & Video Productions Inc, pg 863
Lucerne Media, pg 925

NEW MEXICO

National Information Center for Educational Media (NICEM)/MediaSleuth, pg 952

NEW YORK

Michael Blackwood Productions Inc, pg 808
De Nonno Productions Inc (DPI), pg 844
Downtown Community Television Center (DCTV), pg 851
Fanlight Productions, pg 865
Films for the Humanities & Sciences, pg 868
Films Media Group, pg 868
William Greaves Productions Inc, pg 882
Guidance Associates Inc Center for Humanities, pg 883
Hallel Communications, pg 884
HB-Content, pg 886
Human Relations Media, pg 892
Irish Music Corp, pg 902
Janson Media, pg 904
KickedUp Media Group Inc, pg 910
Maryknoll Productions, pg 933
Meridian Education Corp, pg 939
Monad Trainer's Aide Inc, pg 945
MRG Productions Inc, pg 948
News Broadcast Network, pg 956
Select Media Inc, pg 1006
Shopware, pg 1009
VIEW Inc (Video International Entertainment World Inc), pg 1058
White Buffalo Multimedia, pg 1065
Women Make Movies Inc, pg 1069
Wonderwomen™ Enterprises, pg 1069

NORTH CAROLINA

Vide-O-Go/That's Infotainment!, pg 1054

OHIO

Treehaus Communications Inc, pg 1044

OREGON

TeleVideos, pg 1036

PENNSYLVANIA

FMP Media Solutions Inc, pg 870
Media Inc, pg 936

SOUTH CAROLINA

BJU Press, pg 808

TENNESSEE

American Blackguard Inc, pg 784
Center for Southern Folklore Inc, pg 822
Marine Geographic, pg 931
Spring Arbor Distributors, pg 1022

TEXAS

Educational Video Network, pg 857
The Samuels Co, pg 1002

VIRGINIA

National Audiovisual Center - National Technical Information Service (NTIS), pg 952
PBS Video, pg 970

WASHINGTON

Intermedia Inc, pg 900

WEST VIRGINIA

Focus on Animals, pg 870

WISCONSIN

Knowledge Unlimited Inc, pg 912

ONTARIO

BBC Worldwide Canada Ltd, pg 803
Canadian Learning Co Inc, pg 818
Canamedia Inc, pg 818
Kineticvideo.com, pg 911
Life Cycle Books Ltd, pg 920
McIntyre Media Inc, pg 935

Documentary Producers

ALABAMA

Media Visions Inc, pg 937

ARIZONA

Aardvark Productions LLC, pg 772
Candee Productions Inc, pg 819
Creative Backstage, pg 838

ARKANSAS

Live'N'Loud, pg 923
White Diamond Productions, pg 1065

CALIFORNIA

AM Productions, pg 783
Les Blank Films Inc, pg 809
California/International Arts Foundation, pg 817
Crystal Pyramid Productions™, pg 840
Design Media, pg 845
Direct Images Interactive Inc, pg 848
Discovery Education - Los Angeles, pg 848
Dogma Studios, pg 850
imageReal Pictures LLC, pg 896
Lynch Communications, pg 926
Madera Video, pg 927
Main Street Media Inc, pg 929
The Media Staff Inc, pg 937
New Circuit Films LLC, pg 955
Panorama Productions, pg 968
PM Productions, pg 977
Point Lobos Productions, pg 977
Prime Cut Productions, pg 982
Regent Press Publishers & Printers, pg 994
SBS Productions, pg 1003

PROGRAMMING — AUDIO/VISUAL

Documentary Producers (continued)

ONTARIO

BBC Worldwide Canada Ltd, pg 803
Canamedia Inc, pg 818
DebsVoice, pg 844

QUEBEC

Kerrigan Productions Inc, pg 910

Documentary Rentals

CALIFORNIA

Les Blank Films Inc, pg 809
Glenn Photo Supply, pg 878

ILLINOIS

Discovery Education - Chicago, pg 848
Terra Nova Films Inc, pg 1037

MARYLAND

James Agee Film Project, pg 904

MASSACHUSETTS

Documentary Educational Resources Inc, pg 850

MICHIGAN

Digi Sign Design LLC, pg 847

MISSOURI

The Phoenix Learning Group Inc, pg 974

NEW HAMPSHIRE

Chip Taylor Communications LLC, pg 1032

NEW JERSEY

Euro-Pacific Film & Video Productions Inc, pg 863

NEW YORK

Downtown Community Television Center (DCTV), pg 851
Fanlight Productions, pg 865
William Greaves Productions Inc, pg 882
Hallel Communications, pg 884
Historic Films, pg 889
Select Media Inc, pg 1006

WASHINGTON

Intermedia Inc, pg 900

Educational Program Distributors

ARIZONA

BeachWare Inc, pg 804
Video Learning Library, pg 1055

CALIFORNIA

Academy Savant, pg 773
Astronomical Society of the Pacific, pg 792
Les Blank Films Inc, pg 809
California Newsreel, pg 817
Crystal Productions, pg 840
Crystal Pyramid Productions™, pg 840
Davidson Films Inc, pg 843
Deja View Video, pg 845
Discovery Education - Los Angeles, pg 848
Geddes Productions LLC, pg 876
Glenn Photo Supply, pg 878
Bruce Goldberg Inc, pg 880
Golden State Dance Teachers Association (GSDTA), pg 880
Griggs Productions Inc, pg 882
Joyce Media Inc, pg 906
Kantola Productions LLC, pg 908
Learn Quickly, pg 917
Madera Video, pg 927
MarVista Entertainment Inc, pg 933
monterey video, pg 946
Moose School Productions, pg 946
Music World/Vocal Power School, pg 951
New & Unique Videos™, pg 955
Point Lobos Productions, pg 977
Regent Press Publishers & Printers, pg 994
Sea Studios Foundation, pg 1005
TMW Media Group, pg 1041
The Wine Appreciation Guild Ltd, pg 1067

COLORADO

Vital Learning LLC, pg 1060

CONNECTICUT

Cine-Med Inc, pg 826
Hartley Film Foundation, pg 885
Pictures of Record Inc, pg 975
Weston Woods Studios Inc, pg 1064

DISTRICT OF COLUMBIA

Art Museum of the Americas, pg 791
Biblical Archaeology Society (BAS), pg 806
Systems Impact Inc, pg 1031

FLORIDA

ACE Video Resources Software, pg 774
Allegro Productions Inc, pg 781
Capital Communications Inc, pg 819

GEORGIA

School Media Associates LLC, pg 1004

HAWAII

Media Bridge Gamekids, pg 936
Source School of Tantra Yoga Inc, pg 1019

ILLINOIS

Britannica Film & Video, pg 812
CCH Continuing Education, pg 821
CCore Media Inc, pg 821
Discovery Education - Chicago, pg 848
Educational Insights, pg 857
Encyclopaedia Britannica Inc, pg 861
Film Ideas, pg 867
Learning Seed, pg 917
National Safety Council (NSC), pg 953
Questar Inc, pg 989
RADMAR Inc, pg 990
Terra Nova Films Inc, pg 1037

INDIANA

Agency for Instructional Technology (AIT), pg 778
Herff Jones | Nystrom, pg 888
Solution Tree, pg 1015

KANSAS

Sagebrush Video Productions, pg 1001

KENTUCKY

KET The Kentucky Network, pg 910
National Geographic Learning, pg 952

MARYLAND

Department of Education Resources, pg 845
James Agee Film Project, pg 904
MMI Corp, pg 944

MASSACHUSETTS

Cheng & Tsui Co, pg 824
Davis Art Images, pg 843
Documentary Educational Resources Inc, pg 850
The New Film Company Inc, pg 955
WGBH Production Group, pg 1065

MICHIGAN

Digi Sign Design LLC, pg 847
Emery-Pratt Co, pg 860
HighScope Press, pg 889
Meuninck's Media Methods Inc, pg 940
MSU Technologies, pg 949
The Program Source International, pg 985
Resource Development Co LLC, pg 995
Technology Learning Services, pg 1035

MINNESOTA

American Choral Catalog Ltd, pg 784
EMC/Paradigm Publishing, pg 860
Hazelden Publishing & Educational Services, pg 886

MISSOURI

Marsh Media, pg 931
Phoenix/BFA/Coronet, pg 974
The Phoenix Learning Group Inc, pg 974
SOM Publishing Co, pg 1015

MONTANA

High Plains Films, pg 889

NEW HAMPSHIRE

Captain Fiddle Music & Publications, pg 820
Frey Scientific, pg 873
Heinemann, pg 887
Chip Taylor Communications LLC, pg 1032

NEW JERSEY

Educational Impressions, pg 857
Graphics Depot Inc, pg 881
Lucerne Media, pg 925
A W Peller & Associates Inc, pg 971

NEW MEXICO

National Information Center for Educational Media (NICEM)/MediaSleuth, pg 952

NEW YORK

Beekman Books Inc, pg 804
Michael Blackwood Productions Inc, pg 808
Brooklyn Botanic Garden, pg 814
The Bureau for At-Risk Youth, pg 815
Cornell Laboratory of Ornithology, pg 836
Criterion Collection, pg 839
De Nonno Productions Inc (DPI), pg 844
Downtown Community Television Center (DCTV), pg 851
Educational Activities Inc, pg 857
Fanlight Productions, pg 865
Films Media Group, pg 868
William Greaves Productions Inc, pg 882
Guidance Associates Inc Center for Humanities, pg 883
Hallel Communications, pg 884
Homespun Video, pg 890
Human Relations Media, pg 892
Irish Music Corp, pg 902
Janson Media, pg 904
Listening Library, pg 923
March of Dimes Foundation, pg 930
Maryknoll Productions, pg 933
MRG Productions Inc, pg 948
Practising Law Institute, pg 980
Select Media Inc, pg 1006
TeleTime Productions, pg 1036
VIEW Inc (Video International Entertainment World Inc), pg 1058
White Buffalo Multimedia, pg 1065
Women Make Movies Inc, pg 1069
Wonderwomen™ Enterprises, pg 1069

NORTH CAROLINA

Carolina Biological Supply Co, pg 820
Do It Yourself Inc - DIY Video Corp, pg 849
Hart Inc, pg 885
Vide-O-Go/That's Infotainment!, pg 1054

OHIO

Alegra House Publishers, pg 780
Franciscan Media, pg 872
McGraw-Hill School Education Group, pg 935
South-Western Publishing Co, pg 1019
Treehaus Communications Inc, pg 1044

OREGON

CNS Productions Inc, pg 830
Getty-Dubay Productions, pg 877
International Loving Touch Foundation Inc, pg 901
The Keyboard Workshop, pg 910
TeleVideos, pg 1036

PENNSYLVANIA

Discovery Education - South Burlington, pg 848
FMP Media Solutions Inc, pg 870
Karol Media Inc, pg 908
Media Inc, pg 936

SOUTH CAROLINA

BJU Press, pg 808

TENNESSEE

American Blackguard Inc, pg 784
Center for Southern Folklore Inc, pg 822
National School Products, pg 953
Spring Arbor Distributors, pg 1022

TEXAS

Educational Video Network, pg 857
Institute of Texan Cultures, pg 899
InterCom, pg 900
University of Texas at Austin - Petroleum Extension Service, pg 1050

VERMONT

Dialect Accent Specialists Inc, pg 846
Wilson McLeran Inc, pg 1067

VIRGINIA

Design & Production Inc, pg 845
National Audiovisual Center - National Technical Information Service (NTIS), pg 952
PBS Video, pg 970

WASHINGTON

Intermedia Inc, pg 900

WEST VIRGINIA

Focus on Animals, pg 870
Harpers Ferry Historical Association, pg 885

WISCONSIN

Her Own Words LLC, pg 888
Knowledge Unlimited Inc, pg 912

BRITISH COLUMBIA

Credo Interactive Inc, pg 839

ONTARIO

BBC Worldwide Canada Ltd, pg 803
Canadian Learning Co Inc, pg 818
Canamedia Inc, pg 818
Kineticvideo.com, pg 911
Life Cycle Books Ltd, pg 920
McIntyre Media Inc, pg 935
Novalis, pg 959
The Resource Centre, pg 995

QUEBEC

Editions Hurtubise HMH Ltee, pg 892

Educational Program Producers

ALABAMA

AVS Media Group, pg 800
Media Visions Inc, pg 937

ARIZONA

Aardvark Productions LLC, pg 772
BeachWare Inc, pg 804
Candee Productions Inc, pg 819

ARKANSAS

White Diamond Productions, pg 1065

CALIFORNIA

Academy Savant, pg 773
AM Productions, pg 783
Animax, pg 787
Astronomical Society of the Pacific, pg 792
Les Blank Films Inc, pg 809
Crystal Productions, pg 840
Crystal Pyramid Productions™, pg 840
Davidson Films Inc, pg 843
Design Media, pg 845
Direct Images Interactive Inc, pg 848
Discovery Education - Los Angeles, pg 848
Dolphin MultiMedia Inc, pg 850
Geddes Productions LLC, pg 876
imageReal Pictures LLC, pg 896
Joyce Media Inc, pg 906
KABA Audio Productions, pg 907
Kantola Productions LLC, pg 908
Lynch Communications, pg 926
Madera Video, pg 927
Main Street Media Inc, pg 929
Media Magic, pg 937
The Media Staff Inc, pg 937
Music World/Vocal Power School, pg 951
National Lampoon, pg 953
PM Productions, pg 977
Point Lobos Productions, pg 977
Prime Cut Productions, pg 982
Regent Press Publishers & Printers, pg 994
SBS Productions, pg 1003
Sea Studios Foundation, pg 1005
SNAP, pg 1014
Tam Communications Inc, pg 1031
Tigar Hare Studios, pg 1040
TMW Media Group, pg 1041
Total Media Group, pg 1042
Vineyard Video & Photography, pg 1058
Wavemaker Media Design, pg 1062
Webster Communications, pg 1063
West Coast Projections Inc, pg 1063

COLORADO

Paul L Anderson Productions Inc, pg 786
Flashback Media Productions, pg 869
Jeppesen, pg 905
Phelan Productions Inc, pg 973
Vital Learning LLC, pg 1060

CONNECTICUT

Applebox Studio, pg 788
Biomedical Media Communications Dept, pg 807
Broadcast Video Productions LLC, pg 813
Cine-Med Inc, pg 826
Hartley Film Foundation, pg 885
MCC Films, pg 935
Pictures of Record Inc, pg 975
Weston Woods Studios Inc, pg 1064

DISTRICT OF COLUMBIA

Art Museum of the Americas, pg 791
Biblical Archaeology Society (BAS), pg 806
Hillmann & Carr Inc, pg 889
O'Keefe Communications Inc, pg 961
Systems Impact Inc, pg 1031

FLORIDA

Accel Video Productions, pg 773
ACE Video Resources Software, pg 774
Allegro Productions Inc, pg 781
Audio Visual Imagineering Inc, pg 795
Capital Communications Inc, pg 819
Home Shopping Network (HSN), pg 890
Sunfire Communications Inc, pg 1028
Teach America Corp, pg 1033
Tricycle Studios, pg 1044

GEORGIA

Beachwood Productions, pg 804
Continental Film & Video, pg 835
Guerrilla Productions LLC, pg 883

HAWAII

Hyperspective Studios Inc, pg 893
Media Bridge Gamekids, pg 936
Source School of Tantra Yoga Inc, pg 1019

ILLINOIS

Accenture, pg 773
Airways Digital Media, pg 779
Audio Visual Services Corp, pg 796
Britannica Film & Video, pg 812
CCH Continuing Education, pg 821
CCore Media Inc, pg 821
Chicago Satellite & Video, pg 825
Cresta Creative, pg 839
Discovery Education - Chicago, pg 848
1st Financial Training Services Inc, pg 868
Learning Seed, pg 917
Major Media Productions Inc, pg 929
Manning Productions, pg 930
National Safety Council (NSC), pg 953
The Pepper Group, pg 972
PSAV® Presentation Services (Hotel Services Division), pg 987
Questar Inc, pg 989
Rand McNally Education, pg 991
Steven Samler Music & Sound, pg 1002
SCI Television Productions LLC, pg 1004
Terra Nova Films Inc, pg 1037
20/20 Communications Inc, pg 1047
Video Impressions, pg 1055

INDIANA

Agency for Instructional Technology (AIT), pg 778
Digital Rain LLC, pg 847
Herff Jones | Nystrom, pg 888
Solution Tree, pg 1015

IOWA

The Production House, pg 984

KANSAS

Chapman Recording & Mastering, pg 824
Sagebrush Video Productions, pg 1001

KENTUCKY

KET The Kentucky Network, pg 910
National Geographic Learning, pg 952
NIMCO Inc, pg 957

LOUISIANA

Disk Productions, pg 849

MARYLAND

The Cutting Corp, pg 841
dbF a Media Company, pg 844
Department of Education Resources, pg 845
The Image Generators, pg 895
Instructional Resources Corp, pg 899
James Agee Film Project, pg 904
Lehigh Phoenix™, pg 918
MMI Corp, pg 944
Mobile-Video Productions Inc, pg 944

MASSACHUSETTS

Cheng & Tsui Co, pg 824
Documentary Educational Resources Inc, pg 850
Monadnock Media Inc, pg 945
The New Film Company Inc, pg 955
Soundtrack Recording Studios, pg 1018
Triumph Learning LLC, pg 1045
TVN-The Video Network, pg 1046
WGBH Production Group, pg 1065

MICHIGAN

Digi Sign Design LLC, pg 847
HighScope Press, pg 889
K&R All Media Productions Inc, pg 908
K&R's Recording Studios Inc, pg 908
Resource Development Co LLC, pg 995
Technology Learning Services, pg 1035
Universal Images, pg 1049

MINNESOTA

American Choral Catalog Ltd, pg 784
EMC/Paradigm Publishing, pg 860
Hazelden Publishing & Educational Services, pg 886
Master Communications Group, pg 933
Media Loft Inc, pg 937
MultiMedia, pg 950
Vaddio, pg 1051

MISSOURI

Marsh Media, pg 931
Phoenix/BFA/Coronet, pg 974
The Phoenix Learning Group Inc, pg 974
SOM Publishing Co, pg 1015

PROGRAMMING — AUDIO/VISUAL

Educational Program Producers (continued)

MONTANA

High Plains Films, pg 889
North Country Media Group, pg 959

NEBRASKA

Dog & Pony Productions Inc, pg 850

NEVADA

HDTV Productions Inc, pg 886
JCS Video Productions, pg 904

NEW HAMPSHIRE

Academic & Campus Technology Services, pg 773
Apertura, pg 788
Captain Fiddle Music & Publications, pg 820
Heinemann, pg 887
Chip Taylor Communications LLC, pg 1032

NEW JERSEY

Educational Impressions, pg 857
Half Moon Video Productions, pg 883
Laurel Video Productions, pg 916
Optisonics Productions, pg 965

NEW MEXICO

Michael Dunn Productions, pg 853

NEW YORK

American History Workshop (NY) Inc, pg 784
Blue Barn Pictures Inc, pg 809
Broad Street Inc, pg 812
Brooklyn Botanic Garden, pg 814
The Bureau for At-Risk Youth, pg 815
Cornell Laboratory of Ornithology, pg 836
Criterion Collection, pg 839
De Nonno Productions Inc (DPI), pg 844
dM works, pg 849
Downtown Community Television Center (DCTV), pg 851
Duggal Visual Solutions, pg 853
Educational Activities Inc, pg 857
Fanlight Productions, pg 865
Films Media Group, pg 868
The Food & Beverage Institute, pg 871
Karen Frankel Productions, pg 872
William Greaves Productions Inc, pg 882
Greyfalcon House, pg 882
Guidance Associates Inc Center for Humanities, pg 883
Hallel Communications, pg 884
Havas Worldwide, pg 886
Human Relations Media, pg 892
Irish Music Corp, pg 902
Ketchum Pleon Change, pg 910
Lavine Production Group, pg 917
Listening Library, pg 923
Long Island Video Enterprises Live Inc, pg 924
Manhattan Center Studios Inc, pg 930
March of Dimes Foundation, pg 930
Neal Marshad Productions, pg 931
Maryknoll Productions, pg 933
Jack Morton Worldwide, pg 946
MRG Productions Inc, pg 948
MRY, pg 949
New York Audio Productions, pg 956
News Broadcast Network, pg 956
Shelly Palmer Production, pg 968
Polestar Films & Associated Arts Ltd, pg 978
Practising Law Institute, pg 980
Spoken Arts Inc, pg 1021
Sunrise Media LLC, pg 1028
TBA Global Events, pg 1032
VIEW Inc (Video International Entertainment World Inc), pg 1058
Weigl Publishers Inc, pg 1063
White Buffalo Multimedia, pg 1065
Wonderwomen™ Enterprises, pg 1069
Zelman Studios Ltd, pg 1073

NORTH CAROLINA

Pat Appleson Studios Inc, pg 788
Carolina Biological Supply Co, pg 820
The Communications Group Inc, pg 833
Do It Yourself Inc - DIY Video Corp, pg 849
Humanities Extension Publications, pg 892
Kino Mountain Productions LLC, pg 911
Laurel Hill Press, pg 916
LCW Productions LLC, pg 917
Moving Pictures, pg 948
PACE Worldwide, pg 966
Sinclair Institute, pg 1012

OHIO

Advent Media Inc, pg 778
Alegra House Publishers, pg 780
Creative Technology, pg 838
Cuyahoga Community College Media Center, pg 841
Franciscan Media, pg 872
Lyon Video Inc, pg 927
MainSail Production Services Inc, pg 929
McGraw-Hill School Education Group, pg 935
R&B Communications Inc, pg 991
South-Western Publishing Co, pg 1019
Take 1 Media Services, pg 1031
Treehaus Communications Inc, pg 1044
Vista Color Imaging Inc, pg 1059

OKLAHOMA

CSI/Orion, pg 840

OREGON

A KTVA Production LLC, pg 771
CNS Productions Inc, pg 830
Getty-Dubay Productions, pg 877
Ideascape Inc, pg 894
The Keyboard Workshop, pg 910
Odyssey Productions Inc, pg 961
TeleVideos, pg 1036

PENNSYLVANIA

AiH Group Inc, pg 779
Bang Pictures, pg 802
Discovery Education - South Burlington, pg 848
FMP Media Solutions Inc, pg 870
JPL, pg 906
Kensington Falls Animation, pg 909
Main Point Productions, pg 929
Media Inc, pg 936
Muderick Media, pg 949
Panta Rhei Media Inc, pg 968
Production Masters Inc (PMI), pg 984

RHODE ISLAND

Sound-FX-Design, pg 1017

SOUTH CAROLINA

BJU Press, pg 808

TENNESSEE

American Blackguard Inc, pg 784
Running Pony Productions LLC, pg 1000
Russ Sturgeon Productions/RSVP, pg 1027
WKPT-TV, pg 1068

TEXAS

Educational Video Network, pg 857
Institute of Texan Cultures, pg 899
InterCom, pg 900
Mediaforce Productions, pg 937
Romar Learning, pg 999
Stage Directions, pg 1022
Stockyard Photos/Jim Olive Photography, pg 1025
Tropikal Productions, pg 1045
University of Texas at Austin - Petroleum Extension Service, pg 1050

UTAH

K-SAR Video & DVD Productions, pg 907

VERMONT

Dialect Accent Specialists Inc, pg 846
Wilson McLeran Inc, pg 1067

VIRGINIA

CALIBRE, pg 816
D&B Television & Video Productions Inc, pg 842
ITC Learning LLC, pg 903
Lion Recording Services Inc, pg 922
Metro Productions, pg 939

WASHINGTON

Intermedia Inc, pg 900
Laser Fantasy/HECK Industries/Photon Manufacturing, pg 916

WEST VIRGINIA

Altruist Media LLC, pg 783
Focus on Animals, pg 870

WISCONSIN

Her Own Words LLC, pg 888
Knowledge Unlimited Inc, pg 912
Rucinski & Reetz Communications LLC, pg 1000
USAV Group Inc, pg 1050
Video Wisconsin Inc, pg 1056
Watts Communications Inc, pg 1062
Wisconsin Public Television, pg 1068

WYOMING

Bridger Productions Inc, pg 812

ALBERTA

Black Media Works, pg 808

BRITISH COLUMBIA

West Eagle Films Inc, pg 1064

NEWFOUNDLAND AND LABRADOR

Vidcraft Productions Ltd, pg 1054

NORTHWEST TERRITORIES

Yellowknife Films Inc, pg 1072

ONTARIO

Art Gallery of Ontario, pg 791
BBC Worldwide Canada Ltd, pg 803
Canamedia Inc, pg 818
DebsVoice, pg 844
Doomsday Studios Ltd, pg 850
McIntyre Media Inc, pg 935
Pearson Education Canada, pg 970

QUEBEC

Kerrigan Productions Inc, pg 910

Educational Program Rentals

CALIFORNIA

Les Blank Films Inc, pg 809
Davidson Films Inc, pg 843
Glenn Photo Supply, pg 878

ILLINOIS

Discovery Education - Chicago, pg 848
1st Financial Training Services Inc, pg 868
National Safety Council (NSC), pg 953
Terra Nova Films Inc, pg 1037

MARYLAND

James Agee Film Project, pg 904

MASSACHUSETTS

Documentary Educational Resources Inc, pg 850

MICHIGAN

Digi Sign Design LLC, pg 847
HighScope Press, pg 889

MINNESOTA

American Choral Catalog Ltd, pg 784
Hazelden Publishing & Educational Services, pg 886

MISSOURI

The Phoenix Learning Group Inc, pg 974

NEW HAMPSHIRE

Academic & Campus Technology Services, pg 773
Heinemann, pg 887
Chip Taylor Communications LLC, pg 1032

NEW YORK

Brooklyn Botanic Garden, pg 814
Downtown Community Television Center (DCTV), pg 851
Fanlight Productions, pg 865
William Greaves Productions Inc, pg 882
Hallel Communications, pg 884
Historic Films, pg 889
Select Media Inc, pg 1006

OHIO

Franciscan Media, pg 872
Treehaus Communications Inc, pg 1044

PENNSYLVANIA

Karol Media Inc, pg 908

TEXAS

InterCom, pg 900

WASHINGTON

ChristianAnswers.Net™, pg 825
Intermedia Inc, pg 900

WEST VIRGINIA

Harpers Ferry Historical Association, pg 885

WISCONSIN

Her Own Words LLC, pg 888

Feature Program Distributors

CALIFORNIA

Ben Barry & Associates Inc, pg 803
Les Blank Films Inc, pg 809
Crystal Pyramid Productions™, pg 840
Glenn Photo Supply, pg 878
Bruce Goldberg Inc, pg 880
Madera Video, pg 927
MarVista Entertainment Inc, pg 933
monterey video, pg 946
Moose School Productions, pg 946
National Lampoon, pg 953

FLORIDA

Capital Communications Inc, pg 819

GEORGIA

Visioneering International Inc, pg 1058

IOWA

Right Stuf Inc, pg 997

KENTUCKY

KET The Kentucky Network, pg 910

MONTANA

High Plains Films, pg 889

NEW HAMPSHIRE

Chip Taylor Communications LLC, pg 1032

NEW YORK

Criterion Collection, pg 839
Guidance Associates Inc Center for Humanities, pg 883
HB-Content, pg 886
Janson Media, pg 904
MRG Productions Inc, pg 948
VIEW Inc (Video International Entertainment World Inc), pg 1058
Women Make Movies Inc, pg 1069

NORTH CAROLINA

Vide-O-Go/That's Infotainment!, pg 1054

SOUTH CAROLINA

BJU Press, pg 808

TENNESSEE

American Blackguard Inc, pg 784
Spring Arbor Distributors, pg 1022

TEXAS

The Samuels Co, pg 1002

ONTARIO

Canadian Learning Co Inc, pg 818
Life Cycle Books Ltd, pg 920

Feature Program Producers

ARIZONA

Aardvark Productions LLC, pg 772

CALIFORNIA

Animax, pg 787
Ben Barry & Associates Inc, pg 803
Les Blank Films Inc, pg 809
Crystal Pyramid Productions™, pg 840
imageReal Pictures LLC, pg 896
Jaguar Distribution Corp, pg 903
Lynch Communications, pg 926
National Lampoon, pg 953
PM Productions, pg 977
RKO Pictures Inc, pg 997
Screen Door Entertainment Inc, pg 1005
Tigar Hare Studios, pg 1040
Total Media Group, pg 1042
Vineyard Video & Photography, pg 1058

COLORADO

Flashback Media Productions, pg 869
Tatum Video, pg 1032

CONNECTICUT

Applebox Studio, pg 788
Broadcast Video Productions LLC, pg 813
Hartley Film Foundation, pg 885
MCC Films, pg 935

FLORIDA

Capital Communications Inc, pg 819
Communications Concepts Inc (CCI), pg 833
Sunfire Communications Inc, pg 1028

GEORGIA

Guerrilla Productions LLC, pg 883
Visioneering International Inc, pg 1058

HAWAII

Hyperspective Studios Inc, pg 893

ILLINOIS

Chicago Satellite & Video, pg 825
Manning Productions, pg 930
The Pepper Group, pg 972

INDIANA

Digital Rain LLC, pg 847

IOWA

Right Stuf Inc, pg 997

KENTUCKY

KET The Kentucky Network, pg 910

MASSACHUSETTS

Soundtrack Recording Studios, pg 1018

MICHIGAN

K&R All Media Productions Inc, pg 908
K&R's Recording Studios Inc, pg 908

MONTANA

High Plains Films, pg 889

NEVADA

HDTV Productions Inc, pg 886

NEW HAMPSHIRE

Chip Taylor Communications LLC, pg 1032

NEW JERSEY

Half Moon Video Productions, pg 883
Optisonics Productions, pg 965

NEW YORK

Blue Barn Pictures Inc, pg 809
Broad Street Inc, pg 812
CompuWeather Inc, pg 834
Criterion Collection, pg 839
Duggal Visual Solutions, pg 853
William Greaves Productions Inc, pg 882
Greyfalcon House, pg 882
Havas Worldwide, pg 886
HB-Content, pg 886
Neal Marshad Productions, pg 931
Jack Morton Worldwide, pg 946
MRG Productions Inc, pg 948
News Broadcast Network, pg 956
Shelly Palmer Production, pg 968
Shadow Pictures Inc, pg 1007
Vanguard Documentaries, pg 1051
VIEW Inc (Video International Entertainment World Inc), pg 1058
Zelman Studios Ltd, pg 1073

NORTH CAROLINA

Pat Appleson Studios Inc, pg 788
LCW Productions LLC, pg 917

OHIO

Advent Media Inc, pg 778
Creative Technology, pg 838
Image Video Teleproductions Inc, pg 895
Lyon Video Inc, pg 927
R&B Communications Inc, pg 991
Vista Color Imaging Inc, pg 1059

OREGON

Ideascape Inc, pg 894

PENNSYLVANIA

Kensington Falls Animation, pg 909
Production Masters Inc (PMI), pg 984

RHODE ISLAND

Sound-FX-Design, pg 1017

SOUTH CAROLINA

BJU Press, pg 808

TENNESSEE

American Blackguard Inc, pg 784
Running Pony Productions LLC, pg 1000

TEXAS

Epic Software Group Inc, pg 862
The Samuels Co, pg 1002
Stage Directions, pg 1022
Stockyard Photos/Jim Olive Photography, pg 1025

VIRGINIA

D&B Television & Video Productions Inc, pg 842
Lion Recording Services Inc, pg 922
Metro Productions, pg 939

WASHINGTON

Laser Fantasy/HECK Industries/Photon Manufacturing, pg 916

WISCONSIN

Wisconsin Public Television, pg 1068

WYOMING

Bridger Productions Inc, pg 812

NEWFOUNDLAND AND LABRADOR

Vidcraft Productions Ltd, pg 1054

ONTARIO

Doomsday Studios Ltd, pg 850

QUEBEC

Kerrigan Productions Inc, pg 910

Feature Program Rentals

CALIFORNIA

Ben Barry & Associates Inc, pg 803
Les Blank Films Inc, pg 809
Glenn Photo Supply, pg 878

FLORIDA

Cifex Corp, pg 826

PROGRAMMING — AUDIO/VISUAL

Feature Program Rentals (continued)

NEW HAMPSHIRE

Chip Taylor Communications LLC, pg 1032

NEW YORK

Historic Films, pg 889

Film Loop Distributors

CALIFORNIA

Ametron Audio/Video, pg 785
QRS Software Services, pg 988

INDIANA

Lee Co Inc, pg 918

NEW YORK

Janus Films Inc, pg 904
Visual Technologies Corp, pg 1060

VIRGINIA

Filmdex Inc, pg 867

Film Loop Producers

CALIFORNIA

Dogma Studios, pg 850
International Contact Inc, pg 900
The Kitchen, pg 911
QRS Software Services, pg 988

COLORADO

The Cinema Lab, pg 827

CONNECTICUT

Broadcast Video Productions LLC, pg 813

FLORIDA

Blackburst Entertainment, pg 808

GEORGIA

Continental Film & Video, pg 835
Guerrilla Productions LLC, pg 883

ILLINOIS

Cresta Creative, pg 839

IOWA

The Production House, pg 984

MASSACHUSETTS

TR Productions, pg 1043

MICHIGAN

K&R All Media Productions Inc, pg 908
K&R's Recording Studios Inc, pg 908

MINNESOTA

Aggressive Records Audio Duplication LLC, pg 778

MISSOURI

Celebrities Productions, pg 822

NEW YORK

Duggal Visual Solutions, pg 853
MRG Productions Inc, pg 948
Split Image Productions, pg 1021
Zelman Studios Ltd, pg 1073

TENNESSEE

Memphis Communications Corp, pg 938
Running Pony Productions LLC, pg 1000

TEXAS

Romar Learning, pg 999

WISCONSIN

USAV Group Inc, pg 1050

Film Loop Rentals

CALIFORNIA

Ametron Audio/Video, pg 785

Filmstrip—Silent Distributors

Ametron Audio/Video, pg 785
Discovery Education - Los Angeles, pg 848
QRS Software Services, pg 988
Sea Studios Foundation, pg 1005

COLORADO

Gaiam Inc, pg 875
National Teaching Aids Inc, pg 953

DISTRICT OF COLUMBIA

Biblical Archaeology Society (BAS), pg 806

FLORIDA

Tallahassee Audio Visual, pg 1031

MICHIGAN

Michigan Office Solutions, pg 941
Wayne State University Media Services, pg 1063

NEW MEXICO

National Information Center for Educational Media (NICEM)/MediaSleuth, pg 952

NEW YORK

Visual Technologies Corp, pg 1060

TENNESSEE

Spring Arbor Distributors, pg 1022

TEXAS

Audio Visual Technologies Group, pg 796

VIRGINIA

Colonial Williamsburg Foundation, pg 831

WISCONSIN

School Specialty Inc, pg 1004

Filmstrip—Silent Producers

ALABAMA

Media Visions Inc, pg 937

CALIFORNIA

Discovery Education - Los Angeles, pg 848
Lynch Communications, pg 926
QRS Software Services, pg 988
SBS Productions, pg 1003
Sea Studios Foundation, pg 1005

COLORADO

Gaiam Inc, pg 875
National Teaching Aids Inc, pg 953

CONNECTICUT

Broadcast Video Productions LLC, pg 813

DISTRICT OF COLUMBIA

Biblical Archaeology Society (BAS), pg 806

GEORGIA

Guerrilla Productions LLC, pg 883
Symmes Systems, pg 1030

INDIANA

OMNI Productions, pg 962

MASSACHUSETTS

CommCreative, pg 832
Emergency Film Group, pg 860
TR Productions, pg 1043
Triumph Learning LLC, pg 1045

MICHIGAN

Blue Mouse Studio, pg 809
K&R All Media Productions Inc, pg 908
Wayne State University Media Services, pg 1063

MISSOURI

Celebrities Productions, pg 822

NEW HAMPSHIRE

Apertura, pg 788

NEW JERSEY

Optisonics Productions, pg 965

NEW YORK

Applause Learning Resources, pg 788
Duggal Visual Solutions, pg 853
Jack Morton Worldwide, pg 946
Peter Schleger Co, pg 1004
Split Image Productions, pg 1021
Zelman Studios Ltd, pg 1073

OHIO

Treehaus Communications Inc, pg 1044

PENNSYLVANIA

FMP Media Solutions Inc, pg 870

TENNESSEE

Memphis Communications Corp, pg 938
Running Pony Productions LLC, pg 1000

TEXAS

Romar Learning, pg 999

VIRGINIA

Blair Inc, pg 809

WISCONSIN

USAV Group Inc, pg 1050

Filmstrip—Silent Rentals

CALIFORNIA

Ametron Audio/Video, pg 785

MICHIGAN

Wayne State University Media Services, pg 1063

Filmstrip—Sound Distributors

CALIFORNIA

Ametron Audio/Video, pg 785
Discovery Education - Los Angeles, pg 848
QRS Software Services, pg 988
Sea Studios Foundation, pg 1005
Visual Communications - Southern California Asian American Studies Central Inc, pg 1059

FLORIDA

Tallahassee Audio Visual, pg 1031

GEORGIA

School Media Associates LLC, pg 1004

KENTUCKY

National Geographic Learning, pg 952

MASSACHUSETTS

Triumph Learning LLC, pg 1045

MICHIGAN

Michigan Office Solutions, pg 941

MISSOURI

Mosby Inc, pg 947

NEW HAMPSHIRE

Frey Scientific, pg 873

NEW JERSEY

Educational Impressions, pg 857
A W Peller & Associates Inc, pg 971

NEW MEXICO

National Information Center for Educational Media (NICEM)/MediaSleuth, pg 952

NEW YORK

Brooklyn Botanic Garden, pg 814
Visual Technologies Corp, pg 1060

NORTH CAROLINA

Carolina Biological Supply Co, pg 820

OHIO

McGraw-Hill School Education Group, pg 935
South-Western Publishing Co, pg 1019
Treehaus Communications Inc, pg 1044

PENNSYLVANIA

Discovery Education - South Burlington, pg 848

TENNESSEE

Spring Arbor Distributors, pg 1022

TEXAS

Audio Visual Technologies Group, pg 796
Stage Directions, pg 1022

WISCONSIN

School Specialty Inc, pg 1004

ONTARIO

Canadian Learning Co Inc, pg 818

Filmstrip—Sound Producers

ALABAMA

Media Visions Inc, pg 937

CALIFORNIA

Discovery Education - Los Angeles, pg 848
Lynch Communications, pg 926
QRS Software Services, pg 988
SBS Productions, pg 1003
Sea Studios Foundation, pg 1005
Steve Shapiro Music, pg 1008

CONNECTICUT

Broadcast Video Productions LLC, pg 813

DISTRICT OF COLUMBIA

Educational Film Center, pg 857

GEORGIA

Guerrilla Productions LLC, pg 883
Symmes Systems, pg 1030

ILLINOIS

Communications Corporation of America, pg 833
Universal Training, pg 1049

INDIANA

OMNI Productions, pg 962

KENTUCKY

National Geographic Learning, pg 952

MASSACHUSETTS

CommCreative, pg 832
Emergency Film Group, pg 860
TR Productions, pg 1043

MICHIGAN

K&R All Media Productions Inc, pg 908
K&R's Recording Studios Inc, pg 908

MINNESOTA

Aggressive Records Audio Duplication LLC, pg 778
Jamieson & Associates Inc, pg 904

MISSOURI

Celebrities Productions, pg 822
Mosby Inc, pg 947
Switch, pg 1030

NEW HAMPSHIRE

Apertura, pg 788
Frey Scientific, pg 873

NEW JERSEY

Educational Impressions, pg 857
Optisonics Productions, pg 965

NEW YORK

Applause Learning Resources, pg 788
Brooklyn Botanic Garden, pg 814
Campus Film Distributors Corp, pg 818
Duggal Visual Solutions, pg 853
Greyfalcon House, pg 882
Jack Morton Worldwide, pg 946
David Rapkin Audio Production, pg 991
Peter Schleger Co, pg 1004
Split Image Productions, pg 1021
Zelman Studios Ltd, pg 1073

OHIO

McGraw-Hill School Education Group, pg 935
South-Western Publishing Co, pg 1019
Treehaus Communications Inc, pg 1044

PENNSYLVANIA

FMP Media Solutions Inc, pg 870

TENNESSEE

Memphis Communications Corp, pg 938
Running Pony Productions LLC, pg 1000

TEXAS

Romar Learning, pg 999
The Sound Lab Inc, pg 1017
Tropikal Productions, pg 1045

VIRGINIA

Blair Inc, pg 809

WASHINGTON

Kostov Productions, pg 913

WISCONSIN

USAV Group Inc, pg 1050

BRITISH COLUMBIA

West Eagle Films Inc, pg 1064

ONTARIO

Weston Woods Canada, pg 1064

Filmstrip—Sound Rentals

CALIFORNIA

Ametron Audio/Video, pg 785
Visual Communications - Southern California Asian American Studies Central Inc, pg 1059

NEW YORK

Brooklyn Botanic Garden, pg 814

Foreign Program Distributors

CALIFORNIA

Crystal Pyramid Productions™, pg 840
Discovery Education - Los Angeles, pg 848
Glenn Photo Supply, pg 878
Madera Video, pg 927
MarVista Entertainment Inc, pg 933
New & Unique Videos™, pg 955
Point Lobos Productions, pg 977
The Wine Appreciation Guild Ltd, pg 1067

DISTRICT OF COLUMBIA

Biblical Archaeology Society (BAS), pg 806

FLORIDA

Capital Communications Inc, pg 819
Cifex Corp, pg 826

GEORGIA

Visioneering International Inc, pg 1058

ILLINOIS

International Historic Films Inc, pg 901

IOWA

Right Stuf Inc, pg 997

MASSACHUSETTS

Cheng & Tsui Co, pg 824
Documentary Educational Resources Inc, pg 850

MICHIGAN

Digi Sign Design LLC, pg 847

NEW HAMPSHIRE

Chip Taylor Communications LLC, pg 1032

NEW JERSEY

Euro-Pacific Film & Video Productions Inc, pg 863

NEW YORK

Applause Learning Resources, pg 788
Hallel Communications, pg 884
Janson Media, pg 904
MRG Productions Inc, pg 948
VIEW Inc (Video International Entertainment World Inc), pg 1058
Women Make Movies Inc, pg 1069

NORTH CAROLINA

Vide-O-Go/That's Infotainment!, pg 1054

PENNSYLVANIA

FMP Media Solutions Inc, pg 870

TENNESSEE

Spring Arbor Distributors, pg 1022

TEXAS

Educational Video Network, pg 857

VIRGINIA

National Audiovisual Center - National Technical Information Service (NTIS), pg 952

ONTARIO

Canadian Learning Co Inc, pg 818

Foreign Program Producers

ARIZONA

Aardvark Productions LLC, pg 772

CALIFORNIA

Crystal Pyramid Productions™, pg 840
Discovery Education - Los Angeles, pg 848
Dolphin MultiMedia Inc, pg 850
International Contact Inc, pg 900
Jaguar Distribution Corp, pg 903
Lynch Communications, pg 926
Point Lobos Productions, pg 977
Prime Cut Productions, pg 982
Total Media Group, pg 1042
Vineyard Video & Photography, pg 1058
Webster Communications, pg 1063

CONNECTICUT

Broadcast Video Productions LLC, pg 813

DISTRICT OF COLUMBIA

Biblical Archaeology Society (BAS), pg 806
Hillmann & Carr Inc, pg 889

FLORIDA

Sunfire Communications Inc, pg 1028

GEORGIA

Guerrilla Productions LLC, pg 883
Visioneering International Inc, pg 1058

ILLINOIS

Chicago Satellite & Video, pg 825
Manning Productions, pg 930
The Pepper Group, pg 972
20/20 Communications Inc, pg 1047

PROGRAMMING — AUDIO/VISUAL

Foreign Program Producers (continued)

IOWA

Right Stuf Inc, pg 997

MASSACHUSETTS

Documentary Educational Resources Inc, pg 850
Soundtrack Recording Studios, pg 1018

MICHIGAN

Digi Sign Design LLC, pg 847
K&R All Media Productions Inc, pg 908
K&R's Recording Studios Inc, pg 908

MINNESOTA

Master Communications Group, pg 933

NEVADA

HDTV Productions Inc, pg 886

NEW HAMPSHIRE

Apertura, pg 788
Chip Taylor Communications LLC, pg 1032

NEW YORK

Applause Learning Resources, pg 788
Greyfalcon House, pg 882
Hallel Communications, pg 884
Havas Worldwide, pg 886
Manhattan Center Studios Inc, pg 930
Neal Marshad Productions, pg 931
Maryknoll Productions, pg 933
Jack Morton Worldwide, pg 946
MRG Productions Inc, pg 948
Shelly Palmer Production, pg 968
Shadow Pictures Inc, pg 1007
VIEW Inc (Video International Entertainment World Inc), pg 1058
Zelman Studios Ltd, pg 1073

NORTH CAROLINA

Pat Appleson Studios Inc, pg 788

OHIO

Creative Technology, pg 838
Take 1 Media Services, pg 1031
VGI Productions, pg 1053
Vista Color Imaging Inc, pg 1059

PENNSYLVANIA

FMP Media Solutions Inc, pg 870

RHODE ISLAND

Sound-FX-Design, pg 1017

TEXAS

Educational Video Network, pg 857
Stage Directions, pg 1022
Tropikal Productions, pg 1045

VIRGINIA

D&B Television & Video Productions Inc, pg 842
Lion Recording Services Inc, pg 922
Metro Productions, pg 939

WASHINGTON

Kostov Productions, pg 913

WISCONSIN

Wisconsin Public Television, pg 1068

WYOMING

Bridger Productions Inc, pg 812

ONTARIO

Doomsday Studios Ltd, pg 850

QUEBEC

Kerrigan Productions Inc, pg 910

Foreign Program Rentals

CALIFORNIA

Ben Barry & Associates Inc, pg 803
Glenn Photo Supply, pg 878

FLORIDA

Cifex Corp, pg 826

MASSACHUSETTS

Documentary Educational Resources Inc, pg 850

MICHIGAN

Digi Sign Design LLC, pg 847

NEW HAMPSHIRE

Chip Taylor Communications LLC, pg 1032

NEW JERSEY

Euro-Pacific Film & Video Productions Inc, pg 863

NEW YORK

Fanlight Productions, pg 865
Hallel Communications, pg 884

Globe Distributors

CALIFORNIA

Angstrom Lighting, pg 786
QRS Software Services, pg 988
Social Studies School Service, pg 1015

ILLINOIS

Educational Insights, pg 857

INDIANA

Herff Jones | Nystrom, pg 888

KENTUCKY

National Geographic Learning, pg 952

MARYLAND

Absolute Hollywood, pg 772
MMI Corp, pg 944

NEW JERSEY

A W Peller & Associates Inc, pg 971

NEW YORK

Magnaplan Corp, pg 928

NORTH CAROLINA

Carolina Biological Supply Co, pg 820

WISCONSIN

Demco Inc, pg 845
School Specialty Inc, pg 1004

Globe Producers

CALIFORNIA

QRS Software Services, pg 988
Total Media Group, pg 1042

CONNECTICUT

Broadcast Video Productions LLC, pg 813

ILLINOIS

LightCraft Graphics Inc, pg 920
Rand McNally Education, pg 991

INDIANA

Herff Jones | Nystrom, pg 888

KENTUCKY

National Geographic Learning, pg 952

MARYLAND

Absolute Hollywood, pg 772

MICHIGAN

K&R's Recording Studios Inc, pg 908

MISSOURI

Celebrities Productions, pg 822

OHIO

Creative Technology, pg 838
Vista Color Imaging Inc, pg 1059

PENNSYLVANIA

Main Point Productions, pg 929

TENNESSEE

Running Pony Productions LLC, pg 1000

TEXAS

The Music Bakery, pg 950

VIRGINIA

Advance Concepts Inc, pg 777

Globe Rentals

MARYLAND

Absolute Hollywood, pg 772

Government Program Distributors

CALIFORNIA

Ben Barry & Associates Inc, pg 803
Crystal Pyramid Productions™, pg 840
Discovery Education - Los Angeles, pg 848
Glenn Photo Supply, pg 878

COLORADO

Vital Learning LLC, pg 1060

FLORIDA

ACE Video Resources Software, pg 774
Allegro Productions Inc, pg 781
Capital Communications Inc, pg 819

GEORGIA

Visioneering International Inc, pg 1058

ILLINOIS

CCH Inc, A Wolters Kluwer business, pg 821
CCore Media Inc, pg 821
Film Ideas, pg 867

MARYLAND

Special Archives Division, Motion Picture Branch, pg 1020

MICHIGAN

Digi Sign Design LLC, pg 847

NEW HAMPSHIRE

Chip Taylor Communications LLC, pg 1032

NEW MEXICO

National Information Center for Educational Media (NICEM)/MediaSleuth, pg 952

NEW YORK

Monad Trainer's Aide Inc, pg 945
MRG Productions Inc, pg 948
Women Make Movies Inc, pg 1069

NORTH CAROLINA

Vide-O-Go/That's Infotainment!, pg 1054

OHIO

Treehaus Communications Inc, pg 1044

PENNSYLVANIA

FMP Media Solutions Inc, pg 870

VIRGINIA

National Audiovisual Center - National Technical Information Service (NTIS), pg 952

ONTARIO

Kineticvideo.com, pg 911

Government Program Producers

Government Program Rentals

Industrial Program Distributors

PROGRAMMING — AUDIO/VISUAL

Industrial Program Distributors (continued)

FLORIDA

ACE Video Resources Software, pg 774
Allegro Productions Inc, pg 781
Capital Communications Inc, pg 819

GEORGIA

Convergent Media Systems, pg 836
Thompson-Mitchell & Associates Inc, pg 1039
Visioneering International Inc, pg 1058

ILLINOIS

CCore Media Inc, pg 821
National Safety Council (NSC), pg 953
Woodside Avenue Music Productions Inc, pg 1069

KENTUCKY

Hammond Communications Group, pg 884

MASSACHUSETTS

Preston Productions Inc, pg 981

MICHIGAN

Digi Sign Design LLC, pg 847
Resource Development Co LLC, pg 995

NEW HAMPSHIRE

Chip Taylor Communications LLC, pg 1032

NEW JERSEY

Advanced Imaging Concepts Inc, pg 777
Euro-Pacific Film & Video Productions Inc, pg 863

NEW MEXICO

National Information Center for Educational Media (NICEM)/MediaSleuth, pg 952

NEW YORK

Fanlight Productions, pg 865
Guidance Associates Inc Center for Humanities, pg 883
HB-Content, pg 886
KickedUp Media Group Inc, pg 910
Monad Trainer's Aide Inc, pg 945
MRG Productions Inc, pg 948
TeleTime Productions, pg 1036

NORTH CAROLINA

Vide-O-Go/That's Infotainment!, pg 1054

OHIO

South-Western Publishing Co, pg 1019
Treehaus Communications Inc, pg 1044

PENNSYLVANIA

FMP Media Solutions Inc, pg 870
Media Inc, pg 936

SOUTH CAROLINA

DaviSound, pg 843

TENNESSEE

Marine Geographic, pg 931

TEXAS

The Samuels Co, pg 1002
University of Texas at Austin - Petroleum Extension Service, pg 1050

WISCONSIN

Wisconsin Technical College System Foundation Inc, pg 1068

ONTARIO

BBC Worldwide Canada Ltd, pg 803
Canadian Learning Co Inc, pg 818
Kineticvideo.com, pg 911

Industrial Program Producers

ALABAMA

Media Visions Inc, pg 937

ARIZONA

Aardvark Productions LLC, pg 772
Candee Productions Inc, pg 819

ARKANSAS

Live'N'Loud, pg 923
White Diamond Productions, pg 1065

CALIFORNIA

Academy Savant, pg 773
AM Productions, pg 783
Crystal Pyramid Productions™, pg 840
Design Media, pg 845
Direct Images Interactive Inc, pg 848
Discovery Education - Los Angeles, pg 848
Dolphin MultiMedia Inc, pg 850
imageReal Pictures LLC, pg 896
Jaguar Distribution Corp, pg 903
KABA Audio Productions, pg 907
Kavich Reynolds Productions Inc, pg 908
Lynch Communications, pg 926
Media Magic, pg 937
The Media Staff Inc, pg 937
Panorama Productions, pg 968
PM Productions, pg 977
SBS Productions, pg 1003
Screen Door Entertainment Inc, pg 1005
SNAP, pg 1014
Tam Communications Inc, pg 1031
Tigar Hare Studios, pg 1040
Total Media Group, pg 1042
Vineyard Video & Photography, pg 1058
Wavemaker Media Design, pg 1062
Webster Communications, pg 1063
West Coast Projections Inc, pg 1063

COLORADO

Paul L Anderson Productions Inc, pg 786
Daylight Productions & Rentals, pg 844
Flashback Media Productions, pg 869
Phelan Productions Inc, pg 973
Vital Learning LLC, pg 1060

CONNECTICUT

Applebox Studio, pg 788
Biomedical Media Communications Dept, pg 807
Broadcast Video Productions LLC, pg 813
MCC Films, pg 935

DISTRICT OF COLUMBIA

Hillmann & Carr Inc, pg 889
O'Keefe Communications Inc, pg 961

FLORIDA

Accel Video Productions, pg 773
ACE Video Resources Software, pg 774
Allegro Productions Inc, pg 781
Capital Communications Inc, pg 819
Sunfire Communications Inc, pg 1028
Tricycle Studios, pg 1044
Universal Studios Florida® Production Group, pg 1049
Video Techniques Inc, pg 1056

GEORGIA

Beachwood Productions, pg 804
Continental Film & Video, pg 835
Guerrilla Productions LLC, pg 883
Visioneering International Inc, pg 1058

HAWAII

Hyperspective Studios Inc, pg 893

ILLINOIS

Airways Digital Media, pg 779
Audio Visual Services Corp, pg 796
CCore Media Inc, pg 821
Chicago Satellite & Video, pg 825
Cresta Creative, pg 839
1st Financial Training Services Inc, pg 868
Major Media Productions Inc, pg 929
National Safety Council (NSC), pg 953
The Pepper Group, pg 972
PSAV® Presentation Services (Hotel Services Division), pg 987
20/20 Communications Inc, pg 1047
Video Impressions, pg 1055
Woodside Avenue Music Productions Inc, pg 1069

INDIANA

AVA Productions, pg 798
Digital Rain LLC, pg 847

KANSAS

Chapman Recording & Mastering, pg 824
Sagebrush Video Productions, pg 1001

KENTUCKY

NIMCO Inc, pg 957

LOUISIANA

Digital FX Inc, pg 847
Disk Productions, pg 849

MARYLAND

The Cutting Corp, pg 841
dbF a Media Company, pg 844
The Image Generators, pg 895
Mobile-Video Productions Inc, pg 944

MASSACHUSETTS

CommCreative, pg 832
Cramer Productions, pg 837
Soundtrack Recording Studios, pg 1018
TVN-The Video Network, pg 1046

MICHIGAN

Digi Sign Design LLC, pg 847
K&R All Media Productions Inc, pg 908
K&R's Recording Studios Inc, pg 908
Resource Development Co LLC, pg 995
Universal Images, pg 1049

MINNESOTA

Big Event Productions LLC, pg 807
Live Spark Inc, pg 923
Master Communications Group, pg 933
MultiMedia, pg 950

MONTANA

North Country Media Group, pg 959

NEBRASKA

Dog & Pony Productions Inc, pg 850

NEVADA

HDTV Productions Inc, pg 886
JCS Video Productions, pg 904
Tanglewood Productions, pg 1031

NEW HAMPSHIRE

Apertura, pg 788
Chip Taylor Communications LLC, pg 1032

NEW JERSEY

Advanced Imaging Concepts Inc, pg 777
Half Moon Video Productions, pg 883
Laurel Video Productions, pg 916
Optisonics Productions, pg 965
Suede Interactive, pg 1027

NEW MEXICO

Michael Dunn Productions, pg 853

NEW YORK

Norman N Axelrod Associates, pg 800
Blue Barn Pictures Inc, pg 809
Broad Street Inc, pg 812
Castillo Theater, pg 820
dM works, pg 849

Duggal Visual Solutions, pg 853
Fanlight Productions, pg 865
Guidance Associates Inc Center for Humanities, pg 883
Havas Worldwide, pg 886
HB-Content, pg 886
Hello World Communications, pg 888
Image Zone Inc, pg 896
Ketchum Pleon Change, pg 910
KickedUp Media Group Inc, pg 910
Long Island Video Enterprises Live Inc, pg 924
Manhattan Center Studios Inc, pg 930
Neal Marshad Productions, pg 931
Jack Morton Worldwide, pg 946
MRG Productions Inc, pg 948
MRY, pg 949
New York Audio Productions, pg 956
News Broadcast Network, pg 956
Northeast Video Productions Inc, pg 959
Shelly Palmer Production, pg 968
Polestar Films & Associated Arts Ltd, pg 978
Sunrise Media LLC, pg 1028
TBA Global Events, pg 1032
Zelman Studios Ltd, pg 1073

NORTH CAROLINA

Pat Appleson Studios Inc, pg 788
The Communications Group Inc, pg 833
Kino Mountain Productions LLC, pg 911
LCW Productions LLC, pg 917
Moving Pictures, pg 948
PACE Worldwide, pg 966

OHIO

Advent Media Inc, pg 778
Creative Technology, pg 838
Cuyahoga Community College Media Center, pg 841
Image Video Teleproductions Inc, pg 895
Lyon Video Inc, pg 927
MainSail Production Services Inc, pg 929
R&B Communications Inc, pg 991
South-Western Publishing Co, pg 1019
Take 1 Media Services, pg 1031
Treehaus Communications Inc, pg 1044
Vista Color Imaging Inc, pg 1059

OREGON

A KTVA Production LLC, pg 771
Ideascape Inc, pg 894
Odyssey Productions Inc, pg 961

PENNSYLVANIA

AiH Group Inc, pg 779
Audio Visual Communications Inc, pg 795
Bang Pictures, pg 802
FMP Media Solutions Inc, pg 870
JPL, pg 906
Kensington Falls Animation, pg 909
Main Point Productions, pg 929
Muderick Media, pg 949
Panta Rhei Media Inc, pg 968
Pemcor LLC, pg 971
Production Masters Inc (PMI), pg 984

RHODE ISLAND

Sound-FX-Design, pg 1017

SOUTH CAROLINA

DaviSound, pg 843

TENNESSEE

Continental Film, pg 835
Marine Geographic, pg 931
Running Pony Productions LLC, pg 1000
WKPT-TV, pg 1068

TEXAS

Biway Media, pg 808
Dykeman Associates Inc, pg 854
Epic Software Group Inc, pg 862
Mediaforce Productions, pg 937
Romar Learning, pg 999
The Samuels Co, pg 1002
South Coast Film & Video, pg 1019
Stage Directions, pg 1022
Stockyard Photos/Jim Olive Photography, pg 1025
Tropikal Productions, pg 1045
University of Texas at Austin - Petroleum Extension Service, pg 1050

VIRGINIA

Advance Concepts Inc, pg 777
CALIBRE, pg 816
D&B Television & Video Productions Inc, pg 842
ITC Learning LLC, pg 903
Lion Recording Services Inc, pg 922
Metro Productions, pg 939

WASHINGTON

Adams Creative & Production Services, pg 775
Kostov Productions, pg 913

WEST VIRGINIA

Altruist Media LLC, pg 783

WISCONSIN

Audio Visual of Milwaukee Inc, pg 795
AVS Group, pg 800
Logan Productions Inc, pg 924
Rucinski & Reetz Communications LLC, pg 1000
USAV Group Inc, pg 1050
Video Wisconsin Inc, pg 1056
Watts Communications Inc, pg 1062
Wisconsin Public Television, pg 1068
Wisconsin Technical College System Foundation Inc, pg 1068

WYOMING

Bridger Productions Inc, pg 812

ALBERTA

Black Media Works, pg 808

BRITISH COLUMBIA

West Eagle Films Inc, pg 1064

NEWFOUNDLAND AND LABRADOR

Vidcraft Productions Ltd, pg 1054

ONTARIO

BBC Worldwide Canada Ltd, pg 803
DebsVoice, pg 844
Mediaimage Communications Group, pg 937

QUEBEC

Kerrigan Productions Inc, pg 910

Industrial Program Rentals

CALIFORNIA

Glenn Photo Supply, pg 878

GEORGIA

Convergent Media Systems, pg 836
ON Event Services, pg 963

ILLINOIS

National Safety Council (NSC), pg 953
Woodside Avenue Music Productions Inc, pg 1069

MASSACHUSETTS

Preston Productions Inc, pg 981

MICHIGAN

Digi Sign Design LLC, pg 847

NEW HAMPSHIRE

Chip Taylor Communications LLC, pg 1032

NEW JERSEY

Euro-Pacific Film & Video Productions Inc, pg 863

NEW YORK

Fanlight Productions, pg 865
Historic Films, pg 889
TBA Global Events, pg 1032

UTAH

Webb Audio Visual Communication, pg 1063

Literature, *see* Feature Program

Map Distributors

ARIZONA

Arizona Cine Equipment, pg 789

CALIFORNIA

Astronomical Society of the Pacific, pg 792
Health Education Services, pg 887
QRS Software Services, pg 988
Social Studies School Service, pg 1015

FLORIDA

Kappa Map Group LLC, pg 908

INDIANA

Herff Jones | Nystrom, pg 888

KENTUCKY

National Geographic Learning, pg 952

MARYLAND

MMI Corp, pg 944

NEW HAMPSHIRE

Frey Scientific, pg 873

NEW JERSEY

A W Peller & Associates Inc, pg 971

NEW MEXICO

National Information Center for Educational Media (NICEM)/MediaSleuth, pg 952

NEW YORK

Magnaplan Corp, pg 928

NORTH CAROLINA

Carolina Biological Supply Co, pg 820

PENNSYLVANIA

AccuWeather Inc, pg 774

SOUTH CAROLINA

BJU Press, pg 808

TENNESSEE

B&H Publishing Group, pg 802
Randall House Publications, pg 991
Spring Arbor Distributors, pg 1022

WISCONSIN

School Specialty Inc, pg 1004

Map Producers

CALIFORNIA

QRS Software Services, pg 988
Total Media Group, pg 1042
The Wine Appreciation Guild Ltd, pg 1067

COLORADO

Flashback Media Productions, pg 869

CONNECTICUT

Broadcast Video Productions LLC, pg 813

FLORIDA

Kappa Map Group LLC, pg 908

GEORGIA

Imagers, pg 896

ILLINOIS

LightCraft Graphics Inc, pg 920
Quartet Manufacturing Co, pg 989
Rand McNally Education, pg 991

INDIANA

Bright Ideas Creative Services, pg 812
Herff Jones | Nystrom, pg 888

PROGRAMMING — AUDIO/VISUAL

Map Producers (continued)

KENTUCKY

National Geographic Learning, pg 952

MASSACHUSETTS

CommCreative, pg 832

MICHIGAN

K&R's Recording Studios Inc, pg 908

MISSOURI

Celebrities Productions, pg 822

NEW JERSEY

Fiber Optic Systems Inc (FOSI), pg 866

NEW YORK

Applause Learning Resources, pg 788

OHIO

Creative Technology, pg 838
Vista Color Imaging Inc, pg 1059

OREGON

InterVision Media, pg 902

PENNSYLVANIA

AccuWeather Inc, pg 774
Kensington Falls Animation, pg 909
Main Point Productions, pg 929

SOUTH CAROLINA

BJU Press, pg 808

TENNESSEE

Running Pony Productions LLC, pg 1000

VIRGINIA

Advance Concepts Inc, pg 777
Blair Inc, pg 809

WISCONSIN

USAV Group Inc, pg 1050

Medical Program Distributors

ARIZONA

Video Learning Library, pg 1055

CALIFORNIA

Academy Savant, pg 773
Crystal Pyramid Productions™, pg 840
Davies Publishing Inc, pg 843
Discovery Education - Los Angeles, pg 848
Geddes Productions LLC, pg 876
Glenn Photo Supply, pg 878
Bruce Goldberg Inc, pg 880
Joyce Media Inc, pg 906
Madera Video, pg 927
Medcom Inc, pg 936
New & Unique Videos™, pg 955
TMW Media Group, pg 1041

COLORADO

Vital Learning LLC, pg 1060

CONNECTICUT

Cine-Med Inc, pg 826

FLORIDA

Allegro Productions Inc, pg 781
Capital Communications Inc, pg 819
Motion Image Group LLC, pg 947

ILLINOIS

CCore Media Inc, pg 821
Film Ideas, pg 867

LOUISIANA

Louisiana State University Health Sciences Center - Shreveport, pg 925

MASSACHUSETTS

Gyrus ACMI, pg 883
Preston Productions Inc, pg 981

MICHIGAN

Digi Sign Design LLC, pg 847
Emery-Pratt Co, pg 860
MSU Technologies, pg 949
Phoenix Society for Burn Survivors Inc, pg 974

MISSOURI

Mosby Inc, pg 947
University of Missouri-Kansas City School of Dentistry, pg 1050

NEW HAMPSHIRE

Frey Scientific, pg 873
Chip Taylor Communications LLC, pg 1032

NEW JERSEY

Advanced Imaging Concepts Inc, pg 777
Euro-Pacific Film & Video Productions Inc, pg 863

NEW MEXICO

National Information Center for Educational Media (NICEM)/ MediaSleuth, pg 952
Uncharted Country Publishing, pg 1048

NEW YORK

Fanlight Productions, pg 865
Guidance Associates Inc Center for Humanities, pg 883
HB-Content, pg 886
KickedUp Media Group Inc, pg 910
Monad Trainer's Aide Inc, pg 945
MRG Productions Inc, pg 948
News Broadcast Network, pg 956
Select Media Inc, pg 1006
VIEW Inc (Video International Entertainment World Inc), pg 1058
Women Make Movies Inc, pg 1069

NORTH CAROLINA

Sinclair Institute, pg 1012
Vide-O-Go/That's Infotainment!, pg 1054

OHIO

South-Western Publishing Co, pg 1019

PENNSYLVANIA

FMP Media Solutions Inc, pg 870
Lippincott Williams & Wilkins, pg 922
Media Inc, pg 936
TouchStar Productions Inc, pg 1042

VIRGINIA

PBS Video, pg 970

WASHINGTON

Medical Media Systems, pg 938

ONTARIO

BBC Worldwide Canada Ltd, pg 803
Canadian Learning Co Inc, pg 818
Kineticvideo.com, pg 911
Life Cycle Books Ltd, pg 920

Medical Program Producers

ALABAMA

Media Visions Inc, pg 937

ARIZONA

Aardvark Productions LLC, pg 772
Candee Productions Inc, pg 819

ARKANSAS

White Diamond Productions, pg 1065

CALIFORNIA

Academy Savant, pg 773
Crystal Pyramid Productions™, pg 840
Design Media, pg 845
Direct Images Interactive Inc, pg 848
Discovery Education - Los Angeles, pg 848
Dolphin MultiMedia Inc, pg 850
Geddes Productions LLC, pg 876
imageReal Pictures LLC, pg 896
Jaguar Distribution Corp, pg 903
Joyce Media Inc, pg 906
KABA Audio Productions, pg 907
Lynch Communications, pg 926
Madera Video, pg 927
Medcom Inc, pg 936
The Media Staff Inc, pg 937
Panorama Productions, pg 968
PM Productions, pg 977
SNAP, pg 1014
Tigar Hare Studios, pg 1040
TMW Media Group, pg 1041
Total Media Group, pg 1042
Vineyard Video & Photography, pg 1058
Wavemaker Media Design, pg 1062
West Coast Projections Inc, pg 1063

COLORADO

Paul L Anderson Productions Inc, pg 786
Daylight Productions & Rentals, pg 844
Flashback Media Productions, pg 869
Vital Learning LLC, pg 1060

CONNECTICUT

Biomedical Media Communications Dept, pg 807
Broadcast Video Productions LLC, pg 813
Cine-Med Inc, pg 826
MCC Films, pg 935
New London Media, pg 956

DISTRICT OF COLUMBIA

Hillmann & Carr Inc, pg 889
O'Keefe Communications Inc, pg 961

FLORIDA

Accel Video Productions, pg 773
Capital Communications Inc, pg 819
Home Shopping Network (HSN), pg 890
Motion Image Group LLC, pg 947
Sunfire Communications Inc, pg 1028
Teach America Corp, pg 1033
Tricycle Studios, pg 1044
Video Techniques Inc, pg 1056

GEORGIA

Beachwood Productions, pg 804
Guerrilla Productions LLC, pg 883

HAWAII

Hyperspective Studios Inc, pg 893

ILLINOIS

Airways Digital Media, pg 779
CCore Media Inc, pg 821
Chicago Satellite & Video, pg 825
Major Media Productions Inc, pg 929
Manning Productions, pg 930
The Pepper Group, pg 972
SCI Television Productions LLC, pg 1004
20/20 Communications Inc, pg 1047
Video Impressions, pg 1055

INDIANA

AVA Productions, pg 798
Digital Rain LLC, pg 847

KANSAS

Chapman Recording & Mastering, pg 824

LOUISIANA

Digital FX Inc, pg 847
Louisiana State University Health Sciences Center - Shreveport, pg 925

MARYLAND

The Cutting Corp, pg 841
dbF a Media Company, pg 844
The Image Generators, pg 895
Mobile-Video Productions Inc, pg 944

Medical Program Rentals

Model & Mock-up Distributors

Model & Mock-up Producers

PROGRAMMING — AUDIO/VISUAL

Model & Mock-up Producers (continued)

CONNECTICUT

Broadcast Video Productions LLC, pg 813

HAWAII

ATTCO Inc, pg 793
Hyperspective Studios Inc, pg 893

ILLINOIS

LightCraft Graphics Inc, pg 920

INDIANA

AVA Productions, pg 798
Herff Jones | Nystrom, pg 888

LOUISIANA

Moxie Media, pg 948

MICHIGAN

Digi Sign Design LLC, pg 847
K&R All Media Productions Inc, pg 908
K&R's Recording Studios Inc, pg 908

MISSOURI

Celebrities Productions, pg 822
Switch, pg 1030

NEW JERSEY

Fiber Optic Systems Inc (FOSI), pg 866

NEW YORK

MRG Productions Inc, pg 948

OHIO

Creative Technology, pg 838
Vista Color Imaging Inc, pg 1059

OREGON

InterVision Media, pg 902

VIRGINIA

Blair Inc, pg 809

WISCONSIN

USAV Group Inc, pg 1050

Model & Mock-up Rentals

MICHIGAN

Digi Sign Design LLC, pg 847

Multimedia, CD-ROM & DVD Interactive Program Distributors

CALIFORNIA

Astronomical Society of the Pacific, pg 792
California Language Laboratories, pg 817
Crystal Pyramid Productions™, pg 840
Davies Publishing Inc, pg 843
Discovery Education - Los Angeles, pg 848
Dogma Studios, pg 850
Future US Inc, pg 874
Griggs Productions Inc, pg 882
MarVista Entertainment Inc, pg 933
Medcom Inc, pg 936
QRS Software Services, pg 988
Rovi Corp, pg 1000
The Wine Appreciation Guild Ltd, pg 1067

COLORADO

National Teaching Aids Inc, pg 953
Vital Learning LLC, pg 1060

CONNECTICUT

Cine-Med Inc, pg 826
Crossroads Video, pg 840
Pictures of Record Inc, pg 975

FLORIDA

ACE Video Resources Software, pg 774
Allegro Productions Inc, pg 781
CD ROM™ Inc, pg 822

GEORGIA

Convergent Media Systems, pg 836
School Media Associates LLC, pg 1004
Visioneering International Inc, pg 1058

HAWAII

Media Bridge Gamekids, pg 936

ILLINOIS

Britannica Film & Video, pg 812
CCore Media Inc, pg 821
Educational Insights, pg 857
National Safety Council (NSC), pg 953

INDIANA

Agency for Instructional Technology (AIT), pg 778
Herff Jones | Nystrom, pg 888

IOWA

Right Stuf Inc, pg 997

KENTUCKY

National Geographic Learning, pg 952

MARYLAND

MMI Corp, pg 944

MASSACHUSETTS

Documentary Educational Resources Inc, pg 850
Preston Productions Inc, pg 981
Sinauer Associates Inc, pg 1011

MICHIGAN

Digi Sign Design LLC, pg 847
MSU Technologies, pg 949
Zondervan, A HarperCollins Company, pg 1074

MINNESOTA

Beyers Sound & Essay Audio, pg 806
EMC/Paradigm Publishing, pg 860
JIST Publishing, pg 905

MISSOURI

The Phoenix Learning Group Inc, pg 974

NEW HAMPSHIRE

Frey Scientific, pg 873
Chip Taylor Communications LLC, pg 1032

NEW JERSEY

Euro-Pacific Film & Video Productions Inc, pg 863

NEW MEXICO

National Information Center for Educational Media (NICEM)/MediaSleuth, pg 952

NEW YORK

Brooklyn Botanic Garden, pg 814
The Bureau for At-Risk Youth, pg 815
Educational Images Ltd, pg 857
Films for the Humanities & Sciences, pg 868
Guidance Associates Inc Center for Humanities, pg 883
HB-Content, pg 886
Human Relations Media, pg 892
Interactive International Inc, pg 899
Magnetic Music Publishing Co, pg 928
Meridian Education Corp, pg 939
Monad Trainer's Aide Inc, pg 945
MRG Productions Inc, pg 948
Scholastic Media, pg 1004
Shopware, pg 1009
Trans-Lux Multimedia Corp, pg 1043
Video Aided Instruction Inc, pg 1054
WorldView Software, pg 1070

NORTH CAROLINA

Vide-O-Go/That's Infotainment!, pg 1054

OREGON

Wilderness Video, pg 1066

PENNSYLVANIA

AccuWeather Inc, pg 774
Discovery Education - South Burlington, pg 848
FMP Media Solutions Inc, pg 870
MVD Entertainment Group, pg 951
New Horizons Computer Learning Centers Inc, pg 955
Science for Kids, pg 1005

TENNESSEE

Marine Geographic, pg 931
Spring Arbor Distributors, pg 1022

TEXAS

Replicopy Digital Media Center, pg 995

UTAH

Strata™, pg 1025

VERMONT

Ashgate Publishing Co, pg 792
Multicultural Media, pg 950

VIRGINIA

National Audiovisual Center - National Technical Information Service (NTIS), pg 952

WASHINGTON

Intermedia Inc, pg 900

WISCONSIN

Wisconsin Technical College System Foundation Inc, pg 1068

MANITOBA

Inland Audio Visual Ltd, pg 898
Tek Gear, pg 1035

ONTARIO

Canadian Learning Co Inc, pg 818
The Children's Book Store Distribution (CBSD), pg 825
McIntyre Media Inc, pg 935

Multimedia, CD-ROM & DVD Interactive Program Producers

ALABAMA

Media Visions Inc, pg 937

ARIZONA

Aardvark Productions LLC, pg 772

CALIFORNIA

Ancient Future, pg 786
Animax, pg 787
Astronomical Society of the Pacific, pg 792
California Language Laboratories, pg 817
Crystal Pyramid Productions™, pg 840
Design Media, pg 845
Direct Images Interactive Inc, pg 848
Discovery Education - Los Angeles, pg 848
Dogma Studios, pg 850
Dolphin MultiMedia Inc, pg 850
Future US Inc, pg 874
IEEE Computer Society Press, pg 894
Lumeni Productions Inc, pg 926
Lynch Communications, pg 926
Medcom Inc, pg 936
Media Magic, pg 937
The Media Staff Inc, pg 937
New Circuit Films LLC, pg 955
Panorama Productions, pg 968
QRS Software Services, pg 988
SBS Productions, pg 1003
SNAP, pg 1014
Tam Communications Inc, pg 1031
Tigar Hare Studios, pg 1040
Total Media Group, pg 1042
Towards 2000 Inc, pg 1043
Video Movie Magic, pg 1056
Vineyard Video & Photography, pg 1058
Wavemaker Media Design, pg 1062
Webster Communications, pg 1063
West Coast Projections Inc, pg 1063
WMS Media Inc, pg 1069

PROGRAMMING — AUDIO/VISUAL

Multimedia, CD-ROM & DVD Interactive Program Producers (continued)

WISCONSIN

Audio Visual of Milwaukee Inc, pg 795
Logan Productions Inc, pg 924
Rucinski & Reetz Communications LLC, pg 1000
USAV Group Inc, pg 1050
Video Wisconsin Inc, pg 1056
Watts Communications Inc, pg 1062
Wisconsin Public Television, pg 1068
Wisconsin Technical College System Foundation Inc, pg 1068

WYOMING

Bridger Productions Inc, pg 812

ALBERTA

Black Media Works, pg 808
HBW Entertainment Inc, pg 886

BRITISH COLUMBIA

West Eagle Films Inc, pg 1064

MANITOBA

Tek Gear, pg 1035

NEWFOUNDLAND AND LABRADOR

Vidcraft Productions Ltd, pg 1054

ONTARIO

DebsVoice, pg 844
GAPC (General Assembly Production Centre), pg 875
Gesturetek, pg 877
JFB Communications, pg 905
Mediaimage Communications Group, pg 937
Purefire Communications Inc, pg 987
SLI Manufacturing Inc, pg 1013

QUEBEC

Kerrigan Productions Inc, pg 910

Multimedia, CD-ROM & DVD Interactive Program Rentals

CONNECTICUT

Pictures of Record Inc, pg 975

DELAWARE

Side Door Studio Inc, pg 1010

GEORGIA

Convergent Media Systems, pg 836

MASSACHUSETTS

Documentary Educational Resources Inc, pg 850
Preston Productions Inc, pg 981

MICHIGAN

Digi Sign Design LLC, pg 847

NEW HAMPSHIRE

Chip Taylor Communications LLC, pg 1032

NEW JERSEY

Euro-Pacific Film & Video Productions Inc, pg 863

NEW YORK

Brooklyn Botanic Garden, pg 814
Interactive International Inc, pg 899

UTAH

Webb Audio Visual Communication, pg 1063

WASHINGTON

Intermedia Inc, pg 900

MANITOBA

Tek Gear, pg 1035

Multimedia Kit Distributors

ARIZONA

Arizona Cine Equipment, pg 789

CALIFORNIA

Ametron Audio/Video, pg 785
Astronomical Society of the Pacific, pg 792
Crystal Productions, pg 840
Discovery Education - Los Angeles, pg 848
QRS Software Services, pg 988
Social Studies School Service, pg 1015
The Wine Appreciation Guild Ltd, pg 1067

COLORADO

National Teaching Aids Inc, pg 953
Vital Learning LLC, pg 1060

CONNECTICUT

Crossroads Video, pg 840

GEORGIA

School Media Associates LLC, pg 1004

ILLINOIS

Educational Insights, pg 857
National Safety Council (NSC), pg 953
Sunburst Digital, pg 1028

INDIANA

Agency for Instructional Technology (AIT), pg 778
Herff Jones | Nystrom, pg 888

KENTUCKY

National Geographic Learning, pg 952

MARYLAND

Department of Education Resources, pg 845
Kids on the Block Inc, pg 910
MMI Corp, pg 944
Nicholas P Pipino Associates Inc, pg 976

MASSACHUSETTS

Cheng & Tsui Co, pg 824
Triumph Learning LLC, pg 1045

MICHIGAN

Digi Sign Design LLC, pg 847

MISSOURI

Marsh Media, pg 931
Mosby Inc, pg 947

NEW HAMPSHIRE

Frey Scientific, pg 873

NEW JERSEY

Educational Impressions, pg 857
A W Peller & Associates Inc, pg 971

NEW MEXICO

National Information Center for Educational Media (NICEM)/ MediaSleuth, pg 952
Uncharted Country Publishing, pg 1048

NEW YORK

Brooklyn Botanic Garden, pg 814
Criterion Collection, pg 839
Educational Activities Inc, pg 857
Educational Images Ltd, pg 857
Guidance Associates Inc Center for Humanities, pg 883
Human Relations Media, pg 892
Magnetic Music Publishing Co, pg 928
Voyetra Turtle Beach, pg 1061

NORTH CAROLINA

Carolina Biological Supply Co, pg 820

OHIO

McGraw-Hill School Education Group, pg 935
South-Western Publishing Co, pg 1019
Treehaus Communications Inc, pg 1044

PENNSYLVANIA

Discovery Education - South Burlington, pg 848
TRC Interactive Inc, pg 1044

TEXAS

Lamb & Lion Ministries, pg 915
Stage Directions, pg 1022

VERMONT

Taylor Associates, pg 1032
Wilson McLeran Inc, pg 1067

VIRGINIA

National Audiovisual Center - National Technical Information Service (NTIS), pg 952

WISCONSIN

Knowledge Unlimited Inc, pg 912
Plank Road Publishing Inc, pg 976
School Specialty Inc, pg 1004

ONTARIO

Canadian Learning Co Inc, pg 818
The Resource Centre, pg 995

QUEBEC

National Film Board of Canada/Office National du Film du Canada, pg 952

Multimedia Kit Producers

ARIZONA

Aardvark Productions LLC, pg 772

ARKANSAS

Live'N'Loud, pg 923

CALIFORNIA

Astronomical Society of the Pacific, pg 792
Custom Video Productions Inc, pg 841
Design Media, pg 845
Direct Images Interactive Inc, pg 848
Discovery Education - Los Angeles, pg 848
Dogma Studios, pg 850
Dolphin MultiMedia Inc, pg 850
International Contact Inc, pg 900
Main Street Media Inc, pg 929
Media Magic, pg 937
Panorama Productions, pg 968
piXvfm, pg 976
QRS Software Services, pg 988
Rhythms Productions (Tom Thumb Music), pg 996
SBS Productions, pg 1003
Tam Communications Inc, pg 1031
Wavemaker Media Design, pg 1062

COLORADO

National Teaching Aids Inc, pg 953
Starwest Productions, pg 1024
Vital Learning LLC, pg 1060

CONNECTICUT

Antenna International, pg 787
Broadcast Video Productions LLC, pg 813
Crossroads Video, pg 840

DISTRICT OF COLUMBIA

Hillmann & Carr Inc, pg 889
O'Keefe Communications Inc, pg 961

FLORIDA

Tricycle Studios, pg 1044

GEORGIA

First Cut Communications LLC, pg 868
Guerrilla Productions LLC, pg 883
Imagers, pg 896

HAWAII

Hyperspective Studios Inc, pg 893

ILLINOIS

ABS Enterprises, pg 772
Airways Digital Media, pg 779
LightCraft Graphics Inc, pg 920
National Safety Council (NSC), pg 953
Rand McNally Education, pg 991
Sparkfactor, pg 1019
Sunburst Digital, pg 1028

INDIANA

Agency for Instructional Technology (AIT), pg 778
Herff Jones | Nystrom, pg 888
OMNI Productions, pg 962

IOWA

The Production House, pg 984

KENTUCKY

National Geographic Learning, pg 952
Prosper Media Group Inc, pg 986

LOUISIANA

Louisiana State University Health Sciences Center - Shreveport, pg 925

MARYLAND

Department of Education Resources, pg 845
Kids on the Block Inc, pg 910
Milner-Fenwick Inc, pg 943

MASSACHUSETTS

Capron Lighting & Sound Co Inc, pg 819
TR Productions, pg 1043

MICHIGAN

Digi Sign Design LLC, pg 847
K&R All Media Productions Inc, pg 908
K&R's Recording Studios Inc, pg 908
MessageMakers, pg 939

MINNESOTA

Jamieson & Associates Inc, pg 904

MISSOURI

Celebrities Productions, pg 822
Marsh Media, pg 931
Mosby Inc, pg 947
Switch, pg 1030

NEVADA

Encore Productions Inc, pg 861
JCS Video Productions, pg 904

NEW HAMPSHIRE

Frey Scientific, pg 873

NEW JERSEY

Educational Impressions, pg 857
Optisonics Productions, pg 965
Outside The Box Interactive LLC, pg 966

NEW MEXICO

Uncharted Country Publishing, pg 1048

NEW YORK

Blue Barn Pictures Inc, pg 809
Broad Street Inc, pg 812
Criterion Collection, pg 839
dM works, pg 849
Educational Activities Inc, pg 857
Educational Images Ltd, pg 857
Greyfalcon House, pg 882
Guidance Associates Inc Center for Humanities, pg 883
Havas Worldwide, pg 886
Human Relations Media, pg 892
Ketchum Pleon Change, pg 910
L A Bruell Inc, pg 914
Magnetic Music Publishing Co, pg 928
Neal Marshad Productions, pg 931
Jack Morton Worldwide, pg 946
MRG Productions Inc, pg 948
MRY, pg 949
Scholastic Media, pg 1004
Sunrise Media LLC, pg 1028
WorldView Software, pg 1070
Zelman Studios Ltd, pg 1073

NORTH CAROLINA

Carolina Biological Supply Co, pg 820
The Communications Group Inc, pg 833
Image Associates Inc, pg 894
2BruceStudio, pg 1047
World Class Learning Materials Inc, pg 1069

OHIO

Advent Media Inc, pg 778
McGraw-Hill School Education Group, pg 935
South-Western Publishing Co, pg 1019
Treehaus Communications Inc, pg 1044
Vista Color Imaging Inc, pg 1059

OREGON

ERA Learning, pg 862
Ideascape Inc, pg 894
NeoSoft Corp, pg 954

PENNSYLVANIA

Audio Visual Communications Inc, pg 795
Beholder Productions Inc, pg 804
Discovery Education - South Burlington, pg 848
FMP Media Solutions Inc, pg 870
JPL, pg 906
Main Point Productions, pg 929
Production Masters Inc (PMI), pg 984
Scala Inc, pg 1003

TENNESSEE

Center for Southern Folklore Inc, pg 822
Memphis Communications Corp, pg 938

TEXAS

Lamb & Lion Ministries, pg 915
Mediaforce Productions, pg 937
The Music Bakery, pg 950
Omni Intercommunications Inc, pg 962
Romar Learning, pg 999

VERMONT

Wilson McLeran Inc, pg 1067

VIRGINIA

Advance Concepts Inc, pg 777
CALIBRE, pg 816

WISCONSIN

Knowledge Unlimited Inc, pg 912
Plank Road Publishing Inc, pg 976
USAV Group Inc, pg 1050
Video Wisconsin Inc, pg 1056
Watts Communications Inc, pg 1062

NEWFOUNDLAND AND LABRADOR

Vidcraft Productions Ltd, pg 1054

ONTARIO

Art Gallery of Ontario, pg 791
Image Video Services & Productions, pg 895

QUEBEC

Group PVP, pg 882
National Film Board of Canada/Office National du Film du Canada, pg 952

Multimedia Kit Rentals

ARIZONA

Arizona Cine Equipment, pg 789

CALIFORNIA

Ametron Audio/Video, pg 785
deKramer Productions Inc, pg 845

ILLINOIS

The Pepper Group, pg 972

MICHIGAN

Digi Sign Design LLC, pg 847

NEW JERSEY

PLS Staging, pg 977

NEW YORK

Interactive International Inc, pg 899

WYOMING

Bridger Productions Inc, pg 812

News Program Distributors

CALIFORNIA

Crystal Pyramid Productions™, pg 840

FLORIDA

Allegro Productions Inc, pg 781

ILLINOIS

CCore Media Inc, pg 821

MICHIGAN

Digi Sign Design LLC, pg 847

NEW HAMPSHIRE

Chip Taylor Communications LLC, pg 1032

NEW YORK

HB-Content, pg 886
MRG Productions Inc, pg 948
News Broadcast Network, pg 956
Women Make Movies Inc, pg 1069

NORTH CAROLINA

Vide-O-Go/That's Infotainment!, pg 1054

VIRGINIA

PBS Video, pg 970

News Program Producers

ALABAMA

Media Visions Inc, pg 937

ARIZONA

Aardvark Productions LLC, pg 772

CALIFORNIA

Crystal Pyramid Productions™, pg 840
Direct Images Interactive Inc, pg 848
Jaguar Distribution Corp, pg 903
Lynch Communications, pg 926
PM Productions, pg 977
Total Media Group, pg 1042
Vineyard Video & Photography, pg 1058
Webster Communications, pg 1063

COLORADO

Flashback Media Productions, pg 869
Tatum Video, pg 1032

CONNECTICUT

Broadcast Video Productions LLC, pg 813
Fox Connecticut, pg 872

FLORIDA

Accel Video Productions, pg 773
Allegro Productions Inc, pg 781
CD ROM™ Inc, pg 822
Communications Concepts Inc (CCI), pg 833
Sunfire Communications Inc, pg 1028
Video Techniques Inc, pg 1056

GEORGIA

Beachwood Productions, pg 804
Guerrilla Productions LLC, pg 883

ILLINOIS

CCore Media Inc, pg 821
Chicago Satellite & Video, pg 825
Comtech Multimedia Marketing, pg 834
Manning Productions, pg 930
The Pepper Group, pg 972

INDIANA

Digital Rain LLC, pg 847

LOUISIANA

Digital FX Inc, pg 847

MARYLAND

The Image Generators, pg 895

PROGRAMMING — AUDIO/VISUAL

News Program Producers (continued)

MASSACHUSETTS

Soundtrack Recording Studios, pg 1018

MICHIGAN

Benjamin Creative Productions, pg 805
Digi Sign Design LLC, pg 847
K&R All Media Productions Inc, pg 908
K&R's Recording Studios Inc, pg 908

MINNESOTA

MultiMedia, pg 950
Vaddio, pg 1051

NEVADA

JCS Video Productions, pg 904

NEW HAMPSHIRE

Chip Taylor Communications LLC, pg 1032

NEW JERSEY

Half Moon Video Productions, pg 883
Laurel Video Productions, pg 916
Optisonics Productions, pg 965

NEW MEXICO

Michael Dunn Productions, pg 853

NEW YORK

Castillo Theater, pg 820
CompuWeather Inc, pg 834
Havas Worldwide, pg 886
HB-Content, pg 886
Hello World Communications, pg 888
Manhattan Center Studios Inc, pg 930
Jack Morton Worldwide, pg 946
MRG Productions Inc, pg 948
News Broadcast Network, pg 956
Northeast Video Productions Inc, pg 959
Shelly Palmer Production, pg 968
SMP Digital Graphics, pg 1014
Zelman Studios Ltd, pg 1073

NORTH CAROLINA

Pat Appleson Studios Inc, pg 788
LCW Productions LLC, pg 917
Moving Pictures, pg 948

OHIO

Advent Media Inc, pg 778
Creative Technology, pg 838
MainSail Production Services Inc, pg 929
R&B Communications Inc, pg 991
Take 1 Media Services, pg 1031
Vista Color Imaging Inc, pg 1059

PENNSYLVANIA

FMP Media Solutions Inc, pg 870
Main Point Productions, pg 929

RHODE ISLAND

Sound-FX-Design, pg 1017

TENNESSEE

Running Pony Productions LLC, pg 1000
WKPT-TV, pg 1068

TEXAS

Epic Software Group Inc, pg 862
Romar Learning, pg 999
The Samuels Co, pg 1002
Stage Directions, pg 1022

VIRGINIA

D&B Television & Video Productions Inc, pg 842
Lion Recording Services Inc, pg 922

WISCONSIN

Video Wisconsin Inc, pg 1056
Watts Communications Inc, pg 1062
Wisconsin Public Television, pg 1068

WYOMING

Bridger Productions Inc, pg 812

ALBERTA

Black Media Works, pg 808

QUEBEC

Kerrigan Productions Inc, pg 910

News Program Rentals

MICHIGAN

Digi Sign Design LLC, pg 847

NEW HAMPSHIRE

Chip Taylor Communications LLC, pg 1032

UTAH

Webb Audio Visual Communication, pg 1063

Overhead Transparency Distributors

ALABAMA

Media Visions Inc, pg 937

ARIZONA

Arizona Cine Equipment, pg 789

CALIFORNIA

Ametron Audio/Video, pg 785
QRS Software Services, pg 988

CONNECTICUT

USI Inc, pg 1051

FLORIDA

AVI-SPL, pg 798
Pro Stage Inc, pg 983
Tallahassee Audio Visual, pg 1031

GEORGIA

Audio Visual Resources Inc, pg 795
ON Event Services, pg 963
School Media Associates LLC, pg 1004

ILLINOIS

Educational Insights, pg 857

INDIANA

Herff Jones | Nystrom, pg 888

MAINE

Headlight Audio Visual Inc, pg 887

MARYLAND

Nicholas P Pipino Associates Inc, pg 976

MICHIGAN

Michigan Office Solutions, pg 941

MISSOURI

Southwest Binding & Laminating, pg 1019

NEW HAMPSHIRE

Frey Scientific, pg 873

NEW JERSEY

A W Peller & Associates Inc, pg 971

NEW MEXICO

National Information Center for Educational Media (NICEM)/MediaSleuth, pg 952

NEW YORK

Human Relations Media, pg 892
Magnaplan Corp, pg 928
Visual Technologies Corp, pg 1060

OHIO

McGraw-Hill School Education Group, pg 935
South-Western Publishing Co, pg 1019

PENNSYLVANIA

TRC Interactive Inc, pg 1044

TENNESSEE

Randall House Publications, pg 991
Spring Arbor Distributors, pg 1022

TEXAS

Endtime Inc, pg 861

VIRGINIA

Filmdex Inc, pg 867
Microtraining LLC, pg 942

WISCONSIN

Demco Inc, pg 845
Knowledge Unlimited Inc, pg 912
School Specialty Inc, pg 1004

ONTARIO

Nelson Education Ltd, pg 954

Overhead Transparency Producers

ARIZONA

Merestone, pg 938

CALIFORNIA

Geddes Productions LLC, pg 876
Lynch Communications, pg 926
QRS Software Services, pg 988
The Studio Center, pg 1026

CONNECTICUT

Broadcast Video Productions LLC, pg 813

FLORIDA

Image Technical Services, pg 895

GEORGIA

Guerrilla Productions LLC, pg 883
Imagers, pg 896

ILLINOIS

CCore Media Inc, pg 821
LightCraft Graphics Inc, pg 920
Jim Passin Productions, pg 970
QuickSet International Inc, pg 989
Rand McNally Education, pg 991
Universal Training, pg 1049

INDIANA

Herff Jones | Nystrom, pg 888
OMNI Productions, pg 962

IOWA

The Production House, pg 984

KANSAS

Genigraphics®, pg 877

KENTUCKY

NIMCO Inc, pg 957

LOUISIANA

Digital FX Inc, pg 847
Louisiana State University Health Sciences Center - Shreveport, pg 925
Primary Color Laboratory Inc, pg 982

MAINE

Headlight Audio Visual Inc, pg 887

MARYLAND

Lehigh Phoenix™, pg 918

MASSACHUSETTS

DGI-Invisuals LLC, pg 846
TR Productions, pg 1043

MICHIGAN

K&R All Media Productions Inc, pg 908
K&R's Recording Studios Inc, pg 908

MINNESOTA

Aggressive Records Audio Duplication LLC, pg 778
Jamieson & Associates Inc, pg 904

Overhead Transparency Rentals

Public Relations Program Distributors

Public Relations Program Producers

PROGRAMMING — AUDIO/VISUAL

Public Relations Program Producers (continued)

NEW YORK (continued)

Karen Frankel Productions, pg 872
Hallel Communications, pg 884
Havas Worldwide, pg 886
HB-Content, pg 886
Ketchum Pleon Change, pg 910
KickedUp Media Group Inc, pg 910
Manhattan Center Studios Inc, pg 930
Neal Marshad Productions, pg 931
Maryknoll Productions, pg 933
Jack Morton Worldwide, pg 946
MRG Productions Inc, pg 948
News Broadcast Network, pg 956
Northeast Video Productions Inc, pg 959
Shelly Palmer Production, pg 968
SMP Digital Graphics, pg 1014
TBA Global Events, pg 1032
Zelman Studios Ltd, pg 1073

NORTH CAROLINA

Pat Appleson Studios Inc, pg 788
The Communications Group Inc, pg 833
Kino Mountain Productions LLC, pg 911

OHIO

Advent Media Inc, pg 778
Creative Technology, pg 838
MainSail Production Services Inc, pg 929
R&B Communications Inc, pg 991
Take 1 Media Services, pg 1031
Thread Marketing Group, pg 1039
Treehaus Communications Inc, pg 1044
Vista Color Imaging Inc, pg 1059

OREGON

Ideascape Inc, pg 894
Odyssey Productions Inc, pg 961
Rex, pg 995

PENNSYLVANIA

AiH Group Inc, pg 779
FMP Media Solutions Inc, pg 870
JPL, pg 906
Main Point Productions, pg 929
Panta Rhei Media Inc, pg 968
Production Masters Inc (PMI), pg 984

RHODE ISLAND

Sound-FX-Design, pg 1017

TENNESSEE

American Blackguard Inc, pg 784
Continental Film, pg 835
Running Pony Productions LLC, pg 1000

TEXAS

Epic Software Group Inc, pg 862
Mediaforce Productions, pg 937
The Samuels Co, pg 1002
South Coast Film & Video, pg 1019
Stage Directions, pg 1022
Stockyard Photos/Jim Olive Photography, pg 1025

VIRGINIA

Advance Concepts Inc, pg 777
CALIBRE, pg 816
D&B Television & Video Productions Inc, pg 842
Lion Recording Services Inc, pg 922
Metro Productions, pg 939

WASHINGTON

Adams Creative & Production Services, pg 775
Kostov Productions, pg 913

WEST VIRGINIA

Altruist Media LLC, pg 783

WISCONSIN

AVS Group, pg 800
Rucinski & Reetz Communications LLC, pg 1000
USAV Group Inc, pg 1050
Video Wisconsin Inc, pg 1056
Watts Communications Inc, pg 1062
Wisconsin Public Television, pg 1068

WYOMING

Bridger Productions Inc, pg 812

ALBERTA

Black Media Works, pg 808

BRITISH COLUMBIA

West Eagle Films Inc, pg 1064

NEWFOUNDLAND AND LABRADOR

Vidcraft Productions Ltd, pg 1054

ONTARIO

BBC Worldwide Canada Ltd, pg 803
Mediaimage Communications Group, pg 937

QUEBEC

Kerrigan Productions Inc, pg 910

Public Relations Program Rentals

GEORGIA

Convergent Media Systems, pg 836

MICHIGAN

Digi Sign Design LLC, pg 847

NEW HAMPSHIRE

Chip Taylor Communications LLC, pg 1032

NEW YORK

Hallel Communications, pg 884

UTAH

Webb Audio Visual Communication, pg 1063

Public Service Announcement Distributors

CALIFORNIA

Crystal Pyramid Productions™, pg 840
New & Unique Videos™, pg 955

LOUISIANA

Louisiana State University Health Sciences Center - Shreveport, pg 925

MICHIGAN

Digi Sign Design LLC, pg 847

NEW HAMPSHIRE

Chip Taylor Communications LLC, pg 1032

NEW YORK

HB-Content, pg 886
KickedUp Media Group Inc, pg 910
March of Dimes Foundation, pg 930
MRG Productions Inc, pg 948
News Broadcast Network, pg 956

OHIO

Franciscan Media, pg 872

TENNESSEE

American Blackguard Inc, pg 784

TEXAS

Institute of Texan Cultures, pg 899

WISCONSIN

Wisconsin Public Television, pg 1068

Public Service Announcement Producers

ALABAMA

Media Visions Inc, pg 937

ARIZONA

Candee Productions Inc, pg 819
Tellens Inc, pg 1037

ARKANSAS

Live'N'Loud, pg 923

CALIFORNIA

AM Productions, pg 783
Crystal Pyramid Productions™, pg 840
Direct Images Interactive Inc, pg 848
Tom Donald Films, pg 850
Lynch Communications, pg 926
Media Magic, pg 937
The Media Staff Inc, pg 937
New & Unique Videos™, pg 955
New Circuit Films LLC, pg 955
Panorama Productions, pg 968
PM Productions, pg 977
Total Media Group, pg 1042
Vineyard Video & Photography, pg 1058
Wavemaker Media Design, pg 1062

COLORADO

Flashback Media Productions, pg 869
Phelan Productions Inc, pg 973
Tatum Video, pg 1032

CONNECTICUT

Applebox Studio, pg 788
Broadcast Video Productions LLC, pg 813
Fox Connecticut, pg 872
MCC Films, pg 935

DISTRICT OF COLUMBIA

Hillmann & Carr Inc, pg 889

FLORIDA

Allegro Productions Inc, pg 781
Communications Concepts Inc (CCI), pg 833
Home Shopping Network (HSN), pg 890
Paradise Video & Film, pg 969
Sunfire Communications Inc, pg 1028
Tricycle Studios, pg 1044
Video Techniques Inc, pg 1056

GEORGIA

Beachwood Productions, pg 804
Continental Film & Video, pg 835
Guerrilla Productions LLC, pg 883
Visioneering International Inc, pg 1058

HAWAII

Hyperspective Studios Inc, pg 893

ILLINOIS

Chicago Satellite & Video, pg 825
Comtech Multimedia Marketing, pg 834
Cresta Creative, pg 839
Major Media Productions Inc, pg 929
The Pepper Group, pg 972
SCI Television Productions LLC, pg 1004
Sparkfactor, pg 1019
20/20 Communications Inc, pg 1047

INDIANA

AVA Productions, pg 798
Covenant Productions®, pg 837
Digital Rain LLC, pg 847

IOWA

Hellman Associates Inc, pg 887

KANSAS

Chapman Recording & Mastering, pg 824

LOUISIANA

Digital FX Inc, pg 847
Louisiana State University Health Sciences Center - Shreveport, pg 925

MARYLAND

dbF a Media Company, pg 844
The Image Generators, pg 895

Public Service Announcement Rentals

Realia Distributors

Realia Producers

Religious Program Distributors

PROGRAMMING — AUDIO/VISUAL

Religious Program Distributors (continued)

OHIO

Franciscan Media, pg 872
Treehaus Communications Inc, pg 1044

TENNESSEE

Abingdon Press, pg 772
EMI CMG Distribution, pg 860
Randall House Publications, pg 991
Spring Arbor Distributors, pg 1022
Zion Music Group, pg 1074

TEXAS

Endtime Inc, pg 861
Lamb & Lion Ministries, pg 915

ONTARIO

Broughton's Church Supplies, Religious Books & Gifts, pg 814
Canadian Learning Co Inc, pg 818
Gospel Folio Press, pg 880
Kineticvideo.com, pg 911
Life Cycle Books Ltd, pg 920
Novalis, pg 959

Religious Program Producers

ALABAMA

AVS Media Group, pg 800
Media Visions Inc, pg 937

ARIZONA

BeachWare Inc, pg 804

ARKANSAS

White Diamond Productions, pg 1065

CALIFORNIA

Clarity Sound & Light, pg 829
Discovery Education - Los Angeles, pg 848
Dolphin MultiMedia Inc, pg 850
Joyce Media Inc, pg 906
Lynch Communications, pg 926
PM Productions, pg 977
SNAP, pg 1014
Total Media Group, pg 1042
Vineyard Video & Photography, pg 1058

COLORADO

Flashback Media Productions, pg 869

CONNECTICUT

Applebox Studio, pg 788
Broadcast Video Productions LLC, pg 813
Fox Connecticut, pg 872
MCC Films, pg 935

DISTRICT OF COLUMBIA

Biblical Archaeology Society (BAS), pg 806

FLORIDA

Audio Visual Imagineering Inc, pg 795
Capital Communications Inc, pg 819
Home Shopping Network (HSN), pg 890
Sunfire Communications Inc, pg 1028

GEORGIA

Beachwood Productions, pg 804
Continental Film & Video, pg 835
Guerrilla Productions LLC, pg 883

HAWAII

Hyperspective Studios Inc, pg 893
Media Bridge Gamekids, pg 936

ILLINOIS

ACTA Publications, pg 775
CCore Media Inc, pg 821
Chicago Satellite & Video, pg 825
Comtech Multimedia Marketing, pg 834
Major Media Productions Inc, pg 929
The Pepper Group, pg 972
20/20 Communications Inc, pg 1047
Video Impressions, pg 1055

INDIANA

Covenant Productions®, pg 837
InterComm, pg 900

KANSAS

Chapman Recording & Mastering, pg 824

MARYLAND

Lehigh Phoenix™, pg 918

MASSACHUSETTS

Pauline Books & Media, pg 970
Soundtrack Recording Studios, pg 1018

MICHIGAN

Digi Sign Design LLC, pg 847
K&R All Media Productions Inc, pg 908
K&R's Recording Studios Inc, pg 908
Zondervan, A HarperCollins Company, pg 1074

MINNESOTA

Augsburg Fortress Publishers, pg 796
MultiMedia, pg 950
Vaddio, pg 1051

MONTANA

North Country Media Group, pg 959

NEBRASKA

Dog & Pony Productions Inc, pg 850

NEVADA

JCS Video Productions, pg 904

NEW HAMPSHIRE

Apertura, pg 788
Chip Taylor Communications LLC, pg 1032

NEW JERSEY

Half Moon Video Productions, pg 883
Laurel Video Productions, pg 916
Optisonics Productions, pg 965

NEW YORK

Havas Worldwide, pg 886
Manhattan Center Studios Inc, pg 930
Maryknoll Productions, pg 933
Jack Morton Worldwide, pg 946
MRG Productions Inc, pg 948
Shelly Palmer Production, pg 968
Spoken Arts Inc, pg 1021
Zelman Studios Ltd, pg 1073

NORTH CAROLINA

Pat Appleson Studios Inc, pg 788
Howard Hanger, pg 884
LCW Productions LLC, pg 917

OHIO

Advent Media Inc, pg 778
Franciscan Media, pg 872
MainSail Production Services Inc, pg 929
Take 1 Media Services, pg 1031
Treehaus Communications Inc, pg 1044
Vista Color Imaging Inc, pg 1059

PENNSYLVANIA

Audio Visual Communications Inc, pg 795
Bang Pictures, pg 802
FMP Media Solutions Inc, pg 870
JPL, pg 906

RHODE ISLAND

Sound-FX-Design, pg 1017

SOUTH CAROLINA

BJU Press, pg 808

TENNESSEE

Abingdon Press, pg 772
Continental Film, pg 835
EMI CMG Distribution, pg 860
Running Pony Productions LLC, pg 1000
Spring Arbor Distributors, pg 1022
Russ Sturgeon Productions/RSVP, pg 1027
WKPT-TV, pg 1068

TEXAS

Endtime Inc, pg 861
Lamb & Lion Ministries, pg 915
Mediaforce Productions, pg 937
Stage Directions, pg 1022

VIRGINIA

D&B Television & Video Productions Inc, pg 842
Lion Recording Services Inc, pg 922
Metro Productions, pg 939

WASHINGTON

Kostov Productions, pg 913

WISCONSIN

Rucinski & Reetz Communications LLC, pg 1000
Video Wisconsin Inc, pg 1056

WYOMING

Bridger Productions Inc, pg 812

ONTARIO

Novalis, pg 959

QUEBEC

Kerrigan Productions Inc, pg 910

Religious Program Rentals

CALIFORNIA

Glenn Photo Supply, pg 878

INDIANA

InterComm, pg 900

MICHIGAN

Digi Sign Design LLC, pg 847

NEW HAMPSHIRE

Chip Taylor Communications LLC, pg 1032

NORTH CAROLINA

World Wide Pictures Inc, pg 1070

OHIO

Franciscan Media, pg 872
Treehaus Communications Inc, pg 1044

UTAH

Webb Audio Visual Communication, pg 1063

Research—Technical Program, *see* Technical Research Program

Sales Promotion & Training Program Distributors

ARIZONA

Video Learning Library, pg 1055

CALIFORNIA

Crystal Pyramid Productions™, pg 840
Discovery Education - Los Angeles, pg 848
Kantola Productions LLC, pg 908

COLORADO

Vital Learning LLC, pg 1060

FLORIDA

ACE Video Resources Software, pg 774
Allegro Productions Inc, pg 781
Capital Communications Inc, pg 819

GEORGIA

Thompson-Mitchell & Associates Inc, pg 1039

ILLINOIS

CCore Media Inc, pg 821
1st Financial Training Services Inc, pg 868

MICHIGAN

Digi Sign Design LLC, pg 847

NEW HAMPSHIRE

Chip Taylor Communications LLC, pg 1032

NEW JERSEY

Graphics Depot Inc, pg 881

NEW MEXICO

National Information Center for Educational Media (NICEM)/MediaSleuth, pg 952

NEW YORK

HB-Content, pg 886
KickedUp Media Group Inc, pg 910
Monad Trainer's Aide Inc, pg 945
MRG Productions Inc, pg 948

NORTH CAROLINA

Vide-O-Go/That's Infotainment!, pg 1054

OHIO

South-Western Publishing Co, pg 1019

PENNSYLVANIA

FMP Media Solutions Inc, pg 870

TENNESSEE

American Blackguard Inc, pg 784
Marine Geographic, pg 931

TEXAS

InterCom, pg 900

ONTARIO

BBC Worldwide Canada Ltd, pg 803
Canadian Learning Co Inc, pg 818
Kineticvideo.com, pg 911

Sales Promotion & Training Program Producers

ALABAMA

Media Visions Inc, pg 937

ARIZONA

Aardvark Productions LLC, pg 772
Candee Productions Inc, pg 819
Creative Backstage, pg 838

CALIFORNIA

Aaron Marcus & Associates Inc, pg 772
AM Productions, pg 783
Crystal Pyramid Productions™, pg 840
Design Media, pg 845
Direct Images Interactive Inc, pg 848
Discovery Education - Los Angeles, pg 848
Dogma Studios, pg 850
Dolphin MultiMedia Inc, pg 850
IEEE Computer Society Press, pg 894
KABA Audio Productions, pg 907
Kantola Productions LLC, pg 908
Kavich Reynolds Productions Inc, pg 908
Lynch Communications, pg 926
Media Magic, pg 937
The Media Staff Inc, pg 937
New & Unique Videos™, pg 955
Panorama Productions, pg 968
PM Productions, pg 977
SBS Productions, pg 1003
SNAP, pg 1014
Tam Communications Inc, pg 1031
Total Media Group, pg 1042
Vineyard Video & Photography, pg 1058
Wavemaker Media Design, pg 1062
Webster Communications, pg 1063
West Coast Projections Inc, pg 1063

COLORADO

Paul L Anderson Productions Inc, pg 786
Daylight Productions & Rentals, pg 844
Flashback Media Productions, pg 869
Phelan Productions Inc, pg 973
Vital Learning LLC, pg 1060

CONNECTICUT

Applebox Studio, pg 788
Broadcast Video Productions LLC, pg 813
Cine-Med Inc, pg 826
Fox Connecticut, pg 872
MCC Films, pg 935

DISTRICT OF COLUMBIA

O'Keefe Communications Inc, pg 961

FLORIDA

Accel Video Productions, pg 773
ACE Video Resources Software, pg 774
Allegro Productions Inc, pg 781
Audio Visual Imagineering Inc, pg 795
Capital Communications Inc, pg 819
CD ROM™ Inc, pg 822
Communications Concepts Inc (CCI), pg 833
Gulf Coast Audio Visual Producers Inc, pg 883
Home Shopping Network (HSN), pg 890
Paradise Video & Film, pg 969
Sunfire Communications Inc, pg 1028
Teach America Corp, pg 1033
Tricycle Studios, pg 1044
Universal Studios Florida® Production Group, pg 1049
Video Techniques Inc, pg 1056

GEORGIA

Beachwood Productions, pg 804
Continental Film & Video, pg 835
Guerrilla Productions LLC, pg 883

HAWAII

Hyperspective Studios Inc, pg 893

ILLINOIS

Airways Digital Media, pg 779
Audio Visual Services Corp, pg 796
CCore Media Inc, pg 821
Chicago Satellite & Video, pg 825
Comtech Multimedia Marketing, pg 834
Cresta Creative, pg 839
1st Financial Training Services Inc, pg 868
LightCraft Graphics Inc, pg 920
Major Media Productions Inc, pg 929
Manning Productions, pg 930
The Pepper Group, pg 972
PSAV® Presentation Services (Hotel Services Division), pg 987
SCI Television Productions LLC, pg 1004
Sparkfactor, pg 1019
20/20 Communications Inc, pg 1047
Video Impressions, pg 1055

INDIANA

AVA Productions, pg 798
Covenant Productions®, pg 837
Digital Rain LLC, pg 847

IOWA

Hellman Associates Inc, pg 887

KANSAS

Chapman Recording & Mastering, pg 824

KENTUCKY

Hammond Communications Group, pg 884

LOUISIANA

Digital FX Inc, pg 847

MARYLAND

The Cutting Corp, pg 841
The Image Generators, pg 895
Lehigh Phoenix™, pg 918
Mobile-Video Productions Inc, pg 944

MASSACHUSETTS

CommCreative, pg 832
Cramer Productions, pg 837
Soundtrack Recording Studios, pg 1018
TVN-The Video Network, pg 1046
Veritech Corp, pg 1053

MICHIGAN

Benjamin Creative Productions, pg 805
Digi Sign Design LLC, pg 847
K&R All Media Productions Inc, pg 908
K&R's Recording Studios Inc, pg 908
Universal Images, pg 1049

MINNESOTA

Badiyan Inc, pg 801
Big Event Productions LLC, pg 807
Live Spark Inc, pg 923
Media Loft Inc, pg 937
MultiMedia, pg 950

MISSOURI

The Phoenix Learning Group Inc, pg 974

MONTANA

North Country Media Group, pg 959

NEBRASKA

Dog & Pony Productions Inc, pg 850
Rainbow Video Productions Inc, pg 991

NEVADA

HDTV Productions Inc, pg 886
JCS Video Productions, pg 904

NEW HAMPSHIRE

Apertura, pg 788
Chip Taylor Communications LLC, pg 1032

NEW JERSEY

Half Moon Video Productions, pg 883
Laurel Video Productions, pg 916
Optisonics Productions, pg 965
Outside The Box Interactive LLC, pg 966

NEW MEXICO

Michael Dunn Productions, pg 853

NEW YORK

American Management Association International, pg 784
Blue Barn Pictures Inc, pg 809
dM works, pg 849
Duggal Visual Solutions, pg 853
Karen Frankel Productions, pg 872
Havas Worldwide, pg 886
HB-Content, pg 886
Hello World Communications, pg 888
Ketchum Pleon Change, pg 910
KickedUp Media Group Inc, pg 910
Manhattan Center Studios Inc, pg 930
Neal Marshad Productions, pg 931
Jack Morton Worldwide, pg 946
MRG Productions Inc, pg 948
News Broadcast Network, pg 956
Northeast Video Productions Inc, pg 959
Shelly Palmer Production, pg 968
SMP Digital Graphics, pg 1014
TBA Global Events, pg 1032
Total Impact Multimedia Group Ltd, pg 1042
WorldView Software, pg 1070
Zelman Studios Ltd, pg 1073

NORTH CAROLINA

Pat Appleson Studios Inc, pg 788
The Communications Group Inc, pg 833
Image Associates Inc, pg 894
Kino Mountain Productions LLC, pg 911
LCW Productions LLC, pg 917
Moving Pictures, pg 948
PACE Worldwide, pg 966

OHIO

Advent Media Inc, pg 778
Creative Technology, pg 838

PROGRAMMING — AUDIO/VISUAL

Sales Promotion & Training Program Producers (continued)

OHIO (continued)

Cuyahoga Community College Media Center, pg 841
Image Video Teleproductions Inc, pg 895
MainSail Production Services Inc, pg 929
R&B Communications Inc, pg 991
South-Western Publishing Co, pg 1019
Take 1 Media Services, pg 1031
Thread Marketing Group, pg 1039
Vista Color Imaging Inc, pg 1059

OREGON

A KTVA Production LLC, pg 771
Ideascape Inc, pg 894
Odyssey Productions Inc, pg 961

PENNSYLVANIA

AiH Group Inc, pg 779
Audio Visual Communications Inc, pg 795
Bang Pictures, pg 802
FMP Media Solutions Inc, pg 870
JPL, pg 906
Kensington Falls Animation, pg 909
Main Point Productions, pg 929
New Horizons Computer Learning Centers Inc, pg 955
Panta Rhei Media Inc, pg 968
Pemcor LLC, pg 971
Production Masters Inc (PMI), pg 984
Scala Inc, pg 1003

RHODE ISLAND

Sound-FX-Design, pg 1017

TENNESSEE

American Blackguard Inc, pg 784
Continental Film, pg 835
Marine Geographic, pg 931
Running Pony Productions LLC, pg 1000
WKPT-TV, pg 1068

TEXAS

Biway Media, pg 808
Epic Software Group Inc, pg 862
Horizon Film + Video Productions, pg 891
InterCom, pg 900
Mediaforce Productions, pg 937
Romar Learning, pg 999
The Samuels Co, pg 1002
Stage Directions, pg 1022
Stockyard Photos/Jim Olive Photography, pg 1025

VIRGINIA

Advance Concepts Inc, pg 777
CALIBRE, pg 816
D&B Television & Video Productions Inc, pg 842
Lion Recording Services Inc, pg 922
Metro Productions, pg 939

WASHINGTON

Adams Creative & Production Services, pg 775
Kostov Productions, pg 913
Medical Media Systems, pg 938
White Rain Films Ltd, pg 1065

WEST VIRGINIA

Altruist Media LLC, pg 783

WISCONSIN

Audio Visual of Milwaukee Inc, pg 795
AVS Group, pg 800
Logan Productions Inc, pg 924
Rucinski & Reetz Communications LLC, pg 1000
USAV Group Inc, pg 1050
Video Wisconsin Inc, pg 1056
Watts Communications Inc, pg 1062
Wisconsin Public Television, pg 1068

WYOMING

Bridger Productions Inc, pg 812

ALBERTA

Black Media Works, pg 808

NEWFOUNDLAND AND LABRADOR

Vidcraft Productions Ltd, pg 1054

ONTARIO

BBC Worldwide Canada Ltd, pg 803
DebsVoice, pg 844
JFB Communications, pg 905
Mediaimage Communications Group, pg 937

QUEBEC

Kerrigan Productions Inc, pg 910

Sales Promotion & Training Program Rentals

ILLINOIS

1st Financial Training Services Inc, pg 868

MICHIGAN

Digi Sign Design LLC, pg 847

NEW HAMPSHIRE

Chip Taylor Communications LLC, pg 1032

NEW YORK

TBA Global Events, pg 1032

NORTH CAROLINA

Image Associates Inc, pg 894

TEXAS

InterCom, pg 900

UTAH

Webb Audio Visual Communication, pg 1063

Scientific Program Distributors

CALIFORNIA

Academy Savant, pg 773
Astronomical Society of the Pacific, pg 792
Crystal Pyramid Productions™, pg 840
Deja View Video, pg 845
Discovery Education - Los Angeles, pg 848
Glenn Photo Supply, pg 878
Bruce Goldberg Inc, pg 880
Joyce Media Inc, pg 906
Sea Studios Foundation, pg 1005
The Wine Appreciation Guild Ltd, pg 1067

COLORADO

National Teaching Aids Inc, pg 953

FLORIDA

ACE Video Resources Software, pg 774
Allegro Productions Inc, pg 781
Capital Communications Inc, pg 819
Psychological Assessment Resources Inc (PAR), pg 987

GEORGIA

School Media Associates LLC, pg 1004

INDIANA

Agency for Instructional Technology (AIT), pg 778
Herff Jones | Nystrom, pg 888

KENTUCKY

National Geographic Learning, pg 952

MARYLAND

MMI Corp, pg 944

MASSACHUSETTS

Documentary Educational Resources Inc, pg 850
Sinauer Associates Inc, pg 1011

MICHIGAN

Digi Sign Design LLC, pg 847
Emery-Pratt Co, pg 860
Meuninck's Media Methods Inc, pg 940
MSU Technologies, pg 949

MISSOURI

Phoenix/BFA/Coronet, pg 974

NEW HAMPSHIRE

Chip Taylor Communications LLC, pg 1032

NEW JERSEY

Advanced Imaging Concepts Inc, pg 777
Lucerne Media, pg 925

NEW YORK

Films for the Humanities & Sciences, pg 868
Human Relations Media, pg 892
Janson Media, pg 904
March of Dimes Foundation, pg 930
Meridian Education Corp, pg 939
MRG Productions Inc, pg 948
Shopware, pg 1009

NORTH CAROLINA

Carolina Biological Supply Co, pg 820

PENNSYLVANIA

AccuWeather Inc, pg 774
FMP Media Solutions Inc, pg 870
Media Inc, pg 936
Science for Kids, pg 1005

TENNESSEE

Marine Geographic, pg 931

VIRGINIA

PBS Video, pg 970

ONTARIO

BBC Worldwide Canada Ltd, pg 803
Canadian Learning Co Inc, pg 818
Kineticvideo.com, pg 911
McIntyre Media Inc, pg 935

Scientific Program Producers

ALABAMA

Media Visions Inc, pg 937

ARIZONA

Aardvark Productions LLC, pg 772

CALIFORNIA

Academy Savant, pg 773
Astronomical Society of the Pacific, pg 792
Crystal Pyramid Productions™, pg 840
Direct Images Interactive Inc, pg 848
Discovery Education - Los Angeles, pg 848
Dolphin MultiMedia Inc, pg 850
imageReal Pictures LLC, pg 896
Joyce Media Inc, pg 906
Lynch Communications, pg 926
The Media Staff Inc, pg 937
New & Unique Videos™, pg 955
PM Productions, pg 977
Sea Studios Foundation, pg 1005
Total Media Group, pg 1042
Vineyard Video & Photography, pg 1058
Wavemaker Media Design, pg 1062
Webster Communications, pg 1063
West Coast Projections Inc, pg 1063

COLORADO

Paul L Anderson Productions Inc, pg 786
Daylight Productions & Rentals, pg 844
Flashback Media Productions, pg 869
National Teaching Aids Inc, pg 953

CONNECTICUT

Broadcast Video Productions LLC, pg 813
Fox Connecticut, pg 872

DISTRICT OF COLUMBIA

Hillmann & Carr Inc, pg 889

FLORIDA

Accel Video Productions, pg 773
ACE Video Resources Software, pg 774
Allegro Productions Inc, pg 781
Capital Communications Inc, pg 819
CD ROM™ Inc, pg 822
Home Shopping Network (HSN), pg 890
Sunfire Communications Inc, pg 1028
Tricycle Studios, pg 1044

GEORGIA

Beachwood Productions, pg 804
Guerrilla Productions LLC, pg 883

HAWAII

Hyperspective Studios Inc, pg 893

ILLINOIS

Airways Digital Media, pg 779
Chicago Satellite & Video, pg 825
Comtech Multimedia Marketing, pg 834
Major Media Productions Inc, pg 929
The Pepper Group, pg 972
20/20 Communications Inc, pg 1047
Video Impressions, pg 1055

INDIANA

Agency for Instructional Technology (AIT), pg 778
Digital Rain LLC, pg 847
Herff Jones | Nystrom, pg 888

KENTUCKY

National Geographic Learning, pg 952

LOUISIANA

Louisiana State University Health Sciences Center - Shreveport, pg 925

MARYLAND

The Image Generators, pg 895
MMI Corp, pg 944

MASSACHUSETTS

Documentary Educational Resources Inc, pg 850
Monadnock Media Inc, pg 945
Sinauer Associates Inc, pg 1011
Soundtrack Recording Studios, pg 1018
TVN-The Video Network, pg 1046
Veritech Corp, pg 1053

MICHIGAN

Digi Sign Design LLC, pg 847
K&R All Media Productions Inc, pg 908
K&R's Recording Studios Inc, pg 908

MONTANA

North Country Media Group, pg 959

NEVADA

HDTV Productions Inc, pg 886
JCS Video Productions, pg 904

NEW HAMPSHIRE

Apertura, pg 788
Chip Taylor Communications LLC, pg 1032

NEW JERSEY

Advanced Imaging Concepts Inc, pg 777
Half Moon Video Productions, pg 883
Laurel Video Productions, pg 916
Optisonics Productions, pg 965

NEW YORK

Norman N Axelrod Associates, pg 800
Blue Barn Pictures Inc, pg 809
Broad Street Inc, pg 812
CompuWeather Inc, pg 834
Duggal Visual Solutions, pg 853
Florentine Films, pg 870
Havas Worldwide, pg 886
Hello World Communications, pg 888
Human Relations Media, pg 892
March of Dimes Foundation, pg 930
Neal Marshad Productions, pg 931
Jack Morton Worldwide, pg 946
MRG Productions Inc, pg 948
MRY, pg 949
News Broadcast Network, pg 956
Shelly Palmer Production, pg 968
Zelman Studios Ltd, pg 1073

NORTH CAROLINA

Pat Appleson Studios Inc, pg 788
Carolina Biological Supply Co, pg 820
Kino Mountain Productions LLC, pg 911

OHIO

Advent Media Inc, pg 778
Creative Technology, pg 838
R&B Communications Inc, pg 991
Take 1 Media Services, pg 1031
Vista Color Imaging Inc, pg 1059

OREGON

Ideascape Inc, pg 894
Odyssey Productions Inc, pg 961

PENNSYLVANIA

AccuWeather Inc, pg 774
AiH Group Inc, pg 779
Audio Visual Communications Inc, pg 795
FMP Media Solutions Inc, pg 870
JPL, pg 906
Panta Rhei Media Inc, pg 968
Production Masters Inc (PMI), pg 984
Science for Kids, pg 1005

RHODE ISLAND

Sound-FX-Design, pg 1017

TENNESSEE

Continental Film, pg 835
Marine Geographic, pg 931
Running Pony Productions LLC, pg 1000
WKPT-TV, pg 1068

TEXAS

Epic Software Group Inc, pg 862
Mediaforce Productions, pg 937
Romar Learning, pg 999
Stage Directions, pg 1022
Texas Heart Institute Visual Communication Services, pg 1037

VIRGINIA

D&B Television & Video Productions Inc, pg 842
Lion Recording Services Inc, pg 922
Metro Productions, pg 939

WISCONSIN

Rucinski & Reetz Communications LLC, pg 1000
USAV Group Inc, pg 1050
Video Wisconsin Inc, pg 1056
Wisconsin Public Television, pg 1068

WYOMING

Bridger Productions Inc, pg 812

BRITISH COLUMBIA

West Eagle Films Inc, pg 1064

ONTARIO

BBC Worldwide Canada Ltd, pg 803

QUEBEC

Kerrigan Productions Inc, pg 910

Scientific Program Rentals

CALIFORNIA

Glenn Photo Supply, pg 878

INDIANA

Agency for Instructional Technology (AIT), pg 778

MASSACHUSETTS

Documentary Educational Resources Inc, pg 850

MICHIGAN

Digi Sign Design LLC, pg 847

NEW HAMPSHIRE

Chip Taylor Communications LLC, pg 1032

UTAH

Webb Audio Visual Communication, pg 1063

Silent Filmstrip, *see* Filmstrip—Silent

Slide Distributors

ALABAMA

Media Visions Inc, pg 937

ARIZONA

Arizona Cine Equipment, pg 789

CALIFORNIA

Academy Savant, pg 773
Ametron Audio/Video, pg 785
Astronomical Society of the Pacific, pg 792
Discovery Education - Los Angeles, pg 848
Medcom Inc, pg 936
QRS Software Services, pg 988
RJ Video Productions, pg 997
Sea Studios Foundation, pg 1005
Social Studies School Service, pg 1015

CONNECTICUT

Pictures of Record Inc, pg 975

DISTRICT OF COLUMBIA

Grocery Manufacturers Association (GMA), pg 882

FLORIDA

Gulf Coast Audio Visual Producers Inc, pg 883
Pro Stage Inc, pg 983

GEORGIA

First Cut Communications LLC, pg 868
School Media Associates LLC, pg 1004
Symmes Systems, pg 1030

ILLINOIS

CCore Media Inc, pg 821
National Safety Council (NSC), pg 953

MARYLAND

Department of Education Resources, pg 845
Milner-Fenwick Inc, pg 943
MMI Corp, pg 944

MASSACHUSETTS

Emergency Film Group, pg 860
Triumph Learning LLC, pg 1045

MICHIGAN

Michigan Office Solutions, pg 941
MSU Technologies, pg 949

MISSOURI

Mosby Inc, pg 947

NEW HAMPSHIRE

Frey Scientific, pg 873

NEW JERSEY

A W Peller & Associates Inc, pg 971

NEW MEXICO

National Information Center for Educational Media (NICEM)/MediaSleuth, pg 952

NEW YORK

Educational Images Ltd, pg 857
Janus Films Inc, pg 904
Light Impressions, pg 920
United Nations Department of Public Information-News & Media Division, pg 1048
Visual Technologies Corp, pg 1060

PROGRAMMING — AUDIO/VISUAL

Slide Distributors (continued)

NORTH CAROLINA

Carolina Biological Supply Co, pg 820

OHIO

South-Western Publishing Co, pg 1019

PENNSYLVANIA

Karol Media Inc, pg 908
Lippincott Williams & Wilkins, pg 922

TENNESSEE

Marine Geographic, pg 931
Spring Arbor Distributors, pg 1022

TEXAS

Stage Directions, pg 1022
University of Texas at Austin - Petroleum Extension Service, pg 1050

VIRGINIA

Colonial Williamsburg Foundation, pg 831
Filmdex Inc, pg 867

WISCONSIN

Demco Inc, pg 845
School Specialty Inc, pg 1004

QUEBEC

Editions Hurtubise HMH Ltee, pg 892

Slide Producers

ALABAMA

Media Visions Inc, pg 937

ARIZONA

Video Learning Library, pg 1055

CALIFORNIA

Astronomical Society of the Pacific, pg 792
Auslender Productions/Celestial Images, pg 797
deKramer Productions Inc, pg 845
Design Media, pg 845
Discovery Education - Los Angeles, pg 848
Dolphin MultiMedia Inc, pg 850
Geddes Productions LLC, pg 876
The Kenwood Group, pg 909
Lynch Communications, pg 926
Fred Lyon Pictures, pg 927
QRS Software Services, pg 988
Dick Reizner Film & Video, pg 994
SBS Productions, pg 1003
Sea Studios Foundation, pg 1005
The Studio Center, pg 1026
Webster Communications, pg 1063

COLORADO

Starwest Productions, pg 1024

CONNECTICUT

Broadcast Video Productions LLC, pg 813
Pictures of Record Inc, pg 975

DISTRICT OF COLUMBIA

Biblical Archaeology Society (BAS), pg 806
Hillmann & Carr Inc, pg 889
National Education Association (NEA), pg 952
O'Keefe Communications Inc, pg 961

FLORIDA

Gulf Coast Audio Visual Producers Inc, pg 883
Roger Scruggs Films, pg 1005

GEORGIA

First Cut Communications LLC, pg 868
Imagers, pg 896
Symmes Systems, pg 1030

HAWAII

Hyperspective Studios Inc, pg 893

ILLINOIS

Audio Visual Services Corp, pg 796
CCore Media Inc, pg 821
LightCraft Graphics Inc, pg 920
National Safety Council (NSC), pg 953
Jim Passin Productions, pg 970
PSAV® Presentation Services (Hotel Services Division), pg 987
QuickSet International Inc, pg 989
Universal Training, pg 1049

INDIANA

AVA Productions, pg 798
Communication Ministries, pg 833
OMNI Productions, pg 962

IOWA

Iowa State University-Information Technology Services, pg 902
The Production House, pg 984

KANSAS

Genigraphics®, pg 877

LOUISIANA

Digital FX Inc, pg 847
Louisiana State University Health Sciences Center - Shreveport, pg 925

MARYLAND

Department of Education Resources, pg 845
Milner-Fenwick Inc, pg 943
MMI Corp, pg 944

MASSACHUSETTS

CommCreative, pg 832
DGI-Invisuals LLC, pg 846
Emergency Film Group, pg 860
Preston Productions Inc, pg 981
TR Productions, pg 1043

MICHIGAN

K&R All Media Productions Inc, pg 908
K&R's Recording Studios Inc, pg 908
MessageMakers, pg 939
Michigan Office Solutions, pg 941
MSU Technologies, pg 949

MINNESOTA

Linhoff Photo & Digital Imaging, pg 922

MISSOURI

Celebrities Productions, pg 822
Fambrough & Associates Inc, pg 865
Mosby Inc, pg 947
Switch, pg 1030

NEBRASKA

Telepro Video Inc, pg 1036

NEVADA

Encore Productions Inc, pg 861

NEW HAMPSHIRE

Academic & Campus Technology Services, pg 773
Apertura, pg 788

NEW JERSEY

The Bergman Collection of Medical/Technical/Scientific Stock Images, pg 805
Laurel Video Productions, pg 916
Optisonics Productions, pg 965

NEW YORK

Applause Learning Resources, pg 788
Blue Barn Pictures Inc, pg 809
Broad Street Inc, pg 812
Campus Film Distributors Corp, pg 818
Cornell Laboratory of Ornithology, pg 836
Educational Images Ltd, pg 857
Karen Frankel Productions, pg 872
Greyfalcon House, pg 882
Icontent, pg 893
Jack Morton Worldwide, pg 946
MRG Productions Inc, pg 948
Peter Schleger Co, pg 1004
SMP Digital Graphics, pg 1014
TBA Global Events, pg 1032
White Buffalo Multimedia, pg 1065
Zelman Studios Ltd, pg 1073

NORTH CAROLINA

Aon Hewitt, pg 787
Carolina Biological Supply Co, pg 820
Image Associates Inc, pg 894

OHIO

Cuyahoga Community College Media Center, pg 841
Maslowski Productions, pg 933
South-Western Publishing Co, pg 1019
Treehaus Communications Inc, pg 1044
Vista Color Imaging Inc, pg 1059

OREGON

Ideascape Inc, pg 894

PENNSYLVANIA

Audio Visual Communications Inc, pg 795
FMP Media Solutions Inc, pg 870
JPL, pg 906
Kensington Falls Animation, pg 909
Lippincott Williams & Wilkins, pg 922
Main Point Productions, pg 929

TENNESSEE

Center for Southern Folklore Inc, pg 822
Marine Geographic, pg 931
Memphis Communications Corp, pg 938
WKPT-TV, pg 1068

TEXAS

Omni Intercommunications Inc, pg 962
Romar Learning, pg 999
Stage Directions, pg 1022
Texas Heart Institute Visual Communication Services, pg 1037
University of Texas at Austin - Petroleum Extension Service, pg 1050

VIRGINIA

Advance Concepts Inc, pg 777
Blair Inc, pg 809
CALIBRE, pg 816

WASHINGTON

Kostov Productions, pg 913

WISCONSIN

AVS Group, pg 800
USAV Group Inc, pg 1050
Video Wisconsin Inc, pg 1056

NORTHWEST TERRITORIES

Yellowknife Films Inc, pg 1072

ONTARIO

Art Gallery of Ontario, pg 791

QUEBEC

Editions Hurtubise HMH Ltee, pg 892

Slide Rentals

ARIZONA

Arizona Cine Equipment, pg 789

CALIFORNIA

Ametron Audio/Video, pg 785
Medcom Inc, pg 936

FLORIDA

Gulf Coast Audio Visual Producers Inc, pg 883
Pro Stage Inc, pg 983

GEORGIA

Symmes Systems, pg 1030

MASSACHUSETTS

Tom Pantages, pg 968
Preston Productions Inc, pg 981

Slide Show Distributors

Slide Show Producers

PROGRAMMING — AUDIO/VISUAL

Slide Show Producers (continued)

VIRGINIA

Advance Concepts Inc, pg 777
CALIBRE, pg 816
Lion Recording Services Inc, pg 922

WASHINGTON

Adams Creative & Production Services, pg 775
Inland Audio Visual Co, pg 898
Kostov Productions, pg 913

WISCONSIN

AVS Group, pg 800
USAV Group Inc, pg 1050
Watts Communications Inc, pg 1062
Wisconsin Public Television, pg 1068

WYOMING

Bridger Productions Inc, pg 812

ONTARIO

Mediaimage Communications Group, pg 937
Purefire Communications Inc, pg 987

QUEBEC

Kerrigan Productions Inc, pg 910

Slide Show Rentals

GEORGIA

Symmes Systems, pg 1030

ILLINOIS

National Safety Council (NSC), pg 953

MASSACHUSETTS

Preston Productions Inc, pg 981

MICHIGAN

Digi Sign Design LLC, pg 847

NEW HAMPSHIRE

Chip Taylor Communications LLC, pg 1032

NEW YORK

Brooklyn Botanic Garden, pg 814
TBA Global Events, pg 1032

NORTH CAROLINA

Image Associates Inc, pg 894

UTAH

Webb Audio Visual Communication, pg 1063

Sound Filmstrip, *see* Filmstrip—Sound

Sponsored Program Distributors

CALIFORNIA

Crystal Pyramid Productions™, pg 840
Medcom Inc, pg 936
New & Unique Videos™, pg 955

FLORIDA

Allegro Productions Inc, pg 781
Capital Communications Inc, pg 819

ILLINOIS

CCore Media Inc, pg 821
Terra Nova Films Inc, pg 1037

MASSACHUSETTS

Preston Productions Inc, pg 981

MICHIGAN

Digi Sign Design LLC, pg 847

NEW HAMPSHIRE

Chip Taylor Communications LLC, pg 1032

NEW JERSEY

Euro-Pacific Film & Video Productions Inc, pg 863

NEW YORK

William Greaves Productions Inc, pg 882
HB-Content, pg 886
KickedUp Media Group Inc, pg 910
MRG Productions Inc, pg 948

TENNESSEE

American Blackguard Inc, pg 784
Marine Geographic, pg 931

ONTARIO

Canadian Learning Co Inc, pg 818

Sponsored Program Producers

ARIZONA

Candee Productions Inc, pg 819
Tellens Inc, pg 1037

CALIFORNIA

Animax, pg 787
Crystal Pyramid Productions™, pg 840
Direct Images Interactive Inc, pg 848
Dogma Studios, pg 850
imageReal Pictures LLC, pg 896
Lynch Communications, pg 926
The Media Staff Inc, pg 937
New & Unique Videos™, pg 955
Panorama Productions, pg 968
Screen Door Entertainment Inc, pg 1005
Total Media Group, pg 1042
Vineyard Video & Photography, pg 1058
Webster Communications, pg 1063

COLORADO

Flashback Media Productions, pg 869
Tatum Video, pg 1032

CONNECTICUT

Applebox Studio, pg 788
Broadcast Video Productions LLC, pg 813
Cine-Med Inc, pg 826
Fox Connecticut, pg 872
MCC Films, pg 935

FLORIDA

Allegro Productions Inc, pg 781
Audio Visual Imagineering Inc, pg 795
Capital Communications Inc, pg 819
Communications Concepts Inc (CCI), pg 833
Sunfire Communications Inc, pg 1028
Tricycle Studios, pg 1044

GEORGIA

Beachwood Productions, pg 804
Guerrilla Productions LLC, pg 883
Visioneering International Inc, pg 1058

HAWAII

Hyperspective Studios Inc, pg 893

ILLINOIS

Audio Visual Services Corp, pg 796
CCore Media Inc, pg 821
Chicago Satellite & Video, pg 825
Comtech Multimedia Marketing, pg 834
Manning Productions, pg 930
The Pepper Group, pg 972
PSAV® Presentation Services (Hotel Services Division), pg 987
Terra Nova Films Inc, pg 1037
Video Impressions, pg 1055

INDIANA

AVA Productions, pg 798
Digital Rain LLC, pg 847

IOWA

The Production House, pg 984

MARYLAND

The Image Generators, pg 895

MASSACHUSETTS

Soundtrack Recording Studios, pg 1018

MICHIGAN

Digi Sign Design LLC, pg 847
K&R All Media Productions Inc, pg 908
K&R's Recording Studios Inc, pg 908

MINNESOTA

MultiMedia, pg 950

MONTANA

North Country Media Group, pg 959

NEVADA

HDTV Productions Inc, pg 886
JCS Video Productions, pg 904

NEW HAMPSHIRE

Apertura, pg 788
Chip Taylor Communications LLC, pg 1032

NEW JERSEY

Half Moon Video Productions, pg 883
Laurel Video Productions, pg 916
Optisonics Productions, pg 965

NEW YORK

Blue Barn Pictures Inc, pg 809
Broad Street Inc, pg 812
Castillo Theater, pg 820
dM works, pg 849
William Greaves Productions Inc, pg 882
Havas Worldwide, pg 886
HB-Content, pg 886
Ketchum Pleon Change, pg 910
KickedUp Media Group Inc, pg 910
Neal Marshad Productions, pg 931
Jack Morton Worldwide, pg 946
MRG Productions Inc, pg 948
News Broadcast Network, pg 956
Shelly Palmer Production, pg 968
Zelman Studios Ltd, pg 1073

NORTH CAROLINA

Pat Appleson Studios Inc, pg 788
Kino Mountain Productions LLC, pg 911
Moving Pictures, pg 948

OHIO

Advent Media Inc, pg 778
Creative Technology, pg 838
R&B Communications Inc, pg 991
Take 1 Media Services, pg 1031
VGI Productions, pg 1053
Vista Color Imaging Inc, pg 1059

OREGON

Ideascape Inc, pg 894
Odyssey Productions Inc, pg 961
Rex, pg 995

PENNSYLVANIA

Bang Pictures, pg 802
FMP Media Solutions Inc, pg 870
JPL, pg 906
Kensington Falls Animation, pg 909
Main Point Productions, pg 929
Production Masters Inc (PMI), pg 984

RHODE ISLAND

Sound-FX-Design, pg 1017

TENNESSEE

American Blackguard Inc, pg 784
Continental Film, pg 835
Marine Geographic, pg 931
Running Pony Productions LLC, pg 1000
WKPT-TV, pg 1068

TEXAS

Epic Software Group Inc, pg 862
Mediaforce Productions, pg 937
Romar Learning, pg 999

Sponsored Program Rentals

Sports Program Distributors

Sports Program Producers

PROGRAMMING — AUDIO/VISUAL

Sports Program Producers (continued)

VIRGINIA

D&B Television & Video Productions Inc, pg 842
Lion Recording Services Inc, pg 922
Metro Productions, pg 939

WISCONSIN

Watts Communications Inc, pg 1062
Wisconsin Public Television, pg 1068

WYOMING

Bridger Productions Inc, pg 812

ALBERTA

Black Media Works, pg 808

NEWFOUNDLAND AND LABRADOR

Vidcraft Productions Ltd, pg 1054

QUEBEC

Kerrigan Productions Inc, pg 910

Sports Program Rentals

INDIANA

InterComm, pg 900

MICHIGAN

Digi Sign Design LLC, pg 847

NEW HAMPSHIRE

Chip Taylor Communications LLC, pg 1032

UTAH

Webb Audio Visual Communication, pg 1063

VIRGINIA

Once Around, pg 963

Talking Filmstrip, *see* Filmstrip—Sound

Technical Research Program Distributors

CALIFORNIA

Crystal Pyramid Productions™, pg 840

DISTRICT OF COLUMBIA

American Chemical Society (ACS), pg 784

FLORIDA

Capital Communications Inc, pg 819

ILLINOIS

CCH Continuing Education, pg 821

MASSACHUSETTS

Documentary Educational Resources Inc, pg 850

MICHIGAN

Digi Sign Design LLC, pg 847

NEW HAMPSHIRE

Chip Taylor Communications LLC, pg 1032

NEW YORK

MRG Productions Inc, pg 948

PENNSYLVANIA

FMP Media Solutions Inc, pg 870

VIRGINIA

National Audiovisual Center - National Technical Information Service (NTIS), pg 952

ONTARIO

BBC Worldwide Canada Ltd, pg 803

Technical Research Program Producers

ALABAMA

Media Visions Inc, pg 937

ARIZONA

Aardvark Productions LLC, pg 772
Candee Productions Inc, pg 819

CALIFORNIA

Crystal Pyramid Productions™, pg 840
Design Media, pg 845
IEEE Computer Society Press, pg 894
Lynch Communications, pg 926
New & Unique Videos™, pg 955
StereoScope International, pg 1024
Total Media Group, pg 1042
Vineyard Video & Photography, pg 1058
Wavemaker Media Design, pg 1062
West Coast Projections Inc, pg 1063

COLORADO

Paul L Anderson Productions Inc, pg 786
Daylight Productions & Rentals, pg 844
Flashback Media Productions, pg 869

CONNECTICUT

Broadcast Video Productions LLC, pg 813
Fox Connecticut, pg 872

DISTRICT OF COLUMBIA

American Chemical Society (ACS), pg 784

FLORIDA

Allegro Productions Inc, pg 781
Capital Communications Inc, pg 819
Sunfire Communications Inc, pg 1028

GEORGIA

Beachwood Productions, pg 804
Guerrilla Productions LLC, pg 883
Visioneering International Inc, pg 1058

HAWAII

Hyperspective Studios Inc, pg 893

ILLINOIS

Accenture, pg 773
CCH Continuing Education, pg 821
Chicago Satellite & Video, pg 825
Major Media Productions Inc, pg 929
The Pepper Group, pg 972
20/20 Communications Inc, pg 1047
Video Impressions, pg 1055

INDIANA

AVA Productions, pg 798

LOUISIANA

Louisiana State University Health Sciences Center - Shreveport, pg 925

MASSACHUSETTS

Documentary Educational Resources Inc, pg 850
Soundtrack Recording Studios, pg 1018

MICHIGAN

Digi Sign Design LLC, pg 847
K&R All Media Productions Inc, pg 908
K&R's Recording Studios Inc, pg 908

MINNESOTA

Badiyan Inc, pg 801

MONTANA

North Country Media Group, pg 959

NEBRASKA

Rainbow Video Productions Inc, pg 991

NEW HAMPSHIRE

Apertura, pg 788
Chip Taylor Communications LLC, pg 1032

NEW JERSEY

Broadcast Center Studios, pg 813
Optisonics Productions, pg 965

NEW YORK

Norman N Axelrod Associates, pg 800
dM works, pg 849
Havas Worldwide, pg 886
Jack Morton Worldwide, pg 946
MRG Productions Inc, pg 948
Shelly Palmer Production, pg 968
TBA Global Events, pg 1032
Zelman Studios Ltd, pg 1073

NORTH CAROLINA

Pat Appleson Studios Inc, pg 788
Kino Mountain Productions LLC, pg 911

OHIO

Advent Media Inc, pg 778
Creative Technology, pg 838
R&B Communications Inc, pg 991
Take 1 Media Services, pg 1031
Vista Color Imaging Inc, pg 1059

OREGON

Ideascape Inc, pg 894

PENNSYLVANIA

AiH Group Inc, pg 779
FMP Media Solutions Inc, pg 870
Panta Rhei Media Inc, pg 968
Production Masters Inc (PMI), pg 984

RHODE ISLAND

Sound-FX-Design, pg 1017

TENNESSEE

Continental Film, pg 835
Running Pony Productions LLC, pg 1000
WKPT-TV, pg 1068

TEXAS

Mediaforce Productions, pg 937
Romar Learning, pg 999
Stage Directions, pg 1022
Stockyard Photos/Jim Olive Photography, pg 1025

VIRGINIA

D&B Television & Video Productions Inc, pg 842
Lion Recording Services Inc, pg 922

WISCONSIN

Wisconsin Public Television, pg 1068

WYOMING

Bridger Productions Inc, pg 812

ONTARIO

BBC Worldwide Canada Ltd, pg 803

QUEBEC

Kerrigan Productions Inc, pg 910

Technical Research Program Rentals

MASSACHUSETTS

Documentary Educational Resources Inc, pg 850

MICHIGAN

Digi Sign Design LLC, pg 847

NEW HAMPSHIRE

Chip Taylor Communications LLC, pg 1032

NEW YORK

TBA Global Events, pg 1032

UTAH

Webb Audio Visual Communication, pg 1063

Training Program Distributors

ARIZONA

Video Learning Library, pg 1055

CALIFORNIA

Academy Savant, pg 773
Crystal Pyramid Productions™, pg 840
Deja View Video, pg 845
Discovery Education - Los Angeles, pg 848
Kantola Productions LLC, pg 908
Medcom Inc, pg 936
Players Press, pg 977
Melvin Powers Television Marketing, pg 979
Semiconductor Services, pg 1006
University of Southern California, pg 1050
The Wine Appreciation Guild Ltd, pg 1067

COLORADO

National Teaching Aids Inc, pg 953
Vital Learning LLC, pg 1060

CONNECTICUT

Crossroads Video, pg 840

DISTRICT OF COLUMBIA

Theatrical Technicians Inc (TTI), pg 1038

FLORIDA

ACE Video Resources Software, pg 774
Capital Communications Inc, pg 819
Motion Image Group LLC, pg 947
Psychological Assessment Resources Inc (PAR), pg 987

GEORGIA

Thompson-Mitchell & Associates Inc, pg 1039

HAWAII

Media Bridge Gamekids, pg 936
Source School of Tantra Yoga Inc, pg 1019

ILLINOIS

CCH Continuing Education, pg 821
CCore Media Inc, pg 821
Film Ideas, pg 867
National Safety Council (NSC), pg 953

KENTUCKY

KET The Kentucky Network, pg 910

MARYLAND

MMI Corp, pg 944

MICHIGAN

Digi Sign Design LLC, pg 847
The Program Source International, pg 985
Resource Development Co LLC, pg 995

NEW HAMPSHIRE

Captain Fiddle Music & Publications, pg 820
Chip Taylor Communications LLC, pg 1032

NEW JERSEY

FlagHouse, pg 869

NEW MEXICO

National Information Center for Educational Media (NICEM)/ MediaSleuth, pg 952
Uncharted Country Publishing, pg 1048

NEW YORK

Guidance Associates Inc Center for Humanities, pg 883
HB-Content, pg 886
Interactive International Inc, pg 899
Monad Trainer's Aide Inc, pg 945
MRG Productions Inc, pg 948
VIEW Inc (Video International Entertainment World Inc), pg 1058

NORTH CAROLINA

Vide-O-Go/That's Infotainment!, pg 1054

OHIO

South-Western Publishing Co, pg 1019

OREGON

International Loving Touch Foundation Inc, pg 901

PENNSYLVANIA

American Law Institute Continuing Legal Education (ALICLE), pg 784
FMP Media Solutions Inc, pg 870
Media Inc, pg 936
TRC Interactive Inc, pg 1044

TENNESSEE

American Blackguard Inc, pg 784
Spring Arbor Distributors, pg 1022
Zion Music Group, pg 1074

TEXAS

InterCom, pg 900
MVP International Inc, pg 951
University of Texas at Austin - Petroleum Extension Service, pg 1050

VERMONT

Dialect Accent Specialists Inc, pg 846

WASHINGTON

Intermedia Inc, pg 900

WISCONSIN

Wisconsin Technical College System Foundation Inc, pg 1068

ONTARIO

BBC Worldwide Canada Ltd, pg 803
Canadian Learning Co Inc, pg 818
Kineticvideo.com, pg 911

Training Program Producers

ALABAMA

Media Visions Inc, pg 937

ARIZONA

Aardvark Productions LLC, pg 772
Candee Productions Inc, pg 819
Creative Backstage, pg 838
Tellens Inc, pg 1037
Video Media Productions (VMP), pg 1055

ARKANSAS

Live'N'Loud, pg 923
White Diamond Productions, pg 1065

CALIFORNIA

Aaron Marcus & Associates Inc, pg 772
Academy Savant, pg 773
AM Productions, pg 783
Animax, pg 787
California Language Laboratories, pg 817
Crystal Pyramid Productions™, pg 840
Design Media, pg 845
Direct Images Interactive Inc, pg 848
Discovery Education - Los Angeles, pg 848
Dolphin MultiMedia Inc, pg 850
imageReal Pictures LLC, pg 896
International Contact Inc, pg 900
Kantola Productions LLC, pg 908
Kavich Reynolds Productions Inc, pg 908
Lynch Communications, pg 926
Medcom Inc, pg 936
Media Magic, pg 937
The Media Staff Inc, pg 937
New & Unique Videos™, pg 955
New Circuit Films LLC, pg 955
Panorama Productions, pg 968
Players Press, pg 977
Prime Cut Productions, pg 982
SBS Productions, pg 1003
Tam Communications Inc, pg 1031
Total Media Group, pg 1042
University of Southern California, pg 1050
Vineyard Video & Photography, pg 1058
Wavemaker Media Design, pg 1062
Webster Communications, pg 1063
West Coast Projections Inc, pg 1063

COLORADO

Paul L Anderson Productions Inc, pg 786
Daylight Productions & Rentals, pg 844
Flashback Media Productions, pg 869
National Teaching Aids Inc, pg 953
Vital Learning LLC, pg 1060

CONNECTICUT

Applebox Studio, pg 788
Broadcast Video Productions LLC, pg 813
Cine-Med Inc, pg 826
Fox Connecticut, pg 872
MCC Films, pg 935

DISTRICT OF COLUMBIA

O'Keefe Communications Inc, pg 961
Theatrical Technicians Inc (TTI), pg 1038

FLORIDA

Accel Video Productions, pg 773
ACE Video Resources Software, pg 774
Allegro Productions Inc, pg 781
Capital Communications Inc, pg 819
CD ROM™ Inc, pg 822
Communications Concepts Inc (CCI), pg 833
Home Shopping Network (HSN), pg 890
Motion Image Group LLC, pg 947
Paradise Video & Film, pg 969
Sunfire Communications Inc, pg 1028
Teach America Corp, pg 1033
Tricycle Studios, pg 1044
Video Techniques Inc, pg 1056

GEORGIA

Beachwood Productions, pg 804
Continental Film & Video, pg 835
Guerrilla Productions LLC, pg 883
Thompson-Mitchell & Associates Inc, pg 1039

HAWAII

Hyperspective Studios Inc, pg 893
Media Bridge Gamekids, pg 936
Source School of Tantra Yoga Inc, pg 1019

ILLINOIS

Accenture, pg 773
Airways Digital Media, pg 779
Audio Visual Services Corp, pg 796
CCH Continuing Education, pg 821
CCore Media Inc, pg 821
Chicago Satellite & Video, pg 825
Comtech Multimedia Marketing, pg 834
1st Financial Training Services Inc, pg 868
LightCraft Graphics Inc, pg 920
Major Media Productions Inc, pg 929
Manning Productions, pg 930
National Safety Council (NSC), pg 953
The Pepper Group, pg 972
PSAV® Presentation Services (Hotel Services Division), pg 987
Roadworthy Image Magnification, pg 998
SCI Television Productions LLC, pg 1004
Sparkfactor, pg 1019
20/20 Communications Inc, pg 1047
Video Impressions, pg 1055

PROGRAMMING — AUDIO/VISUAL

Training Program Producers (continued)

INDIANA

AVA Productions, pg 798
Covenant Productions®, pg 837
Digital Rain LLC, pg 847

IOWA

The Production House, pg 984

KENTUCKY

KET The Kentucky Network, pg 910
NIMCO Inc, pg 957

LOUISIANA

Digital FX Inc, pg 847
Louisiana State University Health Sciences Center - Shreveport, pg 925

MARYLAND

The Cutting Corp, pg 841
dbF a Media Company, pg 844
The Image Generators, pg 895
Lehigh Phoenix™, pg 918
Mobile-Video Productions Inc, pg 944

MASSACHUSETTS

CommCreative, pg 832
Cramer Productions, pg 837
Soundtrack Recording Studios, pg 1018
TVN-The Video Network, pg 1046
Veritech Corp, pg 1053

MICHIGAN

Benjamin Creative Productions, pg 805
Digi Sign Design LLC, pg 847
K&R All Media Productions Inc, pg 908
K&R's Recording Studios Inc, pg 908
Resource Development Co LLC, pg 995
Universal Images, pg 1049

MINNESOTA

Badiyan Inc, pg 801
Big Event Productions LLC, pg 807
Live Spark Inc, pg 923
Master Communications Group, pg 933
Media Loft Inc, pg 937
MultiMedia, pg 950

MONTANA

North Country Media Group, pg 959

NEBRASKA

Dog & Pony Productions Inc, pg 850

NEVADA

HDTV Productions Inc, pg 886
JCS Video Productions, pg 904

NEW HAMPSHIRE

Apertura, pg 788
Chip Taylor Communications LLC, pg 1032

NEW JERSEY

Broadcast Center Studios, pg 813
Half Moon Video Productions, pg 883
Laurel Video Productions, pg 916
Optisonics Productions, pg 965
Selden Associates, pg 1006
Telemanagement Resources International Inc (TRI), pg 1036

NEW MEXICO

Michael Dunn Productions, pg 853
Uncharted Country Publishing, pg 1048

NEW YORK

American Management Association International, pg 784
Blue Barn Pictures Inc, pg 809
Broad Street Inc, pg 812
dM works, pg 849
Duggal Visual Solutions, pg 853
Guidance Associates Inc Center for Humanities, pg 883
Havas Worldwide, pg 886
HB-Content, pg 886
Hello World Communications, pg 888
Interactive International Inc, pg 899
Ketchum Pleon Change, pg 910
Neal Marshad Productions, pg 931
Jack Morton Worldwide, pg 946
MRG Productions Inc, pg 948
MRY, pg 949
News Broadcast Network, pg 956
Northeast Video Productions Inc, pg 959
Shelly Palmer Production, pg 968
TBA Global Events, pg 1032
VIEW Inc (Video International Entertainment World Inc), pg 1058
WorldView Software, pg 1070
Zelman Studios Ltd, pg 1073

NORTH CAROLINA

Pat Appleson Studios Inc, pg 788
The Communications Group Inc, pg 833
Image Associates Inc, pg 894
Kino Mountain Productions LLC, pg 911
LCW Productions LLC, pg 917
Moving Pictures, pg 948
PACE Worldwide, pg 966

OHIO

Advent Media Inc, pg 778
Creative Technology, pg 838
Cuyahoga Community College Media Center, pg 841
MainSail Production Services Inc, pg 929
R&B Communications Inc, pg 991
South-Western Publishing Co, pg 1019
Take 1 Media Services, pg 1031
Thread Marketing Group, pg 1039
Treehaus Communications Inc, pg 1044
VGI Productions, pg 1053
Vista Color Imaging Inc, pg 1059

OREGON

A KTVA Production LLC, pg 771
Ideascape Inc, pg 894
Rex, pg 995

PENNSYLVANIA

AiH Group Inc, pg 779
American Law Institute Continuing Legal Education (ALICLE), pg 784
Audio Visual Communications Inc, pg 795
Bang Pictures, pg 802
FMP Media Solutions Inc, pg 870
JPL, pg 906
Main Point Productions, pg 929
Panta Rhei Media Inc, pg 968
Pemcor LLC, pg 971
Production Masters Inc (PMI), pg 984

RHODE ISLAND

Sound-FX-Design, pg 1017

TENNESSEE

American Blackguard Inc, pg 784
Continental Film, pg 835
Running Pony Productions LLC, pg 1000
Spring Arbor Distributors, pg 1022
WKPT-TV, pg 1068

TEXAS

Biway Media, pg 808
Horizon Film + Video Productions, pg 891
InterCom, pg 900
Mediaforce Productions, pg 937
MVP International Inc, pg 951
Romar Learning, pg 999
Stage Directions, pg 1022
Stockyard Photos/Jim Olive Photography, pg 1025
University of Texas at Austin - Petroleum Extension Service, pg 1050

VERMONT

Dialect Accent Specialists Inc, pg 846

VIRGINIA

Advance Concepts Inc, pg 777
CALIBRE, pg 816
D&B Television & Video Productions Inc, pg 842
ITC Learning LLC, pg 903
Lion Recording Services Inc, pg 922
Metro Productions, pg 939

WASHINGTON

Adams Creative & Production Services, pg 775
Intermedia Inc, pg 900
Kostov Productions, pg 913
Media Resources Inc, pg 937

WEST VIRGINIA

Altruist Media LLC, pg 783

WISCONSIN

Audio Visual of Milwaukee Inc, pg 795
Rucinski & Reetz Communications LLC, pg 1000
USAV Group Inc, pg 1050
Watts Communications Inc, pg 1062
Wisconsin Public Television, pg 1068
Wisconsin Technical College System Foundation Inc, pg 1068

WYOMING

Bridger Productions Inc, pg 812

ALBERTA

Black Media Works, pg 808

NEWFOUNDLAND AND LABRADOR

Vidcraft Productions Ltd, pg 1054

NORTHWEST TERRITORIES

Yellowknife Films Inc, pg 1072

ONTARIO

BBC Worldwide Canada Ltd, pg 803
JFB Communications, pg 905
Purefire Communications Inc, pg 987

QUEBEC

Kerrigan Productions Inc, pg 910

Training Program Rentals

CALIFORNIA

Academy Savant, pg 773
Medcom Inc, pg 936
Semiconductor Services, pg 1006
University of Southern California, pg 1050

ILLINOIS

1st Financial Training Services Inc, pg 868
National Safety Council (NSC), pg 953

MICHIGAN

Digi Sign Design LLC, pg 847

NEW HAMPSHIRE

Chip Taylor Communications LLC, pg 1032

NEW YORK

Interactive International Inc, pg 899
TBA Global Events, pg 1032

TEXAS

InterCom, pg 900
MVP International Inc, pg 951

UTAH

Webb Audio Visual Communication, pg 1063

WASHINGTON

Intermedia Inc, pg 900

Transparency, *see* Overhead Transparency

Travelog Distributors

ARIZONA

Video Learning Library, pg 1055

CALIFORNIA

Crystal Pyramid Productions™, pg 840
Glenn Photo Supply, pg 878
Global Village Productions, pg 879
Jaguar Distribution Corp, pg 903
New & Unique Videos™, pg 955
Melvin Powers Television Marketing, pg 979

DISTRICT OF COLUMBIA

Biblical Archaeology Society (BAS), pg 806

FLORIDA

Capital Communications Inc, pg 819

ILLINOIS

Film Ideas, pg 867

KENTUCKY

Horizon Films & Media LLC, pg 891

MICHIGAN

Digi Sign Design LLC, pg 847

NEW HAMPSHIRE

Chip Taylor Communications LLC, pg 1032

NEW JERSEY

Euro-Pacific Film & Video Productions Inc, pg 863

NEW MEXICO

National Information Center for Educational Media (NICEM)/MediaSleuth, pg 952

NEW YORK

Irish Music Corp, pg 902
Janson Media, pg 904
MRG Productions Inc, pg 948
Videofashion Network, pg 1056

NORTH CAROLINA

Vide-O-Go/That's Infotainment!, pg 1054

OREGON

TeleVideos, pg 1036

PENNSYLVANIA

FMP Media Solutions Inc, pg 870

TENNESSEE

American Blackguard Inc, pg 784
Marine Geographic, pg 931

TEXAS

Educational Video Network, pg 857

VIRGINIA

Once Around, pg 963

ONTARIO

Canadian Learning Co Inc, pg 818

Travelog Producers

ALABAMA

AVS Media Group, pg 800
Media Visions Inc, pg 937

ARIZONA

Aardvark Productions LLC, pg 772
Tellens Inc, pg 1037

CALIFORNIA

Crystal Pyramid Productions™, pg 840
Dogma Studios, pg 850
Dolphin MultiMedia Inc, pg 850
Global Village Productions, pg 879
Jaguar Distribution Corp, pg 903
Lynch Communications, pg 926
New & Unique Videos™, pg 955
Prime Cut Productions, pg 982
SBS Productions, pg 1003
Screen Door Entertainment Inc, pg 1005
Total Media Group, pg 1042
Vineyard Video & Photography, pg 1058
Wavemaker Media Design, pg 1062
Webster Communications, pg 1063
West Coast Projections Inc, pg 1063

COLORADO

Flashback Media Productions, pg 869
Tatum Video, pg 1032

CONNECTICUT

Applebox Studio, pg 788
Broadcast Video Productions LLC, pg 813
Fox Connecticut, pg 872
MCC Films, pg 935

DISTRICT OF COLUMBIA

O'Keefe Communications Inc, pg 961

FLORIDA

Allegro Productions Inc, pg 781
Sunfire Communications Inc, pg 1028

GEORGIA

Beachwood Productions, pg 804
Continental Film & Video, pg 835
Guerrilla Productions LLC, pg 883

HAWAII

Hyperspective Studios Inc, pg 893

ILLINOIS

Audio Visual Services Corp, pg 796
Chicago Satellite & Video, pg 825
Comtech Multimedia Marketing, pg 834
The Pepper Group, pg 972
PSAV® Presentation Services (Hotel Services Division), pg 987
SCI Television Productions LLC, pg 1004
20/20 Communications Inc, pg 1047
Video Impressions, pg 1055

INDIANA

Digital Rain LLC, pg 847

KANSAS

Chapman Recording & Mastering, pg 824

KENTUCKY

Horizon Films & Media LLC, pg 891

MARYLAND

The Image Generators, pg 895

MASSACHUSETTS

Soundtrack Recording Studios, pg 1018
TVN-The Video Network, pg 1046

MICHIGAN

Digi Sign Design LLC, pg 847
K&R All Media Productions Inc, pg 908
K&R's Recording Studios Inc, pg 908

MINNESOTA

MultiMedia, pg 950
Stoney-Wolf Productions Inc, pg 1025

MONTANA

North Country Media Group, pg 959

NEVADA

HDTV Productions Inc, pg 886

NEW HAMPSHIRE

Chip Taylor Communications LLC, pg 1032

NEW JERSEY

Broadcast Center Studios, pg 813
Optisonics Productions, pg 965

NEW YORK

Edgeware Associates/Travel Arts Syndicate, pg 856
Irish Music Corp, pg 902
Neal Marshad Productions, pg 931
Jack Morton Worldwide, pg 946
MRG Productions Inc, pg 948
MRY, pg 949
News Broadcast Network, pg 956
Shelly Palmer Production, pg 968
Videofashion Network, pg 1056
Zelman Studios Ltd, pg 1073

NORTH CAROLINA

Pat Appleson Studios Inc, pg 788
Kino Mountain Productions LLC, pg 911

OHIO

Advent Media Inc, pg 778
MainSail Production Services Inc, pg 929
R&B Communications Inc, pg 991
Take 1 Media Services, pg 1031
Treehaus Communications Inc, pg 1044

OREGON

Odyssey Productions Inc, pg 961
TeleVideos, pg 1036

PENNSYLVANIA

FMP Media Solutions Inc, pg 870
JPL, pg 906
Muderick Media, pg 949
Production Masters Inc (PMI), pg 984

RHODE ISLAND

Sound-FX-Design, pg 1017

TENNESSEE

American Blackguard Inc, pg 784
Marine Geographic, pg 931
Running Pony Productions LLC, pg 1000
WKPT-TV, pg 1068

TEXAS

Educational Video Network, pg 857
Horizon Film + Video Productions, pg 891
Mediaforce Productions, pg 937
Stage Directions, pg 1022

VIRGINIA

D&B Television & Video Productions Inc, pg 842
Lion Recording Services Inc, pg 922

WASHINGTON

White Rain Films Ltd, pg 1065

WISCONSIN

Rucinski & Reetz Communications LLC, pg 1000
Wisconsin Public Television, pg 1068

WYOMING

Bridger Productions Inc, pg 812

ALBERTA

HBW Entertainment Inc, pg 886

NEWFOUNDLAND AND LABRADOR

Vidcraft Productions Ltd, pg 1054

NORTHWEST TERRITORIES

Yellowknife Films Inc, pg 1072

QUEBEC

Kerrigan Productions Inc, pg 910

Travelog Rentals

CALIFORNIA

Glenn Photo Supply, pg 878
Global Village Productions, pg 879

MICHIGAN

Digi Sign Design LLC, pg 847

NEW HAMPSHIRE

Chip Taylor Communications LLC, pg 1032

PROGRAMMING — AUDIO/VISUAL

Travelog Rentals (continued)

NEW JERSEY

Euro-Pacific Film & Video Productions Inc, pg 863

UTAH

Webb Audio Visual Communication, pg 1063

VIRGINIA

Once Around, pg 963

Vocational Program Distributors

ARIZONA

Video Learning Library, pg 1055

CALIFORNIA

Crystal Pyramid Productions™, pg 840
Discovery Education - Los Angeles, pg 848
Players Press, pg 977

FLORIDA

ACE Video Resources Software, pg 774
Capital Communications Inc, pg 819

GEORGIA

Convergent Media Systems, pg 836
School Media Associates LLC, pg 1004

ILLINOIS

Film Ideas, pg 867
National Safety Council (NSC), pg 953

INDIANA

Agency for Instructional Technology (AIT), pg 778

MICHIGAN

Digi Sign Design LLC, pg 847

NEW HAMPSHIRE

Frey Scientific, pg 873
Chip Taylor Communications LLC, pg 1032

NEW JERSEY

Lucerne Media, pg 925

NEW MEXICO

National Information Center for Educational Media (NICEM)/MediaSleuth, pg 952

NEW YORK

Films for the Humanities & Sciences, pg 868
Films Media Group, pg 868
Guidance Associates Inc Center for Humanities, pg 883
Human Relations Media, pg 892
March of Dimes Foundation, pg 930
Meridian Education Corp, pg 939
MRG Productions Inc, pg 948
Penguin Audiobooks, pg 971
Shopware, pg 1009
VIEW Inc (Video International Entertainment World Inc), pg 1058

NORTH CAROLINA

Do It Yourself Inc - DIY Video Corp, pg 849
Vide-O-Go/That's Infotainment!, pg 1054

OHIO

McGraw-Hill School Education Group, pg 935
South-Western Publishing Co, pg 1019

PENNSYLVANIA

FMP Media Solutions Inc, pg 870

TENNESSEE

American Blackguard Inc, pg 784

TEXAS

University of Texas at Austin - Petroleum Extension Service, pg 1050

WISCONSIN

Wisconsin Technical College System Foundation Inc, pg 1068

ONTARIO

Canadian Learning Co Inc, pg 818
Kineticvideo.com, pg 911
McIntyre Media Inc, pg 935

Vocational Program Producers

ALABAMA

Media Visions Inc, pg 937

ARIZONA

Aardvark Productions LLC, pg 772

CALIFORNIA

Aaron Marcus & Associates Inc, pg 772
Crystal Pyramid Productions™, pg 840
Discovery Education - Los Angeles, pg 848
imageReal Pictures LLC, pg 896
Lynch Communications, pg 926
The Media Staff Inc, pg 937
New & Unique Videos™, pg 955
Players Press, pg 977
SBS Productions, pg 1003
Total Media Group, pg 1042
Vineyard Video & Photography, pg 1058
Wavemaker Media Design, pg 1062
Webster Communications, pg 1063
West Coast Projections Inc, pg 1063

COLORADO

Flashback Media Productions, pg 869

CONNECTICUT

Applebox Studio, pg 788
Broadcast Video Productions LLC, pg 813
Fox Connecticut, pg 872

FLORIDA

ACE Video Resources Software, pg 774
Allegro Productions Inc, pg 781
Capital Communications Inc, pg 819
Sunfire Communications Inc, pg 1028

GEORGIA

Beachwood Productions, pg 804
Continental Film & Video, pg 835
Guerrilla Productions LLC, pg 883

HAWAII

Hyperspective Studios Inc, pg 893

ILLINOIS

Chicago Satellite & Video, pg 825
1st Financial Training Services Inc, pg 868
Major Media Productions Inc, pg 929
National Safety Council (NSC), pg 953
The Pepper Group, pg 972
20/20 Communications Inc, pg 1047

INDIANA

Agency for Instructional Technology (AIT), pg 778

KENTUCKY

NIMCO Inc, pg 957

MARYLAND

dbF a Media Company, pg 844
The Image Generators, pg 895

MASSACHUSETTS

Soundtrack Recording Studios, pg 1018
Triumph Learning LLC, pg 1045

MICHIGAN

Digi Sign Design LLC, pg 847
K&R All Media Productions Inc, pg 908
K&R's Recording Studios Inc, pg 908

MINNESOTA

Badiyan Inc, pg 801
Master Communications Group, pg 933

MONTANA

North Country Media Group, pg 959

NEBRASKA

Dog & Pony Productions Inc, pg 850

NEVADA

JCS Video Productions, pg 904

NEW HAMPSHIRE

Apertura, pg 788
Frey Scientific, pg 873
Chip Taylor Communications LLC, pg 1032

NEW JERSEY

Half Moon Video Productions, pg 883
Laurel Video Productions, pg 916
Optisonics Productions, pg 965

NEW YORK

dM works, pg 849
Films Media Group, pg 868
The Food & Beverage Institute, pg 871
Guidance Associates Inc Center for Humanities, pg 883
Havas Worldwide, pg 886
Hello World Communications, pg 888
Human Relations Media, pg 892
Ketchum Pleon Change, pg 910
March of Dimes Foundation, pg 930
Jack Morton Worldwide, pg 946
MRG Productions Inc, pg 948
Shelly Palmer Production, pg 968
Penguin Audiobooks, pg 971
VIEW Inc (Video International Entertainment World Inc), pg 1058
Zelman Studios Ltd, pg 1073

NORTH CAROLINA

Pat Appleson Studios Inc, pg 788
Do It Yourself Inc - DIY Video Corp, pg 849
Kino Mountain Productions LLC, pg 911
LCW Productions LLC, pg 917
Moving Pictures, pg 948

OHIO

Advent Media Inc, pg 778
MainSail Production Services Inc, pg 929
McGraw-Hill School Education Group, pg 935
R&B Communications Inc, pg 991
South-Western Publishing Co, pg 1019
Take 1 Media Services, pg 1031
Treehaus Communications Inc, pg 1044
VGI Productions, pg 1053
Vista Color Imaging Inc, pg 1059

OREGON

A KTVA Production LLC, pg 771
ERA Learning, pg 862
Ideascape Inc, pg 894

PENNSYLVANIA

FMP Media Solutions Inc, pg 870
JPL, pg 906
Muderick Media, pg 949
Production Masters Inc (PMI), pg 984

RHODE ISLAND

Sound-FX-Design, pg 1017

TENNESSEE

American Blackguard Inc, pg 784
Continental Film, pg 835

TEXAS

VIRGINIA

WISCONSIN

WYOMING

NEWFOUNDLAND AND LABRADOR

QUEBEC

Vocational Program Rentals

GEORGIA

ILLINOIS

MICHIGAN

NEW HAMPSHIRE

UTAH

PROGRAMMING — FILM

Business Program Distributors

ARIZONA

Video Learning Library, pg 1055

CALIFORNIA

Allied Artists International Inc, pg 781
Crystal Pyramid Productions™, pg 840
Direct Cinema Ltd Inc, pg 848
eFootage LLC, pg 858
Jaguar Distribution Corp, pg 903
New & Unique Videos™, pg 955
TMW Media Group, pg 1041

FLORIDA

Capital Communications Inc, pg 819

GEORGIA

Convergent Media Systems, pg 836

HAWAII

Media Bridge Gamekids, pg 936

ILLINOIS

ABSA Productions Inc, pg 772
Chicago Satellite & Video, pg 825

MASSACHUSETTS

Emergency Film Group, pg 860

MICHIGAN

Emery-Pratt Co, pg 860

MINNESOTA

Service Quality Institute, pg 1007

MISSOURI

Phoenix/BFA/Coronet, pg 974

NEVADA

DVDs4Less, pg 854

NEW MEXICO

National Information Center for Educational Media (NICEM)/MediaSleuth, pg 952

NEW YORK

Broad Street Inc, pg 812
Films Media Group, pg 868
Guidance Associates Inc Center for Humanities, pg 883
HB-Content, pg 886
Richter Productions Inc, pg 996
VIEW Inc (Video International Entertainment World Inc), pg 1058

PENNSYLVANIA

FMP Media Solutions Inc, pg 870

VIRGINIA

CACI Productions Group, pg 816

ONTARIO

Kineticvideo.com, pg 911
McNabb & Connolly, pg 935

Business Program Producers

ALABAMA

Leo Ticheli Productions, pg 1040

ALASKA

Aurora Films, pg 797

ARIZONA

Candee Productions Inc, pg 819
Film Creations Ltd, pg 867

CALIFORNIA

Classic Images, pg 829
Crystal Pyramid Productions™, pg 840
Dogma Studios, pg 850
Dolphin MultiMedia Inc, pg 850
Havas Edge, pg 885
imageReal Pictures LLC, pg 896
Kavich Reynolds Productions Inc, pg 908
The Kenwood Group, pg 909
Main Street Media Inc, pg 929
The Media Staff Inc, pg 937
New & Unique Videos™, pg 955
Panorama Productions, pg 968
Dick Reizner Film & Video, pg 994
Glenn Roland Films, pg 998
Tam Communications Inc, pg 1031
TMW Media Group, pg 1041
Utopia Films, pg 1051
Vineyard Video & Photography, pg 1058
Webster Communications, pg 1063

COLORADO

Apogee Communications Group, pg 788
The Cinema Lab, pg 827
Flashback Media Productions, pg 869
Transtar Entertainment Co Inc, pg 1043

CONNECTICUT

ACM Productions Ltd, pg 774
Broadcast Video Productions LLC, pg 813
MCC Films, pg 935
Moving Pictures, pg 947

DISTRICT OF COLUMBIA

Hillmann & Carr Inc, pg 889
Yellow Cat Productions Inc, pg 1072

FLORIDA

Capital Communications Inc, pg 819
Civins Productions Inc, pg 828
Eastern Video, pg 856
Jordan Klein Film & Video (JKFV), pg 906
Universal Studios Florida® Production Group, pg 1049

GEORGIA

Beachwood Productions, pg 804
Burst Video/Film Inc, pg 815
Continental Film & Video, pg 835
Guerrilla Productions LLC, pg 883
Myriad Productions, pg 951

HAWAII

Hyperspective Studios Inc, pg 893
Media Bridge Gamekids, pg 936
1013 Integrated, pg 1037

ILLINOIS

ABSA Productions Inc, pg 772
Comtech Multimedia Marketing, pg 834
Cresta Creative, pg 839
Film Police, pg 867
Manning Productions, pg 930
MIGHTYbYTES Inc, pg 942
SCI Television Productions LLC, pg 1004
Winter Productions, pg 1068

INDIANA

AVA Productions, pg 798
Road Pictures, pg 997

LOUISIANA

Digital FX Inc, pg 847

MARYLAND

The Ahern Group, pg 779
Richard Chisolm Cinematography, pg 825
dbF a Media Company, pg 844
The Image Generators, pg 895

MASSACHUSETTS

CommCreative, pg 832
Emergency Film Group, pg 860
Green Mountain Post Films (GMP), pg 882
Heliotrope Studios, pg 887

MICHIGAN

Maritz Performance Improvement Co, pg 931

MINNESOTA

Blue 60 Pictures, pg 810
House of Cinemagraphics, pg 891
Service Quality Institute, pg 1007

MISSISSIPPI

Dollarhide Film Inc, pg 850

MISSOURI

Phoenix/BFA/Coronet, pg 974

MONTANA

North Country Media Group, pg 959

NEBRASKA

Dog & Pony Productions Inc, pg 850

NEVADA

DVDs4Less, pg 854

NEW HAMPSHIRE

Apertura, pg 788

NEW JERSEY

Half Moon Video Productions, pg 883
Bill Quinn Productions, pg 989
Telequest Inc, pg 1036
TimeSteps Productions Inc, pg 1041

NEW MEXICO

Michael Dunn Productions, pg 853

NEW YORK

aurora productions, pg 797
Brian Film Productions LLC, pg 812
Broad Street Inc, pg 812
De Nonno Productions Inc (DPI), pg 844
Fanlight Productions, pg 865
Films Media Group, pg 868
Florentine Films, pg 870
Karen Frankel Productions, pg 872
Havas Worldwide, pg 886
HB-Content, pg 886
Hello World Communications, pg 888
Image Zone Inc, pg 896
Ketchum Pleon Change, pg 910
Neal Marshad Productions, pg 931
Jack Morton Worldwide, pg 946
MRY, pg 949
New Horizon Studios, pg 955
News Broadcast Network, pg 956
Northeast Video Productions Inc, pg 959
Shelly Palmer Production, pg 968
Pat Kogan Productions Inc, pg 970
Polestar Films & Associated Arts Ltd, pg 978
PrimeLight Productions Inc, pg 982
Richter Productions Inc, pg 996
Suggs Media Productions Inc, pg 1028
TBA Global Events, pg 1032
VIEW Inc (Video International Entertainment World Inc), pg 1058
Zelman Studios Ltd, pg 1073

NORTH CAROLINA

The Communications Group Inc, pg 833
Kino Mountain Productions LLC, pg 911
Unifour Productions Inc, pg 1048

OHIO

Creative Technology, pg 838
Take 1 Media Services, pg 1031

OREGON

Ideascape Inc, pg 894
Odyssey Productions Inc, pg 961

PENNSYLVANIA

Bang Pictures, pg 802
FMP Media Solutions Inc, pg 870
Goodman Associates Inc, pg 880
JPL, pg 906
Main Point Productions, pg 929
Muderick Media, pg 949
Production Masters Inc (PMI), pg 984
Video/Film Associates, pg 1055

RHODE ISLAND

Sound-FX-Design, pg 1017

TENNESSEE

Continental Film, pg 835
Memphis Communications Corp, pg 938
Scripps Networks, pg 1005

Business Program Rentals

Children's Program Distributors

Children's Program Producers

PROGRAMMING — FILM

Children's Program Producers (continued)

KENTUCKY

National Geographic Learning, pg 952

MARYLAND

dbF a Media Company, pg 844

MASSACHUSETTS

Green Mountain Post Films (GMP), pg 882
Heliotrope Studios, pg 887

MINNESOTA

House of Cinemagraphics, pg 891

MISSOURI

Cable Films & Video, pg 816
Phoenix/BFA/Coronet, pg 974

MONTANA

North Country Media Group, pg 959

NEW HAMPSHIRE

Apertura, pg 788

NEW JERSEY

Bill Quinn Productions, pg 989
Telequest Inc, pg 1036

NEW MEXICO

Rainbow International Inc/Rainbow Productions Inc, pg 990

NEW YORK

American History Workshop (NY) Inc, pg 784
aurora productions, pg 797
Brian Film Productions LLC, pg 812
Brooklyn Botanic Garden, pg 814
Billy Budd Films Inc, pg 814
Buzzco Associates Inc, pg 816
De Nonno Productions Inc (DPI), pg 844
Fanlight Productions, pg 865
Florentine Films, pg 870
Karen Frankel Productions, pg 872
Greyfalcon House, pg 882
Hallel Communications, pg 884
Havas Worldwide, pg 886
Hearst Entertainment & Syndication, pg 887
Hello World Communications, pg 888
Neal Marshad Productions, pg 931
Metropolitan Museum of Art, pg 940
Jack Morton Worldwide, pg 946
Shelly Palmer Production, pg 968
Pat Kogan Productions Inc, pg 970
Polestar Films & Associated Arts Ltd, pg 978
Scholastic Media, pg 1004
Third World Newsreel/Camera News Inc, pg 1039
VIEW Inc (Video International Entertainment World Inc), pg 1058
Zelman Studios Ltd, pg 1073

NORTH CAROLINA

The Communications Group Inc, pg 833
Crystal Pictures Inc, pg 840
Kino Mountain Productions LLC, pg 911

OHIO

Creative Technology, pg 838
Take 1 Media Services, pg 1031

OREGON

Ideascape Inc, pg 894

PENNSYLVANIA

Kensington Falls Animation, pg 909
Production Masters Inc (PMI), pg 984

RHODE ISLAND

Sound-FX-Design, pg 1017

TENNESSEE

American Blackguard Inc, pg 784

TEXAS

Alexander Media Productions, pg 780
Cerutti Productions Inc, pg 823
Marx InDigital, pg 933
Earl Miller Productions Inc, pg 943

VERMONT

Marlboro Film & Video Productions, pg 931

VIRGINIA

BES Studios, pg 805

WASHINGTON

ChristianAnswers.Net™, pg 825

WEST VIRGINIA

Altruist Media LLC, pg 783

WISCONSIN

Wisconsin Public Television, pg 1068

WYOMING

Bridger Productions Inc, pg 812

ALBERTA

Global Television Station, pg 879
HBW Entertainment Inc, pg 886

BRITISH COLUMBIA

West Eagle Films Inc, pg 1064

ONTARIO

Epitome Pictures Inc, pg 862

QUEBEC

Kerrigan Productions Inc, pg 910
Les Productions Via Le Monde (Daniel Bertolino) Inc, pg 985

SASKATCHEWAN

plan9films, pg 976

Children's Program Rentals

CALIFORNIA

Direct Cinema Ltd Inc, pg 848
Em Gee Film Library, pg 860
Glenn Photo Supply, pg 878
Visual Communications - Southern California Asian American Studies Central Inc, pg 1059

ILLINOIS

Discovery Education - Chicago, pg 848

INDIANA

InterComm, pg 900

MISSOURI

Cable Films & Video, pg 816
Phoenix/BFA/Coronet, pg 974
University of Missouri-Columbia, pg 1050

NEW YORK

Brooklyn Botanic Garden, pg 814
Hallel Communications, pg 884
Select Media Inc, pg 1006
Third World Newsreel/Camera News Inc, pg 1039
VIEW Inc (Video International Entertainment World Inc), pg 1058

NORTH CAROLINA

Crystal Pictures Inc, pg 840

PENNSYLVANIA

Bullfrog Films Inc, pg 815

WASHINGTON

ChristianAnswers.Net™, pg 825

ONTARIO

Kineticvideo.com, pg 911

QUEBEC

Les Productions Via Le Monde (Daniel Bertolino) Inc, pg 985

Classic Program Distributors

CALIFORNIA

Anchor Bay Entertainment LLC, pg 786
Ben Barry & Associates Inc, pg 803
Increase Video/Silver Mine Video, pg 897
MarVista Entertainment Inc, pg 933
MGM Home Video, pg 941
National Lampoon, pg 953
Rhino Home Video, pg 996
TMW Media Group, pg 1041
Visual Communications - Southern California Asian American Studies Central Inc, pg 1059
Worldwide Entertainment Corp, pg 1070

IDAHO

Lagoon Video, pg 915

ILLINOIS

Cool-Lux, pg 836
International Historic Films Inc, pg 901

MASSACHUSETTS

Documentary Educational Resources Inc, pg 850

MISSOURI

Cable Films & Video, pg 816

NEW JERSEY

Lucerne Media, pg 925

NEW MEXICO

National Information Center for Educational Media (NICEM)/MediaSleuth, pg 952

NORTH CAROLINA

Crystal Pictures Inc, pg 840
Vide-O-Go/That's Infotainment!, pg 1054

PENNSYLVANIA

Library Video Company, pg 920
Movies Unlimited, pg 947
MVD Entertainment Group, pg 951

TENNESSEE

Spring Arbor Distributors, pg 1022

TEXAS

Marengo Films, pg 931

WASHINGTON

Media Resources Inc, pg 937

ONTARIO

Cambium Catalyst International (CCI), pg 817
Universal Studios Canada Inc, pg 1049

Classic Program Producers

CALIFORNIA

Backstage Pass Entertainment Inc, pg 801
National Lampoon, pg 953
Glenn Roland Films, pg 998
TMW Media Group, pg 1041
Total Media Group, pg 1042
Visual Communications - Southern California Asian American Studies Central Inc, pg 1059

COLORADO

The Cinema Lab, pg 827

FLORIDA

Chatterbox Productions Inc, pg 824

GEORGIA

Guerrilla Productions LLC, pg 883

MARYLAND

dbF a Media Company, pg 844

MASSACHUSETTS

Heliotrope Studios, pg 887

Classic Program Rentals

Commercial, *see* Test Commercial

Current Event Program Distributors

Current Event Program Producers

PROGRAMMING — FILM

Current Event Program Producers (continued)

WEST VIRGINIA

Altruist Media LLC, pg 783

WISCONSIN

5th Floor Recording Co, pg 867
Wisconsin Public Television, pg 1068

WYOMING

Bridger Productions Inc, pg 812

ALBERTA

Black Media Works, pg 808
Global Television Station, pg 879

BRITISH COLUMBIA

West Eagle Films Inc, pg 1064

ONTARIO

VO2 Mix Studios, pg 1060

QUEBEC

Kerrigan Productions Inc, pg 910
Les Productions Via Le Monde (Daniel Bertolino) Inc, pg 985

Current Event Program Rentals

CALIFORNIA

Direct Cinema Ltd Inc, pg 848
Visual Communications - Southern California Asian American Studies Central Inc, pg 1059

MISSOURI

Phoenix/BFA/Coronet, pg 974

NEW YORK

Pennebaker Hegedus Films Inc, pg 972
Richter Productions Inc, pg 996
Third World Newsreel/Camera News Inc, pg 1039
VIEW Inc (Video International Entertainment World Inc), pg 1058

PENNSYLVANIA

Bullfrog Films Inc, pg 815

ONTARIO

Kineticvideo.com, pg 911

QUEBEC

Les Productions Via Le Monde (Daniel Bertolino) Inc, pg 985

Documentary Distributors

ARIZONA

Tellens Inc, pg 1037

CALIFORNIA

Allied Artists International Inc, pg 781
Les Blank Films Inc, pg 809
California Newsreel, pg 817
Cambridge Documentary Films Inc, pg 818
Crystal Pyramid Productions™, pg 840
Direct Cinema Ltd Inc, pg 848
eFootage LLC, pg 858
Em Gee Film Library, pg 860
FXF Productions Inc, pg 874
Glenn Photo Supply, pg 878
Goal Productions, pg 879
Ishtar Films, pg 902
Main Street Media Inc, pg 929
MarVista Entertainment Inc, pg 933
Millennium Entertainment LLC, pg 943
New & Unique Videos™, pg 955
Regent Press Publishers & Printers, pg 994
TMW Media Group, pg 1041
Universal Studios Home Entertainment, pg 1049
Visual Communications - Southern California Asian American Studies Central Inc, pg 1059
The Wine Appreciation Guild Ltd, pg 1067

COLORADO

Tatum Video, pg 1032

CONNECTICUT

Hartley Film Foundation, pg 885

DELAWARE

University Media Services, pg 1049

FLORIDA

Accord Productions, pg 773
Capital Communications Inc, pg 819
Cifex Corp, pg 826
Motion Image Group LLC, pg 947

HAWAII

Media Bridge Gamekids, pg 936

IDAHO

Lagoon Video, pg 915

ILLINOIS

ABSA Productions Inc, pg 772
Film Ideas, pg 867
Terra Nova Films Inc, pg 1037

KENTUCKY

Horizon Films & Media LLC, pg 891
National Geographic Learning, pg 952

MARYLAND

DSR Computer Technology Specialists Inc, pg 853
James Agee Film Project, pg 904
Special Archives Division, Motion Picture Branch, pg 1020

MASSACHUSETTS

Documentary Educational Resources Inc, pg 850
Emergency Film Group, pg 860
Green Mountain Post Films (GMP), pg 882
The New Film Company Inc, pg 955
Northern Light Productions, pg 959

MINNESOTA

Festival Films, pg 866

MISSOURI

Cable Films & Video, pg 816
Phoenix/BFA/Coronet, pg 974
The Phoenix Learning Group Inc, pg 974

NEVADA

DVDs4Less, pg 854

NEW HAMPSHIRE

Captain Fiddle Music & Publications, pg 820

NEW JERSEY

Alden Films, pg 780
Euro-Pacific Film & Video Productions Inc, pg 863
Milestone Film & Video Inc, pg 943

NEW MEXICO

National Information Center for Educational Media (NICEM)/ MediaSleuth, pg 952
SouthWest Organizing Project (SWOP), pg 1019

NEW YORK

Michael Blackwood Productions Inc, pg 808
Broad Street Inc, pg 812
Billy Budd Films Inc, pg 814
Circulating Film & Video Library, pg 828
Fanlight Productions, pg 865
Films Media Group, pg 868
First Run Features, pg 869
French American Cultural Exchange (FACE), pg 873
William Greaves Productions Inc, pg 882
Hallel Communications, pg 884
HB-Content, pg 886
Hearst Entertainment & Syndication, pg 887
Icarus Film Inc, pg 893
Janson Media, pg 904
Richard Kaplan Productions, pg 908
Kino International Corp, pg 911
Maryknoll Productions, pg 933
Mastervision Inc, pg 933
New Day Films, pg 955
News Broadcast Network, pg 956
Pennebaker Hegedus Films Inc, pg 972
Richter Productions Inc, pg 996
Select Media Inc, pg 1006
Third World Newsreel/Camera News Inc, pg 1039
VIEW Inc (Video International Entertainment World Inc), pg 1058
Women Make Movies Inc, pg 1069
Wonderwomen™ Enterprises, pg 1069
Zeitgeist Films Ltd, pg 1073

NORTH CAROLINA

Crystal Pictures Inc, pg 840

OHIO

Griesinger Films LLC, pg 882

PENNSYLVANIA

Bullfrog Films Inc, pg 815
FMP Media Solutions Inc, pg 870
Goodman Associates Inc, pg 880
Karol Media Inc, pg 908
Rahlic Publishing Co, pg 990

TENNESSEE

American Blackguard Inc, pg 784
Center for Southern Folklore Inc, pg 822
Spring Arbor Distributors, pg 1022

VERMONT

Dorothy Tod Films, pg 1041

VIRGINIA

CACI Productions Group, pg 816
Water Bearer Films Inc, pg 1062

WASHINGTON

North-by-Northwest Productions, pg 958
White Rain Films Ltd, pg 1065

WEST VIRGINIA

Focus on Animals, pg 870

WISCONSIN

Wisconsin Public Television, pg 1068

ALBERTA

Global Television Station, pg 879

NORTHWEST TERRITORIES

Yellowknife Films Inc, pg 1072

ONTARIO

Cambium Catalyst International (CCI), pg 817
Canadian Filmmakers Distribution Center (CFMDC), pg 818
IMAX Corp, pg 896
Kineticvideo.com, pg 911
McIntyre Media Inc, pg 935
McNabb & Connolly, pg 935
Sullivan Home Entertainment, pg 1028

QUEBEC

National Film Board of Canada/ Office National du Film du Canada, pg 952
Les Productions Via Le Monde (Daniel Bertolino) Inc, pg 985

Documentary Producers

ALASKA

Aurora Films, pg 797

ARIZONA

Candee Productions Inc, pg 819
Film Creations Ltd, pg 867
MediaWorks, pg 938
Phoenix VideoFilms®, pg 974
Tellens Inc, pg 1037

PROGRAMMING — FILM

Documentary Producers (continued)

OHIO (continued)

Maslowski Productions, pg 933
Take 1 Media Services, pg 1031

OREGON

Ideascape Inc, pg 894
Odyssey Productions Inc, pg 961
Producers Studio, pg 984

PENNSYLVANIA

Argentine Productions Inc, pg 789
Bang Pictures, pg 802
FMP Media Solutions Inc, pg 870
Goodman Associates Inc, pg 880
Innovision Media Group, pg 899
Main Point Productions, pg 929
Production Masters Inc (PMI), pg 984
Rahlic Publishing Co, pg 990
Video/Film Associates, pg 1055

RHODE ISLAND

Sound-FX-Design, pg 1017

TENNESSEE

American Blackguard Inc, pg 784
Center for Southern Folklore Inc, pg 822
Continental Film, pg 835
Scripps Networks, pg 1005

TEXAS

Alexander Media Productions, pg 780
Castleview Productions, pg 821
Cerutti Productions Inc, pg 823
Dykeman Associates Inc, pg 854
The Editing Co, pg 857
Horizon Film + Video Productions, pg 891
Earl Miller Productions Inc, pg 943
Rich-Heape Films Inc, pg 996
South Coast Film & Video, pg 1019
Stage Directions, pg 1022
Texas Heart Institute Visual Communication Services, pg 1037

VERMONT

Marlboro Film & Video Productions, pg 931
Dorothy Tod Films, pg 1041

VIRGINIA

BES Studios, pg 805
CACI Productions Group, pg 816
CALIBRE, pg 816
Dorst MediaWorks Inc, pg 851
Metro Productions, pg 939

WASHINGTON

Hamilton Studio, pg 884
North-by-Northwest Productions, pg 958
Pal Productions Inc, pg 967
White Rain Films Ltd, pg 1065

WEST VIRGINIA

Altruist Media LLC, pg 783

WISCONSIN

5th Floor Recording Co, pg 867
University of Wisconsin-Oshkosh Radio-TV-Film Dept, pg 1050
Wisconsin Public Television, pg 1068

WYOMING

Bridger Productions Inc, pg 812

ALBERTA

Black Media Works, pg 808
Global Television Station, pg 879
HBW Entertainment Inc, pg 886

BRITISH COLUMBIA

Network Entertainment Inc, pg 954
West Eagle Films Inc, pg 1064

MANITOBA

Lank/Beach Productions Inc, pg 916

NORTHWEST TERRITORIES

Yellowknife Films Inc, pg 1072

ONTARIO

Doomsday Studios Ltd, pg 850
IMAX Corp, pg 896
VO2 Mix Studios, pg 1060

QUEBEC

Kerrigan Productions Inc, pg 910
National Film Board of Canada/ Office National du Film du Canada, pg 952
Productions Grand Nord Quebec Inc, pg 985
Les Productions Via Le Monde (Daniel Bertolino) Inc, pg 985

Documentary Rentals

CALIFORNIA

Auslender Productions/Celestial Images, pg 797
Les Blank Films Inc, pg 809
Cambridge Documentary Films Inc, pg 818
Direct Cinema Ltd Inc, pg 848
Em Gee Film Library, pg 860
Glenn Photo Supply, pg 878
Point of View Productions, pg 977
Visual Communications - Southern California Asian American Studies Central Inc, pg 1059

COLORADO

Tatum Video, pg 1032

DELAWARE

University Media Services, pg 1049

FLORIDA

Cifex Corp, pg 826

ILLINOIS

Terra Nova Films Inc, pg 1037

KENTUCKY

National Geographic Learning, pg 952

MARYLAND

James Agee Film Project, pg 904

MASSACHUSETTS

Documentary Educational Resources Inc, pg 850
Emergency Film Group, pg 860

MISSOURI

Cable Films & Video, pg 816
Phoenix/BFA/Coronet, pg 974
University of Missouri-Columbia, pg 1050

NEW JERSEY

Alden Films, pg 780
Euro-Pacific Film & Video Productions Inc, pg 863
Milestone Film & Video Inc, pg 943

NEW YORK

American Museum of Natural History (AMNH), pg 784
Circulating Film & Video Library, pg 828
Fanlight Productions, pg 865
Film-Makers Cooperative, pg 867
Films Media Group, pg 868
First Run Features, pg 869
William Greaves Productions Inc, pg 882
Hallel Communications, pg 884
Icarus Film Inc, pg 893
Kino International Corp, pg 911
New Day Films, pg 955
Pennebaker Hegedus Films Inc, pg 972
Richter Productions Inc, pg 996
Select Media Inc, pg 1006
Third World Newsreel/Camera News Inc, pg 1039
VIEW Inc (Video International Entertainment World Inc), pg 1058

NORTH CAROLINA

Crystal Pictures Inc, pg 840

PENNSYLVANIA

Bullfrog Films Inc, pg 815
Karol Media Inc, pg 908
Rahlic Publishing Co, pg 990

TENNESSEE

Center for Southern Folklore Inc, pg 822

ONTARIO

Kineticvideo.com, pg 911
McNabb & Connolly, pg 935

QUEBEC

Les Productions Via Le Monde (Daniel Bertolino) Inc, pg 985

Educational Program Distributors

ARIZONA

Tellens Inc, pg 1037

CALIFORNIA

Allied Artists International Inc, pg 781
Les Blank Films Inc, pg 809
California Newsreel, pg 817
Cambridge Documentary Films Inc, pg 818
Crystal Productions, pg 840
Crystal Pyramid Productions™, pg 840
Davidson Films Inc, pg 843
Direct Cinema Ltd Inc, pg 848
eFootage LLC, pg 858
Em Gee Film Library, pg 860
Glenn Photo Supply, pg 878
Ishtar Films, pg 902
Joyce Media Inc, pg 906
Main Street Media Inc, pg 929
MarVista Entertainment Inc, pg 933
Millennium Entertainment LLC, pg 943
Moose School Productions, pg 946
New & Unique Videos™, pg 955
Players Press, pg 977
TMW Media Group, pg 1041
Visual Communications - Southern California Asian American Studies Central Inc, pg 1059
The Wine Appreciation Guild Ltd, pg 1067

COLORADO

Inferno Film Productions LLC, pg 897

CONNECTICUT

Hartley Film Foundation, pg 885
Weston Woods Studios Inc, pg 1064

DELAWARE

University Media Services, pg 1049

FLORIDA

Allegro Productions Inc, pg 781
Capital Communications Inc, pg 819
Cifex Corp, pg 826
Global Video Distributors Inc, pg 879
Motion Image Group LLC, pg 947

HAWAII

Media Bridge Gamekids, pg 936

ILLINOIS

ABSA Productions Inc, pg 772
Discovery Education - Chicago, pg 848
Encyclopaedia Britannica Inc, pg 861
Film Ideas, pg 867
National Safety Council (NSC), pg 953
Terra Nova Films Inc, pg 1037

KENTUCKY

Horizon Films & Media LLC, pg 891
The Learning House Inc, pg 917
National Geographic Learning, pg 952

MARYLAND

Department of Education Resources, pg 845
DSR Computer Technology Specialists Inc, pg 853
James Agee Film Project, pg 904

MASSACHUSETTS

Documentary Educational Resources Inc, pg 850
Emergency Film Group, pg 860
Green Mountain Post Films (GMP), pg 882

Educational Program Producers

PROGRAMMING — FILM

Educational Program Producers (continued)

MARYLAND (continued)

dbF a Media Company, pg 844
Department of Education Resources, pg 845
DSR Computer Technology Specialists Inc, pg 853
The Image Generators, pg 895
James Agee Film Project, pg 904

MASSACHUSETTS

Cramer Productions, pg 837
Documentary Educational Resources Inc, pg 850
Emergency Film Group, pg 860
Green Mountain Post Films (GMP), pg 882
Heliotrope Studios, pg 887
Monadnock Media Inc, pg 945
The New Film Company Inc, pg 955
Northern Light Productions, pg 959

MICHIGAN

HighScope Press, pg 889
K&R All Media Productions Inc, pg 908
Lawrence Productions Inc, pg 917

MINNESOTA

Hazelden Publishing & Educational Services, pg 886
House of Cinemagraphics, pg 891

MISSISSIPPI

Dollarhide Film Inc, pg 850

MISSOURI

Cable Films & Video, pg 816
Fambrough & Associates Inc, pg 865
Hardcastle Films & Video, pg 885
Phoenix/BFA/Coronet, pg 974

NEBRASKA

Dog & Pony Productions Inc, pg 850
Peak Performance Publishing, pg 970

NEVADA

The Larry Little Co, pg 923

NEW HAMPSHIRE

Academic & Campus Technology Services, pg 773
Apertura, pg 788
Captain Fiddle Music & Publications, pg 820

NEW JERSEY

Broadcast Center Studios, pg 813
MIB Mediaworks, pg 941
Telequest Inc, pg 1036
TimeSteps Productions Inc, pg 1041

NEW MEXICO

Michael Dunn Productions, pg 853

NEW YORK

Ace Video, pg 774
American History Workshop (NY) Inc, pg 784
aurora productions, pg 797
Michael Blackwood Productions Inc, pg 808
Blue Barn Pictures Inc, pg 809
Brian Film Productions LLC, pg 812
Broad Street Inc, pg 812
Brooklyn Botanic Garden, pg 814
Billy Budd Films Inc, pg 814
Buzzco Associates Inc, pg 816
De Nonno Productions Inc (DPI), pg 844
Fanlight Productions, pg 865
Films Media Group, pg 868
Florentine Films, pg 870
Four Corners Productions, pg 871
Karen Frankel Productions, pg 872
William Greaves Productions Inc, pg 882
Greyfalcon House, pg 882
Hallel Communications, pg 884
Havas Worldwide, pg 886
Ketchum Pleon Change, pg 910
Lavine Production Group, pg 917
Neal Marshad Productions, pg 931
Maryknoll Productions, pg 933
Mastervision Inc, pg 933
Jack Morton Worldwide, pg 946
News Broadcast Network, pg 956
Shelly Palmer Production, pg 968
Pat Kogan Productions Inc, pg 970
Peckham Productions Inc, pg 970
Polestar Films & Associated Arts Ltd, pg 978
R/GA, pg 990
Richter Productions Inc, pg 996
Scholastic Media, pg 1004
Suggs Media Productions Inc, pg 1028
Third World Newsreel/Camera News Inc, pg 1039
VIEW Inc (Video International Entertainment World Inc), pg 1058
Wonderwomen™ Enterprises, pg 1069
Zelman Studios Ltd, pg 1073

NORTH CAROLINA

Pat Appleson Studios Inc, pg 788
The Communications Group Inc, pg 833
Crystal Pictures Inc, pg 840
Horizon Video Productions Inc, pg 891
Kino Mountain Productions LLC, pg 911
Sinclair Institute, pg 1012
Unifour Productions Inc, pg 1048

OHIO

Creative Technology, pg 838
Franciscan Media, pg 872
Griesinger Films LLC, pg 882
Maslowski Productions, pg 933
Take 1 Media Services, pg 1031

OKLAHOMA

CSI/Orion, pg 840

OREGON

Ideascape Inc, pg 894
Odyssey Productions Inc, pg 961
Wilderness Video, pg 1066

PENNSYLVANIA

Argentine Productions Inc, pg 789
Bang Pictures, pg 802
FMP Media Solutions Inc, pg 870
Fusion Brand Experiences, pg 874
Innovision Media Group, pg 899
JPL, pg 906
Kensington Falls Animation, pg 909
Main Point Productions, pg 929
Muderick Media, pg 949
Production Masters Inc (PMI), pg 984
Rahlic Publishing Co, pg 990
Video/Film Associates, pg 1055

RHODE ISLAND

Sound-FX-Design, pg 1017

TENNESSEE

American Blackguard Inc, pg 784
Center for Southern Folklore Inc, pg 822
Continental Film, pg 835
Memphis Communications Corp, pg 938
Scripps Networks, pg 1005

TEXAS

Castleview Productions, pg 821
Cerutti Productions Inc, pg 823
CEV Multimedia Ltd, pg 823
The Editing Co, pg 857
Horizon Film + Video Productions, pg 891
Marx InDigital, pg 933
Earl Miller Productions Inc, pg 943
Romar Learning, pg 999
South Coast Film & Video, pg 1019
Stage Directions, pg 1022
Texas Heart Institute Visual Communication Services, pg 1037
University of Texas at Austin - Petroleum Extension Service, pg 1050

UTAH

K-SAR Video & DVD Productions, pg 907

VERMONT

Marlboro Film & Video Productions, pg 931
Dorothy Tod Films, pg 1041

VIRGINIA

BES Studios, pg 805
CACI Productions Group, pg 816
CALIBRE, pg 816
Metro Productions, pg 939

WASHINGTON

ChristianAnswers.Net™, pg 825
North-by-Northwest Productions, pg 958
White Rain Films Ltd, pg 1065

WEST VIRGINIA

Altruist Media LLC, pg 783

WISCONSIN

Equiservices Publishing, pg 862
5th Floor Recording Co, pg 867
Meridian Studios, pg 939
University of Wisconsin-Oshkosh Radio-TV-Film Dept, pg 1050
Video Wisconsin Inc, pg 1056
Wisconsin Public Television, pg 1068

WYOMING

Bridger Productions Inc, pg 812

ALBERTA

Black Media Works, pg 808
Global Television Station, pg 879
HBW Entertainment Inc, pg 886

BRITISH COLUMBIA

West Eagle Films Inc, pg 1064

MANITOBA

Lank/Beach Productions Inc, pg 916

ONTARIO

Epitome Pictures Inc, pg 862
IMAX Corp, pg 896
Pearson Education Canada, pg 970
VO2 Mix Studios, pg 1060

QUEBEC

Kerrigan Productions Inc, pg 910
National Film Board of Canada/ Office National du Film du Canada, pg 952
Productions Grand Nord Quebec Inc, pg 985
Les Productions Via Le Monde (Daniel Bertolino) Inc, pg 985

Educational Program Rentals

CALIFORNIA

Les Blank Films Inc, pg 809
Cambridge Documentary Films Inc, pg 818
Davidson Films Inc, pg 843
Direct Cinema Ltd Inc, pg 848
Em Gee Film Library, pg 860
Glenn Photo Supply, pg 878
Point of View Productions, pg 977
Visual Communications - Southern California Asian American Studies Central Inc, pg 1059

DELAWARE

University Media Services, pg 1049

ILLINOIS

Custom Medical Stock Photo Inc, pg 841
National Safety Council (NSC), pg 953
Terra Nova Films Inc, pg 1037

KENTUCKY

National Geographic Learning, pg 952

MARYLAND

James Agee Film Project, pg 904

MASSACHUSETTS

Documentary Educational Resources Inc, pg 850
Emergency Film Group, pg 860

MICHIGAN

HighScope Press, pg 889

Eight mm Films, *see* Films—8mm

Feature Program Distributors

Feature Program Producers

PROGRAMMING — FILM

Feature Program Producers (continued)

COLORADO (continued)

Tatum Video, pg 1032
Transtar Entertainment Co Inc, pg 1043

CONNECTICUT

Broadcast Video Productions LLC, pg 813
Essex Television Group Inc, pg 862
The Gary-Paul Agency, pg 875
MCC Films, pg 935

FLORIDA

Blackburst Entertainment, pg 808
Capital Communications Inc, pg 819
Chatterbox Productions Inc, pg 824
Cifex Corp, pg 826
Communications Concepts Inc (CCI), pg 833
CopShopMiami.com, pg 836
Jordan Klein Film & Video (JKFV), pg 906

GEORGIA

Burst Video/Film Inc, pg 815
Guerrilla Productions LLC, pg 883
Myriad Productions, pg 951

HAWAII

Hyperspective Studios Inc, pg 893

IDAHO

Lagoon Video, pg 915

ILLINOIS

Comtech Multimedia Marketing, pg 834
Film Police, pg 867
Mimi Productions, pg 943
Winter Productions, pg 1068

IOWA

Right Stuf Inc, pg 997

KENTUCKY

Donna Lawrence Productions, pg 917

MARYLAND

Absolute Hollywood, pg 772
dbF a Media Company, pg 844
DSR Computer Technology Specialists Inc, pg 853

MASSACHUSETTS

Green Mountain Post Films (GMP), pg 882
Heliotrope Studios, pg 887

MICHIGAN

K&R All Media Productions Inc, pg 908

MINNESOTA

House of Cinemagraphics, pg 891

MISSOURI

Cable Films & Video, pg 816
Fambrough & Associates Inc, pg 865

NEBRASKA

Leo Films, pg 919

NEW JERSEY

Broadcast Center Studios, pg 813
CELCO-Constantine Engineering Labs Co, pg 822
Bill Quinn Productions, pg 989

NEW MEXICO

I-25 Studios, pg 893

NEW YORK

Blue Barn Pictures Inc, pg 809
Broad Street Inc, pg 812
Brooklyn Films, pg 814
De Nonno Productions Inc (DPI), pg 844
FilmNation Entertainment, pg 867
William Greaves Productions Inc, pg 882
Greyfalcon House, pg 882
Havas Worldwide, pg 886
HB-Content, pg 886
Richard Kaplan Productions, pg 908
Kinetic Arts, pg 911
Neal Marshad Productions, pg 931
Jack Morton Worldwide, pg 946
New Horizon Studios, pg 955
NSR Productions Inc & Capricorn Five Films, pg 960
Shelly Palmer Production, pg 968
Pennebaker Hegedus Films Inc, pg 972
Scholastic Media, pg 1004
Shadow Pictures Inc, pg 1007
Suggs Media Productions Inc, pg 1028
VIEW Inc (Video International Entertainment World Inc), pg 1058
The Visual Studies Workshop (VSW), pg 1059
Zelman Studios Ltd, pg 1073

NORTH CAROLINA

The Communications Group Inc, pg 833

OHIO

Creative Technology, pg 838

OREGON

Ideascape Inc, pg 894
Pacific International Enterprises Inc (PIE), pg 967
Producers Studio, pg 984

PENNSYLVANIA

Goodman Associates Inc, pg 880
Innovision Media Group, pg 899
Kensington Falls Animation, pg 909
Production Masters Inc (PMI), pg 984

RHODE ISLAND

Sound-FX-Design, pg 1017

TENNESSEE

American Blackguard Inc, pg 784

TEXAS

Aries Productions, pg 789
Castleview Productions, pg 821
Cerutti Productions Inc, pg 823
Rich-Heape Films Inc, pg 996

VERMONT

Edgewood Studios, pg 857

VIRGINIA

BES Studios, pg 805
CACI Productions Group, pg 816
Metro Productions, pg 939

WASHINGTON

Hamilton Studio, pg 884
North-by-Northwest Productions, pg 958
Pal Productions Inc, pg 967
Victory Studios, pg 1054

WISCONSIN

5th Floor Recording Co, pg 867
Wisconsin Public Television, pg 1068

WYOMING

Bridger Productions Inc, pg 812

ALBERTA

Global Television Station, pg 879
HBW Entertainment Inc, pg 886

BRITISH COLUMBIA

Network Entertainment Inc, pg 954

MANITOBA

Lank/Beach Productions Inc, pg 916

ONTARIO

Doomsday Studios Ltd, pg 850
IMAX Corp, pg 896
VO2 Mix Studios, pg 1060

QUEBEC

Kerrigan Productions Inc, pg 910
Max Films Inc, pg 934
Productions Grand Nord Quebec Inc, pg 985
Les Productions Via Le Monde (Daniel Bertolino) Inc, pg 985

Feature Program Rentals

CALIFORNIA

Ben Barry & Associates Inc, pg 803
Les Blank Films Inc, pg 809
Direct Cinema Ltd Inc, pg 848
Em Gee Film Library, pg 860
Glenn Photo Supply, pg 878
Palardo Productions, pg 968
Visual Communications - Southern California Asian American Studies Central Inc, pg 1059
Worldwide Entertainment Corp, pg 1070

IDAHO

Lagoon Video, pg 915

MISSOURI

Cable Films & Video, pg 816
University of Missouri-Columbia, pg 1050

NEW YORK

Circulating Film & Video Library, pg 828
Film-Makers Cooperative, pg 867
First Run Features, pg 869
Icarus Film Inc, pg 893
Kino International Corp, pg 911
Pennebaker Hegedus Films Inc, pg 972
Third World Newsreel/Camera News Inc, pg 1039
VIEW Inc (Video International Entertainment World Inc), pg 1058

NORTH CAROLINA

Crystal Pictures Inc, pg 840
World Wide Pictures Inc, pg 1070

OREGON

Pacific International Enterprises Inc (PIE), pg 967

PENNSYLVANIA

Bullfrog Films Inc, pg 815

ONTARIO

McNabb & Connolly, pg 935
WESCAM Inc, pg 1063

QUEBEC

Les Productions Via Le Monde (Daniel Bertolino) Inc, pg 985

Film Short, *see* Theatrical Short

Films—8mm Distributors

CALIFORNIA

Adolph Gasser Inc, pg 776
Canyon Cinema Inc, pg 819
Players Press, pg 977
QRS Software Services, pg 988
Visual Communications - Southern California Asian American Studies Central Inc, pg 1059

CONNECTICUT

EagleVision Inc, pg 855

FLORIDA

Tallahassee Audio Visual, pg 1031

INDIANA

InterComm, pg 900

KENTUCKY

National Geographic Learning, pg 952

MARYLAND

Milner-Fenwick Inc, pg 943
Nicholas P Pipino Associates Inc, pg 976

NEW MEXICO

National Information Center for Educational Media (NICEM)/MediaSleuth, pg 952

NEW YORK

Film Emporium, pg 867
Janus Films Inc, pg 904
MRG Productions Inc, pg 948
Visual Technologies Corp, pg 1060

NORTH CAROLINA

Crystal Pictures Inc, pg 840

PENNSYLVANIA

Karol Media Inc, pg 908

VIRGINIA

Filmdex Inc, pg 867

WASHINGTON

White Rain Films Ltd, pg 1065

ONTARIO

Canadian Filmmakers Distribution Center (CFMDC), pg 818

Films—8mm Producers

ARIZONA

Phoenix VideoFilms®, pg 974

ARKANSAS

White Diamond Productions, pg 1065

CALIFORNIA

Concrete Images, pg 835
Custom Video Productions Inc, pg 841
Design Media, pg 845
Main Street Media Inc, pg 929
New Circuit Films LLC, pg 955
Players Press, pg 977
QRS Software Services, pg 988
SBS Productions, pg 1003
Visual Communications - Southern California Asian American Studies Central Inc, pg 1059

COLORADO

Starwest Productions, pg 1024

CONNECTICUT

The Gary-Paul Agency, pg 875

FLORIDA

Chatterbox Productions Inc, pg 824

INDIANA

InterComm, pg 900
OMNI Productions, pg 962

IOWA

The Production House, pg 984

MARYLAND

Milner-Fenwick Inc, pg 943

MICHIGAN

Maritz Performance Improvement Co, pg 931

MINNESOTA

Jamieson & Associates Inc, pg 904

MISSOURI

Celebrities Productions, pg 822
Fambrough & Associates Inc, pg 865

NEW YORK

aurora productions, pg 797
Blue Barn Pictures Inc, pg 809
MRG Productions Inc, pg 948
Shadow Pictures Inc, pg 1007
Split Image Productions, pg 1021
TBA Global Events, pg 1032
Zelman Studios Ltd, pg 1073

NORTH CAROLINA

The Communications Group Inc, pg 833

PENNSYLVANIA

Argentine Productions Inc, pg 789
Production Masters Inc (PMI), pg 984

TENNESSEE

American Blackguard Inc, pg 784
Memphis Communications Corp, pg 938

TEXAS

South Coast Film & Video, pg 1019

WASHINGTON

Adams Creative & Production Services, pg 775
White Rain Films Ltd, pg 1065

WYOMING

Bridger Productions Inc, pg 812

Films—8mm Rentals

CALIFORNIA

Canyon Cinema Inc, pg 819
Classic Images, pg 829
New Circuit Films LLC, pg 955
Visual Communications - Southern California Asian American Studies Central Inc, pg 1059

FLORIDA

Jordan Klein Film & Video (JKFV), pg 906

GEORGIA

Staging Directions Inc, pg 1023

NEW MEXICO

National Information Center for Educational Media (NICEM)/MediaSleuth, pg 952

NEW YORK

Film-Makers Cooperative, pg 867

Films—16mm Distributors

ALABAMA

Media Visions Inc, pg 937

CALIFORNIA

Adolph Gasser Inc, pg 776
Ametron Audio/Video, pg 785
Ben Barry & Associates Inc, pg 803
Cambridge Documentary Films Inc, pg 818
Canyon Cinema Inc, pg 819
Digital Media West, pg 847
Direct Cinema Ltd Inc, pg 848
Discovery Education - Los Angeles, pg 848
Em Gee Film Library, pg 860
Glenn Photo Supply, pg 878
MGM United Artists, pg 941
New & Unique Videos™, pg 955
Palardo Productions, pg 968
Paulist Productions, pg 970
Players Press, pg 977
Point Lobos Productions, pg 977
Point of View Productions, pg 977
QRS Software Services, pg 988
Sony Pictures Entertainment, pg 1016
Twentieth Century Fox Film Corp, pg 1046
Visual Communications - Southern California Asian American Studies Central Inc, pg 1059
The Walt Disney Co, pg 1061
Warner Bros Entertainment Inc, pg 1062

COLORADO

Inferno Film Productions LLC, pg 897

CONNECTICUT

EagleVision Inc, pg 855

DELAWARE

University Media Services, pg 1049

DISTRICT OF COLUMBIA

Grocery Manufacturers Association (GMA), pg 882
National Council of Churches, pg 952

FLORIDA

Courter Films LLC, pg 837
Tallahassee Audio Visual, pg 1031

ILLINOIS

Communications Corporation of America, pg 833
Film Ideas, pg 867
National Safety Council (NSC), pg 953
Terra Nova Films Inc, pg 1037

INDIANA

InterComm, pg 900

KANSAS

Day Star Productions, pg 844

KENTUCKY

National Geographic Learning, pg 952

MAINE

Headlight Audio Visual Inc, pg 887

MARYLAND

Department of Education Resources, pg 845
DSR Computer Technology Specialists Inc, pg 853
Milner-Fenwick Inc, pg 943
Nicholas P Pipino Associates Inc, pg 976

MASSACHUSETTS

Documentary Educational Resources Inc, pg 850
Emergency Film Group, pg 860
Green Mountain Post Films (GMP), pg 882
National Fire Protection Association (NFPA), pg 952

MISSOURI

Cable Films & Video, pg 816
Phoenix/BFA/Coronet, pg 974
Swank Audio Visuals, pg 1029

NEBRASKA

Leo Films, pg 919

NEVADA

DVDs4Less, pg 854

NEW JERSEY

Films of the Nations, pg 868
Lucerne Media, pg 925
Milestone Film & Video Inc, pg 943

NEW MEXICO

National Information Center for Educational Media (NICEM)/MediaSleuth, pg 952

NEW YORK

Applause Learning Resources, pg 788
ATA Trading Corp/Favorite TV Inc, pg 792
Campus Film Distributors Corp, pg 818
The Cinema Guild Inc, pg 827
Circulating Film & Video Library, pg 828
Thomas Craven Film Corp, pg 837
Film Emporium, pg 867
First Run Features, pg 869
French American Cultural Exchange (FACE), pg 873
Gene Friedman, pg 873
Hallel Communications, pg 884
HB-Content, pg 886
Icarus Film Inc, pg 893
Janus Films Inc, pg 904
Richard Kaplan Productions, pg 908
Kino International Corp, pg 911
MRG Productions Inc, pg 948
New Day Films, pg 955
Richter Productions Inc, pg 996
Third World Newsreel/Camera News Inc, pg 1039
Timed Exposures Films, pg 1040
Tisch School of the Arts, pg 1041
United Nations Department of Public Information-News & Media Division, pg 1048
Visual Technologies Corp, pg 1060
Women Make Movies Inc, pg 1069
Worldview Entertainment Holdings Inc, pg 1070

NORTH CAROLINA

Crystal Pictures Inc, pg 840

OHIO

Griesinger Films LLC, pg 882
South-Western Publishing Co, pg 1019

PROGRAMMING — FILM

Films—16mm Distributors (continued)

Films—16mm Producers

Films—16mm Rentals

Films—35mm Distributors

PROGRAMMING — FILM

Films—35mm Distributors (continued)

NEW YORK (continued)

Kino International Corp, pg 911
MRG Productions Inc, pg 948
Paramount Motion Pictures Group, pg 969
Pennebaker Hegedus Films Inc, pg 972
Telemotions LLC, pg 1036
Third World Newsreel/Camera News Inc, pg 1039
United Nations Department of Public Information-News & Media Division, pg 1048
Visual Technologies Corp, pg 1060
Women Make Movies Inc, pg 1069
Worldview Entertainment Holdings Inc, pg 1070

NORTH CAROLINA

Crystal Pictures Inc, pg 840

OREGON

Wilderness Video, pg 1066

TENNESSEE

American Blackguard Inc, pg 784

VIRGINIA

Filmdex Inc, pg 867

WISCONSIN

School Specialty Inc, pg 1004

ONTARIO

Canadian Filmmakers Distribution Center (CFMDC), pg 818

QUEBEC

National Film Board of Canada/ Office National du Film du Canada, pg 952
Les Productions Via Le Monde (Daniel Bertolino) Inc, pg 985

Films—35mm Producers

ARIZONA

Phoenix VideoFilms®, pg 974

ARKANSAS

Jones Film Video, pg 906

CALIFORNIA

Artichoke Productions, pg 791
Big Door, pg 807
Big Time Picture Company Inc, pg 807
Cinevest, pg 828
Concrete Images, pg 835
deKramer Productions Inc, pg 845
Design Media, pg 845
Direct Cinema Ltd Inc, pg 848
Goal Productions, pg 879
Hope Productions, pg 891
imageReal Pictures LLC, pg 896
Kavich Reynolds Productions Inc, pg 908
The Kenwood Group, pg 909
Keystone Entertainment, pg 910
KTVU-Retail Services, pg 914
Main Street Media Inc, pg 929
Moving Art by Louie Schwartzberg, pg 947
New & Unique Videos™, pg 955
New Circuit Films LLC, pg 955
Palardo Productions, pg 968
Players Press, pg 977
Prime Cut Productions, pg 982
Producers Group Ltd, pg 983
RetinaVision Productions, pg 995
Rhythm & Hues, pg 996
Glenn Roland Films, pg 998
SBS Productions, pg 1003
SNAP, pg 1014
Tam Communications Inc, pg 1031
Visual Communications - Southern California Asian American Studies Central Inc, pg 1059
Zamacona Productions, pg 1073

COLORADO

The Cinema Lab, pg 827
Inferno Film Productions LLC, pg 897
National Teaching Aids Inc, pg 953
Phelan Productions Inc, pg 973
Tatum Video, pg 1032
Transtar Entertainment Co Inc, pg 1043

CONNECTICUT

ACM Productions Ltd, pg 774
The Gary-Paul Agency, pg 875
MCC Films, pg 935

DISTRICT OF COLUMBIA

Hillmann & Carr Inc, pg 889

FLORIDA

Chatterbox Productions Inc, pg 824
Cifex Corp, pg 826
Parallax Productions Inc, pg 969
Roger Scruggs Films, pg 1005
Tel-Air Interests Inc, pg 1035

GEORGIA

COMPRO Productions Inc, pg 834
Continental Film & Video, pg 835
Myriad Productions, pg 951

IDAHO

Lagoon Video, pg 915

ILLINOIS

Communications Corporation of America, pg 833
Film Police, pg 867
Universal Training, pg 1049
Winter Productions, pg 1068

INDIANA

AVA Productions, pg 798
Perennial Pictures Film Corp, pg 973
Road Pictures, pg 997

IOWA

Hellman Associates Inc, pg 887

KENTUCKY

Donna Lawrence Productions, pg 917

LOUISIANA

Digital FX Inc, pg 847
Moxie Media, pg 948

MARYLAND

Department of Education Resources, pg 845
Milner-Fenwick Inc, pg 943

MASSACHUSETTS

CommCreative, pg 832
Emergency Film Group, pg 860
Green Mountain Post Films (GMP), pg 882
Heliotrope Studios, pg 887
ICL Imaging Inc, pg 893
Monadnock Media Inc, pg 945
TR Productions, pg 1043

MICHIGAN

Lawrence Productions Inc, pg 917
Maritz Performance Improvement Co, pg 931
Michigan Office Solutions, pg 941
Tri-Color, pg 1044

MINNESOTA

Badiyan Inc, pg 801
House of Cinemagraphics, pg 891
Jamieson & Associates Inc, pg 904

MISSISSIPPI

Dollarhide Film Inc, pg 850

MISSOURI

Celebrities Productions, pg 822
Fambrough & Associates Inc, pg 865

NEBRASKA

Leo Films, pg 919

NEVADA

DVDs4Less, pg 854

NEW HAMPSHIRE

Apertura, pg 788

NEW JERSEY

Euro-Pacific Film & Video Productions Inc, pg 863
Half Moon Video Productions, pg 883
Bill Quinn Productions, pg 989
Telequest Inc, pg 1036

NEW MEXICO

Michael Dunn Productions, pg 853

NEW YORK

aurora productions, pg 797
Blue Barn Pictures Inc, pg 809
Brooklyn Films, pg 814
Buzzco Associates Inc, pg 816
Campus Film Distributors Corp, pg 818
Thomas Craven Film Corp, pg 837
William Greaves Productions Inc, pg 882
HB-Content, pg 886
Icontent, pg 893
Richard Kaplan Productions, pg 908
Kinetic Arts, pg 911
Neal Marshad Productions, pg 931
MRG Productions Inc, pg 948
Northeast Video Productions Inc, pg 959
Shelly Palmer Production, pg 968
Paramount Motion Pictures Group, pg 969
Peckham Productions Inc, pg 970
Polestar Films & Associated Arts Ltd, pg 978
Scholastic Media, pg 1004
Shadow Pictures Inc, pg 1007
Suggs Media Productions Inc, pg 1028
TBA Global Events, pg 1032
Zelman Studios Ltd, pg 1073

NORTH CAROLINA

The Communications Group Inc, pg 833
Crystal Pictures Inc, pg 840
Moving Pictures, pg 948
Trailblazer Studios®, pg 1043

OHIO

Commercial Video, pg 832
Creative Technology, pg 838
Lyon Video Inc, pg 927

OREGON

Odyssey Productions Inc, pg 961
Pacific International Enterprises Inc (PIE), pg 967
Producers Studio, pg 984
Production West, pg 985
Wilderness Video, pg 1066

PENNSYLVANIA

Argentine Productions Inc, pg 789
Aztech Productions LLC, pg 801
Bang Pictures, pg 802
Fusion Brand Experiences, pg 874
Goodman Associates Inc, pg 880
JPL, pg 906
Kensington Falls Animation, pg 909
Production Masters Inc (PMI), pg 984
Video/Film Associates, pg 1055

SOUTH CAROLINA

Venture Media, pg 1052

TENNESSEE

American Blackguard Inc, pg 784
Memphis Communications Corp, pg 938
Scripps Networks, pg 1005

TEXAS

Alexander Media Productions, pg 780
AMS Pictures, pg 786
Marx InDigital, pg 933
Phil Lights, pg 973
South Coast Film & Video, pg 1019
Stage Directions, pg 1022

VERMONT

Edgewood Studios, pg 857

VIRGINIA

BES Studios, pg 805
CACI Productions Group, pg 816
CALIBRE, pg 816

WASHINGTON

Adams Creative & Production Services, pg 775
Getty Images, pg 877

WISCONSIN

Video Wisconsin Inc, pg 1056

WYOMING

Bridger Productions Inc, pg 812

ALBERTA

Global Television Station, pg 879

BRITISH COLUMBIA

West Eagle Films Inc, pg 1064

ONTARIO

Doomsday Studios Ltd, pg 850

QUEBEC

National Film Board of Canada/ Office National du Film du Canada, pg 952
Les Productions Via Le Monde (Daniel Bertolino) Inc, pg 985

Films—35mm Rentals

CALIFORNIA

Auslender Productions/Celestial Images, pg 797
Canyon Cinema Inc, pg 819
Classic Images, pg 829
Direct Cinema Ltd Inc, pg 848
New Line Cinema, pg 956
Palardo Productions, pg 968
Visual Communications - Southern California Asian American Studies Central Inc, pg 1059

FLORIDA

Cifex Corp, pg 826
Jordan Klein Film & Video (JKFV), pg 906

GEORGIA

Staging Directions Inc, pg 1023

MISSOURI

Swank Audio Visuals, pg 1029

NEW JERSEY

Bill Quinn Productions, pg 989

NEW YORK

Film-Makers Cooperative, pg 867
Icarus Film Inc, pg 893
Kino International Corp, pg 911
Pennebaker Hegedus Films Inc, pg 972
Third World Newsreel/Camera News Inc, pg 1039

NORTH CAROLINA

Crystal Pictures Inc, pg 840

OREGON

Pacific International Enterprises Inc (PIE), pg 967

QUEBEC

National Film Board of Canada/ Office National du Film du Canada, pg 952
Les Productions Via Le Monde (Daniel Bertolino) Inc, pg 985

Films—70mm Distributors

CALIFORNIA

Cinevest, pg 828
MacGillivray Freeman Films Inc, pg 927
Players Press, pg 977
Sony Pictures Entertainment, pg 1016

FLORIDA

Cifex Corp, pg 826

NEW YORK

French American Cultural Exchange (FACE), pg 873
Janus Films Inc, pg 904
MRG Productions Inc, pg 948
Paramount Motion Pictures Group, pg 969
Visual Technologies Corp, pg 1060

VIRGINIA

Filmdex Inc, pg 867

ONTARIO

IMAX Corp, pg 896

Films—70mm Producers

CALIFORNIA

Cinevest, pg 828
MacGillivray Freeman Films Inc, pg 927
Moving Art by Louie Schwartzberg, pg 947
Players Press, pg 977
Producers Group Ltd, pg 983
RetinaVision Productions, pg 995
Rhythm & Hues, pg 996
Sony Pictures Entertainment, pg 1016

GEORGIA

Continental Film & Video, pg 835

KENTUCKY

Donna Lawrence Productions, pg 917

MINNESOTA

Jamieson & Associates Inc, pg 904

MISSISSIPPI

Dollarhide Film Inc, pg 850

MISSOURI

Celebrities Productions, pg 822

NEW YORK

aurora productions, pg 797
Blue Barn Pictures Inc, pg 809
Guidance Associates Inc Center for Humanities, pg 883
MRG Productions Inc, pg 948
Shelly Palmer Production, pg 968
Paramount Motion Pictures Group, pg 969
Scholastic Media, pg 1004
Split Image Productions, pg 1021
TBA Global Events, pg 1032

OHIO

Creative Technology, pg 838

PENNSYLVANIA

Argentine Productions Inc, pg 789

WYOMING

Bridger Productions Inc, pg 812

BRITISH COLUMBIA

West Eagle Films Inc, pg 1064

ONTARIO

IMAX Corp, pg 896

Films—70mm Rentals

CALIFORNIA

Classic Images, pg 829

GEORGIA

Staging Directions Inc, pg 1023

Foreign Program Distributors

CALIFORNIA

Allied Artists International Inc, pg 781
Les Blank Films Inc, pg 809
Coastline Licensing International Inc, pg 831
Crystal Pyramid Productions™, pg 840
Em Gee Film Library, pg 860
Glenn Photo Supply, pg 878
MarVista Entertainment Inc, pg 933
Millennium Entertainment LLC, pg 943
New & Unique Videos™, pg 955

CONNECTICUT

Really Good Stuff, pg 992

FLORIDA

Capital Communications Inc, pg 819
Cifex Corp, pg 826

IDAHO

Lagoon Video, pg 915

IOWA

Right Stuf Inc, pg 997

MARYLAND

DSR Computer Technology Specialists Inc, pg 853
Recorded Books LLC, pg 993

MASSACHUSETTS

Documentary Educational Resources Inc, pg 850

MINNESOTA

Festival Films, pg 866

MISSOURI

Cable Films & Video, pg 816
Swank Audio Visuals, pg 1029

NEBRASKA

Leo Films, pg 919

NEW JERSEY

Alden Films, pg 780
Films of the Nations, pg 868
Milestone Film & Video Inc, pg 943

NEW MEXICO

National Information Center for Educational Media (NICEM)/MediaSleuth, pg 952

NEW YORK

Applause Learning Resources, pg 788
Circulating Film & Video Library, pg 828
Fanlight Productions, pg 865
First Run Features, pg 869
French American Cultural Exchange (FACE), pg 873
Hallel Communications, pg 884
Icarus Film Inc, pg 893
Janson Media, pg 904
Kino International Corp, pg 911
Mastervision Inc, pg 933
Richter Productions Inc, pg 996
SISU Home Entertainment Inc, pg 1012
Third World Newsreel/Camera News Inc, pg 1039
VIEW Inc (Video International Entertainment World Inc), pg 1058
Women Make Movies Inc, pg 1069
Zeitgeist Films Ltd, pg 1073

NORTH CAROLINA

Crystal Pictures Inc, pg 840

OHIO

Network Technologies Inc, pg 955
Ohio State University Foreign Language Publications, pg 961

PENNSYLVANIA

Bullfrog Films Inc, pg 815
FMP Media Solutions Inc, pg 870

VIRGINIA

Water Bearer Films Inc, pg 1062

ALBERTA

Global Television Station, pg 879

ONTARIO

Cambium Catalyst International (CCI), pg 817
Canadian Filmmakers Distribution Center (CFMDC), pg 818
IMAX Corp, pg 896

QUEBEC

Les Productions Via Le Monde (Daniel Bertolino) Inc, pg 985

Foreign Program Producers

CALIFORNIA

Classic Images, pg 829
Crystal Pyramid Productions™, pg 840
Custom Video Productions Inc, pg 841
International Contact Inc, pg 900
Jaguar Distribution Corp, pg 903

PROGRAMMING — FILM

Foreign Program Producers (continued)

CALIFORNIA (continued)

Main Street Media Inc, pg 929
New & Unique Videos™, pg 955
QRS Software Services, pg 988
SBS Productions, pg 1003
Vineyard Video & Photography, pg 1058

CONNECTICUT

Broadcast Video Productions LLC, pg 813
The Gary-Paul Agency, pg 875

DISTRICT OF COLUMBIA

Hillmann & Carr Inc, pg 889

FLORIDA

Blackburst Entertainment, pg 808
Jordan Klein Film & Video (JKFV), pg 906

GEORGIA

Guerrilla Productions LLC, pg 883

IOWA

Right Stuf Inc, pg 997

LOUISIANA

Moxie Media, pg 948

MARYLAND

Absolute Hollywood, pg 772
Richard Chisolm Cinematography, pg 825
dbF a Media Company, pg 844
DSR Computer Technology Specialists Inc, pg 853

MASSACHUSETTS

Documentary Educational Resources Inc, pg 850
Heliotrope Studios, pg 887

MICHIGAN

K&R All Media Productions Inc, pg 908

MINNESOTA

House of Cinemagraphics, pg 891

MISSOURI

Fambrough & Associates Inc, pg 865

MONTANA

North Country Media Group, pg 959

NEW HAMPSHIRE

Apertura, pg 788

NEW YORK

Ace Video, pg 774
Applause Learning Resources, pg 788
Blue Barn Pictures Inc, pg 809
Hallel Communications, pg 884
Havas Worldwide, pg 886
Kinetic Arts, pg 911
Maryknoll Productions, pg 933
Mastervision Inc, pg 933
Jack Morton Worldwide, pg 946
Shelly Palmer Production, pg 968
Pat Kogan Productions Inc, pg 970
Richter Productions Inc, pg 996
Shadow Pictures Inc, pg 1007
VIEW Inc (Video International Entertainment World Inc), pg 1058
Zelman Studios Ltd, pg 1073

NORTH CAROLINA

Pat Appleson Studios Inc, pg 788
The Communications Group Inc, pg 833

OHIO

Creative Technology, pg 838

PENNSYLVANIA

FMP Media Solutions Inc, pg 870

RHODE ISLAND

Sound-FX-Design, pg 1017

TEXAS

Cerutti Productions Inc, pg 823
Stage Directions, pg 1022

VIRGINIA

Metro Productions, pg 939

WISCONSIN

5th Floor Recording Co, pg 867
Wisconsin Public Television, pg 1068

WYOMING

Bridger Productions Inc, pg 812

ALBERTA

Global Television Station, pg 879
HBW Entertainment Inc, pg 886

BRITISH COLUMBIA

West Eagle Films Inc, pg 1064

QUEBEC

Kerrigan Productions Inc, pg 910

Foreign Program Rentals

CALIFORNIA

Les Blank Films Inc, pg 809
Em Gee Film Library, pg 860
Glenn Photo Supply, pg 878

FLORIDA

Cifex Corp, pg 826

MASSACHUSETTS

Documentary Educational Resources Inc, pg 850

MISSOURI

Cable Films & Video, pg 816
Swank Audio Visuals, pg 1029
University of Missouri-Columbia, pg 1050

NEW JERSEY

Alden Films, pg 780

NEW YORK

Circulating Film & Video Library, pg 828
Film-Makers Cooperative, pg 867
First Run Features, pg 869
Hallel Communications, pg 884
Icarus Film Inc, pg 893
Kino International Corp, pg 911
Richter Productions Inc, pg 996
Third World Newsreel/Camera News Inc, pg 1039
VIEW Inc (Video International Entertainment World Inc), pg 1058

NORTH CAROLINA

Crystal Pictures Inc, pg 840

QUEBEC

Les Productions Via Le Monde (Daniel Bertolino) Inc, pg 985

Government Program Distributors

CALIFORNIA

Crystal Pyramid Productions™, pg 840
Em Gee Film Library, pg 860
Glenn Photo Supply, pg 878

FLORIDA

Capital Communications Inc, pg 819

ILLINOIS

ABSA Productions Inc, pg 772

MARYLAND

DSR Computer Technology Specialists Inc, pg 853
Special Archives Division, Motion Picture Branch, pg 1020

MISSOURI

Phoenix/BFA/Coronet, pg 974

NEVADA

DVDs4Less, pg 854

NEW MEXICO

National Information Center for Educational Media (NICEM)/MediaSleuth, pg 952

NEW YORK

Broad Street Inc, pg 812
Films Media Group, pg 868
VIEW Inc (Video International Entertainment World Inc), pg 1058
Women Make Movies Inc, pg 1069

PENNSYLVANIA

FMP Media Solutions Inc, pg 870

TEXAS

CEV Multimedia Ltd, pg 823

VIRGINIA

CACI Productions Group, pg 816

WISCONSIN

Wisconsin Public Television, pg 1068

ONTARIO

Kineticvideo.com, pg 911

Government Program Producers

ALASKA

Aurora Films, pg 797

ARIZONA

Film Creations Ltd, pg 867
MediaWorks, pg 938
Phoenix VideoFilms®, pg 974

ARKANSAS

Jones Film Video, pg 906

CALIFORNIA

Big Door, pg 807
Classic Images, pg 829
Crystal Pyramid Productions™, pg 840
Custom Video Productions Inc, pg 841
Design Media, pg 845
Dogma Studios, pg 850
Goal Productions, pg 879
Havas Edge, pg 885
The Media Staff Inc, pg 937
New & Unique Videos™, pg 955
QRS Software Services, pg 988
Dick Reizner Film & Video, pg 994
Glenn Roland Films, pg 998
Santa Barbara Location Services, pg 1002
SBS Productions, pg 1003
Utopia Films, pg 1051
Video Resources Inc, pg 1056
Vineyard Video & Photography, pg 1058

COLORADO

Blue River Productions, pg 810
Flashback Media Productions, pg 869
Tatum Video, pg 1032
Transtar Entertainment Co Inc, pg 1043

CONNECTICUT

Broadcast Video Productions LLC, pg 813
The Gary-Paul Agency, pg 875
Moving Pictures, pg 947
New London Media, pg 956

DISTRICT OF COLUMBIA

Hillmann & Carr Inc, pg 889
O'Keefe Communications Inc, pg 961

FLORIDA

Accord Productions, pg 773
Blackburst Entertainment, pg 808
Capital Communications Inc, pg 819
Communications Concepts Inc (CCI), pg 833
CopShopMiami.com, pg 836

Government Program Rentals

Industrial Program Distributors

Industrial Program Producers

PROGRAMMING — FILM

Industrial Program Producers (continued)

ARIZONA

Candee Productions Inc, pg 819
Film Creations Ltd, pg 867
MediaWorks, pg 938
Phoenix VideoFilms®, pg 974
Tellens Inc, pg 1037

ARKANSAS

Jones Film Video, pg 906

CALIFORNIA

A Go Go Films, pg 771
Big Door, pg 807
Classic Images, pg 829
Concrete Images, pg 835
Crystal Pyramid Productions™, pg 840
Custom Video Productions Inc, pg 841
Davidson Films Inc, pg 843
Design Media, pg 845
Dogma Studios, pg 850
Dolphin MultiMedia Inc, pg 850
FXF Productions Inc, pg 874
Goal Productions, pg 879
Havas Edge, pg 885
imageReal Pictures LLC, pg 896
Jaguar Distribution Corp, pg 903
Kavich Reynolds Productions Inc, pg 908
The Kenwood Group, pg 909
KION-TV, pg 911
Main Street Media Inc, pg 929
The Media Staff Inc, pg 937
New & Unique Videos™, pg 955
Panorama Productions, pg 968
Point of View Productions, pg 977
QRS Software Services, pg 988
Dick Reizner Film & Video, pg 994
RetinaVision Productions, pg 995
Glenn Roland Films, pg 998
Santa Barbara Location Services, pg 1002
SBS Productions, pg 1003
SNAP, pg 1014
Tam Communications Inc, pg 1031
Tigar Hare Studios, pg 1040
Video Resources Inc, pg 1056
Vineyard Video & Photography, pg 1058
Webster Communications, pg 1063

COLORADO

Flashback Media Productions, pg 869
Transtar Entertainment Co Inc, pg 1043

CONNECTICUT

Broadcast Video Productions LLC, pg 813
The Gary-Paul Agency, pg 875
MCC Films, pg 935
Moving Pictures, pg 947
New London Media, pg 956

DISTRICT OF COLUMBIA

Hillmann & Carr Inc, pg 889

FLORIDA

Accord Productions, pg 773
Blackburst Entertainment, pg 808
Capital Communications Inc, pg 819
Civins Productions Inc, pg 828
CopShopMiami.com, pg 836
Eastern Video, pg 856
Home Shopping Network (HSN), pg 890
Jordan Klein Film & Video (JKFV), pg 906
Motion Image Group LLC, pg 947
Tel-Air Interests Inc, pg 1035
Universal Studios Florida® Production Group, pg 1049

GEORGIA

Beachwood Productions, pg 804
Burst Video/Film Inc, pg 815
COMPRO Productions Inc, pg 834
Continental Film & Video, pg 835
Guerrilla Productions LLC, pg 883
Myriad Productions, pg 951

HAWAII

Hyperspective Studios Inc, pg 893

ILLINOIS

ABSA Productions Inc, pg 772
Comtech Multimedia Marketing, pg 834
Cresta Creative, pg 839
Film Police, pg 867
Manning Productions, pg 930
National Safety Council (NSC), pg 953
Richter Studios, pg 996
SCI Television Productions LLC, pg 1004
Winter Productions, pg 1068

INDIANA

Road Pictures, pg 997

IOWA

Hellman Associates Inc, pg 887

LOUISIANA

Digital FX Inc, pg 847
Moxie Media, pg 948

MARYLAND

Absolute Hollywood, pg 772
The Ahern Group, pg 779
dbF a Media Company, pg 844
The Image Generators, pg 895

MASSACHUSETTS

CommCreative, pg 832
Emergency Film Group, pg 860
Green Mountain Post Films (GMP), pg 882
Heliotrope Studios, pg 887
Northern Light Productions, pg 959

MICHIGAN

K&R All Media Productions Inc, pg 908
Lawrence Productions Inc, pg 917
Maritz Performance Improvement Co, pg 931

MINNESOTA

House of Cinemagraphics, pg 891

MISSISSIPPI

Dollarhide Film Inc, pg 850

MISSOURI

Fambrough & Associates Inc, pg 865
Hardcastle Films & Video, pg 885

MONTANA

North Country Media Group, pg 959

NEBRASKA

Dog & Pony Productions Inc, pg 850

NEVADA

DVDs4Less, pg 854

NEW HAMPSHIRE

Apertura, pg 788

NEW JERSEY

MIB Mediaworks, pg 941
Suede Interactive, pg 1027
Telequest Inc, pg 1036
TimeSteps Productions Inc, pg 1041

NEW MEXICO

Michael Dunn Productions, pg 853

NEW YORK

Ace Video, pg 774
aurora productions, pg 797
Norman N Axelrod Associates, pg 800
Blue Barn Pictures Inc, pg 809
Brian Film Productions LLC, pg 812
Broad Street Inc, pg 812
Mark Druck Productions, pg 852
Fanlight Productions, pg 865
Films Media Group, pg 868
Florentine Films, pg 870
Karen Frankel Productions, pg 872
Havas Worldwide, pg 886
HB-Content, pg 886
Ketchum Pleon Change, pg 910
Neal Marshad Productions, pg 931
Jack Morton Worldwide, pg 946
News Broadcast Network, pg 956
Shelly Palmer Production, pg 968
Pat Kogan Productions Inc, pg 970
Peckham Productions Inc, pg 970
Polestar Films & Associated Arts Ltd, pg 978
PrimeLight Productions Inc, pg 982
R/GA, pg 990
Suggs Media Productions Inc, pg 1028
TBA Global Events, pg 1032
Third World Newsreel/Camera News Inc, pg 1039
VIEW Inc (Video International Entertainment World Inc), pg 1058
Zelman Studios Ltd, pg 1073

NORTH CAROLINA

Pat Appleson Studios Inc, pg 788
The Communications Group Inc, pg 833
Horizon Video Productions Inc, pg 891
Kino Mountain Productions LLC, pg 911
Unifour Productions Inc, pg 1048

OHIO

Creative Technology, pg 838
Lyon Video Inc, pg 927
Take 1 Media Services, pg 1031

OREGON

Ideascape Inc, pg 894
Odyssey Productions Inc, pg 961
Producers Studio, pg 984
Production West, pg 985

PENNSYLVANIA

Bang Pictures, pg 802
FMP Media Solutions Inc, pg 870
Fusion Brand Experiences, pg 874
Goodman Associates Inc, pg 880
Innovision Media Group, pg 899
JPL, pg 906
Kensington Falls Animation, pg 909
Main Point Productions, pg 929
Muderick Media, pg 949
Production Masters Inc (PMI), pg 984
Video/Film Associates, pg 1055

RHODE ISLAND

Sound-FX-Design, pg 1017

TENNESSEE

Continental Film, pg 835
Memphis Communications Corp, pg 938
Scripps Networks, pg 1005

TEXAS

Alexander Media Productions, pg 780
AMS Pictures, pg 786
Aries Productions, pg 789
Biway Media, pg 808
Castleview Productions, pg 821
Cerutti Productions Inc, pg 823
CEV Multimedia Ltd, pg 823
Dykeman Associates Inc, pg 854
The Editing Co, pg 857
Epic Software Group Inc, pg 862
Horizon Film + Video Productions, pg 891
Marx InDigital, pg 933
Earl Miller Productions Inc, pg 943
Romar Learning, pg 999
South Coast Film & Video, pg 1019
Stage Directions, pg 1022
Tecfilms Inc, pg 1033
University of Texas at Austin - Petroleum Extension Service, pg 1050

VERMONT

Marlboro Film & Video Productions, pg 931

VIRGINIA

BES Studios, pg 805
CACI Productions Group, pg 816
CALIBRE, pg 816
Metro Productions, pg 939

WASHINGTON

Adams Creative & Production Services, pg 775
Hamilton Studio, pg 884
North-by-Northwest Productions, pg 958
Pal Productions Inc, pg 967
Victory Studios, pg 1054
White Rain Films Ltd, pg 1065

WEST VIRGINIA

Altruist Media LLC, pg 783

WISCONSIN

Audio Visual of Milwaukee Inc, pg 795
5th Floor Recording Co, pg 867
Meridian Studios, pg 939
University of Wisconsin-Oshkosh Radio-TV-Film Dept, pg 1050
Video Wisconsin Inc, pg 1056
Wisconsin Public Television, pg 1068

WYOMING

Bridger Productions Inc, pg 812

ALBERTA

Black Media Works, pg 808

BRITISH COLUMBIA

West Eagle Films Inc, pg 1064

MANITOBA

Lank/Beach Productions Inc, pg 916

NORTHWEST TERRITORIES

Yellowknife Films Inc, pg 1072

ONTARIO

Mediaimage Communications Group, pg 937
Shaw Street Productions, pg 1008

QUEBEC

Kerrigan Productions Inc, pg 910
Les Productions Via Le Monde (Daniel Bertolino) Inc, pg 985

Industrial Program Rentals

CALIFORNIA

Em Gee Film Library, pg 860
Glenn Photo Supply, pg 878

GEORGIA

Convergent Media Systems, pg 836

ILLINOIS

National Safety Council (NSC), pg 953

MASSACHUSETTS

Emergency Film Group, pg 860

MISSOURI

Phoenix/BFA/Coronet, pg 974
University of Missouri-Columbia, pg 1050

NEW YORK

Fanlight Productions, pg 865
Films Media Group, pg 868
Richter Productions Inc, pg 996
VIEW Inc (Video International Entertainment World Inc), pg 1058

ONTARIO

Kineticvideo.com, pg 911

Kinescope Distributors

NEW JERSEY

Films of the Nations, pg 868

Kinescope Producers

ARIZONA

Phoenix VideoFilms®, pg 974

KENTUCKY

Donna Lawrence Productions, pg 917

MISSOURI

Celebrities Productions, pg 822

NEW YORK

Shelly Palmer Production, pg 968

Kinescope Rentals

CALIFORNIA

Classic Images, pg 829

GEORGIA

Staging Directions Inc, pg 1023

Literature, *see* Feature Program

Medical Program Distributors

ARIZONA

Tellens Inc, pg 1037

CALIFORNIA

Crystal Pyramid Productions™, pg 840
Davidson Films Inc, pg 843
Direct Cinema Ltd Inc, pg 848
Glenn Photo Supply, pg 878
Joyce Media Inc, pg 906
TMW Media Group, pg 1041

FLORIDA

Capital Communications Inc, pg 819
Motion Image Group LLC, pg 947

ILLINOIS

Chicago Satellite & Video, pg 825
Film Ideas, pg 867

MARYLAND

DSR Computer Technology Specialists Inc, pg 853

MASSACHUSETTS

Emergency Film Group, pg 860

MICHIGAN

Emery-Pratt Co, pg 860
Phoenix Society for Burn Survivors Inc, pg 974

MISSOURI

Phoenix/BFA/Coronet, pg 974

NEW JERSEY

MIB Mediaworks, pg 941

NEW MEXICO

National Information Center for Educational Media (NICEM)/MediaSleuth, pg 952

NEW YORK

Broad Street Inc, pg 812
Fanlight Productions, pg 865
Films Media Group, pg 868
HB-Content, pg 886
News Broadcast Network, pg 956
Richter Productions Inc, pg 996
Select Media Inc, pg 1006
VIEW Inc (Video International Entertainment World Inc), pg 1058
Women Make Movies Inc, pg 1069

NORTH CAROLINA

Sinclair Institute, pg 1012

PENNSYLVANIA

Bullfrog Films Inc, pg 815
FMP Media Solutions Inc, pg 870
Karol Media Inc, pg 908
TouchStar Productions Inc, pg 1042

TEXAS

CEV Multimedia Ltd, pg 823
Texas Heart Institute Visual Communication Services, pg 1037

VIRGINIA

CACI Productions Group, pg 816

WISCONSIN

Equiservices Publishing, pg 862

ONTARIO

Kineticvideo.com, pg 911

Medical Program Producers

ALABAMA

Leo Ticheli Productions, pg 1040

ARIZONA

Film Creations Ltd, pg 867
MediaWorks, pg 938
Phoenix VideoFilms®, pg 974
Tellens Inc, pg 1037

ARKANSAS

Jones Film Video, pg 906

CALIFORNIA

Big Door, pg 807
Classic Images, pg 829
Crystal Pyramid Productions™, pg 840
Custom Video Productions Inc, pg 841
Davidson Films Inc, pg 843
Design Media, pg 845
Dogma Studios, pg 850
Dolphin MultiMedia Inc, pg 850
Havas Edge, pg 885
imageReal Pictures LLC, pg 896
Joyce Media Inc, pg 906
Kavich Reynolds Productions Inc, pg 908
The Kenwood Group, pg 909
KION-TV, pg 911
Main Street Media Inc, pg 929
The Media Staff Inc, pg 937
New & Unique Videos™, pg 955
Panorama Productions, pg 968
Point of View Productions, pg 977
QRS Software Services, pg 988
Dick Reizner Film & Video, pg 994
RetinaVision Productions, pg 995
Glenn Roland Films, pg 998
SNAP, pg 1014
Tam Communications Inc, pg 1031
Tigar Hare Studios, pg 1040
TMW Media Group, pg 1041
Video Resources Inc, pg 1056

COLORADO

Flashback Media Productions, pg 869
Transtar Entertainment Co Inc, pg 1043

CONNECTICUT

Broadcast Video Productions LLC, pg 813
The Gary-Paul Agency, pg 875
MCC Films, pg 935
Moving Pictures, pg 947
New London Media, pg 956

DISTRICT OF COLUMBIA

Hillmann & Carr Inc, pg 889
O'Keefe Communications Inc, pg 961

FLORIDA

Accord Productions, pg 773
Blackburst Entertainment, pg 808
Capital Communications Inc, pg 819
CopShopMiami.com, pg 836
Home Shopping Network (HSN), pg 890
Jordan Klein Film & Video (JKFV), pg 906
Motion Image Group LLC, pg 947

GEORGIA

Beachwood Productions, pg 804
Burst Video/Film Inc, pg 815
COMPRO Productions Inc, pg 834
Guerrilla Productions LLC, pg 883

HAWAII

Hyperspective Studios Inc, pg 893

ILLINOIS

Comtech Multimedia Marketing, pg 834
Film Police, pg 867
Manning Productions, pg 930
SCI Television Productions LLC, pg 1004
Winter Productions, pg 1068

INDIANA

Road Pictures, pg 997

KENTUCKY

Idle Minds Productions Inc, pg 894

LOUISIANA

Digital FX Inc, pg 847
Moxie Media, pg 948

PROGRAMMING — FILM

Medical Program Producers (continued)

MARYLAND

Absolute Hollywood, pg 772
The Ahern Group, pg 779
Richard Chisolm Cinematography, pg 825
dbF a Media Company, pg 844
DSR Computer Technology Specialists Inc, pg 853
The Image Generators, pg 895

MASSACHUSETTS

Emergency Film Group, pg 860
Green Mountain Post Films (GMP), pg 882
Heliotrope Studios, pg 887
Northern Light Productions, pg 959

MICHIGAN

K&R All Media Productions Inc, pg 908

MINNESOTA

House of Cinemagraphics, pg 891

MISSISSIPPI

Dollarhide Film Inc, pg 850

MISSOURI

Fambrough & Associates Inc, pg 865
Phoenix/BFA/Coronet, pg 974

NEBRASKA

Dog & Pony Productions Inc, pg 850

NEW HAMPSHIRE

Apertura, pg 788

NEW JERSEY

MIB Mediaworks, pg 941
Suede Interactive, pg 1027
Telequest Inc, pg 1036
TimeSteps Productions Inc, pg 1041

NEW MEXICO

Michael Dunn Productions, pg 853
Rainbow International Inc/Rainbow Productions Inc, pg 990

NEW YORK

Ace Video, pg 774
aurora productions, pg 797
Norman N Axelrod Associates, pg 800
Brian Film Productions LLC, pg 812
Broad Street Inc, pg 812
Fanlight Productions, pg 865
Films Media Group, pg 868
Havas Worldwide, pg 886
HB-Content, pg 886
Image Zone Inc, pg 896
Ketchum Pleon Change, pg 910
Neal Marshad Productions, pg 931
Jack Morton Worldwide, pg 946
News Broadcast Network, pg 956
Shelly Palmer Production, pg 968
Pat Kogan Productions Inc, pg 970
Peckham Productions Inc, pg 970
R/GA, pg 990
Richter Productions Inc, pg 996
VIEW Inc (Video International Entertainment World Inc), pg 1058
Zelman Studios Ltd, pg 1073

NORTH CAROLINA

Pat Appleson Studios Inc, pg 788
The Communications Group Inc, pg 833
Horizon Video Productions Inc, pg 891
Kino Mountain Productions LLC, pg 911
Sinclair Institute, pg 1012
Unifour Productions Inc, pg 1048

OHIO

Creative Technology, pg 838
Take 1 Media Services, pg 1031

OKLAHOMA

CSI/Orion, pg 840

OREGON

Ideascape Inc, pg 894

PENNSYLVANIA

Bang Pictures, pg 802
FMP Media Solutions Inc, pg 870
Fusion Brand Experiences, pg 874
Goodman Associates Inc, pg 880
Innovision Media Group, pg 899
JPL, pg 906
Kenexa, pg 909
Kensington Falls Animation, pg 909
Production Masters Inc (PMI), pg 984
TouchStar Productions Inc, pg 1042
Video/Film Associates, pg 1055

RHODE ISLAND

Sound-FX-Design, pg 1017

TENNESSEE

Continental Film, pg 835
Memphis Communications Corp, pg 938
Scripps Networks, pg 1005

TEXAS

Alexander Media Productions, pg 780
AMS Pictures, pg 786
Castleview Productions, pg 821
Cerutti Productions Inc, pg 823
CEV Multimedia Ltd, pg 823
Dykeman Associates Inc, pg 854
The Editing Co, pg 857
Horizon Film + Video Productions, pg 891
Marx InDigital, pg 933
Earl Miller Productions Inc, pg 943
Romar Learning, pg 999
South Coast Film & Video, pg 1019
Texas Heart Institute Visual Communication Services, pg 1037

VERMONT

Marlboro Film & Video Productions, pg 931

VIRGINIA

BES Studios, pg 805
CACI Productions Group, pg 816
Metro Productions, pg 939

WASHINGTON

Adams Creative & Production Services, pg 775
Hamilton Studio, pg 884
North-by-Northwest Productions, pg 958
Victory Studios, pg 1054

WEST VIRGINIA

Altruist Media LLC, pg 783

WISCONSIN

Audio Visual of Milwaukee Inc, pg 795
Equiservices Publishing, pg 862
5th Floor Recording Co, pg 867
Meridian Studios, pg 939
Video Wisconsin Inc, pg 1056
Wisconsin Public Television, pg 1068

WYOMING

Bridger Productions Inc, pg 812

MANITOBA

Lank/Beach Productions Inc, pg 916

ONTARIO

VO2 Mix Studios, pg 1060

QUEBEC

Kerrigan Productions Inc, pg 910

Medical Program Rentals

CALIFORNIA

Davidson Films Inc, pg 843
Direct Cinema Ltd Inc, pg 848
Glenn Photo Supply, pg 878
Point of View Productions, pg 977

MASSACHUSETTS

Emergency Film Group, pg 860

MISSOURI

Phoenix/BFA/Coronet, pg 974
University of Missouri-Columbia, pg 1050

NEW YORK

Fanlight Productions, pg 865
Films Media Group, pg 868
Richter Productions Inc, pg 996
Select Media Inc, pg 1006

NORTH CAROLINA

Sinclair Institute, pg 1012

PENNSYLVANIA

Bullfrog Films Inc, pg 815

ONTARIO

Kineticvideo.com, pg 911

Multimedia, CD-ROM & DVD Interactive Program Distributors

CALIFORNIA

Crystal Pyramid Productions™, pg 840
Focus Features, pg 870
MarVista Entertainment Inc, pg 933
Rovi Corp, pg 1000

FLORIDA

Allegro Productions Inc, pg 781
Motion Image Group LLC, pg 947

GEORGIA

Convergent Media Systems, pg 836

ILLINOIS

ABSA Productions Inc, pg 772
Britannica Film & Video, pg 812
National Safety Council (NSC), pg 953

MASSACHUSETTS

Documentary Educational Resources Inc, pg 850

NEBRASKA

Leo Films, pg 919

NEW MEXICO

National Information Center for Educational Media (NICEM)/MediaSleuth, pg 952

NEW YORK

Brooklyn Botanic Garden, pg 814
Films Media Group, pg 868
HB-Content, pg 886
Interactive International Inc, pg 899

OREGON

Wilderness Video, pg 1066

PENNSYLVANIA

FMP Media Solutions Inc, pg 870
New Horizons Computer Learning Centers Inc, pg 955
Science for Kids, pg 1005

TENNESSEE

Center for Southern Folklore Inc, pg 822
Spring Arbor Distributors, pg 1022

TEXAS

CEV Multimedia Ltd, pg 823
Replicopy Digital Media Center, pg 995

UTAH

Strata™, pg 1025

ONTARIO

McIntyre Media Inc, pg 935

Multimedia, CD-ROM & DVD Interactive Program Producers

ARIZONA

Film Creations Ltd, pg 867
MediaWorks, pg 938

CALIFORNIA

Animax, pg 787
Big Door, pg 807
Concrete Images, pg 835
Crystal Pyramid Productions™, pg 840
Custom Video Productions Inc, pg 841
Design Media, pg 845
Direct Images Interactive Inc, pg 848
Dogma Studios, pg 850
Dolphin MultiMedia Inc, pg 850
Focus Features, pg 870
Havas Edge, pg 885
Kavich Reynolds Productions Inc, pg 908
The Kenwood Group, pg 909
Lumeni Productions Inc, pg 926
Main Street Media Inc, pg 929
The Media Staff Inc, pg 937
New Circuit Films LLC, pg 955
Palardo Productions, pg 968
Panorama Productions, pg 968
QRS Software Services, pg 988
RetinaVision Productions, pg 995
Glenn Roland Films, pg 998
SBS Productions, pg 1003
SNAP, pg 1014
Tam Communications Inc, pg 1031
Tigar Hare Studios, pg 1040
Toon Makers, pg 1042
Video Movie Magic, pg 1056
Webster Communications, pg 1063

COLORADO

Flashback Media Productions, pg 869

CONNECTICUT

Broadcast Video Productions LLC, pg 813
Moving Pictures, pg 947
New London Media, pg 956
T & M Digital Services, pg 1031
VRSim Inc, pg 1061

DISTRICT OF COLUMBIA

Hillmann & Carr Inc, pg 889
O'Keefe Communications Inc, pg 961
USCCB Publishing, pg 1051

FLORIDA

Allegro Productions Inc, pg 781
Blackburst Entertainment, pg 808
CD ROM™ Inc, pg 822
Civins Productions Inc, pg 828
Communications Concepts Inc (CCI), pg 833
Jordan Klein Film & Video (JKFV), pg 906
Motion Image Group LLC, pg 947
Video Techniques Inc, pg 1056

GEORGIA

Beachwood Productions, pg 804
Burst Video/Film Inc, pg 815
Continental Film & Video, pg 835
Guerrilla Productions LLC, pg 883
Myriad Productions, pg 951

HAWAII

Hyperspective Studios Inc, pg 893

ILLINOIS

ABSA Productions Inc, pg 772
Accenture, pg 773
Britannica Film & Video, pg 812
Comtech Multimedia Marketing, pg 834
Cresta Creative, pg 839
Manning Productions, pg 930
MIGHTYbYTES Inc, pg 942
National Safety Council (NSC), pg 953
Richter Studios, pg 996
SCI Television Productions LLC, pg 1004

IOWA

The Production House, pg 984

KENTUCKY

Donna Lawrence Productions, pg 917

LOUISIANA

Digital FX Inc, pg 847

MARYLAND

Absolute Hollywood, pg 772
dbF a Media Company, pg 844
Satellite Media Production, pg 1003

MASSACHUSETTS

CommCreative, pg 832
Documentary Educational Resources Inc, pg 850
Northern Light Productions, pg 959
Veritech Corp, pg 1053

MICHIGAN

K&R All Media Productions Inc, pg 908
Tri-Color, pg 1044

MINNESOTA

House of Cinemagraphics, pg 891

NEBRASKA

Dog & Pony Productions Inc, pg 850
Leo Films, pg 919

NEW HAMPSHIRE

Apertura, pg 788

NEW JERSEY

Outside The Box Interactive LLC, pg 966
Suede Interactive, pg 1027

NEW YORK

American Management Association International, pg 784
Blue Barn Pictures Inc, pg 809
Broad Street Inc, pg 812
Brooklyn Botanic Garden, pg 814
Films Media Group, pg 868
Greyfalcon House, pg 882
Havas Worldwide, pg 886
HB-Content, pg 886
Image Zone Inc, pg 896
Interactive International Inc, pg 899
Neal Marshad Productions, pg 931
Jack Morton Worldwide, pg 946
MRY, pg 949
Shelly Palmer Production, pg 968
Pat Kogan Productions Inc, pg 970
R/GA, pg 990
Judson Rosebush Co Inc, pg 999
Suggs Media Productions Inc, pg 1028
Zelman Studios Ltd, pg 1073

NORTH CAROLINA

Pat Appleson Studios Inc, pg 788
The Communications Group Inc, pg 833
Horizon Video Productions Inc, pg 891
Moving Pictures, pg 948
NASCAR Media Group LLC, pg 952
Unifour Productions Inc, pg 1048

OHIO

Creative Technology, pg 838
Take 1 Media Services, pg 1031

OREGON

Ideascape Inc, pg 894
Odyssey Productions Inc, pg 961
Wilderness Video, pg 1066

PENNSYLVANIA

Argentine Productions Inc, pg 789
FMP Media Solutions Inc, pg 870
Innovision Media Group, pg 899
JPL, pg 906
New Horizons Computer Learning Centers Inc, pg 955
Production Masters Inc (PMI), pg 984
Science for Kids, pg 1005

RHODE ISLAND

Sound-FX-Design, pg 1017

TENNESSEE

Anode Inc, pg 787
Continental Film, pg 835
Memphis Communications Corp, pg 938
Scripps Networks, pg 1005

TEXAS

Castleview Productions, pg 821
CEV Multimedia Ltd, pg 823
The Editing Co, pg 857
Epic Software Group Inc, pg 862
Horizon Film + Video Productions, pg 891
InterCom, pg 900
Romar Learning, pg 999
South Coast Film & Video, pg 1019

VIRGINIA

CALIBRE, pg 816
Metro Productions, pg 939

WASHINGTON

Adams Creative & Production Services, pg 775
Hamilton Studio, pg 884
North-by-Northwest Productions, pg 958
Victory Studios, pg 1054

WEST VIRGINIA

Altruist Media LLC, pg 783

WISCONSIN

Audio Visual of Milwaukee Inc, pg 795
5th Floor Recording Co, pg 867
Video Wisconsin Inc, pg 1056
Wisconsin Public Television, pg 1068

WYOMING

Bridger Productions Inc, pg 812

ALBERTA

Black Media Works, pg 808
HBW Entertainment Inc, pg 886

ONTARIO

GAPC (General Assembly Production Centre), pg 875
Purefire Communications Inc, pg 987
Shaw Street Productions, pg 1008
SLI Manufacturing Inc, pg 1013

QUEBEC

Kerrigan Productions Inc, pg 910

Multimedia, CD-ROM & DVD Interactive Program Rentals

DELAWARE

Side Door Studio Inc, pg 1010

GEORGIA

Convergent Media Systems, pg 836

MASSACHUSETTS

Documentary Educational Resources Inc, pg 850

NEW YORK

Brooklyn Botanic Garden, pg 814
Films Media Group, pg 868
Interactive International Inc, pg 899
Select Media Inc, pg 1006

OREGON

Wilderness Video, pg 1066

News Program Distributors

CALIFORNIA

Crystal Pyramid Productions™, pg 840

GEORGIA

School Media Associates LLC, pg 1004

ILLINOIS

Chicago Satellite & Video, pg 825

MISSOURI

Cable Films & Video, pg 816

NEW JERSEY

MIB Mediaworks, pg 941

NEW YORK

Icarus Film Inc, pg 893
News Broadcast Network, pg 956

PROGRAMMING — FILM

News Program Distributors (continued)

NEW YORK (continued)
Richter Productions Inc, pg 996
Women Make Movies Inc, pg 1069

VIRGINIA
CACI Productions Group, pg 816

ALBERTA
Global Television Station, pg 879

News Program Producers

CALIFORNIA
Big Door, pg 807
Crystal Pyramid Productions™, pg 840
Jaguar Distribution Corp, pg 903
KION-TV, pg 911
New & Unique Videos™, pg 955
QRS Software Services, pg 988
SNAP, pg 1014
Vineyard Video & Photography, pg 1058
Webster Communications, pg 1063

COLORADO
Flashback Media Productions, pg 869
Tatum Video, pg 1032

CONNECTICUT
Broadcast Video Productions LLC, pg 813
Essex Television Group Inc, pg 862
New London Media, pg 956

DISTRICT OF COLUMBIA
Hillmann & Carr Inc, pg 889
O'Keefe Communications Inc, pg 961

FLORIDA
Blackburst Entertainment, pg 808
Civins Productions Inc, pg 828
Communications Concepts Inc (CCI), pg 833
CopShopMiami.com, pg 836
Eastern Video, pg 856
Jordan Klein Film & Video (JKFV), pg 906
Motion Image Group LLC, pg 947
Video Techniques Inc, pg 1056

GEORGIA
Beachwood Productions, pg 804
Guerrilla Productions LLC, pg 883
Myriad Productions, pg 951

ILLINOIS
Comtech Multimedia Marketing, pg 834
SCI Television Productions LLC, pg 1004

KENTUCKY
Idle Minds Productions Inc, pg 894

LOUISIANA
Digital FX Inc, pg 847

MARYLAND
Absolute Hollywood, pg 772
Richard Chisolm Cinematography, pg 825
dbF a Media Company, pg 844

MICHIGAN
K&R All Media Productions Inc, pg 908

MINNESOTA
House of Cinemagraphics, pg 891

MISSOURI
Cable Films & Video, pg 816
Fambrough & Associates Inc, pg 865

NEW JERSEY
MIB Mediaworks, pg 941
Bill Quinn Productions, pg 989
Telequest Inc, pg 1036

NEW MEXICO
Michael Dunn Productions, pg 853

NEW YORK
Ace Video, pg 774
aurora productions, pg 797
De Nonno Productions Inc (DPI), pg 844
Havas Worldwide, pg 886
Neal Marshad Productions, pg 931
Jack Morton Worldwide, pg 946
News Broadcast Network, pg 956
Shelly Palmer Production, pg 968
Richter Productions Inc, pg 996
TBA Global Events, pg 1032
Zelman Studios Ltd, pg 1073

NORTH CAROLINA
Pat Appleson Studios Inc, pg 788
The Communications Group Inc, pg 833

PENNSYLVANIA
Innovision Media Group, pg 899
Production Masters Inc (PMI), pg 984

RHODE ISLAND
Sound-FX-Design, pg 1017

TENNESSEE
Continental Film, pg 835

TEXAS
Cerutti Productions Inc, pg 823
Horizon Film + Video Productions, pg 891
Romar Learning, pg 999
Stage Directions, pg 1022
Texas Heart Institute Visual Communication Services, pg 1037

VIRGINIA
CACI Productions Group, pg 816
Metro Productions, pg 939

WISCONSIN
5th Floor Recording Co, pg 867
Wisconsin Public Television, pg 1068

WYOMING
Bridger Productions Inc, pg 812

ALBERTA
Black Media Works, pg 808
Global Television Station, pg 879
HBW Entertainment Inc, pg 886

QUEBEC
Kerrigan Productions Inc, pg 910

News Program Rentals

NEW YORK
Richter Productions Inc, pg 996

ONTARIO
WESCAM Inc, pg 1063

Public Relations Program Distributors

CALIFORNIA
Christian Media Network, pg 825
Crystal Pyramid Productions™, pg 840
Direct Cinema Ltd Inc, pg 848
eFootage LLC, pg 858
Joseph Nicoletti Consulting-Promotion/California International Records/Global Village Records, pg 957

FLORIDA
Allegro Productions Inc, pg 781
Capital Communications Inc, pg 819

GEORGIA
Convergent Media Systems, pg 836

ILLINOIS
ABSA Productions Inc, pg 772
Chicago Satellite & Video, pg 825

NEVADA
DVDs4Less, pg 854

NEW YORK
Broad Street Inc, pg 812
HB-Content, pg 886
News Broadcast Network, pg 956

PENNSYLVANIA
FMP Media Solutions Inc, pg 870
Karol Media Inc, pg 908

TENNESSEE
American Blackguard Inc, pg 784

VIRGINIA
CACI Productions Group, pg 816

ALBERTA
Global Television Station, pg 879

Public Relations Program Producers

ALABAMA
Leo Ticheli Productions, pg 1040

ALASKA
Aurora Films, pg 797

ARIZONA
Candee Productions Inc, pg 819
MediaWorks, pg 938
Metropolitan Audio-Visual Inc, pg 940
Tellens Inc, pg 1037

ARKANSAS
Jones Film Video, pg 906

CALIFORNIA
Big Door, pg 807
Christian Media Network, pg 825
Classic Images, pg 829
Crystal Pyramid Productions™, pg 840
Dogma Studios, pg 850
Dolphin MultiMedia Inc, pg 850
Goal Productions, pg 879
Kavich Reynolds Productions Inc, pg 908
KION-TV, pg 911
Main Street Media Inc, pg 929
The Media Staff Inc, pg 937
New & Unique Videos™, pg 955
Joseph Nicoletti Consulting-Promotion/California International Records/Global Village Records, pg 957
Panorama Productions, pg 968
Point of View Productions, pg 977
QRS Software Services, pg 988
Dick Reizner Film & Video, pg 994
Glenn Roland Films, pg 998
Santa Barbara Location Services, pg 1002
SBS Productions, pg 1003
SNAP, pg 1014
Tam Communications Inc, pg 1031
Vineyard Video & Photography, pg 1058
Webster Communications, pg 1063
Zamacona Productions, pg 1073

COLORADO
Flashback Media Productions, pg 869
Tatum Video, pg 1032
Transtar Entertainment Co Inc, pg 1043

CONNECTICUT
Broadcast Video Productions LLC, pg 813
The Gary-Paul Agency, pg 875
MCC Films, pg 935
New London Media, pg 956

DISTRICT OF COLUMBIA
Hillmann & Carr Inc, pg 889

FLORIDA
Accord Productions, pg 773
Allegro Productions Inc, pg 781
Blackburst Entertainment, pg 808
Civins Productions Inc, pg 828
Communications Concepts Inc (CCI), pg 833
Eastern Video, pg 856
Home Shopping Network (HSN), pg 890
Jordan Klein Film & Video (JKFV), pg 906
Motion Image Group LLC, pg 947

Tel-Air Interests Inc, pg 1035
Video Techniques Inc, pg 1056

GEORGIA

Beachwood Productions, pg 804
Burst Video/Film Inc, pg 815
COMPRO Productions Inc, pg 834
Continental Film & Video, pg 835
Guerrilla Productions LLC, pg 883
Myriad Productions, pg 951

HAWAII

Hyperspective Studios Inc, pg 893
1013 Integrated, pg 1037

ILLINOIS

ABSA Productions Inc, pg 772
Comtech Multimedia Marketing, pg 834
Cresta Creative, pg 839
Film Police, pg 867
Manning Productions, pg 930
SCI Television Productions LLC, pg 1004
WEEK TV, pg 1063
Winter Productions, pg 1068

INDIANA

Road Pictures, pg 997

IOWA

Hellman Associates Inc, pg 887

KENTUCKY

Horizon Films & Media LLC, pg 891
Idle Minds Productions Inc, pg 894
Donna Lawrence Productions, pg 917

LOUISIANA

Digital FX Inc, pg 847
Moxie Media, pg 948

MARYLAND

Absolute Hollywood, pg 772
Richard Chisolm Cinematography, pg 825
dbF a Media Company, pg 844

MASSACHUSETTS

Green Mountain Post Films (GMP), pg 882
Heliotrope Studios, pg 887
Monadnock Media Inc, pg 945

MICHIGAN

K&R All Media Productions Inc, pg 908

MINNESOTA

House of Cinemagraphics, pg 891

MISSISSIPPI

Dollarhide Film Inc, pg 850

MISSOURI

Fambrough & Associates Inc, pg 865

MONTANA

North Country Media Group, pg 959

NEBRASKA

Dog & Pony Productions Inc, pg 850

NEVADA

DVDs4Less, pg 854

NEW HAMPSHIRE

Apertura, pg 788

NEW JERSEY

Concepts TV Production, pg 834
Bill Quinn Productions, pg 989
Telequest Inc, pg 1036
TimeSteps Productions Inc, pg 1041

NEW MEXICO

Michael Dunn Productions, pg 853

NEW YORK

Ace Video, pg 774
aurora productions, pg 797
Blue Barn Pictures Inc, pg 809
Brian Film Productions LLC, pg 812
Broad Street Inc, pg 812
Buzzco Associates Inc, pg 816
Florentine Films, pg 870
Karen Frankel Productions, pg 872
Havas Worldwide, pg 886
HB-Content, pg 886
Ketchum Pleon Change, pg 910
Kinetic Arts, pg 911
Neal Marshad Productions, pg 931
Jack Morton Worldwide, pg 946
News Broadcast Network, pg 956
Northeast Video Productions Inc, pg 959
Shelly Palmer Production, pg 968
Peckham Productions Inc, pg 970
Richter Productions Inc, pg 996
Suggs Media Productions Inc, pg 1028
Zelman Studios Ltd, pg 1073

NORTH CAROLINA

Pat Appleson Studios Inc, pg 788
The Communications Group Inc, pg 833
Horizon Video Productions Inc, pg 891
Kino Mountain Productions LLC, pg 911
Unifour Productions Inc, pg 1048

OHIO

Maslowski Productions, pg 933

OREGON

Ideascape Inc, pg 894
Odyssey Productions Inc, pg 961
Producers Studio, pg 984

PENNSYLVANIA

FMP Media Solutions Inc, pg 870
Fusion Brand Experiences, pg 874
Goodman Associates Inc, pg 880
Innovision Media Group, pg 899
JPL, pg 906
Main Point Productions, pg 929
Production Masters Inc (PMI), pg 984
Video/Film Associates, pg 1055

RHODE ISLAND

Sound-FX-Design, pg 1017

TENNESSEE

American Blackguard Inc, pg 784
Continental Film, pg 835
Memphis Communications Corp, pg 938
Scripps Networks, pg 1005

TEXAS

AMS Pictures, pg 786
Biway Media, pg 808
Castleview Productions, pg 821
Cerutti Productions Inc, pg 823
The Editing Co, pg 857
Horizon Film + Video Productions, pg 891
Marx InDigital, pg 933
Earl Miller Productions Inc, pg 943
South Coast Film & Video, pg 1019
Stage Directions, pg 1022
Texas Heart Institute Visual Communication Services, pg 1037

VIRGINIA

BES Studios, pg 805
CACI Productions Group, pg 816
CALIBRE, pg 816
Metro Productions, pg 939

WASHINGTON

Adams Creative & Production Services, pg 775
Hamilton Studio, pg 884
North-by-Northwest Productions, pg 958

WEST VIRGINIA

Altruist Media LLC, pg 783

WISCONSIN

5th Floor Recording Co, pg 867
Meridian Studios, pg 939
Video Wisconsin Inc, pg 1056
Wisconsin Public Television, pg 1068

WYOMING

Bridger Productions Inc, pg 812

ALBERTA

Black Media Works, pg 808
Global Television Station, pg 879
HBW Entertainment Inc, pg 886

NORTHWEST TERRITORIES

Yellowknife Films Inc, pg 1072

ONTARIO

Shaw Street Productions, pg 1008

QUEBEC

Kerrigan Productions Inc, pg 910

Public Relations Program Rentals

CALIFORNIA

Direct Cinema Ltd Inc, pg 848

GEORGIA

Convergent Media Systems, pg 836

Public Service Announcement Distributors

CALIFORNIA

Crystal Pyramid Productions™, pg 840
New & Unique Videos™, pg 955

FLORIDA

Allegro Productions Inc, pg 781

ILLINOIS

ABSA Productions Inc, pg 772
Chicago Satellite & Video, pg 825

NEVADA

DVDs4Less, pg 854

NEW YORK

HB-Content, pg 886
News Broadcast Network, pg 956
Select Media Inc, pg 1006

OHIO

Franciscan Media, pg 872

PENNSYLVANIA

Karol Media Inc, pg 908

TENNESSEE

American Blackguard Inc, pg 784

VIRGINIA

CACI Productions Group, pg 816

WISCONSIN

Wisconsin Public Television, pg 1068

ALBERTA

Global Television Station, pg 879

Public Service Announcement Producers

ALASKA

Aurora Films, pg 797

ARIZONA

Candee Productions Inc, pg 819
Film Creations Ltd, pg 867
MediaWorks, pg 938
Metropolitan Audio-Visual Inc, pg 940
Phoenix VideoFilms®, pg 974

CALIFORNIA

Big Door, pg 807
Classic Images, pg 829
Concrete Images, pg 835
Crystal Pyramid Productions™, pg 840
Custom Video Productions Inc, pg 841
Dogma Studios, pg 850
Tom Donald Films, pg 850
GAMfilm Productions, pg 875
imageReal Pictures LLC, pg 896
Kavich Reynolds Productions Inc, pg 908

PROGRAMMING — FILM

Public Service Announcement Producers (continued)

CALIFORNIA (continued)

KION-TV, pg 911
KTVU-Retail Services, pg 914
Main Street Media Inc, pg 929
The Media Staff Inc, pg 937
New & Unique Videos™, pg 955
New Circuit Films LLC, pg 955
Panorama Productions, pg 968
Point of View Productions, pg 977
QRS Software Services, pg 988
Glenn Roland Films, pg 998
Santa Barbara Location Services, pg 1002
SBS Productions, pg 1003
SNAP, pg 1014
Tam Communications Inc, pg 1031
Video Resources Inc, pg 1056
Vineyard Video & Photography, pg 1058
Webster Communications, pg 1063
Zamacona Productions, pg 1073

COLORADO

Flashback Media Productions, pg 869
Transtar Entertainment Co Inc, pg 1043

CONNECTICUT

ACM Productions Ltd, pg 774
Broadcast Video Productions LLC, pg 813
The Gary-Paul Agency, pg 875
MCC Films, pg 935
Moving Pictures, pg 947

DISTRICT OF COLUMBIA

Hillmann & Carr Inc, pg 889

FLORIDA

Accord Productions, pg 773
Allegro Productions Inc, pg 781
Blackburst Entertainment, pg 808
Civins Productions Inc, pg 828
Communications Concepts Inc (CCI), pg 833
CopShopMiami.com, pg 836
Eastern Video, pg 856
Home Shopping Network (HSN), pg 890
Jordan Klein Film & Video (JKFV), pg 906
Motion Image Group LLC, pg 947
Tel-Air Interests Inc, pg 1035
Video Techniques Inc, pg 1056

GEORGIA

Beachwood Productions, pg 804
Burst Video/Film Inc, pg 815
Continental Film & Video, pg 835
Guerrilla Productions LLC, pg 883

HAWAII

Hyperspective Studios Inc, pg 893

ILLINOIS

ABSA Productions Inc, pg 772
Comtech Multimedia Marketing, pg 834
Film Police, pg 867
Manning Productions, pg 930
Mimi Productions, pg 943
SCI Television Productions LLC, pg 1004
Winter Productions, pg 1068

INDIANA

Road Pictures, pg 997

KENTUCKY

Idle Minds Productions Inc, pg 894

LOUISIANA

Digital FX Inc, pg 847
Moxie Media, pg 948

MARYLAND

Absolute Hollywood, pg 772
The Ahern Group, pg 779
Richard Chisolm Cinematography, pg 825
dbF a Media Company, pg 844
The Image Generators, pg 895

MASSACHUSETTS

Green Mountain Post Films (GMP), pg 882
Heliotrope Studios, pg 887
MotionArt Studios, pg 947
Northern Light Productions, pg 959

MICHIGAN

K&R All Media Productions Inc, pg 908

MINNESOTA

House of Cinemagraphics, pg 891

MISSISSIPPI

Dollarhide Film Inc, pg 850

MISSOURI

Fambrough & Associates Inc, pg 865

MONTANA

North Country Media Group, pg 959

NEVADA

DVDs4Less, pg 854

NEW HAMPSHIRE

Apertura, pg 788

NEW JERSEY

TimeSteps Productions Inc, pg 1041

NEW MEXICO

Michael Dunn Productions, pg 853

NEW YORK

aurora productions, pg 797
Blue Barn Pictures Inc, pg 809
Broad Street Inc, pg 812
De Nonno Productions Inc (DPI), pg 844
Fanlight Productions, pg 865
Florentine Films, pg 870
Havas Worldwide, pg 886
HB-Content, pg 886
Ketchum Pleon Change, pg 910
Kinetic Arts, pg 911
Neal Marshad Productions, pg 931
Jack Morton Worldwide, pg 946
News Broadcast Network, pg 956
Shelly Palmer Production, pg 968
Pat Kogan Productions Inc, pg 970
Polestar Films & Associated Arts Ltd, pg 978
Shadow Pictures Inc, pg 1007
Suggs Media Productions Inc, pg 1028
Alan Weiss Productions, pg 1063
Zelman Studios Ltd, pg 1073

NORTH CAROLINA

Pat Appleson Studios Inc, pg 788
The Communications Group Inc, pg 833
Horizon Video Productions Inc, pg 891
Kino Mountain Productions LLC, pg 911
Unifour Productions Inc, pg 1048

OHIO

Franciscan Media, pg 872
Lyon Video Inc, pg 927
Take 1 Media Services, pg 1031

OREGON

Ideascape Inc, pg 894
Odyssey Productions Inc, pg 961
Producers Studio, pg 984
Production West, pg 985

PENNSYLVANIA

Bang Pictures, pg 802
Fusion Brand Experiences, pg 874
Goodman Associates Inc, pg 880
Innovision Media Group, pg 899
JPL, pg 906
Kensington Falls Animation, pg 909
Muderick Media, pg 949
Production Masters Inc (PMI), pg 984
Video/Film Associates, pg 1055

RHODE ISLAND

Sound-FX-Design, pg 1017

TENNESSEE

American Blackguard Inc, pg 784
Continental Film, pg 835

TEXAS

AMS Pictures, pg 786
Biway Media, pg 808
Castleview Productions, pg 821
Cerutti Productions Inc, pg 823
The Editing Co, pg 857
Horizon Film + Video Productions, pg 891
Stage Directions, pg 1022
Texas Heart Institute Visual Communication Services, pg 1037

UTAH

K-SAR Video & DVD Productions, pg 907

VIRGINIA

BES Studios, pg 805
CACI Productions Group, pg 816
CALIBRE, pg 816
Metro Productions, pg 939
Studio Center Corp, pg 1026

WASHINGTON

Hamilton Studio, pg 884
Victory Studios, pg 1054
White Rain Films Ltd, pg 1065

WEST VIRGINIA

Altruist Media LLC, pg 783

WISCONSIN

5th Floor Recording Co, pg 867
Meridian Studios, pg 939
University of Wisconsin-Oshkosh Radio-TV-Film Dept, pg 1050
Wisconsin Public Television, pg 1068

WYOMING

Bridger Productions Inc, pg 812

ALBERTA

Black Media Works, pg 808
Global Television Station, pg 879
HBW Entertainment Inc, pg 886

ONTARIO

Mediaimage Communications Group, pg 937
Shaw Street Productions, pg 1008

QUEBEC

Kerrigan Productions Inc, pg 910

Public Service Announcement Rentals

NEW YORK

Select Media Inc, pg 1006

Religious Program Distributors

ARIZONA

Tellens Inc, pg 1037

CALIFORNIA

Christian Media Network, pg 825
Direct Cinema Ltd Inc, pg 848
Joyce Media Inc, pg 906

CONNECTICUT

Hartley Film Foundation, pg 885

DISTRICT OF COLUMBIA

USCCB Publishing, pg 1051

FLORIDA

Capital Communications Inc, pg 819

HAWAII

Media Bridge Gamekids, pg 936

ILLINOIS

Baha'i Distribution Service (BDS), pg 801
Film Ideas, pg 867

INDIANA

InterComm, pg 900

Religious Program Producers

Religious Program Rentals

Research—Technical Program, *see* Technical Research Program

Sales Promotion & Training Program Distributors

PROGRAMMING — FILM

Sales Promotion & Training Program Distributors (continued)

PENNSYLVANIA

FMP Media Solutions Inc, pg 870
Karol Media Inc, pg 908
New Horizons Computer Learning Centers Inc, pg 955

TENNESSEE

American Blackguard Inc, pg 784

VIRGINIA

CACI Productions Group, pg 816

ONTARIO

Kineticvideo.com, pg 911

Sales Promotion & Training Program Producers

ALABAMA

Leo Ticheli Productions, pg 1040

ARIZONA

Candee Productions Inc, pg 819
Film Creations Ltd, pg 867
MediaWorks, pg 938
Metropolitan Audio-Visual Inc, pg 940
Phoenix VideoFilms®, pg 974

ARKANSAS

Jones Film Video, pg 906

CALIFORNIA

Aaron Marcus & Associates Inc, pg 772
AM Productions, pg 783
Big Door, pg 807
Christian Media Network, pg 825
Classic Images, pg 829
Concrete Images, pg 835
Crystal Pyramid Productions™, pg 840
Custom Video Productions Inc, pg 841
Design Media, pg 845
Dogma Studios, pg 850
Dolphin MultiMedia Inc, pg 850
Kavich Reynolds Productions Inc, pg 908
The Kenwood Group, pg 909
KION-TV, pg 911
KTVU-Retail Services, pg 914
Main Street Media Inc, pg 929
The Media Staff Inc, pg 937
New & Unique Videos™, pg 955
Panorama Productions, pg 968
People Skills International, pg 972
Point of View Productions, pg 977
QRS Software Services, pg 988
Dick Reizner Film & Video, pg 994
RetinaVision Productions, pg 995
Glenn Roland Films, pg 998
Santa Barbara Location Services, pg 1002
SBS Productions, pg 1003
SNAP, pg 1014
Tam Communications Inc, pg 1031
Vineyard Video & Photography, pg 1058
Webster Communications, pg 1063
Zamacona Productions, pg 1073

COLORADO

Flashback Media Productions, pg 869
Transtar Entertainment Co Inc, pg 1043

CONNECTICUT

Broadcast Video Productions LLC, pg 813
The Gary-Paul Agency, pg 875
MCC Films, pg 935

FLORIDA

Accord Productions, pg 773
Allegro Productions Inc, pg 781
Blackburst Entertainment, pg 808
Capital Communications Inc, pg 819
Communications Concepts Inc (CCI), pg 833
Eastern Video, pg 856
Home Shopping Network (HSN), pg 890
Jordan Klein Film & Video (JKFV), pg 906
Tel-Air Interests Inc, pg 1035
Video Techniques Inc, pg 1056

GEORGIA

Beachwood Productions, pg 804
Burst Video/Film Inc, pg 815
COMPRO Productions Inc, pg 834
Continental Film & Video, pg 835
Guerrilla Productions LLC, pg 883
Myriad Productions, pg 951

HAWAII

Hyperspective Studios Inc, pg 893

ILLINOIS

ABSA Productions Inc, pg 772
Comtech Multimedia Marketing, pg 834
Cresta Creative, pg 839
Film Police, pg 867
Manning Productions, pg 930
MIGHTYbYTES Inc, pg 942
Richter Studios, pg 996
SCI Television Productions LLC, pg 1004
Winter Productions, pg 1068

INDIANA

Road Pictures, pg 997

IOWA

Hellman Associates Inc, pg 887

KENTUCKY

Idle Minds Productions Inc, pg 894

LOUISIANA

Digital FX Inc, pg 847
Moxie Media, pg 948

MARYLAND

Absolute Hollywood, pg 772
The Ahern Group, pg 779
Richard Chisolm Cinematography, pg 825
dbF a Media Company, pg 844
The Image Generators, pg 895

MASSACHUSETTS

CommCreative, pg 832
Green Mountain Post Films (GMP), pg 882
Northern Light Productions, pg 959

MICHIGAN

K&R All Media Productions Inc, pg 908
Lawrence Productions Inc, pg 917
Maritz Performance Improvement Co, pg 931

MINNESOTA

House of Cinemagraphics, pg 891

MISSISSIPPI

Dollarhide Film Inc, pg 850

MISSOURI

Fambrough & Associates Inc, pg 865
Hardcastle Films & Video, pg 885

MONTANA

North Country Media Group, pg 959

NEBRASKA

Dog & Pony Productions Inc, pg 850

NEVADA

DVDs4Less, pg 854

NEW HAMPSHIRE

Apertura, pg 788

NEW JERSEY

Concepts TV Production, pg 834
MIB Mediaworks, pg 941
Bill Quinn Productions, pg 989
Telequest Inc, pg 1036
TimeSteps Productions Inc, pg 1041

NEW MEXICO

Michael Dunn Productions, pg 853
Rainbow International Inc/Rainbow Productions Inc, pg 990

NEW YORK

Ace Video, pg 774
American Management Association International, pg 784
aurora productions, pg 797
Blue Barn Pictures Inc, pg 809
Brian Film Productions LLC, pg 812
Broad Street Inc, pg 812
Havas Worldwide, pg 886
HB-Content, pg 886
Ketchum Pleon Change, pg 910
Neal Marshad Productions, pg 931
Jack Morton Worldwide, pg 946
News Broadcast Network, pg 956
Northeast Video Productions Inc, pg 959
Shelly Palmer Production, pg 968
Pat Kogan Productions Inc, pg 970
Peckham Productions Inc, pg 970
Suggs Media Productions Inc, pg 1028
TBA Global Events, pg 1032
Zelman Studios Ltd, pg 1073

NORTH CAROLINA

Pat Appleson Studios Inc, pg 788
The Communications Group Inc, pg 833
Horizon Video Productions Inc, pg 891
Kino Mountain Productions LLC, pg 911
Unifour Productions Inc, pg 1048

OHIO

Lyon Video Inc, pg 927
Take 1 Media Services, pg 1031

OREGON

Ideascape Inc, pg 894
Odyssey Productions Inc, pg 961
Producers Studio, pg 984

PENNSYLVANIA

Argentine Productions Inc, pg 789
FMP Media Solutions Inc, pg 870
Fusion Brand Experiences, pg 874
Goodman Associates Inc, pg 880
Innovision Media Group, pg 899
JPL, pg 906
Kensington Falls Animation, pg 909
Main Point Productions, pg 929
Muderick Media, pg 949
New Horizons Computer Learning Centers Inc, pg 955
Production Masters Inc (PMI), pg 984
Video/Film Associates, pg 1055

RHODE ISLAND

Sound-FX-Design, pg 1017

TENNESSEE

American Blackguard Inc, pg 784
Continental Film, pg 835
Memphis Communications Corp, pg 938
Scripps Networks, pg 1005
Stage Post, pg 1022

TEXAS

Aries Productions, pg 789
Biway Media, pg 808
Castleview Productions, pg 821
Cerutti Productions Inc, pg 823
The Editing Co, pg 857
Horizon Film + Video Productions, pg 891
Marx InDigital, pg 933
Earl Miller Productions Inc, pg 943
Romar Learning, pg 999
South Coast Film & Video, pg 1019
Tecfilms Inc, pg 1033

VERMONT

Marlboro Film & Video Productions, pg 931

VIRGINIA

BES Studios, pg 805
CACI Productions Group, pg 816
Metro Productions, pg 939

WASHINGTON

Adams Creative & Production Services, pg 775
Hamilton Studio, pg 884
North-by-Northwest Productions, pg 958
Victory Studios, pg 1054
White Rain Films Ltd, pg 1065

Sales Promotion & Training Program Rentals

Scientific Program Distributors

Scientific Program Producers

PROGRAMMING — FILM

Scientific Program Producers (continued)

TEXAS (continued)
Romar Learning, pg 999
Texas Heart Institute Visual Communication Services, pg 1037

VIRGINIA
CACI Productions Group, pg 816
Metro Productions, pg 939

WEST VIRGINIA
Altruist Media LLC, pg 783

WISCONSIN
Equiservices Publishing, pg 862
5th Floor Recording Co, pg 867
Wisconsin Public Television, pg 1068

WYOMING
Bridger Productions Inc, pg 812

ALBERTA
Black Media Works, pg 808

BRITISH COLUMBIA
West Eagle Films Inc, pg 1064

NORTHWEST TERRITORIES
Yellowknife Films Inc, pg 1072

ONTARIO
IMAX Corp, pg 896

QUEBEC
Kerrigan Productions Inc, pg 910
Les Productions Via Le Monde (Daniel Bertolino) Inc, pg 985

Scientific Program Rentals

CALIFORNIA
Direct Cinema Ltd Inc, pg 848
Em Gee Film Library, pg 860
Glenn Photo Supply, pg 878

KENTUCKY
National Geographic Learning, pg 952

MASSACHUSETTS
Documentary Educational Resources Inc, pg 850
Emergency Film Group, pg 860

MINNESOTA
Science Museum of Minnesota, pg 1005

MISSOURI
University of Missouri-Columbia, pg 1050

NEW YORK
American Museum of Natural History (AMNH), pg 784
Films Media Group, pg 868
Richter Productions Inc, pg 996
Select Media Inc, pg 1006

PENNSYLVANIA
Bullfrog Films Inc, pg 815

QUEBEC
Les Productions Via Le Monde (Daniel Bertolino) Inc, pg 985

Seventy mm Films, *see* Films—70mm

Short Film, *see* Theatrical Short

Sixteen mm Films, *see* Films—16mm

Sponsored Program Distributors

CALIFORNIA
Crystal Pyramid Productions™, pg 840
Direct Cinema Ltd Inc, pg 848
New & Unique Videos™, pg 955
Visual Communications - Southern California Asian American Studies Central Inc, pg 1059

FLORIDA
Allegro Productions Inc, pg 781
Capital Communications Inc, pg 819
Motion Image Group LLC, pg 947

ILLINOIS
Chicago Satellite & Video, pg 825
Terra Nova Films Inc, pg 1037

MARYLAND
DSR Computer Technology Specialists Inc, pg 853

MISSOURI
Cable Films & Video, pg 816

NEVADA
DVDs4Less, pg 854

NEW YORK
Broad Street Inc, pg 812
William Greaves Productions Inc, pg 882
HB-Content, pg 886
VIEW Inc (Video International Entertainment World Inc), pg 1058

PENNSYLVANIA
Bullfrog Films Inc, pg 815
Karol Media Inc, pg 908

TENNESSEE
American Blackguard Inc, pg 784

QUEBEC
Les Productions Via Le Monde (Daniel Bertolino) Inc, pg 985

Sponsored Program Producers

ALABAMA
Leo Ticheli Productions, pg 1040

ARIZONA
MediaWorks, pg 938
Phoenix VideoFilms®, pg 974

CALIFORNIA
A Go Go Films, pg 771
Animax, pg 787
Big Door, pg 807
Classic Images, pg 829
Crystal Pyramid Productions™, pg 840
Custom Video Productions Inc, pg 841
Davidson Films Inc, pg 843
Dogma Studios, pg 850
imageReal Pictures LLC, pg 896
KION-TV, pg 911
KTVU-Retail Services, pg 914
Main Street Media Inc, pg 929
The Media Staff Inc, pg 937
New & Unique Videos™, pg 955
Panorama Productions, pg 968
Point of View Productions, pg 977
QRS Software Services, pg 988
Glenn Roland Films, pg 998
SNAP, pg 1014
Visual Communications - Southern California Asian American Studies Central Inc, pg 1059

COLORADO
Flashback Media Productions, pg 869
Transtar Entertainment Co Inc, pg 1043

CONNECTICUT
Broadcast Video Productions LLC, pg 813
MCC Films, pg 935

DISTRICT OF COLUMBIA
Hillmann & Carr Inc, pg 889

FLORIDA
Accord Productions, pg 773
Allegro Productions Inc, pg 781
Blackburst Entertainment, pg 808
Capital Communications Inc, pg 819
Communications Concepts Inc (CCI), pg 833
Courter Films LLC, pg 837
Eastern Video, pg 856
Home Shopping Network (HSN), pg 890
Jordan Klein Film & Video (JKFV), pg 906
Karst Productions Inc, pg 908
Motion Image Group LLC, pg 947
Tel-Air Interests Inc, pg 1035

GEORGIA
Beachwood Productions, pg 804
Burst Video/Film Inc, pg 815
Guerrilla Productions LLC, pg 883
Myriad Productions, pg 951

HAWAII
Hyperspective Studios Inc, pg 893
1013 Integrated, pg 1037

ILLINOIS
Comtech Multimedia Marketing, pg 834
Film Police, pg 867
Mimi Productions, pg 943
SCI Television Productions LLC, pg 1004
Terra Nova Films Inc, pg 1037
Winter Productions, pg 1068

INDIANA
Road Pictures, pg 997

KENTUCKY
Donna Lawrence Productions, pg 917

LOUISIANA
Moxie Media, pg 948

MARYLAND
Absolute Hollywood, pg 772
Richard Chisolm Cinematography, pg 825
dbF a Media Company, pg 844
DSR Computer Technology Specialists Inc, pg 853

MASSACHUSETTS
Green Mountain Post Films (GMP), pg 882
Heliotrope Studios, pg 887

MICHIGAN
K&R All Media Productions Inc, pg 908

MINNESOTA
House of Cinemagraphics, pg 891

MISSOURI
Fambrough & Associates Inc, pg 865

MONTANA
North Country Media Group, pg 959

NEVADA
DVDs4Less, pg 854

NEW HAMPSHIRE
Apertura, pg 788

NEW JERSEY
Telequest Inc, pg 1036
TimeSteps Productions Inc, pg 1041

NEW MEXICO
Michael Dunn Productions, pg 853

NEW YORK
Ace Video, pg 774
aurora productions, pg 797
Blue Barn Pictures Inc, pg 809
Brian Film Productions LLC, pg 812
Broad Street Inc, pg 812
Florentine Films, pg 870

Sponsored Program Rentals

Sports Program Distributors

Sports Program Producers

PROGRAMMING — FILM

Sports Program Producers (continued)

MINNESOTA

House of Cinemagraphics, pg 891

MISSOURI

Fambrough & Associates Inc, pg 865

MONTANA

North Country Media Group, pg 959

NEBRASKA

The Recruiters Library, pg 993

NEW HAMPSHIRE

Apertura, pg 788
YMAA Publication Center Inc, pg 1072

NEW JERSEY

Euro-Pacific Film & Video Productions Inc, pg 863
Bill Quinn Productions, pg 989

NEW MEXICO

Michael Dunn Productions, pg 853

NEW YORK

aurora productions, pg 797
Blue Barn Pictures Inc, pg 809
Brian Film Productions LLC, pg 812
Broad Street Inc, pg 812
Corbis Motion, pg 836
Florentine Films, pg 870
Havas Worldwide, pg 886
HB-Content, pg 886
Jalbert Productions International, pg 903
Neal Marshad Productions, pg 931
Mastervision Inc, pg 933
Jack Morton Worldwide, pg 946
Shelly Palmer Production, pg 968
Peckham Productions Inc, pg 970
Penguin Audiobooks, pg 971
TBA Global Events, pg 1032
VIEW Inc (Video International Entertainment World Inc), pg 1058
Zelman Studios Ltd, pg 1073

NORTH CAROLINA

Pat Appleson Studios Inc, pg 788
The Communications Group Inc, pg 833
Kino Mountain Productions LLC, pg 911
Unifour Productions Inc, pg 1048

OREGON

Odyssey Productions Inc, pg 961

PENNSYLVANIA

Bang Pictures, pg 802
FMP Media Solutions Inc, pg 870
Fusion Brand Experiences, pg 874
Innovision Media Group, pg 899
Kensington Falls Animation, pg 909
Production Masters Inc (PMI), pg 984

RHODE ISLAND

Sound-FX-Design, pg 1017

TENNESSEE

Continental Film, pg 835

TEXAS

Cerutti Productions Inc, pg 823
Horizon Film + Video Productions, pg 891
Earl Miller Productions Inc, pg 943

VIRGINIA

CACI Productions Group, pg 816
Metro Productions, pg 939

WASHINGTON

Victory Studios, pg 1054

WISCONSIN

5th Floor Recording Co, pg 867
Wisconsin Public Television, pg 1068

WYOMING

Bridger Productions Inc, pg 812

ALBERTA

Black Media Works, pg 808
Global Television Station, pg 879

BRITISH COLUMBIA

Network Entertainment Inc, pg 954

QUEBEC

Kerrigan Productions Inc, pg 910

Sports Program Rentals

CALIFORNIA

Direct Cinema Ltd Inc, pg 848
Em Gee Film Library, pg 860
Glenn Photo Supply, pg 878

COLORADO

Tatum Video, pg 1032

INDIANA

InterComm, pg 900

MISSOURI

University of Missouri-Columbia, pg 1050

NEW JERSEY

Euro-Pacific Film & Video Productions Inc, pg 863

PENNSYLVANIA

Bullfrog Films Inc, pg 815

ONTARIO

WESCAM Inc, pg 1063

Technical Research Program Distributors

CALIFORNIA

Crystal Pyramid Productions™, pg 840

DISTRICT OF COLUMBIA

American Chemical Society (ACS), pg 784

FLORIDA

Capital Communications Inc, pg 819

ILLINOIS

ABSA Productions Inc, pg 772

MASSACHUSETTS

Documentary Educational Resources Inc, pg 850
Emergency Film Group, pg 860

PENNSYLVANIA

FMP Media Solutions Inc, pg 870

VIRGINIA

CACI Productions Group, pg 816

Technical Research Program Producers

ARIZONA

Phoenix VideoFilms®, pg 974

CALIFORNIA

Big Door, pg 807
Classic Images, pg 829
Crystal Pyramid Productions™, pg 840
Custom Video Productions Inc, pg 841
Design Media, pg 845
Havas Edge, pg 885
New & Unique Videos™, pg 955
QRS Software Services, pg 988
Glenn Roland Films, pg 998
SNAP, pg 1014
StereoScope International, pg 1024

COLORADO

Flashback Media Productions, pg 869
Transtar Entertainment Co Inc, pg 1043

CONNECTICUT

Broadcast Video Productions LLC, pg 813

DISTRICT OF COLUMBIA

American Chemical Society (ACS), pg 784

FLORIDA

Accord Productions, pg 773
Capital Communications Inc, pg 819
Civins Productions Inc, pg 828
Courter Films LLC, pg 837
Jordan Klein Film & Video (JKFV), pg 906

GEORGIA

Beachwood Productions, pg 804
Guerrilla Productions LLC, pg 883

HAWAII

Hyperspective Studios Inc, pg 893

ILLINOIS

ABSA Productions Inc, pg 772
Accenture, pg 773

LOUISIANA

Moxie Media, pg 948

MARYLAND

Absolute Hollywood, pg 772
The Ahern Group, pg 779
dbF a Media Company, pg 844

MASSACHUSETTS

Documentary Educational Resources Inc, pg 850
Emergency Film Group, pg 860
Green Mountain Post Films (GMP), pg 882
Heliotrope Studios, pg 887
Northern Light Productions, pg 959

MICHIGAN

K&R All Media Productions Inc, pg 908

MINNESOTA

House of Cinemagraphics, pg 891

MISSOURI

Fambrough & Associates Inc, pg 865

MONTANA

North Country Media Group, pg 959

NEW HAMPSHIRE

Apertura, pg 788

NEW MEXICO

Michael Dunn Productions, pg 853

NEW YORK

Ace Video, pg 774
Norman N Axelrod Associates, pg 800
Jack Morton Worldwide, pg 946
Shelly Palmer Production, pg 968
Peckham Productions Inc, pg 970
Zelman Studios Ltd, pg 1073

NORTH CAROLINA

Pat Appleson Studios Inc, pg 788
The Communications Group Inc, pg 833
Kino Mountain Productions LLC, pg 911
Moving Pictures, pg 948

OHIO

Creative Technology, pg 838
Take 1 Media Services, pg 1031

PENNSYLVANIA

FMP Media Solutions Inc, pg 870
Goodman Associates Inc, pg 880
Innovision Media Group, pg 899

Technical Research Program Rentals

Test Commercial Distributors

Test Commercial Producers

Theatrical Short Distributors

PROGRAMMING — FILM

Theatrical Short Distributors (continued)

NEW YORK (continued)

VIEW Inc (Video International Entertainment World Inc), pg 1058
Women Make Movies Inc, pg 1069

NORTH CAROLINA

Crystal Pictures Inc, pg 840

TENNESSEE

American Blackguard Inc, pg 784

VIRGINIA

CACI Productions Group, pg 816

WASHINGTON

White Rain Films Ltd, pg 1065

BRITISH COLUMBIA

Credo Interactive Inc, pg 839

ONTARIO

Canadian Filmmakers Distribution Center (CFMDC), pg 818
IMAX Corp, pg 896

QUEBEC

Les Productions Via Le Monde (Daniel Bertolino) Inc, pg 985

Theatrical Short Producers

ARKANSAS

Live'N'Loud, pg 923

CALIFORNIA

Animax, pg 787
Artichoke Productions, pg 791
Auslender Productions/Celestial Images, pg 797
Big Door, pg 807
Cinevest, pg 828
Classic Images, pg 829
Concrete Images, pg 835
Crystal Pyramid Productions™, pg 840
Custom Video Productions Inc, pg 841
Direct Cinema Ltd Inc, pg 848
FXF Productions Inc, pg 874
GAMfilm Productions, pg 875
imageReal Pictures LLC, pg 896
Jaguar Distribution Corp, pg 903
Main Street Media Inc, pg 929
Moving Art by Louie Schwartzberg, pg 947
New & Unique Videos™, pg 955
New Deal Studios, pg 955
Palardo Productions, pg 968
Point of View Productions, pg 977
QRS Software Services, pg 988
RetinaVision Productions, pg 995
Rhythm & Hues, pg 996
Glenn Roland Films, pg 998
Santa Barbara Location Services, pg 1002
SNAP, pg 1014
Tigar Hare Studios, pg 1040
Visual Communications - Southern California Asian American Studies Central Inc, pg 1059

COLORADO

The Cinema Lab, pg 827
Starwest Productions, pg 1024
Transtar Entertainment Co Inc, pg 1043

CONNECTICUT

ACM Productions Ltd, pg 774
Broadcast Video Productions LLC, pg 813
EagleVision Inc, pg 855
The Gary-Paul Agency, pg 875
MCC Films, pg 935

FLORIDA

Accord Productions, pg 773
Chatterbox Productions Inc, pg 824
CopShopMiami.com, pg 836
Courter Films LLC, pg 837
Home Shopping Network (HSN), pg 890
Jordan Klein Film & Video (JKFV), pg 906
Tel-Air Interests Inc, pg 1035

GEORGIA

Burst Video/Film Inc, pg 815
Guerrilla Productions LLC, pg 883
Myriad Productions, pg 951

HAWAII

Hyperspective Studios Inc, pg 893

ILLINOIS

ABS Enterprises, pg 772
Comtech Multimedia Marketing, pg 834
Film Police, pg 867
Winter Productions, pg 1068

INDIANA

Perennial Pictures Film Corp, pg 973

LOUISIANA

Moxie Media, pg 948

MARYLAND

Absolute Hollywood, pg 772
Richard Chisolm Cinematography, pg 825
dbF a Media Company, pg 844

MASSACHUSETTS

Green Mountain Post Films (GMP), pg 882
Heliotrope Studios, pg 887

MICHIGAN

K&R All Media Productions Inc, pg 908

MINNESOTA

House of Cinemagraphics, pg 891
Jamieson & Associates Inc, pg 904

MISSISSIPPI

Dollarhide Film Inc, pg 850

MISSOURI

Cable Films & Video, pg 816
Celebrities Productions, pg 822
Fambrough & Associates Inc, pg 865

MONTANA

North Country Media Group, pg 959

NEW HAMPSHIRE

Apertura, pg 788

NEW JERSEY

Bill Quinn Productions, pg 989

NEW MEXICO

Rainbow International Inc/Rainbow Productions Inc, pg 990

NEW YORK

aurora productions, pg 797
Blue Barn Pictures Inc, pg 809
Brian Film Productions LLC, pg 812
Brooklyn Films, pg 814
Thomas Craven Film Corp, pg 837
Florentine Films, pg 870
William Greaves Productions Inc, pg 882
Greyfalcon House, pg 882
HB-Content, pg 886
Kinetic Arts, pg 911
Neal Marshad Productions, pg 931
Jack Morton Worldwide, pg 946
Shelly Palmer Production, pg 968
Peckham Productions Inc, pg 970
Pennebaker Hegedus Films Inc, pg 972
Polestar Films & Associated Arts Ltd, pg 978
R/GA, pg 990
Richter Productions Inc, pg 996
Shadow Pictures Inc, pg 1007
Split Image Productions, pg 1021
Suggs Media Productions Inc, pg 1028
Third World Newsreel/Camera News Inc, pg 1039
VIEW Inc (Video International Entertainment World Inc), pg 1058
Zelman Studios Ltd, pg 1073

NORTH CAROLINA

The Communications Group Inc, pg 833
Crystal Pictures Inc, pg 840
Kino Mountain Productions LLC, pg 911
Trailblazer Studios®, pg 1043

OHIO

Creative Technology, pg 838

OREGON

Ideascape Inc, pg 894

PENNSYLVANIA

Innovision Media Group, pg 899
JPL, pg 906
Kensington Falls Animation, pg 909
Production Masters Inc (PMI), pg 984

RHODE ISLAND

Sound-FX-Design, pg 1017

TENNESSEE

American Blackguard Inc, pg 784

TEXAS

Biway Media, pg 808
Cerutti Productions Inc, pg 823

VIRGINIA

CACI Productions Group, pg 816
Metro Productions, pg 939

WEST VIRGINIA

Altruist Media LLC, pg 783

WISCONSIN

5th Floor Recording Co, pg 867
Wisconsin Public Television, pg 1068

WYOMING

Bridger Productions Inc, pg 812

ALBERTA

Black Media Works, pg 808
HBW Entertainment Inc, pg 886

MANITOBA

Lank/Beach Productions Inc, pg 916

ONTARIO

IMAX Corp, pg 896

QUEBEC

Kerrigan Productions Inc, pg 910
Les Productions Via Le Monde (Daniel Bertolino) Inc, pg 985

Theatrical Short Rentals

CALIFORNIA

Auslender Productions/Celestial Images, pg 797
Direct Cinema Ltd Inc, pg 848
Em Gee Film Library, pg 860
Glenn Photo Supply, pg 878
Palardo Productions, pg 968
Point of View Productions, pg 977
Visual Communications - Southern California Asian American Studies Central Inc, pg 1059

FLORIDA

Cifex Corp, pg 826

MISSOURI

Cable Films & Video, pg 816
University of Missouri-Columbia, pg 1050

NEW YORK

Circulating Film & Video Library, pg 828
Kino International Corp, pg 911
Pennebaker Hegedus Films Inc, pg 972
Richter Productions Inc, pg 996
Third World Newsreel/Camera News Inc, pg 1039
VIEW Inc (Video International Entertainment World Inc), pg 1058

NORTH CAROLINA

Crystal Pictures Inc, pg 840

PROGRAMMING — FILM

Training Program Distributors (continued)

WISCONSIN

Equiservices Publishing, pg 862

ONTARIO

Kineticvideo.com, pg 911

Training Program Producers

ALABAMA

Leo Ticheli Productions, pg 1040

ALASKA

Aurora Films, pg 797

ARIZONA

Candee Productions Inc, pg 819
Film Creations Ltd, pg 867
MediaWorks, pg 938
Metropolitan Audio-Visual Inc, pg 940
Phoenix VideoFilms®, pg 974
Tellens Inc, pg 1037

ARKANSAS

Jones Film Video, pg 906

CALIFORNIA

Aaron Marcus & Associates Inc, pg 772
AM Productions, pg 783
Animax, pg 787
Big Door, pg 807
Classic Images, pg 829
Concrete Images, pg 835
Crystal Pyramid Productions™, pg 840
Custom Video Productions Inc, pg 841
Design Media, pg 845
Dogma Studios, pg 850
Dolphin MultiMedia Inc, pg 850
Goal Productions, pg 879
Havas Edge, pg 885
imageReal Pictures LLC, pg 896
Jossey-Bass, pg 906
Kavich Reynolds Productions Inc, pg 908
The Kenwood Group, pg 909
KION-TV, pg 911
KTVU-Retail Services, pg 914
Main Street Media Inc, pg 929
The Media Staff Inc, pg 937
New & Unique Videos™, pg 955
New Circuit Films LLC, pg 955
ODC Publishing, pg 961
QRS Software Services, pg 988
RetinaVision Productions, pg 995
Glenn Roland Films, pg 998
SBS Productions, pg 1003
SNAP, pg 1014
Tam Communications Inc, pg 1031
Videografix LLC, pg 1057
Webster Communications, pg 1063

COLORADO

CSI Films, pg 840
Flashback Media Productions, pg 869
Inferno Film Productions LLC, pg 897
Transtar Entertainment Co Inc, pg 1043

CONNECTICUT

ACM Productions Ltd, pg 774
Broadcast Video Productions LLC, pg 813
The Gary-Paul Agency, pg 875
MCC Films, pg 935

DELAWARE

University Media Services, pg 1049

DISTRICT OF COLUMBIA

O'Keefe Communications Inc, pg 961

FLORIDA

Accord Productions, pg 773
Blackburst Entertainment, pg 808
Capital Communications Inc, pg 819
Communications Concepts Inc (CCI), pg 833
CopShopMiami.com, pg 836
Courter Films LLC, pg 837
Jordan Klein Film & Video (JKFV), pg 906
Motion Image Group LLC, pg 947
Video Techniques Inc, pg 1056

GEORGIA

Beachwood Productions, pg 804
COMPRO Productions Inc, pg 834
Continental Film & Video, pg 835
Guerrilla Productions LLC, pg 883
Myriad Productions, pg 951

HAWAII

Hyperspective Studios Inc, pg 893

ILLINOIS

ABSA Productions Inc, pg 772
Accenture, pg 773
CCH Inc, A Wolters Kluwer business, pg 821
Comtech Multimedia Marketing, pg 834
Film Police, pg 867
Manning Productions, pg 930
MIGHTYbYTES Inc, pg 942
National Safety Council (NSC), pg 953
SCI Television Productions LLC, pg 1004
Winter Productions, pg 1068

IOWA

The Production House, pg 984

KENTUCKY

Idle Minds Productions Inc, pg 894

LOUISIANA

Digital FX Inc, pg 847
Moxie Media, pg 948

MARYLAND

Absolute Hollywood, pg 772
The Ahern Group, pg 779
dbF a Media Company, pg 844

MASSACHUSETTS

CommCreative, pg 832
Documentary Educational Resources Inc, pg 850
Emergency Film Group, pg 860
Green Mountain Post Films (GMP), pg 882
Northern Light Productions, pg 959

MICHIGAN

K&R All Media Productions Inc, pg 908
Maritz Performance Improvement Co, pg 931

MINNESOTA

House of Cinemagraphics, pg 891

MISSISSIPPI

Dollarhide Film Inc, pg 850

MISSOURI

Fambrough & Associates Inc, pg 865
The Phoenix Learning Group Inc, pg 974

NEBRASKA

Dog & Pony Productions Inc, pg 850

NEVADA

DVDs4Less, pg 854

NEW HAMPSHIRE

Apertura, pg 788
Captain Fiddle Music & Publications, pg 820

NEW JERSEY

Broadcast Center Studios, pg 813
Concepts TV Production, pg 834
Half Moon Video Productions, pg 883
Selden Associates, pg 1006
Telemanagement Resources International Inc (TRI), pg 1036
Telequest Inc, pg 1036
TimeSteps Productions Inc, pg 1041

NEW MEXICO

Michael Dunn Productions, pg 853

NEW YORK

American Management Association International, pg 784
aurora productions, pg 797
Blue Barn Pictures Inc, pg 809
Broad Street Inc, pg 812
Karen Frankel Productions, pg 872
HB-Content, pg 886
Interactive International Inc, pg 899
Ketchum Pleon Change, pg 910
Neal Marshad Productions, pg 931
Jack Morton Worldwide, pg 946
News Broadcast Network, pg 956
Shelly Palmer Production, pg 968
Peckham Productions Inc, pg 970
Suggs Media Productions Inc, pg 1028
Zelman Studios Ltd, pg 1073

NORTH CAROLINA

Pat Appleson Studios Inc, pg 788
The Communications Group Inc, pg 833
Horizon Video Productions Inc, pg 891
Kino Mountain Productions LLC, pg 911
Unifour Productions Inc, pg 1048

OHIO

Creative Technology, pg 838
Take 1 Media Services, pg 1031

OREGON

Ideascape Inc, pg 894

PENNSYLVANIA

Bang Pictures, pg 802
FMP Media Solutions Inc, pg 870
Fusion Brand Experiences, pg 874
Goodman Associates Inc, pg 880
Innovision Media Group, pg 899
JPL, pg 906
Kensington Falls Animation, pg 909
Main Point Productions, pg 929
Muderick Media, pg 949
Video/Film Associates, pg 1055

RHODE ISLAND

Sound-FX-Design, pg 1017

TENNESSEE

American Blackguard Inc, pg 784
Continental Film, pg 835
Memphis Communications Corp, pg 938
Scripps Networks, pg 1005
Stage Post, pg 1022

TEXAS

Aries Productions, pg 789
Castleview Productions, pg 821
Cerutti Productions Inc, pg 823
CEV Multimedia Ltd, pg 823
The Editing Co, pg 857
Horizon Film + Video Productions, pg 891
Marx InDigital, pg 933
Earl Miller Productions Inc, pg 943
Romar Learning, pg 999
Stage Directions, pg 1022
Tecfilms Inc, pg 1033
Telemetrics International, pg 1036
University of Texas at Austin - Petroleum Extension Service, pg 1050

VIRGINIA

CACI Productions Group, pg 816
CALIBRE, pg 816
Metro Productions, pg 939

WASHINGTON

Adams Creative & Production Services, pg 775
North-by-Northwest Productions, pg 958

WEST VIRGINIA

Altruist Media LLC, pg 783

WISCONSIN

Audio Visual of Milwaukee Inc, pg 795
Equiservices Publishing, pg 862
5th Floor Recording Co, pg 867
Meridian Studios, pg 939
Wisconsin Public Television, pg 1068

Training Program Rentals

Travelog Distributors

Travelog Producers

PROGRAMMING — FILM

Travelog Producers (continued)

QUEBEC

Kerrigan Productions Inc, pg 910

Travelog Rentals

CALIFORNIA

Direct Cinema Ltd Inc, pg 848
Em Gee Film Library, pg 860
Glenn Photo Supply, pg 878

MISSOURI

University of Missouri-Columbia, pg 1050

NEW YORK

VIEW Inc (Video International Entertainment World Inc), pg 1058

OREGON

Wilderness Video, pg 1066

PENNSYLVANIA

Karol Media Inc, pg 908

Vocational Program Distributors

CALIFORNIA

Crystal Pyramid Productions™, pg 840
Direct Cinema Ltd Inc, pg 848
Increase Video/Silver Mine Video, pg 897
New & Unique Videos™, pg 955
Players Press, pg 977
The Wine Appreciation Guild Ltd, pg 1067

DELAWARE

University Media Services, pg 1049

FLORIDA

Capital Communications Inc, pg 819

GEORGIA

Convergent Media Systems, pg 836

ILLINOIS

Film Ideas, pg 867
National Safety Council (NSC), pg 953

MASSACHUSETTS

Emergency Film Group, pg 860

NEW MEXICO

National Information Center for Educational Media (NICEM)/MediaSleuth, pg 952

NEW YORK

Films Media Group, pg 868
Maryknoll Productions, pg 933
Penguin Audiobooks, pg 971
VIEW Inc (Video International Entertainment World Inc), pg 1058

PENNSYLVANIA

Bullfrog Films Inc, pg 815
FMP Media Solutions Inc, pg 870
Karol Media Inc, pg 908

TEXAS

CEV Multimedia Ltd, pg 823
University of Texas at Austin - Petroleum Extension Service, pg 1050

VIRGINIA

CACI Productions Group, pg 816

ONTARIO

Kineticvideo.com, pg 911

Vocational Program Producers

ALASKA

Aurora Films, pg 797

ARIZONA

MediaWorks, pg 938

CALIFORNIA

Aaron Marcus & Associates Inc, pg 772
Big Door, pg 807
Classic Images, pg 829
Crystal Pyramid Productions™, pg 840
imageReal Pictures LLC, pg 896
KION-TV, pg 911
Main Street Media Inc, pg 929
The Media Staff Inc, pg 937
New & Unique Videos™, pg 955
Players Press, pg 977
QRS Software Services, pg 988
Dick Reizner Film & Video, pg 994
Glenn Roland Films, pg 998
Santa Barbara Location Services, pg 1002
SBS Productions, pg 1003
SNAP, pg 1014
Webster Communications, pg 1063

COLORADO

Flashback Media Productions, pg 869

CONNECTICUT

Broadcast Video Productions LLC, pg 813
The Gary-Paul Agency, pg 875

DELAWARE

University Media Services, pg 1049

FLORIDA

Blackburst Entertainment, pg 808
Capital Communications Inc, pg 819
Civins Productions Inc, pg 828
CopShopMiami.com, pg 836
Courter Films LLC, pg 837
Jordan Klein Film & Video (JKFV), pg 906

GEORGIA

Beachwood Productions, pg 804
Continental Film & Video, pg 835
Guerrilla Productions LLC, pg 883

HAWAII

Hyperspective Studios Inc, pg 893

ILLINOIS

National Safety Council (NSC), pg 953

INDIANA

Road Pictures, pg 997

LOUISIANA

Moxie Media, pg 948

MARYLAND

Absolute Hollywood, pg 772
The Ahern Group, pg 779
dbF a Media Company, pg 844

MASSACHUSETTS

Emergency Film Group, pg 860

MICHIGAN

K&R All Media Productions Inc, pg 908

MINNESOTA

House of Cinemagraphics, pg 891

MISSOURI

Fambrough & Associates Inc, pg 865

MONTANA

North Country Media Group, pg 959

NEBRASKA

Dog & Pony Productions Inc, pg 850

NEW HAMPSHIRE

Apertura, pg 788

NEW JERSEY

Broadcast Center Studios, pg 813
Telequest Inc, pg 1036

NEW YORK

aurora productions, pg 797
Blue Barn Pictures Inc, pg 809
Films Media Group, pg 868
Neal Marshad Productions, pg 931
Maryknoll Productions, pg 933
Jack Morton Worldwide, pg 946
Shelly Palmer Production, pg 968
Pat Kogan Productions Inc, pg 970
Peckham Productions Inc, pg 970
Penguin Audiobooks, pg 971
VIEW Inc (Video International Entertainment World Inc), pg 1058
Zelman Studios Ltd, pg 1073

NORTH CAROLINA

Pat Appleson Studios Inc, pg 788
The Communications Group Inc, pg 833
Kino Mountain Productions LLC, pg 911
Unifour Productions Inc, pg 1048

OHIO

Take 1 Media Services, pg 1031

OREGON

Ideascape Inc, pg 894

PENNSYLVANIA

FMP Media Solutions Inc, pg 870
JPL, pg 906

RHODE ISLAND

Sound-FX-Design, pg 1017

TENNESSEE

Continental Film, pg 835
Memphis Communications Corp, pg 938

TEXAS

Cerutti Productions Inc, pg 823
CEV Multimedia Ltd, pg 823
The Editing Co, pg 857
Horizon Film + Video Productions, pg 891
Earl Miller Productions Inc, pg 943
University of Texas at Austin - Petroleum Extension Service, pg 1050

VIRGINIA

CACI Productions Group, pg 816
Metro Productions, pg 939

WEST VIRGINIA

Altruist Media LLC, pg 783

WISCONSIN

5th Floor Recording Co, pg 867
Wisconsin Public Television, pg 1068

WYOMING

Bridger Productions Inc, pg 812

ALBERTA

Global Television Station, pg 879

QUEBEC

Kerrigan Productions Inc, pg 910

Vocational Program Rentals

CALIFORNIA

Direct Cinema Ltd Inc, pg 848

DELAWARE

University Media Services, pg 1049

GEORGIA

Convergent Media Systems, pg 836

ILLINOIS

National Safety Council (NSC), pg 953

MASSACHUSETTS

Emergency Film Group, pg 860

MISSOURI

University of Missouri-Columbia, pg 1050

NEW YORK

Films Media Group, pg 868

PENNSYLVANIA

Bullfrog Films Inc, pg 815

PROGRAMMING — VIDEO

Animated Television Commercials, *see* Television Commercial—Animated

Business Program Distributors

ARIZONA

CyberIconics International, pg 841
Video Learning Library, pg 1055

CALIFORNIA

Chesney Communications, pg 824
Crystal Pyramid Productions™, pg 840
Custom Video Productions Inc, pg 841
Direct Cinema Ltd Inc, pg 848
Discovery Education - Los Angeles, pg 848
411 Video Information, pg 872
Increase Video/Silver Mine Video, pg 897
Jossey-Bass, pg 906
Kantola Productions LLC, pg 908
KPBS TV FM-San Diego, pg 913
Learning Communications LLC, pg 917
New & Unique Videos™, pg 955
ODC Publishing, pg 961
People Skills International, pg 972
Melvin Powers Television Marketing, pg 979
Pyramid Media, pg 987
QCI International, pg 988
Sonoma Valley Chamber of Commerce, pg 1016
Thinking Allowed Productions, pg 1038
TMW Media Group, pg 1041
University of Southern California, pg 1050
Valley Media, pg 1051

COLORADO

Jeppesen, pg 905

CONNECTICUT

Book Marketing Works LLC, pg 810

FLORIDA

ACE Video Resources Software, pg 774
Capital Communications Inc, pg 819
Liberty Publishing Co Inc, pg 919
ThirdWave Learning Inc, pg 1039

GEORGIA

Convergent Media Systems, pg 836
LYRASIS, pg 927
School Media Associates LLC, pg 1004
Thompson-Mitchell & Associates Inc, pg 1039

ILLINOIS

ABSA Productions Inc, pg 772
CCH Continuing Education, pg 821
CCH Inc, A Wolters Kluwer business, pg 821
CCore Media Inc, pg 821
Centrax Corp, pg 823
Chicago Satellite & Video, pg 825
Film Ideas, pg 867
Moviecraft Inc, pg 947
Nightingale-Conant Corp, pg 957
Questar Inc, pg 989

INDIANA

Educational Video Group Inc, pg 857

KENTUCKY

KET The Kentucky Network, pg 910
WaxWorks VideoWorks, pg 1063

MARYLAND

Total AV Systems, pg 1042

MASSACHUSETTS

Commonwealth Films Inc, pg 832
Emergency Film Group, pg 860
Enterprise Media LLC, pg 861
Merrimack Films, pg 939
Penfield Productions Ltd, pg 971

MICHIGAN

Digi Sign Design LLC, pg 847
Emery-Pratt Co, pg 860
MSU Technologies, pg 949
The Program Source International, pg 985
Society of Manufacturing Engineers (SME), pg 1015

MINNESOTA

JIST Publishing, pg 905
Service Quality Institute, pg 1007

MISSOURI

Phoenix/BFA/Coronet, pg 974
The Phoenix Learning Group Inc, pg 974

NEBRASKA

B & B Video Productions Inc, pg 801

NEVADA

Aardvark Video & Media Productions, pg 772
DVDs4Less, pg 854

NEW HAMPSHIRE

Channell One Video, pg 824
Frey Scientific, pg 873
Chip Taylor Communications LLC, pg 1032

NEW JERSEY

Euro-Pacific Film & Video Productions Inc, pg 863
MIB Mediaworks, pg 941
SES World Skies, pg 1007

NEW MEXICO

National Information Center for Educational Media (NICEM)/MediaSleuth, pg 952

NEW YORK

American Management Association®, pg 784
Broad Street Inc, pg 812
De Nonno Productions Inc (DPI), pg 844
Films for the Humanities & Sciences, pg 868
Films Media Group, pg 868
Guidance Associates Inc Center for Humanities, pg 883
HB-Content, pg 886
Loftin Productions, pg 924
Mastervision Inc, pg 933
Meridian Education Corp, pg 939
MRG Productions Inc, pg 948
Practising Law Institute, pg 980
Richter Productions Inc, pg 996
Shopware, pg 1009
Synaptic Digital, pg 1030
Video Catalogue Co Inc, pg 1054
VIEW Inc (Video International Entertainment World Inc), pg 1058

NORTH CAROLINA

Baker & Taylor Inc, pg 801
Crystal Pictures Inc, pg 840
Eli Research Group, pg 859
Vide-O-Go/That's Infotainment!, pg 1054

OHIO

Curtis Inc, pg 841
South-Western Publishing Co, pg 1019

OREGON

InterVision Media, pg 902
The Keyboard Workshop, pg 910

PENNSYLVANIA

Beholder Productions Inc, pg 804
FMP Media Solutions Inc, pg 870
Karol Media Inc, pg 908
Library Video Company, pg 920
Movies Unlimited, pg 947
S I Video Sales Group, pg 1001

SOUTH CAROLINA

American Production Services LLC, pg 785

TENNESSEE

National School Products, pg 953
Zion Music Group, pg 1074

TEXAS

CEV Multimedia Ltd, pg 823
Dallas Learning Solutions, pg 842
Educational Video Network, pg 857

VERMONT

Perceptions Inc, pg 973
University of Vermont, Instructional Television Dept, pg 1050
Wilson McLeran Inc, pg 1067

VIRGINIA

CACI Productions Group, pg 816
WETA Production Center, pg 1064

WASHINGTON

AEON Communications Inc, pg 778
Bennett-Watt HD Productions Inc, pg 805
Intermedia Inc, pg 900
Media Resources Inc, pg 937

WEST VIRGINIA

Sweetsong Productions, pg 1029

ONTARIO

Canadian Learning Co Inc, pg 818
Kineticvideo.com, pg 911
McIntyre Media Inc, pg 935
McNabb & Connolly, pg 935

Business Program Producers

ALABAMA

CMEInfo, pg 830
Media Visions Inc, pg 937
Leo Ticheli Productions, pg 1040

ALASKA

Aurora Films, pg 797

ARIZONA

Aardvark Productions LLC, pg 772
American Audio Visual Center, pg 783
Candee Productions Inc, pg 819
Creative Backstage, pg 838
CyberIconics International, pg 841
Direct Current Video Productions, pg 848
Fox 10 Productions (KSAZ-TV), pg 872
MediaWorks, pg 938
Metropolitan Audio-Visual Inc, pg 940
On-Site Video, pg 963
Phoenix VideoFilms®, pg 974
Tellens Inc, pg 1037
Video Media Productions (VMP), pg 1055

ARKANSAS

Cedar Crest Studio, pg 822
Jones Film Video, pg 906

CALIFORNIA

Access Video in Berkeley, pg 773
Action Video, pg 775
Animax, pg 787
Artichoke Productions, pg 791
Barbosa Video Services, pg 802
Big Door, pg 807
Cavalcade Productions Inc, pg 821
Chesney Communications, pg 824
Classic Images, pg 829
Coastline Productions, pg 831
Cox Media, pg 837
Crystal Pyramid Productions™, pg 840
Custom Video Productions Inc, pg 841
Digital Outpost, pg 847
Direct Images Interactive Inc, pg 848
Discovery Education - Los Angeles, pg 848
Dogma Studios, pg 850
Dolphin MultiMedia Inc, pg 850
Face Digital Post, pg 865
First Camera, pg 868
Goal Productions, pg 879
Havas Edge, pg 885
imageReal Pictures LLC, pg 896
Imageworks, pg 896
ITV Productions, pg 903
Jossey-Bass, pg 906

PROGRAMMING — VIDEO

Business Program Producers (continued)

MONTANA

North Country Media Group, pg 959

NEBRASKA

B & B Video Productions Inc, pg 801
Dog & Pony Productions Inc, pg 850
Envision Communications Inc, pg 861
Rainbow Video Productions Inc, pg 991

NEVADA

Aardvark Video & Media Productions, pg 772
DVDs4Less, pg 854
Encore Productions Inc, pg 861
HDTV Productions Inc, pg 886
JCS Video Productions, pg 904
Skyfire Video, pg 1013
Tanglewood Productions, pg 1031

NEW HAMPSHIRE

Apertura, pg 788
Channell One Video, pg 824
Chip Taylor Communications LLC, pg 1032
The Troupe, pg 1045

NEW JERSEY

Broadcast Center Studios, pg 813
CFP Video Productions Inc, pg 823
DWJ Television, pg 854
Euro-Pacific Film & Video Productions Inc, pg 863
Half Moon Video Productions, pg 883
Laurel Video Productions, pg 916
MediaNow, pg 938
Megavideo Productions, pg 938
MIB Mediaworks, pg 941
Ray Mueller Productions, pg 949
Optisonics Productions, pg 965
Producer East Productions, pg 983
Public Eye Productions, pg 987
Bill Quinn Productions, pg 989
Reider Photography & Video Productions, pg 994
Suede Interactive, pg 1027
Telequest Inc, pg 1036
TimeSteps Productions Inc, pg 1041
VCSvideo, pg 1052
VTS Video & Media, pg 1061

NEW MEXICO

Michael Dunn Productions, pg 853
Production Outfitters, pg 984
Rainbow International Inc/Rainbow Productions Inc, pg 990

NEW YORK

Ace Video, pg 774
American Management Association®, pg 784
Associated Press Television News, pg 792
aurora productions, pg 797
Blue Barn Pictures Inc, pg 809
Brian Film Productions LLC, pg 812
Broad Street Inc, pg 812
Charlex Inc, pg 824
Cohn Creative Group LLC, pg 831
De Nonno Productions Inc (DPI), pg 844
Duplication Depot Inc, pg 853
Fanlight Productions, pg 865
Films Media Group, pg 868
Florentine Films, pg 870
Karen Frankel Productions, pg 872
Guidance Associates Inc Center for Humanities, pg 883
Havas Worldwide, pg 886
HB-Content, pg 886
Hello World Communications, pg 888
Image Zone Inc, pg 896
Ketchum Pleon Change, pg 910
L A Bruell Inc, pg 914
Long Island Video Enterprises Live Inc, pg 924
Neal Marshad Productions, pg 931
Mastervision Inc, pg 933
Jack Morton Worldwide, pg 946
MRG Productions Inc, pg 948
MRM Worldwide, pg 948
MRY, pg 949
New Horizon Studios, pg 955
News Broadcast Network, pg 956
Northeast Video Productions Inc, pg 959
NSR Productions Inc & Capricorn Five Films, pg 960
Shelly Palmer Production, pg 968
Pat Kogan Productions Inc, pg 970
Peckham Productions Inc, pg 970
Polestar Films & Associated Arts Ltd, pg 978
Practising Law Institute, pg 980
PrimaLux Video Inc, pg 982
PrimeLight Productions Inc, pg 982
Richter Productions Inc, pg 996
Spoken Arts Inc, pg 1021
Suggs Media Productions Inc, pg 1028
Synaptic Digital, pg 1030
TBA Global Events, pg 1032
TeleTime Productions, pg 1036
Video Catalogue Co Inc, pg 1054
VIEW Inc (Video International Entertainment World Inc), pg 1058
Alan Weiss Productions, pg 1063
WNET/NET TELECON, pg 1069
Zelman Studios Ltd, pg 1073

NORTH CAROLINA

All Pro Media Inc, pg 780
Pat Appleson Studios Inc, pg 788
J Arnold Productions Inc, pg 790
Bill Barnes Video Productions LLC, pg 803
The Communications Group Inc, pg 833
Eli Research Group, pg 859
Kino Mountain Productions LLC, pg 911
LCW Productions LLC, pg 917
Moving Pictures, pg 948
Sinclair Institute, pg 1012
Unifour Productions Inc, pg 1048

OHIO

Advent Media Inc, pg 778
Russ Beckner Pictures, pg 804
CET, pg 823
Commercial Video, pg 832
Creative Technology, pg 838
Curtis Inc, pg 841
EDR Media LLC, pg 857
Electronic Vision Inc (EV), pg 859
Image Video Teleproductions Inc, pg 895
Lyon Video Inc, pg 927
MainSail Production Services Inc, pg 929
South-Western Publishing Co, pg 1019
Take 1 Media Services, pg 1031
Treehaus Communications Inc, pg 1044
VGI Productions, pg 1053
Vista Color Imaging Inc, pg 1059

OKLAHOMA

Institute for Teaching & Learning Excellence (ITLE), pg 899

OREGON

A KTVA Production LLC, pg 771
Creative Media Development, pg 838
ERA Learning, pg 862
InterVision Media, pg 902
The Keyboard Workshop, pg 910
KPDX-TV Production Center, pg 913
KVAL, pg 914
Odyssey Productions Inc, pg 961
Production West, pg 985
Rex, pg 995

PENNSYLVANIA

AiH Group Inc, pg 779
Audio Visual Communications Inc, pg 795
Bang Pictures, pg 802
Beholder Productions Inc, pg 804
CCI Communications Inc, pg 821
FMP Media Solutions Inc, pg 870
Goodman Associates Inc, pg 880
JPL, pg 906
Main Point Productions, pg 929
Muderick Media, pg 949
Panta Rhei Media Inc, pg 968
Pemcor LLC, pg 971
Production Masters Inc (PMI), pg 984
Video Communication Productions Inc, pg 1054
Video/Film Associates, pg 1055
The Videohouse Inc, pg 1057
Visual Sound Inc, pg 1059
WHYY Inc, pg 1066

RHODE ISLAND

Sound-FX-Design, pg 1017

SOUTH CAROLINA

American Production Services LLC, pg 785
Encore Video Productions, pg 861
Go To Team, pg 879
Stages Video Productions, pg 1023
Venture Media, pg 1052

TENNESSEE

Continental Film, pg 835
Jaguar Productions, pg 903
Memphis Communications Corp, pg 938
Paradigm Marketing & Creative, pg 969
Running Pony Productions LLC, pg 1000
Scripps Networks, pg 1005

TEXAS

Alpha Video Productions, pg 782
AMS Pictures, pg 786
Biway Media, pg 808
Castleview Productions, pg 821
Cerutti Productions Inc, pg 823
CEV Multimedia Ltd, pg 823
Communication Arts Multimedia Inc, pg 832
Countdown Productions Inc, pg 837
Dallas Learning Solutions, pg 842
Dub King, pg 853
Dykeman Associates Inc, pg 854
The Editing Co, pg 857
Educational Video Network, pg 857
Horizon Film + Video Productions, pg 891
J&S Audio Visual Inc, pg 904
Marx InDigital, pg 933
Matson Multi-Media, pg 934
Mediaforce Productions, pg 937
Earl Miller Productions Inc, pg 943
Julye Newlin Productions Inc, pg 956
Omega Productions, pg 962
Omni Intercommunications Inc, pg 962
Richie Media Productions LLC, pg 996
South Coast Film & Video, pg 1019
Sportsmen on Film Inc, pg 1021
Stage Directions, pg 1022
Tecfilms Inc, pg 1033

VERMONT

Marlboro Film & Video Productions, pg 931
Perceptions Inc, pg 973
University of Vermont, Instructional Television Dept, pg 1050
Wilson McLeran Inc, pg 1067

VIRGINIA

Advance Concepts Inc, pg 777
BES Studios, pg 805
CALIBRE, pg 816
Cinebar Productions Inc, pg 826
Creative Video of Washington Inc, pg 839
D&B Television & Video Productions Inc, pg 842
Gingerbread Productions, pg 878
Limelight Communications Inc, pg 921
Metro Productions, pg 939
National Media Services Inc, pg 953
Rocktown Media, pg 998
Video Solutions, pg 1056
WETA Production Center, pg 1064

WASHINGTON

Adams Creative & Production Services, pg 775
Bennett-Watt HD Productions Inc, pg 805
Global Net Productions Inc, pg 879
Intermedia Inc, pg 900
Media Resources Inc, pg 937
Pal Productions Inc, pg 967
Victory Studios, pg 1054

WEST VIRGINIA

Altruist Media LLC, pg 783

WISCONSIN

Audio Visual of Milwaukee Inc, pg 795
AVS Group, pg 800
Grassland Media Inc, pg 881
Media Communications Association-International (MCA-I), pg 936
Meridian Studios, pg 939

Midland Video Productions Inc, pg 942
ProVideo, pg 986
Rucinski & Reetz Communications LLC, pg 1000
University of Wisconsin-Oshkosh Radio-TV-Film Dept, pg 1050
USAV Group Inc, pg 1050
Video Wisconsin Inc, pg 1056
Watts Communications Inc, pg 1062
Wisconsin Public Television, pg 1068

WYOMING

Bridger Productions Inc, pg 812

ALBERTA

Global Television Station, pg 879
HBW Entertainment Inc, pg 886

BRITISH COLUMBIA

Triad Communications Ltd, pg 1044

MANITOBA

Spectra Video Productions Ltd, pg 1020

ONTARIO

ADS Media, pg 777
DebsVoice, pg 844
Image Video Services & Productions, pg 895
Jams Productions Inc, pg 904
JFB Communications, pg 905
Mediaimage Communications Group, pg 937
RB Productions, pg 992
Shaw Street Productions, pg 1008
Video Advantage, pg 1054
Video Excellence Productions, pg 1055

QUEBEC

Kerrigan Productions Inc, pg 910

SASKATCHEWAN

plan9films, pg 976

Business Program Rentals

ARIZONA

Video Learning Library, pg 1055

CALIFORNIA

Direct Cinema Ltd Inc, pg 848
Jossey-Bass, pg 906
Learning Communications LLC, pg 917
University of Southern California, pg 1050

GEORGIA

Convergent Media Systems, pg 836

ILLINOIS

1st Financial Training Services Inc, pg 868

MASSACHUSETTS

Commonwealth Films Inc, pg 832
Emergency Film Group, pg 860
Enterprise Media LLC, pg 861
Merrimack Films, pg 939

MICHIGAN

Digi Sign Design LLC, pg 847

MINNESOTA

Service Quality Institute, pg 1007

MISSOURI

The Phoenix Learning Group Inc, pg 974
University of Missouri-Columbia, pg 1050

NEW JERSEY

Euro-Pacific Film & Video Productions Inc, pg 863

NEW YORK

Films for the Humanities & Sciences, pg 868
Films Media Group, pg 868
Richter Productions Inc, pg 996
TBA Global Events, pg 1032
VIEW Inc (Video International Entertainment World Inc), pg 1058

OREGON

The Keyboard Workshop, pg 910

VERMONT

University of Vermont, Instructional Television Dept, pg 1050

ONTARIO

Kineticvideo.com, pg 911
McNabb & Connolly, pg 935

Cable TV Program Distributors

ALABAMA

Eternal Word Television Network (EWTN), pg 862

ARIZONA

Arizona Cine Equipment, pg 789

ARKANSAS

Mullikin Agency, pg 949

CALIFORNIA

Ametron Audio/Video, pg 785
Barbosa Video Services, pg 802
Custom Video Productions Inc, pg 841
411 Video Information, pg 872
Hope Productions, pg 891
Krishnamurti Foundation of America, pg 913
Lions Gate Entertainment Corp, pg 922
National Lampoon, pg 953
New & Unique Videos™, pg 955
Players Press, pg 977
Prime Cut Productions, pg 982
Pyramid Media, pg 987
Rhino Home Video, pg 996
Western Instructional Television Inc, pg 1064

COLORADO

Apogee Communications Group, pg 788

CONNECTICUT

ESPN Inc, pg 862

FLORIDA

Capital Communications Inc, pg 819
Lighting Sales Connections, pg 920

GEORGIA

Turner Broadcasting System Inc, pg 1046

ILLINOIS

Chicago Satellite & Video, pg 825
Communications Corporation of America, pg 833
Moviecraft Inc, pg 947

INDIANA

Communication Ministries, pg 833

IOWA

Right Stuf Inc, pg 997

KENTUCKY

Media Resources, pg 937
Northern Kentucky University, pg 959

MARYLAND

Recorded Books LLC, pg 993
Total AV Systems, pg 1042

MASSACHUSETTS

Documentary Educational Resources Inc, pg 850

MICHIGAN

Digi Sign Design LLC, pg 847

MINNESOTA

American Choral Catalog Ltd, pg 784
Jamieson & Associates Inc, pg 904

MISSOURI

Cable Films & Video, pg 816
Phoenix/BFA/Coronet, pg 974

NEVADA

Aardvark Video & Media Productions, pg 772
DVDs4Less, pg 854

NEW HAMPSHIRE

Channell One Video, pg 824
Chip Taylor Communications LLC, pg 1032

NEW JERSEY

Alden Films, pg 780
Films of the Nations, pg 868
MIB Mediaworks, pg 941
SES World Skies, pg 1007

NEW YORK

A&E Home Video, pg 771
A&E Television Networks LLC, pg 771
ATA Trading Corp/Favorite TV Inc, pg 792
Custom Media Environments, pg 841
HB-Content, pg 886
Lifetime Television®, pg 920
Mastervision Inc, pg 933
MRG Productions Inc, pg 948
Showtime Networks Inc, pg 1010
SISU Home Entertainment Inc, pg 1012
Third World Newsreel/Camera News Inc, pg 1039
Time Warner Cable Business Class, pg 1040
VIEW Inc (Video International Entertainment World Inc), pg 1058

NORTH DAKOTA

UND Television Center, pg 1048

OHIO

VGI Productions, pg 1053

PENNSYLVANIA

AccuWeather Inc, pg 774

TENNESSEE

American Blackguard Inc, pg 784
Center for Southern Folklore Inc, pg 822
Marine Geographic, pg 931
Zion Music Group, pg 1074

TEXAS

Lamb & Lion Ministries, pg 915
Marengo Films, pg 931

WASHINGTON

Bennett-Watt HD Productions Inc, pg 805
Victory Studios, pg 1054

WISCONSIN

Wisconsin Public Television, pg 1068

BRITISH COLUMBIA

Picture Box Distribution Inc, pg 975

QUEBEC

Whalley-Abbey Media Holdings Inc, pg 1065

Cable TV Program Producers

ALABAMA

Eternal Word Television Network (EWTN), pg 862

ARIZONA

Aardvark Productions LLC, pg 772
Direct Current Video Productions, pg 848

ARKANSAS

Jones Film Video, pg 906
Live'N'Loud, pg 923
Mullikin Agency, pg 949

CALIFORNIA

Action Video, pg 775
Animax, pg 787
Barbosa Video Services, pg 802
Big Door, pg 807
Burrud Productions Inc, pg 815
Custom Video Productions Inc, pg 841

PROGRAMMING — VIDEO

Cable TV Program Producers (continued)

Cable TV Program Rentals

Children's Program Distributors

PROGRAMMING — VIDEO

Children's Program Distributors (continued)

NEW YORK (continued)

Mastervision Inc, pg 933
Price Stern Sloan, pg 981
Random House Children's Books, pg 991
Scholastic Media, pg 1004
Select Media Inc, pg 1006
SISU Home Entertainment Inc, pg 1012
Spoken Arts Inc, pg 1021
Synaptic Digital, pg 1030
Third World Newsreel/Camera News Inc, pg 1039
Video Aided Instruction Inc, pg 1054
VIEW Inc (Video International Entertainment World Inc), pg 1058
White Buffalo Multimedia, pg 1065

NORTH CAROLINA

Baker & Taylor Inc, pg 801
Crystal Pictures Inc, pg 840
Ladyslipper Inc, pg 915
Vide-O-Go/That's Infotainment!, pg 1054

OHIO

Alegra House Publishers, pg 780
Curtis Inc, pg 841
Treehaus Communications Inc, pg 1044

OREGON

Encounter Video Inc, pg 861
International Loving Touch Foundation Inc, pg 901
InterVision Media, pg 902
Memory Lane Videos, pg 938
Nostalgia Family Video Inc, pg 959
Sugar Mountain PR, pg 1028

PENNSYLVANIA

Anchor Distributors, pg 786
Beholder Productions Inc, pg 804
Bullfrog Films Inc, pg 815
Corinth Films Inc, pg 836
Discovery Education - South Burlington, pg 848
Karol Media Inc, pg 908
Library Video Company, pg 920
Movies Unlimited, pg 947
MVD Entertainment Group, pg 951
Red Fox Enterprises, pg 993
The Fred Rogers Co, pg 998
S I Video Sales Group, pg 1001
Schlessinger Media, pg 1004
Vision Video, pg 1058
The Whale Video Co, pg 1065

SOUTH CAROLINA

American Production Services LLC, pg 785
BJU Press, pg 808

TENNESSEE

Abingdon Press, pg 772
American Blackguard Inc, pg 784
Cokesbury, pg 831
EMI CMG Distribution, pg 860
National School Products, pg 953
Randall House Publications, pg 991
Spring Arbor Distributors, pg 1022
Word Label Group, pg 1069

TEXAS

Big Kids Productions Inc, pg 807
Educational Video Network, pg 857
Horizon Film + Video Productions, pg 891
Marengo Films, pg 931
Shadow Play Records & Video, pg 1007

VERMONT

Perceptions Inc, pg 973
University of Vermont, Instructional Television Dept, pg 1050

WASHINGTON

ChristianAnswers.Net™, pg 825
Intermedia Inc, pg 900
John McLean Media, pg 905
Victory Studios, pg 1054

WEST VIRGINIA

Focus on Animals, pg 870
Sweetsong Productions, pg 1029

WISCONSIN

Aylmer Press, pg 801
Knowledge Unlimited Inc, pg 912
NEWIST/CESA 7, pg 956
Wisconsin Public Television, pg 1068

ALBERTA

Global Television Station, pg 879

BRITISH COLUMBIA

Picture Box Distribution Inc, pg 975
Thompson Rivers University Open Learning, pg 1039

ONTARIO

BFS Entertainment & Multimedia Limited, pg 806
Broughton's Church Supplies, Religious Books & Gifts, pg 814
Cambium Catalyst International (CCI), pg 817
Canadian Filmmakers Distribution Center (CFMDC), pg 818
Canadian Learning Co Inc, pg 818
Canamedia Inc, pg 818
The Children's Book Store Distribution (CBSD), pg 825
Kineticvideo.com, pg 911
Life Cycle Books Ltd, pg 920
McIntyre Media Inc, pg 935
McNabb & Connolly, pg 935
Sullivan Home Entertainment, pg 1028
Universal Studios Canada Inc, pg 1049

QUEBEC

Les Productions Via Le Monde (Daniel Bertolino) Inc, pg 985

Children's Program Producers

ALASKA

Alaska Video Postcards Inc, pg 779

ARIZONA

Aardvark Productions LLC, pg 772
Candee Productions Inc, pg 819
MediaWorks, pg 938
Tellens Inc, pg 1037

CALIFORNIA

Action Video, pg 775
Allied Artists International Inc, pg 781
Animax, pg 787
Barbosa Video Services, pg 802
Big Door, pg 807
Burrud Productions Inc, pg 815
C & M Publishing Co, pg 816
California Language Laboratories, pg 817
Chesney Communications, pg 824
Classic Images, pg 829
Concept Associates Inc, pg 834
Cox Media, pg 837
Crystal Productions, pg 840
Crystal Pyramid Productions™, pg 840
Custom Video Productions Inc, pg 841
Digital Media West, pg 847
Discovery Education - Los Angeles, pg 848
Dogma Studios, pg 850
Face Digital Post, pg 865
Glenray Productions Inc, pg 878
Increase Video/Silver Mine Video, pg 897
ITV Productions, pg 903
Joyce Media Inc, pg 906
KION-TV, pg 911
Lightyear Entertainment, pg 921
Live Wire Media, pg 923
Ludlow Media Solutions, pg 926
Main Street Media Inc, pg 929
MarVista Entertainment Inc, pg 933
Maximus Media Inc, pg 934
McCune Audio-Video-Lighting, pg 935
Media Magic, pg 937
The Media Staff Inc, pg 937
Mist Media Inc, pg 944
monterey media inc, pg 945
Moose School Productions, pg 946
Music Rhapsody, pg 951
New & Unique Videos™, pg 955
ODC Publishing, pg 961
Players Press, pg 977
Pyramid Media, pg 987
Regent Press Publishers & Printers, pg 994
Glenn Roland Films, pg 998
Russ InVision Co/AbridgeClub.com, pg 1001
Saturn Studios, pg 1003
Screen Door Entertainment Inc, pg 1005
Sea Studios Foundation, pg 1005
SNAP, pg 1014
Staylor-Made Communications Inc, pg 1024
Still N'Motion, pg 1025
Tam Communications Inc, pg 1031
Tigar Hare Studios, pg 1040
TMW Media Group, pg 1041
Toon Makers, pg 1042
Total Media Group, pg 1042
TVA Productions, pg 1046
Twin Peaks Creative, pg 1047
Universal Studios Home Entertainment, pg 1049
Videowerks, pg 1057
Vineyard Video & Photography, pg 1058
Visual Communications - Southern California Asian American Studies Central Inc, pg 1059
Webster Communications, pg 1063
Xenon Pictures Inc, pg 1071
Zamacona Productions, pg 1073

COLORADO

Apogee Communications Group, pg 788
Centre Communications Inc, pg 823
CSI Films, pg 840
Flashback Media Productions, pg 869
Gaiam Inc, pg 875
InJoy Birth & Parenting Education, pg 898
Transtar Entertainment Co Inc, pg 1043

CONNECTICUT

ACM Productions Ltd, pg 774
Applebox Studio, pg 788
Broadcast Video Productions LLC, pg 813
Fox Connecticut, pg 872
Geomatrix Productions, pg 877
Ironik Design & Post, pg 902
MCC Films, pg 935
Twenty-Third Publications/Bayard, pg 1047
Weston Woods Studios Inc, pg 1064

DELAWARE

So Smart Productions, pg 1015

DISTRICT OF COLUMBIA

Durrin Productions Inc, pg 854
Hillmann & Carr Inc, pg 889
Systems Impact Inc, pg 1031

FLORIDA

Accel Video Productions, pg 773
ACE Video Resources Software, pg 774
Blackburst Entertainment, pg 808
Chatterbox Productions Inc, pg 824
Civins Productions Inc, pg 828
Courter Films LLC, pg 837
Ed Ethridge Productions Inc, pg 863
Global Cyber-Visions, pg 879
Jordan Klein Film & Video (JKFV), pg 906
National Teleproductions Inc, pg 953
Paradise Video & Film, pg 969
Sunfire Communications Inc, pg 1028
Sunrise Studios, pg 1028
Tricycle Studios, pg 1044

GEORGIA

Beachwood Productions, pg 804
Burst Video/Film Inc, pg 815
Gingerbread Group, pg 878
Guerrilla Productions LLC, pg 883
Little Mammoth Media, pg 923
Malcolm Neal Productions, pg 954
On-Line Productions, pg 963

HAWAII

Hyperspective Studios Inc, pg 893

IDAHO

Brad Shaw Productions Inc, pg 1008
Wide Eye Productions, pg 1066

PROGRAMMING — VIDEO

Children's Program Producers (continued)

TEXAS (continued)

Shadow Play Records & Video, pg 1007
South Coast Film & Video, pg 1019

VERMONT

Marlboro Film & Video Productions, pg 931
Perceptions Inc, pg 973
University of Vermont, Instructional Television Dept, pg 1050

VIRGINIA

BES Studios, pg 805
D&B Television & Video Productions Inc, pg 842
Gingerbread Productions, pg 878
Limelight Communications Inc, pg 921
Rocktown Media, pg 998
Video Solutions, pg 1056

WASHINGTON

ChristianAnswers.Net™, pg 825
Global Net Productions Inc, pg 879
Pal Productions Inc, pg 967

WEST VIRGINIA

Sweetsong Productions, pg 1029

WISCONSIN

Aylmer Press, pg 801
Midland Video Productions Inc, pg 942
NEWIST/CESA 7, pg 956
ProVideo, pg 986
Watts Communications Inc, pg 1062
Wisconsin Public Television, pg 1068

WYOMING

Bridger Productions Inc, pg 812

ALBERTA

Global Television Station, pg 879
HBW Entertainment Inc, pg 886

BRITISH COLUMBIA

Thompson Rivers University Open Learning, pg 1039
Triad Communications Ltd, pg 1044

MANITOBA

Spectra Video Productions Ltd, pg 1020

ONTARIO

ADS Media, pg 777
Canamedia Inc, pg 818
Jams Productions Inc, pg 904
Marblemedia, pg 930
Mediaimage Communications Group, pg 937
Weston Woods Canada, pg 1064

QUEBEC

Kerrigan Productions Inc, pg 910
Les Productions Via Le Monde (Daniel Bertolino) Inc, pg 985

SASKATCHEWAN

plan9films, pg 976

Children's Program Rentals

ARIZONA

Video Learning Library, pg 1055

CALIFORNIA

Direct Cinema Ltd Inc, pg 848
Visual Communications - Southern California Asian American Studies Central Inc, pg 1059

DISTRICT OF COLUMBIA

Durrin Productions Inc, pg 854

ILLINOIS

Discovery Education - Chicago, pg 848
Facets Multi-Media Inc, pg 865

INDIANA

Agency for Instructional Technology (AIT), pg 778
InterComm, pg 900

MASSACHUSETTS

Pauline Books & Media, pg 970

MICHIGAN

Digi Sign Design LLC, pg 847

MISSOURI

Cable Films & Video, pg 816
University of Missouri-Columbia, pg 1050

NEBRASKA

Vision Maker Media, pg 1058

NEW YORK

Brooklyn Botanic Garden, pg 814
Hallel Communications, pg 884
Third World Newsreel/Camera News Inc, pg 1039
VIEW Inc (Video International Entertainment World Inc), pg 1058

NORTH CAROLINA

Crystal Pictures Inc, pg 840

OHIO

Treehaus Communications Inc, pg 1044

OREGON

Nostalgia Family Video Inc, pg 959

PENNSYLVANIA

Bullfrog Films Inc, pg 815

VERMONT

University of Vermont, Instructional Television Dept, pg 1050

WASHINGTON

ChristianAnswers.Net™, pg 825

WISCONSIN

NEWIST/CESA 7, pg 956

MANITOBA

Spectra Video Productions Ltd, pg 1020

ONTARIO

Kineticvideo.com, pg 911
McNabb & Connolly, pg 935

QUEBEC

Les Productions Via Le Monde (Daniel Bertolino) Inc, pg 985

Classic Television Program, *see* Television Program—Classic

Commercial, *see* Test Commercial

Commercials—Animated, Television, *see* Television Commercial—Animated

Commercials—Live, Television, *see* Television Commercial—Live

Current Event Program Distributors

ARIZONA

Video Learning Library, pg 1055

ARKANSAS

Master Books, pg 933

CALIFORNIA

Bennett Media Corp, pg 805
Crystal Pyramid Productions™, pg 840
Direct Cinema Ltd Inc, pg 848
eFootage LLC, pg 858
411 Video Information, pg 872
New & Unique Videos™, pg 955
Publishers Group West Inc, pg 987
Pyramid Media, pg 987
Regent Press Publishers & Printers, pg 994
TMW Media Group, pg 1041
Visual Communications - Southern California Asian American Studies Central Inc, pg 1059

CONNECTICUT

Really Good Stuff, pg 992

DISTRICT OF COLUMBIA

Durrin Productions Inc, pg 854

FLORIDA

Allegro Productions Inc, pg 781
Capital Communications Inc, pg 819
Distribution Video & Audio (DVA), pg 849
Global Video Distributors Inc, pg 879

GEORGIA

School Media Associates LLC, pg 1004

ILLINOIS

CCore Media Inc, pg 821
Chicago Satellite & Video, pg 825
Film Ideas, pg 867
Moviecraft Inc, pg 947
Questar Inc, pg 989

INDIANA

Educational Video Group Inc, pg 857
Our Sunday Visitor Inc, pg 966

KENTUCKY

WaxWorks VideoWorks, pg 1063

MARYLAND

Recorded Books LLC, pg 993

MASSACHUSETTS

WGBH Production Group, pg 1065

MICHIGAN

Digi Sign Design LLC, pg 847

MISSOURI

Phoenix/BFA/Coronet, pg 974
The Phoenix Learning Group Inc, pg 974

MONTANA

High Plains Films, pg 889

NEVADA

Aardvark Video & Media Productions, pg 772

NEW HAMPSHIRE

Channell One Video, pg 824
Chip Taylor Communications LLC, pg 1032

NEW JERSEY

MIB Mediaworks, pg 941

NEW YORK

ATA Trading Corp/Favorite TV Inc, pg 792
Broad Street Inc, pg 812
De Nonno Productions Inc (DPI), pg 844
Films for the Humanities & Sciences, pg 868
Guidance Associates Inc Center for Humanities, pg 883
HB-Content, pg 886
Icarus Film Inc, pg 893
Janson Media, pg 904
KickedUp Media Group Inc, pg 910
Kino International Corp, pg 911
Mastervision Inc, pg 933
Meridian Education Corp, pg 939
MRG Productions Inc, pg 948
News Broadcast Network, pg 956
Richter Productions Inc, pg 996
Shopware, pg 1009

Current Event Program Producers

PROGRAMMING — VIDEO

Current Event Program Producers (continued)

NEW YORK (continued)

Hello World Communications, pg 888
KickedUp Media Group Inc, pg 910
Manhattan Center Studios Inc, pg 930
Neal Marshad Productions, pg 931
Mastervision Inc, pg 933
Jack Morton Worldwide, pg 946
MRG Productions Inc, pg 948
MRY, pg 949
News Broadcast Network, pg 956
Shelly Palmer Production, pg 968
PrimaLux Video Inc, pg 982
PrimeLight Productions Inc, pg 982
Richter Productions Inc, pg 996
Suggs Media Productions Inc, pg 1028
Sunrise Media LLC, pg 1028
Synaptic Digital, pg 1030
Third World Newsreel/Camera News Inc, pg 1039
Videograf, pg 1057
VIEW Inc (Video International Entertainment World Inc), pg 1058
WNET/NET TELECON, pg 1069
Zelman Studios Ltd, pg 1073

NORTH CAROLINA

Pat Appleson Studios Inc, pg 788
Bill Barnes Video Productions LLC, pg 803
The Communications Group Inc, pg 833
LCW Productions LLC, pg 917

OHIO

Advent Media Inc, pg 778
CET, pg 823
Creative Technology, pg 838
Image Video Teleproductions Inc, pg 895
Lyon Video Inc, pg 927
MainSail Production Services Inc, pg 929
R&B Communications Inc, pg 991
Take 1 Media Services, pg 1031
VGI Productions, pg 1053
Vista Color Imaging Inc, pg 1059

OREGON

InterVision Media, pg 902
KPDX-TV Production Center, pg 913
Odyssey Productions Inc, pg 961
Production West, pg 985

PENNSYLVANIA

Beholder Productions Inc, pg 804
CCI Communications Inc, pg 821
FMP Media Solutions Inc, pg 870
Innovision Media Group, pg 899
Muderick Media, pg 949
Production Masters Inc (PMI), pg 984
The Videohouse Inc, pg 1057
WHYY Inc, pg 1066

RHODE ISLAND

Sound-FX-Design, pg 1017

SOUTH CAROLINA

Go To Team, pg 879
Venture Media, pg 1052

TENNESSEE

Running Pony Productions LLC, pg 1000
UMCom Productions, pg 1048

TEXAS

Cerutti Productions Inc, pg 823
Countdown Productions Inc, pg 837
Epic Software Group Inc, pg 862
Horizon Film + Video Productions, pg 891
Mediaforce Productions, pg 937
Earl Miller Productions Inc, pg 943
Julye Newlin Productions Inc, pg 956
Omega Productions, pg 962
South Coast Film & Video, pg 1019
Stage Directions, pg 1022

VIRGINIA

BES Studios, pg 805
CALIBRE, pg 816
Close Up Foundation, pg 830
D&B Television & Video Productions Inc, pg 842
Gingerbread Productions, pg 878
Limelight Communications Inc, pg 921
Metro Productions, pg 939
Rocktown Media, pg 998
Video Solutions, pg 1056
WETA Production Center, pg 1064

WASHINGTON

Bennett-Watt HD Productions Inc, pg 805
Global Net Productions Inc, pg 879
Intermedia Inc, pg 900

WEST VIRGINIA

Blackwater Video Productions, pg 808
Sweetsong Productions, pg 1029

WISCONSIN

5th Floor Recording Co, pg 867
Grassland Media Inc, pg 881
Midland Video Productions Inc, pg 942
ProVideo, pg 986
Rucinski & Reetz Communications LLC, pg 1000
Wisconsin Public Television, pg 1068

WYOMING

Bridger Productions Inc, pg 812

ALBERTA

Black Media Works, pg 808
Global Television Station, pg 879

BRITISH COLUMBIA

Image Media Farm, pg 895
Triad Communications Ltd, pg 1044

NEWFOUNDLAND AND LABRADOR

Vidcraft Productions Ltd, pg 1054

ONTARIO

Canamedia Inc, pg 818
GAPC (General Assembly Production Centre), pg 875
Image Video Services & Productions, pg 895
Video Excellence Productions, pg 1055

QUEBEC

Kerrigan Productions Inc, pg 910
Les Productions Via Le Monde (Daniel Bertolino) Inc, pg 985

Current Event Program Rentals

ARIZONA

Video Learning Library, pg 1055

CALIFORNIA

Direct Cinema Ltd Inc, pg 848
Visual Communications - Southern California Asian American Studies Central Inc, pg 1059

MICHIGAN

Digi Sign Design LLC, pg 847

MISSOURI

The Phoenix Learning Group Inc, pg 974
University of Missouri-Columbia, pg 1050

NEW YORK

Films for the Humanities & Sciences, pg 868
Icarus Film Inc, pg 893
Kino International Corp, pg 911
Richter Productions Inc, pg 996
Third World Newsreel/Camera News Inc, pg 1039
VIEW Inc (Video International Entertainment World Inc), pg 1058

PENNSYLVANIA

Bullfrog Films Inc, pg 815

VIRGINIA

Filmakers Library, pg 867

BRITISH COLUMBIA

Video In Studios/Video Out Distribution, pg 1055

ONTARIO

Kineticvideo.com, pg 911

QUEBEC

Les Productions Via Le Monde (Daniel Bertolino) Inc, pg 985

Documentary Distributors

ALASKA

Skyriver Films, pg 1013

ARIZONA

Drumbeat Indian Arts Inc, pg 852
Tellens Inc, pg 1037
Video Learning Library, pg 1055

ARKANSAS

Master Books, pg 933

CALIFORNIA

Allied Artists International Inc, pg 781
Anchor Bay Entertainment LLC, pg 786
Ark Media Group Ltd, pg 790
Astronomical Society of the Pacific, pg 792
Bennett Media Corp, pg 805
Les Blank Films Inc, pg 809
Blue Dolphin Multimedia, pg 809
California/International Arts Foundation, pg 817
Cambridge Documentary Films Inc, pg 818
Crystal Pyramid Productions™, pg 840
Deja View Video, pg 845
Direct Cinema Ltd Inc, pg 848
Discovery Education - Los Angeles, pg 848
Eagle Multimedia, pg 855
ECONEWS (Environmental Television Series) & (Environmental Directions Radio Series), pg 856
Em Gee Film Library, pg 860
411 Video Information, pg 872
FXF Productions Inc, pg 874
Glenn Photo Supply, pg 878
Glenn Video Vistas Ltd, pg 878
Global Village Stock Footage Library, pg 879
Increase Video/Silver Mine Video, pg 897
Ishtar Films, pg 902
KPBS TV FM-San Diego, pg 913
Learning Communications LLC, pg 917
Madera Video, pg 927
Main Street Media Inc, pg 929
MarVista Entertainment Inc, pg 933
MGM Home Video, pg 941
monterey media inc, pg 945
monterey video, pg 946
New & Unique Videos™, pg 955
North Atlantic Books, pg 958
Pacific Media, pg 967
Pentrex Media Group LLC, pg 972
Players Press, pg 977
Point Lobos Productions, pg 977
Pyramid Media, pg 987
Regent Press Publishers & Printers, pg 994
Rhino Home Video, pg 996
Sea Studios Foundation, pg 1005
TMW Media Group, pg 1041
Universal Studios Home Entertainment, pg 1049
The Video Project, pg 1056
Visual Communications - Southern California Asian American Studies Central Inc, pg 1059
Warner Home Video Inc, pg 1062
The Wine Appreciation Guild Ltd, pg 1067
Xenon Pictures Inc, pg 1071

COLORADO

Tatum Video, pg 1032

CONNECTICUT

Creative Arts Television, pg 838
Crossroads Video, pg 840
Hartley Film Foundation, pg 885
Pictures of Record Inc, pg 975
Really Good Stuff, pg 992

DELAWARE

University Media Services, pg 1049

DISTRICT OF COLUMBIA

Art Museum of the Americas, pg 791
Biblical Archaeology Society (BAS), pg 806
Durrin Productions Inc, pg 854
US Holocaust Memorial Museum, pg 1050
USCCB Publishing, pg 1051
VSA, pg 1061

FLORIDA

Accord Productions, pg 773
Allegro Productions Inc, pg 781
America By Air Stock Footage Library, pg 783
Capital Communications Inc, pg 819
Distribution Video & Audio (DVA), pg 849
Global Video Distributors Inc, pg 879

GEORGIA

On-Line Productions, pg 963
School Media Associates LLC, pg 1004
Skyhoundz, pg 1013

HAWAII

Ka Io Productions Inc, pg 907
Tropical Visions Video Inc, pg 1045

IDAHO

Lagoon Video, pg 915

ILLINOIS

ABSA Productions Inc, pg 772
Facets Multi-Media Inc, pg 865
Film Ideas, pg 867
International Historic Films Inc, pg 901
Moviecraft Inc, pg 947
Perspectives Media, pg 973
Questar Inc, pg 989
Terra Nova Films Inc, pg 1037
Theosophical Publishing House, pg 1038

INDIANA

Educational Video Group Inc, pg 857

IOWA

American Visions, pg 785

KENTUCKY

Horizon Films & Media LLC, pg 891
KET The Kentucky Network, pg 910
National Geographic Learning, pg 952
WaxWorks VideoWorks, pg 1063

LOUISIANA

Great Chefs/Leisure Jazz Video, pg 881
Leisure Video, pg 918

MAINE

Down East Books, pg 851

MARYLAND

Adventure Productions LLC, pg 778
DSR Computer Technology Specialists Inc, pg 853
James Agee Film Project, pg 904
MMI Corp, pg 944
Recorded Books LLC, pg 993
RLJ Entertainment Inc, pg 997
Special Archives Division, Motion Picture Branch, pg 1020
Total AV Systems, pg 1042

MASSACHUSETTS

Award Productions, pg 800
Documentary Educational Resources Inc, pg 850
Emergency Film Group, pg 860
Enterprise Media LLC, pg 861
Media Marketing Associates Inc, pg 937
Merrimack Films, pg 939
The New Film Company Inc, pg 955
Pauline Books & Media, pg 970
Penfield Productions Ltd, pg 971
WGBH Production Group, pg 1065

MICHIGAN

Digi Sign Design LLC, pg 847
The Program Source International, pg 985
Zondervan, A HarperCollins Company, pg 1074

MINNESOTA

Festival Films, pg 866
Harris Communications Inc, pg 885
Llewellyn Publications, pg 923

MISSOURI

Cable Films & Video, pg 816
Phoenix/BFA/Coronet, pg 974
SOM Publishing Co, pg 1015
Vedanta Society of St Louis, pg 1052

MONTANA

High Plains Films, pg 889

NEBRASKA

B & B Video Productions Inc, pg 801
Vision Maker Media, pg 1058

NEVADA

DVDs4Less, pg 854

NEW HAMPSHIRE

Channell One Video, pg 824
NH Movies Inc, pg 957
Chip Taylor Communications LLC, pg 1032

NEW JERSEY

Alden Films, pg 780
Comex Systems Inc, pg 832
Dance Horizons Video, pg 842
Ergo Media Inc, pg 862
Euro-Pacific Film & Video Productions Inc, pg 863
Kultur International Films Ltd Inc, pg 914
Lucerne Media, pg 925
MIB Mediaworks, pg 941
Milestone Film & Video Inc, pg 943
Princeton Book Company, Publishers, pg 982
Shanachie Entertainment Corp, pg 1008
VTS Video & Media, pg 1061

NEW MEXICO

National Information Center for Educational Media (NICEM)/MediaSleuth, pg 952

NEW YORK

A&E Home Video, pg 771
Ambrose Video Publishing Inc, pg 783
Artistic Video, pg 791
ATA Trading Corp/Favorite TV Inc, pg 792
Benchmark Media, pg 805
Michael Blackwood Productions Inc, pg 808
Billy Budd Films Inc, pg 814
Circulating Film & Video Library, pg 828
Downtown Community Television Center (DCTV), pg 851
Film-Makers Cooperative, pg 867
Films for the Humanities & Sciences, pg 868
Films Media Group, pg 868
First Run Features, pg 869
French American Cultural Exchange (FACE), pg 873
William Greaves Productions Inc, pg 882
Guidance Associates Inc Center for Humanities, pg 883
Hallel Communications, pg 884
HB-Content, pg 886
Hearst Entertainment & Syndication, pg 887
Human Relations Media, pg 892
IAI Video, pg 893
Icarus Film Inc, pg 893
The Institute Inc, pg 899
Irish Music Corp, pg 902
Janson Media, pg 904
Richard Kaplan Productions, pg 908
KickedUp Media Group Inc, pg 910
Kino International Corp, pg 911
L & S Video Inc, pg 914
Maryknoll Productions, pg 933
Mastervision Inc, pg 933
Meridian Education Corp, pg 939
Monad Trainer's Aide Inc, pg 945
MRG Productions Inc, pg 948
New Day Films, pg 955
News Broadcast Network, pg 956
Parabola Audio/Video, pg 968
Richter Productions Inc, pg 996
Select Media Inc, pg 1006
Shopware, pg 1009
SISU Home Entertainment Inc, pg 1012
Synaptic Digital, pg 1030
Third World Newsreel/Camera News Inc, pg 1039
Transformational Education Initiatives, pg 1043
United Nations Department of Public Information-News & Media Division, pg 1048
Video Artists International & VAI Audio, pg 1054
Video Catalogue Co Inc, pg 1054
VIEW Inc (Video International Entertainment World Inc), pg 1058
White Buffalo Multimedia, pg 1065
Willow Mixed Media Inc, pg 1067
Women Make Movies Inc, pg 1069
Wonderwomen™ Enterprises, pg 1069
Zeitgeist Films Ltd, pg 1073

NORTH CAROLINA

Baker & Taylor Inc, pg 801
Carolina Biological Supply Co, pg 820
Crystal Pictures Inc, pg 840
Ladyslipper Inc, pg 915
Media Consultants Inc, pg 936
Vide-O-Go/That's Infotainment!, pg 1054
World Wide Pictures Inc, pg 1070

OHIO

Franciscan Media, pg 872
Griesinger Films LLC, pg 882
Shelburne Films, pg 1008
Treehaus Communications Inc, pg 1044

OKLAHOMA

University of Oklahoma Academic Media & Digital Services, pg 1050
VCI Entertainment, pg 1052

OREGON

InterVision Media, pg 902
Nostalgia Family Video Inc, pg 959
Wilderness Video, pg 1066

PENNSYLVANIA

Anchor Distributors, pg 786
Beholder Productions Inc, pg 804
Bullfrog Films Inc, pg 815
Corinth Films Inc, pg 836
FMP Media Solutions Inc, pg 870
Gary Gentile Productions (GGP), pg 877
Goodman Associates Inc, pg 880
Himalayan Institute Audio/Video, pg 889
Karol Media Inc, pg 908
Library Video Company, pg 920
Movies Unlimited, pg 947
MVD Entertainment Group, pg 951
Rahlic Publishing Co, pg 990
The Fred Rogers Co, pg 998
S I Video Sales Group, pg 1001
Schlessinger Media, pg 1004
Vision Video, pg 1058
The Whale Video Co, pg 1065

TENNESSEE

American Blackguard Inc, pg 784
Center for Southern Folklore Inc, pg 822
Marine Geographic, pg 931
National School Products, pg 953
Spring Arbor Distributors, pg 1022

TEXAS

Dallas Learning Solutions, pg 842
Educational Video Network, pg 857
EduMedia of Sugar Land, Texas, pg 857
Three Rivers Publishing Co, pg 1040

VERMONT

Multicultural Media, pg 950
Perceptions Inc, pg 973
Dorothy Tod Films, pg 1041
University of Vermont, Instructional Television Dept, pg 1050

PROGRAMMING — VIDEO

Documentary Distributors (continued)

VIRGINIA

CACI Productions Group, pg 816
CDR Communications Inc, pg 822
Filmakers Library, pg 867
National Audiovisual Center - National Technical Information Service (NTIS), pg 952
Once Around, pg 963
Water Bearer Films Inc, pg 1062

WASHINGTON

Bennett-Watt HD Productions Inc, pg 805
Global Net Productions Inc, pg 879
Intermedia Inc, pg 900
John McLean Media, pg 905
North-by-Northwest Productions, pg 958
Terra Productions LLC, pg 1037
Victory Studios, pg 1054
White Rain Films Ltd, pg 1065

WISCONSIN

Her Own Words LLC, pg 888
NEWIST/CESA 7, pg 956
Wisconsin Public Television, pg 1068

ALBERTA

Global Television Station, pg 879

BRITISH COLUMBIA

Norlynn Audio Visual Services, pg 958
Picture Box Distribution Inc, pg 975
Timeless Books, pg 1040
Video In Studios/Video Out Distribution, pg 1055

NORTHWEST TERRITORIES

Yellowknife Films Inc, pg 1072

ONTARIO

BFS Entertainment & Multimedia Limited, pg 806
Cambium Catalyst International (CCI), pg 817
Canadian Filmmakers Distribution Center (CFMDC), pg 818
Canadian Learning Co Inc, pg 818
Canamedia Inc, pg 818
Doomsday Studios Ltd, pg 850
Kineticvideo.com, pg 911
Life Cycle Books Ltd, pg 920
McIntyre Media Inc, pg 935
McNabb & Connolly, pg 935
Sullivan Home Entertainment, pg 1028

QUEBEC

National Film Board of Canada/ Office National du Film du Canada, pg 952
Les Productions Via Le Monde (Daniel Bertolino) Inc, pg 985

Documentary Producers

ALABAMA

CMEInfo, pg 830
Media Visions Inc, pg 937

ALASKA

Alaska Film Services Inc, pg 779
Aurora Films, pg 797
Skyriver Films, pg 1013

ARIZONA

Aardvark Productions LLC, pg 772
Candee Productions Inc, pg 819
Creative Backstage, pg 838
Film Creations Ltd, pg 867
Forensic Video Deposition Service, pg 871
Fox 10 Productions (KSAZ-TV), pg 872
MediaWorks, pg 938
Merestone, pg 938
Phoenix VideoFilms®, pg 974
Tellens Inc, pg 1037
Video Media Productions (VMP), pg 1055

ARKANSAS

Jones Film Video, pg 906
Live'N'Loud, pg 923
White Diamond Productions, pg 1065

CALIFORNIA

Access Video in Berkeley, pg 773
Action Video, pg 775
Allied Artists International Inc, pg 781
Artichoke Productions, pg 791
Big Door, pg 807
Les Blank Films Inc, pg 809
Burrud Productions Inc, pg 815
California/International Arts Foundation, pg 817
Cambridge Documentary Films Inc, pg 818
Cavalcade Productions Inc, pg 821
Chesney Communications, pg 824
Classic Images, pg 829
Coastline Productions, pg 831
Concept Associates Inc, pg 834
Concoction Lab, pg 835
Concrete Images, pg 835
Cox Media, pg 837
Crystal Pyramid Productions™, pg 840
Custom Video Productions Inc, pg 841
Deja View Video, pg 845
Design Media, pg 845
Digital Outpost, pg 847
Direct Images Interactive Inc, pg 848
Discovery Education - Los Angeles, pg 848
Dogma Studios, pg 850
ECONEWS (Environmental Television Series) & (Environmental Directions Radio Series), pg 856
Face Digital Post, pg 865
FIDM Productions, pg 866
First Camera, pg 868
FXF Productions Inc, pg 874
GAMfilm Productions, pg 875
Global Village Stock Footage Library, pg 879
Goal Productions, pg 879
Howard Hall Productions, pg 883
Image Integration, pg 895
imageReal Pictures LLC, pg 896
Imageworks, pg 896
Increase Video/Silver Mine Video, pg 897
Ishtar Films, pg 902
ITV Productions, pg 903
Kavich Reynolds Productions Inc, pg 908
KION-TV, pg 911
Learning Communications LLC, pg 917
Madera Video, pg 927
Main Street Media Inc, pg 929
Maximus Media Inc, pg 934
McCune Audio-Video-Lighting, pg 935
Media Magic, pg 937
The Media Staff Inc, pg 937
Mist Media Inc, pg 944
monterey media inc, pg 945
Moving Art by Louie Schwartzberg, pg 947
New & Unique Videos™, pg 955
New Circuit Films LLC, pg 955
New Era Media, pg 955
Nolte Media, pg 958
North Atlantic Books, pg 958
On-Trax Inc, pg 963
Pacific Media, pg 967
Panorama Productions, pg 968
Penrose Productions, pg 972
Pentrex Media Group LLC, pg 972
Players Press, pg 977
PM Productions, pg 977
Point Lobos Productions, pg 977
Point of View Productions, pg 977
Prime Cut Productions, pg 982
Pyramid Media, pg 987
QRS Software Services, pg 988
Regent Press Publishers & Printers, pg 994
Dick Reizner Film & Video, pg 994
Rhino Home Video, pg 996
RJ Video Productions, pg 997
Glenn Roland Films, pg 998
SBS Productions, pg 1003
Screen Door Entertainment Inc, pg 1005
Sea Studios Foundation, pg 1005
SNAP, pg 1014
Still N'Motion, pg 1025
The Studio Center, pg 1026
Tam Communications Inc, pg 1031
Tele-Video Production Services (TVPS), pg 1036
Tigar Hare Studios, pg 1040
Timestream Video, pg 1041
TMW Media Group, pg 1041
Total Media Group, pg 1042
TVA Productions, pg 1046
Twin Peaks Creative, pg 1047
Universal Studios Home Entertainment, pg 1049
Utopia Films, pg 1051
Videolady, pg 1057
Videowerks, pg 1057
Vineyard Video & Photography, pg 1058
Visions Plus, pg 1058
Visual Communications - Southern California Asian American Studies Central Inc, pg 1059
WalkerVision Interarts, pg 1061
Wavemaker Media Design, pg 1062
Webster Communications, pg 1063
The Wine Appreciation Guild Ltd, pg 1067
Xenon Pictures Inc, pg 1071
Zamacona Productions, pg 1073

COLORADO

Paul L Anderson Productions Inc, pg 786
Apogee Communications Group, pg 788
Blue River Productions, pg 810
Centre Communications Inc, pg 823
Daylight Productions & Rentals, pg 844
Flashback Media Productions, pg 869
Greg Hensley Productions, pg 888
Renaissance Media, pg 994
Rocky Mountain Audio/Video Productions Inc, pg 998
Side 3 Studios, pg 1010
Tatum Video, pg 1032
Transtar Entertainment Co Inc, pg 1043

CONNECTICUT

Applebox Studio, pg 788
Biomedical Media Communications Dept, pg 807
Broadcast Video Productions LLC, pg 813
Creative Arts Television, pg 838
Crossroads Video, pg 840
Essex Television Group Inc, pg 862
Fox Connecticut, pg 872
The Gary-Paul Agency, pg 875
Geomatrix Productions, pg 877
Hartley Film Foundation, pg 885
Ironik Design & Post, pg 902
MCC Films, pg 935
Moving Pictures, pg 947
New London Media, pg 956
P&P Studios Inc, pg 968
Pictures of Record Inc, pg 975

DELAWARE

University Media Services, pg 1049

DISTRICT OF COLUMBIA

Art Museum of the Americas, pg 791
Biblical Archaeology Society (BAS), pg 806
Durrin Productions Inc, pg 854
Hillmann & Carr Inc, pg 889
O'Keefe Communications Inc, pg 961
US Holocaust Memorial Museum, pg 1050
VSA, pg 1061
Yellow Cat Productions Inc, pg 1072

FLORIDA

Accel Video Productions, pg 773
Accord Productions, pg 773
Allegro Productions Inc, pg 781
America By Air Stock Footage Library, pg 783
Big Byte Video Productions, pg 806
Blackburst Entertainment, pg 808
Capital Communications Inc, pg 819
Civins Productions Inc, pg 828
Communications Concepts Inc (CCI), pg 833
CopShopMiami.com, pg 836
Courter Films LLC, pg 837
EarthDesign Inc, pg 855
Eastern Video, pg 856
Ed Ethridge Productions Inc, pg 863
Global Cyber-Visions, pg 879
Home Shopping Network (HSN), pg 890
Jordan Klein Film & Video (JKFV), pg 906

Media Entertainment Inc, pg 936
Motion Image Group LLC, pg 947
National Teleproductions Inc, pg 953
Paradise Video & Film, pg 969
Sunfire Communications Inc, pg 1028
Sunrise Studios, pg 1028
Tel-Air Interests Inc, pg 1035

GEORGIA

Beachwood Productions, pg 804
Burst Video/Film Inc, pg 815
COMPRO Productions Inc, pg 834
Continental Film & Video, pg 835
ECG Productions, pg 856
Guerrilla Productions LLC, pg 883
Memory Lane Productions, pg 938
Myriad Productions, pg 951
Malcolm Neal Productions, pg 954
On-Line Productions, pg 963
Showcase Photo & Video, pg 1009
Skyhoundz, pg 1013

HAWAII

Hyperspective Studios Inc, pg 893
Ka Io Productions Inc, pg 907
Sight & Sound Studios, pg 1010
1013 Integrated, pg 1037
Tropical Visions Video Inc, pg 1045
TV Juice Productions Inc, pg 1046

IDAHO

Brad Shaw Productions Inc, pg 1008
Wide Eye Productions, pg 1066

ILLINOIS

ABSA Productions Inc, pg 772
Airways Digital Media, pg 779
The Chicago Production Center, pg 825
Chicago Satellite & Video, pg 825
Film Police, pg 867
IV Media Resources, pg 903
Manning Productions, pg 930
The Market Place, pg 931
Mimi Productions, pg 943
Rob Orr Productions Ltd, pg 965
The Pepper Group, pg 972
Perspectives Media, pg 973
Questar Inc, pg 989
QuickSet International Inc, pg 989
SCI Television Productions LLC, pg 1004
Southern Illinois University, pg 1019
Terra Nova Films Inc, pg 1037
Theosophical Publishing House, pg 1038
20/20 Communications Inc, pg 1047
Waveland Software Inc, pg 1062
WEEK TV, pg 1063
Winter Productions, pg 1068

INDIANA

AVA Productions, pg 798
Bright Ideas Creative Services, pg 812
Covenant Productions®, pg 837
Digital Rain LLC, pg 847
Educational Video Group Inc, pg 857
Explore Media LLC, pg 864
Lighthouse Photo & Video Productions, pg 920
PentaVision Communications Inc, pg 972

IOWA

American Visions, pg 785
Iowa State University-Information Technology Services, pg 902
Kuhn Productions LLC, pg 914
The Production House, pg 984

KANSAS

KAKE-TV, pg 907

KENTUCKY

Horizon Films & Media LLC, pg 891
Idle Minds Productions Inc, pg 894
KET The Kentucky Network, pg 910
Donna Lawrence Productions, pg 917
The Media Collaboratory, pg 936
National Geographic Learning, pg 952
Prosper Media Group Inc, pg 986

LOUISIANA

Digital FX Inc, pg 847
Great Chefs/Leisure Jazz Video, pg 881
Launch Media, pg 916
Leisure Video, pg 918
Moxie Media, pg 948

MAINE

WGME-TV, pg 1065

MARYLAND

Absolute Hollywood, pg 772
Adventure Productions LLC, pg 778
The Ahern Group, pg 779
CAS Video Productions, pg 820
Richard Chisolm Cinematography, pg 825
CPR MultiMedia Solutions, pg 837
dbF a Media Company, pg 844
DSR Computer Technology Specialists Inc, pg 853
James Agee Film Project, pg 904
Kramer Communications Video Production, pg 913
Media Dimensions Inc, pg 936

MASSACHUSETTS

Award Productions, pg 800
CommCreative, pg 832
Documentary Educational Resources Inc, pg 850
Emergency Film Group, pg 860
Enterprise Media LLC, pg 861
Green Mountain Post Films (GMP), pg 882
Heliotrope Studios, pg 887
Home Inc, pg 890
In the Wild Productions, pg 897
Inter-Media Electronics, pg 899
Merrimack Films, pg 939
Monadnock Media Inc, pg 945
The New Film Company Inc, pg 955
Northern Light Productions, pg 959
Pauline Books & Media, pg 970
Penfield Productions Ltd, pg 971
TVN-The Video Network, pg 1046
Veritech Corp, pg 1053
WGBH Production Group, pg 1065
WVP Boston, pg 1071

MICHIGAN

Benjamin Creative Productions, pg 805
Digi Sign Design LLC, pg 847
K&R All Media Productions Inc, pg 908
K&R's Recording Studios Inc, pg 908
The Program Source International, pg 985
WTVS-Station Enterprises, pg 1071
Zondervan, A HarperCollins Company, pg 1074

MINNESOTA

Aggressive Records Audio Duplication LLC, pg 778
Blue 60 Pictures, pg 810
House of Cinemagraphics, pg 891
Llewellyn Publications, pg 923
Master Communications Group, pg 933
Media Loft Inc, pg 937
MultiMedia, pg 950
Stoney-Wolf Productions Inc, pg 1025
Worthwhile Films, pg 1070

MISSISSIPPI

Dollarhide Film Inc, pg 850

MISSOURI

Cable Films & Video, pg 816
Fambrough & Associates Inc, pg 865
Hardcastle Films & Video, pg 885
Phoenix/BFA/Coronet, pg 974
The Phoenix Learning Group Inc, pg 974
SOM Publishing Co, pg 1015
Vedanta Society of St Louis, pg 1052

MONTANA

High Plains Films, pg 889
KUSM TV, pg 914
North Country Media Group, pg 959

NEBRASKA

B & B Video Productions Inc, pg 801
Dog & Pony Productions Inc, pg 850
Envision Communications Inc, pg 861
Mason Video, pg 933
Rainbow Video Productions Inc, pg 991
Vision Maker Media, pg 1058

NEVADA

Aardvark Video & Media Productions, pg 772
DVDs4Less, pg 854
Encore Productions Inc, pg 861
HDTV Productions Inc, pg 886
JCS Video Productions, pg 904
Tanglewood Productions, pg 1031

NEW HAMPSHIRE

Apertura, pg 788
Channell One Video, pg 824
NH Movies Inc, pg 957
Chip Taylor Communications LLC, pg 1032
The Troupe, pg 1045

NEW JERSEY

Alden Films, pg 780
Audio Vistas LLC, pg 795
CELCO-Constantine Engineering Labs Co, pg 822
CFP Video Productions Inc, pg 823
Comex Systems Inc, pg 832
Dance Horizons Video, pg 842
DWJ Television, pg 854
Euro-Pacific Film & Video Productions Inc, pg 863
Half Moon Video Productions, pg 883
Laurel Video Productions, pg 916
MIB Mediaworks, pg 941
Ray Mueller Productions, pg 949
Optisonics Productions, pg 965
Producer East Productions, pg 983
Public Eye Productions, pg 987
Bill Quinn Productions, pg 989
Shanachie Entertainment Corp, pg 1008
Suede Interactive, pg 1027
Telequest Inc, pg 1036
TimeSteps Productions Inc, pg 1041
VCSvideo, pg 1052
VTS Video & Media, pg 1061

NEW MEXICO

Michael Dunn Productions, pg 853
Production Outfitters, pg 984

NEW YORK

A&E Home Video, pg 771
Ace Video, pg 774
Air Sea Land Productions Inc (ASL), pg 779
American History Workshop (NY) Inc, pg 784
American Montage Inc, pg 784
Artistic Video, pg 791
aurora productions, pg 797
BC Video Inc, pg 803
Benchmark Media, pg 805
Michael Blackwood Productions Inc, pg 808
Blue Barn Pictures Inc, pg 809
Brian Film Productions LLC, pg 812
Broad Street Inc, pg 812
Brooklyn Films, pg 814
Billy Budd Films Inc, pg 814
Clarity Media Group, pg 829
Downtown Community Television Center (DCTV), pg 851
Fanlight Productions, pg 865
Films for the Humanities & Sciences, pg 868
Films Media Group, pg 868
Florentine Films, pg 870
Karen Frankel Productions, pg 872
William Greaves Productions Inc, pg 882
Greyfalcon House, pg 882
Guidance Associates Inc Center for Humanities, pg 883
Hallel Communications, pg 884
Havas Worldwide, pg 886
HB-Content, pg 886
Hearst Entertainment & Syndication, pg 887
Hello World Communications, pg 888
Human Relations Media, pg 892
IAI Video, pg 893
The Institute Inc, pg 899
Irish Music Corp, pg 902
Janson Media, pg 904
Richard Kaplan Productions, pg 908
Kavanagh Productions Inc, pg 908
Ketchum Pleon Change, pg 910
KickedUp Media Group Inc, pg 910
Kinetic Arts, pg 911
L A Bruell Inc, pg 914
L & S Video Inc, pg 914
Lavine Production Group, pg 917
LightHouse Films, pg 920

PROGRAMMING — VIDEO

Documentary Producers (continued)

NEW YORK (continued)

Magnetic Music Publishing Co, pg 928
Manhattan Center Studios Inc, pg 930
Neal Marshad Productions, pg 931
Maryknoll Productions, pg 933
Mastervision Inc, pg 933
Meridian Education Corp, pg 939
Mood Creations Ltd, pg 946
Jack Morton Worldwide, pg 946
MRG Productions Inc, pg 948
MRY, pg 949
New Horizon Studios, pg 955
News Broadcast Network, pg 956
Northeast Video Productions Inc, pg 959
Shelly Palmer Production, pg 968
Parabola Audio/Video, pg 968
Pat Kogan Productions Inc, pg 970
Peckham Productions Inc, pg 970
Polestar Films & Associated Arts Ltd, pg 978
PrimaLux Video Inc, pg 982
PrimeLight Productions Inc, pg 982
RAVA Films, pg 991
Richter Productions Inc, pg 996
Shadow Pictures Inc, pg 1007
Shopware, pg 1009
Suggs Media Productions Inc, pg 1028
Sunrise Media LLC, pg 1028
Third World Newsreel/Camera News Inc, pg 1039
Time Warner Cable, pg 1040
Tobin Productions Inc, pg 1041
Video Catalogue Co Inc, pg 1054
Videograf, pg 1057
VIEW Inc (Video International Entertainment World Inc), pg 1058
Alan Weiss Productions, pg 1063
White Buffalo Multimedia, pg 1065
Willow Mixed Media Inc, pg 1067
WNET/NET TELECON, pg 1069
Wonderwomen™ Enterprises, pg 1069
Zelman Studios Ltd, pg 1073

NORTH CAROLINA

All Pro Media Inc, pg 780
Pat Appleson Studios Inc, pg 788
J Arnold Productions Inc, pg 790
Bill Barnes Video Productions LLC, pg 803
The Communications Group Inc, pg 833
Crystal Pictures Inc, pg 840
Horizon Video Productions Inc, pg 891
Kino Mountain Productions LLC, pg 911
LCW Productions LLC, pg 917
Media Consultants Inc, pg 936
Moving Pictures, pg 948
Unifour Productions Inc, pg 1048

OHIO

Advent Media Inc, pg 778
Russ Beckner Pictures, pg 804
CET, pg 823
Clear Choice Creative Corp, pg 829
Commercial Video, pg 832
Creative Technology, pg 838
Franciscan Media, pg 872
Griesinger Films LLC, pg 882
Image Video Teleproductions Inc, pg 895
Lyon Video Inc, pg 927
MainSail Production Services Inc, pg 929
Maslowski Productions, pg 933
R&B Communications Inc, pg 991
Shelburne Films, pg 1008
Take 1 Media Services, pg 1031
Treehaus Communications Inc, pg 1044
VGI Productions, pg 1053
Vista Color Imaging Inc, pg 1059

OKLAHOMA

University of Oklahoma Academic Media & Digital Services, pg 1050
VCI Entertainment, pg 1052

OREGON

Ideascape Inc, pg 894
Inner Explorations, pg 898
InterVision Media, pg 902
KPDX-TV Production Center, pg 913
Odyssey Productions Inc, pg 961
Producers Studio, pg 984
Production West, pg 985
TeleVideos, pg 1036
Wilderness Video, pg 1066

PENNSYLVANIA

AiH Group Inc, pg 779
Argentine Productions Inc, pg 789
Bang Pictures, pg 802
Beholder Productions Inc, pg 804
CCI Communications Inc, pg 821
FMP Media Solutions Inc, pg 870
Goodman Associates Inc, pg 880
Himalayan Institute Audio/Video, pg 889
Innovision Media Group, pg 899
Main Point Productions, pg 929
Muderick Media, pg 949
Panta Rhei Media Inc, pg 968
Production Masters Inc (PMI), pg 984
Rahlic Publishing Co, pg 990
S I Video Sales Group, pg 1001
Schlessinger Media, pg 1004
Video Communication Productions Inc, pg 1054
Video/Film Associates, pg 1055
The Videohouse Inc, pg 1057
Vision Video, pg 1058
The Whale Video Co, pg 1065
WHYY Inc, pg 1066

RHODE ISLAND

Sound-FX-Design, pg 1017

SOUTH CAROLINA

Go To Team, pg 879
Stages Video Productions, pg 1023
Venture Media, pg 1052

TENNESSEE

American Blackguard Inc, pg 784
Center for Southern Folklore Inc, pg 822
Continental Film, pg 835
EMI CMG Distribution, pg 860
Griffith Productions, pg 882
Jaguar Productions, pg 903
Marine Geographic, pg 931
Running Pony Productions LLC, pg 1000
Scripps Networks, pg 1005
Russ Sturgeon Productions/RSVP, pg 1027
UMCom Productions, pg 1048

TEXAS

Alpha Video Productions, pg 782
AMS Pictures, pg 786
Biway Media, pg 808
Castleview Productions, pg 821
Cerutti Productions Inc, pg 823
Communication Arts Multimedia Inc, pg 832
Countdown Productions Inc, pg 837
Dallas Learning Solutions, pg 842
Dykeman Associates Inc, pg 854
The Editing Co, pg 857
Educational Video Network, pg 857
EduMedia of Sugar Land, Texas, pg 857
Epic Software Group Inc, pg 862
Horizon Film + Video Productions, pg 891
J&S Audio Visual Inc, pg 904
Mediaforce Productions, pg 937
Earl Miller Productions Inc, pg 943
Julye Newlin Productions Inc, pg 956
Omega Productions, pg 962
Phil Lights, pg 973
Richie Media Productions LLC, pg 996
South Coast Film & Video, pg 1019
Sportsmen on Film Inc, pg 1021
Stage Directions, pg 1022
Three Rivers Publishing Co, pg 1040

UTAH

ImageWorks Communications, pg 896

VERMONT

Marlboro Film & Video Productions, pg 931
Multicultural Media, pg 950
Perceptions Inc, pg 973
Dorothy Tod Films, pg 1041
University of Vermont, Instructional Television Dept, pg 1050

VIRGINIA

BES Studios, pg 805
CALIBRE, pg 816
CDR Communications Inc, pg 822
Cinebar Productions Inc, pg 826
D&B Television & Video Productions Inc, pg 842
Gingerbread Productions, pg 878
Limelight Communications Inc, pg 921
Metro Productions, pg 939
Rocktown Media, pg 998
Video Solutions, pg 1056

WASHINGTON

Bennett-Watt HD Productions Inc, pg 805
Global Net Productions Inc, pg 879
Hamilton Studio, pg 884
Intermedia Inc, pg 900
North-by-Northwest Productions, pg 958
Pal Productions Inc, pg 967
Terra Productions LLC, pg 1037
White Rain Films Ltd, pg 1065

WEST VIRGINIA

Blackwater Video Productions, pg 808
Sweetsong Productions, pg 1029

WISCONSIN

5th Floor Recording Co, pg 867
Grassland Media Inc, pg 881
Her Own Words LLC, pg 888
Midland Video Productions Inc, pg 942
NEWIST/CESA 7, pg 956
ProVideo, pg 986
Rucinski & Reetz Communications LLC, pg 1000
University of Wisconsin-Oshkosh Radio-TV-Film Dept, pg 1050
USAV Group Inc, pg 1050
Watts Communications Inc, pg 1062
Wisconsin Public Television, pg 1068

WYOMING

Bridger Productions Inc, pg 812

ALBERTA

Black Media Works, pg 808
Global Television Station, pg 879
HBW Entertainment Inc, pg 886

BRITISH COLUMBIA

Image Media Farm, pg 895
Norlynn Audio Visual Services, pg 958
Timeless Books, pg 1040
West Eagle Films Inc, pg 1064

MANITOBA

Spectra Video Productions Ltd, pg 1020

NEWFOUNDLAND AND LABRADOR

Vidcraft Productions Ltd, pg 1054

NORTHWEST TERRITORIES

Yellowknife Films Inc, pg 1072

ONTARIO

ADS Media, pg 777
Associated Producers Ltd, pg 792
Canamedia Inc, pg 818
DebsVoice, pg 844
Doomsday Studios Ltd, pg 850
GAPC (General Assembly Production Centre), pg 875
Image Video Services & Productions, pg 895
Iron Ring Communications Ltd, pg 902
Jams Productions Inc, pg 904
Marblemedia, pg 930
Pendulum Entertainment, pg 971
Triune Arts, pg 1045
Video Excellence Productions, pg 1055
YAP Films, pg 1072

QUEBEC

Group PVP, pg 882
Kerrigan Productions Inc, pg 910
National Film Board of Canada/ Office National du Film du Canada, pg 952
Productions Grand Nord Quebec Inc, pg 985
Les Productions Via Le Monde (Daniel Bertolino) Inc, pg 985

SASKATCHEWAN

plan9films, pg 976

Documentary Rentals

ARIZONA

Video Learning Library, pg 1055

CALIFORNIA

Auslender Productions/Celestial Images, pg 797
Les Blank Films Inc, pg 809
Cambridge Documentary Films Inc, pg 818
Direct Cinema Ltd Inc, pg 848
ECONEWS (Environmental Television Series) & (Environmental Directions Radio Series), pg 856
Learning Communications LLC, pg 917
Point of View Productions, pg 977
Visual Communications - Southern California Asian American Studies Central Inc, pg 1059

COLORADO

Tatum Video, pg 1032

CONNECTICUT

Crossroads Video, pg 840

DELAWARE

University Media Services, pg 1049

DISTRICT OF COLUMBIA

Durrin Productions Inc, pg 854

GEORGIA

On-Line Productions, pg 963

ILLINOIS

Facets Multi-Media Inc, pg 865
Terra Nova Films Inc, pg 1037

MARYLAND

James Agee Film Project, pg 904

MASSACHUSETTS

Documentary Educational Resources Inc, pg 850
Emergency Film Group, pg 860
Enterprise Media LLC, pg 861
Merrimack Films, pg 939
Pauline Books & Media, pg 970

MICHIGAN

Digi Sign Design LLC, pg 847

MISSOURI

Cable Films & Video, pg 816
The Phoenix Learning Group Inc, pg 974
University of Missouri-Columbia, pg 1050

NEBRASKA

Vision Maker Media, pg 1058

NEW JERSEY

Euro-Pacific Film & Video Productions Inc, pg 863

NEW YORK

BC Video Inc, pg 803
Circulating Film & Video Library, pg 828
Downtown Community Television Center (DCTV), pg 851
Fanlight Productions, pg 865
Ronald Feldman Fine Arts Inc, pg 866
Films for the Humanities & Sciences, pg 868
Films Media Group, pg 868
First Run Features, pg 869
William Greaves Productions Inc, pg 882
Hallel Communications, pg 884
Icarus Film Inc, pg 893
Kino International Corp, pg 911
New Day Films, pg 955
Richter Productions Inc, pg 996
Third World Newsreel/Camera News Inc, pg 1039
VIEW Inc (Video International Entertainment World Inc), pg 1058

NORTH CAROLINA

Crystal Pictures Inc, pg 840
World Wide Pictures Inc, pg 1070

OREGON

Nostalgia Family Video Inc, pg 959
Wilderness Video, pg 1066

PENNSYLVANIA

Bullfrog Films Inc, pg 815
Rahlic Publishing Co, pg 990

TENNESSEE

Center for Southern Folklore Inc, pg 822

TEXAS

Three Rivers Publishing Co, pg 1040

VERMONT

University of Vermont, Instructional Television Dept, pg 1050

VIRGINIA

Filmakers Library, pg 867
Once Around, pg 963

WASHINGTON

Intermedia Inc, pg 900

WISCONSIN

Her Own Words LLC, pg 888
NEWIST/CESA 7, pg 956

BRITISH COLUMBIA

Video In Studios/Video Out Distribution, pg 1055

MANITOBA

Spectra Video Productions Ltd, pg 1020

ONTARIO

Kineticvideo.com, pg 911
McNabb & Connolly, pg 935

QUEBEC

Les Productions Via Le Monde (Daniel Bertolino) Inc, pg 985

DVD Distributors

ALABAMA

Eternal Word Television Network (EWTN), pg 862

ALASKA

Skyriver Films, pg 1013

ARIZONA

Arizona Public Media, pg 790
Celestial Harmonies/Fortuna Records/Kuckuck Schallplatten/ Black Sun Music/MonteVideo, pg 822
Coyote Cowboy Co, pg 837
Drumbeat Indian Arts Inc, pg 852
Tom Hopkins International Inc, pg 891
Mother Basilea Films, pg 947
Valley of the Sun Publishing Co, pg 1051

CALIFORNIA

Adolph Gasser Inc, pg 776
Anchor Bay Entertainment LLC, pg 786
Ariztical Entertainment Inc, pg 790
Ark Media Group Ltd, pg 790
Astronomical Society of the Pacific, pg 792
Barbosa Video Services, pg 802
Les Blank Films Inc, pg 809
Blind Pig Records, pg 809
California/International Arts Foundation, pg 817
California Language Laboratories, pg 817
California Newsreel, pg 817
Cambridge Documentary Films Inc, pg 818
Canyon Cinema Inc, pg 819
Cavalcade Productions Inc, pg 821
Coast Learning Systems, pg 830
Crystal Productions, pg 840
Davidson Films Inc, pg 843
DawnSignPress, pg 844
Deja View Video, pg 845
Direct Cinema Ltd Inc, pg 848
Eastman Corp, pg 856
ECONEWS (Environmental Television Series) & (Environmental Directions Radio Series), pg 856
Em Gee Film Library, pg 860
Focus Features, pg 870
Forte Productions, pg 871
411 Video Information, pg 872
FXF Productions Inc, pg 874
Glenn Photo Supply, pg 878
Glenray Productions Inc, pg 878
Global Village Stock Footage Library, pg 879
Golden State Dance Teachers Association (GSDTA), pg 880
Griggs Productions Inc, pg 882
Steven Halpern's Inner Peace Music, pg 884
Hay House Inc, pg 886
Health Education Services, pg 887
Image Entertainment, pg 895
Increase Video/Silver Mine Video, pg 897
Ishtar Films, pg 902
Joyce Media Inc, pg 906
Latham Foundation Publications, pg 916
Learn Quickly, pg 917
Lightworks Audio & Video Inc, pg 921
Live Wire Media, pg 923
MarVista Entertainment Inc, pg 933
monterey media inc, pg 945
Motion Picture Licensing Corp (MPLC), pg 947
Nilgiri Press, pg 957
Pacific Media, pg 967
Paulist Productions, pg 970
Point Lobos Productions, pg 977
Pyramid Media, pg 987
Randolf Productions Inc, pg 991
Rhino Home Video, pg 996
RM Films International, pg 997
Ron Roy Productions/Moodtapes, pg 1000
Sea Studios Foundation, pg 1005
Shokus Video, pg 1009
Staylor-Made Communications Inc, pg 1024
Theatre Arts Video Library, pg 1038
Thinking Allowed Productions, pg 1038
Valley Media, pg 1051
Visual Communications - Southern California Asian American Studies Central Inc, pg 1059
Walt Disney Studio, pg 1061
Warner Bros Entertainment Inc, pg 1062
Warner Home Video Inc, pg 1062
Western Instructional Television Inc, pg 1064
The Wine Appreciation Guild Ltd, pg 1067
The Writing Co, pg 1070
Xenon Pictures Inc, pg 1071
Zamacona Productions, pg 1073

COLORADO

Paul L Anderson Productions Inc, pg 786
Crown Ministries International, pg 840
Greg Hensley Productions, pg 888
Inferno Film Productions LLC, pg 897
InJoy Birth & Parenting Education, pg 898
Jeppesen, pg 905
Meriwether Publishing Ltd, pg 939
National Institute for Trial Advocacy (NITA), pg 953
Stretching Inc, pg 1026
Tatum Video, pg 1032
White Swan Music Inc, pg 1065

CONNECTICUT

Cine-Med Inc, pg 826
Crossroads Video, pg 840
Ironik Design & Post, pg 902
Twenty-Third Publications/Bayard, pg 1047
Video Design Group, pg 1055
Weston Woods Studios Inc, pg 1064

DISTRICT OF COLUMBIA

Sano Videos, pg 1002

FLORIDA

Allegro Productions Inc, pg 781
Alliance Entertainment Corp (AEC) LLC, pg 781
America By Air Stock Footage Library, pg 783
Capital Communications Inc, pg 819
Catholic Books & Tapes, pg 821
Children of Mary, pg 825
Global Video Distributors Inc, pg 879
Karst Productions Inc, pg 908

PROGRAMMING — VIDEO

DVD Distributors (continued)

FLORIDA (continued)

Motion Image Group LLC, pg 947
MTI Home Video, pg 949
Photomart Cine-Video Inc, pg 975

GEORGIA

The Alliance for Christian Media, pg 781
New Leaf Distributing Co, pg 955
Skyhoundz, pg 1013
Thompson-Mitchell & Associates Inc, pg 1039

HAWAII

Ka Io Productions Inc, pg 907

IDAHO

University of Idaho Engineering Outreach, pg 1049

ILLINOIS

ABSA Productions Inc, pg 772
Analog Free Media, pg 786
Bolchazy - Carducci Publishers Inc, pg 810
Encyclopaedia Britannica Inc, pg 861
Film Ideas, pg 867
Learning Seed, pg 917
Prevent Blindness America, pg 981
Questar Inc, pg 989
Rediscover Music, pg 993
Research Press Co, pg 995
Terra Nova Films Inc, pg 1037

INDIANA

Agency for Instructional Technology (AIT), pg 778
Educational Video Group Inc, pg 857
Folkcraft Instruments, pg 871
Optical Disc Solutions Inc, pg 964

KANSAS

Day Star Productions, pg 844
Yarn Barn of Kansas, pg 1072

KENTUCKY

Horizon Films & Media LLC, pg 891
WaxWorks VideoWorks, pg 1063

LOUISIANA

Great Chefs/Leisure Jazz Video, pg 881
Leisure Video, pg 918
Moxie Media, pg 948

MARYLAND

Crunch Bird Studios Inc, pg 840
dbF a Media Company, pg 844
Human Circuit, pg 892
Kids on the Block Inc, pg 910
Library Video Network (LVN), pg 920
MMI Corp, pg 944
Nicholas P Pipino Associates Inc, pg 976
Recorded Books LLC, pg 993
RLJ Entertainment Inc, pg 997
Total AV Systems, pg 1042

MASSACHUSETTS

Cheng & Tsui Co, pg 824
Documentary Educational Resources Inc, pg 850
Education Development Center Inc (EDC), pg 857
Merrimack Films, pg 939
National Fire Protection Association (NFPA), pg 952
The New Film Company Inc, pg 955
Video Express, pg 1055

MICHIGAN

Digi Sign Design LLC, pg 847
Meuninck's Media Methods Inc, pg 940
MSU Technologies, pg 949
The Program Source International, pg 985
Society of Manufacturing Engineers (SME), pg 1015
Jack Van Impe Ministries International, pg 1051
Zondervan, A HarperCollins Company, pg 1074

MINNESOTA

Aggressive Records Audio Duplication LLC, pg 778
Festival Films, pg 866
Harris Communications Inc, pg 885
Hazelden Publishing & Educational Services, pg 886
Llewellyn Publications, pg 923
Master Communications Group, pg 933

MISSOURI

American Optometric Association (AOA), pg 785
Annenberg Learner, pg 787
Marsh Media, pg 931
Phoenix/BFA/Coronet, pg 974
SOM Publishing Co, pg 1015
Vedanta Society of St Louis, pg 1052

NEBRASKA

AdventSource, pg 778
Leo Films, pg 919
Peak Performance Publishing, pg 970
The Recruiters Library, pg 993

NEVADA

DVDs4Less, pg 854

NEW HAMPSHIRE

Captain Fiddle Music & Publications, pg 820
Channell One Video, pg 824
French American Music Enterprises, pg 873
Heinemann, pg 887
Chip Taylor Communications LLC, pg 1032
YMAA Publication Center Inc, pg 1072

NEW JERSEY

Alden Films, pg 780
Business Education Films, pg 815
Comex Systems Inc, pg 832
Dance Horizons Video, pg 842
Educational Impressions, pg 857
Ergo Media Inc, pg 862
Euro-Pacific Film & Video Productions Inc, pg 863
Films of the Nations, pg 868
Jointure for Community Adult Education Inc, pg 906
Kimbo Educational, pg 910
Lucerne Media, pg 925
Shanachie Entertainment Corp, pg 1008
VTS Video & Media, pg 1061

NEW MEXICO

National Information Center for Educational Media (NICEM)/ MediaSleuth, pg 952
Uncharted Country Publishing, pg 1048

NEW YORK

A&E Home Video, pg 771
A&E Television Networks LLC, pg 771
Applause Learning Resources, pg 788
Benchmark Media, pg 805
Michael Blackwood Productions Inc, pg 808
Billy Budd Films Inc, pg 814
The Bureau for At-Risk Youth, pg 815
The Christophers, pg 826
The Cinema Guild Inc, pg 827
Cornell Laboratory of Ornithology, pg 836
Criterion Collection, pg 839
Educational Activities Inc, pg 857
Entertainment One Distribution, pg 861
Film Emporium, pg 867
William Greaves Productions Inc, pg 882
Guilford Publications, pg 883
HB-Content, pg 886
HBO Home Video Inc, pg 886
Homespun Video, pg 890
Human Relations Media, pg 892
Icarus Film Inc, pg 893
Irish Music Corp, pg 902
Lylofilm Productions, pg 926
Magnetic Music Publishing Co, pg 928
Mastervision Inc, pg 933
Monad Trainer's Aide Inc, pg 945
MRG Productions Inc, pg 948
New Day Films, pg 955
Random House Children's Books, pg 991
Richter Productions Inc, pg 996
Saturn Productions Inc, pg 1003
SISU Home Entertainment Inc, pg 1012
Third World Newsreel/Camera News Inc, pg 1039
Tommy Boy Entertainment LLC, pg 1042
Transformational Education Initiatives, pg 1043
United Nations Department of Public Information-News & Media Division, pg 1048
Video Aided Instruction Inc, pg 1054
Video Artists International & VAI Audio, pg 1054
Video Catalogue Co Inc, pg 1054
VIEW Inc (Video International Entertainment World Inc), pg 1058
Visual Technologies Corp, pg 1060
Women Make Movies Inc, pg 1069
Wonderwomen™ Enterprises, pg 1069
Zim Records, pg 1074

NORTH CAROLINA

Baker & Taylor Inc, pg 801
Carolina Biological Supply Co, pg 820
Eli Research Group, pg 859
Sinclair Institute, pg 1012
World Wide Pictures Inc, pg 1070

OHIO

The American Classical League, pg 784
Griesinger Films LLC, pg 882
Red Onion Records, pg 993
VGI Productions, pg 1053

OKLAHOMA

VCI Entertainment, pg 1052

OREGON

CNS Productions Inc, pg 830
Getty-Dubay Productions, pg 877
Medifecta Healthcare Training, pg 938
Memory Lane Videos, pg 938
Norman Beerger Productions, pg 958
TeleVideos, pg 1036

PENNSYLVANIA

Bergwall Productions Inc, pg 805
Corinth Films Inc, pg 836
Himalayan Institute Audio/Video, pg 889
Vision Video, pg 1058
The Whale Video Co, pg 1065

SOUTH CAROLINA

American Production Services LLC, pg 785
BJU Press, pg 808

TENNESSEE

Abingdon Press, pg 772
American Blackguard Inc, pg 784
B&H Publishing Group, pg 802
Cokesbury, pg 831
Ingram Entertainment Inc, pg 898
Marine Geographic, pg 931
Word Label Group, pg 1069
Zion Music Group, pg 1074

TEXAS

Big Kids Productions Inc, pg 807
CEV Multimedia Ltd, pg 823
Chalk Dust Co, pg 823
Dallas Learning Solutions, pg 842
Educational Video Network, pg 857
Executive Development Systems, pg 864
First Group Communications Inc, pg 868
Marengo Films, pg 931
Replicopy Digital Media Center, pg 995
TopCat Records LLC, pg 1042

VERMONT

Dialect Accent Specialists Inc, pg 846
Multicultural Media, pg 950
Wilson McLeran Inc, pg 1067

VIRGINIA

County Sales, pg 837
Dorst MediaWorks Inc, pg 851
Filmakers Library, pg 867
Rocktown Media, pg 998

WASHINGTON

Bennett-Watt HD Productions Inc, pg 805
ChristianAnswers.Net™, pg 825
College of Nursing, Washington State University, pg 831
Intermedia Inc, pg 900

WEST VIRGINIA

Focus on Animals, pg 870
Harpers Ferry Historical Association, pg 885

WISCONSIN

Aylmer Press, pg 801
Her Own Words LLC, pg 888
NEWIST/CESA 7, pg 956
Plank Road Publishing Inc, pg 976

BRITISH COLUMBIA

Norlynn Audio Visual Services, pg 958

ONTARIO

Canadian Learning Co Inc, pg 818
Canamedia Inc, pg 818
The Children's Book Store Distribution (CBSD), pg 825
ETHOS Ltd, pg 863
Life Cycle Books Ltd, pg 920
McIntyre Media Inc, pg 935
McNabb & Connolly, pg 935
Nelson Education Ltd, pg 954
Random House of Canada Limited, pg 991
TVO/Ontario Educational Communications Authority (OECA), pg 1046

QUEBEC

National Film Board of Canada/Office National du Film du Canada, pg 952

DVD Producers

ALABAMA

Eternal Word Television Network (EWTN), pg 862

ALASKA

Aurora Films, pg 797

ARIZONA

Aardvark Productions LLC, pg 772
Arizona Public Media, pg 790
Celestial Harmonies/Fortuna Records/Kuckuck Schallplatten/ Black Sun Music/MonteVideo, pg 822
Film Creations Ltd, pg 867
Forensic Video Deposition Service, pg 871
Merestone, pg 938
Valley of the Sun Publishing Co, pg 1051
Video Media Productions (VMP), pg 1055

ARKANSAS

Live'N'Loud, pg 923
White Diamond Productions, pg 1065

CALIFORNIA

Access Video in Berkeley, pg 773
ACDC Audio CD & Cassette, pg 774
Animax, pg 787
Arhoolie Productions Inc (aka Arhoolie Records), pg 789
Ariztical Entertainment Inc, pg 790
Artichoke Productions, pg 791
Astronomical Society of the Pacific, pg 792
Auslender Productions/Celestial Images, pg 797
Barbosa Video Services, pg 802
Big Door, pg 807
Les Blank Films Inc, pg 809
Blind Pig Records, pg 809
California/International Arts Foundation, pg 817
California Language Laboratories, pg 817
Cambridge Documentary Films Inc, pg 818
Cavalcade Productions Inc, pg 821
Coast Learning Systems, pg 830
Concrete Images, pg 835
Creativity Unlimited Press®, pg 839
Custom Video Productions Inc, pg 841
Davidson Films Inc, pg 843
DawnSignPress, pg 844
Deja View Video, pg 845
Digital Outpost, pg 847
Direct Cinema Ltd Inc, pg 848
Direct Images Interactive Inc, pg 848
Dogma Studios, pg 850
Dynamic Digital Depth Inc (DDD), pg 854
Eastman Corp, pg 856
ECONEWS (Environmental Television Series) & (Environmental Directions Radio Series), pg 856
Face Digital Post, pg 865
Focus Features, pg 870
Forte Productions, pg 871
411 Video Information, pg 872
FXF Productions Inc, pg 874
Geddes Productions LLC, pg 876
Glenray Productions Inc, pg 878
Global Village Stock Footage Library, pg 879
Gold Standard Productions, pg 880
Griggs Productions Inc, pg 882
Steven Halpern's Inner Peace Music, pg 884
Havas Edge, pg 885
imageReal Pictures LLC, pg 896
Imageworks, pg 896
Increase Video/Silver Mine Video, pg 897
ITV Productions, pg 903
Joyce Media Inc, pg 906
K2B2 Records, pg 907
Latham Foundation Publications, pg 916
Learn Quickly, pg 917
Live Wire Media, pg 923
Ludlow Media Solutions, pg 926
Main Street Media Inc, pg 929
Maximus Media Inc, pg 934
Media Magic, pg 937
Mist Media Inc, pg 944
monterey media inc, pg 945
M2 Communications, pg 949
Multi-Media Mathematics, pg 949
Music World/Vocal Power School, pg 951
New Era Media, pg 955
Nilgiri Press, pg 957
On-Trax Inc, pg 963
Pacific Media, pg 967
Paulist Productions, pg 970
Pentrex Media Group LLC, pg 972
PM Productions, pg 977
Point Lobos Productions, pg 977
Pyramid Media, pg 987
QRS Software Services, pg 988
Randolf Productions Inc, pg 991
RetinaVision Productions, pg 995
Rhino Home Video, pg 996
RM Films International, pg 997
Glenn Roland Films, pg 998
Ron Roy Productions/Moodtapes, pg 1000
Saturn Studios, pg 1003
Screen Door Entertainment Inc, pg 1005
Sea Studios Foundation, pg 1005
Shokus Video, pg 1009
Staylor-Made Communications Inc, pg 1024
Tam Communications Inc, pg 1031
Theatre Arts Video Library, pg 1038
Thinking Allowed Productions, pg 1038
Timestream Video, pg 1041
Total Media Group, pg 1042
Vedanta Press & Catalog, pg 1052
Video Resources Inc, pg 1056
Videolady, pg 1057
Videowerks, pg 1057
WalkerVision Interarts, pg 1061
Warner Bros Entertainment Inc, pg 1062
Wavemaker Media Design, pg 1062
Western Instructional Television Inc, pg 1064
Xenon Pictures Inc, pg 1071
Zamacona Productions, pg 1073

COLORADO

Alpine Media, pg 782
Paul L Anderson Productions Inc, pg 786
blue onion, pg 810
The Cinema Lab, pg 827
Crown Ministries International, pg 840
Flashback Media Productions, pg 869
Inferno Film Productions LLC, pg 897
InJoy Birth & Parenting Education, pg 898
Jeppesen, pg 905
Meriwether Publishing Ltd, pg 939
National Institute for Trial Advocacy (NITA), pg 953
Rocky Mountain Audio/Video Productions Inc, pg 998
Side 3 Studios, pg 1010
Tatum Video, pg 1032

CONNECTICUT

ACM Productions Ltd, pg 774
Applebox Studio, pg 788
Biomedical Media Communications Dept, pg 807
Broadcast Video Productions LLC, pg 813
Cine-Med Inc, pg 826
Crossroads Video, pg 840
Essex Television Group Inc, pg 862
Geomatrix Productions, pg 877
Ironik Design & Post, pg 902
MCC Films, pg 935
New London Media, pg 956
Twenty-Third Publications/Bayard, pg 1047
Weston Woods Studios Inc, pg 1064

DISTRICT OF COLUMBIA

USCCB Publishing, pg 1051

FLORIDA

Accord Productions, pg 773
Allegro Productions Inc, pg 781
America By Air Stock Footage Library, pg 783
Big Byte Video Productions, pg 806
Blackburst Entertainment, pg 808
Chatterbox Productions Inc, pg 824
Civins Productions Inc, pg 828
Courter Films LLC, pg 837
Easy Edit Video Inc, pg 856
Ed Ethridge Productions Inc, pg 863
Motion Image Group LLC, pg 947
MTI Home Video, pg 949
Multivision Video & Film, pg 950
National Teleproductions Inc, pg 953
Sound & Vision Communications Inc, pg 1016
Sunfire Communications Inc, pg 1028
Sunrise Studios, pg 1028
Tight Line Productions, pg 1040
Tricycle Studios, pg 1044
Universal Studios Florida® Production Group, pg 1049
Video Techniques Inc, pg 1056

GEORGIA

Burst Video/Film Inc, pg 815
Continental Film & Video, pg 835
ECG Productions, pg 856
Guerrilla Productions LLC, pg 883
Myriad Productions, pg 951
On-Line Productions, pg 963
Skyhoundz, pg 1013

HAWAII

Hyperspective Studios Inc, pg 893
Ka Io Productions Inc, pg 907
Sight & Sound Studios, pg 1010

IDAHO

Brad Shaw Productions Inc, pg 1008

ILLINOIS

ABSA Productions Inc, pg 772
Airways Digital Media, pg 779
American Hospital Association, pg 784
Analog Free Media, pg 786
Beatty TeleVisual Productions, pg 804
Cresta Creative, pg 839
Encyclopaedia Britannica Inc, pg 861
Extraordinary Demos, pg 864
Film Police, pg 867
IV Media Resources, pg 903
Learning Seed, pg 917
Major Media Inc, pg 929
Manning Productions, pg 930
Jim Passin Productions, pg 970
Prevent Blindness America, pg 981
Questar Inc, pg 989
RADMAR Inc, pg 990
Research Press Co, pg 995
Richter Studios, pg 996
Sparkfactor, pg 1019
Terra Nova Films Inc, pg 1037
Universal Training, pg 1049

PROGRAMMING — VIDEO

DVD Producers (continued)

ILLINOIS (continued)

Video Impressions, pg 1055
Winter Productions, pg 1068

INDIANA

Agency for Instructional Technology (AIT), pg 778
AVA Productions, pg 798
Bright Ideas Creative Services, pg 812
Covenant Productions®, pg 837
Digital Rain LLC, pg 847
Educational Video Group Inc, pg 857
InterComm, pg 900
Optical Disc Solutions Inc, pg 964
PentaVision Communications Inc, pg 972
Road Pictures, pg 997

IOWA

American Visions, pg 785

KANSAS

KAKE-TV, pg 907
Yarn Barn of Kansas, pg 1072

KENTUCKY

Horizon Films & Media LLC, pg 891
Northern Kentucky University, pg 959
Prosper Media Group Inc, pg 986

LOUISIANA

Great Chefs/Leisure Jazz Video, pg 881
Leisure Video, pg 918
Louisiana State University Health Sciences Center - Shreveport, pg 925
Moxie Media, pg 948

MARYLAND

CPR MultiMedia Solutions, pg 837
dbF a Media Company, pg 844
The Image Generators, pg 895
Kids on the Block Inc, pg 910
Kramer Communications Video Production, pg 913
Library Video Network (LVN), pg 920
Lion & Fox Recording Studios, pg 922
Media Dimensions Inc, pg 936
RLJ Entertainment Inc, pg 997
Video Labs, pg 1055

MASSACHUSETTS

Cheng & Tsui Co, pg 824
Education Development Center Inc (EDC), pg 857
Heliotrope Studios, pg 887
In the Wild Productions, pg 897
Inter-Media Electronics, pg 899
Merrimack Films, pg 939
Monadnock Media Inc, pg 945
Preston Productions Inc, pg 981

MICHIGAN

Benjamin Creative Productions, pg 805
Digi Sign Design LLC, pg 847
International Tae Kwon Do Association (ITA Institute), pg 901
K&R All Media Productions Inc, pg 908
Meuninck's Media Methods Inc, pg 940
MSU Technologies, pg 949
The Program Source International, pg 985
Society of Manufacturing Engineers (SME), pg 1015
TGA Recording Co, pg 1038
Universal Images, pg 1049
Zondervan, A HarperCollins Company, pg 1074

MINNESOTA

Aggressive Records Audio Duplication LLC, pg 778
Hazelden Publishing & Educational Services, pg 886
House of Cinemagraphics, pg 891
Llewellyn Publications, pg 923
MultiMedia, pg 950
Babe Winkelman Productions Inc, pg 1068
Worthwhile Films, pg 1070

MISSOURI

American Optometric Association (AOA), pg 785
Annenberg Learner, pg 787
Celebrities Productions, pg 822
Fambrough & Associates Inc, pg 865
Marsh Media, pg 931
SOM Publishing Co, pg 1015
Vedanta Society of St Louis, pg 1052

NEBRASKA

AdventSource, pg 778
American Gramaphone LLC, pg 784
Dog & Pony Productions Inc, pg 850
Envision Communications Inc, pg 861
Leo Films, pg 919
Peak Performance Publishing, pg 970
Rainbow Video Productions Inc, pg 991
The Recruiters Library, pg 993

NEVADA

Encore Productions Inc, pg 861
JCS Video Productions, pg 904
The Larry Little Co, pg 923
Tanglewood Productions, pg 1031

NEW HAMPSHIRE

Captain Fiddle Music & Publications, pg 820
Channell One Video, pg 824
NH Movies Inc, pg 957
Chip Taylor Communications LLC, pg 1032
YMAA Publication Center Inc, pg 1072

NEW JERSEY

Audio Vistas LLC, pg 795
Comex Systems Inc, pg 832
Dance Horizons Video, pg 842
Educational Impressions, pg 857
Euro-Pacific Film & Video Productions Inc, pg 863
Kimbo Educational, pg 910
Lucerne Media, pg 925
Midnight Media Group Inc, pg 942
Ray Mueller Productions, pg 949
Outside The Box Interactive LLC, pg 966
Shanachie Entertainment Corp, pg 1008
TimeSteps Productions Inc, pg 1041
VCSvideo, pg 1052
VTS Video & Media, pg 1061

NEW MEXICO

Production Outfitters, pg 984
Uncharted Country Publishing, pg 1048

NEW YORK

A&E Home Video, pg 771
Air Sea Land Productions Inc (ASL), pg 779
Applause Learning Resources, pg 788
Asia Society, pg 792
BC Video Inc, pg 803
Benchmark Media, pg 805
Michael Blackwood Productions Inc, pg 808
Blue Barn Pictures Inc, pg 809
Bridge Records Inc, pg 812
Brooklyn Films, pg 814
Billy Budd Films Inc, pg 814
The Bureau for At-Risk Youth, pg 815
Conversation Arts Media, pg 836
Cornell Laboratory of Ornithology, pg 836
Thomas Craven Film Corp, pg 837
Criterion Collection, pg 839
dM works, pg 849
Duplication Depot Inc, pg 853
Educational Activities Inc, pg 857
Entertainment One Distribution, pg 861
Eye on Dance, pg 865
The Food & Beverage Institute, pg 871
Greyfalcon House, pg 882
Guidance Associates Inc Center for Humanities, pg 883
Guilford Publications, pg 883
HB-Content, pg 886
HBO Home Video Inc, pg 886
Homespun Video, pg 890
Human Relations Media, pg 892
International Digital Centre, pg 901
Irish Music Corp, pg 902
Richard Kaplan Productions, pg 908
L A Bruell Inc, pg 914
Live Oak Media, pg 923
Lylofilm Productions, pg 926
Lyrichord Discs Inc, pg 927
Magnetic Music Publishing Co, pg 928
Mastervision Inc, pg 933
Jack Morton Worldwide, pg 946
MRG Productions Inc, pg 948
Pat Kogan Productions Inc, pg 970
PrimaLux Video Inc, pg 982
Random House Children's Books, pg 991
Reinhardt Productions Inc, pg 994
Richter Productions Inc, pg 996
Saturn Productions Inc, pg 1003
Shadow Pictures Inc, pg 1007
Sunrise Media LLC, pg 1028
Third World Newsreel/Camera News Inc, pg 1039
Tommy Boy Entertainment LLC, pg 1042
United Nations Multimedia Resources Unit, pg 1048
Video Aided Instruction Inc, pg 1054
Video Catalogue Co Inc, pg 1054
VIEW Inc (Video International Entertainment World Inc), pg 1058
Willow Mixed Media Inc, pg 1067
Wonderwomen™ Enterprises, pg 1069

NORTH CAROLINA

All Pro Media Inc, pg 780
Pat Appleson Studios Inc, pg 788
Carolina Biological Supply Co, pg 820
The Communications Group Inc, pg 833
Creative Services Inc, pg 838
Eli Research Group, pg 859
Horizon Video Productions Inc, pg 891
Moving Pictures, pg 948
Sinclair Institute, pg 1012
2BruceStudio, pg 1047

OHIO

Advent Media Inc, pg 778
CET, pg 823
EDR Media LLC, pg 857
Griesinger Films LLC, pg 882
Maslowski Productions, pg 933
Musicol Recording, pg 951
R&B Communications Inc, pg 991
Red Onion Records, pg 993
VGI Productions, pg 1053
Vista Color Imaging Inc, pg 1059

OKLAHOMA

VCI Entertainment, pg 1052

OREGON

Allegro Corp/Allegro Entertainment Canada Ltd, pg 781
CNS Productions Inc, pg 830
Getty-Dubay Productions, pg 877
Ideascape Inc, pg 894
InterVision Media, pg 902
Medifecta Healthcare Training, pg 938
Memory Lane Videos, pg 938
Norman Beerger Productions, pg 958
Odyssey Productions Inc, pg 961
Producers Studio, pg 984
Rex, pg 995
TeleVideos, pg 1036

PENNSYLVANIA

Argentine Productions Inc, pg 789
Bang Pictures, pg 802
Beholder Productions Inc, pg 804
Bergwall Productions Inc, pg 805
Himalayan Institute Audio/Video, pg 889
Innovision Media Group, pg 899
JPL, pg 906
Main Point Productions, pg 929
Video Communication Productions Inc, pg 1054
Video/Film Associates, pg 1055
The Videohouse Inc, pg 1057
Videosmith Inc, pg 1057
Vision Video, pg 1058
The Whale Video Co, pg 1065

SOUTH CAROLINA

American Production Services LLC, pg 785
BJU Press, pg 808
Encore Video Productions, pg 861
Go To Team, pg 879
Stages Video Productions, pg 1023
Venture Media, pg 1052

TENNESSEE

Abingdon Press, pg 772
American Blackguard Inc, pg 784
Cokesbury, pg 831
Marine Geographic, pg 931
Running Pony Productions LLC, pg 1000
Word Label Group, pg 1069

TEXAS

CEV Multimedia Ltd, pg 823
Chalk Dust Co, pg 823
Communication Arts Multimedia Inc, pg 832
Dallas Learning Solutions, pg 842
The Editing Co, pg 857
Educational Video Network, pg 857
First Group Communications Inc, pg 868
McNee Productions Inc, pg 935
Mediaforce Productions, pg 937
Julye Newlin Productions Inc, pg 956
Sportsmen on Film Inc, pg 1021
Stage Directions, pg 1022
TopCat Records LLC, pg 1042
Writer's AudioShop/Davenport Productions, pg 1070

UTAH

K-SAR Video & DVD Productions, pg 907
One Stop CD Shop LLC, pg 963
San Juan School District Heritage Language Resource Center, pg 1002

VERMONT

Dialect Accent Specialists Inc, pg 846
Multicultural Media, pg 950
Wilson McLeran Inc, pg 1067

VIRGINIA

CALIBRE, pg 816
Cinebar Productions Inc, pg 826
County Sales, pg 837
D&B Television & Video Productions Inc, pg 842
Dorst MediaWorks Inc, pg 851
Limelight Communications Inc, pg 921
Metro Productions, pg 939
Rocktown Media, pg 998

WASHINGTON

Bennett-Watt HD Productions Inc, pg 805
Center for Touch Drawing, pg 822
ChristianAnswers.Net™, pg 825
College of Nursing, Washington State University, pg 831
Victory Studios, pg 1054

WISCONSIN

Audio Visual of Milwaukee Inc, pg 795
Aylmer Press, pg 801
Excel Duplication Services, pg 864
Her Own Words LLC, pg 888
Knowledge Unlimited Inc, pg 912
Meridian Studios, pg 939
NEWIST/CESA 7, pg 956
Plank Road Publishing Inc, pg 976
USAV Group Inc, pg 1050
Video Wisconsin Inc, pg 1056
Watts Communications Inc, pg 1062

ALBERTA

Black Media Works, pg 808

BRITISH COLUMBIA

Norlynn Audio Visual Services, pg 958
Triad Communications Ltd, pg 1044
West Eagle Films Inc, pg 1064

NEWFOUNDLAND AND LABRADOR

Vidcraft Productions Ltd, pg 1054

ONTARIO

ADS Media, pg 777
Art Gallery of Ontario, pg 791
DebsVoice, pg 844
ETHOS Ltd, pg 863
GAPC (General Assembly Production Centre), pg 875
Image Video Services & Productions, pg 895
McNabb & Connolly, pg 935
Purefire Communications Inc, pg 987
RB Productions, pg 992
Shaw Street Productions, pg 1008
Weston Woods Canada, pg 1064

QUEBEC

National Film Board of Canada/Office National du Film du Canada, pg 952

SASKATCHEWAN

plan9films, pg 976

DVD Rentals

ARIZONA

Arizona Public Media, pg 790

CALIFORNIA

Auslender Productions/Celestial Images, pg 797
Les Blank Films Inc, pg 809
Cavalcade Productions Inc, pg 821
Griggs Productions Inc, pg 882
Visual Communications - Southern California Asian American Studies Central Inc, pg 1059
Western Instructional Television Inc, pg 1064

GEORGIA

Thompson-Mitchell & Associates Inc, pg 1039

ILLINOIS

RBR Productions, pg 992
Terra Nova Films Inc, pg 1037

INDIANA

Agency for Instructional Technology (AIT), pg 778
InterComm, pg 900

MARYLAND

Kramer Communications Video Production, pg 913

MASSACHUSETTS

Documentary Educational Resources Inc, pg 850
Merrimack Films, pg 939

MICHIGAN

Digi Sign Design LLC, pg 847
Meuninck's Media Methods Inc, pg 940

MISSOURI

Cable Films & Video, pg 816
Show-Me Audio-Visual, pg 1009

NEW HAMPSHIRE

Chip Taylor Communications LLC, pg 1032

NEW JERSEY

Alden Films, pg 780
Business Education Films, pg 815
Euro-Pacific Film & Video Productions Inc, pg 863
Films of the Nations, pg 868

NEW MEXICO

National Information Center for Educational Media (NICEM)/MediaSleuth, pg 952

NEW YORK

Icarus Film Inc, pg 893
New Day Films, pg 955
Third World Newsreel/Camera News Inc, pg 1039

VIRGINIA

Filmakers Library, pg 867

WASHINGTON

ChristianAnswers.Net™, pg 825

WISCONSIN

Her Own Words LLC, pg 888
NEWIST/CESA 7, pg 956

ONTARIO

McNabb & Connolly, pg 935

QUEBEC

National Film Board of Canada/Office National du Film du Canada, pg 952

Educational Program Distributors

ALASKA

Skyriver Films, pg 1013

ARIZONA

CyberIconics International, pg 841
Drumbeat Indian Arts Inc, pg 852
Tellens Inc, pg 1037
TSG Publishing Foundation Inc USA, pg 1046

ARKANSAS

Master Books, pg 933
Mullikin Agency, pg 949

CALIFORNIA

Allied Artists International Inc, pg 781
Anchor Bay Entertainment LLC, pg 786
Ark Media Group Ltd, pg 790
Astronomical Society of the Pacific, pg 792
Backstage Pass Entertainment Inc, pg 801
Barbosa Video Services, pg 802
Bennett Media Corp, pg 805
Les Blank Films Inc, pg 809
Blue Dolphin Multimedia, pg 809
C & M Publishing Co, pg 816
California Language Laboratories, pg 817
Cambridge Documentary Films Inc, pg 818
Chesney Communications, pg 824
Clarity Sound & Light, pg 829
Coast Learning Systems, pg 830
Concept Associates Inc, pg 834
Crystal Productions, pg 840
Crystal Pyramid Productions™, pg 840
Davidson Films Inc, pg 843
DawnSignPress, pg 844
Deja View Video, pg 845
Direct Cinema Ltd Inc, pg 848
Discovery Education - Los Angeles, pg 848
Eastman Corp, pg 856
ECONEWS (Environmental Television Series) & (Environmental Directions Radio Series), pg 856
eFootage LLC, pg 858
Em Gee Film Library, pg 860
Feldenkrais® Movement Institute, pg 866
Forte Productions, pg 871
411 Video Information, pg 872
Geddes Productions LLC, pg 876
Glenn Photo Supply, pg 878
Glenn Video Vistas Ltd, pg 878
Global Village Productions, pg 879
Golden State Dance Teachers Association (GSDTA), pg 880
Hay House Inc, pg 886
Increase Video/Silver Mine Video, pg 897
Institute of Precision Muscle Balancing, pg 899
Ishtar Films, pg 902
Joyce Media Inc, pg 906
Kantola Productions LLC, pg 908
KPBS TV FM-San Diego, pg 913
Krishnamurti Foundation of America, pg 913
Latham Foundation Publications, pg 916
Learn Quickly, pg 917
Learning Communications LLC, pg 917
Live Wire Media, pg 923
Madera Video, pg 927
Main Street Media Inc, pg 929
MarVista Entertainment Inc, pg 933
Medcom Inc, pg 936
monterey media inc, pg 945
monterey video, pg 946
Moose School Productions, pg 946
Multi-Media Mathematics, pg 949
Music World/Vocal Power School, pg 951
New & Unique Videos™, pg 955
Nolte Media, pg 958

PROGRAMMING — VIDEO

Educational Program Distributors (continued)

CALIFORNIA (continued)

Noontide Press, pg 958
ODC Publishing, pg 961
Pacific Media, pg 967
Panorama Publishing Co, pg 968
Pentrex Media Group LLC, pg 972
People Skills International, pg 972
Players Press, pg 977
Point Lobos Productions, pg 977
Pyramid Media, pg 987
QCI International, pg 988
Regent Press Publishers & Printers, pg 994
Revelli, pg 995
Rhino Home Video, pg 996
Russ InVision Co/AbridgeClub.com, pg 1001
Sea Studios Foundation, pg 1005
SevenStar Communications, pg 1007
Sodanceabit, pg 1015
Theatre Arts Video Library, pg 1038
Thinking Allowed Productions, pg 1038
TMW Media Group, pg 1041
University of Southern California, pg 1050
The Video Project, pg 1056
Visual Communications - Southern California Asian American Studies Central Inc, pg 1059
ViVi Co, pg 1060
Warner Home Video Inc, pg 1062
White Lotus Foundation, pg 1065
Xenon Pictures Inc, pg 1071

COLORADO

Crown Ministries International, pg 840
Gaiam Inc, pg 875
Inferno Film Productions LLC, pg 897
InJoy Birth & Parenting Education, pg 898
Jeppesen, pg 905
Meriwether Publishing Ltd, pg 939
National Institute for Trial Advocacy (NITA), pg 953
Stretching Inc, pg 1026

CONNECTICUT

Cine-Med Inc, pg 826
Creative Arts Television, pg 838
Crossroads Video, pg 840
Hartley Film Foundation, pg 885
Pictures of Record Inc, pg 975
Really Good Stuff, pg 992
The Taunton Press Inc, pg 1032
Weston Woods Studios Inc, pg 1064

DELAWARE

Intercollegiate Studies Institute Inc (ISI), pg 900
So Smart Productions, pg 1015
University Media Services, pg 1049

DISTRICT OF COLUMBIA

American Chemical Society (ACS), pg 784
Art Museum of the Americas, pg 791
Biblical Archaeology Society (BAS), pg 806
Durrin Productions Inc, pg 854
Grocery Manufacturers Association (GMA), pg 882
Sano Videos, pg 1002
Systems Impact Inc, pg 1031
USCCB Publishing, pg 1051
VSA, pg 1061

FLORIDA

ACE Video Resources Software, pg 774
Allegro Productions Inc, pg 781
America By Air Stock Footage Library, pg 783
Bisk Education, pg 808
Capital Communications Inc, pg 819
Cifex Corp, pg 826
EarthDesign Inc, pg 855
Global Video Distributors Inc, pg 879
I M P A C T Publishing Inc, pg 893
Liberty Publishing Co Inc, pg 919
Potentials Unlimited, pg 979
ThirdWave Learning Inc, pg 1039

GEORGIA

American Association for Vocational Instructional Materials (AAVIM), pg 783
Robert Benedetto, pg 805
Gingerbread Group, pg 878
Little Mammoth Media, pg 923
LYRASIS, pg 927
New Leaf Distributing Co, pg 955
School Media Associates LLC, pg 1004
Skyhoundz, pg 1013

HAWAII

Ka Io Productions Inc, pg 907
Source School of Tantra Yoga Inc, pg 1019

IDAHO

University of Idaho Engineering Outreach, pg 1049

ILLINOIS

ABSA Productions Inc, pg 772
African American Images, pg 778
Britannica Film & Video, pg 812
Cahokia Mounds Museum Society, pg 816
CCH Continuing Education, pg 821
CCore Media Inc, pg 821
Centrax Corp, pg 823
Chicago Satellite & Video, pg 825
Discovery Education - Chicago, pg 848
Encyclopaedia Britannica Inc, pg 861
Film Ideas, pg 867
1st Financial Training Services Inc, pg 868
International Historic Films Inc, pg 901
Learning Seed, pg 917
Liturgy Training Publications, pg 923
Magna Systems Inc, pg 928
Moviecraft Inc, pg 947
National Safety Council (NSC), pg 953
Nightingale-Conant Corp, pg 957
Perspectives Media, pg 973
Prevent Blindness America, pg 981
Questar Inc, pg 989
Research Press Co, pg 995
Terra Nova Films Inc, pg 1037
Theosophical Publishing House, pg 1038

INDIANA

Agency for Instructional Technology (AIT), pg 778
Career & Self Directed Extended Programs at Purdue University, pg 820
Educational Video Group Inc, pg 857
Herff Jones | Nystrom, pg 888
Solution Tree, pg 1015

IOWA

Accelerated Learning Foundation, pg 773
Championship Productions Inc, pg 823
Kendall/Hunt Publishing Co, pg 909
Kirkwood Community College, pg 911
Perfection Learning Corp, pg 973

KANSAS

Day Star Productions, pg 844
Yarn Barn of Kansas, pg 1072

KENTUCKY

Hammond Communications Group, pg 884
KET The Kentucky Network, pg 910
The Learning House Inc, pg 917
Media Resources, pg 937
National Geographic Learning, pg 952
WaxWorks VideoWorks, pg 1063

MAINE

Slim Goodbody Corp, pg 1013
WoodenBoat Publications, pg 1069

MARYLAND

Adventure Productions LLC, pg 778
Paul H Brookes Publishing Co, pg 814
DSR Computer Technology Specialists Inc, pg 853
Hearing Loss Association of America (HLAA), pg 887
James Agee Film Project, pg 904
Library Video Network (LVN), pg 920
MMI Corp, pg 944
Recorded Books LLC, pg 993
RLJ Entertainment Inc, pg 997
Sign Media Inc, pg 1011
Total AV Systems, pg 1042

MASSACHUSETTS

Award Productions, pg 800
Cheng & Tsui Co, pg 824
Commonwealth Films Inc, pg 832
Documentary Educational Resources Inc, pg 850
Education Development Center Inc (EDC), pg 857
Emergency Film Group, pg 860
Home Inc, pg 890
In the Wild Productions, pg 897
Limelight Productions Inc, pg 921
Media Marketing Associates Inc, pg 937
Merrimack Films, pg 939
The New Film Company Inc, pg 955
Penfield Productions Ltd, pg 971
Sinauer Associates Inc, pg 1011
WGBH Production Group, pg 1065

MICHIGAN

Digi Sign Design LLC, pg 847
Emery-Pratt Co, pg 860
HighScope Press, pg 889
MSU Technologies, pg 949
Prakken Publications Inc, pg 980
The Program Source International, pg 985
Resource Development Co LLC, pg 995
Society of Manufacturing Engineers (SME), pg 1015
Technology Learning Services, pg 1035
VMS Inc, pg 1060
Zondervan, A HarperCollins Company, pg 1074

MINNESOTA

American Choral Catalog Ltd, pg 784
EMC/Paradigm Publishing, pg 860
Festival Films, pg 866
Harris Communications Inc, pg 885
Hazelden Publishing & Educational Services, pg 886
JIST Publishing, pg 905
Llewellyn Publications, pg 923
Whole Person Associates Inc, pg 1066

MISSOURI

Annenberg Learner, pg 787
Cable Films & Video, pg 816
Marsh Media, pg 931
Phoenix/BFA/Coronet, pg 974
SOM Publishing Co, pg 1015
Vedanta Society of St Louis, pg 1052

MONTANA

High Plains Films, pg 889

NEBRASKA

B & B Video Productions Inc, pg 801
Vision Maker Media, pg 1058

NEVADA

DVDs4Less, pg 854
The Larry Little Co, pg 923

NEW HAMPSHIRE

Captain Fiddle Music & Publications, pg 820
French American Music Enterprises, pg 873
Frey Scientific, pg 873
Heinemann, pg 887
Chip Taylor Communications LLC, pg 1032

NEW JERSEY

Alden Films, pg 780
Comex Systems Inc, pg 832
Dance Horizons Video, pg 842
Educational Impressions, pg 857
Ergo Media Inc, pg 862
Euro-Pacific Film & Video Productions Inc, pg 863
Jointure for Community Adult Education Inc, pg 906

Kultur International Films Ltd Inc, pg 914
Lucerne Media, pg 925
MIB Mediaworks, pg 941
Milestone Film & Video Inc, pg 943
A W Peller & Associates Inc, pg 971
Princeton Book Company, Publishers, pg 982
SES World Skies, pg 1007
Shanachie Entertainment Corp, pg 1008
John Wiley & Sons Inc, pg 1066

NEW MEXICO

National Information Center for Educational Media (NICEM)/ MediaSleuth, pg 952
Uncharted Country Publishing, pg 1048

NEW YORK

Ambrose Video Publishing Inc, pg 783
American Management Association®, pg 784
Artistic Video, pg 791
Asia Society, pg 792
ATA Trading Corp/Favorite TV Inc, pg 792
Beekman Books Inc, pg 804
Benchmark Media, pg 805
Michael Blackwood Productions Inc, pg 808
Broad Street Inc, pg 812
Brooklyn Botanic Garden, pg 814
Billy Budd Films Inc, pg 814
The Bureau for At-Risk Youth, pg 815
Criterion Collection, pg 839
Cross-Cultural Communications, pg 839
De Nonno Productions Inc (DPI), pg 844
Downtown Community Television Center (DCTV), pg 851
Educational Activities Inc, pg 857
Albert Ellis Institute (AEI), pg 859
Film-Makers Cooperative, pg 867
Films for the Humanities & Sciences, pg 868
Films Media Group, pg 868
French American Cultural Exchange (FACE), pg 873
William Greaves Productions Inc, pg 882
Guidance Associates Inc Center for Humanities, pg 883
Guilford Publications, pg 883
Hallel Communications, pg 884
Homespun Video, pg 890
Human Relations Media, pg 892
IAI Video, pg 893
Icarus Film Inc, pg 893
Image Makers of Pittsford/Image Maker Productions, pg 895
The Institute Inc, pg 899
Irish Music Corp, pg 902
Janson Media, pg 904
L & S Video Inc, pg 914
Lifetime Television®, pg 920
March of Dimes Foundation, pg 930
Maryknoll Productions, pg 933
Mastervision Inc, pg 933
Mathmadeeasy.com, pg 934
McGraw Hill Financial, pg 935
Meridian Education Corp, pg 939
Metropolitan Opera Guild, pg 940
MRG Productions Inc, pg 948
Practising Law Institute, pg 980
Random House Children's Books, pg 991
Richter Productions Inc, pg 996
Science Television Co, pg 1005
Select Media Inc, pg 1006
Shopware, pg 1009
SISU Home Entertainment Inc, pg 1012
Third World Newsreel/Camera News Inc, pg 1039
Transformational Education Initiatives, pg 1043
Video Aided Instruction Inc, pg 1054
Video Catalogue Co Inc, pg 1054
Videofashion Network, pg 1056
VIEW Inc (Video International Entertainment World Inc), pg 1058
White Buffalo Multimedia, pg 1065
Willow Mixed Media Inc, pg 1067
Women Make Movies Inc, pg 1069
Wonderwomen™ Enterprises, pg 1069
Zeitgeist Films Ltd, pg 1073

NORTH CAROLINA

Carolina Biological Supply Co, pg 820
Crystal Pictures Inc, pg 840
Do It Yourself Inc - DIY Video Corp, pg 849
Eli Research Group, pg 859
Hart Inc, pg 885
Ladyslipper Inc, pg 915
Laurel Hill Press, pg 916
Media Consultants Inc, pg 936
Sinclair Institute, pg 1012
Thinking Maps Inc, pg 1038
Vide-O-Go/That's Infotainment!, pg 1054
World Wide Pictures Inc, pg 1070

NORTH DAKOTA

UND Television Center, pg 1048

OHIO

Alegra House Publishers, pg 780
Curtis Inc, pg 841
Electronic Vision Inc (EV), pg 859
Franciscan Media, pg 872
Griesinger Films LLC, pg 882
McGraw-Hill School Education Group, pg 935
Shelburne Films, pg 1008
South-Western Publishing Co, pg 1019
Treehaus Communications Inc, pg 1044
WOUB Public Media, pg 1070
The Wright Group, pg 1070

OKLAHOMA

University of Oklahoma Academic Media & Digital Services, pg 1050
VCI Entertainment, pg 1052

OREGON

CNS Productions Inc, pg 830
Cooking by the Book, pg 836
Encounter Video Inc, pg 861
Garden Valley Productions, pg 875
Getty-Dubay Productions, pg 877
International Loving Touch Foundation Inc, pg 901
InterVision Media, pg 902
The Keyboard Workshop, pg 910
Medifecta Healthcare Training, pg 938
Memory Lane Videos, pg 938
Sugar Mountain PR, pg 1028

PENNSYLVANIA

Bergwall Productions Inc, pg 805
Bullfrog Films Inc, pg 815
Corinth Films Inc, pg 836
Discovery Education - South Burlington, pg 848
FMP Media Solutions Inc, pg 870
Karol Media Inc, pg 908
Movies Unlimited, pg 947
MVD Entertainment Group, pg 951
Rahlic Publishing Co, pg 990
Red Fox Enterprises, pg 993
The Fred Rogers Co, pg 998
S I Video Sales Group, pg 1001
Schlessinger Media, pg 1004
Vision Video, pg 1058
The Whale Video Co, pg 1065

SOUTH CAROLINA

American Production Services LLC, pg 785

TENNESSEE

Abingdon Press, pg 772
American Blackguard Inc, pg 784
Center for Southern Folklore Inc, pg 822
Marine Geographic, pg 931
National School Products, pg 953
Spring Arbor Distributors, pg 1022

TEXAS

CEV Multimedia Ltd, pg 823
Chalk Dust Co, pg 823
Critical Information Network, pg 839
Dallas Learning Solutions, pg 842
db interactive Inc, pg 844
Educational Video Network, pg 857
EduMedia of Sugar Land, Texas, pg 857
Executive Development Systems, pg 864
Language Plus Inc, pg 916
Shadow Play Records & Video, pg 1007
Teleometrics International, pg 1036
University of Texas at Austin - Petroleum Extension Service, pg 1050

UTAH

San Juan School District Heritage Language Resource Center, pg 1002

VERMONT

Dialect Accent Specialists Inc, pg 846
Multicultural Media, pg 950
Perceptions Inc, pg 973
Dorothy Tod Films, pg 1041
University of Vermont, Instructional Television Dept, pg 1050
Wilson McLeran Inc, pg 1067

VIRGINIA

CACI Productions Group, pg 816
CDR Communications Inc, pg 822
Close Up Foundation, pg 830
Filmakers Library, pg 867
National Audiovisual Center - National Technical Information Service (NTIS), pg 952
Once Around, pg 963

WASHINGTON

AEON Communications Inc, pg 778
Bennett-Watt HD Productions Inc, pg 805
ChristianAnswers.Net™, pg 825
College of Nursing, Washington State University, pg 831
Global Net Productions Inc, pg 879
Intermedia Inc, pg 900
John McLean Media, pg 905
Media Resources Inc, pg 937
Ritchie's Perfect Press, pg 997
Terra Productions LLC, pg 1037

WEST VIRGINIA

Focus on Animals, pg 870
Harpers Ferry Historical Association, pg 885

WISCONSIN

Attainment Co Inc, pg 793
Aylmer Press, pg 801
Equiservices Publishing, pg 862
Her Own Words LLC, pg 888
Knowledge Unlimited Inc, pg 912
Nancy's Notions, pg 952
NEWIST/CESA 7, pg 956
Plank Road Publishing Inc, pg 976
Willow Creek Press Inc, pg 1067

WYOMING

Trance Formations Unlimited, pg 1043

ALBERTA

Global Television Station, pg 879

BRITISH COLUMBIA

Credo Interactive Inc, pg 839
Thompson Rivers University Open Learning, pg 1039

ONTARIO

BFS Entertainment & Multimedia Limited, pg 806
Canadian Filmmakers Distribution Center (CFMDC), pg 818
Canadian Learning Co Inc, pg 818
Canamedia Inc, pg 818
Entertainment One Distribution, pg 861
Kineticvideo.com, pg 911
Life Cycle Books Ltd, pg 920
McIntyre Media Inc, pg 935
McNabb & Connolly, pg 935
Scholastic Canada Ltd, pg 1004
Sullivan Home Entertainment, pg 1028
TVO/Ontario Educational Communications Authority (OECA), pg 1046
University of Toronto, Classroom Technology Support, pg 1050
Wintergreen Learning Materials, pg 1068

QUEBEC

National Film Board of Canada/ Office National du Film du Canada, pg 952
Les Productions Via Le Monde (Daniel Bertolino) Inc, pg 985
Whalley-Abbey Media Holdings Inc, pg 1065

PROGRAMMING — VIDEO

Educational Program Producers

ALABAMA

AVS Media Group, pg 800
CMEInfo, pg 830
Leo Ticheli Productions, pg 1040

ALASKA

Alaska Film Services Inc, pg 779
Aurora Films, pg 797

ARIZONA

Aardvark Productions LLC, pg 772
Candee Productions Inc, pg 819
CyberIconics International, pg 841
Direct Current Video Productions, pg 848
Film Creations Ltd, pg 867
Fox 10 Productions (KSAZ-TV), pg 872
MediaWorks, pg 938
Merestone, pg 938
Phoenix VideoFilms®, pg 974
Tellens Inc, pg 1037
TSG Publishing Foundation Inc USA, pg 1046
Video Media Productions (VMP), pg 1055

ARKANSAS

Cedar Crest Studio, pg 822
Jones Film Video, pg 906
Live'N'Loud, pg 923
Mullikin Agency, pg 949
White Diamond Productions, pg 1065

CALIFORNIA

A Go Go Films, pg 771
Access Video in Berkeley, pg 773
Action Video, pg 775
Allied Artists International Inc, pg 781
Animax, pg 787
Artichoke Productions, pg 791
Astronomical Society of the Pacific, pg 792
Backstage Pass Entertainment Inc, pg 801
Barbosa Video Services, pg 802
Big Door, pg 807
Les Blank Films Inc, pg 809
Burrud Productions Inc, pg 815
C & M Publishing Co, pg 816
California Language Laboratories, pg 817
Cambridge Documentary Films Inc, pg 818
Cavalcade Productions Inc, pg 821
Chesney Communications, pg 824
Chick Russell Communications, pg 825
Clarity Sound & Light, pg 829
Classic Images, pg 829
Coast Learning Systems, pg 830
Coastline Productions, pg 831
Concept Associates Inc, pg 834
Concrete Images, pg 835
Cox Media, pg 837
Crystal Productions, pg 840
Crystal Pyramid Productions™, pg 840
Custom Video Productions Inc, pg 841
Davidson Films Inc, pg 843
DawnSignPress, pg 844
Deja View Video, pg 845
Design Media, pg 845
Developmental Studies Center, pg 846
Digital Outpost, pg 847
Direct Images Interactive Inc, pg 848
Discovery Education - Los Angeles, pg 848
Dogma Studios, pg 850
Dolphin MultiMedia Inc, pg 850
Duck Studios, pg 853
Eastman Corp, pg 856
ECONEWS (Environmental Television Series) & (Environmental Directions Radio Series), pg 856
Face Digital Post, pg 865
Feldenkrais® Movement Institute, pg 866
First Camera, pg 868
Forte Productions, pg 871
Gateways Books & Tapes, pg 876
Geddes Productions LLC, pg 876
Global Village Productions, pg 879
Goal Productions, pg 879
Bruce Goldberg Inc, pg 880
Havas Edge, pg 885
Hay House Inc, pg 886
imageReal Pictures LLC, pg 896
Images in Motion Media Inc, pg 896
Imageworks, pg 896
Increase Video/Silver Mine Video, pg 897
Institute of Precision Muscle Balancing, pg 899
Ishtar Films, pg 902
ITV Productions, pg 903
Joyce Media Inc, pg 906
Kantola Productions LLC, pg 908
Kavich Reynolds Productions Inc, pg 908
KION-TV, pg 911
KPBS TV FM-San Diego, pg 913
Krishnamurti Foundation of America, pg 913
Latham Foundation Publications, pg 916
Learn Quickly, pg 917
Learning Communications LLC, pg 917
Live Wire Media, pg 923
Madera Video, pg 927
Main Street Media Inc, pg 929
Maximus Media Inc, pg 934
McCune Audio-Video-Lighting, pg 935
Medcom Inc, pg 936
Media Magic, pg 937
The Media Staff Inc, pg 937
Mist Media Inc, pg 944
monterey media inc, pg 945
Moose School Productions, pg 946
Multi-Media Mathematics, pg 949
Music World/Vocal Power School, pg 951
New & Unique Videos™, pg 955
New Circuit Films LLC, pg 955
New Era Media, pg 955
Nolte Media, pg 958
Noontide Press, pg 958
ODC Publishing, pg 961
On-Trax Inc, pg 963
Pacific Media, pg 967
Panorama Publishing Co, pg 968
Penrose Productions, pg 972
Pentrex Media Group LLC, pg 972
Players Press, pg 977
PM Productions, pg 977
Point Lobos Productions, pg 977
Point of View Productions, pg 977
Prime Cut Productions, pg 982
Pyramid Media, pg 987
QCI International, pg 988
QRS Software Services, pg 988
Quilt in a Day, pg 989
Regent Press Publishers & Printers, pg 994
Dick Reizner Film & Video, pg 994
RetinaVision Productions, pg 995
Revelli, pg 995
Rhythms Productions (Tom Thumb Music), pg 996
Glenn Roland Films, pg 998
Russ InVision Co/AbridgeClub.com, pg 1001
SBS Productions, pg 1003
Sea Studios Foundation, pg 1005
SevenStar Communications, pg 1007
SNAP, pg 1014
Sodanceabit, pg 1015
Staylor-Made Communications Inc, pg 1024
Still N'Motion, pg 1025
The Studio Center, pg 1026
Tam Communications Inc, pg 1031
Tele-Video Production Services (TVPS), pg 1036
Theatre Arts Video Library, pg 1038
Thinking Allowed Productions, pg 1038
Tigar Hare Studios, pg 1040
Timestream Video, pg 1041
TMW Media Group, pg 1041
Toon Makers, pg 1042
Total Media Group, pg 1042
Twin Peaks Creative, pg 1047
University of Southern California, pg 1050
Videolady, pg 1057
Videowerks, pg 1057
Vineyard Video & Photography, pg 1058
Visions Plus, pg 1058
Visual Communications - Southern California Asian American Studies Central Inc, pg 1059
ViVi Co, pg 1060
WalkerVision Interarts, pg 1061
Wavemaker Media Design, pg 1062
Webster Communications, pg 1063
West Coast Projections Inc, pg 1063
The Wine Appreciation Guild Ltd, pg 1067
Xenon Pictures Inc, pg 1071
Zamacona Productions, pg 1073

COLORADO

Paul L Anderson Productions Inc, pg 786
Apogee Communications Group, pg 788
Centre Communications Inc, pg 823
Crown Ministries International, pg 840
Daylight Productions & Rentals, pg 844
Flashback Media Productions, pg 869
Gaiam Inc, pg 875
Greg Hensley Productions, pg 888
Inferno Film Productions LLC, pg 897
InJoy Birth & Parenting Education, pg 898
Jeppesen, pg 905
Meriwether Publishing Ltd, pg 939
National Institute for Trial Advocacy (NITA), pg 953
Renaissance Media, pg 994
Rocky Mountain Audio/Video Productions Inc, pg 998
Scott Resources Inc, pg 1005
Stretching Inc, pg 1026
Transtar Entertainment Co Inc, pg 1043
Visual Communications Group Inc, pg 1059

CONNECTICUT

Antenna International, pg 787
Applebox Studio, pg 788
Biomedical Media Communications Dept, pg 807
Broadcast Video Productions LLC, pg 813
Cine-Med Inc, pg 826
Creative Arts Television, pg 838
Crossroads Video, pg 840
Essex Television Group Inc, pg 862
Fox Connecticut, pg 872
The Gary-Paul Agency, pg 875
Geomatrix Productions, pg 877
Hartley Film Foundation, pg 885
Ironik Design & Post, pg 902
MCC Films, pg 935
Moving Pictures, pg 947
New London Media, pg 956
P&P Studios Inc, pg 968
Pictures of Record Inc, pg 975
The Taunton Press Inc, pg 1032
Weston Woods Studios Inc, pg 1064

DELAWARE

So Smart Productions, pg 1015
University Media Services, pg 1049

DISTRICT OF COLUMBIA

American Chemical Society (ACS), pg 784
Art Museum of the Americas, pg 791
Biblical Archaeology Society (BAS), pg 806
Durrin Productions Inc, pg 854
Grocery Manufacturers Association (GMA), pg 882
Hillmann & Carr Inc, pg 889
O'Keefe Communications Inc, pg 961
Sano Videos, pg 1002
Systems Impact Inc, pg 1031
VSA, pg 1061
Yellow Cat Productions Inc, pg 1072

FLORIDA

Accel Video Productions, pg 773
Accord Productions, pg 773
ACE Video Resources Software, pg 774
Allegro Productions Inc, pg 781
America By Air Stock Footage Library, pg 783
Bisk Education, pg 808
Blackburst Entertainment, pg 808
Capital Communications Inc, pg 819
Civins Productions Inc, pg 828
CopShopMiami.com, pg 836
Courter Films LLC, pg 837
DME Studios, pg 849
EarthDesign Inc, pg 855
Eastern Video, pg 856
Easy Edit Video Inc, pg 856
Ed Ethridge Productions Inc, pg 863
Global Cyber-Visions, pg 879
Gulf Coast Audio Visual Producers Inc, pg 883
Home Shopping Network (HSN), pg 890

PROGRAMMING — VIDEO

Educational Program Producers (continued)

NEVADA

Aardvark Video & Media Productions, pg 772
DVDs4Less, pg 854
Encore Productions Inc, pg 861
HDTV Productions Inc, pg 886
JCS Video Productions, pg 904
The Larry Little Co, pg 923
Tetrahedron LLC, pg 1037

NEW HAMPSHIRE

Academic & Campus Technology Services, pg 773
Apertura, pg 788
Captain Fiddle Music & Publications, pg 820
Channell One Video, pg 824
Chip Taylor Communications LLC, pg 1032
The Troupe, pg 1045

NEW JERSEY

Alden Films, pg 780
CFP Video Productions Inc, pg 823
Comex Systems Inc, pg 832
Dance Horizons Video, pg 842
DWJ Television, pg 854
Educational Impressions, pg 857
Euro-Pacific Film & Video Productions Inc, pg 863
Half Moon Video Productions, pg 883
Laurel Video Productions, pg 916
Lucerne Media, pg 925
Megavideo Productions, pg 938
MIB Mediaworks, pg 941
Ray Mueller Productions, pg 949
Optisonics Productions, pg 965
Producer East Productions, pg 983
Public Eye Productions, pg 987
Bill Quinn Productions, pg 989
Reider Photography & Video Productions, pg 994
Selden Associates, pg 1006
Shamrock Communications, pg 1008
Shanachie Entertainment Corp, pg 1008
Suede Interactive, pg 1027
Telequest Inc, pg 1036
TimeSteps Productions Inc, pg 1041
VCSvideo, pg 1052
John Wiley & Sons Inc, pg 1066

NEW MEXICO

Michael Dunn Productions, pg 853
Production Outfitters, pg 984
Rainbow International Inc/Rainbow Productions Inc, pg 990
Uncharted Country Publishing, pg 1048

NEW YORK

American History Workshop (NY) Inc, pg 784
American Management Association®, pg 784
American Montage Inc, pg 784
Artistic Video, pg 791
Asia Society, pg 792
aurora productions, pg 797
BC Video Inc, pg 803
Benchmark Media, pg 805
Bevilacqua Studios, pg 806
Michael Blackwood Productions Inc, pg 808
Brian Film Productions LLC, pg 812
Broad Street Inc, pg 812
Brooklyn Botanic Garden, pg 814
Billy Budd Films Inc, pg 814
The Bureau for At-Risk Youth, pg 815
Buzzco Associates Inc, pg 816
Clarity Media Group, pg 829
Conversation Arts Media, pg 836
Criterion Collection, pg 839
Cross-Cultural Communications, pg 839
De Nonno Productions Inc (DPI), pg 844
dM works, pg 849
Downtown Community Television Center (DCTV), pg 851
Educational Activities Inc, pg 857
Eye on Dance, pg 865
Fanlight Productions, pg 865
Films for the Humanities & Sciences, pg 868
Films Media Group, pg 868
Florentine Films, pg 870
Karen Frankel Productions, pg 872
William Greaves Productions Inc, pg 882
Greyfalcon House, pg 882
Guidance Associates Inc Center for Humanities, pg 883
Guilford Publications, pg 883
Hallel Communications, pg 884
Hello World Communications, pg 888
Homespun Video, pg 890
Human Relations Media, pg 892
IAI Video, pg 893
Image Makers of Pittsford/Image Maker Productions, pg 895
The Institute Inc, pg 899
Kamen Entertainment Group Inc, pg 908
Ketchum Pleon Change, pg 910
L A Bruell Inc, pg 914
L & S Video Inc, pg 914
Lavine Production Group, pg 917
Lifetime Television®, pg 920
Long Island Video Enterprises Live Inc, pg 924
March of Dimes Foundation, pg 930
Neal Marshad Productions, pg 931
Maryknoll Productions, pg 933
Mastervision Inc, pg 933
Mathmadeeasy.com, pg 934
Meridian Education Corp, pg 939
Mood Creations Ltd, pg 946
Jack Morton Worldwide, pg 946
MRG Productions Inc, pg 948
MRY, pg 949
New Horizon Studios, pg 955
News Broadcast Network, pg 956
Northeast Video Productions Inc, pg 959
Shelly Palmer Production, pg 968
Pat Kogan Productions Inc, pg 970
Peckham Productions Inc, pg 970
Polestar Films & Associated Arts Ltd, pg 978
Practising Law Institute, pg 980
PrimaLux Video Inc, pg 982
PrimeLight Productions Inc, pg 982
Random House Children's Books, pg 991
Richter Productions Inc, pg 996
Science Television Co, pg 1005
Shopware, pg 1009
D S Simon Productions, pg 1011
SISU Home Entertainment Inc, pg 1012
Spoken Arts Inc, pg 1021
Suggs Media Productions Inc, pg 1028
Sunrise Media LLC, pg 1028
TBA Global Events, pg 1032
TeleTime Productions, pg 1036
Third World Newsreel/Camera News Inc, pg 1039
Tobin Productions Inc, pg 1041
Video Aided Instruction Inc, pg 1054
Video Catalogue Co Inc, pg 1054
Videofashion Network, pg 1056
Videograf, pg 1057
Vidicom Inc, pg 1057
VIEW Inc (Video International Entertainment World Inc), pg 1058
Weigl Publishers Inc, pg 1063
Alan Weiss Productions, pg 1063
White Buffalo Multimedia, pg 1065
Willow Mixed Media Inc, pg 1067
WNET/NET TELECON, pg 1069
Wonderwomen™ Enterprises, pg 1069
Zelman Studios Ltd, pg 1073

NORTH CAROLINA

All Pro Media Inc, pg 780
Pat Appleson Studios Inc, pg 788
The Communications Group Inc, pg 833
Crystal Pictures Inc, pg 840
Do It Yourself Inc - DIY Video Corp, pg 849
Eli Research Group, pg 859
Horizon Video Productions Inc, pg 891
Kino Mountain Productions LLC, pg 911
Laurel Hill Press, pg 916
LCW Productions LLC, pg 917
Media Consultants Inc, pg 936
Moving Pictures, pg 948
PACE Worldwide, pg 966
Sinclair Institute, pg 1012
Unifour Productions Inc, pg 1048

NORTH DAKOTA

UND Television Center, pg 1048

OHIO

Advent Media Inc, pg 778
Alegra House Publishers, pg 780
Russ Beckner Pictures, pg 804
CET, pg 823
Creative Technology, pg 838
Curtis Inc, pg 841
Cuyahoga Community College Media Center, pg 841
Electronic Vision Inc (EV), pg 859
Franciscan Media, pg 872
Griesinger Films LLC, pg 882
Image Video Teleproductions Inc, pg 895
Lyon Video Inc, pg 927
MainSail Production Services Inc, pg 929
Maslowski Productions, pg 933
McGraw-Hill School Education Group, pg 935
R&B Communications Inc, pg 991
Shelburne Films, pg 1008
South-Western Publishing Co, pg 1019
Take 1 Media Services, pg 1031
Treehaus Communications Inc, pg 1044
VGI Productions, pg 1053
Vista Color Imaging Inc, pg 1059
WOUB Public Media, pg 1070
The Wright Group, pg 1070

OKLAHOMA

CSI/Orion, pg 840
Institute for Teaching & Learning Excellence (ITLE), pg 899
University of Oklahoma Academic Media & Digital Services, pg 1050
VCI Entertainment, pg 1052

OREGON

A KTVA Production LLC, pg 771
ADD Plus, pg 776
CNS Productions Inc, pg 830
Cooking by the Book, pg 836
Encounter Video Inc, pg 861
Garden Valley Productions, pg 875
Getty-Dubay Productions, pg 877
Ideascape Inc, pg 894
Inner Explorations, pg 898
International Loving Touch Foundation Inc, pg 901
InterVision Media, pg 902
The Keyboard Workshop, pg 910
KPDX-TV Production Center, pg 913
KVAL, pg 914
Medifecta Healthcare Training, pg 938
Memory Lane Videos, pg 938
Odyssey Productions Inc, pg 961
Producers Studio, pg 984
Production West, pg 985
Spirit Media, pg 1021

PENNSYLVANIA

AiH Group Inc, pg 779
Argentine Productions Inc, pg 789
Bang Pictures, pg 802
Beholder Productions Inc, pg 804
Bergwall Productions Inc, pg 805
CCI Communications Inc, pg 821
Discovery Education - South Burlington, pg 848
FMP Media Solutions Inc, pg 870
Fusion Brand Experiences, pg 874
Innovision Media Group, pg 899
JPL, pg 906
Kensington Falls Animation, pg 909
Main Point Productions, pg 929
Muderick Media, pg 949
Panta Rhei Media Inc, pg 968
Pemcor LLC, pg 971
Production Masters Inc (PMI), pg 984
Rahlic Publishing Co, pg 990
S I Video Sales Group, pg 1001
Scala Inc, pg 1003
Schlessinger Media, pg 1004
Video Communication Productions Inc, pg 1054
Video/Film Associates, pg 1055
The Videohouse Inc, pg 1057
Vision Video, pg 1058
Visual Sound Inc, pg 1059
The Whale Video Co, pg 1065
WHYY Inc, pg 1066

RHODE ISLAND

Sound-FX-Design, pg 1017

SOUTH CAROLINA

American Production Services LLC, pg 785
BJU Press, pg 808
Encore Video Productions, pg 861
Stages Video Productions, pg 1023
Venture Media, pg 1052

Educational Program Rentals

PROGRAMMING — VIDEO

Educational Program Rentals (continued)

NEW YORK (continued)

Films Media Group, pg 868
William Greaves Productions Inc, pg 882
Hallel Communications, pg 884
Icarus Film Inc, pg 893
Image Makers of Pittsford/Image Maker Productions, pg 895
Richter Productions Inc, pg 996
Third World Newsreel/Camera News Inc, pg 1039
VIEW Inc (Video International Entertainment World Inc), pg 1058

NORTH CAROLINA

Crystal Pictures Inc, pg 840
Sinclair Institute, pg 1012
World Wide Pictures Inc, pg 1070

OHIO

Franciscan Media, pg 872
Treehaus Communications Inc, pg 1044
WOUB Public Media, pg 1070

OREGON

The Keyboard Workshop, pg 910

PENNSYLVANIA

Bullfrog Films Inc, pg 815
Rahlic Publishing Co, pg 990

TENNESSEE

Center for Southern Folklore Inc, pg 822

VERMONT

University of Vermont, Instructional Television Dept, pg 1050

VIRGINIA

Filmakers Library, pg 867
Once Around, pg 963

WASHINGTON

ChristianAnswers.Net™, pg 825
Intermedia Inc, pg 900

WISCONSIN

Her Own Words LLC, pg 888
NEWIST/CESA 7, pg 956

MANITOBA

Spectra Video Productions Ltd, pg 1020

ONTARIO

Kineticvideo.com, pg 911
McNabb & Connolly, pg 935
University of Toronto, Classroom Technology Support, pg 1050

QUEBEC

Les Productions Via Le Monde (Daniel Bertolino) Inc, pg 985

Feature Program Distributors

ARIZONA

Drumbeat Indian Arts Inc, pg 852

CALIFORNIA

Allied Artists International Inc, pg 781
Anchor Bay Entertainment LLC, pg 786
Ariztical Entertainment Inc, pg 790
Ben Barry & Associates Inc, pg 803
Les Blank Films Inc, pg 809
Coastline Licensing International Inc, pg 831
Crystal Pyramid Productions™, pg 840
Direct Cinema Ltd Inc, pg 848
Em Gee Film Library, pg 860
411 Video Information, pg 872
Glenn Photo Supply, pg 878
Glenn Video Vistas Ltd, pg 878
Increase Video/Silver Mine Video, pg 897
MarVista Entertainment Inc, pg 933
MGM Home Video, pg 941
monterey media inc, pg 945
monterey video, pg 946
National Lampoon, pg 953
Noontide Press, pg 958
Pacific Media, pg 967
Palardo Productions, pg 968
Players Press, pg 977
Rhino Home Video, pg 996
Universal Studios Home Entertainment, pg 1049
Warner Home Video Inc, pg 1062
Worldwide Entertainment Corp, pg 1070
Xenon Pictures Inc, pg 1071

COLORADO

Crown Ministries International, pg 840
Inferno Film Productions LLC, pg 897

CONNECTICUT

Really Good Stuff, pg 992

FLORIDA

Cifex Corp, pg 826
Distribution Video & Audio (DVA), pg 849
Global Video Distributors Inc, pg 879

IDAHO

Lagoon Video, pg 915

ILLINOIS

CCore Media Inc, pg 821
Chicago Satellite & Video, pg 825
Facets Multi-Media Inc, pg 865
Film Ideas, pg 867
Moviecraft Inc, pg 947

IOWA

Right Stuf Inc, pg 997

KENTUCKY

KET The Kentucky Network, pg 910
WaxWorks VideoWorks, pg 1063

MARYLAND

DSR Computer Technology Specialists Inc, pg 853
Recorded Books LLC, pg 993
RLJ Entertainment Inc, pg 997

MASSACHUSETTS

Award Productions, pg 800
Penfield Productions Ltd, pg 971

MINNESOTA

Festival Films, pg 866

MISSOURI

Cable Films & Video, pg 816
Swank Audio Visuals, pg 1029

MONTANA

High Plains Films, pg 889

NEBRASKA

B & B Video Productions Inc, pg 801
Leo Films, pg 919

NEVADA

DVDs4Less, pg 854

NEW HAMPSHIRE

Chip Taylor Communications LLC, pg 1032

NEW JERSEY

Dance Horizons Video, pg 842
Ergo Media Inc, pg 862
MIB Mediaworks, pg 941
Milestone Film & Video Inc, pg 943

NEW YORK

A&E Television Networks LLC, pg 771
ATA Trading Corp/Favorite TV Inc, pg 792
Criterion Collection, pg 839
Film-Makers Cooperative, pg 867
First Run Features, pg 869
French American Cultural Exchange (FACE), pg 873
Guidance Associates Inc Center for Humanities, pg 883
HB-Content, pg 886
HBO Home Video Inc, pg 886
Icarus Film Inc, pg 893
Janson Media, pg 904
Kino International Corp, pg 911
Mastervision Inc, pg 933
MRG Productions Inc, pg 948
Parabola Audio/Video, pg 968
SISU Home Entertainment Inc, pg 1012
Synaptic Digital, pg 1030
Third World Newsreel/Camera News Inc, pg 1039
VIEW Inc (Video International Entertainment World Inc), pg 1058
Women Make Movies Inc, pg 1069

NORTH CAROLINA

Baker & Taylor Inc, pg 801
Crystal Pictures Inc, pg 840
Ladyslipper Inc, pg 915
Vide-O-Go/That's Infotainment!, pg 1054
World Wide Pictures Inc, pg 1070

OHIO

Network Technologies Inc, pg 955

OKLAHOMA

VCI Entertainment, pg 1052

OREGON

InterVision Media, pg 902
Nostalgia Family Video Inc, pg 959
Pacific International Enterprises Inc (PIE), pg 967

PENNSYLVANIA

Corinth Films Inc, pg 836
Movies Unlimited, pg 947
MVD Entertainment Group, pg 951

SOUTH CAROLINA

BJU Press, pg 808

TENNESSEE

American Blackguard Inc, pg 784
Spring Arbor Distributors, pg 1022

TEXAS

Marengo Films, pg 931

VIRGINIA

CACI Productions Group, pg 816

WASHINGTON

Bennett-Watt HD Productions Inc, pg 805
White Rain Films Ltd, pg 1065

WISCONSIN

Knowledge Unlimited Inc, pg 912

ALBERTA

Global Television Station, pg 879

ONTARIO

BFS Entertainment & Multimedia Limited, pg 806
Cambium Catalyst International (CCI), pg 817
Canadian Filmmakers Distribution Center (CFMDC), pg 818
Canadian Learning Co Inc, pg 818
Entertainment One Distribution, pg 861
Life Cycle Books Ltd, pg 920
McNabb & Connolly, pg 935
Sullivan Home Entertainment, pg 1028
Universal Studios Canada Inc, pg 1049

QUEBEC

Les Productions Via Le Monde (Daniel Bertolino) Inc, pg 985

Feature Program Producers

ALABAMA

CMEInfo, pg 830

ALASKA

Aurora Films, pg 797

PROGRAMMING — VIDEO

Feature Program Producers (continued)

VIRGINIA

BES Studios, pg 805
D&B Television & Video Productions Inc, pg 842
Gingerbread Productions, pg 878
Metro Productions, pg 939
Water Bearer Films Inc, pg 1062

WASHINGTON

Bennett-Watt HD Productions Inc, pg 805
Hamilton Studio, pg 884
Victory Studios, pg 1054

WISCONSIN

5th Floor Recording Co, pg 867
Knowledge Unlimited Inc, pg 912
Wisconsin Public Television, pg 1068

WYOMING

Bridger Productions Inc, pg 812

ALBERTA

Global Television Station, pg 879
HBW Entertainment Inc, pg 886

NEWFOUNDLAND AND LABRADOR

Vidcraft Productions Ltd, pg 1054

ONTARIO

GAPC (General Assembly Production Centre), pg 875
Image Video Services & Productions, pg 895

QUEBEC

Kerrigan Productions Inc, pg 910
Productions Grand Nord Quebec Inc, pg 985
Les Productions Via Le Monde (Daniel Bertolino) Inc, pg 985

Feature Program Rentals

CALIFORNIA

Les Blank Films Inc, pg 809
Direct Cinema Ltd Inc, pg 848

ILLINOIS

Facets Multi-Media Inc, pg 865

MISSOURI

Cable Films & Video, pg 816
The Phoenix Learning Group Inc, pg 974
Swank Audio Visuals, pg 1029
University of Missouri-Columbia, pg 1050

NEW YORK

First Run Features, pg 869
Icarus Film Inc, pg 893
Kino International Corp, pg 911
Third World Newsreel/Camera News Inc, pg 1039
VIEW Inc (Video International Entertainment World Inc), pg 1058

NORTH CAROLINA

Crystal Pictures Inc, pg 840
World Wide Pictures Inc, pg 1070

OREGON

Nostalgia Family Video Inc, pg 959

BRITISH COLUMBIA

Video In Studios/Video Out Distribution, pg 1055

ONTARIO

McNabb & Connolly, pg 935
WESCAM Inc, pg 1063

QUEBEC

Les Productions Via Le Monde (Daniel Bertolino) Inc, pg 985

Film on Videocassette Distributors

CALIFORNIA

Adolph Gasser Inc, pg 776
Ametron Audio/Video, pg 785
California Language Laboratories, pg 817
Cambridge Documentary Films Inc, pg 818
411 Video Information, pg 872
FXF Productions Inc, pg 874
Increase Video/Silver Mine Video, pg 897
Ishtar Films, pg 902
MarVista Entertainment Inc, pg 933
MGM Home Video, pg 941
monterey media inc, pg 945
National Lampoon, pg 953
Pacific Media, pg 967
Players Press, pg 977
Point Lobos Productions, pg 977
QRS Software Services, pg 988
Regent Press Publishers & Printers, pg 994
Revelli, pg 995
Rhino Home Video, pg 996
RM Films International, pg 997
Visual Communications - Southern California Asian American Studies Central Inc, pg 1059
Western Instructional Television Inc, pg 1064

COLORADO

Gaiam Inc, pg 875
InJoy Birth & Parenting Education, pg 898

CONNECTICUT

Cine-Med Inc, pg 826
Ironik Design & Post, pg 902

DISTRICT OF COLUMBIA

Library of Congress, Motion Picture, Broadcasting & Recorded Sound Division, pg 919

FLORIDA

Global Video Distributors Inc, pg 879

GEORGIA

School Media Associates LLC, pg 1004

ILLINOIS

Britannica Film & Video, pg 812
Film Ideas, pg 867

IOWA

Right Stuf Inc, pg 997

MARYLAND

dbF a Media Company, pg 844

MASSACHUSETTS

The New Film Company Inc, pg 955

MINNESOTA

Aggressive Records Audio Duplication LLC, pg 778
Harris Communications Inc, pg 885

MISSOURI

Cable Films & Video, pg 816
SOM Publishing Co, pg 1015

NEBRASKA

Leo Films, pg 919

NEW HAMPSHIRE

Chip Taylor Communications LLC, pg 1032

NEW MEXICO

National Information Center for Educational Media (NICEM)/ MediaSleuth, pg 952
SouthWest Organizing Project (SWOP), pg 1019

NEW YORK

Michael Blackwood Productions Inc, pg 808
DRG Records Inc, pg 852
Flash Electronics Inc, pg 869
French American Cultural Exchange (FACE), pg 873
HB-Content, pg 886
Human Relations Media, pg 892
Mastervision Inc, pg 933
SISU Home Entertainment Inc, pg 1012
Spoken Arts Inc, pg 1021
Tisch School of the Arts, pg 1041
Women Make Movies Inc, pg 1069

NORTH CAROLINA

Vide-O-Go/That's Infotainment!, pg 1054

OREGON

Nostalgia Family Video Inc, pg 959

TEXAS

Dallas Learning Solutions, pg 842
Lamb & Lion Ministries, pg 915

VERMONT

Multicultural Media, pg 950

VIRGINIA

National Audiovisual Center - National Technical Information Service (NTIS), pg 952
Water Bearer Films Inc, pg 1062

WASHINGTON

Global Net Productions Inc, pg 879
Intermedia Inc, pg 900
White Rain Films Ltd, pg 1065

WEST VIRGINIA

Focus on Animals, pg 870

ONTARIO

Entertainment One Distribution, pg 861
Life Cycle Books Ltd, pg 920

Film on Videocassette Producers

ARIZONA

Merestone, pg 938
Phoenix VideoFilms®, pg 974

ARKANSAS

Live'N'Loud, pg 923

CALIFORNIA

ACDC Audio CD & Cassette, pg 774
Artichoke Productions, pg 791
ATV Video Center Inc, pg 793
Auslender Productions/Celestial Images, pg 797
Big Door, pg 807
Les Blank Films Inc, pg 809
California Language Laboratories, pg 817
Cambridge Documentary Films Inc, pg 818
Concrete Images, pg 835
Dogma Studios, pg 850
FXF Productions Inc, pg 874
Havas Edge, pg 885
Ishtar Films, pg 902
Main Street Media Inc, pg 929
MGM Home Video, pg 941
monterey media inc, pg 945
National Lampoon, pg 953
Pacific Media, pg 967
Players Press, pg 977
Point Lobos Productions, pg 977
QRS Software Services, pg 988
Regent Press Publishers & Printers, pg 994
RetinaVision Productions, pg 995
Revelli, pg 995
RM Films International, pg 997
Glenn Roland Films, pg 998
Tam Communications Inc, pg 1031
TVA Productions, pg 1046
Vedanta Press & Catalog, pg 1052
Video Resources Inc, pg 1056
Visual Communications - Southern California Asian American Studies Central Inc, pg 1059
Wavemaker Media Design, pg 1062

COLORADO

The Cinema Lab, pg 827
CSI Films, pg 840
Gaiam Inc, pg 875
InJoy Birth & Parenting Education, pg 898

CONNECTICUT

Cine-Med Inc, pg 826
The Gary-Paul Agency, pg 875
Ironik Design & Post, pg 902
MCC Films, pg 935

DISTRICT OF COLUMBIA

Hillmann & Carr Inc, pg 889
USCCB Publishing, pg 1051

FLORIDA

Chatterbox Productions Inc, pg 824
Civins Productions Inc, pg 828
Courter Films LLC, pg 837
Motion Image Group LLC, pg 947
Sunfire Communications Inc, pg 1028
Tight Line Productions, pg 1040

GEORGIA

Continental Film & Video, pg 835
Guerrilla Productions LLC, pg 883

HAWAII

Hyperspective Studios Inc, pg 893

ILLINOIS

Analog Free Media, pg 786
Britannica Film & Video, pg 812
Cresta Creative, pg 839
QuickSet International Inc, pg 989
Richter Studios, pg 996
Video Impressions, pg 1055

INDIANA

AVA Productions, pg 798
Digital Rain LLC, pg 847

IOWA

Right Stuf Inc, pg 997

KENTUCKY

Idle Minds Productions Inc, pg 894
Donna Lawrence Productions, pg 917
Prosper Media Group Inc, pg 986

MARYLAND

The Ahern Group, pg 779
dbF a Media Company, pg 844

MASSACHUSETTS

Heliotrope Studios, pg 887
In the Wild Productions, pg 897

MICHIGAN

K&R All Media Productions Inc, pg 908

MINNESOTA

Aggressive Records Audio Duplication LLC, pg 778
House of Cinemagraphics, pg 891
Worthwhile Films, pg 1070

MISSOURI

Fambrough & Associates Inc, pg 865
SOM Publishing Co, pg 1015

NEBRASKA

Leo Films, pg 919

NEW HAMPSHIRE

Chip Taylor Communications LLC, pg 1032

NEW JERSEY

Producer East Productions, pg 983
Suede Interactive, pg 1027

NEW YORK

Michael Blackwood Productions Inc, pg 808
Blue Barn Pictures Inc, pg 809
DRG Records Inc, pg 852
Duplication Depot Inc, pg 853
William Greaves Productions Inc, pg 882
HB-Content, pg 886
Human Relations Media, pg 892
Kinetic Arts, pg 911
Mastervision Inc, pg 933
Polestar Films & Associated Arts Ltd, pg 978
Shadow Pictures Inc, pg 1007
SISU Home Entertainment Inc, pg 1012
Spoken Arts Inc, pg 1021

NORTH CAROLINA

Pat Appleson Studios Inc, pg 788
The Communications Group Inc, pg 833
Moving Pictures, pg 948

OHIO

Advent Media Inc, pg 778
Creative Technology, pg 838
Lyon Video Inc, pg 927
Maslowski Productions, pg 933
Musicol Recording, pg 951
R&B Communications Inc, pg 991
Take 1 Media Services, pg 1031

OREGON

Ideascape Inc, pg 894
Odyssey Productions Inc, pg 961
Rex, pg 995

PENNSYLVANIA

Argentine Productions Inc, pg 789
FMP Media Solutions Inc, pg 870
Innovision Media Group, pg 899

SOUTH CAROLINA

Encore Video Productions, pg 861

TENNESSEE

American Blackguard Inc, pg 784

TEXAS

Dallas Learning Solutions, pg 842
The Editing Co, pg 857
Lamb & Lion Ministries, pg 915
Julye Newlin Productions Inc, pg 956
Romar Learning, pg 999
Stage Directions, pg 1022

UTAH

K-SAR Video & DVD Productions, pg 907

VERMONT

Edgewood Studios, pg 857
Multicultural Media, pg 950

VIRGINIA

Metro Productions, pg 939

WASHINGTON

Bennett-Watt HD Productions Inc, pg 805
White Rain Films Ltd, pg 1065

WISCONSIN

Meridian Studios, pg 939
Video Wisconsin Inc, pg 1056

ALBERTA

Black Media Works, pg 808

BRITISH COLUMBIA

Triad Communications Ltd, pg 1044

NEWFOUNDLAND AND LABRADOR

Vidcraft Productions Ltd, pg 1054

NORTHWEST TERRITORIES

Yellowknife Films Inc, pg 1072

Film on Videocassette Rentals

ARIZONA

Video Learning Library, pg 1055

CALIFORNIA

Ametron Audio/Video, pg 785
Les Blank Films Inc, pg 809
Cambridge Documentary Films Inc, pg 818
Regent Press Publishers & Printers, pg 994
Visual Communications - Southern California Asian American Studies Central Inc, pg 1059

MASSACHUSETTS

Documentary Educational Resources Inc, pg 850

NEW HAMPSHIRE

Chip Taylor Communications LLC, pg 1032

NEW MEXICO

National Information Center for Educational Media (NICEM)/MediaSleuth, pg 952

NEW YORK

William Greaves Productions Inc, pg 882

OREGON

Nostalgia Family Video Inc, pg 959

Film Short, *see* Theatrical Short

Film—Television, *see* Television Film

Foreign Program Distributors

ARIZONA

Drumbeat Indian Arts Inc, pg 852

CALIFORNIA

Allied Artists International Inc, pg 781
Ariztical Entertainment Inc, pg 790
Backstage Pass Entertainment Inc, pg 801
Ben Barry & Associates Inc, pg 803
Les Blank Films Inc, pg 809
Crystal Pyramid Productions™, pg 840
Discovery Education - Los Angeles, pg 848
Em Gee Film Library, pg 860
411 Video Information, pg 872
Glenn Photo Supply, pg 878
Glenn Video Vistas Ltd, pg 878
Glenray Productions Inc, pg 878
Madera Video, pg 927
MarVista Entertainment Inc, pg 933
New & Unique Videos™, pg 955
Pacific Media, pg 967
Rhino Home Video, pg 996

CONNECTICUT

Really Good Stuff, pg 992

DISTRICT OF COLUMBIA

Art Museum of the Americas, pg 791
Biblical Archaeology Society (BAS), pg 806
Sano Videos, pg 1002

FLORIDA

Cifex Corp, pg 826
Distribution Video & Audio (DVA), pg 849
Global Video Distributors Inc, pg 879

GEORGIA

On-Line Productions, pg 963

ILLINOIS

Facets Multi-Media Inc, pg 865
International Historic Films Inc, pg 901
Moviecraft Inc, pg 947

IOWA

Right Stuf Inc, pg 997

KENTUCKY

WaxWorks VideoWorks, pg 1063

MARYLAND

DSR Computer Technology Specialists Inc, pg 853
Recorded Books LLC, pg 993

MASSACHUSETTS

Cheng & Tsui Co, pg 824
Documentary Educational Resources Inc, pg 850

MICHIGAN

Digi Sign Design LLC, pg 847

PROGRAMMING — VIDEO

Foreign Program Distributors (continued)

MINNESOTA

Festival Films, pg 866

MISSOURI

Cable Films & Video, pg 816

NEBRASKA

Leo Films, pg 919

NEW HAMPSHIRE

Chip Taylor Communications LLC, pg 1032

NEW JERSEY

Ergo Media Inc, pg 862
Euro-Pacific Film & Video Productions Inc, pg 863
Films of the Nations, pg 868
Kultur International Films Ltd Inc, pg 914
Milestone Film & Video Inc, pg 943

NEW MEXICO

National Information Center for Educational Media (NICEM)/MediaSleuth, pg 952

NEW YORK

Applause Learning Resources, pg 788
ATA Trading Corp/Favorite TV Inc, pg 792
Criterion Collection, pg 839
Cross-Cultural Communications, pg 839
Downtown Community Television Center (DCTV), pg 851
Fanlight Productions, pg 865
Film-Makers Cooperative, pg 867
Films for the Humanities & Sciences, pg 868
First Run Features, pg 869
French American Cultural Exchange (FACE), pg 873
Hallel Communications, pg 884
Icarus Film Inc, pg 893
Irish Music Corp, pg 902
Janson Media, pg 904
Kino International Corp, pg 911
Maryknoll Productions, pg 933
Mastervision Inc, pg 933
Meridian Education Corp, pg 939
MRG Productions Inc, pg 948
Richter Productions Inc, pg 996
Shopware, pg 1009
SISU Home Entertainment Inc, pg 1012
Third World Newsreel/Camera News Inc, pg 1039
VIEW Inc (Video International Entertainment World Inc), pg 1058
Women Make Movies Inc, pg 1069

NORTH CAROLINA

Crystal Pictures Inc, pg 840
Vide-O-Go/That's Infotainment!, pg 1054

OHIO

Network Technologies Inc, pg 955
Ohio State University Foreign Language Publications, pg 961

OREGON

Nostalgia Family Video Inc, pg 959

PENNSYLVANIA

Anchor Distributors, pg 786
Bullfrog Films Inc, pg 815
Corinth Films Inc, pg 836
FMP Media Solutions Inc, pg 870
Movies Unlimited, pg 947
MVD Entertainment Group, pg 951
S I Video Sales Group, pg 1001

TENNESSEE

Spring Arbor Distributors, pg 1022

TEXAS

Educational Video Network, pg 857
Marengo Films, pg 931

VIRGINIA

National Audiovisual Center - National Technical Information Service (NTIS), pg 952
Water Bearer Films Inc, pg 1062

WASHINGTON

Bennett-Watt HD Productions Inc, pg 805

WISCONSIN

Plank Road Publishing Inc, pg 976

BRITISH COLUMBIA

Video In Studios/Video Out Distribution, pg 1055

ONTARIO

BFS Entertainment & Multimedia Limited, pg 806
Cambium Catalyst International (CCI), pg 817
Canadian Filmmakers Distribution Center (CFMDC), pg 818
Entertainment One Distribution, pg 861

QUEBEC

Les Productions Via Le Monde (Daniel Bertolino) Inc, pg 985

Foreign Program Producers

ARIZONA

Aardvark Productions LLC, pg 772
Candee Productions Inc, pg 819

CALIFORNIA

Classic Images, pg 829
Crystal Pyramid Productions™, pg 840
Custom Video Productions Inc, pg 841
Discovery Education - Los Angeles, pg 848
Glenray Productions Inc, pg 878
International Contact Inc, pg 900
ITV Productions, pg 903
Lightyear Entertainment, pg 921
Madera Video, pg 927
McCune Audio-Video-Lighting, pg 935
New & Unique Videos™, pg 955
New Circuit Films LLC, pg 955
Pacific Media, pg 967
Prime Cut Productions, pg 982
QRS Software Services, pg 988
Total Media Group, pg 1042
TVA Productions, pg 1046
Twin Peaks Creative, pg 1047
Videowerks, pg 1057
Vineyard Video & Photography, pg 1058
Webster Communications, pg 1063

COLORADO

Rocky Mountain Audio/Video Productions Inc, pg 998

CONNECTICUT

Broadcast Video Productions LLC, pg 813
Ironik Design & Post, pg 902

DISTRICT OF COLUMBIA

Art Museum of the Americas, pg 791
Biblical Archaeology Society (BAS), pg 806
Hillmann & Carr Inc, pg 889
Sano Videos, pg 1002
Yellow Cat Productions Inc, pg 1072

FLORIDA

Blackburst Entertainment, pg 808
Civins Productions Inc, pg 828
CopShopMiami.com, pg 836
Courter Films LLC, pg 837
Eastern Video, pg 856
Jordan Klein Film & Video (JKFV), pg 906
Sunfire Communications Inc, pg 1028

GEORGIA

Guerrilla Productions LLC, pg 883
Malcolm Neal Productions, pg 954
On-Line Productions, pg 963
Showcase Photo & Video, pg 1009

IDAHO

Wide Eye Productions, pg 1066

ILLINOIS

Chicago Satellite & Video, pg 825
Film Police, pg 867
The Pepper Group, pg 972
20/20 Communications Inc, pg 1047

INDIANA

AVA Productions, pg 798
Road Pictures, pg 997

IOWA

Right Stuf Inc, pg 997

LOUISIANA

Moxie Media, pg 948

MARYLAND

Absolute Hollywood, pg 772
Richard Chisolm Cinematography, pg 825
dbF a Media Company, pg 844
DSR Computer Technology Specialists Inc, pg 853
Kramer Communications Video Production, pg 913

MASSACHUSETTS

Documentary Educational Resources Inc, pg 850
Heliotrope Studios, pg 887
Inter-Media Electronics, pg 899

MICHIGAN

Digi Sign Design LLC, pg 847
K&R All Media Productions Inc, pg 908
K&R's Recording Studios Inc, pg 908

MINNESOTA

Aggressive Records Audio Duplication LLC, pg 778
House of Cinemagraphics, pg 891
Master Communications Group, pg 933
Worthwhile Films, pg 1070

MISSOURI

Cable Films & Video, pg 816
Fambrough & Associates Inc, pg 865

NEVADA

Aardvark Video & Media Productions, pg 772
Encore Productions Inc, pg 861
HDTV Productions Inc, pg 886

NEW HAMPSHIRE

Apertura, pg 788
Chip Taylor Communications LLC, pg 1032

NEW JERSEY

Euro-Pacific Film & Video Productions Inc, pg 863
Half Moon Video Productions, pg 883
MIB Mediaworks, pg 941
Bill Quinn Productions, pg 989
Suede Interactive, pg 1027
Video Ideas Productions, pg 1055

NEW YORK

Applause Learning Resources, pg 788
Blue Barn Pictures Inc, pg 809
Criterion Collection, pg 839
Cross-Cultural Communications, pg 839
Downtown Community Television Center (DCTV), pg 851
Hallel Communications, pg 884
Manhattan Center Studios Inc, pg 930
Neal Marshad Productions, pg 931
Maryknoll Productions, pg 933
Mastervision Inc, pg 933
Jack Morton Worldwide, pg 946
MRG Productions Inc, pg 948
Shelly Palmer Production, pg 968
Pat Kogan Productions Inc, pg 970
PrimaLux Video Inc, pg 982
Richter Productions Inc, pg 996
Shadow Pictures Inc, pg 1007
VIEW Inc (Video International Entertainment World Inc), pg 1058

NORTH CAROLINA

Pat Appleson Studios Inc, pg 788
The Communications Group Inc, pg 833

OHIO

Advent Media Inc, pg 778
Creative Technology, pg 838
Take 1 Media Services, pg 1031
VGI Productions, pg 1053

PENNSYLVANIA

FMP Media Solutions Inc, pg 870
Muderick Media, pg 949
S I Video Sales Group, pg 1001

RHODE ISLAND

Sound-FX-Design, pg 1017

TENNESSEE

Scripps Networks, pg 1005

TEXAS

Alpha Video Productions, pg 782
Cerutti Productions Inc, pg 823
Educational Video Network, pg 857
Omega Productions, pg 962
Omni Intercommunications Inc, pg 962
South Coast Film & Video, pg 1019
Stage Directions, pg 1022

VIRGINIA

CALIBRE, pg 816
D&B Television & Video Productions Inc, pg 842
Gingerbread Productions, pg 878
Metro Productions, pg 939
Water Bearer Films Inc, pg 1062

WASHINGTON

Bennett-Watt HD Productions Inc, pg 805

WISCONSIN

5th Floor Recording Co, pg 867
Midland Video Productions Inc, pg 942
Wisconsin Public Television, pg 1068

WYOMING

Bridger Productions Inc, pg 812

ONTARIO

GAPC (General Assembly Production Centre), pg 875

QUEBEC

Kerrigan Productions Inc, pg 910

Foreign Program Rentals

CALIFORNIA

Les Blank Films Inc, pg 809

GEORGIA

On-Line Productions, pg 963

ILLINOIS

Facets Multi-Media Inc, pg 865

MASSACHUSETTS

Documentary Educational Resources Inc, pg 850

MICHIGAN

Digi Sign Design LLC, pg 847

MISSOURI

Cable Films & Video, pg 816
University of Missouri-Columbia, pg 1050

NEW JERSEY

Euro-Pacific Film & Video Productions Inc, pg 863

NEW YORK

Downtown Community Television Center (DCTV), pg 851
Fanlight Productions, pg 865
First Run Features, pg 869
Hallel Communications, pg 884
Icarus Film Inc, pg 893
Kino International Corp, pg 911
Richter Productions Inc, pg 996
Third World Newsreel/Camera News Inc, pg 1039
VIEW Inc (Video International Entertainment World Inc), pg 1058

NORTH CAROLINA

Crystal Pictures Inc, pg 840

OREGON

Nostalgia Family Video Inc, pg 959

PENNSYLVANIA

Bullfrog Films Inc, pg 815

BRITISH COLUMBIA

Video In Studios/Video Out Distribution, pg 1055

QUEBEC

Les Productions Via Le Monde (Daniel Bertolino) Inc, pg 985

Game, *see* Video Game

Government Program Distributors

CALIFORNIA

Crystal Pyramid Productions™, pg 840
Discovery Education - Los Angeles, pg 848
Em Gee Film Library, pg 860
411 Video Information, pg 872
Glenn Video Vistas Ltd, pg 878
Learning Communications LLC, pg 917
Pyramid Media, pg 987

FLORIDA

ACE Video Resources Software, pg 774
Allegro Productions Inc, pg 781
Bisk Education, pg 808
ThirdWave Learning Inc, pg 1039

ILLINOIS

ABSA Productions Inc, pg 772
CCH Inc, A Wolters Kluwer business, pg 821
CCore Media Inc, pg 821
Film Ideas, pg 867

KENTUCKY

WaxWorks VideoWorks, pg 1063

MARYLAND

DSR Computer Technology Specialists Inc, pg 853
Special Archives Division, Motion Picture Branch, pg 1020

MASSACHUSETTS

Enterprise Media LLC, pg 861
Merrimack Films, pg 939
Penfield Productions Ltd, pg 971

MICHIGAN

Digi Sign Design LLC, pg 847

MINNESOTA

Service Quality Institute, pg 1007

MISSOURI

Phoenix/BFA/Coronet, pg 974
The Phoenix Learning Group Inc, pg 974

NEVADA

DVDs4Less, pg 854

NEW HAMPSHIRE

Chip Taylor Communications LLC, pg 1032

NEW JERSEY

Comex Systems Inc, pg 832

NEW MEXICO

National Information Center for Educational Media (NICEM)/MediaSleuth, pg 952

NEW YORK

Broad Street Inc, pg 812
Downtown Community Television Center (DCTV), pg 851
Films Media Group, pg 868
Monad Trainer's Aide Inc, pg 945
MRG Productions Inc, pg 948
Synaptic Digital, pg 1030
VIEW Inc (Video International Entertainment World Inc), pg 1058
Women Make Movies Inc, pg 1069

NORTH CAROLINA

Baker & Taylor Inc, pg 801
Vide-O-Go/That's Infotainment!, pg 1054

OHIO

Curtis Inc, pg 841

OKLAHOMA

University of Oklahoma Academic Media & Digital Services, pg 1050

OREGON

InterVision Media, pg 902

PENNSYLVANIA

FMP Media Solutions Inc, pg 870

TEXAS

CEV Multimedia Ltd, pg 823

VERMONT

Perceptions Inc, pg 973
University of Vermont, Instructional Television Dept, pg 1050

VIRGINIA

CACI Productions Group, pg 816
National Audiovisual Center - National Technical Information Service (NTIS), pg 952
WETA Production Center, pg 1064

WASHINGTON

Bennett-Watt HD Productions Inc, pg 805

WEST VIRGINIA

Sweetsong Productions, pg 1029

ONTARIO

Entertainment One Distribution, pg 861
Kineticvideo.com, pg 911

Government Program Producers

ALABAMA

CMEInfo, pg 830

ALASKA

Aurora Films, pg 797

ARIZONA

Aardvark Productions LLC, pg 772
Direct Current Video Productions, pg 848
Film Creations Ltd, pg 867
MediaWorks, pg 938
Phoenix VideoFilms®, pg 974
Video Media Productions (VMP), pg 1055

ARKANSAS

White Diamond Productions, pg 1065

CALIFORNIA

Access Video in Berkeley, pg 773
Action Video, pg 775
Animax, pg 787
Barbosa Video Services, pg 802
Big Door, pg 807
Cavalcade Productions Inc, pg 821
Classic Images, pg 829
Concrete Images, pg 835
Cox Media, pg 837
Crystal Pyramid Productions™, pg 840
Custom Video Productions Inc, pg 841
Design Media, pg 845
Digital Outpost, pg 847
Discovery Education - Los Angeles, pg 848

PROGRAMMING — VIDEO

Government Program Producers (continued)

CALIFORNIA (continued)

Dogma Studios, pg 850
Face Digital Post, pg 865
Global Village Productions, pg 879
Goal Productions, pg 879
Havas Edge, pg 885
Imageworks, pg 896
ITV Productions, pg 903
Learning Communications LLC, pg 917
Maximus Media Inc, pg 934
McCune Audio-Video-Lighting, pg 935
Media Magic, pg 937
The Media Staff Inc, pg 937
New & Unique Videos™, pg 955
On-Trax Inc, pg 963
Opticomm-EMCORE, pg 964
PM Productions, pg 977
QRS Software Services, pg 988
Dick Reizner Film & Video, pg 994
Glenn Roland Films, pg 998
SBS Productions, pg 1003
SNAP, pg 1014
Staylor-Made Communications Inc, pg 1024
Still N'Motion, pg 1025
The Studio Center, pg 1026
Tam Communications Inc, pg 1031
Tele-Video Production Services (TVPS), pg 1036
Timestream Video, pg 1041
Total Media Group, pg 1042
TVA Productions, pg 1046
Twin Peaks Creative, pg 1047
Utopia Films, pg 1051
Videowerks, pg 1057
Vineyard Video & Photography, pg 1058
Visions Plus, pg 1058
Zamacona Productions, pg 1073

COLORADO

Apogee Communications Group, pg 788
Daylight Productions & Rentals, pg 844
Flashback Media Productions, pg 869
Rocky Mountain Audio/Video Productions Inc, pg 998
Tatum Video, pg 1032
Transtar Entertainment Co Inc, pg 1043

CONNECTICUT

Applebox Studio, pg 788
Biomedical Media Communications Dept, pg 807
Broadcast Video Productions LLC, pg 813
Fox Connecticut, pg 872
The Gary-Paul Agency, pg 875
Ironik Design & Post, pg 902
Moving Pictures, pg 947
New London Media, pg 956

DISTRICT OF COLUMBIA

Durrin Productions Inc, pg 854
Hillmann & Carr Inc, pg 889
O'Keefe Communications Inc, pg 961
Yellow Cat Productions Inc, pg 1072

FLORIDA

ACE Video Resources Software, pg 774
Allegro Productions Inc, pg 781
Bisk Education, pg 808
Blackburst Entertainment, pg 808
Capital Communications Inc, pg 819
Civins Productions Inc, pg 828
Communications Concepts Inc (CCI), pg 833
CopShopMiami.com, pg 836
Courter Films LLC, pg 837
Eastern Video, pg 856
Easy Edit Video Inc, pg 856
Ed Ethridge Productions Inc, pg 863
Gulf Coast Audio Visual Producers Inc, pg 883
Image Technical Services, pg 895
Jordan Klein Film & Video (JKFV), pg 906
Motion Image Group LLC, pg 947
Roger Scruggs Films, pg 1005
Sunfire Communications Inc, pg 1028
Sunrise Studios, pg 1028
Tel-Air Interests Inc, pg 1035
Video Techniques Inc, pg 1056

GEORGIA

Beachwood Productions, pg 804
Burst Video/Film Inc, pg 815
COMPRO Productions Inc, pg 834
Continental Film & Video, pg 835
Guerrilla Productions LLC, pg 883
Memory Lane Productions, pg 938
On-Line Productions, pg 963
Showcase Photo & Video, pg 1009

HAWAII

Hyperspective Studios Inc, pg 893

IDAHO

Brad Shaw Productions Inc, pg 1008
Wide Eye Productions, pg 1066

ILLINOIS

ABSA Productions Inc, pg 772
Accenture, pg 773
Airways Digital Media, pg 779
Analog Free Media, pg 786
Audio Visual Services Corp, pg 796
Beatty TeleVisual Productions, pg 804
CCH Inc, A Wolters Kluwer business, pg 821
CCore Media Inc, pg 821
Chicago Satellite & Video, pg 825
Film Police, pg 867
IV Media Resources, pg 903
Manning Productions, pg 930
The Pepper Group, pg 972
PSAV® Presentation Services (Hotel Services Division), pg 987
Richter Studios, pg 996
SCI Television Productions LLC, pg 1004
Southern Illinois University, pg 1019
Video I-D Teleproductions Inc, pg 1055
Video Impressions, pg 1055

INDIANA

Advanced Media Integration, pg 777
AVA Productions, pg 798
Covenant Productions®, pg 837
Digital Rain LLC, pg 847
Road Pictures, pg 997

IOWA

The Production House, pg 984

KENTUCKY

Hammond Communications Group, pg 884
Idle Minds Productions Inc, pg 894
The Media Collaboratory, pg 936

LOUISIANA

Moxie Media, pg 948

MAINE

WGME-TV, pg 1065

MARYLAND

Absolute Hollywood, pg 772
The Ahern Group, pg 779
CAS Video Productions, pg 820
CPR MultiMedia Solutions, pg 837
dbF a Media Company, pg 844
DSR Computer Technology Specialists Inc, pg 853
The Image Generators, pg 895
Kramer Communications Video Production, pg 913
Mobile-Video Productions Inc, pg 944

MASSACHUSETTS

Award Productions, pg 800
Enterprise Media LLC, pg 861
Merrimack Films, pg 939
Monadnock Media Inc, pg 945
Northern Light Productions, pg 959
Penfield Productions Ltd, pg 971
TVN-The Video Network, pg 1046
Veritech Corp, pg 1053

MICHIGAN

Benjamin Creative Productions, pg 805
Digi Sign Design LLC, pg 847
K&R All Media Productions Inc, pg 908
K&R's Recording Studios Inc, pg 908

MINNESOTA

Aggressive Records Audio Duplication LLC, pg 778
House of Cinemagraphics, pg 891
Master Communications Group, pg 933
Service Quality Institute, pg 1007
Stoney-Wolf Productions Inc, pg 1025
Vaddio, pg 1051
Worthwhile Films, pg 1070

MISSISSIPPI

Dollarhide Film Inc, pg 850

MISSOURI

Audio-VideoGraphics Inc, pg 795
Fambrough & Associates Inc, pg 865
Hardcastle Films & Video, pg 885

MONTANA

North Country Media Group, pg 959

NEBRASKA

Dog & Pony Productions Inc, pg 850
Rainbow Video Productions Inc, pg 991

NEVADA

Aardvark Video & Media Productions, pg 772
DVDs4Less, pg 854
Encore Productions Inc, pg 861
JCS Video Productions, pg 904

NEW HAMPSHIRE

Apertura, pg 788
Channell One Video, pg 824
NH Movies Inc, pg 957
Chip Taylor Communications LLC, pg 1032
The Troupe, pg 1045

NEW JERSEY

Broadcast Center Studios, pg 813
Comex Systems Inc, pg 832
DWJ Television, pg 854
Half Moon Video Productions, pg 883
Laurel Video Productions, pg 916
MIB Mediaworks, pg 941
Optisonics Productions, pg 965
Bill Quinn Productions, pg 989
Reider Photography & Video Productions, pg 994
Suede Interactive, pg 1027
VCSvideo, pg 1052

NEW MEXICO

Production Outfitters, pg 984

NEW YORK

Ace Video, pg 774
Associated Press Television News, pg 792
aurora productions, pg 797
Blue Barn Pictures Inc, pg 809
Brian Film Productions LLC, pg 812
Clarity Media Group, pg 829
Downtown Community Television Center (DCTV), pg 851
Films Media Group, pg 868
Golden Lamb Productions, pg 880
Hello World Communications, pg 888
Ketchum Pleon Change, pg 910
Mood Creations Ltd, pg 946
Jack Morton Worldwide, pg 946
MRG Productions Inc, pg 948
MRY, pg 949
Northeast Video Productions Inc, pg 959
Shelly Palmer Production, pg 968
PrimaLux Video Inc, pg 982
PrimeLight Productions Inc, pg 982
Richter Productions Inc, pg 996
Suggs Media Productions Inc, pg 1028
Synaptic Digital, pg 1030
Third World Newsreel/Camera News Inc, pg 1039
Time Warner Cable, pg 1040
Tobin Productions Inc, pg 1041
VIEW Inc (Video International Entertainment World Inc), pg 1058
Alan Weiss Productions, pg 1063
WNET/NET TELECON, pg 1069

Government Program Rentals

Industrial Program Distributors

PROGRAMMING — VIDEO

Industrial Program Distributors (continued)

NEVADA

DVDs4Less, pg 854

NEW HAMPSHIRE

Channell One Video, pg 824
Frey Scientific, pg 873
Chip Taylor Communications LLC, pg 1032

NEW JERSEY

MIB Mediaworks, pg 941

NEW MEXICO

National Information Center for Educational Media (NICEM)/MediaSleuth, pg 952

NEW YORK

Broad Street Inc, pg 812
Fanlight Productions, pg 865
Films Media Group, pg 868
Guidance Associates Inc Center for Humanities, pg 883
HB-Content, pg 886
KickedUp Media Group Inc, pg 910
Monad Trainer's Aide Inc, pg 945
MRG Productions Inc, pg 948
Richter Productions Inc, pg 996
Synaptic Digital, pg 1030
VIEW Inc (Video International Entertainment World Inc), pg 1058

NORTH CAROLINA

Baker & Taylor Inc, pg 801
The International Society of Automation (ISA), pg 901
Media Consultants Inc, pg 936
Vide-O-Go/That's Infotainment!, pg 1054

NORTH DAKOTA

UND Television Center, pg 1048

OHIO

Curtis Inc, pg 841
South-Western Publishing Co, pg 1019

OREGON

InterVision Media, pg 902

PENNSYLVANIA

Bergwall Productions Inc, pg 805
FMP Media Solutions Inc, pg 870
Karol Media Inc, pg 908

TENNESSEE

Marine Geographic, pg 931
Zion Music Group, pg 1074

TEXAS

CEV Multimedia Ltd, pg 823
Critical Information Network, pg 839
Dykeman Associates Inc, pg 854
University of Texas at Austin - Petroleum Extension Service, pg 1050

VERMONT

Perceptions Inc, pg 973
University of Vermont, Instructional Television Dept, pg 1050
Wilson McLeran Inc, pg 1067

VIRGINIA

CACI Productions Group, pg 816
Coastal Training Technologies Corp, pg 831
WETA Production Center, pg 1064

WASHINGTON

Bennett-Watt HD Productions Inc, pg 805
Media Resources Inc, pg 937

ONTARIO

Canadian Learning Co Inc, pg 818
Kineticvideo.com, pg 911

QUEBEC

Les Productions Via Le Monde (Daniel Bertolino) Inc, pg 985

Industrial Program Producers

ALABAMA

CMEInfo, pg 830
Media Visions Inc, pg 937
Leo Ticheli Productions, pg 1040

ALASKA

Alaska Video Postcards Inc, pg 779
Aurora Films, pg 797

ARIZONA

Aardvark Productions LLC, pg 772
Candee Productions Inc, pg 819
CyberIconics International, pg 841
Direct Current Video Productions, pg 848
Film Creations Ltd, pg 867
Fox 10 Productions (KSAZ-TV), pg 872
MediaWorks, pg 938
Merestone, pg 938
On-Site Video, pg 963
Phoenix VideoFilms®, pg 974
Video Media Productions (VMP), pg 1055

ARKANSAS

Cedar Crest Studio, pg 822
Jones Film Video, pg 906
Live'N'Loud, pg 923
Mullikin Agency, pg 949
White Diamond Productions, pg 1065

CALIFORNIA

A Go Go Films, pg 771
Academy Savant, pg 773
Access Video in Berkeley, pg 773
Action Video, pg 775
AM Productions, pg 783
Artichoke Productions, pg 791
Barbosa Video Services, pg 802
Big Door, pg 807
Cavalcade Productions Inc, pg 821
Chesney Communications, pg 824
Chick Russell Communications, pg 825
Classic Images, pg 829
Coastline Productions, pg 831
Concrete Images, pg 835
Cox Media, pg 837
Crystal Pyramid Productions™, pg 840
Custom Video Productions Inc, pg 841
Davidson Films Inc, pg 843
Deja View Video, pg 845
Design Media, pg 845
Digital Outpost, pg 847
Direct Images Interactive Inc, pg 848
Discovery Education - Los Angeles, pg 848
Dogma Studios, pg 850
Dolphin MultiMedia Inc, pg 850
Face Digital Post, pg 865
First Camera, pg 868
FXF Productions Inc, pg 874
Global Village Productions, pg 879
Goal Productions, pg 879
Havas Edge, pg 885
Image Integration, pg 895
imageReal Pictures LLC, pg 896
Imageworks, pg 896
Increase Video/Silver Mine Video, pg 897
ITV Productions, pg 903
Kavich Reynolds Productions Inc, pg 908
The Kenwood Group, pg 909
KION-TV, pg 911
Main Street Media Inc, pg 929
Maximus Media Inc, pg 934
McCune Audio-Video-Lighting, pg 935
Media Magic, pg 937
The Media Staff Inc, pg 937
Mist Media Inc, pg 944
New & Unique Videos™, pg 955
Nolte Media, pg 958
On-Trax Inc, pg 963
Panorama Productions, pg 968
Penrose Productions, pg 972
PM Productions, pg 977
Point of View Productions, pg 977
PSI Inc, pg 987
QRS Software Services, pg 988
Dick Reizner Film & Video, pg 994
RetinaVision Productions, pg 995
Glenn Roland Films, pg 998
Ron Roy Productions/Moodtapes, pg 1000
SBS Productions, pg 1003
Screen Door Entertainment Inc, pg 1005
SNAP, pg 1014
Staylor-Made Communications Inc, pg 1024
Still N'Motion, pg 1025
The Studio Center, pg 1026
Tam Communications Inc, pg 1031
Tele-Video Production Services (TVPS), pg 1036
Tigar Hare Studios, pg 1040
Timestream Video, pg 1041
Total Media Group, pg 1042
TVA Productions, pg 1046
Twin Peaks Creative, pg 1047
Videografix LLC, pg 1057
Videolady, pg 1057
Videowerks, pg 1057
Vineyard Video & Photography, pg 1058
Visions Plus, pg 1058
WalkerVision Interarts, pg 1061
Wavemaker Media Design, pg 1062
Webster Communications, pg 1063
West Coast Projections Inc, pg 1063
Yada/Levine Video Productions, pg 1071
Zamacona Productions, pg 1073

COLORADO

Paul L Anderson Productions Inc, pg 786
Apogee Communications Group, pg 788
Daylight Productions & Rentals, pg 844
Flashback Media Productions, pg 869
Rocky Mountain Audio/Video Productions Inc, pg 998
Transtar Entertainment Co Inc, pg 1043
Visual Communications Group Inc, pg 1059

CONNECTICUT

Applebox Studio, pg 788
Biomedical Media Communications Dept, pg 807
Broadcast Video Productions LLC, pg 813
Business & Legal Reports Inc, pg 815
Czar Productions Inc, pg 842
Fox Connecticut, pg 872
The Gary-Paul Agency, pg 875
Geomatrix Productions, pg 877
Ironik Design & Post, pg 902
MCC Films, pg 935
Moving Pictures, pg 947
New London Media, pg 956
P&P Studios Inc, pg 968
Video Production Associates Inc, pg 1056

DISTRICT OF COLUMBIA

Durrin Productions Inc, pg 854
Hillmann & Carr Inc, pg 889
O'Keefe Communications Inc, pg 961
Yellow Cat Productions Inc, pg 1072

FLORIDA

Accel Video Productions, pg 773
Accord Productions, pg 773
ACE Video Resources Software, pg 774
Allegro Productions Inc, pg 781
America By Air Stock Footage Library, pg 783
Blackburst Entertainment, pg 808
Capital Communications Inc, pg 819
Civins Productions Inc, pg 828
CopShopMiami.com, pg 836
Courter Films LLC, pg 837
Eastern Video, pg 856
Easy Edit Video Inc, pg 856
Ed Ethridge Productions Inc, pg 863
Gulf Coast Audio Visual Producers Inc, pg 883
Home Shopping Network (HSN), pg 890
Jordan Klein Film & Video (JKFV), pg 906
Media Entertainment Inc, pg 936
Motion Image Group LLC, pg 947
National Teleproductions Inc, pg 953
Paradise Video & Film, pg 969
Sound & Vision Communications Inc, pg 1016
Sunfire Communications Inc, pg 1028
Sunrise Studios, pg 1028
Tel-Air Interests Inc, pg 1035
Tricycle Studios, pg 1044
Universal Studios Florida® Production Group, pg 1049

PROGRAMMING — VIDEO

Industrial Program Producers (continued)

NORTH CAROLINA

All Pro Media Inc, pg 780
Pat Appleson Studios Inc, pg 788
J Arnold Productions Inc, pg 790
Bill Barnes Video Productions LLC, pg 803
The Communications Group Inc, pg 833
Horizon Video Productions Inc, pg 891
Kino Mountain Productions LLC, pg 911
LCW Productions LLC, pg 917
Media Consultants Inc, pg 936
Moving Pictures, pg 948
Unifour Productions Inc, pg 1048

NORTH DAKOTA

UND Television Center, pg 1048

OHIO

Advent Media Inc, pg 778
Russ Beckner Pictures, pg 804
CET, pg 823
Commercial Video, pg 832
Creative Technology, pg 838
Curtis Inc, pg 841
Cuyahoga Community College Media Center, pg 841
Electronic Vision Inc (EV), pg 859
Image Video Teleproductions Inc, pg 895
Lyon Video Inc, pg 927
MainSail Production Services Inc, pg 929
R&B Communications Inc, pg 991
Shelburne Films, pg 1008
South-Western Publishing Co, pg 1019
Take 1 Media Services, pg 1031
Treehaus Communications Inc, pg 1044
VGI Productions, pg 1053
Vista Color Imaging Inc, pg 1059

OKLAHOMA

Institute for Teaching & Learning Excellence (ITLE), pg 899

OREGON

A KTVA Production LLC, pg 771
Ideascape Inc, pg 894
InterVision Media, pg 902
KPDX-TV Production Center, pg 913
KVAL, pg 914
Odyssey Productions Inc, pg 961
Producers Studio, pg 984
Production West, pg 985
Rex, pg 995

PENNSYLVANIA

AiH Group Inc, pg 779
Audio Visual Communications Inc, pg 795
Beholder Productions Inc, pg 804
Bergwall Productions Inc, pg 805
CCI Communications Inc, pg 821
FMP Media Solutions Inc, pg 870
Fusion Brand Experiences, pg 874
Goodman Associates Inc, pg 880
Innovision Media Group, pg 899
JPL, pg 906
Kensington Falls Animation, pg 909
Main Point Productions, pg 929
Muderick Media, pg 949
Panta Rhei Media Inc, pg 968
Pemcor LLC, pg 971
Production Masters Inc (PMI), pg 984
Video Communication Productions Inc, pg 1054
Video/Film Associates, pg 1055
The Videohouse Inc, pg 1057
Visual Sound Inc, pg 1059
WHYY Inc, pg 1066

RHODE ISLAND

Sound-FX-Design, pg 1017

SOUTH CAROLINA

Encore Video Productions, pg 861
Go To Team, pg 879
Stages Video Productions, pg 1023
Venture Media, pg 1052

TENNESSEE

Continental Film, pg 835
Griffith Productions, pg 882
Jaguar Productions, pg 903
Marine Geographic, pg 931
Memphis Communications Corp, pg 938
Paradigm Marketing & Creative, pg 969
Running Pony Productions LLC, pg 1000
Scripps Networks, pg 1005

TEXAS

Alpha Video Productions, pg 782
Biway Media, pg 808
Castleview Productions, pg 821
Cerutti Productions Inc, pg 823
CEV Multimedia Ltd, pg 823
Communication Arts Multimedia Inc, pg 832
Countdown Productions Inc, pg 837
Critical Information Network, pg 839
Dykeman Associates Inc, pg 854
The Editing Co, pg 857
Epic Software Group Inc, pg 862
First Group Communications Inc, pg 868
Horizon Film + Video Productions, pg 891
J&S Audio Visual Inc, pg 904
Marx InDigital, pg 933
Mediaforce Productions, pg 937
Earl Miller Productions Inc, pg 943
Julye Newlin Productions Inc, pg 956
Omega Productions, pg 962
Omni Intercommunications Inc, pg 962
Richie Media Productions LLC, pg 996
Romar Learning, pg 999
South Coast Film & Video, pg 1019
Sportsmen on Film Inc, pg 1021
Stage Directions, pg 1022
Tecfilms Inc, pg 1033
University of Texas at Austin - Petroleum Extension Service, pg 1050

UTAH

ImageWorks Communications, pg 896

VERMONT

Marlboro Film & Video Productions, pg 931
Perceptions Inc, pg 973
University of Vermont, Instructional Television Dept, pg 1050
Wilson McLeran Inc, pg 1067

VIRGINIA

Advance Concepts Inc, pg 777
BES Studios, pg 805
CALIBRE, pg 816
Cinebar Productions Inc, pg 826
Coastal Training Technologies Corp, pg 831
Computer Sciences Corp, pg 834
Creative Video of Washington Inc, pg 839
D&B Television & Video Productions Inc, pg 842
Gingerbread Productions, pg 878
ITC Learning LLC, pg 903
Limelight Communications Inc, pg 921
Metro Productions, pg 939
National Media Services Inc, pg 953
Rocktown Media, pg 998
Video Solutions, pg 1056
WETA Production Center, pg 1064

WASHINGTON

Adams Creative & Production Services, pg 775
Bennett-Watt HD Productions Inc, pg 805
Hamilton Studio, pg 884
North-by-Northwest Productions, pg 958
Sparkworks Media, pg 1019
Victory Studios, pg 1054
White Rain Films Ltd, pg 1065

WEST VIRGINIA

Altruist Media LLC, pg 783
Blackwater Video Productions, pg 808

WISCONSIN

AVS Group, pg 800
5th Floor Recording Co, pg 867
Grassland Media Inc, pg 881
Logan Productions Inc, pg 924
Media Communications Association-International (MCA-I), pg 936
Meridian Studios, pg 939
Midland Video Productions Inc, pg 942
ProVideo, pg 986
Rucinski & Reetz Communications LLC, pg 1000
University of Wisconsin-Oshkosh Radio-TV-Film Dept, pg 1050
USAV Group Inc, pg 1050
Watts Communications Inc, pg 1062
Wisconsin Public Television, pg 1068

WYOMING

Bridger Productions Inc, pg 812

ALBERTA

Black Media Works, pg 808
Global Television Station, pg 879

BRITISH COLUMBIA

Image Media Farm, pg 895
Triad Communications Ltd, pg 1044

MANITOBA

Spectra Video Productions Ltd, pg 1020

NEWFOUNDLAND AND LABRADOR

Vidcraft Productions Ltd, pg 1054

NORTHWEST TERRITORIES

Yellowknife Films Inc, pg 1072

ONTARIO

ADS Media, pg 777
DebsVoice, pg 844
GAPC (General Assembly Production Centre), pg 875
Image Video Services & Productions, pg 895
Iron Ring Communications Ltd, pg 902
Jams Productions Inc, pg 904
JFB Communications, pg 905
Mediaimage Communications Group, pg 937
Purefire Communications Inc, pg 987
RB Productions, pg 992
Shaw Street Productions, pg 1008
Video Excellence Productions, pg 1055

QUEBEC

Group PVP, pg 882
Kerrigan Productions Inc, pg 910
Les Productions Via Le Monde (Daniel Bertolino) Inc, pg 985

SASKATCHEWAN

plan9films, pg 976

Industrial Program Rentals

ARIZONA

Video Learning Library, pg 1055

GEORGIA

Convergent Media Systems, pg 836

ILLINOIS

National Safety Council (NSC), pg 953

LOUISIANA

WVLA-TV, pg 1071

MASSACHUSETTS

Emergency Film Group, pg 860

MICHIGAN

Digi Sign Design LLC, pg 847

MISSOURI

The Phoenix Learning Group Inc, pg 974
University of Missouri-Columbia, pg 1050

NEW YORK

BC Video Inc, pg 803
Fanlight Productions, pg 865
Films Media Group, pg 868

Richter Productions Inc, pg 996
VIEW Inc (Video International Entertainment World Inc), pg 1058

NORTH CAROLINA

The International Society of Automation (ISA), pg 901

VERMONT

University of Vermont, Instructional Television Dept, pg 1050

VIRGINIA

Coastal Training Technologies Corp, pg 831

ONTARIO

Kineticvideo.com, pg 911

Kinescope Distributors

ARIZONA

Arizona Cine Equipment, pg 789

CALIFORNIA

Shokus Video, pg 1009

Kinescope Producers

QRS Software Services, pg 988

FLORIDA

Courter Films LLC, pg 837

KENTUCKY

Donna Lawrence Productions, pg 917

NEW YORK

Shelly Palmer Production, pg 968

Kinescope Rentals

GEORGIA

Staging Directions Inc, pg 1023

PENNSYLVANIA

FMP Media Solutions Inc, pg 870
Muderick Media, pg 949

Literature, *see* Feature Program

Live Television Commercials, *see* Television Commercial—Live

Medical Program Distributors

ARIZONA

Video Learning Library, pg 1055

CALIFORNIA

Academy Savant, pg 773
Ark Media Group Ltd, pg 790
Cavalcade Productions Inc, pg 821
Crystal Pyramid Productions™, pg 840
Davidson Films Inc, pg 843
Davies Publishing Inc, pg 843
Direct Cinema Ltd Inc, pg 848
Discovery Education - Los Angeles, pg 848
411 Video Information, pg 872
Geddes Productions LLC, pg 876
Steven Halpern's Inner Peace Music, pg 884
Increase Video/Silver Mine Video, pg 897
Institute of Precision Muscle Balancing, pg 899
Joyce Media Inc, pg 906
KPBS TV FM-San Diego, pg 913
Learning Communications LLC, pg 917
Medcom Inc, pg 936
New & Unique Videos™, pg 955
Pyramid Media, pg 987
Regent Press Publishers & Printers, pg 994
TMW Media Group, pg 1041
University of Southern California, pg 1050

COLORADO

Apogee Communications Group, pg 788
InJoy Birth & Parenting Education, pg 898

CONNECTICUT

Cine-Med Inc, pg 826

FLORIDA

ACE Video Resources Software, pg 774
Allegro Productions Inc, pg 781
Bisk Education, pg 808
Capital Communications Inc, pg 819

ILLINOIS

ABSA Productions Inc, pg 772
CCore Media Inc, pg 821
Chicago Satellite & Video, pg 825
Film Ideas, pg 867

INDIANA

Career & Self Directed Extended Programs at Purdue University, pg 820

KENTUCKY

WaxWorks VideoWorks, pg 1063

MARYLAND

Paul H Brookes Publishing Co, pg 814
DSR Computer Technology Specialists Inc, pg 853
Total AV Systems, pg 1042

MASSACHUSETTS

Award Productions, pg 800
Emergency Film Group, pg 860
Gyrus ACMI, pg 883
Penfield Productions Ltd, pg 971

MICHIGAN

Digi Sign Design LLC, pg 847
Emery-Pratt Co, pg 860
MSU Technologies, pg 949
Phoenix Society for Burn Survivors Inc, pg 974
VMS Inc, pg 1060

MINNESOTA

Harris Communications Inc, pg 885
Service Quality Institute, pg 1007

MISSOURI

Mosby Inc, pg 947
Phoenix/BFA/Coronet, pg 974
The Phoenix Learning Group Inc, pg 974
University of Missouri-Kansas City School of Dentistry, pg 1050

NEBRASKA

B & B Video Productions Inc, pg 801

NEVADA

DVDs4Less, pg 854

NEW HAMPSHIRE

Frey Scientific, pg 873
Chip Taylor Communications LLC, pg 1032

NEW JERSEY

Euro-Pacific Film & Video Productions Inc, pg 863
MIB Mediaworks, pg 941
SES World Skies, pg 1007

NEW MEXICO

National Information Center for Educational Media (NICEM)/MediaSleuth, pg 952
Uncharted Country Publishing, pg 1048

NEW YORK

ATA Trading Corp/Favorite TV Inc, pg 792
Broad Street Inc, pg 812
Fanlight Productions, pg 865
Films Media Group, pg 868
Guidance Associates Inc Center for Humanities, pg 883
Guilford Publications, pg 883
HB-Content, pg 886
KickedUp Media Group Inc, pg 910
Monad Trainer's Aide Inc, pg 945
MRG Productions Inc, pg 948
News Broadcast Network, pg 956
Richter Productions Inc, pg 996
Select Media Inc, pg 1006
Synaptic Digital, pg 1030
VIEW Inc (Video International Entertainment World Inc), pg 1058
Willow Mixed Media Inc, pg 1067

NORTH CAROLINA

Sinclair Institute, pg 1012
Vide-O-Go/That's Infotainment!, pg 1054

OHIO

Curtis Inc, pg 841
Edward Feil Productions, pg 866
South-Western Publishing Co, pg 1019

OREGON

InterVision Media, pg 902
Medifecta Healthcare Training, pg 938

PENNSYLVANIA

Bullfrog Films Inc, pg 815
FMP Media Solutions Inc, pg 870
Karol Media Inc, pg 908
Lippincott Williams & Wilkins, pg 922
S I Video Sales Group, pg 1001
TouchStar Productions Inc, pg 1042

TENNESSEE

National School Products, pg 953

TEXAS

CEV Multimedia Ltd, pg 823
Texas Heart Institute Visual Communication Services, pg 1037

VERMONT

University of Vermont, Instructional Television Dept, pg 1050

VIRGINIA

Alexander Street Press, pg 780
CACI Productions Group, pg 816
Coastal Training Technologies Corp, pg 831
Family Health Media, pg 865
Filmakers Library, pg 867

WASHINGTON

Bennett-Watt HD Productions Inc, pg 805
College of Nursing, Washington State University, pg 831
Medical Media Systems, pg 938

WISCONSIN

Equiservices Publishing, pg 862

BRITISH COLUMBIA

Thompson Rivers University Open Learning, pg 1039

ONTARIO

Canadian Learning Co Inc, pg 818
Kineticvideo.com, pg 911
Life Cycle Books Ltd, pg 920

Medical Program Producers

ALABAMA

CMEInfo, pg 830
Leo Ticheli Productions, pg 1040

ALASKA

Alaska Film Services Inc, pg 779

ARIZONA

Aardvark Productions LLC, pg 772
Direct Current Video Productions, pg 848
Film Creations Ltd, pg 867
Fox 10 Productions (KSAZ-TV), pg 872
MediaWorks, pg 938
Phoenix VideoFilms®, pg 974
Video Media Productions (VMP), pg 1055

PROGRAMMING — VIDEO

Medical Program Producers (continued)

ARKANSAS

Cedar Crest Studio, pg 822
Jones Film Video, pg 906
White Diamond Productions, pg 1065

CALIFORNIA

Academy Savant, pg 773
Access Video in Berkeley, pg 773
Action Video, pg 775
Artichoke Productions, pg 791
Big Door, pg 807
Cavalcade Productions Inc, pg 821
Chesney Communications, pg 824
Classic Images, pg 829
Coastline Productions, pg 831
Concrete Images, pg 835
Cox Media, pg 837
Crystal Pyramid Productions™, pg 840
Custom Video Productions Inc, pg 841
Davidson Films Inc, pg 843
Design Media, pg 845
Digital Outpost, pg 847
Direct Images Interactive Inc, pg 848
Discovery Education - Los Angeles, pg 848
Dogma Studios, pg 850
Dolphin MultiMedia Inc, pg 850
Face Digital Post, pg 865
First Camera, pg 868
Geddes Productions LLC, pg 876
Global Village Productions, pg 879
Steven Halpern's Inner Peace Music, pg 884
Havas Edge, pg 885
imageReal Pictures LLC, pg 896
Imageworks, pg 896
Increase Video/Silver Mine Video, pg 897
Institute of Precision Muscle Balancing, pg 899
ITV Productions, pg 903
Joyce Media Inc, pg 906
Kavich Reynolds Productions Inc, pg 908
The Kenwood Group, pg 909
KION-TV, pg 911
KPBS TV FM-San Diego, pg 913
Main Street Media Inc, pg 929
Maximus Media Inc, pg 934
McCune Audio-Video-Lighting, pg 935
Medcom Inc, pg 936
Media Magic, pg 937
The Media Staff Inc, pg 937
Mist Media Inc, pg 944
New & Unique Videos™, pg 955
On-Trax Inc, pg 963
Opticomm-EMCORE, pg 964
Panorama Productions, pg 968
PM Productions, pg 977
Point of View Productions, pg 977
Pyramid Media, pg 987
QRS Software Services, pg 988
Regent Press Publishers & Printers, pg 994
Dick Reizner Film & Video, pg 994
RetinaVision Productions, pg 995
Glenn Roland Films, pg 998
Ron Roy Productions/Moodtapes, pg 1000
Screen Door Entertainment Inc, pg 1005
SNAP, pg 1014
Staylor-Made Communications Inc, pg 1024
Still N'Motion, pg 1025
The Studio Center, pg 1026
Tam Communications Inc, pg 1031
Tele-Video Production Services (TVPS), pg 1036
Tigar Hare Studios, pg 1040
Timestream Video, pg 1041
TMW Media Group, pg 1041
Total Media Group, pg 1042
Twin Peaks Creative, pg 1047
University of Southern California, pg 1050
Videowerks, pg 1057
Vineyard Video & Photography, pg 1058
Visions Plus, pg 1058
Wavemaker Media Design, pg 1062
Webster Communications, pg 1063
West Coast Projections Inc, pg 1063
Zamacona Productions, pg 1073

COLORADO

Paul L Anderson Productions Inc, pg 786
Apogee Communications Group, pg 788
Centre Communications Inc, pg 823
Daylight Productions & Rentals, pg 844
Flashback Media Productions, pg 869
InJoy Birth & Parenting Education, pg 898
Rocky Mountain Audio/Video Productions Inc, pg 998
Transtar Entertainment Co Inc, pg 1043

CONNECTICUT

Applebox Studio, pg 788
Biomedical Media Communications Dept, pg 807
Broadcast Video Productions LLC, pg 813
Cine-Med Inc, pg 826
Essex Television Group Inc, pg 862
Fox Connecticut, pg 872
The Gary-Paul Agency, pg 875
Geomatrix Productions, pg 877
Ironik Design & Post, pg 902
MCC Films, pg 935
Moving Pictures, pg 947
New London Media, pg 956
P&P Studios Inc, pg 968
Video Production Associates Inc, pg 1056

DISTRICT OF COLUMBIA

Hillmann & Carr Inc, pg 889
O'Keefe Communications Inc, pg 961
Yellow Cat Productions Inc, pg 1072

FLORIDA

Accel Video Productions, pg 773
Accord Productions, pg 773
ACE Video Resources Software, pg 774
Allegro Productions Inc, pg 781
Bisk Education, pg 808
Blackburst Entertainment, pg 808
Capital Communications Inc, pg 819
Civins Productions Inc, pg 828
CopShopMiami.com, pg 836
Courter Films LLC, pg 837
DME Studios, pg 849
Easy Edit Video Inc, pg 856
Ed Ethridge Productions Inc, pg 863
Gulf Coast Audio Visual Producers Inc, pg 883
Home Shopping Network (HSN), pg 890
Jordan Klein Film & Video (JKFV), pg 906
Motion Image Group LLC, pg 947
National Teleproductions Inc, pg 953
Paradise Video & Film, pg 969
Sound & Vision Communications Inc, pg 1016
Sunfire Communications Inc, pg 1028
Sunrise Studios, pg 1028
Tight Line Productions, pg 1040
Tricycle Studios, pg 1044

GEORGIA

ADAM Inc, pg 775
Beachwood Productions, pg 804
Burst Video/Film Inc, pg 815
COMPRO Productions Inc, pg 834
Georgia-Pacific Television & Photography, pg 877
Guerrilla Productions LLC, pg 883
Memory Lane Productions, pg 938
On-Line Productions, pg 963

HAWAII

Hyperspective Studios Inc, pg 893

IDAHO

Brad Shaw Productions Inc, pg 1008
Wide Eye Productions, pg 1066

ILLINOIS

ABSA Productions Inc, pg 772
Airways Digital Media, pg 779
American Hospital Association, pg 784
Analog Free Media, pg 786
CCore Media Inc, pg 821
The Chicago Production Center, pg 825
Chicago Satellite & Video, pg 825
Comtech Multimedia Marketing, pg 834
Film Police, pg 867
IV Media Resources, pg 903
Major Media Productions Inc, pg 929
Manning Productions, pg 930
The Market Place, pg 931
Rob Orr Productions Ltd, pg 965
The Pepper Group, pg 972
SCI Television Productions LLC, pg 1004
20/20 Communications Inc, pg 1047
Universal Training, pg 1049
Video I-D Teleproductions Inc, pg 1055
Video Impressions, pg 1055
WEEK TV, pg 1063
Winter Productions, pg 1068

INDIANA

Advanced Media Integration, pg 777
AVA Productions, pg 798
Bright Ideas Creative Services, pg 812
Covenant Productions®, pg 837
Digital Rain LLC, pg 847
Explore Media LLC, pg 864
PentaVision Communications Inc, pg 972
Road Pictures, pg 997

KANSAS

KAKE-TV, pg 907

KENTUCKY

Idle Minds Productions Inc, pg 894
The Media Collaboratory, pg 936
Northern Kentucky University, pg 959

LOUISIANA

Digital FX Inc, pg 847
Louisiana State University Health Sciences Center - Shreveport, pg 925
Moxie Media, pg 948

MAINE

WGME-TV, pg 1065

MARYLAND

Adventure Productions LLC, pg 778
The Ahern Group, pg 779
CAS Video Productions, pg 820
Richard Chisolm Cinematography, pg 825
dbF a Media Company, pg 844
DSR Computer Technology Specialists Inc, pg 853
The Image Generators, pg 895
Kramer Communications Video Production, pg 913
Mobile-Video Productions Inc, pg 944

MASSACHUSETTS

Award Productions, pg 800
Emergency Film Group, pg 860
Green Mountain Post Films (GMP), pg 882
Heliotrope Studios, pg 887
Northern Light Productions, pg 959
Pauline Books & Media, pg 970
Penfield Productions Ltd, pg 971
PixMix Video Services, pg 976
Preston Productions Inc, pg 981
TVN-The Video Network, pg 1046
Veritech Corp, pg 1053
VideoLink Inc, pg 1057
WVP Boston, pg 1071

MICHIGAN

Benjamin Creative Productions, pg 805
Digi Sign Design LLC, pg 847
K&R All Media Productions Inc, pg 908
K&R's Recording Studios Inc, pg 908
MSU Technologies, pg 949
Phoenix Society for Burn Survivors Inc, pg 974

MINNESOTA

Aggressive Records Audio Duplication LLC, pg 778
House of Cinemagraphics, pg 891
Master Communications Group, pg 933
Media Loft Inc, pg 937
MultiMedia, pg 950
Service Quality Institute, pg 1007
Vaddio, pg 1051
Worthwhile Films, pg 1070

MISSISSIPPI

Dollarhide Film Inc, pg 850

MISSOURI

Audio-VideoGraphics Inc, pg 795
Communitronics Corp, pg 833
Fambrough & Associates Inc, pg 865
Mosby Inc, pg 947
Phoenix/BFA/Coronet, pg 974
University of Missouri-Kansas City School of Dentistry, pg 1050

MONTANA

North Country Media Group, pg 959

NEBRASKA

B & B Video Productions Inc, pg 801
Dog & Pony Productions Inc, pg 850
Rainbow Video Productions Inc, pg 991

NEVADA

Aardvark Video & Media Productions, pg 772
DVDs4Less, pg 854
Encore Productions Inc, pg 861
HDTV Productions Inc, pg 886
JCS Video Productions, pg 904
Tetrahedron LLC, pg 1037

NEW HAMPSHIRE

Apertura, pg 788
Chip Taylor Communications LLC, pg 1032

NEW JERSEY

Amerinex Applied Imaging Inc, pg 785
Broadcast Center Studios, pg 813
CFP Video Productions Inc, pg 823
DWJ Television, pg 854
Euro-Pacific Film & Video Productions Inc, pg 863
Half Moon Video Productions, pg 883
Laurel Video Productions, pg 916
MediaNow, pg 938
Megavideo Productions, pg 938
MIB Mediaworks, pg 941
Midnight Media Group Inc, pg 942
Optisonics Productions, pg 965
Producer East Productions, pg 983
Projects in Knowledge Inc, pg 986
Public Eye Productions, pg 987
Bill Quinn Productions, pg 989
Reider Photography & Video Productions, pg 994
Telequest Inc, pg 1036
TimeSteps Productions Inc, pg 1041
VCSvideo, pg 1052

NEW MEXICO

Michael Dunn Productions, pg 853
Production Outfitters, pg 984
Rainbow International Inc/Rainbow Productions Inc, pg 990
Uncharted Country Publishing, pg 1048

NEW YORK

Ace Video, pg 774
Associated Press Television News, pg 792
aurora productions, pg 797
Norman N Axelrod Associates, pg 800
BC Video Inc, pg 803
Brian Film Productions LLC, pg 812
Broad Street Inc, pg 812
Clarity Media Group, pg 829
Cohn Creative Group LLC, pg 831
dM works, pg 849
Fanlight Productions, pg 865
Films Media Group, pg 868
Guidance Associates Inc Center for Humanities, pg 883
Guilford Publications, pg 883
HB-Content, pg 886
Hello World Communications, pg 888
Image Zone Inc, pg 896
Ketchum Pleon Change, pg 910
KickedUp Media Group Inc, pg 910
L A Bruell Inc, pg 914
Long Island Video Enterprises Live Inc, pg 924
Neal Marshad Productions, pg 931
Mood Creations Ltd, pg 946
MRG Productions Inc, pg 948
MRY, pg 949
The Napoleon Group, pg 952
News Broadcast Network, pg 956
Northeast Video Productions Inc, pg 959
Shelly Palmer Production, pg 968
Pat Kogan Productions Inc, pg 970
Peckham Productions Inc, pg 970
PrimaLux Video Inc, pg 982
PrimeLight Productions Inc, pg 982
Richter Productions Inc, pg 996
Suggs Media Productions Inc, pg 1028
Sunrise Media LLC, pg 1028
Synaptic Digital, pg 1030
TeleTime Productions, pg 1036
Tobin Productions Inc, pg 1041
Videograf, pg 1057
VIEW Inc (Video International Entertainment World Inc), pg 1058
Alan Weiss Productions, pg 1063
Willow Mixed Media Inc, pg 1067
WNET/NET TELECON, pg 1069

NORTH CAROLINA

All Pro Media Inc, pg 780
Pat Appleson Studios Inc, pg 788
Bill Barnes Video Productions LLC, pg 803
The Communications Group Inc, pg 833
Horizon Video Productions Inc, pg 891
Kino Mountain Productions LLC, pg 911
Moving Pictures, pg 948
Sinclair Institute, pg 1012
Unifour Productions Inc, pg 1048

OHIO

Advent Media Inc, pg 778
CET, pg 823
Creative Technology, pg 838
Curtis Inc, pg 841
Electronic Vision Inc (EV), pg 859
Edward Feil Productions, pg 866
Image Video Teleproductions Inc, pg 895
Lyon Video Inc, pg 927
MainSail Production Services Inc, pg 929
R&B Communications Inc, pg 991
South-Western Publishing Co, pg 1019
Take 1 Media Services, pg 1031
VGI Productions, pg 1053
Vista Color Imaging Inc, pg 1059

OKLAHOMA

CSI/Orion, pg 840
University of Oklahoma Academic Media & Digital Services, pg 1050

OREGON

Ideascape Inc, pg 894
InterVision Media, pg 902
Medifecta Healthcare Training, pg 938
Producers Studio, pg 984
Production West, pg 985

PENNSYLVANIA

AiH Group Inc, pg 779
Audio Visual Communications Inc, pg 795
Beholder Productions Inc, pg 804
CCI Communications Inc, pg 821
FMP Media Solutions Inc, pg 870
Fusion Brand Experiences, pg 874
Goodman Associates Inc, pg 880
Innovision Media Group, pg 899
JPL, pg 906
Kensington Falls Animation, pg 909
Lippincott Williams & Wilkins, pg 922
Muderick Media, pg 949
Panta Rhei Media Inc, pg 968
Pemcor LLC, pg 971
Production Masters Inc (PMI), pg 984
S I Video Sales Group, pg 1001
TouchStar Productions Inc, pg 1042
Video Communication Productions Inc, pg 1054
Video/Film Associates, pg 1055
The Videohouse Inc, pg 1057
Videosmith Inc, pg 1057
WHYY Inc, pg 1066

RHODE ISLAND

Sound-FX-Design, pg 1017

SOUTH CAROLINA

Encore Video Productions, pg 861
Go To Team, pg 879
Venture Media, pg 1052

TENNESSEE

Continental Film, pg 835
Griffith Productions, pg 882
Jaguar Productions, pg 903
Memphis Communications Corp, pg 938
Paradigm Marketing & Creative, pg 969
Running Pony Productions LLC, pg 1000
Scripps Networks, pg 1005
Russ Sturgeon Productions/RSVP, pg 1027

TEXAS

Alpha Video Productions, pg 782
Castleview Productions, pg 821
Cerutti Productions Inc, pg 823
CEV Multimedia Ltd, pg 823
Communication Arts Multimedia Inc, pg 832
The Editing Co, pg 857
Epic Software Group Inc, pg 862
Horizon Film + Video Productions, pg 891
Mediaforce Productions, pg 937
Earl Miller Productions Inc, pg 943
Julye Newlin Productions Inc, pg 956
Omega Productions, pg 962
Omni Intercommunications Inc, pg 962
Romar Learning, pg 999
South Coast Film & Video, pg 1019
Sportsmen on Film Inc, pg 1021
Stage Directions, pg 1022
Texas Heart Institute Visual Communication Services, pg 1037

VERMONT

Marlboro Film & Video Productions, pg 931
Perceptions Inc, pg 973
University of Vermont, Instructional Television Dept, pg 1050

VIRGINIA

Advance Concepts Inc, pg 777
Alexander Street Press, pg 780
BES Studios, pg 805
CALIBRE, pg 816
Coastal Training Technologies Corp, pg 831
Creative Video of Washington Inc, pg 839
D&B Television & Video Productions Inc, pg 842
Family Health Media, pg 865
Gingerbread Productions, pg 878
Limelight Communications Inc, pg 921
Metro Productions, pg 939
Rocktown Media, pg 998
Video Solutions, pg 1056

WASHINGTON

Adams Creative & Production Services, pg 775
Bennett-Watt HD Productions Inc, pg 805
College of Nursing, Washington State University, pg 831
Hamilton Studio, pg 884
Medical Media Systems, pg 938
North-by-Northwest Productions, pg 958
Sparkworks Media, pg 1019
Victory Studios, pg 1054

WEST VIRGINIA

Altruist Media LLC, pg 783
Blackwater Video Productions, pg 808

WISCONSIN

Equiservices Publishing, pg 862
5th Floor Recording Co, pg 867
Grassland Media Inc, pg 881
Media Communications Association-International (MCA-I), pg 936
Meridian Studios, pg 939
Midland Video Productions Inc, pg 942
ProVideo, pg 986
Rucinski & Reetz Communications LLC, pg 1000
USAV Group Inc, pg 1050
Video Wisconsin Inc, pg 1056
Watts Communications Inc, pg 1062
Wisconsin Public Television, pg 1068

WYOMING

Bridger Productions Inc, pg 812

PROGRAMMING — VIDEO

Medical Program Producers (continued)

ALBERTA

Global Television Station, pg 879

BRITISH COLUMBIA

Image Media Farm, pg 895
Thompson Rivers University Open Learning, pg 1039
Triad Communications Ltd, pg 1044

MANITOBA

Spectra Video Productions Ltd, pg 1020

NEWFOUNDLAND AND LABRADOR

Vidcraft Productions Ltd, pg 1054

ONTARIO

ADS Media, pg 777
Associated Producers Ltd, pg 792
GAPC (General Assembly Production Centre), pg 875
Image Video Services & Productions, pg 895
JFB Communications, pg 905
Shaw Street Productions, pg 1008
Video Excellence Productions, pg 1055
YAP Films, pg 1072

QUEBEC

Kerrigan Productions Inc, pg 910

Medical Program Rentals

ARIZONA

Video Learning Library, pg 1055

CALIFORNIA

Cavalcade Productions Inc, pg 821
Davidson Films Inc, pg 843
Direct Cinema Ltd Inc, pg 848
Learning Communications LLC, pg 917
Medcom Inc, pg 936
Point of View Productions, pg 977
University of Southern California, pg 1050

MASSACHUSETTS

Emergency Film Group, pg 860

MICHIGAN

Digi Sign Design LLC, pg 847

MINNESOTA

Service Quality Institute, pg 1007

MISSOURI

The Phoenix Learning Group Inc, pg 974
University of Missouri-Columbia, pg 1050
University of Missouri-Kansas City School of Dentistry, pg 1050

NEW JERSEY

Euro-Pacific Film & Video Productions Inc, pg 863

NEW YORK

BC Video Inc, pg 803
Fanlight Productions, pg 865
Films for the Humanities & Sciences, pg 868
Films Media Group, pg 868
Richter Productions Inc, pg 996

NORTH CAROLINA

Sinclair Institute, pg 1012

PENNSYLVANIA

Bullfrog Films Inc, pg 815

VERMONT

University of Vermont, Instructional Television Dept, pg 1050

VIRGINIA

Alexander Street Press, pg 780
Coastal Training Technologies Corp, pg 831
Filmakers Library, pg 867

ONTARIO

Kineticvideo.com, pg 911

Multimedia, CD-ROM & DVD Interactive Program Distributors

ARIZONA

Valley of the Sun Publishing Co, pg 1051

ARKANSAS

Master Books, pg 933

CALIFORNIA

Ariztical Entertainment Inc, pg 790
Astronomical Society of the Pacific, pg 792
California Language Laboratories, pg 817
Christian Media Network, pg 825
Crystal Productions, pg 840
Crystal Pyramid Productions™, pg 840
Davies Publishing Inc, pg 843
411 Video Information, pg 872
MarVista Entertainment Inc, pg 933
Music World/Vocal Power School, pg 951
QRS Software Services, pg 988
Rovi Corp, pg 1000
Sea Studios Foundation, pg 1005
Videobotics, pg 1056

COLORADO

Paul L Anderson Productions Inc, pg 786
National Teaching Aids Inc, pg 953

CONNECTICUT

Cine-Med Inc, pg 826
Really Good Stuff, pg 992

FLORIDA

ACE Video Resources Software, pg 774
Allegro Productions Inc, pg 781
ThirdWave Learning Inc, pg 1039

GEORGIA

Convergent Media Systems, pg 836
School Media Associates LLC, pg 1004

ILLINOIS

Britannica Film & Video, pg 812
CCore Media Inc, pg 821
National Safety Council (NSC), pg 953

INDIANA

Educational Video Group Inc, pg 857
Herff Jones | Nystrom, pg 888

IOWA

Right Stuf Inc, pg 997

KENTUCKY

WaxWorks VideoWorks, pg 1063

LOUISIANA

Great Chefs/Leisure Jazz Video, pg 881
Leisure Video, pg 918

MASSACHUSETTS

Cheng & Tsui Co, pg 824
Documentary Educational Resources Inc, pg 850
Penfield Productions Ltd, pg 971

MICHIGAN

Digi Sign Design LLC, pg 847
MSU Technologies, pg 949
Prakken Publications Inc, pg 980
VMS Inc, pg 1060

MINNESOTA

Beyers Sound & Essay Audio, pg 806
Harris Communications Inc, pg 885
JIST Publishing, pg 905

MISSOURI

Cable Films & Video, pg 816
The Phoenix Learning Group Inc, pg 974

NEBRASKA

B & B Video Productions Inc, pg 801
Leo Films, pg 919

NEW HAMPSHIRE

French American Music Enterprises, pg 873
Frey Scientific, pg 873
Chip Taylor Communications LLC, pg 1032

NEW JERSEY

Comex Systems Inc, pg 832
MIB Mediaworks, pg 941

NEW MEXICO

National Information Center for Educational Media (NICEM)/MediaSleuth, pg 952

NEW YORK

Benchmark Media, pg 805
Broad Street Inc, pg 812
Brooklyn Botanic Garden, pg 814
The Bureau for At-Risk Youth, pg 815
Films for the Humanities & Sciences, pg 868
Films Media Group, pg 868
French American Cultural Exchange (FACE), pg 873
Guidance Associates Inc Center for Humanities, pg 883
HB-Content, pg 886
Human Relations Media, pg 892
IAI Video, pg 893
Interactive International Inc, pg 899
Magnetic Music Publishing Co, pg 928
Meridian Education Corp, pg 939
Monad Trainer's Aide Inc, pg 945
MRG Productions Inc, pg 948
Shopware, pg 1009
SISU Home Entertainment Inc, pg 1012
Videofashion Network, pg 1056
Women Make Movies Inc, pg 1069

NORTH CAROLINA

Vide-O-Go/That's Infotainment!, pg 1054

OHIO

Electronic Vision Inc (EV), pg 859
Treehaus Communications Inc, pg 1044

OREGON

InterVision Media, pg 902

PENNSYLVANIA

Anchor Distributors, pg 786
Bullfrog Films Inc, pg 815
Discovery Education - South Burlington, pg 848
FMP Media Solutions Inc, pg 870
Library Video Company, pg 920
MVD Entertainment Group, pg 951
S I Video Sales Group, pg 1001
Schlessinger Media, pg 1004

SOUTH CAROLINA

American Production Services LLC, pg 785

TENNESSEE

Center for Southern Folklore Inc, pg 822
Marine Geographic, pg 931
National School Products, pg 953
Spring Arbor Distributors, pg 1022

TEXAS

CEV Multimedia Ltd, pg 823
Critical Information Network, pg 839
Dallas Learning Solutions, pg 842

UTAH

Strata™, pg 1025

VERMONT

Multicultural Media, pg 950
University of Vermont, Instructional Television Dept, pg 1050

VIRGINIA

National Audiovisual Center - National Technical Information Service (NTIS), pg 952

WASHINGTON

Bennett-Watt HD Productions Inc, pg 805
Global Net Productions Inc, pg 879
Intermedia Inc, pg 900

ALBERTA

Global Television Station, pg 879

ONTARIO

Canadian Learning Co Inc, pg 818
McIntyre Media Inc, pg 935
Universal Studios Canada Inc, pg 1049

Multimedia, CD-ROM & DVD Interactive Program Producers

ALABAMA

Media Visions Inc, pg 937

ALASKA

Alaska Film Services Inc, pg 779

ARIZONA

Aardvark Productions LLC, pg 772
Film Creations Ltd, pg 867
Forensic Video Deposition Service, pg 871
MediaWorks, pg 938
Merestone, pg 938
Valley of the Sun Publishing Co, pg 1051
Video Media Productions (VMP), pg 1055

ARKANSAS

Live'N'Loud, pg 923

CALIFORNIA

Access Video in Berkeley, pg 773
Action Video, pg 775
Animax, pg 787
Artichoke Productions, pg 791
Astronomical Society of the Pacific, pg 792
Big Door, pg 807
California Language Laboratories, pg 817
Christian Media Network, pg 825
Classic Images, pg 829
Coastline Productions, pg 831
Concrete Images, pg 835
Crystal Pyramid Productions™, pg 840
Custom Video Productions Inc, pg 841
Design Media, pg 845
Digital Outpost, pg 847
Direct Images Interactive Inc, pg 848
Dogma Studios, pg 850
Dolphin MultiMedia Inc, pg 850
Duck Studios, pg 853
Dynamic Digital Depth Inc (DDD), pg 854
First Camera, pg 868
Gateways Books & Tapes, pg 876
Havas Edge, pg 885
Imageworks, pg 896
ITV Productions, pg 903
Kavich Reynolds Productions Inc, pg 908
The Kenwood Group, pg 909
Lieberman Productions, pg 920
Lumeni Productions Inc, pg 926
Main Street Media Inc, pg 929
Maximus Media Inc, pg 934
McCune Audio-Video-Lighting, pg 935
Media Magic, pg 937
Mist Media Inc, pg 944
Music World/Vocal Power School, pg 951
Nolte Media, pg 958
Panorama Productions, pg 968
Prime Cut Productions, pg 982
PSI Inc, pg 987
QRS Software Services, pg 988
RetinaVision Productions, pg 995
Glenn Roland Films, pg 998
SBS Productions, pg 1003
Sea Studios Foundation, pg 1005
SNAP, pg 1014
Staylor-Made Communications Inc, pg 1024
Still N'Motion, pg 1025
Tam Communications Inc, pg 1031
Tele-Video Production Services (TVPS), pg 1036
Tigar Hare Studios, pg 1040
Toon Makers, pg 1042
Total Media Group, pg 1042
Towards 2000 Inc, pg 1043
Video Movie Magic, pg 1056
Videowerks, pg 1057
Vineyard Video & Photography, pg 1058
Visions Plus, pg 1058
ViVi Co, pg 1060
WalkerVision Interarts, pg 1061
Wavemaker Media Design, pg 1062
Webster Communications, pg 1063
West Coast Projections Inc, pg 1063
The Wine Appreciation Guild Ltd, pg 1067
WMS Media Inc, pg 1069
Zamacona Productions, pg 1073

COLORADO

Paul L Anderson Productions Inc, pg 786
Daylight Productions & Rentals, pg 844
Flashback Media Productions, pg 869
National Teaching Aids Inc, pg 953

CONNECTICUT

ACM Productions Ltd, pg 774
Applebox Studio, pg 788
Broadcast Video Productions LLC, pg 813
Cine-Med Inc, pg 826
Ironik Design & Post, pg 902
Moving Pictures, pg 947
New London Media, pg 956
P&P Studios Inc, pg 968
VRSim Inc, pg 1061

DISTRICT OF COLUMBIA

Hillmann & Carr Inc, pg 889
O'Keefe Communications Inc, pg 961
USCCB Publishing, pg 1051

FLORIDA

Accel Video Productions, pg 773
Accord Productions, pg 773
ACE Video Resources Software, pg 774
Allegro Productions Inc, pg 781
Big Byte Video Productions, pg 806
Blackburst Entertainment, pg 808
Civins Productions Inc, pg 828
Communications Concepts Inc (CCI), pg 833
Courter Films LLC, pg 837
DME Studios, pg 849
Gulf Coast Audio Visual Producers Inc, pg 883
Home Shopping Network (HSN), pg 890
Image Technical Services, pg 895
Jordan Klein Film & Video (JKFV), pg 906
Motion Image Group LLC, pg 947
Skystorm Productions, pg 1013
Sound & Vision Communications Inc, pg 1016
Sunfire Communications Inc, pg 1028
Sunrise Studios, pg 1028
Teach America Corp, pg 1033
Tricycle Studios, pg 1044
Video Techniques Inc, pg 1056

GEORGIA

ADAM Inc, pg 775
Beachwood Productions, pg 804
Burst Video/Film Inc, pg 815
Continental Film & Video, pg 835
ECG Productions, pg 856
Guerrilla Productions LLC, pg 883
Myriad Productions, pg 951
On-Line Productions, pg 963

HAWAII

Hyperspective Studios Inc, pg 893
1013 Integrated, pg 1037

IDAHO

Brad Shaw Productions Inc, pg 1008
Wide Eye Productions, pg 1066

ILLINOIS

Airways Digital Media, pg 779
Analog Free Media, pg 786
APTE Inc, pg 789
Audio Visual Services Corp, pg 796
Britannica Film & Video, pg 812
CCore Media Inc, pg 821
Centrax Corp, pg 823
Chicago Satellite & Video, pg 825
Comtech Multimedia Marketing, pg 834
Cresta Creative, pg 839
Extraordinary Demos, pg 864
IV Media Resources, pg 903
Major Media Productions Inc, pg 929
Manning Productions, pg 930
MIGHTYbYTES Inc, pg 942
National Safety Council (NSC), pg 953
Jim Passin Productions, pg 970
The Pepper Group, pg 972
PSAV® Presentation Services (Hotel Services Division), pg 987
QuickSet International Inc, pg 989
Richter Studios, pg 996
Roadworthy Image Magnification, pg 998
SCI Television Productions LLC, pg 1004
Southern Illinois University, pg 1019
Sparkfactor, pg 1019
20/20 Communications Inc, pg 1047
Universal Training, pg 1049
Video I-D Teleproductions Inc, pg 1055
Video Impressions, pg 1055

INDIANA

Advanced Media Integration, pg 777
AVA Productions, pg 798
Bright Ideas Creative Services, pg 812
Explore Media LLC, pg 864
PentaVision Communications Inc, pg 972

IOWA

The Production House, pg 984
Right Stuf Inc, pg 997

KANSAS

KAKE-TV, pg 907

KENTUCKY

Hammond Communications Group, pg 884
Idle Minds Productions Inc, pg 894
Donna Lawrence Productions, pg 917
Northern Kentucky University, pg 959
Prosper Media Group Inc, pg 986

LOUISIANA

Digital FX Inc, pg 847
Leisure Video, pg 918
Louisiana State University Health Sciences Center - Shreveport, pg 925

MARYLAND

Absolute Hollywood, pg 772
The Ahern Group, pg 779
CPR MultiMedia Solutions, pg 837
dbF a Media Company, pg 844
Kramer Communications Video Production, pg 913
Media Dimensions Inc, pg 936
Mobile-Video Productions Inc, pg 944
Video Labs, pg 1055

MASSACHUSETTS

Cheng & Tsui Co, pg 824
CommCreative, pg 832
Documentary Educational Resources Inc, pg 850
Green Mountain Post Films (GMP), pg 882
Inter-Media Electronics, pg 899
Northern Light Productions, pg 959
Penfield Productions Ltd, pg 971
Preston Productions Inc, pg 981
TVN-The Video Network, pg 1046
Veritech Corp, pg 1053
WGBH Production Group, pg 1065

MICHIGAN

Digi Sign Design LLC, pg 847
K&R All Media Productions Inc, pg 908
K&R's Recording Studios Inc, pg 908
TGA Recording Co, pg 1038
Universal Images, pg 1049
VMS Inc, pg 1060

PROGRAMMING — VIDEO

Multimedia, CD-ROM & DVD Interactive Program Producers (continued)

MINNESOTA

Aggressive Records Audio Duplication LLC, pg 778
Badiyan Inc, pg 801
Beyers Sound & Essay Audio, pg 806
House of Cinemagraphics, pg 891
JIST Publishing, pg 905
Live Spark Inc, pg 923
Master Communications Group, pg 933
MultiMedia, pg 950
Worthwhile Films, pg 1070

NEBRASKA

B & B Video Productions Inc, pg 801
Dog & Pony Productions Inc, pg 850
Leo Films, pg 919
Rainbow Video Productions Inc, pg 991

NEVADA

Aardvark Video & Media Productions, pg 772
Encore Productions Inc, pg 861
JCS Video Productions, pg 904

NEW HAMPSHIRE

Apertura, pg 788
Chip Taylor Communications LLC, pg 1032

NEW JERSEY

Comex Systems Inc, pg 832
DWJ Television, pg 854
Euro-Pacific Film & Video Productions Inc, pg 863
Half Moon Video Productions, pg 883
Laurel Video Productions, pg 916
MediaNow, pg 938
MIB Mediaworks, pg 941
Midnight Media Group Inc, pg 942
Optisonics Productions, pg 965
Outside The Box Interactive LLC, pg 966
Producer East Productions, pg 983
Public Eye Productions, pg 987
Bill Quinn Productions, pg 989
Suede Interactive, pg 1027
VCSvideo, pg 1052
Video Ideas Productions, pg 1055

NEW MEXICO

Production Outfitters, pg 984
Rainbow International Inc/Rainbow Productions Inc, pg 990

NEW YORK

Ace Video, pg 774
American Management Association International, pg 784
Big Fish Productions Inc, pg 807
Blue Barn Pictures Inc, pg 809
Broad Street Inc, pg 812
Brooklyn Botanic Garden, pg 814
Brooklyn Films, pg 814
The Bureau for At-Risk Youth, pg 815
Cohn Creative Group LLC, pg 831
Digital Force, pg 847
dM works, pg 849
Duplication Depot Inc, pg 853
Films for the Humanities & Sciences, pg 868
Films Media Group, pg 868
Greyfalcon House, pg 882
Guidance Associates Inc Center for Humanities, pg 883
Havas Worldwide, pg 886
HB-Content, pg 886
Human Relations Media, pg 892
IAI Video, pg 893
Image Zone Inc, pg 896
Interactive International Inc, pg 899
Ketchum Pleon Change, pg 910
L A Bruell Inc, pg 914
Long Island Video Enterprises Live Inc, pg 924
Magnetic Music Publishing Co, pg 928
Neal Marshad Productions, pg 931
Meridian Education Corp, pg 939
MRG Productions Inc, pg 948
MRY, pg 949
New Horizon Studios, pg 955
Northeast Video Productions Inc, pg 959
Shelly Palmer Production, pg 968
PrimaLux Video Inc, pg 982
R/GA, pg 990
Judson Rosebush Co Inc, pg 999
Shopware, pg 1009
Suggs Media Productions Inc, pg 1028
Sunrise Media LLC, pg 1028
TBA Global Events, pg 1032
Tiki Recording Studios Inc, pg 1040
Tobin Productions Inc, pg 1041
Videofashion Network, pg 1056
Vidicom Inc, pg 1057

NORTH CAROLINA

All Pro Media Inc, pg 780
Pat Appleson Studios Inc, pg 788
The Communications Group Inc, pg 833
Horizon Video Productions Inc, pg 891
Image Associates Inc, pg 894
Moving Pictures, pg 948
NASCAR Media Group LLC, pg 952
Unifour Productions Inc, pg 1048

OHIO

Advent Media Inc, pg 778
Creative Technology, pg 838
Cuyahoga Community College Media Center, pg 841
EDR Media LLC, pg 857
Electronic Vision Inc (EV), pg 859
Lyon Video Inc, pg 927
R&B Communications Inc, pg 991
Take 1 Media Services, pg 1031
Treehaus Communications Inc, pg 1044
VGI Productions, pg 1053
Vista Color Imaging Inc, pg 1059

OKLAHOMA

BCD Associates Inc, pg 803

OREGON

A KTVA Production LLC, pg 771
ERA Learning, pg 862
Ideascape Inc, pg 894
InterVision Media, pg 902
Odyssey Productions Inc, pg 961
Rex, pg 995
Wallace Creative Inc, pg 1061

PENNSYLVANIA

AiH Group Inc, pg 779
Argentine Productions Inc, pg 789
Audio Visual Communications Inc, pg 795
Beholder Productions Inc, pg 804
CCI Communications Inc, pg 821
Discovery Education - South Burlington, pg 848
FMP Media Solutions Inc, pg 870
Innovision Media Group, pg 899
JPL, pg 906
Kenexa, pg 909
Kensington Falls Animation, pg 909
Muderick Media, pg 949
Panta Rhei Media Inc, pg 968
Production Masters Inc (PMI), pg 984
S I Video Sales Group, pg 1001
Scala Inc, pg 1003
Visual Sound Inc, pg 1059

RHODE ISLAND

Sound-FX-Design, pg 1017

SOUTH CAROLINA

American Production Services LLC, pg 785

TENNESSEE

Anode Inc, pg 787
Center for Southern Folklore Inc, pg 822
Continental Film, pg 835
Griffith Productions, pg 882
Marine Geographic, pg 931
Memphis Communications Corp, pg 938
Paradigm Marketing & Creative, pg 969
Running Pony Productions LLC, pg 1000
Scripps Networks, pg 1005
Spring Arbor Distributors, pg 1022
Russ Sturgeon Productions/RSVP, pg 1027

TEXAS

Biway Media, pg 808
Castleview Productions, pg 821
CEV Multimedia Ltd, pg 823
Communication Arts Multimedia Inc, pg 832
Critical Information Network, pg 839
Dallas Learning Solutions, pg 842
Dykeman Associates Inc, pg 854
The Editing Co, pg 857
Epic Software Group Inc, pg 862
First Group Communications Inc, pg 868
Horizon Film + Video Productions, pg 891
InterCom, pg 900
J&S Audio Visual Inc, pg 904
Mediaforce Productions, pg 937
Julye Newlin Productions Inc, pg 956
Omega Productions, pg 962
Omni Intercommunications Inc, pg 962
Romar Learning, pg 999
South Coast Film & Video, pg 1019
Stage Directions, pg 1022
Texas Heart Institute Visual Communication Services, pg 1037

UTAH

K-SAR Video & DVD Productions, pg 907

VERMONT

University of Vermont, Instructional Television Dept, pg 1050

VIRGINIA

Advance Concepts Inc, pg 777
CALIBRE, pg 816
Computer Sciences Corp, pg 834
D&B Television & Video Productions Inc, pg 842
Gingerbread Productions, pg 878
ITC Learning LLC, pg 903
Metro Productions, pg 939
Video Solutions, pg 1056

WASHINGTON

Adams Creative & Production Services, pg 775
Bennett-Watt HD Productions Inc, pg 805
Global Net Productions Inc, pg 879
Hamilton Studio, pg 884
Intermedia Inc, pg 900
North-by-Northwest Productions, pg 958
Tri-Digital Software Inc, pg 1044
Victory Studios, pg 1054

WEST VIRGINIA

Altruist Media LLC, pg 783

WISCONSIN

AVS Group, pg 800
5th Floor Recording Co, pg 867
Logan Productions Inc, pg 924
Media Communications Association-International (MCA-I), pg 936
Rucinski & Reetz Communications LLC, pg 1000
USAV Group Inc, pg 1050
Video Wisconsin Inc, pg 1056
Watts Communications Inc, pg 1062
Wisconsin Public Television, pg 1068

WYOMING

Bridger Productions Inc, pg 812

ALBERTA

Black Media Works, pg 808
HBW Entertainment Inc, pg 886

BRITISH COLUMBIA

Triad Communications Ltd, pg 1044

NEWFOUNDLAND AND LABRADOR

Vidcraft Productions Ltd, pg 1054

ONTARIO

ADS Media, pg 777
DebsVoice, pg 844
GAPC (General Assembly Production Centre), pg 875
Gesturetek, pg 877
Image Video Services & Productions, pg 895
Iron Ring Communications Ltd, pg 902
JFB Communications, pg 905

Multimedia, CD-ROM & DVD Interactive Program Rentals

Music Video Distributors

Music Video Producers

PROGRAMMING — VIDEO

Music Video Producers (continued)

CALIFORNIA (continued)

Tranquil Technology Music, pg 1043
Twin Peaks Creative, pg 1047
Videolady, pg 1057
Vineyard Video & Photography, pg 1058
Wavemaker Media Design, pg 1062
Webster Communications, pg 1063
West Coast Projections Inc, pg 1063
Xenon Pictures Inc, pg 1071

COLORADO

Flashback Media Productions, pg 869
Rocky Mountain Audio/Video Productions Inc, pg 998

CONNECTICUT

Applebox Studio, pg 788
Broadcast Video Productions LLC, pg 813
Fox Connecticut, pg 872
The Gary-Paul Agency, pg 875
Ironik Design & Post, pg 902
MCC Films, pg 935
New London Media, pg 956
P&P Studios Inc, pg 968

DISTRICT OF COLUMBIA

Sano Videos, pg 1002

FLORIDA

Accord Productions, pg 773
Big Byte Video Productions, pg 806
Blackburst Entertainment, pg 808
CD ROM™ Inc, pg 822
Chatterbox Productions Inc, pg 824
Communications Concepts Inc (CCI), pg 833
CopShopMiami.com, pg 836
Courter Films LLC, pg 837
Eastern Video, pg 856
Ed Ethridge Productions Inc, pg 863
Everlast Productions, pg 863
Home Shopping Network (HSN), pg 890
Jordan Klein Film & Video (JKFV), pg 906
Motion Image Group LLC, pg 947
Paradise Video & Film, pg 969
Sunfire Communications Inc, pg 1028
Sunrise Studios, pg 1028
Tel-Air Interests Inc, pg 1035
Tight Line Productions, pg 1040
Tricycle Studios, pg 1044
Universal Studios Florida® Production Group, pg 1049
Video Techniques Inc, pg 1056

GEORGIA

Beachwood Productions, pg 804
Continental Film & Video, pg 835
ECG Productions, pg 856
Guerrilla Productions LLC, pg 883
Myriad Productions, pg 951
Malcolm Neal Productions, pg 954
On-Line Productions, pg 963
Showcase Photo & Video, pg 1009

HAWAII

Hyperspective Studios Inc, pg 893
Sight & Sound Studios, pg 1010
1013 Integrated, pg 1037

IDAHO

Wide Eye Productions, pg 1066

ILLINOIS

ABSA Productions Inc, pg 772
CCore Media Inc, pg 821
The Chicago Production Center, pg 825
Chicago Satellite & Video, pg 825
Comtech Multimedia Marketing, pg 834
Delmark Records, pg 845
Film Police, pg 867
IV Media Resources, pg 903
MIGHTYbYTES Inc, pg 942
Rob Orr Productions Ltd, pg 965
The Pepper Group, pg 972
Richter Studios, pg 996
Roadworthy Image Magnification, pg 998
SCI Television Productions LLC, pg 1004
20/20 Communications Inc, pg 1047
Video Impressions, pg 1055
WEEK TV, pg 1063
Winter Productions, pg 1068

INDIANA

AVA Productions, pg 798
Covenant Productions®, pg 837
Digital Rain LLC, pg 847
Explore Media LLC, pg 864

KANSAS

KAKE-TV, pg 907

KENTUCKY

Hammond Communications Group, pg 884
Idle Minds Productions Inc, pg 894
Prosper Media Group Inc, pg 986
Trusty Tuneshop Recording Studios, pg 1045

LOUISIANA

Digital FX Inc, pg 847
Great Chefs/Leisure Jazz Video, pg 881
Leisure Video, pg 918
Moxie Media, pg 948

MARYLAND

Absolute Hollywood, pg 772
Adventure Productions LLC, pg 778
CPR MultiMedia Solutions, pg 837
dbF a Media Company, pg 844
Kramer Communications Video Production, pg 913
Quality Film & Video, pg 988

MASSACHUSETTS

Green Mountain Post Films (GMP), pg 882
Heliotrope Studios, pg 887
Home Inc, pg 890
Penfield Productions Ltd, pg 971
TVN-The Video Network, pg 1046
Veritech Corp, pg 1053

MICHIGAN

Digi Sign Design LLC, pg 847
K&R All Media Productions Inc, pg 908
K&R's Recording Studios Inc, pg 908
Universal Images, pg 1049

MINNESOTA

Aggressive Records Audio Duplication LLC, pg 778
Big Event Productions LLC, pg 807
House of Cinemagraphics, pg 891
Master Communications Group, pg 933
MultiMedia, pg 950

MISSISSIPPI

Dollarhide Film Inc, pg 850

MISSOURI

Fambrough & Associates Inc, pg 865

MONTANA

North Country Media Group, pg 959

NEVADA

Aardvark Video & Media Productions, pg 772
DVDs4Less, pg 854
Encore Productions Inc, pg 861
HDTV Productions Inc, pg 886
JCS Video Productions, pg 904
Tanglewood Productions, pg 1031

NEW HAMPSHIRE

Apertura, pg 788
Captain Fiddle Music & Publications, pg 820
Channell One Video, pg 824
Chip Taylor Communications LLC, pg 1032
The Troupe, pg 1045

NEW JERSEY

Broadcast Center Studios, pg 813
CFP Video Productions Inc, pg 823
Half Moon Video Productions, pg 883
Megavideo Productions, pg 938
MIB Mediaworks, pg 941
Optisonics Productions, pg 965
Public Eye Productions, pg 987
Bill Quinn Productions, pg 989
Shanachie Entertainment Corp, pg 1008
Suede Interactive, pg 1027
TimeSteps Productions Inc, pg 1041
VCSvideo, pg 1052

NEW MEXICO

Production Outfitters, pg 984

NEW YORK

Ace Video, pg 774
American Montage Inc, pg 784
aurora productions, pg 797
BC Video Inc, pg 803
Blue Barn Pictures Inc, pg 809
Broad Street Inc, pg 812
Brooklyn Films, pg 814
Charlex Inc, pg 824
De Nonno Productions Inc (DPI), pg 844
Hallel Communications, pg 884
Havas Worldwide, pg 886
HB-Content, pg 886
Hello World Communications, pg 888
Homespun Video, pg 890
IAI Video, pg 893
Image Zone Inc, pg 896
Irish Music Corp, pg 902
Kinetic Arts, pg 911
Lavine Production Group, pg 917
LightHouse Films, pg 920
Long Island Video Enterprises Live Inc, pg 924
Lylofilm Productions, pg 926
Magnetic Music Publishing Co, pg 928
Manhattan Center Studios Inc, pg 930
Neal Marshad Productions, pg 931
Mastervision Inc, pg 933
Mood Creations Ltd, pg 946
MRG Productions Inc, pg 948
MRY, pg 949
New Horizon Studios, pg 955
Northeast Video Productions Inc, pg 959
Shelly Palmer Production, pg 968
Peckham Productions Inc, pg 970
Pennebaker Hegedus Films Inc, pg 972
Polestar Films & Associated Arts Ltd, pg 978
PrimaLux Video Inc, pg 982
R/GA, pg 990
Shadow Pictures Inc, pg 1007
Suggs Media Productions Inc, pg 1028
Third World Newsreel/Camera News Inc, pg 1039
Tiki Recording Studios Inc, pg 1040
Tobin Productions Inc, pg 1041
VIEW Inc (Video International Entertainment World Inc), pg 1058

NORTH CAROLINA

All Pro Media Inc, pg 780
Pat Appleson Studios Inc, pg 788
The Communications Group Inc, pg 833
LCW Productions LLC, pg 917
Moving Pictures, pg 948

OHIO

Advent Media Inc, pg 778
CET, pg 823
Clear Choice Creative Corp, pg 829
Creative Technology, pg 838
Image Video Teleproductions Inc, pg 895
Lyon Video Inc, pg 927
MainSail Production Services Inc, pg 929
R&B Communications Inc, pg 991
Red Onion Records, pg 993
Take 1 Media Services, pg 1031
VGI Productions, pg 1053
Vista Color Imaging Inc, pg 1059
WOUB Public Media, pg 1070

OREGON

Ideascape Inc, pg 894
The Keyboard Workshop, pg 910
KPDX-TV Production Center, pg 913
Production West, pg 985
Rex, pg 995
TeleVideos, pg 1036
Wallace Creative Inc, pg 1061
Wilderness Video, pg 1066

PENNSYLVANIA

Bang Pictures, pg 802
Discovery Education - South Burlington, pg 848
FMP Media Solutions Inc, pg 870

Music Video Rentals

News Program Distributors

News Program Producers

PROGRAMMING — VIDEO

News Program Producers (continued)

FLORIDA (continued)

Communications Concepts Inc (CCI), pg 833
CopShopMiami.com, pg 836
Eastern Video, pg 856
Ed Ethridge Productions Inc, pg 863
Jordan Klein Film & Video (JKFV), pg 906
Media Entertainment Inc, pg 936
Motion Image Group LLC, pg 947
National Teleproductions Inc, pg 953
Roger Scruggs Films, pg 1005
Sunfire Communications Inc, pg 1028
Mike Vasilinda Productions Inc, pg 1052
Video Techniques Inc, pg 1056
WCJB TV20, pg 1063

GEORGIA

Beachwood Productions, pg 804
Guerrilla Productions LLC, pg 883
KEF Media, pg 908
Myriad Productions, pg 951
On-Line Productions, pg 963

IDAHO

Brad Shaw Productions Inc, pg 1008
Wide Eye Productions, pg 1066

ILLINOIS

Abacus Group of Saint Louis LLC, pg 772
ABSA Productions Inc, pg 772
Audio Visual Services Corp, pg 796
CCore Media Inc, pg 821
The Chicago Production Center, pg 825
Chicago Satellite & Video, pg 825
Communications Corporation of America, pg 833
Film Police, pg 867
Manning Productions, pg 930
Mimi Productions, pg 943
The Pepper Group, pg 972
Production Craft Inc, pg 984
PSAV® Presentation Services (Hotel Services Division), pg 987
SCI Television Productions LLC, pg 1004

INDIANA

AVA Productions, pg 798
Digital Rain LLC, pg 847

KANSAS

KAKE-TV, pg 907

KENTUCKY

Idle Minds Productions Inc, pg 894

LOUISIANA

Digital FX Inc, pg 847

MAINE

WGME-TV, pg 1065

MARYLAND

Adventure Productions LLC, pg 778
The Ahern Group, pg 779
Richard Chisolm Cinematography, pg 825
CPR MultiMedia Solutions, pg 837
dbF a Media Company, pg 844
The Image Generators, pg 895
Kramer Communications Video Production, pg 913

MASSACHUSETTS

Award Productions, pg 800
Home Inc, pg 890
TVN-The Video Network, pg 1046
Veritech Corp, pg 1053
VideoLink Inc, pg 1057
WVP Boston, pg 1071

MICHIGAN

Benjamin Creative Productions, pg 805
Digi Sign Design LLC, pg 847
K&R All Media Productions Inc, pg 908
K&R's Recording Studios Inc, pg 908

MINNESOTA

Aggressive Records Audio Duplication LLC, pg 778
House of Cinemagraphics, pg 891
Master Communications Group, pg 933
MultiMedia, pg 950
Worthwhile Films, pg 1070

MISSOURI

Cable Films & Video, pg 816
Fambrough & Associates Inc, pg 865

NEBRASKA

Mason Video, pg 933

NEVADA

Aardvark Video & Media Productions, pg 772
Encore Productions Inc, pg 861
JCS Video Productions, pg 904

NEW HAMPSHIRE

Apertura, pg 788
Chip Taylor Communications LLC, pg 1032

NEW JERSEY

Broadcast Center Studios, pg 813
CFP Video Productions Inc, pg 823
DWJ Television, pg 854
Half Moon Video Productions, pg 883
Laurel Video Productions, pg 916
MIB Mediaworks, pg 941
Optisonics Productions, pg 965
Public Eye Productions, pg 987
Bill Quinn Productions, pg 989
Telequest Inc, pg 1036
VCSvideo, pg 1052

NEW MEXICO

Michael Dunn Productions, pg 853
Production Outfitters, pg 984

NEW YORK

Ace Video, pg 774
Associated Press Television News, pg 792
aurora productions, pg 797
Clarity Media Group, pg 829
CompuWeather Inc, pg 834
De Nonno Productions Inc (DPI), pg 844
Downtown Community Television Center (DCTV), pg 851
Havas Worldwide, pg 886
HB-Content, pg 886
Hello World Communications, pg 888
Manhattan Center Studios Inc, pg 930
Neal Marshad Productions, pg 931
MRG Productions Inc, pg 948
MRY, pg 949
News Broadcast Network, pg 956
Northeast Video Productions Inc, pg 959
Shelly Palmer Production, pg 968
PrimaLux Video Inc, pg 982
Richter Productions Inc, pg 996
Tobin Productions Inc, pg 1041
VIEW Inc (Video International Entertainment World Inc), pg 1058
Alan Weiss Productions, pg 1063
WNET/NET TELECON, pg 1069

NORTH CAROLINA

Pat Appleson Studios Inc, pg 788
J Arnold Productions Inc, pg 790
Bill Barnes Video Productions LLC, pg 803
The Communications Group Inc, pg 833
LCW Productions LLC, pg 917

NORTH DAKOTA

UND Television Center, pg 1048

OHIO

Advent Media Inc, pg 778
CET, pg 823
Commercial Video, pg 832
Creative Technology, pg 838
Image Video Teleproductions Inc, pg 895
Lyon Video Inc, pg 927
MainSail Production Services Inc, pg 929
R&B Communications Inc, pg 991
Shelburne Films, pg 1008
VGI Productions, pg 1053
Vista Color Imaging Inc, pg 1059

OREGON

Production West, pg 985

PENNSYLVANIA

AccuWeather Inc, pg 774
Beholder Productions Inc, pg 804
CCI Communications Inc, pg 821
FMP Media Solutions Inc, pg 870
Innovision Media Group, pg 899
Muderick Media, pg 949
Production Masters Inc (PMI), pg 984
The Videohouse Inc, pg 1057

RHODE ISLAND

Sound-FX-Design, pg 1017

SOUTH CAROLINA

Encore Video Productions, pg 861
Go To Team, pg 879
Stages Video Productions, pg 1023
Venture Media, pg 1052

TENNESSEE

Continental Film, pg 835
Jaguar Productions, pg 903
Running Pony Productions LLC, pg 1000

TEXAS

Cerutti Productions Inc, pg 823
Communication Arts Multimedia Inc, pg 832
Countdown Productions Inc, pg 837
Epic Software Group Inc, pg 862
Horizon Film + Video Productions, pg 891
Julye Newlin Productions Inc, pg 956
Omega Productions, pg 962
South Coast Film & Video, pg 1019
Stage Directions, pg 1022
Texas Heart Institute Visual Communication Services, pg 1037

VIRGINIA

CACI Productions Group, pg 816
CALIBRE, pg 816
D&B Television & Video Productions Inc, pg 842
Gingerbread Productions, pg 878
Limelight Communications Inc, pg 921
Metro Productions, pg 939
Rocktown Media, pg 998
Video Solutions, pg 1056

WASHINGTON

Bennett-Watt HD Productions Inc, pg 805
North-by-Northwest Productions, pg 958
Sparkworks Media, pg 1019

WEST VIRGINIA

Blackwater Video Productions, pg 808

WISCONSIN

5th Floor Recording Co, pg 867
Grassland Media Inc, pg 881
ProVideo, pg 986
University of Wisconsin-Oshkosh Radio-TV-Film Dept, pg 1050
Wisconsin Public Television, pg 1068

WYOMING

Bridger Productions Inc, pg 812

ALBERTA

Black Media Works, pg 808
Global Television Station, pg 879

BRITISH COLUMBIA

Image Media Farm, pg 895
Triad Communications Ltd, pg 1044

NEWFOUNDLAND AND LABRADOR

Vidcraft Productions Ltd, pg 1054

NORTHWEST TERRITORIES

Yellowknife Films Inc, pg 1072

ONTARIO

GAPC (General Assembly Production Centre), pg 875
Video Excellence Productions, pg 1055

QUEBEC

Kerrigan Productions Inc, pg 910

News Program Rentals

ARIZONA

Video Learning Library, pg 1055

MICHIGAN

Digi Sign Design LLC, pg 847

NEW YORK

Downtown Community Television Center (DCTV), pg 851
Icarus Film Inc, pg 893
Richter Productions Inc, pg 996
VIEW Inc (Video International Entertainment World Inc), pg 1058

ONTARIO

WESCAM Inc, pg 1063

Program—Television, *see* Television Program

Public Relations Program Distributors

ARIZONA

Video Learning Library, pg 1055

ARKANSAS

Mullikin Agency, pg 949

CALIFORNIA

Crystal Pyramid Productions™, pg 840
Direct Cinema Ltd Inc, pg 848
eFootage LLC, pg 858
411 Video Information, pg 872
New & Unique Videos™, pg 955

FLORIDA

Allegro Productions Inc, pg 781
Capital Communications Inc, pg 819

GEORGIA

Convergent Media Systems, pg 836
On-Line Productions, pg 963

ILLINOIS

ABSA Productions Inc, pg 772
CCore Media Inc, pg 821
Chicago Satellite & Video, pg 825

KENTUCKY

WaxWorks VideoWorks, pg 1063

MASSACHUSETTS

Penfield Productions Ltd, pg 971

MICHIGAN

Digi Sign Design LLC, pg 847

NEBRASKA

B & B Video Productions Inc, pg 801

NEVADA

DVDs4Less, pg 854

NEW HAMPSHIRE

Channell One Video, pg 824
Chip Taylor Communications LLC, pg 1032

NEW JERSEY

MIB Mediaworks, pg 941
SES World Skies, pg 1007

NEW YORK

Broad Street Inc, pg 812
HB-Content, pg 886
KickedUp Media Group Inc, pg 910
Maryknoll Productions, pg 933
MRG Productions Inc, pg 948
News Broadcast Network, pg 956
Synaptic Digital, pg 1030

NORTH CAROLINA

Baker & Taylor Inc, pg 801

OHIO

Treehaus Communications Inc, pg 1044

OKLAHOMA

University of Oklahoma Academic Media & Digital Services, pg 1050

OREGON

Sugar Mountain PR, pg 1028

PENNSYLVANIA

FMP Media Solutions Inc, pg 870
Karol Media Inc, pg 908

TENNESSEE

American Blackguard Inc, pg 784

VERMONT

Perceptions Inc, pg 973
University of Vermont, Instructional Television Dept, pg 1050

VIRGINIA

CACI Productions Group, pg 816
WETA Production Center, pg 1064

WASHINGTON

Bennett-Watt HD Productions Inc, pg 805

ALBERTA

Global Television Station, pg 879

Public Relations Program Producers

ALABAMA

CMEInfo, pg 830

ALASKA

Aurora Films, pg 797

ARIZONA

Aardvark Productions LLC, pg 772
Candee Productions Inc, pg 819
Direct Current Video Productions, pg 848
Fox 10 Productions (KSAZ-TV), pg 872
MediaWorks, pg 938
Merestone, pg 938
Metropolitan Audio-Visual Inc, pg 940
Video Media Productions (VMP), pg 1055

ARKANSAS

Cedar Crest Studio, pg 822
Jones Film Video, pg 906
Live'N'Loud, pg 923
Mullikin Agency, pg 949
White Diamond Productions, pg 1065

CALIFORNIA

Aaron Marcus & Associates Inc, pg 772
Action Video, pg 775
AM Productions, pg 783
Big Door, pg 807
Cavalcade Productions Inc, pg 821
Chesney Communications, pg 824
Chick Russell Communications, pg 825
Classic Images, pg 829
Crystal Pyramid Productions™, pg 840
Custom Video Productions Inc, pg 841
Design Media, pg 845
Digital Outpost, pg 847
Direct Images Interactive Inc, pg 848
Dogma Studios, pg 850
Dolphin MultiMedia Inc, pg 850
Face Digital Post, pg 865
First Camera, pg 868
Goal Productions, pg 879
Imageworks, pg 896
ITV Productions, pg 903
Kavich Reynolds Productions Inc, pg 908
KION-TV, pg 911
Main Street Media Inc, pg 929
Maximus Media Inc, pg 934
McCune Audio-Video-Lighting, pg 935
Media Magic, pg 937
The Media Staff Inc, pg 937
Mist Media Inc, pg 944
Nolte Media, pg 958
On-Trax Inc, pg 963
Panorama Productions, pg 968
Prime Cut Productions, pg 982
QRS Software Services, pg 988
Dick Reizner Film & Video, pg 994
Glenn Roland Films, pg 998
SBS Productions, pg 1003
SNAP, pg 1014
Staylor-Made Communications Inc, pg 1024
Still N'Motion, pg 1025
The Studio Center, pg 1026
Tam Communications Inc, pg 1031
Tele-Video Production Services (TVPS), pg 1036
Total Media Group, pg 1042
TVA Productions, pg 1046
Twin Peaks Creative, pg 1047
Videolady, pg 1057
Videowerks, pg 1057
Vineyard Video & Photography, pg 1058
Visions Plus, pg 1058
WalkerVision Interarts, pg 1061
Wavemaker Media Design, pg 1062
West Coast Projections Inc, pg 1063
WMS Media Inc, pg 1069
Yada/Levine Video Productions, pg 1071
Zamacona Productions, pg 1073

COLORADO

Apogee Communications Group, pg 788
Daylight Productions & Rentals, pg 844
Flashback Media Productions, pg 869
Rocky Mountain Audio/Video Productions Inc, pg 998
Tatum Video, pg 1032
Transtar Entertainment Co Inc, pg 1043

CONNECTICUT

Applebox Studio, pg 788
Biomedical Media Communications Dept, pg 807
Broadcast Video Productions LLC, pg 813
Fox Connecticut, pg 872
The Gary-Paul Agency, pg 875
Geomatrix Productions, pg 877
Ironik Design & Post, pg 902
MCC Films, pg 935
Moving Pictures, pg 947
New London Media, pg 956
P&P Studios Inc, pg 968
Video Production Associates Inc, pg 1056

DISTRICT OF COLUMBIA

Hillmann & Carr Inc, pg 889
O'Keefe Communications Inc, pg 961
Yellow Cat Productions Inc, pg 1072

FLORIDA

Accel Video Productions, pg 773
Accord Productions, pg 773
Allegro Productions Inc, pg 781
Blackburst Entertainment, pg 808
Civins Productions Inc, pg 828
Communications Concepts Inc (CCI), pg 833
CopShopMiami.com, pg 836
Courter Films LLC, pg 837
Eastern Video, pg 856
Easy Edit Video Inc, pg 856
Ed Ethridge Productions Inc, pg 863
Home Shopping Network (HSN), pg 890
Jordan Klein Film & Video (JKFV), pg 906
Media Entertainment Inc, pg 936
Motion Image Group LLC, pg 947
National Teleproductions Inc, pg 953
Paradise Video & Film, pg 969
Sound & Vision Communications Inc, pg 1016
Sound*Light, pg 1017
Sunfire Communications Inc, pg 1028
Sunrise Studios, pg 1028
Tel-Air Interests Inc, pg 1035
Tricycle Studios, pg 1044
Universal Studios Florida® Production Group, pg 1049

PROGRAMMING — VIDEO

Public Relations Program Producers (continued)

FLORIDA (continued)

Mike Vasilinda Productions Inc, pg 1052
Video Techniques Inc, pg 1056

GEORGIA

Beachwood Productions, pg 804
Burst Video/Film Inc, pg 815
COMPRO Productions Inc, pg 834
Continental Film & Video, pg 835
ECG Productions, pg 856
Georgia-Pacific Television & Photography, pg 877
Guerrilla Productions LLC, pg 883
Memory Lane Productions, pg 938
Myriad Productions, pg 951
Malcolm Neal Productions, pg 954
On-Line Productions, pg 963
Showcase Photo & Video, pg 1009

HAWAII

Hyperspective Studios Inc, pg 893
1013 Integrated, pg 1037

IDAHO

Brad Shaw Productions Inc, pg 1008
Wide Eye Productions, pg 1066

ILLINOIS

Abacus Group of Saint Louis LLC, pg 772
ABSA Productions Inc, pg 772
Airways Digital Media, pg 779
Audio Visual Services Corp, pg 796
Beatty TeleVisual Productions, pg 804
CCore Media Inc, pg 821
The Chicago Production Center, pg 825
Chicago Satellite & Video, pg 825
Comtech Multimedia Marketing, pg 834
Cresta Creative, pg 839
Extraordinary Demos, pg 864
Film Police, pg 867
IV Media Resources, pg 903
Major Media Productions Inc, pg 929
Manning Productions, pg 930
Mimi Productions, pg 943
Rob Orr Productions Ltd, pg 965
The Pepper Group, pg 972
Production Craft Inc, pg 984
PSAV® Presentation Services (Hotel Services Division), pg 987
QuickSet International Inc, pg 989
Roadworthy Image Magnification, pg 998
SCI Television Productions LLC, pg 1004
20/20 Communications Inc, pg 1047
Universal Training, pg 1049
Video I-D Teleproductions Inc, pg 1055
Video Impressions, pg 1055
WEEK TV, pg 1063
Winter Productions, pg 1068

INDIANA

AVA Productions, pg 798
Covenant Productions®, pg 837
Explore Media LLC, pg 864
PentaVision Communications Inc, pg 972

KANSAS

KAKE-TV, pg 907

KENTUCKY

Horizon Films & Media LLC, pg 891
Idle Minds Productions Inc, pg 894
Donna Lawrence Productions, pg 917
The Media Collaboratory, pg 936

LOUISIANA

Digital FX Inc, pg 847
Louisiana State University Health Sciences Center - Shreveport, pg 925
Moxie Media, pg 948

MAINE

WGME-TV, pg 1065

MARYLAND

Absolute Hollywood, pg 772
Adventure Productions LLC, pg 778
The Ahern Group, pg 779
CAS Video Productions, pg 820
Richard Chisolm Cinematography, pg 825
CPR MultiMedia Solutions, pg 837
dbF a Media Company, pg 844
The Image Generators, pg 895
Kramer Communications Video Production, pg 913

MASSACHUSETTS

Award Productions, pg 800
CommCreative, pg 832
Green Mountain Post Films (GMP), pg 882
Heliotrope Studios, pg 887
Home Inc, pg 890
Inter-Media Electronics, pg 899
Monadnock Media Inc, pg 945
Northern Light Productions, pg 959
Penfield Productions Ltd, pg 971
Preston Productions Inc, pg 981
TVN-The Video Network, pg 1046
Veritech Corp, pg 1053
WVP Boston, pg 1071

MICHIGAN

Benjamin Creative Productions, pg 805
Digi Sign Design LLC, pg 847
K&R All Media Productions Inc, pg 908
K&R's Recording Studios Inc, pg 908
Universal Images, pg 1049

MINNESOTA

Aggressive Records Audio Duplication LLC, pg 778
Big Event Productions LLC, pg 807
GMI Productions, pg 879
House of Cinemagraphics, pg 891
Master Communications Group, pg 933
Media Loft Inc, pg 937
MultiMedia, pg 950
Worthwhile Films, pg 1070

MISSISSIPPI

Dollarhide Film Inc, pg 850

MISSOURI

Audio-VideoGraphics Inc, pg 795
Communitronics Corp, pg 833
Fambrough & Associates Inc, pg 865

MONTANA

KUSM TV, pg 914
North Country Media Group, pg 959

NEBRASKA

B & B Video Productions Inc, pg 801
Dog & Pony Productions Inc, pg 850
Envision Communications Inc, pg 861
Rainbow Video Productions Inc, pg 991

NEVADA

Aardvark Video & Media Productions, pg 772
DVDs4Less, pg 854
Encore Productions Inc, pg 861
HDTV Productions Inc, pg 886
JCS Video Productions, pg 904

NEW HAMPSHIRE

Apertura, pg 788
Channell One Video, pg 824
NH Movies Inc, pg 957
Chip Taylor Communications LLC, pg 1032
The Troupe, pg 1045

NEW JERSEY

CFP Video Productions Inc, pg 823
DWJ Television, pg 854
Euro-Pacific Film & Video Productions Inc, pg 863
Half Moon Video Productions, pg 883
Laurel Video Productions, pg 916
MediaNow, pg 938
Megavideo Productions, pg 938
MIB Mediaworks, pg 941
Midnight Media Group Inc, pg 942
Ray Mueller Productions, pg 949
Optisonics Productions, pg 965
Producer East Productions, pg 983
Public Eye Productions, pg 987
Bill Quinn Productions, pg 989
Reider Photography & Video Productions, pg 994
Suede Interactive, pg 1027
Telequest Inc, pg 1036
TimeSteps Productions Inc, pg 1041
VCSvideo, pg 1052

NEW MEXICO

Michael Dunn Productions, pg 853
Production Outfitters, pg 984

NEW YORK

Ace Video, pg 774
Artistic Video, pg 791
Associated Press Television News, pg 792
aurora productions, pg 797
Blue Barn Pictures Inc, pg 809
Brian Film Productions LLC, pg 812
Broad Street Inc, pg 812
Clarity Media Group, pg 829
Cohn Creative Group LLC, pg 831
dM works, pg 849
Florentine Films, pg 870
Karen Frankel Productions, pg 872
Golden Lamb Productions, pg 880
Havas Worldwide, pg 886
HB-Content, pg 886
Hello World Communications, pg 888
Ketchum Pleon Change, pg 910
KickedUp Media Group Inc, pg 910
Kinetic Arts, pg 911
L A Bruell Inc, pg 914
Long Island Video Enterprises Live Inc, pg 924
Neal Marshad Productions, pg 931
Mood Creations Ltd, pg 946
MRG Productions Inc, pg 948
MRY, pg 949
News Broadcast Network, pg 956
Northeast Video Productions Inc, pg 959
Shelly Palmer Production, pg 968
Peckham Productions Inc, pg 970
Polestar Films & Associated Arts Ltd, pg 978
PrimaLux Video Inc, pg 982
Richter Productions Inc, pg 996
Suggs Media Productions Inc, pg 1028
Synaptic Digital, pg 1030
TeleTime Productions, pg 1036
Time Warner Cable, pg 1040
Tobin Productions Inc, pg 1041
Alan Weiss Productions, pg 1063
WNET/NET TELECON, pg 1069

NORTH CAROLINA

All Pro Media Inc, pg 780
Pat Appleson Studios Inc, pg 788
J Arnold Productions Inc, pg 790
Bill Barnes Video Productions LLC, pg 803
The Communications Group Inc, pg 833
Horizon Video Productions Inc, pg 891
Kino Mountain Productions LLC, pg 911
Moving Pictures, pg 948
Unifour Productions Inc, pg 1048

OHIO

Advent Media Inc, pg 778
Russ Beckner Pictures, pg 804
CET, pg 823
Commercial Video, pg 832
Creative Technology, pg 838
EDR Media LLC, pg 857
Electronic Vision Inc (EV), pg 859
Image Video Teleproductions Inc, pg 895
Lyon Video Inc, pg 927
MainSail Production Services Inc, pg 929
Maslowski Productions, pg 933
R&B Communications Inc, pg 991
Take 1 Media Services, pg 1031
Treehaus Communications Inc, pg 1044
VGI Productions, pg 1053
Vista Color Imaging Inc, pg 1059

OKLAHOMA

University of Oklahoma Academic Media & Digital Services, pg 1050

OREGON

Ideascape Inc, pg 894
InterVision Media, pg 902
KPDX-TV Production Center, pg 913

Public Relations Program Rentals

Public Service Announcement Distributors

PROGRAMMING — VIDEO

Public Service Announcement Producers

ALABAMA

CMEInfo, pg 830

ALASKA

Alaska Film Services Inc, pg 779
Aurora Films, pg 797

ARIZONA

Aardvark Productions LLC, pg 772
Candee Productions Inc, pg 819
Direct Current Video Productions, pg 848
Film Creations Ltd, pg 867
Fox 10 Productions (KSAZ-TV), pg 872
MediaWorks, pg 938
Metropolitan Audio-Visual Inc, pg 940
On-Site Video, pg 963
Phoenix VideoFilms®, pg 974
Video Media Productions (VMP), pg 1055

ARKANSAS

Cedar Crest Studio, pg 822
Jones Film Video, pg 906
Live'N'Loud, pg 923
Mullikin Agency, pg 949
White Diamond Productions, pg 1065

CALIFORNIA

Access Video in Berkeley, pg 773
Action Video, pg 775
AM Productions, pg 783
Artichoke Productions, pg 791
Barbosa Video Services, pg 802
Big Door, pg 807
Cavalcade Productions Inc, pg 821
Chesney Communications, pg 824
Classic Images, pg 829
Coastline Productions, pg 831
Concrete Images, pg 835
Cox Media, pg 837
Crystal Pyramid Productions™, pg 840
Custom Video Productions Inc, pg 841
Direct Images Interactive Inc, pg 848
Dogma Studios, pg 850
Tom Donald Films, pg 850
Duck Studios, pg 853
ECONEWS (Environmental Television Series) & (Environmental Directions Radio Series), pg 856
Face Digital Post, pg 865
First Camera, pg 868
FXF Productions Inc, pg 874
GAMfilm Productions, pg 875
Global Village Productions, pg 879
Image Integration, pg 895
imageReal Pictures LLC, pg 896
Imageworks, pg 896
ITV Productions, pg 903
Kavich Reynolds Productions Inc, pg 908
KION-TV, pg 911
KTVU-Retail Services, pg 914
Main Street Media Inc, pg 929
Maximus Media Inc, pg 934
McCune Audio-Video-Lighting, pg 935
Media Magic, pg 937
The Media Staff Inc, pg 937
Mist Media Inc, pg 944
New & Unique Videos™, pg 955
New Circuit Films LLC, pg 955
Nolte Media, pg 958
On-Trax Inc, pg 963
Point of View Productions, pg 977
QRS Software Services, pg 988
Dick Reizner Film & Video, pg 994
Glenn Roland Films, pg 998
SBS Productions, pg 1003
Screen Door Entertainment Inc, pg 1005
SNAP, pg 1014
Staylor-Made Communications Inc, pg 1024
Still N'Motion, pg 1025
The Studio Center, pg 1026
Tam Communications Inc, pg 1031
Tele-Video Production Services (TVPS), pg 1036
Timestream Video, pg 1041
Total Media Group, pg 1042
Twin Peaks Creative, pg 1047
Videolady, pg 1057
Videowerks, pg 1057
Vineyard Video & Photography, pg 1058
Visions Plus, pg 1058
Visual Communications - Southern California Asian American Studies Central Inc, pg 1059
WalkerVision Interarts, pg 1061
Wavemaker Media Design, pg 1062
The Wyland Group, pg 1071
Zamacona Productions, pg 1073

COLORADO

Daylight Productions & Rentals, pg 844
Flashback Media Productions, pg 869
Rocky Mountain Audio/Video Productions Inc, pg 998
Tatum Video, pg 1032
Transtar Entertainment Co Inc, pg 1043

CONNECTICUT

ACM Productions Ltd, pg 774
Applebox Studio, pg 788
Biomedical Media Communications Dept, pg 807
Broadcast Video Productions LLC, pg 813
Fox Connecticut, pg 872
The Gary-Paul Agency, pg 875
Geomatrix Productions, pg 877
Ironik Design & Post, pg 902
MCC Films, pg 935
Moving Pictures, pg 947
P&P Studios Inc, pg 968
Video Production Associates Inc, pg 1056

DISTRICT OF COLUMBIA

Hillmann & Carr Inc, pg 889
O'Keefe Communications Inc, pg 961
US Holocaust Memorial Museum, pg 1050
Yellow Cat Productions Inc, pg 1072

FLORIDA

Allegro Productions Inc, pg 781
Blackburst Entertainment, pg 808
Civins Productions Inc, pg 828
Communications Concepts Inc (CCI), pg 833
CopShopMiami.com, pg 836
Courter Films LLC, pg 837
Eastern Video, pg 856
Ed Ethridge Productions Inc, pg 863
Home Shopping Network (HSN), pg 890
Jordan Klein Film & Video (JKFV), pg 906
Motion Image Group LLC, pg 947
National Teleproductions Inc, pg 953
Paradise Video & Film, pg 969
Sunfire Communications Inc, pg 1028
Sunrise Studios, pg 1028
Tel-Air Interests Inc, pg 1035
Tricycle Studios, pg 1044
Mike Vasilinda Productions Inc, pg 1052
Video Techniques Inc, pg 1056

GEORGIA

Beachwood Productions, pg 804
Burst Video/Film Inc, pg 815
Continental Film & Video, pg 835
Georgia-Pacific Television & Photography, pg 877
Guerrilla Productions LLC, pg 883
Memory Lane Productions, pg 938
On-Line Productions, pg 963

HAWAII

Hyperspective Studios Inc, pg 893
1013 Integrated, pg 1037

IDAHO

Brad Shaw Productions Inc, pg 1008
Wide Eye Productions, pg 1066

ILLINOIS

ABSA Productions Inc, pg 772
Airways Digital Media, pg 779
Audio Visual Services Corp, pg 796
CCore Media Inc, pg 821
The Chicago Production Center, pg 825
Chicago Satellite & Video, pg 825
Film Police, pg 867
IV Media Resources, pg 903
Major Media Productions Inc, pg 929
Manning Productions, pg 930
Mimi Productions, pg 943
The Pepper Group, pg 972
Production Craft Inc, pg 984
PSAV® Presentation Services (Hotel Services Division), pg 987
SCI Television Productions LLC, pg 1004
Sparkfactor, pg 1019
20/20 Communications Inc, pg 1047
Universal Training, pg 1049
Video I-D Teleproductions Inc, pg 1055
WEEK TV, pg 1063
Winter Productions, pg 1068

INDIANA

AVA Productions, pg 798
Bright Ideas Creative Services, pg 812
Covenant Productions®, pg 837
Digital Rain LLC, pg 847
Explore Media LLC, pg 864
Road Pictures, pg 997

IOWA

Kuhn Productions LLC, pg 914

KANSAS

KAKE-TV, pg 907

KENTUCKY

Idle Minds Productions Inc, pg 894
Media Resources, pg 937
Northern Kentucky University, pg 959
Prosper Media Group Inc, pg 986

LOUISIANA

Digital FX Inc, pg 847
Louisiana State University Health Sciences Center - Shreveport, pg 925
Moxie Media, pg 948

MAINE

WGME-TV, pg 1065

MARYLAND

Adventure Productions LLC, pg 778
The Ahern Group, pg 779
CAS Video Productions, pg 820
Richard Chisolm Cinematography, pg 825
CPR MultiMedia Solutions, pg 837
dbF a Media Company, pg 844
The Image Generators, pg 895
Kramer Communications Video Production, pg 913
Media Dimensions Inc, pg 936
Producers Video, pg 984
Recorded Books LLC, pg 993
Sign Media Inc, pg 1011

MASSACHUSETTS

Award Productions, pg 800
Documentary Educational Resources Inc, pg 850
Green Mountain Post Films (GMP), pg 882
Heliotrope Studios, pg 887
Home Inc, pg 890
Inter-Media Electronics, pg 899
Monadnock Media Inc, pg 945
MotionArt Studios, pg 947
Penfield Productions Ltd, pg 971
Preston Productions Inc, pg 981
TVN-The Video Network, pg 1046
Veritech Corp, pg 1053
VideoLink Inc, pg 1057

MICHIGAN

Benjamin Creative Productions, pg 805
Digi Sign Design LLC, pg 847
K&R All Media Productions Inc, pg 908
K&R's Recording Studios Inc, pg 908
Universal Images, pg 1049
WTVS-Station Enterprises, pg 1071

MINNESOTA

Aggressive Records Audio Duplication LLC, pg 778
Big Event Productions LLC, pg 807
GMI Productions, pg 879
House of Cinemagraphics, pg 891
Master Communications Group, pg 933
MultiMedia, pg 950
Worthwhile Films, pg 1070

MISSISSIPPI

Dollarhide Film Inc, pg 850

MISSOURI

Audio-VideoGraphics Inc, pg 795
Communitronics Corp, pg 833
Fambrough & Associates Inc, pg 865
Hardcastle Films & Video, pg 885
University of Missouri-Columbia, pg 1050

MONTANA

KUSM TV, pg 914
North Country Media Group, pg 959

NEBRASKA

Rainbow Video Productions Inc, pg 991

NEVADA

Aardvark Video & Media Productions, pg 772
DVDs4Less, pg 854
Encore Productions Inc, pg 861
HDTV Productions Inc, pg 886
JCS Video Productions, pg 904

NEW HAMPSHIRE

Apertura, pg 788
Channell One Video, pg 824
Chip Taylor Communications LLC, pg 1032

NEW JERSEY

Broadcast Center Studios, pg 813
CFP Video Productions Inc, pg 823
DWJ Television, pg 854
Euro-Pacific Film & Video Productions Inc, pg 863
Half Moon Video Productions, pg 883
Laurel Video Productions, pg 916
MIB Mediaworks, pg 941
Midnight Media Group Inc, pg 942
Ray Mueller Productions, pg 949
Optisonics Productions, pg 965
Public Eye Productions, pg 987
Bill Quinn Productions, pg 989
Reider Photography & Video Productions, pg 994
Suede Interactive, pg 1027
Telequest Inc, pg 1036
TimeSteps Productions Inc, pg 1041
VCSvideo, pg 1052

NEW MEXICO

Michael Dunn Productions, pg 853
Production Outfitters, pg 984

NEW YORK

Ace Video, pg 774
aurora productions, pg 797
BC Video Inc, pg 803
Blue Barn Pictures Inc, pg 809
Broad Street Inc, pg 812
Brooklyn Botanic Garden, pg 814
Buzzco Associates Inc, pg 816
Clarity Media Group, pg 829
De Nonno Productions Inc (DPI), pg 844
Fanlight Productions, pg 865
Florentine Films, pg 870
HB-Content, pg 886
Hello World Communications, pg 888
Ketchum Pleon Change, pg 910
KickedUp Media Group Inc, pg 910
Kinetic Arts, pg 911
Long Island Video Enterprises Live Inc, pg 924
March of Dimes Foundation, pg 930
Neal Marshad Productions, pg 931
Mood Creations Ltd, pg 946
MRG Productions Inc, pg 948
MRM Worldwide, pg 948
MRY, pg 949
News Broadcast Network, pg 956
Northeast Video Productions Inc, pg 959
Shelly Palmer Production, pg 968
Pat Kogan Productions Inc, pg 970
Polestar Films & Associated Arts Ltd, pg 978
PrimaLux Video Inc, pg 982
Shadow Pictures Inc, pg 1007
Suggs Media Productions Inc, pg 1028
Synaptic Digital, pg 1030
TeleTime Productions, pg 1036
Third World Newsreel/Camera News Inc, pg 1039
Time Warner Cable, pg 1040
Tobin Productions Inc, pg 1041
Vidicom Inc, pg 1057
Alan Weiss Productions, pg 1063
Willow Mixed Media Inc, pg 1067
WNET/NET TELECON, pg 1069

NORTH CAROLINA

All Pro Media Inc, pg 780
Pat Appleson Studios Inc, pg 788
The Communications Group Inc, pg 833
Horizon Video Productions Inc, pg 891
Kino Mountain Productions LLC, pg 911
LCW Productions LLC, pg 917
Unifour Productions Inc, pg 1048

OHIO

Advent Media Inc, pg 778
Russ Beckner Pictures, pg 804
CET, pg 823
Creative Technology, pg 838
Cuyahoga Community College Media Center, pg 841
Electronic Vision Inc (EV), pg 859
Image Video Teleproductions Inc, pg 895
Lyon Video Inc, pg 927
MainSail Production Services Inc, pg 929
Maslowski Productions, pg 933
R&B Communications Inc, pg 991
Take 1 Media Services, pg 1031
Treehaus Communications Inc, pg 1044
VGI Productions, pg 1053
Vista Color Imaging Inc, pg 1059

OKLAHOMA

University of Oklahoma Academic Media & Digital Services, pg 1050

OREGON

A KTVA Production LLC, pg 771
Ideascape Inc, pg 894
InterVision Media, pg 902
KPDX-TV Production Center, pg 913
Odyssey Productions Inc, pg 961
Producers Studio, pg 984
Production West, pg 985
Spirit Media, pg 1021

PENNSYLVANIA

AiH Group Inc, pg 779
Audio Visual Communications Inc, pg 795
CCI Communications Inc, pg 821
FMP Media Solutions Inc, pg 870
Fusion Brand Experiences, pg 874
Goodman Associates Inc, pg 880
Innovision Media Group, pg 899
JPL, pg 906
Kensington Falls Animation, pg 909
Muderick Media, pg 949
Panta Rhei Media Inc, pg 968
Pemcor LLC, pg 971
Producers Management Television (PMTV), pg 983
Production Masters Inc (PMI), pg 984
Video/Film Associates, pg 1055
The Videohouse Inc, pg 1057
Visual Sound Inc, pg 1059

RHODE ISLAND

Sound-FX-Design, pg 1017

SOUTH CAROLINA

Encore Video Productions, pg 861
Stages Video Productions, pg 1023
Venture Media, pg 1052

TENNESSEE

American Blackguard Inc, pg 784
Continental Film, pg 835
Griffith Productions, pg 882
Jaguar Productions, pg 903
Running Pony Productions LLC, pg 1000

TEXAS

Biway Media, pg 808
Castleview Productions, pg 821
Cerutti Productions Inc, pg 823
Communication Arts Multimedia Inc, pg 832
Dykeman Associates Inc, pg 854
The Editing Co, pg 857
Epic Software Group Inc, pg 862
First Group Communications Inc, pg 868
Horizon Film + Video Productions, pg 891
Mediaforce Productions, pg 937
Julye Newlin Productions Inc, pg 956
Omega Productions, pg 962
Phil Lights, pg 973
The Samuels Co, pg 1002
South Coast Film & Video, pg 1019
Texas Heart Institute Visual Communication Services, pg 1037

UTAH

K-SAR Video & DVD Productions, pg 907

VERMONT

Perceptions Inc, pg 973
University of Vermont, Instructional Television Dept, pg 1050

VIRGINIA

CACI Productions Group, pg 816
CALIBRE, pg 816
CDR Communications Inc, pg 822
Cinebar Productions Inc, pg 826
Creative Video of Washington Inc, pg 839
D&B Television & Video Productions Inc, pg 842
Gingerbread Productions, pg 878
Limelight Communications Inc, pg 921
Metro Productions, pg 939
National Media Services Inc, pg 953
Rocktown Media, pg 998
Studio Center Corp, pg 1026
Video Solutions, pg 1056

WASHINGTON

Bennett-Watt HD Productions Inc, pg 805
Hamilton Studio, pg 884
Victory Studios, pg 1054
White Rain Films Ltd, pg 1065

WEST VIRGINIA

Blackwater Video Productions, pg 808

WISCONSIN

5th Floor Recording Co, pg 867
Media Communications Association-International (MCA-I), pg 936
Meridian Studios, pg 939
Midland Video Productions Inc, pg 942
ProVideo, pg 986
Rucinski & Reetz Communications LLC, pg 1000
University of Wisconsin-Oshkosh Radio-TV-Film Dept, pg 1050
USAV Group Inc, pg 1050
Video Wisconsin Inc, pg 1056
Watts Communications Inc, pg 1062
Wisconsin Public Television, pg 1068

WYOMING

Bridger Productions Inc, pg 812

ALBERTA

Black Media Works, pg 808
Global Television Station, pg 879
HBW Entertainment Inc, pg 886

BRITISH COLUMBIA

Image Media Farm, pg 895

MANITOBA

Spectra Video Productions Ltd, pg 1020

NEWFOUNDLAND AND LABRADOR

Vidcraft Productions Ltd, pg 1054

NORTHWEST TERRITORIES

Yellowknife Films Inc, pg 1072

ONTARIO

ADS Media, pg 777
DebsVoice, pg 844
GAPC (General Assembly Production Centre), pg 875
Image Video Services & Productions, pg 895
Shaw Street Productions, pg 1008
Video Excellence Productions, pg 1055

QUEBEC

Kerrigan Productions Inc, pg 910

PROGRAMMING — VIDEO

Public Service Announcement Producers (continued)

SASKATCHEWAN

plan9films, pg 976

Public Service Announcement Rentals

CALIFORNIA

ECONEWS (Environmental Television Series) & (Environmental Directions Radio Series), pg 856
Visual Communications - Southern California Asian American Studies Central Inc, pg 1059

GEORGIA

On-Line Productions, pg 963

MICHIGAN

Digi Sign Design LLC, pg 847

NEW YORK

BC Video Inc, pg 803

VERMONT

University of Vermont, Instructional Television Dept, pg 1050

Religious Program Distributors

ALABAMA

Eternal Word Television Network (EWTN), pg 862

ARIZONA

Mother Basilea Films, pg 947
TSG Publishing Foundation Inc USA, pg 1046

ARKANSAS

Mullikin Agency, pg 949

CALIFORNIA

Blue Dolphin Multimedia, pg 809
Christian Media Network, pg 825
Clarity Sound & Light, pg 829
Direct Cinema Ltd Inc, pg 848
Discovery Education - Los Angeles, pg 848
411 Video Information, pg 872
Glenray Productions Inc, pg 878
Increase Video/Silver Mine Video, pg 897
monterey media inc, pg 945
monterey video, pg 946
Nilgiri Press, pg 957
Osho Viha Information Center & Book Distributors, pg 965
People Skills International, pg 972
Pyramid Media, pg 987
Thinking Allowed Productions, pg 1038
Vedanta Press & Catalog, pg 1052
The Wyland Group, pg 1071
Xenon Pictures Inc, pg 1071

COLORADO

Crown Ministries International, pg 840

CONNECTICUT

Hartley Film Foundation, pg 885

DISTRICT OF COLUMBIA

Biblical Archaeology Society (BAS), pg 806
USCCB Publishing, pg 1051

FLORIDA

Children of Mary, pg 825

GEORGIA

Gingerbread Group, pg 878
New Leaf Distributing Co, pg 955

ILLINOIS

ACTA Publications, pg 775
Baha'i Distribution Service (BDS), pg 801
CCore Media Inc, pg 821
Film Ideas, pg 867
International Historic Films Inc, pg 901
Liturgy Training Publications, pg 923
The Market Place, pg 931
Questar Inc, pg 989
Theosophical Publishing House, pg 1038

INDIANA

InterComm, pg 900

KENTUCKY

WaxWorks VideoWorks, pg 1063

MARYLAND

RLJ Entertainment Inc, pg 997
Total AV Systems, pg 1042

MASSACHUSETTS

Pauline Books & Media, pg 970

MICHIGAN

Digi Sign Design LLC, pg 847
Emery-Pratt Co, pg 860
The Program Source International, pg 985
Jack Van Impe Ministries International, pg 1051
Zondervan, A HarperCollins Company, pg 1074

MINNESOTA

Augsburg Fortress Publishers, pg 796
Harris Communications Inc, pg 885

MISSOURI

Cable Films & Video, pg 816
Vedanta Society of St Louis, pg 1052

NEBRASKA

B & B Video Productions Inc, pg 801

NEW HAMPSHIRE

Chip Taylor Communications LLC, pg 1032

NEW JERSEY

Ergo Media Inc, pg 862
SES World Skies, pg 1007

NEW YORK

The Christophers, pg 826
First Run Features, pg 869
Hallel Communications, pg 884
Irish Music Corp, pg 902
Janson Media, pg 904
Maryknoll Productions, pg 933
Mastervision Inc, pg 933
MRG Productions Inc, pg 948
Parabola Audio/Video, pg 968
The Fulton J Sheen Co Inc, pg 1008
SISU Home Entertainment Inc, pg 1012
Women Make Movies Inc, pg 1069

NORTH CAROLINA

World Wide Pictures Inc, pg 1070

OHIO

Franciscan Media, pg 872
Treehaus Communications Inc, pg 1044

OKLAHOMA

VCI Entertainment, pg 1052

OREGON

Cooking by the Book, pg 836

PENNSYLVANIA

Anchor Distributors, pg 786
Bullfrog Films Inc, pg 815
Chinmaya Publications, pg 825
FMP Media Solutions Inc, pg 870
Himalayan Institute Audio/Video, pg 889
Karol Media Inc, pg 908
Movies Unlimited, pg 947
MVD Entertainment Group, pg 951
Vision Video, pg 1058

SOUTH CAROLINA

ACS Technologies, pg 775
American Production Services LLC, pg 785

TENNESSEE

Abingdon Press, pg 772
Cokesbury, pg 831
EMI CMG Distribution, pg 860
Randall House Publications, pg 991
Spring Arbor Distributors, pg 1022
Zion Music Group, pg 1074

TEXAS

Endtime Inc, pg 861
Lamb & Lion Ministries, pg 915

VIRGINIA

Shakticom, pg 1008

WASHINGTON

ChristianAnswers.Net™, pg 825
Global Net Productions Inc, pg 879
Linguist's Software Inc, pg 922

BRITISH COLUMBIA

Norlynn Audio Visual Services, pg 958
Timeless Books, pg 1040

ONTARIO

Broughton's Church Supplies, Religious Books & Gifts, pg 814
Canadian Learning Co Inc, pg 818
Gospel Folio Press, pg 880
Life Cycle Books Ltd, pg 920
Novalis, pg 959

Religious Program Producers

ALABAMA

AVS Media Group, pg 800
CMEInfo, pg 830
Eternal Word Television Network (EWTN), pg 862

ALASKA

Aurora Films, pg 797

ARIZONA

Aardvark Productions LLC, pg 772
CyberIconics International, pg 841
Merestone, pg 938
Mother Basilea Films, pg 947
Phoenix VideoFilms®, pg 974
TSG Publishing Foundation Inc USA, pg 1046

ARKANSAS

Mullikin Agency, pg 949
White Diamond Productions, pg 1065

CALIFORNIA

Action Video, pg 775
Barbosa Video Services, pg 802
Cavalcade Productions Inc, pg 821
Christian Media Network, pg 825
Clarity Sound & Light, pg 829
Classic Images, pg 829
Cox Media, pg 837
Custom Video Productions Inc, pg 841
Discovery Education - Los Angeles, pg 848
Dogma Studios, pg 850
Face Digital Post, pg 865
Gateways Books & Tapes, pg 876
Glenray Productions Inc, pg 878
ITV Productions, pg 903
KION-TV, pg 911
Maximus Media Inc, pg 934
McCune Audio-Video-Lighting, pg 935
Mist Media Inc, pg 944
Nilgiri Press, pg 957
Osho Viha Information Center & Book Distributors, pg 965
Parallax Press, pg 969
PM Productions, pg 977
QRS Software Services, pg 988
Dick Reizner Film & Video, pg 994
Glenn Roland Films, pg 998
Screen Door Entertainment Inc, pg 1005
SNAP, pg 1014
Still N'Motion, pg 1025
Tele-Video Production Services (TVPS), pg 1036
Total Media Group, pg 1042
TVA Productions, pg 1046
Vedanta Press & Catalog, pg 1052
Videowerks, pg 1057
Vineyard Video & Photography, pg 1058
WalkerVision Interarts, pg 1061
The Wyland Group, pg 1071
Xenon Pictures Inc, pg 1071

COLORADO

Centre Communications Inc, pg 823
Crown Ministries International, pg 840
Flashback Media Productions, pg 869
Rocky Mountain Audio/Video Productions Inc, pg 998

CONNECTICUT

Applebox Studio, pg 788
Broadcast Video Productions LLC, pg 813
Fox Connecticut, pg 872
Geomatrix Productions, pg 877
Hartley Film Foundation, pg 885
Ironik Design & Post, pg 902
MCC Films, pg 935
Twenty-Third Publications/Bayard, pg 1047

DISTRICT OF COLUMBIA

Biblical Archaeology Society (BAS), pg 806
USCCB Publishing, pg 1051

FLORIDA

Blackburst Entertainment, pg 808
Civins Productions Inc, pg 828
CopShopMiami.com, pg 836
Courter Films LLC, pg 837
Eastern Video, pg 856
Ed Ethridge Productions Inc, pg 863
Home Shopping Network (HSN), pg 890
Jordan Klein Film & Video (JKFV), pg 906
Motion Image Group LLC, pg 947
Sound*Light, pg 1017
Sunfire Communications Inc, pg 1028
Sunrise Studios, pg 1028
Tel-Air Interests Inc, pg 1035

GEORGIA

Beachwood Productions, pg 804
Burst Video/Film Inc, pg 815
Continental Film & Video, pg 835
Gingerbread Group, pg 878
Guerrilla Productions LLC, pg 883
Malcolm Neal Productions, pg 954
On-Line Productions, pg 963

HAWAII

Hyperspective Studios Inc, pg 893

ILLINOIS

ACTA Publications, pg 775
Analog Free Media, pg 786
Audio Visual Services Corp, pg 796
Beatty TeleVisual Productions, pg 804
CCore Media Inc, pg 821
Chicago Satellite & Video, pg 825
Film Police, pg 867
IV Media Resources, pg 903
Liturgy Training Publications, pg 923
The Pepper Group, pg 972
PSAV® Presentation Services (Hotel Services Division), pg 987
Questar Inc, pg 989
QuickSet International Inc, pg 989
RADMAR Inc, pg 990
SCI Television Productions LLC, pg 1004
Theosophical Publishing House, pg 1038
20/20 Communications Inc, pg 1047
Video Impressions, pg 1055
WEEK TV, pg 1063
Winter Productions, pg 1068

INDIANA

AVA Productions, pg 798
Covenant Productions®, pg 837
Explore Media LLC, pg 864
InterComm, pg 900
PentaVision Communications Inc, pg 972

IOWA

Kuhn Productions LLC, pg 914

KANSAS

KAKE-TV, pg 907

KENTUCKY

Idle Minds Productions Inc, pg 894
Prosper Media Group Inc, pg 986
Trusty Tuneshop Recording Studios, pg 1045

LOUISIANA

Moxie Media, pg 948

MARYLAND

Adventure Productions LLC, pg 778
CPR MultiMedia Solutions, pg 837
dbF a Media Company, pg 844

MASSACHUSETTS

Award Productions, pg 800
Heliotrope Studios, pg 887
Inter-Media Electronics, pg 899
Pauline Books & Media, pg 970
VideoLink Inc, pg 1057

MICHIGAN

Digi Sign Design LLC, pg 847
K&R All Media Productions Inc, pg 908
K&R's Recording Studios Inc, pg 908
Zondervan, A HarperCollins Company, pg 1074

MINNESOTA

Aggressive Records Audio Duplication LLC, pg 778
Augsburg Fortress Publishers, pg 796
House of Cinemagraphics, pg 891
Llewellyn Publications, pg 923
Master Communications Group, pg 933
MultiMedia, pg 950
Vaddio, pg 1051

MISSOURI

Audio-VideoGraphics Inc, pg 795
Communitronics Corp, pg 833
Fambrough & Associates Inc, pg 865
Vedanta Society of St Louis, pg 1052

MONTANA

North Country Media Group, pg 959

NEBRASKA

B & B Video Productions Inc, pg 801
Dog & Pony Productions Inc, pg 850
Rainbow Video Productions Inc, pg 991

NEVADA

Aardvark Video & Media Productions, pg 772
Encore Productions Inc, pg 861
JCS Video Productions, pg 904

NEW HAMPSHIRE

Apertura, pg 788
Chip Taylor Communications LLC, pg 1032

NEW JERSEY

CFP Video Productions Inc, pg 823
Euro-Pacific Film & Video Productions Inc, pg 863
Half Moon Video Productions, pg 883
MIB Mediaworks, pg 941
Ray Mueller Productions, pg 949
Optisonics Productions, pg 965
Paulist Press, pg 970
Bill Quinn Productions, pg 989
VCSvideo, pg 1052

NEW MEXICO

Production Outfitters, pg 984

NEW YORK

aurora productions, pg 797
Brian Film Productions LLC, pg 812
Golden Lamb Productions, pg 880
Hallel Communications, pg 884
Manhattan Center Studios Inc, pg 930
Maryknoll Productions, pg 933
Mastervision Inc, pg 933
MRG Productions Inc, pg 948
Shelly Palmer Production, pg 968
Parabola Audio/Video, pg 968
Richter Productions Inc, pg 996
The Fulton J Sheen Co Inc, pg 1008
SISU Home Entertainment Inc, pg 1012
Time Warner Cable, pg 1040
Tobin Productions Inc, pg 1041

NORTH CAROLINA

All Pro Media Inc, pg 780
Pat Appleson Studios Inc, pg 788
The Communications Group Inc, pg 833
Horizon Video Productions Inc, pg 891
LCW Productions LLC, pg 917

OHIO

Advent Media Inc, pg 778
Russ Beckner Pictures, pg 804
Franciscan Media, pg 872
Image Video Teleproductions Inc, pg 895
MainSail Production Services Inc, pg 929
Take 1 Media Services, pg 1031
Treehaus Communications Inc, pg 1044
Vista Color Imaging Inc, pg 1059

OKLAHOMA

VCI Entertainment, pg 1052

OREGON

A KTVA Production LLC, pg 771
Inner Explorations, pg 898
Production West, pg 985

PENNSYLVANIA

Beholder Productions Inc, pg 804
CCI Communications Inc, pg 821
Chinmaya Publications, pg 825
FMP Media Solutions Inc, pg 870
Fusion Brand Experiences, pg 874
Himalayan Institute Audio/Video, pg 889
JPL, pg 906
Muderick Media, pg 949
The Videohouse Inc, pg 1057
Vision Video, pg 1058
Visual Sound Inc, pg 1059

RHODE ISLAND

Sound-FX-Design, pg 1017

SOUTH CAROLINA

ACS Technologies, pg 775
BJU Press, pg 808

TENNESSEE

Abingdon Press, pg 772
Continental Film, pg 835
EMI CMG Distribution, pg 860
Jaguar Productions, pg 903
Memphis Communications Corp, pg 938
Running Pony Productions LLC, pg 1000
Russ Sturgeon Productions/RSVP, pg 1027
UMCom Productions, pg 1048

TEXAS

Alpha Video Productions, pg 782
Cerutti Productions Inc, pg 823
Communication Arts Multimedia Inc, pg 832
The Editing Co, pg 857
Endtime Inc, pg 861
Horizon Film + Video Productions, pg 891
Lamb & Lion Ministries, pg 915
Mediaforce Productions, pg 937
Earl Miller Productions Inc, pg 943
Omega Productions, pg 962
Reelsound Recording Co, pg 994
South Coast Film & Video, pg 1019

VERMONT

Perceptions Inc, pg 973

VIRGINIA

Creative Video of Washington Inc, pg 839
D&B Television & Video Productions Inc, pg 842
Gingerbread Productions, pg 878
Metro Productions, pg 939
National Media Services Inc, pg 953
Rocktown Media, pg 998
Shakticom, pg 1008

WASHINGTON

Bennett-Watt HD Productions Inc, pg 805
ChristianAnswers.Net™, pg 825

PROGRAMMING — VIDEO

Religious Program Producers (continued)

WASHINGTON (continued)

Global Net Productions Inc, pg 879
Linguist's Software Inc, pg 922

WISCONSIN

5th Floor Recording Co, pg 867
Media Communications Association-International (MCA-I), pg 936
Midland Video Productions Inc, pg 942
Rucinski & Reetz Communications LLC, pg 1000
Video Wisconsin Inc, pg 1056
Watts Communications Inc, pg 1062

WYOMING

Bridger Productions Inc, pg 812

BRITISH COLUMBIA

Image Media Farm, pg 895
Norlynn Audio Visual Services, pg 958
Timeless Books, pg 1040

ONTARIO

ADS Media, pg 777
GAPC (General Assembly Production Centre), pg 875
Image Video Services & Productions, pg 895
Jams Productions Inc, pg 904
Novalis, pg 959

QUEBEC

Kerrigan Productions Inc, pg 910

Religious Program Rentals

ARIZONA

Video Learning Library, pg 1055

CALIFORNIA

Clarity Sound & Light, pg 829
Direct Cinema Ltd Inc, pg 848

INDIANA

InterComm, pg 900

MASSACHUSETTS

Pauline Books & Media, pg 970

MICHIGAN

Digi Sign Design LLC, pg 847

MISSOURI

University of Missouri-Columbia, pg 1050

NEW YORK

Films for the Humanities & Sciences, pg 868
First Run Features, pg 869
Hallel Communications, pg 884
Icarus Film Inc, pg 893

NORTH CAROLINA

World Wide Pictures Inc, pg 1070

OHIO

Franciscan Media, pg 872
Treehaus Communications Inc, pg 1044

PENNSYLVANIA

Bullfrog Films Inc, pg 815

WASHINGTON

ChristianAnswers.Net™, pg 825

Research—Technical Program, *see* Technical Research Program

Sales Promotion & Training Program Distributors

ARIZONA

Video Learning Library, pg 1055

ARKANSAS

Mullikin Agency, pg 949

CALIFORNIA

Crystal Pyramid Productions™, pg 840
Deja View Video, pg 845
Direct Cinema Ltd Inc, pg 848
Discovery Education - Los Angeles, pg 848
411 Video Information, pg 872
Learning Communications LLC, pg 917
New & Unique Videos™, pg 955
Melvin Powers Television Marketing, pg 979
TMW Media Group, pg 1041

CONNECTICUT

Cine-Med Inc, pg 826

FLORIDA

ACE Video Resources Software, pg 774
Allegro Productions Inc, pg 781
Potentials Unlimited, pg 979

GEORGIA

On-Line Productions, pg 963
Thompson-Mitchell & Associates Inc, pg 1039

ILLINOIS

ABSA Productions Inc, pg 772
CCore Media Inc, pg 821
Centrax Corp, pg 823
Chicago Satellite & Video, pg 825
1st Financial Training Services Inc, pg 868
Nightingale-Conant Corp, pg 957

KENTUCKY

KET The Kentucky Network, pg 910

MARYLAND

Sign Media Inc, pg 1011
Total AV Systems, pg 1042

MASSACHUSETTS

Penfield Productions Ltd, pg 971

MICHIGAN

Digi Sign Design LLC, pg 847
VMS Inc, pg 1060

NEBRASKA

B & B Video Productions Inc, pg 801

NEVADA

DVDs4Less, pg 854

NEW HAMPSHIRE

Chip Taylor Communications LLC, pg 1032

NEW MEXICO

National Information Center for Educational Media (NICEM)/MediaSleuth, pg 952

NEW YORK

Broad Street Inc, pg 812
HB-Content, pg 886
KickedUp Media Group Inc, pg 910
Monad Trainer's Aide Inc, pg 945
MRG Productions Inc, pg 948
Video Catalogue Co Inc, pg 1054

NORTH CAROLINA

Baker & Taylor Inc, pg 801
Eli Research Group, pg 859
Vide-O-Go/That's Infotainment!, pg 1054

OHIO

South-Western Publishing Co, pg 1019
Speakers Unlimited, pg 1020

PENNSYLVANIA

FMP Media Solutions Inc, pg 870
Karol Media Inc, pg 908

TENNESSEE

American Blackguard Inc, pg 784
Marine Geographic, pg 931

TEXAS

Executive Development Systems, pg 864

VERMONT

Perceptions Inc, pg 973
University of Vermont, Instructional Television Dept, pg 1050
Wilson McLeran Inc, pg 1067

VIRGINIA

CACI Productions Group, pg 816
CDR Communications Inc, pg 822
WETA Production Center, pg 1064

WASHINGTON

AEON Communications Inc, pg 778
Bennett-Watt HD Productions Inc, pg 805
Media Resources Inc, pg 937

ONTARIO

Kineticvideo.com, pg 911

Sales Promotion & Training Program Producers

ALABAMA

CMEInfo, pg 830
Media Visions Inc, pg 937
Leo Ticheli Productions, pg 1040

ARIZONA

Aardvark Productions LLC, pg 772
Candee Productions Inc, pg 819
Creative Backstage, pg 838
Direct Current Video Productions, pg 848
Film Creations Ltd, pg 867
Fox 10 Productions (KSAZ-TV), pg 872
MediaWorks, pg 938
Merestone, pg 938
Metropolitan Audio-Visual Inc, pg 940
On-Site Video, pg 963
Phoenix VideoFilms®, pg 974
Video Media Productions (VMP), pg 1055

ARKANSAS

Cedar Crest Studio, pg 822
Jones Film Video, pg 906
Live'N'Loud, pg 923
Mullikin Agency, pg 949
White Diamond Productions, pg 1065

CALIFORNIA

Aaron Marcus & Associates Inc, pg 772
Access Video in Berkeley, pg 773
Action Video, pg 775
AM Productions, pg 783
Animax, pg 787
Artichoke Productions, pg 791
Barbosa Video Services, pg 802
Big Door, pg 807
Cavalcade Productions Inc, pg 821
Chesney Communications, pg 824
Chick Russell Communications, pg 825
Classic Images, pg 829
Coastline Productions, pg 831
Cox Media, pg 837
Crystal Pyramid Productions™, pg 840
Custom Video Productions Inc, pg 841
Deja View Video, pg 845
Design Media, pg 845
Digital Outpost, pg 847
Direct Images Interactive Inc, pg 848
Discovery Education - Los Angeles, pg 848
Dogma Studios, pg 850
Dolphin MultiMedia Inc, pg 850
Duck Studios, pg 853
Dynamic Digital Depth Inc (DDD), pg 854
Face Digital Post, pg 865
Global Village Productions, pg 879
Imageworks, pg 896
International Contact Inc, pg 900
ITV Productions, pg 903
Kavich Reynolds Productions Inc, pg 908
The Kenwood Group, pg 909

PROGRAMMING — VIDEO

Sales Promotion & Training Program Producers (continued)

MANITOBA

Spectra Video Productions Ltd, pg 1020

NEWFOUNDLAND AND LABRADOR

Vidcraft Productions Ltd, pg 1054

ONTARIO

DebsVoice, pg 844
GAPC (General Assembly Production Centre), pg 875
Image Video Services & Productions, pg 895
Jams Productions Inc, pg 904
JFB Communications, pg 905
Mediaimage Communications Group, pg 937
Purefire Communications Inc, pg 987
RB Productions, pg 992
Shaw Street Productions, pg 1008
Video Excellence Productions, pg 1055

QUEBEC

Kerrigan Productions Inc, pg 910

SASKATCHEWAN

plan9films, pg 976

Sales Promotion & Training Program Rentals

ARIZONA

Video Learning Library, pg 1055

CALIFORNIA

Direct Cinema Ltd Inc, pg 848
Learning Communications LLC, pg 917

ILLINOIS

1st Financial Training Services Inc, pg 868

MICHIGAN

Digi Sign Design LLC, pg 847

MISSOURI

The Phoenix Learning Group Inc, pg 974

NEW YORK

BC Video Inc, pg 803
Image Makers of Pittsford/Image Maker Productions, pg 895

NORTH CAROLINA

Image Associates Inc, pg 894

VERMONT

University of Vermont, Instructional Television Dept, pg 1050

Scientific Program Distributors

ARIZONA

Video Learning Library, pg 1055

CALIFORNIA

Academy Savant, pg 773
Allied Artists International Inc, pg 781
Astronomical Society of the Pacific, pg 792
Crystal Pyramid Productions™, pg 840
Deja View Video, pg 845
Direct Cinema Ltd Inc, pg 848
Discovery Education - Los Angeles, pg 848
Increase Video/Silver Mine Video, pg 897
New & Unique Videos™, pg 955
North Atlantic Books, pg 958
Pyramid Media, pg 987
Sea Studios Foundation, pg 1005
TMW Media Group, pg 1041
The Video Project, pg 1056
The Wine Appreciation Guild Ltd, pg 1067

DISTRICT OF COLUMBIA

American Chemical Society (ACS), pg 784

FLORIDA

ACE Video Resources Software, pg 774
Allegro Productions Inc, pg 781
Distribution Video & Audio (DVA), pg 849
Psychological Assessment Resources Inc (PAR), pg 987

HAWAII

Ka Io Productions Inc, pg 907

ILLINOIS

ABSA Productions Inc, pg 772
Cahokia Mounds Museum Society, pg 816
Chicago Satellite & Video, pg 825
Film Ideas, pg 867

INDIANA

Agency for Instructional Technology (AIT), pg 778
Herff Jones | Nystrom, pg 888

KANSAS

Day Star Productions, pg 844

KENTUCKY

National Geographic Learning, pg 952
WaxWorks VideoWorks, pg 1063

MARYLAND

MMI Corp, pg 944

MASSACHUSETTS

Documentary Educational Resources Inc, pg 850
Emergency Film Group, pg 860
Media Marketing Associates Inc, pg 937
Penfield Productions Ltd, pg 971
Sinauer Associates Inc, pg 1011

MICHIGAN

Digi Sign Design LLC, pg 847
Emery-Pratt Co, pg 860
Meuninck's Media Methods Inc, pg 940
MSU Technologies, pg 949

MISSOURI

Phoenix/BFA/Coronet, pg 974

NEVADA

DVDs4Less, pg 854

NEW HAMPSHIRE

Chip Taylor Communications LLC, pg 1032

NEW JERSEY

Lucerne Media, pg 925

NEW MEXICO

National Information Center for Educational Media (NICEM)/ MediaSleuth, pg 952
Uncharted Country Publishing, pg 1048

NEW YORK

Films Media Group, pg 868
French American Cultural Exchange (FACE), pg 873
Guilford Publications, pg 883
Human Relations Media, pg 892
Janson Media, pg 904
March of Dimes Foundation, pg 930
Mastervision Inc, pg 933
MRG Productions Inc, pg 948
Richter Productions Inc, pg 996
Science Television Co, pg 1005
Synaptic Digital, pg 1030
VIEW Inc (Video International Entertainment World Inc), pg 1058

NORTH CAROLINA

Baker & Taylor Inc, pg 801
Carolina Biological Supply Co, pg 820

PENNSYLVANIA

Bullfrog Films Inc, pg 815
Discovery Education - South Burlington, pg 848
FMP Media Solutions Inc, pg 870
Karol Media Inc, pg 908

TENNESSEE

Marine Geographic, pg 931

TEXAS

CEV Multimedia Ltd, pg 823

VERMONT

Perceptions Inc, pg 973
University of Vermont, Instructional Television Dept, pg 1050

VIRGINIA

CACI Productions Group, pg 816
Filmakers Library, pg 867
WETA Production Center, pg 1064

WASHINGTON

Bennett-Watt HD Productions Inc, pg 805
Linguist's Software Inc, pg 922
Terra Productions LLC, pg 1037

WISCONSIN

Equiservices Publishing, pg 862

BRITISH COLUMBIA

Thompson Rivers University Open Learning, pg 1039

ONTARIO

BFS Entertainment & Multimedia Limited, pg 806
Canadian Learning Co Inc, pg 818
Kineticvideo.com, pg 911
Life Cycle Books Ltd, pg 920
McIntyre Media Inc, pg 935

QUEBEC

Les Productions Via Le Monde (Daniel Bertolino) Inc, pg 985

Scientific Program Producers

ALABAMA

CMEInfo, pg 830
Media Visions Inc, pg 937

ALASKA

Alaska Film Services Inc, pg 779

ARIZONA

Aardvark Productions LLC, pg 772
Film Creations Ltd, pg 867
MediaWorks, pg 938
Phoenix VideoFilms®, pg 974

ARKANSAS

Cedar Crest Studio, pg 822

CALIFORNIA

Academy Savant, pg 773
Access Video in Berkeley, pg 773
Action Video, pg 775
Allied Artists International Inc, pg 781
Artichoke Productions, pg 791
Astronomical Society of the Pacific, pg 792
Big Door, pg 807
Classic Images, pg 829
Cox Media, pg 837
Creativity Unlimited Press®, pg 839
Crystal Pyramid Productions™, pg 840
Custom Video Productions Inc, pg 841
Davidson Films Inc, pg 843
Deja View Video, pg 845
Direct Images Interactive Inc, pg 848
Discovery Education - Los Angeles, pg 848
Dogma Studios, pg 850
Dolphin MultiMedia Inc, pg 850
Face Digital Post, pg 865
imageReal Pictures LLC, pg 896
ITV Productions, pg 903
Kavich Reynolds Productions Inc, pg 908
KION-TV, pg 911
Main Street Media Inc, pg 929
Maximus Media Inc, pg 934
McCune Audio-Video-Lighting, pg 935
The Media Staff Inc, pg 937
New & Unique Videos™, pg 955
Penrose Productions, pg 972
QRS Software Services, pg 988
Dick Reizner Film & Video, pg 994
SBS Productions, pg 1003
Screen Door Entertainment Inc, pg 1005

PROGRAMMING — VIDEO

Scientific Program Producers (continued)

CALIFORNIA (continued)

Sea Studios Foundation, pg 1005
SNAP, pg 1014
Staylor-Made Communications Inc, pg 1024
Still N'Motion, pg 1025
Tam Communications Inc, pg 1031
Tele-Video Production Services (TVPS), pg 1036
TMW Media Group, pg 1041
Total Media Group, pg 1042
Twin Peaks Creative, pg 1047
Videowerks, pg 1057
Vineyard Video & Photography, pg 1058
Visions Plus, pg 1058
WalkerVision Interarts, pg 1061
Wavemaker Media Design, pg 1062
West Coast Projections Inc, pg 1063

COLORADO

Paul L Anderson Productions Inc, pg 786
Apogee Communications Group, pg 788
Daylight Productions & Rentals, pg 844
Flashback Media Productions, pg 869
Transtar Entertainment Co Inc, pg 1043

CONNECTICUT

Broadcast Video Productions LLC, pg 813
Fox Connecticut, pg 872
Ironik Design & Post, pg 902
P&P Studios Inc, pg 968

DISTRICT OF COLUMBIA

American Chemical Society (ACS), pg 784
Hillmann & Carr Inc, pg 889
Yellow Cat Productions Inc, pg 1072

FLORIDA

Accel Video Productions, pg 773
ACE Video Resources Software, pg 774
Allegro Productions Inc, pg 781
Blackburst Entertainment, pg 808
Capital Communications Inc, pg 819
Civins Productions Inc, pg 828
CopShopMiami.com, pg 836
Courter Films LLC, pg 837
Ed Ethridge Productions Inc, pg 863
Home Shopping Network (HSN), pg 890
Jordan Klein Film & Video (JKFV), pg 906
Motion Image Group LLC, pg 947
National Teleproductions Inc, pg 953
Sound & Vision Communications Inc, pg 1016
Sunfire Communications Inc, pg 1028
Sunrise Studios, pg 1028
Tricycle Studios, pg 1044

GEORGIA

Beachwood Productions, pg 804
COMPRO Productions Inc, pg 834
Georgia-Pacific Television & Photography, pg 877
Guerrilla Productions LLC, pg 883
On-Line Productions, pg 963

HAWAII

Hyperspective Studios Inc, pg 893
Ka Io Productions Inc, pg 907
Sight & Sound Studios, pg 1010

IDAHO

Brad Shaw Productions Inc, pg 1008
Wide Eye Productions, pg 1066

ILLINOIS

ABSA Productions Inc, pg 772
Cahokia Mounds Museum Society, pg 816
Chicago Satellite & Video, pg 825
Film Police, pg 867
IV Media Resources, pg 903
Manning Productions, pg 930
The Pepper Group, pg 972
SCI Television Productions LLC, pg 1004
20/20 Communications Inc, pg 1047
Video Impressions, pg 1055

INDIANA

Agency for Instructional Technology (AIT), pg 778
AVA Productions, pg 798
Explore Media LLC, pg 864
Road Pictures, pg 997

KANSAS

KAKE-TV, pg 907

KENTUCKY

Idle Minds Productions Inc, pg 894
Donna Lawrence Productions, pg 917
National Geographic Learning, pg 952

LOUISIANA

Louisiana State University Health Sciences Center - Shreveport, pg 925
Moxie Media, pg 948

MARYLAND

Adventure Productions LLC, pg 778
The Ahern Group, pg 779
Richard Chisolm Cinematography, pg 825
dbF a Media Company, pg 844
The Image Generators, pg 895
Kramer Communications Video Production, pg 913
MMI Corp, pg 944

MASSACHUSETTS

Award Productions, pg 800
Documentary Educational Resources Inc, pg 850
Emergency Film Group, pg 860
Green Mountain Post Films (GMP), pg 882
Heliotrope Studios, pg 887
In the Wild Productions, pg 897
Monadnock Media Inc, pg 945
Northern Light Productions, pg 959
Penfield Productions Ltd, pg 971
Sinauer Associates Inc, pg 1011
TVN-The Video Network, pg 1046
Veritech Corp, pg 1053
VideoLink Inc, pg 1057
WVP Boston, pg 1071

MICHIGAN

Digi Sign Design LLC, pg 847
K&R All Media Productions Inc, pg 908
K&R's Recording Studios Inc, pg 908
Meuninck's Media Methods Inc, pg 940

MINNESOTA

Aggressive Records Audio Duplication LLC, pg 778
House of Cinemagraphics, pg 891
Master Communications Group, pg 933
Worthwhile Films, pg 1070

MISSOURI

Fambrough & Associates Inc, pg 865

MONTANA

North Country Media Group, pg 959

NEBRASKA

Rainbow Video Productions Inc, pg 991

NEVADA

Aardvark Video & Media Productions, pg 772
DVDs4Less, pg 854
Encore Productions Inc, pg 861
HDTV Productions Inc, pg 886
JCS Video Productions, pg 904
Tetrahedron LLC, pg 1037

NEW HAMPSHIRE

Apertura, pg 788
Channell One Video, pg 824
Chip Taylor Communications LLC, pg 1032

NEW JERSEY

Amerinex Applied Imaging Inc, pg 785
CFP Video Productions Inc, pg 823
DWJ Television, pg 854
Euro-Pacific Film & Video Productions Inc, pg 863
Half Moon Video Productions, pg 883
Laurel Video Productions, pg 916
MIB Mediaworks, pg 941
Midnight Media Group Inc, pg 942
Optisonics Productions, pg 965
Producer East Productions, pg 983
Public Eye Productions, pg 987
Bill Quinn Productions, pg 989
VCSvideo, pg 1052

NEW MEXICO

Production Outfitters, pg 984
Uncharted Country Publishing, pg 1048

NEW YORK

aurora productions, pg 797
Norman N Axelrod Associates, pg 800
Brian Film Productions LLC, pg 812
Clarity Media Group, pg 829
CompuWeather Inc, pg 834
Criterion Collection, pg 839
Films Media Group, pg 868
Florentine Films, pg 870
Guilford Publications, pg 883
Hello World Communications, pg 888
Human Relations Media, pg 892
Ketchum Pleon Change, pg 910
L A Bruell Inc, pg 914
March of Dimes Foundation, pg 930
Neal Marshad Productions, pg 931
Mastervision Inc, pg 933
MRG Productions Inc, pg 948
MRY, pg 949
News Broadcast Network, pg 956
NSR Productions Inc & Capricorn Five Films, pg 960
Shelly Palmer Production, pg 968
Pat Kogan Productions Inc, pg 970
Peckham Productions Inc, pg 970
PrimaLux Video Inc, pg 982
Richter Productions Inc, pg 996
Science Television Co, pg 1005
Synaptic Digital, pg 1030
Tobin Productions Inc, pg 1041
Videograf, pg 1057
VIEW Inc (Video International Entertainment World Inc), pg 1058

NORTH CAROLINA

Pat Appleson Studios Inc, pg 788
Carolina Biological Supply Co, pg 820
The Communications Group Inc, pg 833
Horizon Video Productions Inc, pg 891
Kino Mountain Productions LLC, pg 911

OHIO

Advent Media Inc, pg 778
Creative Technology, pg 838
Image Video Teleproductions Inc, pg 895
Lyon Video Inc, pg 927
MainSail Production Services Inc, pg 929
Maslowski Productions, pg 933
R&B Communications Inc, pg 991
Take 1 Media Services, pg 1031
VGI Productions, pg 1053
Vista Color Imaging Inc, pg 1059

OREGON

Ideascape Inc, pg 894
Odyssey Productions Inc, pg 961
Production West, pg 985

PENNSYLVANIA

AiH Group Inc, pg 779
Audio Visual Communications Inc, pg 795
Beholder Productions Inc, pg 804
CCI Communications Inc, pg 821
Discovery Education - South Burlington, pg 848
FMP Media Solutions Inc, pg 870
Fusion Brand Experiences, pg 874
Goodman Associates Inc, pg 880
Innovision Media Group, pg 899
Muderick Media, pg 949
Panta Rhei Media Inc, pg 968
Production Masters Inc (PMI), pg 984
The Videohouse Inc, pg 1057

Scientific Program Rentals

Short Film, *see* Theatrical Short

Sponsored Program Distributors

Sponsored Program Producers

PROGRAMMING — VIDEO

Sponsored Program Producers (continued)

CALIFORNIA (continued)

Custom Video Productions Inc, pg 841
Direct Images Interactive Inc, pg 848
Dogma Studios, pg 850
Face Digital Post, pg 865
FXF Productions Inc, pg 874
imageReal Pictures LLC, pg 896
ITV Productions, pg 903
Kavich Reynolds Productions Inc, pg 908
KION-TV, pg 911
KTVU-Retail Services, pg 914
Main Street Media Inc, pg 929
Maximus Media Inc, pg 934
McCune Audio-Video-Lighting, pg 935
Medcom Inc, pg 936
Media Magic, pg 937
The Media Staff Inc, pg 937
Mist Media Inc, pg 944
New & Unique Videos™, pg 955
Panorama Productions, pg 968
Point of View Productions, pg 977
QRS Software Services, pg 988
Dick Reizner Film & Video, pg 994
Glenn Roland Films, pg 998
Screen Door Entertainment Inc, pg 1005
SNAP, pg 1014
Staylor-Made Communications Inc, pg 1024
Still N'Motion, pg 1025
The Studio Center, pg 1026
Total Media Group, pg 1042
Twin Peaks Creative, pg 1047
Videowerks, pg 1057
Vineyard Video & Photography, pg 1058
Visual Communications - Southern California Asian American Studies Central Inc, pg 1059
Wavemaker Media Design, pg 1062
Zamacona Productions, pg 1073

COLORADO

Apogee Communications Group, pg 788
Flashback Media Productions, pg 869
Tatum Video, pg 1032
Transtar Entertainment Co Inc, pg 1043

CONNECTICUT

Applebox Studio, pg 788
Broadcast Video Productions LLC, pg 813
Cine-Med Inc, pg 826
Fox Connecticut, pg 872
Ironik Design & Post, pg 902
MCC Films, pg 935
Moving Pictures, pg 947

DISTRICT OF COLUMBIA

Durrin Productions Inc, pg 854
Hillmann & Carr Inc, pg 889
VSA, pg 1061

FLORIDA

Allegro Productions Inc, pg 781
Blackburst Entertainment, pg 808
Capital Communications Inc, pg 819
CD ROM™ Inc, pg 822
Civins Productions Inc, pg 828
Communications Concepts Inc (CCI), pg 833
CopShopMiami.com, pg 836
Courter Films LLC, pg 837
Eastern Video, pg 856
Ed Ethridge Productions Inc, pg 863
Home Shopping Network (HSN), pg 890
Jordan Klein Film & Video (JKFV), pg 906
National Teleproductions Inc, pg 953
Paradise Video & Film, pg 969
Sound & Vision Communications Inc, pg 1016
Sunfire Communications Inc, pg 1028
Sunrise Studios, pg 1028
Tel-Air Interests Inc, pg 1035
Tricycle Studios, pg 1044

GEORGIA

Beachwood Productions, pg 804
Burst Video/Film Inc, pg 815
Guerrilla Productions LLC, pg 883
Memory Lane Productions, pg 938
Myriad Productions, pg 951
Malcolm Neal Productions, pg 954
On-Line Productions, pg 963

HAWAII

Hyperspective Studios Inc, pg 893
Sight & Sound Studios, pg 1010
1013 Integrated, pg 1037

IDAHO

Brad Shaw Productions Inc, pg 1008
Wide Eye Productions, pg 1066

ILLINOIS

Airways Digital Media, pg 779
Audio Visual Services Corp, pg 796
Chicago Satellite & Video, pg 825
Film Police, pg 867
Manning Productions, pg 930
Mimi Productions, pg 943
Rob Orr Productions Ltd, pg 965
The Pepper Group, pg 972
Professional Education Institute (PEI), pg 985
PSAV® Presentation Services (Hotel Services Division), pg 987
QuickSet International Inc, pg 989
SCI Television Productions LLC, pg 1004
Terra Nova Films Inc, pg 1037
Universal Training, pg 1049
Video Impressions, pg 1055
WEEK TV, pg 1063
Winter Productions, pg 1068

INDIANA

Advanced Media Integration, pg 777
AVA Productions, pg 798
Digital Rain LLC, pg 847
Road Pictures, pg 997

IOWA

The Production House, pg 984

KANSAS

KAKE-TV, pg 907

KENTUCKY

Idle Minds Productions Inc, pg 894
Donna Lawrence Productions, pg 917

LOUISIANA

Moxie Media, pg 948

MAINE

WGME-TV, pg 1065

MARYLAND

Adventure Productions LLC, pg 778
Richard Chisolm Cinematography, pg 825
CPR MultiMedia Solutions, pg 837
dbF a Media Company, pg 844
DSR Computer Technology Specialists Inc, pg 853
Kramer Communications Video Production, pg 913

MASSACHUSETTS

Award Productions, pg 800
Green Mountain Post Films (GMP), pg 882
Heliotrope Studios, pg 887
Home Inc, pg 890
Penfield Productions Ltd, pg 971
TVN-The Video Network, pg 1046

MICHIGAN

Digi Sign Design LLC, pg 847
K&R All Media Productions Inc, pg 908
K&R's Recording Studios Inc, pg 908

MINNESOTA

Aggressive Records Audio Duplication LLC, pg 778
House of Cinemagraphics, pg 891
Master Communications Group, pg 933
MultiMedia, pg 950

MISSOURI

Fambrough & Associates Inc, pg 865

MONTANA

KUSM TV, pg 914
North Country Media Group, pg 959

NEVADA

Aardvark Video & Media Productions, pg 772
DVDs4Less, pg 854
Encore Productions Inc, pg 861
HDTV Productions Inc, pg 886
JCS Video Productions, pg 904

NEW HAMPSHIRE

Apertura, pg 788
Channell One Video, pg 824
Chip Taylor Communications LLC, pg 1032

NEW JERSEY

Broadcast Center Studios, pg 813
CFP Video Productions Inc, pg 823
DWJ Television, pg 854
Euro-Pacific Film & Video Productions Inc, pg 863
Half Moon Video Productions, pg 883
Laurel Video Productions, pg 916
MIB Mediaworks, pg 941
Midnight Media Group Inc, pg 942
Optisonics Productions, pg 965
Public Eye Productions, pg 987
Bill Quinn Productions, pg 989
Telequest Inc, pg 1036
VCSvideo, pg 1052

NEW MEXICO

Michael Dunn Productions, pg 853
Production Outfitters, pg 984

NEW YORK

Associated Press Television News, pg 792
aurora productions, pg 797
Brian Film Productions LLC, pg 812
Broad Street Inc, pg 812
Cohn Creative Group LLC, pg 831
dM works, pg 849
Florentine Films, pg 870
William Greaves Productions Inc, pg 882
HB-Content, pg 886
Ketchum Pleon Change, pg 910
KickedUp Media Group Inc, pg 910
Neal Marshad Productions, pg 931
Mastervision Inc, pg 933
MRG Productions Inc, pg 948
MRY, pg 949
News Broadcast Network, pg 956
NSR Productions Inc & Capricorn Five Films, pg 960
Shelly Palmer Production, pg 968
Pat Kogan Productions Inc, pg 970
Peckham Productions Inc, pg 970
PrimaLux Video Inc, pg 982
Richter Productions Inc, pg 996
Suggs Media Productions Inc, pg 1028
Synaptic Digital, pg 1030
TeleTime Productions, pg 1036
Third World Newsreel/Camera News Inc, pg 1039
Tobin Productions Inc, pg 1041
Video Catalogue Co Inc, pg 1054
Videograf, pg 1057
VIEW Inc (Video International Entertainment World Inc), pg 1058
WNET/NET TELECON, pg 1069

NORTH CAROLINA

All Pro Media Inc, pg 780
Pat Appleson Studios Inc, pg 788
The Communications Group Inc, pg 833
Horizon Video Productions Inc, pg 891
Kino Mountain Productions LLC, pg 911
Moving Pictures, pg 948
NASCAR Media Group LLC, pg 952
Unifour Productions Inc, pg 1048

OHIO

Advent Media Inc, pg 778
Russ Beckner Pictures, pg 804
Creative Technology, pg 838
EDR Media LLC, pg 857
Electronic Vision Inc (EV), pg 859
Image Video Teleproductions Inc, pg 895
Lyon Video Inc, pg 927
MainSail Production Services Inc, pg 929

Sponsored Program Rentals

Sports Program Distributors

PROGRAMMING — VIDEO

Sports Program Distributors (continued)

PENNSYLVANIA (continued)

Movies Unlimited, pg 947
S I Video Sales Group, pg 1001

SOUTH CAROLINA

American Production Services LLC, pg 785
Yoga 1 Inc, pg 1072

TENNESSEE

Marine Geographic, pg 931
Spring Arbor Distributors, pg 1022

TEXAS

Oncourt Offcourt Ltd, pg 963

VERMONT

Trafalgar Square Books, pg 1043

VIRGINIA

CACI Productions Group, pg 816

WASHINGTON

Bennett-Watt HD Productions Inc, pg 805
John McLean Media, pg 905

WYOMING

Bridger Productions Inc, pg 812

ALBERTA

Global Television Station, pg 879

ONTARIO

BFS Entertainment & Multimedia Limited, pg 806
Canadian Learning Co Inc, pg 818
Canamedia Inc, pg 818

Sports Program Producers

ALASKA

Aurora Films, pg 797

ARIZONA

Aardvark Productions LLC, pg 772
Candee Productions Inc, pg 819
Film Creations Ltd, pg 867
Fox 10 Productions (KSAZ-TV), pg 872
Phoenix VideoFilms®, pg 974
Rodeo Video Inc, pg 998

ARKANSAS

Jones Film Video, pg 906
Live'N'Loud, pg 923
White Diamond Productions, pg 1065

CALIFORNIA

A Go Go Films, pg 771
Allied Artists International Inc, pg 781
Animax, pg 787
Bennett Media Corp, pg 805
Big Door, pg 807
Classic Images, pg 829
Cox Media, pg 837
Crystal Pyramid Productions™, pg 840
Custom Video Productions Inc, pg 841
Deja View Video, pg 845
Discovery Education - Los Angeles, pg 848
Dogma Studios, pg 850
First Camera, pg 868
FXF Productions Inc, pg 874
Global Village Productions, pg 879
Goal Productions, pg 879
Havas Edge, pg 885
Image Integration, pg 895
ITV Productions, pg 903
Kavich Reynolds Productions Inc, pg 908
KION-TV, pg 911
McCune Audio-Video-Lighting, pg 935
New & Unique Videos™, pg 955
New Circuit Films LLC, pg 955
New Wave Entertainment, pg 956
On-Trax Inc, pg 963
Penrose Productions, pg 972
QRS Software Services, pg 988
Glenn Roland Films, pg 998
Screen Door Entertainment Inc, pg 1005
SNAP, pg 1014
Sodanceabit, pg 1015
Tigar Hare Studios, pg 1040
TMW Media Group, pg 1041
Total Media Group, pg 1042
Twin Peaks Creative, pg 1047
Universal Studios Home Entertainment, pg 1049
Videowerks, pg 1057
Vineyard Video & Photography, pg 1058

COLORADO

Apogee Communications Group, pg 788
Centre Communications Inc, pg 823
CSI Films, pg 840
Flashback Media Productions, pg 869
Gaiam Inc, pg 875
Tatum Video, pg 1032
Transtar Entertainment Co Inc, pg 1043

CONNECTICUT

Broadcast Video Productions LLC, pg 813
Fox Connecticut, pg 872
Golf Digest, pg 880
Ironik Design & Post, pg 902
Video Production Associates Inc, pg 1056

DISTRICT OF COLUMBIA

VSA, pg 1061

FLORIDA

Accord Productions, pg 773
Allegro Productions Inc, pg 781
Blackburst Entertainment, pg 808
Capital Communications Inc, pg 819
Civins Productions Inc, pg 828
Communications Concepts Inc (CCI), pg 833
CopShopMiami.com, pg 836
Courter Films LLC, pg 837
DME Studios, pg 849
Eastern Video, pg 856
Easy Edit Video Inc, pg 856
Ed Ethridge Productions Inc, pg 863
Home Shopping Network (HSN), pg 890
I M P A C T Publishing Inc, pg 893
Jordan Klein Film & Video (JKFV), pg 906
Motion Image Group LLC, pg 947
National Teleproductions Inc, pg 953
Olympusat Entertainment, pg 962
Peak Performance Sports LLC, pg 970
Sunfire Communications Inc, pg 1028
Sunrise Studios, pg 1028
Tel-Air Interests Inc, pg 1035
WCJB TV20, pg 1063

GEORGIA

Beachwood Productions, pg 804
ECG Productions, pg 856
Georgia-Pacific Television & Photography, pg 877
Guerrilla Productions LLC, pg 883
Memory Lane Productions, pg 938
Myriad Productions, pg 951
On-Line Productions, pg 963

HAWAII

Hyperspective Studios Inc, pg 893
Sight & Sound Studios, pg 1010

IDAHO

Brad Shaw Productions Inc, pg 1008
Wide Eye Productions, pg 1066

ILLINOIS

Chicago Satellite & Video, pg 825
Film Police, pg 867
IV Media Resources, pg 903
Nightingale-Conant Corp, pg 957
The Pepper Group, pg 972
SCI Television Productions LLC, pg 1004
20/20 Communications Inc, pg 1047
Video I-D Teleproductions Inc, pg 1055
WEEK TV, pg 1063

INDIANA

AVA Productions, pg 798
Digital Rain LLC, pg 847
Explore Media LLC, pg 864
PentaVision Communications Inc, pg 972

IOWA

Championship Productions Inc, pg 823

KANSAS

KAKE-TV, pg 907

KENTUCKY

Idle Minds Productions Inc, pg 894
Donna Lawrence Productions, pg 917
Northern Kentucky University, pg 959

LOUISIANA

Moxie Media, pg 948

MARYLAND

Absolute Hollywood, pg 772
Adventure Productions LLC, pg 778
dbF a Media Company, pg 844
Kramer Communications Video Production, pg 913
Quality Film & Video, pg 988

MASSACHUSETTS

Award Productions, pg 800
Green Mountain Post Films (GMP), pg 882
Penfield Productions Ltd, pg 971
TVN-The Video Network, pg 1046
Veritech Corp, pg 1053
VideoLink Inc, pg 1057

MICHIGAN

Benjamin Creative Productions, pg 805
Digi Sign Design LLC, pg 847
K&R All Media Productions Inc, pg 908
K&R's Recording Studios Inc, pg 908
Lawrence Productions Inc, pg 917

MINNESOTA

Aggressive Records Audio Duplication LLC, pg 778
House of Cinemagraphics, pg 891
Stoney-Wolf Productions Inc, pg 1025

MISSOURI

Fambrough & Associates Inc, pg 865

MONTANA

North Country Media Group, pg 959

NEBRASKA

Mason Video, pg 933

NEVADA

Aardvark Video & Media Productions, pg 772
Encore Productions Inc, pg 861
HDTV Productions Inc, pg 886
JCS Video Productions, pg 904
Skyfire Video, pg 1013

NEW HAMPSHIRE

Apertura, pg 788
Channell One Video, pg 824
Chip Taylor Communications LLC, pg 1032
YMAA Publication Center Inc, pg 1072

NEW JERSEY

CFP Video Productions Inc, pg 823
DWJ Television, pg 854
Euro-Pacific Film & Video Productions Inc, pg 863
Half Moon Video Productions, pg 883
MIB Mediaworks, pg 941
NBA Entertainment Inc, pg 953
Optisonics Productions, pg 965
Public Eye Productions, pg 987
Bill Quinn Productions, pg 989
VCSvideo, pg 1052

NEW MEXICO

Michael Dunn Productions, pg 853
Production Outfitters, pg 984
Uncharted Country Publishing, pg 1048

NEW YORK

Ace Video, pg 774
Associated Press Television News, pg 792
aurora productions, pg 797
Brian Film Productions LLC, pg 812
Broad Street Inc, pg 812
Florentine Films, pg 870
HB-Content, pg 886
Jalbert Productions International, pg 903
Kamen Entertainment Group Inc, pg 908
Neal Marshad Productions, pg 931
Mastervision Inc, pg 933
MRG Productions Inc, pg 948
MRY, pg 949
Shelly Palmer Production, pg 968
Peckham Productions Inc, pg 970
PrimaLux Video Inc, pg 982
Synaptic Digital, pg 1030
Time Warner Cable, pg 1040
Tobin Productions Inc, pg 1041
VIEW Inc (Video International Entertainment World Inc), pg 1058

NORTH CAROLINA

Pat Appleson Studios Inc, pg 788
The Communications Group Inc, pg 833
NASCAR Media Group LLC, pg 952
Unifour Productions Inc, pg 1048

NORTH DAKOTA

UND Television Center, pg 1048

OHIO

CET, pg 823
Creative Technology, pg 838
Image Video Teleproductions Inc, pg 895
Lyon Video Inc, pg 927
MainSail Production Services Inc, pg 929
R&B Communications Inc, pg 991
VGI Productions, pg 1053

OKLAHOMA

Institute for Teaching & Learning Excellence (ITLE), pg 899
VCI Entertainment, pg 1052

OREGON

KPDX-TV Production Center, pg 913
KVAL, pg 914
Odyssey Productions Inc, pg 961
Production West, pg 985

PENNSYLVANIA

Bang Pictures, pg 802
CCI Communications Inc, pg 821
FMP Media Solutions Inc, pg 870
Fusion Brand Experiences, pg 874
Innovision Media Group, pg 899
Kensington Falls Animation, pg 909
Muderick Media, pg 949
Producers Management Television (PMTV), pg 983
Production Masters Inc (PMI), pg 984
S I Video Sales Group, pg 1001
The Videohouse Inc, pg 1057

RHODE ISLAND

Sound-FX-Design, pg 1017

SOUTH CAROLINA

American Production Services LLC, pg 785
Encore Video Productions, pg 861
Go To Team, pg 879
Yoga 1 Inc, pg 1072

TENNESSEE

Continental Film, pg 835
Jaguar Productions, pg 903
Marine Geographic, pg 931
Running Pony Productions LLC, pg 1000
Russ Sturgeon Productions/RSVP, pg 1027

TEXAS

AMS Pictures, pg 786
Cerutti Productions Inc, pg 823
Communication Arts Multimedia Inc, pg 832
Countdown Productions Inc, pg 837
Dub King, pg 853
Epic Software Group Inc, pg 862
Horizon Film + Video Productions, pg 891
Mediaforce Productions, pg 937
Earl Miller Productions Inc, pg 943
Omega Productions, pg 962
Oncourt Offcourt Ltd, pg 963
South Coast Film & Video, pg 1019
Sportsmen on Film Inc, pg 1021

UTAH

ImageWorks Communications, pg 896

VERMONT

Perceptions Inc, pg 973
Trafalgar Square Books, pg 1043

VIRGINIA

CACI Productions Group, pg 816
Creative Video of Washington Inc, pg 839
D&B Television & Video Productions Inc, pg 842
Gingerbread Productions, pg 878
Limelight Communications Inc, pg 921
Metro Productions, pg 939

WASHINGTON

Bennett-Watt HD Productions Inc, pg 805
Pal Productions Inc, pg 967
Victory Studios, pg 1054

WEST VIRGINIA

Blackwater Video Productions, pg 808

WISCONSIN

5th Floor Recording Co, pg 867
Watts Communications Inc, pg 1062
Wisconsin Public Television, pg 1068

WYOMING

Bridger Productions Inc, pg 812

ALBERTA

Black Media Works, pg 808
Global Television Station, pg 879

BRITISH COLUMBIA

Image Media Farm, pg 895

NEWFOUNDLAND AND LABRADOR

Vidcraft Productions Ltd, pg 1054

ONTARIO

ADS Media, pg 777
Image Video Services & Productions, pg 895
Video Excellence Productions, pg 1055

QUEBEC

Kerrigan Productions Inc, pg 910

SASKATCHEWAN

plan9films, pg 976

Sports Program Rentals

ARIZONA

Video Learning Library, pg 1055

CALIFORNIA

Direct Cinema Ltd Inc, pg 848

COLORADO

Tatum Video, pg 1032

MICHIGAN

Digi Sign Design LLC, pg 847

MISSOURI

University of Missouri-Columbia, pg 1050

NEW HAMPSHIRE

Channell One Video, pg 824

NEW JERSEY

Euro-Pacific Film & Video Productions Inc, pg 863

NEW YORK

VIEW Inc (Video International Entertainment World Inc), pg 1058

PENNSYLVANIA

Bullfrog Films Inc, pg 815

ONTARIO

WESCAM Inc, pg 1063

Technical Research Program Distributors

CALIFORNIA

Astronomical Society of the Pacific, pg 792
Crystal Pyramid Productions™, pg 840

COLORADO

Paul L Anderson Productions Inc, pg 786

DISTRICT OF COLUMBIA

American Chemical Society (ACS), pg 784

ILLINOIS

ABSA Productions Inc, pg 772
CCH Continuing Education, pg 821

MASSACHUSETTS

Documentary Educational Resources Inc, pg 850
Emergency Film Group, pg 860
Penfield Productions Ltd, pg 971

MICHIGAN

Digi Sign Design LLC, pg 847

NEVADA

DVDs4Less, pg 854

NEW HAMPSHIRE

Chip Taylor Communications LLC, pg 1032

NEW JERSEY

Avtech Systems Inc, pg 800

NEW YORK

MRG Productions Inc, pg 948
Science Television Co, pg 1005
Synaptic Digital, pg 1030

NORTH CAROLINA

Baker & Taylor Inc, pg 801

PENNSYLVANIA

FMP Media Solutions Inc, pg 870

VERMONT

University of Vermont, Instructional Television Dept, pg 1050

VIRGINIA

CACI Productions Group, pg 816

WASHINGTON

Bennett-Watt HD Productions Inc, pg 805

Technical Research Program Producers

ALASKA

Alaska Film Services Inc, pg 779

ARIZONA

Aardvark Productions LLC, pg 772
Candee Productions Inc, pg 819
Film Creations Ltd, pg 867
Phoenix VideoFilms®, pg 974

ARKANSAS

Cedar Crest Studio, pg 822

CALIFORNIA

Access Video in Berkeley, pg 773
Astronomical Society of the Pacific, pg 792
Big Door, pg 807
Classic Images, pg 829
Cox Media, pg 837

PROGRAMMING — VIDEO

Technical Research Program Producers (continued)

CALIFORNIA (continued)

Crystal Pyramid Productions™, pg 840
Custom Video Productions Inc, pg 841
Design Media, pg 845
ITV Productions, pg 903
Main Street Media Inc, pg 929
Maximus Media Inc, pg 934
McCune Audio-Video-Lighting, pg 935
Mist Media Inc, pg 944
New & Unique Videos™, pg 955
QRS Software Services, pg 988
Dick Reizner Film & Video, pg 994
SNAP, pg 1014
StereoScope International, pg 1024
Still N'Motion, pg 1025
Tele-Video Production Services (TVPS), pg 1036
Timestream Video, pg 1041
Total Media Group, pg 1042
TVA Productions, pg 1046
Videowerks, pg 1057
Vineyard Video & Photography, pg 1058
WalkerVision Interarts, pg 1061
West Coast Projections Inc, pg 1063

COLORADO

Paul L Anderson Productions Inc, pg 786
Daylight Productions & Rentals, pg 844
Flashback Media Productions, pg 869
Transtar Entertainment Co Inc, pg 1043

CONNECTICUT

Fox Connecticut, pg 872
Ironik Design & Post, pg 902
Video Production Associates Inc, pg 1056

DISTRICT OF COLUMBIA

American Chemical Society (ACS), pg 784

FLORIDA

Accel Video Productions, pg 773
Accord Productions, pg 773
Civins Productions Inc, pg 828
CopShopMiami.com, pg 836
Courter Films LLC, pg 837
Ed Ethridge Productions Inc, pg 863
Home Shopping Network (HSN), pg 890
Jordan Klein Film & Video (JKFV), pg 906
National Teleproductions Inc, pg 953
Sunfire Communications Inc, pg 1028
Sunrise Studios, pg 1028

GEORGIA

Beachwood Productions, pg 804
Guerrilla Productions LLC, pg 883
On-Line Productions, pg 963

HAWAII

Hyperspective Studios Inc, pg 893
Sight & Sound Studios, pg 1010

ILLINOIS

ABSA Productions Inc, pg 772
Accenture, pg 773
Airways Digital Media, pg 779
CCH Continuing Education, pg 821
Chicago Satellite & Video, pg 825
Film Police, pg 867
IV Media Resources, pg 903
The Pepper Group, pg 972
20/20 Communications Inc, pg 1047
Video Impressions, pg 1055

INDIANA

AVA Productions, pg 798
PentaVision Communications Inc, pg 972

LOUISIANA

Louisiana State University Health Sciences Center - Shreveport, pg 925
Moxie Media, pg 948

MARYLAND

The Ahern Group, pg 779
dbF a Media Company, pg 844
Kramer Communications Video Production, pg 913

MASSACHUSETTS

Award Productions, pg 800
Documentary Educational Resources Inc, pg 850
Emergency Film Group, pg 860
Green Mountain Post Films (GMP), pg 882
Heliotrope Studios, pg 887
Northern Light Productions, pg 959
Penfield Productions Ltd, pg 971
TVN-The Video Network, pg 1046

MICHIGAN

Digi Sign Design LLC, pg 847
K&R All Media Productions Inc, pg 908
K&R's Recording Studios Inc, pg 908

MINNESOTA

Aggressive Records Audio Duplication LLC, pg 778
House of Cinemagraphics, pg 891

MISSOURI

Fambrough & Associates Inc, pg 865

MONTANA

North Country Media Group, pg 959

NEBRASKA

Rainbow Video Productions Inc, pg 991

NEVADA

Aardvark Video & Media Productions, pg 772
DVDs4Less, pg 854
Encore Productions Inc, pg 861
JCS Video Productions, pg 904

NEW HAMPSHIRE

Apertura, pg 788
ProPhotonix Ltd, pg 986
Chip Taylor Communications LLC, pg 1032
The Troupe, pg 1045

NEW JERSEY

CFP Video Productions Inc, pg 823
Half Moon Video Productions, pg 883
Laurel Video Productions, pg 916
MIB Mediaworks, pg 941
Optisonics Productions, pg 965
Bill Quinn Productions, pg 989
Suede Interactive, pg 1027
VCSvideo, pg 1052

NEW MEXICO

Michael Dunn Productions, pg 853
Production Outfitters, pg 984

NEW YORK

aurora productions, pg 797
Norman N Axelrod Associates, pg 800
Broad Street Inc, pg 812
dM works, pg 849
Neal Marshad Productions, pg 931
MRG Productions Inc, pg 948
Shelly Palmer Production, pg 968
Peckham Productions Inc, pg 970
Science Television Co, pg 1005
Synaptic Digital, pg 1030
TeleTime Productions, pg 1036
Tobin Productions Inc, pg 1041
Videograf, pg 1057

NORTH CAROLINA

Pat Appleson Studios Inc, pg 788
The Communications Group Inc, pg 833
Kino Mountain Productions LLC, pg 911
Moving Pictures, pg 948

OHIO

Advent Media Inc, pg 778
Creative Technology, pg 838
Image Video Teleproductions Inc, pg 895
Lyon Video Inc, pg 927
MainSail Production Services Inc, pg 929
R&B Communications Inc, pg 991
Take 1 Media Services, pg 1031
Vista Color Imaging Inc, pg 1059

OREGON

Ideascape Inc, pg 894
Production West, pg 985

PENNSYLVANIA

AiH Group Inc, pg 779
FMP Media Solutions Inc, pg 870
Goodman Associates Inc, pg 880
Muderick Media, pg 949
Panta Rhei Media Inc, pg 968
Production Masters Inc (PMI), pg 984

RHODE ISLAND

Sound-FX-Design, pg 1017

SOUTH CAROLINA

Venture Media, pg 1052

TENNESSEE

Continental Film, pg 835
Memphis Communications Corp, pg 938
Running Pony Productions LLC, pg 1000

TEXAS

Biway Media, pg 808
Horizon Film + Video Productions, pg 891
Mediaforce Productions, pg 937
Omega Productions, pg 962
Romar Learning, pg 999
South Coast Film & Video, pg 1019
Texas Heart Institute Visual Communication Services, pg 1037

VERMONT

Perceptions Inc, pg 973
University of Vermont, Instructional Television Dept, pg 1050

VIRGINIA

CACI Productions Group, pg 816
Computer Sciences Corp, pg 834
D&B Television & Video Productions Inc, pg 842
Gingerbread Productions, pg 878
Limelight Communications Inc, pg 921
Metro Productions, pg 939
Rocktown Media, pg 998
Video Solutions, pg 1056

WASHINGTON

Bennett-Watt HD Productions Inc, pg 805

WISCONSIN

5th Floor Recording Co, pg 867
Media Communications Association-International (MCA-I), pg 936
Midland Video Productions Inc, pg 942
Wisconsin Public Television, pg 1068

WYOMING

Bridger Productions Inc, pg 812

BRITISH COLUMBIA

Image Media Farm, pg 895

ONTARIO

Image Video Services & Productions, pg 895

QUEBEC

Kerrigan Productions Inc, pg 910

Technical Research Program Rentals

MASSACHUSETTS

Documentary Educational Resources Inc, pg 850
Emergency Film Group, pg 860

MICHIGAN

Digi Sign Design LLC, pg 847

Television Commercial—Animated Distributors

Television Commercial—Animated Producers

PROGRAMMING — VIDEO

Television Commercial—Animated Producers (continued)

OKLAHOMA

KFOR-TV, pg 910

OREGON

KPDX-TV Production Center, pg 913
Odyssey Productions Inc, pg 961
Wallace Creative Inc, pg 1061

PENNSYLVANIA

AiH Group Inc, pg 779
Bang Pictures, pg 802
FMP Media Solutions Inc, pg 870
Fusion Brand Experiences, pg 874
Innovision Media Group, pg 899
JPL, pg 906
Kensington Falls Animation, pg 909
Muderick Media, pg 949
Production Masters Inc (PMI), pg 984
The Videohouse Inc, pg 1057

RHODE ISLAND

Sound-FX-Design, pg 1017

SOUTH CAROLINA

American Production Services LLC, pg 785

TENNESSEE

Continental Film, pg 835
Paradigm Marketing & Creative, pg 969
Running Pony Productions LLC, pg 1000
Scripps Networks, pg 1005

TEXAS

Biway Media, pg 808
The Editing Co, pg 857
Horizon Film + Video Productions, pg 891
Omega Productions, pg 962
Omni Intercommunications Inc, pg 962
The Samuels Co, pg 1002
South Coast Film & Video, pg 1019
Stage Directions, pg 1022

UTAH

K-SAR Video & DVD Productions, pg 907

VIRGINIA

Gingerbread Productions, pg 878
Metro Productions, pg 939

WASHINGTON

Bennett-Watt HD Productions Inc, pg 805
Hamilton Studio, pg 884
North-by-Northwest Productions, pg 958
Victory Studios, pg 1054

WISCONSIN

5th Floor Recording Co, pg 867
Meridian Studios, pg 939
Midland Video Productions Inc, pg 942
ProVideo, pg 986
Rucinski & Reetz Communications LLC, pg 1000
USAV Group Inc, pg 1050
Video Wisconsin Inc, pg 1056
Watts Communications Inc, pg 1062

WYOMING

Bridger Productions Inc, pg 812

ALBERTA

Black Media Works, pg 808
Global Television Station, pg 879

NEWFOUNDLAND AND LABRADOR

Vidcraft Productions Ltd, pg 1054

ONTARIO

ADS Media, pg 777
GAPC (General Assembly Production Centre), pg 875
Shaw Street Productions, pg 1008

QUEBEC

Kerrigan Productions Inc, pg 910

SASKATCHEWAN

plan9films, pg 976

Television Commercial—Animated Rentals

MICHIGAN

Digi Sign Design LLC, pg 847

MISSOURI

University of Missouri-Columbia, pg 1050

Television Commercial—Live Distributors

ARKANSAS

Mullikin Agency, pg 949

CALIFORNIA

Crystal Pyramid Productions™, pg 840
Digital Media West, pg 847
Far West Media Services Inc, pg 865
Shokus Video, pg 1009

FLORIDA

Allegro Productions Inc, pg 781

ILLINOIS

ABS Enterprises, pg 772
ABSA Productions Inc, pg 772
Chicago Satellite & Video, pg 825
Communications Corporation of America, pg 833

MARYLAND

Total AV Systems, pg 1042

MASSACHUSETTS

Penfield Productions Ltd, pg 971

MICHIGAN

Digi Sign Design LLC, pg 847

NEVADA

DVDs4Less, pg 854

NEW HAMPSHIRE

Chip Taylor Communications LLC, pg 1032

NEW JERSEY

MIB Mediaworks, pg 941
SES World Skies, pg 1007

NEW YORK

HB-Content, pg 886
Janus Films Inc, pg 904
Lifetime Television®, pg 920
MRG Productions Inc, pg 948
Reinhardt Productions Inc, pg 994

NORTH CAROLINA

Baker & Taylor Inc, pg 801

PENNSYLVANIA

FMP Media Solutions Inc, pg 870
Movies Unlimited, pg 947

TENNESSEE

American Blackguard Inc, pg 784
Marine Geographic, pg 931

VERMONT

Perceptions Inc, pg 973

VIRGINIA

CACI Productions Group, pg 816

ALBERTA

Global Television Station, pg 879

Television Commercial—Live Producers

ALABAMA

CMEInfo, pg 830

ALASKA

Alaska Film Services Inc, pg 779
Aurora Films, pg 797

ARIZONA

Aardvark Productions LLC, pg 772
Candee Productions Inc, pg 819
Direct Current Video Productions, pg 848
Film Creations Ltd, pg 867
Fox 10 Productions (KSAZ-TV), pg 872
MediaWorks, pg 938
Metropolitan Audio-Visual Inc, pg 940
Phoenix VideoFilms®, pg 974
Rodeo Video Inc, pg 998
Video Media Productions (VMP), pg 1055

ARKANSAS

Cedar Crest Studio, pg 822
Jones Film Video, pg 906
Live'N'Loud, pg 923
Mullikin Agency, pg 949
White Diamond Productions, pg 1065

CALIFORNIA

A Go Go Films, pg 771
Artichoke Productions, pg 791
Big Door, pg 807
Chesney Communications, pg 824
Classic Images, pg 829
Concrete Images, pg 835
Cox Media, pg 837
Crystal Pyramid Productions™, pg 840
Custom Video Productions Inc, pg 841
Direct Images Interactive Inc, pg 848
Dogma Studios, pg 850
Dolphin MultiMedia Inc, pg 850
Tom Donald Films, pg 850
Far West Media Services Inc, pg 865
GAMfilm Productions, pg 875
Global Village Productions, pg 879
Groovy Like a Movie, pg 882
Havas Edge, pg 885
Hope Productions, pg 891
Images in Motion Media Inc, pg 896
Imageworks, pg 896
ITV Productions, pg 903
Kavich Reynolds Productions Inc, pg 908
KION-TV, pg 911
KTVU-Retail Services, pg 914
Lieberman Productions, pg 920
Linsman Film, pg 922
Main Street Media Inc, pg 929
Maximus Media Inc, pg 934
McCune Audio-Video-Lighting, pg 935
Media Magic, pg 937
Mist Media Inc, pg 944
Moving Art by Louie Schwartzberg, pg 947
New & Unique Videos™, pg 955
New Deal Studios, pg 955
Nolte Media, pg 958
On-Trax Inc, pg 963
Opticomm-EMCORE, pg 964
Panorama Productions, pg 968
Penrose Productions, pg 972
PM Productions, pg 977
Producers Group Ltd, pg 983
QRS Software Services, pg 988
Dick Reizner Film & Video, pg 994
RetinaVision Productions, pg 995
Glenn Roland Films, pg 998
Ron Roy Productions/Moodtapes, pg 1000
Sahara Records & Filmworks Entertainment Co, pg 1001
Santa Barbara Location Services, pg 1002
Santa Clarita Studios, pg 1002
SBS Productions, pg 1003
SNAP, pg 1014
Staylor-Made Communications Inc, pg 1024
Still N'Motion, pg 1025
The Studio Center, pg 1026
Tam Communications Inc, pg 1031
Timestream Video, pg 1041
Total Media Group, pg 1042
TVA Productions, pg 1046
Videolady, pg 1057
Videowerks, pg 1057
Vineyard Video & Photography, pg 1058
Wavemaker Media Design, pg 1062

Yada/Levine Video Productions, pg 1071
Zamacona Productions, pg 1073

COLORADO

Apogee Communications Group, pg 788
Blue River Productions, pg 810
CSI Films, pg 840
Daylight Productions & Rentals, pg 844
Flashback Media Productions, pg 869
Rocky Mountain Audio/Video Productions Inc, pg 998
Side 3 Studios, pg 1010
Starwest Productions, pg 1024
Transtar Entertainment Co Inc, pg 1043

CONNECTICUT

ACM Productions Ltd, pg 774
Applebox Studio, pg 788
EagleVision Inc, pg 855
Fox Connecticut, pg 872
Ironik Design & Post, pg 902
MCC Films, pg 935
Moving Pictures, pg 947
P&P Studios Inc, pg 968
Powerstation Events, pg 979
Video Production Associates Inc, pg 1056

FLORIDA

Allegro Productions Inc, pg 781
Astoria Communications Inc, pg 792
Big Byte Video Productions, pg 806
Blackburst Entertainment, pg 808
CD ROM™ Inc, pg 822
Chatterbox Productions Inc, pg 824
Civins Productions Inc, pg 828
CopShopMiami.com, pg 836
Courter Films LLC, pg 837
Digital Zoetrope Productions, pg 848
Eastern Video, pg 856
Ed Ethridge Productions Inc, pg 863
Gulf Coast Audio Visual Producers Inc, pg 883
Home Shopping Network (HSN), pg 890
Jordan Klein Film & Video (JKFV), pg 906
Media Entertainment Inc, pg 936
National Teleproductions Inc, pg 953
Olympusat Entertainment, pg 962
Roger Scruggs Films, pg 1005
Skystorm Productions, pg 1013
Sunfire Communications Inc, pg 1028
Sunrise Studios, pg 1028
Tel-Air Interests Inc, pg 1035
Tight Line Productions, pg 1040
Tricycle Studios, pg 1044
Universal Studios Florida® Production Group, pg 1049
Mike Vasilinda Productions Inc, pg 1052

GEORGIA

Beachwood Productions, pg 804
Burst Video/Film Inc, pg 815
Continental Film & Video, pg 835
ECG Productions, pg 856
Georgia-Pacific Television & Photography, pg 877
Guerrilla Productions LLC, pg 883
Memory Lane Productions, pg 938
On-Line Productions, pg 963
Pogo Pictures, pg 977
Sirius Images Corp dba WaveGuide Studios, pg 1012

HAWAII

Hyperspective Studios Inc, pg 893
Sight & Sound Studios, pg 1010
1013 Integrated, pg 1037

IDAHO

Brad Shaw Productions Inc, pg 1008

ILLINOIS

Abacus Group of Saint Louis LLC, pg 772
ABS Enterprises, pg 772
ABSA Productions Inc, pg 772
Audio Producers Group, pg 794
The Chicago Production Center, pg 825
Chicago Satellite & Video, pg 825
Communications Corporation of America, pg 833
Comtech Multimedia Marketing, pg 834
Cresta Creative, pg 839
Film Police, pg 867
IV Media Resources, pg 903
Manning Productions, pg 930
The Market Place, pg 931
Mimi Productions, pg 943
Jim Passin Productions, pg 970
The Pepper Group, pg 972
The Prairie Production Group, pg 980
Roadworthy Image Magnification, pg 998
SCI Television Productions LLC, pg 1004
Sparkfactor, pg 1019
Video Impressions, pg 1055
WEEK TV, pg 1063
Winter Productions, pg 1068

INDIANA

Advanced Media Integration, pg 777
AVA Productions, pg 798
Covenant Productions®, pg 837
Digital Rain LLC, pg 847
Explore Media LLC, pg 864
OMNI Productions, pg 962
PentaVision Communications Inc, pg 972
Road Pictures, pg 997

KANSAS

KAKE-TV, pg 907
Walterscheid Productions, pg 1062

KENTUCKY

Idle Minds Productions Inc, pg 894
Prosper Media Group Inc, pg 986
Trusty Tuneshop Recording Studios, pg 1045

LOUISIANA

Digital FX Inc, pg 847
Moxie Media, pg 948

MARYLAND

Adventure Productions LLC, pg 778
Richard Chisolm Cinematography, pg 825
CPR MultiMedia Solutions, pg 837
dbF a Media Company, pg 844
The Image Generators, pg 895
Kramer Communications Video Production, pg 913
Media Dimensions Inc, pg 936
Producers Video, pg 984

MASSACHUSETTS

Award Productions, pg 800
Cramer Productions, pg 837
Green Mountain Post Films (GMP), pg 882
Heliotrope Studios, pg 887
Penfield Productions Ltd, pg 971
PixMix Video Services, pg 976
Gabriel Polonsky Studio, pg 978
TVN-The Video Network, pg 1046
Veritech Corp, pg 1053
VideoLink Inc, pg 1057

MICHIGAN

Digi Sign Design LLC, pg 847
K&R All Media Productions Inc, pg 908
K&R's Recording Studios Inc, pg 908
Lawrence Productions Inc, pg 917

MINNESOTA

Aggressive Records Audio Duplication LLC, pg 778
Big Event Productions LLC, pg 807
Blue 60 Pictures, pg 810
GMI Productions, pg 879
House of Cinemagraphics, pg 891
Jamieson & Associates Inc, pg 904
Stoney-Wolf Productions Inc, pg 1025

MISSISSIPPI

Dollarhide Film Inc, pg 850

MISSOURI

Avatar Studios, pg 798
Celebrities Productions, pg 822
Fambrough & Associates Inc, pg 865
Hardcastle Films & Video, pg 885

NEBRASKA

Mason Video, pg 933
Telepro Video Inc, pg 1036

NEVADA

Aardvark Video & Media Productions, pg 772
DVDs4Less, pg 854
Encore Productions Inc, pg 861
HDTV Productions Inc, pg 886
JCS Video Productions, pg 904
Tanglewood Productions, pg 1031

NEW HAMPSHIRE

Apertura, pg 788
Channell One Video, pg 824
NH Movies Inc, pg 957
Chip Taylor Communications LLC, pg 1032
The Troupe, pg 1045

NEW JERSEY

Broadcast Center Studios, pg 813
Color Leasing Studios, pg 831
Concepts TV Production, pg 834
Euro-Pacific Film & Video Productions Inc, pg 863
Half Moon Video Productions, pg 883
MediaNow, pg 938
MIB Mediaworks, pg 941
Optisonics Productions, pg 965
Producer East Productions, pg 983
Public Eye Productions, pg 987
Bill Quinn Productions, pg 989
Reider Photography & Video Productions, pg 994
Shamrock Communications, pg 1008
Suede Interactive, pg 1027
TimeSteps Productions Inc, pg 1041
VCSvideo, pg 1052

NEW MEXICO

Stevens Design & Animation LLC, pg 1024

NEW YORK

Air Sea Land Productions Inc (ASL), pg 779
American Montage Inc, pg 784
aurora productions, pg 797
Avekta Productions Inc, pg 798
Big Fish Productions Inc, pg 807
BioMedia Inc, pg 807
Blue Barn Pictures Inc, pg 809
Broad Street Inc, pg 812
Brooklyn Films, pg 814
Charlex Inc, pg 824
De Nonno Productions Inc (DPI), pg 844
dM works, pg 849
Mark Druck Productions, pg 852
East of Hollywood NY, pg 855
Golden Lamb Productions, pg 880
HB-Content, pg 886
Hello World Communications, pg 888
HOThead, pg 891
Kinetic Arts, pg 911
L A Bruell Inc, pg 914
Lifetime Television®, pg 920
Long Island Video Enterprises Live Inc, pg 924
Neal Marshad Productions, pg 931
McGuane Studio Inc, pg 935
Mood Creations Ltd, pg 946
MRG Productions Inc, pg 948
The Napoleon Group, pg 952
New Horizon Studios, pg 955
News Broadcast Network, pg 956
Northeast Video Productions Inc, pg 959
NSR Productions Inc & Capricorn Five Films, pg 960
Shelly Palmer Production, pg 968
Pat Kogan Productions Inc, pg 970
Peckham Productions Inc, pg 970
PrimaLux Video Inc, pg 982
Production Central, pg 984
R/GA, pg 990
Shadow Pictures Inc, pg 1007
Split Image Productions, pg 1021
Suggs Media Productions Inc, pg 1028
TBA Global Events, pg 1032
TeleTime Productions, pg 1036
Tobin Productions Inc, pg 1041
Zelman Studios Ltd, pg 1073

NORTH CAROLINA

All Pro Media Inc, pg 780
The Communications Group Inc, pg 833
Kino Mountain Productions LLC, pg 911
LCW Productions LLC, pg 917
Moving Pictures, pg 948
Trailblazer Studios®, pg 1043
Unifour Productions Inc, pg 1048

OHIO

Russ Beckner Pictures, pg 804
CET, pg 823

PROGRAMMING — VIDEO

Television Commercial—Live Producers (continued)

OHIO (continued)

Clear Choice Creative Corp, pg 829
Commercial Video, pg 832
EDR Media LLC, pg 857
Image Video Teleproductions Inc, pg 895
Lyon Video Inc, pg 927
R&B Communications Inc, pg 991
Shelburne Films, pg 1008
Take 1 Media Services, pg 1031
Treehaus Communications Inc, pg 1044
VGI Productions, pg 1053
Vista Color Imaging Inc, pg 1059

OKLAHOMA

KFOR-TV, pg 910

OREGON

Creative Media Development, pg 838
Ideascape Inc, pg 894
InterVision Media, pg 902
KPDX-TV Production Center, pg 913
KVAL, pg 914
Odyssey Productions Inc, pg 961
Production West, pg 985
Rex, pg 995

PENNSYLVANIA

AiH Group Inc, pg 779
Bang Pictures, pg 802
Beholder Productions Inc, pg 804
CCI Communications Inc, pg 821
FMP Media Solutions Inc, pg 870
Fusion Brand Experiences, pg 874
Goodman Associates Inc, pg 880
Innovision Media Group, pg 899
JPL, pg 906
Muderick Media, pg 949
Production Masters Inc (PMI), pg 984
The Videohouse Inc, pg 1057
Visual Sound Inc, pg 1059
WHYY Inc, pg 1066

RHODE ISLAND

Sound-FX-Design, pg 1017

SOUTH CAROLINA

Encore Video Productions, pg 861
Stages Video Productions, pg 1023
Venture Media, pg 1052

TENNESSEE

American Blackguard Inc, pg 784
Continental Film, pg 835
Marine Geographic, pg 931
Paradigm Marketing & Creative, pg 969
Running Pony Productions LLC, pg 1000
Scripps Networks, pg 1005
Stage Post, pg 1022
Russ Sturgeon Productions/RSVP, pg 1027

TEXAS

Alexander Media Productions, pg 780
AMS Pictures, pg 786
Biway Media, pg 808
Cerutti Productions Inc, pg 823
Communication Arts Multimedia Inc, pg 832
Countdown Productions Inc, pg 837
Dykeman Associates Inc, pg 854
The Editing Co, pg 857
Horizon Film + Video Productions, pg 891
Marx InDigital, pg 933
Mediaforce Productions, pg 937
Earl Miller Productions Inc, pg 943
Omega Productions, pg 962
Omni Intercommunications Inc, pg 962
Phil Lights, pg 973
Radio Vision Inc, pg 990
The Samuels Co, pg 1002
South Coast Film & Video, pg 1019
Stage Directions, pg 1022
Zachry Associates Inc, pg 1073

UTAH

K-SAR Video & DVD Productions, pg 907

VERMONT

Marlboro Film & Video Productions, pg 931
Perceptions Inc, pg 973

VIRGINIA

CACI Productions Group, pg 816
D&B Television & Video Productions Inc, pg 842
Dorst MediaWorks Inc, pg 851
Gingerbread Productions, pg 878
Limelight Communications Inc, pg 921
Metro Productions, pg 939
Rocktown Media, pg 998
Video Solutions, pg 1056

WASHINGTON

Adams Creative & Production Services, pg 775
Bennett-Watt HD Productions Inc, pg 805
Hamilton Studio, pg 884
North-by-Northwest Productions, pg 958
Pal Productions Inc, pg 967
Victory Studios, pg 1054

WEST VIRGINIA

Blackwater Video Productions, pg 808

WISCONSIN

5th Floor Recording Co, pg 867
Logan Productions Inc, pg 924
Meridian Studios, pg 939
Midland Video Productions Inc, pg 942
ProVideo, pg 986
Rucinski & Reetz Communications LLC, pg 1000
University of Wisconsin-Oshkosh Radio-TV-Film Dept, pg 1050
USAV Group Inc, pg 1050
Watts Communications Inc, pg 1062

WYOMING

Bridger Productions Inc, pg 812

ALBERTA

Black Media Works, pg 808
Global Television Station, pg 879

BRITISH COLUMBIA

Image Media Farm, pg 895

MANITOBA

Lank/Beach Productions Inc, pg 916
Spectra Video Productions Ltd, pg 1020

NEWFOUNDLAND AND LABRADOR

Vidcraft Productions Ltd, pg 1054

ONTARIO

ADS Media, pg 777
DebsVoice, pg 844
GAPC (General Assembly Production Centre), pg 875
Image Video Services & Productions, pg 895
Iron Ring Communications Ltd, pg 902
Pendulum Entertainment, pg 971
RB Productions, pg 992
Video Excellence Productions, pg 1055

QUEBEC

Auriga Productions Ltd, pg 797
Kerrigan Productions Inc, pg 910

SASKATCHEWAN

plan9films, pg 976

Television Commercial—Live Rentals

MICHIGAN

Digi Sign Design LLC, pg 847

MISSOURI

University of Missouri-Columbia, pg 1050

Television Film Distributors

CALIFORNIA

Agrama Film Enterprises Inc, pg 778
Astronomical Society of the Pacific, pg 792
Digital Media West, pg 847
Direct Cinema Ltd Inc, pg 848
ECONEWS (Environmental Television Series) & (Environmental Directions Radio Series), pg 856
eFootage LLC, pg 858
FXF Productions Inc, pg 874
Glenn Photo Supply, pg 878
Glenn Video Vistas Ltd, pg 878
Glenray Productions Inc, pg 878
Hope Productions, pg 891
MarVista Entertainment Inc, pg 933
MGM Home Video, pg 941
National Lampoon, pg 953
Paulist Productions, pg 970
Players Press, pg 977
Pyramid Media, pg 987
Regent Press Publishers & Printers, pg 994
Universal Studios Home Entertainment, pg 1049

DISTRICT OF COLUMBIA

VSA, pg 1061

FLORIDA

Capital Communications Inc, pg 819
Cifex Corp, pg 826
Distribution Video & Audio (DVA), pg 849
Global Video Distributors Inc, pg 879

ILLINOIS

Communications Corporation of America, pg 833
Moviecraft Inc, pg 947

KENTUCKY

WaxWorks VideoWorks, pg 1063

MARYLAND

RLJ Entertainment Inc, pg 997

MASSACHUSETTS

Documentary Educational Resources Inc, pg 850

MISSOURI

Cable Films & Video, pg 816
Phoenix/BFA/Coronet, pg 974

NEBRASKA

Leo Films, pg 919

NEVADA

DVDs4Less, pg 854

NEW HAMPSHIRE

Chip Taylor Communications LLC, pg 1032

NEW JERSEY

Ergo Media Inc, pg 862
Euro-Pacific Film & Video Productions Inc, pg 863

NEW YORK

ATA Trading Corp/Favorite TV Inc, pg 792
William Greaves Productions Inc, pg 882
HB-Content, pg 886
Hearst Entertainment & Syndication, pg 887
Janus Films Inc, pg 904
Kino International Corp, pg 911
Mastervision Inc, pg 933
MRG Productions Inc, pg 948
Richter Productions Inc, pg 996
SISU Home Entertainment Inc, pg 1012
United Nations Multimedia Resources Unit, pg 1048
VIEW Inc (Video International Entertainment World Inc), pg 1058
Women Make Movies Inc, pg 1069

NORTH CAROLINA

Baker & Taylor Inc, pg 801
Crystal Pictures Inc, pg 840

Television Film Producers

PROGRAMMING — VIDEO

Television Film Producers (continued)

OREGON

Ideascape Inc, pg 894
Odyssey Productions Inc, pg 961
Production West, pg 985
Rex, pg 995

PENNSYLVANIA

Bang Pictures, pg 802
FMP Media Solutions Inc, pg 870
Goodman Associates Inc, pg 880
Innovision Media Group, pg 899
JPL, pg 906
Kensington Falls Animation, pg 909
Muderick Media, pg 949
Production Masters Inc (PMI), pg 984
Video/Film Associates, pg 1055

RHODE ISLAND

Sound-FX-Design, pg 1017

TENNESSEE

American Blackguard Inc, pg 784
Running Pony Productions LLC, pg 1000
Scripps Networks, pg 1005

TEXAS

Cerutti Productions Inc, pg 823
Horizon Film + Video Productions, pg 891
Julye Newlin Productions Inc, pg 956
Omega Productions, pg 962
Stage Directions, pg 1022

VERMONT

Marlboro Film & Video Productions, pg 931
Perceptions Inc, pg 973

VIRGINIA

CACI Productions Group, pg 816
CALIBRE, pg 816
Gingerbread Productions, pg 878
Metro Productions, pg 939

WASHINGTON

Bennett-Watt HD Productions Inc, pg 805
North-by-Northwest Productions, pg 958
Pal Productions Inc, pg 967

WISCONSIN

5th Floor Recording Co, pg 867
Video Wisconsin Inc, pg 1056
Wisconsin Public Television, pg 1068

WYOMING

Bridger Productions Inc, pg 812

ALBERTA

Black Media Works, pg 808
Global Television Station, pg 879
HBW Entertainment Inc, pg 886

MANITOBA

Spectra Video Productions Ltd, pg 1020

ONTARIO

Canamedia Inc, pg 818
Doomsday Studios Ltd, pg 850
RB Productions, pg 992

QUEBEC

Kerrigan Productions Inc, pg 910
Max Films Inc, pg 934
Les Productions Via Le Monde (Daniel Bertolino) Inc, pg 985

Television Film Rentals

CALIFORNIA

Auslender Productions/Celestial Images, pg 797
Direct Cinema Ltd Inc, pg 848
Paulist Productions, pg 970
Point of View Productions, pg 977

MASSACHUSETTS

Documentary Educational Resources Inc, pg 850

MISSOURI

University of Missouri-Columbia, pg 1050

NEW JERSEY

Alden Films, pg 780

NEW YORK

Kino International Corp, pg 911
Richter Productions Inc, pg 996
VIEW Inc (Video International Entertainment World Inc), pg 1058

NORTH CAROLINA

Crystal Pictures Inc, pg 840

PENNSYLVANIA

Bullfrog Films Inc, pg 815

QUEBEC

Les Productions Via Le Monde (Daniel Bertolino) Inc, pg 985

Television Program Distributors

ALABAMA

Eternal Word Television Network (EWTN), pg 862

CALIFORNIA

Anchor Bay Entertainment LLC, pg 786
Ariztical Entertainment Inc, pg 790
Astronomical Society of the Pacific, pg 792
Digital Media West, pg 847
Direct Cinema Ltd Inc, pg 848
411 Video Information, pg 872
FXF Productions Inc, pg 874
Glenray Productions Inc, pg 878
Global Village Stock Footage Library, pg 879
Lions Gate Entertainment Corp, pg 922
Live Wire Media, pg 923
MarVista Entertainment Inc, pg 933
MGM Home Video, pg 941
National Lampoon, pg 953
Paramount Pictures Corporation, pg 969
Melvin Powers Television Marketing, pg 979
Prime Cut Productions, pg 982
Pyramid Media, pg 987
Regent Press Publishers & Printers, pg 994
Rhino Home Video, pg 996
Sahara Records & Filmworks Entertainment Co, pg 1001
Shokus Video, pg 1009
Thinking Allowed Productions, pg 1038
Universal Studios Home Entertainment, pg 1049
Warner Home Video Inc, pg 1062
Western Instructional Television Inc, pg 1064
The Wyland Group, pg 1071

DISTRICT OF COLUMBIA

National Council of Churches, pg 952
VSA, pg 1061

FLORIDA

Accord Productions, pg 773
Capital Communications Inc, pg 819
Global Video Distributors Inc, pg 879

GEORGIA

New Leaf Distributing Co, pg 955
On-Line Productions, pg 963

ILLINOIS

Chicago Satellite & Video, pg 825
Facets Multi-Media Inc, pg 865
Questar Inc, pg 989

INDIANA

Agency for Instructional Technology (AIT), pg 778
Communication Ministries, pg 833
Perennial Pictures Film Corp, pg 973

IOWA

American Visions, pg 785
Right Stuf Inc, pg 997

LOUISIANA

Great Chefs/Leisure Jazz Video, pg 881
Leisure Video, pg 918

MARYLAND

Adventure Productions LLC, pg 778
RLJ Entertainment Inc, pg 997
Total AV Systems, pg 1042

MASSACHUSETTS

Award Productions, pg 800
Documentary Educational Resources Inc, pg 850
Enterprise Media LLC, pg 861
Penfield Productions Ltd, pg 971

MICHIGAN

Digi Sign Design LLC, pg 847
VMS Inc, pg 1060

MISSOURI

Cable Films & Video, pg 816
World Events Productions Ltd, pg 1069

MONTANA

High Plains Films, pg 889

NEBRASKA

Vision Maker Media, pg 1058

NEW HAMPSHIRE

Channell One Video, pg 824
Chip Taylor Communications LLC, pg 1032

NEW JERSEY

Euro-Pacific Film & Video Productions Inc, pg 863
MIB Mediaworks, pg 941
SES World Skies, pg 1007
Shanachie Entertainment Corp, pg 1008

NEW YORK

A&E Home Video, pg 771
A&E Television Networks LLC, pg 771
ATA Trading Corp/Favorite TV Inc, pg 792
The Christophers, pg 826
CMI Media Management, pg 830
HB-Content, pg 886
Hearst Entertainment & Syndication, pg 887
Icarus Film Inc, pg 893
Janson Media, pg 904
Janus Films Inc, pg 904
Lifetime Television®, pg 920
Maryknoll Productions, pg 933
Mastervision Inc, pg 933
MRG Productions Inc, pg 948
Scholastic Media, pg 1004
SISU Home Entertainment Inc, pg 1012
Third World Newsreel/Camera News Inc, pg 1039
Timed Exposures Films, pg 1040
United Nations Multimedia Resources Unit, pg 1048
Videofashion Network, pg 1056
VIEW Inc (Video International Entertainment World Inc), pg 1058

NORTH CAROLINA

Baker & Taylor Inc, pg 801

NORTH DAKOTA

UND Television Center, pg 1048

OHIO

VGI Productions, pg 1053

OREGON

Cooking by the Book, pg 836
Nostalgia Family Video Inc, pg 959

PENNSYLVANIA

Beholder Productions Inc, pg 804
Corinth Films Inc, pg 836
Movies Unlimited, pg 947
MVD Entertainment Group, pg 951
Penn State University MediaTech, pg 972
Rahlic Publishing Co, pg 990

Television Program Producers

PROGRAMMING — VIDEO

Television Program Producers (continued)

INDIANA (continued)

AVA Productions, pg 798
Communication Ministries, pg 833
Covenant Productions®, pg 837
Digital Rain LLC, pg 847
Explore Media LLC, pg 864
OMNI Productions, pg 962

IOWA

American Visions, pg 785
The Production House, pg 984
Right Stuf Inc, pg 997

KANSAS

KAKE-TV, pg 907

KENTUCKY

Idle Minds Productions Inc, pg 894
Donna Lawrence Productions, pg 917
Northern Kentucky University, pg 959
Prosper Media Group Inc, pg 986

LOUISIANA

Great Chefs/Leisure Jazz Video, pg 881
Launch Media, pg 916
Leisure Video, pg 918
Louisiana State University Health Sciences Center - Shreveport, pg 925
Moxie Media, pg 948

MAINE

WGME-TV, pg 1065

MARYLAND

Adventure Productions LLC, pg 778
CAS Video Productions, pg 820
Richard Chisolm Cinematography, pg 825
CPR MultiMedia Solutions, pg 837
dbF a Media Company, pg 844
Kramer Communications Video Production, pg 913
WMAR-TV, pg 1068

MASSACHUSETTS

Award Productions, pg 800
Documentary Educational Resources Inc, pg 850
Emergency Film Group, pg 860
Enterprise Media LLC, pg 861
Green Mountain Post Films (GMP), pg 882
Heliotrope Studios, pg 887
Northern Light Productions, pg 959
Penfield Productions Ltd, pg 971
PixMix Video Services, pg 976
VideoLink Inc, pg 1057

MICHIGAN

Benjamin Creative Productions, pg 805
Digi Sign Design LLC, pg 847
K&R All Media Productions Inc, pg 908
K&R's Recording Studios Inc, pg 908
Lawrence Productions Inc, pg 917
WTVS-Station Enterprises, pg 1071

MINNESOTA

Aggressive Records Audio Duplication LLC, pg 778
Big Event Productions LLC, pg 807
House of Cinemagraphics, pg 891
Jamieson & Associates Inc, pg 904
Master Communications Group, pg 933
Worthwhile Films, pg 1070

MISSOURI

Cable Films & Video, pg 816
Celebrities Productions, pg 822
Fambrough & Associates Inc, pg 865
World Events Productions Ltd, pg 1069

MONTANA

High Plains Films, pg 889
North Country Media Group, pg 959

NEBRASKA

Mason Video, pg 933
Rainbow Video Productions Inc, pg 991
Vision Maker Media, pg 1058

NEVADA

Aardvark Video & Media Productions, pg 772
Encore Productions Inc, pg 861
HDTV Productions Inc, pg 886
JCS Video Productions, pg 904

NEW HAMPSHIRE

Apertura, pg 788
Channell One Video, pg 824
NH Movies Inc, pg 957
Chip Taylor Communications LLC, pg 1032

NEW JERSEY

Broadcast Center Studios, pg 813
CFP Video Productions Inc, pg 823
DWJ Television, pg 854
Euro-Pacific Film & Video Productions Inc, pg 863
Half Moon Video Productions, pg 883
MIB Mediaworks, pg 941
Newark Beth Israel Medical Center, pg 956
Optisonics Productions, pg 965
Public Eye Productions, pg 987
Bill Quinn Productions, pg 989
Shamrock Communications, pg 1008
Shanachie Entertainment Corp, pg 1008
Suede Interactive, pg 1027
Telequest Inc, pg 1036
VCSvideo, pg 1052

NEW MEXICO

Michael Dunn Productions, pg 853
I-25 Studios, pg 893
Production Outfitters, pg 984

NEW YORK

A&E Home Video, pg 771
A&E Television Networks LLC, pg 771
aurora productions, pg 797
Avekta Productions Inc, pg 798
Big Fish Productions Inc, pg 807
Brian Film Productions LLC, pg 812
Broad Street Inc, pg 812
Brooklyn Films, pg 814
C2 Imaging LLC, pg 841
De Nonno Productions Inc (DPI), pg 844
East of Hollywood NY, pg 855
Florentine Films, pg 870
Golden Lamb Productions, pg 880
William Greaves Productions Inc, pg 882
HB-Content, pg 886
Hearst Entertainment & Syndication, pg 887
Hello World Communications, pg 888
HOThead, pg 891
Janson Media, pg 904
Lifetime Television®, pg 920
Lylofilm Productions, pg 926
Manhattan Center Studios Inc, pg 930
Neal Marshad Productions, pg 931
Maryknoll Productions, pg 933
Mastervision Inc, pg 933
MRG Productions Inc, pg 948
News Broadcast Network, pg 956
NSR Productions Inc & Capricorn Five Films, pg 960
Shelly Palmer Production, pg 968
Pat Kogan Productions Inc, pg 970
Peckham Productions Inc, pg 970
PrimaLux Video Inc, pg 982
Scholastic Media, pg 1004
Split Image Productions, pg 1021
Suggs Media Productions Inc, pg 1028
Sunrise Media LLC, pg 1028
Third World Newsreel/Camera News Inc, pg 1039
Timed Exposures Films, pg 1040
United Nations Multimedia Resources Unit, pg 1048
Videofashion Network, pg 1056
Vidicom Inc, pg 1057
VIEW Inc (Video International Entertainment World Inc), pg 1058
Alan Weiss Productions, pg 1063
WNET/NET TELECON, pg 1069

NORTH CAROLINA

J Arnold Productions Inc, pg 790
Bill Barnes Video Productions LLC, pg 803
The Communications Group Inc, pg 833
LCW Productions LLC, pg 917
Moving Pictures, pg 948
NASCAR Media Group LLC, pg 952
Trailblazer Studios®, pg 1043
Unifour Productions Inc, pg 1048

NORTH DAKOTA

UND Television Center, pg 1048

OHIO

CET, pg 823
Clear Choice Creative Corp, pg 829
Commercial Video, pg 832
Creative Technology, pg 838
Cuyahoga Community College Media Center, pg 841
EDR Media LLC, pg 857
Image Video Teleproductions Inc, pg 895
Lyon Video Inc, pg 927
MainSail Production Services Inc, pg 929
Maslowski Productions, pg 933
R&B Communications Inc, pg 991
Take 1 Media Services, pg 1031
VGI Productions, pg 1053
Vista Color Imaging Inc, pg 1059

OKLAHOMA

University of Oklahoma Academic Media & Digital Services, pg 1050

OREGON

A KTVA Production LLC, pg 771
Creative Media Development, pg 838
Ideascape Inc, pg 894
KPDX-TV Production Center, pg 913
Odyssey Productions Inc, pg 961
Production West, pg 985
Rex, pg 995

PENNSYLVANIA

Bang Pictures, pg 802
Beholder Productions Inc, pg 804
CCI Communications Inc, pg 821
FMP Media Solutions Inc, pg 870
Fusion Brand Experiences, pg 874
Goodman Associates Inc, pg 880
Innovision Media Group, pg 899
Kensington Falls Animation, pg 909
Muderick Media, pg 949
Production Masters Inc (PMI), pg 984
Rahlic Publishing Co, pg 990
Schlessinger Media, pg 1004
Video Communication Productions Inc, pg 1054
Video/Film Associates, pg 1055
The Videohouse Inc, pg 1057
Videosmith Inc, pg 1057
WHYY Inc, pg 1066
WQED-Multimedia, pg 1070

RHODE ISLAND

Sound-FX-Design, pg 1017

SOUTH CAROLINA

American Production Services LLC, pg 785
Go To Team, pg 879
Venture Media, pg 1052

TENNESSEE

American Blackguard Inc, pg 784
Jaguar Productions, pg 903
Marine Geographic, pg 931
Running Pony Productions LLC, pg 1000
Scripps Networks, pg 1005
UMCom Productions, pg 1048

TEXAS

Biway Media, pg 808
Central Texas College KNCT-TV & Radio FM, pg 823
Cerutti Productions Inc, pg 823
Communication Arts Multimedia Inc, pg 832
Countdown Productions Inc, pg 837
Dub King, pg 853
The Editing Co, pg 857
Horizon Film + Video Productions, pg 891
Mediaforce Productions, pg 937
Earl Miller Productions Inc, pg 943

Television Program Rentals

Television Program—Classic Distributors

Television Program—Classic Producers

PROGRAMMING — VIDEO

Television Program—Classic Producers (continued)

NORTH CAROLINA

The Communications Group Inc, pg 833

OHIO

Creative Technology, pg 838
R&B Communications Inc, pg 991
Take 1 Media Services, pg 1031

PENNSYLVANIA

Bang Pictures, pg 802
FMP Media Solutions Inc, pg 870
Production Masters Inc (PMI), pg 984

RHODE ISLAND

Sound-FX-Design, pg 1017

TEXAS

Mediaforce Productions, pg 937

VIRGINIA

Metro Productions, pg 939
Rocktown Media, pg 998

WASHINGTON

Bennett-Watt HD Productions Inc, pg 805

WISCONSIN

5th Floor Recording Co, pg 867
Watts Communications Inc, pg 1062

WYOMING

Bridger Productions Inc, pg 812

BRITISH COLUMBIA

Image Media Farm, pg 895

ONTARIO

Canamedia Inc, pg 818
GAPC (General Assembly Production Centre), pg 875

QUEBEC

Kerrigan Productions Inc, pg 910

Television Program—Classic Rentals

MICHIGAN

Digi Sign Design LLC, pg 847

Test Commercial Distributors

CALIFORNIA

Far West Media Services Inc, pg 865

FLORIDA

Allegro Productions Inc, pg 781

MASSACHUSETTS

Penfield Productions Ltd, pg 971

MICHIGAN

Digi Sign Design LLC, pg 847

NEVADA

DVDs4Less, pg 854

NEW HAMPSHIRE

Chip Taylor Communications LLC, pg 1032

NEW YORK

HB-Content, pg 886
MRG Productions Inc, pg 948

VIRGINIA

CACI Productions Group, pg 816

Test Commercial Producers

ARIZONA

Aardvark Productions LLC, pg 772
Candee Productions Inc, pg 819
Film Creations Ltd, pg 867
Phoenix VideoFilms®, pg 974
Rodeo Video Inc, pg 998
Video Media Productions (VMP), pg 1055

ARKANSAS

Jones Film Video, pg 906
Live'N'Loud, pg 923

CALIFORNIA

A Go Go Films, pg 771
Action Video, pg 775
Animax, pg 787
Artichoke Productions, pg 791
Big Door, pg 807
Chesney Communications, pg 824
Classic Images, pg 829
Concrete Images, pg 835
Custom Video Productions Inc, pg 841
Design Media, pg 845
Direct Images Interactive Inc, pg 848
Tom Donald Films, pg 850
Far West Media Services Inc, pg 865
Havas Edge, pg 885
ITV Productions, pg 903
KION-TV, pg 911
KTVU-Retail Services, pg 914
Main Street Media Inc, pg 929
Maximus Media Inc, pg 934
McCune Audio-Video-Lighting, pg 935
Media Magic, pg 937
Mist Media Inc, pg 944
New & Unique Videos™, pg 955
New Circuit Films LLC, pg 955
QRS Software Services, pg 988
Dick Reizner Film & Video, pg 994
RetinaVision Productions, pg 995
Glenn Roland Films, pg 998
SNAP, pg 1014
Still N'Motion, pg 1025
Tam Communications Inc, pg 1031
Timestream Video, pg 1041
Total Media Group, pg 1042
Videowerks, pg 1057
Vineyard Video & Photography, pg 1058
Zamacona Productions, pg 1073

COLORADO

Flashback Media Productions, pg 869
Transtar Entertainment Co Inc, pg 1043

CONNECTICUT

Applebox Studio, pg 788
Fox Connecticut, pg 872
Ironik Design & Post, pg 902
MCC Films, pg 935
P&P Studios Inc, pg 968
Video Production Associates Inc, pg 1056

FLORIDA

Allegro Productions Inc, pg 781
Blackburst Entertainment, pg 808
Chatterbox Productions Inc, pg 824
Civins Productions Inc, pg 828
CopShopMiami.com, pg 836
Courter Films LLC, pg 837
Eastern Video, pg 856
Ed Ethridge Productions Inc, pg 863
Gulf Coast Audio Visual Producers Inc, pg 883
Home Shopping Network (HSN), pg 890
Jordan Klein Film & Video (JKFV), pg 906
Sunfire Communications Inc, pg 1028
Sunrise Studios, pg 1028
Tricycle Studios, pg 1044
Universal Studios Florida® Production Group, pg 1049

GEORGIA

Beachwood Productions, pg 804
ECG Productions, pg 856
Georgia-Pacific Television & Photography, pg 877
Guerrilla Productions LLC, pg 883
On-Line Productions, pg 963
WATL-TV Inc, pg 1062

HAWAII

Hyperspective Studios Inc, pg 893

IDAHO

Brad Shaw Productions Inc, pg 1008
Wide Eye Productions, pg 1066

ILLINOIS

Audio Visual Services Corp, pg 796
Chicago Satellite & Video, pg 825
Film Police, pg 867
The Pepper Group, pg 972
PSAV® Presentation Services (Hotel Services Division), pg 987
Richter Studios, pg 996
Roadworthy Image Magnification, pg 998
SCI Television Productions LLC, pg 1004
20/20 Communications Inc, pg 1047
Video Impressions, pg 1055
WEEK TV, pg 1063
Winter Productions, pg 1068

INDIANA

AVA Productions, pg 798
Digital Rain LLC, pg 847
Road Pictures, pg 997

KANSAS

KAKE-TV, pg 907

LOUISIANA

Moxie Media, pg 948

MARYLAND

CPR MultiMedia Solutions, pg 837
dbF a Media Company, pg 844
The Image Generators, pg 895
Kramer Communications Video Production, pg 913

MASSACHUSETTS

Green Mountain Post Films (GMP), pg 882
Penfield Productions Ltd, pg 971

MICHIGAN

Digi Sign Design LLC, pg 847
K&R All Media Productions Inc, pg 908
K&R's Recording Studios Inc, pg 908
Universal Images, pg 1049

MINNESOTA

Aggressive Records Audio Duplication LLC, pg 778
Big Event Productions LLC, pg 807
GMI Productions, pg 879
House of Cinemagraphics, pg 891
Master Communications Group, pg 933

MISSOURI

Fambrough & Associates Inc, pg 865
Hardcastle Films & Video, pg 885

MONTANA

North Country Media Group, pg 959

NEVADA

DVDs4Less, pg 854
Encore Productions Inc, pg 861
JCS Video Productions, pg 904

NEW HAMPSHIRE

Chip Taylor Communications LLC, pg 1032

NEW JERSEY

Broadcast Center Studios, pg 813
CFP Video Productions Inc, pg 823
DWJ Television, pg 854
Euro-Pacific Film & Video Productions Inc, pg 863
Half Moon Video Productions, pg 883
Laurel Video Productions, pg 916
MediaNow, pg 938
MIB Mediaworks, pg 941
Optisonics Productions, pg 965
Producer East Productions, pg 983
Public Eye Productions, pg 987
Bill Quinn Productions, pg 989
Suede Interactive, pg 1027
VCSvideo, pg 1052

NEW MEXICO

Production Outfitters, pg 984

NEW YORK

aurora productions, pg 797
Blue Barn Pictures Inc, pg 809
Brooklyn Films, pg 814
Charlex Inc, pg 824

Test Commercial Rentals

Theatrical Short Distributors

Theatrical Short Producers

PROGRAMMING — VIDEO

Theatrical Short Producers (continued)

MARYLAND

Absolute Hollywood, pg 772
Richard Chisolm Cinematography, pg 825
CPR MultiMedia Solutions, pg 837
dbF a Media Company, pg 844
Kramer Communications Video Production, pg 913

MASSACHUSETTS

Green Mountain Post Films (GMP), pg 882
Heliotrope Studios, pg 887
Home Inc, pg 890
Preston Productions Inc, pg 981

MICHIGAN

Digi Sign Design LLC, pg 847
K&R All Media Productions Inc, pg 908
K&R's Recording Studios Inc, pg 908

MINNESOTA

Aggressive Records Audio Duplication LLC, pg 778
House of Cinemagraphics, pg 891

MISSOURI

Cable Films & Video, pg 816
Fambrough & Associates Inc, pg 865

NEVADA

Aardvark Video & Media Productions, pg 772
Encore Productions Inc, pg 861

NEW HAMPSHIRE

Apertura, pg 788
Chip Taylor Communications LLC, pg 1032

NEW JERSEY

Broadcast Center Studios, pg 813
CFP Video Productions Inc, pg 823
Half Moon Video Productions, pg 883
MIB Mediaworks, pg 941
Optisonics Productions, pg 965
Producer East Productions, pg 983
Bill Quinn Productions, pg 989

NEW YORK

Air Sea Land Productions Inc (ASL), pg 779
aurora productions, pg 797
Big Fish Productions Inc, pg 807
Blue Barn Pictures Inc, pg 809
Brooklyn Films, pg 814
Buzzco Associates Inc, pg 816
Castillo Theater, pg 820
dM works, pg 849
HB-Content, pg 886
Kinetic Arts, pg 911
Neal Marshad Productions, pg 931
MRG Productions Inc, pg 948
Shelly Palmer Production, pg 968
Peckham Productions Inc, pg 970
Third World Newsreel/Camera News Inc, pg 1039
VIEW Inc (Video International Entertainment World Inc), pg 1058

NORTH CAROLINA

The Communications Group Inc, pg 833
Crystal Pictures Inc, pg 840

OHIO

Advent Media Inc, pg 778
Creative Technology, pg 838
R&B Communications Inc, pg 991
Vista Color Imaging Inc, pg 1059

OKLAHOMA

Institute for Teaching & Learning Excellence (ITLE), pg 899

OREGON

Ideascape Inc, pg 894

PENNSYLVANIA

Bang Pictures, pg 802
FMP Media Solutions Inc, pg 870
Innovision Media Group, pg 899
Kensington Falls Animation, pg 909
Muderick Media, pg 949
Production Masters Inc (PMI), pg 984

RHODE ISLAND

Sound-FX-Design, pg 1017

TENNESSEE

American Blackguard Inc, pg 784
Continental Film, pg 835

TEXAS

Cerutti Productions Inc, pg 823
Horizon Film + Video Productions, pg 891
Mediaforce Productions, pg 937
Omega Productions, pg 962
Stage Directions, pg 1022

VIRGINIA

CACI Productions Group, pg 816
Gingerbread Productions, pg 878
Limelight Communications Inc, pg 921
Metro Productions, pg 939

WASHINGTON

Bennett-Watt HD Productions Inc, pg 805
Intermedia Inc, pg 900

WISCONSIN

5th Floor Recording Co, pg 867
Wisconsin Public Television, pg 1068

WYOMING

Bridger Productions Inc, pg 812

ALBERTA

HBW Entertainment Inc, pg 886

BRITISH COLUMBIA

Image Media Farm, pg 895

ONTARIO

Doomsday Studios Ltd, pg 850
GAPC (General Assembly Production Centre), pg 875
Image Video Services & Productions, pg 895
RB Productions, pg 992

QUEBEC

Kerrigan Productions Inc, pg 910
Les Productions Via Le Monde (Daniel Bertolino) Inc, pg 985

SASKATCHEWAN

plan9films, pg 976

Theatrical Short Rentals

CALIFORNIA

Auslender Productions/Celestial Images, pg 797
Direct Cinema Ltd Inc, pg 848
Point of View Productions, pg 977
Visual Communications - Southern California Asian American Studies Central Inc, pg 1059

GEORGIA

On-Line Productions, pg 963

MICHIGAN

Digi Sign Design LLC, pg 847

MISSOURI

Cable Films & Video, pg 816

NEW YORK

Circulating Film & Video Library, pg 828
Kino International Corp, pg 911
Third World Newsreel/Camera News Inc, pg 1039
VIEW Inc (Video International Entertainment World Inc), pg 1058

NORTH CAROLINA

Crystal Pictures Inc, pg 840

ONTARIO

Doomsday Studios Ltd, pg 850

QUEBEC

Les Productions Via Le Monde (Daniel Bertolino) Inc, pg 985

Training Program Distributors

ARIZONA

Rodeo Video Inc, pg 998
Valley of the Sun Publishing Co, pg 1051
Video Learning Library, pg 1055

ARKANSAS

Mullikin Agency, pg 949

CALIFORNIA

Academy Savant, pg 773
Backstage Pass Entertainment Inc, pg 801
Barbosa Video Services, pg 802
Bennett Media Corp, pg 805
California Language Laboratories, pg 817
Cavalcade Productions Inc, pg 821
Deja View Video, pg 845
Direct Cinema Ltd Inc, pg 848
Discovery Education - Los Angeles, pg 848
Forte Productions, pg 871
Golden State Dance Teachers Association (GSDTA), pg 880
Increase Video/Silver Mine Video, pg 897
Jossey-Bass, pg 906
Kantola Productions LLC, pg 908
Learning Communications LLC, pg 917
MarVista Entertainment Inc, pg 933
Medcom Inc, pg 936
Moose School Productions, pg 946
New & Unique Videos™, pg 955
ODC Publishing, pg 961
Pacific Media, pg 967
People Skills International, pg 972
Captain J Charles Plumb, pg 977
Pyramid Media, pg 987
QCI International, pg 988
Revelli, pg 995
Russ InVision Co/AbridgeClub.com, pg 1001
Semiconductor Services, pg 1006
SevenStar Communications, pg 1007
Theatre Arts Video Library, pg 1038
TMW Media Group, pg 1041
University of Southern California, pg 1050
White Lotus Foundation, pg 1065
The Wine Appreciation Guild Ltd, pg 1067

COLORADO

Inferno Film Productions LLC, pg 897
InJoy Birth & Parenting Education, pg 898
Jeppesen, pg 905
National Institute for Trial Advocacy (NITA), pg 953

CONNECTICUT

Crossroads Video, pg 840

DELAWARE

University Media Services, pg 1049

DISTRICT OF COLUMBIA

American Chemical Society (ACS), pg 784

FLORIDA

ACE Video Resources Software, pg 774
Psychological Assessment Resources Inc (PAR), pg 987
ThirdWave Learning Inc, pg 1039

GEORGIA

LYRASIS, pg 927
On-Line Productions, pg 963
Thompson-Mitchell & Associates Inc, pg 1039

HAWAII

Source School of Tantra Yoga Inc, pg 1019

Training Program Producers

PROGRAMMING — VIDEO

Training Program Producers (continued)

CALIFORNIA (continued)

The Media Staff Inc, pg 937
Mist Media Inc, pg 944
Moose School Productions, pg 946
New & Unique Videos™, pg 955
New Circuit Films LLC, pg 955
Nolte Media, pg 958
ODC Publishing, pg 961
On-Trax Inc, pg 963
Pacific Media, pg 967
Panorama Productions, pg 968
Penrose Productions, pg 972
PM Productions, pg 977
Pyramid Media, pg 987
QCI International, pg 988
QRS Software Services, pg 988
Dick Reizner Film & Video, pg 994
RetinaVision Productions, pg 995
Revelli, pg 995
Glenn Roland Films, pg 998
Russ InVision Co/AbridgeClub.com, pg 1001
SBS Productions, pg 1003
SevenStar Communications, pg 1007
SNAP, pg 1014
Staylor-Made Communications Inc, pg 1024
Still N'Motion, pg 1025
The Studio Center, pg 1026
Tam Communications Inc, pg 1031
Theatre Arts Video Library, pg 1038
TMW Media Group, pg 1041
Total Media Group, pg 1042
TVA Productions, pg 1046
Twin Peaks Creative, pg 1047
University of Southern California, pg 1050
Videografix LLC, pg 1057
Videolady, pg 1057
Videowerks, pg 1057
Vineyard Video & Photography, pg 1058
Visions Plus, pg 1058
WalkerVision Interarts, pg 1061
Wavemaker Media Design, pg 1062
West Coast Projections Inc, pg 1063
Zamacona Productions, pg 1073

COLORADO

Paul L Anderson Productions Inc, pg 786
Daylight Productions & Rentals, pg 844
Flashback Media Productions, pg 869
Inferno Film Productions LLC, pg 897
InJoy Birth & Parenting Education, pg 898
National Institute for Trial Advocacy (NITA), pg 953
Rocky Mountain Audio/Video Productions Inc, pg 998
Transtar Entertainment Co Inc, pg 1043
Visual Communications Group Inc, pg 1059

CONNECTICUT

ACM Productions Ltd, pg 774
Applebox Studio, pg 788
Biomedical Media Communications Dept, pg 807
Business & Legal Reports Inc, pg 815
Cine-Med Inc, pg 826
Crossroads Video, pg 840
Fox Connecticut, pg 872
The Gary-Paul Agency, pg 875
Geomatrix Productions, pg 877
Ironik Design & Post, pg 902
MCC Films, pg 935
Moving Pictures, pg 947
P&P Studios Inc, pg 968
Video Production Associates Inc, pg 1056

DELAWARE

University Media Services, pg 1049

DISTRICT OF COLUMBIA

American Chemical Society (ACS), pg 784
O'Keefe Communications Inc, pg 961
Yellow Cat Productions Inc, pg 1072

FLORIDA

Accel Video Productions, pg 773
Accord Productions, pg 773
ACE Video Resources Software, pg 774
Astoria Communications Inc, pg 792
Blackburst Entertainment, pg 808
Capital Communications Inc, pg 819
Civins Productions Inc, pg 828
Communications Concepts Inc (CCI), pg 833
CopShopMiami.com, pg 836
Courter Films LLC, pg 837
Eastern Video, pg 856
Easy Edit Video Inc, pg 856
Ed Ethridge Productions Inc, pg 863
Gulf Coast Audio Visual Producers Inc, pg 883
Home Shopping Network (HSN), pg 890
Jordan Klein Film & Video (JKFV), pg 906
Media Entertainment Inc, pg 936
National Teleproductions Inc, pg 953
Paradise Video & Film, pg 969
Roger Scruggs Films, pg 1005
Skystorm Productions, pg 1013
Sound & Vision Communications Inc, pg 1016
Sunfire Communications Inc, pg 1028
Sunrise Studios, pg 1028
Teach America Corp, pg 1033
Tel-Air Interests Inc, pg 1035
Tight Line Productions, pg 1040
Tricycle Studios, pg 1044
Universal Studios Florida® Production Group, pg 1049
Mike Vasilinda Productions Inc, pg 1052
Video Techniques Inc, pg 1056

GEORGIA

Beachwood Productions, pg 804
COMPRO Productions Inc, pg 834
Continental Film & Video, pg 835
ECG Productions, pg 856
Georgia-Pacific Television & Photography, pg 877
Guerrilla Productions LLC, pg 883
Myriad Productions, pg 951
On-Line Productions, pg 963
Showcase Photo & Video, pg 1009
Thompson-Mitchell & Associates Inc, pg 1039

HAWAII

Hyperspective Studios Inc, pg 893
Source School of Tantra Yoga Inc, pg 1019
TV Juice Productions Inc, pg 1046

IDAHO

Brad Shaw Productions Inc, pg 1008
Wide Eye Productions, pg 1066

ILLINOIS

ABSA Productions Inc, pg 772
Accenture, pg 773
Airways Digital Media, pg 779
Audio Visual Services Corp, pg 796
Beatty TeleVisual Productions, pg 804
CCH Continuing Education, pg 821
CCore Media Inc, pg 821
The Chicago Production Center, pg 825
Chicago Satellite & Video, pg 825
Comtech Multimedia Marketing, pg 834
Extraordinary Demos, pg 864
Film Police, pg 867
1st Financial Training Services Inc, pg 868
IV Media Resources, pg 903
Major Media Productions Inc, pg 929
Manning Productions, pg 930
MIGHTYbYTES Inc, pg 942
National Safety Council (NSC), pg 953
Nightingale-Conant Corp, pg 957
The Pepper Group, pg 972
The Prairie Production Group, pg 980
Production Craft Inc, pg 984
PSAV® Presentation Services (Hotel Services Division), pg 987
QuickSet International Inc, pg 989
RADMAR Inc, pg 990
Richter Studios, pg 996
Roadworthy Image Magnification, pg 998
SCI Television Productions LLC, pg 1004
Southern Illinois University, pg 1019
Sparkfactor, pg 1019
20/20 Communications Inc, pg 1047
Video I-D Teleproductions Inc, pg 1055
Video Impressions, pg 1055
WEEK TV, pg 1063
Winter Productions, pg 1068

INDIANA

Advanced Media Integration, pg 777
AVA Productions, pg 798
Covenant Productions®, pg 837
Digital Rain LLC, pg 847
Lighthouse Photo & Video Productions, pg 920
PentaVision Communications Inc, pg 972

IOWA

Kirkwood Community College, pg 911
The Production House, pg 984

KENTUCKY

Idle Minds Productions Inc, pg 894
KET The Kentucky Network, pg 910
The Media Collaboratory, pg 936
Media Resources, pg 937
Northern Kentucky University, pg 959
Prosper Media Group Inc, pg 986

LOUISIANA

Digital FX Inc, pg 847
Launch Media, pg 916
Louisiana State University Health Sciences Center - Shreveport, pg 925
Moxie Media, pg 948

MAINE

WGME-TV, pg 1065

MARYLAND

Adventure Productions LLC, pg 778
The Ahern Group, pg 779
CAS Video Productions, pg 820
Richard Chisolm Cinematography, pg 825
CPR MultiMedia Solutions, pg 837
dbF a Media Company, pg 844
The Image Generators, pg 895
Kramer Communications Video Production, pg 913
Library Video Network (LVN), pg 920
Media Dimensions Inc, pg 936
Mobile-Video Productions Inc, pg 944
Quality Film & Video, pg 988

MASSACHUSETTS

Award Productions, pg 800
CommCreative, pg 832
Commonwealth Films Inc, pg 832
Emergency Film Group, pg 860
Enterprise Media LLC, pg 861
Green Mountain Post Films (GMP), pg 882
Home Inc, pg 890
Inter-Media Electronics, pg 899
Northern Light Productions, pg 959
Penfield Productions Ltd, pg 971
TVN-The Video Network, pg 1046
Veritech Corp, pg 1053
VideoLink Inc, pg 1057
WVP Boston, pg 1071

MICHIGAN

Benjamin Creative Productions, pg 805
Digi Sign Design LLC, pg 847
K&R All Media Productions Inc, pg 908
K&R's Recording Studios Inc, pg 908
Lawrence Productions Inc, pg 917
Maritz Performance Improvement Co, pg 931
Prakken Publications Inc, pg 980
The Program Source International, pg 985
Resource Development Co LLC, pg 995
Society of Manufacturing Engineers (SME), pg 1015
TGA Recording Co, pg 1038
Universal Images, pg 1049
VMS Inc, pg 1060

MINNESOTA

Aggressive Records Audio Duplication LLC, pg 778
Big Event Productions LLC, pg 807
GMI Productions, pg 879
House of Cinemagraphics, pg 891
JIST Publishing, pg 905
Live Spark Inc, pg 923
Master Communications Group, pg 933
Media Loft Inc, pg 937
MultiMedia, pg 950
Service Quality Institute, pg 1007
Whole Person Associates Inc, pg 1066
Worthwhile Films, pg 1070

MISSISSIPPI

Dollarhide Film Inc, pg 850

MISSOURI

Annenberg Learner, pg 787
Audio-VideoGraphics Inc, pg 795
Communitronics Corp, pg 833
Fambrough & Associates Inc, pg 865
Hardcastle Films & Video, pg 885
The Phoenix Learning Group Inc, pg 974

MONTANA

North Country Media Group, pg 959

NEBRASKA

B & B Video Productions Inc, pg 801
Dog & Pony Productions Inc, pg 850
Envision Communications Inc, pg 861
Rainbow Video Productions Inc, pg 991

NEVADA

Aardvark Video & Media Productions, pg 772
DVDs4Less, pg 854
Encore Productions Inc, pg 861
HDTV Productions Inc, pg 886
JCS Video Productions, pg 904
Tanglewood Productions, pg 1031

NEW HAMPSHIRE

Apertura, pg 788
Channell One Video, pg 824
Chip Taylor Communications LLC, pg 1032
The Troupe, pg 1045

NEW JERSEY

Broadcast Center Studios, pg 813
CFP Video Productions Inc, pg 823
Color Leasing Studios, pg 831
DWJ Television, pg 854
Euro-Pacific Film & Video Productions Inc, pg 863
Half Moon Video Productions, pg 883
Laurel Video Productions, pg 916
MIB Mediaworks, pg 941
Midnight Media Group Inc, pg 942
Ray Mueller Productions, pg 949
Optisonics Productions, pg 965
Producer East Productions, pg 983
Public Eye Productions, pg 987
Bill Quinn Productions, pg 989
Reider Photography & Video Productions, pg 994
Selden Associates, pg 1006
Shamrock Communications, pg 1008
Suede Interactive, pg 1027
Telemanagement Resources International Inc (TRI), pg 1036
Telequest Inc, pg 1036
TimeSteps Productions Inc, pg 1041
VCSvideo, pg 1052
Video Ideas Productions, pg 1055

NEW MEXICO

Michael Dunn Productions, pg 853
Production Outfitters, pg 984
Uncharted Country Publishing, pg 1048

NEW YORK

American Management Association®, pg 784
Artistic Video, pg 791
aurora productions, pg 797
BC Video Inc, pg 803
Blue Barn Pictures Inc, pg 809
Broad Street Inc, pg 812
Buzzco Associates Inc, pg 816
Cohn Creative Group LLC, pg 831
dM works, pg 849
Karen Frankel Productions, pg 872
Guidance Associates Inc Center for Humanities, pg 883
Guilford Publications, pg 883
Havas Worldwide, pg 886
HB-Content, pg 886
Image Makers of Pittsford/Image Maker Productions, pg 895
Interactive International Inc, pg 899
Ketchum Pleon Change, pg 910
L A Bruell Inc, pg 914
LightHouse Films, pg 920
Neal Marshad Productions, pg 931
Mastervision Inc, pg 933
Mood Creations Ltd, pg 946
MRG Productions Inc, pg 948
MRM Worldwide, pg 948
MRY, pg 949
News Broadcast Network, pg 956
Northeast Video Productions Inc, pg 959
Shelly Palmer Production, pg 968
Pat Kogan Productions Inc, pg 970
Peckham Productions Inc, pg 970
PrimaLux Video Inc, pg 982
PrimeLight Productions Inc, pg 982
Shopware, pg 1009
Suggs Media Productions Inc, pg 1028
TeleTime Productions, pg 1036
Tobin Productions Inc, pg 1041
Video Aided Instruction Inc, pg 1054
Video Catalogue Co Inc, pg 1054
Videograf, pg 1057
Alan Weiss Productions, pg 1063
Willow Mixed Media Inc, pg 1067
WNET/NET TELECON, pg 1069

NORTH CAROLINA

All Pro Media Inc, pg 780
Pat Appleson Studios Inc, pg 788
J Arnold Productions Inc, pg 790
Bill Barnes Video Productions LLC, pg 803
The Communications Group Inc, pg 833
Do It Yourself Inc - DIY Video Corp, pg 849
Eli Research Group, pg 859
Horizon Video Productions Inc, pg 891
Image Associates Inc, pg 894
Kino Mountain Productions LLC, pg 911
LCW Productions LLC, pg 917
Media Consultants Inc, pg 936
Moving Pictures, pg 948
NASCAR Media Group LLC, pg 952
PACE Worldwide, pg 966
Unifour Productions Inc, pg 1048

OHIO

Advent Media Inc, pg 778
Russ Beckner Pictures, pg 804
CET, pg 823
Clear Choice Creative Corp, pg 829
Commercial Video, pg 832
Creative Technology, pg 838
Cuyahoga Community College Media Center, pg 841
EDR Media LLC, pg 857
Electronic Vision Inc (EV), pg 859
Image Video Teleproductions Inc, pg 895
Lyon Video Inc, pg 927
MainSail Production Services Inc, pg 929
R&B Communications Inc, pg 991
Shelburne Films, pg 1008
South-Western Publishing Co, pg 1019
Take 1 Media Services, pg 1031
VGI Productions, pg 1053
Vista Color Imaging Inc, pg 1059

OKLAHOMA

University of Oklahoma Academic Media & Digital Services, pg 1050

OREGON

A KTVA Production LLC, pg 771
Creative Media Development, pg 838
Ideascape Inc, pg 894
International Loving Touch Foundation Inc, pg 901
InterVision Media, pg 902
KPDX-TV Production Center, pg 913
Medifecta Healthcare Training, pg 938
Memory Lane Videos, pg 938
Production West, pg 985

PENNSYLVANIA

AiH Group Inc, pg 779
American Law Institute Continuing Legal Education (ALICLE), pg 784
Audio Visual Communications Inc, pg 795
Beholder Productions Inc, pg 804
Bergwall Productions Inc, pg 805
FMP Media Solutions Inc, pg 870
Fusion Brand Experiences, pg 874
Goodman Associates Inc, pg 880
Innovision Media Group, pg 899
JPL, pg 906
Kensington Falls Animation, pg 909
Main Point Productions, pg 929
Muderick Media, pg 949
Panta Rhei Media Inc, pg 968
Pemcor LLC, pg 971
Production Masters Inc (PMI), pg 984
The Fred Rogers Co, pg 998
S I Video Sales Group, pg 1001
Video Communication Productions Inc, pg 1054
Video/Film Associates, pg 1055
The Videohouse Inc, pg 1057
Videosmith Inc, pg 1057
Visual Sound Inc, pg 1059

RHODE ISLAND

Sound-FX-Design, pg 1017

SOUTH CAROLINA

Encore Video Productions, pg 861
Stages Video Productions, pg 1023
Venture Media, pg 1052

TENNESSEE

American Blackguard Inc, pg 784
Continental Film, pg 835
Jaguar Productions, pg 903
Marine Geographic, pg 931
Memphis Communications Corp, pg 938
Paradigm Marketing & Creative, pg 969
Running Pony Productions LLC, pg 1000
Scripps Networks, pg 1005
Stage Post, pg 1022
Russ Sturgeon Productions/RSVP, pg 1027

TEXAS

Alpha Video Productions, pg 782
AMS Pictures, pg 786
Biway Media, pg 808
Castleview Productions, pg 821
Cerutti Productions Inc, pg 823
CEV Multimedia Ltd, pg 823
Chalk Dust Co, pg 823
Communication Arts Multimedia Inc, pg 832
Countdown Productions Inc, pg 837
Critical Information Network, pg 839
Dub King, pg 853
Dykeman Associates Inc, pg 854
The Editing Co, pg 857
Epic Software Group Inc, pg 862
Horizon Film + Video Productions, pg 891
J&S Audio Visual Inc, pg 904
Language Plus Inc, pg 916
Marx InDigital, pg 933
Mediaforce Productions, pg 937
Earl Miller Productions Inc, pg 943
Julye Newlin Productions Inc, pg 956
Omega Productions, pg 962
Omni Intercommunications Inc, pg 962
Phil Lights, pg 973
R&O Studios, pg 991
Richie Media Productions LLC, pg 996
Romar Learning, pg 999
South Coast Film & Video, pg 1019
Sportsmen on Film Inc, pg 1021
Stage Directions, pg 1022
Tecfilms Inc, pg 1033
Telemetrics International, pg 1036
University of Texas at Austin - Petroleum Extension Service, pg 1050

UTAH

K-SAR Video & DVD Productions, pg 907

VERMONT

Dialect Accent Specialists Inc, pg 846
Perceptions Inc, pg 973
Wilson McLeran Inc, pg 1067

PROGRAMMING — VIDEO

Training Program Producers (continued)

VIRGINIA

American Counseling Association, pg 784
CACI Productions Group, pg 816
CALIBRE, pg 816
CDR Communications Inc, pg 822
Cinebar Productions Inc, pg 826
Coastal Training Technologies Corp, pg 831
Computer Sciences Corp, pg 834
Creative Video of Washington Inc, pg 839
D&B Television & Video Productions Inc, pg 842
Gingerbread Productions, pg 878
ITC Learning LLC, pg 903
Limelight Communications Inc, pg 921
Metro Productions, pg 939
Microtraining LLC, pg 942
National Association of Elementary School Principals (NAESP), pg 952
National Media Services Inc, pg 953
Rocktown Media, pg 998
Video Solutions, pg 1056
WETA Production Center, pg 1064

WASHINGTON

Adams Creative & Production Services, pg 775
Bennett-Watt HD Productions Inc, pg 805
Global Net Productions Inc, pg 879
Hamilton Studio, pg 884
Intermedia Inc, pg 900
Media Resources Inc, pg 937
North-by-Northwest Productions, pg 958
Sparkworks Media, pg 1019
White Rain Films Ltd, pg 1065

WEST VIRGINIA

Altruist Media LLC, pg 783
Blackwater Video Productions, pg 808
Sweetsong Productions, pg 1029

WISCONSIN

AVS Group, pg 800
Equiservices Publishing, pg 862
5th Floor Recording Co, pg 867
Grassland Media Inc, pg 881
Logan Productions Inc, pg 924
Media Communications Association-International (MCA-I), pg 936
Meridian Studios, pg 939
Midland Video Productions Inc, pg 942
ProVideo, pg 986
Rucinski & Reetz Communications LLC, pg 1000
USAV Group Inc, pg 1050
Video Wisconsin Inc, pg 1056
Watts Communications Inc, pg 1062
Wisconsin Public Television, pg 1068

WYOMING

Bridger Productions Inc, pg 812

ALBERTA

Black Media Works, pg 808

BRITISH COLUMBIA

Image Media Farm, pg 895
Thompson Rivers University Open Learning, pg 1039
Triad Communications Ltd, pg 1044

NEWFOUNDLAND AND LABRADOR

Vidcraft Productions Ltd, pg 1054

ONTARIO

ADS Media, pg 777
GAPC (General Assembly Production Centre), pg 875
Image Video Services & Productions, pg 895
Iron Ring Communications Ltd, pg 902
JFB Communications, pg 905
Purefire Communications Inc, pg 987
RB Productions, pg 992
Video Excellence Productions, pg 1055

QUEBEC

Kerrigan Productions Inc, pg 910

SASKATCHEWAN

plan9films, pg 976

Training Program Rentals

CALIFORNIA

Cavalcade Productions Inc, pg 821
Direct Cinema Ltd Inc, pg 848
Jossey-Bass, pg 906
Learning Communications LLC, pg 917
Medcom Inc, pg 936
Semiconductor Services, pg 1006
University of Southern California, pg 1050

DELAWARE

University Media Services, pg 1049

ILLINOIS

1st Financial Training Services Inc, pg 868
National Safety Council (NSC), pg 953

MASSACHUSETTS

Commonwealth Films Inc, pg 832
Emergency Film Group, pg 860
Enterprise Media LLC, pg 861

MICHIGAN

Digi Sign Design LLC, pg 847

MINNESOTA

Service Quality Institute, pg 1007

MISSOURI

The Phoenix Learning Group Inc, pg 974

NEW JERSEY

Euro-Pacific Film & Video Productions Inc, pg 863

NEW YORK

BC Video Inc, pg 803
Interactive International Inc, pg 899

NORTH CAROLINA

Image Associates Inc, pg 894

VIRGINIA

Coastal Training Technologies Corp, pg 831

WASHINGTON

Intermedia Inc, pg 900

Travelog Distributors

ALASKA

Alaska Video Postcards Inc, pg 779
Skyriver Films, pg 1013

ARIZONA

Video Learning Library, pg 1055

CALIFORNIA

Direct Cinema Ltd Inc, pg 848
ECONEWS (Environmental Television Series) & (Environmental Directions Radio Series), pg 856
eFootage LLC, pg 858
Em Gee Film Library, pg 860
411 Video Information, pg 872
Glenn Video Vistas Ltd, pg 878
Global Village Productions, pg 879
Global Village Stock Footage Library, pg 879
MarVista Entertainment Inc, pg 933
New & Unique Videos™, pg 955
Point Lobos Productions, pg 977
Melvin Powers Television Marketing, pg 979
TMW Media Group, pg 1041

COLORADO

Tatum Video, pg 1032

DISTRICT OF COLUMBIA

Biblical Archaeology Society (BAS), pg 806

FLORIDA

America By Air Stock Footage Library, pg 783
Distribution Video & Audio (DVA), pg 849
Global Video Distributors Inc, pg 879

GEORGIA

On-Line Productions, pg 963

ILLINOIS

ABSA Productions Inc, pg 772
Chicago Satellite & Video, pg 825
Film Ideas, pg 867
Moviecraft Inc, pg 947
Questar Inc, pg 989

IOWA

American Visions, pg 785

KENTUCKY

Horizon Films & Media LLC, pg 891
WaxWorks VideoWorks, pg 1063

MAINE

Down East Books, pg 851

MARYLAND

Recorded Books LLC, pg 993
RLJ Entertainment Inc, pg 997

MASSACHUSETTS

Penfield Productions Ltd, pg 971

MICHIGAN

Digi Sign Design LLC, pg 847
The Program Source International, pg 985

NEW HAMPSHIRE

Chip Taylor Communications LLC, pg 1032

NEW JERSEY

Ergo Media Inc, pg 862
Euro-Pacific Film & Video Productions Inc, pg 863
MIB Mediaworks, pg 941

NEW MEXICO

National Information Center for Educational Media (NICEM)/MediaSleuth, pg 952

NEW YORK

Irish Music Corp, pg 902
Janson Media, pg 904
Metropolitan Opera Guild, pg 940
MRG Productions Inc, pg 948
Random House Children's Books, pg 991
SISU Home Entertainment Inc, pg 1012
VIEW Inc (Video International Entertainment World Inc), pg 1058

NORTH CAROLINA

Baker & Taylor Inc, pg 801
Vide-O-Go/That's Infotainment!, pg 1054

OHIO

Shelburne Films, pg 1008

OREGON

Encounter Video Inc, pg 861
Wilderness Video, pg 1066

PENNSYLVANIA

Beholder Productions Inc, pg 804
CCI Communications Inc, pg 821
FMP Media Solutions Inc, pg 870
Karol Media Inc, pg 908
Library Video Company, pg 920
Movies Unlimited, pg 947

SOUTH CAROLINA

American Production Services LLC, pg 785

Travelog Producers

PROGRAMMING — VIDEO

Travelog Producers (continued)

NEW YORK (continued)

Videograf, pg 1057
VIEW Inc (Video International Entertainment World Inc), pg 1058

NORTH CAROLINA

Pat Appleson Studios Inc, pg 788
J Arnold Productions Inc, pg 790
The Communications Group Inc, pg 833
Kino Mountain Productions LLC, pg 911

OHIO

Advent Media Inc, pg 778
Creative Technology, pg 838
MainSail Production Services Inc, pg 929
R&B Communications Inc, pg 991
Shelburne Films, pg 1008
Treehaus Communications Inc, pg 1044
VGI Productions, pg 1053

OREGON

Encounter Video Inc, pg 861
KPDX-TV Production Center, pg 913
Odyssey Productions Inc, pg 961
Production West, pg 985
Rex, pg 995
Wilderness Video, pg 1066

PENNSYLVANIA

Bang Pictures, pg 802
Beholder Productions Inc, pg 804
CCI Communications Inc, pg 821
FMP Media Solutions Inc, pg 870
Innovision Media Group, pg 899
JPL, pg 906
Main Point Productions, pg 929
Muderick Media, pg 949
Production Masters Inc (PMI), pg 984
The Videohouse Inc, pg 1057

RHODE ISLAND

Sound-FX-Design, pg 1017

SOUTH CAROLINA

American Production Services LLC, pg 785
Stages Video Productions, pg 1023
Venture Media, pg 1052

TENNESSEE

American Blackguard Inc, pg 784
Griffith Productions, pg 882
Marine Geographic, pg 931
Running Pony Productions LLC, pg 1000
Scripps Networks, pg 1005

TEXAS

Cerutti Productions Inc, pg 823
Communication Arts Multimedia Inc, pg 832
Educational Video Network, pg 857
Horizon Film + Video Productions, pg 891
Mediaforce Productions, pg 937
Earl Miller Productions Inc, pg 943
Julye Newlin Productions Inc, pg 956
Omega Productions, pg 962
South Coast Film & Video, pg 1019
Sportsmen on Film Inc, pg 1021
Stage Directions, pg 1022

VERMONT

Marlboro Film & Video Productions, pg 931
Perceptions Inc, pg 973

VIRGINIA

CACI Productions Group, pg 816
Cinebar Productions Inc, pg 826
D&B Television & Video Productions Inc, pg 842
Gingerbread Productions, pg 878
Limelight Communications Inc, pg 921
Metro Productions, pg 939
Rocktown Media, pg 998

WASHINGTON

Bennett-Watt HD Productions Inc, pg 805
Small World Productions Inc, pg 1013
Terra Productions LLC, pg 1037
White Rain Films Ltd, pg 1065

WISCONSIN

5th Floor Recording Co, pg 867
ProVideo, pg 986
Rucinski & Reetz Communications LLC, pg 1000
Wisconsin Public Television, pg 1068

WYOMING

Bridger Productions Inc, pg 812

BRITISH COLUMBIA

Image Media Farm, pg 895

NEWFOUNDLAND AND LABRADOR

Vidcraft Productions Ltd, pg 1054

ONTARIO

Canamedia Inc, pg 818
GAPC (General Assembly Production Centre), pg 875
Image Video Services & Productions, pg 895
Video Excellence Productions, pg 1055

QUEBEC

Kerrigan Productions Inc, pg 910

Travelog Rentals

ARIZONA

Video Learning Library, pg 1055

CALIFORNIA

Direct Cinema Ltd Inc, pg 848
ECONEWS (Environmental Television Series) & (Environmental Directions Radio Series), pg 856
Global Village Productions, pg 879

COLORADO

Tatum Video, pg 1032

MICHIGAN

Digi Sign Design LLC, pg 847

NEW JERSEY

Euro-Pacific Film & Video Productions Inc, pg 863

NEW YORK

VIEW Inc (Video International Entertainment World Inc), pg 1058

OREGON

Wilderness Video, pg 1066

VIRGINIA

Once Around, pg 963

Video Game Distributors

CALIFORNIA

Allied Artists International Inc, pg 781
Digital Media West, pg 847
MGM Home Video, pg 941
National Lampoon, pg 953

FLORIDA

Distribution Video & Audio (DVA), pg 849

KENTUCKY

WaxWorks VideoWorks, pg 1063

MARYLAND

Recorded Books LLC, pg 993

MINNESOTA

Aggressive Records Audio Duplication LLC, pg 778

NEW YORK

MRG Productions Inc, pg 948

TENNESSEE

Spring Arbor Distributors, pg 1022

WISCONSIN

Aylmer Press, pg 801

ONTARIO

Gesturetek, pg 877

Video Game Producers

CALIFORNIA

Allied Artists International Inc, pg 781
Animax, pg 787
Classic Images, pg 829
Cox Media, pg 837
Dogma Studios, pg 850
Gateways Books & Tapes, pg 876
ITV Productions, pg 903
Kavich Reynolds Productions Inc, pg 908
McCune Audio-Video-Lighting, pg 935
National Lampoon, pg 953
Opticomm-EMCORE, pg 964
Palardo Productions, pg 968
QRS Software Services, pg 988
Tigar Hare Studios, pg 1040
Total Media Group, pg 1042

CONNECTICUT

Fox Connecticut, pg 872

FLORIDA

Jordan Klein Film & Video (JKFV), pg 906
Tricycle Studios, pg 1044

GEORGIA

Beachwood Productions, pg 804
Guerrilla Productions LLC, pg 883

HAWAII

Hyperspective Studios Inc, pg 893

ILLINOIS

The Pepper Group, pg 972

MARYLAND

Absolute Hollywood, pg 772

MICHIGAN

K&R All Media Productions Inc, pg 908
Universal Images, pg 1049

MINNESOTA

Aggressive Records Audio Duplication LLC, pg 778
House of Cinemagraphics, pg 891

MISSOURI

Celebrities Productions, pg 822

NEVADA

Encore Productions Inc, pg 861

NEW HAMPSHIRE

The Troupe, pg 1045

NEW JERSEY

Optisonics Productions, pg 965
Outside The Box Interactive LLC, pg 966

NEW YORK

Lylofilm Productions, pg 926
MRG Productions Inc, pg 948
MRY, pg 949
Shelly Palmer Production, pg 968
R/GA, pg 990
Split Image Productions, pg 1021

NORTH CAROLINA

Pat Appleson Studios Inc, pg 788
Moving Pictures, pg 948

OHIO

Creative Technology, pg 838
Vista Color Imaging Inc, pg 1059

OREGON

InterVision Media, pg 902

PENNSYLVANIA

Innovision Media Group, pg 899
Muderick Media, pg 949

SOUTH CAROLINA

Venture Media, pg 1052

TEXAS

Omega Productions, pg 962
Romar Learning, pg 999

VIRGINIA

Advance Concepts Inc, pg 777
CACI Productions Group, pg 816

WISCONSIN

Aylmer Press, pg 801

BRITISH COLUMBIA

Credo Interactive Inc, pg 839

ONTARIO

Gesturetek, pg 877
RB Productions, pg 992

Video Game Rentals

Gesturetek, pg 877

Videocassette Distributors

ALABAMA

CMEInfo, pg 830

ARIZONA

Arizona Cine Equipment, pg 789
Arizona Public Media, pg 790
Mother Basilea Films, pg 947
Valley of the Sun Publishing Co, pg 1051
Video Learning Library, pg 1055

CALIFORNIA

Adolph Gasser Inc, pg 776
Ametron Audio/Video, pg 785
Les Blank Films Inc, pg 809
Blind Pig Records, pg 809
Cambridge Documentary Films Inc, pg 818
Cavalcade Productions Inc, pg 821
Coast Learning Systems, pg 830
Deja View Video, pg 845
Direct Cinema Ltd Inc, pg 848
Discovery Education - Los Angeles, pg 848
Eastman Corp, pg 856
Educational Technology Services (ETS), pg 857
Em Gee Film Library, pg 860
Forte Productions, pg 871
411 Video Information, pg 872
FXF Productions Inc, pg 874
Glenn Photo Supply, pg 878
Bruce Goldberg Inc, pg 880
Gordon Productions Inc, pg 880
Steven Halpern's Inner Peace Music, pg 884
Hay House Inc, pg 886
Health Education Services, pg 887
Increase Video/Silver Mine Video, pg 897
Ishtar Films, pg 902
Joyce Media Inc, pg 906
Krishnamurti Foundation of America, pg 913
Learning Communications LLC, pg 917
Live Wire Media, pg 923
Madera Video, pg 927
MarVista Entertainment Inc, pg 933
MGM Home Video, pg 941
monterey media inc, pg 945
Motion Picture Licensing Corp (MPLC), pg 947
Music World/Vocal Power School, pg 951
New & Unique Videos™, pg 955
Joseph Nicoletti Consulting-Promotion/California International Records/Global Village Records, pg 957
Nilgiri Press, pg 957
ODC Publishing, pg 961
Osho Viha Information Center & Book Distributors, pg 965
Pacific Media, pg 967
Palardo Productions, pg 968
Panorama Publishing Co, pg 968
Point Lobos Productions, pg 977
Point of View Productions, pg 977
Prime Cut Productions, pg 982
Regent Press Publishers & Printers, pg 994
Rhino Home Video, pg 996
RJ Video Productions, pg 997
Sea Studios Foundation, pg 1005
Shokus Video, pg 1009
Social Studies School Service, pg 1015
Sodanceabit, pg 1015
Theatre Arts Video Library, pg 1038
Universal Music Group, pg 1049
University of Southern California, pg 1050
Valley Media, pg 1051
Visual Communications - Southern California Asian American Studies Central Inc, pg 1059
Walt Disney Studio, pg 1061
Warner Home Video Inc, pg 1062
Western Instructional Television Inc, pg 1064
The Wine Appreciation Guild Ltd, pg 1067
The Writing Co, pg 1070
The Wyland Group, pg 1071

COLORADO

Gaiam Inc, pg 875
Greg Hensley Productions, pg 888
Meriwether Publishing Ltd, pg 939
Tatum Video, pg 1032

CONNECTICUT

Crossroads Video, pg 840
EagleVision Inc, pg 855
Ironik Design & Post, pg 902
Pictures of Record Inc, pg 975
Scholastic Library Publishing, pg 1004
The Taunton Press Inc, pg 1032
Twenty-Third Publications/Bayard, pg 1047

DELAWARE

So Smart Productions, pg 1015
University Media Services, pg 1049

DISTRICT OF COLUMBIA

Biblical Archaeology Society (BAS), pg 806
Durrin Productions Inc, pg 854
Grocery Manufacturers Association (GMA), pg 882
National Council of Churches, pg 952
Sano Videos, pg 1002

FLORIDA

Capital Communications Inc, pg 819
Distribution Video & Audio (DVA), pg 849
Global Video Distributors Inc, pg 879
Motion Image Group LLC, pg 947
Photomart Cine-Video Inc, pg 975

GEORGIA

American Association for Vocational Instructional Materials (AAVIM), pg 783
Audio Visual Resources Inc, pg 795
Dixie Theatre Service & Supply Co Inc, pg 849
First Cut Communications LLC, pg 868
Gingerbread Group, pg 878
School Media Associates LLC, pg 1004

IDAHO

Lagoon Video, pg 915

ILLINOIS

ABSA Productions Inc, pg 772
Britannica Film & Video, pg 812
CCore Media Inc, pg 821
Communications Corporation of America, pg 833
Encyclopaedia Britannica Inc, pg 861
Film Ideas, pg 867
Learning Seed, pg 917
Moviecraft Inc, pg 947
National Safety Council (NSC), pg 953
Nightingale-Conant Corp, pg 957
Research Press Co, pg 995
Sunburst Digital, pg 1028
Terra Nova Films Inc, pg 1037
Theosophical Publishing House, pg 1038

INDIANA

Agency for Instructional Technology (AIT), pg 778
Communication Ministries, pg 833
Educational Video Group Inc, pg 857
InterComm, pg 900
Lee Co Inc, pg 918
Our Sunday Visitor Inc, pg 966
Perennial Pictures Film Corp, pg 973

IOWA

Perfection Learning Corp, pg 973
Right Stuf Inc, pg 997

KANSAS

Day Star Productions, pg 844

KENTUCKY

American Recordable Media, pg 785
Media Resources, pg 937
National Geographic Learning, pg 952
WaxWorks VideoWorks, pg 1063

LOUISIANA

Great Chefs/Leisure Jazz Video, pg 881
Leisure Video, pg 918
Moxie Media, pg 948

MAINE

Headlight Audio Visual Inc, pg 887

MARYLAND

Crunch Bird Studios Inc, pg 840
The Cutting Corp, pg 841
Discovery Education - Silver Spring, pg 848
DSR Computer Technology Specialists Inc, pg 853
Human Circuit, pg 892
Library Video Network (LVN), pg 920
Milner-Fenwick Inc, pg 943
MMI Corp, pg 944
Nicholas P Pipino Associates Inc, pg 976
Sign Media Inc, pg 1011

MASSACHUSETTS

Emergency Film Group, pg 860
Green Mountain Post Films (GMP), pg 882
Pauline Books & Media, pg 970
Penfield Productions Ltd, pg 971
Video Express, pg 1055

MICHIGAN

Jack Van Impe Ministries International, pg 1051
Wayne State University Media Services, pg 1063

MINNESOTA

Aggressive Records Audio Duplication LLC, pg 778
Hazelden Publishing & Educational Services, pg 886

MISSOURI

Annenberg Learner, pg 787
Cable Films & Video, pg 816
Marsh Media, pg 931
Mosby Inc, pg 947
Phoenix/BFA/Coronet, pg 974
The Phoenix Learning Group Inc, pg 974
SOM Publishing Co, pg 1015
Swank Audio Visuals, pg 1029
Vedanta Society of St Louis, pg 1052

NEBRASKA

Leo Films, pg 919
The Recruiters Library, pg 993
Vision Maker Media, pg 1058

NEVADA

DVDs4Less, pg 854

NEW HAMPSHIRE

Channell One Video, pg 824
Frey Scientific, pg 873
Heinemann, pg 887
Chip Taylor Communications LLC, pg 1032

NEW JERSEY

Business Education Films, pg 815
Educational Impressions, pg 857
Lucerne Media, pg 925
Milestone Film & Video Inc, pg 943
A W Peller & Associates Inc, pg 971
Shanachie Entertainment Corp, pg 1008
John Wiley & Sons Inc, pg 1066

PROGRAMMING — VIDEO

Videocassette Distributors (continued)

NEW MEXICO

National Information Center for Educational Media (NICEM)/ MediaSleuth, pg 952
Uncharted Country Publishing, pg 1048

NEW YORK

ATA Trading Corp/Favorite TV Inc, pg 792
Benchmark Media, pg 805
Brooklyn Botanic Garden, pg 814
Campus Film Distributors Corp, pg 818
Circulating Film & Video Library, pg 828
Thomas Craven Film Corp, pg 837
DRG Records Inc, pg 852
Educational Activities Inc, pg 857
Educational Images Ltd, pg 857
Fanlight Productions, pg 865
Film-Makers Cooperative, pg 867
First Run Features, pg 869
Flash Electronics Inc, pg 869
French American Cultural Exchange (FACE), pg 873
Guidance Associates Inc Center for Humanities, pg 883
Guilford Publications, pg 883
Hallel Communications, pg 884
HB-Content, pg 886
Human Relations Media, pg 892
Icarus Film Inc, pg 893
Irish Music Corp, pg 902
Janus Films Inc, pg 904
Kino International Corp, pg 911
L & S Video Inc, pg 914
Live Oak Media, pg 923
Magnetic Music Publishing Co, pg 928
Maryknoll Productions, pg 933
Mastervision Inc, pg 933
MRG Productions Inc, pg 948
Richter Productions Inc, pg 996
The Fulton J Sheen Co Inc, pg 1008
SISU Home Entertainment Inc, pg 1012
Third World Newsreel/Camera News Inc, pg 1039
Timed Exposures Films, pg 1040
Tommy Boy Entertainment LLC, pg 1042
United Nations Department of Public Information-News & Media Division, pg 1048
Video Catalogue Co Inc, pg 1054
Videofashion Network, pg 1056
Visual Technologies Corp, pg 1060
White Buffalo Multimedia, pg 1065
WNET/NET TELECON, pg 1069
Women Make Movies Inc, pg 1069

NORTH CAROLINA

Baker & Taylor Inc, pg 801
Carolina Biological Supply Co, pg 820
Hart Inc, pg 885
Ladyslipper Inc, pg 915
Vide-O-Go/That's Infotainment!, pg 1054
World Wide Pictures Inc, pg 1070

NORTH DAKOTA

UND Television Center, pg 1048

OHIO

Curtis Inc, pg 841
Franciscan Media, pg 872
Griesinger Films LLC, pg 882
McGraw-Hill School Education Group, pg 935
Ohio State University Foreign Language Publications, pg 961
South-Western Publishing Co, pg 1019
Speakers Unlimited, pg 1020
Treehaus Communications Inc, pg 1044
VGI Productions, pg 1053
WOUB Public Media, pg 1070

OREGON

CNS Productions Inc, pg 830
InterVision Media, pg 902
The Keyboard Workshop, pg 910
Norman Beerger Productions, pg 958
Pacific International Enterprises Inc (PIE), pg 967
Wilderness Video, pg 1066

PENNSYLVANIA

Corinth Films Inc, pg 836
Discovery Education - South Burlington, pg 848
Dreambox Media Inc, pg 852
FMP Media Solutions Inc, pg 870
Himalayan Institute Audio/Video, pg 889
Karol Media Inc, pg 908
Library Video Company, pg 920
Lippincott Williams & Wilkins, pg 922
Rahlic Publishing Co, pg 990
Schlessinger Media, pg 1004
TRC Interactive Inc, pg 1044

TENNESSEE

Marine Geographic, pg 931
Randall House Publications, pg 991
Spring Arbor Distributors, pg 1022
Word Label Group, pg 1069

TEXAS

Astro Audio Visual, pg 792
Big Kids Productions Inc, pg 807
Dallas Learning Solutions, pg 842
db interactive Inc, pg 844
Educational Video Network, pg 857
Executive Development Systems, pg 864
Stage Directions, pg 1022
Texas Heart Institute Visual Communication Services, pg 1037

VERMONT

Dorothy Tod Films, pg 1041
University of Vermont, Instructional Television Dept, pg 1050
Wilson McLeran Inc, pg 1067

VIRGINIA

County Sales, pg 837
Microtraining LLC, pg 942
National Media Services Inc, pg 953
WETA Production Center, pg 1064

WASHINGTON

Bennett-Watt HD Productions Inc, pg 805
ChristianAnswers.Net™, pg 825
College of Nursing, Washington State University, pg 831
Intermedia Inc, pg 900
Ritchie's Perfect Press, pg 997
Victory Studios, pg 1054

WEST VIRGINIA

Focus on Animals, pg 870
Harpers Ferry Historical Association, pg 885

WISCONSIN

Aylmer Press, pg 801
Full Compass Systems, pg 874
NEWIST/CESA 7, pg 956
Wisconsin Public Television, pg 1068

BRITISH COLUMBIA

Thompson Rivers University Open Learning, pg 1039
Video In Studios/Video Out Distribution, pg 1055

ONTARIO

BBC Worldwide Canada Ltd, pg 803
Canadian Learning Co Inc, pg 818
Novalis, pg 959
Scholastic Canada Ltd, pg 1004
University of Toronto, Classroom Technology Support, pg 1050

QUEBEC

Les Productions Via Le Monde (Daniel Bertolino) Inc, pg 985
Whalley-Abbey Media Holdings Inc, pg 1065

Videocassette Producers

ALABAMA

CMEInfo, pg 830
Media Visions Inc, pg 937

ARIZONA

Arizona Public Media, pg 790
Phoenix VideoFilms®, pg 974
Valley of the Sun Publishing Co, pg 1051
Video Media Productions (VMP), pg 1055

ARKANSAS

Jones Film Video, pg 906
Live'N'Loud, pg 923
White Diamond Productions, pg 1065

CALIFORNIA

Access Video in Berkeley, pg 773
ACDC Audio CD & Cassette, pg 774
Barbosa Video Services, pg 802
Big Door, pg 807
Blind Pig Records, pg 809
Cambridge Documentary Films Inc, pg 818
Cavalcade Productions Inc, pg 821
Coast Learning Systems, pg 830
Custom Video Productions Inc, pg 841
Deja View Video, pg 845
Design Media, pg 845
Direct Cinema Ltd Inc, pg 848
Discovery Education - Los Angeles, pg 848
Dogma Studios, pg 850
Dolphin MultiMedia Inc, pg 850
Eastman Corp, pg 856
Educational Technology Services (ETS), pg 857
Em Gee Film Library, pg 860
Forte Productions, pg 871
411 Video Information, pg 872
FXF Productions Inc, pg 874
Gateways Books & Tapes, pg 876
Geddes Productions LLC, pg 876
Goal Productions, pg 879
Gold Standard Productions, pg 880
Bruce Goldberg Inc, pg 880
Gordon Productions Inc, pg 880
Steven Halpern's Inner Peace Music, pg 884
Havas Edge, pg 885
Hay House Inc, pg 886
Hope Productions, pg 891
Imageworks, pg 896
Increase Video/Silver Mine Video, pg 897
Ishtar Films, pg 902
ITV Productions, pg 903
Joyce Media Inc, pg 906
K2B2 Records, pg 907
The Kenwood Group, pg 909
KPBS TV FM-San Diego, pg 913
Krishnamurti Foundation of America, pg 913
KTVU-Retail Services, pg 914
Learning Communications LLC, pg 917
Live Wire Media, pg 923
Ludlow Media Solutions, pg 926
Lynch Communications, pg 926
Madera Video, pg 927
Main Street Media Inc, pg 929
Maximus Media Inc, pg 934
Media Magic, pg 937
MGM Home Video, pg 941
monterey media inc, pg 945
Music World/Vocal Power School, pg 951
New & Unique Videos™, pg 955
Nilgiri Press, pg 957
ODC Publishing, pg 961
On-Trax Inc, pg 963
Pacific Media, pg 967
Palardo Productions, pg 968
Panorama Productions, pg 968
Panorama Publishing Co, pg 968
Penrose Productions, pg 972
piXvfm, pg 976
PM Productions, pg 977
Point Lobos Productions, pg 977
Point of View Productions, pg 977
Prime Cut Productions, pg 982
Producers Group Ltd, pg 983
QRS Software Services, pg 988
Randolf Productions Inc, pg 991
Regent Press Publishers & Printers, pg 994
RetinaVision Productions, pg 995
Rhino Home Video, pg 996
Glenn Roland Films, pg 998
SBS Productions, pg 1003
Screen Door Entertainment Inc, pg 1005
Sea Studios Foundation, pg 1005
Shokus Video, pg 1009
SNAP, pg 1014
Sodanceabit, pg 1015
The Studio Center, pg 1026
Tam Communications Inc, pg 1031
Tele-Video Production Services (TVPS), pg 1036
Theatre Arts Video Library, pg 1038
Timestream Video, pg 1041
Total Media Group, pg 1042

PROGRAMMING — VIDEO

Videocassette Producers (continued)

NEW YORK (continued)

Greyfalcon House, pg 882
Guidance Associates Inc Center for Humanities, pg 883
Guilford Publications, pg 883
Hallel Communications, pg 884
HB-Content, pg 886
Human Relations Media, pg 892
Icontent, pg 893
International Digital Centre, pg 901
Kamen Entertainment Group Inc, pg 908
L A Bruell Inc, pg 914
L & S Video Inc, pg 914
Live Oak Media, pg 923
Long Island Video Enterprises Live Inc, pg 924
Magnetic Music Publishing Co, pg 928
Maryknoll Productions, pg 933
Mastervision Inc, pg 933
Jack Morton Worldwide, pg 946
MRG Productions Inc, pg 948
Shelly Palmer Production, pg 968
Pat Kogan Productions Inc, pg 970
Richter Productions Inc, pg 996
Peter Schleger Co, pg 1004
Scholastic Media, pg 1004
The Fulton J Sheen Co Inc, pg 1008
SISU Home Entertainment Inc, pg 1012
Split Image Productions, pg 1021
Suggs Media Productions Inc, pg 1028
Sunrise Media LLC, pg 1028
TeleTime Productions, pg 1036
Third World Newsreel/Camera News Inc, pg 1039
Tisch School of the Arts, pg 1041
Tommy Boy Entertainment LLC, pg 1042
United Nations Multimedia Resources Unit, pg 1048
Video Catalogue Co Inc, pg 1054
Videofashion Network, pg 1056
White Buffalo Multimedia, pg 1065
Zelman Studios Ltd, pg 1073

NORTH CAROLINA

Pat Appleson Studios Inc, pg 788
J Arnold Productions Inc, pg 790
Carolina Biological Supply Co, pg 820
The Communications Group Inc, pg 833
Moving Pictures, pg 948
Trailblazer Studios®, pg 1043

NORTH DAKOTA

UND Television Center, pg 1048

OHIO

CET, pg 823
Commercial Video, pg 832
Creative Technology, pg 838
Curtis Inc, pg 841
Cuyahoga Community College Media Center, pg 841
EDR Media LLC, pg 857
Franciscan Media, pg 872
Griesinger Films LLC, pg 882
Lyon Video Inc, pg 927
MainSail Production Services Inc, pg 929
Maslowski Productions, pg 933
McGraw-Hill School Education Group, pg 935
Musicol Recording, pg 951
R&B Communications Inc, pg 991
South-Western Publishing Co, pg 1019
Take 1 Media Services, pg 1031
VGI Productions, pg 1053
Vista Color Imaging Inc, pg 1059
WOUB Public Media, pg 1070

OKLAHOMA

University of Oklahoma Academic Media & Digital Services, pg 1050

OREGON

CNS Productions Inc, pg 830
Ideascape Inc, pg 894
InterVision Media, pg 902
The Keyboard Workshop, pg 910
KPDX-TV Production Center, pg 913
Norman Beerger Productions, pg 958
Odyssey Productions Inc, pg 961
Pacific International Enterprises Inc (PIE), pg 967
Rex, pg 995
Wilderness Video, pg 1066

PENNSYLVANIA

Argentine Productions Inc, pg 789
Audio Visual Communications Inc, pg 795
Discovery Education - South Burlington, pg 848
Dreambox Media Inc, pg 852
FMP Media Solutions Inc, pg 870
Fusion Brand Experiences, pg 874
Goodman Associates Inc, pg 880
Himalayan Institute Audio/Video, pg 889
Innovision Media Group, pg 899
JPL, pg 906
Lippincott Williams & Wilkins, pg 922
Main Point Productions, pg 929
Muderick Media, pg 949
Production Masters Inc (PMI), pg 984
Rahlic Publishing Co, pg 990
Schlessinger Media, pg 1004
Video/Film Associates, pg 1055
Visual Sound Inc, pg 1059

SOUTH CAROLINA

Stages Video Productions, pg 1023
Venture Media, pg 1052

TENNESSEE

Continental Film, pg 835
Jaguar Productions, pg 903
Marine Geographic, pg 931
Memphis Communications Corp, pg 938
Scripps Networks, pg 1005
UMCom Productions, pg 1048
WKPT-TV, pg 1068
Word Label Group, pg 1069

TEXAS

Communication Arts Multimedia Inc, pg 832
Dallas Learning Solutions, pg 842
db interactive Inc, pg 844
The Editing Co, pg 857
Educational Video Network, pg 857
J&S Audio Visual Inc, pg 904
Language Plus Inc, pg 916
Marx InDigital, pg 933
Mediaforce Productions, pg 937
Earl Miller Productions Inc, pg 943
Julye Newlin Productions Inc, pg 956
Romar Learning, pg 999
Stage Directions, pg 1022
Texas Heart Institute Visual Communication Services, pg 1037

UTAH

K-SAR Video & DVD Productions, pg 907

VERMONT

University of Vermont, Instructional Television Dept, pg 1050
Wilson McLeran Inc, pg 1067

VIRGINIA

BES Studios, pg 805
CACI Productions Group, pg 816
CALIBRE, pg 816
Creative Video of Washington Inc, pg 839
Limelight Communications Inc, pg 921
Microtraining LLC, pg 942
National Media Services Inc, pg 953
WETA Production Center, pg 1064

WASHINGTON

Bennett-Watt HD Productions Inc, pg 805
ChristianAnswers.Net™, pg 825
College of Nursing, Washington State University, pg 831
Intermedia Inc, pg 900
Ritchie's Perfect Press, pg 997
Victory Studios, pg 1054

WISCONSIN

Aylmer Press, pg 801
Excel Duplication Services, pg 864
Grassland Media Inc, pg 881
Meridian Studios, pg 939
NEWIST/CESA 7, pg 956
ProVideo, pg 986
University of Wisconsin-Oshkosh Radio-TV-Film Dept, pg 1050
USAV Group Inc, pg 1050
Video Wisconsin Inc, pg 1056
Watts Communications Inc, pg 1062
Wisconsin Public Television, pg 1068

WYOMING

Bridger Productions Inc, pg 812

ALBERTA

Black Media Works, pg 808

BRITISH COLUMBIA

Thompson Rivers University Open Learning, pg 1039
Triad Communications Ltd, pg 1044

NEWFOUNDLAND AND LABRADOR

Vidcraft Productions Ltd, pg 1054

ONTARIO

BBC Worldwide Canada Ltd, pg 803
Purefire Communications Inc, pg 987
RB Productions, pg 992
University of Toronto, Classroom Technology Support, pg 1050

QUEBEC

Les Productions Via Le Monde (Daniel Bertolino) Inc, pg 985
Whalley-Abbey Media Holdings Inc, pg 1065

SASKATCHEWAN

plan9films, pg 976

Videocassette Rentals

ARIZONA

Arizona Public Media, pg 790
Video Learning Library, pg 1055

CALIFORNIA

Ametron Audio/Video, pg 785
Auslender Productions/Celestial Images, pg 797
Cambridge Documentary Films Inc, pg 818
Cavalcade Productions Inc, pg 821
Direct Cinema Ltd Inc, pg 848
ECONEWS (Environmental Television Series) & (Environmental Directions Radio Series), pg 856
Educational Technology Services (ETS), pg 857
Learning Communications LLC, pg 917
Medcom Inc, pg 936
Palardo Productions, pg 968
Regent Press Publishers & Printers, pg 994
University of Southern California, pg 1050
Visual Communications - Southern California Asian American Studies Central Inc, pg 1059
Western Instructional Television Inc, pg 1064
The Wyland Group, pg 1071

CONNECTICUT

Crossroads Video, pg 840

DELAWARE

University Media Services, pg 1049

DISTRICT OF COLUMBIA

Durrin Productions Inc, pg 854
National Council of Churches, pg 952

GEORGIA

Staging Directions Inc, pg 1023

ILLINOIS

National Safety Council (NSC), pg 953
Research Press Co, pg 995
Terra Nova Films Inc, pg 1037

INDIANA

Agency for Instructional Technology (AIT), pg 778
InterComm, pg 900

MASSACHUSETTS

Documentary Educational Resources Inc, pg 850
Emergency Film Group, pg 860
Pauline Books & Media, pg 970

MICHIGAN

The Program Source International, pg 985
Wayne State University Media Services, pg 1063

MINNESOTA

Hazelden Publishing & Educational Services, pg 886

MISSOURI

Cable Films & Video, pg 816
Swank Audio Visuals, pg 1029

NEBRASKA

Vision Maker Media, pg 1058

NEW HAMPSHIRE

Chip Taylor Communications LLC, pg 1032

NEW JERSEY

Business Education Films, pg 815
Euro-Pacific Film & Video Productions Inc, pg 863

NEW MEXICO

National Information Center for Educational Media (NICEM)/MediaSleuth, pg 952

NEW YORK

Adwar Video, pg 778
Brooklyn Botanic Garden, pg 814
Circulating Film & Video Library, pg 828
Downtown Community Television Center (DCTV), pg 851
Fanlight Productions, pg 865
First Run Features, pg 869
Hallel Communications, pg 884
Icarus Film Inc, pg 893
Kino International Corp, pg 911
Richter Productions Inc, pg 996
Third World Newsreel/Camera News Inc, pg 1039

OHIO

Franciscan Media, pg 872

OREGON

The Keyboard Workshop, pg 910
Wilderness Video, pg 1066

PENNSYLVANIA

Penn State University MediaTech, pg 972
Rahlic Publishing Co, pg 990

VERMONT

University of Vermont, Instructional Television Dept, pg 1050

WASHINGTON

ChristianAnswers.Net™, pg 825

WISCONSIN

NEWIST/CESA 7, pg 956
Wisconsin Public Television, pg 1068

BRITISH COLUMBIA

Video In Studios/Video Out Distribution, pg 1055

QUEBEC

Les Productions Via Le Monde (Daniel Bertolino) Inc, pg 985

Videodisc Distributors

ARIZONA

Arizona Cine Equipment, pg 789

CALIFORNIA

Ametron Audio/Video, pg 785
Blind Pig Records, pg 809
Health Education Services, pg 887
Joyce Media Inc, pg 906
Medcom Inc, pg 936
MGM Home Video, pg 941
QRS Software Services, pg 988
Rhino Home Video, pg 996
Social Studies School Service, pg 1015
Valley Media, pg 1051
Warner Home Video Inc, pg 1062
The Writing Co, pg 1070

CONNECTICUT

Ironik Design & Post, pg 902
Scholastic Library Publishing, pg 1004

DELAWARE

University Media Services, pg 1049

FLORIDA

Global Video Distributors Inc, pg 879
Media Concepts Inc, pg 936

GEORGIA

School Media Associates LLC, pg 1004

ILLINOIS

Britannica Film & Video, pg 812
Encyclopaedia Britannica Inc, pg 861
Film Ideas, pg 867
Sunburst Digital, pg 1028

IOWA

Right Stuf Inc, pg 997

KENTUCKY

National Geographic Learning, pg 952

LOUISIANA

Great Chefs/Leisure Jazz Video, pg 881
Leisure Video, pg 918

MARYLAND

Discovery Education - Silver Spring, pg 848

MINNESOTA

Aggressive Records Audio Duplication LLC, pg 778

MISSOURI

Phoenix/BFA/Coronet, pg 974
The Phoenix Learning Group Inc, pg 974

NEW HAMPSHIRE

Academic & Campus Technology Services, pg 773

NEW JERSEY

Milestone Film & Video Inc, pg 943

NEW MEXICO

National Information Center for Educational Media (NICEM)/MediaSleuth, pg 952

NEW YORK

Thomas Craven Film Corp, pg 837
Film-Makers Cooperative, pg 867
Flash Electronics Inc, pg 869
Human Relations Media, pg 892
Janus Films Inc, pg 904
Mastervision Inc, pg 933
Visual Technologies Corp, pg 1060
Women Make Movies Inc, pg 1069

NORTH CAROLINA

Baker & Taylor Inc, pg 801
Carolina Biological Supply Co, pg 820
Hart Inc, pg 885

OHIO

Electronic Vision Inc (EV), pg 859

PENNSYLVANIA

Bullfrog Films Inc, pg 815
Schlessinger Media, pg 1004

TEXAS

Astro Audio Visual, pg 792
Stage Directions, pg 1022

VERMONT

University of Vermont, Instructional Television Dept, pg 1050

ONTARIO

Entertainment One Distribution, pg 861
Technovision® Interactive Inc, pg 1035

Videodisc Producers

ARIZONA

Film Creations Ltd, pg 867
Tellens Inc, pg 1037

ARKANSAS

White Diamond Productions, pg 1065

CALIFORNIA

Big Door, pg 807
Blind Pig Records, pg 809
Custom Video Productions Inc, pg 841
Joyce Media Inc, pg 906
The Kenwood Group, pg 909
Main Street Media Inc, pg 929
MGM Home Video, pg 941
piXvfm, pg 976
PM Productions, pg 977
Producers Group Ltd, pg 983
QRS Software Services, pg 988
RetinaVision Productions, pg 995
Rhino Home Video, pg 996
Glenn Roland Films, pg 998
SBS Productions, pg 1003
Screen Door Entertainment Inc, pg 1005
Sea Studios Foundation, pg 1005
SNAP, pg 1014
Tam Communications Inc, pg 1031
Total Media Group, pg 1042
Videowerks, pg 1057
WalkerVision Interarts, pg 1061
Wavemaker Media Design, pg 1062
WMS Media Inc, pg 1069

COLORADO

The Cinema Lab, pg 827
Daylight Productions & Rentals, pg 844
Flashback Media Productions, pg 869
Tatum Video, pg 1032

CONNECTICUT

ACM Productions Ltd, pg 774
Broadcast Video Productions LLC, pg 813
Ironik Design & Post, pg 902
Scholastic Library Publishing, pg 1004

DELAWARE

University Media Services, pg 1049

DISTRICT OF COLUMBIA

Hillmann & Carr Inc, pg 889

FLORIDA

Big Byte Video Productions, pg 806
Blackburst Entertainment, pg 808
National Teleproductions Inc, pg 953
Sunfire Communications Inc, pg 1028

GEORGIA

Beachwood Productions, pg 804
Guerrilla Productions LLC, pg 883
Sirius Images Corp dba WaveGuide Studios, pg 1012

HAWAII

1013 Integrated, pg 1037

IDAHO

Brad Shaw Productions Inc, pg 1008

ILLINOIS

Britannica Film & Video, pg 812
Comtech Multimedia Marketing, pg 834
Encyclopaedia Britannica Inc, pg 861

PROGRAMMING — VIDEO

Videodisc Producers (continued)

ILLINOIS (continued)

Major Media Inc, pg 929
QuickSet International Inc, pg 989
Universal Training, pg 1049
Video Impressions, pg 1055

INDIANA

AVA Productions, pg 798

IOWA

Right Stuf Inc, pg 997

KENTUCKY

Donna Lawrence Productions, pg 917
National Geographic Learning, pg 952

LOUISIANA

Digital FX Inc, pg 847
Great Chefs/Leisure Jazz Video, pg 881
Moxie Media, pg 948

MARYLAND

The Ahern Group, pg 779
Discovery Education - Silver Spring, pg 848

MASSACHUSETTS

Capron Lighting & Sound Co Inc, pg 819
CommCreative, pg 832
Penfield Productions Ltd, pg 971

MICHIGAN

K&R All Media Productions Inc, pg 908
K&R's Recording Studios Inc, pg 908
Maritz Performance Improvement Co, pg 931
Universal Images, pg 1049

MINNESOTA

Aggressive Records Audio Duplication LLC, pg 778
House of Cinemagraphics, pg 891
Jamieson & Associates Inc, pg 904

MISSOURI

Fambrough & Associates Inc, pg 865
The Phoenix Learning Group Inc, pg 974

NEVADA

Encore Productions Inc, pg 861

NEW HAMPSHIRE

Academic & Campus Technology Services, pg 773
Apertura, pg 788
The Troupe, pg 1045

NEW JERSEY

CFP Video Productions Inc, pg 823

NEW MEXICO

Michael Dunn Productions, pg 853

NEW YORK

BioMedia Inc, pg 807
Thomas Craven Film Corp, pg 837
Eastco Multimedia Solutions Inc, pg 856
Human Relations Media, pg 892
Mastervision Inc, pg 933
Jack Morton Worldwide, pg 946
MRY, pg 949
Shelly Palmer Production, pg 968
Split Image Productions, pg 1021
Suggs Media Productions Inc, pg 1028
TeleTime Productions, pg 1036

NORTH CAROLINA

Pat Appleson Studios Inc, pg 788
Carolina Biological Supply Co, pg 820
The Communications Group Inc, pg 833

OHIO

Creative Technology, pg 838
Electronic Vision Inc (EV), pg 859
Take 1 Media Services, pg 1031

OREGON

Odyssey Productions Inc, pg 961
Rex, pg 995

PENNSYLVANIA

Goodman Associates Inc, pg 880
Innovision Media Group, pg 899
Production Masters Inc (PMI), pg 984
Schlessinger Media, pg 1004
Video/Film Associates, pg 1055
Videosmith Inc, pg 1057

SOUTH CAROLINA

Venture Media, pg 1052

TENNESSEE

Scripps Networks, pg 1005

TEXAS

The Editing Co, pg 857
Mediaforce Productions, pg 937
Romar Learning, pg 999
Stage Directions, pg 1022
Tecfilms Inc, pg 1033

VERMONT

University of Vermont, Instructional Television Dept, pg 1050

VIRGINIA

Computer Sciences Corp, pg 834

WASHINGTON

Sparkworks Media, pg 1019
Victory Studios, pg 1054

WISCONSIN

USAV Group Inc, pg 1050
Video Wisconsin Inc, pg 1056
Wisconsin Public Television, pg 1068

ALBERTA

Black Media Works, pg 808

NEWFOUNDLAND AND LABRADOR

Vidcraft Productions Ltd, pg 1054

ONTARIO

Technovision® Interactive Inc, pg 1035

Videodisc Rentals

CALIFORNIA

Ametron Audio/Video, pg 785
Medcom Inc, pg 936

DELAWARE

University Media Services, pg 1049

FLORIDA

Media Concepts Inc, pg 936

GEORGIA

Staging Directions Inc, pg 1023

NEW MEXICO

National Information Center for Educational Media (NICEM)/MediaSleuth, pg 952

NEW YORK

Interactive International Inc, pg 899

TEXAS

Stage Directions, pg 1022

VERMONT

University of Vermont, Instructional Television Dept, pg 1050

VIRGINIA

Lee Hartman & Sons Inc, pg 918

ONTARIO

Technovision® Interactive Inc, pg 1035

Videotape Distributors

ALABAMA

CMEInfo, pg 830

ARIZONA

Arizona Cine Equipment, pg 789
Tellens Inc, pg 1037

CALIFORNIA

Adolph Gasser Inc, pg 776
Ametron Audio/Video, pg 785
Anchor Bay Entertainment LLC, pg 786
Coast Learning Systems, pg 830
DawnSignPress, pg 844
Deja View Video, pg 845
Digital Media West, pg 847
Direct Cinema Ltd Inc, pg 848
FXF Productions Inc, pg 874
Global Village Productions, pg 879
Bruce Goldberg Inc, pg 880
Golden State Dance Teachers Association (GSDTA), pg 880
Griggs Productions Inc, pg 882
Steven Halpern's Inner Peace Music, pg 884
Increase Video/Silver Mine Video, pg 897
Joyce Media Inc, pg 906
Keystone Entertainment, pg 910
Learning Communications LLC, pg 917
Main Street Media Inc, pg 929
Medcom Inc, pg 936
monterey media inc, pg 945
Music World/Vocal Power School, pg 951
Joseph Nicoletti Consulting-Promotion/California International Records/Global Village Records, pg 957
Nilgiri Press, pg 957
ODC Publishing, pg 961
Pacific Media, pg 967
Point of View Productions, pg 977
Regent Press Publishers & Printers, pg 994
Rhino Home Video, pg 996
Sahara Records & Filmworks Entertainment Co, pg 1001
Sea Studios Foundation, pg 1005
Technicolor, pg 1034
Valley Media, pg 1051
Warner Bros Production Sound & Video Services, pg 1062
Warner Home Video Inc, pg 1062
Western Instructional Television Inc, pg 1064

COLORADO

Stretching Inc, pg 1026

CONNECTICUT

Cine-Med Inc, pg 826
Crossroads Video, pg 840
EagleVision Inc, pg 855
Ironik Design & Post, pg 902
Video Design Group, pg 1055

DELAWARE

University Media Services, pg 1049

DISTRICT OF COLUMBIA

Durrin Productions Inc, pg 854
Library of Congress, Motion Picture, Broadcasting & Recorded Sound Division, pg 919

FLORIDA

AVI-SPL, pg 798
Capital Communications Inc, pg 819
Courter Films LLC, pg 837
Distribution Video & Audio (DVA), pg 849
EarthDesign Inc, pg 855
Global Video Distributors Inc, pg 879
MTI Home Video, pg 949
Photomart Cine-Video Inc, pg 975

GEORGIA

Audio Visual Resources Inc, pg 795
First Cut Communications LLC, pg 868
School Media Associates LLC, pg 1004

ILLINOIS

CCore Media Inc, pg 821
Chicago Satellite & Video, pg 825
Communications Corporation of America, pg 833
Encyclopaedia Britannica Inc, pg 861

Videotape Producers

PROGRAMMING — VIDEO

Videotape Producers (continued)

CALIFORNIA (continued)

Goal Productions, pg 879
Gold Standard Productions, pg 880
Bruce Goldberg Inc, pg 880
Griggs Productions Inc, pg 882
Steven Halpern's Inner Peace Music, pg 884
Havas Edge, pg 885
Imageworks, pg 896
Increase Video/Silver Mine Video, pg 897
International Contact Inc, pg 900
ITV Productions, pg 903
Joyce Media Inc, pg 906
K2B2 Records, pg 907
Kavich Reynolds Productions Inc, pg 908
The Kenwood Group, pg 909
Keystone Entertainment, pg 910
KPBS TV FM-San Diego, pg 913
KTVU-Retail Services, pg 914
Learning Communications LLC, pg 917
Ludlow Media Solutions, pg 926
Lynch Communications, pg 926
Main Street Media Inc, pg 929
Maximus Media Inc, pg 934
Media Magic, pg 937
Mist Media Inc, pg 944
monterey media inc, pg 945
Music World/Vocal Power School, pg 951
New & Unique Videos™, pg 955
Nilgiri Press, pg 957
ODC Publishing, pg 961
On-Trax Inc, pg 963
Pacific Media, pg 967
Palardo Productions, pg 968
Panorama Productions, pg 968
Penrose Productions, pg 972
piXvfm, pg 976
Point of View Productions, pg 977
Producers Group Ltd, pg 983
QCI International, pg 988
QRS Software Services, pg 988
Regent Press Publishers & Printers, pg 994
RetinaVision Productions, pg 995
Glenn Roland Films, pg 998
Sahara Records & Filmworks Entertainment Co, pg 1001
SBS Productions, pg 1003
Screen Door Entertainment Inc, pg 1005
Sea Studios Foundation, pg 1005
SevenStar Communications, pg 1007
SNAP, pg 1014
The Studio Center, pg 1026
Technicolor, pg 1034
Tele-Video Production Services (TVPS), pg 1036
Timestream Video, pg 1041
Total Media Group, pg 1042
Videolady, pg 1057
Videowerks, pg 1057
Warner Bros Production Sound & Video Services, pg 1062
Wavemaker Media Design, pg 1062
Webster Communications, pg 1063
Western Instructional Television Inc, pg 1064
WMS Media Inc, pg 1069
The Wyland Group, pg 1071

COLORADO

Centre Communications Inc, pg 823
The Cinema Lab, pg 827
Daylight Productions & Rentals, pg 844
Flashback Media Productions, pg 869
Rocky Mountain Audio/Video Productions Inc, pg 998
Tatum Video, pg 1032
Transtar Entertainment Co Inc, pg 1043

CONNECTICUT

ACM Productions Ltd, pg 774
Antenna International, pg 787
Applebox Studio, pg 788
Broadcast Video Productions LLC, pg 813
Cine-Med Inc, pg 826
Crossroads Video, pg 840
EagleVision Inc, pg 855
Geomatrix Productions, pg 877
Ironik Design & Post, pg 902
New London Media, pg 956
Pictures of Record Inc, pg 975
Video Design Group, pg 1055

DELAWARE

Ken-Del Productions Inc, pg 909
University Media Services, pg 1049

DISTRICT OF COLUMBIA

Durrin Productions Inc, pg 854
Educational Film Center, pg 857
Hillmann & Carr Inc, pg 889
USCCB Publishing, pg 1051
Yellow Cat Productions Inc, pg 1072

FLORIDA

Accel Video Productions, pg 773
Capital Communications Inc, pg 819
Civins Productions Inc, pg 828
Courter Films LLC, pg 837
Ed Ethridge Productions Inc, pg 863
Home Shopping Network (HSN), pg 890
I M P A C T Publishing Inc, pg 893
MTI Home Video, pg 949
National Teleproductions Inc, pg 953
PRI Productions, pg 981
Roger Scruggs Films, pg 1005
Sound & Vision Communications Inc, pg 1016
Sunfire Communications Inc, pg 1028
Video Techniques Inc, pg 1056

GEORGIA

Beachwood Productions, pg 804
Burst Video/Film Inc, pg 815
COMPRO Productions Inc, pg 834
Continental Film & Video, pg 835
ECG Productions, pg 856
First Cut Communications LLC, pg 868
Guerrilla Productions LLC, pg 883
Memory Lane Productions, pg 938
Myriad Productions, pg 951
Sirius Images Corp dba WaveGuide Studios, pg 1012

IDAHO

Brad Shaw Productions Inc, pg 1008

ILLINOIS

Analog Free Media, pg 786
Audio Visual Services Corp, pg 796
CCore Media Inc, pg 821
Chicago Satellite & Video, pg 825
Don Cohen - The Mathman, pg 831
Communications Corporation of America, pg 833
Comtech Multimedia Marketing, pg 834
Cresta Creative, pg 839
Encyclopaedia Britannica Inc, pg 861
IV Media Resources, pg 903
Major Media Inc, pg 929
Manning Productions, pg 930
Moviecraft Inc, pg 947
National Safety Council (NSC), pg 953
Nightingale-Conant Corp, pg 957
Jim Passin Productions, pg 970
The Pepper Group, pg 972
PSAV® Presentation Services (Hotel Services Division), pg 987
QuickSet International Inc, pg 989
Sparkfactor, pg 1019
Terra Nova Films Inc, pg 1037
Universal Training, pg 1049
Video Impressions, pg 1055

INDIANA

Agency for Instructional Technology (AIT), pg 778
AVA Productions, pg 798
OMNI Productions, pg 962
PentaVision Communications Inc, pg 972

IOWA

Accelerated Learning Foundation, pg 773
Kirkwood Community College, pg 911
The Production House, pg 984
Right Stuf Inc, pg 997

KENTUCKY

Donna Lawrence Productions, pg 917
Media Resources, pg 937
National Geographic Learning, pg 952
Prosper Media Group Inc, pg 986

LOUISIANA

Digital FX Inc, pg 847
Great Chefs/Leisure Jazz Video, pg 881
Leisure Video, pg 918
Louisiana State University Health Sciences Center - Shreveport, pg 925
Moxie Media, pg 948

MAINE

WGME-TV, pg 1065

MARYLAND

The Ahern Group, pg 779
CPR MultiMedia Solutions, pg 837
Library Video Network (LVN), pg 920
Media Dimensions Inc, pg 936
Milner-Fenwick Inc, pg 943
Mobile-Video Productions Inc, pg 944
Sign Media Inc, pg 1011

MASSACHUSETTS

Capron Lighting & Sound Co Inc, pg 819
CommCreative, pg 832
Cramer Productions, pg 837
Education Development Center Inc (EDC), pg 857
Emergency Film Group, pg 860
Heliotrope Studios, pg 887
Home Inc, pg 890
The New Film Company Inc, pg 955
Penfield Productions Ltd, pg 971
Preston Productions Inc, pg 981

MICHIGAN

Benjamin Creative Productions, pg 805
Digi Sign Design LLC, pg 847
K&R All Media Productions Inc, pg 908
K&R's Recording Studios Inc, pg 908
Lawrence Productions Inc, pg 917
Maritz Performance Improvement Co, pg 931
MessageMakers, pg 939
MSU Technologies, pg 949
Prakken Publications Inc, pg 980
Universal Images, pg 1049
Wayne State University Media Services, pg 1063
WTVS-Station Enterprises, pg 1071

MINNESOTA

Aggressive Records Audio Duplication LLC, pg 778
American Choral Catalog Ltd, pg 784
GMI Productions, pg 879
House of Cinemagraphics, pg 891
Jamieson & Associates Inc, pg 904
JIST Publishing, pg 905
Llewellyn Publications, pg 923
Whole Person Associates Inc, pg 1066
Worthwhile Films, pg 1070

MISSOURI

Cable Films & Video, pg 816
Celebrities Productions, pg 822
Fambrough & Associates Inc, pg 865
Marsh Media, pg 931
The Phoenix Learning Group Inc, pg 974
SOM Publishing Co, pg 1015

MONTANA

KUSM TV, pg 914

NEBRASKA

Envision Communications Inc, pg 861
Rainbow Video Productions Inc, pg 991
Telepro Video Inc, pg 1036
Vision Maker Media, pg 1058

NEVADA

DVDs4Less, pg 854
Encore Productions Inc, pg 861
JCS Video Productions, pg 904
The Larry Little Co, pg 923
Tanglewood Productions, pg 1031

NEW HAMPSHIRE

Apertura, pg 788
Channell One Video, pg 824

Chip Taylor Communications LLC, pg 1032
The Troupe, pg 1045
YMAA Publication Center Inc, pg 1072

NEW JERSEY

Alden Films, pg 780
Broadcast Center Studios, pg 813
CFP Video Productions Inc, pg 823
Comex Systems Inc, pg 832
DWJ Television, pg 854
Euro-Pacific Film & Video Productions Inc, pg 863
Films of the Nations, pg 868
Half Moon Video Productions, pg 883
Laurel Video Productions, pg 916
MIB Mediaworks, pg 941
Midnight Media Group Inc, pg 942
Ray Mueller Productions, pg 949
Newark Beth Israel Medical Center, pg 956
Optisonics Productions, pg 965
Telequest Inc, pg 1036
VCSvideo, pg 1052

NEW MEXICO

Michael Dunn Productions, pg 853
Production Outfitters, pg 984
Rainbow International Inc/Rainbow Productions Inc, pg 990
Uncharted Country Publishing, pg 1048

NEW YORK

Ace Video, pg 774
aurora productions, pg 797
Blue Barn Pictures Inc, pg 809
Buzzco Associates Inc, pg 816
Campus Film Distributors Corp, pg 818
Thomas Craven Film Corp, pg 837
dM works, pg 849
Duplication Depot Inc, pg 853
Eastco Multimedia Solutions Inc, pg 856
Femme Productions Inc, pg 866
The Food & Beverage Institute, pg 871
Four Corners Productions, pg 871
Karen Frankel Productions, pg 872
William Greaves Productions Inc, pg 882
Hallel Communications, pg 884
Homespun Video, pg 890
Human Relations Media, pg 892
IAI Video, pg 893
Icontent, pg 893
International Digital Centre, pg 901
Richard Kaplan Productions, pg 908
L A Bruell Inc, pg 914
Long Island Video Enterprises Live Inc, pg 924
Lylofilm Productions, pg 926
Manhattan Center Studios Inc, pg 930
Mastervision Inc, pg 933
Jack Morton Worldwide, pg 946
MRG Productions Inc, pg 948
MRM Worldwide, pg 948
MRY, pg 949
News Broadcast Network, pg 956
Shelly Palmer Production, pg 968
Pat Kogan Productions Inc, pg 970
Peckham Productions Inc, pg 970
PrimaLux Video Inc, pg 982
PrimeLight Productions Inc, pg 982
Richter Productions Inc, pg 996
Peter Schleger Co, pg 1004
Shadow Pictures Inc, pg 1007
SISU Home Entertainment Inc, pg 1012
Split Image Productions, pg 1021
Suggs Media Productions Inc, pg 1028
Sunrise Media LLC, pg 1028
TeleTime Productions, pg 1036
Videofashion Network, pg 1056
The Visual Studies Workshop (VSW), pg 1059
White Buffalo Multimedia, pg 1065
Zelman Studios Ltd, pg 1073

NORTH CAROLINA

Pat Appleson Studios Inc, pg 788
Carolina Biological Supply Co, pg 820
The Communications Group Inc, pg 833
Horizon Video Productions Inc, pg 891
NASCAR Media Group LLC, pg 952
Trailblazer Studios®, pg 1043

OHIO

CET, pg 823
Commercial Video, pg 832
Creative Technology, pg 838
Curtis Inc, pg 841
Cuyahoga Community College Media Center, pg 841
EDR Media LLC, pg 857
Franciscan Media, pg 872
Lyon Video Inc, pg 927
MainSail Production Services Inc, pg 929
Maslowski Productions, pg 933
Musicol Recording, pg 951
R&B Communications Inc, pg 991
South-Western Publishing Co, pg 1019
Take 1 Media Services, pg 1031
VGI Productions, pg 1053

OREGON

Creative Media Development, pg 838
Garden Valley Productions, pg 875
InterVision Media, pg 902
KPDX-TV Production Center, pg 913
Medifecta Healthcare Training, pg 938
Norman Beerger Productions, pg 958
Odyssey Productions Inc, pg 961
Rex, pg 995
Wilderness Video, pg 1066

PENNSYLVANIA

Argentine Productions Inc, pg 789
Audio Visual Communications Inc, pg 795
FMP Media Solutions Inc, pg 870
Fusion Brand Experiences, pg 874
Goodman Associates Inc, pg 880
Main Point Productions, pg 929
Muderick Media, pg 949
Production Masters Inc (PMI), pg 984
Rahlic Publishing Co, pg 990
Schlessinger Media, pg 1004
Video Communication Productions Inc, pg 1054
Video/Film Associates, pg 1055
The Videohouse Inc, pg 1057

SOUTH CAROLINA

American Production Services LLC, pg 785
Stages Video Productions, pg 1023
Venture Media, pg 1052

TENNESSEE

Center for Southern Folklore Inc, pg 822
Marine Geographic, pg 931
Memphis Communications Corp, pg 938
Running Pony Productions LLC, pg 1000
Scripps Networks, pg 1005
UMCom Productions, pg 1048
WKPT-TV, pg 1068

TEXAS

Biway Media, pg 808
Communication Arts Multimedia Inc, pg 832
Dallas Learning Solutions, pg 842
The Editing Co, pg 857
First Group Communications Inc, pg 868
Lamb & Lion Ministries, pg 915
Marx InDigital, pg 933
Mediaforce Productions, pg 937
Earl Miller Productions Inc, pg 943
Julye Newlin Productions Inc, pg 956
Omni Intercommunications Inc, pg 962
Romar Learning, pg 999
Stage Directions, pg 1022
Tecfilms Inc, pg 1033
Texas Heart Institute Visual Communication Services, pg 1037
University of Texas at Austin - Petroleum Extension Service, pg 1050

UTAH

K-SAR Video & DVD Productions, pg 907
One Stop CD Shop LLC, pg 963

VERMONT

Edgewood Studios, pg 857
Multicultural Media, pg 950
Dorothy Tod Films, pg 1041
Wilson McLeran Inc, pg 1067

VIRGINIA

BES Studios, pg 805
CACI Productions Group, pg 816
CALIBRE, pg 816
Cinebar Productions Inc, pg 826
Coastal Training Technologies Corp, pg 831
Computer Sciences Corp, pg 834
D&B Television & Video Productions Inc, pg 842
Limelight Communications Inc, pg 921

WASHINGTON

Adams Creative & Production Services, pg 775
Bennett-Watt HD Productions Inc, pg 805
Center for Touch Drawing, pg 822
Victory Studios, pg 1054

WEST VIRGINIA

Altruist Media LLC, pg 783

WISCONSIN

Excel Duplication Services, pg 864
Meridian Studios, pg 939
ProVideo, pg 986
USAV Group Inc, pg 1050
Video Wisconsin Inc, pg 1056
Watts Communications Inc, pg 1062
Wisconsin Public Television, pg 1068

WYOMING

Bridger Productions Inc, pg 812

ALBERTA

Black Media Works, pg 808
Global Television Station, pg 879

BRITISH COLUMBIA

Timeless Books, pg 1040
Triad Communications Ltd, pg 1044

NEWFOUNDLAND AND LABRADOR

Vidcraft Productions Ltd, pg 1054

NORTHWEST TERRITORIES

Yellowknife Films Inc, pg 1072

ONTARIO

CBC/Radio-Canada, pg 821
Jams Productions Inc, pg 904
Purefire Communications Inc, pg 987
RB Productions, pg 992

QUEBEC

Les Productions Via Le Monde (Daniel Bertolino) Inc, pg 985

SASKATCHEWAN

plan9films, pg 976

Videotape Rentals

ARIZONA

Video Learning Library, pg 1055

CALIFORNIA

Ametron Audio/Video, pg 785
Direct Cinema Ltd Inc, pg 848
ECONEWS (Environmental Television Series) & (Environmental Directions Radio Series), pg 856
Griggs Productions Inc, pg 882
Learning Communications LLC, pg 917
Medcom Inc, pg 936
Regent Press Publishers & Printers, pg 994
Western Instructional Television Inc, pg 1064
The Wyland Group, pg 1071

CONNECTICUT

Crossroads Video, pg 840
Ironik Design & Post, pg 902

DELAWARE

University Media Services, pg 1049

DISTRICT OF COLUMBIA

Durrin Productions Inc, pg 854

PROGRAMMING — VIDEO

Videotape Rentals (continued)

FLORIDA

Courter Films LLC, pg 837
Jordan Klein Film & Video (JKFV), pg 906

GEORGIA

Staging Directions Inc, pg 1023

ILLINOIS

National Safety Council (NSC), pg 953
RBR Productions, pg 992

INDIANA

Agency for Instructional Technology (AIT), pg 778

MARYLAND

Kids on the Block Inc, pg 910

MASSACHUSETTS

Documentary Educational Resources Inc, pg 850
Emergency Film Group, pg 860

MICHIGAN

Digi Sign Design LLC, pg 847
Wayne State University Media Services, pg 1063

MINNESOTA

American Choral Catalog Ltd, pg 784
Science Museum of Minnesota, pg 1005

MISSOURI

Cable Films & Video, pg 816
Swank Audio Visuals, pg 1029

NEBRASKA

Vision Maker Media, pg 1058

NEW HAMPSHIRE

Chip Taylor Communications LLC, pg 1032

NEW JERSEY

Business Education Films, pg 815
Euro-Pacific Film & Video Productions Inc, pg 863

NEW MEXICO

National Information Center for Educational Media (NICEM)/MediaSleuth, pg 952

NEW YORK

Adwar Video, pg 778
Fanlight Productions, pg 865
William Greaves Productions Inc, pg 882
Hallel Communications, pg 884
Icarus Film Inc, pg 893
Kino International Corp, pg 911
New Day Films, pg 955
Richter Productions Inc, pg 996
Timed Exposures Films, pg 1040

OHIO

Franciscan Media, pg 872

OREGON

Nostalgia Family Video Inc, pg 959
Wilderness Video, pg 1066

PENNSYLVANIA

Rahlic Publishing Co, pg 990

TENNESSEE

Center for Southern Folklore Inc, pg 822

TEXAS

University of Texas at Austin - Petroleum Extension Service, pg 1050

VIRGINIA

Coastal Training Technologies Corp, pg 831

WISCONSIN

Wisconsin Public Television, pg 1068

ALBERTA

Global Television Station, pg 879

BRITISH COLUMBIA

Video In Studios/Video Out Distribution, pg 1055

ONTARIO

Kineticvideo.com, pg 911

QUEBEC

Les Productions Via Le Monde (Daniel Bertolino) Inc, pg 985

Vocational Program Distributors

ARIZONA

Video Learning Library, pg 1055

CALIFORNIA

Barbosa Video Services, pg 802
Direct Cinema Ltd Inc, pg 848
Discovery Education - Los Angeles, pg 848
411 Video Information, pg 872
Increase Video/Silver Mine Video, pg 897
New & Unique Videos™, pg 955
Panorama Publishing Co, pg 968
Players Press, pg 977
Pyramid Media, pg 987
TMW Media Group, pg 1041
The Wine Appreciation Guild Ltd, pg 1067

COLORADO

InJoy Birth & Parenting Education, pg 898

CONNECTICUT

The Taunton Press Inc, pg 1032

DELAWARE

University Media Services, pg 1049

DISTRICT OF COLUMBIA

VSA, pg 1061

FLORIDA

ACE Video Resources Software, pg 774
EarthDesign Inc, pg 855
Psychological Assessment Resources Inc (PAR), pg 987
ThirdWave Learning Inc, pg 1039

GEORGIA

Convergent Media Systems, pg 836
On-Line Productions, pg 963

ILLINOIS

ABSA Productions Inc, pg 772
Film Ideas, pg 867
National Safety Council (NSC), pg 953

INDIANA

Agency for Instructional Technology (AIT), pg 778
Career & Self Directed Extended Programs at Purdue University, pg 820

IOWA

Kirkwood Community College, pg 911

KENTUCKY

WaxWorks VideoWorks, pg 1063

MAINE

WoodenBoat Publications, pg 1069

MARYLAND

Gypsum Association, pg 883
Library Video Network (LVN), pg 920

MASSACHUSETTS

Media Marketing Associates Inc, pg 937
Penfield Productions Ltd, pg 971

MICHIGAN

Digi Sign Design LLC, pg 847
Prakken Publications Inc, pg 980
Society of Manufacturing Engineers (SME), pg 1015
VMS Inc, pg 1060

MINNESOTA

EMC/Paradigm Publishing, pg 860
JIST Publishing, pg 905

MISSOURI

The Phoenix Learning Group Inc, pg 974

NEVADA

DVDs4Less, pg 854

NEW HAMPSHIRE

Chip Taylor Communications LLC, pg 1032

NEW JERSEY

Alden Films, pg 780
Comex Systems Inc, pg 832
Lucerne Media, pg 925
MIB Mediaworks, pg 941

NEW MEXICO

National Information Center for Educational Media (NICEM)/MediaSleuth, pg 952

NEW YORK

Brooklyn Botanic Garden, pg 814
The Bureau for At-Risk Youth, pg 815
Films Media Group, pg 868
Guidance Associates Inc Center for Humanities, pg 883
Human Relations Media, pg 892
March of Dimes Foundation, pg 930
MRG Productions Inc, pg 948
Shopware, pg 1009
SISU Home Entertainment Inc, pg 1012
Video Catalogue Co Inc, pg 1054
VIEW Inc (Video International Entertainment World Inc), pg 1058
Willow Mixed Media Inc, pg 1067

NORTH CAROLINA

Baker & Taylor Inc, pg 801
Do It Yourself Inc - DIY Video Corp, pg 849
Vide-O-Go/That's Infotainment!, pg 1054

OHIO

McGraw-Hill School Education Group, pg 935
Shelburne Films, pg 1008
South-Western Publishing Co, pg 1019
WOUB Public Media, pg 1070

PENNSYLVANIA

Bergwall Productions Inc, pg 805
Bullfrog Films Inc, pg 815
Discovery Education - South Burlington, pg 848
FMP Media Solutions Inc, pg 870
Karol Media Inc, pg 908
Movies Unlimited, pg 947

TENNESSEE

American Blackguard Inc, pg 784

TEXAS

CEV Multimedia Ltd, pg 823
Critical Information Network, pg 839
University of Texas at Austin - Petroleum Extension Service, pg 1050

VERMONT

Perceptions Inc, pg 973
University of Vermont, Instructional Television Dept, pg 1050
Wilson McLeran Inc, pg 1067

VIRGINIA

CACI Productions Group, pg 816

WASHINGTON

Media Resources Inc, pg 937

ONTARIO

Canadian Learning Co Inc, pg 818
Kineticvideo.com, pg 911
McIntyre Media Inc, pg 935

Vocational Program Producers

ALASKA

Aurora Films, pg 797

ARIZONA

Aardvark Productions LLC, pg 772
MediaWorks, pg 938

CALIFORNIA

Access Video in Berkeley, pg 773
Action Video, pg 775
Big Door, pg 807
Classic Images, pg 829
Coastline Productions, pg 831
Cox Media, pg 837
Creativity Unlimited Press®, pg 839
Custom Video Productions Inc, pg 841
Design Media, pg 845
Discovery Education - Los Angeles, pg 848
Dogma Studios, pg 850
Face Digital Post, pg 865
FXF Productions Inc, pg 874
imageReal Pictures LLC, pg 896
ITV Productions, pg 903
KION-TV, pg 911
Main Street Media Inc, pg 929
Maximus Media Inc, pg 934
McCune Audio-Video-Lighting, pg 935
Media Magic, pg 937
The Media Staff Inc, pg 937
Mist Media Inc, pg 944
New & Unique Videos™, pg 955
New Circuit Films LLC, pg 955
Nolte Media, pg 958
On-Trax Inc, pg 963
Panorama Publishing Co, pg 968
Penrose Productions, pg 972
Players Press, pg 977
PM Productions, pg 977
Point of View Productions, pg 977
QRS Software Services, pg 988
Dick Reizner Film & Video, pg 994
Glenn Roland Films, pg 998
SBS Productions, pg 1003
SNAP, pg 1014
The Studio Center, pg 1026
Tam Communications Inc, pg 1031
Tele-Video Production Services (TVPS), pg 1036
Timestream Video, pg 1041
TMW Media Group, pg 1041
Total Media Group, pg 1042
Videolady, pg 1057
Videowerks, pg 1057
Vineyard Video & Photography, pg 1058
WalkerVision Interarts, pg 1061
Wavemaker Media Design, pg 1062
West Coast Projections Inc, pg 1063
Zamacona Productions, pg 1073

COLORADO

Daylight Productions & Rentals, pg 844
Flashback Media Productions, pg 869
InJoy Birth & Parenting Education, pg 898
Rocky Mountain Audio/Video Productions Inc, pg 998

CONNECTICUT

Fox Connecticut, pg 872
The Gary-Paul Agency, pg 875
Ironik Design & Post, pg 902
The Taunton Press Inc, pg 1032

DELAWARE

University Media Services, pg 1049

DISTRICT OF COLUMBIA

Hillmann & Carr Inc, pg 889
VSA, pg 1061

FLORIDA

Accel Video Productions, pg 773
ACE Video Resources Software, pg 774
Blackburst Entertainment, pg 808
Capital Communications Inc, pg 819
Civins Productions Inc, pg 828
CopShopMiami.com, pg 836
Courter Films LLC, pg 837
EarthDesign Inc, pg 855
Easy Edit Video Inc, pg 856
Ed Ethridge Productions Inc, pg 863
Home Shopping Network (HSN), pg 890
Jordan Klein Film & Video (JKFV), pg 906
Sunfire Communications Inc, pg 1028
Sunrise Studios, pg 1028
Tricycle Studios, pg 1044

GEORGIA

Beachwood Productions, pg 804
Continental Film & Video, pg 835
Guerrilla Productions LLC, pg 883
On-Line Productions, pg 963

HAWAII

Hyperspective Studios Inc, pg 893
Source School of Tantra Yoga Inc, pg 1019

IDAHO

Brad Shaw Productions Inc, pg 1008
Wide Eye Productions, pg 1066

ILLINOIS

ABSA Productions Inc, pg 772
Chicago Satellite & Video, pg 825
Film Police, pg 867
IV Media Resources, pg 903
Major Media Productions Inc, pg 929
National Safety Council (NSC), pg 953
The Pepper Group, pg 972
SCI Television Productions LLC, pg 1004
Southern Illinois University, pg 1019
20/20 Communications Inc, pg 1047
Universal Training, pg 1049

INDIANA

Agency for Instructional Technology (AIT), pg 778
AVA Productions, pg 798
Digital Rain LLC, pg 847
PentaVision Communications Inc, pg 972
Road Pictures, pg 997

IOWA

Kirkwood Community College, pg 911
The Production House, pg 984

KENTUCKY

Idle Minds Productions Inc, pg 894
NIMCO Inc, pg 957

LOUISIANA

Moxie Media, pg 948

MARYLAND

CPR MultiMedia Solutions, pg 837
dbF a Media Company, pg 844
Gypsum Association, pg 883
The Image Generators, pg 895
Kramer Communications Video Production, pg 913
Library Video Network (LVN), pg 920

MASSACHUSETTS

Award Productions, pg 800
Green Mountain Post Films (GMP), pg 882
Penfield Productions Ltd, pg 971
Triumph Learning LLC, pg 1045

MICHIGAN

Digi Sign Design LLC, pg 847
K&R All Media Productions Inc, pg 908
K&R's Recording Studios Inc, pg 908
Prakken Publications Inc, pg 980
Society of Manufacturing Engineers (SME), pg 1015
VMS Inc, pg 1060

MINNESOTA

Aggressive Records Audio Duplication LLC, pg 778
EMC/Paradigm Publishing, pg 860
House of Cinemagraphics, pg 891
JIST Publishing, pg 905
Master Communications Group, pg 933
MultiMedia, pg 950

MISSOURI

Audio-VideoGraphics Inc, pg 795
Fambrough & Associates Inc, pg 865

MONTANA

KUSM TV, pg 914
North Country Media Group, pg 959

NEBRASKA

Dog & Pony Productions Inc, pg 850

NEVADA

Aardvark Video & Media Productions, pg 772
DVDs4Less, pg 854
Encore Productions Inc, pg 861
JCS Video Productions, pg 904
Tanglewood Productions, pg 1031

NEW HAMPSHIRE

Apertura, pg 788
Chip Taylor Communications LLC, pg 1032

NEW JERSEY

Alden Films, pg 780
Broadcast Center Studios, pg 813
CFP Video Productions Inc, pg 823
Comex Systems Inc, pg 832
Half Moon Video Productions, pg 883
Laurel Video Productions, pg 916
MIB Mediaworks, pg 941
Optisonics Productions, pg 965
Producer East Productions, pg 983
Bill Quinn Productions, pg 989
Suede Interactive, pg 1027
Telequest Inc, pg 1036
VCSvideo, pg 1052

NEW MEXICO

Production Outfitters, pg 984

NEW YORK

aurora productions, pg 797
BC Video Inc, pg 803
Blue Barn Pictures Inc, pg 809
Brooklyn Botanic Garden, pg 814
The Bureau for At-Risk Youth, pg 815
dM works, pg 849
Films Media Group, pg 868
Guidance Associates Inc Center for Humanities, pg 883
Hello World Communications, pg 888
Human Relations Media, pg 892
March of Dimes Foundation, pg 930
Neal Marshad Productions, pg 931
MRG Productions Inc, pg 948
Shelly Palmer Production, pg 968
Pat Kogan Productions Inc, pg 970
Peckham Productions Inc, pg 970
PrimaLux Video Inc, pg 982
Shopware, pg 1009
TeleTime Productions, pg 1036
Tobin Productions Inc, pg 1041
Video Catalogue Co Inc, pg 1054
Videograf, pg 1057
VIEW Inc (Video International Entertainment World Inc), pg 1058
Alan Weiss Productions, pg 1063
Willow Mixed Media Inc, pg 1067

NORTH CAROLINA

Pat Appleson Studios Inc, pg 788
The Communications Group Inc, pg 833
Do It Yourself Inc - DIY Video Corp, pg 849
Kino Mountain Productions LLC, pg 911
LCW Productions LLC, pg 917
Media Consultants Inc, pg 936
Moving Pictures, pg 948
Unifour Productions Inc, pg 1048

OHIO

Advent Media Inc, pg 778
Creative Technology, pg 838
EDR Media LLC, pg 857
Lyon Video Inc, pg 927
MainSail Production Services Inc, pg 929
McGraw-Hill School Education Group, pg 935
R&B Communications Inc, pg 991
Shelburne Films, pg 1008
South-Western Publishing Co, pg 1019
Treehaus Communications Inc, pg 1044

PROGRAMMING — VIDEO

Vocational Program Producers (continued)

OHIO (continued)

VGI Productions, pg 1053
Vista Color Imaging Inc, pg 1059
WOUB Public Media, pg 1070

OREGON

A KTVA Production LLC, pg 771
ERA Learning, pg 862
Ideascape Inc, pg 894
KPDX-TV Production Center, pg 913
Production West, pg 985
Rex, pg 995

PENNSYLVANIA

Bergwall Productions Inc, pg 805
CCI Communications Inc, pg 821
FMP Media Solutions Inc, pg 870
Innovision Media Group, pg 899
JPL, pg 906
Muderick Media, pg 949
Panta Rhei Media Inc, pg 968
The Videohouse Inc, pg 1057

RHODE ISLAND

Sound-FX-Design, pg 1017

SOUTH CAROLINA

Stages Video Productions, pg 1023
Venture Media, pg 1052

TENNESSEE

American Blackguard Inc, pg 784
Continental Film, pg 835
Jaguar Productions, pg 903
Memphis Communications Corp, pg 938
Running Pony Productions LLC, pg 1000
Scripps Networks, pg 1005

TEXAS

Cerutti Productions Inc, pg 823
CEV Multimedia Ltd, pg 823
Communication Arts Multimedia Inc, pg 832
Countdown Productions Inc, pg 837
Critical Information Network, pg 839
The Editing Co, pg 857
Epic Software Group Inc, pg 862
Horizon Film + Video Productions, pg 891
Mediaforce Productions, pg 937
Earl Miller Productions Inc, pg 943
Julye Newlin Productions Inc, pg 956
Omega Productions, pg 962
Sportsmen on Film Inc, pg 1021
Stage Directions, pg 1022
University of Texas at Austin - Petroleum Extension Service, pg 1050

VERMONT

Perceptions Inc, pg 973
University of Vermont, Instructional Television Dept, pg 1050
Wilson McLeran Inc, pg 1067

VIRGINIA

CACI Productions Group, pg 816
CALIBRE, pg 816
D&B Television & Video Productions Inc, pg 842
Gingerbread Productions, pg 878
Limelight Communications Inc, pg 921
Metro Productions, pg 939
Rocktown Media, pg 998
Video Solutions, pg 1056

WASHINGTON

Bennett-Watt HD Productions Inc, pg 805
Hamilton Studio, pg 884

WISCONSIN

5th Floor Recording Co, pg 867
ProVideo, pg 986
Rucinski & Reetz Communications LLC, pg 1000
USAV Group Inc, pg 1050
Video Wisconsin Inc, pg 1056
Wisconsin Public Television, pg 1068

WYOMING

Bridger Productions Inc, pg 812

BRITISH COLUMBIA

Triad Communications Ltd, pg 1044

MANITOBA

Spectra Video Productions Ltd, pg 1020

NEWFOUNDLAND AND LABRADOR

Vidcraft Productions Ltd, pg 1054

ONTARIO

DebsVoice, pg 844
GAPC (General Assembly Production Centre), pg 875
Image Video Services & Productions, pg 895
Video Excellence Productions, pg 1055

QUEBEC

Kerrigan Productions Inc, pg 910

Vocational Program Rentals

ARIZONA

Video Learning Library, pg 1055

CALIFORNIA

Direct Cinema Ltd Inc, pg 848

DELAWARE

University Media Services, pg 1049

GEORGIA

Convergent Media Systems, pg 836

ILLINOIS

National Safety Council (NSC), pg 953

INDIANA

Agency for Instructional Technology (AIT), pg 778

MAINE

WoodenBoat Publications, pg 1069

MICHIGAN

Digi Sign Design LLC, pg 847

MISSOURI

The Phoenix Learning Group Inc, pg 974

NEW YORK

BC Video Inc, pg 803
Brooklyn Botanic Garden, pg 814
Films for the Humanities & Sciences, pg 868
Films Media Group, pg 868

OHIO

WOUB Public Media, pg 1070

PENNSYLVANIA

Bullfrog Films Inc, pg 815

VERMONT

University of Vermont, Instructional Television Dept, pg 1050

PROGRAMMING — MISCELLANEOUS

Computer Multimedia, CD-ROM & DVD Interactive Program Distributors

ARIZONA

BeachWare Inc, pg 804

CALIFORNIA

Academy Savant, pg 773
Ametron Audio/Video, pg 785
Animated Software Co, pg 786
Astronomical Society of the Pacific, pg 792
Barbosa Video Services, pg 802
Christian Media Network, pg 825
Deja View Video, pg 845
Electronic Arts, pg 859
Eye & I Productions, pg 864
Steven Halpern's Inner Peace Music, pg 884
Learning Communications LLC, pg 917
MarVista Entertainment Inc, pg 933
Rovi Corp, pg 1000
Staylor-Made Communications Inc, pg 1024
Videobotics, pg 1056

COLORADO

Paul L Anderson Productions Inc, pg 786
Aspen Systems Inc, pg 792
Meriwether Publishing Ltd, pg 939

CONNECTICUT

Cine-Med Inc, pg 826
Crossroads Video, pg 840
Ironik Design & Post, pg 902
Market Data Retrieval (MDR), pg 931
Twenty-Third Publications/Bayard, pg 1047

DISTRICT OF COLUMBIA

Theatrical Technicians Inc (TTI), pg 1038

FLORIDA

Allegro Productions Inc, pg 781
Capital Communications Inc, pg 819
CD ROM™ Inc, pg 822
Communications Concepts Inc (CCI), pg 833
Image Technical Services, pg 895
ThirdWave Learning Inc, pg 1039
Times-Square Fantasy Theatre, pg 1041

ILLINOIS

Britannica Film & Video, pg 812
CCore Media Inc, pg 821
Educational Insights, pg 857
Encyclopaedia Britannica Inc, pg 861
Film Ideas, pg 867
Learning Seed, pg 917
Rand McNally Education, pg 991
Richter Studios, pg 996

INDIANA

Agency for Instructional Technology (AIT), pg 778
Herff Jones | Nystrom, pg 888
Optical Disc Solutions Inc, pg 964

IOWA

Perfection Learning Corp, pg 973
Right Stuf Inc, pg 997

KANSAS

Genigraphics®, pg 877

LOUISIANA

Great Chefs/Leisure Jazz Video, pg 881
Leisure Video, pg 918

MARYLAND

dbF a Media Company, pg 844
Discovery Education - Silver Spring, pg 848
MMI Corp, pg 944

MASSACHUSETTS

Cramer Productions, pg 837
Documentary Educational Resources Inc, pg 850
Pauline Books & Media, pg 970
Penfield Productions Ltd, pg 971

MICHIGAN

Digi Sign Design LLC, pg 847
Prakken Publications Inc, pg 980
Zondervan, A HarperCollins Company, pg 1074

MINNESOTA

Aggressive Records Audio Duplication LLC, pg 778
Beyers Sound & Essay Audio, pg 806
Harris Communications Inc, pg 885

NEW JERSEY

Lucerne Media, pg 925
Paulist Press, pg 970

NEW MEXICO

National Information Center for Educational Media (NICEM)/MediaSleuth, pg 952

NEW YORK

The Bureau for At-Risk Youth, pg 815
Criterion Collection, pg 839
Digital Force, pg 847
Educational Images Ltd, pg 857
French American Cultural Exchange (FACE), pg 873
HB-Content, pg 886
Human Relations Media, pg 892
Monad Trainer's Aide Inc, pg 945
SISU Home Entertainment Inc, pg 1012
Voyetra Turtle Beach, pg 1061

NORTH CAROLINA

Vide-O-Go/That's Infotainment!, pg 1054

OHIO

Electronic Vision Inc (EV), pg 859

OREGON

Wilderness Video, pg 1066

PENNSYLVANIA

AccuWeather Inc, pg 774
Bullfrog Films Inc, pg 815
Discovery Education - South Burlington, pg 848
FMP Media Solutions Inc, pg 870
Library Video Company, pg 920
MVD Entertainment Group, pg 951
Scala Inc, pg 1003
Schlessinger Media, pg 1004
Science for Kids, pg 1005

SOUTH DAKOTA

Sencore Inc, pg 1006

TENNESSEE

American Blackguard Inc, pg 784
Spring Arbor Distributors, pg 1022
Zion Music Group, pg 1074

TEXAS

CEV Multimedia Ltd, pg 823
Dallas Learning Solutions, pg 842
Epic Software Group Inc, pg 862
Lamb & Lion Ministries, pg 915
Replicopy Digital Media Center, pg 995

UTAH

Strata™, pg 1025

VERMONT

Ashgate Publishing Co, pg 792

VIRGINIA

Design & Production Inc, pg 845

WASHINGTON

Global Net Productions Inc, pg 879

WISCONSIN

Meridian Studios, pg 939

BRITISH COLUMBIA

Credo Interactive Inc, pg 839

Computer Multimedia, CD-ROM & DVD Interactive Program Producers

ARIZONA

Aardvark Productions LLC, pg 772
BeachWare Inc, pg 804
Merestone, pg 938
MindPlay, pg 943

ARKANSAS

Live'N'Loud, pg 923

CALIFORNIA

Animated Software Co, pg 786
Animax, pg 787
Astronomical Society of the Pacific, pg 792
Big Door, pg 807
Christian Media Network, pg 825
Coloredge, pg 832
Custom Video Productions Inc, pg 841
Deja View Video, pg 845
Digital Outpost, pg 847
Direct Images Interactive Inc, pg 848
Dogma Studios, pg 850
Dolphin MultiMedia Inc, pg 850
Dynamic Digital Depth Inc (DDD), pg 854
Electronic Arts, pg 859
Eye & I Productions, pg 864
Gateways Books & Tapes, pg 876
Steven Halpern's Inner Peace Music, pg 884
Havas Edge, pg 885
Imageworks, pg 896
International Contact Inc, pg 900
Ludlow Media Solutions, pg 926
Lumeni Productions Inc, pg 926
Lynch Communications, pg 926
Main Street Media Inc, pg 929
Maximus Media Inc, pg 934
Media Magic, pg 937
Mist Media Inc, pg 944
Panorama Productions, pg 968
QRS Software Services, pg 988
RetinaVision Productions, pg 995
Glenn Roland Films, pg 998
Staylor-Made Communications Inc, pg 1024
Still N'Motion, pg 1025
Tam Communications Inc, pg 1031
Three D Graphics Inc, pg 1039
Tickets.com, pg 1040
Tigar Hare Studios, pg 1040
Total Media Group, pg 1042
Towards 2000 Inc, pg 1043
Videobotics, pg 1056
Videowerks, pg 1057
Wavemaker Media Design, pg 1062
WMS Media Inc, pg 1069

COLORADO

Paul L Anderson Productions Inc, pg 786
Flashback Media Productions, pg 869
Meriwether Publishing Ltd, pg 939

CONNECTICUT

Broadcast Video Productions LLC, pg 813
Cine-Med Inc, pg 826
Crossroads Video, pg 840
Geomatrix Productions, pg 877
Ironik Design & Post, pg 902
Market Data Retrieval (MDR), pg 931
Musivision Inc, pg 951
New London Media, pg 956
Palace Digital Studios, pg 967
Twenty-Third Publications/Bayard, pg 1047

DISTRICT OF COLUMBIA

Hillmann & Carr Inc, pg 889
Theatrical Technicians Inc (TTI), pg 1038
USCCB Publishing, pg 1051

FLORIDA

Allegro Productions Inc, pg 781
AVI-SPL, pg 798
Blackburst Entertainment, pg 808
CD ROM™ Inc, pg 822
Civins Productions Inc, pg 828
Motion Image Group LLC, pg 947
Sunfire Communications Inc, pg 1028
Sunrise Studios, pg 1028
Teach America Corp, pg 1033

PROGRAMMING — MISCELLANEOUS

Computer Multimedia, CD-ROM & DVD Interactive Program Producers (continued)

FLORIDA (continued)

Times-Square Fantasy Theatre, pg 1041
Tricycle Studios, pg 1044
Video Techniques Inc, pg 1056

GEORGIA

Beachwood Productions, pg 804
Continental Film & Video, pg 835
ECG Productions, pg 856
Guerrilla Productions LLC, pg 883
Imagers, pg 896
On-Line Productions, pg 963

HAWAII

Hyperspective Studios Inc, pg 893

IDAHO

Marketron Broadcast Solutions, pg 931

ILLINOIS

ABSA Productions Inc, pg 772
Advanced Audio Technology, pg 777
Airways Digital Media, pg 779
Analog Free Media, pg 786
AnswersMedia, pg 787
Britannica Film & Video, pg 812
CCore Media Inc, pg 821
Centrax Corp, pg 823
Comtech Multimedia Marketing, pg 834
Cresta Creative, pg 839
Encyclopaedia Britannica Inc, pg 861
Extraordinary Demos, pg 864
IV Media Resources, pg 903
Learning Seed, pg 917
Major Media Inc, pg 929
MIGHTYbYTES Inc, pg 942
QuickSet International Inc, pg 989
RADMAR Inc, pg 990
Rand McNally Education, pg 991
Richter Studios, pg 996
Roadworthy Image Magnification, pg 998
Sparkfactor, pg 1019
Video Impressions, pg 1055

INDIANA

Agency for Instructional Technology (AIT), pg 778
AVA Productions, pg 798
Bright Ideas Creative Services, pg 812
Herff Jones | Nystrom, pg 888
Optical Disc Solutions Inc, pg 964
PentaVision Communications Inc, pg 972

IOWA

Right Stuf Inc, pg 997

KANSAS

Genigraphics®, pg 877
KAKE-TV, pg 907

KENTUCKY

Donna Lawrence Productions, pg 917
Northern Kentucky University, pg 959

LOUISIANA

Leisure Video, pg 918

MARYLAND

The Ahern Group, pg 779
CPR MultiMedia Solutions, pg 837
dbF a Media Company, pg 844
Discovery Education - Silver Spring, pg 848
Media Dimensions Inc, pg 936
Mobile-Video Productions Inc, pg 944
Video Labs, pg 1055

MASSACHUSETTS

Cramer Productions, pg 837
Documentary Educational Resources Inc, pg 850
In the Wild Productions, pg 897
Pauline Books & Media, pg 970
Penfield Productions Ltd, pg 971
PixMix Video Services, pg 976
Preston Productions Inc, pg 981
Veritech Corp, pg 1053

MICHIGAN

Digi Sign Design LLC, pg 847
K&R All Media Productions Inc, pg 908
K&R's Recording Studios Inc, pg 908
Zondervan, A HarperCollins Company, pg 1074

MINNESOTA

Aggressive Records Audio Duplication LLC, pg 778
Badiyan Inc, pg 801
Beyers Sound & Essay Audio, pg 806
The Richard Diercks Co Inc, pg 846
Hopkins Technology LLC, pg 891
House of Cinemagraphics, pg 891
Worthwhile Films, pg 1070

MISSOURI

Fambrough & Associates Inc, pg 865

NEVADA

Encore Productions Inc, pg 861
JCS Video Productions, pg 904

NEW JERSEY

CD Meyer Inc, pg 822
Euro-Pacific Film & Video Productions Inc, pg 863
Jeep Jazz Media Solutions, pg 905
Laurel Video Productions, pg 916
Megavideo Productions, pg 938
MIB Mediaworks, pg 941
Midnight Media Group Inc, pg 942
Optisonics Productions, pg 965
Outside The Box Interactive LLC, pg 966
Paulist Press, pg 970
Producer East Productions, pg 983

NEW MEXICO

Production Outfitters, pg 984

NEW YORK

AMV/Unitel, pg 786
Blue Barn Pictures Inc, pg 809
The Bureau for At-Risk Youth, pg 815
Criterion Collection, pg 839
Digital Force, pg 847
dM works, pg 849
Duplication Depot Inc, pg 853
Eastco Multimedia Solutions Inc, pg 856
Educational Images Ltd, pg 857
Fingerpaint, pg 868
Greyfalcon House, pg 882
Havas Worldwide, pg 886
HB-Content, pg 886
Human Relations Media, pg 892
iCrossing Inc, pg 893
International Digital Centre, pg 901
L A Bruell Inc, pg 914
Neal Marshad Productions, pg 931
Northeast Video Productions Inc, pg 959
PrimeLight Productions Inc, pg 982
Judson Rosebush Co Inc, pg 999
Sunrise Media LLC, pg 1028
Total Impact Multimedia Group Ltd, pg 1042

NORTH CAROLINA

All Pro Media Inc, pg 780
Pat Appleson Studios Inc, pg 788
The Communications Group Inc, pg 833
Horizon Video Productions Inc, pg 891
Moving Pictures, pg 948
SAS Institute Inc, pg 1002
2BruceStudio, pg 1047

OHIO

Advent Media Inc, pg 778
Creative Technology, pg 838
EDR Media LLC, pg 857
Electronic Vision Inc (EV), pg 859
R&B Communications Inc, pg 991
Take 1 Media Services, pg 1031
Thread Marketing Group, pg 1039

OREGON

Ideascape Inc, pg 894
InterVision Media, pg 902
NeoSoft Corp, pg 954
Odyssey Productions Inc, pg 961
Rex, pg 995
Wilderness Video, pg 1066

PENNSYLVANIA

AccuWeather Inc, pg 774
AiH Group Inc, pg 779
Beholder Productions Inc, pg 804
Discovery Education - South Burlington, pg 848
FMP Media Solutions Inc, pg 870
Innovision Media Group, pg 899
JPL, pg 906
Kenexa, pg 909
New Horizons Computer Learning Centers Inc, pg 955
Panta Rhei Media Inc, pg 968
Production Masters Inc (PMI), pg 984
Scala Inc, pg 1003
Science for Kids, pg 1005
Video/Film Associates, pg 1055

RHODE ISLAND

Sound-FX-Design, pg 1017

SOUTH DAKOTA

Sencore Inc, pg 1006

TENNESSEE

American Blackguard Inc, pg 784
Anode Inc, pg 787
Running Pony Productions LLC, pg 1000
Scripps Networks, pg 1005
Spring Arbor Distributors, pg 1022

TEXAS

Biway Media, pg 808
CEV Multimedia Ltd, pg 823
Communication Arts Multimedia Inc, pg 832
Dallas Learning Solutions, pg 842
The Editing Co, pg 857
Epic Software Group Inc, pg 862
First Group Communications Inc, pg 868
Lamb & Lion Ministries, pg 915
Mediaforce Productions, pg 937
Julye Newlin Productions Inc, pg 956
Omni Intercommunications Inc, pg 962
Romar Learning, pg 999
South Coast Film & Video, pg 1019

UTAH

K-SAR Video & DVD Productions, pg 907
Strata™, pg 1025

VERMONT

Ashgate Publishing Co, pg 792

VIRGINIA

Advance Concepts Inc, pg 777
CALIBRE, pg 816
D&B Television & Video Productions Inc, pg 842
ITC Learning LLC, pg 903
Lion Recording Services Inc, pg 922
Metro Productions, pg 939

WASHINGTON

Adams Creative & Production Services, pg 775
Victory Studios, pg 1054

WISCONSIN

Audio Visual of Milwaukee Inc, pg 795
Logan Productions Inc, pg 924
Meridian Studios, pg 939
Rucinski & Reetz Communications LLC, pg 1000
USAV Group Inc, pg 1050
Video Wisconsin Inc, pg 1056
Watts Communications Inc, pg 1062

BRITISH COLUMBIA

Triad Communications Ltd, pg 1044

NEWFOUNDLAND AND LABRADOR

Vidcraft Productions Ltd, pg 1054

ONTARIO

ADS Media, pg 777
GAPC (General Assembly Production Centre), pg 875
Gesturetek, pg 877

Computer Multimedia, CD-ROM & DVD Interactive Program Rentals

CALIFORNIA

DELAWARE

MASSACHUSETTS

MICHIGAN

OREGON

Coursewear & Software—Microcomputer, *see* Microcomputer Software & Courseware

Diorama Distributors

CALIFORNIA

MARYLAND

VIRGINIA

Diorama Producers

CALIFORNIA

CONNECTICUT

HAWAII

INDIANA

KENTUCKY

MICHIGAN

MISSOURI

NEVADA

NEW JERSEY

NEW YORK

OHIO

RHODE ISLAND

VIRGINIA

Diorama Rentals

GEORGIA

ILLINOIS

Learning System, *see* Reading & Tachistoscopic Equipment & Learning System

Microcomputer Software & Courseware Distributors

ARIZONA

CALIFORNIA

CONNECTICUT

DELAWARE

DISTRICT OF COLUMBIA

FLORIDA

GEORGIA

ILLINOIS

INDIANA

IOWA

KENTUCKY

MARYLAND

MASSACHUSETTS

MICHIGAN

MINNESOTA

NEW HAMPSHIRE

NEW JERSEY

NEW MEXICO

NEW YORK

NORTH CAROLINA

OHIO

PENNSYLVANIA

RHODE ISLAND

SOUTH CAROLINA

TENNESSEE

TEXAS

UTAH

VERMONT

WISCONSIN

BRITISH COLUMBIA

ONTARIO

Microcomputer Software & Courseware Producers

ARIZONA

PROGRAMMING — MISCELLANEOUS

Microcomputer Software & Courseware Producers (continued)

CALIFORNIA

Academy Savant, pg 773
Adobe Systems Inc, pg 776
Apple Inc, pg 788
Astronomical Society of the Pacific, pg 792
Autodesk Inc, pg 797
Joyce Media Inc, pg 906
Palardo Productions, pg 968
QRS Software Services, pg 988
Three D Graphics Inc, pg 1039
Unique Business Systems, pg 1048
Videobotics, pg 1056
Xytech Systems Corp, pg 1071

COLORADO

Scriptware, pg 1005

CONNECTICUT

Scholastic Library Publishing, pg 1004

DELAWARE

University Media Services, pg 1049

FLORIDA

Medina Software Inc, pg 938
Teach America Corp, pg 1033

ILLINOIS

Centrax Corp, pg 823
Encyclopaedia Britannica Inc, pg 861
1st Financial Training Services Inc, pg 868
Follett Software Co, pg 871
Major Media Inc, pg 929
National Safety Council (NSC), pg 953
Rand McNally Education, pg 991
Sunburst Digital, pg 1028
Video Impressions, pg 1055

INDIANA

Agency for Instructional Technology (AIT), pg 778
OMNI Productions, pg 962

IOWA

Accelerated Learning Foundation, pg 773
The Production House, pg 984

KENTUCKY

National Geographic Learning, pg 952

MARYLAND

CSPMedia.com, pg 840

MASSACHUSETTS

Cheng & Tsui Co, pg 824
Duxbury Systems Inc, pg 854
Lotus Development Corp, an IBM Company, pg 925
Monotype Inc, pg 945

MICHIGAN

Digi Sign Design LLC, pg 847
K&R All Media Productions Inc, pg 908
Wayne State University Media Services, pg 1063
Zondervan, A HarperCollins Company, pg 1074

MINNESOTA

Badiyan Inc, pg 801
Beyers Sound & Essay Audio, pg 806
Hopkins Technology LLC, pg 891
Llewellyn Publications, pg 923

MISSOURI

Celebrities Productions, pg 822

NEVADA

Encore Productions Inc, pg 861

NEW JERSEY

Advanced Imaging Concepts Inc, pg 777
Educational Impressions, pg 857
Outside The Box Interactive LLC, pg 966
John Wiley & Sons Inc, pg 1066

NEW MEXICO

VidCAD by Commsys Design LLC, pg 1054

NEW YORK

Norman N Axelrod Associates, pg 800
Criterion Collection, pg 839
Educational Images Ltd, pg 857
Neal Marshad Productions, pg 931
McGraw Hill Financial, pg 935
MRY, pg 949
Shelly Palmer Production, pg 968
Judson Rosebush Co Inc, pg 999
WorldView Software, pg 1070

NORTH CAROLINA

Alien Skin Software LLC, pg 780
SAS Institute Inc, pg 1002

OHIO

Advent Media Inc, pg 778
Creative Technology, pg 838
Electronic Vision Inc (EV), pg 859
McGraw-Hill School Education Group, pg 935
R&B Communications Inc, pg 991
South-Western Publishing Co, pg 1019

OREGON

ERA Learning, pg 862
InterVision Media, pg 902
NeoSoft Corp, pg 954

PENNSYLVANIA

AccuWeather Inc, pg 774
AiH Group Inc, pg 779
FMP Media Solutions Inc, pg 870
Innovision Media Group, pg 899
JPL, pg 906
Kenexa, pg 909
Scala Inc, pg 1003
Science for Kids, pg 1005

RHODE ISLAND

Sound-FX-Design, pg 1017

SOUTH CAROLINA

ACS Technologies, pg 775
BJU Press, pg 808

TENNESSEE

Cokesbury, pg 831
Memphis Communications Corp, pg 938

TEXAS

CEV Multimedia Ltd, pg 823
Communication Arts Multimedia Inc, pg 832
Compass Learning Inc, pg 833
Epic Software Group Inc, pg 862
Image Innovations Inc, pg 895
Romar Learning, pg 999
Videotex Systems Inc, pg 1057

UTAH

HEC Reading Horizons, pg 887
Novell Inc, pg 959

VIRGINIA

Computer Sciences Corp, pg 834
SoftWright LLC, pg 1015

WISCONSIN

DNASTAR Inc, pg 849
USAV Group Inc, pg 1050
Wisconsin Technical College System Foundation Inc, pg 1068

WYOMING

Bridger Productions Inc, pg 812

BRITISH COLUMBIA

Thompson Rivers University Open Learning, pg 1039

ONTARIO

Canadian Learning Co Inc, pg 818
Open Text Corp, pg 964
RB Productions, pg 992
Technovision® Interactive Inc, pg 1035

QUEBEC

Orion Software, pg 965

Microcomputer Software & Courseware Rentals

ARIZONA

CADint, pg 816

DELAWARE

University Media Services, pg 1049

FLORIDA

Micro Innovations Inc, pg 941

GEORGIA

Staging Directions Inc, pg 1023

ILLINOIS

1st Financial Training Services Inc, pg 868

MICHIGAN

Wayne State University Media Services, pg 1063

WISCONSIN

Wisconsin Technical College System Foundation Inc, pg 1068

QUEBEC

Orion Software, pg 965

Print—Study, *see* Study Print

Reading & Tachistoscopic Equipment & Learning System Distributors

CALIFORNIA

Ametron Audio/Video, pg 785

COLORADO

Vital Learning LLC, pg 1060

ILLINOIS

Educational Insights, pg 857

MARYLAND

Nicholas P Pipino Associates Inc, pg 976

MASSACHUSETTS

Duxbury Systems Inc, pg 854

NEW YORK

Visual Technologies Corp, pg 1060

UTAH

HEC Reading Horizons, pg 887

ONTARIO

Technovision® Interactive Inc, pg 1035

Reading & Tachistoscopic Equipment & Learning System Producers

CALIFORNIA

QRS Software Services, pg 988
SBS Productions, pg 1003

COLORADO

Vital Learning LLC, pg 1060

GEORGIA

Guerrilla Productions LLC, pg 883

MASSACHUSETTS

Duxbury Systems Inc, pg 854

MICHIGAN

K&R All Media Productions Inc, pg 908

MISSOURI

Celebrities Productions, pg 822

MISCELLANEOUS

Analyzer, *see* Battery, Charger & Analyzer

Battery, Charger & Analyzer Distributors

ALABAMA

Media Visions Inc, pg 937

ARIZONA

EAR Professional Audio/Video, pg 855
Metropolitan Audio-Visual Inc, pg 940
Troxell Communications Inc, pg 1045

CALIFORNIA

Adolph Gasser Inc, pg 776
Ametron Audio/Video, pg 785
Audio/Video Supply Inc, pg 795
Band Pro Film & Digital Inc, pg 802
BroadcastStore.com, pg 813
California Tape Products Inc, pg 817
Christy's Editorial, pg 826
Cinema Engineering Co, pg 827
Delicate Electronics Sales Inc, pg 845
Diversified Imaging Supply, pg 849
FXC Communications, pg 874
Gluskin's Custom Audio Video, pg 879
Alan Gordon Enterprises Inc, pg 880
Hooper Camera & Imaging, pg 891
IDX System Technology Inc, pg 894
Jameco Electronics, pg 903
JD Audio Visual Inc, pg 904
Kappa optronics Inc, pg 908
LibertyPak Co Inc, pg 919
Mobilized Tech Systems, pg 944
Mole-Richardson Co, pg 945
Orvac Electronics, pg 965
Pacific Radio Electronics, pg 967
Point of View Productions, pg 977
Power-Sonic Corp, pg 979
Pro Camera Repair, pg 982
Pro Power Products Inc, pg 983
Promax Systems, pg 986
SNAP, pg 1014
Sound Service Co, pg 1017
SSL Industries Inc, pg 1022
Total Concept Sales, pg 1042
Tri-Ed, pg 1044
Victory Cinevideo Battery Corp, pg 1054
Video Gear Rentals Inc, pg 1055
VTP Inc, pg 1061
Zack Electronics Inc, pg 1073

COLORADO

Daylight Productions & Rentals, pg 844
Spectrum Audio Visual Services, pg 1020
Stanco Sales LLC, pg 1023

CONNECTICUT

MAVCO, pg 934
Sennheiser Electronic Corp, pg 1006

FLORIDA

Access Media Group, pg 773
Allstar Audio Systems Inc, pg 782
Digital Video Systems Inc, pg 848
Enhanced View Services Inc, pg 861
Griffiths Broadcast Co Inc, pg 882
Hi-Tech Enterprises Inc, pg 888
Hi-Tech Import Export Corp, pg 888
Hunter Electronics LLC, pg 892
Media Concepts Inc, pg 936
Midtown Video Inc, pg 942
Photomart Cine-Video Inc, pg 975
Pro Stage Inc, pg 983
Recording Media & Equipment Inc (RM&E), pg 993
Reef Photo & Video, pg 993
TAI Audio, pg 1031
Techni-Lux Inc, pg 1033
Videoscope, pg 1057

GEORGIA

Blue Media Supply Inc, pg 809
Lighting & Production Equipment Inc, pg 920
Stage Front Presentation Systems, pg 1022
Synergistic Batteries Inc, pg 1030

ILLINOIS

Joseph Electronics, pg 906
RAM Systems LLC, pg 991
Tape Resources, pg 1031
Tele-Time Systems, pg 1036

INDIANA

Jack's Camera Shop, pg 903
Lee Co Inc, pg 918
Victoria Supply Inc/Topbulb.com, pg 1054

IOWA

Sitler's Supplies Inc, pg 1012

KANSAS

Smith Audio-Visual Inc, pg 1014

KENTUCKY

Barney Miller's Inc, pg 943
NOR-COM Inc, pg 958

MARYLAND

Noventri, pg 960
Shadowstone R & R™, pg 1008

MASSACHUSETTS

Advanced Battery Systems Inc, pg 777
Camera Co Inc/Broadcast Divison, pg 818
Terry Hanley Audio Systems Inc, pg 884
HMC Electronics, pg 889
Hunt's Photo, Video & Digital, pg 892
Rule Broadcast Systems, pg 1000
Stanley Supply & Services Inc, pg 1023

MICHIGAN

Lowing Light & Grip Inc, pg 925

MINNESOTA

Alpha Video & Audio Inc, pg 782
Lights On, pg 921

MISSISSIPPI

Bowie Audio Visual Enterprises Inc, pg 811

MISSOURI

Communitronics Corp, pg 833
Southwest Audio-Visual Inc, pg 1019

NEVADA

Aardvark Video & Media Productions, pg 772
L E Nelson Sales Corp, pg 954

NEW JERSEY

Alltec Stores, a Vcom IMC Company, pg 782
Argraph Corp, pg 789
Audio Visual Associates, pg 795
AV Bluebook, pg 797
Comprehensive Cable & Connectivity Co, pg 833
Frezzi Energy Systems, pg 873
G&G Technologies Inc, pg 875
Hakuba Sunpak Velbon, pg 883
Hamilton Buhl, pg 884
Herbach & Rademan Co Inc, pg 888
HP Marketing Corp, pg 892
MCCOM Inc, pg 935
National Audio-Visual Supply, pg 952
Bill Quinn Productions, pg 989
Starlite Productions, pg 1024
SYMCO Inc, pg 1030
Total Video Products Inc, pg 1042

NEW YORK

Adwar Video, pg 778
Audio-Video Corp, pg 795
AV Workshop, pg 797
B&H Photo & Video Pro Audio, pg 802
Barbizon Electric Co Inc, pg 802
BTX Technologies, pg 814
Bulb Direct, pg 815
Bulbtronics Inc, pg 815
Communication Corner Inc, pg 832
Creative Stage Lighting Co Inc, pg 838
Edmund Scientific, pg 857
Film Emporium, pg 867
Gaylord Brothers, pg 876
HAVE Inc, pg 886
Long Island Video Enterprises Live Inc, pg 924
Markertek Video Supply, pg 931
MDS Power Inc, pg 936
Neptune Photo Inc, pg 954
Northern Lights, pg 959
Production Radio Rentals Inc, pg 984
RNJ Electronics, pg 997
RTS Inc, pg 1000
Russell Industries Inc, pg 1001
Technisphere Corp, pg 1034
TecNec Distributing, pg 1035
The Tiffen Co LLC, pg 1040
Varta Microbattery Inc, pg 1052
Visual Technologies Corp, pg 1060
Visual Word Systems Inc, pg 1060
Vitec Videocom Inc, pg 1060
Xtech Inc, pg 1071

NORTH CAROLINA

Harrison Brothers, pg 885
Strategic Connections, pg 1026

OHIO

Copp Integrated Systems, pg 836
Midwest Photo Exchange, pg 942
Parts Express, pg 969
Smithall Electronics Inc, pg 1014
Tri-State Audio Visual Co, pg 1044
Vanner Inc, pg 1051

PENNSYLVANIA

Advanced AV, pg 777
Audio Visions Inc, pg 795
Bernie's Photo Center, pg 805
J E Foss Co, pg 871
Garcia Marketing Inc, pg 875
The Lerro Corp, pg 919
Morefield Communications Inc, pg 946
New York Camera & Video, pg 956
Techni-Tool Inc, pg 1033

TENNESSEE

Lowrance Sound Co Inc, pg 925

TEXAS

Astro Audio Visual, pg 792
Audio Visual Technologies Group, pg 796
Horizon Worldwide, pg 891
Industrial Audio/Video Inc, pg 897
International Fun-Shop, pg 901
MarathonNorco Aerospace Inc, pg 930
Omega Broadcast Group, pg 962
Precision Camera & Video, pg 980
Pro Video & Film Equipment Co Inc, pg 983
RadioShack Corp, pg 990
Specialized Products Co, pg 1020
TapeWorks Texas Inc, pg 1032
Tarpley Media Systems, pg 1032

UTAH

Redman Movies & Stories, pg 993
RIA Corp, pg 996

VERMONT

Production Advantage Inc, pg 984

VIRGINIA

Avitecture Inc, pg 799
Boitnott Visual Communications Corp (BVC), pg 810
Communications Specialists Inc, pg 833
D&B Television & Video Productions Inc, pg 842
Filmdex Inc, pg 867
Lee Hartman & Sons Inc, pg 918
Thomas & Betts Power Solutions, pg 1039

WASHINGTON

Alpha Technologies, pg 782
Oppenheimer Camera Products, pg 964

WISCONSIN

Alpha Source Inc, pg 782
Audio Visual of Milwaukee Inc, pg 795
Camera Corner Connecting Point, pg 818
Full Compass Systems, pg 874
Pro Studio Supply, pg 983
Safe Harbor Computers, pg 1001

PUERTO RICO

Bonnin Electronics Inc, pg 810

ALBERTA

Infosat Communications Inc, pg 898
Matrix Video Communications Corp (MVCC), pg 934
McBain Audio Visual Ltd, pg 935

BRITISH COLUMBIA

Cadex Electronics Inc, pg 816
ProVision Video Sales & Rentals Inc, pg 986

MANITOBA

Inland Audio Visual Ltd, pg 898

ONTARIO

Edcom Multimedia Products, pg 856
HD Source, pg 886
Henry's Camera, pg 888
Nationwide Audio Visual Co, pg 953

QUEBEC

Panavideo Inc, pg 968
SC Media Canada, pg 1003

Battery, Charger & Analyzer Manufacturers

CALIFORNIA

Apogee Electronics Corp, pg 788
IDX System Technology Inc, pg 894
Kappa optronics Inc, pg 908
LibertyPak Co Inc, pg 919
Power-Sonic Corp, pg 979
Pro Power Products Inc, pg 983
Victory Cinevideo Battery Corp, pg 1054
Visual Instrumentation Corp, pg 1059

CONNECTICUT

Anton/Bauer Inc, pg 787

GEORGIA

Synergistic Batteries Inc, pg 1030

ILLINOIS

Cool-Lux, pg 836
Smith-Victor Corp, pg 1014
Tripp Lite, pg 1045

NEW JERSEY

Dyna-Lite Inc, pg 854
Frezzi Energy Systems, pg 873
Hakuba Sunpak Velbon, pg 883
Nova Electric, pg 959

NEW YORK

Cine 60 Inc, pg 826
Sima Products Corp, pg 1011
Ultralife Corporation, pg 1047
Varta Microbattery Inc, pg 1052

OHIO

Vanner Inc, pg 1051

RHODE ISLAND

APC by Schneider Electric, pg 788

TEXAS

Exeltech Inc, pg 864
Horizon Worldwide, pg 891
MarathonNorco Aerospace Inc, pg 930

VIRGINIA

Thomas & Betts Power Solutions, pg 1039

WASHINGTON

Oppenheimer Camera Products, pg 964

WISCONSIN

Marinco Electrical Group, pg 931

BRITISH COLUMBIA

Cadex Electronics Inc, pg 816

Battery, Charger & Analyzer Rentals

ARIZONA

Merestone, pg 938
Metropolitan Audio-Visual Inc, pg 940
Reel Men Rentals Inc, pg 994

ARKANSAS

White Diamond Productions, pg 1065

CALIFORNIA

Aaron & Le Duc, pg 772
Action Audio & Visual, pg 775
Adolph Gasser Inc, pg 776
Alternative Rentals, pg 783
Ametron Audio/Video, pg 785
Artichoke Productions, pg 791
Bexel Corp, pg 806
Chater Camera Inc, pg 824
Cineworks Inc, pg 828
Crystal Pyramid Productions™, pg 840
Express Media Inc, pg 864
First Camera, pg 868
Full Moon & High Tide Productions & Studios, pg 874
Gear Monkey, pg 876
Gold Standard Productions, pg 880
Alan Gordon Enterprises Inc, pg 880
iCorpTv, pg 893
Image Integration, pg 895
Location Sound Corp, pg 924
Main Street Media Inc, pg 929
Munday & Collins AV, pg 950
Otto Nemenz International Inc, pg 954
Next Arts, pg 957
Old School Cameras, pg 961
Phoebus Lighting, pg 974
Prime Cut Productions, pg 982
Pro HD Rentals, pg 983
Radiant Images, pg 990
RetinaVision Productions, pg 995
Samy's Camera, pg 1002
Shooting Star Video, pg 1009
Slate Media Group, pg 1013
SNAP, pg 1014
Stray Angel Films, pg 1026
T-stop Inc, pg 1031
Total Media Group, pg 1042
Tri-Ed, pg 1044
Twin Peaks Creative, pg 1047
VER-Video Equipment Rentals, pg 1053
Video Gear Rentals Inc, pg 1055
Visual Instrumentation Corp, pg 1059
VMI Inc, pg 1060
Voice & Video Rentals, pg 1060
Westcoast Video Productions Inc, pg 1064

COLORADO

Daylight Productions & Rentals, pg 844
Tatum Video, pg 1032

CONNECTICUT

A/V Davey, pg 797
Fox Connecticut, pg 872
Videofilm Systems Inc, pg 1057

FLORIDA

Access Media Group, pg 773
Allstar Audio Systems Inc, pg 782
Budget Video Rentals, pg 815
Cinema East, pg 827
Eastern Video, pg 856
Jordan Klein Film & Video (JKFV), pg 906
Knowles Video Inc (KVI), pg 912
Midtown Video Inc, pg 942
Pro Stage Inc, pg 983
Skyline Broadcast, pg 1013
Universal Studios Florida® Production Group, pg 1049

GEORGIA

Lighting & Production Equipment Inc, pg 920
Stage Front Presentation Systems, pg 1022

HAWAII

Sight & Sound Studios, pg 1010

ILLINOIS

Backstar Creative Media Inc, pg 801
Beatty TeleVisual Productions, pg 804
Chicago Satellite & Video, pg 825
On Site Video, pg 963
RC Communications, pg 992
Show Department Inc, pg 1009
Tele-Time Systems, pg 1036

KENTUCKY

Audio Visual Techniques Inc, pg 796
Kentucky Grip & Lighting, pg 909

LOUISIANA

Pace Systems, pg 966

MARYLAND

Archai Media, pg 789
Shadowstone R & R™, pg 1008

MASSACHUSETTS

Camera Co Inc/Broadcast Divison, pg 818
Capron Lighting & Sound Co Inc, pg 819
Terry Hanley Audio Systems Inc, pg 884
WVP Boston, pg 1071

MICHIGAN

Digi Sign Design LLC, pg 847
K&R All Media Productions Inc, pg 908
K&R's Recording Studios Inc, pg 908
Lowing Light & Grip Inc, pg 925

MINNESOTA

Lights On, pg 921
Pro Media Productions, pg 983

MISSISSIPPI

Bowie Audio Visual Enterprises Inc, pg 811

MISSOURI

Show-Me Audio-Visual, pg 1009

NEBRASKA

Lights On Nebraska, pg 921

NEW HAMPSHIRE

Apertura, pg 788

NEW JERSEY

CFP Video Productions Inc, pg 823
Dyna-Lite Inc, pg 854
Bill Quinn Productions, pg 989
Video Corporation of America (VCA), pg 1055

NEW MEXICO

Production Outfitters, pg 984

NEW YORK

Adorama Rental Co, pg 776
Adwar Video, pg 778
Big Foot Productions Inc, pg 807
Bond Street Studio, pg 810
Cine 60 Inc, pg 826
Cinema-Vision, pg 827
CPT Rental Inc, pg 837
CSI Rentals, pg 840
Hand Held Films, pg 884
LightHouse Films, pg 920
Long Island Video Enterprises Live Inc, pg 924
Scheimpflug Digital, pg 1004
TBA Global Events, pg 1032
Technisphere Corp, pg 1034
Visual Technologies Corp, pg 1060
Xtech Inc, pg 1071

NORTH CAROLINA

A&V Company, pg 772
The Communications Group Inc, pg 833
Duke Media Services, pg 853
Moving Pictures, pg 948
On Location North Carolina, pg 963
Special Event Services, pg 1020
Take One Productions Ltd, pg 1031

NORTH DAKOTA

Media Productions, pg 937

OHIO

ITA Audio Visual Solutions, pg 902
Lyon Video Inc, pg 927
Ohio HD Video, pg 961
R&B Communications Inc, pg 991

OKLAHOMA

PDC Productions, pg 970

MISCELLANEOUS

Battery, Charger & Analyzer Rentals (continued)

OREGON

Koerner Camera Systems, pg 912
Northwest Film Center, pg 959

PENNSYLVANIA

Advanced AV, pg 777
Bernie's Photo Center, pg 805
Fusion Brand Experiences, pg 874
JPL, pg 906
Location Camera Ltd, pg 923
Location Lighting Ltd, pg 924
Muderick Media, pg 949
New York Camera & Video, pg 956
The Videohouse Inc, pg 1057
Visual Sound Inc, pg 1059

TENNESSEE

RentACamera.com, pg 995

TEXAS

Bright Giant Creative Group, pg 812
GEAR Cameras & Lighting, pg 876
Omega Broadcast Group, pg 962
South Coast Film & Video, pg 1019
Stage Directions, pg 1022
Texcam Inc, pg 1038
Video Perspective, pg 1056

UTAH

Ron Hill Imagery, pg 889
Redman Movies & Stories, pg 993

VERMONT

Dark Star Lighting & Production, pg 842

WASHINGTON

Oppenheimer Camera Products, pg 964
Victory Studios, pg 1054

WISCONSIN

Camera Corner Connecting Point, pg 818
Full Compass Systems, pg 874

WYOMING

Bridger Productions Inc, pg 812

ALBERTA

Global Television Station, pg 879

BRITISH COLUMBIA

Image Media Farm, pg 895
ProVision Video Sales & Rentals Inc, pg 986
Triad Communications Ltd, pg 1044
Video In Studios/Video Out Distribution, pg 1055

ONTARIO

Edcom Multimedia Products, pg 856
HD Source, pg 886
JIB Shots Equipment Inc, pg 905
RB Productions, pg 992
ZTV Broadcast Services Inc, pg 1074

QUEBEC

Group PVP, pg 882

Battery, Charger & Analyzer Repairs

CALIFORNIA

Ametron Audio/Video, pg 785
BroadcastStore.com, pg 813
McAlister Electronics, pg 935
Pro Power Products Inc, pg 983
TEK Media Group, pg 1035
Victory Cinevideo Battery Corp, pg 1054
Visual Instrumentation Corp, pg 1059

FLORIDA

ELC Sales & Service Inc, pg 858

GEORGIA

Stage Front Presentation Systems, pg 1022

ILLINOIS

Midwest Digital Corp, pg 942
On Site Video, pg 963

KENTUCKY

NOR-COM Inc, pg 958

MICHIGAN

Lowing Light & Grip Inc, pg 925

NEW JERSEY

Dyna-Lite Inc, pg 854
Frezzi Energy Systems, pg 873

NEW YORK

Adwar Video, pg 778
Cine 60 Inc, pg 826
CPT Rental Inc, pg 837
Visual Technologies Corp, pg 1060
Vitec Videocom Inc, pg 1060
Xtech Inc, pg 1071

OHIO

Vanner Inc, pg 1051

PENNSYLVANIA

Bernie's Photo Center, pg 805

TEXAS

MarathonNorco Aerospace Inc, pg 930
Pro Video & Film Equipment Co Inc, pg 983
Tarpley Media Systems, pg 1032

UTAH

RIA Corp, pg 996

WASHINGTON

Oppenheimer Camera Products, pg 964

WISCONSIN

Camera Corner Connecting Point, pg 818
Full Compass Systems, pg 874

ALBERTA

Infosat Communications Inc, pg 898

ONTARIO

Edcom Multimedia Products, pg 856
HD Source, pg 886

Blinds, *see* Room-Darkening Drape & Blind

Cabinet—Storage, *see* Storage Cabinet

Carrying Case, *see* Shipping, Packaging, Carrying & Storage Case

Charger, *see* Battery, Charger & Analyzer

Clock, *see* Timer & Clock

Control Equipment, *see* Lighting Fixture & Control Equipment

Drapes, *see* Room-Darkening Drape & Blind

Dust Elimination Equipment Distributors

ALABAMA

Media Visions Inc, pg 937

CALIFORNIA

Adolph Gasser Inc, pg 776
Diversified Imaging Supply, pg 849
Educational Technology Services (ETS), pg 857
Gluskin's Custom Audio Video, pg 879
Jameco Electronics, pg 903
Location Sound Corp, pg 924
Media Fabricators Inc, pg 936
Samy's Camera, pg 1002
Tri-Ed, pg 1044

CONNECTICUT

MAVCO, pg 934

FLORIDA

Hunter Electronics LLC, pg 892
Midtown Video Inc, pg 942
Projector Protector Inc, pg 986

GEORGIA

Stage Front Presentation Systems, pg 1022

KENTUCKY

K&R Photo Digital, pg 908
NOR-COM Inc, pg 958
WaxWorks VideoWorks, pg 1063

MARYLAND

Shadowstone R & R™, pg 1008

MASSACHUSETTS

Hunt's Photo, Video & Digital, pg 892
Spirig Advanced Technologies Inc (SAT), pg 1021

NEW JERSEY

Argraph Corp, pg 789
AV Bluebook, pg 797
Falcon Safety Products Inc, pg 865
National Audio-Visual Supply, pg 952

NEW YORK

AV Workshop, pg 797
Communication Corner Inc, pg 832
Get Smart Products, pg 877
Light Impressions, pg 920
Markertek Video Supply, pg 931
NRD LLC, A Mark IV Industries Co, pg 960
TecNec Distributing, pg 1035

PENNSYLVANIA

Bernie's Photo Center, pg 805
Charles Beseler Co, pg 824
Techni-Tool Inc, pg 1033

TEXAS

RadioShack Corp, pg 990
Specialized Products Co, pg 1020

VIRGINIA

Filmdex Inc, pg 867
Lee Hartman & Sons Inc, pg 918

WISCONSIN

Full Compass Systems, pg 874

PUERTO RICO

Bonnin Electronics Inc, pg 810

ALBERTA

McBain Audio Visual Ltd, pg 935

QUEBEC

SC Media Canada, pg 1003

Dust Elimination Equipment Manufacturers

FLORIDA

Kinetronics Corp, pg 911
Projector Protector Inc, pg 986

ILLINOIS

Sprayway Inc, pg 1022

MASSACHUSETTS

Spirig Advanced Technologies Inc (SAT), pg 1021

NEW JERSEY

Falcon Safety Products Inc, pg 865

NEW YORK

NRD LLC, A Mark IV Industries Co, pg 960

PENNSYLVANIA

Nilfisk-Advance America Inc, pg 957

Dust Elimination Equipment Rentals

FLORIDA

Jordan Klein Film & Video (JKFV), pg 906

GEORGIA

Stage Front Presentation Systems, pg 1022

NEW YORK

TBA Global Events, pg 1032

NORTH CAROLINA

Take One Productions Ltd, pg 1031

PENNSYLVANIA

Bernie's Photo Center, pg 805

UTAH

Redman Movies & Stories, pg 993

Dust Elimination Equipment Repairs

GEORGIA

Stage Front Presentation Systems, pg 1022

KENTUCKY

NOR-COM Inc, pg 958

PENNSYLVANIA

Bernie's Photo Center, pg 805

Electrical Generator Distributors

ALABAMA

Media Visions Inc, pg 937

CALIFORNIA

Ametron Audio/Video, pg 785
Angstrom Lighting, pg 786
Mole-Richardson Co, pg 945
Phoebus Lighting, pg 974

FLORIDA

Allstar Audio Systems Inc, pg 782
Pro Stage Inc, pg 983
Recording Media & Equipment Inc (RM&E), pg 993

GEORGIA

Lighting & Production Equipment Inc, pg 920

ILLINOIS

Joseph Electronics, pg 906

MARYLAND

Absolute Hollywood, pg 772

MASSACHUSETTS

ASACA/ShibaSoku Corp of America, pg 791
High Output Inc, pg 888

NEW YORK

Long Island Video Enterprises Live Inc, pg 924

PENNSYLVANIA

Techni-Tool Inc, pg 1033

TEXAS

MQ Power Corp, pg 948
Pro Video & Film Equipment Co Inc, pg 983
Specialized Products Co, pg 1020

UTAH

RIA Corp, pg 996

PUERTO RICO

Bonnin Electronics Inc, pg 810

ALBERTA

McBain Audio Visual Ltd, pg 935

BRITISH COLUMBIA

DL Sound & Lighting Productions Ltd, pg 849

ONTARIO

Nationwide Audio Visual Co, pg 953

Electrical Generator Manufacturers

CALIFORNIA

Mole-Richardson Co, pg 945

FLORIDA

Compuvideo Sales USA Ltd, pg 834
PowerTechnology Southeast Inc, pg 979

MARYLAND

Teledyne Energy Systems Inc, pg 1036

MASSACHUSETTS

ASACA/ShibaSoku Corp of America, pg 791

NEW JERSEY

Nova Electric, pg 959

OHIO

Norlake Manufacturing Co, pg 958

TEXAS

MQ Power Corp, pg 948

Electrical Generator Rentals

ALABAMA

Audio-Video Resources Inc, pg 795

ARIZONA

Arizona Cine Equipment, pg 789

CALIFORNIA

AGF Media Services, pg 778
Ametron Audio/Video, pg 785
Angstrom Lighting, pg 786
Cherry Multimedia, pg 824
Cineworks Inc, pg 828
Dadco, pg 842
DTC Lighting & Grip, pg 853
Gear Monkey, pg 876
JD Audio Visual Inc, pg 904
Main Street Media Inc, pg 929
McCune Audio-Video-Lighting, pg 935
Mole-Richardson Co, pg 945
Phoebus Lighting, pg 974
PSAV® Presentation Services, pg 986
RetinaVision Productions, pg 995
Total Media Group, pg 1042
Video Gear Rentals Inc, pg 1055

COLORADO

Zelo Productions Inc, pg 1073

CONNECTICUT

A/V Davey, pg 797
Videofilm Systems Inc, pg 1057

FLORIDA

Allstar Audio Systems Inc, pg 782
Budget Video Rentals, pg 815
Jordan Klein Film & Video (JKFV), pg 906
MAPS Production House, pg 930
Pro Stage Inc, pg 983

GEORGIA

Continental Film & Video, pg 835
Lighting & Production Equipment Inc, pg 920
Stage Front Presentation Systems, pg 1022

HAWAII

ATTCO Inc, pg 793
FOTON Hawaii, pg 871

ILLINOIS

AV Chicago Inc, pg 797
LITE-IT Grip Truck Rentals, pg 923
On Site Video, pg 963

KENTUCKY

Audio Visual Techniques Inc, pg 796

LOUISIANA

Moxie Media, pg 948
Pace Systems, pg 966

MARYLAND

Event Tech, pg 863

MASSACHUSETTS

Advanced Lighting & Production Services Inc (ALPS), pg 777
Capron Lighting & Sound Co Inc, pg 819
High Output Inc, pg 888
Limelight Productions Inc, pg 921
massAV, pg 933

MICHIGAN

Digi Sign Design LLC, pg 847
Lowing Light & Grip Inc, pg 925
On Stage Visuals, pg 963

MINNESOTA

Lights On, pg 921

MISSOURI

Show-Me Audio-Visual, pg 1009
Sight & Sound Production Services Inc, pg 1010

NEVADA

PRG Lighting, pg 981

NEW JERSEY

CFP Video Productions Inc, pg 823
Ironbound Film & Television Studios LLC, pg 902
Starlite Productions, pg 1024
Turner Engineering Inc, pg 1046

NEW YORK

All Terrain Power Co Inc, pg 781
Bond Street Studio, pg 810
Thomas Cestare Inc, pg 823
Design Audio Visual Inc, pg 845
Eastern Effects Inc, pg 856
Gearhead Rentals, pg 876
LightSpace Studios, pg 921
Long Island Video Enterprises Live Inc, pg 924
RGH Lighting LLC, pg 996

NORTH CAROLINA

On Location North Carolina, pg 963
Take One Productions Ltd, pg 1031

OKLAHOMA

PDC Productions, pg 970

OREGON

Pacific Grip & Lighting Inc, pg 967
Picture This Production Services, pg 975

PENNSYLVANIA

Location Camera Ltd, pg 923
Location Lighting Ltd, pg 924

SOUTH CAROLINA

Studio Charleston, pg 1026

TENNESSEE

DR&A Inc, pg 852

TEXAS

GEAR Cameras & Lighting, pg 876
Light Tec, pg 920
Muller Entertainment, pg 949
Panavision Dallas, pg 968
Texcam Inc, pg 1038

UTAH

Redman Movies & Stories, pg 993

WASHINGTON

Victory Studios, pg 1054

PUERTO RICO

Stage Crew Audiovisual Inc, pg 1022

MISCELLANEOUS

Electrical Generator Rentals (continued)

ALBERTA

Global Television Station, pg 879
MTM Equipment Rentals Ltd, pg 949

BRITISH COLUMBIA

DL Sound & Lighting Productions Ltd, pg 849

ONTARIO

JIB Shots Equipment Inc, pg 905

MASSACHUSETTS

Rule Broadcast Systems, pg 1000
Stanley Supply & Services Inc, pg 1023

MICHIGAN

ASC Systems, pg 791

NEW JERSEY

Starlite Productions, pg 1024

NEW YORK

Edmund Scientific, pg 857
Gage-Line Technology Inc, pg 874
Markertek Video Supply, pg 931

OHIO

Parts Express, pg 969
Smithall Electronics Inc, pg 1014

PENNSYLVANIA

Techni-Tool Inc, pg 1033

SOUTH DAKOTA

Sencore Inc, pg 1006

TEXAS

Specialized Products Co, pg 1020

VIRGINIA

Lee Hartman & Sons Inc, pg 918

WISCONSIN

Full Compass Systems, pg 874

Electrical Generator Repairs

CALIFORNIA

Ametron Audio/Video, pg 785
Mole-Richardson Co, pg 945
Phoebus Lighting, pg 974

GEORGIA

Lighting & Production Equipment Inc, pg 920

MARYLAND

Teledyne Energy Systems Inc, pg 1036

MASSACHUSETTS

Capron Lighting & Sound Co Inc, pg 819
Limelight Productions Inc, pg 921

TEXAS

Pro Video & Film Equipment Co Inc, pg 983

UTAH

RIA Corp, pg 996

Equipment Inspection & Testing Device Distributors

CALIFORNIA

Addlogix, pg 776
Ametron Audio/Video, pg 785
Cinematography Electronics Inc, pg 828
Jameco Electronics, pg 903
VTP Inc, pg 1061

CONNECTICUT

Gold Line/TEF, pg 880

FLORIDA

Access Media Group, pg 773
Alcorn McBride Inc, pg 780
Digital Video Systems Inc, pg 848
Pro Stage Inc, pg 983

ILLINOIS

Joseph Electronics, pg 906

KENTUCKY

NOR-COM Inc, pg 958

MASSACHUSETTS

Rule Broadcast Systems, pg 1000
Stanley Supply & Services Inc, pg 1023

MICHIGAN

ASC Systems, pg 791

NEW JERSEY

Starlite Productions, pg 1024

NEW YORK

Edmund Scientific, pg 857
Gage-Line Technology Inc, pg 874
Markertek Video Supply, pg 931

OHIO

Parts Express, pg 969
Smithall Electronics Inc, pg 1014

PENNSYLVANIA

Techni-Tool Inc, pg 1033

SOUTH DAKOTA

Sencore Inc, pg 1006

TEXAS

Specialized Products Co, pg 1020

VIRGINIA

Lee Hartman & Sons Inc, pg 918

WISCONSIN

Full Compass Systems, pg 874

Equipment Inspection & Testing Device Manufacturers

ARIZONA

Applied Integration Corp, pg 789

CALIFORNIA

Ametek Programmable Power, pg 785
Cinematography Electronics Inc, pg 828
Emlight Design, pg 860
Extron Electronics, pg 864

CONNECTICUT

Gold Line/TEF, pg 880

FLORIDA

Alcorn McBride Inc, pg 780
Compuvideo Sales USA Ltd, pg 834

INDIANA

R B Annis Instruments Inc, pg 787

NEW HAMPSHIRE

Monarch Instrument, pg 945

NEW JERSEY

Prism Media Products Inc, pg 982

NEW YORK

Norman N Axelrod Associates, pg 800
Broadcast Devices Inc, pg 813
Gage-Line Technology Inc, pg 874
Navitar Inc, pg 953

PENNSYLVANIA

Tobias Associates Inc, pg 1041

SOUTH DAKOTA

Sencore Inc, pg 1006

TEXAS

National Instruments Corp, pg 953

Equipment Inspection & Testing Device Rentals

CALIFORNIA

Ametron Audio/Video, pg 785
Express Media Inc, pg 864
RetinaVision Productions, pg 995
Twin Peaks Creative, pg 1047

CONNECTICUT

Videofilm Systems Inc, pg 1057

FLORIDA

Access Media Group, pg 773
Pro Stage Inc, pg 983

GEORGIA

Stage Front Presentation Systems, pg 1022

NEW JERSEY

Starlite Productions, pg 1024

NORTH CAROLINA

Take One Productions Ltd, pg 1031

OHIO

Lyon Video Inc, pg 927

TEXAS

GEAR Cameras & Lighting, pg 876
Texcam Inc, pg 1038

WISCONSIN

Full Compass Systems, pg 874

Equipment Inspection & Testing Device Repairs

CALIFORNIA

Ametron Audio/Video, pg 785

KENTUCKY

NOR-COM Inc, pg 958

WISCONSIN

Full Compass Systems, pg 874

Generator, *see* Electrical Generator

Kiosk Distributors

ARKANSAS

Jay S Stanley & Associates Inc, pg 1023

CALIFORNIA

Cibola Systems, pg 826
Delicate Electronics Sales Inc, pg 845

COLORADO

KD Kanopy Inc, pg 908

FLORIDA

Alcorn McBride Inc, pg 780
Digital Video Systems Inc, pg 848

KENTUCKY

Axxis Inc, pg 800
NOR-COM Inc, pg 958

MARYLAND

Noventri, pg 960

MASSACHUSETTS

Veritech Corp, pg 1053

MICHIGAN

Digi Sign Design LLC, pg 847

NEW JERSEY

MIB Mediaworks, pg 941

NEW YORK

Custom Media Environments, pg 841
General Audio-Visual Inc (GAVI), pg 876
Visual Technologies Corp, pg 1060

PENNSYLVANIA

Advanced AV, pg 777
Innovision Media Group, pg 899

TENNESSEE

Spring Arbor Distributors, pg 1022

TEXAS

DNP Photo Imaging America Corp, pg 849

WISCONSIN

Spectrum Industries Inc, pg 1021

MANITOBA

Tek Gear, pg 1035

ONTARIO

Cinema Stage Inc, pg 827
Gesturetek, pg 877
Technovision® Interactive Inc, pg 1035

Kiosk Manufacturers

ALABAMA

ExpoDisplays, pg 864
Marco Inc, pg 930

CALIFORNIA

Electrorack Legrand Division, pg 859
Grande Vitesse Systems Inc (GVS), pg 881
International E-Z UP Inc, pg 901
POP TV, pg 978

COLORADO

Display Devices, pg 849

CONNECTICUT

Alarmco Intelligent Message Repeaters, pg 779

FLORIDA

Alcorn McBride Inc, pg 780
CD ROM™ Inc, pg 822

ILLINOIS

Bretford Manufacturing Inc, pg 812
Marshall Furniture Inc, pg 932
The Miller Group, Multiplex Division, pg 943

KANSAS

Keywest Technology Inc, pg 910

MARYLAND

Quatrefoil Associates Inc, pg 989

MASSACHUSETTS

Veritech Corp, pg 1053

MINNESOTA

Emcor Enclosures-Crenlo, pg 860

NEW YORK

Eastco Multimedia Solutions Inc, pg 856

OHIO

Mills James Productions, pg 943

OKLAHOMA

Digital Designs, pg 847

TENNESSEE

Adtec Digital Inc, pg 777
Spring Arbor Distributors, pg 1022

TEXAS

DNP Photo Imaging America Corp, pg 849

VIRGINIA

Optikinetics Ltd - The Americas, pg 964

WISCONSIN

Spectrum Industries Inc, pg 1021

BRITISH COLUMBIA

Kodak Canada Inc, pg 912

MANITOBA

Big Deal Custom Casings, pg 807
Tek Gear, pg 1035

ONTARIO

Gesturetek, pg 877
Technovision® Interactive Inc, pg 1035
Versatruss, pg 1053

Kiosk Rentals

CALIFORNIA

Muse Presentation Technologies, pg 950

GEORGIA

Stage Front Presentation Systems, pg 1022

MICHIGAN

Digi Sign Design LLC, pg 847

NEW YORK

Design Audio Visual Inc, pg 845
Interactive International Inc, pg 899
Visual Technologies Corp, pg 1060

PENNSYLVANIA

Advanced AV, pg 777
FMP Media Solutions Inc, pg 870
Innovision Media Group, pg 899

WISCONSIN

Logan Productions Inc, pg 924

MANITOBA

Tek Gear, pg 1035

Kiosk Repairs

KENTUCKY

Axxis Inc, pg 800
NOR-COM Inc, pg 958

MANITOBA

Big Deal Custom Casings, pg 807
Tek Gear, pg 1035

Learning System, *see* Reading & Tachistoscopic Equipment & Learning System

Light Meter Distributors

ARIZONA

Troxell Communications Inc, pg 1045

CALIFORNIA

Adolph Gasser Inc, pg 776
Ametron Audio/Video, pg 785
Angstrom Lighting, pg 786
Educational Technology Services (ETS), pg 857
FXC Communications, pg 874
Alan Gordon Enterprises Inc, pg 880
Hooper Camera & Imaging, pg 891
Mole-Richardson Co, pg 945
Point of View Productions, pg 977
Sacramento Theatrical Lighting Ltd (STL), pg 1001

CONNECTICUT

Connecticut Audio & Theatrical Supply, pg 835

FLORIDA

Access Media Group, pg 773
Bay Stage Lighting Co Inc, pg 803
Digital Video Systems Inc, pg 848
Eastern Video, pg 856
Media Concepts Inc, pg 936
Photomart Cine-Video Inc, pg 975
Pro Stage Inc, pg 983
Recording Media & Equipment Inc (RM&E), pg 993

ILLINOIS

Chicago Spotlight Inc, pg 825
Joseph Electronics, pg 906

KENTUCKY

NOR-COM Inc, pg 958

MASSACHUSETTS

HMC Electronics, pg 889
Hunt's Photo, Video & Digital, pg 892
International Light Technologies Inc, pg 901
Rule Broadcast Systems, pg 1000
Stanley Supply & Services Inc, pg 1023
University Products Inc, pg 1050

MICHIGAN

Fantasee Lighting Inc, pg 865

MINNESOTA

Lights On, pg 921

NEVADA

MeshTel-Intelite, pg 939

NEW JERSEY

Argraph Corp, pg 789
Manfrotto Distribution Inc, pg 930
Starlite Productions, pg 1024

NEW MEXICO

Quickbeam Systems Inc (QSI), pg 989

NEW YORK

B&H Photo & Video Pro Audio, pg 802
Barbizon Electric Co Inc, pg 802
Creative Stage Lighting Co Inc, pg 838
Edmund Scientific, pg 857
Markertek Video Supply, pg 931
Neptune Photo Inc, pg 954
RTS Inc, pg 1000
Sekonic, pg 1006
TecNec Distributing, pg 1035

OHIO

Midwest Photo Exchange, pg 942

PENNSYLVANIA

Bernie's Photo Center, pg 805
Techni-Tool Inc, pg 1033

SOUTH DAKOTA

Sencore Inc, pg 1006

TEXAS

Olden Lighting, pg 962
Precision Camera & Video, pg 980
Pro Video & Film Equipment Co Inc, pg 983
RadioShack Corp, pg 990

VIRGINIA

Filmdex Inc, pg 867
Lee Hartman & Sons Inc, pg 918

WASHINGTON

Oppenheimer Camera Products, pg 964

WISCONSIN

Full Compass Systems, pg 874
Pro Studio Supply, pg 983

BRITISH COLUMBIA

ProVision Video Sales & Rentals Inc, pg 986

MANITOBA

Inland Audio Visual Ltd, pg 898

ONTARIO

Henry's Camera, pg 888

Light Meter Manufacturers

CALIFORNIA

Spectra Cine Inc, pg 1020

MASSACHUSETTS

AEMC Instruments, pg 778
International Light Technologies Inc, pg 901

MICHIGAN

PCO-TECH Inc, pg 970

NEVADA

MeshTel-Intelite, pg 939

NEW YORK

RTS Inc, pg 1000

OREGON

Grass Valley, pg 881

SOUTH DAKOTA

Sencore Inc, pg 1006

ONTARIO

The Optikon Corp, pg 964

Light Meter Rentals

ARIZONA

Arizona Cine Equipment, pg 789

ARKANSAS

White Diamond Productions, pg 1065

CALIFORNIA

Adolph Gasser Inc, pg 776
Artichoke Productions, pg 791
Cherry Multimedia, pg 824
Full Moon & High Tide Productions & Studios, pg 874
Golden Gate Studios, pg 880
New Circuit Films LLC, pg 955
PIX, pg 976

MISCELLANEOUS

Light Meter Rentals (continued)

FLORIDA

Cinema East, pg 827
MAPS Production House, pg 930
Pro Stage Inc, pg 983

GEORGIA

Stage Front Presentation Systems, pg 1022

HAWAII

FOTON Hawaii, pg 871

LOUISIANA

Available Lighting & Motion Picture Services Inc, pg 798

MICHIGAN

Fantasee Lighting Inc, pg 865
Lowing Light & Grip Inc, pg 925

NEW JERSEY

Bill Quinn Productions, pg 989
Starlite Productions, pg 1024

NEW YORK

Bond Street Studio, pg 810

NORTH CAROLINA

Take One Productions Ltd, pg 1031

OHIO

Lyon Video Inc, pg 927

TEXAS

Muller Entertainment, pg 949
Precision Camera & Video, pg 980

UTAH

Redman Movies & Stories, pg 993

BRITISH COLUMBIA

ProVision Video Sales & Rentals Inc, pg 986

MANITOBA

Inland Audio Visual Ltd, pg 898

Light Meter Repairs

CALIFORNIA

Pro Camera Repair, pg 982
Spectra Cine Inc, pg 1020

KENTUCKY

NOR-COM Inc, pg 958

MARYLAND

Strauss Photo Technical Service Inc, pg 1026

MASSACHUSETTS

International Light Technologies Inc, pg 901

MICHIGAN

Fantasee Lighting Inc, pg 865

NEW YORK

Sekonic, pg 1006

TEXAS

Pro Video & Film Equipment Co Inc, pg 983

Lighting Fixture & Control Equipment Distributors

ARIZONA

Metropolitan Audio-Visual Inc, pg 940
Tempe Camera, pg 1037
David Wexler & Co, pg 1064

ARKANSAS

Carlton-Bates Co, pg 820
Jay S Stanley & Associates Inc, pg 1023

CALIFORNIA

Adolph Gasser Inc, pg 776
Advanced Systems Group LLC, pg 778
Ametron Audio/Video, pg 785
Angstrom Lighting, pg 786
ARRI Inc, pg 790
Audio/Video Supply Inc, pg 795
Automated Entertainment, pg 797
Barger-Lite, pg 803
Birns & Sawyer Inc, pg 808
California Stage & Lighting, pg 817
ChronTrol Corp, pg 826
Cinemills Corp, pg 828
Delicate Electronics Sales Inc, pg 845
DTC Lighting & Grip, pg 853
Eco-Greenlighting Inc, pg 856
Freestyle Photographic Supplies, pg 872
FXC Communications, pg 874
Gearhouse Broadcast LLC, pg 876
Gluskin's Custom Audio Video, pg 879
Alan Gordon Enterprises Inc, pg 880
Intel-A-Jib™, pg 899
Kino Flo Lighting Systems, pg 911
LTM Corp of America, pg 925
Matthews Studio Equipment Inc, pg 934
Mole-Richardson Co, pg 945
Phoebus Lighting, pg 974
Photoflex Inc, pg 974
Premier Lighting & Production Co, pg 980
Sacramento Theatrical Lighting Ltd (STL), pg 1001
San Diego Stage & Lighting Supply Inc, pg 1002
Slow Motion Film & Digital Inc, pg 1013
SNAP, pg 1014
Thin-Lite Corp, pg 1038
Tri-Ed, pg 1044
Visual Instrumentation Corp, pg 1059
VTP Inc, pg 1061
Wildfire Lighting & Visual Effects, pg 1066

COLORADO

Ceavco Audio/Visual Co, pg 822
Chimera®, pg 825
Plume Ltd, pg 977
Spectrum Audio Visual Services, pg 1020

CONNECTICUT

Concord Communications, pg 835
Connecticut Audio & Theatrical Supply, pg 835
Digital Video Productions, pg 848
MAVCO, pg 934
Revolution Lighting Technologies Inc, pg 995
Rockwell Communications Inc, pg 998

DELAWARE

Actors Attic, pg 775

DISTRICT OF COLUMBIA

Theatrical Technicians Inc (TTI), pg 1038

FLORIDA

Access Media Group, pg 773
Alcorn McBride Inc, pg 780
Allstar Audio Systems Inc, pg 782
A2D Solutions Inc, pg 793
Bay Stage Lighting Co Inc, pg 803
Christie Lites, pg 825
Crystalite Industries Inc, pg 840
Digital Lighting Systems Inc, pg 847
Digital Video Systems Inc, pg 848
Enhanced View Services Inc, pg 861
General Projection Systems Inc, pg 877
Gulf Coast Audio Visual Producers Inc, pg 883
Hi-Tech Enterprises Inc, pg 888
Martin Professional Inc, pg 932
Miami Stagecraft Inc, pg 941
Midtown Video Inc, pg 942
P&H Chrystalite Inc, pg 968
Photomart Cine-Video Inc, pg 975
Pro Stage Inc, pg 983
Reef Photo & Video, pg 993
Stage Equipment & Lighting Inc, pg 1022
Techni-Lux Inc, pg 1033
Union Connector Co Inc, pg 1048
Videoscope, pg 1057

GEORGIA

AVForSale, pg 798
Convergent Media Systems, pg 836
Lighting & Production Equipment Inc, pg 920
MAGNUM Companies Ltd, pg 929
Stage Front Presentation Systems, pg 1022
Technical Innovation, pg 1033

HAWAII

ATTCO Inc, pg 793

ILLINOIS

Aero-Tech Light Bulb Co Inc, pg 778
Chicago Spotlight Inc, pg 825
Grand Stage Co Inc, pg 881
Leedal Inc, pg 918
Photogenic Professional Lighting, pg 974
Robertson Worldwide, pg 998
Tele-Time Systems, pg 1036

INDIANA

Heart Breaker Entertainment LLC, pg 887
Lee Co Inc, pg 918
Victoria Supply Inc/Topbulb.com, pg 1054

KANSAS

EiKO Ltd, pg 858
Smith Audio-Visual Inc, pg 1014
Theatrical Services Inc, pg 1038

KENTUCKY

NOR-COM Inc, pg 958
Theatre Effects, pg 1038
Theatre House Inc, pg 1038

LOUISIANA

Available Lighting & Motion Picture Services Inc, pg 798

MARYLAND

Cannon Stage Lighting Inc, pg 819
Event Tech, pg 863
Noventri, pg 960
Parlights Inc, pg 969
RTZ Audio Visual, pg 1000
Shadowstone R & R™, pg 1008
Theatre Service & Supply Corp, pg 1038
Visual Aids Electronics Corp, pg 1059

MASSACHUSETTS

Advanced Lighting & Production Services Inc (ALPS), pg 777
Capron Lighting & Sound Co Inc, pg 819
High Output Inc, pg 888
Limelight Productions Inc, pg 921
Osram Sylvania Inc, pg 965
Rule Broadcast Systems, pg 1000
Savant Systems LLC, pg 1003

MICHIGAN

Ascom Communications Contractors, pg 791
Fantasee Lighting Inc, pg 865
Lowing Light & Grip Inc, pg 925
On Stage Visuals, pg 963
TeL Systems, pg 1035
Tobins Lake Sales, pg 1041

MINNESOTA

Alpha Video & Audio Inc, pg 782
AVI Systems, pg 799
Cinequipt Inc, pg 828
Norcostco Inc, pg 958

MISSISSIPPI

Jasper Ewing & Sons Inc, pg 864

MISSOURI

A to Z Theatrical Supply & Service, pg 771
Communitronics Corp, pg 833
Conference Technologies Inc, pg 835
Image Technologies Corp, pg 895
MIS Technologies, pg 944
Production Support Services Inc, pg 985
The RapcoHorizon Co, pg 991
Southwest Audio-Visual Inc, pg 1019
Swank Audio Visuals, pg 1029

NEBRASKA

Dog & Pony Productions Inc, pg 850

Lighting Fixture & Control Equipment Manufacturers

MISCELLANEOUS

Lighting Fixture & Control Equipment Manufacturers (continued)

MISSOURI

Dazor Manufacturing Corp, pg 844

NEBRASKA

Strong Cinema Products, pg 1026
Strong Entertainment Lighting, pg 1026

NEW HAMPSHIRE

ProPhotonix Ltd, pg 986

NEW JERSEY

Crescent/Stonco, pg 839
Crestron Electronics Inc, pg 839
De Sisti Lighting/Desmar Corp, pg 844
Dyna-Lite Inc, pg 854
Estiluz Inc, pg 862
Frezzi Energy Systems, pg 873
Hanovia Specialty Lighting LLC, pg 884
Leucos USA Inc, pg 919
Pro-Tape & Specialities Inc, pg 983

NEW YORK

Creative Stage Lighting Co Inc, pg 838
Edison Price Lighting, pg 857
Gagne Inc, pg 875
Group One Ltd, pg 882
GTI (Graphic Technology Inc), pg 883
Legion Lighting Co Inc, pg 918
Levy Lighting NYC Inc, pg 919
Lighting Services Inc, pg 921
Lighttech Group Inc, pg 921
Lowel-Light Manufacturing Inc, pg 925
Navitar Inc, pg 953
Production Resource Group LLC (PRG), pg 984
Swivelier, pg 1030
Theatrical Services & Supplies Inc, pg 1038
The Tiffen Co LLC, pg 1040
TPR Enterprises Ltd, pg 1043
WAC Lighting Co, pg 1061
Zelco Industries Inc, pg 1073

NORTH CAROLINA

Strategic Connections, pg 1026
Sunnex Inc, pg 1028

OHIO

EPRAD Inc, pg 862
Future Light Inc, pg 874
Janson Industries, pg 904
The Will-Burt Co, pg 1066

OREGON

Leviton LES, pg 919
Magic Gadgets™, pg 928

PENNSYLVANIA

Brightline LP, pg 812
Charles Beseler Co, pg 824
Lehigh Electric Products Co, pg 918
Simkar Corporation, pg 1011

SOUTH CAROLINA

Columbia Lighting, pg 832
Prescolite, pg 981

TENNESSEE

Kozmic Lazer Show LLC, pg 913
Mystery Electronics, pg 951
TOMCAT USA Inc, pg 1041

TEXAS

AMX, pg 786
High End Systems Inc, pg 888
Philips Lighting Controls, pg 974
Sky-View Co, pg 1013
Strand Lighting Inc, pg 1025
Vari-Lite, pg 1052

UTAH

Vantage/Legrand, pg 1051

VERMONT

Verilux® - The Healthy Lighting Co, pg 1053

VIRGINIA

Applied Electronics, pg 788
Lightronics Inc, pg 921
Optikinetics Ltd - The Americas, pg 964

ALBERTA

Johnson Systems Inc (JSI), pg 906
Pathway Connectivity Inc, pg 970

NEW BRUNSWICK

Kabuki, pg 907

ONTARIO

The Fluorescent Co Inc, pg 870
Osram Sylvania Ltd/LTEE, pg 966
Technovision® Interactive Inc, pg 1035

Lighting Fixture & Control Equipment Rentals

ARIZONA

American Audio Visual Center, pg 783
Arizona Cine Equipment, pg 789
AV Concepts, pg 797
Broadcast Rentals, pg 813
Creative Backstage, pg 838
Glendale Media Center, pg 878
Merestone, pg 938
Metropolitan Audio-Visual Inc, pg 940
Reel Men Rentals Inc, pg 994
Tempe Camera, pg 1037
Video West Inc, pg 1056

ARKANSAS

Jones Film Video, pg 906

CALIFORNIA

Action Audio & Visual, pg 775
Alternative Rentals, pg 783
Ametron Audio/Video, pg 785
Angstrom Lighting, pg 786
Arc Light Efx Inc, pg 789
Arctek Studios, pg 789
Artichoke Productions, pg 791
Automated Entertainment, pg 797
AV Guys, pg 797
Best Bet Camera Rentals, pg 805
Birns & Sawyer Inc, pg 808
California Stage & Lighting, pg 817
Chater Camera Inc, pg 824
Cherry Multimedia, pg 824
Cinema Camera Rentals, pg 827
Cinemills Corp, pg 828
Cineworks Inc, pg 828
Clean Slate Video, pg 829
Crash Video Productions, pg 837
Crystal Pyramid Productions™, pg 840
Dadco, pg 842
Digital Film Studios, pg 847
Division Camera, pg 849
DTC Lighting & Grip, pg 853
Dystopian Studios, pg 854
Eco-Greenlighting Inc, pg 856
Flip 2 Media Inc, pg 870
Fuller Street Productions, pg 874
Gear Monkey, pg 876
Gold Standard Productions, pg 880
Golden Gate Studios, pg 880
Alan Gordon Enterprises Inc, pg 880
Greenery Studios, pg 882
Groovy Like a Movie, pg 882
HDrental.com, pg 886
Hollywood Center Studios, pg 890
Hollywood Loft, pg 890
iCorpTv, pg 893
Illuminate Studios, pg 894
Imagecraft Productions, pg 896
Images in Motion Media Inc, pg 896
Intel-A-Jib™, pg 899
InVision Productions, pg 902
JFA Studio, pg 905
KESSPRO Studios, pg 910
Laurel Canyon Stages, pg 916
Loyal Studios, pg 925
Luminys Systems Corp, pg 926
LW Media Group, pg 926
Main Street Media Inc, pg 929
McCune Audio-Video-Lighting, pg 935
Mole-Richardson Co, pg 945
Next Arts, pg 957
North County Media Center, pg 959
On-Trax Inc, pg 963
Phoebus Lighting, pg 974
Photo Film Stage, pg 974
PIX, pg 976
Pollution Studios, pg 978
Premier Lighting & Production Co, pg 980
Pro HD Rentals, pg 983
The Producer's Loft, pg 983
Production Gear Rentals (PGR), pg 984
Pyxis Industries Inc, pg 988
RED Studios Hollywood, pg 993
The Rosenthal Group, pg 999
Sacramento Theatrical Lighting Ltd (STL), pg 1001
Samy's Camera, pg 1002
San Diego Stage & Lighting Supply Inc, pg 1002
Santa Clarita Studios, pg 1002
Shooting Star Video, pg 1009
Shoulder High Productions, pg 1009
Slate Media Group, pg 1013
Slow Motion Film & Digital Inc, pg 1013
SNAP, pg 1014
Source Film Studio, pg 1018
Stray Angel Films, pg 1026
Studio 1444, pg 1026
Studio 637, pg 1027
The Studios at Paramount, pg 1027
T-stop Inc, pg 1031
Towards 2000 Inc, pg 1043
Tri-Ed, pg 1044
Twin Peaks Creative, pg 1047
Universal Studios, pg 1049
Valencia Studios, pg 1051
Video Gear Rentals Inc, pg 1055
Visual Instrumentation Corp, pg 1059
Vitruvian Entertainment, pg 1060
VMI Inc, pg 1060
Voice & Video Rentals, pg 1060
Warner Bros Entertainment Inc, pg 1062
Wildfire Lighting & Visual Effects, pg 1066
Z-Ville Productions, pg 1073

COLORADO

Chimera®, pg 825
Denver Media Center, pg 845
Maniac Productions, pg 930
Tatum Video, pg 1032
Westworks Studios, pg 1064
Zelo Productions Inc, pg 1073

CONNECTICUT

Concord Communications, pg 835
Connecticut Audio & Theatrical Supply, pg 835
Fox Connecticut, pg 872
KJfilms LLC, pg 911
Revolution Lighting Technologies Inc, pg 995
Videofilm Systems Inc, pg 1057

DELAWARE

Actors Attic, pg 775
Cornerstone Media Productions Inc, pg 836

DISTRICT OF COLUMBIA

Metro Teleproductions Inc (MTI), pg 939

FLORIDA

Access Media Group, pg 773
Adrenaline Films, pg 777
All Communications Rentals Inc (ALLCOMM), pg 780
Allstar Audio Systems Inc, pg 782
Aperture Studios Miami, pg 788
Bay Stage Lighting Co Inc, pg 803
Budget Video Rentals, pg 815
Canavan Scenic & Light LLC, pg 819
Christie Lites, pg 825
Cinema East, pg 827
Cinema Entertainment Inc, pg 827
Steven Cohen Motion Picture Production, pg 831
Digital Zoetrope Productions, pg 848
Facet Media, pg 865
Fiddler Films, pg 866
HD House, pg 886
Illuminart Lighting, pg 894
Jordan Klein Film & Video (JKFV), pg 906
JungleTV, pg 906
Knowles Video Inc (KVI), pg 912
MAPS Production House, pg 930
Miami Daylight Studios, pg 941
Miami Stagecraft Inc, pg 941
Moving Picture, pg 947
Paradise Show & Design Inc, pg 969
Photosound of Orlando Inc, pg 975
Pro Stage Inc, pg 983
Stage Equipment & Lighting Inc, pg 1022
10-20 Productions, pg 1037
Universal Studios Florida® Production Group, pg 1049
Zebedee Productions, pg 1073

GEORGIA

Continental Film & Video, pg 835
Convergent Media Systems, pg 836
First Cut Communications LLC, pg 868
In Concert Production Inc (ICP), pg 897
Lighting & Production Equipment Inc, pg 920
Magick Lantern, pg 928
MAGNUM Companies Ltd, pg 929
See Production Services, pg 1006
Stage Front Presentation Systems, pg 1022
Studio Space Atlanta, pg 1027

HAWAII

ATTCO Inc, pg 793
FOTON Hawaii, pg 871
Hawaii Sound & Vision, pg 886
Sight & Sound Studios, pg 1010

ILLINOIS

Audio Visual Services Corp, pg 796
Chicago Spotlight Inc, pg 825
Firehouse Studios, pg 868
Grand Stage Co Inc, pg 881
Helix Camera & Video, pg 887
LITE-IT Grip Truck Rentals, pg 923
Magnanimous Media, pg 928
Product Productions, pg 984
PSAV® Presentation Services (Hotel Services Division), pg 987
2nd Cine, pg 1006
Show Department Inc, pg 1009
Staging Resources Inc, pg 1023
Tele-Time Systems, pg 1036
Zacuto, pg 1073

INDIANA

Heart Breaker Entertainment LLC, pg 887
Jack's Camera Shop, pg 903
OMNI Productions, pg 962

IOWA

Central Lighting & Equipment Inc (CLE), pg 823
Musco Lighting, pg 950
Pro Video, pg 983

KANSAS

KAKE-TV, pg 907
Theatrical Services Inc, pg 1038

KENTUCKY

Audio Visual Techniques Inc, pg 796
Kentucky Grip & Lighting, pg 909
Theatre House Inc, pg 1038

LOUISIANA

Available Lighting & Motion Picture Services Inc, pg 798
Pace Systems, pg 966

MARYLAND

Archai Media, pg 789
Cannon Stage Lighting Inc, pg 819
CPR MultiMedia Solutions, pg 837
RTZ Audio Visual, pg 1000
Shadowstone R & R™, pg 1008

MASSACHUSETTS

Advanced Lighting & Production Services Inc (ALPS), pg 777
AVFX Inc, pg 798
Capron Lighting & Sound Co Inc, pg 819
Fastlane Productions LLC, pg 866
Green Mountain Post Films (GMP), pg 882
High Output Inc, pg 888
Home Inc, pg 890
Limelight Productions Inc, pg 921
Preston Productions Inc, pg 981

MICHIGAN

Fantasee Lighting Inc, pg 865
K&R All Media Productions Inc, pg 908
Lowing Light & Grip Inc, pg 925
On Stage Visuals, pg 963
TeL Systems, pg 1035

MINNESOTA

Aggressive Records Audio Duplication LLC, pg 778
Area 19, pg 789
AVI Systems, pg 799
House of Cinemagraphics, pg 891
Lights On, pg 921
Norcostco Inc, pg 958
Pro Media Productions, pg 983

MISSOURI

A to Z Theatrical Supply & Service, pg 771
Cashmark Media Inc, pg 820
Production Support Services Inc, pg 985
Show-Me Audio-Visual, pg 1009
Sight & Sound Production Services Inc, pg 1010
Swank Audio Visuals, pg 1029
Switch, pg 1030
Wise Audio Video, pg 1068

MONTANA

Filmlites Montana, pg 867

NEBRASKA

Dog & Pony Productions Inc, pg 850
Lights On Nebraska, pg 921

NEVADA

4 Wall Entertainment, pg 872
GES Audio Visual, pg 877
MG Studio, pg 940
PRG Lighting, pg 981

NEW HAMPSHIRE

Apertura, pg 788
APS Lighting-Sound-AV, pg 789

NEW JERSEY

Audio Visual Dynamics®, pg 795
Butter Tree Studio, pg 816
CFP Video Productions Inc, pg 823
Dyna-Lite Inc, pg 854
Earl Girls Inc, pg 855
Euro-Pacific Film & Video Productions Inc, pg 863
Ironbound Film & Television Studios LLC, pg 902
Leucos USA Inc, pg 919
Nelson Enterprises Theatrical Supply Co, pg 954
SLD Lighting, pg 1013
Soundtracks Production Services LLC, pg 1018
Starlite Productions, pg 1024
Video Corporation of America (VCA), pg 1055

NEW MEXICO

Production Outfitters, pg 984
Quickbeam Systems Inc (QSI), pg 989

NEW YORK

Ace Video, pg 774
Adorama Rental Co, pg 776
Adwar Video, pg 778
Albany Theatre Supply Co Inc, pg 780
BC Video Inc, pg 803
Bestek Lighting & Staging, pg 806
Bond Street Studio, pg 810
Bravo Studios, pg 812
Brooklyn Fire Proof, pg 814
Brooklyn Studios, pg 814
Camart, pg 817
C&C Studios Corp, pg 819
Thomas Cestare Inc, pg 823
City Stage, pg 828
CMI Communications, pg 830
Colortone Audio Visual, pg 832
Creative Stage Lighting Co Inc, pg 838
CSI Rentals, pg 840
Design Audio Visual Inc, pg 845
East of Hollywood NY, pg 855
Eastern Effects Inc, pg 856
Gearhead Rentals, pg 876
Group One Ltd, pg 882
Hand Held Films, pg 884
KVL Audio Visual Services Inc, pg 914
Levy Lighting NYC Inc, pg 919
LightHouse Films, pg 920
LightSpace Studios, pg 921
Long Island Video Enterprises Live Inc, pg 924
Manhattan Center Studios Inc, pg 930
Metromotion Productions LLC, pg 940
Neo Studios, pg 954
Northern Lights, pg 959
Production Central, pg 984
Production Resource Group LLC (PRG), pg 984
Rollin Studios, pg 998
Scheimpflug Digital, pg 1004
Steiner Studios, pg 1024
Syracuse Scenery & Stage Lighting Co Inc, pg 1031
TBA Global Events, pg 1032
Theatrical Services & Supplies Inc, pg 1038
Umbra of Newburgh LLC, pg 1048
Visual Technologies Corp, pg 1060

NORTH CAROLINA

A&V Company, pg 772
Audio & Light, pg 794
Camcor Inc, pg 818
The Communications Group Inc, pg 833
Duke Media Services, pg 853
On Location North Carolina, pg 963
Special Event Services, pg 1020
Strategic Connections, pg 1026
Take One Productions Ltd, pg 1031
Visual Aids Electronics of North Carolina Inc, pg 1059

OHIO

Bartha, pg 803
Hughie's Event Production Services, pg 892
ITA Audio Visual Solutions, pg 902
Lyon Video Inc, pg 927
Ohio HD Video, pg 961
Partech Lighting Systems Inc, pg 969
Vincent Lighting Systems, pg 1058
Vista Color Imaging Inc, pg 1059

OKLAHOMA

PDC Productions, pg 970

OREGON

Hollywood Lights Inc, pg 890
Pacific Grip & Lighting Inc, pg 967
Picture This Production Services, pg 975
Rose City Sound, pg 999

PENNSYLVANIA

Argentine Productions Inc, pg 789
Audio Visions Inc, pg 795
FirstGeneration Audio/Visual Services, pg 869
Fusion Brand Experiences, pg 874
Grise Audio Visual Center Inc, pg 882
Innovision Media Group, pg 899
JPL, pg 906
Location Camera Ltd, pg 923
Location Lighting Ltd, pg 924
Muderick Media, pg 949
New York Camera & Video, pg 956
Philadelphia Soundstages, pg 974
The Videohouse Inc, pg 1057
Viewpoint Production Services Inc, pg 1058

SOUTH CAROLINA

Sound & Images Inc, pg 1016
Studio Charleston, pg 1026

TENNESSEE

DR&A Inc, pg 852
Kozmic Lazer Show LLC, pg 913
Nashville Production Rentals (NPR), pg 952
NuMynd Studios, pg 960
RentACamera.com, pg 995

TEXAS

Big House Sound Inc, pg 807
Bright Giant Creative Group, pg 812
Communilux Productions, pg 833
Freeman, pg 872
Industrial Audio/Video Inc, pg 897
Light Tec, pg 920
Earl Miller Productions Inc, pg 943
Olden Lighting, pg 962
Omega Broadcast Group, pg 962
Onstage Systems, pg 963
Panavision Dallas, pg 968
Phil Lights, pg 973
Photogroup Studios, pg 975
Power Factory Productions, pg 979
Precision Camera & Video, pg 980
Sky-View Co, pg 1013
South Coast Film & Video, pg 1019
Stage Directions, pg 1022
Texcam Inc, pg 1038

UTAH

Ron Hill Imagery, pg 889
Redman Movies & Stories, pg 993

VERMONT

Dark Star Lighting & Production, pg 842
Parlato Productions, pg 969

MISCELLANEOUS

Lighting Fixture & Control Equipment Rentals (continued)

VIRGINIA

Audio Visual Actions Inc (AVA), pg 795
D&B Television & Video Productions Inc, pg 842
Projection Presentation Technology, pg 985
Rainbow Rentals, pg 991
StageSound, pg 1023

WASHINGTON

The House Studios, pg 891
Oppenheimer Camera Products, pg 964
Pacific Northwest Theatre Associates Inc (PNTA), pg 967
Victory Studios, pg 1054

WEST VIRGINIA

Blackwater Video Productions, pg 808
United Sound & Electronics, pg 1048

WISCONSIN

Camera Corner Connecting Point, pg 818
Event Essentials, pg 863
Full Compass Systems, pg 874
MKE Production Rental, pg 944
Wisconsin Public Television, pg 1068

PUERTO RICO

Stage Crew Audiovisual Inc, pg 1022

ALBERTA

Allstar Show Industries Inc, pg 782
Global Television Station, pg 879
Johnson Systems Inc (JSI), pg 906
MTM Equipment Rentals Ltd, pg 949

BRITISH COLUMBIA

DL Sound & Lighting Productions Ltd, pg 849
ProVision Video Sales & Rentals Inc, pg 986
Video In Studios/Video Out Distribution, pg 1055

MANITOBA

Inland Audio Visual Ltd, pg 898
MidCanada Production Services Inc (MidCan), pg 942

NEW BRUNSWICK

Kabuki, pg 907

NOVA SCOTIA

Atlantic Illumination Entertainment Lighting, pg 793

ONTARIO

Boxcar Studio, pg 811
The Fluorescent Co Inc, pg 870
HD Source, pg 886
JIB Shots Equipment Inc, pg 905
RB Productions, pg 992
Wallace Film Studios, pg 1061
Westbury National Show Systems Ltd, pg 1064
ZTV Broadcast Services Inc, pg 1074

Lighting Fixture & Control Equipment Repairs

CALIFORNIA

Ametron Audio/Video, pg 785
Angstrom Lighting, pg 786
ARRI Inc, pg 790
Cinemills Corp, pg 828
Digitron Electronics, pg 848
LTM Corp of America, pg 925
Matthews Studio Equipment Inc, pg 934
Lloyd F McKinney Associates Inc, pg 935
Mole-Richardson Co, pg 945
Phoebus Lighting, pg 974
Premier Lighting & Production Co, pg 980
Sacramento Theatrical Lighting Ltd (STL), pg 1001
San Diego Stage & Lighting Supply Inc, pg 1002
Spectra Cine Inc, pg 1020
Towards 2000 Inc, pg 1043
Visual Instrumentation Corp, pg 1059
Wildfire Lighting & Visual Effects, pg 1066

DELAWARE

Actors Attic, pg 775

FLORIDA

Bay Stage Lighting Co Inc, pg 803
Christie Lites, pg 825
JT Communications, pg 906
Miami Stagecraft Inc, pg 941
Tel-Test, pg 1035

GEORGIA

Lighting & Production Equipment Inc, pg 920
MAGNUM Companies Ltd, pg 929
Stage Front Presentation Systems, pg 1022

HAWAII

ATTCO Inc, pg 793

ILLINOIS

Chicago Spotlight Inc, pg 825
Grand Stage Co Inc, pg 881

KANSAS

Theatrical Services Inc, pg 1038

KENTUCKY

NOR-COM Inc, pg 958

MARYLAND

RTZ Audio Visual, pg 1000
Shadowstone R & R™, pg 1008

MASSACHUSETTS

Advanced Lighting & Production Services Inc (ALPS), pg 777
Capron Lighting & Sound Co Inc, pg 819
Dedotec USA Inc, pg 844
Limelight Productions Inc, pg 921

MICHIGAN

Fantasee Lighting Inc, pg 865
Lowing Light & Grip Inc, pg 925
On Stage Visuals, pg 963

MINNESOTA

AVI Systems, pg 799
Norcostco Inc, pg 958

MISSOURI

A to Z Theatrical Supply & Service, pg 771

NEVADA

4 Wall Entertainment, pg 872
PRG Lighting, pg 981

NEW JERSEY

Dyna-Lite Inc, pg 854
Earl Girls Inc, pg 855
Frezzi Energy Systems, pg 873
Nelson Enterprises Theatrical Supply Co, pg 954
Starlite Productions, pg 1024

NEW MEXICO

Quickbeam Systems Inc (QSI), pg 989

NEW YORK

Adwar Video, pg 778
Bowens USA, pg 811
Flash Clinic Inc, pg 869
Levy Lighting NYC Inc, pg 919
Lowel-Light Manufacturing Inc, pg 925
Northern Lights, pg 959
Theatrical Services & Supplies Inc, pg 1038
Vitec Videocom Inc, pg 1060

NORTH CAROLINA

Strategic Connections, pg 1026

OHIO

Partech Lighting Systems Inc, pg 969
Smithall Electronics Inc, pg 1014
Vincent Lighting Systems, pg 1058

OREGON

All Service Musical Electronics Repair, pg 780
Hollywood Lights Inc, pg 890

PENNSYLVANIA

Location Lighting Ltd, pg 924

TENNESSEE

Kozmic Lazer Show LLC, pg 913
Technical Support Systems LLC, pg 1034

TEXAS

Communilux Productions, pg 833
Crossroads Audio Inc, pg 840
Data Display Audio Visual Co LP, pg 843
Industrial Audio/Video Inc, pg 897
Olden Lighting, pg 962
Pro Video & Film Equipment Co Inc, pg 983
Sky-View Co, pg 1013
Strand Lighting Inc, pg 1025
Tarpley Media Systems, pg 1032

UTAH

RIA Corp, pg 996

VIRGINIA

Hoppmann Audio Visual, pg 891
Intellidyne LLC, pg 899

WEST VIRGINIA

United Sound & Electronics, pg 1048

WISCONSIN

Full Compass Systems, pg 874

ALBERTA

Allstar Show Industries Inc, pg 782

NOVA SCOTIA

Atlantic Illumination Entertainment Lighting, pg 793

ONTARIO

Edcom Multimedia Products, pg 856
The Fluorescent Co Inc, pg 870
Westbury National Show Systems Ltd, pg 1064

Microform Projector & Reader Distributors

ALABAMA

Media Visions Inc, pg 937

ARIZONA

Troxell Communications Inc, pg 1045

CALIFORNIA

Ametron Audio/Video, pg 785
Media Fabricators Inc, pg 936

COLORADO

Ceavco Audio/Visual Co, pg 822

CONNECTICUT

MAVCO, pg 934

GEORGIA

Technical Innovation, pg 1033

INDIANA

Victoria Supply Inc/Topbulb.com, pg 1054

KENTUCKY

NOR-COM Inc, pg 958

MARYLAND

Nicholas P Pipino Associates Inc, pg 976

MICHIGAN

Michigan Office Solutions, pg 941

NEVADA

Bulbman Inc, pg 815

NEW YORK

Gaylord Brothers, pg 876

OHIO

Audio Visual Media, pg 795
Thread Marketing Group, pg 1039

PENNSYLVANIA

Brodart Co, pg 813
IMR Limited, pg 897

TENNESSEE

Spring Arbor Distributors, pg 1022
Tennessee Visual Service Co, pg 1037

TEXAS

Audio Visual Technologies Group, pg 796

VIRGINIA

Filmdex Inc, pg 867
Lee Hartman & Sons Inc, pg 918
The Whitlock Group, pg 1065

WISCONSIN

Demco Inc, pg 845
Indus International Inc, pg 897

ONTARIO

Carr McLean Ltd, pg 820
Edcom Multimedia Products, pg 856

Microform Projector & Reader Manufacturers

WISCONSIN

Indus International Inc, pg 897

BRITISH COLUMBIA

Kodak Canada Inc, pg 912

Microform Projector & Reader Rentals

CALIFORNIA

Ametron Audio/Video, pg 785
Crystal Pyramid Productions™, pg 840
Media Fabricators Inc, pg 936

COLORADO

Ceavco Audio/Visual Co, pg 822

FLORIDA

Jordan Klein Film & Video (JKFV), pg 906

GEORGIA

Stage Front Presentation Systems, pg 1022

OHIO

Audio Visual Media, pg 795
Thread Marketing Group, pg 1039

PENNSYLVANIA

IMR Limited, pg 897

VIRGINIA

Projection Presentation Technology, pg 985

ALBERTA

Global Television Station, pg 879

Microform Projector & Reader Repairs

CALIFORNIA

Ametron Audio/Video, pg 785

COLORADO

Ceavco Audio/Visual Co, pg 822

KENTUCKY

NOR-COM Inc, pg 958

OHIO

Audio Visual Media, pg 795

PENNSYLVANIA

IMR Limited, pg 897

VIRGINIA

The Whitlock Group, pg 1065

WASHINGTON

Inland Audio Visual Co, pg 898

ONTARIO

Edcom Multimedia Products, pg 856
Premier A/V Sales Ltd, pg 980

Microform Reader, *see* Microform Projector & Reader

Phase Converter—Rotary Distributors

CALIFORNIA

FXC Communications, pg 874

FLORIDA

Access Media Group, pg 773

KENTUCKY

NOR-COM Inc, pg 958

NEW JERSEY

Earl Girls Inc, pg 855

Phase Converter—Rotary Manufacturers

CALIFORNIA

OnLine Power Inc, pg 963

INDIANA

Kay Industries Inc, pg 908

Phase Converter—Rotary Rentals

CALIFORNIA

PSAV® Presentation Services, pg 986

GEORGIA

Stage Front Presentation Systems, pg 1022

MICHIGAN

Lowing Light & Grip Inc, pg 925

NEW JERSEY

Earl Girls Inc, pg 855

Phase Converter—Rotary Repairs

KENTUCKY

NOR-COM Inc, pg 958

MICHIGAN

Lowing Light & Grip Inc, pg 925

Power Quality & Control Equipment Distributors

CALIFORNIA

Ametron Audio/Video, pg 785
Delicate Electronics Sales Inc, pg 845
Furman, pg 874
Orvac Electronics, pg 965
Promax Systems, pg 986
Skjonberg Controls Inc, pg 1012
Yanchar Design & Consulting Group, pg 1072
Zack Electronics Inc, pg 1073

COLORADO

Lightning Eliminators & Consultants Inc, pg 921

CONNECTICUT

Connecticut Audio & Theatrical Supply, pg 835

FLORIDA

Access Media Group, pg 773
Digital Video Systems Inc, pg 848

GEORGIA

Stage Front Presentation Systems, pg 1022

ILLINOIS

AmpliVox Portable Sound Systems, pg 785
Chicago Spotlight Inc, pg 825
Joseph Electronics, pg 906

KENTUCKY

NOR-COM Inc, pg 958

MASSACHUSETTS

Stanley Supply & Services Inc, pg 1023

MICHIGAN

ASC Systems, pg 791

NEVADA

Selco Products Co, pg 1006

NEW JERSEY

Earl Girls Inc, pg 855
Total Video Products Inc, pg 1042

NEW YORK

BTX Technologies, pg 814
Emerson Network Power Surge Protection Inc, pg 860
MDS Power Inc, pg 936

NORTH CAROLINA

Innocinema, pg 898
Power Integrity Corporation, pg 979
SurgeX, pg 1029

PENNSYLVANIA

Techni-Tool Inc, pg 1033

TENNESSEE

Lowrance Sound Co Inc, pg 925
Technical Support Systems LLC, pg 1034

TEXAS

Juice Goose, pg 906
Specialized Products Co, pg 1020

VIRGINIA

Avitecture Inc, pg 799
Filmdex Inc, pg 867
Lee Hartman & Sons Inc, pg 918

WASHINGTON

Asentria Corp, pg 792

WISCONSIN

Alpha Source Inc, pg 782
Full Compass Systems, pg 874

ALBERTA

Johnson Systems Inc (JSI), pg 906

ONTARIO

Cinema Stage Inc, pg 827
VFGadgets Inc, pg 1053
Westbury National Show Systems Ltd, pg 1064

Power Quality & Control Equipment Manufacturers

CALIFORNIA

Ametek Programmable Power, pg 785
Furman, pg 874
Henry Engineering, pg 888
MGE UPS Systems, pg 940
J P Nolan & Co, pg 958
OnLine Power Inc, pg 963
Skjonberg Controls Inc, pg 1012

COLORADO

Lightning Eliminators & Consultants Inc, pg 921

CONNECTICUT

Hubbell Wiring Device-Kellems, pg 892
Superior Electric, pg 1029

MISCELLANEOUS

Power Quality & Control Equipment Manufacturers (continued)

FLORIDA

Compuvideo Sales USA Ltd, pg 834
Vutec Corp, Video Products Division, pg 1061

IDAHO

PolyPhaser Corp, pg 978
Transtector Systems Inc, pg 1043

ILLINOIS

AmpliVox Portable Sound Systems, pg 785
Tripp Lite, pg 1045

MASSACHUSETTS

AEMC Instruments, pg 778

MISSOURI

Lowell Manufacturing, pg 925

NEW JERSEY

FSR Inc, pg 873
Nova Electric, pg 959

NEW YORK

Creative Stage Lighting Co Inc, pg 838
Emerson Network Power Surge Protection Inc, pg 860
MDS Power Inc, pg 936

NORTH CAROLINA

Eaton Corp, pg 856
Power Integrity Corporation, pg 979

OHIO

Staco Energy Products Co, pg 1022

OREGON

Equi=Tech Corp, pg 862
Leviton LES, pg 919
Magic Gadgets™, pg 928

PENNSYLVANIA

Kalglo Electronics Co Inc, pg 907

RHODE ISLAND

APC by Schneider Electric, pg 788

TEXAS

ETA Systems, pg 862
Exeltech Inc, pg 864
Juice Goose, pg 906

WASHINGTON

Alpha Technologies, pg 782

ALBERTA

Johnson Systems Inc (JSI), pg 906

Power Quality & Control Equipment Rentals

CALIFORNIA

AGF Media Services, pg 778
Ametron Audio/Video, pg 785
Imagecraft Productions, pg 896
Main Street Media Inc, pg 929
Muse Presentation Technologies, pg 950
Next Arts, pg 957
PSAV® Presentation Services, pg 986

COLORADO

Zelo Productions Inc, pg 1073

GEORGIA

Stage Front Presentation Systems, pg 1022

ILLINOIS

Chicago Spotlight Inc, pg 825
Show Department Inc, pg 1009

KENTUCKY

Audio Visual Techniques Inc, pg 796

MARYLAND

CPR MultiMedia Solutions, pg 837

MICHIGAN

Lowing Light & Grip Inc, pg 925

MONTANA

Jereco Studios Inc, pg 905

NEW JERSEY

Earl Girls Inc, pg 855

OHIO

Bartha, pg 803

OKLAHOMA

PDC Productions, pg 970

VERMONT

Dark Star Lighting & Production, pg 842

ALBERTA

Johnson Systems Inc (JSI), pg 906

ONTARIO

Westbury National Show Systems Ltd, pg 1064

Power Quality & Control Equipment Repairs

CALIFORNIA

Ametron Audio/Video, pg 785
TEK Media Group, pg 1035

GEORGIA

Stage Front Presentation Systems, pg 1022

ILLINOIS

Chicago Spotlight Inc, pg 825

KENTUCKY

NOR-COM Inc, pg 958

MICHIGAN

Lowing Light & Grip Inc, pg 925

OHIO

ITA Audio Visual Solutions, pg 902

TENNESSEE

Technical Support Systems LLC, pg 1034

WISCONSIN

Full Compass Systems, pg 874

ONTARIO

Westbury National Show Systems Ltd, pg 1064

Properties (Props) Distributors

ARIZONA

Arizona Cine Equipment, pg 789
Mardi Gras Costume Shop, pg 930

CALIFORNIA

Ametron Audio/Video, pg 785
Apex Jr, pg 788
Automated Entertainment, pg 797
Omnirax, pg 963
Silvestri California, pg 1011
Studio Dynamics, pg 1026
Stunt Wings Adventure Sports Talent & Equipment, pg 1027
Weapons of Choice™, pg 1063

CONNECTICUT

MAVCO, pg 934

FLORIDA

The Great Southern Studios, pg 882
Pro Stage Inc, pg 983

HAWAII

ATTCO Inc, pg 793

ILLINOIS

Grand Stage Co Inc, pg 881

MASSACHUSETTS

Limelight Productions Inc, pg 921

MICHIGAN

AirBrands Event & Marketing Group, pg 779
Digi Sign Design LLC, pg 847
Tobins Lake Sales, pg 1041

MISSOURI

A to Z Theatrical Supply & Service, pg 771
Production Support Services Inc, pg 985

NEVADA

DVDs4Less, pg 854

NEW HAMPSHIRE

APS Lighting-Sound-AV, pg 789

NEW JERSEY

Earl Girls Inc, pg 855
Starlite Productions, pg 1024

NEW YORK

Barbizon Electric Co Inc, pg 802
Gettinger Feather Corp, pg 877
MRG Productions Inc, pg 948
Rafik, pg 990
Showman Fabricators Inc, pg 1010
Uniset Co LLC, pg 1048

NORTH CAROLINA

The Godfrey Group Inc, pg 880

OHIO

Cleveland Costume & Display Corp, pg 830

PENNSYLVANIA

Shore Manufacturing Co, pg 1009

TEXAS

Pro Video & Film Equipment Co Inc, pg 983
Starline Costume, pg 1024

VERMONT

Dark Star Lighting & Production, pg 842

VIRGINIA

Blair Inc, pg 809

WISCONSIN

Demco Inc, pg 845
Pro Studio Supply, pg 983
Wisconsin Public Television, pg 1068

Properties (Props) Manufacturers

ARIZONA

Merestone, pg 938

CALIFORNIA

The Set Shop, pg 1007

NEW YORK

Cobalt Studios Inc, pg 831
Uniset Co LLC, pg 1048

OREGON

Magic Gadgets™, pg 928

TEXAS

Communilux Productions, pg 833

Properties (Props) Rentals

ARIZONA

Arizona Cine Equipment, pg 789
Mardi Gras Costume Shop, pg 930
Merestone, pg 938

CALIFORNIA

Ametron Audio/Video, pg 785
Antelope Valley Locations & Production Services, pg 787
Arctek Studios, pg 789
Artichoke Productions, pg 791

Automated Entertainment, pg 797
Digital Film Studios, pg 847
Dystopian Studios, pg 854
Fuller Street Productions, pg 874
Golden Gate Studios, pg 880
JFA Studio, pg 905
Loyal Studios, pg 925
McCune Design, pg 935
Palace Costume & Prop Co, pg 967
Pro HD Rentals, pg 983
The Mack Sennett Studios, pg 1006
Studio Dynamics, pg 1026
Stunt Wings Adventure Sports Talent & Equipment, pg 1027
Universal Studios, pg 1049
Warner Bros Entertainment Inc, pg 1062
Weapons of Choice™, pg 1063

CONNECTICUT

MAVCO, pg 934

DISTRICT OF COLUMBIA

Metro Teleproductions Inc (MTI), pg 939

FLORIDA

Canavan Scenic & Light LLC, pg 819
The Great Southern Studios, pg 882
Jordan Klein Film & Video (JKFV), pg 906
Pro Stage Inc, pg 983
Sight & Sound Productions, pg 1010
Universal Studios Florida® Production Group, pg 1049
Zebedee Productions, pg 1073

GEORGIA

Continental Film & Video, pg 835
Lighting & Production Equipment Inc, pg 920
Special Projects, pg 1020
Studio Space Atlanta, pg 1027

HAWAII

ATTCO Inc, pg 793

ILLINOIS

Broadway Costumes Inc, pg 813
WEEK TV, pg 1063

MASSACHUSETTS

Capron Lighting & Sound Co Inc, pg 819

MICHIGAN

AirBrands Event & Marketing Group, pg 779
Digi Sign Design LLC, pg 847
K&R All Media Productions Inc, pg 908
K&R's Recording Studios Inc, pg 908
On Stage Visuals, pg 963

MINNESOTA

Area 19, pg 789

MISSOURI

A to Z Theatrical Supply & Service, pg 771
Production Support Services Inc, pg 985

NEW HAMPSHIRE

APS Lighting-Sound-AV, pg 789

NEW JERSEY

Earl Girls Inc, pg 855
Starlite Productions, pg 1024

NEW YORK

Brooklyn Studios, pg 814
Cobalt Studios Inc, pg 831
East of Hollywood NY, pg 855
modprop.com, pg 945
MRG Productions Inc, pg 948
The Old Rhinebeck Aerodome®, pg 961
RGH Lighting LLC, pg 996

NORTH CAROLINA

The Godfrey Group Inc, pg 880
Take One Productions Ltd, pg 1031

OHIO

Cleveland Costume & Display Corp, pg 830

PENNSYLVANIA

Innovision Media Group, pg 899

TENNESSEE

Center for Southern Folklore Inc, pg 822

TEXAS

Communilux Productions, pg 833
Starline Costume, pg 1024
The Yesterday USA Radio Networks, pg 1072

WASHINGTON

The House Studios, pg 891
Osum Event Rentals, pg 966
Pacific Northwest Theatre Associates Inc (PNTA), pg 967

WISCONSIN

Wisconsin Public Television, pg 1068

ALBERTA

Global Television Station, pg 879

BRITISH COLUMBIA

MicrophoneRentals.com, pg 941

ONTARIO

RB Productions, pg 992

Properties (Props) Repairs

ARIZONA

Merestone, pg 938

NEW YORK

Cobalt Studios Inc, pg 831

Reading & Tachistoscopic Equipment & Learning System Distributors

CALIFORNIA

Ametron Audio/Video, pg 785
FXC Communications, pg 874
Instructional Materials & Equipment Distributors (I-Med), pg 899

CONNECTICUT

MAVCO, pg 934

MARYLAND

Nicholas P Pipino Associates Inc, pg 976

MASSACHUSETTS

Duxbury Systems Inc, pg 854

NEW YORK

Langie Audio Visual Systems, pg 915

RHODE ISLAND

Custom Computer Specialists Inc, pg 841

TENNESSEE

Memphis Communications Corp, pg 938

ONTARIO

Carr McLean Ltd, pg 820
Edcom Multimedia Products, pg 856

Reading & Tachistoscopic Equipment & Learning System Manufacturers

MASSACHUSETTS

Duxbury Systems Inc, pg 854

Reading & Tachistoscopic Equipment & Learning System Rentals

CALIFORNIA

Ametron Audio/Video, pg 785
Instructional Materials & Equipment Distributors (I-Med), pg 899

TENNESSEE

Memphis Communications Corp, pg 938

Reading & Tachistoscopic Equipment & Learning System Repairs

CALIFORNIA

Ametron Audio/Video, pg 785
Instructional Materials & Equipment Distributors (I-Med), pg 899

MINNESOTA

AVI Systems, pg 799

TENNESSEE

Memphis Communications Corp, pg 938
Tennessee Visual Service Co, pg 1037

ONTARIO

Edcom Multimedia Products, pg 856

Room-Darkening Drape & Blind Distributors

ALABAMA

Media Visions Inc, pg 937

ARIZONA

Metropolitan Audio-Visual Inc, pg 940

ARKANSAS

Jay S Stanley & Associates Inc, pg 1023

CALIFORNIA

Ametron Audio/Video, pg 785
Camera Essentials, pg 818
Delicate Electronics Sales Inc, pg 845
Instructional Materials & Equipment Distributors (I-Med), pg 899
Matthews Studio Equipment Inc, pg 934
San Diego Stage & Lighting Supply Inc, pg 1002

CONNECTICUT

MAVCO, pg 934

DELAWARE

Actors Attic, pg 775

FLORIDA

Bay Stage Lighting Co Inc, pg 803
Gulf Coast Audio Visual Producers Inc, pg 883
Pro Stage Inc, pg 983
Tallahassee Audio Visual, pg 1031

GEORGIA

Lighting & Production Equipment Inc, pg 920

HAWAII

ATTCO Inc, pg 793

ILLINOIS

Grand Stage Co Inc, pg 881

INDIANA

Lee Co Inc, pg 918

KANSAS

KK Office Solutions Inc, pg 911

KENTUCKY

Barney Miller's Inc, pg 943
NOR-COM Inc, pg 958

LOUISIANA

Intermedia Technologies, pg 900

MISCELLANEOUS

Room-Darkening Drape & Blind Distributors (continued)

MARYLAND

Nicholas P Pipino Associates Inc, pg 976
Theatre Service & Supply Corp, pg 1038

MASSACHUSETTS

Advanced Lighting & Production Services Inc (ALPS), pg 777
International Display & Exhibit Corp, pg 901
Rule Broadcast Systems, pg 1000

MICHIGAN

Ascom Communications Contractors, pg 791
Fantasee Lighting Inc, pg 865
Lowing Light & Grip Inc, pg 925

MISSOURI

A to Z Theatrical Supply & Service, pg 771
Production Support Services Inc, pg 985
Southwest Audio-Visual Inc, pg 1019

NEW HAMPSHIRE

APS Lighting-Sound-AV, pg 789

NEW JERSEY

Argraph Corp, pg 789
Audio Visual Associates, pg 795
Audio Visual Dynamics®, pg 795
Dazian Inc, pg 844
Wired 4 Sound Inc, pg 1068

NEW MEXICO

Quickbeam Systems Inc (QSI), pg 989

NEW YORK

AV Workshop, pg 797
Bestek Lighting & Staging, pg 806
BMI Supply, pg 810
Colortone Audio Visual, pg 832
Communication Corner Inc, pg 832
Design Audio Visual Inc, pg 845
Mutual Hardware, pg 951
Novelty Scenic Studios Inc, pg 959
PASCO, pg 969
Visual Technologies Corp, pg 1060
Visual Word Systems Inc, pg 1060

OHIO

Copp Integrated Systems, pg 836
ITA Audio Visual Solutions, pg 902

PENNSYLVANIA

Audio Visions Inc, pg 795
Bernie's Photo Center, pg 805
SAPSIS Rigging Inc, pg 1002

TENNESSEE

Memphis Communications Corp, pg 938
Technical Support Systems LLC, pg 1034

TEXAS

Audio Visual Technologies Group, pg 796
Heffernan Audio Visual, pg 887
Tarpley Media Systems, pg 1032

VERMONT

Production Advantage Inc, pg 984

VIRGINIA

Boitnott Visual Communications Corp (BVC), pg 810
Communications Specialists Inc, pg 833
Filmdex Inc, pg 867

WISCONSIN

Audio Visual of Milwaukee Inc, pg 795
Pro Studio Supply, pg 983

MANITOBA

Inland Audio Visual Ltd, pg 898

ONTARIO

Cinema Stage Inc, pg 827
Edcom Multimedia Products, pg 856
Westbury National Show Systems Ltd, pg 1064

Room-Darkening Drape & Blind Manufacturers

ARIZONA

Merestone, pg 938

CALIFORNIA

Automated Entertainment, pg 797
Camera Essentials, pg 818
Matthews Studio Equipment Inc, pg 934

FLORIDA

Vutec Corp, Video Products Division, pg 1061

ILLINOIS

Chicago Spotlight Inc, pg 825

INDIANA

Draper Inc, pg 852

MARYLAND

Baron Stage Curtain & Equipment Co Inc, pg 803
Theatre Service & Supply Corp, pg 1038

MICHIGAN

North Coast Studios Inc, pg 959

MISSOURI

A to Z Theatrical Supply & Service, pg 771

NEW JERSEY

Dazian Inc, pg 844
Gerriets International, pg 877

NEW YORK

Novelty Scenic Studios Inc, pg 959
Showman Fabricators Inc, pg 1010
Syracuse Scenery & Stage Lighting Co Inc, pg 1031

OHIO

Janson Industries, pg 904

PENNSYLVANIA

Automatic Devices Co, pg 797

TEXAS

Communilux Productions, pg 833

WASHINGTON

Pacific Northwest Theatre Associates Inc (PNTA), pg 967

WISCONSIN

Regal Photo Products Inc/Arkay Corp, pg 994

Room-Darkening Drape & Blind Rentals

ARIZONA

American Audio Visual Center, pg 783
Merestone, pg 938
Metropolitan Audio-Visual Inc, pg 940

CALIFORNIA

Fuller Street Productions, pg 874
Golden Gate Studios, pg 880
McCune Audio-Video-Lighting, pg 935
Next Arts, pg 957
San Diego Stage & Lighting Supply Inc, pg 1002
Warner Bros Entertainment Inc, pg 1062

FLORIDA

All Communications Rentals Inc (ALLCOMM), pg 780
Paradise Show & Design Inc, pg 969
Pro Stage Inc, pg 983

GEORGIA

Lighting & Production Equipment Inc, pg 920
Stage Front Presentation Systems, pg 1022

HAWAII

ATTCO Inc, pg 793

ILLINOIS

Grand Stage Co Inc, pg 881

MASSACHUSETTS

AVFX Inc, pg 798

MICHIGAN

Lowing Light & Grip Inc, pg 925

MISSOURI

Production Support Services Inc, pg 985
Swank Audio Visuals, pg 1029

NEW HAMPSHIRE

APS Lighting-Sound-AV, pg 789

NEW JERSEY

Dazian Inc, pg 844

NEW MEXICO

Quickbeam Systems Inc (QSI), pg 989

NEW YORK

Albany Theatre Supply Co Inc, pg 780
Bestek Lighting & Staging, pg 806
Design Audio Visual Inc, pg 845
Showman Fabricators Inc, pg 1010
Visual Word Systems Inc, pg 1060

NORTH CAROLINA

A&V Company, pg 772
Special Event Services, pg 1020
Take One Productions Ltd, pg 1031
Visual Aids Electronics of North Carolina Inc, pg 1059

OKLAHOMA

PDC Productions, pg 970

PENNSYLVANIA

Bernie's Photo Center, pg 805
The Videohouse Inc, pg 1057

TENNESSEE

Memphis Communications Corp, pg 938

TEXAS

Communilux Productions, pg 833

VIRGINIA

StageSound, pg 1023

ALBERTA

Global Television Station, pg 879

BRITISH COLUMBIA

Clark's Audio Visual Services Ltd, pg 829

ONTARIO

Westbury National Show Systems Ltd, pg 1064

QUEBEC

AVW-TELAV Audio Visual Solutions, a Freeman Company, pg 800

Room-Darkening Drape & Blind Repairs

ARIZONA

Merestone, pg 938

CALIFORNIA

Matthews Studio Equipment Inc, pg 934
Lloyd F McKinney Associates Inc, pg 935
San Diego Stage & Lighting Supply Inc, pg 1002

DELAWARE

Actors Attic, pg 775

GEORGIA

Lighting & Production Equipment Inc, pg 920

ILLINOIS

Chicago Spotlight Inc, pg 825

KENTUCKY

NOR-COM Inc, pg 958

MARYLAND

Baron Stage Curtain & Equipment Co Inc, pg 803

MICHIGAN

Fantasee Lighting Inc, pg 865
Lowing Light & Grip Inc, pg 925

NEW JERSEY

Dazian Inc, pg 844

NEW YORK

Showman Fabricators Inc, pg 1010

PENNSYLVANIA

Bernie's Photo Center, pg 805

TENNESSEE

Memphis Communications Corp, pg 938
Technical Support Systems LLC, pg 1034

TEXAS

Tarpley Media Systems, pg 1032

VIRGINIA

Avitecture Inc, pg 799

ONTARIO

Edcom Multimedia Products, pg 856

Satellite Earth Station Equipment Distributors

CALIFORNIA

SNAP, pg 1014

COLORADO

Vexcel Corp, pg 1053

DISTRICT OF COLUMBIA

NPR Satellite Services, pg 960

FLORIDA

Digital Video Systems Inc, pg 848
Multicom Inc, pg 949
Recording Media & Equipment Inc (RM&E), pg 993

IOWA

EASI, pg 855
Winegard Co, pg 1067

MASSACHUSETTS

Antronics Inc, pg 787

MICHIGAN

DAWNco, pg 843

NEBRASKA

ATV Research Inc, pg 793

NEW JERSEY

Diversified Systems Inc, pg 849

NEW YORK

L-3 GCS, pg 915

PENNSYLVANIA

North Star Satellite Communications Inc, pg 959

TEXAS

Pro Video & Film Equipment Co Inc, pg 983

VIRGINIA

Lee Hartman & Sons Inc, pg 918

WISCONSIN

DH Satellite, pg 846

BRITISH COLUMBIA

Norsat International Inc, pg 958

Satellite Earth Station Equipment Manufacturers

CALIFORNIA

Broadcast Microwave Services (BMS), pg 813
Communications & Power Industries, Satcom Division, pg 833
CPI Malibu, pg 837
FM Systems Inc, pg 870
Intersil Americas LLC, pg 901
Pico Digital, pg 975

COLORADO

Vexcel Corp, pg 1053

GEORGIA

Wegener Communications, pg 1063

IDAHO

PolyPhaser Corp, pg 978

IOWA

EASI, pg 855
Winegard Co, pg 1067

MICHIGAN

DAWNco, pg 843

NEW JERSEY

CELCO-Constantine Engineering Labs Co, pg 822

NORTH CAROLINA

Eaton Corp, pg 856

PENNSYLVANIA

North Star Satellite Communications Inc, pg 959

WISCONSIN

DH Satellite, pg 846

BRITISH COLUMBIA

Norsat International Inc, pg 958

ONTARIO

International Datacasting, pg 900

Satellite Earth Station Equipment Rentals

CALIFORNIA

Cosumnes River College, pg 836
FJ Productions Inc, pg 869
Lynch Communications, pg 926
PSSI, pg 987

GEORGIA

Stage Front Presentation Systems, pg 1022

ILLINOIS

Assignment Desk, pg 792
Chicago Satellite & Video, pg 825

KANSAS

KAKE-TV, pg 907

NORTH CAROLINA

Microspace Communications Corp, pg 942

PENNSYLVANIA

North Star Satellite Communications Inc, pg 959

Satellite Earth Station Equipment Repairs

CALIFORNIA

Communications & Power Industries, Satcom Division, pg 833

IOWA

EASI, pg 855

PENNSYLVANIA

North Star Satellite Communications Inc, pg 959

TEXAS

The Yesterday USA Radio Networks, pg 1072

Satellite News Vehicle Distributors

CALIFORNIA

Satellite Digital Teleproductions (SDTV), pg 1003
SNAP, pg 1014

FLORIDA

Digital Video Systems Inc, pg 848

MICHIGAN

DAWNco, pg 843

NEW JERSEY

Diversified Systems Inc, pg 849

OHIO

Sure Shot Transmissions Inc, pg 1029

TEXAS

Pro Video & Film Equipment Co Inc, pg 983
Shook Mobile Technology LP, pg 1009

Satellite News Vehicle Manufacturers

CALIFORNIA

Broadcast Microwave Services (BMS), pg 813

FLORIDA

Frontline Communications, pg 873

GEORGIA

Wegener Communications, pg 1063

TEXAS

Shook Mobile Technology LP, pg 1009

Satellite News Vehicle Rentals

CALIFORNIA

PSSI, pg 987

GEORGIA

Stage Front Presentation Systems, pg 1022

ILLINOIS

Assignment Desk, pg 792
Chicago Satellite & Video, pg 825

KANSAS

KAKE-TV, pg 907

LOUISIANA

Satellite Center, pg 1003

MICHIGAN

Digi Sign Design LLC, pg 847

NEW JERSEY

Vision Quest Productions Inc, pg 1058

NEW MEXICO

Production Outfitters, pg 984

NEW YORK

Direct Broadcast Services Inc (DBS), pg 848

NORTH CAROLINA

Microspace Communications Corp, pg 942

TEXAS

AMS Pictures, pg 786

MISCELLANEOUS

Satellite News Vehicle Repairs

Shook Mobile Technology LP, pg 1009
The Yesterday USA Radio Networks, pg 1072

Satellite Teleport Service Distributors

FLORIDA

Digital Video Systems Inc, pg 848

MICHIGAN

ASC Systems, pg 791
DAWNco, pg 843

NEW JERSEY

Diversified Systems Inc, pg 849
MIB Mediaworks, pg 941
SES World Skies, pg 1007

NEW YORK

L-3 GCS, pg 915

ONTARIO

International Datacasting, pg 900

Satellite Teleport Service Manufacturers

NEW YORK

L-3 GCS, pg 915

Satellite Teleport Service Rentals

ARIZONA

Crew West Inc, pg 839

CALIFORNIA

PSSI, pg 987
Universal Satellite Communications Inc, pg 1049

COLORADO

Maniac Productions, pg 930

FLORIDA

Mike Vasilinda Productions Inc, pg 1052

GEORGIA

Stage Front Presentation Systems, pg 1022

ILLINOIS

Chicago Satellite & Video, pg 825
Satellite Technology Systems Inc, pg 1003

INDIANA

Midwest Uplink Inc, pg 942

MISSOURI

Show-Me Audio-Visual, pg 1009

NORTH CAROLINA

Microspace Communications Corp, pg 942

OHIO

Mills James Productions, pg 943

PENNSYLVANIA

Liberty Uplink, pg 919

Satellite Teleport Service Repairs

TEXAS

The Yesterday USA Radio Networks, pg 1072

Satellite Transmission Equipment Distributors

CALIFORNIA

Computer Modules Inc, pg 834
Satellite Digital Teleproductions (SDTV), pg 1003

CONNECTICUT

Newtec America Inc, pg 957

DISTRICT OF COLUMBIA

NPR Satellite Services, pg 960

FLORIDA

Digital Video Systems Inc, pg 848
Multicom Inc, pg 949
Pro Stage Inc, pg 983
PTL Test Equipment Inc, pg 987
Recording Media & Equipment Inc (RM&E), pg 993

IOWA

EASI, pg 855

MICHIGAN

DAWNco, pg 843

NEW JERSEY

Diversified Systems Inc, pg 849
DSI RF Systems Inc, pg 853
MIB Mediaworks, pg 941

NEW YORK

Image Management Systems Inc, pg 895
L-3 GCS, pg 915

OHIO

Sure Shot Transmissions Inc, pg 1029

PENNSYLVANIA

North Star Satellite Communications Inc, pg 959

TEXAS

Pro Video & Film Equipment Co Inc, pg 983

BRITISH COLUMBIA

Norsat International Inc, pg 958

Satellite Transmission Equipment Manufacturers

CALIFORNIA

Antex Electronics Corp, pg 787
Communications & Power Industries, Satcom Division, pg 833
FM Systems Inc, pg 870
Intersil Americas LLC, pg 901
Rovi Corp, pg 1000

CONNECTICUT

Newtec America Inc, pg 957

GEORGIA

Wegener Communications, pg 1063

IDAHO

PolyPhaser Corp, pg 978

NEW YORK

L-3 GCS, pg 915

PENNSYLVANIA

North Star Satellite Communications Inc, pg 959

TENNESSEE

Adtec Digital Inc, pg 777

ONTARIO

International Datacasting, pg 900

Satellite Transmission Equipment Rentals

CALIFORNIA

Cosumnes River College, pg 836
Golden Gate Studios, pg 880
Lynch Communications, pg 926
PSSI, pg 987

FLORIDA

Pro Stage Inc, pg 983

ILLINOIS

Chicago Satellite & Video, pg 825
QuickSet International Inc, pg 989

KANSAS

KAKE-TV, pg 907

LOUISIANA

Satellite Center, pg 1003

MICHIGAN

Digi Sign Design LLC, pg 847
K&R All Media Productions Inc, pg 908

NEW JERSEY

Vision Quest Productions Inc, pg 1058

NEW YORK

Image Management Systems Inc, pg 895

NORTH CAROLINA

Microspace Communications Corp, pg 942

OHIO

Cuyahoga Community College Media Center, pg 841

PENNSYLVANIA

FMP Media Solutions Inc, pg 870
North Star Satellite Communications Inc, pg 959

Satellite Transmission Equipment Repairs

CALIFORNIA

Communications & Power Industries, Satcom Division, pg 833

DISTRICT OF COLUMBIA

NPR Satellite Services, pg 960

PENNSYLVANIA

North Star Satellite Communications Inc, pg 959

Satellite Transponder Space Segment Distributors

CALIFORNIA

Satellite Digital Teleproductions (SDTV), pg 1003

NEW JERSEY

Diversified Systems Inc, pg 849
SES World Skies, pg 1007

NEW YORK

Associated Press Television News, pg 792
L-3 GCS, pg 915

OHIO

Sure Shot Transmissions Inc, pg 1029

PENNSYLVANIA

North Star Satellite Communications Inc, pg 959

Satellite Transponder Space Segment Rentals

CALIFORNIA

PSSI, pg 987

DISTRICT OF COLUMBIA

NPR Satellite Services, pg 960

ILLINOIS

Chicago Satellite & Video, pg 825
QuickSet International Inc, pg 989

MICHIGAN

Digi Sign Design LLC, pg 847

NEW JERSEY

Vision Quest Productions Inc, pg 1058

NEW YORK

Associated Press Television News, pg 792
Direct Broadcast Services Inc (DBS), pg 848

NORTH CAROLINA

Microspace Communications Corp, pg 942

PENNSYLVANIA

North Star Satellite Communications Inc, pg 959

Shipping, Packaging, Carrying & Storage Case Distributors

ALABAMA

Media Visions Inc, pg 937

ARIZONA

EAR Professional Audio/Video, pg 855
Troxell Communications Inc, pg 1045

CALIFORNIA

Adolph Gasser Inc, pg 776
Ametron Audio/Video, pg 785
Audio/Video Supply Inc, pg 795
Christy's Editorial, pg 826
Delicate Electronics Sales Inc, pg 845
FXC Communications, pg 874
Gearhouse Broadcast LLC, pg 876
J & R Film Co, pg 903
Jameco Electronics, pg 903
Location Sound Corp, pg 924
McCune Audio-Video-Lighting, pg 935
Media Fabricators Inc, pg 936
Melmat Inc, pg 938
Mole-Richardson Co, pg 945
Nalpak Inc, pg 952
Orvac Electronics, pg 965
Related Visual Inc, pg 994
San Diego Stage & Lighting Supply Inc, pg 1002
Thermodyne Cases, pg 1038
Zack Electronics Inc, pg 1073

COLORADO

Case Logic Inc, pg 820
Ceavco Audio/Visual Co, pg 822
Lightware Inc, pg 921
Rose Packaging & Design Inc, pg 999
Stanco Sales LLC, pg 1023

CONNECTICUT

Calzone Anvil Case Co, pg 817
Concord Communications, pg 835
MAVCO, pg 934
Monaco LLC, pg 945
Rockwell Communications Inc, pg 998

DELAWARE

Actors Attic, pg 775

FLORIDA

Access Media Group, pg 773
Digital Video Systems Inc, pg 848
Gulf Coast Audio Visual Producers Inc, pg 883
Olympic Case Co, pg 962
Pro Stage Inc, pg 983
Recording Media & Equipment Inc (RM&E), pg 993
TAI Audio, pg 1031
Tallahassee Audio Visual, pg 1031

GEORGIA

Audio Visual Resources Inc, pg 795
Lighting & Production Equipment Inc, pg 920
Technical Innovation, pg 1033

ILLINOIS

Chicago Spotlight Inc, pg 825
Creative Technology, pg 838
Joseph Electronics, pg 906
Platt Luggage Inc, pg 977
Polyline LLC, pg 978
RC Communications, pg 992
Research Technology International (RTI), pg 995
Tele-Time Systems, pg 1036

INDIANA

Jack's Camera Shop, pg 903
Lee Co Inc, pg 918
Porter Case Inc, pg 978

KENTUCKY

Axxis Inc, pg 800
NOR-COM Inc, pg 958

LOUISIANA

Intermedia Technologies, pg 900

MARYLAND

Cardinal Sound & Video, pg 820
Professional Label Inc, pg 985
RTZ Audio Visual, pg 1000

MASSACHUSETTS

Camera Co Inc/Broadcast Divison, pg 818
Terry Hanley Audio Systems Inc, pg 884
High Output Inc, pg 888
HMC Electronics, pg 889
Rule Broadcast Systems, pg 1000
Stanley Supply & Services Inc, pg 1023
University Products Inc, pg 1050

MICHIGAN

Aarmor Case Co, pg 772
On Stage Visuals, pg 963
TeL Systems, pg 1035

MINNESOTA

AVI Systems, pg 799
Phil Sykes & Associates Inc, pg 974

MISSISSIPPI

Bowie Audio Visual Enterprises Inc, pg 811
Jasper Ewing & Sons Inc, pg 864

MISSOURI

A to Z Theatrical Supply & Service, pg 771
Communitronics Corp, pg 833
Southwest Audio-Visual Inc, pg 1019

NEBRASKA

Wilson Case Inc, pg 1067

NEW HAMPSHIRE

Channell One Video, pg 824

NEW JERSEY

Audio Visual Associates, pg 795
Comprehensive Cable & Connectivity Co, pg 833
Hakuba Sunpak Velbon, pg 883
Nelson Enterprises Theatrical Supply Co, pg 954
Starlite Productions, pg 1024
Total Video Products Inc, pg 1042

NEW YORK

Barbizon Electric Co Inc, pg 802
Colortone Audio Visual, pg 832
Design Audio Visual Inc, pg 845
DSan Corp, pg 852
Gotham Sound & Communications Inc, pg 881
Hybrid Cases, pg 892
Island Cases, pg 902
Langie Audio Visual Systems, pg 915
Light Impressions, pg 920
Long Island Video Enterprises Live Inc, pg 924
Magnaplan Corp, pg 928
Motion Picture Enterprises Inc, pg 947
Rafik, pg 990
Talas, pg 1031
TecNec Distributing, pg 1035
Tenba, pg 1037
Visual Technologies Corp, pg 1060
Visual Word Systems Inc, pg 1060

NORTH CAROLINA

Camcor Inc, pg 818
Dudley Theatrical, pg 853

OHIO

Copp Integrated Systems, pg 836
Tri-State Audio Visual Co, pg 1044
Univenture Inc, pg 1049

PENNSYLVANIA

Audio Visions Inc, pg 795
Brodart Co, pg 813
Charles Beseler Co, pg 824
Electron Microscopy Sciences (EMS), pg 859
J E Foss Co, pg 871
The Lerro Corp, pg 919
New York Camera & Video, pg 956
RSS Distributors, pg 1000
Techni-Tool Inc, pg 1033

RHODE ISLAND

Custom Computer Specialists Inc, pg 841

TENNESSEE

Memphis Communications Corp, pg 938
Spring Arbor Distributors, pg 1022
Technical Support Systems LLC, pg 1034
Tennessee Visual Service Co, pg 1037

TEXAS

Audio Visual Technologies Group, pg 796
J&S Audio Visual Inc, pg 904
Pro Video & Film Equipment Co Inc, pg 983
Specialized Products Co, pg 1020

VERMONT

Production Advantage Inc, pg 984

VIRGINIA

Avitecture Inc, pg 799
Boitnott Visual Communications Corp (BVC), pg 810
Communications Specialists Inc, pg 833
Lee Hartman & Sons Inc, pg 918
The Whitlock Group, pg 1065

WASHINGTON

Inland Audio Visual Co, pg 898

WEST VIRGINIA

United Sound & Electronics, pg 1048

WISCONSIN

Associated Bag Co, pg 792
Audio Visual of Milwaukee Inc, pg 795
Full Compass Systems, pg 874
Pro Studio Supply, pg 983
USAV Group Inc, pg 1050

PUERTO RICO

Bonnin Electronics Inc, pg 810

ALBERTA

Sharp's Audio-Visual Ltd, pg 1008
Unique Communications Ltd, pg 1048

ONTARIO

Carr McLean Ltd, pg 820
Edcom Multimedia Products, pg 856
Nationwide Audio Visual Co, pg 953
Premier A/V Sales Ltd, pg 980
Westbury National Show Systems Ltd, pg 1064

Shipping, Packaging, Carrying & Storage Case Manufacturers

ALABAMA

ExpoDisplays, pg 864

CALIFORNIA

A & J Cases, pg 771
A&S Case Co Inc, pg 771
Anvil Cases, pg 787
Creative Custom Cases, pg 838
Encore Cases, pg 861
Extron Electronics, pg 864
J & R Film Co, pg 903
Jan-Al Cases, pg 904
Melmat Inc, pg 938

MISCELLANEOUS

Shipping, Packaging, Carrying & Storage Case Manufacturers (continued)

CALIFORNIA (continued)

Mole-Richardson Co, pg 945
Nalpak Inc, pg 952
Tasman Group Pacific Rim, pg 1032
Thermodyne Cases, pg 1038

COLORADO

Lightware Inc, pg 921
ProLine Digital, pg 986
Rose Packaging & Design Inc, pg 999

CONNECTICUT

Calzone Anvil Case Co, pg 817
Monaco LLC, pg 945

FLORIDA

Myton Industries Inc, pg 952
Olympic Case Co, pg 962
Viking Cases, pg 1058

GEORGIA

Lighting & Production Equipment Inc, pg 920

ILLINOIS

Bretford Manufacturing Inc, pg 812
Calumet Carton Co, pg 817
Elegant Packaging Corp, pg 859
Flight Form Cases Inc, pg 870
Kart-A-Bag Manufacturing Inc, pg 908
Platt Luggage Inc, pg 977
R & R Cases & Cabinets, pg 989
Research Technology International (RTI), pg 995

INDIANA

Porter Case Inc, pg 978
Star Case Manufacturing Co Inc, pg 1023

IOWA

Winegard Co, pg 1067

KENTUCKY

Salesmaker Carts, pg 1001

MARYLAND

Delta Consolidated Industries Inc, pg 845
Professional Label Inc, pg 985

MASSACHUSETTS

ATS Cases Inc, pg 793
Pelican Products, pg 971

MICHIGAN

Aarmor Case Co, pg 772
Harnel Case Co, pg 885

MINNESOTA

Chief, pg 825
Phil Sykes & Associates Inc, pg 974
Sunrise Packaging Inc, pg 1028

MISSOURI

Blair Packaging, pg 809

NEBRASKA

Wilson Case Inc, pg 1067

NEW JERSEY

Nelson Enterprises Theatrical Supply Co, pg 954
Pioneer Research Inc, pg 976
Reed Presentations Inc (RPI), pg 993

NEW YORK

Albumx Corp, pg 780
Fibre Case Corp, pg 866
Hybrid Cases, pg 892
Island Cases, pg 902
Light Impressions, pg 920
Magnaplan Corp, pg 928
Northern Lights, pg 959
Tenba, pg 1037
The Tiffen Co LLC, pg 1040

NORTH CAROLINA

US Case Corp, pg 1050

OHIO

Bud Industries, pg 814
Cabbage Cases Inc, pg 816
LM Cases/LM Engineering Inc, pg 923
Univenture Inc, pg 1049

PENNSYLVANIA

American Thermoplastic Co, pg 785
Case Design Corp, pg 820
Charles Beseler Co, pg 824
Electron Microscopy Sciences (EMS), pg 859
Media Supply Inc, pg 937
Production Solutions Inc, pg 985

TEXAS

Opti-Case Inc, pg 964

UTAH

ZERO Manufacturing Inc, pg 1073

VERMONT

PortaBrace Inc, pg 978

WISCONSIN

Full Compass Systems, pg 874

MANITOBA

Big Deal Custom Casings, pg 807

QUEBEC

STIL Casing Solution, pg 1025

Shipping, Packaging, Carrying & Storage Case Rentals

ARIZONA

Metropolitan Audio-Visual Inc, pg 940

CALIFORNIA

Adolph Gasser Inc, pg 776
Ametron Audio/Video, pg 785
Crystal Pyramid Productions™, pg 840
Gold Standard Productions, pg 880
Location Sound Corp, pg 924
Media Fabricators Inc, pg 936
Mole-Richardson Co, pg 945
Shooting Star Video, pg 1009
Total Media Group, pg 1042
Twin Peaks Creative, pg 1047
VMI Inc, pg 1060

COLORADO

Ceavco Audio/Visual Co, pg 822

CONNECTICUT

A/V Davey, pg 797

FLORIDA

Access Media Group, pg 773
Pro Stage Inc, pg 983
Technomedia Solutions, pg 1035

GEORGIA

Lighting & Production Equipment Inc, pg 920
Stage Front Presentation Systems, pg 1022

ILLINOIS

Creative Technology, pg 838
RC Communications, pg 992
Show Department Inc, pg 1009
Tele-Time Systems, pg 1036

MARYLAND

RTZ Audio Visual, pg 1000

MASSACHUSETTS

Capron Lighting & Sound Co Inc, pg 819
Terry Hanley Audio Systems Inc, pg 884

MICHIGAN

On Stage Visuals, pg 963

MISSISSIPPI

Bowie Audio Visual Enterprises Inc, pg 811

NEW HAMPSHIRE

Apertura, pg 788

NEW JERSEY

Audio Visual Dynamics®, pg 795
Nelson Enterprises Theatrical Supply Co, pg 954
Starlite Productions, pg 1024

NEW YORK

Design Audio Visual Inc, pg 845
Gotham Sound & Communications Inc, pg 881
Langie Audio Visual Systems, pg 915
Long Island Video Enterprises Live Inc, pg 924
Motion Picture Enterprises Inc, pg 947
Visual Word Systems Inc, pg 1060

NORTH CAROLINA

A&V Company, pg 772

OKLAHOMA

PDC Productions, pg 970

PENNSYLVANIA

Audio Visions Inc, pg 795
New York Camera & Video, pg 956
Production Solutions Inc, pg 985

TENNESSEE

Memphis Communications Corp, pg 938
Technical Support Systems LLC, pg 1034

TEXAS

Light Tec, pg 920

UTAH

Redman Movies & Stories, pg 993

WISCONSIN

Full Compass Systems, pg 874

ALBERTA

Unique Communications Ltd, pg 1048

MANITOBA

Big Deal Custom Casings, pg 807

ONTARIO

Westbury National Show Systems Ltd, pg 1064

Shipping, Packaging, Carrying & Storage Case Repairs

CALIFORNIA

A & J Cases, pg 771
A&S Case Co Inc, pg 771
Anvil Cases, pg 787
Jan-Al Cases, pg 904
Mole-Richardson Co, pg 945

COLORADO

Ceavco Audio/Visual Co, pg 822

CONNECTICUT

Calzone Anvil Case Co, pg 817

FLORIDA

Olympic Case Co, pg 962
Viking Cases, pg 1058

GEORGIA

Lighting & Production Equipment Inc, pg 920

ILLINOIS

R & R Cases & Cabinets, pg 989

KENTUCKY

Axxis Inc, pg 800
NOR-COM Inc, pg 958

NEBRASKA

Wilson Case Inc, pg 1067

Stage Distributors

Stage Manufacturers

Stage Rentals

MISCELLANEOUS

Stage Rentals (continued)

FLORIDA (continued)

Pro Stage Inc, pg 983
Universal Studios Florida® Production Group, pg 1049
Mike Vasilinda Productions Inc, pg 1052
Zebedee Productions, pg 1073

GEORGIA

Continental Film & Video, pg 835
In Concert Production Inc (ICP), pg 897
Lighting & Production Equipment Inc, pg 920
MAGNUM Companies Ltd, pg 929
PC&E, pg 970
Stage Front Presentation Systems, pg 1022

HAWAII

ATTCO Inc, pg 793

ILLINOIS

Chicago Satellite & Video, pg 825
Chicago Scenic Studios Inc, pg 825
Communications Corporation of America, pg 833
QuickSet International Inc, pg 989
Show Department Inc, pg 1009

IOWA

Central Lighting & Equipment Inc (CLE), pg 823

LOUISIANA

Pace Systems, pg 966

MARYLAND

CPR MultiMedia Solutions, pg 837

MASSACHUSETTS

Advanced Lighting & Production Services Inc (ALPS), pg 777
High Output Inc, pg 888
Limelight Productions Inc, pg 921

MICHIGAN

AirBrands Event & Marketing Group, pg 779
Digi Sign Design LLC, pg 847
Fantasee Lighting Inc, pg 865
K&R All Media Productions Inc, pg 908
On Stage Visuals, pg 963

MISSOURI

Cashmark Media Inc, pg 820
Switch, pg 1030

NEW JERSEY

Audio Visual Dynamics®, pg 795
Earl Girls Inc, pg 855
MIB Mediaworks, pg 941
PLS Staging, pg 977
SLD Lighting, pg 1013
Starlite Productions, pg 1024

NEW MEXICO

Quickbeam Systems Inc (QSI), pg 989

NEW YORK

Bestek Lighting & Staging, pg 806
Design Audio Visual Inc, pg 845
KVL Audio Visual Services Inc, pg 914
Manhattan Center Studios Inc, pg 930
Mood Creations Ltd, pg 946
NBC Production Facilities, pg 953
Northern Lights, pg 959
Showman Fabricators Inc, pg 1010
Studio Instrument Rentals (SIR), pg 1027
TBA Global Events, pg 1032
Visual Word Systems Inc, pg 1060

NORTH CAROLINA

Moving Pictures, pg 948
Special Event Services, pg 1020

OHIO

Bartha, pg 803
CET, pg 823
EDR Media LLC, pg 857
Mills James Productions, pg 943
Thread Marketing Group, pg 1039
Vista Color Imaging Inc, pg 1059

OREGON

Pacific Grip & Lighting Inc, pg 967

PENNSYLVANIA

Advanced AV, pg 777
FMP Media Solutions Inc, pg 870
Fusion Brand Experiences, pg 874
Production Solutions Inc, pg 985
Stagestep Inc, pg 1023
WQED-Multimedia, pg 1070

TENNESSEE

Brantley Sound Associates Inc, pg 812
UMCom Productions, pg 1048

TEXAS

Big House Sound Inc, pg 807
Communilux Productions, pg 833
Freeman, pg 872
Onstage Systems, pg 963
Phillips MediaSource, pg 974
Power Factory Productions, pg 979
South Coast Film & Video, pg 1019
Stage Directions, pg 1022
Texcam Inc, pg 1038

VERMONT

Dark Star Lighting & Production, pg 842
Parlato Productions, pg 969

VIRGINIA

American AV, pg 783
Creative Video of Washington Inc, pg 839
Rainbow Rentals, pg 991
StageSound, pg 1023
WETA Production Center, pg 1064

WASHINGTON

Pacific Northwest Theatre Associates Inc (PNTA), pg 967

WEST VIRGINIA

United Sound & Electronics, pg 1048

WISCONSIN

Event Essentials, pg 863
Full Compass Systems, pg 874
Logan Productions Inc, pg 924

ALBERTA

Global Television Station, pg 879

BRITISH COLUMBIA

DL Sound & Lighting Productions Ltd, pg 849

ONTARIO

HD Source, pg 886
Westbury National Show Systems Ltd, pg 1064

Stage Repairs

CALIFORNIA

San Diego Stage & Lighting Supply Inc, pg 1002
Steeldeck® Inc, pg 1024

FLORIDA

Tel-Test, pg 1035

GEORGIA

Lighting & Production Equipment Inc, pg 920

HAWAII

ATTCO Inc, pg 793

MICHIGAN

Fantasee Lighting Inc, pg 865
Studio Consulting & Construction Inc, pg 1026

WISCONSIN

Full Compass Systems, pg 874

ONTARIO

Westbury National Show Systems Ltd, pg 1064

Static Eliminator Distributors

ALABAMA

Media Visions Inc, pg 937

CALIFORNIA

Ametron Audio/Video, pg 785
Christy's Editorial, pg 826
Jameco Electronics, pg 903

COLORADO

Stanco Sales LLC, pg 1023

CONNECTICUT

MAVCO, pg 934

FLORIDA

Lightning Master Corp, pg 921

ILLINOIS

FUJIFILM Graphic Systems Division, pg 873

INDIANA

Lee Co Inc, pg 918

KANSAS

Nazdar®, pg 953

KENTUCKY

NOR-COM Inc, pg 958

MASSACHUSETTS

HMC Electronics, pg 889
Spirig Advanced Technologies Inc (SAT), pg 1021

NEBRASKA

ATV Research Inc, pg 793

NEW JERSEY

Argraph Corp, pg 789
Falcon Safety Products Inc, pg 865
Herbach & Rademan Co Inc, pg 888
VCom International Multimedia Corp, pg 1052

NEW YORK

Colortone Audio Visual, pg 832
Communication Corner Inc, pg 832
Light Impressions, pg 920
NRD LLC, A Mark IV Industries Co, pg 960

PENNSYLVANIA

Techni-Tool Inc, pg 1033

RHODE ISLAND

Custom Computer Specialists Inc, pg 841

VIRGINIA

Filmdex Inc, pg 867
Lee Hartman & Sons Inc, pg 918

WISCONSIN

Associated Bag Co, pg 792
School Specialty Inc, pg 1004

PUERTO RICO

Bonnin Electronics Inc, pg 810

Static Eliminator Manufacturers

ARIZONA

Zippertubing® Co, pg 1074

FLORIDA

Kinetronics Corp, pg 911
Lightning Master Corp, pg 921

ILLINOIS

Sprayway Inc, pg 1022

MASSACHUSETTS

Spirig Advanced Technologies Inc (SAT), pg 1021

NEW JERSEY

Falcon Safety Products Inc, pg 865
Master Bond, pg 933

NEW YORK

NRD LLC, A Mark IV Industries Co, pg 960

PENNSYLVANIA

Simco-Ion, pg 1011

Static Eliminator Rentals

GEORGIA

Stage Front Presentation Systems, pg 1022

OHIO

Hughie's Event Production Services, pg 892

Static Eliminator Repairs

KENTUCKY

NOR-COM Inc, pg 958

Storage Cabinet Distributors

ALABAMA

Media Visions Inc, pg 937

ARIZONA

Troxell Communications Inc, pg 1045

ARKANSAS

Jay S Stanley & Associates Inc, pg 1023

CALIFORNIA

Advanced Systems Group LLC, pg 778
ARS Electronics, pg 791
Christy's Editorial, pg 826
Compact Storage Systems Inc, pg 833
FXC Communications, pg 874
Instructional Materials & Equipment Distributors (I-Med), pg 899
Media Fabricators Inc, pg 936
Promax Systems, pg 986
Russ Bassett Corp, pg 1001
Zack Electronics Inc, pg 1073

COLORADO

Ceavco Audio/Visual Co, pg 822
Stanco Sales LLC, pg 1023

CONNECTICUT

Concord Communications, pg 835
MAVCO, pg 934
Rockwell Communications Inc, pg 998

FLORIDA

Access Media Group, pg 773
Digital Video Systems Inc, pg 848
Hi-Tech Import Export Corp, pg 888
Multicom Inc, pg 949
Photosound of Orlando Inc, pg 975

GEORGIA

Audio Visual Resources Inc, pg 795
Technical Innovation, pg 1033

ILLINOIS

Joseph Electronics, pg 906
G T Luscombe Co Inc, pg 926
Research Technology International (RTI), pg 995
H Wilson Co, pg 1067
Woodside Avenue Music Productions Inc, pg 1069

INDIANA

Lee Co Inc, pg 918

KANSAS

Nazdar®, pg 953

MARYLAND

Cardinal Sound & Video, pg 820
Nicholas P Pipino Associates Inc, pg 976
RTZ Audio Visual, pg 1000

MASSACHUSETTS

Camera Co Inc/Broadcast Divison, pg 818
Gyrus ACMI, pg 883
HMC Electronics, pg 889
Rule Broadcast Systems, pg 1000
University Products Inc, pg 1050

MICHIGAN

Aarmor Case Co, pg 772
Olson Anderson Co, pg 786

MINNESOTA

Alpha Video & Audio Inc, pg 782

MISSISSIPPI

Bowie Audio Visual Enterprises Inc, pg 811
Jasper Ewing & Sons Inc, pg 864

MISSOURI

Image Technologies Corp, pg 895
Southwest Audio-Visual Inc, pg 1019

NEW JERSEY

Audio Visual Associates, pg 795
Audio Visual Dynamics®, pg 795
Comprehensive Cable & Connectivity Co, pg 833
Hannecke Display Systems Inc, pg 884
Total Video Products Inc, pg 1042
VCom International Multimedia Corp, pg 1052
Video Corporation of America (VCA), pg 1055

NEW YORK

AV Workshop, pg 797
Biomorph Desks, pg 807
Colortone Audio Visual, pg 832
Communication Corner Inc, pg 832
Design Audio Visual Inc, pg 845
Flash Electronics Inc, pg 869
Light Impressions, pg 920
A Liss & Co, pg 922
Long Island Video Enterprises Live Inc, pg 924
Magnaplan Corp, pg 928
Markertek Video Supply, pg 931
Motion Picture Enterprises Inc, pg 947
Neptune Photo Inc, pg 954
Sentry Industries Inc, pg 1007
Talas, pg 1031
Visual Technologies Corp, pg 1060
Willoughby's Imaging Center, pg 1067

NORTH CAROLINA

Camcor Inc, pg 818
Carolina Biological Supply Co, pg 820

OHIO

Copp Integrated Systems, pg 836
Jimmy Rea Electronics Inc, pg 992

PENNSYLVANIA

Audio Visions Inc, pg 795
Brodart Co, pg 813
The Lerro Corp, pg 919
Morefield Communications Inc, pg 946
Techni-Tool Inc, pg 1033
Wespen Audio Visual Co, pg 1063

RHODE ISLAND

Custom Computer Specialists Inc, pg 841

TENNESSEE

Lowrance Sound Co Inc, pg 925
Memphis Communications Corp, pg 938

TEXAS

Audio Visual Technologies Group, pg 796
Heffernan Audio Visual, pg 887
J&S Audio Visual Inc, pg 904
Specialized Products Co, pg 1020
TopCat Records LLC, pg 1042

UTAH

RIA Corp, pg 996

VIRGINIA

Avitecture Inc, pg 799
Boitnott Visual Communications Corp (BVC), pg 810
Communications Specialists Inc, pg 833
Filmdex Inc, pg 867
Lee Hartman & Sons Inc, pg 918
Metropolitan Audio Visual Co LLC, pg 940

WASHINGTON

Inland Audio Visual Co, pg 898

WISCONSIN

Demco Inc, pg 845
Full Compass Systems, pg 874
School Specialty Inc, pg 1004
Spectrum Industries Inc, pg 1021

PUERTO RICO

Bonnin Electronics Inc, pg 810

ALBERTA

McBain Audio Visual Ltd, pg 935

ONTARIO

Carr McLean Ltd, pg 820
CBM Metal, pg 821
Edcom Multimedia Products, pg 856

Storage Cabinet Manufacturers

ALABAMA

Omni International Inc, pg 962

CALIFORNIA

A & J Cases, pg 771
Electrorack Legrand Division, pg 859
Russ Bassett Corp, pg 1001
Tasman Group Pacific Rim, pg 1032

COLORADO

ProLine Digital, pg 986

FLORIDA

Harris Corp, pg 885

ILLINOIS

Bretford Manufacturing Inc, pg 812
Luxor, pg 926
Lyon Workspace Products LLC, pg 927
Magnetic Shield Corp, pg 928
Marshall Furniture Inc, pg 932
Smith-Victor Corp, pg 1014
Tripp Lite, pg 1045
H Wilson Co, pg 1067

INDIANA

General Devices Co Inc, pg 876
Star Case Manufacturing Co Inc, pg 1023

MICHIGAN

Aarmor Case Co, pg 772

MINNESOTA

Emcor Enclosures-Crenlo, pg 860
Winsted Corp, pg 1068

MISSOURI

Shure Manufacturing Corp, pg 1010

NEW JERSEY

Hannecke Display Systems Inc, pg 884

NEW YORK

Biomorph Desks, pg 807
Hybrid Cases, pg 892
Magnaplan Corp, pg 928
TBC Consoles Inc, pg 1033

OHIO

Roconex Corp, pg 998

PENNSYLVANIA

A/S Custom Furniture, pg 771
Electron Microscopy Sciences (EMS), pg 859
Sandusky Lee Corp, pg 1002

TENNESSEE

Mystery Electronics, pg 951

TEXAS

Smith System Inc, pg 1014
TopCat Records LLC, pg 1042

WASHINGTON

Watson Desking, pg 1062

MISCELLANEOUS

Storage Cabinet Manufacturers (continued)

WISCONSIN

Spectrum Industries Inc, pg 1021

MANITOBA

Big Deal Custom Casings, pg 807

ONTARIO

Can-Am Merchandising Systems, pg 818
CBM Metal, pg 821
Egan Visual Inc/Egan TeamBoard Inc, pg 858

Storage Cabinet Rentals

FLORIDA

Jordan Klein Film & Video (JKFV), pg 906

GEORGIA

Stage Front Presentation Systems, pg 1022

ILLINOIS

Woodside Avenue Music Productions Inc, pg 1069

NEW YORK

Visual Technologies Corp, pg 1060

NORTH CAROLINA

A&V Company, pg 772
Take One Productions Ltd, pg 1031

TENNESSEE

Memphis Communications Corp, pg 938

VIRGINIA

Lee Hartman & Sons Inc, pg 918

Storage Cabinet Repairs

TENNESSEE

Memphis Communications Corp, pg 938

VIRGINIA

Avitecture Inc, pg 799
Lee Hartman & Sons Inc, pg 918

WISCONSIN

Full Compass Systems, pg 874

ONTARIO

Edcom Multimedia Products, pg 856

Storage Case, *see* Shipping, Packaging, Carrying & Storage Case

Studio Furniture Distributors

ARIZONA

EAR Professional Audio/Video, pg 855
Troxell Communications Inc, pg 1045

CALIFORNIA

Christy's Editorial, pg 826
Eurotech Seating, pg 863
FXC Communications, pg 874
Marketec, pg 931
Mobilized Tech Systems, pg 944
Steeldeck® Inc, pg 1024
VTP Inc, pg 1061
Zack Electronics Inc, pg 1073

FLORIDA

Access Media Group, pg 773
Digital Video Systems Inc, pg 848
Hunter Electronics LLC, pg 892
Media Concepts Inc, pg 936
Recording Media & Equipment Inc (RM&E), pg 993

GEORGIA

Lighting & Production Equipment Inc, pg 920

ILLINOIS

Chicago Spotlight Inc, pg 825
Leedal Inc, pg 918
Woodside Avenue Music Productions Inc, pg 1069

INDIANA

Lee Co Inc, pg 918

KENTUCKY

Axxis Inc, pg 800
NOR-COM Inc, pg 958

MARYLAND

Cardinal Sound & Video, pg 820

MASSACHUSETTS

Professional Audio Design Inc, pg 985
Rule Broadcast Systems, pg 1000

MICHIGAN

Ascom Communications Contractors, pg 791

MINNESOTA

Alpha Video & Audio Inc, pg 782

MISSOURI

Production Support Services Inc, pg 985

NEW HAMPSHIRE

Technet® Systems Group, pg 1033

NEW JERSEY

Alltec Stores, a Vcom IMC Company, pg 782
Diversified Systems Inc, pg 849
PatchAmp, pg 970
Princeton Acoustics Corp, pg 982
Starlite Productions, pg 1024
Total Video Products Inc, pg 1042
Wired 4 Sound Inc, pg 1068

NEW YORK

Biomorph Desks, pg 807
BTX Technologies, pg 814
Design Audio Visual Inc, pg 845
A Liss & Co, pg 922
Markertek Video Supply, pg 931
Neptune Photo Inc, pg 954
TecNec Distributing, pg 1035

OHIO

Jimmy Rea Electronics Inc, pg 992

OREGON

Anthro Corp, pg 787
ASC-Tube Trap, pg 791

PENNSYLVANIA

A/S Custom Furniture, pg 771
Audio Visions Inc, pg 795
The Lerro Corp, pg 919

SOUTH CAROLINA

DaviSound, pg 843

TENNESSEE

Lowrance Sound Co Inc, pg 925
Technical Support Systems LLC, pg 1034

VIRGINIA

Avitecture Inc, pg 799
Communications Specialists Inc, pg 833
Lee Hartman & Sons Inc, pg 918

WASHINGTON

CCI Solutions, pg 821
Pacific Northwest Theatre Associates Inc (PNTA), pg 967

WISCONSIN

Full Compass Systems, pg 874
Pro Studio Supply, pg 983
Spectrum Industries Inc, pg 1021

ALBERTA

Infosat Communications Inc, pg 898

ONTARIO

Cinema Stage Inc, pg 827

Studio Furniture Manufacturers

ALABAMA

Marco Inc, pg 930

ARIZONA

David Wexler & Co, pg 1064

CALIFORNIA

Electrorack Legrand Division, pg 859
Enright Co, pg 861
Steeldeck® Inc, pg 1024

COLORADO

Arrakis Systems, pg 790

FLORIDA

Harris Corp, pg 885

ILLINOIS

Bretford Manufacturing Inc, pg 812
Chicago Scenic Studios Inc, pg 825
Leedal Inc, pg 918
Marshall Furniture Inc, pg 932

INDIANA

HSA Inc, pg 892

MARYLAND

RPG Diffusor Systems Inc, pg 1000

MINNESOTA

Artograph Inc, pg 791
Winsted Corp, pg 1068

NEW JERSEY

Middle Atlantic Products Inc, pg 942

NEW YORK

Biomorph Desks, pg 807
TBC Consoles Inc, pg 1033
Uniset Co LLC, pg 1048

NORTH CAROLINA

Audioarts Engineering, pg 796
Wheatstone Corp, pg 1065

OREGON

Anthro Corp, pg 787
ASC-Tube Trap, pg 791

PENNSYLVANIA

A/S Custom Furniture, pg 771

SOUTH CAROLINA

DaviSound, pg 843

TEXAS

Smith System Inc, pg 1014

WASHINGTON

Pacific Northwest Theatre Associates Inc (PNTA), pg 967

WISCONSIN

Spectrum Industries Inc, pg 1021

MANITOBA

Big Deal Custom Casings, pg 807

Studio Furniture Rentals

ARIZONA

Merestone, pg 938

CALIFORNIA

Golden Gate Studios, pg 880
Steeldeck® Inc, pg 1024

CONNECTICUT

Videofilm Systems Inc, pg 1057

GEORGIA

Stage Front Presentation Systems, pg 1022

MISCELLANEOUS

Timer & Clock Rentals (continued)

CALIFORNIA (continued)

Lynch Communications, pg 926
McCune Audio-Video-Lighting, pg 935
VER-Video Equipment Rentals, pg 1053

COLORADO

Daylight Productions & Rentals, pg 844
Spectrum Audio Visual Services, pg 1020

DELAWARE

Ken-Del Productions Inc, pg 909

FLORIDA

Jordan Klein Film & Video (JKFV), pg 906
Sight & Sound Productions, pg 1010

GEORGIA

Stage Front Presentation Systems, pg 1022

ILLINOIS

AV Chicago Inc, pg 797
Show Department Inc, pg 1009

LOUISIANA

Pace Systems, pg 966

MASSACHUSETTS

Capron Lighting & Sound Co Inc, pg 819

NEVADA

GES Audio Visual, pg 877

NEW YORK

KVL Audio Visual Services Inc, pg 914
Visual Word Systems Inc, pg 1060

NORTH CAROLINA

A&V Company, pg 772
Special Event Services, pg 1020

OHIO

Bartha, pg 803
Mills James Productions, pg 943

PENNSYLVANIA

Bernie's Photo Center, pg 805
FMP Media Solutions Inc, pg 870

VIRGINIA

Quince Imaging Inc, pg 989

WISCONSIN

Event Essentials, pg 863

BRITISH COLUMBIA

Clark's Audio Visual Services Ltd, pg 829

Timer & Clock Repairs

CALIFORNIA

Ametron Audio/Video, pg 785
HM Electronics Inc (HME), pg 889

KENTUCKY

NOR-COM Inc, pg 958

MASSACHUSETTS

Capron Lighting & Sound Co Inc, pg 819

PENNSYLVANIA

Bernie's Photo Center, pg 805

VIRGINIA

Quince Imaging Inc, pg 989

WEST VIRGINIA

United Sound & Electronics, pg 1048

WISCONSIN

Full Compass Systems, pg 874

Sections

AV Product & Service Providers

This section contains full entries for companies active in the AV trade. Entries are sorted by company name and generally contain name, address, telecommunications data, key personnel, branch office and catalog information.

A & J Cases
11121 Hindry Ave, Los Angeles, CA 90045
Mailing Address: PO Box 90596, Airport Sta, Los Angeles, CA 90009-0596
Tel: 310-216-2170 *Toll Free Tel:* 800-537-4000 *Fax:* 310-216-2694
Web Site: www.ajcases.com
Key Personnel
Pres: Patrick Doucette
Sr Engr: Keith Bell
Mktg Mgr: Janet DeVita
Online catalog(s) available

A Cut Above Video Productions Inc
4450 W Eau Gallie Blvd, Suite 220, Melbourne, FL 32934
Tel: 321-253-5677 *Fax:* 321-253-5611
Web Site: www.acutabovevideo.com
Key Personnel
Pres: Bill Williams *E-mail:* bill@acutabovevideo.com
Founded: 1988
Video production company. Broadcast HD ENG/EFP camera, cinema style camera/lenses, insert studio, Premiere & Final Cut post.
Membership(s): American Advertising Federation

A Go Go Films
4324 Via Marina, Marina Del Rey, CA 90292
Tel: 310-576-4992
E-mail: art@agogofilms.com
Web Site: www.agogofilms.com
Key Personnel
Pres: Art Brown *E-mail:* artieb60@gmail.com
Founded: 1997
Commercial, music video production & fitness videos.

A KTVA Production LLC
9818 SE 17 Ave, Suite B, Milwaukie, OR 97222
Mailing Address: PO Box 22911, Portland, OR 97269
Tel: 503-659-4417 *Toll Free Tel:* 800-282-KTVA (282-5882, OR & WA only)
E-mail: mail@ktvavideo.com
Web Site: www.ktvavideo.com
Key Personnel
Owner: Rick Phillips
Founded: 1987
Video production services.
Membership(s): Oregon Media Production Association

A M Graphics Products, dba Affton Graphics Inc
2500 Third Ave, Bronx, NY 10454
Tel: 718-401-4040 *Toll Free Tel:* 800-777-0539 *Fax:* 718-401-3322
E-mail: amproducts@aol.com
Web Site: www.amdba.com
Key Personnel
Pres: A V Classe
Founded: 1973
Specialize in the manufacturing of interior architectural signage.
Catalog(s) available

A Musical Buffet, see SOS Worldwide Productions Inc

A/S Custom Furniture
364-C Valley Rd, Warrington, PA 18976
Tel: 215-491-3100 *Fax:* 215-491-3107
E-mail: sales@ascustom.com
Web Site: www.ascustom.com
Key Personnel
Co-Owner: Matt Smith; Roy Smith, Sr
Design & manufacturing of custom technical furniture; control rooms & audio rooms.
Membership(s): SBE

A T Products Inc
1600 S Division St, Harvard, IL 60033
Tel: 815-943-3590 *Toll Free Tel:* 800-848-2205 *Fax:* 815-943-3604
E-mail: atprod@mc.net
Web Site: atproducts.com
Key Personnel
CEO, Pres & Chief Design Engr: Mike Rose
VP, Busn Devt & Govt Sales: Lynn Stoughton *E-mail:* lynnstou@mc.net
Mgr, Opers: Becky Zalud *E-mail:* bzalud@mc.net
Founded: 1986
Designer & manufacturer of teleconferencing & audience response equipment.
Membership(s): IMCCA; USDLA

A to Z Theatrical Supply & Service
307 W 80 St, Kansas City, MO 64114-2376
Tel: 816-523-1655 *Toll Free Tel:* 800-732-8252 *Fax:* 816-523-1690
E-mail: atoz@atoztheatrical.com
Web Site: www.atoztheatrical.com
Key Personnel
Pres: Alex Perry
VP, Sales: Brad Schmitz
A theatrical supply company offering design, sales, installation, service & rentals in lighting, rigging, curtain, costume & scenic supplies. Lighting & costume rentals for individuals, schools, churches & corporate productions. 2,000 inventory items from make-up to paint, lamps to hardware are available for immediate shipping.
Catalog(s) available
Membership(s): National Costumers Association; Professional Lighting & Sound Association; USITT

A-V Services Inc
99 Fairfield Rd, Fairfield, NJ 07004
Tel: 973-575-5222 *Fax:* 973-575-0857
E-mail: sales@avservices.net
Web Site: www.avservices.net
Key Personnel
CEO: Charles Rodriguez *E-mail:* crodriguez@avservices.net
Pres: Ralph Capria *E-mail:* rcapria@avservices.net
VP, Engg: Joseph Shewchuk *E-mail:* jshewchuk@avservices.net
VP, Fin: Stephen J Inge *E-mail:* singe@avservices.net
VP, Sales: Gary Lanzet *E-mail:* glanzet@avservices.net
Founded: 1960
Branch Office(s)
250 W 57 St, Suite 1229, New York, NY 10107 *Tel:* 212-686-9666

A-Ware Software Inc
330 S Executive Dr, Suite 205, Brookfield, WI 53005-4215
Tel: 262-717-2220 *Toll Free Tel:* 800-326-2609 *Fax:* 262-717-2230
E-mail: info@musicmaster.com; sales@musicmaster.com
Web Site: www.a-ware.com
Key Personnel
Pres: Joe Knapp *E-mail:* joe@musicmaster.com
We sell & manufacture music scheduling software for use by radio stations, video channels & Internet music providers. Also background music providers (non-broadcast).

A&E Home Video
Subsidiary of A&E Networks
235 E 45 St, New York, NY 10017
Tel: 212-210-1400 *Toll Free Tel:* 877-447-4253 *Fax:* 212-907-9418
Web Site: www.aetv.com
Key Personnel
SVP, Consumer Prods, A&E Networks: Kate Winn
Catalog(s) available

A&E Networks, see A&E Television Networks LLC

A&E Television Networks LLC
Affiliate of Hearst/Disney-ABC Television Group
235 E 45 St, New York, NY 10017
Tel: 212-210-1400
Web Site: www.aetv.com
Key Personnel
Chairman: Abbe Raven
CEO & Pres: Nancy Dubuc
SVP, Publicity: Dan Silberman
Branch Office(s)
1925 Century Park E, Suite 900, Los Angeles, CA 90067 *Tel:* 310-201-6060
111 E Wacker Dr, Chicago, IL 60601 *Tel:* 312-819-0191
201 W Big Beaver Rd, Suite 1010, Troy, MI 48084 *Tel:* 248-740-1300

A&I
257 S Lake St, Burbank, CA 91502
Tel: 323-856-5280; 818-848-9001 *Fax:* 323-856-5110
E-mail: mail@aandi.com
Web Site: www.aandi.com
Key Personnel
Owner: Baret Lepejian
Founded: 2004
Photographic & digital processing & printing services. Fine art photographic printing, photobooks, cards & calendars.

A&M Productions
86 Weybosset St, 5th fl, Providence, RI 02903
Tel: 401-453-6161 *Fax:* 401-421-6443
E-mail: info@a-mproductions.com
Web Site: www.a-mproductions.com
Key Personnel
Owner, Pres & Exec Prodr: Michelle S Ahlborg *E-mail:* michelle@a-mproductions.com

A&S Case Co Inc
5260 Vineland Ave, North Hollywood, CA 91601

Tel: 818-509-5920 *Toll Free Tel:* 800-394-6181
Fax: 818-509-1397
E-mail: info@ascase.com
Web Site: www.ascase.com
Key Personnel
Gen Mgr: Denise Berry
Mgr, Sales & Opers: Bill Waskey
Founded: 1975
Online catalog(s) available
Membership(s): NAMM, the National Association of Music Merchants; SMPTE

A&V Company
4238 Piedmont Pkwy, Greensboro, NC 27410-8111
Tel: 336-292-9700 *Toll Free Tel:* 800-292-9700
Fax: 336-854-5282
E-mail: info@avcompany.com
Web Site: www.avcompany.com
Key Personnel
Pres: Amin Haghighat
VP: Chris Alford *E-mail:* calford@avcompany.com
Founded: 1980
AV events & rentals.
Online catalog(s) available
Branch Office(s)
4209-C Stuart Andrew Blvd, Charlotte, NC 28217 *Tel:* 704-940-4045 *Fax:* 704-940-4047
100 Southcenter Ct, Suite 400, Morrisville, NC 27560 *Tel:* 919-462-0720 *Fax:* 919-462-0166
Membership(s): InfoComm International®; International Special Events Society; MPI

Aardvark Productions LLC
6738 S La Rosa Dr, Tempe, AZ 85283-3737
Tel: 480-775-8237 *Fax:* 480-775-8237
E-mail: aardvarkproductions@cox.net
Web Site: www.aardvarkproductionsllc.com
Key Personnel
Pres: Jeff H Haymes *Tel:* 310-301-3040 (cell)
World class TV crew, pre-production & production staff. Full line of television production equipment available as well as still production equipment.
Membership(s): IBEW; International Alliance of Theatrical Stage Employees; NABET-CWA; NATAS; Television Academy

Aardvark Video & Media Productions
17 Winding Rd, Henderson, NV 89052
Tel: 702-897-4477 *Toll Free Tel:* 800-692-4445
E-mail: creators@computer.net
Web Site: aardvarkvideolasvegas.com
Founded: 1987 (in NY, 2001 in NV)
Video production in Las Vegas.
Membership(s): Las Vegas Metro Chamber of Commerce; Las Vegas Videographers Association; WEVA

Aarmor Case Co
2100 Lapo Rd, Lake Odessa, MI 48849
Toll Free Tel: 800-722-5763
E-mail: scat@sell104.com
Founded: 1978
Catalog(s) available

Aaron & Le Duc
Subsidiary of Le Duc Productions
2210 Third St, No 316, Santa Monica, CA 90405
Tel: 310-452-2034
Key Personnel
Owner & Dir: Greg Le Duc
Founded: 1972
Video rental, HDTV, Sony HD-Cam & lenses, 3D production & post-production. Rent 3D cameras, monitors & production accessories.
Catalog(s) available
Membership(s): AES; SAG-AFTRA; SMPTE

Aaron Marcus & Associates Inc
1196 Euclid Ave, Suite 1-F, Berkeley, CA 94708-1640
Tel: 510-601-0994 *Fax:* 510-527-1994
Web Site: www.amanda.com
Key Personnel
Pres: Aaron Marcus *E-mail:* aaron.marcus@amanda.com
Founded: 1982
User-interface design, web design & information visualization. Video editing (conceptual, visual, verbal & story boarding). Interactive media & presentation editing (conceptual, visual & verbal).
Catalog(s) available
Membership(s): AIGA, the professional association for design; Association for Computing Machinery; Special Interest Group for Computer Human Interaction; User Experience Professionals Association

AAVIM, see American Association for Vocational Instructional Materials (AAVIM)

AB Audio Visual Entertainment Inc
PO Box 8020, Long Beach, CA 90808
Tel: 562-429-1042 *Toll Free Tel:* 877-222-8346
Fax: 562-429-2401
E-mail: media@abaudio.com
Web Site: www.abaudio.com
Key Personnel
Pres: Arlan Boll
Founded: 1990

AB Systems Amplifiers
6120 Brace Rd, Loomis, CA 95650
Tel: 916-223-1133
E-mail: absales@abamps.com
Web Site: www.abamps.net
Key Personnel
Owner: Bob Hennige
Founded: 1978
High end home theater, studio & home audio amplifiers.
Membership(s): AES; NAMM, the National Association of Music Merchants; NSCA

Abacus Group of Saint Louis LLC
No 11 Tower, Glen Carbon, IL 62034
Tel: 314-583-3747
E-mail: abacusgroup@agstl.com
Web Site: www.agstl.com
Key Personnel
Owner: Ramey Elliot
Founded: 1971

Abel Cine Tech Los Angeles
801 S Main St, Suite 104, Burbank, CA 91506
Tel: 818-972-9078 *Toll Free Tel:* 888-700-4416
Fax: 818-972-2673
E-mail: orders@abelcine.com
Web Site: www.abelcine.com
Key Personnel
Head, West Coast Prodn Sales: Jerrod Haarstad *E-mail:* jerrod@abelcine.com
Movie camera manufacturing.
Branch Office(s)
17W662 Butterfield Rd, Suite 302, Oakbrook Terrace, IL 60181 *Tel:* 630-359-5778 *Toll Free Tel:* 877-880-4267 *Fax:* 630-359-5793
609 Greenwich St, New York, NY 10014 *Tel:* 212-462-0100 *Toll Free Tel:* 888-223-1599 *Fax:* 212-462-0199

Aberdeen Broadcast Services
22362 Gilberto, Suite 120, Rancho Santa Margarita, CA 92688
Tel: 949-858-4463 *Toll Free Tel:* 800-688-6621
Fax: 949-420-2431
E-mail: info@abercap.com
Web Site: www.abercap.com
Founded: 2001
Digital file delivery, closed captioning & subtitling, multi-language subtitling.
Membership(s): NRB

Abingdon Press
201 Eighth Ave S, Nashville, TN 37203
Mailing Address: PO Box 801, Nashville, TN 37202-0801
Tel: 615-749-6000 *Toll Free Tel:* 800-251-3320
Fax: 615-749-6061
E-mail: orders@abingdonpress.com
Web Site: www.abingdonpress.com
Key Personnel
Exec Dir, Mktg: Tamara Crabtree
Catalog(s) available

ABS Enterprises
PO Box 5127, Evanston, IL 60204-5127
Tel: 847-982-1414
Key Personnel
Owner: Alan Soell *E-mail:* alansoell@comcast.net
Full service marketing communications firm.
Membership(s): AECT; AMC; Biomedical Photographers Association; Chicago Audio-Visual Association; Cinema Chicago; IIAC; MCA-I

ABSA Productions Inc
125 N Halsted St, Chicago, IL 60661
Tel: 312-382-1029
Web Site: www.absaproductions.com
Key Personnel
Owner & Exec Prodr: Yamil Ahuile
Founded: 1999
Full service video production company.

Absolute Hollywood
10232 Harvest Fields Dr, Woodstock, MD 21163
Tel: 443-341-6424
E-mail: events@absolutehollywood.com
Web Site: www.absolutehollywood.com
Key Personnel
CEO: James Lanier
Founded: 1993
3D video projection, filming & event production. World's largest video dome, air structures & immersive 360 video display screen structures.
Branch Office(s)
Hollywood, CA *Tel:* 323-952-8400

Absolute Rentals
2633 N San Fernando Blvd, Burbank, CA 91504
Tel: 818-842-2828
Web Site: www.absoluterentals.com
Key Personnel
CEO: Dave Rosen *E-mail:* dave@absoluteliveproductions.com
Founded: 1995
Production & post-production equipment rentals.

Ac-cetera Inc
5049 Center Dr, Bldg D-1, Latrobe, PA 15650
Mailing Address: PO Box 900, Luxor, PA 15662
Tel: 724-532-3363 *Fax:* 724-532-3364
E-mail: contact@ez-clamp.net
Web Site: www.ac-cetera.com
Key Personnel
Owner & Pres: Mike Kairys
Manufactures work lights, microphone holders & goosenecks, iPads, iPhone & Smart Phone holders.

AC Lighting Inc
88 Horner Ave, Toronto, ON M8Z 5Y3, Canada
Tel: 416-255-9494 *Fax:* 416-255-3514
E-mail: northamerica@aclighting.com
Web Site: www.aclighting.com
Key Personnel
COO: Penny Watier
CFO: Rick Bradley

VP, US Sales & Mktg: Fred Mikeska *Tel:* 518-494-9988
Mng Dir: J F Canuel
Gen Mgr: Tracey Hill
Distribute stage, studio & event lighting, accessories & consumables.

Academic & Campus Technology Services
Division of Dartmouth College
37 Dewey Field Rd, Hanover, NH 03755
Tel: 603-646-2999 *Fax:* 603-646-1343
Web Site: dartmouth.edu
Key Personnel
Assoc Dir, Classroom Technol Servs: Andrew Faunce *Tel:* 603-646-3614 *E-mail:* andrew.g.faunce@dartmouth.edu

Academy Savant
524 W Commonwealth Ave, Suite E, Fullerton, CA 92832
Mailing Address: PO Box 3670, Fullerton, CA 92834-3670
Tel: 714-870-7880 *Toll Free Tel:* 800-472-8268 *Fax:* 714-526-7400
E-mail: info@academysavant.com
Web Site: www.academysavant.com
Key Personnel
Pres: Robin D Lai
Founded: 1977
Develop, publish & distribute computer based AV training programs for analytical laboratories.
Catalog(s) available

Accel Video Productions
14056 Golden Eagle Dr, Jacksonville, FL 32226
Tel: 904-677-9063; 848-467-6299
E-mail: accelv@yahoo.com
Web Site: www.accelvideo.com
Key Personnel
Pres: John R Markert
HD video acquisition, non-linear editing, duplication, DVD authoring & web video.

Accelerated Learning Foundation
118 N Court St, Fairfield, IA 52556
Tel: 641-954-5443 *Toll Free Tel:* 800-289-2377 *Fax:* 641-954-5851
E-mail: info@gamesforthinkers.org
Web Site: gamesforthinkers.org
Key Personnel
Pres & Dir, Sales & Training: Layman G (Buzz) Allen
Central Off & Warehouse Mgr: Gail Crotta
Produce & distribute educational games & puzzles.
Catalog(s) available

Accenture
161 N Clark St, Chicago, IL 60601
Tel: 312-693-0161 *Toll Free Tel:* 877-889-9009 *Fax:* 312-693-0507
Web Site: www.accenture.com
Branch Office(s)
3200 E Camelback, Suite 245, Phoenix, AZ 85018 *Tel:* 602-337-4000 *Fax:* 602-337-4444
2141 Rosecrans Ave, Suite 3100, El Segundo, CA 90245 *Tel:* 310-726-2700 *Fax:* 310-726-2950
1800 Third St, Suite 215, Sacramento, CA 95811 *Tel:* 916-557-2200
750 "B" St, Suite 2820, San Diego, CA 92101
1615 Murray Canyon Rd, Suite 400, San Diego, CA 92108 *Tel:* 619-574-2400
18300 Von Karman Ave, Suite 820, San Diego, CA 92612
560 Mission St, Suite 1200, San Francisco, CA 94105 *Tel:* 415-537-5000 *Fax:* 415-537-5042
50 W San Fernando St, Suite 1200, San Jose, CA 95113 *Tel:* 408-817-2700
1400 16 St, Suite 500, Denver, CO 80202 *Tel:* 720-359-6500 *Fax:* 720-359-6750
One Financial Plaza, Suite 1600, Hartford, CT 06103 *Tel:* 860-756-2000 *Fax:* 860-756-2890
501 Carr Rd, Wilmington, DE 19809 *Tel:* 302-830-5800 *Fax:* 302-830-5801
800 Connecticut Ave NW, Suite 600, Washington, DC 20006 *Tel:* 202-533-1100 *Fax:* 202-533-1111
5201 Blue Lagoon Dr, Suite 250, Miami, FL 33126 *Tel:* 786-425-7000 *Fax:* 305-358-3122
140 Fountain Pkwy, Suite 400, St Petersburg, FL 33716 *Tel:* 727-897-7000 *Fax:* 727-897-7099
2002 Old Saint Augustine Rd, Suite E-45, Tallahassee, FL 32301 *Tel:* 850-513-0620 *Fax:* 850-513-3500
75 Fifth St NW, Suite 1100, Atlanta, GA 30308 *Tel:* 678-657-8000 *Fax:* 678-657-4050
Bank One Ctr/Tower, Suite 2100, 111 Monument Circle, Indianapolis, IN 46204 *Tel:* 317-267-3400 *Fax:* 317-267-3450
7500 College Blvd, Suite 1400, Overland Park, KS 66210 *Tel:* 913-319-1000 *Fax:* 913-319-1900
Prudential Tower, Suite 2300, 800 Boylston St, Boston, MA 02199 *Tel:* 617-488-4000 *Fax:* 617-488-4001
3000 Town Ctr, Suite 2400, Southfield, MI 48075 *Tel:* 313-887-2000 *Fax:* 313-887-2050
333 S Seventh St, Minneapolis, MN 55402 *Tel:* 612-277-0000 *Fax:* 612-277-1010
1807 Jones St, Bolivar, MO 65613 *Tel:* 417-777-6970
211 N Broadway, Suite 2950, St Louis, MO 63102 *Tel:* 314-345-3000 *Fax:* 314-345-3505
300 Campus Dr, Florham Park, NJ 07932 *Tel:* 973-301-1000 *Fax:* 973-301-1005
5 Spring St, Murray Hill, NJ 07974 *Tel:* 908-898-5000 *Fax:* 908-898-5044
111 Washington St, Albany, NY 12210 *Tel:* 518-462-4762 *Fax:* 518-462-1576
1345 Avenue of the Americas, New York, NY 10105 *Tel:* 917-452-4400 *Fax:* 917-527-9915
201 S College St, Suite 1900, Charlotte, NC 28244 *Tel:* 704-332-6411 *Fax:* 704-370-5700
One Renaissance Ctr, Suite 503, 3301 Benson Dr, Raleigh, NC 27609 *Tel:* 919-836-1200 *Fax:* 919-821-0561
Atrium One, 201 E Fourth St, Suite 1600, Cincinnati, OH 45202-1604 *Tel:* 513-455-1000 *Fax:* 513-455-1604
200 Public Sq, Suite 1900, Cleveland, OH 44114 *Tel:* 216-535-5000 *Fax:* 216-535-5350
250 West St, Suite 150, Columbus, OH 43215 *Tel:* 614-629-2000 *Fax:* 614-629-2001
One Commerce Sq, 15th fl, 2005 Market St, Philadelphia, PA 19103 *Tel:* 267-216-1000 *Fax:* 267-216-0100
K&L Gates Ctr, 210 Sixth Ave, Suite 3650, Pittsburgh, PA 15222 *Tel:* 412-937-6000 *Fax:* 412-937-6005
1441 Main St, Columbia, SC 29201 *Tel:* 803-223-7040
1501 S MoPac Expwy, Suite 300, Austin, TX 78746 *Tel:* 512-732-5300 *Fax:* 512-476-7765
1301 Fannin St, Suite 1900, Houston, TX 77002 *Tel:* 713-483-9090 *Fax:* 713-483-9091
5221 N O'Connor Blvd, Suite 1400, Irving, TX 75039 *Tel:* 469-665-0000 *Fax:* 469-665-2000
800 N Glebe Rd, Suite 300, Arlington, VA 22203 *Tel:* 703-947-2000 *Fax:* 703-947-2200
818 Stewart St, Suite 400, Seattle, WA 98101 *Tel:* 206-839-2000 *Fax:* 206-839-2008
111 E Kilbourn, Suite 1200, Milwaukee, WI 53202 *Tel:* 414-212-1000 *Fax:* 414-212-3620

Access Media Group
Division of Hi-Tech Enterprises Inc
4250 114 Terr N, Clearwater, FL 33762
Tel: 727-573-9600 *Toll Free Tel:* 888-354-2510 *Fax:* 727-573-9606
E-mail: hitech@videoequipment.com
Web Site: www.videoequipment.com
Founded: 1984
Video production, rentals, editing & duplication.
Membership(s): Media Professionals of Florida Inc

Access Video in Berkeley
1442 A Walnut St, Berkeley, CA 94709
Tel: 510-528-6044
E-mail: accessvideo@hotmail.com
Web Site: www.accessvideoproductions.com
Key Personnel
Prodn: David Karp
A full service video production & post-production facility. Services include event videography, live video streaming & AVID video editing.

ACCO Brands Corp
4 Corporate Dr, Lake Zurick, IL 60047-8997
Toll Free Tel: 800-541-0094 *Toll Free Fax:* 800-941-4463
E-mail: contactus@gbc.com
Web Site: www.accobrands.com
Key Personnel
Chmn & CEO: Robert J Keller
Pres & COO: Boris Elisman
EVP & CFO: Neal V Fenwick
EVP & Pres, Computer Prods Group: Christopher Franey
EVP & Pres, Intl: Neil McLachlan
EVP & Pres, US Off & Consumer Prods: Thomas W Tedford
SVP & Pres, Emerging Mkts: Patrick Buchenroth
SVP & Pres, Europe: James Mitchell
SVP, Corp Devt: Mark C Anderson
SVP, Fin & Acctg & Chief Acctg Offr: Thomas P O'Neill, Jr
SVP, Gen Coun & Corp Secy: Pamela R Schneider
VP, Corp Communs: Richard Nelson
VP, Investor Rel: Jennifer Rice
Catalog(s) available
Membership(s): Business Technology Association; InfoComm International®; NAB; NOPA; Photo Marketing Association

Accord Productions
2140 S Dixie Hwy, Suite 301, Miami, FL 33133
Tel: 305-856-1245 *Toll Free Tel:* 800-833-1245 *Fax:* 305-856-9101
Web Site: www.accordvideo.com
Key Personnel
Pres: William Wyler
VP: Rocky Wyler
Mktg Dir: Max Wyler *E-mail:* max@accordvideo.com
Catalog(s) available
Membership(s): Independent Media Producers Association; MCA-I

Accu-Tech
11350 Old Roswell Rd, Suite 100, Roswell, GA 30009
Tel: 770-740-2240 *Toll Free Tel:* 800-221-4767; 888-222-8832 *Fax:* 770-740-2260
Web Site: www.accu-tech.com
Key Personnel
Pres: Bill Geary
VP, Sales: Keith Hopkins
Dir, Low Voltage Solutions: Joe Essma
Founded: 1984
Catalog(s) available
Branch Office(s)
6600 Hembree Pkwy, Suite 100, Roswell, GA 30076, Mgr: Todd Delavie *Tel:* 770-751-9473 *Toll Free Tel:* 800-221-4767 *Fax:* 770-475-4659
241 Lyon Lane, Birmingham, AL 35211, Mgr: Brad Moore *Tel:* 205-942-0366 *Toll Free Tel:* 800-368-0265 *Fax:* 205-290-9395
2360 W Broadway Rd, Suite 102, Mesa, AZ 85202-1885, Mgr: John Ittu *Tel:* 480-615-4804 *Toll Free Tel:* 800-824-0180 *Fax:* 480-615-4909

30631 San Antonio St, Hayward, CA 94544, Mgr: Jesse Friedman *Tel:* 510-477-8060 *Toll Free Tel:* 855-868-8801 *Fax:* 510-477-8071
16801 Knott Ave, No D, La Mirada, CA 90638, Mgr: Shannon Van Maisen *Tel:* 714-994-8000 *Toll Free Tel:* 866-293-2514 *Fax:* 714-994-8008
830 W National Dr, Suite 100, Sacramento, CA 95834, Mgr: Jesse Friedman *Tel:* 916-574-9257 *Toll Free Tel:* 800-470-2759 *Fax:* 916-928-7066
7025 S Revere Pkwy, Suite 300, Centennial, CO 80112, Mgr: Jennifer Hall *Tel:* 720-460-3400 *Toll Free Tel:* 844-209-9273
6631 Executive Park Ct, Suite 208, Jacksonville, FL 32216, Mgr: Chris Havel *Tel:* 904-281-9834 *Toll Free Tel:* 855-291-0393 *Fax:* 904-281-9162
701 NW 33 St, Suite 100, Pompano Beach, FL 33064, Mgr: Tim Cullinane *Tel:* 954-788-0016 *Toll Free Tel:* 800-951-5966 *Fax:* 954-788-1095
119 Hamilton Dr, Tallahassee, FL 32304, Mgr: John Campbell *Tel:* 850-210-0168 *Toll Free Tel:* 888-838-3166 *Fax:* 850-210-0194
9220 Palm River Rd, Bldg 1, Suite 103, Tampa, FL 33619-4426, Mgr: Brent Campbell *Tel:* 813-664-1919 *Toll Free Tel:* 800-493-8328 *Fax:* 813-664-1434
1109 Windham Pkwy, Romeoville, IL 60446, Mgr: Jon Park *Tel:* 630-226-0133 *Toll Free Tel:* 866-417-0133 *Fax:* 630-226-0523
15731 W 100 Terr, Bldg 3, Lenexa, KS 66219, Mgr: Kevin Weiss *Tel:* 913-894-0444 *Toll Free Tel:* 800-810-5666 *Fax:* 913-894-0011
1328 Charwood Rd, Suite 600, Hanover, MD 21076-3113, Mgr: Josh McCullough *Tel:* 410-694-9621 *Toll Free Tel:* 800-490-4580 *Fax:* 410-694-9737
23R Rainin Rd, Woburn, MA 01801, Mgr: Chris DeFeo *Tel:* 781-938-4002 *Toll Free Tel:* 866-822-8656 *Fax:* 781-938-4007
11853 Belden Ct, Livonia, MI 48150-1460, Mgr: Dan Walker *Tel:* 734-524-8385 *Toll Free Tel:* 800-228-1016 *Fax:* 734-524-8386
13231 Centennial Rd, Suite 3, Omaha, NE 68138, Mgr: Tom Regan *Tel:* 402-408-4580 *Toll Free Tel:* 855-533-7260 *Fax:* 402-408-4581
109 Amfresco Dr, Plainview, NY 11803, Mgr: John Park *Tel:* 516-249-5790 *Toll Free Tel:* 800-880-9517 *Fax:* 516-249-8275
2801-A Hutchison-McDonald Rd, Charlotte, NC 28269, Mgr: Dion Roberts *Tel:* 704-599-9997 *Toll Free Tel:* 800-770-0006 *Fax:* 704-599-9987
200 Innovation Ave, Suite 110, Morrisville, NC 27560, Mgr: Darrell Davis *Tel:* 919-484-8500 *Toll Free Tel:* 866-243-3916 *Fax:* 919-484-8550
2305 International St, Columbus, OH 43228-4622, Mgr: Joshua Dempsey *Tel:* 614-527-9600 *Toll Free Tel:* 800-414-3777 *Fax:* 614-527-9633
11358 E 60 Place, Tulsa, OK 74146, Mgr: Eric Esses *Tel:* 918-872-1438 *Toll Free Tel:* 866-212-4937
Essex Bldg, Darby Commons, Bay 6, Folcroft, PA 19032, Mgr: Vince Rizzo *Tel:* 610-583-7789 *Toll Free Tel:* 866-858-0838 *Fax:* 610-583-8997
Foster Plaza 5, 651 Holiday Dr, Suite 300, Pittsburgh, PA 15220, Mgr: Jeff Smullin *Tel:* 412-928-4713
7260 Peppermill Pkwy, Charleston, SC 29418, Mgr: Wes Moore *Tel:* 843-767-1771 *Toll Free Tel:* 866-851-9468 *Fax:* 843-767-1747
5200 Pelham Rd, Suite B, Greenville, SC 29615, Mgr: Brian Hughes *Tel:* 864-288-3765 *Toll Free Tel:* 888-457-2900 *Fax:* 864-288-3850
1417 Donelson Pike, Nashville, TN 37217-2957, Mgr: Tim Flannagan *Tel:* 615-399-2123 *Toll Free Tel:* 800-227-0628 *Fax:* 615-399-3494
1500 Luna Rd, Suite 108, Carrollton, TX 75006, Mgr: Eric Esses *Tel:* 972-428-4800 *Toll Free Tel:* 800-895-5792 *Fax:* 972-428-4801
1812 Brittmoore Rd, Suite 200, Houston, TX 77043-2216, Mgr: Steve Bellew *Tel:* 713-647-9995 *Toll Free Tel:* 800-909-5995 *Fax:* 713-647-9743
1421 Wells Branch Pkwy, Suite 100, Pflugerville, TX 78660, Mgr: Spencer Bergeron *Tel:* 512-719-3155 *Toll Free Tel:* 800-432-0325 *Fax:* 512-719-3160
12625 Wetmore Rd, Suite 207, San Antonio, TX 78247, Mgr: Bobby Lee *Tel:* 210-402-0316 *Fax:* 210-490-0062
901 Live Oak Dr, Chesapeake, VA 23320, Mgr: Scott McCallum *Tel:* 757-523-4100 *Toll Free Tel:* 800-362-6612 *Fax:* 757-523-4004
2256 Dabney Rd, Suite A, Richmond, VA 23230, Mgr: Walter Baker *Tel:* 804-204-1507 *Toll Free Tel:* 866-255-7876 *Fax:* 804-204-1517
1109 Andover Park W, Tukwila, WA 98188, Mgr: Sean Mallery *Tel:* 206-575-2820 *Toll Free Tel:* 866-423-2590 *Fax:* 206-575-2830

Accusoft
4001 N Riverside Dr, Tampa, FL 33603
Tel: 813-875-7575 *Toll Free Tel:* 800-875-7009 *Fax:* 813-875-7705
E-mail: sales@accusoft.com
Web Site: www.accusoft.com
Key Personnel
Founder, CEO & Pres: Jack Berlin
VP, Sales & Mktg: Russ Puskaric
VP, Technol Infrastructure: Chris Lubeck
Founded: 1991
Provide imaging technology.
Branch Office(s)
4 Mount Royal Ave, Suite 110, Marlborough, MA 01752 *Tel:* 508-948-0939

AccuWeather Inc
385 Science Park Rd, State College, PA 16803
Tel: 814-235-8600 *Toll Free Tel:* 800-566-6606 *Fax:* 814-235-8609
E-mail: sales@accuweather.com
Web Site: www.accuweather.com
Key Personnel
Founder & Pres: Dr Joel N Myers
CEO: Barry Myers
COO & SVP: Evan A Myers
Founded: 1962

ACDC Audio CD & Cassette
606 Alamo Pintado Rd, Suite 3-281, Solvang, CA 93463
Tel: 818-762-ACDC (762-2232)
Web Site: www.acdc-cdr.com
Key Personnel
Owner: Steve Mitchell *E-mail:* steve@acdc-cdr.com
Founded: 1983
Audio & video duplication.

Ace Video
178 Columbus Ave, No 237072, New York, NY 10023
Tel: 212-727-7969 *Toll Free Fax:* 888-315-9596
E-mail: acevideonyc@gmail.com
Web Site: www.acevideonyc.com
Online catalog(s) available
Membership(s): AES; SMPTE

ACE Video Resources Software
11767 S Dixie Hwy, Suite 222, Miami, FL 33156
Tel: 305-596-6908 *Toll Free Tel:* 888-223-6284 *Fax:* 305-256-0467
E-mail: mailroom@tutorace.com
Web Site: www.tutorace.com
Catalog(s) available

Acey Decy Lighting
200 Parkside Dr, San Fernando, CA 91340
Tel: 818-408-4444 *Fax:* 818-408-2777
E-mail: rcarranza@aceydecy.com
Web Site: www.aceydecy.com; www.lighttrader.com
Founded: 1963
Equipment, rental, sales & service for film, television, theatre, concerts & events. Specializing in grip trucks, moving lights, special effects & dimmers. Factory authorized sales & service center for high end, ETC & strand lighting. Complete line of expendables for all your needs.

ACM Productions Ltd
38 Bob Hill Rd, Ridgefield, CT 06877
Tel: 203-431-9575
E-mail: info@acmproductions.tv
Web Site: www.acmproductions.tv
Key Personnel
Pres: A J Mikhitarian
VP: Craig Mikhitarian

Acme Filmworks
3347 Motor Ave, Suite 100, Los Angeles, CA 90034
Tel: 323-464-7805 *Fax:* 323-464-6614
Web Site: www.acmefilmworks.com
Key Personnel
Exec Prodr: Ron Diamond *E-mail:* rjd@acmefilmworks.com

Acme Recording Studios Inc
112 W Boston Post Rd, Mamaroneck, NY 10543
Tel: 914-381-4141
Web Site: www.acmerec.com
Key Personnel
Owner, Prodr & Engr: Peter Denenberg *E-mail:* pdenenberg@acmerec.com
Founded: 1979

ACO Pacific Inc
2604 Read Ave, Belmont, CA 94002
Tel: 650-595-8588 *Fax:* 650-591-2891
E-mail: sales@acopacific.com; info@acopacific.com; support@acopacific.com
Web Site: www.acopacific.com
Key Personnel
Pres: Noland L Lewis
Founded: 1978
Manufacturer of measurement mics & systems, sound level alarms & monitors, noise generators.
Catalog(s) available
Membership(s): AES; ASA; CAS; INCE

Acorn Media Group Inc, see RLJ Entertainment Inc

Acorn Productions
620 Homewood Dr, Plano, TX 75025
Tel: 972-385-9977 *Fax:* 972-385-9944
E-mail: acornprod@aol.com
Key Personnel
Owner & Pres: Tony Metcalfe
Video production, AV services, sound & lighting for corporate events.

Acoustic Systems
Division of ETS-Lindgren
1301 Arrow Point Dr, Cedar Park, TX 78613
Tel: 512-531-6400 *Toll Free Tel:* 800-749-1460 *Fax:* 512-531-6500
E-mail: sales@ets-lindgren.com
Web Site: www.ets-lindgren.com
Key Personnel
Mktg Dir: Glenn Watkins
Founded: 2002
Manufacture modular sound enclosures.
Catalog(s) available

Acoustical Solutions Inc
2420 Grenoble Rd, Richmond, VA 23294
Tel: 804-346-8350 *Toll Free Tel:* 800-782-5742 *Fax:* 804-346-8808
E-mail: info@acousticalsolutions.com
Web Site: www.acousticalsolutions.com
Key Personnel
Pres: Michael Binns
Sales Mgr: Gary Hudson

Sound & noise control products & acoustical materials.
Catalog(s) available
Membership(s): InfoComm International®; NAB

Acoustics First Corp
2247 Tomlyn St, Richmond, VA 23230-3334
Tel: 804-342-2900 *Toll Free Tel:* 888-765-2900 *Fax:* 804-342-1107
E-mail: info@acousticsfirst.com
Web Site: www.acousticsfirst.com
Key Personnel
Pres, Sales: Rebecca Colleran
Accoustical materials.
Catalog(s) available

Acoustone Corp
140 58 St, Unit 9 W, Bldg A, Brooklyn, NY 11220
Tel: 718-782-5560 *Fax:* 718-782-7367
E-mail: acoustone@newcastlefabrics.com
Web Site: www.acoustonegrillecloth.com
Key Personnel
VP: Larry Lubliner
Manufacturer of grille cloth.
Catalog(s) available

ACS Professional Education, see American Chemical Society (ACS)

ACS Technologies
180 N Dunbarton Dr, Florence, SC 29501
Tel: 843-662-1681 *Toll Free Tel:* 800-736-7425 *Fax:* 843-669-3198
E-mail: info@acstechnologies.com
Web Site: www.acstechnologies.com
Key Personnel
CFO: Craig Hearon
Pres: Marvin Owen
VP: Paige Tuttle
Sr Dir, Enterprise Churches: Pattie White
Busn Devt & Strategic Initiatives: Tom Carringer
Founded: 1978
Information management solutions for churches, schools & other faith-based organizations.
Catalog(s) available

Act One Video
PO Box 342076, Kailua, HI 96734-8997
Tel: 808-220-3625
E-mail: info@actonevideo.tv
Web Site: www.actonevideo.tv
Key Personnel
Owner: Steve Katz
Founded: 1983
Video production & duplication. Broadcast quality cameras & editing suite. Shooting, editing, duplication & format transfers services.

ACT Productions
407 Lincoln Rd, Suite 302, Miami Beach, FL 33139
Tel: 305-538-3809 *Fax:* 305-538-3814
E-mail: info@actproductions.com
Web Site: www.actproductions.com
Key Personnel
CEO & Pres: Bruce Orosz
Dir, Opers: Barbara Goicoechea
Digital Media Dir: Aram Velazquez
Commercial, corporate video, documentary, film, photo shoot & TV production support.

ACTA Publications
4848 N Clark St, Chicago, IL 60640
Tel: 773-271-1030 *Toll Free Tel:* 800-397-2282 *Fax:* 773-271-7399 *Toll Free Fax:* 800-397-0079
Web Site: www.actapublications.com
Key Personnel
Pres & Publr: Gregory F Augustine-Pierce *E-mail:* gpierce@actapublications.com
Founded: 1957
A religious book, audio & video publishing company & distributor of select religious AV products produced by others.
Catalog(s) available
Membership(s): Association of Catholic Publishers Inc

Action Audio & Visual
10834 Burbank Blvd, Suite A-100, North Hollywood, CA 91601
Tel: 818-760-2585 *Toll Free Tel:* 888-406-8164 *Fax:* 818-760-2175
E-mail: info@actionaudioandvisual.com
Web Site: www.actionaudioandvisual.com
Founded: 2001
Audio, camera, AV presentation, lighting & grip rentals. Crew & event services.

Action Photo Service Inc
1741 Clayton Rd, Concord, CA 94520
Tel: 925-676-7777 *Fax:* 925-676-9275
E-mail: actionps@sbcglobal.net
Web Site: www.actionphotoservice.com
Key Personnel
Owner: Dennis Hamilton
Founded: 1963
Catalog(s) available
Membership(s): AIE™; Photo Marketing Association

Action Sports Adventure Inc, see Corbis Motion

Action Sports/All Stock
Subsidiary of All-Stock
PO Box 301, Malibu, CA 90265-0301
Tel: 310-459-2526 *Fax:* 310-456-1743
E-mail: info@sdfilms.com
Web Site: www.actionsportsstockfootage.com
Key Personnel
Owner & Pres: Scott Dittrich
Content Mgr: Bill Lauten
Ed: Ellen Renell
Founded: 1985
Stock library & production services.

Action Video
2373 Walnut Blvd, Walnut Creek, CA 94597
Tel: 925-934-4366
E-mail: actvid@aol.com
Web Site: actionvideo.biz
Key Personnel
Owner: Lester Howard
Founded: 1983
Video production & duplication.

Activu Corp
301 Roundhill Dr, Rockaway, NJ 07866
Tel: 973-366-5550 *Toll Free Tel:* 888-ACTIVU1 (228-4881) *Fax:* 973-625-7775
E-mail: info@activu.com
Web Site: www.activu.com
Key Personnel
CEO: Paul Noble
Founded: 1983
Delivers a scalable visualization platform for control rooms & mobile devices. Our solution integrates with other applications to provide information when & where it's needed in order to provide greater situational awareness & collaboration.
Catalog(s) available
Branch Office(s)
1100 Wilson Blvd, Suite 1225, Arlington, VA 22209 *Tel:* 703-527-4440 *Fax:* 571-312-7581
Membership(s): InfoComm International®

Actors Attic
540 Otis Dr, Dover, DE 19901
Tel: 302-734-8214 *Fax:* 302-734-8207
E-mail: sales@actorsattic.com
Web Site: www.actorsattic.com
Key Personnel
Owner: Susan Betts; Mark Fels

ADAM Inc
Unit of Ebix Inc
5 Concourse Pkwy, Suite 3200, Atlanta, GA 30328
Tel: 404-604-2757 *Toll Free Tel:* 800-755-ADAM (755-2326)
E-mail: editorialdirector@adamcorp.com
Web Site: www.adam.com
Key Personnel
CEO & Pres: Robin Raina
CFO: Robert F Kerris
Health care information & multimedia visual learning assets.

Adams Creative & Production Services
PO Box 98636, Des Moines, WA 98198-0636
Tel: 206-824-6970 *Fax:* 206-824-7036
E-mail: adamscreative@isomedia.com
Web Site: www.adamscreative.net
Key Personnel
Owner: Dan Adams
Founded: 1976
Business communications media design & production.
Shipping Address: 24039 Ninth Place S, Des Moines, WA 98198

D L Adams Associates Inc
1536 Augden St, Denver, CO 80218
Tel: 303-455-1900 *Fax:* 303-455-9187
E-mail: denver@dlaa.com
Web Site: www.dlaa.com
Key Personnel
VP: Ed Logsdon *E-mail:* elogsdon@dlaa.com
Founded: 1979
Acoustical, AV & technology engineering consultants.
Branch Office(s)
970 N Kalaheo Ave, Suite A-311, Kailua, HI 96734 *Tel:* 808-254-3318 *Fax:* 808-254-5295 *E-mail:* hawaii@dlaa.com
Membership(s): AES; ASA; InfoComm International®; USITT

DL Adams Associates Ltd
970 N Kalaheo Ave, Suite A-311, Kailua, HI 96734
Tel: 808-254-3318 *Fax:* 808-254-5295
E-mail: infohawaii@dlaa.com
Web Site: www.dlaa.com
Key Personnel
Principal Engr: David L Adams
Founded: 1979
Consulting & designing services for audio, AV, teleconferencing & video conferencing.
Branch Office(s)
1536 Ogden St, Denver, CO 80218 *Tel:* 303-455-1900 *E-mail:* infodenver@dlaa.com

Adams Evidence Grade Technology Inc
4123 N Little Creek Rd, Utopia, TX 78884
Mailing Address: PO Box 1217, Utopia, TX 78884-1217
Tel: 830-966-4210 *Toll Free Tel:* 877-643-4900 *Fax:* 830-966-4214
E-mail: info1@evidencegrade.com; customerservice@evidencegrade.com
Web Site: www.evidencegrade.com
Key Personnel
VP, Fin: Anne Mauel
Founded: 1981
Recording media & equipment for government & law enforcement.
Catalog(s) available

Adaptive Video Walls & Displays
Division of Adaptive Technologies Group Inc

1635 E Burnett St, Signal Hill, CA 90755
Tel: 562-424-1100 *Fax:* 562-424-3520
E-mail: info@adapttechgroup.com
Web Site: www.adapttechgroup.com
Key Personnel
Pres: Paul Allen
Founded: 2004
Video wall frames & display hardware.
Catalog(s) available
Membership(s): ICTA; InfoComm International®; NAMM, the National Association of Music Merchants; NSCA

Adcom LLC
PO Box 54096, Phoenix, AZ 85078
Tel: 480-607-2277 *Fax:* 623-505-9523
E-mail: sales@adcom-usa.com
Web Site: www.adcom-usa.com
Designs, develops, manufactures, markets & distributes worldwide high performance consumer electronics.

ADD Plus
488 Glacier Way S, Monmouth, OR 97361
Toll Free Tel: 800-847-1233 *Fax:* 503-838-1608
Web Site: www.add-plus.com
Key Personnel
Dir: Dr John Taylor *E-mail:* drtaylor@add-plus.com
Founded: 1993

Addlogix
47 Peters Canyon Rd, Irvine, CA 92606
Tel: 949-341-0888 *Toll Free Tel:* 800-344-6921 *Fax:* 949-341-0669
E-mail: sales@addlogix.com
Web Site: www.addlogix.com
Key Personnel
Sr Sales Mgr: Doug Johnson
Founded: 1979
Catalog(s) available

Adelphi Records Inc
PO Box 7688, Silver Spring, MD 20907-7688
Tel: 301-434-6958 *Fax:* 301-434-3056
E-mail: adelphi@adelphirecords.com
Web Site: www.adelphirecords.com
Key Personnel
CEO & Pres: Gene Rosenthal *E-mail:* gene@adelphirecords.com
Busn Mgr: Hap Passman *E-mail:* hap@adelphirecords.com

ADI Systems Inc
3144 Thunderbird Crescent, Burnaby, BC V5A 3G4, Canada
Tel: 604-291-1839 *Toll Free Tel:* 800-663-1042 *Fax:* 604-294-5782
E-mail: burnaby.ca@adiglobal.com
Web Site: www.adiglobal.ca
Key Personnel
Branch Mgr: Jeremy Taylor
Closed circuit TV, commercial sound & intercom products, video surveillance.

Adobe Systems Inc
345 Park Ave, San Jose, CA 95110-2704
Tel: 408-536-6000 *Fax:* 408-537-6000
Web Site: www.adobe.com
Key Personnel
Founder & Chmn of the Bd: Dr Charles M Geschke; Dr John E Warnock
CEO & Pres: Shantanu Narayen
EVP & Gen Mgr, Mobile & Devices: Alan S Ramadan
EVP & Chief Software Architect: Kevin Lynch
SVP & Gen Coun: Karen Cottle
SVP, Corp Devt: John Brennan
SVP, Global Mktg: Ann Lewnes
SVP, HR: Donna Morris
SVP, Print & Classic Publg Solutions Busn Unit & Mng Dir, India R&D: Naresh Gupta
SVP, Engg Technol Group: Digby Horner
SVP, Chief Software Architect, Advanced Technol Labs: Tom Malloy
Founded: 1982
Branch Office(s)
601 Townsend St, San Francisco, CA 94103 *Tel:* 415-832-2000 *Fax:* 415-832-2020
275 Washington St, 3rd fl, Newton, MA 02458 *Tel:* 617-766-2360 *Fax:* 617-658-2190 (Boston office)
3900 Northwoods, 3rd fl, Arden Hills, MN *Tel:* 651-766-4700 *Fax:* 651-766-4750
1540 Broadway, 17th fl, New York, NY 10036 *Tel:* 212-471-0904 *Fax:* 212-471-0990
532 Broadway, 7th fl, New York, NY 10036 *Tel:* 646-918-7738 *Fax:* 646-861-6495
18 E 16 St, 7th fl, New York, NY 10003 *Tel:* 646-480-3670 *Fax:* 212-242-3273
3900 Adobe Way, Lehi, UT 84043 *Tel:* 385-345-0000
7930 Jones Branch Dr, 5th fl, McLean, VA 22102 *Tel:* 571-765-5400 *Fax:* 571-765-5450 (Washington, DC office)
801 N 34 St, Seattle, WA 98103 *Tel:* 206-675-7000
Adobe Systems Canada, 343 Preston St, Ottawa, ON K1S 1N4, Canada *Tel:* 613-940-3676 *Fax:* 613-594-8886
Foreign Office(s): Adobe Systems Pty Ltd, Tower 2, Level 27, 201 Sussex St, Sydney, NSW 2000, Australia *Tel:* (02) 9778 4100 *Fax:* (02) 9778 4190
Adobe Systems Pty Ltd, One Queens Rd, Suite 1001, Melbourne, Victoria 3004, Australia *Tel:* (03) 9778 4162 *Fax:* (03) 9863 8010
Adobe Systems Benelux BV, Park Lane Bldg F, 1st fl, Culliganlaan 2F, 1831 Diegem, Belgium *Tel:* (02) 416 40 00 *Fax:* (02) 416 40 09
Adobe Systems Brazil, Rua James Joule 65, Conjunto 141, Condominio Edificio Torre Sul, 04576-080 Sao Paulo-SP, Brazil *Tel:* (011) 2175 9595 *Fax:* (011) 3842 9539
0909, 9/F, China World Tower, No 1 JianGuoMenWai Ave, Beijing 100004, China *Tel:* (010) 58657700 *Fax:* (010) 58657701
35/F Citic Sq, 1168 Nanjing Rd W, Shanghai 200041, China *Tel:* (010) 58657700 *Fax:* (021) 52524616
Avenir Business Park, Radlicka 714/113a, 158 00 Prague 5, Czech Republic *Tel:* 225 020 900 *Fax:* 225 020 909
Adobe Systems Danmark ApS, Islands Brygge 57, 2300 Copenhagen, Denmark *Tel:* 3231 6000 *Fax:* 3231 6001
Adobe Systems France SAS, Tour Maine Montparnasse, 112, ave Kleber, 75784 Paris Cedex 16, France *Tel:* 01 56 54 99 00 *Fax:* 01 56 54 99 01
Adobe Sytems Engineering GmbH, Grosse Elbstr 27, 22767 Hamburg, Germany *Tel:* (040) 306 36 0 *Fax:* (040) 306 36 333
Adobe Systems GmbH, Georg-Brauchle-Ring 58, 80992 Munich, Germany *Tel:* (089) 31 70 50 *Fax:* (089) 31 70 57 05
The Lee Gardens, Suite 4102, 41/F, 33 Hysan Ave, Causeway Bay, Hong Kong *Tel:* 2916 2100 *Fax:* 2970 2277
Salarpuria Infinity, 3rd fl, 5 Bannerghatta Rd, Bangalore 560 029, India *Tel:* (080) 41939500 *Fax:* (080) 41939505 *Web Site:* www.adobeindia.com
518/519 Midas Sahar Plaza Complex, Andheri (E), Mumbai 400 059, India *Tel:* (022) 40308809 *Fax:* (022) 28365167
Adobe Systems India Pvt Ltd, Adobe Towers, I-1A City Centre, Sector 25A, Noida 201 301, India *Tel:* (0120) 244 4711 *Fax:* (0120) 433 3427 *Web Site:* www.adobeindia.com
Adobe Systems Software Ireland Ltd, 4-6 Riverwalk, Citywest Business Campus, Dublin 24, Ireland *Tel:* (01) 242 6700 *Fax:* (01) 242 6711
Adobe Systems Israel, 8 Aba Even Blvd, 46725 Herzlia, Israel *Tel:* (09) 9614025
Adobe Systems Italia SRL, Viale Colleoni 5, Centro Direzlionale Colleoni, Palazzo Taurus A3, 20041 Milan MI, Italy *Tel:* (02) 039 6550 1 *Fax:* (02) 039 6550 50
Adobe Systems Roma, c/o Tiempo Business Ctr, Via Leone XIII 95, 00165 Rome, Italy *Tel:* (06) 3280 3650 *Fax:* (06) 454 39899
Adobe Systems Co Ltd, Gate City Osaki, East Tower, 1-11-2 Osaki, Shinagawa-ku, Tokyo 141-0032, Japan *Tel:* (03) 5740 2400
ICS Adobe Systems SRL, Business Center Le Roi, 29 Sfatul Tarii St, 2012 Chisinau, Moldova *Tel:* (032) 283 9878 *Fax:* (032) 283 9877
Adobe Systems Benelux BV, Europlaza, Hoogoorddreef 54a, 1101 BE Amsterdam, Netherlands *Tel:* (020) 65 11 200 *Fax:* (020) 65 11 300
171 Featherston St, Wellington 6011, New Zealand *Tel:* (04) 894 8538
Adobe Systems Norge AS, Karenslyst alle 8 B, 0278 Oslo, Norway *Tel:* 23 16 28 81 *Fax:* 23 16 28 82
Regus Business Ctr, ul Prusa 2, 00-493 Warsaw, Poland *Tel:* (022) 657 0173 *Fax:* (022) 657 0111
Adobe Systems Romania, Anchor Plaza, 9th fl, 26Z Timisoara Blvd, 061331 Bucharest, Romania *Tel:* (031) 413 35 00 *Fax:* (021) 413 36 26
Adobe Systems Russia, Kosmodamianskaya nab 52, Bldg 1B, 115054 Moscow, Russia *Tel:* (495) 782 97 00 *Fax:* (495) 503 66 90
No 8 Temasek Blvd, Suntec Tower 3, 06-02, Singapore 038988, Singapore *Tel:* 6511 5500 *Fax:* 6333 8023
Adobe Systems South Africa (Pty) Ltd, The Campus Twickenham Bldg, Corner Sloane & Main Rd, Bryanston 2021, South Africa *Tel:* (011) 573 0008 *Fax:* (011) 541 0842
16F, A, Kyobo Kangnam Tower, 1303-22 Seochodong, Seocho-gu, Seoul 137-070, South Korea *Tel:* (02) 530 8000 *Fax:* (02) 530 8001
Adobe Systems Iberica SL, Torre Mapfre, Villa Olimpica C/ Marina 16-18, Planta 20, 08005 Barcelona, Spain *Tel:* 933 268 400 *Fax:* 933 268 420
Adobe Systems Nordic AB, Knarrarnasgatan 7, 164 93 Kista, Sweden *Tel:* (08) 752 3300 *Fax:* (08) 751 4955
Adobe Research Schweiz AG, Barfusserplatz 6, 4051 Basel, Switzerland *Tel:* (061) 226 5500 *Fax:* (061) 226 5539
Buyukdere Cad No 191, Apa Giz Ofis Binasi Kat 16, 34394 Levent Istanbul, Turkey *Tel:* (0212) 371 05 00 *Fax:* (0212) 371 05 99
Festival City, Festival Business Tower 19th fl, PO Box 36605, Dubai, United Arab Emirates *Tel:* (04) 293 26 13 *Fax:* (04) 293 25 25
Adobe Systems Europe Ltd, 34-38 Market St, Maidenhead, Berks SL6 8AD, United Kingdom *Tel:* (01628) 590 000 *Fax:* (01628) 590 100

Adolph Gasser Inc
181 Second St, San Francisco, CA 94105
Tel: 415-495-3852 *Toll Free Tel:* 800-994-2773 *Fax:* 415-543-8510
E-mail: agivideo@yahoo.com
Web Site: www.gasserphoto.com
Key Personnel
Owner: John Gasser
Video Sales Mgr: Michael O'Connor
Founded: 1950
Photographic & video equipment rental & sales.

Adorama Rental Co
42 W 18 St, 6th fl, New York, NY 10011
Tel: 212-627-8487
E-mail: rent@adorama.com
Web Site: www.adoramarentals.com

Founded: 1988
Rents & supports a full range of still & motion cameras & accessories, lighting & grip equipment.

Adrenaline Films
5224 S Orange Ave, Orlando, FL 32809
Tel: 407-850-0711 *Fax:* 407-859-6527
E-mail: contact@adrenalinefilms.com
Web Site: www.adrenalinefilms.com
Key Personnel
Pres: Michael Murray
Gen Mgr: Tim Bartlett
Prodn Mgr & Prodr: Mary Rosa
Post Mgr: Dennis Larkin
Location production, specialty shooting, camera crews, lighting & grip equipment. Post-production services include video editing, sound design, color grading & visual effects.

Adrienne Electronics Corp (AEC)
901 American Pacific Dr, Suite 170, Henderson, NV 89014
Tel: 702-896-1858 *Toll Free Tel:* 800-782-2321 *Fax:* 702-896-3034
E-mail: info@adrielec.com; orders@adrielec.com; support@adrielec.com
Web Site: www.adrielec.com
Key Personnel
Founder & Owner: Bruce E Waggoner
Pres: Tracey Ruesch
Founded: 1986
Manufacturer of computer based time code products.

The ADS Group
2155 Niagara Lane N, Suite 120, Plymouth, MN 55447
Tel: 763-449-5500 *Toll Free Tel:* 800-759-0992 *Fax:* 763-449-5555
E-mail: sales@theadsgroup.com
Web Site: www.theadsgroup.com
Key Personnel
COO: Connie Comeau
Exec Prodr: Mitch Waters
Prodr: Dave Friend; Kerry Johnson
Founded: 1989
Full service AV production company, including a music library. Manufacture DVDs, CDs & USB drives.
Catalog(s) available
Membership(s): AVDA; Content Delivery & Storage Association; InfoComm International®

ADS Media
Division of ADS Studio Productions Inc
620 Trinity Church Rd, Hamilton, ON L0R 1P0, Canada
Tel: 905-692-2960 *Fax:* 905-692-2961
E-mail: info@adsmedia.ca
Web Site: www.adsmedia.ca
Key Personnel
CEO & Pres: Ken Vandevrie
Founded: 1990
AV production.

ADS Technologies
Division of Adesso Inc
160 Commerce Way, Walnut, CA 91789
Tel: 909-839-2929 *Fax:* 909-839-2930
E-mail: sales@adesso.com
Web Site: www.adesso.com
Founded: 1992
Catalog(s) available

Adtec Digital Inc
408 Russell St, Nashville, TN 37206
Tel: 615-256-6619 *Fax:* 615-256-6593
E-mail: sales@adtecinc.com
Web Site: www.adtecinc.com
Founded: 1985
Manufacturer of MPEG-2 based digital video players, single-channel commercial insertion controllers, automated video control systems & streaming video encoders.
Catalog(s) available
Branch Office(s)
2231-3 Corporate Square Blvd, Jacksonville, FL 32216 *Tel:* 904-720-2003 ext 4606 *Fax:* 904-239-3199
Sales Office(s): 8009 NW 36 St, Suite 210, Doral, FL 33166 *Tel:* 305-720-2363 *Fax:* 305-720-2371 (Latin America sales off)

Advance Audiovisual Presentation Ltd
5 Rothschild Ct, Gaithersburg, MD 20878
Tel: 301-937-0900 *Fax:* 301-330-2937
E-mail: aaplav@outlook.com
Web Site: aaplav.com
Key Personnel
Pres: Robert J Ziobro
Founded: 1993
AV equipment rentals & sales.
Catalog(s) available
Membership(s): InfoComm International®

Advance Concepts Inc
8453 Tyco Rd, Suite N, Vienna, VA 22182-2623
Tel: 703-448-0445 *Fax:* 703-893-8049
Web Site: www.advanceconcepts.com
Key Personnel
Pres: Philip Joseph *E-mail:* phil@advanceconcepts.com
VP, Servs: Rebecca Draznin *E-mail:* rebecca@advanceconcepts.com
Founded: 1982
Membership(s): InfoComm International®; Media Communications Association

Advance Pro
Division of Advance Electronics
1300 Portage Ave, Winnipeg, MB R3G 0V1, Canada
Tel: 204-772-0386 *Toll Free Tel:* 800-392-1295 *Fax:* 204-783-2177
E-mail: ap@advance.mb.ca
Web Site: www.advance-pro.com
Key Personnel
Mng Partner & Opers Mgr: Peter Bernatsky
Founded: 1971
Shipping Address: 613 Erin St, Winnipeg, MB R3G 2W1, Canada
Membership(s): InfoComm International®; Manitoba Electrical League; NAB; NSCA

Advanced Audio Technology
200 Easy St, Carol Stream, IL 60188
Tel: 630-665-3344 *Fax:* 630-665-3347
E-mail: info@advancedaudio.net
Web Site: www.advancedaudio.net
CD & DVD production, USB duplication, onsite recording, media conversion, specialty printing & multimedia authoring.

Advanced Audio-Visual Inc
11978 Riverwood Dr, Burnsville, MN 55337
Tel: 952-881-4500
Web Site: www.aavmn.com
Key Personnel
Owner: Larry Pierce *E-mail:* larry@aavmn.com

Advanced AV
208 Carter Dr, Suite 7, West Chester, PA 19382
Toll Free Tel: 877-696-7700 *Fax:* 610-692-8421
E-mail: sales@advancedav.com
Web Site: www.advancedav.com
Key Personnel
Founder: Paul Grafinger
CEO: Michael Boettcher
VP, Sales & Mktg: John P Green
VP, Tech Opers: Travis A Lisk
Founded: 1985
Specialized integrator of professional AV systems for business, education, government & worship facilities.
Catalog(s), sales
Membership(s): InfoComm International®; MCA-I

Advanced Battery Systems Inc
516 Bedford St, East Bridgewater, MA 02333
Tel: 508-378-2284 *Toll Free Tel:* 800-634-8132
E-mail: abs@batteryprice.com
Web Site: www.batteryprice.com
Key Personnel
Gen Mgr: Brian Kmito
Portable equipment batteries.
Online catalog(s) available
Branch Office(s)
254 Church St, Unit 3, Pembroke, MA 02359 *Tel:* 781-924-5672

Advanced Designs Corp
1169 W Second St, Bloomington, IN 47403
Tel: 812-333-1922 *Fax:* 812-333-2030
Web Site: www.doprad.com
Key Personnel
Pres: Matt McGrath *E-mail:* mmcgrath@doprad.com
Doppler weather radar, weather display systems & computer graphics.
Membership(s): AMS; NAB; TAB

Advanced Digital Design, see Studio 6429

Advanced Imaging Concepts Inc
301 N Harrison St, Bldg B, Suite 266, Princeton, NJ 08540
Tel: 609-921-3629; 609-529-9200 *Fax:* 609-924-3010
E-mail: info@aic-imagecentral.com; sales@aic-imagecentral.com
Web Site: www.aic-imagecentral.com
Key Personnel
Sales Mgr: Scott E Berman *E-mail:* sberman@aic-imagecentral.com
Founded: 1989
Digital imaging for optical microscopes.

Advanced Lighting & Production Services Inc (ALPS)
65 Teed Dr, Randolph, MA 02368
Tel: 781-961-3066 *Toll Free Tel:* 866-961-3066 *Fax:* 781-961-3256
E-mail: info@alpsweb.com
Web Site: www.alpsweb.com
Key Personnel
Pres: Steven F Way
VP: James A deVeer
Mgr: Chad Winship
Founded: 1981
Sales, installations, rentals, repairs & production services of theatrical lighting supplies & related equipment. Rigging & truss, staging & production management.
Online catalog(s) available
Membership(s): International Special Events Society; Professional Lighting & Sound Association

Advanced Media Integration
2300 Meyer Rd, Fort Wayne, IN 46805
Tel: 260-428-2698 *Toll Free Tel:* 877-428-2610 *Fax:* 260-428-2699
E-mail: info@advancedmediaintegration.com
Web Site: www.advancedmediaintegration.com
Key Personnel
Owner: Vince Tippmann
Founded: 1976
Membership(s): Independent Television Companies Association; InfoComm International®; MCA-I

Advanced Media LLC
369 N Fairfax Ave, Suite A, Los Angeles, CA 90036
Tel: 323-469-0707 *Fax:* 323-461-3715
E-mail: info@advancedmediallc.com
Web Site: www.advancedmediallc.com
Founded: 1984
Video, DVD, film & media services.

Advanced Sound
4611 Central Ave Pike, Suite F, Knoxville, TN 37912
Tel: 865-661-5961 *Fax:* 865-637-6694
Web Site: www.advancedsound.com
Key Personnel
Owner: Robert Craton *E-mail:* bobcraton@advancedsound.com
Founded: 1983

Advanced Systems Group LLC
1226 Powell St, Emeryville, CA 94608-2618
Tel: 510-654-8300 *Fax:* 510-654-8370
Web Site: www.asgllc.com
Key Personnel
Pres & Sales: Dave Van Hoy *E-mail:* dvh@asgllc.com
Opers Mgr: Kristina Caspari *E-mail:* kristina@asgllc.com
Cont: Amy Zeno *E-mail:* amy@asgllc.com
Founded: 1997
Membership(s): SMPTE

Advent Media Inc
5629 Fraley Ct, Columbus, OH 43235
Tel: 614-538-1622 *Toll Free Tel:* 877-538-1622 *Fax:* 614-538-1621
Web Site: www.adventmediainc.com
Key Personnel
Owner & Pres: Stephen F Puffenberger
VP: David Puffenberger
Founded: 1982
Helps with technology communication.

AdventSource
5120 Prescott Ave, Lincoln, NE 68506
Tel: 402-486-8800 *Toll Free Tel:* 800-328-0525 *Fax:* 402-486-8819
E-mail: service@adventsource.org
Web Site: www.adventsource.org
Key Personnel
Exec Dir: Brad Forbes
Catalog(s) available

Adventure Productions LLC
5910 York Rd, Lower Level, Baltimore, MD 21212
Tel: 410-878-1261; 410-961-5942 (cell) *Fax:* 410-878-1263
Web Site: www.adventureproductions.com
Key Personnel
Owner & Dir, Photog: George A Stover, III *E-mail:* george@adventureproductions.com
Mktg Dir: Carol L Stover *E-mail:* carol@adventureproductions.com
Founded: 1993
Full service TV & video production company. Complete electronic gathering equipment & editing facilities, lighting & audio packages, green screen studio, music libraries.
Membership(s): ASCAP; IBEW; NATAS

Adwar Video
125 Gazza Blvd, Farmingdale, NY 11735
Tel: 631-777-7070 *Toll Free Tel:* 877-GOADWAR (462-3927) *Fax:* 631-777-7011
E-mail: sales@adwarvideo.com
Web Site: adwarvideo.com
Key Personnel
Pres: Michael Adwar
Supplier of professional AV equipment & services.
Catalog(s) available

AEMC Instruments
200 Foxborough Blvd, Foxborough, MA 02035
Tel: 508-698-2115 *Toll Free Tel:* 800-343-1391 *Fax:* 508-698-2118
E-mail: sales@aemc.com
Web Site: www.aemc.com
Founded: 1893
Installation testers.

AEON Communications Inc
PO Box 96, Mountlake Terrace, WA 98043
Tel: 425-672-8222
E-mail: winningcolors@mindspring.com
Web Site: winningcolors.com
Key Personnel
Pres: Stefan Neilson
Winning class process identifies in minutes, the behaviors required by the situation, job description, or relationships for executives, managers & sales persons. Leadership, team-building, communication. Music to live by & communicate (CD & audiotape).
Branch Office(s)
PO Box 100, Harrison Hot Springs, BC V0M 1K0, Canada

Aerial Imaging Productions
12001 E 33 Ave, Unit R, Aurora, CO 80010
Tel: 720-255-1195
E-mail: info@aerialimagingproductions.com
Web Site: www.aerialimagingproductions.com
Founded: 2007
HD low-altitude videography.

Aerial Video Systems
712 S Main St, Burbank, CA 91506
Tel: 818-954-8842 *Fax:* 818-954-8842
Web Site: aerialvideo.com
Key Personnel
Founder: Randy Hermes
Customized HD solutions for the broadcasting industry. Specialize in aerial camera platforms, point-of-view cameras, microwave systems & HD wireless video.

Aero-Tech Light Bulb Co Inc
534 Pratt Ave N, Schaumburg, IL 60193
Tel: 847-352-4900 *Toll Free Tel:* 800-955-2376 *Fax:* 847-352-4999
E-mail: info@aerolights.com
Web Site: www.aerolights.com
Key Personnel
Pres: Ray M Schlosser
VP, Sales: Kathy M Schlosser *E-mail:* kathy@aerolights.com
Founded: 1987
Manufacturer of long-life light bulbs.
Catalog(s) available
Membership(s): NAILD; NALMCO

Affton Graphics Inc, see A M Graphics Products, dba Affton Graphics Inc

African American Images
PO Box 1799, Chicago Heights, IL 60412
Tel: 708-672-4909 *Toll Free Tel:* 800-552-1991 *Fax:* 708-672-0466
E-mail: customersvc@africanamericanimages.com
Web Site: www.africanamericanimages.com
Key Personnel
Pres: Jawanza Kunjufu
Online catalog(s) available
Membership(s): The Association of Publishers for Special Sales; PMA International; Reading Recovery Council of North America

Agency for Instructional Technology (AIT)
8111 N Lee Paul Rd, Bloomington, IN 47404-7916
Tel: 812-339-2203 *Toll Free Tel:* 800-457-4509 *Fax:* 812-333-4218
E-mail: info@ait.net
Web Site: www.ait.net
Key Personnel
Exec Dir: Charles Wilson *E-mail:* cwilson@ait.net
Dir, Educ: Elaine Larson
Dir, Opers & Fin: Barb Jackson
Founded: 1962
Online catalog(s) available

AGF Media Services
14932 Delano St, Van Nuys, CA 91411-2122
Tel: 818-780-7400; 818-780-8085 (24 hours) *Fax:* 818-904-9905
E-mail: info@agfmedia.com
Web Site: www.agfmedia.com
Key Personnel
CEO: Aaron J Baker
Pres: Jeffrey Baker
VP, Sales: J P Brozyna
Founded: 1967
Catalog(s) available
Branch Office(s)
555 Universal Terrace Pkwy, Universal City, CA 91608 *Tel:* 818-505-8620 *Fax:* 818-505-8640
Membership(s): InfoComm International®

Agfa Graphics
Unit of Agfa-Gevaert Group
611 River Dr, Ctr 3, Elmwood Park, NJ 07407
Tel: 201-440-2500 *Toll Free Tel:* 800-540-2432
Web Site: www.agfagraphics.com; www.agfa.com
Key Personnel
CFO & VP: Gunther Muertens
VP, North America Opers: Jonathan Ashton
Dir, Opers: Jeffrey Aurichio
Sr HR Mgr: Nadine Lauzon-Rosato
Prodn Mgr: Adam Szewc
Prepress imaging.
Online catalog(s) available

Aggressive Records Audio Duplication LLC
1951 University Ave W, Suite 107, St Paul, MN 55104
Tel: 651-645-7805
E-mail: sales@aggressiverecords.com
Web Site: www.aggressiverecords.com
Founded: 1992
DVD, CD & video duplication, printing & graphics.
Membership(s): The Film & Digital Media Group

Agrama Film Enterprises Inc
Division of Harmony Gold USA Inc
7655 Sunset Blvd, Los Angeles, CA 90046
Tel: 323-851-4900 *Fax:* 323-851-5599
E-mail: sales@harmonygold.com
Web Site: harmonygold.com
Key Personnel
Chmn & CEO: Frank Agrama
VP, Busn & Legal Aff: Christy Duran
Online catalog(s) available

Ahead Stereo Inc
7428 Beverly Blvd, Los Angeles, CA 90036
Tel: 323-931-8873 *Fax:* 323-937-7285
E-mail: mrstereo@pacbell.net
Web Site: www.aheadstereo.com
Key Personnel
Owner & Custom Design Mgr: Phil Werbin *Tel:* 323-939-8081
Sales Mgr: Brian Bloom
Founded: 1971

AheadTeK
6410 Via Del Oro, San Jose, CA 95119

Tel: 408-226-9800; 408-226-9991
Toll Free Tel: 800-971-9191 *Fax:* 408-226-9195
Web Site: www.aheadtek.com
Key Personnel
Pres: Tim Higgins
VP: Patrick Johnston *E-mail:* patj@aheadtek.com
Catalog(s) available

The Ahern Group
3701 Malden Ave, Unit A, Baltimore, MD 21211
Tel: 410-367-9660 *Fax:* 410-367-9661
E-mail: videoahern@aol.com
Web Site: www.theaherngroup.com
Key Personnel
Pres: Donald Ahern *E-mail:* don@theaherngroup.com
VP: Lynne Ahern
Chief Engr: Robert Ahern
Founded: 1955
Digital media production for government, corporate & nonprofit clients.

The Charles Aidikoff Screening Room
150 S Rodeo Dr, Suite 140, Beverly Hills, CA 90212
Tel: 310-274-0866 *Fax:* 310-550-1794
E-mail: info@aidikoff.com
Web Site: www.aidikoff.tv
Key Personnel
Gen Mgr: Josh Aidikoff
Founded: 1966
Screening room for people in the movie industry.

AiH Group Inc
709 S Aiken Ave, Pittsburgh, PA 15232
Tel: 412-687-5700
E-mail: aih@aihgroup.com
Web Site: www.aihgroup.com
Key Personnel
Pres: Alan I Harris
Founded: 1974
Writers, designers & producers of print & electronic media.
Membership(s): Apple Consultants Network; Macromedia Developers

Aiphone Corp
1700 130 Ave NE, Bellevue, WA 98005
Mailing Address: PO Box 90075, Bellevue, WA 98009
Tel: 425-455-0510 *Toll Free Tel:* 800-692-0200
Fax: 425-455-0516 (sales); 425-455-0071
Toll Free Fax: 800-525-3372 (cust serv)
E-mail: info@aiphone.com; cs@aiphone.com
Web Site: www.aiphone.com
Key Personnel
Sr Mktg Specialist: Brad Kamcheff
Manufacture intercom solutions for communication & security.
Catalog(s) available

Air Sea Land Productions Inc (ASL)
19-69 Steinway St, Astoria, NY 11105-1108
Tel: 718-626-2646 *Toll Free Tel:* 888-ASL-LENS (275-5367) *Fax:* 718-626-1493
E-mail: sales@airsealand.com
Web Site: www.airsealand.com
Key Personnel
CEO & Pres: Anthony S Lenzo
E-mail: anthonyl@airsealand.com
VP: Edward Lenzo *E-mail:* camraguy@gmail.com
Dir, Opers: Michael Warner *E-mail:* mwarner@airsealand.com
Opers Mgr: Gary Costantino *E-mail:* gary@airsealand.com
Founded: 1994
Production company & rental house. DVD & digital programming.

AirBrands Event & Marketing Group
6470 Wyoming St, Dearborn, MI 48126
Tel: 519-254-9563 *Toll Free Tel:* 800-411-6200 (ext 26)
E-mail: service@airbrandsmarketing.com
Web Site: www.airbrandsmarketing.com
Key Personnel
Pres: Steve Thomson *Tel:* 519-254-9563 ext 26
E-mail: steve@airbrandsmarketing.com
Founded: 1962
Online catalog(s) available
Branch Office(s)
8612 Larthorn Dr, Huntington Beach, CA 92646
AirBrands Event & Marketing Co, 1805 Wilson Ave, No 212, Toronto, ON M9M 1A2, Canada
1776 Sylvestre Dr, Windsor, ON N9A 5C9, Canada *Tel:* 519-254-9563 *Fax:* 519-258-0767

Aircraft Music Library, see AirCraft Production Libraries

AirCraft Production Libraries
Division of CAV Corp
162 Columbus Ave, Boston, MA 02116-5222
Tel: 617-303-7600 *Toll Free Tel:* 800-343-2514
Fax: 617-303-7666
E-mail: info@aircraftmusiclibrary.com; acsales@aircraftmusiclibrary.com
Web Site: www.aircraftmusiclibrary.com
Key Personnel
Engr & Prodr: Tim Reppert
Founded: 1985
Production music: aircraft, The American Music Series, Ads Up-Music for Commercials, Cinemusic & Rock Sweepers.
Online catalog(s) available

Airshow Mastering
3063 Sterling Circle, Suite 3, Boulder, CO 80301
Tel: 303-247-9035 *Toll Free Tel:* 888-545-9035
Toll Free Fax: 888-545-9035
E-mail: studio@airshowmastering.com
Web Site: www.airshowmastering.com
Key Personnel
Founder & Chief Engr: David Glasser
Mgr: Karen Maye *E-mail:* karen@airshowmastering.com
Founded: 1983
Branch Office(s)
7014-C Westmoreland Ave, Tacoma Park, MD 20913, Mgr: Mike Petillo *Tel:* 301-891-9035 *Fax:* 301-891-9036 *E-mail:* mike@airshowmastering.com

Airwave Recording Studio
5176 Hollow Log Lane, Birmingham, AL 35244
Tel: 205-427-4675
Key Personnel
Pres: Marc Phillips

Airways Digital Media
4055 W Peterson Ave, Chicago, IL 60646
Tel: 773-539-8400
E-mail: info@airwaysdigital.com
Web Site: www.airwaysdigital.com
Key Personnel
Pres: Steve Zaransky
Founded: 1981
Membership(s): MCA-I

AIT, see Agency for Instructional Technology (AIT)

AITech International
1288 Kifer Rd, Suite 203, Sunnyvale, CA 94086
Tel: 408-991-9699 *Fax:* 408-991-9691
E-mail: info@aitech.com; aitechproducts@aitech.com
Web Site: www.aitech.com
Key Personnel
Chmn & CEO: Michael Chen
SVP: Jennifer Chen
Dir, Opers: Jason M Chiu *E-mail:* jason@aitech.com
Founded: 1987
Manufacturer of video conversion, connection, convergence for presentation, education & training, home entertainment. Manufacture HDMI related products.

AJA Video Systems Inc
180 Litton Dr, Grass Valley, CA 95945
Mailing Address: PO Box 1033, Grass Valley, CA 95945-1033
Tel: 530-274-2048 *Fax:* 530-274-9442
E-mail: sales@aja.com
Web Site: www.aja.com
Key Personnel
PR: Karen Raz *E-mail:* karen@razpr.com
Founded: 1993

Akai Professional
Subsidiary of inMusic Brands Inc
200 Scenic View Dr, Suite 201, Cumberland, RI 02864
Tel: 401-658-4032
E-mail: info@akaipro.com
Web Site: www.akaipro.com
Founded: 1984
Digital personal studios, digital audio recording & editing systems. Samplers, the MPC & Midi production center.
Catalog(s) available
Foreign Office(s): 437 Ave Larco, Miraflores, Lima, Peru *Tel:* (01) 998325179
Naking East Rd, 7th fl, No 165, Section 4, Taipei 105, Taiwan *Tel:* (02) 2717 2389 *Fax:* (02) 2717 2734

AKG Acoustics US
Division of Harman Pro Group
8500 Balboa Blvd, Northridge, CA 91329
Tel: 818-920-3212 *Fax:* 818-920-3208
E-mail: akgusa@harman.com
Web Site: www.akg.com/us
Key Personnel
Dir, Mktg: Brian Divine
Founded: 1947
Manufacture high-quality microphones, headphones & wireless equipment.
Catalog(s) available

Alarmco Intelligent Message Repeaters
One Bailey Dr, Guilford, CT 06437
Tel: 203-458-2646 *Toll Free Tel:* 800-824-5006
E-mail: info@messagerepeaters.com
Web Site: www.messagerepeaters.com
Message repeaters, paging system feedback eliminator.
Catalog(s) available
Membership(s): International Planned Music Association; IPMA; NSCA

Alaska Film Services Inc
11050 Cange St, Anchorage, AK 99516
Tel: 907-230-6870 *Fax:* 907-272-6778
E-mail: filmservices@alaska.net
Web Site: www.alaskafilmservices.com
Key Personnel
Owner: Deborah Schildt *Tel:* 907-230-8839 (cell)
Founded: 1983
A boutique production company. HD camera, editing suite. Location scouting, casting, producing, directing & editing. Digital video (HD & Digi Beta & DV). Television, educational-commercials & documentary. Sales offices in Alaska & Kenora, ON, CN.
Membership(s): Alaska Film Group; International Alliance of Theatrical Stage Employees

Alaska Video Postcards Inc
PO Box 112808, Anchorage, AK 99511-2808
Tel: 907-349-8002 *Toll Free Tel:* 800-248-2624

E-mail: mail@akvideo.com
Web Site: www.akvideo.com
Key Personnel
Pres: Todd Hardesty
Online catalog(s) available

Albany Theatre Supply Co Inc
445 N Pearl St, Albany, NY 12204
Tel: 518-465-8895 *Fax:* 518-465-8908
E-mail: sales@albanytheatresupply.com
Web Site: www.albanytheatresupply.com
Key Personnel
Pres: Dick McGrath
VP: Thomas McGrath *E-mail:* tom@albanytheatresupply.com
Founded: 1946

Albinson Reprographics, see Thomas Reprographics

Albumx Corp
21 Grace Church St, Port Chester, NY 10573
Tel: 914-939-6878 *Toll Free Tel:* 800-961-6710 *Fax:* 914-939-8047
E-mail: info@renaissancealbums.com
Web Site: www.renaissancealbums.com
Key Personnel
Pres: Terry Huang
Founded: 1988
Catalog(s) available
Online catalog(s) available

ALC (Auernheimer Labs & Co)
4561 E Florence Ave, Fresno, CA 93725
Tel: 559-442-1048
Key Personnel
Owner & Pres: C Curly Auernheimer
Catalog(s) available

Alcorn McBride Inc
3300 S Hiawassee Rd, Bldg 105, Orlando, FL 32835
Tel: 407-296-5800 *Fax:* 407-296-5801
E-mail: info@alcorn.com; sales@alcorn.com
Web Site: www.alcorn.com
Key Personnel
COO: Jeremy Scheinberg
Dir, Sales: Larry Howard
Prod Mgr: Mike Polder
Founded: 1986
Largest manufacturer of show control, audio/video playback & lighting control equipment used in theme parks, museums, retail stores, casinos, visitor centers, themed restaurants & transportation systems worldwide. Our systems are reliable & cost effective.
Catalog(s) available

Alden Films
Division of Paulicia Enterprises
PO Box 449, Clarksburg, NJ 08510-0449
Tel: 732-462-3522 *Toll Free Tel:* 800-832-0980 *Fax:* 732-294-0330
E-mail: info@aldenfilms.com
Web Site: www.aldenfilms.com
Key Personnel
Pres: Paul Weinberg
VP: Felicia Weinberg
Founded: 1952
Video & audio programming on Israel, Judaica & Jewish studies.

Alegra House Publishers
Subsidiary of Kaya Books
PO Box 1443, Warren, OH 44482-1443
Tel: 330-372-2951 *Fax:* 330-399-1619
Key Personnel
Pres: Robert Prokop
Ed-in-Chief: Linda Marado
Mng Ed: Robert C Peters
Catalog(s) available
Shipping Address: 641 Fairway NE, Warren, OH 44483
Membership(s): IBPA, the Independent Book Publishers Association

Alexander Media Productions
1901 Diamond Ridge Dr, Carrollton, TX 75010
Tel: 214-274-3456
Web Site: www.heatheralexander.net
Key Personnel
Prodn Coord: Heather Alexander *E-mail:* halexander74@gmail.com
Film & commercial production service company. Also produces programming in HD & writes content for screenplays.

Alexander Street Press
3212 Duke St, Alexandria, VA 22314
Tel: 703-212-8520
E-mail: sales@alexanderstreet.com
Web Site: academicvideostore.com
Media producers on healthcare issues. Over 800 films on healthcare issues, including new films on DVD streaming & online education.
Catalog(s) available

Alford Media Services
296 Freeport Pkwy, Coppell, TX 75019
Tel: 972-538-9400 *Toll Free Tel:* 800-554-9144 *Fax:* 972-538-0800
E-mail: info@alfordmedia.com; sales@alfordmedia.com
Web Site: www.alfordmedia.com
Key Personnel
Founder & Pres: Steve Alford
Gen Mgr: Tom Alford
Founded: 1984
Audio/video/lighting rental & event staging.
Membership(s): IABC; InfoComm International®; National Foundation of Independent Businesses

Alien Skin Software LLC
1111 Haynes St, Suite 113, Raleigh, NC 27604
Tel: 919-832-4124 *Toll Free Tel:* 888-921-7546 *Fax:* 919-832-4065
E-mail: sales@alienskin.com
Web Site: www.alienskin.com
Key Personnel
CEO: Finley Lee
Founded: 1993
Manufacture graphics software.

Aliso Creek Productions Inc
4106 W Burbank Blvd, Burbank, CA 91510
Mailing Address: PO Box 10006, Burbank, CA 91510-0006
Tel: 818-954-9931
Web Site: www.alisocreek.net
Key Personnel
Founder: William Williams
Founded: 1987
Voice over workshops, live action & animation shorts, web site design.

All Access Staging & Productions
1320 Storm Pkwy, Torrance, CA 90501
Tel: 310-784-2464 *Toll Free Tel:* 877-784-2464 *Fax:* 310-517-0899
E-mail: usinfo@allaccessinc.com
Web Site: www.allaccessinc.com
Key Personnel
CEO: Clive Forrester *E-mail:* clivef@allaccessinc.com
Pres: Erik Eastland *E-mail:* erike@allaccessinc.com
VP: Robert Achlimbari *E-mail:* roberta@allaccessinc.com
Sales Exec: Bryan Schluntz *E-mail:* bryans@allaccessinc.com
Founded: 1991
Rental & sales of custom staging,-sets, camera platforms & accessories. Additional services include custom low-res & high-res displays, soft goods, lifts, elevators, turntables & plexidecks. Versastage, CM hoists, hippotizer media server, colorkinetics, SL Flex power supplies & video system management. Branch office in New Jersey, sales offices in Los Angeles & New Jersey.
Branch Office(s)
2 N Park Dr, Newton, NJ 07860 *Tel:* 973-579-0067 *Toll Free Tel:* 866-840-7387 *Fax:* 973-579-0068
Foreign Office(s): 23 Demand Ave, Arundel, Qld 4214, Australia *Tel:* (0411) 656 462 *E-mail:* auinfo@allaccessinc.com
Unit 5/8 Kerr Rd, Ingleburn, NSW 2565, Australia *Tel:* (02) 4872 1232 *Fax:* (02) 4871 2954 *E-mail:* auinfo@allaccessinc.com
Unit 12, Woking Business Park, Albert Dr, Woking, Surrey GU21 5JY, United Kingdom *Tel:* (01483) 765 305 *Fax:* (01483) 762 594 *E-mail:* ukinfo@allaccessinc.com
Membership(s): Professional Lighting & Sound Association; USITT

All Communications Rentals Inc (ALLCOMM)
1402 SW 13 Ct, Pompano Beach, FL 33069
Tel: 954-788-9555
Web Site: www.allcommrentals.com
Key Personnel
Pres: Lou Selesnich *E-mail:* louis@allcommrentals.com
Dir, Audio Visual: Steve McBrayer *E-mail:* steve@allcommrentals.com
Tech Dir: Kris Bauersfeld *E-mail:* kris@allcommrentals.com
Founded: 1993
Rental of audio, video & lighting equipment. Also provides full production services.

All Jersey Studios
Subsidiary of All Jersey Video LLC
222 Cavour St, Colonia, NJ 07067
Tel: 732-382-2333
E-mail: info@alljerseystudios.com
Web Site: www.alljerseystudios.com
Key Personnel
Pres: James J O'Keefe

All Mobile Video Inc
221 W 26 St, New York, NY 10001
Tel: 212-727-1234 *Fax:* 212-255-6644
E-mail: contact@amvchelsea.com
Web Site: allmobilevideo.com
Key Personnel
Pres: Eric Duke *E-mail:* eduke@amvchelsea.com
Mobile production, post-production, equipment sales & rental.
Branch Office(s)
AMV Field Operations, 272 State Rte 17 S, Lodi, NJ 07644 *Tel:* 201-488-4181 *Fax:* 201-488-3709

All Pro Media Inc
422 S Spring St, Burlington, NC 27216
Mailing Address: PO Box 2566, Burlington, NC 27216-2566
Tel: 336-229-7700 *Toll Free Tel:* 800-270-2207 *Fax:* 336-229-7778
Web Site: www.allpromedia.com
Key Personnel
Pres: Alan Kirby *E-mail:* alan@allpromedia.com
Founded: 1990
Video production, web design, advertising & equipment rental.

All Service Musical Electronics Repair
617 SE Morrison St, Portland, OR 97214
Tel: 503-231-6552 *Fax:* 503-239-7157
E-mail: service@asmusic.org
Web Site: www.all-service-musical.com
Key Personnel
Owner: Randy Morgan

Founded: 1981
Electronic repair.

All Terrain Power Co Inc
PO Box 18, Bellport, NY 11713
Tel: 718-852-4922 *Fax:* 718-267-0002
Web Site: www.allterrainpower.com
Key Personnel
Pres: John Kuegel *E-mail:* jwkco@yahoo.com
Founded: 2000
On location electric power generator & distribution rentals.

All Video Productions
726 Santa Monica Blvd, Suite 212, Santa Monica, CA 90401
Tel: 310-666-5606 *Fax:* 310-656-1155
E-mail: info@allvideoproductions.com
Web Site: www.allvideoproductions.com
Key Personnel
Pres: Pascal Sangary *E-mail:* pascalproduction@msn.com
Founded: 1989

Allegro Corp/Allegro Entertainment Canada Ltd
20048 NE San Rafael St, Portland, OR 97230-7459
Tel: 503-491-8480 *Toll Free Tel:* 800-288-2007 (ext 2500, cust serv) *Fax:* 503-491-8488
E-mail: mailcs@allegro-music.com (cust serv)
Web Site: www.allegromediagroup.com
Key Personnel
CEO: Joseph Micallef *E-mail:* joe.micallef@allegromediagroup.com
Founded: 1982
Online catalog(s) available
Branch Office(s)
105 Consumers Dr, Unit 2, Whitby, ON L1N 1C4, Canada *Tel:* 289-316-0513 *Fax:* 647-277-9007

Allegro Productions Inc
1000 Clint Moore Rd, Suite 108, Boca Raton, FL 33487
Tel: 561-994-9111 *Toll Free Tel:* 800-232-2133 (ext 201) *Fax:* 561-241-0707
Web Site: www.allegrovideo.com
Key Personnel
Pres: Scott J Forman *Tel:* 561-994-9111 ext 201 *E-mail:* scott@allegrovideo.com
VP: Glenn A Forman *Tel:* 561-994-9111 ext 202 *E-mail:* glenn@allegrovideo.com
Busn Mgr: Judith Sitkin *Tel:* 561-994-9111 ext 200 *E-mail:* judi@allegrovideo.com
Founded: 1957
Online catalog(s) available

Allen & Heath USA, see American Music & Sound (AM&S)

Allen Avionics Inc
255 E Second St, Mineola, NY 11501
Tel: 516-248-8080 *Fax:* 516-747-6724
E-mail: info@allenavionics.com
Web Site: www.allenavionics.com
Key Personnel
VP: Jim Lyons *E-mail:* jim@allenavionics.com
Online catalog(s), info@allenavionics.com
Membership(s): AES; NAB; SMPTE

John E Allen Inc
PO Box 452, Newfoundland, PA 18445
Tel: 570-676-4152 *Fax:* 570-676-9194
E-mail: jeainc@gmail.com
Web Site: www.allenarchive.com/wordpress
Key Personnel
Pres: John E Allen
Online catalog(s) available
Stock shot(s), by specific request
Membership(s): Association of Moving Image Archivists

Allen Products Co Inc
Division of Adaptive Technologies Group Inc
1635 E Burnett St, Signal Hill, CA 90755
Tel: 562-424-1100 *Fax:* 562-424-3520
E-mail: info@adapttechgroup.com
Web Site: www.adapttechgroup.com
Key Personnel
Pres: Paul Allen
Founded: 1987
Speaker mounting hardware design & manufacturing. Distribute loud speaker mounting equipment & rigging hardware.
Catalog(s) available
Membership(s): InfoComm International®; NAMM, the National Association of Music Merchants; NSCA

Allen Visual Systems Inc
1405 Busch Pkwy, Buffalo Grove, IL 60089
Tel: 847-520-4960 *Fax:* 847-520-7370
E-mail: sales@allenvisual.com
Web Site: www.allenvisual.com
Founded: 1971
Catalog(s) available
Membership(s): ASSE; ATD; InfoComm International®; International Facilities Management Association; NSCA; Professional Systems Network Inc

Alliance Entertainment Corp (AEC) LLC
4250 Coral Ridge Dr, Coral Springs, FL 33065
Tel: 954-346-4024 *Toll Free Tel:* 800-356-2049 (ext 4600)
Web Site: www.aent.com
Key Personnel
CEO: Jeff Walker *Tel:* 954-255-4403 *E-mail:* jeffw@sdcd.com
CFO: George Campagna *Tel:* 954-255-4031 *E-mail:* george.campagna@aent.com
Retail Sales & Busn Devt: Mike Donohue *Tel:* 954-255-4450 *E-mail:* michael.donohue@aent.com
Founded: 1990
Wholesale distributor of home entertainment audio & video software.

The Alliance for Christian Media
2715 Peachtree Rd NE, Atlanta, GA 30305
Tel: 404-815-0640 *Toll Free Tel:* 800-229-3788
E-mail: contact@allianceforchristianmedia.org
Web Site: www.allianceforchristianmedia.org
Key Personnel
Dir, Mktg: Thomas Keuneke
Founded: 2004
Distribute DVDs for Christian education.
Online catalog(s) available

Alliance Publications Inc (API)/Sinsinawa Studios Productions
585 County Rd Z, Sinsinawa, WI 53824-0157
Tel: 608-748-4411 (ext 124) *Fax:* 608-748-4491
E-mail: api@apimusic.org
Web Site: www.apimusic.org
Key Personnel
Pres: Anita Smisek
Founded: 1989
Publish sheet music for band, orchestra, choirs & keyboard instruments. Classical, folk, sacred & secular, specialty, Czech & Slovak music.
Catalog(s) available

Alliant Event Services
196 University Pkwy, Pomona, CA 91768
Tel: 909-622-3306 *Toll Free Tel:* 800-851-5415 *Fax:* 909-622-3917
E-mail: marketing@alliantevents.com
Web Site: www.alliantevents.com
Key Personnel
Pres: Sanjay Patel *E-mail:* sanjay.patel@alliantevents.com
Opers Mgr: Reuben Harrison *E-mail:* reuben.harrison@alliantevents.com
Founded: 1984
Complete audio, visual, lighting, computer, display rental & staging services.

Allied Artists International Inc
Production Services Ctr, 15810 E Gale Ave, Suite 133, Hacienda Heights, CA 91745
Tel: 626-330-0600 *Fax:* 626-961-0411
E-mail: info@alliedartists.net
Web Site: us.alliedartists.com
Key Personnel
Chmn of the Bd & CEO: Kim Richards
CFO, Entertainment Group: Jerry Sifuentes
CTO & VP: Greg Hammond
Pres: Robert Fitzpatrick
Catalog(s) available
Branch Office(s)
Allied Artists Music Group, Attn: A & R, PO Box 2035, Industry, CA 91746 (demo submissions)
Membership(s): Entertainment Merchants Association

Allied Media Corp
5252 Cherokee Ave, Suite 200, Alexandria, VA 22312
Tel: 703-333-2008 *Fax:* 703-997-7539 *Toll Free Fax:* 888-747-0957
E-mail: info@allied-media.com; contact@allied-media.com
Web Site: www.allied-media.com
Key Personnel
Pres & Sales & Mktg Mgr: Mostapha Saout *E-mail:* saout@allied-media.com
Founded: 1998
Communication & creative production.

Allied Photo Color Co
4221 Forest Park Ave, St Louis, MO 63108
Tel: 314-652-4000 *Fax:* 314-652-8203
Web Site: alliedphotocolor.com
Key Personnel
Pres: Robert Little
Digital photographic imaging services.
Catalog(s) available
Membership(s): AIE™; Photo Marketing Association; PPA

Alligator Records & Artist Management Inc
1441 W Devon Ave, Chicago, IL 60660
Mailing Address: PO Box 60234, Chicago, IL 60660
Tel: 773-973-7736 *Fax:* 773-973-2088
E-mail: info@allig.com
Web Site: www.alligator.com
Key Personnel
Pres: Bruce Iglauer
Natl Sales & Ad Dir: Kerry Peace
Dir, Publicity: Marc Lipkin *E-mail:* publicity@allig.com
Founded: 1971
Blues & roots rock record label.
Catalog(s) available
Online catalog(s) available

Allsop Inc
PO Box 23, Bellingham, WA 98227-0023
Tel: 360-734-9090 *Toll Free Tel:* 800-426-4303 *Fax:* 360-734-9858 (sales); 360-733-4302 (corp)
E-mail: info@allsop.com
Web Site: www.allsop.com
Key Personnel
Co-Pres: James Allsop
PR Mgr: Kelli Veening *Tel:* 360-734-9090 ext 306 *E-mail:* kelli.veening@allsop.com
Founded: 1965
Online catalog(s) available

Foreign Office(s): Allsop Europe Ltd, IDA Industrial Park, Cort Rd, Butlerstown, Co Waterford, Ireland, Sales & Mktg Mgr: Ciaran Duffy *Tel:* (051) 355091 *Fax:* (051) 377717 *E-mail:* info@allsop.eu *Web Site:* www.allsop.eu

Allstar Audio Systems Inc
PO Box 541964, Merritt Island, FL 32954-1964
Tel: 321-455-2202 *Fax:* 321-455-2224
E-mail: info@allstaraudio.com
Web Site: www.allstaraudio.com; allstarsystems.net
Key Personnel
Pres: Mike Borne *E-mail:* mike@allstaraudio.com
Founded: 1984

Allstar Show Industries Inc
10331 176 St, Edmonton, AB T5S 2E4, Canada
Tel: 780-486-4000 *Toll Free Tel:* 800-663-4063 (CN & US) *Fax:* 780-414-5724
E-mail: allsales@allstar-show.com
Web Site: www.allstar-show.com
Key Personnel
Dir: Rodger Boyce
Purchaser: Bob Gregory *E-mail:* bobg@allstar-show.com
Founded: 1979
AV integrator, audio, video & lighting design, sales, service, installation & production services. AV lighting, event production, corporate events & theatre.
Catalog(s) available
Branch Office(s)
Bay 5, 6325 11 St SE, Calgary, AB T2H 2L6, Canada *Tel:* 403-258-2000 *Toll Free Tel:* 888-618-2489 *Fax:* 403-258-1334
1131 William St, Vancouver, BC V6A 2J1, Canada *Tel:* 604-247-4550 *Toll Free Tel:* 888-618-2487 *Fax:* 604-247-4552
Membership(s): AES; International Special Events Society; NAMM, the National Association of Music Merchants; NSCA

Alltec Stores, a Vcom IMC Company
80 Little Falls Rd, Fairfield, NJ 07004
Toll Free Tel: 800-637-3181 *Toll Free Fax:* 800-965-7836
E-mail: sales@alltecstores.com
Web Site: www.alltecstores.com
Key Personnel
Pres: Shelly Goldstein
Sales: Ezra Hiller *Tel:* 800-637-3181 ext 1046
Founded: 1958
AV & technology equipment distributors.
Catalog(s) available
CD-ROM catalog(s) available
Membership(s): Custom Electronic Design & Installation Association; NSCA

Allusion Studios & Pure Wave Audio
Division of Allusion Enterprises
248 W Elm St, Tucson, AZ 85705
Tel: 520-622-3895 *Fax:* 520-622-3895
E-mail: contact@allusionstudios.com
Web Site: www.allusionstudios.com; www.purewaveaudio.com
Key Personnel
Owner & Operator: Jim Pavett
Commercial studio including transfers & forensic audio.

ALOM Technologies Corp
48105 Warm Springs Blvd, Fremont, CA 94539-7498
Tel: 510-360-3600 *Toll Free Tel:* 800-500-9991 *Fax:* 510-226-7617
E-mail: customerservice@alom.com
Web Site: www.alom.com
Key Personnel
CEO & Pres: Hannah Kain
CFO: Phil Roloff
VP, Opers: Subu Subramanian
Dir, Acct Mgmt: Rick Mizzo
Dir, IT: Brandon Marugg
Quality: Michelle Remoaldo
Founded: 1997
A logistics company, packaging, shipping & duplication.

Alpec®
1231 Midas Way, Sunnyvale, CA 94085
Tel: 408-735-6180 *Toll Free Tel:* 800-854-6686 *Fax:* 408-735-6190
Web Site: www.alpec.com
Key Personnel
Pres: Sunil Prafullchandra
Founded: 1991
Manufacturer of laser pointer, laser projection equipment & presentation systems.
Online catalog(s) available

Alpha & Omega Recording
150 Bellam Blvd, Suite 255, San Rafael, CA 94901
Key Personnel
Dir, Opers: Sandy Pearlman

Alpha Source Inc
6619 W Calumet Rd, Milwaukee, WI 53223-4186
Tel: 414-760-2222 *Toll Free Tel:* 800-654-9845 *Fax:* 414-760-2070 *Toll Free Fax:* 888-654-9840
E-mail: customer.service@alphasource.com; info@alphasource.com
Web Site: www.alphasource.com
Key Personnel
Founder & CEO: Norine Carlson-Weber
CFO: Sherri L Huff
HR Mgr: Ivan Brown
Founded: 1986
LCD projector lamps, AV lamps & batteries for medical equipment.
Online catalog(s) available

Alpha Technologies
3767 Alpha Way, Bellingham, WA 98226
Tel: 360-647-2360 *Fax:* 360-671-4936
E-mail: alpha@alpha.com
Web Site: www.alpha.com
Key Personnel
Chmn & CEO: Fred Kaiser
Pres & COO: Drew Zogby
VP, North American Cable TV: John Hewitt
Mktg Dir: Eric Wentz
Mktg Servs Mgr: Andrew Azure
Full line of power supplies, status monitoring products, surge suppressors, batteries & enclosures for use in cable TV, telecommunications & data networks.
Catalog(s) available
Branch Office(s)
7700 Riverfront Gate, Burnaby, BC V5J 5M4, Canada *Tel:* 604-430-1476 *Fax:* 604-436-1233
Foreign Office(s): Alpha Technologies SA, Blvd de l'Europe, 131, 1301 Wavre, Belgium *Tel:* (010) 438510 *Fax:* (010) 438213 *Web Site:* www.alphatechnologies.eu
Alphatec Ltd, 339 Saint Andrews St, 3307 Limassol, Cyprus *Tel:* (025) 375 675 *Fax:* (025) 359 595
Alpha Technologies GmbH, Hansastr 8, 91126 Schwabach, Germany *Tel:* (09122) 798890 *Fax:* (09122) 7988921
Alphatec Baltics, S Konarskio G 49, LT-03123 Vilnius, Lithuania *Tel:* (05) 210 5291 *Fax:* (05) 210 5292 *E-mail:* info@alphatec.lt
AlphaTek Russia, Boytsovaya ul, dom 22 Stroenie 3, 107150 Moscow, Russia *Tel:* (495) 916 1854 *Fax:* (495) 916 1349 *Web Site:* www.alpha-group.ru
Alpha Technologies Europe Ltd, Bishop's Stortford, Twyford House, Thorley, Herts CM22 7PA, United Kingdom *Tel:* (01279) 501110 *Fax:* (01279) 659870
Membership(s): SCTE

Alpha Video & Audio Inc
7711 Computer Ave, Edina, MN 55435
Tel: 952-896-9898 *Toll Free Tel:* 800-388-0008 *Fax:* 952-896-9899
E-mail: info@alphavideo.com
Web Site: www.alphavideo.com
Key Personnel
Pres: Stan Stanek *E-mail:* stan.stanek@alphavideo.com
Sales Mgr & Partner: Kevin Groves *E-mail:* kevin.groves@alphavideo.com
Founded: 1970
Leading video systems integrator & provider of visual communications solutions.
Membership(s): InfoComm International®; NSCA; PSNI

Alpha Video Productions
441 Biscay Dr, Garland, TX 75043
Tel: 972-497-9959
E-mail: alphaghb@sbcglobal.net
Web Site: www.alphavideo.net
Key Personnel
Founder & Owner: Gary H Bauer
Founder, Writer & Prodr: Susan Bauer
Founded: 1981
Award winning video production company serving the US & international clients, including broadcast, corporate & nonprofit. HD & HDDVcam camera packages & AVID Media Composer edit system.
Catalog(s) available

Alpha Wire Co
Division of Belden Wire & Cable Co
711 Lidgerwood Ave, Elizabeth, NJ 07207-0711
Tel: 908-925-8000 *Toll Free Tel:* 800-52-ALPHA (522-5742) *Fax:* 908-925-6923
E-mail: info@alphawire.com
Web Site: www.alphawire.com
Key Personnel
Dir, Mktg: Tim Howett
Catalog(s) available
Online catalog(s) available
Foreign Office(s): Silver Ctr, Rm 1708, N Shanxi Rd 1388, Shanghai 200060, China *Tel:* (021) 61498201 *Fax:* (021) 61498001 *E-mail:* apac@alphawire.com
Alpha Wire International, Saxon House, One Downside, Sudbury-on-Thames, Middx TW16 6RT, United Kingdom *Toll Free Tel:* 800-288-8809 *Toll Free Fax:* 800-288-8810 *E-mail:* europe@alphawire.com

AlphaDogs Inc
1612 W Olive Ave, Suite 200, Burbank, CA 91506-2462
Tel: 818-729-9262 *Fax:* 818-729-8537
Web Site: www.alphadogs.tv
Key Personnel
Founder & Pres: Terence Curren
VP, Sales & Gen Mgr: Paul De Cham *E-mail:* paul@alphadogs.tv
Founded: 2002
Full service post-production & design boutique.
Membership(s): Hollywood Post Alliance

Alpine Media
Subsidiary of Quality Data Systems Inc
1644 Conestoga St, Suite 3, Boulder, CO 80301
Tel: 303-444-1257 *Toll Free Tel:* 800-475-0872
E-mail: info@alpinemedia.com; production@alpinemedia.com; av@alpinemedia.com
Web Site: www.alpinemedia.com
Key Personnel
CEO & Pres: Jeanne K Phipps *E-mail:* theboss@alpinemedia.com
Gen Mgr: Keith Heinzmann *E-mail:* production@alpinemedia.com

Founded: 1984 (as Quality Data Systems)
Duplication of CD, DVD, USB Flash & Blu-ray. Transfers from VHS, 8mm, 16mm, Mini-DV, etc to DVD. Transfers from audio tape, vinyl, reel to reel, etc to CD. Digital editing & international conversions. Professional custom editing available by the hour. Post-production services including duplication, packaging & shrink-wrapping.
Membership(s): Better Business Bureau; Boulder Chamber of Commerce

Alpine Optics Inc
150 View Rd, Brevard, NC 28712
Tel: 828-884-5822 *Fax:* 828-884-5884
E-mail: toalpine_optics@citcom.net
Key Personnel
Secy: Gabriela Jung
Catalog(s) available

ALPS, see Advanced Lighting & Production Services Inc (ALPS)

Altaria Inc, see Alpec®

ALTEL Systems Inc
601 N Main St, Brewster, NY 10509
Tel: 845-278-4400 *Toll Free Tel:* 800-88ALTEL (882-5835) *Fax:* 845-278-2824
E-mail: info@altel-av.com
Web Site: www.altel-av.com
Key Personnel
Pres: Andrew M Musci
Founded: 1954
Branch Office(s)
27 N Church St, Cortland, NY 13045 *Tel:* 607-756-6565 *E-mail:* tmcnerney@altel-av.com
Altel Systems Group Inc, 2856 Broadway Center Blvd, Brandon, FL 33510 *Tel:* 813-628-6100 *Fax:* 813-628-8949 *E-mail:* avitale@asq-av.com
Membership(s): AES; InfoComm International®; NSCA; SMPTE

Alternative Rentals
5805 W Jefferson Blvd, Los Angeles, CA 90016
Tel: 310-204-3388 *Fax:* 310-204-3384
E-mail: info@alternativerentals.com
Web Site: www.alternativerentals.com
Rents high-end digital equipment for the feature film, television & commercial industries.
Branch Office(s)
1600 Roswell St, Suite 5, Smyrna, GA 30080 *Tel:* 770-438-0912 *Fax:* 770-438-0916
1109 N Al Davis Rd, Suite A, Harahan, LA 70123 *Tel:* 504-736-1426 *Fax:* 504-734-2441

ALTINEX Inc
592 Apollo St, Brea, CA 92821
Tel: 714-990-2300 *Toll Free Tel:* 800-ALTINEX (258-4639) *Fax:* 714-990-3303
E-mail: sales@altinex.com
Web Site: www.altinex.com
Key Personnel
Pres: Jack Gershfield
Founded: 1993
Leading manufacturer of AV signal management equipment & design software.
Online catalog(s) available
Membership(s): InfoComm International®; NSCA

Altruist Media LLC
1023 Williamsport Pike, Martinsburg, WV 25404
Tel: 703-812-8813 *Fax:* 703-812-9710
E-mail: frank@altruistmedia.com
Web Site: www.altruistmedia.com
Key Personnel
Owner & CEO: Jan Dearth *E-mail:* jan@altruistmedia.com

AM Productions
1141 S Pasadena Ave, Pasadena, CA 91105
Tel: 626-403-0258 *Fax:* 626-403-0138
Key Personnel
Owner & Pres: Arthur C Michaud
Founded: 1975

AM Stock-Cameo Film Library
1663 Sawtelle Blvd, Suite 305, Los Angeles, CA 90025
Tel: 310-479-4800 *Fax:* 310-933-6979
E-mail: researcher@amstockcameo.com
Web Site: www.amstockcameo.com
Key Personnel
Pres: Chris Angelich *E-mail:* chris@amstockcameo.com
Head Libn: Ada Cottrell
35mm & HD stock footage film library; over 1.5 million feet of 35mm film. Shoot custom stock & second unit footage for over 50 different series.
Catalog(s) available

AMA, see American Management Association®

AMA Nystrom Printing/Finishing
920 N Valley Mills Dr, Waco, TX 76710
Tel: 254-776-8860 *Toll Free Tel:* 800-369-9226 *Fax:* 254-751-2127
E-mail: info@amanystrom.com
Web Site: www.amanystrom.com
Key Personnel
Pres: Morris Shaw
Branch Office(s)
8535 Jackrabbit Rd, Suite G, Houston, TX 77095 *Tel:* 713-681-3752 *Toll Free Tel:* 800-276-0441 *Fax:* 713-681-4234

Ambrose Video Publishing Inc
145 W 45 St, Suite 1115, New York, NY 10036
Tel: 212-768-7373 *Toll Free Tel:* 800-526-4663 *Fax:* 212-768-9282
E-mail: customerservice@ambrosevideo.com
Web Site: www.ambrosevideo.com
Key Personnel
Pres: William V Ambrose
Catalog(s) available
Shipping Address: SRM Distribution Services Inc, 75 W Century Rd, Paramus, NJ 07652

America By Air Stock Footage Library
154 Euclid Blvd, Lantana, FL 33462
Toll Free Tel: 800-488-6359 *Fax:* 413-235-1462
E-mail: footage@americabyair.com
Web Site: www.americabyair.com; www.hdfootage.com
Key Personnel
Owner: Douglas Kahan
Aerial footage shots on film, HD & digital motion picture formats.

American Artist Studio
1114 W 26 St, Erie, PA 16508-1518
Mailing Address: PO Box 131, Erie, PA 16512-0131
Tel: 814-455-4796 *Toll Free Tel:* 888-462-7813
Web Site: americanartiststudio.com
Key Personnel
Owner: Carl "Skip" Niebauer
Founded: 1972
Catalog(s) available
Membership(s): The Recording Academy

American Artists Representatives Inc
4700 Mamaroneck Ave, White Plains, NY 10605
Tel: 212-682-2462; 646-286-5633 (cell)
E-mail: info@aareps.com
Web Site: www.aareps.com
Key Personnel
Mng Dir: Michael R Mendelsohn
Sales Mgr: Antonio Adriao
Digital creative production for interactive, motion & print.

American Association for Vocational Instructional Materials (AAVIM)
220 Smithonia Rd, Winterville, GA 30683
Tel: 706-742-5355 *Fax:* 706-742-7005
E-mail: sales@aavim.com
Web Site: www.aavim.com
Key Personnel
Dir: Gary Farmer
Founded: 1949
Produce instructional materials in the vocational areas including agriculture education. Distribute CD-ROMs & videos.
Catalog(s) available
Membership(s): National Association of Agriculture Educators

American Audio Prose Library Inc (AAPL)
600 Crestland Ave, Columbia, MO 65203
Mailing Address: PO Box 842, Columbia, MO 65205-0842
Tel: 573-443-0361 *Fax:* 573-499-0579
E-mail: aaplinc@centurytel.net
Web Site: www.americanaudioprose.org
Key Personnel
Exec Dir: Kay Callison
Founded: 1980
Nonprofit literary audio publisher.

American Audio Visual Center
7434 E Monte Cristo Ave, Scottsdale, AZ 85260
Tel: 480-596-9880 *Fax:* 480-596-0942
Web Site: www.americanavc.com
Key Personnel
CEO & Pres: Jim Carlson
COO & SVP: Jeff Winkler
CFO & SVP: John Radonovich
Chief Mktg Offr & SVP: Duane Tornquist
Chief Strategy Offr & SVP: Tim Brady
Founded: 1993
Premier hospitality AV & production company.
Branch Office(s)
389 Oyster Point Blvd, Suite 1, South San Francisco, CA 94080 *Tel:* 650-866-3017 *Fax:* 650-866-3038
3225 Broadmoor Valley Rd, Colorado Springs, CO 80906 *Tel:* 719-538-4039; 719-538-4000 *Fax:* 719-576-4711
464 Armour Dr NE, Atlanta, GA 30324 *Tel:* 404-458-3677 *Fax:* 404-458-3678

American AV
2862 Hartland Rd, Falls Church, VA 22043
Tel: 703-573-6910 *Fax:* 703-573-3539
E-mail: sales@aavevents.com
Web Site: www.aavevents.com
Key Personnel
Owner & Pres: John Eltzroth *E-mail:* eltzroth@aavevents.com
Sales: Colin Bobby *E-mail:* cbobby@aavevents.com
Founded: 1972
Branch Office(s)
800 Briar Creek Rd, Suite EE-206, Charlotte, NC 28205, Sales: Colin Bobby *Tel:* 704-339-0030 *Fax:* 704-339-0506 *E-mail:* cbobby@aavevents.com
Sheraton Imperial Hotel, 4700 Emperor Blvd, Durham, NC 27703, Opers: Eric Hauge *Tel:* 919-941-8112 *Fax:* 919-941-9109 *E-mail:* ehauge@aavevents.com
151 Kitty Hawk Dr, Morrisville, NC 27560, Opers: Michael Murphy *Tel:* 919-361-1151 *Fax:* 919-405-2380 *E-mail:* mmurphy@aavevents.com

American AVC, see American Audio Visual Center

American Blackguard Inc
PO Box 680686, Franklin, TN 37068-0686
Tel: 615-599-4032
E-mail: contact@americanblackguard.com
Web Site: www.americanblackguard.com
Key Personnel
CEO & Pres: Clay Stafford
Founded: 1978
Motion picture & television development, production & support.

American Chemical Society (ACS)
Dept of Professional Education, 1155 16 St NW, Washington, DC 20036
Tel: 202-872-4508 *Toll Free Tel:* 800-ACS-5558 (227-5558 ext 4508) *Fax:* 202-872-6336
E-mail: proed@acs.org
Web Site: proed.acs.org
Key Personnel
Admin: Andrea Adams
Founded: 1876

American Choral Catalog Ltd
205 S Water St, Northfield, MN 55057
Mailing Address: PO Box 528, Northfield, MN 55057-0528
Tel: 507-645-4695 *Toll Free Tel:* 800-246-7257 *Fax:* 507-645-2474
E-mail: info@americanchoral.com
Web Site: www.americanchoral.com
Key Personnel
Pres: Peter Dahlen
Catalog(s) available
Membership(s): Music Business Association; The Recording Academy

The American Classical League
Miami University, 422 Wells Mill Dr, Oxford, OH 45056
Tel: 513-529-7741 *Fax:* 513-529-7742
E-mail: info@aclclassics.org
Web Site: www.aclclassics.org
Key Personnel
Pres: Kathy Elifrits *E-mail:* president@aclclassics.org
Admin Secy: Sherwin Little
VP: Donald Connor *E-mail:* vicepresident@aclclassics.org
Founded: 1919
Educational materials, books, software & student resources.
Catalog(s) available

American Color Imaging (ACI)
715 E 18 St, Cedar Falls, IA 50613
Tel: 319-277-3655 *Toll Free Tel:* 800-728-2722 *Fax:* 319-277-6522
E-mail: sales@acilab.com
Web Site: www.acilab.com
Key Personnel
Pres: Mark Lane
VP: Lisa Lane
HR Dir: Jenny Gerrans
Cust Serv Mgr: Teresa Tjaden
Mktg Mgr: Len Searfoss
Natl Sales Mgr: Pat Cahill
Founded: 1967
Membership(s): AIE™; Photo Marketing Association; PPA

American Counseling Association
6101 Stevenson Ave, Alexandria, VA 22304
Tel: 703-823-9800 (ext 222) *Toll Free Tel:* 800-422-2648 (ext 222) *Fax:* 703-370-4833 *Toll Free Fax:* 800-473-2329
E-mail: membership@counseling.org
Web Site: www.counseling.org
Key Personnel
Exec Dir: Richard Yep
Assoc Publr: Carolyn C Baker *Tel:* 703-823-9800 ext 356 *E-mail:* cbaker@counseling.org
Founded: 1952
Professional association. Produce online educational & training programs.
Catalog(s), annual, free

American Fibertek Inc
120 Belmont Dr, Somerset, NJ 08873-4243
Tel: 732-302-0660 *Toll Free Tel:* 877-234-7200 *Fax:* 732-302-0667
E-mail: sales@americanfibertek.com; techinfo@americanfibertek.com
Web Site: www.americanfibertek.com
Key Personnel
Pres: Jack Fernandes
VP: Edward Davis
VP, Sales: Ray Sooley
Founded: 1984
Manufacture IP video systems & video management systems. CCTV - Fiber optic transmission.
Catalog(s) available
Membership(s): American Society for Industrial Security

American Gramaphone LLC
9130 Mormon Bridge Rd, Omaha, NE 68152
Tel: 402-457-4341 *Fax:* 402-457-4332
E-mail: mailbox@mannheimsteamroller.com
Web Site: www.mannheimsteamroller.com
Key Personnel
Owner: Chip Davis
Record company best known for albums from Mannheim Steamroller.

American Harlequin Corp
1531 Glen Ave, Moorestown, NJ 08057
Tel: 856-234-5505 *Toll Free Tel:* 800-642-6440 *Fax:* 856-231-4403
E-mail: dance@harlequinfloors.com
Web Site: www.harlequinfloors.com
Key Personnel
VP & Gen Mgr: Patricia Basileo
Mktg Mgr: Karla Johnson
Mktg Coord: Kristyn Burns
Catalog(s) available

American History Workshop (NY) Inc
588 Seventh St, Brooklyn, NY 11215-3707
Tel: 718-499-6500
E-mail: info@americanhistoryworkshop.com
Web Site: www.americanhistoryworkshop.com
Key Personnel
Pres: Richard Rabinowitz
Media Dir & Planner: Lynda B Kaplan *E-mail:* lbkahw@earthlink.net
Founded: 1980
Membership(s): AASCH; American Alliance of Museums; NAME

American Hospital Association
155 N Wacker Dr, Suite 400, Chicago, IL 60606-1725
Tel: 312-422-3000 *Fax:* 312-422-4700
Web Site: www.aha.org
Key Personnel
Dir, AHA Resource Center: Sara Beazley *Tel:* 312-422-2017 *E-mail:* sbeazley@aha.org
Founded: 1898
Online catalog(s) available
Branch Office(s)
800 Tenth St NW, Two CityCenter, Suite 400, Washington, DC 20001-4956 *Tel:* 202-638-1100

American Law Institute Continuing Legal Education (ALICLE)
4025 Chestnut St, Philadelphia, PA 19104-3099
Toll Free Tel: 800-253-6397 *Fax:* 215-243-1664
Web Site: www.ali-cle.org
Key Personnel
HR: Diane Schnitzer
Founded: 1947
Legal training products & services.

American Management Association®
1601 Broadway, New York, NY 10019
Tel: 212-586-8100 *Toll Free Tel:* 877-566-9441 (cust serv) *Fax:* 212-903-8168; 518-891-0368 (cust serv)
E-mail: customerservice@amanet.org
Web Site: www.amanet.org
Key Personnel
CEO & Pres: Edward T Reilly
PR Mgr: Roger Kelleher *Tel:* 212-903-7976 *E-mail:* rkelleher@amanet.org
Founded: 1923
Brochure(s) available

American Management Association International
600 AMA Way, Saranac Lake, NY 12983
Tel: 518-891-1500 (ext 300) *Toll Free Tel:* 877-566-9441 (cust serv) *Fax:* 518-891-0368
E-mail: customerservice@amanet.org
Web Site: www.amanet.org
Key Personnel
Mgr, HR: Patrick Redman
Founded: 1923
Catalog(s) available
Foreign Office(s): Rue de l'Aqueduc 118, 1050 Brussels, Belgium *Tel:* (02) 543-2100 *Fax:* (02) 543-2400 *E-mail:* info@mce.be *Web Site:* www.mce-ama.com
State Apartment Henderson Ctr, Suite 2202, 18 Jianguomennei Ave, Beijing 100005, China *Tel:* (010) 65187081; (010) 65187082; (010) 65187083 *Fax:* (010) 65187083-102
Tianyu Garden, Suite 1106, Bldg D, No 138 Linghe Zhong Rd, Guangzhou 510613, China *Tel:* (020) 38852627; (020) 38852767 *E-mail:* service@amagmt.com.cn *Web Site:* www.amachina.com
Ming Yuan Business Ctr, Rm 501, 1199 Fu Xing Rd Middle, Shanghai 200031, China *Tel:* (021) 62528678-330; (021) 62528678-321 *Fax:* (021) 62529505
Global Knowledge Management Ctr Ltd, 19F, Sumitomo Fudosan Shinjyuku Oak Tower, 6-8-1 Nishishinjyuku, Shinguku-ku, Tokyo 163-6019, Japan *Tel:* (03) 3347-9740 *Fax:* (03) 3347-9701 *E-mail:* gkmc_info@globalknowledge.co.jp *Web Site:* www.amajapan.co.jp
AC Mexico, Av Paseo de la Reforma 350, Piso 14, Colonia Juarez, 06600 Mexico, DF, Mexico *Tel:* (0155) 3098 3300 *E-mail:* info@amamex.org.mx *Web Site:* www.amamex.org.mx

American Melody
PO Box 270, Guilford, CT 06437-0270
Tel: 203-457-0881
Web Site: www.americanmelody.com
Key Personnel
Pres: Phil Rosenthal *E-mail:* phil@americanmelody.com
Founded: 1985
Record labels: children's recordings (stories & music) as well as folk & bluegrass music & CDs.

American Montage Inc
PO Box 1042, New York, NY 10003
Tel: 212-334-8283
Web Site: americanmontage.com
Key Personnel
Pres: Eric A Marciano *E-mail:* eric@americanmontage.com

American Museum of Natural History (AMNH)
c/o Moving Image Collection, Library Services Dept, Central Park W & 79 St, New York, NY 10024-5192
Tel: 212-769-5420 *Fax:* 212-769-5009

E-mail: speccol@amnh.org
Web Site: www.amnh.org
Key Personnel
Head, Lib Spec Collections: Barbara Mathe
E-mail: bmathe@amnh.org
Spec Collections & Res Libn: Gregory Raml
E-mail: graml@amnh.org
Online catalog(s) available

American Music & Sound (AM&S)
925 Broadbeck Dr, No 220, Newbury Park, CA 91320
Toll Free Tel: 800-431-2609 *Toll Free Fax:* 866-707-0717
E-mail: info@americanmusicandsound.com
Web Site: www.americanmusicandsound.com
Key Personnel
Pres: Lynn Martin
Sales Mgr: Michael Palmer
Independent publisher of pro audio, music creation & musical instrument products.

American Music Environments Inc (AME)
1133 W Long Lake Rd, Suite 200, Bloomfield Hills, MI 48302
Tel: 248-646-2020 *Toll Free Tel:* 888-AME-5005 (263-5005) *Toll Free Fax:* 888-AME-6006 (263-6006)
E-mail: info@amemusic.com
Web Site: www.amemusic.com
Founded: 1996
Background music & messaging & in-store video services. Full line of audio equipment including speakers, amplifiers, wire, microphones & much more.

American Optometric Association (AOA)
243 N Lindbergh Blvd, 1st fl, St Louis, MO 63141-7881
Tel: 314-991-4100 *Toll Free Tel:* 800-365-2219 *Fax:* 314-991-4101
Web Site: www.aoa.org
Online catalog(s) available
Branch Office(s)
1505 Prince St, Suite 300, Alexandria, VA 22314, Contact: Debbie Espinoza *Tel:* 703-739-9200 *Fax:* 703-739-9497

American Playback Images
27748 Caraway Lane, Santa Clarita, CA 91350
Tel: 818-427-8292 *Fax:* 661-263-2387
E-mail: americanplayback@aol.com
Key Personnel
Mgr: Mike Anglim

American Power Conversion Corp, see APC by Schneider Electric

American Production Services LLC
150 Nims Spring Dr, Fort Mill, SC 29715
Tel: 803-548-2290 *Toll Free Tel:* 888-506-2400 *Fax:* 803-548-3406
Web Site: www.apsvideo.com
Key Personnel
Pres: Bruce A Moody *E-mail:* bmoody@apsvideo.com
Founded: 1995
Creative & cost-effective video solutions. Corporate, legal & special interest video production services.
Catalog(s) available

American Recordable Media
110 Dewey Dr, Suite A, Nicholasville, KY 40356
Toll Free Tel: 800-598-8273
E-mail: info@americanrecordablemedia.com
Web Site: www.americanrecordablemedia.com
Key Personnel
Mgr: Ryan Wendt
Founded: 1982

American Thermoplastic Co
106 Gamma Dr, Pittsburgh, PA 15238
Tel: 412-967-0900 *Toll Free Tel:* 800-245-6600 *Fax:* 412-967-9990
E-mail: atc@binders.com
Web Site: www.binders.com
Key Personnel
Ad Mgr: Joseph Sprumont
Founded: 1954
Manufacture custom-imprinted ring binders & albums for audio, videocassette, CD, DVD, etc.
Catalog(s) available

The American University
Dept of Performing Arts, 4400 Massachusetts Ave NW, Washington, DC 20016-8053
Tel: 202-885-2746 *Fax:* 202-885-1092
E-mail: audiotech@american.edu
Web Site: www.american.edu
Key Personnel
Dir, Audio Technol Progs: Paul Oehlers

American Video Inc
780 Third Ave, 5th fl, New York, NY 10017-2024
Tel: 212-527-9000 *Toll Free Tel:* 800-582-4184
E-mail: sales@accnewyork.com
Web Site: www.americanvideo.com
Key Personnel
Pres: Greg Sherman *E-mail:* greg@americanvideo.com
Founded: 1979
Design, produce, install & manage display advertising, augmented reality, video conferencing facilities, webcasting services, webinars, conference AV & lighting, technical services.
Catalog(s) available
Membership(s): InfoComm International®

American Visions
One Deerfield Lane, Cedar Rapids, IA 52403
Tel: 319-360-3211
E-mail: info@americanvisions.org
Web Site: www.americanvisions.org
Key Personnel
Exec Prodr & Dir: Thomas D Hedges
Exec Prodr & Dir, Busn Devt: Stevie Ballard
E-mail: stevie.ballard@stamats.com
Prodr & Dir, New Media: Scott Leamon
Creators & producers of public television programming.

Amerinex Applied Imaging Inc
PO Box 6473, Monroe Township, NJ 08831-6473
Tel: 609-944-8855 *Toll Free Tel:* 877-664-8772 *Fax:* 609-944-8855
E-mail: info@amerineximaging.com
Web Site: www.amerineximaging.com
Key Personnel
Pres: Richard Kretschmann
VP, Mktg & Sales: Bruno Lay
Founded: 1986
Develop & market image processing/analysis software products. Office in France.

Ames Recording Studios
840 Danit St, Prescott, AZ 86301
Tel: 928-830-2313
Web Site: www.amesrecordingstudios.com
Key Personnel
Owner: Justin Ames *E-mail:* justin.d.ames@outlook.com
Founded: 2012
Full service professional recording studio.

Ametek Programmable Power
9250 Brown Deer Rd, San Diego, CA 92121
Tel: 858-450-0085 *Toll Free Tel:* 800-733-5427 *Fax:* 858-458-0267
E-mail: sales.ppd@amtek.com
Web Site: programmablepower.com
Founded: 1961
Manufacturer of precision AC & DC power supplies & test instrumentation products for applications where stable, controllable & reliable power is needed.

Ametron Audio/Video
Division of Ametron/American Electronic Supply Inc
1546 N Argyle Ave, Hollywood, CA 90028-6410
Tel: 323-466-4321 *Fax:* 323-871-0127
E-mail: info@ametron.com
Web Site: www.ametron.com
Key Personnel
Owner: Fred Rosenthal
Online catalog(s) available

AMG Studios-Los Angeles
2225 E 28 St, Suite 511, Signal Hill, CA 90755
Tel: 562-424-0824
Web Site: www.amgstudiosla.com
Studio rental for film production or photography.

Amherst Records Inc
1762 Main St, Suite A, Buffalo, NY 14208
Tel: 716-883-9520 *Toll Free Tel:* 800-836-0751 *Fax:* 716-884-1432
E-mail: info@amherstrecords.com
Web Site: www.amherstrecords.com
Key Personnel
Owner & Pres: Leonard Silver
Independent music label.

AMP Services Inc
3111 Fortune Way, Suite B-18, West Palm Beach, FL 33414
Tel: 561-333-0335 *Fax:* 561-333-0370
Web Site: www.audiomagnetics.com
Key Personnel
Pres: Tom Rappolt *E-mail:* tomampservices@comcast.net
Founded: 1985
Head relapping, DAT, ADAT & DA88 repair, reel to reel & motor rebuilding for AV equipment, keyboards, mixing consoles, speakers, amplifiers & most professional audio equipment.
Catalog(s) available

Ampex Data Systems Corp
500 Broadway, Redwood City, CA 94063
Tel: 650-367-2011 *Fax:* 650-367-2444
E-mail: info@ampex.com
Web Site: www.ampex.com
Key Personnel
Pres: Lawrence Chiarella
Founded: 1944

Amplifier Technologies Inc (ATI)
1749 Chapin Rd, Montebello, CA 90640
Tel: 323-278-0001 *Fax:* 323-278-0083
E-mail: sales@ati-amp.com
Web Site: www.ati-amp.com
Key Personnel
Founder & Pres: Morris Kessler
VP, Sales & Mktg: Jeff Hipps
Founded: 1993

AmpliVox Portable Sound Systems
650 Anthony Trail, Suite D, Northbrook, IL 60062-2512
Tel: 847-498-9000 *Toll Free Tel:* 800-267-5486 *Toll Free Fax:* 800-267-5489
E-mail: info@ampli.com
Web Site: www.ampli.com
Key Personnel
CEO & Pres: Don Roth
Founded: 1952
Design engineering, manufacturing all electronics & audio, UL/CUL & CE, portable sound systems & lecterns.

Online catalog(s) available
Membership(s): BPIA; Business Technology Association; Education Market Association; InfoComm International®

AMPLUS Productions
1484 Liveoak Dr, Mississauga, ON L5E 2X1, Canada
Tel: 416-889-7664 *Fax:* 905-274-7687
Web Site: www.amplusproductions.com
Key Personnel
Pres: Brian Allen *E-mail:* brian@amplusproductions.com
Music production, composition, business consultation.
Membership(s): Canadian Country Music Association; Country Music Association of Ontario; The Society of Composers, Authors and Music Publishers of Canada; Songwriters Association of Canada

AMS Pictures
16986 N Dallas Pkwy, Dallas, TX 75248
Tel: 972-818-7400 *Toll Free Tel:* 866-691-3660 *Fax:* 972-818-1257
Web Site: www.amspictures.com
Key Personnel
Founder & CEO: Andy Streitfeld
VP, Creative Servs: Mark McGovern
Founded: 1982
Premiere film, video, HD interactive services & multimedia production company in the Southwestern US. Specialize in creative communication solutions for clients.
Catalog(s) available
Branch Office(s)
4407 Bee Caves Rd, Suite 612, Austin, TX 78746 *Tel:* 512-330-9434 *Toll Free Tel:* 866-691-3660

AMV/Unitel
515 W 57 St, New York, NY 10019
Tel: 212-265-3600 (studios); 212-586-8616 (sales) *Fax:* 212-246-5059
E-mail: hdsales@allmobilevideo.com
Web Site: www.allmobilevideo.com
Key Personnel
Gen Mgr: Ron Ranieri *Tel:* 212-265-3600 ext 361
Sales: Eric Thielking
Television production facility.
Catalog(s) available

AMX
3000 Research Dr, Richardson, TX 75082
Tel: 469-624-8000 *Toll Free Tel:* 800-222-0193 *Fax:* 469-624-7153
E-mail: service@amx.com
Web Site: www.amx.com
Key Personnel
CEO & Pres: Rashid Skaf
Catalog(s) available
Online catalog(s) available
Membership(s): Consumer Electronics Association; Custom Electronic Design & Installation Association; InfoComm International®; NSCA; US Green Building Council

Analog Free Media
111 E Ninth St, Lockport, IL 60441
Tel: 815-588-5000 *Toll Free Tel:* 877-4MYVIDEO (469-8433)
E-mail: analogfreemedia@yahoo.com
Web Site: www.analogfreemedia.com
Key Personnel
Pres: Timothy L Montague
Founded: 2003
Multimedia & post-production.

Analog Man Recording Studio
PO Box 70245, Nashville, TN 37207
Tel: 615-242-2908
Key Personnel
Engr & Prodr: Mark Hughes *E-mail:* mrmarksmusic@aol.com
Analog electronics with over 25 pieces of vintage mike preamps (most of which have been customized by Stephen Hazelton from The Mastering Lab in LA), console & effects, recording to digital recorders. Get that special, standout, phat vocal sound at Analog Man. Production & musicians also available.

Analog Way Inc
299 Broadway, Suite 1620, New York, NY 10007
Tel: 212-269-1902 *Fax:* 212-269-1943
E-mail: salesusa@analogway.com
Web Site: www.analogway.com
Founded: 1989
Manufacturer of innovative signal converters & AV switchers.
CD-ROM catalog(s), annual, free
Online catalog(s) available
Foreign Office(s): Analog Way SAS, 2/4 rue Georges Besse, 92160 Antony, France *Tel:* 01 81 89 08 60 *Fax:* 01 57 19 04 54
Analog Way Italy, Via Volta N 18, 20026 Novate Milanese MI, Italy *Tel:* (02) 39493943 *Fax:* (02) 39493943
Analog Way Pte Ltd, 152 Beach Rd, 15-03 Gateway E, Singapore 189721, Singapore *Tel:* 6292 5800 *Fax:* 6292 5202
Analog Way UK, North London Business Park, Oakleigh Rd S, N11 1NP London, United Kingdom *Tel:* (020) 36 68 15 74
Membership(s): IEEE; InfoComm International®; NAB; SMPTE; VESA

Anchor Audio Inc
5931 Darwin Ct, Carlsbad, CA 92008
Tel: 760-827-7100 *Toll Free Tel:* 800-262-4671 *Fax:* 760-827-7105
E-mail: sales@anchoraudio.com
Web Site: www.anchoraudio.com
Key Personnel
Pres: Janet Jacobs
VP, Sales: Alex Jacobs
Dir, Mktg: Emily Golding
Founded: 1975
Portable sound system manufacturer. Wired & wireless intercom manufacturer.
Online catalog(s) available
Membership(s): InfoComm International®

Anchor Bay Entertainment LLC
Division of Starz Media LLC
9242 Beverly Blvd, Suite 201, Beverly Hills, CA 90210
Tel: 424-204-4166
E-mail: questions@anchorbayent.com
Web Site: www.anchorbayentertainment.com
Key Personnel
EVP & Gen Mgr: Bill Clark
EVP, Consumer & Brand Mktg: Julie Cartwright
EVP, Worldwide Acqs & Co-Productions: Kevin Kasha
EVP, Worldwide Sales & Retail Mktg: Raymond J Zinar
SVP, Mktg: Jennifer Roberts
Founded: 2008
Distributes feature films, children's entertainment, fitness programming, TV series, documentaries, anime & other filmed entertainment on Blu-ray & DVD.
Branch Office(s)
1699 Stutz Dr, Troy, MI 48084 *Tel:* 248-816-0909

Anchor Distributors
Division of Whitaker House
1030 Hunt Valley Circle, New Kensington, PA 15068
Tel: 724-334-7000 *Toll Free Tel:* 800-444-4484 *Fax:* 724-334-1200 *Toll Free Fax:* 800-765-1960
E-mail: marketing@anchordistributors.com
Web Site: www.anchordistributors.com; www.whitakerhouse.com
Key Personnel
Pres: Robert Whitaker, Sr
Dir, Mktg: John Whitaker
Founded: 1970
Distributors of Christian products.
Catalog(s), biannual, free, available upon request
Membership(s): CBA: The Association for Christian Retail

Ancient Future
PO Box 264, Kentfield, CA 94914-0264
Tel: 415-459-1892
E-mail: info@ancient-future.com
Web Site: www.ancient-future.com
Key Personnel
Dir: Matthew Montfort
Catalog(s) available

Olson Anderson Co
3124 Kochville Rd, Suite 121, Saginaw, MI 48604-9305
Tel: 989-399-3024
E-mail: oac100@aol.com
Web Site: www.olsonanderson.com
Key Personnel
CFO & Cont: Michael Bracey
Founded: 1931
Membership(s): National Association of Sound Contractors

Paul L Anderson Productions Inc
2107 Constitution Ave, Fort Collins, CO 80526
Web Site: www.paulanderson.com
Key Personnel
Owner & Pres: Paul Anderson *E-mail:* paul@paulanderson.com
Founded: 1982
Online catalog(s) available

Angenieux
40-G Commerce Way, Totowa, NJ 07512
Tel: 973-812-3858 *Fax:* 973-812-9049
E-mail: angenieux@tccus.com
Web Site: www.angenieux.com
Key Personnel
Sales Mgr: Eva Paryzka
Founded: 1935
Online catalog(s) available
Membership(s): NAB; SBE; SMPTE

Angstrom Lighting
837 N Cahuenga Blvd, Hollywood, CA 90038
Tel: 323-462-4246 *Fax:* 323-462-8190
Web Site: www.angstromlighting.com
Key Personnel
CEO & Pres: Alton Butler *E-mail:* alton@angstromlighting.com
CFO: Tina Newsome *Tel:* 323-960-0113 *E-mail:* tnewsome@line204.com
Opers Mgr: John McQuay *Tel:* 323-960-0113 *E-mail:* john@line204.com
Founded: 1977
Full service lighting & special effects supplier serving the entertainment industry. Rentals, sales, service, design & education.
Membership(s): Professional Lighting & Sound Association; USITT

Animated Software Co
PO Box 1936, Carlsbad, CA 92018-1936
Tel: 760-720-7261 *Toll Free Tel:* 800-551-2726
Web Site: www.animatedsoftware.com
Key Personnel
Owner: Ace Hoffman *E-mail:* rhoffman@animatedsoftware.com
Founded: 1984
Interactive & educational animation.
Online catalog(s) available

Animax
6627 Valjean Ave, Van Nuys, CA 91406
Tel: 818-787-4444
E-mail: hello@animaxent.com
Web Site: www.animaxent.com
Key Personnel
Founder & Exec Creative Dir: Dave Thomas
CEO: Michael Bellavia
Prodr: David Logan
Founded: 2001
Animation studio.
Membership(s): Producers Guild of America

Animotion Inc
501 W Fayette St, Syracuse, NY 13204
Tel: 315-471-3533 *Fax:* 315-471-2730
E-mail: info@animotioninc.com
Web Site: animotioninc.com
Key Personnel
Pres: David Hicock; Larry Royer
VP, Opers: Peter Wynn
Founded: 1983
Traditional animation & animation for the web.

Anixter Inc
2301 Patriot Blvd, Glenview, IL 60026
Tel: 224-521-8000 *Toll Free Tel:* 800-323-8167 *Fax:* 224-521-8100
Web Site: www.anixter.com
Key Personnel
CEO & Pres: Bob Eck
Founded: 1957
Global supplier of communications & security products.

Annenberg Learner
Division of Annenberg Foundation
PO Box 26983, St Louis, MO 63118
Tel: 202-783-0500 (outside US) *Toll Free Tel:* 800-LEARNER (532-7637) *Fax:* 202-783-0333
E-mail: order@learner.org
Web Site: www.learner.org
Key Personnel
Gen Mgr: Pete Neal *E-mail:* pneal@learner.org
Sr Prog Offr: Michele McLeod *E-mail:* mmcleod@learner.org
Mgr, Interactive Servs: Yolanda Odunsi *E-mail:* yodunsi@learner.org
Educational programming distributor.
Online catalog(s) available

The Annex
PO Box 2390, Los Gatos, CA 95031
Tel: 650-328-8338
E-mail: info@theannex.us
Web Site: theannexstudios.com
Founded: 2003
Media services, production management services, music recording/album production, audio for multimedia technologies & marketing, audio format transfers & duplication.

R B Annis Instruments Inc
117 W Franklin St, Greencastle, IN 46135-1223
Tel: 765-848-1621 *Fax:* 765-848-1625
E-mail: info@rbannis.com
Web Site: www.rbannis.com
Key Personnel
Pres: Michael Scott
Online catalog(s) available

Anode Inc
926 Main St, Nashville, TN 37206
Tel: 615-742-1490 *Toll Free Tel:* 866-802-2436 *Fax:* 615-742-1487
E-mail: inquiry@anode.com
Web Site: www.anode.com
Key Personnel
Pres: Mark Magnuson
Founded: 1991
Provides clients with digital solutions, develops marketing & sales tools, produces meetings & create interactive media for corporations & institutions.

Ansonia Prompting Inc
251 W 30 St, Suite 11-FE, New York, NY 10001
Tel: 212-594-0500 *Fax:* 212-202-4925
E-mail: info@ansoniaprompting.com
Web Site: www.ansoniaprompting.com
Key Personnel
Owner & Pres: Sandy Garfunkel
Founded: 1995
Offer complete teleprompter services. Branch office in Orlando, FL.

AnswersMedia
30 N Racine Ave, Suite 300, Chicago, IL 60607
Tel: 312-421-0113 *Fax:* 312-421-1457
E-mail: contactus@answersmediainc.com
Web Site: www.answersmediainc.com
Key Personnel
CEO: Jeff Bohnson
COO: Sean Murray
Founded: 2004
Full service video production & post-production company.
Online catalog(s) available

Antelope Valley Locations & Production Services
42848 150 St E, Lancaster, CA 93535
Tel: 661-946-1515 *Fax:* 661-946-0454
E-mail: clubed@avlocations.com
Web Site: www.avlocations.com
Key Personnel
Owner & Mgr: Randy Czajkowski *Tel:* 661-917-1587 (cell)
Founded: 1990
Provide locations, services & props to movie, commercial & still photography.

Antenna International
383 Main Ave, Norwalk, CT 06851
Tel: 203-523-0320 *Fax:* 203-354-5519
E-mail: inquiry@antennainternational.com
Web Site: www.antennainternational.com
Key Personnel
CEO & Pres: David A Falter
COO, CFO & EVP: Ira Morgenstern
CIO, CTO & VP: Sean Lentner
SVP, Global Opers: David Rowlands
SVP, Human Capital & Chief Admin Offr: Bob Moran
VP, Experience Design & Gen Mgr, Antenna Lab: Jessica Taylor
VP, Global Fin Opers: Mark Norris
VP, Sales Effectiveness, Global Strategic Accts & Busn Devt: Christopher Bazley
Creates handheld audio, multimedia & virtual tours for museums, historic & cultural sites & tourist attractions.
Online catalog(s) available

Antex Electronics Corp
19160 Van Ness Ave, Torrance, CA 90501
Tel: 310-532-3092 *Toll Free Tel:* 800-338-4231 *Fax:* 310-532-8509
E-mail: ainfo@antex.com; asales@antex.com
Web Site: www.antex.com
Key Personnel
CEO & Pres: David Antrim *Tel:* 310-532-3092 ext 24 *E-mail:* dantrim@antex.com
Cont: Rodney Dunbar
Mfg Mgr: Frank Martinez
Tech Support Mgr: Christopher Mankins
Founded: 1983
Design & manufacture courtroom recording products, AV client/servers for retail & commercial applications, satellite receiving systems, XM & Sirius satellite radios.
Membership(s): AES; Custom Electronic Design & Installation Association; NAB; NSCA

Anthro Corp
10450 SW Manhasset Dr, Tualatin, OR 97062
Tel: 503-691-2556 *Toll Free Tel:* 800-325-3841 (cust serv) *Fax:* 503-691-2409 *Toll Free Fax:* 800-325-0045
E-mail: sales@anthro.com
Web Site: www.anthro.com
Key Personnel
VP: Catherine Filgas
Founded: 1984
Design & manufacture modular computer furniture.
Catalog(s), free

Anton/Bauer Inc
Division of Vitec Videocom Inc
14 Progress Dr, Shelton, CT 06484
Tel: 203-929-1100 *Toll Free Tel:* 800-422-3473 *Fax:* 203-929-9935
E-mail: sales@antonbauer.com; americas@antonbauer.com
Web Site: www.antonbauer.com
Portable power systems for professional broadcast, digital cinema, video & healthcare industries.
Online catalog(s) available
Foreign Office(s): Anton/Bauer Europe BV, Eurode Business Ctr, Eurode Park 1-2, 6461 KB Kerkrade, Netherlands, Contact: Martyn Sly-Jex *Tel:* (045) 5639220 *Fax:* (045) 5639222 *E-mail:* eurosupport@antonbauer.com
Anton/Bauer Singapore, No 02-02 Hoe Huat Industrial Bldg, 6 New Industrial Rd, Singapore 536199, Singapore, Contact: Martin Soh *Tel:* 6297 5784 *Fax:* 6282 5235 *E-mail:* asia@antonbauer.com

Antronics Inc
25 Summer Ave, Waltham, MA 02452-5634
Mailing Address: PO Box 540429, Waltham, MA 02454-0429
Tel: 781-891-7525 *Fax:* 781-647-3667
E-mail: info@antronics.net
Web Site: www.antronics.net
Key Personnel
Pres: Chris Karimbakas
Gen Mgr: Jim Karimbakas
Founded: 1955
Sales, service & systems integration.

Anvil Cases
Subsidiary of Calzone Anvil Case Co
15730 Salt Lake Ave, City of Industry, CA 91745
Tel: 626-968-4100 *Toll Free Tel:* 800-359-2684 *Fax:* 626-968-1703
E-mail: web.sales@anvilcase.com
Web Site: www.anvilcase.com
Key Personnel
Pres: Joseph Calzone
Founded: 1952
Manufacture & repair reusable shipping, packaging, carrying & storage cases & containers.
Catalog(s) available
Membership(s): InfoComm International®; NAB; NAMM, the National Association of Music Merchants; Percussive Arts Society; Professional Lighting & Sound Association

Aon Hewitt
Affiliate of Aon Corp
1100 Reynolds Blvd, Winston-Salem, NC 27105-3400
Mailing Address: PO Box 66, Winston-Salem, NC 27102-0066
Tel: 336-748-1120 *Fax:* 847-953-4854
Web Site: www.aon.com
Key Personnel
Local Mkt Leader: Madeline Cashdollar

Produce sales presentations with slides.
Membership(s): American Business Communication Association; IABC; Industrial Communication Council

AP/Images
Division of The Associated Press
450 W 33 St, 15th fl, New York, NY 10001
Tel: 212-621-1930 *Fax:* 212-621-1955
Web Site: www.apimages.com
Visual content for purchase (historical & contemporary photographs). Still photography & assignment photography.

APC by Schneider Electric
132 Fairgrounds Rd, West Kingston, RI 02892
Tel: 401-789-5735 *Toll Free Tel:* 800-788-2208 *Fax:* 401-789-3710
Web Site: www.apc.com
Key Personnel
SVP, IT Busn, Mktg & Sales Process: Chris Hanley
Founded: 1981
Worldwide leader in the designing, manufacturing & marketing of power protection & management solutions for nonstop networking. The product range includes surge suppressors, uninterruptible power supplies, DC power supplies, power conditioning equipment & related software for computer & computer-related equipment.
Online catalog(s) available

Apertura
535 Main St, Orford, NH 03777
Mailing Address: PO Box 12, Orford, NH 03777-0012
Tel: 603-353-9067 *Fax:* 603-353-4646
Web Site: www.apertura.org
Key Personnel
Prodr & Filmmaker: John Karol *E-mail:* karol@apertura.org
Founded: 1969
Film/video/sound production & production services.
Catalog(s) available
Membership(s): SMPTE

Aperture Studios Miami
385 NE 59 St, Miami, FL 33137
Tel: 305-759-4327 *Fax:* 305-757-1198
E-mail: rental@aperturepro.com
Web Site: aperturepro.com
Founded: 1993
Studio & equipment rentals, including cameras, computer & DSLR accessories, lighting & grip.

Apex Jr
1450 W 228 St, Unit 4, Torrance, CA 90501
Tel: 818-248-0416 *Fax:* 424-263-4614
E-mail: steve.apexjr@prodigy.net
Web Site: www.apexjr.com
Founded: 1992
New surplus electronics.

Apex Machine Co
3000 NE 12 Terr, Fort Lauderdale, FL 33334
Tel: 954-566-1572 *Fax:* 954-563-2844
E-mail: email@apexmachine.com
Web Site: www.apexmachine.com
Key Personnel
CEO: A Robert Coningsby, III
Pres: Todd Coningsby
Founded: 1903
Custom printing for CD-ROMs.
Brochure(s) available
Membership(s): Content Delivery & Storage Association; PMMI: The Association for Packaging and Processing Technologies; WIMA

Aphex LLC
Division of DWV Entertainment
PO Box 711674, Salt Lake City, UT 84171
Tel: 818-767-2929
E-mail: sales@aphex.com
Web Site: www.aphex.com
Key Personnel
Chmn & CEO: David Wiener
Audio system manufacturer.
Online catalog(s) available
Membership(s): AES; NAB; NAMM, the National Association of Music Merchants; NSCA; SMPTE

API
8301 Patuxent Range Rd, Jessup, MD 20794
Tel: 301-776-7879 *Fax:* 301-776-8117
E-mail: service@apiaudio.com
Web Site: www.apiaudio.com
Key Personnel
Pres: Larry Droppa *E-mail:* larry@apiaudio.com
Mng Dir: Gordon Smart *E-mail:* gordon@apiaudio.com
Dir, Engg: Jeff Bork *E-mail:* jbork@apiaudio.com
Dir, Sales: Dan Zimbelman *Tel:* 410-330-8079 *E-mail:* zimbel@apiaudio.com
Sales: Mark Seman *Tel:* 301-776-7879 *E-mail:* mark@apiaudio.com
Founded: 1968
Membership(s): AES

Apogee Communications Group
159 Alpine Way, Boulder, CO 80304
Tel: 303-443-8473 *Toll Free Tel:* 800-210-5700 *Fax:* 303-443-0500
E-mail: sales@apogeevideo.com; orders@apogeevideo.com
Web Site: www.apogeevideo.com
Key Personnel
Owner & Dir, Photog & Prodr: Arthur J Levy
Health & safety videos & DVDs.
Online catalog(s) available

Apogee Electronics Corp
1715 Berkeley St, Santa Monica, CA 90404
Tel: 310-584-9394 *Fax:* 310-584-9385
Web Site: www.apogeedigital.com
Key Personnel
Pres: Betty Bennett
Creative Dir: Sean McArthur
Founded: 1985
Design, manufacture & distribute analog & digital converters.

Apogee Sound International LLC
Subsidiary of Bogen Communications International Inc
50 Spring St, Ramsey, NJ 07446
Toll Free Tel: 800-443-3979 *Toll Free Fax:* 800-999-9016
E-mail: info@apogee-sound.com
Web Site: www.apogee-sound.com
Key Personnel
Intl Sales: Dave Chambers *E-mail:* dchambers@bogen.com
Founded: 1985
Membership(s): AES; NAMM, the National Association of Music Merchants; NSCA

Apollo Design Technology Inc
4130 Fourier Dr, Fort Wayne, IN 46818
Tel: 260-497-9191 *Toll Free Tel:* 800-288-4626 *Fax:* 260-497-9192
E-mail: sales@apollodesign.net
Web Site: www.apollodesign.net
Founded: 1992
Custom design products (gobos) that go with lighting accessories.
Catalog(s) available
Membership(s): Professional Lighting & Sound Association; USITT

Applause Learning Resources
85 Fernwood Lane, Roslyn, NY 11576
Tel: 516-625-1145 *Toll Free Tel:* 800-277-5287 *Toll Free Fax:* 877-365-7484
E-mail: info@applauselearning.com
Web Site: www.applauselearning.com
Key Personnel
Dir: Michael Pollack
Sales Dir: Evelyn Pollack
Sales Mgr: Karen Minguez
Foreign language teaching videos & DVDs.
Catalog(s) available
Membership(s): American Council on the Teaching of Foreign Languages

Applause Productions & Publications
PO Box 820024, Dallas, TX 75382-0024
Tel: 214-652-4300 *Fax:* 214-652-4075
E-mail: info@applauseproductions.com
Web Site: applauseproductions.com
Key Personnel
Pres: Lisa Owen *E-mail:* lisa@applauseproductions.com
Founded: 1983
Specialize in corporate event production. Producer of the annual Partyfest Extravaganza Tradeshow.
Catalog(s) available

Apple Inc
One Infinite Loop, Cupertino, CA 95014
Tel: 408-996-1010
Web Site: www.apple.com
Key Personnel
CEO: Timothy D Cook
CFO & SVP: Luca Maestri
SVP, Internet Software & Servs: Eddy Cue
SVP, Software Engg: Craig Federighi
SVP, Worldwide Mktg: Philip W Schiller
Founded: 1976

Applebox Studio
48 Kingswood Dr, Bethel, CT 06801
Tel: 203-762-7333 *Toll Free Fax:* 888-624-2829
E-mail: info@appleboxstudio.com; info@appleboxvideo.com
Web Site: www.appleboxstudio.com
Key Personnel
Pres: Jim Jontz
Founded: 1990
Video production company.

Pat Appleson Studios Inc
2359 Hwy 70 SE, Suite 102, Hickory, NC 28602
Tel: 828-994-4361; 828-461-3003 (cell)
Web Site: www.appleson.com
Key Personnel
Pres: Patrick G Appleson *E-mail:* pat@appleson.com
PR Dir: Jayne Kilgore
Natl Sales Mgr: Alan Muller
Membership(s): International Television Association; NAB; NATAS; SBE; SMPTE

Applied Electronics
722 Blue Crab Rd, Newport News, VA 23606
Tel: 757-591-9371 *Toll Free Tel:* 800-883-0008 *Fax:* 757-591-9514
E-mail: sales@appliednn.com
Web Site: www.appliednn.com
Key Personnel
COO: Mike Rampmeyer *E-mail:* mike@appliednn.com
Lifts, custom truss, lighting control & motors.
Catalog(s) available

Applied Electronics Ltd
1260 Kamato Rd, Mississauga, ON L4W 1Y1, Canada
Tel: 905-625-4321 *Fax:* 905-625-4333
E-mail: ael.toronto@appliedelectronics.com
Web Site: www.appliedelectronics.com

Key Personnel
Pres: Paul Stechly
VP, AV Systs Div: Mike Dalton
Designer, supplier & integrator of professional AV, broadcast & post-production technology.

Applied Integration Corp
3930 W New York Dr, Tucson, AZ 85745
Tel: 520-743-3095
E-mail: info@appliedi.com
Web Site: www.appliedi.com
Key Personnel
Pres: Frederick Pingal
Dir: Karen Bock
Founded: 1992
Developer & manufacturer of mobile & remote access digital video surveillance systems.

Applied Research & Technology Inc, see ART (Applied Research & Technology Inc)

APS Lighting-Sound-AV
901 Columbia Circle, Merrimack, NH 03054
Tel: 603-424-9198 *Toll Free Tel:* 800-837-0005 *Fax:* 603-423-9816
E-mail: info@apslightingnh.com
Web Site: www.apslightingnh.com
Key Personnel
Owner: Norm St Germain
Founded: 2000
Full service theatrical & special event production company providing the sale, installation & rental of quality stage/video lighting, AV, special effects & theatrical equipment.
Product sheet(s), free
Membership(s): National Foundation of Independent Businesses; Professional Lighting & Sound Association; USITT

APTE Inc
1424 Wesley Ave, Suite A, Evanston, IL 60201
Tel: 847-866-1872 *Fax:* 847-866-1873
E-mail: mail@apte.com
Web Site: www.apte.com
Key Personnel
CEO: Sally De Vincentis
Founded: 1989
Publish educational software, market software & digital cameras to the education market.
Online catalog(s) available
Membership(s): Photo Marketing Association

Aquarius Healthcare Media, see Alexander Street Press

ARC Document Solutions
1981 N Broadway, Suite 385, Walnut Creek, CA 94596
Tel: 925-949-5100 *Fax:* 925-949-5101
E-mail: info@e-arc.com
Web Site: www.e-arc.com
Key Personnel
Chmn, Pres & CEO: K Suriyakumar
COO: Dilantha Wijesuriya
CFO: John E D Toth
CTO: Rahul Roy
Founded: 1988 (as Ford Graphics)
Reprographics company which provides business-to-business document management services.
Catalog(s) available
Online catalog(s) available

Arc Light Efx Inc
9338 San Fernando Rd, Sun Valley, CA 91352
Tel: 818-394-6330 *Fax:* 818-252-3486
E-mail: gaslights@arclightefx.com
Web Site: www.arclightefx.com
Key Personnel
CEO & Pres: Greg Smith
CFO: Kary Smith
Founded: 1989
Lighting equipment rental company.
Online catalog(s) available

Archai Media
31E Patrick St, Frederick, MD 21701
Tel: 301-401-8117
E-mail: rentals@archaimedia.com
Web Site: archaimedia.com
Rent cameras & accessories for any production.

Arcor Electronics Co
5689 W Howard St, Niles, IL 60714
Tel: 847-588-0088 *Fax:* 847-588-0080
E-mail: sales@arcorelectronics.com
Web Site: www.arcorelectronics.com
Key Personnel
Pres: Chuck Coren
Founded: 2009
Membership(s): MCA-I

Arctek Studios
140 E Chestnut Ave, Monrovia, CA 91016
Tel: 626-509-2123
E-mail: info@arctekstudios.com
Web Site: arctekstudios.com
Commercial video & photography production studio offering lighting, equipment, furniture, backdrops, stage walls, accessories & more.

Arcube Multimedia Inc
959 E Collins Blvd, Suite 123, Richardson, TX 75081
Tel: 972-267-1800 *Toll Free Tel:* 877-677-9582 *Fax:* 972-267-1922
E-mail: sales@arcube.com
Web Site: www.arcube.com
Founded: 1994
CD/DVD manufacturing services.

Ardent Music LLC
2000 Madison Ave, Memphis, TN 38104
Tel: 901-725-0855 *Fax:* 901-725-7011
E-mail: info@ardentmusic.com
Web Site: www.ardentmusic.com
Key Personnel
Pres: John Fry
Gen Mgr: Jody Stephens *E-mail:* jstephens@ardentmusic.com
Founded: 1959
Catalog(s) available
Membership(s): The Recording Academy

Ardent Studios Inc
2000 Madison Ave, Memphis, TN 38104
Tel: 901-725-0855 *Fax:* 901-725-7011
E-mail: info@ardentstudios.com
Web Site: www.ardentstudios.com
Key Personnel
Pres: John Fry
Gen Mgr: Jody Stephens *E-mail:* jstephens@ardentmusic.com
Studio Mgr: Dan Russo *E-mail:* drusso@ardentmusic.com
Full service recording & mixing studio.

Area 19
24562 County Rd 75, St Augusta, MN 56301
Tel: 320-253-9493 *Toll Free Tel:* 888-334-4825 *Fax:* 320-257-8788
E-mail: info@areanineteen.com
Web Site: www.areanineteen.com
Still photography & video rental studio. Offer props, backdrops & lighting rentals.

ARF!ARF!
PO Box 465, Middleboro, MA 02346-0465
Tel: 508-947-7387 *Fax:* 508-947-7387
E-mail: page@arfarfrecords.com
Web Site: www.arfarfrecords.com
Key Personnel
Pres: Erik Lindgren
Re-issues of 60's rock.
Catalog(s) available

Argentine Productions Inc
603 Washington Rd, Suite 501, Pittsburgh, PA 15228
Tel: 412-341-6448
E-mail: info@argentineproductions.com
Web Site: www.argentineproductions.com
Key Personnel
Prodr & Writer: Peter Argentine
Provide creative media services for corporations, the nonprofit community (including museums, hospitals & educational institutions) cable & broadcast. Also offer services for media professionals such as equipment rentals, production management & stock footage.

Argraph Corp
111 Asia Place, Carlstadt, NJ 07072
Tel: 201-939-7722 *Toll Free Tel:* 800-526-6290 *Fax:* 201-939-7782
E-mail: info@argraph.com; sales@argraph.com
Web Site: www.argraph.com
Key Personnel
CEO: Mark Roth
Natl Sales Mgr: Martin Lipton
Founded: 1953
Manufacturer & distributor of photographic & imaging products.
Catalog(s) available
Membership(s): Photo Marketing Association; Photoimaging Manufacturers & Distributors Association

Argyle Post
Affiliate of Absolute Rentals
2633 N San Fernando Blvd, Burbank, CA 91504
Tel: 818-845-5555; 310-560-2373 *Fax:* 818-842-8115
E-mail: info@argylepost.com
Web Site: www.argylepost.com
Key Personnel
Dir, Opers: Misty Tamburelli *E-mail:* mistyxo@gmail.com
Client Servs: Dave Rosen *E-mail:* dave.absolute@gmail.com
Founded: 2009
Post sound facility with ProTools, mix stage, ADR/Foley stage, live streaming.

Arhoolie Productions Inc (aka Arhoolie Records)
10341 San Pablo Ave, El Cerrito, CA 94530
Tel: 510-525-7471 *Fax:* 510-525-1204
E-mail: info@arhoolie.com
Web Site: www.arhoolie.com

Aries Productions
1110 Avenue "H" E, Suite 200, Arlington, TX 76011
Tel: 817-640-9955; 817-300-5255 (cell) *Fax:* 817-649-2529
E-mail: inform@aries-prods.com
Web Site: www.aries-prods.com
Key Personnel
Pres & Prodn Mgr: Wynn Winberg *E-mail:* wynn@aries-prods.com
Video, film & multimedia production.
Online catalog(s) available
Membership(s): Dallas Producers Association

Arizona Cine Equipment
2125 E 20 St, Tucson, AZ 85719
Tel: 520-623-8268 *Fax:* 520-623-1092
Web Site: www.azcine.com
Key Personnel
Pres: Lee Oliver
Convention Servs Sales Mgr: Linda Oliver

AV equipment sales & rentals.
Branch Office(s)
3532 E Elwood St, Phoenix, AZ 85040 *Tel:* 602-437-0221

Arizona Public Media
1423 E University, MLB67, Rm 223, Tucson, AZ 85719
Mailing Address: PO Box 210067, MLB67, Tucson, AZ 85721
Tel: 520-621-5828; 520-621-5836 (sales) *Fax:* 520-621-3360
Web Site: www.azpm.org
Key Personnel
Dir & Gen Mgr: Jack Gibson
Prodr: Christopher Conover
Television & radio production & broadcast.
Online catalog(s) available

Arizona Virtual Studios
4614 E McDowell Rd, Phoenix, AZ 85008
Tel: 602-275-9100
E-mail: john@azvirtualstudios.com
Web Site: azvirtualstudios.com
Full service video production studio offering 3D animation, graphic design, motion graphics, web development & video effects.

Ariztical Entertainment Inc
12400 Ventura Blvd, Suite 686, Studio City, CA 91604-2406
Tel: 818-760-3739 *Fax:* 818-760-3581
E-mail: info@ariztical.com
Web Site: www.ariztical.com
Key Personnel
Pres: Michael Jack Shoel *E-mail:* mjshoel@ariztical.com
Distribute & produce LGBT, independent & art house films.

Ark Media Group Ltd
PO Box 410685, San Francisco, CA 94141-0685
Tel: 415-863-7200 *Fax:* 415-864-5437
E-mail: sales@arkmedia.com
Web Site: www.arkmedia.com
Key Personnel
Pres: Allan Kessler
Founded: 1985
Multi-media sales company.
Catalog(s) available
Shipping Address: 425 Alabama St, San Francisco, CA 94110

Arkon Resources Inc
20 La Porte St, Arcadia, CA 91006
Tel: 626-254-9005 *Toll Free Tel:* 800-841-0884 *Fax:* 626-254-9266
E-mail: arkon5@arkon.com
Web Site: www.arkon.com
Key Personnel
VP, Sales & Mktg: Aaron Roth
Sr Acct Mgr: Benjamin Arana *Tel:* 626-400-6767
Founded: 1988
Manufacture & supplier of mobile mounting solutions & accessories designed for use with tablets, smartphones, cameras, GPS, satellite radios & other mobile communication & portable devices.
Online catalog(s) available
Foreign Office(s): Beveren, Belgium, Sr Acct Mgr: Hendrik Heyman *Tel:* (0107) 99-4143
14F-14 Byucksan Digital Valley 5th, 60-73, Gasandong, Geumchean-gu, Seoul, South Korea, Opers Mgr: Juliana Kim *Tel:* (02) 839-5701 *Fax:* (02) 830-5703 *Web Site:* www.arkonkorea.co.kr
5B16-17, No 5, Hsin-Yi Rd, Section 5, Taipei, Taiwan, Gen Mgr: Caroline Chang *Tel:* (02) 8789 8796 *Fax:* (02) 8789 8795

Arkwright Advanced Coating Inc
538 Main St, Fiskeville, RI 02823
Tel: 401-821-1000 *Toll Free Tel:* 800-556-6866
Web Site: www.sihlusa.com
Key Personnel
Pres: Christian Steeb
Founded: 1810
Produce film & specialty papers.
Online catalog(s) available
Membership(s): AECT; ATD; Education Market Association; InfoComm International®; NOPA

Arms Communications
1517 Maurice Dr, Woodbridge, VA 22191
Tel: 703-690-3338 *Fax:* 703-490-3810 (call first)
E-mail: info@armscomm.com
Web Site: www.armscomm.com
Key Personnel
VP, Opers: Diane Arms *E-mail:* diane@armscomm.com
Stock photography agency with special emphasis on military photos.

J Arnold Productions Inc
147 Cove Creek Rd, Mooresville, NC 28117-8910
Tel: 704-663-4444
Web Site: www.jarnoldproductions.com
Key Personnel
Dir, Sales & Mktg: Lori Arnold *E-mail:* lori@jarnoldproductions.com
Produce national network TV shows: ABC News, A&E, PBS, FOX, HGTV, History Channel, Travel Channel, etc. Behind the Scenes & electronic press kits for movies.
Online catalog(s) available
Branch Office(s)
25 Stanley Ave, Medford, MA 02155 *Tel:* 781-391-2300

Arrakis Systems
6604 Powell St, Loveland, CO 80538
Tel: 970-461-0730 *Fax:* 970-663-1010
E-mail: support@arrakis-systems.com
Web Site: www.arrakis-systems.com
Key Personnel
VP, Sales: Ben Palmer
Catalog(s) available
Online catalog(s) available

ARRI Inc
Subsidiary of Arnold & Richter Cine Technik
600 N Victory Blvd, Burbank, CA 91502-1639
Tel: 818-841-7070 *Fax:* 818-848-4028
E-mail: info@arri.com
Web Site: www.arri.com
Key Personnel
Pres: Glenn Kennel
VP: Bill Russell
VP, Intl Mktg: Franz Wieser *E-mail:* fwieser@arri.com
Founded: 1917
Catalog(s) available
Membership(s): AICP; NAB; Professional Film & Video Equipment Association; SMPTE

ARRIS Group Inc
3871 Lakefield Dr, Suwanee, GA 30024
Tel: 678-473-2907 *Toll Free Tel:* 866-36-ARRIS (362-7747) *Fax:* 678-473-8470
Web Site: www.arrisi.com
Digital & AM fiber optics, RF amplifiers, network management systems, modems, passives & 90-volt powering options. Services include network analysis & design, field engineering, installation & maintenance assistance, technical training, equipment repair, 48-hour emergency repair service & a 24-hour emergency hotline.
Catalog(s) available
Branch Office(s)
6450 Sequence Dr, San Diego, CA 92121 *Toll Free Tel:* 800-225-9446
ARRIS General Instrument Corp, 2450 Walsh Ave, Santa Clara, CA 95051 *Tel:* 408-235-5500
9800 E Geddes Ave, Suite A-100, Englewood, CO 80112 *Tel:* 720-895-7000 *Toll Free Tel:* 888-353-9473 *Fax:* 720-895-7106
ARRIS Group-Operations, 15 Sterling Dr, Wallingford, CT 06492 *Tel:* 203-303-6400 *Fax:* 203-303-6411
2400 Ogden Ave, Suite 180, Lisle, IL 60532 *Tel:* 630-281-3000 *Fax:* 630-281-3362
1321 Wakarusa Dr, Lawrence, KS 66049
900 Chelmsford St, Lowell, MA 01851 *Tel:* 978-614-2900
8 Technology Dr, Westborough, MA 01581 *Tel:* 508-870-2500 *Fax:* 508-836-2677
ARRIS Group-Global Strategies, 1825 NW 167 Place, Beaverton, OR 97006 *Tel:* 503-495-9240
101 Tournament Dr, Horsham, PA 19044 *Tel:* 215-323-1000
100 N 18 St, Suite 1810, Philadelphia, PA 19103 *Tel:* 215-209-6160
60 Decibel Rd, State College, PA 16801 *Tel:* 814-238-2461 *Toll Free Tel:* 800-233-2267 *Fax:* 814-238-4065
8815 122 Ave NE, Kirkland, WA 98033 *Tel:* 425-896-6000 *Fax:* 425-896-6060
Foreign Office(s): ARRIS do Brasil, Cond Edificio Dumez Av Alfredo Egidio de Souza Aranha 75, 4º andar - conjunto 42, 04726-170 Sao Paulo-SP, Brazil *Tel:* (011) 2737-6206
ARRIS Group Telecommunications Cia Ltda, Av Cerro el Plomo 5680, Torre 6, oficina 1901, 7500742 Las Condes, Santiago, Chile *Tel:* (02) 26784500 *Fax:* (02) 23352791
ARRIS Beijing, No 1 Wang King East Rd, Chao Yang District, Beijing 100102, China
2/F Back Area, Bldg D, No 68 Eastcom Rd, Bin Jiang District, Hangzhou 310053, China
ARRIS International, 300 Huaihai Mid Rd, Suite 9, 47th fl, Shanghai 200021, China *Tel:* (021) 5116 2945 *Fax:* (021) 5116 2960
ARRIS Technology (Shenzhen) Co, South & East Wing, 4/F, Block 2, Vision (Shenzhen) Business Park, Shenzhen, China *Tel:* (0755) 2671 6300 *Fax:* (0755) 2671 6307
General Instrument Corp India Pvt Ltd, Level 7 & 8, Lakeview Bldg, Block A, No 66/1, Bagmane Tech Park, C V Raman Nagar, Bangalore 560 093, India
General Instrument Corp India Pvt Ltd, Regus I-Tech Business Ctr Private Ltd, 9th fl, Space I-Tech Park, Tower-A1, Sector-49, Gurgaon Sohna Rd, Gurgaon 122 018, India
ARRIS Communications Ireland Ltd, Bldg 4300, Cork Airport Business Park, Kinsale Rd, Co Cork, Ireland *Tel:* (021) 7305800 *Fax:* (021) 4321972
ARRIS Research & Development, 28 Ha Barzel St, 69710 Tel-Aviv, Israel *Tel:* (03) 607 1111 *Fax:* (03) 607 1222
ARRIS Group Japan KK, Shinagawa East One Tower 21F, 2-16-1 Konan, Minato-ku, Tokyo 108-0075, Japan *Tel:* (03) 5461-7300 *Fax:* (03) 5461-2270
Paseo de la Reforma No 350, Piso 10 y 11, Col Juarez, 06600 Mexico, DF, Mexico
ARRIS Instrumentos Generales de Mexico SA de CV, Via de Innovacion 402, Parque de Investigacion e Innocasion Tecnologica, 66628 Apodaca, Nuevo Leon, Mexico *Tel:* (0181) 2281 8500
ARRIS Manufacturing Facility, ARRIS Group de Mexico SA de CV, Av De La Paz 11721, Parque Industrial Pacifico, 22643 Tijuana, Mexico *Tel:* (0664) 104-7200 *Fax:* (0664) 104-7294
ARRIS Group BV, Atlas Arena Bldg Azie, Hoogoorddreef 5, 1101 BA Amsterdam, Netherlands *Tel:* (020) 311 2500 *Fax:* (020) 311 2501
ARRIS Russia General Instrument LLC, Testovskaya 10, 13th fl, 123317 Moscow, Russia *Tel:* (495) 988 47 64
ARRIS Russia General Instrument LLC, Sedova 12, 192019 St Petersburg, Russia *Tel:* (812) 329 19 00 *Fax:* (812) 329 19 12

ARRIS Korea, No 1507, Parkview Office Tower, Jeongja-dong, Bundang-gu, Seongnam-si, Gyeonggi-do 463-863, South Korea *Tel:* (031) 740-4217 *Fax:* (031) 783-4896
General Instrument Espana SLU, Calle Garrotxa No 10-12, Floor 1, Mod 4B, Oceano 1, Barcelona, Spain *Tel:* 93 378 9140 *Fax:* 93 378 9147
General Instrument Espana SLU, Calle Martinez Villergas 52, Bldg 3, 2nd fl, Madrid, Spain *Tel:* 91 4233800 *Fax:* 91 4233901
General Instrument Sweden AB, Teknikringen 2, 583 30 Linkoping, Sweden *Tel:* (013) 367600
ARRIS Taiwan Site, General Instrument of Taiwan Ltd, No 1, Lane 232, Baoqiao Rd, Xindian Dist, New Taipei City 23145, Taiwan *Tel:* (02) 29189145 *Fax:* (02) 29159561
General Instrument UK Ltd, 710 Wharfedale Rd, Wokingham, Berks RG41 5TP, United Kingdom *Tel:* (0118) 921 5500

ARS Electronics
7110 DeCelis Place, Van Nuys, CA 91406
Tel: 818-997-6279 *Fax:* 818-997-6158
E-mail: info@arselectronics.com
Web Site: www.arselectronics.com
Key Personnel
Sales Mgr: Martin Sanett
Founded: 1947
Catalog(s) available

ART (Applied Research & Technology Inc)
Division of Yorkville Group Inc
4625 Witmer Industrial Estate, Niagara Falls, NY 14305
Tel: 716-297-2920 *Fax:* 716-297-3689
E-mail: usa@yorkville.com
Web Site: www.artproaudio.com; www.yorkville.com
Key Personnel
Pres: Betty VanDenBosch
Founded: 1984
Audio equipment manufacturer.
Online catalog(s) available
Branch Office(s)
215 Tremont St, Rochester, NY 14608 *Tel:* 585-436-2720 *Fax:* 585-436-3942

Art Gallery of Ontario
317 Dundas St W, Toronto, ON M5T 1G4, Canada
Tel: 416-979-6660 *Toll Free Tel:* 877-225-4246 *Fax:* 416-979-6674
E-mail: danny_winchester@ago.net
Web Site: www.ago.net
Key Personnel
CEO: Matthew Teitelbaum
Pres: Tony Gagliano
Catalog(s) available
Membership(s): Visual Resources Association

Art Museum of the Americas
201 18 St, Washington, DC 20006
Mailing Address: 1889 "F" St NW, Washington, DC 20006
Tel: 202-370-0147
E-mail: artmus@oas.org
Web Site: www.amamuseum.org
Key Personnel
PR: Gregory Svitil *E-mail:* gsvitil@oas.org
Online catalog(s) available

Art Resource
536 Broadway, 5th fl, New York, NY 10012
Tel: 212-505-8700 *Fax:* 212-505-2053
E-mail: requests@artres.com
Web Site: www.artres.com
Key Personnel
Gen Mgr: Ryan Jensen
Electronic Rts & Reproductions: Alison Strum
Founded: 1968
Fine art images, digital & analog.
Online catalog(s) available
Membership(s): American Society of Picture Professionals; ASMP; Picture Agency Council of America

Artaflex Inc
96 Steelcase Rd W, Markham, ON L3R 1B5, Canada
Tel: 905-470-0109 *Toll Free Tel:* 866-502-3378 *Fax:* 905-470-0621
Web Site: www.artaflex.com
Key Personnel
CEO: Paul Walker
Pres: Gerry Iuliano
Founded: 1985
Online catalog(s) available
Branch Office(s)
1402 Star Top Rd, Gloucester, ON K1B 4V7, Canada *Tel:* 613-744-3043 *Toll Free Tel:* 888-773-7832 *Fax:* 613-744-1993
Membership(s): AES; IEEE; PEO; SMPTE

Artbeats
1405 N Myrtle Rd, Myrtle Creek, OR 97457
Mailing Address: PO Box 709, Myrtle Creek, OR 97457-0110
Tel: 541-863-4429 *Toll Free Tel:* 800-444-9392 *Fax:* 541-863-4547
E-mail: info@artbeats.com
Web Site: www.artbeats.com
Key Personnel
CEO: Phil Bates
COO: Laura Hollifield
Dir, Technol: Sebastian Rabern
Global Dist Mgr: Peggy Nichols *E-mail:* pnichols@artbeats.com
Ad & Mktg: Julie Hill *E-mail:* julie@artbeats.com
Founded: 1989
Leading provider of royalty free stock-footage for broadcast, desktop video & multimedia.

Artech Electronics Ltd
PO Box 1547, Williston, VT 05495-1547
Toll Free Tel: 800-631-6448 *Toll Free Fax:* 800-934-7166
E-mail: info@artech-electronics.com
Web Site: www.artech-electronics.com
Key Personnel
Pres: David Lang
Founded: 1971
Importer & distributor of high quality audio & AV consumer products.
Online catalog(s) available
Branch Office(s)
PO Box 218, Sta CSL, Montreal, QC H4V 2Y4, Canada

Artel Video Systems
5B Lyberty Way, Westford, MA 01886
Tel: 978-263-5775 *Toll Free Tel:* 800-225-0228 *Fax:* 978-263-9755
E-mail: sales@artel.com
Web Site: www.artel.com
Key Personnel
Mktg Mgr: Karen Menard *E-mail:* kmenard@artel.com
Founded: 1981
Manufacture & distribute video & Ethernet transport equipment.
Online catalog(s) available
Membership(s): NAB; SCTE; SMPTE; Video Services Forum

Artichoke Productions
4114 Linden St, Oakland, CA 94608
Tel: 510-655-1283
Web Site: www.artichokepro.com
Key Personnel
Prodr & Dir: Paul Kalbach
Founded: 1981

Artistic Video
87 Tyler Ave, Dept V, Sound Beach, NY 11789
Tel: 631-744-5999 *Toll Free Tel:* 888-982-4244 *Fax:* 631-744-5993
E-mail: info@movementsofmagic.com
Web Site: www.movementsofmagic.com
Key Personnel
Pres: Bob Klein *E-mail:* bobklein5@yahoo.com
Founded: 1975
Over 100 instructional videos & DVDs on health & fitness, martial arts & Tai-Chi.
Catalog(s) available

Artograph Inc
525 Ninth St S, Delano, MN 55328-8624
Tel: 763-553-1112 *Toll Free Tel:* 888-975-9555 *Fax:* 763-553-1262
E-mail: sales@artograph.com; info@artograph.com
Web Site: www.artograph.com
Key Personnel
Pres: Donald Dow
Founded: 1947
Art projector manufacturers.
Online catalog(s) available
Sales list(s) available
Membership(s): NAMTA

Arts & Entertainment Network, see A&E Television Networks LLC

ASA Custom Cases Inc, see Creative Custom Cases

ASACA/ShibaSoku Corp of America
Subsidiary of ShibaSoku Co Ltd (Japan)
33 Boston Post Rd W, Suite 130, Marlborough, MA 01752
Tel: 508-229-0107 *Toll Free Tel:* 800-423-6347 *Fax:* 508-229-0721
Founded: 1971

ASC Systems
Mack Place, 566, St Clair Shores, MI 48080-0566
Tel: 313-882-1133
E-mail: ascsystems@live.com
Web Site: www.airi.com
Key Personnel
Mktg Mgr: D Leadore
Systems Mgr: R Martin
Video graphics systems, imaging systems, facilities & security monitoring & video Internet broadcasting & web broadcasting, wireless/video networking, broadband networks & cloud computing.
Catalog(s) available

ASC-Tube Trap
Division of Acoustic Sciences Corp
4275 W Fifth Ave, Eugene, OR 97402
Mailing Address: PO Box 1189, Eugene, OR 97440
Tel: 541-343-9727 *Toll Free Tel:* 800-272-8823 *Fax:* 541-343-9245
E-mail: info@acousticsciences.com
Web Site: www.acousticsciences.com
Key Personnel
Pres: Arthur Noxon
CFO: Pearl Chang
Distribute & manufacture acoustic control products.
Online catalog(s) available
Membership(s): AES; Custom Electronic Design & Installation Association

Ascom Communications Contractors
11952 James St, Holland, MI 49424
Tel: 616-820-1289 *Toll Free Tel:* 800-968-2444 *Fax:* 616-538-4311
E-mail: info@ascominc.com

Web Site: www.ascomllc.com
Key Personnel
Pres: Todd Billin
Founded: 1960
Communications contractor, AV systems integrator.
Membership(s): ABC; American Subcontractors Association of Western Michigan; NSCA

Asentria Corp
1200 N 96 St, Seattle, WA 98103
Tel: 206-344-8800 *Fax:* 206-344-2116
E-mail: sales@asentria.com
Web Site: www.asentria.com
Remote site monitoring & telecommunications equipment.
Online catalog(s) available

ASET - The Neurodiagnostic Society
402 E Bannister Rd, Suite A, Kansas City, MO 64131-3019
Tel: 816-931-1120 *Fax:* 816-931-1145
E-mail: info@aset.org
Web Site: www.aset.org
Key Personnel
Exec Dir: Arlen Reimnitz
Mktg & Communs Coord: Sarah Ecker
Founded: 1959
Nonprofit organization. Distribute continuing education programs.
Catalog(s), lists our available videos online

Ashgate Publishing Co
110 Cherry St, Suite 3-1, Burlington, VT 05401-3818
Tel: 802-865-7641 *Toll Free Tel:* 800-535-9544 (distribution) *Fax:* 802-865-7847
E-mail: info@ashgate.com
Web Site: www.ashgate.com
Key Personnel
Mktg Asst: Elizabeth Sutton *Tel:* 802-865-7641 ext 317
Foreign Office(s): Ashgate Publishing Ltd, Wey Ct E, Union Rd, Farnham, Surrey GU9 7PT, United Kingdom, Promo Mgr: Sarah Stilwell *Tel:* (01252) 736600 *Fax:* (01252) 736736 *E-mail:* info@ashgatepub.co.uk

Ashly Audio Inc
Division of Jam Industries
847 Holt Rd, Webster, NY 14580-9103
Tel: 585-872-0010 *Toll Free Tel:* 800-828-6308 *Fax:* 585-872-0739
E-mail: info@ashly.com; sales@ashly.com
Web Site: www.ashly.com
Key Personnel
CEO: Mark Wentling
Dir, Mktg: Anthony Errigo *Tel:* 585-872-0010 ext 106
Founded: 1974
Design & manufacture quality signal processing equipment.
Catalog(s) available
Online catalog(s) available
Membership(s): AES; InfoComm International®; NAMM, the National Association of Music Merchants; NSCA

Asia Society
725 Park Ave, New York, NY 10021
Tel: 212-288-6400 *Fax:* 212-517-8315
E-mail: pr@asiasociety.org
Web Site: www.asiasociety.org; www.asiasociety.org/video
Key Personnel
CEO & Pres: Josette Sheeran
CFO & SVP, Opers: Don Nagle
EVP: Tom Nagorski
Communs & Mktg Mgr: Preeti Bhuyan *E-mail:* preetib@asiasociety.org
Founded: 1956
Videos online.

Aspen Systems Inc
3900 Youngfield St, Wheat Ridge, CO 80033-3865
Tel: 303-431-4606 *Toll Free Tel:* 800-992-9242 *Fax:* 303-431-7196
E-mail: sales@aspsys.com
Web Site: www.aspsys.com
Key Personnel
CEO: Steven L Spring
VP, Sales: Jaime McIntyre
Founded: 1982

Assignment Desk
820 N Orleans St, Suite 205, Chicago, IL 60610
Tel: 312-464-8600 *Toll Free Tel:* 800-959-DESK (959-3375) *Fax:* 312-464-8605
E-mail: crew@assignmentdesk.com
Web Site: www.assignmentdesk.com
Founded: 1992
Booking agency for video production personnel & camera crews worldwide.

Associated Bag Co
400 W Boden St, Milwaukee, WI 53207
Tel: 414-769-1000 *Toll Free Tel:* 800-926-6100 *Fax:* 414-769-6530 *Toll Free Fax:* 800-926-4610
E-mail: customerservice@associatedbag.com
Web Site: www.associatedbag.com
Key Personnel
Pres: Herb Rubenstein
Cust Serv Mgr: Ellen Virta
Mktg Secy: Donna Keckeisen *Tel:* 800-926-6100 ext 291
Packaging & shipping products.
Catalog(s) available

Associated Drapery & Equipment Co, see Novelty Scenic Studios Inc

Associated Press Television News
450 W 33 St, New York, NY 10001
Tel: 212-621-1500 *Fax:* 212-621-7419
Web Site: www.aptn.com
Key Personnel
Dir, Natl Networks & Major Accts: Sara White *Tel:* 212-621-7863 *E-mail:* swhite@ap.org
Mgr, Natl Networks & Major Accts: Ivett Chicas *Tel:* 212-621-1876 *E-mail:* ichicas@ap.org
SNTV North America Ed: Rick Haas *Tel:* 212-621-7417 *E-mail:* rhaas@ap.org
News production services for media clients.
Membership(s): Media Communications Association

Associated Producers Ltd
18 Dupont St, Toronto, ON M5R 1V2, Canada
Tel: 416-504-6662 *Fax:* 416-504-6667
E-mail: general@apltd.ca
Web Site: www.apltd.ca
Key Personnel
Partner & Dir: Simcha Jacobovici *Tel:* 416-504-6662 ext 230
Also produce reality TV programs & episodic television. Documentary & factual programming for cable & digital broadcasters.

Associated Production Music LLC
6255 Sunset Blvd, Suite 900, Hollywood, CA 90028
Tel: 323-461-3211 *Fax:* 323-461-9102
E-mail: info@apmmusic.com
Web Site: www.apmmusic.com
Key Personnel
Pres: Adam Taylor
Source of production music services.
Branch Office(s)
381 Park Ave S, Suite 1101, New York, NY 10016 *Tel:* 212-856-9800 *Fax:* 212-856-9807 *E-mail:* clientservices@apmmusic.com
Membership(s): BME; Entertainment Merchants Association; MCA-I; NAB; NATPE; NCTA; PromaxBDA

Associated Sound
1417 Del Paso Blvd, Sacramento, CA 95815
Tel: 916-649-8040 *Toll Free Tel:* 800-492-6800 *Fax:* 916-649-0243
E-mail: sales@associatedsound.com
Web Site: www.associatedsound.com
Key Personnel
Rental Dept Mgr: Will Updegraff
Sales Mgr: Anthony Brown
Founded: 1968
Pro audio & AV systems & equipment. Media & sports events a specialty.
Membership(s): NAMM, the National Association of Music Merchants

Associated Video
2542 MacLaren Circle, Atlanta, GA 30360
Tel: 404-873-6411
Key Personnel
Pres: Jim Ruppert
Video production company, news monitoring.

Astoria Communications Inc
12054 Miramar Pkwy, Miami, FL 33025
Tel: 305-728-4280 *Toll Free Tel:* 877-GETMEAV (438-6328) *Fax:* 305-728-4285
Web Site: www.getmeav.com
Key Personnel
Pres: Ron Spiegal *E-mail:* ron@getmeav.com
Sr Proj Mgr: Hector Arocho *E-mail:* hectorjr@getmeav.com
Founded: 1997
Rent professional video & AV live event products & crew.

Astro Audio Visual
1336 W Clay St, Houston, TX 77019
Tel: 713-528-7119 *Fax:* 713-526-0607
AV equipment rentals & sales.
Catalog(s) available
Membership(s): InfoComm International®

Astronomical Society of the Pacific
390 Ashton Ave, San Francisco, CA 94112
Tel: 415-337-1100 *Toll Free Tel:* 800-335-2624 *Fax:* 415-337-5205
E-mail: service@astrosociety.org
Web Site: astrosociety.org
Key Personnel
Exec Dir: James Manning *Tel:* 415-715-1411 *E-mail:* jmanning@astrosociety.org
Dir, Devt & Commun: Kathryn Harper *Tel:* 415-715-1406 *E-mail:* kharper@astrosociety.org
Dir, Educ: Greg Schultz *Tel:* 415-715-1425 *E-mail:* gschultz@astrosociety.org
Dir, Fin & Opers: Michael Sowle *Tel:* 415-715-1412 *E-mail:* msowle@astrosociety.org
Founded: 1889
Design & deliver astronomy & space science education & outreach programs, workshops, materials, toolkits & publications throughout the Unites States.

ATA Trading Corp/Favorite TV Inc
877 Oceanfront, Long Beach, NY 11561-1542
Tel: 516-431-2302 *Fax:* 516-431-2302
E-mail: atat@verizon.net
Key Personnel
Pres: Harold G Lewis
Will sell rights to entire library of prgrams in perpetuity.
Catalog(s) available

ATCi (Antenna Technology Communication Solutions Inc)
450 N McKemy Ave, Chandler, AZ 85226
Tel: 480-844-8501 *Fax:* 480-898-7667
Web Site: www.atci.com
Key Personnel
CEO: Gary S Hatch
Mktg Dir: Kristen Love
Founded: 1979
Supplier & integrator of ground-based fixed & mobile satellite communications systems, commercial video broadcast systems, satellite teleport services & fiber optic links.
Online catalog(s) available
Membership(s): NAB; NCTA; SCTE; World Teleport Association

ATD Northwest Inc
17 N 100 W, Lehi, UT 84043
Tel: 801-407-8310 *Toll Free Fax:* 866-870-3697
E-mail: sales@atdnw.com
Web Site: www.atdnw.com; www.atdnorthwest.com
Manufactures products for portable surveillance. Designs & constructs specialized electro-optical systems for the aerospace & simulator segments of the industry.
Membership(s): AEA; SMPTE; SPIE

ATI Audio
Subsidiary of DaySequerra Corp
154 Cooper Rd, Bldg 902, West Berlin, NJ 08091
Tel: 856-719-9900
E-mail: info@daysequerra.com; sales@daysequerra.com
Web Site: www.atiaudio.com
Founded: 1979
Audio equipment manufacturer.
Membership(s): NAB; NSCA; SBE

Atlanta Filmworks
4280 Northeast Expwy, Atlanta, GA 30340
E-mail: info@atlantafilmworks.com
Web Site: atlantafilmworks.com
Key Personnel
Partner: Mark Henderson *Tel:* 678-677-1257; Daniel Minchew *Tel:* 404-630-0508
Founded: 2013
Feature film & TV program production studio.

Atlantic Illumination Entertainment Lighting
80 Fairbanks St, Dartmouth, NS B3A 1C4, Canada
Tel: 902-463-7418
E-mail: aiel@chebucto.biz
Web Site: aiel.chebucto.biz/
Key Personnel
Dir: Richard Bonner
Founded: 1977
Sales, rental & repair of stage lighting, special effects & related equipment.

Atlas Sound
4545 E Baseline Rd, Phoenix, AZ 85042
Toll Free Tel: 800-876-3333 *Toll Free Fax:* 800-765-3435
Web Site: www.atlassound.com
Founded: 1934
Manufacture UL listed racks for AV equipment.
Online catalog(s) available
Membership(s): AES; Custom Electronic Design & Installation Association; IBMA; InfoComm International®; IPMA; NAMM, the National Association of Music Merchants; NSCA

ATM Fly-Ware
Division of Adaptive Technologies Group Inc
1635 E Burnett St, Signal Hill, CA 90755
Tel: 562-424-1100 *Fax:* 562-424-3520
E-mail: info@adapttechgroup.com; marketing@adapttechgroup.com
Web Site: www.adapttechgroup.com/atmflyware.html
Key Personnel
Pres: Paul Allen
Founded: 1983
Designer of certified, pre-engineered professional loudspeaker rigging systems & flying hardware for permanent installations & live performances.
Catalog(s) available
Membership(s): InfoComm International®; NAMM, the National Association of Music Merchants; NSCA

Atma-Sphere Music Systems Inc
1742 Selby Ave, St Paul, MN 55104
Tel: 651-690-2246
Web Site: www.atma-sphere.com
Key Personnel
Founder, Owner & CEO: Ralph Karsten
E-mail: ralph@atma-sphere.com
Founded: 1978
Manufacture preamplifiers & amplifiers.

ATS Cases Inc
172 Otis St, Northborough, MA 01532
Tel: 508-393-9110 *Toll Free Tel:* 800-451-4242; 800-519-2771 *Fax:* 508-393-9508
E-mail: casemakers@mac.com
Web Site: atscases.com
Key Personnel
Founder & Pres: Ron Orlando
Founded: 1975
Designs & manufactures custom shipping cases, OEM carrying cases, material handling containers & reusable packaging for commercial & military applications.

Attainment Co Inc
504 Commerce Pkwy, Verona, WI 53593
Mailing Address: PO Box 930160, Verona, WI 53593-0160
Tel: 608-845-7880 *Toll Free Tel:* 800-327-4269 *Fax:* 608-845-8040 *Toll Free Fax:* 800-942-3865
E-mail: customerservice@attainmentcompany.com; international@attainmentcompany.com
Web Site: www.attainmentcompany.com
Key Personnel
Founder, CEO & Pres: Don Bastian
Dir, Opers: Sue Lockard *E-mail:* sue@attainmentcompany.com
Dir, Software Devt: Scott Meister *E-mail:* scott@attainmentcompany.com
Writer & Ed: Tom Kinney *E-mail:* tom@attainmentcompany.com
Founded: 1979
Creating, scripting, producing, editing, distributing & soliciting distributors for in-house video products; do not produce for others. The areas covered are youth at risk, early childhood & special education, especially people with developmental disabilities.
Catalog(s), free
Online catalog(s), PDF

ATTCO Inc
825 Ilaniwai St, Honolulu, HI 96813
Tel: 808-836-1191 *Fax:* 808-834-1046
E-mail: information@attcoinc.com
Web Site: www.attcoinc.com
Key Personnel
VP: Daniel Anderson *E-mail:* dander@attcoinc.com
Sales Mgr: Debbie Urasaki
Founded: 1964
Conventions & trade show supply, industrial staging, theatrical sales & services.
Membership(s): EDPA; Exposition Service Contractors' Association; Hawaii Association of Exposition Managers; National Association of Exposition Managers

ATTO Technology Inc
155 CrossPoint Pkwy, Amherst, NY 14068
Tel: 716-691-1999 *Fax:* 716-691-9353
Web Site: www.attotech.com
Key Personnel
Co-Founder, CEO & Pres: Timothy J Klein
Co-Founder, CTO & VP, Opers: David A Snell
VP, Fin & HR: James F Masiello
VP, Mktg: Wayne P Arvidson
VP, Opers: Timothy J Boser
Founded: 1988
Provide storage connectivity & infrastructure solutions for data intensive computing environments.
Brochure(s), PDF downloads
Data sheet(s) available

ATV Research Inc
1301 Broadway, Dakota City, NE 68731
Mailing Address: PO Box 620, Dakota City, NE 68731-0620
Tel: 402-987-3771 *Toll Free Tel:* 800-392-3922 *Fax:* 402-987-3709
E-mail: sales@atvresearch.com
Web Site: www.atvresearch.com
Key Personnel
Pres: Melvin Shadbolt
VP: Scott Shadbolt
Founded: 1964
Nationwide video distributors & system consultants on CCTV, MATV & SMATV.
Catalog(s), annual, free

ATV Video Center Inc
2424 Glendale Lane, Sacramento, CA 95825
Tel: 916-973-9100 *Toll Free Tel:* 800-635-1266 *Fax:* 916-973-8100
E-mail: info@atv.net
Web Site: www.atv.net
Key Personnel
Owner & Pres: Gary Jones
Founded: 1986
Professional AV sales, rental, production & installation.
Branch Office(s)
4310 S Cameron St, Las Vegas, NV 89103 *Toll Free Tel:* 800-635-1266
Foreign Office(s): Cabo Villas - 1209/1506, Fraccionamiento Miramar, mz 30, lote 17, Cabo San Lucas, Mexico
Membership(s): InfoComm International®

A2D Solutions Inc
Member of Fedele Group
20200 NW Second Ave, Suite 403, Miami Gardens, FL 33169
Tel: 305-895-5888 *Toll Free Tel:* 866-223-7253
E-mail: sales@a2dsolutions.com
Web Site: a2dsolutions.com
Founded: 2000
Worldwide business-to-business equipment supplier, distributor & systems integration firm serving clients from high end broadcast & film to defense & security systems.

Audacity Creative
2734 Polk St, Suite B, Hollywood, FL 33020
Tel: 954-920-4418 *Toll Free Fax:* 877-229-6298
E-mail: info@audacitycreative.com; audacityrecording@mac.com
Web Site: audacitycreative.com; audacityrecording.com
Key Personnel
Pres & Exec Prodr: Linda Thornberg
Creative Dir: John Martyn
Founded: 1986
HD video & audio post-production, original music & sound design, web videos, ADR & ISDN capable.
Membership(s): Advertising Federation of America; AICP; The Recording Academy

Audico Labels, see Lighthouse Photo & Video Productions

Audience Response Systems Inc
5611-C E Morgan Ave, Evansville, IN 47715
Tel: 812-479-7507 *Toll Free Tel:* 800-INVOLVE (468-6583) *Fax:* 812-479-1057
Web Site: www.audienceresponse.com
Key Personnel
Pres: Steve Campus
EVP: Steve Knapp
VP, Sales: Debbie Minor
IT Mgr: Jeff Osborn
Pulse Systems Mgr: Brad Copes
Founded: 1984
Membership(s): InfoComm International®

Audio Accessories Inc
25 Mill St, Marlow, NH 03456
Mailing Address: PO Box 360, Marlow, NH 03456-0360
Tel: 603-446-3335 *Fax:* 603-446-7543
E-mail: audioacc@patchbays.com
Web Site: www.patchbays.com
Key Personnel
Pres: M B Hall
Opers Mgr: Timothy J Symonds
Audio patch panels & video panels.
Catalog(s) available
Membership(s): NAB

Audio & Light
2209 Randleman Rd, Greensboro, NC 27406
Tel: 336-274-1234 *Fax:* 336-274-4022
E-mail: info@audio-light.com
Web Site: www.audio-light.com
Key Personnel
Pres: Jim Hoyle *E-mail:* jhoyle@audio-light.com
VP, Sales: Brian Cox
Dir, Opers/Rental Div: Ernest Grey *E-mail:* egrey@audio-light.com
Tech Dir: Charlie Starr
Prodn Mgr: Natalie Vail
Founded: 1984
Audio, video & lighting systems. Specialize in live events.

Audio Art
124 Forsythe Dr, Chapel Hill, NC 27517
Tel: 919-260-1507
Key Personnel
Owner: Jon Paul McClellan *E-mail:* jonpaulmcclellan@gmail.com
Sound mixing for concerts.

Audio Book Contractors LLC
PO Box 96, Riverdale, MD 20738-0096
Tel: 301-439-5830 *Fax:* 301-439-5830
E-mail: info@audiobookcontractors.com
Web Site: www.audiobookcontractors.com
Key Personnel
Owner & Mgr: Robert Butler
Founded: 1983
Sells unabridged classic novels, children's books, poetry, plays & collections of short stories for use by the general public, schools & libraries on cassette & CD. Downloads available on audible.com.
Online catalog(s) available

Audio Consultant Services Inc
2133 S Bellair, Suite 5, Denver, CO 80222
Tel: 303-296-1885
Web Site: www.audio-consultants.com
Key Personnel
Pres: David Soran *E-mail:* dsoran@qwest.net
Founded: 1993
Engineering services for location recording.
Catalog(s) available

The Audio Department Inc
119 W 57 St, Suite 400, New York, NY 10019
Tel: 212-586-3503 *Fax:* 212-245-1675
E-mail: scheduling@theaudiodepartment.com
Web Site: www.theaudiodepartment.com
Key Personnel
Pres: Robert Chapman
Studio Mgr: Aimee Christie
Sound Engr: Donald Hoffman

Audio Editions Books-On-Cassette & CD
Division of The Audio Partners Inc
131 E Placer St, Auburn, CA 95603
Mailing Address: PO Box 6930, Auburn, CA 95604-6930
Tel: 530-888-7801 *Toll Free Tel:* 800-231-4261 *Toll Free Fax:* 800-882-1840
E-mail: info@audioeditions.com
Web Site: audioeditions.com; audioeditionslibrary.com
Key Personnel
Mgr & Lib Servs Supv: Kirby Desha
Founded: 1987
Audio book supplier offering personal customer service for 19,000 audio books from 100 publishers. Also distributes MP3 CDs & Playaways.
Catalog(s), monthly
Membership(s): ALA; Audio Publishers Association

Audio Graphic Services
1516 Ferris Ave, Royal Oak, MI 48067
Tel: 248-544-1793
E-mail: netmail@audiographicservices.com
Web Site: www.audiographicservices.com
Key Personnel
Owner, COO & Pres: Edward J Wolfrum
Owner: Susan E Wolfrum
Founded: 1967
Audio, technical & recording services.
Online catalog(s) available
Membership(s): The Recording Academy

Audio Images Corp
701 Bryant St, 2nd fl, San Francisco, CA 94107
Tel: 415-957-9131 *Fax:* 415-957-1531
Web Site: www.audioimages.com
Key Personnel
Partner: James C Chen
Founded: 1986
Retail professional audio store. AV system installation & service.

Audio Mechanics
1200 W Magnolia Blvd, Burbank, CA 91506
Tel: 818-846-5525 *Fax:* 818-846-5501
E-mail: info@audiomechanics.com
Web Site: audiomechanics.com
Key Personnel
Owner & Chief Engr: John Polito *E-mail:* john@audiomechanics.com
Mng Dir: Bob Sky
Founded: 1991
Music mastering & sound restoration.

Audio Media Productions
6739 Kirby Trace Cove, Memphis, TN 38119
Tel: 901-751-2363
E-mail: ampman@aol.com
Web Site: www.audiomediaprod.com
Key Personnel
Owner: Andy Black
Soundmixer: Nathan Black; Michael Hunkele
Founded: 1994
Specialize in sound for film, video & radio. Location sound mixing. Complete sound packages for film & video.

Audio Network US Inc
48 W 25 St, 10th fl, New York, NY 10010
Tel: 646-688-4320
E-mail: nyoffice@audionetwork.com
Web Site: us.audionetwork.com
Key Personnel
Founder & Chmn: Andrew Sunnucks
Founder & CEO: Robert Hurst
Mng Dir: Juliette Squair
VP, Sales: Ian Ginsberg
US Head, Mktg: Eric Morse
Sr Mgr, Creative Licensing: Matt McMullian
Founded: 2001
Production & stock music for TV, film advertising & corporate video.
Branch Office(s)
9465 Wilshire Blvd, Suite 300, Beverly Hills, CA 90212 *Tel:* 310-889-0109

Audio Precision
5750 SW Arctic Dr, Beaverton, OR 97005
Tel: 503-627-0832 *Toll Free Tel:* 800-231-7350 *Fax:* 503-469-0336
E-mail: sales@ap.com
Web Site: www.ap.com
Key Personnel
Co-Founder & Chmn: Bruce E Hofer
Pres: David Schmoldt
VP, Engg: Tom Kite
VP, Sales & Mktg: Spyros Lazaris
Founded: 1984
Audio test & measurement equipment manufacturer.
Foreign Office(s): South Fens Business Ctr, Suite L13, Fenton Way, Chatteris, Cambs PE16 6TT, United Kingdom, Dir: James Kelly *Tel:* (0740) 307 9426 *E-mail:* jamesk@ap.com
Membership(s): AES

Audio Producers Group
200 N Dearborn St, Suite 2705, Chicago, IL 60601
Tel: 312-977-9400 *Fax:* 312-977-9494
E-mail: info@apgaudio.com
Web Site: www.audioproducersgroup.com
Key Personnel
Partner & Prodr: David Kaplan *E-mail:* david@apgaudio.com; Mindy Verson *E-mail:* mindy@apgaudio.com
Founded: 2004
Full service audio post-production facility, voice casting, voice record, sound design, digital mix & duplication.

Audio Rents
1541 N Wilcox Ave, Hollywood, CA 90028
Tel: 323-874-1000 *Fax:* 323-460-2676
E-mail: info@audiorents.com
Web Site: www.audiorents.com
Key Personnel
Mgr: Traci Bradford
Founded: 1986
Post-production audio rentals.
Price list(s), free, upon request

Audio Resource Honolulu
1750 Kalakaua Ave, Suite 201, Honolulu, HI 96826
Tel: 808-944-9400 *Toll Free Fax:* 866-774-4184
E-mail: information@audioresourcehonolulu.com
Web Site: www.audioresourcehonolulu.com
Key Personnel
Mktg Dir: Tony Hugar *E-mail:* tonyhugar@me.com
Recording studios.

Audio-Technica US Inc
Subsidiary of Audio-Technica Corp
1221 Commerce Dr, Stow, OH 44224
Tel: 330-686-2600 *Fax:* 330-686-0719
E-mail: pro@atus.com
Web Site: www.audio-technica.com
Key Personnel
Pres: Philip Cajka

Natl Dir, Sales & Mktg, Prof Mkts: Doug Swan
Membership(s): AES; NAB; NAMM, the National Association of Music Merchants; NSCA

Audio Upgrades
6982 Mimosa Dr, Carlsbad, CA 92011
Tel: 818-780-1222
Web Site: www.audioupgrades.com
Key Personnel
Owner: Jim Williams *E-mail:* jwilliams3@earthlink.net
Founded: 1990
Component level upgrades for the recording industry & design services.

Audio-Video Corp
213 Broadway, Albany, NY 12204
Tel: 518-449-7213 *Fax:* 518-449-1205
E-mail: info@audiovideocorp.com; sales@audiovideocorp.com
Web Site: www.audiovideocorp.com
Key Personnel
Pres & CEO: Ted Klarsfeld
Provider of high-end AV presentation equipment.
Online catalog(s) available
Branch Office(s)
6365 Collamer Dr, East Syracuse, NY 13057
Tel: 315-463-1946 *Fax:* 315-463-2999
145 Pine Haven Shores Rd, Suite 1053, Shelburne, VT 05482 *Tel:* 802-316-6375 *Fax:* 315-463-2999

Audio Video Resources
4323 E Cotton Center Blvd, Phoenix, AZ 85040
Tel: 602-643-4200; 602-643-4300 (rentals)
Toll Free Tel: 877-643-4204 *Fax:* 602-643-4270
E-mail: sales@avrinc.com; rentals@avrinc.com
Web Site: www.avrinc.com
Key Personnel
CEO & Owner: Mark Temen
Membership(s): InfoComm International®; PSNI

Audio-Video Resources Inc
1043 Adams Ave, Montgomery, AL 36104
Mailing Address: PO Box 2371, Montgomery, AL 36102-2371
Tel: 334-262-4806 *Fax:* 334-240-0000
E-mail: avrinc@bellsouth.net
Key Personnel
Owner & Pres: Rick Martin
Sr Partner & VP: Charles E McCoy
Founded: 1990
Industrial AV rental house only.

Audio/Video Supply Inc
4575 Ruffner St, San Diego, CA 92111
Tel: 858-565-1101 *Toll Free Tel:* 800-284-2288
Fax: 858-565-7845
E-mail: sales@avsupply.com
Web Site: www.avsupply.com
Key Personnel
Pres: R T Moore, Jr
Membership(s): InfoComm International®; MCA-I

Audio-VideoGraphics Inc
17501 E 40 Hwy, Suite 219, Independence, MO 64055
Tel: 816-350-0800 *Toll Free Tel:* 800-322-2832
Fax: 816-350-0804
E-mail: mail@avginc.com
Web Site: www.avginc.com
Key Personnel
Pres: Greg Azorsky
Online catalog(s) available

Audio Visions Inc
1501 N George St, York, PA 17404
Tel: 717-843-1561 *Fax:* 717-848-3289
Web Site: www.audiovisionsinc.com
Key Personnel
Pres: Daniel R Snyder *E-mail:* dan@audiovisionsinc.com

Audio Vistas LLC
170 N Woods Dr, South Orange, NJ 07079
Tel: 212-586-2177
E-mail: info@audiovistas.com
Web Site: www.audiovistas.com
Key Personnel
Pres: Charles D Wantman *E-mail:* charles@audiovistas.com
Founded: 1977
Produce HD video.
Online catalog(s) available

Audio Visual Actions Inc (AVA)
5641-C General Washington Dr, Alexandria, VA 22312
Tel: 703-750-0950 *Toll Free Tel:* 866-893-5382
Fax: 703-750-0954
E-mail: info@avactions.com
Web Site: avactions.com
Event staging. Video, audio equipment, conferencing, lighting & general AV rentals.

Audio Visual Associates
One Stewart Ct, Denville, NJ 07834
Toll Free Tel: 888-435-6678 *Fax:* 973-442-0888
E-mail: sales@avaonline.com; info@avaonline.com
Web Site: www.avaonline.com
Key Personnel
Pres: Ed Susco *E-mail:* esusco@avaonline.com
Founded: 1988
AV sales, service, design, installation & rental.
Membership(s): InfoComm International®

Audio Visual Communications Inc
1336 Cherry St, Boothwyn, PA 19061
Tel: 610-272-8500
E-mail: audiovc@verizon.net
Web Site: www.audiovc.com
Key Personnel
Pres: Frank Matys

The Audio Visual Co (AVCO)
98-810 Moanalua Rd, Aiea, HI 96701
Tel: 808-485-3200 *Fax:* 808-487-0733
Web Site: www.theavco.com
Key Personnel
Pres: Thomas Lee *E-mail:* tlee@theavco.net
Proj Mgr: Wade Higa *Tel:* 808-485-3238
E-mail: whiga@theavco.net
Founded: 1970

Audio Visual Concepts Inc
PO Box 3915, Guaynabo, PR 00970-3915
Tel: 787-753-7700 *Fax:* 787-766-7712
Web Site: www.mig-avc.com
Key Personnel
Partner & VP: Tony Alvarado *E-mail:* talvarado@mig-avc.com
Founded: 1982
AV/IT/System Integrators.
Membership(s): ICTA; PR Industrial Association

Audio Visual Consultants
3640 Grand Ave, Suite 105, Oakland, CA 94610
Tel: 510-839-2020 *Fax:* 510-839-6464
E-mail: info@avconsultants.com
Web Site: www.avconsultants.com
Key Personnel
Owner: Stuart Sweetow *E-mail:* sweetow@avconsultants.com
Founded: 1983

Audio Visual Dynamics®
Division of B B Productions
8 Budd St, Morristown, NJ 07960
Tel: 973-993-8500 *Fax:* 973-984-0644
Web Site: www.avdusa.com
Key Personnel
Pres: Chris Broening *E-mail:* cbroening@avdusa.com
EVP: Elliott Gillman *E-mail:* egillman@avdusa.com
Founded: 1964
Full service AV staging & rental company.
Online catalog(s) available
Membership(s): InfoComm International®

Audio Visual Dynamics Ltd
2360 23 Ave, Lachine, QC H8T 0A3, Canada
Tel: 514-332-6440 *Fax:* 514-332-2009
E-mail: service@avd.ca
Web Site: www.avd.ca
Key Personnel
Owner: Philip Hamilton
AV staging & rentals.

Audio Visual Imagineering Inc
6565 Hazeltine National Dr, Suite 2, Orlando, FL 32822
Tel: 407-859-8166 *Fax:* 407-859-8254
Web Site: www.av-imagineering.com
Key Personnel
Owner & Mng Dir: Joanne Young
E-mail: joanne@av-imagineering.com
Founded: 1978
Manufacture laser projection equipment & produce laser shows. Full animation studio producing classical 2D animation & computer graphics. Exclusive US agent for Konica Minolta Planetarium.
Membership(s): Association of Science & Technology Centers; International Laser Display Association; International Planetarium Society

Audio Visual Management Group, see Freeman

Audio Visual Media
1141 Lexington Ave, Mansfield, OH 44907
Mailing Address: PO Box 3526, Mansfield, OH 44907-0526
Tel: 419-756-2698 *Fax:* 419-756-1560
E-mail: avm2698@aol.com
Web Site: audiovisualmedia.net
Key Personnel
Owner: Mark Stallsmith
Founded: 1957
Services include videography, film transfer, video editing, format conversion & video photo montages. Rents AV presentation equipment for business meetings & special events.

Audio Visual of Milwaukee Inc
285 N Janacek Rd, Brookfield, WI 53045
Tel: 262-432-1077 *Toll Free Tel:* 800-236-6909
Fax: 262-432-1078
E-mail: avm@avmonline.com
Web Site: www.avmonline.com
Key Personnel
Sales Mgr: Tim Rouse
Founded: 1980

Audio Visual Resources Inc
3932 Ogeechee Rd, Savannah, GA 31405
Tel: 912-447-5656 *Fax:* 912-447-5655
E-mail: aaavr@aol.com
Web Site: www.avrsav.com
Catalog(s) available
Membership(s): InfoComm International®

Audio Visual Resources LLC
1000 N Division St, Suite 2F, Peekskill, NY 10566
Tel: 914-526-2698 *Fax:* 914-526-3060
E-mail: info@avrny.com
Web Site: www.avrny.com

Key Personnel
Pres & Founder: Jeffrey Werner
Founded: 2001
AV production services & equipment.

Audio Visual Sales & Service Inc
2601 Curry Rd, Schenectady, NY 12303
Tel: 518-688-0640 *Fax:* 518-688-0634
E-mail: info@avssi.com
Key Personnel
Pres: Leo Lupien

Audio Visual Services Corp
1700 E Golf Rd, Suite 400, Schaumburg, IL 60173
Tel: 847-222-9800 *Toll Free Tel:* 800-486-9509 *Fax:* 847-222-1600
Web Site: www.psav.com
Catalog(s) available
Membership(s): InfoComm International®; MCA-I; NAPTE

Audio Visual Services Inc, see Impact Group

Audio Visual Supply LLC, see RSS Distributors

Audio Visual Systems Rental Centres
Pennjerdel House, 449 High St, Burlington, NJ 08016-4514
Tel: 609-387-3636 *Toll Free Tel:* 800-416-3636 *Fax:* 609-871-3636
Web Site: www.avsgroup.com
Key Personnel
Pres: Erik L Burro *E-mail:* eburro@comcast.net

Audio Visual Techniques Inc
1489 Leestown Rd, Lexington, KY 40511
Tel: 859-254-8954 *Fax:* 859-233-4754
E-mail: info@avtav.com
Web Site: avtav.com
Key Personnel
Pres: Bradley Abney *E-mail:* brad@avtav.com
Founded: 1983
AV rentals & staging.
Membership(s): InfoComm International®

Audio Visual Technologies Group
12502 Exchange Dr, Stafford, TX 77477
Mailing Address: PO Box 2307, Stafford, TX 77497-2307
Tel: 281-240-2100 *Toll Free Tel:* 800-522-3687
E-mail: avtginfo@avtg.com
Web Site: www.avtg.com
Key Personnel
Pres: Ashley Brown *E-mail:* abrown@avtg.com
Founded: 1952
Online catalog(s) available
Membership(s): InfoComm International®; NSCA

Audioarts Engineering
Division of Wheatstone Corp
600 Industrial Dr, New Bern, NC 28562
Tel: 252-638-7000 *Fax:* 252-637-1285; 252-635-4857 (sales)
E-mail: sales@wheatstone.com
Web Site: www.wheatstone.com
Key Personnel
Dir, Intl Sales: Brad Harrison

AudioControl®
22410 70 Ave W, Mountlake Terrace, WA 98043
Tel: 425-775-8461 *Fax:* 425-778-3166
E-mail: sound.better@audiocontrol.com; superio.sound@audiocontrol.com
Web Site: www.audiocontrol.com
Key Personnel
CEO: Alex Camara
Mgr, Sales & Mktg: Chris Kane
Founded: 1977
Designer & manufacturer of audio & video measurement equipment.
Online catalog(s) available
Membership(s): AES; Consumer Electronics Association; Custom Electronic Design & Installation Association; IASCA; NSCA

AudioGO, see Downpour.com

AudioImage Recording
110 N Jefferson St, Richmond, VA 23220-5022
Tel: 804-644-7700 *Fax:* 804-644-8801
E-mail: info@audioimagerecording.com
Web Site: www.audioimagerecording.com
Key Personnel
Pres: John Valentine *E-mail:* john@audioimagerecording.com
Chief Engr/Studio Mgr: Joe Horner *E-mail:* joe@audioimagerecording.com
Client Servs: Coral Preston *E-mail:* coral@audioimagerecording.com
Founded: 1980
Digital production studio, also do ISDN.

Audiomoxie®
PO Box 304, Georgetown, TX 78627
E-mail: info@audiomoxie.com
Web Site: www.audiomoxie.com
Key Personnel
Founder & Creative Dir: James Laurance
Founded: 2000
Music production.
Membership(s): ASCAP; BMI

AudioTransitions
6429 N Talman Ave, Chicago, IL 60645
Tel: 773-338-8813 *Fax:* 773-338-8813
Web Site: www.judithwest.com
Key Personnel
Owner & Prodr: Judith West *E-mail:* judith@judithwest.com
Founded: 2000
Full service audiobook development & production; diverse talent pool. Custom in-house studio; free estimates. Special consulting for publishers new to audiobooks: concept & design, abridgment, manufacturing/packaging, alternative digital formats, reviewers, special markets, digital downloads.
Membership(s): The Association of Publishers for Special Sales; Audio Publishers Association; The Authors Guild; Chicago Women in Publishing

Audiovox
180 Marcus Blvd, Hauppauge, NY 11788
Tel: 631-231-7750 *Toll Free Tel:* 800-645-4994 *Fax:* 631-231-4006
Web Site: www.voxxelectronics.com; www.voxxintl.com
VOXX International brand.

Audix Corp
9400 SW Barber St, Wilsonville, OR 97070
Mailing Address: PO Box 4010, Wilsonville, OR 97070-4010
Tel: 503-682-6933 *Toll Free Tel:* 800-966-8261 *Fax:* 503-682-7114
E-mail: info@audixusa.com
Web Site: www.audixusa.com
Key Personnel
VP, Sales & Mktg: Clifford J Castle
Founded: 1984
Catalog(s) available
Membership(s): AES

Augsburg Fortress Publishers
Division of Publishing House of Evangelical Lutheran Church in America
100 S Fifth St, Suite 600, Minneapolis, MN 55402
Mailing Address: PO Box 1209, Minneapolis, MN 55440-1209
Tel: 612-330-3300 *Toll Free Tel:* 800-328-4648 *Fax:* 612-330-3455 *Toll Free Fax:* 800-722-7766
E-mail: info@augsburgfortress.org
Web Site: www.augsburgfortress.org
Key Personnel
CEO & Pres: Beth A Lewis *E-mail:* ceo@augsburgfortress.org
Newsletter(s), free, web-based
Membership(s): ICVM

August House Audio
Subsidiary of August House Publishers Inc
3500 Piedmont Rd NE, Suite 310, Atlanta, GA 30305
Tel: 404-442-4420 *Toll Free Tel:* 800-284-8784 *Fax:* 404-442-4435
E-mail: ahinfo@augusthouse.com
Web Site: www.augusthouse.com
Key Personnel
CEO: Steve Floyd
EVP & Creative Dir: Graham Anthony
Dir, Devt: Rob Cleveland
Online catalog(s) available
Membership(s): Audio Publishers Association

Aura Sonic Ltd
PO Box 520791, Flushing, NY 11352-0791
Tel: 718-886-6500
E-mail: somebody@aurasonic.com
Web Site: www.aurasonicltd.com
Key Personnel
Owner: Steven Remote
Aura Sonic Ltd (ASL) was established in the late 70s to provide a variety of location audio recording & production ventures. ASL provides an efficient & economical way to integrate quality audio components with the finest "On Location" audio production techniques. ASL is dedicated to satisfying the needs of our colleagues & clients. We invite you to call +/or e-mail us with any questions, concerns or suggestions you may have. Analog & digital recording is available via three mobile audio trucks & various remote recording packages. Additional services include sound reinforcement, audio production & audio equipment sales.

Aural Gratification Inc
32 Nissen Lane, West Hurley, NY 12491-5903
Tel: 845-679-5674
E-mail: auralg@gmail.com
Key Personnel
Pres: Kevin Bartlett
Recording studio & record label. Specialize in custom music production for TV & film as well as album production & recording for artists.
Online catalog(s) available
Membership(s): BMI

Auralex Acoustics Inc
9955 Westpoint Dr, Suite 101, Indianapolis, IN 46256
Tel: 317-842-2600 *Toll Free Tel:* 800-95-WEDGE (959-3343, orders) *Fax:* 317-842-2760
E-mail: info@auralex.com
Web Site: www.auralex.com
Key Personnel
Pres: Eric Smith
Founded: 1977
Manufacture & distribute acoustical foams, sound barriers, diffusors, adhesives & related sound control items.
Online catalog(s) available

Auratron Systems
3716 N Broadway, Knoxville, TN 37917-3120
Tel: 865-687-6060; 865-687-6006 *Fax:* 865-687-6020

Web Site: www.auratronsystems.com
Key Personnel
Sr Engr: Alex Copeland
Ultra high-end audio equipment for home & professional use.
Catalog(s) available
Online catalog(s) available

Auriga Productions Ltd
2856 rue du Comtois, Ste-Lazare, QC J7T 0E7, Canada
Tel: 514-984-4202
E-mail: aurigapix@gmail.com
Web Site: www.aurigapix.com
Key Personnel
Founder & Pres: Francois Ouimet

Aurora Films
324 E Dowling Rd, Suite 4, Anchorage, AK 99518
Tel: 907-258-4686 *Fax:* 907-561-6622
E-mail: aurorafilms@acsalaska.net
Key Personnel
Prodr: Laurence Goldin
Founded: 1974
Membership(s): Alaska Film Group; International Documentary Association; Writers Guild of America West

aurora productions
315 Walt Whitman Rd, Suite 210, Huntington Station, NY 11746-4112
Tel: 631-549-8933
E-mail: info@auroraproductions.tv
Web Site: www.auroraproductions.tv
Key Personnel
Founder & Prodr/Dir: Richard H Poggioli *E-mail:* richpogg@optonline.net
Membership(s): MCA-I; SMPTE

Auslender Productions/Celestial Images
Subsidiary of Leland Auslender Photography
6036 Comey Ave, Los Angeles, CA 90034-2204
Tel: 323-931-3277 *Fax:* 323-937-1720
Web Site: celestial-images.net; auslender.com
Key Personnel
Owner & Mgr: Leland Auslender *E-mail:* auslender@ca.rr.com
Founded: 1961
Fine art photography/motion pictures.
Catalog(s) available

Autodesk Inc
111 McInnis Pkwy, San Rafael, CA 94903
Tel: 415-507-5000 *Fax:* 415-507-5100
Web Site: www.autodesk.com
Key Personnel
CEO & Pres: Carl Bass

AutoDesSys Inc
3518 Riverside Dr, Suite 102, Columbus, OH 43221
Tel: 614-488-8838 *Fax:* 614-488-0848
E-mail: formz@formz.com; sales@formz.com; sales@autodessys.com
Web Site: www.formz.com
Key Personnel
CEO & Pres: Chris Yessios
SVP, Devt: Dave Krop
Founded: 1989
3D modeling software development.

Autogram/Crl
920 Edison Ave, Suite 4, Benton, AR 72015
Tel: 480-893-7080 *Fax:* 501-776-0357
Web Site: www.orban.com
Key Personnel
Mktg: Terry Nall *E-mail:* tnall@orban.com
Catalog(s) available
Membership(s): NAB

Automated Entertainment
PO Box 1079, Little Rock, CA 95343-1079
Tel: 661-944-2299 *Toll Free Tel:* 800-880-6567 (orders) *Fax:* 661-944-2348
E-mail: questions@automatedhd.com
Web Site: www.automatedhd.com
Key Personnel
Principal & Owner: Jeffrey W Hillinger
Founded: 1987
Catalog(s) available

Automatic Devices Co
2121 S 12 St, Allentown, PA 18103
Tel: 610-797-6000 *Toll Free Tel:* 800-360-2321 *Fax:* 610-797-4088
E-mail: info@automaticdevices.com
Web Site: www.automaticdevices.com
Key Personnel
COO/Engg: Dennis Lopez *Tel:* 610-797-6000 ext 18 *E-mail:* eeadc@automaticdevices.com
Cont: Kathleen Schock *Tel:* 610-797-6000 ext 22 *E-mail:* ks@automaticdevices.com
Sales: Caryn Anderson *Tel:* 610-797-6000 ext 14 *E-mail:* caryn@automaticdevices.com
Founded: 1919
Catalog(s) available

Automobile Film Club of America Inc
10 Cross St, Staten Island, NY 10304
Tel: 718-447-2255 *Fax:* 718-447-2289
E-mail: autofilm@aol.com
Web Site: www.autofilmclub.com
Key Personnel
Founder: Ralph Lucci
Founded: 1992

Auton Motorized Systems
29102 Hancock Pkwy, Valencia, CA 91355
Tel: 661-257-9282 *Fax:* 661-295-5638
E-mail: tvlifts@auton.com
Web Site: www.auton.com
Key Personnel
Founder & Pres: Virgil Walker
Founded: 1955
World's first manufacturer of television lifts.
Catalog(s), on request
CD-ROM catalog(s) available
Membership(s): Custom Electronic Design & Installation Association

AV Bluebook
80 Little Falls Rd, Fairfield, NJ 07004
Mailing Address: PO Box 10005, Fairfield, NJ 07004
Toll Free Tel: 800-631-7791 *Toll Free Fax:* 800-332-5871
E-mail: info@avbluebook.com
Web Site: www.avbluebook.com
Founded: 1976
Catalog(s) available
Membership(s): BPIA; InfoComm International®; National Art Materials Trade Association; NSCA; Photo Marketing Association

AV Chicago Inc
619 W Taylor St, Chicago, IL 60607
Tel: 312-229-4100 *Toll Free Tel:* 888-709-9599
Web Site: www.avchicago.com
Founded: 1982
Membership(s): Better Business Bureau; Chicago Convention & Tourism Bureau (Choose Chicago®); InfoComm International®

AV Concepts
1917 W First St, Tempe, AZ 85281
Tel: 480-557-6000 *Toll Free Tel:* 866-927-7590 *Fax:* 480-894-8376
E-mail: info@avconcepts.com
Web Site: www.avconcepts.com
Key Personnel
Pres: Nick Smith
Founded: 1987
Branch Office(s)
9340 Dowdy Dr, Suite 102, San Diego, CA 92126 *Tel:* 619-229-2901 *Fax:* 619-229-2910

AV Conferencing
PO Box 21606, Concord, CA 94521
Tel: 925-216-6319 *Fax:* 801-382-5573
E-mail: sales@avconferencing.com
Web Site: www.avconferencing.com
Key Personnel
Gen Mgr: Bob Kearns
Contact: Gregg R Kearns *E-mail:* grkearns@avconferencing.com
Founded: 1987

A/V Davey
71 Clifton Place, Bridgeport, CT 06606
Tel: 203-372-3286 *Toll Free Tel:* 877-AVDAVEY (283-2839) *Fax:* 203-372-3307
Web Site: avdavey.com
Key Personnel
Pres: David M Katz *Tel:* 203-372-3286 ext 12 *E-mail:* davey@avdavey.com
Founded: 1989
Online catalog(s) available

AV Guys
1641 Pacific Rim Ct, Suite AB, San Diego, CA 92154
Tel: 619-474-5050 *Fax:* 619-474-5454
Web Site: www.avguys.com
Founded: 2000
AV equipment rentals & sales.
Foreign Office(s): SAV Mision de Loreto No 26-B, Zona Rio, 22320 Tijuana, Mexico, Contact: Carlos Portilla *Tel:* (664) 634 21 81 *Fax:* (664) 634 39 71 *E-mail:* sav@solucionesaudiovisuales.com *Web Site:* www.solucionesaudiovisuales.com

AV Metro Inc
5401 Etta Burke Ct, Raleigh, NC 27606
Tel: 919-233-1901 *Fax:* 919-233-1804
E-mail: info@avmetro.com
Web Site: www.avmetro.com
Key Personnel
Pres: Frank Thompson *E-mail:* ft@avmetro.com
Sr Proj Mgr: Jon Singletary *E-mail:* jon@avmetro.com
Proj Mgr: Chris Wallace *E-mail:* chris@avmetro.com
Brochure(s) available
Membership(s): InfoComm International®

A/V Presentations Inc
104 Otis St, Suite 30, Northborough, MA 01532
Tel: 508-393-9767 *Toll Free Tel:* 800-648-7176 *Fax:* 508-393-6698
Web Site: www.avpresentations.com
Key Personnel
Owner: Morris Beverly *E-mail:* morrisb@avpresentations.com; Rod Callahan *E-mail:* rodc@avpresentations.com

AV Toolbox
Division of TV One Multimedia Solutions
2791 Circleport Dr, Erlanger, KY 41018
Tel: 859-282-7303 *Toll Free Tel:* 800-235-3280; 800-721-4044
E-mail: sales@avtoolbox.com
Web Site: www.avtoolbox.com

AV Workshop
500 W 37 St, 3rd fl, New York, NY 10018
Tel: 212-643-0040 *Fax:* 212-564-5277
E-mail: sales@avworkshop.com
Web Site: avworkshop.com
Key Personnel
VP: Jason Lieberman *E-mail:* jlieberman@avworkshop.com

Founded: 1978
Catalog(s) available
Membership(s): InfoComm International®

AVA Electronics Corp
4000 Bridge St, Drexel Hill, PA 19026
Tel: 610-284-2500 *Fax:* 610-259-8379
Key Personnel
Off Mgr: Jen Schiavo

AVA Productions
Subsidiary of Audio-Visual Associates
4760 E 65 St, Indianapolis, IN 46220
Tel: 317-255-6457
E-mail: avaprods@comcast.net
Web Site: www.avavideoproductions.com
Key Personnel
Owner: Bud Osborne
Founded: 1980
Catalog(s) available
Membership(s): AES; PPA

Available Light
Division of JT Services
5251 Dixon Rd, Oceanside, CA 92056-2319
Tel: 760-505-1605; 760-505-1600
E-mail: availablelight@jtservices.com
Web Site: www.jtservices.com
Key Personnel
Owner & Operator: James Teiper
Founded: 1986
Mobile grip & lighting.

Available Light
29-20 37 Ave, Long Island City, NY 11101
Tel: 718-707-9670; 718-707-9671 *Fax:* 718-707-9693
E-mail: info@alny.net
Web Site: www.alny.net

Available Lighting & Motion Picture Services Inc
826 Jefferson Hwy, New Orleans, LA 70120
Tel: 504-831-5214 *Fax:* 504-831-5361
E-mail: avlight@bellsouth.net
Web Site: www.availablelighting.com
Key Personnel
Pres: Billy Bragg
Rental Mgr: Jose Sanchez
Founded: 1984
Lighting, grip, generators for rental.
Catalog(s), available by request

Avalon Acoustics
2800 Wilderness Place, Boulder, CO 80301
Tel: 303-440-0422 *Fax:* 303-440-4396
E-mail: sales@avalonacoustics.com
Web Site: www.avalonacoustics.com

Avast! Recording Co
601 NW 80 St, Seattle, WA 98117
Tel: 206-633-3926 *Fax:* 206-789-7569
E-mail: avast@comcast.net
Web Site: www.avastrecording.com
Key Personnel
Owner: Stuart Hallerman
Staff Engr: Adam Burd
Recording studio.

Avatar Studios
2675 Scott Ave, Suite G, St Louis, MO 63103
Tel: 314-533-2242 *Fax:* 314-533-3349
Web Site: www.avatar-studios.com
Key Personnel
Pres: Bill Faris
VP, Opers: Brad Shelton *E-mail:* bshelton@avatar-studios.com
Dir, Photog: Doug Hastings
Ed: Jack Larson

Founded: 1999
Provides creative & engaging video, audio & interactive communications solutions for clients across all media delivery platforms.

Avaya Inc
211 Mount Airy Rd, Basking Ridge, NJ 07920
Tel: 908-953-6000 *Toll Free Tel:* 866-GO-AVAYA (462-8292 US & CN)
Web Site: www.avaya.com
Key Personnel
CEO & Pres: Kevin Kennedy
CFO & SVP: Dave Vellequette
Chief Admin Offr: Pamela Craven
EVP, Busn Opers: Jim Chirico
SVP, Worldwide Sales: Pierre-Paul Allard
Founded: 2000
Global provider of business collaboration & communications solutions.
Branch Office(s)
4655 Great America Pkwy, Santa Clara, CA 95054-1233
8744 Lucent Blvd, Highlands Ranch, CO 80129
1300 W 120 Ave, Westminster, CO 80234
1000 NW 57 Ct, Suite 500, Miami, FL 33126
1145 Sanctuary Pkwy, Alpharetta, GA 30009
Two Penn Plaza, New York, NY 10121
4001 E Chapel Hill-Nelson Hwy, Research Triangle Park, NC 27709
1111 Freeport Pkwy, Coppell, TX 75019-4451

Avekta Productions Inc
One Rock Place, Yonkers, NY 10705
Tel: 914-378-8000
Web Site: avekta.com
Key Personnel
Pres: Maria Avgerakis *E-mail:* maria@avekta.com
VP & Creative Dir: George Avgerakis
Prodr: Carlyle Gifford; Patricia Pastorelli
Founded: 1976
E-media consultancy producing video, Internet content & print in English & all foreign languages.
Sales Office(s): 147 E 48 St, New York, NY 10017 *Tel:* 212-308-8000 *E-mail:* george@avekta.com
Membership(s): IABC

AVerMedia Technologies Inc
47358 Fremont Blvd, Fremont, CA 94538
Tel: 510-403-0006 (sales) *Fax:* 510-403-0022
E-mail: avtsales.usa@avermedia.com; avt.pmk@avermedia.com
Web Site: www.avermedia-usa.com
Key Personnel
Chmn & CEO: Michael Kuo
Founded: 1990
Scan converters, TV tuners & capture cards.
Catalog(s) available

AVES Audio Visual Systems Inc
PO Box 500, Sugar Land, TX 77487-0500
Tel: 281-295-1300 *Toll Free Tel:* 800-365-AVES (365-2837) *Fax:* 281-295-1310
E-mail: sales@avesav.com
Web Site: www.avesav.com
Key Personnel
Pres: Frank Rabinovitz
VP & Mgr: Sandra Ramos
Founded: 1963
Catalog(s) available
Membership(s): InfoComm International®

AVForSale
1222 Logan Cir, Atlanta, GA 30318
Tel: 404-355-6147 *Toll Free Tel:* 866-634-5296 *Fax:* 404-355-7462
E-mail: customerservice@avforsale.com
Web Site: www.avforsale.com
Key Personnel
Prod Inquiries: Greg Scheuer *Tel:* 404-355-6147 ext 7554

Contact: Bob Buchanan *Tel:* 404-355-6147 ext 7555
Retailer of new & used professional AV equipment.

AVFX Inc
96 Holton St, Boston, MA 02135
Tel: 617-254-0770 *Toll Free Tel:* 888-254-0770
E-mail: info@avfx.com
Web Site: www.avfx.com
Key Personnel
Founder & CEO: Murray Lapides
Pres: Steve Halling
VP, Busn Devt: Cecil Dorman
Gen Mgr: Tom Peckham
Systems Design Mgr: Robert Sicklick
Sr Tech Prodr: Kevin Reilly
Tech Prodr: Rich Keefe; Ken Quigley
Founded: 1984
Membership(s): EDPA; InfoComm International®; MCA-I; MPI; TESA

AVI-SPL
6301 Benjamin Rd, Suite 101, Tampa, FL 33634
Tel: 813-884-7168 *Toll Free Tel:* 866-708-5034; 800-282-6733; 866-925-8298 (cust serv); 866-559-8197 (sales) *Fax:* 813-882-9508
E-mail: questions@avispl.com; sales@avispl.com; customerservice@avispl.com
Web Site: www.avispl.com
Key Personnel
Exec Chmn: Martin Schaffel
VChmn: Chad Gillenwater
CEO: John Zettel
CFO: Raj Dani
Founded: 1979
Full service AV company providing the following services: AV system design/build & installation, product sales, rental & repair, rental & event staging & logistic management.
Online catalog(s), PDF
Branch Office(s)
337 Northlake Blvd, Suite 1004, Altamonte Springs, FL 32701 *Tel:* 407-786-5000 *Toll Free Tel:* 877-550-6205 *Fax:* 407-786-5033
772 S Military Trail, Deerfield Beach, FL 33442 *Tel:* 954-938-9382 *Toll Free Tel:* 888-284-8913 *Fax:* 954-776-4772
9143 Philips Hwy, Suite 350, Jacksonville, FL 32256 *Tel:* 904-281-2714 *Toll Free Tel:* 888-387-9572 *Fax:* 904-281-2716
Bradfordville Ctr, 6753 Thomasville Rd, Tallahassee, FL 32312 *Tel:* 850-894-3030 *Toll Free Tel:* 877-325-7331 *Toll Free Fax:* 800-244-8630
4705 Alton Ct, Irondale, AL 35210 *Tel:* 205-951-1951 *Toll Free Tel:* 866-847-5188 *Fax:* 205-951-1341
11095 Knott Ave, Suite E, Cypress, CA 90630 *Tel:* 714-799-7166 *Toll Free Tel:* 866-772-3153 *Fax:* 714-799-7616
5880 W Las Positas Blvd, Suite 39, Pleasanton, CA 94588 *Tel:* 925-404-0440 *Fax:* 925-551-7630
15700 Parkerhouse Rd, Suite 200, Parker, CO 80134 *Tel:* 303-792-3090 *Toll Free Tel:* 866-279-2584 *Fax:* 303-792-3094
3079 Premier Pkwy, Suite 170, Duluth, GA 30096 *Tel:* 678-542-2201 *Toll Free Tel:* 800-501-0366 *Fax:* 678-542-2206
2266 Palmer Dr, Schaumburg, IL 60173 *Tel:* 847-437-7712 *Fax:* 847-437-0271
9160 Rumsey Rd, Suite B-12, Columbia, MD 21045 *Tel:* 410-964-8100 *Fax:* 410-964-8920
9701 Philadelphia Ct, Suite J, Lanham, MD 20706 *Tel:* 301-306-0120 *Toll Free Tel:* 877-373-6848 *Fax:* 301-306-7540
45 South St, Suite F, Hopkinton, MA 01748 *Toll Free Tel:* 866-296-0418 *Toll Free Fax:* 866-296-0419
28900 Beck Rd, Wixom, MI 48393 *Tel:* 248-669-4286 *Toll Free Tel:* 866-843-0536 *Fax:* 248-669-4541

2730 Arthur St, Roseville, MN 55113 *Tel:* 651-287-7000 *Toll Free Tel:* 800-292-4125 *Fax:* 651-287-7001
4065 W Mesa Vista Ave, Suite A, Las Vegas, NV 89118 *Tel:* 702-597-2323 *Toll Free Tel:* 866-634-7210 *Fax:* 702-739-6052
10-40 45 Ave, Long Island City, NY 11101 *Tel:* 718-806-4040 *Fax:* 718-806-4041
8301 Arrowridge Blvd, Suite B, Charlotte, NC 28273 *Tel:* 704-523-5886 *Toll Free Tel:* 800-501-0366 *Fax:* 704-523-5389
4524 Green Point Dr, Suite 104, Greensboro, NC 27410 *Tel:* 336-605-4760 *Fax:* 336-605-4798
335 Ken-Mar Industrial Pkwy, Broadview Heights, OH 44147 *Tel:* 440-740-0630 *Toll Free Tel:* 800-569-5269 *Fax:* 440-740-0891
35 Rockridge Rd, Suite B, Englewood, OH 45322 *Tel:* 937-832-6900 (video network opers ctr)
761 Crossroads Ct, Vandalia, OH 45377 *Tel:* 937-847-5558 *Fax:* 937-847-7481
207 Commerce Park Dr, Cranberry Township, PA 16066 *Tel:* 724-776-3877 *Toll Free Tel:* 866-847-5186 *Fax:* 724-776-3890
780 Fifth Ave, Suite 175, King of Prussia, PA 19406 *Tel:* 610-270-1545 *Fax:* 484-688-0249
13859 Diplomat Dr, Suite 180, Dallas, TX 75234 *Tel:* 972-243-4422 *Toll Free Tel:* 800-630-4022 *Fax:* 972-243-5450
11275 W Sam Houston Pkwy S, Suite 300, Houston, TX 77031 *Tel:* 281-902-3933 *Fax:* 281-902-3937
100 Carpenter Dr, Suite 204, Sterling, VA 20164 *Tel:* 703-796-9011 *Fax:* 703-796-9047
21312 30 Dr SE, Suite 102, Bothell, WA 98021 *Tel:* 425-861-5564 *Fax:* 425-861-5784
2923 Fifth Ave NE, Calgary, AB T2A 6T8, Canada *Tel:* 403-457-1994
355 Burrard St, Suite 1000, Vancouver, BC V6C 2G8, Canada *Tel:* 604-638-4961 *Fax:* 604-608-6163
30 Duke St W, Kitchener, ON N2H 3W5, Canada *Tel:* 226-339-0828 *Fax:* 905-731-7135
505 Industrial Ave, Unit 6, Ottawa, ON K1G 0Z1, Canada *Tel:* 613-288-5839 *Fax:* 613-247-7045
35 E Beaver Creek Rd, Unit 1, Richmond Hill, ON L4B 1B3, Canada *Tel:* 905-695-2202 *Fax:* 905-731-7135
3500 Rue Ashby, Ville-Sainte-Laurent, QC H4R 2C1, Canada *Tel:* 514-228-1350
Foreign Office(s): Dubai Investments Park Phase 2, Plot 597-4858, Bldg 8, Unit 10, PO Box 502508, Dubai, United Arab Emirates *Tel:* (04) 448 9202 *Fax:* (04) 448 9203
Armstrong Mall, Unit 12, Farnborough, Hants GU14 0NR, United Kingdom *Tel:* 0800 181 4425 (European headquarters)
Membership(s): ABC; AES; AFCEA; American Institute of Architects; ASA; Buy-Out Music Association; Illuminating Engineering Society; InfoComm International®; International Facilities Management Association; NSCA

AVI Systems
9675 W 76 St, Suite 200, Eden Prairie, MN 55344
Tel: 952-949-3700 *Toll Free Tel:* 800-488-4954 *Fax:* 952-949-6000
E-mail: info@avisystems.com
Web Site: www.avisystems.com
Key Personnel
Chmn: Joe Stoebner
CEO & Pres: Jeff Stoebner
CFO: Randi Borth
Catalog(s) available
Branch Office(s)
7270 Trade St, Suite 102, San Diego, CA 92121 *Tel:* 858-653-4300 *Fax:* 858-695-7844
355 Inverness Dr S, Unit 355-A, Englewood, CO 80112 *Tel:* 303-704-6911
621 Busse Rd, Suite 101, Bensenville, IL 60106 *Tel:* 630-477-2300 *Fax:* 630-477-2301
3131 W 76 St, Suite 5, Davenport, IA 52806 *Tel:* 563-333-3000 *Fax:* 515-254-9981
3001 104 St, Urbandale, IA 50322-3830 *Tel:* 515-254-9850 *Fax:* 215-254-9981
8052 Flint St, Lenexa, KS 66214-1486 *Tel:* 913-495-9494 *Fax:* 913-495-9479
1000 100 St SW, Suite D, Byron Center, MI 49315 *Tel:* 616-631-4500 *Fax:* 616-631-4501
27280 Haggerty Rd, Suite C2, Farmington Hills, MI 48331 *Tel:* 248-957-6150 *Fax:* 248-957-6151
5055 S 111 St, Omaha, NE 68137-2232 *Tel:* 402-593-6500 *Fax:* 402-593-8500
1930 E Century Ave, Bismarck, ND 58503 *Tel:* 701-258-6360 *Fax:* 701-258-2015
4575 23 Ave S, Fargo, ND 58104 *Tel:* 701-237-4427 *Fax:* 701-237-0166
2868 E Kemper Rd, Cincinnati, OH 45241 *Tel:* 513-578-6550 *Fax:* 513-578-6551
2300 E 54 St N, Suite 2, Sioux Falls, SD 57104 *Tel:* 605-782-4141
3275 Intertech Dr, Suite 500, Brookfield, WI 53045 *Tel:* 262-207-1300 *Toll Free Tel:* 800-800-7086 (serv) *Fax:* 262-207-1301 *E-mail:* wiservice@avisystems.com
5201 Femrite Dr, Madison, WI 53718 *Tel:* 608-221-8888 *Toll Free Tel:* 800-800-7086 (serv) *Fax:* 608-221-9252 *E-mail:* wiservice@avisystems.com
Membership(s): InfoComm International®

Avid Technology Inc
65-75 Network Dr, Burlington, MA 01830
Tel: 978-640-6789 *Fax:* 978-640-3366
Web Site: www.avid.com
Key Personnel
CEO & Pres: Louis Hernandez, Jr
CFO, EVP & Chief Admin Offr: John Frederick
SVP & Chief Mktg Offr: Jennifer Smith
SVP, Cust Success & Prof Servs: Rick Lowenstein
SVP, HR: Jay Blackington
SVP, Prods & Technol: Chris Gahagan
SVP, Worldwide Field Opers: Jeff Rosica
VP, Gen Coun & Corp Secy: Jason Duva
VP, Supply & Hardware Technol: Bruce Yaung
Founded: 1987
Audio & video technology for media organizations & independent professionals.
Branch Office(s)
2600 Tenth St, Suite 200, Berkeley, CA 94710 *Tel:* 510-229-1000 *Fax:* 510-229-1010
101 S First St, Suite 200, Burbank, CA 91502 *Tel:* 818-557-2520 *Fax:* 818-557-2558
280 Bernardo Ave, Suites A & B, Mountain View, CA 94043, VP, Audio Strategy: Martin Kloiber *Tel:* 650-526-1600 *Fax:* 650-526-1601
1101 Pennsylvania Ave NW, Suite 600, Washington DC, DC 20004 *Tel:* 202-756-7724 *Toll Free Tel:* 800-497-AVID (497-2843) *Fax:* 202-318-4593
90 Park Ave, 17th fl, New York, NY 10016 *Tel:* 212-983-2424 *Fax:* 212-430-0378
3510 St Laurent Blvd, Suite 300, Montreal, QC H2X 2V2, Canada *Tel:* 514-845-1636 *Fax:* 514-845-5676
Foreign Office(s): Northpoint Tower, 100 Miller St, North Sydney 2060, Australia *Tel:* (02) 9931 6841; (02) 9420 3066 (support)
Regus Brussels Airport, Pegasuslaan 5, 1831 Diegem, Belgium *Tel:* (02) 709 20 28 *Fax:* (02) 709 22 22
Parkview Green, 9 Dongdaqiao Rd, Off Bldg A, Beijing 100020, China *Tel:* (010) 67096116 *Fax:* (010) 67096113
Televisiokatu 3, 00100 Helsinki, Finland *Tel:* (040) 511 9477
Immeuble Place de Seine, 157 rue Anatole France, 8ieme etage, 92300 Levallois-Perret, France *Tel:* 01 41 49 40 00 *Fax:* 01 47 57 15 27
Europallee 10, 67657 Kaiserslautern, Germany *Tel:* (0631) 303 5200 *Fax:* (0631) 303 5209
Paul-Heyse Str 29, 2nd fl, 80336 Munich, Germany *Tel:* (089) 50 20 60 *Fax:* (089) 50 20 6140
88 Gloucester Rd, Unit 801, Wan Chai, Hong Kong *Tel:* 3973 8503 *Fax:* 3973 8589
311/326, Regus, Level 3, Neo Vikram New Link Rd, Andheri West, Mumbai 400 053, India *Tel:* (022) 6198 4549
Carman Hall Rd, Unit 38, Sandyford Industrial Estate, Dublin 18, Ireland *Tel:* (01) 207 8200 *Fax:* (01) 295 0079
ATT Bldg 4F, 2-11-7 Akasaka, Minato-Ku, Tokyo 107-0052, Japan *Tel:* (03) 3505 7937 *Fax:* (03) 3505 7938
Vreelandseweg 42A, 1216 CH Hilversum, Netherlands *Tel:* (035) 772 35 61 *Fax:* (035) 625 00 90
Northern Tower, Testovskaya ul 10, 123317 Moscow, Russia *Tel:* (495) 662 6390
Sime Darby Business Ctr, 315 Alexandra Rd, Suite 03-01, Singapore 159944, Singapore *Tel:* 6476 7666 *Fax:* 6475 7666
3F, DongSung Bldg, 17-8 Youido-dong, Youngdeugpo-gu, Seoul 150-874, South Korea *Tel:* (02) 782 4210 *Fax:* (02) 782 4214
Centro Empresarial VK, Locales A & B, Camino de la Zarzuela 21, 3a Plata, 28023 Madrid, Spain *Tel:* 91 762 86 00 *Fax:* 91 183 66 50
Hus E, Plan 3, Linnegatan 87B, 11523 Stockholm, Sweden *Tel:* (08) 442 55 70 *Fax:* (08) 442 55 87
36/F CRC Tower, All Seasons Place, Office 46, 87/2 Wireless Rd, Phathumwan, Bangkok 10330, Thailand *Tel:* (02) 625 3119
Al Thuraya Tower 2, 19th fl, 1903, PO Box 500646, Dubai Media City, United Arab Emirates *Tel:* (04) 361 6260 *Fax:* (04) 366 1055
Pinewood Studios, West Side Complex, Pinewood Rd, Iver Heath, Bucks SL0 0NH, United Kingdom *Tel:* (01753) 655 999 *Fax:* (01753) 654 999
Membership(s): NAB

Avidex Inc
Subsidiary of ITOCHU International Inc
13555 Bel-Red Rd, Suite 226, Bellevue, MA 98005
Tel: 425-643-0330 *Fax:* 425-274-7091
E-mail: info@avidexav.com
Web Site: www.avidexav.com
Key Personnel
CEO: Joel Harris
Provides project management, equipment procurement, programming, installation, rental & staging services.
Branch Office(s)
6100 Stewart Ave, Fremont, CA 94538 *Tel:* 510-279-7100 *Toll Free Tel:* 800-999-8590 *Fax:* 510-279-7101
2009 S 4130 W, Suite D, Salt Lake City, UT 84104 *Tel:* 801-973-6483 *Fax:* 801-908-5674

Aviom Inc
1157 Phoenixville Pike, Suite 201, West Chester, PA 19380-4254
Tel: 610-738-9005 *Fax:* 610-738-9950
E-mail: info@aviom.com
Web Site: www.aviom.com
Key Personnel
Founder & CEO: Carl Bader
VP, Sales & Mktg: Chandler Collison
Dir, Sales US & CN: Mark Meding
Devt Mgr & Prod Res: Ray Legnini
Founded: 2002
Manufacturer of distributed audio network products.

Avitecture Inc
One Export Dr, Sterling, VA 20164-4421
Tel: 703-404-8900 *Fax:* 703-404-8940
E-mail: info@avitecture.com
Web Site: www.avitecture.com

Key Personnel
Chmn: Sidney L Lissner *E-mail:* sidney.lissner@avitecture.com
CTO & VP: Jason Nichols *E-mail:* jason.nichols@avitecture.com
Pres: Greg Boyd *E-mail:* greg.boyd@avitecture.com
VP, Sales & Mktg: Bruce Pittman *E-mail:* bruce.pittman@avitecture.com
Founded: 1979 (as AVWashington)
Design, build, install & support integrated AV-IT systems.
Membership(s): American Alliance of Museums; American Institute of Architects; BICSI; InfoComm International®; International Facilities Management Association; Mid-Atlantic Association of Museums; Northern Virginia Technology Council (NVTC); NSCA; SEMC; US Green Building Council; VAM

AVL Systems Design LLC
14901 Bristol Park Blvd, Edmond, OK 73013
Tel: 405-749-1866 *Fax:* 405-749-1851
E-mail: dnix@avl1.com
Web Site: www.avl1.com
Key Personnel
Pres: Marc Pierce
CFO: Stacy Pierce
VP, Accts: Kenny Kendrick
Dir, Engg: Ryan Zemke
Cust Rel & Mktg Mgr: Danny Nix
Founded: 2000
Provides quality designs for audio, acoustics, video projection, production video, intercom systems & lighting systems.
Membership(s): AES; American Institute of Architects; BICSI; HAA; IEEE; Imaging Science Foundation; InfoComm International®; LDI; NAB; NFPA; NSCA; Synergetic Audio Concepts

AVP Mfg & Supply Inc
2288-B7 Dumfries Rd RR2, Cambridge, ON N1R 5S3, Canada
Tel: 519-740-7966 *Toll Free Tel:* 800-481-2493 *Fax:* 519-740-0131
E-mail: sales@jackfields.com
Web Site: www.jackfields.com
Key Personnel
Dir, Admin: Gord Heidman
Dir, Sales: Brian Ferri *Tel:* 416-529-3623 (cell) *E-mail:* brian.ferri@jackfields.com
Founded: 1985
Manufacturer of commercial broadcast, telecom & satellite equipment.
Catalog(s), free, PDF download

AVS Group
3120 South Ave, La Crosse, WI 54601
Tel: 608-787-1010 *Fax:* 608-787-0012
E-mail: info@avsgroup.com
Web Site: www.avsgroup.com
Key Personnel
Owner & Gen Mgr: Ed Wais
Founded: 1988
Full service video production, from pre-planning & script writing to filming, editing & duplication.
Membership(s): MCA-I

AVS Media Group
11193 Old Hwy 31, Suite 1, Spanish Fort, AL 36527
Tel: 251-621-1200
E-mail: info@avsmediagroup.com
Web Site: www.avsmediagroup.com
Key Personnel
Pres: Steve King *E-mail:* steve@avsmediagroup.com
Video production & post-production.

AVS Technologies Inc
Division of Synnex Canada Ltd
2100 Place Transcanadienne, Dorval, QC H4R 2B7, Canada
Tel: 514-683-1771
Founded: 1979
Catalog(s) available

Avtech Systems Inc
7-01 Bellair Ave, Fairlawn, NJ 07410
Tel: 201-833-8777 *Fax:* 201-833-4995
E-mail: sales@avtechsystems.com
Web Site: www.avtechsystems.com
Key Personnel
Pres: Fred M Samuel *E-mail:* fred@avtechsystems.com
Founded: 1978
Catalog(s) available

AVW-TELAV Audio Visual Solutions, a Freeman Company
2056 32 Ave, Montreal, QC H8T 3H7, Canada
Tel: 514-631-1821 *Toll Free Tel:* 800-868-6886
Web Site: freemanav-ca.com
Key Personnel
Gen Mgr, Montreal & Regl Dir, Eastern Reg: Bernard Carignan *E-mail:* bernard.carignan@freemanco.com
Dir, Sales: Danielle Piche *E-mail:* danielle.piche@freemanco.com
Founded: 1959
Offers a full range of AV & presentation technology services in over 30 cities throughout North America.
Catalog(s) available
Branch Office(s)
2025 Rue Lavoisier, Suite 100, Quebec, QC G1N 4L6, Canada, Gen Mgr: Mr Jean Fortin *Tel:* 418-687-9055 *E-mail:* jean.fortin@freemanco.com
105 Falcon St, Banff, AB T1L 1J2, Canada, Tech Servs Mgr: Matt Luttrell *Tel:* 403-760-4440 *E-mail:* matt.luttrell@freemanco.com
2931 Fifth Ave NE, Calgary, AB T2A 6T8, Canada, Gen Mgr: Nozer Bhathena *Tel:* 403-235-1563 *E-mail:* nozer.bhathena@freemanco.com
12868 184 St NW, Edmonton, AB T5V 1T4, Canada, Gen Mgr: Lori Arndt *Tel:* 780-454-8840 *E-mail:* lori.arndt@freemanco.com
395 W Eighth Ave, Vancouver, BC V5Y 1N7, Canada, Gen Mgr: Michael Dosch *Tel:* 604-255-1151 *E-mail:* mike.dosch@freemanco.com
26 Bunting St, Winnipeg, MB R2X 2P6, Canada *Tel:* 204-775-6198
125 Whiting Rd, Unit 2G, Fredericton, NB E3B 5Y5, Canada, Admin Asst: Kim Morgan *Tel:* 506-459-1117 *E-mail:* kim.morgan@freemanco.com
100 Ilsley Ave, Unit K, Dartmouth, NS B3B 1L3, Canada, Gen Mgr: Angie Ambrose *Tel:* 902-468-4485 *E-mail:* angie.ambrose@freemanco.com
1110 Dearness Dr, Unit 13, London, ON N6E 1N9, Canada, Br Mgr: Dan McGrath *Tel:* 519-668-7745 *E-mail:* dan.mcgrath@freemanco.com
2365 Matheson Blvd E, Mississauga, ON L4W 5B3, Canada, Gen Mgr: Dianne King *Tel:* 905-366-9200 *E-mail:* dianne.king@freemanco.com
3020 Hawthorne Rd, No 300A-300, Ottawa, ON K1G 3J6, Canada, Gen Mgr: Kevin Wolfe *Tel:* 613-526-3121 *E-mail:* kevin.wolfe@freemanco.com
901 E South St, Anaheim, CA 82805 *Tel:* 714-254-3400
2616 Commerce Park Dr, Suite 600, Orlando, FL 32819 *Tel:* 407-816-1005
841 Joseph E Lowery Blvd NW, Atlanta, GA 30318 *Tel:* 404-253-6400
9260 W 55 St, McCook, IL 60525 *Tel:* 708-255-7100
3325 Sunset Rd, Suite A, Las Vegas, NV 89118 *Tel:* 702-263-1484
4801 Freidrich Lane, Bldg 1, Suite 100, Austin, TX 78744 *Tel:* 512-827-3200
4545 W Davis St, Dallas, TX 75211 *Tel:* 214-623-1300
1001 Avenida de las Americas, Houston, TX 77010 *Tel:* 713-853-8180
Membership(s): Global Presence Alliance; InfoComm International®

Award Productions
164 Great Rd, Acton, MA 01720
Tel: 978-667-3335
E-mail: web@awardproductions.com
Web Site: www.awardproductions.com
Key Personnel
Founder & Dir, Prodn: Al Ward
Dir, Creative Devt: Darren Garnick
VP, Prodn: Peter Koziell
Prodr: Ursula Kane
HD video & TV production.

Norman N Axelrod Associates
445 E 86 St, New York, NY 10028
Tel: 212-741-6302
E-mail: naxelrod@axelrodassociates.com
Web Site: www.axelrodassociates.com
Key Personnel
VP, Display Systems: V A Grant
Engg Mgr: Dr Norman N Axelrod
Mgr, Software Devt: C Chang
Provides simple, effective solutions to complex problems involving imaging, optics processing & system integration. Computer automated & manual systems. Turn-key systems, consulting & development.

Axis Films
3138 Cumberland Rd, Berkley, MI 48072
Tel: 248-722-1734
Web Site: www.axisfilms.tv
Key Personnel
Owner: Steve Oatley
Founded: 1991
Film & video production.

Axxis Inc
845 S Ninth St, Louisville, KY 40203
Tel: 502-568-6030 *Fax:* 502-568-6204
E-mail: info@axxisinc.com
Web Site: www.axxisinc.com
Key Personnel
VP, Opers: Erik Knappenberger *E-mail:* eknappenberger@axxisinc.com
VP, Prodn: Stewart Davis *E-mail:* sdavis@axxisinc.com
Dir, Prodn Servs: Chuck Rogers *E-mail:* crogers@axxisinc.com
Prodn Coord: Jamie Belicove *E-mail:* jbelicove@axxisinc.com; Barbara Hayes *E-mail:* bhayes@axxisinc.com
Full service production company.
Membership(s): InfoComm International®; MCA-I; NSCA

Aydin Displays Inc
Subsidiary of Video Display Corp
One Riga Lane, Birdsboro, PA 19508
Tel: 610-404-7400; 610-404-5353 (sales) *Toll Free Tel:* 866-367-2934 *Fax:* 610-404-8190
E-mail: sales1@aydindisplays.com; orders@aydindisplays.com
Web Site: www.aydindisplays.com
Key Personnel
Pres: Arthur V Mengel
Mgr, Mktg & Communs: Dan Spollen
Founded: 1967
Catalog(s) available

Cliff Ayers Enterprises
Subsidiary of The Entertainer Network
American Big Band Hall of Fame, 608 SW 75 Terr, North Lauderdale, FL 33068

Tel: 615-361-7902 *Fax:* 615-336-2480
E-mail: info@entertainernet.net
Web Site: www.entertainernet.net
Key Personnel
Pres: Cliff Ayers
Founded: 1953
Consists of Emerald Records Music City Entertainer News - Music Town Distributors. "Record Row Review" TV show (10 years); Cliff Ayers Productions. Member of the American Big Band Hall of Fame.
Branch Office(s)
608 SW 75 Terr, North Lauderdale, FL 33068

Aylmer Press
PO Box 2302, Madison, WI 53701-2302
Tel: 608-441-5277 *Fax:* 608-251-0890
Web Site: www.signit2.com
Key Personnel
Pres: Steve Kokette *E-mail:* steve@signit2.com
Founded: 1992
Produces videos & DVDs to teach kids sign language.
Catalog(s) available

AZ Spectrum
53-53 62 St, Maspeth, NY 11378
Tel: 718-779-1892 *Fax:* 718-779-1892
E-mail: az@az-spectrum.com; azspectrum@aol.com
Web Site: www.az-spectrum.com
Founded: 1994
Accessories for professional motion picture cameras as well as electronics repair services.

Aztec Video Productions
2967 Montana Ave, Cincinnati, OH 45211
Tel: 513-481-5004
E-mail: aztec@fuse.net
Web Site: www.aztecvideo.com
Key Personnel
Owner: Van Cottengim
Founded: 1980
Manufacturing & reproducing magnetic & optical media.
Catalog(s) available
Branch Office(s)
9435 Waterstone Blvd, Suite 140, Cincinnati, OH 45249 *Tel:* 513-489-5554

Aztech Productions LLC
400 Bethlehem Pike, Erdenheim, PA 19038
Tel: 215-836-5490 *Fax:* 215-836-0577
Web Site: aztechproductions.com
Key Personnel
Owner & CEO: Linda Mattice *E-mail:* lmattice@aztechproductions.com
Owner: Kevin Mattice
Film & video production, multimedia design & post-production studio.

Aztek Inc
13765-F Alton Pkwy, Irvine, CA 92618
Tel: 949-770-8787 *Toll Free Tel:* 800-GRAPH-55 (472-7455) *Fax:* 949-770-4986
E-mail: mail@aztek.com
Web Site: www.aztek.com
Key Personnel
Founder & Pres: Phil Lippincott
VP & VP, Engg: Evan Lippincott
Founded: 1980
Provide professional, quality integrated turnkey image production systems & software.
Catalog(s) available
Membership(s): ACM/SIGGRAPH; DIMA; InfoComm International®; Photo Marketing Association

B & B Video Productions Inc
233 N Main St, West Point, NE 68788
Mailing Address: PO Box 33, West Point, NE 68788
Tel: 402-372-2628
E-mail: info@bandbvideo.com
Web Site: www.bandbvideo.com
Key Personnel
Pres: Brian Kreikemeier *E-mail:* brian@bandbvideo.com
Founded: 1987
Documentary style productions for businesses & organizations.

B-K Lighting
40429 Brickyard Dr, Madera, CA 93636
Tel: 559-438-5800 *Fax:* 559-438-5900
E-mail: info@bklighting.com
Web Site: www.bklighting.com
Key Personnel
Founder & CEO: Doug Hagen
Founded: 1984
Catalog(s) available

The Baby School, see So Smart Productions

Back to the Bible
6400 Cornhusker Hwy, Lincoln, NE 68507
Mailing Address: PO Box 82808, Lincoln, NE 68501-2808
Tel: 402-464-7200 *Toll Free Tel:* 800-759-6655 (inquires); 800-759-2425 (orders) *Fax:* 402-464-7474
E-mail: info@backtothebible.org
Web Site: www.backtothebible.org
Key Personnel
CEO: Dr Arnie Cole
Founded: 1939
Worldwide Christian ministry bringing people together through media & technology.

Backdrop Outlet
3540 Seagate Way, Oceanside, CA 92056
Tel: 760-547-2900 *Toll Free Tel:* 800-466-1755 *Fax:* 760-547-2899
E-mail: cs@backdropoutlet.com
Web Site: www.backdropoutlet.com
Key Personnel
Owner: Jay Gupta
Founded: 1991
Backgrounds, props, lighting & studio accessories for photography & video.

Backstage Equipment Inc
8052 Lankershim Blvd, North Hollywood, CA 91605
Tel: 818-504-6026 *Toll Free Tel:* 800-692-2787 *Fax:* 818-504-6180
E-mail: info@backstageweb.com
Web Site: www.backstageweb.com
Key Personnel
Pres & Chief Designer: Cary Griffith
Opers Mgr: Sig Guzman
Founded: 1979
Manufacture specialized carts to transport motion picture equipment.
Catalog(s), free

Backstage Pass Entertainment Inc
Unit of Hailing Frequency Productions Inc
7438 Shoshone Ave, Lake Balboa, CA 91406-2340
Tel: 818-881-9888 *Toll Free Tel:* 800-664-6555 *Fax:* 818-881-0555
E-mail: blowinsmokeband@ktb.net
Key Personnel
Owner & Pres: Larry Weisberg
Catalog(s) available

Backstar Creative Media Inc
676 N La Salle Dr, Suite 424, Chicago, IL 60654
Tel: 312-467-0425 *Toll Free Tel:* 800-955-8900
E-mail: solutions@backstar.com
Web Site: www.backstar.com
Key Personnel
Pres: Mitch Norinsky
Founded: 2002

Badiyan Inc
720 W 94 St, Bloomington, MN 55420
Tel: 952-888-5507 *Fax:* 952-888-0360
E-mail: info@badiyan.com
Web Site: www.badiyan.com
Key Personnel
Owner & Pres: Fred Badiyan
VP, Sales & Mktg: Janiece Haglund
Founded: 1974

Bag End Loudspeakers
1201 Armstrong St, Algonquin, IL 60102
Tel: 847-658-8888 *Fax:* 847-658-5008
E-mail: info@bagend.com; usedcars@bagend.com (sales)
Web Site: www.bagend.com
Key Personnel
Pres: Jim Wischmeyer
Founded: 1976
Online catalog(s) available

Baha'i Distribution Service (BDS)
Subsidiary of Baha'i Publishing Trust of India
401 Greenleaf Ave, Wilmette, IL 60091
Tel: 847-425-7950 *Toll Free Tel:* 800-999-9019 *Fax:* 847-425-7951
E-mail: bds@usbnc.org
Web Site: www.bahaibookstore.com
Key Personnel
Gen Mgr: Tim Moore
Founded: 1902

BAI Distributors Inc
2312 NE 29 Ave, Ocala, FL 34470-3999
Tel: 352-732-7009 *Toll Free Tel:* 888-224-3446 *Fax:* 352-732-1616
E-mail: sales@baionline.com
Web Site: www.baionline.com
Key Personnel
Gen Mgr: Jim Ritchhart
Founded: 1983
Wholesale distribution of electronic systems equipment including sound, AV & CCTV products.
Catalog(s), annual, free
Membership(s): BICSI; Custom Electronic Design & Installation Association; InfoComm International®; NAMM, the National Association of Music Merchants; NSCA; SIA

Baker & Taylor Inc
Division of Castle Harlan Partners IV LP
2550 W Tyvola Rd, Suite 300, Charlotte, NC 28217
Tel: 704-998-3100 *Toll Free Tel:* 800-775-1800
E-mail: btinfo@baker-taylor.com
Web Site: www.btol.com
Key Personnel
CEO & Pres: George F Coe
CFO: Jeff Leonard
CIO & EVP: Matt Carroll
EVP, Merchandising/Digital Media Servs: David Cully
SVP, Opers: Gary Dayton
Founded: 1828
Distribution of books, videos & music products to libraries, institutions & retailers.
Catalog(s) available
Membership(s): Entertainment Merchants Association; Music Business Association; National Association of Video Distributors

Baker Audio Inc
2195 N Norcross Tucker Rd, Norcross, GA 30071
Tel: 770-441-2000 *Toll Free Tel:* 800-847-3523 *Fax:* 770-449-7719

E-mail: sales@bakeraudiovisual.com
Web Site: www.bakeraudiovisual.com
Key Personnel
Owner & VP: Joe Schuch
Dir, Sales & Proj Devt: B Dave Davis
Proj Mgr: Moses Kohn
Mktg & Admin Coord: Kasie Barnett
Busn Devt: Jacob Dylan
Founded: 1953
Provide innovative sight & sound communication solutions.

Balboa Capital Corp
2010 Main St, Suite 1100, Irvine, CA 92614
Tel: 949-756-0800 *Toll Free Tel:* 888-BALBOA1 (225-2621) *Fax:* 949-756-2565
E-mail: customerservice@balboacapital.com
Web Site: www.balboacapital.com
Key Personnel
CEO: Patrick Byrne
COO: Robert Rasmussen
CFO: David Chiurazzi
Pres: Phil Silva
Founded: 1988
Provide equipment leasing & working capital loans.
Branch Office(s)
2410 Camino Ramon, Suite 275, San Ramon, CA 94583 *Toll Free Tel:* 800-950-7650
15279 N Scottsdale Rd, Suite B 245, Scottsdale, AZ 85254 *Toll Free Tel:* 800-280-5624
8833 Perimeter Park Blvd, Suite 902, Jacksonville, FL 32216

Baldwin Productions
160 Tioga Lane, Greenbrae, CA 94904
Tel: 415-925-9262 *Fax:* 415-925-1040
Web Site: www.baldwinproductions.com
Key Personnel
Owner: Jim Baldwin *E-mail:* jim@baldwinproductions.com
Location services, post-production, film & still photography.

Ballantyne Strong Inc
13710 FNB Pkwy, Suite 400, Omaha, NE 68154
Tel: 402-453-4444 *Toll Free Tel:* 800-424-1215 *Fax:* 402-453-7238
E-mail: info@btn-inc.com
Web Site: ballantynestrong.com
Key Personnel
CEO & Pres: Gary L Cavey
COO & SVP: Chris D Stark
Founded: 1932
Brochure(s), free, PDF download
Shipping Address: 975 Old Norcross Rd, Suite D, Lawrenceville, GA 30045 *Tel:* 770-369-9333
Membership(s): ICTA; Theatre Equipment Association

Band Pro Film & Digital Inc
3403 W Pacific Ave, Burbank, CA 91505
Tel: 818-841-9655 *Toll Free Tel:* 888-BANDPRO (226-3776) *Fax:* 818-841-7649
Web Site: www.bandpro.com
Key Personnel
CEO & Pres: Amnon H Band *E-mail:* amnon.band@bandpro.com
COO & EVP: Renee Contreras *E-mail:* rene.contreras@bandpro.com
Cont: Sandra Graves *E-mail:* sandra.graves@bandpro.com
Sales Mgr: Nir Reches *E-mail:* nir.reches@bandpro.com
Mktg Mgr: Brett Gillespie *E-mail:* brett.gillespie@bandpro.com
Founded: 1984
Digital cinematography, broadcast & ENG equipment.
Branch Office(s)
100 Hartsfield Center Pkwy, Suite 508, Atlanta, GA 30354, Sales Mgr: Nir Reches *Tel:* 818-841-9655 *E-mail:* nir.reches@bandpro.com
1115 Broadway, 11th fl, Suite 1136, New York, NY 10010, Sales Mgr: John Fishburn *Tel:* 212-227-8577 *Fax:* 212-564-5540 *E-mail:* john.fishburn@bandpro.com
Foreign Office(s): Wrangelstr 4, 10997 Berlin, Germany, Tech Sales Mgr: Vojtech Pokorny *Tel:* (0170) 3174794 *E-mail:* vojtech@bandpro.de *Web Site:* www.bandpro.de
Max-Planck-Str 6, 85609 Dornach, Munich, Germany, Mng Dir: Christopher Hantel *Tel:* (089) 94548490 *Fax:* (089) 94548499 *E-mail:* christopher@bandpro.de *Web Site:* www.bandpro.de
3 Hasolelim St, 67897 Tel Aviv, Israel, Sales Mgr: Arnon Shemer *Tel:* (03) 5621631 *Fax:* (03) 5621632 *E-mail:* arnon@bandpro.co.il *Web Site:* www.bandpro.co.il

B&B Electronics Manufacturing Co
707 Dayton Rd, Ottawa, IL 61350
Mailing Address: PO Box 1040, Ottawa, IL 61350-6040
Tel: 815-433-5100 *Toll Free Tel:* 800-346-3119 *Fax:* 815-433-5109
E-mail: info@bb-elec.com; orders@bb-elec.com
Web Site: www.bb-elec.com
Key Personnel
CEO & Pres: Jerry O'Gorman
Founded: 1981
Manufacturer of rugged, reliable, wired & wireless connectivity & communications solutions.
Catalog(s), semiannual, free
Online catalog(s) available
Foreign Office(s): Westlink Commercial Park, Oranmore, Co Galway, Ireland, Contact: Jerry O'Gorman *Tel:* (091) 792444 *Fax:* (091) 792445

B&H Photo & Video Pro Audio
420 Ninth Ave, New York, NY 10001
Tel: 212-444-5000; 212-444-6615 *Toll Free Tel:* 800-606-6969 *Fax:* 212-239-7770 *Toll Free Fax:* 800-947-7008
Web Site: www.bhphotovideo.com
Key Personnel
Pres: Samuel Goldstein
Founded: 1973
Catalog(s) available

B&H Publishing Group
Division of LifeWay Christian Resources
One Lifeway Plaza, Nashville, TN 37234
Toll Free Tel: 800-251-3225 (retailers); 800-448-8032 (consumers); 800-458-2772 (churches) *Fax:* 615-251-3914 (consumers); 615-251-5933 (churches) *Toll Free Fax:* 800-296-4036 (retailers)
Web Site: www.bhpublishinggroup.com
Key Personnel
SVP, Mktg: Amanda Sloan
Publisher of Bible-centered content, including religious & children's programming on DVD.
Catalog(s) available
Online catalog(s) available

B&K Components Ltd
Division of Amplifier Technologies Inc
1749 Chapin Rd, Montebello, CA 90640
Tel: 323-278-0001 *Fax:* 323-278-0083
Web Site: www.bkcomp.com
Key Personnel
SVP: Jeff Hipps *E-mail:* jeff@ati-amp.com
Founded: 1981
Manufacturer of high end audio & home theater components.

Bang Pictures
78 Graterford Rd, Schwenksville, PA 19473
Tel: 610-357-1015
Web Site: www.bangpictures.com
Key Personnel
Exec Prodr & Dir: Mark Eaton *E-mail:* mark@bangpictures.com; John Swarr *Tel:* 610-888-5656 *Fax:* 610-489-2626 *E-mail:* john@bangpictures.com
Dir: Gerry Creighton

The Banquet Sound Studios
5870 McFarland Rd, Sebastopol, CA 95472
Tel: 707-823-3500
E-mail: info@banquetstudios.com
Web Site: www.banquetstudios.com
Key Personnel
Owner & Prodr: Warren Dennis Kahn *E-mail:* warren@banquetstudios.com
Mgr: Shanin Jones
Digital audio recording studio.
Membership(s): AES; The Recording Academy

Bantam Doubleday Dell Audio Publishing
Division of Random House Inc
1745 Broadway, New York, NY 10019
Tel: 212-782-9000
E-mail: audio@randomhouse.com
Web Site: www.randomhouse.com; bantam-dell.atrandom.com
Founded: 1945
Publisher of adult fiction & nonfiction.
Online catalog(s) available
Membership(s): Audio Publishers Association

Barber Tech Video Products
205 E Anaheim St, Long Beach, CA 90813
Tel: 818-982-7775 *Toll Free Tel:* 877-887-6388
E-mail: info@barbertvp.com
Web Site: www.barbertvp.com
Key Personnel
Owner: Eddie Barber

Barbizon Electric Co Inc
456 W 55 St, New York, NY 10019-4403
Tel: 212-586-1620 *Toll Free Tel:* 800-582-9941 *Fax:* 212-247-8818
E-mail: benysales@barbizon.com
Web Site: www.barbizon.com
Key Personnel
Dir, Intl Sales: Michael Lieberman
Sales Mgr: Danny Quiles
Founded: 1947
Branch Office(s)
8269 E 23 Ave, Suite 111, Denver, CO 80238, Contact: Rick Loudenberg *Tel:* 303-394-9875 *Fax:* 303-355-5996 *E-mail:* bwrsales@barbizon.com
11551 Interchange Circle S, Miramar, FL 33025, Sales: Ted Doyle *Tel:* 954-919-6495 *Fax:* 954-919-6606 *E-mail:* flasales@barbizon.com
1483 Chattahoochee Ave NW, Suite D, Atlanta, GA 30318, Contact: Damian Vaudo *Tel:* 404-681-5124 *Fax:* 404-681-5315 *E-mail:* atlsales@barbizon.com
3 Draper St, Woburn, MA 01801, Gen Mgr: Peter McNamee *Tel:* 781-935-3920 *Fax:* 781-935-9273 *E-mail:* blonesales@barbizon.com
1016 McClelland Ct, Charlotte, NC 28206, Contact: Jeff Montgomerie *Tel:* 704-372-2122 *Fax:* 704-372-7422 *E-mail:* charsales@barbizon.com

Barbizon Lighting Co, see Barbizon Electric Co Inc

Barbosa Video Services
11 Plaza, Suite E, Patterson, CA 95363
Mailing Address: PO Box 1545, Patterson, CA 95363-1545
Tel: 209-324-5327
Web Site: barbosavideo.com
Key Personnel
Owner: Gordon Barbosa

Founded: 1990
Provide affordable, quality media services to families, businesses & public agencies such as transfer of 8mm & videotapes to DVDs.

Barco Inc
3059 Premiere Pkwy, Suite 400, Duluth, GA 30097
Tel: 916-859-2500; 678-475-8000
Toll Free Tel: 888-414-7226
E-mail: sales.events.us@barco.com
Web Site: www.barco.com
Key Personnel
Dir, Corp Mktg-North America: Tyler West
E-mail: tyler.west@barco.com
Designs & develops visualization solutions for the medical imaging, media & entertainment, infrastructure & utilities, traffic & transportation, defense & security, education & training & corporate AV markets.
Branch Office(s)
3078 Prospect Park Dr, Rancho Cordova, CA 95670 *Toll Free Tel:* 888-414-7226
1287 Anvilwood Ave, Sunnyvale, CA 94089
600 Bellbrook Ave, Xenia, OH 45385 *Tel:* 937-372-7579

Bardes Products Inc
5245 W Clinton Ave, Milwaukee, WI 53223
Tel: 414-354-9000 *Toll Free Tel:* 800-223-1357
Fax: 414-354-1921
E-mail: sales@bardes.com
Web Site: www.bardes.com
Key Personnel
Custom Prods Mgr: Scott Hallberg
Founded: 1978
Manufacturer of heat-sealed vinyl envelopes, pouches, production jackets, sleeves etc.
Catalog(s), annual, free, by request
Membership(s): Ophthalmic Photographers Society

Barger-Lite
PO Box 90294, Venice, CA 90294
Tel: 310-401-0633 *Fax:* 310-392-6791
Web Site: www.bargerlite.com
Key Personnel
Owner: Ed Barger
Founded: 2000
Manufacture, sell & rent lighting equipment for motion picture & TV production.

Jake Barner Studio
120 S Barner Dr, Centralia, WA 98531
Tel: 360-736-1764
Key Personnel
Mgr & Engr: Allen Fadness
From 2 to 32 tracks. Automated console. By appointment only.

Bill Barnes Video Productions LLC
14238 Honeysuckle Ridge, Matthews, NC 28105-6403
Tel: 704-847-8685 *Toll Free Tel:* 888-893-7331
Fax: 704-847-7279
E-mail: bill@bbvp.tv
Web Site: bbvp.tv
Key Personnel
Owner: William R Barnes
Prodr: Charlotte Barnes
Founded: 1988

Baron Stage Curtain & Equipment Co Inc
3218 Noble St, Baltimore, MD 21224
Tel: 410-327-6962 *Fax:* 410-327-7077
E-mail: curtains@baronstage.com
Web Site: www.baronstage.com
Key Personnel
Pres: Joe Stelmack
Catalog(s) available

Barron's Educational Series Inc
250 Wireless Blvd, Hauppauge, NY 11788
Tel: 631-434-3311 *Toll Free Tel:* 800-645-3476
Fax: 631-434-3723
E-mail: barrons@barronseduc.com
Web Site: www.barronseduc.com
Key Personnel
Chmn & CEO: Manuel H Barron
Pres: Ellen Sibley
VP, Sales: Alex Holtz
Dir, Mktg: Lonny Stein
Acqs Ed: Wayne Barr
Founded: 1941
Catalog(s) available
Branch Office(s)
Georgetown Book Warehouse, 34 Armstrong Ave, Georgetown, ON L7G 4R9, Canada, Contact: Brian Cox *Toll Free Tel:* 800-247-7160

Ben Barry & Associates Inc
10246 Briarwood Dr, Los Angeles, CA 90077
Tel: 310-274-1523 *Fax:* 310-274-1523
E-mail: benbarryfilms@sbcglobal.net
Key Personnel
Chmn & CEO: Ben Barry
Pres: Mimi Barry

Carl Barth Images
PO Box 5325, Santa Barbara, CA 93150-5325
Tel: 805-637-0881
E-mail: carlbarthimages@cox.net
Key Personnel
Owner: Carl Barth

Bartha
600 N Cassady Ave, Columbus, OH 43219
Tel: 614-252-7455 *Toll Free Tel:* 800-363-2698
Fax: 614-252-7641
E-mail: info@bartha.com
Web Site: www.bartha.com
Key Personnel
Owner & Pres: Dan Bashore
Owner: Tom Gabbert; John Killacky
Founded: 1946
Catalog(s) available
Membership(s): InfoComm International®

Bartok Records & Publications
PO Box 399, Homosassa, FL 34487
Tel: 352-382-2015 *Fax:* 352-382-0341
E-mail: bartok@atlantic.net
Web Site: www.bartokrecords.com
Key Personnel
Owner: Peter Bartok
Prepare corrected editions of Bela Bartok's compositions, based on his manuscripts or copies of them, as well as the publication of books & sheet music.
Online catalog(s) available

Bay Photo Lab
920 Disc Dr, Scotts Valley, CA 95066
Tel: 831-475-6686 *Toll Free Tel:* 800-435-6686
Fax: 831-475-5275
E-mail: support@bayphoto.com (cust serv)
Web Site: www.bayphoto.com
Key Personnel
Owner & Pres: Larry Abitbol *E-mail:* larry@bayphoto.com
Catalog(s) available
Membership(s): AIE™

Bay Records
3365 S Lucille Lane, Lafayette, LA 94549
Tel: 925-284-7797
Web Site: www.bayrec.com
Key Personnel
Owner: Michael Cogan *E-mail:* mcogan@bayrec.com
Audio recording, mastering & CD production.
Catalog(s) available
Membership(s): The Recording Academy

Bay Stage Lighting Co Inc
4008 W Alva St, Tampa, FL 33614
Tel: 813-877-1089 *Fax:* 813-875-8837
Web Site: www.baystagelighting.com
Key Personnel
Co-Owner & Pres: Yvonne Felicione Justo
E-mail: yvonne@baystagelighting.com
Co-Owner: Brian Justo *E-mail:* brian@baystagelighting.com
Dir, Busn Devt: Nicole Justo Carballa
E-mail: nicole@baystagelighting.com
Founded: 1957
Rental & production of stage lighting equipment.

BBC Motion Gallery, see BBC Worldwide Learning

BBC Worldwide Canada Ltd
Subsidiary of British Broadcasting Corp (BBC)
409 King St W, 5th fl, Toronto, ON M5V 1K1, Canada
Tel: 416-204-0500
Web Site: www.bbcworldwide.com
Key Personnel
VP, Digital: Reeshma Tejani *E-mail:* reeshma.tajani@bbc.com
Catalog(s) available

BBC Worldwide Learning
1120 Avenue of the Americas, 5th fl, New York, NY 10036
Tel: 212-339-1700 *Fax:* 212-705-9530
E-mail: education.us@bbc.com
Web Site: www.bbcworldwidelearning.com
Rights-cleared video solutions tailored for education, from clip licensing to fully produced short form video segments.

BBE Sound Inc
2548 Fender Ave, Fullerton, CA 92831
Tel: 714-897-6766 *Toll Free Tel:* 800-233-8346
Fax: 714-895-6728
Web Site: www.bbesound.com
Key Personnel
Chmn & CEO: John C McLaren
EVP: David C McLaren *E-mail:* dmclaren@bbesound.com
VP, Technol: Paul Gagon
Founded: 1985
Audio technology company.
Online catalog(s) available

BC Video Inc
Affiliate of BC Studio
152 W 25 St, 2nd fl, New York, NY 10001
Tel: 212-242-4065 *Toll Free Tel:* 800-846-9682
Fax: 212-242-4190
Web Site: www.bcvideo.com
Key Personnel
Pres: Bill Cote *E-mail:* bcote@nyc.rr.com
Founded: 1981
Cameras, video, film & final cut pro editing. Complete production for videos, DVDs & television & DVD authoring. BC Studio soundstage for film & video, including green screen.
Catalog(s) available

BCD Associates Inc
2800 NW 36 St, Suite 220, Oklahoma City, OK 73112
Tel: 405-702-6888 *Toll Free Tel:* 800-223-6734
E-mail: salesweb@bcdusa.com; sales@bcdusa.com
Web Site: www.bcdusa.com
Key Personnel
Pres: Diane Howard *E-mail:* diane@bcdusa.com
VP, Devt: Robert Howard
Founded: 1980

Manufacture pushbutton interface devices & produce interactive video DVDs.
Catalog(s) available
Membership(s): Association for Computing Machinery; InfoComm International®

The BD Co
PO Box 2048, Chandler, AZ 85225-2048
Tel: 480-632-1160 *Toll Free Tel:* 800-704-3072
Fax: 480-632-1163
E-mail: info@bdcompany.com
Web Site: www.bdcompany.com
Key Personnel
Export Mgr: Cindy Graves
Catalog(s) available
Membership(s): National Association of Display Industries; Photo Marketing Association; PPA

Be Media
9729 Lurline Ave, Chatsworth, CA 91311
Tel: 310-725-8500 *Toll Free Tel:* 877-210-7664
Fax: 310-725-9500
Web Site: www.bemedia.com
Key Personnel
CEO & Pres: Mohammad Ahmadi
VP, Opers: David Sayah
Founded: 1998
AV & lighting systems integration, design, engineer, install & service. Sales offices located in Atlanta, GA, Columbus, OH, Toronto, ON & Nassau, Bahamas.
Membership(s): International Association of Amusement Parks & Attractions; NSCA; Themed Entertainment Association

BeachTek Inc
480 Osprey Ave, Kelowna, BC V1Y 5A5, Canada
Tel: 416-690-9457
E-mail: info@beachtek.com
Web Site: www.beachtek.com
Key Personnel
Pres: Harry Kaufmann
Founded: 1997
Manufacturer of audio adapters for camcorders.

BeachWare Inc
4980 N Campbell Ave, Tucson, AZ 85718
Tel: 520-577-8945 *Fax:* 520-577-8945
Web Site: www.beachware.com
Key Personnel
Pres: Tom Gilliland *E-mail:* tom@beachware.com
Catalog(s) available

Beachwood Productions
1500 Mill Creek Ct SW, Marietta, GA 30008
Tel: 770-432-6563; 404-324-7271 (cell)
Web Site: www.beachwoodproductions.com
Key Personnel
Contact: Peter Wilcox *E-mail:* beachwoodpeter@comcast.net
Full service video production.

Beachwood Studios, see EDR Media LLC

Bear Creek Studio & Music Production Inc
6313 Maltby Rd, Woodinville, WA 98072
Tel: 425-481-4100 *Fax:* 425-486-2718
E-mail: bearcreek@seanet.com
Web Site: bearcreekstudio.com
Key Personnel
Prodr, Composer & Engr: Joe Hadlock
E-mail: joehadlock@hotmail.com; Ryan Hadlock *E-mail:* ryanhadlock@hotmail.com
Studio Mgr & Engr: Jerry Streeter
E-mail: jeremiahstreeter@gmail.com
Busn Aff: Manny Hadlock
E-mail: mannyhadlock@hotmail.com
Founded: 1977
Music production, licensing & supervision. Full analog & digital studio for music recording.

Beast Atlanta
Division of Deluxe Entertainment Services Group
3399 Peachtree Rd NE, Suite 200, Atlanta, GA 30326-1149
Tel: 404-237-9977 *Fax:* 404-237-3923
E-mail: info@riotatlanta.com
Web Site: www.beast.tv
Key Personnel
Exec Prodr: Molly Baroco
Sr Creative Ed: Matt Barron; Eddie Kesler
Ed: Jeff Jay
Audio Engr: Chris Basta
Founded: 1984
Offers content, concept & design creation services in a boutique work environment.
Membership(s): AICE; AICP; MCA-I

Beatty TeleVisual Productions
Division of Beatty TeleVisual Inc
1287 Wabash Ave, Springfield, IL 62704
Tel: 217-787-4747 *Toll Free Tel:* 800-777-2043
Fax: 217-787-4857
E-mail: bargins@beattytelevisual.com
Web Site: www.beattytelevisual.com
Key Personnel
CEO: David E Beatty
Pres: Wilma Beatty
Founded: 1958
Audio & video equipment sales & rentals.
Catalog(s) available

Russ Beckner Pictures
2100 Heatherwood Ct, Middletown, OH 45042
Tel: 513-422-9552
Web Site: www.russbecknerpictures.com
Key Personnel
Owner & Exec Prodr: Russ Beckner
E-mail: russ@russbecknerpictures.com
Busn Mgr: Jenni Beckner
Founded: 2003

Beekman Books Inc
300 Old All Angels Hill Rd, Wappingers Falls, NY 12590
Tel: 845-297-2690 *Fax:* 845-297-1002
E-mail: manager@beekmanbooks.com
Web Site: www.beekmanbooks.com
Key Personnel
Pres: Michael Arthur
Founded: 1972
Online catalog(s) available

Beholder Productions Inc
1515 Market St, Suite 1200, Philadelphia, PA 19102
Toll Free Tel: 844-BEHOLD-R (234-6537)
E-mail: info@beholderproductions.com
Web Site: www.beholderproductions.com
Key Personnel
Co-Founder, CEO & Pres: Craig Andrews
Co-Founder & COO: Emilia Andrews
Founded: 1999
Award-winning, full service premier video production company.
Membership(s): Alliance for Women in Media; Business Clubs America

Lawrence Behr Associates Inc
Division of LBA Group Inc
3400 Tupper Dr, Greenville, NC 27834
Mailing Address: PO Box 8026, Greenville, NC 27835-8026
Tel: 252-757-0279 *Toll Free Tel:* 800-522-4464
Fax: 252-752-9155
E-mail: lbassc@lbagroup.com
Web Site: www.lbagroup.com/associates
Key Personnel
COO & VP, Sales: Mike Britner *E-mail:* mike.britner@lbagroup.com
CTO: Chris Horne *E-mail:* chris.horne@lbagroup.com
Busn Devt: Byron Johnson *E-mail:* byron.johnson@lbagroup.com
Founded: 1963
Offer infrastructure support services for the wireless communications industry worldwide.

Belar Electronics Laboratory Inc
1140 McDermott Dr, Suite 105, West Chester, PA 19380-4043
Mailing Address: PO Box 1689, West Chester, PA 19380-0055
Tel: 610-687-5550 *Fax:* 610-687-2686
E-mail: sales@belar.com
Web Site: www.belar.com
Key Personnel
Pres: Arno Meyer
Founded: 1964
Manufacture modulation monitors & related equipment for the broadcast industry.
Membership(s): NAB

Belden
401 Pennsylvania Pkwy, Suite 200, Indianapolis, IN 46280
Tel: 317-818-6300 (ext 6334) *Toll Free Tel:* 800-235-3362; 800-BELDEN-1 (235-3361)
Fax: 317-818-6365
E-mail: info@belden.com
Web Site: www.belden.com
Key Personnel
Pres: Glenn Pennycook
Founded: 1902
Manufactures speciality cables for AV applications.
Catalog(s) available

Belew Enterprises
524 Vance Dr, Bristol, TN 37620
Mailing Address: PO Box 3167, Bristol, TN 37625
Tel: 423-764-4116
E-mail: bsv@tricon.net
Key Personnel
Pres: Sam B Belew

Bell & Howell LLC
760 S Wolf Rd, Wheeling, IL 60090
Tel: 847-675-7600 *Toll Free Tel:* 800-220-3030 (cust serv)
E-mail: marketing@bhemail.com
Web Site: www.bellhowell.net
Key Personnel
CEO: Ramesh Ratan
CFO: Arthur Bergens
VP & Gen Coun: Blake Eaddy
VP, Busn Devt: Mark Van Gorp
VP, Software Mktg: Chris Lien
VP, Sorting & Postal Software: Mike Swift
Provider of solutions & services for paper-based & digital messaging.
Branch Office(s)
3791 S Alston Ave, Durham, NC 27713-1803
Tel: 919-767-4401 (inserting & field servs)
30 Mural St, Unit 6, Richmond Hill, ON L4B 1B5, Canada *Toll Free Tel:* 800-889-6245; 800-850-3023 (cust serv-English); 800-850-3018 (cust serv-French) *Fax:* 416-228-2438
Foreign Office(s): Mergenthaleralle 73, 65760 Frankfurt, Germany
Brinkworth House, Brinkworth, Chippenham, Wilts SN15 5DF, United Kingdom

Bella Faccia Inc
6521 Chillum Place NW, Washington, DC 20012
Mailing Address: PO Box 11069, Takoma Park, MD 20913
Tel: 202-291-1932 *Fax:* 202-301-7716
E-mail: contact@bellafaccia.net
Web Site: www.bellafaccia.net
Key Personnel
Pres: Paul Falcon
Sound Stage Mgr: Rebecca Salms

Founded: 2000
Soundstage rental, production design & voice talent for the television, film & theatrical industries.

Bellin Productions
812 Hickory Grove Dr, Larchmont, NY 10538
Tel: 914-834-5520 *Fax:* 914-834-5477
E-mail: info@bellinproductions.com
Web Site: www.bellinproductions.com
Membership(s): NATAS

Ben Nye Makeup
3655 Lenawee Ave, Los Angeles, CA 90016
Tel: 310-839-1984 *Fax:* 310-839-2640
E-mail: sales1@bennyemakeup.com
Web Site: www.bennye.com
Make-up for theater, film & video.
Catalog(s) available

Benchmark Media
72 N State Rd, Suite 415, Briarcliff Manor, NY 10510
Tel: 914-762-3838 *Fax:* 914-762-3895
E-mail: benchmarkmedia.info@gmail.com
Web Site: www.benchmarkmedia.info
Key Personnel
Pres: Mike Solin
Producer & distributor of curricular videos for schools.
Catalog(s) available
Membership(s): International Council for Educational Media; National Media Market

Benchmark Media Systems Inc
203 E Hampton Place, Suite 2, Syracuse, NY 13206
Tel: 315-437-6300 *Toll Free Tel:* 800-262-4675 *Fax:* 315-437-5119
E-mail: info@benchmarkmedia.com
Web Site: www.benchmarkmedia.com
Key Personnel
Sales Mgr: Rory Rall
Membership(s): AES; NAMM, the National Association of Music Merchants

Robert Benedetto
10 Mall Terr, Suite A, Savannah, GA 31406
Tel: 912-692-1400 *Fax:* 912-692-1403
Web Site: www.benedettoguitars.com
Key Personnel
Owner: Robert Benedetto
Dir, Mktg: Cindy Benedetto *E-mail:* cbenedetto@benedettoguitars.com
Founded: 1968
Guitar making & consulting.
Catalog(s) available
Membership(s): Association of Stringed Instrument Artisans; NAMM, the National Association of Music Merchants

Benjamin Creative Productions
577 Lakeside Dr, Waterford, MI 48328
Tel: 248-682-6566 *Fax:* 248-682-0508
Web Site: www.benjaminvideo.com
Key Personnel
Owner: Chris Benjamin *E-mail:* chris@benjaminvideo.com
Founded: 1990
Full service creative shop specializing in television programs. Write, produce & direct. Also multiple camera direction for live shows & events.
Membership(s): MCA-I

Bennett Media Corp
2321 Abbot Kinney Blvd, Venice, CA 90291
Tel: 310-827-8064 *Toll Free Tel:* 800-733-8862 *Fax:* 310-827-8074
E-mail: sale@bennettmarine.com
Web Site: www.bennettmarine.com
Key Personnel
Dir, Mktg: Elaine Dochard
Founded: 1989
Outdoor instructional programming for recreational enthusiasts.
Catalog(s) available
Membership(s): Entertainment Merchants Association; NMMA

Bennett-Watt HD Productions Inc
Affiliate of Bennett-Watt Entertainment Inc
13021 244 Ave SE, Issaquah, WA 98027
Tel: 425-392-3935 *Toll Free Tel:* 800-327-2893 *Fax:* 425-526-5851
E-mail: info@bennett-watt.com
Web Site: www.bennett-watt.com
Key Personnel
Pres: Jim Watt
VP: Kelly Watt
Founded: 1978
Complete HD video production services for broadcast, in-house or media. Aerial drone service available.

Benro
Division of MAC Group
75 Virginia Rd, Suite 1, North White Plains, NY 10603
Tel: 914-347-3300 *Fax:* 914-347-3309
E-mail: info@benrousa.com
Web Site: www.benrousa.com
Key Personnel
Pres, MAC Group: Jan Lederman
Photographic tripods, monopods, heads & photographic support gear.

The Bergman Collection of Medical/Technical/Scientific Stock Images
Division of Project Masters Inc
134 Leabrook Lane, Princeton, NJ 08540-3622
Tel: 609-921-0749
E-mail: information@pmiprinceton.com
Web Site: pmiprinceton.com
Key Personnel
Owner & Pres: Richard I Bergman
Owner & VP: Victoria B Bergman

Bergwall Productions Inc
120 N Church St, Suite 106, West Chester, PA 19380
Mailing Address: PO Box 1481, Chadds Ford, PA 19317
Tel: 610-436-4017 *Toll Free Tel:* 800-934-8696 *Fax:* 610-436-4018
Web Site: www.bergwall.com
Founded: 1970
Provide training to vocational/career & technical education teachers & students by providing online training videos & DVDs.
Online catalog(s) available

Berke Creative Inc
50 Mendell St, Suite 11, San Francisco, CA 94124
Tel: 415-285-8800 *Fax:* 415-285-8847
Web Site: www.berkesound.com
Key Personnel
Pres: Nancy Berke *E-mail:* nancy@berkesound.com
Founded: 1970

Berke Sound, see Berke Creative Inc

Berkeley Sound Artists Inc
2600 Tenth St, Suite 312, Berkeley, CA 94710
Tel: 510-486-2290 *Fax:* 510-549-0287
E-mail: info@berkeleysoundartists.com
Web Site: www.berkeleysoundartists.com
Key Personnel
Pres: James LeBrecht
Founded: 1996
Full service post-production audio facility serving film, television, multimedia, corporate, exhibition & music. Audio forensics & media transfers.
Membership(s): IDA; International Game Developers Association; San Francisco Film Society

Bernie's Photo Center
525 E Ohio St, Pittsburgh, PA 15212
Tel: 412-231-1717 *Toll Free Tel:* 800-346-8884 *Fax:* 412-231-1217
E-mail: info@berniesphoto.com
Web Site: www.berniesphoto.com
Key Personnel
Pres: Bruce M Klein
Off Mgr: Donna Downie
Photographic equipment & supplies.
Catalog(s) available

Berry & Homer
2035 Richmond St, Philadelphia, PA 19125
Tel: 215-425-0888 *Fax:* 215-425-2701
E-mail: info@berryandhomer.com
Web Site: www.berryandhomer.com
Key Personnel
Pres: Joseph B Thompson, III
Founded: 1898
Large format digital printing.
Branch Office(s)
4390 Parliament Place, Suite G, Lanham, MD 20706 *Tel:* 301-459-4500 *Fax:* 301-459-9813
Membership(s): EDPA

Daniel Bertolino Inc, see Les Productions Via Le Monde (Daniel Bertolino) Inc

BES Studios
6829 Atmore Dr, Suite E, Richmond, VA 23225
Tel: 804-276-0806 *Toll Free Tel:* 800-995-2371
E-mail: info@besstudios.com
Web Site: www.besstudios.com
Key Personnel
Exec Prodr: Mark Remes *E-mail:* mark@besstudios.com

Beseler Photo
Division of Charles Beseler Co
2018 W Main St, Stroudsburg, PA 18360
Mailing Address: PO Box 431, Stroudsburg, PA 18360
Toll Free Tel: 800-237-3537 *Toll Free Fax:* 800-966-4515
Web Site: www.beselerphoto.com
Key Personnel
Pres: Hank Gasikowski *E-mail:* hank@beselerphoto.com
Membership(s): Photo Marketing Association; Photoimaging Manufacturers & Distributors Association

Best Bet Camera Rentals
5247 Agnes Ave, Unit 5, Valley Village, CA 91607
Tel: 818-508-9249
E-mail: info@bestbetcamera.com
Web Site: www.bestbetcamera.com
Rental assortment of camera packages for filmmaking.

Best Film & Video
3913 Fall Wheat Dr, Plano, TX 75075
Tel: 214-395-4070
Web Site: www.bestfilmandvideo.com
Key Personnel
Owner: Alan J Lefebvre *E-mail:* alan@bestfilmandvideo.com
Turn key film & video production, all formats. Individual services include: acquisition, writing & editing. Production in HD.

Best Shot
4301 W Cayuga St, Tampa, FL 33614
Tel: 813-454-5768
E-mail: request@bestshotfootage.com
Web Site: www.bestshotfootage.com
Key Personnel
Pres: Ronald Ceyrolles
Stock footage library, videography.

Bestek Lighting & Staging
98 Mahan St, West Babylon, NY 11704
Tel: 631-643-0707 *Fax:* 631-643-0764
E-mail: production@bestek.com
Web Site: www.bestek.com
Key Personnel
Pres: Van Allen Rice
Gen Mgr: Ken Bush
Membership(s): International Special Events Society; MPI; Professional Lighting & Sound Association

Bestwell Optical Instrument Corp
46 Henry St, Merrick, NY 11566
Tel: 516-379-2280 *Fax:* 516-706-1744
Web Site: www.bestwelloptical.com
Key Personnel
Founder & Inventor: Murray Rosenberg
CEO & Pres: Irene Rosenfeld
COO & VP: Lisa Weingarten
E-mail: lisaweingarten@bestwelloptical.com
Founded: 1950
Manufacture grain focusers & image magnifiers for darkroom photography.

Beta Electronics Inc
130 S Barranca St, Apt 314, West Covina, CA 91791-2279
Tel: 614-538-8207 *Toll Free Tel:* 800-546-2382 *Fax:* 614-538-8209 *Toll Free Fax:* 888-329-2382
E-mail: sales@betalaser.com
Web Site: www.betalaser.com
Key Personnel
Pres: Ming Liou
Manufacture laser pointers. Produces electronic interactive whiteboards.
Catalog(s) available

Bethesda Softworks LLC
Division of ZeniMax Media Inc
1370 Piccard Dr, Suite 120, Rockville, MD 20850
Tel: 301-926-8300
E-mail: info@bethsoft.com
Web Site: www.bethsoft.com
Key Personnel
Pres: Vlatko Andonov
Publisher of interactive entertainment software.
Catalog(s) available
Membership(s): AES; SMPTE

Bevilacqua Studios
202 E 42 St, New York, NY 10017
Tel: 212-490-0355 *Fax:* 212-490-0355
Key Personnel
Pres & Prodr: Joe Bevilacqua
E-mail: joebev202@aol.com
Feature film production.
Membership(s): ASMP

Bexel Corp
Division of Vitec Group
2701 N Ontario St, Burbank, CA 91504
Tel: 818-565-4322 *Toll Free Tel:* 800-225-6185 (tech support)
E-mail: rentals@bexel.com
Web Site: www.bexel.com
Key Personnel
CTO: Tom Dickinson
Pres & Gen Mgr: Halid Hatic
VP, Engg & Opers: Craig Schiller
VP, Fin: John Schrieber
VP, Opers: Kristen Ballard
VP, Sales & Mktg: Greg Bragg
VP & Gen Mgr, Bexel ESS: Scott Nardelli
Founded: 1981
Provider of broadcast services.
Catalog(s) available
Branch Office(s)
700 Penhorn Ave, Secaucus, NJ 07094 *Tel:* 201-558-7101
1001 N Union Bower Rd, Suite 130, Irving, TX 75061 *Tel:* 972-870-2339
22626 Sally Ride Dr, Suite 110, Sterling, VA 20164 *Tel:* 703-796-5980
Sales Office(s): 5555 Glenridge Connector, Suite 200, Atlanta, GA 30342 *Tel:* 770-448-3000
Foreign Office(s): Rua Quintana 950 cj 32, Booklin Novo, 04569-011 Sao Paulo, Brazil *Tel:* (011) 5102-4001
Membership(s): NAB

Bext Inc
1045 Tenth Ave, San Diego, CA 92101
Tel: 619-BEXTINC (239-8462) *Toll Free Tel:* 888-BEXTINC (239-8462) *Fax:* 619-239-8474
E-mail: bext@bext.com
Web Site: www.bext.com
Key Personnel
CEO: Dennis Pieri
Founded: 1985
Specialize in high quality RF equipment for radio, television & industrial or scientific applications.
Membership(s): NAB

beyerdynamic Inc
56 Central Ave, Farmingdale, NY 11735
Tel: 631-293-3200 *Toll Free Tel:* 800-293-4463 *Fax:* 631-293-3288
E-mail: info@beyerdynamic-usa.com
Web Site: north-america.beyerdynamic.com
Key Personnel
Gen Mgr: Wolfgang Luckhardt
Busn Unit Mgr: Alan Feckanin
Founded: 1924
Data sheet(s) available
Online catalog(s) available
Membership(s): AES; NAB; NAMM, the National Association of Music Merchants; NSCA; SBE

Beyers Sound & Essay Audio
Division of Beyersound Computing
PO Box 120442, St Paul, MN 55112-0018
Tel: 651-633-3933
E-mail: info@essayaudio.com
Web Site: www.essayaudio.com
Key Personnel
Owner & Founder: Scott Beyers
Founded: 1989
Audio post-production with focus on live & remote recording.

BFS Entertainment & Multimedia Limited
360 Newkirk Rd, Richmond Hill, ON L4C 3G7, Canada
Tel: 905-884-2323 *Fax:* 905-884-8292
E-mail: info@bfsent.com; contact@bfsent.com
Web Site: www.bfsent.com
Key Personnel
CEO & Pres: Denis BE Donnelly
CFO: John Grzybowski
Secy: David E Chapman
Founded: 1980
Independent entertainment company focusing on the acquisition, distribution & production of film & television media.
Membership(s): Entertainment Merchants Association; Music Business Association

BGW Systems, an Amplifier Technologies Inc Company
1749 Chapin Rd, Montebello, CA 90640
Tel: 323-278-0001 *Fax:* 323-278-0083
E-mail: sales@bgw.com; info@bgw.com
Web Site: www.bgw.com
Key Personnel
Pres: Morris Kessler
Founded: 1971
Membership(s): Consumer Electronics Association; Custom Electronic Design & Installation Association; International Theatre Equipment Association; NAMM, the National Association of Music Merchants; NSCA

BIAMP Systems
9300 SW Gemini Dr, Beaverton, OR 97008
Tel: 503-641-7287 *Toll Free Tel:* 800-826-1457 (US & CN) *Fax:* 503-626-0281
E-mail: biampinfo@biamp.com; salesteam@biamp.com
Web Site: www.biamp.com
Key Personnel
CEO & Pres: Steve Metzger
EVP, Opers: Matt Czyzewski
EVP, Mktg: Graeme Harrison
VP, Global Sales: Ron Camden
Founded: 1976
Manufacture AV systems & products.
Catalog(s), PDF download
Membership(s): AES; NSCA

Bias Studios
5400 Carolina Place, Springfield, VA 22151
Tel: 703-941-3333
E-mail: info@biasstudios.com
Web Site: www.biasstudios.com
Key Personnel
Owner, Prodr & Engr: Bob Dawson
Prodr & Engr: Jim Robeson
Studio Mgr: Gloria Dawson
Founded: 1973
Audio recording, two multi-track audio studios.

Biblical Archaeology Society (BAS)
4710 41 St NW, Washington, DC 20016
Tel: 202-364-3300 *Toll Free Tel:* 800-221-4644 *Fax:* 202-364-2636
E-mail: bas@bib-arch.org; merchandise@bib-arch.org
Web Site: www.biblicalarchaeology.org
Key Personnel
Publr: Susan Laden
Ed: Hershel Shanks
Prodn Mgr: Heather Metzger
Founded: 1974
A nonprofit, nondenominational educational organization dedicated to the dissemination of information about archaeology in the Bible lands.
Online catalog(s) available

Big Apple Films
636 W 28 St, New York, NY 10001
Tel: 212-368-1111 *Fax:* 347-689-1604
Web Site: www.bigapplefilms.com
Key Personnel
CEO: Daniel Dacian *Tel:* 917-386-8322 (cell)
E-mail: daniel@bigapplefilms.com
Mng Dir: Corey Scott Rutledge *E-mail:* corey@bigapplefilms.com
Rents cameras & accessories. Also provides editing & color correction services.

Big Byte Video Productions
223 Washington Blvd, Lake Placid, FL 33852
Tel: 863-699-6229 *Fax:* 863-699-0145
E-mail: bigbytevideo@yahoo.com
Web Site: www.bigbytevideo.us
Key Personnel
Owner: Rick Shorrock
Founded: 2000
Video production.

Big Deal Custom Casings
100 Durand Rd, Winnipeg, MB R2J 3T2, Canada
Tel: 204-663-4870 *Toll Free Tel:* 800-337-3325
Fax: 204-668-7404
E-mail: info@bigdealcases.com
Web Site: bigdealcases.ca
Key Personnel
Pres: Gary Dealey *E-mail:* gdealy@bigdealcases.com
Founded: 1976
Design & manufacture custom cases ranging from aerospace & utilities to theatre & sports clubs. Specialize in large theatre productions & complete show packaging.
Online catalog(s) available

Big Door
114 Sheldon St, El Segundo, CA 90245
Tel: 310-546-6100 *Fax:* 310-906-4585
E-mail: sales@bigdoor.tv
Web Site: www.bigdoor.tv; www.bigdoorstudio.tv
Key Personnel
Principal, Prodr & Dir: Max Yoffe *E-mail:* max@bigdoor.tv
SVP, Digital Media: Scot Rubin *E-mail:* scot@bigdoor.tv
Dir, IT: Oscar Chavez *E-mail:* oscar@bigdoor.tv
Dir, Prodn: Jaromy Siporen *E-mail:* js@bigdoor.tv
Founded: 1993
Full service production company. Specialize in live streaming, video & post-production, web series & branded entertainment.

Big Event Productions LLC
77 13 Ave NE, Studio 101, Minneapolis, MN 55413
Tel: 612-623-7800 *Fax:* 612-455-0450
Web Site: www.bigeventpros.com
Key Personnel
Prodr & Tech Dir: Bob Chouinard *E-mail:* bobc@bigeventpros.com
Prodr/Video: Steve Friederichsen
Audio Design & Prodn Mgmt: Tom Bothof
Lighting Designer: Ross Gish
Founded: 2003
Video production & event staging company.

Big Film Design
375 S End Ave, No 9S, New York, NY 10280
Tel: 212-627-3430
E-mail: info@bigfilmdesign.com
Web Site: www.bigfilmdesign.com
Key Personnel
Owner, Pres & Chief Creative Offr: Randall Balsmeyer
Founded: 2001
Design & production of title sequences & visual effects for feature films & television.
Membership(s): International Alliance of Theatrical Stage Employees & Moving Picture Machine Operators of the United States & Canada; Visual Effects Society

Big Fish Productions Inc
PO Box 782, Bronx, NY 10462-0782
Tel: 212-860-3639
Web Site: www.bigfishproductioninc.com
Key Personnel
CEO, Pres & Gen Mgr: James Carter
Artists management, recording label, productions & business management.
Membership(s): Actors' Equity Association; ASCAP; BMI; Music Business Association; SAG-AFTRA

Big Foot Productions Inc
37-09 36 Ave, Long Island City, NY 11101
Tel: 718-729-1900 *Fax:* 718-729-8638
E-mail: info@bigfootnyc.com
Web Site: www.bigfootnyc.com
Key Personnel
Exec Prodr: Steven Mosovic *E-mail:* steve@bigfootnyc.com
Dir & Writer: Rob Cohen
Dir, Photog: Joe Livolsi *E-mail:* joe@bigfootnyc.com
Prodn Mgr: Marcia Hahn Foley *E-mail:* marcia@bigfootnyc.com
Prodr & Sound Engr: Paul Turlick *E-mail:* paul@bigfootnyc.com
Prodr & Writer: Brad Rothschild
Prodr: Martin Pohl
Founded: 1994
Video production services.

The Big House Group
17 Waller Ave, Ossining, NY 10562
Tel: 914-944-4011 *Fax:* 914-944-8044
Web Site: www.bighousetv.com
Key Personnel
Pres: Jacqueline Weir *Tel:* 914-589-1660 (cell) *E-mail:* jackie@bighousetv.com
Founded: 1993
Emmy award winning production company. AVID Symphony, creative editorial, graphic design & visual effects.

Big House Sound Inc
4001 Drossett Dr, Austin, TX 78744
Tel: 512-443-0019 *Fax:* 512-443-0916
Web Site: www.bighousesound.com
Key Personnel
Principal: Roy Kircher *E-mail:* roy@bighousesound.com; Rod Nielsen *E-mail:* rod@bighousesound.com
Opers Mgr: Bobby Filarowicz *E-mail:* bobby@bighousesound.com
Founded: 1991
Specialize in production services for concerts & corporate events. Provides sound systems, video production, staging, backline & lighting equipment.

Big Kids Productions Inc
2620 Barton Hills Dr, Austin, TX 78704
Tel: 512-441-0737 *Toll Free Tel:* 800-477-7811
Fax: 512-441-0339
E-mail: customerservice@bigkids.com
Web Site: bigkids.com
Key Personnel
Pres: Michele Roi
Founded: 1995
Distributor of children's DVDs & music.

Big Shoulders Digital Video Productions
875 N Michigan Ave, Suite 3750, Chicago, IL 60611
Tel: 312-540-5400
E-mail: info@bigshoulders.com; sales@bigshoulders.com
Web Site: www.bigshoulders.com
Key Personnel
Pres: Frank Hanes *Tel:* 312-540-5400 ext 222 *E-mail:* frankh@bigshoulders.com
VP: Brad Fox *Tel:* 312-540-5400 ext 218 *E-mail:* bradf@bigshoulders.com
Dir, Photog: Don Murphy
Equip Mgr: Matt Hacker
Intl Sales Mgr: Maria Colapinto
Prodn Mgr: Amy Stewart
Founded: 1995
Specialize in remote video production. Full editing & post-production services, design & audio sound engineering. Television studio available. Webcasting, time lapse video & other additional services available.

Big Time Picture Company Inc
12210 1/2 Nebraska Ave, Los Angeles, CA 90025
Tel: 310-207-0921 *Fax:* 310-826-0071
E-mail: info@bigtimepic.com
Web Site: www.bigtimepic.com
Key Personnel
Pres & Owner: Susan Klos
CTO: John Klos
Founded: 1978
Motion picture film & digital post-production facility & services. Systems integration & web hosting. Apple authorized reseller.

Bil-Jax Inc
125 Taylor Pkwy, Archbold, OH 43502
Tel: 419-445-8915 *Toll Free Tel:* 800-537-0540
Fax: 419-445-0367
E-mail: sales@biljax.com
Web Site: www.biljax.com
Key Personnel
VP, Scaffolding Sales: Doug Beck
Catalog(s), free, PDF downloads

Bill Bachmann Studios
PO Box 950833, Lake Mary, FL 32795
Tel: 407-333-9988
Web Site: www.billbachmann.com
Key Personnel
Owner & Photog: Bill Bachmann
Studio Mgr: Michele Rene
PR: Bob Schlussler
Founded: 1984
Photography & videography studios.
Membership(s): ASMP; PPA

BingoLewis
203 NE Weidler St, Portland, OR 97232
Tel: 503-223-2224
E-mail: info@bingolewis.com
Web Site: www.bingolewis.com
Key Personnel
Pres: Nancy Anderson
VP: Rob Anderson *E-mail:* rob@bingolewis.com
Multimedia & post-production services, CD-ROM authoring & digital video encoding.

BioMedia Inc
PO Box 918, Franklin, NY 13775
Tel: 917-754-3274 (cell)
E-mail: andy@bio-media.com
Web Site: bio-media.com
Key Personnel
Exec Prodr: Andy Bobrow
Video production & post-production & DVD authoring, graphic design & animation, content & script development for science, medicine & technology.

Biomedical Media Communications Dept
Division of University of Connecticut Health Center
263 Farmington Ave, Farmington, CT 06030-2910
Tel: 860-679-2119; 860-679-2433 *Fax:* 860-679-4034
Web Site: video.uchc.edu
Key Personnel
Univ Dir & Dept Head: Bill Hengstenberg
Video, multimedia & computer-assisted communications programs. Video teleconferencing production services.

Biomorph Desks
11 Broadway, Rm 905, New York, NY 10004
Tel: 212-809-4323 *Toll Free Tel:* 888-302-DESK (302-3375) *Toll Free Fax:* 888-652-7137
E-mail: info@biomorphdesk.com
Web Site: www.biomorphdesk.com
Key Personnel
Pres & Design Dir: Stephen Lawson
Founded: 1978
Ergonomic height-adjustable office/studio furniture designing & manufacturing business. Showroom located in New York City.
Catalog(s) available

Birds & Animals Unlimited
34145 Pacific Coast Hwy, No 761, Dana Point, CA 92629
Tel: 661-269-0148 *Toll Free Tel:* 877-542-1355 *Toll Free Fax:* 866-212-7899
E-mail: california@birdsandanimals.com
Web Site: www.birdsandanimals.com
35mm original stock film of North American & African wildlife in their natural habitat.

Birns & Sawyer Inc
5275 Craner Ave, North Hollywood, CA 91601
Tel: 323-466-8211 *Fax:* 323-466-1868; 818-358-4395 (rental)
E-mail: info@birnsandsawyer.com
Web Site: www.birnsandsawyer.com
Key Personnel
Owner & Cinematographer: Bill Meurer
Dir, Sales & Mktg: Ramzi Abed
Gen Mgr: Jason Stuckey
Online catalog(s), PDF download
Membership(s): SMPTE

Bisk Education
9417 Princess Palm Ave, Tampa, FL 33619
Toll Free Tel: 800-280-9718
E-mail: customerservice@bisk.com
Web Site: www.bisk.com
Key Personnel
Founder & Chmn: Nathan Bisk
CEO: Andrew Titen
COO & EVP: Joseph Smith
Chief Mktg Offr & EVP, Sales: Adrian Marrullier
Pres: Michael D Bisk
Founded: 1971
Online education.
Catalog(s) available

Bismeaux Studio
PO Box 463, Austin, TX 78767-0463
Tel: 512-444-9885 *Fax:* 512-444-4699
Web Site: www.bismeauxstudio.com
Key Personnel
Studio Mgr & Engg: Sam Seifert *E-mail:* sam@asleepatthewheel.com
Founded: 1992
A front-line recording facility. Multitrack recording, mixing, stereo mastering & analog tape restoration. Classic API main console, AMD 64-bit dual processing system, Nuendo, Cubase, MCI 2 inch, Ampex 1/4 inch, Adat M20, Mackie HD24, wide selection of microphones & grand pianos. Arranging, scoring, musician referral & production.
Membership(s): The Recording Academy

Bitcentral Inc
4340 Von Karman Ave, Suite 400, Newport Beach, CA 92660
Tel: 949-253-9000
E-mail: sales@bitcentral.com; support@bitcentral.com
Web Site: www.bitcentral.com
Key Personnel
Founder, CEO & Pres: Fred Fourcher *E-mail:* fred@bitcentral.com
Cont: Mike Healey
VP & Gen Mgr, Sales & Busn Devt: Rick Young *E-mail:* ryoung@bitcentral.com
VP, Prof Engg Servs: John King
VP, Software Devt: Daniel Pugh
VP, Support & Opers: Sameer Mohiuddin
Founded: 1998
Provides a new (file-based) management & play-to-air solution including digital archiving & clip-sharing solutions for TV broadcasters.
Catalog(s), PDF download

BitFlow Inc
400 W Cummings Park, Suite 5050, Woburn, MA 01801
Tel: 781-932-2900 *Fax:* 781-933-9965
E-mail: sales@bitflow.com
Web Site: www.bitflow.com
Key Personnel
Co-Founder & CEO: Avner Butnaru
Co-Founder & Pres: Reynold Dodson
Dir, Sales: Donal Wade
Founded: 1993
Membership(s): Automated Imaging Association; SPIE

Biway Media
5803 Sovereign, Suite 204, Houston, TX 77036
Tel: 713-271-4036 *Toll Free Tel:* 877-BIWAY DV (249-2938) *Fax:* 713-271-4240
E-mail: info@biwaymedia.com; sales@biwaymedia.com; audiosales@biwaymedia.com
Web Site: www.biwaymedia.com
Key Personnel
Mgr: Joseph Wang *E-mail:* joseph@biwaymedia.com
Founded: 1995
Provide turnkey Non-Linear Video Editing (NLE) systems for professional video & film production applications & turnkey Digital Audio Workstation (DAW) systems for musicians & audio production applications. We are a turnkey provider & also provide video production services with 20X30 studio w/light grid & edit suites with latest NLE & DAW systems. We are not a company of sales persons, but rather a company of production professionals & engineers, allowing clients to be fully supported on hardware as well as software applications. We also host 3D animation user groups & daily training sessions for production tools. Our fame has led to accolades from industry publications & peers alike.
Membership(s): Texas Association of Motion Media Professionals

BJU Press
1700 Wade Hampton Blvd, Greenville, SC 29614
Tel: 864-770-1317 *Toll Free Tel:* 800-845-5731 *Fax:* 864-271-8151 *Toll Free Fax:* 800-525-8398
E-mail: bjupinfo@bjupress.com
Web Site: www.bjupress.com; www.bjupresshomeschool.com
Founded: 1974
Provides K-12 educational materials that are academically rigorous, develop a biblical worldview, promote critical thinking & inspire a love of learning.
Catalog(s) available

The Black Academy of Arts & Letters Inc
Dallas Convention Ctr Theater Complex, 1309 Canton St, Dallas, TX 75201
Mailing Address: Dallas Convention Ctr Theater Complex, 650 S Griffin St, Dallas, TX 75202
Tel: 214-743-2440 *Fax:* 214-743-2451
E-mail: info@tbaal.org
Web Site: www.tbaal.org
Key Personnel
Founder & Pres: Curtis L King
Founded: 1977
Create & enhance awareness & understanding of artistic, cultural & aesthetic differences utilizing the framework of African-American arts & letters.

Black Film Center Archive
Unit of Indiana University
Indiana University, Wells Library, Rm 044, 1320 E Tenth St, Bloomington, IN 47405
Tel: 812-855-6041 *Fax:* 812-856-5832
E-mail: bfca@indiana.edu
Web Site: www.indiana.edu/~bfca
Key Personnel
Dir: Michael T Martin, PhD *E-mail:* martinmt@indiana.edu
Head, Public & Technol Servs: Brian Graney *E-mail:* bpgraney@indiana.edu
Founded: 1981
Collect, preserve & make available historically & culturally significant films by & about black people.
Newsletter(s), biannual, PDF download

Black Media Works
534 21 Ave SW, Calgary, AB T2S 0H1, Canada
Tel: 403-802-0010
E-mail: info@blackmediaworks.com
Web Site: www.blackmediaworks.com
Key Personnel
Prodr & Dir: Darold Black
Writer & Prodr: John Nursall
Videography & non-linear editing, full production services from script to screen.
Membership(s): Director's Guild of Canada

Black Star Publishing Co Inc
333 Mamaroneck Ave, PMB 175, White Plains, NY 10605
Tel: 212-679-3288 *Fax:* 212-889-2052
Web Site: www.blackstar.com
Key Personnel
Pres: Benjamin J Chapnick
EVP: John P Chapnick
Provide location photography, stock photography & Internet development.

Blackburst Entertainment
1830 Longwood Lake Mary Rd, No 1024, Longwood, FL 32750
Tel: 407-599-5353
E-mail: info@blackburst.net
Web Site: www.blackburstentertainment.com
Key Personnel
Founder & Pres: Walter Lowe
Founded: 2001
Full service television, film, commercial & video production company.

Blacklight Films, see Moving Art by Louie Schwartzberg

Blackstone Audio Inc
31 Mistletoe Rd, Ashland, OR 97520
Toll Free Tel: 800-621-0182 *Toll Free Fax:* 877-492-0793
E-mail: libraryservices@blackstoneaudio.com
Web Site: www.blackstoneaudio.com; www.blackstonelibrary.com
Key Personnel
Founder & Pres: Craig Black
Founded: 1987
Audiobooks on CD, MP3-CD & digital download.
Online catalog(s), PDF download

Blackstone Magik Enterprises Inc
12800 Puesta Del Sol, Redlands, CA 92373
Tel: 909-792-1227 *Fax:* 909-794-2737
E-mail: magik@blackstonemagic.com
Web Site: www.blackstonemagic.com
Key Personnel
Pres & Owner: Gay Blackstone
Founded: 1971
Magic effects, prop rentals, design & production of events (both corporate & public).

Blackwater Video Productions
PO Box 909, Morgantown, WV 26507
Tel: 304-296-4048
E-mail: blackwatervideo@hotmail.com
Web Site: www.blackwatervideo.com
Key Personnel
Owner & Founder: Daniel McMullen

Michael Blackwood Productions Inc
6 W 18 St, Suite 2B, New York, NY 10011

Tel: 212-242-1805 *Fax:* 212-242-1671
E-mail: blackwoodfilm@aol.com
Web Site: www.michaelblackwoodproductions.com
Key Personnel
CEO, Prodr & Dir: Michael Blackwood
Dist Mgr: Elinor Feist
Founded: 1966
Producer of documentaries on the arts. HD equipment & facilities, complete HD services.

Blair Inc
7001 Loisdale Rd, Springfield, VA 22150
Tel: 703-922-0200 *Fax:* 703-924-0765
E-mail: info@blairinc.com
Web Site: www.blairinc.com
Key Personnel
VP: R Scott Jackson
Founded: 1952

Blair Packaging
1515 Independence St, Cape Girardeau, MO 63703
Tel: 573-264-2146 *Toll Free Tel:* 800-624-3150 *Fax:* 573-264-3730
E-mail: info@blairpkg.com
Web Site: www.blairpkg.com
Key Personnel
Dir, Mktg: Joe Bullock *Tel:* 800-624-3150 ext 144 *E-mail:* jbullock@blairpkg.com
Founded: 1952
Manufacture media packaging solutions for the distribution of media products.
Catalog(s), free
Membership(s): Binding Industries Association International; Entertainment Merchants Association; Printing Industries of America

Blaise Media
3400 "J" St, Sacramento, CA 95816
Tel: 916-446-3126 *Fax:* 916-446-8089
Web Site: blaisemedia.com
Key Personnel
Owner & Pres: Paul Blaise *E-mail:* paul@blaisemedia.com
Art Dir: Elizabeth Blaise
Founded: 1976
Marketing video - design & production. Full broadcast production & post-production.

Les Blank Films Inc
10341 San Pablo Ave, El Cerrito, CA 94530-3123
Tel: 510-525-0942 *Toll Free Tel:* 800-572-7618 *Fax:* 510-525-1204
E-mail: lesblankfilmsinc@gmail.com
Key Personnel
Pres: Harrod Blank
Dir & Ed: Gina Leibrecht
Dir & Prodr: David Silberberg
Founded: 1967
Films by Les Blank & others, nonfiction, music, art, cooking, filmmaking, folklore, creativity & vitality.
Catalog(s) available
Membership(s): American Film & Video Association; International Documentary Association

Blind
1702 Olympic Blvd, Santa Monica, CA 90404
Tel: 310-314-1618 *Fax:* 310-314-1718
Web Site: www.blind.com
Key Personnel
Founder & CEO: Chris Do
Exec Prodr/Busn Devt: S Tobin Kirk *E-mail:* tobin@blind.com
Creative Dir: Matthew Encina; Greg Gunn
Digital Strategy Dir: Jose Caballer
Head, Prodn: Amy Knerl
Prodr: Scott Rothstein
Mktg Assoc: Archi Prudencio
Founded: 1995
Motion graphics studio & design consultancy.

Blind Pig Records
Division of Whole Hog Inc
PO Box 2344, San Francisco, CA 94126
Tel: 415-550-6484 *Toll Free Tel:* 888-474-4736 *Fax:* 415-550-6485
E-mail: info@blindpigrecords.com
Web Site: www.blindpigrecords.com
Key Personnel
Pres: Edward Chmelewski *E-mail:* edward@blindpigrecords.com
Founded: 1977
Blues & roots music.
Catalog(s), free
Branch Office(s)
PO Box 18461, Chicago, IL 60618-0461, Contact: Jerry Del Giudice *Tel:* 773-772-0043 *E-mail:* info@wholehoginc.com
Membership(s): BMA; Music Business Association

Blonder Tongue Laboratories Inc
One Jake Brown Rd, Old Bridge, NJ 08857
Tel: 732-679-4000 *Toll Free Tel:* 800-523-6049 *Fax:* 732-679-4353
E-mail: custsvc@blondertongue.com; btglobalsales@blondertongue.com (other than US & CN)
Web Site: www.blondertongue.com
Key Personnel
CEO: James A Luksch
Pres: Robert J Palle
EVP: Emily M Nikoo
VP, Sales: Jeff Smith *Tel:* 512-238-6973; 858-531-2997 (cell) *E-mail:* jsmith@blondertongue.com
Dir, CATV Sales & Spec Mkts: Steve Cimino *Tel:* 858-505-1318; 858-531-2997 (cell) *E-mail:* scimino@blondertongue.com
Dir, Cust Serv: Lynne Russo *Tel:* 732-679-400 ext 4261 *E-mail:* lrusso@blondertongue.com
Dir, Tech Solutions: Steve Hegge *Tel:* 800-523-6049 ext 4358 *E-mail:* shegge@blondertongue.com
Founded: 1950
Provide system operators & integrators serving the cable, broadcast, satellite, IPTV, institutional & professional video markets with comprehensive solutions for the provision of content contribution, distribution & video delivery to homes & businesses.
Online catalog(s) available

Blood-Horse Publications
Subsidiary of Thoroughbred Owners & Breeders Association
3101 Beaumont Centre Circle, Lexington, KY 40513
Toll Free Tel: 800-866-2361; 800-582-5604
E-mail: customerservice@bloodhorse.com; advertise@bloodhorse.com
Web Site: www.bloodhorse.com
Key Personnel
Ed-in-Chief: Eric Mitchell *Tel:* 859-276-6770 *E-mail:* emitchell@bloodhorse.com
Online Mng Ed: Ron Mitchell *Tel:* 859-276-6729 *E-mail:* rmitchell@bloodhorse.com
News Ed: Tom Lamarra *Tel:* 859-276-6795 *E-mail:* tlamarra@bloodhorse.com
Founded: 1916
Offer a vast selection of thoroughbred & equine publications, products & services.
Catalog(s) available

Blue Barn Pictures Inc
68 Jay St, Suite 311, Brooklyn, NY 11201
Tel: 718-852-1403
Web Site: www.bluebarnpictures.com
Key Personnel
CEO: Jim Baker
Dir: Andrea Fumagalli; Matt Weckel
Creative Dir: David Castillo
Multimedia production company including HD, green screen, editing & effects.

Blue Dolphin Multimedia
Subsidiary of Blue Dolphin Publishing Inc
13340-D Grass Valley Ave, Grass Valley, CA 95945
Mailing Address: PO Box 8, Nevada City, CA 95959
Tel: 530-477-1503 *Toll Free Tel:* 800-643-0765 (orders) *Fax:* 530-477-8342
E-mail: bdolphin@bluedolphinpublishing.com
Web Site: www.bluedolphinpublishing.com
Key Personnel
Pres & Publr: Paul M Clemens *E-mail:* clemens@bluedolphinpublishing.com
Dir: Sean Mikuriya *E-mail:* pelicanpondstudios@hotmail.com
Catalog(s), semiannual, 1 full catalog & 1 mini-catalog of new titles

Blue Earth Pictures
5532 Code Ave, Minneapolis, MN 55436
Tel: 612-619-5909
E-mail: missioncontrol@blueearthpictures.com
Web Site: www.blueearthpictures.com
Key Personnel
Pres & Dir: James Ankeny *E-mail:* jankeny@blueearthpictures.com

Blue Lotus Temple Studio
PO Box 888, Boulder Creek, CA 95006
Tel: 831-338-2544
E-mail: info@bluelotustemple.com
Web Site: www.bluelotustemple.com
Key Personnel
Art Dir: Penny Slinger
Design & Prodn: Dhiren Dasu
Studio facilities include a chromakey video studio/photo studio, control room, vocal booth, edit suite, scoring studio & viewing/projection lounge. Digital film & video cameras for rent on a project basis.

Blue Media Supply Inc
3511 Church St, Suite F, Atlanta, GA 30021
Tel: 404-622-6709 *Toll Free Tel:* 866-717-6334 *Fax:* 404-622-1008
E-mail: sales@bluemediasupply.com
Web Site: www.bluemediasupply.com
Distributor of recordable media products, duplication equipment, audio video equipment & accessories.
Branch Office(s)
208 Production Ct, Louisville, KY 40299 *Tel:* 502-491-9084 *Fax:* 502-491-9085

Blue Mouse Studio
26829 37 St, Gobles, MI 49055
Tel: 269-628-5160
E-mail: frogville@earthlink.net; mwivi@earthlink.net
Key Personnel
Mgr: Chris Buchman
Art Dir: Rex Schneider
Founded: 1979
Creates all manner of illustrations but specializing in children's picture books, classic children's literature & educational material; cel animation & backgrounds for filmstrips & animated films; title artwork; slides from original artwork; computer graphics & also restores old photographs. We now offer the following: Computer Graphics, Power Point Presentation, Storyboards, Art (DVD, CD) Covers, DVD Production-enquire.
Catalog(s) available

blue onion
940 Wadsworth Blvd, 3rd fl, Lakewood, CO 80214
Tel: 303-232-1100 *Fax:* 303-232-2241
E-mail: info@digourideas.com
Web Site: www.digourideas.com
Key Personnel
VP, Busn Devt: Peter TenEyck
Founded: 1985
Branding, design, production & editing.
Catalog(s) available
Membership(s): Colorado Film & Video Association

Blue River Productions
Subsidiary of Lukacs & Associates
PO Box 1535, Breckenridge, CO 80424-1535
Tel: 970-390-8568
E-mail: filmbreckenridge@gmail.com
Web Site: www.filmcolorado.com
Key Personnel
Dir: Ann Lukacs *E-mail:* alukacs@earthlink.net
Handles permits, scouting & locations, hotel accommodations, production support & casting.

Blue Room Post
MBS Raleigh Studios, Bldg 5-A, Suite 100, 1600 Rosecrans Ave, Manhattan Beach, CA 90266
Tel: 310-727-2600
Web Site: www.blueroompost.com
Key Personnel
Owner: John Harris *Tel:* 310-941-0221 (cell) *E-mail:* john@blueroompost.com
Founded: 2010
DVD & Blu-ray authoring services, 5.1 audio encoding, CD & DVD replication, graphic design, visual effects, offline & online.
Branch Office(s)
Raleigh Studios, Chaplin Bldg, 2nd fl, 5300 Melrose Ave, Hollywood, CA 90038

Blue 60 Pictures
555 First Ave NE, Suite 200, Minneapolis, MN 55413
Tel: 612-871-6800
E-mail: info@blue-60.com
Web Site: www.blue-60.com
Key Personnel
Exec Prodr: Ridge Henderson
Dir & Dir, Photog: Greg Winter
Dir & Prodr: Fritz Basgen *Tel:* 612-871-6800 ext 103
Dir & Writer: Tom Bloom *Tel:* 612-871-6800 ext 102
Production services company.

Blue Sky Stock Footage
PO Box 177, Santa Fe, NM 87504-0177
Tel: 310-859-4709 *Toll Free Tel:* 877-992-5477 *Fax:* 310-823-0924
E-mail: sales@blueskyfootage.com
Web Site: www.blueskyfootage.com
Key Personnel
Owner & Cinematographer: Bill Mitchell
COO: Laurie Schrader
Prodn Mgr: Linda Giella
Founded: 1993
DV & HD royalty free stock footage that downloads immediately.

Blue Wave Records
3221 Perryville Rd, Baldwinsville, NY 13027
Tel: 315-638-4286 *Fax:* 315-635-4757
E-mail: bluewave@localnet.com
Web Site: www.bluewaverecords.com
Key Personnel
Owner: Greg Spencer
Founded: 1985
Artist oriented, non-commercial independent music label with a common thread of blues related music.

Blueyed Pictures Inc
8950 W Olympic Blvd, Suite 324, Beverly Hills, CA 90211
Tel: 310-295-0848 *Fax:* 310-295-0260
E-mail: la@blueyedpictures.com
Web Site: www.blueyedpictures.com
Key Personnel
Founder & Exec Prodr: Jamee Natella *E-mail:* jnatella@blueyedpictures.com
Exec Prodr: Chris Ellis *E-mail:* chrisellis@blueyedpictures.com
Prodr & Head, Prodn: Jon Goldberg
Prodr: Darrin Ball
Founded: 1998
Specialize in creating award-winning commercials, digital branded content, corporate films & multimedia entertainment.
Foreign Office(s): MBE No 316, Atago Green Hills, Mori Tower 1F, 2-5-1 Atago, Minato-ku, Tokyo 105-0002, Japan *Tel:* (0904) 4745 7121 (cell) *Fax:* (03) 3431 6233 *E-mail:* tokyo@blueyedpictures.com
77 Beak St, Suite 160, Soho, London W1F 7QP, United Kingdom, Exec Prodr: Chris Ellis *Tel:* (07534) 32 6559 (cell) *Fax:* (020) 8043 2154 *E-mail:* london@blueyedpictures.com
Membership(s): AICP; DGA; Producers Guild of America; Women in Film

BMI Supply
571 Queensbury Ave, Queensbury, NY 12804
Tel: 518-793-6706 *Toll Free Tel:* 800-836-0524 *Fax:* 518-793-6181
E-mail: bminy@bmisupply.com
Web Site: www.bmisupply.com
Key Personnel
Pres: Cindy Barber *E-mail:* cindy.barber@bmisupply.com
Dir, Mktg & Devt: Steve Roudebush *E-mail:* steve.roudebush@bmisupply.com
Sr Sales Mgr: Matt Williams *E-mail:* matt.williams@bmisupply.com
Sales Mgr: Jim Koehnle; Paul Martini *E-mail:* paul.martini@bmisupply.com; Mark Ross *E-mail:* mark.ross@bmisupply.com
Founded: 1987
Theatrical supply & installation company that offers stage lighting, rigging, stage hardware, paint, special effects, draperies, stage/studio lamps, intercom & more.
Catalog(s), annual, free, US only
Online catalog(s) available
Membership(s): Professional Lighting & Sound Association; USITT

Boeckeler Instruments Inc
4650 S Butterfield Dr, Tucson, AZ 85714
Tel: 520-745-0001 *Toll Free Tel:* 800-552-2262 *Fax:* 520-745-0004
E-mail: support@pointmaker.com
Web Site: www.boeckeler.com
Key Personnel
Pres: Pat Brey
Founded: 1942
Manufacturer of precision measuring devices, video measuring & software.
Data sheet(s) available
Membership(s): InfoComm International®; PRSA; RTDNA

Bogen Communications Inc
50 Spring St, Ramsey, NJ 07446
Mailing Address: PO Box 575, Ramsey, NJ 07446-0575
Tel: 201-934-8500 *Fax:* 201-934-9832
E-mail: info@bogen.com
Web Site: www.bogen.com
Founded: 1932
Catalog(s), annual, free
Membership(s): IPMA; NSCA

Boitnott Visual Communications Corp (BVC)
14201 Justice Rd, Midlothian, VA 23113
Mailing Address: PO Box 655, Midlothian, VA 23113-0655
Tel: 804-379-9400 *Fax:* 804-379-9413
Web Site: www.boitnottvisual.com
Key Personnel
CEO: L Harrell Boitnott
Pres: Keith Boitnott *E-mail:* kboitnott@boitnottvisual.com
Founded: 1969
AV rentals, systems integrators & LED projection screen rentals.

Boland Communications
16 Rancho Circle, Lake Forest, CA 92630
Tel: 949-465-9911 *Toll Free Tel:* 800-918-9090 *Fax:* 949-465-9944
E-mail: sales@bolandcom.com
Web Site: www.bolandcom.com
Key Personnel
Pres: Michael J Boland
Dir, Sales: Gary Litwin
Premium quality LCD monitor manufacturer.
Brochure(s), online
Membership(s): InfoComm International®; NAB; SID; SMPTE

Bolchazy - Carducci Publishers Inc
1570 Baskin Rd, Mundelein, IL 60060
Tel: 847-526-4344 *Toll Free Tel:* 800-392-6453 *Fax:* 847-526-2867
E-mail: info@bolchazy.com
Web Site: www.bolchazy.com
Key Personnel
Owner & Pres: Marie C Bolchazy, EdD *E-mail:* marie@bolchazy.com
VP: Allan Bolchazy *E-mail:* abolchazy@bolchazy.com
Online catalog(s) available

Bond Street Studio
235 Bond St, Brooklyn, NY 11217
Tel: 718-858-2238 *Fax:* 718-858-2239
E-mail: info@bondstreetstudio.com
Web Site: www.bondstreetstudio.com
Key Personnel
Owner: Robert DiScalfani
Studio Mgr: Cassandra St George
Studio space for film, still photography & music video shoots. Full array of professional camera, lighting & grip equipment available.

Bonnin Electronics Inc
617 Hipodromo St, San Juan, PR 00909
Mailing Address: PO Box 13846, San Juan, PR 00908-3846
Tel: 787-725-4765 *Fax:* 787-725-0840
Web Site: www.bonninelectronics.com
Key Personnel
CEO & Pres: Carlos Bonnin *E-mail:* carlos@bonninelectronics.com
Servs Mgr: Sebastian Bonnin
Founded: 1970
Multimedia & broadcast sound system, intercoms, CCTV installation & teleconference, prosound, home theater, integrator.
Catalog(s) available

Book Marketing Works LLC
50 Lovely St, Avon, CT 06001
Mailing Address: PO Box 715, Avon, CT 06001-0715
Tel: 860-675-1344
Web Site: www.bookmarketingworks.com
Key Personnel
Pres & Publr: Brian Jud *E-mail:* brianjud@bookmarketing.com
Book marketing products & services.
Catalog(s) available

Membership(s): The Association of Publishers for Special Sales; Connecticut Authors & Publishers Association; IBPA, the Independent Book Publishers Association

Books In Motion
Division of Classic Ventures Ltd
9922 E Montgomery Dr, Suite 31, Spokane Valley, WA 99206
Tel: 509-922-1646 *Toll Free Tel:* 800-752-3199 *Fax:* 509-922-1445
E-mail: sales@booksinmotion.com
Web Site: www.booksinmotion.com
Key Personnel
Pres: Gary Challender
Founded: 1980
Also distribute & produce MP3 downloads.

Books on Tape®
Division of Random House Inc
c/o Library & School Servs, 400 Hahn Rd, Westminster, MD 21157
Toll Free Tel: 800-733-3000 *Toll Free Fax:* 800-940-7046
E-mail: csbot@randomhouse.com
Web Site: www.booksontape.com
Key Personnel
Mktg Dir: Cheryl Herman *Tel:* 212-782-9000 ext 829462 *E-mail:* cherman@randomhouse.com
Founded: 1975
Adult, children's & teen unabridged audiobook productions of bestselling, award-winning titles. CDs, digital downloads & flexible standing order plan available.
Catalog(s), seasonal

Boonton Electronics
Subsidiary of Wireless Telecom Group Co
25 Eastmans Rd, Parsippany, NJ 07054
Tel: 973-386-9696 *Fax:* 973-386-9191
E-mail: info@boonton.com
Web Site: www.boonton.com
Key Personnel
CEO & Pres: Paul Genova
CFO & Corp Secy: Robert Censullo
SVP, Global Sales & Mktg: Joe Debold
Founded: 1947
Manufacturer of test equipment for RF & microwave systems used in both military & commercial sectors. Also manufactures impendance measuring instruments, RF voltmeters & audio analyzers.
Catalog(s) available
Foreign Office(s): Landmark House, Station Rd, Cheadle Hulme, Cheadle, Cheshire SK8 7BS, United Kingdom *Tel:* (0161) 486 3380 *Fax:* (0161) 486 3301 *E-mail:* info.uk@boonton.com

Bosch Security Systems North America
Subsidiary of Bosch Group
130 Perinton Pkwy, Fairport, NY 14450
Tel: 585-223-4060 *Toll Free Tel:* 800-289-0096 *Fax:* 585-223-9180
Web Site: us.boschsecurity.com
Key Personnel
Pres: Christopher Gerace
Pres, Sales Americas: Brian Wiser
Supplier of equipment for the global electronic protection & communications systems industries.
Catalog(s) available

Bose Corp
The Mountain, MS 2C3, Framingham, MA 01701-8863
Tel: 508-879-7330; 508-766-1099 (sales outside US) *Toll Free Tel:* 800-999-2673; 800-869-1855 (sales) *Fax:* 508-820-3465
E-mail: support@bose.com
Web Site: www.bose.com
Founded: 1964
Audio solutions for the home, office & mobile devices.
Membership(s): AES; ASA; NSCA

Boston Acoustics
Subsidiary of D+M Group
7 Constitution Way, Woburn, MA 01801
Tel: 201-762-6429 *Fax:* 978-538-6237
E-mail: weborders@bostonacoustics.com
Web Site: www.bostonacoustics.com
Key Personnel
Pres: Charlie Randall
SVP, Sales & Mktg: Phil Cohn
VP, Fin: Debra A Ricker-Rosato
Founded: 1979
Design & manufacture high-performance loudspeakers & tabletop products.

The Boston Connection Inc
PO Box 1835, Cotuit, MA 02635
Tel: 617-908-6258 *Fax:* 508-428-2036
E-mail: bconnect@cutfilm.com
Web Site: www.cutfilm.com
Key Personnel
Owner: Dwight Cody
Founded: 1983
Film editing equipment supplier.

Boston Light & Sound Inc
290 N Beacon St, Boston, MA 02135-1990
Tel: 617-787-3131 *Fax:* 617-787-4257
E-mail: info@blsi.com
Web Site: www.blsi.com
Key Personnel
Prodn Mgr: Celine Larimer *Tel:* 617-787-3131 ext 115 *E-mail:* celine@blsi.com
Design, installation & integration of sound systems along with film/video projection systems.

Boston Productions Inc
290 Vanderbilt Ave, Suite 1, Norwood, MA 02062
Tel: 781-255-1555
E-mail: imagine@bostonproductions.com
Web Site: www.bostonproductions.com
Key Personnel
Pres: Robert Noll
Full service production services.

Bowens USA
Division of MAC Group
75 Virginia Rd, North White Plains, NY 10603
Tel: 914-347-3300 *Fax:* 914-347-3309
Web Site: www.bowensusa.com
Key Personnel
Pres, MAC Group: Jan Lederman
Photographic lighting & light modifiers.

Bowers Media Group Inc
6035 Florence Ave, Suite 100, Charlotte, NC 28212
Mailing Address: PO Box 470352, Charlotte, NC 28247
Tel: 704-542-8754 *Fax:* 704-532-1058
Web Site: www.bowersmediagroup.com
Key Personnel
Pres: Bruce Bowers *E-mail:* bruce@bowersmediagroup.com
Founded: 1989
Provide crews-complete video production services, scripting & post-production.
Membership(s): British-American Business Association; Charlotte Film & Video Association; Charlotte World Trade Association; French American Business Alliance

Bowie Audio Visual Enterprises Inc
290 Highpoint Dr, Ridgeland, MS 39157
Tel: 601-957-6566 *Toll Free Tel:* 800-748-9030 *Fax:* 601-957-7042
E-mail: sales@bowieav.com
Web Site: www.bowieav.com
Key Personnel
Pres: Bob Smylie
Founded: 1976
Sales & rentals of AV equipment.
Catalog(s) available
Membership(s): InfoComm International®

Boxcar Studio
1444 Dupont St W, Bldg C, Suite 21, Toronto, ON M6P 4H3, Canada
Tel: 416-465-8094
E-mail: info@boxcarstudio.ca
Web Site: www.boxcarstudio.ca
Studio, grip, lighting, cameras, audio equipment & computer rentals.

Boxlight Inc
NE 151 Hwy 300, Suite A, Belfair, WA 98528
Mailing Address: PO Box 2609, Belfair, WA 98528-2609
Tel: 360-464-2119 *Fax:* 360-282-6141
E-mail: sales@boxlight.com
Web Site: www.boxlight.com
Key Personnel
Pres: Hank Nance
Founded: 1985
AV digital projection equipment.
Catalog(s) available
Membership(s): InfoComm International®

Boyce Nemec Designs
PO Box 566, Norfolk, CT 06058-0566
Tel: 860-542-5937
Web Site: www.boycenemec.com
Key Personnel
Principal: Andrew Smith *E-mail:* andy@boycenemec.com
Design & consulting services or e-mail.

Bradley Broadcast & Pro Audio
Division of SCMS Inc
PO Box 756, New Market, MD 21774
Tel: 301-682-8700 *Toll Free Tel:* 800-732-7665 *Fax:* 301-263-7042
E-mail: beburg@bradleybroadcast.com
Web Site: www.bradleybroadcast.com
Key Personnel
Gen Mgr: Art Reed *E-mail:* areed@bradleybroadcast.com
Audio, RF & broadcast equipment supplier.
Online catalog(s) available

Brady Corp
6555 W Good Hope Rd, Milwaukee, WI 53201-0571
Mailing Address: PO Box 571, Milwaukee, WI 53201-0571
Tel: 414-358-6600 *Toll Free Tel:* 800-541-1686 *Toll Free Fax:* 800-292-2289
Web Site: www.bradycorp.com
Key Personnel
CEO & Dir: J Michael Nauman
Pres: Thomas J Felmer
SVP, HR: Helena Nelligan
Founded: 1914
Manufacturer & marketer of complete solutions that identify & protect premises, products & people.
Catalog(s) available
Membership(s): Content Delivery & Storage Association

Branam Enterprises Inc
9152 Independence Ave, Chatsworth, CA 91311
Tel: 818-885-6474 *Toll Free Tel:* 877-295-3390 *Fax:* 818-885-6475
E-mail: info@branament.com
Web Site: www.branament.com

Key Personnel
CEO: Kristy Branam Farrell *E-mail:* kristy@branament.com
Founded: 1978
Theatrical rigging & special effects. Rigging & grip equipment rental, fabrication, special flying effects & stunts. Aerial camera rigs, CM chain motors, truss, curtain track, decks, I-beam track, fall protection & rigging accessories.
Online catalog(s) available

The Brand Gallery
701 W Putnam Ave, Greenwich, CT 06830
Tel: 203-422-3900 *Fax:* 203-531-1394
Web Site: www.thebrandgallery.com
Key Personnel
CEO: Phil McIntyre *E-mail:* philm@thebrandgallery.com
Chief Creative Offr: Iain Greenway
Founded: 2005

Brantley Sound Associates Inc
115 Duluth Ave, Nashville, TN 37209-1207
Tel: 615-256-6260
E-mail: ccussick@brantleysound.com
Web Site: www.brantleysound.com
Key Personnel
Owner & CEO: Bobby Brantley
Founded: 1973
Provider of high-end full production services.

Bravo Studios
40 W 27 St, 2nd fl, New York, NY 10001
Tel: 212-563-0054
E-mail: info@newyorkgreenscreen.com
Web Site: www.newyorkgreenscreen.com
Two film studios with production support. Cameras, lighting & grip equipment as well as video production & post-production services.
Branch Office(s)
145 W 28 St, 2nd fl, New York, NY 10001

BRB Audiovisual Productions
135 Punkup Rd, Oxford, CT 06478-1747
Tel: 203-881-3577 *Toll Free Tel:* 800-587-7521
E-mail: services@brbaudiovisual.com
Web Site: brbaudiovisual.com
Founded: 1984
Audio & video production company.
Membership(s): NAB; WEVA

Breeze Productions Inc
1660 Edgewood Rd, Highland Park, IL 60035
Tel: 312-860-1710
Web Site: www.breezeprod.com
Key Personnel
Founder & Pres: Mel Levy *E-mail:* mel@breezeprod.com
Founded: 1998
Corporate visual communications.

Bretford Manufacturing Inc
11000 Seymour Ave, Franklin Park, IL 60131
Tel: 847-678-2545 *Toll Free Tel:* 800-521-9614 *Fax:* 847-678-0852 *Toll Free Fax:* 800-343-1779
E-mail: customerservice@bretford.com
Web Site: bretford.com
Key Personnel
CEO & Pres: Chris Petrick
Dir, Mktg Communs: Cindy Weinschreider
Founded: 1948
Design & manufacture dependable furniture products.
Catalog(s), free, PDF download
Foreign Office(s): Bretford Manufacturing Ltd, 2 Eatongate, 110 Windsor Rd, Slough, Berks, United Kingdom *Tel:* (01753) 539955 *Fax:* (01753) 539478 *E-mail:* ukmarketing@bretford.com
Membership(s): Education Market Association; InfoComm International®

BRg Music Works
Division of Premiere Networks
111 Presidential Blvd, Suite 100, Bala Cynwyd, PA 19004
Tel: 610-971-9490
Web Site: brg.sourceaudio.com
Founded: 1972
Produce jingles for local & regional advertisers.

Brian Film Productions LLC
254 W 25 St, Suite 6-A, New York, NY 10001-7325
Tel: 212-645-8795
Key Personnel
Owner: Brian Kellman
Membership(s): New York Women in Film & Television

The Brick Studio
414 Raymond Blvd, Studio 5, Newark, NJ 07105
Tel: 646-801-4449
E-mail: info@thebrickstudio.com
Web Site: www.thebrickstudio.com
Studio & equipment rental, post-production services.

Bridge Publications Inc
5600 E Olympic Blvd, Los Angeles, CA 90022
Tel: 323-953-3320; 323-888-6200 *Toll Free Tel:* 800-722-1733 *Fax:* 323-888-6202
E-mail: info@bridgepub.com
Web Site: www.bridgepub.com
Founded: 1981
Publish audio books.
Catalog(s) available
Membership(s): Audio Publishers Association

Bridge Records Inc
200 Clinton Ave, New Rochelle, NY 10801
Tel: 914-654-9270
E-mail: bridgerec@bridgerecords.com
Web Site: www.bridgerecords.com
Key Personnel
Pres: Becky Starobin
VP: Robert Starobin
Dir, Artists & Repertoire: David Starobin
Founded: 1981
Issue CDs, DVDs & digital downloads. Also a publishing arm & artist management.
Online catalog(s) available

Bridger Productions Inc
4150 Glory View Lane, Jackson, WY 83001
Mailing Address: PO Box 8131, Jackson, WY 83002
Tel: 307-733-7871 *Fax:* 307-734-1947
E-mail: info@bridgerproductions.com
Web Site: www.bridgerproductions.com
Key Personnel
Founder & Pres: Michael Emmer
Full service film & video production company.

Bright Giant Creative Group
7600 Burnet Rd, Suite 180, Austin, TX 78757
Tel: 512-535-7855
E-mail: info@brightgiantstudios.com
Web Site: brightgiantcg.com
Services include video production, instructional design, eLearning development, video editing & post-production, visual communications, motion graphics & script writing.

Bright Ideas Creative Services
107 W Maple St, Suite 206, Jeffersonville, IN 47130
Mailing Address: PO Box 446, Jeffersonville, IN 47131
Tel: 812-282-9900; 502-693-9900 (cell) *Toll Free Fax:* 866-593-5753
Web Site: www.brightideascreative.com
Key Personnel
Owner: William Tyler Thomas *E-mail:* bill@brightideascreative.com
Founded: 1986
Complete AV production services.

Bright Star Productions Inc
2420 Center St, Houston, TX 77007
Tel: 713-529-2757 *Fax:* 713-529-2329
Web Site: www.brightstarproductions.com
Key Personnel
Prodn Mgr: Larry Huff *E-mail:* larryh@brightstarproductions.com

Brightline LP
580 Mayer St, Bldg 7, Bridgeville, PA 15017
Tel: 412-206-0106 *Fax:* 412-206-0146
E-mail: information@brightlines.com
Web Site: www.brightlines.com
Founded: 1997
Energy efficient specialty lighting manufacturer. Light fixtures for broadcast, video conference, telemedicine, telepsychology, distance ed & architectural applications.
Catalog(s), as requested, free, full line binder

Brilliance Audio
1704 Eaton Dr, Grand Haven, MI 49417
Mailing Address: PO Box 887, Grand Haven, MI 49417-0887
Tel: 616-846-5256 *Toll Free Tel:* 800-648-2312 (orders) *Fax:* 616-846-0630
E-mail: customerservice@brillianceaudio.com
Web Site: www.brillianceaudio.com
Key Personnel
Pres & Publr: Mark Pereira *Tel:* 616-846-5256 ext 701
Sales Mgr: Steve Woessner
Studio Mgr: Colleen Rocky
Founded: 1984
Audio publishing; CDs, MP3 CDs & downloads.
Catalog(s), consumer; retail; library products
Membership(s): Audio Publishers Association; The Recording Academy

Brim Electronics
120 Home Place, Lodi, NJ 07644
Tel: 201-796-2886 *Fax:* 973-778-2792
E-mail: info@brimelectronics.com
Web Site: www.brimelectronics.com
Key Personnel
Sales Mgr: B Brown
Founded: 1975

Britannica Film & Video
Division of Encyclopaedia Britannica Inc
331 N LaSalle St, Chicago, IL 60654
Toll Free Tel: 800-621-3900 *Toll Free Fax:* 800-344-9624
E-mail: contact@eb.com
Web Site: info.eb.com
Key Personnel
Exec Dir, Sales: Rick Lumsden
Catalog(s) available

Broad Street Inc
242 W 30 St, 2nd fl, New York, NY 10001
Tel: 212-780-5700
E-mail: newyork@broadstreet.com
Web Site: www.broadstreet.com
Key Personnel
CEO & Mng Partner: Mark Baltazar
CFO & Partner: Ed Gibbons
SVP & Partner: Claudia Rodriguez Tressler
Full service production company.

Broadcast Center Studios
700 Millbridge Gardens, Clementon, NJ 08021
Tel: 856-751-3500
Web Site: www.broadcastcenterstudios.com
Key Personnel
Pres: Larry Scott

Broadcast Devices Inc
Westchester Industrial Complex, 3199 Albany Post Rd, Suite 122, Buchanan, NY 10511-1639
Tel: 914-737-5032 *Fax:* 914-736-6916
E-mail: sales@broadcast-devices.com
Web Site: www.broadcast-devices.com
Key Personnel
Owner & Pres: Bob Tarsio
Founded: 1985
Equipment for the broadcast industry; RF & audio products, RF monitor protection systems.

Broadcast Electronics
4100 N 24 St, Quincy, IL 62305
Tel: 217-224-9600 *Fax:* 217-224-9607
E-mail: bdcast@bdcast.com
Web Site: www.bdcast.com
Key Personnel
Pres: Joseph Roark
Mktg Mgr: Jim Roberts
Founded: 1959
Radio broadcast equipment manufacturer.
Online catalog(s) available
Membership(s): NAB; SBE; TAB

Broadcast Management Group
1625 Eye St NW, Suite 620, Washington, DC 20006
Tel: 202-609-7757
E-mail: info@broadcastmgmt.com
Web Site: www.broadcastmgmt.com
Key Personnel
CEO: Todd Mason
EVP, Prodn: Max J Schindler
VP & Prodn Mgr: Andrew Ryback
VP, West Coast Opers: Steve McIntire
Acctg Mgr: Abel Darg
Founded: 2005
Television production management services, studio facility management, remote production services & social media integration.
Branch Office(s)
2600 W Olive Ave, 5th fl, Burbank, CA 91505 *Tel:* 310-807-4635
One Rockefeller Ctr, 10th fl, New York, NY 10020 *Tel:* 212-784-6020

Broadcast Microwave Services (BMS)
Subsidiary of Cohu Inc
12367 Crosthwaite Circle, Poway, CA 92064
Tel: 858-391-3050 *Toll Free Tel:* 800-669-9667 *Fax:* 858-391-3049
E-mail: sales@bms-inc.com
Web Site: www.bms-inc.com
Key Personnel
Pres: Graham Bunney
Founded: 1984
System customization services including: portable & fixed site microwave communication equipment links & manufacturing.
Online catalog(s) available
Foreign Office(s): Georg-Ohm-Str-2, 65232 Taunesstein, Germany *Tel:* (06128) 7408-200 *Fax:* (06128) 7408-229

Broadcast Rentals
2343 W University Dr, Suite 101, Tempe, AZ 85281
Tel: 480-894-1456 *Toll Free Tel:* 888-686-7368 *Fax:* 480-894-1023
E-mail: rent@broadcastrentals.com
Web Site: www.broadcastrentals.com
Key Personnel
Owner: Deborah Oslund; Steve Oslund
Founded: 1994
Rents broadcast & support equipment. Supply projection, teleprompting, audio & support equipment for corporate meetings & events. Also media duplication & replication services & used gear for sale.

Broadcast Supply World Wide
2237 S 19 St, Tacoma, WA 98405
Tel: 253-565-2301 (intl) *Toll Free Tel:* 800-426-8434 *Fax:* 253-565-8114 (intl) *Toll Free Fax:* 800-231-7055
E-mail: sales@bswusa.com; info@bswusa.com; customersupport@bswusa.com
Web Site: www.bswusa.com
Key Personnel
Pres: Tim Schwieger
Sales Mgr: Shannon Nichols *E-mail:* shannon@bswusa.com
Audio equipment dealer.
Catalog(s) available
Online catalog(s) available
Membership(s): NAMM, the National Association of Music Merchants; SBE

Broadcast Video Productions LLC
61 Briarwood Dr, Old Saybrook, CT 06475
Tel: 860-575-7247 *Fax:* 860-395-2036
E-mail: bvpusa@comcast.net
Key Personnel
Pres: Debra Ann Soudan; Kenneth Soudan
Founded: 1984
30 years experience in AV productions, DVD, CD, Betacam DV formats, corporate, event & cable programming.
Membership(s): AP; CAPP; IBEW; MCA-I

Broadcast Video Systems Corp
25 Forest Ridge Rd, Richmond Hill, ON L4E 3L8, Canada
E-mail: broadcastvideosystems@gmail.com
Web Site: www.bvs.ca
Key Personnel
Pres: Bert Verwey
VP: Jill Verwey *E-mail:* jill@bvs.ca
Founded: 1975
Manufacturers of innovative video equipment for the television broadcast & video production industries.

Broadcasters General Store Inc
2480 SE 52 St, Ocala, FL 34480
Tel: 352-622-7700 *Fax:* 352-629-7000
E-mail: sales@bgs.cc (orders)
Web Site: www.bgs.cc
Key Personnel
Pres: Dave Kerstin
Sales Mgr: Buck Waters *E-mail:* buck@bgs.cc
Sales: Jonathan Shute *E-mail:* jon@bgs.cc
Founded: 1979
Audio & video equipment sales.
Membership(s): NAB; SBE

BroadcastStore.com
9420 Lurline Ave, Unit C, Chatsworth, CA 91311
Tel: 818-998-9100 *Fax:* 818-998-9106
E-mail: sales@broadcaststore.com
Web Site: www.broadcaststore.com
Key Personnel
Owner & Pres: Lou Claude
Sales Mgr: Norm Hoffman *E-mail:* nhoffman@alterantech.com
Founded: 1984
Online catalog(s) available
Membership(s): NAB; SMPTE; STE

Broadview Media
4455 W 77 St, Minneapolis, MN 55435
Tel: 952-835-4455; 612-280-6947 *Fax:* 952-835-0971
E-mail: sales@broadviewmedia.com; corporate@broadviewmedia.com
Web Site: www.broadviewmedia.com
Key Personnel
Gen Mgr: Red White *E-mail:* rwhite@globeuniversity.edu
Studio & equipment rental.
Membership(s): SMPTE

Broadview Software Inc
110 Adelaide St E, Toronto, ON M5C 1K9, Canada
Tel: 416-778-0623 *Fax:* 416-778-0648
E-mail: sales@broadviewsoftware.com
Web Site: www.broadviewsoftware.com
Key Personnel
Pres: Michael Atkin *E-mail:* michael@broadviewsoftware.com
Provide software for television & radio broadcasters with a solution for traffic, scheduling, programming, rights management & ad management.

Broadway Costumes Inc
1100 W Cermak Rd, 2nd fl, Chicago, IL 60608
Tel: 312-829-6400 *Toll Free Tel:* 800-397-3316 *Fax:* 312-829-8621
E-mail: rentals@broadwaycostumes.com
Web Site: www.broadwaycostumes.com
Key Personnel
Pres: R C Schramm
Rentals Mgr: Amanda Lifvendahl
Founded: 1886
Costume rentals.

Broadway Digital
1014 E Broadway, Louisville, KY 40204
Mailing Address: 1611 Deerwood Ave, Louisville, KY 40205
Tel: 502-540-5301 *Fax:* 502-540-5565
E-mail: msworkscm@mindspring.com
Web Site: www.broadwaydigital.us
Key Personnel
Pres: Charles Miesner
Fiber & satellite uplinks. Studios in Louisville, KY, Indianapolis, IN, Austin, TX & Dallas, TX.

Brodart Co
500 Arch St, Williamsport, PA 17701
Tel: 570-769-3265 *Toll Free Tel:* 888-820-4377 *Toll Free Fax:* 800-283-6087
E-mail: supplies.customerservice@brodart.com
Web Site: www.shopbrodart.com
Key Personnel
CEO & Pres: Joseph Largen
Mktg Mgr: Jolie Conahan
AV equipment, media supplies & cases.
Catalog(s) available
Online catalog(s) available
Membership(s): ALA

Brodsky & Treadway
69 Warehouse Lane, Rowley, MA 01969
Mailing Address: PO Box 335, Rowley, MA 01969-0735
Tel: 978-948-7985
Web Site: www.LittleFilm.com
Key Personnel
Mgr: Toni Treadway
Small gauge film specialists. Film restoration & preservation.
Membership(s): Association of Moving Image Archivists; National Alliance for Media Arts & Culture

Bromwell Marketing
3 Allegheny Ctr, Suite 111, Pittsburgh, PA 15212
Tel: 412-321-4118
E-mail: bromwell@earthlink.net
Web Site: www.bromwellmarketing.com

Key Personnel
Owner: Theodore R Bromwell
AV marketing.
Online catalog(s) available

Paul H Brookes Publishing Co
PO Box 10624, Baltimore, MD 21285-0624
Tel: 410-337-9580 *Toll Free Tel:* 800-638-3775 (cust serv) *Fax:* 410-337-8539
E-mail: custserv@brookespublishing.com
Web Site: www.brookespublishing.com
Key Personnel
Mktg Dir: Jessica Reighard *E-mail:* jreighard@brookespublishing.com
Founded: 1978
Early childhood education products.
Catalog(s), annual, free, books & videos

Brookline Books
8 Trumbull Rd, Suite B-001, Northampton, MA 01060
Tel: 413-584-0184; 603-669-7032 (orders) *Toll Free Tel:* 800-666-BOOK (666-2665 cust serv) *Fax:* 413-584-6184
E-mail: brbooks@yahoo.com
Web Site: www.brooklinebooks.com
Key Personnel
Pres: Michael Beattie
Founded: 1983
Distribute educational programs; readability software for MAC & PC.
Online catalog(s) available

Brooklyn Botanic Garden
1000 Washington Ave, Brooklyn, NY 11225
Tel: 718-623-7200
E-mail: feedback@bbg.org
Web Site: www.bbg.org

Brooklyn College Television Center
Division of City University of New York (CUNY)
Whitehead Hall, 2900 Bedford Ave, Rm 018-A, Brooklyn, NY 11210-2889
Tel: 718-951-5585 *Fax:* 718-951-5558
Web Site: www.bctvr.org/tvcenter_base.php
Key Personnel
Dir: Richard Grossberg
Opers Mgr: Jeanine Corbert *E-mail:* jcorbert@brooklyn.cuny.edu
TV post-production facility that supports academic functions.

Brooklyn Films
PO Box 20412, New York, NY 10021-0066
Tel: 212-744-2845
E-mail: inquiries@brooklynfilms.com
Web Site: www.brooklynfilms.com
Key Personnel
Founding Partner: Robin C Adams *E-mail:* robin.adams@brooklynfilms.com; Michael Helman
Founded: 1987
Entertainment & technology company.

Brooklyn Fire Proof
119 Ingraham St, Brooklyn, NY 11237
Tel: 718-456-7570
E-mail: hello@brooklynfireproof.com
Web Site: www.brooklynfireproof.com
Rents full service film & television sound & workspaces.

Brooklyn Studios
211 Meserole Ave, 2nd fl, Brooklyn, NY 11222
Tel: 718-392-1007 *Fax:* 718-392-1008
E-mail: brooklynstudios@verizon.net
Web Site: www.brooklynstudios.net
Rental studios & equipment for photography, video, film, commercials & music videos.

The Brookwood Studio Inc
6870 N Territorial Rd, Plymouth, MI 48170
Tel: 734-358-6071
E-mail: info@brookwoodstudio.com
Web Site: www.brookwoodstudio.com
Key Personnel
Owner, Pres & Chief Engr: David Lau *E-mail:* david@brookwoodstudio.com
Founded: 1978
Fine arts audio recording.

Broughton's Church Supplies, Religious Books & Gifts
322 Consumers Rd, North York, ON M2J 1P8, Canada
Tel: 416-690-4777 *Toll Free Tel:* 800-268-4449 *Fax:* 416-690-5357
E-mail: sales@bbroughton.com
Web Site: www.bbroughton.com
Key Personnel
Owner: Brian Broughton
Founded: 1970
Books & AV materials on religious education for church, home & school.
Catalog(s), every 5 yrs

Brown Bag Imaging
Subsidiary of Premiere Radio Networks Inc
111 Presidential Blvd, Suite 100, Bala Cynwyd, PA 19004
Toll Free Tel: 800-533-8686
E-mail: sales@brownbagimaging.com
Web Site: brownbag.sourceaudio.com
Key Personnel
Gen Mgr: Doug Reed *Tel:* 610-784-5517
Barter production services available for radio & TV imaging, radio imaging, TV promo use.
Online catalog(s) available

Brown United
PO Box 362, Monrovia, CA 91017-0362
Tel: 626-357-1161 *Toll Free Tel:* 800-44-BROWN (442-7696) *Fax:* 626-358-3064 *Toll Free Fax:* 800-26-BROWN (262-7696)
E-mail: info@brownunited.com
Web Site: www.brownunited.com
Key Personnel
CEO: John Brown
Pres: Mike Zwaal
VP, Sales: Jeff Llamas
AV support (structural) services, four plus post roofs, staging & more.

Nicholas Browse & Associates, see Cavanaugh Tocci Associates Inc

Brush Industries Inc
301 Reagan St, Sunbury, PA 17801
Mailing Address: PO Box 638, Sunbury, PA 17801-0638
Tel: 570-286-5611 *Fax:* 570-286-2649
E-mail: info@brushindustries.com
Web Site: www.brushindustries.com
Key Personnel
Pres: Karen Nickolauson
Dir, Sales & Mktg: Jeff Myers
Magnetic read & write heads & long life magnetic readers.
Catalog(s) available
Membership(s): AIM; ICMA

Bryce Corp
4505 Old Lamar Ave, Memphis, TN 38118
Tel: 901-369-4400 *Toll Free Tel:* 800-238-7277
Web Site: www.brycecorp.com
Key Personnel
Chmn & CEO: Tom Bryce
Founded: 1976

Bryston Ltd
677 Neal Dr, Peterborough, ON K9J 6X7, Canada
Mailing Address: PO Box 2170, Peterborough, ON K9J 7Y4, Canada
Tel: 705-742-5325 *Fax:* 705-742-0882
Web Site: bryston.com
Key Personnel
CEO: Christopher Russell
Pres: Brian W Russell *E-mail:* bwrussell@bryston.com
VP, Sales: James Tanner *E-mail:* jamestanner@bryston.com
High-end audio equipment manufacturer.
Brochure(s) available

BSW Records
PO Box 2297, Universal City, TX 78148-1297
Tel: 210-653-3989 *Fax:* 210-653-3989
E-mail: bswr18@att.net
Web Site: www.bsw-records.com
Key Personnel
CEO & Pres: Frank Willson
VP, Nashville Off: Earl E Owens *E-mail:* earlowens@bellsouth.net
VP, Europe: Regina Willson
Founded: 1987
Record label.
Catalog(s), annual, free
Branch Office(s)
124 Lakeview Dr, Hendersonville, TN 37075 *Tel:* 615-824-1578
Membership(s): Instructional Systems Association; The Recording Academy

BTX Technologies
5 Skyline Dr, Hawthorne, NY 10532
Tel: 914-592-1800 *Toll Free Tel:* 800-666-0996 *Toll Free Fax:* 800-569-4244
E-mail: info@btx.com
Web Site: www.btx.com
Key Personnel
Sr Mktg Mgr: Kim Robbins *E-mail:* kimr@btx.com
Founded: 1967
Distributor & manufacturer of the industry's cutting edge interface & integration products for audio, video & data systems.
Catalog(s) available
Online catalog(s) available
Membership(s): Custom Electronic Design & Installation Association; Electronic Components Industry Association; InfoComm International®; NSCA; SMPTE

Bud Industries
4605 E 355 St, Willoughby, OH 44094
Tel: 440-946-3200 *Fax:* 440-951-4015
E-mail: saleseast@budind.com
Web Site: www.budind.com
Key Personnel
Pres: B K Haas
Online catalog(s) available

Billy Budd Films Inc
235 E 57 St, New York, NY 10022
Tel: 212-755-3968
E-mail: info@billybuddfilms.com
Web Site: www.billybuddfilms.com
Key Personnel
Pres: Frank Moynihan
Produce clay animated classics.

Budget Films Stock Footage Inc
706 N Vendome St, Suite 6, Los Angeles, CA 90026
Tel: 323-660-0187 *Fax:* 323-660-5571
E-mail: filmclip@aol.com; info@budgetfilms.com
Web Site: www.budgetfilms.com
Key Personnel
Mgr: Layne J Drebin-Murphy
Founded: 1962
Stock footage library.
Membership(s): Association of Moving Image Archivists

Budget Video Rentals
Division of SuperGroup International
1825 NE 149 St, Miami, FL 33181
Tel: 305-945-8888 *Toll Free Tel:* 800-772-1111
Fax: 305-945-0300
E-mail: rentals@budgetvideo.com
Web Site: budgetvideo.com
Rental house for cameras, accessories & production tools.

BUF Technology
12335 World Trade Dr, Suite 11, San Diego, CA 92128
Tel: 858-451-1350 *Fax:* 858-451-6589
E-mail: info@buftek.com
Web Site: www.buftek.com
Key Personnel
VP, Mktg: Tracey H Bredon
Founded: 1991
Manufacturer of control systems for broadcast & professional television equipment. Instant replay systems, Server Control, VTR/DDR Control & Router Controls.
Membership(s): NAB; SMPTE

Bulb Direct
7911 Rae Blvd, Victor, NY 14564
Tel: 585-385-3540 *Toll Free Tel:* 800-772-5267
Fax: 585-385-4976 *Toll Free Fax:* 800-257-0760
E-mail: info@bulbdirect.com
Web Site: www.bulbdirect.com
Key Personnel
VP: Deb Smith
Opers Mgr: Connie Taylor *E-mail:* connie@bulbdirect.com
Replacement lamp distributor specializing in bulbs for audio visual, photographic, stage studio & video equipment. We offer the brand names GE, Osram Sylvania, Philips, Eiko & Ushio along with Duracell batteries & Pyramex safety glasses.

Bulbman Inc
630 Sunshine Lane, Reno, NV 89502
Mailing Address: PO Box 12280, Reno, NV 89510-2280
Tel: 775-788-5661 *Toll Free Tel:* 800-648-1163
Fax: 775-329-6599 *Toll Free Fax:* 800-548-6216
E-mail: service@bulbman.com
Web Site: www.bulbman.com
Key Personnel
CEO: Dee Ann Harn
Replacement bulbs for all projectors; stage & studio lighting.
Branch Office(s)
Bulbman Vegas, 4230 Cameron St, Las Vegas, NV 89103 *Tel:* 702-364-9000 *Fax:* 702-364-0138 *Toll Free Fax:* 800-548-6216
Bulbman Sacramento, 3101 Orange Grove, North Highlands, CA 95660, Contact: Dennis Curran *Tel:* 916-920-3234 *Toll Free Tel:* 800-648-1163 *Toll Free Fax:* 800-548-6216

Bulbtronics Inc
45 Banfi Plaza N, Farmingdale, NY 11735
Tel: 631-249-2272 *Toll Free Tel:* 800-654-8542 (sales); 800-588-2852 *Fax:* 631-249-6066
E-mail: marketing@bulbtronics.com
Web Site: www.bulbtronics.com
Key Personnel
CEO & Pres: Bruce R Thaw
Dir, Sales & Mktg: Barbara Kaplan
Founded: 1976
Replacement lamps, bulbs & batteries for all applications.
Online catalog(s) available
Branch Office(s)
415 W 50 St, New York, NY 10019 *Tel:* 212-765-6190 *Fax:* 212-765-6195
2210 N Screenland Dr, Burbank, CA 91505 *Tel:* 323-461-6262 *Fax:* 323-461-7307
9990 NW 14 St, Suite 106, Miami, FL 33172, VP: John Dahdouh *Tel:* 305-704-7163 *Fax:* 305-704-7076 *E-mail:* jdahdouh@bulbtronics.com
9460 Delegates Dr, Suite 108, Orlando, FL 32837 *Tel:* 407-857-1777 *Toll Free Tel:* 866-675-2852 *Fax:* 407-857-1115
6185 S Valley View Dr, Suite O, Las Vegas, NV 89118 *Tel:* 702-586-9993 *Fax:* 702-586-9999

Bullfrog Films Inc
PO Box 149, Oley, PA 19547-0149
Tel: 610-779-8226 *Toll Free Tel:* 800-543-3764
Fax: 610-370-1978
E-mail: video@bullfrogfilms.com
Web Site: www.bullfrogfilms.com
Key Personnel
Pres: John Hoskyns-Abrahall *E-mail:* john@bullfrogfilms.com
VP: Winifred Scherrer
Educational video & DVD distributor.
Catalog(s) available
Shipping Address: 372 Dautrich Rd, Reading, PA 19606
Membership(s): ALA; Consortium of College & University Media Centers; National Association of Media & Technology Centers; PAECT

Richard W Burden Associates
20944 Sherman Way, Canoga Park, CA 91303
Tel: 818-340-4590
Key Personnel
Principal: Richard W Burden
Low power broadcast systems for theatres; equipment & facilities consulting.
Catalog(s) available
Membership(s): AES; SBE; SMPTE

The Bureau for At-Risk Youth
Division of The Guidance Group
PO Box 170, Farmingdale, NY 11738
Toll Free Tel: 800-99-YOUTH (999-6884)
Toll Free Fax: 800-262-1886
Web Site: www.at-risk.com; www.guidance-group.com
Educational publishing company that develops guidance & health videos, DVD games, activity books, curricula, pamphlets & print materials for the K-12 school market.
Catalog(s) available
Online catalog(s) available

Burk Technology Inc
7 Beaver Brook Rd, Littleton, MA 01460
Tel: 978-486-0086 *Toll Free Tel:* 800-255-8090
Fax: 978-486-0081
E-mail: sales@burk.com; orders@burk.com
Web Site: www.burk.com
Key Personnel
Opers Mgr: Kevin Frappier
Sales Dir: Matt Leland
Remote monitoring & control system manufacturer.
Online catalog(s) available

Burlington A/V Recording Media
106 Mott St, Oceanside, NY 11572
Tel: 516-678-4414 *Toll Free Tel:* 800-331-3191
Fax: 516-678-8959
E-mail: burlington@optonline.net
Web Site: www.recordingstore.com
Key Personnel
Pres: Jan Schwartz
Gen Mgr: Tom Marchetti *Tel:* 800-331-3191 ext 122
Founded: 1970
Distributor of pro audio, recording & DJ equipment, musical gear, musical instruments, recording media, audio/video tape formats & hard drives. Leading seller of air products, such as air cleaners, humidifiers, etc. In business over 40 years with a top reputation serving the consumer & professional.

Larry Burr
602 Via Casitas, Greenbrae, CA 94904
Tel: 415-925-0822
E-mail: jabarni@yahoo.com
Founded: 1983
Stock photos.

Burrud Productions Inc
468 N Camden Dr, 2nd fl, Beverly Hills, CA 90210
Tel: 310-860-5158 *Fax:* 562-595-5986
E-mail: info@burrud.com
Web Site: www.burrud.com
Key Personnel
CEO & Pres: John Burrud
Founded: 1954
Branch Office(s)
3620 Long Beach Blvd, Suite C1, Long Beach, CA 90807 (prodn facility & billing)

Burst Electronics Inc
PO Box 65947, Albuquerque, NM 87193
Tel: 505-898-1455
E-mail: sales@burstelectronics.com
Web Site: www.burstelectronics.com
Key Personnel
Pres: Brad Hamlin
Founded: 1985
Manufacture professional video & broadcasting equipment.
Online catalog(s) available
Shipping Address: 6105 Coronado Ave NE, Suite E, Albuquerque, NM 87109
Membership(s): NAB; SMPTE

Burst Video/Film Inc
PO Box 5354, Atlanta, GA 31107-0354
Key Personnel
Dir & Prodr: Fran Burst
Founded: 1981
Membership(s): Georgia Production Partnership; NATAS

Business & Legal Reports Inc
141 Mill Rock Rd E, Old Saybrook, CT 06475
Tel: 860-510-0100 *Toll Free Tel:* 800-727-5257
Fax: 860-510-7224
E-mail: service@blr.com
Web Site: www.blr.com
Key Personnel
CEO & Pres: Dan Oswald
VP: Bobby Edgil
Membership(s): Instructional Systems Association

Business Education Films
Division of Paulicia Enterprises
PO Box 449, Clarksburg, NJ 08510-0449
Tel: 732-462-3522 *Fax:* 732-294-0330
E-mail: info@aldenfilms.com
Web Site: www.aldenfilms.com
Key Personnel
Pres: Paul Weinberg
VP: Felicia Weinberg
Films & audios of Israel & Judaica.
Membership(s): InfoComm International®

Butler Films Inc
108 Old Solomons Island Rd, Suite L-10, Annapolis, MD 21401
Tel: 410-280-1160 *Fax:* 443-458-5315
E-mail: info@butlerfilm.com
Web Site: www.butlerfilm.com
Key Personnel
Dir & Exec Prodr: David Butler
Prodr: Lynda Meier
TV commercials & corporate communication.

Butter Tree Studio
32 Merry Lane, East Hanover, NJ 07936
Tel: 973-585-7632 *Fax:* 973-585-7633
Web Site: www.buttertreestudios.com
Film & sound stage rental for video, film & photography shoots.

Buttercup Pictures
2415 Michigan Ave, Bldg H, Santa Monica, CA 90404
Tel: 323-692-0909
E-mail: info@buttercuppictures.com
Web Site: buttercuppictures.com
Key Personnel
Exec Prodr: Carolyn Bates *E-mail:* carolyn@buttercuppictures.com
Specialize in complex 2D animation, CG visual effects, live-action production & compositing for feature films, commercials & specialty venue projects.

Buzzco Associates Inc
33 Bleecker St, New York, NY 10012
Tel: 212-473-8800 *Fax:* 212-473-8891
E-mail: info@buzzzco.com
Web Site: www.buzzzco.com
Key Personnel
Owner, Dir & Prodr: Candy Kugel
Founded: 1985
Animation production, complete 2D animation.

BZ/Rights & Permissions Inc
145 W 86 St, New York, NY 10024
Tel: 212-924-3000 *Fax:* 212-924-2525
E-mail: info@bzrights.com
Web Site: www.bzrights.com; www.thepublicdomainsite.com
Key Personnel
Pres: Barbara Zimmerman *E-mail:* bz@bzrights.com
Rights clearance service - books, lyrics, music, film & TV clips, photos & art - anything that is copyrighted, plus celebrities. A subsidiary, The BZ/Rights Stuff, Inc publishes lists of music & literature in the public domain. Articles on rights clearance on web site.
Membership(s): Association of Independent Music Publishers; Copyright Society

C & M Publishing Co
Subsidiary of Curriculum Media Inc
1076 Torrey Pines Rd, Chula Vista, CA 91915
Tel: 619-656-6462
Key Personnel
CEO: Robert Pike *E-mail:* rpike63@aol.com
Children's video programming.
Membership(s): American Checker Federation

C-Ducer/C T Audio
54 Old Lakeside Rd S, Hewitt, NJ 07421
Tel: 973-728-1743 *Toll Free Tel:* 800-282-8346 *Toll Free Fax:* 866-548-7683
E-mail: meow54@rocketmail.com
Web Site: www.c-ducer.com
Key Personnel
Owner: Jack Waligora

C Vision Productions
5533 144 Ave NW, Ramsey, MN 55303-5646
Tel: 763-577-1358 *Toll Free Tel:* 888-827-3287 *Fax:* 763-577-1359
Web Site: www.cvisionproductions.com
Key Personnel
Owner: Chris Laskowski *E-mail:* clasko@cvisionproductions.com
Founded: 1990
Multimedia video production company.

CA Technologies
520 Madison Ave, 22nd fl, New York, NY 10022
Toll Free Tel: 800-225-5224
Web Site: www.ca.com
Key Personnel
CEO: Michael P Gregoire
Chief Mktg Offr & EVP: Lauren Flaherty
Founded: 1976
IT management software & solutions company with expertise across all IT environments, from mainframe & physical to virtual & cloud.

Cabbage Cases Inc
1166-C Steelwood Rd, Columbus, OH 43212-1356
Tel: 614-486-2495 *Toll Free Tel:* 800-888-2495 *Fax:* 614-486-2788
E-mail: sales@cabbagecases.com
Web Site: www.cabbagecases.com
Key Personnel
Sales Mgr: Michael Hannah *E-mail:* mhannah@cabbagecases.com
Founded: 1974
Manufacturer of custom shipping & carrying cases.

Cable Films & Video
PO Box 7171, Country Club Sta, Kansas City, MO 64113-0171
Tel: 913-362-2804 *Toll Free Tel:* 800-514-2804 *Fax:* 913-362-2804
E-mail: cablefilms@kc.rr.com
Key Personnel
CEO & Pres: Herb Miller
VP & Opers Mgr: Todd Randall
Founded: 1976
Three hundred classic films, 1915-1960. Catalog describes films, actors, directors & story lines.
Catalog(s), annual, free
Shipping Address: 2026 W 63 St, Mission Hills, KS 66208
Membership(s): Mid-America Cable Telecommunications Association; NATAS; NATPE; NCTA

CACI Productions Group
Subsidiary of CACI International Inc
14370 Newbrook Dr, Chantilly, VA 20151
Tel: 703-679-3100
Web Site: www.caci.com
Key Personnel
Exec Chmn & Chmn of the Bd: Dr Jack P London
CEO & Pres: Kenneth Asbury
EVP, PR, Corp Communs & Congressional Rel: Jody A Brown *Tel:* 703-841-7801 *E-mail:* jbrown@caci.com
Founded: 1985
Video production & duplication.
Catalog(s) available

CAD Audio
6573 Cochran Rd, Bldg I, Solon, OH 44139
Tel: 440-349-4900 *Toll Free Tel:* 800-762-9266 (ext 211) *Fax:* 440-248-4902
E-mail: sales@cadaudio.com
Web Site: www.cadaudio.com
Key Personnel
VP, Sales & Mktg: Tony O'Keefe
Manufacture professional microphones for stage & studio.
Catalog(s) available

Cadence Jazz Records
Subsidiary of Cadnor Ltd
Cadence Bldg, Redwood, NY 13679
Tel: 315-287-2852 *Fax:* 315-287-2860
E-mail: cjr@cadencebuilding.com; cadence@cadencebuilding.com; info@cadencemagazine.com
Web Site: www.cadencebuilding.com
Founded: 1980
Catalog(s) available

Cadex Electronics Inc
22000 Fraserwood Way, Richmond, BC V6W 1J6, Canada
Tel: 604-231-7777 *Toll Free Tel:* 800-565-5228 *Fax:* 604-231-7755
E-mail: info@cadex.com
Web Site: www.cadex.com
Key Personnel
VP, Sales: Bruce Adams
Design & manufacture battery chargers & analyzers, as well as advanced rapid-test & monitoring systems.

CADint
10517 W Bellarose Dr, Sun City, AZ 85351-2241
Tel: 303-520-0907 *Toll Free Tel:* 800-553-1177 (ext 12) *Fax:* 707-924-0907
E-mail: info@cadint.com; sales@cadint.com
Web Site: www.cadint.com
Key Personnel
Pres: Mary Leasure
Online catalog(s) available

Cahokia Mounds Museum Society
Affiliate of Cahokia Mounds World Heritage Site
30 Ramey Dr, Collinsville, IL 62234
Tel: 618-344-7316 *Fax:* 618-346-5162
E-mail: museumsociety@cahokiamounds.org
Web Site: www.cahokiamounds.org
Key Personnel
Exec Dir: Lori Belknap
Founded: 1976
Catalog(s) available

Calbor Enterprises Two Inc
10646 Chiquita St, Toluca Lake, CA 91602
Tel: 818-760-3222
E-mail: pyro-fx@sbcglobal.net
Web Site: www.pyro-fx.net
Key Personnel
SFX Technician: John Bordeaux
Founded: 1973
Pyrotechnic special effects & design effects for film, video, theatrical & concerts & provide licensed operator.

Calculated Industries Inc
4840 Hytech Dr, Carson City, NV 89706
Tel: 775-885-4900 *Toll Free Tel:* 800-854-8075 *Fax:* 775-885-4949
E-mail: info@calculated.com
Web Site: www.calculated.com
Key Personnel
Mktg & Communs Mgr: Jennifer Goedde *E-mail:* jenniferg@calculated.com
Founded: 1978
Advanced time-code calculator for film, video & audio editing.
Catalog(s) available
Membership(s): NAB

Calger Lighting Inc
200 Lexington Ave, Suite 434, New York, NY 10016
Tel: 212-689-9511 *Fax:* 212-779-0721
E-mail: sales@calgerlighting.com
Web Site: www.calgerlighting.com
Key Personnel
Pres & Mgr: Carmela Califano *E-mail:* carmela@calgerlighting.com
Founded: 1981
Catalog(s) available

CALIBRE
Metro Park, 6354 Walker Lane, Alexandria, VA 22310-3252
Tel: 703-797-8500 *Toll Free Tel:* 888-CALIBRE (225-4273) *Fax:* 703-797-8501
E-mail: info@calibresys.com
Web Site: www.calibresys.com

Key Personnel
CEO & Pres: Joseph A Martore
EVP & COO: John C Mutarelli
EVP & CFO: Pamela A Little
EVP & Chief Admin Offr: Robert W Larrick, Jr
EVP & Corp Devt Offr: W Michael Polster
SVP, Busn Devt: Jeffrey E Giangiuli
SVP, Strategy Devt: Dr Craig E College
Founded: 1982
Video production/digital multimedia communications company.
Branch Office(s)
4900 University Sq, Suite 28, Huntsville, AL 35816-1829
12001 Research Pkwy, Suite 236, Orlando, FL 32826 *Tel:* 407-792-0057
1777 NE Loop 410, Suite 628, San Antonio, TX 78217
Membership(s): AFCEA; MCA-I; Women in Film & Video

Califone International Inc
1145 Arroyo Ave, No A, San Fernando, CA 91340
Tel: 818-407-2400 *Toll Free Tel:* 800-722-0500 *Fax:* 818-407-2405 *Toll Free Fax:* 877-402-2248
Web Site: www.califone.com
Key Personnel
VP, Mktg: Tim Ridgway *E-mail:* timr@califone.com
Founded: 1946
Manufacture document cameras.
Catalog(s) available
Online catalog(s) available
Membership(s): InfoComm International®

California Communications Inc, see CCI Digital

California/International Arts Foundation
2737 Outpost Dr, Los Angeles, CA 90068
Tel: 323-874-4107 *Fax:* 323-874-8195
Key Personnel
Pres: Lyn Kienholz *E-mail:* lkienholz@gmail.com
Founded: 1981
Nonprofit arts organization which produces filmed interviews with artists. DVDs of interviews with artists. Exhibitions in museums worldwide.

California Language Laboratories
6170 Palmero Circle, Cameron Park, CA 95682
Toll Free Tel: 800-327-1147 *Fax:* 530-350-8072
E-mail: info@esltapes.com
Web Site: www.esltapes.com
Key Personnel
Owner & Dir: Barbara Sullivan *E-mail:* bsullivan@esltapes.com
Founded: 1980
English as a second language materials from 30 languages. Interactive Citizenship DVDs for the new citizenship exam in 28 languages plus English only. Job seekers DVDs in 25 languages plus English only.
Catalog(s), annual, free

California Newsreel
44 Gough St, Suite 303, San Francisco, CA 94103
Tel: 415-284-7800 *Fax:* 415-284-7801
E-mail: contact@newsreel.org
Web Site: www.newsreel.org
Key Personnel
Dir: Lawrence Daressa *E-mail:* lgd@newsreel.org
Nonprofit organization distributing social change educational documentaries to institutional theme markets.
Online catalog(s) available

Sales Office(s): PO Box 3400, Lancaster, PA 17604-3400 *Toll Free Tel:* 877-811-7495 *Fax:* 717-285-6363 (order dept)
PO Box 2284, South Burlington, VT 05407-2284 *Toll Free Tel:* 877-811-7495 *Fax:* 802-846-1850 (fulfillment ctr)

California Stage & Lighting
3601 W Garry Ave, Santa Ana, CA 92704
Tel: 714-966-1852 *Fax:* 714-966-0104
E-mail: sales@calstage.com
Web Site: www.calstage.com
Key Personnel
CFO: Irene Hutton *E-mail:* ihutton@calstage.com
Founded: 1982
Sale & rental of theatrical equipment & supplies.

California Stainless Manufacturing Inc
32 N Wood Rd, Camarillo, CA 93010
Tel: 805-484-1038 *Toll Free Tel:* 888-712-7035 *Fax:* 805-484-1030
E-mail: contact@calstainless.com
Web Site: www.calstainless.com
Key Personnel
Sales Mgr: James R Carr, Jr
Founded: 1960
Manufacture revolving darkroom doors & stainless steel photographic sinks.
Catalog(s) available
Online catalog(s) available

California Tape Products Inc
Subsidiary of Kollner Corp
PO Box 177, Forest Falls, CA 92339-0177
Tel: 909-794-6524
E-mail: info@caltape.com
Web Site: www.caltape.com
Key Personnel
Pres: David Druck
Supplies magnetic media & related products throughout the nation to the video professional as well as government, education & the entertainment industry.

California Teleprompter
PO Box 13024, La Jolla, CA 92039-3024
Tel: 858-945-2076
E-mail: caprompter@aol.com
Web Site: www.sandiegoteleprompter.com
Key Personnel
Owner: Maia McQuillan
Teleprompter equipment rental & services for southern California, San Diego, Palm Springs & Orange County.

Callen Photo Mount
185 Sixth Ave, Paterson, NJ 07524
Tel: 973-925-2390 *Toll Free Tel:* 800-225-5360 *Fax:* 973-925-9615
Web Site: www.callencorp.com
Key Personnel
VP: Dennis Callen
Founded: 1938
Online catalog(s) available

Calrad Electronics
819 N Highland Ave, Los Angeles, CA 90038
Tel: 323-465-2131 *Toll Free Tel:* 800-821-8536 *Fax:* 323-465-3504
E-mail: calradelectronics@calrad.com
Web Site: www.calrad.com
Key Personnel
Pres: Robert Shupper
VP, Sales: Alma Munoz
Gen Mgr: Mike Karten
Founded: 1951
Online catalog(s) available

Calumet Carton Co
16920 State St, South Holland, IL 60473
Mailing Address: PO Box 405, South Holland, IL 60473-0405
Tel: 708-333-6521 *Fax:* 708-333-8540
E-mail: info@calumetcarton.com
Web Site: www.calumetcarton.com
Key Personnel
Pres: John Inwood
Mktg Dir: Gina Inwood
Founded: 1930
Packaging manufacturer.
Catalog(s) available
Online catalog(s) available

Calumet College of Saint Joseph
2400 New York Ave, Whiting, IN 46394
Tel: 219-473-7770 *Fax:* 219-473-4259
Web Site: www.ccsj.edu
Key Personnel
Pres: Dr Dan Lowery *Tel:* 219-473-4333 *E-mail:* dlowery@ccsj.edu

Calzone Anvil Case Co
225 Black Rock Ave, Bridgeport, CT 06605
Tel: 203-367-5766 *Toll Free Tel:* 800-243-5152 *Fax:* 203-336-4406
E-mail: info@calzonecase.com
Web Site: www.calzonecase.com
Key Personnel
Pres: Joe Calzone
EVP: Vincent Calzone
Founded: 1975
Manufacture re-usable shipping, packaging, carrying, storage cases & containers, including: racks, monitor cases, plasma screen cases, video camera cases, audio console cases, etc.
Catalog(s) available
Branch Office(s)
Anvil Cases, 15730 Salt Lake Ave, City of Industry, CA 91745-1115, Gen Mgr: Deborah Visokay *Tel:* 626-968-4100 *E-mail:* sales@anvilcase.com
Calzone Case Co, 1430 Bradley Lane, Carrollton, TX 75007, Sales Mgr: Frank Bravico *Tel:* 972-241-3998 *Fax:* 972-241-3998 *E-mail:* frank@calzonecase.com
Membership(s): InfoComm International®; NAB; NAMM, the National Association of Music Merchants; Percussive Arts Society

CAM Audio Inc
2210 Executive Dr, Garland, TX 75041
Tel: 972-271-2800 *Toll Free Tel:* 800-527-3458 *Fax:* 972-271-1555
E-mail: sales@camaudio.com
Web Site: www.camaudio.com
Founded: 1968
Discount audio, video, sound, media & packaging dealer.
Branch Office(s)
WM Sales, 124 W Fairmeadows, Duncanville, TX 75116 *Tel:* 972-296-2773 *Toll Free Tel:* 800-836-7745 *Fax:* 972-709-1514 *E-mail:* sales@wmsales.com *Web Site:* www.wmsales.com

Camart
6 W 20 St, New York, NY 10011
Tel: 212-691-8840
E-mail: rentals@camart.com
Web Site: www.camart.com
Key Personnel
Owner: John Carriglio
Photography studio rental, including cameras, lighting & accessories.

Cambium Catalyst International (CCI)
18 Dupont St, Toronto, ON M5R 1V2, Canada
Tel: 416-964-8750 *Fax:* 416-964-1980
E-mail: info@ccientertainment.com
Web Site: www.ccientertainment.com
Key Personnel
Chmn: Charles Falzon
CEO & Pres: Arnie Zipursky
Founded: 2002

Producer & distributor of children's, family, TV movies & lifestyle programming.
Membership(s): Canadian Film & Television Production Association; NATPE

Cambridge Documentary Films Inc
3099 Hidden Valley Lane, Santa Barbara, CA 93108
Mailing Address: PO Box 390385, Cambridge, MA 02139-0004
Tel: 617-484-3993
E-mail: info@cambridgedocumentaryfilms.org
Web Site: www.cambridgedocumentaryfilms.org
Key Personnel
Pres: Carol Belding
Exec Dir: Margaret Lazarus
Prodr: R Wunderlich
Secy: E Shub
Treas: Joan Sawyer
Founded: 1974
Nonprofit production & distribution organizations.
Online catalog(s) available
Membership(s): AMPAS

Cambridge Educational, see Films Media Group

Cambridge University Press
32 Avenue of the Americas, New York, NY 10013-2473
Tel: 212-337-5000 *Toll Free Tel:* 800-221-4512 *Fax:* 212-691-3239
E-mail: information@cambridge.org; newyork@cambridge.org
Web Site: www.cambridge.org
Key Personnel
Mng Dir: Michael Peluse
Dir, Content Strategy: Janet Aitchison
Distributor of educational & scientific programming.
Online catalog(s) available
Membership(s): American Association of University Presses; Association of American Publishers

Camcor Inc
2273 S Church St, Burlington, NC 27215
Mailing Address: PO Box 1899, Burlington, NC 27216-1899
Tel: 336-228-0251 *Toll Free Tel:* 800-868-2462 *Fax:* 336-222-8011 *Toll Free Fax:* 800-298-1181
E-mail: info@camcor.com
Web Site: www.camcor.com
Key Personnel
Pres: Ray E Bailey, Sr
Treas: Glenda Bailey
Founded: 1949

Camera Co Inc/Broadcast Divison
858 Boston-Providence Tpke, Norwood, MA 02062
Tel: 781-769-7810 *Toll Free Tel:* 866-769-0210 *Fax:* 781-769-5750
Web Site: www.cameraco.com
Key Personnel
Pres: David Katz
VP: Martin P Feldman *E-mail:* mfeldman@cameraco.com
Digital Video Sales: Gary Pink
Founded: 1989
Sales, service, rental broadcast; professional & industrial video equipment. Specialize in Apple Computer, Sony Broadcast Professional Video, Q-GEAR Prompters & Tightrope Media systems, Panasonic Broadcast, JVC Professional, Leightronix, Sennheiser, Shure & Lowel Light, Cannon Video, Fujinon Lenses; DVD duplication.
Online catalog(s) available
Membership(s): SMPTE

Camera Corner Connecting Point
PO Box 248, Green Bay, WI 54305-0248
Tel: 920-435-5353 *Toll Free Tel:* 800-236-4950 (orders) *Fax:* 920-435-6984
E-mail: contactus@cccp.com; salessupport@cccp.com
Web Site: www.cccp.com
Key Personnel
CEO: Rick Chernick
Founded: 1953
Online catalog(s) available
Shipping Address: 529 N Monroe Ave, Green Bay, WI 54301
Membership(s): InfoComm International®

Camera Dynamics, see Vitec Videocom Inc

Camera Essentials
91 N Daisy Ave, Pasadena, CA 91107-3705
Tel: 626-844-3722 *Fax:* 323-686-5830
E-mail: info@cameraessentials.com
Web Site: www.cameraessentials.com
Founded: 1987
Manufacture & distributor of Harrison Film changing tents, Harrison changing bags & photographic accessories, film equipment & accessories & large format photographic accessories.
Catalog(s), upon request

CamMate Systems
425 E Comstock, Chandler, AZ 85225
Tel: 480-813-9500 *Fax:* 480-813-9292
E-mail: cammate@cammate.com
Web Site: www.cammate.com
Key Personnel
CEO: Linda Mitchell
CFO: Richard Laitinen
Founded: 1987
Manufacture, sell & service camera cranes & accessories for video & film cameras.
Online catalog(s) available
Membership(s): A2 Production Association; MCA-I; NAB

The Campbell Agency
3838 Oak Lawn Ave, Suite 900, Dallas, TX 75219
Tel: 214-522-8991 *Fax:* 214-522-8997
Web Site: www.thecampbellagency.com
Key Personnel
Pres: Nancy Campbell *E-mail:* nancycampbell@thecampbellagency.com
Agent: Sharon Howell *E-mail:* sharonhowell@thecampbellagency.com
Founded: 1989
Full service model/talent agency.
Membership(s): Women in Film

Campus Film Distributors Corp
Division of Campus Group Co
42 Oak Ave, Tuckahoe, NY 10707
Tel: 914-961-1900 *Fax:* 914-395-1091
Web Site: www.campusgroup.com
Key Personnel
Pres: Steven Campus
VP: Jordan Campus

CamTec Motion Picture Cameras
4221 W Magnolia Blvd, Burbank, CA 91505
Tel: 818-841-8700 *Fax:* 818-841-8777
Web Site: www.camtec.tv
Key Personnel
Rental Dept Mgr: Scott Travers *E-mail:* scott@camtec.tv
Rental Agent: Tracy Morse *E-mail:* tracy@camtec.tv
Founded: 1989
Rents cameras, new & vintage lenses & accessories for the film industry.

Can-Am Merchandising Systems
70 Shields Ct, Markham, ON L3R 9T5, Canada
Tel: 905-475-6622 *Toll Free Tel:* 800-387-9790 *Fax:* 905-475-1154
E-mail: mail@can-am.ca
Web Site: www.can-am.ca
Key Personnel
Pres: Jerry Pila
Founded: 1979
Modular media furniture manufacturer.
Online catalog(s) available

Canadian American Records
Division of Caprice International Recording Studios
PO Box 808, Lititz, PA 17543-0538
Tel: 717-627-4800 *Fax:* 717-627-4800
E-mail: canadianamerican@dejazzd.com
Web Site: www.canadianamericanrecords.net; www.joeywelz.com
Key Personnel
Owner & CEO: Joey Welz *E-mail:* joeywelz@dejazzd.com
Pres, A & R: Phil Schwartz
VP, A & R: Gabriel Maciocia
VP, Catalog: Danny Burden
VP, Engg: Bill Zimmerman
Founded: 1958
Record label, publishing, production & CD manufacturing & recording studio.
Catalog(s), oldies & current artists
Membership(s): AF of M; ASCAP; BMI; The Recording Academy; ROPE

Canadian Filmmakers Distribution Center (CFMDC)
401 Richmond St W, Suite 245, Toronto, ON M5V 3A8, Canada
Tel: 416-588-0725 *Fax:* 416-588-7956
Web Site: www.cfmdc.org
Key Personnel
Exec Dir: Lauren Howes *E-mail:* director@cfmdc.org
Distribute independent short cinema.
Online catalog(s) available

Canadian Learning Co Inc
95 Vansittart Ave, Woodstock, ON N4S 6E3, Canada
Tel: 519-537-2360 *Toll Free Tel:* 800-267-2977 (CN) *Fax:* 519-537-1035
Web Site: www.canlearn.com
Key Personnel
Pres: Michael Harding
Founded: 1978
Producer & distributor of educational media.
Online catalog(s) available
Membership(s): Educational Media Producers & Distributors Association of Canada

Canamedia Inc
Division of Magic Lantern Media Inc
1540 Cornwall Rd, Suite 216, Oakville, ON L6J 7W5, Canada
Tel: 416-363-6765 *Toll Free Tel:* 866-999-5292 *Fax:* 416-363-7834
Web Site: www.canamedia.com
Key Personnel
COO & Pres: Doug Connolly *Tel:* 416-363-6147 *E-mail:* doug.connolly@distributionaccess.com
EVP, Prodn: Less Harris *Tel:* 416-214-9779 *E-mail:* less.harris@canamedia.com
Sr Exec Prodr, Content Devt: Daniel D'or *E-mail:* dan.or@canamedia.com
Mng Dir, Intl Sales & Acqs: Andrea Stokes *Tel:* 416-363-8683 *E-mail:* andrea_stokes@canamedia.com
Acctg Mgr: Victoria Yuvminina *E-mail:* victoria.yuvminina@canamedia.com
Prodn Servs & Busn Devt: Brad Schroeder *Tel:* 416-363-5681 *E-mail:* brad.schroder@canamedia.com
Founded: 1978

Television, music & archive film distribution. TV production. Pump audio music library.
Online catalog(s), PDF download
Branch Office(s)
7820 Venture St, Burnaby, BC V5A 1V3, Canada, VP, Global Sales & Acqs: Bill McGowan *Tel:* 604-523-6677 *Toll Free Tel:* 800-665-4121 *Fax:* 604-523-6688 *Toll Free Fax:* 800-665-2909 *E-mail:* bill.mcgowan@distributionaccess.com
Hilyard Place Bldg A, Suite 120, 560 Main St, St John, NB E2K 1J5, Canada, Dir, Access Digital Media: Greg Abrams *Tel:* 506-633-6038 *Toll Free Tel:* 800-595-MPEG (595-6734) *Fax:* 506-633-7493 *E-mail:* greg.abrams@distributionaccess.com
Membership(s): Canadian Film & Television Production Association

Canare Corporation of America
45 Commerce Way, Unit C, Totowa, NJ 07512
Tel: 973-837-0070 *Fax:* 973-837-0080
E-mail: sales@canare.com
Web Site: www.canare.com
Key Personnel
CEO & Pres: Junichiro Oono
Founded: 1983
Manufacture broadcasting cables & connectors including SMPTE hybrid fiberoptic cables & assemblies & panels.
Catalog(s) available
Online catalog(s) available
Membership(s): InfoComm International®

Canavan Scenic & Light LLC
2440 Dinneen Ave, Orlando, FL 32804
Tel: 407-888-8002 *Fax:* 407-888-8171
Web Site: www.csandl.com
Key Personnel
CEO: Michael Canavan *E-mail:* mikec@csandl.com
Founded: 1996
Scenery & lighting services for business meetings & trade shows.

C&C Studios Corp
20 W 37 St, New York, NY 10018
Tel: 212-967-6427
Web Site: www.candcstudios.tv
Key Personnel
Contact: Clinton Kennet *E-mail:* clinton@candcstudios.tv
Founded: 2007
Studio rentals for a variety of production needs, including post-production & satellite media tours. Full array of audio, video & lighting equipment.

Candee Productions Inc
301 W Deer Valley Rd, Suite 7, Phoenix, AZ 85027
Tel: 623-266-3070 *Fax:* 623-581-7020
Web Site: www.candeeproductions.com
Key Personnel
Pres & Dir: Rees W Candee *E-mail:* rwcandee@gmail.com
Founded: 1979
TV production.
Membership(s): MCA-I

C&I Studios
541 NW First Ave, Fort Lauderdale, FL 33301
Tel: 954-357-3934
E-mail: contact@c-istudios.com
Web Site: www.c-istudios.com
Key Personnel
Exec Dir: Joshua Miller
Opers Mgr: Abbie Cessna
Studio Mgr: Brandon Baker
Pre- to post-production services in the photographic, design, audio & video/film industries.
Branch Office(s)
716 Broadway, 2nd fl, Baltimore, MD 21231 *Tel:* 240-893-0177

Cannon Stage Lighting Inc
1717 Whitehead Rd, Baltimore, MD 21207
Tel: 410-298-0636 *Fax:* 410-298-7950
Web Site: www.cannonstage.com
Key Personnel
Pres: George Cannon, Jr *E-mail:* george@cannonstage.com
Founded: 1981
Provide rental, sales & service of stage light equipment.

Canon Broadcast & Communications Division
One Canon Park, Melville, NY 11747-3336
Toll Free Tel: 800-321-4388
E-mail: bctv@cusa.canon.com
Web Site: www.canon.com/bctv; www.usa.canon.com/cusa/professional
Key Personnel
Regl Acct Mgr: John Rose *E-mail:* jrosejr@cusa.canon.com
Catalog(s) available
Sales Office(s): 15955 Alton Pkwy, Irvine, CA 92618 *Tel:* 949-753-4330 *Fax:* 949-753-4337
5625 Oakbrook Pkwy, Norcross, GA 30093 *Tel:* 770-849-7890 *Fax:* 770-849-7888
100 Park Blvd, Itasca, IL 60143 *Tel:* 630-250-6236 *Fax:* 630-250-0399
3200 Regent Blvd, Irving, TX 75063 *Tel:* 972-409-8871 *Fax:* 972-409-8869
Membership(s): InfoComm International®; NAB; SBE; SMPTE

Canon USA Inc, see Canon Broadcast & Communications Division

Canon USA Inc
One Canon Park, Melville, NY 11747
Tel: 613-330-5000
E-mail: pr@cusa.canon.com
Web Site: www.usa.canon.com
Key Personnel
Chmn & CEO: Joe Adachi
Pres & COO: Yuichi Ishizuka
EVP, Chief Admin Offr, Gen Coun & Secy: Seymour Liebman
SVP, CFO & Treas: Kunihiko Tedo
SVP, Busn Imaging Solutions Group: Junichi Yoshitake
SVP, Corp HR: Joseph G Warren
SVP, Imaging Technologies & Communs Group: Eliott Peck
Leading provider of consumer, business-to-business & industrial digital imaging solutions.
Online catalog(s) available

Cantrax Recorders
2119 Fidler Ave, Long Beach, CA 90815
Tel: 562-498-6492
E-mail: cantrax@verizon.net
Key Personnel
Owner & Pres: Richard Cannata
Chief Engr: Martin Carman
All recording services.

Canvys™
Division of Richardson Electronics
40W267 Keslinger Rd, La Fox, IL 60147-0393
Mailing Address: PO Box 393, La Fox, IL 60147-0393
Toll Free Tel: 888-735-7373 *Fax:* 630-208-2830
Web Site: www.canvys.com
Key Personnel
EVP & Gen Mgr: Wendy Diddell
VP & Gen Mgr, North America Custom OEM: Steven Stamper
Founded: 1988
Design, development & manufacturing of high res/high bright CRT & LCD displays for government, military, medical & scientific applications.
Branch Office(s)
753 Forest St, Suite 100, Marlborough, MA 01752 *Tel:* 508-460-5400 *Toll Free Tel:* 800-291-1344 *Fax:* 508-460-5470 *E-mail:* steven.stamper@canvys.com
12975 16 Ave N, Suite 300, Plymouth, MN 55441 *Tel:* 763-550-9001 *Toll Free Tel:* 888-753-7373 *Fax:* 763-550-9002 *E-mail:* david.sorensen@canvys.com
Foreign Office(s): Raiffeisenstr 5, 78166 Donaueschingen, Germany *Tel:* (0771) 8300-0 *Fax:* (0771) 8300-80 *E-mail:* info-europe@canvys.com
St Swithin's Ct, Suite 2, One Flavian Rd, Nettleham Rd, Lincoln LN2 4GR, United Kingdom, Sales Mgr: Andrew Perez *Tel:* (01522) 548598 *Fax:* (01522) 524265 *E-mail:* andrew.perez@canvys.com

Canyon Cinema Inc
1777 Yosemite Ave, Suite 210, San Francisco, CA 94124
Tel: 415-626-2255
E-mail: info@canyoncinema.com
Web Site: www.canyoncinema.com
Key Personnel
Dir, Opers: Denah Johnston *E-mail:* denah@canyoncinema.com
Founded: 1967
Rental distribution of Super 8mm, 16mm & 35mm films by independent film artists. Also lease those films & their DVD transfers.
Online catalog(s) available

Capital Communications Inc
2357-3, S Tamiami Trail, Venice, FL 34293
Tel: 941-539-6741
E-mail: cap5678@isp.com
Key Personnel
Pres: Jim Springer
Film Libn: Ronda Armour
Catalog(s), free

Capitol Records
Member of Universal Music Group
1750 N Vine St, Hollywood, CA 90028
Tel: 323-871-5001
E-mail: mark.moreno@emimusic.com
Web Site: www.capitalstudios.com; www.capitolrecords.com
Founded: 1942

Caprock Developments Inc
475 Speedwell, Morris Plains, NJ 07950
Mailing Address: PO Box 95, Morris Plains, NJ 07950
Tel: 973-267-9292 *Toll Free Tel:* 800-222-0325 *Fax:* 973-292-0614
E-mail: info@caprockdev.com
Web Site: www.caprockdev.com
Key Personnel
Pres: Alan Schwartz
Founded: 1953
Supplier of speciality lamps, magnifiers & microscopes, hanna PH, conductivity & ORP (Redux) meters, thickness gages & digital micrometers, anti-moire filters & other measuring devices.
Online catalog(s), PDF download
Membership(s): NACASA; National Association for Printing Leadership; NPES; Specialty Graphic Imaging Association

Capron Lighting & Sound Co Inc
278 West St, Needham, MA 02494
Tel: 781-444-8850 *Fax:* 781-444-1408
E-mail: info@capron.net
Web Site: www.capron.net

Key Personnel
Pres: Richard Larond
Full service special events contractor.

Captain Fiddle Music & Publications
94 Wiswall Rd, Lee, NH 03861
Tel: 603-659-2658
E-mail: cfiddle@tiac.net
Web Site: captainfiddle.com
Key Personnel
Owner: Ryan Thomson
Founded: 1985
Publisher of books packaged with audio & video recordings.
Catalog(s), upon request

Caption Colorado LLC
5690 DTC Blvd, Suite 500W, Greenwood Village, CO 80111
Tel: 720-489-5662 *Toll Free Tel:* 800-775-7838 *Fax:* 720-489-5664
Web Site: www.captioncolorado.com
Key Personnel
CEO & Pres: Tad Polumbus *E-mail:* tpolumbus@captioncolorado.com
CFO: Kurt Suppes *E-mail:* kurtsuppes@captioncolorado.com
CIO: James Barker *E-mail:* jimb@captioncolorado.com
SVP, Busn Devt: Randy Holyfield *E-mail:* randyh@captioncolorado.com; Jeff Wennberg *E-mail:* jeffw@captioncolorado.com
SVP, Sales & Mktg: John Irwin *E-mail:* johni@captioncolorado.com
VP, Mktg: Lindsay Condon *E-mail:* lindsayc@captioncolorado.com
VP, Sales: Brenda Nowicki *E-mail:* brendan@captioncolorado.com
Founded: 1991
Closed captioning products & services.
Online catalog(s) available

CaptionMax
2438 27 Ave S, Minneapolis, MN 55406
Tel: 612-341-3566 *Toll Free Tel:* 800-822-3566 *Fax:* 612-341-2345
Web Site: www.captionmax.com
Key Personnel
Founder & CEO: Max Duckler
COO & Pres: Gerald Freda
EVP, Busn Devt: Donna Horn
Busn Devt Mgr: Lindsay Beiriger; Maridelle Hannah
Mgr, Tech Sales & Servs: Emily Bell
Founded: 1993
Closed captioning & audio description production services.
Branch Office(s)
441 N Varney, Burbank, CA 91502 *Tel:* 818-295-2500 *Fax:* 818-295-2509
5 Columbus Circle, Suite 810, New York, NY 10019 *Tel:* 212-462-0060 *Fax:* 212-462-0061

Captions & Subtitle Services Ltd
101 Hempstead Place, Suite 1A, Joliet, IL 60433
Tel: 815-740-1009 *Toll Free Tel:* 866-230-1009
E-mail: info@capsubservices.com; quote@capsubservices.com
Web Site: www.capsubservices.com
Key Personnel
Owner: Terry Thomas
Pres: Angie Russell
Founded: 2000
Captions & subtitles produced for video, DVD & webcasts.

Cardinal Sound & Video
2219 Kansas Ave, Silver Spring, MD 20910
Tel: 301-589-3700 *Fax:* 301-589-4284
E-mail: info@cardinalsound.us
Web Site: www.cardinalsound.us
Key Personnel
Pres: Scott Reidinger
Founded: 1970
Professional sound & video system design, sales, installation & service. Offer sound system rentals for small to medium sized events.
Online catalog(s) available
Membership(s): NSCA

Career & Self Directed Extended Programs at Purdue University
Stewart Ctr, G-53, 128 Memorial Mall, West Lafayette, IN 47907-2034
Tel: 765-494-8619 *Toll Free Tel:* 800-830-0269 *Fax:* 765-496-2484
E-mail: distance@purdue.edu
Web Site: www.distance.purdue.edu/training
Key Personnel
Asst Dean, Extended Campus: Michael Eddy *Tel:* 765-494-4654 *E-mail:* mmeddy@purdue.edu
Catalog(s) available

Carlton-Bates Co
Subsidiary of Wesco International Inc
3600 W 69 St, Little Rock, AR 72209
Tel: 501-562-9100 *Toll Free Tel:* 866-600-6040
E-mail: customerservicecb@carltonbates.com; sales@carltonbates.com
Web Site: www.carltonbates.com
Founded: 1957
Offers electrical OEM products to the electronic & electromechanical industries.
Catalog(s), free
Online catalog(s) available

Carolina Biological Supply Co
2700 York Rd, Burlington, NC 27215-3398
Tel: 336-584-0381 (outside US & CN) *Toll Free Tel:* 800-334-5551 *Toll Free Fax:* 800-222-7112
E-mail: customer_service@carolina.com; internationalsales@carolina.com
Web Site: www.carolina.com
Key Personnel
Direct Mktg Mgr: Gray Amick
Founded: 1927
Curriculum resources for science & math classrooms.
Catalog(s) available
Online catalog(s) available
Membership(s): National Science Teachers Association

Carpel Video Inc
429 E Patrick St, Frederick, MD 21701
Tel: 301-694-3500 *Toll Free Tel:* 800-238-4300 *Fax:* 301-694-9510
Web Site: www.carpelvideoonline.com
Key Personnel
Pres: Andy Carpel *E-mail:* acarpel@aol.com
Sales Mgr: Vicki Fearnow *E-mail:* vfearnow@carpelvideo.com
Prodn: Andrew Mulieri *E-mail:* amulieri@carpelvideo.com
Founded: 1978
Video production, film & tape transferring, DVD & CD duplication & video tape wholesaling.
Online catalog(s) available

Carr McLean Ltd
461 Horner Ave, Toronto, ON M8W 4X2, Canada
Tel: 416-252-3371 *Toll Free Tel:* 800-268-2123 (CN) *Fax:* 416-252-9203 *Toll Free Fax:* 800-871-2397
E-mail: sales@carrmclean.ca
Web Site: www.carrmclean.ca
Key Personnel
Pres: Paul Barclay
Mktg Mgr: David Gudnason
Purch Offr: Nicole Van Engelen
National library & museum supply distributor.
Catalog(s), free, PDF download
Membership(s): ALA; InfoComm International®; NOPA

Carvin Corp
12340 World Trade Dr, San Diego, CA 92128
Tel: 858-487-1600 *Toll Free Tel:* 800-854-2235 *Fax:* 858-487-8160
Web Site: www.carvin.com
Key Personnel
Pres: Carson Kiesel
Founded: 1946
Professional sound equipment & guitars.
Catalog(s), free, US & CN only
Online catalog(s) available

CAS Video Productions
820 White Marsh Ct, Huntingtown, MD 20639
Tel: 301-760-7301; 301-674-2000 (cell)
Web Site: www.casvideo.com
Key Personnel
Owner: Chris Sciannella *E-mail:* chris@casvideo.com
Founded: 1988
TV & video production.
Membership(s): Television, Internet & Video Association of DC Inc; Women in Film & Video

Case Design Corp
333 School Lane, Telford, PA 18969
Tel: 215-703-0130 *Toll Free Tel:* 800-847-4176 *Fax:* 215-703-0139
E-mail: sales@casedesigncorp.com
Web Site: www.casedesigncorp.com
Key Personnel
Pres: Roger Ernst
VP, Sales: Paul Lowman
Catalog(s), free
Membership(s): InfoComm International®; NAB

Case Logic Inc
6303 Dry Creek Pkwy, Longmont, CO 80503
Tel: 303-652-1000 *Toll Free Tel:* 800-925-8111 *Fax:* 303-652-1094
E-mail: customer.service@caselogic.com
Web Site: www.caselogic.com
Founded: 1984
Online catalog(s) available

Cashmark Media Inc
4702 Eastern Ave, Kansas City, MO 64129
Tel: 816-861-4200 *Fax:* 816-861-4205
E-mail: info@cashmarkmedia.com
Web Site: www.cashmarkmedia.com
Key Personnel
Owner: Daryn Cashmark *E-mail:* daryn@cashmarkmedia.com
Specialize in live event video production services, including image magnification & multimedia presentations. Offer digital video & electronic media production support services including AV & video production equipment rental.

Casio America Inc
570 Mount Pleasant Ave, Dover, NJ 07801
Tel: 973-361-5400 *Fax:* 973-537-8929
E-mail: projectors@casio.com
Web Site: www.casioprojector.com
Key Personnel
Dir, Prod Mktg: Joseph Gillio *Tel:* 973-361-5400 ext 4145 *E-mail:* jgillio@casio.com
Founded: 1957

Casslee Corp, see Clever Cleaver Productions

Castillo Theater
543 W 42 St, New York, NY 10036
Tel: 212-941-5800 *Toll Free Tel:* 800-435-7453
E-mail: castillo@allstars.org
Web Site: www.castillo.org

Key Personnel
VP, Theater All Stars Proj: Diane Stiles
Artistic Dir: Dan Friedman
Founded: 1984
Theatre production company.

Castleview Productions
1100 W 41 St, Austin, TX 78756
Tel: 512-442-9944 *Fax:* 512-442-8823
E-mail: contact@castleviewproductions.com
Web Site: www.castleviewproductions.com
Key Personnel
Pres & Exec Prodr: Ted Barnhill
Prodn Mgr: Sonia Anguiano
Founded: 1999
Video, film & interactive media production.

Catapult Films Inc
832 Third St, Suite 303, Santa Monica, CA 90403
Tel: 310-395-1470
Key Personnel
Pres: Lawrence Levy
Prodr: Lisa Josefsberg
Membership(s): DGA; Independent Film Project/West; Writers Guild of America

Catholic Books & Tapes
Subsidiary of Children of Mary
PO Box 350333, Fort Lauderdale, FL 33335-0333
Tel: 954-583-5108 *Fax:* 954-583-5108
E-mail: mascmen7@yahoo.com
Web Site: www.catholicbook.com
Key Personnel
Owner & CEO: John Walsh
Catholic traditional books & conspiracy books on who rules the world. DVDs of royal weddings in UK & Spain, with choral music.
Catalog(s), annual, free

Catman & Mary Productions
336 W 37 St, Suite 800, New York, NY 10018
Tel: 212-947-4777 *Fax:* 212-947-4779
Web Site: www.catmanandmary.com
Key Personnel
Contact: Gregor Clark *E-mail:* gregor@catmanandmary.com
Film & TV production company.

Cavalcade Productions Inc
PO Box 2480, Nevada City, CA 95959-1948
Tel: 530-477-0701 (outside US & CN) *Toll Free Tel:* 800-345-5530 *Fax:* 530-477-0701 (outside US & CN) *Toll Free Fax:* 800-345-5530
E-mail: info@cavalcadeproductions.com
Web Site: www.cavalcadeproductions.com
Key Personnel
Pres: Bruce McCulley
Founded: 1948
Video production & distribution, specializing in programs on psychological trauma.
Online catalog(s) available

Cavanaugh Tocci Associates Inc
327F Boston Post Rd, Sudbury, MA 01776
Tel: 978-443-7871
E-mail: cta@cavtocci.com
Web Site: www.cavtocci.com
Key Personnel
Pres: Douglas Bell
Sr Principal Consultant: Nicholas Browse
Founded: 1975
Acoustical, theatrical & AV consulting firm.

Cavision Enterprises Ltd
2323 Boundary Rd, Suite 210, Vancouver, BC V5M 4V8, Canada
Tel: 604-298-9053 *Fax:* 604-298-9051
E-mail: info@cavision.com
Web Site: www.cavision.com
Founded: 1993
Design & manufacture a wide variety of accessories for professional cameras.
Online catalog(s) available
Membership(s): NAB

CBC/Radio-Canada
181 Queen St, Ottawa, ON K1P 1K9, Canada
Mailing Address: PO Box 3220, Sta C, Ottawa, ON K1Y 1E4, Canada
Toll Free Tel: 866-306-4636 (CN) *Fax:* 613-288-6245
E-mail: liaison@cbc.ca; liaison@radio-canada.ca
Web Site: www.cbc.radio-canada.ca
Key Personnel
CEO & Pres: Hubert T Lacroix
Chair: Remi Racine
Broadcast company.
Catalog(s) available
Branch Office(s)
Communications-English Services, PO Box 500, Sta A, 250 Front St W, Toronto, ON M5W 1E6, Canada *Tel:* 416-205-3311 *Fax:* 416-205-3714 *E-mail:* cbcfeedback@cbc.ca
The Ombudsman, CBC English Services, PO Box 500, Sta A, Toronto, ON M5W 1E6, Canada *Tel:* 416-205-2959 *Fax:* 416-205-2825 *E-mail:* ombudsman@cbc.ca (audience relations)
Communications-French Services, PO Box 6000, 1400 Rene-Levesque Blvd E, Montreal, QC H3C 3A8, Canada *Tel:* 514-597-6000 *Fax:* 514-597-5545 *E-mail:* auditoire@radio-canada.ca
Sales Office(s): Ombudsman de Radio Canada-French Services, PO Box 6000, 1400 Rene-Levesque Blvd E, Montreal, QC H3C 3A8, Canada *Tel:* 514-597-4757 *Fax:* 514-597-5253 *E-mail:* ombudsman@radio-canada.ca

CBM Metal
High Point Business Park, 8750 Holgate Cresent, Milton, ON L9T 0K3, Canada
Tel: 905-878-0648 *Toll Free Tel:* 800-387-4834 *Fax:* 905-878-6748 *Toll Free Fax:* 888-554-5501
E-mail: sales@cbmmetal.com
Web Site: www.cbmmetal.com
Key Personnel
VP, Sales & Mktg: Jeff Williams *E-mail:* jeff.williams@cbmmetal.com
Busn Devt Mgr: Bruce Hosker
Founded: 1927
Design driven manufacturing.
Catalog(s) available
Membership(s): InfoComm International®

CCH Continuing Education
Division of CCH Inc, A Wolters Kluwer business
4025 W Peterson Ave, Chicago, IL 60646-6085
Tel: 773-866-3648 *Toll Free Tel:* 800-248-3248 *Fax:* 773-866-3084
Web Site: www.cch.com
Key Personnel
Mng Ed: Gwen Hefty *E-mail:* gwen.hefty@wolterskluwer.com
Tax & legal publications.

CCH Inc, A Wolters Kluwer business
2700 Lake Cook Rd, Riverwoods, IL 60015
Tel: 847-267-7000
Web Site: www.cch.com
Key Personnel
CEO & Pres: Karen Abramson
Dir, PR: Leslie Bonacum
Founded: 1913
Provider of tax information & software solutions for tax & accounting professionals.
Catalog(s) available
Branch Office(s)
4025 W Peterson Ave, Chicago, IL 60646-6085 *Toll Free Tel:* 800-334-3734 (cust support)
CCH Washington Service Bureau, 1015 15 St NW, 10th fl, Washington, DC 20005 *Tel:* 202-842-7355 *Toll Free Tel:* 800-289-1057 *Web Site:* www.wsb.com
CCH Canada Ltd, 90 Sheppard Ave E, Suite 300, Toronto, ON M2N 6X1, Canada, Pres: Doug Finley *Tel:* 416-224-2248 *Fax:* 416-224-2243 *E-mail:* cservice@cch.ca *Web Site:* www.cch.ca
Foreign Office(s): CCH Australia Ltd, 101 Waterloo Rd, Level 2, North Ryde, NSW 2113, Australia *Tel:* (02) 9857 1300 *Fax:* (02) 9857 1601 *E-mail:* support@cch.com.au *Web Site:* www.cch.com.au
CCH Asia Pte Ltd, 03-00 Link (THM) Bldg, 8 Chang Charn Rd, Singapore 159637, Singapore *E-mail:* support@cch.com.sg *Web Site:* www.cch.com.sg
Croner CCH Group Ltd, 145 London Rd, Kingston-Upon-Thames, Surrey KT2 6SR, United Kingdom *Tel:* (020) 8547 3333 *Fax:* (020) 8547 2638 *Web Site:* www.cch.co.uk

CCI, see Cambium Catalyst International (CCI)

CCI Communications Inc
1440 Phoenixville Pike, West Chester, PA 19380
Tel: 610-296-7233 *Fax:* 610-296-7358
E-mail: info@ccivideo.com
Web Site: www.ccivideo.com
Key Personnel
Pres: Kenneth R Selinger
Founded: 1982
Television production facility including location shooting, mobile production unit & studio.
Membership(s): MCA-I

CCI Digital
2921 W Alameda Ave, Burbank, CA 91505
Tel: 818-562-6300 *Fax:* 818-562-8222
E-mail: info@ccidigital.com
Web Site: www.ccidigital.com
Key Personnel
Pres: Ruben Veloso
Full service post-production facility.
Online catalog(s) available
Membership(s): IAAVC; MCA-I

CCI Solutions
1342 88 Ave SE, Olympia, WA 98501
Mailing Address: PO Box 481, Olympia, WA 98507
Tel: 360-943-5378 *Toll Free Tel:* 800-562-6006 *Fax:* 360-754-1566
E-mail: info@ccisolutions.com
Web Site: www.ccisolutions.com
Key Personnel
Pres: Bob Schmidt
EVP: Mark Bradley; Jerry Lamb
Dir, Church Rel: Duke DeJong
Founded: 1976
Acoustical consulting, equipment sales, recording media & design-build/installation services to churches, schools & government agencies.
Branch Office(s)
1247 85 Ave SE, Olympia, WA 98501 (warehouse)

CCore Media Inc
Formerly Creative Core Inc
1421 Lowe Dr, Algonquin, IL 60102
Tel: 847-854-1111
Web Site: www.creativecore.com
Key Personnel
Exec Prodr: Robert L Sandidge *E-mail:* bobsdesk@ccoremedia.com
Founded: 1982
Media producer, publisher & distributor.
Catalog(s) available
Membership(s): Chicago Area Producers Association; SPARC

CD Meyer Inc
91 Clinton Rd, Suite 2C, Fairfield, NJ 07004
Tel: 973-882-9411 *Fax:* 973-808-4087
E-mail: info@cdmeyer.com
Web Site: www.cdmeyer.com; www.point2explore.com; museumdigitalsignage.com
Key Personnel
Pres: Chris Meyer *Tel:* 973-882-9411 ext 13
Founded: 1988
Corporate web site development, digital signage content creation, exhibit multimedia, DVD & video production services.

The CD Recycling Center of America
68 Stiles Rd, Salem, NH 03079
Tel: 603-894-5553 *Fax:* 603-898-4319
E-mail: info@cdrecyclingcenter.org
Web Site: www.cdrecyclingcenter.org
Key Personnel
Founder & Pres: Lisa Bennett
Founded: 2006
Founded to promote public awareness of the importance of recycling CDs & DVDs & their packaging. Collection center will accept unwanted & obsolete CDs, DVDs & their packaging. Online information center, with onsite collection of materials.

CD ROM™ Inc
3131 E Riverside Dr, Fort Myers, FL 33916
Tel: 952-832-5424 (sales) *Toll Free Tel:* 866-662-3766 (orders) *Fax:* 239-332-2808; 715-372-6702 (orders)
E-mail: sales@cdrominc.com
Web Site: www.cdrominc.com
Key Personnel
CEO & Pres: Roger S Hutchison, PhD *E-mail:* rshutch@cdrominc.com
Founded: 1988
Manufactures DX-CD2 optical disc destruction device & DX-CD manual optical disc destruction device. Distributes Hammer, hard drive secure ease device, SCSI Hammer, hard drive secure erase device & PSI Clone, hard drive forensic imaging device.
Catalog(s) available
Foreign Office(s): CRSI Pte Ltd, International Plaza, No 23-14, 10 Anson Rd, Singapore, Singapore, Consultant: Dr Philip Teo *Tel:* 9616 5632 *Fax:* 745 2009

CDAI Innovative Design Solutions
4279 Roswell Rd NE, Suite 102, No 135, Atlanta, GA 30342
Tel: 404-633-8861 *Fax:* 404-636-5089
E-mail: info@cdai.com
Web Site: www.cdai.com
Key Personnel
Pres: Rogers Dixson
Founded: 1988
Specialty consultants in audio, video & control system design, construction, installation & monitoring; acoustics & lighting design & consulting; presentation; facility consulting & planning.
Brochure(s), upon request
Online catalog(s) available
Membership(s): ASA; Association of Science & Technology Centers; Illuminating Engineering Society; InfoComm International®; SMPTE

CDR Communications Inc
9310-B Old Keene Mill Rd, Burke, VA 22015
Tel: 703-569-3400 *Toll Free Tel:* 800-729-2237 *Fax:* 703-569-3448
E-mail: info@cdrcommunications.com
Web Site: www.cdrcommunications.com
Key Personnel
Pres: Christopher D Rogers *E-mail:* chris@cdrcommunications.com
VP & Mgr: Nancy Rogers *E-mail:* nancy@cdrcommunications.com
Founded: 1984
Full service film & video production company.
Membership(s): ICVM

Ceavco Audio/Visual Co
6240 W 54 Ave, Arvada, CO 80002
Tel: 303-539-3500 *Fax:* 303-539-3501
E-mail: solutions@ceavco.com
Web Site: www.ceavco.com
Key Personnel
Owner: Matt Emerson
Founded: 1961
Full service audio/video solutions provider specializing in audiovisual production for live events & system integration for clients nationwide.
Online catalog(s) available
Branch Office(s)
5078 List Dr, Colorado Springs, CO 80919 *Tel:* 719-636-2866 *Fax:* 719-636-2857
Membership(s): InfoComm International®; PSNI

Cedar Crest Studio
17 CR 830, Henderson, AR 72544
Tel: 870-488-5777
E-mail: cedarcrest@springfield.net
Web Site: www.cedarcreststudio.com
Key Personnel
Owner: Bob Ketchum
Mktg Dir: Jane Ketchum
Founded: 1976
Audio video production studio.
Video(s) available

CELCO-Constantine Engineering Labs Co
14 Industrial Ave, Suite 3, Mahwah, NJ 07430
Tel: 201-327-1123 *Fax:* 201-327-7047
E-mail: info@celco-nj.com
Web Site: www.celco.com; www.celco-nj.com
Key Personnel
VP, Yokes: John Constantine, Jr
Founded: 1950
CRT digital display equipment designers & manufacturers. State-of-the-art CRT deflection components including Raster Calligraphic Projection, flight simulators, planetarium displays, night vision, TANK, Head-Up (HUD), image tube applications & digital film recorders to the film industry worldwide & digital filmout service.
Online catalog(s), yokes, coils, deflection components
Branch Office(s)
CELCO Pacific, 10291-A Trademark St, Rancho Cucamonga, CA 91730, Mng Dir: Michael Constantine *Tel:* 909-481-4648 *Fax:* 909-481-6899 *E-mail:* info@celco.com
Membership(s): IBC; IEEE; NAB; SID; SMPTE; SPIE

Celebrities Productions
Division of Clayton-Davis & Associates
c/o Clayton-Davis & Associates, 230 S Bemiston Ave, Suite 1400, St Louis, MO 63105
Tel: 314-862-7800 *Fax:* 314-721-5171
E-mail: idcda@aol.com
Web Site: www.claytondavis.com
Key Personnel
CEO & Pres: Irvin Davis
VP: Jennifer Davis
Art Dir: Steve Pezald
Secy: Adele Solit
Catalog(s) available
Membership(s): SAG-AFTRA

Celebrity Helicopters Inc
961 W Alondra Blvd, Compton, CA 90220
Tel: 310-618-1155 *Toll Free Tel:* 877-999-2099 *Fax:* 424-785-8768 *Toll Free Fax:* 877-999-2099
Web Site: www.celebheli.com
Key Personnel
CEO: Robin Petgrave *E-mail:* robin@celebheli.com
Aerial production services, executive transportation & location scouting, flight training & sightseeing flights.

Celestial Harmonies/Fortuna Records/Kuckuck Schallplatten/Black Sun Music/MonteVideo
Division of Mayflower Music Corp
1951 N Wilmot Rd, Bldg 2, Unit 7, Tucson, AZ 85712-8000
Mailing Address: PO Box 30122, Tucson, AZ 85751-0122
Tel: 520-326-4400 *Fax:* 520-326-3333
E-mail: celestial@harmonies.com
Web Site: www.harmonies.com
Key Personnel
Pres: Eckart Rahn
Gen Mgr: Tony Eckstat
Online catalog(s) available
Membership(s): Music Business Association; RIAA

Celestial Mechanix Inc, see CMI

Centaur Records Inc
136 Saint Joseph St, Baton Rouge, LA 70802
Tel: 225-336-4877 *Fax:* 225-336-9678
E-mail: info@centaurrecords.com
Web Site: www.centaurrecords.com
Key Personnel
Pres: Victor E Sachse
VP: Dan Cassin
Founded: 1976
Audio production.
Membership(s): The Recording Academy

Centennial Electric Sound Co Ltd
545 W 45 St, New York, NY 10036
Tel: 212-581-4150 *Fax:* 212-581-4152
Cassette tape recorders & hand held megaphones.

Center City Film & Video Inc
1501-1503 Walnut St, Philadelphia, PA 19102
Tel: 215-568-4134 *Fax:* 215-568-6011
E-mail: info@ccfv.com; sales@ccfv.com
Web Site: www.ccfv.com
Key Personnel
Founder, CEO & Pres: Jordan M Schwartz
Full service video & interactive production company.
Membership(s): MCA-I; Television Radio Advertising Club

Center for Southern Folklore Inc
119 S Main St, Memphis, TN 38103
Tel: 901-525-3655 *Fax:* 901-544-9965
E-mail: info@southernfolklore.com
Web Site: www.southernfolklore.com
Key Personnel
Exec Dir: Judy Peiser *E-mail:* jlpeiser@gmail.com
Nonprofit multimedia organization documenting culture of the Memphis Delta Region of the South.

Center for Touch Drawing
PO Box 1595, Langley, WA 98260
Tel: 360-221-5745 *Toll Free Tel:* 800-989-6334 (orders)
E-mail: center@touchdrawing.com
Web Site: www.touchdrawing.com
Key Personnel
Founder & Owner: Deborah Koff-Chapin
Online catalog(s) available
Shipping Address: 628 First St, Langely, WA 98260

CenterStaging LLC
3407 Winona Ave, Burbank, CA 91504

Tel: 818-559-4333 *Fax:* 818-848-4016
E-mail: info@centerstaging.com
Web Site: centerstaging.com
Key Personnel
Co-Owner & Pres: Mitch Clark
Co-Owner: Scott Scovill
Audio Mgr: Doug Dubin
Busn Mgr: Will Kerlick
Opers Mgr: Jr Estrada
Prodn Support Mgr: Kerry Jensen
Founded: 2009
Studio, soundstage & equipment rentals. Specialize in production & technical support for television & live performances.

Central Audio-Visual Equipment Inc
375 Roma Jean Pkwy, Streamwood, IL 60107
Tel: 630-372-8100 *Toll Free Tel:* 800-323-4239 *Fax:* 630-372-9281
Web Site: www.cavinc.com
Key Personnel
Pres: Michael Bashir
VP: Irene Bashir
Sales: Jonathan Bashir *E-mail:* jbashir@cavinc.com
Founded: 1958
Catalog(s) available

Central Lighting & Equipment Inc (CLE)
4103 E 16 St, Des Moines, IA 50313
Tel: 515-277-4190 *Toll Free Tel:* 877-977-4190 *Fax:* 515-277-2295
E-mail: info@cleproductions.com
Web Site: www.cleproductions.com
Key Personnel
Pres: Arren C Wetzel *E-mail:* arren.wetzel@clelights.com
Founded: 2002
Full service production company including indoor/outdoor LED walls, floating screens & wall-to-wall video displays.
Branch Office(s)
5055 S 111 St, Omaha, NE 68137 *Tel:* 402-593-6500 *Fax:* 402-593-8500
Membership(s): Professional Lighting & Sound Association

Central Texas College KNCT-TV & Radio FM
PO Box 1800, Killeen, TX 76540-1800
Tel: 254-526-1176 *Fax:* 254-526-1850
E-mail: knct@knct.org
Web Site: www.knct.org
Key Personnel
Gen Mgr: Max Rudolph *E-mail:* max.rudolph@knct.org
Radio & TV programming.
Program guide(s) available

Centralite Systems Inc
1000 Cody Rd S, Mobile, AL 36695
Tel: 251-607-9119 *Toll Free Tel:* 877-466-5483 *Fax:* 251-607-9117
Web Site: www.centralite.com

Centrax Corp
22 W Washington, Suite 1500, Chicago, IL 60602
Tel: 312-946-2000 *Toll Free Tel:* 800-556-1909 *Toll Free Fax:* 888-661-7030
E-mail: info@centrax.com
Web Site: www.centrax.com
Founded: 1985
Membership(s): American Society of Association Executives

Centre Communications Inc
75 Manhattan Dr, Suite 200, Boulder, CO 80303
Tel: 303-444-1166
E-mail: centre@ecentral.com
Web Site: www.centrecommunicationinc.com; www.centredm.com
Key Personnel
Pres: Ron Meyer
Online catalog(s) available
Membership(s): IAAVC

Century Business Solutions
Division of New Century Direct LLC
2340 Brighton Henrietta Town Line Rd, Rochester, NY 14623
Toll Free Tel: 800-975-6429 *Toll Free Fax:* 800-975-6429
E-mail: customerservice@ncd-brands.com
Web Site: www.centurybusinesssolutions.com
Founded: 1954
Products for organization, presentation & display.
Catalog(s) available
Online catalog(s) available

Century Color Labs Inc
494 School St, East Hartford, CT 06108
Tel: 860-289-9501 *Toll Free Tel:* 800-242-9501 *Fax:* 860-291-9098
E-mail: production@centurycolor.com
Web Site: www.centurycolor.com
Key Personnel
Pres: Greg Der Boghosian
Founded: 1968
Online catalog(s) available

Cerutti Productions Inc
18211 Bulverde Rd, Suite 10202, San Antonio, TX 78259
Tel: 210-403-0800 *Fax:* 210-403-0801
Web Site: www.cerutti.org
Key Personnel
Pres: Marc Cerutti *E-mail:* marc@cerutti.org
Catalog(s) available
Membership(s): International Alliance of Theatrical Stage Employees; NATAS

Cerwin-Vega! Inc
Division of Gibson Pro Audio
309 Plus Park Blvd, Nashville, TN 37217
Tel: 615-871-4500 *Toll Free Tel:* 800-444-2766
Web Site: www.cerwinvega.com
Founded: 1954
Online catalog(s) available

CES, see Cinema Equipment & Supplies Inc

Thomas Cestare Inc
188 Herricks Rd, Mineola, NY 11502
Tel: 516-742-5550 *Fax:* 516-742-5551
E-mail: cestare@aol.com
Web Site: www.thomascestareinc.com
Key Personnel
Owner: Thomas Cestare
Pres: Gary Haspel
Founded: 1972
Catalog(s) available

CET
Division of Public Media Connect
1223 Central Pkwy, Cincinnati, OH 45214
Tel: 513-381-4033 *Fax:* 513-381-7520
E-mail: wcet@cetconnect.org
Web Site: www.cetconnect.org
Key Personnel
Dir of Prodn: Taylor Feltner *Tel:* 513-345-6560 *E-mail:* tfeltner@cetconnect.org

CEV Multimedia Ltd
1020 SE Loop 289, Lubbock, TX 79404
Toll Free Tel: 800-922-9965 *Toll Free Fax:* 800-243-6398
E-mail: cev@cevmultimedia.com
Web Site: www.cevmultimedia.com
Key Personnel
Partner & Pres: Jeff Lansdell *E-mail:* jeff.lansdell@cevmultimedia.com
Founded: 1984
Online catalog(s) available

CFP Video Productions Inc
PO Box 86, Caldwell, NJ 07006-0086
Tel: 973-226-2481 *Fax:* 973-226-2480
Web Site: cfpvideo.com
Key Personnel
Pres: Don Spitzmiller *E-mail:* don.spitzmiller@verizon.net
Founded: 1983
Shipping Address: 68 Anderson Pkwy, Cedar Grove, NJ 07009
Membership(s): American Guild of Court Videographers; IEEE; MCA-I; NAB

Chace Audio by Deluxe
Division of Deluxe Media Services
201 S Victory Blvd, Burbank, CA 91502-2349
Toll Free Tel: 800-842-8346
Web Site: www.chace.com
Key Personnel
VP, Audio/DDM: Robert J Heiber
Gen Mgr: James R C Eccles
Founded: 1984
Full audio post-production services.
Branch Office(s)
The Rick Chace Film Center, 1150 W Olive Ave, Burbank, CA 91506
Membership(s): AES; Association of Moving Image Archivists; SMPTE

Chalk Dust Co
16107 Kensington Dr, PMB 256, Sugar Land, TX 77479-4401
Tel: 281-265-2495 *Toll Free Tel:* 800-588-7564 *Fax:* 281-265-3197
E-mail: sales@chalkdust.com
Web Site: www.chalkdust.com
Key Personnel
Owner & Pres: Dana Mosely *E-mail:* dana@chalkdust.com
Owner & VP: Richard Mosely *E-mail:* richard@chalkdust.com
Founded: 1994
Manufacturing & marketing of comprehensive math DVDs for eleven separate courses including Basic Math, Prealgebra, Algebra 1, Geometry, SAT*Math Review, Algebra 2, College Algebra, Trigonometry, Precalculus, Calculus 1 & Statistics.
Online catalog(s) available

Challenge Productions
400 E George St, Marion, OH 43302
Tel: 740-531-3077
E-mail: info@challenge-pro.com
Web Site: challenge-pro.com
Key Personnel
Owner: Terry Cline *E-mail:* terry@challenge-pro.com

Championship Productions Inc
Ames Community Development Park, 2730 Graham St, Ames, IA 50010
Tel: 515-232-3687 *Toll Free Tel:* 800-873-2730 *Fax:* 515-232-3739
E-mail: info@championshipproductions.com
Web Site: www.championshipproductions.com
Key Personnel
Founder & Pres: William Bergan
Founded: 1976
Catalog(s), upon request

Channel Productions
1964 Filer Ave E, Twin Falls, ID 83301
Fax: 208-734-6550
E-mail: chanpro@mindspring.com
Key Personnel
Owner: Kelly Yost
Founded: 1987
Cross-over classical record label & music CDs.

Channell One Video
PO Box 399, Epping, NH 03042-0399
Tel: 603-679-6796 *Toll Free Tel:* 888-722-3843 (natl)
E-mail: racevid@earthlink.net
Web Site: www.racevideo.com
Key Personnel
Pres: Bill Channell
VP: Kathleen Channell
VP, Prodn: Bill Harris
Founded: 1971
Catalog(s) available
Shipping Address: 9 Old State Rd, Epping, NH 03042
Membership(s): Alliance for Community Media; Race Videographers Association; Seacoast Professional Videographers Association

Chapman/Leonard Studios & Production Center
12950 Raymer St, North Hollywood, CA 91605
Tel: 818-764-6726 *Toll Free Tel:* 888-883-6559 *Fax:* 818-764-6730
Web Site: www.chapman-leonard.com
Key Personnel
COO: Charles Huenergardt *E-mail:* chuckh@chapman-leonard.com
CFO: Michael Chapman *E-mail:* mchapman@chapman-leonard.com
VP & Dir, Mktg & Sales: Christine Chapman-Huenergardt *E-mail:* christine@chapman-leonard.com
Mktg Asst: Jaqueline Sunshine *E-mail:* jackies@chapman-leonard.com
Specialize in camera cranes, arms, bases, dollies, pedestals & remote camera systems for motion picture & TV production. State-of-the-art sound stage & production center at the Orlando location.
Catalog(s) available
Branch Office(s)
9460 Delegates Dr, Orlando, FL 32837, Contact: Juan Escribano *Tel:* 407-851-3456 *Toll Free Tel:* 888-337-8243 *Fax:* 407-855-1653 *E-mail:* juane@chapman-leonard.com
500 Sandy Creek Rd, Bldg 2004, Suite 101, Fayetteville, GA 30214, Contact: Rusty Bishop *Toll Free Tel:* 888-758-4826 *Fax:* 678-583-1858 *E-mail:* rustyb@chapman-leonard.com
Elmwood Business Park, 668 Distributors Row, Suite E, New Orleans, LA 70123, Contact: David Bullard *Tel:* 504-731-6050 *Toll Free Tel:* 888-758-4826 *Fax:* 504-731-6051 *E-mail:* davidb@chapman-leonard.com
5650 University Blvd SE, Albuquerque, NM 87106, Contact: Ian Curry *Toll Free Tel:* 888-758-4826 *Fax:* 505-227-2578 *E-mail:* ianc@chapman-leonard.com
15919 Industrial Pkwy, Cleveland, OH 44135, Contact: Fulton Dawson *Tel:* 216-241-4800 *Toll Free Tel:* 888-758-4826 *Fax:* 216-241-4805 *E-mail:* fultond@chapman-leonard.com
1901 E 51 St, Austin, TX 78723, Contact: James Marks *Tel:* 512-473-0084 *Toll Free Tel:* 888-758-4826 *Fax:* 512-473-0042 *E-mail:* jmarks@chapman-leonard.com
Foreign Office(s): Chapman/Leonard Studio Equipment Ltd, North Orbital Commercial Park, Unit 2, Napsbury Lane, Saint Albans, Herts AL1 1XB, United Kingdom, Mng Dir: Dennis Fraser *Tel:* (01727) 838424 *Fax:* (01727) 852241 *E-mail:* dennis@chapman-leonard.com
Membership(s): AICP; ASC; SMPTE; Society of Camera Operators; Women in Film

Chapman Recording & Mastering
8805 Monrovia, Lenexa, KS 66215
Tel: 913-894-6854 *Fax:* 913-894-6857
Web Site: www.chapmanrecording.com
Key Personnel
Owner: Chuck Chapman *E-mail:* chuck@chapmanrecording.com
Bookings Rep: Neil Simpson *E-mail:* neil@chapmanrecording.com
Studio hours: 24/7 by appointment only.

Charles Beseler Co
2018 W Main St, Stroudsburg, PA 18360
Mailing Address: PO Box 431, Stroudsburg, PA 18360
Toll Free Tel: 800-237-3537 *Toll Free Fax:* 800-966-4515
Web Site: www.beselerphoto.com
Key Personnel
Pres: Hank Gasikowski *E-mail:* hank@beselerphoto.com
Membership(s): Photo Marketing Association

Charlex Inc
2 W 45 St, 7th fl, New York, NY 10036
Tel: 212-719-4600 *Fax:* 212-840-2747
Web Site: www.charlex.com

Chartpak Inc
Subsidiary of GPC International
One River Rd, Leeds, MA 01053
Tel: 413-584-5446 *Toll Free Tel:* 800-628-1910 *Fax:* 413-584-6781
E-mail: info@chartpak.com
Web Site: www.chartpak.com
Key Personnel
Pres: Steven Roth
VP & Gen Mgr: Bob Rodak
Founded: 1949
Catalog(s) available
Online catalog(s) available

Chater Camera Inc
1336 Ninth St, Berkeley, CA 94710
Tel: 510-525-5400 *Fax:* 510-295-2478
E-mail: rentals@chatercamera.com
Web Site: www.chatercamera.com
Key Personnel
Owner: John Chater *E-mail:* john@chatercamera.com
Owner & Engr: Jay Farrington *E-mail:* jay@chatercamera.com
Busn Mgr: Erin Anderson *E-mail:* erin@chatercamera.com
Full service film, video, digital cinema & 35mm lens rental house.

Chatterbox Productions Inc
2311 S Bayshore Dr, Coconut Grove, FL 33133-4728
Tel: 305-285-1058
Web Site: www.ampersandcom.com/chatterbox
Key Personnel
Prodr & Script Writer: Marjory E Leposky *E-mail:* meleposky@gmail.com
Founded: 1996
TV & film production, music videos, infomercials, casting, short films & feature films.

Chauvet Lighting
5200 NW 108 Ave, Sunrise, FL 33351-8040
Tel: 954-577-4455 *Toll Free Tel:* 800-762-1084 *Fax:* 954-929-5560 *Toll Free Fax:* 800-544-4898
E-mail: info@chauvetlighting.com
Web Site: www.chauvetlighting.com
Key Personnel
Mktg Mgr: Len Quist
Founded: 1989
Lighting manufacturer.
Catalog(s), semiannual, free
Online catalog(s) available

Checkers Industrial Products LLC
620 Compton St, Broomfield, CO 80020
Tel: 720-890-1187 *Toll Free Tel:* 800-438-9336 *Fax:* 720-890-1191
E-mail: sales@checkersindustrial.com
Web Site: www.checkersindustrial.com
Key Personnel
VP, Sales & Mktg: Ray Torres
Founded: 1967
Manufacture cable protectors & grip equipment.
Newsletter(s) available
Membership(s): IAAPA

Chelsea Decorative Metal Co
Division of Pressed Tin Ceiling Co
8212 Braewick Dr, Dept AV, Houston, TX 77074
Tel: 713-721-9200 *Fax:* 713-776-8661
E-mail: tinman83@earthlink.net
Web Site: www.tinman.com
Key Personnel
Owner: Glenn Eldridge
Ceiling material backdrops; Victorian styles & scenic accessories for movie sets or backgrounds.
Catalog(s) available

Chelsea Green Publishing Co
85 N Main St, Suite 120, White River Junction, VT 05001
Tel: 802-295-6300 *Toll Free Tel:* 800-639-4099 *Fax:* 802-295-6444
Web Site: www.chelseagreen.com
Key Personnel
Pres & Publr: Margo Baldwin *E-mail:* mbaldwin@chelseagreen.com
Busn & Dist Mgr: Sandi Eaton *Fax:* 802-229-4900 ext 105 *E-mail:* seaton@chelseagreen.com
Founded: 1984
Online catalog(s) available

Cheng & Tsui Co
25 West St, 2nd fl, Boston, MA 02111-1213
Tel: 617-988-2400 *Toll Free Tel:* 800-554-1963 (orders) *Fax:* 617-426-3669
E-mail: orders@cheng-tsui.com
Web Site: www.cheng-tsui.com
Key Personnel
Pres: Jill Cheng
Founded: 1987
Catalog(s) available
Online catalog(s) available
Shipping Address: c/o PSSC, 46 Development Rd, Fitchburg, MA 01420

Cherry Multimedia
2129 Colorado Blvd, Los Angeles, CA 90041
Toll Free Tel: 800-378-7598
E-mail: info@cherrymultimedia.com
Web Site: cherrymultimedia.com
Key Personnel
CEO: Lee Cherry
Provides cameras for video production & post-production.

Chesney Communications
PO Box 61945, Irvine, CA 92602-1945
Tel: 949-263-5500
E-mail: videocc@aol.com
Web Site: www.speakersdemos.com; www.videocc.com
Key Personnel
Pres: Robert Chesney *Tel:* 949-263-5500
Online catalog(s) available

Cheuvront Studios
4607 NW Sixth St Ext, Studio I, Gainesville, FL 32609
Tel: 352-378-4671 *Fax:* 352-338-9215
E-mail: allen@cheuvront.com
Web Site: www.cheuvront.com
Full service commercial photography studio.

Bruce Chianese
719 S Main St, Burbank, CA 91506
Tel: 818-841-6607

E-mail: bruce@brucechianese.com
Web Site: www.brucechianese.com
Film & TV composing, audio production.
Catalog(s) available
Membership(s): IAAVC; The Recording Academy

The Chicago Production Center
Division of WTTW Communications Inc
5400 N Saint Louis Ave, Chicago, IL 60625-4698
Tel: 773-509-5571 *Fax:* 773-509-5303
Web Site: www.wttw.com
Key Personnel
CEO & Pres: Daniel J Schmidt
CFO & EVP: Reese P Marcusson
SVP: Parke Richeson
SVP, Prodn: V J McAleer
Dir, Prodn Servs: Kim Mattes
Online catalog(s) available
Membership(s): MCA-I; NAB; NATAS

Chicago Satellite & Video
6749 N Keeler Ave, Lincolnwood, IL 60712-3513
Tel: 312-907-3057
E-mail: chicagosatellite@hotmail.com
Key Personnel
Owner & Pres: Brad S Fox
Television production company.

Chicago Scenic Studios Inc
1315 N Branch St, Chicago, IL 60642
Tel: 312-274-9900 *Fax:* 312-274-9901
E-mail: info@chicagoscenic.com
Web Site: www.chicagoscenic.com
Key Personnel
Pres: Bob Doepel *E-mail:* rdoepel@chicagoscenic.com
Mktg Dir: Diane Langhorst
Founded: 1978
A full service organization providing design, fabrication & production management to the special event, trade show, theatrical & entertainment industries.

Chicago Spotlight Inc
1658 W Carroll St, Chicago, IL 60612
Tel: 312-455-1171 *Fax:* 312-455-1744
Web Site: www.chicagospotlight.com
Key Personnel
Pres: Marty Lazarus *E-mail:* marty@chicagospotlight.com
Rental Mgr: Joe Mohamed *E-mail:* joe@chicagospotlight.com
Sales Mgr: Hope Kass *E-mail:* hope@chicagospotlight.com
Mktg Mgr: Todd Koeppl *E-mail:* todd@chicagospotlight.com
Sales: Ruth Hudson *E-mail:* ruth@chicagospotlight.com
Online catalog(s) available
Membership(s): Illinois Theatre Association; Professional Lighting & Sound Association; USITT

Chick Russell Communications
490 Castano Ave, Pasadena, CA 91107
Tel: 407-406-2899
E-mail: info@chickrussell.com
Web Site: www.chickrussell.com
Key Personnel
Pres: Chick Russell
Inspirational video production: museums, visitor centers & theme parks.

Chief
Division of Milestone AV Technologies
6436 City West Pkwy, Eden Prairie, MN 55344
Tel: 952-894-6280 *Toll Free Tel:* 800-582-6480 *Fax:* 952-894-6918 *Toll Free Fax:* 877-894-6918
E-mail: chief@chiefmfg.com; orders@chiefmfg.com
Web Site: www.chiefmfg.com
Key Personnel
Dir, Facilities: Ron Jensen
Founded: 1978
Catalog(s) available
Branch Office(s)
8401 Eagle Creek Pkwy, Savage, MN 55378
Membership(s): InfoComm International®

Children of Mary
PO Box 350333, Fort Lauderdale, FL 33335-0333
Tel: 954-583-5108 *Fax:* 954-583-5108
E-mail: mascmen7@yahoo.com
Web Site: www.catholicbook.com
Key Personnel
Owner & CEO: John R Walsh
Distribute DVDs, Catholic traditional books & conspiracy books on who rules the world.
Catalog(s), annual, free

The Children's Book Store Distribution (CBSD)
14-3245 Harvester Rd, Burlington, ON L7N 3T7, Canada
Tel: 905-681-8160; 905-831-1995 (intl) *Toll Free Tel:* 800-668-0242; 800-757-8372 (cust serv-CN & US) *Fax:* 905-831-1142 (intl)
E-mail: info@childrensgroup.com
Web Site: www.childrensgroup.com
Key Personnel
Pres: Geoff Kulawick *E-mail:* geoff@linusent.ca
Dir, Opers: Lee Mizzi *E-mail:* lee@linusent.ca
Gen Mgr: Laura Hunter *E-mail:* lhunter@childrensgroup.com
Classical music entertainment for children through a collection of CDs, DVDs, illustrated books, live concerts & educational resources.
Online catalog(s) available
Membership(s): Education Market Association; NAMM, the National Association of Music Merchants

Chimera®
1812 Valtec Lane, Boulder, CO 80301
Tel: 303-444-8000 *Toll Free Tel:* 888-444-1812 *Fax:* 303-444-8303
E-mail: salesinfo@chimeralighting.com
Web Site: chimeralighting.com
Key Personnel
VP, Sales: Eileen Healy *Tel:* 303-444-8000 ext 103
Mgr, Mktg & Prodn Devt: Terry Monahan *Tel:* 303-444-8000 ext 115
Sales, Cust Care Rep: Laura Plantell *Tel:* 303-444-8000 ext 104
Catalog(s) available
Online catalog(s) available
Membership(s): NAB

Chinmaya Publications
Division of Chinmaya Mission West
560 Bridgetown Pike, Langhorne, PA 19053-7210
Tel: 215-396-0390 *Toll Free Tel:* 888-CMW-READ (269-7323) *Fax:* 215-396-9710
E-mail: publications@chinmayamission.org
Web Site: www.chinmayamission.org; www.chinmayapublications.org
Key Personnel
Dir: Rev Swami Siddhananda
Catalog(s) available
Online catalog(s) available

Richard Chisolm Cinematography
300 Oakdale Rd, Baltimore, MD 21210
Tel: 410-467-2997
E-mail: mail@richardchisolm.com
Web Site: www.richardchisolm.com
Key Personnel
Dir, Photog: Richard Chisolm

CHK Electronics
6021 SW 29 St, Suite A311, Topeka, KS 66614
Tel: 785-862-2543 *Fax:* 707-361-0230
E-mail: sales@chk-electronics.com
Web Site: www.chk-electronics.com
Founded: 1991
Warehouse & distribute professional quality electronic components & connectors throughout North & South America.
Membership(s): NAMM, the National Association of Music Merchants

Christian Media Network
PO Box 728, Garberville, CA 95542-8728
Web Site: www.christianmedianetwork.com
Key Personnel
Owner: James Lloyd *E-mail:* james@christianmedianetwork.com
Christian music & videos.

Christian TV Services of Ellicottville, NY
6490 Pine Tree Rd, Bldg 5, Apt 315, Ellicottville, NY 14731-9603
Mailing Address: PO Box 209, Ellicottville, NY 14731-0209
Tel: 716-699-2549 (off & home); 716-257-2096 (cell); 716-397-9825 (cell)
Web Site: www.christiantvservices.com; www.angelfire.com/ny/christiantvservices; home.sbu.edu/christ; www.christiantvservices.net; www.sauen.com/george/adm; www.christiantvservices.us; www.christiantvservices.info
Key Personnel
CEO & Pres: Rev George Allan Thayer *E-mail:* geothayer@yahoo.com
Founded: 1974 (incorporated in 1981)
Independent consultant for Christian media.

ChristianAnswers.Net™
Division of Films for Christ Inc
PO Box 1167, Marysville, WA 98270-1167
Tel: 480-507-3621 *Toll Free Tel:* 800-332-2261 (orders only) *Fax:* 480-507-3623
E-mail: mail@eden.org
Web Site: www.christiananswers.net; www.christiananswers.net/eden/home.html
Key Personnel
Exec Dir: Paul S Taylor
Catalog(s) available
Membership(s): ICVM; National Religious Broadcasters

Christie Digital Systems USA Inc
10550 Camden Dr, Cypress, CA 90630
Tel: 714-236-8610 *Toll Free Tel:* 866-880-4462 (cust serv) *Fax:* 714-503-3375
E-mail: sales-us@christiedigital.com
Web Site: www.christiedigital.com
Key Personnel
Chmn, CEO & Pres: Jack Kline
Sales Admin, US Busn Prods: Leigh Shanks
Founded: 1929
Manufacturers of high resolution projection systems for digital & film applications.

Christie Lites
6990 Lake Ellenor Dr, Orlando, FL 32809
Tel: 407-856-0016 *Fax:* 407-856-0765
Web Site: www.christielites.com
Key Personnel
CEO: Huntly Christie *E-mail:* hchri@christielites.com
VP, Fin: Larry Winchowky *E-mail:* lwinc@christielites.com
Mktg Coord: Sheila Grant *E-mail:* sgran@christielites.com
Founded: 1985
Stage lighting rentals & production for theater, concerts, trade shows, TV & film, corporate presentations & special events.
Catalog(s) available

Branch Office(s)
Christie Lites Orlando, 7662 Currency Dr, Orlando, FL 32809, Opers Mgr: Fred Foster *E-mail:* ffost@christielites.com
Christie Lites Chicago, 1000 Davey Rd, Suite 500, Woodbridge, IL 60517, Opers Mgr: Thomas Cowdery *Tel:* 630-863-7067 *E-mail:* tcowd@christielites.com
Christie Lites Las Vegas, 4850 Statz St, Suite 103, North Las Vegas, NV 89081, Opers Mgr: Mike Gaynor *Tel:* 702-222-0363 *E-mail:* mgayn@christielites.com
Christie Lites Broadway, 40 Whelan Rd, East Rutherford, NJ 07073, Opers Mgr: Pete Hulin *Tel:* 201-438-6700 *E-mail:* phuli@christielites.com
Christie Lites New York, 13B Division St, Fairview, NJ 07022, Opers Mgr: Mark Wolverton *Tel:* 201-941-8370 *E-mail:* mwolv@christielites.com
Christie Lites Nashville, 6050 Dana Way, Suite 250, Antioch, TN 37013, Opers Mgr: Troy Rigney *Tel:* 615-280-5450 *Fax:* 615-641-5143 *E-mail:* trign@christielites.com
Christie Lites Dallas, 4801 Sharp St, Dallas, TX 75247, Opers Mgr: Mike Kennedy *Tel:* 214-637-3535 *Fax:* 214-637-4343 *E-mail:* mkenn@christielites.com
Christie Lites Seattle, 7815 S 208 St, Suite 101, Kent, WA 98032, Opers Mgr: Tim Reel *Tel:* 206-223-7200 *Fax:* 206-244-0000 *E-mail:* treel@christielites.com
Christie Lites Calgary, 4900 64 Ave SE, Bay 60, Calgary, AB T2C 4V3, Canada, Opers Mgr: Todd Hucul *Tel:* 403-243-2688 *E-mail:* thucu@christielites.com
Christie Lites Vancouver, 4154 McConnell Dr, Burnaby, BC V5A 3Y9, Canada, Opers Mgr: Kevan Bull *Tel:* 604-255-9943 *Fax:* 604-420-1130 *E-mail:* kbull@christielites.com
Christie Lites Winnipeg, 25 Terracon Place, Winnipeg, MB R2J 4B3, Canada, Regl Opers Mgr: A-Lynn Thompson *Tel:* 204-231-3921 *Fax:* 204-233-7965 *E-mail:* athom@christielites.com
Christie Lites Halifax, 100 Ilsley Ave, Unit BB, Darmouth, NS B3B 1L3, Canada, Regl Opers Mgr: Laura Smith *Tel:* 902-468-8887 *Fax:* 902-468-7778 *E-mail:* lsmit@christielites.com
Christie Lites Ottawa, 1230 Old Innes Rd, Unit 404, Ottawa, ON K1B 3V3, Canada, Regl Opers Mgr: Dennis Dagenais *Tel:* 613-594-5804 *E-mail:* ddage@christielites.com
Christie Lites Toronto, 100 Carson St, Unit A, Toronto, ON M8W 3R9, Canada, Opers Mgr: Naveed Khan *Tel:* 416-644-1010 *Fax:* 416-644-0404; 416-644-0408 (warehouse) *E-mail:* nkhan@christielites.com
Membership(s): Professional Lighting & Sound Association

Christopher Gray Post Production
3918 Michael Ave, Los Angeles, CA 90066
Tel: 310-395-9845
E-mail: cgray@cgpost.com
Web Site: www.cgpost.com
Founded: 1980
Post-production services.
Membership(s): SMPTE

The Christophers
5 Hanover Sq, 22nd fl, New York, NY 10004
Tel: 212-759-4050 *Toll Free Tel:* 888-298-4050 (orders) *Fax:* 212-838-5073
E-mail: mail@christophers.org
Web Site: www.christophers.org
Key Personnel
Prodr: Tony Rossi *E-mail:* t.rossi@christophers.org
Founded: 1945
Brochure(s) available
Online catalog(s) available

Christy's Editorial
Affiliate of Atomic Film Co
3625 W Pacific Ave, Burbank, CA 91505
Tel: 818-845-1755 *Toll Free Tel:* 800-468-6391; 800-556-5706 (CA) *Fax:* 818-845-1756
E-mail: info@christys.net
Web Site: www.christys.net
Key Personnel
Pres & Ad Mgr: Craig Christy
Founded: 1969
Rent, sell & repair traditional film equipment & supplies. Also rent Avid editing systems, storage & decks.
Online catalog(s) available

Chromavision Corp
The Radio Wave Bldg, 8th fl, 49 W 27 St, New York, NY 10001
Tel: 212-686-7366
E-mail: info@chromavision.net
Web Site: www.chromavision.net
Key Personnel
Owner & Pres: Bruce Testa *E-mail:* btesta@chromavision.net
Online catalog(s) available

ChronTrol Corp
7525-D Mission Gorge Rd, San Diego, CA 92120
Mailing Address: PO Box 19537, San Diego, CA 92159-0537
Tel: 619-282-8686 *Toll Free Tel:* 800-854-1999 *Fax:* 619-563-6563
E-mail: info@chrontrol.com
Web Site: www.chrontrol.com
Key Personnel
VP, Engg: James G Durham *E-mail:* jgd@chrontrol.com
Mgr, Prodn: Chris McDuff
Founded: 1977
Online catalog(s) available

Chyron Corp, see ChyronHego Corp

ChyronHego Corp
5 Hub Dr, Melville, NY 11747
Tel: 631-845-2000 *Fax:* 631-845-2058
E-mail: usa@chyronhego.com
Web Site: www.chyronhego.com
Key Personnel
CEO: Johan Apel
SVP, Worldwide Sales: Kathleen Power *Tel:* 631-845-3858 *E-mail:* kathleen.power@chyronhego.com
Online catalog(s) available

Cibola Systems
180 S Cypress St, Orange, CA 92866
Tel: 714-480-0272 *Fax:* 714-480-0768
E-mail: info@cibolasystems.com
Web Site: cibolasystems.com
Key Personnel
Owner & CEO: Lisa Perrine *Tel:* 714-480-0272 ext 101
VP, Engg: Diana Theron
Sr AV Engr: Tom Francis
Sr Design Engr: Benjamin Djou
Sr Field Engr: Viktor Shafer
Purchasing Mgr: Doug Kotkin
Service Coord: Ramon Duran
Founded: 1971
AV design & integration.
Brochure(s) available

Cifex Corp
20547 Linksview Way, Boca Raton, FL 33434
Tel: 561-883-5548 *Fax:* 561-883-2712
E-mail: 2cifex@gmail.com
Key Personnel
Pres: Jerry Rappoport
VP: Beulah Rappoport
VP, Foreign Dist: Dorothy Clarke
Founded: 1977
Producers & distributors.
Membership(s): University Film & Video Association

Cine Audio Visual Sales & Service Ltd
10251 106 St, Edmonton, AB T5J 1H5, Canada
Tel: 780-423-5081 *Toll Free Tel:* 877-423-5081 *Fax:* 780-424-0309
E-mail: cineav@cineav.com; sales@cineav.com; info@cineav.com
Web Site: www.cineav.com
Key Personnel
Gen Mgr: Scott Zubko
Founded: 1958
Branch Office(s)
5655 Tenth St NE, Bay No 131, Calgary, AB T2E 8W7, Canada, Gen Mgr: Daryl Zubko *Tel:* 403-777-1070 *Toll Free Tel:* 877-777-1070 *Fax:* 403-777-1074

Cine Magnetics Inc, see CMI Media Management

Cine-Med Inc
127 Main St N, Woodbury, CT 06798
Mailing Address: PO Box 745, Woodbury, CT 06798
Tel: 203-263-0006 *Toll Free Tel:* 800-253-7657 *Fax:* 203-263-4839
E-mail: support@cine-med.net
Web Site: www.cine-med.com
Key Personnel
Pres: Kevin McGovern *E-mail:* kmcgovern@cine-med.net
Founded: 1980
Book publishing providing continuing medical education DVDs, books & meeting services.
Catalog(s) available

Cine Photo Tech
1240 Oakleigh Dr, Atlanta, GA 30344
Tel: 404-684-7100 *Fax:* 404-684-7080
E-mail: info@cinephototech.com
Web Site: www.cinephototech.com
Key Personnel
Owner: Frank Battaglia; Brian McGraw
Rents camera equipment to the motion picture, commercial & music video industry.

Cine 60 Inc
630 Ninth Ave, New York, NY 10036
Tel: 347-460-3971
E-mail: cine60nyc@gmail.com
Web Site: cine60.jimdo.com
Key Personnel
Sales Liaison: Vidal Ortiz
Founded: 1960
Manufacture & distribute film, video, lighting equipment & supplies.
Catalog(s) available

CineBags Inc
825 Western Ave, Suite 17, Glendale, CA 91201
Tel: 818-662-0605 *Fax:* 818-662-0613
Web Site: www.cinebags.com
Key Personnel
Pres: Markus Davids
Founded: 2001
Production bags.
Catalog(s) available

Cinebar Productions Inc
763 J Clyde Morris Blvd, Suite 1-C, Newport News, VA 23601
Tel: 757-873-3232 *Fax:* 757-873-3790
E-mail: cinebar@cinebarproductions.com
Web Site: www.cinebarproductions.com
Key Personnel
Principal: Richard D Borenstein *E-mail:* rich@

cinebarproductions.com; Sherri Fisher-Staples *E-mail:* sherri@cinebarproductions.com
Museum, historical society, arts programming & documentaries. Also streaming live online.
Membership(s): SEMC; VAM

Cinecraft Productions Inc
2515 Franklin Blvd, Cleveland, OH 44113
Tel: 216-781-2300 *Toll Free Tel:* 800-959-2463 *Fax:* 216-781-1067
E-mail: info@cinecraft.com
Web Site: cinecraft.com
Key Personnel
Chmn: Neil G McCormick *E-mail:* neil@cinecraft.com
Founded: 1939
Corporate & film video production company that also produces DVDs & provides web development.
Membership(s): AMA; IABC; SME

CineFilm Lab
2156 Faulkner Rd NE, Atlanta, GA 30324
Tel: 404-633-1448 *Toll Free Tel:* 800-633-1448 *Fax:* 404-633-3867
E-mail: csr@cinefilmlab.com
Web Site: www.cinefilmlab.com
Key Personnel
Gen Mgr: Jim Ogburn *E-mail:* jim@cinefilmlab.com
Founded: 1976
Film lab (16mm & 35mm) & transfer to video & HD.

Cinema Camera Rentals
113 Fleet St, Marina del Rey, CA 90292
Tel: 310-574-1524
E-mail: info@cinemacamerarentals.com
Web Site: www.cinemacamerarentals.com
Camera rental facility carrying ARRI Alexa, RED Epic, RED Scarlet, RED MX & a wide selection of lenses.

Cinema Concepts
Subsidiary of Cinema Concepts Theater Service Co Inc
2030 Powers Ferry Rd, Suite 214, Atlanta, GA 30339
Tel: 770-956-7460 *Toll Free Tel:* 800-SHOWADS (746-9237) *Fax:* 770-956-8358
E-mail: info@cinemaconcepts.com
Web Site: www.cinemaconcepts.com
Key Personnel
CEO: Stewart D Harnell
EVP: Teresa Dickey
VP Studio Dir: John Price
Creative Dir: Mike Tremble
Founded: 1977
Film, D-Cinema, 3D Stereoscopic & HD resolution post-production, digital intermediate solutions, 35mm, DCI-compliant & HD theatre with on-screen editing & finishing. Film recording & digital encoding services. Smoke 2K, Avid DS/HD Nitris, DVS Clipster 4K, Final Cut HD, 2D & 3D animation suites, multiresolution conversion, D-Cinema encoding, DVD replication, Fulfillment.
Catalog(s) available
Membership(s): Cinema Advertising Council; Digital Cinema Initiatives; SMPTE; Women in Film/Atlanta

Cinema East
7111 Biscayne Blvd, Miami, FL 33138
Tel: 305-757-5859 *Fax:* 305-751-2329
Web Site: www.cinemaeast.com
Key Personnel
Pres: Charles Allen *E-mail:* callen@cinemaeast.com
Prodr: Deny Chang *E-mail:* dchang@cinemaeast.com
Founded: 1979
Online catalog(s) available

Cinema Engineering Co
Affiliate of CinemaGear.com
14737 Arminta St, Unit B, Panorama City, CA 91402
Tel: 818-780-5404 *Fax:* 818-780-5405
E-mail: cinemaengineering@tcsn.net; cinemagear@cinemagear.com
Web Site: www.cinema-engineering.com; www.cinemagear.com
Key Personnel
Pres: Richard Bennett
Founded: 1975
Motion picture camera sales & repair, motion picture lens sales & repairs, motion picture equipment supply & sales. Film camera repair, modifications & sales. Live action DP & visual effects DP.
Online catalog(s) available
Membership(s): AFI; Cinematographers Guild Local 600; SMPTE; Television Academy

Cinema Entertainment Inc
1779 NW 79 Ave, Doral, FL 33126
Tel: 561-899-0721
E-mail: info@cinemaent.com
Web Site: cinemaent.com
Key Personnel
Dir: Fernando Lugo; Jordan Stavrev
Prodr: Rafael Gutierrez
Cinematographer: Denis Dufresne
Full production support for music videos, commercials, documentaries & film production.

Cinema Equipment & Supplies Inc
12457 SW 130 St, Miami, FL 33186
Tel: 305-232-8182 *Toll Free Tel:* 800-759-5905
E-mail: sales@cinemaequip.com
Web Site: www.cinemaequip.com
Key Personnel
Sales: Alex Younger
Founded: 1984
Distributor of movie theatre equipment.
Membership(s): Theatre Equipment Association

Cinema Equipment Sales of California Inc
24881 Alicia Pkwy, Suite E-326, Laguna Hills, CA 92653
Tel: 949-470-0298 *Fax:* 949-470-0835
E-mail: cinemadealer@cinemadealer.com
Web Site: www.cinema-equip.com
Key Personnel
Pres: Paula Smith *E-mail:* paula@cinemadealer.com
Gen Mgr: Michael Smith *E-mail:* mike@cinemadealer.com
Founded: 1986
Provide & install all equipment, furnishings & accessories for commercial cinemas, professional screening rooms & home cinemas (worldwide).

The Cinema Guild Inc
115 W 30 St, Suite 800, New York, NY 10001-4061
Tel: 212-685-6242 *Toll Free Tel:* 800-723-5522 *Fax:* 212-685-4717
E-mail: info@cinemaguild.com
Web Site: www.cinemaguild.com
Key Personnel
Founder: Philip Hobel; Mary-Ann Hobel
Founded: 1984

The Cinema Lab
2735 S Raritan St, Englewood, CO 80110-1101
Tel: 303-783-1020 *Fax:* 303-806-0555
Web Site: www.cinemalab.com
Key Personnel
CEO: Robert David
COO: Dan Clark *E-mail:* dan@thecinemalab.com
Founded: 2003
Also offers DVD production services.
Branch Office(s)
333 N Front, Burbank, CA 91502
Membership(s): Association of Moving Image Archivists; Colorado Film & Video Association

Cinema Rentals Inc
25876 The Old Rd, Suite 174, Stevenson Ranch, CA 91381
Tel: 661-222-7342
E-mail: ocxinc@gmail.com
Web Site: www.cinemarentals.com
Key Personnel
Owner & CEO: Jim Pearson *E-mail:* jpearson@cinemaaquatics.com
Founded: 1969
Filming service.

Cinema Stage Inc
110 Saunders Rd, Unit 4, Barrie, ON L4N 9A8, Canada
Tel: 705-733-8740 *Toll Free Tel:* 800-387-6205 *Fax:* 705-733-8742
E-mail: info@cinemastage.ca
Web Site: www.cinemastage.ca
Key Personnel
Sales Mgr: Karl Hergert
Founded: 1981
Supply & install motion picture systems, sound systems, specialty lighting systems, complex control systems, board rooms, training facilities, simulator theatres, lecture theatres, specialized video walls & plasma LCD technology, digital signage video projection, rigging, large projection screens, wall acoustical treatment & motorized drapery systems.
Membership(s): InfoComm International®; NSCA

Cinema-Vision
424 W 33 St, Suite 370, New York, NY 10001
Tel: 212-620-8191 *Fax:* 212-620-8198
E-mail: info@motionpicturerentals.com
Web Site: www.motionpicturerentals.com
Rental house for digital & film cameras, lenses, filters & more.

Cinema Xenon International Inc
261 Valley Vista Dr, Camarillo, CA 93010-1655
Tel: 805-383-5548 *Toll Free Tel:* 888-669-7271 *Fax:* 805-389-9611
E-mail: info@cxilamps.com
Web Site: www.cxilamps.com
Key Personnel
Founder & Pres: Dick Stockton
Founded: 1995
Exclusive distributor for YUMEX™ Xenon arc lamps. Complete line of high quality, competitvely priced quartz body & ceramic body lamps for Follow Spots & all Xenon projection equipment. Re-lamp service for BARCO, Christie, Digital, DPI & NEC-Large Venue Xenon Digital.
Membership(s): Professional Lighting & Sound Association

Cinemarr Entertainment
104 Church St, Sevierville, TN 37862
E-mail: cinemarrstudios@aol.com
Web Site: cinemarrstudios.com
Key Personnel
Prodr & Dir: Shane Marr
Contact: Doris Marr
Production & post-production.

Cinemat Inc
2350 NW 96 Ave, Doral, FL 33172
Tel: 305-887-7726
E-mail: info@cinematusa.com
Web Site: cinematusa.com
Key Personnel
Owner: Eduardo Scheuren; Jose Vicente Scheuren

Founded: 1997
Television production company that produces original scripted & non-scripted programming.

Cinematography Electronics Inc
5321 Derry Ave, Suite G, Agoura Hills, CA 91301
Tel: 818-706-3334 *Fax:* 818-706-3335
E-mail: info@cinemaelec.com
Web Site: www.cinematographyelectronics.com
Key Personnel
Pres: Larry Barton
Founded: 1976
Catalog(s) available

Cinemills Corp
2021 N Lincoln St, Burbank, CA 91504
Tel: 818-843-4560 *Toll Free Tel:* 877-CMC-HMIS (262-4647) *Fax:* 818-843-7834
E-mail: sales@cinemills.com
Web Site: www.cinemills.com
Key Personnel
Dir, Sales & Mktg: Matthew M De Mattos
Catalog(s) available
Branch Office(s)
1720 Redwood Rd, Suite B, San Marcos, TX 78666 *Tel:* 210-347-4012; 210-347-4013 *Web Site:* www.cinemillstx.com

Cinequipt Inc
2601 49 Ave N, Suite 500, Minneapolis, MN 55430
Tel: 612-627-9080 *Toll Free Tel:* 800-809-9080 *Fax:* 612-627-9789
Web Site: www.cinequipt.com
Key Personnel
Pres: Dawn Mans *E-mail:* dawn@cinequipt.com
Membership(s): AICP; Production Equipment Rental Association

Cinetel Films Inc
8255 Sunset Blvd, Los Angeles, CA 90046-2432
Tel: 323-654-4000 *Fax:* 323-650-6400
E-mail: info@cinetelfilms.com
Web Site: cinetelfilms.com
Key Personnel
CEO & Pres: Paul Hertzberg
Pres, Prodn: Lisa M Hansen
Founded: 1988
Film production & distribution.
Catalog(s) available
Membership(s): Independent Film & Television Alliance®

CineVantage LLC
8560 W Sunset Blvd, 5th fl, West Hollywood, CA 90069
Toll Free Tel: 888-518-7571
Web Site: www.cinevantage.com
Key Personnel
Founder & Prodr: Honnie Korngold
Full service television production company, supplying reality & nonfiction programming to networks in the US & internationally.
Branch Office(s)
PO Box 399, Larkspur, CO 80118
1776 Park Ave, No 4-469, Park City, UT 84060

Cinevest
21956 Carbon Mesa Rd, Malibu, CA 90265
Tel: 310-913-0284
Web Site: www.cinevest.com
Key Personnel
CEO & Pres: Andrew Gellis *E-mail:* agellis@cinevest.com
Distribute & produce IMAX/large format films & 3D.
Membership(s): AMPAS

CineVideotech Inc
7330 NE Fourth Ct, Miami, FL 33138
Tel: 305-754-2611 *Fax:* 305-759-2463
Web Site: www.cinevideotech.com
Key Personnel
Pres: Egon Stephan, Jr *E-mail:* estephanjr@cinevideotech.com
Founded: 1968
Catalog(s) available
Branch Office(s)
3600 W Lake Hamilton Dr, Winter Haven, FL 33881 *Tel:* 727-421-2997
Membership(s): AICP; Professional Film & Video Equipment Association; SMPTE

Cinevision Corp
3300 Northeast Expwy NE, Bldg 2-A, Atlanta, GA 30341
Tel: 770-455-8988 *Fax:* 770-455-4066
E-mail: cvcorp@bellsouth.net
Key Personnel
Pres: Stephen A Newton
VP: Saundra Conner
Also distributes digital video equipment.
Catalog(s) available

Cineworks Inc
8125 Lankershim Blvd, North Hollywood, CA 91605
Tel: 818-252-0001 *Fax:* 818-252-0003
E-mail: cineworks@cineworksinc.com
Web Site: www.cineworksinc.com
Key Personnel
Owner: Deborah Maxwell *E-mail:* deborah@cineworksinc.com
Founded: 1969
Provide lighting, grip & trucks.
Catalog(s) available
Membership(s): Production Equipment Rental Association; Women in Film

Cinram Inc
2255 Markham Rd, Scarborough, ON M1B 2W3, Canada
Tel: 416-298-8190 *Fax:* 416-298-0612
E-mail: sales@cinram.com
Web Site: www.cinramgroup.com
Key Personnel
Pres: Steven Brown
EVP: David Ashton; Fred Rudolph
Branch Office(s)
4905 Moores Mill Rd, Huntsville, AL 35811 *Tel:* 256-859-9042 *Fax:* 256-859-9932
2 JVC Rd, Tuscaloosa, AL 35405
2750 Barrett Lakes Blvd NW, Kennesaw, GA 30144
Cinram Business Solutions, 2800 Livernois Rd, Bldg D, Suite 230, Troy, MI 48083
1400 E Lackawanna Ave, Olyphant, PA 18448
Sanford Rd, LaVergne, TN 37086

Cintrex Audio Visual
656 Axminister Dr, Fenton, MO 63026
Tel: 636-343-0178 *Toll Free Tel:* 800-325-9541 *Fax:* 636-343-3513
E-mail: websales@cintrexav.com
Web Site: www.cintrexav.com
Founded: 1979
Media conversion.
Membership(s): MCA-I

CircuitWerkes Inc
2805 NW Sixth St, Gainesville, FL 32609
Tel: 352-335-6555 *Fax:* 352-380-0230
E-mail: sales@circuitwerkes.com
Web Site: www.broadcastboxes.com; www.circuitwerkes.com
Key Personnel
Pres: Kyle Magrill
Electronic interface gear for professional broadcasting & industrial use. Product line includes telecommunication & audio signaling devices & remote controls.
Online catalog(s) available

Circulating Film & Video Library
Affiliate of The Museum of Modern Art
11 W 53 St, New York, NY 10019-5401
Tel: 212-708-9530 *Fax:* 212-708-9531
E-mail: circfilm@moma.org
Web Site: www.moma.org
Key Personnel
Contact: Kitty Cleary
Catalog(s) available

Tim Cissell Music
10732 W 107 Circle, Westminster, CO 80021
Tel: 303-955-4436
E-mail: tcissell@wt.net
Web Site: web.wt.net/~tcissell
Key Personnel
Owner: Tim Cissell
Founded: 1989
Original music composition & production.

Citizens Systems America Corp
363 Van Ness Way, Suite 404, Torrance, CA 90501
Tel: 310-781-1460 *Toll Free Tel:* 800-421-6516 *Fax:* 310-781-9152
Web Site: www.citizen-systems.com
Key Personnel
Mktg Dir: Glenn Williams *E-mail:* gwilliams@citizen-systems.com
Catalog(s) available

City Color
1825 W Mockingbird Lane, Dallas, TX 75235
Tel: 214-951-9696 *Fax:* 214-951-9697
Web Site: www.citycolor.com
Founded: 1982
Catalog(s) available
Branch Office(s)
233 SW Naito Pkwy, Suite 100, Portland, OR 97204 *Tel:* 503-646-5750

City Events Group
57 Park Dr, Troy, MI 48083-2724
Tel: 248-589-0600 *Toll Free Tel:* 800-872-8295 *Fax:* 248-589-2020
E-mail: info@cityeventsgroups.com
Web Site: www.cityeventsgroup.com
Key Personnel
CEO & Pres: Eric D Schultz *E-mail:* eschultz@cityeventsgroup.com
Founded: 1959
Full service AV rental & staging.
Catalog(s) available
Membership(s): InfoComm International®; NSCA

City Stage
435 W 19 St, New York, NY 10011
Tel: 212-627-3400 *Fax:* 212-633-1228
Web Site: www.citystage.com
Key Personnel
Dir, Opers: Brian Coles *Tel:* 917-846-6164 (cell) *E-mail:* brian@citystage.com
Soundstage rental for film, television, web & photography productions, equipment rentals & sales of expendables.

Civins Productions Inc
5881 NW 122 Dr, Coral Springs, FL 33076
Tel: 954-938-8600
E-mail: info@civins.com
Web Site: www.civins.com
Key Personnel
Pres: Gary Civins *E-mail:* gary@civins.com
Founded: 1984
HD, Beta SP, DV, Insert Stage w/Bluescreen & Avid Media Computer XL. Full service CD-ROM & DVD production working in film, video or computer graphics. Catalog includes demo tapes, CD-ROMs & DVDs. All materials are available as streaming media at civins.com.

Clair Brothers Audio Systems Inc
One Clair Blvd, Manheim, PA 17545
Tel: 717-665-4000 *Fax:* 717-665-8000
Web Site: www.clairsystems.com
Key Personnel
EVP, Sales-Corp: Gene Pelland
E-mail: gpelland@clairsystems.com
Design & install comprehensive AV & lighting systems.
Online catalog(s), PDF
Branch Office(s)
331 SW 20 Rd, Miami, FL 33129 *Tel:* 305-929-8461
9225 Trinity Dr, Unit E/F, Lake in the Hills, IL 60156 *Tel:* 717-665-4000 ext 211 *Fax:* 847-649-1703
3335 Ambrose Ave, Nashville, TN 37207 *Tel:* 615-227-9881
4904 Sharp St, Dallas, TX 75247 *Tel:* 214-922-0289 *Fax:* 214-922-9225

Clairmont Camera Inc
4343 Lankershim Blvd, North Hollywood, CA 91602
Tel: 818-761-4440 *Fax:* 818-761-0861
E-mail: hollywood@clairmont.com
Web Site: www.clairmont.com
Key Personnel
Pres: Denny Clairmont *E-mail:* dennyc@clairmont.com
Sr EVP: Alan Albert *E-mail:* alana@clairmont.com
Founded: 1976
Motion picture camera rental company.
Online catalog(s) available
Branch Office(s)
5650 University Blvd SE, Bldg A, Suite 201 & 202, Albuquerque, NM 87106, Dir, Client Opers: Dillon Glazebrook *Tel:* 505-227-2525 *Fax:* 505-227-2527 *E-mail:* albuquerque@clairmont.com
1225 E Keith Rd, Suite 2, North Vancouver, BC V7J 1J3, Canada, VP, Rentals: Garry Gosnell *Tel:* 604-984-4563 *Fax:* 604-984-4693 *E-mail:* vancouver@clairmont.com
16 Overlea Blvd, Toronto, ON M4H 1A4, Canada, Opers Mgr: James Piper *Tel:* 416-467-1700 *Fax:* 416-467-8006 *E-mail:* toronto@clairmont.com
Membership(s): ASC; Production Equipment Rental Association; The Society of Composers, Authors and Music Publishers of Canada

Clarity Media Group
166 Fifth Ave, 6th fl, New York, NY 10010
Tel: 212-262-7015
E-mail: info@claritymediagroup.com
Web Site: www.claritymediagroup.com
Key Personnel
Founder & CEO: Bill McGowan
Founded: 1996
Full service television production, media training, corporate writing.

Clarity Sound & Light
Division of Crystal Clarity Publishers
14618 Tyler Foote Rd, Nevada City, CA 95959
Tel: 530-478-7600 *Toll Free Tel:* 800-424-1055 *Fax:* 530-478-7610
E-mail: clarity@crystalclarity.com
Web Site: www.crystalclarity.com
Teach principles & practices that help individuals develop an expanded, divine awareness & to demonstrate practically how to apply these principles to every facet of life.
Catalog(s), free, US & CN only
Membership(s): Reading Recovery Council of North America

Clark
1225 Old Alpharetta Rd, Suite 295, Alpharetta, GA 85296
Tel: 770-888-5088 *Toll Free Tel:* 888-621-8841 *Fax:* 678-513-8206
Web Site: www.clark.is
Key Personnel
Off Mgr: Anna Cardinal
Founded: 2009
National performance engineering firm, headquartered in Atlanta, specializing in solutions for venues in the 1,500-8,000 seat range. Clients are primarily churches, ranging from contemporary to traditional, who value technical excellence as a key part of their overall worship experience.
Branch Office(s)
2803 Taylor St, Dallas, TX 75226 *Tel:* 214-317-0573

Clark Services Audio Visual & Exhibit Inc
113 Board Rd, Lafayette, LA 70508
Mailing Address: PO Box 91265, Lafayette, LA 70509-1265
Tel: 337-234-5653 *Fax:* 337-232-0243
E-mail: clarkservices@bellsouth.net
Web Site: www.clarkservices.biz
Key Personnel
Owner & Pres: James M Clark
Founded: 1981
Convention services.
Membership(s): Greater Lafayette Chamber of Commerce; Lafayette Convention & Visitors Commission; Louisianna Society of Association Executives

Clark Wire & Cable
408 Washington Blvd, Mundelein, IL 60060-3102
Tel: 847-949-9944 *Toll Free Tel:* 800-222-5348 *Fax:* 847-949-9595
E-mail: sales@clarkwire.com
Web Site: www.clarkwire.com
Key Personnel
Accts Receivable: Amanda Whiting
Founded: 1989
Membership(s): NAB; SBE

Clark's Audio Visual Services Ltd
1615 Venables St, Vancouver, BC V5L 2H1, Canada
Tel: 604-877-8558 *Toll Free Tel:* 800-667-1819 *Fax:* 604-879-2993 *Toll Free Fax:* 800-665-2932
E-mail: info@clarksav.com
Web Site: www.clarksav.com
Key Personnel
CEO & Pres: Les Clark *E-mail:* les@clarksav.com
Gen Mgr: Mark Happeney *E-mail:* mark@clarksav.com
Founded: 1981
Supplier of AV equipment & technical support services for the convention & meeting industry.
Branch Office(s)
702 Kentucky St, Suite 332, Bellingham, WA 98225-4200
Membership(s): AMA; InfoComm International®; International Congress & Convention Association; MPI

Clarkson Studio
401 N Hoback St, Helena, MT 59601
Tel: 406-442-2046
Web Site: www.clarksonstudio.com
Key Personnel
Owner: Robert N Clarkson *Tel:* 406-410-2013 (cell) *E-mail:* clarkson@mt.net
Founded: 1974
Imaging for commercial media & public relations, private portraiture, stock images & Internet web pages.

Classic Images
469 S Bedford Dr, Beverly Hills, CA 90212
Tel: 310-277-0400 *Toll Free Tel:* 800-949-CLIP (949-2547) *Fax:* 310-277-0412
E-mail: sales@classicimg.com
Web Site: www.classicimg.com
Key Personnel
Pres: Marcie Alexander

Clayton-Davis & Associates
230 S Bemiston Ave, St Louis, MO 63105
Tel: 314-862-7800
E-mail: info@claytondavis.com
Web Site: www.claytondavis.com
Key Personnel
Chmn of the Bd: Irvin Davis
Pres: Jennifer Davis
Founded: 1953
Full-circle service in advertising, public relations & marketing.

Clean Slate Video
3070 Kerner Blvd, Unit O, San Rafael, CA 94901
Tel: 415-485-0727
E-mail: info@cleanslatevideo.com
Web Site: www.cleanslatevideo.com
Key Personnel
Owner: Eli Adler
Dir, Opers: Benjamin Little
Founded: 1981
Full service video production rentals & staffing.

Clear Blue Audio Video
Affiliate of Clear Blue Engineering
1650 Cold Creek Dr, Layafette, CO 80026
Tel: 303-412-9477 *Fax:* 303-412-9457
Key Personnel
Pres: Dan Minardi
Manufacture AV control systems.
Membership(s): InfoComm International®; NSCA

Clear Choice Creative Corp
4013 E Market St, Warren, OH 44484
Tel: 330-469-9542; 330-469-9524
Web Site: www.clearchoicecreative.com
Web design, search engine optimization, marketing & advertising, social media marketing, video production, public relations & graphic design.

Clear-Com®
Division of HM Electronics Inc (HME)
1301 Marina Village Pkwy, Suite 105, Alameda, CA 94501
Tel: 510-337-6600 *Toll Free Tel:* 800-462-HELP (462-4357) *Fax:* 510-337-6699
E-mail: CustomerServicesUS@clearcom.com
Web Site: www.clearcom.com
Key Personnel
Pres: Bob Boster
Mktg Dir: Judy Cheng *Tel:* 510-337-6676
E-mail: judy.cheng@clearcom.com
Founded: 1968
Brochure(s), PDF
Data sheet(s), PDF
Branch Office(s)
1430 Hocquart, Suite 101, St-Bruno-de-Montarville, QC J3V 6E1, Canada *Tel:* 450-653-9669
Foreign Office(s): Clear-Com LLC, Rm 518, Tower A, He Qiao Plaza, No 8A Guanghua Rd, Chaoyang District, Beijing 100026, China *Tel:* (010) 65811360; (010) 65815577 *Fax:* (010) 65811360
HME Clear-Com LTD, Cambridge Research Park, 2000 Beach Dr, Cambridge CB25 9TP, United Kingdom *Tel:* (01223) 815000 *Fax:* (01223) 815099 *E-mail:* SalesSupportEMEA@clearcom.com (Africa, Europe & Middle East headquarters)

Clear Gravy Productions
PO Box 270, Frederick, CO 80530-0270
Tel: 303-833-2029

E-mail: studio@cleargravy.com
Web Site: www.cleargravy.com
Founded: 2001
Full service recording studio.

Clearlast, see Bardes Products Inc

ClearOne Inc
Edgewater Corporate Park, South Tower, Suite 500, 5225 Wiley Post Way, Salt Lake City, UT 84116
Tel: 801-974-3760 *Toll Free Tel:* 800-705-2103 (tech sales) *Fax:* 801-977-0087
E-mail: techsales@clearone.com
Web Site: www.clearone.com
Key Personnel
Chmn of the Bd & CEO: Ms Zee Hakimoglu
Design, develop & sell conferencing, collaboration, streaming & digital signage solutions for AV communications.
Catalog(s) available
Membership(s): IMCCA; InfoComm International®; NSCA; US Green Building Council; USDLA

ClearOne MagicBox Inc
408 SW Monroe, Suite M236, Corvallis, OR 97333
Tel: 541-752-5654 (sales); 541-752-5542 (tech support) *Fax:* 541-752-5614
E-mail: info@magicboxinc.com; sales@magicboxinc.com; support@magicboxinc.com
Web Site: www.magicboxinc.com
Key Personnel
VP, Digital Signage: Tom Searcy
Founded: 1995
CD-ROM catalog(s), annual, free
Literature available
Membership(s): DSA; InfoComm International®; NSCA; SCTE

Wally Cleaver's Recording Service
2200 Airport Ave, Fredericksburg, VA 22401-7220
Tel: 540-373-6511 *Fax:* 540-370-0645
E-mail: wallycleavers@mac.com
Web Site: www.facebook.com/wallycleavers
Key Personnel
Owner: Jeff Covert
Catalog(s) available
Membership(s): AES; AFM

Cleveland Costume & Display Corp
18489 Pearl Rd, Strongsville, OH 44136
Tel: 440-846-9292
E-mail: info@clevelandcostume.com
Web Site: www.clevelandcostume.com
Key Personnel
Dir: Maria Costa
Also rents costumes.

Clever Cleaver Productions
Division of Casslee Corp
11397 Legacy Canyon Place, San Diego, CA 92131
Tel: 619-522-6760 *Fax:* 619-522-6763
E-mail: info@clevercleaver.com
Web Site: www.clevercleaver.com
Key Personnel
Pres: Lee Gerovitz *E-mail:* lee@clevercleaver.com
VP: Stephen Cassarino *E-mail:* steve@clevercleaver.com
Founded: 1984
Produce 3-minute cooking vignettes, 2 1/2-minute tailgate cooking vignettes, 30 minute cooking shows, cookbooks, cooking videotapes, tailgate/BBQ DVD & 90 second HD cooking segments.
Membership(s): NATPE; RTDNA

Clever Devices Ltd
300 Crossways Park Dr, Woodburg, NY 11797
Tel: 516-433-6100 *Toll Free Tel:* 800-872-6129
Web Site: www.cleverdevices.com
Key Personnel
CEO & Pres: Frank Ingrassia
COO: Andrew Stanton
EVP: Buddy Coleman
Helping the transit industry work with products that keep buses on track & on time, monitor fuel consumption & emissions & keep rider comfortable. Some products are: SmartBus™ IVM®; BusTime™-Bus arrival prediction technology; AVM™2; Computer Aided Dispatch Technology-CLENERCAD™; Clever Analytics™; APC; Speak Easy; Automatic Voice Annunciation (AVA). Fully compliant with the Americans with Disabilities Act of 1990.
Branch Office(s)
8770 W Bryn Mawr Ave, Suite 1300, Chicago, IL 60631-3515 *Tel:* 773-867-8022
1703 N Parham Rd, Suite 201, Richmond, VA 23229 *Tel:* 804-673-5220

Close Up Foundation
1330 Braddock Place, Suite 400, Alexandria, VA 22314
Tel: 703-706-3300 *Toll Free Tel:* 800-CLOSEUP (256-7387)
E-mail: info@closeup.org
Web Site: www.closeup.org
Key Personnel
CEO & Pres: Timothy S Davis, Esq
CFO & Treas: Stephen Dougherty
VP, Prog Servs: Larry Tait
Founded: 1971
Partner with educators, schools & youth organizations throughout the country to help young people develop the skills & attitudes to become informed & engaged citizens.

CMEInfo
Division of Oakstone Publishing LLC
2700 Corporate Dr, Suite 100, Birmingham, AL 35242
Tel: 205-991-5188 *Toll Free Tel:* 800-284-8433 *Toll Free Fax:* 800-284-5964
Web Site: www.cmeinfo.com
Founded: 1989
Home-study medical continuing education.
Catalog(s), free

CMI
612 Hampton Dr, Venice, CA 90291
Tel: 310-392-8771 *Fax:* 310-392-5704
E-mail: cmi@cmifilms.com
Web Site: www.cmifilms.com
Key Personnel
Prog Prodr: Chuck Blore
VP, Mktg: Holly Cantos
Make commercials for radio stations & the radio industry.
Membership(s): AICP

CMI Communications
400 Mile Crossing Blvd, Rochester, NY 14624
Tel: 585-424-1900 *Toll Free Tel:* 888-736-8264 *Fax:* 585-424-1913
E-mail: info@cmiav.com
Web Site: www.cmiav.com
Key Personnel
Pres: Eric M Smith *E-mail:* esmith@cmiav.com
Audio visual services for tradeshows, conferences & corporate events.
Branch Office(s)
10 Walker Way, Suite 6, Albany, NY 12205, Mgr: Eric DeYoung *Tel:* 518-867-3288 *Fax:* 518-867-3290 *E-mail:* ecdeyoung@cmiav.com
Membership(s): ASAE; InfoComm International®; MPI; Professional Convention Management Association

CMI Media Management
Division of Cine Magnetics Inc
100 Business Park Dr, Armonk, NY 10504-1750
Tel: 914-273-7500 *Toll Free Tel:* 800-431-1102 *Fax:* 914-273-7575
Web Site: www.cinemagnetics.com
Key Personnel
CEO: Haitham Wahab
Pres: Kenneth Wynne
Founded: 1961
DVD authoring & compression, DVD replication, content streaming & digital asset management.
Branch Office(s)
3765 Cahuenga Blvd W, Studio City, CA 91604-3504 *Tel:* 818-623-2560 *Fax:* 818-623-2565
Membership(s): Airline Passenger Experience Association; American Independent Media Manufacturers Association; International Disc Duplicating Association; MCA-I; National Veteran-Owned Business Association

CNIB Library for the Blind
Division of Canadian National Institute for the Blind (CNIB)
1929 Bayview Ave, Toronto, ON M4G 3E8, Canada
Toll Free Tel: 800-563-2642 *Fax:* 416-480-7700
E-mail: library@cnib.ca; info@cnib.ca
Web Site: www.cnib.ca
Key Personnel
CEO & Pres, CNIB: John Rafferty
Founded: 1918
Production audio mastering, duplicating.
Catalog(s) available
Branch Office(s)
Calgary District Office, 15 Colonial Baker Place NE, Calgary, AB T2E 4Z3, Canada *Tel:* 403-266-8831 *Toll Free Tel:* 800-376-2642 *Fax:* 403-265-5029
Edmonton District Office, 12010 Jasper Ave, Edmonton, AB T5K 0P3, Canada *Tel:* 780-488-4871 *Toll Free Tel:* 866-459-2648 *Fax:* 780-482-0017
Grande Prairie District Office, 105-9919 99 Ave, Grande Prairie, AB T8V 0R6, Canada *Tel:* 780-539-4719 *Fax:* 780-539-3331
Lethbridge District Office, 100-410 Stafford Dr S, Lethbridge, AB T1J 2L2, Canada *Tel:* 403-327-1044 *Fax:* 403-380-2672
Medicine Hat District Office, 102-520 Second St SE, Medicine Hat, AB T1A 0C6, Canada *Tel:* 403-527-2211 *Fax:* 403-526-3548
Red Deer District Office, 4, 5015 48 St, Red Deer, AB T4N 1S9, Canada *Tel:* 403-346-0037 *Fax:* 403-341-3925
Yellowknife District Office, 5003 48 St, No 4, Yellowknife, NT X1A 2N6, Canada *Tel:* 867-873-2647 *Fax:* 867-873-2657
Membership(s): AER; ALA; Canadian Library Association; International Federation of Library Associations & Institutions; Ontario Library Association

CNS Productions Inc
11 Almond St, Medford, OR 97504
Tel: 541-779-3361 *Toll Free Tel:* 800-888-0617 *Fax:* 541-773-5905
E-mail: info@cnsproductions.com
Web Site: www.cnsproductions.com
Key Personnel
Principal: William Cohen; Paul J Steinbroner
Founded: 1980
Catalog(s) available

Coast Learning Systems
Division of Coastline Community College/Coast Community College District
11460 Warner Ave, Fountain Valley, CA 92708
Tel: 714-241-6109 *Toll Free Tel:* 800-547-4748 *Fax:* 714-241-6286
Web Site: www.coastlearning.org

Key Personnel
Dir, Mktg & Partnerships: Lynn M Dahnke
Tel: 714-241-6231
Founded: 1973
Educational courseware producer. Full production. Products sold online.
Online catalog(s) available

Coastal Training Technologies Corp
Subsidiary of DuPont Sustainable Solutions
500 Studio Dr, Virginia Beach, VA 23452
Tel: 757-498-9014 *Toll Free Tel:* 877-262-7825
Fax: 757-498-3657
E-mail: info@training.dupont.com
Web Site: www.training.dupont.com
Founded: 1984
Offer collaborative consulting services, technologies & blended learning solutions which reflect market needs in the areas of workplace safety, sustainable operations, employee training & clean technologies.

Coastline Licensing International Inc
7345 Topanga Canyon Blvd, Canoga Park, CA 91303
Tel: 818-226-0488 *Fax:* 818-226-0489
Web Site: www.coastlinelicensing.com
Key Personnel
Pres: David B Kravis *E-mail:* david@coastlinelicensing.com
Founded: 1981
Rights licensing, DVD editing & authoring for broadcast media; worldwide pay TV-satellite-Pay Per View systems; video on demand; IPTV; streaming Internet; mobile for the general & adult audience.

Coastline Productions
2647 Gateway Rd, No 105-355, Carlsbad, CA 92009
Tel: 760-598-1860 *Toll Free Tel:* 888-781-5714
E-mail: productions@coastlinevideo.com
Web Site: www.coastlinevideo.com
Key Personnel
Owner & Prodr: Simone Hogan *Tel:* 760-599-9792 (cell)
Founded: 1993
Video production company providing video location production services & HD recording.

Cobalt Studios Inc
134 Royce Rd, White Lake, NY 12786
Mailing Address: PO Box 79, White Lake, NY 12786-0079
Tel: 845-583-7025 *Fax:* 845-583-7025
E-mail: mail@cobaltstudios.net; rentals@cobaltstudios.net
Web Site: www.cobaltstudios.net
Key Personnel
Co-Founder & Owner: Rachel Keebler
Founded: 1988
Professional scenic painting/decorative painting school & studio, custom-painted backdrops & rental backdrops.
Membership(s): Association for Theatre in Higher Education; Educational Theatre Association; USITT

Cobham Tactical Communications & Surveillance
3845 Gateway Centre Blvd, Pinellas Park, FL 33782
Tel: 571-392-2500
Web Site: www.cobham.com
Key Personnel
CEO & Pres: Chet Claudon
Audio concealments; video & audio solid state recorders; wired & wireless analogue & digital audio surveillance systems.
Catalog(s) available

Don Cohen - The Mathman
809 Stratford Dr, Champaign, IL 61821-4140
Tel: 217-356-4555
Web Site: www.mathman.biz
Key Personnel
Contact: Donald Cohen
E-mail: doncohenmathman@gmail.com
Founded: 1988
Produce videos, CDs, books for children's math & educational programs, infinite series & iteration ages 7 & up. Tutor ages 3-73; summer gifted program. Produce video programming of CDs.

Steven Cohen Motion Picture Production
1182 Coral Club Dr, Coral Springs, FL 33071
Tel: 954-346-7370 *Fax:* 954-346-7370
Membership(s): International Alliance of Theatrical Stage Employees; NATAS; SMPTE

Cohn Creative Group LLC
244 W 54 St, 5th fl, New York, NY 10019
Tel: 212-333-3241 *Fax:* 212-246-5727
E-mail: info@cohncreative.com
Web Site: www.cohncreativegroup.com
Key Personnel
Pres: Roy B Cohn *E-mail:* roy@cohncreative.com
Founded: 1986
Corporate video & meeting production.

CohuHD
Division of Cohu Inc
12367 Crosthwaite Circle, Poway, CA 92064
Tel: 858-391-1800
E-mail: info@cohuhd.com
Web Site: www.cohuhd.com
Key Personnel
Pres & Gen Mgr: Thomas D Kampfer
Mktg Mgr: Dana Varga *Tel:* 858-391-1712
E-mail: dvarga@cohuhd.com
Founded: 1946
Manufacturer of HD surveillance camera systems for use in mission-critical sensitive environments.
Online catalog(s) available

Cokesbury
Division of United Methodist Publishing House
201 Eighth Ave, Nashville, TN 37203
Mailing Address: PO Box 801, Nashville, TN 37202-0801
Tel: 615-749-6000 *Toll Free Tel:* 800-672-1789
Fax: 615-749-6079
E-mail: cokes_serv@cokesbury.com
Web Site: www.cokesbury.com
Key Personnel
Pres: Neil Alexander
Producers of religious & children's programs.

Colby Systems Corp
2991 Alexis Dr, Palo Alto, CA 94304
Tel: 650-941-9090
Web Site: www.colbysystems.com
Key Personnel
Pres: Charles Colby *E-mail:* chuckcolby@colbysystems.com
Founded: 1982
Manufacturer of AV systems.

Cole Wire & Cable Co Inc
620 Margate Dr, Lincolnshire, IL 60069-4247
Toll Free Tel: 800-323-1403 *Fax:* 847-634-4988
E-mail: sales@colewire.com
Web Site: www.colewire.com
Key Personnel
Owner & Pres: Leo Cole
Founded: 1979

College of Nursing, Washington State University
Division of Washington State University/Eastern Washington/University Whitworth University
103 E Spokane Falls Blvd, Spokane, WA 99202
Mailing Address: PO Box 1495, Spokane, WA 99210-1495
Tel: 509-324-7360 *Fax:* 509-324-7341
Web Site: nursing.wsu.edu
Key Personnel
Multimedia Servs Coord: Jerry Reynolds
Tel: 509-324-7322 *E-mail:* reynolds@wsu.edu
Provider of educational videos & CDs.
Membership(s): AAN; ANA; STT

Colonel Buster Doss Music Group
341 Billy Goat Hill Rd, Winchester, TN 37398
Tel: 931-649-2577
E-mail: cbd@united.net
Web Site: www.stardustcountrymusic.com
Key Personnel
CEO & Owner: Barbara Doss Brewer
E-mail: badgranny@united.net
Founded: 1959
A major country music record company consisting of Stardust, Wizard & Thunderhawk labels.
Membership(s): CMAA; DJ Association; ICMA; LSSCMA; NCMO

Colonial Williamsburg Foundation
PO Box 1776, Williamsburg, VA 23187-1776
Tel: 757-229-1000
E-mail: geninfo@cwf.org
Web Site: www.colonialwilliamsburg.org
Key Personnel
Pres: Colin G Campbell

The Color Lab Inc
4442 Lawnview Ave, Dallas, TX 75227
Tel: 214-381-2105 *Fax:* 214-381-5168
E-mail: color.lab@airmail.net
Web Site: thecolorlab.com
Key Personnel
Pres: Robert L Messina
Catalog(s) available
Membership(s): AIE™; PMA International

Color Leasing Studios
330 Rte 46 E, Fairfield, NJ 07004
Tel: 973-575-1118 *Fax:* 973-575-1170
Web Site: www.colorleasingstudios.com
Key Personnel
Prodr: Jack Berberian
Founded: 1966
Product demos, TV spots & corporate marketing; video NLE post services; video location & studio recording & rental.

Colorado Display Systems
Division of Colorado Time Systems LLC
1551 E 11 St, Loveland, CO 80537
Tel: 970-667-1000 *Toll Free Tel:* 800-279-0111
Fax: 970-667-5876
E-mail: info@coloradotime.com
Web Site: www.coloradotime.com
Key Personnel
Gen Mgr, Colorado Time Systems: Anita Sayed
Founded: 1972
A wide range of displays for commerical & sporting applications.
Catalog(s) available

Colorado Sound Recording Studios
3100 W 71 Ave, Westminster, CO 80030
Tel: 303-430-8811
E-mail: colosnd@coloradosound.com
Web Site: www.coloradosound.com
Key Personnel
Owner & Studio Mgr: Kevin Clock
Founded: 1977
Full service recording studio with video lock.

Colorado Studios
8269 E 23 Ave, Denver, CO 80238
Fax: 303-388-9600
E-mail: info@coloradostudios.com
Web Site: www.coloradostudios.com
Key Personnel
COO & Pres: Phillip Garvin *E-mail:* phillip@coloradostudios.com
Contact: Karl Siebrecht *Tel:* 303-388-8500 *E-mail:* ksiebrecht@coloradostudios.com
Equipped soundstage for video or film production. Post-production services, crew available. Location production packages.

Colorado Video Inc
6595 Odell Place, Mezzanine S, Boulder, CO 80301
Mailing Address: PO Box 928, Boulder, CO 80306-0928
Tel: 303-530-9580 *Fax:* 303-530-9569
E-mail: sales@colorado-video.com
Web Site: www.colorado-video.com
Key Personnel
Pres & Mktg Mgr: Kirk Fowler
Founded: 1965
Video equipment manufacturer with the ability to provide custom designs for special requirements.
Online catalog(s) available

Coloredge
Division of Merisel Inc
1919 Empire Ave, Burbank, CA 91504
Tel: 818-842-1121 *Fax:* 818-840-0185
Web Site: coloredge.com
Key Personnel
VP, Sales: David Esqueda *E-mail:* david.esqueda@coloredge.com
Mktg Communs: Patty Bolten *Tel:* 818-842-1121 ext 3058 *E-mail:* patty.bolten@coloredge.com
Founded: 1946
Full service graphic arts & visual communications agency.
Catalog(s) available
Branch Office(s)
1100 Northside Dr, Atlanta, GA 30318, Sr Acct Exec: Cheridi Candela *Tel:* 404-876-3330 *E-mail:* cheridi.candela@coloredge.com
190 Jony Dr, Carlstadt, NJ 07072 *Tel:* 201-716-5200 *E-mail:* jim.bonaventura@coloredge.com (production)
132 W 31 St, New York, NY 10001, SVP, Sales: Jim Bonaventura *Tel:* 212-594-4800 *Fax:* 646-924-3921 *E-mail:* jim.bonaventura@coloredge.com
Membership(s): AIE™; Bay Area Association of Professional Laboratories; Bay Area Association of Professional Photographers; Society of Industrial Photographers

Colortek of Boston
727 Atlantic Ave, Boston, MA 02111
Tel: 617-451-0894 *Fax:* 617-451-2714
E-mail: info@colortekofboston.com
Web Site: www.colortekofboston.com
Key Personnel
Owner: Jackie Anderson *E-mail:* jackie@colortekofboston.com
Full service color lab.
Membership(s): AIE™; Photo Marketing Association

Colortone Audio Visual
75 Virginia Rd, White Plains, NY 10603
Tel: 914-592-4151 *Fax:* 914-592-2833
Web Site: www.colortone-av.com
Key Personnel
Pres: Marvin Lederman
VP: Don Silver *E-mail:* don@colortone-av.com
Specialists in custom design & installation.
Catalog(s) available
Membership(s): InfoComm International®

Columbia Lighting
Division of Hubbell Lighting
701 Millennium Blvd, Greenville, SC 29607
Tel: 864-678-1000; 864-678-1664 (cust support) *Toll Free Fax:* 866-898-0131
Web Site: www.columbialighting.com
Founded: 1897
Lighting manufacturer. Manufacturing factories in Bristol, PA & Juarez, Mexico.

Columbia Pictures Inc
Division of Sony Pictures Entertainment
10202 W Washington Blvd, Culver City, CA 90232
Tel: 310-244-4000; 310-244-6926 (studio opers) *Fax:* 310-244-8090
Web Site: www.sonypicturesstudios.com; www.sonypictures.com
Key Personnel
Chmn, Sony Pictures Entertainment: Amy Pascal
Chmn & CEO, Sony Pictures Entertainment: Michael Lynton
Pres: Doug Belgrad
Founded: 1918

Comex Systems Inc
101 Pleasant Hill Rd, Chester, NJ 07930
Tel: 908-881-6301 (cell) *Toll Free Tel:* 800-543-6959 *Fax:* 908-879-0070
E-mail: mail@comexsystems.com
Web Site: www.comexsystems.com
Key Personnel
VP: Doug Prybylowski
Producer of educational videos & CD-ROMs.
Catalog(s) available

Comm-Arts
2512 E 71 St, Suite A, Tulsa, OK 74136
Tel: 918-493-5700 *Fax:* 918-493-3526
E-mail: info@comm-arts.com
Web Site: www.comm-arts.com
Key Personnel
Pres: Linda C Godfrey *E-mail:* linda@comm-arts.com
Founded: 1985
Full service marketing, communications & advertising company. Broadcasts TV documentaries & commercials.

CommCreative
345 Union Ave, Framingham, MA 01702
Tel: 508-620-6664 *Toll Free Tel:* 877-620-6664 *Fax:* 508-620-0592
Web Site: www.commcreative.com
Key Personnel
Pres: Bob Fields *E-mail:* robertfields@commcreative.com
Chief Mktg Offr: Myles Bristow
Founded: 1990

Commercial Electronics Ltd
1565 W Seventh St, Vancouver, BC V6J 1S1, Canada
Tel: 604-669-5525; 604-669-6626 *Fax:* 604-669-6347
E-mail: info@commercialelectronics.ca
Web Site: commercialelectronics.ca
Key Personnel
Pres: Susanne Adam
Founded: 1957
Electronic sales, installation, service & rental company.
Membership(s): AES; Custom Electronic Design & Installation Association; InfoComm International®; NSCA

Commercial Video
PO Box 360247, Cleveland, OH 44136-0005
Tel: 330-273-8795
E-mail: info@comvid.com
Web Site: www.comvid.com
Key Personnel
Pres: J R Burroughs *E-mail:* jeff@comvid.com
Membership(s): Apple Consultants Network; International Alliance of Theatrical Stage Employees

Commonwealth Films Inc
223 Commonwealth Ave, Boston, MA 02116
Tel: 617-262-5634
E-mail: info@commonwealthfilms.com
Web Site: www.commonwealthfilms.com
Key Personnel
Pres: Thomas McCann
Gen Mgr: David Burke
Produce & distribute corporate training videos.
Online catalog(s) available

CommScope Inc
1100 CommScope Place SE, Hickory, NC 28602
Mailing Address: PO Box 339, Hickory, NC 28603-0339
Tel: 828-324-2200 *Toll Free Tel:* 800-982-1708
Web Site: www.commscope.com
Key Personnel
Chmn & Founder: Frank M Drendel
CEO & Pres: Marvin S Edwards, Jr
COO & EVP: Randall W Crenshaw
CFO & EVP: Mark A Olson
Founded: 1976
Enterprise cabling solutions & high-performance, high-bandwidth coaxial cable.
Branch Office(s)
6519 CommScope Rd, PO Box 199, Catawba, NC 28609-0199 *Tel:* 828-241-3142 *Fax:* 828-241-6168
3642 US Hwy 70 E, PO Box 879, Claremont, NC 28610-0879 *Tel:* 828-459-5000 *Fax:* 828-459-5099
CommScope Cable Technology Center, 1545 St James Church Rd, PO Box 150, Newton, NC 28658 *Tel:* 828-466-8600 *Fax:* 828-466-8617
125 CommScope Way, Statesville, NC 28625-1876 *Tel:* 704-873-3519 *Fax:* 704-832-7548
2700 Ellis Rd, Joliet, IL 60433-8459 *Tel:* 779-435-6000
CommScope Nevada Operations LLC, 775 Waltham Way, Suite 101, Sparks, NV 89434 *Tel:* 775-352-8917
11312 S Pipeline Rd, Euless, TX 76040 *Tel:* 817-864-4100 *Fax:* 817-864-4199
CommScope Solutions Inc, 1300 E Lookout Dr, Richardson, TX 75082 *Tel:* 972-792-3000 *Fax:* 972-792-3010
2601 Telecom Pkwy, Richardson, TX 75082-3521 *Tel:* 972-952-9700 *Fax:* 972-952-0000
140 Vista Centre Dr, Forest, VA 24551 *Tel:* 434-386-5300
Foreign Office(s): 1256 Av Com Camilo Julio, Predio B Zonal Industrial CP597, 18086-000 Sorocaba SP, Brazil, Reg Sales Mgr: Roberto Mangullo *Tel:* (015) 2102-4000 *Fax:* (015) 2102-4001 *E-mail:* roberto.mangullo@andrew.com
Ave Industrial Reynosa Lote 3, 4 y 5 Col Parque Reynosa Industrial Ctr, 88780 Reynosa, Tamaulipas, Mexico *Tel:* (0899) 921-1700 *Fax:* (0899) 921-1740

Communication Arts Multimedia Inc
1618 Williams Dr, No 5, Georgetown, TX 78628
Tel: 512-868-0548 *Toll Free Tel:* 888-742-0074 *Fax:* 512-868-0548
E-mail: mail@commartsmultimedia.com
Web Site: commartsmultimedia.com
Key Personnel
Pres: Eugene Vasconi
Catalog(s) available

Communication Corner Inc
PO Box 210, Brightwater, NY 11718
Tel: 631-567-2626 *Fax:* 631-665-3473

Web Site: www.commcorner.com
Key Personnel
Pres: William E Brown *E-mail:* bill@commcorner.com
Catalog(s) available

Communication Ministries
Division of Christian Church (Disciples of Christ)
PO Box 1986, Indianapolis, IN 46206-1986
Tel: 317-713-2492 *Fax:* 317-635-3700
Toll Free Fax: 800-458-3318
Web Site: disciples.org/dns
Shipping Address: 1099 N Meridian, Suite 700, Indianapolis, IN 46204
Membership(s): National Council of Churches Communication Commission; Religious Public Relations Council; World Association for Christian Communication

Communications & Power Industries, Satcom Division
811 Hansen Way, Bldg 2, Palo Alto, CA 94304-1031
Tel: 650-846-3803; 650-846-2801 *Fax:* 650-424-1744
E-mail: satcommarketing@cpii.com
Web Site: www.cpii.com
Key Personnel
Mktg: JoAnne Meacham
Catalog(s) available

Communications Concepts Inc (CCI)
7980 N Atlantic Ave, Cape Canaveral, FL 32920
Mailing Address: PO Box 661, Cape Canaveral, FL 32920-0661
Tel: 321-783-5232 *Toll Free Tel:* 800-783-2368
Fax: 321-799-1016
E-mail: info@cciflorida.com
Web Site: www.cciflorida.com
Key Personnel
Pres & Prodr: Jim Lewis *E-mail:* jlewis@cciflorida.com
Opers Mgr: Robin Champagne
E-mail: rchampagne@cciflorida.com
Founded: 1978
AV production company (Production & Rentals).
Catalog(s) available
Membership(s): ADFED; Florida Motion Picture & Television Association; MCA-I

Communications Corporation of America
PO Box 14262, Chicago, IL 60614-0262
Tel: 773-348-0001
E-mail: comcorp30@aol.com
Key Personnel
Exec Prodr: Fred Strauss
Founded: 1960
Audio live productions & talent casting. Also produce "Festival Hall of Fame" & live TV political debates. Produces documentaries for the Library of Congress.
Literature available
Sample(s) available
Membership(s): NATAS; The Recording Academy

The Communications Department Inc
3724 Amherst Ave, Dallas, TX 75225-7201
Tel: 214-369-1281
Key Personnel
Pres: Betty Jo Taylor *E-mail:* bjtwhcsb@aol.com
Founded: 1982
Production company - video, online visuals & meeting production.

Communications Design Associates
437 Turnpike St, Canton, MA 02021
Tel: 339-502-6551 *Fax:* 339-502-6595
E-mail: information@cdaconsultants.com
Web Site: www.cdaconsultants.com
Key Personnel
Principal Consultant: James C Davis; Stewart B Randall *E-mail:* srandall@cdaconsultants.com; Greg T Vincent
Founded: 1993
Consultants for audio & video system design, engineering & management services.
Membership(s): The Boston Society of Architects; InfoComm International®; NSCA

The Communications Group Inc
502 S West St, Raleigh, NC 27601
Mailing Address: PO Box 50157, Raleigh, NC 27650-6157
Tel: 919-828-4086 *Toll Free Tel:* 800-595-2937
E-mail: info@cgfilm.com
Web Site: www.cgfilm.com
Key Personnel
Principal: Jay Spain *E-mail:* jay@cgfilm.com
Founded: 1982
Video, film & media production & consultation.
Catalog(s) available
Membership(s): Independent Documentary Association; Media Communications Association

Communications Plus Digital, see CPdigital

Communications Specialists Inc
7272 Jackson Ave, Mechanicsville, VA 23111
Tel: 804-559-4274 *Fax:* 804-559-4479
E-mail: info@csisystems.net
Web Site: www.csisystems.net
Key Personnel
CEO & Pres: Ron Pusey *E-mail:* ron.pusey@csisystems.net
EVP: Jack Tuck *E-mail:* jack.tuck@csisystems.net
Gen Mgr: Danielle Hagen *E-mail:* danielle.hagen@csisystems.net
Founded: 1986
Full sprectrum of integrated voice, data & video systems.
Membership(s): InfoComm International®

Communications Specialties Inc
125 Comac St, Ronkonkoma, NY 11779
Tel: 631-273-0404 *Fax:* 631-273-1638
E-mail: info@commspecial.com
Web Site: www.commspecial.com
Key Personnel
Co-Founder, CEO & Pres: John Lopinto
Co-Founder & COO: Larry Schulman
Dir, Sales: Paul Seiden *Tel:* 813-653-1686
E-mail: pauls@commspecial.com
Sales Mgr: Michael Fazzi *Tel:* 503-287-3248
E-mail: mikef@commspecial.com
Founded: 1983
Manufacturing of computer-video peripherals & fiber optic transmission systems.
CD-ROM catalog(s) available
Printed material(s) available

Communilux Productions
4001 East Side Ave, Dallas, TX 75226
Tel: 214-821-8706 *Toll Free Tel:* 877-323-5189
E-mail: info@communilux.com
Web Site: www.communilux.com
Key Personnel
Owner & Pres: Warren Cunningham
Founded: 1982
Theatrical production services.
Membership(s): Professional Lighting & Sound Association

Communitronics Corp
970 Bolger Ct, Fenton, MO 63026
Tel: 314-771-7160 *Fax:* 314-771-9144
E-mail: info@communitronics.com
Web Site: www.communitronics.com
Key Personnel
Pres: Rita Leitensdorfer
Founded: 1969
Newsletter(s), quarterly

Community Professional Loudspeakers
333 E Fifth St, Chester, PA 19013-4511
Tel: 610-876-3400 *Toll Free Tel:* 800-523-4934
Fax: 610-874-0190
E-mail: info@communitypro.com
Web Site: www.communitypro.com
Key Personnel
Dir, Sales & Mktg: Julia Lee *E-mail:* sales@communitypro.com
Founded: 1968
Manufacturer of sound devices.
Catalog(s) available
Membership(s): AES; InfoComm International®; International Association of Assembly Managers; NAMM, the National Association of Music Merchants; NSCA

Compact Storage Systems Inc
9757 Reseda Blvd, Suite 68, Northridge, CA 91324
Tel: 818-772-0996
E-mail: info@halfthespace.com
Web Site: www.halfthespace.com
Key Personnel
Co-Owner: Paul Jemielita *E-mail:* paul@halfthespace.com; Betty M Leonard *Tel:* 818-772-0883 *E-mail:* betty@halfthespace.com
Distribute AV cabinetry & storage.

Compass Learning Inc
203 Colorado St, Austin, TX 78701
Tel: 512-478-9600 *Toll Free Tel:* 866-586-7387 (sales); 800-678-1412 (cust support)
Web Site: www.compasslearning.com
Key Personnel
CEO: Eric Loeffel
CFO: Trey Chambers
VP, Busn Strategy & Devt: Arthur Vanderveen
VP, Content Devt: Lynelle Morgenthaler
VP, HR: Tammy Deal
VP, Mktg & Prod Mgmt: Eileen Shihadeh
VP, Sales: Eric Wasser
Founded: 1969
K-12 learning acceleration software.
Membership(s): InfoComm International®

Compix Media
26 Edelman, Irvine, CA 92618
Tel: 949-585-0055 *Fax:* 949-585-0320
E-mail: info@compix.tv
Web Site: www.compix.tv
Key Personnel
Sales: Lan Merrill
Manufacture & distribution of video character generators.

Comprehensive Cable & Connectivity Co
Division of Vcom International Multimedia Corp
80 Little Falls Rd, Fairfield, NJ 07004
Toll Free Tel: 800-526-0242 *Fax:* 201-814-0510
E-mail: sales@comprehensivecable.com; customerservice@comprehensivecable.com
Web Site: www.comprehensivecable.com
Key Personnel
Pres: Scott Schaefer
Founded: 1974
Multimedia sales solutions.
Catalog(s), annual
Membership(s): InfoComm International®; NAB; NSCA; SBE

Comprehensive Technical Group
2030 Powers Ferry Rd SE, Suite 130, Atlanta, GA 30339
Tel: 404-352-3000 *Toll Free Tel:* 888-557-4284
Fax: 404-352-2962
E-mail: info@ctgatlanta.com
Web Site: www.ctgatlanta.com
Founded: 1991
Professional broadcast & AV solutions, including sales & consultation, system design & integration, service & repair.

Branch Office(s)
2715 Marietta St, Kenner, LA 70062 *Tel:* 504-466-4454 *Fax:* 504-466-9875
Membership(s): PSNI

COMPRO Productions Inc
Division of Communication Projects Inc
2055 Boar Tusk Rd NE, Conyers, GA 30012-3801
Tel: 770-918-8163
E-mail: compro@compro-atl.com
Web Site: www.compro-atl.com
Key Personnel
Pres & Dir: Nels Anderson
EVP: Kim Anderson
VP & Sr Prodr: Steve Brinson
Founded: 1977
Full service production company.
Membership(s): AICP; IABC; MCA-I

Comprompter Inc
1601 Caledonia St, Suite E, La Crosse, WI 54603
Tel: 608-785-7766
E-mail: sales@comprompter.com
Web Site: www.comprompter.com
Key Personnel
Pres: Ralph King *E-mail:* ralph@compromter.com
Founded: 1985
Newsroom & automation systems.
Catalog(s) available
Membership(s): Minnesota Broadcasters Association; NAB; RTDNA; Wisconsin Broadcasters Association

Computer Dynamics
Division of CIMTEC Automation LLC
3030 Whitehall Park Dr, Charlotte, NC 28273
Tel: 704-227-4600 *Toll Free Tel:* 866-599-6512 *Fax:* 704-583-9671
Web Site: www.cdynamics.com
Founded: 1981
Manufacture flat panel display systems, both computers & monitors.
Catalog(s) available

The Computer Language Co Inc
5521 State Park Rd, Point Pleasant, PA 18950
Tel: 215-297-8082
E-mail: sales@computerlanguage.com; comments@computerlanguage.com
Web Site: www.computerlanguage.com
Key Personnel
Pres: Alan Freedman
VP: Irma Morrison
Founded: 1978
Distributor of the computer desktop encyclopedia for Windows, iPhone & Android.

Computer Modules Inc
11409 W Bernardo Ct, San Diego, CA 92127
Tel: 858-613-1818 *Fax:* 858-613-1815
E-mail: info@computermodules.com
Web Site: www.dveo.com
Key Personnel
Pres: Laszlo "Les" Zoltan
Founded: 1982
AV sales & service.
Membership(s): ATSC; Electronic Retailing Association; NAB; SBE; SMPTE

Computer Prompting & Captioning Co (CPC), see Telestream Inc

Computer Sciences Corp
3170 Fairview Park Dr, Falls Church, VA 22042
Tel: 703-876-1000
Web Site: www.csc.com
Key Personnel
CEO & Pres: Mike Lawrie
CFO & EVP: Paul N Saleh
CTO: Dan Hushon
CIO: Doug Tracy
Chief Mktg & Communs Offr: Gary Stockman
EVP & Chief HR Offr: Donna Lesch
EVP & Gen Coun: William L Deckelman, Jr
Founded: 1959
Provides technology-enabled business solutions & services.
Foreign Office(s): 26 Talavera Rd, Macquarie Park, NSW 2113, Australia *Tel:* (02) 9034 3000
Retortvej 8, 2500 Valby, Denmark *Tel:* 36144000
Immeuble Balzac, 10 place des Vosges, 92072 Paris la Defense Cedex, France *Tel:* 01 55 70 70 70
Abraham-Lincoln-Park 1, 65189 Wiesbaden, Germany *Tel:* (0611) 1420
Level 9, UE Biz Hub E, 6 Changi Business Park Ave 1, Singapore 468017, Singapore *Tel:* 68099 000
One Pancras Sq, 4th fl, London N1C 4AG, United Kingdom *Tel:* (020) 3696 3000

Computing & Information Technology
Affiliate of State University of New York at Geneseo
South Hall 119, One College Circle, Geneseo, NY 14454
Tel: 585-245-5577 *Fax:* 585-245-5579
Web Site: www.geneseo.edu/cit
Key Personnel
CIO & Dir: Sue Chichester *E-mail:* sue@geneseo.edu
Catalog(s) available

Compuvideo Sales USA Ltd
7255 Brunswick Circle, Boynton Beach, FL 33472
Tel: 561-733-4780
E-mail: sales@compuvideo.com; customerservice@compuvideo.com
Web Site: www.compuvideo.com
Manufacture professional test & measurement video equipment.

CompuWeather Inc
Member of FleetWeather Group
2566 Rte 52, Hopewell Junction, NY 12533
Tel: 845-227-8500 *Toll Free Tel:* 800-825-4445 *Fax:* 845-227-8400 *Toll Free Fax:* 800-825-4441
Web Site: www.compuweather.com
Key Personnel
CTO & Dir, Sales & Mktg: Jess Hurwitz
Forensic Acct Exec: Patti Robertson
Founded: 1976
Membership(s): AICP; CWSA

Comrex Corp
19 Pine Rd, Devens, MA 01434
Tel: 978-784-1776 (intl) *Toll Free Tel:* 800-237-1776 *Fax:* 978-784-1717
E-mail: info@comrex.com
Web Site: www.comrex.com
Key Personnel
Pres: Mrs Kris Bobo
Dir, Sales: Mr Chris Crump
Founded: 1961
Innovator in communications & telephony technologies for over 40 years, providing reliable solutions to meet the demands of live broadcast. Thousands of radio & TV stations trust the quality of our products every day for news, sports & entertainment audio. Headquartered near Boston, MA, our products are offered & supported by a worldwide network of dealers.
Online catalog(s) available
Membership(s): SBE

Comtech Multimedia Marketing
6048 Broadcast Pkwy, Loves Park, IL 61111
Tel: 779-774-3188 *Fax:* 779-423-0090
E-mail: info@comtechcorporation.com
Web Site: www.comtechcorporation.com
Key Personnel
Pres & Dir: Joseph Arco
Prodr: Susan Arco
Founded: 1984
A full service video production studio. Produce broadcast quality programs on DVD & HD/SD.

Comtek Communications Technology Inc
357 W 2700 S, Salt Lake City, UT 84115
Tel: 801-466-3463 *Toll Free Tel:* 800-496-3463 *Fax:* 801-484-6906
E-mail: sales@comtek.com
Web Site: www.comtek.com
Key Personnel
Pres: Ralph Belgique
Sales Dir: Laurel Robertson
Communs Dir: Jon Belgique
Assistive listening supplies & professional sound systems.
Membership(s): NAB; NSCA

Comtel Inc
14901 NE 20 Ave, Miami, FL 33181
Tel: 305-948-9116 *Fax:* 305-947-9306
E-mail: info@comtelinc.com
Web Site: www.comtelinc.com
Key Personnel
CEO & Pres: Dolores Sukhdeo
Founded: 1981
AV studio.

Concept Associates Inc
5371 Punta Alta, Unit 1-E, Laguna Woods, CA 92637
Toll Free Tel: 800-333-8252
E-mail: customerservice@preschoolpower.com
Web Site: www.preschoolpower.com
Key Personnel
Pres: William J Connell *Tel:* 949-855-3710 *E-mail:* wjconnell@preschoolpower.com
Founded: 1972
Award winning children's programming.
Catalog(s) available

Concept Audio-Visual
4295 rue d'Iberville, Montreal, QC H2H 2L5, Canada
Tel: 514-954-0000 *Toll Free Tel:* 800-567-7076 (CN only) *Fax:* 514-954-1425
E-mail: info@conceptav.ca
Web Site: www.conceptav.ca
Key Personnel
Pres: Vanessa Arsenault *Tel:* 514-954-0000 ext 224 *E-mail:* vanessa@conceptav.ca
VP & Dir, Opers: Chill Arsenault *Tel:* 514-954-0000 ext 242 *E-mail:* c.arsenault@conceptav.ca
Sales & rental of AV equipment.
Catalog(s) available

Concept Productions Inc
7878 Big Sky Dr, Madison, WI 53719
Tel: 608-833-8273
E-mail: info@conceptpro.biz
Web Site: www.conceptpro.biz
Key Personnel
Prodn Mgr & Audio Designer: Doug Schoebel
Digital sound recording.
Rate card(s) available
Membership(s): American Advertising Federation

Concept Videos Inc, see Concept Associates Inc

Concepts TV Production
328 W Main St, Boonton, NJ 07005
Tel: 973-331-1500 *Fax:* 973-331-1550
E-mail: sales@conceptstv.com
Web Site: www.conceptstv.com
Key Personnel
Pres: Collette Liantonio *E-mail:* collette@conceptstv.com

VP, Sales & Mktg: Kristy Pinand-Dumpert *E-mail:* kristy@conceptstv.com
Dir, Fin: Laraine Lamicella
Founded: 1983
Direct Response Television experts specializing in the production of commercials & infomercials for over 25 years. Most recent award winners include: Bottle Top, Emery Cat & Amish Heat Surge Fireplace. Production & post-production facilities.
Membership(s): Direct Marketing Association; Electronic Retailing Association

Concoction Lab
520 Frederick St, No 8, San Francisco, CA 94117
Tel: 415-294-2032 *Fax:* 415-294-2178
E-mail: info@concoctionlab.com
Web Site: www.concoctionlab.com
Theatrical & TV trailers, documentaries, broadcast promos, product launches, sizzle reels.

Concord Communications
26 Denise Place, Stamford, CT 06905
Tel: 203-322-9322
Key Personnel
Pres: Gerald Rich
AV equipment & supplies; specialty furniture; AV rentals.
Catalog(s) available
Membership(s): IEEE; InfoComm International®

Concord Jazz Inc
Member of Concord Music Group Inc
100 N Crescent Dr, Garden Level, Beverly Hills, CA 90210
Tel: 310-385-4455 *Fax:* 310-385-4466
Web Site: www.concordmusicgroup.com
Key Personnel
CEO & Pres: Glen Barros
Founded: 1973
Cassette & CD producers.
Catalog(s) available
Membership(s): Music Business Association

Concord Records Inc
Member of Concord Music Group Inc
100 N Crescent Dr, Garden Level, Beverly Hills, CA 90210
Tel: 310-385-4455 *Fax:* 310-385-4466
Web Site: www.concordmusicgroup.com
Key Personnel
CEO & Pres: Glen Barros
Founded: 1969
Cassette & CD producers.

Concrete Images
1301 Main St, Venice, CA 90291
Tel: 310-452-9655 *Fax:* 310-452-9866
E-mail: office@concreteimages.com
Web Site: www.concreteimages.com
Key Personnel
Pres & Exec Prodr: Hani Selim *E-mail:* hs@concreteimages.com
Founded: 1998
Line production services.
Membership(s): AICP; IFP

Conex Electro-Systems Inc
789 W Smith Rd, Bellingham, WA 98226-9613
Tel: 360-734-4323 *Fax:* 360-676-4822
E-mail: sales@conex-electro.com
Web Site: www.conex-electro.com
Key Personnel
Sales Mgr: John Plattner *E-mail:* john@conex-electro.com
Broadcast equipment manufacturer.

Conference Technologies Inc
11653 Adie Rd, Maryland Heights, MO 63043
Tel: 314-993-1400 *Toll Free Tel:* 800-743-6051 *Toll Free Fax:* 855-329-2844
Web Site: www.conferencetech.com
Design & install presentation systems; also rent & service.
Catalog(s) available
Branch Office(s)
1419 Westpark Dr, Suite B, Little Rock, AR 72204 *Tel:* 501-375-2800
512 High Point Lane, East Peoria, IL 61611 *Tel:* 309-698-8150
1501 Ardmore Ave, Itasca, IL 60143 *Tel:* 630-467-1500
5010 Brady St, Davenport, IA 52806 *Tel:* 563-359-1825
333 SW Ninth St, Suite N, Des Moines, IA 50309 *Tel:* 515-280-9800
1950 Boyson Rd, Hiawatha, IA 52233 *Tel:* 319-363-8144
8830 Bond St, Overland Park, KS 66214 *Tel:* 913-894-2500
248 N Cleveland Ave, Wichita, KS 67214 *Tel:* 316-651-0119
11205 S 150 St, Suite 500, Omaha, NE 68138 *Tel:* 402-593-6750
520 Third Ave, Suite 1, Brookings, SD 57006 *Tel:* 605-692-2667
5425 E Raines Rd, Suite 2, Memphis, TN 38115 *Tel:* 901-360-8332
555 W Estabrook Blvd, Suite 100, Milwaukee, WI 53212 *Tel:* 414-906-3335
Membership(s): InfoComm International®

Conly Productions
1563 Oneida St, Denver, CO 80220
Tel: 303-393-6240 *Fax:* 303-393-6240
Key Personnel
CEO: Paul Conly
Mktg Dir: Maura Adler
Founded: 1980
Recording studio & equipment.
Membership(s): Colorado Film & Video Association

Connecticut Audio & Theatrical Supply
775 Bloomfield Ave, Windsor, CT 06095
Tel: 860-298-9141 *Fax:* 860-298-9142
Web Site: www.ctaudio.com
Key Personnel
Owner & Pres: Douglas Fay *E-mail:* doug@ctaudio.com
Sound system, stages, lighting, LCD video projectors & plasma screens.
Membership(s): International Alliance of Theatrical Stage Employees

Connections Film & Video Inc
PO Box 110929, Anchorage, AK 99511
Tel: 907-561-6450
Web Site: www.filmalaska.com
Key Personnel
Owner: Jerry LaVine
HD & film production services.

Conquest Sound Co Inc
26113 S Ridgeland Ave, Monee, IL 60449
Tel: 708-534-0390 *Toll Free Tel:* 800-323-7671 *Fax:* 708-534-0398
E-mail: info@conquestsound.com; customerservice@conquestsound.com
Web Site: www.conquestsound.com
Key Personnel
Opers: Sue Woolum *E-mail:* sue@conquestsound.com
Purch: Michelle Borvan *E-mail:* michelle@conquestsound.com
Designer & manufacturer of audio, video & data wiring systems & cables.
Online catalog(s), PDF download
Membership(s): NAB; NAMM, the National Association of Music Merchants; NSCA

Consolidated Communications Consultants
1837 SE Harold St, Portland, OR 97202-4932
Tel: 503-232-9787 *Toll Free Tel:* 800-929-5119 *Fax:* 503-232-9787 *Toll Free Fax:* 800-929-5119
E-mail: acmrl@myexcel.com
Web Site: www.acmusicresearch.com
Key Personnel
VP & Gen Mgr: Eric Norberg
Founded: 1980
Radio programming, management consulting & music research.

Consolidated Display Co Inc
1210 US Hwy 34, Oswego, IL 60543
Mailing Address: PO Box 4108, Naperville, IL 60567-4108
Tel: 630-851-8666 *Toll Free Tel:* 888-851-7669 *Fax:* 630-851-8756
E-mail: info@letitsnow.com
Web Site: www.letitsnow.com
Key Personnel
Pres: Sebastian J Puccio
Full service display company.
Catalog(s) available

Contemporary Research
4355 Excel Pkwy, Suite 600, Addison, TX 75001
Tel: 972-931-2728 *Toll Free Tel:* 888-972-2728 *Fax:* 972-931-2765
E-mail: contact@crwww.com
Web Site: contemporaryresearch.com
Key Personnel
Pres & Chief Engr: Scott Hetzler
Founded: 1994
Designs & manufactures HD AV control products, HD tuners, HD modulators & software for integrated systems solutions applicable to stadiums, arenas, control rooms, corporate facilities, education & church facilities, to name a few.
CD-ROM catalog(s), annual, free, updated frequently
Membership(s): InfoComm International®; NAB; SCTE

Continental Film
1466 Riverside Dr, Suite E, Chattanooga, TN 37406
Mailing Address: PO Box 5126, Chattanooga, TN 37406-0126
Tel: 423-622-1193 *Toll Free Tel:* 888-909-3456 *Fax:* 423-629-0853
Web Site: www.continentalfilm.com
Key Personnel
Pres: James L Webster *E-mail:* jim.webster@continentalfilm.com
Online catalog(s) available
Membership(s): InfoComm International®

Continental Film & Video
PO Box 250627, Atlanta, GA 30325
Tel: 404-844-6374
Web Site: www.continentalfilmvideo.com
Key Personnel
Pres: J B Hockersmith *E-mail:* hockersmith1970@continentalfilmvideo.com
Founded: 1998
Complete film & video production services.

Continental Recordings Inc
23 Mirimichi St, Plainville, MA 02762
Tel: 508-699-0003 *Toll Free Tel:* 888-729-3130 *Fax:* 508-699-0004
Key Personnel
Pres & Sales Mgr: L Daniel Flynn *E-mail:* danf31@earthlink.net
Founded: 1963
Recording studio.

Convenience
3012 N Long Ave, Chicago, IL 60641-4930
Tel: 773-545-3073 *Fax:* 773-545-3073

Key Personnel
Owner & Dir: John A Mazovick
Founded: 1984
Price list(s) available

Convergent Media Systems
Division of Ballantyne Strong Inc
190 Bluegrass Valley Pkwy, Alpharetta, GA 30005-2204
Tel: 770-369-9000 *Toll Free Tel:* 800-877-7804 *Fax:* 770-369-9100
E-mail: convergent@convergent.com
Web Site: www.convergent.com
Key Personnel
CEO & Pres: Gary L Cavey
CFO: Nate Legband
Deputy Pres: Mitsuru Ito
SVP, Engg: Trevor Davies
SVP, Mktg & Busn Devt: Jay Dishong
SVP, Sales & Mktg: Gary Johns
SVP, Strategy & Innovation: Kenneth J Boyle
VP & Gen Mgr, Acct Opers: Haig Megerian
VP, HR: Lori Bruckner
VP, IT: Rob Harwood
VP, Sales, Eastern Reg: Kevin Fenton
Mng Dir, Digital Media Opers: Craig Leathers
Provider of broadband platforms.
Brochure(s) available
Branch Office(s)
49 Ontario St, 5th fl, Toronto, ON M5A 2V1, Canada *Tel:* 647-349-0723 *Fax:* 770-369-9100
Membership(s): IMCCA; MCA-I

Conversation Arts Media
PO Box 715, Brooklyn, NY 11215
Tel: 718-768-0824
Web Site: www.dongabor.com
Key Personnel
Pres: Don Gabor *E-mail:* don@dongabor.com
Founded: 1991
Writer of communication books & CDs.
Membership(s): National Speakers Association

Cooking by the Book
13475 N Applegate Rd, Grants Pass, OR 97527
Tel: 541-846-0654 *Toll Free Tel:* 800-655-9071 *Fax:* 541-846-0654
Web Site: www.atasteofnature.org
Key Personnel
Owner & Author: Marcella O Lynch *E-mail:* lynchmarcella@gmail.com
Vegetarian cookbook, vegetarian cooking DVDs & television programs.
Brochure(s) available

Cool-Lux™
Division of PromarkBRANDS
1268 Humbracht Circle, Bartlett, IL 60103
Toll Free Tel: 800-ACDC-LUX (223-2589) *Fax:* 630-830-2525
Web Site: www.cool-lux.com
Key Personnel
Pres: Ken Orlando
Founded: 1977
Products & services for professional videographers.

Cooper Controls
Division of Eaton Corp
203 Cooper Circle, Peachtree City, GA 30269
Tel: 770-486-4782 *Toll Free Tel:* 800-553-3879 *Toll Free Fax:* 800-954-7016
E-mail: controlssales@cooperindustries.com
Web Site: www.coopercontrol.com
Key Personnel
Mktg Mgr: Angela Maddox *E-mail:* angela.maddox@cooperindustries.com
Lighting control solutions for energy management.
Catalog(s) available

Copp Integrated Systems
123 S Keowee St, Dayton, OH 45402
Tel: 937-228-4188 *Toll Free Tel:* 877-450-2677 *Fax:* 937-228-2901
Web Site: www.copp.com
Key Personnel
Owner & CEO: William DeFries
Pres & Gen Mgr: Thomas Frericks, Jr *E-mail:* tjf@copp.com
Production & repair services.
Membership(s): IBMA; InfoComm International®; NSCA

CopShopMiami.com
160 E 35 St, Hialeah, FL 33013
Tel: 305-333-5791
E-mail: omar@copshopmiami.com
Web Site: www.copshopmiami.com
Founded: 1989
One stop police props.
Online catalog(s) available
Membership(s): DGA; SAG-AFTRA; Writers Guild of America

Corbis
710 Second Ave, Suite 200, Seattle, WA 98104
Tel: 206-373-6000 *Fax:* 206-373-6100
Web Site: www.corbisimages.com
Key Personnel
CEO: Gary Shenk
Provide visual solutions.
Catalog(s) available
Branch Office(s)
6060 Center Dr, Suite 100, Los Angeles, CA 90045 *Tel:* 323-602-5700 *Fax:* 323-602-5701
250 Hudson St, 4th fl, New York, NY 10013 *Tel:* 212-777-6200 *Toll Free Tel:* 800-260-0444 *Fax:* 212-375-7700 *Toll Free Fax:* 877-297-7977 *E-mail:* sales@corbis.com
Corbis Film Preservation Facility, PO Box 67, Boyers, PA 16020-0067 (US mail only)
Foreign Office(s): 9, rue du Quatre Septembre, 75002 Paris, France *Tel:* 01 53 33 38 00 *Fax:* 01 53 33 38 02
Rosenthaler Str 42, 10178 Berlin, Germany *Tel:* (030) 600 310 001 *Fax:* (030) 600 310 250
Stephanienstr 36, 40221 Dusseldorf, Germany *Tel:* (0211) 912 8230 *Fax:* (0211) 912 8234
Via Lombardini 13, 20143 Milan MI, Italy *Tel:* (02) 58105551 *Fax:* (02) 83242493
Greenlight, 149 Shibuya Mark City West 22F, 1-12-1 Doginzaka, Shibuya-ku, Tokyo 150-0002, Japan *Tel:* (03) 4360-5415 *Fax:* (03) 4360-5781
111 Salusbury Rd, London NW6 6RG, United Kingdom *Tel:* (020) 7644 7400 *Fax:* (020) 7644 7401
Membership(s): Picture Agency Council of America

Corbis Motion
Member of Corbis Corporation
250 Hudson St, 4th fl, New York, NY 10013-1413
Tel: 212-375-7622 *Toll Free Tel:* 800-260-0444 *Fax:* 212-375-7700 *Toll Free Fax:* 877-297-7977
E-mail: sales@corbis.com
Web Site: www.corbismotion.com
Key Personnel
CEO: Gary Shenk
High quality moving images.
Catalog(s) available
Branch Office(s)
6060 Center Dr, Los Angeles, CA 90045 *E-mail:* infola@corbismotion.com

Corinth Films Inc
3117 Bursonville Rd, Riegelsville, PA 18077
Tel: 610-346-7446 *Fax:* 610-346-6345
E-mail: sales@corinthfilms.com
Web Site: www.corinthreleasing.com; www.corinthfilms.com
Key Personnel
Owner & Pres: John M Poole *E-mail:* johnpool5@verizon.net
EVP, Opers: Richard Evangelista *Tel:* 908-686-9230 *E-mail:* rich@corinthfilms.com
Dir, Visual & Social Media: Crystal Goodwin
Film Engagements & Res: John M Poole, Jr *E-mail:* john@corinthfilms.com
Founded: 1977
Distribution of classic movies & TV shows.
Catalog(s), quarterly

Cornell Laboratory of Ornithology
Division of Cornell University Audio-Visual Resource Center
Cornell University, 159 Sapsucker Woods Rd, Ithaca, NY 14850
Tel: 607-254-BIRD (254-2473) *Toll Free Tel:* 800-843-BIRD (843-2473) *Fax:* 607-254-2415
E-mail: cornellbirds@cornell.edu
Web Site: www.birds.cornell.edu
Key Personnel
Dir: John Fitzpatrick
Educational programming.
Catalog(s) available

Cornerstone Media Productions Inc
41 Bramhall St, Georgetown, DE 19947
Tel: 302-855-9380
Web Site: www.cornerstonemedia.com
Key Personnel
CEO: Rick Greenberg *E-mail:* rick@cornerstonemedia.com
Video, audio & multimedia production services.

Coronet/MTI Film & Video, see The Phoenix Learning Group Inc

Corplex
Subsidiary of NEP Group Inc
915 Sherwood Dr, Lake Bluff, IL 60044
Tel: 847-582-8800 *Fax:* 847-582-8730
Web Site: www.nepinc.com/welcome/corplex
Key Personnel
Mgr, Strategic Sales: Carter Ruehrdanz
Digital & HD mobile broadcast production facilities & services.

Corporate Color Graphics Inc
3525 Lousma Dr SE, Grand Rapids, MI 49548
Tel: 616-774-9583 *Toll Free Tel:* 800-776-9583 *Fax:* 616-774-8235
E-mail: production@corpcolor.com
Web Site: www.corpcolor.com
Key Personnel
Sr Acct Exec: Kevin Wells *Tel:* 616-774-9583 ext 3117 *E-mail:* kevin.wells@corpcolor.com
Large format printing company.
Catalog(s) available
Membership(s): Photo Marketing Association

Cosumnes River College
Subsidiary of Los Rios Community College District
8401 Center Pkwy, Sacramento, CA 95823
Tel: 916-691-7289 *Fax:* 916-691-7375
Web Site: www.crc.losrios.edu
Key Personnel
Media Resources Supv: Chris Beck *E-mail:* beckc@crc.losrios.edu
College resource center, including fiber optics & satellite transmission capabilities.

Council on Foundations
2121 Crystal Dr, Suite 700, Arlington, VA 22202
Toll Free Tel: 800-673-9036
Web Site: www.cof.org

Key Personnel
CEO & Pres: Vicki Spruill
Catalog(s) available

Countdown Productions Inc
PO Box 180220, Dallas, TX 75218
Tel: 214-321-3233; 214-808-9988 (cell)
Web Site: www.countdownproductions.com
Key Personnel
Pres: Thomas C Crocker *E-mail:* tom@countdownproductions.com
Founded: 1986
Professional video, web & corporate productions.

Countryman Associates Inc
195 Constitution Dr, Menlo Park, CA 94025
Tel: 650-364-9988 *Toll Free Tel:* 800-669-1422 *Fax:* 650-364-2794
E-mail: sales@countryman.com
Web Site: www.countryman.com
Key Personnel
Mktg Dir: Mary Anderson
Microphone manufacturers.
Catalog(s) available

County Sales
117A W Main St, Floyd, VA 24091
Mailing Address: PO Box 191, Floyd, VA 24091-0191
Tel: 540-745-2001 *Fax:* 540-745-2008
E-mail: sales@countysales.com; info@countysales.com
Web Site: www.countysales.com
Key Personnel
Pres: David Freeman
Founded: 1965
Bluegrass, old time & country music distributor.
Catalog(s) available

Courter Films LLC
121 NW Crystal St, Crystal River, FL 34428
Tel: 352-795-2156 *Fax:* 352-795-6144
E-mail: info@courterfilms.com
Web Site: www.courterfilms.com
Key Personnel
Dir & Ed: Philip R Courter *E-mail:* phil@courterfilms.com
Exec Prodr: Gay Courter *E-mail:* gay@courterfilms.com
Founded: 1971
Full service production company.
Catalog(s) available

Coustic Car Audio
4545 E Baseline Rd, Phoenix, AZ 85042
Tel: 602-438-2020 *Toll Free Tel:* 800-225-5689
E-mail: coustic@coustic.com
Web Site: www.coustic.com
Key Personnel
CEO: Loyd Ivey
Automobile audio systems.
Catalog(s) available

Covenant Productions®
Division of Anderson University
c/o Anderson University, 1100 E Fifth St, Anderson, IN 46012
Tel: 765-641-4348 *Fax:* 765-641-3825
Web Site: www.covenantproductions.com
Key Personnel
Gen Mgr: Donald Boggs
Opers Dir: David Armstrong *E-mail:* dsarmstrong@covenantproductions.com
Video production.
Rate card(s) available
Membership(s): NATAS

Covid Inc
1723 W Fourth St, Tempe, AZ 85281
Tel: 480-966-2221 *Toll Free Tel:* 800-638-6104 *Fax:* 480-966-6728
E-mail: sales@covid.com
Web Site: www.covid.com
Key Personnel
Pres: Norm Carson *E-mail:* normc@covid.com
Opers Mgr: John Sullivan
Mktg Coord: Joseph Ramirez *E-mail:* joer@covid.com
Manufacturer of AV integration products.
Catalog(s) available
Membership(s): InfoComm International®; NSCA

Cox Creative Studios
17602 N Black Canyon Hwy, Phoenix, AZ 85053
Tel: 623-328-4778
Web Site: www.coxcreativestudios.com
Founded: 1982
HDTV production & broadcast facility. Studio, equipment & truck rentals.

Cox Media
350 Tenth Ave, Suite 500, San Diego, CA 92101
Tel: 619-686-1900 *Toll Free Tel:* 855-755-2691 *Fax:* 619-867-4996
Web Site: www.coxmedia.com
Key Personnel
Mktg Mgr: Laurin Boutin
Cable entertainment & broadband services.

Coyote Cowboy Co
PO Box 2190, Benson, AZ 85602-2190
Tel: 520-586-1077 *Toll Free Tel:* 800-654-2550
Web Site: baxterblack.com
Key Personnel
Contact: Cindy Black *E-mail:* cindylou@baxterblack.com
Founded: 1982
AV distributor.
Catalog(s), annual

CP Communications
200 Clearbrook Rd, Suite 148, Elmsford, NY 10523
Tel: 914-345-9292 *Toll Free Tel:* 800-762-4254 *Fax:* 914-345-9222
E-mail: info@cpcomms.com; sales@cpcomms.com
Web Site: www.cpcomms.com
Key Personnel
Pres: Michael Mason *E-mail:* michael.mason@cpcomms.com
CTO & Pres: Tim Fisher *E-mail:* tim.fisher@cpcomms.com
SVP: Kurt Heitmann *E-mail:* kurt.heitmann@cpcomms.com
Gen Mgr: Aaron Segarra *E-mail:* aaron.segarra@cpcomms.com
Founded: 1980
Production communications equipment rentals & custom engineering solutions.
Branch Office(s)
15 Ninnie Dr, Wappingers Falls, NY 12590, SVP: Kurt Heitmann *Tel:* 845-440-0525 *E-mail:* kurt.heitmann@cpcomms.com
3506 St Valentine Way, Unit 6, Orlando, FL 32811, CEO: David Goldsmith *Tel:* 407-843-4225 *Toll Free Tel:* 800-373-6827 *Fax:* 407-843-4921 *E-mail:* david.goldsmith@cpcomms.com

CPdigital
102 Madison Ave, New York, NY 10016
Tel: 212-328-5177
Web Site: www.cpdigital.com
Key Personnel
EVP: Franco Fiore *E-mail:* ffiore@cpdigital.com
Full service production company. Also provides non-linear editing, SD & HD editing, live event production, trade shows & digital file transfers.

CPI Malibu
Division of Communications & Power Industries (CPI)
3760-A Calle Tecate, Camarillo, CA 93012-5060
Tel: 805-383-1829 *Fax:* 805-383-1859
E-mail: malibu.sales@cpii.com
Web Site: www.cpii.com/division.cfm/10
Key Personnel
Dir, Busn Devt: Anthony Macari *Tel:* 805-383-1829 ext 108 *E-mail:* anthony.macari@cpii.com
Aftermarket Specialist: Whitney K Ordelheide *Tel:* 805-383-1829 ext 209 *E-mail:* whitney.ordelheide@cpii.com
Founded: 1975
Satellite terminal provider.

CPR MultiMedia Solutions
7812 Cessna Ave, Gaithersburg, MD 20879
Tel: 301-590-9400 *Fax:* 301-590-9402
E-mail: info@cprmms.com
Web Site: www.cprmms.com
Key Personnel
Pres: Jeff Studley *E-mail:* jstudley@cprmms.com
Founded: 1988
Full service media component distributor.
Catalog(s) available
Membership(s): ASAE; InfoComm International®; International Special Events Society; MPI

CPT Rental Inc
36-01A 48 Ave, Long Island City, NY 11101
Tel: 718-424-1600 *Fax:* 718-457-4778
E-mail: rental@cptrental.com
Web Site: www.cptrental.com
Key Personnel
Pres: Aaron Fidan
Rent & repair movie equipment.

Craig Recording Studios
2381 Philmont Ave, Suite 112, Huntingdon Valley, PA 19006
Tel: 215-947-8900
Web Site: www.craigrecording.com; www.craigrecordingstudios.com
Key Personnel
Owner: Michael Gallagher *E-mail:* mike@craigrecording.com
Recording studios.

Cramer Productions
425 University Ave, Norwood, MA 02062
Tel: 781-278-2300 *Fax:* 781-255-0721
E-mail: info@cramer.com
Web Site: cramer.com
Key Personnel
Chmn: Thomas Martin
CEO: Thom Faria
Full service AV production company & digital marketing.

Crash Video Productions
713 N Mansfield Ave, Los Angeles, CA 90038
Tel: 310-489-6848
E-mail: crash@crashproductions.com
Web Site: www.crashproductions.com
Key Personnel
Owner: Michael Levine

Thomas Craven Film Corp
5 W 19 St, New York, NY 10011-4216
Tel: 212-463-7190 *Fax:* 212-627-4761
E-mail: info@cravenfilms.com
Web Site: cravenfilms.com
Key Personnel
Pres: Michael Craven *E-mail:* michael@cravenfilms.com
VP, Prodn: Penny Craven
VP, Sales: Ernest Barbieri
Founded: 1952

Complete video, film & webcasting services from script & development through duplication & distribution.
Catalog(s) available

Crawford Media Services
6 W Druid Hills Dr NE, Atlanta, GA 30329
Tel: 404-876-0333 *Toll Free Tel:* 800-831-8029 *Fax:* 678-536-4912
Web Site: www.crawford.com
Key Personnel
CEO: Jesse Crawford
VP, Post Prodn: Kathleen Fitch
Founded: 1981
Electronic media services industry, offering domestic & international clients a full spectrum of television, post-production, satellite, IP-media & digitizing & archiving services.
Membership(s): AES; MCA-I; NATAS; The Recording Academy; SMPTE; SPARS

Creation Technologies Inc
102-8977 Fraserton Ct, Burnaby, BC V5J 5H8, Canada
Tel: 604-430-4336 *Toll Free Tel:* 800-736-1271 *Fax:* 604-430-4337
E-mail: info@creationtech.com
Web Site: www.creationtech.com
Key Personnel
Regl Leader, West: Jeff Kuypers
Gen Mgr: Ana Cantu; Stan Krzyczkowski
Electronics manufacturer.
Catalog(s) available
Membership(s): AES; NAMM, the National Association of Music Merchants

Creative Arts Television
PO Box 739, Kent, CT 06757-0739
Tel: 860-868-1771 *Fax:* 860-868-9999
E-mail: catarchive@aol.com; info@catarchive.com
Web Site: www.catarchive.com
Key Personnel
Pres: Stephan Chodorov
Founded: 1950
Educational programming.

Creative Backstage
4829 S 36 St, Suite 1, Phoenix, AZ 85040
Tel: 480-580-2222
E-mail: sales@creativebackstage.com
Web Site: www.creativebackstage.com
Key Personnel
Owner: John Garberson *E-mail:* john@creativebackstage.com
Creative production services: lighting, sound, video & staging.

Creative Color Services, see Ferrari Color®

Creative Core Inc, see CCore Media Inc

Creative Custom Cases
Formerly ASA Custom Cases Inc
14946 Shoemaker Ave, Suite D, Santa Fe Springs, CA 90670
Tel: 562-404-5500 *Fax:* 562-404-5505
E-mail: info@creativecc.net
Web Site: www.creativecc.net
Key Personnel
Mgr: Roofi Bhure *E-mail:* roofi@creativecc.net
Founded: 1994
Manufacture ATA cases.

Creative Light, see Bowens USA

Creative Media Development
1631 NW Thurman St, Portland, OR 97209
Tel: 503-223-6794 *Fax:* 503-223-2430
E-mail: info@cmdpdx.com
Web Site: www.cmdpdx.com
Key Personnel
Print Prodn Mgr: Laura Huber
Mid-sized full service agency.
Catalog(s) available
Membership(s): Oregon Media Production Association; SMPTE

Creative Media Recording
11105 Knott Ave, Suite G, Cypress, CA 90630
Tel: 714-892-9469
E-mail: info@creativemediarecording.com
Web Site: www.creativemediarecording.com
Key Personnel
Opers Dir: Tim Keenan
Prodn Coord: Linda Keenan
Founded: 1970
Digital audio post-production.
Brochure(s) available
Membership(s): MCA-I

Creative Realities Inc
55 Broadway, 9th fl, New York, NY 10006
Tel: 212-324-6660 *Toll Free Tel:* 888-432-7328
E-mail: info@cri.com
Web Site: www.cri.com
Key Personnel
CEO & Dir: Paul Price *E-mail:* paul.price@cri.com
COO & CFO: John Walpuck
Pres: Scott Koller
Digital in-store merchandising, digital signage & marketing solutions for retailers & brands using the latest technologies.
Branch Office(s)
22 Audrey Place, Fairfield, NJ 07004 *Tel:* 973-244-9911

Creative Services Inc
806 Westchester Dr, High Point, NC 27262
Tel: 336-889-3010; 336-883-8800 *Toll Free Tel:* 800-989-3010 *Fax:* 336-885-1829
E-mail: info@nidoqubein.com
Web Site: www.nidoqubein.com; www.getcreativeservices.com
Key Personnel
CEO: Dr Deena Qubein *E-mail:* deena@getcreativeservices.com
Produce marketing materials, including posters, brochures, invitations, web sites & multimedia presentations. Nido Qubein recorded AV learning systems.
Catalog(s) available

Creative Sound Corp
5515 Medea Valley Dr, Agoura Hills, CA 91301
Tel: 818-707-8986
E-mail: info@csoundcorp.com
Web Site: www.csoundcorp.com
Key Personnel
CEO: Bob Cotterell
Founded: 1983
Manufacture CDs & DVDs - replication, graphics, printing & packaging.

Creative Specialists Inc, see CSI/Orion

Creative Stage Lighting Co Inc
149 Rte 28 N, North Creek, NY 12853
Mailing Address: PO Box 567, North Creek, NY 12853-0567
Tel: 518-251-3302 *Fax:* 518-251-2908
E-mail: info@creativestagelighting.com
Web Site: www.creativestagelighting.com
Lighting distributor & manufacturer.
Membership(s): Professional Lighting & Sound Association; USITT

Creative Support Services/CSS Music
1948 Riverside Dr, Los Angeles, CA 90039
Tel: 323-666-7968 *Toll Free Tel:* 800-468-6874 *Fax:* 323-660-2070
E-mail: info@cssmusic.com
Web Site: www.cssmusic.com
Key Personnel
Owner & Chief Mktg Offr: Michael M Fuller *E-mail:* mfuller@cssmusic.com
Catalog(s) available
Membership(s): AES; Buy-Out Music Association; Copyright Society; IAAVC; InfoComm International®; NAB; NATPE

Creative Technology
1455 Estes Ave, Elk Grove Village, IL 60007
Tel: 847-671-9670 *Toll Free Tel:* 800-826-4761 *Fax:* 847-640-6559
E-mail: info@ctchicago.com
Web Site: us.ct-group.com
Key Personnel
Natl Dir, Sales: Kristi Ventura *E-mail:* kventura@ctus.com
Dir, Opers: Dominic Tosterud *E-mail:* dtosterud@ctus.com
Gen Mgr: Sim Elwood *E-mail:* selwood@ctus.com
Professional full service audio visual staging company providing turn key solutions for corporate & special events, tradeshows & exhibits, conferences & general sessions, product launches & award ceremonies.
Catalog(s) available
Branch Office(s)
14000 Arminita St, Panorama City, CA 91402, Dir, Mktg: Sandra De Mond *Tel:* 818-779-2400 *Fax:* 818-779-2401 *E-mail:* sdemond@ctus.com
14072 Catalina St, San Leandro, CA 94577, Gen Mgr: David Skaff *Tel:* 510-618-5100 *Fax:* 510-618-5118 *E-mail:* dskaff@ctus.com
Patrick Commerce Ctr, Bldg E, 6171 S McLeod Dr, Las Vegas, NV 89120, Gen Mgr: Herb Brandt *Tel:* 702-450-3600 *Fax:* 702-450-3602 *E-mail:* hbrandt@ctus.com
Foreign Office(s): In der Au 11, 72622 Nurtingen, Germany, Gen Mgr: Georg Rossler *Tel:* (0722) 253-0 *Fax:* (0722) 253-100 *E-mail:* info@ctgermany.com
15 Changi North St One, No 01-04, Singapore 493765, Singapore, Mng Dir: Charlie Whitlock *Tel:* 6546 6240 *Fax:* 6543 4251 *E-mail:* cwhitlock@ctasiapacific.com
Dubai Investment Park, Bldg 11, Unit 5, PO Box 282572, Jebel Ali, Dubai, United Arab Emirates, Gen Mgr: Damien McGurn *Tel:* (04) 885 6020 *Fax:* (04) 885 6131 *E-mail:* dmcgurn@ctdubai.com
Sussex Manor Business Park, Unit E2, Gatwick Rd, Crawley RH10 9NH, United Kingdom *Tel:* (01293) 582000 *Fax:* (01293) 582010 *E-mail:* info@ctlondon.com
Membership(s): InfoComm International®

Creative Technology
137 Heritage Woods Dr, Akron, OH 44321
Tel: 330-668-7777 *Fax:* 330-665-3718
Web Site: www.creativetechnology.com
Key Personnel
Pres: Roger Berk
VP: Robert C Berk
Sr Exec Prodr: Kelly Seiberling *E-mail:* kelly@creativetechnology.com
Founded: 1980
Full scale media production company offering end-to-end service from conception to final delivery.
Branch Office(s)
222 Front St, 2nd fl, San Francisco, CA 94111 *Tel:* 415-513-5918 *E-mail:* studio@ct-sf.com

Creative Video
26 Colonial Ave, Woodbury, NJ 08096
Tel: 856-848-0046 *Toll Free Tel:* 888-988-2877 *Fax:* 856-848-8905

E-mail: contact@creativevideo.org
Web Site: www.creativevideo.org
Founded: 1991
Full service corporate video production company. Production studio & equipment rentals.

Creative Video of Washington Inc
1410 Spring Hill Rd, Suite 100, McLean, VA 22102
Tel: 703-891-2620 *Fax:* 703-891-2625
Web Site: www.creativevideo.com
Key Personnel
Pres: Kirby Whyte *E-mail:* kw@creativevideo.com
Founded: 1981
Video production, presentation, duplication & post-production.
Membership(s): MCA-I; Television, Internet & Video Association of DC Inc

Creativity Unlimited Press®
30819 Casilina Dr, Rancho Palos Verdes, CA 90275
Tel: 310-541-4844 *Fax:* 310-377-7946
E-mail: ihf@cox.net
Web Site: drshelleynicholas.com; hypnosisfederation.com
Key Personnel
Publr-in-Chief: Shelley Stockwell-Nicholas, PhD
Founded: 1978
Hypnosis & other self-help CDs & DVDs.

Cre-a-tv Studios
1332 Londontown Blvd, Suite 102, Eldesburg, MD 21784
Toll Free Tel: 800-628-0112
E-mail: production@cre-a-tv.com
Web Site: cre-a-tv.com
Key Personnel
Pres: Tina Apellaniz Waganer
Dir & Prodr: Richard Waganer *E-mail:* rich@cre-a-tv.com
Premier live events arena & video production studio.

Credo Interactive Inc
4612 Strathcona Rd, North Vancouver, BC V7O 1G3, Canada
Tel: 604-291-6717
E-mail: info@charactermotion.com
Web Site: www.charactermotion.com
Key Personnel
CEO: Tom Calvert
Founded: 1995

Crescendo Designs Inc
641 County Rd 39-A, Southampton, NY 11968
Tel: 631-283-2133 *Fax:* 631-204-1066
E-mail: sales@crescendodesigns.com
Web Site: www.crescendodesigns.com
Key Personnel
Founder & Pres: Chris Brody
Founder & VP: Mike Brody
Sales & installation of home theatre equipment.

Crescent/Stonco
Division of Philips Group
200 Franklin Square Dr, Somerset, NJ 08873
Toll Free Tel: 800-334-2212
Web Site: www.crescent-stonco.com/led; www.csgreenlightingsolutions.com
Key Personnel
Gen Mgr, Outdoor Group: Chuck Havers *E-mail:* chuck.havers@philips.com
Dir, Mktg: Barret Gorman *E-mail:* barret.gorman@philips.com
Lighting manufacturer.
Catalog(s) available

Crest Audio Inc
5022 Hwy 493, Meridian, MS 39305
Toll Free Tel: 866-812-7378 *Fax:* 601-486-1380
E-mail: webmaster@crestaudio.com
Web Site: www.crestaudio.com
Manufacture amps, consoles & control products.
Foreign Office(s): Crest Audio Asia, 20, Hasip Pee Rd, Patong-Kathu, Phuket 83150, Thailand *Tel:* (076) 296 644 *Fax:* (076) 296 646 *E-mail:* crestphu@ksc.th.com (Asia, Australia & Far East)
Crest Audio Europe, Great Folds Rd, Oakley Hay Corby NN18 9ET, United Kingdom *Tel:* (01536) 424612 *Fax:* (01536) 747222 *E-mail:* mbecker@crestaudio.co.uk (Africa, Eastern Europe, Europe & Middle East)

Crest Electronics Inc
3706 Alliance Dr, Greensboro, NC 27407
Tel: 336-855-6422 *Toll Free Tel:* 888-502-7378 *Fax:* 336-855-6676
E-mail: info@crestelectronics.com; custserv@crestelectronics.com
Web Site: www.crestelectronics.com
Key Personnel
Off Mgr: Suzie Woodring *E-mail:* suziew@crestelectronics.com
Founded: 1974
Video component manufacturer.
Catalog(s) available

Cresta Creative
1050 N State St, Chicago, IL 60610
Tel: 312-944-4700 *Fax:* 312-944-1582
E-mail: info@crestagroup.com
Web Site: www.crestacreative.com
Key Personnel
Mng Partner: Joan Beugen
Founded: 1987
Corporate & marketing communications.
Branch Office(s)
6815 Willoughby Ave, Suite 102, Los Angeles, CA 90038 *Tel:* 323-939-7003
Membership(s): BMA; IABC

Crestron Electronics Inc
15 Volvo Dr, Rockleigh, NJ 07647
Tel: 201-767-3400 *Toll Free Tel:* 800-237-2041 *Fax:* 201-767-1903
E-mail: crestronhq@crestron.com
Web Site: www.crestron.com
Key Personnel
CEO: Randy Klein
Cust Support: Abby Davis
Sales Support: Ray Coneys
Control & automation systems manufacturer.
Catalog(s) available
Foreign Office(s): Crestron International, Oude Keerbergsebaan 2, 2820 Rijmenam, Belgium *Tel:* (015) 50 99 50 *Fax:* (015) 50 99 40 *E-mail:* info@crestron.eu
Crestron Asia Ltd, 25/F Westin Ctr, Rm 2501, No 26 Hung To Rd, Kwun Tong, Kowloon, Hong Kong *Tel:* 2341 2016 *Fax:* 2344 0889 *E-mail:* support@crestronasia.com *Web Site:* www.crestronasia.com
Crestron Latin America, Blvd M Avila Camacho 37 - 1A, 11560 Col Lomas de Chapultepec, Mexico *Tel:* (0155) 5093 2160 *Fax:* (0155) 5093 2165 *E-mail:* contacto@crestronlatin.com *Web Site:* www.crestron.com.mx
Membership(s): American Institute of Architects; Consortium of College & University Media Centers; Consumer Electronics Association; Custom Electronic Design & Installation Association; EDUCAUSE®; IALD; Illuminating Engineering Society; InfoComm International®; NSCA; Society for College and University Planning; US Green Building Council

Crew West Inc
1515 W Deer Valley Rd, Suite C109, Phoenix, AZ 85027
Mailing Address: PO Box 22147, Phoenix, AZ 85028-3201
Tel: 480-367-6888 *Toll Free Tel:* 888-444-2739 *Fax:* 480-367-6688
E-mail: tvcrews@crewwestinc.com
Web Site: www.crewwestinc.com
Key Personnel
Corp Pres & Dir, Photog: Jim Farrell *E-mail:* jimf@crewwestinc.com
VP: Dustin Farrell *E-mail:* dustinf@crewwestinc.com
Busn Mgr: Nancy Morningstar *E-mail:* nancym@crewwestinc.com
Opers & Prodn Coord: Laura Farrell *E-mail:* lauraf@crewwestinc.com
Network level HDTV & production video crews. Satellite trucks & live uplink studio.

Crispin Corp
600 Wade Ave, Raleigh, NC 27605
Tel: 919-845-7744 *Fax:* 919-845-7766
E-mail: welisten@crispincorp.com
Web Site: www.crispincorp.com
Key Personnel
COO: David Jones
CTO: Jim Zagrobelny
Pres: Alan DeVaney
Founded: 1997
Broadcast automation solutions.

Criterion Collection
215 Park Ave S, 5th fl, New York, NY 10003
Tel: 212-756-8822
E-mail: orders@criterion.com
Web Site: www.criterion.com
Key Personnel
CEO: Jonathan Turell
Pres: Robert Stein
Founded: 1984
Film publishing & video distribution.
Online catalog(s) available

Critical Information Network
17300 N Dallas Pkwy, Suite 3010, Dallas, TX 75248
Tel: 972-309-4000 *Toll Free Tel:* 800-624-2272 *Fax:* 972-309-5402; 972-309-5432
E-mail: info@criticalinfonet.com
Web Site: www.criticalinfonet.com
Key Personnel
CFO: David Porter
Founded: 1986
Interactive online training modules, including real-world video, animated graphics, pop-up descriptions, demonstrations & simulations.
Catalog(s) available

Cross-Cultural Communications
Subsidiary of Cross-Cultural Communications Publications Corp
239 Wynsum Ave, Merrick, NY 11566-4725
Tel: 516-868-5635 *Fax:* 516-379-1901
E-mail: info@cross-culturalcommunications.com
Web Site: www.cross-culturalcommunications.com
Key Personnel
Publr & Ed-in-Chief: Stanley H Barkan
Art Dir: Bebe Barkan
Publicity Dir: Mia Barkan Clarke
AV: Scott Randall
Founded: 1972
Distribute & publish audiocassettes, videocassettes, CDs, records & DVDs.
Flyer(s), continuous, free
Foreign Office(s): Via Tripoli 13, 90138 Palermo PA, Italy, Contact: Nicolo D'Alessandro *Tel:* (091) 322030
Membership(s): American Literary Translators Association

Crosscreek Television Productions Inc
100 Airpark Ct, Alabaster, AL 35007
Tel: 205-663-4411 *Fax:* 205-621-1389
E-mail: tvmcree@gmail.com

Web Site: www.crosscreektv.com
Lease production vehicles to network, entertainment & corporate clients.

Crossroads Audio Inc
2623 Myrtle Springs Ave, Dallas, TX 75220
Tel: 214-358-2623 *Toll Free Tel:* 800-287-0436 *Fax:* 214-358-0185
E-mail: mail@crossroadsaudio.com
Web Site: www.crossroadsaudio.com
Key Personnel
Dir, Opers: Ed Spoto *E-mail:* espoto@crossroadsaudio.com
Gen Mgr: Robin Magruder *E-mail:* rmagruder@crossroadsaudio.com
Tech Dir: Stewart Bennett
Concerts Dept Mgr: Mike Ponczek *E-mail:* mponczek@crossroadsaudio.com
Rental Dept Mgr: Jeff Oakley *E-mail:* joakley@crossroadsaudio.com
Sr Staff Engr, Concerts Dept: Dave Bell *E-mail:* dbell@crossroadsaudio.com
Off Mgr: Ashley Spoto *E-mail:* aspoto@crossroadsaudio.com
Founded: 1972
Audio & lighting equipment - rentals, sales, repairs & production services.
Membership(s): AES; NAMM, the National Association of Music Merchants

Crossroads Video
65 Church Rd, Sherman, CT 06784-1334
Tel: 860-350-0010 *Toll Free Tel:* 866-746-7111 (orders) *Fax:* 860-350-0010
E-mail: info@crossroadsvideo.com; crossroadsvideo@charter.net
Web Site: www.crossroadsvideo.com
Key Personnel
Pres: Elliot Glass
Founded: 1984
Catalog(s) available

Crown Audio Inc
Unit of Harman International
1718 W Mishawaka Rd, Elkhart, IN 46517
Tel: 574-294-8000 *Toll Free Tel:* 800-342-6939 *Fax:* 574-294-8301
Web Site: www.crownaudio.com
Key Personnel
Mktg Dir: Daniel Saenz
Founded: 1947
Power amplifier manufacturer.
Membership(s): AES; IAAPA; International Technology and Engineering Educators Association; NAMM, the National Association of Music Merchants; NSCA; SMPTE

Crown Ministries International
Division of Youth With a Mission's International Communications Network
PO Box 26479, Colorado Springs, CO 80936-6479
Tel: 719-591-2767 *Toll Free Tel:* 800-433-4685
E-mail: crownmin@intlcom.org
Web Site: www.crownmin.org
Founded: 1979
Religious educational programming.
Catalog(s) available
Membership(s): ICVM

CRT Custom Products Inc
7532 Hickory Hills Ct, Whites Creek, TN 37189
Tel: 615-876-5490 *Toll Free Tel:* 800-453-2533 *Fax:* 615-876-0096
E-mail: sales@crtcustomproducts.com
Web Site: www.crtcustomproducts.com
Key Personnel
Pres: Cheryl J Hutchinson *Tel:* 615-876-5490 ext 111 *E-mail:* cheryl@crtcustomproducts.com
Mktg Dir: Ron Brower *Tel:* 615-876-5490 ext 152 *E-mail:* rbrower@crttoybox.com
Founded: 1979
Manufacturing, printing, packaging & fulfillment.

Crunch Bird Studios Inc
9537 Whetstone Dr, Montgomery Village, MD 20886
Tel: 301-947-2927
Web Site: www.crunchbirdstudios.com
Key Personnel
Owner: Fred Petok *E-mail:* fpetok@verizon.net
Commercial studio.
Catalog(s) available

Crush Creative, see Coloredge

Crystal Clear Media Group
6737 E 30 St, Indianapolis, IN 46219
Toll Free Tel: 800-880-0073
E-mail: info@crystalclearcds.com
Web Site: www.crystalclearcds.com
Key Personnel
Br Mgr: Jim Cocke *Tel:* 214-349-0081 *Fax:* 214-349-3819 *E-mail:* jim@crystalclearcds.com
Manufacturer & distributor of CDs & DVDs.
Catalog(s) available

Crystal Pictures Inc
2000 Riverside Dr, Asheville, NC 28804
Tel: 828-285-9995 *Toll Free Tel:* 800-669-4057 *Fax:* 828-285-9997
E-mail: cryspic@aol.com
Web Site: www.ivyvideo.com
Key Personnel
Pres: Joshua Tager
Video sales & rentals.
Catalog(s), free

Crystal Productions
5320 Carpinteria Ave, Suite K, Carpinteria, CA 93013-2107
Tel: 847-657-8144 *Toll Free Tel:* 800-255-8629 *Fax:* 847-657-8149 *Toll Free Fax:* 800-657-8149
E-mail: custserv@crystalproductions.com
Web Site: www.crystalproductions.com
Key Personnel
Pres: Amy Woodworth
Founded: 1973
Produces & distributes educational materials pertaining to art.
Catalog(s), annual, art

Crystal Pyramid Productions™
Affiliate of New & Unique Videos™
7323 Rondel Ct, San Diego, CA 92119-1530
Tel: 619-644-3000
E-mail: cpp@newuniquevideos.com
Web Site: www.crystalpyramid.com
Key Personnel
CEO: Mark Schulze
CFO & COO: Patty Mooney
Catalog(s) available
Membership(s): MCA-I

Crystal Records Inc
28818 NE Hancock Rd, Camas, WA 98607
Tel: 360-834-7022 *Fax:* 360-834-9680
E-mail: info@crystalrecords.com
Web Site: www.crystalrecords.com
Key Personnel
Pres: Peter Christ
Founded: 1966
Record producers.
Catalog(s), 1-2 times/yr, free

Crystalite Industries Inc
101 Palm Harbor Pkwy, Unit 117, Palm Coast, FL 32137
Tel: 561-330-8742; 561-330-8660 *Toll Free Tel:* 800-328-5483; 800-468-8673 *Fax:* 561-330-8659; 561-330-8665
E-mail: phcrystalite@aol.com
Web Site: www.phcled.com
Key Personnel
VP, Sales & Mktg: Anna Robin
Founded: 1980
Decorative & task lighting products. Manufacture & distribute LED lighting.
Catalog(s) available

CSI Films
1913 Sonora St, Fort Collins, CO 80525
Tel: 970-282-1622
E-mail: mail@airhat.com
Web Site: www.airhat.com
Key Personnel
Prodr & Dir: Blake Miller *E-mail:* blake248@airhat.com
Children's programming.

CSI/Orion
1709 Utica Sq, Tulsa, OK 74114
Tel: 918-743-7881 *Toll Free Tel:* 888-579-1850
Web Site: www.csihealthcarecommunications.com; www.csiorion.com
Founded: 1970
Web-based communications tools to organizations in healthcare & other key industries.

CSI Rentals
133 W 19 St, Ground Level, New York, NY 10011
Tel: 212-243-7368 *Fax:* 212-243-2102
E-mail: info@csirentals.com; orders@csirentals.com
Web Site: www.csirentals.com
Photo & video equipment featuring camera & lighting rentals for still & video as well as expendables, photo & video supplies.
Branch Office(s)
1138 Flushing Ave, Ground Level, Brooklyn, NY 11237 *Tel:* 718-366-7368 *Fax:* 718-366-1721 *E-mail:* ordersbk@csirentals.com

CSPI
43 Manning Rd, Billerica, MA 01821
Tel: 978-663-7598 *Toll Free Tel:* 800-325-3110 *Fax:* 978-663-0150
E-mail: info@cspi.com
Web Site: www.cspi.com
Key Personnel
CEO & Pres: Victor Dellovo
Founded: 1968
Provide IT solutions, systems integration services & dense cluster computing services.
Catalog(s) available

CSPMedia.com
PO Box 3474, Capitol Heights, MD 20791-3474
Tel: 301-350-3181
Web Site: www.soundstore.com
Key Personnel
Owner: Nolan C Church
Children's programming & audio books.
Online catalog(s) available

CTG Audio
2100 Constitution Blvd, Sarasota, FL 34231
Tel: 941-922-2322 *Fax:* 941-922-5445
E-mail: orders@ctgaudio.com; info@ctgaudio.com
Web Site: www.ctgaudio.com
Key Personnel
CEO & Pres: Dave J Newman
Founded: 1995
Manufacture installed sound systems for teleconferencing.
Brochure(s), annual
Membership(s): InfoComm International®

CTL Communications Televideo Ltd, see Total AV Systems

C2 Imaging LLC
423 W 55 St, New York, NY 10019
Tel: 646-557-6300 *Fax:* 646-557-6400
Web Site: www.vomela.com/locations/c2_imaging
Key Personnel
Pres: Tim Wieland
E-business provider of media graphics.
Brochure(s) available
Price list(s) available

Cue Tech Teleprompting
5527 Satsuma Ave, North Hollywood, CA 91601
Tel: 818-487-2700 *Fax:* 818-487-2750
E-mail: info@cue-tech.com
Web Site: www.cue-tech.com
Key Personnel
Pres: Pamela Kutsunai
Teleprompter systems.

Culver Pictures Inc
51-02 21 St, Suite 4B, Long Island City, NY 11101
Tel: 718-752-9393 *Fax:* 718-752-9394
E-mail: research@culverpictures.com
Web Site: www.culverpictures.com
Key Personnel
Pres: Harriet Culver
Founded: 1926
Vintage & historical stock images leased for reproduction.
Historical archives available

Cupit Music Group
PO Box 121904, Nashville, TN 37212
Tel: 615-731-0100 *Fax:* 615-731-3005
Web Site: www.cupitmusic.com
Key Personnel
SVP: Dan Hagar *Tel:* 615-731-0100 ext 13 *E-mail:* dan@cupitmusic.com
Founded: 1980
Complete entertainment company including a record label, booking agency, radio & video promotions, recording facility & music publishing/production.

Curb Entertainment International Corp
Unit of Curb Records Inc
3907 W Alameda Ave, Burbank, CA 91505
Tel: 818-843-8580 *Fax:* 818-566-1719
Web Site: www.curbentertainment.com
Key Personnel
Chmn: Mike Curb
Pres: Carole Curb Nemoy *E-mail:* ccurb@curb.com
Founded: 1984
Film production & distribution.

Curious Pictures
440 Lafayette St, 5th fl, New York, NY 10003
Founded: 1993
Animation company.

Curtis Company
PO Box 210-215, Montgomery, AL 36121
Tel: 334-279-7127 *Toll Free Tel:* 800-228-5937 *Fax:* 334-270-8787 *Toll Free Fax:* 800-325-6341
Web Site: www.curtisav.com
Key Personnel
Owner & Pres: Larry Huffstetter *E-mail:* larryh@curtisav.com
Reseller of educational AV equipment.

Curtis Inc
1105 Western Ave, Cincinnati, OH 45203
Tel: 513-621-8895 *Toll Free Tel:* 800-733-2878 *Fax:* 513-621-0942
E-mail: info@curtisinc.com; clientservices@curtisinc.com
Web Site: www.curtisinc.com
Key Personnel
VP: Karen Sellers
Founded: 1985
Visual communications provider.

Custom Color Corp
14320 W 101 Terr, Lenexa, KS 66215
Tel: 913-730-3100 *Toll Free Tel:* 888-605-4050 *Fax:* 913-730-3101
E-mail: info@customcolor.com
Web Site: www.customcolor.com
Key Personnel
Chmn & CEO: Matt Keith
Founded: 1969
Large format printing company.
Catalog(s) available

Custom Computer Specialists Inc
6 Blackstone Valley Place, Suite 402, Lincoln, RI 02865
Tel: 401-765-3000 *Toll Free Tel:* 800-556-2828 *Fax:* 401-765-6440
Web Site: www.customonline.com
Key Personnel
CEO & Pres: Gregory G Galdi
CFO: Richard Kolberg
COO: Alan Lacher
SVP: Dennis Callagy
Founded: 1946
Leading computer technology services firm.
Membership(s): InfoComm International®

Custom Media Environments
299 Duffy Ave, Hicksville, NY 11801
Tel: 516-586-3600 *Toll Free Tel:* 800-80-SOUND (807-6863) *Fax:* 516-586-3487
E-mail: info@custommediaenvironments.com; sales@custommediaenvironments.com
Web Site: custommediaenvironments.com
Key Personnel
Owner & CEO: Amanda Jankelovics
VP, Opers: Vincenzo Giordano
Founded: 1979
Leading provider of turnkey AV system design, integration & installation solutions.

Custom Medical Stock Photo Inc
Division of MediaMD.com
3660 W Irving Park Rd, Chicago, IL 60618
Tel: 773-267-3100 *Toll Free Tel:* 800-373-2677 *Fax:* 773-267-6071
E-mail: info@cmsp.com
Web Site: www.cmsp.com
Key Personnel
CEO: Mike Fisher *E-mail:* mfisher@cmsp.com
Founded: 1986
Photographic services: location & studio. Still photo studio, thermography, surgical & clinical photography & video.
Catalog(s) available
Membership(s): Picture Agency Council of America

Custom Video Productions Inc
Division of South Bay Custom Video Productions Inc
707 Torrance Blvd, Suite 105, Redondo Beach, CA 90277
Tel: 310-543-4901
E-mail: info@customvideo.tv
Web Site: www.customvideo.tv
Founded: 1989
Video production, duplication, transfer, replication & packaging services. Media placement.

Custom Video Productions Inc
15 Lake Shore Dr, Red Bank, NJ 07701
Tel: 732-936-1001 *Fax:* 732-741-9204
E-mail: info@cvpnj.com
Web Site: www.cvpnj.com
Key Personnel
Pres: Frank Farrell *E-mail:* frank@cvpnj.com
Busn Devt Mgr: Noreen Miller *E-mail:* cvpnj.noreen@cvpnj.com
Founded: 1978
Full service multimedia production company offering services to corporations. Complete music & sound effects library, scripting, camera, editing, multimedia, high quality duplication, professional narrators & studio sound booth.

The Cutting Corp
4940 Hampden Lane, Suite 300, Bethesda, MD 20814
Tel: 301-654-CUTS (654-2887) *Fax:* 301-654-3271
E-mail: info@cuttingarchives.com
Web Site: www.cuttingarchives.com
Key Personnel
Div Dir: Angie Cornette *Tel:* 301-654-2887 ext 22
Founded: 1971
Audio production including audiobooks & sound production.
Catalog(s) available

Cutting Edge Productions
22904 Lockness Ave, Torrance, CA 90501
Tel: 310-326-4500; 818-503-0400
E-mail: info@cuttingedgeproductions.tv
Web Site: www.cuttingedgeproductions.tv
Full service broadcast, meeting & event technology company. Supplies video, audio & lighting services nationwide & operates a TV studio.

Cuyahoga Community College Media Center
2900 Community College Ave, Cleveland, OH 44115
Tel: 216-987-6000 *Toll Free Tel:* 800-954-8742
Web Site: www.tri-c.edu
Key Personnel
Exec Dir, TV & Video Servs: Robert Bryan
Full production services available.
Membership(s): Content Delivery & Storage Association

CyberIconics International
1752 N 74 Place, Mesa, AZ 85207-2932
Tel: 480-396-8731
Key Personnel
Pres: Ron L McIntyre
Religious educational programming producer.

Cybernetics
111 Cybernetics Way, Yorktown, VA 23693
Tel: 757-833-9000 *Fax:* 757-833-9300
E-mail: customer_service@cybernetics.com; techsales@cybernetics.com
Web Site: www.cybernetics.com
Founded: 1978
Manufacture & sell high performance disk & tape sub-systems.

CyberOptics
5900 Golden Hills Dr, Minneapolis, MN 55416
Tel: 763-542-5000 *Fax:* 763-542-5100
E-mail: info@cyberoptics.com
Web Site: cyberoptics.com
Key Personnel
CEO & Pres: Dr Subodh Kulkami
COO, CFO & VP, Fin: Jeffrey Bertelsen
VP, Sales & Mktg: Dennis Rutherford
VP, Technol & Busn Devt: Timothy Skunes
VP, Worldwide Opers: Corey Felber
Founded: 1984
Supplier of precision optical sensor solutions to the manufacturers of automated assembly, inspection & metrology equipment.

Foreign Office(s): No 1395 Hengshan Rd, Kunshan, Jiangsu 215300, China *Tel:* (0512) 50156306
No 21 Ubi Rd 1, Suite 02-01, Singapore 408724, Singapore *Tel:* 6744 3021 *Fax:* 6844 5331
15a, Hornbeam Park Oval, Hornbeam Park, Harrogate, N Yorks HG2 8RB, United Kingdom *Tel:* (01423) 871411 *Fax:* (01756) 700440

Czar Productions Inc
809 New Britain Ave, Hartford, CT 06106
Tel: 860-953-0809
E-mail: czar.productions@snet.net
Key Personnel
Owner & Mktg Mgr: Gene Czarnecki
Video production company.
Membership(s): MCA-I

D A S Audio of America Inc
Sunset Palmetto Park, 6900 NW 52 St, Miami, FL 33166
Tel: 305-436-0521 *Fax:* 305-436-0528
E-mail: sales@dasaudio.com
Web Site: www.dasaudio.com
Key Personnel
Gen Mgr: Jaime Villegas
Speaker distributor.

D A Sound
12932 SE Kent Kangley Rd, Box 460, Kent, WA 98030
Tel: 206-632-7773 *Toll Free Tel:* 855-DASOUND (327-6863) *Toll Free Fax:* 866-859-8650
E-mail: info@dasound.biz
Web Site: www.dasound.biz
Key Personnel
Owner: David Hunter *Tel:* 253-569-5560 *E-mail:* david@dasound.biz; Mark Szczerba *Tel:* 253-880-4699 *E-mail:* mark@dasound.biz
Founded: 1987
Audio sales & rentals.

Da-Lite
3100 N Detroit St, Warsaw, IN 46582
Tel: 574-267-8101 *Toll Free Tel:* 800-622-3737 *Fax:* 574-267-7804 *Toll Free Fax:* 877-325-4832
E-mail: info@da-lite.com
Web Site: www.da-lite.com
Key Personnel
Dir, Cust Serv & Training: Wendy Cox *E-mail:* wendy.cox@milestone.com
Sr Mktg Mgr: Melissa Rone *E-mail:* melissa.rone@milestone.com
Founded: 1909
World leader in projection screen design & surface technology. Product lines include custom surface solutions, manual & electric front projection screens as well as rear projection screens, lecterns, computer furniture, easels, projection carts & stands, TV/AV carts & simulation.
Catalog(s), free
Online catalog(s), PDF
Branch Office(s)
Advance Division, 1199 E Central, Wichita, KS 67214 *Tel:* 316-263-4231 *Fax:* 316-263-4245
Polacoat Division, 11500 Williamson Rd, Cincinnati, OH 45241 *Tel:* 513-489-3222 *Fax:* 513-489-4247
Foreign Office(s): Procolor, Rue Rene Pinsard, 45310 ZI de Patay, France *Tel:* 02 38 80 98 02 *Fax:* 02 38 80 90 92 *E-mail:* infoscreen@procolor.fr *Web Site:* www.procolor.fr
Projecta BV, Franklinstr 14, 6003 DK Weert, Netherlands *Tel:* (0495) 580 850 *Fax:* (0495) 580 860 *E-mail:* screens@projecta.nl *Web Site:* www.projectascreens.com
Membership(s): Consumer Electronics Association; Custom Electronic Design & Installation Association; InfoComm International®; NAB; NAPM; NSCA

Daburn Electronics & Cable Corp
44 Richboynton Rd, Dover, NJ 07801
Tel: 973-328-3200 *Fax:* 973-328-3130
E-mail: daburn@daburn.com
Web Site: www.daburn.com
Founded: 1964
Supplier of wire, cable & associated hardware, shrinkable tubing, sleeving & cold shrinking tape.
Online catalog(s) available

daCapo Productions
516 Hargrave St, Winnipeg, MB R3A 0X8, Canada
Tel: 204-956-2867 *Fax:* 204-956-2869
Web Site: www.dacapo.ca
Key Personnel
Mgr, Opers: Clinton Skibitzky *E-mail:* clinton@dacapo.ca
Founded: 1998
Complete digital audio service from original music to voice-overs for everything from TV & film to advertising campaigns.

Dadco
11078 Fleetwood St, Sun Valley, CA 91352
Tel: 818-768-8886 *Fax:* 818-765-0914
Web Site: www.dadcopowerandlights.com
Key Personnel
Gen Mgr: Ted Conroy *E-mail:* ted@dadcopowerandlights.com
Founded: 1995
Manufacturer of portable power distribution systems & cable assemblies. Lighting & equipment rentals & sales. Generator rentals, tractor rentals & production vehicle rentals. Manufacturer of Sunray Lighting. Repair department available.

Dage-MTI
701 N Roeske Ave, Michigan City, IN 46360
Tel: 219-872-5514 *Fax:* 219-872-5559
E-mail: info@dagemti.com; sales@dagemti.com; service@dagemti.com
Web Site: www.dagemti.com
Key Personnel
Owner: John Moore; Peggy Moore
Founded: 1952
AV equipment manufacturer.

Daily Electronics Corp
PO Box 822437, Vancouver, WA 98682-0053
Tel: 360-896-8856 *Toll Free Tel:* 800-346-6667 *Fax:* 360-896-5476
E-mail: daily@worldaccessnet.com
Web Site: dailyelectronics.net
Key Personnel
Pres: Jim Grimes
Transmitting & camera tubes, electron tubes & accessories.

Dake Publishing Inc
764 Martins Chapel Rd, Lawrenceville, GA 30045
Toll Free Tel: 800-241-1239 *Fax:* 770-963-7700
E-mail: info@dake.com
Web Site: www.dake.com
Key Personnel
Dir, Prod Devt: Mark Allison *E-mail:* mark@dake.com
Gen Mgr: Derrick Germaine *E-mail:* derrick@dake.com
Founded: 1961
Religious publishing.
Catalog(s) available
Membership(s): CBA: The Association for Christian Retail; Evangelical Christian Publishers Association

Dalet Digital Media Systems
100 Wall St, 15th fl, New York, NY 10005
Tel: 212-269-6700 *Fax:* 212-269-6709
E-mail: ddms@dalet.com
Web Site: www.dalet.com
Founded: 1990
Developer of audio, video & multimedia software solutions for the broadcast industry, government agencies, corporations & educational institutions.
Membership(s): NAB; RTDNA

Dallas Learning Solutions
Division of Dallas County Community College District
9596 Walnut St, Dallas, TX 75243-2112
Tel: 972-669-6650 *Toll Free Tel:* 866-DISTLRN (347-8576) *Fax:* 972-669-6668
E-mail: tlearn@dcccd.edu
Web Site: dls.dcccd.edu
Key Personnel
Provost, LeCroy Center for Educational Telecommunications: Pamela K Quinn *Tel:* 972-669-6550 *E-mail:* pquinn@dcccd.edu
Mgr, Academic Partnerships: Becky Stinson *Tel:* 972-669-6666 *E-mail:* bstinson@dcccd.edu; Cristin Thomas *Tel:* 972-669-6651 *E-mail:* cjthomas@dcccd.edu
Founded: 1972
Educational video & CD-ROM producer & distributor.
Online catalog(s) available
Membership(s): ITC

Dallas Prompter
PO Box 571233, Dallas, TX 75357
Tel: 214-275-9000
Web Site: www.dallasprompter.com
Key Personnel
Pres: Greg Stephenson *E-mail:* g@dallasprompter.com
Founded: 1985
Provide teleprompter services & equipment for meetings, conventions & video projects.
Membership(s): Dallas Producers Association; Texas Association of Motion Media Professionals

Dance Horizons Video
Division of Princeton Book Company, Publishers
614 Rte 130, Hightstown, NJ 08520
Tel: 609-426-0602 *Toll Free Tel:* 800-220-7149 *Fax:* 609-426-1344
E-mail: pbc@dancehorizons.com
Web Site: www.dancehorizons.com
Key Personnel
Pres: Charles H Woodford
Cust Serv: Marcia Sylvester
Online catalog(s) available

D&B Television & Video Productions Inc
1400 Riverbend Dr, Rocky Mount, VA 24151
Tel: 305-542-7000
Web Site: www.dbvideoproductions.net
Key Personnel
CEO & Exec Prodr: Derek Anderson *E-mail:* derek4tv@gmail.com
Founded: 1995
TV & video production company. Provider of AV crew & broadcast crews & equipment.
Online catalog(s) available
Membership(s): American Guild of Court Videographers

Dark Star Lighting & Production
102 Commerce St, Hinesburg, VT 05461
Tel: 802-482-4802 *Toll Free Tel:* 877-375-7827 *Fax:* 802-482-4803
E-mail: sales@darkstarlighting.com
Web Site: www.darkstarlighting.com

Founded: 1995
Technical design, equipment rentals & sales, on-site event management. Specialize in corporate event AV & mobile stage rentals.

Data Check Video Inc
Division of Lavi Systems
5148-E Commerce Ave, Moorpark, CA 93021
Tel: 805-517-1907 *Fax:* 805-552-0744
E-mail: mail@datacheck.com
Web Site: www.datacheck.com
Key Personnel
CEO & Dir, Prod Devt: Darrel Bevan *Tel:* 805-208-8231 (cell) *E-mail:* dbevan@datacheck.com
CFO & Dir, Busn Devt: Bill Acosta *Tel:* 858-335-6592 (cell) *E-mail:* bacosta@datacheck.com
Manufacture video monitoring.
Catalog(s) available
Membership(s): American Electronics Association

Data Display Audio Visual Co LP
3720 Dacoma, Houston, TX 77092-8906
Tel: 713-688-7900 *Toll Free Tel:* 800-840-2500 *Fax:* 713-688-5840
E-mail: tech@ddav.com
Web Site: www.ddav.com
Key Personnel
Pres: Collin G Loewen *E-mail:* collin@ddav.com
VP: Shawn Rockefeller *E-mail:* shawn@ddav.com
Founded: 1988
Audio visual equipment sales, service & rental.
Catalog(s) available
Membership(s): InfoComm International®; NSCA

Data Projections Inc
3700 W Sam Houston Pkwy S, Suite 525, Houston, TX 77042
Tel: 713-781-1999 *Toll Free Tel:* 866-225-5374 *Fax:* 713-781-3338
Web Site: www.dataprojections.com
Key Personnel
CEO: Linda C Zaleski
Principal: Billy Zaleski
Pres: Matthew Zaleski *E-mail:* mzaleski@dataprojections.com
EVP, Sales & Mktg: Robby Turner
VP, Opers: Megan Stasio
Founded: 1987
Integrated AV & display solutions.
Branch Office(s)
4616 W Howard Lane, Austin, TX 78728, Regl VP: Kris Begnaud *Tel:* 512-420-8856 *Fax:* 512-420-9185 *E-mail:* kbegnaud@dataprojections.com
14452 W Beltwood Pkwy, Dallas, TX 75244, Regl VP: Scott Birdsong *Tel:* 972-386-7686 *Fax:* 972-386-7685 *E-mail:* sbirdsong@dataprojections.com
16120 College Oak, Suite 107, San Antonio, TX 78249, Regl VP: Robby Turner *Tel:* 210-408-2860 *Fax:* 210-408-4598 *E-mail:* rturner@dataprojections.com

Data Security Inc
300 S Seventh St, Lincoln, NE 68508
Tel: 402-434-5959 *Toll Free Tel:* 800-225-7554 *Fax:* 402-434-3291
E-mail: sales@telesis-inc.com
Web Site: www.datasecurityinc.com
Key Personnel
CEO: Brian K Boles
Dir, Sales & Mktg: Renee Schafer
Founded: 1985
Manufacturer & supplier of hard drive degaussers, magnetic tape degaussers & hard drive & solid state destruction devices.

Data Translation Inc
100 Locke Dr, Marlboro, MA 01752-1192
Tel: 508-481-3700 *Toll Free Tel:* 800-525-8528 (sales) *Fax:* 508-481-8620
E-mail: info@datatranslation.com
Web Site: www.datatranslation.com
Key Personnel
CEO & Pres: Fred Molinari
Founded: 1973
Design, manufacture & provide data acquisition solutions for test & measurement.
Foreign Office(s): IM Weilerlen 10, 74321 Bietigheim-Bissingen, Germany, Sales & Mgmt: Winfried Klass *Tel:* (07142) 9531-0 *Fax:* (07142) 9531-13 *E-mail:* info@datatranslation.eu *Web Site:* www.datatranslation.eu

DataDirect Networks
2929 Patrick Henry Dr, Santa Clara, CA 95054
Tel: 818-700-4000 *Toll Free Tel:* 800-TERABYTE (837-2298)
E-mail: info@ddn.com; sales@ddn.com
Web Site: www.ddn.com
Key Personnel
Founder, Chmn & CEO: Alex Bouzari
Founder & Pres: Paul Bloch
Founded: 1998
Manufacture high-performance, cross-platform data storage & networking systems for the open systems, network attached computer environment.
Branch Office(s)
9351 Deering Ave, Chatsworth, CA 91311 *Tel:* 818-700-7600
9960 Federal Dr, Suite 180, Colorado Springs, CO 80921 *Tel:* 719-598-9792
8320 Guilford Rd, Suite D, Columbia, MD 21046 *Tel:* 410-309-9300
Foreign Office(s): Level 36 Riparian Plaza, 71 Eagle St, Brisbane, Qld 4000, Australia *Tel:* (07) 243 280 248
Immeuble le Dynasteur, 1er etage, gauche, 10 rue Andras Beck, 92360 Meudon La foret, France *Tel:* 01 84 01 03 30
Noerdlicher Zubringer 9, 40470 Duesseldorf, Germany *Tel:* (06196) 5868580
Plaza 256, Suite 7, Blanchardstown Corporate Business Park, Ballycoolin, Dublin 15, Ireland *Tel:* (01) 5255653
Tokyo Bancho Bldg 8F, 6-2 Yonban-cho, Chiyoda-ku, Tokyo 102-0081, Japan *Tel:* (03) 3261-9101 *Fax:* (03) 3261-9140
Dubai Media City, Al Thuraya Tower 1, Off 504, Dubai, United Arab Emirates *Tel:* (04) 390-2576 *Fax:* (04) 454-8507
The Innovation Centre, Sci-Tech Daresbury, Keckwick Lane, Daresbury, Cheshire WA4 4FS, United Kingdom *Tel:* (01925) 607270

Dav Tronics Ltd
Subsidiary of S W Davis Broadcast Technical Services Ltd
1543 Venables St, Suite 200, Vancouver, BC V5L 2G8, Canada
Tel: 604-255-2200 *Fax:* 604-255-4083
Web Site: www.broadcasttechnical.com
Key Personnel
Supv: Dan Roach
Manufacture broadcasting equipment.
Data sheet(s) available

Davenport Music Library
PO Box 690536, Charlotte, NC 28227-7009
E-mail: info@davenportmusic.com
Web Site: www.davenportmusic.com
Key Personnel
Owner & Pres: Neal Davenport
Founded: 1992
Royalty free tracks & CDs.
Catalog(s) available

David Clark Co Inc
360 Franklin St, Worcester, MA 01604
Mailing Address: PO Box 15054, Worcester, MA 01615-0054
Tel: 508-751-5800 *Toll Free Tel:* 800-900-3434 *Fax:* 508-753-5827
E-mail: sales@davidclark.com
Web Site: www.davidclark.com
Key Personnel
Pres: Robert A Vincent
Prod Mgr: Bryce Clark *E-mail:* bclark@davidclark.com
Manufacturer of communication equipment.
Catalog(s) available

Davidson Films Inc
PO Box 664, Santa Margarita, CA 93453
Toll Free Tel: 888-437-4200 *Fax:* 805-594-0532
E-mail: dfi@davidsonfilms.com
Web Site: davidsonfilms.com
Key Personnel
CEO & Pres: Frances W Davidson
Founded: 1955
Produce & distribute educational documentaries for the university market specializing in psychology, neuroscience & education.
Online catalog(s), PDF

Davies Publishing Inc
32 S Raymond Ave, Suite 4, Pasadena, CA 91105-1935
Tel: 626-792-3046 *Toll Free Tel:* 877-792-0005 *Fax:* 626-792-5308
E-mail: order@daviespublishing.com
Web Site: daviespublishing.com
Key Personnel
Pres & Publr: Michael Davies *E-mail:* mikedavies@daviespublishing.com
Opers Mgr: Janet Heard *E-mail:* janetheard@daviespublishing.com
Founded: 1981
Full service publishing company.
Catalog(s), annual, free upon request

Davis Art Images
Division of Davis Publications Inc
50 Portland St, Worcester, MA 01608
Tel: 508-754-7201 *Toll Free Tel:* 800-533-2847 *Fax:* 508-753-3834
E-mail: das@davisart.com
Web Site: www.davisartimages.com
Key Personnel
Curator: Karl Cole
Pres: Wyatt Wade
Assoc Curator: Lydia Keene-Kendrick *E-mail:* lkeenekendrick@davisart.com
Founded: 1901
Educational resources. Produce digital images from artwork & from other media.
Online catalog(s) available
Membership(s): Visual Resources Association

John J Davis & Associates Consulting Engineers
PO Box 128, Sierra Madre, CA 91025-0128
Tel: 626-355-6909
Key Personnel
Owner & Pres: John J Davis

DaviSound
1504 Sunset Ave, Newberry, SC 29108
Mailing Address: PO Box 521, Newberry, SC 29108-0521
Tel: 803-944-7972 (messages only)
E-mail: davisound@davisound.com; davisound@hotmail.com
Web Site: www.davisound.com
Key Personnel
Founder: Hayne Davis
Founded: 1970

DAWNco
3340 S Lapeer Rd, Orion, MI 48359

Tel: 248-391-9200 *Fax:* 248-391-9206
E-mail: sales@dawnco.com
Web Site: www.dawnco.com
Key Personnel
Dir, Sales & Mktg: John A Joslin
Providing satellite & fiber optic communication products.
Catalog(s), semiannual

DawnSignPress
6130 Nancy Ridge Dr, San Diego, CA 92121-3223
Tel: 858-625-0600 *Toll Free Tel:* 800-549-5350 *Fax:* 858-625-2336
E-mail: contactus@dawnsign.com
Web Site: www.dawnsign.com
Key Personnel
Mktg Dir: Becky Ryan *E-mail:* beckyr@dawnsign.com
Founded: 1979
Creates, develops & publishes American Sign Language (ASL) & Deaf culture-related DVDs & books.
Catalog(s), annual, free

Day Star Productions
1042 S 130 St, Bonner Springs, KS 66012
Tel: 913-422-3400 *Fax:* 913-422-3401
E-mail: daystar@day-star.org
Web Site: www.day-star.org
Key Personnel
Off Mgr: Edwin Bowden

Daylight Productions & Rentals
4700 Sterling Dr, Suite I, Boulder, CO 80301
Tel: 303-440-3334 *Fax:* 303-442-8180
E-mail: info@daylightav.com
Web Site: www.daylightav.com
Key Personnel
Pres: Brian Day
Founded: 2004
Video production, video & AV rentals.
Catalog(s) available
Membership(s): InfoComm International®; Mountain Film & Video Association

Dazian Inc
18 Central Blvd, South Hackensack, NJ 07606
Toll Free Tel: 877-232-9426 *Fax:* 201-641-2728; 201-549-1055
E-mail: info@dazian.com
Web Site: www.dazian.com
Key Personnel
CFO: Chris Diaz
Mktg Dir: Karen Loftus
Founded: 1842
Manufacture, sell, install & rent theatrical drapery.
Online catalog(s) available
Branch Office(s)
10671 Lorne St, Sun Valley, CA 91352 *Toll Free Tel:* 877-432-9426 *Fax:* 818-287-3810; 818-287-3812 (rentals)
2438 Viscount Row, Orlando, FL 32809 *Toll Free Tel:* 888-318-2904
Membership(s): Professional Lighting & Sound Association

Dazor Manufacturing Corp
2079 Congressional, St Louis, MO 63146
Tel: 314-652-2400 *Toll Free Tel:* 800-345-9103 *Fax:* 314-652-2069
E-mail: info@dazor.com
Web Site: www.dazor.com
Founded: 1938
Illumination & magnification tools.

db interactive Inc
PO Box 302064, Austin, TX 78703
Tel: 512-436-8586
E-mail: info@dbinteractive.com
Web Site: dbinteractive.com
Key Personnel
Founder: Dan Brown
Founded: 1999
Web site design.

dbF a Media Company
9683 Charles St, La Plata, MD 20646
Tel: 301-645-6110 *Fax:* 301-392-6111
E-mail: service@dbfmedia.com
Web Site: dbfmedia.com
Key Personnel
Pres: Randy Runyon
Founded: 1981
Audio & video production services.
Membership(s): Business Alliance of Charles County

DBM Communications Inc
606 Baltimore Ave, Suite 200, Towson, MD 21204
Mailing Address: PO Box 20115, Towson, MD 21284
Tel: 410-825-7400 *Fax:* 443-269-0213
Web Site: www.dbmcommunications.com
Key Personnel
Dir, Prodr & Exec Prodr: Douglas B Maddox
Offer production services including film, video, marketing design, print, new media & web.

dbx Professional Products
Subsidiary of Harman International Industries Inc
8760 S Sandy Pkwy, Sandy, UT 84070
Tel: 801-566-8800; 801-568-7660 (cust serv) *Fax:* 801-568-7662
E-mail: customer@dbxpro.com
Web Site: www.dbxpro.com
Key Personnel
Sr Sales Dir: Craig Paller
Founded: 1971
Offer complete equalization & speaker management systems, powered speaker optimizers, direct boxes, zone controllers, equalizers & more.

DCTV, see Downtown Community Television Center (DCTV)

De Nonno Productions Inc (DPI)
7119 Shore Rd, Suite 6-F, Brooklyn, NY 11209
Tel: 917-304-6610
E-mail: info@denonnoproductions.com
Web Site: www.denonnoproductions.com; www.denonnocelebrityphotos.com
Key Personnel
Pres & Dir: Tony De Nonno
Founded: 1978
Video, TV, film, music, photographic production & distribution.
Online catalog(s) available

De Sisti Lighting/Desmar Corp
1011 Rte 22 E, Unit D, Mountainside, NJ 07092
Tel: 908-317-0020 *Fax:* 908-317-0021
Web Site: www.desisti.it
Key Personnel
Gen Mgr: Frank Kosuda *E-mail:* frank_kosuda@desistiusa.com
Founded: 1982
Lighting equipment manufacturer.
Catalog(s) available
Foreign Office(s): De Sisti Lighting SpA, via Cancelliera 10/A, 00041 Albano Laziale, Rome RM, Italy, Contact: Fabio De Sisti *Tel:* (06) 902901 *Fax:* (06) 90231051 *E-mail:* desisti@desisti.it
Membership(s): NAB; Professional Lighting & Sound Association

De Wolfe Music USA
37 W 17 St, 7th fl, Suite E, New York, NY 10011
Tel: 212-259-0524
E-mail: info@dewolfmusicusa.com
Web Site: dewolfemusic.com
Catalog(s) available
Membership(s): MCA-I; NAB

Debbie Regan Locations Ltd
PO Box 353, Old Westbury, NY 11568
Tel: 516-626-1928 *Fax:* 516-626-2337
E-mail: info@debbiereganlocations.com
Web Site: www.debbiereganlocations.com
Key Personnel
Owner & Pres: Debbie Regan
NYC location scout with 20 years experience. 5,000 locations in NYC, NY, NJ & CT. Location library online. Film photo, TV, video & events.

DebsVoice
19 Park Trail, Midhurst, ON L0L 1X0, Canada
Tel: 604-459-5559 (cell)
E-mail: info@debsvoice.com
Web Site: www.debsvoice.com
Key Personnel
Owner & Voiceover Talent: Debbie Munro
Passionate production company for audio & video needs. International full-time voice talent & voice instructor & motivational speaker.
Membership(s): AMPIA; WIFT

DecisionOne
426 W Lancaster Ave, Devon, PA 19333
Tel: 610-296-6000 *Toll Free Tel:* 800-767-2876; 800-777-8800 (cust serv); 888-287-9202 (sales); 800-554-5179 (CN) *Fax:* 610-296-2910
Web Site: www.decisionone.com
Key Personnel
CEO: Nick Sharma
CFO & EVP: Marc Krasuski
Branch Office(s)
25 Kinnear Ct, Richmond Hill, ON L4B 1H9, Canada *Toll Free Tel:* 800-554-5179 *Fax:* 905-882-1579

Deck Hand Inc
1905 Victory Blvd, Suite 8, Glendale, CA 91201
Tel: 818-557-8403 *Fax:* 818-557-8406
E-mail: info@deckhand.com
Web Site: www.deckhand.com
Key Personnel
Owner: Joseph Mealey
Founded: 2002
Digital filmmaking equipment rentals.

Dedotec USA Inc
48 Sheffield Business Park, Ashley Falls, MA 01222
Tel: 413-229-2550 *Fax:* 413-229-2556
E-mail: info@dedolight.com
Web Site: www.dedolight.com
Key Personnel
Pres: Paul Tepper
Manufacture Dedolight precision lighting instruments.
Catalog(s) available
Membership(s): NAB

Deerfield Laboratory Inc
524 San Anselmo Ave, Suite 136, San Anselmo, CA 94960
Tel: 650-632-4090 *Fax:* 650-632-4091
E-mail: info@deerfieldlab.com
Web Site: www.deerfieldlab.com
Key Personnel
CEO & Pres: Daniel Krakauer *E-mail:* danielk@deerfieldlab.com
Founded: 1995
Video isolation transformer.

Definitive Technology LLP
11433 Cronridge Dr, Suite K, Owings Mills, MD 21117-2294
Tel: 410-363-7148 *Toll Free Tel:* 800-228-7148 *Fax:* 410-363-9998
E-mail: info@definitivetech.com
Web Site: www.definitivetech.com
Key Personnel
Cust Serv Mgr: Chet Pelkowski *Tel:* 410-363-7148 ext 5562 *E-mail:* chet.pelkowski@definitivetech.com
Founded: 1990
Manufacturer of high end loudspeakers.
Catalog(s) available
Membership(s): Consumer Electronics Association; Custom Electronic Design & Installation Association

Deja View Video
417 S Eldorado St, San Mateo, CA 94402-1374
Tel: 650-343-8899
Web Site: www.dejaview.com
Key Personnel
Owner: William Krone
Producing video programs & distributor of instructional videos.
Catalog(s) available
Membership(s): CLVS; NABET-CWA; SMPTE

deKramer Productions Inc
515 Western Ave, Petaluma, CA 94952
Tel: 707-765-0888
E-mail: dekramer@sonic.net
Web Site: www.dekramerproductions.com
Key Personnel
Pres: Peter deKramer *E-mail:* peter@dekramerproductions.com
Founded: 1978
Stage, film & video direction.

Delaware Audio Visual Inc, see Indigo Productions

Delicate Electronics Sales Inc
Subsidiary of Delicate Productions Inc
874 Verdulera St, Camarillo, CA 93010
Tel: 805-484-8139 *Toll Free Tel:* 800-350-3555 *Fax:* 805-388-1037
Web Site: www.delicatesales.com
Key Personnel
Dir & Cust Serv Mgr: Tom Akoury *E-mail:* tom@delicate.com
Sales Mgr: Bill Sage *E-mail:* bill@delicate.com
Cust Serv: Coty Shipe *E-mail:* coty@delicate.com
Electronics distribution.

deLise Studios
83 Park Dr, Cherry Hill, NJ 08002-3002
Tel: 856-616-2867
E-mail: info@delisestudios.com
Web Site: www.delisestudios.com
Key Personnel
Owner: Louis deLise
Composer of concert music, arranger & conductor for pop records, film composer & teacher at Boyer College of Music & Dance, Temple University & Rowan University.

Delmark Records
4121 N Rockwell, Chicago, IL 60618
Tel: 773-539-5001 *Fax:* 773-539-5004
E-mail: delmark@delmark.com; jazzmart@delmark.com
Web Site: www.delmark.com
Key Personnel
Prop: Bob Koester
Founded: 1953
Recording studio & record company. Provide sound recordings - magnetic & digital.
Catalog(s), quarterly
Sales Office(s): Jazz Record Mart, 27 E Illinois, Chicago, IL 60611 *Tel:* 312-222-1467 *Fax:* 312-222-0497 *E-mail:* info@jazzmart.com *Web Site:* jazzmart.com

Delta Consolidated Industries Inc
Division of Apex Tool Group
14600 York Rd, Suite A, Sparks, MD 21152
Toll Free Tel: 800-643-0084 (cust serv) *Fax:* 870-935-4994 *Toll Free Fax:* 877-356-4081
Web Site: www.deltastorage.com; www.apextoolgroup.com
Catalog(s) available
Membership(s): National Truck Equipment Association; Specialty Equipment Market Association; Specialty Tools & Fasteners Distributors Association

Delta Electronics Inc
5730 General Washington Dr, Alexandria, VA 22312
Mailing Address: PO Box 11268, Alexandria, VA 22312
Tel: 703-354-3350 *Toll Free Tel:* 800-833-5828 *Fax:* 703-354-0216
E-mail: sales@deltaelectronics.com
Web Site: www.deltaelectronics.com
Key Personnel
VP, Mktg: Joseph Novak *E-mail:* jsnovak@deltaelectronics.com
Founded: 1962
Manufacture test equipment, high power RF switches & meters & operating impedence bridges.
Catalog(s) available

Deluxe Laboratories Inc
5433 Fernwood Ave, Hollywood, CA 90027
Tel: 323-960-3600 *Fax:* 323-960-7016
Web Site: www.bydeluxe.com
Key Personnel
CEO & Pres: Cyril Drabinsky
VP, Sales: Bob Bianco
Founded: 1919
Photo processing.
Catalog(s) available
Membership(s): SMPTE

Deluxe Media Services
235 Pegasus Ave, Northvale, NJ 07647
Tel: 201-767-3800 *Fax:* 201-784-2769
Web Site: www.bydeluxe.com
Key Personnel
SVP, Opers: Andre Macaluso
Branch Office(s)
2400 W Empire Ave, Burbank, CA 91504 *Tel:* 818-565-3600

Demco Inc
4810 Forest Run Rd, Madison, WI 53704
Mailing Address: PO Box 7488, Madison, WI 53707-7488
Tel: 608-241-1201 *Toll Free Tel:* 800-962-4463; 800-279-1586 *Toll Free Fax:* 800-245-1329
Web Site: www.demco.com
Key Personnel
Pres: Nedra Sadorf *E-mail:* president@demco.com
Founded: 1905
Catalog(s) available
Membership(s): NOPA

Denecke Inc
25209 Ave Tibbitts, Valencia, CA 91355
Tel: 661-607-0206 *Fax:* 661-257-2236
E-mail: info@denecke.com
Web Site: www.denecke.com
Key Personnel
Off Mgr: Kimberly Parra
Catalog(s) available

Denver Media Center
3853 S Broadway, Englewood, CO 80113
Tel: 303-872-9993
Web Site: denvermediacenter.com
Key Personnel
Founder & Exec Prodr: Blaine Howerton *Tel:* 303-872-9993 ext 101 *E-mail:* blaine@denvermediacenter.com; Whei Wong
Founder & Chief Ed: Nick Arnold
Founded: 2013
Full service audio & video recording studio. Mixing, mastering, replicating & distribution services, video production equipment rental & closed captioning services.

Department of Education Resources
Division of National Gallery of Art
2000-B S Club Dr, Landover, MD 20785
Tel: 202-842-6280 *Fax:* 202-842-6935
E-mail: edresources@nga.gov
Web Site: www.nga.gov; www.nga.gov/education
Key Personnel
Head, Dept of Educ Resources: Leo Kasun
Catalog(s), free

Derksen (USA) Inc
4934 Pathway Ct, Fair Oaks, CA 95628
Tel: 916-903-7275 *Fax:* 916-903-7022
E-mail: info@derksen.com
Web Site: www.derksen.com
Distributor of Derksen line of projection systems.
Catalog(s) available

Deschamps Recording Studios Ltd, see Wanted! Sound + Picture

Design & Production Inc
7110 Rainwater Place, Lorton, VA 22079
Tel: 703-550-8640 *Fax:* 703-339-0296
E-mail: email@d-and-p.com
Web Site: www.d-and-p.com
Key Personnel
SVP: L Sue Lepp *E-mail:* lslepp@d-and-p.com
Membership(s): EDPA; InfoComm International®; NSCA

Design Audio Visual Inc
195-A Central Ave, Farmingdale, NY 11735
Tel: 631-694-3334 *Toll Free Tel:* 800-886-1328 *Fax:* 631-694-3549
Web Site: www.design-av.com
Key Personnel
Pres: Chuck Weinstein *E-mail:* chuck@design-av.com
Founded: 1981
Catalog(s), rental & sales
Membership(s): ATD; HSMAI; IABC; InfoComm International®; International Special Events Society; MCA-I; MPI

Design FX Audio
PO Box 491087, Los Angeles, CA 90049
Tel: 818-843-6555 *Toll Free Tel:* 800-441-4415 *Fax:* 818-562-6978
Web Site: www.dfxaudio.com
Key Personnel
Owner: Gary Ladinsky *E-mail:* gary@dfxaudio.com
Rentals Dept Mgr: Tony Pinnick *E-mail:* tony@dfxaudio.com
Audio equipment rentals, sales & services for the recording, film & TV industries.

Design Media
650 Alabama St, Suite 203, San Francisco, CA 94110-2038
Tel: 415-641-4848 *Fax:* 415-641-5245
E-mail: info@designmedia.com
Web Site: www.designmedia.com

Key Personnel
CEO & Pres: Pamela May *E-mail:* pmay@designmedia.com
Multimedia solutions for business, education & government.

Designomotion
67 E 11 St, Suite 324, New York, NY 10003
Tel: 917-532-0738
E-mail: info@designomotion.com
Web Site: designomotion.com
Key Personnel
Founder & Creative Dir: Joseph Silver *E-mail:* jsilver@designomotion.com
Founded: 2001
Motion graphics production.

Desktop Video Systems
9052 Parkhill, Lenexa, KS 66215
Tel: 913-782-8888 *Toll Free Tel:* 800-662-6901 *Fax:* 913-492-6908
E-mail: sales@desktopvideosystems.com
Web Site: www.desktopvideosystems.com
Key Personnel
Owner: Tom O'Connor
Professional video equipment sales - nonlinear editing equipment manufacture.

Destiny Recordings, see Inner Traditions International

Developmental Studies Center
1250 53 St, Suite 3, Emeryville, CA 94608
Tel: 510-533-0213 *Toll Free Tel:* 800-666-7270 *Fax:* 510-464-3670
E-mail: info@devstu.org; customer_service@devstu.org
Web Site: www.devstu.org
Key Personnel
Pres: Frank Snyder, PhD *Tel:* 510-533-0213 ext 237 *E-mail:* frank_snyder@devstu.org
Dir, Dissemination & Mktg: Jan Berman *Tel:* 510-533-0213 ext 303 *E-mail:* jan_berman@devstu.org
Founded: 1980
Educational products.
Catalog(s) available

Devlin Video International
1501 Broadway, Suite 408, New York, NY 10036
Tel: 212-391-1313 *Fax:* 212-391-2744
Web Site: www.devlinvideo.com
Key Personnel
EVP: Cari Davis *E-mail:* cdavis@devlinvideo.com
Video production services.
Catalog(s) available

DG FastChannel, see Extreme Reach Inc

DG Generation Inc, see Extreme Reach Inc

DG Mijo
Formerly MIJO Thunder North Broadcast Services Ltd
635 E Queen St, East Toronto, ON M4M 1G4, Canada
Tel: 416-964-7539 *Toll Free Tel:* 800-463-MIJO (463-6456) *Fax:* 416-964-5920
Web Site: www.mijo.com
Key Personnel
Mgr: Willie Maxwell
Founded: 1978
Film & video tape storage & archival.

DGI-Invisuals LLC
101 Billerica Ave, Bldg 6, North Billerica, MA 01862
Toll Free Tel: 800-344-0432 *Fax:* 781-270-3663
E-mail: sales@dgi-invisuals.com
Web Site: www.dgi-invisuals.com
Key Personnel
Owner & Pres: James Dadmun
Gen Mgr: Glen Fairbanks *E-mail:* gfairbanks@dgi-invisuals.com
Founded: 1994
Large format digital printing & photo imaging.
Brochure(s) available
Membership(s): AIE™

DH Satellite
Division of Design Homes Inc
600 N Marquette Rd, Prairie du Chien, WI 53821
Mailing Address: PO Box 239, Prairie du Chien, WI 53821-0239
Tel: 608-326-8406 *Toll Free Tel:* 800-627-9443 *Fax:* 608-326-4233
E-mail: dhsat@mhtc.net
Web Site: www.dhsatellite.com
Key Personnel
VP: Michael Doll *E-mail:* mdoll@mhtc.net
Sales: Cindy Wille *E-mail:* cwille@dhsatellite.com
Manufacture satellite equipment.
Catalog(s) available

Dialect Accent Specialists Inc
PO Box 44, Lyndonville, VT 05851-0044
Toll Free Tel: 800-753-1016
E-mail: dasinc@kingcon.com; info@dialectaccentspecialists.com
Web Site: www.dialectaccentspecialists.com; www.learnaccent.com
Key Personnel
Mgr: Peggy Voakes
Mail order educational audiotapes, booklets & CDs teaching learning/losing accents, dialects & general speech improvement.

Diamond Dreams Music Productions
North Ocean County, Carbon Canyon, Chino Hills, CA 91709
Tel: 909-393-6120 *Fax:* 909-606-5779
E-mail: info@diamonddreamsmusic.com
Web Site: www.diamonddreamsmusic.com
Key Personnel
Owner & Prodr: Raphael DeGiorgio *E-mail:* raphael@diamonddreamsmusic.com
Founded: 1999
Membership(s): ASCAP

Diamond Studios
Woods Point 1, 1855 Data Dr, Suite 255, Hoover, AL 35244
Tel: 205-987-2121 *Fax:* 205-987-2128
Web Site: www.tvstuff.com
Key Personnel
CEO: Joe Miele *Tel:* 205-987-2121 ext 3
Pres & Exec Prodr: Barbara Fowler *Tel:* 205-987-2121 ext 2
Founded: 1982
HD & web video, TV, multimedia & technology company. Viral, corporate, marketing, training & orientation videos.
Catalog(s) available

Diaquest
Subsidiary of Advanced Systems Group
5808 Vallejo St, Emeryville, CA 94608
Tel: 510-547-4544 *Fax:* 510-654-8370
E-mail: sales@diaquest.com; support@diaquest.com
Web Site: www.diaquest.com
Key Personnel
Pres: David Van Hoy
Founded: 1982
Develop mission critical software for the video, film & broadcast industries. Develop software as an OEM for several manufacturers as well as custom software tools for a variety of clients. Also provide professional-level support of related software & hardware products.
Online catalog(s) available
Membership(s): SMPTE; Special Interest Group on Computer Graphics

Dickensheets Design Associates
12335 Hymeadow Dr, Suite 200, Austin, TX 78750
Tel: 512-331-8977 *Toll Free Tel:* 800-545-5734
Web Site: www.dickensheets.com
Key Personnel
VP: Ken Dickensheets *E-mail:* ken@dickensheets.com
Founded: 1985
Design of AV systems, acoustics, noise control & IT.
Membership(s): AES; ASA; NCAC; NSCA; SMPTE

DiCon Fiberoptics Inc
1689 Regatta Blvd, Richmond, CA 94804
Tel: 510-620-5000; 510-620-5200 (sales) *Fax:* 510-620-4100; 510-620-4102 (sales)
E-mail: info@diconfiber.com; sales@diconfiber.com
Web Site: www.diconfiberoptics.com
Key Personnel
CEO & Dir: Ho-Shang Lee
Dir, Mfg & Opers: Paul Lo
Founded: 1986
Fiber optic manufacturer.
Catalog(s) available
Foreign Office(s): 6F 248-28 Hsing Shen Rd, Cheng-Jeng District, Kaohsiung, Taiwan *Tel:* (07) 815-8055 *Fax:* (07) 815-8456

Dielectric Communications
Division of Sinclair Broadcast Group Inc
22 Tower Rd, Raymond, ME 04071
Tel: 207-655-4555 *Toll Free Tel:* 800-341-9678 *Fax:* 207-655-8174
E-mail: dcsales@dielectric.com
Web Site: www.dielectric.com
Key Personnel
Dir, Busn Devt: Kim Savage *E-mail:* kim.savage@dielectric.com
Founded: 1942
Manufacturer of radio equipment.
Catalog(s) available

Diemer Amp & Keyboard Repair
12814 Landale St, Studio City, CA 91604-1351
Tel: 818-762-0804
Web Site: bustedgear.com
Key Personnel
Owner: Richard Diemer *E-mail:* rich@bustedgear.com
Catalog(s) available

The Richard Diercks Co Inc
3140 Harbor Lane N, Suite 223, Minneapolis, MN 55447
Tel: 763-231-3303 *Fax:* 763-231-3307
E-mail: rdiercks@diercks.com
Web Site: www.dvdauthor.com
Key Personnel
Pres: Richard Diercks

Different Fur Recording Ltd
3470 19 St, San Francisco, CA 94110
Tel: 415-864-1967; 415-828-4060 (bookings) *Fax:* 415-864-1965
Web Site: www.differentfurstudios.com
Key Personnel
Owner: Patrick Brown *E-mail:* patrick@differentfurstudios.com
Engr: Nic Pope *E-mail:* nic@differentfurstudios.com
Studio Mgr: Lindsey Cundiff *E-mail:* lindsey@differentfurstudios.com

Recording studio.
Brochure(s) available

Digi-matics
4472 Spring Valley Rd, Dallas, TX 75244
Tel: 469-644-1390
Web Site: www.digi-matics.com
Key Personnel
Owner & Pres: Josh Hurst *E-mail:* josh@digi-matics.com
Broadcast graphics, animation, web development & video production.

Digi Sign Design LLC
Subsidiary of K&R All Media Productions Inc
28533 Greenfield Rd, Suite 2, Southfield, MI 48076
Tel: 248-569-5422
Web Site: www.digisigndesign.com
Key Personnel
Pres: Ken Glaza
Outside & inside digital signage design & networking.
Online catalog(s) available

Digimation
250 International Pkwy, Suite 320, Lake Mary, FL 32746
Tel: 407-833-0600 *Toll Free Tel:* 800-854-4496 *Fax:* 813-283-4906
E-mail: sales@digimation.com
Web Site: www.digimation.com
Key Personnel
CEO: David Avigkos
Founded: 1992
Develops the industry's most realistic virtual training, interactive marketing & serious game solutions. Using our own proprietary tools & popular 3D technologies such as CryENGINE 3 & Unity, we develop maintenance training solutions, virtual environments, small arms training & work instructions on desktop, laptops & tablet devices such as the iPad.

Digital Art Video Inc
8506 60 Ave, 3rd fl, Middle Village, NY 11379-5430
Tel: 718-457-5388
Web Site: www.digital-art.com
Key Personnel
Founder & Pres: Kim E Wang
Full service film & video production & post-production.

Digital Audio Labs
1266 Park Rd, Chanhassen, MN 55317
Tel: 952-401-7700 *Fax:* 952-401-7725
E-mail: sales@digitalaudio.com
Web Site: www.digitalaudio.com
Key Personnel
Pres: Ted Klein
Opers Mgr: Jeff Gedden
Founded: 1988
Developer & manufacturer of Livemix personal monitoring system, PowerShape integrated amplifiers, Stompblox modular pedalboards & CardDeluxe.
Membership(s): InfoComm International®; NAMM, the National Association of Music Merchants

Digital Comm Link Inc
10450 W State Rd 84, Davie, FL 33324-4206
Tel: 954-236-2993 *Toll Free Tel:* 877-532-5438 *Fax:* 954-236-3633
E-mail: booking@dclinc.net
Web Site: www.dclinc.net
Key Personnel
Engr: Michael Kohler *E-mail:* mkohler@dclinc.net
Sales: Said Khan *E-mail:* skhan@dclinc.net
Founded: 1995
Full service video, voice & data transmission company. Two satellite trucks & 6 studio live shot & play-out facilities.
Branch Office(s)
3401 S Congress Ave, Boynton Beach, FL 33426
2140 S Dixie Hwy, Suite 301, Miami, FL 33133-2463
3435 Tenth St N, Suite 101, Naples, FL 34103-3815
246 E Sixth Ave, Tallahassee, FL 32303
1034 S Brentwood Blvd, 17th fl, St Louis, MO 63117
701 Sawdust Rd, Unit 2, The Woodlands, TX 77380

Digital Designs
Division of Resonance Inc
1141 NW First St, Oklahoma City, OK 73106
Tel: 405-239-2800 *Fax:* 405-239-7100
E-mail: ddtech@ddaudio.com
Web Site: www.ddaudio.com
Key Personnel
Engr: Jassa Langford
Founded: 1986
Car audio systems.
Catalog(s) available
Membership(s): NAMM, the National Association of Music Merchants

Digital Display Solutions Inc
12081 Starcrest, San Antonio, TX 78216
Tel: 210-404-1233; 210-523-7368 (rentals) *Fax:* 210-979-6585
E-mail: lharbert@ddssa.com
Web Site: www.ddssa.com
Key Personnel
Pres: Roger Harbert *E-mail:* rharbert@ddssa.com
Founded: 2001

Digital Film Studios
11800 Sheldon St, Unit C/D, Sun Valley, CA 91352
Tel: 818-771-0019 *Fax:* 818-351-1155
E-mail: info@digitalfilmstudios.com
Web Site: www.digitalfilmstudios.com
Key Personnel
Owner: Ted Hayash
Owner & Mgr: Dan Toback
Complete lighting, grip & small stage rental.

Digital Force
149 Madison Ave, 12th fl, New York, NY 10016
Tel: 212-252-9300 *Toll Free Tel:* 877-DISC-USA (347-2872) *Fax:* 212-252-7377
E-mail: frontdesk@digitalforce.com
Web Site: www.digitalforce.com
Key Personnel
Pres: Jerome Bunke *E-mail:* jerry@digitalforce.com
Founded: 1994
Specialize in media replication & duplication.
Membership(s): The Recording Academy

Digital FX Inc
6010 Perkins Rd, Suite B, Baton Rouge, LA 70808
Tel: 225-763-6010 *Toll Free Tel:* 888-898-6010 *Fax:* 225-763-6059
E-mail: info@digitalfx.tv; rentals@digitalfx.tv
Web Site: www.digitalfx.tv
Key Personnel
Founder & Pres: Greg Milneck
Full service AV production company.
Membership(s): MCA-I; PPA

Digital Image Studios LLC
23400 Commerce Dr, Farmington Hills, MI 48335
Tel: 248-477-5600 *Toll Free Tel:* 888-434-7839 *Fax:* 248-477-4322
Web Site: www.dimage.com
Key Personnel
VP, Sales & Mktg: Chuck Kaiser *Tel:* 248-477-5600 ext 103 *E-mail:* chuck@dimage.com
Founded: 1990

Digital Jungle
6363 Santa Monica Blvd, Hollywood, CA 90038
Tel: 323-962-0867 *Fax:* 323-962-9960
E-mail: info@digijungle.com
Web Site: www.digijungle.com
4K, 2K, HD & SD post-production services for film, television & commercials-servicing studios, networks & independent content providers.

Digital Lighting Systems Inc
12302 SW 128 Ct, Suite 105, Miami, FL 33186
Tel: 305-969-8442 *Fax:* 305-969-8675
E-mail: info@digitallighting.com; sales@digitallighting.com
Web Site: www.digitallighting.com
Key Personnel
Pres: Elie Khawand
Founded: 1978
Lighting systems & laser projection.
Catalog(s) available

Digital Media West
573 Jones St, Ventura, CA 93003
Tel: 805-559-1318
Web Site: www.digitalmediawest.com
Key Personnel
Pres: Gary Guenot *E-mail:* garyg@digitalmediawest.com
Media duplication services & authoring.

Digital Music Corp
3165 Coffey Lane, Santa Rosa, CA 95403
Tel: 707-545-0600 *Fax:* 707-545-9777
E-mail: info@voodoolab.com
Web Site: www.voodoolab.com
Key Personnel
Pres & Mktg Mgr: Josh Fiden
Sales Mgr: Jessica Luther
Founded: 1986
Guitar effects & electronics.

Digital Outpost
2772 Loker Ave W, Carlsbad, CA 92010
Tel: 760-431-3575 *Toll Free Tel:* 800-464-6434 *Fax:* 760-431-8717
E-mail: info@dop.com; sales@dop.com
Web Site: www.dop.com
Key Personnel
Pres: Brian Douglas
Founded: 1996
DVD authoring, post-production facility, full production, multimedia design, encoding house & video for the web.

Digital Projection
55 Chastain Rd, Suite 115, Kennesaw, GA 30144
Tel: 770-420-1350 *Fax:* 770-420-1360
E-mail: contact@digitalprojection.com
Web Site: www.digitalprojection.com
Key Personnel
VP, Mktg: Michael Bridwell *E-mail:* mbridwell@digitalprojection.com
Founded: 1987
Projection equipment manufacturer.
Membership(s): Custom Electronic Design & Installation Association; InfoComm International®

Digital Rain LLC
640 Wilson St, Danville, IN 46122
Tel: 317-563-1208
E-mail: avmarket@digitalrainllc.com
Web Site: www.digitalrainllc.com
Key Personnel
Owner: Rodney A Myers

Founded: 1998
Video & TV production, integration & consultation.

Digital Services Recording Studios
1601 S Cherry St, Tomball, TX 77375
Tel: 281-290-8500 *Fax:* 281-290-8510
E-mail: studio@dsrecordings.com
Web Site: www.dsrecordings.com
Key Personnel
Owner: Charlie Ray *E-mail:* charlie@dsrecordings.com
Full service recording, mixing, mastering & production services.
Membership(s): AES

Digital Video Arts
7775 Belfort Pkwy, Jacksonville, FL 32256
Tel: 904-281-1001 *Toll Free Tel:* 888-340-1010 *Fax:* 904-281-0051
Web Site: www.digitalvideoarts.com
Key Personnel
Pres, Prodn: Clark Fivek
VP & Dir, Creative Design: Britt McTammany
Founded: 1994
Musical scoring & design.

Digital Video Productions
257 Federal Rd, Brookfield, CT 06804
Tel: 203-743-7663 *Fax:* 203-743-1658
E-mail: info@dvpllc.com
Web Site: www.dvpllc.com
Key Personnel
Owner: Paul Ayoub *E-mail:* paul@dvpllc.com
Founded: 1995
Video production services, including HD.
Membership(s): WEVA

Digital Video Systems Inc
3270 Executive Way, Miramar, FL 33025
Tel: 954-239-4410 *Fax:* 954-239-4485
E-mail: info@digitalvideosystems.net
Web Site: www.digitalvideosystems.net
Key Personnel
VP, Sales: Jorge J Necuze
Founded: 1975
Broadcast, satellite & AV systems integrator.
Online catalog(s) available
Membership(s): InfoComm International®; NAB; SMPTE

Digital Zoetrope Productions
1902 Oak St, Melbourne, FL 32901
Tel: 321-821-7404 *Fax:* 321-821-2287
Web Site: digitalzoetrope.com
Key Personnel
Owner: Michael Misconi
Full service video production company & advertising agency. Video production equipment rental.

DigiTech
Division of Harman Signal Processing
10653 S River Front Pkwy, Suite 300, South Jordan, UT 84095
Tel: 801-566-8800 *Toll Free Tel:* 800-999-9363
E-mail: support@digitech.com
Web Site: www.digitech.com
Key Personnel
Mktg Dir: Jason Kunz
Exec Admin: Brenda Perez
Manufacturer of guitar products.
Membership(s): AES; NAMM, the National Association of Music Merchants; NSCA

Digitron Electronics
7801 E Telegraph Rd, Montebello, CA 90640
Tel: 323-629-4518 *Fax:* 323-887-0891
E-mail: repairs@digitronelectronics.com
Web Site: digitronelectronics.com
Founded: 1991
Repairs for broadcast & film, musicians & DJs, studio & event production, projectors, CCTV cameras, industrial & medical imaging equipment.

DimcoGray Co
900 Dimco Way, Centerville, OH 45458-2710
Tel: 937-433-7600 *Fax:* 937-433-0520
E-mail: dgsales@dimcogray.com; dginfo@dimcogray.com
Web Site: www.dimcogray.com
Founded: 1924
Custom molded thermoplastic parts.
Catalog(s) available
Membership(s): Photo Marketing Association

Direct Broadcast Services Inc (DBS)
711 Executive Blvd, Suite F, Valley Cottage, NY 10989
Tel: 845-267-2800 *Fax:* 845-267-2123
E-mail: dbs@directbroadcast.com
Web Site: www.directbroadcast.com
Key Personnel
Pres: Leo Rosenberg
Founded: 1988
Transportable satellite uplinking & downlinking (truck & fly-away), microwave (news van & portable), multichannel laser (canobeam) & portable fiber optics.
Catalog(s) available
Membership(s): NAB

Direct Cinema Ltd Inc
PO Box 10003, Santa Monica, CA 90410-1003
Tel: 310-636-8200 *Toll Free Tel:* 800-525-0000 *Fax:* 310-636-8228
E-mail: dclvideo@aol.com
Web Site: www.directcinema.com
Key Personnel
Pres: Mitchell W Block
Founded: 1974
Video production & rentals.
Catalog(s) available
Membership(s): AECT; ALA; American Association for the Arts; AMPAS; Consortium of College & University Media Centers; National Association of Media & Technology Centers; NFM; University Film & Video Association

Direct Current Video Productions
1928 E Highland, Suite F-104-448, Phoenix, AZ 85016
Tel: 602-263-7717 *Fax:* 602-263-7719
Web Site: www.directcurrentproductions.com
Key Personnel
Owner: Ginny Temple *E-mail:* ginny@directcurrentproductions.com
Founded: 1988
Complete video production services for television, corporations & independent producers.
Membership(s): Arizona Production Association; MCA-I

Direct Images Interactive Inc
1933 Davis St, Suite 308, San Leandro, CA 94577
Tel: 510-613-8299
E-mail: info@directimages.com
Web Site: www.directimages.com
Key Personnel
Prodr: Bill Knowland
Founded: 1988
Multimedia design & video production.

Directed Electronics
One Viper Way, Vista, CA 92081
Tel: 760-598-6200 *Toll Free Tel:* 800-876-0800 *Fax:* 760-598-6400
E-mail: customerfeedback@directed.com
Web Site: www.directed.com
Key Personnel
COO: Julien Joly
Pres: Michael Simmons
SVP, Global Sales: Glen R Busse
Founded: 1982
Branch Office(s)
2750 Alphonse Gariepy, Lachine, QC H8T 3M2, Canada *Toll Free Tel:* 800-361-7271
E-mail: customers@directed.ca

Disc Makers
Division of Audio & Video Labs Inc
7905 N Rte 130, Pennsauken, NJ 08110-1402
Tel: 856-663-9030 *Toll Free Tel:* 800-468-9353 *Fax:* 856-661-3450
E-mail: info@discmakers.com
Web Site: www.discmakers.com
Key Personnel
SVP, Sales: David Olinsky
Founded: 1946
CD & DVD manufacturer.
Catalog(s) available
Branch Office(s)
4425 W Riverside Dr, Suite 204, Burbank, CA 91505 *Toll Free Tel:* 800-468-9353 *Fax:* 856-661-3450
560 W Washington Blvd, Suite 410, Chicago, IL 60661 *Toll Free Tel:* 800-468-9355
36 Prospect St, Cambridge, MA 02139
16 W 18 St, New York, NY 10011-5504, Contact: Jeff Epstein
1305 16 Ave S, 1st fl, Nashville, TN 37212
701 Richmond Ave, Suite 150, Houston, TX 77006
16300 Christensen Rd, Suite 310, Tukwila, WA 98188, Contact: Mimi Crocker
Ave Blvd Arturo Cadillo, EB18, Levittown, Toa Baja 00949-2701, Puerto Rico, Contact: David Rodriguez
Membership(s): Content Delivery & Storage Association; The Recording Academy; SPARS

Discovery Education - Chicago
Division of Discovery Communications LLC
111 E Wacker Dr, Suite 3000, Chicago, IL 60601
Web Site: www.discoveryeducation.com
Key Personnel
SVP, Educ Partnerships: Coni Rechner
Catalog(s) available

Discovery Education - Los Angeles
Division of Discovery Communications LLC
10100 Santa Monica Blvd, Suite 1500, Los Angeles, CA 90067
Tel: 310-551-1611 *Fax:* 310-551-1684
Web Site: www.discoveryeducation.com
Catalog(s) available

Discovery Education - Silver Spring
Division of Discovery Communications LLC
One Discovery Place, Silver Spring, MD 20910
Toll Free Tel: 800-323-9084 *Fax:* 847-328-6706
Web Site: discoveryeducation.com
Key Personnel
CEO: Bill Goodwyn
SVP: Scott Kinney
Video(s), K-8

Discovery Education - South Burlington
Division of Discovery Communications LLC
PO Box 3400, Lancaster, PA 17604
Toll Free Tel: 888-892-3484 *Toll Free Fax:* 877-324-6830
E-mail: education_info@discovery.com
Web Site: teacherstore.discovery.com
Catalog(s) available

Discovery Toys
3037 Independence Dr, Suite G, Livermore, CA 94551

Tel: 925-606-2600 *Toll Free Tel:* 800-341-TOYS (341-8697, sales) *Fax:* 925-447-0626
E-mail: contact@discoverytoys.net
Web Site: www.discoverytoys.net
Key Personnel
VP, Sales: Leslie Boyd-Bradley
Founded: 1978
Catalog(s) available

Disk Productions
1100 Perkins Rd, Baton Rouge, LA 70802
Tel: 225-343-5438
E-mail: disk_productions@yahoo.com
Key Personnel
Owner: Joe Decker
Audio production studio.
Membership(s): AES; American Advertising Association

DiskFaktory Direct
Division of Innovative Diversified Technologies Inc
17173 Gillette Ave, Suite A, Irvine, CA 92614
Tel: 949-477-1700 *Toll Free Tel:* 888-464-9664
E-mail: customercare@diskfaktory.com
Web Site: www.direct.diskfaktory.com
Founded: 1997
Catalog(s) available

Display Devices
10828 Hwy 93, Golden, CO 80403
Tel: 303-412-0399 *Toll Free Tel:* 877-862-6865 *Fax:* 303-412-9346
E-mail: sales@displaydevices.com
Web Site: www.displaydevices.com
Key Personnel
Founder & Owner: Mervin Perkins *E-mail:* merv@displaydevices.com
Gen Mgr: Eric Perkins *Tel:* 303-412-0399 ext 19 *E-mail:* eric@displaydevices.com
Mktg: Lawrence Brinton *Tel:* 303-412-0399 ext 48 *E-mail:* lrb@displaydevices.com
Manufacturer of AV products.
Catalog(s) available
Membership(s): Custom Electronic Design & Installation Association; InfoComm International®; NAB; NSCA

Display Systems International
2214 Hanselman Ave, Saskatoon, SK S7L 6A4, Canada
Tel: 306-934-6884 *Toll Free Tel:* 877-934-6884 *Fax:* 306-934-6447
E-mail: sales@displaysystemsintl.com
Web Site: www.displaysystemsintl.com
Key Personnel
Owner, CEO & Pres: Dale Lemke
Founded: 1983
Catalog(s) available

Les Disques Artiste
154 Grande Cote, Rosemere, QC J7A 1H3, Canada
Tel: 450-437-7625
Web Site: www.disquesartiste.com
Key Personnel
Pres: Paul Levesque
Prod Mgr: Claude Marcheterre
Independent record label.
Online catalog(s) available
Membership(s): ADISQ; The Society of Composers, Authors and Music Publishers of Canada; UDA

Distribution Video & Audio (DVA)
15232 US 19 N, Suite B, Clearwater, FL 33764
Tel: 727-447-4147 *Toll Free Tel:* 800-683-4147 *Fax:* 727-441-3069
Web Site: www.dvaspecial.com
Key Personnel
CFO & Pres: Brad Kugler *E-mail:* brad@dva.com
Secy & Treas: Gina Kugler *E-mail:* gina@dva.com
Founded: 1988
Full service media distributor.
Catalog(s), monthly, free
Membership(s): ALA; Entertainment Merchants Association; Public Library Association

Scott Dittrich Films, see Action Sports/All Stock

Diversified Imaging Supply
333 Alondra Blvd, Gardena, CA 90248
Key Personnel
Pres: Darrell Benton
Founded: 1988
Wholesale distributor of photo, video, digital film, equipment & supplies.
Catalog(s) available
CD-ROM catalog(s) available
Online catalog(s) available
Membership(s): AIE™; PPA; PPC

Diversified Systems Inc
363 Market St, Kenilworth, NJ 07033
Tel: 908-245-4833 *Fax:* 908-245-0011
E-mail: info@divsystems.com
Web Site: www.divsystems.com
Key Personnel
COO & EVP: Kevin Collins *E-mail:* kcollins@divsystems.com
Pres: Fred D'Alessandro
Founded: 1993
AV design integration.
Branch Office(s)
3275 Edward Ave, Santa Clara, CA 95054 *Tel:* 408-969-1972
23475 Rockhaven Way, Suite 140, Dulles, VA 20166 *Tel:* 703-661-8870
4000 Aurora Ave N, Suite 225, Seattle, WA 98103 *Tel:* 206-547-0251
Membership(s): InfoComm International®; NAB; SBE; SMPTE

Division Camera
7022 W Sunset Blvd, Hollywood, CA 90028
Tel: 323-465-7700 *Fax:* 323-293-2773
E-mail: rent@divisioncamera.com
Web Site: divisioncamera.com
Founded: 2004
Rents digital cinema cameras, lenses & support technology for productions of all sizes.
Branch Office(s)
10000 Celtic Dr, Suite 600, Baton Rouge, LA 70809 *Tel:* 225-308-9990 *Fax:* 225-308-9993 *E-mail:* gayle@divisioncamera.com

Dixie Theatre Service & Supply Co Inc
311 N Washington, Albany, GA 31701
Tel: 229-435-4566
E-mail: dixietheatre@aol.com
Key Personnel
Pres: Linda C Appleman
Distribute DSLR video.

DL Sound & Lighting Productions Ltd
450 Banga Place, Victoria, BC V8Z 6X5, Canada
Mailing Address: PO Box 1173, Victoria, BC V8W 2T6, Canada
Tel: 250-216-7898 *Fax:* 250-590-1280
Web Site: www.dlsound.net
Key Personnel
Owner & Pres: Doug Lyngard *E-mail:* doug@dlsound.net
Founded: 1984
Sales, rentals & productions.
Branch Office(s)
Vancouver, BC, Canada *Tel:* 604-561-3528

dM works
246 Rockaway Ave, Valley Stream, NY 11580
Tel: 516-255-0100 *Toll Free Tel:* 888-914-6639
E-mail: info@dmworks.com
Web Site: www.dmworks.com
Key Personnel
Mng Partner: Ken Fleischer
Founded: 1996
Produces high impact HD, 3D, 4K, multi-screen videos, motion graphics & dynamic content for broadcast, web, entertainment, film, marketing & advertising campaigns.
Membership(s): Long Island Association

DME Studios
1025 Greenwood Blvd, Suite 191, Lake Mary, FL 32746
Tel: 407-585-7500
E-mail: creativeteam@dmestudios.com
Web Site: www.dmestudios.com
Key Personnel
Pres: Ben Dyon
Dir, Busn Devt: John Armistead
Dir, Photog: Mike Lopez
Gen Mgr: Carmen Treffiletti
Integrated marketing communications & video production.

DNASTAR Inc
3801 Regent St, Madison, WI 53705-5204
Tel: 608-258-7420 *Toll Free Tel:* 866-511-5090 *Fax:* 608-258-7439
E-mail: info@dnastar.com
Web Site: www.dnastar.com
Key Personnel
Pres: Frederick Blattner
Founded: 1984
Catalog(s) available

DNP Photo Imaging America Corp
Subsidiary of DNP Group
101 Uhland Rd, Suite 210, San Marcos, TX 78666
Mailing Address: PO Box 767, San Marcos, TX 78667
Tel: 512-753-7280 *Toll Free Tel:* 800-467-4935 *Fax:* 512-753-7299
E-mail: info@pixelmagic.com; sales@pixelmagic.com; customercare@pixelmagic.com
Web Site: www.dnpphoto.com; www.pixelmagic.com; www.pmimaging.com
Key Personnel
CEO: Kazuhiro Kawabata
Dir, Opers: Takahito Tatsumi
Founded: 1992
Catalog(s) available
Foreign Office(s): DNP Photo Imaging Europe SAS, 22 Ave des Nations-Villepointe, BP 51077, 95948 Roissy CDG Cedex, France *Tel:* 01 49 38 65 50 *Fax:* 01 49 89 00 81
DNP Photo Marketing, CS Tower, 5-20-8 Asakusabashi, Taitou-ku, Tokyo 111-0053, Japan
Membership(s): Photo Marketing Association

Do It Yourself Inc - DIY Video Corp
200 N Greensboro St, Suite A5, Carrboro, NC 27510
Tel: 919-904-7343; 828-773-8878 (cell)
Web Site: www.do-it-yourself-dvds.com
Key Personnel
Pres: Robert Roskind *E-mail:* roskind@boone.net
Woodworking, craft, real estate & home improvement videos & DVDs.
Catalog(s) available

Docter Optics Inc
Subsidiary of Docter Optics GmbH
1425 W Elliot Rd, Suite A-105, Gilbert, AZ 85233
Tel: 480-844-7585 *Fax:* 480-844-7826
E-mail: doi@docteroptics.com
Web Site: www.docteroptics.com
Key Personnel
CEO: Jan Hamkens
COO: Hans-Juergen Brandt

VP & Exec Mgr: Bruce Nielsen *E-mail:* bruce.nielsen@docteroptics.com
Dir, Sales: Harry Steger
Catalog(s) available

Documentary Educational Resources Inc
101 Morse St, Watertown, MA 02472
Tel: 617-926-0491 *Toll Free Tel:* 800-569-6621 *Fax:* 617-926-9519
E-mail: docued@der.org
Web Site: www.der.org
Key Personnel
Pres & Exec Dir: Alice Apley *E-mail:* alice@der.org
Dist Mgr: Julia Perciasepe *E-mail:* juliap@der.org
Founded: 1968
Produce, distribute & promote quality ethnographic & documentary films from around the world.
Catalog(s), free on request
Online catalog(s) available
Printed material(s), free, new releases
Membership(s): American Anthropological Association; ICAES; IFP; International Documentary Association; National Alliance for Media Arts & Culture

Dog & Pony Productions Inc
8928 "L" St, Omaha, NE 68127
Tel: 402-391-7691 *Fax:* 402-341-2751
Web Site: dogandponyinc.com
Key Personnel
CFO: Susan Gilstrap
Pres: Mike Gilstrap
Founded: 1988
AV rentals & productions.

Dogma Studios
10559 Jefferson Blvd, Culver City, CA 90232
Mailing Address: PO Box 11941, Marina del Rey, CA 90295-2941
Tel: 310-838-2973 *Fax:* 310-838-2975
E-mail: info@dogmastudios.com
Web Site: www.dogmastudios.com
Key Personnel
CTO: Brian Alvarez *E-mail:* tech@dogmastudios.com
Pres: Scott Schlichter *E-mail:* scott@dogmastudios.com
Dir, Busn Devt/Sales: Jon Woydziak *E-mail:* jon@dogmastudios.com
Dir, Content Devt/Sales: Terrence Coles *E-mail:* terrence@dogmastudios.com
Creative & Edit Dir: Eric McHugh *E-mail:* eric@dogmastudios.com
Sales Mgr: Curtis Bole *E-mail:* curtis@dogmastudios.com
Founded: 1996
New media post, editorial, DVD, post-production, graphic design & video on demand.

Dogwood Recording Studios
Division of Dogwood Productions Inc
757 Government St, Mobile, AL 36602
Tel: 251-476-0858 *Toll Free Tel:* 800-254-9903 *Fax:* 251-479-0364
E-mail: info@dogwoodproductions.com
Web Site: www.dogwoodproductions.com
Key Personnel
Audio Dir: Ray Norman
Founded: 1981

Dolby Labs Inc
100 Potrero Ave, San Francisco, CA 94103-4813
Tel: 415-558-0200 *Fax:* 415-645-4000
E-mail: info@dolby.com
Web Site: www.dolby.com
Key Personnel
CEO & Pres: Kevin Yeaman
CFO & EVP: Lewis Chew
SVP, Worldwide Sales & Field Opers: Mike Bergeron
Founded: 1965
Catalog(s) available
Branch Office(s)
175 S Hill Dr, Brisbane, CA 94005-1272 *Tel:* 415-715-2500
3601 W Alameda Ave, Burbank, CA 91505 *Tel:* 818-823-2800 *Fax:* 818-557-0890
475 Brannan St, Suite 300, San Francisco, CA 94107-5420 *Tel:* 415-357-7000
999 Brannan St, San Francisco, CA 94103-4938 *Tel:* 415-645-5000
432 Lakeside Dr, Santa Clara, CA 94085 *Tel:* 408-330-3300 *Fax:* 408-330-3200
1350 Avenue of the Americas, 20th fl, New York, NY 10019-4703 *Tel:* 212-767-1700 *Fax:* 212-767-1705
Foreign Office(s): Dolby Australia Pty Ltd, 35 Mitchell St, Level 3, McMahons Point, NSW 2060, Australia *Tel:* (02) 9101-7900 *Fax:* (02) 9101-7800
Av das Nacoes Unidas, 12551, 17 andar, 04578-000 Sao Paulo-SP, Brazil *Tel:* (011) 3443-7443 *Fax:* (011) 3443-1401
Dolby Laboratories International Services (Beijing) Co Ltd, World Financial Ctr, West Bldg, Rm 907-916, Level 9, No 1 E 3rd Ring Middle Rd, Chaoyang District, Beijing 100020, China *Tel:* (010) 5910-3000 *Fax:* (010) 5910-3001
Dolby Laboratories International Services (Shanghai) Co Ltd, The Center, 05-07A, fl 18, 989 Chang Le Rd, Shanghai 200031, China *Tel:* (021) 6113-3456 *Fax:* (021) 6113-3400
Dolby Laboratories International Services Inc, Kerry Plaza, 18F, Tower 1, No 1 Zhong Xin Si Rd, Futian District, Shenzhen 518048, China *Tel:* (0755) 3698-5900 *Fax:* (0755) 3698-5901
Dolby France, 28 Rue de Londres, 75009 Paris, France *Tel:* 01 78 42 40 43 *Fax:* 01 78 42 35 00
Dolby Germany GmbH, Rheinstr 45, Aufgang 1, 12161 Berlin, Germany *Tel:* (030) 89061-8000 *Fax:* (030) 89061-8001
Dolby Germany GmbH, Maximilianstr 35a, 80539 Munich, Germany *Tel:* (089) 24218-0 *Fax:* (089) 24218-305
Dolby Germany GmbH, Deutschherrnstr 15-19, 90429 Nuernberg, Germany *Tel:* (0911) 928-91-0 *Fax:* (0911) 928-91-99
Dolby Laboratories Hong Kong Ltd, Central Plaza, Suite 5407, 18 Harbour Rd, Wanchai, Hong Kong *Tel:* 2519 0888 *Fax:* 2519 8988
Dolby Technology India Pvt Ltd, Regus Shyamala Gardens, Shyamala Tower, 3rd fl, No 136 Arcot Rd, Saligramam, Chennai 600 093, India *Tel:* (044) 6686-4949 *Fax:* (044) 6686-4567
Dolby Technology India Pvt Ltd, No 331-332, Regus, Level 3, Neo Vikram, New Link Rd, Andheri (West), Mumbai 400 053, India *Tel:* (022) 6198-4940 *Fax:* (022) 6198 4950
Dolby Technology India Pvt Ltd, Level 15, Eros Corporate Tower, Nehru Place, New Delhi 110 019, India *Tel:* (011) 4223 5051 *Fax:* (011) 4223-5222
Dolby Japan KK, Level 19 Hilton Plaza West Office Tower, 2-2-2 Umeda, Kita-ku, Osaka 530-0001, Japan *Tel:* (06) 6133-5415 *Fax:* (06) 6133-5416
Dolby Japan KK, NBF Higashi-Ginza Sq 3F, 1-13-14 Tsukiji, Chuo-ku, Tokyo 104-0045, Japan *Tel:* (03) 3524-7300 *Fax:* (03) 3524-7389
Dolby International AB, Apollo Bldg, 3E, Herikerbergweg 1-35, 1101 CN Amesterdam Zuidoost, Netherlands *Tel:* (020) 6511 800 *Fax:* (020) 6511 801
Dolby CIS LLC, Smolensky Passage, Smolenskaya Sq, 3, 7th fl, Off 716-718, 121099 Moscow, Russia *Tel:* (495) 937-8485 *Fax:* (495) 937-8290
Dolby Singapore Pte Ltd, UOB Plaza 1, No 35-05, 80 Raffles Place, Singapore 048624, Singapore *Tel:* 6248 4597 *Fax:* 6248 4960
Dolby Laboratories International Services Inc, The Executive Ctr 41/F, Gangnam Finance Ctr, 737 Yeoksam-dong, Gangnam-gu, Seoul 135-984, South Korea *Tel:* (02) 2008-4650 *Fax:* (02) 2008-4555
IMM Sound, SA, a Dolby Company, Barcelona Media Bldg, Avinguda Diagonal, 177, 08018 Barcelona, Spain *Tel:* 934-867-600 *Fax:* 934-867-601
Dolby Iberia SL, Paseo de la Castellana 141, Planta 20, Edificio Cuzco IV, 28046 Madrid, Spain *Tel:* 91-7498-009 *Fax:* 91-5705-199
Dolby Sweden AB, Gavlegatan 12A, 113 30 Stockholm, Sweden *Tel:* (08) 442 91 60 *Fax:* (08) 442 91 90
Dolby Laboratories International Services Inc, Suite 3733, Level 37, 7 Xinyi Rd, Sec 5, Taipei, Taiwan *Tel:* (02) 8758 2785 *Fax:* (02) 8758 2999
Dolby Middle East FZ LLC, Dubai Media City, Bldg 5, Off 110, 502444 Dubai, United Arab Emirates *Tel:* (04) 455-6900 *Fax:* (040 455-6901
Dolby Europe Ltd, 4-6 Soho Sq, London W1D 3PZ, United Kingdom *Tel:* (020) 7406 3200 *Fax:* (020) 7406 3201
Dolby Europe Ltd, Royal Wootton Bassett, Swindon, Wilts SN4 8QJ, United Kingdom *Tel:* (01793) 842100 *Fax:* (01793) 842101
Membership(s): AES; SMPTE

Dollarhide Film Inc
764 Lake Cavalier Rd, Madison, MS 39110
Tel: 601-946-8407
Web Site: www.dollarhide.net
Key Personnel
Dir & Founder: Jim Dollarhide *E-mail:* jim@dollarhide.net
Membership(s): IQ; MCA-I

Dolphin MultiMedia Inc
1660 Belleville Way, Sunnyvale, CA 94087
Tel: 650-354-0800 *Fax:* 408-737-8404
E-mail: dolphin@dolphinmm.com
Web Site: www.dolphinmm.com
Key Personnel
Pres: Cynthia Kondratieff *E-mail:* cynthia@dolphinmm.com
Founded: 1972

Domino Film Ltd
4004 Grey Ave, Montreal, QC H4A 3P1, Canada
Tel: 514-484-0446 *Fax:* 514-484-0468
E-mail: domino@dominofilm.ca
Web Site: www.dominofilm.ca
Key Personnel
Pres: Jeanne Ritter *E-mail:* jritter@dominofilm.ca
Founded: 1983
Feature film & television, distribution & video sales.
Catalog(s) available

Tom Donald Films
601 Fourth St, Suite 320, San Francisco, CA 94107
Tel: 415-546-4966 *Fax:* 415-546-5145
Web Site: www.tomdonaldfilms.com
Key Personnel
Principal & Dir: Tom Donald *Tel:* 415-377-1065 (cell) *E-mail:* tom@tomdonaldfilms.com
Founded: 1994
TV commercial production company.

Doomsday Studios Ltd
212 James St, Ottawa, ON K1R 5M7, Canada
Tel: 613-230-9769 *Fax:* 613-230-6004
E-mail: info@doomsdaystudios.com
Key Personnel
Pres & Exec Prodr: Ramona Macdonald
Founded: 1978
Membership(s): Canadian Media Production Association; WIFT

Doppler Studios
1922 Piedmont Circle, Atlanta, GA 30324
Tel: 404-873-6941 *Fax:* 404-249-7148
E-mail: info@dopplerstudios.com
Web Site: www.dopplerstudios.com
Key Personnel
Pres, Studio & Schedule Mgr: Bill Quinn
Founded: 1969
Sound recording & mixing services.
Membership(s): AES; SPARS

Doremi Labs
Division of Dolby Labs Inc
1020 Chestnut St, Burbank, CA 91506
Tel: 818-562-1101 *Fax:* 818-562-1109
E-mail: info@doremilabs.com
Web Site: www.doremilabs.com
Key Personnel
Mng Dir: Emil Rizko
Founded: 1985
Foreign Office(s): Fukunishi Bldg, 6F, 2-6-21 Nishi Ikuta, Tama-Ku, Kawasaki-Shi, Kanagawa 214-0037, Japan *Tel:* (044) 966-4855 *Fax:* (044) 966-4856 *E-mail:* sales@doremilabs.co.jp

Dorfman Museum Figures Inc
6224 Holabird Ave, Baltimore, MD 21224
Tel: 410-284-3248 *Toll Free Tel:* 800-634-4873 *Fax:* 410-284-3249
E-mail: info@museumfigures.com
Web Site: www.museumfigures.com
Key Personnel
Pres: Robert Dorfman
Founded: 1957
Create lifesize life-like human figures for museums, visitor centers & collectors & ETHAFOAM™ conservation forms for display & storage of high value artifacts.
Online catalog(s) available

Dorian Color
24 Mill St, Arlington, MA 02476
Tel: 781-648-8040 *Fax:* 781-641-1231
E-mail: images@dorianlabcolor.com (gallery)
Web Site: www.doriancolor.com
Key Personnel
Founder & Owner: Alan Asadorian *E-mail:* alan@doriancolor.com
Prod Mgr: Jim Munn *E-mail:* jim@doriancolor.com
Prodn & Cust Serv: Eric Bailey *E-mail:* eric@doriancolor.com
Acctg: Mary Russo
Founded: 1973
Full service, professional, digital imaging & photographic printing company.
Catalog(s) available
Membership(s): AIE™

Dorrough Electronics Inc
5221 Collier Place, Woodland Hills, CA 91364
Tel: 818-998-2824 *Fax:* 818-998-1507
E-mail: dorroughel@aol.com
Web Site: www.dorrough.com
Key Personnel
Partner: Kay Dorrough
Pres: Michael Dorrough
Contact: Sergio Plasenia
Manufacture audio level meters & sound recording.
Catalog(s) available
Membership(s): AES; NAB

Dorst MediaWorks Inc
209 N Filmore St, Arlington, VA 22201
Tel: 202-258-9612 *Fax:* 571-312-9212
Web Site: www.stevedorst.com
Key Personnel
Pres, Dir, Prodr & Ed: Steve Dorst *E-mail:* steve@dorstmediaworks.com
Founded: 2000
Script-to-screen full service video production company.
Membership(s): Women in Film & Video

Dot C Software Inc
117 Waihili Place, Honolulu, HI 96825
Tel: 808-744-0836
E-mail: info@dotcsw.com
Web Site: www.dotcsw.com
Key Personnel
CEO & Pres: Cheryl M LaMont *E-mail:* cheryl@dotcsw.com
CTO & VP: Rick LaMont *E-mail:* lamont@dotcsw.com
Founded: 1992
Software Graphics tools: RenderDotC & MaiTai.

Dot Hill Systems Corp
1351 S Sunset St, Longmont, CO 80501-6533
Tel: 303-845-3200 *Toll Free Tel:* 800-872-2783 *Fax:* 303-845-3655
E-mail: support@dothill.com; websales@dothill.com
Web Site: www.dothill.com
Key Personnel
CEO & Pres: Dana W Kammersgard
CFO & SVP: Hanif I Jamal
CTO: Kenneth F Day
SVP, Prods & Solutions: William J Wuertz
SVP, Quality & Cust Advocacy: Mike Flood
SVP, Worldwide Mfg & Supply Base Mgmt: William Haskins
VP & Gen Mgr, HP Busn Unit: Cooper Cowart
VP, Channel Sales: Brad Painter
VP, Worldwide OEM Sales: Garrett Wein
Founded: 1984
Offer software & hardware solutions for storing, sharing, protecting & managing data.
Catalog(s) available
Branch Office(s)
Minnesota Technology Center, 2905 NW Blvd, Suite 20, Plymouth, MN 55441
Foreign Office(s): 607 Ronggui Postal Mansion, 6 Rongqi Ave Central, Ronggui Shunde District, Foshan City, Guangdong Province 528300, China *Tel:* (0757) 26610832
Jin Luan Da Sha, Unit 09-968, Hepingdonglu, Longhua Jiedao, Shenzhen City, Baoan District 518109, China *Tel:* (0755) 33045303 *E-mail:* apac@dothill.com
AM Weinberg 2, 34454 Bad Arolsen, Germany *Tel:* (05691) 914-380 *Fax:* (05691) 914-381 *E-mail:* channeleurope@dothill.com
Obere Bahnhofstr 41, 82110 Germering, Germany *Tel:* (089) 92587052 *Fax:* (089) 89459817 *E-mail:* oemeurope@dothill.com
7F ASK Bldg, 2-8 Kanda, Sudac-cho, Chiyoda-ku, Tokyo 101-0041, Japan *Tel:* (03) 3251-1690 *Fax:* (03) 3251-1691 *E-mail:* nihon@dothill.com
54 Genting Lane, 06-01 Ruby Land Complex, Singapore 349562, Singapore *Tel:* 6844 5861
Hassocks Wood Business Ctr, Unit 14, Stroudley Rd, Basingstoke, Hants RG24 8UQ, United Kingdom *Tel:* (01256) 840600 *Fax:* (01256) 814462 *E-mail:* uk@dothill.com
Membership(s): NAB

Dotronix Technology Inc
160 First St SE, New Brighton, MN 55112
Tel: 651-633-1742 *Fax:* 651-633-2152
E-mail: service@dotronix.com; sales@dotronix.com
Web Site: www.dotronix.com
Key Personnel
Owner: Kurt Sadler *E-mail:* ksadler@dotronix.com
Founded: 1980
Sell new replacement monitors & service nearly any CRT-based monitor.

Douglas House Inc
275 Kings Hwy, Orangeburg, NY 10962
Tel: 845-359-1477 *Fax:* 845-359-2945
E-mail: thedouglashouse@earthlink.net
Web Site: www.thedouglashouse.com
Key Personnel
Pres: Marjorie Douglas
Mgr: Heather Douglas
Founded: 1981
Commercial, fully propped film production facility.

Dover Publications Inc
31 E Second St, Mineola, NY 11501
Tel: 516-294-7000 *Fax:* 516-742-5049 (wholesale orders); 516-742-6953 (cust care)
Web Site: store.doverpublications.com
Key Personnel
Contact: Ken Katzman *Tel:* 516-294-7000 ext 121
Founded: 1941
Catalog(s) available

Dow-Key Microwave Corp
Subsidiary of Dover Corp
4822 McGrath St, Ventura, CA 93003
Tel: 805-650-0260 *Toll Free Tel:* 800-266-3695 *Fax:* 805-650-1734
E-mail: askdk@dowkey.com
Web Site: www.dowkey.com
Key Personnel
Pres: David Wightman
Gen Mgr: Adolf Cheung *Tel:* 805-650-2329
Founded: 1945
Manufacture switches for the commercial, military, wireless & high reliability space industries.
Catalog(s) available

Down East Books
Division of Down East Enterprises Inc
680 Commercial St, Rockport, ME 04856
Mailing Address: c/o Down East Enterprises Inc, PO Box 679, Camden, ME 04843
Tel: 207-594-9544 *Toll Free Tel:* 800-766-1670 *Fax:* 207-594-0147
E-mail: editorial@downeast.com
Web Site: www.downeast.com
Key Personnel
CEO, Pres & Publr: Bob Fernald *E-mail:* bfernald@downeast.com
Ed-in-Chief: Paul Doiron
Prodn Rep: Dawn Rasmussen
Founded: 1977
Publish books by Maine authors & artists.
Membership(s): The Association of Publishers for Special Sales; NEBA

Downpour.com
31 Mistletoe Rd, Ashland, OR 97520
Toll Free Tel: 855-369-6768 *Toll Free Fax:* 800-482-9294
E-mail: customercare@downpour.com
Web Site: www.downpour.com
Founded: 2012
Produce audiobooks in CD & download.

Downtown Community Television Center (DCTV)
87 Lafayette St, New York, NY 10013
Tel: 212-966-4510 *Fax:* 212-226-3053
E-mail: info@dctvny.org
Web Site: www.dctvny.org
Key Personnel
Founder, Exec Dir & Prodr: Jon Alpert *E-mail:* jonny@dctvny.org
Founder & Exec Dir: Keiko Tsuno *Tel:* 212-996-4510 ext 622 *E-mail:* ktsuno@dctvny.org
Mng Dir: Catherine Martinez *Tel:* 212-966-4510 ext 645 *E-mail:* cmartinez@dctvny.org
Founded: 1972
Foster diverse viewpoints by providing professional training, state-of-the-industry resources & by creating outstanding documentary produc-

tions, with the belief that diversity of expression strengthens our democracy & enhances civil society.

R L Drake Co
9900 Springboro Pike, Miamisburg, OH 45342
Tel: 937-746-4556 *Fax:* 937-806-1510 (sales); 937-806-1511 (gen)
E-mail: salesgroup@rldrake.net
Web Site: www.rldrake.com
Key Personnel
VP, Sales & Mktg: Andy Ruffin
Inside Sales Mgr: Philip Hawkins
Founded: 1943
Manufacturer of assistive listening products, cable television products & classroom amplification systems.
CD-ROM catalog(s), annual, free on request
Branch Office(s)
Drake Canada, 655 The Queensway, Unit 16, Peterborough, ON K9J 7M1, Canada *Tel:* 705-742-3122 *Fax:* 705-742-2838 *Web Site:* www.drakecanada.com

DR&A Inc
45 Willow St, Nashville, TN 37210
Tel: 615-256-6200 *Fax:* 615-256-6236
Web Site: www.griptruck.com
Key Personnel
Contact: Shaun Anweiler *E-mail:* shaun@griptruck.com; Doug Rice *E-mail:* drice@griptruck.com
Founded: 1985
Television & film production services.

Draper Inc
411 S Pearl St, Spiceland, IN 47385
Tel: 765-987-7999 *Toll Free Tel:* 800-238-7999 *Fax:* 765-987-7142
Web Site: www.draperinc.com; blog.draperinc.com
Key Personnel
Pres: John D Pidgeon *E-mail:* jpidgeon@draperinc.com
Ad Mgr: Penny R Sitler *E-mail:* psitler@draperinc.com
Cust Serv Mgr: Beverly Ferguson *E-mail:* bferguson@draperinc.com
Mktg Admin: Amy Bradway *Tel:* 765-987-7999 ext 2329 *E-mail:* abradway@draperinc.com
Founded: 1902
Manufacture AV equipment, home theater, front projection, rear projection & portable projection screens, fixed screens & more.
Online catalog(s) available
Sales Office(s): 151 N Kraemer Blvd, Suite 101, Placenta, CA 92870, AV Regl Sales Mgr: Randy Reece *Tel:* 714-577-0088 *Fax:* 714-577-0044 *E-mail:* rreece@draperinc.com
Membership(s): AECT; Custom Electronic Design & Installation Association; Education Market Association; InfoComm International®

Drastic Technologies Ltd
523 The Queensway, Suite 102, Toronto, ON M8Y 1J7, Canada
Tel: 416-255-5636 *Fax:* 416-255-8780
Web Site: www.drastic.tv
Key Personnel
Pres: Robert Brooks *E-mail:* bob@drastictech.com
Sales Support Coord: Corey D Cousineau *E-mail:* sales@drastictech.com
Founded: 1991
Offer hardware & software products for digital video capture, control, conversion & output.

Dreambox Media Inc
PO Box 8132, Philadelphia, PA 19101-8132
E-mail: mail@dreamboxmedia.com
Web Site: www.dreamboxmedia.com
Key Personnel
Founder: James Miller *Tel:* 267-250-8506
Founded: 1995
Independent musicians' recording label dedicated to promoting the rich tradition of distinctively original & creative Philadelphia Jazz artists.

Dreamhire LLC
36-36 33 St, Suite 102, Long Island City, NY 11106
Tel: 212-691-5544 *Toll Free Tel:* 800-234-7536
E-mail: info@dreamhire.com
Web Site: www.dreamhire.com
Key Personnel
CEO: Chris Dunn
Founded: 1984
Professional audio equipment rentals & audio transfer services.

The Dreaming Tree
1112 Chestnut St, Unit B, Burbank, CA 91506
Tel: 818-845-3230 *Fax:* 818-333-0795
E-mail: info@dreamingtreeproductions.com
Web Site: www.dreamingtreeproductions.com
Key Personnel
Dir & Dir, Photog: Oktay Ortabasi
Ed/Colorist: Leslie Ortabasi
Production company.

Dreamscape Lighting Mfg Inc
5521 W Washington Blvd, Los Angeles, CA 90016
Tel: 323-933-5760 *Fax:* 323-933-3607
E-mail: info@dreamscapelighting.com
Web Site: www.dreamscapelighting.com
Key Personnel
Gen Mgr: Victor Kelmelis
Founded: 1988
Manufacture linear, landscape, architechtural lighting & linear LED.
Online catalog(s), PDF

DreamWorks Animation SKG Inc
1000 Flower St, Glendale, CA 91201
Tel: 818-695-5000 *Fax:* 818-695-4190
Web Site: www.dreamworksanimation.com
Key Personnel
CEO & Dir: Jeffrey Katzenberg
COO: Mark Zoradi
CFO: Fazal Merchant
Chief Creative Offr: Bill Damaschke
Chief Global Brand Offr: Michael R Francis
Chief Mktg Offr: Dawn Taubin
VChmn & Acting Chief Acctg Offr: Lew Coleman
Pres: Ann Daly
Gen Coun & Corp Secy: Andrew Chang
Head, HR: Dan Satterthwaite
Head, TV: Margie Cohn
Creates animated feature films & television programs.

DRG Records Inc
22 Harbor Park Dr, Port Washington, NY 11050
Tel: 516-484-1000 (ext 147); 212-614-2800 *Toll Free Tel:* 866-293-2854 *Fax:* 516-484-2365
E-mail: info@drgrecords.com
Web Site: drgrecords.com
Key Personnel
Pres: Hugh Fordin
Founded: 1976
Online catalog(s) available
Membership(s): Music Business Association; The Recording Academy

DRM: sir reel sound
10520 Beard Ave, Austin, TX 78748
Tel: 214-752-5000 (studio)
E-mail: drmuzik@mac.com
Web Site: www.drm-sirreelsound.com
Key Personnel
Founder, Pres, Sound Designer & Music Prodr: David Rosenblad
Founded: 1989
Provide a variety of sound & music production services for film, video & music media.
Membership(s): AES; AFM; The Recording Academy

DRT Mastering
20 Vine St, Peterborough, NH 03458
Tel: 603-924-2277
Web Site: www.drtmastering.com
Key Personnel
Owner & Chief Engr: David Torrey *E-mail:* davidt@drtmastering.com

Mark Druck Productions
300 E 40 St, New York, NY 10016
Tel: 212-682-5980 *Fax:* 212-682-5981
Key Personnel
Pres: Mark Druck *E-mail:* markdruck@aol.com
VP: Lisa Dodenhoff
Founded: 1969

Drumbeat Indian Arts Inc
4143 N 16 St, Phoenix, AZ 85016
Tel: 602-266-4823 *Toll Free Tel:* 800-895-4859 *Fax:* 602-265-2402
E-mail: info@drumbeatindianarts.com
Web Site: www.drumbeatindianarts.com
Key Personnel
Owner & Pres: Robert Nuss
Founded: 1984
Wholesale & retail source for authentic traditional & contemporary American Indian music. Also a major supplier of American Indian religious herbs, craft supplies & books.
Online catalog(s), PDF

Drytac Corp
5601 Eastport Blvd, Richmond, VA 23231
Toll Free Tel: 800-280-6013
E-mail: customerservice@drytac.com
Web Site: www.drytac.com
Key Personnel
CEO & Chmn: Richard Kelley
Pres, Drytac Group: Marc Oosterhuis
VP, New Mkt Busn Devt: Jerry Hill
Founded: 1976
Manufacturer & distributor of mounting & laminating materials & equipment.
Online catalog(s), PDF download
Branch Office(s)
10600 Shoemaker Ave, Suite D, Santa Fe Springs, CA 90670 *Tel:* 562-941-9630
140 S Pinnacle Dr, Romeoville, IL 60446 *Tel:* 815-838-0226
11425 Mathis Ave, Suite 400, Dallas, TX 75234 *Tel:* 972-910-8811
220 Caldari Rd, Concord, ON L4K 4L1, Canada *Toll Free Tel:* 800-353-2883 *E-mail:* toronto@drytac.com
Foreign Office(s): Filwood Rd, Fishponds, Bristol BS16 3RY, United Kingdom *Tel:* (0117) 958-6500 *Web Site:* www.drytac.co.uk
Membership(s): AIE™; International Reprographic Association; International Sign Association; Photo Marketing Association; PPFA; Specialty Graphic Imaging Association

DSan Corp
142 Mineola Ave, Roslyn Heights, NY 11577
Tel: 516-625-5608 *Fax:* 516-625-0878
E-mail: sales@dsan.com
Web Site: www.dsan.com
Key Personnel
Pres: Kelvin J Swarth
Mktg Dir: Rodger Swarth
Manufacturer of unique presentation tools. Speaker timers are used by the US Congress,

Supreme Court, city councils, government agencies & corporations everywhere. Cue lights for remote control of presentations have become industry standards for their solid RF links & flexible setups. Ultra bright green laser pointers suitable for institutions & the rental market & several handy audio adapters for getting sound-accompanied presentations into house audio systems. Sells direct worldwide & through AV dealers.
Catalog(s) available

DSI RF Systems Inc
26-H World's Fair Dr, Somerset, NJ 08873
Tel: 732-563-1144 *Toll Free Tel:* 888-374-7388 *Fax:* 732-563-1818
E-mail: info@dsirf.com; sales@dsirf.com
Web Site: www.dsirf.com
Key Personnel
Pres: Judy Mueller *E-mail:* jmueller@dsirf.com
Provide technical & engineering solutions to the broadcast industry.

DSR Computer Technology Specialists Inc
921-P Mercantile Dr, Hanover, MD 21076
Tel: 410-579-4508 *Toll Free Tel:* 800-875-0037 *Fax:* 410-579-8412
E-mail: dsr@dsr-inc.com
Web Site: www.dsr-inc.com
Key Personnel
CEO & Pres: Dan Hogan *Tel:* 410-579-4508 ext 121 *E-mail:* dhogan@dsr-inc.com
Founded: 1986
Business computer sales, networking & computer repair.
Online catalog(s) available

DTC Communications Inc, see Cobham Tactical Communications & Surveillance

DTC Grip & Electric, see DTC Lighting & Grip

DTC Lighting & Grip
1280 65 St, Emeryville, CA 94608
Tel: 510-595-0770 *Toll Free Tel:* 877-382-3456 *Fax:* 510-595-0772
E-mail: sales@dtcgrip.com; rentals@dtcgrip.com
Web Site: www.dtcgrip.com
Key Personnel
Gen Mgr & COO: Tadd Sibley *E-mail:* tsibley@dtcgrip.com
Pres: Steve Condiotti *E-mail:* stevec@dtcgrip.com
Founded: 1983
Lighting & grip equipment rentals & sales.
Catalog(s) available

DuArt
245 W 55 St, New York, NY 10019
Tel: 212-757-4580 *Fax:* 212-977-5609
E-mail: info@duart.com
Web Site: www.duart.com
Key Personnel
COO: Charles Darby
VP, Opers: Joe Monge *E-mail:* jmonge@duart.com
VP, Prodn & Sales: Ron Harris *Tel:* 917-522-5645 *E-mail:* rharris@duart.com
Founded: 1922
Post-production facility. Specialize in broadcast post-production, editing, finishing, equipment rentals & other services.
Membership(s): IAAVC; MCA-I; SMPTE

Dub King
8133 Callaghan Rd, San Antonio, TX 78230
Tel: 210-979-8779 *Toll Free Tel:* 800-542-1187
E-mail: dubking@dubking.com
Web Site: www.dubking.com
Key Personnel
Pres: Kimble Dement
Founded: 1981
Membership(s): Association of Professional Videographers

The DubHouse
404 SE 15 St, Fort Lauderdale, FL 33316
Tel: 954-524-3658 *Toll Free Tel:* 877-900-DUBS (900-3827) *Fax:* 954-522-1905
Web Site: www.thedubhouse.net
Key Personnel
Pres: Michael Pardo *E-mail:* mike@thedubhouse.net
VP, Sales: Stu Goldstein *E-mail:* stu@thedubhouse.com
Proj Mgr/Graphics: Sue Tracy *E-mail:* sue@thedubhouse.com
Founded: 2002
DVD & CD replication & duplication, DVD & CD-ROM authoring, printing of innovative packaging, book & magazine printing & USB duplication. Facilities in CA, FL, IN, MD, NY, NC & Asia.

Duck Studios
2205 Stoner Ave, Los Angeles, CA 90064
Tel: 310-478-0771 *Fax:* 310-478-0773
E-mail: info@duckstudios.com
Web Site: www.duckstudios.com
Key Personnel
Exec Prodr: Mark Medernach *E-mail:* mark@duckstudios.com

Dudley Theatrical
3401 Indiana Ave, Winston-Salem, NC 27105
Tel: 336-722-3255 *Fax:* 336-722-4641
E-mail: sales@dudleytheatrical.com
Web Site: www.dudleytheatrical.com
Key Personnel
Mgr: McCoy Hill *E-mail:* mccoy@dudleytheatrical.com
Provide products for creating or enhancing stage settings.
Online catalog(s) available

Dan Dugan Sound Design Inc
290 Napoleon St, Suite E, San Francisco, CA 94124
Tel: 415-821-9776 *Fax:* 415-826-7699
Web Site: www.dandugan.com
Key Personnel
Prop: Dan Dugan *E-mail:* dan@dandugan.com
Manufacturing, editing & CD mastering.
Membership(s): AES; NAB; NSCA; SMPTE

Duggal Visual Solutions
29 W 23 St, New York, NY 10010
Tel: 212-924-8100 *Fax:* 212-242-6660
E-mail: info@duggal.com
Web Site: duggal.com
Key Personnel
CEO: Michael Duggal
VP, Mktg: Glenn Rabbach
Founded: 1963
Supplier of printing, computer imaging & multimedia, wide format graphics & display services.

Dukane Corp, Audio Visual Products Division
Division of Dukane Corp
2900 Dukane Dr, St Charles, IL 60174
Tel: 630-762-4040 *Toll Free Tel:* 888-245-1966 *Fax:* 630-584-5156
E-mail: avsales@dukane.com
Web Site: dukaneav.com
Key Personnel
Pres: James Locascio *Tel:* 800-265-4607; 630-846-1102 (cell) *E-mail:* jlocascio@dukane.com
Dir, Prods & Technol: Ron Ohlhaber
Natl Sales Mgr: Scott Doornbos *Tel:* 800-269-9715 *E-mail:* sdoornbos@dukane.com
Intl Sales: Ryan Pitterle *Tel:* 630-762-4022 *E-mail:* rpitterle@dukane.com
Founded: 1945
Membership(s): BPIA; Computer Technology Industry Association; Education Market Association; InfoComm International®; NSCA

Duke Media Services
Division of Duke University
0052 Bryan Ctr, Durham, NC 27708
Tel: 919-660-1740 *Fax:* 919-660-1719
Web Site: sites.duke.edu/mediaservices
Key Personnel
Prodn Supv: Tom Wilson *E-mail:* t.wilson@duke.edu
Membership(s): MCA-I

Michael Dunn Productions
25 Sunlit Dr W, Santa Fe, NM 87508
Tel: 847-940-0150
Key Personnel
Owner & Pres: Michael Dunn *E-mail:* mdunn@mc.net

Dunning Photo Equipment Inc
605 W Needles St, Bixby, OK 74008
Tel: 918-366-4917 *Fax:* 918-366-4918
Web Site: www.dunningphoto.com
Key Personnel
Owner & Sales: Ernie Dunning *E-mail:* ernie@dunningphoto.com
Founded: 1975
Dealer & rebuilder of kreonite color print processors & color film processors.
Membership(s): AIE™; Photo Marketing Association; PPA

Duplication Depot Inc
7 Brookstan Rd, Nesconset, NY 11767
Tel: 631-752-0608
E-mail: copymydisc@gmail.com
Web Site: www.duplicationdepot.com
Key Personnel
VP: Bob Weisen
Founded: 2010
CD/DVD duplication & replication, media conversions & video production.
Price sheet(s) available

Duplication Media
8126 Douglas Ave, Urbandale, IA 50322
Tel: 515-334-DUPS (334-3877)
E-mail: info@duplicationmedia.com
Web Site: www.duplicationmedia.com
Key Personnel
Owner: Jason Olson
Founded: 2003
Duplication service company offering CD, DVD & videotape duplications, audio to CD transfers, video to DVD transfers, picture videos, USB flash stick duplication & more.

Duplication Specialists Inc
843 Merrick Rd, Baldwin, NY 11510
Tel: 516-867-7300; 212-754-2044 *Toll Free Tel:* 800-227-1382 *Fax:* 516-867-7597
E-mail: sales@dupespec.com
Web Site: www.dupespec.com
Key Personnel
Pres: David Schwartz
Founded: 1986
Catalog(s) available

DuQuaine Manufacturing
PO Box 56, Kewaunee, WI 54216-0056
Tel: 920-388-3790
Web Site: www.duquaine.com
Key Personnel
Pres: Doug Charles *E-mail:* doug@duquaine.com
Founded: 1949
Custom lectern, podiums & cabinetry.
Brochure(s) available

Duray Lighting
Division of Weslite Inc
500 E Touhy Ave, Suite F, Des Plaines, IL 60018
Tel: 773-271-2800 *Fax:* 773-271-4410
E-mail: info@duraylighting.com; sales@duraylighting.com
Web Site: www.duraylighting.com
Key Personnel
COO: Jack Conway
Founded: 1946
Designer & manufacturer of standard & custom flourescent lighting & LED fixtures.
Catalog(s), upon request

Durrell LLC
801 Fifth Ave S, Nashville, TN 37203
Tel: 615-313-8877 *Fax:* 615-313-8873
Web Site: www.durrellsports.com
Key Personnel
Pres: John Horrell *E-mail:* jhorrell@durrellsports.com
VP: Chris Horrell *E-mail:* chorrell@durrellsports.com
Membership(s): NSCA

Durrenberger Engineering Inc
2037 Powell Dr, El Cajon, CA 92020
Tel: 858-578-3363
Web Site: www.dfrfx.com
Key Personnel
CEO & Pres: Robert S Durrenberger *E-mail:* bobdur@gmail.com
Founded: 1989
Provide post-production services for the motion picture industry. Additional services offered include: film transfer service of digital video to 35mm motion picture film & DCP (Digital Cinema Package) transfer service; audio transfers of Dolby Cinema 5.1, SR, SRD & DTS Cinema; film recording services of any digital files, animation projects, photos etc.

Durrin Productions Inc
4926 Sedgwick St NW, Washington, DC 20016
Tel: 202-237-6700 *Toll Free Tel:* 800-536-6843 *Fax:* 202-237-6738
E-mail: info@durrinproductions.com
Web Site: www.durrinproductions.com
Key Personnel
Owner & Pres: Ginny Durrin *E-mail:* gdurrin@durrinproductions.com
Catalog(s) available
Membership(s): Women in Film & Video

Duxbury Systems Inc
270 Littleton Rd, Unit 6, Westford, MA 01886-3523
Tel: 978-692-3000 *Fax:* 978-692-7912
E-mail: info@duxsys.com
Web Site: www.duxburysystems.com
Key Personnel
Pres: Joe Sullivan
VP, Software Devt: Peter Sullivan
Mktg Dir: Neal Kuniansky
Founded: 1976
Software engineering, Braille software, Braille translation software, 3195 & NT, Macintosh, DOS & UNIX.
Online catalog(s) available

DV Post
505 N Tustin Ave, Suite 220, Santa Ana, CA 92705
Tel: 714-550-0925
Web Site: www.dvpostvideo.com
Key Personnel
Owner: John Primm *E-mail:* john@dvpostvideo.com
Founded: 1999
Nonlinear video editing & production services.
Membership(s): MCA-I; Media Alliance of Orange County

DVDs4Less
6519 Jamon Dr, Sparks, NV 89436-9142
Mailing Address: PO Box 2266, Sparks, NV 89432-2266
Tel: 775-323-0965 *Toll Free Tel:* 800-852-2330 *Fax:* 775-323-1055
E-mail: info@dvds4less.net
Web Site: www.dvds4less.net
Key Personnel
Pres: James F Mitchell
Prodn Mgr: Ramm Francis
Founded: 1967
Production & post-production.
Membership(s): AICP; American Marketing Association

The DVI Group
1486 Mecaslin St NW, Atlanta, GA 30309
Tel: 404-873-6283 *Toll Free Tel:* 888-736-7384
E-mail: makeitbetter@thedvigroup.com
Web Site: www.thedvigroup.com
Key Personnel
Partner, Prodr & Edit: Matthew Lopes
Partner & Busn Devt: Suzanne Kosak
Founded: 1999
Visual communications company which specializes in video production & has built a reputation on a proven ability to create effective video productions driven by innovative creative concepts, designed to reach the target audience. Full service corporate productions from creative to all delivery formats: broadcast, promotional videos, training, event & trade show on disc, web, iPod, e-mail & mobile phones. Multilingual & formats that offer advanced tracking technology for marketing or training analysis.

DVS InteleStream
2600 W Olive Ave, Burbank, CA 91505
Tel: 818-566-4151 *Fax:* 818-566-4453
E-mail: info@dvs.tv
Web Site: www.dvs.tv
Key Personnel
Pres: Richard Appell
Online digital asset management, DVD services, electronic distribution, international standards conversion, vault management system, quality control services, mastering, editing suites, film transfers, color correction & telecine audio services.
Catalog(s) available
Branch Office(s)
216 E 45 St, 7th fl, New York, NY 10017 *Tel:* 212-629-6971 *Fax:* 212-629-6976

DW Electrochemicals Ltd
3-97 Newkirk Rd N, Richmond Hill, ON L4C 3G4, Canada
Tel: 905-508-7500 *Fax:* 905-508-7502
E-mail: dwel@stabilant.com
Web Site: www.stabilant.com
Key Personnel
Pres: Wm M Wright
Intl Mktg Mgr: Betty Gordon
Founded: 1986
Handle the Stabilant 22, which is an electronic contact enhancer used to ensure long-term connector reliability. It is an easy to use, cost-effective, active resident contact treatment when assembling or servicing audio & video equipment. Stabilant 22 can improve sound quality by increasing the signal-to-noise ratio as well as reducing thin-film rectification effects which cause RF demodulation.
Information sheet(s) available

DWD Theatre Design & Consulting
Suite 485, 425 Carrall St, Vancouver, BC V6B 6E3, Canada
Tel: 604-874-0552
E-mail: info@d-w-d.com
Web Site: www.d-w-d.com
Key Personnel
Co-Owner: Robert Hamilton; Scott Miller
Design & technical consulting for the performing arts & related industries.

DWJ Television
One Robinson Lane, Ridgewood, NJ 07450
Tel: 201-445-1711 *Toll Free Tel:* 800-766-1711 *Fax:* 201-445-8352
Key Personnel
EVP: Michael L Friedman *Tel:* 201-445-1711 ext 136 *E-mail:* mfriedman@dwjtv.com
SVP & Gen Mgr: Cynthia Wagner Boseski *Tel:* 201-445-1711 ext 272 *E-mail:* cboseski@dwjtv.com
SVP & Sr Prodr: Gloria Wolford Johnson
Broadcast public relations company producing TV, Internet, video & radio projects.
Catalog(s) available
Branch Office(s)
Box 996, 22 Division St, Sag Harbor, NY 11961 *Tel:* 631-899-4500 *Fax:* 631-899-4499

Dyer-Bennet Records
792 Columbus Ave, Rm 16-0, New York, NY 10025
Tel: 212-866-3675
Key Personnel
Mgr: Harvey Cort *E-mail:* hcort@msn.com
Distributed by the Smithsonian Folkways.
Membership(s): BMI

Dykeman Associates Inc
4115 Rawlins St, Dallas, TX 75219
E-mail: info@dykemanassociates.com
Web Site: www.dykemanassociates.com
Founded: 1974
Full service results-oriented firm which provides public relations, advertising, video production & other related services.
Brochure(s), free
Membership(s): Public Relations Society of America; Religion Communicators Council

Dyna-Lite Inc
1050 Commerce Ave, Union, NJ 07083
Tel: 908-687-8800 *Toll Free Tel:* 800-722-6638 *Fax:* 908-686-6682
E-mail: flash@dynalite.com
Web Site: www.dynalite.com
Key Personnel
Pres: Peter Poremba *Tel:* 908-687-8800 ext 207
Founded: 1970
Catalog(s) available
Membership(s): Photo Marketing Association

Dynamic Digital Depth Inc (DDD)
6100 Center Dr W, Suite 1100, Los Angeles, CA 90045
Tel: 310-566-3340 *Toll Free Tel:* 877-884-4333 *Fax:* 310-566-3380
E-mail: info@ddd.com
Web Site: www.ddd.com
Key Personnel
CEO & Exec Dir: Christopher Yewdall *Tel:* 310-566-3340 ext 355
CFO: Victoria Stull
CTO: Dr Julien Flack
Founded: 1993
3D "glasses-free" LCD & plasma display sale, rental & content.
Foreign Office(s): Technology Park, 6-A Brodie Hall Dr, Bentley, WA 6102, Australia *Tel:* (08) 9355 6888 *Fax:* (08) 9355 6988

Dystopian Studios
651 Clover St, Bldg 1, Los Angeles, CA 90031
Tel: 310-503-2365
Web Site: dystopianstudios.com

Key Personnel
Owner: Kevin Flint *E-mail:* kevin@dystopianstudios.com
Founded: 2004
Facility & equipment rentals, including cameras, lighting & sound recording equipment.
Branch Office(s)
670 Moulton Ave, No 9, Los Angeles, CA 90031

e-MEDIAtely
6778 Cibola, San Diego, CA 92120
Tel: 619-583-2008 *Toll Free Tel:* 866-816-6845 *Fax:* 619-501-1425
E-mail: sdweb@cox.net
Web Site: www.e-mediately.com
Key Personnel
Art Dir: Greg Raymond
Founded: 1976
CD duplication & graphic design.
Catalog(s), on request

E Video Productions
17 Washington St, Toms River, NJ 08753
Mailing Address: PO Box 322, Forked River, NJ 08731
Tel: 732-349-4762 *Toll Free Tel:* 877-384-3365
Web Site: www.evideoproductions.net
Key Personnel
Exec Prodr & Opers Mgr: Darcie King
Exec Prodr: Star Young
Dir, Photog & Post-Prodn Mgr: Kristopher King
Founded: 2001
Corporate video production. Specialize in Webmercials. In-studio & mobile studio rental.

Eagle Camera Support Systems Ltd
1783 Draycott Rd, North Vancouver, BC V7J 1W5, Canada
Tel: 604-649-6350
Web Site: eaglecss.com
Key Personnel
Owner & CEO: Ken Woznow *E-mail:* kwoz123@gmail.com
Founded: 1995
Camera support & cranes rental.

Eagle Films
2806 Cameron Rd, Falls Church, VA 22042-2004
Tel: 703-237-8160
Web Site: www.eaglefilms.com
Key Personnel
Owner: Phillip Cook *E-mail:* philcook@eaglefilms.com
Visual effects & animation.

Eagle Inc
PO Box 579, Clarkdale, AZ 86324
Tel: 928-204-2597 *Fax:* 928-204-2568
E-mail: hier_bosch@yahoo.com
Web Site: www.eagle-1st.com
Key Personnel
Pres: James Beck
Catalog(s) available

Eagle Multimedia
Division of Riden International Corp
6024 Paseo Palmilla, Goleta, CA 93117
Tel: 805-964-7041 *Fax:* 805-964-1338
E-mail: dicepoo@aol.com
Web Site: www.eaglemultimedia.com
Key Personnel
Pres: Richard Dennison
Founded: 1978
Distribute motion pictures internationally.
Membership(s): NATPE

Eagle Photographics & Digital Imaging Inc
3612 W Swann Ave, Tampa, FL 33609
Tel: 813-870-2495 *Fax:* 813-876-5093
Web Site: www.eaglefineartimaging.com
Key Personnel
Owner & Pres: George Cott *E-mail:* george@eaglefineartimaging.com
Inkjet prints, photographic digital prints, large format display, high-resolution scanning & digital scanning.
Membership(s): AIE™

EagleVision Inc
1200 High Ridge Rd, 2nd fl, Stamford, CT 06905
Tel: 203-359-8777 *Fax:* 203-348-6000
E-mail: info@evtv.net
Web Site: www.evtv.net
Key Personnel
Exec Prodr: Michael Macari, Jr *E-mail:* michael@evtv.net
Brochure(s) available

EAR Professional Audio/Video
2641 E McDowell Rd, Phoenix, AZ 85008
Tel: 602-267-0600 *Toll Free Tel:* 800-473-6914 *Fax:* 602-275-3277
E-mail: info@ear.net
Web Site: www.ear.net
Key Personnel
Pres: Edward Vogt
Founded: 1978
AV consulting, design, installation, sales & support.
Catalog(s) available
Membership(s): MCA-I

Earl Girls Inc
1648 White Horse Pike, Egg Harbor City, NJ 08215
Mailing Address: PO Box 297, Egg Harbor City, NJ 08215-0297
Tel: 609-965-6900 *Toll Free Tel:* 888-777-EARL (777-3275) *Fax:* 609-965-3330
E-mail: sales@earlgirlsinc.com
Web Site: earlgirlsinc.com
Key Personnel
Pres: Don Earl *Tel:* 609-965-6900 ext 117 *E-mail:* donearl@earlgirlsinc.com
Proj Specialist: Robert Thorpe *Tel:* 609-965-6900 ext 116
Founded: 1991
Sales, rental, installation & production services of entertainment audio, video, lighting, drapery & rigging.
Membership(s): International Special Events Society; Professional Lighting & Sound Association

Early Films
9 Richter St, Randolph, NJ 07869-3309
Tel: 973-361-5817 *Fax:* 973-361-2748
E-mail: info@earlyfilms.net
Web Site: www.earlyfilms.net
Key Personnel
Owner: Bruce Bertrand *E-mail:* bruceb@earlyfilms.net

Earmark LLC
1125 Dixwell Ave, Hamden, CT 06514
Tel: 203-777-2130 *Toll Free Tel:* 888-327-6275 *Fax:* 203-777-2886
E-mail: staff@earmark.com
Web Site: www.earmark.com
Founded: 1973
Catalog(s) available

Earth Mother Productions Inc™
PO Box 43204, Tucson, AZ 85733-3204
Tel: 520-790-7061 *Fax:* 801-740-6397
E-mail: art4wall@aol.com
Web Site: www.earthmotherproductions.com
Key Personnel
Pres: Pamala Ballingham
VP: Tim Ballingham
Catalog(s) available

EarthDesign Inc
9 Riverfront Dr, Venice, FL 34293
Tel: 941-276-8689 *Toll Free Tel:* 800-327-8433
E-mail: gp@jamilin.com
Web Site: www.jamilin.com
Key Personnel
Owner: Jami Lin
Production of decorating, design, landscaping, educational, documentary & vocational videos.
Catalog(s) available

Earthworks Inc
37 Wilton Rd, Milford, NH 03055
Mailing Address: PO Box 517, Wilton, NH 03086-0517
Tel: 603-654-6427 (sales); 603-654-2433 *Fax:* 603-654-6107
E-mail: info@earthworksaudio.com
Web Site: www.earthworksaudio.com
Key Personnel
COO: Bill Norton
Pres: Heidi B Robichaud
Membership(s): AES; InfoComm International®; NAMM, the National Association of Music Merchants

Earwax Productions Inc
916 Kearny St, San Francisco, CA 94133
Tel: 415-860-9403
Web Site: www.earwaxproductions.com
Key Personnel
Owner & Prodr: Jim McKee *E-mail:* jim@earwaxproductions.com
Founded: 1984
Two full pro tool studios; audio production & voice casting.

Earwig Music Co Inc
2054 W Farwell Ave, Unit G, Chicago, IL 60645-4963
Tel: 773-262-0278
E-mail: orders@earwigmusic.com
Web Site: www.earwigmusic.com
Key Personnel
CEO & Pres: Michael Frank *E-mail:* mfrank@earwigmusic.com
Founded: 1978
Produce & distribute blues, jazz & folktales on CD & cassette. Shipping is billed to customer.
Catalog(s), annual, free
Online catalog(s) available
Membership(s): The Blues Foundation; The Recording Academy

EASI
2296 Country Club Dr, Mason City, IA 50401
Tel: 641-424-5079 *Toll Free Tel:* 888-327-4797 *Fax:* 641-424-8869
Web Site: www.easisat.com
Key Personnel
Principal: Tim Hedrick *Tel:* 888-424-5079 *E-mail:* thedrick@easisat.com
Contact: Tom Head *Tel:* 888-515-2960 *Fax:* 608-648-3776 *E-mail:* thead@easisat.com
Founded: 1993
Satellite equipment, systems & integration from conception to completion.

East of Hollywood NY
140 53 St, Brooklyn, NY 11232
Tel: 718-492-7400 *Fax:* 718-439-3930
E-mail: info@eastofhollywoodny.com
Web Site: www.eastofhollywoodny.com
Key Personnel
Owner: Michael Tadross
Contact: Lucille Ascanio
Founded: 1996
Film & television production facility. Sound stages offer onsite production offices & extensive set, prop & wardrobe storage areas.

Eastco Multimedia Solutions Inc
3646 California Rd, Orchard Park, NY 14127
Tel: 716-662-0536 *Toll Free Tel:* 800-365-8273 (orders) *Fax:* 716-662-3360
E-mail: info@eastcomultimedia.com
Web Site: www.eastcomultimedia.com
Key Personnel
Pres: Holt Vaughn *E-mail:* holt@eastcomultimedia.com
Founded: 1985
Manufacturer of CDs & DVDs. Also does VHS duplication, commercial print, packaging & authoring.
Catalog(s), free, full color

Eastern Acoustic Works Inc (EAW)
One Main St, Whitinsville, MA 01588-2238
Tel: 508-234-6158 *Toll Free Tel:* 800-992-5013 *Fax:* 508-234-8251 *Toll Free Fax:* 800-322-8251
E-mail: info@eaw.com
Web Site: www.eaw.com
Key Personnel
EVP, Strategic Prod Devt: Kenton Forsythe
Founded: 1978
Catalog(s) available
Foreign Office(s): Century Point, Halifax Rd, High Wycombe, Bucks HP12 3SL, United Kingdom *Tel:* (01494) 552790 *Fax:* (01494) 552791
Membership(s): NSCA

Eastern Effects Inc
99 Ninth St, Brooklyn, NY 11215
Tel: 718-855-1197 *Fax:* 212-504-9534
E-mail: geteffected@easterneffects.com
Web Site: www.easterneffects.com
Key Personnel
Lead Mng Partner & Pres: Scott Levy *Tel:* 718-855-5167 ext 108 *E-mail:* scott@easterneffects.com
Mng Partner & Dir, Opers: Laura Gahrahmat *Tel:* 718-855-5167 ext 107 *E-mail:* laura@easterneffects.com
Founded: 1998
Lighting & grip equipment rental.

Eastern Video
7111 Biscayne Blvd, Miami, FL 33138
Tel: 305-759-7111 *Fax:* 305-759-7111; 305-751-2329
E-mail: miami@easternvideo.com
Web Site: www.easternvideo.com
Key Personnel
Owner & Pres: Susan Allen *E-mail:* sallen@easternvideo.com
Catalog(s) available
Branch Office(s)
1240 Oakleigh Dr, Atlanta, GA 30344, Mgr: John Edenfield *Tel:* 404-761-6111 *E-mail:* atlanta@easternvideo.com

Eastman Corp
7447 Via de Fortuna, Carlsbad, CA 92009
Tel: 760-603-8646
Web Site: www.kbwfoundation.com
Key Personnel
Pres: Kay Weiner *E-mail:* kayeastman@aol.com
Founded: 1992
Flyer(s) available

Eastman Kodak Professional
Division of Eastman Kodak Co
343 State St, Rochester, NY 14650
Toll Free Tel: 800-698-3324
Web Site: www.kodak.com
Key Personnel
Chmn & CEO: Jeff Clarke
VP & Dir, Commercial Mktg: Chris Payne
Catalog(s) available

Easy Edit Video Inc
8431 Baymeadows Way, Jacksonville, FL 32256
Tel: 904-730-9999 *Fax:* 904-730-0412
Web Site: www.easyeditvideo.com
Key Personnel
Owner & Pres: David Zuckerman *E-mail:* david@easyeditvideo.com
Founded: 1993
Professionally operated, affordably priced, we are northeast Florida's largest DVD duplication center, also offering production & post-production services for business clients. Two non-linear edit suites equipped with Final Cut Pro 7.0 & Adobe Creative Suite 6.0.

Easy Street Productions
118 Redhaven Ct, Thurmont, MD 21788
Tel: 301-471-8058
E-mail: info@publicdomainfootage.com
Web Site: www.publicdomainfootage.com
Key Personnel
Pres & Creative Dir: Peter Ferraro
Provider of public domain & royalty free contemporary & archival stock footage. Writing, producing & stock footage archival research.
Membership(s): NATAS

Eaton Corp
8609 Six Forks Rd, Raleigh, NC 27615
Tel: 919-872-3020 *Toll Free Tel:* 800-356-5794
E-mail: powerquality@eaton.com
Web Site: powerquality.eaton.com
Key Personnel
Pres, Power Quality Opers: Brian Brickhouse
Power distribution solution company.
Catalog(s) available

ECG Productions
120 Interstate N Pkwy SE, Suite 435, Atlanta, GA 30339
Tel: 678-855-5169
E-mail: info@ecgprod.com
Web Site: www.ecgprod.com
Key Personnel
Partner: Jason Sirotin *E-mail:* sirotin@ecgprod.com
Pres: Jason Marraccini *E-mail:* jason@ecgprod.com
CFO & VP: Trey Gregory *E-mail:* trey@ecgprod.com
Founded: 2006
Full service HD production & post. National & international shipping. Greenscreen & Cyc wall facility. Also offers compositing & 3D animation services as well as Blu-ray programming.
Membership(s): Georgia Production Partnership; Metro Atlanta Chamber of Commerce

Eco-Greenlighting Inc
7718 San Fernando Rd N, Sun Valley, CA 91352
Tel: 818-768-4300 *Fax:* 818-768-4988
E-mail: info@eco-greenlighting.com
Web Site: www.eco-greenlighting.com
Key Personnel
VP: Scott Hunter *Tel:* 818-768-4300 ext 102
Founded: 1992
Glass illumination, special effect lighting & fiber optic lighting.
Catalog(s) available
Membership(s): Illuminating Engineering Society

ECONEWS (Environmental Television Series) & (Environmental Directions Radio Series)
Subsidiary of Educational Communications
PO Box 351419, Los Angeles, CA 90035-9119
Tel: 310-559-9160 *Fax:* 310-559-9160
E-mail: ecnp@aol.com
Web Site: www.ecoprojects.org
Key Personnel
Exec Prodr & Dir: Nancy Pearlman
Founded: 1958
Produce & distribute Econews television series & Environmental Directions radio series. Produce, distribute & give away both DVDs & CDs of environmental radio & television programs. We also do documentaries & public service announcements & have an archive of over 3,000 tapes from 1977 to present.
Catalog(s), listing over 600 video programs in series & 2,000 radio shows

ECS Inc
5665 Tremont Ave, Davenport, IA 52807-2658
Tel: 563-322-1525 *Fax:* 563-322-5920
Web Site: www.ecsdav.com
Key Personnel
Pres: Rex Lawrence
VP, Opers: Nate Lawrence
Rental Mgr: Ben Villareal
Founded: 1971 (as Video Midwest)
Specialize in custom design, engineering, installation, rental, sales & service of commercial & broadcast quality communication systems.
Catalog(s) available
Membership(s): InfoComm International®; NSCA; PSNI

EcuFilm, see Kingswood Productions

Edcom Multimedia Products
2386 Main St, Unit 1, London, ON N6P 1A9, Canada
Tel: 519-652-3533 *Toll Free Tel:* 800-265-1069 *Fax:* 519-652-5045
E-mail: sales-l@edcom.ca; info@edcom.ca
Web Site: www.edcom.ca
Key Personnel
Pres: Wayne Gowanlock *E-mail:* wgowanlock@edcom.ca
Founded: 1979
Digital signage solutions, collaborative meeting spaces with interactive solutions.
Catalog(s) available
Branch Office(s)
31 Durwood Place, Unit C, Waterloo, ON N2L 4E5, Canada *Tel:* 519-578-2260 *Fax:* 519-578-8101 *E-mail:* sales-w@edcom.ca
4320 Seminole St, Windsor, ON N8Y 1Z6, Canada *Tel:* 519-256-7772 *Fax:* 519-256-1899 *E-mail:* sales-w@edcom.ca

EDCOR Electronics Corp
7130 National Parks Hwy, Carlsbad, NM 88220
Tel: 575-887-6790 *Toll Free Tel:* 800-854-0259 *Fax:* 575-887-6880
E-mail: sales@edcorusa.com
Web Site: www.edcorusa.com
Key Personnel
Pres: Brian Weston *E-mail:* bweston@edcorusa.com
VP: Phyllis Weston
CD-ROM catalog(s), free

Edgeware Associates/Travel Arts Syndicate
377 Rector Place, Suite 10-H, New York, NY 10280
Tel: 212-807-7509
Web Site: www.travelartssyndicate.blogspot.com
Key Personnel
Pres: Terese Loeb Kreuzer *E-mail:* tereseloeb10@gmail.com
Founded: 1979
Multi-media program for web use.
Brochure(s) available

Edgewise Media Inc
602 N Cypress St, Orange, CA 92867
Toll Free Tel: 800-959-5156 *Fax:* 323-466-6815
E-mail: sales@edgewise-media.com
Web Site: www.edgewise-media.com
Key Personnel
Owner & CEO: David Cohen
Founded: 1993

Broadcast video tape supplier. Products include AV data media. Authorized distributor for Sony, Fuji & Maxell.
Catalog(s) available
Branch Office(s)
4518 W Vanowen St, Burbank, CA 91505
630 Ninth Ave, Suite 800, New York, NY 10036 *Toll Free Tel:* 800-444-9330

Edgewood Studios
Howe Ctr, Unit 12-B, Suite 90, Rutland, VT 05701-4459
Tel: 802-773-0510 *Fax:* 802-773-3481
Web Site: www.edgewoodstudios.com
Key Personnel
Owner: David Giancola
Studio Mgr: Jeremy Jackson
Founded: 1987

Edison Price Lighting
41-50 22 St, Long Island City, NY 11101
Tel: 718-685-0700 *Fax:* 718-786-8530
E-mail: info@epl.com
Web Site: www.epl.com
Key Personnel
Pres: Emma Price *E-mail:* eprice@epl.com
EVP, Mktg & Sales: Joel R Siegel *E-mail:* jsiegel@epl.com
Catalog(s) available

Edit House Chicago
5325 W Berenice Ave, Chicago, IL 60641
Tel: 773-725-1525
Web Site: www.edithousechicago.com
Key Personnel
Ed: Jeff Hellyer *E-mail:* jeff@edithousechicago.com
Editing, post-production, graphics & open captioning services for video, television & DVD productions.

The Editing Co
7030 Empire Central Dr, Houston, TX 77040
Tel: 713-783-2655 *Fax:* 713-783-8642
Web Site: www.editingco.com
Key Personnel
Pres: Nancy Clinton
Founded: 1979
All new award-winning television & corporate communications facility with 3 edit suites, Pro Tools audio suite, large area network server & film/video production services. Fast closed captioning in HD, 14 video formats, compressions, web development, DVD/CD authoring & duplication. Subtitling & narrations in 60 languages, 30' x 30' studio.
Catalog(s) available
Membership(s): WIFT

Les Editions CEC Inc
Affiliate of Quebecor Media
9001 boul Louis-H-La Fontaine, Anjou, QC H1J 2C5, Canada
Tel: 514-351-6010 *Toll Free Tel:* 800-363-0494 *Fax:* 514-351-3534
Web Site: www.editionscec.com
Key Personnel
Pres: Christian Jette
VP, Sales & Mktg: Gilles Lefebvre *Tel:* 514-351-6010 ext 320 *E-mail:* gilles.lefebvre@ceceditions.com
Founded: 1956
Catalog(s) available

Edmund Scientific
532 Main St, Tonawanda, NY 14150
Toll Free Tel: 800-728-6999; 800-818-4955 *Toll Free Fax:* 800-828-3299
E-mail: scientifics@edsci.com
Web Site: www.scientificsonline.com
Key Personnel
Dir: Tim Burns *E-mail:* tim.burns@scientificsdierect.com
Catalog(s) available

EDR Media LLC
23330 Commerce Park, Beachwood, OH 44122-5811
Tel: 216-292-7300
Web Site: www.edrmedia.com; www.beachwoodstudios.com
Key Personnel
CEO: Peter T Vrettas *E-mail:* vrettas@edrmedia.com
Chief Engr: Ray Leporati
Develops & produces digital media including broadcast TV shows, radio & TV spots of ad agencies, corporate video & interactive programs & content for retail media networks. Motion graphics, flame compositing, digital signage & sound design.
Branch Office(s)
4616 W Sahara Ave, No 608, Las Vegas, NV 89102 *Tel:* 702-228-2022 (exec off)

Education Development Center Inc (EDC)
43 Foundry Ave, Waltham, MA 02453-8313
Tel: 617-969-7100 *Fax:* 617-969-5979
E-mail: contact@edc.org
Web Site: www.edc.org
Key Personnel
CEO & Pres: Luther Luedtke
VP & Deputy to Pres: Siobhan Murphy
Founded: 1958
Branch Office(s)
1025 Thomas Jefferson St NW, Suite 700, Washington, DC 20007 *Tel:* 202-572-3700 *Fax:* 202-223-4059
96 Morton St, 7th fl, New York, NY 10014 *Tel:* 212-807-4200 *Fax:* 212-633-8804

Education Works
735 Iwilei Rd, Suite 330, Honolulu, HI 96817
Tel: 808-237-5350 *Toll Free Tel:* 800-573-3822 *Fax:* 808-545-8341
E-mail: info@educationworkshawaii.com
Web Site: catalog.educationworkshawaii.com
Catalog(s) available
Membership(s): InfoComm International®

Educational Activities Inc
PO Box 87, Baldwin, NY 11510-0087
Tel: 516-223-4666 *Toll Free Tel:* 800-797-3223 *Fax:* 516-623-9282
E-mail: learn@edact.com
Web Site: www.edact.com
Key Personnel
Off Mgr: Roni Hofbauer
Founded: 1948
Catalog(s) available

Educational Film Center
3314 Newark St NW, Washington, DC 20008
Tel: 202-243-1048 *Fax:* 202-243-1048
Web Site: www.efcvideo.com
Key Personnel
CEO: Ruth Pollak *E-mail:* ruthpollak@verizon.net
CEO, Prodn Div: Ira H Klugerman *Tel:* 703-250-3393 *E-mail:* efc3ira@mac.com

Educational Images Ltd
660 Fassett Rd, Elmira, NY 14901
Tel: 607-732-1090 *Toll Free Tel:* 800-527-4264
Key Personnel
CEO: Charles R Belinky, PhD
Produce & distribute educational media & stock photo library-education, science & natural history.

Educational Impressions
Affiliate of A W Peller & Associates Inc
785 Franklin Ave, Franklin Lakes, NJ 07417
Mailing Address: PO Box 377, Franklin Lakes, NJ 07417-0377
Tel: 201-644-0908 *Toll Free Tel:* 800-451-7450 *Fax:* 201-644-0907
E-mail: awpeller@optonline.net
Web Site: www.edimpressions.com
Key Personnel
Pres: Allan W Peller
Dir, Sales & Mktg: Neil Peller
Secy: Barbara Peller
Founded: 1973
Catalog(s) available
Membership(s): Education Market Association

Educational Insights
380 N Fairway Dr, Vernon Hills, IL 60061
Toll Free Tel: 888-591-9334 (cust serv) *Toll Free Fax:* 888-995-0506 (cust serv)
E-mail: info@edin.com; cs@educationalinsights.com
Web Site: www.educationalinsights.com
Key Personnel
Mktg Mgr: Thao Truong *Tel:* 847-968-3710
Founded: 1962
Catalog(s) available
Membership(s): ASTRA; Education Market Association; InfoComm International®

Educational Media LLC
1300 W Main St, Oklahoma City, OK 73106
Tel: 405-239-2955 *Toll Free Tel:* 800-654-8428 *Fax:* 405-236-4261
E-mail: mail@educationalmediallc.com
Web Site: www.educationalmediallc.com
Founded: 1970
Distribute & manufacture language lab equipment.
Catalog(s) available

Educational Technology Services (ETS)
Division of University of California, San Francisco
Medical Sciences, Rm SB-43, 513 Parnassus Ave, San Francisco, CA 94143-0702
Tel: 415-476-4310 *Fax:* 415-514-3735
E-mail: edtech@ucsf.edu
Web Site: edtech.ucsf.edu
Key Personnel
Dir: John DeAngelo
Catalog(s) available
Membership(s): HeSCA

Educational Video Group Inc
291 Southwind Way, Greenwood, IN 46142-9190
Tel: 317-889-8253 *Fax:* 317-888-5857
E-mail: service@evgonline.com
Web Site: www.evgonline.com
Key Personnel
VP: Roger Cook
Online catalog(s) available

Educational Video Network
1401 19 St, Huntsville, TX 77340
Tel: 936-295-5767 *Toll Free Tel:* 800-762-0060 *Fax:* 936-294-0233 *Toll Free Fax:* 866-814-1714
Web Site: www.evndirect.com
Key Personnel
CEO: George H Russell
Catalog(s) available
Membership(s): Entertainment Merchants Association

EduMedia of Sugar Land, Texas
PO Box 2428, Sugar Land, TX 77487-2428
Tel: 281-277-3970
E-mail: service@history2u.com
Web Site: www.history2u.com
Key Personnel
Pres: Bryan Hardesty
Founded: 1995

EEG Enterprises Inc
586 Main St, Farmingdale, NY 11735
Tel: 516-293-7472 *Fax:* 516-293-7417
E-mail: sales@eegent.com
Web Site: www.eegent.com
Key Personnel
Dir, Sales: Eric McErlain *E-mail:* ericm@eegent.com
Manufacture TV broadcast equipment, closed caption decoders & encoders.
Catalog(s) available
Branch Office(s)
20 Jay St, Brooklyn, NY 11201
Membership(s): NAB

Effective Engineering
2805 W Empire Ave, Burbank, CA 91504
Tel: 818-841-4437 *Fax:* 818-841-4389
E-mail: info@effeng.com
Web Site: www.effeng.com
Key Personnel
Off Mgr: Shirley Fuentes
Catalog(s) available
Membership(s): NAB; SMPTE

Effective Learning Systems Inc
7740 W 78 St, Bloomington, MN 55439
Tel: 952-943-1660 *Toll Free Tel:* 800-966-5683 (orders)
E-mail: info@efflearn.com
Web Site: www.efflearn.com
Key Personnel
Founder: Bob Griswold
Gen Mgr: Jeff Griswold
Founded: 1972
Catalog(s) available

eFootage LLC
65 N Raymond Ave, Suite 220, Pasadena, CA 91103
Tel: 626-395-9593 *Fax:* 626-792-5394
E-mail: info@efootage.com
Web Site: www.efootage.com
Key Personnel
Owner: Paul Risey
Founded: 1967
Premier DV, film & video, digital & HD stock footage archive.
Foreign Office(s): Chronos-Media GmbH/eFootage LLC, Alt Nowawes 116-118, 14482 Potsdam-Babelsberg Brandenburg, Germany, Head, Sales: Christel Gass *Tel:* (0331) 70493 0 *Fax:* (0331) 70493 15 *E-mail:* info@chronos-media.de *Web Site:* www.chronos-media.de
Membership(s): Association of Moving Image Archivists

EFX Media
2300 S Ninth St, Suite 136, Arlington, VA 22204
Tel: 703-486-2303 *Fax:* 703-553-9813
E-mail: info@efxmedia.com; sales@efxmedia.com
Web Site: www.efxmedia.com
Key Personnel
CEO & Pres: James Franco
Founded: 1983
Core business revolves around full service video production, interactive solutions, media services & online video.
Membership(s): MCA-I; Women in Film & Video

Egan Visual Inc/Egan TeamBoard Inc
300 Hanlan Rd, Woodbridge, ON L4L 3P6, Canada
Tel: 905-851-2826 *Toll Free Tel:* 800-263-2387 (US & CN) *Toll Free Fax:* 888-609-8886
E-mail: marketing@egan.com
Web Site: www.egan.com; www.teamboard.com
Key Personnel
Cont: Chris Garlock
Founded: 1967
Manufacture interactive white boards.
Catalog(s) available
Branch Office(s)
Egan Visual West, 6085 Rickenbacker Rd, Commerce, CA 90040 *Toll Free Tel:* 800-826-1778 *Toll Free Fax:* 800-726-1314

Egripment USA Inc
201 Center Park Dr, Suite 1010, Knoxville, TN 37922
Tel: 865-357-7535 *Fax:* 865-357-7536
Web Site: www.egripment.com
Manufacturer of camera support equipment, including remote systems.
Product sheet(s) available
Membership(s): IBC; NAB

18 Label Studios
18 Label St, Montclair, NJ 07042
Tel: 973-744-7382
E-mail: info@18label.com
Web Site: 18label.com
Key Personnel
Contact: Elizabeth Sardinsky *E-mail:* elizabethsardinsky@gmail.com
Photography studio & event space designed to cater to photographers, agencies, producers, filmmakers & brands.

8K Productions
11952 Blue Heron Dr, Draper, UT 84020
Tel: 801-671-8357
E-mail: rentals@8kproductions.com
Web Site: www.8kproductions.com
Key Personnel
Dir: Jeffrey S Farrell *E-mail:* jeff@8kproductions.com
Provides rental of video cameras, lenses & accessories.

Eiki International
Subsidiary of Eiki Industrial Co Ltd (Japan)
30251 Esperanza, Rancho Santa Margarita, CA 92688-2130
Tel: 949-457-0200 *Toll Free Tel:* 800-242-3454 *Fax:* 949-457-7877 *Toll Free Fax:* 800-457-3454
E-mail: usa@eiki.com
Web Site: www.eiki.com
Key Personnel
CEO & Pres: Bill Blair
Catalog(s) available
Branch Office(s)
PO Box 156, Midland, ON L4R 4K8, Canada *Toll Free Tel:* 800-563-3454 *Toll Free Fax:* 800-567-4069
Membership(s): Association of Audio-Visual Service Technicians; InfoComm International®; SMPTE

EiKO Ltd
23220 W 84 St, Shawnee Mission, KS 66227
Tel: 913-441-8500 *Toll Free Tel:* 800-852-2217 *Fax:* 913-441-6679
E-mail: eiko@eiko.com
Web Site: www.eiko-ltd.com
Key Personnel
CEO: Gary Withers
Pres: Rick Laird
Mktg Dir & Natl Sales Mgr: Andy Poorman *Tel:* 913-441-8500 ext 8550 *E-mail:* andyp@eiko-ltd.com
Founded: 1978
Primary lighting manufacturer.
Branch Office(s)
81 King St, Barrie, ON L4N 6B5, Canada *Tel:* 705-721-5189 *Fax:* 705-721-7855 *E-mail:* orderdesk@eiko.com
Membership(s): Education Market Association; InfoComm International®; NAILD; Photo Marketing Association

eInstruction Corp
14400 N 87 St, Suite 250, Scottsdale, AZ 85260
Tel: 480-948-6540 *Toll Free Tel:* 800-856-0732 *Fax:* 480-948-5508
Web Site: www.einstruction.com
Key Personnel
CEO & Pres: Rich Fennessy
CFO: Tim Torno
SVP, Global Sales & Mktg: Samir Joglekar
VP, Mktg: Shelly Bodine
VP, Prod Mgmt: Eric Rohy
Founded: 1980
Branch Office(s)
1717 Dixie Hwy, Suite 450, Fort Wright, KY 41011 *Tel:* 859-446-7040 *Toll Free Tel:* 800-549-3415 *Fax:* 859-331-2360
1330 Teasley Lane, Denton, TX 76205 *Tel:* 940-565-0004 *Toll Free Tel:* 888-707-6819 *Fax:* 940-565-0959
1450 O'Connor Dr, Suite 210, Toronto, ON M4B 2T8, Canada *Toll Free Tel:* 877-690-5001 *Fax:* 416-691-3873 *E-mail:* canada@einstruction.com
Foreign Office(s): 26/36 rue Alfred Nobel, 93600 Aulnay-sous-Bois, France

El Mar Plastics Inc
967 E Sandhill Ave, Carson, CA 90746
Tel: 310-436-6444 *Toll Free Tel:* 800-255-5210 *Fax:* 310-436-6445
E-mail: sales@elmarplastics.com
Web Site: www.elmarplastics.com
Key Personnel
Pres: Allen Schor *E-mail:* allen@elmarplastics.com
Founded: 1966
Manufacture audio jewel boxes, handle & ship spindles for video. Also distribute DVD boxes.
Catalog(s) available

ELC Sales & Service Inc
3100 S Congress Ave, Suite 6, Boynton Beach, FL 33426
Tel: 561-756-2210
E-mail: tvman@gate.net
Key Personnel
Pres: Gary Braisted

Electric Lady Studios
52 W Eighth St, New York, NY 10011
Tel: 212-677-4700
Web Site: electricladystudios.com
Key Personnel
Gen & Artist Mgr: Lee Foster *E-mail:* lee.foster@electricladystudios.com
Asst Mgr: Vira Byramji *E-mail:* vira@electricladystudios.com
Artist Mgr: Paul Bannister *E-mail:* paul@electricladystudios.com
Founded: 1970
Oldest working & flourishing recording studio in NYC made famous by Jimi Hendrix.

Electriduct Inc
6250 NW 27 Way, Fort Lauderdale, FL 33309
Tel: 954-867-9100 *Toll Free Tel:* 866-673-9590 *Fax:* 954-206-0799
E-mail: sales@electriduct.com
Web Site: www.electriduct.com
Key Personnel
Pres: Joseph Proto *E-mail:* joe@electriduct.com
Founded: 2006
Online catalog(s) available

Electro Impulse Laboratory Inc
1805 Rte 33, Neptune, NJ 07754
Mailing Address: PO Box 278, Neptune, NJ 07754-0278
Tel: 732-776-5800 *Fax:* 732-776-6793
E-mail: sales@electroimpulse.com
Web Site: www.electroimpulse.com

Key Personnel
CEO & Pres: Mark Rubin
Founded: 1949
Catalog(s) available

Electron Microscopy Sciences (EMS)
Subsidiary of Negafile Systems
1560 Industry Rd, Hatfield, PA 19440
Mailing Address: PO Box 550, Hatfield, PA 19440
Tel: 215-412-8400 *Toll Free Tel:* 800-523-5874 *Fax:* 215-412-8450
E-mail: sgkcck@aol.com
Web Site: www.emsdiasum.com/microscopy
Key Personnel
Pres: Stacie Kirsch
Founded: 1988
Furniture quality wood storage files for cassettes, viewmaster-stereo slides, archival, glassine envelopes, acetate sleeves.
Catalog(s) available

Electronic Arts
209 Redwood Shores Pkwy, Redwood City, CA 94065
Tel: 650-628-1500
Web Site: www.ea.com
Key Personnel
CEO: Andrew Wilson
Chief Mktg Offr: Chris Bruzzo
EVP: Frank Gibeau
EVP, HR: Gabrielle Toledano
Founded: 1982
Publishing, developing & distributing interactive entertainment & education software worldwide.

Electronic Communications Systems, see ECS Inc

Electronic Theatre Controls Inc, see ETC

Electronic Vision Inc (EV)
5 Depot St, Athens, OH 45701
Tel: 740-592-2433 *Fax:* 740-592-2650
E-mail: info@ev.net
Web Site: www.electronicvision.com
Key Personnel
CEO: Dan Krivicich *Tel:* 740-592-2433 ext 111 *E-mail:* dkriv@ev.net
COO: Tony Presti *Tel:* 740-592-2433 ext 112 *E-mail:* tpresti@ev.net
Catalog(s) available

Electrorack Legrand Division
1443 S Sunkist St, Anaheim, CA 92806
Tel: 714-776-5420 *Toll Free Tel:* 800-433-6745 *Fax:* 714-776-9683
E-mail: sales@electrorack.com
Web Site: www.electrorack.com
Key Personnel
VP: Jeff Shew
Founded: 1955
Manufacture server racks, consoles, 19 inch EIA equipment & accessories.
Catalog(s) available
CD-ROM catalog(s) available
Membership(s): NAB

Electrosonic Inc
3320 N San Fernando Blvd, Burbank, CA 91504
Tel: 818-333-3600 *Toll Free Tel:* 888-343-3604 (sales) *Fax:* 818-230-1017
E-mail: info@electrosonic.com
Web Site: www.electrosonic.com
Key Personnel
Pres: Jim Bowie
Sr Mktg Mgr: Ramzi Shakra
Mktg Coord: Pamela Manlulu *E-mail:* pamela.manlulu@electrosonic.com
Founded: 1964
AV company providing systems integration services, engineering, project management & AV design.
Branch Office(s)
4501 Vineland Rd, Suite 105, Orlando, FL 32811 *Tel:* 407-839-1154 *Fax:* 407-839-2055
10320 Bren Rd E, Minnetonka, MN 55343-9048 *Tel:* 952-931-7500 *Toll Free Tel:* 800-328-6202 *Fax:* 952-938-9311
318 W 39 St, 9th fl, New York, NY 10018 *Tel:* 212-206-7711 *Fax:* 212-206-7333
Foreign Office(s): Electrosonic Ltd, Hawley Mill, Hawley Rd, Dartford, Kent DA2 7SY, United Kingdom *Tel:* (01322) 222211 *Fax:* (01322) 282215 *Web Site:* www.electrosonic.co.uk
Membership(s): AFCEA; American Institute of Architects; ASTC; IAAPA; InfoComm International®; NSCA; Themed Entertainment Association

Elegant Packaging Corp
5253 W Roosevelt Rd, Cicero, IL 60804
Tel: 708-652-3400 *Toll Free Tel:* 800-367-5493 *Fax:* 708-652-6444
E-mail: info@elegantpackaging.com
Web Site: www.elegantpackaging.com
Key Personnel
Pres: Mario Denado
VP: Stan Guillaume
Founded: 1910
Design & manufacture audio-video CDs, DVDs, VHS, direct mail, presentation kits & folders.
Catalog(s) available

Elektrashock
1320 Main St, Venice, CA 90291
Tel: 310-399-4985 *Fax:* 310-399-4972
E-mail: info@elektrashock.com
Web Site: www.elektrashock.com
Key Personnel
Dir: Darnell Williams
Founded: 1997
Computer animation, special effects & motion capture services.

Eli Research Group
2222 Sedwick Rd, Suite 102, Durham, NC 27713
Toll Free Tel: 800-223-8720 *Toll Free Fax:* 800-508-2592
E-mail: customerservice@dartnellcorp.com
Web Site: www.dartnellcorp.com
Key Personnel
Founder & CEO: Greg E Lindberg
Educational training programs.
Catalog(s) available
Membership(s): Instructional Systems Association

Elite Video
209 E Emerson Rd, Lexington, MA 02420
Tel: 781-862-6606
E-mail: sales@elitevision.com
Web Site: www.elitevision.com
Key Personnel
Pres: Eric Geller *E-mail:* egeller@elitevision.com
VP, Engg: Walter Allen *E-mail:* wallen@elitevision.com
Founded: 1999
Manufacturer/Distributor/VAR/Installer of large screen displays for home & business.
Membership(s): Custom Electronic Design & Installation Association

Elite Video & Photography Services Inc
Division of Elite Video Services Corp
250 Mount Sinai Coram Rd, Coram, NY 11727
Tel: 631-696-1635
E-mail: info@cantbeatelite.com
Web Site: www.cantbeatelite.com
Key Personnel
Pres: Cheryl Collik
Mktg Mgr: Bob Collik
Founded: 1979
Video production, post-production & digital imaging.

Albert Ellis Institute (AEI)
145 E 32 St, 9th fl, New York, NY 10016
Tel: 212-535-0822 *Fax:* 212-249-3582
E-mail: info@albertellis.org
Web Site: www.albertellis.org
Key Personnel
Exec Dir: Kristene Doyle
Founded: 1959

Ellison Educational Equipment Inc
25862 Commercentre Dr, Lake Forest, CA 92630-8804
Tel: 949-598-8822 *Toll Free Tel:* 800-253-2238 *Fax:* 949-598-8840 *Toll Free Fax:* 800-253-2240
E-mail: customersupport@ellison.com
Web Site: www.ellison.com
Key Personnel
CEO: Kristin Highberg
Art Dir: E L Smith *Tel:* 949-598-8822 ext 190 *E-mail:* esmith@ellison.com
Founded: 1977
Catalog(s) available
Foreign Office(s): Ellison Europe Ltd, Whitegate Industrial Estate, Unit 3, Wrexham LL13 8UG, United Kingdom *Tel:* (0845) 345 2277 *Fax:* (0845) 345 0111 *E-mail:* europecustomerservice@ellison.com
Membership(s): Pacific Educational Marketing Association

ELMO USA Corp
Subsidiary of ELMO Co Ltd
1478 Old Country Rd, Plainview, NY 11803
Tel: 516-501-1400 *Toll Free Tel:* 800-947-3566 *Fax:* 516-501-0429
E-mail: elmo@elmousa.com
Web Site: www.elmousa.com
Catalog(s) available
Branch Office(s)
5555 Garden Grove Blvd, Suite 375, Westminster, CA 92683 *Tel:* 714-828-8457 *Fax:* 714-828-8429
Foreign Office(s): ELMO (Beijing) Co Ltd, Xiaoyun Rd, Chaoyang District, Beijing, China *Tel:* (010) 5716-3481 *Fax:* (010) 6462-6605 *Web Site:* www.elmochina.com.cn
ELMO Europe SAS, Immeuble Elysees la Defense, 7C, Place du Dome, 92056 Paris la Defense, France *Tel:* 01 73 02 67 06 *Fax:* 01 73 02 67 10 *E-mail:* info@elmoeurope.fr *Web Site:* www.elmoeurope.com
ELMO Europe SAS, Hansaallee 201, 40549 Dusseldorf, Germany *Tel:* (0211) 544 756 40 *Fax:* (0211) 544 756 60 *E-mail:* info@elmo-germany.de *Web Site:* elmo-germany.de
ELMO Co Ltd, 3-12-16 Mita, Minato-ku, Tokyo 108-0073, Japan *Tel:* (03) 3453 6471 *Fax:* (03) 3453 6479 *Web Site:* www.elmo.co.jp
ELMO Russia, 121170 Moscow, Russia *Tel:* (495) 743 2620 *E-mail:* info@elmorussia.com *Web Site:* elmorussia.com

Elo TouchSystems
1033 McCarthy Blvd, Milpitas, CA 95035
Toll Free Tel: 800-356-8682; 800-557-1458 *Fax:* 650-361-4722
E-mail: eloinfo@elotouch.com; customerservice@elotouch.com
Web Site: www.elotouch.com
Key Personnel
CEO: Craig Witsoe
Founded: 1971
Branch Office(s)
250 Metro Park, Rochester, NY 14623-2617 *Tel:* 585-272-3100
Membership(s): SID

ELS Productions Inc
3287 Sanborn Dr, Riverton, UT 84065
Tel: 801-676-0807 *Toll Free Tel:* 800-927-3472
E-mail: customerservice@elsproductions.com
Web Site: www.elsproductions.com
Key Personnel
Owner: Dawn McLelland
Owner & Pres: Mark McLelland *E-mail:* mark@elsproductions.com
Short run CD & DVD duplication & retail packaging.
Printed material(s), free

Em Gee Film Library
13502 Erwin St, Van Nuys, CA 91401
Tel: 818-997-0410
Key Personnel
Owner & Mgr: Murray Glass *E-mail:* murray713@hotmail.com
Founded: 1954
16mm film rental library; 16mm film sales; video sales.
Affiliate companies: Glenn Photo Supply; Glenn Video Vistas.
Catalog(s), $5

eMagin Corp
3006 Northup Way, Suite 103, Bellevue, WA 98004
Tel: 425-284-5200 *Toll Free Tel:* 877-362-4461 *Fax:* 425-284-5201
E-mail: info@emagin.com
Web Site: www.emagin.com
Key Personnel
CEO & Pres: Andrew G Sculley
CFO: Paul C Campbell
Founded: 1996
Catalog(s) available
Branch Office(s)
2070 Rte 52, Bldg 334, Hopewell Junction, NY 12533 *Tel:* 845-838-7900 *Fax:* 845-838-7901 (display mfg opers & R&D)
PO Box 121, Vienna, VA 22183, Contact: Doug Hughes *Tel:* 202-664-2222 *E-mail:* dhughes@emagin.com (govt progs & congressional rel)
Foreign Office(s): 6-4-9-201 Minami-Aoyama, Minato-ku, Tokyo 107-0062, Japan *Tel:* (03) 5766 0244 *Fax:* (03) 5766 0258 *E-mail:* ysnakazaki@e-mail.jp

Emanuel Audiovisual Consultants
Division of Emanuel Associates Inc
303 County Rd, Cresskill, NJ 07626
Tel: 201-569-5328 *Toll Free Fax:* 888-397-1302
E-mail: emanuelav@att.net
Web Site: www.audiovisualconsultant.com
Key Personnel
Pres & AV Consultant: Frank Emanuel
Founded: 1980
Emanuel creates AV budgets & designs, bid documents & punch lists.
Catalog(s), on written request
Membership(s): American Society of Professional Engineers; Distance Learning Association; InfoComm International®

EMC/Paradigm Publishing
Division of EMC Corp
875 Montreal Way, St Paul, MN 55102
Tel: 651-290-2800 (corp) *Toll Free Tel:* 800-535-6865 (cust care); 800-328-1452 *Fax:* 651-290-2899 *Toll Free Fax:* 800-328-4564 (cust care)
E-mail: educate@emcp.com
Web Site: www.emcp.com
Founded: 1954
Catalog(s) available

Emcor Enclosures-Crenlo
1600 Fourth Ave NW, Rochester, MN 55901
Tel: 507-287-3535 *Fax:* 507-287-3405
E-mail: emcorenclosures@crenlo.com
Web Site: www.emcorenclosures.com
Catalog(s) available

Emedia Studios, see Gurrilla Video Solutions

Emerald Records
Subsidiary of The Entertainer Network
PO Box 17059, Nashville, TN 37217-0059
Tel: 615-361-7902
E-mail: entertainernet@comcast.net
Web Site: www.entertainernet.net
Key Personnel
Pres: Cliff Ayers *E-mail:* cliffayersostermeyer@gmail.com
Founded: 1961
Over 1,200 tracks with & without music. Recorded tracks over 30 years. Internet radio programming-WHIR (Wildhorse Internet Radio).
Branch Office(s)
608 SW 75 Terr, North Lauderdale, FL 33068
Foreign Office(s): Berlinstr 5, 34513 Waldeck, Germany
Membership(s): ASCAP; BMI

Emergency Film Group
Division of Detrick Lawrence Corp
140 Cooke St, Edgartown, MA 02539
Mailing Address: PO Box 1928, Edgartown, MA 02539-1928
Tel: 508-627-8844 *Toll Free Tel:* 800-842-0999 *Fax:* 508-627-8863
E-mail: info@efilmgroup.com
Web Site: www.efilmgroup.com
Key Personnel
Pres & Dir: Gordon Massingham *E-mail:* gordon@efilmgroup.com
VP, Mktg: Kerry O'Donnell *E-mail:* kerry@efilmgroup.com
Founded: 1987
Videos, DVDs & software.
Membership(s): IAFC; ISFSI; NFPA

Emerson Network Power Surge Protection Inc
Division of Emerson
100 Emerson Pkwy, Binghamton, NY 13905
Mailing Address: PO Box 1380, Binghamton, NY 13902-1380
Tel: 607-721-8840 *Toll Free Tel:* 800-288-6169 *Fax:* 607-722-8713
E-mail: contactsurge@emerson.com
Web Site: www.emersonnetworkpower.com
Key Personnel
Dir, Mktg: Sarah Beadle
Power quality & lightning protection equipment.
Catalog(s) available
Membership(s): NEMRA-Manufacturers Group

Emerson Radio Corp
Affiliate of H H Scott Division Audio Equipment
3 University Plaza, Suite 405, Hackensack, NJ 07601
Tel: 973-884-5800 *Toll Free Tel:* 800-909-1240 (cust serv) *Fax:* 973-428-2067
E-mail: internet@emersonradio.com
Web Site: www.emersonradio.com
Key Personnel
CEO: Duncan Hon
EVP: Andrew L Davis
Treas & Asst Secy: Barry Smith
Founded: 1948
Consumer electronic sales including home theater systems, DVD players & televisions.

Emery-Pratt Co
1966 W M-21, Owosso, MI 48867-1379
Tel: 989-723-5291 *Toll Free Tel:* 800-248-3887 *Fax:* 989-723-4677 *Toll Free Fax:* 800-523-6379
E-mail: mail@emery-pratt.com
Web Site: www.emery-pratt.com
Key Personnel
Natl Sales Mgr: Avery Weaver
Acct Mgr: Byron E Shattuck *E-mail:* byron.shattuck@emery-pratt.com
Membership(s): ALA

EMI CMG Distribution
Division of EMI Christian Music Group
101 Winners Circle, Brentwood, TN 37027
Mailing Address: PO Box 5084, Brentwood, TN 37024-5084
Tel: 615-371-4300 *Toll Free Tel:* 800-877-4443 *Fax:* 615-371-6555; 615-371-6980 (sales)
E-mail: distribution@emicmg.com
Web Site: www.emicmg.com; www.emicmgdistribution.com
Key Personnel
SVP, Sales & Mktg: Greg Bays
Founded: 1994
Catalog(s), annual

Emlight Design
1179 N Eastman Ave, Suite 1, Los Angeles, CA 90063
Tel: 323-261-5162 *Toll Free Fax:* 866-728-9164
E-mail: service@dimmer.com
Web Site: www.dimmer.com; www.emlightdesign.com
Key Personnel
Owner: Maurice Garcia
Founded: 1999
Service dimmers: architectural, theatrical, motion picture & television lighting.

eMotion Studios
85 Liberty Ship Way, Suite 110, Sausalito, CA 94965
Tel: 415-331-6975 *Fax:* 415-331-6124
E-mail: sales@emotionstudios.com
Web Site: www.emotionstudios.com
Key Personnel
CEO & Dir: Glen Janssens *E-mail:* glen@emotionstudios.com
Pres & Creative Dir: Paul Lundahl *E-mail:* paul@emotionstudios.com
Founded: 1993
Marketing, communications & creative services agency.

Empire Wholesale Inc
5675 Mansfield Way, Bell, CA 90201
Tel: 213-748-5200 *Toll Free Tel:* 866-748-5200 *Fax:* 213-748-5505
E-mail: sales@empirepro.com
Web Site: www.empirepro.com
Key Personnel
Pres: Edmond Khanian *Tel:* 213-748-5200 ext 103
Membership(s): InfoComm International®; NAMM, the National Association of Music Merchants

ENCO Systems Inc
29444 Northwestern Hwy, Southfield, MI 48034
Tel: 248-827-4440 *Toll Free Tel:* 800-362-6797 (sales) *Fax:* 248-827-4441
E-mail: sales@enco.com
Web Site: www.enco.com
Key Personnel
Pres: Eugene Novacek *Tel:* 248-827-4440 ext 144
VP, Sales & Mktg: Don Backus *Tel:* 248-827-4440 ext 130 *E-mail:* backus@enco.com
Gen Mgr: Patrick Campion
Founded: 1983
Foreign Office(s): Mithilesh Mishra, F-7 (Basement) Sector-27, Noida, Uttar Pradesh 201301, India *Tel:* (010) 4277920 *E-mail:* mithilesh@enco.com

Encore Broadcast Solutions
2104 W Kennedy Blvd, Tampa, FL 33606

Tel: 813-253-2774 *Toll Free Tel:* 800-780-8857 *Fax:* 813-254-5907
Web Site: www.encorebroadcast.com
Founded: 1992
Serving all broadcast, government, education, religion & corporate markets. Video equipment sales, design, installation & services.
Branch Office(s)
1255 Belle Ave, Suite 171, Winter Springs, FL 32708 *Tel:* 407-327-9006 *Toll Free Tel:* 800-567-0438 *Fax:* 407-327-2202
213 Hoffman Ave, Bridgeport, AL 35740 *Tel:* 423-544-1821 (cell) *Toll Free Tel:* 888-260-5999
107 Stratford Way, Signal Mountain, TN 37377 *Tel:* 423-544-1821 *Toll Free Tel:* 888-260-5999 *Fax:* 256-495-2931

Encore Cases
8818 Lankershim Blvd, Sun Valley, CA 91352
Tel: 818-768-8803 *Toll Free Tel:* 800-743-6267 *Fax:* 818-768-3993
Web Site: www.encorecases.com; www.giantcases.com
Key Personnel
Founder & Pres: Gary Peterson *E-mail:* gary@encorecases.com
CFO: Susan Herman
Sales: Rusty Scott
Founded: 1988
Catalog(s) available

Encore Home Video
PO Box 25, Frankenmuth, MI 48734-0025
Tel: 989-652-9699
E-mail: sales@encorehomevideo.com
Web Site: www.encorehomevideo.com
Key Personnel
Owner: Dennis Atkinson *E-mail:* dennis@encorehomevideo.com
Duplicating & transfering services.

Encore Productions Inc
5150 S Decatur Blvd, Las Vegas, NV 89119
Tel: 702-739-8803 *Toll Free Tel:* 800-287-7469 *Fax:* 702-739-8831
Web Site: www.encore-us.com
Key Personnel
CEO: Phillip Cooper

Encore Video Productions
811 Main St, Myrtle Beach, SC 29577
Tel: 843-448-9900
E-mail: crew@encorevideo.biz
Web Site: www.encorevideo.biz
Key Personnel
Pres: Rik Dickinson *E-mail:* rik@encorevideo.biz
VP: Frank Payne *E-mail:* frank@encorevideo.biz
Founded: 1980
Full service video production, AV equipment & operation.

Encounter Video Inc
14825 NW Ash St, Portland, OR 97231-2620
Tel: 503-285-8974 *Fax:* 503-285-3726
E-mail: encountvid@aol.com
Web Site: www.encountervideo.com
Key Personnel
Pres: Dennis Burkhart
Founded: 1983
Catalog(s) available

Encyclomedia
1526 Dekalb Ave, Atlanta, GA 30307
Tel: 404-527-3600 *Fax:* 404-584-5171
E-mail: info@encyclomedia.net
Web Site: www.encyclomedia.net
Key Personnel
Mng Partner/Prodr: Lance Holland
Mktg Dir: Tiffany Farmer
Dir, Photog: Kent Maxey
Prodr: Burt Holland
Soundstage & editing suite rental. Camera crew for hire.

Encyclopaedia Britannica Inc
331 N La Salle St, Chicago, IL 60654
Tel: 312-347-7000 (all other countries) *Toll Free Tel:* 800-323-1229 (US & CN) *Fax:* 312-294-2104
Web Site: www.britannica.com
Catalog(s) available
Membership(s): ALA; InfoComm International®

Endtime Inc
2701 E George Bush Tpke, Suite 100, Plano, TX 75074
Mailing Address: PO Box 940729, Plano, TX 75094-0729
Tel: 972-422-0857 *Toll Free Tel:* 800-363-8463 (cust serv) *Fax:* 972-423-4370
E-mail: questions@endtime.com; customerservice@endtime.com
Web Site: www.endtime.com
Key Personnel
CEO & Ed: Irvin Baxter, Jr
Sr Mgr: Dave Robbins
Founded: 1991
Programming by Type (Audio & Audio Visual) includes distributing & producing religious & political radio programs, specifically Prophecy.

Enhanced View Services Inc
12360 SW 132 Ct, Suite 114, Miami, FL 33186
Tel: 305-971-2916 *Toll Free Tel:* 877-873-3843
Web Site: www.usedvideogear.com
Dealers of professional broadcast audio & video equipment.

Enright Co
1801-I Parkcourt Place, Suite 100, Santa Ana, CA 92701
Toll Free Tel: 888-334-7773 *Fax:* 714-285-1905
E-mail: admin@enrightcompany.com
Web Site: www.enrightcompany.com
Key Personnel
Owner: Logan Enright *E-mail:* logan@enrightcompany.com
Contact: Patti Enright *E-mail:* patti@enrightcompany.com; David Fahrbach *E-mail:* dave@enrightcompany.com; Steve McNeil *E-mail:* stephen@enrightcompany.com
Manufacturer's representative in professional video, AV & imaging equipment.
Membership(s): InfoComm International®

Ensemble Designs Inc
870 Gold Flat Rd, Nevada City, CA 95959
Mailing Address: PO Box 993, Grass Valley, CA 95945-0993
Tel: 530-478-1830 *Fax:* 530-478-1832
E-mail: info@ensembledesigns.com
Web Site: www.ensembledesigns.com
Key Personnel
Pres: David Wood
Sales: Mondae Hott *E-mail:* mondae@ensembledesigns.com
Founded: 1989
Catalog(s), free
CD-ROM catalog(s), free
Membership(s): IABM; NAB; SMPTE

Entel Systems Inc
230 W Parkway, Pompton Plains, NJ 07444
Tel: 201-447-2000 *Toll Free Tel:* 888-914-7100 *Fax:* 201-447-2880
E-mail: service@entelsystems.com
Web Site: www.entelsystems.com
Key Personnel
Owner & VP: Don Giordano
Owner: Enzo Stampone
Founded: 1992
Branch Office(s)
17 Arcadian Way, Paramus, NJ 07652

Enterprise Media LLC
91 Harvey St, Cambridge, MA 02140
Tel: 617-354-0017 *Toll Free Tel:* 800-423-6021 *Fax:* 617-354-1637
E-mail: orders@enterprisemedia.com
Web Site: www.enterprisemedia.com
Key Personnel
Pres: Stewart B Clifford *E-mail:* stewart@enterprisemedia.com
VP: Dini Coffin *E-mail:* dini@enterprisemedia.com
Cont: Susan Dissley *E-mail:* susan@enterprisemedia.com
Founded: 1986
Catalog(s) available

Entertainment One Distribution
Formerly E1 Entertainment
70 Driver Rd, Unit 1, Brampton, ON L6T 5V2, Canada
Tel: 905-624-7337 *Toll Free Tel:* 800-387-0184 *Fax:* 905-624-7310; 905-463-9755 (cust serv)
E-mail: info@entertainmentone.ca
Web Site: entertainmentone.com; ca.eonedistribution.com
Key Personnel
CEO: Darren Throop *Tel:* 905-624-7337 ext 7878
Founded: 1973
Acquisition, production & distribution of film & television content.
Branch Office(s)
Bay 105, 10905-48 St SE, Calgary, AB T2C 1G8, Canada *Tel:* 403-258-3880 *Toll Free Tel:* 800-352-8245 *Fax:* 403-252-3176
Videoglobe 1, 6000 Chemin de la Cote de Liesse, Saint-Laurent, QC H4T 1E3, Canada *Tel:* 514-738-6665 *Toll Free Tel:* 800-361-7151 *Fax:* 514-738-3923
Membership(s): Canadian Academy of Recording Arts & Sciences

Entertainment One Distribution
Formerly E1 Entertainment
22 Harbor Park Dr, Port Washington, NY 11050
Tel: 516-484-1000
E-mail: musicdistribution@entonegroup.com; videosales@entonegroup.com
Web Site: entertainmentone.com; us.eonedistribution.com
Physical & digital music & video distribution company for independent record labels & studios.
Catalog(s) available
Membership(s): Music Business Association

Envirovision
Division of Beverly Factor Photography
PO Box 4136, Laguna Beach, CA 92652-4136
Tel: 949-673-2555 *Fax:* 949-673-2555
Web Site: www.beverlyfactor.com
Key Personnel
Owner & Pres: Beverly Factor *E-mail:* bfactor@beverlyfactor.com
Underwater photography, location & product shoots. Stock image library: 10,000.
Catalog(s) available
Shipping Address: 3408 Via Oporto, Suite 204, Newport Beach, CA 92663
Membership(s): ASMP

Envision Communications Inc
2002 N 204 St, Elkhorn, NE 68022
Tel: 402-289-2220
Key Personnel
Pres: Verle G Peterson *Tel:* 402-289-2220 ext 201 *E-mail:* verle@envision-com.com

eOne Distribution, see Entertainment One Distribution

eOne Distribution, see Entertainment One Distribution

E1 Entertainment, see Entertainment One Distribution

E1 Entertainment, see Entertainment One Distribution

Epic Software Group Inc
701 Sawdust Rd, The Woodlands, TX 77380
Tel: 281-363-3742 *Fax:* 281-419-4509
E-mail: epic@epicsoftware.com
Web Site: www.epicsoftware.com
Key Personnel
Pres: Vic Cherubini
3D animation & multimedia production studio & NewTek reseller.
Membership(s): BMA

Epitome Pictures Inc
220 Bartley Dr, Toronto, ON M4A 1G1, Canada
Tel: 416-752-7627 *Fax:* 416-752-7837
E-mail: info@epitomepictures.com
Web Site: www.epitomepictures.com
Key Personnel
CEO & Exec Prodr: Linda Schuyler
Pres & Exec Prodr: Stephen Stohn

EPIX Inc
381 Lexington Dr, Buffalo Grove, IL 60089
Tel: 847-465-1818 *Fax:* 847-465-1919
E-mail: epix@epixinc.com
Web Site: epixinc.com
Key Personnel
Off Mgr: Kirsten Gimm
Sales: Charlie Dijak
Founded: 1983
Catalog(s) available

Kat Epple Music Productions
PO Box 3156, North Fort Myers, FL 33918-3156
Tel: 239-997-0323
E-mail: music@katepple.com
Web Site: www.katepple.com
Key Personnel
Pres: Kat Epple *E-mail:* katepple@comcast.net
Sound track composition & production.

EPRAD Inc
6979 Wales Rd, Northwood, OH 43619
Tel: 419-666-3266 *Fax:* 419-666-8109
E-mail: info@eprad.com
Web Site: www.eprad.com
Founded: 1946

Equi=Tech Corp
PO Box 249, Selma, OR 97538-0249
Toll Free Tel: 877-378-4832 *Fax:* 541-787-8740
E-mail: sales@equitech.com
Web Site: www.equitech.com
Key Personnel
Pres: Martin Glasband *E-mail:* martin.g@equitech.com
Founded: 1992
Shipping Address: 18258 Redwood Hwy, Selma, OR 97538

Equiservices Publishing
4343 Garfoot Rd, Cross Plains, WI 53528
Tel: 608-798-4910
E-mail: info@equipub.com
Web Site: www.equipub.com
Key Personnel
Mgr: Jane Ginther
Produce & distribute books, videos & posters of ultrasonography for veterinarians, veterinary students & veterinary technicians.
Catalog(s) available

ERA Learning
Division of Educational Research Associates
PO Box 8795, Portland, OR 97207-8795
Tel: 503-228-6345 *Toll Free Tel:* 800-827-2499 (orders) *Fax:* 810-885-5811
E-mail: info@eralearning.com; customerservice@eralearning.com
Web Site: www.eralearning.com
Key Personnel
Dir: Mark Salser *E-mail:* mark@eralearning.com
Founded: 1965
Catalog(s) available

Ergo Media Inc
668 American Legion Dr, Teaneck, NJ 07666
Mailing Address: PO Box 2132, Teaneck, NJ 07666-1437
Tel: 201-692-0404 *Fax:* 201-692-0663
E-mail: info@jewishvideo.com
Web Site: www.jewishvideo.com; www.ergomedia.com
Key Personnel
Pres: Eric Goldman
Founded: 1986
Jewish oriented videos & DVDs.
Online catalog(s) available

ESE
142 Sierra St, El Segundo, CA 90245
Tel: 310-322-2136 *Fax:* 310-322-8127
E-mail: ese@ese-web.com
Web Site: www.ese-web.com
Key Personnel
Pres: William Kaiser
VP: Brian Way
Off Mgr: Teena Rael
Founded: 1971
Provider of time control solutions & distribution products: GPS based master clocks, SMPTE Time Code products, audio & video distribution amplifiers, analog & digital remote displays, NTP Time Servers, frequency standards & audio level indicators & interfaces.
Catalog(s) available
Membership(s): NAB

ESECO Speedmaster
730 E Eseco Rd, Cushing, OK 74023-5505
Tel: 918-225-1266 *Toll Free Tel:* 800-331-5904 (US & CN) *Fax:* 918-225-1284
E-mail: info@eseco-speedmaster.com
Web Site: www.eseco-speedmaster.com
Key Personnel
Pres: Wallace Hallman *E-mail:* wallace@eseco-speedmaster.com
EVP: Jerry Kaminshine *E-mail:* jerry@eseco-speedmaster.com
Founded: 1956
Electronic systems engineering company. Manufactures & markets in the photographic, graphic arts & x-ray industries.

Esoteric Sound
1608 Hemstock Ave, Wheaton, IL 60189
Tel: 630-933-9801 *Fax:* 630-933-9801
E-mail: esoterictt@aol.com
Web Site: www.esotericsound.com
Key Personnel
Owner: Michael Stosich
Founded: 1981
Catalog(s) available

ESPN Inc
Subsidiary of ABC Inc
ESPN Plaza, 545 Middle St, Bristol, CT 06010
Tel: 860-766-2000
Web Site: espn.go.com
Founded: 1979
Membership(s): Cable Television Advertising Bureau; NAB; NATAS; NCTA; SMPTE

Essex Television Group Inc
7 Vista Dr, Old Lyme, CT 06371
Mailing Address: PO Box 454, Old Lyme, CT 06371-0454
Tel: 860-434-7200 *Fax:* 860-434-7210
E-mail: contact@essextelevision.com
Web Site: www.essextelevision.com
Key Personnel
Pres: Daniel Carey *E-mail:* dcarey@essextelevision.com
Busn Mgr: Jennifer Gobey *E-mail:* jgobey@essextelevision.com
Founded: 1998
Full production company. Corporate video, documentaries & HD programs.

Estiluz Inc
235 Moonachie Rd, Moonachie, NJ 07074
Tel: 201-641-1997 *Fax:* 201-641-2092
E-mail: estiluzinc@estiluz.com
Web Site: www.estiluzusa.com
Key Personnel
EVP: Albert Grabulosa
Founded: 1993
Catalog(s), annual

ETA Systems
Subsidiary of MiTek Corp
1601 Jack McKay Blvd, Ennis, TX 75119
Tel: 972-875-8413 *Toll Free Tel:* 800-321-6699 *Toll Free Fax:* 800-996-3821
E-mail: etacustomerrelations@etasys.com
Web Site: www.mitekcorp.com; www.etasys.com
Founded: 1977
Manufacturer of power conditioners for audio & video.

ETC
3031 Pleasant View Rd, Middleton, WI 53562-4809
Mailing Address: PO Box 620979, Middleton, WI 53562-0979
Tel: 608-831-4116 *Toll Free Tel:* 800-688-4116 *Fax:* 608-836-1736
E-mail: mail@etcconnect.com; americas@etcconnect.com
Web Site: www.etcconnect.com
Key Personnel
CEO: Fred Foster
Pres: Dick Titus
VP, Fin: Mark Veldey
VP, World Sales: Mark Vassallo
Founded: 1975
Catalog(s) available
Branch Office(s)
4201 Vineland Rd, Suite I-1, Orlando, FL 32811, Contact: Leonard Wittn *Tel:* 407-843-7770 *Fax:* 407-843-0337 (southeast regl off)
Foreign Office(s): Enterprise Sq, 18/F, Tower I, Rm 1801, 9 Sheung Yuet Rd, Kowloon Bay, Kowloon, Hong Kong *Tel:* 2799 1220 *Fax:* 2799 9325 *E-mail:* asia@etcconnect.com
26-28 Victoria Industrial Estate, Victoria Rd, London W3 6UU, United Kingdom *Tel:* (020) 8896 1000 *Fax:* (020) 8896 2000 *E-mail:* uk@etcconnect.com

Eternal Word Television Network (EWTN)
5817 Old Leeds Rd, Irondale, AL 35210-2164
Tel: 205-271-2900 *Fax:* 205-271-2920
E-mail: viewer@ewtn.com
Web Site: www.ewtn.com
Key Personnel
Chmn of the Bd & CEO: Michael P Warsaw
COO & Pres: Doug Keck
Dir, Mktg Support: Julia Muscari

Founded: 1981
Now offer in-house production on EWTN Home Video.
Branch Office(s)
PO Box 157, Sta A, Etobicoke, ON M9C 4V2, Canada
Membership(s): NCTA

ETHOS Ltd
Division of Robert B Mansour Ltd
4981 Hwy 7 E, Unit 12-A, Suite 235, Markham, ON L3R 1N1, Canada
Tel: 905-471-7654 *Toll Free Tel:* 800-471-0737 *Fax:* 905-471-7976
E-mail: ethoseducation@rogers.com
Web Site: www.ethoseducation.ca
Key Personnel
Pres: Robert Mansour
Founded: 1972
Producer & distributor of educational interactive DVDs.

Ed Ethridge Productions Inc
1215 E Broward Blvd, Suite 200, Fort Lauderdale, FL 33301
Tel: 954-533-7100 *Fax:* 954-306-3261
Web Site: www.ethridgeproductions.com
Key Personnel
Founder & Pres: Ed Ethridge *E-mail:* ed@ethridgeproductions.com
Acctg Mgr: Kerry L York *E-mail:* accounting@ethridgeproductions.com
Founded: 2007

EUE/Screen Gems Studios
Division of EUE/Screen Gems Ltd
1223 N 23 St, Wilmington, NC 28405
Tel: 910-343-3500 *Fax:* 910-343-3574
E-mail: info@euescreengems.com
Web Site: euescreengems.com
Key Personnel
COO & Pres: Chris Cooney *Tel:* 212-450-1600
EVP: Bill Vassar
Film, television & commercial production.
Branch Office(s)
175 Lakewood Way, Atlanta, GA 30315, EVP: Kris Bagwell *Tel:* 404-333-6506 *E-mail:* kbagwell@euescreengems.com
603 Greenwich St, New York, NY 10014, EVP: Doug Wedeck *Tel:* 212-450-1600 *Fax:* 212-450-1610 *E-mail:* doug@euescreengems.com

Euphonix Inc, see Avid Technology Inc

Euro-Pacific Film & Video Productions Inc
PO Box 7986, Shrewsbury, NJ 07702
Tel: 732-530-4451 *Toll Free Tel:* 800-387-6776
E-mail: info@euro-pacific.com
Web Site: www.euro-pacific.com
Key Personnel
Pres & Exec Sr Prodr: David Calderwood *E-mail:* david@euro-pacific.com
VP & Exec Sr Prodr: Lisa Moss Calderwood
Promos Mktg Specialist: E B Moss
Founded: 1990
Multimedia production & web site development. Foreign offices located in Auckland, New Zealand & London, England.
Membership(s): DVDA; MCA-I; NATAS

Euro RSCG EDGE, see Havas Edge

Euro RSCG Magnet, see Havas Worldwide

Eurotech Seating
c/o Marketec, 419 S Flower St, Burbank, CA 91502
Tel: 818-847-0200 *Toll Free Tel:* 800-557-8861 *Toll Free Fax:* 888-262-1726
E-mail: info@marketec.com
Web Site: www.marketec.com
Key Personnel
Pres: Penny Russell
AV seating.

Event Essentials
Division of A to Z RentAll & Sales Inc
6485 Blanchar's Crossing, Windsor, WI 53598
Tel: 608-846-5004 *Toll Free Tel:* 800-220-4991 *Fax:* 608-222-5063
Web Site: www.eventessentials.com
Key Personnel
Owner: Kevin Hoffman
Gen Mgr: Farrah Slinger *E-mail:* farrah@eventessentials.com
Catalog(s) available
Membership(s): InfoComm International®

Event Tech
7601 Brandon Woods Blvd, Baltimore, MD 21226
Tel: 410-360-5006 *Toll Free Tel:* 866-950-8343 *Fax:* 410-360-5002
E-mail: info@eventtech.com
Web Site: www.eventtech.com
Key Personnel
Pres: Eric Maynard
VP, Opers: Matt Totaro
VP, Sales & Mktg: Mike Aug
Founded: 1986
Full production services & equipment rentals for special events nationwide.
Membership(s): International Special Events Society; Professional Lighting & Sound Association

Eventide Inc
One Alsan Way, Little Ferry, NJ 07643
Tel: 201-641-1200 *Fax:* 201-641-1640
E-mail: audio@eventide.com; support@eventide.com
Web Site: www.eventide.com
Key Personnel
VP, Sales & Mktg: Ray Maxwell
Manufacture audio hardware & software, including stompboxes.
Catalog(s) available
Membership(s): AES; NAB; NAMM, the National Association of Music Merchants

Ever-Ready Media Packaging
Unit of Reliance Corrugated Container Corp
8192 Gatherly Circle, Easton, MD 21601
Mailing Address: PO Box 40, Haworth, NJ 07641
Tel: 973-566-9333 *Fax:* 201-387-1530
E-mail: packages@erpack.com
Web Site: www.erpack.com
Key Personnel
Pres: Marshall Weingarden
Founded: 1963
Manufacture & distribute CD & DVD packaging.
Online catalog(s) available
Sample(s), annual, free
Shipping Address: 920 N Ridge Ave, Unit C-3, Lombard, IL 60148

Everett Hall Associates Inc
76 Progress Dr, Stamford, CT 06902
Tel: 203-325-4328 *Fax:* 203-323-8078
E-mail: info@everetthall.com
Web Site: www.everetthall.com
Key Personnel
Gen Mgr: Joel R Rollins
Founded: 1975
AV rental, staging, systems design & installation.
Catalog(s) available
Membership(s): InfoComm International®; SMPTE

Everlast Productions
59 SW 12 Ave, Unit 109, Dania Beach, FL 33004
Tel: 954-456-7167 *Fax:* 954-456-1243
E-mail: info@everlastproductions.com
Web Site: everlastproductions.com
Key Personnel
CEO: Washington Arias
Sales Dir: Letty Dexter
Tech Dir: David McCrainie
Gen Mgr: Dave Jones

Evertz Microsystems Ltd
5292 John Lucas Dr, Burlington, ON L7L 5Z9, Canada
Tel: 905-335-3700 *Toll Free Tel:* 877-995-3700 *Fax:* 905-335-3573
E-mail: sales@evertz.com
Web Site: www.evertz.com
Key Personnel
Sr Regl Sales Mgr: Paul Soares *E-mail:* paul@evertz.com
Founded: 1966
Design & manufacture audio & video infrastructure equipment for the television broadcast & film industry. Offers HD, 3G & Ultra HD end to end solutions including: master control systems, large, medium & small routers, branding, RF, master sync generation, terminal gear, fiber optics, multi-display monitoring, production tools & interfaces & closed captioning. Also provides solutions for post-production, production & mobile production, IPTV, OTT, transport & distribution equipment & broadcast, satellite & cable applications. Branch offices in Los Angeles & San Jose, CA, Washington, DC & New York, NY. Foreign offices in Australia, Germany, Hong Kong, India, New Zealand, United Arab Emirates & UK.
Catalog(s), annual, free
Membership(s): IABM; SMPTE

Evidence Audio Inc
PO Box 473, Lake Oswego, OR 97034
Tel: 949-306-7390
E-mail: info@evidenceaudio.com
Web Site: www.evidenceaudio.com
Key Personnel
Founder & Pres: Tony Farinella
Founded: 1997
Cable & wire for the MI & studio market.
Catalog(s) available

Evolution Presentation Technologies
6910 Farrell Rd SE, Calgary, AB T2H 0T1, Canada
Tel: 403-259-3793 *Toll Free Tel:* 800-561-9820 *Fax:* 403-259-2374
Web Site: www.evolutionav.ca
Key Personnel
Pres: Steve Read
Founded: 1980
AV rentals & staging.
Membership(s): InfoComm International®; MPI; Professional Systems Network Inc

Evolution Presentation Technologies
971 Wall St, Winnipeg, MB R3G 2V4, Canada
Tel: 204-775-6662 *Toll Free Fax:* 888-775-4693
E-mail: sstephens@evolutionav.com
Web Site: www.evolutionav.ca
Key Personnel
Pres: Duncan Pimlott *Tel:* 204-775-6662 ext 4001
Acct Mgr, Integrated Solutions: Peter Pomialowski *Tel:* 204-775-6662 ext 4006
AV equipment sales & rentals.
Catalog(s) available
Membership(s): InfoComm International®

Evolve Inc
1210 E Arlington Blvd, Greenville, NC 27858
Tel: 252-754-2957 *Fax:* 252-754-2832
Web Site: www.evolveinc.com
Key Personnel
Pres: Will Daugherty
Creative Dir: Brian Taylor
Media Dir: Shari Tourlitis

Founded: 2002
Full service advertising agency. Specialize in brand management & marketing strategy through the integrated use of marketing, advertising & public relations. Video & radio production.

Jasper Ewing & Sons Inc
1220 E Northside Dr, Suite 370, Jackson, MS 39211
Tel: 601-981-2178 *Fax:* 601-981-2178
E-mail: jasperewing@comcast.net
Web Site: jasperewing.com
Key Personnel
Pres: Malcolm P Ewing, Jr
Founded: 1906

EWTN, see Eternal Word Television Network (EWTN)

Excel Duplication Services
1219 N Cass St, Milwaukee, WI 53202
Tel: 414-225-9235 *Fax:* 414-225-9236
E-mail: info@excelduplication.com
Web Site: www.excelduplication.com
Key Personnel
Owner: Tom Gripp
Founded: 1986
DVD & CD duplication.
Membership(s): MCA-I

Executive Development Systems
3818 Vinecrest Dr, Dallas, TX 75229
Tel: 214-351-0055 *Toll Free Tel:* 800-955-7353 *Fax:* 214-351-5024
Web Site: www.edforeman.com
Key Personnel
Founder & Pres: Ed Foreman *E-mail:* edf@edforeman.com
Founder & EVP: Earlene Vining *E-mail:* earlene@edoreman.com
Contact: Linda Barrett *E-mail:* linda@edforeman.com
Brochure(s) available

Exeltech Inc
7317 Jack Newell Blvd N, Fort Worth, TX 76118
Tel: 817-595-4969 *Toll Free Tel:* 800-886-4683 *Fax:* 817-595-1290
E-mail: exlsales@exeltech.com
Web Site: www.exeltech.com
Founded: 1990
Manufacture inverters.
Catalog(s) available

Explore Media LLC
113 1/2 E Lexington Ave, Elkhart, IN 46516
Tel: 574-875-5565 *Fax:* 574-830-0200
E-mail: info@explore-media.com
Web Site: www.explore-media.com
Key Personnel
Exec Prodr: Jeremy Pinckert

ExpoDisplays
Division of Diamond Displays International
3401 Mary Taylor Rd, Birmingham, AL 35235
Tel: 205-439-8200 *Toll Free Tel:* 800-367-3976 *Fax:* 205-439-8201
E-mail: info@expodisplays.com
Web Site: www.expodisplays.com
Key Personnel
Pres: David Holiday
VP: Jay Burkette
Founded: 1970
Displays & exhibits.
Branch Office(s)
Huntsville Showroom, 1003 Production Ct, Suite 600, Madison, AL 35758

Express Media Inc
2225 Palou Ave, San Francisco, CA 94124
Tel: 415-255-9883 *Fax:* 415-255-0139
Web Site: www.rentvideo.com; www.expressmedia.tv
Key Personnel
Pres: Steven Barger
Dir: Buddy Scauzzo
Founded: 1989
Broadcast & professional video gear rental & offering a wide range of production & post services. Multicam & ENG field production & Avid editing for here or to go. Philips DD-10, 10-bit digital flypack, DFS-700 analog component & SDI digital flypack. Avid media Composer 9000XL & DXC-D35 camera heads with triax studio packages. Folsom Scan Converters, Canon Sports lenses, BETASP, DVCam & Digital Betacam ENG Camera packages.
Rate card(s), quarterly, free
Membership(s): Northern California Production Community

Express Media Inc
2225 Palou Ave, San Francisco, CA 94124
Tel: 415-255-9883 *Fax:* 415-255-0139
Web Site: www.expressmedia.tv
Key Personnel
CFO: Maria Stepaneko
Pres: Steven Barger
Dir: Buddy Scauzzo
Founded: 1989
Video & digital media duplication services. Have nonlinear video editing facilities & CD & DVD authoring facilities. Provide video consulting services.

Express Video Supply Inc
1819 Victory Blvd, Glendale, CA 91201
Tel: 818-552-4590 *Toll Free Tel:* 800-238-8480 *Fax:* 818-552-4591
E-mail: rentals@evsonline.com; sales@evsonline.com
Web Site: www.evsonline.com
Founded: 1991
Catalog(s) available

Extraordinary Demos
2131 Yellowstar Lane, Naperville, IL 60564-5330
Tel: 630-904-3636
Web Site: www.extraordinarydemos.com
Key Personnel
Owner & Pres: Fred Harms *E-mail:* demofred@aol.com
Founded: 1985
Multimedia & training-audio, video animations.

Extreme Reach Inc
75 Second Ave, Suite 720, Needham, MA 02494
Tel: 781-577-2016
E-mail: sales@extremereach.com; press@extremereach.com
Web Site: www.extremereach.com
Key Personnel
Co-Founder & CEO: John Roland
Co-Founder & COO: Tim Conley
Co-Founder & CTO: Dan Brackett
CFO: Nancy Lazaros
Chief Digital Offr: Avi Brown
Chief Mktg Offr: Robert Haskitt
Chief Revenue Offr: Patrick Hanavan
Chief Talent Offr: Tim Hale
TV & digital video advertising.
Branch Office(s)
2323 N Valley St, Burbank, CA 91505 *Tel:* 818-729-2900
6005 Shellmound St, Suite 200, Emeryville, CA 94608 *Tel:* 510-400-8200
3330 Cahuenga Blvd W, 4th fl, Los Angeles, CA 90068 *Tel:* 323-603-5220 *Fax:* 323-603-5300
1777 Montgomery St, San Francisco, CA 94111 *Fax:* 415-989-0349
450 Corporate Blvd, Newark, DE 19702 *Tel:* 302-368-0002 *Toll Free Tel:* 888-275-4001 *Fax:* 302-368-5436
1499 W Palmetto Pk Rd, No 220, Boca Raton, FL 33486 *Toll Free Tel:* 800-525-0230 *Fax:* 561-392-9919 *E-mail:* requests@sourceecreative.com
245 Hembree Park Dr, Roswell, GA 30076 *Tel:* 770-619-0801 *Fax:* 770-619-0802 *E-mail:* syndsupport@extremereach.com
111 W Jackson Blvd, Suite 1525, Chicago, IL 60604 *Tel:* 312-846-6255
8130 River Dr, Morton Grove, IL 60053 *Tel:* 312-624-7539 *Fax:* 312-624-7493
100 High Rise Dr, Louisville, KY 40213
3309 Gilmore Industrial Blvd, Louisville, KY 40213 *Toll Free Tel:* 877-769-9382
200 Galleria Officentre, Suite 109, Southfield, MI 48034
721 Second St S, Great Falls, MT 59405 *Tel:* 406-761-7877
1633 Broadway, New York, NY 10019 *Tel:* 212-868-3820 (talent & traffic servs) *Toll Free Tel:* 888-326-8733 (direct response) *Fax:* 212-868-3821 (talent & traffic servs) *Toll Free Fax:* 877-302-8633 (opers) *E-mail:* directresponse@extremereach.com
2525 McKinnon St, Suite 530, Dallas, TX 75201 *Tel:* 972-581-1990 *Fax:* 214-965-9435
1518 First Ave S, Suite 300, Seattle, WA 98134
Extreme Reach Canada, 635 Queen St E, Toronto, ON M4M 1G4, Canada *Tel:* 647-436-0563 *Fax:* 416-964-5920 *E-mail:* canadasupport@extremereach.com
Extreme Reach Mijo, 635 Queen St E, Toronto, ON M4M 1G4, Canada *Tel:* 416-964-7539 *Fax:* 416-964-5920 *E-mail:* info@mijo.com

Extron Electronics
1025 E Ball Rd, Suite 100, Anaheim, CA 92805-5957
Tel: 714-491-1500 *Toll Free Tel:* 800-633-9876 (sales & tech support); 800-633-9873 (order support) *Fax:* 714-491-1517
E-mail: sales-usa@extron.com
Web Site: www.extron.com
Key Personnel
VP: Art Garcia
VP, Sales & Mktg-North America: Casey Hall
PR Mgr: Christine Fowler
Founded: 1983
Catalog(s) available
Branch Office(s)
2500 N Raleigh Blvd, Raleigh, NC 27604 *Tel:* 919-850-1000 *Fax:* 919-850-1001
3855 Centerview Dr, Suite 400A, Chantilly, VA 20151
Foreign Office(s): Extron Europe, Hanzeboulevard 10, 3825 PH Amersfoort, Netherlands *Tel:* (033) 453 4040 *Toll Free Tel:* 800 3987 6673 (inside Europe only) *Fax:* (033) 453 4050
Extron Electronics Asia Pte Ltd, PM Industrial Bldg, Suite 04-01, 135 Joo Seng Rd, Singapore 368363, Singapore *Tel:* 6383 4400 *Fax:* 6383 4664
Membership(s): Custom Electronic Design & Installation Association; InfoComm International®; NAB; NSCA

Eye & I Productions
1250 Kay Lane, Oakley, CA 94561
Tel: 925-625-7888 *Toll Free Tel:* 800-720-9014
E-mail: contact@voicecrystal.com
Web Site: www.voicecrystal.com
Key Personnel
Pres: Mark Wiens
Founded: 1987
Music synthesizer, sampler, midi & multimedia products & sound design consultants. Synthesizer spec & implementation & general midi soundset design. Full sound design studio Mac & PC. Full line of sample CDs & synthesizer

sound banks & cards, SoundFont libraries & DLS.
Online catalog(s) available

Eye on Dance
Subsidiary of Arts Resources in Collaboration
70 E Tenth St, Suite 19-D, New York, NY 10003
Tel: 212-206-6492
E-mail: eyeonthearts@gmail.com
Web Site: www.eyeondance.org
Key Personnel
Prog Dir: Celia Ipiotis
Tech Dir: Jeff Bush
Founded: 1981
Arts television series & video library.
Online catalog(s) available

Eyecon Video Productions
1865 Summit Ave, Suite 605, Plano, TX 75074
Tel: 972-881-3200 *Toll Free Tel:* 877-704-1517
E-mail: info@eyeconvideo.com
Web Site: www.eyeconvideo.com
Key Personnel
Owner: Greg Coon *E-mail:* greg@eyeconvideo.com
Founded: 1991
Full service video production.
Membership(s): MCA-I; National Press Photographers Association; Texas Association of Motion Media Professionals

Eyeline Teleprompting
1313 Mound St, Alameda, CA 94501
Tel: 510-205-6762
Web Site: www.eyeline.tv
Key Personnel
Owner & Operator: Conchita Perales *E-mail:* conchita@eyeline.tv
Founded: 2000
Teleprompting equipment rental & operator services for video, film, events, conventions & webcasts. Bilingual operators.

EZ FX Inc
Division of EZ FX Jib Arm
324 Maguire Rd, Ocoee, FL 34761
Tel: 407-877-2335 *Toll Free Tel:* 800-541-5706 *Fax:* 407-877-6603
E-mail: sales@ezfx.com
Web Site: www.ezfx.com
Key Personnel
Contact: Steve G Bonin *E-mail:* steve@ezfx.com
Founded: 1993
Manufacture camera cranes, jib arms & slider dolly.
Catalog(s) available
Demo video(s) available

FACE, see French American Cultural Exchange (FACE)

Face Digital Post
9753 Via Roma, Burbank, CA 91504
Tel: 818-842-9081 *Fax:* 818-768-6313
E-mail: face@facedigitalpost.com
Web Site: www.facedigitalpost.com
Key Personnel
Partner & Sr Ed: Ron Malvin; Jamie Tullo
Graphic Artist: Justin Malvin
Founded: 1983
Boutique production & post facility, specializing in electronic publicity. Videotape archiving.
Membership(s): Television Academy

Facet Media
5821 Rodman St, Hollywood, FL 33023
Tel: 954-589-0535 *Fax:* 954-593-0411
E-mail: info@facetmedia.com
Web Site: www.facetmedia.com
Key Personnel
Dir: Max Sainvil
Digital cinema services & RED EPIC rentals. Lighting & grip services & crews, studio rental, camera rentals & accessories.

Facets Multi-Media Inc
1517 W Fullerton Ave, Chicago, IL 60614
Tel: 773-281-9075 (ext 3011) *Toll Free Tel:* 800-331-6197 *Fax:* 773-929-5437
E-mail: sales@facets.org
Web Site: www.facets.org
Key Personnel
Exec Dir: Milos Stehlik
Founded: 1975
Catalog(s), bimonthly
Membership(s): Entertainment Merchants Association

Faith Fellowship Ministries World Outreach Center
2707 Main St Ext, Sayreville, NJ 08872
Tel: 732-727-9500
E-mail: information@ffmwoc.org
Web Site: www.ffmwoc.org
Key Personnel
Head, Audio Dept: Mike Marulli *Tel:* 732-727-9500 ext 3106 *E-mail:* mmarulli@ffmwoc.org
Ministry Mgr: Rev Maryanne Percy *Tel:* 732-727-9500 ext 1201 *E-mail:* mpercy@ffmwoc.org
TV broadcasting.

Falcon Safety Products Inc
25 Imclone Dr, Branchburg, NJ 08876
Tel: 908-707-4900 *Toll Free Tel:* 800-332-5266 (cust serv ext 1) *Fax:* 908-707-8855
Web Site: www.falconsafety.com
Key Personnel
Pres: Philip Lapin
Founded: 1953
Catalog(s) available

Fambrough & Associates Inc
13501 Leatha's Ct, Suite 100, Kansas City, MO 64089-7701
Tel: 816-471-1717 *Fax:* 816-256-5283
E-mail: we_work_for_you@fambrough.com
Web Site: www.fambrough.com
Key Personnel
CEO & Pres: William Fambrough
Founded: 1927
Visual media services including photography, video & film. Digital, HD, film & video equipment & facilities.
Membership(s): PPA

Family Health Media
PO Box 5832, Charlottesville, VA 22905-5832
Tel: 434-566-0123 *Toll Free Tel:* 800-366-3641 *Toll Free Fax:* 888-234-2579
E-mail: support@familyhealthmedia.com
Web Site: www.familyhealthmedia.com
Key Personnel
Owner: Andy Spratt *E-mail:* andy@familyhealthmedia.com
Founded: 1992
Produce & publish health education media.
Catalog(s) available
Shipping Address: 4320 Burton Rd, North Garden, VA 22959

F&F Productions
Subsidiary of Hubbard Broadcasting Inc
14333 Myerlake Circle, Clearwater, FL 33760
Tel: 727-530-5000 *Fax:* 727-535-6547
Web Site: www.fandfhd.tv
Key Personnel
CEO & Pres: George Orgera *E-mail:* georgeo@fandfhd.tv
EVP: Ryan Hatch *E-mail:* ryanh@fandfhd.tv
VP, Engg: Bill McKechney *E-mail:* billm@fandfhd.tv
Founded: 1981
Mobile television production.
Catalog(s) available
Membership(s): NAB

Fanlight Productions
Subsidiary of First Run/Icarus Films Inc
c/o Icarus Films, 32 Court St, Brooklyn, NY 11201
Tel: 718-488-8900 *Toll Free Tel:* 800-876-1710 *Fax:* 781-488-8642
E-mail: info@fanlight.com
Web Site: www.fanlight.com; www.icarusfilms.com
Focus on healthcare.
Catalog(s) available
Membership(s): IMDA

Fanon Courier
Subsidiary of Shelly Associates
17171 Murphy Ave, Irvine, CA 92614-5915
Tel: 949-417-8085 *Toll Free Tel:* 800-345-1354 *Fax:* 949-417-8075
E-mail: info@fanon.com
Web Site: www.fanon.com
Key Personnel
Contact: Diane Cross
Catalog(s) available

Fantasee Lighting Inc
14857 Martinsville Rd, Belleville, MI 48111
Tel: 734-699-7200 *Fax:* 734-699-7400
E-mail: info@fantaseelighting.com
Web Site: www.fantaseelighting.com
Key Personnel
Opers Dir: Kevin Phail *E-mail:* kphail@fantaseelighting.com
Founded: 1977
Rent, sell & service theatrical lighting systems & special effects.
Membership(s): Professional Lighting & Sound Association; USITT

Fantasy Creations FX
Division of Studio 2060
2060 E McDaniel St, Springfield, MO 65802
Tel: 417-619-1138
E-mail: fcfxmike@yahoo.com
Web Site: www.fantasycreationsfx.com
Key Personnel
Owner: Mike Strain, Jr
Founded: 1987
Create special makeup effects & pyrotechnics.
Catalog(s), annual, $2, make-up FX & expendables
Online catalog(s), make-up FX & expendables

Fantasy Studios
2600 Tenth St, Berkeley, CA 94710
Tel: 510-486-2038 *Fax:* 510-486-2248
Web Site: www.fantasystudios.com
Key Personnel
Studio Dir: Jeffrey Wood *E-mail:* jwood@fantasystudios.com
Studio Mgr: Allison Gomer *E-mail:* agomer@fantasystudios.com
Founded: 1949
Recording studio.
Catalog(s) available

Far West Media Services Inc
4140 Norse Way, Long Beach, CA 90808
Tel: 562-496-3342 *Fax:* 562-496-4329
Web Site: www.farwestmedia.com
Key Personnel
Pres & Dir: Robert Ranaldi
Radio & television advertising short & long form.

Fastlane Productions LLC
7 Riverdale Rd, Billerica, MA 01821
Tel: 978-667-8399 *Fax:* 978-667-8398
E-mail: info@fastlaneproductions.net
Web Site: www.fastlaneproductions.net
Sound, lighting & production company. Services include sales, installations & rentals for all audio & lighting needs.

Fax Animation Co
Division of Alan Gordon Enterprises Inc
5625 Melrose Ave, Hollywood, CA 90038
Tel: 323-466-3561 *Fax:* 323-871-2193
E-mail: contactus@alangordon.com
Web Site: www.alangordon.com
Key Personnel
Pres: Grant Loucks
VP: Don Sahlein
Manufacture, sales & rental of animation stands, animation desks, animation discs, backlites, peg boards & peg bars.
Catalog(s) available

D W Fearn
PO Box 57, Pocopson, PA 19366
Tel: 610-793-2526 *Fax:* 610-793-1479
E-mail: dwfearn@dwfearn.com
Web Site: www.dwfearn.com
Key Personnel
Pres: Douglas W Fearn
Manufacturer of professional vacuum tube audio recording equipment.
Catalog(s) available
Shipping Address: 182 Bragg Hill Rd, West Chester, PA 19382

Feature Systems Inc
223 Veterans Blvd, Carlstadt, NJ 07072
Tel: 201-531-2299; 212-736-0447 *Fax:* 201-531-2290; 212-465-1987
Web Site: www.featuresystems.com
Key Personnel
CEO & Pres: Robert Bailin
COO & Gen Mgr: Jay Karasick *E-mail:* jay@featuresystems.com
Founded: 1972
Rental of lighting equipment, 3-, 5- & 10-ton trucks, dollies, generators & expendable items.
Branch Office(s)
Feature Systems Baltimore LLC, 2615 C Willow Ave, Baltimore, MD 21227 *Tel:* 410-242-4030

Edward Feil Productions
36980 Wallace Creek Rd, Springfield, OH 97478
Mailing Address: PO Box 2243, Jasper, OR 97438
Tel: 541-521-2411 *Toll Free Fax:* 877-582-1158
Web Site: www.edwardfeilproductions.com
Key Personnel
Pres: Edward R Feil
VP: Naomi Feil
Res Dir: Edward G Feil *E-mail:* ed@edwardfeilproductions.com
Founded: 1952
Catalog(s) available
Branch Office(s)
21987 Byron E, Shaker Heights, OH 44122 *Tel:* 216-561-0357
Membership(s): MCA-I; University Film & Video Association

Feldenkrais® Movement Institute
721 The Alameda, Berkeley, CA 94707
Tel: 510-527-2634 *Toll Free Tel:* 800-342-3424 *Fax:* 510-528-1332
E-mail: info@feldenkraisinstitute.org
Web Site: www.feldenkraisinstitute.org
Key Personnel
Founder & Educ Dir: Dr Frank Wildman, PhD
Audio & video tapes, as well as practitioner training & workshops based on the Feldenkrais Method, a somatic approach to neuro-muscular education & training.
Catalog(s) available

Ronald Feldman Fine Arts Inc
31 Mercer St, New York, NY 10013
Tel: 212-226-3232 *Fax:* 212-941-1536
E-mail: info@feldmangallery.com
Web Site: www.feldmangallery.com
Key Personnel
Owner: Frayda Feldman *E-mail:* frayda@feldmangallery.com; Ron Feldman
Founded: 1971
Membership(s): Art Dealers Association of America

Femme Productions Inc
PO Box 268, New York, NY 10012
Toll Free Tel: 800-456-LOVE (456-5683); 800-955-0888 (CN)
E-mail: inquiries@candidaroyalle.com
Web Site: candidaroyalle.com
Key Personnel
Pres: Candida Royalle
Founded: 1984
Woman-friendly erotic videos.
Catalog(s) available

Fender Musical Instruments Corp
17600 N Perimeter Dr, Suite 100, Scottsdale, AZ 85255
Tel: 480-596-9690 *Fax:* 480-596-1384
E-mail: consumerrelations@fender.com
Web Site: www.fender.com
Key Personnel
SVP: Jason Padgitt
SVP, HR: Keith Davis
Founded: 1946
Catalog(s) available

Ferrari Color®
1550 S Gladiola St, Salt Lake City, UT 84104
Tel: 801-355-4124 *Toll Free Tel:* 888-312-6567 *Fax:* 801-355-4152
E-mail: info.slc@ferraricolor.com
Web Site: www.ferraricolor.com
Key Personnel
CEO: Kirk Green
Dir, Mktg: Heidi Hall *E-mail:* hhall@ferraricolor.com
Founded: 1978
Digital graphics production facility, offering large & grand format printing, trade show graphics & digital laser prints.
Catalog(s) available
Branch Office(s)
1330 Ninth St, Berkeley, CA 94710 *Tel:* 510-740-0234 *Toll Free Tel:* 888-695-4382 *Fax:* 510-740-0240 *E-mail:* info.sf@ferraricolor.com
900 National Dr, Sacramento, CA 95834 *Tel:* 916-444-9600 *Toll Free Tel:* 800-533-6333 *Fax:* 916-444-2567 *E-mail:* info.sac@ferraricolor.com
Membership(s): AIE™; DPI; PMA International

Ferrari Productions
11717 Sorrento Valley Rd, San Diego, CA 92121
Tel: 858-792-8011 *Fax:* 858-481-6499
E-mail: info@ferrariproductions.com
Web Site: www.ferrariproductions.com
Key Personnel
Owner: Phillip Ferrari *E-mail:* phil@ferrariproductions.com
Founded: 1989
AV production & staging, video production & editing.
Membership(s): MCA-I

Festival Films
6115 Chestnut Terr, Shorewood, MN 55331
Tel: 952-470-2172 *Fax:* 952-470-2172
E-mail: fesfilms@aol.com
Web Site: www.fesfilms.com
Key Personnel
Pres: Ron Hall
Distribute public domain films.
Catalog(s) available

FFMWOC, see Faith Fellowship Ministries World Outreach Center

Fiber Optic Cable Shop
Affiliate of Support Systems International Corp
136 S Second St, Richmond, CA 94804
Tel: 510-234-9090 *Toll Free Tel:* 800-777-6269 *Fax:* 510-233-8888
E-mail: sales@fibermailbox.com
Web Site: www.fiberopticcableshop.com
Key Personnel
Gen Mgr: Ben Parsons
Founded: 1976
Manufactures & distributes custom & standard fiber optic cable assemblies, media converters, switches, patch panels, enclosures & associated equipment.

Fiber Optic Systems Inc (FOSI)
2 Railroad Ave, Whitehouse Station, NJ 08889
Tel: 908-534-5500 *Toll Free Tel:* 800-809-3674 *Fax:* 908-534-2272
E-mail: info@fosi.com
Web Site: www.fosi.com
Key Personnel
Owner: Cyr A Ryan
Founded: 1970
Design & manufacture interactive fiber optic exhibits, optic lighting & special effects.
Catalog(s) available

Fibre Case Corp
160 Broadway, Suite 1105, New York, NY 10038
Tel: 212-566-2720 *Toll Free Tel:* 800-394-6871 *Fax:* 212-566-2726
E-mail: sales@fibrecase.com
Web Site: www.fibrecase.com
Key Personnel
Pres: Elliot Kozer
Busn Contact: Richard Rubin
Founded: 1894
Manufacture shipping, transportation & equipment cases.
Catalog(s) available

Fiddler Films
1111 Fifth Ave S, Naples, FL 34102
Tel: 239-435-1818
E-mail: lou@fiddlerfilms.com
Web Site: www.fiddlerfilms.com
Provides rental of facilities & lighting. Offers DVD & Blu-ray production, aerial & underwater shooting & voiceover casting.

Fidelity Information Services (FIS)
601 Riverside Ave, Jacksonville, FL 32204
Tel: 904-438-6000 *Toll Free Tel:* 888-323-0310 (US only) *Fax:* 904-357-1105
E-mail: moreinformation@fisglobal.com
Web Site: www.fisglobal.com
Key Personnel
Dir, Enterprise Prog Mgmt: Lucky Caves
Founded: 1968 (as Systematics)

FIDM Productions
Division of Fashion Institute of Design & Merchandising
919 S Grand Ave, Los Angeles, CA 90015-1421
Tel: 213-624-1201 *Toll Free Tel:* 800-624-1200 *Fax:* 213-624-4799 *Toll Free Fax:* 800-624-1200
Web Site: fidm.edu
Key Personnel
Exec Dir: Dena Stitt

Founded: 1969
Catalog(s) available

5th Floor Recording Co
316 N Milwaukee St, Suite 501, Milwaukee, WI 53202
Tel: 414-276-1919 *Fax:* 414-271-6621
Web Site: www.5thfloorrecording.com
Key Personnel
Owner & Engr: Ray Fister *Tel:* 414-412-4056 (cell) *E-mail:* ray@5thfloorrecording.com
Founded: 1997
Offers professional commercial & industrial audio for advertising agencies as well as the corporate world. Produce TV & radio commercials, industrial DVD/videos & original music.

FILM Archives Inc
35 W 35 St, Suite 904, New York, NY 10001-2238
Tel: 212-696-2616 *Fax:* 503-210-9927
E-mail: info@filmarchives.com
Web Site: www.filmarchivesonline.com
Key Personnel
CEO & Pres: Mark Trost
Founded: 1988
Stock footage library.
Online catalog(s) available

Film Bank Inc, see Corbis Motion

Film Converter Co of America Inc
10 W Burbank Blvd, Burbank, CA 91502
Mailing Address: PO Box 110, Burbank, CA 91503
Tel: 818-845-7651 *Fax:* 818-845-7651
Web Site: www.filmconverterco.com
Key Personnel
Pres: Lynne Plambeck *E-mail:* lynne@filmconverterco.com
Editorial leaders & supplies. Film destruction/recycling.
Catalog(s) available

Film Creations Ltd
2021 E Broadway Blvd, Tucson, AZ 85719
Tel: 520-624-4444 *Toll Free Tel:* 888-877-2490 *Fax:* 520-624-9659
E-mail: info@filmcreations.com
Web Site: www.filmcreations.com
Key Personnel
CEO & Pres: Richard A Rose *E-mail:* rarose@filmcreations.com
VP: Paul Rose *E-mail:* paul@filmcreations.com
Founded: 1978
Video production & post-production.

Film Emporium
1890 Palmer Ave, Suite 403, Larchmont, NY 10538
Tel: 914-833-2433 *Toll Free Tel:* 800-371-2555 *Fax:* 914-833-2430
E-mail: info@filmemporium.com
Web Site: www.filmemporium.com
Founded: 1995
Motion picture film stock, video/audio tape & production insurance. Competitive rates.

Film House Inc
810 Dominican Dr, Nashville, TN 37228
Tel: 615-255-4000 *Fax:* 615-255-4111
E-mail: results@filmhouse.com
Web Site: www.filmhouse.com
Key Personnel
CEO: Curt Hahn *E-mail:* curthahn@filmhouse.com
CFO: Andy Cohen *E-mail:* andycohen@filmhouse.com
COO & Pres: Ron Routson *E-mail:* ronroutson@filmhouse.com
SVP: Wayne Campbell *E-mail:* waynecampbell@filmhouse.com
Founded: 1976

Film Ideas
308 N Wolf Rd, Wheeling, IL 60090
Tel: 847-419-0255 *Toll Free Tel:* 800-475-3456 (US only) *Fax:* 847-419-8933
E-mail: info@filmideas.com
Web Site: www.filmideas.com
Key Personnel
Pres: Mike Collins *E-mail:* mikec@filmideas.com
Founded: 1979
DVD & MPEG 1, 2.
Catalog(s) available
Membership(s): Consortium of College & University Media Centers; National Association of Media & Technology Centers

Film-Makers Cooperative
Division of New American Cinema Group Inc
475 Park Ave S, 6th fl, New York, NY 10016
Tel: 212-267-5665 *Fax:* 212-267-5666
E-mail: film6000@aol.com; filmmakerscoop@gmail.com
Web Site: film-makerscoop.com
Key Personnel
Exec Dir: M M Serra
Founded: 1962
Distributor of independent & avant-garde films.
Catalog(s) available
Membership(s): Media Alliance; National Association of Media Arts Centers

Film Marketing Services Inc
4640 Admiralty Way, Suite 500, Marina del Rey, CA 90292
E-mail: info@filmmarketingservices.com
Web Site: filmmarketingservices.com
Film contract negotiations for international & domestic distribution.

Film Police
Division of Koch/Marschall Productions Inc
4310 Mozart St, Chicago, IL 60618-1528
Tel: 773-463-4010
E-mail: info@filmpolice.com
Web Site: www.filmpolice.com
Key Personnel
Pres: Phillip Koch *E-mail:* phil@filmpolice.com
VP: Sally Marschall *E-mail:* sally@filmpolice.com
Founded: 1980
Full service film & video production company specializing in high quality programs.
Catalog(s) available
Membership(s): DGA; Independent Feature Project

Film Technology Co Inc
726 N Cole Ave, Hollywood, CA 90038
Tel: 323-464-3456 *Fax:* 323-464-7439
Web Site: www.filmtech.com
Key Personnel
Pres: Ralph Sargent
Gen Mgr: Zac Fink *Tel:* 323-464-3456 ext 18 *E-mail:* zac@filmtech.com
Catalog(s) available
Membership(s): Association of Moving Image Archivists

Film TV Sound
Division of EQE Media & Consulting Group
PO Box 950207, Mission Hills, CA 91395-0207
Tel: 818-231-1038 *Fax:* 818-892-9236
E-mail: editorial@filmtvsound.com; eqe-media@filmtvsound.com
Web Site: www.filmtvsound.com
Key Personnel
Pres: Fred Ginsburg
Educational web site for production sound & video production. Tips, tricks, tutorials. Workshops & seminars. Online articles & tutorials available.
Membership(s): BKSTS; Cinema Audio Society; Law Enforcement Video Association; University Film & Video Association

Filmakers Library
3212 Duke St, Alexandria, VA 22314
Tel: 703-212-8520
E-mail: sales@alexanderstreet.com; orders@alexanderstreet.com
Web Site: www.academicvideostore.com/filmakers; www.academicvideostore.com
Key Personnel
Dir: Andrea Traubner *E-mail:* andrea@filmakers.com
Educational distributors.
Catalog(s), annual, free
Membership(s): AFVA; ALA; Consortium of College & University Media Centers; National Association of Media & Technology Centers; New York Film/Video Council; New York Women in Film & Television

Filmdex Inc
14016 Sullyfield Circle, Chantilly, VA 20151
Tel: 703-631-0600 *Toll Free Tel:* 888-FILMDEX (345-6339) *Fax:* 703-818-0237
E-mail: webinquiry@filmdex.com
Web Site: www.filmdex.com
Key Personnel
Contact: Catherine Slattery *Tel:* 703-631-0600 ext 669
Founded: 1955
Catalog(s) available
Membership(s): AIM

Filmlites Montana
6465 River Rd, Bozeman, MT 59718
Tel: 406-587-0226 *Fax:* 406-551-4555
E-mail: info@filmlitesmt.com
Web Site: www.filmlitesmt.com
Key Personnel
Founder & Dir: J P Gabriel
Founded: 1989
Film & video production rental equipment; HD video/film production; events & lighting.

FilmNation Entertainment
150 W 22 St, 9th fl, New York, NY 10011
Web Site: www.filmnation.com
Key Personnel
CEO: Glen Basner
COO: Milan Popelka
Pres, Prodn: Aaron Ryder
Co-Pres, Prodn: Ben Browning
EVP, Mktg & Dist: Richard Baker
EVP, Prodn: Karen Lunder
EVP, Post-Prodn: Mike Jackman
SVP, Intl Dist & Strategy: Gregoire Gensollen
SVP, Intl Dist Servs: Stefan Zorich
SVP, Mktg & Dist: Pauline Piechota
SVP, Sales: Tara Erer
VP, Sales: Robert Carney
Dir, Prodn: Patrick Chu
Dir, Publicity: Selena Saldana
Mgr, Intl Dist Servs: Anaite Shields
Coord, Intl Dist Servs: Alexandra Balino
Coord, Mktg, Publicity & Dist: Colby Leopard
Founded: 2008
Film production company & international film sales agent.
Branch Office(s)
345 N Maple Dr, Suite 202, Beverly Hills, CA 90210

Films by Huey
103 Montrose Ave, Portland, ME 04103
Tel: 207-773-1130
E-mail: huey@filmsbyhuey.com
Web Site: www.filmsbyhuey.com

Key Personnel
Dir: James "Huey" Coleman
Award winning independent film & video producer, also does artist-in-residencies, K-12 & college.

Films for the Humanities & Sciences
Division of Infobase Learning
132 W 31 St, 17th fl, New York, NY 10001
Toll Free Tel: 800-257-5126 *Fax:* 609-671-0266
E-mail: custserv@films.com
Web Site: ffh.films.com
Key Personnel
Chmn: Mark McDonnell
Chief Content Offr & VP: Kathy Tan *Tel:* 212-967-8800 *E-mail:* ktan@infobaselearning.com
VP, Digital Strategy: Wendy Collins *Tel:* 212-967-8800 *E-mail:* wcollins@infobaselearning.com
Dir, Sales: Doug Humphrey *Tel:* 212-967-8800 *E-mail:* dhumphrey@infobaselearning.com
Prodn Ed: Diane Rhodes *Tel:* 609-647-7651 ext 4372 *E-mail:* drhodes@infobaselearning.com
Founded: 1959
Provider of media for advanced education. Films for the Humanities & Sciences (FFH&S) creates & distributes products designed especially for discerning high school & college-level educators. FFH&S is the flagship brand of Films Media Group, an award-winning source of over 13,000 titles & exclusive US distributor for BBC Educational Collections, the Bill Moyers Collection, PBS, HBO & NewsHour, as well as many offerings from ABC News.
Catalog(s), weekly, free, over 100 unique catalogs mailed throughout the year

Films Media Group
Division of Infobase Learning
132 W 31 St, 17th fl, New York, NY 10001
Tel: 212-967-8800 *Toll Free Tel:* 800-322-8755 *Toll Free Fax:* 800-678-3633
E-mail: custserv@films.com; order@films.com
Web Site: www.films.com
DVDs & streaming video on academic, vocational & life skills topics.

Films of the Nations
Division of Paulicia Enterprises
PO Box 449, Clarksburg, NJ 08510-0449
Tel: 732-462-3522 *Toll Free Tel:* 800-832-0980 *Fax:* 732-294-0330
E-mail: info@aldenfilms.com
Web Site: www.aldenfilms.com
Key Personnel
Owner & Pres: Paul Weinberg
Booking: Felicia Weinberg
Founded: 1952
Catalog(s) available

Filmtools®
1400 W Burbank Blvd, Burbank, CA 91506
Tel: 818-845-8066 *Toll Free Tel:* 888-807-1900 *Fax:* 818-845-8138
Web Site: www.filmtools.com
Key Personnel
Owner & CFO: Stan McClain
Owner: Kim McClain
Founded: 1986
Grip & lighting bags.
Catalog(s) available

Filmworkers
232 E Ohio, Chicago, IL 60611
Tel: 312-664-9333
Web Site: www.filmworkersastro.com
Key Personnel
Gen Mgr: Manuela Hung *E-mail:* manuelah@filmworkers.com
Post Prodn Coord: Chad Rohrback *E-mail:* chadr@filmworkers.com
Catalog(s) available
Membership(s): AICP; ITVS; SMPTE

FilmWorks Pacific
PO Box 61281, Honolulu, HI 96839-1281
Tel: 808-599-6403 (studio) *Fax:* 808-537-9272
E-mail: studio@filmworkspacific.com
Web Site: www.filmworkspacific.com
Key Personnel
Writer & Dir: Edgy Lee

Final Draft Inc
26707 W Agoura Rd, Suite 205, Calabasas, CA 91302
Tel: 818-995-8995; 818-906-8930 (tech support) *Toll Free Tel:* 800-231-4055 *Fax:* 818-995-4422
E-mail: info@finaldraft.com
Web Site: www.finaldraft.com
Key Personnel
CEO & Pres: Marc Madnick
CFO: Al Belmont
COO: Yan Vinterfeld
Chief Strategy Offr: Josh C Kline
VP, Events & Servs: Shelly Mellott
VP, Sales: Scott McMenamin
VP, Tech Support: Joel Levin
Founded: 1991

Finale Editworks
2339 Columbia, Suite 100, Vancouver, BC V5Y 3V5, Canada
Tel: 604-876-7678 *Fax:* 604-876-3299
E-mail: info@finale.tv
Web Site: www.finale.tv
Key Personnel
Pres: Don Thompson *E-mail:* don@finale.tv
Founded: 1988
Fully integrated HD post-production facility offering creative editorial, HD online finishing, sound post, VFX, DVD authoring & duplication. Full service rental department.

Fingerpaint
13 Walker Way, Albany, NY 12205
Tel: 518-869-1968 *Fax:* 518-869-1969
Web Site: fingerpaintmarketing.com
Key Personnel
Audio & Video Servs: Margherita Petti Krug *E-mail:* mkrug@fingerpaintmarketing.com; Ray Rettig
Founded: 2008
Branch Office(s)
395 Broadway, Saratoga Springs, NY 12866
Membership(s): The Ad Club; Alliance for Women in Media; AMA; SPARS

Stuart Finley Films
3428 Mansfield Rd, Falls Church, VA 22041
Tel: 703-820-7700
Web Site: www.stufin.com
Key Personnel
Pres: Robert Finley *E-mail:* rsf@stufin.com
Stock footage.
Catalog(s) available

Fire Power Music Inc
9913 E Main St, No 171, Tempe, AZ 85207
Tel: 602-463-2988
Key Personnel
CEO: Douglas Robertson
Founded: 2005
Recording studio specializing in all types of music & vocal presentation.

Fire Station Studios
224 N Guadalupe St, San Marcos, TX 78666
Tel: 512-396-1144 *Fax:* 512-396-1169
E-mail: info@firestationstudios.com
Web Site: www.firestationstudios.com
Key Personnel
Studio Mgr: Mark C Erickson *E-mail:* mark@firestationstudios.com
Engr: Gary Hickinbotham *E-mail:* gary@firestationstudios.com

Firefly Book Club
Division of Scholastic Inc
557 Broadway, New York, NY 10012
Tel: 212-343-6100 *Toll Free Tel:* 800-724-6527 (cust serv) *Fax:* 212-343-4535
E-mail: info@scholastic.com; custserv@scholastic.com
Web Site: www.scholastic.com
Key Personnel
Pres, Book Clubs: Judith A Newman
Founded: 1920

Firehouse Studios
155 W Rosemont Ave, Chicago, IL 60660
Tel: 773-271-3100 *Toll Free Fax:* 866-540-1091
E-mail: folks@firehousestudios.com
Web Site: firehousestudios.com
Studio, lighting, video & audio equipment rentals & crew.

First Camera
2472 Third St, San Francisco, CA 94107
Tel: 415-647-3400 *Fax:* 415-647-3410
E-mail: sfvideo@firstcamera.com
Web Site: www.firstcamera.com
Key Personnel
Owner: Vaughn Kilgore *E-mail:* vaughn@firstcamera.com

First Cut Communications LLC
301 W Broome St, Suite 100, LaGrange, GA 30240
Mailing Address: PO Box 49, LaGrange, GA 30241
Tel: 706-882-5581
E-mail: info@firstcutcommunications.com
Web Site: www.firstcutcommunications.com
Key Personnel
Client Devt Mgmt & Opers: Matt French
Video production specializing in contract negotiations videos, employee orientations/onboarding videos, employee benefit videos, labor relations videos, positive employee relations videos, plant tours videos, sales meeting videos, training videos, union avoidance videos & web sites.

1st Financial Training Services Inc
1515 E Woodfield Rd, Suite 3730, Schaumburg, IL 60173
Tel: 847-969-0900 *Toll Free Tel:* 800-442-8662 *Fax:* 847-969-0521
E-mail: sales@1stfinancialtraining.com
Web Site: www.1stfinancialtraining.com
Key Personnel
CEO & Pres: Bonnie Eidsin
Founded: 1986
Catalog(s) available

First Group Communications Inc
10994 Ranch Stone Dr, Houston, TX 77064
Tel: 281-890-9999 *Fax:* 281-890-9989
E-mail: info@firstgroupmedia.com
Web Site: www.firstgroupmedia.com
Key Personnel
Pres: Dalton Knight *Tel:* 281-728-7003 (cell) *E-mail:* dalt@firstgroupmedia.com
Founded: 1981
Production studio (8,000 sq ft) & training consultants.
Catalog(s), free

First Person™
550 Bryant St, San Francisco, CA 94107
Tel: 415-495-5595 *Fax:* 415-543-8370

Key Personnel
Principal: Drew Fiero
Bldg Mgr: Andre Custodio
Post Prodr: Carlos Cabrales
Client Servs: Kelsey Bryant
Brochure(s) available
Membership(s): AICP; MCA-I; San Francisco Ad Club

First Run Features
The Film Center Bldg, Suite 1213, 630 Ninth Ave, New York, NY 10036-3708
Tel: 212-243-0600 *Fax:* 212-989-7649
E-mail: info@firstrunfeatures.com
Web Site: www.firstrunfeatures.com
Key Personnel
Pres: Seymour Wishman
Dir, Home Video Sales: John Bione
Founded: 1979
Catalog(s) available
Membership(s): Entertainment Merchants Association

1st Wave Productions
2017 Pacific Ave, Venice, CA 90291
Tel: 310-474-2439 *Fax:* 310-474-5282
Web Site: www.1stwaveproductions.com
Key Personnel
Owner: Luann Barry *E-mail:* luann@1stwaveproductions.com
Founded: 1999
Production services, co-production & office space.

FirstCom Music
1325 Capital Pkwy, Suite 109, Carrollton, TX 75006
Tel: 972-446-8742 *Toll Free Tel:* 800-858-8880 *Fax:* 972-242-6526
E-mail: info@firstcom.com
Web Site: www.firstcom.com
Key Personnel
SVP & Exec Prodr: Ken Nelson
VP & Gen Mgr: Carol Riffert
Dir, Mktg: Cristy Coffey
Founded: 1980
Nineteen world-class production music libraries empower your creativity with over 135,000 tracks & over 6,000 new track releases every year. Our diverse repertoire includes high quality, easy-to-use production music that reflects today's charts. Hear the difference at www.firstcom.com today.
Catalog(s) available
Branch Office(s)
FirstCom Film/TV Music, 9255 W Sunset Blvd, 2nd fl, Los Angeles, CA 90069 *Tel:* 310-865-4436 *Toll Free Tel:* 800-778-1574 *Fax:* 310-865-4454
Membership(s): MCA-I; NAB

FirstGeneration Audio/Visual Services
410 Allentown Dr, Allentown, PA 18109
Tel: 610-437-4300 *Fax:* 610-437-3200
E-mail: information@firstgencom.com; contact@firstgencom.com
Web Site: www.firstgenav.com
Equipment rentals - audio, data projection & video, event lighting & general presentation AV.

Fish Films Footage World
4548 Van Noord Ave, Studio City, CA 91604
Tel: 818-905-1071
E-mail: footageworld@aol.com
Web Site: www.footageworld.com
Key Personnel
Pres: D Fishbein
Secy/Treas: Gloria Lopez
Catalog(s) available

FitzCo Sound Inc
4300 W Wall St, Bldg B, Midland, TX 79703
Mailing Address: PO Box 710, Midland, TX 79702
Tel: 432-684-0861 *Fax:* 432-682-9978
Web Site: www.fitzcosound.com
Key Personnel
Owner: Milt Hathaway
Founded: 1981

5 Alarm Music
Division of Imagem Production Music LLC
35 W Dayton St, Pasadena, CA 91105
Tel: 626-304-1698 *Toll Free Tel:* 800-322-7879 *Fax:* 626-795-2058
E-mail: info@5alarmmusic.com
Web Site: www.5alarmmusic.com
Key Personnel
VP: Cassie Lord *Tel:* 626-304-1698 ext 5503 *E-mail:* cassie@5alarmmusic.com
Exec Dir: J D Adams *Tel:* 626-304-1698 ext 5511 *E-mail:* jd@5alarmmusic.com
Dir, Opers: TerriLynn Rosa *Tel:* 626-304-1698 ext 5542 *E-mail:* terrilynn@rescuerecords.com
Founded: 1997
Production music library.
Catalog(s), licensed library
Membership(s): Association of Independent Music Publishers; PMA International

FJ Productions Inc
14900 Ventura Blvd, Suite 350, Sherman Oaks, CA 91403-3465
Tel: 818-788-0153 *Fax:* 818-788-0186
Web Site: www.fjproductions.com
Key Personnel
Chief Creative Offr: Harlan Freedman *E-mail:* hfreedman@fjproductions.com
Exec Prodr: Fabio Golombek *Tel:* 818-788-0153 ext 16 *E-mail:* fgolombek@fjproductions.com
Prodr & Ad Dir: Adriana Saboya *Tel:* 818-788-0153 ext 14 *E-mail:* asaboya@fjproductions.com
Assoc Prodr: Luiza Florence *Tel:* 818-788-0153 ext 15 *E-mail:* lflorence@fjproductions.com

FJW Optical Systems Inc
322 N Woodwork Lane, Palatine, IL 60067-4933
Tel: 847-358-2500 *Toll Free Tel:* 800-355-4FJW (355-4359) *Fax:* 847-358-2533
E-mail: irsales@findrscope.com
Web Site: www.findrscope.com
Key Personnel
Owner & Pres: Frank Warzak
Founded: 1945
Manufacture infrared video camera.
Catalog(s) available

FlagHouse
601 Flaghouse Dr, Hasbrouck Heights, NJ 07604-3116
Tel: 201-288-7600 *Toll Free Tel:* 800-793-7900 *Fax:* 201-288-7887 *Toll Free Fax:* 800-793-7922
E-mail: sales@flaghouse.com
Web Site: www.flaghouse.com
Key Personnel
Owner: Douglas Carmel; George Carmel
Founded: 1954
Catalog(s) available
Membership(s): EDSA; Education Market Association

Paul Flanagan Productions
1623 S Hearthside Dr, Richmond, TX 77406-1369
Tel: 281-799-4832
Web Site: www.productionhub.com
Key Personnel
Owner: Paul Flanagan *E-mail:* paul.flanagan@att.net
Founded: 1999
Video production company; video & audio equipment; video shoots, editing, tape duplications.

Flash Clinic Inc
164 W 25 St, New York, NY 10001
Tel: 212-337-0447 *Toll Free Tel:* 800-752-7536 *Fax:* 212-337-8088
E-mail: info@flashclinic.com
Web Site: www.flashclinic.com
Key Personnel
Owner: Janet Lederman
Founded: 1973
Professional photographic equipment, rentals, sales & service.
Catalog(s) available

Flash Electronics Inc
Brooklyn Army Terminal, Suite 1-A, Mail Box 3, 140 58 St, Brooklyn, NY 11220
Tel: 718-492-4040 *Toll Free Tel:* 800-831-3127 *Fax:* 718-492-4590
E-mail: flashdistr@aol.com; customercare@flashdistributors.com
Web Site: www.flashdistributors.com
Key Personnel
Pres: Steven V Scavelli
VP: Frank Rampino
Catalog(s) available
Membership(s): Entertainment Merchants Association; National Association of Video Distributors

Flashback Media Productions
Division of Strassner Entertainment Group LLC
510 E Sutton Circle, Lafayette, CO 80026
Tel: 303-545-9955 *Fax:* 303-545-6658
E-mail: info@flashback.tv
Web Site: www.flashback.tv
Key Personnel
Pres: Bunnie Strassner *E-mail:* bunnie@flashbackmedia.tv
Prodn: Norman Strassner
Founded: 1987
Video & film production services.

Flashback Stage Lighting
8151 Commercial St, La Mesa, CA 91924
Tel: 619-697-2729 *Fax:* 619-697-2782
E-mail: mail@flashbackstagelighting.com
Web Site: www.flashbackstagelighting.com
Key Personnel
Pres: Matthew Short
Founded: 1979

Flat Town Music Co
Division of Swallow Publications Inc
238 E Main St, Ville Platte, LA 70856
Mailing Address: PO Drawer 10, Ville Platte, LA 70586-0010
Tel: 337-363-2177 *Fax:* 337-363-2094
E-mail: info@flattownmusic.com
Web Site: www.flattownmusic.com
Key Personnel
Pres: Floyd Soileau
Founded: 1957
Music libraries, Cajun, Zydeco, "Swamp-Pop" music publisher.
Catalog(s) available

Doug Fleenor Design Inc
396 Corbett Canyon Rd, Arroyo Grande, CA 93420
Tel: 805-481-9599 *Toll Free Tel:* 888-436-9512 *Fax:* 805-481-9599
E-mail: info@dfd.com
Web Site: www.dfd.com
Key Personnel
Pres: Doug Fleenor
Cont: Cindy Fleenor *E-mail:* cindy@dfd.com
Opers Mgr: Matt Walker *E-mail:* matt@dfd.com

Founded: 1990
Manufacture lighting control equipment.

Fleetwood Group Inc
11832 James St, Holland, MI 49424
Mailing Address: PO Box 1259, Holland, MI 49422-1259
Tel: 616-396-1142 *Toll Free Tel:* 800-257-6390 *Fax:* 616-820-8301
E-mail: sales@fleetwoodgroup.com
Web Site: www.fleetwoodgroup.com; www.replysystems.com (electronics div)
Key Personnel
Prod Mgr: Heather Waller
Manufacture audience response products.

Flex-A-Lite West
10250 Aldebaran Dr, Reno, NV 89508
Tel: 775-677-7711 *Fax:* 775-677-7577
Key Personnel
Owner: Mike Ross *Tel:* 775-742-7600 (cell) *E-mail:* mikeaspen@aol.com
Stage lighting, curtains, rigging, projection screens, mounts & projectors.
Catalog(s) available

Flight Form Cases Inc
6543 S Laramie Ave, Bedford Park, IL 60638
Tel: 708-458-8989 *Toll Free Tel:* 800-334-4884 *Fax:* 708-458-9023
E-mail: info@flightform.com; info@caseyguys.net; sales@caseguys.com
Web Site: www.flightform.com
Key Personnel
Pres: Edward Otrusina
Founded: 1962
Catalog(s) available
Membership(s): GAMMA; Music Distributors Association; NAMM, the National Association of Music Merchants

Flip 2 Media Inc
1067 Serpentine Lane, Pleasanton, CA 94566-4759
Tel: 925-417-1420
E-mail: info@flip2media.com
Web Site: www.flip2media.com
Key Personnel
CTO: Doug Mann
Sr Prodr/Dir: Thaddeus Coburg
Dir, Post Prodn: Glen Shockley
Founded: 2014
Full service media & video production company offering content development, production, post-production & electronic file delivery. Also marketing & advertising services.

FLIR Systems Inc
27700 SW Parkway Ave, Wilsonville, OR 97070
Tel: 503-498-3547 *Toll Free Tel:* 800-322-3731 *Fax:* 503-498-3904
E-mail: marketing@flir.com
Web Site: www.flir.com
Key Personnel
Mgr: Ashley Walker
Global leader in infrared technology.
Catalog(s) available
Branch Office(s)
25 Esquire Rd, North Billerica, MA 01862 *Toll Free Tel:* 800-464-6372
108 Kountz Lane, Freeport, PA 16229, Contact: Michael Matzko *Tel:* 724-295-2880 *E-mail:* michael.matzko@flir.com
5230 S Service Rd, Suite 125, Burlington, ON L7L 5K2, Canada *Toll Free Tel:* 800-613-0507
Foreign Office(s): FLIR Systems AB, Antennvagen 6, 187 66 Taby, Sweden *Tel:* (08) 753 2500 *Fax:* (08) 753 0752

Flo-Co, see The Fluorescent Co Inc

Florentine Films
136 E 56 St, Suite 4-B, New York, NY 10022
Tel: 212-980-5966 *Fax:* 212-980-5944
Web Site: www.florentinefilms.com/sherman
Key Personnel
Prodr & Dir: Roger Sherman *E-mail:* rogersherman@florentinefilms.com
Founded: 1976
Catalog(s) available

Florical Systems Inc
Division of Clear Channel Communications Inc
4500 NW 27 Ave, Bldg B-1, Gainesville, FL 32606
Tel: 352-372-8326 *Toll Free Tel:* 800-372-4613 *Fax:* 352-375-0859
E-mail: support@florical.com
Web Site: www.florical.com
Key Personnel
VP & Gen Mgr, Opers: Shawn Maynard *Tel:* 352-372-8326 ext 318 *E-mail:* shawn.maynard@florical.com
TV automation for TV stations & cable networks.

Florida Digital Studios
10781 75 St, Largo, FL 33777
Tel: 727-546-7900 *Fax:* 727-546-8640
Web Site: www.floridadigitalstudios.com
Key Personnel
Gen Mgr: Jay Gross
Dir, Sales & Mktg: Kathy Fishback *E-mail:* kathy@floridadigitalstudios.com
Founded: 1982
Free standing 12,000 sq ft studio offering post-production tape & disc duplication.

Florida Film & Tape
3417 Lake Breeze Rd, Orlando, FL 32808
Tel: 407-297-0091 *Fax:* 407-297-0094
Web Site: www.ffandt.com
Key Personnel
Pres: Brad Fuller *E-mail:* brad@ffandt.com
Dir: Mike Fuller
Founded: 1980

Florida Film & Video
4461 38 Way S, St Petersburg, FL 33711
Tel: 727-369-0732
E-mail: info@flhd.tv
Web Site: www.flhd.tv
Key Personnel
Pres: Bill Mills
Founded: 1985
Film & video production.

Fluke Corp
Subsidiary of Danaher Corp
6920 Seaway Blvd, Everett, WA 98203
Mailing Address: PO Box 9090, Everett, WA 98206-9090
Tel: 425-347-6100 *Toll Free Tel:* 800-443-5853 *Fax:* 425-446-5116
E-mail: fluke-info@fluke.com
Web Site: www.fluke.com
Key Personnel
PR Mgr: Leah Friberg
Electronics test & measurement co.
Catalog(s) available
Foreign Office(s): PO Box 1186, Eindhoven, Netherlands *Tel:* (040) 267 5200 *Fax:* (040) 267 5222

The Fluorescent Co Inc
c/o Red*D*Mix Rentals Inc, 388 Carlaw Ave, Suite 116, Toronto, ON M4M 2T4, Canada
Tel: 416-879-3761 *Fax:* 905-681-8520
E-mail: reddmix@cogeco.ca
Web Site: www.flo-co.com
Key Personnel
Contact: Ray McMillian
Catalog(s) available

Flying Colors Broadcasts
2000 "M" St NW, Suite 345, Washington, DC 20036
Tel: 202-293-5300
E-mail: info@fc-tv.com
Web Site: www.fc-tv.com
Key Personnel
Co-Owner & Pres: Constance Chatfield-Taylor
Co-Owner & VP: Lynn Hanford
Dir, Prodn: Erin Murphy
Sales & Satellite Servs Dir: Susan Chavarria
Specialize in video production, live domestic & international event broadcasts, business television networks & broadcasting.

FM Systems Inc
3877 S Main St, Santa Ana, CA 92707
Tel: 714-979-3355 *Toll Free Tel:* 800-235-6960 *Fax:* 714-979-0913
E-mail: fmsystemsinc@sbcglobal.net
Web Site: www.fmsystems-inc.com
Key Personnel
COO: Donald McClatchie
Pres: Frank McClatchie
Sales Mgr: Mr Billings
Founded: 1978
Catalog(s) available

FMP Media Solutions Inc
1010 Spring Mill Ave, Suite 100, Conshohocken, PA 19428
Tel: 610-825-4000 *Toll Free Tel:* 800-346-5071 *Fax:* 610-825-4430
E-mail: info@fmpmedia.com
Web Site: www.fmpmedia.com
Key Personnel
Pres: Ronald Giannone
VP, Creative Media: Don Cox
Dir, FMP Languages Translation/Narration: Bill Groce
Founded: 1966
Digital media & event production company that develops visually-driven business communications for their clients. Outfit productions & video shoots but do not rent equipment without providing management & staff.
Catalog(s) available
Membership(s): AFI; MCA-I; SMPTE

Focus Features
Division of NBC Universal
1540 Second St, No 200, Santa Monica, CA 90401
Web Site: www.focusfeatures.com
Founded: 2002
Branch Office(s)
c/o NBC Universal, 30 Rockefeller Plaza, Bldg 5TS, 10th fl, New York, NY 10112

Focus on Animals
Division of National Humane Education Society (NHES)
PO Box 340, Charles Town, WV 25414-0340
Tel: 304-725-0506 *Fax:* 304-725-1523
E-mail: information@nhes.org
Web Site: www.nhes.org
Key Personnel
Humane Educator: Megan Moore
Founded: 1948
Educational videos & films for people with a reverence for life, animal rights & welfare issues.
Catalog(s), free

Folk Era Productions Inc
705 S Washington St, Suite 3, Naperville, IL 60540-6654
Tel: 630-637-2303; 630-305-0770 (cust serv) *Toll Free Tel:* 800-232-7328 (orders) *Fax:* 630-305-0782
E-mail: info@folkera.com
Web Site: www.rediscovermusic.com

Key Personnel
Pres: Allan Shaw *E-mail:* allan@folkera.com
Catalog(s) available
Membership(s): International Bluegrass Music Association; The Recording Academy

Folk-Legacy
85 Sharon Mountain Rd, Sharon, CT 06069
Mailing Address: PO Box 1148, Sharon, CT 06069-1148
Tel: 860-364-5661 *Toll Free Tel:* 800-836-0901 (orders) *Fax:* 860-364-1050
E-mail: sales@folk-legacy.com
Web Site: www.folk-legacy.com
Key Personnel
Pres: Caroline Paton
Founded: 1961
Catalog(s) available

Folkcraft Instruments
22133 Main St, Woodburn, IN 46797
Mailing Address: PO Box 302, Woodburn, IN 46797
Tel: 317-522-1635 *Toll Free Tel:* 800-433-3655 *Fax:* 317-245-2378
E-mail: sales@folkcraft.com
Web Site: www.folkcraft.com; www.richardash.com
Key Personnel
Owner: Richard Ash
Catalog(s) available

Follett Software Co
Division of Follett Corp
1391 Corporate Dr, McHenry, IL 60050-7041
Tel: 815-344-8700 *Toll Free Tel:* 800-323-3397 *Fax:* 815-344-8774; 815-578-5575 *Toll Free Fax:* 800-807-3623 (cust serv)
Web Site: www.follettsoftware.com
Key Personnel
Pres: Simona Rollinson
VP, Sales: Jerry Perez
VP, Servs & Opers: Mike Gedzyk
VP, Software Devt: Tim Rogers
Run library automation, textbook distribution management, asset management for school grades K-12.
Catalog(s) available

The Food & Beverage Institute
Division of The Culinary Institute of America
1946 Campus Dr, Hyde Park, NY 12538-1499
Tel: 845-905-4417 *Toll Free Tel:* 800-888-7850 *Fax:* 845-451-1078
E-mail: ciaprochef@culinary.edu
Web Site: www.ciachef.edu; www.ciaprochef.com
Key Personnel
Admin Coord, Continuing Educ Dept: Debbie Bailey *Tel:* 845-451-1396 *E-mail:* d_bailey@culinary.edu
Catalog(s) available

FootageBank HD
13470 Washington Blvd, Suite 210, Marina Del Rey, CA 90292
Tel: 310-822-1400 *Toll Free Tel:* 888-653-1400 *Fax:* 310-822-4100
E-mail: info@footagebank.com
Web Site: www.footagebank.com
Key Personnel
Founder & Pres: Paula Lumbard *Tel:* 310-822-1400 ext 105 *E-mail:* paulal@footagebank.com
VP: Carol Martin *Tel:* 310-822-1400 ext 102 *E-mail:* carolm@footagebank.com
Founded: 2002
Supplier of large format & HD images to television, theatrical, mobile, independent & corporate media buyers.

Foothill Digital Inc
217 Storer Ave, New Rochelle, NY 10801
Tel: 914-235-5670
E-mail: info@foothilldigital.com
Web Site: www.foothilldigital.com; www.tuckersound.com
Key Personnel
Owner: Allan Tucker *E-mail:* tucker@foothilldigital.com
Founded: 1988
Digital mastering & authoring for CD & DVD.

For-A Corp of America
Subsidiary of For-A Co Ltd
11155 Knott Ave, Suite G & H, Cypress, CA 90630
Tel: 714-894-3311 *Fax:* 714-894-5399
E-mail: info@for-a.com
Web Site: www.for-a.com
Key Personnel
Pres: Mr Hiro Tanoue
Catalog(s) available
Branch Office(s)
2400 NE Waldo Rd, Gainesville, FL 32609-3329 *Tel:* 352-371-1505 *Fax:* 352-378-5320 (dist & serv ctr)
5200 Blue Lagoon Dr, Suite 760, Miami, FL 33126 *Tel:* 305-931-1700 *Fax:* 305-264-7890 *E-mail:* silvestre@for-a.com
Fort Lee Executive Park, 2 Executive Dr, Suite 670, Fort Lee, NJ 07024 *Tel:* 201-944-1120
346-A Queen St W, Toronto, ON M5V 2A2, Canada *Tel:* 416-977-0343 *Fax:* 416-977-0657
Membership(s): InfoComm International®; NAB

Forensic Video Deposition Service
2823 N 48 St, Suite 8, Phoenix, AZ 85008
Tel: 602-840-1222 *Fax:* 602-840-1313
Web Site: forensicvideo.net
Key Personnel
Pres: John Lynch *E-mail:* jlynch@forensicvideo.net
Legal video & video conferencing.

Foresight Imaging
One Executive Dr, Suite 102, Chelmsford, MA 01824
Tel: 978-458-4624 *Fax:* 978-458-5488
E-mail: info@fi-llc.com
Web Site: www.fi-llc.com
Key Personnel
Founder & CEO & Pres: Mark Mariotti
Founder & VP, Engg: Jack Melville
Founder & VP, Sales & Mktg: Tony Molinari *Tel:* 978-458-4624 ext 223
Co-Owner & VP, Procurement & Mfg: Mike Carroll
Founded: 1985
Catalog(s) available

Forge Recording LLC
100 Mill Rd, Oreland, PA 19075
Tel: 215-885-7000 *Toll Free Tel:* 800-331-0405 *Fax:* 215-887-3501
E-mail: info@forgerecording.com
Web Site: www.forgerecording.com
Founded: 1979
Recording, graphic design & duplication services.
Catalog(s) available
Membership(s): AES

Forte Productions
PO Box 17, San Geronimo, CA 94963-0325
Tel: 415-488-9446 *Fax:* 415-488-9446
Web Site: www.pianovideos.com
Key Personnel
Pres: Talc Tolchin *E-mail:* talc.tolchin@gmail.com
Catalog(s) available

48 Windows
1661 N Lincoln Blvd, Suite 220, Santa Monica, CA 90404
Tel: 310-392-9545 *Fax:* 310-392-9445
E-mail: ziv@48windows.com
Web Site: www.48windows.com
Key Personnel
Owner: Eric Garcia *E-mail:* ericg@48windows.com

J E Foss Co
3328-B Industrial Blvd, Bethel Park, PA 15102
Mailing Address: PO Box 357, Bethel Park, PA 15102-0357
Tel: 412-564-5644 *Toll Free Tel:* 800-245-6240 *Fax:* 412-564-5646
E-mail: jefoss@earthlink.net
Web Site: www.jefoss.com
Key Personnel
Pres: Gary Spezialetti
Founded: 1925
Multimedia projectors.
Catalog(s) available

FotoKem Film & Video
2801 W Alameda Ave, Burbank, CA 91505
Tel: 818-846-3101 *Fax:* 818-841-2130
E-mail: sales@fotokem.com
Web Site: www.fotokem.com
Key Personnel
Pres: William F Brodersen *Fax:* 818-840-0946
EVP: Bob Semmer
Founded: 1963
Full service motion picture & video post-production facility: 35mm & 16mm film processing, answer prints, digital intermediates, preservation & restoration, telecine, duplication, scanning & recording, HD transfers, DVD pre-mastering & tape-to-film transfer.
Branch Office(s)
Pershing Point Plaza, 1375 Peachtree St NE, Suite A12, Atlanta, GA 30309 *Tel:* 404-334-3660
935 Gravier St, Suite 670, New Orleans, LA 70112 *Tel:* 504-299-4545
1841 Broadway, Suite 801, New York, NY 10023 *Tel:* 646-578-8670

FOTON Hawaii
98-021 Kamehameha Hwy, Aiea, HI 96701
Tel: 808-206-5244
Web Site: www.fotonhawaii.com
Lighting & grip rentals, serving the needs of professional photographers & still photo shoots. Other services include photo assistant referral, studio rental, motorhomes & production supplies.

Fotosearch Stock Photography
21155 Watertown Rd, Waukesha, WI 53186
Tel: 262-717-0740 *Toll Free Tel:* 800-827-3920 *Fax:* 262-717-0745
E-mail: fotosearch@fotosearch.com
Web Site: www.fotosearch.com
Provider of royalty fee & rights managed stock photography, illustrations, maps, video & audio.

Four Corners Productions
38 W Tenth St, New York, NY 10011
Tel: 212-228-6492 *Fax:* 212-228-6492
Web Site: www.operatitles.net; www.gracepaleyvideo.com
Key Personnel
Owner: Sonya Friedman *E-mail:* friedman4c@verizon.net
Opera supertitles. Subtitles for film & video. Producer & director for film & video.
Membership(s): New York Women in Film & Television

4-D Creative Media
16 W 46 St, 12th fl, New York, NY 10036
Tel: 212-994-3300 *Fax:* 212-499-9081
Web Site: www.4-dcreative.com

Key Personnel
Owner & Pres: Rob Carbone
Sales/Prodn Mgr: Peter Cascone *E-mail:* peter@4-dcreative.com
Ed/Prodr: Michael Griffin
Creative production film/video. Avid, Final Cut Pro, Combustion, Hal, Digi Beta Deck. Branch office in Madrid, Spain.
Online catalog(s), NY411 Production Guide

411 Video Information
PO Box 1223, Pebble Beach, CA 93953-1223
Tel: 831-656-0553 *Fax:* 831-656-0555
Web Site: www.411videoinfo.com
Key Personnel
Pres: Leslie McClure *E-mail:* leslie@411videoinfo.com
Founded: 1988
Health & fitness, how-to, special interest, theatrical & non-theatrical video sales & marketing, as well as DVD, CD-ROM, VHS, Blu-ray, Internet, etc. Publicity, marketing & consulting.
Catalog(s) available
Shipping Address: 1013 Sombrero Rd, Pebble Beach, CA 93953

4 Wall Entertainment
3325 W Sunset Rd, Suite F, Las Vegas, NV 89118
Tel: 702-263-3858 *Toll Free Tel:* 877-789-8167 (Western US); 866-492-5540 (Eastern US) *Fax:* 702-263-3863
E-mail: info@4wall.com
Web Site: www.4wall.com; www.usedlighting.com
Key Personnel
CEO: Michael Cannon
CFO: Mark Fletcher
COO: Kathy Torjman
Dir, Used Sales: Mike Mancuso *E-mail:* mmancuso@4wall.com
Founded: 1999
Provider of architectural & entertainment lighting systems - including rentals, sales, service, design, consultation & project management.
Branch Office(s)
5435 W San Fernando Rd, Los Angeles, CA 90039, Gen Mgr: Jim Riendeau *Tel:* 818-252-7481 *Fax:* 818-252-7642 *E-mail:* jriendeau@4wall.com
9525 Berger Rd, Suite G, Colombia, MD 21046, Gen Mgr: Scott Church *Tel:* 410-242-3322 *Toll Free Tel:* 866-242-6625 *Fax:* 410-247-5589 *E-mail:* schurch@4wall.com
35 State St, Moonachie, NJ 07074, Gen Mgr: Jim Cannon *Tel:* 201-329-9878 *Fax:* 201-329-9890 *E-mail:* jcannon@4wall.com
820 Cowan St, Nashville, TN 37207, Gen Mgr: Cathie Berbena Lloyd *Tel:* 615-453-2332 *E-mail:* clloyd@4wall.com
Membership(s): Professional Lighting & Sound Association

4th Street Recording
1211 Fourth St, Santa Monica, CA 90401
Tel: 310-395-9114
E-mail: info@4thstreetrecording.com
Web Site: www.4thstreetrecording.com
Key Personnel
Studio Mgr: Kathleen Wirt *E-mail:* kathleen@4thstreetrecording.com
Founded: 1989
Recording studio.

Fox Connecticut
Subsidiary of Tribune
285 Broad St, Hartford, CT 06115
Tel: 860-527-6161 *Fax:* 860-727-0158
Web Site: www.ctnow.com
Key Personnel
Prodn Mgr: Frank Zakrzewski *Tel:* 860-723-2171
TV program productions.

Fox 40 KTXL TV
Subsidiary of Tribune Co
4655 Fruitridge Rd, Sacramento, CA 95820
Tel: 916-454-4422 *Fax:* 916-739-8139
Web Site: www.fox40.com
Key Personnel
VP & Gen Mgr: Jerry Del Core *E-mail:* jerry.delcore@fox40.com
Television programming.

Fox Television Center
Division of Fox Television Stations Inc
1999 S Bundy Dr, Los Angeles, CA 90025
Tel: 310-584-2000 *Fax:* 310-584-2023
Web Site: www.myfoxla.com
Key Personnel
VP & Gen Mgr: Kevin Hale
Television programming.
Membership(s): NATPE

Fox 10 Productions (KSAZ-TV)
511 W Adams, Phoenix, AZ 85003
Tel: 602-257-1234 *Fax:* 602-262-0177
E-mail: fox10.desk@foxtv.com
Web Site: www.myfoxphoenix.com; www.my45.com
Key Personnel
Creative Servs: Bill Lucas *E-mail:* bill.lucas@foxtv.com
TV station.

Foxtrot Teleprompt
20 Clifford Place, East Norwich, NY 11732-1306
Tel: 516-428-3063 (cell) *Toll Free Tel:* 888-365-0808
E-mail: nyprompter@hotmail.com
Web Site: foxtrotteleprompt.com
Key Personnel
Pres: Robert Burford

Frame 30 Productions Ltd
10816A-82 Ave, No 202, Edmonton, AB T6E 2B3, Canada
Tel: 780-439-5322
E-mail: frame30@frame30.com
Web Site: www.frame30.com
Key Personnel
Prodr & Dir: Michael Hamm *E-mail:* michael@frame30.com
Prodr: Kerrie Long
Prodn: Marie Guerrette
Founded: 1980

Framepool
150 Alhambre Circle, Suite 800, Miami, FL 33134
Tel: 305-401-8597 *Toll Free Tel:* 800-331-1314 *Fax:* 305-428-2800
E-mail: americas@framepool.com
Web Site: usa2.framepool.com
Key Personnel
COO: Peter Carstens *E-mail:* peter.carstens@framepool.com
Founded: 2001
Stock footage library & agency.

Franciscan Media
28 W Liberty St, Cincinnati, OH 45202-6498
Tel: 513-241-5615 *Toll Free Tel:* 800-488-0488 *Fax:* 513-241-0399
Web Site: www.americancatholic.org
Key Personnel
CEO & Publr: Fr Dan Kroger
COO: Thomas Shumate
Catalog(s) available

Karen Frankel Productions
520 E 84 St, New York, NY 10028
Tel: 212-744-6446 *Fax:* 212-570-2820
E-mail: izcrystal@aol.com

Franklin Video Inc
931 Marilyn Dr, Raleigh, NC 27607
Tel: 919-833-8888
Web Site: www.franklinvideo.com
Key Personnel
Pres: Frank Smith *E-mail:* frank@franklinvideo.com
Founded: 1985
Full service production company also offering non-linear editing, digital video & web design.

Freeman
1600 Viceroy, Suite 100, Dallas, TX 75235
Mailing Address: PO Box 660613, Dallas, TX 75266-0613
Tel: 214-445-1000 *Fax:* 214-445-0200
Web Site: www.freemanco.com
Key Personnel
Chmn: Donald S Freeman
CEO: Joseph V Popolo, Jr
Vice Chair: Carrie Freeman Parsons
Pres & COO: Bob Priest-Heck
Pres, Expositions: Albert Chew
Pres, Freeman Audio Visual Solutions: Ken Sanders
Pres, FreemanXP: Daniel Hoffend, Jr
EVP & Chief Admin Offr: Ellis Moseley
EVP & CFO: Julio Ramirez
EVP & CIO: Richard Maranville
EVP & COO, Western Region: Chris Schimek
EVP & COO, Eastern Region: Mike O'Neil
EVP & Chief Sales Offr, Exposition Servs: Martin Moggre
EVP, Busn Devt: Steve Anderson
EVP, Busn Devt-Freeman Audio Visual: Ron Graham
EVP, Cust Experience: Katy Wild
EVP, Logistics & Supply Chain: Jay Atherton
Founded: 1927
Integrated marketing solutions for live engagements including expositions, conventions, corporate events & exhibits. State-of-the-art AV equipment & production services.

Freeman Pictures Inc
1234 Sherman Ave, Suite 201, Evanston, IL 60602
Tel: 847-733-0717
Web Site: www.freemanpictures.com
Key Personnel
Dir: Barbara Freeman *E-mail:* barbarafreeman@freemanpictures.com
Founded: 1991
Film & video production & post-production.

Freestyle Photographic Supplies
5124 Sunset Blvd, Los Angeles, CA 90027
Tel: 323-660-3460 *Toll Free Tel:* 800-292-6137 *Fax:* 323-660-4885
Web Site: www.freestylephoto.biz
Founded: 1946
Photographic equipment & supplies, including cameras, films, papers & darkroom supplies.

Freestyle Productions Inc
7160 Madison Ave W, Minneapolis, MN 55427
Tel: 763-417-9575 *Fax:* 763-417-9576
E-mail: info@freestyle-productions.com
Web Site: freestyleproductions.com
Key Personnel
VP, Sales: Carrie O'Keefe *E-mail:* carrie@freestyle-productions.com

Freewheelin' Films
44895 Hwy 82, Aspen, CO 81611
Tel: 970-925-2640 *Fax:* 970-925-9369
Web Site: www.fwf.com
Key Personnel
Principal & Exec Prodr: Rodney H Jacobs

SVP: Kayla B Hoffman-Cook *E-mail:* kayla@fwf.com
Dir: Peter Sellers

FremantleMedia
Division of RTL Group
4000 W Alameda Ave, 3rd fl, Burbank, CA 91505
Tel: 818-748-1100 *Fax:* 818-563-6410
E-mail: contactus@fremantlemedia.com
Web Site: www.fremantlemedia.com
Key Personnel
Mktg Mgr: Ada Lagreca
Founded: 1917
Television producers.
Foreign Office(s): Fremantle Media Ltd, One Stephen St, London W1T 1AL, United Kingdom *Tel:* (020) 7691 6000
Membership(s): Television Academy

French American Cultural Exchange (FACE)
972 Fifth Ave, New York, NY 10021
Tel: 212-439-1449 *Fax:* 212-439-1455
E-mail: info@facecouncil.org
Web Site: www.facecouncil.org
Key Personnel
Exec Dir: Elizabeth Hayes *Tel:* 212-439-1437
Art Dir: Laurent Auffret
Admin Mgr: Oisin Muldowney
Founded: 1955
Catalog(s), annual or biennial, free, two catalogues: Eclairage & Tournees

French American Music Enterprises
5 Junkins Ave, Suite 106, Portsmouth, NH 03801
Tel: 603-430-9524
Web Site: www.luciet.com
Key Personnel
Owner: Lucie Therrien *E-mail:* LT@star.net
Distribute CDs, DVDs & publications.
Catalog(s) available

Fresh Music Library
320 South St, Agawam, MA 01001
Toll Free Tel: 888-211-8576
Web Site: www.freshmusic.com
Key Personnel
Owner: Bob Casinghino *E-mail:* bob@freshmusic.com
Founded: 1990
Royalty free music.

Frey Scientific
Division of School Specialty Inc
80 Northwest Blvd, Nashua, NH 03063-4067
Mailing Address: PO Box 3000, Nashua, NH 03061-3000
Toll Free Tel: 800-225-3739 *Toll Free Fax:* 877-256-3739
E-mail: customercare@freyscientific.com
Web Site: www.freyscientific.com
Key Personnel
VP: Doug Welles *Tel:* 215-499-7451 *E-mail:* doug.welles@schoolspecialty.com
Founded: 1962
Educational programs.
Catalog(s) available
Membership(s): InfoComm International®

Frezzi Energy Systems
Division of Frezzolini Electronics Inc
7 Valley St, Hawthorne, NJ 07506
Tel: 973-427-1160 *Fax:* 973-427-0934
E-mail: info@frezzi.com
Web Site: www.frezzi.com
Key Personnel
Chmn of the Bd & Pres: James Crawford
VP, Engg & New Prods: Kevin Crawford
VP, Sales: Edward Kuhn
Lighting & power equipment & robotics P/T camera systems manufacturer for broadcast industry, system integration.
Online catalog(s) available
Membership(s): NAB

Fricon Entertainment Co Inc
134 Bluegrass Circle, Hendersonville, TN 37075
Tel: 615-826-2288 *Fax:* 615-826-0500
Key Personnel
Pres: Terri Fricon *E-mail:* fricon@comcast.net
Dir, Opers: Jan Morales
Founded: 1981
Contact for quote on catalog. Music clearances.
Membership(s): American Federation of Musicians; ASCAP; BMI; SESAC

Robert Fried Photography
610 Eldridge Ct, Novato, CA 94947
Tel: 415-898-6153 *Fax:* 415-897-0353
Web Site: www.robertfriedphotography.com
Key Personnel
CEO: Robert Fried *E-mail:* rob@robertfriedphotography.com

Gene Friedman
PO Box 275, Wainscott, NY 11975-0275
Tel: 631-537-0178
E-mail: genfried@optonline.net
Shipping Address: 425 Montauk Hwy, Wainscott, NY 11975

Frontier Communications Corp
PO Box 939, Portland, OR 97207-0939
Tel: 503-246-8080 *Fax:* 541-549-1809
Key Personnel
Pres: Bob McClanathan
Founded: 1974
Designing & building radio & TV broadcast systems & operating communication towers.
Branch Office(s)
PO Box 1810, Sisters, OR 97759-1810

Frontier Software Inc
PO Box 56505, Houston, TX 77256
Tel: 713-622-8167 *Toll Free Tel:* 800-634-3306 *Fax:* 713-622-0058
E-mail: webmaster@frontiertex.com
Web Site: www.frontiertex.com
Key Personnel
Pres: Charles Beard
Distribute tutorial & test practice software & computer software.

Frontline Communications
Division of Pierce Manufacturing Inc
12770 44 St N, Clearwater, FL 33762
Tel: 727-573-0400 *Fax:* 727-571-3295
Web Site: www.frontlinecomm.com
Key Personnel
Gen Mgr: Andy Callaway *Tel:* 727-573-0400 ext 38803 *E-mail:* acallaway@frontlinecomm.com
Founded: 1985
Catalog(s) available
Membership(s): NAB; RTDNA

FSL Media Inc
122 Amity St, Suite 1, Brooklyn, NY 11201
Tel: 347-463-9729
E-mail: info@fslmedia.com
Web Site: www.fslmedia.com
Key Personnel
Pres: John Duff
Duplication of CD-ROMs, DVDs, packaging & fulfillment.

FSR Inc
244 Bergen Blvd, West Paterson, NJ 07424
Tel: 973-785-4347 *Toll Free Tel:* 800-332-3771 (tech support) *Fax:* 973-785-4207
E-mail: sales@fsrinc.com
Web Site: www.fsrinc.com
Key Personnel
Pres: Janice Sandri *E-mail:* jan@fsrinc.com
Founded: 1981
Catalog(s) available
Membership(s): BICSI; InfoComm International®; NSCA

Fugro EarthData
7320 Executive Way, Frederick, MD 21704
Tel: 301-948-8550 *Fax:* 301-963-2064
E-mail: info@fugroearthdata.com
Web Site: www.fugroearthdata.com
Founded: 1955 (as PhotoScience Inc)
Collects & transforms information about the earth's surface into spacially accurate mapping & GIS products for use in GIS, engineering design & other land & information management environments.
Branch Office(s)
18227 Airpark Rd, Hagerston, MD 21742 *Tel:* 301-733-1176 *Fax:* 301-733-4906 *E-mail:* aviation@earthdata.com
5761 Silverado Way, Suite O, Anchorage, AK 99518 *Tel:* 907-561-3478 *Fax:* 907-561-5123
3600 Jet Dr, Rapid City, SD 57703 *Tel:* 605-343-0280 *Fax:* 605-343-0305

FUJIFILM Canada Inc
Subsidiary of FUJIFILM North America Corp
600 Suffolk Ct, Mississauga, ON L5R 4G4, Canada
Tel: 905-890-6611 *Toll Free Tel:* 800-263-5018 *Fax:* 905-890-6446
Web Site: www.fujifilm.ca
Key Personnel
Pres: Nobuhiko Koshimizu
Founded: 1934
Photographic film & paper, film cameras, digital cameras. minilab systems, graphic systems, recording media, motion picture films.

FUJIFILM Graphic Systems Division
Division of FUJIFILM North America Corp
850 Central Ave, Hanover Park, IL 60133
Tel: 630-259-7200 *Toll Free Tel:* 800-877-0555 *Fax:* 630-259-7078
E-mail: contact@fujifilmgs.com
Web Site: www.fujifilmgs.com
Key Personnel
Regl Sales Mgr: John Briar

FUJIFILM North America Corp
Subsidiary of FUJIFILM Holdings America Corp
200 Summit Lake Dr, Valhalla, NY 10595-1356
Tel: 914-789-8100 *Toll Free Tel:* 800-755-3854 *Fax:* 914-789-8530
Web Site: www.fujifilmusa.com/northamerica
Key Personnel
CEO & Pres: Go Miyazaki
AV media, cameras, film & graphics.
Membership(s): NAB; SBE; SMPTE

FUJIFILM Optical Devices Division
Division of FUJIFILM North America Corp
10 High Point Dr, Wayne, NJ 07470
Tel: 973-633-5600 *Fax:* 973-633-5216
Web Site: www.fujifilmusa.com/products/optical_devices
Key Personnel
Dir, Mktg & Prod Devt: Thom Calabro *E-mail:* tcalabro@fujifilm.com
Broadcast lenses, Cine lenses & pan & tilt systems.
Catalog(s) available
Branch Office(s)
2621 Manhattan Beach Blvd, Redondo Beach, CA 90278-1604, Contact: Miles Shozuya *Tel:* 310-536-0800 *Fax:* 310-536-0022 *E-mail:* mshozya@fujifilm.com

18601 LBJ Fwy, Suite 100, Mesquite, TX 75150, Contact: David Waddell *Tel:* 972-385-8902 *Fax:* 972-392-3251 *E-mail:* dwaddell@fujifilm.com

Full Compass Systems
9770 Silicon Prairie Pkwy, Madison, WI 53593
Tel: 608-831-7330 *Toll Free Tel:* 800-356-5844 *Fax:* 608-831-8846
E-mail: customerservice@fullcompass.com
Web Site: www.fullcompass.com
Key Personnel
Chmn: Susan W Lipp
CEO: Jonathan Lipp *E-mail:* jon@fullcompass.com
Founded: 1977
Dealer of professional audio, video, lighting & musical instrument equipment; rents audio & video equipment. Rentals in WI only.
Catalog(s), biannual
Membership(s): AES; GSA; InfoComm International®; NAB; NAMM, the National Association of Music Merchants; NSCA; SBE

Full Moon & High Tide Productions & Studios
424 Main St, El Segundo, CA 90245-3002
Tel: 310-647-1958 *Fax:* 310-647-1960
Web Site: fmht.net
Key Personnel
Dir, Devt: Jake Pentland *E-mail:* jakep@fmht.net
Production studio.

Full Scale Effects
6869 Tujunga Ave, North Hollywood, CA 91605
Tel: 818-760-0875; 818-760-0042 *Fax:* 818-760-0876
Web Site: fullscalefx.com
Key Personnel
Gen Mgr: Dave Peterson *E-mail:* dave@fullscalefx.com
Opers Mgr: Mike Craven *E-mail:* mike@fullscalefx.com
Full service special effects company that specializes in the highest quality physical effects, design, manufacturing, rentals & set operations.

Full Spectrum Arts & Services
PO Box 1032, Littleton, CO 80160
Tel: 303-798-7906
Web Site: www.fullspectrumarts.com
Key Personnel
Owner: David Magoun *E-mail:* dave@fullspectrumarts.com
Founded: 1989
A "one stop shop" for all your creative needs. Graphic arts, fine arts, animation, advertising, multi-media or recording.

Fuller Street Productions
10702 Hathaway Dr, No 2, Santa Fe Springs, CA 90670
Toll Free Tel: 877-637-8733 *Toll Free Fax:* 877-637-8733
E-mail: contact@fullerstreet.com
Web Site: www.fullerstreet.com
Key Personnel
Dir, Sales: Daniel Smith *E-mail:* daniel@fullerstreet.com
Prodn Mgr: Brad Cook *E-mail:* brad@fullerstreet.com
Founded: 2005
Full service event production & equipment rental company.

Furman
Division of Panamax
1800 S McDowell Blvd, Petaluma, CA 94954
Tel: 707-763-1010 *Fax:* 707-763-1310
E-mail: info@furmansound.com
Web Site: www.furmansound.com
Key Personnel
Pres: Bill Pollock
EVP, Sales & Mktg: Dave Keller
Dir, Mktg: Bill Hensley
Founded: 1974
Manufacturing power conditioning & distribution systems.
Catalog(s) available
Membership(s): AES; Custom Electronic Design & Installation Association; NAMM, the National Association of Music Merchants; NSCA

Furnace MFG
2719-B Dorr Ave, Fairfax, VA 22031
Mailing Address: PO Box 3268, Merrifield, VA 22116
Tel: 703-205-0007 *Toll Free Tel:* 888-599-9883 *Fax:* 703-205-2951
E-mail: sales@furnacemfg.com
Web Site: www.furnacemfg.com
Key Personnel
CEO & Pres: Eric Astor
Prodn Mgr: Ali Miller
Founded: 1996
Small disc manufacturing business. CD/DVD replication & duplication (graphic design, mastering & DVD authoring services), vinyl LP production.

Fusion Brand Experiences
421 Chestnut St, Philadelphia, PA 19123
Tel: 215-629-2000
Web Site: www.fusionexperiences.com
Key Personnel
Owner & Pres: Steve Lajoie *Tel:* 917-453-8803 *E-mail:* slajoie@fusionexperiences.com
Catalog(s) available
Membership(s): MCA-I; NATPE; SMPTE

Future Disc LLC
15851 NW Willis Rd, McMinnville, OR 97128
Tel: 213-361-0603 *Fax:* 503-472-1951
Web Site: www.futurediscsystems.com
Key Personnel
Owner & Mastering Engr: Steve Hall *E-mail:* steve@futurediscsystems.com
Studio Coord: Laura Hall *E-mail:* laura@futurediscsystems.com
Founded: 1981
Surround & stereo mastering.

Future Light Inc
23420 Lorain Rd, Suite 200, North Olmsted, OH 44070
Tel: 440-801-1310 *Toll Free Tel:* 800-581-5536 *Fax:* 440-779-4159
E-mail: info@future-light.com
Web Site: www.future-light.com
Key Personnel
Pres: John Seaman *E-mail:* jseaman@future-light.com
Manufacturing lighting equipment.
Catalog(s) available
Membership(s): Illuminating Engineering Society; MCA-I; Professional Lighting & Sound Association; SBE

Future US Inc
4000 Shoreline Ct, Suite 400, South San Francisco, CA 94080
Tel: 650-872-1642 *Fax:* 650-872-2207
Web Site: www.futureus.com
Key Personnel
Pres: Rachelle Considine
Founded: 1985
PC games & mobile PCs.
Catalog(s) available
Branch Office(s)
41 Madison Ave, Suite 3128 & 3129, New York, NY 10010

Future View Inc
6035 Blair Rd NW, Washington, DC 20011
Tel: 202-882-7400 *Fax:* 202-882-7450
E-mail: info@futureview.com
Web Site: www.futureview.com
Key Personnel
CEO: Dave Hanrahan
Provide video production services & equipment, large screen display & event staging.

FutureVideo
28202 Cabot Rd, Suite 300, Laguna Niguel, CA 92677
Mailing Address: PO Box 6251, Laguna Niguel, CA 92607-6251
Tel: 949-363-1286 *Toll Free Fax:* 866-261-1686
E-mail: sales@futurevideo.com
Web Site: www.futurevideo.com
Key Personnel
Dir, Busn Devt: Stephen Godfrey
Founded: 1986
Design, engineer & manufacture control products for AV applications.
Catalog(s) available

FWT LLC
5750 E I-20, Fort Worth, TX 76119
Mailing Address: PO Box 8597, Fort Worth, TX 76124-0597
Tel: 817-255-3060 *Toll Free Tel:* 800-433-1816 *Fax:* 817-255-2957
E-mail: info@fwtllc.com
Web Site: fwtllc.com
Key Personnel
CEO: Fred Moore
EVP, Sales: Bill Sales *E-mail:* bsales@fwtllc.com
Founded: 1959
Manufacturer of telecommunications structures & utility structures.
Catalog(s) available
Branch Office(s)
761 W High St, Hicksville, OH 43526-1052

FXC Communications
Affiliate of Service of Foxcorp-California Inc
970 S Second St, San Jose, CA 95112-5825
Tel: 408-293-2000 *Fax:* 408-294-2000
Key Personnel
VP, Engg: James Becher
Founded: 1965
Full service AV distributor & manufacturer.
Membership(s): AES; NSCA; SMPTE

FXF Productions Inc
1024 Harding Ave, Suite 201, Venice Beach, CA 90291
Mailing Address: 2554 Lincoln Blvd, No 1062, Venice Beach, CA 90291
Tel: 310-577-5009 *Fax:* 310-577-1960
E-mail: info@fxfproductions.com
Web Site: www.fxfproductions.com
Key Personnel
Dir & Prodr: L Lonnie Peralta *E-mail:* lonnie@fxfproductions.com
Exec Prodr & Ed: Eric Alan Donaldson *E-mail:* eric@fxfproductions.com
Founded: 1997
Production & post-production.
Membership(s): Music Video Production Association

Gage-Line Technology Inc
121 LaGrange Ave, Rochester, NY 14613-1577
Tel: 585-458-2000 *Toll Free Tel:* 800-291-3724 *Fax:* 585-458-0524
E-mail: sales@gage-line.com
Web Site: www.gage-line.com
Key Personnel
Pres: Frank Dombrowski
Founded: 1972
Design & manufacture precision imaged, optical, gaging & calibration products, test arrays & used photographic equipment.

Catalog(s) available
Membership(s): Optics & Electro Optics Standards Counsel; Rochester Regional Photomics Cluster; SPIE

Gagne Inc
41 Commercial Dr, Johnson City, NY 13790
Tel: 607-729-3366 *Toll Free Tel:* 800-800-5954 *Fax:* 607-729-7644
E-mail: sales@gagneinc.com
Web Site: www.gagneinc.com
Key Personnel
Pres: Mary Ann Holland
Natl Sales Mgr: Kim Prentice
Sales Engr: Dick Fletcher
Founded: 1950
Manufacturers of portable light boxes & free-standing light tables.
Catalog(s) available

Gaiam Inc
833 W South Boulder Rd, PO Box 3095, Boulder, CO 80307-3095
Tel: 303-222-3600 *Toll Free Tel:* 877-989-6321 (cust serv) *Fax:* 303-222-3700
E-mail: customerservice@gaiam.com
Web Site: www.gaiam.com
Key Personnel
Founder & Chmn: Jirka Rysavy
CEO: Lynn Powers
Pres: Bill Sonheim
Founded: 1988
Producer & marketer of lifestyle media & fitness accessories for eco-conscious living.
Catalog(s) available

Gaither Studios LLC
1705 S Park Ave, Alexandria, IN 46001
Mailing Address: PO Box 119, Alexandria, IN 46001
Toll Free Tel: 800-333-7859
E-mail: info@gaitherstudios.com
Web Site: www.gaitherstudios.com
Key Personnel
Owner: Bill Gaither; Gloria Gaither
Music equipment sales & rentals.

Galaxy Audio
601 E Pawnee Ave, Wichita, KS 67211
Mailing Address: PO Box 16285, Wichita, KS 67216-0285
Tel: 316-263-2852 *Toll Free Tel:* 800-369-7768 *Fax:* 316-263-0642
E-mail: sales@galaxyaudio.com; orders@galaxyaudio.com
Web Site: www.galaxyaudio.com
Key Personnel
Founder & Pres: Brock M Jabara *E-mail:* brock@galaxyaudio.com
Founded: 1977
Audio sound systems.
Catalog(s) available
Membership(s): AES; NAMM, the National Association of Music Merchants; NSCA

Gallien/Krueger
2234 Industrial Dr, Stockton, CA 95206
Tel: 209-234-7300 *Fax:* 209-234-8420
E-mail: sales@gallien.com
Web Site: www.gallien.com
Key Personnel
Pres: Robert Gallien *E-mail:* bob@gallien.com
Founded: 1968
Manufacture & distribute sound systems-guitar bass amplifiers & cabinets.
Catalog(s) available
Membership(s): AES

GAMfilm Productions
7559 Willoughby Ave, Suite 5, Los Angeles, CA 90046
Tel: 213-840-6212
E-mail: gamfilm@gmail.com
Web Site: director-writer-producer.com
Key Personnel
Dir & Prodr: A G Melkom

Gamma Imaging
222 N DesPlaines St, Chicago, IL 60661
Tel: 312-441-0091 *Toll Free Tel:* 877-441-4830 *Fax:* 312-441-0092
E-mail: digital@gammaimaging.com
Web Site: gammaimaging.com
Key Personnel
Pres: Doug Goddard
Founded: 1962
Digital & graphic imaging services.
Catalog(s) available
Membership(s): AIE™; American Association of Magazine Photographers

G&G Technologies Inc
280 N Midland Ave, Bldg F, Suite 202, Saddle Brook, NJ 07663
Tel: 201-791-1400 *Toll Free Tel:* 800-422-2920 *Fax:* 201-791-1401
E-mail: staff@ggvideo.com
Web Site: www.ggvideo.com
Key Personnel
Pres: Robert Greenberg
Founded: 1988
Professional AV equipment sales & rentals.
Catalog(s) available

GAPC (General Assembly Production Centre)
1550 Laperriere Ave, Suite 102, Ottawa, ON K1Z 7T2, Canada
Tel: 613-723-3316 *Fax:* 613-723-8583
Web Site: www.gapc.com
Key Personnel
Pres & Exec Prodr: Ken Stewart *Tel:* 613-723-3316 ext 224 *E-mail:* kstewart@gapc.com
Sr Prodr: Hoda Elatawi *E-mail:* helatawi@gapc.com
Prod Coord: Veronica Davidson *E-mail:* vdavidson@gapc.com
Catalog(s) available
Membership(s): Canadian Media Production Association

Garcia Marketing Inc
400 Ninth St, Conway, PA 15027-1663
Tel: 724-869-0100 *Toll Free Tel:* 800-683-1925 *Fax:* 724-869-1925
E-mail: gmavfoto@verizon.net
Key Personnel
Owner: Jean Garcia
VP: Thomas C Garcia
Mgr: Cathy Stewart
AV equipment distribution & installation.
Catalog(s) available
Membership(s): InfoComm International®; Photo Marketing Association

Garden Valley Productions
240 Crystal Springs Lane, Roseburg, OR 97471
Tel: 541-440-1926 *Fax:* 541-440-1008
Key Personnel
Partner & Opers Mgr: Woody Lane *E-mail:* woody@woodylane.com

Garman Productions LLC
2828 NW 58 St, Oklahoma City, OK 73112
Tel: 405-254-2500 *Toll Free Tel:* 800-747-5699 *Fax:* 405-254-2507
E-mail: info@garman.com
Web Site: www.garman.com
Key Personnel
Owner & CEO: Steve Garman *E-mail:* steve@garman.com
Founded: 1981
Full service AV production, post-production & new media company. Facilities include 3 non-linear, 2 digital audio, new media & graphics animation suites. Additional production services available are DVD authoring, DVD burning, video compression, web site development, closed captioning, remote & studio shooting, ISDN & Pro Tools 11 HD.
Membership(s): Media Communications Association

Garner Products Inc
10620 Industrial Ave, Suite 100, Roseville, CA 95678
Tel: 916-784-0200 *Toll Free Tel:* 800-624-1903 *Fax:* 916-784-1425
E-mail: info@garner-products.com
Web Site: www.garner-products.com
Key Personnel
CEO: Ronald A Stofan *E-mail:* ron@garner-products.com
Founded: 1959
Manufacturer of degaussing equipment for audio, video, hard drive & computer industries.

Gary Camera & Digital
6750 Broadway Ave, Merrillville, IN 46410
Tel: 219-769-2451 *Fax:* 219-769-2488
Web Site: garycameradigital.com
Key Personnel
VP: Barry Blane; Mark Blane
Founded: 1940
Catalog(s) available

The Gary-Paul Agency
1549 Main St, Stratford, CT 06615
Tel: 203-345-6167
Web Site: www.thegarypaulagency.com
Key Personnel
Owner: Gary Maynard *E-mail:* garret@thegarypaulagency.com
Founded: 1991
Full service production company: post-production, avid editing suite & archivist.
Membership(s): Writers Guild of America East

Joe Gastwirt Mastering
4750 Rhapsody Dr, Oak Park, CA 91377
Tel: 310-444-9904
Web Site: www.gastwirtmastering.com
Key Personnel
Pres: Joe Gastwirt *E-mail:* joe@gastwirtmastering.com
Founded: 1990
Complete state-of-the-art mastering services. Call for equipment information.

GatesAir
5300 Kings Island Dr, Suite 101, Mason, OH 45040
Tel: 513-459-3400 *Fax:* 513-459-3796
E-mail: information@gatesair.com; orders@gatesair.com; support@gatesair.com
Web Site: www.gatesair.com
Key Personnel
CEO: Phil Argyris
CFO: L R "Skip" Sorenson
Chief Prod Offr: Rich Redmond
VP, HR: Kim Ratcliffe
VP, Opers: Bryant Burke
VP, Sales-Americas: Joseph Mack
VP, Sales-Europe, Middle East, Asia & Africa: Alain Pecot
Global Servs Dir: John Howell
Founded: 1922 (as Gates Radio & Supply Co)
Over-the-air TV & radio technology, including transmitters, exciters & shelters.
Company formed from the rebranding of Harris Broadcast which split into two companies, GatesAir & Imagine Communications.
Branch Office(s)
3200 Wismann Lane, Quincy, IL 62301 *Tel:* 217-222-8200

Gateways
Subsidiary of G W Fulfillment
PO Box 1706, Ojai, CA 93024-1706
Tel: 805-649-5367 *Toll Free Tel:* 800-477-8908
Fax: 805-649-5302
E-mail: gwgateways@sbcglobal.net
Key Personnel
Owner: Karen Schumann
Gen Mgr: Martin William
Children's self-improvement & educational audio programs.
Catalog(s) available
Shipping Address: 699 Highland Dr, Ojai, CA 93023

Gateways Books & Tapes
Division of Institute for the Development of the Harmonious Human Being Inc
PO Box 370, Nevada City, CA 95959
Tel: 530-271-2239 *Toll Free Tel:* 800-869-0658
Fax: 530-272-0184
E-mail: info@gatewaysbooksandtapes.com
Web Site: www.gatewaysbooksandtapes.com
Key Personnel
Ed & Dist Mgr: Iven Lourie *Tel:* 530-477-8101
Founded: 1971
Educational & religious programs.
Catalog(s) available
Membership(s): Reading Recovery Council of North America

Gaylord Brothers
PO Box 4901, Syracuse, NY 13221-4901
Tel: 315-634-8243 (intl) *Toll Free Tel:* 800-962-9580 (cust serv) *Fax:* 315-453-5030 (intl)
Toll Free Fax: 800-272-3412
E-mail: customerservice@gaylord.com
Web Site: www.gaylord.com
Key Personnel
CEO: Guy Marhewka
VP, Busn Devt: Henry Orr
VP, Mktg: Coleen Gagliardo
VP, Opers: Keith George
Regl Sales Mgr: Stephen Scicchitano
E-mail: stephen.sciccitano@gaylord.com
Founded: 1896
Provide library supplies including archival supplies.
Catalog(s) available
Shipping Address: 7282 William Barry Blvd, North Syracuse, NY 13212 *Web Site:* www.gaylord.com

GBC Document Finishing
Division of ACCO Brands Corp
4 Corporate Dr, Lake Zurich, IL 60047
Toll Free Tel: 800-723-4000 (orders)
Toll Free Fax: 800-914-8178
Web Site: www.gbcconnect.com; www.gbcoffice.com
Key Personnel
VP, Corp Communs: Richard Nelson *E-mail:* rich.nelson@acco.com
Founded: 1947
Complete document finishing solutions.
Branch Office(s)
GBC Canada, 7381 Bramalea Rd, Mississauga, ON L5S 1C4, Canada *Toll Free Tel:* 800-463-2545 *Toll Free Fax:* 800-463-2545 *E-mail:* custserv@gbccanada.com *Web Site:* www.gbccanada.com
Foreign Office(s): GBC Australia, Unit 1, Block Q, Regents Park Estate, Princes Rd E, Regents Park, NSW 2143, Australia *Tel:* (02) 9738 4000 *Fax:* (02) 9738 4100 *E-mail:* product.info@gbcaustralia.com.au *Web Site:* www.gbcaustralia.com.au
Ibico Chile SA, Av San Josemaria Escriva de Balaguer 5773, 7640870 Vitacura, Santiago, Chile, Gen Mgr: Gonzalo Anais *Tel:* (02) 2876 9700 *Fax:* (02) 2876 9715 *E-mail:* ventas@gbc.cl *Web Site:* www.gbc.cl
ACCO Brands Japan K K, 14F Harmony Tower Bldg, 1-32-2 Honcho, Nakano-Ku, Tokyo 164-8721, Japan, Mng Dir: Ted Fukudome *Tel:* (03) 5351 1810 *Fax:* (03) 5351 1831 *E-mail:* tfukudome@accobrands.co.jp *Web Site:* www.accobrands.co.jp
GBC Mexicana S A de C V, Neptuno No 43, Col Nueva Industrial Vallejo, Delegacion Gustavo A Madero, 07700 Mexico, DF, Mexico *Tel:* (0155) 1500-5700 *Fax:* (0155) 1500-5701 *Web Site:* www.gbc.com.mx
GBC Asia Pte Ltd, 47 Ayer Rajah Crescent, No 05-08/17, Singapore 139947, Singapore *Tel:* 6776 0195 *Fax:* 6779 1041 *E-mail:* webmaster@accobrandsasia.com *Web Site:* www.accobrandsasia.com
GBC Asian Films Group, 98-18 Shin Hang Ri, Doon Po Myun, Asan City, Choong Nam 336-873, South Korea, Mktg Mgr: Stewart Kim *Tel:* (041) 531 1830 *Fax:* (041) 531 1831 *E-mail:* stkim@gbcasia.co.kr
Acco Brands Europe, Oxford House, Oxford Rd, Aylesbury, Bucks HP21 8SZ, United Kingdom *Tel:* (01296) 397444 *Fax:* (01296) 311000 *E-mail:* informationeurope@acco.com *Web Site:* www.gbceurope.com

GEAR Cameras & Lighting
4822 E Cesar Chavez, Austin, TX 78702
Tel: 512-485-3131 *Fax:* 512-474-6098
E-mail: austin@hdgear.tv
Web Site: www.hdgear.tv
Rents cameras, lenses, support, lighting & grip equipment.

Gear Monkey
630 The City Dr, Suite 175, Orange, CA 92868
Tel: 714-705-6088 *Toll Free Tel:* 877-411-4445
Fax: 714-705-6080
Web Site: www.gearmonkey.tv
Production equipment rentals & sales.

Gearhead Rentals
69 O'Conner Rd, Suite 6, Fairport, NY 14450
Tel: 585-236-4272
Web Site: www.gearheadrentals.com
Key Personnel
Contact: Mike Drago *E-mail:* mdrago@gearheadrentals.com
Rents cameras, lenses, filters, tripods, monitors, recorders, microphones, teleprompters, lighting, grip equipment.

Gearhouse Broadcast LLC
9440 Chivers Ave, Sun Valley, CA 91352
Tel: 818-955-9449 *Fax:* 818-955-9779
E-mail: sales@gearhousebroadcast.us
Web Site: www.gearhousebroadcast.com
Founded: 2002
Television broadcast services. Specialize in equipment rental & sales, outside broadcast, project solutions & systems integration.

Geddes Productions LLC
PO Box 41761, Los Angeles, CA 90041-0761
Tel: 323-344-8045 *Fax:* 323-257-7209
E-mail: orders@geddesproduction.com
Web Site: www.geddesproduction.com
Key Personnel
Pres: Kittie Frantz
Founded: 1986
Produce & distribute informational materials (videos, DVDs, slides, overheads, patient handouts, pocket cards, CDs, posters & books) related to breast feeding. Breastfeeding or lactation would be key words.
Online catalog(s) available

Gefen
Subsidiary of Nortek Inc
20600 Nordhoff St, Chatsworth, CA 91311
Tel: 818-772-9100 *Toll Free Tel:* 800-545-6900
Fax: 818-772-9120
E-mail: gsinfo@gefen.com
Web Site: www.gefen.com
Key Personnel
Pres: Sean Burke
PR: Linda Morgan *Tel:* 818-534-8254
Founded: 1995 (as Gefen Systems)
Supplies a wide selection of signal switchers, splitters, extenders, scalers, converters, KVM, digital signage & home theater accessories that enable audio/video & computer systems to be easily integrated, extended, distributed & optimized to maximize performance.
Catalog(s) available
Foreign Office(s): Gefen Distribution GmbH & Co KG, Landshuter Allee 162a, 80637 Munich, Germany, Gen Mgr: Florian Goebel *Tel:* (089) 143 451 880 *Fax:* (089) 143 451 8899 *Web Site:* www.gefen.de
Membership(s): AES; Consumer Electronics Association; Custom Electronic Design & Installation Association; InfoComm International®; NAB; NSCA

Gemini
2000 Penncraft Ct, Ann Arbor, MI 48103
Tel: 734-665-0165 *Toll Free Tel:* 800-317-9929
Fax: 734-786-4007
E-mail: info@geminichildrensmusic.com
Web Site: www.geminichildrensmusic.com
Key Personnel
Owner: Sandor Slomovits
Recordings & videos for children & families.
Catalog(s) available

Gemini Sound
107 Trumbull St, Bldg F8, 2nd fl, Elizabeth, NJ 07206-2171
Tel: 732-346-0061 *Fax:* 732-346-0065
E-mail: sales@geminisound.com
Web Site: www.geminisound.com
Key Personnel
CEO: Artie Cabasso
Founded: 1974
Manufacturer of equipment including studio monitors, media controllers, DJ mixers, headphones, power amps, passive & active loud speakers, CD players, turntables.
Catalog(s) available

General Audio-Visual Inc (GAVI)
92 E Merrick Rd, Freeport, NY 11520
Tel: 516-623-8500 *Fax:* 516-623-9155
E-mail: miked@gavi.com
Web Site: www.gavi.com
Key Personnel
Pres: Angelo Dituri
VP & Sales Mgr: Michael Dituri *E-mail:* miked@gavi.com
Catalog(s) available
Membership(s): InfoComm International®; NSCA

General Binding Corp Document Finishing, see GBC Document Finishing

General Devices Co Inc
1410 S Post Rd, Indianapolis, IN 46239
Tel: 317-897-7000 *Fax:* 317-898-2917
E-mail: sales@generaldevices.com
Web Site: www.generaldevices.com
Key Personnel
Owner & EVP: Martin Fall
CEO: Maxwell Fall
Dir, Sales & Mktg: Dan McCauley
Catalog(s), free

General Electric Co
3135 Easton Tpke, Fairfield, CT 06828
Tel: 203-373-2211 *Fax:* 203-373-3131
Web Site: www.ge.com

Key Personnel
Chmn & CEO: Jeffrey Immelt
SVP & Chief Mktg Offr: Beth Comstock
SVP & Gen Counsel: Brackett B Denniston, III
Projection systems.
Branch Office(s)
Lighting Division, Nela Park, Bldg 308, Cleveland, OH 44112 *Tel:* 216-266-2121 *Fax:* 216-266-2310

General Production Services
Division of GPS Inc
883 S East St, Anaheim, CA 92805
Tel: 714-535-2271 *Fax:* 714-535-0952
E-mail: lensclens@yahoo.com
Web Site: www.lensclens.com
Key Personnel
Pres: Jerry Tochilin
Founded: 1971
Manufacturer of cleaning solutions & supplies for optics.
Online catalog(s) available

General Projection Systems Inc
707 Platinum Point, Lake Mary, FL 32746-5702
Tel: 407-260-5511 *Toll Free Tel:* 888-GENPROJ (436-7765) *Fax:* 407-833-4990
E-mail: solutions@genproj.com
Web Site: www.genproj.com
Key Personnel
Owner: Cheryl Walker *Tel:* 407-260-5511 ext 312
Systems integrator.
Membership(s): InfoComm International®; NSCA

Genesis Creative
1006 Hafely Ct, Cayce, SC 29033
Tel: 803-796-9666
E-mail: geninfo@gencreative.com
Web Site: genesisstudiossc.com
Key Personnel
Pres & Prodn Dir: Cliff Springs *E-mail:* cliff@gencreative.com
Founded: 1993
Full service advertising & production. Graphic design, animation, web design, interactive, video & film production - all in-house. 4,000 feet of studio space. DVCPRO-50, Beta SP, DVCAM, 1 inch & more. 5 non-linear work stations. Work with clients from concept to completion or as a production resource for other agencies.

Genigraphics®
PO Box 860111, Shawnee, KS 66286-0111
Tel: 913-441-1410 *Toll Free Tel:* 800-790-4001 (cust serv)
E-mail: info@genigraphics.com
Web Site: www.genigraphics.com
Key Personnel
Mng Partner: Jay Larson
Founded: 1982
Provider of 35mm slides, transparencies & large format posters produced directly from digital files. We also offer slide-scanning, CD-ROM duplication, graphic design services & digital projector rentals. Next day delivery is available throughout the US & Canada.
Catalog(s) available

Gary Gentile Productions (GGP)
3 Lehigh Gorge Dr, Jim Thorpe, PA 18229
Tel: 252-394-6974
Web Site: www.ggentile.com
Key Personnel
Owner: Gary Gentile *E-mail:* gary@ggentile.com
Founded: 1989
Video distribution.

A Gentle Wind
14 S Pine Ave, Albany, NY 12208
Mailing Address: PO Box 3103, Albany, NY 12203-0103
Tel: 518-FUN-SONG (482-9023)
Toll Free Tel: 888-386-7664 (orders)
E-mail: hello@gentlewind.com
Web Site: www.gentlewind.com
Key Personnel
Owner: Jill Person
Catalog(s), annual or by request, free

Geomatrix Productions
270 Amity Rd, Woodbridge, CT 06525-2267
Tel: 203-389-0001
Web Site: www.geomatrixproductions.com
Key Personnel
Pres: Cathie Reese *E-mail:* cathie@geomatrixproductions.com
Prodr: Edgar Smith; Patrick Volk
Founded: 1978
Video production company.
Membership(s): MCA-I

Georgia-Pacific Television & Photography
Subsidiary of Georgia-Pacific LLC
133 Peachtree St NE, Atlanta, GA 30303
Tel: 404-652-5690 *Fax:* 404-487-5352
Web Site: www.gp.com; g-ptv.com
Key Personnel
Mgr: Bradford Hinton *E-mail:* brhinton@gapac.com
Video production.
Video(s) available
Membership(s): MCA-I

Gepco®, a General Cable brand
500 Thorndale Ave, Suite F, Wood Dale, IL 60191-1267
Tel: 847-795-9555 *Toll Free Tel:* 800-966-0069
Fax: 847-795-8770
Web Site: www.gepco.com; www.generalcable.com
Founded: 1981
Catalog(s) available
Branch Office(s)
6850 Vineland Ave, Unit N, North Hollywood, CA 91605 *Tel:* 818-506-5590
Membership(s): AES; MCA-I; NAB; NSCA; SBE; SMPTE

Bob Gerardi Music Productions
160 W 73 St, New York, NY 10023-3012
Tel: 212-874-6436
Key Personnel
Owner: Bob Gerardi *E-mail:* bobgmusic@aol.com
Musical scoring & production.
Catalog(s) available
Membership(s): AFM; ASCAP; The Recording Academy; SAG-AFTRA; SCL

Gerriets International
130 Winterwood Ave, Ewing, NJ 08638
Tel: 609-771-8111 *Toll Free Tel:* 800-369-3695
Fax: 609-771-8118
E-mail: info@gerriets.us
Web Site: www.gerriets.us
Key Personnel
New Prods Mgr: Nick Pagliante
Manufacturer of front & rear projection screens.
Catalog(s) available

GES Audio Visual
Subsidiary of The Viad Corp
7000 Lindell Rd, Las Vegas, NV 89118
Tel: 702-515-5500 *Toll Free Tel:* 800-443-9767
Fax: 702-515-5765
E-mail: lasvegas@ges.com
Web Site: ges.com
Key Personnel
Opers: Brian Larson
Full service AV equipment rentals.

Gesturetek
317 Adelaide St W, Suite 903, Toronto, ON M5V 1P9, Canada
Tel: 416-340-9290 *Toll Free Tel:* 800-315-1189
Fax: 416-348-9809
E-mail: info@gesturetek.com
Web Site: www.gesturetek.com
Key Personnel
Founder & CEO: John Vincent
Pres: Erol Vekil
Founded: 1986
Video(s) available
Branch Office(s)
530 Lakeside Dr, Suite 280, Sunnyvale, CA 94085 *Tel:* 408-216-8087 *Fax:* 408-732-3977
240 Catherine St, Suite 305, Ottawa, ON K2P 2G8, Canada *Tel:* 613-233-2022 *Fax:* 815-361-4123

Get Organized
328 Canham Rd, Scotts Valley, CA 95066
Tel: 831-438-0259 *Fax:* 831-438-0359
Key Personnel
Owner: Robby Frank
Home organizational supplies & wire management systems.
Catalog(s) available

Get Smart Products
30 S Highland Ave, Ossining, NY 10562
Mailing Address: PO Box 0018, Maryknoll, NY 10545
Tel: 914-762-3500 *Toll Free Tel:* 800-827-0673
Fax: 914-923-5818 *Toll Free Fax:* 866-827-0673
E-mail: getsmart@pfile.com
Web Site: www.pfile.com
Key Personnel
Pres: Steve Weisbart
Founded: 1988
Retailer for archival photo storage supplies.
Catalog(s) available
Shipping Address: 807 Airport Access Rd, Unit D, Traverse City, MI 49686

Gettinger Feather Corp
Subsidiary of AA Feather Co
16 W 36 St, New York, NY 10018
Tel: 212-695-9470 *Fax:* 212-695-9471
E-mail: gettfeath@aol.com
Web Site: www.gettingerfeather.com
Key Personnel
Pres: Daniel Gettinger
Founded: 1915
Wholesale feathers, plumes, fans & boas.
Catalog(s), free

Getty-Dubay Productions
PO Box 91084, Portland, OR 97291-0084
Tel: 503-223-7268 (orders) *Toll Free Tel:* 800-777-2844 *Fax:* 503-223-9182 (orders)
E-mail: info@handwritingsuccess.com; info@allport.com (orders)
Web Site: www.handwritingsuccess.com; www.allport.com (orders)
Key Personnel
Owner: Inga Dubay *Tel:* 503-228-0809 *Fax:* 503-225-9094 *E-mail:* idubay@teleport.com; Barbara Getty *E-mail:* ellyfont@frontier.com
Founded: 1995
Educational program in DVD-handwriting.
Online catalog(s) available

Getty Images
605 Fifth Ave S, Suite 400, Seattle, WA 98104
Tel: 206-925-5000 *Toll Free Tel:* 888-888-5889; 800-462-4379 (sales) *Fax:* 206-925-5001
E-mail: sales@gettyimages.com
Web Site: www.gettyimages.com
Key Personnel
Founder & CEO: Jonathan Klein
Founder & Chmn: Mark Getty
Founded: 1995

Provide imagery, film & digital services.
Catalog(s) available
Branch Office(s)
6300 Wilshire Blvd, 16th fl, Los Angeles, CA 90048 *Tel:* 323-202-4200
122 S Michigan Ave, Suite 900, Chicago, IL 60603 *Tel:* 312-344-4500
75 Varick St, New York, NY 10013 *Tel:* 646-613-4000
Foreign Office(s): 101 Bayham St, London NW1 0AG, United Kingdom *Tel:* (020) 7428 6109 *Fax:* (020) 7267 6540 *E-mail:* filmsales@gettyimages.com (headquarters for Africa, Europe & Middle East)

GGP, see Gary Gentile Productions (GGP)

Ghent Manufacturing
Affiliate of GMi
2999 Henkle Dr, Lebanon, OH 45036-9260
Tel: 513-932-3445 *Toll Free Tel:* 800-543-0550 *Fax:* 513-932-9252
E-mail: customer_service@ghent.com
Web Site: www.ghent.com
Key Personnel
VP, Sales: Jim Harter *E-mail:* jharter@ghent.com
Dir, Mktg: Scott Bowers *E-mail:* bowers@ghent.com
Dir, Mfg: John Kurtz
Founded: 1976
Produce visual communication products.
Catalog(s) available

GHO Group LLC
Formerly VDO Ltd
340 W 55 St, Suite 5E, New York, NY 10019
Tel: 212-319-7716
E-mail: info@ghogroup.com
Web Site: www.ghogroup.com
Key Personnel
Principal: Gary H Olson
Owner representative & project management.
Catalog(s) available

Giant Audio Visual Inc
111 Canfield Ave, Unit B-6, Randolph, NJ 07869-1114
Tel: 973-927-1112 *Toll Free Tel:* 866-GIANTAV (442-6828) *Fax:* 973-927-9977
E-mail: staging@giantav.com
Web Site: www.giantav.com
Key Personnel
Pres: Guy Nadeau
Founded: 1982
Specialize in AV production services & comprehensive AV technology solutions for corporate meetings & other live events.
Membership(s): InfoComm International®

Giant Interactive
88 Tenth Ave, Suite 6-W, New York, NY 10011
Tel: 212-675-7300 *Fax:* 212-765-9336
E-mail: info@giant-interactive.com
Web Site: www.giant-interactive.com
Key Personnel
Founder & Pres: Jeff Stabenau *E-mail:* jeffs@giant-interactive.com
Founder & VP: David Anthony *E-mail:* davida@giant-interactive.com
Founded: 2005
Designs & produces DVDs for the entertainment & music industry.
Branch Office(s)
6100 Wilshire Blvd, Suite 1550, Los Angeles, CA 90048, Dir, Sales: Jeff Jewett *Tel:* 323-938-6100 *Fax:* 323-934-7783 *E-mail:* jjewett@giant-interactive.com
2710 Walnut St, Denver, CO 80205, Creative Dir: Sean Anderson *Tel:* 303-458-6000 *Fax:* 303-458-6002 *E-mail:* sean@giant-interactive.com

GigaSonic
260 E Gish Rd, San Jose, CA 95112
Tel: 408-573-1400 *Toll Free Tel:* 888-246-4442 *Fax:* 408-573-0602
Web Site: www.gigasonic.com
Music recording equipment & musical instrument distributor.

Gilderfluke & Co Inc
205 S Flower St, Burbank, CA 91502
Tel: 818-840-9484 *Toll Free Tel:* 800-776-5972 *Fax:* 818-840-9485
E-mail: info@gilderfluke.com
Web Site: www.gilderfluke.com
Key Personnel
CEO & Pres: Douglas C Mobley
CFO & VP: Carolyn Rowley *E-mail:* carolyn@gilderfluke.com
Founded: 1981
Designs & manufactures animation control systems, CD-quality digital audio repeaters & intelligent public address systems for themed amusement park, themed restaurants, museums, churches & movies. PC MAC systems, using Microsoft Windows & a standard PC compatible computer, creates a complete animation control system.
Catalog(s) available

Jim Gill Music Inc
PO Box 2263, Oak Park, IL 60303-2263
Tel: 708-763-9864 *Fax:* 708-763-9888
Web Site: www.jimgill.com
Key Personnel
Owner: Jim Gill *E-mail:* jimgill@jimgill.com
Produce children's music.
Catalog(s) available

Gingerbread Group
1337 Kittredge Ct, Atlanta, GA 30329
Tel: 404-634-8678; 404-663-9050 *Fax:* 404-601-9387
E-mail: books2gogh@gmail.com
Key Personnel
Exec Prodr & Dir, Mktg: Evi Reznick
Founded: 1996
Produce & distribute children's videos.

Gingerbread Productions
1323 Shepard Dr, Unit I, Sterling, VA 20164
Tel: 703-450-7722; 571-432-6920 *Toll Free Tel:* 877-219-3562 *Fax:* 703-450-6836
E-mail: bakegingerbread@aol.com
Web Site: www.gingerbreadproductions.com
Key Personnel
Prod Mgr: Bob Vanjani
Founded: 1987
Professional full service video taping.

GKM Broadcast Racks
Division of Ultimate Precision Metal Products Inc
200 Finn Ct, Farmingdale, NY 11735
Tel: 631-249-7816 *Fax:* 631-249-9450
E-mail: info@gkmbroadcastracks.com
Web Site: www.gkmbroadcastracks.com
Founded: 1958
Catalog(s) available

Glanz Technologies Inc
687 NE 124 St, North Miami, FL 33161
Tel: 305-893-1269 *Fax:* 305-899-8526
E-mail: mglanz@glanztech.com
Web Site: www.glanztechnologies.com
Key Personnel
Pres: Mark Glanz
Founded: 1981
Rent & distribute video equipment & projection systems.

Glendale Media Center
9494 W Maryland Ave, Glendale, AZ 85305
Tel: 623-930-4510
Web Site: www.glendalemediacenter.com
Key Personnel
Gen Mgr: Laurie Berg Sapp *E-mail:* lsapp@glendaleaz.com
Chief Broadcast Engr: Dave Rainey *Tel:* 623-930-4512 *E-mail:* drainey@glendaleaz.com
Rental studios & HD production for video, films, advertising, commercials, studio audience shows & more.

Glendale Production Centre
1239 S Glendale Ave, Glendale, CA 91205
Tel: 818-550-6000
E-mail: info@glendalestudios.com
Web Site: www.glendalestudios.com
Soundstages, production office & AV rentals.

Glenn Photo Supply
13502 Erwin St, Van Nuys, CA 91401
Tel: 818-997-0410
Web Site: www.emgee.freeyellow.com
Key Personnel
Owner & Mgr: Murray Glass *E-mail:* murray713@hotmail.com
Founded: 1950
16mm film sales.
Afflilate companies: Em Gee Film Library; Glenn Video Vistas Ltd.
Catalog(s), $5

Glenn Video Vistas Ltd
13502 Erwin St, Van Nuys, CA 91401
Tel: 818-997-0410
Web Site: www.emgee.freeyellow.com
Key Personnel
Owner & Mgr: Murray Glass *E-mail:* murray713@hotmail.com
Video sales.
Affiliate companies: Em Gee Film Library; Glenn Photo Supply.
Catalog(s), $5

Glenray Productions Inc
1265 E Calaveras St, Altadena, CA 91001-2535
Mailing Address: PO Box 40400, Pasadena, CA 91114-7400
Tel: 626-797-5462
E-mail: 2glenray@sbcglobal.net
Web Site: www.childrensmedia.com
Key Personnel
Pres: C Ray Carlson
Founded: 1983
Produce & distribute visual media for kids, tweens, teens & families.
Catalog(s) available

GLI Sound Systems
2691 W 15 St, Brooklyn, NY 11224
Tel: 718-372-7849 *Toll Free Tel:* 800-GLI-PRO-1 (454-7761) *Fax:* 718-946-4151
E-mail: info@glipro.com; sales@glipro.com
Web Site: www.glipro.com
Key Personnel
Pres: David Harari
Dir, Opers: Paul Arking *Tel:* 718-946-4134
Sales: Morris Shalom *E-mail:* mshalom@glipro.com
Manufacture DJ equipment.
Catalog(s) available

Glidecam Industries Inc
23 Joseph St, Kingston, MA 02364
Tel: 781-585-7900 *Toll Free Tel:* 800-949-2089; 800-600-2011 *Fax:* 781-585-7903
E-mail: sales@glidecam.com
Web Site: www.glidecam.com
Key Personnel
VP, Sales & Mktg: Thomas Howie
Founded: 1992
Manufacture camera stabilizers & cranes.

Catalog(s) available
Membership(s): NAB

Glix Studios
437 N Varney St, Burbank, CA 91502
Tel: 818-441-4065
E-mail: info@glixstudios.com
Web Site: www.glixstudios.com
Video production, post-production, Blu-ray & DVD authoring.

Global Communications Solutions (GCS), see L-3 GCS

Global Cyber-Visions
Subsidiary of The Venus Project
21 Valley Lane, Venus, FL 33960
Tel: 863-465-0321
E-mail: tvp@thevenusproject.com
Web Site: www.thevenusproject.com
Key Personnel
Founder & Mktg Dir: Roxanne Meadows *E-mail:* meadows@thevenusproject.com
Produce educational programs.

Global ImageWorks LLC
65 Beacon St, Haworth, NJ 07641
Tel: 201-384-7715 *Fax:* 201-501-8971
E-mail: info@globalimageworks.com
Web Site: www.globalimageworks.com
Key Personnel
Pres: Jessica Berman-Bogdan *E-mail:* jessica@globalimageworks.com
Independent multi-service media business that licenses Rights Managed & Royalty Free contemporary & historic footage. Footage includes: 9/11, aerials, climate change, destinations, extreme sports, fire, global conflict, historic travel films, home movies, interviews, lifestyle, music, nature, pop culture, re-enactments, rock n roll, extreme weather, science, time lapse, US cities, wildlife. Premium collections include *Soul Train, The Dick Cavett Show, Austin City Limits & Omnibus.* Provides research & music clearance services to outside productions.
Catalog(s) available
Membership(s): Association of Commercial Stock Image Licensors; Association of Moving Image Archivists; BAFTA; The Federation of Commercial Audiovisual Libraries Ltd; IDA

Global Net Productions Inc
568 Iverson Beach Rd, Camano Island, WA 98282-8597
Tel: 360-387-8222 *Toll Free Tel:* 800-862-6247
E-mail: contact@globalnetproductions.com
Web Site: www.globalnetproductions.com
Key Personnel
Pres: Michael Lienau
Television & video production.
Catalog(s) available

Global Television
Division of Shaw Media
222 23 St NE, Calgary, AB T2E 7N2, Canada
Tel: 403-235-7777 *Fax:* 403-248-0252
E-mail: globalnews.calg@globaltv.com
Web Site: www.globaltv.com
Key Personnel
Prodn Mgr: Norm Michaelis *Fax:* 403-248-0258
Sales Mgr: Greg Campbell
Creative Servs Mgr: Jeff Eisler

Global Television Station
Subsidiary of Global TV Group Ltd
5325 Allard Way, Edmonton, AB T6H 5B8, Canada
Tel: 780-436-1250; 780-989-4683 *Fax:* 780-989-4686
E-mail: globalnews.ed@globaltv.com
Web Site: www.globaltv.com
Key Personnel
Gen Mgr: Tim Spellisey
News Dir: Michael Fulmes
Produce TV programs.

Global Video Distributors Inc
8181 NW 91 Terr, Suite 7, Medley, FL 33166
Tel: 305-887-2000 *Fax:* 305-887-2000
Web Site: global.myvideostore.com
Key Personnel
Pres: Angel Tamargo
Founded: 1985
International distribution for video, television & merchandising rights. Also distribute DVDs (HD, Blu-ray & 3D).
Catalog(s) available

Global Village Productions
Division of Videosource.com/HDEnvironments.com
6914 B Sebastapol Ave, Sebastopol, CA 95472
Mailing Address: PO Box 1818, Sebastopol, CA 95473-1818
Tel: 707-823-1451 *Toll Free Tel:* 800-798-FIND (798-3463) *Fax:* 707-829-5545
E-mail: production@videosource.com; video@videosource.com
Web Site: www.videosource.com
Key Personnel
Owner & Pres: Michael Heumann
Founded: 1979
Distribution & production, DVD & streaming.
Membership(s): Entertainment Merchants Association

Global Village Stock Footage Library
1717 Darby Rd, Sebastopol, CA 95472
Mailing Address: PO Box 1818, Sebastopol, CA 95473-1818
Tel: 707-823-1451 *Toll Free Tel:* 800-798-FIND (798-3463) *Fax:* 707-829-5545
E-mail: contact@hdenvironments.com
Web Site: www.videosource.com; hdenvironments.com
Key Personnel
Owner & Prodr: Michael Heumann
Searchable stock footage database on Internet. Royalty free footage collections & HD footage & production.
Catalog(s) available

GlobalStreams™ Corp
20353 W 108 St, Olathe, KS 66061
Tel: 314-423-6700 *Toll Free Tel:* 800-788-7205; 866-558-7830 (cust support) *Fax:* 314-423-6705
E-mail: gsinfo@globalstreams.com; support@globalstreams.com; sales@globalstreams.com
Web Site: www.globalstreams.com
Key Personnel
CEO & Pres: J Thomas Webb
Founded: 2000
Provider of video communications hardware & software; turnkey TV studio systems.

Globe Photos Inc
24 Edmore Lane S, West Islip, NY 11795
Tel: 631-661-3131 *Fax:* 631-321-4063
E-mail: info@globephotos.com
Web Site: www.globephotos.com
Key Personnel
Pres: Mary Beth Whelan
Sales Mgr: Raymond F Whelan
Founded: 1939
Stock celebrity photos.
Catalog(s) available

Globe Video Services Inc, see Set To Go Studios

Gluskin's Custom Audio Video
Division of Gluskins Inc
2087 Grand Canal Blvd, Suite 11, Stockton, CA 95204
Tel: 209-888-4609 *Fax:* 209-888-4629
E-mail: audio@gluskins.com
Web Site: www.gluskins.com
Key Personnel
Owner: Greg Dooley
Proj Mgr: Ben Palakovich
Photographic equipment service & repair.

GMF Sound Inc
1961 N Main, Orange, CA 92865
Tel: 714-282-1559 *Fax:* 714-282-1942
E-mail: generalinfo@gmfsound.com; sales@gmfsound.com
Web Site: www.gmfsound.com
Key Personnel
Pres: James Carroll *E-mail:* jimc@gmfsound.com
Founded: 1972
Distribute AV equipment.

GMI Productions
Division of General Mills Inc
One General Mills Blvd, Minneapolis, MN 55426
Mailing Address: PO Box 9452, Minneapolis, MN 55440
Tel: 763-764-7600 *Toll Free Tel:* 800-248-7310 *Fax:* 763-764-2739
Web Site: www.generalmills.com
Key Personnel
Prodn Supv: Eric Swenson *E-mail:* eric.swenson@genmills.com
Audio & video resources relating to General Mills brands.
Membership(s): MCA-I

GMP, see Green Mountain Post Films (GMP)

GMP Music
Division of Gene Michael Productions Inc
1103 North St, Niles, MI 49120
Tel: 269-687-9100 *Toll Free Tel:* 800-955-0619 *Fax:* 269-687-9200
E-mail: info@gmpmusic.com
Web Site: www.gmpmusic.com; www.reservemusic.com
Key Personnel
Owner: Gene Ort
Founded: 1989
Production music library.
Catalog(s) available

GNP Crescendo Records
1405 N Avon St, Burbank, CA 91505-1885
Tel: 818-566-8900
E-mail: gnp@pacificnet.net
Web Site: www.gnpcrescendo.com
Key Personnel
Pres: Neil Norman
Founded: 1954
Music & soundtracks.
Catalog(s), free

Go To Team
359-C Wando Place Dr, Mount Pleasant, SC 29464
Tel: 843-884-6222 *Toll Free Tel:* 888-455-4333
E-mail: crew@gototeam.com
Web Site: www.gototeam.com
Key Personnel
Mng Partner: Shawn Moffatt *E-mail:* smoffatt@gototeam.com
Partner: Patrick Bryant
Dir, Photog: Dave Baker
Founded: 1997
On location videography. High-end broadcast video crews located throughout the country.

Goal Productions
1905 Victory Blvd, Suite 6, Glendale, CA 91201
Tel: 818-588-3900 *Fax:* 818-588-3903

E-mail: info@goalproductions.com
Web Site: www.goalproductions.com
Key Personnel
Pres: Robert Ballo *E-mail:* rballo@goalproductions.com
Mktg Dir: Alysia Camp *E-mail:* acamp@goalproductions.com
Prodr: Griff Partington *E-mail:* gpartington@goalproductions.com
Founded: 1969
Digital video & film production company.
Membership(s): Television Academy

Goddard Design Co
51 Nassau Ave, Brooklyn, NY 11222
Tel: 718-599-0170 *Fax:* 718-599-0172
E-mail: sales@goddarddesign.com
Web Site: www.goddarddesign.com
Key Personnel
Owner: Bob Goddard
Off Mgr: Rosemary F Heath
Manufacture & sales of electronic test & control equipment for theater. Manufacture DMX 512 test equipment & DMX 512 processing & distribution equipment. We ship worldwide.
Online catalog(s) available
Membership(s): Professional Lighting & Sound Association; USITT

The Godfrey Group Inc
4102 S Miami Blvd, Durham, NC 27703
Tel: 919-544-6504 *Toll Free Tel:* 800-789-9394 *Fax:* 919-544-6729
E-mail: sales@godfreygroup.com
Web Site: www.godfreygroup.com
Key Personnel
Pres: Will Daniel Godfrey
Custom design graphics & photography.
Catalog(s) available

Goin' Mobile
PO Box 470627, Brookline, MA 02447
Tel: 617-232-7969 (cell)
Web Site: www.goin-mobile.com
Key Personnel
Owner: Lonnie Bedell *E-mail:* lbedell@goin-mobile.com
Founded: 1985
Audio mobile recording truck.

Gold Line/TEF
PO Box 500, West Redding, CT 06896-0500
Tel: 203-938-2588 *Fax:* 203-938-8740
E-mail: sales@gold-line.com
Web Site: www.gold-line.com
Key Personnel
VP, Sales: Marjorie Miller *E-mail:* mdmiller@gold-line.com
Founded: 1961
Manufacture audio test equipment & equalizers for the sound installer.
Catalog(s) available
Membership(s): AES; Custom Electronic Design & Installation Association; NSCA

Gold Link Productions Inc
176 Ridge Rd, Bolton, ON L7E 4V4, Canada
Tel: 416-560-3864
Web Site: www.toronto-cameraman.com
Key Personnel
Camera Operator: Silvio Bulgaretti *E-mail:* spyroe@sympatico.ca
Founded: 1993
Freelance camera operator: EFP for broadcast & corporate.

Gold Standard Productions
Division of Gold Standard Enterprises
12952 Miriam Place, Santa Ana, CA 92705-1334
Tel: 714-544-7000 *Fax:* 714-544-7010
Web Site: www.goldstandardproductions.com
Key Personnel
Dir, Photog: Gary Stone *E-mail:* gkstone@earthlink.net
Full service audio & video production.
Membership(s): AOPA; MCA-I

Goldberg Brothers Inc
8000 E 40 Ave, Denver, CO 80207
Tel: 303-321-1099 *Fax:* 303-388-0749
E-mail: reelservice@goldbergbrothers.com
Web Site: www.goldbergbrothers.com
Key Personnel
Pres: Russ Brown
VP: John Golesh
Founded: 1897
Manufacturing of products for film & film memorability.
Catalog(s) available
Membership(s): International Technology and Engineering Educators Association; SMPTE; Tech Council

Bruce Goldberg Inc
5354 Quakertown Ave, Woodland Hills, CA 91364
Tel: 818-713-8190 *Toll Free Tel:* 800-527-6248 *Fax:* 818-704-9189
E-mail: drbg@sbcglobal.net
Web Site: www.drbrucegoldberg.com
Key Personnel
Dir: Bruce Goldberg
Catalog(s) available

Golden Gate Studios
Division of KTLN-TV
100 Pelican Way, Suite E, San Rafael, CA 94901
Tel: 415-485-5856 *Fax:* 415-256-9262
Web Site: www.goldengatestudios.com
Key Personnel
Admin Asst: Lara Peterson *E-mail:* lpeterson@tln.com
Founded: 1974

Golden Lamb Productions
47 Schoolhouse Rd, Nassau, NY 12123
Tel: 518-766-4358
Web Site: www.glpvideoproduction.com
Key Personnel
Pres: Dow Haynor
Founded: 1986
Provide SD & HD camera crews throughout the Northeast. Complete SD & HD production.

Golden State Dance Teachers Association (GSDTA)
Division of Alterra Publishing
10804 Woodruff Ave, Downey, CA 90241-3910
Tel: 562-869-8949
Web Site: www.swingworld.com
Key Personnel
Owner: Skippy Blair *E-mail:* skippy@skippyblair.com
Dance education.
Catalog(s) available

Golf Digest
Division of Conde Nast Publications
20 Westport Rd, Wilton, CT 06897
Mailing Address: PO Box 850, Wilton, CT 06897-0580
Tel: 203-761-5100 *Toll Free Tel:* 800-727-4653 *Fax:* 203-761-5129
Web Site: www.golfdigest.com
Key Personnel
Chmn & Ed-in-Chief: Jerry Tarde *Tel:* 203-761-5225
Educational golf videos & books.
Catalog(s) available

Goodman Associates Inc
718 S 22 St, Philadelphia, PA 19146
Tel: 215-546-1448
E-mail: goodman@histories.com
Key Personnel
Pres: Robert Goodman
VP: Daniel Goodman
Membership(s): IFP

Goose Creek Music & Entertainment
17723 Tranquility Rd, Purcellville, VA 20132
Tel: 540-751-1395
E-mail: info@goosecreekmusic.com
Web Site: www.goosecreekmusic.com
Key Personnel
COO & Pres: Mike Pugh
Head, Busn Devt: Paul Shreve
Founded: 2008
Audio & video recordings of original Americana music by emerging artists. Specialize in recording live performances.

Alan Gordon Enterprises Inc
5625 Melrose Ave, Hollywood, CA 90038
Tel: 323-466-3561 *Fax:* 323-871-2193
E-mail: contactus@alangordon.com
Web Site: www.alangordon.com
Key Personnel
Pres: Grant Loucks
VP & Mktg Mgr: Don Sahlein
Founded: 1947
Manufacture, sales & rental of professional motion picture & video equipment.
Online catalog(s) available
Membership(s): American Society for Photogrammetry and Remote Sensing; American Society of Cinematographers; NAB

Gordon Productions Inc
1730 Pacheco St, San Francisco, CA 94116
Tel: 415-776-7484
Web Site: www.gpvideo.com
Key Personnel
Pres: John T Gordon *E-mail:* john@gpvideo.com
Corporate video production.
Membership(s): National Association of Broadcast Communications

Gordon Visual Solutions
504 Reiman St, Buffalo, NY 14212-2250
Tel: 716-894-5930 *Fax:* 630-839-5930
E-mail: info@gordonvisualsolutions.com; service@gordonvisualsolutions.com
Web Site: www.gordonvisualsolutions.com
Key Personnel
Pres: Richard Whipple
VP: James Chorazak
Sales: John Savage
Mktg Dir: Antoinette Baczkowski
Founded: 1974
Catalog(s) available

Gospel Folio Press
304 Killaly St W, Port Colborne, ON L3K 6A6, Canada
Tel: 905-835-9166 *Toll Free Tel:* 800-952-2382 *Fax:* 905-834-0012
E-mail: info@gospelfolio.com; orders@gospelfolio.com
Web Site: www.gospelfolio.com
Key Personnel
Sales Mgr: Sam Cairns
Religious programming distribution.
Catalog(s) available
Membership(s): Canadian Booksellers Association

Gotham City Studios
2219 Freedom Dr, Charlotte, NC 28208
Tel: 704-333-2349
E-mail: info@gothamcitystudios.us
Web Site: www.gothamcitystudios.us
Rents soundstage, post-production facility, offices & meeting spaces. Post-production services. Audio recording & sound design.

Gotham Sound & Communications Inc
330 W 38 St, No 105, New York, NY 10018
Tel: 212-629-9430 *Toll Free Tel:* 866-468-4268 *Fax:* 212-629-9436
E-mail: nyc@gothamsound.com
Web Site: www.gothamsound.com
Key Personnel
Owner: Jim Guzzi; Peter Schneider
Gen Mgr: Joe Mulica
Founded: 2002
Audio solution company that rents, sells & repairs audio equipment.
Branch Office(s)
500 Bishop St NW, Suite F-5, Atlanta, GA 30318 *Tel:* 404-855-2255 *Fax:* 404-855-2256 *E-mail:* atl@gothamsound.com

Grace Church - St Louis
2695 Creve Coeur Mill Rd, Maryland Heights, MO 63043
Tel: 314-292-8300 *Fax:* 314-291-0918
E-mail: info@gracestl.org
Web Site: www.gracestl.org
Key Personnel
Sr Pastor: Ron Tucker *Tel:* 314-292-8300 ext 2119 *E-mail:* ront@gracestl.org
Personnel Dir: Mike Schmidt *Tel:* 314-292-8300 ext 2115 *E-mail:* mikes@gracestl.org
Tech Dir: Ron Krause *Tel:* 314-292-8300 ext 2196 *E-mail:* ronk@gracestl.org
Audio Recording Specialist: Reba Holt *Tel:* 314-292-8300 ext 2166 *E-mail:* rholt@gracestl.org
Founded: 1978
Religious audio programs (pastor's sermons).

Grafco Inc
PO Box 431, Stroudsburg, PA 18360
Toll Free Tel: 800-367-6169 *Toll Free Fax:* 800-443-4329
E-mail: grafcofurniture@grafco.com
Web Site: www.grafco.com
Key Personnel
Pres: Steve Mavin
Computer tables for schools with cable management.
Catalog(s) available

Graftek Imaging Inc
8900 Shoal Creek Blvd, Bldg 300, Suite B, Austin, TX 78757
Tel: 512-416-1099 *Toll Free Tel:* 800-441-2118 *Fax:* 512-416-1014
E-mail: graftek@graftek.com
Web Site: www.graftek.com
Key Personnel
CFO: Jane Sims *Tel:* 512-416-1099 ext 103
Founded: 1984
Machine vision hardware & software solutions.
Catalog(s) available

Graham-Patten
Division of The ISIS Group Inc
119 E McKnight Way, Unit A, Grass Valley, CA 95949
Tel: 530-477-2984 *Fax:* 530-477-2986
E-mail: support@isis-group.com
Web Site: www.gpsys.com
Key Personnel
CEO & Pres: Bob Stillwaugh *Tel:* 530-477-2984 ext 211 *E-mail:* bob.stillwaugh@isis-group.com
Acctg: Kay Stillwaugh *E-mail:* kay.stillwaugh@isis-group.com
Founded: 1980
Manufacture digital audio products including audio monitors.
Catalog(s) available

Grand Stage Co Inc
630 W Lake St, Chicago, IL 60661
Tel: 312-332-5611 *Toll Free Tel:* 800-621-2181 *Fax:* 312-258-0056
E-mail: info@grandstage.com
Web Site: www.grandstage.com
Key Personnel
Pres & Sales: Glenn Becker *Tel:* 312-332-5611 ext 135 *E-mail:* gbecker@grandstage.com
Founded: 1947
Stage lighting distribution.
Catalog(s) available

Grande Vitesse Systems Inc (GVS)
390 Fremont St, San Francisco, CA 94105-9275
Tel: 415-777-0320 *Toll Free Tel:* 800-794-4622 (sales) *Fax:* 415-777-9544
Web Site: www.gvs9000.com
Founded: 1989
Branch Office(s)
2503 N Ontario St, Burbank, CA 91504 *Tel:* 818-823-1760 (sales)

Granger
25 Chapel St, Suite 605, New York, NY 11201
Tel: 212-447-1789 *Fax:* 212-447-1492
E-mail: info@granger.com
Web Site: www.granger.com
Founded: 1964
Collection of historical prints & photographs from prehistoric times through the 20th century. NB stills only, no film footage.
Membership(s): American Society of Picture Professionals; Digital Media Licensing Association

Granny Press LLC
101 Gedney St, Apt 5-D, Nyack, NY 10960
Tel: 845-875-4422; 845-875-4423
E-mail: webmaster@grannypress.com
Web Site: www.grannypress.com
Key Personnel
Pres & Owner: Davida Hirsch
Owner: Esther Nelson *Tel:* 718-548-6112
Founded: 1999
Publishing children's music cassettes & books & workshops.
Catalog(s) available

Graphic Laminating LLC
6185 Cochran Rd, Solon, OH 44139
Tel: 440-498-3400 *Toll Free Tel:* 800-345-5300 *Fax:* 440-498-3410
E-mail: info@graphiclaminating.com
Web Site: www.graphiclaminating.com
Key Personnel
Pres: Michael Hannon
Admin Mgr: Ginger Hannon
Manufactures laminating equipment (LEDCO Division), films & paper. Also provides laminating services.
Catalog(s) available
Membership(s): Education Market Association

Graphic Products Corp
455 Maple Ave, Carpentersville, IL 60110
Tel: 847-836-9600 *Toll Free Tel:* 800-323-1660 (cust serv) *Fax:* 847-836-9666
E-mail: info@gpcpapers.com
Web Site: www.gpcpapers.com
Key Personnel
Pres: Robert Serafin
Founded: 1962
Graphic supplies manufacturing.

Graphics Depot Inc
11 Middlebury Blvd, Unit 4, Randolph, NJ 07869
Tel: 973-927-8200 *Fax:* 973-927-8253
E-mail: info@graphicsdepotinc.com; sales@graphicsdepotinc.com
Web Site: www.graphicsdepotinc.com
Key Personnel
Pres: David Bernstein
Copy services both color & B&W, bindery, 4-color Heidelberg printing press, large format 60 inch printing & lamination & graphic design capability. All work is done in-house.
Brochure(s) available

Graphx Inc
400 W Cummings Park, Suite 3900, Woburn, MA 01801
Tel: 781-932-0430 *Fax:* 781-932-0855
E-mail: info@graphx.com
Web Site: www.graphx.com
Key Personnel
Founder & CTO: Pete Traversy
CEO & Pres: Joseph Kowalik
Founded: 1985
Software digital printers & RIP for digital printers. Web based print fulfillment for digital mini-labs.
Membership(s): DIMA; Photo Marketing Association

Grass Valley
3030 NW Aloclek Dr, Hillsboro, OR 97124
Mailing Address: PO Box 599000, Nevada City, CA 95959-7900
Tel: 503-526-8160 *Fax:* 503-526-8109
Key Personnel
Corp Mktg Communs Mgr: Tiffany Haley *E-mail:* tiffany.haley@grassvalley.com
Video & film graphics experts.
Catalog(s) available
Membership(s): SMPTE

Grassland Media Inc
5944 Seminole Centre Ct, Suite 120, Fitchburg, WI 53711-5019
Tel: 608-238-7575 *Toll Free Tel:* 800-236-7575 *Fax:* 608-270-9301
Web Site: www.grasslandmedia.com
Key Personnel
Pres: Stewart Stroup *E-mail:* sstroup@grasslandmedia.com
Founded: 1978
Complete provider of video production services.
Membership(s): MCA-I

Great Chefs/Leisure Jazz Video
Division of GCI Inc
747 Magazine St, New Orleans, LA 70130
Tel: 504-581-5000 *Toll Free Tel:* 800-321-1499 *Fax:* 504-581-1188
E-mail: info@greatchefs.com
Web Site: www.greatchefs.com
Key Personnel
Chmn & CEO: John Shoup *E-mail:* shoup@greatchefs.com
Cooking technique shows.
Membership(s): Entertainment Merchants Association; MIP; NATPE

Great Recordings LLC
1812 Procter St, Port Arthur, TX 77640
Mailing Address: PO Box 1436, Port Arthur, TX 77641-1436
Tel: 409-982-7121 *Fax:* 409-982-0643
E-mail: music@great-recordings.com
Web Site: www.great-recordings.com
Key Personnel
Owner: Floyd J Badeaux
Founded: 1957
CD pre-mastering & audio noise reduction.

Great River Electronics
164 Hardman Ave S, South St Paul, MN 55075
Tel: 651-455-1846 *Fax:* 651-455-3224
E-mail: info@greweb.com
Web Site: www.greatriverelectronics.com
Key Personnel
Founder & CEO: Dan Kennedy *E-mail:* dkennedy@greweb.com
Founded: 1994

The Great Southern Studios
Division of Dunright Productions
15221 NE 21 Ave, North Miami Beach, FL 33162
Tel: 305-944-2464 *Fax:* 305-944-9920
E-mail: info@gssmiami.com
Web Site: www.greatsouthernstudios.com
Key Personnel
Pres: Arlene Gillen
Scenery, studios, concept & design & lighting equipment rentals.
Catalog(s) available
Membership(s): AICP

William Greaves Productions Inc
475 W 57 St, No 17A, New York, NY 10019
Toll Free Tel: 800-874-8314 *Fax:* 212-315-0027
Web Site: www.williamgreaves.com
Key Personnel
Pres: Louise Greaves
Founded: 1964
Production of educational videos & documentaries.
Catalog(s) available

Green Dot Audio Electronics
PO Box 290609, Nashville, TN 37229-0609
Tel: 615-366-5964 *Fax:* 615-366-7069
E-mail: greendotaudio@bellsouth.net
Web Site: www.greendotaudio.com
Key Personnel
Owner: Mark Nadlin
Founded: 1989
Dealer/contractor. Professional audio parts & patch bays.

Green Linnet Records
Division of Compass Records
916 19 Ave S, Nashville, TN 37212
Tel: 615-320-7672 *Toll Free Tel:* 800-468-6644 *Fax:* 615-320-7378
E-mail: info@compassrecords.com
Web Site: greenlinnet.com; www.compassrecords.com
Key Personnel
Dir: Alison Brown; Garry West
Founded: 1976
Produces & markets Celtic music.
Catalog(s), free

Green Mountain Audio Inc
955 E Fillmore St, Colorado Springs, CO 80907-6315
Tel: 719-636-2500
E-mail: greenmountainaudio@comcast.net
Web Site: www.greenmountainaudio.com
Key Personnel
CEO: Roy Johnson
Founded: 1988
Manufacture hand-crafted & acoustically-correct time coherent loudspeakers & subwoofers that are each a work of art, inside & out. We set the world standard for time coherent sound & have maintained that number 1 position since 1988.

Green Mountain Post Films (GMP)
PO Box 229, Turners Falls, MA 01376-0229
Tel: 413-863-4754 *Fax:* 413-863-8248
E-mail: info@gmpfilms.com
Web Site: www.gmpfilms.com
Key Personnel
Pres: Daniel Keller
VP & Ad Mgr: Charles Light
Founded: 1975
Complete film & video production & distribution.
Catalog(s) available
Shipping Address: 23 Unity St, Turners Falls, MA 01376

Dr Ida Greene, see People Skills International

Greenery Studios
7764 San Fernando Rd, Burbank, CA 91352
Tel: 818-253-9990
E-mail: info@greenerystudios.com
Web Site: greenerystudios.com
Service for motion pictures, TV, commercials, music videos & photography.

GretagMacbeth, see X-Rite

Greyfalcon House
124 Waverly Place, New York, NY 10011
Tel: 212-777-9042
Key Personnel
Dir & Prodr: Ann Grifalconi
Founded: 1980
Children's & educational programming producer/writer. Artwork services.
Membership(s): The Authors Guild

Griesinger Films LLC
7300 Old Mill Rd, Gates Mills, OH 44040
Tel: 440-423-1601 *Toll Free Tel:* 800-872-4456 *Fax:* 440-423-1601
E-mail: orders@griesingerfilms.com
Web Site: www.griesingerfilms.com
Key Personnel
Prodr & Dir: Peter Root Griesinger *E-mail:* peterg@griesingerfilms.com
Founded: 1974
Unique environmental films from an economic perspective.
Catalog(s) available

Griffith Productions
1750 Donelson Dr, Eads, TN 38028
Tel: 901-351-1899 *Fax:* 901-465-1787
E-mail: info@griffithproductions.tv
Web Site: www.griffithproductions.tv
Key Personnel
Pres: Ed Griffith
Founded: 1992
Corporate video/event.

Griffiths Broadcast Co Inc
2981 Le Conte St, Viera, FL 32940
Tel: 321-622-4619 *Fax:* 321-622-4619
E-mail: griffiths.broadcast@usa.net
Web Site: www.griffithsbroadcast.com
Key Personnel
CEO: Naomi Griffiths
VP, Sales: Bob Griffiths
Mktg Dir: Dara Touma
Regl Mgr: Lisa Vachna
Founded: 1989
Broadcast, cable, telephone, education, government & industry are the prime markets served. Manufacture Hum eliminators & distribute EAS equipment & velcro cable ties under the name "Griff-Wrap".
Catalog(s), annual, free
Branch Office(s)
665 Linda Ave, Thornwood, NY 10594
Membership(s): Armed Forces Communications & Electronics Association; SBE; SMPTE

Griggs Productions Inc
Kappas Marina, 29 W Pier, Sausalito, CA 94965
Tel: 415-999-1079 *Toll Free Tel:* 800-210-4200
Web Site: www.griggs.com
Key Personnel
CEO & Prodr: Lewis Brown Griggs *E-mail:* lewis@griggs.com
Founded: 1983
Diversity, culture & relationship training. Videos, DVDs, CD-ROMs & online programs as well as workshops & speaking.
Catalog(s) available

Grise Audio Visual Center Inc
2402 Cherry St, Erie, PA 16502
Mailing Address: PO Box 546, Erie, PA 16512-0546
Tel: 814-452-4465 *Toll Free Tel:* 888-404-2719 *Fax:* 814-452-4479
E-mail: grise@erie.net
Web Site: www.griseav.com
Key Personnel
CEO: Jim Grise
Pres: Donald J Grise
Founded: 1947
Full service AV sales center.
Catalog(s) available
Membership(s): InfoComm International®

Grocery Manufacturers Association (GMA)
1350 "I" St NW, Suite 300, Washington, DC 20005
Tel: 202-639-5900 *Toll Free Tel:* 800-355-0983 *Fax:* 202-639-5932
E-mail: info@gmaonline.org
Web Site: gmaonline.org
Key Personnel
EVP, Communs & Membership Servs: Sean McBride *E-mail:* smcbride@gmaonline.org
Catalog(s) available

GrooveWorx
1418 Second St, Santa Monica, CA 90401
Tel: 310-260-2626 *Toll Free Tel:* 800-400-6767 *Fax:* 310-260-2662
E-mail: contact@grooveworx.com
Web Site: www.grooveworx.com
Key Personnel
VP & Gen Mgr: Bill Stollier *E-mail:* bill@grooveworx.com
Founded: 1997
Motion picture, television & radio.

Groovy Like a Movie
5205 Kearny Villa Way, Suite 100, San Diego, CA 92123
Tel: 858-715-0300
E-mail: info@groovylikeamovie.com
Web Site: www.groovylikeamovie.com
Key Personnel
Exec Prodr: Brent Altomare
Prodr/Dir: Tom Antl
Dir, Photog: Stephen Scavulli
Provides rental of soundstage, lighting & grip. Also provides pre-production, production & post-production services.

Ground Support Equipment (US) Ltd, see Biomorph Desks

Group One Ltd
70 Sea Lane, Farmingdale, NY 11735
Tel: 516-249-1399 *Fax:* 516-249-8870
E-mail: sales@g1limited.com
Web Site: www.g1limited.com
Key Personnel
Pres: Jack Kelly *E-mail:* jackk@g1limited.com
VP, US Sales-Audio: Chris Fichera *E-mail:* chris@abluesky.com
VP, US Sales-Lighting: Vincent Finnegan *E-mail:* vinnyf@g1limited.com
Distribute audio & lighting products.
Catalog(s) available
Membership(s): AES; NAB; NAMM, the National Association of Music Merchants; Professional Lighting & Sound Association

Group PVP
296 Saint Pierre St, Matane, QC G4W 2B9, Canada
Tel: 418-566-2040 *Toll Free Tel:* 877-320-2040 *Fax:* 418-562-4643
E-mail: info@pvp.ca
Web Site: www.pvp.ca

Key Personnel
Pres & Prodr: Vic Pelletier
VP & Prodr: Vincent Leroux
VP, Devt: Robert Tremblay
Founded: 1985
Produce documentaries for television, animation film & series, fiction, web sites.
Branch Office(s)
6 Desaulniers Blvd, Burea 408, Ste-Lambert, QC J4P 1L3, Canada *Tel:* 450-672-2913 *Fax:* 450-672-6901
Membership(s): APFTQ

GTI (Graphic Technology Inc)
PO Box 3138, Newburgh, NY 12550-0651
Tel: 845-562-7066 *Toll Free Tel:* 888-562-7066 *Fax:* 845-562-2543
E-mail: sales@gtilite.com
Web Site: www.gtilite.com
Key Personnel
VP, Sales: Robert McCurdy
Sales Mktg Coord: Linda Sutherland
Catalog(s) available
Shipping Address: 211 Dupont Ave, Newburgh, NY 12550

Guerrilla Productions LLC
1119 E 50 St, Savannah, GA 31404
Mailing Address: PO Box 20852, Raleigh, NC 27619
Tel: 919-349-7643; 912-354-4518 *Fax:* 912-354-1176
E-mail: info@guerrillapro.com
Web Site: www.guerrillapro.com
Key Personnel
Pres: Wil Kazary
Founded: 2001
Video & television production.

Guidance Associates Inc Center for Humanities
31 Pine View Rd, Mount Kisco, NY 10549
Tel: 914-666-4100 *Toll Free Tel:* 800-431-1242 *Fax:* 914-666-5319
Web Site: www.guidanceassociates.com
Key Personnel
Pres: Will Goodman *E-mail:* willg1961@gmail.com
Publish educational videos & DVDs.
Catalog(s) available
Membership(s): American Personnel & Guidance Association; InfoComm International®

Guilford Publications
72 Spring St, 4th fl, New York, NY 10012
Tel: 212-431-9800 *Toll Free Tel:* 800-365-7006 *Fax:* 212-966-6708
E-mail: info@guilford.com
Web Site: www.guilford.com
Key Personnel
Mktg Dir: Marian Robinson
Acct Mgr: Estefeni Estremera *Tel:* 212-431-9800 ext 258 *E-mail:* estefeni.estremera@guilford.com
Sales Mgr: Anne Patota *E-mail:* anne.patota@guilford.com
Publisher.
Catalog(s) available
Foreign Office(s): Footprint Books, 1/6a Prosperity Parade, Warriewood, NSW 2102, Australia *Tel:* (02) 9997 3973 *Fax:* (02) 9997 3185 *E-mail:* info@footprint.com.au *Web Site:* www.footprint.com.au
Taylor & Francis Asia Pacific, No 06-09 Siemens Ctr, Block 1, 60 MacPherson Rd, Singapore 348574, Singapore *Tel:* 6741 5166 *Fax:* 6742 9356 *E-mail:* info@tandf.com.sg (Brunei, Cambodia, China, Hong Kong, Indonesia, Korea, Laos, Malaysia, Myanmar, Philippines, Singapore, Thailand, Vietnam)
Juta & Co Ltd, Sunclare Bldg, 1st fl, 21 Dreyer St, Claremont, Cape Town 7708, South Africa *Tel:* (021) 659 2300 *Fax:* (021) 659 2360 *E-mail:* orders@juta.co.za
Unifacmanu Trading, 4F, No 19 Ho-Ping E Rd, Section 1, Taipei 10609, Taiwan *Tel:* (02) 2391 4280 *Fax:* (02) 2394 3103 *E-mail:* unifacmu@ms34.hinet.net *Web Site:* www.unifacmanu.com.tw
Taylor & Francis, c/o Bookpoint Ltd, 130 Milton Park, Abingdon, Oxon OX14 4SB, United Kingdom *Tel:* (01235) 400 524 *Fax:* (01235) 400 525 *E-mail:* tandf@bookpoint.co.uk *Web Site:* www.guilfordpress.co.uk

Gulf Coast Audio Visual Producers Inc
c/o National Park Bookshop, 3720 N Pace Blvd, Pensacola, FL 32506
Tel: 850-433-3016 *Toll Free Tel:* 800-722-2057 *Fax:* 850-438-4807
E-mail: gcavp@aol.com
Web Site: www.gcavp.com
Key Personnel
Owner: Chuck Edwards
Full service AV producing & distributing.
Catalog(s) available
Membership(s): InfoComm International®

Gurrilla Video Solutions
Formerly Emedia Studios
233 Fillmore Ave, Suite 8, Tonawanda, NY 14150
Tel: 716-692-0064
E-mail: info@gvideosolutions.com
Web Site: www.gvideosolutions.com
Key Personnel
Owner & Exec Prodr: Katherine Lucas *E-mail:* katherine@gvideosolutions.com

Guymark Studios LLC
3019 Dixwell Ave, Hamden, CT 06518
Mailing Address: PO Box 5037, Hamden, CT 06518-5037
Tel: 203-248-9323 *Fax:* 203-248-9325
E-mail: guymark.studios@snet.net
Web Site: www.guymarkstudios.com
Key Personnel
Owner & VP: Mark L Guarino
Pres: Anthony Guy Guarino
Off Mgr: Susan Guarino
Founded: 1950
Full AV production studio.
Catalog(s) available

GVISION USA Inc
20532 Crescent Bay Dr, Lake Forest, CA 92630
Tel: 949-586-3338 *Fax:* 949-586-3398
E-mail: info@gvision-usa.com; gsales@gvision-usa.com
Web Site: www.gvision-usa.com
Key Personnel
Sales Dir: Darren Somo
Founded: 1999
LCD monitors, touch screens, open frame units, stands & mounts.

Gypsum Association
6525 Belcrest Rd, Suite 480, Hyattsville, MD 20782
Tel: 301-277-8686 *Fax:* 301-277-8747
E-mail: info@gypsum.org
Web Site: www.gypsum.org
Key Personnel
Exec Dir: Michael Gardner
Founded: 1930
Distribute & produce CD-ROM training & vocational training videos.
Catalog(s), annual

Gyration
3601-B Calle Tecate, Camarillo, CA 93012
Toll Free Tel: 888-340-0033 (tech support)
E-mail: gsupport@smkusa.com
Web Site: www.gyration.com
Founded: 1989
Manufacture & distribute motion-sensing technology for in-air navigation & cursor control on a television screen or monitor.
Catalog(s) available

Gyrus ACMI
Subsidiary of Olympus Corp
136 Turnpike Rd, Southborough, MA 01772-2104
Tel: 508-804-2600 *Toll Free Tel:* 800-852-9361 (cust serv) *Fax:* 508-804-2624; 763-416-3001 (cust serv)
E-mail: customercare@gyrusacmi.com
Web Site: www.gyrusacmi.com
Key Personnel
Sr Mgr, Mktg Communs: Lorna Piche *E-mail:* lorna.piche@gyrusacmi.com
Catalog(s) available
Branch Office(s)
300 Stillwater Ave, Stamford, CT 06902-3695 *Tel:* 203-357-8300 *Fax:* 203-328-8618
6655 Wedgewood Rd, Suite 160, Maple Grove, MN 55311 *Tel:* 763-416-3000 *Toll Free Tel:* 866-724-3101 *Fax:* 763-463-1200
93 N Pleasant St, Norwalk, OH 44857 *Tel:* 419-668-8201 *Fax:* 419-660-4151
2925 Appling Rd, Bartlett, TN 38133 *Tel:* 901-373-0200 *Toll Free Tel:* 800-773-4301 *Fax:* 901-373-0220 *E-mail:* customerserviceent@gyrusacmi.com
Sales Office(s): Gyrus ACMI LP, 6655 Wedgwood Rd, Suite 160, Maple Grove, MN 55311 *Tel:* 763-416-3000 *Fax:* 763-463-1200
Olympus Canada Inc, 25 Leek Crescent, Richmond Hill, ON L4B 4B3, Canada *Toll Free Tel:* 800-387-0437 *Toll Free Fax:* 888-240-2607
Olympus Australia, 31 Gilby Rd, Mount Waverley, Victoria 3149, Australia *Tel:* 1300 132 992 (toll free)
Olympus Medical Systems Europa GmbH, Wendenstr 14-18, 20097 Hamburg, Germany *Tel:* (040) 23773-0 *Fax:* (040) 23773-4656 *Web Site:* www.olympus-europa.com (Europe)
KeyMed Ltd, KeyMed House, Stock Rd, Southend-on-Sea, Essex SS2 5QH, United Kingdom *Tel:* (01702) 616333 *Fax:* (01702) 465677
Foreign Office(s): Parque Industrial La Angostrua, Carretera Saltillo Zacatacas Km.4.5, 25315 Saltillo, Coahuila, Mexico *Tel:* (844) 986-6000 *Fax:* (844) 482-9150
Gyrus Medical Ltd, Fortran Rd, St Mellons, Cardiff CF3 0LT, United Kingdom *Tel:* (029) 2077 6300 *Fax:* (029) 2077 6301

Hakuba Sunpak Velbon
Division of ToCAD America Inc
53 Green Pond Rd, Suite 5, Rockaway, NJ 07866
Tel: 973-627-9600 *Toll Free Tel:* 800-886-2236 *Fax:* 973-664-2438
E-mail: info@tocad.com
Web Site: www.tocad.com
Key Personnel
Pres: Richard Darrow *Tel:* 972-627-9600 ext 103
VP, Sales: Nick Cheremsak
Photographic equipment manufacturer.
Catalog(s) available

Half Moon Video Productions
79 Central Ave, Jersey City, NJ 07306-2124
Tel: 201-792-1066 *Fax:* 201-792-1523
E-mail: pavonia@home.com
Key Personnel
Gen Mgr: Tom Horan

Howard Hall Productions
2171 La Amatista Rd, Del Mar, CA 92014-3031
Tel: 858-259-8989 *Fax:* 858-792-1467
E-mail: info@howardhall.com
Web Site: www.howardhall.com
Key Personnel
Owner: Howard Hall; Michele Hall
Founded: 1988

TV & IMAX film production; natural history wildlife stock footage library - originated in HD. Shoot special assignments. Time lapse underwater & topside photography.
Membership(s): AMPAS; DGA; Television Academy

Hall Productions
951 Front St, Grover Beach, CA 93433
Mailing Address: PO Box 645, Grover Beach, CA 93483
Tel: 805-473-1042 *Toll Free Tel:* 800-366-6057 *Fax:* 805-473-2202
Web Site: hallpro.com
Key Personnel
Pres: Dan Hall *E-mail:* dan@hallpro.com
Handcrafted light boxes & light tables.
Catalog(s) available
Membership(s): Photo Marketing Association

HallBrook Productions
565 Dutch Valley Rd, Atlanta, GA 30324
Tel: 404-892-0042
E-mail: hallbrook@hallbrookproductions.com
Web Site: hallbrookproductions.com
Key Personnel
Dir: Anita Hallman
Prodr: George Martin
Founded: 1995
Full service video production facility, edit suites & office space. Production services.

Hallel Communications
Hallel Institute, 175 Rte 340, Sparkill, NY 10976-1047
Tel: 845-365-2277 *Toll Free Tel:* 800-445-7477 *Fax:* 845-365-2279
E-mail: hallel@hallel.net
Web Site: www.hallelvideos.com
Key Personnel
Pres: George Torok
Founded: 1974
Catalog(s) available

Steven Halpern's Inner Peace Music
PO Box 2644, San Anselmo, CA 94979-2644
Tel: 541-488-7870 *Toll Free Tel:* 888-765-9697 (shipping); 800-909-0707 (orders) *Fax:* 541-488-7870
E-mail: info@innerpeacemusic.com
Web Site: www.innerpeacemusic.com
Key Personnel
Contact: Diana Ziegler *Tel:* 415-485-5321 *E-mail:* dvz@innerpeacemusic.com
Catalog(s) available
Shipping Address: 701 Mistletoe Rd, Ashland, OR 97520

Hamilton Buhl
Division of Vcom International Multimedia Corp
80 Little Falls Rd, Fairfield, NJ 07004
Toll Free Tel: 800-631-0868 *Toll Free Fax:* 800-398-1812 (cust serv & sales)
E-mail: customerservice@hamiltonbuhl.com
Web Site: www.hamiltonbuhl.com
Key Personnel
Sales Assoc: Denise Lisch *Tel:* 800-631-0868 ext 1074 *E-mail:* dlisch@hamiltonbuhl.com
Founded: 1933
Educational AV equipment.
Catalog(s) available
Membership(s): Education Market Association; InfoComm International®

Hamilton Studio
1427 W Dean Ave, Spokane, WA 99201
Tel: 509-327-9501
Web Site: www.hamiltonstudio.com
Key Personnel
Prodr: Don Hamilton *E-mail:* don@hamiltonstudio.com; Lorna St John *E-mail:* lorna@hamiltonstudio.com
Film/video production & commercial photography.
Membership(s): ASMP

Hammond Communications Group
173 Trade St, Lexington, KY 40511-2608
Tel: 859-254-1878
E-mail: info@hammondcg.com
Web Site: www.hammondcg.com
Key Personnel
Pres: Ron Mossotti
VP, Interactive Media: Craig Miller
Prodr & Dir: Jesse Kelsey *E-mail:* jkelsey@hammondcg.com
Dir, Video Prodn: Angie Poole
Founded: 1980

Hampshire Street Studios
540A Hampshire St, San Francisco, CA 94110
Tel: 415-643-5580
E-mail: info@hampshirestreetstudios.com
Web Site: www.hampshirestreetstudios.com
Soundstage & facilities rental.

Hand Held Films
129 W 27 St, New York, NY 10001
Tel: 212-627-2781; 212-502-0900 (rentals) *Fax:* 212-502-0906
E-mail: rentals@handheldfilms.com
Web Site: handheldfilms.com
Founded: 1987
Offers rental of digital HD cameras, lenses & accessories, film equipment, grip & lighting.

Howard Hanger
Affiliate of Jazz Fantasy
31 Park Ave N, Asheville, NC 28801
Tel: 828-280-8419 *Fax:* 828-280-8419
E-mail: hangerhall@prodigy.net
Web Site: www.howardhanger.com
Catalog(s) available

Terry Hanley Audio Systems Inc
20 Industrial Pkwy, Woburn, MA 01801
Tel: 781-932-5300 *Fax:* 781-932-5354
E-mail: mail@terryhanleyaudio.com
Web Site: www.terryhanleyaudio.com
Key Personnel
CEO & Pres: Terrence Hanley
Gen Mgr & Acct Mgr: John Doerschuk *E-mail:* john@terryhanleyaudio.com
Sales Mgr & Chief Engr: Daniel Kidwell
Founded: 1969

G W Hannaway & Associates
839 Pearl St, Boulder, CO 80302
Tel: 303-440-9631 *Fax:* 303-440-4421
E-mail: sales@gwha.com; services@gwha.com; technology@gwha.com
Web Site: www.gwha.com
Key Personnel
Busn Mgr: Sarah Anderson
Founded: 1975

Hannay Reels Inc
553 State Rte 143, Westerlo, NY 12193-0159
Tel: 518-797-3791 *Toll Free Tel:* 877-467-3357 *Fax:* 518-797-3259 *Toll Free Fax:* 800-733-5464
E-mail: reels@hannay.com
Web Site: www.hannay.com
Key Personnel
Pres: Eric Hannay
Mktg Mgr: Edward Rash *E-mail:* ed@hannay.com
Founded: 1933
World's leading manufacturer of quality cable reels & AV reels. Offers infinite variety, built to order & delivered on time.
Catalog(s), free
Online catalog(s) available

Hannecke Display Systems Inc
91 Fulton St, Boonton, NJ 07005
Tel: 973-335-0434 *Toll Free Tel:* 800-345-8631 *Fax:* 973-335-1274
E-mail: info.usa@hannecke.com
Web Site: www.hannecke.com
Key Personnel
CEO: Cuno Goetz von Olenhusen
Catalog(s) available
Foreign Office(s): Hannecke Display Systems GmbH & Co KG, Rischenauweg 6, 37154 Northeim, Germany *Tel:* (05551) 599-0 *Fax:* (05551) 599-27 *E-mail:* info@hannacke.de
Membership(s): Canadian Booksellers Association; Evangelical Christian Publishers Association; NASFM; National Association of College Stores; POPAI; Reading Recovery Council of North America

Hanovia Specialty Lighting LLC
Subsidiary of Gaven Co
6 Evans St, Fairfield, NJ 07004
Tel: 973-651-5510 *Fax:* 973-651-5550
E-mail: sales@hanovia-uv.com
Web Site: www.hanovia-uv.com
Key Personnel
Mng Dir: Liming Du
Founded: 1905
Manufacture UV lamps & equipment.
Catalog(s) available
Foreign Office(s): 27-B Yifu Rd, Jiuting Songjiang, Shanghai 201615, China *Tel:* (021) 6762 7720 *Fax:* (021) 6762 7730

Har-Ken Specialties
PO Box 37, Parkesburg, PA 19365-0037
Tel: 610-384-2161 *Fax:* 610-384-8258
E-mail: harken1@comcast.net
Web Site: www.har-kenspecialties.com; www.har-ken.com
Key Personnel
Pres: Harry Smith
Founded: 1980
Manufacture audio adapters.
Catalog(s), free, on request

Harbor House Studios
Division of Harbour Studios LLP
2525 Florence Rd, Suite B, Keller, TX 76262
Tel: 817-379-1500 *Fax:* 817-337-5104
E-mail: info@harborhousestudios.com
Web Site: www.harborhousestudios.com
Key Personnel
Owner: Hyman Stansky *E-mail:* hstansky@mac.com
Founded: 2001
TDM protools facility; mastering, video recording, DVD authoring, CD/DVD replication & analog to DVD restoration.
Online catalog(s) available
Membership(s): The Recording Academy

Harbro Corp
2691 W 15 St, Brooklyn, NY 11224-2705
Tel: 718-946-4134 *Fax:* 718-946-4151
Key Personnel
Chief Salesman: Morris Shalom

Hard Hat Radio Music Service
519 N Halifax Ave, Daytona Beach, FL 32118-4017
Tel: 386-252-0381 *Fax:* 386-252-0381
E-mail: hardhatrecords@aol.com
Web Site: www.hardhatrecords.com
Key Personnel
CEO: Bobby Lee Cude
Founded: 1948

Membership(s): Alliance of Artists & Recording Companies; BMI; National Music Publishers' Association; The Recording Academy; SoundExchange

Hardcastle Films & Video
7319 Wise Ave, St Louis, MO 63117-1718
Tel: 314-647-4200 *Fax:* 314-647-4201
Key Personnel
Partner: Jeff Hardcastle
Founded: 1930

Hargrove Inc
One Hargrove Dr, Lanham, MD 20706
Tel: 301-306-9000 *Fax:* 301-306-9318
E-mail: exhibitorservices@hargroveinc.com
Web Site: www.hargroveinc.com
Key Personnel
CEO: Tim McGill
Pres & COO: Carla Hargrove McGill
Special events, exhibits & trade show company.
Catalog(s) available
Membership(s): EDPA; IAEM

Harman/Becker, see Harman Pro North America

Harman International Industries Inc
400 Atlantic St, 15th fl, Stamford, CT 06901
Tel: 203-328-3500
Web Site: www.harman.com
Key Personnel
CEO: Dinesh C Paliwal
CFO: Herbert K Parker

Harman Pro North America
Subsidiary of Harman International Industries
8500 Balboa Blvd, Northridge, CA 91329
Tel: 818-894-8850; 818-893-8411 *Fax:* 818-920-3208
E-mail: info@harman.com
Web Site: www.harman.com
US distributor for AMEK, BSS Audio & Soundcraft.
Catalog(s) available
Membership(s): AES; NSCA

Harmonia Mundi USA
1117 Chestnut St, Burbank, CA 91506
Tel: 818-333-1500 *Fax:* 818-333-1502
E-mail: info-usa@harmoniamundi.com
Web Site: www.harmoniamundi.com
Key Personnel
Pres: Rene Goiffon
Founded: 1958
Catalog(s) available

Harmon's Audio-Visual Services
Division of Jim Harmon Enterprises Inc
2533 Crystal Dr, Fort Myers, FL 33966
Mailing Address: PO Box 61127, Fort Myers, FL 33906-1127
Tel: 239-939-2273 *Fax:* 239-939-5966
E-mail: info@harmonsav.com
Web Site: www.harmonsav.com
Key Personnel
Owner: James R Harmon *E-mail:* jim@harmonsav.com
Prodn Mgr: Bobby Harmon *E-mail:* bobby@harmonsav.com
Founded: 2003
Catalog(s) available
Membership(s): InfoComm International®

Harnel Case Co
1600 Marshall Ave SE, Grand Rapids, MI 49507
Tel: 616-452-4522 *Fax:* 616-452-5514
E-mail: info@harnelcase.com
Web Site: www.harnelcase.com
Key Personnel
VP, Mktg & Sales: Jim Tuffs *E-mail:* jtuffboy@yahoo.com
Founded: 1947
Quality custom case manufacturer.
Product sheet(s) available

HarperAudio
Division of HarperCollins Publishers Inc
10 E 53 St, New York, NY 10022
Tel: 212-207-7000 *Toll Free Tel:* 800-242-7737 *Fax:* 212-207-2582 *Toll Free Fax:* 800-822-4090
Web Site: www.harpercollins.com
Key Personnel
Chief Digital Offr: Chantal Restivo-Alessi
VP, Digital Innovation: Ana Marie Allessi
Sr Dir: Sean McManus
Sr Prodr: Caitlin Garing
Prodr: Erin Wicks
Mktg Dir, Audio: Beth Ives *Tel:* 212-207-7286
Audio Coord: Karen Radner
Catalog(s) available

Harpers Ferry Historical Association
c/o National Park Bookshop, 723 Shenandoah St, Harpers Ferry, WV 25425
Mailing Address: PO Box 197, Harpers Ferry, WV 25425-0197
Tel: 304-535-6881 *Fax:* 304-535-6749
E-mail: hfha@earthlink.net
Web Site: www.harpersferryhistory.org
Key Personnel
Film Libn: Stephanie Sager
Founded: 1971
Catalog(s) available

Harrah's Theatre Equipment Co
25613 Dollar St, Unit 1, Hayward, CA 94544
Tel: 510-881-4989 *Fax:* 510-881-0448
Key Personnel
Pres: Jerry Harrah
Distribute theatre equipment.

Harris Canada Systems
26 Peppler St, Waterloo, ON N2J 3C4, Canada
Tel: 519-570-9111 *Toll Free Tel:* 800-363-3400 *Fax:* 519-570-9140
E-mail: info@inscriber.com
Web Site: www.broadcast.harris.com
Founded: 1986
Catalog(s) available

Harris Communications Inc
15155 Technology Dr, Eden Prairie, MN 55344
Tel: 952-906-1180 *Toll Free Tel:* 800-825-6758 *Fax:* 952-906-1099
E-mail: info@harriscomm.com
Web Site: www.harriscomm.com
Key Personnel
Pres: Robert Harris
Mktg Dir: Lori Foss *Tel:* 952-974-4744 *E-mail:* lfoss@harriscomm.com
Distribution of products including videotapes, for deaf & hard-of-hearing individuals as well as the interpreters & hearing healthcare workers who associate with them.
Catalog(s), annual, free

Harris Corp
1025 W NASA Blvd, Melbourne, FL 32919-0001
Tel: 321-727-9100 *Toll Free Tel:* 800-442-7747
E-mail: webmaster@harris.com
Web Site: www.harris.com
Key Personnel
CEO & Pres: William Brown
CFO & SVP: Gary L McArthur
An international communications & information technology company that serves government & commercial markets throughout the world.
Catalog(s) available

Harrison Brothers
47 N Chatham Pkwy, Chapel Hill, NC 27517
Toll Free Tel: 866-386-8335; 800-327-4414 *Toll Free Fax:* 800-327-6651
E-mail: info@harrisonbros.com
Web Site: www.thetapeworks.com
Key Personnel
Contact: Jeff Harrison *E-mail:* jeff@harrisonbros.com
Founded: 1986
Catalog(s) available

Harrison Consoles
1024 Firestone Pkwy, La Vergne, TN 37086-3505
Tel: 615-641-7200 *Fax:* 615-641-7224
E-mail: info@harrisonconsoles.com
Web Site: www.harrisonconsoles.com
Key Personnel
Sales/Advanced Prod Mgr: Gary Thielman *E-mail:* mixbus@harrisonconsoles.com
Founded: 1971
Brochure(s) available

Hart Inc
320 New Stock Rd, Asheville, NC 28804
Tel: 828-645-4734 *Toll Free Tel:* 800-654-8012 *Fax:* 828-645-4294 *Toll Free Fax:* 866-390-4278
E-mail: mail@hart-inc.com
Web Site: www.hart-inc.com
Key Personnel
Pres: Brett Eaker
Educational software distributor.

Hartley Film Foundation
49 Richmondville Ave, Suite 204, Westport, CT 06880
Tel: 203-226-9500 *Toll Free Tel:* 800-937-1819 *Fax:* 203-227-6938
E-mail: info@hartleyfoundation.org
Web Site: www.hartleyfoundation.org
Key Personnel
Mng Dir: Sarah Masters
Off Mgr: Laura Healy
Documentary & audio meditation sales.
Online catalog(s) available

Harvest Studios
2880 Vision Ct, Aurora, IL 60506
Tel: 630-801-3658 *Fax:* 630-801-3839
E-mail: info@harveststudios.org
Web Site: harveststudios.org
Key Personnel
Opers Mgr: Pete McDonough
Full service production facility.

Hasselblad Bron Inc
Subsidiary of Victor Hasselblad AB (Denmark)
1080A Garden State Rd, Union, NJ 07083
Tel: 908-754-5800 *Toll Free Tel:* 800-456-0203; 800-367-6434 *Fax:* 908-754-5807
E-mail: production@hasselbladbron.com; sales@hasselbladbron.com; servicedept@hasselbladbron.com
Web Site: www.hasselbladbron.com
Key Personnel
Pres & CEO: Michael Hejtmanek
VP: Joe Robinson *Tel:* 800-367-6434 ext 231
Catalog(s) available

Havas Edge
6922 Hollywood Blvd, Hollywood, CA 90028
Tel: 310-734-1333
E-mail: info@havasedge.com
Web Site: www.havasedge.com
Key Personnel
CEO: Steve Netzley
COO & Pres: Greg Johnson
CFO: Eric Bush
EVP, Busn Devt: Shannon Ellis *Tel:* 760-603-1520 *E-mail:* shannon.ellis@havasedge.com

Founded: 1988
Full service direct response agency with expertise across all digital, broadcast & media domains.

Havas Worldwide
200 Hudson St, New York, NY 10013
Tel: 212-886-2000 *Fax:* 212-886-5013
Web Site: havasworldwide.com
Key Personnel
Global Chief Mktg Offr: Matt Weiss
E-mail: matt.weiss@havasww.com
Advertising, marketing, corporate communications, design, digital & social media solutions.

HAVE Inc
309 Power Ave, Hudson, NY 12534
Tel: 518-828-2000 *Toll Free Tel:* 888-999-HAVE (999-4283) *Fax:* 518-828-2008
E-mail: pro_sales@haveinc.com; have@haveinc.com
Web Site: www.haveinc.com
Key Personnel
Pres: Nancy Gordon *E-mail:* ngordon@haveinc.com
VP: Paul Swedenburg
Mktg Mgr: Kevin Stein *E-mail:* kstein@haveinc.com
Founded: 1977
Catalog(s) available
Membership(s): MCA-I; SBE

Hawaii Sound & Vision
PO Box 2267, Kailua-Kona, HI 96745
Tel: 808-982-8330 *Toll Free Tel:* 877-982-8330
Fax: 808-982-8340
E-mail: aloha@hawaiisav.com
Web Site: www.hawaiisav.com
AV equipment rental, full service entertainment crew & event enhancements.

Hay House Inc
PO Box 5100, Carlsbad, CA 92018-5100
Tel: 760-431-7695 (ext 2, intl) *Toll Free Tel:* 800-654-5126 (ext 2, US); 800-650-5115 *Fax:* 760-431-6948
Web Site: www.hayhouse.com
Key Personnel
Pres: Reid Tracy
Founded: 1984
International leader in inspirational & self-help publishing.
Catalog(s) available
Branch Office(s)
250 Park Ave S, Suite 201, New York, NY 10003
Tel: 646-484-4950 *Fax:* 646-484-4956

Hayden 5 Media LLC
22 W 27 St, 6th fl, New York, NY 10001
Tel: 212-871-9316
E-mail: info@hayden5.com
Web Site: www.hayden5.com
Key Personnel
Co-Founder & Exec Prodr: Milos Silber; Todd Wiseman, Jr
Provides rental of studio & services for production & post-production.

Hazelden Publishing & Educational Services
Division of Hazelden Foundation
15251 Pleasant Valley Rd, Center City, MN 55012-0011
Mailing Address: PO Box 176, Center City, MN 55012-0176
Tel: 651-213-4200 *Toll Free Tel:* 800-328-9000
Fax: 651-213-4590
E-mail: info@hazelden.org; customersupport@hazelden.org
Web Site: www.hazelden.org
Key Personnel
SVP, Publg & Mktg Mgr: Nick Motu
Catalog(s) available

HB Communications Inc
Affiliate of HB Group Inc
60 Dodge Ave, North Haven, CT 06473
Tel: 203-234-9246 *Toll Free Tel:* 800-243-4414
Fax: 203-234-2013
E-mail: info@hbcommunications.com
Web Site: www.hbcommunications.com
Key Personnel
CEO & Pres: Dana Barron
Chmn: Mackey Barron
VP: Bob Anderson
VP, Sales: James Burke
Founded: 1946
Premier AV systems integration company. Satellite offices in New York, NY, Providence, RI & Waterford, VT.
Catalog(s) available
Branch Office(s)
1432 Main St, Waltham, MA 02451 *Tel:* 781-890-6046 *Fax:* 781-890-6048
1130 Globe Ave, Mountainside, NJ 07092
Tel: 908-654-3600 *Toll Free Tel:* 800-524-0610
Fax: 908-654-9273
Membership(s): ATD; InfoComm International®; International Facilities Management Association; MCA-I; NSCA

HB-Content
105 Butler St, Suite 2B, Brooklyn, NY 11231
Tel: 212-213-8824
E-mail: hb@hb-content.com
Web Site: www.hb-content.com
Key Personnel
Founder & Creative Dir: David Ragsdale
E-mail: david@hb-content.com
Dir, Photog: Michael De Mita
Writer, Ed & Prodr: Cynthia Lowen
Full service film, video, new media & event production; video/film editing, audio editing & original music production.

HBO Archives
1100 Avenue of the Americas, New York, NY 10036
Toll Free Tel: 877-426-1121
Web Site: www.hboarchives.com
Licenses commercial/professional footage.

HBO Home Video Inc
1100 Avenue of the Americas, New York, NY 10036
Tel: 212-512-1000 *Fax:* 212-512-7458
Web Site: www.hbo.com
Key Personnel
CFO: Rob Roth

HBO Studio Productions
Division of Home Box Office
120-A E 23 St, New York, NY 10010
Tel: 212-512-7800
E-mail: hsp@hsptv.com
Web Site: www.hbo.com
Key Personnel
Dir, Studio & Graphic Opers: Peter Consiglio
Founded: 1972
Full service production & post-production facility, studio & stage.
Brochure(s) available
Shipping Address: 115 E 22 St, New York, NY 10010

HBW Entertainment Inc
62 Massey Place, SW, T2V 2G5 Calgary, AB T2H 2H1, Canada
Tel: 403-228-1900 *Fax:* 403-259-3860
Key Personnel
Pres: Helene B White *E-mail:* hbwftv@shaw.ca
Founded: 1982
HBW Entertainment Inc & its group of companies has international recognition & top awards for film & TV production to their credit. A solid, yet exciting production & distribution company that seeks co-productions, offers production services to offshore companies & develops & produces original material.
Membership(s): AMPIA; Canadian Film & Television Production Association; WGC

HD Cinema
12233 W Olympic Blvd, Suite 120, Los Angeles, CA 90064
Tel: 310-434-9500 *Fax:* 310-499-5237 (efax)
Web Site: www.hd-cinema.com
Key Personnel
Contact: Jeff Blauvelt *E-mail:* jeff@hd-cinema.com
Founded: 1998
Production & post-production rental house with a vision for the creative use of 4K & HD technology for digital cinema & broadcast programming.
Branch Office(s)
1771 Post Rd E, Suite 220, Westport, CT 06880
Tel: 203-221-0233

HD House
6312 NW 77 Ct, Miami, FL 33166
Tel: 305-597-7359 *Fax:* 305-597-7027
Web Site: thehdhouse.com
Key Personnel
CEO: Tony Perez *E-mail:* tony@thehdhouse.com
CTO: Gaston Fazio *E-mail:* gaston@thehdhouse.com
Dir, Opers: Samantha Harter *E-mail:* samantha@thehdhouse.com
Rental Mgr: Carlos Martinez *E-mail:* carlos@thehdhouse.com
Founded: 2008
Provides HD & digital cinema equipment rental packages, audio & lighting gear, portable post-production suites, crewing, technical & logistical support & studio space.

HD Source
1333 Matheson Blvd E, Mississauga, ON L4W 1R1, Canada
Tel: 416-449-3030; 905-890-6905 *Fax:* 416-449-5230
Web Site: www.hdsource.ca
Key Personnel
Owner: Steve Zajaczkiwsky
Catalog(s) available
Membership(s): Canadian Society of Cinematographers; CCTA; Meeting Planners International; MTCVA; SMPTE

HDrental.com
Division of United Broadcast Group
16129 Covello St, Van Nuys, CA 91406
Tel: 818-994-3461 *Fax:* 818-994-3471
Web Site: hdrental.com
Key Personnel
CEO: John Schneider *Tel:* 818-625-4231 (cell)
E-mail: jon@hdrental.com
Sales Mgr: Nick Teti *Tel:* 484-390-0279 (cell)
E-mail: nick@hdrental.com
Film & television production equipment rentals.

HDTV Productions Inc
2620 S Maryland Pkwy, Suite 816, Las Vegas, NV 89109
Tel: 702-499-4880
E-mail: hdtv@hdtvproductions.com
Web Site: www.hdtvproductions.com
Key Personnel
Pres: Douglas Munro
Ed: Margot McMaster
Founded: 1980
HD production services, cameras & HD editing.
Branch Office(s)
132-250 Shawville Blvd SE, No 209, Calgary,

AB T2Y 2Z7, Canada *Tel:* 403-226-3727
Fax: 403-931-2352
Membership(s): International Alliance of Theatrical Stage Employees

Headlight Audio Visual Inc
74 Evergreen Dr, Portland, ME 04103-1066
Tel: 207-774-5998 *Toll Free Tel:* 800-247-0540
Fax: 207-774-4917
Web Site: www.headlightaudiovisual.com
Key Personnel
Pres: Robert G Bruns
VP: Andrew Bruns
Founded: 1975
Catalog(s) available
Membership(s): InfoComm International®

Headroom Digital Audio
Subsidiary of Plotkin Music Associates Inc
11 E 26 St, 19th fl, New York, NY 10010
Tel: 212-246-8400 *Fax:* 212-245-0370
E-mail: info@headroomdigi.com
Web Site: www.headroomdigi.com
Key Personnel
Pres: Jerry Plotkin *E-mail:* jerry@headroomdigi.com
Sample(s) available

Health Communications Inc
3201 SW 15 St, Deerfield Beach, FL 33442-8124
Tel: 954-360-0909 *Toll Free Tel:* 800-441-5569
Fax: 954-360-0034
Web Site: www.hcibooks.com
Key Personnel
Pres: Peter Vegso
Founded: 1977
Catalog(s) available

Health Education Services
Division of Social Studies School Service
10200 Jefferson Blvd, Culver City, CA 90232
Mailing Address: PO Box 802, Culver City, CA 90232-0802
Tel: 310-839-2436 *Toll Free Tel:* 800-421-4246
Fax: 310-839-2249 *Toll Free Fax:* 800-944-5432
E-mail: access@socialstudies.com
Web Site: www.socialstudies.com
Key Personnel
CEO: David Weiner
Chief Educ Offr: Dr Aaron Willis
Founded: 1965
Distributing supplementary educational materials.
Catalog(s) available

Hearing Loss Association of America (HLAA)
7910 Woodmont Ave, Suite 1200, Bethesda, MD 20814
Tel: 301-657-2248; 301-657-2249 (TTY)
Fax: 301-913-9413
E-mail: info@hearingloss.org
Web Site: www.hearingloss.org
Key Personnel
Exec Dir: Anna Gilmore Hall
Deputy Exec Dir: Barbara Kelley
Dir, Events & Mktg: Nancy Macklin
E-mail: nmacklin@hearingloss.org
Founded: 1979
Distributor of educational programming.
Catalog(s) available

Hearst Entertainment & Syndication
Subsidiary of The Hearst Corp
300 W 57 St, New York, NY 10019-5238
Tel: 212-969-7553 *Toll Free Tel:* 800-526-5464
Fax: 646-280-1553
E-mail: hearstentertainment@hearst.com
Web Site: www.hearst.com
Key Personnel
Co-Pres: Neerja Khemlani; George Kliavkoff
SVP: Stacey Valenza *Fax:* 646-280-1553
E-mail: svalenza@hearst.com
Catalog(s) available
Membership(s): Entertainment Merchants Association; INTV; NAB; NATPE

Heart Breaker Entertainment LLC
10094 Lacy Rd, Hagerstown, IN 47346
Tel: 765-489-4048; 765-489-5558
Toll Free Tel: 800-843-3635 *Fax:* 765-489-4899
E-mail: info@videodj.com
Web Site: videodj.com
Key Personnel
Owner: Larry Black *E-mail:* larry@videodj.com
Founded: 1978
Service provider for production services such as stage, lighting, audio rentals & also a retailer for top brands in the industry.

Heart Music Inc
PO Box 160326, Austin, TX 78716-0326
Tel: 512-795-2375 *Fax:* 512-795-9573
E-mail: info@heartmusic.com
Web Site: www.heartmusic.com
Key Personnel
Owner: Tab Bartling *E-mail:* tab@heartmusic.com
Phonograph record label.
Catalog(s) available
Membership(s): BMI; The Recording Academy

Heavy Melody
307 Seventh Ave, Suite 1203, New York, NY 10001
Tel: 212-675-9585 *Fax:* 212-675-9565
E-mail: contact_hm@heavymelodymusic.com (studio inquiries)
Web Site: www.heavymelodymusic.com
Key Personnel
Creative Dir: Dave Fraser
Contact: Neil Goldberg
Founded: 2003
Composing original music for film, TV & video games.

HEC Reading Horizons
60 N Cutler Dr, Suite 101, North Salt Lake, UT 84054
Tel: 801-295-7054 *Toll Free Tel:* 800-333-0054
Fax: 801-295-7088
E-mail: info@readinghorizons.com
Web Site: www.readinghorizons.com
Key Personnel
Pres: Tyson Smith
Gen Mgr: Alisha Thomas *E-mail:* alisha@readinghorizons.com
Mktg Mgr: Jonathan Diaz
Sales Mgr: Quin Kofford
Founded: 1984
Phonics computer software designers.
Catalog(s) available

Hedquist Productions Inc
PO Box 1475, Fairfield, IA 52556-1475
Tel: 641-472-6708 *Toll Free Fax:* 855-510-5726
Web Site: www.hedquist.com
Key Personnel
Pres & Creative Dir: Jeffrey P Hedquist
E-mail: jeffrey@hedquist.com
Founded: 1985
Audio creation & production for all media. Casting, directing, talent payment, recording, editing & distribution.
Catalog(s) available
Shipping Address: 1827 223 St, Libertyville, IA 52567
Membership(s): RAMA

Heffernan Audio Visual
616 W Rhapsody, San Antonio, TX 78216
Tel: 210-732-4333 *Fax:* 210-732-5906
E-mail: sales@heffernanav.com
Web Site: www.heffernanav.com
Key Personnel
Pres: Paul Heffernan *E-mail:* paul@heffernanav.com
Presentation AV dealer & distributor.
Catalog(s) available

Heffernan Supply Co Inc, see Heffernan Audio Visual

Grant Heilman Photography Inc
506 W Lincoln Ave, Lititz, PA 17543
Mailing Address: PO Box 317, Lititz, PA 17543
Tel: 717-626-0296 *Toll Free Tel:* 800-622-2046
Fax: 717-626-0971
E-mail: info@heilmanphoto.com
Web Site: www.heilmanphoto.com
Key Personnel
Chmn of the Bd: Grant Heilman
Pres: Sonia S Wasco *E-mail:* sw@heilmanphoto.com
Founded: 1948
Stock photography.
Membership(s): AAAE; American Society of Picture Professionals; North American Nature Photography Association; Picture Agency Council of America

Heinemann
Division of Houghton Mifflin Harcourt
361 Hanover St, Portsmouth, NH 03801-3912
Mailing Address: PO Box 6926, Portsmouth, NH 03802-6926
Tel: 603-431-7894 *Toll Free Tel:* 800-225-5800
Fax: 603-431-2214 *Toll Free Fax:* 877-231-6980
E-mail: custserv@heinemann.com
Web Site: www.heinemann.com
Key Personnel
Pres: Lesa Scott
SVP & Publr: Vicky Boyd
VP, Mktg & Prod Devt: Charles McQuillen
Dir, Sales: William Rhodes
Sales Serv Mgr: Lori Lampert *Tel:* 603-431-7894 ext 1115 *E-mail:* lori.lampert@heinmann.com
Founded: 1978
Publisher of professional resources for teachers.
Catalog(s) available

Heliotrope Studios
44 Oak St, Newton Upper Falls, MA 02464
Tel: 617-964-8181 *Fax:* 617-964-8030
E-mail: heliotropestudios@earthlink.net
Web Site: www.heliotropestudios.com
Key Personnel
Pres: Boyd Estus *E-mail:* boydestus@sprintmail.com
Founded: 1984
Film & video production services; all formats: film, digital video, analogue video & HD.
Membership(s): International Alliance of Theatrical Stage Employees

Helix Camera & Video
310 S Racine Ave, Chicago, IL 60607
Tel: 312-421-6000 *Toll Free Tel:* 800-33-HELIX (334-3549 orders) *Fax:* 312-421-1586
E-mail: info@helixcamera.com
Web Site: www.helixcamera.com
Key Personnel
Pres: Paul Schutt
Founded: 1963
Catalog(s) available

Hellman Associates Inc
1225 W Fourth St, Waterloo, IA 50702-2903
Mailing Address: PO Box 627, Waterloo, IA 50704-0627
Tel: 319-234-7055 *Toll Free Tel:* 800-747-7055
Fax: 319-234-2089
E-mail: info@hellman.com
Web Site: www.hellman.com

Key Personnel
Founder & Chmn: Robert B Hellman
VP, Busn Devt: Ross Bruno
Founded: 1981
Demo reel(s) available

Hello World Communications
118 W 22 St, 2nd fl, New York, NY 10011
Tel: 212-243-8800 *Fax:* 212-691-6961
E-mail: excitable01@gmail.com
Web Site: www.hwc.tv
Key Personnel
Dir: Ron Yoshida *Tel:* 917-566-0000 (cell) *E-mail:* elronyo@msn.com
Founded: 1991
Video production, editing, duplication DVD authoring & audio/video/communications rental.
Membership(s): AICP; IFP

HeloAir Inc
5721 Gulfstream Rd, Richmond, VA 23250
Tel: 804-226-3400 *Toll Free Tel:* 888-FLY-HELO (359-4356) *Fax:* 804-226-3494
E-mail: info@heloair.com
Web Site: www.heloair.com
Key Personnel
Pres: Whit Baldwin *E-mail:* whit@heloair.com
Founded: 1992
Six Bell helicopter aerials, WESCAM, FLIR, Cineflex. Branch offices in Norfolk, VA & Washington, DC.

Henninger Media Services
2601-A Wilson Blvd, Arlington, VA 22201
Tel: 703-243-3444 *Toll Free Tel:* 888-243-3444 *Fax:* 703-243-5697
E-mail: hmsinfo@henninger.com; hmsquotes@henninger.com
Web Site: www.henninger.com
Key Personnel
CEO & Pres: Robert L Henninger
Founded: 1983
Catalog(s) available
Membership(s): IABC; MCA-I

Henry Engineering
PO Box 3796, Seal Beach, CA 90740
Tel: 562-493-3589
E-mail: info@henryeng.com
Web Site: www.henryeng.com
Key Personnel
CEO & Pres: Hank Landsberg
Founded: 1982
Manufacturer of professional audio & broadcast studio equipment.
Catalog(s) available
Membership(s): NAB

Henry's Camera
119 Church St, Toronto, ON M5C 2G5, Canada
Tel: 416-941-0579 *Toll Free Tel:* 800-461-7960 *Fax:* 416-868-4951 *Toll Free Fax:* 800-645-6431
E-mail: info@henrys.com
Web Site: www.henrys.com
Founded: 1909
Photographic & digital retailer.

Greg Hensley Productions
200 S "E" Ave, Unit 113, New Castle, CO 81647
Tel: 970-984-3158
E-mail: hensley@sopris.net
Web Site: www.greghensley.com
Key Personnel
Owner & Filmmaker: Greg Hensley
Founded: 1991
35mm film shot, Arriflex, video HD cameras. Stock footage library available as HD & SD. Produce wildlife nature films, plus all video formats & subjects. Multimedia as available, stills production services, illustration, art work, music & made to order wildlife sounds.
Catalog(s), weekly

Her Own Words LLC
PO Box 5264, Madison, WI 53705-0264
Tel: 608-271-7083 *Fax:* 608-271-0209
Web Site: herownwords.com; nontraditionalcareers.com
Key Personnel
Pres: Jocelyn Riley
Founded: 1986
Catalog(s) available

Herbach & Rademan Co Inc
353 Crider Ave, Moorestown, NJ 08057
Tel: 856-802-0422 *Toll Free Tel:* 800-848-8001 *Fax:* 856-802-0465
E-mail: sales@herbach.com
Web Site: www.herbach.com
Key Personnel
Pres: Frank Lobasco *Tel:* 856-802-0422 ext 311 *E-mail:* lobasco@voicenet.com
Founded: 1934
Catalog(s) available

Here-in Our Motives Evolve Inc, see Home Inc

Herff Jones | Nystrom
Division of Herff Jones Inc
4719 W 62 St, Indianapolis, IN 46268-2593
Toll Free Tel: 800-621-8086 *Fax:* 317-329-3305
Web Site: www.herffjonesnystrom.com
Catalog(s) available

Ken Herkes Productions & Entertainment (KHPE)
PO Box 313, Volcano, HI 96785
Tel: 808-640-0730
Web Site: www.khpe-hawaii.com
Key Personnel
Owner: Ken Herkes *E-mail:* ken@khpe-hawaii.com

Herman Pro AV
10110 USA Today Way, Miramar, FL 33025
Tel: 305-477-0063 *Toll Free Tel:* 888-736-6888 *Fax:* 305-392-3377
E-mail: sales@hermanproav.com; info@hermanproav.com
Web Site: www.hermanproav.com
Key Personnel
Owner & Pres: David Wolf
Owner & EVP: Jeffrey Wolf
Founded: 1963
Leading provider of professional AV products & labor resources to the commercial AV industry. Distribution facilities in FL, GA, NV & NJ.
Membership(s): InfoComm International®; NAB; NSCA

Hewlett-Packard Co
3000 Hanover St, Palo Alto, CA 94304-1185
Tel: 650-857-1501 *Toll Free Tel:* 800-752-0900 *Fax:* 650-857-5518
Web Site: www.hp.com
Key Personnel
CEO & Pres: Meg Whitman
Catalog(s) available

Hi-Tech Audio Systems Inc
3382 Enterprise Ave, Hayward, CA 94545
Tel: 650-742-9166 *Fax:* 650-648-0573
E-mail: consoles@hi-techaudio.com
Web Site: www.hi-techaudio.com
Key Personnel
Pres: Louis Adamo

Hi-Tech Enterprises Inc
4250 114 Terr, Clearwater, FL 33762
Tel: 727-573-9600 *Toll Free Tel:* 800-350-4862 *Fax:* 727-573-9606
E-mail: hitech@videoequipment.com
Web Site: www.videoequipment.com
Key Personnel
Opers Mgr: Angela Reischmann
Founded: 1984
New & used broadcast equipment & services.
Catalog(s) available
Membership(s): NAB

Hi-Tech Import Export Corp
1101 W McNab Rd, Pompano Beach, FL 33069
Tel: 954-946-0603 *Fax:* 954-946-0652
Key Personnel
Pres: Jay Shah *E-mail:* jayhitec@bellsouth.net
Catalog(s) available

Hi-Tech Lamps Inc
922 San Leandro Ave, Suite B, Mountain View, CA 94043
Tel: 650-961-9031 *Toll Free Tel:* 800-229-6509 *Fax:* 650-961-9033
E-mail: info@hi-techlamps.com
Web Site: www.hi-techlamps.com
Key Personnel
Pres: Wes Moloney
Distributor specializing in technical lamps, bulbs, sockets, photo-detectors & optical equipment for customers in manufacturing, science, education & government.
Catalog(s) available

HiFi House
Division of HiFi House Group
2304 Concord Pike, Wilmington, DE 19803
Tel: 302-655-4780 *Toll Free Tel:* 800-990-HIFI (990-4434)
Web Site: www.hifihousegroup.com; www.hifihouse.com
Key Personnel
Mktg Mgr: Brian David *Tel:* 302-655-4780 ext 103
Founded: 1955

High End Systems Inc
2105 Gracy Farms Lane, Austin, TX 78758
Tel: 512-836-2242 *Toll Free Tel:* 800-890-8989 *Fax:* 512-837-5290
E-mail: info@highend.com
Web Site: www.highend.com
Key Personnel
Founder & CTO: Richard Belliveau
Founder: Lowell Fowler
CEO & Sales: Bill Morris
VP, Sales & Servs: Jeff Pelzl
Dir, Opers: David Hansen
Cust Serv Mgr: Christy Willemin *Tel:* 512-836-2242 ext 1108 *E-mail:* christy_willemin@highend.com
Catalog(s) available
Membership(s): IALD; Professional Lighting & Sound Association

High Output Inc
495 Turnpike St, Canton, MA 02021
Tel: 781-364-1800 *Fax:* 781-364-1900
Web Site: www.highoutput.com
Key Personnel
System Sales Mgr: Mark Shore
Catalog(s) available
Branch Office(s)
4 Warren Ave, Suite 6, Westbrook, ME 04092, Regl Mgr: J P Gagnone *Tel:* 207-854-4737 *Fax:* 207-854-4746
301 Iron Horse Way, Bldg 62, Providence, RI 02908, Acct Mgr: Patrick Adam *Tel:* 401-521-0676 *Fax:* 401-521-0776

62 Bridge St, Suite A-5, Charleston, SC 29403, Regl Mgr: Martin Bluford *Tel:* 843-772-3600 *Toll Free Tel:* 888-744-1400 *Fax:* 843-722-3607
Membership(s): Production Equipment Rental Association; Professional Lighting & Sound Association; USITT

High Plains Films
PO Box 8796, Missoula, MT 59807
Tel: 406-543-6726
E-mail: yak@highplainsfilms.org
Web Site: www.highplainsfilms.org
Key Personnel
Dir & Ed: Drury Gunn Carr *E-mail:* dru@highplainsfilms.org; Doug Hawes-Davis *E-mail:* dhd@highplainsfilms.org
Founded: 1992

High-Tech Special Effects Inc
PO Box 193, Eads, TN 38028-0193
Tel: 901-850-5522 *Fax:* 901-850-8317
Web Site: www.hightechspecialeffects.com
Key Personnel
Owner & Pres: Randy Bast *E-mail:* randybast@bellsouth.net
VP: Melissa Wasaman
Off Mgr: Rick Inghram
Provide special effects, fireworks, pyrotechnics & lasers to the corporate & entertainment industry. Fog & gas systems.

High Water
Division of University of Memphis
University of Memphis, Rudi E Scheidt School of Music, Memphis, TN 38152
Tel: 901-678-3317 *Fax:* 901-678-3096
Key Personnel
Exec Prodr: Richard Ranta
Prodr: David Evans *E-mail:* dhevans@memphis.edu
Founded: 1980
Catalog(s) available

High Windy Audio/Banjoman Inc
PO Box 553, Fairview, NC 28730
Tel: 828-628-1728 *Toll Free Tel:* 800-637-8679 *Fax:* 828-628-4435
E-mail: office@davidholt.com
Web Site: www.davidholt.com
Key Personnel
Owner & Pres: David Holt
Booking: Betty Nichols *E-mail:* office@highwindy.com
Founded: 1986
Catalog(s), annual, free
Membership(s): ABA; Audio Publishers Association

HighBridge Audio
201 Sixth St, Suite 220, Minneapolis, MN 55414
Toll Free Tel: 800-755-8532 *Fax:* 612-436-4005
E-mail: highbridge@highbridgeaudio.com
Web Site: www.highbridgeaudio.com
Key Personnel
Pres: Sallie Neall *E-mail:* sallie.neall@highbridgeaudio.com
Catalog(s) available
Membership(s): Audio Publishers Association; Reading Recovery Council of North America

HighScope Press
Division of HighScope Educational Research Foundation
600 N River St, Ypsilanti, MI 48198-2898
Tel: 734-485-2000 *Toll Free Tel:* 800-407-7377 *Fax:* 734-485-0704 *Toll Free Fax:* 800-442-4329
E-mail: info@highscope.org; press@highscope.org
Web Site: www.highscope.org
Key Personnel
Pres: Larry Schweinhart *E-mail:* lschweinhart@highscope.org
Dir, Sales & Mktg: Carrie Hernandez *Tel:* 734-485-2000 ext 255 *E-mail:* chernandez@highscope.org
Founded: 1970
Books, videos, CDs, cassettes & software for the early childhood market.
Catalog(s) available

Hilferty & Associates Inc
14240 State Rte 550, Athens, OH 45701
Tel: 740-448-3821 *Fax:* 740-448-2331
E-mail: gha@hilferty.com
Web Site: www.hilferty.com
Key Personnel
Pres: Gerard Hilferty
Museum planning & exhibit design.
Membership(s): ASTEC; ICON

Jerry Hill Steadicam Products
19160 Arminta St, Reseda, CA 91335-1105
Tel: 818-772-9256 *Fax:* 818-772-9251
E-mail: jerry@steadimoves.com
Web Site: www.steadimoves.com
Key Personnel
Owner: Jerry Hill
Founded: 1980
Manufacturer of Steadicam accessories & camera related products.
Online catalog(s) available

Ron Hill Imagery
2994 S Richards St, Salt Lake City, UT 84115
Tel: 801-486-3300 *Fax:* 801-486-3310
Web Site: ronhillimagery.com
Television, film & video production equipment rentals, directing, crewing, on-site technical assistance, pre & post-production services, web/graphic design & support, photography.

Hillmann & Carr Inc
2233 Wisconsin Ave, Washington, DC 20007
Tel: 202-342-0001 *Fax:* 202-342-0117
E-mail: mail@hillmanncarr.com
Web Site: www.hillmanncarr.com
Key Personnel
Pres: Alfred J Hillmann
VP & Treas: Michal Brand Carr *E-mail:* michalcarr@hillmanncarr.com
Founded: 1975
Production of film, video, interactive, audio, videowall & multimedia & new media presentations. Full service production & project management. Creative track record with expertise in expositions, museums, visitor centers, special exhibits & multi-language international projects in traditional & non-traditional standard formats. Experience includes AV systems, design, integration & installation.
Membership(s): AASLH; American Alliance of Museums; ASIFA; ASTEC; CINE Board; InfoComm International®; Washington Film & Video Council; Women in Film & Video

Himalayan Institute Audio/Video
Division of Himalayan Institute
952 Bethany Tpke, Honesdale, PA 18431
Tel: 570-253-5551 *Toll Free Tel:* 800-822-4547 *Fax:* 570-253-9078
E-mail: info@himalayaninstitute.org
Web Site: www.himalayaninstitute.org
Key Personnel
Mktg Mgr: Todd Wolfenberg *E-mail:* twolfenberg@himalayaninstitute.org
Founded: 1971
Catalog(s) available

Historic Films
211 Third St, Greenport, NY 11944
Tel: 631-477-9700 *Toll Free Tel:* 800-249-1940 *Fax:* 631-477-9800
E-mail: info@historicfilms.com
Web Site: www.historicfilms.com
Key Personnel
Pres: Joseph Lauro
Sales Dir: Mark Heidemann *E-mail:* mark@historicfilms.com
Founded: 1991
Catalog(s) available
Demo reel(s) available
Membership(s): The Federation of Commercial Audiovisual Libraries Ltd

Hitachi Kokusai Electric America Ltd
Subsidiary of Hitachi Kokusai Electric Inc
150 Crossways Park Dr, Woodbury, NY 11797
Tel: 516-921-7200 *Fax:* 516-496-3718
E-mail: info@hitachikokusai.us
Web Site: hitachikokusai.us
Key Personnel
Pres: Yuichi Otsuka
Natl Sales Mgr: Sean Moran
Branch Office(s)
11258 Monarch St, Unit H, Garden Grove, CA 92841, Regl Sales Mgr: Dave Morris *Tel:* 714-895-6116 *Fax:* 714-895-6252
197 Great Oaks Trail, No 110, Wadsworth, OH 44281, Regl Sales Mgr: Bob Johnston *Tel:* 330-334-4115 *Fax:* 330-334-0574
One Select Ave, Unit 11, Scarborough, ON M1V 5J3, Canada, Natl Sales Mgr: Richard Kraemer *Tel:* 416-299-5900 ext 223 *Fax:* 416-299-0450
Membership(s): MCA-I; NAB; SMPTE

Hite Co
3101 Beale Ave, Altoona, PA 16601
Mailing Address: PO Box 1754, Altoona, PA 16603-1754
Tel: 814-944-6121 *Toll Free Tel:* 800-252-3598 *Fax:* 814-944-3052
Web Site: www.hiteco.com
Key Personnel
COO & SVP: Ronald Eberhart
CFO & VP: Scott Lawhead
Cont: Brenda Fix
Pres: R Lee Hite
VP, Mktg: Katherine Hite Brouse
Dir, Opers: Rick Gavin
Prod Specialist, Video & Electronic: Tim Merritts *E-mail:* timmer@hiteco.com
Tech Specialist, Electronics: Gordie Hein
Founded: 1949
Catalog(s) available

HM Electronics Inc (HME)
14110 Stowe Dr, Poway, CA 92064
Tel: 858-535-6000 *Toll Free Tel:* 800-848-4468 (domestic sales) *Fax:* 858-452-7207; 858-552-0139 (domestic sales)
E-mail: info@hme.com
Web Site: www.hme.com
Key Personnel
CEO: Chuck Miyahira
VP, Sales: Paul Foley
Dir, Mktg: Daren Haas
Founded: 1971
Brochure(s) available
Membership(s): American Electronics Association

HMC Electronics
33 Springdale Ave, Canton, MA 02021
Mailing Address: PO Box 526, Canton, MA 02021-0526
Tel: 781-821-1870 *Toll Free Tel:* 800-482-4440 *Fax:* 781-821-4133
E-mail: sales@hmcelectronics.com
Web Site: www.hmcelectronics.com
Key Personnel
VP & Gen Mgr: Howard Chase *Tel:* 781-821-1870 ext 141 *E-mail:* hchase@hmcelectronics.com

Founded: 1927
Catalog(s), annual

Hogpenny Studios
Ship Bottom Studio Ctr, 123 E 14 St, Ship Bottom, Long Beach Island, NJ 08008
Tel: 609-494-6640
E-mail: hogpenny@verizon.net; info@hogpenny.com
Web Site: mysite.verizon.net/vzep5xhw
Key Personnel
Exec Prodr: Jim De Francesco
Founded: 1975
Video & audio production & duplication.

The Hollaender Manufacturing Co
10285 Wayne Ave, Cincinnati, OH 45215
Mailing Address: PO Box 156399, Cincinnati, OH 45215-6399
Tel: 513-772-8800 *Toll Free Tel:* 800-772-8800 (orders) *Fax:* 513-772-8806
Web Site: www.hollaender.com
Key Personnel
CEO: Robert P Hollaender, II
COO & Pres: Marc E Cetrulo
VP, Sales & Mktg: Ron Crebo
Admin Asst: Robin Keller *E-mail:* robink@hollaender.com
Founded: 1946
Manufacturer of structural aluminum slip-on pipe fittings & handrail systems.
Catalog(s) available

Hollywood Center Studios
1040 N Las Palmas, Los Angeles, CA 90038
Tel: 323-860-0000
E-mail: info@hollywoodcenter.com
Web Site: www.hollywoodcenter.com
Key Personnel
CEO & Pres: Alan Singer *E-mail:* alan@hollywoodcenter.com
COO & EVP: Tim Mahoney *E-mail:* tmahoney@hollywoodcenter.com
VP, Prodn: Pat Mahoney *E-mail:* patm@hollywoodcenter.com
Studio Opers: J L Singer *E-mail:* jl@hollywoodcenter.com
Founded: 1919
Provides grip, lighting & production facilities for film, television & commercial shoots.

The Hollywood Edge
Subsidiary of Soundelux Entertainment Group
7080 Hollywood Blvd, Suite 519, Hollywood, CA 90028
Tel: 323-603-3252 *Toll Free Tel:* 800-292-3755 *Fax:* 323-603-3298
E-mail: info@hollywoodedge.com; sales@hollywoodedge.com
Web Site: www.hollywoodedge.com
Key Personnel
Mng Dir: John C Moran *Tel:* 323-603-3253 *E-mail:* jmoran@hollywoodedge.com
Catalog(s) available

Hollywood Lights Inc
5251 SE McLoughlin Blvd, Portland, OR 97202-4836
Tel: 503-232-9001; 503-232-8855 *Toll Free Tel:* 800-826-9881 *Fax:* 503-517-8686
E-mail: portland@hollywoodlights.biz
Web Site: www.hollywoodlights.biz
Key Personnel
Pres: Frank Locke *E-mail:* frank@hollywoodlights.biz
AV Servs Mgr: Craig Fazzone *E-mail:* craig@hollywoodlights.biz
Electrical Servs Mgr: Nai Saechow *E-mail:* nai@hollywoodlights.biz
Electrical Servs Mgr, Seattle Branch: Star Moser *E-mail:* star@hollywoodlights.biz
Lighting Prodn Mgr: Greg Eggen *E-mail:* greg@hollywoodlights.biz
Lighting Prodn Mgr, Seattle Branch: Kerrigan O'Neill *E-mail:* kerrigan@hollywoodlights.biz
Rentals Mgr: Edward Borromeo *E-mail:* ed@hollywoodlights.biz
Rentals Mgr, Seattle Branch: Scott Rode *E-mail:* scott@hollywoodlights.biz
Sales Mgr/System Sales & Design: Emily Stadulis *E-mail:* emily@hollywoodlights.biz
Sales Mgr, Seattle Branch: Robin Woodburn *E-mail:* robin@hollywoodlights.biz
Systems Sales & Design Mgr, Seattle Branch: Jim Graham *E-mail:* jimg@hollywoodlights.biz
Founded: 1948
Full service stage & event lighting design, production, rentals & sales.
Catalog(s), upon request, rental catalog
Branch Office(s)
660 S Dakota St, Seattle, WA 98108-5226, Contact: Craig Fazzone *Tel:* 503-232-9001 *Toll Free Tel:* 800-826-9881 *Fax:* 503-232-8505 *E-mail:* craig@hollywoodlights.biz
Membership(s): CIC-APEX; International Special Events Society; Meeting Professionals International; Professional Lighting & Sound Association; Trade Show Exhibitions Association; USITT

Hollywood Loft
6161 Santa Monica Blvd, Los Angeles, CA 90038
Tel: 323-957-9398
Web Site: hollywoodloft.com
Key Personnel
Contact: Michael Lohr
Studio rentals for television, film & still photography.

Hollywood Rentals Production Services
Division of The Raleigh Family of Companies
12800 Foothill Blvd, Sylmar, CA 91342
Tel: 818-407-7800 *Toll Free Tel:* 800-233-7830 *Fax:* 818-407-7868
E-mail: info@hollywoodrentals.com
Web Site: www.hollywoodrentals.com
Key Personnel
Pres: Kelly Koskella *E-mail:* kkoskella@hollywoodrentals.com
Catalog(s) available
Branch Office(s)
2616 Commerce Park Dr, Suite 100, Orlando, FL 32819 *Tel:* 407-354-2555 *Fax:* 407-354-2255
4950 S Royal Atlanta Dr, Tucker, GA 30084 *Tel:* 770-939-0475 *Fax:* 770-939-8803
16333 George O'Neal Rd, Baton Rouge, LA 70817 *Tel:* 225-752-8965 *Fax:* 225-752-8984
9100-C Perimeter Woods Dr, Charlotte, NC 28216 *Tel:* 704-597-1808 *Fax:* 704-597-1829
Membership(s): MCA-I; NAB; Professional Film & Video Equipment Association; SMPTE

Hollywood Sound Systems
1541 N Wilcox Ave, Hollywood, CA 90028
Tel: 323-466-2416 *Fax:* 323-460-2676
Web Site: www.hollywoodsound.com
Key Personnel
Pres: Les Harrison
Professional audio equipment rentals & sales. Full range of production services.

Hollywood Theatre Equipment Inc
1941 N 66 Ave, Hollywood, FL 33024
Tel: 954-920-2832 *Fax:* 954-986-6914
E-mail: hwdtheatre@aol.com
Key Personnel
Owner & Pres: Don Gallagher
Founded: 1979
Sale of motion picture theatre equipment.
Branch Office(s)
231 Steeple Chase Trail, Dallas, GA 30132, Contact: Don Gallagher, Jr
Membership(s): Theatre Equipment Association

Hollywood Vaults Inc
742 N Seward St, Hollywood, CA 90038-3504
Tel: 323-461-6464 *Toll Free Tel:* 800-569-5336 *Fax:* 323-461-6479
E-mail: vault@hollywoodvaults.com
Web Site: www.hollywoodvaults.com
Key Personnel
Founder & Owner: David Wexler *E-mail:* david@hollywoodvaults.com
VP: Julie Wexler *E-mail:* juliewexler@mac.com
Opers Mgr: Raymond Barber *E-mail:* raymond@hollywoodvaults.com
Founded: 1985
Preservation-quality storage of film, tape & digital media.
Catalog(s) available
Branch Office(s)
1780 Prospect Ave, Santa Barbara, CA 93103-1948 *Tel:* 805-569-5336 *Fax:* 805-569-1657
Membership(s): ASIS; Association of Moving Image Archivists; SMPTE; SPARS

Holo-Spectra Inc
7742B Gloria Ave, Van Nuys, CA 91406
Tel: 818-994-9577 *Fax:* 818-994-4709
E-mail: info@lasershs.com
Web Site: www.lasershs.com
Key Personnel
Pres: William Arkin *E-mail:* bill@lasershs.com
VP, Engg: Robert Arkin
Founded: 1974
Laser & display projection equipment; laser shows.
Catalog(s) available
Membership(s): ILDA

Home Inc
566 Columbus Ave, Boston, MA 02118
Tel: 617-427-4663 *Fax:* 617-427-4664
Web Site: homeinc.org
Key Personnel
Co-Founder & Dir: Alan Michel *E-mail:* alanmichel@homeinc.org
Catalog(s) available

Home Shopping Network (HSN)
PO Box 9090, Clearwater, FL 33758
Tel: 727-872-1000 *Toll Free Tel:* 800-933-2887 (cust serv, orders online); 800-284-3900 (cust serv, orders by phone); 800-557-0714 (cust serv, auto ship orders); 800-284-5757 (orders) *Fax:* 727-872-6559
Web Site: www.hsn.com
Key Personnel
CEO: Mindy Grossman
Shipping Address: 18495 US 19 N, Clearwater, FL 34624

Homespun Video
Division of Homespun Tapes Ltd
1610 Rte 212, Saugerties, NY 12477
Mailing Address: PO Box 340, Woodstock, NY 12498-0340
Tel: 845-246-2550 *Toll Free Tel:* 800-338-2737 (orders-US & CN) *Fax:* 845-246-5282
E-mail: info@homespuntapes.com
Web Site: www.homespuntapes.com
Key Personnel
Founder & Pres: Happy Traum
Founder & VP: Jane Traum
Founded: 1967
Distribute & produce music video, instructional.
Catalog(s), monthly, free
Online catalog(s) available

Hoodman Corp
20445 Gramercy Place, Suite 201, Torrence, CA 90501
Tel: 310-222-8608 *Toll Free Tel:* 800-818-3946 *Fax:* 310-222-8623
E-mail: sales@hoodmanusa.com
Web Site: www.hoodmanusa.com
Key Personnel
VP, Mktg: Lou Schmidt *E-mail:* lou@hoodmanusa.com
Founded: 1986
Manufacture flash memory cards, i.e. CF, SD, SxS adapters, monitor hoods.
Catalog(s) available
Membership(s): NAB

Hooper Camera & Imaging
Division of GKM Enterprises Inc
21902 Devonshire St, Chatsworth, CA 91311-2907
Tel: 818-709-0014 *Fax:* 818-709-0130
E-mail: sales@hoopercamera.com
Web Site: hoopercamera.com
Key Personnel
Opers Mgr: Dean Lawrence *Tel:* 818-292-5532 *E-mail:* mgr@hoopercamera.com
Founded: 1951
Digital photo supplies & photo finishing. Rent, repair & sell digital cameras.

Hope Productions
3116 Arrowhead Dr, Hollywood, CA 90068
Tel: 323-460-4995
Key Personnel
Pres: Mark Hope
Catalog(s) available

Hopkins Technology LLC
421 Hazel Lane, Hopkins, MN 55343-7116
Tel: 952-856-0467
E-mail: infodesk5@hoptechno.com
Web Site: www.hoptechno.com
Key Personnel
Pres: Carol Dunn *E-mail:* cjdunn@hoptechno.com
Founded: 1986
Catalog(s) available

Tom Hopkins International Inc
465 E Chilton Dr, Suite 4, Chandler, AZ 85225
Tel: 480-949-0786 *Toll Free Tel:* 800-528-0446 *Fax:* 480-949-1590
E-mail: info@tomhopkins.com
Web Site: www.tomhopkins.com
Key Personnel
CEO: Tom O Hopkins
Pres: Laura Oien
Founded: 1976
Seminars, CDs & DVDs on selling & selling skills.

Hoppmann Audio Visual
4170 Lafayette Center Dr, Suite 100, Chantilly, VA 20151-1255
Tel: 703-502-4080 *Toll Free Tel:* 800-220-3038 *Fax:* 703-222-0038
E-mail: info@hoppmann-av.com; sales@hoppmann-av.com
Web Site: www.hoppmann-av.net
Key Personnel
VP, Opers: Joe Whiteside
Founded: 1955
Information package(s) available
Membership(s): InfoComm International®

Horita Co Inc
PO Box 3993, Mission Viejo, CA 92690-3993
Tel: 949-489-0240 *Fax:* 949-489-0242
E-mail: sales@horita.com
Web Site: www.horita.com
Key Personnel
Pres: Gerald Hester
Sales Mgr & Mktg Dir: Christopher L Lovallo
Founded: 1986
Catalog(s) available
Membership(s): NAB; SMPTE

Horizon Film + Video Productions
808 E 34 St, Austin, TX 78705
Tel: 512-459-3100 *Toll Free Tel:* 800-540-2785 *Fax:* 512-459-3477
Web Site: www.horizonvideo.com
Key Personnel
Prodr & Dir: Nicole Simonion *E-mail:* ns@horizonvideo.com
Dir, Photog & Ed: Paul Murski *E-mail:* pm@horizonvideo.com
Ed, Motion Picture Graphics: Chris Westerman
Founded: 1982
Full service video production company which provides script to screen services as well as duplication. A well seasoned, creative team who's been around for over 25 years. Delivers high quality innovative videos.
Catalog(s) available
Membership(s): MCA-I

Horizon Films & Media LLC
PO Box 1087, Shelbyville, KY 40066
Tel: 502-647-9966 *Fax:* 502-647-9968
E-mail: horizonfilms@insightbb.com
Web Site: www.horizon-films.com
Key Personnel
Owner: Sandy Mortimer
Educational videos.
Catalog(s) available

Horizon Video Productions Inc
6114 Fayetteville St, Suite 106, Durham, NC 27713
Tel: 919-941-0901 *Toll Free Tel:* 800-768-3776 *Fax:* 919-941-1939
E-mail: info@horizonvp.com
Web Site: www.horizonvp.com
Key Personnel
Dir, Multimedia: Jason Cooper *E-mail:* jason@horizonvp.com
Proj Mgr: Steve Braaten *E-mail:* steve@horizonvp.com
Off Mgr: Brenda Dejewski *E-mail:* brenda@horizonvp.com
Founded: 1982
Full service agency providing turnkey video, film & multimedia production.

Horizon Worldwide
1765 Stebbins Dr, Houston, TX 77043
Tel: 713-647-7400 *Fax:* 713-647-6664
E-mail: info@horizonworldwide.com
Web Site: horizonworldwide.com
Key Personnel
Owner & Pres: Gary M Seline *Tel:* 713-647-7400 ext 101 *E-mail:* gary-seline@horizonworldwide.com
Founded: 1979

Susan Hormuth, Visual Resource Consultant
3356 Pennsylvania Ave SE, Washington, DC 20020
Tel: 202-584-3994
E-mail: susanhormuth@verizon.net
Founded: 1990
Still picture & footage research, specializing in historical images & public domain sources.

Hosa Technology Inc
6650 Caballero Blvd, Buena Park, CA 90620
Tel: 714-522-8878 *Fax:* 714-522-4540
E-mail: info@hosatech.com; sales@hosatech.com; orders@hosatech.com
Web Site: www.hosatech.com
Founded: 1984
Online catalog(s) available

Hot Buttered Content, see HB-Content

Hot House Professional Audio
275 Martin Ave, Highland, NY 12528
Tel: 845-691-6077
E-mail: info@hothousepro.com
Web Site: www.hothousepro.com
Key Personnel
Owner: Richard Rose

HOThead
56 W 45 St, 17th fl, New York, NY 10036
Tel: 212-575-5566 *Fax:* 212-575-1070
E-mail: info@hothead.tv
Web Site: www.hothead.tv
Key Personnel
Owner & Dir: Jim Stauffer
Audio postproduction facility.

Hotronic Inc
1875 S Winchester Blvd, Campbell, CA 95008
Tel: 408-378-3883 *Fax:* 408-378-3888
E-mail: sales@hotronics.com
Web Site: www.hotronics.com
Founded: 1982
Catalog(s) available

Hottrax Records
1957 Kilburn Dr, Atlanta, GA 30324-4852
Mailing Address: PO Box 13584, Atlanta, GA 30324-0584
Tel: 770-662-6661
E-mail: info@hottrax.com; hotwax@hottrax.com
Web Site: www.hottrax.com
Key Personnel
CEO: Aleck Janoulis *E-mail:* ajanoulis@hottrax.com
Founded: 1975
Catalog(s) available

House of Cinemagraphics
4802 Quail Ave N, Minneapolis, MN 55429
Tel: 612-339-7803; 763-458-8244 *Toll Free Tel:* 888-813-0413
E-mail: film@visi.com
Web Site: www.houseofcinemagraphics.com
Key Personnel
Owner: Bill Felker
Founded: 1975
Motion picture services & rentals.

House of Grace, see Sound*Light

House of Moves
Division of Vicon Industries Inc
5419 McConnell Ave, Los Angeles, CA 90066-7027
Tel: 310-306-6131
E-mail: info@moves.com
Web Site: www.moves.com
Key Personnel
CEO: Brian Rausch *E-mail:* rausch@moves.com
Sr Prodr: Heather McCann
Busn Devt Mgr: Jimmy Corvan *E-mail:* jimmy@moves.com
Founded: 1997
Motion capture studio.

The House Studios
325 Second Ave W, Seattle, WA 98119
Tel: 206-218-6810
E-mail: book@thehousestudios.com
Web Site: thehousestudios.com
Key Personnel
Founder & Owner: Emily Goodnight *E-mail:* emily@thehousestudios.com
Commercial photography & visual media studio. Equipment & prop rentals & on-site production team.

Houston Photo Imaging
5250 Gulfton, Suite 3-B, Houston, TX 77081
Tel: 713-666-0282 *Toll Free Tel:* 800-664-0282
Fax: 713-667-9625
E-mail: info@houstonphotoimaging.com
Web Site: www.houstonphotoimaging.com
Key Personnel
Pres: Steve Hogan
Founded: 1976
Catalog(s) available
Membership(s): AIE™; Photo Marketing Association

Hover-Views Unlimited
PO Box 1164, Syosset, NY 11791
Tel: 516-496-2946 *Fax:* 516-496-8029
Web Site: www.hoverviews.com
Key Personnel
Owner: Al Cerullo *Tel:* 516-315-8063
Aerial cinematography for feature films, television, commercials, documentaries & specials, print ads & music videos.

HP Marketing Corp
16 Chapin Rd, Unit 908, Pine Brook, NJ 07058
Mailing Address: PO Box 715, Pine Brook, NJ 07058-0715
Tel: 973-808-9010 *Toll Free Tel:* 800-735-4373
Fax: 973-808-9004
E-mail: info@hpmarketingcorp.com
Web Site: www.hpmarketingcorp.com
Key Personnel
Pres: Roger Bartzke
Sales Mgr: Robert Salomon *E-mail:* bob@hpmarketingcorp.com
Founded: 1971
AV opaque projectors.
Catalog(s) available
Membership(s): Photoimaging Manufacturers & Distributors Association

HSA Inc
1717 E Sixth St, Mishawaka, IN 46544
Tel: 574-255-6100 *Fax:* 574-255-8131
E-mail: hsainfo@hsarolltops.com
Web Site: www.hsarolltops.com
Key Personnel
CEO & Pres: Richard Johnson
Sales: Alan Oglesby
Manufacture a line of oak rolltop desks & 19 inch equipment racks for the AV industry.

Hubbard Supply Co
901 W Second St, Flint, MI 48503
Tel: 810-234-8681 *Toll Free Tel:* 800-875-4811
Fax: 810-234-6142
E-mail: information@hubbardsupply.com
Web Site: www.hubbardsupply.com
Key Personnel
CEO: Jeff Bigelow
COO: Tim Brooks
Mgr: Jane Knapp *E-mail:* jknapp@hubbardsupply.com
Founded: 1865
Closed channel TV for security purposes.
Catalog(s) available
Branch Office(s)
4560 W Dickman Rd, Battle Creek, MI 49037
Tel: 269-965-2211 *Toll Free Tel:* 800-632-9606
Fax: 269-965-3164
3900 E Washington Rd, Saginaw, MI 48601
Tel: 989-753-2453 *Toll Free Tel:* 800-875-4812
Fax: 989-753-3266
Membership(s): MCA-I

Hubbell Wiring Device-Kellems
Division of Hubbell Inc
40 Waterview Dr, Shelton, CT 06484
Tel: 475-882-4800 *Toll Free Tel:* 800-288-6000 (cust serv) *Fax:* 475-882-4849
Toll Free Fax: 800-255-1031 (cust serv)
E-mail: techserv@hubbell.com
Web Site: www.hubbell-wiring.com
Key Personnel
Dir, Intl Sales: Steve Consolo *E-mail:* sconsolo@hubbell.com
Catalog(s) available

Hughie's Event Production Services
1260 E 38 St, Cleveland, OH 44114
Tel: 216-361-4600 *Toll Free Tel:* 800-449-4115
Fax: 216-361-2570
Web Site: www.hughies.com
Key Personnel
Pres: David M Wheeler *E-mail:* dwheeler@hughies.com
VP, Opers: Bill Reeder *E-mail:* breeder@hughies.com
Dir, Mktg: Julie Felder *E-mail:* jfelder@hughies.com
Founded: 1953
Catalog(s) available
Branch Office(s)
7034 Worthington-Galena Rd, Worthington, OH 43805, Contact: Nathan Shireman
Tel: 614-436-5273 *Toll Free Tel:* 800-643-2959
Fax: 614-436-5290
333 33 St, Pittsburgh, PA 15201, Contact: Michael Steinmetz *Tel:* 412-621-1220
Fax: 412-621-7260
Membership(s): InfoComm International®

Charles A Hulcher Co Inc
909 "G" St, Hampton, VA 23661
Tel: 757-245-6190 *Fax:* 757-245-2882
E-mail: hulcher@hulchercamera.com
Web Site: www.hulchercamera.com
Key Personnel
Pres: Betty H Giles
VP: Richard Hill
Founded: 1952
Manufacturer of sequence & panoramic cameras.
Catalog(s) available

Human Circuit
9120 Gaither Rd, Gaithersburg, MD 20877
Tel: 240-864-4000 *Toll Free Tel:* 800-638-8071
Fax: 240-864-4000
E-mail: info@humancircuit.com
Web Site: www.humancircuit.com
Key Personnel
CEO & Pres: Bruce Kaufmann *Tel:* 240-864-4000 ext 4058
Founded: 1965
Membership(s): InfoComm International®; SMPTE

Human Relations Media
41 Kensico Dr, Mount Kisco, NY 10549
Tel: 914-666-9151 *Toll Free Tel:* 800-431-2050 (cust serv) *Fax:* 914-666-9506
E-mail: service@hrmvideo.com; orders@hrmvideo.com; help@hrmvideo.com; letters@hrmvideo.com
Web Site: www.hrmvideo.com
Key Personnel
CEO & Pres: Anson W Schloat
Founded: 1976
Videos on substance abuse prevention, health education, career education, math & science.
Catalog(s) available

Humanities Extension Publications
Unit of North Carolina State University
North Carolina State Univ, Campus Box 8101, Raleigh, NC 27695
Tel: 919-515-2468 *Fax:* 919-515-9419
Web Site: www.ncsu.edu/chass/extension
Key Personnel
Prog Coord: Eileen Hannan Ferrell *Tel:* 919-513-0596 *E-mail:* eileen_ferrell@ncsu.edu
Produce & distribute video programs for grades 4-7.

David Hunter, see D A Sound

Hunter Electronics LLC
7553 Lake Harbor Terr, Lake Worth, FL 33467
Tel: 561-568-2063 *Fax:* 561-491-8030
E-mail: hunterelectronics@comcast.net; hunterelectronics201@gmail.com
Key Personnel
VP: Robert Manzo
Catalog(s) available

Hunt's Photo, Video & Digital
100 Main St, Melrose, MA 02176-6104
Tel: 781-662-8822 (retail sales)
Toll Free Tel: 800-924-8682 (retail sales); 800-221-1830 (ext 2340, corp sales) *Fax:* 781-662-6524
E-mail: ecommerce@wbhunt.com (retail online sales)
Web Site: www.huntsphotoandvideo.com
Key Personnel
Pres: Scott Farber
Corp Sales Mgr: Marty Weiskoff *Tel:* 781-462-2339 *E-mail:* mweiskoff@wbhunt.com
Catalog(s) available

Frank D Hurst Corp dba Pechman Imaging
106 E Second St, Kaukauna, WI 54130
Tel: 920-766-6160 *Toll Free Tel:* 800-777-0221
Fax: 920-766-6161
E-mail: customerservice@pechmanimaging.com
Web Site: www.pechmanimaging.com
Key Personnel
Pres: Frank Hurst
VP: Andrea Hurst
Providers of innovative digital & optical printing.
Catalog(s) available
Membership(s): AIE™; Photo Marketing Association

Editions Hurtubise HMH Ltee
1815 Avenue De Lorimier, Montreal, QC H2K 3W6, Canada
Tel: 514-523-1523 *Toll Free Tel:* 800-361-1664
Fax: 514-523-9969
Web Site: www.editionshurtubise.com
Key Personnel
Pres: Herve Foulon
VP, Opers: Arnaud Foulon *E-mail:* arnaud.foulon@editionshurtubise.com
Admin Dir: Johanne Livernoche *E-mail:* johanne.livernoche@distributionhmh.com
Prodn Mgr: Dominique Thuillot
E-mail: dominique.thuillot@editionshurtubise.com
Founded: 1960
Catalog(s) available
Membership(s): Association Nationale des Editeurs de Livres; UELF

Hybrid Cases
1121-20 Lincoln Ave, Holbrook, NY 11741
Tel: 631-563-1181 *Toll Free Tel:* 800-645-1707 (orders) *Fax:* 631-563-1390
E-mail: sales@hybridcases.com
Web Site: www.hybridcases.com
Key Personnel
Mktg & Sales Mgr: Bruce Papa
E-mail: brucepapa77@optonline.net
Catalog(s) available
Membership(s): NAMM, the National Association of Music Merchants

Hybrid Studios
3021 S Shannon St, Santa Ana, CA 92704
Tel: 714-850-1499
E-mail: info@hybridstudiosca.com; rentals@hybridstudiosca.com
Web Site: hybridstudiosca.com

Key Personnel
Founder & Co-Owner: Patrick Akhamlich *E-mail:* patrick@hybridstudiosca.com; Bill Klein *E-mail:* billy@hybridstudiosca.com
Studio Opers Supv: Mike Miller *E-mail:* mike@hybridstudiosca.com
Founded: 2012
Multimedia production facility with digital & analog recording studio, soundstage, gear & staff.

Hydrogen Whiskey Studios
Subsidiary of Dragonlight Productions Inc
1640 Fifth St, Suite 226, Santa Monica, CA 90401
Tel: 310-394-8130 *Fax:* 310-394-8129
Web Site: www.hydrogenwhiskey.com
Key Personnel
Chief Creative Offr: Ron Franco *E-mail:* ron@hwhiskey.com
Founded: 1992
Full service 3D animation & audio production.

Hyperspective Studios Inc
2800 Woodlawn Dr, Suite 253, Honolulu, HI 96822
Tel: 808-353-3618
E-mail: info@hyperspective.com
Web Site: www.hyperspective.com
Key Personnel
CEO & Pres: Todd J Robertson *Tel:* 808-741-1292 *E-mail:* todd@hyperspective.com
COO: Charisse Lindsey *Tel:* 808-386-7172
Founded: 1996
Visual production services, multimedia, video FX, graphics illustration. 3D & 2D animation, video production & special effects.

I M P A C T Publishing Inc
3409 47 Ave E, Bradenton, FL 34203
Mailing Address: PO Box 10058, Bradenton, FL 34282-0058
Tel: 941-739-2611 *Toll Free Tel:* 800-221-6121; 800-426-3963 *Fax:* 941-756-0315
E-mail: potentialsunlimitedcs@gmail.com
Web Site: www.potentialsunlimited.com
Key Personnel
Pres: Stephanie Banfill *E-mail:* skonicov@potentialsunlimited.com
Exclusive licensee of Potentials Unlimited subliminal persuasion & self-hypnosis audio & video products.
Catalog(s), free

I-25 Studios
9201 Pan American Fwy NE, Albuquerque, NM 87113
Tel: 505-822-7115 *Fax:* 505-314-7094
E-mail: info@i-25studios.com
Web Site: i-25studios.com
Key Personnel
CEO: Rick Clemente *Tel:* 505-688-4148 (cell) *E-mail:* rick@i-25studios.com
Mng Dir: Drew Dolan
Full service motion picture production facility.

IAC Acoustics
1160 Commerce Ave, Bronx, NY 10462
Tel: 718-931-8000 *Fax:* 718-863-1138
E-mail: newyork@iac-acoustics.com
Web Site: www.iac-acoustics.com/us
Key Personnel
VP, Americas: Paul Conover
Dir of Sales, Americas: Richard Alfano
Founded: 1949
Manufacture noise control equipment.
Catalog(s) available

IAI Video
Division of Improvising Artists International
33 Lancaster St, Cherry Valley, NY 13320
Mailing Address: PO Box 496, Cherry Valley, NY 13320-0496
Tel: 646-696-5645
E-mail: iai@improvart.com
Web Site: www.improvart.com
Key Personnel
Prodr & Dir: Carol Goss
Mktg: A I Goss-Bley
Founded: 1974
Produce & distribute jazz & video art, long play music video, documentary & educational programs for the home video, educational & cable markets & Internet.
Catalog(s) available

IAMP Professional Audio
218 Reindollar, Marina, CA 93933
Tel: 831-884-9558 *Fax:* 831-643-2131
E-mail: iamp-pro-audio@comcast.net
Web Site: www.iampproaudio.com
Key Personnel
Owner: Anthony Nocita *Tel:* 831-224-2201 (cell)

IAPC Inc, see Imageworks

IBM SPSS
200 W Madison Ave, 23rd fl, Chicago, IL 60606
Toll Free Tel: 800-543-2185 *Toll Free Fax:* 800-841-0064
E-mail: salesbox@us.ibm.com
Web Site: www-01.ibm.com/software/analytics/spss
Global provider of predictive analytics software & solutions.

Icarus Film Inc
32 Court St, 21st fl, Brooklyn, NY 11201
Tel: 718-488-8900 *Toll Free Tel:* 800-876-1710 *Fax:* 718-488-8642
E-mail: mail@icarusfilms.com
Web Site: www.icarusfilms.com
Key Personnel
Pres: Jonathan Miller
Founded: 1978
Catalog(s) available
Membership(s): Consortium of College & University Media Centers; National Alliance for Media Arts & Culture

ICL Imaging Inc
51 Mellen St, Framingham, MA 01702
Tel: 508-872-3280 *Toll Free Tel:* 800-660-3280 *Fax:* 508-872-7364
E-mail: csr@icl-imaging.com
Web Site: www.icl-imaging.com
Key Personnel
Pres: Larry Capodilupo, III
Dir, Sales & Mktg: Bill Smith
Prodn Mgr: Jim Lyon
Founded: 1956

Icom Multimedia
294 E Long St, Columbus, OH 43215-1829
Tel: 614-224-4400 *Fax:* 614-457-8050
Web Site: www.icommultimedia.com
Key Personnel
Pres: Phil Yoder *E-mail:* phil@icom-multimedia.com
Web casting meeting products.
Catalog(s) available

Icontent
149 Fifth Ave, New York, NY 10010
Tel: 212-462-0022
E-mail: info@icontent.tv; tania@icontent.tv
Web Site: www.icontent.tv
Key Personnel
Dir: Douglas Sloan
Catalog(s) available

iCorpTv
PO Box 461172, Los Angeles, CA 90046
Tel: 818-492-4623
E-mail: contact@icorptv.com
Web Site: www.icorptv.com
Key Personnel
Dir & Prodr: Gregory McDonald
Founded: 1996
Scriptwriting, video & film production & post-production, DVD/CD & flash authoring.

iCrossing Inc
300 W 57 St, New York, NY 10019
Tel: 212-649-3900 *Fax:* 646-280-1091
Web Site: www.icrossing.com
Key Personnel
Global Pres: Bryan Powley
CD-ROM manufacturer.
Branch Office(s)
15169 N Scottsdale Rd, Suite C-400, Scottsdale, AZ 85254 *Tel:* 480-505-5800 *Fax:* 480-505-5801
550 Kearny St, 4th fl, San Francisco, CA 94108 *Tel:* 415-869-1120 *Fax:* 415-869-1121
3000 Ocean Park Blvd, 2nd fl, Santa Monica, CA 90405 *Tel:* 310-664-2930 *Fax:* 310-664-2931
333 Wacker Dr, Suite 950, Chicago, IL 60606 *Tel:* 312-277-4700 *Fax:* 312-277-4740
2828 Routh St, Suite 777, Dallas, TX 75201 *Tel:* 214-210-6800 *Fax:* 214-210-6783
1902 Campus Commons, Suite 600, Reston, VA 20191 *Tel:* 703-262-3200 *Fax:* 703-262-3201
Foreign Office(s): Av Maipu 1210, Piso 8, Retiro, Buenos Aires, Argentina *Tel:* (011) 5275 6311
Av Presidente Kennedy 5118, Piso 4, Vitacura, 7630423 Santiago, Chile *Tel:* (02) 432 3220
3GNet GmbH, Tal 11, Rear Bldg, 80331 Munich, Germany, CEO: Patrick Bertermann *Tel:* (089) 24 20 53-0 *Fax:* (089) 24 20 53-151 *Web Site:* icrossing.de
Av Patriotismo no 229, Piso 8, San Pedros de los Pinos, 03800 Mexico, DF, Mexico *Tel:* (0155) 28 81 0239
516 Ave Dos de Mayo, Off 603, Miraflores, Lima, Peru *Tel:* (01) 628 0550
275 Gongdeok-dong, Mapo-gu, Seoul 121-721, South Korea *Tel:* (02) 3782 6813
Calle Lezama 16, 28034 Madrid, Spain, CEO: Gonzaga Valdes *Tel:* 917288751
13 Black Lion St, Brighton, East Sussex BN1 1ND, United Kingdom *Tel:* (01273) 827700 *Fax:* (01273) 827701 *Web Site:* icrossing.co.uk
22 Chapter St, 2nd fl, London SW1P 4NP, United Kingdom *Tel:* (020) 7821 2300 *Fax:* (020) 8433 7005 *Web Site:* icrossing.co.uk
Stamford House, Northenden Rd, Sale, Cheshire M33 2DH, United Kingdom *Tel:* (016) 1451 0822 *Web Site:* icrossing.co.uk

Idaho Camera Inc
1310 N Orchard Ave, Boise, ID 83706
Tel: 208-377-3686 (corp) *Toll Free Tel:* 877-323-8734
E-mail: info@idahocamera.com; orchard@idahocamera.com; sales@idahocamera.com
Web Site: www.idahocamera.com
Key Personnel
Pres: Patrick F Nagel
Compt: Dennis Nagel
Founded: 1946
Catalog(s) available
Branch Office(s)
Vista Village Shopping Center, 1036 Vista Ave, Boise, ID 83705 *Tel:* 208-343-8075 *E-mail:* vista@idahocamera.com
Boise Towne Square Mall, 350 N Milwaukee Ave, Boise, ID 83704 *Tel:* 208-375-5220 *E-mail:* townesquare@idahocamera.com

IDC, see International Datacasting

Ideal Large Format Imaging Services
15737 Crabbs Branch Way, Rockville, MD 20855

Tel: 301-468-0123 *Toll Free Tel:* 800-76IDEAL (764-3325) *Fax:* 301-230-0813
E-mail: sales@ideal.com
Web Site: www.ideal.com
Key Personnel
Pres: Jay Magenheim *Tel:* 301-468-0123 ext 1201
E-mail: jmagenheim@ideal.com
Cont: Ellen Berne
Provide large format color printing, ideal plan rooms & large/small document scanning services.

Ideascape Inc
PO Box 1966, Lake Oswego, OR 97035
Tel: 503-246-2439
E-mail: info@ideascapeinc.com
Web Site: www.ideascapeinc.com
Key Personnel
VP: Douglas Freeman *E-mail:* dfreeman@ideascapeinc.com
Prodr & Prodn Asst: MacKenzie Freeman
E-mail: mfreeman@ideascapeinc.com
Founded: 1997
Media scripting & production services.
Membership(s): Oregon Media Production Association

IDenticard Systems Inc
Division of Brady Corp
25 Race Ave, 1st fl, Lancaster, PA 17603
Tel: 717-569-5797 *Toll Free Tel:* 800-233-0298
Fax: 717-427-1654
E-mail: identicard.info@identicard.com
Web Site: www.identicard.com
Key Personnel
Gen Mgr: Jeff Bill
Founded: 1970
Digital imaging systems, Security 10, Access Control Systems, Smart Card, Biometrics.
Catalog(s) available

Idle Minds Productions Inc
3405 Pepperhill Rd, Lexington, KY 40502
Tel: 859-268-8500 *Fax:* 859-268-8500
E-mail: idleminds@twc.com
Key Personnel
Pres & Owner: Timothy Asher
Membership(s): Kentucky Film & Video Professionals; MCA-I

IDX System Technology Inc
19001 Harborgate Way, Suite 105, Torrance, CA 90501
Tel: 310-328-2850 *Fax:* 310-328-8202
E-mail: idx.usa@idx.tv
Web Site: www.idx.tv
Key Personnel
Western Regl Sales Mgr: Cathy Fercano
E-mail: cathy@idx.tv
Eastern Regl Sales Mgr: Don Mainardi
E-mail: don@idx.tv
Founded: 1989
Manufacturer & distributor of batteries, chargers & power supplies.
Foreign Office(s): IDX Co Ltd (Japan), 6-28-11 Shukugawara, Tama-ku Kawasaki-shi, Kanagawa-ken 214-0021, Japan *Tel:* (044) 850 8801 *Fax:* (044) 850 8838 *E-mail:* idx.japan@idx.tv
IDX Technology Europe (UK), Langley Park, Unit 9, Waterside Dr, Langley, Berks SL3 6AD, United Kingdom *Tel:* (01753) 547 692 *Fax:* (01753) 546 660 *E-mail:* idx.europe@idx.tv
Membership(s): NAB

IEEE Computer Society Press
10662 Los Vaqueros Circle, Los Alamitos, CA 90720-1314
Tel: 714-821-8380 *Toll Free Tel:* 800-272-6657 (cust serv) *Fax:* 714-821-4010
E-mail: help@computer.org
Web Site: www.computer.org
Key Personnel
Dir, Sales & Mktg: Chris Jensen
E-mail: cjensen@computer.org
Catalog(s) available

IFM World Releasing Inc
1328 E Palmer Ave, Glendale, CA 91205
Tel: 818-243-4976 *Fax:* 818-550-9728
E-mail: contact@ifmfilm.com
Web Site: www.ifmfilm.com
Key Personnel
Pres: Antony I Ginnane
EVP: Anthony J Lyons
VP, Intl: David Makhlout
Founded: 1995
International film & TV distribution. Executive production, theatrical, video, TV, feature film, TV movies & factual.
Foreign Office(s): 25 Second St, Unit 2, Clayton, Victoria 3169, Australia *Tel:* (03) 9515 9249 *Fax:* (03) 9515 9248
Membership(s): Independent Film & Television Alliance®

Ikegami Electronics (USA) Inc
37 Brook Ave, Maywood, NJ 07607
Tel: 201-368-9171 *Fax:* 201-569-1626
E-mail: sales@ikegami.com; service@ikegami.com
Web Site: www.ikegami.com
Key Personnel
CEO & Pres (US): Akira Harada
Pres (Japan): Masaki Matsubara
VP & Dir, Engg: Alan Keil
Catalog(s) available
Branch Office(s)
2633 Manhattan Beach Blvd, Redondo Beach, CA 90278, Contact: Tom Carr *Tel:* 310-297-1900 *Fax:* 310-536-9550 *E-mail:* tcarr@ikegami.com
710 E Hillsboro Blvd, Suite 100, Deerfield Beach, FL 33441, Contact: Bill Munoz *Tel:* 954-571-7177 *Fax:* 954-571-7760 *E-mail:* gmunoz@ikegami.com
16206 Hunter Ct, Orland Hills, IL 60487, Contact: James Daniel *Tel:* 708-460-1451 *E-mail:* jdaniels@ikegami.com
773 Bearden, Waxahachie, TX 75167, Contact: John Webb *Tel:* 972-869-2363 *Fax:* 972-556-1057 *E-mail:* jwebb@ikegami.com
Membership(s): NAB; SMPTE

ILFORD America Inc
Division of ILFORD Imaging Switzerland GmbH
30 Tower Lane, Avon, CT 06001
Tel: 860-321-7602 *Toll Free Tel:* 888-453-6731 *Fax:* 860-321-7519
E-mail: usinfo@ilford.com
Web Site: www.ilford.ch/en/contact/contactusa.asp
Catalog(s) available
Membership(s): InfoComm International®

Ilio Enterprises LLC
PO Box 6211, Malibu, CA 90265
Tel: 818-707-7222; 818-707-3655
Toll Free Tel: 800-747-4546 *Fax:* 818-707-8552
E-mail: security@ilio.com
Web Site: www.ilio.com
Key Personnel
Dir, Retail Mktg & Sales: Aaron Neimann
Founded: 1994
Sample sound effects libraries & virtual instruments.
Catalog(s) available

Illuma Studios
16601 N 90 St, Scottsdale, AZ 85260
Tel: 480-222-4396
E-mail: info@illumastudios.com
Web Site: www.illumastudios.com
Key Personnel
Partner: Matthew Gould; Louis Silberman
Studio Mgr: Amanda Smith
Prodr: Gay Gilbert
Founded: 1998
Provides rental of studio & lighting. Offers production & post-production services.

Illuminart Lighting
7320 Griffin Rd, Suite 111, Davie, FL 33314
Tel: 954-327-0564 *Fax:* 954-327-0367
E-mail: lightisart@aol.com
Web Site: www.illuminart-inc.com
Key Personnel
Owner: Marco Rose *Tel:* 954-529-3720 (cell)
E-mail: marcolight@aol.com
Catalog(s) available

Illuminate Post/Digital Finishing
3575 Cahuenga Blvd W, 4th fl, Hollywood, CA 90068
Tel: 323-969-8822 *Fax:* 323-969-8860
Web Site: illuminatehollywood.com
Key Personnel
CEO: Jim Hardy
EVP, Sales: Steve Tannen
Post-production facility offering digital finishing for independent films & television.

Illuminate Studios
10900 Ventura Blvd, Studio City, CA 90068
Tel: 818-769-4500 *Fax:* 818-769-7150
Web Site: illuminatehollywood.com
Key Personnel
CEO: Jim Hardy
EVP & Gen Mgr: Sandy Crawford
EVP, Sales: Steve Tannen
Opers Mgr: Manuel Garcia
Fully equipped stage rentals with satellite broadcasting capabilities. Multiple HD camera shoots for live & taped productions. RED cameras available for rent.

Illusion Television Productions, see ITV Productions

Image Associates Inc
5311 S Miami Blvd, Suite G, Durham, NC 27703
Tel: 919-876-6400 *Fax:* 919-876-6400
E-mail: info@imageassociates.com
Web Site: www.imageassociates.com
Key Personnel
CEO & Pres: Carla Davenport
Multimedia Prodr: John Maruca
Founded: 1964
Catalog(s) available
Membership(s): Photo Marketing Association; Special Interest Group on Computer Graphics

Image Audiovisuals
2130 S Dahlia St, Denver, CO 80222
Tel: 303-758-1818 *Toll Free Tel:* 800-818-1857 *Fax:* 303-758-5722
E-mail: commercialsales@imageav.com
Web Site: www.imageav.com
Key Personnel
CEO: Diana Mueller *E-mail:* diana@imageav.com
Pres: David Mueller *E-mail:* dmueller@imageav.com
Dir, Opers: David Kreutz
Dir, Sales: Scott Cornelius
Designs, engineers & installs AV systems for corporate, healthcare, government & educational clients.

Image Craft LLC
3401 E Broadway Rd, Phoenix, AZ 85040
Tel: 602-276-2082 *Toll Free Tel:* 800-274-2422 *Fax:* 602-232-0719
E-mail: designgroup@imcraft.com
Web Site: www.imcraft.com

Key Personnel
Owner: Doug Olson
Founded: 1979
Digital imaging, large format printing & photographic imaging.
Catalog(s) available
Branch Office(s)
12503 E Euclid Dr, Suite 10, Centennial, CO 80111 *Tel:* 303-274-1011 *Fax:* 303-274-7605
Membership(s): Arizona Industrial Photographers; ASMP; Photo Marketing Association

Image Entertainment
Subsidiary of RLJ Entertainment Inc
20525 Nordhoff St, Suite 200, Chatsworth, CA 91311
Tel: 818-407-9100 *Toll Free Tel:* 800-473-3475
E-mail: inquiries@rljentertainment.com
Web Site: www.image-entertainment.com
Independent films, music, documentaries, stand-up comedy, stage plays, classic TV/movies & African American movies in theaters, on TV, on DVD, digital streaming & digital downloads.
Catalog(s) available

Image G
28490 Westinghouse Place, Unit 160, Valencia, CA 91355
Tel: 818-761-6644 *Fax:* 661-775-8900
E-mail: production@imageg.com
Web Site: sites.google.com/site/imagegwebsite
Key Personnel
Dir: Tom Barron
Founded: 1984
Membership(s): AICP

The Image Generators
18156 Darnell Dr, Olney, MD 20832
Tel: 301-924-5700 *Fax:* 240-363-0062
E-mail: info@imagegenerators.com
Web Site: www.imagegenerators.com
Key Personnel
CEO & Pres: Michael J Weiner *E-mail:* mike@imagegenerators.com
Founded: 1985
Voice-over services with ISDN.
Membership(s): MCA-I; SAG-AFTRA; Women in Film & Video

Image Innovations Inc
Division of Slidescribe Products LLC
8607 Wurzbach Rd, San Antonio, TX 78240
Tel: 210-696-5900
Web Site: www.slidescribe.com
Key Personnel
Gen Mgr: Lamont Stewart
Catalog(s), quarterly, free

Image Integration
2619 Benvenue Ave, No A, Berkeley, CA 94704
Tel: 510-504-2605
Key Personnel
Pres: Vincent Casalaina *Tel:* 510-504-2605 (cell) *E-mail:* vincesail@aol.com
Founded: 1973
Documentary production of sailing events.
Membership(s): DGA; Television Academy

Image Labs Corp
20 Arden Dr, Garrison, NY 10524
Mailing Address: PO Box 749, Peekskill, NY 10524
Tel: 845-737-4420 *Fax:* 845-737-0426
E-mail: imagelabs@optonline.net
Key Personnel
Pres: Christopher Rimm
VP: Robert Rimm
Manufacture audio & video equipment.
Catalog(s) available
Shipping Address: 37 Arden Dr, Garrison, NY 10524

Image Logic Corp
6807 Brennon Lane, Chevy Chase, MD 20815-3255
Tel: 202-223-2888
E-mail: info@imagelogic.com
Web Site: www.imagelogic.com
Key Personnel
Mktg Dir: Rick Hofmann
Manufacture & distribute captioning systems.
Membership(s): NAB

Image Makers of Pittsford/Image Maker Productions
6 Wood Gate, Pittsford, NY 14534-1826
Tel: 585-385-4567 *Fax:* 585-586-6568
Key Personnel
Pres: Richard H Roberts
Videos on the subject of optics.
Catalog(s) available

Image Management Systems Inc
239 W 15 St, New York, NY 10011
Tel: 212-741-8765 *Fax:* 212-243-2344
E-mail: ims@imagemgt.com
Web Site: www.imagemgt.com
Key Personnel
Pres: Jack Berry
Founded: 1980
System solutions for information capture, storage, access & communication. Satellite phone sales & rentals. Satellite video phone systems. DVD equipment & jukes.
Membership(s): New York DVD Association; SMPTE

Image Marketing Corp
1636 N 24 St, Mesa, AZ 85213
Tel: 480-969-7032 *Fax:* 480-969-0939
E-mail: info@image4u.com
Web Site: www.image4u.com
Key Personnel
Owner: Rik W Beimfohr
Founded: 1979
Distribute light boxes & magnifiers.
Catalog(s), on request
Membership(s): DIMA; Photo Marketing Association

Image Media Farm
1090 E Georgia St, Vancouver, BC V6A 2A7, Canada
Tel: 604-874-7513 *Toll Free Tel:* 800-352-1454 (prodn rentals); 800-567-0037 (equip rentals) *Fax:* 604-874-7516
E-mail: info@imagemediafarm.com
Web Site: www.imagemediafarm.com
Key Personnel
CEO, Pres & Exec Prodr: Roger Williams
Television production & rental facility for broadcasting & HD equipment.
Branch Office(s)
40 Torlake Cresent, Toronto, ON M8Z 1B3, Canada *Tel:* 416-405-9977 *Fax:* 416-405-9969
Membership(s): International Alliance of Theatrical Stage Employees

Image Technical Services
720 Crown Point Cross Rd, Winter Garden, FL 34787
Tel: 407-905-2100 *Toll Free Tel:* 800-393-4300 *Fax:* 407-905-2150
E-mail: moreinfo@goimage.com
Web Site: www.goimage.com
Key Personnel
Pres: Randy Noble
Founded: 1979
Full service AV & creative communications provider.
Catalog(s) available
Shipping Address: 611 Susan B Britt Ct, Winter Garden, FL 34787
Membership(s): InfoComm International®; International Association of Speakers Bureaus; OCCVB

Image Technologies Corp
523 Hanley Industrial Ct, St Louis, MO 63144
Tel: 314-646-1800 *Toll Free Tel:* 800-962-2344 *Fax:* 314-646-1818
Web Site: www.imagetechnologies.com
Key Personnel
Pres: Tom Kuntz
VP: Dennis Snow *Tel:* 816-221-7663 *E-mail:* dsnow@imagetechnologies.com
Brochure(s) available
Branch Office(s)
2540 W Pennway St, Kansas City, MO 64108 *Tel:* 816-221-7663 *Fax:* 816-221-5512
Membership(s): HSMAI; MPI

Image Up
176 Main St, Metuchen, NJ 08840
Tel: 732-549-1845
Web Site: www.imageup.com
Key Personnel
Pres: David Glasofer *E-mail:* david@imageup.com
Founded: 1978

Image Video
Division of 1077541 Ontario Ltd
1620 Midland Ave, Scarborough, ON M1P 3C2, Canada
Tel: 416-750-8872 *Fax:* 416-750-8015
E-mail: sales@imagevideo.com
Web Site: www.imagevideo.com
Key Personnel
VP: David Russell
Founded: 1974
Manufacture & distribute tally systems, alarm systems & multi-image display systems.
Catalog(s) available
Membership(s): NAB; SMPTE

Image Video Services & Productions
1210 Southview Dr, Sudbury, ON P3E 2L6, Canada
Tel: 705-698-1212 *Fax:* 705-805-0110
E-mail: info@imagevideo.ca
Web Site: www.imagevideo.ca
Key Personnel
Media Prodr: Daniel Thomson
Ed: Susan Thomson
Founded: 1998
Video production for live event, corporate, instructional & marketing purposes.
Sample(s), free, DVD samples
Branch Office(s)
Maple Beach Rd, RR 1, Beaverton, ON L0K 1A0, Canada
Membership(s): Ontario Professional Videographer Association

Image Video Teleproductions Inc
6755 Freedom Ave NW, North Canton, OH 44720
Tel: 330-494-9303 *Fax:* 330-966-1792
E-mail: info@image-video.com
Web Site: www.image-video.com
Key Personnel
Pres: Michael A Tonges
Gen Mgr: Dean Marini
Sales & Mktg: Mike Simon
Rent 2 GHZ portable microwave transmitters & receivers.
Catalog(s) available

Image Zone Inc
11 W 69 St, Suite 10A, New York, NY 10023
Tel: 212-924-8804
Web Site: www.imagezone.com
Key Personnel
Mng Dir: Douglas Ehrlich *E-mail:* dehrlich@imagezone.com
Creative Dir: Peter Smallman
Founded: 1987
Provide full service interactive & multimedia products.

Imagecraft Productions
3318 Burton Ave, Burbank, CA 91504
Tel: 818-954-0187 *Fax:* 818-954-0189
Web Site: www.imagecraftproductions.com
Key Personnel
Founder & Dir, Photog: Robin Hirsch *E-mail:* robin@imagecraftproductions.com
Pres: Jason Been
Rentals Mgr: Ben Fuller *E-mail:* ben@imagecraftproductions.com
Sales & Mktg Mgr: Gene Duggan *E-mail:* gene@imagecraftproductions.com
Founded: 1984
Full service production rental house; cameras, video/engineering, audio, grip, electric, gear, services, crewing.

imageReal Pictures LLC
4 Lighthouse St, No 8, Marina del Rey, CA 90292
E-mail: info@imagereal.com
Web Site: www.imagereal.com
Key Personnel
Founder & Exec Prodr: Katie Cadigan
Founded: 1997
Nonfiction media production.
Membership(s): IDA

Imagers
1575 Northside Dr, Bldg 400, Suite 490, Atlanta, GA 30318-5411
Tel: 404-351-5800 *Toll Free Tel:* 800-232-5411 *Fax:* 404-351-9020
E-mail: imagers@imagers.com
Web Site: www.imagers.com
Key Personnel
Owner: Thomas S Lines
VP, Sales: Joe Edwards
Founded: 1947
Provide printing, prepress, color laser & photo print services.
Catalog(s) available
Membership(s): PMA International

Images in Motion Media Inc
720 Ladera Dr, Sonoma, CA 95476
Tel: 707-996-9474
E-mail: images@vom.com
Web Site: www.imagesmedia.com
Key Personnel
Co-Owner & Prodr: Lee Armstrong
Co-Owner & Prodn Designer: Kamela Portuges
TV/film production using live action, puppets & animation. Complete video production studio rental.

Images II Inc
1700 "O" St, Lincoln, NE 68508
Tel: 402-475-4000 *Toll Free Tel:* 800-669-4001
E-mail: graphics@images2.com
Web Site: www.images2.com
Key Personnel
Gen Mgr: Redge Johnson
Founded: 1974
Design of imaging technology equipment.
Membership(s): AIE™; Photo Marketing Association

Imageworks
1039 Meade Ave, San Diego, CA 92116-1038
Tel: 619-239-6161
E-mail: info@imageworks.tv
Web Site: www.imageworks.tv
Key Personnel
Prodr/Dir/Writer: Craig Bentley
Founded: 1986
Video production company.
Membership(s): MCA-I

ImageWorks Communications
10155 High Point Lane, Suite 100, Sandy, UT 84092
Tel: 801-231-7234 (cell)
Web Site: www.imageworkscommunications.com
Key Personnel
Owner & CEO: Walt Winters *E-mail:* walt@imageworkscommunications.com
Founded: 1995
Full service multimedia production company. Acquire footage on HD & edit on Final Cut Pro. Shooting, producing, directing & writing. Manage large conferences & meetings with AV needs.
Membership(s): MCA-I

Imagine Communications Corp
3001 Dallas Pkwy, Suite 300, Frisco, TX 75034
Tel: 469-803-4900 *Toll Free Tel:* 866-4-IMAGINE (446-2446) *Fax:* 469-803-4899
E-mail: insidesales@imaginecommunications.com
Web Site: www.imaginecommunications.com
Key Personnel
CEO: Charlie Vogt
CFO: L R "Skip" Sorenson
CTO: Steve Reynolds
Chief Legal Offr: Chuck Gilbert
Chief People Offr: Sean Huurman
Chief Strategy Offr: Brian Cabeceiras
Pres, Global Opers: Steve Foreman
Pres, Global Sales: Pablo Gargiulo
Media software & video infrastructure solutions serving broadcast, multichannel video programming distributor, government & enterprise customers.
Company formed from the rebranding of Harris Broadcast which split into two companies, Imagine Communications & GatesAir.
Branch Office(s)
3400 W Olive Ave, Suite 220, Burbank, CA 91504 *Tel:* 818-717-6800 *Fax:* 818-842-8945
1493 Poinsettia Ave, Suite 143, Vista, CA 92081 *Tel:* 760-936-4000 *Fax:* 760-936-4001
101 W Colfax Ave, Suite 600, Denver, CO 80202 *Tel:* 303-476-5000 *Fax:* 303-568-4715
CALA Regional Ctr, 703 Waterford Way, Suite 810, Miami, FL 33126 *Tel:* 786-437-1960 *Fax:* 305-267-4154
1160 US Hwy 22, Bridgewater, NJ 08807-2931 *Tel:* 908-927-1200
One Penn Plaza, 39th fl, Suite 3915, New York, NY 10119 *Tel:* 212-303-4200 *Fax:* 212-779-8719
Volvo Off Park, 1228 Progressive Dr, Suite 101, Chesapeake, VA 23320 *Tel:* 757-548-2300 *Fax:* 757-548-4088
25 Dyas Rd, North York, ON M3B 1V7, Canada *Tel:* 416-445-9640 *Fax:* 416-445-0595
390 rue Le Moyne, Montreal, QC H2Y 1Y3, Canada *Tel:* 514-842-0101 *Fax:* 514-842-0111

Imagivations
11314 Sheldon St, Sun Valley, CA 91352
Tel: 818-767-6767 *Fax:* 818-767-3637
E-mail: info@imagivations.com
Web Site: www.imagivations.com
Key Personnel
Owner: Michael Fuller; Andrew Menschik
Founded: 1996
Entertainment - custom fabrication; custom, construction, scenic & design.
Online catalog(s) available

Imation Corp
One Imation Way, Oakdale, MN 55128-3421
Tel: 651-704-4000 *Toll Free Tel:* 888-466-3456 *Fax:* 651-704-3444 *Toll Free Fax:* 888-704-4200
E-mail: info@imation.com
Web Site: www.imation.com
Key Personnel
CEO & Pres: Mark Lucas
CFO & SVP: Paul R Zeller
Admin Asst: Kathy Brackey

IMAX Corp
2525 Speakman Dr, Mississauga, ON L5K 1B1, Canada
Tel: 905-403-6500 *Fax:* 905-403-6450
E-mail: info@imax.com
Web Site: www.imax.com
Key Personnel
CEO: Richard L Gefond
Chmn: Bradley J Wechsler
CFO & EVP: Joseph Sparacio

IME, see Inter-Media Electronics

Imig Audio/Video Inc
2611 Fairbanks St, Suite 100, Anchorage, AK 99503
Tel: 907-274-2161 *Fax:* 907-279-0219
E-mail: info@imigav.com
Web Site: www.imigav.com
Key Personnel
Pres: Charles Imig
Commercial AV Equip & Design Consultant: Eric Imig *E-mail:* eric@imigav.com

Immersion Corp
310 Rio Robles, San Jose, CA 95134
Tel: 408-467-1900 *Fax:* 408-467-1901
E-mail: info@immersion.com
Web Site: www.immersion.com
Key Personnel
CEO & Pres: Victor Viegas
CFO: Paul Norris
SVP, Sales & Mktg: Dennis Sheehan
VP, Engg: Rob Lacroix
VP, HR: Janice Passarello
Catalog(s) available
Branch Office(s)
4200 Blvd Ste-Laurent, Suite 1105, Montreal, QC H2W 2R2, Canada *Tel:* 514-987-9800 *Fax:* 514-987-9808
Foreign Office(s): Tallberginkatu 2B, 00180 Helsinki, Finland
Level 20, Marunouchi Trust Tower - Main, 1-8-3 Marunouchi, Chiyoda-ku, Tokyo 100-0005, Japan *Tel:* (03) 6269-3430
ERW Bldg, 5th fl, 1330-8 Seocho-dong, Seocho-gu, Seoul 137-85, South Korea *Tel:* (02) 3472 3141 *Fax:* (02) 3472 3145
12F-3 No 866, ZhongZheng Rd, ZhongHe City, Taipei County 235, Taiwan *Tel:* (02) 32345467

IMP Digital Studios
120 Rte 17N, Paramus, NJ 07652
Tel: 201-261-3959 *Fax:* 201-261-3959
E-mail: info@impdigital.us
Web Site: impdigitalstudios.com
Key Personnel
Chief Engr & Prodr: Mike Goldberg
Founded: 1995
Video production services from concept development through post-production. Audio recording facility & production services. App & web site development.

Impact Christian Books Inc
332 Leffingwell Ave, Suite 101, Kirkwood, MO 63122
Tel: 314-822-3309
E-mail: info@impactchristianbooks.com
Web Site: www.impactchristianbooks.com
Key Personnel
Founder & Pres: William D Banks
Founded: 1971
Catalog(s) available
Membership(s): CBA: The Association for Christian Retail

Impact Group
410 Bryant Circle, Bldg F, Ojai, CA 93023
Toll Free Tel: 800-675-2200
E-mail: sales@impact-group.com
Web Site: impact-group.com
Key Personnel
VP, Opers: Chris Gearhart *E-mail:* chrisg@impact-group.com
Branch Office(s)
1833 Crossbeam Dr, Bldg D, Charlotte, NC 28217

IMR Limited
1104 Fernwood Ave, 4th fl, Camp Hill, PA 17011
Tel: 717-364-3700 *Toll Free Tel:* 800-446-2826 *Fax:* 717-364-3750
E-mail: information@imrdigital.com
Web Site: www.imrdigital.com
Key Personnel
Pres: Scott McCabe *Tel:* 717-364-3783 *E-mail:* smccabe@imrdigital.com
Imaging Specialist: Dawson E Flinchbaugh *Tel:* 717-364-3726 *E-mail:* dflinchbaugh@imrdigital.com
Capture, storage, retrieval, distribution & conversion of documents, data & microforms.
Catalog(s) available
Membership(s): AIIM; ARMA; Custom Electronic Design & Installation Association

Imtronics Industries Inc
11930 31 Ct N, St Petersburg, FL 33716
Tel: 727-572-9010 *Fax:* 727-572-9012
E-mail: imtronics@imtronics.com
Web Site: imtronics.com
Key Personnel
Pres: Steven B Cohen
VP: Oliver Cohen
Founded: 1972
Manufacture electronic parts & testing equipment.
Catalog(s) available

In Concert Production Inc (ICP)
2750 S Cobb Industrial Blvd, Smyrna, GA 30082
Tel: 404-355-7943 *Fax:* 404-350-9045
Web Site: icpatlanta.com
Key Personnel
Pres: Jay Rabbitt
Sound, lighting & stage production.

In the Wild Productions
PO Box 1443, Provincetown, MA 02657-5443
Tel: 508-241-5990; 508-487-2887
E-mail: info@inthewildproductions.com
Web Site: www.inthewildproductions.com
Key Personnel
Exec Dir & Prodr: Christopher P Hamilton *E-mail:* chris@inthewildproductions.com
Founded: 1999
Supplier of wildlife stock footage, particularly whales & dolphins.

InCharge Systems, see Applied Integration Corp

Increase Video/Silver Mine Video
Division of Silver Mine Inc
5776 D Lindero Canyon Rd, Westlake Village, CA 91362
Tel: 805-480-0303 *Fax:* 805-375-1606
Key Personnel
Pres: Howard Silvers
Mgr, Mktg: Stefan Silvers
Catalog(s) available
Membership(s): Entertainment Merchants Association; Music Business Association

Independent Audio Inc
43 Deerfield Rd, Portland, ME 04101
Tel: 207-773-2424 *Fax:* 207-773-2422
E-mail: info@independentaudio.com
Web Site: www.independentaudio.com
Key Personnel
Owner & Pres: Fraser Jones
Owner & Treas: Jean Todd *E-mail:* jean@independentaudio.com
Founded: 1993
Brochure(s), free

Independent Studios
4701 Conti, New Orleans, LA 70119
Tel: 504-915-IJOE (915-4563)
Key Personnel
Contact: Joseph J Catalanotto
Founded: 1960

Indian House
PO Box 472, Taos, NM 87571-0472
Tel: 575-776-2953 *Toll Free Tel:* 800-748-0522 *Fax:* 575-776-2804
E-mail: music@indianhouse.com
Web Site: www.indianhouse.com
Key Personnel
Prop: Tony Isaacs
Founded: 1966
Traditional American Indian music.
Catalog(s) available

Indiana University Press
Office of Scholarly Publishing, Herman B Wells Library 350, 1320 E Tenth St, Bloomington, IN 47405-3907
Tel: 812-855-8817 *Toll Free Tel:* 800-842-6796 *Fax:* 812-855-8507
E-mail: iupress@indiana.edu
Web Site: www.iupress.indiana.edu
Key Personnel
CFO & Dir, Opers: Dan Nichols *Tel:* 812-855-4901 *E-mail:* nichodan@indiana.edu
Founded: 1950
Catalog(s) available
Shipping Address: 802 E 13 St, Bloomington, IN 47408-2101 *Tel:* 812-855-4362 *Fax:* 812-855-8507
Membership(s): Association of American University Presses

Indie Aerials
16425 Hart St, Van Nuys, CA 91406
Tel: 818-988-9382
E-mail: info@indieaerials.com
Web Site: indieaerials.com
Aerial production company serving the film industry.

Indigo Productions
313 Kensington Ave, Buffalo, NY 14214
Tel: 716-836-2930 *Fax:* 716-836-6830
E-mail: indigo@indigoproductions.net
Web Site www.indigoproductions.net
Concert grade professional audio equipment.
Catalog(s) available

Induro
Division of MAC Group
75 Virginia Rd, North White Plains, NY 10603
Tel: 914-347-3300 *Fax:* 914-347-3309
E-mail: info@indurogear.com
Web Site: www.indurogear.com
Key Personnel
Pres, MAC Group: Jan Lederman
Photographic tripods, monopods, heads & photographic support gear.

Indus International Inc
340 S Oak St, West Salem, WI 54669
Mailing Address: PO Box 890, West Salem, WI 54669
Tel: 608-786-0300 *Toll Free Tel:* 800-843-9377 *Fax:* 608-786-0786
E-mail: info@indususa.com
Web Site: www.indususa.com
Key Personnel
Pres: Ameen Ayoob
Founded: 1985
Manufacture opaque microcard reader printer & micrographic products.

Industrial Acoustics Co (IAC), see IAC Acoustics

Industrial Audio/Video Inc
2617 Bissonnet, Houston, TX 77005
Tel: 713-524-1956 *Toll Free Tel:* 800-392-4384 (TX only) *Fax:* 713-524-2823
E-mail: info@iavdigital.com
Web Site: www.iavdigital.com
Key Personnel
Pres: David Lopez *Tel:* 713-535-2350 *E-mail:* dlopez@iavdigital.com
Founded: 1971
AV systems design, sales, integration, maintenance & support services.
Catalog(s) available
Online catalog(s) available
Membership(s): InfoComm International®; NSCA; SMPTE

Industrial Light & Magic (ILM)
Division of Lucasfilm Ltd Co
1110 Gorgas St, San Francisco, CA 94129
Tel: 415-746-3000 *Fax:* 415-746-3015
E-mail: prdepartment@ilm.com
Web Site: www.ilm.com
Key Personnel
Pres & Gen Mgr: Lynwen Brennan
Founded: 1975
Visual effects.

Industrial Strength Inc
3232 44 Ave N, St Petersburg, FL 33714
Tel: 727-528-2877 *Toll Free Fax:* 888-804-7680
E-mail: sales@industrialstrengthstaging.com
Web Site: www.worryfreeav.com
Full service, audio, video, lighting & production/staging source.
Catalog(s) available
Membership(s): InfoComm International®

Industrial Timer Co
30 Industrial Park Rd, Centerbrook, CT 06409
Tel: 860-767-7130 *Toll Free Tel:* 800-394-7130 *Fax:* 860-767-9137 *Toll Free Fax:* 800-767-9137
E-mail: sales@epg-inc.com
Web Site: www.industrialtimercompany.com
Key Personnel
Pres: Peter Griffin
Founded: 1938
Manufacture timers for industrial use.
Catalog(s) available

Inferno Film Productions LLC
PO Box 696, Littleton, CO 80160-0696
Tel: 303-587-9792
E-mail: sales@infernofilm.com
Web Site: www.infernofilm.com
Key Personnel
Owner: Darlene Cypser; Mark Steven Grove; Trygve Lode
Develops & produces its own movies in-house.

Inferno Films
3404 Guadalupe St, Austin, TX 78705
Tel: 512-302-9009 *Fax:* 512-302-9022
Web Site: www.infernofilms.com
Key Personnel
Partner & Dir: Layton Blaylock
E-mail: lblaylock@infernofilms.com
Exec Prodr: Jeff Hastings; Quincy Lowman
Founded: 1999
Full service commercial film & video production company. Three edit suites equipped with AVID & Final Cut systems, Panasonic AF-100, HDX-170 & HDX-900 camera packages.
Membership(s): ADFED

Inferno Motion Pictures, see Inferno Film Productions LLC

InFocus Corp
13190 SW 68 Pkwy, Suite 200, Portland, OR 97223-8368
Tel: 503-207-4700 *Toll Free Tel:* 877-388-8385 *Fax:* 503-207-4707
E-mail: sales@infocus.com
Web Site: www.infocus.com
Key Personnel
Pres: Raymond Yu
Founded: 1986
Catalog(s) available
Foreign Office(s): InFocus International, 4 Teck Lim Rd, Singapore 088382, Singapore *Tel:* 6513 9600 *Fax:* 6238 0535 *E-mail:* asiapacific@infocus.com

Infonics Inc
Subsidiary of Phoenix Enterprise Inc
2302 E Michigan Blvd, Michigan City, IN 46360
Mailing Address: PO Box 1111, Michigan City, IN 46361-8311
Tel: 219-879-3381 *Fax:* 219-879-3383
E-mail: infonics@sbcglobal.net
Key Personnel
Pres: Carol Lant
Founded: 1975
Manufacture audio tape duplicators, digital & analog & rewinders.
Catalog(s) available

Infosat Communications Inc
3130 114 Ave SE, Calgary, AB T2Z 3V6, Canada
Tel: 403-543-8188 *Toll Free Tel:* 888-524-3038 *Fax:* 403-289-8133
Web Site: infosat.com
Key Personnel
CEO & Pres: Justin de Vlieg
VP, Opers: Bryan Hetlinger
Founded: 1986
Catalog(s) available
Branch Office(s)
Able Infosat Communications, 5906 Broadway St, Pearland, TX 77581, Gen Mgr: Michelle Williamson *Tel:* 281-485-8800 *Fax:* 281-485-8230 *Web Site:* www.ableinfosat.com
Membership(s): InfoComm International®

Ingram Book Group
Subsidiary of Ingram Content Group Inc
One Ingram Blvd, La Vergne, TN 37086
Tel: 615-793-5000
E-mail: customer.service@ingramcontent.com; inquiry@ingramcontent.com
Web Site: www.ingramcontent.com
Key Personnel
Chmn & CEO: John R Ingram
Distribute books, music, hard to find titles & Spanish language products.
Catalog(s) available
Membership(s): Audio Publishers Association

Ingram Entertainment Inc
2 Ingram Blvd, La Vergne, TN 37089-7006
Tel: 615-287-4000 (corp) *Toll Free Tel:* 800-621-1333 (sales & cust serv) *Fax:* 615-287-4982
Web Site: www.ingramentertainment.com
Key Personnel
Chmn: David Ingram
Pres & CEO: Bob Webb
EVP & CFO: Donnie Daniel
VP, Sales: Bill Bryant
National distributor of entertainment software & hardware, including Blu-ray, DVD, audiobooks, games & music players.
Catalog(s) available
Branch Office(s)
1130 Iron Point Rd, Suite 288, Folsom, CA 95630 *Tel:* 916-605-1500 *Toll Free Tel:* 800-366-2111 *Fax:* 916-605-1760; 916-605-2383
Membership(s): Entertainment Merchants Association; National Association of Video Distributors

Ingram Micro
1600 E Saint Andrew Place, Santa Ana, CA 92705
Mailing Address: PO Box 25125, Santa Ana, CA 92799
Tel: 714-566-1000
Web Site: www.ingrammicro.com
Key Personnel
CEO: Alain Monie
Sr EVP, Corp: Alain Maquet
Founded: 1979
Distribute & market a large variety of technology & mobility products.
Branch Office(s)
1759 Wehrle Dr, Williamsville, NY 14221 *Tel:* 716-633-3600 (east coast corp off)
Shipping Address: 12510 Micro Dr, Mira Loma, CA 91752 *Tel:* 909-727-3300; 415 E Lies Rd, Carol Stream, IL 60188 *Tel:* 630-668-0106; 80 Micro Dr, Jonestown, PA 17038 *Tel:* 717-865-0800; 3820 Micro Dr, Millington, TN 38053 *Tel:* 901-873-7000; 1809 W Frankford, Suite 100, Carrollton, TX 75007 *Tel:* 972-512-2700
Membership(s): Global Technology Distribution Council

InJoy Birth & Parenting Education
7107 La Vista Place, Longmont, CO 80503
Tel: 303-447-2082 (ext 2) *Toll Free Tel:* 800-326-2082 (ext 2) *Fax:* 303-449-8788
E-mail: custserv@injoyvideos.com
Web Site: www.injoyvideos.com
Key Personnel
Pres: Charlie Stein
Founded: 1988
Producers of prenatal, labor & delivery & postpartum curriculum. Offers DVDs, parent guides, PowerPoint programs & online education.
Online catalog(s) available

Inland Audio Visual Co
1414 N Fiske St, Suite E, Spokane, WA 99202
Tel: 509-328-0706 *Toll Free Tel:* 888-9INLAND (946-5263) *Fax:* 509-328-0730
E-mail: inland@inlandav.com
Web Site: www.inlandav.com
Key Personnel
Owner: Tracy Cahalan
Founded: 1946
AV rentals, set-up & production work.
Membership(s): IABC; InfoComm International®; MCA-I

Inland Audio Visual Ltd
422 Lucas Ave, Box 102, Group 200, RR 2, Winnipeg, MB R3C 2E6, Canada
Tel: 204-786-6521 *Toll Free Tel:* 800-933-6006 *Fax:* 204-783-6281
E-mail: winnipeg@inlandav.ca
Web Site: www.inlandav.ca
Key Personnel
Owner, CEO & Pres: Kim E Werbowski
E-mail: kwerbowski@inlandav.ca
Founded: 1937
Catalog(s) available
Branch Office(s)
700 58 Ave SE, Bay 1, Calgary, AB T2H 2E2, Canada *Tel:* 403-252-7726 *Toll Free Tel:* 800-495-6006 *Fax:* 403-253-1716 *E-mail:* calgary@inlandav.ca
17893 106-A Ave, No 100, Edmonton, AB T5S 1V8, Canada, Mgr: Ben Mejia *Tel:* 780-423-4833 *Toll Free Tel:* 800-587-4004 *Fax:* 780-423-1671 *E-mail:* edmonton@inlandav.ca
2501 Seventh Ave, Regina, SK S4R 1C7, Canada, Mgr: Tim Wiest *Tel:* 306-525-8726 *Toll Free Tel:* 800-743-8008 *Fax:* 306-525-0690 *E-mail:* regina@inlandav.ca
21-1738 Quebec Ave, Saskatoon, SK S7K 1V9, Canada, Mgr: Ralph Niekamp *Tel:* 306-664-8622 *Toll Free Tel:* 800-925-6006 *Fax:* 306-664-2809 *E-mail:* saskatoon@inlandav.ca
Membership(s): InfoComm International®

Inner Explorations
PO Box 37, Midland, OR 97634-0037
Tel: 541-851-1534
Web Site: www.innerexplorations.com
Key Personnel
Owner: Tyra Arraj *E-mail:* arraj@innerexplorations.com
Online catalog(s) available
Shipping Address: 301 Old Midland Rd, Midland, OR 97634

Inner Traditions International
One Park St, Rochester, VT 05767
Mailing Address: PO Box 388, Rochester, VT 05767-0388
Tel: 802-767-3174 *Toll Free Tel:* 800-246-8648 *Fax:* 802-767-3726
E-mail: customerservice@innertraditions.com
Web Site: www.innertraditions.com
Key Personnel
Pres: Ehud Sperling
Dir, Sales & Mktg: John Hays
Sales & Mktg Assoc: Jessica Arsenault *Tel:* 802-767-3174 ext 118 *E-mail:* jessa@innertraditions.com
Publicity: Manzanita Carpenter
Catalog(s), free

Innocinema
10130 Perimeter Pkwy, Suite 180, Charlotte, NC 28216
Tel: 704-665-1945 *Fax:* 704-665-1956
E-mail: info@innocinema.com; sales@innocinema.com
Web Site: www.innocinema.com
Key Personnel
Founder & Partner: Justin Goff
Partner: Brian Goff; Daryl Goff
Founded: 2010
Equipment & accessories for professionals working in large-scale movie & video production.

Innovative Electronic Designs LLC
9701 Taylorsville Rd, Louisville, KY 40299
Tel: 502-267-7436 *Fax:* 502-267-9070
E-mail: info@iedaudio.com
Web Site: www.iedaudio.com
Key Personnel
Gen Mgr, IED Support Servs: Dick Snider *E-mail:* dsnider@iedaudio.com
Intl Sales Mgr: Steve Youngson *Tel:* 502-287-0043 *E-mail:* syoungson@iedaudio.com
Founded: 1978
Manufacture commercial audio systems & computer-controlled sound systems.
Membership(s): AAAE; AES; International Association of Assembly Managers; NFPA; NSCA

Innovision Media Group
307 W Johnson Hwy, Norristown, PA 19401
Tel: 484-688-1200 *Fax:* 484-688-0148
E-mail: info@innovision.net; sales@innovision.net
Web Site: www.innovision.net
Key Personnel
Pres: Dan Fried *Tel:* 610-662-2688 (cell)
Founded: 1990

Innovision Optics
1719 21 St, Santa Monica, CA 90404
Tel: 310-453-4866 *Fax:* 310-453-4677
Web Site: www.innovision-optics.com
Key Personnel
Pres: Mark Centkowski *E-mail:* mark@innovisionoptics.com
Founded: 1987
Catalog(s) available

Institute for Teaching & Learning Excellence (ITLE)
Division of Oklahoma State University
100 ITLE, Oklahoma State University, Stillwater, OK 74078
Tel: 405-744-1000 *Fax:* 405-744-8563
E-mail: itle@okstate.edu
Web Site: itle.okstate.edu
Key Personnel
Prodr/Dir: Wade A Pearson *Tel:* 405-744-3936 *E-mail:* wade.pearson@okstate.edu

The Institute Inc
787 East Ave, Brockport, NY 14420
Tel: 585-637-6531
Web Site: www.the-institute-ny.com
Key Personnel
Pres: Jack Rollwagen
Founded: 1972

Institute of Precision Muscle Balancing
6035 Vantage Ave, North Hollywood, CA 91616-4637
Tel: 818-766-8555 *Fax:* 818-766-8645
Web Site: www.dralexander.com
Key Personnel
Owner: Dr Ric D Alexander *E-mail:* ricalexander@dralexander.com
Distribute unique self-treatment videos.

Institute of Texan Cultures
Division of University of Texas at San Antonio
UTSA HemisFair Park Campus, 801 E Cesar E Chavez Blvd, San Antonio, TX 78205-3296
Tel: 210-458-2300 *Toll Free Tel:* 800-776-7651 *Fax:* 210-458-2205
Web Site: www.texancultures.com
Key Personnel
VP, Community Servs: Dr Jude Valdez *Tel:* 210-458-2401
Asst Exec Dir: Aaron Parks *Tel:* 210-458-2329 *E-mail:* aaron.parks@utsa.edu
Founded: 1968
History & diverse cultures of Texas.
Catalog(s), biennial

Institute on Religious Life Inc
PO Box 7500, Libertyville, IL 60048-7500
Tel: 847-573-8975 *Fax:* 847-573-8960
Web Site: www.religiouslife.com
Key Personnel
Exec Dir: Michael Wick
Dir, Opers: M Kathleen O'Brien *E-mail:* kit@religiouslife.com
Founded: 1974
Distribute audio & video material on vocations to the religious life.
Catalog(s) available

Instructional Materials & Equipment Distributors (I-Med)
1520 Cotner Ave, Los Angeles, CA 90025
Tel: 323-879-0377; 323-272-5260; 310-473-5558 *Toll Free Tel:* 800-352-7423 (CA only) *Fax:* 310-312-1743
Web Site: www.i-med-inc.com
Key Personnel
Pres: Donald H Parson, Jr
Distribute school AV equipment & supplies.
Catalog(s) available
Membership(s): InfoComm International®

Instructional Resources Corp
1819 Bay Ridge Ave, Annapolis, MD 21403
Tel: 410-263-0025 *Toll Free Tel:* 800-922-1711 *Fax:* 410-268-8320
Web Site: www.historypictures.com
Key Personnel
CEO: Bill White *E-mail:* bwhite@historypictures.com
Catalog(s) available

Instrumentation Marketing Corp
Subsidiary of Photo-Sonics Inc
820 S Mariposa St, Burbank, CA 91506-3196
Tel: 818-842-2141 *Fax:* 818-842-2610
E-mail: mail@photosonics.com
Web Site: www.photosonics.com/imc.htm
Key Personnel
CFO: Kate Treesuwan *Tel:* 818-531-3246 *E-mail:* kate@photosonics.com
Pres: Philip Kiel *Tel:* 818-531-3219 *E-mail:* pkiel@photosonics.com
Dir, Busn Devt: Rudy Nunez *Tel:* 818-531-3234 *E-mail:* rnunez@photosonics.com
Engg Mgr: Ken Rhodes *Tel:* 818-531-3221 *E-mail:* krhodes@photosonics.com
Founded: 1971
Photographic equipment, photo-optical instrumentation, high-speed digital camera & trucking mounts.
Catalog(s) available
Membership(s): OSG; SFTE; SPIE

IntegraColor
3210 Innovative Way, Mesquite, TX 75149
Tel: 972-289-0705 *Toll Free Tel:* 800-933-9511 *Fax:* 972-285-4881
E-mail: salesinfo@integracolor.com
Web Site: www.integracolor.com
Key Personnel
CEO & Pres: Larry C King
Founded: 1972
Creative & design service, film scanning, volume-film scanning, scanning for web, digital asset management, digital file access-ordering systems, digital procurement systems, CD duplication, trade show graphics, 4-color printing-sales collateral.
Catalog(s) available
Membership(s): AIE™; Digital Imaging Association; Photo Marketing Association

Integrated Event Management
1239 Vista Leaf Dr, Decatur, GA 30033
Tel: 404-633-8541 *Fax:* 404-633-8691
Web Site: www.integratedevents.com
Key Personnel
Pres: Thomas Kann *E-mail:* kann@integratedevents.com
Founded: 1999
Full service creative & technical event production.
Branch Office(s)
Orlando, FL, Dir, Mktg & Prodn Servs: Nancy McFarland *Tel:* 407-353-4513 *Fax:* 407-622-8851 *E-mail:* mcfarland@integratedevents.com
Membership(s): ASAE; InfoComm International®; International Association of Speakers Bureaus

Intel-A-Jib™
409 Calle San Pablo, No 108, Camarillo, CA 93012
Web Site: www.intel-a-jib.com
Key Personnel
Contact: Jim Vetkos *E-mail:* jvetkos@intelajib.com
Founded: 1996

Intelix LLC
Division of Liberty AV Solutions
8001 Terrace Ave, Suite 201, Middleton, WI 53562
Tel: 608-831-0880 *Toll Free Tel:* 866-4-MATMIX (462-8649) *Fax:* 608-831-1833
E-mail: intelix@intelix.com
Web Site: www.intelix.com
Key Personnel
Prod Mgr: Christopher Melendy
Founded: 1986
Manufacture AV UTP wire.
Catalog(s) available
Membership(s): AES; Custom Electronic Design & Installation Association; InfoComm International®; NSCA

The Intellications Co
1110 Northshore Dr, Roswell, GA 30076-2812
Tel: 678-643-8468
Web Site: www.johnatwood.com
Key Personnel
Pres: John Atwood *E-mail:* john@johnatwood.com
Founded: 1978
Providing scripting services for business communcations.

Intellidyne LLC
5203 Leesburg Pike, Suite 400, 2 Skyline Place, Falls Church, VA 22041
Tel: 703-575-9715 *Fax:* 703-575-9718
Web Site: www.intellidyne-llc.com
Key Personnel
Founder & Pres: Robert L Grey
CEO: Tony Crescenzo
COO: William Maguire
CFO: Carlos Salazar
Gen Coun: Fern Ward
SVP: Shirl Jenkins; Brian Mortweet
VP: Bill Boyd; Carolyn Coffey; Joanne Surico
VP, Technol: Ric Sears

Inter-Media Electronics
192 Willard St, Quincy, MA 02169
Tel: 617-773-9688 *Fax:* 617-696-6327
E-mail: intermedia.ex@verizon.net; info@ime-imaging.com
Web Site: www.viapolonia.net/IME
Key Personnel
Pres: Tad Walkowiak
Mktg Dir: Andy Warot
Video production.

Inter Video
2000 N Lincoln St, Burbank, CA 91504
Tel: 818-843-3624 *Fax:* 818-843-6884
Web Site: www.intervideo24.com
3D & 2D video services & AV support for the motion picture & television industry.

Interactive International Inc
290 West End Ave, New York, NY 10023-8106
Tel: 212-580-5015 *Fax:* 212-580-5017
E-mail: ivie@erols.com
Key Personnel
Pres: George M Bulow
Catalog(s) available
Membership(s): ATD; InfoComm International®

Interactive Products
Division of Numonics Corp

101 Commerce Dr, Montgomeryville, PA 18936
Mailing Address: PO Box 1005, Montgomeryville, PA 18936
Tel: 215-362-2766 *Toll Free Tel:* 800-523-6716 *Fax:* 215-361-0167
E-mail: numonics@numonics.com
Web Site: www.numonics.com
Key Personnel
Dir, Software & Electrical Engg: Ellis Lauman
Mfg Opers Mgr: Pat Burns
Mgr, Sales Admin: Phyllis Ulrich
Manufacture interactive whiteboards.
Catalog(s) available

InterAmerica Stage Inc
4300 St Johns Pkwy, Sanford, FL 32771
Tel: 407-302-0881 *Toll Free Tel:* 877-302-4274 *Fax:* 407-302-0882
E-mail: info@iastage.com
Web Site: www.iastage.com
Key Personnel
Sales Mgr: Jack Hoffend *Tel:* 407-302-0881 ext 18
Designers & manufacturers of custom rigging systems. Speaker hoist & installation, format projection screens, frames & rigging.
Membership(s): Entertainment Technician Certification Program; InfoComm International®; International Association of Music Ministries; NAB; Professional Lighting & Sound Association; USITT

Intercollegiate Studies Institute Inc (ISI)
3901 Centerville Rd, Wilmington, DE 19807
Tel: 302-652-4600 *Toll Free Tel:* 800-526-7022 *Fax:* 302-652-1760
E-mail: info@isi.org
Web Site: www.isi.org
Key Personnel
Pres: Chris Long
Founded: 1953
Nonprofit, tax exempt educational organization with online lectures that can be downloaded.
Brochure(s) available

InterCom
3 Grogan's Park, Suite 200, The Woodlands, TX 77380
Tel: 281-367-4277 *Toll Free Tel:* 800-298-7070 *Fax:* 281-364-7032
E-mail: intercom@intercomtraining.com
Web Site: www.intercom-interactive.com
Key Personnel
Gen Mgr: Margo Pearson *Tel:* 281-367-4277 ext 103 *E-mail:* margo@intercomtraining.com
Founded: 1978
Produce educational training programs delivered on the web.
Catalog(s) available
Membership(s): ATD

InterComm
1520 E Winona Ave, Warsaw, IN 46590
Mailing Address: PO Box 618, Winona Lake, IN 46590
Tel: 574-267-5774 *Fax:* 574-267-5876
E-mail: info@intercommedia.org
Web Site: www.intercommedia.org
Key Personnel
Secy: Mr Lane Anderson
Produce Christian films, videos & filmstrips in 40 languages.
Catalog(s) available

Intercon 1
Division of Nortech Systems Inc
7746 Goedderz Rd, Suite 110, Baxter, MN 56425
Tel: 218-828-3157 *Toll Free Tel:* 800-237-9576 *Fax:* 218-828-1096
E-mail: intercon@nortechsys.com
Web Site: www.intercon-1.com
Key Personnel
Busn Mgr: Ron Folkeringa *E-mail:* rfolkeringa@nortechsys.com
Founded: 1978
Manufacture AV cables.
Online catalog(s) available

Interface Media Group
1233 20 St NW, Washington, DC 20036
Tel: 202-861-0500
E-mail: info@interfacevideo.com
Web Site: www.interfacevideo.com
Key Personnel
CEO & Pres: Jeff Weingarten
EVP, Strategic Partnerships: Adam Hurst *E-mail:* ahurst@interfacevideo.com
Founded: 1977
Full service production/post-production facility.
Catalog(s) available
Membership(s): MCA-I; PromaxBDA

Interlink Technologies
139 W Indiana Ave, Suite 203, Perrysburg, OH 43552
Mailing Address: PO Box 970, Perrysburg, OH 43552
Tel: 419-893-9011 *Toll Free Tel:* 800-655-5465 *Fax:* 419-893-7280
E-mail: info@interlinktech.com; info@thinkinterlink.com
Web Site: www.interlinktech.com; www.thinkinterlink.com
Key Personnel
CEO & Pres: Jessie Miller
Founded: 1986
Warehouse management software solutions for the supply chain industry.
Membership(s): APICS –The Association for Operations Management; Council of Supply Chain Management Professionals; International Warehouse Logistics Association; Material Handling Industry of America; Warehousing Education and Research Council

Intermark Industries Inc
2980 NW 74 Ave, Miami, FL 33122
Tel: 305-591-8930 *Fax:* 305-593-1091
E-mail: info@intermarkindustries.com
Web Site: www.intermarkindustries.com
Key Personnel
EVP: Dan Kremen *E-mail:* dan@intermarkindustries.com
Manufacturing & wholesale distribution of electronic equipment.
Catalog(s) available

Intermed Video Technologies Inc
18 Commerce Rd, Newtown, CT 06470
Tel: 203-270-0677; 203-270-9100 *Fax:* 203-270-9619
E-mail: sales@intermedvideo.com
Web Site: www.intermedvideo.com
Key Personnel
Prodn Mgr: Bob Strong *E-mail:* strong@intermedvideo.com
Sales: Tim Dye
Founded: 1991
Manufacture monitors for the military.

Intermedia Inc
5600 Rainier Ave S, Suite 203, Seattle, WA 98118
Tel: 206-284-2995 *Toll Free Tel:* 800-553-8336 *Toll Free Fax:* 800-553-1655
E-mail: info@intermedia-inc.com
Web Site: www.intermedia-inc.com
Key Personnel
Pres: Susan Hoffman *E-mail:* shoffman@intermedia-inc.com
Gen Mgr: Ted Fitch
Catalog(s) available
Membership(s): MCA-I

Intermedia Technologies
1720 Kaliste Saloom, Bldg 2, Suite B-2, Lafayette, LA 70508
Tel: 337-406-9428 *Toll Free Tel:* 877-268-9574 *Fax:* 337-406-9582
Web Site: www.intermedia-technologies.com
Key Personnel
CEO & Pres: Bobby Cobb
COO & VP: Gerald Broussard
Cont: Carol Bourque
Founded: 2001
Design & installation of multimedia presentation systems, projectors, conferencing, white boards & all AV & professional audio equipment.
Membership(s): InfoComm International®

InterNation Inc
299 Broadway, Suite 1400, New York, NY 10007
Tel: 212-619-5545 *Toll Free Tel:* 800-222-8799 *Fax:* 212-619-5887
E-mail: info@internation.com
Web Site: www.internation.com
Key Personnel
Pres: Erick Derkatsch
Founded: 1990
Foreign language translations, voice-over recording, subtitling & web localization.

International Audio Visual Inc
622 Rte 10, Unit 21, Whippany, NJ 07981
Tel: 973-887-7744 *Toll Free Tel:* 888-887-7749 *Fax:* 973-887-7272
E-mail: iav@iavnj.com
Web Site: www.iavnj.com
Key Personnel
Pres: Martin Dalakian
Founded: 1986
Catalog(s) available
Membership(s): InfoComm International®

International Cellulose Corp
12315 Robin Blvd, Houston, TX 77045
Tel: 713-433-6701 *Toll Free Tel:* 800-444-1252 *Fax:* 713-433-2029
E-mail: icc@spray-on.com
Web Site: www.spray-on.com
Key Personnel
Regl Sales Mgr: Joey Dickey
Develop & manufacture cellulose spray-applied thermal insulation & acoustical finishes.
Catalog(s) available

International Contact Inc
351 15 St, Oakland, CA 94612
Tel: 510-836-1180 *Toll Free Tel:* 800-430-7705 *Fax:* 510-835-1314
E-mail: info@intlcontact.com
Web Site: www.intlcontact.com
Key Personnel
Chmn & Creative Dir: Norma Armon *E-mail:* norma@intlcontact.com
Pres: C Itzkowich
Founded: 1982
Membership(s): ATA; IABC; PINC

International Datacasting
50 Frank Nighbor Place, Kanata, ON K2V 1B9, Canada
Tel: 613-596-4120 *Fax:* 613-596-4863
E-mail: marketing@datacast.com
Web Site: www.datacast.com
Key Personnel
CEO & Pres: Doug Lowther
CFO: Steven Archambault
CTO & VP: Gary Carter
Founded: 1984
Manufacture & distribute satellite data broadcasting equipment.
Brochure(s) available

Branch Office(s)
6215 Ferris Sq, Suite 100, San Diego, CA 92121
Foreign Office(s): Marga Klompelaan 18, 6836 BH Arnhem, Netherlands *Tel:* (026) 323-6969

International Digital Centre
216 E 45 St, 7th fl, New York, NY 10017
Tel: 212-581-3940 *Fax:* 212-581-3979
E-mail: info@idcdigital.com
Web Site: www.idcdigital.com
Key Personnel
CEO & Pres: Marcy Gilbert *E-mail:* marcy@idcdigital.com
VP, Opers & Scheduling: Amy Alfonzo *E-mail:* amy@idcdigital.com
Prodr: Scott Carroll *E-mail:* scott@idcdigital.com
Founded: 1988
Multi-format, audio-video duplication, standards conversion, digital video compression HD transfers & DVD authoring. Digital delivery via Smart Jog.

International Display & Exhibit Corp
60 Shawmut Rd, Suite 5, Canton, MA 02021
Tel: 617-527-7878 *Toll Free Tel:* 800-533-7878 *Fax:* 617-964-5099
E-mail: sales@idec-displays.com
Web Site: www.idecdisplays.com
Key Personnel
Pres: Steve Levin *E-mail:* slevin@idec-displays.com
Founded: 1967
Manufacturer of all types of flip-chart easels & flip-chart pads: plain, graph & ruled. Also manufacture all types of display stands & equipment. Tradeshow exhibits & booths, folding screens, drapes all types.
Catalog(s) available

International E-Z UP Inc
1900 Second St, Norco, CA 92860
Tel: 951-279-0999 *Toll Free Tel:* 800-45SHADE (457-4233) *Fax:* 951-279-0888
Web Site: www.ezup.com
Founded: 1983
Instant shelters, shelter accessories, flags, directors chairs, tables, table covers & banner displays.
Catalog(s) available
Sales Office(s): E-Z UP Europe BV, Ringveste 7, 3992 DD Houten, Netherlands *Tel:* (030) 635 4100 *Fax:* (030) 634 1767 *E-mail:* euinfo@ezup.com *Web Site:* ezup.nl (European sales)

International Electro-Magnetics Inc
1033A S Noel Ave, Wheeling, IL 60090
Tel: 847-358-4622 *Toll Free Tel:* 800-227-4323 (sales) *Fax:* 847-947-8239
E-mail: information@iemmag.com; service@iemmag.com; sales@iemmag.com
Web Site: www.iemmag.com
Key Personnel
Pres: Anthony Pretto
Founded: 1976

International Fun-Shop
2114 Seabrook Circle, Seabrook, TX 77586
Tel: 281-291-0707 *Fax:* 281-291-0718
E-mail: fssales@fun-shop.com
Web Site: www.fun-shop.com
Key Personnel
CEO: Gary Douglas
Founded: 1979
Theatrical & stage supply company.

International Historic Films Inc
3533 S Archer Ave, Chicago, IL 60609
Mailing Address: PO Box 5796, Chicago, IL 60680
Tel: 773-927-2900 *Fax:* 773-927-9211
E-mail: info@ihffilm.com
Web Site: www.ihffilm.com
Key Personnel
Pres: Peter Bernotas
Catalog(s) available

International Light Technologies Inc
10 Technology Dr, Peabody, MA 01960-7976
Tel: 978-818-6180 *Fax:* 978-818-6181
E-mail: ilsales@intl-lighttech.com
Web Site: www.intl-lighttech.com
Key Personnel
Sales Mgr: Jill Fowler
Founded: 1965
Catalog(s) available

International Loving Touch Foundation Inc
2122 SE Division St, Portland, OR 97202
Mailing Address: PO Box 16374, Portland, OR 97292-0374
Tel: 503-253-8482 *Fax:* 503-256-6753
E-mail: info@lovingtouch.com
Web Site: www.lovingtouch.com
Key Personnel
Pres: Diana Moore
Founded: 1992
Health education & training; parenting & baby massage.
Catalog(s) available
Membership(s): AMTA

International Marketing Group
1900 Elm Hill Pike, Nashville, TN 37210
Tel: 615-889-8000 *Fax:* 615-871-4817
Key Personnel
CEO: Moe Lytle
Distributes music on CDs.

International Robotics Inc
2001 Palmer Ave, Suite LL-1, Larchmont, NY 10538
Tel: 914-630-1060 *Fax:* 203-630-1733
E-mail: info@internationalrobotics.com
Web Site: www.internationalrobotics.com
Key Personnel
CEO: Robert Doornick *E-mail:* doornickr@internationalrobotics.com
Off Mgr: Christopher Briggs *E-mail:* iriny@aol.com
Social robots for marketing & communication, education & special needs groups & film stage entertainment.

The International Society of Automation (ISA)
67 T W Alexander Dr, Research Triangle Park, NC 27709
Mailing Address: PO Box 12277, Research Triangle Park, NC 27709-2277
Tel: 919-549-8411 *Fax:* 919-549-8288
E-mail: info@isa.org
Web Site: www.isa.org
Key Personnel
Exec Dir: Patrick Gouhin *Tel:* 919-990-9240 *E-mail:* pgouhin@isa.org
Exec Off Mgr: Debbie Eby *Tel:* 919-990-9241 *E-mail:* deby@isa.org
Founded: 1945
Membership society for automation professionals.
Catalog(s) available

International Tae Kwon Do Association (ITA Institute)
PO Box 281, Grand Blanc, MI 48480
Tel: 810-232-6482 *Fax:* 810-235-8594
E-mail: hq@itatkd.com
Web Site: www.itatkd.com
Key Personnel
Founder & Pres: James S Benko
Founded: 1974
Catalog(s) available

Interscope, Geffen, A&M Records
Member of Universal Music Group
2220 Colorado Ave, Santa Monica, CA 90404
Tel: 310-865-4500
Web Site: www.interscope.com
Founded: 1999

Interscreen America Inc
13191 56 Ct, Suite 104, Clearwater, FL 33760
Tel: 727-546-8515 *Toll Free Tel:* 800-520-9642 *Toll Free Fax:* 866-476-0440
E-mail: info@interscreen.tv
Web Site: www.interscreen.us
Key Personnel
Mng Dir: Keith Olsen
Broadcast & professional video equipment for rent & sale.

Intersect Video
Subsidiary of Road's End Films Inc
25749 SW Canyon Creek Rd, Suite 300, Wilsonville, OR 97070
Tel: 971-224-4808
E-mail: info@intersectvideo.com
Web Site: www.intersectvideo.com
Key Personnel
Pres & Creative Dir: Robert Bruce
Dir, Opers: Sterling Flock
Prodr & Post Prodn Supv: Carey Flock
Professional video production, audio production & motion graphics, as well as multimedia localization & professional post-production for corporate, business & industrial customers.

Intersil Americas LLC
1001 Murphy Ranch Rd, Milpitas, CA 95035
Tel: 408-432-8888 *Toll Free Tel:* 888-INTERSIL (468-3774) *Fax:* 408-434-5351
Web Site: www.intersil.com
Key Personnel
CEO, Pres & Dir: Necip Sayiner
CFO & SVP: Rick Crowley
Founded: 1967
Analog circuit, semi-conductors.
Branch Office(s)
1650 Robert J Conlan Blvd NE, Palm Bay, FL 32905 *Tel:* 321-724-7000 *Fax:* 321-729-7320
Foreign Office(s): Unit 1507-11, One ICC, Shanghai ICC, 999 Middle Huaihai Rd, Shanghai 200031, China *Tel:* (021) 6335-1198 *Fax:* (021) 6335-1958
Han Tang Bldg, Suite 701, Overseas Chinese Town, Shenzhen 518053, China *Tel:* (0755) 8246-5118 *Fax:* (0755) 8246-1718
Oskar-Messter-Str 29, 85737 Ismaning, Germany *Tel:* (089) 46263-0 *Fax:* (089) 46263-148
8F, Nihon Seimei, Kyoto Santetsu Bldg, 608-9, Higashi Shiokoji-cho, Nishinotoin-Dori, Shiokoji-Agaru, Shimogyo-ku, Kyoto 600-8216, Japan *Tel:* (075) 342-2381 *Fax:* (075) 342-2380
6F, Mita Nitto Daibiru, 3-11-36, Mita, Minato-ku, Tokyo 108-0073, Japan *Tel:* (03) 5439-2311 *Fax:* (03) 5439-2300
Hampshire Place Off, Suite A-13-1, 157 Hampshire, No 1, Jl Mayang Sari, 50450 Kuala Lumpur, Malaysia *Tel:* (03) 2180 7888 *Fax:* (03) 2180 7840
Warwick House, Roydon Rd, Harlow, Essex CM19 5DX, United Kingdom *Tel:* (01279) 630900 *Fax:* (01279) 630938

Interstate Connecting Components
Division of Heilind Mil-Aero LLC
120 Mount Holly Bypass, Lumberton, NJ 08048-1112
Tel: 856-722-5535 *Toll Free Tel:* 888-881-5420 *Fax:* 856-813-5419
E-mail: info@connecticc.com
Web Site: www.connecticc.com
Key Personnel
Pres: Scott Jacobs *Tel:* 856-722-5535 ext 102 *E-mail:* scott@connecticc.com

Founded: 1985
Distribution of audio connectors & custom cable assemblies.
Catalog(s) available
Branch Office(s)
6701 Katella Ave, Suite 200, Cypress, CA 90630 *Toll Free Tel:* 888-913-3509 *Toll Free Fax:* 888-913-3578
6565 Americas Pkwy NE, Suite 232, Albuquerque, NM 87110 *Toll Free Tel:* 888-913-3598 *Fax:* 856-813-5401
200 Broadhollow Rd, Suite 207, Melville, NY 11747 *Toll Free Tel:* 888-881-5419 *Fax:* 856-813-5454

Intervideo Duplication Services
Division of International Historic Films Inc
3533 S Archer Ave, Chicago, IL 60609
Tel: 773-927-9091 *Fax:* 773-927-9211
E-mail: info@intervideoduplication.com
Web Site: www.intervideoduplication.com
Key Personnel
Pres: Peter Bernotas
DVD & CD duplication. Film to video transfers. Format conversions & archival tape transfers.
Membership(s): Entertainment Merchants Association

InterVision Media
44 W Broadway, Suite 426, Eugene, OR 97401
Tel: 541-343-7993 *Fax:* 541-345-5951
E-mail: info@intervisionmedia.com
Web Site: www.intervisionmedia.com
Key Personnel
Principal: Steve Christiansen
Founded: 1983
Full service design & development for web, interactive media & video.
Catalog(s) available
Membership(s): Mid-Oregon Production Arts Network

InVision Productions
821 Las Colindas Rd, San Rafael, CA 94903
Tel: 415-492-0414
E-mail: invision@goinvision.com
Web Site: www.goinvision.com
Key Personnel
Partner: Andrew Neddermeyer *Tel:* 415-497-1651 (cell) *E-mail:* andy@goinvision.com; Elaine G Trotter *Tel:* 415-328-9423 (cell) *E-mail:* et@goinvision.com
Production services, video assistance for film, location shooting & video engineering.

Iowa State University-Information Technology Services
1200 Communications Bldg, Ames, IA 50011-3243
Tel: 515-294-6014 (multimedia & streaming prodn) *Fax:* 515-294-8089
Web Site: www.it.iastate.edu
Key Personnel
Asst Dir, Academic Technologies: James Twetten *Tel:* 515-294-2317 *E-mail:* jtwetten@iastate.edu

Ipitek
2330 Faraday Ave, Carlsbad, CA 92008
Tel: 760-438-1010 *Toll Free Tel:* 888-4-IPITEK (447-4835, US) *Fax:* 760-438-2412
E-mail: sales@ipitek.com
Web Site: www.ipitek.com
Key Personnel
Founder, Chmn of the Bd & CEO: Michael Salour *E-mail:* msalour@ipitek.com
Cust Serv Mgr: Mary Ellen Mann *Tel:* 760-438-1010 ext 3284
Founded: 1980
Digital video transport for analog video or HDTV.
Catalog(s), free, paper
CD-ROM catalog(s), free
Membership(s): SCTE; Video Services Forum

iProbe Multilingual Solutions Inc
273 E Third St, New York, NY 10009
Mailing Address: PO Box 77, New York, NY 10156
Tel: 212-489-6035 *Toll Free Tel:* 888-489-6035 *Fax:* 212-202-4790
E-mail: info@iprobesolutions.com
Web Site: www.iprobesolutions.com
Founded: 2001
Sale & rental of simultaneous interpretation equipment including Williams Sound, Listen Technologies, Telex SoundMate, Bosch Integrus, Bosch Next Generation, Danish Interpretation Systems (DIS); interpreter booths, wireless systems (Shure).
Services: Translation, language dubbing; video closed captioning, subtitling & transcription.

iQstor Networks Inc
2001 Corporate Center Dr, Newbury Park, CA 91320
Tel: 805-376-1000
E-mail: sales@iqstor.com
Web Site: www.iqstor.com
Key Personnel
Founder & CEO: Jason Lo
Founded: 2002
Provide network & storage technology.
Foreign Office(s): iQstor Technology (Beijing) Ltd, 5 E Shangdi Rd, Haidan, Beijing 100085, China *Tel:* (010) 6297 4477 *Fax:* (010) 6296 7772 *E-mail:* info@iqstor.com.cn
iQstor Asia Ltd, Hong Kong Science Park West Ave, Unit 217, 2/F, Shatin, NT, Hong Kong *Tel:* 2155 6488 *Fax:* 2155 9488

Irish Music Corp
PO Box 1515, Green Island, NY 12183-1515
Tel: 518-266-0765 *Toll Free Tel:* 800-458-7346; 800-854-3746 (sales)
E-mail: info@regorecords.com
Web Site: www.regorecords.com
Founded: 1916
Irish music on CD & DVD.
Catalog(s) available

Iron Ring Communications Ltd
431 Brookmill Rd, Unit 1, Oakville, ON L6J 5K6, Canada
Tel: 905-849-5922 *Fax:* 905-849-6188
Web Site: www.ironringltd.com
Key Personnel
Pres: Dennis Towell *E-mail:* dtowell@ironringltd.com
Founded: 1988

Ironbound Film & Television Studios LLC
Newark Arts & Entertainment Bldg, 169 Malvern St, Newark, NJ 07105
Tel: 201-456-4754
Web Site: www.ironboundfilmstudios.com
Key Personnel
Contact: Peter Meister *E-mail:* peter.meister@ironboundfilmstudios.com; Mary Beth O'Connor *Tel:* 917-842-9571 (cell) *E-mail:* mb@luckyviii.com
Offers facilities for television, motion picture & digital media productions.

Ironik Design & Post
56 E Main St, Suite 203, Avon, CT 06001
Tel: 860-404-2386 *Fax:* 860-404-2735
E-mail: info@ironikdesign.com
Web Site: www.ironikdesign.com
Key Personnel
Pres: Sean E Stall *E-mail:* sean@ironikdesign.com
Prodn & Facility Mgr: Angela Pace-Stall *E-mail:* angela@ironikdesign.com
Graphic design & post-production company specializing in editorial & finishing processes of standard definition & HD content. Avid Media Composer, Avid DS, Discreet Combustion, DVD authoring, Avid Xpress Pro & Adobe Suite.

Ironstone Technologies
534 Berry St, Winnipeg, MB R3H 0R9, Canada
Tel: 204-697-0159 *Toll Free Tel:* 800-665-4766 *Fax:* 204-694-9355
E-mail: info@ironstone.ca
Web Site: www.ironstone.ca
Key Personnel
Pres: Joel Remis *E-mail:* jremis@ironstone.ca
Founded: 1992
CD & DVD duplication service bureau & DVD authoring. Manufacture digital storage solutions.

ISCAN Inc
21 Cabot Rd, Woburn, MA 01801
Tel: 781-932-1199 *Fax:* 781-932-1155
E-mail: info@iscaninc.com
Web Site: www.iscaninc.com
Key Personnel
Pres: Rikki Razdan
Founded: 1980
Manufacture motion sensors.
Catalog(s) available

Ishtar Films
12400 Moorpark St, Suite 2, Studio City, CA 91604
Toll Free Tel: 800-428-7136 *Fax:* 818-985-0567
E-mail: ishtarfilms2@sbcglobal.net
Web Site: www.ishtarfilms.com
Key Personnel
Owner & Pres: Martha Wheelock
Founded: 1976
Catalog(s) available
Membership(s): Alliance of Women Directors; International Documentary Association

Island Cases
1121-20 Lincoln Ave, Holbrook, NY 11741
Tel: 631-563-0633 *Toll Free Tel:* 877-824-3199 *Fax:* 631-563-1390; 631-563-0608
E-mail: sales@roadcasesusa.com
Web Site: www.islandcases.com; www.roadcasesusa.com
Key Personnel
Sales: Bruce Papa
Founded: 1978
Manufacture & distribute shipping cases.
Catalog(s) available

ITA Audio Visual Solutions
2162 Dana Ave & I-71, Cincinnati, OH 45207
Tel: 513-631-7000 *Toll Free Tel:* 800-899-8877 *Fax:* 513-631-3290; 513-631-8877
E-mail: csr@ita.com
Web Site: www.ita.com
Key Personnel
Pres: Mark Greene
Dir, Tech Servs: Marcus Davies
Regl Mgr, Rental Opers: Dennis Segrist
Founded: 1982
AV equipment rental, sales & service; creative & convention services & video production. Edit & record DVDs.
Catalog(s) available
Branch Office(s)
3033 E 14 Ave, Columbus, OH 43219 *Tel:* 614-258-2900
2309 Dryden Rd, Dayton, OH 45439 *Tel:* 937-298-8880
Membership(s): InfoComm International®; NSCA

ITC Learning LLC
1616 Anderson Rd, Suite 109, McLean, VA 22102
Toll Free Tel: 800-638-3757
E-mail: sales@itclearning.com
Web Site: www.itclearning.com
Key Personnel
Co-Founder: Bill Walton *E-mail:* bwalton@itclearning.com
Cust Support: Adam Kovic *E-mail:* akovic@itclearning.com
Founded: 1977
Industrial skills training courseware.
Catalog(s) available

ITEC Entertainment Corp
8544 Commodity Circle, Orlando, FL 32819
Tel: 407-226-0200 *Fax:* 407-226-0201
E-mail: productionsinfo@itec.com
Web Site: www.itec.com
Key Personnel
Owner: Bill Coan
Computer graphic design company.
Membership(s): IAAPA; National Association of Display Industries

ITT Veam LLC
Division of ITT Industries
100 New Wood Rd, Watertown, CT 06795
Tel: 860-274-9681 *Fax:* 860-274-4963
Web Site: www.ittcannon.com
Manufacture electrical connectors.
Catalog(s) available

ITV Productions
1649 S Robertson Blvd, Los Angeles, CA 90035
Tel: 310-204-1234
E-mail: itvproductions1@gmail.com
Web Site: www.itvproductions.com
Key Personnel
Owner & Pres: Cid Hunter
Founded: 1971

IV Media Resources
910 Redwing Dr, Geneva, IL 60134
Tel: 630-389-0000 *Fax:* 630-389-0208
E-mail: info@infinitevideo.com
Web Site: www.infinitevideo.com
Key Personnel
Owner: Nancy Ellen Temple
Founded: 1982
Corporate/industrial video production, multimedia DVD duplication & related services. Transfer slides & film to DVD.

iVideo Technologies
14885 Sprague Rd, Cleveland, OH 44136
Tel: 440-891-9440 *Toll Free Tel:* 800-352-6150 *Fax:* 440-891-9450
E-mail: info@ivideo.com
Web Site: www.ivideo.com
Key Personnel
Pres: Timothy Czyzak
Serv Dir: Ron McGlothlin
Regl Sales Mgr: David Walters
Founded: 1968
Systems integration.
Catalog(s) available
Branch Office(s)
659 Lakeview Plaza, Suite C, Columbus, OH 43085 *Tel:* 614-509-2360 *Fax:* 614-825-1003
Sales Office(s): 6851 Steger Dr, Cincinatti, OH 45237 *Tel:* 513-624-8666 *Fax:* 513-624-6407
Membership(s): ITVG; National Foundation of Independent Businesses; NSCA; SBE; SMPTE

Ivie Technologies Inc
1195 Spring Creek Place, Suite B, Springville, UT 84663
Tel: 801-489-8703 *Toll Free Fax:* 877-829-6567
E-mail: ivie@ivie.com
Web Site: www.ivie.com
Key Personnel
CEO & Pres: Scott Merrell
CFO: Don Merrell
Dir, Mktg: Bill Raventos
Founded: 1965
Foreign Office(s): Ivie Europe, Milan, Pzza Bonaparte 22/E, 20030 Bovisio M MI, Italy *Tel:* (0362) 571116 *Fax:* (0362) 596220 *E-mail:* info@audionetwork.it

Ivory Productions
529 Plymouth Rd, Gwynedd Valley, PA 19437
Mailing Address: PO Box 679, Gwynedd Valley, PA 19437-0679
Tel: 215-591-9900
E-mail: divory@comcast.net
Web Site: www.ivoryproductions.com
Key Personnel
Owner: David Ivory *E-mail:* david@ivoryproductions.com
Musical production & engineering.
Membership(s): The Recording Academy

IVS Imaging
Division of Costar Video Systems LLC
101 Wrangler Dr, Suite 201, Coppell, TX 75019
Toll Free Tel: 888-446-1301 *Fax:* 469-635-6800
E-mail: info@ivsimaging.com
Web Site: www.ivsimaging.com
Key Personnel
Div Mgr: Steve Belden *E-mail:* steveb@ivsimaging.com
Video parts distributor. Machine/industrial camera & accessories distributor.
Catalog(s) available
Membership(s): Automated Imaging Association

J & D Laboratories Inc
27 E 21 St, New York, NY 10010
Tel: 212-982-3330 *Toll Free Tel:* 800-535-2201 *Fax:* 212-982-3332
E-mail: jdvideolab@aol.com
Web Site: jdvideolab.com
Key Personnel
Pres: Joseph David *E-mail:* joe@jdvideolab.com
VP: Patricia David
Founded: 1966
Video duplication & editing, CD & DVD replication.
Catalog(s) available

J & R Film Co
1135 N Mansfield Ave, Hollywood, CA 90038
Tel: 323-467-1116 *Toll Free Tel:* 877-668-4652 *Fax:* 323-464-1518
Web Site: www.moviola.com
Key Personnel
CEO: Joe Paskal
Pres: Randy Paskal
SVP: Michael Mostin *E-mail:* mmostin@moviola.com
Cust Serv: Michelle Frazier
Founded: 1924
Total solutions provider for production, post editing & education.
Catalog(s) available
Branch Office(s)
545 W 45 St, 4th fl, New York, NY 10036 *Tel:* 212-247-8722 *Fax:* 212-265-0972
Membership(s): InfoComm International®; SMPTE

J K Audio Inc
1311 E Sixth St, Sandwich, IL 60548
Tel: 815-786-2929 *Toll Free Tel:* 800-552-8346 *Fax:* 815-786-8502
E-mail: info@jkaudio.com
Web Site: www.jkaudio.com
Key Personnel
Owner: Joseph Klinger
Founded: 1992
Manufacture telephone audio interface products.
Catalog(s) available

Jack's Camera Shop
300 E Main St, Muncie, IN 47305
Tel: 765-282-0204 *Fax:* 765-284-6405
E-mail: info@jackscamera.com
Web Site: jackscamera.com
Founded: 1948
Sells & rents photographic & video equipment & supplies.

JaffeHolden
114-A Washington St, Norwalk, CT 06854
Tel: 203-838-4167 *Fax:* 203-838-4168
Web Site: www.jaffeholden.com
Key Personnel
Chmn: Mark Holden
Pres: Russell Cooper *Tel:* 203-838-4167 ext 113 *E-mail:* rcooper@jaffeholden.com
Principal, Acoustics: Mark Reber *E-mail:* mreber@jaffeholden.com
Founded: 1968
Catalog(s) available

Jaguar Distribution Corp
12711 Ventura Blvd, Suite 300, Studio City, CA 91604
Tel: 818-508-3377 *Fax:* 818-508-3340
Web Site: www.jaguardc.com
Key Personnel
Pres: Jeff Klein
VP: Peter George
Dir, Acq & Publicity: Mona Kwan
Founded: 1982

Jaguar Productions
PO Box 121014, Nashville, TN 37212-1014
Tel: 615-391-4393 (off); 615-390-4161 (cell)
Web Site: www.jaguarvideoproductions.com
Key Personnel
Owner & Pres: Jerry Gibbs *E-mail:* jerry@jaguarproductions.com
Founded: 1990
Production, acquisition services, electronic news gathering & electronic field production crew.

Jalbert Productions International
230 New York Ave, Huntington, NY 11743
Tel: 631-351-5878 *Fax:* 631-351-5875
E-mail: info@jalbertfilm.com
Web Site: www.jalbertfilm.com
Key Personnel
VP, Syndication Sales: Carol Randel
Founded: 1970
Producer of sports videos & sports TV programming.
Catalog(s) available

JAM Industries Ltd
21000 Trans-Canadienne, Baie D'Urfe, QC H9X 4B7, Canada
Tel: 514-457-2555 *Fax:* 514-457-0055
E-mail: info@jamindustries.com
Web Site: www.jamindustries.com
Key Personnel
VP, Erikson Audio: Jeff Carman
Founded: 1972
Distributor.

Jameco Electronics
1355 Shoreway Rd, Belmont, CA 94002-4105
Tel: 650-592-8097 *Toll Free Tel:* 800-831-4242 (orders); 800-536-4316 (cust serv) *Fax:* 650-592-2503 *Toll Free Fax:* 800-237-6948
E-mail: info@jameco.com; sales@jameco.com
Web Site: www.jameco.com
Key Personnel
CEO: James Farrey
VP, Mktg & Sales: Greg Harris

Mktg Dir: Angela Avanzino *Tel:* 650-592-8097 ext 507 *E-mail:* angela@jameco.com
Mgr, IT: Matt Smith
Mgr, Fin & Acctg: Ester Baldovino
Founded: 1974
Distributing electronic components.
Catalog(s), quarterly, free

James Agee Film Project
PO Box 73, Riverdale, MD 20738-0073
Tel: 301-277-3880
E-mail: jagee@cstone.net
Web Site: www.ageefilms.org
Key Personnel
Dir & Pres: Ross Spears
Catalog(s) available
Branch Office(s)
913 Althea St, Johnson City, TN 37601

Jamieson & Associates Inc
Affiliate of AVSense Productions Division
4133 W 45 St, Minneapolis, MN 55424-1040
Tel: 952-920-3770
E-mail: info@jamieson.com
Web Site: www.jamieson.com
Key Personnel
Pres: Richard N Jamieson
VP: Marjorie Jamieson
VP, Sales & Mktg: Richard S Jamieson
Founded: 1972
AV & system design.
Membership(s): AES; SID; SMPTE

Jams Productions Inc
Production Trailer No 1, 2206 Holt Rd, Bowmanville, ON L1C 3K7, Canada
Tel: 647-273-4844 *Fax:* 905-623-2895
E-mail: info@jamsproductions.ca
Web Site: www.jamsproductions.ca
Key Personnel
Prodr: Alan J Schwarz *E-mail:* alan@jamsproductions.ca; Susan Schwarz *E-mail:* susan@jamsproductions.ca
Founded: 1990
Independent TV production company.

JamSync
Music Row, 1232 17 Ave S, Nashville, TN 37212-2802
Mailing Address: PO Box 120969, Nashville, TN 37212-0969
Tel: 615-320-5050 *Fax:* 615-340-9559
E-mail: info@jamsync.com
Web Site: www.jamsync.com
Key Personnel
Pres: K K Proffitt *E-mail:* kk@jamsync.com
Founded: 1997
Membership(s): AES; Nashville Film Festival; WIFT

Jan-Al Cases
3339 Union Pacific Ave, Los Angeles, CA 90023
Mailing Address: PO Box 23337, Los Angeles, CA 90023
Tel: 323-260-7212 *Toll Free Tel:* 800-735-2625 *Fax:* 323-260-4696
Web Site: www.janalcase.com
Key Personnel
Owner & Corp Sales: Jan M Alejandro *Tel:* 323-260-7212 ext 140 *E-mail:* jan@janalcase.com
Pres: Miriam (Muffie) Alejandro *Tel:* 323-260-7212 ext 120 *E-mail:* muffie@janalcase.com
Founded: 1983
Manufacture ATA 300 CAT 1 custom cases & design solutions for any tradeshow. Thousands of designs on file.
Membership(s): Institute of Packaging Professionals; NAMM, the National Association of Music Merchants

J&S Audio Visual Inc
9150 N Royal Lane, Suite 150, Irving, TX 75063
Tel: 972-241-5444 *Toll Free Tel:* 800-852-8771 *Fax:* 972-247-2590
E-mail: info@jsav.com
Web Site: www.jsav.com
Key Personnel
CEO & Pres: Monroe Jost
VP: Kevin Jost *E-mail:* kevinj@jsav.com; Todd Jost
Purch Agent: Kris Gutz
Shipping Contact: Mauro Castillo
Founded: 1986
Catalog(s) available
Branch Office(s)
1301 S Jason St, Unit A, Denver, CO 80223, Contact: Chris Brennan *Tel:* 303-792-5588 *Toll Free Tel:* 800-835-7966 *Fax:* 303-792-5599
5849 Westview, Houston, TX 77055, Contact: Jeff Wilson *Tel:* 713-957-4567 *Toll Free Tel:* 800-795-2244 *Fax:* 713-957-4622

Janson Industries
1200 Garfield Ave SW, Canton, OH 44706
Tel: 330-455-7029 *Toll Free Tel:* 800-548-8982 *Fax:* 330-455-5919
Web Site: www.jansonindustries.com
Key Personnel
Owner & Mktg Mgr: R K Janson
Founded: 1936
Manufacture & design of stage equipment.
Catalog(s) available

Janson Media
118 Main St, Tappan, NY 10983
Tel: 845-359-8488
E-mail: info@janson.com
Web Site: www.janson.com
Key Personnel
Pres: Stephen Janson *E-mail:* stephen.janson@janson.com
VP: Zara Janson *E-mail:* zara.janson@janson.com
Mktg Dir: Betsy Van Ost *E-mail:* betsy.vanost@janson.com
Founded: 1989
Distribute videos, DVDs & films.
Catalog(s) available
Membership(s): NATPE

January Productions, see Educational Impressions

Janus Films Inc
215 Park Ave S, 5th fl, New York, NY 10003
Tel: 212-756-8822 *Fax:* 212-756-8850
Web Site: www.criterion.com
Key Personnel
Mng Dir: Jon Mulvaney *E-mail:* mulvaney@criterion.com
Distribute contemporary & classical film.
Brochure(s) available
Catalog(s) available

Javboy Records
408 Kingston Dr, Douglassville, PA 19518
Tel: 215-285-7444
E-mail: contact@javboyrecords.com
Web Site: www.javboyrecords.com
Key Personnel
Pres & Chief Engr: Ben Blakesley
Founded: 2001
Recording studio & production facility, audio recording & production, audio mixing, editing & mastering.

Jay Jay Record & Tape Co
102 Brookfield Lane, Geneva, IL 60134
Tel: 305-758-0000 *Fax:* 305-758-0000
Key Personnel
VP: Dorothy Flanagan
Founded: 1951
Nationwide distribution of Jay Jay records, tapes, CDs, cassettes, albums, 45 RPMs & home videos; also Drum Boy, Bonfire Records, White Eagle Records & many more.
Catalog(s) available
Membership(s): The Recording Academy

Jazzology
Division of George H Buck Junior Jazz Foundation
61 French Market Place, New Orleans, LA 70116
Tel: 504-525-5000 *Fax:* 504-525-1776
E-mail: info@jazzology.com
Web Site: www.jazzology.com
Key Personnel
Pres: George H Buck, Jr *E-mail:* geobuck@bellsouth.net
Parent of GHB, Audiophile, Circle, Southland, Progressive, Black Swan Records & Solo Art & American Music.
Catalog(s) available

JBK Cinequipt LLC
17940 N Tamiami Trail, No 222, North Fort Myers, FL 33903
Tel: 954-607-8440
E-mail: jbkfilm@yahoo.com; jbkcine@gmail.com
Web Site: www.jbkcinequipt.com
Founded: 1980
Design & manufacture accessories for film & video HD cameras. Repair cinema products & motion picture equipment.

JBL Professional
Division of JBL Inc
8500 Balboa Blvd, Northridge, CA 91329
Tel: 818-894-8850; 818-895-3498 *Fax:* 818-894-3479; 818-830-7865 (mktg); 818-830-7801 (sales)
E-mail: info@jblpro.com
Web Site: www.jblpro.com; www.harman.com
Key Personnel
Marcom Coord: Kerry Kapin
Manufacture & design professional loud speakers.
Catalog(s) available
Membership(s): AES; ASA; International Background Music Association; NAB; NSCA

JCS Video Productions
Division of Vosburgh Ventures
4617 Sequoia Park Ave, Las Vegas, NV 89139
Tel: 702-596-9291 (cell); 702-546-0150 *Toll Free Tel:* 800-791-8671 *Fax:* 702-546-0150
E-mail: jcsvideo@cox.net
Web Site: www.jcsvideo.com
Key Personnel
Owner & Pres: Jack M Vosburgh
Founded: 1987
Video production business, Betacam SP, DV, 36 inch media 100xR NLE, multimedia, commercials, local & cable TV programming.
Membership(s): MCA-I

JD Audio Visual Inc
1713 E Walnut St, Pasadena, CA 91106
Tel: 626-792-6682 *Toll Free Tel:* 800-532-8346 *Fax:* 626-796-6635
E-mail: sales@jdav.com
Web Site: www.jdav.com
Key Personnel
Owner: Kenneth L Dymmel *E-mail:* ken@jdav.com
Founded: 1959
Full service AV equipment company offering sales & rentals.
Catalog(s) available
Membership(s): InfoComm International®

JDS Video & Media Productions Inc
39870 Camden Ct, Temecula, CA 92591
Tel: 951-296-6715 *Toll Free Fax:* 866-737-2239

E-mail: info@jds-productions.com
Web Site: www.jds-productions.com
Key Personnel
Owner & Pres: Diane Strand
Full service video production company. HD production & post-production.
Membership(s): Media Communications Association

JDSU
430 N McCarthy Blvd, Milpitas, CA 95035
Tel: 408-546-5000 *Fax:* 408-546-4300
Web Site: www.jdsu.com
Key Personnel
CEO & Pres: Thomas Waechter
Exec Opers: Judith Kay

Jeep Jazz Media Solutions
8 Graham Terr, Montclair, NJ 07042
Tel: 973-222-5737
E-mail: jeepjazz@hotmail.com
Web Site: www.jeepjazz.com
Key Personnel
Pres: Shane Faber
Producer of jazz music tapes & CDs.

JEM Smoke Machine Co Ltd
Division of Martin Professional Inc
700 Sawgrass Corporate Pkwy, Sunrise, FL 33325
Tel: 954-858-1800 *Toll Free Tel:* 800-832-4180 *Fax:* 954-858-1811
E-mail: martinus@martinpro.com
Web Site: www.martinpro.com
Key Personnel
Pres: Brian Friborg *Tel:* 954-375-2813
Smoke & haze machines.
Catalog(s) available
Membership(s): Illuminating Engineering Society; Professional Lighting & Sound Association; USITT

Jensen Transformers Inc
9304 Deering Ave, Chatsworth, CA 91311
Tel: 818-374-5857 *Toll Free Tel:* 866-476-6291 *Fax:* 818-374-5856
E-mail: sales@jensen-transformers.com
Web Site: www.jensen-transformers.com
Key Personnel
Pres: Bill Whitlock
VP, Opers & Gen Mgr: Dave Hill
Manufacture audio equipment.
Catalog(s) available
Membership(s): AES; Custom Electronic Design & Installation Association; IEEE; InfoComm International®

Jeppesen
Division of Boeing Co
55 Inverness Dr E, Englewood, CO 80112
Tel: 303-799-9090 *Toll Free Tel:* 800-621-5377; 800-353-2107 *Fax:* 303-328-4153
Web Site: www.jeppesen.com
Key Personnel
CEO & Pres: Mark Van Tine
COO & SVP: Brad Thoman
Founded: 1934
Producing private pilot training kits.
Catalog(s) available

Jereco Studios Inc
627 E Peach St, Suite E, Bozeman, MT 59715
Tel: 406-586-5262 *Fax:* 406-586-5262
Web Site: www.jerecostudios.com
Key Personnel
Prodr & Sound Engr: Jeremiah Slovarp *E-mail:* jeremiah@jerecostudios.com
Dist Mgr: Luke Flansburg *E-mail:* luke@jerecostudios.com
Founded: 2002

Jeron Electronic Systems Inc
1743-55 W Rosehill Dr, Chicago, IL 60660
Tel: 773-275-1900 *Toll Free Tel:* 800-621-1903 *Fax:* 773-275-0283
E-mail: sales@jeron.com
Web Site: www.jeron.com
Key Personnel
VP, Mktg: Ericka C Baran *E-mail:* ebaran@jeron.com
Founded: 1965

JFA Studio
3062 N Lima St, Burbank, CA 91504
Tel: 818-861-9090
E-mail: info@jfastudio.com
Web Site: www.jfastudio.com
Studio facility for the film & TV industry. Equipment rental & full production & post-production services.

JFB Communications
3 Haig Ave, Toronto, ON M1N 2W2, Canada
Tel: 416-691-5001
E-mail: jfb@jfb.ca
Web Site: jfb.ca
Key Personnel
Pres: John Fulford-Brown
Founded: 1991
Corporate communications, film & television production.

JFW Industries Inc
5134 Commerce Square Dr, Indianapolis, IN 46237
Tel: 317-887-1340 *Toll Free Tel:* 877-887-4539 *Fax:* 317-881-6790
E-mail: sales@jfwindustries.com; jfwengr@jfwindustries.com
Web Site: www.jfwindustries.com
Key Personnel
Pres: Fred Walker
VP: Jim Leach
Mktg: Connie Ventress
Founded: 1979
Catalog(s) available

JIB Shots Equipment Inc
1828 Lorraine Ave, Ottawa, ON K1H 6Z8, Canada
Tel: 613-293-3318 *Fax:* 613-521-9312
Web Site: www.jibshots.com
Key Personnel
Owner: Graham Dunnell *E-mail:* graham@jibshots.com
Founded: 1999
Rentals & operation of specialized camera support (jibs, galaxy crane, golf carts).

Jin
Division of Swallow Publications Inc
238 E Main St, Ville Platte, LA 70586
Mailing Address: PO Drawer 10, Ville Platte, LA 70586-0010
Tel: 337-363-2177 *Fax:* 337-363-2094
E-mail: info@flattownmusic.com
Web Site: www.flattownmusic.com
Key Personnel
Pres: Floyd Soileau
Founded: 1957
Catalog(s) available

JIST Publishing
Division of EMC/Paradigm Publishing
875 Montreal Way, St Paul, MN 55102
Toll Free Tel: 800-328-1452 *Toll Free Fax:* 800-328-4564
E-mail: info@jist.com
Web Site: www.jist.com
Key Personnel
Mktg: Jelena Dehn
Founded: 1981
Career & job search books, videos & CD-ROMs.
Catalog(s) available

JL Recording Studios
270 Adelaide St W, Suite 202, Toronto, ON M5H 1X6, Canada
Tel: 416-598-7979
Web Site: www.jlstudios.ca; www.facebook.com/jlrecordingstudios; twitter.com/JLStudios
Key Personnel
Owner: Jeffrey LeClair
Proj Engr: Lorne Mower
Founded: 1994
Professional audio recording, editing & sound mixing studio.

JLCooper Electronics
142 Arena St, El Segundo, CA 90245-3901
Tel: 310-322-9990 *Fax:* 310-335-0110
E-mail: sales@jlcooper.com; service@jlcooper.com
Web Site: www.jlcooper.com
Founded: 1979
Catalog(s) available
Membership(s): AES; IBC; NAB; NAMM, the National Association of Music Merchants

JLG Industries
One JLG Dr, McConnellsburg, PA 17233
Tel: 717-485-5161 *Toll Free Tel:* 877-JLG-LIFT (554-5438) *Fax:* 717-485-6417
E-mail: comments@jlg.com
Web Site: www.jlg.com
Key Personnel
Multimedia Developer: Travis Abbott
Manufacturer of vertical personnel lifts.
Catalog(s), on request
Membership(s): ARA; NAB

JMC Photo & Digital Services Inc
10 Westport Ct, Bloomington, IL 61704-8233
Tel: 309-663-4677 *Fax:* 309-664-3973
E-mail: jmcpds@jmcpds.com
Web Site: www.jmcpds.com
Key Personnel
Owner: Ann Charback
Photofinishing, film processing & large format printing.
Brochure(s) available

JoeAudio
10850 John Galt Blvd, Omaha, NE 68137
Tel: 402-341-9153 *Toll Free Tel:* 866-JOE-AUDIO (563-2834)
Web Site: www.joeaudioproductions.com
Key Personnel
Pres & Prodr: Joe Wolf *E-mail:* joe@joeaudioproductions.com
Founded: 1992
Recording studio services for voiceover & audio post; ISDN, ProTools.

John McLean Media
802 Newton, Penthouse 3, Seattle, WA 98109
Tel: 206-285-2603
E-mail: info@johnmcleanmedia.com
Web Site: www.johnmcleanmedia.com
Key Personnel
Founder & Pres: John McLean
Founded: 1999
Video program distribution.

Alan Johnson Recording
5763 Park Plaza Ct, Indianapolis, IN 46220
Tel: 317-439-6521
E-mail: alan@alanjohnsonrecording.com
Web Site: www.alanjohnsonrecording.com
Key Personnel
Contact: Alan Johnson

Johnson Systems Inc (JSI)
1923 Highfield Crescent SE, Calgary, AB T2G 5M1, Canada
Tel: 403-287-8003 *Fax:* 403-287-9003
E-mail: info@johnsonsystems.com
Web Site: www.johnsonsystems.com
Key Personnel
Pres: Shaun Johnson
Founded: 1987
Manufactures lighting systems, lighting control products & equipment.
Catalog(s) available

Pamela Johnston Voice Talent
249 Eighth Ave, Cramerton, NC 28032
Tel: 703-371-7341 *Fax:* 703-997-8971
Web Site: www.pjvoicetalent.com
Key Personnel
Voice Talent: Pamela Johnston *E-mail:* pamela@pjvoicetalent.com
Founded: 1995
Voice talent, providing narrations & voiceovers for educational, e-learning, IVR, film, video, web, radio, TV & audiobook projects in English, Spanish & German.
Membership(s): Women in Film & Video; Women in Film/Atlanta

Jointure for Community Adult Education Inc
Centre at Raritan, Suite B-11, 1124 US Hwy 202 S, Raritan, NJ 08869
Tel: 908-722-0233; 908-874-4852 *Fax:* 908-722-0388
E-mail: jcaeinc@aol.com
Web Site: www.jointure.org
Key Personnel
Exec Dir: Erica Condon
Dir, Opers: Dianne Lewis *Tel:* 908-722-0233 ext 10
Founded: 1914
Adult education courses.
Catalog(s) available

JoLida Inc
21310 Ridgecroft Dr, Brookeville, MD 20833
Tel: 301-953-2014 *Fax:* 301-498-0554
E-mail: jolidacorp@msn.com
Web Site: www.jolida.com
Key Personnel
CEO: Mike Allen
Founded: 1983
Catalog(s) available

Jones Film Video
Subsidiary of CJRW
916 W Sixth St, Little Rock, AR 72201
Tel: 501-372-1981 *Toll Free Tel:* 800-880-1981 *Fax:* 501-372-4286
E-mail: info@jonesfilmvideo.com
Web Site: www.jonesfilmvideo.com
Key Personnel
Pres: Gary W Jones *E-mail:* gary@jonesfilmvideo.com
Sr Ed: Les Galusha
Founded: 1981
Film & video production company.
Membership(s): ADFED

Jordan Klein Film & Video (JKFV)
10197 SE 144 Place, Summerfield, FL 34491
Tel: 352-288-3999 *Fax:* 352-288-5538
Web Site: www.jordy.com
Key Personnel
Owner & Pres: Jordan Klein, Jr *Tel:* 352-427-2560 (cell) *E-mail:* jordy@jordy.com
Film & video production.
Catalog(s) available

Joseph Electronics
6633 W Howard St, Niles, IL 60714
Tel: 847-588-3800 *Toll Free Tel:* 800-323-5925 *Fax:* 847-588-3300 *Toll Free Fax:* 800-446-8366
E-mail: sales@josephelectronics.com
Web Site: www.josephelectronics.com
Key Personnel
CEO & Pres: Yohay Hahamy
Mktg Mgr: Chris Annella *E-mail:* chrisa@josephelectronics.com
Founded: 2001
Distributor of broadcast products & value added services.
Catalog(s) available
Branch Office(s)
Joseph Electronics West, 3045 Teagarden St, San Leandro, CA 94577 *Tel:* 510-352-7500 *Fax:* 510-352-7510
Membership(s): NAB; SBE; Sports Video Group; TAB; Wisconsin Broadcasters Association

Harry Joseph & Associates Inc
PO Box 20993, New York, NY 10025
Tel: 212-244-5900
E-mail: harry@hja.com
Web Site: www.hja.com
Key Personnel
Pres: Harry Joseph
Founded: 1974
Membership(s): SMPTE

Josephson Engineering Inc
329-A Ingalls St, Santa Cruz, CA 95060
Tel: 831-420-0888 *Fax:* 831-420-0890
E-mail: info@josephson.com
Web Site: www.josephson.com
Key Personnel
CEO & Dir: David Josephson
Founded: 1988
Catalog(s) available

Jossey-Bass
Division of John Wiley & Sons Inc
One Montgomery St, Suite 1200, San Francisco, CA 94104
Tel: 415-433-1740 *Fax:* 415-433-0499
Web Site: www.josseybass.com; www.wiley.com
Publishes books, training products & subscription materials in business, education & general interest.
Catalog(s) available

Joyce Media Inc
3413 Soledad Canyon Rd, Acton, CA 93510
Mailing Address: PO Box 57, Acton, CA 93510-0057
Tel: 661-269-1169 *Fax:* 661-269-2139
E-mail: help@joycemediainc.com
Web Site: www.joycemediainc.com
Key Personnel
CEO: John Joyce
Pres: Gayle Joyce
Founded: 1969
Educational DVDs including sign language songs & stories.
Online catalog(s), updated weekly

JPL
471 JPL Wick Dr, Harrisburg, PA 17111-2504
Tel: 717-558-8048 *Toll Free Tel:* 800-421-7697 *Fax:* 717-558-8349
E-mail: jpl@jplcreative.com
Web Site: www.jplcreative.com; www.facebook.com/jplcreative
Key Personnel
Dir of Communs: Susan Cort *E-mail:* scort@jplcreative.com
Founded: 1989
Strategic integrated communications. Video & media production.
Branch Office(s)
3355 Keswick Rd, Suite 300, Baltimore, MD 21211 *Tel:* 410-630-8440

JR Media Services
2501 W Burbank Blvd, Suite 200, Burbank, CA 91505
Tel: 818-557-0200 *Fax:* 818-557-0201
E-mail: info@jrmediaservices.com
Web Site: www.jrmediaservices.com
Key Personnel
Chmn & CEO: Max Beno
Pres: Robert Troy
Founded: 1979
Film editing.
Brochure(s) available
Membership(s): IDA; IFP West; Reel Black Women; Women in Film

JRF Magnetic Sciences Inc
249 Kennedy Rd, Greendell, NJ 07839
Mailing Address: PO Box 309, Greendell, NJ 07839-0309
Tel: 973-579-5773 *Fax:* 973-579-6021
E-mail: jrf@jrfmagnetics.com
Web Site: www.jrfmagnetics.com
Key Personnel
Pres: John French
Secy & Treas: Cookie French
Founded: 1979
Distribution & repair of magnetic recording equipment.
Catalog(s) available
Membership(s): AES; The Recording Academy

JSC Wire & Cable
Division of Seminole Wire & Cable
7861 Airport Hwy, Pennsauken, NJ 08109
Tel: 856-324-2929 *Toll Free Tel:* 800-572-9473 *Fax:* 973-694-8297
E-mail: sales@jscwire.com
Web Site: www.jscwire.com
Key Personnel
Pres: Michael Genzel
Founded: 1942
Manufacturer of wire & cable for the audio & video market.
Printed material(s), free

JT Communications
579 NE 44 Ave, Ocala, FL 34470-1421
Tel: 352-236-0744 *Fax:* 352-236-5130
E-mail: general_info@jtcomms.com
Web Site: www.jtcomms.com
Key Personnel
Owner: Jim Trapani
Founded: 1990
Manufacture & repair of audio equipment.
Catalog(s) available
Membership(s): AES

Juice
1648 Tenth St, Santa Monica, CA 90404
Tel: 310-460-7830 *Fax:* 310-460-7845
Web Site: www.juicewest.com
Key Personnel
Opers Mgr: Oscar Morales *E-mail:* oscar@juicewest.com
Founded: 1985
Audio recording & mixing facility.

Juice Goose
7320 Ashcroft, Suite 104, Houston, TX 77081
Tel: 713-772-1404 *Fax:* 713-772-7360
E-mail: info@juicegoose.com
Web Site: www.juicegoose.com
Key Personnel
VP: Peter M Cook *E-mail:* pcook@juicegoose.com
Catalog(s) available
Membership(s): InfoComm International®

JungleTV
571 NW Mercantile Place, Port St Lucie, FL 34986

Mailing Address: PO Box 881122, Port St Lucie, FL 34988-1122
Tel: 772-370-0043
E-mail: info@jungletv.com
Web Site: www.jungletv.com
Key Personnel
Dir & Exec Prodr: Michael Stankoski
Dir, Photog: Jon Schellenger
Founded: 1998
Offers a comprehensive suite of video & visual arts services that includes video production, post-production, commercial photography, file conversion services & video transfers/duplication.

Jupiter Moon Productions
53 Grand Haven Dr, Commack, NY 11725
Tel: 631-553-9750
Web Site: www.jupitermoonproductions.com
Key Personnel
Owner: Laura Serpico
Videography, producing & editing.

Jupiter Systems
31015 Huntwood Ave, Hayward, CA 94544
Tel: 510-675-1000 *Fax:* 510-675-1001
E-mail: sales@jupiter.com
Web Site: www.jupiter.com
Key Personnel
Co-Founder & Pres: Eric Wogsberg
Co-Founder & VP: Jack Klingelhofer
CFO: Bob Worthington
SVP, Worldwide Sales: Scott Sullivan
VP, Engg: Bob Gardyne
VP, Mktg & Strategic Alliances: Brady O Bruce
VP, Opers: Chuck Kelley
Founded: 1982
Worldwide supplier of visualization & collaboration solutions for video walls, PCs & mobile devices.
Foreign Office(s): Jupiter Systems China (Shenzhen) Ltd, Rm D501-503, 5th fl, Shenzhen Tech-Innovation Intl Bldg, 10 Kejinan Rd, Nashan, Shenzhen, China, Gen Mgr: Guomin Zhang *Tel:* (0755) 2672-7856 *E-mail:* gzhang@jupiter.com

Just Bulbs - The Light Bulb Store
220 E 60 St, New York, NY 10022
Tel: 212-888-5707 *Fax:* 212-888-5704
E-mail: sales@justbulbsnyc.com
Web Site: www.justbulbsnyc.com
Key Personnel
Pres: David Brooks *E-mail:* dbrooks@justbulbsnyc.com
Founded: 1980
Light bulbs of every description.

Juston Records
PO Box 362, New York, NY 10113-0362
Tel: 973-379-5538 *Fax:* 973-379-5538
E-mail: justonrecords@att.net
Key Personnel
Rep: Diana Sabatino *E-mail:* d.sabatino@att.net

JVC Professional Products Co
Division of JVC Americas Corp
1700 Valley Rd, Wayne, NJ 07470
Tel: 973-317-5000 *Toll Free Tel:* 800-582-5825; 800-247-3608; 800-252-5722 *Fax:* 973-317-5030 *Toll Free Fax:* 800-582-5825 (option 2)
E-mail: proinfo@jvc.com
Web Site: www.jvc.com
Key Personnel
SVP: Larry Librach
Catalog(s) available
Membership(s): AES; Content Delivery & Storage Association; MCA-I; NAB; NCTA; PPA; SBE; SMPTE; SPARS

JWP Inc
PO Box 14867, Fort Worth, TX 76117
Tel: 817-233-6462 *Fax:* 817-439-2353
Web Site: www.jwproductions.org
Key Personnel
Owner & Exec Prodr: Jeff Watts
E-mail: jeffwatts@jwproductions.org
Full service production company. Equipment includes both HD & SD cameras.

K-SAR Video & DVD Productions
Center for Persons with Disabilities, Utah Univ Ctr of Excellence, 6800 Old Main Hill, Logan, UT 84322-6800
Tel: 435-797-1981 *Fax:* 435-797-3944
Web Site: www.cpdusa.org
Key Personnel
Contact: Todd Newman *Tel:* 435-797-2020

K2B2 Records
1748 Roosevelt Ave, Los Angeles, CA 90006
Web Site: k2b2.com
Key Personnel
Pres: Marty Krystall *Tel:* 213-705-1248 (cell)
E-mail: marty@k2b2.com
Founded: 1979
On-site mastering, production, editing, jazz record label.
Catalog(s) available
Membership(s): American Federation of Musicians; ASCAP; Recording Musicians of America

Ka Io Productions Inc
PO Box 5150, Hilo, HI 96720-1150
Tel: 808-959-3885 *Toll Free Tel:* 888-458-7538
Fax: 808-959-3885
E-mail: lava@volcanovideo.com
Web Site: www.volcanovideo.com
Key Personnel
Pres: Cheryl Gansecki
VP: Jenda Johnson
Founded: 1987
Produce & distribute educational & scientific videos on DVD & Blu-ray; production of stock footage, particularly of volcanic eruptions.

KABA Audio Productions
Subsidiary of KABA Enterprises Inc
PO Box 5357, Petaluma, CA 94955
Tel: 707-765-9900
E-mail: info@kabaaudio.com
Web Site: www.kabaaudio.com
Key Personnel
Pres: Paul Bacon
Founded: 1974
Reproduction services (audio); distribute & produce replication CDs, DVDs, graphics, music, health program, self-improvement training tapes.
Catalog(s) available
Membership(s): AES; Raggae Ambassadors Worldwide; The Recording Academy

Kaboom Productions
1465 Illinois St, San Francisco, CA 94107
Tel: 415-434-2666 *Fax:* 415-970-8548
E-mail: updates@kaboomproductions.com
Web Site: kaboomproductions.com
Key Personnel
Dir: Michele Atkins; Brandon Dickerson; Matt Fackrell; Kent Harvey; Reynir Lyngdal; Joe Meade; Erik Moe; Gary Shaffer; Joe Stevens; Doug Werby
Exec Prodr: Lauren Schwartz *E-mail:* lauren@kaboomproductions.com
Head, Prodn: Steven Sills
Founded: 1996
Full service television, music video, feature film & commercial production company.
Branch Office(s)
13045 Pacific Promenade, Loft 320, Los Angeles, CA 90094 *Tel:* 818-985-2666

Kabuki
63 rue Gaudet, Cap-Pele, NB E4N 1T8, Canada
Tel: 506-577-6326 *Toll Free Tel:* 800-461-7625
Fax: 506-577-2875 *Toll Free Fax:* 800-461-4329
E-mail: info@kabuki.com
Web Site: www.kabuki.com
Key Personnel
Pres: Ray Hebert
Founded: 1990
Manufacturer.
Catalog(s) available

KAE Corp
955 E 500 S, Salt Lake City, UT 84102
Tel: 801-238-2300 *Fax:* 801-238-3900
E-mail: kaecorp@xmission.com
Web Site: www.kaecorp.com
Key Personnel
Pres: Ed Scott
Founded: 1998
Rack accessory products.
Catalog(s) available
Membership(s): NAB

Kajo Co
2081 E Bellerive Place, Chandler, AZ 85249-4131
Tel: 480-830-9798 *Fax:* 480-883-3022
Web Site: www.kajoco.com
Key Personnel
Owner: John McGuire *E-mail:* john@kajoco.com
Founded: 1993
Distribute velcro reusable slotted tie wraps for bundling cords & cables, anti-slip glow-in-the dark adhesive tape & Gaffer's & tunnel tape.
Catalog(s) available

KAKE-TV
Subsidiary of Gray Television Inc
1500 N West St, Wichita, KS 67203-1323
Tel: 316-943-4221; 316-946-1314 (sales)
Fax: 316-943-5493
Web Site: kake.com
Key Personnel
Dir, Opers: Patrick G Myers *Tel:* 316-946-1328
E-mail: patrick.myers@kake.com
News Dir: Michael Sipes *E-mail:* michael.sipes@kake.com
Asst News Dir: Dave Grant *E-mail:* dave.grant@kake.com
Gen Sales Mgr: George Brown *E-mail:* george.brown@kake.com
Founded: 1954

Kaleidosound
3883 Campolindo Dr, Moraga, CA 94556
Tel: 925-283-9901
Web Site: www.k-sound.com
Key Personnel
Owner & Consultant: Forrest G Patten
E-mail: forrest@k-sound.com
Founded: 1978
Membership(s): ASCAP; NATAS

Kalglo Electronics Co Inc
5911 Colony Dr, Bethlehem, PA 18017-9348
Tel: 610-837-0700 *Fax:* 610-837-7978
E-mail: kalglo@kalglo.com
Web Site: www.kalglo.com
Key Personnel
Pres: R Bruce MacDougall
Founded: 1969
Manufacture surge protectors, voltage & power line protectors.

Kamen Entertainment Group Inc
200 E 94 St, New York, NY 10128
Tel: 212-575-4660 *Fax:* 212-575-4799
E-mail: kamen@kamen.com
Web Site: www.kamen.com
Key Personnel
Owner & Creative Dir: Marina Kamen
Owner & Tech Dir: Roy Kamen
Full service recording & live entertainment company, including music & audio production.
Membership(s): The Recording Academy; SPARS

K&R All Media Productions Inc
28533 Greenfield, Southfield, MI 48076
Tel: 248-557-8276 *Toll Free Tel:* 888-802-0420
Web Site: www.knr.net
Key Personnel
Prodr & Engr: Dan Hanley
Engg: Ken Glaza *E-mail:* ken@kandrforensic.com
Founded: 1973
Recording studio with forensic expertise.
Online catalog(s) available

K&R Photo Digital
538 Terry Lane, Fort Mitchell, KY 41017
Tel: 859-341-6998 *Fax:* 859-341-6987
E-mail: photodigitalpro@mac.com
Web Site: www.krphotodigital.com
Key Personnel
Owner: Rob Kumler
Membership(s): AIE™

K&R's Recording Studios Inc
28533 Greenfield, Southfield, MI 48076
Tel: 248-557-8276
E-mail: recordav@knr.net
Web Site: www.knr.net
Key Personnel
Owner & Pres: Kenneth Glaza
Recording studio providing forensic qualifications & services.
Online catalog(s) available

Kangaroo Cases
4027 Main St, Dallas, TX 75226
Tel: 214-823-5264 *Toll Free Tel:* 800-890-1073 *Fax:* 214-824-1179
E-mail: info@kangaroocases.com
Web Site: www.kangaroocases.com
Key Personnel
Pres & CEO: David Chandler
Case manufacturing.
Catalog(s), upon request

Kantola Productions LLC
55 Sunnyside Ave, Mill Valley, CA 94941
Tel: 415-381-9363 *Toll Free Tel:* 800-280-1180 *Fax:* 415-381-9801
E-mail: kantola@kantola.com
Web Site: www.kantola.com
Key Personnel
Pres: Steve Kantola
Founded: 1985
Business training videos.
Catalog(s) available

Richard Kaplan Productions
455 N End Ave, Apt 1114, New York, NY 10282-1139
Tel: 212-787-0258 *Fax:* 212-787-0268
E-mail: richardkaplan33@gmail.com
Web Site: www.richardkaplanproductions.com
Key Personnel
Pres: Richard Kaplan

Kappa Map Group LLC
112 E New York Ave, Deland, FL 32724
Tel: 386-873-3010 *Toll Free Tel:* 800-829-6277 (cust serv) *Fax:* 386-873-3011
E-mail: info@kappamapgroup.com
Web Site: kappamapgroup.com
Key Personnel
Mktg Mgr: Christine Ecarius
Branch Office(s)
Kappa Publishing Group Inc, 6198 Butler Pike, Suite 200, Blue Bell, PA 19422 (corp off)
Membership(s): Education Market Association; International Map Dealers Association

Kappa optronics Inc
Subsidiary of Kappa optronics GmbH
825 S Primrose Ave, Suite I, Monrovia, CA 91016
Tel: 626-256-4343 *Fax:* 626-256-6484
E-mail: info@kappa-optronics.com
Web Site: www.kappa-optronics.com
Key Personnel
Dir, Sales: Christian Koziol
Catalog(s) available

Karol Media Inc
Hanover Industrial Estates, 375 Stewart Rd, Wilkes-Barre, PA 18703
Tel: 570-822-8899 *Toll Free Tel:* 800-526-4773 *Fax:* 570-822-8226
E-mail: sales@karolmedia.com
Web Site: www.karolmedia.com
Key Personnel
VP: Michael Kincheloe
Founded: 1976
Full duplication services.
Catalog(s) available

Karst Productions Inc
5779 NE County Rd 340, High Springs, FL 32643
Tel: 386-454-2376 *Fax:* 386-454-2369
E-mail: images@karstproductions.com
Web Site: www.karstproductions.com

Kart-A-Bag Manufacturing Inc
Division of Remin Laboratories Inc
510 Manhattan Rd, Joliet, IL 60433
Tel: 815-723-1940 *Toll Free Tel:* 800-423-9328 *Fax:* 815-723-2495
E-mail: bks@kart-a-bag.com
Web Site: www.kart-a-bag.com
Key Personnel
Pres: Eugene Kazmark, Jr
VP, Mktg & Ad: Barbara Kazmark Starner
Founded: 1967
Manufacture heavy duty telescoping carts & hand trucks.
Catalog(s) available
Membership(s): LLGMA; NAB; Photo Marketing Association

KAS Music & Sound
Subsidiary of Kaufman Astoria Studios
34-12 36 St, Astoria, NY 11106
Tel: 718-786-3400 *Fax:* 718-729-3007
Web Site: www.kasmusic.com
Key Personnel
Exec Creative Dir: Joe Castellon *E-mail:* joe@kasmusic.com
Membership(s): AES; AFM; The Recording Academy; SPARS

Kavanagh Productions Inc
32 Broadway, Suite 1711-12, New York, NY 10004
Tel: 212-480-0065 *Fax:* 212-480-0149
E-mail: mail@kavanaghproductions.com
Web Site: www.kavanaghproductions.com
Key Personnel
Dir & Prodr: Bill Kavanagh
Ed: Sylke Froechtenigt
Production company & post-production house that specializes in documentary, live event video & corporate projects. Avid media composer, final cut pro. Field & multicamera production.
Membership(s): DCTV; Film Video Arts

Kavich Reynolds Productions Inc
6381 Hollywood Blvd, Suite 580, Hollywood, CA 90028
Tel: 323-466-2490 *Fax:* 323-466-3655
E-mail: info@kavichreynolds.com
Web Site: www.kavichreynolds.com
Key Personnel
CEO: Steve Kavich
Pres: John Reynolds
Full service AV production company.

Kay Industries Inc
227 N Dixie Way, South Bend, IN 46637
Tel: 574-236-6220 *Toll Free Tel:* 800-348-5257 *Fax:* 574-289-5932
E-mail: phasemaster@kayind.com; techsupp@kayind.com
Web Site: www.kayind.com
Catalog(s) available
Branch Office(s)
Power Solutions, 4127 Bay St, Suite 6, Fremont, CA 94538, Contact: Larry Katz *Tel:* 510-656-8766 *Fax:* 510-657-7283

KB Systems
10407 62 Place W, Mukilteo, WA 98275
Tel: 425-355-8740
E-mail: kbsystem@kbsystem.com
Web Site: www.kbsystem.com
Key Personnel
Mktg Mgr: Kay Reid
Contact: Bill Reid
Founded: 1970
Manufacture quality wood tripods for telescopes & cameras.
Catalog(s) available
Membership(s): PMA International

KCFW Television
401 First Ave E, Kalispell, MT 59901
Mailing Address: PO Box 857, Kalispell, MT 59903
Tel: 406-755-5239 *Fax:* 406-752-8002
E-mail: news@kcfw.com
Web Site: www.nbcmontana.com; www.kcfw.com
Key Personnel
News Dir: Chris Grogan *E-mail:* cgrogan@kcfw.com

KD Kanopy Inc
1921 E 68 Ave, Denver, CO 80229
Tel: 303-650-1310 *Toll Free Tel:* 800-432-4435 *Fax:* 303-650-5211
E-mail: sales@kdkanopy.com
Web Site: www.kdkanopy.com
Key Personnel
CEO & Pres: Matt Kayser
Founded: 1984
Manufacture canopies & tents used for remotes, concerts & on-location shoots, etc.
Catalog(s) available
Membership(s): GSA; NAB

KDM Electronics Inc
55 Mills Rd, Unit 3, Ajax, ON L1S 2H2, Canada
Tel: 416-439-7158 *Toll Free Tel:* 800-567-6282 *Fax:* 416-439-7232
E-mail: kdm@octasound.com
Web Site: www.octasound.com
Key Personnel
Pres: Ron Bull *E-mail:* ron@octasound.com
Gen Mgr: Martin Bull *E-mail:* martin@octasound.com
Sales & Mktg Mgr: Kevin Bull *E-mail:* kevin@octasound.com
Founded: 1976

KEF Media
1161 Concord Rd, Smyrna, GA 30080

Tel: 404-605-0009 *Toll Free Tel:* 866-219-2477 *Fax:* 404-605-0639
Web Site: www.kefmedia.com
Key Personnel
CEO, Founder: Kevin Foley
Co-Pres, Gen Mgr: Yvonne Goforth-Hanak
Co-Pres, Cust Serv, Sales & Mktg: Linda Buckley
SVP, Exec Prodr: Audrey Kelsey
Founded: 1986
Catalog(s) available

Kelmscott Communications
1665 Mallette Rd, Aurora, IL 60505-1354
Tel: 630-898-0800 *Fax:* 630-898-2183
Web Site: kelmscottcommunications.com
Key Personnel
VP, Mktg: Jason Tews *E-mail:* jtews@kelmscottcommunications.com
Founded: 1982
CD audio, CD-ROM replication/CD-R duplication services.

Ken-A-Vision Manufacturing Co Inc
5615 Raytown Rd, Kansas City, MO 64133
Tel: 816-353-4787 *Toll Free Tel:* 800-501-7366; 800-627-1953 (cust serv) *Fax:* 816-358-5072
E-mail: info@ken-a-vision.com
Web Site: www.ken-a-vision.com
Key Personnel
Pres: Steven M Dunn
Founded: 1954
Catalog(s) available
Membership(s): InfoComm International®

Ken-Del Productions Inc
1500 First State Blvd, Wilmington, DE 19804-3596
Tel: 302-999-1111; 302-999-1110; 302-999-1164 *Toll Free Tel:* 800-249-1110 *Fax:* 302-999-1656
E-mail: info@ken-del.com
Web Site: www.ken-del.com
Key Personnel
Pres & Gen Mgr: H Edwin Kennedy
Dir, Sales: Rose Burke
Opers Mgr: William Burgess, III
Founded: 1950
AV & staging facilities installation & rental, productions, vault storage, shrink wrapping, printing, graphic design & fulfillment. Rent 16mm, 8mm, S8mm, 35mm projectors, equipment & facility lights.
Membership(s): AES; ASA; Delaware Media Association; SMPTE; SPARS

Ken-Del Studios
Division of Ken-Del Productions Inc
1500 First State Blvd, Wilmington, DE 19804-3596
Tel: 302-999-1111 *Toll Free Tel:* 800-249-1110 *Fax:* 302-999-1656
E-mail: info@ken-del.com
Web Site: www.ken-del.com
Key Personnel
Pres & Gen Mgr: H Edwin Kennedy
Opers Mgr: William Burgess, III
Prodr & Engr: Paul Janocha
Sales: Rose Burke
Founded: 1950
All allied services, CD replication & recording studios, control rooms, duplication equipment & music libraries. Both analog & digital 64 track recording by 2 inch tape & professional tools computer. Graphic design & printing.
Catalog(s) available
Membership(s): AES; ASA; ASC; SMPTE; SPARS

Kendall/Hunt Publishing Co
4050 Westmark Dr, Dubuque, IA 52002
Mailing Address: PO Box 1840, Dubuque, IA 52004-1840
Tel: 563-589-1000 *Toll Free Tel:* 800-228-0810 *Fax:* 563-589-1237 *Toll Free Fax:* 800-772-9165
E-mail: orders@kendallhunt.com
Web Site: www.kendallhunt.com
Key Personnel
VP: David Tart *Tel:* 563-589-1000 ext 1195
Mktg Servs Asst: Kristy Malone *Tel:* 563-589-1128 *E-mail:* kmalone@kendallhunt.com
Founded: 1994
Textbook publishing with CD supplements.
Online catalog(s) available
Branch Office(s)
26242 Dimension Dr, Suite 210, Lake Forest, CA 92630-7802, Contact: John V Coniglio *Tel:* 949-830-0833 *Fax:* 949-830-0828
28570 Marguerite Pkwy, Suite 226, Mission Viejo, CA 92692-3733, Contact: Janice M Samuells *Tel:* 949-364-9557 *Fax:* 949-364-2101

Kenexa
650 E Swedesford Rd, 2nd fl, Wayne, PA 19087
Tel: 407-548-1444 *Fax:* 610-971-9181
E-mail: kenexa_learn_sales@kenexa.com
Web Site: www.outstart.com
Key Personnel
Founder & CTO: John Alonso
CEO & Pres: Massood Zarrabian
CFO: Rob Lubash
VP, Servs & Chief Learning Offr: Michelle Bruce
VP, Devt: Randy McLean
Dir, HR: Maria D'Alessandro
VP, Mktg: Jeffrey Whitney
VP, Sales: Jeff Heine
Founded: 1999
Producers of multimedia, CD-ROM & DVD programs.
Catalog(s) available
Branch Office(s)
100 Colonial Center Pkwy, Suite 150, Lake Mary, FL 32746 *Tel:* 407-548-0444 *Fax:* 407-548-0555
3755 Riverside Dr, Ottawa, ON K1G 4K9, Canada *Tel:* 416-478-3111 *Fax:* 613-738-0682
Foreign Office(s): MLC Ctr, Level 57, 19 Martin Place, Sydney, NSW 2000, Australia *Tel:* (02) 9225 7842 *Fax:* (02) 9238 7633
Franzoesische Str 24, 10117 Berlin, Germany *Tel:* (030) 20648551 *Fax:* (030) 20648556 *E-mail:* info@outstart.de
47 Mark Lane, London EC3R 7QQ, United Kingdom *Tel:* (020) 3545 8000 *Fax:* (020) 3545 8001

Keng Seng Enterprises Inc
4000 Rue St Ambroise, Suite 103, Montreal, QC H4C 2C7, Canada
Tel: 514-939-3971 *Fax:* 514-989-1922
E-mail: canada@kengseng.com
Web Site: www.kengseng.com
Key Personnel
Pres & Prod Mgr: David Chen
VP: Charles Cheng
Dir: Virginia Poon
Graphic art book & color reference guide book distributor. Also X-Rite distributor.
Catalog(s) available
Branch Office(s)
315 Traders Blvd E, Unit 9, Mississauga, ON L4Z 3E4, Canada, Dir: Lisia Tjhia *Tel:* 905-568-8567 *Fax:* 905-568-9158
Foreign Office(s): 8 Wu Si St, Don Cheng District, Beijing 100010, China *Tel:* (010) 6524-2907 *Fax:* (010) 5622-1076 *E-mail:* china@kengseng.com
Oriental Plaza, 20th fl, Rm 2011, 1072 Jian She Rd, Shenzhen, Guangdong 518001, China *Tel:* (0755) 823-11588 *Fax:* (0755) 8222-3992 *E-mail:* china@kengseng.com
Pantone-Keng Seng, Rm 1507, 225 Fujian Zhong Rd, Shanghai 200001, China *Tel:* (021) 6360-6889 *Fax:* (021) 6350-7710 *E-mail:* china@kengseng.com
Winner Commercial Bldg, 1/F, 401-403 Lockhart Rd, Hong Kong, Hong Kong *Tel:* 2591 1068 *Fax:* 2893 2259 *E-mail:* hongkong@kengseng.com
Rua Do General Rodrigues, Suite 11-A, R/C, Macau, Macau *Tel:* 522813 *Fax:* 522812 *E-mail:* macau@kengseng.com

Kensington Falls Animation
1680 Hillsdale Ave, Ambridge, PA 15003
Tel: 724-266-0329 *Fax:* 724-266-4016
E-mail: kensingtonfalls@aol.com
Web Site: kensingtonfalls.com
Key Personnel
Prodr & Dir: Michael C Schwab
Sales & Mktg Dir: Toby Schwab
Founded: 1979
Full service animation production.

Kensington Technology Group
Division of ACCO Brands Corp
333 Twin Dolphin Dr, 6th fl, Redwood Shores, CA 94065
Tel: 650-572-2700 *Toll Free Tel:* 800-235-6708 (cust serv); 800-535-4242 (tech support) *Fax:* 650-267-2800
E-mail: sales@kensington.com
Web Site: www.kensington.com
Key Personnel
Dir, Mktg: Rob Humphrey
Founded: 1981
Computer accesssory products.
Branch Office(s)
3731 N Fraser Way, Unit 550, Burnaby, BC V5J 5J2, Canada *Tel:* 604-431-5020 (R&D Ctr)
ACCO Brands Inc, 5 Precidio Ct, Brampton, ON, Canada *Toll Free Tel:* 800-266-3447 *Toll Free Fax:* 800-263-1063

Norman Kent Productions
PO Box 1749, Flagler Beach, FL 32136
Tel: 386-446-0505
Web Site: www.normankent.com
Key Personnel
Owner: Norman Kent *E-mail:* norman@normankent.com
Aerial cinematography & photography for feature films, television, commercials, sports events & printed media.

Kentucky Grip & Lighting
Subsidiary of Cabin Hill Communications Inc
1340 Connor Station Rd, Simpsonville, KY 40067
Tel: 502-548-5833
E-mail: sstaley@iglou.com
Web Site: www.kentuckyvideo.net; www.kentuckygrip.com
Key Personnel
Owner: Steve Staley *E-mail:* steve@kentuckygrip.com
Founded: 1987
Freelance cameraman (owner operator), grip & lighting trucks.

The Kenwood Group
75 Varney Place, San Francisco, CA 94107
Tel: 415-957-5333 *Fax:* 415-957-5311
E-mail: newbusiness@kenwoodgroup.com
Web Site: www.kenwoodgroup.com
Key Personnel
Sr Acct Exec: Skip Jansen *Tel:* 415-957-5333 ext 214
Founded: 1978
Creative production agency specializing in meeting & trade show exhibits.

Kenyon Laboratories LLC
12 Scovil Rd, Higganum, CT 06441
Tel: 860-345-2097 *Toll Free Tel:* 800-253-4681 *Fax:* 860-345-8652
E-mail: kenyonlabs@comcast.net

Web Site: www.ken-lab.com
Key Personnel
Owner: Ron Denman
Manufacture, rent, sell & repair gyro stabilizers.
Catalog(s) available

Kerrigan Productions Inc
3877 Draper Ave, Montreal, QC H4A 2N9, Canada
Tel: 514-486-8456 *Fax:* 514-488-4550
Web Site: www.kerrigan.ca
Key Personnel
Dir: Bill Kerrigan *E-mail:* bill@kerrigan.ca
Founded: 1986
A film & video production company.

Keslow Camera Inc
11260 Playa Ct, Culver City, CA 90230
Tel: 310-636-4600 *Fax:* 310-915-5335
E-mail: info@keslowcamera.com
Web Site: www.keslowcamera.com
Key Personnel
CEO: Robert Keslow *E-mail:* robert@keslowcamera.com
COO: Dennis McDonald *E-mail:* dennis@keslowcamera.com
CFO: Denny Taing *E-mail:* dtaing@keslowcamera.com
Film & digital camera rentals. Offices in Miami, FL, Chicago, IL & New Orleans, LA.

KESSPRO Studios
435 S Molino St, Los Angeles, CA 90013
Tel: 213-253-2623 *Fax:* 213-253-2629
E-mail: info@kessprostudios.com
Web Site: www.kessprostudios.com
Key Personnel
Contact: David Kessinger *E-mail:* david@kessprostudios.com; Matt Kessinger *E-mail:* matt@kessprostudios.com
Founded: 2009
Studio rental for filming, video, photography & special events.

KET The Kentucky Network
600 Cooper Dr, Lexington, KY 40502
Tel: 859-258-7000 *Toll Free Tel:* 800-432-0951 *Fax:* 859-258-7396
E-mail: adulted@ket.org
Web Site: www.ket.org
Key Personnel
CEO & Exec Dir: Shae Hopkins *Tel:* 859-258-7220 *E-mail:* shopkins@ket.org
Dir, Enterprise Div: Ron Griffin *Tel:* 859-258-7218 *E-mail:* rgriffin@ket.org
Adult education video-based learning material: GED preparation, pre-GED, workplace skills, life skills & ESL. Video, workbooks & online.
Catalog(s) available

Ketchum Pleon Change
1285 Avenue of the Americas, 3rd fl, New York, NY 10019
Tel: 646-935-3900
Web Site: www.ketchum.com/change
Key Personnel
Sr Partner & Chmn: Ray Kotcher *E-mail:* ray.kotcher@ketchum.com
Sr Partner & CEO: Rob Flaherty *E-mail:* rob.flaherty@ketchum.com
Production & consulting company.
Branch Office(s)
10960 Wilshire Blvd, Suite 400, Los Angeles, CA 90024, Partner: Dave Chapman *E-mail:* dave.chapman@ketchum.com
3500 Lenox Rd, Suite 1250, Atlanta, GA 30326, Partner: Hilary Hanson McKean *E-mail:* hilary.mckean@ketchum.com

Key Digital Systems
521 E Third St, Mount Vernon, NY 10553
Tel: 914-667-9700 *Fax:* 914-668-8666
E-mail: info@keydigital.com
Web Site: www.keydigital.com
Key Personnel
Founder & Pres: Mike Tsinberg
VP, Sales: Michael Lakhter *Tel:* 914-667-9700 ext 210 *E-mail:* michael@keydigital.com
VP, Mktg: Masha Lakhter *Tel:* 914-667-9700 ext 211 *E-mail:* marketing@keydigital.com

Key of David Publications
PO Box 153, Merion, PA 19066
Tel: 610-896-1970 *Fax:* 610-896-1970
Web Site: www.keyofdavidpublications.org
Key Personnel
Secy: Kathy DiPrinzio *E-mail:* diprinzio-revival@voicenet.com
Religious books & tapes.
Catalog(s) available

The Keyboard Workshop
PO Box 700, Medford, OR 97501
Tel: 541-664-7052 *Fax:* 541-664-7052
Web Site: www.playpiano.com
Key Personnel
Owner: Duane Shinn *E-mail:* duane@playpiano.com
Founded: 1965
Sale of educational audio & video programs.
Catalog(s) available

Keystone Entertainment
23410 Civic Ctr Way, Suite E-9, Malibu, CA 90265
Tel: 310-317-4883 *Fax:* 310-317-4903
E-mail: films@keypics.com
Web Site: www.keypics.com
Key Personnel
CEO: Robert Vince
Pres: Anna McRoberts
Founded: 1996
Film producers & post-production facility.
Branch Office(s)
300-2339 Columbia St, Vancouver, BC V5Y 3Y3, Canada *Tel:* 604-873-9739 *Fax:* 604-873-5919

Keystone View
2200 Dickerson Rd, Reno, NV 89503
Tel: 775-324-2799; 510-931-7747 *Toll Free Tel:* 866-574-6360 *Fax:* 775-324-5375 *Toll Free Fax:* 866-574-6395
E-mail: sales@keystoneview.com
Web Site: www.keystoneview.com
Key Personnel
Contact: Al Fleming
Catalog(s) available

Keywest Technology Inc
14563 W 96 Terr, Lenexa, KS 66215
Tel: 913-492-4666 *Toll Free Tel:* 800-331-2019 *Fax:* 913-322-1864
E-mail: info@keywesttechnology.com; sales@keywesttechnology.com
Web Site: www.keywesttechnology.com
Key Personnel
Pres: Koytt O Nichols
Engg Dir: John Macan
Mktg Dir: David Little *E-mail:* davidl@keywesttechnology.com
Sales Dir: Wes Dixon
Sales: Sam Ruggles
Founded: 1999
Catalog(s) available
Membership(s): Digital Screenmedia Association; InfoComm International®

KFOR-TV
Subsidiary of Local TV LLC
444 E Britton Rd, Oklahoma City, OK 73114
Tel: 405-424-4444 *Fax:* 405-478-6337
Web Site: www.kfor.com
Key Personnel
Pres & Gen Mgr: Wes Milbourn
Promos: Todd Rich

KHNL/KGMB
Affiliate of Raycom Media Inc
420 Waiakamilo Rd, Suite 205, Honolulu, HI 96817
Tel: 808-847-3246 *Fax:* 808-845-3616
E-mail: info8@khnl.com; news8@khnl.com
Web Site: www.hawaiinewsnow.com
Key Personnel
Gen Mgr: Rick Blangiardi *E-mail:* rblangiardi@hawaiinewsnow.com
Catalog(s) available

KickedUp Media Group Inc
2 Amherst Dr, Hastings-on-Hudson, NY 10706
Tel: 914-693-KICK (693-5425)
E-mail: info@kickedupmediagroup.com
Web Site: www.kickedupmediagroup.com
Key Personnel
Pres & Founder: Larry Saperstein *E-mail:* lsaperstein@kickedupmediagroup.com
VP, Prodn: Laura DeAngelis *E-mail:* ldeangelis@kickedupmediagroup.com
Dir, Opers: Allison Lehman *E-mail:* alehman@kickedupmediagroup.com
NY area based company specializing in satellite & radio media tours, video production of PSAs, corporate & social videos, media training & Hispanic media outreach. The company was founded by Larry Saperstein, the former head of broadcast & production services at West Glen Communications.

Kids on the Block Inc
9 Westminster Shopping Ctr, Suite 344, Westminster, MD 21157
Tel: 443-297-9564 *Toll Free Tel:* 800-368-KIDS (368-5437) *Fax:* 410-290-9358
E-mail: kob@kotb.com
Web Site: www.kotb.com
Key Personnel
Pres: Aric-James Darroe
Founded: 1977
Catalog(s) available

Killer Tracks
Unit of Universal Music Publishing Group
2110 Colorado Ave, Suite 110, Santa Monica, CA 90404
Tel: 310-865-4455 *Toll Free Tel:* 800-4-KILLER (454-5537) *Fax:* 310-865-4470 *Toll Free Fax:* 800-787-2257
E-mail: info@killertracks.com; sales@killertracks.com
Web Site: www.killertracks.com
Key Personnel
VP/Head, Music Prodn: Carl Peel *E-mail:* cpeel@killertracks.com
VP/ Head, Music Licensing: Anna Maria Hall *E-mail:* ahall@killertracks.com
Founded: 1989

Kimbo Educational
Division of United Sound Arts Inc
10 N Third Ave, Long Branch, NJ 07740
Mailing Address: PO Box 477, Long Branch, NJ 07740-0477
Tel: 732-229-4949 *Toll Free Tel:* 800-631-2187 *Fax:* 732-870-3340
E-mail: kimboed@aol.com
Web Site: www.kimboed.com
Key Personnel
CEO: Gertrude S Kimble
Pres: James A Kimble
Sales & Mktg: Elaine Murphy
Catalog Ed: Amy Laufer
Founded: 1954
CDs & DVDs for children; educational market.
Catalog(s) available

Sales Office(s): 504 Via Ventana Dr, Mesquite, NV 89027, Contact: Elaine Murphy *Toll Free Tel:* 800-848-6099
Membership(s): Education Market Association

Kimono Surf Studios
401 Logan Ave, Suite 109, Toronto, ON M4M 1S1, Canada
Tel: 416-405-8111 *Fax:* 416-405-8751
E-mail: studio@kimonosurf.com
Web Site: www.kimonosurf.com
Key Personnel
Studio Mgr: Susie Rucska *Tel:* 416-405-8111 ext 336
Small turn-key production studio with equipment rental & HD post-production services.

Kinetic Arts
306 Gold St, No 5-I, Brooklyn, NY 11201
Tel: 917-439-4008
E-mail: info@kineticarts.tv
Web Site: www.kineticarts.tv
Key Personnel
Partner: Alex Twersky
Founded: 1997
Film production & development.

Kinetic Corp
200 Distillery Commons, Suite 200, Louisville, KY 40206-1990
Tel: 502-719-9500 *Fax:* 502-719-9509
E-mail: info@thetechnologyagency.com
Web Site: kinetic.thetechnologyagency.com
Key Personnel
Founder & CEO: G Raymond Schuhmann
Cont: Ron Hess
VP, Tech Servs: Bob Poston, III
Dir, Digital Servs: Tim Pitts
Visual communications for business.
Membership(s): APGU; Photo Marketing Association

Kineticvideo.com
16 Munition St, Toronto, ON M5A 1G7, Canada
Tel: 416-538-6613 *Toll Free Tel:* 800-263-6910 (CN only) *Fax:* 416-538-9984
E-mail: info@kineticvideo.com
Web Site: www.kineticvideo.com
Key Personnel
Pres: Frances Broome *E-mail:* fmb@kineticvideo.com
VP, Sales & Cust Serv: Gary Malloy *E-mail:* gmt@kineticvideo.com
Acctg: Michael Phillips *E-mail:* mp@kineticvideo.com
Founded: 1976
Catalog(s) available
Branch Office(s)
255 Great Arrow Ave, Suite F, Buffalo, NY 14202 *Tel:* 716-856-7631 *Toll Free Tel:* 800-466-7631 *Fax:* 716-856-7838
Membership(s): Educational Media Producers & Distributors Association of Canada

Kinetronics Corp
1459 Tallevast Rd, Sarasota, FL 34243
Tel: 941-951-2432 *Toll Free Tel:* 800-624-3204 (US & CN) *Fax:* 941-955-5992
E-mail: info@kinetronics.com; order@kinetronics.com
Web Site: www.kinetronics.com
Key Personnel
Off Mgr: Sally Robbins
Founded: 1973
Catalog(s) available
Membership(s): AIE™; International Technology and Engineering Educators Association; Mini Lab Association; National Association of Theatre Owners; Photo Marketing Association; SMPTE

Kingsway Motion Picture Ltd
200 Evans Ave, Unit 4, Toronto, ON M8Z 1J7, Canada
Tel: 416-463-4345 *Fax:* 416-469-2609
E-mail: info@kingswaycanada.com
Web Site: kingswaycanada.com
Key Personnel
Pres: Doug Macaulay

Kingswood Productions
Subsidiary of United Methodist Communications
810 12 Ave S, Nashville, TN 37203
Toll Free Tel: 800-476-7766
E-mail: info@kingswoodproductions.com
Web Site: kingswoodproductions.com
Key Personnel
Proj Coord: Kim Sanderson
Audio & video development, webcast production, video streaming & editing.

Kino Flo Lighting Systems
2840 N Hollywood Way, Burbank, CA 91505
Tel: 818-767-6528 *Fax:* 818-252-0290 (rental); 818-767-7517 (sales)
E-mail: sales@kinoflo.com
Web Site: www.kinoflo.com
Key Personnel
Founder & Pres: Frieder Hochheim *E-mail:* fhochheim@kinoflo.com
Gen Mgr: Ray Goitiandia *E-mail:* rgoitiandia@kinoflo.com
Catalog(s) available
Membership(s): ASC; NAB; Professional Lighting & Sound Association; SMPTE

Kino International Corp
333 W 39 St, Suite 503, New York, NY 10018
Tel: 212-629-6880 *Toll Free Tel:* 800-562-3330 *Fax:* 212-714-0871
E-mail: contact@kino.com
Web Site: www.kinolorber.com
Key Personnel
Pres: Richard Lorber
Theatre Mgr: Gary Palmucci
Founded: 1977
Catalog(s) available
Membership(s): Entertainment Merchants Association

Kino Mountain Productions LLC
307 S Salem St, No 311, Apex, NC 27502
Tel: 919-210-1379
Web Site: www.kinomountain.com
Key Personnel
Owner: Greg Winters *E-mail:* greg@kinomountain.com
Prodr: Ray Gantt *E-mail:* ray@kinomountain.com
Founded: 2010

KION-TV
1550 Moffett St, Salinas, CA 93905
Tel: 831-784-1702; 831-422-3500 *Fax:* 831-757-1766
Web Site: www.kionrightnow.com
Key Personnel
Asst News Dir: Brooke Holmquist

Kipp Visual Systems Inc
3600 Clipper Mill Rd, Suite 105, Baltimore, MD 21211
Tel: 410-235-9900 *Toll Free Tel:* 800-278-6912 *Fax:* 410-235-7122
Web Site: kippvisual.com
Key Personnel
Pres: Ryan Lessans *E-mail:* ryan.lessans@kippvisual.com
Catalog(s) available
Membership(s): InfoComm International®

Kirkwood Community College
Linn Hall, Rm 102, 6301 Kirkwood Blvd SW, Cedar Rapids, IA 52406
Tel: 319-398-5517 *Toll Free Tel:* 800-363-2220 *Fax:* 319-398-5413
E-mail: info@kirkwood.edu
Web Site: www.kirkwood.edu
Key Personnel
AV Servs Coord: Allan Schau *Tel:* 319-398-5620 *E-mail:* allan.schau@kirkwood.edu

The Kitchen
Division of TM Systems
4119 W Burbank Blvd, Burbank, CA 91505
Tel: 818-306-5300 *Fax:* 305-415-6201
E-mail: info@thekitchen.tv
Web Site: www.thekitchen.tv
Key Personnel
CEO & Pres: Ken Lorber *E-mail:* ken@thekitchen.tv
CFO: Don Denkhaus *E-mail:* don@thekitchen.tv
CTO: Carlos Contreras *E-mail:* carlos@thekitchen.tv
EVP: Deeny Kaplan *E-mail:* deeny@thekitchen.tv
VP, Opers: Tim Fox *E-mail:* tim@thekitchen.tv
Mgr, Opers: Kevin Varnell *E-mail:* kevin@thekitchen.tv
Gen Mgr: Maritza Alvarado *E-mail:* maritza@thekitchen.tv
Founded: 2001
Emmy Award winning language translation, dubbing, subtitling & closed captioning services facility. Transfer & conversion services.
Branch Office(s)
265 NE 24 St, Suite 401, Miami, FL 33137 *Tel:* 305-415-6200 *Fax:* 305-415-6201
Foreign Office(s): La Cuadra Creativa-Talleres 7B, Los Palos Grandes, Caracas 1060, Venezuela *Tel:* (0212) 899-0848 *Fax:* (0212) 286-9146
Membership(s): NAB; NATPE; SMPTE; Television Academy

Kitchen Sync, see Optix Digital Pictures & Sound

Kits & Expendables
45-27 37 St, Long Island, NY 11101
Tel: 718-482-1824; 718-482-1993; 917-842-8394 (emergencies after hrs) *Fax:* 718-482-1853
E-mail: orders@kitsandexpendables.com
Web Site: www.kitsandexpendables.com
Key Personnel
Gen Mgr: Steve Woodroffe *E-mail:* steve@kitsandexpendables.com
Founded: 1995
Rents production supplies, tables & chairs, tents, coolers, heaters, A/C units & packaged kits of expendables. Sells gels & tape.

KJfilms LLC
33 Serra Dr, Middletown, CT 06457
Tel: 860-894-2363; 860-995-5106 (cell)
E-mail: info@kjfilms.com
Web Site: www.kjfilms.com
Key Personnel
Dir, Photog: Jeff Hoyt *E-mail:* jeff@kjfilms.com
Founded: 1998

KK Office Solutions Inc
3910 N Bridgeport Circle, Wichita, KS 67219
Tel: 316-944-5464 *Toll Free Tel:* 800-362-1317 *Fax:* 316-944-0605 *Toll Free Fax:* 888-319-9600
E-mail: info@kkofficesolutions.com
Web Site: kkosinc.com
Key Personnel
CEO: Matthew Brandt
Founded: 1994 (as The Kartridge King)
Educational supplier of AV needs.
Branch Office(s)
1302 Adams St, Kansas City, MO 64116 *Tel:* 913-754-5434 *Fax:* 913-754-5433

Klipsch Audio Technologies
3502 Woodview Trace, Suite 200, Indianapolis, IN 46268
Tel: 317-860-8100 *Toll Free Tel:* 877-412-7467 (orders); 800-544-1482 *Fax:* 317-860-9170 (sales & mktg)
E-mail: support@klipsch.com
Web Site: www.klipsch.com
Key Personnel
CEO & Chmn of the Bd: Fred Klipsch
CEO & Pres: Paul Jacobs
CFO & Treas: Fred Farrar
Pres, Global Opers: Mike Klipsch
Pres, Global Sales: David Kelley
Founded: 1946
Shipping Address: 137 Hempstead, No 278, Dock 2, Hope, AR 71801 *Fax:* 870-777-3376
Membership(s): Consumer Electronics Association

Kloss Studios Co
1441 Jericho Rd, Abington, PA 19001
Tel: 215-885-1203 *Toll Free Tel:* 800-885-1203 (PA only)
E-mail: kloss@kloss-studios.com
Web Site: kloss-studios.com
Key Personnel
Owner & CEO: John P Kloss
Founded: 1985
Catalog(s) available

Klutz
Division of Scholastic Inc
450 Lambert Ave, Palo Alto, CA 94306
Tel: 650-857-0888 *Toll Free Tel:* 800-737-4123 *Fax:* 650-857-9110
E-mail: thefolks@klutz.com
Web Site: www.klutz.com
Key Personnel
Chief Creative Offr & Pres: Jeff Pinsker
Founded: 1977
Activity products for kids.
Catalog(s), semiannual, free

Knowledge Unlimited Inc
2320 Pleasant View, Middleton, WI 53562
Mailing Address: PO Box 52, Madison, WI 53701-0052
Tel: 608-661-5666 *Toll Free Tel:* 800-356-2303 *Fax:* 608-836-6684 *Toll Free Fax:* 800-618-1570
E-mail: csis@newscurrents.com
Web Site: www.knowledgeunlimited.com
Key Personnel
Pres: Judith Laitman
Founded: 1983
Writing, editing & video production of educational materials for social studies, science, language arts & current events.
Catalog(s), biannual
Membership(s): National Council for the Social Studies

Knowles Video Inc (KVI)
5450 Buck Lake Rd, Tallahassee, FL 32317
Mailing Address: PO Box 12127, Tallahassee, FL 32317-2127
Tel: 850-878-2298
E-mail: info@knowlesvideo.com
Web Site: www.knowlesvideo.com
Key Personnel
Pres: Karl Knowles
Membership(s): Florida Motion Picture & Television Association

Knox Video Technologies
15875 Crabbs Branch Way, Suite A, Rockville, MD 20855
Tel: 301-840-5805 *Fax:* 301-840-2946
E-mail: sales@knoxvideo.com
Web Site: www.knoxvideo.com
Key Personnel
Sales & Mktg Mgr: Ken Nottingham
Founded: 1975
Manufacturer of professional & residential matrix routing switchers, scalers, CAT5 distribution equipment & other AV necessities.
Membership(s): Consumer Electronics Association; Custom Electronic Design & Installation Association; InfoComm International®; NAB; NSCA

KO Creative
465 S Beverly Dr, 3rd fl, Beverly Hills, CA 90212
Tel: 310-288-3820
Web Site: www.ko-creative.com
Key Personnel
CEO: Kristi Kilday *E-mail:* kristi@ko-creative.com
Founded: 1993
Entertainment marketing company specializing in theatrical marketing, television marketing, festival marketing, home entertainment & company branding/identity.

Kodak Canada Inc
Subsidiary of Eastman Kodak Co
4225 Kincaid St, Burnaby, BC V5G 4P5, Canada
Tel: 604-320-1777 *Toll Free Tel:* 800-465-6325 *Fax:* 604-570-3501
Web Site: www.kodak.ca
Founded: 1899
Branch Office(s)
4225 Kincaid St, Burnaby, BC V5G 4P5, Canada *Tel:* 604-320-1777 *Fax:* 604-570-3501
4 Place du Commerce, Suite 100, Ile des Soeurs, Verdun, QC H3E 1J4, Canada *Tel:* 514-761-3481 *Fax:* 514-768-3637

Koerner Camera Systems
2323 N Williams Ave, Portland, OR 97227
Tel: 503-274-6533 *Toll Free Tel:* 800-377-1132 *Fax:* 503-274-5446
E-mail: michael@koernercamera.com
Web Site: www.koernercamera.com
Founded: 1996
Digital cinema camera rental house.
Branch Office(s)
101 Nickerson, Suite B500, Seattle, WA 98109 *Tel:* 206-285-7334 *Toll Free Tel:* 855-285-7334 *Fax:* 206-285-7335 *E-mail:* seattle@koernercamera.com

Kofax Image Products
15211 Laguna Canyon Rd, Irvine, CA 92618-3603
Tel: 949-727-1733 *Fax:* 949-727-3144
E-mail: info@kofax.com
Web Site: www.kofax.com
Founded: 1985
Catalog(s) available
Branch Office(s)
36 Cosby Dr, Bedord, MA 01730 *Tel:* 781-743-1900 *Fax:* 781-743-2200
Foreign Office(s): Kofax Australia Pty Ltd, Norwich House, Level 7, 6 O'Connell St, Sydney, NSW 2000, Australia *Tel:* (02) 8916 0200 *Fax:* (02) 8916 0299 *E-mail:* mailbox.au@kofax.com
Kofax Australia Pty Ltd, One Queens Rd, Suite 246-248, Level 2, Melbourne, Victoria 3004, Australia *Tel:* (03) 8807 9924 *Fax:* (03) 8807 9928 *E-mail:* mailbox.au@kofax.com
Kofax Austria GmbH, Talpagasse 1, A-1230 Vienna, Austria *Tel:* (01) 86645-55000 *Fax:* (01) 86645-58001 *E-mail:* mailbox.at@kofax.com
Kofax Benelux NV/SA, Mechelen Campus, Schalienhoevedreef 20 E, 2800 Mechelen, Belgium *Tel:* (015) 444 900 *Fax:* (015) 444 901 *E-mail:* mailbox.be@kofax.com
Kofax Produtos de Imagem do Brasil Ltda, Rua Gomes de Carvalho, 1069 cj 102, 04547-004 Sao Paulo-SP, Brazil *Tel:* (011) 3047 4000 *E-mail:* kofax.brasil@kofax.com
Kofax Danmark A/S, Ringager 4, C, 2605 Brondby, Denmark *Tel:* 4342-4150 *Fax:* 4342-4180 *E-mail:* mailbox.dk@kofax.com
Kofax France SAS, 8 Blvd Dubreuil, 91400 Orsay, France *Tel:* 01 60 92 18 50 *Fax:* 01 69 28 77 38 *E-mail:* mailbox.fr@kofax.com
Kofax Deutschland AG, Unterschweinstiege 8 (Main Airport Ctr), 60549 Frankfurt, Germany *Tel:* (0761) 45269-0 *Fax:* (0761) 45269-90 *E-mail:* mailbox.de@kofax.com
Kofax Deutschland AG, Business Bldg, Haid Park, Wentzingerstr 19, 79106 Freiberg, Germany *Tel:* (0761) 45269-0 *Fax:* (0761) 45269-90 *E-mail:* mailbox.de@fofax.com
Kofax Asia Holdings Pte Ltd, 2902 Shui On Ctr, No 6-8 Harbour Rd, Wan Chai, Hong Kong *Tel:* 9368 6795 *E-mail:* mailbox.asia@kofax.com
Kofax India Pvt Ltd, The V, Auriga Bldg, 2nd fl, B-Wing, Plot No 17, Software Units Layout, Madhapur, Hyderabad 500 081, India *Tel:* (040) 4545 9949 *Fax:* (040) 4545 9922 *E-mail:* mailbox.asia@kofax.com
Kofax India Pvt Ltd, The Capital, Plot No C-70, G-Block, 7th fl, Bandra Kurla Complex, Bandra East, Mumbai 400 051, India *Tel:* (022) 6712 8588 *E-mail:* mailbox.asia@kofax.com
Kofax Asia Holdings Pte Ltd, Indonesia Rep Off, Suite 5, 48th fl, Jl Jendral Sudiman Kav 1, Jakarta 10220, Indonesia *Tel:* (021) 574 8862 *Fax:* (021) 574 8888 *E-mail:* mailbox.asia@kofax.com
Kofax Italia SRL, Viale Morza, 270, 20128 Milan MI, Italy *Tel:* (02) 252051 *Fax:* (02) 2570534 *E-mail:* mailbox.it@kofax.com
Kofax Japan Co Ltd, 9F Soc Takanawa Bldg, 3-19-26 Takanawa, Minato-ku, Tokyo 108-0074, Japan *Tel:* (03) 6853 0001 *Fax:* (03) 6853 0002 *E-mail:* mailbox.jp@kofax.com
Kofax Malaysia Sdn Bhd, The Gardens South Tower, Suite 12, Level 12, Mid Valley City, Lingkaran Syed Putra, 59200 Kuala Lumpur, Malaysia *Tel:* (03) 2092 0202 *Fax:* (03) 2092 0211 *E-mail:* mailbox.my@kofax.com
Ave Presidente Masaryk 111-1, Col Chapultepec Morales, 11560 Mexico, DF, Mexico *Tel:* (0155) 33 00 58 86 *Fax:* (0155) 91 99 72 26
Kofax Benelux NV/SA, Meidoornkade 19, 3992 AG Houten, Netherlands *Tel:* (030) 26 26 206 *Fax:* (030) 26 73 928 *E-mail:* mailbox.nl@kofax.com
Kofax Portugal SA, Centro de Congressos de Estoril, 4-A, Av Clotilde, 2765-211 Estoril, Portugal *Tel:* 214646190 *Fax:* 214646191 *E-mail:* mailbox.pt@kofax.com
Kofax Singapore Pte Ltd, Republic Plaza I, No 53-01, 9 Raffles Place, Singapore 048619, Singapore *Tel:* 6278 7662 *Fax:* 6278 4345 *E-mail:* mailbox.asia@kofax.com
Kofax South Africa Pty Ltd, Gillooly's View Off Park, Block C, 1st fl, One Osborne Lane, Bedfordview 2007, South Africa *Tel:* (011) 417 8629 *Fax:* (011) 417 8761 *E-mail:* mailbox.za@kofax.com
Kofax Software Iberica SAU, Torre Mapfre, C/ de la Marina 16-18, 11-B, 08005 Barcelona, Spain *Tel:* 934 09 20 63 *Fax:* 934 09 20 64 *E-mail:* mailbox.es@kofax.com
Kofax Sverige AB, Energigatan 11, 43437 Kungsbacka, Sweden *Tel:* (030) 03 58 80 *Fax:* (030) 03 58 99 *E-mail:* mailbox.se@kofax.com
Kofax Sverige AB, Frosundaviks Alle 15, 169 70 Solna, Sweden *Tel:* (08) 5444 0480 *E-mail:* mailbox.se@kofax.com
Kofax Schweiz AG, Business Bldg Forren W, Grundstr 14, 6343 Rotkreuz, Switzerland *Tel:* (041) 799 82 82 *Fax:* (041) 799 82 95 *E-mail:* mailbox.ch@kofax.com
Kofax ME FZE, Dubai Airport Free Zone & Busn Park, E Wing 3E GO7, PO Box 54574, Dubai, United Arab Emirates *Tel:* (04) 2306

800 *Fax:* (04) 2306 899 *E-mail:* mailbox.ae@kofax.com
Kofax PLC, One Cedarwood, Chineham Business Park, Basingstoke, Hants RG24 8WD, United Kingdom *Tel:* (0870) 777 3767 *Fax:* (0870) 777 3768 *E-mail:* mailbox.uk@kofax.com
Kofax Northern Ireland Ltd, 26 Linenhall St, Belfast BT2 8BG, United Kingdom *Tel:* (028) 9072 7000 *Fax:* (028) 9072 7038
Kofax Northern Ireland Ltd, 113-118 Duncreggan Rd, Derry BT48 0AA, United Kingdom *Tel:* (028) 7126 7767 *Fax:* (028) 7126 8085
Kofax Northern Ireland Ltd, 85 London Wall, Ground fl, London EC2M 7AD, United Kingdom *Tel:* (020) 7496 1760 *Fax:* (020) 7256 8151
Kofax Vietnam Co Ltd, RESCO Bldg, A Tower, 11th fl, 521 Kim Ma St, Ba Dinh District, Hanoi, Vietnam *Tel:* (03) 771 2546 *Fax:* (03) 771 2543 *E-mail:* mailbox.vn@kofax.com

KOH Design Inc
540 Barnum Ave, Bridgeport, CT 06608
Tel: 203-336-1334 *Fax:* 203-335-9361
E-mail: info@kohdesign.com
Web Site: www.kohdesign.com
Key Personnel
Mktg Dir: Karl Hasselrot

Konica Minolta Business Solutions
100 Williams Dr, Ramsey, NJ 07446
Tel: 201-825-4000 *Fax:* 201-825-7567
Web Site: kmbs.konicaminolta.us
Key Personnel
Pres: Tom Taiko
EVP, Busn Planning: Keith Okamoto
Catalog(s) available

Kontron America
14118 Stowe Dr, Poway, CA 92064-7147
Tel: 858-677-0877 *Toll Free Tel:* 888-294-4558; 800-480-0044 (cust serv & tech support) *Fax:* 858-677-0898
E-mail: sales@us.kontron.com
Web Site: www.kontron.com
Key Personnel
EVP, Americas: Kevin Rhoads
Catalog(s), semiannual
Branch Office(s)
6505 Dumbarton Circle, Fremont, CA 94538 *Tel:* 510-284-1100 *Toll Free Tel:* 800-995-7579 *Fax:* 510-284-1111
4555 Rue Ambroise-Lafortune, Boisbriand, QC J7H 0A4, Canada *Tel:* 450-437-5682 *Toll Free Tel:* 800-387-4222 *Fax:* 450-437-8053
Foreign Office(s): Oskar-von-Miller-Str 1, 85386 Eching, Munich, Germany *Tel:* (081) 65 77 0 *Fax:* (081) 65 77 385 *Web Site:* www.kontron.de
Membership(s): PICMG

KOOL FM Radio
Division of CBS Radio Inc
840 N Central Ave, Phoenix, AZ 85004
Tel: 602-452-1000; 602-260-9494 (request line) *Fax:* 602-440-6530
Web Site: www.koolradio.com
Key Personnel
Prog Dir: Dave Shakes *E-mail:* dave.shakes@cbsradio.com

Kool Music
9 Hector Ave, Toronto, ON M6G 3G2, Canada
Tel: 416-533-3520
E-mail: host@koolmusic.com
Web Site: www.koolmusic.com
Key Personnel
Pres: Al Kussin
Founded: 1999
Production music provider.
CD-ROM catalog(s), royalty free production music, $39 per single song download
Membership(s): The Society of Composers, Authors and Music Publishers of Canada

Kopp Glass
2108 Palmer St, Pittsburgh, PA 15218
Tel: 412-271-0190 *Fax:* 412-271-4103
E-mail: sales@koppglass.com
Web Site: www.koppglass.com
Key Personnel
Dir, Tech Servs: Jim Forish
Founded: 1926
Manufacturer of specialty & technical glass including clear & colored borosilicate glass.

Korg USA Inc
Subsidiary of Korg Inc Japan
316 S Service Rd, Melville, NY 11747
Tel: 631-390-6500; 631-390-8737 *Fax:* 631-390-6501
Web Site: www.korgusa.com
Key Personnel
Pres: Joseph Castronovo
Founded: 1963
Distribute recorders, converters, players & amplifiers.
Catalog(s) available

Koss Corp
4129 N Port Washington Ave, Milwaukee, WI 53212
Tel: 414-964-5000 *Toll Free Tel:* 800-USA-KOSS (872-5677) *Fax:* 414-964-8615
E-mail: customersupport@koss.com
Web Site: www.koss.com
Key Personnel
CEO & Pres: Michael Koss
VP, Sales: John Koss, Jr
Founded: 1958
Catalog(s) available

Kostov Productions
Division of CP Production Inc
Whispering Wind Ranch, 16320 High Bridge Rd, Monroe, WA 98272
Tel: 206-755-0050
E-mail: info@kostov.com
Web Site: www.kostov.com
Key Personnel
Pres: Michael Kostov *E-mail:* michael@hotmail.com
Founded: 1981
Membership(s): CIA

Kozmic Lazer Show LLC
PO Box 140197, Nashville, TN 37214-0197
Tel: 615-391-3226 *Toll Free Tel:* 800-MRLASER (675-2737) *Fax:* 615-391-3265
E-mail: mrlaser800@aol.com
Web Site: www.kozmiclazershow.com
Key Personnel
Pres: Patrick Sittnick
Provider of laser light show & pyrotechnic systems.
Online catalog(s) available
Membership(s): NFPA

KPBS TV FM-San Diego
5200 Campanille Dr, San Diego, CA 92182
Tel: 619-594-1515; 619-265-6438 (newsroom) *Toll Free Tel:* 888-399-5727 *Fax:* 619-594-3812
Web Site: www.kpbs.org
Key Personnel
Dir, Interactive Strategy: Tammy Carpowich *Tel:* 619-594-1237 *E-mail:* tcarpowich@kpbs.org
Membership(s): IMCCA; NAB; NATPE; PromaxBDA

KPDX-TV Production Center
Division of Meredith Corp
14975 NW Greenbrier Pkwy, Beaverton, OR 97006-5731
Tel: 503-906-1249 *Fax:* 503-548-6920
E-mail: ezone@kpdx.com; fox12news@kptv.com
Web Site: www.kptv.com; www.kpdx.com
Key Personnel
EVP & Gen Mgr: Patrick McCreery
Dir, Sales Content: Linda Johns

KPHO-TV5
Subsidiary of Meredith Corp
4016 N Black Canyon Hwy, Phoenix, AZ 85017
Tel: 602-264-1000 *Fax:* 602-274-1596
E-mail: cbs5news@kpho.com
Web Site: www.news5.tv
Key Personnel
Dir, HR & Acctg: Judy Wallace
Central Cast Dir: Mark Nutini

KPLR-TV
Affiliate of CW Television Network
2250 Ball Dr, St Louis, MO 63146
Tel: 314-213-2222; 314-213-7831 (newsroom)
E-mail: kplradmin@tribune.com
Web Site: www.cw11tv.com; www.kplr11.com
Key Personnel
Pres & Gen Mgr: Spencer Koch

Kramer Communications Video Production
12504 Quarterhorse Dr, Bowie, MD 20720
Tel: 301-352-3042 *Fax:* 301-352-3559
E-mail: kcam@his.com
Web Site: www.kramercommunications.tv
Key Personnel
Exec Prodr: Jeffrey T Kramer
Script writing & video production. Editing DVDs, CDs & web streaming.
Membership(s): Baltimore Videographers Association; International Television Video Association; MCA-I; NATAS

Kramer Electronics USA Inc
Subsidiary of Kramer Electronics Ltd
6 Rte 173 W, Clinton, NJ 08809
Tel: 908-735-0018 *Toll Free Tel:* 888-275-6311 *Fax:* 908-735-0515
E-mail: info@kramerus.com
Web Site: www.kramerus.com
Key Personnel
VP, Mktg: Clint Hoffman
VP, Sales: Kent Cawthorne
Founded: 1981
Catalog(s) available
Membership(s): Custom Electronic Design & Installation Association; InfoComm International®; NAB; NSCA

Joan Kramer & Associates Inc
10490 Wilshire Blvd, Suite 1701, Los Angeles, CA 90024
Tel: 310-446-1866 *Fax:* 310-446-1856
E-mail: ekeeeek@earthlink.net
Key Personnel
Pres: Joan Kramer
Membership(s): Picture Agency Council of America

Krishnamurti Foundation of America
1070 McAndrew Rd, Ojai, CA 93023
Mailing Address: PO Box 1560, Ojai, CA 93024
Tel: 805-646-2726 (ext 10) *Fax:* 805-646-6674
E-mail: kfa@kfa.org
Web Site: www.kfa.org
Key Personnel
Exec Dir: Jaap Sluijter
Dir, K Pubns: Derek Dodds *E-mail:* derek@kfa.org
Produce & distribute Krishnamurti's work.
Catalog(s), biannual, free

Foreign Office(s): Krishnamurti Foundation Trust Ltd, Brockwood Park, Bramdean, Hants SO24 0LQ, United Kingdom *Tel:* (01962) 771 525 *Fax:* (01962) 771 159 *Web Site:* www.kfoundation.org

KRK Systems
Division of Gibson Pro Audio
c/o Gibson Pro Audio, 309 Plus Park Blvd, Nashville, TN 37217
Toll Free Tel: 800-444-2799
E-mail: service@gibson.com
Web Site: www.krksys.com
Founded: 1986
Provider of monitors & control room solutions.
Catalog(s) available

Kroy LLC
3830 Kelley Ave, Cleveland, OH 44114
Tel: 216-426-5600 *Toll Free Tel:* 888-888-5769 (cust serv) *Fax:* 216-426-5601
Web Site: www.kroy.com
Key Personnel
Sales: Mark Mallett *E-mail:* mallett@kroy.com
Catalog(s) available
Foreign Office(s): 14 Worton Grange, Reading, Berks RG2 0LZ, United Kingdom *Tel:* (0118) 986 5200 *Fax:* (0118) 986 5205 *E-mail:* sales@kroyeurope.com *Web Site:* www.kroyeurope.com

KTHV Television, a Gannett Company
720 Izard St, Little Rock, AR 72201
Tel: 501-376-1111 *Fax:* 501-376-9928 (sales); 501-376-3324 (admin); 501-376-1645 (news)
Web Site: www.todaysthv.com
Key Personnel
Pres & Gen Mgr: Michael Caplan

KTVA Productions, see A KTVA Production LLC

KTVB-TV
Subsidiary of Gannett Co Inc
5407 Fairview Ave, Boise, ID 83706
Mailing Address: PO Box 7, Boise, ID 83707
Tel: 208-375-7277 *Toll Free Tel:* 800-559-7277 *Fax:* 208-378-1762; 208-375-7770 (news fax)
E-mail: info@ktvb.com; ktvbnews@ktvb.com
Web Site: www.ktvb.com
Key Personnel
Gen Mgr: Doug Armstrong
Community Serv Dir: Sally Craven

KTVU-Retail Services
Subsidiary of Cox Communications
2 Jack London Sq, Oakland, CA 94607
Tel: 510-834-1212
Web Site: www.ktvu.com
Key Personnel
Acting Dir, Mktg: Greg Randall
Catalog(s) available

K2 Productions
4214 Shoal Creek Dr, Greensboro, NC 27410
Tel: 336-664-8036
E-mail: info@k2production.com
Web Site: www.k2production.com
Key Personnel
Exec Prodr: April Eller
Prodr & Dir: Kevin Eller
Creative Dir: Mechelle La Velle
Film & video production company, from pre- to post-production.

Kuhn Productions LLC
321 E Walnut St, Suite 340, Des Moines, IA 50309
Tel: 515-244-1618
Key Personnel
Owner: Bill Kuhn *E-mail:* bill@kuhnproductions.com

Kultur International Films Ltd Inc
195 Hwy 36, West Long Branch, NJ 07764
Tel: 732-229-2343 *Toll Free Tel:* 800-573-3782 *Toll Free Fax:* 866-205-2744
E-mail: support@kultur.com
Web Site: www.kultur.com
Key Personnel
Chmn: Dennis M Hedlund
Catalog(s) available
Membership(s): Entertainment Merchants Association

KUSM TV
Visual Communications Bldg 183, Montana State University, Bozeman, MT 59717
Tel: 406-994-3437 *Toll Free Tel:* 866-832-0829 *Fax:* 406-994-6545
E-mail: kusm@montanapbs.org
Web Site: www.montanapbs.org

KVAL
Affiliate of Fisher Broadcasting
4575 Blanton Rd, Eugene, OR 97405
Mailing Address: PO Box 1313, Eugene, OR 97440
Tel: 541-342-4961 *Fax:* 541-342-2635
E-mail: kvalnews@kval.com
Web Site: www.kval.com
Key Personnel
VP & Gen Mgr: Greg Raschio *E-mail:* raschio@kval.com
Gen Sales Mgr: Steve Murray *E-mail:* murray@kval.com

KVIE-Channel 6
2030 W El Camino Ave, Sacramento, CA 95833
Tel: 916-929-5843 *Toll Free Tel:* 800-347-5843 *Fax:* 916-929-7215
E-mail: member@kvie.org
Web Site: www.kvie.org
Key Personnel
Pres & Gen Mgr: David Lowe
Catalog(s) available

KVL Audio Visual Services Inc
466 Saw Mill River Rd, Ardsley, NY 10502-2112
Tel: 914-479-3300 *Toll Free Tel:* 800-862-3210 *Fax:* 914-479-3395
E-mail: info@kvlav.com
Web Site: www.kvlav.com
Key Personnel
CEO & Pres: Les Lieberman *Tel:* 914-479-3300 ext 333
Founded: 1976
Branch Office(s)
Conrad New York, 102 N End Ave, New York, NY 10282, Contact: John Henriques *Tel:* 646-769-4230 *E-mail:* jhenriques@kvlav.com
Park Central Hotel, Seventh Ave & 56 St, New York, NY 10019, Site Mgr: James Cote *Tel:* 212-707-4230 *E-mail:* jcote@kvlav.com
500 W 37 St, New York, NY 10018 *Tel:* 212-643-0040 *Fax:* 212-582-6409
Hilton Pearl River, 500 Veterans Memorial Dr, Pearl River, NY, Mgr: Aaron Gagnon *Tel:* 845-620-0749 *Fax:* 845-620-0749 *E-mail:* agagnon@kvlav.com
Holiday Inn Chicago Mart Plaza, 350 W Mart Center Dr, Chicago, IL 60654, Site Mgr: Greg Holman *Tel:* 312-529-1138 *Fax:* 312-529-1135 *E-mail:* gholman@kvlav.com
Hilton Newark Airport, 1170 Spring St, Elizabeth, NJ 07201, Site Mgr: Mario Garcia *Tel:* 908-352-3990 *Fax:* 908-352-5507 *E-mail:* mgarcia@kvlav.com
Hilton Woodbridge, 120 Wood Ave S, Iselin, NJ 08830, Mgr: Bill Ward *Tel:* 732-548-5591 *Fax:* 732-548-5591 *E-mail:* bward@kvlav.com
Meadowlands Exposition Ctr, 355 Plaza Dr, Secaucus, NJ 07094, Site Mgr: Martin Kennedy *Tel:* 201-866-5220 *Fax:* 201-866-5218 *E-mail:* mkennedy@kvlav.com
Hilton Houston Westchase, 9999 Westheimer Rd, Houston, TX 77042-3802, Jose Villanueva *Tel:* 713-735-5926 *Fax:* 713-735-5974 *E-mail:* jvillanueva@kvlav.com
Founders Inn, 5641 Indian River Rd, Virginia Beach, VA 23464, Site Mgr: Krista Farley *Tel:* 757-366-5776 *Fax:* 757-424-6437 *E-mail:* kfarley@kvlav.com

L A Bruell Inc
30 W 26 St, New York, NY 10010
Tel: 646-336-5977 *Fax:* 646-336-8317
Web Site: www.labruell.com
Key Personnel
Pres, Dir & Prodr: Lucy Bruell *E-mail:* lucy@labruell.com
Medical Educ Writer & Healthcare Communs Consultant: Ned Putnam *E-mail:* ned@labruell.com
Founded: 1986
Video production, multimedia & interactive design & development. Healthcare communications, continuing medical education, training & educational programs.

L A Management Co LLC
8131 Bay Pointe Dr, Denver, NC 28037
Tel: 704-560-6274 *Toll Free Tel:* 800-651-7818 *Fax:* 704-973-7968
E-mail: info@managementco.com
Web Site: lamanagementco.com
Key Personnel
Pres: Lou Amico
VP: Joe Zammit
Video Prodr: Steven Huff
Video production services, including script writing, narration, music, graphics, animation & editing.
Branch Office(s)
4201 Congress St, Suite 440, Charlotte, NC 28209

L Acoustics US
2201 Celsius Ave, Unit E, Oxnard, CA 93030
Tel: 805-604-0577 *Fax:* 805-604-0858
E-mail: info@l-acoustics-us.com
Web Site: www.l-acoustics.com
Key Personnel
VP, Sales & Mktg: Paul Tillman *E-mail:* paul.tillman@l-acoustics-us.com
Founded: 1984
Loudspeaker manufacturer.
Catalog(s) available
Membership(s): AES; NAMM, the National Association of Music Merchants; NSCA

L'AIR International
117 Vacek St, Fort Worth, TX 76107
Tel: 817-237-9390 *Toll Free Tel:* 844-243-8574 *Fax:* 817-237-9407
E-mail: info@lairfloors.com
Web Site: www.lairfloors.com
Key Personnel
Pres: Kenneth Snipes
Busn Mgr: Serena West-Snipes *E-mail:* swestsnipe@aol.com
Founded: 1989
Manufacturer of suspended dance flooring.
Catalog(s) available
Membership(s): ISPA; USITT

L & S Video Inc
45 Stornowaye, Chappaqua, NY 10514
Tel: 914-238-9366 *Fax:* 914-238-6324

E-mail: videopaint2@msn.com
Web Site: www.landsvideo.com
Key Personnel
Principal: Linda Freeman
Founded: 1987
Catalog(s) available
Membership(s): CAA; NAEA

L R Light & Sound
5317 54 St, Drayton Valley, AB T7A 1R6, Canada
Mailing Address: Box 6067, Drayton Valley, AB T7A 1R6, Canada
Tel: 780-542-4242; 780-542-9363 *Fax:* 780-542-4283
E-mail: lrlightandsound@yahoo.ca
Web Site: www.lrlightandsound.ca
Key Personnel
Owner: Lonnie Ross

L-3 ESSCO
Subsidiary of L-3 Communications
90 Nemco Way, Ayer, MA 01432
Tel: 978-568-5100 *Fax:* 978-772-7581
Web Site: www2.l-3com.com/essco/wolfcoach
Manufacturer of mobile production units.

L-3 GCS
7640 Omnitech Place, Victor, NY 14564
Tel: 585-742-9100 *Toll Free Tel:* 888-SAT1USA (728-1872); 877-247-1207 (tech support) *Fax:* 585-742-1914
E-mail: gcs.info@l-3com.com
Web Site: www.globalcoms.com
Key Personnel
Sales: Rick Vernetti
Founded: 1995
Remote satellite communications for a variety of applications.
Catalog(s) available
Branch Office(s)
L-3 3Di, 961 Mercantile Dr, Suite Q, Hanover, MD 21076 *Tel:* 703-621-4568 *Fax:* 703-673-7356 *E-mail:* 3di.info@1-3com.com

L-3 Integrated Optical Systems
4040 Lakeside Dr, Richmond, CA 94806-1963
Tel: 510-222-8110 *Fax:* 510-223-4534
E-mail: sales@asphere.com
Web Site: www.asphere.com
Key Personnel
CEO: Dan Desmond
Founded: 1926
Photo optical equipment manufacturer.
Catalog(s) available
Branch Office(s)
65 Jonspin Rd, Wilmington, MA 01187 *Tel:* 978-694-9991 *E-mail:* salesios@l-3com.com
615 Epsilon Dr, Pittsburgh, PA 15238 *Tel:* 412-967-7700 *E-mail:* salesios@l-3com.com
Membership(s): MCA-I; NAB; SMPTE; SPIE

LA Castle Studios
154 S Victory Blvd, Burbank, CA 91502
Tel: 818-861-7317
Web Site: lacastlestudios.com
Key Personnel
Owner/Prodr: Tim Pipher
Founded: 2012
HDTV & feature film studios. Full studio configuration. 3D virtual studio system.

La Paloma Films
Division of Stillman Productions Ltd
719 Dorr Edson Rd, Suite 1, Oneonta, NY 13820
Tel: 607-287-5175
E-mail: lapalomafilms@yahoo.com
Web Site: www.lapalomafilms.net
Key Personnel
CEO & Pres: Joseph C Stillman
Founded: 1974
Full service motion picture/video production company.

LA Sound Co
9001 Canoga Ave, Canoga Park, CA 91304
Tel: 818-772-9200 *Fax:* 818-772-9977
E-mail: rentals@lasoundco.com; sales@lasoundco.com
Web Site: lasoundco.com
Key Personnel
Pres: Richard Ralke
Founded: 1977
Supply production sound systems to the event & entertainment industry. Offer turnkey system design, installation & operation.

Labor Saving Devices Inc
5678 Eudora St, Commerce City, CO 80022-3809
Tel: 303-287-2121 *Toll Free Tel:* 800-648-4714 *Fax:* 303-287-9044
E-mail: info@lsdinc.com
Web Site: www.lsdinc.com
Key Personnel
Cust Devt Lead: Jennifer Garcia
Founded: 1982
Manufacturer & supplier of professional specialty tools for wire & cable installation.
Catalog(s) available
Membership(s): Canadian Alarm & Security Association; Consumer Electronics Association; Electronic Security Association; National Alarm Association of America; SIA

Labrecque Creative Sound
2825 Main St, Becket, MA 01223
Key Personnel
Owner & Prodr: David Labrecque *Tel:* 520-240-6001 (cell) *E-mail:* dave@labrecquecreativesound.com
Founded: 1993
Audio post-production studio & engineer/producer. ISDN/phone patch/voice booth.
Membership(s): Arizona Production Association

Lacquer-Mat Inc
13035 Wayne Rd, Livonia, MI 48150
Toll Free Tel: 800-942-2223 (cust serv) *Fax:* 734-422-4205 (orders)
Web Site: www.lacquer-mat.com
Key Personnel
Pres: Allan Tyndell
Membership(s): AIE™; PPA

Ladyslipper Inc
PO Box 14, Cedar Grove, NC 27231
Tel: 919-245-3737
E-mail: info@ladyslipper.org
Web Site: www.ladyslipper.org
Key Personnel
Dir: Laurie Fuchs
Founded: 1976
Catalog(s), free

Lagoon Video
Division of Circle Associates Ltd
3323 Marble Front Rd, Caldwell, ID 83605
Tel: 208-455-3457 *Fax:* 208-453-1136
E-mail: kapsm@aol.com
Key Personnel
Pres: Mike Kaplan *E-mail:* mike@circlelagoon.com
Founded: 1987

Laird Digital Cinema
One Tower Dr, Saugerties, NY 12477
Mailing Address: PO Box 720, Mount Marion, NY 12456-0720
Tel: 845-339-9555 *Toll Free Tel:* 800-898-0759 *Fax:* 845-339-0231
E-mail: info@lairddigitalcinema.com; sales@lairddigitalcinema.com
Web Site: www.lairddigitalcinema.com
Founded: 1971

Lakeshore Productions
8625 Indiana Place, Merriville, IN 46410
Tel: 219-756-5656 *Toll Free Tel:* 888-694-5253 *Fax:* 219-755-4312
Web Site: lakeshoreproduction.com
Mobile production, satellite uplink, production management.

Lamb & Lion Ministries
PO Box 919, McKinney, TX 75070
Tel: 972-736-3567 *Toll Free Tel:* 800-705-8316 (sales)
E-mail: lamblion@lamblion.com
Web Site: www.lamblion.com
Key Personnel
Founder & Dir: Dr David R Reagan
Founded: 1980
Catalog(s) available
Shipping Address: 2067 County Rd 463, Princeton, TX 75407
Membership(s): ECFA; NRB

Laminex Inc
4209 Pleasant Rd, Fort Mill, SC 29708
Tel: 704-679-4170 *Toll Free Tel:* 800-438-8850 *Fax:* 704-679-8453
E-mail: info@laminex.com
Web Site: www.laminex.com
Key Personnel
Pres: Tim Long
Founded: 1945
AV laminating equipment & supplies.
Spec sheet(s) available

Landmark Media Inc
3450 Slade Run Dr, Falls Church, VA 22042
Tel: 703-241-2030 *Toll Free Tel:* 800-342-4336 *Fax:* 703-536-9540
E-mail: info@landmarkmedia.com; landmrkmed@aol.com
Web Site: www.landmarkmedia.com
Key Personnel
Owner: Joan Hartogs; Michael Hartogs
VP, Acqs: Richard Hartogs *E-mail:* richard@landmarkmedia.com
VP, New Busn & Devt: Peter Hartogs *E-mail:* peter@landmarkmedia.com
Sales: Eric Miller *Tel:* 800-889-3939 *Fax:* 800-889-3939 *E-mail:* eric@landmarkmedia.com; Beverly Weisenberg *Tel:* 847-279-8761 *Fax:* 847-279-8055 *E-mail:* bev@landmarkmedia.com
Catalog(s) available

L&P Media
255 River St, Troy, NY 12180
Tel: 518-880-0300 *Toll Free Tel:* 800-201-5949 *Fax:* 518-880-0390
E-mail: information@lpmedia.net
Web Site: www.light-power.com
Key Personnel
Pres: John Daniels
Founded: 1977
Total solutions via electronic media.
Branch Office(s)
11 Pruyn St, 3 E Comm Sq, Albany, NY 12207
36 Russet Dr, Guilford, CT 06437

Langie Audio Visual Systems
Piano Works Mall, 349 W Commercial St, East Rochester, NY 14445
Mailing Address: PO Box 147, East Rochester, NY 14445-0147
Tel: 585-385-4880 *Fax:* 585-385-4882
E-mail: info@langieav.com; sales@langieav.com; rental@langieav.com

Web Site: www.langieav.com
Key Personnel
Pres: Ed Ali
Founded: 1970
Catalog(s) available
Membership(s): Greater Rochester Chamber of Commerce; InfoComm International®; MPI

Language Plus Inc
4110 Rio Bravo, Suite 202, El Paso, TX 79902
Tel: 915-544-8600 *Fax:* 915-544-8640
E-mail: speak@languageplus.com
Web Site: www.languageplus.com
Key Personnel
Owner & Dir: Connie Gyenis
Catalog(s) available
Membership(s): ATA; International Association of Language Centers

LANGUAGE/30™
Division of MPS Multimedia Inc
1222 S Amphlett Blvd, San Mateo, CA 94403
Tel: 650-872-7100 *Fax:* 650-872-7133
Web Site: www.lang30.com
Founded: 1948
Publish LANGUAGE/30 self-teaching audio CD & MP3 language courses.

Lank/Beach Productions Inc
341 Wardlaw Ave, Winnipeg, MB R3L 0L5, Canada
Tel: 204-452-9422
E-mail: info@lankbeach.com
Web Site: www.lankbeach.com
Key Personnel
Pres & Dir: Barry Lank
Prodr: Luanne Lank
Founded: 1983
Equipment & facilities include Digital Betacam SP.
Catalog(s) available
Membership(s): Academy of Canadian Cinema & Television/AFI; Alliance of Canadian Regional Motion Picture Industry Associations; Manitoba Motion Picture Industry Association/Manitoba Film Producers' Association

Lannan Foundation
313 Read St, Santa Fe, NM 87501-2628
Tel: 505-986-8160 *Fax:* 505-986-8195
E-mail: info@lannan.org
Web Site: www.lannan.org
Key Personnel
Pres: J Patrick Lannan, Jr
VP & Dir, Opers: Frank C Lawler
Catalog(s), annual

Larrabee Sound Studio
4162 Lankershim Blvd, North Hollywood, CA 91602
Tel: 818-753-0717 *Fax:* 818-753-8046
E-mail: info@larrabeestudios.com
Web Site: www.larrabeestudios.com
Key Personnel
Owner: Kevin Mills
Studio Mgr: Amy Butt *E-mail:* amyb@larrabeestudios.com

Laser Fantasy/HECK Industries/Photon Manufacturing
4228 159 Ave SE, Bellevue, WA 98006
Tel: 425-890-6026 (software & creative support); 425-214-0771 (hardware & tech support)
Fax: 425-296-4255
E-mail: info@heckindustries.com; info@photonmanufacturing.com
Web Site: www.heckindustries.com; www.photonmanufacturing.com
Key Personnel
Owner & Creative Dir, HECK Industries: Jay Heck

Founded: 1977
Laser entertainment, manufacturing & engineering.
Membership(s): IAAPA; ILDA; LDI

Laser Magic Productions
722 N Orlando Ave, No 207, Los Angeles, CA 90069
Tel: 323-951-9392
Web Site: www.laser-magic.com
Key Personnel
Pres & Owner: Gene Baum *E-mail:* gbaum@laser-magic.com
Founded: 1981

Laser Rentals Inc
1953 S County Lane 282, Joplin, MO 64804
Tel: 417-782-8484; 417-437-9149 (after hours)
Toll Free Tel: 800-285-2737
Web Site: www.laserrentalsinc.com
Key Personnel
Pres: Walter Meador
Laser lighting shows.
Catalog(s) available

Laser Spectacles Inc
PO Box 1535, San Marcos, TX 78667
Tel: 512-392-4600 *Fax:* 512-392-4601
E-mail: laserinfo@laserspectacles.com
Web Site: www.laserspectacles.com
Key Personnel
Pres: Timothy Walsh
Founded: 1985
Producer of laser light shows.
Shipping Address: 415 N Guadalupe St, No 430, San Marcos, TX 78666
Membership(s): IFEA; ILDA; Texas Association of Fairs & Events; Texas Chamber of Commerce Executives

Laser Video Corp
401 Germantown Pike, Lafayette Hill, PA 19444
Tel: 610-825-2500 *Toll Free Tel:* 800-448-8772
Fax: 610-941-9989
E-mail: customerservice@laservideousa.com
Web Site: www.lvconline.com
Key Personnel
Pres: Ken O'Neill; Trudie O'Neill
Founded: 1985
Nielson Sigma encoding, encoding, web, Flash, Quicktime, Windows Media Files, H 264, Sorenson, MPEG, distribution & fulfillment, USB flashdrives & bulk shipping.

Lasergraphics Inc
20 Ada, Irvine, CA 92618
Tel: 949-753-8282 *Fax:* 949-727-9282
E-mail: info@lasergraphics.com
Web Site: www.lasergraphics.com
Key Personnel
CEO: Dr Stefan Demetrescu
CFO & VP: David T Boyd
Founded: 1981
Spec sheet(s) available

Laserium
6911 Hayvenhurst Ave, Suite 102, Van Nuys, CA 91406
Tel: 818-429-0454
E-mail: info@laserium.com
Web Site: www.laserium.com
Key Personnel
Founder & CEO: Ivan Dryer *E-mail:* ivan@laserium.com
Founded: 1973
Catalog(s) available

The LAST Factory
Subsidiary of Gamma Omega Associates Inc
2015 Research Dr, Livermore, CA 94550-3803
Tel: 925-449-9449 *Fax:* 925-447-0662
E-mail: thelastfactory@gmail.com
Web Site: thelastfactory.com
Key Personnel
Owner: Walter Davies *E-mail:* wdavies@lastfactory.com
Founded: 1979
Audio mag tape preservation treatment & tape head treatment, record preservative for vinyl records, stylus cleaner & treatment, CD/DVD cleaner & treatment, CD/DVD shields. Our goal is to provide quality cleaners & treatments for all commercial media & to help maintain media whether it be a personal collection or an archive for a museum or library.
Catalog(s), annual, free
Membership(s): ARSC

Latham Foundation Publications
Latham Plaza Bldg, 1826 Clement Ave, Alameda, CA 94501
Tel: 510-521-0920 *Fax:* 510-521-9861
E-mail: info@latham.org
Web Site: www.latham.org
Key Personnel
Pres: Hugh Tebault, III
Admin Assist: Sue Spiersch
Founded: 1918
Produce & distribute DVD educational programs.

Laughing Dog Studio Inc
59 Hylan Blvd, Apt 1C, Staten Island, NY 10305
Tel: 917-496-7752
E-mail: lafndog@inch.com
Web Site: billdonnelly.com
Key Personnel
Owner & Pres: Bill Donnelly
Founded: 1986
Sound designer & audio engineer mixer.
Membership(s): AES

Launch Media
Celtic Media Ctr, 10000 Celtic Dr, Baton Rouge, LA 70809
Tel: 225-612-2112
E-mail: contactus@launchmedia.tv
Web Site: www.launchmedia.tv
Key Personnel
Partner & Coordinating Prodr: Michael Trufant
Pres & Exec Prodr: John E Jackson *Tel:* 225-612-2112 ext 1
Dir, Prodn Servs: Wes Kennison *Tel:* 225-612-2112 ext 2
Multimedia production company. Specialize in developing & producing strategies & communication tools through customized video & experiential event production.

Laurel Canyon Stages
9337 Laurel Canyon Blvd, Arleta, CA 91331-4315
Tel: 818-768-8935 *Fax:* 818-768-6852
E-mail: info@lcstages.com
Web Site: www.lcstages.com
Facility, grip, lighting & electrical equipment rentals.

Laurel Hill Press
PO Box 16516, Chapel Hill, NC 27516-6516
Toll Free Tel: 800-942-6516 *Fax:* 919-942-9533
E-mail: plantsforus@gmail.com
Web Site: www.laurelhillpress.com
Key Personnel
Owner: Dr C Ritchie Bell
Publisher of colorful & informative natural history books, videos & DVDs.
Catalog(s) available

Laurel Video Productions
1999 Marlton Pike, Suite 11, Cherry Hill, NJ 08003
Tel: 856-424-3300
E-mail: inquiries@laurelvideo.net

Web Site: www.laurelvideo.net
Key Personnel
Founder & Owner: Steven Tadzynski
Catalog(s) available
Membership(s): IABC; MCA-I; SBE; SMPTE

Lavine Production Group
189 Dean St, Brooklyn, NY 11217
Tel: 917-804-1870
Web Site: www.lavinegroup.com
Key Personnel
Pres & Exec Prodr: Miriam Lewin
E-mail: miriamlewin@lavinegroup.com

Donna Lawrence Productions
624 Baxter Ave, Louisville, KY 40204
Tel: 502-589-9617
E-mail: dlp@dlproductions.com
Web Site: www.dlproductions.com
Key Personnel
Principal: Donna Lawrence
Administrator: Carol Mooney *Tel:* 502-589-9617 ext 225
Full service production company.

Lawrence Productions Inc
6146 W Main St, Suite A, Kalamazoo, MI 49009
Tel: 269-903-2395
E-mail: sales@lpi.com
Web Site: www.lpi.com
Key Personnel
VP: Curtis Cunningham *Tel:* 269-903-2395 ext 28
E-mail: ccunningham@lpi.com
Film & video production company.
Catalog(s) available
Membership(s): American Marketing Association

Lex Lawson Associates
2002 Platinum St, Garland, TX 75042
Tel: 972-272-8482 *Toll Free Tel:* 800-783-9395
Fax: 972-276-8120
Web Site: www.lexlawson.com
Key Personnel
Owner: David Lawson *E-mail:* david@lexlawson.com
Off Mgr: Sandy McCleary *E-mail:* sandy@lexlawson.com
Founded: 1974
Manufacturers, representatives & consultants for AV systems. Provides systems training for dealers.
Membership(s): InfoComm International®

LBA Technology Inc
Division of LBA Group Inc
3400 Tupper Dr, Greenville, NC 27834
Mailing Address: PO Box 8026, Greenville, NC 27835-8026
Tel: 252-757-0279 *Toll Free Tel:* 800-522-4464
Fax: 252-752-9155
E-mail: lbagrp@lbagroup.com
Web Site: www.lbagroup.com
Key Personnel
CEO, LBA Group: Lawrence Behr
E-mail: lbwireless@lbagroup.com
CFO: Wayne Hildebrandt *E-mail:* whildebrandt@lbagroup.com
Pres: Jerry Brown *E-mail:* jbrown@lbagroup.com
Founded: 1963
Manufacturer of high power digital ready antenna systems.
Catalog(s) available

LCW Productions LLC
3019 Hayden Dr, Wilmington, NC 28411-9625
Tel: 910-681-0835 *Fax:* 910-524-2736
Web Site: www.lcwproductions.com
Key Personnel
CEO & Pres: Linda C Warden
E-mail: lcwarden@yahoo.com
Founded: 2005
HD video production & still photography services.

LEA International
Member of Smiths Power Protection Technology Group
10701 Airport Rd, Hayden, ID 83835
Tel: 208-762-6121 *Toll Free Tel:* 800-882-9110
Founded: 1971
Surge suppressor manufacturer.
Catalog(s) available
Membership(s): NAB; SBE

LEAD Technologies Inc
1927 S Tryon St, Suite 200, Charlotte, NC 28203
Tel: 704-332-5532 *Toll Free Tel:* 800-637-4699
Fax: 704-372-8161
E-mail: sales@leadtools.com
Web Site: www.leadtools.com
Key Personnel
Pres: Richard Little
Founded: 1990
Our primary focus is providing digital imaging & compression technology to programmers.

Leader Instruments Corp
Subsidiary of Leader Electronics Corp
6484 Commerce Dr, Cypress, CA 90630
Tel: 714-527-9300 *Toll Free Tel:* 800-645-5104
Fax: 714-527-7490
E-mail: sales@leaderusa.com
Web Site: www.leaderusa.com
Key Personnel
Dir, Sales: George Gonos
Prod Mktg Mgr: Christian Young
Monitoring system manufacturer.
Catalog(s) available

Learn Quickly
PO Box 3114, Palm Springs, CA 92263-3114
Toll Free Tel: 888-LRN-FAST (576-3278)
Toll Free Fax: 888-LRN-FAST (576-3278)
Web Site: www.learnquickly.com
Key Personnel
Owner & Creator: Janet Scarpone *E-mail:* janet@learnquickly.com
Founded: 1996
Educational books & videos in math, communication, writing & grammar. Online format available.
Brochure(s) available

Learning Ally
20 Roszel Rd, Princeton, NJ 08540
Tel: 609-750-1830 *Toll Free Tel:* 800-221-4792 (memb support)
E-mail: custserv@learningally.org
Web Site: www.learningally.org
Key Personnel
Dir, Media Rel: Doug Sprei *Tel:* 609-243-5865 *Fax:* 609-452-2585 *E-mail:* dsprei@learningally.org
Producer of accessible recorded educational materials for people who cannot read standard print because of a learning disability, visual impairment or other physical disability. Both CDs & tapes available.
Online catalog(s) available
Branch Office(s)
5022 Hollywood Blvd, Los Angeles, CA 90027 *Tel:* 323-210-1454
2445 Faber Place, Suite 103, Palo Alto, CA 94303 *Tel:* 650-493-3717
1355 S Colorado Blvd, Suite C-406, Denver, CO 80222 *Tel:* 303-757-0787
5225 Wisconsin Ave NW, Suite 312, Washington, DC 20015 *Tel:* 202-244-8990
Gladys Davis Pavilion, Bldg 49, 777 Glades Rd, Boca Raton, FL 33431 *Tel:* 561-297-4444
120 Florida Ave, Athens, GA 30605 *Tel:* 706-549-1313
14600 S Ravinia Ave, Orland Park, IL 60462 *Tel:* 708-349-9356
2067 Massachusetts Ave, 3rd fl, Cambridge, MA 02140 *Tel:* 617-500-2706
545 Fifth Ave, Suite 1005, New York, NY 10017 *Tel:* 212-557-5720
1314 W 45 St, Austin, TX 78756 *Tel:* 512-323-9390

Learning Communications LLC
5520 Trabuco Rd, Irvine, CA 92620
Toll Free Tel: 800-622-3610 *Fax:* 949-727-4323
E-mail: sales@learncom.com
Web Site: www.learncom.com
Key Personnel
VP, Sales: Mike Johnson
Founded: 1998
Provides employee & management training resources & services to corporate, government & nonprofit customers.
Catalog(s) available
Sales Office(s): 8345 University Blvd, Suite G-1, Clive, IA 50325 *Fax:* 515-221-3149
Shipping Address: 450-B Frontier Way, Bensenville, IL 60106 *Tel:* 630-227-1080 *Fax:* 630-238-9088 *E-mail:* distributors@learncom.com
Membership(s): ATD

The Learning House Inc
427 S Fourth St, Suite 300, Louisville, KY 40202
Tel: 502-589-9878 *Fax:* 502-589-9825
E-mail: sales@learninghouse.com
Web Site: www.learninghouse.com
Key Personnel
Founder: Denzil Edge
CEO & Pres: David T Richardson
COO: Todd Zipper
VP, Curriculum: Victoria Alexander
VP, Fin: Jim Lintner
Founded: 1999
Creators of online degree courses.
Catalog(s) available
Shipping Address: 1548 Cherokee Rd, Louisville, KY 40205

Learning Seed
208 S Jefferson St, Suite 402, Chicago, IL 60661
Toll Free Tel: 800-634-4941 *Toll Free Fax:* 800-998-0854
E-mail: info@learningseed.com
Web Site: www.learningseed.com
Key Personnel
Pres: Christine Schrank
Educational programming.
Catalog(s) available

Learning Strategies Corp
2000 Plymouth Rd, Minnetonka, MN 55305-2335
Tel: 952-767-9800 *Toll Free Tel:* 888-800-2688 (cust serv); 866-292-1861 (24 hour order line)
Fax: 952-475-2373
E-mail: info@learningstrategies.com
Web Site: www.learningstrategies.com
Key Personnel
Pres: Peter Bissonette
Founded: 1981
Provider of self-improvement, education & health programs on audio programs & through events.
Catalog(s) available

Learning Technology Services
Affiliate of University of Wisconsin-Stout
301 Millennium Hall, Menomonie, WI 54751
Tel: 715-232-1289 *Fax:* 715-232-2456
E-mail: helpdesk@uwec.edu
Web Site: www.unwec.edu/lts
Key Personnel
Dir: Jane Henderson *Tel:* 715-232-1289 ext 5005
E-mail: hendersonj@uwstout.edu

Lectrosonics Inc
581 Laser Rd NE, Rio Rancho, NM 87124
Mailing Address: PO Box 15900, Rio Rancho, NM 87174
Tel: 505-892-4501 *Toll Free Tel:* 800-821-1121 *Fax:* 505-892-6243
E-mail: sales@lectrosonics.com
Web Site: www.lectrosonics.com
Key Personnel
Pres: Larry Fisher
VP, Engg: Bob Cunnings
VP, Mfg: Wes Herron
VP, Mktg: Bruce Jones
VP, Sales: Gordon Moore
Mktg Coord: Kathy Baca
Founded: 1971
Catalog(s), annual
Branch Office(s)
49 Spadina Ave, Suite 303A, Toronto, ON M5V 2J1, Canada *Tel:* 416-596-2202 *Toll Free Tel:* 877-7LECTRO (753-2876) *Fax:* 416-596-6648
Membership(s): InfoComm International®; NAB; NAMM, the National Association of Music Merchants; NSCA

LEDtronics Inc
23105 Kashiva Ct, Torrance, CA 90505
Tel: 310-534-1505 *Toll Free Tel:* 800-579-4875 *Fax:* 310-534-1424
E-mail: info@ledtronics.com
Web Site: www.ledtronics.com
Founded: 1983
Manufacturer of LED bulbs & LED lamps.
Catalog(s) available

Lee Co Inc
27 S 12 St, Terre Haute, IN 47807
Tel: 812-235-8155 *Fax:* 812-235-3587
E-mail: leeco@leecompanyinc.com
Web Site: www.leecompanyinc.com
Key Personnel
Pres: Ken Senseman
Founded: 1932
Catalog(s) available

Lee Dan® Communications Inc
155 Adams Ave, Hauppauge, NY 11788-3699
Tel: 631-231-1414 *Toll Free Tel:* 800-231-1414 *Fax:* 631-231-1498
E-mail: info@leedan.com
Web Site: www.leedan.com
Key Personnel
VP: David H Goldberg
Founded: 1955
Intercom manufacturer.
Catalog(s) available

Lee Filters
Division of Panavision
2237 N Hollywood Way, Burbank, CA 91505
Tel: 818-238-1220 *Toll Free Tel:* 800-576-5055 *Fax:* 818-238-1228
E-mail: mail@leefiltersusa.com
Web Site: www.leefilters.com
Key Personnel
VP & Gen Mgr: Jessie Friend
Catalog(s) available

Lee Hartman & Sons Inc
3236 Cove Rd NW, Roanoke, VA 24017
Mailing Address: PO Box 13365, Roanoke, VA 24033-3365
Tel: 540-366-3493 *Toll Free Tel:* 800-344-1832 *Fax:* 540-362-4659
E-mail: info@leehartman.com
Web Site: www.leehartman.com
Key Personnel
Pres & Gen Mgr: Steve M Hartman
Rental Mgr: Rob Hartman
Founded: 1936
Retail/wholesale audio visual products. Consultation services, delivery, installation & rental department. Education, government, religious & business specialists.
Catalog(s), annual, free
Branch Office(s)
11861 Canon Blvd SW, Suite R, Newport News, VA 23606, Contact: Lou Ensley *Tel:* 757-873-4944 *Fax:* 757-873-0915 *E-mail:* lensley@leehartman.com
8839 Kelso St, Suite J, Baltimore, MD 21221, Contact: Quentin Mills *Tel:* 410-686-6975 *Fax:* 410-686-5170 *E-mail:* qmills@leehartman.com
3 Davis Ct, Hurricane, WV 25526, Contact: Larry Cox *Tel:* 304-397-4100 *Fax:* 304-397-4101 *E-mail:* lcox@leehartman.com
Membership(s): Chamber of Commerce; Custom Electronic Design & Installation Association; InfoComm International®

Leedal Inc
Affiliate of Matrix Division
3453 Commercial Ave, Northbrook, IL 60062
Tel: 847-498-0111 *Fax:* 847-498-0198
E-mail: sink@leedal.com
Web Site: www.leedal.com
Key Personnel
Pres: Sheldon Levin
VP & Dir, Mktg: A J Levin
Founded: 1946
Catalog(s) available
Membership(s): InfoComm International®; Photo Marketing Association

Lefco Video Services Inc
600 W Sunset Rd, Suite 103, Henderson, NV 89011
Tel: 702-566-1770 *Fax:* 702-566-1798
E-mail: info1@lefco.com
Web Site: www.lefco.com
Key Personnel
Pres & Gen Mgr: Michael Minkoff *Tel:* 702-400-1120 (cell) *E-mail:* mm@lefco.com
Broadcast equipment rentals & systems.
Catalog(s) available

Legendary Entertainment
160 Torrance Woods, Brampton, ON L6Y 4K2, Canada
Tel: 416-712-9994
E-mail: info@legendaryentertainment.com
Web Site: legendaryentertainment.com
Record label & media company.

Legendary Pictures LLC
2900 W Alameda Ave, 15th fl, Burbank, CA 91505
Tel: 818-688-7003
E-mail: info@legendary.com
Web Site: www.legendary.com
Key Personnel
Founder & CEO: Thomas Tull
Pres & Chief Creative Offr: Jon Jashni
Founded: 2000
Film production company. Co-production & co-financing of films with Universal Studios. Legendary Television & Digital Media division.

Legion Lighting Co Inc
221 Glenmore Ave, Brooklyn, NY 11207
Tel: 718-498-1770 *Fax:* 718-498-0128 *Toll Free Fax:* 800-4-LEGION (453-4466)
E-mail: sales@legionlighting.com
Web Site: www.legionlighting.com
Key Personnel
CEO: Sheldon Bellovin
Founded: 1946
Manufacture energy efficient fluorescent lighting fixtures & exit lighting.
Catalog(s) available
CD-ROM catalog(s) available

Lehigh Electric Products Co
6265 Hamilton Blvd, Allentown, PA 18106
Tel: 610-395-3386 *Fax:* 610-395-7735
E-mail: sales@lehighdim.com
Web Site: www.lehighdim.com
Key Personnel
Pres: Lloyd H Jones
Founded: 1961
Lighting control equipment manufacturer.
Catalog(s) available
Membership(s): Professional Lighting & Sound Association; USITT

Lehigh Phoenix™
18249 Phoenix Dr, Hagerstown, MD 21742
Tel: 301-733-0018 *Toll Free Tel:* 800-632-4111 *Fax:* 301-733-1733
Web Site: www.phoenixcolor.com
Key Personnel
SVP, Natl Sales-Educ: Mike Phippard *Tel:* 240-527-2572
SVP, Natl Sales-Trade & Children's Books: John A Sabella *Tel:* 240-527-2543
Catalog(s) available
Branch Office(s)
350 Seventh Ave, New York, NY 10001 *Tel:* 240-527-2533 *Fax:* 240-527-2534

Leica Camera Inc
Subsidiary of Leica Camera Group (Germany)
One Pearl Ct, Unit A, Allendale, NJ 07401
Toll Free Tel: 800-222-0118 *Fax:* 201-995-1686
Web Site: en.leica-camera.com
Key Personnel
VP, Mktg: Christian Erhardt
Manufacturer & distributor of camera equipment.
Catalog(s) available

Leightronix Inc
2330 Jarco Dr, Holt, MI 48842
Tel: 517-694-8000 *Toll Free Tel:* 800-243-5589 *Fax:* 517-694-1600
E-mail: support@leightronix.com; sales@leightronix.com
Web Site: www.leightronix.com
Key Personnel
Dir, Mktg: Sherri Powers
Founded: 1981
Manufacture IPTV System Solutions & hardware & software (middleware).

Leisure Video
747 Magazine St, New Orleans, LA 70130
Tel: 504-299-9000 *Toll Free Tel:* 800-432-3853 *Fax:* 504-299-9090
E-mail: info@dukesofdixieland.com
Web Site: www.dukesofdixieland.com; www.leisurejazz.com
Key Personnel
Pres: John Shoup
Membership(s): Entertainment Merchants Association; NATPE

LEMO USA Inc
Subsidiary of LEMO SA (Switzerland)
635 Park Ct, Rohnert Park, CA 94928
Mailing Address: PO Box 2408, Rohnert Park, CA 94927-2408
Tel: 707-578-8811 *Toll Free Tel:* 800-444-LEMO (444-5366) *Fax:* 707-578-0869
E-mail: info@lemousa.com
Web Site: www.lemousa.com; www.lemo.com
Key Personnel
Mktg Communs Mgr: Julie Carlson *Tel:* 707-206-3776 *E-mail:* jcarlson@lemo.com
Founded: 1946
Electronic connectors for headsets, microphones & professional cameras.
Catalog(s) available

Lenel Systems International Inc
1212 Pittsford-Victor Rd, Pittsford, NY 14534-3820
Tel: 585-248-9720 *Toll Free Tel:* 866-788-5095 *Fax:* 585-248-9185
E-mail: pr@lenel.com
Web Site: www.lenel.com
Key Personnel
Pres: Louise Orbegoso
Dir, Mktg: Julie Shanahan *Tel:* 585-267-8071

Lensless Camera Manufacturing Co
809 Lark Dr, Fernley, NV 89408
Mailing Address: PO Box 261, Fernley, NV 89408-0261
Tel: 775-575-5189
E-mail: info@pinholecamera.com
Web Site: www.pinholecamera.com
Key Personnel
Owner: Charles Levy
Single shot lensless camera made available in 4x5, 5x7, 8x10 & 11x14 formats. These cameras take film holders & Polaroid backs.
Brochure(s) available

Leo Films
6548 Country Squire Lane, Omaha, NE 68152
Tel: 323-459-5574
Web Site: www.leofilms.com
Key Personnel
Pres: Steve Lustgarten *E-mail:* lustgar@pacbell.net
Catalog(s) available

Leonardo Software
11726 San Vicente Blvd, Suite 520, Los Angeles, CA 90049
Tel: 310-820-9961 *Toll Free Tel:* 800-606-4536 *Fax:* 310-820-9970
E-mail: info@leonardosoft.com
Web Site: www.leonardosoft.com
Key Personnel
Owner: Louis Benioff *E-mail:* lbenioff@leonardosoft.com
Founded: 1986
Resell sound effects libraries.
Catalog(s) available

Leprecon®
Division of CAE Inc
10087 Industrial Dr, Hamburg, MI 48139
Mailing Address: PO Box 218, Hamburg, MI 48139-0430
Tel: 810-852-4300 *Toll Free Tel:* 888-422-3537 *Fax:* 810-231-1631
E-mail: lepsls@leprecon.com
Web Site: www.leprecon.com
Key Personnel
Pres: James Fackert
Sales/Mktg Mgr: Julie Sanders *E-mail:* juliesanders@leprecon.com
Sales: Peter Stewart *E-mail:* pstewart@leprecon.com
Off Mgr: Lois Riske
Catalog(s) available
Membership(s): Professional Lighting & Sound Association; USITT

The Lerro Corp
Valley Forge Corporate Ctr, 905 Madison Ave, Norristown, PA 19403
Tel: 610-650-4100 *Fax:* 610-650-4110
E-mail: lerrocorp@lerro.com
Web Site: www.lerro.com
Key Personnel
Pres: Matthew E Murphy *E-mail:* mattm@lerro.com
Secy & Treas: Marion E Murphy *Tel:* 610-650-4100 ext 217 *E-mail:* marionm@lerro.com
Founded: 1949
Catalog(s) available
Branch Office(s)
3510 Margo Rd, Camp Hill, PA 17011, Patrick Bucher *Tel:* 717-763-1580 *E-mail:* patb@lerro.com
400 Penn Center Blvd, Suite 721, Pittsburgh, PA 15235, Joe SeNay *Tel:* 412-824-5222 *Fax:* 412-824-5190 *E-mail:* joes@lerro.com
13 Kintore Ct, Baltimore, MD 21234 *Tel:* 410-668-9800 *E-mail:* mmcintyre@lerro.com

Leucos USA Inc
Subsidiary of Leucos SpA
11 Mayfield Ave, Edison, NJ 08837
Tel: 732-225-0010 *Toll Free Tel:* 800-832-3360 *Fax:* 732-225-0250
E-mail: info@leucosusa.com
Web Site: www.leucos.com
Key Personnel
Pres: Josie A Anthony
Founded: 1991
Distributor of contemporary glass lighting.
Catalog(s) available
Foreign Office(s): Leucos SpA, Via Maglionese 29/31, 30037 Scorze/Venezia, Italy *Tel:* (041) 5859111 *Fax:* (041) 447598 *E-mail:* info@leucos.it

Level 3 Communications Inc
1025 Eldorado Blvd, Broomfield, CO 80021
Tel: 720-888-1000 *Toll Free Tel:* 877-2LEVEL3 (253-8357)
Web Site: www.level3.com
Key Personnel
CEO & Pres: Jeff Storey
CFO & EVP: Sunit Patel
AV teleconferencing service.

Leviton LES
Division of Leviton Manufacturing Co Inc
20497 SW Teton Ave, Tualatin, OR 97062
Toll Free Tel: 800-736-6682 *Fax:* 503-404-5594
Web Site: www.leviton.com
Founded: 1906
Advanced architectural lighting control systems.
Catalog(s) available
Branch Office(s)
Levitron Manufacturing Co Inc, 201 N Service Rd, Melville, NY 11747 *Toll Free Tel:* 800-323-8920 *Toll Free Fax:* 800-832-9538
Levitron Network Solutions, 2222-222 St SE, Bothell, WA 98021-4422 *Toll Free Tel:* 800-722-2082 *Fax:* 425-483-5270
Levitron Manufacturing of Canada Ltd, 165, Boul Hymus Blvd, Pointe-Claire, QC H9R 1E9, Canada *Toll Free Tel:* 800-461-2002 *Toll Free Fax:* 800-563-1853

C H Levy & Co, see Lensless Camera Manufacturing Co

Levy Lighting NYC Inc
347 W 36 St, Ground fl, New York, NY 10018
Tel: 212-925-4640 *Fax:* 212-925-4216
E-mail: info@levylighting.com
Web Site: www.levylighting.com
Key Personnel
Pres: Ira Levy
Chief, Opers: Liz Kirschner *E-mail:* lkirschner@levylighting.com
Lighting designers.

Lex Products Corp
15 Progress Dr, Shelton, CT 06484
Tel: 203-363-3738 *Toll Free Tel:* 800-643-4460 *Fax:* 203-363-3742
E-mail: info@lexproducts.com
Web Site: www.lexproducts.com
Key Personnel
CEO: Bob Luther *Tel:* 203-274-9910 *E-mail:* bluther@lexproducts.com
VP, Sales: Tom Siko *Tel:* 203-815-3700 *E-mail:* tsiko@lexproducts.com
Founded: 1989
Manufacturer & distributor of portable power distribution systems including cable assemblies.
Catalog(s) available
Branch Office(s)
11847 Sheldon St, Sun Valley, CA 91352 *Tel:* 818-768-4474 *Fax:* 818-768-4040
Membership(s): Production Equipment Rental Association; Professional Lighting & Sound Association

LHV Audio Services
3417 Lake Breeze Rd, Orlando, FL 32808
Tel: 407-295-3565
E-mail: service@lhvaudio.com
Web Site: www.lhvaudio.com
Key Personnel
Pres & Chief Engr: Laurence Vexler
Founded: 1990
Membership(s): AES; The Recording Academy

Liberty Photo Products
1041 Calle Trepadora, San Clemente, CA 92673
Tel: 949-361-1100 *Toll Free Tel:* 800-572-3600 *Fax:* 949-498-4441
E-mail: info@liberty2create.com; sales-info@libertyphoto.com
Web Site: www.liberty2create.com
Founded: 1984
Catalog(s) available
Membership(s): International Mini Lab Association; Photo Marketing Association

Liberty Publishing Co Inc
PO Box 4485, Deerfield Beach, FL 33442-4248
Tel: 954-573-7236
Web Site: www.bullsorbears.com
Key Personnel
Pres & Edit Dir: Jeffrey B Little *E-mail:* jblittle@bellsouth.net
VP, Opers: Judith A Little
Publicity Dir: Suzanne Little
Distributes & produces DVD - "Understanding Wall Street".
Catalog(s) available

Liberty Uplink
2547 Yellow Springs Rd, Malvern, PA 19355
Tel: 215-964-5222; 917-254-0155
E-mail: info@libertyuplink.com
Web Site: www.libertyuplink.com
Key Personnel
Founder & Partner: Adam Sirkin
Partner: Chuck Ranney
Founded: 1999
Pre-production scouting services, satellite time booking, production coordination, camera crews & transmission services.

LibertyPak Co Inc
420 Bryant Circle, Bldg B, Ojai, CA 93023
Tel: 805-640-6700
E-mail: sales@libertypak.com; service@libertypak.com
Web Site: www.libertypak.com
Key Personnel
Owner: Stuart Lennox
Founded: 2002
Design & manufacture new technology battery belts & blocks.

Library of Congress, Motion Picture, Broadcasting & Recorded Sound Division
Division of Library of Congress
James Madison Bldg, LM 336, 101 Independence Ave SE, Washington, DC 20540-1000
Tel: 202-707-8572 *Fax:* 202-707-2371
Web Site: www.loc.gov/rr/mopic

Key Personnel
Admin Offr: Jo Ellen Marcel *Tel:* 202-707-1762 *E-mail:* jmarcel@loc.gov
Catalog(s), for sound recordings only; includes folk music & poetry readings

Library Video Company
7 E Wynnewood Rd, Wynnewood, PA 19096
Tel: 610-645-4000 *Toll Free Tel:* 800-843-3620 *Fax:* 610-645-4040
E-mail: sales@libraryvideo.com; comments@libraryvideo.com
Web Site: www.libraryvideo.com
Key Personnel
CEO: Andrew Schlessinger
Founded: 1985
Leading publisher of educational media to schools & libraries.
Catalog(s), 5 times/yr, free, educational media
Membership(s): ALA; Entertainment Merchants Association

Library Video Network (LVN)
320 York Rd, Towson, MD 21204
Tel: 410-887-2090 *Toll Free Tel:* 800-441-8273 *Fax:* 410-887-2091
E-mail: lvn@bcpl.net
Web Site: www.lvn.org
Key Personnel
Video Prodr: Carl Birkmeyer
Video Prodn Specialist: Brenda Kinzinger *E-mail:* bkinzing@bcpl.net
Provider of library-specific training media.
Catalog(s), free

Ken Lieberman Labs Inc
69 Fairview Dr, Albertson, NY 11507-1007
Tel: 212-633-0500
Web Site: lieberman-labs.com
Key Personnel
Pres: Ken Lieberman *E-mail:* kenlieberman@gmail.com
Founded: 1965
Custom photo lab & production services film, digital & conventional, custom print making.
Membership(s): ASMP; PAI

Lieberman Productions
455 Ninth St, San Francisco, CA 94103-4410
Tel: 415-955-0855 *Fax:* 415-955-0822
E-mail: lpinfo@lieberman.com
Web Site: www.lieberman.com
Key Personnel
Pres: Lenny Lieberman
Full service production company. Specialize in infomercials.

Life Cycle Books Ltd
1085 Bellamy Rd N, Unit 20, Toronto, ON M1H 1H7, Canada
Tel: 416-690-5860 *Toll Free Tel:* 866-880-5860 *Fax:* 416-690-8532 *Toll Free Fax:* 866-690-8532
E-mail: support@lifecyclebooks.com; billing@lifecyclebooks.com; orders@lifecyclebooks.com
Web Site: www.lifecyclebooks.com
Key Personnel
Founder & Pres: Paul Broughton *E-mail:* paulb@lifecyclebooks.com
Catalog(s) available
Branch Office(s)
PO Box 799, Fort Collins, CO 80522 *Toll Free Tel:* 800-214-5849 *Toll Free Fax:* 888-690-8532

Life House Productions LLC
PO Box 4007, Manchester, CT 06045-4007
Tel: 860-432-9177
Web Site: www.lifehouseproductions.com
Key Personnel
Partner & Pres: William Matthews *E-mail:* bill@lifehouseproductions.com
Partner: Dena Matthews *E-mail:* dena@lifehouseproductions.com
Founded: 1998
Medical & scientific 3D computer animation & graphics.

Lifetime Television®
Unit of Lifetime Entertainment Services LLC
235 E 45 St, New York, NY 10017
Tel: 212-424-7000
Web Site: www.mylifetime.com
Key Personnel
EVP & Gen Mgr: Rob Sharenow
VP, Scripted Series: Jennifer Breslow
Founded: 1984
TV programming.
Branch Office(s)
2049 Century Park E, Suite 840, Los Angeles, CA 90067 *Tel:* 310-556-7500
444 N Michigan Ave, Suite 3270, Chicago, IL 60611 *Tel:* 312-464-1991

Light Impressions
Division of New Century Direct LLC
2340 Brighton Henrietta Town Line Rd, Rochester, NY 14623
Toll Free Tel: 800-975-6429 *Toll Free Fax:* 800-975-6429 (orders)
E-mail: info@lightimpressionsdirect.com
Web Site: www.lightimpressionsdirect.com
Founded: 1969
Manufacturer & distributor of archival supplies.
Catalog(s), monthly

The Light Source
3935 Westinghouse Blvd, Charlotte, NC 28273
Tel: 704-504-8399 *Fax:* 704-588-4693 (acctg); 704-588-4637 (orders)
E-mail: mail@thelightsource.com; sales@thelightsource.com
Web Site: www.thelightsource.com
Key Personnel
Owner: Eric Von Fange *E-mail:* ericvf@thelightsource.com
Manufacture lighting clamps.
Catalog(s) available
Membership(s): Professional Lighting & Sound Association

Light Tec
1311 Chemical St, Dallas, TX 75207
Tel: 214-350-8990 *Toll Free Tel:* 888-548-3832 *Fax:* 214-638-2038
E-mail: info@lighttec.com
Web Site: www.lighttec.com
Founded: 1980
Lighting, equipment & studio rentals.

LightBox-NY
841 Barretto St, Bronx, NY 10474
Tel: 718-759-6419
E-mail: lightboxny@gmail.com
Web Site: www.lightbox-ny.com
Daylight studio rental for film, photography & music videos.

LightCraft Graphics Inc
1269 Rand Rd, Des Plaines, IL 60016
Tel: 847-759-8500 *Fax:* 847-759-8540
Web Site: www.lightcraft.com
Key Personnel
Pres: Rick Vogeney *E-mail:* rick@lightcraft.com
Premier printing & large format graphics company.
Catalog(s) available
Membership(s): IAPP

LightHouse Films
115 W 29 St, Suite 903, New York, NY 10001
Tel: 646-649-3600 *Fax:* 646-398-7122
E-mail: contact@lhfny.com; rent@lhfny.com
Web Site: www.light-house-films.com
Key Personnel
Founder & Partner: Camille De Galbert
Partner & Prodr: Thibaut Estellon
Dir: Nick Everhart
Founded: 2008
Commercial, corporate & music video production services. Camera & accessories rental.

Lighthouse Photo & Video Productions
1100 Chicago Ave, Suite 2C, Goshen, IN 46528
Tel: 574-533-1400 (off); 574-202-5502 (studio)
E-mail: lighthousevideo@gmail.com
Web Site: www.lighthousephotoandvideo.com
Key Personnel
Owner & Pres: William Landow
Photography & videography for family & corporate events. Film & video transfer service. Documentary production for promotion, training or TV broadcast.

Lighting & Production Equipment Inc
590 Travis St, Atlanta, GA 30318
Tel: 404-352-0464 *Toll Free Tel:* 800-275-3721 *Fax:* 404-351-4399
Web Site: www.lpe.com
Key Personnel
Founder & CEO: W Bruce Harlan *Tel:* 404-924-7600 *E-mail:* bharlan@lpe.com
Catalog(s) available
Online catalog(s) available
Membership(s): AICP; NABET-CWA; NATAS

The Lighting Design Alliance
2830 Temple Ave, Long Beach, CA 90806-2213
Tel: 562-989-3843 *Fax:* 562-989-3847
E-mail: info@lightingdesignalliance.com
Web Site: www.lightingdesignalliance.com
Key Personnel
Pres: Chip Israel *E-mail:* cisrael@lightingdesignalliance.com
Founded: 1992
Lighting designers.

Lighting Design Group
49 W 27 St, Suite 920, New York, NY 10001
Tel: 212-685-4940 *Fax:* 212-685-4927
E-mail: lighting@ldg.com
Web Site: www.ldg.com
Key Personnel
EVP, Design: Dennis M Size
Founded: 1989
Lighting design & lighting production service company.
Catalog(s) available
Membership(s): IALD; Illuminating Engineering Society; International Alliance of Theatrical Stage Employees; NABET-CWA; NATAS; SMPTE; United Scenic Artists; USITT

Lighting Industry Resource Council
Affiliate of The International Association of Lighting Designers (IALD)
440 N Wells St, Suite 210, Chicago, IL 60654
Tel: 312-527-3677 *Fax:* 312-527-3680
E-mail: iald@iald.org
Web Site: www.iald.org/council
Key Personnel
CEO: Marsha L Turner *Tel:* 312-527-3677 ext 106 *E-mail:* marsha@iald.org
Membership Mgr: Ashley Robbins *E-mail:* ashley@iald.org
Founded: 1996
Manufacturer of lighting equipment.

Lighting Sales Connections
757 SE 17 St, PMB 254, Fort Lauderdale, FL 33316
Tel: 954-764-6928 *Fax:* 954-791-8450
E-mail: info@lightingsales.com
Web Site: www.lightingsales.com

Key Personnel
Pres: Richard J Blanco
Catalog(s) available

Lighting Services Inc
2 Holt Dr, Stony Point, NY 10980-1996
Tel: 845-942-2800 *Toll Free Tel:* 800-999-9574 (US & CN) *Fax:* 845-942-2177
E-mail: applications@maillsi.com; sales@maillsi.com
Web Site: www.lightingservicesinc.com
Founded: 1958
Manufacture track lighting, accent lighting, display lighting & LED lighting systems.
Catalog(s) available

Lightning Eliminators & Consultants Inc
6687 Arapahoe Rd, Boulder, CO 80303
Tel: 303-447-2828 *Toll Free Tel:* 800-521-6101 *Fax:* 303-447-8122
E-mail: info@lightningprotection.com
Web Site: www.lightningprotection.com
Key Personnel
CEO & Pres: Avram Saunders *Tel:* 303-951-3120 *E-mail:* avrams@lecglobal.com
EVP & Dir, Applied Engg: Peter A Carpenter *Tel:* 303-951-3155 *E-mail:* peterc@lecglobal.com
VP, Opers: Joe Lanzoni *Tel:* 303-951-3156 *E-mail:* jlanzoni@lecglobal.com
Dir, Engg: Kirk S Chynoweth *E-mail:* kirkc@lecglobal.com
Mgr, Intl Solutions: Nate Mascarenas *Tel:* 303-951-3126
Founded: 1971
Lightning prevention systems & products, application engineering, consulting & educational services.

Lightning Master Corp
1770 Calumet St, Clearwater, FL 33765
Tel: 727-447-6800 *Toll Free Tel:* 877-334-8006 *Fax:* 727-499-0138
E-mail: info@lightningmaster.com
Web Site: www.lightningmaster.com
Key Personnel
Pres: Bruce Kaiser
Founded: 1984
Manufacturer of full spectrum static solutions & lightning & transient protection systems, serving the oil, gas & chemical industries.
Catalog(s) available
Membership(s): American Petroleum Institute; IEEE; NFPA

Lightning Media
1415 Cahuenga Blvd, Hollywood, CA 90028
Tel: 323-957-9255
E-mail: info@lightningmedia.com
Web Site: www.lightningmedia.com
Post-production services to media & entertainment clients.

Lightolier
Subsidiary of Philips Lighting Business Unit-Professional Luminaires North America
631 Airport Rd, Fall River, MA 02720
Tel: 508-679-8131 *Toll Free Tel:* 800-215-1068 *Fax:* 508-674-4710
Web Site: www.lightolier.com
Key Personnel
VP, Sales-Midwest Zone: Jeff Ridgell
Founded: 1904
Membership(s): American Lighting Association; Illuminating Engineering Society

Lightolier® Controls, see Philips Lighting Controls

Lightronics Inc
509 Central Dr, Virginia Beach, VA 23454
Tel: 757-486-3588 *Toll Free Tel:* 800-472-8541 *Fax:* 757-486-3391
Web Site: www.lightronics.com
Key Personnel
Natl Dir, Sales: Dennis Degen *Tel:* 301-788-3667
Sales & Mktg Mgr: Chris Pease
Manufacture lighting control equipment.

Lights On
61 Bedford St SE, Minneapolis, MN 55414
Tel: 612-331-6620 *Toll Free Tel:* 800-336-6620 *Fax:* 612-331-6601
E-mail: minneapolis@lightson.com
Web Site: www.lightson.com
Rental & sales of film & video production supplies.
Branch Office(s)
1720 Merriam Lane, Kansas City, KS 66106 *Tel:* 913-362-6940 *Toll Free Tel:* 800-229-6876 *Fax:* 913-362-6958 *E-mail:* kansascity@lightson.com

Lights On Nebraska
7520 Burlington St, Omaha, NE 68127
Tel: 402-331-4340 *Fax:* 402-331-4556
E-mail: ne@lightsonrentals.com
Web Site: www.lightsonrentals.com
Founded: 1992
Lighting/grip rental house, full studio sound stage & production office.

LightSpace Studios
1115 Flushing Ave, Brooklyn, NY 11237
Tel: 212-202-0372
E-mail: reserve@lightspace.tv
Web Site: www.lightspace.tv
Full service photo & film production facility. Offers large inventory of lighting, grip, camera, digital capture & crew roster.

Lightspeed Technologies Inc
11509 SW Herman Rd, Tualatin, OR 97062
Tel: 503-684-5538 *Toll Free Tel:* 800-732-8999 *Fax:* 503-684-3197
Web Site: www.lightspeed-tek.com
Key Personnel
EVP, Sales & Mktg: David Solomon
Mktg Resource Mgr: Bruce Bebb *E-mail:* bruce.bebb@lightspeed-tek.com
Founded: 1990
Classroom audio technology, a low volume amplification system providing clarity of speech & even-sound distribution throughout the learning environment.
Catalog(s), free, educational
Online catalog(s), educational

Lighttech Group Inc
161-15 Rockaway Blvd, Jamaica, NY 11434
Tel: 718-525-2900 *Fax:* 718-525-2488
E-mail: info@lighttech.com
Web Site: www.lighttech.com
Key Personnel
Pres: Leon R Saddler *E-mail:* leon@lighttech.com
VP: Jacques F Pardovany *E-mail:* jacques@lighttech.com
Founded: 1992
Lighting manufacturing company.
Catalog(s) available

Lightware Inc
1329 W Byers Place, Denver, CO 80223-1723
Tel: 303-744-0202 *Fax:* 303-722-4545
E-mail: info@lightwareinc.com
Web Site: www.lightwareinc.com; www.lightwaredirect.com
Key Personnel
Pres: Paul Peregrine
Lightweight airline shippable equipment cases for the still & video photographer. Film or digital still photography - studio & location; cases for computers & monitors.
Online catalog(s) available
Membership(s): ASMP; National Press Photographers Association; PMA International

Lightworks Audio & Video Inc
PO Box 661593, Los Angeles, CA 90066
Tel: 310-398-4949 *Fax:* 310-397-4401
E-mail: sales1@lightworksav.com
Web Site: www.lightworksav.com
Key Personnel
Pres & CEO: Harry DeLigter
Founded: 1992
Distribution of enlightening media.

Lightyear Entertainment
4011 Alcove Ave, Studio City, CA 91604
Tel: 818-855-1318 *Fax:* 818-855-1320
E-mail: mail@lightyear.com
Web Site: www.lightyear.com
Key Personnel
Owner: Arnie Holland
Producer & distributor of entertainment software products.
Catalog(s) available
Membership(s): Music Business Association

Ligos Corporation
6001 Chatham Ctr Dr, Suite 300, Savannah, GA 31405
Mailing Address: PO Box 15387, Savannah, GA 31416
Tel: 912-236-8993 *Fax:* 912-234-1366
Web Site: www.ligos.com
Founded: 1997
MPEG encoder systems.

Limbo Films
2223 NE Martin Luther King Jr Blvd, Portland, OR 97212
Tel: 503-228-0844 *Fax:* 503-228-0857
E-mail: info@limbofilms.com
Web Site: www.limbofilms.com
Key Personnel
Owner & Dir: Gary Nolton *E-mail:* gary@limbofilms.com
Exec Prodr: Judy Kettler *E-mail:* judy@limbofilms.com
Off Mgr: Kelly Paterson *E-mail:* kelly@limbofilms.com
Prodr: Howard Kennedy *E-mail:* howard@limbofilms.com
Founded: 1995
Full service production company.
Membership(s): AICP

Limelight Communications Inc
2812 Roesh Way, Vienna, VA 22181
Tel: 703-242-4596 *Fax:* 703-991-0616
E-mail: moreinfo@limelightdc.com
Web Site: www.limelightdc.com
Key Personnel
Pres & Exec Prodr: Kenny Reff
Founded: 1985
Video production & digital media solutions.
Membership(s): International Television Video Association; MCA-I; Television, Internet & Video Association of DC Inc

Limelight Productions Inc
471 Pleasant St, Lee, MA 01238-9322
Tel: 413-243-4950 *Toll Free Tel:* 800-243-4950 *Fax:* 413-243-4993 *Toll Free Fax:* 800-243-4951
E-mail: info@limelightproductions.com
Web Site: www.limelightproductions.com
Key Personnel
Pres: William Beautyman *E-mail:* wbeautyman@limelightproductions.com
Curtain Fabrication: Ginny Bentley
Founded: 1972

Designer & installer of stage lighting & rigging systems for theatre, film/video, studio & display.
Catalog(s) available
Membership(s): International Alliance of Theatrical Stage Employees; Professional Lighting & Sound Association; USITT

Linear LLC
Subsidiary of Nortek Inc
1950 Camino Vida Roble, Suite 150, Carlsbad, CA 92008-6517
Tel: 760-438-7000 *Toll Free Tel:* 800-421-1587 *Fax:* 760-931-1340 *Toll Free Fax:* 800-468-1340
E-mail: sales@linearcorp.com
Web Site: www.linearcorp.com
Key Personnel
Chmn & CEO: Grant Rummell
VP, Busn Devt Group: Todd Hokunson
Founded: 1961
Wired & wireless products serving the security & access control markets as well as health & wellness & home technology needs.
Catalog(s) available

Lineco
Division of University Products Inc
517 Main St, Holyoke, MA 01040
Mailing Address: PO Box 2604, Holyoke, MA 01041-2604
Toll Free Tel: 800-322-7775 *Fax:* 413-532-9281 *Toll Free Fax:* 800-298-7815
E-mail: info@lineco.com
Web Site: www.lineco.com
Key Personnel
COO & Pres: Scott Magoon
Key Accts Mgr: Joanne Buzzell
Catalog(s) available
Membership(s): PMA International

Linguistic Systems Inc
201 Broadway, Cambridge, MA 02139
Tel: 617-528-7400 *Toll Free Tel:* 877-654-5006 *Fax:* 617-528-7491
Web Site: linguist.com
Key Personnel
Pres & AV Mgr: Martin Roberts *Tel:* 617-528-7412 *E-mail:* mroberts@linguist.com
Dir, Mktg: Bill Lawson
Founded: 1967
Create foreign language versions of AV.
Catalog(s) available

Linguist's Software Inc
PO Box 580, Edmonds, WA 98020-0580
Tel: 425-775-1130 *Fax:* 425-771-5911
E-mail: fonts@linguistsoftware.com
Web Site: www.linguistsoftware.com
Key Personnel
Pres: Philip B Payne *E-mail:* phil@linguistsoftware.com
Founded: 1984
Create & sell foreign language fonts (Unicode & ASCII) & input software for over 2,600 languages.
Catalog(s), free

Linhoff Photo & Digital Imaging
4400 France Ave S, Edina, MN 55410
Tel: 952-927-7333
E-mail: info@linhoff.com
Web Site: linhoff.com
Key Personnel
Owner: John Linhoff
Founded: 1954
Catalog(s) available
Membership(s): AIE™; Minnesota Commercial Industrial Photographers Association; Photo Marketing Association

Link Electronics Inc
2137 Rust Ave, Cape Girardeau, MO 63703-7668
Tel: 573-334-4433 *Toll Free Tel:* 800-776-4411 *Fax:* 573-334-9255
E-mail: sales@linkelectronics.com
Web Site: www.linkelectronics.com
Key Personnel
Pres: Bob Henson *E-mail:* bhenson@linkelectronics.com
Founded: 1989
Electronic products manufacturer.
Catalog(s) available
Membership(s): NAB

Linkabit
Division of L-3 Communications
9890 Towne Centre Dr, San Diego, CA 92121
Toll Free Tel: 800-331-9401
E-mail: linkabitproducts@l-3com.com
Web Site: www2.l-3com.com/linkabit
Founded: 1968
Video exploitation & management systems. Reconfigurable video/image processing technologies.
Brochure(s) available
Membership(s): AFCEA

Linker Systems Inc
13612 Onkayha Circle, Irvine, CA 92620
Tel: 949-552-1904 *Toll Free Tel:* 800-315-1174
Web Site: linkersystems.com
Key Personnel
Owner & Pres: Toni Poper
CTO & VP: Sheldon Linker *E-mail:* sol@linker.com
Animation system manufacturer, custom software developer & consultant & manufactures special effects generators.
Online catalog(s) available

Linsman Film
329 N Windsor Blvd, Los Angeles, CA 90004
Tel: 310-903-3009
Web Site: www.linsman.com
Key Personnel
Owner & Dir: William Linsman *E-mail:* bill@linsman.com
Founded: 1976
Directs & produces commercials & industrial films.
Membership(s): DGA; SMPTE

Lion & Fox Recording Studios
Affiliate of Lion Recording Services Inc
9517 Baltimore Ave, College Park, MD 20740
Tel: 301-982-4431
E-mail: mail@lionfox.com
Web Site: www.lionfox.com
Key Personnel
Gen Mgr, Prodr & Engr: Mike Caplan *E-mail:* mike@lionfox.com
Prodr & Engr: Rob Buhrman *E-mail:* rb@lionfox.com; Jim Fox
Founded: 1979
Digital audio recording & post-production - CD, CD-ROM, DVD & 3 digital recording studios.
Membership(s): AES; MCA-I; Washington Film & Video Council

Lion Recording Services Inc
Division of Lion & Fox Recording Inc
7532 Fullerton Ct, Springfield, VA 22153
Tel: 703-569-3200 *Fax:* 703-891-3220
E-mail: mail@lionrecording.com
Web Site: www.lionrecording.com
Key Personnel
Pres: Richard Lion
Founded: 1967
AV duplication service.
Membership(s): Content Delivery & Storage Association

Lions Gate Entertainment Corp
2700 Colorado Ave, Santa Monica, CA 90404
Tel: 310-449-9200 *Fax:* 310-255-3870
E-mail: general-inquiries@lionsgate.com
Web Site: www.lionsgate.com; corporate.lionsgate.com
Key Personnel
SVP, Investor Rel & Exec Communs: Peter Wilkes *Tel:* 310-255-3998
Motion picture production & distribution, television programming & syndication, home entertainment, family entertainment, digital distribution, new channel platforms & international distribution & sales.
Membership(s): Entertainment Merchants Association; National Association of Video Distributors

Lippincott Williams & Wilkins
Unit of Wolters Kluwer Health
Two Commerce Sq, 2001 Market St, Philadephia, PA 19103
Tel: 215-521-8300; 301-223-2300 (cust serv) *Toll Free Tel:* 800-638-3030 (cust serv) *Fax:* 215-521-8902
E-mail: orders@lww.com
Web Site: www.lww.com
Key Personnel
Exec Dir, Prodn: Kathy Dunn *Tel:* 215-521-8300 ext 18906
Catalog(s) available
Branch Office(s)
Ambler, 323 Norristown Rd, Suite 200, Ambler, PA 19022-2758 *Tel:* 215-646-8700 *Fax:* 215-654-1328
351 W Camden St, Baltimore, MD 21201 *Tel:* 410-528-4000
16522 Hunters Green Pkwy, Hagerstown, MD 21740 *Fax:* 301-223-2400
Healthcare Group, 333 Seventh Ave, 19th & 20th fl, New York, NY 10001 *Toll Free Tel:* 800-933-6525
Foreign Office(s): Lippincott Williams & Wilkins Pty Ltd, 9 Hunter St, Level 18, Suite 1801, Sydney, NSW 2000, Australia *Tel:* (02) 9276-6600 *Fax:* (02) 9231-1255
Lippincott Williams & Wilkins Asia Ltd, 15F W Sq, 314-324 Hennessy Rd, Wan Chai, Hong Kong *Tel:* 2610 7000 *Fax:* 2610 7098
250 Waterloo Rd, London SE1 8RD, United Kingdom *Tel:* (020) 7981 0600 *Fax:* (020) 7981 0601

Lipsner-Smith Co
Subsidiary of Research Technology International (RTI)
4700 Chase Ave, Lincolnwood, IL 60712-1689
Tel: 847-677-3000 *Toll Free Tel:* 800-323-7520 *Fax:* 847-677-1311 *Toll Free Fax:* 800-784-6733
E-mail: sales@lipsner.com; sales@rtico.com
Web Site: www.lipsner.com
Key Personnel
Pres, RTI Film Group: Jonathan A Banks
Sales & Ad: Sherwin Berger
Founded: 1958
Catalog(s) available
Membership(s): AECT; AIIM; ALA; British Kinematograph Sound & Television Society; Consortium of College & University Media Centers; ICVM; InfoComm International®; NAB; National Association of Media & Technology Centers; SMPTE

A Liss & Co
51-55 59 Place, Woodside, NY 11377-7408
Tel: 718-728-0600 *Toll Free Tel:* 800-221-0938 *Fax:* 718-728-1227
E-mail: sales@alissco.com
Web Site: www.alissco.com
Key Personnel
Pres: Jeffery Liss

Founded: 1936
Materials handling company.
Catalog(s) available

Listec Video Corp
Unit of The Tiffen Co LLC
90 Oser Ave, Hauppauge, NY 11788
Tel: 631-273-2500 *Toll Free Tel:* 800-645-2522 *Fax:* 631-273-2557
E-mail: orders@tiffen.com; techsupport@tiffen.com
Web Site: www.tiffen.com
Key Personnel
VP: Raymond Blumenthal
Founded: 1967
Teleprompting hardware & software, light & medium weight tripod systems.
Membership(s): NAB

Listen & Live Audio Inc
1700 Manhattan Ave, Union City, NJ 07068
Tel: 201-558-9000 *Toll Free Tel:* 800-653-9400 (orders) *Fax:* 201-558-9800
Web Site: www.listenandlive.com
Key Personnel
Pres: Alfred C Martino *E-mail:* alfred@listenandlive.com
Publr: Alisa S Weberman
Founded: 1993

Listen Technologies Corp
14912 Heritage Crest Way, Bluffdale, UT 84065-4818
Tel: 801-233-8992 *Toll Free Tel:* 800-330-0891 *Fax:* 801-233-8995
E-mail: info@listentech.com
Web Site: www.listentech.com
Key Personnel
Chmn, CEO & Pres: Russell Gentner
VP, Sales Worldwide: Cory Schaeffer

Listening Library
Division of Random House Audio Publishing Group
1745 Broadway, New York, NY 10019
Tel: 212-782-9000 *Toll Free Tel:* 800-733-3000
E-mail: audio@randomhouse.com
Web Site: www.randomhouse.com/audio/listeninglibrary
Founded: 1955
Educational audiotapes.
Catalog(s) available
Membership(s): American Booksellers for Children

LITE-IT Grip Truck Rentals
450 Saint Andrews Ct, West Chicago, IL 60185
Tel: 630-231-1671 *Fax:* 630-231-1672
E-mail: liteit1@sbcglobal.net
Web Site: www.liteit1.com
Key Personnel
Owner: Tom Scott
Lighting & grip equipment rentals.

Little Big Bang Design Inc
287 NE 90 St, Miami, FL 33138
Tel: 786-218-0713
E-mail: info@littlebigbangdesign.com
Web Site: www.littlebigbangdesign.com
Specialize in motion graphics & animation.

The Larry Little Co
10120 W Flamingo Rd, Suite 4-160, Las Vegas, NV 89147
Tel: 262-518-2014 *Toll Free Fax:* 800-452-8273
E-mail: larrylittlecompany@gmail.com
Web Site: www.larrylittle.com
Key Personnel
Owner: Larry Little
Music instruction DVDs & books.
Catalog(s) available

Little Mammoth Media
Division of VanDerKloot Film & Television Inc
750 Ralph McGill Blvd, NE, Atlanta, GA 30312
Toll Free Tel: 800-KIDVIDEO (543-8433)
E-mail: bv@vanderkloot.com
Web Site: www.littlemammoth.com
Children's videos.
Catalog(s) available

The Little Warehouse Inc
900 Resource Dr, Suite 8, Brooklyn Heights, OH 44131
Tel: 216-398-0022 *Toll Free Tel:* 800-445-8273 *Fax:* 216-398-9980
E-mail: tlwtape@sbcglobal.net
Web Site: www.thelittlewarehouse.com
Key Personnel
Pres: Jim Lesnick
Founded: 1972
Distribute DVD & CD duplicators & supplies.
Catalog(s) available

Littlite LLC
Division of CAE Inc
PO Box 430, Hamburg, MI 48139-0430
Tel: 810-852-4242 *Fax:* 810-231-1631
E-mail: sales@littlite.com
Web Site: www.littlite.com
Key Personnel
Pres: James H Fackert *E-mail:* jfackert@littlite.com
Ad Dir: Barbara Burns *Tel:* 810-852-4242 ext 214 *E-mail:* bburns@littlite.com
Spec Prods, Mktg: Donn Deniston *Tel:* 810-852-4242 ext 212 *E-mail:* ddeniston@littlite.com
Manufacture miniature task lamps.
Catalog(s) available
Membership(s): NAMM, the National Association of Music Merchants; NSCA; Professional Lighting & Sound Association; USITT

Liturgy Training Publications
Division of Archdiocese of Chicago
3949 S Racine Ave, Chicago, IL 60609-2523
Tel: 773-579-4900 *Toll Free Tel:* 800-933-1800 (orders) *Fax:* 773-579-4929
E-mail: orders@ltp.org
Web Site: www.ltp.org
Key Personnel
Dir: John A Thomas *Tel:* 773-579-4900 ext 3557 *E-mail:* jthomas@ltp.org
Busn Mgr: Maureen Como *Tel:* 773-579-4900 ext 3533 *E-mail:* mcomo@ltp.org
Religious education programs.
Catalog(s) available
Membership(s): Association of Catholic Publishers Inc

Live Oak Media
PO Box 652, Pine Plains, NY 12567-0652
Toll Free Tel: 800-788-1121 *Toll Free Fax:* 866-398-1070
E-mail: info@liveoakmedia.com
Web Site: www.liveoakmedia.com
Key Personnel
Owner & Pres: Arnold M Cardillo
Owner & Publr: Debra Cardillo
Catalog(s) available
Membership(s): ALA; Audio Publishers Association

Live Spark Inc
700 Raymond Ave, Suite 100, St Paul, MN 55114
Tel: 651-289-7375
E-mail: info@live-spark.com
Web Site: www.live-spark.com
Key Personnel
VP, Busn Devt: Kristina Gooding *E-mail:* kristina@live-spark.com
Live production of events.

Live Wire Media
Division of Elkind & Sweet Communications Inc
PO Box 848, Mill Valley, CA 94942
Tel: 415-564-9500 *Toll Free Tel:* 800-359-KIDS (359-5437) *Fax:* 415-552-4087
E-mail: sales@livewiremedia.com
Web Site: www.livewiremedia.com
Key Personnel
Cofounder: David Elkind; Freddy Sweet *E-mail:* sweet@livewiremedia.com
Online catalog(s) available
Membership(s): ASCD

Live'N'Loud
One Lindsay Way, Hot Springs Village, AR 71909
Mailing Address: PO Box 9436, Hot Springs Village, AR 71910
Tel: 501-414-2845
Web Site: www.livenloud.net
Key Personnel
Owner, Dir, Ed & Writer: Ethan Nahte *E-mail:* nahteboy@livenloud.net
Founded: 1993
Production/post-production video company.

LKG Industries Inc
3660 Publishers Dr, Rockford, IL 61109
Tel: 815-874-2301 *Toll Free Tel:* 800-645-2262 *Fax:* 815-874-2896
E-mail: sales-lkgindustries@t6b.com
Web Site: www.philmore-datak.com
Key Personnel
Pres: Kittikarn Mejudhon
Manufacturer of electronic products.
Catalog(s) available

Llewellyn Publications
Division of Llewellyn Worldwide Ltd
2143 Wooddale Dr, Woodbury, MN 55125-2989
Tel: 651-291-1970 *Toll Free Tel:* 877-NEWWRLD (639-9753) *Fax:* 651-291-1908
E-mail: publicity@llewellyn.com; customerservice@llewellyn.com
Web Site: www.llewellyn.com
Key Personnel
Chmn: Carl L Weschcke
Treas: Sandra K Weschcke
Founded: 1901
Catalog(s) available

C V Lloyde
102 S Neil St, Champaign, IL 61820
Tel: 217-352-7031 *Toll Free Tel:* 800-779-7031
E-mail: sales@cvlloyde.com
Web Site: www.cvlloyde.com
Key Personnel
Pres: Stephen Morris
Catalog(s) available
Membership(s): InfoComm International®; NAMM, the National Association of Music Merchants; NSCA

LM Cases/LM Engineering Inc
2720 Intertech Dr, Youngstown, OH 44509
Tel: 330-270-2400 *Toll Free Tel:* 800-874-8326 *Fax:* 330-270-2424
E-mail: info@lmcases.com
Web Site: www.lmcases.com
Key Personnel
CEO: William La Guardia
CFO & Pres: Jo Ann La Guardia *E-mail:* jlaguard@lmengineering.com
Opers Mgr: Joe Listorti
Founded: 1985
Custom case manufacturer.
Catalog(s) available

Location Camera Ltd
300 Pennsylvania Ave, Oreland, PA 19075

Tel: 215-576-5600 *Fax:* 215-576-6022
E-mail: mail@locationcamera.com
Web Site: www.locationcamera.com
Key Personnel
Owner & Pres: Brad Shapiro
Owner & VP: Tom Greco
Founded: 1998
Rental & sales of cameras for video & film production including Arriflex 16mm SR3 & Panasonic Vericam HD camcorder.

The Location Connection Inc
1600 Rosecrans Ave, Bldg 5, Manhattan Beach, CA 90266
Tel: 310-376-9797 *Fax:* 310-376-9796
E-mail: lconnect@aol.com
Web Site: www.locationconnection.com
Key Personnel
Pres & Creator: Darian Mathias *Tel:* 818-422-8127 (cell)
Founded: 1991
Offer privately owned mansions & unique homes for film shoots, weddings & other special events.

Location Lighting Ltd
300 Pennsylvania Ave, Oreland, PA 19075
Tel: 215-576-5600 *Fax:* 215-576-6022
E-mail: mail@locationlighting.com; rentals@locationlighting.com
Web Site: www.locationlighting.com
Key Personnel
Owner & Pres: Brad Shapiro *Tel:* 215-353-0543 *E-mail:* bradshapiro@locationlighting.com
Rental Mgr: Allison Ruff *Tel:* 215-200-5083
Founded: 1998
Lighting & grip equipment rental & sales for film & video production. Dealer for many leading manufacturers.

Location Sound Corp
10639 Riverside Dr, North Hollywood, CA 91602
Tel: 818-980-9891 *Toll Free Tel:* 800-228-4429 *Fax:* 818-980-9911
E-mail: information@locationsound.com; salesdept@locationsound.com
Web Site: www.locationsound.com
Key Personnel
Sales Mgr: Steve Joachim *Tel:* 818-980-9891 ext 302
Asst Mgr, Rental: Robert Anzalone *Tel:* 818-980-9891 ext 354 *E-mail:* anzalone@locationsound.com
Founded: 1977
Membership(s): AES; NAB; SMPTE

Location 05 Studios
509 W 34 St, 2nd fl, New York, NY 10001
Tel: 212-219-2144 *Fax:* 212-344-8032
E-mail: info@location05.com
Web Site: location05.com
Founded: 1991
Photo studio, location rental & meeting venue. Provides photography needs for film & video production & provides event space.

Loft 19
21618 N Ninth Ave, Suite A, Phoenix, AZ 85027
Tel: 623-434-3791 *Fax:* 623-434-5003
E-mail: info@loft19.com
Web Site: loft19.com
Key Personnel
Co-Owner: Brian Bannister; Floyd Bannister
Founded: 2003
Sound studios equipped with lights & grip for film & video production.

Loftin Productions
PO Box 78, New York, NY 10116
Tel: 917-825-5412
E-mail: loftin.productions@gmail.com
Web Site: www.loftinpro.com
Founded: 1999
Our company provides a cost effective cameraman for your video advertising & events. Camera operator, videographer, lighting cameraman or crew. Audio restoration & post-production services is based in the NY area. It includes audio post, sound design, editing, original production music & more. Visit www.loftinpro.com.
Video(s) available

Logan Productions Inc
8035 N Port Washington Rd, Milwaukee, WI 53217
Tel: 414-352-9691 *Fax:* 414-352-4993
E-mail: sales@loganproductions.com
Web Site: www.loganproductions.com
Key Personnel
CEO: Beth Logan *E-mail:* beth@loganproductions.com
Pres: Jim Logan
Busn Mgr: Peggy Rytman
Soc Media & Mktg Mgr: Holly Butz *E-mail:* holly@loganproductions.com
Founded: 1978
Full service rentals, live events, multilingual web broadcasting, video production company.
Membership(s): MCA-I

Logitech
7600 Gateway Blvd, Newark, CA 94560
Tel: 510-795-8500 *Toll Free Tel:* 800-231-7717 (sales)
Web Site: www.logitech.com
Founded: 1981
Catalog(s) available
Branch Office(s)
Logitech Audio Group, 4700 NW Camas Meadows Dr, Camas, WA 98607 *Tel:* 360-817-1200

Logitek Electronic Systems Inc
5622 Edgemoor Dr, Houston, TX 77081
Tel: 713-664-4470 *Toll Free Tel:* 800-231-5870 (sales); 877-231-5870 (tech support) *Fax:* 713-664-4479
E-mail: northamericansales@logitekaudio.com
Web Site: www.logitekaudio.com
Key Personnel
Pres: Tag Borland
VP: Susan Borland
Sales Dir: Frank Grundstein
Founded: 1979
Manufacture digital audio equipment - audio routers, consoles & meters.
Catalog(s) available
Membership(s): AES; NAB

Loma Scientific International (LSI)
Subsidiary of JP Associates Inc
3115 Kashiwa St, Torrance, CA 90505
Tel: 310-539-8655 *Fax:* 310-539-8634
E-mail: info@lomasci.com
Web Site: www.lomasci.com
Key Personnel
Founder, Pres & Sales Mgr: Patrick Loughboro
VP, Engg & Opers: Jeff Loughboro
Founded: 1957
Transmitters, antennas, microwave, MMDS, complete analog & digital headends, reception, encode/decode.
Online catalog(s) available
Membership(s): NAB

Long Island University Media Arts Dept
One University Plaza, Brooklyn, NY 11201-8423
Tel: 718-488-1052 *Fax:* 718-780-4578
E-mail: mediart@brooklyn.liu.edu
Web Site: www.liu.edu/brooklyn.aspx
Key Personnel
Chmn, Media Arts Dept: Larry Banks *Tel:* 718-488-1343 *E-mail:* larry.banks@liu.edu

Long Island Video Enterprises Live Inc
110 Pratt Oval, Glen Cove, NY 11542
Tel: 516-759-5483 *Fax:* 516-671-5874
E-mail: info@longislandvideo.com
Web Site: www.longislandvideo.com
Key Personnel
Pres: Peter L Warzer
VP, Sales: Lori Di Giacomo
Founded: 1982
Video & audio sales, rentals, design & installation services.
Flyer(s) available
Membership(s): InfoComm International®; Long Island Association; MCA-I

Long-Term Success Publishing
766 Ninth Ave N, Suite 1, Fort Dodge, IA 50501
Tel: 515-571-8880
Web Site: judypayne.com
Key Personnel
Owner: Judy Payne *E-mail:* judypayne@mchsi.com
Catalog(s) available

Loopmedia Inc
401 Richmond St W, Suite 243, Toronto, ON M5V 3A8, Canada
Tel: 416-595-6496 *Fax:* 416-595-0306
E-mail: info@loopmedia.com
Web Site: www.loopmedia.com
Key Personnel
Co-Founder & Pres: Sonja Perovic *E-mail:* sonja@loopmedia.com
Dir, Mktg & Busn Devt: Jan King *E-mail:* jan@loopmedia.com
Founded: 1995
Design & commercial production studio specializing in end-to-end brand solutions for all platforms geared towards broadcasters, advertising agencies & entertainment companies.

Los Angeles Center Studios
450 S Bixel St, Los Angeles, CA 90017
Mailing Address: 1201 W Fifth St, Suite T-110, Los Angeles, CA 90017
Tel: 213-534-3000
E-mail: productionservices@lacenterstudios.com
Web Site: lacenterstudios.com
Key Personnel
Pres: Sam Nicassio *E-mail:* snicassio@lacenterstudios.com
Dir, Mktg: Dolly Greene *Tel:* 213-534-2334 *E-mail:* dgreene@lacenterstudios.com
Prodn Servs Mgr: Bobby Hunt *Tel:* 213-534-2370 *E-mail:* bhunt@lacenterstudios.com
Full service studio for TV, film & commercial production.

Los Angeles Post Music Inc
4340 E Kentucky Ave, Suite 308, Glendale, CO 80246
Tel: 310-896-5176
Web Site: www.lapostmusic.com
Key Personnel
Agent: Vel Lewis *E-mail:* hammondjammin@aol.com
Founded: 1995
Nationally & internationally recognized music provider. Production music & original composition.

Los Feliz Post
6767 Forest Lawn Dr, Suite 211, Los Angeles, CA 90068
Tel: 818-859-3500
Key Personnel
Pres: John Kazaroff *E-mail:* jhanik@yahoo.com
Quantel & AVID bays in Glendale, CA.

The Lot (Skye Partners)
1041 N Formosa Ave, West Hollywood, CA 90046
Tel: 323-850-3180 *Fax:* 323-850-3190
E-mail: info@skyepartners.com
Web Site: www.thelotstudios.com
Key Personnel
Dir, Stage Opers: Tricia Bodak-Smith *E-mail:* tsmith@skyepartners.com
Full service studio for TV, film & commercial production. Sound stage & equipment rentals.

Lotus Development Corp, an IBM Company
One Rogers St, Cambridge, MA 02142
Tel: 617-693-4235; 914-499-1900 (IBM)
Web Site: www.lotus.com

LOUD Technologies Inc
16220 Wood-Red Rd NE, Woodinville, WA 98072
Tel: 425-487-4333; 415-892-6500 *Toll Free Tel:* 866-858-LTEC (858-5832) *Fax:* 425-487-4337
Web Site: www.mackie.com; www.loudtechinc.com
Key Personnel
CEO & Pres: Mark Graham
CFO & SVP: Case Kuehn
Professional audio & music products.
Catalog(s) available
Branch Office(s)
One Main St, Whitinsville, MA 01588 *Tel:* 508-234-6158 *Fax:* 508-234-8251
560 Johnson St, Suite 320, Victoria, BC V8W 3C6, Canada *Tel:* 425-892-6500 *Fax:* 250-382-7737
Foreign Office(s): 8 Eu Tong Sen St, No 14-93, The Central, Singapore 059818, Singapore
Loud Technologies PLC, Cressex Business Park, Unit 2, Century Point, Halifax Rd, High Wycombe, Bucks HP12 3SL, United Kingdom *Tel:* (01494) 557398 *Fax:* (01494) 557396

Louisiana State University Health Sciences Center - Shreveport
Dept of Video Servs & TeleHealth, 1501 Kings Hwy, Shreveport, LA 71103-4228
Mailing Address: PO Box 33932, Shreveport, LA 71103-3932
Tel: 318-675-5268 *Fax:* 318-675-7757
Web Site: www.lsuhscshreveport.edu
Key Personnel
Dir, Video Servs & Telehealth: Donna Haas *E-mail:* dhaas@lsuhsc.edu
Medical school & health sciences center - provide video conferencing & video production services.

James Loupas Associates Inc
134 Carrington Dr, Coppell, TX 75019
Tel: 972-304-0455
Web Site: jimloupas.com
Key Personnel
Pres: James Loupas *E-mail:* jim@jimloupas.com
Founded: 1976
Audio & technology consulting - psychoacoustic services.

Love Shack Recording Studios
Division of EMG LLC
909 18 Ave S, Nashville, TN 37212
Tel: 615-843-0019
E-mail: book@loveshackstudios.com
Web Site: loveshackstudios.com
Key Personnel
CEO & COO: Andrew Kautz
Contact: Chris Rowe; Jeff Socher

Lowel-Light Manufacturing Inc
90 Oser Ave, Hauppauge, NY 11788
Tel: 631-273-2500 *Toll Free Tel:* 800-645-2522 *Fax:* 631-273-2557
E-mail: info@lowel.com
Web Site: www.lowel.com
Key Personnel
Dir, Communs: Duane Sherwood
Location lighting equipment for professional imaging.
Catalog(s) available
CD-ROM catalog(s) available

Lowell Manufacturing
100 Integram Dr, Pacific, MO 63069-3476
Toll Free Tel: 800-325-9660 *Toll Free Fax:* 800-456-9355
E-mail: sales@lowellmfg.com
Web Site: www.lowellmfg.com
Key Personnel
CEO & Pres: John Lowell
Natl Sales Mgr: Jeff Garstick *E-mail:* jgarstick@lowellmfg.com
Founded: 1947
Designs & manufactures audio, rack & power products for professional systems integration.

Lowing Light & Grip Inc
1500 Whiting St SW, Wyoming, MI 49509-1056
Tel: 616-530-7440 *Toll Free Tel:* 888-530-7440 *Fax:* 616-249-8947
Web Site: www.lowinglight.com
Key Personnel
Owner & Pres: David R Lowing *E-mail:* dave@lowinglight.com
Founded: 1985
Grip, electric, camera support, staff, gear & expendables for the filmed entertainment industry.
Online catalog(s) available
Membership(s): International Alliance of Theatrical Stage Employees

Lowrance Sound Co Inc
2132 Nailling Dr, Union City, TN 38261
Tel: 731-885-4504 *Toll Free Tel:* 800-852-5418
E-mail: info@lowrancesoundcompany.com
Web Site: www.lowrancesoundcompany.com
Key Personnel
Pres: Mark Lowrance
Founded: 1975
AV design, sales & installations.
Membership(s): InfoComm International®; NFPA; NSCA

Loyal Studios
3513 W Pacific Ave, Burbank, CA 91505
Tel: 818-845-5123 (studio); 818-399-9499
Web Site: www.loyalstudios.tv
Key Personnel
Prodr: Bob Bekian *E-mail:* bob@loyalstudios.tv
Studio with control room & edit bay. Specialize in greenscreen commercials, interviews & web content.

LT Sound Inc
7980 LT Pkwy, Lithonia, GA 30058
Tel: 770-482-4836
E-mail: info3@ltsound.com
Web Site: www.ltsound.com
Key Personnel
Pres: Lacy Thompson, Jr
Founded: 1976
Distribute audio-digital signal processing & professional audio equipment.
Catalog(s) available

LTM Corp of America
Subsidiary of LTM France
7357 1/2 Atoll Ave, North Hollywood, CA 91605
Tel: 818-780-9828 *Toll Free Tel:* 800-762-4291 *Fax:* 818-780-9848
E-mail: sales@ltmlighting.com; info@ltmlighting.com
Key Personnel
EVP: Richard Espinoza
Founded: 1976
Broad selection of Hml lights.
Catalog(s) available
Foreign Office(s): 10 rue de Longjumeau, SILIC 452, 94593 Rungis Cedex, France *Tel:* 01 41 73 42 42 *Fax:* 01 41 73 42 40 *E-mail:* ltmfrance@dial.oleane.com
Membership(s): American Society of Cinematographers; NAB; SMPTE

Lubbock Audio Visual Inc
2120 Ave "Q", Lubbock, TX 79405
Mailing Address: PO Box 1935, Lubbock, TX 79408-1935
Tel: 806-744-2559 *Toll Free Tel:* 800-850-2559 *Fax:* 806-747-6939
E-mail: sales@lav.com
Web Site: www.lav.com
Key Personnel
Pres: Stan Wagnon *E-mail:* swagnon@lav.com
Founded: 1978
Authorized for over 300 manufacturers of professional video, audio & telecommunications products.
Catalog(s) available
Branch Office(s)
2505 Lakeview Dr, Suite 209, Amarillo, TX 79109, Acct Mgr: Dennis Smith *Tel:* 806-358-0795 *Fax:* 806-351-2800
1030 Andrews Hwy, Suite 202, Midland, TX 79701 *Tel:* 432-218-9829 *Fax:* 432-218-9830
Membership(s): InfoComm International®; NSCA; Professional Systems Network Inc; Texas Association of Broadcasters; Western Texas Association of General Contractors

Lubell Labs Inc
21 N Stanwood Rd, Columbus, OH 43209
Tel: 614-235-6740
E-mail: lubell_labs@wowway.com
Web Site: www.lubell.com
Key Personnel
Pres: Alan H Lubell
Speaker manufacturer.

David Lubman Acoustics
14301 Middletown Lane, Westminster, CA 92683
Tel: 714-373-3050 *Fax:* 714-373-3050
Web Site: www.dlacoustics.com
Key Personnel
Pres: David Lubman *E-mail:* dlubman@dlacoustics.com
Acoustical consultant specializing in certified sound measurement & analysis.
Membership(s): ASA; INCE; National Council of Acoustical Consultants

Lucasey Manufacturing Corp
2744 E 11 St, Oakland, CA 94601
Mailing Address: PO Box 14023, Oakland, CA 94614
Tel: 510-534-1435 *Toll Free Tel:* 800-582-2739 *Fax:* 510-534-6828
E-mail: sales@lucasey.com
Web Site: www.lucasey.com
Key Personnel
CEO: Charles Lucasey
Founded: 1954
Manufacture mounts.
Catalog(s) available

Lucerne Media
37 Ground Pine Rd, Morris Plains, NJ 07950
Tel: 973-538-1401 *Fax:* 973-538-0855
E-mail: lucernemedia@optonline.net
Key Personnel
Pres: Franklin J Visco
Founded: 1974
Membership(s): Florida Educational Media Association; Iowa Educational Media Association; Michigan Educational Media Association;

National Association of Media & Technology Centers; Pennsylvania Learning Resources Association; Texas Educational Media Association

Ludlow Media Solutions
Division of Brevidia
15501 San Pablo Ave, Suite G320, San Pablo, CA 94806
Tel: 415-927-1300
E-mail: info@ludlowmedia.com
Web Site: www.ludlowmedia.com
Key Personnel
Founder & Sr Prodr: Rhys Ludlow *E-mail:* rhys@ludlowmedia.com
Content Ed & Prodr: Alec Oyung *E-mail:* alec@ludlowmedia.com
Founded: 1997

Lumalaser
84777 Charlottes Way, Eugene, OR 97405
Tel: 541-687-1414 *Toll Free Tel:* 800-606-2597 *Fax:* 541-687-1438
E-mail: info@lumalaser.com
Web Site: www.lumalaser.com
Key Personnel
Pres: Tim Ziegerbein *E-mail:* tim@lumalaser.com
Proj Mgr: Nicole Poisson
Quality laser projectors.
Catalog(s) available
Membership(s): ILDA

Lumedyne Inc
6010 Wall St, Port Richey, FL 34668
Tel: 727-847-2777; 727-847-5394 *Toll Free Tel:* 800-586-3396 *Fax:* 727-841-0000
E-mail: info@lumedyne.com; sales@lumedyne.com; service@lumedyne.com
Web Site: www.lumedyne.com
Key Personnel
Sales Mgr: D J La Dez *E-mail:* dj@lumedyne.com
Founded: 1972
Manufacture & distribute portable flash equipment for photographers.
Catalog(s) available
Membership(s): Photo Marketing Association

Lumeni Productions Inc
1632 Flower St, Glendale, CA 91201
Tel: 818-956-2200 *Fax:* 818-956-3298
E-mail: info@lumeni.com
Web Site: www.lumeni.com
Key Personnel
Pres & Creative Dir: Tony Valdez
VP & Chief Tech Dir: Gilbert Yablon
Dir, Mktg: Dennis Kull
Catalog(s) available
Sample(s) available

Luminaud Inc
8688 Tyler Blvd, Mentor, OH 44060
Tel: 440-255-9082 *Toll Free Tel:* 800-255-3408 *Fax:* 440-255-2250
E-mail: info@luminaud.com
Web Site: www.luminaud.com
Key Personnel
Pres: Thomas Lennox
Founded: 1972
Manufacture & distribute battery powered, portable systems.
Catalog(s) available

Luminys Systems Corp
Subsidiary of Imagility Inc
11961 Sherman Rd, North Hollywood, CA 91605
Tel: 323-461-6361 *Toll Free Tel:* 800-321-3644 *Fax:* 323-461-3067
E-mail: info@luminyscorp.com
Web Site: www.luminyscorp.com
Key Personnel
Chmn & CTO: David Pringle *E-mail:* dpringle@luminyscorp.com
CEO: Eric Golden
Pres: Richard Amadril
Premier provider of lighting fixtures.
Catalog(s) available

Lumisphere™ USA
9429 Everett Ct, Spotsylvania, VA 22553
Tel: 540-582-7897 *Fax:* 540-582-5233
E-mail: jrbent@starpower.net
Web Site: www.lumisphereusa.com
Key Personnel
Pres: John Bernard
Low-voltage festoon lighting.
Catalog(s) available

G T Luscombe Co Inc
106 Kansas St, Frankfort, IL 60423
Mailing Address: PO Box 722, Frankfort, IL 60423-0722
Tel: 815-469-2478 *Toll Free Tel:* 800-435-7855 *Fax:* 815-469-5429 *Toll Free Fax:* 888-469-5429
E-mail: info@gtluscombe.com
Web Site: www.gtluscombe.com
Key Personnel
Founder: George Luscombe
CEO & Pres: John Luscombe *E-mail:* john@gtluscombe.com
Founded: 1974
AV wholesale distribution.
Catalog(s) available
Membership(s): CBA: The Association for Christian Retail; Evangelical Christian Publishers Association

Lux Mundi Production House
1405 16 St, Racine, WI 53403
Tel: 262-619-1622
E-mail: producer@luxmundistudio.com
Web Site: www.luxmundistudio.com
Key Personnel
Owner & Prodr: Richard Sosa
Video Ed: Edward Sosa
Full video productions services, product & corporate photography & marketing visuals.

Luxor
Subsidiary of EBSCO Industries
2245 Delany Rd, Waukegan, IL 60087
Tel: 847-244-1800 *Toll Free Tel:* 800-323-4656 *Fax:* 847-244-1818 *Toll Free Fax:* 800-327-1698
E-mail: info@luxorfurn.com; customerservice@luxorfurn.com
Web Site: www.luxorfurn.com
Key Personnel
Div Gen Mgr: Steve Hill *Tel:* 847-244-1800 ext 128 *E-mail:* shill@luxorfurn.com
Quality Assurance: Randy Douglas
Catalog(s) available
Membership(s): Education Market Association; InfoComm International®; NSCA

LuXout Brand Stage Curtains
Division of The Specialty Group Ltd
1221 Admiral St, Richmond, VA 23220
Tel: 804-264-3000; 804-264-3700 *Toll Free Tel:* 800-817-1204 *Toll Free Fax:* 888-227-8064
E-mail: luxoutinfo@luxout.com
Web Site: www.luxout.com
Key Personnel
Pres: Tony Lovette
VP, Sales: Ned Dunford
Founded: 1948
Manufacturer of staging products; stage curtains, TV studio curtains & photo backdrop curtains.
Catalog(s) available

Luzerne County Community College
1333 S Prospect St, Nanticoke, PA 18634-3899
Tel: 570-740-0200 *Toll Free Tel:* 800-377-5222 *Fax:* 570-740-0250
Web Site: www.luzerne.edu/index.jsp
Key Personnel
HR: Kim Hogan *E-mail:* khogan@luzerne.edu
Founded: 1967
Online educational programs.
Catalog(s) available

LVN, see Library Video Network (LVN)

LW Media Group
107 W Valencia Ave, Burbank, CA 91502
Tel: 818-439-2989
E-mail: lwmgbooking@gmail.com
Web Site: www.lwmgstudios.com
Key Personnel
Owner & Dir: Chaaz Williams
Owner & Prodr: Max Rose
Dir, Photog: Justyn Moro
Founded: 2009
Music & film production company. Studio rentals for film, photography & recording.

Lylofilm Productions
Division of Graphissimo Entertainment
503 Beech St, New Hyde Park, NY 11040
Tel: 516-587-0567
E-mail: lylofilm@gmail.com; cdigitalv@yahoo.com
Web Site: www.lylofilm.com
Key Personnel
Owner & Dir: Simona Lyriti *E-mail:* simona@graphissimo.com
Prodr: Stanley Lozowski *E-mail:* stanley@graphissimo.com

Lyn Norstad & Associates Inc
2470 E Oakton St, Arlington Heights, IL 60005
Tel: 847-640-6400 *Fax:* 847-640-1677
E-mail: contact@lnainc.com
Web Site: www.lnainc.com
Key Personnel
CEO & Pres: Mr Lyn Norstad
Founded: 1981
Computer system sales.
Membership(s): ICM; InfoComm International®; NAB

Lynch Communications
22 Canada Cove Ave, Half Moon Bay, CA 94019
Tel: 678-939-1212
Web Site: www.lynchcommunications.com
Key Personnel
Principal: Paul Lynch *E-mail:* paul@lynchcommunications.com
Web cast services.
Membership(s): MPI

Lynx Broadband
12219 Wood Lake Dr, Burnsville, MN 55337
Tel: 952-894-9590 *Fax:* 952-894-9380
E-mail: info@lynxbroadband.com
Web Site: www.lynxbroadband.com
Key Personnel
Natl Sales & Mktg Mgr: Gregg Kelley *Tel:* 952-808-1576
Founded: 1967
Manufacture products that distribute television (RF) on Cat 6 cable.

LYNX Signal Management Systems LLC
4407 Vineland Rd, Suite D-18, Orlando, FL 32811
Tel: 407-428-1071 *Fax:* 407-428-1075
E-mail: sales1@intelligentmedia.us; support1@intelligentmedia.us
Web Site: www.intelligentmedia.us

Key Personnel
Pres: Robert Proctor
CFO: Thomas Makofske
Founded: 1988
Designer of digital audio & video transmission equipment for CAT5 & fiber optic networks.
Catalog(s) available
Membership(s): AES; NSCA

Lynx Studio Technology Inc
190 McCormick Ave, Costa Mesa, CA 92626-3307
Tel: 714-545-4700 *Fax:* 714-545-4777
E-mail: sales@lynxstudio.com
Web Site: www.lynxstudio.com
Founded: 1998
Manufacture high end audio PCI cards & converters.
Catalog(s), free
Online catalog(s) available
Branch Office(s)
2900 Government Way, Suite 42, Coeur d'Alene, ID 83815-3751

Fred Lyon Pictures
3609 Buchanan St, San Francisco, CA 94123
Tel: 415-922-5100 *Fax:* 415-922-5762
E-mail: images@winetravelandfood.com
Web Site: www.fredlyon.com; www.winetravelandfood.com
Key Personnel
Pres: Fred Lyon *E-mail:* fred@fredlyon.com
Primarily a still stock-shot library.

Lyon Video Inc
2091 Arlingate Lane, Columbus, OH 43228
Tel: 614-297-0001
Web Site: www.lyonvideo.com
Key Personnel
Prodr & Dir: Robert Lyon *E-mail:* rlyon@lyonvideo.com
Founded: 1986
Video production & rentals.

Lyon Workspace Products LLC
420 N Main St, Montgomery, IL 60538
Mailing Address: PO Box 671, Aurora, IL 60507-0671
Tel: 630-892-8941 *Toll Free Tel:* 800-433-8488 *Fax:* 630-892-8966 *Toll Free Fax:* 800-367-6681
E-mail: lyon@lyonworkspace.com
Web Site: www.lyonworkspace.com
Key Personnel
Dir, Mktg: Bryce Hiner
Founded: 1901
Storage solutions company.
Catalog(s) available
Branch Office(s)
350 Nevada St, Redlands, CA 92373
524-B Imperial Ct, Bensalem, PA 19020
2725 S State Hwy 360, Suite 400, Grand Prairie, TX 75052

LYRASIS
1438 W Peachtree NW, Suite 200, Atlanta, GA 30309
Mailing Address: PO Box 116179, Atlanta, GA 30368
Tel: 404-892-0943 *Toll Free Tel:* 800-999-8558 *Fax:* 404-892-7879
Web Site: www.lyrasis.org
Key Personnel
Exec Dir: Kate Nevins *Tel:* 404-892-0943 ext 4898 *E-mail:* kate.nevins@lyrasis.org
Founded: 2009
Membership association for libraries formed by the merger of PALINET, SOLINET & NELINET.

Lyrichord Discs Inc
PO Box 1977, Old Chelsea Sta, New York, NY 10011-1726
Tel: 212-404-8290 *Fax:* 212-404-8291
E-mail: info@lyrichord.com
Web Site: www.lyrichord.com
Key Personnel
Pres: Nick Fritsch *E-mail:* nick@lyrichord.com
Founded: 1950
CDs & DVDs of classical & world music.
Catalog(s) available

M-Audio
Subsidiary of inMusic Brands Inc
2000 Scenic View Dr, Cumberland, RI 02864
Tel: 401-658-5765 *Fax:* 401-658-3640
Web Site: www.m-audio.com
Founded: 1988
Professional audio hardware manufacturer & software distributor.
Catalog(s) available
Foreign Office(s): Rua General Flores, 290-cj 134/135, 01129-010 San Paulo-SP, Brazil *Tel:* (011) 32234820 *Fax:* (011) 33370579
Halskestr 16-18, 47877 Willich, Germany *Tel:* (02154) 81299-0 *Fax:* (02154) 81299-9
6F, 3-19-23, Minami Azabu, Minato-ku, Tokyo 106-0047, Japan *Tel:* (03) 6277-2230 *Fax:* (03) 6277-0025 *Web Site:* numark.co.jp
7th fl, No 165, Nanking East Rd, Section 4, Taipei 105, Taiwan *Tel:* (02) 2717-2389 *Fax:* (02) 2717-2734
Unit 3, Nexus Park, Lysons Ave, Ash Vale, Hampshire GU12 5QE, United Kingdom *Tel:* (01252) 896090 *Fax:* (01252) 896021
Membership(s): NAMM, the National Association of Music Merchants

M M Newman Corp
24 Tioga Way, Marblehead, MA 01945
Mailing Address: PO Box 615, Marblehead, MA 01945-0615
Tel: 781-631-7100 *Toll Free Tel:* 800-777-6309 *Fax:* 781-631-8887
E-mail: sales@mmnewman.com
Web Site: www.mmnewman.com
Founded: 1956
Manufacture spirally cut plastic tubing.
Catalog(s) available

M Works Mastering Studios
1035 Cambridge St, Suite 17-B, Cambridge, MA 02141
Tel: 617-577-0089 *Fax:* 617-577-0098
E-mail: studio@m-works.com
Web Site: www.m-works.com
Key Personnel
Pres & Chief Engr: Jonathan Wyner
Engr: Nick Dragoni
Full service mastering offering engineering, restoration, editing, transfers & replication services.
Catalog(s) available
Membership(s): AES

MAC Production Group
3172 Greenwood St, Winter Park, FL 32792
Tel: 407-234-8898 *Fax:* 407-671-5360
E-mail: info@macproav.com
Web Site: macproav.com
Audio, lighting, video, design, pre- & post-production services for event presentation needs.

MacGillivray Freeman Films Inc
PO Box 205, Laguna Beach, CA 92652-0205
Tel: 949-494-1055 *Fax:* 949-494-2079
E-mail: info@macfreefilms.com
Web Site: www.macfreefilms.com
Catalog(s) available
Shipping Address: 2470 S Coast Hwy, Unit F, Laguna Beach, CA 92651

Mach 1 Productions
1101 N Himes Ave, Tampa, FL 33607
Tel: 813-873-7700 *Fax:* 813-875-6633
E-mail: info@mach1pro.com
Web Site: www.mach1pro.com
Key Personnel
Pres: Darren Howard
Gen Mgr: Dan Mockensturm
Audio recording & production, sound design, music composition, scoring, arranging, audio post & mix-to-picture in stereo or multiple surround formats.

Mackenzie Laboratories Inc
1163 Nicole Ct, Glendora, CA 91740
Tel: 909-394-9007 *Fax:* 909-394-9411
E-mail: info@macklabs.com
Web Site: www.macklabs.com
Key Personnel
Pres: Nagy Khattar
Natl Sales Mgr: Joe Vitale *E-mail:* jvitale@macklabs.com
Founded: 1954
Manufacture digital audio messaging equipment. Applications served include Message-On-Hold, Storecasting, Overhead Paging, Public Address Announcement, Exhibit/Kiosk Announcements, Intercom & transit Communications.
Catalog(s) available
Membership(s): AES; APTA; NFPA; NSCA

Macmillan Audio
Division of Macmillan
175 Fifth Ave, New York, NY 10010
Tel: 646-600-7856; 646-307-5742 *Toll Free Tel:* 888-330-8477 (orders); 800-221-7945 *Toll Free Fax:* 800-672-7703 (orders)
E-mail: macmillan.audio@macmillanusa.com
Web Site: us.macmillan.com/audio.aspx
Key Personnel
VP & Publr: Mary Beth Roche *E-mail:* marybeth.roche@macmillan.com
Pres, Sales Div: Alison Lazarus
Edit Dir: Robert Allen
Dir, Prodn: Laura Wilson
Founded: 1987
Publisher of audiobooks of general interest in fiction & nonfiction for adults & children. Produce digital downloads.
Catalog(s), 3 times/yr
Membership(s): Audio Publishers Association

Macrosystem US Inc
5541 Central Ave, Suite 135, Boulder, CO 80301
Tel: 303-440-5311 *Toll Free Tel:* 877-554-2846 *Fax:* 303-440-5396
E-mail: info@macrosystem.us
Web Site: www.macrosystem.us
Key Personnel
CEO & Pres: Erik Kloor
Founded: 1990
Design, manufacture & distribute stand-alone digital video editors & HDV storage devices & security products.

Madera Video
501 N E St, Suite A, Madera, CA 93638-3102
Tel: 559-661-6000 *Toll Free Tel:* 800-828-8118 *Fax:* 559-674-3650
Key Personnel
Owner: Louie Fimbrez
Video sales & distribution.
Online catalog(s) available

Madison Square Garden
Division of Cablevision Systems Corp
4 Pennsylvania Plaza, New York, NY 10001
Tel: 212-465-6000; 212-465-6741 *Fax:* 212-465-4416
E-mail: msgnetpr@msgnetwork.com

Web Site: www.thegarden.com; www.msg.com
Key Personnel
Exec Chmn of the Bd: James L Dolan

Madisound Speaker Components Inc
8608 University Green, Suite 10, Middleton, WI 53562
Tel: 608-831-3433 *Toll Free Tel:* 866-883-1488 (orders) *Fax:* 608-831-3771
E-mail: info@madisound.com
Web Site: www.madisound.com
Key Personnel
Mgr: Lawrence Hitch

Magic By Bruce Chadwick
PO Box 12345, Fort Worth, TX 76110-8345
Tel: 817-832-6062
E-mail: chadwickillusionist@yahoo.com
Web Site: www.magicbybrucechadwick.com
Key Personnel
Owner: Bruce Chadwick
Full time illusionist.
Catalog(s) available
Branch Office(s)
PO Box 218503, Houston, TX 77218 *Tel:* 713-823-9845

Magic Gadgets™
Division of William A McIntire Enterprises
12986 Mapleleaf Ct NE, Aurora, OR 97002-8418
Tel: 503-678-6236; 818-655-5465 (rentals) *Fax:* 503-678-6237
E-mail: info@magicgadgets.com
Web Site: www.magicgadgets.com
Key Personnel
Contact: Bill McIntire; Kathryn McIntire
Catalog(s) available

Magic Teleprompting Inc
1390 Waller St, San Francisco, CA 94117
Tel: 415-626-5283 *Toll Free Tel:* 800-646-6244 *Fax:* 415-626-2762
E-mail: info@magicscroll.com
Web Site: www.magicscroll.com
Key Personnel
Founder: Japji Khalsa
Founded: 1989
Teleprompting service company.

Magick Lantern
750 Ralph McGill Blvd, Atlanta, GA 30312
Tel: 404-688-3348 *Fax:* 404-584-5247
E-mail: info@magicklantern.com
Web Site: magicklantern.com
Key Personnel
CEO: Chris Fogg
Exec Prodr: Lisa Farrell *E-mail:* lisa@magicklantern.com
Opers Mgr: Joe Spenneberg *E-mail:* joe@magicklantern.com
Founded: 1990
Video production & post-production services, including editorial, design, motion graphics, audio, Blu-ray authoring & studio services.

Magna Systems Inc
208 S Jefferson St, Suite 402, Chicago, IL 60661
Toll Free Tel: 800-634-4941 *Toll Free Fax:* 800-998-0854
E-mail: info@magnasystems.com
Web Site: www.learningseed.com
Key Personnel
Exec Prodr: Joseph Lombardo
Off Mgr: Kari McCarthy
Founded: 1978
Videos for classrooms & telecourses (Tele-Web).
Catalog(s) available

Magna-Tech Electronic Co Inc
1998 NE 150 St, North Miami, FL 33181
Tel: 305-573-7339 *Fax:* 305-573-8101
E-mail: magnatech@iceco.com; sales@iceco.com
Web Site: www.magna-tech.com
Key Personnel
Founder & Pres: Steven H Krams
VP, 21st Century Cinemas: Barney L Kaufman
Founded: 1975
Catalog(s) available
Membership(s): InfoComm International®; NAB; SMPTE

Magna Visual Inc
9400 Watson Rd, St Louis, MO 63126-1596
Tel: 314-843-9000 *Toll Free Tel:* 800-843-3399 *Fax:* 314-843-0000
E-mail: magna@magnavisual.com
Web Site: www.magnavisual.com
Key Personnel
VP, Sales & Mktg: Frank Venturella
Founded: 1961
Manufacture white boards & magnetic accessories.
Catalog(s), annual, free

Magnanimous Media
600 W Cermak, Chicago, IL 60616
Tel: 312-465-2366
E-mail: rentals@magnanimous.biz; production@magnanimous.biz
Web Site: www.magnanimous.biz
Offers professional HD video production assistance. Rents cameras, accessories & equipment & offers repair service.

Magnaplan Corp
1320 Rte 9, No 3314, Champlain, NY 12919
Tel: 518-298-8404 *Toll Free Tel:* 800-361-1192 *Fax:* 518-298-2368 *Toll Free Fax:* 888-563-8730
E-mail: info@visualplanning.com
Web Site: www.visualplanning.com
Key Personnel
Pres: J P Josephson
Ad Mgr: Boris Polanski
AV presentation equipment.
Catalog(s) available
Branch Office(s)
2209 Tucker St, Burlington, NC 27215, Contact: Vernon Moore *Tel:* 336-228-0188 *Fax:* 336-227-9211 *E-mail:* magnaplan@triad.twcbc.com
1716 Woodward Dr, Suite 106, Ottawa, ON K2C 0P8, Canada, Contact: Egon Hummel *Tel:* 613-563-8727 *Fax:* 613-563-8730 *Toll Free Fax:* 888-563-8730 *E-mail:* ottawa@visualplanning.com
6805 Decarie Blvd, Montreal, QC H3W 3E4, Canada, Contact: Joseph Josephson *Tel:* 514-739-3116 *Toll Free Tel:* 800-361-1192 *Fax:* 514-739-0085 *E-mail:* info@visualplanning.com

Magnepan Inc
1645 Ninth St, White Bear Lake, MN 55110
Tel: 651-426-1645 *Toll Free Tel:* 800-474-1646 *Fax:* 651-426-0441
Web Site: www.magnepan.com
Key Personnel
Pres: Mark Winey
Mktg Mgr: Wendell Diller
Founded: 1969
Speaker manufacturer.
Catalog(s) available

Magnet Sales & Manufacturing Co Inc
11248 Playa Ct, Culver City, CA 90230
Tel: 310-391-7213 *Toll Free Tel:* 800-421-6692 *Fax:* 310-391-7463
E-mail: info@magnetsales.com
Web Site: www.magnetsales.com
Key Personnel
Pres: Anil Nanji
Founded: 1955
Catalog(s) available

Magnetek Inc
N49 W13650 Campbell Dr, Menomonee Falls, WI 53051
Tel: 262-783-3500 *Toll Free Tel:* 800-288-8178 *Toll Free Fax:* 800-298-3503
E-mail: sales@magnetek.com
Web Site: www.magnetek.com
Key Personnel
CEO & Pres: Peter M McCormick
CFO & VP: Marty J Schwenner
Dir, Communs: Lynn Bostrom *Tel:* 262-252-2903 *Fax:* 262-783-0006 *E-mail:* lbostrom@magnetek.com
Founded: 1984
Catalog(s) available

Magnetic Music Publishing Co
20 Jane St, Suite 2-C, New York, NY 10014-1945
Tel: 212-255-8527 *Fax:* 212-595-2067
E-mail: info@magneticmusic.ws
Web Site: magneticmusic.ws
Key Personnel
Composer & Prodr: Reynold Weidenaar *Tel:* 212-769-1514
Music producer.
Catalog(s) available
Membership(s): Media Alliance

Magnetic Post Production
4 Marshall Rd, Wappingers Falls, NY 12590-4105
Tel: 212-598-3000 *Fax:* 212-228-3664
E-mail: contact@magneticimage.com
Web Site: www.magneticimage.com
Key Personnel
Owner & Ed: Harry Douglas *E-mail:* harry@magneticimage.com
Founded: 1990
Production & post-production services.

Magnetic Reference Laboratory Inc
165 Wyandotte Dr, San Jose, CA 95123
Tel: 408-227-8631 *Fax:* 408-227-8631
E-mail: mrltapes@comcast.net
Web Site: www.mrltapes.com
Key Personnel
Pres: Jay McKnight
Founded: 1972
Manufacture & sell open reel calibration tapes for analog audio tape recorders.
Online catalog(s) available
Membership(s): AES

Magnetic Shield Corp
740 N Thomas Dr, Bensenville, IL 60106
Tel: 630-766-7800 *Toll Free Tel:* 888-766-7800 *Fax:* 630-766-2813
E-mail: shields@magnetic-shield.com
Web Site: www.magnetic-shield.com
Key Personnel
Chief Engr: Don Lammersseld
Eastern Regl Mgr: Brad Friestedt *E-mail:* bfriestedt@magnetic-shield.com
Western Regl Mgr: Robert Dasso *E-mail:* rdasso@magnetic-shield.com
Founded: 1941
Manufacture magnetic shielding products & materials.
Catalog(s) available

Magnicon Media/Image d'Or
PO Box 1898, Dearborn, MI 48121-1898
Tel: 313-846-8694; 313-574-3546 (cell) *Fax:* 815-361-2869
Key Personnel
Tech Prodr: Peter Herb *E-mail:* pahl@usa.net

Founded: 1983
Field production services, film/video, camera & lighting equipment & crew services, AV technician services.

Magno Sound & Video
729 Seventh Ave, New York, NY 10019
Tel: 212-302-2505 *Fax:* 212-819-1282
E-mail: staff@magnosound.com
Web Site: www.magnosoundandvideo.com
Key Personnel
EVP: David Friedman *E-mail:* david@magnosound.com
Founded: 1950
Full service production company.

MAGNUM Companies Ltd
205 Armour Dr NE, Atlanta, GA 30324
Tel: 404-872-0553 *Toll Free Tel:* 800-255-1774 *Fax:* 404-875-5629
E-mail: buy@magnumco.com; rent@magnumco.com; design@magnumco.com; production@magnumco.com
Web Site: www.magnumco.com
Key Personnel
Pres & Gen Mgr: Todd Finch *E-mail:* tfinch@magnumco.com
Mktg Mgr: Ingrid Magnuson *E-mail:* imagnuson@magnumco.com
Founded: 1980
Lighting design & technical production company.
Catalog(s) available
Membership(s): International Special Events Society; MPI; Professional Lighting & Sound Association

Magnum Towers Inc
9370 Elder Creek Rd, Sacramento, CA 95829
Tel: 916-381-5053 *Fax:* 916-381-2144
E-mail: office@magnumtowers.com
Web Site: www.magnumtowers.com
Key Personnel
Pres: Ronald Kardokus
Off Mgr: Lori Morris
Catalog(s) available

Mailing Avenue Stageworks
1144 Mailing Ave, Atlanta, GA 30315
Tel: 404-601-9500 (ext 11)
Web Site: www.mailingavenuestageworks.com
Key Personnel
Owner: Tyler Edgarton; John Raulet *Tel:* 404-353-1118 (cell) *E-mail:* john@raulet.com; Paul Raulet
Motion picture & television production facility.

Main Point Productions
295 Lobachsville Rd, Oley, PA 19547
Tel: 610-987-9320
E-mail: mainpoint@dejazzd.com
Key Personnel
Writer & Prodr: William Stanton
Full service production company.

Main Street Media Inc
185 Pier Ave, Suite 105, Santa Monica, CA 90405
Tel: 310-450-1846
E-mail: info@mainstreetmediainc.com
Web Site: www.mainstreetmediainc.com
Key Personnel
Owner & CEO: Robert Newell *E-mail:* robnc60@gmail.com
Owner & Pres: Christopher Blakely *E-mail:* chris@mainstreetmediainc.com
Founded: 1982
Motion picture production, services & equipment.

Maine Imaging
PO Box 753, Wiscasset, ME 04578
Tel: 207-380-6343
Web Site: maineaerial.com
Key Personnel
Owner: Dave Cleaveland *E-mail:* dave@maineimaging.com
Full service custom aerial photography in Maine & New England.

MainSail Production Services Inc
521 Byers Rd, Suite 109, Miamisburg, OH 45342
Tel: 937-866-7800 *Toll Free Tel:* 800-877-0093 *Fax:* 937-866-8088
E-mail: discover@mainsailproductions.com
Web Site: www.mainsailproductions.com
Key Personnel
Pres: Mark D Morgan
Membership(s): IABC; MCA-I

Maison de Soul Records
Subsidiary of Flat Town Music Co
238 E Main St, Ville Platte, LA 70586
Mailing Address: PO Drawer 10, Ville Platte, LA 70586-0010
Tel: 337-363-2177 *Fax:* 337-363-2094
E-mail: info@flattownmusic.com
Web Site: www.flattownmusic.com
Key Personnel
Founder & Pres: Floyd Soileau
VP: Chris Soileau
Catalog(s) available

Major Media Inc
PO Box 209, Deerfield, IL 60015
Tel: 847-433-1682
E-mail: webmaster@major-media.com
Web Site: www.major-media.com
Key Personnel
Pres: Jay Steinberg *E-mail:* jay@major-media.com
Duplication services.
Brochure(s) available

Major Media Productions Inc
PO Box 209, Deerfield, IL 60015
Tel: 847-433-1682
E-mail: webmaster@major-media.com
Web Site: www.major-media.com
Key Personnel
Pres: Jay Steinberg *E-mail:* jay@major-media.com
Production services.

Major Reproductions Equipment Co
PO Box 209, Deerfield, IL 60015
Tel: 847-433-1682
E-mail: webmaster@major-media.com
Web Site: www.major-media.com
Key Personnel
Pres: Jay Steinberg *E-mail:* jay@major-media.com
Audio & video equipment & supplies.

Majortech Inc
8464 Ninth Line RR-1, Norval, ON L0P 1K0, Canada
Tel: 905-873-0778 *Fax:* 905-873-1244
Web Site: www.majortech.com
Key Personnel
Pres: Ken Stelmakowich *E-mail:* kens@majortech.com
Cont: John Nettleton *E-mail:* johnn@majortech.com
Sales Mgr, Broadcast: Mike Sandwell *E-mail:* michaels@majortech.com
Sales Support Specialist: Konstantin Fedotchev *E-mail:* konstantinf@majortech.com; Ernie Medori *E-mail:* emedori@majortech.com
Broadcast, production & post-production, system design, consultation & installation.
Membership(s): SMPTE; WABE

MakeMusic® Inc
7615 Golden Triangle Dr, Suite M, Eden Prairie, MN 55344
Tel: 952-937-9611 *Toll Free Tel:* 800-843-2066 (cust serv) *Fax:* 952-937-9760
Web Site: www.makemusic.com
Key Personnel
CEO: Karen Van Der Bosch

MALCO Electronics
5 Wolcott Ave, Lawrence, MA 01844
Tel: 978-685-4383 *Toll Free Tel:* 800-937-6252 *Fax:* 978-975-4038
E-mail: info@malcoelectronics.com
Web Site: www.malcoelectronics.com
Key Personnel
Pres: Joseph Musumarra
Industrial AV.
Catalog(s) available

MAM-A Inc
4250 Buckingham Dr, Suite 100, Colorado Springs, CO 80907
Toll Free Tel: 888-626-3472 *Fax:* 719-592-0057 *Toll Free Fax:* 888-923-7203
E-mail: info@mam-a.com
Web Site: www.mam-a.com
Key Personnel
Sales & Mktg: Lora Swenson *Tel:* 888-626-3472 ext 430 *E-mail:* lora.swenson@mam-a.com
Cust Serv: Cydney Smoote *Tel:* 888-626-3472 ext 465 *E-mail:* cydney.smoote@mam-a.com
Founded: 1996
Manufacturer of quality recordable CDs & DVDs.
Membership(s): OSTA

Mamiya
Division of MAC Group
75 Virginia Rd, Suite 1, North White Plains, NY 10603
Tel: 914-347-3300 *Fax:* 914-347-3309
E-mail: info@mamiya-usa.com
Web Site: www.mamiya-usa.com; www.mamiyaleaf.com
Key Personnel
Pres, MAC Group: Jan Lederman
Medium format cameras & lenses.

Mammoth HD
PO Box 2064, Evergreen, CO 80437
Tel: 303-670-7973
E-mail: mammothhd@me.com; info@mammothhd.com
Web Site: www.mammothhd.com
Key Personnel
CEO & Creative Dir: Clark Dunbar *E-mail:* clark@mammothhd.com
Gen Mgr: Andy Klingelhoefer *E-mail:* andy@mammothhd.com
Original HD & RED stock footage, 3D animation & motion graphics for broadcast film, advertising, corporate, educational videos & digital screen signage/display.
Membership(s): Global Society for Asset Management; Hollywood Post Alliance; NAB

Manchester Music Library Inc
26 Ivalou St, Somerville, MA 02143
Tel: 413-369-4331
Web Site: www.manchestermusiclibrary.com
Key Personnel
Pres: John Manchester *E-mail:* johnkmanchester@gmail.com
Founded: 1994
Catalog(s) available
Membership(s): ASCAP

maney-logic
6117 Thornebury Dr, Madison, WI 53719-4834
Tel: 608-277-8001 *Fax:* 608-277-8001
Web Site: maney-logic.com

Key Personnel
Owner & Design Engr: Dan Maney
E-mail: dan@maney-logic.com
Custom software & electronics for TV stations, etc.
Online catalog(s) available
Membership(s): SBE

Manfrotto Distribution Inc
Subsidiary of Vitec Group
10 Mountainview Rd, Suite 320 S, Upper Saddle River, NJ 07458
Tel: 201-818-9500 *Fax:* 201-818-9177
E-mail: info@manfrottodistribution.us
Web Site: www.manfrottodistribution.us
Key Personnel
Dir, Prod Mktg: Paul Zakrzewski
Trade Mktg Mgr: Diane Divincenzo
Catalog(s) available

Manhattan Center Studios Inc
311 W 34 St, New York, NY 10001
Tel: 212-279-7740 *Fax:* 212-564-1072
E-mail: info@mcstudios.com
Web Site: www.mcstudios.com
Key Personnel
EVP: Marcus Karr
Gen Counsel: Peter D Ross *Tel:* 212-279-7740 ext 300
Dir, Audio & Television: Obie O'Brien *Tel:* 212-695-6600 ext 212 *E-mail:* oobrien@mcstudios.com
Dir, Video Engg & Opers: Marvin Williams *Tel:* 212-695-6600 ext 312 *E-mail:* marvin@mcstudios.com
Sales & Mktg: Clifton Pierce *Tel:* 212-279-7740 ext 219 *E-mail:* cpierce@mcstudios.com
Founded: 1986
Full service production & post-production facility.
Brochure(s) available

Manhattan Production Music Inc
Division of Chesky Productions Inc
1650 Broadway, Suite 900, New York, NY 10019
Tel: 212-333-5766 *Fax:* 212-262-0814
E-mail: info@mpmmusic.com
Web Site: www.mpmmusic.com
Key Personnel
Pres: Norman Chesky
VP, Mktg & Sales: Ron Goldberg
Catalog(s), free

Maniac Productions
3888 Viewpoint Way, Lafayette, CO 80026
Tel: 303-661-0920 *Toll Free Tel:* 888-626-4227 *Fax:* 303-661-0995
E-mail: mpcl@aol.com; info@maniacproductions.com
Web Site: www.maniacproductions.com
Key Personnel
Founder: Mani Boniek *E-mail:* mani@maniacproductions.com; Patrisha Boniek *E-mail:* patrisha@maniacproductions.com
Complete service AV production company.

Maniglia Media
7925 Jones Branch Dr, Suite LL110, Tysons, VA 22102
Tel: 703-283-8532
Web Site: www.manigliamedia.com
Key Personnel
CEO, Pres: Frank Maniglia, Jr *E-mail:* frank@manigliamedia.com
Media production services including Avid, FCP & HD production.
Brochure(s) available
Price list(s) available

Manios Digital & Film
Division of Ste-Man Inc
10663 Burbank Blvd, North Hollywood, CA 91601
Tel: 818-760-8290 *Toll Free Tel:* 800-845-6619 *Fax:* 818-760-8805
E-mail: sales@maniosdigital.com
Web Site: www.maniosdigital.com
Key Personnel
Pres: Steven Manios, Jr *E-mail:* steve@maniosdigital.com
Natl Sales Mgr: David Butler *E-mail:* david@maniosdigital.com
Founded: 1991
Camera equipment.

Manitoba Film & Music
410-93 Lombard Ave, Suite 410, Winnipeg, MB R3B 3B1, Canada
Tel: 204-947-2040 *Fax:* 204-956-5261
E-mail: info@mbfilmmusic.ca
Web Site: www.mbfilmmusic.ca
Key Personnel
CEO & Film Commissioner: Carole Vivier *E-mail:* carole@mbfilmmusic.ca
Communs & Mktg Dir: Ginny Collins *Tel:* 204-947-2040 ext 16 *E-mail:* ginny@mbfilmmusic.ca
Mgr, Fin & Opers: Kevin Gabriel *Tel:* 204-947-2040 ext 15 *E-mail:* kevin@mbfilmmusic.ca
Founded: 1998
Provincial funding agency & film commission.

Manley Laboratories Inc
13880 Magnolia Ave, Chino, CA 91710
Tel: 909-627-4256 *Fax:* 909-628-2482
Web Site: www.manley.com
Key Personnel
Owner & Pres: EveAnna Manley *E-mail:* emanley@manleylabs.com
Founded: 1993
Catalog(s), free, 4-color
Membership(s): NAMM, the National Association of Music Merchants

Manning Productions
115 N Morgan St, Chicago, IL 60607
Tel: 312-756-1100 *Fax:* 312-756-1200
E-mail: info@manningproductions.com
Web Site: www.manningproductions.com
Key Personnel
Pres & Exec Prodr: Douglas Manning *E-mail:* dmanning@manningproductions.com
VP: Char Manning
Founded: 1985
Web site design & development; iPad development.
Membership(s): DGA

Map Resources
50 S Union St, Lambertville, NJ 08530
Mailing Address: PO Box 334, Lambertville, NJ 08530
Tel: 609-397-1611 *Toll Free Tel:* 800-334-4291 *Fax:* 609-751-9378
E-mail: info@mapresources.com; sales@mapresources.com
Web Site: www.mapresources.com
Key Personnel
Mktg Dir: Barbara Fordyce
Founded: 1984
Maps for graphic design applications.
Catalog(s) available

MAPS Production House
212 Collins Ave, Miami Beach, FL 33139
Tel: 305-532-7880; 786-245-2491 (equipment rentals) *Fax:* 305-532-7673
E-mail: info@mapsproduction.com; equipment@mapsproduction.com
Web Site: mapsproduction.com
Founded: 1991
Studios available for photo shoots, film & commercial shoots as well as private events. Equipment rental.
Branch Office(s)
Studio 255, Wynwood Arts District, 255 NW 25 St, Miami, FL 33127

MarathonNorco Aerospace Inc
c/o Christie Electric Div, 8301 Imperial Dr, Waco, TX 76712-6588
Mailing Address: PO Box 8233, Waco, TX 76714-8233
Tel: 254-776-0650 *Fax:* 254-776-6558
E-mail: marathon@mptc.com
Web Site: www.mnaerospace.com
Key Personnel
CEO: Sergio Rodriguez *Tel:* 254-776-0650 ext 409
Founded: 2003
Catalog(s) available
Membership(s): NAB; SMPTE

Marblemedia
74 Fraser Ave, Suite 100, Toronto, ON M6K 3E1, Canada
Tel: 416-646-2711
E-mail: connect@marblemedia.com
Web Site: www.marblemedia.com
Key Personnel
Co-CEO & Exec Prodr: Mark Bishop; Matt Hornburg
Exec Asst: Kerri Grasser
Founded: 1998
Television, film & new media production. Specialize children's, music, documentary, drama & new media production.
Membership(s): Academy of Canadian Cinema & Television; Canadian Film & Television Production Association

March Manufacturing Inc
1819 Pickwick Ave, Glenview, IL 60026
Tel: 847-729-5300 *Fax:* 847-729-7062
E-mail: sales@marchpump.com
Web Site: www.marchpump.com
Key Personnel
Mktg Mgr: Otto Zimmerman *Tel:* 847-729-5300 ext 40 *E-mail:* ozimmermann@marchpump.com
Founded: 1954
Catalog(s) available

March of Dimes Foundation
1275 Mamaroneck Ave, White Plains, NY 10605
Tel: 914-997-4488 *Toll Free Tel:* 888-663-4637
E-mail: contactus@marchofdimes.com
Web Site: www.marchofdimes.com
Key Personnel
Pres: Jennifer Howse
Founded: 1939
Educational video producer & distributor.
Catalog(s) available

Marco Inc
451 Carson Rd N, Birmingham, AL 35215
Tel: 205-856-1110 *Toll Free Tel:* 888-465-2514 *Fax:* 205-856-1136
E-mail: marco@marcoconsoles.com
Web Site: www.marcoconsoles.com
Key Personnel
Pres: John Matthews *E-mail:* john@marcoconsoles.com
Founded: 1973
Technical furniture design & manufacturer.
Catalog(s) available

Mardi Gras Costume Shop
5895 N Granite Reef Rd, Scottsdale, AZ 85250
Tel: 480-948-4030 *Fax:* 480-948-0754
E-mail: info@mardigrascostumeshop.com
Web Site: mardigrascostumeshop.com

Key Personnel
Owner: Oscar Gibson
Founded: 1974
Sales & rentals.
Membership(s): National Costumers Association

Marengo Films
27206 Waterfall Hill Pkwy, Spicewood, TX 78669
Tel: 972-365-0406 *Fax:* 830-693-0949
E-mail: marengodvd@texasdata.net
Web Site: www.marengofilms.com
Key Personnel
Pres: Craig Cosgray
Founded: 1996
Manufacture & distribute movies on DVD to retail markets.
Catalog(s), $9.98

Marinco Electrical Group
N85 W12545 Westbrook Crossing, Menomonee Falls, WI 53051-3330
Mailing Address: PO Box 3241, Milwaukee, WI 53201-3241
Tel: 262-293-0600 *Toll Free Tel:* 800-307-6702 *Fax:* 262-293-7022
E-mail: swdsales@marinco.com
Web Site: www.marinco.com
Key Personnel
Prod Mgr: Shaun Horan
Nema type wiring devices 15-50 amp, including all black devices.
Catalog(s) available

Marine Geographic
3636 Division St, Knoxville, TN 37919
Mailing Address: PO Box 11171, Knoxville, TN 37939
Tel: 865-237-0291; 865-524-0001
Web Site: www.marinegeographic.net; www.marinegeographic.com
Key Personnel
Owner: Jim McNutt *E-mail:* jim@marinegeographic.com
Founded: 1982
Photography, travel videos, television productions & underwater stock footage. Branch offices in West Palm Beach, FL & Tulum, Mexico.
Membership(s): The Florida Office of Film & Entertainment; MCA-I; Tennessee Film, Entertainment & Music Commission

Maritz Performance Improvement Co
Division of Maritz Inc
1000 Town Ctr, Suite 1200, Southfield, MI 48075
Tel: 248-948-4500 *Toll Free Tel:* 877-462-7489 *Fax:* 248-948-4598
Web Site: www.maritz.com
Key Personnel
CEO: Steve Maritz
Busn Mgr: Dan Holbrook
Integrated performance improvement & marketing.
Branch Office(s)
6900 Maritz Dr, Mississauga, ON L5W 1L8, Canada *Tel:* 905-696-9400
Foreign Office(s): Borselstr 18, 22765 Hamburg, Germany *Tel:* (040) 369-8330 *Fax:* (040) 369-8333
Alexander House, Globe Park, Marlow, Bucks SL7 1YW, United Kingdom *Tel:* (01628) 95600 *Fax:* (01628) 495601

Mark Custom Recording Service Inc
10815 Bodine Rd, Clarence, NY 14031-2252
Mailing Address: PO Box 406, Clarence, NY 14031-0406
Tel: 716-759-2600 *Fax:* 716-759-2329
E-mail: info@markcustom.com
Web Site: www.markcustom.com
Key Personnel
Owner & Pres: Mark J Morette
Owner: Cecilia M Morette
Founded: 1962
Catalog(s) available
Membership(s): American Band Masters Association; American School Band Directors Association; Association of Concert Bands; Florida Music Educators Association; Grammy Foundation; Illinois Music Educators Association; Kentucky Music Educators Association; NBA; New York State Band Directors Association; New York State School Music Association; Texas Bandmasters Association; Texas Choral Directors Association; Texas Music Educators Association; Women Band Directors International

Mark Sonder Productions Inc
2479 Freezeland Rd, Linden, VA 22642
Tel: 540-636-1640
E-mail: inquiry@marksonderproductions.com
Web Site: www.marksonderproductions.com
Key Personnel
CEO: Mark Sonder *E-mail:* msonder@marksonderproductions.com
Founded: 1985
Entertainment producer.

Markertek Video Supply
Division of Tower Products Inc
One Tower Dr, Saugerties, NY 12477
Mailing Address: PO Box 397, Saugerties, NY 12477-0397
Tel: 845-246-3036 *Toll Free Tel:* 800-522-2025 *Fax:* 845-246-1757
E-mail: sales@markertek.com
Web Site: www.markertek.com
Key Personnel
Natl Sales Mgr: Tom Moretti *E-mail:* tomm@towerpower.com
Broadcast AV supply company.
Catalog(s) available
Foreign Office(s): Willow Lane Industrial Estate, Unit 4, Falcon Business Ctr, 2-4 Willow Lane, Mitcham, Surrey CR4 4NA, United Kingdom *Tel:* (020) 8687 9700 *Fax:* (020) 8787 9707 *Web Site:* www.markertek.co.uk
Membership(s): AES; MCA-I; NAB; NSCA; SBE

Market Data Retrieval (MDR)
Subsidiary of Scholastic Inc
6 Armstrong Rd, Suite 301, Shelton, CT 06484
Tel: 203-926-4800 *Toll Free Tel:* 800-333-8802 *Toll Free Fax:* 866-532-7097
E-mail: mdrinfo@dnb.com
Web Site: www.schooldata.com
Key Personnel
Pres: Faday Khairallah
VP, Sales: John Durkin
Educational marketing solutions.
Catalog(s) available

The Market Place
PO Box 4126, Rockford, IL 61110-0626
Tel: 815-877-1514
Key Personnel
Pres: Max Anderson *E-mail:* mander8813@aol.com
Children's programming.
Shipping Address: 4112 Marsh Ave, Rockford, IL 61114

Marketec
Division of Rack Innovations Inc
419 S Flower St, Burbank, CA 91502
Tel: 818-847-0200 *Toll Free Tel:* 800-557-8861 *Toll Free Fax:* 888-262-1726
E-mail: info@marketec.com
Web Site: www.marketec.com
Key Personnel
Pres: Penny Russell
AV chairs. Distributor of technical furniture & electronics.

Marketron Broadcast Solutions
101 Empty Saddle Trail, Hailey, ID 83333
Tel: 208-788-6800 *Toll Free Tel:* 888-239-8878 (support); 800-476-7226
E-mail: info@wicksbroadcastsolutions.com
Web Site: www.wicksbroadcastsolutions.com; www.marketron.com
Key Personnel
CEO & Pres: Jeff Haley
CTO: Tony Gaughan
Produce software for radio.
Branch Office(s)
201 California St, Suite 600, San Francisco, CA 94111
4576 Yonge St, Suite 400, Toronto, ON M2N 6N4, Canada *Tel:* 416-221-9944 *Fax:* 416-821-4845
Sales Office(s): 508 S Seventh St, Opelika, AL 36801-4910, Gen Mgr: Bill Price *Tel:* 334-749-5666
Membership(s): NAB; National Religious Broadcasters; SBE

Marlboro Film & Video Productions
1076 Moss Hollow Rd, Marlboro, VT 05344
Tel: 802-257-0743 *Toll Free Tel:* 888-867-7581 (orders) *Fax:* 802-257-0743
E-mail: mfilmpro@sover.net
Web Site: marlboroproductions.com
Key Personnel
Owner & Pres: Alan Dater

Marsand Inc
6100 S IH-35W, Alvarado, TX 76009
Mailing Address: PO Box 485, Alvarado, TX 76009-0485
Tel: 817-783-5566 *Fax:* 817-783-5577
Web Site: www.marsand.com
Key Personnel
Pres: Matthew A Sanderford, Jr *E-mail:* tvcowboy@marsand.com
VP: David Sanderford *E-mail:* david@marsand.com
Broadcasting engineering consulting firm.
Membership(s): AFCCE; IEEE; NAB; PBE; SBE; TAB

Marsh Media
200 Avila Circle, Kansas City, MO 64114
Mailing Address: PO Box 8082, Shawnee Mission, KS 66208-0082
Tel: 816-523-1059 *Toll Free Tel:* 800-821-3303 *Fax:* 816-333-7421 *Toll Free Fax:* 866-333-7421
E-mail: order@marshmedia.com; info@marshmedia.com
Web Site: www.marshmedia.com
Key Personnel
VP: Dan Witcher
Mgr: Brenna Witcher
Founded: 1969
Catalog(s), annual, free
Membership(s): PMA International

Neal Marshad Productions
Division of Marshad Technology Group
99 Hudson St, 5th fl, New York, NY 10013
Tel: 212-925-8656 *Fax:* 212-292-8912
E-mail: info@marshad.com
Web Site: www.marshad.com
Key Personnel
CEO & Pres: Neal Marshad *E-mail:* neal@marshad.com
Producers of television & Internet content.
Catalog(s) available

Marshad Technology Group
99 Hudson St, 5th fl, New York, NY 10013
Tel: 212-925-8656
E-mail: info@marshad.com
Web Site: www.marshad.com
Key Personnel
CEO & Pres: Neal Marshad *E-mail:* neal@marshad.com
Sr Prodr: Tim Cassidy
Providers of proprietary & third party software.

Marshall Electronics Inc
1910 E Maple Ave, El Segundo, CA 90245
Tel: 310-333-0606 *Toll Free Tel:* 800-800-6608 *Fax:* 310-333-0688
E-mail: sales@mars-cam.com; sales@marshall-usa.com
Web Site: www.mars-cam.com; www.marshall-usa.com
Key Personnel
Opers: David Quinlan
Manufacturer of broadcast multimedia products.
Catalog(s) available
Membership(s): AES; NAB

Marshall Furniture Inc
999 Anita Ave, Antioch, IL 60002
Tel: 847-395-9350 *Fax:* 847-395-9351
E-mail: info@marshallfurniture.com
Web Site: www.marshallfurniture.com
Key Personnel
Pres: Richard Mangione *E-mail:* dick@marshallfurniture.com
VP, Sales & Mktg: Michelle Wille *E-mail:* michelle@marshallfurniture.com
Founded: 1986
Custom multimedia lecterns, projection carts, mobile video consoles, video carts & media storage, conference tables & rack boxes.
Catalog(s), annual, free
Online catalog(s), PDF download
Membership(s): Architectural Woodworking Institute; InfoComm International®; NSCA

Martel Electronics Sales Inc
Yorba Linda Hills Business Park, 23221 E La Palma Ave, Yorba Linda, CA 92887
Tel: 714-692-6690 *Toll Free Tel:* 800-553-5536 *Fax:* 714-692-1799
E-mail: martelsales@marteldirect.com
Web Site: www.martelelectronics.com
Key Personnel
Pres: Ron Smith
Founded: 1957
Dictation & recording company.
Catalog(s) available

Marti Electronics Inc
Division of Broadcast Electronics
4100 N 24 St, Quincy, IL 62305
Mailing Address: PO Box 3606, Quincy, IL 62305-3606
Tel: 217-224-9600 *Fax:* 217-224-9607
E-mail: sales@martielectronics.com
Web Site: martielectronics.com
Key Personnel
Pres: Tim Bealor
Mktg Coord: Christine Fasiska
Founded: 1959
Catalog(s) available
Membership(s): NAB; SBE; TAB

The Martin Guitar Co
510 Sycamore St, Nazareth, PA 18064
Mailing Address: PO Box 329, Nazareth, PA 18064-0329
Tel: 610-759-2837 *Toll Free Tel:* 800-633-2060; 888-433-9177 *Fax:* 610-759-5757
E-mail: info@martinguitar.com
Web Site: www.martinguitar.com
Key Personnel
Chmn & CEO: Christian Frederick Martin, IV
VP, HR: Debra Karlowitch
Founded: 1833
Producer of acoustic instruments & recording equipment.
Catalog(s) available

Martin Professional Inc
700 Sawgrass Corporate Pkwy, Sunrise, FL 33325
Tel: 954-858-1800 *Fax:* 954-858-1811
E-mail: martinus@martinpro.com
Web Site: www.martinpro.com
Key Personnel
Pres: Brian Friborg
Lighting company.
Catalog(s) available
Sales Office(s): 3001 San Fernando Blvd, Burbank, CA 91504 *Toll Free Tel:* 888-287-4776
Membership(s): Illuminating Engineering Society; Professional Lighting & Sound Association; USITT

Martinsound Inc
1151 W Valley Blvd, Alhambra, CA 91803-2493
Tel: 626-281-3555 *Toll Free Tel:* 800-582-3555 *Fax:* 626-284-3092
E-mail: info@martinsound.com
Web Site: www.martinsound.com
Key Personnel
Pres: Joe Martinson
Audio equipment manufacturers.
Catalog(s) available
Membership(s): AES; NAMM, the National Association of Music Merchants

Marvel Photo Inc
1720 N Sheridan Rd, Tulsa, OK 74115
Tel: 918-836-0741 *Toll Free Tel:* 800-806-3616 *Fax:* 918-836-0949
Web Site: www.marvelphoto.com
Key Personnel
CEO: Anthony Perrault
Manufacturer of identification equipment.
Catalog(s) available

Marvell Semiconductor Inc
5488 Marvell Lane, Santa Clara, CA 95054
Tel: 408-222-2500 *Fax:* 408-988-8279
Web Site: www.marvell.com
Key Personnel
CEO & Pres: Dr Sehat Sutardja
Catalog(s) available
Branch Office(s)
30 Enterprise, Suite 200, Aliso Viejo, CA 92656 *Tel:* 949-614-7700
890 Glenn Dr, Folsom, CA 95630 *Tel:* 916-605-3700
1750 E Northrop Blvd, Suite 100, Chandler, AZ 85286 *Tel:* 480-612-8700
1365 Garden of the Gods Rd, Suite 105, Colorado Springs, CO 80907 *Tel:* 719-244-9200 *Fax:* 719-244-9222
1921 Corporate Center Circle, Suite 3-A, Longmont, CO 80501 *Tel:* 303-651-5800 *Fax:* 303-684-9248
700 Commerce Dr, 5th fl, Oak Brook, IL 60523 *Tel:* 630-341-4023
293 Boston Post Rd W, Suite 400, Marlborough, MA 01752 *Tel:* 508-573-3274
7825 Washington Ave S, Suite 720, Bloomington, MN 55439 *Tel:* 952-852-4000
4238 SW Research Way, Corvallis, OR 97333 *Tel:* 541-768-3800 *Fax:* 541-768-3855
807 Las Cimas Pkwy, Suite 200, Austin, TX 78746 *Tel:* 512-651-6800
20333 State Hwy 249, Suite 200, Houston, TX 77070 *Tel:* 281-378-1536
Foreign Office(s): Marvell Technology Group Ltd, Canon's Ct, 22 Victoria St, Hamilton HM 12, Bermuda *Tel:* (441) 296-6395 *Fax:* (441) 295-3328
Marvell Technology (Beijing) Ltd, Unit 407, Vision International Ctr, Tsinghua Science Park Bldg 9, No 1, Zhongguancun E Rd, Haidian District, Beijing 100084, China *Tel:* (010) 8215 1511 *Fax:* (010) 8215 1121 *E-mail:* sunw@marvell.com
Marvell Technology (Chengdu) Ltd, Fl 25, Bldg 10, Area C, Tianfu Software Park, Chengdu Hi-Tech Industrial Devt Zone, No 219 Tianhua Second St, Chengdu, Sichuan, China
Marvell Technology (Beijing) Ltd, 26F Buiding C, Tianhui Mansion, No 569 Huizhou Ave, Hefei 230001, China
Marvell Technology (Nanjing) Ltd, 4th fl, 28 Ningshuang Rd, Yuhuatai District, Nanjing, China
Marvell Technology (Shanghai) Ltd, 4F, Bldg 2, 399 Keyuan Rd, Pudong District, Shanghai 201203, China *Tel:* (021) 6109 2800 *Fax:* (021) 5080 9769
Marvell Technology (Beijing) Ltd, Bldg 4, 399 Keyuan Rd, Pudong District, Shanghai 201203, China
Marvell Technology (Beijing) Ltd, 2nd fl, FuCheng Science & Technology Mansion, First Lane, Southern Region, High & New Technology Science Park, NanShan District, GuanDong Province, Shenzhen 518057, China *Tel:* (0755) 8636 9711 *Fax:* (0755) 8636 9733
Marvell Tehnology Denmark, Boge Alle 5, 1.th, 2970 Horsholm, Denmark
Marvell UK, 15, Ave de Norvege, BP 116, 91140 Villebon-sur-Yvette, France *Tel:* 01 60 92 41 41 *Fax:* 01 69 29 09 19
Marvell Semiconductor Germany GmbH, Siemenstr 23, 76275 Ettlingen, Germany *Tel:* (07243) 502 100 *Fax:* (07243) 502 593
Marvell Hong Kong Ltd, Units 45, 47, 49 & 49A, 13th fl, Hong Kong Intl Trade & Exhibition Centre, One Trademart Dr, Kowloon Bay, Hong Kong, Hong Kong *Tel:* 2628 3216 *Fax:* 2628 3215
Marvell India Pvt Ltd, Leela Galleria, 2nd fl, 23 Airport Rd, Bangalore 560 008, India *Tel:* (080) 2502 6000
Marvell India Pvt Ltd, Pioneer Towers, 6th fl, Software Units Layout No 16, Madhapur, Hyderabad 500 081, India *Tel:* (040) 6612 6900 *Fax:* (040) 6612 6901
Marvell India Pvt Ltd, Muttha Towers, 1st fl, Don Bosco Marg off Airport Rd, Pune 411 006, India *Tel:* (020) 4013-0000 *Fax:* (020) 4013-0101
Marvell Israel (MISL) Ltd, 94 Em Hamoshavot way, Azorim Park, PO Box 10097, 49527 Petah Tikva, Israel *Tel:* (040) 909 1500 *Fax:* (040) 970 4999
Marvell Israel (MISL) Ltd, Mordot HaCarmel Industrial Park, 6 Hamada St, 20692 Yokneam, Israel *Tel:* (04) 909 1500 *Fax:* (04) 909 1501
Marvell Japan KK/Marvell Technology Japan YK, Hiratsuka Off, Hiratsuka MN, Bldg 9F, 3-1 Takara-cho, Kenagawa-ken, Hiratsuka 254-0034, Japan *Tel:* (04) 6325-5826 *Fax:* (04) 6325-5838
Marvell Accel Japan KKL, Nankai-nomura Bldg, 1-10-4, Nanba-naka, Naniwa-ku, Osaka 556-0011, Japan *Tel:* (06) 6633-0078 *Fax:* (06) 6633-0087
Marvell Accel Japan KK, 25th Chuo Bldg 2-8-3, Kanda-tsukasamachi, Chiyoda-ku, Japan 101-0048, Japan *Tel:* (03) 5298-1455 *Fax:* (03) 5298-1456
Marvell Japan KK, Shinjuku Center Bldg, 44F, 1-25-1, Nishi-Shinjuku, Shinjuku-ku, Tokyo 163-0644, Japan *Tel:* (03) 5324-0355 *Fax:* (03) 5324-0354
Marvell Technology Japan YK, Shinjuku Center Bldg, 44F, 1-25-1, Nishi-Shinjuku, Shinjuku-ku, Tokyo 163-0644, Japan *Tel:* (03) 5324-0355 *Fax:* (03) 5324-0354
Marvell Accel Japan KK, 7-5-1 Wakabadai-minami, Tottori City 689-1112, Japan *Tel:* (08) 5737-8078 *Fax:* (08) 5737-8077

Marvell Semiconductor SDN BHD, Plot 98, Hala Kampung Jawa Satu, Non Free Industrial Zone, 11900 Bayan Lepas, Penang, Malaysia *Tel:* (04) 615-9335 *Fax:* (04) 615 9304
Marvell Netherlands BV, Laan van Diepenvoorde 4, 5582 LA Waarle, Netherlands *Tel:* (040) 236 6690
Marvell Asia Pte Ltd, 8 Tai Seng Link, Singapore 534158, Singapore *Tel:* 6756 1600 *Fax:* 6756 7600
Marvell Semiconductor Korea Ltd, 15F Pruden-tial Tower, 838 Youksam-Dong, Kangnam-Ku, Seoul 135-982, South Korea
Marvell Hispania SL, Europark Bldg C / Narcis Monturiol l Estarriol 11D, Parque Tecnologico, 46980 Paterna, Spain *Tel:* 961 366 004
Marvell Tehnology Sweden AB, Olof Palmes Gata 29, PO Box 204, 101 24 Stockholm, Sweden *Tel:* (08) 50625700
Marvell Switzerland Sarl, Route de Pallatex 17, 1163 Etoy, Switzerland
Marvell Taiwan Ltd, 5F-3, No 120, Section 2, Gongdaowu Rd, Hsinchu City 300, Taiwan *Tel:* (03) 516 5098 *Fax:* (03) 573 9907
Marvell Taiwan Ltd, 2nd Fl, No 1, Alley 20, Lane 407, Sec 2, Ti-Ding Blvd, Nei Hu District, Taipei 114, Taiwan *Tel:* (02) 8177 7071 *Fax:* (02) 8752 5707

MarVista Entertainment Inc
10277 W Olympic Blvd, 3rd fl, Los Angeles, CA 90067
Tel: 424-274-3000 *Fax:* 424-274-3050
E-mail: info@marvista.net
Web Site: www.marvista.net
Key Personnel
Partner: George Port *E-mail:* gport@marvista.net; Joseph Szew *E-mail:* jszew@marvista.net
CEO: Fernando Szew *E-mail:* fszew@marvista.net
CFO: Susan Young
Founded: 2003
International distribution for video, television & merchandising rights.
Catalog(s) available
Membership(s): Independent Film & Television Alliance®; NATPE

Marx InDigital
7921 Skylake Dr, Fort Worth, TX 76179
Tel: 414-351-5060
Web Site: www.marxindigital.com
Key Personnel
Pres: David Marx
Founded: 1920
Strategic marketing & production specialists.
Membership(s): AICP; NAB; SBE

Maryknoll Productions
PO Box 308, Maryknoll, NY 10545-0308
Tel: 914-941-7590 *Toll Free Tel:* 888-627-9566 *Fax:* 914-944-3613
E-mail: mkweb@maryknoll.org
Web Site: www.maryknoll.org
Key Personnel
Cust Serv: Nancy Keels *E-mail:* nkeels@maryknoll.org
Full service production company.
Catalog(s) available

Maryland Sound International Holding Co LLC
4900 Wetheredsville Rd, Baltimore, MD 21207
Tel: 410-448-1400 *Toll Free Tel:* 800-76SOUND (767-6863) *Fax:* 410-448-1467
E-mail: martha@msihc.com
Web Site: www.marylandsound.com
Key Personnel
Pres: Robert Goldstein
Founded: 1968
Special event production. Concert touring systems & services. System analysis & consultation, equipment sales & rentals, system design.

Maslowski Productions
1219 Eversole Rd, Cincinnati, OH 45230
Tel: 513-231-7301 *Fax:* 513-231-7301
Web Site: www.maslowskiwildlife.com
Key Personnel
Owner: Steve Maslowski
Wildlife photography.
Catalog(s) available
Membership(s): Outdoor Writers Association of America

Mason Video
9632 N 34 St, Omaha, NE 68112
Tel: 402-455-9422
E-mail: mason.video@mac.com
Web Site: www.masonvideo.com
Key Personnel
Owner: Mele Mason *Tel:* 402-680-5802 (cell)
Founded: 1987
HD, XD & SD video production.

massAV
755 Middlesex Tpke, Billerica, MA 01821
Tel: 978-670-0027 *Toll Free Tel:* 800-423-7830 *Fax:* 978-670-0037
E-mail: info@massav.com
Web Site: www.massav.com
Key Personnel
Pres: Patricia Basteri
VP: Jeffrey Robinson
Founded: 1975
A premier event production firm.
Catalog(s) available
Membership(s): InfoComm International®; International Special Events Society; MPI; NACE

Mastech
1000 Commerce Dr, Suite 500, Pittsburgh, PA 15275
Tel: 412-787-2100 *Toll Free Tel:* 800-627-8323 *Fax:* 412-494-9272
E-mail: info@mastech.com
Web Site: www.mastech.com
Key Personnel
CEO & Pres: D Kevin Horner
COO: Scott Aicher
Founded: 1986
Fully integrated technology & operations firm.
Branch Office(s)
39465 Paseo Padre Pkwy, Suite 1200, Fremont, CA 94538 *Tel:* 510-713-1644 *Fax:* 510-713-1615
Foreign Office(s): GYS Heights, 4th fl, Plot No 10 & 11, Sector 125, Noida 201 301, India *Tel:* (0120) 2546 002

Master Bond
154 Hobart St, Hackensack, NJ 07601
Tel: 201-343-8983 *Fax:* 201-343-2132
E-mail: main@masterbond.com
Web Site: www.masterbond.com
Founded: 1976

Master Books
Subsidiary of New Leaf Publishing Group
3142 Hwy 103 N, Green Forest, AR 72638
Mailing Address: PO Box 726, Green Forest, AR 72638-0726
Tel: 870-438-5288 *Toll Free Tel:* 800-999-3777 *Fax:* 870-438-5120
E-mail: nlp@newleafpress.net
Web Site: www.nlpg.com
Key Personnel
Pres, New Leaf Publishing Group: Tim Dudley *E-mail:* tim@newleafpress.net
Founded: 1975
Christian audio books & videos.
Catalog(s), 2 times/yr, free
Membership(s): CBA: The Association for Christian Retail

Master Communications Group
3410 Winnetka Ave, Suite 107, New Hope, MN 55427
Tel: 763-231-1881 *Fax:* 763-231-1885
E-mail: info@mastcom.com
Web Site: www.mastcom.com
Key Personnel
CEO & Pres: Tim Lewis *Tel:* 763-231-1881 ext 311 *E-mail:* tlewis@mastcom.com
Founded: 1977
Digital media content creation.

Master Mind Publishing Co
Division of Renaissance Unity
11200 E 11 Mile Rd, Warren, MI 48089
Tel: 586-353-2300 *Toll Free Tel:* 800-758-3055 *Fax:* 586-758-7249
E-mail: info@renaissanceunity.org
Web Site: www.renaissanceunity.org
Key Personnel
Dir, Opers: Mike Dennis *Tel:* 586-353-2300 ext 2353 *E-mail:* mdennis@renaissanceunity.org
Religious programming.
Catalog(s) available

Master Video Disc & Design
7349 N Via Paseo del Sur, Suite 515-455, Scottsdale, AZ 85238
Tel: 480-948-0305 *Fax:* 480-948-8628
Web Site: www.mastervdd.com
Key Personnel
CEO & Pres: Janita Cooper *E-mail:* janita@mastervdd.com
Founded: 1987
Full service duplicating company.

Masterclock Inc
2484 W Clay St, St Charles, MO 63301-2548
Tel: 636-724-3666 *Toll Free Tel:* 800-940-2248 *Fax:* 636-724-3776
E-mail: info@masterclock.com; sales@masterclock.com
Web Site: www.masterclock.com
Key Personnel
Pres: William J Clark
Founded: 1986
Complete time synchronization solutions.

Masterdisk Corp
545 W 45 St, 5th fl, New York, NY 10036
Tel: 212-541-5022 *Fax:* 212-581-4093
E-mail: info@masterdisk.com
Web Site: www.masterdisk.com
Key Personnel
Pres: Scott Hull *E-mail:* scott@masterdisk.com
Proj Mgr: Peter Cho
Founded: 1973
Audio, video multimedia mastering facilities.

Mastervision Inc
969 Park Ave, New York, NY 10028
Tel: 212-879-0448 *Toll Free Tel:* 800-876-0091 (order info) *Fax:* 212-744-3560
Web Site: www.mastervision.com
Key Personnel
Pres: Richard Stadin *E-mail:* stadin1@aol.com
Video & DVD producers & distributors.
Online catalog(s) available

Mastery Technologies Inc
41216 Bridge St, Novi, MI 48375
Tel: 972-943-9214 *Toll Free Tel:* 800-258-3837 *Fax:* 248-888-8424
E-mail: sales@masterytech.com
Web Site: www.masterytech.com

Key Personnel
VP, Sales: Kirk Berry
Founded: 1974
Interactive training systems.

Mathmadeeasy.com
Subsidiary of Multi Media Tutorial Services Inc
4914 13 Ave, Brooklyn, NY 11219
Mailing Address: PO Box 190846, Brooklyn, NY 11219
Toll Free Tel: 800-USA-MATH (872-6284)
Web Site: www.mathmadeeasy.com
Key Personnel
CEO: Barry Reichman
Membership(s): Direct Marketing Association

MathMastery, see Systems Impact Inc

Matrix Video Communications Corp (MVCC)
120 2331 50 Ave SE, Calgary, AB T2G 0N1, Canada
Tel: 403-640-4490 *Toll Free Tel:* 800-320-3974 *Fax:* 403-640-9012
Web Site: www.matrixvideocom.com
Key Personnel
Pres & Gen Mgr: Glenn Burgess *E-mail:* glennburgess@matrixvideocom.com
Founded: 1994
Reseller of professional & broadcast video products.
Branch Office(s)
17430-106A Ave, Edmonton, AB T5S 1E6, Canada, Contact: Ron Kusick *Tel:* 780-489-8787 *Fax:* 780-489-4496
106-8678 Greenall Ave, Burnaby, BC V5J 3M6, Canada *Tel:* 604-436-4492 *Fax:* 604-436-4482
320 Gardiner Park Ct, Regina, SK S4V 1R9, Canada, Contact: Don Stephens *Tel:* 306-757-5902 *Fax:* 306-761-2620
2358 Ave "C" N, Suite 99, Saskatoon, SK S7L 5X5, Canada, Contact: Bill Redekop *Tel:* 306-652-5033 *Fax:* 306-652-5037

Matrox Video Products Group
Division of Matrox Electronic Systems Ltd
1055 Saint Regis Blvd, Dorval, QC H9P 2T4, Canada
Tel: 514-822-6364; 514-685-7230 *Toll Free Tel:* 800-361-4903 *Fax:* 514-685-2853
Web Site: www.matrox.com/video
Key Personnel
Mktg Communs Dir: Janet Matey
Worldwide Sales Mgr: Albert Cieri
Founded: 1976
Video equipment manufacturer.
Brochure(s) available
Foreign Office(s): 1602, 38-A Zhongguancun Rd, Beijing 100086, China *Tel:* (010) 6256-4853 *Fax:* (010) 6253-6251 *E-mail:* asiapacific@matrox.com
Chaplin House, Moorhall Rd, Harefield, Middlesex UB9 6NS, United Kingdom *Tel:* (01895) 827220 *Fax:* (01895) 827239 *E-mail:* video.info.emea@matrox.com

Matson Multi-Media
403 E Ramsey Rd, Suite 101, San Antonio, TX 78216
Tel: 210-349-3674 *Fax:* 210-340-5710
E-mail: sales@matsonmultimedia.com
Web Site: www.matsonmultimedia.com
Key Personnel
Pres: James Berg *E-mail:* jim@matsoncreative.com
Full AV production & equipment.

Matthews Studio Equipment Inc
4520 W Valerio St, Burbank, CA 91505
Tel: 818-843-6715 *Toll Free Tel:* 800-237-8263 *Fax:* 818-480-5808
E-mail: info@msegrip.com
Web Site: www.msegrip.com
Key Personnel
VP, Sales & Mktg: Robert E Kulesh
Founded: 1970
Catalog(s), biannual, free
CD-ROM catalog(s), biannual, free
Membership(s): InfoComm International®; NAB; Production Equipment Rental Association

MAVCO
77 S Main St, Newtown, CT 06470
Tel: 203-270-8292 *Fax:* 203-270-8292
Key Personnel
Pres: Chris M Helland
AV equipment distributor.
Catalog(s) available

Maverick Video Productions
121 Interpark, Suite 601, San Antonio, TX 78216
Tel: 210-495-1111 *Fax:* 210-495-8033
Web Site: www.maverickstudio.com
Key Personnel
CFO: Patricia Iverson *E-mail:* pat@maverickstudio.com
Pres: Glenn Duchaine
Founded: 1992
Full service film/video production.

Max Films Inc
1751 Richardson St, Suite 5101, Montreal, QC H3K 1G6, Canada
Tel: 514-282-8444 *Fax:* 514-282-9222
E-mail: info@maxfilms.ca
Web Site: www.maxfilms.ca
Key Personnel
Pres & Prodr: Roger Frappier *Tel:* 514-282-8444 ext 222
Prodr: Luc Vandal *Tel:* 514-282-8444 ext 224
Film producers.

Max USA
257 E Second St, Mineola, NY 11501
Tel: 516-741-3151 *Toll Free Tel:* 800-223-4293 *Fax:* 516-741-3272
E-mail: maxcorp@maxusacorp.com
Web Site: www.maxusacorp.com
Key Personnel
Sales Mgr, Off Prods Div: Carolyn Martello
Electronic office equipment producer.
Catalog(s) available

Maxell Corp of America
Subsidiary of Hitachi Maxell Ltd (Japan)
3 Garret Mountain Plaza, Suite 300, Woodland Park, NJ 07424-3352
Tel: 973-653-2400 *Toll Free Tel:* 800-533-2836; 800-377-5887 (tech support) *Fax:* 201-796-8790
E-mail: techsupp@maxell.com
Web Site: www.maxell-usa.com
Founded: 1969
Producer of optical magnetic memory media.
Catalog(s) available
Branch Office(s)
Maxell Canada, 10 Parr Blvd, Unit 106, Bolton, ON L7E 4E9, Canada *Tel:* 905-669-8107 *Toll Free Tel:* 800-661-9500 *Fax:* 905-669-8108 *E-mail:* support@maxellcanada.com
Foreign Office(s): Hitachi Maxell Ltd, Beijing Fortune Bldg 12F, Rm 1203, 5-Dong San Huan Bei Lu, Beijing 100004, China *Tel:* (010) 6501-4318 *Fax:* (010) 6501-4319 (all Asian countries not listed elsewhere)
Maxell AB, Ennekuja 4, 02270 Espoo, Finland *Tel:* (09) 804 2055 *Fax:* (09) 804 2066
Maxell SA, 14 Rue de Petit Albi, BP 8269, 95801 Cergy Pontoise Cedex, France *Tel:* 01 34 24 88 11 *Fax:* 01 30 73 56 77
Maxell Europe GmbH, Mollsfeld 2, 40670 Meerbusch, Germany *Tel:* (02159) 913-0 *Fax:* (02159) 913-150 (Germany, Austria, Czech Republic, Hungary & Switzerland)
Maxell Asia Ltd, 506 World Commerce Ctr, Harbour City, Phase 1, Canton Rd, Kowloon, Hong Kong *Tel:* 2730 9243 *Fax:* 2735 6250 *E-mail:* maxell@maxell.com.hk *Web Site:* www.maxell.com.hk (Hong Kong, China & Vietnam)
Hitachi Maxell Ltd, Totate-Nagai Bldg, 2-18-2 Iidabashi, Chiyada-ku, Tokyo 102-8521, Japan *Tel:* (03) 3515-8211 *Fax:* (03) 3515-8314 *Web Site:* www.maxell.co.jp
Maxell Mexico, Blvd Manuel Avila Camacho, No 32, Piso 2, Col Lomas de Chapultepec, 11000 Mexico, DF, Mexico *Tel:* (0155) 91787991 *E-mail:* cgongalez@maxmelmx.com (consumer products)
Maxell BV, Wamberg 37, 1083 CW Amsterdam, Netherlands *Tel:* (020) 6460346 *Fax:* (020) 6426685
Maxell Latin America SA, Calle 50, Edificio P H Universal, Piso 2, PO Box 0831-0222, Paitilla, Panama City, Panama *Tel:* 269-6291 *Fax:* 263-4413 *E-mail:* maxell@ciabtesh.com *Web Site:* www.maxell-latin.com
Maxell Asia Pte Ltd, 10 Anson Rd, 25-06 International Plaza, Singapore 079 903, Singapore *Tel:* 6220 9291 *Fax:* 6220 6070 *E-mail:* sales@maxell.com.sg *Web Site:* www.maxell.com.sg (Signapore, India, Indonesia, Malaysia & Myanmar)
Maxell Scandinavia AB, Archimedesvaegen 6, Box 20094, 161 02 Bromma, Sweden *Tel:* (08) 445 22 00 *Fax:* (08) 981080 *E-mail:* msa@maxell.se
Maxell Europe Ltd, 3A High St, Rickmansworth, Herts WD3 1HR, United Kingdom *Tel:* (01923) 77-7171 *Fax:* (01923) 77-7710 *Web Site:* www.maxell.eu.com (Belgium, Denmark, Italy, Norway, Portugal & Spain)
Membership(s): Content Delivery & Storage Association; Entertainment Merchants Association; HVA; NAB; SBE; SMPTE

Maximus Media Inc
2727 N Grove Industrial Dr, Suite 111, Fresno, CA 93727
Tel: 559-255-1688 *Toll Free Tel:* 800-2THEMAX (284-3629) *Fax:* 559-255-0323
Web Site: www.tothemax.com
Key Personnel
Pres: Jeff Hall *E-mail:* jeff@maximusmedia.net
Opers Mgr: Raymond Settle
Founded: 1985
Audio & video production & creative services, network & custom scoring.
Membership(s): AAF; AES; The Recording Academy

MAXON Computer Inc
2640 Lavery Ct, Suite A, Newbury Park, CA 91320
Tel: 805-376-3333 *Fax:* 805-376-3331
E-mail: info_us@maxon.net
Web Site: www.maxon.net
Key Personnel
CEO: Paul Babb
VP, Opers: Rick Barrett
Founded: 1986
Develops professional 3D modeling, painting, animation & rendering solutions. Maxon's Cinema 4D & Body Paint 3D are used in entertainment, science, architecture & other industries.
Foreign Office(s): MAXON Computer GmbH, Max-Planckstr 20, 61381 Friedrichsdorf, Germany *Tel:* (01672) 59 06 0 *Fax:* (01672) 59 06 30 *E-mail:* info@maxon.de (headquarters)

MB Productions
4 Edison Place, Fairfield, NJ 07004
Tel: 973-439-0044 *Toll Free Tel:* 800-622-2224 *Fax:* 973-439-9844

E-mail: mbp@mbvideo.com
Web Site: www.mbvideo.com
Key Personnel
Pres: Brian Brooks *Tel:* 973-439-0044 ext 101 *E-mail:* brian@mbvideo.com
Founded: 1979
Video staging services, supplying video projection, camera packages & flat panel displays for the special events & television industries.

McAlister Electronics
926 E Fremont Ave, Sunnyvale, CA 94087
Tel: 408-739-2605 *Fax:* 408-733-2895
E-mail: mcalelect@aol.com
Web Site: www.werepairallbrands.com
Key Personnel
Pres & Mktg Mgr: William McAlister
Founded: 1967
Membership(s): NESDA; Photographic Society of America

McBain Audio Visual Ltd
Subsidiary of McBain Camera Ltd
10805 107 Ave, Edmonton, AB T5H 0W9, Canada
Tel: 780-420-0404 *Toll Free Tel:* 800-661-6980 *Fax:* 780-421-1188
Web Site: www.mcbaincamera.com
Key Personnel
AV Sales Mgr: Michael Williams *E-mail:* mwilliams@mcbaincamera.com
Founded: 1949
AV equipment sales.
Catalog(s) available
Membership(s): InfoComm International®

MCC Films
Affiliate of Glenn Andrew Productions LLC
7 Rabbit Lane, Brookfield, CT 06804
Tel: 203-775-9473 *Fax:* 734-310-6328
E-mail: info@mcc-films.com
Web Site: www.mcc-films.com
Key Personnel
Exec Partner: Glenn McCabe; James McCauley
Founded: 1994
Film, video productions, commercials, corporate & feature films.

McCauley Sound Inc
16607 Meridian Ave E, Puyallup, WA 98375
Tel: 253-848-0363 *Toll Free Tel:* 877-622-2853 *Fax:* 253-841-3050
Web Site: www.mccauleysound.com
Key Personnel
Owner & Pres: Thomas McCauley
Owner & Exec Dir: Evgueni Sam Ocean
Sr Acct Exec: Bruce Anderson *E-mail:* bruce@mccauley.com
Founded: 1979
Design & manufacture loudspeaker systems.
Catalog(s) available
Membership(s): NSCA

MCCOM Inc
383 Rte 206, Chester, NJ 07930
Tel: 908-879-9590 *Fax:* 908-879-9679
E-mail: info@mccominc.com
Web Site: www.mccom.tv
Key Personnel
Owner: Michael Mehalko
COO: Scott Trupp *E-mail:* scott@mccom.tv
Buy, sell & trade new & used video equipment. Panasonic, Hitachi & Fujinon dealer.
Catalog(s) available

Robert McConnell Productions
4303 67 Ave NW, Gig Harbor, WA 98335
Tel: 253-265-3184 *Toll Free Tel:* 800-532-4017 *Fax:* 253-265-1550 *Toll Free Fax:* 800-948-8463
E-mail: info@parli.com; drvideo@earthlink.net
Web Site: parli.com
Key Personnel
Pres: Robert McConnell
Training videos.
Catalog(s) available

McCune Audio-Video-Lighting
101 Utah Ave, South San Francisco, CA 94080
Tel: 650-873-1111 *Toll Free Tel:* 800-899-7686 *Fax:* 650-246-6702
E-mail: info@mccune.com
Web Site: www.mccune.com
Key Personnel
Pres: Allan McCune *E-mail:* amccune@mccune.com
VP: David Molnar *E-mail:* dmolnar@mccune.com
Founded: 1932
Full service equipment rental, production & staging company.
Catalog(s) available
Branch Office(s)
168 E Liberty Ave, Anaheim, CA 92801, Regl Mgr: Hugh O'Donovan *Tel:* 714-578-1900 *Toll Free Tel:* 800-486-7686 *Fax:* 714-525-6022
222 Ramona Ave, No 1, Monterey, CA 93940, Regl Mgr: Pete Bender *Tel:* 831-372-6038 *Toll Free Tel:* 800-372-3611 *Fax:* 831-372-0513
Membership(s): InfoComm International®

McCune Design
6836 Valjean Ave, Van Nuys, CA 91406
Tel: 818-779-1920
Web Site: www.mccune-design.com
Key Personnel
Owner: Grant McCune
Recording facility rental, custom design, fabrication, effects photography, special effects.

McCurdy Radio Ltd
75 First St, Suite 108, Orangeville, ON L9W 5B6, Canada
Tel: 416-248-6155 *Fax:* 416-248-6755
E-mail: sales8800@mcradio.com
Web Site: www.mcradio.com; www.mccurdytel.com
Key Personnel
CEO: Paul Hudson
Gen Mgr: Stuart Hobbs
Founded: 1948
Quality broadcast equipment.

The McGraw-Hill Companies, see McGraw Hill Financial

McGraw Hill Financial
Formerly The McGraw-Hill Companies
1221 Avenue of the Americas, New York, NY 10020-1095
Tel: 212-512-2000; 212-904-2000
Web Site: www.mhfi.com
Founded: 1909

McGraw-Hill School Education Group
Division of McGraw-Hill Education
8787 Orion Place, Columbus, OH 43240-4027
Mailing Address: PO Box 182605, Columbus, OH 43218
Tel: 614-430-4000 *Toll Free Tel:* 800-334-7734 *Fax:* 614-755-5682
E-mail: customer.service@mcgraw-hill.com
Web Site: www.mcgraw-hill.com
Key Personnel
CEO & Pres: Lloyd G Waterhouse
SVP & Gen Counsel: David Stafford *E-mail:* david_stafford@mcgraw-hill.com
Founded: 1971
Educational materials for elementary, middle school & high school.
Catalog(s) available
Branch Office(s)
2 Penn Plaza, New York, NY 10121 *Tel:* 212-904-2000

McGuane Studio Inc
36 Horatio St, Suite 5-B, New York, NY 10014-1691
Tel: 212-463-7259
Key Personnel
Dir, Spec Effects: James P McGuane
Founded: 1972
Television production studio.
Membership(s): AICP

McIntyre Media Inc
203-75 First St, Orangeville, ON L9W 5B6, Canada
Tel: 519-942-9640 *Toll Free Tel:* 800-565-3036 *Fax:* 519-942-8489
E-mail: info@mcintyre.ca
Web Site: www.mcintyre.ca
Key Personnel
Pres: Peter Whyte *E-mail:* peter@mcintyre.ca
Founded: 1965
Children's programming distribution, DVD & digital streaming.
Catalog(s) available

McKay Conant Hoover Inc
5655 Lindero Canyon Rd, Suite 325, Westlake Village, CA 91362
Tel: 818-991-9300 *Fax:* 818-991-2324
E-mail: info@mchinc.com
Web Site: www.mchinc.com
Key Personnel
Sr Consultant: William Chu
Founded: 1987
Consulting services in all areas of building acoustics & AV systems.
Branch Office(s)
3961 N 75 St, Scottsdale, AZ 85251, Supervisory Consultant: Randal B Willis *Tel:* 480-947-3335 *Fax:* 480-947-3416
Membership(s): AES; InfoComm International®; NSCA

Lloyd F McKinney Associates Inc
25350 Cypress Ave, Hayward, CA 94544
Tel: 510-783-8043 *Fax:* 510-783-2130
Web Site: www.mckinneyassoc.com
Key Personnel
CEO & Pres: Betty L Harmoney *E-mail:* betty.harmoney@mckinneyassoc.com
Gen Mgr: Steven A Bailey, Sr *E-mail:* steve.bailey@mckinneyassoc.com
Founded: 1961
System integration specialists.
Membership(s): AES; NSCA

McNabb & Connolly
60 Briarwood Ave, Mississauga, ON L5G 3N6, Canada
Tel: 905-278-0566 *Toll Free Tel:* 866-722-1522 *Fax:* 905-278-2801 *Toll Free Fax:* 866-722-1822
E-mail: info@mcnabbconnolly.ca
Web Site: www.mcnabbconnolly.ca
Key Personnel
Pres: Steve Connolly
Founded: 1986
Educational programming for K-12 schools, post secondary institutions & public libraries on DVD, streaming or digital file.

McNee Productions Inc
3301 W Alabama St, Houston, TX 77098
Mailing Address: PO Box 540367, Houston, TX 77254-0367
Tel: 713-526-5333 *Fax:* 713-526-4634
E-mail: mcnee@mcnee.com

Web Site: www.mcnee.com
Key Personnel
Founder & Dir: Jim McNee
Pres: Doug McNee
Acctg: Sheryl McNee
Founded: 1970
Full service production company.

MCS Recording Studios
550 Queen St E, Suite G100, Toronto, ON M5A 1V2, Canada
Tel: 416-361-1688 *Toll Free Tel:* 866-322-8555 *Fax:* 416-361-5088
E-mail: info@mcsrecording.com
Web Site: www.mcsrecording.com
Key Personnel
Pres & Studio Mgr: Bill Walker *E-mail:* bwalker@mcsrecording.com
Founded: 1969
Recording studio, ISDN patch for audio.

MDR, see Market Data Retrieval (MDR)

MDS Power Inc
PO Box 532, Champlain, NY 12919-0532
Tel: 514-369-4919 *Toll Free Tel:* 800-931-4919 *Fax:* 514-369-4817 *Toll Free Fax:* 800-931-4817
E-mail: sales@mdspower.com; support@mdspower.com
Web Site: www.mdspower.com
Key Personnel
Orders Admin: Jessica Johns
Founded: 1990
Inverters, power supplies, DC to DC converters, UPS, surge protection & frequency converters.
Catalog(s) available
Branch Office(s)
MDS Power Canada, 8255 Mountain Sights, Suite 305, Montreal, QC H4P 2B5, Canada *Tel:* 514-369-4919 *Fax:* 514-369-4817 *Toll Free Fax:* 800-797-9634

Medcom Inc
6060 Phyllis Dr, Cypress, CA 90630-5243
Mailing Address: PO Box 6003, Cypress, CA 90630-0003
Tel: 714-891-1443 *Toll Free Tel:* 800-877-1443; 800-541-0253 *Fax:* 714-891-3140
E-mail: customerservice@medcominc.com
Web Site: www.medcominc.com
Key Personnel
Pres: Larry Gorum
VP, Sales: Michael Zoradi
VP, Opers: Tina Armstrong
Mktg Mgr: Lisa Hammonds
Medical training programs.
Catalog(s) available

Media Bridge Gamekids
PO Box 513, Koloa, HI 96703
Tel: 808-280-9591
Web Site: www.gamekids.com
Key Personnel
Publr & Prodr: Rennie Mau *E-mail:* rmau@gamekids.com
Founded: 2001
Musical production company.
Online catalog(s) available
Membership(s): Multicultural Publishing & Educational Council

The Media Collaboratory
215 E High St, Lexington, KY 40507
Tel: 859-255-9049 *Fax:* 859-281-6537
E-mail: info@veslex.com
Web Site: www.veslex.com
Key Personnel
Owner & Sr Dir: Arthur Rouse
Full service production company.

Media-Comm
9700 S Pine Blvd, Charlotte, NC 28273
Tel: 704-527-8853
Web Site: www.media-comm.com
Key Personnel
Pres: Mark A Kramer *Tel:* 803-578-1409 *E-mail:* mkramer@media-comm.com
VP, Opers: Brack Rogers *Tel:* 704-507-4332 *E-mail:* brogers@media-comm.com
Provides rental of facilities for audio, video production, post-production & captioning.

Media Communications Association-International (MCA-I)
PO Box 5135, Madison, WI 53705-0135
Tel: 608-836-0722 *Toll Free Tel:* 888-899-MCAI (899-6224) *Fax:* 608-443-2474; 608-443-2478 *Toll Free Fax:* 888-862-8150
E-mail: info@mca-i.org
Web Site: www.mca-i.org
Key Personnel
Exec Dir: Connie Terwilliger
Founded: 1968
Nonprofit organization for media professionals.

Media Computing Inc
PO Box 4169, Cave Creek, AZ 85327-4169
Tel: 602-614-2091
E-mail: info@mediacomputing.com
Web Site: www.mediacomputing.com
Key Personnel
Pres: Michael Rich
Founded: 1981
Superior PC-based automation systems.
Membership(s): NAB; SBE; SMPTE

Media Concepts Inc
559 49 St S, St Petersburg, FL 33707
Tel: 727-321-2122 *Toll Free Tel:* 800-330-3873 *Fax:* 727-321-2272
E-mail: mcifl@tampabay.rr.com
Web Site: www.mcifl.com
Key Personnel
Pres: Scott Richardson
Founded: 1974
Full service video specialty house.
Membership(s): Entertainment Merchants Association; MCA-I; Media Professionals of Florida Inc; SMPTE

Media Consultants Inc
3908 E Valley Ct, Raleigh, NC 27606
Tel: 919-821-2190 *Toll Free Tel:* 800-560-7379 *Toll Free Fax:* 866-881-9331
Web Site: www.mediaconsultants.com
Key Personnel
Pres: Carl Gilfillan *Tel:* 919-623-1871 (cell) *E-mail:* carlg@mediaconsultants.com
Founded: 1972
AV production studio.
Catalog(s), annual

Media Control Systems LLC
1050 Pioneer Way, Suite Q, El Cajon, CA 92020
Tel: 619-599-1050 *Fax:* 619-599-1051
Web Site: www.mediacontrolsystems.com
Key Personnel
CEO & Mktg Dir: Thomas Walsh *E-mail:* twalsh@mediacontrolsystems.com
COO: Tracy Cummins *E-mail:* tcummins@mediacontrolsystems.com
Founded: 2000
Manufacturer & television systems integrator.

Media Cybernetics Inc
Subsidiary of Roper Industries Inc
401 N Washington St, Suite 350, Rockville, MD 20850
Tel: 301-495-3305 *Toll Free Tel:* 800-263-2088 *Fax:* 240-328-6193
E-mail: info@mediacy.com
Web Site: www.mediacy.com
Key Personnel
Prod Mgr: Nick Beaver
Founded: 1981
Software creator.

Media Dimensions Inc
2212 Autumn Glow Ct, Bel Air, MD 21015
Tel: 410-561-4550 *Fax:* 410-561-4550
E-mail: info@mediadimensions.com
Web Site: www.mediadimensions.com
Key Personnel
Pres: Thomas Topscher
Founded: 1984
Full service production company.

Media Distributors
4518 W Vanowen St, Burbank, CA 91505
Tel: 818-980-9916 *Toll Free Tel:* 800-851-3113 *Fax:* 818-566-8989
E-mail: la@mediadistributors.com
Web Site: www.mediadistributors.com
Key Personnel
Sales: Jennifer Chorazyczewski *Tel:* 415-321-5939
Founded: 1998
New & evaluated blank tape sales & other media products.
Catalog(s) available

Media Elite Productions
Affiliate of TSG Consulting Co
800 Bellevue Way, Suite 600, Bellevue, WA 98004
Tel: 425-336-3707 *Toll Free Fax:* 877-391-3778
E-mail: mediaeliteproductions@yahoo.com
Web Site: mediaeliteproductions.com
Multimedia, aviation & business consulting.

Media Entertainment Inc
13194 US Hwy 301 S, Suite 320, Riverview, FL 33569
Tel: 813-495-5821 *Toll Free Tel:* 888-886-7793 *Fax:* 813-741-1152
Web Site: www.mediaent.net
Key Personnel
CEO & Pres: Susanne K Emery
VP & Prodr: Bob Emery *E-mail:* media8@verizon.net
Creation of original TV programming.
Catalog(s) available
Membership(s): DGA

Media Event Concepts Inc
2036 Centimeter Circle, Austin, TX 78758
Tel: 512-832-1142 *Toll Free Tel:* 800-299-1142 *Fax:* 512-832-0236
Web Site: www.mecteam.com
Key Personnel
VP: Deb Kobelan
Founded: 1988
Event planners.

Media Fabricators Inc
8509 Washington Blvd, Culver City, CA 90232
Mailing Address: PO Box 78879, Los Angeles, CA 90016-0879
Tel: 323-937-3344 *Fax:* 323-937-1142
E-mail: mediafab@mediafab.com; info@mediafab.com
Web Site: www.mediafab.com; www.mfi-law.com
Key Personnel
Pres: Barry Fluster *Tel:* 323-937-3344 ext 15
Founded: 1970
Sales & rentals of AV, video & computer equipment for presenters & presentation professionals.
Catalog(s) available

Media Inc
PO Box 496, Media, PA 19063

Tel: 610-565-2844 *Fax:* 610-565-3614
Web Site: www.mediaincorporated.com
Producer & distributor of educational & children's programs.

Media Loft Inc
615 First Ave NE, Suite 100, Minneapolis, MN 55413
Tel: 612-375-1086 *Fax:* 612-375-0913
E-mail: info@medialoft.net
Web Site: www.medialoft.net
Key Personnel
CEO: Gene Di Lorenzo
Pres: David Kelsey
Full service production company.
Catalog(s) available
Membership(s): MCA-I; National Professional Photographers Association

Media Magic
11 Tanzanite, Rancho Santa Margarita, CA 92688
Tel: 949-713-9696 *Fax:* 270-716-9696
E-mail: request@mediamagic.tv
Web Site: www.mediamagic.tv
Key Personnel
Owner: Bill Ennis *Tel:* 949-257-8871 (cell) *E-mail:* bill@mediamagic.tv
Founded: 1984
Independent video production from concept to completion. Specialize in nonlinear post, BetaSP, DVCam production, video, DVD & web.
Membership(s): MCA-I

Media Management LLC
1801 Royal Lane, Suite 906, Dallas, TX 75229
Tel: 972-409-0900 *Fax:* 972-409-0903
E-mail: info@mmgt.com
Web Site: www.mmgt.com
Key Personnel
Gen Mgr: Bob Dungan
Founded: 1986
AV systems integration.
Membership(s): InfoComm International®; NSCA

Media Marketing Associates Inc
12 Colgate Rd, Beverly, MA 01915
Key Personnel
Pres: Robert F Hohman, Jr
Video sales.
Catalog(s) available

Media Productions
3241 S University Dr, Fargo, ND 58104
Tel: 701-237-6863 *Toll Free Tel:* 800-480-6863 *Fax:* 701-280-1226
Web Site: www.mediaproductions.com
Key Personnel
Pres & Exec Prodr: Lee Massey *Tel:* 701-237-6863 ext 6981 *E-mail:* lee@mproductions.net
Founded: 1975
Full service audio, video, film & event production company.

Media Resources
Division of Eastern Kentucky University
102 Perkins Bldg, 521 Lancaster Ave, Richmond, KY 40475
Tel: 859-622-6671 *Fax:* 859-622-1116
Web Site: www.mpc.eku.edu
Key Personnel
Prodr & Prodn Mgr: Andre Kinney *Tel:* 859-622-1678 *E-mail:* andre.kinney@eku.edu
Prodn Supv: Estle Dwayne Bolin *Tel:* 859-622-6628 *E-mail:* dwayne.bolin@eku.edu
College resource center.
Catalog(s) available

Media Resources Inc
9012 NW Holly Rd, Bremerton, WA 98312-9595
Tel: 360-830-0302 *Toll Free Tel:* 800-666-0106
Key Personnel
Owner: Ray Jewell
Founded: 1968
Produce & distribute training videos.
Catalog(s) available

The Media Staff Inc
8425 W Third St, Suite 401, Los Angeles, CA 90048
Tel: 323-658-8996 *Fax:* 323-658-8990
E-mail: info@themediastaff.com
Web Site: www.themediastaff.com
Key Personnel
Founder & Pres: Jerry Maybrook *Tel:* 323-541-5900 (cell) *E-mail:* jerry@themediastaff.com
Founded: 1974
Full service production company.

Media Supply Inc
611 Jeffers Circle, Exton, PA 19341
Tel: 610-884-4400 *Toll Free Tel:* 800-944-4237 *Fax:* 610-884-4500
E-mail: info@mediasupply.com
Web Site: www.mediasupply.com
Key Personnel
Sales: Andy McCall *Tel:* 610-884-4400 ext 108
Founded: 1986
CD-R, DVD, CD business cards, diskette duplication, fulfillment, order tracking & packaging services, media & supplies.
Catalog(s) available

Media Systems Design Group
4253 Stewart Ave, Los Angeles, CA 90066
Mailing Address: PO Box 66337, Los Angeles, CA 90066-0337
Tel: 310-398-0281 *Fax:* 310-398-9451
Web Site: www.msd-group.com
Key Personnel
Principal: Timothy S Hart *E-mail:* thart@msd-group.com
Founded: 2000
AV design & consulting.
Membership(s): InfoComm International®; NSCA

Media 3 Ltd
535 Fifth Ave, 13th fl, New York, NY 10017
Tel: 212-983-5200 *Fax:* 212-983-5200
E-mail: media3@liveshots.com
Web Site: liveshots.com
Live broadcast facility to accommodate live shots, satellite media tours, webcasts & other productions.

Media Vision Productions Inc
Subsidiary of Connecticut Public Television
1049 Asylum Ave, Hartford, CT 06105
Tel: 860-278-5310
Web Site: cpbn.org
Key Personnel
CEO & Pres: Jerry Franklin *E-mail:* jfranklin@cptv.org
Program production for television.
Brochure(s) available
Rate card(s) available
Membership(s): CHETA; Connecticut Ad Clubs; Connecticut Business Council; MCA-I

Media Vision USA
1078 60 St, Oakland, CA 94608
Tel: 415-391-9090 *Toll Free Tel:* 877-746-8375 *Fax:* 415-391-9192
E-mail: info@mediavision-usa.com
Web Site: mediavision-usa.com
Founded: 2002
Branch Office(s)
7008 Virginia Manor Rd, Beltsville, MD 20705 *Tel:* 202-688-3588
424 W 33 St, Suite 480, New York, NY 10001 *Tel:* 917-746-4605
Foreign Office(s): Media Vision Sarl, Chemin J-Ph de Sauvage 37, 1219 Chatelain, Switzerland *Tel:* (022) 518 16 17 *Fax:* (022) 594 80 56

Media Visions Inc
5875 Old Leeds Rd, Birmingham, AL 35210
Tel: 205-324-4600 *Toll Free Tel:* 800-254-0876 *Fax:* 205-324-4688
Web Site: www.mediavisions.com
Key Personnel
Owner & Pres: Michael Cruce *E-mail:* mcruce@mediavisions.com
Full service production & distribution company.
Branch Office(s)
1221 Jordan Lane NE, Huntsville, AL 35803, Sales Engr: Bryan Comer *Tel:* 256-714-3656 *E-mail:* bcomer@mediavisions.com
3240 Franklin Limestone Rd, Antioch, TN 37013, Dir, Opers: Chris Bissinger *Tel:* 615-883-4000 *Fax:* 615-837-6775 *E-mail:* cbissinger@mediavisions.com

Mediaforce Productions
5960 W Parker Rd, Suite 278-183, Plano, TX 75093
Tel: 972-473-6888
Web Site: www.mediaforcepro.com
Key Personnel
Owner: Terri Howard-Hughes *Tel:* 972-897-3345 (cell) *E-mail:* terri@mediaforcepro.com
Founded: 2001
Video, multimedia & web.
Membership(s): Dallas Producers Association; Video Association of Dallas; Women in Film

MediaFX
10445 SW Canyon Rd, Suite 220, Beaverton, OR 97005
Tel: 503-646-9884 *Fax:* 503-646-7115
Web Site: www.mediafxvideo.com
Key Personnel
Owner: Lisa Sherman *E-mail:* lisa@mediafxvideo.com
Dir & Prodr: Erik Mayne *E-mail:* erik@mediafxvideo.com
Founded: 1994
Specialize in commercial, marketing, training & custom videos from pre- to post-production & content delivery.

Mediaimage Communications Group
10 Sacks Ave, Grimsby, ON L3M 4Y4, Canada
Tel: 905-309-5554 *Fax:* 905-309-0999
Key Personnel
Pres: Brian E Purdy *E-mail:* brianpurdy@sympatico.ca
Founded: 1966
Production & directing.
Catalog(s) available

MediaMation Inc
387 Maple Ave, Torrance, CA 90503
Tel: 310-320-0696 *Fax:* 310-320-0699
E-mail: sales@mediamation.com
Web Site: www.mediamation.com
Key Personnel
CEO & Pres: Alison Jamele
CTO & VP: Dan Jamele
Founded: 1991
CD-ROM catalog(s) available
Membership(s): American Alliance of Museums; AZA; IAAPA; ICTA; NAMM, the National Association of Music Merchants

MediaMix Inc
4 Pearl Ct, Allendale, NJ 07401
Tel: 201-262-3700 (day); 201-378-3035 (nights/weekends) *Fax:* 201-262-3798
E-mail: info@mmix.net

Web Site: www.mmix.net
Key Personnel
Pres: Joe Vargas *Tel:* 201-262-3700 ext 103
Full service video, film & DVD production facility.

MediaNow
One Maple Ave, 1-E, Netcong, NJ 07857
Tel: 973-347-2155 *Toll Free Tel:* 888-515-2255 *Fax:* 973-215-2121
E-mail: info@medianow.com; rfq@medianow.com (quote)
Web Site: www.medianow.com
Key Personnel
Pres: Marty Pisano
Founded: 1997
Management, delivery & display of digital media.
Branch Office(s)
4214 Third Ave, Brooklyn, NY 11232

MediaOne Services
901 Battery St, Suite 220, San Francisco, CA 94111
Tel: 415-262-4222
E-mail: sales@mediaoneservices.com
Web Site: mediaoneservices.com
Key Personnel
Interim CEO: Stephen Seligman
Gen Mgr & Dir, Prodn: Danny Skarka *E-mail:* danny@m1sf.com
Studio Opers: Fabian Magabni; Drew Nom's
Founded: 1987
Live-to-air studios, video production, webcasting, remote shoots & transmission for TV & Internet applications.

MediaPOINTE
667 Rancho Conejo Blvd, Newbury Park, CA 91320
Tel: 805-480-3700 *Fax:* 805-480-3770
E-mail: info@mediapointe.com; sales@mediapointe.com
Web Site: www.mediapointe.com
Key Personnel
CEO & Pres: Stephen Villoria
Founded: 1979
Membership(s): ACA; AES; American Institute of Architects; IEEE; INCE; InfoComm International®; NSCA; USITT

MediaWorks
843 W Elna Rae St, Tempe, AZ 85281-5421
Tel: 480-968-4392 *Fax:* 480-968-4679
Web Site: www.mediaworks-az.com
Key Personnel
Owner: Barry J Fuller *E-mail:* barry@mediaworks-az.com
Video production, libraries, film or stock shot.

Medical Media Systems
2916 NW Bucklin Hill Rd, No 481, Silverdale, WA 98383
Tel: 360-516-6110 *Fax:* 360-516-6100
Web Site: medicalmediasystems.com
Key Personnel
Founder & Pres: Dr Donald W Novey *E-mail:* dnovey@medicalmediasystems.com
Founded: 1984
Catalog(s) available

Medical Visual Creations (MVC)
1700 California St, Suite 350, San Francisco, CA 94109
Tel: 415-928-1623 *Fax:* 415-928-4642
E-mail: info@lifestyleinmotion.com
Web Site: www.mvcvideodvd.com

Medifecta Healthcare Training
Division of Institute for Professional Care Education (IPCed)
8740 SE Sunnybrook Blvd, Suite 300, Clackamas, OR 97015
Toll Free Tel: 877-843-8374 (sales & prog info) *Fax:* 541-858-6696
E-mail: info@medifecta.com
Web Site: medifecta.com
Founded: 1995
Offer DVDs, textbooks, workbooks & online content to train professional & family caregivers.
Catalog(s) available

Medina Software Inc
PO Box 952440, Lake Mary, FL 32795-2440
Tel: 407-227-4112
E-mail: info@medinasoft.com
Web Site: www.medinasoft.com
Key Personnel
Pres: Carmen Medina
VP, Mktg & Sales: Jorge Medina *E-mail:* jm@medinasoft.com
Founded: 1985
Assists high-technology companies in the production of Spanish language versions of their products.
Catalog(s) available
Membership(s): IEEE Computer Society; IEEE Consultants' Network

The Meetinghouse Companies Inc
781 N Church Rd, Elmhurst, IL 60126-1413
Tel: 630-941-0600 *Fax:* 630-941-7777
E-mail: info@meetinghouse.com
Web Site: www.meetinghouse.com
Key Personnel
CEO & Pres: Deborah Borsum
Founded: 1981
Membership(s): ARA; International Special Events Society

Megatrax
7629 Fulton Ave, North Hollywood, CA 91605
Tel: 818-255-7100 *Toll Free Tel:* 888-MEGA-555 (634-2555) *Fax:* 818-255-7199
E-mail: info@megatrax.com
Web Site: www.megatrax.com
Key Personnel
CEO & Pres: Ron Mendelsohn *Tel:* 818-255-7100 ext 103
Chief Communs Offr & Exec Prodr: J C Dwyer *Tel:* 818-255-7100 ext 105
Founded: 1991
Quality production music, scoring, recording & music editing.
Catalog(s) available
Membership(s): GSA; NAB; PromaxBDA

Megavideo Productions
22 Cedar St, No 2, Garfield, NJ 07026
Tel: 973-478-1921
E-mail: megamail@megadv.com
Web Site: www.megadv.com
Key Personnel
Owner & Pres: Jack Falzarano
Founded: 1983
Full service production company.

Mellow Hollow Studio
3030 River Rd, Ashland City, TN 37015
Tel: 615-971-0146 *Fax:* 615-792-1787
Web Site: www.mellowhollow.com
Key Personnel
Owner, Prodr & Audio Engr: Daniel Glen Timms
Fully equipped rental recording studio.

Melmat Inc
5333 Industrial Dr, Huntington Beach, CA 92649
Tel: 714-379-4555 *Toll Free Tel:* 800-635-6289 *Fax:* 714-379-4554
E-mail: info@melmat.com; sales@melmat.com
Web Site: www.melmat.com
Key Personnel
Pres: John Mellott *E-mail:* john@melmat.com
Founded: 1971
Manufacturer & distributor of custom & stock carrying cases, plastic containers & packaging. Products include metal edge cases as well as Pelican, SKB & Flambeau cases.
Catalog(s) available
Membership(s): Society of Plastics Engineers

Meltzer Media Productions
70 W 36 St, Suite 1000, New York, NY 10018
Tel: 212-868-4600
E-mail: contact@meltzermedia.com
Web Site: www.meltzermedia.com
Key Personnel
Owner: Jeff Meltzer
Full service production.

Memory Lane Productions
4323 Mundymill Rd, Oakwood, GA 30566
Tel: 770-531-1444 *Fax:* 770-531-1444
E-mail: memlane1@aol.com
Key Personnel
Owner: George Collins
Full service production company.
Catalog(s) available
Membership(s): Writers Guild of America

Memory Lane Videos
676 Lone Oak Ave, Eugene, OR 97404
Tel: 541-688-0484 *Fax:* 541-688-0484
Key Personnel
Owner: Gary Marullo *E-mail:* gmarullo@comcast.net
Founded: 1995
Publisher of special interest videos.
Membership(s): Mid-Oregon Production Arts Network

Memphis Communications Corp
4771 Summer Ave, Memphis, TN 38122
Mailing Address: PO Box 770389, Memphis, TN 38177-0389
Tel: 901-725-9271 *Fax:* 901-272-3577
Key Personnel
Chmn: Scot Berry; Shane Berry
VP & Gen Mgr: Randy Turner
Founded: 1972
Full production service company.
Membership(s): Business Technology Association; InfoComm International®

Merck & Hill Consultants Inc
1995 N Park Place, Suite 450, Atlanta, GA 30339
Tel: 770-937-0185 *Fax:* 770-937-0919
E-mail: info@merckhill.com
Web Site: www.merckhill.com
Key Personnel
Principal: Harold Merck
Founded: 1985
Independent acoustics, AV, production lighting, design & consulting services.
Membership(s): ASA; National Council of Acoustical Consultants

Merestone
Division of Unique Inc
7232 E First St, Scottsdale, AZ 85251
Tel: 480-945-4631 *Fax:* 480-945-0590
Web Site: www.merestone.com
Key Personnel
Pres: Camille Hill *E-mail:* camillehill@merestone.com
VP: Rob Hill
Exec Dir: Nancy Waller-Stults
Dir, Prodn & Opers: Robert Roberson
Dir, Creative Servs: Ian Jones
Sr Animator/IT: David Derosier

Founded: 1974
Support & creative services for anyone needing AV, videography, editing, production & scripting. Advanced meeting & event services.

Meridia Audience Response
5207 Militia Hill Rd, Plymouth Meeting, PA 19462
Tel: 610-260-6800 *Fax:* 610-260-6810
E-mail: rsvp@meridiaars.com
Web Site: www.meridiaars.com
Key Personnel
Owner & CEO: Rick Baker
Pres: Keith Reiner
Manufacturer & distributor of audience response systems.
Catalog(s) available
Membership(s): InfoComm International®; Meeting Planners International

Meridian Education Corp
Division of Infobase Learning
c/o Films Media Group, 132 W 31 St, 17th fl, New York, NY 10001
Tel: 609-671-1000 *Toll Free Tel:* 800-257-5126; 800-322-8755 *Toll Free Fax:* 800-678-3633
E-mail: custserv@films.com
Web Site: meridian.films.com
Founded: 1959
Meridian-brand products are ideal for career & technical education instructors who want to teach & reinforce job & employability skills through a multimodal approach to learning. As a leader in educational media for students preparing to enter the workforce, Meridian offers a library of products covering topics such as allied health, culinary arts & child care. Meridian's skills-based, up-to-date educational media thoroughly addresses specific career/job-related skills & prepares students to enter the workforce. Meridian is a trademark of Films Media Group, an award-winning source of over 13,000 titles & exclusive US distributor for BBC Educational Collections, the Bill Moyers Collection, PBS & HBO, as well as many offerings from ABC & NBC News. Infobase Learning is the parent company of Meridian Education.
Catalog(s), weekly, free, over 100 unique catalogs mailed throughout the year

Meridian Studios
1020 Highland Park Rd, Neenah, WI 54956
Tel: 920-720-4200
E-mail: info@meridianstudiosusa.com
Web Site: www.meridianstudiosusa.com
Key Personnel
Partner: Julie Mata *E-mail:* julie@meridianstudiosusa.com; Tony Mata
Founded: 2004
Complete film, video & stage (large venue) production. Full avid media composer 1000XL Editing Suite & digital EFP package plus on-site studio. Specialize in planning, pre-production, field/studio production & post-production, final cut professional HD system & still photography.

Meriwether Publishing Ltd
885 Elkton Dr, Colorado Springs, CO 80907-3522
Mailing Address: PO Box 7710, Colorado Springs, CO 80933-7710
Tel: 719-594-4422 *Toll Free Tel:* 800-937-5297 *Fax:* 719-594-9916 *Toll Free Fax:* 888-594-4436
E-mail: customerservice@meriwether.com; orders@meriwether.com
Web Site: www.meriwether.com
Key Personnel
Pres: Mark Zapel *E-mail:* mzapel@meriwether.com
VP: Ted Zapel *E-mail:* tzapel@aol.com
Produce & distribute educational CDs, videos & DVDs.
Catalog(s), semiannual, free

Mermaid7seas Productions
970 Ninth St, Boulder, CO 80302-7226
Tel: 303-545-0202; 303-818-5771 (cell)
E-mail: mermaid7seas@gmail.com
Key Personnel
Owner: Elizabeth English
Founded: 1999
Script & film consulting.

Merrimack Films
530 Concord Ave, Belmont, MA 02478
Tel: 617-489-4729
E-mail: sales@merrimack-films.com
Web Site: www.merrimack-films.com
Founded: 1983
Produces & distributes educational videos on labor relations.
Catalog(s) available
Membership(s): IDA

MeshTel-Intelite
PO Box 747, Genoa, NV 89411
Tel: 775-267-5959 *Fax:* 775-267-5958
E-mail: info@meshtel.com
Web Site: www.meshtel.com
Key Personnel
Pres: Donna Wilson
Founded: 1990
Manufacturer & supplier of laser projection hardware & software.
Catalog(s) available

MessageMakers
1217 Turner St, Lansing, MI 48906
Tel: 517-482-3333 *Toll Free Tel:* 888-482-6688
E-mail: info@messagemakers.com
Web Site: www.messagemakers.com
Key Personnel
Founder, CEO & Pres: Terry N Terry *E-mail:* terry@messagemakers.com
Sr Video Prodr: Tom Lietz *E-mail:* lietz@messagemakers.com
Founded: 1977
Full service production company specializing in live events, HD video production & learning programs.
Catalog(s) available
Membership(s): ATD; International Society for Performance and Instruction; International Special Events Society; Lansing Chamber of Commerce

Metalworks Recording Studios Inc
3611 Mavis Rd, Mississauga, ON L5C 1T7, Canada
Tel: 905-279-4000 *Fax:* 905-279-4006
Web Site: www.metalworksstudios.com
Key Personnel
Studio Mgr: Chris Crerar *E-mail:* chris@metalworksstudios.com
Founded: 1978
Recording studios.

Meteor, see Tectonics Industries Inc

Method Studios
Division of Deluxe Entertainment Services Group Inc
730 Arizona Ave, Santa Monica, CA 90401
Tel: 310-434-6500
Web Site: www.methodstudios.com
Key Personnel
Pres: Marc Weigert
SVP, Global Opers: Patrick Davenport
SVP of Prodn & Sr Exec Prodr: Gabby Gourrier
Exec Prodr/Head of Prodn: Stephanie Gilgar
Exec Prodr: Robert Owens
Sr Prodr: Cara Farnsworth
Visual Effects Prodr: Heather Saunders
Prodr: Jennie Burnett
Visual effects artist studio.
Catalog(s) available
Branch Office(s)
3399 Peachtree Rd NE, Suite 200, Atlanta, GA 30326 *Tel:* 404-732-1001
435 N Michigan Ave, 22nd fl, Chicago, IL 60611, Prodr: Erica Hilbert *Tel:* 312-725-7990 *E-mail:* erica.hilbert@methodstudios.com
209 W Sixth St, Royal Oak, MI 48067, Mng Dir: Laura Hochthanner *Tel:* 248-837-1700 *E-mail:* laura.hochthanner@methodstudios.com
218 W 18 St, 12th fl, New York, NY 10011, Mng Dir: Stuart Robinson *Tel:* 212-907-1200 *E-mail:* stuart.robinson@methodstudios.com
50 W Second Ave, Vancouver, BC V5Y 1B3, Canada, Visual Effects Prodn Mgr: Naomi Stopa *Tel:* 604-874-8700 *E-mail:* naomi.stopa@methodstudios.com
Foreign Office(s): 706 Mowbray Rd, Unit 3, Lane Cove, NSW 2066, Australia, Gen Mgr: Kath Raphael *Tel:* (02) 9429 7399 *E-mail:* kath.raphael@methodstudios.com *Web Site:* www.methodstudios.com.au
20 Thistlewaite St, South Melbourne, Victoria 3205, Australia, Head of Commercials Asia Pacific: Andrew Shostak *Tel:* (03) 9690 4044 *E-mail:* andrew.shostak@methodstudios.com *Web Site:* www.methodstudios.com.au
8-14 Meard St, London W1F 0EQ, United Kingdom *Tel:* (020) 7878 7878

Metric Splicer Inc
3930 E Miraloma Ave, Suite C, Anaheim, CA 92806
Tel: 714-630-2999 *Fax:* 714-630-2268
Web Site: www.metricsplicer.com
Key Personnel
Pres: Kirby Morrow
Assoc Exec: Trey Morrow *E-mail:* trey.morrow@metricsplicer.com
Editing equipment manufacturer.

Metro Productions
8570 Magellan Pkwy, Suite 400, Richmond, VA 23227
Tel: 804-261-1172 *Toll Free Tel:* 877-669-4687 *Fax:* 804-261-1885
E-mail: contactmetro@metro-productions.com
Web Site: www.metro-productions.com
Key Personnel
CEO & Pres: Ray Walsh
COO: Patrick Bedall *Tel:* 804-261-1172 ext 209 *E-mail:* pbedall@metro-productions.com
Dir, Devt: Jim Miller *Tel:* 804-261-1172 ext 211 *E-mail:* jmiller@metro-productions.com
Communs Mgr: Ashley Warren *Tel:* 804-261-1172 ext 204 *E-mail:* awarren@metro-productions.com
Founded: 1981 (as Metro Video Productions)
Full service video, film, multimedia & animation production.
Branch Office(s)
1000 Cameron St, Alexandria, VA 22314 *Tel:* 571-257-7349
48 W Queen's Way, Hampton, VA 23669 *Tel:* 757-726-0877 *Fax:* 757-726-0876

Metro Teleproductions Inc (MTI)
2500 Virginia Ave NW, 416-S, Washington, DC 20037
Tel: 301-608-9077 *Fax:* 301-608-9078
Web Site: www.mtitv.com
Key Personnel
Owner & Pres: Dave Lilling *Tel:* 301-370-5898 (cell) *E-mail:* dave@mtitv.com
Founded: 1989
Video production, crews & webcasting.

Metro Video Systems Inc
1220 E Imperial Ave, El Segundo, CA 90245
Tel: 310-640-9250 *Fax:* 310-640-9347
E-mail: sales@metrovideosystems.com
Web Site: www.metrovideosystems.com
Key Personnel
Owner: Robert L Weir
Founded: 1969
CCTV distribute & repair.

Metromotion Productions LLC
450 W 31 St, 8th & 9th fl, New York, NY 10001
Tel: 212-967-2000 *Fax:* 212-967-1988
E-mail: info@metromotion.com; pr@metromotion.com
Web Site: www.metromotion.com
Key Personnel
Owner: Marc Chanti
Founded: 1990
Production services for the international commercial photography industry.

Metropolitan Acoustics LLC
40 W Evergreen Ave, Suite 108, Philadelphia, PA 19118
Tel: 215-248-4352 *Fax:* 215-248-4353
E-mail: info@metro-acoustics.com
Web Site: www.metro-acoustics.com
Key Personnel
Founder & Principal Consultant: Felicia Doggett *E-mail:* f.doggett@metro-acoustics.com
Founded: 1990
Acoustical & AV consulting.
Membership(s): American Institute of Architects; ASA; INCE; InfoComm International®; National Council of Acoustical Consultants; NSCA

Metropolitan Audio Visual Co LLC
2862 Hartland Rd, Falls Church, VA 22043
Tel: 703-834-0004 *Toll Free Tel:* 800-966-4333 *Fax:* 703-834-0866
E-mail: sales@metroav.com
Web Site: www.metroav.com
Key Personnel
Owner: David Wilkins
Pres: John Elstrodt
Founded: 1967
Full service AV dealer.
Membership(s): InfoComm International®; Virginia Educational Vendors Association

Metropolitan Audio-Visual Inc
35333 N 27 Lane, Phoenix, AZ 85086
Mailing Address: PO Box 75386, Phoenix, AZ 85087-1024
Tel: 480-948-9008 *Fax:* 480-948-9130
Web Site: www.metroav.tv
Key Personnel
Pres: James A Smidt *E-mail:* jimmetroav@hotmail.com
AV sales & rentals.

Metropolitan Museum of Art
1000 Fifth Ave, New York, NY 10028-0198
Tel: 212-535-7710 *Fax:* 212-472-2764
E-mail: customer.service@metmuseum.org; communications@metmuseum.org
Web Site: www.metmuseum.org
Key Personnel
Pres: Emily K Rafferty *E-mail:* emily.rafferty@metmuseum.org
Founded: 1870

Metropolitan Opera Guild
Samuel B & David Rose Bldg, 70 Lincoln Center Plaza, 6th fl, New York, NY 10023-6593
Tel: 212-769-7000
E-mail: info@metguild.org
Web Site: www.metguild.org
Key Personnel
Mng Dir: Stewart Pearce
Founded: 1935
Shipping Address: 165 W 65 St, New York, NY 10023-6593
Membership(s): Opera Guild International

MetroSonic Recording Studio
143 Roebling St, 3rd fl, Brooklyn, NY 11211
Tel: 718-782-1872
E-mail: manager@metrosonic.net
Web Site: www.metrosonic.net
Key Personnel
Owner: Pete Mignola
Asst Engr: Teruhisa Uchiyama
Founded: 1991
Full service studio & music production facility.

Meuninck's Media Methods Inc
24097 North Shore Dr, Edwardsburg, MI 49112
Web Site: www.herbvideos.com
Key Personnel
Pres & Dir: Jim Meuninck *E-mail:* jim@herbvideos.com
Educational & children's video distributor.
Catalog(s) available

Meyer Sound Laboratories Inc
2832 San Pablo Ave, Berkeley, CA 94702
Tel: 510-486-1166 *Toll Free Tel:* 855-641-3288 (US & CN) *Fax:* 510-486-8356
E-mail: sales@meyersound.com; techsupport@meyersound.com; service@meyersound.com
Web Site: www.meyersound.com
Key Personnel
CEO: John Meyer
Dir, Mktg: Rachel Archibald *Tel:* 510-540-4513
Founded: 1979
Speaker manufacturer.
Catalog(s) available
Branch Office(s)
750 Cowan St, Nashville, TN 37207 *Tel:* 908-377-5384 *E-mail:* nashville@meyersound.com
Meyer Sound Canada, 100 Kalamalka Lake Rd, No 23, Vernon, BC V1T 9G1, Canada *Tel:* 250-549-2588 *Fax:* 250-549-2668 *E-mail:* canada@meyersound.com (R&D only)
Foreign Office(s): Meyer Sound Australia Pty Ltd, Pulse Business Park, Unit 7, 459 Tufnell Rd, Banyo, Qld 4014, Australia *Tel:* (07) 3267 7800 *Fax:* (07) 3267 8733 *E-mail:* australia@meyersound.com *Web Site:* www.meyersound.com.au
Meyer Sound Brasil, Rua Fradique Coutinho 587, C-J, 81-D, Pinheiros, Sao Paulo-SP 05416-010, Brazil, Contact: Sergio Nigro *Tel:* (011) 3816 0401; (011) 9 9658 5272 (cell) *E-mail:* brazil@meyersound.com
Meyer Sound China, C203-16, Beijing Lufthansa Centre Off Bldg, 50 Liangmaqiao Rd, Chaoyang District, Beijing 100125, China *Tel:* (010) 6410 5336 *E-mail:* china@meyersound.com
Meyer Sound Lab Germany GmbH, Horresser Berg 4a, 56410 Montabaur, Germany *Tel:* (02602) 99908-0 *Fax:* (02602) 99908-99 *E-mail:* germany@meyersound.com *Web Site:* www.meyersound.de
Meyer Sound Mexico S de RL de CV, Blvd Picacho-Ajusco, No 130-901A, Col Jardines en la Montana, Delegacion Tlalpan, 14210 Mexico, DF, Mexico *Tel:* (0155) 5631 8137 *Fax:* (0155) 5630 5391 *E-mail:* mexico@meyersound.com *Web Site:* www.meyersound.com/spanish
Meyer Sound Mexico-Monterrey, San Carlos 339, Hacienda los Cantu, Escobedo, Nuevo Leon 66050, Mexico *Tel:* (0181) 8063 3359 *Fax:* (0181) 8340 4355
Meyer Sound Portugal, Multi Business Ctr D12, Estrada Nacional 249, Aboboda, 2785-035 Lisbon, Portugal *Tel:* 91 512 8686 *Web Site:* www.meyersoundportugal.com
Meyer Sound CIS, Marshall Jukov Prospect, 39/1, Off 31, Moscow 123423, Russia *Tel:* 915 270 3010 *Fax:* 095 947 9140 *E-mail:* russia@meyersound.com
Meyer Sound Espana SA, c/ Desarrollo 11, Parque Industrial PISA, Mairena del Aljarafe, Seville 41927, Spain *Tel:* 955 542 111 *Fax:* 954 186 638 *E-mail:* spain@meyersound.com
Meyer Sound Dubai, Shatha Tower, Suite 3018, PO Box 72280, Dubai Media City, Dubai, United Arab Emirates *Tel:* (050) 211 7708 *E-mail:* middleast@meyersound.com
Membership(s): AES; NSCA; SPARS

MFJ Enterprises Inc
300 Industrial Park Rd, Starkville, MS 39759-3992
Mailing Address: PO Box 494, Mississippi State, MS 39762-0494
Tel: 662-323-5869 *Toll Free Tel:* 800-647-1800 *Fax:* 662-323-6551
E-mail: mfjcustserv@mfjenterprises.com
Web Site: www.mfjenterprises.com
Key Personnel
Pres: Martin F Jue
VP: Steven Pan
Founded: 1972
Ham radio communications company.
Catalog(s) available

MG Electronics
32 Ranick Rd, Hauppauge, NY 11788
Tel: 631-582-3400 *Fax:* 631-582-3229
E-mail: info@mgelectronics.com
Web Site: www.mgelectronics.com
Key Personnel
Owner: Elliott Maltz
Founded: 1961
Catalog(s), annual
Membership(s): IPMA; NSCA

MG Studio
6625 S Valley View Blvd, Suite C-304, Las Vegas, NV 89118
Tel: 702-836-3686 *Toll Free Tel:* 866-478-8340
E-mail: office@mgstudio.com
Web Site: mgstudio.com
Key Personnel
Dir: Michael Gaskell *Tel:* 818-681-0808 *E-mail:* michaelg@mgstudio.com
Cinematographer: Ben Ader
Production company. Provides rental of studio, stages, cameras, lighting & grip.

MGE UPS Systems
Unit of APC by Schneider Electric
1660 Scenic Ave, Costa Mesa, CA 92626
Tel: 714-557-1636 *Toll Free Tel:* 800-344-0570
Web Site: www.apc.com
Key Personnel
CEO & Pres, APC: Laurent Vernerey
Founded: 1981
Global provider of power quality solutions.
Catalog(s) available

MGM & Associates Inc
16026 S 36 St, Phoenix, AZ 85048-7322
Tel: 480-759-6251 *Toll Free Tel:* 800-485-0065 *Fax:* 480-759-6257
E-mail: mgm@mgmsuperstar.com
Web Site: www.mgmsuperstar.com; www.thewomensmillionaireclub.com
Key Personnel
CEO & Pres: Maureen G Mulvaney
VP, Mktg: Susan Abernathy
Founded: 1979

International professional speaker on attitude technologies to drive your company to success.
Membership(s): American Society of Association Executives; ATD; MPI; National Speakers Association

MGM Home Video
Division of MGM United Artists
245 N Beverly Dr, Beverly Hills, CA 90210
Tel: 310-449-3000
Web Site: www.mgm.com

MGM United Artists
245 N Beverly Dr, Beverly Hills, CA 90210
Tel: 310-449-3000
Web Site: www.mgm.com
Founded: 1919
Branch Office(s)
655 Third Ave, New York, NY 10017 *Tel:* 212-708-0300 *Fax:* 212-708-0337

MHS-TV
Mamaroneck High School, 1000 W Boston Post Rd, Mamaroneck, NY 10543
Tel: 914-220-3100 *Fax:* 914-220-3115
Web Site: www.mhstv.org; www.mamkschools.org
Catalog(s) available

Mia Mind Music
254 Sixth St, Suite 2, Hoboken, NJ 07030-6916
Toll Free Tel: 800-843-8575 *Fax:* 201-216-1186
E-mail: mimimus@aol.com
Web Site: www.miamindmusic.com
Key Personnel
Owner: Stevie B
Founded: 1984
Entertainment promotion & marketing company.
Membership(s): ASCAP

Miami Daylight Studios
1819 West Ave, Bay 5, Miami Beach, FL 33139
Tel: 305-763-8490
E-mail: info@miamidaylightstudios.com
Web Site: miamidaylightstudios.com
Still & motion equipment rental for professional productions. Offers photographic services, equipment rentals, studio space, transportation & production support, digital tech & creative services.

Miami Stagecraft Inc
2855 E 11 Ave, Hialeah, FL 33013
Tel: 305-836-9356 *Fax:* 305-696-3322
E-mail: info@miamistagecraft.com
Web Site: www.miamistagecraft.com
Key Personnel
Mgr: Andrew Martin *Tel:* 305-836-9356 ext 1
Stage lighting distributor.

MIB Mediaworks
85 Main St, Little Falls, NJ 07424
Tel: 973-403-1133
E-mail: info@mibmediaworks.com
Web Site: www.mibmediaworks.com
Key Personnel
Pres & Dir, Films: Mark Brodie *Tel:* 917-416-4840 (cell) *E-mail:* mark@mibmediaworks.com
Founded: 1986
Video production & technical consulting.

Michigan Office Solutions
2859 Walkent Dr NW, Grand Rapids, MI 49544
Tel: 616-454-1198 *Toll Free Tel:* 800-442-9070 *Fax:* 616-459-8705
Web Site: www.miofficesolutions.com
Key Personnel
EVP, Sales: Bill Orr *Tel:* 616-454-1198 ext 23816
Founded: 1957
Office equipment sales & service company.
Catalog(s) available
Branch Office(s)
431 N Ripley, Alpena, MI 49707 *Tel:* 989-356-9500 *Fax:* 989-356-8427
345 W Lake Lansing Rd, East Lansing, MI 48823 *Tel:* 517-332-2153 *Fax:* 517-332-4074
3800 Covington Rd, Kalamazoo, MI 49001-1882 *Tel:* 269-381-0805 *Fax:* 269-381-2034
116 Court St, Suite 2, Mount Pleasant, MI 48858 *Tel:* 989-773-4910 *Fax:* 989-773-4092
40000 Grand River Ave, Suite 500, Novi, MI 48375 *Tel:* 248-919-3333 *Fax:* 248-919-3334
4177 Fashion Square Blvd, Suite 2, Saginaw, MI 48603 *Tel:* 989-791-1513 *Fax:* 989-791-1525
3281 Racquet Club Dr, Suite B, Traverse City, MI 49686 *Tel:* 231-946-7655 *Fax:* 231-946-5279

Michigan Recording Arts Institute & Technologies
Division of K&R All Media Productions Inc
28533 Greenfield, Southfield, MI 48076
Tel: 248-569-5422 *Toll Free Tel:* 888-802-0402
Web Site: mirecordingarts.com
Key Personnel
Professor: Kenneth Glaza *Tel:* 248-557-8276 *E-mail:* ken@mirecordingarts.com
Founded: 1984
School, institute.
Online catalog(s) available

Michigan State University, Media Services, see MSU Technologies

Micor Analytics
7538 Saint Louis Ave, Skokie, IL 60076
Tel: 847-329-8590 *Fax:* 847-329-8599
Web Site: www.micoranalytics.com
Key Personnel
Sr Analyst: James Minchella *Tel:* 847-329-8590 ext 214
Appraisal, consulting & remarketing of broadcast equipment.
Catalog(s) available

Micro Express
8 Hammond, Suite 105, Irvine, CA 92618-1601
Tel: 949-460-9911 *Toll Free Tel:* 800-989-9900 *Fax:* 949-269-3070
E-mail: info@microexpress.net
Web Site: www.microexpress.net
Founded: 1986
Manufacture computers.

Micro Innovations Inc
910 Belle Ave, Suite 1046, Winter Springs, FL 32708
Tel: 407-696-9800 *Fax:* 407-696-8511
E-mail: avail@avail-software.com
Web Site: www.avail-software.com
Key Personnel
Pres: Harold W Brown
Founded: 1981
"AVAIL" AV/video rental control software.
Membership(s): InfoComm International®

Micro Technology Unlimited
PO Box 80124, Raleigh, NC 27623
Tel: 919-870-0344
Web Site: www.mtu.com
Key Personnel
Pres: David B Cox
Founded: 1977
Audio, video & computer manufacturer & distributor.
Catalog(s) available

Microboards Technology LLC
8150 Mallory Ct, Chanhassen, MN 55317
Tel: 952-556-1600 *Toll Free Tel:* 800-646-8881; 800-290-9012 *Fax:* 952-556-1620
E-mail: sales@microboards.com
Web Site: www.microboards.com
Key Personnel
Sales Mgr: Brian Towey
Founded: 1989
AV equipment distributor.
Foreign Office(s): Mahara Bldg, 410-2, 4-8-4 Ginza, Chuo-ku, Toyko 104-0061, Japan *Tel:* (03) 3561-2266 *Fax:* (03) 3561-2267 *E-mail:* sales@microboards.co.jp *Web Site:* www.microboards.co.jp
Microboards Technology, 7 Harriott Dr, Heathcote Industrial Estate, Warwick CV34 6TJ, United Kingdom *Tel:* (0845) 230 7800 *Fax:* (0845) 230 7900 *E-mail:* sales@microboards.co.uk *Web Site:* www.microboards.co.uk

Microdolly Hollywood
135 N Victory Blvd, Burbank, CA 91502
Tel: 818-845-8383
E-mail: microdolly@microdolly.com
Web Site: www.microdolly.com
Key Personnel
Owner & CEO: Jerry Johnson
Founded: 1996
Manufacture jibs, dollies, mounts & remote heads.
Catalog(s) available
Membership(s): NAB

MicroImage Video Systems
Division of World Video Sales Co Inc
PO Box 331, Boyertown, PA 19512-0331
Tel: 610-754-6800 *Fax:* 610-754-9766
E-mail: sales@mivs.com
Web Site: www.mivs.com
Key Personnel
Pres: John Taylor *E-mail:* jataylor@mivs.com
Founded: 1970
Catalog(s) available
Shipping Address: 625 Hoffmansville Rd, Bechtelsville, PA 19505

MicrophoneRentals.com
103-1075 Marine Dr, Suite 501, North Vancouver, BC V7P 3T6, Canada
Tel: 604-980-5703
E-mail: info@microphonerentals.com
Web Site: www.microphonerentals.com
Key Personnel
Owner: Larry Hennessey
Founded: 1997
Providing vintage microphones & vintage period electronics to the movie & entertainment industry.

Microsemi
2300 Orchard Pkwy, San Jose, CA 95131-1017
Tel: 408-433-0910; 408-428-7907 (tech support) *Fax:* 408-428-6960
E-mail: info@symmetricom.com
Web Site: www.symmetricom.com
Key Personnel
COO & Pres: James J Peterson
CFO: John Hohener
CTO: Steven Litchfield
Catalog(s) available
Branch Office(s)
3750 Westwind Blvd, Santa Rosa, CA 95403 *Tel:* 707-528-1230 *Fax:* 707-527-6640
4775 Walnut St, Suite 1B, Boulder, CO 80301 *Tel:* 303-939-8481 *Fax:* 303-443-5152
Technology Realization Ctr, 34 Tozer Rd, Beverly, MA 01915 *Tel:* 978-927-8220 *Fax:* 978-927-4099
Foreign Office(s): 6/F Derun Tower, No 3A Yongandongli, Jianwai Ave, Chaoyang District, Beijing 100022, China *Tel:* (010) 6566 7800 *Fax:* (010) 6522 9819
Altlaufstr 42, 85635 Hoehenkirchen-Siegertsbrunn, Germany *Tel:* (08102) 89615 0 *Fax:* (08102) 89615 28

Microspace Communications Corp
Subsidiary of Capitol Broadcasting Co Inc
3100 Highwoods Blvd, Suite 120, Raleigh, NC 27604
Tel: 919-850-4500 *Fax:* 919-850-4518
Web Site: www.microspace.com
Key Personnel
VP: Joseph L Amor, III
Mgr, Video Servs: Bonnie Southard McNay *E-mail:* bmcnay@microspace.com
Live shot studio. Branch offices in Charlotte & Wilmington, NC.
Brochure(s) available

Microtraining LLC
3212 Duke St, Alexandria, VA 22314
Tel: 703-212-8520 *Toll Free Tel:* 888-505-5576 *Fax:* 703-212-8540 *Toll Free Fax:* 888-505-5576
E-mail: marketing@astreetpress.com
Web Site: www.academicvideostore.com/microtraining
Key Personnel
Mng Dir: Elizabeth Robey
Founded: 1974
Multicultural & counseling skills professional training videotapes.
Brochure(s), free, 20 pages

Microtran Manufacturing
Division of Tamura Corporation of America
1040 S Andreasen Dr, Suite 100, Escondido, CA 92029
Tel: 951-699-1270 *Toll Free Tel:* 800-472-6624 *Fax:* 951-676-9482
Web Site: www.tamuracorp.com
Key Personnel
Field Sales Rep: Craig Simpson *Tel:* 951-699-1270 ext 105 *E-mail:* simpsonc@tamuracorp.com
Founded: 1987
Manufacture Microtran power/telecom transformers for PCBs. Also manufacture medical/IT power supplies & battery chargers as well as large transformers, inductors & reactors for the renewable energy industry.
Catalog(s) available
Membership(s): Power Sources Manufacturers Association

Microwave Filter Co Inc
6743 Kinne St, East Syracuse, NY 13057
Tel: 315-438-4700 *Toll Free Tel:* 800-448-1666 *Fax:* 315-463-1467 *Toll Free Fax:* 888-411-8860
E-mail: mfcsales@microwavefilter.com
Web Site: www.microwavefilter.com
Key Personnel
Pres: Carl F Fahrenkrug
Founded: 1967
Passive electronic filter design & manufacture.
Catalog(s) available
Membership(s): NAB; National Satellite Programming Network; SCTE; Wireless Communications Association International

Mid-South Color Labs Inc
496 Emmett St, Jackson, TN 38301
Mailing Address: PO Box 2008, Jackson, TN 38302-2008
Tel: 731-422-6691 *Toll Free Tel:* 800-221-3920 *Fax:* 731-424-1902
E-mail: info@midsouthcolor.com
Web Site: www.midsouthcolor.com
Key Personnel
Pres: Brooks Clayton *E-mail:* bclayton@midsouthcolor.com
Lab Mgr: Greg Frye *E-mail:* gfrye@midsouthcolor.com
Founded: 1957
Photographic & digital imaging.
Catalog(s) available
Membership(s): AIE™; PPA

Midas Consoles North America
Unit of Music Group IP Ltd
5270 Procyon St, Las Vegas, NV 89118
Tel: 702-371-0103 *Toll Free Tel:* 866-929-9074 *Fax:* 702-554-2367 *Toll Free Fax:* 800-955-6831
E-mail: custsuppprofus@music-group.com
Web Site: www.midasconsoles.com
Key Personnel
Cust Support: Michael Hill
Founded: 1970

MidCanada Production Services Inc (MidCan)
509 Century St, Winnipeg, MB R3H 0L8, Canada
Tel: 204-772-0368 *Toll Free Tel:* 800-772-0368 *Fax:* 204-772-0360
E-mail: info@midcan.com
Web Site: www.midcan.com
Key Personnel
CEO & Pres: Wayne Sheldon *Tel:* 204-480-0999 *E-mail:* wayne@midcan.com
Equip Sales: Fred Mislawchuk *E-mail:* fred@midcan.com
Founded: 1977
AV rental & production company. Specialize in film, commercial TV & video production.

Middle Atlantic Products Inc
300 Fairfield Rd, Fairfield, NJ 07004
Tel: 973-839-1011 *Fax:* 973-839-1976
E-mail: info@middleatlantic.com
Web Site: www.middleatlantic.com
Key Personnel
Founder & CEO: Bob Schluter
Founded: 1979
Manufacture equipment rack enclosures & related rack-accessories.
Catalog(s) available
Branch Office(s)
Middle Atlantic Canada Inc, 113 Iber Rd, Ottawa, ON K2S 1E7, Canada *Tel:* 613-836-2501 *Fax:* 613-836-2690 *E-mail:* customerservicecanada@middleatlantic.ca *Web Site:* middleatlantic.ca
Membership(s): AES; BICSI; CEMA; Custom Electronic Design & Installation Association; NAMM, the National Association of Music Merchants; NSCA

Midland Video Productions Inc
126 N Jefferson St, Milwaukee, WI 53202
Tel: 414-276-8300
E-mail: request@midlandvideo.com
Web Site: midlandvideo.com
Key Personnel
Pres: George Liberatore *E-mail:* george@midlandvideo.com
VP: Neil Jaehnert *E-mail:* neil@midlandvideo.com
Founded: 1980
Full service production company.
Catalog(s) available

Midnight Media Group Inc
45 E Willow St, Millburn, NJ 07041-1416
Tel: 973-379-5959
E-mail: info@mmgi.tv
Web Site: www.mmgi.tv
Key Personnel
Partner & Prodr: Dave Emmerling *E-mail:* dave@mmgi.tv
Partner: Robert Camitta; Walter Schoeknecht
Founded: 1981
Production & post-production services for business & TV media.

Midtown Video Inc
4824 SW 74 Ct, Miami, FL 33155
Tel: 305-669-1117 *Toll Free Tel:* 800-232-4564 *Fax:* 305-662-2860
E-mail: info@midtownvideo.com
Web Site: www.midtownvideo.com
Key Personnel
CEO & Pres: Kenneth J Miller *Tel:* 305-669-1117 ext 103 *E-mail:* kmiller@midtownvideo.com
CFO & EVP: Debra Miller *E-mail:* dmiller@midtownvideo.com
CTO: Jesse Miller *E-mail:* jmiller@midtownvideo.com
VP, Opers & Sales Engr: Fernando Iglesias *E-mail:* figlesias@midtownvideo.com
Founded: 1984
Sales, rental & integration of AV systems.
Online catalog(s), sales & rental
Membership(s): AICP; InfoComm International®; Production Equipment Rental Association

Midwest Digital Corp
10150 Virginia Ave, Suite H, Chicago Ridge, IL 60415
Tel: 708-790-4040
E-mail: midwestdig@gmail.com
Web Site: www.midwestdigitalcorp.com
Key Personnel
Founder: Brian J Falatovich *E-mail:* midwestdig@gmail.com
Founded: 1996
Service of broadcast video/audio equipment (Sony, Panasonic, JVC, Grass Valley). Used video equipment sales.

Midwest Photo Exchange
3313 N High St, Columbus, OH 43202
Tel: 614-261-1264 *Toll Free Tel:* 866-940-3686 *Fax:* 614-261-1637
E-mail: mpex@mpex.com; orders@mpex.com
Web Site: mpex.com
Key Personnel
Pres: Moshie Appelbaum *Tel:* 614-827-9824 *E-mail:* moshie@mpex.com
Opers Mgr: Andrew Clark *Tel:* 614-827-9832 *E-mail:* andrew@mpex.com
Sales Mgr: Ken Lewis *Tel:* 614-827-9826 *E-mail:* ken@mpex.com
Sells photo, lighting & video equipment.

Midwest Uplink Inc
911 N East St, Indianapolis, IN 46202
Tel: 317-423-8684 *Toll Free Tel:* 866-886-6247 *Fax:* 317-423-3061
Web Site: midwestuplink.com
Key Personnel
Co-Owner: Paul Mpistolarides *Tel:* 317-714-1095 *E-mail:* paulpistol@aol.com; Tony Williams *Tel:* 317-250-4687 *E-mail:* twilliams003@mac.com
Founded: 2002
Fully integrated supplier of television & broadcast logistics & transmission services. Uplink studios & three satellite trucks.

MIGHTYbYTES Inc
4001 N Ravenswood Ave, Suite 404, Chicago, IL 60613
Tel: 773-561-7529
E-mail: info@mightybytes.com
Web Site: www.mightybytes.com
Key Personnel
Principal: Tim Frick *E-mail:* tim@mightybytes.com
Proj Mgr: James Johnston
Founded: 1998
Full service design & digital media communications firm.

MIJO Thunder North Broadcast Services Ltd, see DG Mijo

Milbrodt/Music & Sound Design
1835 US Hwy 9, Howell, NJ 07731
Tel: 848-459-4965
E-mail: info@ideasinmedia.com
Web Site: www.ideasinmedia.com; www.carmusicproject.com
Key Personnel
Owner: Bill Milbrodt
Picture, music & sound services.

Milestone Film & Video Inc
PO Box 128, Harrington Park, NJ 07640-0128
Tel: 201-767-3117 *Toll Free Tel:* 800-603-1104 *Fax:* 201-767-3035
E-mail: milefilms@gmail.com
Web Site: www.milestonefilms.com
Key Personnel
Owner & Pres: Amy Heller
Owner: Dennis Doros
Founded: 1990
Catalog(s) available

Milgrom Productions
50 Kent Rd, Glen Rock, NJ 07452
Tel: 201-444-8838
E-mail: info@milgromproductions.com
Web Site: milgrom.adcstudio.com

Milky Way Press
317 Ridge Run Dr, Georgetown, TX 78628
Mailing Address: PO Box 1047, Georgetown, TX 78627
Tel: 512-869-6455 *Toll Free Tel:* 888-756-6455 (orders only)
Web Site: www.milkywaypress.com
Key Personnel
Owner: Beverly Morgan *E-mail:* bev@bmorgan.com
Publisher of audiobooks on breastfeeding.
Catalog(s), audiobooks on CD & tape priced between $15 & $30

Millennia Media FPC
4600 Missouri Flat Rd, Suite 11, Placerville, CA 95667
Tel: 530-647-0750 *Fax:* 530-647-9921
E-mail: sales@mil-media.com
Web Site: www.mil-media.com
Key Personnel
Mng Dir: Joel Silverman
Catalog(s) available
Membership(s): AES; IEEE; NAMM, the National Association of Music Merchants; The Recording Academy

Millennium Entertainment LLC
5900 Wilshire Blvd, 18th fl, Los Angeles, CA 90036
Tel: 310-893-6289
E-mail: info@millenniumentertainment.me
Web Site: www.millenniumentertainment.me
Key Personnel
EVP, Mktg: Brooke Ford
Founded: 2010
Film distribution.
Catalog(s) available
Membership(s): Independent Film & Television Alliance®

Miller Camera Support LLC
216 Little Falls Rd, Unit 15 & 16, Cedar Grove, NJ 07009-1276
Tel: 973-857-8300 *Fax:* 973-857-8188
E-mail: service@millertripods.us
Web Site: www.millertripods.com
Key Personnel
Sales Mgr: Gus Harilaou *E-mail:* gus@millertripods.us
Founded: 1954
Design professional fluid heads & tripods.
Catalog(s) available
Foreign Office(s): Miller Camera Support Equipment, 30 Hotham Parade, Artarmon, NSW 2064, Australia *Tel:* (02) 9439 6377 *Fax:* (02) 9438 2819 *E-mail:* daniel.sissons@miller.com.au
Miller Fluid Heads Europe, Shepperton Business Park, Unit 2A, Govett Ave, Shepperton, Middx, United Kingdom *Tel:* (01932) 222 888 *Fax:* (01932) 222 211 *E-mail:* sales@millertripods-europe.com
Membership(s): NAB; SMPTE

Earl Miller Productions Inc
1702 W Koenig Lane, Austin, TX 78756
Tel: 512-458-4343 *Fax:* 512-458-4485
E-mail: info@earlmillerproductions.com
Web Site: www.earlmillerproductions.com
Key Personnel
Gen Mgr: Mike Miller
Founded: 1975
Full service production company.

The Miller Group, Multiplex Division
1610 Design Way, Dupo, IL 62239-1820
Tel: 636-343-5700 *Toll Free Tel:* 800-325-3350 *Fax:* 618-286-6202
E-mail: info@miller-group.com
Web Site: www.multiplexdisplays.com
Key Personnel
Pres: Randy Castle *Tel:* 636-343-4648 ext 3308 *E-mail:* randycastle@miller-group.com
VP, Sales & Mktg: Kathy L Webster *Tel:* 636-343-4648 ext 3331 *E-mail:* kathywebster@miller-group.com
Founded: 1903
Manufacture display equipment for photographers-swinging bulletin boards & accessories, display panels-portable systems-counter & floor.
Catalog(s) available
Membership(s): Education Market Association

Robin Miller, Filmaker Inc
606 W Broad St, Bethlehem, PA 18018
Tel: 610-691-0900 *Fax:* 610-691-0952
E-mail: enquire@filmaker.com
Web Site: www.filmaker.com
Key Personnel
Pres: Robin Miller
Founded: 1970
Film company.
Membership(s): AES; SMPTE

Barney Miller's Inc
232 E Main St, Lexington, KY 40507-1310
Tel: 859-252-2216 *Toll Free Tel:* 800-755-6799 *Fax:* 859-253-1115
Web Site: www.barneymillers.com
Key Personnel
Pres: Barney Miller *E-mail:* bmiller@barneymillers.com
Founded: 1922
Home entertainment systems.

Mills James Productions
3545 Fishinger Blvd, Columbus, OH 43026-9489
Tel: 614-777-9933 *Toll Free Tel:* 800-860-8436 *Fax:* 614-777-9943
E-mail: info@mjp.com
Web Site: www.millsjames.com
Key Personnel
VP, Mktg: Scott Rankin *E-mail:* srankin@mjp.com
Sales: Cameron James *E-mail:* cjames@mjp.com
Founded: 1984
Full service production company.
Catalog(s) available
Branch Office(s)
Mills James Experience Group (MJx), 2250 Westbelt Dr, Columbus, OH 43228 *Tel:* 614-777-9933 *Fax:* 614-527-2735
Mills James Cincinnati, 602 Main St, Suite 310, Cincinnati, OH 45202 *Tel:* 513-407-5593 *Fax:* 404-334-5252
Mills James Cleveland, 1220 W Sixth St, Suite 407, Cleveland, OH 44113 *Tel:* 216-443-0468
Membership(s): International Special Events Society; MCA-I; Meeting Planners International

Milner-Fenwick Inc
119 Lakefront Dr, Hunt Valley, MD 21030-2216
Tel: 410-252-1700 *Toll Free Tel:* 800-432-8433 *Fax:* 410-252-6316
E-mail: mail@milner-fenwick.com
Web Site: www.milner-fenwick.com
Key Personnel
CEO: Richard Milner
Pres: David Milner *Tel:* 410-252-1700 ext 266
VP: Michael Quitt
VP, Sales: John Pollara
Catalog(s) available
Membership(s): HeSCA; MCA-I

Mimi Productions
329 W 18 St, Suite 405, Chicago, IL 60616
Tel: 312-829-0162
E-mail: info@mimiproductions.com
Web Site: www.mimiproductions.com
Key Personnel
CEO & Pres: Michelle De Long
Founded: 1997
Television & video production company, including corporate, marketing & viral videos.
Membership(s): International Documentary Association; Women in Film

Mind Over Eye Inc
2221 Rosecrans Ave, Suite 195, El Segundo, CA 90245
Tel: 310-396-4663 *Fax:* 310-297-9526
E-mail: info@mindovereye.com
Web Site: www.mindovereye.com
Key Personnel
CEO: Jack Wignot
Founder, SVP, Exec Creative Dir: Bill Wadsworth
Exec Prodr: Andy Dellenbach *E-mail:* andy@mindovereye.com
VP, Exec Prodr: David Wein
Founded: 2002

Mind Resources Inc
130 Shoemaker St, Unit 1, Kitchener, ON N2E 3G4, Canada
Tel: 519-895-0330 *Toll Free Tel:* 877-414-6463 *Fax:* 519-895-0331 *Toll Free Fax:* 877-585-2992
E-mail: sales@mindresources.com
Web Site: www.mindresources.com
Key Personnel
Pres: Barry Kahl
Founded: 1976

MindPlay
Division of Methods & Solutions Inc
4400 E Broadway Blvd, Suite 400, Tucson, AZ 85711
Tel: 520-888-1800 *Toll Free Tel:* 800-221-7911
E-mail: mail@mindplay.com
Web Site: www.mindplay.com
Key Personnel
CEO: Judith Bliss *Tel:* 520-888-1800 ext 104 *E-mail:* judith@mindplay.com
Founded: 1986
Distribute & produce AV interactive programs focused on literacy.
Catalog(s) available

Saul Mineroff Electronics Inc
574 Meacham Ave, Elmont, NY 11003
Tel: 516-775-1370 *Fax:* 516-775-1371
E-mail: tapenixon@aol.com
Web Site: www.mineroff.com

Key Personnel
Owner & Pres: Saul Mineroff
Founded: 1970
Catalog(s) available

Miranda Technologies
3499 Douglas-B Floreani, Montreal, QC H4S 2C6, Canada
Tel: 514-333-1772 *Toll Free Tel:* 800-224-7882 *Fax:* 514-333-9828
E-mail: salesamericas@miranda.com
Web Site: www.miranda.com; www.belden.com
Key Personnel
Inside Sales Mgr: Sean Murphy *Tel:* 514-333-2126 *E-mail:* sean.murphy@miranda.com
Hardware & software solutions for the television broadcast, cable, satellite & IPTV industry.
Catalog(s) available
Branch Office(s)
125 Crown Point Ct, Grass Valley, CA 95945 *Tel:* 530-265-1000 *Fax:* 530-265-1010
1536 Cole Blvd, Suite 165, Lakewood, CO 80401 *Tel:* 303-237-4868 *Fax:* 303-237-4847
324 Clark St, Worcester, MA 01606 *Tel:* 508-754-4858 *Fax:* 508-752-1520
Foreign Office(s): Rm 15A-O4, Tower 2, North Star New Era, Jira 13 Region, Beiyuanlu, Chaoyang District, Beijing 100107, China *Tel:* (010) 8492 0909; (010) 8493 1010 *Fax:* (010) 8492 8587 *E-mail:* chinasales@miranda.com
Miranda France SAS, 216 Rue De Rosny, 93100 Montreuil, France, Contact: Richard Couzon *Tel:* 01 55 86 87 88 *Fax:* 01 55 86 00 29
Citicorp Ctr, Unit 3602, 18 Whitfield Rd, Causeway Bay, Hong Kong *Tel:* 2539 6987 *Fax:* 2539 0804 *E-mail:* asiasales@miranda.com
Hamacho House, 2-13-9 Nihonbashi Hamacho, Chuo-ku, Tokyo 103-0007, Japan *Tel:* (03) 5644-7533 *Fax:* (03) 3662-7555 *E-mail:* japansales@miranda.com
Level 20 Menara Standard Chartered, 30 Jalan Sultan Ismail, 50250 Kuala Lumpur, Malaysia *Tel:* (03) 2117 5140 *Fax:* (03) 2117 5151 *E-mail:* asiasales@miranda.com
Arena Business Park, Olympia 1 a/b, 1213 NS Hilversum, Netherlands, Contact: Nick Ashley *Tel:* (035) 646 26 68
Unit 01-02 HB Centre 1, 12 Tannery Rd, Singapore 347722, Singapore *Tel:* 6844 2112 *E-mail:* asiasales@miranda.com
Business Central Towers, Office No 903-B, Dubai Media City, Dubai, United Arab Emirates, Contact: Hany Bartella *Tel:* (04) 3754292 *Fax:* (04) 4230863
Miranda Playout Automation, UK, Pembroke House 1st fl, Pegasus Business Park, Castle Donington, Derby DE74 2HN, United Kingdom *Tel:* (01332) 411 300 *Fax:* (01332) 411 353 *E-mail:* europesales@miranda.com
Miranda Subtitling & Captioning, UK, Horseshoe Park, Pangbourne, Berks R68 7JW, United Kingdom *Tel:* (0118) 984 2151 *E-mail:* europesales@miranda.com
Abbey Gate, 57-75 Kings Rd, Reading, Berks RG1 3AB, United Kingdom, Contact: Micky Edwards *Tel:* (0118) 952 3400 *Fax:* (0118) 952 3401 *E-mail:* europesales@miranda.com

Miranda Telecast Fiber Systems Inc
102 Grove St, Worcester, MA 01605
Tel: 508-754-4858 *Fax:* 508-752-1520
E-mail: telecast.sales@belden.com
Web Site: www.miranda.com; www.belden.com
Key Personnel
VP & Gen Mgr: Steve DeFrancesco *E-mail:* steve.defrancesco@belden.com
Spec Proj Mgr, Belden: John Valentine *E-mail:* john.valentine@belden.com
Founded: 1991
Fiber optics for broadcast.
Catalog(s) available
Membership(s): IABM; NAB; NSCA

MIS Technologies
555-B NW Blue Pkwy, Lees Summit, MO 64063
Tel: 816-966-4529 *Fax:* 816-966-2915
Web Site: www.mistechnologies.com
Key Personnel
Partner: Mike Church *E-mail:* mchurch@mistechnologies.com; Brent Marriott *E-mail:* bmarriott@mistechnologies.com
Mktg: Coty Beasley *E-mail:* cbeasley@mistechnologies.com
Founded: 2000
AV systems integrator for business, government, education & religious organizations.
Membership(s): NSCA

MISCO
2637 32 Ave S, Minneapolis, MN 55406-1641
Tel: 612-825-1010 *Toll Free Tel:* 800-276-9955 *Fax:* 612-825-7010
E-mail: info@miscospeakers.com
Web Site: www.miscospeakers.com
Key Personnel
Owner: Dan Digre
Opers Mgr: Dave Wilson
Founded: 1949
Catalog(s) available

Mist Media Inc
10845 Acama St, Toluca Lake, CA 91602
Mailing Address: 827 N Hollywood Way, Suite 208, Burbank, CA 91505
Tel: 818-508-1097 *Fax:* 818-508-1097
E-mail: mistmedia@sbcglobal.net
Web Site: www.mistmedia.tv
Key Personnel
Pres: William Mistretta
VP: Mary Lee Mistretta
Founded: 1988
Video production & post-production.

Mr Mark's Used Musical, Stereo & Studio Equipment Store
109 Grizzard Ave, Nashville, TN 37207-4413
Tel: 615-242-2907
E-mail: mrmarksmusic@aol.com
Key Personnel
Owner: Mark Stephan Hughes
Founded: 1980
Recording & production studio for audio. World's largest trader of used & vintage musical, stereo & recording equipment parts & manuals. Also, country music collectables, CDs, cassettes, posters & other paper products.
Catalog(s) available

Mitchell Acoustics Research
2005B Industrial Blvd, Rockwall, TX 75087
Tel: 214-741-7136 *Toll Free Fax:* 866-492-2470
E-mail: info@frazierspeakers.com
Web Site: www.frazierspeakers.com
Key Personnel
Pres: J E Mitchell
Speaker manufacturing.
Catalog(s) available
Membership(s): AES; NSCA

Mitsubishi Electric Visual Solutions America Inc (MEVSA)
10833 Valley View St, Suite 300, Cypress, CA 90630
Toll Free Tel: 800-332-2119
E-mail: tvsupport@mevsa.com
Web Site: www.mitsubishi-tv.com
Key Personnel
Brand Mgr: Erik Walton
Catalog(s), annual

MKE Production Rental
710 N Plankinton Ave, Suite 300, Milwaukee, WI 53213
Tel: 414-939-3653
E-mail: rent1@mkeproductionrental.com
Web Site: www.mkeproductionrental.com
Key Personnel
Owner: Jon Kline
Founded: 2013
Cameras, lighting & grip rental for photo & video production & events in Milwaukee.

MMI Corp
2950 Wyman Pkwy, Baltimore, MD 21211-2802
Mailing Address: PO Box 19907, Baltimore, MD 21211-0907
Tel: 410-366-1222 *Fax:* 410-366-6311
E-mail: mail@mmicorporation.com
Web Site: www.mmicorporation.com
Key Personnel
Pres: Ralph C Levy
VP: L J Levy
Prodr, Art Dir & Prodn Mgr: Jason Rosenberg
Founded: 1973
AV planetarium (portable & permanent) observatory domes, AV astronomy & earth science.
Catalog(s) available
Membership(s): International Planetarium Society

Mobile Arts Production Services, see MAPS Production House

Mobile-Video Productions Inc
7315 Wisconsin Ave, Suite 1300 W, Bethesda, MD 20814
Tel: 301-656-2525 *Fax:* 301-656-4343
E-mail: mobilevp@verizon.net
Web Site: www.mobilevideoproductions.tv
Key Personnel
Pres: Stephen King
Founded: 1977
Video production services.

Mobilized Tech Systems
4015 Blackthorn Dr, Vacaville, CA 95688
Tel: 707-602-5548 *Toll Free Tel:* 888-293-0869 *Fax:* 707-602-5549
E-mail: info@bigfootmobilecarts.com
Web Site: www.bigfootmobilecarts.com
Key Personnel
Pres: Doug Solis *E-mail:* doug@bigfootmobilecarts.com
Creative Servs Coord: Amber Solis *E-mail:* amber@bigfootmobilecarts.com
AV equipment sales.

Modern Communications Inc
1231 Horan Dr, Fenton, MO 63026
Tel: 636-343-0800 *Toll Free Tel:* 800-428-2442 *Fax:* 636-343-0906
Web Site: www.modcomm.com
Key Personnel
VP, Broadcast & Prof Video Sales: Bill Johnson *E-mail:* bjohnson@modcomm.com
Founded: 1978
Video & audio systems dealer.
Membership(s): MCA-I

Modernage Photographic Services Inc
Division of Modernage
555 Eighth Ave, New York, NY 10018
Tel: 212-997-1800 *Toll Free Tel:* 800-997-2510 *Fax:* 212-869-4796
E-mail: info@modernage.com
Web Site: www.modernage.com
Key Personnel
Pres: Kenneth Troiano *E-mail:* ktroiano@modernage.com
Direct digital printing in color & on fiber base B&W paper, color & B&W ink-jet printing & large murals on paper or vinyl. Digital imaging, retouching, film output & giclee printing.

Catalog(s) available
Membership(s): AIE™; ASMP; DIMA; NYPP; Photo Marketing Association

modprop.com
1044 Madison Ave, New York, NY 10021
Tel: 212-628-7582
E-mail: info@modprop.com
Web Site: www.modprop.com
Key Personnel
CEO & Pres: Stephen Wallis
Founded: 2001
Online modern furniture prop rental company.

Modulation Sciences Inc
14 Worlds Fair Dr, Suite K, Somerset, NJ 08873
Tel: 732-302-3090 *Toll Free Tel:* 800-826-2603 *Fax:* 732-302-0206
E-mail: info@modsci.com; sales@modsci.com
Web Site: www.modsci.com
Key Personnel
CEO: Eric Small
Pres: Hallie Swerdlin
Founded: 1981
CD-ROM catalog(s), free
Membership(s): NAB

Moe AV LLC
133 Deerfield Rd, Sayreville, NJ 08872-1618
Tel: 732-257-3760
Web Site: www.moeco.net
Key Personnel
Owner & Pres: Michael "Moe" Mosakowski *E-mail:* mike@moeco.net
Founded: 1981
Sound systems, AV, corporate meetings, consulting.
Membership(s): Synergetic Audio Concepts

Mohawk
Division of Belden Networking Inc
324 Clark St, Worcester, MA 01606
Tel: 978-537-9961 *Toll Free Tel:* 800-422-9961 *Fax:* 978-537-4358
E-mail: info@mohawk-cable.com
Web Site: www.mohawk-cable.com
Key Personnel
Inside Sales Mgr: Brenda LeBlanc
Founded: 1952
Catalog(s) available
Membership(s): NAB

Mole-Richardson Co
937 N Sycamore Ave, Hollywood, CA 90038-2384
Tel: 323-851-0111 *Fax:* 323-851-5593
E-mail: info@mole.com
Web Site: www.mole.com
Key Personnel
CEO: Michael Parker
VP, Sales: Glenn Weiner
VP, Admin Opers: Andrea Setterstrom
Founded: 1927
Catalog(s) available
Membership(s): American Cinematographers Society; Canadian Society of Cinematographers; NAB; SMPTE; University Film & Video Association

Monaco Digital Films Labs
234 Ninth St, San Francisco, CA 94103
Tel: 415-864-5350 *Fax:* 415-864-5682
E-mail: admin@monacosf.com
Key Personnel
Mng Dir: Rob Monaco *E-mail:* rob@monacosf.com
Catalog(s) available

Monaco LLC
145 Grassy Plain St, Bethel, CT 06801-2806
Mailing Address: PO Box 40, Bethel, CT 06801-0040
Tel: 203-744-3398 *Toll Free Tel:* 800-448-4877 *Fax:* 203-744-3228
E-mail: monaco@hangupbags.com
Web Site: www.hangupbags.com
Key Personnel
Pres: Ed Rabin
Manufacture & distribute storage systems, filing bags & hang-up storage bags & pharmacy bags.
Catalog(s), annual, free

Monad Trainer's Aide Inc
163-60 22 Ave, Whitestone, NY 11357
Tel: 718-352-2314 *Toll Free Tel:* 800-344-6088 *Fax:* 718-352-8276
Web Site: www.monadtrainersaide.com
Key Personnel
CEO & VP: Eugene Richman *E-mail:* gene@monadtrainersaide.com
Pres: Carol Richman *E-mail:* carol@monadtrainersaide.com
Founded: 1973
Distribute all formats & DVD & E-Learning programs for all organizations.
Catalog(s) available
Online catalog(s) available

Monadnock Media Inc
112 Amherst Rd, Sunderland, MA 01375
Mailing Address: PO Box 429, Sunderland, MA 01375-0429
Tel: 413-665-1390 *Fax:* 413-665-1394
E-mail: info@monadnock.org
Web Site: www.monadnock.org
Key Personnel
Exec Dir: Dr Steven H Bressler *E-mail:* steve@monadnock.org
Opers Mgr: Susan Fuller *E-mail:* sue@monadnock.org
Sr Prodr: Claudia Levin *E-mail:* claudia@monadnock.org; Tracy Litwin *E-mail:* tracy@monadnock.org
Founded: 1980
AV experiences for the museum environment.

Monarch Instrument
Division of Monarch International Inc
15 Columbia Dr, Amherst, NH 03031-2305
Tel: 603-883-3390 *Toll Free Tel:* 800-999-3390 *Fax:* 603-886-3300
E-mail: sales@monarchinstrument.com
Web Site: www.monarchinstrument.com
Key Personnel
CEO & Pres: Kenneth Grabeau
Sales & Mktg Mgr: Timothy French
Founded: 1982
Manufacture tachometers, vibration meters, stroboscopes, paperless recorders, data acquisition systems & other meters, as well as diagnostic inspection.
Catalog(s) available

Monotype Inc
500 Unicorn Park Dr, Woburn, MA 01801
Tel: 781-970-6000 *Toll Free Tel:* 800-424-8973 *Fax:* 781-970-6001; 781-970-6002 (gen questions)
Web Site: www.monotype.com
Key Personnel
CEO & Pres: Douglas J Shaw
EVP: John L Seguin
CFO, Treas & SVP: Scott E Landers
Catalog(s) available
Branch Office(s)
1875 S Grant St, Suite 720, San Mateo, CA 94402
4909 Nautilus Ct N, Suite 221, Boulder, CO 80301
25 Northwest Point Blvd, Suite 525, Elk Grove Village, IL 60007 *Tel:* 847-718-0400 *Fax:* 847-718-0500
28 W 44 St, Suite 318, New York, NY 10036 *Tel:* 212-389-6255
Foreign Office(s): Monotype GmbH, Werner-Reimers-Str 2-4, 61352 Bad Homburg, Germany *Tel:* (06172) 484-423 *Fax:* (06172) 484-429
Monotype Hong Kong Ltd, 7A Yardley Commercial Bldg, 3 Connaught Rd W, Sheung Wan, Hong Kong *Tel:* 2575 6789 *Fax:* 2591 9232
Monotype Solutions India Pvt Ltd, Tower B, 4th fl, GYS Universal Plot A-3, 4 & 5, Sector-125, Noida, Uttar Pradesh 201 301, India *Tel:* 4524974
Monotype KK, MG Ichigaya Bldg, 5th fl, 1-9 Gobancho, Chiyoda-ku, Tokyo 102-0076, Japan *Tel:* (03) 5275-6251 *Fax:* (03) 5275-6252
Monotype Korea, No 805, 642-6 Seongji Heights 3-Cha Bldg, Yeoksam-dong, Gangnam-gu, Seoul 135-717, South Korea *Tel:* (02) 2051-9900 *Fax:* (02) 6919-2044
Monotype Ltd, Perrywood Busn Park, Unit 2, Salfords, Redhill, Salfords, Redhill, Surrey RH1 5DZ, United Kingdom *Tel:* (01737) 765959 *Toll Free Tel:* 800 371242 *Fax:* (01737) 769243; 0800 220692
Membership(s): ABCD; MicroComputer Industry Association

Monroe Electronics Inc
100 Housel Ave, Lyndonville, NY 14098
Mailing Address: PO Box 535, Lyndonville, NY 14098
Tel: 585-765-2254 *Fax:* 585-765-9330
Web Site: www.monroe-electronics.com
Key Personnel
COO: Jim Heminway *E-mail:* jfheminway@monroe-electronics.com
Pres: William E Vosteen
Founded: 1954
Catalog(s) available

Monster Cable Products Inc
455 Valley Dr, Brisbane, CA 94005-1209
Tel: 415-840-2000 *Fax:* 415-468-0311
Web Site: www.monstercable.com
Key Personnel
Owner: Noel Lee
Founded: 1979
Manufacture high performance cables that connect AV components for home, car & professional use as well as computers & computer games.
Catalog(s) available
Membership(s): AES; AHFA; Custom Electronic Design & Installation Association; Music Business Association; NAMM, the National Association of Music Merchants

Monster Tracks
Division of Baker Sound Studios Inc
1821 Ranstead St, Philadelphia, PA 19103
Tel: 215-567-0400 *Toll Free Tel:* 800-369-1280 *Fax:* 215-567-0350
Web Site: www.monstertracks.com
Key Personnel
Music Dir: Chuck Butler *E-mail:* chuck@monstertracks.com
Gen Mgr: Ellen Kancher
Founded: 1987
Original music production for film, television, advertising & corporate.

monterey media inc
566 Saint Charles Dr, Thousand Oaks, CA 91360-3953
Tel: 805-494-7199 *Toll Free Tel:* 800-424-2593 *Fax:* 805-496-6061
E-mail: customerservice@montereymedia.com; publicity@montereymedia.com

Web Site: www.montereymedia.com
Key Personnel
CEO & Mng Partner: Scott Mansfield
CFO & Mng Partner: Jere Rae-Mansfield
Dir, Cust Serv & Vendor Rel: Sandy Brown
Publicity Dir: Jennifer Manocchio
Mktg Mgr: Darrell Rae
E-mail: marketingmanager@montereymedia.com
Founded: 1979
Membership(s): American Publishers Association; Coalition for Quality Children's Media; Entertainment Merchants Association; VIAAC

monterey video
Division of monterey media inc
566 Saint Charles Dr, Thousand Oaks, CA 91360-3953
Tel: 805-494-7199 *Toll Free Tel:* 800-424-2593 *Fax:* 805-496-6061
E-mail: customerservice@montereymedia.com; publicity@montereymedia.com
Web Site: www.montereymedia.com
Key Personnel
CEO & Mng Partner: Scott Mansfield
CFO & Mng Partner: Jere Rae-Mansfield
Dir, Cust Serv & Vendor Rel: Sandy Brown
Publicity Dir: Jennifer Manocchio
Mktg Mgr: Darrell Rae
E-mail: marketingmanager@montereymedia.com
Online catalog(s) available
Membership(s): American Publishers Association; Entertainment Merchants Association; VIAAC

Mood Creations Ltd
One Depot Plaza, Ossining, NY 10562
Tel: 914-941-2357 *Fax:* 914-941-3142
E-mail: moodcreations@optonline.net
Web Site: www.moodcreations.com
Key Personnel
Pres: Donald Cohen
Prodr & Prodn Mgr: Scott Cohen

Moodtapes, see Ron Roy Productions/Moodtapes

Moog Music Inc
160 Broadway St, Asheville, NC 28801
Tel: 828-251-0090 *Toll Free Tel:* 800-948-1990 *Fax:* 828-254-6233
E-mail: info@moogmusic.com
Web Site: www.moogmusic.com
Key Personnel
Pres: Mike Adams
Opers Mgr: Dean Cavanaugh
Prod Mktg Mgr: Trent Thompson
Sales: Linda Lafferty
Founded: 1953
Manufacture & distribute electronic musical instruments.
Catalog(s) available
Membership(s): MMA; NAMM, the National Association of Music Merchants

Moore Creative Talent Inc
3130 Excelsior Blvd, Minneapolis, MN 55416
Tel: 612-827-3823
Web Site: www.mooretalent.com
Key Personnel
Pres: Andrea M Hjelm
Founded: 1958

MooreCo Inc
2885 Lorraine Ave, Temple, TX 76501
Tel: 254-778-4727 (CN) *Toll Free Tel:* 800-749-2258 (US) *Fax:* 254-773-0500 (CN) *Toll Free Fax:* 800-697-6258 (US)
Web Site: moorecoinc.com
Key Personnel
CEO: Greg Moore
COO & Pres: Mike Briggs
Visual communication products/manufacturer.
Membership(s): Education Market Association; InfoComm International®

Moose School Productions
Box 960, Topanga, CA 90290-0960
Tel: 310-455-2318 *Toll Free Tel:* 800-676-5480 *Fax:* 310-455-4192
Web Site: www.peteralsop.com
Key Personnel
CEO: Peter Alsop *E-mail:* peter@peteralsop.com
Founded: 1975
Educational materials on child abuse prevention, chemical abuse & co-dependency, loss & grief for children & families. Video production services.
Online catalog(s) available
Shipping Address: 21418 Entrada, Topanga, CA 90290
Membership(s): American Federation of Musicians

Morefield Communications Inc
35 N 35 St, Camp Hill, PA 17011-2707
Tel: 717-761-6170 *Toll Free Tel:* 800-382-1266
E-mail: info@morefield.com
Web Site: www.morefield.com
Key Personnel
Pres: John D Morefield
EVP: Michael E Whiteman
VP: Wesley W Kelly; Nicholas F Spallone
Founded: 1945
Branch Office(s)
801 S Kettle St, Altoona, PA 16602-5521 *Tel:* 814-944-3344
Membership(s): NSCA

Morehouse Publishing
Division of Church Publishing Inc
4775 Linglestown Rd, Harrisburg, PA 17112
Tel: 212-592-1800 (intl) *Toll Free Tel:* 800-242-1918 *Fax:* 717-541-8136
E-mail: churchpublishing@cpg.org
Web Site: www.morehousepublishing.com; churchpublishing.org
Key Personnel
SVP & Publr: David Perkins *E-mail:* dperkins@cpg.org
VP, Prodn: Lorraine Simonello *E-mail:* lsimonello@cpg.org
Founded: 1884
Catalog(s) available

Morning Music Ltd
5200 Dixie Rd, Suite 203, Mississauga, ON L4W 1E4, Canada
Tel: 905-625-2676 *Fax:* 905-625-2092
E-mail: info@morningmusic.ca
Web Site: www.morningmusic.ca
Key Personnel
Pres: Mark Altman *E-mail:* mark@morningmusic.ca
Founded: 1971
Catalog(s) available
Membership(s): ASCAP; National Music Publishers' Association; The Society of Composers, Authors and Music Publishers of Canada

MorphoTrust USA
296 Concord Rd, Billerica, MA 01821
Tel: 978-215-2400 *Fax:* 978-215-2500
Web Site: www.morphotrust.com
Key Personnel
CEO: Robert Eckel
Founded: 2011
Branch Office(s)
5705 W Old Shakopee Rd, Suite 100, Bloomington, MN 55437 *Tel:* 952-932-0888 *Toll Free Tel:* 800-932-0890 *Fax:* 952-932-7181

Rex Morris Productions
5521 S Firethorn Place, Boise, ID 83716
Tel: 208-344-9878 *Fax:* 208-344-9878
Web Site: rexmorrisproductions.com
Key Personnel
Owner & Pres: Rex Morris *Tel:* 208-866-2143 (cell) *E-mail:* rex142@juno.com
Founded: 1981

Morrisound Recording
12111 N 56 St, Tampa, FL 33617
Tel: 813-989-2108 *Fax:* 813-980-6950
E-mail: info@morrisound.com
Web Site: morrisound.com
Key Personnel
Pres: Tom Morris *E-mail:* tom@morrisound.com
Studio Mgr: Lindsay Vitola *E-mail:* lindsay@morrisound.com
Founded: 1981
Digital sound recording.

Jack Morton Worldwide
Member of The Interpublic Group of Companies Inc
909 Third Ave, New York, NY 10022
Tel: 212-401-7000
E-mail: experience@jackmorton.com
Web Site: www.jackmorton.com
Key Personnel
Chmn & CEO: Josh McCall
COO & CFO: Bill Davies
Pres, NY: Tara Back *E-mail:* tara_back@jackmorton.com
Founded: 1939
Catalog(s) available
Branch Office(s)
600 Battery St, 2nd fl, San Francisco, CA 94111, Contact: Edward Scott *Tel:* 415-318-4300 *E-mail:* edward_scott@jackmorton.com
8687 Melrose Ave, Suite G700, West Hollywood, CA 90069, Contact: Edward Scott *Tel:* 310-967-2400 *E-mail:* edward_scott@jackmorton.com
800 Connecticut Ave, Norwalk, CT 06854, Contact: Paula DeFeo *Tel:* 203-851-7800 *E-mail:* paula_defeo@jackmorton.com
875 N Michigan Ave, 27th fl, Chicago, IL 60611, Contact: Matt Pensinger *Tel:* 312-274-6060 *E-mail:* matt_pensinger@jackmorton.com
142 Berkeley St, Boston, MA 02116, Contact: Steve Mooney *Tel:* 617-585-7000 *E-mail:* steve_mooney@jackmorton.com
One Woodward Ave, Detroit, MI 48226, Contact: Brian Patterson *Tel:* 313-596-9100 *E-mail:* brian_patterson@jackmorton.com
Jack Morton Exhibits, 10 Applegate Dr, Robbinsville, NJ 08691, Contact: Cyndi Davis *Tel:* 609-259-0500 *E-mail:* cyndi_davis@jackmorton.com (exhibits)
Foreign Office(s): 520 Burke St, Level 4, Melbourne, Victoria 3000, Australia, Contact: Helen Graney *Tel:* (03) 8644 2100 *E-mail:* helen.graney@jackmorton.com.au
Royal Naval House, 32 Grosvenor St, The Rocks, Sydney, NSW 2000, Australia, Contact: Helen Graney *Tel:* (02) 8231 4500 *E-mail:* helen.graney@jackmorton.com.au
China Life Tower, 17-F, 16 Chao Wai Ave, Beijing 100020, China, Contact: Sheila Shen *Tel:* (010) 8569 9700 *E-mail:* sheila_shen@jackmorton.com.cn
16/F Huai Hai Plaza, 1045 Huaihai Zhong Rd, Shanghai 20031, China, Contact: Adam Charles *Tel:* 2411 0157 *E-mail:* adam_charles@jackmorton.com
Rochusstr 47, 40479 Dusseldorf, Germany, Mng Dir: Jens Oliver Mayer *Tel:* (0211) 49554 501 *E-mail:* jens.mayer@jackmorton.com
10/F Oxford House, TaiKoo Place, Quarry Bay, Hong Kong, Contact: Ben Taylor *Tel:* 2805 1767 *E-mail:* ben_taylor@jackmorton.com
MacDonald House, No 07-01, 40-A Orchard Rd, Singapore 238838, Singapore, Con-

tact: Charles Robinson *Tel:* 6499 8800
E-mail: charles_robinson@jackmorton.com.sg
Bayswater Tower, Off 2201-2202, St 2, Dubai, United Arab Emirates, Contact: Alex Apthorpe *Tel:* (04) 431-2389 *E-mail:* alex_apthorpe@jackmorton.com
16-18 Acton Park Estate, London W3 7QE, United Kingdom, Contact: Julian Pullan *Tel:* (020) 8735 2000 *E-mail:* julian_pullan@jackmorton.co.uk

Mosby Inc
Division of Elsevier, Health Sciences Division
3251 Riverport Lane, Maryland Heights, MO 63043
Tel: 314-872-8370 *Toll Free Tel:* 800-325-4177 *Fax:* 314-432-1380
Web Site: www.us.elsevierhealth.com
Founded: 1906
Catalog(s) available

Mother Basilea Films
Affiliate of Evangelical Sisterhood of Mary
9849 N 40 St, Phoenix, AZ 85028-4099
Tel: 602-996-4040 *Fax:* 602-953-1303
E-mail: cid@integrity.com
Web Site: www.canaaninthedesert.com
Catalog(s) available

Mother West
37 W 20 St, Suite 1006, New York, NY 10011
Tel: 212-807-0405
E-mail: info@motherwest.com
Web Site: www.motherwest.com
Key Personnel
Prodr: Charles Newman *E-mail:* charles@motherwest.com
Head Engr: Rob Stevens *E-mail:* rob@motherwest.com
Founded: 1990

Motion & Graphic Image Corp Inc (MAGIC)
1106 Dauphin St, Mobile, AL 36604
Tel: 251-433-7733
E-mail: magicians@magichd.com
Web Site: magichd.com
Key Personnel
Pres: Chris Meztista
Founded: 1989
HD acquisition & post-production.

Motion Image Group LLC
Subsidiary of Accord Productions
2140 S Dixie Hwy, Suite 301, Coconut Grove, FL 33133
Tel: 305-859-2000 *Fax:* 305-859-2412
Founded: 1988
Video, new media, audio production & graphics.

Motion Picture Enterprises Inc
432 W 45 St, New York, NY 10036
Mailing Address: PO Box 276, Tarrytown, NY 10591-0276
Tel: 212-245-0969 *Toll Free Tel:* 800-673-3348 *Fax:* 212-245-0974
E-mail: sales@mpenyc.com
Web Site: www.mpenyc.com
Founded: 1948
Supplier of post production rental equipment & film supplies.
Publisher of the *Motion Picture TV & Theatre Directory* .
Catalog(s) available
Branch Office(s)
11222 Satellite Blvd, Orlando, FL 32837 *Tel:* 407-704-7859

Motion Picture Licensing Corp (MPLC)
5455 Centinela Ave, Los Angeles, CA 90066
Tel: 310-822-8855 (intl calls) *Toll Free Tel:* 800-462-8855 *Fax:* 310-822-4440
Web Site: www.mplc.org
Key Personnel
Pres, Licensing: Sal Laudicina *Tel:* 310-822-8855 ext 3007
VP, Licensing: Y Julian Eftekar
Opers Mgr: Stephanie Collins
Christian video licensing.
Catalog(s) available

Motion Picture Marine
616 Venice Blvd, Marina Del Rey, CA 90291
Tel: 310-822-1100 *Fax:* 310-822-2679
E-mail: info@motionpicturemarine.com
Web Site: www.motionpicturemarine.com
Key Personnel
Pres: David Grober
Rent camera stabilization equipment.

Motion Picture Services
5121 Ooltewah-Ringgold Rd, Suite E, Ooltewah, TN 37363
Mailing Address: PO Box 22663, Chattanooga, TN 37422-2663
Tel: 423-238-7000
E-mail: info@motionpictureservices.net
Web Site: www.motionpictureservices.net
Key Personnel
Pres: Daniel R Johnson *Tel:* 423-238-7000 *E-mail:* dan@motionpictures.net
Founded: 1980
Motion picture film production serving network TV & motion picture film industry.

MotionArt Studios
27 Common St, Boston, MA 02129
Tel: 617-242-2228
Web Site: www.motionart.org; www.linestorm.com
Key Personnel
Founder & Dir: Pell Osborn *E-mail:* posborn@motionart.org
Founded: 1982
Media & design, animation education & production curriculum. Producers of public service announcements, videowalls & exhibit videos.
Brochure(s) available
Membership(s): Listen Up! National Youth Media Network; Mass Media Alliance; Massachusetts Cultural Council

MotionMasters
2288 Roxalana Rd, Dunbar, WV 25064
Tel: 304-345-8800 *Fax:* 304-345-8809
E-mail: storytellers@motionmasters.com
Web Site: motionmasters.com
Key Personnel
CEO: Diana Sole Walko *E-mail:* dsole@motionmasters.com
Exec Prodr: Brian Peterson *E-mail:* bpeterson@motionmasters.com
Busn Mgr: Pat Legg *E-mail:* plegg@motionmasters.com
Videographer/Ed: Wesley Poole *E-mail:* wpoole@motionmasters.com
Founded: 1987

Motown Record Co
Member of Universal Music Group
c/o Universal Music Group, 1755 Broadway, 6th fl, New York, NY 10019
Tel: 212-841-8000
Web Site: www.motown.com
Founded: 1959

Mountainair Films
1623 Camino De Cruz Blanca, Santa Fe, NM 87505
Tel: 505-471-9293 *Fax:* 505-438-0294
E-mail: produce@mountainairfilms.com
Web Site: mountainairfilms.com
Key Personnel
Owner & Prodr: Alton Walpole *E-mail:* produce@mountainairfilms.com
Founded: 1989
Motion picture, documentary, commercial, feature film & video production services.

Mouser Electronics
1000 N Main St, Mansfield, TX 76063-1514
Tel: 817-804-3888 *Toll Free Tel:* 800-346-6873 *Fax:* 817-804-3899
Web Site: www.mouser.com
Key Personnel
CEO & Pres: Glenn Smith
VP, Busn Devt: Todd S McAtee *Tel:* 817-804-3672
Founded: 1964
Capacitors, resistors, inductors, potentiometers, switches, interconnects, fans, transformers (audio), tranducers, LED knobs, panel meters & switches.
Line card(s) available

Moviecraft Inc
PO Box 438, Orland Park, IL 60462-0438
Tel: 708-460-9082 *Fax:* 708-460-9099
E-mail: stock@moviecraft.com
Web Site: www.moviecraft.com
Key Personnel
Pres: Larry Urbanski
Founded: 1985
Online lists available.
Membership(s): Association of Moving Image Archivists; NATPE

Movies Unlimited
3015 Darnell Rd, Philadelphia, PA 19154
Tel: 215-637-4444 *Toll Free Tel:* 800-4-MOVIES (466-8437) *Fax:* 215-637-2350
E-mail: movies@moviesunlimited.com
Web Site: www.moviesunlimited.com
Key Personnel
Pres: Jerry Frebowitz
Gen Mgr: Ed Weiss
Founded: 1978
Catalog(s) available

Moving Art by Louie Schwartzberg
3371 Cahuenga Blvd W, Los Angeles, CA 90068
Tel: 323-436-7070 *Fax:* 323-436-2230
E-mail: team@movingart.com
Web Site: www.movingart.com
Key Personnel
Founder & Dir: Louis Schwartzberg
Founded: 1997
Catalog(s) available
Membership(s): AMPAS; DGA

Moving Picture
748 N Victoria Park Rd, Fort Lauderdale, FL 33304
Tel: 954-522-1361 *Toll Free Tel:* 800-800-1361 *Fax:* 954-523-1361
E-mail: info@movingpicture.com
Web Site: www.movingpicture.com
Key Personnel
Pres: David Wells *E-mail:* davidwells@movingpicture.com
Post Prodn: Monica Glaysher *E-mail:* monica@movingpicture.com
Founded: 1987
Specialized film & video equipment rentals, including cameras, lenses, lighting, grip equipment, camcorders, photographic equipment & supplies.
Branch Office(s)
139 Fulton St, No 921, New York, NY 10038 *Tel:* 212-203-0218

Moving Pictures
Unit of gener8or communications

200 Court St, Middletown, CT 06457
Tel: 860-704-6900 *Fax:* 860-704-6800
E-mail: inquiry@gener8or.com
Web Site: www.movingpix.com; www.gener8or.com
Key Personnel
Pres: Steve Lovelace
Film, video, multimedia & graphics.

Moving Pictures
Division of Innovative Video Services Inc
655-H Pressley Rd, Charlotte, NC 28217
Tel: 704-676-0868 *Fax:* 704-676-0813
E-mail: info@mpicts.com
Web Site: www.mpicts.com
Key Personnel
Pres & Dir: Christopher Wilson
Founded: 1983
Brochure(s) available
Demo disk(s) available
Price list(s) available
Membership(s): Charlotte Film & Video Association

Moviola
Subsidiary of J&R Film Co Inc
1135 N Mansfield Ave, Hollywood, CA 90038
Tel: 323-467-3107 *Toll Free Tel:* 877-MOVIOLA (668-4652) *Fax:* 323-464-1518
Web Site: www.moviola.com
Key Personnel
Pres: Randy Paskal
SVP: Michael Mostin *E-mail:* mmostin@moviola.com
VP, Data Media: Jerry Pierucci *E-mail:* jpierucci@moviola.com
Principal Instructor/Developer/EPT Prog Mgr: Jim Turner *E-mail:* jturner@moviola.com
Media Sales: Michelle Frazier *E-mail:* mfrazier@moviola.com
Founded: 1923
Catalog(s) available
Branch Office(s)
3000 Olympic Blvd, Santa Monica, CA 90404
11311 Camarillo St, Toluca Lake, CA 91602
545 W 45 St, New York, NY 10036 *Tel:* 212-247-0972

Moviola
Subsidiary of J&R Film Co Inc
545 W 45 St, New York, NY 10036
Tel: 212-247-0972 *Fax:* 212-265-9820
Web Site: www.moviola.com
Key Personnel
Logistics & Purch Mgr: Dennis McShea *E-mail:* dmcshea@moviola.com
Avid System rentals.
Catalog(s) available
Branch Office(s)
1135 N Mansfield Ave, Hollywood, CA 90038 *Tel:* 323-467-3107
Membership(s): Industrial Television Society; MCA-I; SBE; SMPTE

Moxie Media
1301 Dealers Ave, New Orleans, LA 70123
Tel: 504-733-6907 *Toll Free Tel:* 800-346-6943 *Fax:* 504-733-9493
E-mail: info@moxiemedia.com
Web Site: www.moxiemedia.com; www.moxietraining.com
Key Personnel
Pres & Exec Prodr: Martin Glenday
Mktg Dir: Parker Hillery
Busn Mgr: Lucy Glenday
Gen Mgr: Bob Stout
Prodn Mgr: Richard Hofler
Sales Rep: Kim Gallup; Arlene Muller
Founded: 1985
Video & digital media production servicing. Produce & distribute safety & training programs for offshore oil & gas & maritime, marine & general industry. Distribute for other producers.
Catalog(s) available

Moxie Video Productions Inc
7046 Sugar Magnolia Circle, Naples, FL 34109
Tel: 239-682-2129 *Toll Free Fax:* 888-349-8197
Web Site: moxievideo.com
Key Personnel
CEO & Pres: Charles J Liotta
Founded: 1990
Digital post-production mobile editing services. Equipment includes Nitrus Avid, EVS System with IP Director & Announce Booth.

MPLC, see Motion Picture Licensing Corp (MPLC)

MQ Power Corp
Division of Multiquip Inc
1800 Waters Ridge Dr, Suite 500, Lewisville, TX 75057
Tel: 972-459-5650 *Toll Free Tel:* 800-883-2551 *Fax:* 972-315-1847
E-mail: mqpowersales@multiquip.com
Web Site: www.multiquip.com
Key Personnel
SVP, Worldwide Sales: Bob Graydon *E-mail:* bgraydon@multiquip.com
Founded: 1983
Manufacturer of generators for studios, special events, construction, telecommunications, military & emergency standby.
Catalog(s) available
Online catalog(s) available

MRG Productions Inc
286 Horton Hwy, Mineola, NY 11501
Tel: 516-214-6644 *Toll Free Tel:* 866-300-5121
E-mail: info@mrgproductions.com
Web Site: mrgproductions.com
Key Personnel
Pres: Marty Gargiulo
Founded: 1989

MRM Worldwide
Member of McCann Worldgroup
622 Third Ave, New York, NY 10017
Tel: 646-865-6230
E-mail: info@mrmworldwide.com
Web Site: www.mrmworldwide.com
Key Personnel
Chmn: Bill Kolb
CFO: Jon Burleigh
SVP, Global Brand Communs: Sue Geramian *E-mail:* sue.geramian@mrmworldwide.com
Mgr, Global Brand Communs: Erin Hughes *E-mail:* erin.hughes@mrmworldwide.com
Branch Office(s)
600 Battery St, San Francisco, CA 94111 *Tel:* 415-262-5600
360 W Maple Rd, Birmingham, MI 48009 *Tel:* 248-203-8000
105 Carnegie Ctr, Princeton, NJ 08540 *Tel:* 609-895-0200
60 E S Temple, Suite 1400, Salt Lake City, UT 84111 *Tel:* 801-257-7700
10 Bay St, 16th fl, Toronto, ON M5J 2S3, Canada *Tel:* 416-594-6000
Foreign Office(s): Nicaragua 5468 Palermo, C1414BWB Buenos Aires, Argentina *Tel:* (011) 4316 2100
574 St Kilda Rd, Level 7, Melbourne, Victoria 3000, Australia *Tel:* (03) 9993 9333
Rua Loefgreen, 2527, Vila Mariana, 04040-004 Sao Paulo-SP, Brazil *Tel:* (011) 3904 1600 *Web Site:* sun-mrm.com.br
Andres Bello 2711, 7550611 Santiago, Chile *Tel:* (02) 337 6991 *Web Site:* mrm.cl
Zhaowei Bldg, 9th fl, No 14 Jiuxianqiao Rd, Chaoyang District, Beijing 100000, China *Tel:* (010) 6438 0011
Huaihai Plaza, 22nd fl, 1045 Huaihai Zhong Rd, Shanghai 200031, China *Tel:* (021) 2411 1111
69 Blvd du General Leclerc, 92583 Clichy Cedex, Paris, France *Tel:* 01 47 59 41 00 *Web Site:* www.mrmworldwide.fr
Grosser Hasenpfad 44-46, 60598 Frankfurt, Germany *Tel:* (069) 60 50 70 *Web Site:* www.mrm.de
Sunning Plaza, 14th fl, 10 Hysan Ave, Causeway Bay, Hong Kong *Tel:* 2808 7888
New Bridge Business Ctr, 777/D, 100 Feet Rd, Indiranagar, Bangalore (Bengaluru)-Karnataka 560038, India *Tel:* (080) 4204 4043 *E-mail:* india@mrmworldwide.com
61 Dr S S Rao Rd, Parel (East), Mumbai 400012, India *Tel:* (022) 4230 3300 *E-mail:* india@mrmworldwide.com
8 Balaji Estate Guru, Ravidass Marg, Kalkaji, New Delhi 110019, India *Tel:* (011) 2600 2600 *E-mail:* india@mrmworldwide.com
Via Valtelina 15/17, 20159 Milan, Italy *Tel:* (02) 8542 1101
Shin-Aoyama Bldg E, 1-1-1 Minami-Aoyama, Minato-ku, Tokyo 107-0062, Japan *Tel:* (03) 3746 8900
Palo Santo 17, 11950 Lomas Altas, Mexico *Tel:* (055) 5258 5900
Active Fun Bldg, 5/F, 9th Ave, 1634 Taguig City, Philippines *Tel:* (02) 814 0409
Cybernetyki 19, 02-677 Warsaw, Poland *Tel:* (022) 210 11 06
18 Jules Michelet St, 010463 Bucharet, Romania *Tel:* (021) 23 200 *E-mail:* nir_refuah@mnmworldwide.ro
40A Orchard Rd, No 05-01 The MacDonald House, Singapore 238838, Singapore *Tel:* 6737 9911
W Bldg 7th fl, 813-4 Yeoksam-dong, Kangnam-gu, Seoul 135-010, South Korea *Tel:* (02) 2186 9700
Josep Irla i Bosch 1-3, 08034 Barcelona, Spain *Tel:* 932 525 500
Paseo de la Castellana, 165, 28046 Madrid, Spain *Tel:* 914 320 832
Grev Turegatan 11A, 102 49 Stockholm, Sweden *Tel:* (08) 506 500 60
Worldgroup Ctr, 555 Narathiwas Rd, Chongnonsi, Yannawa, Bangkok 10120, Thailand *Tel:* (02) 343 6000
MCN Tecom Section C, PO Box 6834, Dubai, United Arab Emirates *Tel:* (04) 445 4314
Bankside Studios, 76-80 Southwark St, London SE1 0PN, United Kingdom *Tel:* (020) 7153-8000

MRN Radio
Subsidiary of International Speedway Corp
555 MRN Dr, Concord, NC 28027
Tel: 704-262-6700 *Fax:* 704-262-6811
E-mail: sales@mrnradio.com
Web Site: www.mrnradio.com
Key Personnel
Pres: David Hyatt
Founded: 1970
Voice of NASCAR.

MRV Communications Inc
20415 Nordhoff St, Chatsworth, CA 91311
Tel: 818-773-0900 *Toll Free Tel:* 800-338-5316 *Fax:* 818-773-0906
E-mail: info@mrv.com
Web Site: www.mrv-corporate.com
Key Personnel
CEO: David Stehlin
CFO: Stephen Garcia
Founded: 1988
Catalog(s) available
Branch Office(s)
300 Apollo Dr, Chelmsford, MA 01824 *Tel:* 978-674-6800
Foreign Office(s): Hayetzira St, Area 6, Yokneam, Israel *Tel:* (04) 9936200

MRY
11 W 19 St, 3rd fl, New York, NY 10011
Tel: 212-274-0470 *Toll Free Fax:* 888-847-5321
Web Site: mry.com
Key Personnel
CEO: Matt Britton
Founded: 1987
Branch Office(s)
30 Hotaling Place, Suite 200, San Francisco, CA 94111, Mgr: Kingsley Taylor *Tel:* 415-293-2111 *Toll Free Fax:* 888-666-9741
Foreign Office(s): 146 Brick Ln, London E1 6RU, United Kingdom *Tel:* (020) 7063 6465 *Fax:* (020) 7063 6001
Membership(s): AIGA, the professional association for design

MSE Media Solutions
6013 Scott Way, Los Angeles, CA 90040
Tel: 323-721-1656 *Toll Free Tel:* 800-626-1955 *Fax:* 323-721-1506
E-mail: info@msemedia.com
Web Site: www.msemedia.com
Key Personnel
Owner: Fernando Ruballos *E-mail:* fernando@msemedia.com
Founded: 1986
Video tape restoration.
Catalog(s) available
Membership(s): NAB

MSI Productions
9220 Activity Rd, San Diego, CA 92126
Tel: 858-348-0100 *Fax:* 858-348-0076
Web Site: www.msiprod.com
Key Personnel
Owner, Partner & Pres: John Brinkman
Owner, Partner & Dir, Opers: Ray Lucy
Owner, Partner & Dir, Sales: Ed LaFever
Owner, Partner & Tech Dir: Tom Bollard
Founded: 1946
AV equipment sales & rentals.
Catalog(s) available
Membership(s): ASAE; HMA; HSMA; InfoComm International®; NAEM

MSR Mobile Stage Rentals
2331 N State Rd 7, Suite 221, Fort Lauderdale, FL 33313
Toll Free Tel: 877-882-8889 *Toll Free Fax:* 866-704-1194
E-mail: info@mobilestagerentals.com
Web Site: www.mobilestagerentals.com
Mobile hydrolic stage rentals.
Branch Office(s)
4717 Fletcher, Fort Worth, TX 76107 *Tel:* 817-210-0166
827 L'Ange Gardien Blvd, L'Assomption, QC J5W 1T3, Canada

MSU Technologies
Formerly Michigan State University, Media Services
325 E Grand River, Suite 350, East Lansing, MI 48823
Tel: 517-355-2186 *Fax:* 517-432-3880
E-mail: msut@msu.edu
Web Site: www.technologies.msu.edu
Key Personnel
Technol Mgr, Copyright: Kari Haldenwanger *E-mail:* khalden@msu.edu
Distribute & produce faculty produced materials in subjects such as veterinary medicine.
Online catalog(s) available

MTI Home Video
14216 SW 136 St, Miami, FL 33186
Tel: 305-255-8684 *Fax:* 305-233-6943
Web Site: www.mtivideo.com
Key Personnel
CEO & Pres: Larry Brahms *E-mail:* lbrahms@mtivideo.com
VP: Claudia Brahms *E-mail:* cbrahms@mtivideo.com
VP, Sales & Acqs: Jay Grossman *E-mail:* jgrossman@mtivideo.com
Founded: 1984

MTM Equipment Rentals Ltd
604 46 Ave NE, Calgary, AB T2E 8M9, Canada
Tel: 403-276-1505
E-mail: contact@mtmequipment.com
Web Site: www.mtmequipment.com
Founded: 1975
Provides lighting, grip equipment, generators & more to the film industry. Also studio space for commercials, still photography, music videos & corporate videos.

MTV Networks Co
Subsidiary of Viacom
c/o MTV Studios, 1515 Broadway, New York, NY 10036
Tel: 212-258-8000
Web Site: www.mtv.com; www.mtvpress.com
Key Personnel
Pres: Stephen Friedman
EVP, Communs: Jeannie Kedas *Tel:* 212-846-4629 *E-mail:* jeannie.kedas@mtvstaff.com
VP, Communs: Jeff Castaneda *Tel:* 212-846-6774 *E-mail:* jeff.castaneda@mtvstaff.com
SVP, Brand Communs & Pub Aff: Jason Rzepka *Tel:* 212-846-3175 *E-mail:* jason.rzepka@mtvstaff.com

M2 Communications
235 Bellefontaine St, Pasadena, CA 91105
Tel: 626-441-2024 *Toll Free Tel:* 800-423-8273 *Fax:* 626-441-2694
E-mail: m2com@aol.com
Web Site: www.m2com.com
Key Personnel
Pres: Michael McKinney *E-mail:* mckinney@m2com.com
Founded: 1980
Membership(s): National Speakers Association

MTX Audio
Unit of Mitek Consumer Electronics Group
4545 E Baseline Rd, Phoenix, AZ 85042
Tel: 602-438-4545 *Toll Free Tel:* 800-225-5689 *Fax:* 602-438-8692
E-mail: mtx@mtx.com
Web Site: www.mtx.com
Founded: 1983
Catalog(s) available
Membership(s): NAMM, the National Association of Music Merchants

Muderick Media
101 Earlington Rd, Havertown, PA 19083
Tel: 610-449-6970
Key Personnel
Owner: Michael Muderick *E-mail:* michael@muderick.com
Founded: 1984
Membership(s): IABC; MCA-I; SMPTE

Michael Mueller Productions
1654 Airport Rd, Hot Springs, AR 71913
Tel: 501-520-5905
Web Site: muellervideo.com
Key Personnel
Owner & Operator: Michael Mueller *E-mail:* michael@muellervideo.com
Founded: 2000
Professional videography & video services (production, transfers & duplication). HD cameras, digital editing suite, transfers & duplications units.
Membership(s): WEVA

Ray Mueller Productions
5 E Waterloo Rd, Stanhope, NJ 07874
Tel: 973-691-2088; 973-801-6004
Web Site: www.muellerproductions.com
Key Personnel
Owner & Prodr: Ray Mueller *E-mail:* ray.mueller@verizon.net
Founded: 1996
Production & editing of videos, streaming video & DVD authoring for religious & nonprofit organizations. Avid video editing facilities.

Muller Entertainment
540 Commerce St, Southlake, TX 76092
Tel: 972-869-7704 *Fax:* 972-869-7791
E-mail: info@mullerentertainment.com
Web Site: www.mullerentertainment.com
Key Personnel
CEO & Pres: Justin K Muller *E-mail:* justin@mullerentertainment.com
CFO & VP: Alan Medellin *E-mail:* alan@mullerentertainment.com
Founded: 2002
Film/video production service company.
Membership(s): DPA; Texas Association of Motion Media Professionals

Mullikin Agency
1391 Plaza Place, Suite A, Springdale, AR 72764-5225
Tel: 479-750-0871 *Toll Free Tel:* 800-750-0871 *Fax:* 479-750-2685
Web Site: www.mullikinad.com
Key Personnel
Pres: Randy Mullikin *E-mail:* randy@mullikinad.com
VP: Julie Magnuson *E-mail:* julie@mullikinad.com
Founded: 1994

Multi-Media Mathematics
11224 Seawind Cove, San Diego, CA 92126-1119
Tel: 858-578-3421
E-mail: phyl.hil@gmail.com
Web Site: www.miracosta.edu/home/pmcguire
Key Personnel
Pres: Hilary Paul McGuire
Write, produce & disseminate materials to promote education in three categories.
1) Algebraic education with video topics as follows: A) "The Jealousy Method for Addiction & Subtraction of Both Arithmetic & Algebraic Fractions," B) "A Simpler Quadratic Formula," C) "Taking the Trial & Error Out of Factoring Trinomials," D) "A Single Formula for Factoring Cubes," E) "A Simple Generalizing Schema for All Laws of Exponents & Radicals."
2) Education of Chicano youth, especially homeboys with two books *Hopie & the Los Homes Gang: A Gangland Primer & Homeboys in College: Heralds of Progress*.
3) Promotion of tennis for all with the book *Tennis Saves: Stewart Orphans Take World by Racket*.
Catalog(s) available

Multicom Inc
1076 Florida Central Pkwy, Longwood, FL 32750
Tel: 407-331-7779 *Toll Free Tel:* 800-423-2594 *Fax:* 407-339-0204
E-mail: multicom@multicominc.com
Web Site: www.multicominc.com
Key Personnel
Founder & Pres: Sherman G Miller
Dir, Sales & Mktg: Ray Shedden
Mktg & Technol Mgr: Matt Conrad *E-mail:* matt@multicominc.com
Sales Mgr: Scott Brietz
Founded: 1982
Manufacturer & full-line stocking distributor for end-to-end integration of communication solutions. Multicom stocks over 13,000 products from more than 270 of the world's major man-

ufacturers. These products are used to acquire, process & distribute television, data, voice, security & traffic control signals over fiber optic, copper & coax cable.
CD-ROM catalog(s), distributed upon request, free
Printed material(s), distributed upon request, free, product specification sheets, product flyers, manuals
Membership(s): InfoComm International®; NSCA; SCTE

Multicultural Media
56 Browns Mill Rd, Montpelier, VT 05602
E-mail: support@worldmusicstore.com
Web Site: www.worldmusicstore.com; www.multiculturalmedia.com
Key Personnel
Pres: Stephen McArthur
Founded: 1993
Online catalog(s) available

MultiDyne Video & Fiber Optics Systems
191 Forest Ave, Locust Valley, NY 11560
Tel: 516-671-7278 *Toll Free Tel:* 877-MULTIDYNE (685-8439) *Fax:* 516-671-3362
E-mail: sales@multidyne.com
Web Site: www.multidyne.com
Key Personnel
VP, Sales: Glen Powers *E-mail:* glenp@multidyne.com
Sales: Matt Watkins
Founded: 1977
Manufacturer of fiber optic transport for video, audio, data, LAN, Elhbernet, Firewire, SDI & HD-SDI.
Catalog(s) available
Membership(s): NAB; SMPTE

MultiMedia
333 Washington Ave N, Suite 212, Minneapolis, MN 55401
Tel: 612-767-1660 *Fax:* 612-339-5121
E-mail: info@multimedia-inc.com
Web Site: www.multimedia-inc.com
Key Personnel
Owner & Pres: Paul Clements
VP: Diane Thil
Founded: 1968

Multimedia Audio Visual Inc
2640 S Raritan Circle, Denver, CO 80110
Tel: 303-623-2324 *Toll Free Tel:* 800-756-6118 *Fax:* 303-623-0829
E-mail: info@multimedia-av.com
Web Site: www.multimedia-av.com
Key Personnel
Owner & Pres: Neal Cohen *E-mail:* ncohen@multimedia-av.com
Founded: 1992
Stage & event production, rentals.
Brochure(s) available
Membership(s): InfoComm International®; International Special Events Society

Multimedia LED
4225 Prado Rd, Suite 108, Corona, CA 92880
Tel: 951-280-7500 *Toll Free Tel:* 888-98-MMLED (986-6533 sales); 800-888-3007 (cust serv) *Fax:* 951-279-1773
E-mail: info@multimedialed.com
Web Site: www.multimedialed.com
Brochure(s) available
Branch Office(s)
1359 Broadway, Suite 1108, New York, NY 10018 *Tel:* 212-404-7671

Multivision Video & Film
4006 Aurora St, Coral Gables, FL 33146
Tel: 305-662-6011
E-mail: info@multivisionvideo.com
Web Site: www.multivisionvideo.com
Key Personnel
Pres: Robert Berkowitz *E-mail:* bob@multivisionvideo.com
Founded: 1977
Video production.

Munday & Collins AV
2122 Zanker Rd, San Jose, CA 95131-2108
Tel: 408-451-9155 *Toll Free Tel:* 800-834-5551 *Fax:* 408-451-9192
E-mail: info@avevents.com
Web Site: www.avevents.com
Key Personnel
Pres: Robert Munday *E-mail:* rmunday@avevents.com
Founded: 1944
Catalog(s) available

Musco Lighting
100 First Ave W, Oskaloosa, IA 52577
Mailing Address: PO Box 808, Oskaloosa, IA 52577-0808
Tel: 641-673-0411 *Toll Free Tel:* 800-825-6030 *Fax:* 641-673-4852
E-mail: lighting@musco.com
Web Site: www.musco.com
Key Personnel
Mobile Sales Coord: Robyn Anderson *E-mail:* robin.anderson@musco.com
Founded: 1976
Catalog(s) available
Membership(s): NAB

Muse Entertainment Enterprises
3451 Rue Saint Jacques, Montreal, QC H4C 1H1, Canada
Tel: 514-866-6873 *Fax:* 514-876-3911
E-mail: bpalik@muse.ca
Web Site: www.muse.ca
Key Personnel
CEO & Pres: Michael Prupas
Pres of Prodn: Irene Litinsky *E-mail:* ilitinsky@muse.ca
VP, Devt: Jesse Prupas *E-mail:* jprupas@muse.ca
Founded: 1998
Produces & sells TV series, movies, documentaries, mini series & feature films & international co-productions. Also supplies production services for international clients & press kits & "making-of" behind-the-scenes videos.
Brochure(s), annual, free
Branch Office(s)
Muse Entertainment Ontario, 2 Pardee Ave, Suite 102, Toronto, ON M6K 3H5, Canada, Gen Mgr: Jonas Prupas *Tel:* 416-306-6473; 647-919-4711 *E-mail:* jonasprupas@muse.ca
Muse Entertainment USA, 4400 Coldwater Canyon Ave, Suite 355, Studio City, CA 91605, Pres: Joel S Rice *Tel:* 818-358-3615 *Fax:* 818-474-7700 *E-mail:* jrice@muse.ca
Membership(s): Academy of Canadian Cinema & Television; Canadian Film & Television Production Association; Television Academy

Muse Presentation Technologies
3510 S Susan St, Santa Ana, CA 92704
Tel: 714-850-1008 *Toll Free Tel:* 800-950-4955 *Fax:* 714-850-1018
Web Site: www.museprestech.com
Key Personnel
CEO: Jim Muse *Tel:* 714-850-1008 ext 201 *E-mail:* jimmuse@museprestech.com
Off Mgr: Kassandra Newmann *Tel:* 714-850-1008 ext 200 *E-mail:* kassandra@museprestech.com
AV equipment rental/staging/sales.
Membership(s): Exhibition Approved Contractors Association; Healthcare Convention & Exhibitors Association; IAAVC; InfoComm International®; MCA-I

Museum of the City of New York
1220 Fifth Ave, New York, NY 10029
Tel: 212-534-1672 *Fax:* 212-423-0758
E-mail: info@mcny.org
Web Site: www.mcny.org
Key Personnel
Pres: Susan Henshaw Jones
Costume & Textiles Curator: Phyllis Magidson
Founded: 1923

The Music Bakery
7522 Campbell Rd, Suite 113, Dallas, TX 75248
Tel: 972-578-7863 *Toll Free Tel:* 800-229-0313 *Fax:* 214-884-6068
E-mail: helpnow@musicbakery.com
Web Site: www.musicbakery.com
Key Personnel
Pres & Exec Prodr: Jack Waldenmaier
Original music for films, videography, commercials, etc.
Online catalog(s) available

Music Hall LLC
108 Station Rd, Great Neck, NY 11023
Tel: 516-487-3663 *Fax:* 516-773-3891
E-mail: info@musichallaudio.com
Web Site: musichall.biz
Key Personnel
Owner & Pres: Roy Hall
VP, Sales & Mktg: Leland Leard *E-mail:* leland@musichallaudio.com
Founded: 1985
Distributor & manufacturer of speciality audio equipment.
Catalog(s) available
Membership(s): Consumer Electronics Association

The Music Kitchen Inc
12400 Connery Way, Bakersfield, CA 93312
Tel: 661-338-4749 *Fax:* 661-338-2514
Web Site: www.themusickitchen.com
Key Personnel
Pres: Michael Benghiat *E-mail:* michael@themusickitchen.com
Founded: 1991
Music production, production music library, Audio Addiction Music (6,500 tracks).

Music Lab Inc
500 E Saint Elmo Rd, Austin, TX 78745
Tel: 512-707-0560 *Fax:* 512-707-2946
E-mail: rentals@musiclab.net
Web Site: www.musiclab.net
Key Personnel
Pres: Daniel Cabela
Rentals: David Nordyke
Installations: Joe Cabela
Founded: 1992
Retail, rehearsal, rentals & recording; full rehearsal & rental production.
Membership(s): NAMM, the National Association of Music Merchants; The Recording Academy

Music Manufacturing Services
636 King St W, Toronto, ON M5V 1M7, Canada
Tel: 416-364-1943 *Toll Free Tel:* 800-MMS-4CDS (667-4237) *Fax:* 416-364-3616
E-mail: info@musicmanufacturing.com
Web Site: www.musicmanufacturing.com; www.mmsdirect.com
Key Personnel
Dir, Cust Rel: Dave Larson *Tel:* 416-364-1943 ext 228 *E-mail:* dave@musicmanufacturing.com
Founded: 1988
One of North America's largest & most complete CD & DVD manufacturers. Offer a variety of in-house services from creative graphic design, multi-media & DVD authoring facilities, to DMDS digital delivery to radio throughout North America for the independent musician.
Branch Office(s)
MMS Atlantic Disc & DVD, 1266 Kenmount

Rd, Paradise, NL A1L 1N3, Canada, Mng Dir: Robert Buck *Tel:* 709-579-6001 *Toll Free Tel:* 877-579-6001 *Fax:* 709-737-0912 *E-mail:* robert@mmsatlantic.com

MMS Disques et DVD, 6750 Ave de l'Esplanade, Suite 325, Montreal, QC H2V 4M1, Canada, Sales & Cust Rel Mgr: Mike Ionas *Tel:* 514-935-0410 *Toll Free Tel:* 888-838-7129 *Fax:* 514-935-8773 *E-mail:* mike@mmsdisquesetdvd.com *Web Site:* www.mmsdisquesetdvd.com

MMS/Firebrand, 907 NW 50 St, Seattle, WA 98107, Contact: Joel Elder *Tel:* 206-402-4940 *E-mail:* joel@firebrandinc.com *Web Site:* www.mmsdirect.com

The Music People Inc
154 Woodlawn Rd, Suite C, Berlin, CT 06037-1500
Toll Free Tel: 800-289-8889 *Fax:* 860-828-1353
E-mail: sales@musicpeopleinc.com
Web Site: www.musicpeopleinc.com
Key Personnel
Pres: James R Hennessey
SVP, Opers: John Hennessey
SVP, Sales & Mktg: Sharon Hennessey
Founded: 1979
Catalog(s) available
Membership(s): AES; NAMM, the National Association of Music Merchants; NSCA

The Music Place
844 Rte 73, West Berlin, NJ 08091
Tel: 856-768-2226 *Fax:* 856-768-7135
E-mail: zeronemusic@aol.com
Key Personnel
Owner: Tim Zerone
Membership(s): Better Business Bureau; NAMM, the National Association of Music Merchants

Music Rhapsody
1603 Aviation Blvd, Redondo Beach, CA 90278
Tel: 310-376-8646 *Toll Free Tel:* 888-TRY-MUSIC (879-6874) *Fax:* 310-376-8490
E-mail: info@musicrhapsody.com
Web Site: musicrhapsody.com
Key Personnel
Owner & Pres: Lynn Kleiner *E-mail:* lynn@musicrhapsody.com
Founded: 1983
Music classes for babies & young children & retail stores.
Catalog(s) available

Music Sales Corp
180 Madison Ave, 24th fl, New York, NY 10016
Tel: 212-254-2100 *Fax:* 212-254-2013
E-mail: info@musicsales.com
Web Site: www.musicsales.com
Key Personnel
Pres: Tomas Wise
Founded: 1935
Publisher of books with music related DVDs & CDs.
Catalog(s) available
Branch Office(s)
1247 Sixth St, Santa Monica, CA 90401 *Tel:* 310-393-9900 *Fax:* 310-393-9925
Shipping Address: 2 Old State Rte 17, Chester, NY 10918 *Tel:* 845-469-4699 *Fax:* 845-469-7544 (dist)

Music 2 Hues
54 Hazard Ave, Suite 315, Enfield, CT 06082
Tel: 860-745-1312 *Fax:* 860-745-1312 (orders)
E-mail: info@music2hues.com
Web Site: www.music2hues.com
Key Personnel
VP, Sales: Andy Wells
Royalty-free music & sound effects.

Music World/Vocal Power School
9826 Columbus Ave, North Hills, CA 91343
Tel: 818-895-7464 *Toll Free Tel:* 800-929-7464
E-mail: MusicMan@music-world.com
Web Site: www.BornToSing.com
Key Personnel
CEO: Howard Austin
Founded: 1981
Products & services for vocal performance.
Catalog(s) available
Membership(s): AEA; NAMM, the National Association of Music Merchants; NATS; SAG-AFTRA

Musicol Recording
780 Oakland Park Ave, Columbus, OH 43224
Tel: 614-267-3133 *Toll Free Tel:* 800-240-5963 *Fax:* 614-267-3135
E-mail: info@musicolrecording.com
Web Site: www.musicolrecording.com
Key Personnel
Pres: John W Hull
VP: Charlene Hull
Opers Mgr: Warren J Hull *E-mail:* warren1@musicolrecording.com
Founded: 1964

Musikvergnuegen
1545 Wilcox Ave, Suite 202, Hollywood, CA 90028
Tel: 323-856-5900 *Fax:* 323-856-5917
E-mail: info@musikv.com
Web Site: www.musikvergnuegen.com
Key Personnel
Exec Prodr: Julia Trainor *E-mail:* julia@musikv.com
Off Mgr: Adriana Wilbur *E-mail:* adriana@musikv.com

Musivision Inc
8 Deepwood Rd, Weston, CT 06883
Tel: 203-227-1017
E-mail: info@musivision.com
Key Personnel
Pres: Fred Kessler *E-mail:* fred@musivision.com

Mutoh America Inc
Subsidiary of Mutoh Industries Ltd
2602 S 47 St, Phoenix, AZ 85034-7401
Tel: 480-968-7772 *Toll Free Tel:* 800-99-MUTOH (996-8864) *Fax:* 480-968-7990
E-mail: sales@mutoh.com
Web Site: mutoh.com
Key Personnel
Gen Mgr: Brian Phipps
Mtkg Coord: Joseph Anderson
Founded: 1963
Manufacture large format digital printer.
Catalog(s) available
Sales Office(s): 2291 W 205 St, Suite 105, Torrance, CA 90501 *Tel:* 310-783-0281 *Fax:* 310-783-0299
1351 Oakbrook Dr, Suite 180, Norcross, GA 30093 *Tel:* 678-966-9442 *Fax:* 678-966-9443
5410 Newport Dr, Suite 32, Rolling Meadows, IL 60008 *Tel:* 847-483-9107 *Fax:* 847-483-9108
99 Rosewood Dr, Suite 148, Danvers, MA 01923 *Tel:* 978-739-1576
Membership(s): International Reprographic Association; International Sign Association; Specialty Graphic Imaging Association

Mutual Hardware
Subsidiary of Mutual Sales Corp
36-27 Vernon Blvd, Long Island City, NY 11106
Toll Free Tel: 866-361-2480 *Fax:* 718-786-9591
E-mail: info@mutualhardware.com
Web Site: www.mutualhardware.com
Key Personnel
Pres: Mary Piotrowski
Gen Mgr: John Gibbons *E-mail:* john@mutualhardware.com
Founded: 1935
Catalog(s) available
Membership(s): USITT

MVD Entertainment Group
203 Windsor Rd, Pottstown, PA 19464
Tel: 610-650-8200 *Toll Free Tel:* 800-888-0486 *Fax:* 610-650-9102 *Toll Free Fax:* 888-536-7998
Web Site: mvdb2b.com
Key Personnel
CEO: Tom Seaman
Dir, Publicity: Clint Weiler *Tel:* 610-650-8200 ext 115 *E-mail:* clint@mvdb2b.com
Founded: 1986
Catalog(s) available
Membership(s): Entertainment Merchants Association; Music Business Association

MVI Multivision Inc
120 McLevin Ave, Unit 3, Toronto, ON M1B 3E9, Canada
Tel: 416-449-1080 *Toll Free Tel:* 800-563-5902 (ext 228) *Fax:* 416-449-5131
E-mail: business@mvidisplay.com
Web Site: www.mvidisplay.com
Key Personnel
Owner & Chmn: Peter Penkala *E-mail:* penkala@mvidisplay.com
Pres: Christopher Parry *E-mail:* parry@mvidisplay.com
Founded: 1974
Membership(s): InfoComm International®; SMPTE; TESA

MVP International Inc
9000 Southwest Fwy, Suite 320, Houston, TX 77074-1521
Tel: 713-771-1132 *Toll Free Tel:* 800-432-0687 *Fax:* 713-771-3806
E-mail: info@mvp-av.com
Web Site: www.mvp-av.com
Online AV training.
Membership(s): InfoComm International®

Myriad Productions
415 Barlow Ct, Johns Creek, GA 30022
Tel: 678-417-0043 *Fax:* 678-417-0043
Key Personnel
Pres: Ed Harris

Mystery Electronics
6438 Morton Rd, Greenbrier, TN 37073
Tel: 615-643-8460 *Toll Free Tel:* 800-798-2256 *Fax:* 615-643-8464
E-mail: sales@mysteryelectronics.com
Web Site: www.mysteryelectronics.com
Key Personnel
Natl Sales Mgr: Andy Ryan
Founded: 1979
Manufacturer of floor boxes, wall boxes, wall plates & enclosures to accommodate connection for AV & data systems.
Catalog(s) available
Membership(s): InfoComm International®

Mystic Seaport (Film & Video Archives)
75 Greenmanville Ave, Mystic, CT 06355
Mailing Address: PO Box 6000, Mystic, CT 06355-0990
Tel: 860-572-5367 *Toll Free Tel:* 888-973-2767
E-mail: collections@mysticseaport.org; info@mysticseaport.org
Web Site: www.mysticseaport.org
Key Personnel
VP, Collections & Res: Paul O'Pecko *Tel:* 860-572-5366
Catalog(s), featuring maritime videos

Myton Industries Inc
1981 S Park Rd, Pembroke Park, FL 33009
Tel: 954-989-0113 *Toll Free Tel:* 800-544-2406
Fax: 954-989-1488
E-mail: myton@msn.com; sales@mytonindustries.com
Web Site: www.mytonindustries.com
Key Personnel
Pres: Raymond Leone
Founded: 1974
Catalog(s) available

Nady Systems Inc
6701 Shellmound St, Emeryville, CA 94608
Tel: 510-652-2411 *Fax:* 510-652-5075
E-mail: ussales@nady.com
Web Site: www.nady.com
Key Personnel
COO & Mktg Dir: Toby Garten Nady *Tel:* 510-652-2411 ext 270 *E-mail:* tnady@nady.com
Dir, Consumer Sales: Cora Racher
Founded: 1976
Manufacture professional audio & AV equipment.
Catalog(s), free
Membership(s): AES; NAB

Nalpak Inc
1267 Vernon Way, El Cajon, CA 92020
Tel: 619-258-1200 *Toll Free Tel:* 888-488-3372 (help desk) *Fax:* 619-258-0925
E-mail: service@nalpak.com
Web Site: www.nalpak.com
Key Personnel
Pres: Bob Kaplan
Catalog(s) available
Membership(s): NAB

Nancy's Notions
333 Beichl Ave, Beaver Dam, WI 53916
Mailing Address: PO Box 683, Beaver Dam, WI 53916-0683
Tel: 920-887-0391 *Toll Free Tel:* 800-833-0690 (orders) *Fax:* 920-887-2133 *Toll Free Fax:* 800-255-8119 (orders)
E-mail: custserv@nancysnotions.com
Web Site: www.nancysnotions.com
Key Personnel
Pres: Nancy Zieman
Founded: 1979
Catalog(s), monthly, free

Nandar Entertainment Pictures
650 N Bronson Ave, Suite B145, Los Angeles, CA 90004
Toll Free Tel: 800-969-6022
E-mail: mail@nandarent.com
Web Site: nandarentertainment.com
Full service movie/television production & post-production company.

N&N Productions Ltd
5540 High Rock Way, Sparks, NV 89431
Tel: 775-355-9080 *Fax:* 775-355-7859
E-mail: sales@brassgobos.com
Web Site: www.brassgobos.com
Key Personnel
Owner: Rich Norris
Founded: 1982
Manufacture custom gobos for all theatrical lighting instruments. Manufacture custom stencils at a stencilboard & plastic stencils as large as 12 feet x 24 inches.
Membership(s): Professional Lighting & Sound Association

The Napoleon Group
48 W 25 St, New York, NY 10010
Tel: 212-692-9200 *Toll Free Tel:* 800-579-4019
Fax: 212-692-0309
E-mail: info@napny.com
Web Site: www.napny.com
Key Personnel
Owner: Marty Napoleon
Pres: Doug Miller
VP/Busn Mgr: Annabel Salmon
E-mail: annabel@napny.com
Sales: Jane Carter; Paul Johnson
Post-production services in art, test, audio & broadcast.

NASCAR Media Group LLC
550 S Caldwell St, Suite 2000, Charlotte, NC 28202
Tel: 704-348-7100
Web Site: www.nascarmediagroup.com
Key Personnel
Chief Mktg Offr: Steve Phelps
VP, Digital: Marc Jenkins
VP, Broadcasting & Prodn: Steve Herbst
VP, Strategic Devt: Eric Nyquist
Mng Dir, Entertainment Mktg & Busn Devt: Zane Stoddard
Full service video & digital production company.
Branch Office(s)
2049 Century Park E, Suite 3000, Los Angeles, CA 90067 *Tel:* 310-843-2300
Membership(s): BMA; BPAA; IABC; MCA-I

Nashville Production Rentals (NPR)
3401 Ambrose Ave, Nashville, TN 37207
Tel: 615-775-7609 *Fax:* 615-515-5985
E-mail: mail@nashvilleproductionrentals.com
Web Site: www.nashvilleproductionrentals.com
Professional & broadcast HD equipment rentals.

National Association of Elementary School Principals (NAESP)
1615 Duke St, Alexandria, VA 22314
Tel: 703-684-3345 *Toll Free Tel:* 800-386-2377
Fax: 703-549-5568 *Toll Free Fax:* 800-396-2377
E-mail: naesp@naesp.org
Web Site: www.naesp.org
Key Personnel
Asst Exec Dir, Conferences & Exhibits: Deborah M Young *Tel:* 703-684-3345 ext 296
E-mail: dyoung@naesp.org
Founded: 1921
Serving all elementary & middle school principals. Production of instructional videos.
Online catalog(s) available
Membership(s): IAEM; International Association of Speakers Bureaus

National Audio-Visual Supply
80 Little Falls Rd, Fairfield, NJ 07004
Toll Free Tel: 800-222-0109 *Toll Free Fax:* 800-628-1329
E-mail: info@nationalavsupply.com
Web Site: www.nationalaudiovisualsupply.com
Key Personnel
Pres: Sheldon Goldstein
Mgr: Brian Gluck
Founded: 1976
Manufacturer of AV, video & presentation products distributed via catalog & Internet.
Catalog(s), annual, free

National Audiovisual Center - National Technical Information Service (NTIS)
Division of Department of Commerce
5301 Shawnee Rd, Alexandria, VA 22312
Tel: 703-605-6000 *Toll Free Tel:* 800-553-6847
Fax: 703-605-6900
E-mail: info@ntis.gov
Web Site: www.ntis.gov
Key Personnel
Prod Mgr: Christie Langone *Tel:* 703-605-6135
E-mail: clangone@ntis.gov
Catalog(s) available

National Boston
115 Dummer St, Brookline, MA 02446
Tel: 617-734-4800 *Fax:* 617-734-6323
E-mail: info@nationalboston.com
Web Site: www.nationalboston.com
Key Personnel
VP: Dan Cronin
Client Servs Dir: Roger Bayley
Founded: 1992
Film & video services including HD.

National Council of Churches
110 Maryland Ave NE, Suite 10-B, Washington, DC 20002
Tel: 202-544-2350 *Fax:* 202-543-1297
E-mail: info@ncccusa.org
Web Site: www.ncccusa.org
Key Personnel
Pres: Kathryn Mary Lohre
Founded: 1950

National Education Association (NEA)
1201 16 St NW, Washington, DC 20036-3290
Tel: 202-833-4000 *Fax:* 202-822-7974
Web Site: www.nea.org
Key Personnel
Pres: Dennis Van Roekel
Exec Dir: John C Stocks
Secy-Treas: Rebecca S "Becky" Pringle
Founded: 1857
Catalog(s) available

National Event Marketing Inc, see Sky-View Co

National Film Board of Canada/Office National du Film du Canada
Norman-McLaren Bldg, 3155 Cote-de-Liesse Rd, Montreal, QC H4N 2N4, Canada
Mailing Address: Box 6100, Centre-ville Sta, Montreal, QC H3C 3H5, Canada
Tel: 514-283-9000 *Toll Free Tel:* 800-267-7710 (CN only) *Fax:* 514-283-7564
Web Site: www.nfb.ca
Key Personnel
Commissioner: Tom Perlmutter
Contact: Julie Matlin *Tel:* 514-283-5470
Founded: 1939
Online catalog(s) available

National Fire Protection Association (NFPA)
One Batterymarch Park, Quincy, MA 02169-7471
Tel: 617-770-3000 *Toll Free Tel:* 800-344-3555
Fax: 617-770-0700
E-mail: custserv@nfpa.org
Web Site: www.nfpa.org
Key Personnel
Pres & CEO: James M Shannon
Exec Admin: Nancy L Perkins
Founded: 1896
Video & online training.
Catalog(s) available

National Geographic Learning
Unit of Cengage Learning
10650 Toebben Dr, Independence, KY 41051
Toll Free Tel: 888-915-3276
E-mail: schoolcustomerservice@cengage.com
Web Site: ngl.cengage.com
Founded: 1980
Publisher of K-12 language & literary educational materials; Spanish & English.
Catalog(s) available
Membership(s): Association of American Publishers

National Information Center for Educational Media (NICEM)/MediaSleuth
Division of Access Innovations Inc
c/o Access Innovations Inc, 4725 Indian School Rd NE, Suite 100, Albuquerque, NM 87110-3980

Tel: 505-265-3591 *Toll Free Tel:* 800-926-8328 *Fax:* 505-256-1080
E-mail: info-request@nicem.com; orders@mediasleuth.com
Web Site: www.nicem.com; www.mediasleuth.com
Key Personnel
Pres & Chmn, Access Innovations: Marjorie M K Hlava
Founded: 1963
Online database of information about nonprint educational media & training materials from thousands of producers & distributors.
Online catalog(s) available
Membership(s): AECT; AIME; Consortium of College & University Media Centers; National Association of Media & Technology Centers

National Institute for Trial Advocacy (NITA)
1685 38 St, Suite 200, Boulder, CO 80301-2735
Tel: 720-890-4860 *Toll Free Tel:* 800-225-6482 *Fax:* 720-890-7069
E-mail: receptionist@nita.org
Web Site: www.nita.org
Key Personnel
Exec Dir: Karen Lockwood *E-mail:* klockwood@nita.org
Dir, Sales & Mktg: Daniel McHugh *E-mail:* dmchugh@nita.org
Founded: 1971
Online catalog(s) available

National Instruments Corp
11500 N Mopac Expwy, Austin, TX 78759-3504
Toll Free Tel: 888-280-7645 (sales); 800-531-5066 (cust serv) *Fax:* 512-683-8411
Web Site: www.ni.com
Key Personnel
SVP, Sales & Mktg: Pete Zogas
Founded: 1976
Catalog(s) available

National Lampoon
8228 W Sunset Blvd, West Hollywood, CA 90046-2414
Tel: 310-474-5252 *Fax:* 310-474-1219
E-mail: feedback@nationallampoon.com
Web Site: www.nationallampoon.com
Founded: 1970

National Media Services Inc
613 N Commerce Ave, Front Royal, VA 22630
Tel: 540-635-4181 *Fax:* 540-636-4240
E-mail: info@nationalmediaservices.com
Web Site: www.nationalmediaservices.com
Key Personnel
Owner: Michael D McCool *Tel:* 540-635-4181 ext 246 *E-mail:* mike@nationalmediaservices.com
Also does custom packaging.
Catalog(s) available

National Products Inc
8410 Dallas Ave S, Seattle, WA 98108
Tel: 206-763-8361 *Toll Free Tel:* 800-497-7479 *Fax:* 206-763-9615
Web Site: www.rammount.com
Key Personnel
Pres/CEO: Jeff Carnevali *E-mail:* jeffc@rammount.com
VP, Opers: Chad Remmers *E-mail:* chad.remmers@rammount.com
VP, Mktg: Aaron Hersey *E-mail:* aaron.hersey@rammount.com
Founded: 1994
Parent company of RAM (Round-A-Mount) Mounting Systems & PRO PULL (Prop Pulling Tools).

National Safety Council (NSC)
1121 Spring Lake Dr, Itasca, IL 60143-3201
Tel: 630-285-1121 *Toll Free Tel:* 800-621-7615; 800-621-7619 (cust serv) *Fax:* 630-285-1315; 630-285-1434 (cust serv)
E-mail: customerservice@nsc.org
Web Site: www.nsc.org
Key Personnel
Pres & CEO: Deborah Hersman
CFO: Patrick Phelan
VP, Gen Mgr: Shay Gallagher
Founded: 1913
Making our world safer®.
Online catalog(s) available
Branch Office(s)
1025 Connecticut Ave NW, Suite 1210, Washington, DC 20036-5405 *Tel:* 202-293-2270 *Fax:* 202-567-5704 (govt aff)

National School Products
1523 Old Niles Ferry Rd, Maryville, TN 37803
Tel: 865-984-3960 *Toll Free Tel:* 800-627-9393 *Fax:* 865-983-9355 *Toll Free Fax:* 800-289-3960
Web Site: www.nationalschoolproducts.com
Key Personnel
Owner: John Nowell *E-mail:* nowell@nationalschoolproducts.com
Founded: 1974
Online catalog(s), 6 available

National Teaching Aids Inc
Division of American Educational Products LLC
401 Hickory St, Fort Collins, CO 80524
Mailing Address: PO Box 2121, Fort Collins, CO 80522-2121
Tel: 970-484-7445 *Toll Free Tel:* 800-289-9299 *Fax:* 970-484-1198
E-mail: custserv@amep.com
Web Site: www.amep.com
Key Personnel
Pres: Michael Warring
Catalog(s) available

National Teleproductions Inc
PO Box 1804, West Palm Beach, FL 33402-1804
Tel: 561-689-9271 *Fax:* 561-640-4677
E-mail: ntp@ntpworldwide.com
Key Personnel
Pres: Robert M Peterson
Prodn Dir: Mary Eddy

Nationwide Audio Visual Co
4100-B Sladeview Crescent, Units 1 & 2, Mississauga, ON L5L 5Z3, Canada
Tel: 905-608-8899 *Fax:* 905-608-8890
E-mail: sales@nationwideav.com
Web Site: www.nationwideav.com
Key Personnel
Pres: Shawn Quinlan
Founded: 1962
Online catalog(s) available
Membership(s): InfoComm International®

Nautilus Entertainment Design Inc (NED)
1010 Turquoise St, Suite 215, San Diego, CA 92109
Tel: 858-456-6395
E-mail: info@n-e-d.com
Web Site: www.n-e-d.com
Key Personnel
Pres, Principal Consultant & Lighting Designer: W James Tetlow *Tel:* 858-456-6395 ext 18
Founded: 1990
California certified MB consultants (analysis, design, specification, commission systems, drafting).
Membership(s): American Society of Lighting Designers; IALD; International Alliance of Theatrical Stage Employees; NABET-CWA; NATAS; Professional Lighting & Sound Association; STLD

Navigator Systems US
1312 W Main St, Suite E, Lebanon, TN 37087
Tel: 615-547-1895 *Fax:* 615-547-1897
E-mail: sales@hiretrack.com
Web Site: www.hiretrack.com
Key Personnel
Sales & Training Mgr: Greg Smith *E-mail:* gsmith@hiretrack.com
Foreign Office(s): Network Business Ctr, 3 Gloucester St, Bath BAI 2SE, United Kingdom *Tel:* (020) 7183 0011 (sales) *Fax:* (07000) NAVFAX (628329) *E-mail:* enquire@navigator.co.uk *Web Site:* www.navigator.co.uk

Navitar Inc
200 Commerce Dr, Rochester, NY 14623
Tel: 585-359-4000 *Toll Free Tel:* 800-828-6778 *Fax:* 585-359-4999
E-mail: info@navitar.com
Web Site: www.navitar.com
Key Personnel
Pres: Jeremy Goldstein; Julian Goldstein
COO: Thomas McCune
Founded: 1946
Manufacture lighting & inspection equipment.
Online catalog(s) available
Branch Office(s)
Special Optics Division, 315 Richard Mine Rd, Wharton, NJ 07885, Gen Mgr: Steve Morales *Tel:* 973-366-7289 *Fax:* 973-366-7407 *E-mail:* sales@specialoptics.com *Web Site:* www.specialoptics.com
Membership(s): ACIA

Nazdar®
8501 Hedge Lane Terr, Shawnee, KS 66227-3290
Tel: 913-422-1888 *Toll Free Tel:* 800-767-9942 (cust serv) *Fax:* 913-422-2296
E-mail: custserv@nazdar.com
Web Site: www.nazdar.com
Key Personnel
VP, Global Sales & Mktg: Phil McGugan
Founded: 1922
Catalog(s) available
Foreign Office(s): Nazdar Asia, 10, Changi South St 3, No 04-04, Singapore 486147, Singapore *E-mail:* pwong@nazdar.com
Nazdar Ltd, Barton Rd, Heaton Mersey, Stockport SK4 3EG, United Kingdom *Tel:* (0161) 442 2111 *Fax:* (0161) 442 2001 *E-mail:* technicalserviceuk@nazdar.com
Membership(s): SPAI

NBA Entertainment Inc
Subsidiary of NBA Properties Inc
450 Harmon Meadow Blvd, Secaucus, NJ 07094
Tel: 201-865-1500 *Fax:* 201-865-2626
Web Site: www.nba.com
Key Personnel
EVP, Busn Aff & Gen Coun: William S Koenig
EVP, Opers & Technol: Stephen M Hellmuth
Founded: 1982

NBC-5
4805 Amon Carter Blvd, Fort Worth, TX 76155
Mailing Address: PO Box 1780, Fort Worth, TX 76101-1780
Tel: 817-429-5555 *Fax:* 817-654-6325
E-mail: newstips@nbcdfw.com
Web Site: www.nbcdfw.com
Key Personnel
Prog Dir: Brian Hocker
Producer of TV commericals (taped).

NBC Production Facilities
Affiliate of NBC Broadcast & Entertainment Operations
30 Rockefeller Plaza, New York, NY 10112
Tel: 212-664-3687 *Fax:* 212-664-5056
Web Site: www.nbc.com

Catalog(s) available
Branch Office(s)
3000 W Alameda Ave, Burbank, CA 91523

NBCUniversal Archives
Division of NBC News
30 Rockefeller Plaza, New York, NY 10112
Tel: 212-664-5015 *Toll Free Tel:* 855-NBC-VIDEO (622-8433) *Fax:* 212-703-8558; 212-664-4472
E-mail: nbcu.archives@nbcuni.com
Web Site: www.nbcuniversalarchives.com
Key Personnel
Dir: Clara Fon-Sing
Founded: 1948
An economic platform that presents, for the first time, the archives of several NBCUniversal brands. Collections available for licensing include NBC News (with MSNBC & NBC local stations), NBC Sports, NBC Artworks (graphics), Universal Studios stock footage, Telemundo (Spanish language TV network), The Weather Channel & NBC Radio. NBCUniversalArchives.com offers instant access to history, current events, weather, movies, animation, entertainment & sports.
Membership(s): Association of Commercial Stock Image Licensors

NDS Surgical Imaging LLC
5750 Hellyer Ave, San Jose, CA 95138
Tel: 408-776-0085 *Toll Free Tel:* 866-637-5237 *Fax:* 408-776-9878
E-mail: info@ndssi.com
Web Site: www.ndssi.com
Key Personnel
Gen Mgr: Jamie Bader
VP & Chief Legal Offr: Steven Olechny
Design & manufacture comprehensive medical imaging & informatics solutions.
Catalog(s) available
Branch Office(s)
125 Middlesex Tpke, Bedford, MA 01730 *Tel:* 781-266-5700 *Toll Free Tel:* 800-342-3757 *Fax:* 781-266-5114
Foreign Office(s): Nijverheidscentrum 28, 2761 JP Zevenhuizen, Netherlands *Tel:* (0180) 63-43-56 *Fax:* (0180) 63-21-91 *E-mail:* info-emea@ndssi.com

NEA, see National Education Association (NEA)

Malcolm Neal Productions
111 Everest Dr, Thomaston, GA 30286-4603
Tel: 706-646-2749; 706-647-5372 *Fax:* 706-938-1138
E-mail: nealritz@charter.net
Key Personnel
Owner & Prodr: Malcolm Neal
Founded: 1980
Foreign Office(s): 200 Longfellow Rd, Coventry CV2 5HH, United Kingdom, Contact: Pamela Reeve
Membership(s): ACTT

NEC Display Solutions of America
Subsidiary of NEC Corp
500 Park Blvd, Suite 1100, Itasca, IL 60143
Tel: 630-467-3000
Web Site: www.necdisplay.com
Key Personnel
CEO & Pres: Pierre Richier
SVP, Sales: Clark Brown
VP, Channel Sales: Betsy Larson
VP, Mktg: Ashley Flaska
Catalog(s) available

NED, see Nautilus Entertainment Design Inc (NED)

Nelson Education Ltd
1120 Birchmount Rd, Scarborough, ON M1K 5G4, Canada
Tel: 416-752-9100 *Toll Free Tel:* 800-268-2222 (cust support) *Fax:* 416-752-8101 *Toll Free Fax:* 800-430-4445
E-mail: inquire@nelson.com
Web Site: www.nelson.com
Key Personnel
Pres: Greg Nordal

Nelson Enterprises Theatrical Supply Co
1014 Rte 173 E, Bloomsbury, NJ 08804
Tel: 908-479-6902 *Fax:* 908-479-6903
E-mail: sales@nelson-enterprises.com; rentals@nelson-enterprises.com
Web Site: www.nelson-enterprises.com
Key Personnel
Owner/CEO: William A Nelson, III *E-mail:* billnelson@nelson-enterprises.com
Rentals Mgr: Randy Werd
Founded: 1985
Online catalog(s) available

L E Nelson Sales Corp
Division of L E Nelson Corp
6050 S Valley View Blvd, Las Vegas, NV 89118
Tel: 702-367-3656 *Fax:* 702-367-7058
Key Personnel
Pres: Heidi Nelson-Dowd *E-mail:* hdowd@lenelsonsales.com
Catalog(s) available
Branch Office(s)
915 Secaucus Rd, Secaucus, NJ 07094, Mgr: Dan Imfeld *Tel:* 201-794-6700 *Fax:* 201-758-4363 *E-mail:* dimfeld@lenelsonsales.com
Membership(s): NAB; SMPTE; USITT

Scott Nelson HD Productions Inc
PO Box 1198, Bend, OR 97709-1198
Tel: 541-410-8680
E-mail: snp@bendcable.com
Web Site: vimeo.com/scottnelson
Key Personnel
Owner & Pres: Scott Nelson
Founded: 1988
Video production services worldwide. Shoots HD video with 240fps Sony FS5700, stills with Canon 7D HDSLR.

Nelson White Systems Inc
8725-A Loch Raven Blvd, Baltimore, MD 21286
Tel: 410-668-9628 *Toll Free Tel:* 800-296-7555 *Fax:* 410-668-9629
E-mail: sales@nelsonwhite.com; service@nelsonwhite.com; rentals@nelsonwhite.com
Web Site: www.nelsonwhite.com
Key Personnel
Pres: Thomas Wilder *E-mail:* twilder@nelsonwhite.com
Founded: 1955
Systems integrator & AV equipment reseller.
Catalog(s) available
Membership(s): InfoComm International®

Nemal Electronics International Inc
12240 NE 14 Ave, North Miami, FL 33161
Tel: 305-899-0900 *Toll Free Tel:* 800-522-2253 *Fax:* 305-895-8178
E-mail: info@nemal.com
Web Site: www.nemal.com
Key Personnel
CEO & Pres: Benjamin L Nemser *E-mail:* bnemser@nemal.com
Founded: 1977
Manufacturer of electronic cable, connectors, assemblies & panels.
Catalog(s) available
Foreign Office(s): Nemal do Brasil Ltda, Av Morumbi 7948, 04703-001 Sao Paulo-SP, Brazil, Contact: Carlos Heckmann, Jr *Tel:* (011) 5533-4452; (011) 5535-2368 *Fax:* (011) 5049-0378 *E-mail:* nemalbrasil@nemal.com.br *Web Site:* www.nemal.com.br
Membership(s): NAB; SMPTE

Otto Nemenz International Inc
870 N Vine St, Los Angeles, CA 90038
Tel: 323-469-2774 *Fax:* 323-469-1217
E-mail: info@ottonemenz.com
Web Site: www.ottonemenz.com
Key Personnel
Founder & CEO: Otto Nemenz
Gen Mgr: Alex Weingert
Opers Mgr: Marc Gordon
Founded: 1979
Rental & maintenance of motion picture & digital cinema cameras, lenses & accessories.

Neo Studios
628 Broadway, Suite 302, New York, NY 10012
Tel: 212-533-4195
E-mail: mail@neostudiosnyc.com
Web Site: www.neostudiosnyc.com
Video, photo & event production including studios, cameras, lighting, stands & grip, set supplies & expendables.

NeoSoft Corp
PO Box 5667, Bend, OR 97708-5667
Tel: 541-389-5489 *Toll Free Tel:* 877-389-5489 (orders only) *Fax:* 541-388-8221
E-mail: sales@neosoftware.com
Web Site: www.neosoftware.com
Key Personnel
Owner/Pres: David Riley
Founded: 1990
Catalog(s) available
Membership(s): Association of Shareware Professionals

Neptune Photo Inc
130 Seventh St, Garden City, NY 11530
Tel: 516-741-4484 *Toll Free Tel:* 800-955-1110 *Fax:* 516-741-1225
E-mail: sales@neptunephoto.com
Web Site: www.neptunephoto.com
Key Personnel
Pres: Robert K Jacobs
Catalog(s) available
Membership(s): InfoComm International®

Nesbit Systems Inc
243 N Union St, Suite 112, Lambertville, NJ 08530
Tel: 609-397-7720
E-mail: info@nesbit.com
Web Site: www.nesbit.com
Key Personnel
Pres: Irene S Nesbit *E-mail:* irene@nesbit.com
EVP: Ken Michielsen
Providers of media asset tracking software & consulting services.
Sales Office(s): PO Box 106, New York, NY 10021 *Tel:* 212-268-2717

NetWell Noise Control
18525 37 Ave N, Minneapolis, MN 55446-2855
Tel: 763-694-8908 *Toll Free Tel:* 800-638-9355 *Fax:* 763-694-8909
E-mail: help@controlnoise.com
Web Site: www.controlnoise.com
Key Personnel
Pres: Mark Rustad
Founded: 1991
Manufacture & distribute noise reduction products.
Online catalog(s) available

Network Entertainment Inc
23 W Pender St, Suite 290, Vancouver, BC V6B 1R3, Canada

Tel: 604-739-8825 *Fax:* 604-739-8835
E-mail: info@networkentertainment.com
Web Site: www.networkentertainment.ca
Key Personnel
Founder/CEO: Derik Murray
Pres & COO: Paul Gertz
Founded: 1999
Television, feature film production & production service company.
Membership(s): Canadian Film & Television Production Association

Network Technologies Inc
1275 Danner Dr, Aurora, OH 44202
Tel: 330-562-7070 *Toll Free Tel:* 800-742-8324 *Fax:* 330-562-1999
E-mail: sales@ntigo.com
Web Site: www.networktechinc.com
Key Personnel
Sr Acct Exec: Tammy Kuhn *E-mail:* tammy.kuhn@ntigo.com
Catalog(s) available
Online catalog(s) available

Neumann USA
Member of The Sennheiser Group
One Enterprise Dr, Old Lyme, CT 06371
Tel: 860-434-9190 *Fax:* 860-434-1759
E-mail: neumann-help@neumannusa.com
Web Site: www.neumannusa.com
Catalog(s) available
Membership(s): AES

Neutrik® USA Inc
4115 Taggart Creek Rd, Charlotte, NC 28208-5479
Tel: 704-972-3050 *Fax:* 704-438-9202
E-mail: info@neutrikusa.com
Web Site: www.neutrik.us
Key Personnel
Pres: Pete Milbery *E-mail:* pmilbery@neutrikusa.com
Prod Application Mgr: Fred Morgenstern *E-mail:* fmorgenstern@neutrikusa.com
Mktg & Commun Mgr: Mark Boyadjian *E-mail:* mboyadjian@neutrikusa.com
Founded: 1975
Solder or IDC XLR connectors; 1/4 inch jacks/plugs; Combo; EasyPatch TT/TB programmable patchbays; patchcords; PatchLink SPL® or RPM 1/4 inch balanced patchpanels; circular DIN; RCA jacks/plugs; 3.5mm plugs; BNC connectors; full accessory line including DMX adapters. Ethercon® ruggedized RJ45 series, Speakon® SPX & STX, Powercon®. REAN plastic knobs, sliders, buttons; TT/TB quad cords.
Online catalog(s) available

Nevion
1600 Emerson Ave, Oxnard, CA 93033
Tel: 805-247-8560
E-mail: ussales@nevion.com
Web Site: www.nevion.com
Key Personnel
CTO: Eugene Keane
Also manufactures fiber optic transmission equipment.
Foreign Office(s): Nils Hansens vei 2, 0667 Oslo, Norway *Tel:* 22 88 97 50
Nordre Kullerod 1, 3241 Sandefjord, Norway *Tel:* 33 48 99 99 *E-mail:* sales@nevion.com (world headquarters)
The Franklin, No 02-05, 3 Science Park Dr, Singapore 118223, Singapore *Tel:* 6872 9361 *E-mail:* asiasales@nevion.com
Dubai Media City Bldg 8, Media Busn Ctr, Off 60, PO Box 502199, Dubai, United Arab Emirates *Tel:* (04) 390 1018 *E-mail:* middle-east@nevion.com
Unit 5 Church Farm, Church Lane, Eversley, Hook, Hants RG27 0PX, United Kingdom *Tel:* (0118) 973 5831 *E-mail:* uksales@nevion.com
Membership(s): SMPTE

New & Unique Videos™
Subsidiary of Crystal Pyramid Productions™
7323 Rondel Ct, San Diego, CA 92119-1530
Tel: 619-644-3000
E-mail: video@newuniquevideos.com
Web Site: www.newuniquevideos.com
Key Personnel
CEO: Mark Schulze
CFO & COO: Patty Mooney
Acqs: Candace Love
Catalog(s) available
Membership(s): MCA-I; NATAS

New Art Miami
175 SW Seventh St, Suite 2201, Miami, FL 33130
Tel: 305-857-0350 *Fax:* 305-857-0175
E-mail: info@newartmiami.com
Web Site: www.newartmiami.com
Film, audio & video post-production services.

New Circuit Films LLC
403 S Central Ave, No 12, Glendale, CA 91204
Tel: 818-378-0033
E-mail: info@newcircuit.com
Web Site: www.newcircuit.com
Key Personnel
Mgr: Ed Kurt
Full service film & video production company. Camera crews for entertainment, TV & corporations. Rental of HDCAM & film cameras. Camera crews available for union & nonunion projects.

New Cyberian Systems Inc
1919 O'Toole Way, San Jose, CA 95131
Tel: 408-922-0682 *Toll Free Tel:* 877-423-4383 *Fax:* 408-884-2257
E-mail: sales@newcyberian.com
Web Site: www.newcyberian.com
Key Personnel
Pres: Isaac Cheung
Founded: 2000
CD/DVD/Blu-ray replication & duplication with facilities worldwide.
Brochure(s), 4 times/yr, free

New Day Films
190 Rte 17 M, Suite D, Harriman, NY 10926
Toll Free Tel: 888-367-9154 *Fax:* 845-774-2945
E-mail: curator@newday.com; orders@newday.com
Web Site: www.newday.com
Founded: 1971
Collective of independent filmmaker run distribution company with company members selecting the films that are made available.
Catalog(s) available
Online catalog(s) available

New Deal Studios
15392 Cobalt St, Los Angeles, CA 91342
Tel: 310-578-9929
Web Site: www.newdealstudios.com
Key Personnel
CEO: Shannon Blake Gans
Founded: 1995
Design, previsualization, fabrication, photography, production, compositing, 3D animation & post-production services. Visual effects for feature films. Produces features, shorts & commercial spots.

New England Keyboard Inc
One Princeton Rd, Fitchburg, MA 01420
Tel: 978-345-8332 *Fax:* 978-345-4329
E-mail: info@newenglandkeyboard.com
Web Site: www.newenglandkeyboard.com
Key Personnel
Gen Mgr: Mark Yates
Manufacture computer input devices.
Catalog(s) available

New England Technology Group Inc (NETG)
One Davenport St, Cambridge, MA 02140
Tel: 617-864-5551 *Fax:* 520-844-5551
E-mail: teamnetg@netgworld.com
Web Site: netgworld.com
Key Personnel
Pres: Steven Gregory
Multimedia Prodn Mgr: Jennifer Doherty
Founded: 1981

New Era Media
PO Box 410685, San Francisco, CA 94141-0685
Tel: 415-863-3555 *Fax:* 415-864-5437
E-mail: sales@arkmedia.com
Key Personnel
Owner & Pres: Allan Kessler
Multimedia publisher.
Catalog(s) available
Shipping Address: 425 Alabama St, San Francisco, CA 94110

The New Film Company Inc
7 Scott St, Cambridge, MA 02138
Tel: 617-520-5005 *Fax:* 617-491-9201
E-mail: newfilmco@aol.com
Web Site: www.newfilmco.com
Key Personnel
Pres: Christopher Knight
Sales Mgr: Joyce A Zinno
Founded: 1969
Online catalog(s) available

New Harbinger Publications
5674 Shattuck Ave, Oakland, CA 94609
Tel: 510-652-0215 *Toll Free Tel:* 800-748-6273 *Fax:* 510-652-5472
E-mail: customerservice@newharbinger.com
Web Site: www.newharbinger.com
Key Personnel
Pres & Publr: Matthew McKay, PhD
CFO: Kirk Johnson
Sales & Mktg Dir: Julie Bennett
Founded: 1973
The best in self-help psychology & health books & tapes.
Catalog(s), free on request
Online catalog(s) available

New Horizon Studios
202 E 42 St, New York, NY 10017
Tel: 212-490-0355 *Fax:* 212-490-0355
Key Personnel
Pres: Joe Bevilacqua *E-mail:* joebev202@aol.com
Membership(s): ASMP

New Horizons Computer Learning Centers Inc
One W Elm St, Suite 125, Conshohocken, PA 19428
Tel: 484-567-3000 *Toll Free Tel:* 888-236-3625
Web Site: www.newhorizons.com
Key Personnel
CEO: Earle Pratt
Independent IT training company with 300 centers in 70 countries.
Online catalog(s) available
Branch Office(s)
1900 S State College Blvd, Suite 450, Anaheim, CA 92806-6135 (corp off)
Foreign Office(s): One Raffles Place, Level 24, Singapore 048616, Singapore *Tel:* 6408 0587

New Leaf Distributing Co
Subsidiary of Al-Wali Corp
401 Thornton Rd, Lithia Springs, GA 30122-1557

Tel: 770-948-7845 *Toll Free Tel:* 800-326-2665 (orders) *Fax:* 770-944-2313
E-mail: newleaf@newleaf-dist.com
Web Site: www.newleaf-dist.com
Key Personnel
CEO: Alim Thompson *E-mail:* athompson@newleaf-dist.com
CFO: Santosh Krinsky
COO & Pres: Irv Myers *E-mail:* imyers@newleaf-dist.com
Founded: 1975
Catalog(s), monthly

New Letters on the Air
c/o University of Missouri, Kansas City, 5101 Rockhill Rd, Kansas City, MO 64110
Tel: 816-235-1159 *Toll Free Tel:* 888-548-2477 *Fax:* 816-235-2611
E-mail: radio@newletters.org
Web Site: www.newletters.org
Key Personnel
Prodr/Host: Angela Elam
Founded: 1977
Half-hour radio show produced by & audio companion to *New Letters* quarterly literary magazine. Distributed via the Public Radio Satellite System & the Public Radio Exchange (PRX).
Online catalog(s), updated weekly

New Life Communications Inc
905 Hwy 71 NE, Willmar, MN 56201-2654
Mailing Address: PO Box 1075, Willmar, MN 56201-1075
Tel: 320-235-6404 *Toll Free Tel:* 800-233-6470 *Fax:* 320-235-6418
E-mail: nlc@newlifecomm.com
Web Site: www.newlifecomm.com
Key Personnel
VP & Engr: Ron Huisinga
Sales: David Honken
Founded: 1973
AV contractor.
Membership(s): NSCA

New Line Cinema
Division of Warner Bros Entertainment Inc
116 N Robertson Blvd, Suite 200, Los Angeles, CA 90048
Tel: 310-854-5811 *Fax:* 310-854-1824
Web Site: www.warnerbros.com/studio/divisions/motion-pictures/new-line-cinema.html
Key Personnel
Pres & COO: Toby Emmerich
Founded: 1967
Catalog(s) available
Branch Office(s)
4000 Warner Blvd, Burbank, CA 91522 *Tel:* 818-954-6000 (headquarters)
New Line Productions, 888 Seventh Ave, 20th fl, New York, NY 10106-2599 *Tel:* 212-649-4900 *Fax:* 212-649-4966

New London Media
78 Washington St, New London, CT 06320
Tel: 860-961-6300
Web Site: www.andrewclydebell.com
Key Personnel
Owner: Andrew Bell *E-mail:* andrew@newlondonmedia.com

New Wave Entertainment
2660 W Olive Ave, Burbank, CA 91505
Tel: 818-295-5000
E-mail: pr@nwe.com
Web Site: nwe.com
Production, creative marketing & talent management company.
Branch Office(s)
35 W 36 St, 10th fl, New York, NY 10018

New World Records
20 Jay St, Suite 1001, Brooklyn, NY 11201
Tel: 212-290-1680 *Fax:* 646-224-9638
E-mail: info@newworldrecords.org
Web Site: www.newworldrecords.org
Key Personnel
CFO & Pres: Lisa Kahlden *Tel:* 646-442-7929 *E-mail:* lkahlden@dramonline.org
Founded: 1975
Catalog(s) available

New York Audio Productions
344 W 38 St, 6th fl, New York, NY 10018
Tel: 212-244-1114 *Fax:* 212-243-7210
E-mail: info@nyaudio.com
Web Site: www.nyaudio.com
Producing audio books.
Catalog(s) available

New York Camera & Video
1139 Street Rd, Southampton, PA 18966
Tel: 215-357-6222
E-mail: rentals@nycv.com
Web Site: www.nycv.com
Founded: 1978
Sells & rents new & used photographic & video equipment & supplies. Video to DVD transfer, audio transfer, equipment rental, restoration, video editing.

New York Graphic Society
130 Scott Rd, Waterburg, CT 06750
Tel: 203-847-2000 *Toll Free Tel:* 800-677-6947 *Fax:* 203-757-5526
E-mail: mail@nygs.com
Web Site: www.nygs.com
Key Personnel
Pres: Josh Fleischmann
Membership(s): NAEA

The New York Historical Society
170 Central Park W, New York, NY 10024
Tel: 212-873-3400 *Fax:* 212-787-9474
Web Site: www.nyhistory.org
Key Personnel
CEO & Pres: Louise Mirrer *E-mail:* lmirrer@nyhistory.org

New York Sound Inc
166 Fifth Ave, No 6, New York, NY 10010
Tel: 917-523-0770; 212-929-5719
Key Personnel
Pres: Joe Cunningham

New York Times Photo Sales
Division of The New York Times Agency
c/o Redux Pictures, 11 Hanover Sq, 26th fl, New York, NY 10005
Tel: 212-253-0399 *Fax:* 212-253-0397
E-mail: submissions@reduxpictures.com
Web Site: reduxpictures.com
Key Personnel
Dir, Stock Resale: Rosemary Marrow

Newark Beth Israel Medical Center
Affiliate of Barnabas Health
c/o Creative Media Services, 201 Lyons Ave at Osborne Terr, Newark, NJ 07112
Tel: 973-926-7000 *Toll Free Tel:* 800-843-2384
Web Site: www.newarkbeth.com
Key Personnel
Dir, Creative Media Servs: Patricia Mitrano
Founded: 1901

Newbury Media
80 Industrial Way, Wilmington, MA 01887
Tel: 617-267-4095
E-mail: info@newburymedia.com
Web Site: newburymedia.com
Key Personnel
Owner: Ken Kanavos
Founded: 1981
Audio & video recording.

Newdoll Enterprises LLC
3515-B Edison Way, Menlo Park, CA 94025
Tel: 650-365-2843 *Fax:* 650-365-3057
E-mail: info@newdollenterprises.com
Web Site: www.newdollenterprises.com
Key Personnel
Pres: Ronald Newdoll *E-mail:* ron@newdollenterprises.com
Manufacture, sales & service of high-speed audio cassette duplication systems, specializing in digital loop bins.
Catalog(s) available
Membership(s): AES; NAB

The Newhouse Media Group
6907 Silvermill Dr, Tampa, FL 33635
Tel: 813-625-2326
E-mail: newhousemediagroup@yahoo.com
Web Site: www.newhousemediagroup.com
Key Personnel
Owner & Pres: Zack Koczanski *E-mail:* zack@newhousemediagroup.com
VP, Mktg: Kathi Koczanski
Founded: 1985
AV HD video production.

NEWIST/CESA 7
2420 Nicolet Dr, IS 1040, Green Bay, WI 54311
Tel: 920-465-2599 *Toll Free Tel:* 800-633-7445 *Fax:* 920-465-2723
E-mail: newist@cesa7.k12.wi.us
Web Site: www.newist.org/home.html
Founded: 1967
Produces award-winning documentaries on today's social issues.
Catalog(s), free

Julye Newlin Productions Inc
129 E 13 St, Houston, TX 77008
Tel: 713-869-3609; 832-689-3609 (cell)
E-mail: julye@julyenewlin.com
Web Site: www.julyenewlin.com
Key Personnel
Owner: Julye Newlin
Founded: 1992
Video production company; crew, camera, editorial & full production.
Catalog(s) available
Membership(s): MCA-I; The Society of Composers, Authors and Music Publishers of Canada; Texas Association of Motion Media Professionals

News Broadcast Network
75 Broad St, 15th fl, New York, NY 10004
Tel: 212-684-8910 *Fax:* 212-684-9650
Web Site: www.newsbroadcastnetwork.com
Key Personnel
Pres: Michael Hill *Tel:* 212-684-8910 ext 217
Founded: 1968
Catalog(s) available

The News Corp
1211 Avenue of the Americas, 8th fl, New York, NY 10036
Tel: 212-416-3400
Web Site: newscorp.com
Founded: 1923

NewsBank Inc
5801 Pelican Bay Blvd, Suite 600, Naples, FL 34108
Toll Free Tel: 800-762-8182 *Fax:* 239-263-3004
E-mail: sales@newsbank.com; custservice@newsbank.com
Web Site: www.newsbank.com

Key Personnel
SVP: John McDowell
Catalog(s) available
Branch Office(s)
PO Box 219, Chester, VT 05143-0219 *Tel:* 802-875-2910 *Toll Free Tel:* 800-243-7694 (cust serv) *Fax:* 802-875-2904 (opers & prodn facility)

Newtec America Inc
1055 Washington Blvd, Stamford, CT 06901
Tel: 203-323-0042 *Fax:* 203-323-8406
E-mail: sales@newtec.eu
Web Site: www.newtec.eu
Satellite communications company.
Online catalog(s) available
Membership(s): ATSC

Newton Instrument Co Inc
111 E "A" St, Butner, NC 27509-2426
Tel: 919-575-6426 *Fax:* 919-575-4708
Web Site: www.enewton.com
Key Personnel
CEO: Walter Newton
Opers: Mark Zimmerman *Tel:* 919-575-5592
Contract Sales: Patrick Patton *Tel:* 919-575-5573
Founded: 1949
Online catalog(s) available

Newtown Psychological Center
660 Newtown Yardley Rd, Suite 102, Newtown, PA 18940
Tel: 215-968-5378
Key Personnel
Exec Dir: Dr James T Richard
Catalog(s) available

NewWave Technologies Inc
4635 Wedgewood Blvd, Suite 107, Frederick, MD 21703
Tel: 301-624-5300 *Toll Free Tel:* 800-536-5222 *Fax:* 301-948-5883 (sales & serv); 301-668-7808 (acctg, opers & mktg)
E-mail: sales@newwavetech.com; custsupport@newwavetech.com
Web Site: www.newwavetech.com
Key Personnel
Owner & VP: Lenny Martin
Pres: Bill Cordell
Founded: 1992
Membership(s): AIIM

Next Arts
1300 25 St, Unit C, San Francisco, CA 94107
Mailing Address: PO Box 880418, San Francisco, CA 94188
Tel: 415-970-9005
E-mail: mail@nextarts.org
Web Site: www.nextarts.org
Founded: 1998
Full service event production. Certain items for rent on a will call basis.
Branch Office(s)
221 Jana Way, American Canyon, CA 94503 *Tel:* 707-812-3170

NFL Films Inc
One Sabol Way, Mount Laurel, NJ 08054
Tel: 856-222-3500 *Fax:* 856-638-0754
E-mail: nflfilms@nfl.com
Web Site: www.nflfilms.com
Founded: 1962
Catalog(s) available

NFL Films Music Library
Division of NFL Films Inc
One Sabol Way, Mount Laurel, NJ 08054
Tel: 856-222-3500 *Fax:* 856-638-0754
E-mail: nflfilms@nfl.com
Web Site: www.nflfilms.com
Key Personnel
Mgr, Music Admin: Christine Black *E-mail:* christine.black@nfl.com
Catalog(s) available

NH Movies Inc
Subsidiary of Cineworks Production
16 Gulf Rd, Deerfield, NH 03037
Tel: 603-463-5900
E-mail: info@nhmovies.com
Web Site: www.nhmovies.com
Key Personnel
Owner: Gary Anderson
DVD editing & web video production.
Online catalog(s) available

Nickelodeon
Division of MTV Networks Co
1515 Broadway, 44th fl, New York, NY 10036
Tel: 212-258-8000 *Fax:* 212-258-1822
Web Site: www.nick.com
Key Personnel
Pres: Ms Syma Zargharmi
EVP, Corp Communs: Dan Martinsen
Brochure(s) available

Joseph Nicoletti Consulting-Promotion/California International Records/Global Village Records
PO Box 386, Laguna Beach, CA 92652
Tel: 949-446-8005
E-mail: music-film@att.net
Key Personnel
Owner & CEO: Joseph Nicoletti, Jr
Founded: 1976
Offices in England & NSW, Australia.
Membership(s): ASCAP; BMI; ISA; National Association of Music Publishers; National Music Publishers' Association

Nightingale-Conant Corp
1400 S Wolf Rd, Bldg 300, Suite 103, Wheeling, IL 60090
Toll Free Tel: 800-557-1660 (sales); 800-560-6081 (cust serv)
E-mail: customerservice@nightingale.com
Web Site: www.nightingale.com
Key Personnel
Chmn & Pres: Vic Conant
CEO: Gary Chappell
Founded: 1960
Full audio manufacturing & fulfillment services.
Catalog(s) available

Nightingale Music Productions Inc
5460 Yonge St, Suite 1611, Toronto, ON M2N 6K7, Canada
Tel: 416-221-2393 *Fax:* 416-221-2676
E-mail: admin@nightingalemusic.com
Web Site: www.nightingalemusic.com
Key Personnel
Founder & Pres: Caron Nightingale
Founded: 1988
Award winning music & SFX for film, television & multi-media.

Nikon Inc
6420 Wilshire Blvd, Suite 100, Los Angeles, CA 90048-5501
Tel: 323-658-2100 *Toll Free Tel:* 800-NIKONUS (645-6687 - cust rel)
Web Site: www.nikonusa.com
Catalog(s) available
Branch Office(s)
1300 Walt Whitman Rd, Melville, NY 11747 *Tel:* 631-547-4200 (corp headquarters)

Nilfisk-Advance America Inc
740 Hemlock Rd, Suite 100, Morgantown, PA 19543
Toll Free Tel: 800-NILFISK (645-3475) *Fax:* 610-286-7350
E-mail: questions@nilfisk.com
Web Site: www.nilfiskcfm.com
Key Personnel
Inquiry Processor: Gabe DiGiacomo
Catalog(s) available

Nilgiri Press
Division of Blue Mountain Center of Meditation
PO Box 256, Tomales, CA 94971-0256
Tel: 707-878-2369 *Toll Free Tel:* 800-475-2369 *Fax:* 707-878-2375
E-mail: info@easwaran.org
Web Site: www.easwaran.org
Practical resources for leading the spiritual life.
Online catalog(s) available
Shipping Address: 3600 Tomales Rd, Tomales, CA 94971

NIMCO Inc
102 Hwy 81 N, Calhoun, KY 42327
Mailing Address: PO Box 9, Calhoun, KY 42327-0009
Tel: 270-273-5000 *Toll Free Tel:* 800-962-6662 *Fax:* 270-273-5844 *Toll Free Fax:* 800-541-0007
E-mail: info@nimcoinc.com
Web Site: www.nimcoinc.com
Produce health care & guidance programs.
Catalog(s) available

911 Media Arts Center
909 NE 43 St, Suite 206, Seattle, WA 98105
Tel: 206-682-6552
E-mail: info@911media.org
Web Site: www.911media.org
Key Personnel
Exec Dir & Curator, Exhibitions: Steven Vroom *E-mail:* steven@911media.org
Educ Asst: Isaiah Hoban-Halvorsen *E-mail:* isaiah@911media.org
Brochure(s), quarterly, free
Membership(s): National Alliance for Media Arts & Culture

99 Productions LLC
760 Conger St, Suite 1, Eugene, OR 97402
Tel: 541-343-0099
E-mail: email@99productions.com
Web Site: www.99productions.com
Key Personnel
Pres: T J Richard *E-mail:* tj@99productions.com
Production services.

NKK Switches
Subsidiary of Nihon Kaiheki
7850 E Gelding Dr, Scottsdale, AZ 85260
Tel: 480-991-0942 *Toll Free Tel:* 877-228-9655 *Fax:* 480-998-1435
E-mail: sales@nkkswitches.com
Web Site: www.nkkswitches.com
Key Personnel
Mktg Communs: Debra Martin *E-mail:* dmartin@nkkswitches.com
Founded: 1981
Manufacturer of electronic components (switches). Electro-mechanical switches (pushbuttons, toggles, slide, rotary, rocker & LCD programmable).
Brochure(s), Smartswitch LCD pushbutton
Catalog(s), 18-24 months, free
Foreign Office(s): 715-1 Unane, Takatsu-ku, Kawasaki-shi, Japan *Tel:* (044) 813-8008 *Fax:* (044) 813-8038 *Web Site:* www.nikkai.co.jp
Membership(s): Electronic Components Industry Association

No Soap Productions
936 Broadway, 4th fl, New York, NY 10010
Tel: 212-581-5572 *Fax:* 212-586-0045

Web Site: www.nosoap.net
Key Personnel
Pres: Dan Aron *E-mail:* dan@nosoap.net

J P Nolan & Co
4027 E 52 St, Maywood, CA 90270-2298
Tel: 323-581-7158 *Toll Free Tel:* 800-34-NOLAN (346-6526) *Fax:* 323-583-1824
E-mail: jpnolan@jpnolan.com
Web Site: www.jpnolan.com
Key Personnel
Owner: James Nolan
Founded: 1966
Manufacture temporary power equipment.

Nolte Media
12 Pierson St, Santa Rosa, CA 95401
Tel: 707-579-3902
Web Site: www.noltemedia.com
Key Personnel
Owner: Ron Schilling *E-mail:* ron@noltemedia.com
Web design.
Brochure(s) available
Demo video(s) available
Membership(s): MCA-I

Noontide Press
Subsidiary of Legion for the Survival of Freedom Inc
PO Box 2719, Newport Beach, CA 92759
Tel: 714-593-9725
E-mail: orders@noontidepress.com
Web Site: www.noontidepress.com
Key Personnel
Dir: Mark Weber

NOR-COM Inc
2126 Petersburg Rd, Hebron, KY 41048
Tel: 859-689-7451 *Toll Free Tel:* 800-689-6889 *Fax:* 859-689-7483
E-mail: norcom@nor-com.com
Web Site: www.nor-com.com
Key Personnel
CEO & Pres: Dan Van Meter *E-mail:* dvanmeter@nor-com.com
Founded: 1971
Audio/visual & security integrator, core competencies. Include design, engineering, installation support. Branch office in Dayton, OH.
Catalog(s) available
Membership(s): American Institute of Architects; InfoComm International®; NSCA

Noramco Wire & Cable
70 Glacier St, Coquitlam, BC V3K 5Y9, Canada
Tel: 604-472-6980 *Toll Free Tel:* 800-663-8434 *Fax:* 604-472-6973
E-mail: norcorp@noramco.ca
Web Site: www.noramco.ca
Key Personnel
VP & Gen Mgr: Gary McNeil *E-mail:* gary_mcneil@ncsintl.com
Electrical, electronic, wire & cable distributor, Data Comm Products.
Branch Office(s)
480 A Tennyson Place, Victoria, BC V8Z 6S8, Canada *Tel:* 250-389-6066 *Toll Free Tel:* 855-506-6066 *Fax:* 250-389-2824 *E-mail:* norvic@noramco.ca
3529 12 St NE, Suite 1, Calgary, AB T2E 6P4, Canada *Tel:* 403-291-2955 *Toll Free Tel:* 800-661-8530 *Fax:* 403-291-2995 *E-mail:* norcgy@noramco.ca
4328 55 Ave, Edmonton, AB T6B 3S2, Canada *Tel:* 780-468-5678 *Toll Free Tel:* 800-232-7390 *Fax:* 780-465-5614 *E-mail:* noredm@noramco.ca
1266 Border St, Winnipeg, MB R3H 0M6, Canada *Tel:* 204-661-8302 *Toll Free Tel:* 800-706-9519 *Fax:* 204-663-3898 *E-mail:* norwpg@noramco.ca
1031 Hubrey Rd, Unit 8, London, ON N6N 1B4, Canada *Tel:* 519-649-1636 *Toll Free Tel:* 866-387-2564 *Fax:* 519-649-1575 *E-mail:* norldn@noramco.ca
7635 Tranmere Dr, Mississauga, ON L5S IL4, Canada *Tel:* 905-673-3570 *Toll Free Tel:* 800-387-7622 *Fax:* 905-676-9825 *E-mail:* nortor@noramco.ca
1100 S Service Rd, Unit 104, Stoney Creek, ON L8E 0C5, Canada *Tel:* 905-643-9188 *Toll Free Tel:* 866-566-2166 *Fax:* 905-643-9177 *E-mail:* norham@noramco.ca
3490 Griffith St, Ste-Laurent, QC H4T 1A7, Canada *Tel:* 514-595-9595 *Toll Free Tel:* 800-567-9595 *Fax:* 514-595-9599 *E-mail:* normtl@noramco.ca
3703 Millar Ave, Unit 7, Saskatoon, SK S7P 0B3, Canada *Tel:* 306-249-6886 *Toll Free Tel:* 855-249-6886 *Fax:* 306-249-6895

Norcostco Inc
825 Rhode Island Ave S, Minneapolis, MN 55426-1611
Tel: 763-544-0601 *Toll Free Tel:* 800-220-6920 *Fax:* 763-525-8676
E-mail: theatretechmn@norcostco.com; makeupmn@norcostco.com; costumesmn@norcostco.com
Web Site: www.norcostco.com
Key Personnel
Sales Mgr: Rob Koontz *E-mail:* rob.koontz@norcostco.com
Founded: 1884
Theatrical supplies & costumes.
Catalog(s) available
Branch Office(s)
4395 Broadway, Denver, CO 80216-3549, Sales: Ian Floyd *Tel:* 303-620-9734 *Toll Free Tel:* 800-220-6928 *Fax:* 303-615-9115 *E-mail:* denver@norcostco.com
2089 Monroe Dr NE, Atlanta, GA 30324 *Tel:* 404-874-7511 *Toll Free Tel:* 800-241-5356 *Fax:* 404-873-3524 *E-mail:* theatretechatl@norcostco.com
333-A Rte 46 W, Fairfield, NJ 07004-2427, Sales: Steve Schweer *Tel:* 973-575-3503 *Toll Free Tel:* 800-220-6940 *Fax:* 973-575-2563 *E-mail:* newjersey@norcostco.com
1231 Wycliff Ave, Suite 300, Dallas, TX 75207-6205, Sales: Larry Danforth *Tel:* 214-630-4048 *Toll Free Tel:* 800-657-1887 *Fax:* 214-630-4474 *E-mail:* theatretechtx@norcostco.com

Noritsu America Corp
6900 Noritsu Ave, Buena Park, CA 90620
Tel: 714-521-9040 *Toll Free Tel:* 800-521-3686; 888-435-7448 (tech support)
E-mail: sales@noritsu.com
Web Site: www.noritsu.com
Key Personnel
Pres: Hiroki Naruwa
Founded: 1978
Branch Office(s)
Noritsu Canada Ltd, 2680 Argentia Rd, Mississauga, ON L5N 5VA, Canada *Tel:* 289-804-0097

Norlake Manufacturing Co
39301 Taylor Pkwy, Elyria, OH 44036
Mailing Address: PO Box 215, Elyria, OH 44036-0215
Tel: 440-353-3200 *Fax:* 440-353-3232
E-mail: info@norlakemfg.com
Web Site: www.norlakemfg.com
Key Personnel
Pres: James Markus
Founded: 1963
Electrical transformers.
Brochure(s) available

Norlynn Audio Visual Services
1858 Beaulynn Place, North Vancouver, BC V7J 2T1, Canada
Tel: 604-988-4996 *Fax:* 604-988-4996
E-mail: sales@norlynn.ca
Web Site: www.norlynn.ca; www.reason-for-hope.com
Key Personnel
Pres: Stuart Spani
Prodn Mgr: Pat Morten
Founded: 1969
Online catalog(s) available

Norman Beerger Productions
4508 Logan Lane, Tolovana Park, OR 97145
Mailing Address: PO Box 177, Tolovana Park, OR 97145-0177
Tel: 503-919-3453
E-mail: nbeerger@yahoo.com
Web Site: www.thegrandcanyonvideo.com
Key Personnel
Pres: Norman Beerger
Founded: 1984
Produce & distribute nature videos for the home video market.
Catalog(s) available
Branch Office(s)
17585 163 Place SE, Monroe, WA 98272

Norsat International Inc
110-4020 Viking Way, Richmond, BC V6V 2L4, Canada
Tel: 604-821-2800 *Toll Free Tel:* 800-644-4562 *Fax:* 604-821-2801
E-mail: inquiries@norsat.com; support@norsat.com
Web Site: www.norsat.com
Key Personnel
CEO & Pres: Dr Amiee Chan
CFO: Arthur Chin
Founded: 1977
Provider of innovative communication solutions that enable the transmission of data, audio & video for challenging applications & environments. Norsat's products & services include fly-away satellite terminals, M2M Solutions, antennas, Radio Frequency (RF) conditioning products, microwave components, maritime based satellite terminals & remote network connectivity solutions. Additionally, through its Norsat Power Solutions segment, Norsat is a provider of power conversion & energy storage solutions for the communications, transportation & resource sectors. Offices also in Richmond, VA & Lausanne, Switzerland.
Catalog(s) available
Foreign Office(s): Norsat UK, The Old School, South Carlton, Lincoln LN1 2RL, United Kingdom *Tel:* (01522) 730 800 *Fax:* (01522) 730 927

North Atlantic Books
Division of Society of the Study of Native Arts & Science
2526 Martin Luther King Jr Way, Berkeley, CA 94704
Tel: 510-549-4270 *Fax:* 510-549-4276
Web Site: www.northatlanticbooks.com
Key Personnel
CEO & Publr: Richard Grossinger *Tel:* 510-549-4270 ext 11
Assoc Publr & Mng Dir: Doug Reil
Catalog(s) available

North-by-Northwest Productions
903 W Broadway Ave, Spokane, WA 99201
Tel: 509-324-2949 *Fax:* 509-324-2959
E-mail: contact@nxnw.net
Web Site: www.nxnw.net
Key Personnel
CEO & Partner: Dave Tanner *E-mail:* dtanner@nxnw.net

Partner & Prodr: Matt Jaime *E-mail:* mjaime@nxnw.net; Randy Kron *E-mail:* rkron@nxnw.net
Exec Prodr: Val Thomas-Matson *E-mail:* vthomas-matson@nxnw.net
Founded: 1990
Online catalog(s) available
Branch Office(s)
100 Andover Park W, Suite 150-121, Tukwila, WA 98188 *Tel:* 206-293-8860
601 W Broad St, Boise, ID 83702, Contact: Shane Jibben *Tel:* 208-345-7870 *Fax:* 208-345-7999 *E-mail:* sjibben@nxnw.net

North Coast Studios Inc
29181 Calahan Rd, Roseville, MI 48066
Tel: 586-359-6630 *Toll Free Tel:* 888-866-0652 *Fax:* 586-359-6638
E-mail: sales@northcoaststudiosinc.com
Key Personnel
Pres: Steven J Burns
Theatre & stage equipment, projection screens, curtains, tracks & rigging.

North Country Media Group
721 Second St S, Great Falls, MT 59405-1852
Tel: 406-761-7877 *Fax:* 406-761-2029
E-mail: info@ncmg.com
Web Site: www.ncmg.com
Key Personnel
CEO: Sandy Peters *E-mail:* sandy@ncmg.com
Founded: 1979
Rate card(s) available
Membership(s): DRTV; Electronic Retailing Association; MCA-I; NIMA

North County Media Center
1130 N Melrose Dr, Suite 404, Vista, CA 92083
Toll Free Tel: 888-393-0580
E-mail: info@northcountymediacenter.com
Web Site: northcountymediacenter.com
Key Personnel
Exec Prodr: Joel Fieri
Prodr: Jefferson Drexler
Mktg, Sales & Consulting: Andy Jedynak
Video & audio production studio.

North Star Satellite Communications Inc
2547 Yellow Springs Rd, Malvern, PA 19355
Tel: 610-407-9290 *Fax:* 610-407-9304
E-mail: north.star@comcast.net
Web Site: www.northstarsatellite.net
Key Personnel
Pres: Daniel C Gallagher
Founded: 1981

North West Digital Ltd
400-116 W Sixth Ave, Vancouver, BC V5Y 1K6, Canada
Tel: 604-709-3444 *Fax:* 604-687-7600
Web Site: www.nwdigi.com
Key Personnel
Owner: Alex Tkach *E-mail:* alex.tkach@nwdigi.com
Full service visual effects & post-production facility.

NorthCountry Distributors
Subsidiary of Cadence Jazz Ltd
Cadence Bldg, Redwood, NY 13679
Tel: 315-287-2852 *Fax:* 315-287-2860
E-mail: info@ncdsales.com
Web Site: www.ncdsales.com

Northeast Video Productions Inc
Box 8425, Sleepy Hollow, NY 10591
Tel: 914-714-0703
Key Personnel
Dir & Prodr: Henry Steiner *E-mail:* nevsteiner@aol.com
VP: John Herbert; Lucie Rohan
Founded: 1979
Script-to-screen production.
Rate card(s) available
Membership(s): Industrial Television Society; SMPTE

Northeastern Digital Recording Inc
2 Hidden Meadow Lane, Southboro, MA 01772
Tel: 508-481-9322
Web Site: www.northeasterndigital.com
Key Personnel
Pres: Toby Mountain *E-mail:* tm@northeasterndigital.com
Founded: 1985
Mastering for all media: CD, enchanced CD, DVD-video.
Catalog(s) available
Membership(s): AES

Northern Kentucky University
Nunn Dr, Highland Heights, KY 41099
Tel: 859-572-5100 *Fax:* 859-572-6172
Web Site: www.nku.edu
Key Personnel
Pres: Geoffrey Mearns
VP, Admin & Fin: Ken Ramey
Video, editing videocassettes & non-linear.

Northern Light Productions
300 Western Ave, 2nd fl, Boston, MA 02134
Tel: 617-789-4344 *Fax:* 617-789-4744
E-mail: info@nlprod.com
Web Site: www.nlprod.com
Key Personnel
Creative Dir: Bestor Cram
Founded: 1982
Catalog(s) available

Northern Lights
25 Burlingham Rd, Pine Bush, NY 12566
Tel: 845-361-4356 *Toll Free Tel:* 888-353-5134 *Fax:* 845-361-4900
Key Personnel
Partner: James Valenti; Robert Valenti

Northern Lights & Pro Audio
5503 232 St SW, Mountlake Terrace, WA 98043
Tel: 425-774-1905
E-mail: sales@loud.net
Web Site: www.loud.net
Key Personnel
Owner & Pres: Douglas Jones *E-mail:* doug@loud.net
Online catalog(s) available

NorthTown Sounds Inc
275 Wickerberry Hollow, Roswell, GA 30075
Tel: 770-587-9350
E-mail: info@northtownsounds.com
Web Site: www.northtownsounds.com
Key Personnel
Contact: Tom Northrop *E-mail:* tom@northtownsounds.com
Custom music & sound design production.

Northwest Film Center
Division of Portland Art Museum
934 SW Salmon St, Portland, OR 97205
Mailing Address: 1219 SW Park Ave, Portland, OR 97205
Tel: 503-221-1156 (ext 10) *Fax:* 503-294-0874
E-mail: info@nwfilm.org
Web Site: www.nwfilm.org
Key Personnel
Dir: Bill Foster *E-mail:* bill@nwfilm.org
Founded: 1971

Nostalgia Family Video Inc
2345 11 St, Baker City, OR 97814
Tel: 541-523-9034 *Toll Free Tel:* 800-784-3362 *Fax:* 541-523-7115
Key Personnel
Owner: Jeremy Bruner
Founded: 1989
Catalog(s) available
Sample(s) available
Membership(s): Entertainment Merchants Association

Noteworthy Enterprises
3829 NE 167 St, North Miami Beach, FL 33160
Tel: 305-949-9192
E-mail: shenote@comcast.net
Key Personnel
Pres: Sheila Siegel
Founded: 1987
Membership(s): AFM

Nova Electric
Division of Technology Dynamics Inc
100 School St, Bergenfield, NJ 07621-2915
Tel: 201-385-0500 *Fax:* 201-385-0702
E-mail: novasales@theallpower.com
Web Site: www.novaelectric.com
Key Personnel
VP, Mktg: Howard Schrier *Tel:* 201-385-0500 ext 128 *E-mail:* howard@theallpower.com
Founded: 1966
Power conversion equipment including UPS systems inverters & power supplies.
Catalog(s) available

Nova Media Productions, see The Studio Center

Novalis
Division of Bayard Canada
10 Lower Spadina Ave, Suite 400, Toronto, ON M5V 2Z2, Canada
Tel: 416-363-3303 *Toll Free Tel:* 877-702-7773; 800-387-7164 (US & CN only) *Fax:* 416-363-9409 *Toll Free Fax:* 877-702-7775; 800-204-4140 (cust serv)
E-mail: books@novalis.ca; resources@novalis.ca
Web Site: www.novalis.ca
Key Personnel
Publr: Joseph Sinasac *E-mail:* joseph.sinasac@novalis.ca
Catalog(s) available
Membership(s): Association of Catholic Publishers Inc; Canadian Booksellers Association; Canadian Church Press; CBA: The Association for Christian Retail

Novell Inc
1800 S Novell Place, Provo, UT 84606
Tel: 801-861-4272 *Toll Free Tel:* 888-321-4272 (sales); 800-858-4000 (support)
E-mail: crc@novell.com
Web Site: www.novell.com
Key Personnel
Pres & Gen Mgr: Bob Flynn
VP, Engg: Dave Wilkes
VP, North America Sales & Global Mktg: Eric Varness
Branch Office(s)
2400 Lakeview Pkwy, Suite 550, Alpharetta, GA 30004-1976 *Tel:* 678-339-2800
196 Broadway, 3rd fl, Cambridge, MA 02139 *Tel:* 617-613-2000
404 Wyman St, Suite 390, Waltham, MA 02451 *Tel:* 781-464-8000
26677 W Twelve Mile Rd, Suites 166 & 168, Southfield, MI 48037 *Tel:* 248-353-8010
1919 Gallows Rd, Suite 500, Vienna, VA 22182 *Tel:* 703-663-5500
705 Fifth Ave S, Suite 1100, Seattle, WA 98104 *Tel:* 206-217-7100

Novelty Scenic Studios Inc
3 Kosnitz Dr, Unit 111, Monroe, NY 10950-1163

Tel: 516-671-5245
E-mail: noveltyscenic@verizon.net
Key Personnel
VP: Leslie I Kessler
Treas: Howard Kessler
Founded: 1920

Noventri
Division of Specialized Communications Corp
20940 Twin Springs Dr, Smithsburg, MD 21783-1510
Tel: 301-790-0103 *Fax:* 301-790-0173
E-mail: sale@noventri.com
Web Site: www.noventri.com
Key Personnel
Pres: David Linetsky
VP: Andrew Hoffman *E-mail:* andrewh@spec-comm.com
Sales Mgr: Robb Mullen *E-mail:* robertm@noventri.com
Mktg & PR: Judy Hoffman *E-mail:* judyh@noventri.com
Founded: 1985
Broadcast & multimedia video equipment, engineering, maintenance & sales & digital signage manufacturer & provider.
Online catalog(s) available
Membership(s): NAB; SBE

Now Hear This
250 W 49 St, Suite 704, New York, NY 10019
Tel: 212-265-1188 *Fax:* 212-265-6363
E-mail: info@nhtsound.com
Web Site: www.nhtsound.com
Key Personnel
Pres: Larry Buksbaum *E-mail:* larry@nhtsound.com
Studio Mgr: Katie Cassidy *E-mail:* katie@nhtsound.com
Audio post, music, sound design & mixing.

NPR Satellite Services
Division of National Public Radio
1111 N Capitol St NE, Washington, DC 20002
Tel: 202-513-2626 *Fax:* 202-513-3035
Web Site: www.nprss.org
Key Personnel
Dir, Cust Devt: Darlene Holmes *E-mail:* dholmes@npr.org
Founded: 1979
Provides comprehensive satellite communications solutions including space segment, system design, engineering support, equipment, uplink services & 24/7 customer support to commercial radio & television programmers, broadcasters, network operators & other businesses who need a reliable, always on platform for distributing their video, audio or data content.

NPRSS®, see NPR Satellite Services

NRD LLC, A Mark IV Industries Co
2937 Alt Blvd, Grand Island, NY 14072-1285
Mailing Address: PO Box 310, Grand Island, NY 14072-0310
Tel: 716-773-7634 *Toll Free Tel:* 800-525-8076 (US only) *Fax:* 716-773-7744
E-mail: sales@nrdinc.com
Web Site: www.nrdstaticcontrol.com
Key Personnel
Pres: Douglas Fiegel
Dir, Sales & Mktg: Greg Gumkowski *Tel:* 716-773-7634 ext 339 *E-mail:* ggumkowski@nrdinc.com
Founded: 1969

NSI Sound & Video Inc
Division of Conway Recorders
105 S Sparks St, Burbank, CA 91506
Tel: 818-848-1004 *Fax:* 818-848-1571
E-mail: info@nsisound.com
Web Site: www.nsisound.com
Key Personnel
Pres: Ann Parr *E-mail:* ann@nsisound.com; Steve Parr *E-mail:* steve@nsisound.com
Founded: 1969

NSM Surveillance
Subsidiary of SolutionPoint International Inc
2709 Via Orange Way, Suite B, Spring Valley, CA 91978
Tel: 619-670-0616 *Fax:* 619-670-7040
E-mail: sales@nsmsurveillance.com
Web Site: www.nsmsurveillance.com
Key Personnel
CEO & Pres: Carlos Arnero *E-mail:* carnero@nsmsurveillance.com
Supplies, installs & services surveillance systems.
Catalog(s) available

NSR Productions Inc & Capricorn Five Films
Affiliate of AH, Broadway!
110 Second St, Hicksville, NY 11801
Tel: 516-681-2171 *Fax:* 516-681-2171
E-mail: nsrproductions@verizon.net
Key Personnel
Pres: Neal Rubinstein
Founded: 1978
Membership(s): MCA-I; NATAS; SMPTE

NTI Americas Inc
PO Box 231027, Tigard, OR 97281
Tel: 503-684-7050 *Fax:* 503-684-7051
E-mail: americas@nti-audio.com
Web Site: www.nti-audio.com
Key Personnel
Owner & Pres: Thomas E Mintner *E-mail:* tmintner@ntiam.com
Catalog(s) available
Foreign Office(s): NTI China, Lisheng Mansion, Ganglong, Rm 701, No 60 Suli Rd, Wuzhong District, Suzhou, China *Tel:* (0512) 6802 0075 *Fax:* (0512) 6802 0097 *E-mail:* china@nti-audio.com
NTI Audio Prague, Lublanska 9, 120 00 Prague 2, Czech Republic *Tel:* 220 999 992 *E-mail:* czech@nti-audio.com
NTI Japan, Ryogokusakamoto Bldg 1-8-4 Ryogoku, 130-0026, Sumida-ku, Tokyo, Japan *Tel:* (03) 3634-6110 *Fax:* (03) 3634-6160 *E-mail:* japan@nti-audio.com
NTI Audio, Im alten Riet 102, 9494 Schaan, Liechtenstein *Tel:* 239 60 60 *Fax:* 239 60 89 *E-mail:* info@nti-audio.com
NTI Audio Korea, Taekwang Bldg 57-3, Rm 307, Mullaedong 3-ga, Yeongdeungpo-gu, Seoul 150-835, South Korea *Tel:* (02) 6404 4978 *Fax:* (02) 6407 4978 *E-mail:* korea@nti-audio.com

NTS ProMedia
Division of WTS Media
1201 Villa Place, Suite 106, Nashville, TN 37212
Tel: 615-254-8178 *Toll Free Tel:* 800-591-4804
Web Site: www.ntspromedia.com
Distributes recording media. CD & DVD manufacturing & duplication services.

Nuance
One Wayside Rd, Burlington, MA 01803
Tel: 781-565-5000 *Toll Free Tel:* 888-372-1908 (cust serv) *Fax:* 781-565-5001
Web Site: www.nuance.com
Key Personnel
Pres, Sales & Mktg & EVP: Steve Chambers
Speech & imaging software.
Online catalog(s) available

Numark Industries Inc
Subsidiary of inMusic Brands Inc
200 Scenic View Dr, Cumberland, RI 02864
Tel: 401-658-3131 *Fax:* 401-658-3640
Web Site: www.numark.com
Founded: 1971
Manufacture DJ equipment.
Catalog(s) available
Membership(s): LDI; NAMM, the National Association of Music Merchants

NuMynd Studios
915 Twin Elms Ct, Nashville, TN 37210
Tel: 615-259-1143 *Fax:* 615-259-1141
E-mail: hello@numyndstudios.com
Web Site: www.numyndstudios.com
Key Personnel
CEO: Greg Page *E-mail:* greg@numyndstudios.com
Gen Mgr: Jonathan Moore *E-mail:* jonathan@numyndstudios.com
Prodn Mgr: Charity Spencer
Studio & Facility Mgr: Daniel Lewis
Rental of soundstages with lighting, grip & electric included, equipment & personnel rental. Editing & compositing, voice-over & tracking.

Nutmeg Post
45 W 45 St, New York, NY 10036
Tel: 212-921-8005 *Fax:* 212-921-7728
E-mail: info@nutmegpost.com
Web Site: www.nutmegpost.com
Key Personnel
Mng Dir: Jon Adelman *E-mail:* jon@nutmegpost.com
Exec Prodr: Laura Vick *E-mail:* laura@nutmegpost.com
Founded: 1979
Audio post-production services & recording studio.

NVerzion
296 E 3900 S, Salt Lake City, UT 84107-1531
Tel: 801-293-8420 *Fax:* 801-293-8616
E-mail: info@nverzion.com; sales@nverzion.com
Web Site: www.nverzion.com
Key Personnel
CEO & Pres: Scott Murphy
TV station automation.
Membership(s): NAB

OAP Audio Products
Division of Loeber-Hickey Enterprises Inc
310 Peachtree Industrial Blvd, Buford, GA 30518
Tel: 770-945-1033 *Toll Free Tel:* 800-788-1OAP (788-1627) *Fax:* 770-945-1843
E-mail: info@oapaudio.com
Web Site: www.oapaudio.com
Key Personnel
Pres/CEO: Theodore W Hickey
Founded: 1975
Catalog(s) available
Branch Office(s)
1500 Peppertree Dr, Palatine, IL 60067, Dir, Sales & OEM Busn Devt: Kevin Patterson *Tel:* 847-226-9461 *E-mail:* kevin@oapaudio.com
Membership(s): NAM; NAMM, the National Association of Music Merchants; National Foundation of Independent Businesses; NSCA

Oasis Audio
289 S Main Place, Carol Stream, IL 60188-2425
Toll Free Tel: 800-323-2500
E-mail: questions@oasisaudio.com
Web Site: www.oasisaudio.com
Key Personnel
Publr: Steve Smith
Dir, Sales & Mktg: Marianne Gelski
Founded: 1999
Online catalog(s) available

Oasis CD Manufacturing
7905 N Crescent Blvd, Delair, NJ 08110
Toll Free Tel: 888-296-2747 *Fax:* 540-987-8812 *Toll Free Fax:* 866-929-8402

E-mail: info@oasisrecording.com
Web Site: www.oasisrecording.com
Key Personnel
Founder & Pres: Micah Solomon
Founded: 1995
Audio post-production for radio, TV, film & multimedia.
Membership(s): ASCAP; NATAS; The Recording Academy

Oceanic Time Warner Cable
Division of Time Warner
200 Akamainui St, Mililani, HI 96789-3999
Tel: 808-625-2100 *Toll Free Tel:* 800-643-2100 (cust serv) *Fax:* 808-625-5888
Web Site: www.oceanic.com
Key Personnel
VP, Opers: Norman Santos
Founded: 1969

O'Connor Engineering Labs
Division of Vitec Group
2701 N Ontario St, Burbank, CA 91504
Tel: 818-847-8666 *Fax:* 818-847-1205
E-mail: info@ocon.com; sales@ocon.com
Web Site: www.ocon.com
Key Personnel
Pres: Bob Carr *Tel:* 818-847-8666 ext 505 *E-mail:* bob.carr@vitecgroup.com
Mktg Dir: Ali Ahmadi *Tel:* 818-847-8666 ext 506 *E-mail:* ali.ahmadi@vitecgroup.com
Accts Mgr: Bob Low *E-mail:* bob.low@vitecgroup.com
Catalog(s) available
Branch Office(s)
709 Executive Blvd, Valley Cottage, NY 10989 *Tel:* 845-268-0100 *Fax:* 845-268-0113
Foreign Office(s): Derun Bldg, YongAn Dongli A No 8, Rm 706, Jianwai Ave, Chaoyang District, Beijing 100022, China *Tel:* (010) 8528 8748 *Fax:* (010) 8528 8749
171 Ave des Gresillons, 92635 Gennevillers Cedex, France *Tel:* 08 20 82 13 36 *Fax:* 08 25 82 61 81
Planigerstr 34 (Gebaude 16), 55543 Bad Kreuznach, Germany *Tel:* (0671) 483 43-30 *Fax:* (0671) 483 43-40
Erfurterstr 16, 85386 Eching, Germany *Tel:* (089) 321 58 200 *Fax:* (089) 321 58 227
PA Bldg 5F, 3-12-6 Aobadai, Meguro-ku, Tokyo 153-0042, Japan *Tel:* (03) 5456 4155 *Fax:* (03) 5456 4156
No 02-02 Hoe Huat Industrial Bldg, 6 New Industrial Rd, Singapore 536199, Singapore *Tel:* 6297 5776 *Fax:* 6297 5778
William Vinten Bldg, Western Way, Bury St Edmunds, Suffolk IP33 3TB, United Kingdom *Tel:* (01284) 752121 *Fax:* (01284) 750560
Membership(s): MCA-I; NAB; Production Equipment Rental Association; SMPTE

ODC Nimbus Inc
490 E Princeland Ct, Suites 3 & 4, Corona, CA 92879
Tel: 951-372-9800 *Fax:* 951-372-9119
E-mail: sales@odc-nimbus.com
Web Site: www.optical-disc.com
Key Personnel
Pres: Richard Wilkinson
Founded: 1982
Manufacturer of optical disc mastering technology & equipment.
Foreign Office(s): Kowloon Bay, Hoplife Industrial Ctr, Rm 10, 4/F, Block A Line, 3-5 Wang Tai Rd, Kowloon, Hong Kong *Tel:* 2541 1732 *Fax:* 2541 1766 *E-mail:* odchk@odc-nimbus.com
Membership(s): AES; IMA; NAB; SMPTE

ODC Publishing
PO Box 60609, Santa Barbara, CA 93160-0609
Toll Free Tel: 800-551-2800 *Toll Free Fax:* 800-551-2800
Web Site: www.frederickelias.com
Key Personnel
Pres: Dr Frederick G Elias *E-mail:* drfred12@verizon.net
Educator & consultant in human & organizational development.
Catalog(s) available

Oddball Film + Video
275 Capp St, San Francisco, CA 94110
Tel: 415-558-8112 *Fax:* 415-558-8116
E-mail: info@oddballfilm.com
Web Site: www.oddballfilm.com
Key Personnel
Dir: Stephen Parr
Founded: 1984
An eclectic stock footage company featuring a comprehensive collection of historical & contemporary footage in all genres.
Online catalog(s) available
Membership(s): Association of Moving Image Archivists

Odyssey Productions Inc
2800 NW Thurman, Portland, OR 97210
Tel: 503-223-3480 *Fax:* 503-223-3493
E-mail: info@odysseypro.com
Web Site: www.odysseypro.com
Key Personnel
Pres & Dir: Steve Heiser *E-mail:* steve@odysseypro.com
Exec Prodr: Carolyn Zelle *E-mail:* carolyn@odysseypro.com
Prodr/Dir: Adam Heiser *E-mail:* adam@odysseypro.com
Founded: 1973
Full service film/video & interactive multi-media production company, specializing in museum & visitor center programs. Documentary film/video productions from concept to completion.
Membership(s): Oregon Media Production Association

OECA, see TVO/Ontario Educational Communications Authority (OECA)

OGM Production Music
Subsidiary of OGM Inc
6464 Sunset Blvd, Suite 770, Hollywood, CA 90028
Tel: 323-461-2701 *Toll Free Tel:* 800-421-4163 (sales) *Fax:* 323-461-1543
E-mail: ogmmusic@gmail.com
Web Site: www.ogmmusic.com
Key Personnel
Pres: Ole Georg
Production music library.
Catalog(s) available
Membership(s): LEVA; MCA-I; NAB

Ohio HD Video
3465 Noe Bixby Rd, Columbus, OH 43232
Tel: 614-656-1162 *Fax:* 614-656-4343
E-mail: info@ohiohdvideo.com
Web Site: ohiohdvideo.com
Key Personnel
Dir, Photog: Scott Handel
Broadcast & documentary crews. Camera, lens & electronics rentals.

Ohio State University Foreign Language Publications
198 Hagerty Hall, 1775 S College Rd, Columbus, OH 43210-1309
Tel: 614-292-3838 *Toll Free Tel:* 800-678-6999 *Fax:* 614-688-3355
E-mail: flpubs@osu.edu
Web Site: flpubs.osu.edu
Key Personnel
Mgr: Lauren Barrett
Online catalog(s) available

O'Keefe Communications Inc
4301 Connecticut Ave NW, Suite 200, Washington, DC 20008-2304
Tel: 202-363-2101
E-mail: info@okeefecom.com
Web Site: www.okeefecom.com
Key Personnel
CEO: Kevin O'Keefe
Pres: Catie O'Keefe *E-mail:* catie@okeefecom.com
Founded: 1979
A media & event production company serving associations, businesses, government & non-profits.
Membership(s): MCA-I; Women in Film & Video

Oklahoma Sound Corp
149 Entin Rd, Clifton, NJ 07014
Tel: 973-594-9000 *Toll Free Tel:* 800-261-4112 *Fax:* 201-322-2104
E-mail: info@oklahomasound.com
Web Site: www.oklahomasound.com
Key Personnel
Pres: Barry Stauber *E-mail:* barry@oklahomasound.com
Founded: 1981
Manufacture, sells through dealers.
Catalog(s), annual
Online catalog(s) available
Membership(s): Education Market Association; InfoComm International®

Old Army Press (OAP)
218 Alabaster Way, Johnstown, CO 80534
Mailing Address: PO Box 1650, Johnstown, CO 80534-1650
Tel: 970-587-9530 *Toll Free Tel:* 800-627-0079 *Fax:* 970-490-2709
E-mail: oldarmypress@msn.com
Web Site: oldarmypress.com
Key Personnel
Pres: Mike Koury
VP: Dee Koury
Founded: 1968
Catalog(s), free

Old Dominion Broadcasting
Subsidiary of Straus Enterprises Inc
9505 Lakewater Ct, Richmond, VA 23229
Tel: 804-740-4717 *Fax:* 804-740-4717
Key Personnel
CEO & Pres: Sam Straus
Membership(s): SBE

The Old Rhinebeck Aerodome®
9 Norton Rd, Red Hook, NY 12571
Mailing Address: PO Box 229, Rhinebeck, NY 12572
Tel: 845-752-3200 *Fax:* 845-758-6481
E-mail: info@oldrhinebeck.org
Web Site: www.oldrhinebeck.org
Key Personnel
Pres: Michael DiGiacomio
Gift shop sells "Cole Palen's Flying Circus" on DVD.
Online catalog(s) available

Old School Cameras
2819 N San Fernando Blvd, Burbank, CA 91504
Tel: 818-847-1555 *Fax:* 818-847-1556
Web Site: www.oldschoolcameras.com
Key Personnel
Owner: Jesse MacDonald
Founded: 2006
Motion picture cameras, HD & video equipment rental.

Olden Camera & Lens Co Inc
1263 Broadway, 4th fl, New York, NY 10001-3593
Tel: 212-725-1234 *Fax:* 212-725-1325
Key Personnel
Pres: Robert Olden
Sales: Tony Gong
New & used cameras.

Olden Lighting
2008 Alexander Ave, Austin, TX 78722
Tel: 512-416-8080 *Fax:* 512-416-8096
E-mail: rental@oldenlighting.com; sales@oldenlighting.com
Web Site: www.oldenlighting.com
Key Personnel
Owner: Walter L Olden
Founded: 1985
Sales & rental of lighting equipment & supplies.

Jim Olive Photography, see Stockyard Photos/Jim Olive Photography

Olsen Audio Group Inc
7845 E Evans Rd, Scottsdale, AZ 85260-2919
Tel: 480-998-7140 *Fax:* 480-998-7192
E-mail: information@olsenaudio.com
Web Site: www.olsenaudio.com
Founded: 1976
Catalog(s) available
Membership(s): NAMM, the National Association of Music Merchants

Olson Visual Inc
13000 Weber Way, Hawthorne, CA 90250
Tel: 310-355-1681 *Toll Free Tel:* 800-480-6643 *Fax:* 310-263-6980
E-mail: graphics@olsonvisual.com
Web Site: www.olsonvisual.com
Key Personnel
VP: Dan Olson *Tel:* 310-355-1681 ext 212; Tom Olson *Tel:* 310-355-1681 ext 213
Founded: 1954
Production of digital video workstations.
Catalog(s) available
Membership(s): EDPA; Photo Marketing Association

Olympic Case Co
9110 King Palm Dr, Suite 101, Tampa, FL 33619
Tel: 813-246-5525 *Toll Free Tel:* 888-246-5525 *Fax:* 813-246-4748
E-mail: info@olycase.com
Web Site: www.olycase.com
Key Personnel
Natl Sales Mgr: Ralph Gundlach *E-mail:* ralph@olycase.com
Founded: 1996
Provider of ATA & custom cases.

Olympus America Inc
Subsidiary of Olympus Global
3500 Corporate Pkwy, Center Valley, PA 18034
Mailing Address: PO Box 610, Center Valley, PA 18034-0610
Tel: 484-896-5000
Web Site: www.olympusamerica.com
Founded: 1919
Manufacturer & distributor of cameras & equipment.
Brochure(s) available

Olympusat Entertainment
560 Village Blvd, Suite 250W, Palm Beach, FL 33409
Tel: 561-283-2888
E-mail: info@olympusatent.com
Web Site: www.olympusatent.com
Complete film, TV & commercial production.

Omega Broadcast Group
817 W Howard Lane, Austin, TX 78753
Tel: 512-251-7778 *Fax:* 512-251-8633
E-mail: rental@omegabroadcast.com; sales@omegabroadcast.com
Web Site: www.omegabroadcast.com
Key Personnel
Pres: Pam Fry
VP: David Fry
Prodn Mgr: Enrique Garcia
Rental Mgr: Troy Marx
Sales & Mktg: Allan Barnwell
Professional video sales, rentals & services.

Omega Media Group Inc
3100 Medlock Bridge Rd, Suite 100, Norcross, GA 30071
Tel: 770-449-8870
Web Site: www.omegamediagroup.com
Key Personnel
Owner: Cefus McRae *E-mail:* cefus@omegamediagroup.com
Founded: 1985
Full video production facility, pre- & post-production, full in-house studio. Also produces video conferences & live events.

Omega Productions
PO Box 606, Palacios, TX 77465
Tel: 214-891-9585 *Fax:* 214-722-1442
E-mail: getinfo@omegalive.com
Web Site: www.omegalive.com
Key Personnel
Pres: Paul A Christensen
Founded: 1973
Brochure(s) available
Membership(s): Dallas Communications Council; Dallas Producers Association; SPARS

Omega Recording Studios
5609 Fishers Lane, Suite 14-A, Rockville, MD 20852
Tel: 301-230-9100 *Toll Free Tel:* 800-93-OMEGA (936-6342) *Fax:* 301-230-9103
E-mail: omega@omegastudios.com; info@omegastudios.com
Web Site: www.omegastudios.com
Key Personnel
Pres: Edward Peterson
Full service recording studio.
Membership(s): AES; AF of M; National Association for Music Education; The Recording Academy; SAW; WAMA

OmegaBrandess Distribution
626 Hanover Pike, Suite 102, Hampstead, MD 21074-2036
Tel: 410-374-3250 *Fax:* 410-374-3184
E-mail: customerservice@omegabrandess.com
Web Site: www.omegabrandess.com
Key Personnel
Pres: Cindy Wesolowski
Dir, Sales & Serv: Jeff Seidel
Manufacture & distribute photographic equipment.
Online catalog(s) available
Membership(s): Photo Marketing Association

Omni Intercommunications Inc
2825 Wilcrest Dr, Suite 400, Houston, TX 77042
Tel: 713-781-2188 *Toll Free Tel:* 800-777-2304 *Fax:* 713-781-2315
E-mail: info@omni-inter.com
Web Site: www.omni-inter.com
Key Personnel
Pres: Herve F Chain *E-mail:* hchain@omni-inter.com
Founded: 1978
Provide high quality foreign language services.
Membership(s): ATA; ATD; DSA; MCA-I

Omni International Inc
435 12 St SW, Vernon, AL 35592
Mailing Address: PO Box 1409, Vernon, AL 35592-1409
Tel: 205-695-9173 *Toll Free Tel:* 800-844-6664 *Fax:* 205-695-6465
E-mail: omni-brewster@centurytel.net
Web Site: www.omniinternational.com
Key Personnel
Pres: James L Riley
Dir, Support Opers: Donald R Myres
Founded: 1957
Design, manufacture, market & sell contract/commercial furniture to include office, residential life (institutional) & library products.
Catalog(s) available

OMNI Productions
Division of The Omni Corp
PO Box 302, Carmel, IN 46082-0302
Tel: 317-846-2345 (ext 111) *Fax:* 317-846-6664
E-mail: omni@omniproductions.com
Web Site: www.omniproductions.com
Key Personnel
Owner & Gen Mgr: W H Long
VP: S M Long
Prodn Mgr: J A Mullet
Founded: 1976
Full service digital media production company, including windows media streaming services provider.
Membership(s): AECT; NAB

Omnia Audio
Division of Telos Systems
1241 Superior Ave E, Cleveland, OH 44114
Tel: 216-241-7225 *Fax:* 216-241-4103
E-mail: omnia-info@omniaaudio.com
Web Site: www.omniaaudio.com
Key Personnel
Founder & Pres: Frank Foti
Mng Dir: Marty Sacks
Founded: 1988
Foreign Office(s): Omnia Audio Europe, Johannisstr 6, 85354 Freising, Germany *Tel:* (08161) 424-67 *Fax:* (08161) 424-02 *E-mail:* europe-info@omniaaudio.com
Membership(s): AES; NAB

Omnimedia Inc
3085 Maple Cove Dr, Loganville, GA 30052
Toll Free Tel: 800-433-2091 *Fax:* 678-623-3940
E-mail: sales@omni-media.com
Web Site: www.omni-media.com
Key Personnel
Pres: Conrad F Boje
Founded: 1993
Catalog(s) available

OmniMount Systems
4409 E Baseline Rd, Suite 130, Phoenix, AZ 85042
Tel: 480-829-8000 *Toll Free Tel:* 800-MOUNT-IT (668-6848) *Fax:* 480-756-9000
E-mail: info@omnimount.com
Web Site: www.omnimount.com
Key Personnel
Pres: Geoff Miller
SVP, Sales: John Deutsch
VP, Sales Opers: Scott Ashbaugh
Founded: 1978
Manufacturer of audio & video mounts & furniture.

Omnimusic
Subsidiary of Franklin-Douglas Inc
52 Main St, Port Washington, NY 11050
Tel: 516-883-0121 *Toll Free Tel:* 800-828-6664 *Fax:* 516-883-0271
E-mail: omni@omnimusic.com
Web Site: www.omnimusic.com

Key Personnel
CEO & Pres: Doug Wood *E-mail:* daw@omnimusic.com
Founded: 1976
Production music library for film, TV & Internet.
Online catalog(s) available
Membership(s): Media Communications Association

Omnirax
PO Box 1792, Sausalito, CA 94966-1792
Tel: 415-332-3392 *Toll Free Tel:* 800-332-3393 *Fax:* 415-332-2607
E-mail: info@omnirax.com
Web Site: www.omnirax.com
Key Personnel
Dir: Philip Zittell *Tel:* 415-332-3392 ext 102
Multimedia workstation designer & manufacturer.
Shipping Address: 180 Harbor Dr, Suite 202, Sausalito, CA 94965
Membership(s): NAB; NAMM, the National Association of Music Merchants; National Association for Music Education; NSCA

OMNISound Recording Studio
Division of Sounds Perfect LLC
1806 Division St, Nashville, TN 37203
Tel: 615-482-1151 *Fax:* 615-321-5528
Web Site: www.omnisoundstudios.com
Key Personnel
Mgr: Chris Holloway *E-mail:* chris@omnisoundstudios.com
Recording studio.

ON Event Services
Formerly Tech Rentals Inc
6550 McDonough Dr, Norcross, GA 30093-1211
Tel: 404-875-0966 *Fax:* 404-874-7925
E-mail: av@techrentals.com
Web Site: www.oneventservices.com
Key Personnel
Pres: Stan Milner *E-mail:* smilner@oneventservices.com
Founded: 1985
AV rental & staging, sales & installation.
Branch Office(s)
700 Monroe St, Huntsville, AL 35801 *Tel:* 256-348-8592
3085 Directors Row, Memphis, TN 38131 *Tel:* 901-969-0255 *Toll Free Tel:* 866-372-3119 *Fax:* 901-969-2056
1443 Donelson Pike, Nashville, TN 37217 *Tel:* 615-301-6740 *Toll Free Tel:* 877-607-7516 *Fax:* 615-780-2681
Membership(s): HSMAI; InfoComm International®; International Special Events Society; MCA-I; MPI; MPPA; NACE

On-Line Productions
2515 Hawthorne Dr, Atlanta, GA 30345
Tel: 404-634-5572
E-mail: esptv@mindspring.com
Web Site: on-lineproductions.com
Key Personnel
Prodr & Dir: Steven Panayioto
Founded: 1985
Video production & post-production services; provide on location, broadcast quality services as well as editing services for corporate, cable, broadcast & web customers.
Catalog(s), by request
Membership(s): Georgia Production Partnership; MCA-I; NATAS

On Location North Carolina
2121 Atlantic Ave, Suite 106, Raleigh, NC 27604
Mailing Address: PO Box 50157, Raleigh, NC 27650-6157
Tel: 919-755-9488 *Toll Free Tel:* 888-469-4747 *Fax:* 919-832-7797
E-mail: info@onlocation-nc.com
Web Site: www.onlocation-nc.com
Key Personnel
Prodn Coord: John J Spain
Founded: 1982
Supply equipment & crew to out of town producers of video & film who have a shoot in North Carolina.

On Site Video
Subsidiary of Producers Video LLC
PO Box 1865, Palatine, IL 60078-1865
Tel: 847-980-9808 *Fax:* 847-358-8697
E-mail: producersvideo@hotmail.com
Key Personnel
Owner & Pres: Jerry Skora
Founded: 1980
HD video production & post-production.
Catalog(s) available
Membership(s): Digital Cinema Society; IEEE; SBE; SMPTE

On-Site Video
Subsidiary of Video Security Inc
201 E Southern Ave, Suite 112, Tempe, AZ 85282
Tel: 480-967-5062 *Fax:* 480-967-4806
E-mail: on_sitevideo@yahoo.com
Web Site: www.on-sitevideo.com
Key Personnel
VP: John Gruber
Founded: 1979
Full service video production services.

On Stage Audio
Division of OSA International
537 N Edgewood Ave, Wood Dale, IL 60191
Tel: 630-227-1008 *Toll Free Tel:* 877-672-4685 *Toll Free Fax:* 866-OSA-FAX2 (672-3292)
E-mail: welisten@osacorp.com
Web Site: www.osacorp.com
Key Personnel
Sales Mgr: Paul Driggs *E-mail:* pdriggs@osacorp.com
Founded: 1985
Full service sound & technical management company.

On Stage Visuals
420 Baker St, Lansing, MI 48910-1543
Tel: 517-393-7800 *Toll Free Tel:* 800-373-LIVE (373-5483) *Fax:* 517-481-2482
E-mail: support@onstagevisuals.com
Web Site: www.onstagevisuals.com
Founded: 1985
Retail, rental, installations of lighting, pro audio & video equipment.

On-Trax Inc
3052 Vine St, Riverside, CA 92507
Tel: 951-786-3921 *Fax:* 951-786-3922
Web Site: www.on-trax.com
Key Personnel
Owner & Pres: Bradford Williams *E-mail:* bradford@on-trax.com
Founded: 1980
Full service AV production company.
Catalog(s), free

Once Around
194 Castle Lane, Kilmarnock, VA 22482
Tel: 804-436-8904
E-mail: wardjudy56@verizon.net
Key Personnel
Pres: Ward Le Hardy
Data sheet(s) available
Information sheet(s) available
Product sheet(s) available

Oncourt Offcourt Ltd
6301 Gaston Ave, Suite 650, Dallas, TX 75214
Tel: 214-823-3078 *Toll Free Tel:* 888-366-4711 (88-TENNIS-11) *Fax:* 214-823-3082
E-mail: info@oncourtoffcourt.com
Web Site: www.oncourtoffcourt.com
Key Personnel
Founder & Pres: Joe Dinoffer *E-mail:* joe@oncourtoffcourt.com
Founded: 1994
Distribute sports training equipment, books & speaking.
Catalog(s) available

One Stop CD Shop LLC
3149 S State St, Salt Lake City, UT 84115
Tel: 801-303-6100 *Fax:* 801-303-6129
E-mail: info2@1stopcdshop.com
Web Site: www.1stopcdshop.com
Key Personnel
Mktg Dir: Ken Rasmussen
Founded: 1993
Membership(s): UITA

One Touch Systems Inc
2346 Bering Dr, San Jose, CA 95131
Tel: 408-660-8435 *Fax:* 408-436-4699
E-mail: info@onetouchsys.com
Web Site: www.onetouchsys.com
Key Personnel
CEO & Pres: Larry Speckels
CFO & VP: Bob Wilkinson
VP, Enterprise Sales: Michael Schenk
VP, Software Engg: Gopinath Rebala
Founded: 1989
Manufacturer & distributor of audience response systems.
Branch Office(s)
655 Engineering Dr, Norcross, GA 30092 *Tel:* 404-246-0555 *Fax:* 404-246-0051
Membership(s): USDLA

Onkyo USA Corp
Subsidiary of Onkyo Corp
18 Park Way, Upper Saddle River, NJ 07458
Tel: 201-785-2600 *Toll Free Tel:* 800-229-1687 *Fax:* 201-785-2650
Web Site: www.onkyousa.com
Key Personnel
EVP: Tom Ishii
Audio component manufacturer & distributor.
Catalog(s) available

OnLine Power Inc
5701 Smithway St, Commerce, CA 90040
Tel: 323-721-5017 *Toll Free Tel:* 800-227-8899 *Fax:* 323-721-3929
E-mail: sales@onlinepower.com
Web Site: www.onlinepower.com
Key Personnel
Pres: Abbie Gougerchian
Founded: 1975
Manufacturer of medical power products & top switching regulators.
Catalog(s) available
Membership(s): IMSA; ITE

Onstage Systems
10930 Petal St, Dallas, TX 75238
Tel: 972-686-4488 *Fax:* 972-686-7732
E-mail: inquiry@onstagesystems.com
Web Site: www.onstagesystems.com
Key Personnel
Pres: Charles Belcher *E-mail:* charlesb@onstagesystems.com
VP: Vickie Belcher *E-mail:* vickieb@onstagesystems.com
Founded: 1978
Audio equipment rentals.
Membership(s): International Entertainment Buyers Association

Ontario Safety League
2595 Skymark Ave, Suite 212, Mississauga, ON L4W 4Y4, Canada
Tel: 905-625-0556 *Fax:* 905-625-0677
E-mail: info@osl.org
Web Site: www.osl.org; ontariosafetyleague.com
Key Personnel
Pres & Gen Mgr: Brian J Patterson
Founded: 1913
Traffic safety films & videos.

ooLite Media
1702 Nelson Rd, Bozeman, MT 59718
Tel: 406-587-1456 *Toll Free Tel:* 800-798-9980 *Fax:* 406-587-1459
Web Site: www.oolitemedia.com/earthtalk
Key Personnel
CEO & Pres: Daniel J Smith *E-mail:* dan@earthtalk.com
Busn Devt Dir: Kate Bryan *E-mail:* kate@earthtalk.com
Founded: 1990
Multimedia development: commercial & educational.

Opamp Labs Inc
1033 N Sycamore Ave, Los Angeles, CA 90038
Tel: 323-934-3566 *Fax:* 323-462-6490
E-mail: opamplabs@gmail.com
Web Site: www.opamplabs.com
Key Personnel
Pres: Bel Losmandy
Sales Mgr: I Losmandy
Founded: 1965
Manufacture amplifiers, switchers, press boxes, audio transformers, oscillators & power supplies.
Catalog(s) available
Online catalog(s) available

Open Media Foundation
700 Kalamath St, Denver, CO 80204
Tel: 720-222-0159 *Fax:* 303-534-5098
E-mail: info@openmediafoundation.org
Web Site: openmediafoundation.org; denveropenmedia.org
Key Personnel
Founder & Exec Dir: Tony Shawcross

Open Text Corp
275 Frank Tompa Dr, Waterloo, ON N2L 0A1, Canada
Tel: 519-888-7111 *Toll Free Tel:* 800-499-6544; 800-4996-5440 (intl) *Fax:* 519-888-0677
E-mail: support@opentext.com
Web Site: www.opentext.com
Key Personnel
Dir, Industry Analyst Rels: Margaret E Dobbin *Tel:* 519-888-7111 ext 2410 *E-mail:* mdobbin@opentext.com
PR Coord: Julie Hause *Tel:* 519-888-7111 ext 2223 *E-mail:* jhause@opentext.com
Founded: 1991
Provider of enterprise content management solutions.
Catalog(s) available

Oppenheimer Camera Products
7400 Third Ave S, Seattle, WA 98108-4143
Tel: 206-467-8666 *Toll Free Tel:* 877-467-8666 *Fax:* 206-467-9165
Web Site: oppenheimercameraproducts.com
Key Personnel
Pres: Marty Oppenheimer *E-mail:* marty@oppcam.com
Founded: 1979
Film & video equipment rental, sales & service.

Opterna AM
44901 Falcon Place, Suite 116, Sterling, VA 20166-9531
Tel: 703-653-1130 *Toll Free Tel:* 800-248-9004 *Fax:* 703-803-8313
Web Site: www.opterna-am.com
Key Personnel
CFO: Michael Staples
VP & Gen Mgr: Bret A Matz
VP, Mktg: Atikem Haile-Marian
Dir, Opers: Abraham Chandy
Catalog(s) available
Membership(s): PCTA; SCTE

Opti-Case Inc
1175 CR 481 W, Henderson, TX 75654
Tel: 903-657-5666 *Toll Free Tel:* 800-637-6635 *Fax:* 903-657-6030
E-mail: sales@opti-case.net
Web Site: www.opti-case.net
Key Personnel
Contact: Charlotte Thrasher
Founded: 1978

Optibase Inc
Subsidiary of VITEC Multimedia
931 Benecia Ave, Sunnyvale, CA 94085
Toll Free Tel: 800-451-5101 *Fax:* 408-739-1706
Web Site: www.optibase.com
Key Personnel
VP, Prod Mgmt: Eli Garten
Mng Dir: Yaron Comarov
Mgr, R&D: Tomer Carmi
Founded: 1990
Foreign Office(s): Cyber Tower, Bldg A, Rm 2703, 2 Zhong Guan Cun South Ave, Haidian District, Beijing 100086, China *Tel:* (010) 5172-7086 *Fax:* (010) 5172-7096
7 Shenkar St, PO Box 2170, 46120 Herzlia, Israel *Tel:* (09) 9709200 *Fax:* (09) 9709222

Optic Bindery & Packaging
407 Fair Hill Ct, Annapolis, MD 21403-1649
Toll Free Tel: 877-767-0099 *Fax:* 410-295-0079
Web Site: www.pointofpurchasestore.com
Key Personnel
Pres: David Kinlein *Tel:* 410-974-6364 *E-mail:* dakinlein@yahoo.com
Manufacture multimedia packaging products. Duplication, packaging & distribution of cassette, video, CD & DVD.
Catalog(s) available

Optical Disc Solutions Inc
1767 Sheridan St, Richmond, IN 47374
Tel: 765-935-7574 *Toll Free Tel:* 800-704-7648 *Fax:* 765-935-0174
Web Site: www.odiscs.com
Key Personnel
VP, Sales: Brian Klaine *Tel:* 800-704-7648 ext 203 *Fax:* 765-935-1570 *E-mail:* bklaine@odiscs.com

Opticomm-EMCORE
2015 Chestnut St, Alhambra, CA 91803
Tel: 626-293-3400; 626-293-3670 (west coast team); 540-626-3381 (east coast team) *Toll Free Tel:* 800-8OPTICOMM (867-8426) *Fax:* 626-293-3427
E-mail: video-sales@emcore.com
Web Site: www.opticomm.com
Key Personnel
Dir, Busn Devt: Henok Tafese
Founded: 1986
Fiber optic video/audio/data/RGB/sdi comm products.
Catalog(s) available
Branch Office(s)
EMCORE Corp, 10420 Research Rd SE, Albuquerque, NM 87123 *Tel:* 505-332-5000 *Fax:* 505-332-5100 (headquarters)
Foreign Office(s): Camino del tomillaron 59-T8, 28231 Madrid, Spain *Tel:* 916378101
Membership(s): IEEE Computer Society; InfoComm International®; International Technology and Engineering Educators Association; NAB; OFC; OSA; SBE; SPIE

Optics 1 Inc
Subsidiary of Vectronix AG
2 Cooper Lane, Bedford, NH 03110
Tel: 603-296-0469 *Fax:* 603-296-0473
Web Site: www.optics1.com
Founded: 1987
Designers of optical systems & sub-assemblies.
Catalog(s) available

Optikinetics Ltd - The Americas
11211 Air Park Rd, Suite 1, Ashland, VA 23005
Tel: 804-752-2570 *Toll Free Tel:* 800-575-6784 *Fax:* 804-752-2888
E-mail: optius@optikinetics.com
Web Site: www.optikinetics.com
Key Personnel
Owner: Philip Brunker
VP: Arunas Vangas
Mgr: Nick Wallace
Sales Coord: Jennifer Caler *E-mail:* jennifer@optikinetics.com
Manufacturer & distributor of GoBo & solar projection products & aluminum trussing.
Catalog(s), free
Online catalog(s) available
Branch Office(s)
123 Walgreen Rd, Carp, ON K0A 1L0, Canada, Mgr: Ray Turner *Tel:* 613-836-5856 *Fax:* 613-836-6491
Foreign Office(s): Optikinetics Ltd, 38 Cromwell Rd, Luton, Beds LU3 1DN, United Kingdom, Sales Mgr: Idunn Rodziewicz *Tel:* (01582) 411413 *Fax:* (01582) 400613 *E-mail:* optiuk@optikinetics.com *Web Site:* www.optikinetics.co.uk (headquarters)

The Optikon Corp
1099 Guelph St, Kitchener, ON N2B 2E4, Canada
Tel: 519-745-4115 *Fax:* 519-745-6922
E-mail: info@optikon.ca
Web Site: www.optikon.ca
Key Personnel
Admin Mgr & Mktg: Kathy Dietrich *Tel:* 519-745-4115 ext 231
Founded: 1974
Sales of photonic products including light instrumentation: lightmeters, colormeters, spotmeters.
Catalog(s) available

Optimum Production Services Inc
1490 S Sheridan Way, Mississauga, ON L5H 1Z8, Canada
Tel: 905-278-2125 *Toll Free Tel:* 800-461-4979
E-mail: optimum@optimumprod.com
Web Site: www.optimumprod.com
Key Personnel
Mng Dir: Louis Hurtubise
Founded: 1990
Audio, video production & post-production services.
Branch Office(s)
5-1153 Cartier St, Chambly, QC J3L 2K9, Canada
Membership(s): Association of Language Dubbers in Canada

Optimus
161 E Grand Ave, Chicago, IL 60611
Tel: 312-321-0880
Web Site: www.optimus.com
Key Personnel
Pres: Tom Duff
Exec Prodr/Mng Dir: Gretchen Praeger *Tel:* 312-276-2410 *E-mail:* gretchen@optimus.com

Exec Prodr: Brian Hrastar *Tel:* 312-276-2444 *E-mail:* brian@optimus.com
Full service film & video production company.
Catalog(s) available
Branch Office(s)
1237 Seventh St, Santa Monica, CA 90401, VP/Mng Dir: Therese Hunsberger *Tel:* 301-917-2761 *E-mail:* therese@optimus.com
Membership(s): AICP; IAAVC; MCA-I; NAB; SMPTE

Optisonics Productions
311 South Pkwy, Clifton, NJ 07014
Tel: 973-458-0951 *Fax:* 973-458-0983
E-mail: optisonics@aol.com
Web Site: www.optisonics.com
Key Personnel
Pres: Jim Brown *E-mail:* jimbrown@optisonics.com
Graphic & multi-media production & audio recording.
Brochure(s) available

Optix Digital Pictures & Sound
157 Princess St, Toronto, ON M5A 4M4, Canada
Tel: 416-214-9911 *Fax:* 416-214-9912
Web Site: www.optix.ca
Key Personnel
Owner & Head, Post-Prodn: George Levai *E-mail:* george@optix.ca
Founded: 1996
Full service audio & video post-production facility.

Optronics®
Division of Karl Storz Imaging
175 Cremona Dr, Goleta, CA 93117
Tel: 805-968-3568 *Toll Free Tel:* 800-796-8909 *Fax:* 805-968-0933
E-mail: oeinfo@optronics.com
Web Site: www.optronics.com
Key Personnel
Dir, Busn Devt: Richard Crandall *E-mail:* rcrandall@optronics.com
Manufacturer & distributor of video & digital cameras.
Catalog(s) available
Membership(s): National Endowment for the Arts

Opulen Studios
1309 S Flower St, Los Angeles, CA 90015
Tel: 310-867-5023; 310-902-6996
E-mail: info@opulenstudios.com
Web Site: opulenstudios.com
Photography studio, film location & event venue.

Oral Tradition Sound & Music
PO Box 51155, Pacific Grove, CA 93950-6155
Tel: 831-372-0352 *Toll Free Tel:* 800-779-1116 (orders)
Key Personnel
Owner: Richard Chelew *E-mail:* rick@chelew.com
Founded: 1990
Audio books (produce & distribute) & location sound recording.
Catalog(s) available

Orange County Sound Stage
17518 Von Karman Ave, Irvine, CA 92614
Tel: 714-598-6557
E-mail: sm@ocsoundstage.com
Web Site: orangecountysoundstage.com
Video production studio.

Orban
Division of JBL Professionals
8350 E Evans Rd, Suite C-4, Scottsdale, AZ 85260
Tel: 480-403-8300 *Fax:* 480-403-8302
E-mail: info@orban.com; sales@orban.com
Web Site: www.orban.com
Key Personnel
Dir, Sales & Mktg: David Rusch *Tel:* 480-403-8322 *E-mail:* drusch@orban.com
Professional broadcast technology manufacturer.
Catalog(s) available
Branch Office(s)
Orban Northern California Design Center Group, 14798 Wicks Blvd, San Leandro, CA 94577 *Tel:* 510-351-3500 *Fax:* 510-297-2701

Orevox USA Corp
240 N Puente Ave, City of Industry, CA 91746-2303
Mailing Address: PO Box 2655, City of Industry, CA 91746-0655
Tel: 626-336-0516 *Toll Free Tel:* 800-237-0700 *Fax:* 626-336-3748
Web Site: www.dynavox.com
Key Personnel
Pres: Dan Wu
OEM of home theater sound systems, DJ & PA sound systems, sirens & alarms, parts & accessories & flat panel TVs.
Catalog(s), annual

Oriental Records Inc
96 E Williston Ave, East Williston Park, NY 11596-2017
Mailing Address: PO Box 387, Williston Park, NY 11596-0387
Tel: 516-746-0140 *Fax:* 516-747-4285
E-mail: info@orientalrecords.com; orientalcd@aol.com
Web Site: www.orientalrecords.com
Key Personnel
Pres: Mr Rangasami Parthasarthy
Founded: 1977
Classical & "pop" Indian music & CDs for learning Indian language.

Origin Instruments Corp
854 Greenview Dr, Grand Prairie, TX 75050-2438
Tel: 972-606-8740 *Fax:* 972-606-8741
E-mail: support@orin.com; marketing@orin.com
Web Site: www.orin.com
Key Personnel
VP: Mel Dashner
Founded: 1990
Develops & manufactures advanced electro-optical instruments & software.
Catalog(s) available

Original Cast Records
PO Box 496, Georgetown, CT 06829-0496
Tel: 203-544-8288 *Fax:* 203-544-8288
E-mail: originalcast@aol.com
Web Site: www.originalcastrecords.com; footlight.com
Key Personnel
Owner & Pres: Bruce Yeko
Record distributor.
Catalog(s) available
Shipping Address: 33 Irmgard, Wilton, CT 06897
Membership(s): The Recording Academy

Orion Software
6000 Cote-des-Neiges, Suite 240, Montreal, QC H3S 1Z8, Canada
Tel: 514-484-9661 *Toll Free Tel:* 877-755-2012 *Fax:* 514-484-1339
E-mail: info@orion-soft.com
Web Site: www.orion-soft.com
Key Personnel
Pres: Patrice Boivin *E-mail:* pboivin@orion-soft.com
Sales Mgr: Gary Kappel *E-mail:* gkappel@orion-soft.com
Computer software, rental software.

Orlando Special Effects
14222 Lake Mary Jane Rd, Orlando, FL 32832
Tel: 407-648-1867 *Fax:* 407-273-0328
Web Site: www.orlandospfx.com
Key Personnel
Pres: Andrew Nicholls *E-mail:* andy@orlandospfx.com
Founded: 1990
SPFX equipment.
Membership(s): Hollywood Foreign Press Association; IAAPA; International Alliance of Theatrical Stage Employees; Pyrotechnics Guild International

Rob Orr Productions Ltd
1336 Pine St, Glenview, IL 60025
Tel: 847-724-5228 *Fax:* 847-729-7319
E-mail: rob@roborrproductions.com
Web Site: www.roborrproductions.com
Key Personnel
Prodr & Dir: Rob Orr
Founded: 1982
Video production services.

Orvac Electronics
1645 E Orangethorpe Ave, Fullerton, CA 92831
Tel: 714-871-1020 *Fax:* 714-871-1951
E-mail: myorvac@orvac.com
Web Site: www.orvac.com
Key Personnel
CEO & Pres: L J Vaccher
Founded: 1958
Family owned electronics distributor. Stocks a wide variety of products including electronic components, relays & switches, data & networking products, video security, structured cabling, commercial sound equipment, wire & cable, audio & video accessories & test equipment.

Osho Viha Information Center & Book Distributors
Division of America Multi Media Corp
PO Box 352, Mill Valley, CA 94942-0352
Tel: 415-472-5381 *Toll Free Tel:* 866-856-7019 *Fax:* 415-472-5149
E-mail: oshoviha@oshoviha.org
Web Site: www.oshoviha.org
Key Personnel
Pres: Swami Prabodh Dhanyam
Founded: 1986
Catalog(s) available
Membership(s): Reading Recovery Council of North America

Osorio Media, see Video Ideas Productions

Osram Sylvania Inc
100 Endicott St, Danvers, MA 01923
Tel: 978-777-1900 *Toll Free Tel:* 800-842-7010 *Fax:* 978-750-2152
Web Site: www.sylvania.com
Key Personnel
Sales Mgr: Howard Ames
Manufacturer & distributor of lighting fixtures & equipment.
Catalog(s) available
Branch Office(s)
71 Cherry Hill Dr, Beverly, MA 01915 *Tel:* 978-777-1900
54 Cherry Hill Dr, Danvers, MA 01923
800 Church St, Lake Zurich, IL 60047 *Tel:* 847-726-6200
Valeo Sylvania, 1231 A Ave N, Seymour, IN 47274 *Tel:* 812-523-5200 *Fax:* 812-524-5316 (joint venture with Valeo)
1000 Tyrone Pike, Versailles, KY 40383 *Tel:* 859-873-7351
435 E Washington St, Winchester, KY 40391 *Tel:* 859-744-3464
131 Portsmouth Ave, Exeter, NH 03833 *Tel:* 603-772-4331

275 W Main St, Hillsboro, NH 03244 *Tel:* 603-464-5533
655 S Willow St, Manchester, NH 03103 *Tel:* 603-669-5350
835 Washington Rd, St Marys, PA 15857 *Tel:* 814-834-1800
One Jackson St, Wellsboro, PA 16901 *Tel:* 570-724-8200
Osram Sylvania Ltd/LTEE, 2001 Drew Rd, Mississauga L5S 1S4, Canada, Contact: Steven Duff *Tel:* 905-673-6171 *Toll Free Tel:* 800-LIGHTBULB (544-4828) *Fax:* 905-671-5584 (Canadian headquarters)
Sales Office(s): 18725 N Union St, Westfield, IN 46074 *Tel:* 317-867-6000 *Toll Free Tel:* 800-LIGHTBULB (544-4828) (also cust serv)

Osram Sylvania Ltd/LTEE
2001 Drew Rd, Mississauga, ON L5S 1S4, Canada
Tel: 905-673-6171 *Toll Free Tel:* 800-LIGHTBULB (544-4828) *Fax:* 905-671-5584
Web Site: www.sylvania.com
Key Personnel
Dir, Mktg: Steven Duff *Tel:* 905-673-6171 ext 5596
Manufacturer & distributor of lighting fixtures & equipment.
Catalog(s) available
Branch Office(s)
One Sylvan St, Drummondville, QC J2C 2S8, Canada *Tel:* 819-478-6500
Osram Sylvania Inc, 100 Endicott St, Danvers, MA 01923, Sales Mgr: Howard Ames *Tel:* 978-777-1900 *Toll Free Tel:* 800-842-7010 *Fax:* 978-750-2152 (US headquarters)
Membership(s): CITT; CSG; STLD

Ostergaard Acoustical Associates
200 Executive Dr, Suite 350, West Orange, NJ 07052
Tel: 973-731-7002 *Fax:* 973-731-6680
E-mail: info@acousticalconsultant.com
Web Site: www.acousticalconsultant.com
Key Personnel
Principal: Edward M Clark *E-mail:* emclark@acousticalconsultant.com
Sr Consultant: Joe Keefe *E-mail:* jkeefe@acousticalconsultant.com
Founded: 1972
Acoustical engineering.
Membership(s): American Council of Engineering Companies; National Council of Acoustical Consultants

Osum Event Rentals
562 First Ave S, Suite 100, Seattle, WA 98104
Tel: 206-209-2012 *Fax:* 206-209-2013
E-mail: info@osumeventrentals.com
Web Site: osumeventrentals.com
Key Personnel
Owner: Chad Anderson
Event gear & decor rentals.

OSV Studios
29605 Lorain Rd N, Olmsted, OH 44070
Tel: 440-779-1900
Web Site: www.osvstudios.com
Key Personnel
Pres: Craig Smith *E-mail:* csmith@osvstudios.com
Busn Mgr: Kelly Smith *E-mail:* ksmith@osvstudios.com
Consumer Prodn Mgr: Michele Schneider *E-mail:* mschneider@osvstudios.com
Video production facility, including editing & graphics, studio space, audio recording, grip truck & equipment rentals.

OTR Studios
PO Box 874, Belmont, CA 94002
Tel: 650-595-8475
E-mail: info@otrstudios.com
Web Site: www.otrstudios.com
Key Personnel
Owner: Cookie Marenco *E-mail:* cookie@otrstudios.com
Gen Mgr: Patrick O'Connor *Tel:* 650-759-1357 *E-mail:* patrick@otrstudios.com

Ott Film Rentals
6901 Castor Ave, Philadelphia, PA 19149
Tel: 215-745-8964 *Toll Free Tel:* 800-545-4558 *Fax:* 215-745-8965
Key Personnel
Owner: Robert M Ott *E-mail:* robertott6901@yahoo.com
Film & tape transfer to DVD.
Catalog(s) available
Membership(s): PMA International

Our Sunday Visitor Inc
200 Noll Plaza, Huntington, IN 46750
Tel: 260-356-8400 *Toll Free Tel:* 800-348-2440 *Fax:* 260-356-8472
E-mail: osvsales@osv.com
Web Site: www.osv.com
Key Personnel
Dir, Mktg & Ad: John Christensen *E-mail:* jchristensen@osv.com
Distributor of Catholic books & videos.
Catalog(s) available
Membership(s): Catholic Press Association

Out of the BLUE Media
1413 Brenda Lane, Allen, TX 75002
Tel: 469-853-9015
Web Site: www.outofthebluemedia.com
Key Personnel
Prodr: Chuck Andrle *E-mail:* chuck@outofthebluemedia.com

Outland Technology Inc
38190 Commercial Ct, Slidell, LA 70458
Tel: 985-847-1104 *Fax:* 985-847-1106
E-mail: sales@outlandtech.com
Web Site: www.outlandtech.com
Key Personnel
Design Engr: Charles Daussin; Buddy Mayfield
Founded: 1984
Underwater video systems.

Outside The Box Interactive LLC
150 Bay St, Suite 706, Jersey City, NJ 07302
Tel: 201-610-0625 *Fax:* 201-610-0627
E-mail: theoffice@outboxin.com
Web Site: www.outboxin.com
Key Personnel
Founder & Mng Partner: Frank DeMarco
Partner, Creative Servs: Lauren Schwartz
Founded: 1995
Interactive design & marketing.

Outsource Engineering & Manufacturing Inc dba Texscan MSI
11800 Wills Rd, Suite 150, Alpharetta, GA 30009
Tel: 678-689-0146; 770-642-7440 (support)
E-mail: sales@texscan-msi.com
Web Site: www.texscan-msi.com
Key Personnel
Pres: Leonard J Fabiano
Sales & Info Dept: Joe Fabiano
Serv & Support Dept: Corey Kearns
Founded: 1980
Manufacturer & marketer.
Brochure(s), available upon request
Membership(s): NAB; SCTE

Outwater Plastics Industries Inc
Affiliate of Architectural Products by Outwater LLC
24 River Rd, Bogota, NJ 07603
Mailing Address: PO Box 500, Bogota, NJ 07603
Tel: 201-498-8750 *Toll Free Tel:* 800-631-8375 *Fax:* 201-498-8751 *Toll Free Fax:* 800-888-3315
E-mail: info@outwaterplastics.com
Web Site: www.outwater.com
Key Personnel
Mktg: Joey Shimm
Founded: 1972
Stocking more than 65,000 standard & innovative component product essentials which include extrusions, injection molded parts, casters, store fixture components, lighting, engineering plastics, millwork & hardware.
Catalog(s), monthly, free, print (master, supplements)
Sales Office(s): 4720 W Van Buren, PO Box 18190, Phoenix, AZ 85043 *Tel:* 602-447-0936 *Fax:* 602-447-0444
Membership(s): NASFM

Oval Window Audio
33 Wildflower Ct, Nederland, CO 80466
Tel: 303-447-3607 *Fax:* 303-447-3607
E-mail: info@ovalwindowaudio.com
Web Site: www.ovalwindowaudio.com
Key Personnel
Dir, R&D: Norman Lederman *E-mail:* norman@ovalwindowaudio.com
Educ Dir: Paula Hendricks *E-mail:* paula@ovalwindowaudio.com
Founded: 1984
Hearing assistance systems compatible with hearing aids, multisensory sound systems for educational & therapeutic applications.
Catalog(s) available
Online catalog(s) available

OWI Inc
17141 Kingsview Ave, Carson, CA 90746
Tel: 310-515-1900 *Toll Free Tel:* 800-638-1694 *Fax:* 310-515-1606
E-mail: info@owi-inc.com
Web Site: www.owi-inc.com
Key Personnel
Natl Regl Sales Mgr: Giovanni Rossini *Tel:* 954-449-6272 *E-mail:* gio@owi-inc.com
Founded: 1978
Catalog(s) available

Ozam Production
1516 Equestrian Rd, Ozark, MO 65721
Tel: 417-866-3232
Web Site: ozam.com
Key Personnel
Owner & Prodr: Dale DeToni
Founded: 1978
Audio & video production services.

Pace Systems
Division of Pace Sound & Lighting Inc
824 Dakin St, New Orleans, LA 70121
Tel: 504-837-4224 *Toll Free Tel:* 800-722-3797 *Fax:* 504-837-4307
E-mail: info@pacesys.com
Web Site: www.pacesys.com
Key Personnel
Pres: Peter Schulman
VP: Patricia Schulman
Founded: 1976
Technical stage production company.

PACE Worldwide
255 Air Tool Dr, Southern Pines, NC 28387
Tel: 910-695-7223 *Fax:* 910-695-1594
E-mail: support@paceworldwide.com; sales@paceworldwide.com
Web Site: www.paceworldwide.com
Electronic design assembly & productivity solutions company.

Foreign Office(s): Pace Europe Ltd, 11 Holdom Ave, Bletchley, Milton Keyes, Bucks MK1 1QU, United Kingdom *Tel:* (01908) 277666 *Fax:* (01908) 277777

Pacific Audio-Visual Enterprises
3807 E Green St, Pasadena, CA 91107-3904
Tel: 626-449-9353 *Toll Free Tel:* 888-240-8012 *Fax:* 626-395-9793
Web Site: www.stereosoundbook.com
Key Personnel
Prop: Ron Streicher *E-mail:* rs@stereosoundbook.com
Founded: 1972
Audio recording & production services, specializing in on-location "live-to-stereo" & "live surroundsound" audio production.
Membership(s): AES; New York Women in Film & Television

Pacific Grip & Lighting Inc
6550 NE Portland Hwy, Portland, OR 97218
Tel: 503-233-4747 *Fax:* 503-233-5830
E-mail: info@pacific-grip.com
Web Site: pacific-grip.com
Key Personnel
Mgr: Doug Boss
Lighting fixture & equipment distributor.
Catalog(s) available
Branch Office(s)
10401 Martin Luther King Jr Way S, Seattle, WA 98178, Rental Mgr: Ray Hammond *Tel:* 206-622-8540 *Fax:* 206-292-2919
Membership(s): MCA-I; Washington Film & Video Association; Washington Motion Picture Council

Pacific International Enterprises Inc (PIE)
401 Crater Lake Ave, Suite 2, Medford, OR 97504
Mailing Address: PO Box 1727, Medford, OR 97501-0256
Tel: 541-779-0990 *Toll Free Tel:* 800-547-2316 *Fax:* 541-779-0880
E-mail: info@family-films.com
Web Site: www.family-films.com
Key Personnel
Pres: Arthur R Dubs
VP: Arn S Wihtol *E-mail:* arn@piefilm.com
Producer & distributor of videos & films.
Catalog(s) available

Pacific Light Studios
265 Caspian Dr, Sunnyvale, CA 94089
Tel: 408-541-1800
Web Site: www.pacificlightstudios.com
Key Personnel
Owner: Philip Goldworth
Photog: Mel Lindstrom
Founded: 2009
Commercial photo & video agency providing video production assistance, cameras, lenses & lighting.

Pacific Media
Affiliate of Woodland Media Inc
21730 Nordhoff St, Chatsworth, CA 91311
Mailing Address: PO Box 9744, Canoga Park, CA 91309
Tel: 818-341-3156 *Toll Free Tel:* 800-262-7367 *Fax:* 818-341-3562
E-mail: info@pac-media.com
Web Site: www.pac-media.com
Key Personnel
Pres: Scott Brastow *E-mail:* scott@pac-media.com
Catalog(s) available
Membership(s): Reading Recovery Council of North America

Pacific Multimedia Inc
4917 Seaview Way, Everett, WA 98203
Tel: 425-347-4110 *Toll Free Tel:* 888-373-8273 *Fax:* 425-710-9932
Web Site: www.pacmultimedia.com
Key Personnel
Pres: Jim Campbell *E-mail:* jim@pacmultimedia.com

Pacific Northwest Theatre Associates Inc (PNTA)
2414 SW Andover St, Bldg C100, Seattle, WA 98106
Tel: 206-622-7850 *Toll Free Tel:* 800-622-7850 *Fax:* 206-267-1789
E-mail: sales@pnta.com
Web Site: www.pnta.com
Key Personnel
Pres & CEO: Richard Carlson
Founded: 1975
Distribution & rental of audio equipment & lighting equipment.
Catalog(s), annual, free
Membership(s): Associated General Contractors; Professional Lighting & Sound Association; USITT

Pacific Radio Electronics
3031 Thornton Ave, Burbank, CA 91504
Tel: 818-556-4177 *Toll Free Tel:* 800-634-9476 *Fax:* 818-556-4185
E-mail: sales@pacrad.com
Web Site: www.pacrad.com
Key Personnel
Gen Mgr: Kris Snider
Founded: 1932
Catalog(s) available
Online catalog(s) available
Branch Office(s)
2243 Hollywood Way, Burbank, CA 91505, Contact: Hugh Alcaraz *Tel:* 818-556-4177 *Fax:* 818-556-4185
Membership(s): NAB

Pacific Video Image
9065 E Rosecrans Ave, Bellflower, CA 90706
Tel: 562-634-4200 *Fax:* 562-634-4700
E-mail: info@pvideo.com
Web Site: www.pvideo.com
Key Personnel
Owner: Brad Coker
Ed: David Lopez *E-mail:* david@pvideo.com
Founded: 1986
Video concept design, writing, production & post-production.

Pacific Video Products Inc
14312 Franklin Ave, Suite 100, Tustin, CA 92780
Tel: 714-508-2750 *Toll Free Tel:* 800-576-0060 *Fax:* 714-508-2136
Web Site: www.pacvideo.com
Founded: 1975
Professional distributor of video equipment.
Catalog(s) available

Pacifica Radio Archives
Division of Pacifica Foundation
3729 Cahuenga Blvd W, North Hollywood, CA 91604
Tel: 818-506-1077 *Toll Free Tel:* 800-735-0230 *Fax:* 818-506-1084
E-mail: pacarchive@aol.com
Web Site: www.pacificaradioarchives.org
Key Personnel
Dir, Archives: Brian DeShazor *Tel:* 800-735-0230 ext 263 *E-mail:* brian@pacificaradioarchives.org
Sr Prodr/Opers Dir: Mark Torres *Tel:* 800-735-0230 ext 266 *E-mail:* mark@pacificradioarchives.org
Radio/audio archives.
Online catalog(s) available
Membership(s): National Federation of Community Broadcasters

PACSAT
1629 "S" St, Sacramento, CA 95811
Tel: 916-446-7890; 916-335-1649 (after hours) *Toll Free Tel:* 800-672-2728 *Fax:* 916-446-7893
E-mail: pacsat@pacsat.com
Web Site: www.pacsat.com
Key Personnel
Owner & Pres: Steve Mallory *E-mail:* pacsatboss@pacsat.com
CFO & VP: Karen Ross *E-mail:* karen@pacsat.com
VP, Opers: Marcia Calvin *E-mail:* marcia@pacsat.com
Founded: 1987
Full service satellite & production facility.

Padgitt's
7801 N Lamar Blvd, Suite D84, Austin, TX 78752
Tel: 512-832-9900 *Toll Free Tel:* 800-388-3130 *Fax:* 512-832-0003
E-mail: padgitts@padgitts.com
Web Site: www.padgitts.com
Key Personnel
Owner: Chris Schroeder; Karen Schroeder
Mgr: Ben Burson, III
Founded: 1867
Full service communication specialists.
Catalog(s) available

Pak-Wik Corp
128 Tivoli St, Albany, NY 12207
Tel: 518-465-4556 *Toll Free Tel:* 800-372-5945 *Fax:* 518-465-4559
E-mail: sales@pakwik.com
Web Site: www.pakwik.com
Key Personnel
Pres: Samuel Strasser
Founded: 1936
Manufacture cardboard slip cases, mailers, shipping & packaging.
Catalog(s) available

Pal Productions Inc
4056 NE 174 St, Seattle, WA 98155
Tel: 206-361-9366
E-mail: info@paladventurevideos.com
Web Site: www.paladventurevideos.com
Key Personnel
Pres: Laszlo Pal *E-mail:* lazpal123@gmail.com
Founded: 1969
Producer of award-winning outdoor adventure videos.
Membership(s): Director's Guild of Canada; International Alliance of Theatrical Stage Employees & Moving Picture Machine Operators of the United States & Canada; NATAS

Palace Costume & Prop Co
835 N Fairfax Ave, Hollywood, CA 90046
Tel: 323-651-5458 *Fax:* 323-658-7133
E-mail: rentals@palacecostume.com
Web Site: www.palacecostume.com
Key Personnel
Pres: Melody Barnett
Mgr: Valerie Speaks
Founded: 1970
Rent authentic 1850-1990 costumes & props - jewelry & fashion accessories.

Palace Digital Studios
29 N Main St, South Norwalk, CT 06854
Tel: 203-853-1740 *Fax:* 203-855-9608
Web Site: www.palacedigital.com
Key Personnel
COO & Pres: Wendy Lambert *E-mail:* wendy@palacedigital.com

VP, Opers: Maureen Connelly *E-mail:* maureen@palacedigital.com
Full service video post-production center.
Rate card(s) available
Membership(s): PromaxBDA

Palardo Productions
Subsidiary of Palardo Studios
1807 Taft Ave, Suite 4, Hollywood, CA 90028
Tel: 323-469-8991
E-mail: palardo2@msn.com
Key Personnel
Prodr & Dir: Paul Ardolino
Casting Dir: Sandy Sanchez Wright
Dir, Devt: Tommy Ardolino
Music Dir: Bjorn Englen
Dir, Photog: Russell Carpenter
Assoc Prodr: Chip Clements
Chief Audio Engr: Paul Mittenberg
Cust Rels: Deanna Palfrey
Prodn Designer & Modeler: Dr Alan Friedler
Cable Boy: Todd Skelton
Founded: 1971
Full service production company.
Membership(s): DGA; PGA; SMPTE; Writers Guild of America West

Shelly Palmer Production
PO Box 1877, New York, NY 10156-1877
Tel: 212-532-3880
E-mail: info@shellypalmer.com
Web Site: www.shellypalmer.com
Key Personnel
Pres: Shelly Palmer
Founded: 1982
Demo reel(s) available

Panamax
Subsidiary of Core Brands LLC
1800 S McDowell Blvd, 2nd fl, Petaluma, CA 94954
Tel: 707-283-5900 (intl) *Toll Free Tel:* 800-472-5555 (US & CN) *Fax:* 707-283-5901
E-mail: custrelations@panamax.com
Web Site: www.panamax.com
Founded: 1975
Manufactures high-end power protection/filtration products for custom AV installations; power filters, line conditioners, surge protection.
Product sheet(s), online
Branch Office(s)
4064 County Rd, Suite 1, Yarker, ON K0K 3N0, Canada *Tel:* 613-377-1058 *Fax:* 613-377-1034
Foreign Office(s): Concominio Ciudad Vieja, Apto 12 Sur, 8a Calle 1-71, Zona 10, 01010 Guatemala, Guatemala *Tel:* (02) 332-5188

Panasonic Broadcast & Digital Systems Co
Division of Panasonic Corp
3330 Cahuenga Blvd W, Los Angeles, CA 90068
Tel: 323-436-3507 *Fax:* 323-436-3615
Web Site: www.panasonic.com
Key Personnel
CEO & Pres: Rance Poehler
World leader in electronics.
Catalog(s) available
Branch Office(s)
Western Region, 4001 W Alameda, Suite 100, Burbank, CA 91505, Contact: Jim Thibodeaux *Tel:* 818-562-1501
Eastern Region, 50 Meadowlands Pkwy, Secaucus, NJ 07094 *Tel:* 201-348-7975

Panasonic Consumer Electronics Co
Division of Panasonic Corp
One Panasonic Way, Secaucus, NJ 07094
Tel: 201-348-7066 *Toll Free Tel:* 800-211-PANA (211-7262)
Web Site: www.panasonic.com
Key Personnel
CEO & Pres: James Sanduski
World leader in electronics manufacturing.
Catalog(s) available

Panasonic Corp
One Panasonic Way, Secaucus, NJ 07094
Tel: 201-348-7000 *Toll Free Tel:* 800-211-7262; 888-275-2595 *Fax:* 201-348-7807
Web Site: www.panasonic.com
Key Personnel
COO & Pres: Joe Taylor
Founded: 1959

Panasonic Professional Audio Systems
Division of Panasonic Corp
3330 Cahuenga Blvd W, Los Angeles, CA 90068
Tel: 323-436-3616 *Fax:* 323-436-3618
Web Site: www.panasonic.com
Catalog(s) available
Membership(s): AES; NAMM, the National Association of Music Merchants; NSCA

Panavideo Inc
347 Marie de l'Incarnation, Quebec, QC G1N 3G9, Canada
Tel: 418-687-3150 *Toll Free Tel:* 800-463-5076 *Fax:* 418-687-0366
E-mail: info@panavideo.net
Web Site: www.panavideo.net
Key Personnel
Mktg Mgr: Norman Fiset
Full service AV equipment distributor.
Catalog(s) available
Branch Office(s)
3777 Blvd du Tricentenaire, Montreal, QC H1B 5W3, Canada *Tel:* 514-354-3152 *Fax:* 514-354-1728
Membership(s): MCA-I

Panavision Dallas
8000 Jetstar Dr, Irving, TX 75063
Tel: 972-929-8585 *Toll Free Tel:* 800-260-1846 *Fax:* 972-929-8686
Web Site: www.panavision.com
Key Personnel
Gen Mgr: John Schrimpf *E-mail:* john_schrimpf@panavision.com
Founded: 1954
Film equipment rentals.
Catalog(s) available
Membership(s): AICP; DPA; Production Equipment Rental Association; Texas Association of Motion Media Professionals; Women in Film

P&H Chrystalite Inc
101 Palm Harbor Pkwy, Unit 117, Palm Coast, FL 32137
Tel: 561-330-8660 *Fax:* 561-330-8665 *Toll Free Fax:* 800-468-8673
E-mail: phcrystalite@aol.com
Web Site: www.phcled.com
Key Personnel
Pres: Richard Rubin
LED lighting products.
Catalog(s) available

Pandisc Music Corp
247 SW Eighth St, Suite 349, Miami, FL 33130
Tel: 305-557-1914 *Toll Free Fax:* 888-493-7778
Web Site: www.pandisc.com
Key Personnel
Pres: Bo Crane *Tel:* 305-557-1914 ext 128 *E-mail:* bocrane@pandisc.com
Founded: 1982
Catalog(s) available

P&P Studios Inc
110 Lenox Ave, Suite 210, Stamford, CT 06906
Tel: 203-359-9292 *Toll Free Tel:* 888-WEPRODUCE (937-7638)
E-mail: ppstudios@weproduce.com
Web Site: www.weproduce.com
Key Personnel
Pres: John R Fishback
VP, Admin: Abbie Wilson
VP, Mktg: Layne Rodney
Founded: 1970
Full range of AV & multimedia production services.
Catalog(s) available

Pangolin Laser Systems Inc
9501 Satellite Blvd, Suite 109, Orlando, FL 32837
Tel: 407-299-2088 *Toll Free Tel:* 800-PANGOLIN (726-4654) *Fax:* 407-299-6066
E-mail: contact@pangolin.com
Web Site: www.pangolin.com
Key Personnel
CTO & Pres: William R Benner
Founded: 1986
Professional laser show software manufacturer.
Catalog(s) available
Membership(s): ELA; IAAPA; ILDA

Panorama Productions
5320 Croy Rd, Morgan Hill, CA 95037
Tel: 408-727-7500
E-mail: information@panorama-productions.com
Web Site: www.panorama-productions.com
Key Personnel
Pres: Don Dulmage *E-mail:* don@panonet.com
VP: Debbie Dulmage *E-mail:* debbie@panonet.com
Founded: 1965
Membership(s): IAAVC; PPA

Panorama Publishing Co
Subsidiary of Hypnosis Motivation Institute
18607 Ventura Blvd, Suite 310, Tarzana, CA 91356-4158
Tel: 818-758-2747 *Toll Free Tel:* 800-634-5620; 800-479-9464 (home study school) *Fax:* 818-344-2262
Web Site: www.hypnosis.edu
Key Personnel
Dir: George J Kappas
Publishers of self-help books & tapes.
Catalog(s) available

Panta Rhei Media Inc
565 Beulah Rd, Turtle Creek, PA 15145
Tel: 412-824-8858
E-mail: info@panta-rhei.com
Web Site: www.panta-rhei.com
Key Personnel
Pres: Martha O'Grady
Founded: 1983
Multimedia, communication design, videotape, DVD & Internet, production, consultation & training for business, industry & healthcare.

Tom Pantages
87 Short St, Marlboro, MA 01752
Tel: 508-305-2828 *Fax:* 508-305-2828
E-mail: pantages@comcast.net
Catalog(s) available
Membership(s): American Society of Picture Professionals; New England Outdoor Writers Association Inc

Pantomime Pictures Inc
12144 Riverside Dr, North Hollywood, CA 91607
Tel: 818-980-5555
Key Personnel
Pres & Creative Dir: Fred Crippen
VP: Julie Crippen
Prodr: Matt Crippen
Animation production service company.

Parabola Audio/Video
Subsidiary of Society for the Study of Myth & Tradition
20 W 20 St, 2nd fl, New York, NY 10011

Tel: 212-822-8806 (edit & publg); 201-656-7220 (ad) *Toll Free Tel:* 800-560-MYTH (560-6984); 877-593-2521 (subns) *Fax:* 212-822-8823
E-mail: info@parabola.org
Web Site: www.parabola.org
Key Personnel
Ed-in-Chief: Jeff Zaleski
Mng Ed: Dale Fuller
Distribute childrens CDs & DVDs & religious DVDs.
Catalog(s) available
Membership(s): Photo Marketing Association

Paradigm Marketing & Creative
8275 Tournament Dr, Suite 330, Memphis, TN 38125
Tel: 901-685-7703 *Fax:* 901-531-8513
E-mail: info@2dimes.com
Web Site: www.2dimes.com
Key Personnel
Principal & Pres: Charles T Gaushell
Founded: 1992
Marketing, illustration, 3D computer graphics, special effects, animation & interactive multimedia firm serving the real estate, architectural, developer, institutional, aviation & medical professions.

Paradise Show & Design Inc
4653 35 St, Orlando, FL 32811
Tel: 407-649-7220 *Fax:* 407-649-7225
E-mail: info@paradiseshow.com
Web Site: www.paradiseshow.com
Key Personnel
Founder & Pres: Larry Epstein
Production services company specializing in staging, technical design & support.
Membership(s): NSCA

Paradise Video & Film
10148 NW 47 St, Sunrise, FL 33351
Tel: 954-747-1118 *Fax:* 954-747-3380
E-mail: info@paradisevideo.com
Web Site: www.paradisevideo.com
Key Personnel
Prodn Mgr: Sabra Karanian *E-mail:* sabra@paradisevideo.com
Founded: 1984
Membership(s): MCA-I; NATAS; WOMPI

Paradoxal Inc
540 Broadway, New York, NY 10012
Tel: 212-366-5526; 917-400-4507 (cell)
E-mail: contact@paradoxal.net
Web Site: www.paradoxal.net
Key Personnel
Owner: Gaetan Rousseau *E-mail:* gaetan@paradoxal.net
Full service production company offering production services all over the US for foreign production companies when they have a project to shoot in the US. Expertise in producing TV programs, TV series, documentaries, music videos, commercials & feature films.

Paragon Studios Inc
820 W Fulton Market, Chicago, IL 60607-1302
Tel: 312-942-0075 *Fax:* 312-942-2488
E-mail: info@paragonstudiosinc.com
Web Site: www.paragonstudiosinc.com
Key Personnel
Secy/Treas: Ned Englehart
Music recording studio.

Parallax Press
2236-B Sixth St, Berkeley, CA 94710
Mailing Address: PO Box 7355, Berkeley, CA 94707-0355
Tel: 510-525-0101 *Toll Free Tel:* 800-863-5290 (book orders) *Fax:* 510-525-7129
E-mail: info@parallax.org
Web Site: www.parallax.org
Key Personnel
Publr & Publicity: Travis Masch *Tel:* 510-525-0101 ext 104 *E-mail:* travism@parallax.org
Sr Ed: Rachel Neumann *Tel:* 510-525-0101 ext 113 *E-mail:* rachel@parallax.org
Prodn Ed: Terri Saul *E-mail:* terri@parallax.org
Accountant: Leslie Schneider *Tel:* 510-525-0101 ext 105 *E-mail:* leslie@parallax.org
Founded: 1986
Producers of religious AV programs & CDs.
Catalog(s) available

Parallax Productions Inc
1711 Longwood Rd, Suite B, Haverhill, FL 33409
Tel: 561-842-7788 *Toll Free Tel:* 844-892-9289 *Fax:* 561-842-4566
E-mail: parllaxpro@aol.com
Web Site: www.parallaxvideoproductions.com
Key Personnel
Pres: Michael Kintzel
VP & Off Mgr: James W Austin
Full service independent video & film production facility.
Catalog(s) available
Membership(s): Florida Motion Picture & Television Association; MCA-I

Paramount Motion Pictures Group
Division of Paramount Pictures Corporation
1515 Broadway, 3rd fl, New York, NY 10019
Tel: 212-258-6000 *Fax:* 212-846-4315
Web Site: www.viacom.com
Key Personnel
VP: Nancy Bannister
Filmmaker & distributor.

Paramount Pictures Corporation
5555 Melrose Ave, Los Angeles, CA 90038
Tel: 323-956-8398
Web Site: www.paramount.com
Key Personnel
Chmn & CEO: Brad Grey
VChmn: Rob Moore
COO: Frederick Huntsberry
CFO & EVP: Mark Badagliacca
Chief Mktg Offr: Josh Greenstein
Pres, Consumer Prods & EVP, Worldwide Mktg Partnerships: LeeAnne Stables
Pres, Domestic Dist, Motion Pictures Group: Don Harris
Pres, Domestic Mktg & Dist: Megan Colligan
Pres, Home Media Dist: Hal Richardson
Pres, Worldwide Home Media Dist: Dennis Maguire
EVP, Worldwide HR: Catherine Houser
Feature film production & distribution, video & DVD worldwide distribution & production of programs for television broadcast & syndication.

Paramount Studios, see The Studios at Paramount

Parasound Products Inc
2250 McKinnon Ave, San Francisco, CA 94124
Tel: 415-397-7100 *Fax:* 415-397-0144
E-mail: sales@parasound.com; marketing@parasound.com; service@parasound.com
Web Site: www.parasound.com
Key Personnel
Pres: Richard Schram *E-mail:* richard@parasound.com
Founded: 1981
Manufacture & distribute audio equipment.
Catalog(s) available
Membership(s): Consumer Electronics Association; Custom Electronic Design & Installation Association; NAMM, the National Association of Music Merchants; NSCA

Parlato Productions
8632 US Rte 2, North Hero, VT 05474
Tel: 802-264-2902
E-mail: info@parlatoproductions.com
Web Site: www.parlatoproductions.com
Key Personnel
Owner & Pres: Richard Parlato *E-mail:* richard.parlato@gmail.com

Parlights Inc
One Wormans Mill Ct, Suite 7, Frederick, MD 21701
Tel: 301-698-9242 *Fax:* 301-846-0369
E-mail: sales@parlights.com
Web Site: www.parlights.com
Key Personnel
CEO & Pres: Cary Levitt *E-mail:* clevitt@parlights.com
Gen Mgr: Lesley Vandever *E-mail:* lvandever@parlights.com
Distributor of theatrical lighting fixtures & equipment.
Membership(s): Professional Lighting & Sound Association; USITT

Partech Lighting Systems Inc
8711 Reading Rd, Cincinnati, OH 45215
Tel: 513-761-5678 *Toll Free Tel:* 800-701-9551 *Fax:* 513-679-8282
E-mail: info@partechlighting.com
Web Site: www.partechlighting.com
Key Personnel
Pres: David Groh
Founded: 1988
Full entertainment lighting services.
Membership(s): Professional Lighting & Sound Association

Parts Express
725 Pleasant Valley Dr, Springboro, OH 45066-1158
Tel: 937-743-3000 *Toll Free Tel:* 866-366-4909; 800-338-0531 (cust serv & tech support) *Fax:* 937-743-1677 *Toll Free Fax:* 866-755-7557
E-mail: sales@parts-express.com
Web Site: www.parts-express.com
Key Personnel
Wholesale Mgr: Brian L Mitchell
Founded: 1986
Leading suppliers of speakers & AV products in the country. Wholesale program available.
Catalog(s), annual, free
Online catalog(s) available
Membership(s): Consumer Electronics Association; Custom Electronic Design & Installation Association; InfoComm International®; NAMM, the National Association of Music Merchants

PASCO
224 48 St, Brooklyn, NY 11220
Tel: 718-833-9100 *Fax:* 718-833-9118
E-mail: pasco2@aol.com
Key Personnel
Pres: Joseph Anastasi
Photographic lab design & fabrication company.

Paso Sound Products Inc
4750-F Goer Dr, Charleston, SC 29406
Tel: 843-308-9005 *Toll Free Tel:* 800-231-3034 *Fax:* 843-308-0904
E-mail: info@pasosound.com
Web Site: www.pasosound.com
Key Personnel
EVP: Paul Mastrangelo
Founded: 1931
Manufacture audio parts.

Catalog(s) available
Membership(s): AES; InfoComm International®; International Background Music Association; NSCA

Jim Passin Productions
1900 W Berwyn Ave, Chicago, IL 60640
Tel: 773-334-0408

Pat Kogan Productions Inc
615 Half Moon Bay, Croton-on-Hudson, NY 10520
Tel: 914-661-0049
Web Site: www.pkpmedia.com
Key Personnel
Pres: Patricia Kogan *E-mail:* pkogan@mac.com
Production company. Also produces & directs videos.
Membership(s): Media Communications Association; New York Women in Film & Television

PatchAmp
20 E Kennedy St, Hackensack, NJ 07601
Tel: 201-457-1504 *Fax:* 201-457-1507
E-mail: sales@patchamp.com
Web Site: www.patchamp.com
Key Personnel
Pres: James Tronolone
Catalog(s) available
Membership(s): NAB; SBE; SMPTE

Patco Resources Inc
9 Washington Circle, Suffern, NY 10901
Tel: 845-357-5300 *Fax:* 845-357-6427
E-mail: musicinfo@patcoresources.com
Web Site: www.patcoresources.com
Key Personnel
Pres: Peter Tracton
Founded: 1980
Music research, licensing & scoring.

Pathway Connectivity Inc
1439 17 Ave SE, Unit 103, Calgary, AB T2G 1J9, Canada
Tel: 403-243-8110 *Fax:* 403-287-1281
E-mail: sales@pathwayconnect.com
Web Site: www.pathwayconnect.com
Key Personnel
Pres: David Higgins
VP, Admin: Mary Lou Higgins
Off Administrator: Bernie Rooke
Full service DMX products manufacturing company.
Catalog(s) available
Membership(s): Professional Lighting & Sound Association

Pauline Books & Media
50 St Paul's Ave, Boston, MA 02130-3491
Tel: 617-522-8911 *Toll Free Tel:* 800-876-4463 (orders); 800-836-9723 (cust serv) *Fax:* 617-541-9805
E-mail: records@pauline.org
Web Site: www.pauline.org
Key Personnel
Publr: Sister Mary Mark Wickenhiser
Mgr: Sister Bridget Charles Ellis
Catalog(s) available

Paulist Press
997 Macarthur Blvd, Mahwah, NJ 07430-9990
Tel: 201-825-7300 *Toll Free Tel:* 800-218-1903 (orders) *Toll Free Fax:* 800-836-3161
E-mail: info@paulistpress.com
Web Site: www.paulistpress.com
Key Personnel
Edit & Perms: Donna Crilly *E-mail:* dcrilly@paulistpress.com
Sales: Bob Byrns *E-mail:* bbyrns@paulistpress.com
Mktg: Gloria Capik *E-mail:* gcapik@paulistpress.com
Founded: 1913
Distributor of religious books, videos & audios, as well as CDs & DVDs.
Online catalog(s) available
Shipping Address: 39 Ramapo Valley Rd, Mahwah, NJ 07430

Paulist Productions
17575 Pacific Coast Hwy, Pacific Palisades, CA 90272-4128
Mailing Address: PO Box 1057, Pacific Palisades, CA 90272-1057
Tel: 310-454-0688 *Toll Free Tel:* 800-624-8613 *Fax:* 310-459-6549
E-mail: paulistmail@paulistproductions.org
Web Site: www.paulistproductions.org
Key Personnel
Pres: Rev Eric Andrews
EVP: Joseph Kim *E-mail:* jkim@paulistproductions.com
Dir, Devt: Marybeth Sprows
Off Asst: Mark Ortiz
Founded: 1960
Religious film & TV program producers.
Catalog(s) available
Membership(s): DGA; SAG-AFTRA; Writers Guild of America

PBS Video
Division of Public Broadcasting Service
1320 Braddock Place, Alexandria, VA 22314
Tel: 703-739-5021
E-mail: video@pbs.org
Web Site: video.pbs.org; www.shoppbs.org
Key Personnel
Corp Communs: Anne Bentley *E-mail:* awbentley@pbs.org
Founded: 1969
Producers of children's & educational programs & DVDs.
Catalog(s) available

"PBTM" Music
1160 W 26 Ave, Eugene, OR 97405
Tel: 541-345-8117
E-mail: support@pbtmlive.com
Web Site: www.pbtmlive.com; pbtm.com
Key Personnel
Owner: Michael Brewer
Founded: 1989
Catalog(s) available
Online catalog(s) available

PC&E
2235 DeFoor Hills Rd, Atlanta, GA 30318
Tel: 404-609-9001 *Toll Free Tel:* 800-537-4021 *Fax:* 404-609-9926
Web Site: www.pce-atlanta.com
Key Personnel
Camera Mgr: Paul O'Daniel *E-mail:* paul@pce-atlanta.com
Rental Mgr: Jon Omps *E-mail:* jon@pce-atlanta.com
Camera equipment distributor, lighting, stages & studio for TV commercials.

PCO-TECH Inc
6930 Metroplex Dr, Romulus, MI 48174
Tel: 248-276-8820 *Fax:* 248-276-8825
E-mail: info@pco-tech.com; service@pco-tech.com
Web Site: www.pco-tech.com
Key Personnel
Pres: Steve Daicos
Opers Mgr: Barry Brandon
Founded: 1986
Photonic instrumentation & complete systems manufacturer, distributed worldwide.
Catalog(s) available

PDC Productions
3217 N Flood Ave, Norman, OK 73069
Tel: 405-360-5130 *Fax:* 405-360-0524
E-mail: info@pdcproductions.com
Web Site: www.pdcproductions.com
Key Personnel
Owner: Patrick M Boylan
Pres: Jane Anderson *Tel:* 405-360-5130 ext 659
Specializes in live event productioon.

Peak Performance Publishing
Subsidiary of Peak Performance Consultants Inc
14728 Shirley St, Omaha, NE 68144
Tel: 402-334-1676 *Toll Free Tel:* 800-293-1676 *Fax:* 402-334-4437
Web Site: www.peakperformanceconsult.com
Key Personnel
Pres: Stephen J Brennan, PhD *E-mail:* brennan160@cox.net
DVD resources for corporate health & wellness.
Online catalog(s) available

Peak Performance Sports LLC
7380 Sand Lake Rd, PMB 5012, Orlando, FL 32819-5248
Tel: 407-909-1700 *Toll Free Tel:* 888-742-7225 *Fax:* 407-909-1789
E-mail: pgapack@aol.com
Web Site: www.peaksports.com
Key Personnel
Owner: Dr Patrick Cohn
Producers & distributors of sports programs.
Catalog(s), annual, free

Pearson Education Canada
Division of Pearson Canada Inc
26 Prince Andrew Place, North York, ON M3C 2T8, Canada
Tel: 416-447-5101 *Toll Free Tel:* 800-361-6128 *Fax:* 416-447-2551 *Toll Free Fax:* 800-563-9196
Web Site: www.pearsonschoolcanada.ca
Key Personnel
Mktg: Stephanie Villano
Produce educational programs.
Catalog(s) available

Peavey Electronics Corp
5022 Hartley Peavey Dr, Meridian, MS 39305
Tel: 601-483-5365 *Fax:* 601-486-1278
E-mail: domesticsales@peavey.com
Web Site: www.peavey.com
Key Personnel
Mktg Communs Mgr: Scott Mire
Founded: 1965
Manufacturer of audio equipment.
Catalog(s) available
Foreign Office(s): Peavey Electronics Ltd, Great Folds Rd, Oakley Hay, Corby, Northamptonshire NN18 9ET, United Kingdom *Tel:* (01536) 461234 *Fax:* (01536) 747222 *E-mail:* info@peavey-eu.com

Pechman Imaging, see Frank D Hurst Corp dba Pechman Imaging

Peckham Productions Inc
50 S Buckhout St, Irvington, NY 10533
Tel: 914-591-4140 *Fax:* 914-591-4149
E-mail: info@peckhampix.com
Web Site: www.peckhampix.com
Key Personnel
Pres & Exec Prodr: Peter H Peckham *E-mail:* peter@peckhampix.com
Assoc Prodr: Waldine E Peckham
Creative Dir: Russell C Peckham
Founded: 1958

Peerbolte Creative
PO Box 754, Warrensburg, MO 64093
Tel: 660-429-1383 *Fax:* 660-429-3666

E-mail: solutions@peerbolte.com
Web Site: www.peerbolte.com
Key Personnel
Principal: David R Peerbolte
System Designer & Technician: Carl S Hutcherson
Founded: 1994
Theatre rigging & lighting consultation & design.
Branch Office(s)
PO Box 571, Cedar Falls, IA 50613
Membership(s): Professional Lighting & Sound Association

Peerless Industries
2300 White Oak Circle, Aurora, IL 60502
Tel: 630-375-5100 *Toll Free Tel:* 800-865-2112 *Fax:* 630-820-8537 *Toll Free Fax:* 800-359-6500
E-mail: info@peerlessmounts.com
Web Site: www.peerlessmounts.com
Key Personnel
Pres: Mike Campagna
Manufacturer of mounting accessories for AV equipment.
Catalog(s) available
Membership(s): InfoComm International®; SIA

Peerless Lighting
2246 Fifth St, Berkeley, CA 94710
Tel: 510-845-2760 *Fax:* 510-845-2776
Web Site: www.peerless-lighting.com
Catalog(s) available

Pelco
3500 Pelco Way, Clovis, CA 93612-5699
Tel: 559-292-1981 (intl) *Toll Free Tel:* 800-289-9100 (US & CN) *Fax:* 559-348-1120 (intl) *Toll Free Fax:* 800-289-9150 (US & CN)
E-mail: sales@pelco.com
Web Site: www.pelco.com
Key Personnel
Pres & CEO: Dean Meyer
Manufacture digital CCTV systems.
Catalog(s) available
Membership(s): Automated Imaging Association; SIA

Pelican Products
147 N Main St, South Deerfield, MA 01373
Mailing Address: PO Box 201, South Deerfield, MA 01373-0201
Tel: 413-665-2163 *Toll Free Tel:* 800-542-7344 *Fax:* 413-665-8330
Web Site: www.pelican.com
Founded: 1954
Manufacturer of shipping & storage containers for sensitive electronics.
Catalog(s), free
Sales Office(s): 23215 Early Ave, Torrance, CA 90505
Membership(s): NAB

Pelican Publishing Co
1000 Burmaster St, Gretna, LA 70053-2246
Tel: 504-368-1175 *Toll Free Tel:* 800-843-1724; 888-PELICAN (735-4226 - cust serv); 888-5PELICAN (888-573-5422) *Fax:* 504-368-1195
E-mail: sales@pelicanpub.com
Web Site: www.pelicanpub.com
Key Personnel
Sales Mgr: Joseph Billingsley *Tel:* 504-368-1175 ext 322 *E-mail:* jbillingsley@pelicanpub.com
Founded: 1926
Distributing books, videos & audio programs.
Catalog(s) available
Membership(s): Reading Recovery Council of North America

A W Peller & Associates Inc
PO Box 377, Franklin Lakes, NJ 07414-0377
Tel: 201-644-0908 *Toll Free Tel:* 800-451-7450 *Fax:* 201-644-0907
E-mail: awpeller@optonline.net
Web Site: www.brightideascatalog.com
Key Personnel
Pres: Allan W Peller
Contact: Neil Peller
Founded: 1973
Catalog(s) available

Pemcor LLC
2100 State Rd, Lancaster, PA 17601
Tel: 717-898-1555 *Toll Free Tel:* 800-735-1555 *Fax:* 717-898-3191
E-mail: support@pemcor.com
Web Site: www.pemcor.com
Key Personnel
VP, Strategic Mktg Servs: Tim Schauer *E-mail:* tschauer@pemcor.com
Full production service company; commercial printing, mailing & marketing.
Brochure(s) available
Branch Office(s)
Pemcor Conshohocken, 30 Clipper Rd, West Conshohocken, PA 19428 *Tel:* 610-941-7290 *Fax:* 610-941-6649
Membership(s): MCA-I

Pendle Hill Bookstore
338 Plush Mill Rd, Wallingford, PA 19086-6099
Tel: 610-566-4507 (ext 2) *Toll Free Tel:* 800-742-3150 (ext 2) *Fax:* 610-566-3679
E-mail: bookstore@pendlehill.org
Web Site: www.pendlehill.org
Key Personnel
Mgr: Dorothy Day *Tel:* 610-566-4507 ext 125 *E-mail:* dday@pendlehill.org
Distribute religious books.
Catalog(s), annual, free

Pendulum Entertainment
444 Dufferin St, Studio 1, Toronto, ON M6K 2A3, Canada
Tel: 416-721-7593
E-mail: info@pendulumentertainment.com
Web Site: www.pendulumentertainment.com
Key Personnel
Creative Dir: Jacob Troy Miller
Founded: 2001
Boutique production company that produces all forms of broadcast media.

Penfield Productions Ltd
35 Springfield St, Agawam, MA 01001
Tel: 413-786-4454 *Fax:* 413-789-4240
E-mail: info@penfieldprod.com
Web Site: www.penfieldprod.com
Key Personnel
Pres & Gen Mgr: John Shanahan *E-mail:* john@penfieldprod.com
Founded: 1943
Producers of video & interactive media.
Catalog(s) available
Membership(s): MCA-I

Penguin Audiobooks
Subsidiary of Penguin Group (USA) Inc
375 Hudson St, New York, NY 10014
Tel: 212-366-2000
E-mail: online@penguinputnam.com
Web Site: www.penguinputnam.com; us.penguingroup.com
Key Personnel
Exec Prodr: Patti Pirooz *Tel:* 212-366-2402 *E-mail:* patti.pirooz@us.penguingroup.com
Founded: 1990
Multimedia CD-ROM & audio.
Catalog(s) available
Membership(s): Audio Publishers Association

Penn Elcom Inc
Subsidiary of Penn Elcom Ltd
12691 Monarch St, Garden Grove, CA 92841
Tel: 714-230-6200 *Toll Free Tel:* 800-228-9122 (orders) *Fax:* 714-230-6222 *Toll Free Fax:* 800-619-0808
E-mail: california@penn-elcom.com
Web Site: www.penn-elcom.com
Flight case & speaker cabinet solutions.
Catalog(s), annual, free
Branch Office(s)
232 W Parkway, Pompton Plains, NJ 07444 *Tel:* 973-839-7777 *Toll Free Tel:* 800-446-7174 (US orders) *Fax:* 973-839-2277 *E-mail:* new_jersey@penn-elcom.com
5609 Campbell Rd, Houston, TX 77041 *Tel:* 281-855-9772 *Toll Free Tel:* 800-503-8999 (US orders) *Fax:* 281-855-4856 *E-mail:* texas@penn-elcom.com
2020 Halford Dr, Windsor, ON N9A 6J3, Canada *Tel:* 519-737-9494 *Toll Free Tel:* 888-736-6322 (CN orders) *Fax:* 519-737-9499 *E-mail:* canada@penn-elcom.com
Foreign Office(s): Penn Elcom Ltd, 15 Silicon Place, Tullamarine, Victoria 3043, Australia, Contact: Andrew Rushen *Tel:* (03) 9335 6455 *Fax:* (03) 9335 6466 *E-mail:* australia@penn-elcom.com
Verbiest NV, Industriezone Berkenhoek, B-2861 OLV Waver, Belgium *Tel:* (015) 754959 *Fax:* (015) 756288 *E-mail:* info@verbiest.com *Web Site:* www.verbiest.com
Penn Elcom Comercial e Importadora Ltda, Rua Alba, 1872, Vila Santa Catarina, 04360-000 Sao Paulo-SP, Brazil *Tel:* (011) 5678 2000 *Fax:* (011) 5678 2000 *E-mail:* penn-elcom@penn-elcom.com.br *Web Site:* www.penn-elcom.com.br
Comercial e Importadora Penn Elcom Ltda, Cotapos No 1387-A, Independencia, Santiago, Chile *Tel:* (02) 7320212 *Fax:* (02) 7322370 *E-mail:* penn-elcomchile@penn-elcomchile.cl *Web Site:* www.penn-elcomchile.cl
Penn Elcom (Dongguan), Yuquan Industrial Area, Fenggang Town, Dongguan City, Guangdong Province 523681, China *Tel:* (0769) 86803388 *Fax:* (0769) 86803366 *E-mail:* salesperson@penn-elcom.cn
Comercial e Importadora Penn Elcom Ltda, Calle 220 No 127-84 Bodega 17, Barrio Fontibon HB, Centro Empresarial El Dorado, Bogota, Colombia *Tel:* (01) 2982297 *E-mail:* contacto@penn-elcom.com.br *Web Site:* www.penn-elcom.com.co
Holmberg Cases Oy, Pl 65, 95401 Torino, Finland *Tel:* (016) 431 550 *Fax:* (016) 431 555 *E-mail:* arto@hbc.se *Web Site:* www.hbc.se
CP France, 1775 Route De Nimes, 30560 St Hilaire De Brethmas, France *Tel:* 04 66 61 03 03 *Fax:* 04 66 61 03 04 *E-mail:* contact@cpfrance.com *Web Site:* www.cpfrance.com
Penn Elcom GmbH, Dechant-Spruenken-Str 49B, 46446 Emmerich, Germany *Tel:* (02822) 91303-3 *Fax:* (02822) 91303-50 *E-mail:* europe@penn-elcom.com
Penn Elcom (Ghana), 12/7 New Ashanti Rd, Takoradi, Ghana *Tel:* (031) 25065; (020) 8179602 (cell)
Penn Elcom HK Ltd, Ming Sang Industrial Bldg, Rm R, 3rd fl, 21 Hing Yip St, Kwun Tong, Kowloon, Hong Kong *Tel:* 2790 8009 *Fax:* 2343 2656 *E-mail:* info@penn-elcom.hk
Absolute Audio India, Hill Top, Church Rd, Auclet Nest, 2nd fl, Andheri (East), Mumbai 400 059, India *Tel:* (022) 65542334; 9869119110 (cell) *E-mail:* rodney@absoluteaudioindia.com
TGM (G M Cases) Ltd, Industrial Estate Sgula, 3 Nachshon St, 49277 Petah Tikva, Israel *Tel:* (03) 912 4444 *Fax:* (03) 912 4445 *E-mail:* tgm@tgmcases.com *Web Site:* www.tgmcases.com
Valentini SNC, Asti 84/a, Cascine Vica, Rivoli, 10098 Torino TO, Italy *Tel:* (011) 9594160

Fax: (011) 9594166 *E-mail:* info@valentininet.com *Web Site:* www.valentininet.com
Penn Fabrication (Japan), 128-2 Chome, Fujihashi, OME-SH1, Ome-Sh1, Tokyo 198-0022, Japan *Tel:* (0428) 32-5690 *Fax:* (0428) 32-5691 *E-mail:* info@penn-fab.jp *Web Site:* www.penn-fab.jp
Penn Elcom Sdn Bhd, No 15 Jl Meranti Puchong, D25 Meranti Puchong, 47120 Puchong, Seylangor, Malaysia *Tel:* (03) 8052 7967 *Fax:* (03) 8066 7967 *E-mail:* jane.li@penn-elcom.my
Diamant Global Sound Sa de CV, Calle Meave 21-A, Colonia Centro, Delegacion Cuauhtemoc, 06080 Mexico, DF, Mexico *Tel:* (0155) 55126321; (0155) 55127762 *Toll Free Tel:* 800 633 83 31 *Fax:* (0155) 55126321; (0155) 55127762 *E-mail:* contacto@diamant.com.mx *Web Site:* www.diamant.com.mx
Live Sound Manufacturing Ltd, PO Box 68216, 34-C Crummer Rd, Grey Lynn, Auckland, New Zealand *Tel:* (09) 378-0542 *Fax:* (09) 378-9863 *E-mail:* john@livesound.co.nz *Web Site:* www.livesound.co.nz
IBS Woodpros (Nigeria), Butterfly Estate (off Iaswo Rd), 8 Giwa Imale St, Owutu Agric, Ikorodu, Lagos, Nigeria *Tel:* (0802) 3157158 (cell) *E-mail:* elijah@ibsflightcases.com *Web Site:* www.ibsflightcases.com
P A Systems A/S, Normannsgata 25, 0655 Oslo, Norway *Tel:* 22679313 *Fax:* 22682101 *E-mail:* pasystem@online.no *Web Site:* www.pasystem.no
Penn Elcom SAC, Calle Solidaridad Cuadra 2 MZ D2 LT 18, Villa El Salvador, Lima 42, Peru *Tel:* (01) 287-6850 *E-mail:* ricardo@penn-elcom.com.pe *Web Site:* www.penn-elcom.com.pe
Manuel Cunha, Posto de Distribuicao, Rue da Azenba 38, 4200 Porto, Portugal *Tel:* 228300024 *Fax:* 228300024
Penn Fabrication Spain SL, Aralar Bidea 6, 20260 Alegia (Gipuzkoa), Spain *Tel:* 943 655691 *Fax:* 943 655692 *E-mail:* post@penn-elcom.es
Joa Beslag AB, Grabo Industrivag 3, 443 40 Grabo, Sweden *Tel:* (0302) 45300 *Fax:* (0302) 40066 *E-mail:* info@joabeslag.se *Web Site:* www.joabeslag.se
Holmberg Cases Sweden AB, Foretagsvagen 1, 953 33 Haparanda, Sweden *Tel:* (0922) 14640 *Fax:* (0922) 14690 *Web Site:* www.hbc.se
Dinakord Elektronik San VE Tic, Ergenekon Caddesi Sonu, Sahadet Sok No 4, Ferikoy, 80250 Istanbul, Turkey *Tel:* (0212) 2967778 *Fax:* (0212) 2323439 *E-mail:* main@atlantik.com.tr *Web Site:* www.atlantik.com.tr
UMKA-1 Ltd, Ap 3, 37 Yrkovskaya, Kiev 04080, Ukraine *Tel:* (044) 4177575 *Fax:* (044) 4177544 *E-mail:* ymka_@voliacable.com
IBS Flight Cases LLC, PO Box 38365, Al Quoz Industrial 1, Dubai, United Arab Emirates *Tel:* (04) 339 2982 *Fax:* (04) 339 2983 *E-mail:* sales@ibsflightcases.com *Web Site:* www.ibsflightcases.com
Penn Elcom Ltd, Philips House, Drury Lane, Ponswood Industrial Estate, St Leonards-on-Sea, East Sussex TN38 9BA, United Kingdom *Tel:* (01424) 718576; (0191) 416 1717 (sales) *Fax:* (01424) 718572 *E-mail:* info@penn-elcom.com (mfg)
Penn Elcom Ltd, Parsons Industrial Estate, 9-10 Parsons Rd, Tyne & Wear NE37 1HB, United Kingdom *Tel:* (0191) 416 1717 *Fax:* (0191) 419 3715 *E-mail:* info@elcom.com (sales)
Inventos Producciones CA, Ave Pichincha, Centro Comercial Rosal Plaza, Local 18, El Rosal, Caracas, Venezuela *Tel:* (0414) 026 04 32 (cell); (0416) 812 32 44 (cell); (0212) 952 85 06 (cell) *E-mail:* info@ineventos.com.ve *Web Site:* www.ineventos.com.ve
19 Waterfront Dr, Unit 4, Road Town, Tortola, Virgin Islands *Tel:* 284-340-4870 *E-mail:* bvi@penn-elcom.com
Membership(s): NAMM, the National Association of Music Merchants; NSCA

Penn State University MediaTech
14 Wagner Annex, State College, PA 16803-1886
Tel: 814-865-6314; 814-863-3202
Toll Free Tel: 800-826-0132 *Fax:* 814-863-2574
E-mail: mtssmed@psulias.psu.edu
Web Site: www.libraries.psu.edu/mtss; www.medianet.libraries.psu.edu
Key Personnel
Dir: William Bishop *E-mail:* wob1@psu.edu
Asst Dir: Dave Bagley *Tel:* 814-863-0665 *E-mail:* dpb5@psu.edu
Media & technology support services.
Online catalog(s) available
Membership(s): AECT; AFVA; Consortium of College & University Media Centers

Pennebaker Hegedus Films Inc
262 W 91 St, New York, NY 10024
Tel: 212-496-9195 *Fax:* 212-496-8195
Web Site: phfilms.com
Key Personnel
Pres: Frazer Pennebaker *E-mail:* fpenne@aol.com
VP: Chris Hegedus
Catalog(s) available
Foreign Office(s): Flat 2, Crescent Mansions, 122 Elgin Crescent, London WI1 2JN, United Kingdom *Tel:* (020) 7727 1528 *Fax:* (020) 7221 9007 *E-mail:* janebalfour@btconnect.com

Penny + Giles
Unit of Curtiss-Wright Corp
665 N Baldwin Park Blvd, City of Industry, CA 91746
Tel: 626-480-2150 *Fax:* 626-369-6318
E-mail: us.sales@pennyandgiles.com
Web Site: www.pennyandgiles.com
Manufacture faders, T-Bar controllers & joysticks.
Foreign Office(s): Curtiss-Wright Controls - Industrial, Suzhou Industrial Park, No 116 Sumu Rd, Jiangsu 215021, China *Tel:* (0512) 6287-3380 *Fax:* (0512) 6287-3390 *E-mail:* sales@pennyandgiles.com.cn
Penny + Giles GmbH, Straussenlettenstr 7b, 85053 Ingolstadt, Germany *Tel:* (0841) 8855670 *Fax:* (0841) 88556767 *E-mail:* info@penny-giles.de
Penny + Giles Controls Ltd, 15 Airfield Rd, Christchurch, Dorset BH23 3TG, United Kingdom *Tel:* (01202) 409499 *Fax:* (01202) 409475 *E-mail:* sales@pennyandgiles.com
Penny + Giles Controls Ltd, 36 Nine Mile Point Industrial Estate, Cwmfelinfach, Gwent NP11 7HZ, United Kingdom *Tel:* (01495) 202000 *Fax:* (01495) 202006 *E-mail:* sales@pennyandgiles.com

Penrose Productions
1674 N Shoreline Blvd, Suite 130, Mountain View, CA 94043
Tel: 650-969-TAPE (969-8273) *Fax:* 650-969-6816
E-mail: info@penroseproductions.com
Web Site: www.penroseproductions.com
Key Personnel
Owner & Pres: Jim Penrose *E-mail:* jim@penroseproductions.com
Video/multimedia production company.
Catalog(s) available
Membership(s): MCA-I

PentaVision Communications Inc
52303 Emmons Rd, Suite A-4, South Bend, IN 46637
Tel: 574-272-8365 *Fax:* 574-272-8366
Web Site: pentavision.net
Key Personnel
Pres & Sr Prodr: Ryan Geist *E-mail:* ryan@pentavision.net
Founded: 2002
Professional full service video production & communications company.

Pentrex Media Group LLC
2652 E Walnut St, Pasadena, CA 91107-3723
Mailing Address: PO Box 94911, Pasadena, CA 91109-4911
Tel: 626-793-3400 *Toll Free Tel:* 800-950-9333 *Fax:* 626-793-3797
E-mail: pentrex@pentrex.com
Web Site: www.pentrex.com
Key Personnel
Pres: Michael Clayton
Founded: 1984
Produce railroad videos.
Catalog(s) available
Shipping Address: 2926 E Walnut St, Pasadena, CA 91107-3758

People Productions
1737 15 St, Suite 200, Boulder, CO 80302
Tel: 303-449-6086 *Fax:* 303-449-9526
E-mail: info@peopleproductions.com
Web Site: www.peopleproductions.com
Key Personnel
Pres: Brad Gilbert
Prod Mgr, Content: Edie Cheng *E-mail:* edie@peopleproductions.com
Founded: 1984
Video & digital media production company. Specialize in FCP & AVID editing, web video encoding & streaming, DVD authoring & duplication. Integration of video & the web. Music & sound effects library. HD & SD videography.
Membership(s): Colorado Film & Video Association

People Skills International
2910 Baily Ave, San Diego, CA 92105
Tel: 619-262-9951 *Fax:* 619-262-0505
Web Site: www.idagreene.com
Key Personnel
Pres: Ida Greene, PhD *E-mail:* idagreene@earthlink.net
Founded: 1985
Author of 21 books *Light the Fire Within You, Self Esteem: The Essence of You, Soft Power Negotiation Skills, How to Be a Success in Business, How to Improve Self Esteem in Any Child, How to Improve Self Esteem in the African American Child, Money, How to Get It, Keep It, Say Goodbye to Your Smallness, Hello to Your Greatness, Are You Ready for Success?, Anger Management Skills for Children-Elementary, Anger Management Skills for Children-Middle School, Anger Management Skills for Children-Teens, Anger Management Skills for Women, Anger Management Skills for Men, Stirring up the African American Spirit, Secret of Success, Angels Among Us, Earth Angels, Looking for Love in All the Wrong Places, How to Be Alone Without Feeling Lonely, Understanding Relationships and How to Improve Them.*
Catalog(s) available

PeopleVisionFX
311 E First Ave, Bldg A, Roselle, NJ 07203
Tel: 973-509-2056
Web Site: peoplevisionfx.com
Key Personnel
Pres: Wayne Sullivant *E-mail:* waynesullivant@peoplevisionfx.com

The Pepper Group
220 N Smith St, Suite 406, Palatine, IL 60067

Tel: 847-963-0333 *Fax:* 847-963-0888
E-mail: pepper@peppergroup.com
Web Site: www.peppergroup.com
Key Personnel
CEO & Pres: Tim Padgett
VP: George Couris
VP, Fin & Opers: Denise O'Neill
Creative Dir: Cindy Wojdyla
Founded: 1994
Multimedia production; full service marketing provider.
Catalog(s) available

Peppers Ghost HD®
Subsidiary of Bob Thomas Productions Inc
c/o Bob Thomas Productions Inc, 2 Franklin Ct, Montville, NJ 07045
Tel: 973-335-9100
Web Site: www.peppersghosthd.com
Key Personnel
Pres: Robert Thomas *E-mail:* bobthomas@bobthomas.net

Perception Publications
8711 E Pinnacle Peak Rd, PMB 345, Scottsdale, AZ 85255
Toll Free Tel: 800-338-5831 *Fax:* 480-451-9372
E-mail: info@iqbooster.com
Key Personnel
Owner & Pres: David W Richardson
Give your child ages 2-6 the learning advantage no other childhood development program addresses. Increase your child's IQ by enhancing his or her auditory, visual, motor & comprehensive skills. Teach your child to "learn how to learn" before you begin to teach him or her how to read.

Perceptions Inc
1030 Hinesburg Rd, Charlotte, VT 05445
Tel: 802-425-2783 *Fax:* 802-425-3628
E-mail: perceptivt@aol.com
Web Site: perceptionsvermont.com; perceptionsmaple.com; perceptionspics.com
Key Personnel
VP: Betty Ann Lockhart
Video & still image production.
Membership(s): Northeast Historic Film; Vermont Center for Research

Perennial Pictures Film Corp
2102 E 52 St, Indianapolis, IN 46205
Tel: 317-253-1519
E-mail: mail@perennialpictures.com
Web Site: www.perennialpictures.com
Key Personnel
Pres: G Brian Reynolds *E-mail:* brian.reynolds@perennialpictures.com
SVP: Russell Harris *E-mail:* russ.harris@perennialpictures.com
VP: Michael Ruggiero *E-mail:* michael.ruggiero@perennialpictures.com
Founded: 1979
Producers of animated web site logos, television commercials, television specials & limited series for home video.
Membership(s): ASIFA-Hollywood

Perfection Learning Corp
1000 N Second Ave, Logan, IA 51546
Mailing Address: PO Box 500, Logan, IA 51546-0500
Tel: 712-644-2831 *Toll Free Tel:* 800-831-4190 (US & CN) *Toll Free Fax:* 800-543-2745
E-mail: orders@perfectionlearning.com
Web Site: www.perfectionlearning.com
Founded: 1926
Distribute educational programs.
Online catalog(s) available
Membership(s): International Reading Association

Performance Audio
2456 S West Temple St, Salt Lake City, UT 84115
Tel: 801-466-3196 *Toll Free Tel:* 800-771-8330 *Fax:* 801-484-1538
E-mail: sales@performanceaudio.com; rental@performanceaudio.com
Web Site: www.performanceaudio.com
Key Personnel
Opers Mgr, Sales & Servs: Chris Fillmore *Tel:* 801-466-3196 ext 128 *E-mail:* chris@performanceaudio.com
Founded: 1977
Distribute audio systems & equipment.
Branch Office(s)
1420 W Center St, Orem, UT 84057 *Tel:* 801-709-2989 *Fax:* 801-717-2187

Permlight Products Inc
422 W Sixth St, Tustin, CA 92780
Tel: 714-508-0729 *Fax:* 714-508-0920
E-mail: sales@brillialed.com (brillia div); sales@permlightforsigns.com (sign div)
Web Site: www.permlight.com; www.permlightforsigns.com (signs div); www.brillialed.com (brillia div)
Key Personnel
CEO: George Preston
CFO: Kenneth G McCord
VP, Brand Mgmt: Fernando Lynch
Founded: 1995
Thermally managed LED lighting systems.
Catalog(s) available

Personal Achievement Institute
One Speaking Success Rd, Kingman, AZ 86402
Mailing Address: PO Box 6543, Kingman, AZ 86402-6543
Tel: 928-753-5315
Web Site: www.speakingsuccess.com
Key Personnel
Pres: Burt Dubin
Founded: 1989
Audio albums & Speaking Business Success System.
Membership(s): National Speakers Association

Perspectives Media
410 S Michigan Ave, Chicago, IL 60605
Tel: 312-212-1492
Key Personnel
Pres: Judith Paine McBrien
Founded: 1991
History & architecture films, books, audio tapes, public television programs related to design.
Catalog(s) available

PESA
Division of QuStream Corp
103 Quality Circle, Suite 210, Huntsville, AL 35806
Tel: 256-726-9200 *Toll Free Tel:* 800-323-7372
E-mail: sales@pesa.com
Web Site: www.pesa.com
Key Personnel
Exec Chmn: Howard G Sutton
COO & Pres: Chuck D Tillett
CFO: Ricky Ng
Design & manufacture routing & distribution products.
Online catalog(s) available
Branch Office(s)
115 Apple Creek Blvd, Suite 204, Markham, ON LC4 6C9, Canada *Tel:* 905-752-3700 ext 203
Membership(s): HDcctv Alliance® Limited; NAB; SBE

Peterson's Video Transfer Services
10051 E Estates Dr, Cupertino, CA 95014
Tel: 408-255-4925 *Toll Free Tel:* 800-888-0426 *Fax:* 408-255-6404
E-mail: contact@petersonsvideotransfer.com
Web Site: www.petersonsvideotransfer.com
Key Personnel
Pres: Terry Peterson
VP & Partner: Jeff Peterson
Video transfer.
Catalog(s) available
Membership(s): Photo Marketing Association; SMPTE

Petra Productions Ltd
52 Sycamore Rd, Mahopac, NY 10541
E-mail: information@petraproductions.org
Web Site: www.petraproductions.org
Key Personnel
Principal: Jim Libby; Bill Van Nostran *E-mail:* bill.vannostran@petraproductions.org; Eddie Barnett *E-mail:* eddie.barnett@petraproductions.org; Bob de Freitas *E-mail:* bob.defreitas@petraproductions.org
Nonprofit video documentary company.

Phase One Audio Group Inc, see Phase One Studios

Phase One Studios
3015 Kennedy Rd, Suite 10, Toronto, ON M1V 1E7, Canada
Tel: 416-291-9553 *Toll Free Tel:* 888-728-3333 *Fax:* 416-291-7898
E-mail: info@phaseonestudios.com
Web Site: www.phaseonestudios.com
Key Personnel
Pres, Opers & Mktg: Barry Lubotta
Founded: 2000
Membership(s): Canadian Independent Record Production Association

Phase Technology
Subsidiary of United Speaker Systems Inc
6400 Youngerman Circle, Jacksonville, FL 32244
Tel: 913-663-5600 *Toll Free Tel:* 800-874-7076; 888-PHASE-TK (742-7385) *Fax:* 913-663-3200
E-mail: sales@phasetech.com
Web Site: www.phasetech.com
Key Personnel
Pres: Ken Hecht *E-mail:* khecht@unitedspeaker.com
Acct Specialist: Cheryl Susser *E-mail:* csusser@unitedspeaker.com
Founded: 1981

Phat Planet Recording Studios
3473 Parkway Center Ct, Orlando, FL 32808
Tel: 407-295-7270 *Toll Free Tel:* 800-667-4893 *Fax:* 407-295-7207
E-mail: info@phatplanetstudios.com
Web Site: www.phatplanetstudios.com
Key Personnel
Pres & Studio Mgr: Ed Krout *E-mail:* edkrout@phatplanetstudios.com
Founded: 1996
Recording studio offering voice-over sessions, live recording, mixing, production & mastering as well as archiving solutions & audio format transfers; producers on staff in all genres.

Phelan Productions Inc
9201 E Mississippi Ave, Apt C205, Denver, CO 80247-6875
Key Personnel
CEO: James M Phelan *Tel:* 303-888-3657 (cell)
Founded: 1974
Full service film & video production company specializing in advertising, education & corporate communication.

Phil Lights
1903 Redlands, Austin, TX 78757
Tel: 512-452-2930; 512-627-4991 (cell)
Web Site: www.pcurry.com

Key Personnel
Partner: Phil Curry *E-mail:* phil@pcurry.com
Motion picture equipment rental & production services.

Phil Sykes & Associates Inc
692 Sunset Ct, Shoreview, MN 55126
Tel: 651-481-4940 *Fax:* 651-481-3290
E-mail: mail@sykesnet.com
Web Site: www.sykesnet.com
Key Personnel
Pres: Phil Sykes *Tel:* 651-319-2999 (cell)
Catalog(s) available
Membership(s): Content Delivery & Storage Association

Philadelphia Soundstages
1600 N Fifth St, Philadelphia, PA 19122
Tel: 267-773-8971 *Fax:* 267-773-8972
E-mail: info@philastudios.com
Web Site: philastudios.com
Founded: 2007
Studio & production office rental, full service equipment rental for in-house & on-location shoots, production & post-production services.

Philips Lighting Controls
Formerly Lightolier® Controls
Subsidiary of Philips Lighting Business Unit-Professional Luminaires North America
2828 Trade Center Dr, Suite 130B, Carrollton, TX 75007
Toll Free Tel: 800-526-2731 *Fax:* 972-389-6174
E-mail: controls.support@philips.com
Web Site: philipslightingcontrols.com

Phillips MediaSource
750 N St Paul, Suite 1000, Dallas, TX 75201
Mailing Address: PO Box 565246, Dallas, TX 75356-5246
Tel: 214-741-1300 *Toll Free Tel:* 800-TEXAS13 (839-2713) *Fax:* 214-741-3942
Web Site: phillipsmediasource.com
Key Personnel
Owner: Bob Phillips
VP: Jason Anderson *Tel:* 214-741-1300 ext 208
Film & HD video production for TV, radio, web, laptop, table & mobile screens.

PHL17, see WPHL-TV

Phoebus Lighting
Division of The Phoebus Co Inc
2800 Third St, San Francisco, CA 94107
Tel: 415-550-0770 *Fax:* 415-550-2655
Web Site: www.phoebus.com
Key Personnel
Pres: John Tedesco *Tel:* 415-550-0770 ext 110 *E-mail:* jtedesco@phoebus.com
Rental Mgr: Greg Bortolin *E-mail:* gbortolin@phoebus.com
Lighting fixtures & equipment.
Catalog(s) available
Membership(s): AICP

Phoebus Manufacturing
Division of The Phoebus Co Inc
2800 Third St, San Francisco, CA 94107
Tel: 415-550-0770 *Fax:* 415-550-2655
Web Site: www.phoebus.com/phoebusmanufactu.html; www.phoebus.com
Key Personnel
Pres: John Tedesco *Tel:* 415-550-0770 ext 110 *E-mail:* jtedesco@phoebus.com
Founded: 1976
Catalog(s) available
Membership(s): Professional Lighting & Sound Association; USITT

Phoenix Aerial Photography Inc
613 Skyview Dr, Nashville, TN 37206
Mailing Address: PO Box 68432, Nashville, TN 37206
Tel: 615-255-2000; 615-975-4226 (cell)
E-mail: info@phoenixaerialphoto.com
Web Site: www.phoenixaerialphoto.com
Key Personnel
Owner & Pres: Paul Cardel, Jr *E-mail:* paul@phoenixaerialphoto.com
Founded: 1985
Gyros & gyro stabilized video platform.
Membership(s): AOPA; PPA; Professional Aerial Photography Association

Phoenix/BFA/Coronet
Division of The Phoenix Learning Group Inc
141 Milllwell Dr, Suite A, St Louis, MO 63043-2509
Tel: 314-569-0211 (ext 104) *Toll Free Tel:* 800-221-1274 (ext 104) *Fax:* 314-569-2834 (orders)
E-mail: info@phoenixlearninggroup.com; customerservice@phoenixlearninggroup.com
Web Site: www.phoenixlearninggroup.com
Key Personnel
Gen Mgr: Andrew Amir-Fazli
Educational multimedia producer & distributor.
Catalog(s) available
Membership(s): National Association of Media & Technology Centers; National Council for the Social Studies; National Media Market; University Film Consortium

The Phoenix Learning Group Inc
141 Millwell Dr, Suite A, St Louis, MO 63043-2509
Tel: 314-569-0211 *Toll Free Tel:* 800-221-1274 *Fax:* 314-569-2834 (orders)
E-mail: customerservice@phoenixlearninggroup.com; info@phoenixlearninggroup.com
Web Site: www.phoenixlearninggroup.com
Key Personnel
Gen Mgr: Andrew Amir-Fazli
Founded: 1993
Core curriculum educational books, videos & CD-ROMs for sale or rent.
Catalog(s) available
Membership(s): AECT; National Media Market

Phoenix Society for Burn Survivors Inc
1835 RW Berends Dr SW, Grand Rapids, MI 49519-4955
Tel: 616-458-2773 *Toll Free Tel:* 800-888-BURN (888-2876) *Fax:* 616-458-2831
E-mail: info@phoenix-society.org
Web Site: www.phoenix-society.org
Key Personnel
Exec Dir: Amy Acton *E-mail:* amy@phoenix-society.org
Devt Dir: Megan Geerling *E-mail:* megan@phoenix-society.org
Prog Dir: Pam Peterson
Off Mgr: Kerri Hanson *E-mail:* kerri@phoenix-society.org
Produce & distribute medical programs.
Catalog(s) available

Phoenix VideoFilms®
2925 W Indian School Rd, Phoenix, AZ 85017
Tel: 602-266-4198; 801-226-8209
Web Site: www.phoenixvideofilms.com
Key Personnel
Outside Opers: Kelly Karr *E-mail:* kkarr@phoenixvideofilms.com
Contact: Cheryl Karr; Christy Karr; Michael Karr
Founded: 1947
AV production.
Demo video(s) available
Membership(s): AFI; SMPTE

Phonic Ear Inc (FrontRow)
Member of William Demant Group
2080 Lakeville Hwy, Petaluma, CA 94954
Tel: 707-769-1110 *Toll Free Tel:* 800-227-0735 *Fax:* 707-769-9624
E-mail: customerservice@phonicear.com; customercare@gofrontrow.com
Web Site: www.phonicear.com; www.gofrontrow.com
Key Personnel
Sales Dir: Paul Hickey *E-mail:* ph@gofrontrow.com
Founded: 1963
Branch Office(s)
Phonic Ear Ltd, 6950 Creditview Rd, Unit 1, Mississauga, ON L5N 0A6, Canada *Toll Free Tel:* 800-340-9894 *Fax:* 905-677-7760
Foreign Office(s): Kongebakken 9, 2765 Smorum, Denmark *Tel:* 3917 7101 *E-mail:* mail@phonicear.com

Photo Film Stage
820 Thompson Ave, Suite 34, Glendale, CA 91201
Tel: 213-304-5608
E-mail: photofilmstage@yahoo.com
Web Site: photofilmstage.com
Photography & film studio.

Photo Tech Inc
7200 Hudson Blvd N, Suite 170, St Paul, MN 55128
Tel: 651-702-6717 *Toll Free Tel:* 800-525-6486 *Fax:* 651-702-6745
E-mail: rolleasy@juno.com
Web Site: www.phototechinc.com
Key Personnel
Pres: Dan Christiansen
Founded: 1953
Catalog(s) available

Photo Technicians Inc
3664 N River Rd, Freeland, MI 48623
Tel: 989-751-8517
Web Site: www.phototechnicians.com
Key Personnel
Pres: David A Sommers *E-mail:* phototechnicians@charter.net
Catalog(s) available

Photodyne Technologies
8531 Alcott St, Suite 201, Los Angeles, CA 90035
Tel: 310-497-0968 *Toll Free Tel:* 800-660-2147 *Fax:* 310-652-2820
E-mail: info@photodyne.com
Web Site: www.photodyne.com
Key Personnel
Owner & Pres: Henry Corech
Manufacturer of computerized macro-photography equipment & industrial light tables & stands. Z-Axis-Motorized-Copy-Stands.
Catalog(s) available

Photoflex Inc
97 Hangar Way, Watsonville, CA 95076
Tel: 831-786-1370 *Toll Free Tel:* 800-486-2674 *Fax:* 831-786-1372
E-mail: sales@photoflex.com; marketing@photoflex.com
Web Site: www.photoflex.com
Key Personnel
Pres: Sharon Reeves
Founded: 1985
Catalog(s) available
CD-ROM catalog(s) available

Photogenic Professional Lighting
1268 Humbracht Circle, Bartlett, IL 60103-1631
Tel: 630-830-2500 *Toll Free Tel:* 800-682-7668 *Fax:* 630-830-2525
E-mail: sales@photogenicpro.com
Web Site: www.photogenicpro.com

Key Personnel
Sales Mgr: Jim Fennig
Founded: 1903
Catalog(s) available

Photographers' Formulary Inc
7079 Hwy 83 N, Condon, MT 59826
Mailing Address: PO Box 950, Condon, MT 59826-0950
Tel: 406-754-2891 *Toll Free Tel:* 800-922-5255 *Fax:* 406-754-2896
E-mail: formulary@blackfoot.net
Web Site: www.photoformulary.com
Key Personnel
Owner & Pres: William "Bud" G Wilson
Owner & Workshops Prog Dir: Lynn Wilson *E-mail:* lynnw@blackfoot.net
Manufacture & distribute photographic chemicals & supplies.
Catalog(s), free

Photographic Solutions Inc
430-G Ansin Blvd, Hallendale, FL 33009
Tel: 954-458-4744 *Toll Free Tel:* 800-637-3212 *Fax:* 954-458-4745
E-mail: orders@photosol.com
Web Site: www.photosol.com
Key Personnel
Pres: David M Stone *E-mail:* david@photosol.com
Founded: 1983
Manufacture & distribute photographic equipment.
Catalog(s) available

Photogroup Studios
321 W Ben White, Suite 106A & 107, Austin, TX 78704
Tel: 512-373-8547
E-mail: photogroup@photogroupaustin.com
Web Site: www.photogroupaustin.com
Founded: 2011
Rental facility for photographers & videographers. Equipment & grip rental as well as full production services available.

Photomart Cine-Video Inc
6869 Stapoint Ct, Suite 112, Winter Park, FL 32792
Tel: 407-381-5606 *Toll Free Tel:* 800-443-2901 *Fax:* 407-381-5610
E-mail: info@photomartusa.com
Web Site: www.photomartusa.com
Key Personnel
Sales Mgr: Tony De Lia *E-mail:* tony@photomartusa.com
Founded: 1946
Provide high quality video & motion picture equipment, supplies & service to broadcasters & educators.
Online catalog(s) available

Photoquip Inc
3070 S Eighth St, Fernandina Beach, FL 32034-8680
Mailing Address: PO Box 1080, Fernandina Beach, FL 32035-1080
Tel: 904-261-4075
Key Personnel
Pres: J Carter Fletcher
Manufacture photographic equipment.
Tear sheet(s) available

Photosound of Orlando Inc
6438 University Blvd, Unit 14, Winter Park, FL 32792
Mailing Address: PO Box 4370, Winter Park, FL 32793
Tel: 407-898-8841 *Toll Free Tel:* 800-552-8776 *Fax:* 407-898-0300
E-mail: photosound@cfl.rr.com
Web Site: www.photosoundav.com
Key Personnel
Owner: Evan Hossman *E-mail:* ehossman@photosoundav.com
Founded: 1955
Distribute & rent AV presentation equipment.

Phylco Audio Duplication
10431 Blackwell Rd, Central Point, OR 97502
Tel: 541-855-7484 *Toll Free Tel:* 800-348-6194
E-mail: info@phylcoaudio.com
Web Site: www.phylcoaudio.com
Key Personnel
Sales & Graphics: Gail M Husa *E-mail:* gail@phylcoaudio.com
Prodn: Kenneth R Husa *E-mail:* ken@phylcoaudio.com
Founded: 1974
CD & DVD replication & duplication, printing, packaging & fulfillment.
Online catalog(s) available

Physical Optics Corp
1845 E 205 St, Torrance, CA 90501-1510
Tel: 310-320-3088 *Fax:* 310-320-5961
Web Site: www.poc.com
Key Personnel
Pres, Chmn & CEO: Joanna Jannson, PhD
SVP, Chief Mktg Offr: Rick Shie *E-mail:* rshie@poc.com
Mktg & Media Supvr: Emily Campbell *E-mail:* ecampbell@poc.com
Founded: 1985
Holographic Light Shaping Diffuser™ & fiber optic communication products.
Brochure(s) available

Pico Digital
8880 Rehco Rd, San Diego, CA 92121
Tel: 858-546-5050 *Toll Free Tel:* 800-421-6511 *Fax:* 858-546-5051; 858-546-5055 (intl)
E-mail: sales@picodigital.com
Web Site: picodigital.com
Key Personnel
Mktg: Eitan Bendesky *E-mail:* ebendesky@picodigital.com
Founded: 1969
Broadband, broadcast & telecom products.
Catalog(s) available

Picture Box Distribution Inc
141 E 23 Ave, Vancouver, BC V5V 1X1, Canada
Tel: 604-681-3174 *Fax:* 604-608-9081
E-mail: info@picturebox.ca
Web Site: www.picturebox.ca
Key Personnel
Partner & Dir, Sales-Europe: Marilyn Kynaston *E-mail:* marilyn@picturebox.ca
Partner & Dir, Sales-Americas & France: Kate Sanagan *E-mail:* kate@picturebox.ca
Mgr, Busn Aff: Elle Gadsby
Res & Sales Coord: Amanda Laukys *E-mail:* amanda@picturebox.ca
Founded: 2001
International television sales agent & distributor.
Catalog(s), semiannual, free
Sales Office(s): 110 Eastwood Rd, Suite 2, Toronto, ON M4L 2C9, Canada, Dir, North American Sales: Kate Sanagan *Tel:* 416-461-8209 *Fax:* 416-461-6805
Membership(s): Academy of Canadian Cinema & Television

Picture This Production Services
2223 NE Oregon St, Portland, OR 97232
Tel: 503-235-3456 *Fax:* 503-236-2302
E-mail: info@pixthis.com
Web Site: pixthis.com
Specialize in commercial/cable broadcast television, web content & high end corporate events & services. Also provide full post-production services.

PicturePhone Inc
200 Commerce Dr, Rochester, NY 14623
Tel: 585-334-9040 *Toll Free Tel:* 800-521-5454 *Fax:* 585-486-1919
E-mail: info@picturephone.com
Web Site: www.picturephone.com
Key Personnel
EVP: Dave Weber *Tel:* 585-334-9040 ext 2214 *E-mail:* davew@picturephone.com
Purch Mgr: John Wilcoxen *Tel:* 585-334-9040 ext 3227 *E-mail:* johnw@picturephone.com
Founded: 1993
Visual communications & networking solutions.

Pictures of Record Inc
119 Kettle Creek Rd, Weston, CT 06883
Tel: 203-227-3387 *Fax:* 203-222-9673
E-mail: picturesofrecord@aol.com
Web Site: www.picturesofrecord.com
Key Personnel
Pres: Nancy Hammerslough
Founded: 1979
Photograph production services.
Online catalog(s) available
Membership(s): American Anthropological Society; Archeological Institute of America; Society for American Archaeology

Pieces of Learning
Division of Creative Learning Consultants Inc
1990 Market Rd, Marion, IL 62959
Tel: 618-964-9426 *Toll Free Tel:* 800-729-5137 *Toll Free Fax:* 800-844-0455
E-mail: info@piecesoflearning.com
Web Site: www.piecesoflearning.com
Key Personnel
Partner: Kathy Balsamo
Founded: 1989
Educational publisher.
Catalog(s) available
Membership(s): Education Market Association; IBPA, the Independent Book Publishers Association

Pignose-Gorilla
570 W Cheyenne Ave, Suite 80, North Las Vegas, NV 89030
Tel: 702-648-2444 *Toll Free Tel:* 800-9-PIGNOSE (974-4667) *Fax:* 702-648-2440
E-mail: sales@pignoseamps.com
Web Site: www.pignoseamps.com
Key Personnel
Pres: Howard Chatt *E-mail:* hchatt@aol.com
Manufacturer & distributor of amplifiers, PA systems & accessories.
Catalog(s) available
Membership(s): NAMM, the National Association of Music Merchants

Pinewood Sound
555 Brooksbank Ave, Stage S, North Vancouver, BC V7J 3S5, Canada
Tel: 604-669-6900; 604-983-5200 *Fax:* 604-983-5204
E-mail: info@pinewoodsound.com; sales@pinewoodsound.com
Web Site: www.pinewoodsound.com
Key Personnel
Opers Mgr: Jean Turner *E-mail:* jean@pinewoodsound.com
Full service audio post-production services for film & television.

Pinnacle Systems Inc
Division of Corel Corp
385 Ravendale Dr, Mountain View, CA 94043-5240
Tel: 650-526-1600 *Toll Free Tel:* 877-582-6735 *Fax:* 650-526-1601
E-mail: sales@pinnaclesys.com

Web Site: www.pinnaclesys.com; www.corel.com
Founded: 1986
Provides broadcasters & consumers with cutting-edge digital media, creative storage & playback solutions for use at home, in the studio & on the air.
Catalog(s) available
Branch Office(s)
1600 Carling Ave, Ottawa K1Z 8R7, Canada

pinta acoustic inc
Division of pinta elements GmbH
2601 49 Ave N, Suite 400, Minneapolis, MN 55430
Tel: 612-355-4200 *Toll Free Tel:* 800-662-0032 *Fax:* 612-355-4299
E-mail: sales@pinta-acoustic.com; info@pinta-acoustic.com
Web Site: www.pinta-acoustic.com
Key Personnel
Natl Sales Mgr: Eric Johnson *Tel:* 800-438-0685
Sales Mgr: Bob Donahue *Tel:* 866-205-8707
Manufacturer of acoustic wallpanels & ceiling tiles.
Catalog(s) available
Membership(s): NAB; NAMM, the National Association of Music Merchants; NSCA

Pioneer Electronics (USA) Inc
Subsidiary of Pioneer Electronic Corp (Japan)
1925 E Dominguez St, Long Beach, CA 90810
Mailing Address: PO Box 1720, Long Beach, CA 90801-1720
Tel: 310-952-2000 *Toll Free Tel:* 800-421-1404 (cust serv); 800-228-7221 (parts dept) *Fax:* 310-952-2821 (parts dept)
Web Site: www.pioneerelectronics.com
Founded: 1938
Catalog(s) available

Pioneer Research Inc
97 Foster Rd, Suite 5, Moorestown, NJ 08057
Tel: 856-866-9191 *Toll Free Tel:* 800-257-7742 *Fax:* 856-866-8615
E-mail: info@pioneer-research.com
Web Site: www.pioneer-research.com
Key Personnel
VP: Bjorn Harms *E-mail:* bjorn@pioneer-research.com; Sven E Harms *E-mail:* sven@pioneer-research.com
Manufacture & distribute underwater photographic equipment.
Catalog(s) available

PipelineFX LLC
1000 Bishop St, Suite 509, Honolulu, HI 96813
Tel: 808-685-7823 *Toll Free Tel:* 866-856-7823 *Fax:* 808-685-7800
E-mail: sales@pipelinefx.com
Web Site: www.pipelinefx.com
Key Personnel
CEO: Richard Lewis *E-mail:* richard@pipelinefx.com
Founded: 2002
Producer of Qube!, the leading render farm management software for digital media creation.

Piper Media Services Inc
904 W Kenosha St, Broken Arrow, OK 74014
Tel: 918-251-0477 *Toll Free Tel:* 800-752-5346 *Fax:* 918-258-1476
Web Site: www.pipermediaservices.com
Key Personnel
Pres: Daniel B Piper *E-mail:* danny@pipermediaservices.com
Catalog(s) available

Nicholas P Pipino Associates Inc
9159-A Red Branch Rd, Columbia, MD 21045
Tel: 202-603-9319; 301-596-3397; 410-995-0041 *Toll Free Tel:* 888-596-0014 *Fax:* 410-964-1191
Web Site: www.pipinoinc.com
Key Personnel
CEO & Pres: Stephen J Pipino *E-mail:* spipino@pipinoinc.com
Founded: 1969
Sales & service of state-of-the-art audio visual products.

Lee Pitts Enterprises
8765 Azalea Ct, Suite 103, Tamarac, FL 33321
Toll Free Tel: 877-830-0391
E-mail: swimvideo@leepitts.com; speaking@leepitts.com (request speaking engagements)
Web Site: www.leepitts.com
Key Personnel
Contact: Lee Pitts
Distributor of beginners swim lesson video for adults & children.

PIX
1109 S La Brea Ave, Los Angeles, CA 90019
Tel: 323-936-8488 *Toll Free Tel:* 888-697-0081 *Fax:* 323-936-5209
E-mail: rental@pixcamera.com
Web Site: www.pixcamera.com
Sells & rents photographic equipment & supplies.

Pixar Animation Studios
Subsidiary of The Walt Disney Co
1200 Park Ave, Emeryville, CA 94608
Tel: 510-922-3000 *Toll Free Tel:* 800-888-9856 *Fax:* 510-922-3151
E-mail: ir@pixar.com (investor rel)
Web Site: www.pixar.com
Key Personnel
Pres: Dr Edwin E Catmull
Chief Creative Offr: John Lasseter
Animation studio.

PixeLINK
1900 City Park Dr, Suite 410, Ottawa, ON K1J 1A3, Canada
Tel: 613-247-1211 *Fax:* 613-247-2001
E-mail: sales@pixelink.com
Web Site: www.pixelink.com
Key Personnel
CEO: William Legniowski
Prod & Mktg Mgr: Greg Shore
Founded: 1992
Manufacture digital cameras & video converters for scientific/industrial & professional markets.

PixMix Video Services
23 Elm St, Bldg 2, Watertown, MA 02472
Tel: 617-923-0102 *Fax:* 617-923-0105
E-mail: info@pixmix.net
Web Site: www.pixmix.net
Key Personnel
Principal Proj Mgr: Ray Boyer *Tel:* 617-901-7157 (cell) *E-mail:* ray@pixmix.net
Founded: 1998
Video production, single camera ENG production & multi-camera production.
Catalog(s) available
Membership(s): MCA-I

piXvfm
1805 E Dyer, Suite 107, Santa Ana, CA 92705-5701
Tel: 949-250-1749 *Fax:* 949-419-3485
E-mail: infoweb@pixvfm.com
Web Site: www.pixvfm.com
Key Personnel
Pres: Ridgie Barton
Prodr & Dir: Rick Stewart
Web site production, multimedia & industrial training programs.
Membership(s): ATD; IAAVC

PK Photo & Electronic Repair
1760 S Carr St, Lakewood, CO 80232-6643
Tel: 303-777-1311 *Fax:* 303-777-1332
Key Personnel
Owner: Paul Keys *Tel:* keypaul7@msn.com
Repair service.
Catalog(s) available
Membership(s): Society of Photo Technologists

Planet Blue
1250 Sixth St, Suite 102, Santa Monica, CA 90401
Tel: 310-899-3877 *Fax:* 310-899-3787
Web Site: www.planetblue.com
Key Personnel
Cont: Suresh Jain *E-mail:* suresh@planetblue.com
Exec Prodr: Milt Alvarez *E-mail:* milt@planetblue.com
Creative/Tech Dir: Maury Rosenfeld *E-mail:* maury@planetblue.com
Founded: 1988
Post-production visual effects.

Planet Dallas Recording Studios
Division of Planet Dallas Inc
PO Box 110995, Carrollton, TX 75011
Tel: 214-521-2216; 214-893-1130 (cell) *Fax:* 214-528-1299
E-mail: planetd@ix.netcom.com
Web Site: planetdallas.com
Key Personnel
Pres: Rick Rooney
Recording studio.
Membership(s): ASCAP; Austin Songwriters Group; BMI; Dallas Songwriters Association; The Recording Academy

Plank Road Publishing Inc
11111 W Plank Ct, Wauwatosa, WI 53226
Mailing Address: PO Box 26627, Wauwatosa, WI 53226
Tel: 262-790-5210 *Toll Free Tel:* 800-437-0832 *Fax:* 262-781-8818 *Toll Free Fax:* 888-272-0212
E-mail: custsvc@musick8.com
Web Site: www.musick8.com
Key Personnel
Asst Mgr, Opers: Lynn Crowell *E-mail:* lynn@musick8.com
Founded: 1990
Publishers of quality music & vendor of music-related products for elementary & middle school teachers. Audio programming on CD, MP3 & MP4. Shipping via UPS or USPS, rates based on subtotal.
Affiliated with Music K-8 Marketplace, World Music Press, Golden Rule Music & Recorder Classroom.
Catalog(s), annual, interactive +/or downloadable on web site
Membership(s): National Association for Music Education

plan9films
1926B Alberta Ave, Saskatoon, SK S7K 1R9, Canada
Tel: 306-955-6463 *Toll Free Fax:* 866-795-4503
E-mail: info@plan9films.com
Web Site: www.plan9films.com
Key Personnel
CEO & Prodr: Darryl Kesslar

Plantronics Inc
345 Encinal St, Santa Cruz, CA 95060
Tel: 831-426-5858 *Toll Free Tel:* 800-544-4660 *Fax:* 831-426-6098 *Toll Free Fax:* 888-290-4519
E-mail: plantronics@custhelp.com
Web Site: www.plantronics.com
Key Personnel
CEO: Ken Kannappan
EVP, Prods, Technol & Strategy & CTO: Joe Burton
Chief Strategy Offr: Barry Margerum

Founded: 1961
Offers mobile headsets.
Catalog(s) available

Platt Cases, see Platt Luggage Inc

Platt Luggage Inc
4051 W 51 St, Chicago, IL 60632
Tel: 773-838-2000 *Toll Free Tel:* 800-222-1555 *Fax:* 773-838-2010
E-mail: info@plattcases.com
Web Site: www.plattcases.com
Founded: 1921
Manufacture professional cases for business & industry.
Catalog(s), annual, free
CD-ROM catalog(s), annual, free
Online catalog(s) available

Platypi Studios
1245 Champa St, 4th fl, Denver, CO 80204
Tel: 720-935-7497
Web Site: platypistudios.com
Key Personnel
Contact: Brandon Naughton
Studio rental, lighting & production services.

Playback Now
3139 Campus Dr, Suite 700, Norcross, GA 30071-1402
Tel: 770-447-0616 *Toll Free Tel:* 800-241-7785 *Fax:* 770-447-0543
E-mail: sales@playbacknow.com
Web Site: www.playbacknow.com
Key Personnel
Pres: Jonathan Galucki *E-mail:* jon@playbacknow.com
Founded: 1978
Conference programming.

Playback Recording Studio
400 E Gutierrez, Santa Barbara, CA 93101
Tel: 805-730-7529
Web Site: www.playbackrecording.com
Key Personnel
Head Engr: Tucker Bodine *Tel:* 917-331-0429
Sound recording studio & post-production house for the entertainment industry.

Playboy Entertainment Group Inc
Division of Playboy Enterprises Inc
9346 Civic Center Dr, Suite 200, Beverly Hills, CA 90210
Tel: 312-751-8000
Web Site: www.playboy.com; www.playboyenterprises.com
Catalog(s) available

Players Press
PO Box 1132, Studio City, CA 91614-0132
Tel: 818-789-4980
Web Site: ppeps.com
Key Personnel
Busn & Rts Mgr: David Cole
US, UK & Germany libraries & book trade.
Catalog(s), 5 times/yr
Foreign Office(s): 20 Park Dr, Romford, Essex RM1 4LH, United Kingdom

PLS Staging
371 Little Falls Rd, Cedar Grove, NJ 07009-1250
Tel: 973-857-7242 *Toll Free Tel:* 800-783-4757 *Fax:* 973-857-8867
Web Site: www.plsstaging.com
Key Personnel
Owner & Pres: Jim Koziol
Founded: 1979
Audio visual staging company.
Membership(s): AV Alliance; International Special Events Society; MPI

Captain J Charles Plumb
3917 Fairbreeze Circle, Westlake, CA 91361
Tel: 818-991-1964
Web Site: www.charlieplumb.com
Key Personnel
Admin Asst: Susan Runnels *E-mail:* susan@charlieplumb.com
Motivational training tapes.

Plume Ltd
888 Main St, Silver Plume, CO 80476
Mailing Address: PO Box 9, Silver Plume, CO 80476-0009
Tel: 303-569-3236 *Toll Free Tel:* 866-569-3236 *Fax:* 303-569-2932
Web Site: www.plumeltd.com
Key Personnel
Pres: Gary Regester *E-mail:* garyregester@gmail.com
Founded: 1985
Lighting equipment for digital, cine & still photographers.
Catalog(s) available

PLUS Corp of America
9610 SW Sunshine Ct, Suite 100, Beaverton, OR 97005
Tel: 503-748-8700 *Toll Free Tel:* 800-211-9001 *Fax:* 503-643-9756
E-mail: sales@plus-america.com
Web Site: www.plus-america.com
Key Personnel
Pres: Tsutomu (Tom) Oishi
Cont: Russel J Falotico
Natl Sales Mgr: Mike Bluhm
Founded: 1995
Manufacture electronic copyboards & interactive panels.
Foreign Office(s): 1033-1 Oshitate, Inagi-shi Tokyo 206-0811, Japan

Plus 24
1155 N La Brea Ave, West Hollywood, CA 90038
Tel: 323-845-1171; 323-845-1168 (support) *Toll Free Tel:* 800-330-7753 (orders) *Fax:* 323-845-1170
E-mail: info@plus24.net; sales@plus24.net
Web Site: www.plus24.net
Key Personnel
Pres: Jim Pace
Sales & Mktg Mgr: Martin Ucik
Founded: 1989
Distributor for Sanken Microphones, Brainstorm Electronics, Marian Sound Cards, Friend-Chip Studio Electronics & Sommer Cable™.
Online catalog(s) available
Branch Office(s)
407 Stony Point Rd, Santa Rosa, CA 95401 *Tel:* 707-566-2107 *Fax:* 707-566-2106

PM Productions
5882 Bowcroft St, Suite 2, Los Angeles, CA 90016-4907
Tel: 310-559-3127 *Fax:* 310-559-3168
Web Site: www.pmproductionsvideos.com
Key Personnel
Owner: Odell Mack *E-mail:* odellmack@hotmail.com
Founded: 1985
Full service video production.

PM-Systems, see Professional Management Services Inc

PME Audio/Video
2003 S El Camino Rd, Suite 108, Oceanside, CA 92054
Tel: 760-439-0281
E-mail: solutions@pmevideo.com
Web Site: www.pmevideo.com
Key Personnel
Mgr: Angela Macaraeg
Founded: 1998
Manufacture VCR racks & distribute amplifiers & machine control systems for video duplication.
Catalog(s) available
Membership(s): Content Delivery & Storage Association

PMP Marketing Inc
13006 E Philadelphia St, Suite 402, Whittier, CA 90601
Tel: 562-698-0088 *Fax:* 562-320-8139
Web Site: www.pmpmarketing.com
Key Personnel
Pres: Eric Kamayatsu *E-mail:* eric@pmpmarketing.com
Off Mgr: Tiffany Chou *E-mail:* tiffany@pmpmarketing.com
Membership(s): InfoComm International®; NSCA

PMTV, see Producers Management Television (PMTV)

The Pocket Studios
920 Eastern Ave, Top fl, Toronto, ON M4L 1A4, Canada
Tel: 416-466-0029
E-mail: info@thepocketstudios.com
Web Site: www.thepocketstudios.com
Key Personnel
Founding Partner: Mari Dew; Trevor Kustiak; Mike Turner
Recording studios & record production.

Pogo Pictures
114 E Ponce de Leon Ave, Suite B, Decatur, GA 30030
Tel: 404-892-9490 *Fax:* 404-892-9491
E-mail: info@pogopictures.com
Web Site: www.pogopictures.com
Key Personnel
Pres & Dir: Steve Colby
Exec Prodr: Ruth Brown *E-mail:* ruth@pogopictures.com
Dir: Ben Callner; Ryan Smith

Point Lobos Productions
20417 Califa St, Woodland Hills, CA 91367
Tel: 818-340-4201
Key Personnel
Prodr: Brainard Miller *E-mail:* brainardmiller@webtv.net
Catalog(s) available

Point of View Productions
2477 Folsom St, San Francisco, CA 94110
Fax: 415-821-0434
Web Site: www.karildaniels.com
Key Personnel
Pres: Karil Daniels *Tel:* 415-602-0435 (cell) *E-mail:* karil@karildaniels.com
Catalog(s) available
Membership(s): Bay Area Video Coalition; Bay Area Women in Film & Media; NATAS; Women in Multimedia

Point Source Audio
1129 Industrial Ave, No 205, Petaluma, CA 94952
Tel: 415-226-1122 *Fax:* 415-520-2110
E-mail: info@point-sourceaudio.com; sales@point-sourceaudio.com; support@point-sourceaudio.com
Web Site: www.point-sourceaudio.com
Key Personnel
Pres: James Lamb
Manufacture digitial audio systems & ear worn microphones.
Catalog(s) available

Point 360
2701 Media Center Dr, Los Angeles, CA 90065
Tel: 818-565-1400 *Fax:* 818-847-2503
E-mail: sales-point360@point360.com
Web Site: www.point360.com
Key Personnel
CEO & Pres: Haig Bagerdjian
Catalog(s) available
Branch Office(s)
1133 N Hollywood Way, Burbank, CA 91505 *Tel:* 818-556-5700 *Toll Free Tel:* 866-968-4336 *Fax:* 818-556-5753
IVC Digital Film Ctr, 2777 N Ontario St, Burbank, CA 91504 *Tel:* 818-569-4949 *Fax:* 818-569-3659
12421 W Olympic Blvd, Los Angeles, CA 90064 *Tel:* 310-481-7000 *Fax:* 323-466-7406
Membership(s): International Teleproduction Society

Polarity Post Production
69 Green St, San Francisco, CA 94111
Tel: 415-421-6622 *Fax:* 415-391-4995
E-mail: info@polaritypost.com
Web Site: www.polaritypost.com
Key Personnel
Pres: Roger Wiersema
Catalog(s) available
Membership(s): AES; Bay Area Video Coalition; Northern California Production Community; The Recording Academy; San Francisco Film & Tape Council; SMPTE

Polestar Films & Associated Arts Ltd
Subsidiary of Polestar Animation
PO Box 20104, West Village Sta, New York, NY 10014-0708
Tel: 212-352-1375
Key Personnel
Pres & Creative Dir: Irra Verbitsky *E-mail:* irrav@aol.com
VP: Don Duga *E-mail:* donduga@juno.com
Founded: 1976
Animation studio.

Polhemus
40 Hercules Dr, Colchester, VT 05446-5835
Tel: 802-655-3159 *Toll Free Tel:* 800-357-4777 (US & CN)
E-mail: sales@polhemus.com
Web Site: polhemus.com
Key Personnel
Pres & Co-Owner: Skip Rodgers
CEO & Co-Owner: Al Rodgers
Founded: 1969
Catalog(s) available

Pollstar
4697 W Jacquelyn Ave, Fresno, CA 93722-6413
Tel: 559-271-7900 *Fax:* 559-271-7979
E-mail: info@pollstar.com
Web Site: www.pollstar.com; www.pollstarpro.com
Key Personnel
News Ed: Joe Reinartz
Founded: 1981
Concert industry trade publication & database.
Foreign Office(s): Pollstar UK, Leroy House, 436 Essex Rd, Suite 4M, London N1 3QP, United Kingdom, Contact: Brij Gosai *Tel:* (020) 7359 1110 *Fax:* (020) 7359 1131
Membership(s): Academy of Country Music; Country Music Association; IAFE; International Association of Assembly Managers; International Entertainment Buyers Association; NACA

Pollution Studios
3239 Union Pacific Ave, Los Angeles, CA 90023
Mailing Address: 1539 S Grande Vista Ave, Los Angeles, CA 90023
Tel: 323-380-8033
E-mail: info@pollutionstudios.com
Web Site: pollutionstudios.com
Full service studio & equipment rental facilty.

Gabriel Polonsky Studio
33 Harvard Rd, Suite 2, Belmont, MA 02478
Tel: 617-489-3331
E-mail: gp-studio@verizon.net
Web Site: www.gp-studio.com
Key Personnel
Founder & Creative Dir: Gabriel Polonsky
Founded: 1992
Multimedia production company.

Polyline LLC
845 N Church Ct, Elmhurst, IL 60126-1036
Tel: 630-993-2700 *Toll Free Tel:* 800-701-7689 *Toll Free Fax:* 800-816-3330
E-mail: sales@polylinecorp.com
Web Site: www.polylinecorp.com
Key Personnel
CEO & Pres: Mike Cullen
COO: Michael Schlobohm
Catalog(s) available
Shipping Address: 4518 W Vanowen St, Burbank, CA 91505-1135

PolyPhaser Corp
Member of Smiths Interconnect Group
10701 Airport Rd, Hayden, ID 83835
Tel: 208-772-8515 *Toll Free Tel:* 800-882-9110 *Fax:* 208-762-6117
Web Site: www.smithspower.com/brands/polyphaser
Key Personnel
Pres: Shawn Thompson
Founded: 1979
Lightning/EMP protection products & grounding accessories.
Catalog(s) available

PolyScience
Division of Preston Industries Inc
6600 W Touhy Ave, Niles, IL 60714-4516
Tel: 847-647-0611 *Toll Free Tel:* 800-229-7569 *Fax:* 847-647-1155
E-mail: sales@polyscience.com
Web Site: www.polyscience.com
Key Personnel
Pres: Philip Preston
Sales Mgr: Sue Gibbons
Founded: 1963
Manufacturer of temperature control equipment.
Catalog(s) available

PolyVision Corporation
Member of Steelcase Design Partnership
10700 Abbotts Bridge Rd, Suite 100, Duluth, GA 30097
Tel: 678-542-3100 *Toll Free Tel:* 888-325-6351 *Fax:* 678-542-3200
E-mail: info@polyvision.com
Web Site: polyvision.com
Founded: 1954
Creates products & services in the visual communications market.
Catalog(s), annual, free
Branch Office(s)
4301 North Wood Dr, Okmulgee, OK 74447 *Tel:* 918-756-7392 *Fax:* 918-756-6818
Foreign Office(s): Zuiderring 56, 3600 Genk, Belgium *Tel:* (089) 3231 30 *Fax:* (089) 3231 31 *E-mail:* info@polyvision.be
Membership(s): Education Market Association; InfoComm International®; International Multimedia & Collaborative Communications

Pook Diemont & Ohl Inc
Affiliate of acouStaCorp LLC
701 E 132 St, Bronx, NY 10454
Tel: 718-402-2677 *Fax:* 718-402-2859
E-mail: info@pdoinc.com
Web Site: www.pdoinc.com
Key Personnel
Owner: Ted Ohl *E-mail:* tedohl@pdoinc.com
Founded: 1982
The design/build company for theater, television & film facilities, corporate & retail environments. Acoustical & acouroll variable acoustic banners.
Catalog(s) available
Membership(s): DBIA; Professional Lighting & Sound Association

POP TV
5069 Maureen Lane, Moorpark, CA 93021-7127
Tel: 805-499-8513 *Toll Free Tel:* 800-331-4626 *Fax:* 805-499-8206
E-mail: sales@mpo-video.com
Web Site: www.mpo-video.com
Key Personnel
Pres: Larry Kaiser
VP, Corp Devt: Lynn Stearn
Engr: Ray Ward
Mgr, Acctg: Eric Garcia
Installation & Serv: Jill Hogan
Founded: 1947
Visual communication solutions to business & industry. Manufacturer of large & small video displays, using LCD, DLP & CRT technologies. All-weather outdoor LCD TV. Audio/video system integration. National sales & installation. POP displays.
Catalog(s) available
Branch Office(s)
6400 SE Lake Rd, Suite 211, Portland, OR 97222, Contact: Van Faulk *Tel:* 503-659-9868 *Toll Free Tel:* 800-654-8848 *Fax:* 503-659-9727 *E-mail:* vfaulk8996@aol.com
Sales Office(s): 1623 Third Ave, Suite 202, New York, NY 10128, Contact: Allan Armour *Tel:* 212-369-2400 *Fax:* 212-369-5078 *E-mail:* aarmourmpo@aol.com

Popless Voice Screens
PO Box 1014, New Paltz, NY 12561-3063
Tel: 845-255-3367 *Toll Free Tel:* 800-252-1503 *Fax:* 845-255-3367
E-mail: info@popfilter.com
Web Site: www.popfilter.com
Key Personnel
Owner: Brian S Gunn
Founded: 1988
Manufacturer of microphone accessories; variable acoustic compression pop filters.

Porta-Jib
1033 N Sycamore Ave, Los Angeles, CA 90038
Tel: 323-462-2855 *Fax:* 323-462-2682
E-mail: info@porta-jib.com
Web Site: www.porta-jib.com
Key Personnel
Owner: Scott Losmandy
Sales Mgr: Mark Schweickart *Tel:* 323-462-2855 ext 2 *E-mail:* mark@porta-jib.com
Manufacturer of lightweight dollies & jib arms for the film & video camera market.
Catalog(s) available

PortaBrace Inc
PO Box 220, North Bennington, VT 05257-0220
Tel: 802-442-8171 *Fax:* 802-442-9118
E-mail: info@portabrace.com
Web Site: www.portabrace.com
Key Personnel
Pres: Gregg Haythorn
Carrying cases for AV professionals.
Catalog(s) available
Online catalog(s) available

Porter Case Inc
3718 W Western Ave, South Bend, IN 46619

Tel: 574-289-2616 *Toll Free Tel:* 800-356-8348 *Fax:* 574-289-2747
E-mail: sales@portercase.com
Web Site: www.portercase.com
Key Personnel
Pres: Gary E Pond *E-mail:* garypond@portercase.com
Founded: 1990
Brochure(s), free, online
Catalog(s) available

James Porter Photography
211 E Columbine Ave, Suite A-1, Santa Ana, CA 92707
Tel: 714-546-4148
E-mail: info@jamesporterphotography.com
Web Site: www.jamesporterphotography.com
Key Personnel
Owner: James Porter *E-mail:* jim@jamesporterphotography.com
Founded: 1975
Digital photography in studio & on location. Specializing in food, product & people. Full service studio with commercial kitchen.

Porter Productions
211 E Columbine Ave, Suite A-1, Santa Ana, CA 92707
Tel: 714-546-4148
E-mail: studio@porterproductions.info
Web Site: www.porterproductions.info
Key Personnel
Owner: James Porter
Stage rental.

Portland Models & Talent LLC
PO Box 4727, Portland, ME 04112-4727
Tel: 207-741-2850; 207-799-9758
E-mail: PortlandModels@aol.com
Web Site: www.portlandmodels.com
Key Personnel
Dir: Patricia L Campbell; Karen True
Founded: 1984
Our models & actors appear in major catalogues, national print advertisements, national TV commercials including SAG principals & multimedia & international advertising campaigns.
Membership(s): Maine Film & Video Association

Post Josh Productions
375 Greenwich St, New York, NY 10013
Tel: 212-699-2642
E-mail: info@postjosh.com
Web Site: www.postjosh.com
Key Personnel
Prodr & Ed: Joshua Schwarz
Founded: 1998
Avid, digital beta cam & video editing.
Branch Office(s)
40 Worth St, Suite 804, New York, NY 10013 (studio)

Post Production Services, see The PPS Group

Posthorn Recordings
142 W 26 St, 10th fl, New York, NY 10001-6814
Tel: 212-242-3737 *Fax:* 212-924-1243
Web Site: www.posthorn.com
Key Personnel
CEO & Pres: Jerry Bruck *E-mail:* jbruck@posthorn.com
Mgr: Michael P Hesse
PR: Louise A Bloomfield
Founded: 1964
Catalog(s) available
Membership(s): AES

PostWorks
100 Avenue of the Americas, 10th fl, New York, NY 10013
Tel: 212-894-4000 *Fax:* 212-941-0439
E-mail: inquiry@postworks.com
Web Site: www.postworks.com
Key Personnel
Sr Dir of Non-Linear Servs: Dan Porcelli *Tel:* 646-652-3478 *E-mail:* dan@pwny.com
Broadcast Sales: Rob Moriano *Tel:* 646-652-3412 *E-mail:* rmoriano@postworks.com
Founded: 1995
Full service post-production.
Branch Office(s)
Technicolor - Postworks, 110 Leroy St, New York, NY 10014 *Tel:* 212-609-9400 *Fax:* 212-609-9450 *E-mail:* inquiry@technicolorpwny.coom *Web Site:* www.postworks.com/technicolor
609 Greenwich St, New York, NY 10014 *Tel:* 212-399-6342

Potentials Unlimited
Division of I M P A C T Publishing Inc
3409 47 Ave E, Bradenton, FL 34203-3974
Mailing Address: PO Box 10058, Bradenton, FL 34282-0058
Tel: 941-739-2611 *Toll Free Tel:* 800-221-6121; 800-426-3963 *Fax:* 941-756-0315
Web Site: www.potentialsunlimited.com
Key Personnel
Pres: Stephanie Banfill
Catalog(s), free
Online catalog(s) available

Potomac Instruments Inc
7309 Grove Rd, Unit D, Frederick, MD 21704
Tel: 301-696-5550 *Fax:* 301-696-5553
E-mail: comments@pi-usa.com
Web Site: www.pi-usa.com
Key Personnel
Dir, Mktg: Guy Harry
Founded: 1968
Precision measurement & control equipment for the broadcast industry.
Brochure(s), online
Online catalog(s) available

Pounds Photographic Labs Inc
901 Regal Row, Dallas, TX 75247
Mailing Address: PO Box 560308, Dallas, TX 75356-9874
Tel: 214-688-1425 *Toll Free Tel:* 800-350-5671 *Fax:* 214-688-1429
Web Site: www.poundslabs.com
Key Personnel
Founder & Owner: Danny Pounds *Tel:* 512-835-9700
Pres: Steve Oatman
Founded: 1976

Power & Light
1313 Mound St, Alameda, CA 94501
Tel: 510-205-4101 (cell)
Web Site: www.powerlight.net
Key Personnel
Founder & Gaffer: Mike Van Dine *E-mail:* mike@powerlight.net
Founded: 1994
Lighting & grip trucks in northern California.

Power & Telephone Supply Co
44 Hull St, Suite 2, Randolph, VT 05060
Toll Free Tel: 800-451-4381 *Fax:* 802-234-5006
E-mail: cablesales@ptsupply.com
Web Site: www.ptsupply.com
National distributor of wire, cable, fiber optics, tools & test equipment.
Catalog(s), free

Power Factory Productions
14518 Hempstead Rd, No 4CC, Houston, TX 77040
Tel: 281-630-6900
E-mail: info@powerfactoryproductions.com
Web Site: www.powerfactoryproductions.com
Founded: 1995
Professional sound & lighting production. Specialize in concert & touring production, as well as corporate events, AV services, festivals, special events, sales & installation.

Power Integrity Corporation
PO Box 9682, Greensboro, NC 27429-0682
Tel: 336-379-9773 *Toll Free Tel:* 800-237-6260 (tech support)
E-mail: info@powerintegritycorp.com
Web Site: www.powerintegritycorp.com
Key Personnel
Pres: James T Fesmire
VP: Debbie Wilson *E-mail:* d.wilson@powerintegritycorp.com
Founded: 1980
Catalog(s) available
Membership(s): PEI

Power-Sonic Corp
7550 Panasonic Way, San Diego, CA 92154
Tel: 619-661-2020 *Fax:* 619-661-3650
E-mail: customer-service@power-sonic.com; technical-support@power-sonic.com
Web Site: www.power-sonic.com
Key Personnel
Chmn of the Bd & Pres: Guy C Clum
VP, Sales & Mktg: Bruno A Ender
Mktg Dir: Malcolm Jones
Founded: 1970
Design, manufacture & market rechargeable batteries & chargers.
Catalog(s) available

PowerPhysics Inc
877 Production Place, Newport Beach, CA 92663-2809
Tel: 949-371-6202 *Fax:* 815-572-8936
E-mail: contact@powerphysics.com
Web Site: www.powerphysics.com
Key Personnel
Pres: Gordon Wanlass
Founded: 2000
Amplifier & power supply design & manufacture.

Melvin Powers Television Marketing
9731 Variel Ave, Chatsworth, CA 91311-4315
Tel: 818-700-1522
E-mail: mpowers@mpowers.com
Web Site: www.mpowers.com

Powerstation Events
Division of Powerstation LLC
1486 Highland Ave, Bldg 2, Suite 6, Cheshire, CT 06410
Tel: 203-250-8500 *Toll Free Tel:* 800-423-7835 *Fax:* 203-250-8575
E-mail: sales@powerstationevents.com
Web Site: www.powerstationevents.com
Key Personnel
Founder & Pres: Alfred Vagnini *Tel:* 800-423-7835 ext 221 *E-mail:* al@powerstationevents.com
Co-Founder & VP: Jon March *Tel:* 800-423-7835 ext 228
Sales Dir: Rich Gumpert *Tel:* 800-423-7835 ext 225 *E-mail:* richg@powerstationevents.com
Founded: 1983 (by Al Vagnini & Jon March)
Commercial, corporate & event video production.

PowerTechnology Southeast Inc
634 State Rd 44, Leesburg, FL 34748
Tel: 352-365-2777 *Toll Free Tel:* 800-760-0027 *Fax:* 352-787-5545
E-mail: powertech@powertech-gen.com
Web Site: www.powertech-gen.com
Key Personnel
CEO & Pres: Gerald Hayman
CFO & VP: Chris Gray
Founded: 1989

Manufacturer & supplier of mobile diesel generators.
Catalog(s) available
Membership(s): FMCA

PPS, see Precision Projection Systems Inc

The PPS Group
424 Scott St, Covington, KY 41011
Tel: 859-291-5100 *Toll Free Tel:* 800-978-3445 *Fax:* 859-291-5150
E-mail: info@theppsgroup.com
Web Site: www.pps-inc.com; www.theppsgroup.com
Key Personnel
CEO: Bob Gerding
Pres: Jim Bird
VP: Dave Dittgen
Also offers HDTV production & editing, Boomerang interactive & DVD authoring. Film & videotape archiving.

Practising Law Institute
1177 Avenue of the Americas, New York, NY 10036
Tel: 212-824-5700 *Toll Free Tel:* 800-260-4PLI (260-4754, cust serv) *Toll Free Fax:* 800-321-0093
E-mail: info@pli.edu (cust serv)
Web Site: www.pli.edu
Key Personnel
Pres: Victor J Rubino
Dir, Multimedia Servs: Charles Matasker
Founded: 1933
Brochure(s) available
Branch Office(s)
685 Market St, Suite 100, San Francisco, CA 94105-4202 *Tel:* 415-498-2800

Prairie Pictures Film & Video
PO Box 122020, Arlington, TX 76012-8020
Tel: 817-276-9500
E-mail: info@prairiepictures.com
Web Site: prairiepictures.com
Key Personnel
Pres: Martin Lisius *E-mail:* lisius@prairiepictures.com
Founded: 1986
Full service video & film production company. Founded Stormstock in 1993, recognized as the world's premier storm footage library (www.stormstock.com).
Membership(s): Dallas Producers Association; Texas Association of Motion Media Professionals; Texas Film Commission

The Prairie Production Group
509 S Country Fair Dr, Suite A, Champaign, IL 61821
Tel: 217-359-4675 *Fax:* 217-359-4689
E-mail: ppg@prairie-production.com
Web Site: www.prairie-production.com
Key Personnel
Owner & Gen Mgr: Steve Main *E-mail:* stevem@prairie-production.com
Founded: 1989
Full service audio, video & multimedia production company.

Prakken Publications Inc
2851 Boardwalk Dr, Ann Arbor, MI 48104
Mailing Address: PO Box 8623, Ann Arbor, MI 48107-8623
Tel: 734-975-2800 *Toll Free Tel:* 800-530-9673 *Fax:* 734-975-2787
E-mail: matt@techdirections.com
Web Site: www.techdirections.com
Key Personnel
Mng Ed: Susanne Peckham *Tel:* 734-975-2800 ext 303 *E-mail:* susanne@techdirections.com
Founded: 1935
Technology & career technical education publications, books, video, software, CD-ROM & posters.
Catalog(s) available
Membership(s): EdPress

PRC Digital Media
250-A Park St, Jacksonville, FL 32204
Tel: 904-354-1500
E-mail: info@prcdigital.com
Web Site: www.prcdigital.com
Key Personnel
Owner & Pres: Ray Hays *E-mail:* rlhays@prcdigital.com
Founded: 1988
Film, video & interactive media production.

Precision Camera & Video
2438 W Anderson Lane, Suite B-4, Austin, TX 78757
Tel: 512-467-7676 *Toll Free Tel:* 800-677-1023 *Fax:* 512-467-0607
Web Site: www.precision-camera.com
Key Personnel
Founder & CEO: Jerry Sullivan
Gen Mgr: Gregg Burger *E-mail:* gburger@precision-camera.com
Sales Mgr: Mark Cooper *E-mail:* mcooper@precision-camera.com
Founded: 1976
New & used photographic & video equipment for sale & rent. Equipment repair, classes & workshops.

Precision Camera & Video Repair Inc
4 Anngina Dr, Enfield, CT 06082-3222
Tel: 860-749-7380 *Toll Free Tel:* 800-665-6515 *Fax:* 860-763-7100
E-mail: info@precisioncamera.com
Web Site: www.precisioncamera.com
Key Personnel
CEO & Pres: John Malinosky
VP, Opers: Steven Moloney
Exec Offr: David Brooker
Founded: 1948
Factory authorized repair for all major brands.
Branch Office(s)
11500 Rojas Dr, Suite A, El Paso, TX 79936
Membership(s): NESDA; Photo Marketing Association; Photographic Society of America; SPT

Precision Electronics Inc
Division of Grommes
1331 Estes Ave, Gurnee, IL 60031
Tel: 847-599-1799 *Toll Free Tel:* 800-SINCE-46 (746-2346) *Fax:* 847-599-6178
E-mail: info@grommesprecision.com; sales@grommesprecision.com
Web Site: www.grommesprecision.com
Key Personnel
Gen Mgr: J W Franzen
Founded: 1946
Manufacture audio & electronic equipment.
Catalog(s) available

Precision Microproducts of America
One Comac Loop, Unit 13, Ronkonkoma, NY 11779
Tel: 631-580-3456 *Toll Free Tel:* 800-932-9215 *Fax:* 631-580-3003
E-mail: sales@p-m-a.com
Web Site: www.p-m-a.com
Key Personnel
Pres: Carlos Fernandes
Microfilm supplies, equipment & parts-document scanners, supplies & parts.
Catalog(s) available
Membership(s): Photo Marketing Association

Precision Projection Systems Inc
17508 Studebaker Rd, Cerritos, CA 90703
Tel: 562-865-8552 *Fax:* 562-924-7133
E-mail: info@ppsfx.com
Web Site: www.ppsfx.com
Key Personnel
Owner: Carl Hannigan *E-mail:* carl@ppsfx.com
Founded: 1983
Offer specialty lighting products.
Catalog(s) available

Prelinger Archives
PO Box 590622, San Francisco, CA 94159-0622
Tel: 415-750-0445 *Fax:* 415-750-0607
E-mail: footage@panix.com
Web Site: www.prelinger.com
Key Personnel
Pres: Richard Prelinger *E-mail:* rick@well.com
Founded: 1983
Post-production services film/stock footage/still image & graphics libraries.
Catalog(s) available
Membership(s): Association of Moving Image Archivists

Prelinger Associates Inc, see Prelinger Archives

Premier™
Division of Martin Yale Industries Inc
251 Wedcor Ave, Wabash, IN 46992
Tel: 260-563-0641 *Toll Free Tel:* 800-225-5644 *Fax:* 260-563-4575 *Toll Free Fax:* 800-654-8339 (orders)
E-mail: info@martinyale.com
Web Site: www.martinyale.com/premier.aspx
Key Personnel
Gen Mgr: Greg German
Table-top trimmers & office machines.
Catalog(s) available
Membership(s): BPIA; Business Technology Association; Graphic Art Supply Dealers Association; National Art Materials Trade Association; NOPA

Premier A/V Sales Ltd
28 Howden Rd, Scarborough, ON M1R 3E4, Canada
Tel: 416-755-1148 *Toll Free Tel:* 800-267-0700 *Fax:* 416-755-6996
E-mail: sales@premierav.ca
Web Site: www.premierav.ca
Key Personnel
Pres & Gen Mgr: Ron Galea
Founded: 1968

Premier Lighting & Production Co
12023 Victory Blvd, North Hollywood, CA 91606
Tel: 818-762-0884 *Toll Free Tel:* 800-770-0884 *Fax:* 818-762-0896
E-mail: premier@premier-lighting.com
Web Site: www.premier-lighting.com
Key Personnel
Contact: Ryan Medvitz
Founded: 1977
Full service entertainment company.
Catalog(s) available
Online catalog(s) available
Membership(s): Professional Lighting & Sound Association; USITT

Premiere Locations
25 Clyden Rd, Wainscott, NY 11975
Mailing Address: PO Box 308, Wainscott, NY 11975
Tel: 631-537-1669; 917-690-1075 (cell)
E-mail: info@premierelocations.com
Web Site: www.premierelocations.com
Key Personnel
Pres: Roz Block
Founded: 2004
Location library & location/production services in the Hamptons & beyond. Location scout-

ing, casting, permits, pre-production/production, insurance, accommodations, transportations, props, catering, wardrobe supplies & more.

Pres-On Merchandising Corp
2600 E 107 St, Bolingbrook, IL 60440
Toll Free Tel: 800-323-7467 *Fax:* 630-628-8025
Web Site: www.pres-on.com
Key Personnel
VP: Ray Wandolowski
Founded: 1949
Catalog(s) available

Presagis
4700 de la Savane, Suite 300, Montreal, QC H4P 1T7, Canada
Tel: 514-341-3874 *Toll Free Tel:* 800-361-6424
E-mail: info@presagis.com
Web Site: www.presagis.com
Key Personnel
Pres: Guillaume Herve
Global provider of software for the development of modeling, simulation, visualization & embedded display applications.
Catalog(s) available

Prescolite
Division of Hubbell Lighting Inc
701 Millennium Blvd, Greenville, SC 29607
Tel: 864-678-1000 *Fax:* 864-678-1415
Web Site: www.prescolite.com
Key Personnel
Dir of Mktg: Paige Malouche
Founded: 1944
Lighting fixture manufacturer.
Online catalog(s) available

Presence Records
Subsidiary of Presence Productions
67 Candace Lane, Chatham Township, NJ 07928-1115
Tel: 973-701-0707
Web Site: www.paulpayton.com; www.presenceproductions.com
Key Personnel
Owner & Pres: Paul Payton *E-mail:* paul@paulpayton.com
Founded: 1985
Online catalog(s), available on www.presenceproductions.com
Membership(s): MCA-I

Presence Studios Westport
80 Wells Hill Rd, Suite 100, Weston, CT 06883
Tel: 203-221-8061
E-mail: info@presencestudios.com
Web Site: www.presencestudios.com
Key Personnel
Owner: Jon Russell
Founded: 1980

Presentation Products Inc
632 W 28 St, 7th fl, New York, NY 10001
Tel: 212-736-6350 *Toll Free Tel:* 877-774-4523 *Fax:* 212-736-6353
E-mail: info@presentationstore.com; sales@pproducts.com
Web Site: www.ppidirect.com; www.presentationproducts.com
Key Personnel
Pres: Orin Knopp
Founded: 1996
AV systems integrator.

Preston Cinema Systems
1659 11 St, Suite 100, Santa Monica, CA 90404
Tel: 310-453-1852 *Fax:* 310-453-5672
E-mail: sales@prestoncinema.com
Web Site: www.prestoncinema.com
Key Personnel
Pres: Howard Preston

Preston Productions Inc
128 Bartlett St, Marlborough, MA 01752
Toll Free Tel: 800-822-2299
E-mail: ideas@prestonevents.com
Web Site: www.prestonproductions.com; www.prestonevents.com
Key Personnel
CEO & Stage Mgr: Rick Preston
CFO: Susan Preston
Dir of Prodn: Wayne Jackson
Dir of Digital Media: Hannah Fullam
Prodn Supv: Victoria Towne
Dir of Busn Devt: Eric Basta
Founded: 1983
AV equipment rentals.
Brochure(s) available
Catalog(s), on request
Online catalog(s) available
Membership(s): Meeting Planners International

Prevent Blindness America
211 W Wacker Dr, Suite 1700, Chicago, IL 60606
Tel: 312-363-6001 *Toll Free Tel:* 800-331-2020 *Fax:* 312-363-6052
E-mail: info@preventblindness.org
Web Site: www.preventblindness.org
Key Personnel
CEO & Pres: Hugh R Parry
Dir: Sarah Hecker
Founded: 1908
Catalog(s) available
Branch Office(s)
Prevent Blindness Northern California, 169 Hartnell Ave, No 207, Redding, CA 96002 *Tel:* 530-243-0410 *Fax:* 530-243-0414 *E-mail:* msantos@eyeinfo.org
Prevent Blindness Northern California, 1388 Sutter St, Suite 408, San Francisco, CA 94109 *Tel:* 415-567-7500 *Toll Free Tel:* 800-338-3041 (in-state only) *Fax:* 415-567-7600 *E-mail:* q@eyeinfo.org
Prevent Blindness Florida, 76 Fourth St N, No 820, St Petersburg, FL 33731, Contact: Leslie Bailey *Tel:* 813-874-2020 ext 4025 *E-mail:* lbailey@preventblindnessfl.org
Prevent Blindness Georgia, 739 W Peachtree St NW, Suite 200, Atlanta, GA 30308-1137 *Tel:* 404-266-2020 *Toll Free Tel:* 800-477-4448 *Fax:* 404-974-2948
Prevent Blindness Iowa, 1111 Ninth St, Suite 250, Des Moines, IA 50314-2585 *Tel:* 515-244-4341 *Toll Free Tel:* 800-329-8782 (in-state only) *Fax:* 515-244-4718
Prevent Blindness America, Northeast Region, 424 Beacon St, Boston, MA 02115 *Tel:* 312-731-3990 *Fax:* 617-587-5562 *E-mail:* kmajzoub@preventblindness.org
Prevent Blindness North Carolina, 4011 WestChase Blvd, Suite 225, Raleigh, NC 27607 *Tel:* 919-755-5044 *Fax:* 919-755-5013
Prevent Blindness Ohio, 1500 W Third Ave, Suite 200, Columbus, OH 43212 *Tel:* 614-464-2020 *Toll Free Tel:* 800-301-2020 (in-state only) *Fax:* 614-481-9670 *E-mail:* info@pbohio.org
Prevent Blindness Oklahoma, 6 NE 63 St, Suite 150, Oklahoma City, OK 73105 *Tel:* 405-848-7123 *Fax:* 405-848-6935
Prevent Blindness Oklahoma, 2506-B E 21 St, Tulsa, OK 74114 *Tel:* 918-496-3484 *Fax:* 918-496-0469
Prevent Blindness Texas, 2202 Waugh Dr, Houston, TX 77006 *Tel:* 713-526-2559 *Toll Free Tel:* 888-98-SIGHT (in-state only) *Fax:* 713-529-8310 *E-mail:* info@preventblindnesstexas.org
Prevent Blindness Mid-Atlantic, 225 Reinekers Lane, Suite 700, Alexandria, VA 22314 *Tel:* 703-740-2253
Prevent Blindness Mid-Atlantic, 11618 Busy St, Richmond, VA 23236 *Tel:* 804-423-2020 *Toll Free Tel:* 888-790-2020 (in-state only) *Fax:* 804-423-5409
Prevent Blindness America, Northwest Region, 16420 SE McGillivray, Suite 103/645, Vancouver, WA 98683-3599, Dir: Carol R Strong *Tel:* 208-970-0472 *E-mail:* cstrong@preventblindness.org
Prevent Blindness Wisconsin, 759 N Milwaukee St, Suite 305, Milwaukee, WI 53202 *Tel:* 414-765-0505 *Fax:* 414-765-0377 *E-mail:* info@preventblindnesswisconsin.org
Membership(s): National Health Council

Prevention Products & Services Inc, see The Bureau for At-Risk Youth

PRG
1053 Willingham Dr, Atlanta, GA 30344
Tel: 404-214-4800 *Toll Free Tel:* 888-844-4225 *Fax:* 404-214-4801
E-mail: info@hitechrent.com
Web Site: www.prg.com
Key Personnel
Sales & Mktg Specialist: Cindy Hearn
Audio, video, computer, lighting & data display rental & staging solutions.
Catalog(s) available
Branch Office(s)
1902 Cypress Lake Dr, Suite 100, Orlando, FL 32837, Contact: Rodney Brannon *Tel:* 407-855-8060 *Fax:* 407-855-8059

PRG Lighting
Division of Production Resource Group LLC
6050 S Valley View Blvd, Las Vegas, NV 89118
Tel: 702-942-4774 *Fax:* 702-942-4668
E-mail: info@prg.com
Web Site: www.prg.com
Key Personnel
Pres, West Coast Opers: Joe Shenk
VP, Sales: Pat Little
Entertainment lighting & technology equipment.
Branch Office(s)
9111 Sunland Blvd, Sun Valley, CA 91352, Gen Mgr: Brian T Edwards *Tel:* 818-252-2600 *Fax:* 818-252-2620
1902 Cyprus Lake Dr, Suite 100, Orlando, FL 32837, VP, Client Servs: Martee Nurrudin *Tel:* 407-855-8060 *Fax:* 407-855-8059
915 Secaucus Rd, Secaucus, NJ 07094, Gen Mgr, Lighting: Robin Lee *Tel:* 201-758-4000 *Fax:* 201-758-4312
630 Ninth Ave, Suite 610, New York, NY 10036-3748, Chmn & CEO: Jeremiah Harris *Tel:* 212-589-5400 *Fax:* 212-589-5425
2480 Tedlo St, Toronto, ON L5A 3V3, Canada, Gen Mgr: David James *Tel:* 905-270-9050 *Fax:* 905-270-2590
Foreign Office(s): PRG Asia Inc, K1 Bldg, 2nd fl, 6-4-2 Klba, Koto-Ku, Tokyo 135-0042, Japan *Tel:* (03) 5665 3377 *Fax:* (03) 5665 3517
The Cotton Ctr, Groveley Lane, Longbridge, Birmingham B31 4PT, United Kingdom, VP, Opers: Gary Boyd *Tel:* (0845) 470 6400 *Fax:* (0845) 470 6401
Membership(s): Production Equipment Rental Association; Professional Lighting & Sound Association

PRI Productions
1819 Kings Ave, Jacksonville, FL 32207
Tel: 904-398-8179 *Fax:* 904-398-1569
E-mail: generalmailbox@priproductions.com
Web Site: www.priproductions.com
Key Personnel
Pres: Randy Goodwin *E-mail:* rgoodwin@priproductions.com
Event production company of corporate videos, image transfers, photography, audio duplication & computer graphics.

Price Stern Sloan
375 Hudson St, 14th fl, New York, NY 10014

Tel: 212-414-3607; 212-366-2000; 212-366-2372 *Fax:* 212-414-3396; 212-366-2933
Web Site: us.penguingroup.com
Key Personnel
Pres & Publr: Francesco Sedita
Founded: 1960
Imprint: Penguin Group (USA) Inc.
Catalog(s) available

Primacoustic
Division of Radial Engineering Ltd
1588 Kebet Way, Port Coquitlam, BC V3C 5M5, Canada
Tel: 604-942-1001 *Fax:* 604-942-1010
E-mail: info@primacoustic.com
Web Site: www.primacoustic.com
Key Personnel
Busn Devt: Steve Dickson
Busn Devt, CN: James Wright
Acoustic treatment products.
Catalog(s), hard copy or PDF
Membership(s): AES; NAMM, the National Association of Music Merchants

PrimaLux Video Inc
555 Eighth Ave, Suite 1002, New York, NY 10018
Tel: 212-206-1402 *Fax:* 212-206-1826
E-mail: primalux@aol.com
Web Site: www.primalux.com
Key Personnel
Pres: Jeff Schwartz
VP: Jeff Byrd
Prodn Coord: Judy Cashman
Founded: 1982
Catalog(s) available
Membership(s): IBEW; International Alliance of Theatrical Stage Employees; NABET-CWA

Primary Color Laboratory Inc
3550 Williams Blvd, Suite A, Kenner, LA 70065
Tel: 504-468-3750 *Toll Free Tel:* 800-535-7799 *Fax:* 504-468-3751
E-mail: info@primarycolorlab.com
Web Site: www.primarycolorlab.com
Key Personnel
Secy & Treas: Ralph Plaideau, Jr *E-mail:* ralphjr@primarycolorlab.com
Founded: 1958
Catalog(s) available
Membership(s): AIE™; PMA International

Primary Connections, see SLR Enterprises LLC

Primary Press
PO Box 83, St Peters, PA 19470-0083
Tel: 610-469-9029
Key Personnel
Exec Dir & Owner: Thomas Bissinger *E-mail:* tomasbiss@gmail.com
Catalog(s) available

Prime Cut Productions
6418 Via Baron, Rancho Palo Verdes, CA 90275
Tel: 310-750-6109
Web Site: www.primecutproductions.com
Key Personnel
CEO & Exec Prodr: Vikki Loh-Berri *Tel:* 310-308-3584 *E-mail:* vikkiberri@primecutproductions.com
Foreign Office(s): 3 des Ecoles, 75005 Paris, France, Prodn Mgr: Michael Champouret *Tel:* 06 60 90 48 84 *Fax:* 01 41 77 80 44

Prime Image Inc
200 Highpoint Dr, Suite 215, Chalfont, PA 18914
Tel: 215-822-1561; 215-817-2713 (tech support) *Toll Free Tel:* 877-PRIME-40 (774-6340)
E-mail: info@primeimage.com
Web Site: www.primeimage.com
Founded: 1985
Manufacture video equipment.
Catalog(s) available
Branch Office(s)
1415 Koll Circle, Suite 105, San Jose, CA 95112 *Tel:* 408-452-7740 (Mfr & R&D)

PrimeArray Systems Inc
48 Maple St, Lowell, MA 01852
Tel: 978-649-0090 *Toll Free Tel:* 800-433-5133 *Fax:* 978-498-0190
E-mail: info@primearray.com; sales@primearray.com
Web Site: www.primearray.com
Key Personnel
CEO: Willard Rice *E-mail:* rice@primearray.com
CD manufacturers.

PrimeLight Productions Inc
750 Kappock St, Suite 805, Riverdale, NY 10463
Tel: 718-543-3991; 917-680-5780
E-mail: info@primelight.net
Web Site: www.primelight.net
Key Personnel
Owner: Don Forschmidt *E-mail:* don@primelight.net
Founded: 1990
Corporate video production; creative development, studio & location production, post-production, video & DVD.

Princeton Acoustics Corp
40 Benford Dr, Princeton Junction, NJ 08550
Tel: 609-936-0006
Web Site: www.nccnewyork.com
Key Personnel
Pres: Alfred W D'Alessio

Princeton Architectural Press
37 E Seventh St, New York, NY 10003
Tel: 212-995-9620 *Fax:* 212-995-9454
E-mail: sales@papress.com
Web Site: www.papress.com
Key Personnel
Dir, Sales & Mktg: Katharine Myers *Tel:* 212-995-9620 ext 216
Founded: 1981
Manufacturer of CD-ROM equipment.
Catalog(s) available

Princeton Book Company, Publishers
614 Rte 130, Hightstown, NJ 08520
Tel: 609-426-0602 *Toll Free Tel:* 800-220-7149 *Fax:* 609-426-1344
E-mail: pbc@dancehorizons.com
Web Site: www.dancehorizons.com
Key Personnel
Pres: Charles H Woodford
Online catalog(s) available

Print File Inc
1846 S Orange Blossom Trail, Apopka, FL 32703
Tel: 407-886-3100 *Toll Free Tel:* 800-508-8539 *Fax:* 407-886-0008 *Toll Free Fax:* 800-546-4145
E-mail: support@printfile.com
Web Site: www.printfile.com
Key Personnel
VP: Mark Amat
Photographic equipment maker.
Catalog(s) available
Membership(s): Photo Marketing Association; PPA

Prior Scientific Inc
80 Reservoir Park Dr, Rockland, MA 02370-1062
Tel: 781-878-8442 *Toll Free Tel:* 800-877-2234 *Fax:* 781-878-8736
E-mail: info@prior.com; techsupportus@prior.com
Web Site: www.prior.com
Key Personnel
Pres: Thomas Freda *Tel:* 781-878-8442 ext 3003
Founded: 1918
Foreign Office(s): Wildenbruchstr 15, 07745 Jena, Germany *Tel:* (03641) 675 650 *Fax:* (03641) 675 651
Prior Scientific Instruments Inc, 3-4 Fielding Industrial Estate, Wilbraham Rd, Fulbourn, Cambridge CB21 5ET, United Kingdom *Tel:* (01223) 881711 *Fax:* (01223) 881710 *E-mail:* uksales@prior.com

Prism Media Products Inc
21 Pine St, Rockaway, NJ 07866
Tel: 973-983-9577 *Fax:* 973-983-9588
E-mail: sales@prismmpi.com
Web Site: www.prismsound.com
Key Personnel
Mgr, Admin: Janice Norton
Founded: 1992
Catalog(s) available
Branch Office(s)
West Coast Bldg 45, Suite A, 17952 Sky Park Circle, Irvine, CA 92614, Contact: Pat Bowers *Tel:* 949-861-3350 *Fax:* 949-861-3352
7701 Marble Canyon Dr, Fort Worth, TX 76137, Contact: Doug Ordon *Tel:* 817-514-4900 *Fax:* 817-514-4901 *E-mail:* dougordon@hotmail.com
Foreign Office(s): Prism Media Products Ltd, The Old School House, High St, Stretham, Cambridge CB6 3LD, United Kingdom, Contact: Chris Allen *Tel:* (01353) 648 888 *Fax:* (01353) 648 867 *E-mail:* sales@prismsound.com
Membership(s): AES

Pristine Systems Inc
1891 N Gaffey St, Suite I, San Pedro, CA 90731-1268
Tel: 310-831-2234 *Fax:* 310-831-6287
E-mail: sales@pristinesys.com
Web Site: www.pristinesys.com
Key Personnel
Pres: Kevin Loper
Founded: 1984
Digital storage & delivery systems featuring live assist, digital automation, satellite automation, remote control access & live web site content.
Catalog(s) available
Membership(s): NAB

Private Island Trax
Division of Robynopoly
1882 S Cochran Ave, Los Angeles, CA 90019
Tel: 323-856-8729 *Fax:* 323-965-8732
E-mail: info@privateislandtrax.com
Web Site: www.privateislandtrax.com
Key Personnel
Chief Engr: Michael McDonald

Pro Camera Repair
7910 Raytheon Rd, San Diego, CA 92111
Tel: 858-277-3700 *Fax:* 858-277-5332
E-mail: prophotorepair@hotmail.com
Web Site: www.procamerarepair.com
Key Personnel
Gen Mgr: Kelly Chong
Founded: 1978
Professional photographic repair company.
Membership(s): National Foundation of Independent Businesses; Photo Marketing Association

Pro Cuts Editing Services
2138 Priest Bridge Ct, Suite 1, Crofton, MD 21114
Tel: 301-464-5067; 443-274-6115
E-mail: info@procutsediting.com
Web Site: www.procutsediting.com
Key Personnel
Dir, Post-Prodn: Kenneth G Davis *E-mail:* kgd@procutsediting.com
Founded: 2002

Post-production including video editing, DVD & Blu-ray authoring, streaming video, web design consulting, DVD & Blu-ray replication & duplication, digital storage solutions. Editing suites available. Music & sound effects libraries available upon request.
Membership(s): Baltimore Videographers Association; Professional Videographers of Greater Washing DC

Pro8mm
Division of Small Format Film & Video Inc
2805 W Magnolia Blvd, Burbank, CA 91505-3037
Tel: 818-848-5522 *Fax:* 818-848-5956
E-mail: sales@pro8mm.com; info@pro8mm.com
Web Site: www.pro8mm.com
Key Personnel
Pres: Philip Vigeant
VP, Mktg: Rhonda Vigeant
Founded: 1971
AV equipment sales, archival work & compression & decompression service.
Catalog(s) available
Membership(s): Association of Moving Image Archivists; UFVA

Pro HD Rentals
2201 N Hollywood Way, Suite 1, Burbank, CA 91505
Tel: 818-450-1115
E-mail: sales@prohdrentals.com
Web Site: www.prohdrentals.com
Key Personnel
Pres: Bob Bekian
Complete production services, including equipment rental, portable sets/props & crew services.
Branch Office(s)
1448 19 St, Santa Moninca, CA 90404 *Tel:* 310-453-3301

Pro Image
1716 Terrace Ave, Snohomish, WA 98290
Tel: 206-284-5000 *Toll Free Tel:* 888-284-6400
Key Personnel
Owner & Pres: William Wislen *Tel:* 206-321-1100 (cell) *E-mail:* wtwislen@frontier.com
Teleprompting, film to tape transfers, location videography, photos to video transfers, on-camera & podium teleprompting.

Pro Media Productions
2593 Hamline Ave N, Roseville, MN 55113
Tel: 651-631-3681
E-mail: info@promediaproductions.com
Web Site: www.promediaproductions.com
Full service video production, including training videos, product promotion, corporate overviews, employee communications, tradeshow presentations & television commercials.

Pro Media/Ultra Sound
800 Alfred Nobel Dr, Hercules, CA 94547
Tel: 510-741-2925 *Toll Free Tel:* 800-969-7686 (sales) *Fax:* 510-741-0790
E-mail: service@ultrapromedia.com
Web Site: www.promediausa.com
Key Personnel
CEO & Pres: Andrew C Serb *E-mail:* drew@ultrapromedia.com
COO: Ted Leamy *E-mail:* ted@ultrapromedia.com

Pro Power Products Inc
913 S Victory Blvd, Burbank, CA 91502-2430
Tel: 818-558-6222 *Toll Free Tel:* 800-395-8466 *Fax:* 818-558-3999
Web Site: propowerproducts.com
Key Personnel
VP, Sales: Jim Tessmar *E-mail:* jim@propowerproducts.com
Catalog(s) available
Membership(s): NAB; SMPTE

Pro Stage Inc
567 Ocoee Business Pkwy, Ocoee, FL 34761
Tel: 407-654-5822 *Fax:* 407-654-5826
E-mail: info@prostage.com
Web Site: www.prostage.com
Key Personnel
Pres: Timothy Piper
Founded: 1991
Stage equipment sales & rentals.
Branch Office(s)
3655 E Patrick Lane, Suite 1000, Las Vegas, NV 89120 *Tel:* 702-252-8200 *Fax:* 702-252-8201
Membership(s): InfoComm International®

Pro Studio Supply
140 S Park St, Oconomowoc, WI 53066
Tel: 262-567-8047 *Toll Free Tel:* 800-558-0114 *Fax:* 262-567-8479
E-mail: mail2@prostudiousa.com; sales@prostudiousa.com
Web Site: www.prostudiousa.com
Key Personnel
CEO & Pres: Mark A Stall *E-mail:* mark.stall@prostudiousa.com
Founded: 1968
Total photography solutions.
Catalog(s) available
Membership(s): Photo Marketing Association; PPA

Pro-Tape & Specialities Inc
621 Rte 1 S, Suite B, North Brunswick, NJ 08902
Tel: 732-346-0900 *Toll Free Tel:* 800-345-0234 *Fax:* 732-729-7373
Web Site: www.protapes.com
Key Personnel
COO: Barry Hart
Mktg Mgr: Dennis Mirabella *Tel:* 732-346-0900 ext 115 *E-mail:* dennism@protapes.com
Founded: 1977
Pressure sensitive tapes.
Catalog(s) available

Pro Video
600 First Ave NW, Cedar Rapids, IA 52405
Tel: 319-368-7779 *Toll Free Tel:* 800-234-7680
E-mail: service@provideoweb.com
Web Site: www.provideoweb.com
Specialize in film to DVD transfer as well as other media (VHS tape, Mini DV, 8mm cassette, audio recordings, etc) onto DVD & external hard drive. Also videography & video equipment & accessories rentals.

Pro Video & Film Equipment Co Inc
11425 Mathis Ave, Studio 404, Dallas, TX 75234
Tel: 972-869-9990 *Toll Free Tel:* 888-869-9998 *Fax:* 972-869-0145
E-mail: providfilm@aol.com
Web Site: www.provideofilm.com; www.usedequipmentnewsletter.com
Key Personnel
Founder & Pres: Bill Reiter
Ad Mgr: Stephanie Fox
Founded: 1987
Largest used equipment dealer, specializing in film, video, audio, lighting & production equipment.
Catalog(s) available
Membership(s): Chamber of Commerce; NAB

PROCAM
13624 Black Elk Trail, Prescott, AZ 86305
Tel: 928-708-9901 *Fax:* 928-708-9897
E-mail: camradoc@hotmail.com
Web Site: bolex-usa.com
Key Personnel
Owner: Dieter Schaefer
Founded: 1983

Producer East Productions
43 Mandrake Rd, Monroe Township, NJ 08831
Tel: 631-455-9636
Web Site: www.producereast.com
Key Personnel
Prodr & Dir: Harvey M Birnbaum *E-mail:* hmb@producereast.com
Prodn Mgr: Roslyn Birnbaum
Founded: 1982
Catalog(s) available
Membership(s): Suffolk County Motion Picture & Television Film Commission

Producers Group Ltd
713 S Pacific Coast Hwy, Suite B, Redondo Beach, CA 90277-4233
Tel: 310-316-0481 *Fax:* 310-316-1482
Web Site: www.producers-group.tv
Key Personnel
Pres & Exec Prodr: Lee W Gluckman, Jr *E-mail:* lee.gluckman@producers-group.tv
Founded: 1967
Full service production company.
Membership(s): IQ; SMPTE

Producers Library
10832 Chandler Blvd, North Hollywood, CA 91601
Tel: 818-752-9097 *Toll Free Tel:* 800-944-2135 *Fax:* 818-752-9196
E-mail: research@producerslibrary.com
Web Site: www.producerslibrary.com
Key Personnel
Pres: Jeff Goodman *E-mail:* jeff@producerslibrary.com
Founded: 1957
Stock footage & still photos.
Online catalog(s) available

The Producer's Loft
2773 Folsom St, Suite 101, San Francisco, CA 94110
Tel: 415-334-4700
Web Site: theproducersloft.com
Key Personnel
Prodr: Vic Ferrer
Founded: 2006
Full service rental studio, stage & workplace for photography, film & video production.

Producers Management Television (PMTV)
681 Moore Rd, Suite 100, King of Prussia, PA 19406
Tel: 610-768-1770 *Fax:* 610-768-1773
E-mail: info@pmtv.com
Web Site: www.pmtv.com
Key Personnel
Pres: Brian Powers *Tel:* 484-690-9180 *E-mail:* bpowers@pmtv.com
SVP: Rob Schmoll *Tel:* 484-690-9182 *E-mail:* rschmoll@pmtv.com
Opers Mgr: Danna Doo *Tel:* 484-690-9185 *E-mail:* ddoo@pmtv.com
Founded: 1989
TV production trucks, satellite uplink trucks & crewing services.
Membership(s): MCA-I; NATPE

Producers Playhouse
117 NW 142 St, Edmond, OK 73013
Tel: 405-858-0700 *Toll Free Tel:* 888-607-6856 *Fax:* 405-302-0703
Web Site: www.producersplayhouse.com
Key Personnel
Contact: Mark Bauske *E-mail:* mark@

producersplayhouse.com; Matt Bauske
E-mail: matt@producersplayhouse.com
Full service video production company. Services include writing, producing, production coordinating, studio rental, studio & remote production, editing & delivery of projects.

Producers Studio
Subsidiary of International Media Productions Inc
PO Box 7846, Eugene, OR 97401-0032
Tel: 541-683-1400 *Fax:* 541-683-1401
E-mail: producer@cyberis.net
Web Site: www.producers-studio.com
Key Personnel
Pres: Michael S Dilley
Membership(s): Mid-Oregon Production Arts Network; The Recording Academy

Producers Video
3700 Malden Ave, Baltimore, MD 21211
Tel: 410-523-7520 *Fax:* 410-669-3347; 410-523-0281
Web Site: producers.tv
Key Personnel
Pres & Gen Mgr: Rip Lambert
Production & rental company.
Catalog(s) available
Membership(s): AICE; MCA-I

Product Productions
1806 W Grand Ave, Chicago, IL 60622
Tel: 312-421-9030 *Fax:* 312-243-5051
E-mail: info@productproductions.com
Web Site: www.productproductions.com
Production services, location services & production vehicles. Rent video & audio equipment & accessories.

Production Advantage Inc
301 Avenue "D", Suite 10, Williston, VT 05495
Mailing Address: PO Box 1700, Williston, VT 05495-1700
Tel: 802-651-6915 *Toll Free Tel:* 800-424-9991 *Fax:* 802-651-6914 *Toll Free Fax:* 877-424-9991
E-mail: sales@proadv.com; orders@proadv.com
Web Site: www.productionadvantageonline.com
Key Personnel
VP & Admin: David W Schraffenberger *Tel:* 802-651-6915 ext 115 *E-mail:* schraff@proadv.com
Sales: Rocky Harlow *Tel:* 802-651-6915 ext 124; Ron Kline *Tel:* 802-651-6915 ext 201
Theatrical supplies & equipment.
Catalog(s) available
Membership(s): Professional Lighting & Sound Association

Production Central
873 Broadway, Suite 205, New York, NY 10003
Tel: 212-631-0435 *Fax:* 212-631-0436
E-mail: info@prodcentral.com
Web Site: www.prodcentral.com

Production Consultants
1408 Thomas Mason Place, St Louis, MO 63011-4423
Tel: 636-391-8611 *Fax:* 636-391-4044
E-mail: info@productionconsultants.com
Web Site: www.productionconsultants.com
Key Personnel
Pres: Bill Schulenburg
Prodr: David Schulenburg
Founded: 1986
Audio recording, sound design, post-production & video editing.
Membership(s): AES; ASCAP; The Recording Academy; SAG-AFTRA

Production Consultants & Equipment, see PC&E

Production Craft Inc
1437 W Grand Ave, Chicago, IL 60642-6332
Tel: 312-829-0272 *Fax:* 312-829-8936
E-mail: info@productioncraft.com
Web Site: www.productioncraft.com
Key Personnel
Pres: Dawn Arnold *E-mail:* dawn@productioncraft.com
Founded: 1984
Produce children's videos.
Catalog(s) available

Production Garden Music
Division of Taylor Media Productions Inc
510 E Ramsey, Suite 4, San Antonio, TX 78216
Tel: 210-530-5200 *Toll Free Tel:* 800-247-5317 *Fax:* 210-530-5230
E-mail: sales@productiongarden.com
Web Site: www.productiongarden.com
Key Personnel
Pres & Owner: Mel Taylor
Founded: 1990
Production music library.
Demo CD(s), sampler
Membership(s): NAB

Production Gear Rentals (PGR)
16140 Runnymede St, Van Nuys, CA 91406
Tel: 818-989-8640 *Fax:* 818-989-8644
E-mail: oscar@pgr.tv
Web Site: pgr.tv
Video & audio production & post-production equipment rentals.

The Production Group Studios
6767 W Sunset Blvd, No 8-496, Hollywood, CA 90028-7177
Tel: 323-469-8111 *Fax:* 323-962-2182
E-mail: info@productiongroup.tv
Web Site: www.productiongroup.tv
Key Personnel
Chmn: Fred Rheinstein
VP & Gen Mgr: Carol Noorigian *E-mail:* carol@productiongroup.tv
VP, Opers: Mark Biase
Founded: 1981
Full service production stages.

The Production House
Innovative Teaching & Technology Ctr, 108 ITTC Bldg, Cedar Falls, IA 50614
Tel: 319-273-7820 *Fax:* 319-273-2917
E-mail: pro-house@uni.edu
Web Site: www.uni.edu/its/labs/production-house
Key Personnel
Dir: Marilyn Drury *Tel:* 319-273-2309 *E-mail:* marilyn.drury@uni.edu
Mgr, Digital Design & Multimedia Prodn: Keith Kennedy *Tel:* 319-273-6192 *E-mail:* keith.kennedy@uni.edu
Multimedia production facility.
Brochure(s) available
Membership(s): Consortium of College & University Media Centers

Production Intercom Inc
4 Hillview Dr, Unit A, Lake Barrington, IL 60010
Mailing Address: PO Box 3247, Barrington, IL 60011-3247
Tel: 847-381-5350 *Fax:* 847-381-4360
E-mail: beltpack@beltpack.com
Web Site: www.beltpack.com
Key Personnel
Pres: Glenn Mullis
Off Mgr: Sibbelina Mullis
Founded: 1985
Manufacturer of headset communications, distributor of headsets & Icom walkie-talkies.

CD-ROM catalog(s) available
Membership(s): International Association of Assembly Managers; NAB; NSCA; Professional Lighting & Sound Association; USITT

Production Masters Inc (PMI)
202 Fifth Ave, Pittsburgh, PA 15222
Tel: 412-281-8500 *Fax:* 412-391-7529
E-mail: info@pmi.tv
Web Site: www.pmi.tv
Key Personnel
CEO & Pres: David Case *E-mail:* dcase@pmidigital.com
Founded: 1985
TV production.
Catalog(s) available
Membership(s): NAB; NATPE; SMPTE

Production Outfitters
1833 San Mateo Blvd NE, Albuquerque, NM 87110
Tel: 505-237-0770 *Fax:* 505-232-4419
E-mail: info@productionoutfitters.com
Web Site: www.productionoutfitters.com
Key Personnel
Pres & Dir, Photog: Gary Marsh *E-mail:* gary@productionoutfitters.com
Founded: 1995
TV & AV crew services. HD crews, producers, sound packages & lighting. Live single & multicam HDTV & 3D productions. Video equipment rentals.

Production Partners Media
520 Enterprise Dr, Suite C, Lewis Center, OH 43035
Tel: 614-888-4888
Web Site: productionpartnersmedia.com
Key Personnel
Dir & Prodr: Scott Spears *E-mail:* scott@productionpartnersmedia.com
Prodr & Ed: Peter John Ross
Video production, CD/DVD duplication, commercial production, multimedia, corporate video, equipment rental, audio production & feature film production.

Production Radio Rentals Inc
249 Ferris Ave, White Plains, NY 10603-3420
Tel: 914-686-3525 *Fax:* 914-686-3374
E-mail: info@productionradio.com
Web Site: www.productionradio.com
Key Personnel
Gen Mgr: Henry Cohen
Founded: 1991
Wireless networking.

Production Resource Group LLC (PRG)
539 Temple Hill Rd, New Windsor, NY 12553-5533
Tel: 845-567-5700 *Fax:* 845-567-5800
E-mail: info@prg.com
Web Site: www.prg.com
Key Personnel
CEO & Pres, Corp & Trade Show Americas: Scott Hansen
Pres, PRG Servs: Michael Tomkin *E-mail:* mtomkin@prg.com
Pres, Northeast Opers: Darren DeVerna *E-mail:* ddeverna@prg.com
Branch Office(s)
630 Ninth Ave, Suite 610, New York, NY 10036-3708 *Tel:* 212-589-5400 *Fax:* 212-589-5425

Production Solutions Inc
PO Box 49431, Dayton, OH 45449-0431
Tel: 937-866-2028 *Fax:* 253-423-8997
E-mail: proso@worldnet.att.net
Web Site: www.psiohio.com
Key Personnel
Pres: Louis Todd Knopp

Founded: 2001
Sound reinforcement. Sound systems & audio equipment rental & leasing services.

Production Solutions Inc
PO Box 8146, Reading, PA 19603-8146
Tel: 610-374-6998 *Fax:* 610-374-7284
E-mail: info@prod-sol.com
Web Site: www.prod-sol.com
Key Personnel
Gen Mgr: David Neel *E-mail:* dneel@prod-sol.com
AV equipment rentals.
Shipping Address: 135 Juniata St, West Reading, PA 19611

Production Support Services Inc
827 Koeln Ave, St Louis, MO 63111
Tel: 314-535-8548 *Toll Free Tel:* 800-394-1257 *Fax:* 314-236-0735
E-mail: info@productionsupportservices.com
Web Site: www.productionsupportservices.com
Key Personnel
Owner: Robin Nunn *E-mail:* robinnunn@productionsupportservices.com
Founded: 1985
Produces lighting, sounds, staging & special effects for live events, as well as equipment rentals, sales & installation.

Production West
Division of R2C Group Inc
207 NW Park Ave, Portland, OR 97209
Tel: 503-222-0025 *Fax:* 503-573-1941
E-mail: info@r2cgroup.com
Web Site: www.r2cgroup.com
Key Personnel
Dir, Post-Prodn: Brad Grove *Tel:* 971-544-3447
Founded: 1987
Award winning production facility.

Productions Grand Nord Quebec Inc
5141 Notre Dame de Grace Ave, Montreal, QC H4A 1K4, Canada
Tel: 514-521-7433 *Fax:* 514-522-3013
Key Personnel
Pres: Ian McLaren *E-mail:* imclaren@grandnord.ca
Educational programming.

Les Productions Via Le Monde (Daniel Bertolino) Inc
1222 rue MacKay, Suite 201, Montreal, QC H3G 2H4, Canada
Tel: 514-285-1658 *Fax:* 514-285-1970
Web Site: www.vialemonde.com
Key Personnel
Pres: Daniel Bertolino *Tel:* 514-285-1658 ext 222 *E-mail:* daniel.bertolino@vialemonde.qc.ca
VP: Catherine Viau *Tel:* 514-285-1658 ext 223 *E-mail:* catherine.viau@vialemonde.qc.ca
Full service production company.
Catalog(s) available
Membership(s): Academy of Canadian Cinema & Television; Association des Producteurs De Film Et De Television Du Quebec

Productiontrax.com
Division of One Light Music Productions Inc
11811 N Tatum Blvd, Suite 3031, Phoenix, AZ 85028
Tel: 480-331-8729 *Fax:* 480-240-9324
E-mail: sales@productiontrax.com
Web Site: www.productiontrax.com
Key Personnel
Pres: David Negron
Founded: 2003
Library music, stock photos, stock footage & digital multimedia content.

Professional Advancement Enterprises (PAE)
2182 Saginaw SE, Grand Rapids, MI 49506
Tel: 616-956-9443 *Fax:* 616-956-7973
E-mail: paeworld@comcast.net
Web Site: www.paeworld.com
Key Personnel
Founder & Pres: Jorge W Garcia, PhD
Founded: 1981
Translations & DTP in most foreign languages. Voice overs & subtitling.

Professional Audio Design Inc
90 Corporate Park Dr, Suite 1420, Pembroke, MA 02359
Tel: 781-982-2600 *Toll Free Tel:* 877-223-8858 *Fax:* 781-982-2610
E-mail: info@proaudiodesign.com
Web Site: www.proaudiodesign.com
Key Personnel
Pres: Dave Malekpour *E-mail:* davem@proaudiodesign.com
Audio equipment sales & service.

Professional Education Institute (PEI)
7020 High Grove Blvd, Burr Ridge, IL 60527
Tel: 630-382-1000 *Fax:* 630-325-0825
E-mail: kpalmer@pei.com
Web Site: www.thepei.com
Key Personnel
Pres: Michael E Hussey
Founded: 1983

Professional Label Inc
3415 Olandwood Ct, Olney, MD 20832
Tel: 301-570-0774 *Fax:* 301-570-0776
E-mail: prolabel@msn.com
Web Site: www.professionallabel.com; www.prolabel.com
Key Personnel
Owner & Pres: Rick Fry
Founded: 1986
Catalog(s) available
Membership(s): MCA-I

Professional Management Services Inc
100 Lewis Dr, No 2C, Greenville, SC 29605
Mailing Address: PO Box 8599, Greenville, SC 29604-8599
Tel: 864-325-7240; 864-498-5118 *Fax:* 413-683-7431
E-mail: sales@pm-systems.com
Web Site: pm-systems.com
Key Personnel
Pres & Gen Mgr: William B "Beau" Sanders *E-mail:* beau.sanders@pm-systems.com
Founded: 1990
Catalog(s) available

Professional Marketing Services Inc
105 S Southgate Dr, Chandler, AZ 85226
Mailing Address: 4802 E Ray Rd, No 2328, Phoenix, AZ 85044
Tel: 480-940-5400 *Fax:* 480-940-5488
E-mail: pmsi@promarketinc.com
Web Site: www.promarketinc.com
Key Personnel
Pres: Ted C Williams
Founded: 1987
Catalog(s) available

Professional Sound Corp
28085 Smyth Dr, Valencia, CA 91355
Tel: 661-295-9395 *Fax:* 661-295-8398
E-mail: sales@professionalsound.com; service@professionalsound.com
Web Site: www.professionalsound.com
Key Personnel
Pres: Ron Meyer
Founded: 1986
Catalog(s) available
Membership(s): AES; AFI; NAB

Proforma GW Marketing
3839 E 17 Ave, Spokane, WA 99223
Tel: 509-534-9677; 509-534-7477 *Toll Free Tel:* 800-845-6956 *Fax:* 509-534-9703
E-mail: lulupromotion@aol.com
Web Site: www.proforma.com
Key Personnel
Owner & Mktg Dir: Lori Humphrey
Duplicating services.
Catalog(s) available

The Program Source International
2494 Loch Creek Way, Bloomfield Hills, MI 48304
Mailing Address: PO Box 444, Bloomfield Hills, MI 48303-0444
Tel: 248-333-2010
E-mail: info@program-source.com
Web Site: www.program-source.com
Key Personnel
Pres: David A Eicher
Founded: 1983
Television production, post-production service & multimedia production. Location & studio shooting. HD cameras with new editing suite including 3D editing. Also aerial videography.
Catalog(s) available
Membership(s): Content Delivery & Storage Association

Progressive AE
1811 Four Mile Rd NE, Grand Rapids, MI 49525
Tel: 616-361-2664 *Fax:* 616-361-1493
E-mail: info@progressiveae.com
Web Site: www.progressiveae.com
Key Personnel
CEO & Pres: Brad Thomas
Founded: 1987
Design-centered, research-guided, architectural & engineering firm.
Catalog(s) available

Progressive Media & Music
2116 Southview Ave, Tampa, FL 33606
Tel: 813-251-8093 *Fax:* 813-251-6050
E-mail: info@progressivecds.com
Web Site: www.progressivecds.com/index.html
Key Personnel
Pres & Dir, Sales & Mktg: Ken Veenstra
VHS duplication, VHS & DVD transfer. Web design.
Catalog(s) available
Membership(s): AES; SPARS

Projection Presentation Technology
5803 Rolling Rd, Suite 207, Springfield, VA 22152
Tel: 703-912-1334 *Toll Free Tel:* 800-377-7650 *Fax:* 703-912-1350
E-mail: info@projection.com
Web Site: www.projection.com
Key Personnel
Founder & CEO: David Campbell
Founded: 1971
AV & computer rental company.
Branch Office(s)
One S Water St, Mobile, AL 36602 *Tel:* 334-208-2410 *Fax:* 334-208-2412 *E-mail:* mobile@projection.com
300 E Ocean Blvd, Long Beach, CA 9080 *Tel:* 562-499-7546 *Fax:* 562-499-7683 *E-mail:* southerncalifornia@projection.com
747 Howard St, San Francisco, CA 94103 *Tel:* 415-974-4077 *Fax:* 415-882-6452 *E-mail:* sfbayarea@projection.com
1801 Kalakaua Ave, Honolulu, HI 96815 *Tel:* 808-943-3041 *Fax:* 808-943-3042 *E-mail:* honolulu@projection.com
One W Pratt St, Baltimore, MD 21201 *Tel:* 410-649-7314 *Fax:* 410-649-7061 *E-mail:* baltimore@projection.com

8351 Bristol Ct, Suite 511, Jessup, MD 20794
Tel: 301-459-9011 *Fax:* 301-362-9683
E-mail: dcmetro@projection.com
415 Summer St, Boston, MA 02210 *Tel:* 617-954-3333 *Fax:* 617-954-3327 *E-mail:* boston@projection.com
700 Carpenters Crossing, Bay 6B, Folcroft, PA 19032 *Tel:* 610-532-7252 *Fax:* 610-532-7171
E-mail: philadelphia@projection.com
403 N Third St, Richmond, VA 23219
Tel: 804-783-7323 *Fax:* 804-400-7938
E-mail: richmond@projection.com
Membership(s): IAEM; InfoComm International®; International Association of Speakers Bureaus; Meeting Planners International; NAB

Projector Protector Inc
131 SW 35 Terr, Cape Coral, FL 33914
Tel: 239-945-0792 *Fax:* 239-945-0792
E-mail: projectorprotector@excite.com
Web Site: www.projectorprotector.com
Key Personnel
Pres & Inventor: Robert Voorhies
Projector cleaning equipment & plasma & LCD flat screen protectors.
Membership(s): Ohio Satellite Association

Projector SuperStore LLC
17350 N Hartford Dr, Scottsdale, AZ 85255
Tel: 480-922-9420 *Toll Free Tel:* 888-525-6696
Fax: 480-348-0273
Web Site: www.projectorsuperstore.com
Key Personnel
Gen Mgr: Jeff Phillips *Tel:* 480-922-9420 ext 236
E-mail: jeff@projectorsuperstore.com
Founded: 1996
Online direct source for presentation technology equipment. Serve the corporate, education & nonprofit markets.

Projects in Knowledge Inc
290 W Mount Pleasant Ave, Suite 2350, Livingston, NJ 07039
Tel: 973-890-8988 *Toll Free Tel:* 800-772-8277
Fax: 973-992-5810
E-mail: info@projectsinknowledge.com
Web Site: www.projectsinknowledge.com
Key Personnel
CEO & Pres: Robert Stern
SVP, Educ Planning Mgmt: Patricia Peterson
Founded: 1980
Medical programming producer.
Catalog(s) available
Membership(s): ASAE; International Association of Speakers Bureaus; MPI; Photo Marketing Association; SCMP

ProLine Digital
Division of AMI Corp
PO Box 27682, Denver, CO 80227-0682
Tel: 303-761-3999 *Toll Free Tel:* 800-325-0853
Fax: 303-761-1818
E-mail: info@prolinedigital.com
Web Site: www.prolinedigital.com
Key Personnel
Pres: Tony Marcon *E-mail:* tony@prolinedigital.com
Founded: 1993
Technology accessories & produce digital signage. Foreign office in Australia.
Online catalog(s) available
Shipping Address: 3910 S Decatur St, Englewood, CO 80110
Membership(s): Consumer Electronics Association

Promax Systems
2850 S Fairview St, Santa Ana, CA 97204
Tel: 949-861-2700 *Toll Free Tel:* 800-977-6629
Fax: 949-727-2040
E-mail: customer@promax.com; sales@promax.com
Web Site: www.promax.com
Key Personnel
CEO: Jess Hartmann *E-mail:* jess.hartmann@promax.com
Founded: 1994
Video storage systems.
Catalog(s) available
Membership(s): NAB

Promedia Digital
6520 Singletree Dr, Columbus, OH 43229
Tel: 614-274-1600 *Toll Free Tel:* 800-837-3827
Fax: 614-275-0100
E-mail: info@promediaohio.com
Web Site: www.promediadigital.com
Key Personnel
Contact: Jason Homan *Tel:* 614-274-1600 ext 111
E-mail: jhoman@promediaohio.com
Founded: 1985
Branch Office(s)
6800 Lauffer Rd, Columbus, OH 43231 *Tel:* 614-884-6800 *Fax:* 614-275-0100
5335 Far Hills Ave, Suite 108, Dayton, OH 45429, Contact: Mary Collins *Tel:* 937-294-5883 ext 140 *Toll Free Tel:* 888-837-3827
E-mail: mcollins@promediaohio.com

Promidi Music
1980 NE 148 St, Miami, FL 33181
Tel: 305-956-9116 *Fax:* 305-947-8220
E-mail: info@promidi.biz
Web Site: www.promidimusic.com
Music scoring & composing.

Prominent Video, see Deja View Video

Prop Closet LLC, see Theatre Effects

Propeller Music Group
30 Prescott Ave, Mont Clair, NJ 07042
Tel: 212-768-3400
E-mail: info@propellermusic.com
Web Site: www.propellermusic.com
Key Personnel
Owner, Creative Dir & Composer: Doug Hall
E-mail: doug@propellermusic.com

ProPhotonix Ltd
32 Hampshire Rd, Salem, NH 03079
Tel: 603-893-8778 *Toll Free Tel:* 800-472-4633 (North & South America sales) *Fax:* 603-907-0255
E-mail: sales@stockeryale.com
Web Site: www.prophotonix.com
Key Personnel
CEO & Pres: Tim Losik
Founded: 1946 (as Stocker & Yale Inc)
Designs & manufactures LED illumination solutions as well as produces laser modules. Also distribute laser diodes.
Catalog(s) available
Foreign Office(s): LED Solutions, 3020 Euro Business Park, Little Island, Cork, Ireland
Tel: (021) 5001300
Laser Solutions, Pierce Williams Sparrow Lane, Hatfield Broad Oak, Herts CM22 7BA, United Kingdom *Tel:* (01279) 717170
Membership(s): Archeological Institute of America

Prosper Media Group Inc
348 E Main St, Lexington, KY 40507
Mailing Address: PO Box 55182, Lexington, KY 40555
Tel: 859-400-0136 *Toll Free Tel:* 888-528-1999
E-mail: producer@prosperproductions.com
Web Site: www.prospermg.com
Key Personnel
CEO & Exec Prodr: Kyle M Lake
Founded: 1998
Delivers affordable professional multimedia video production services to any business of any size.
Membership(s): Lexington Chamber of Commerce

Protech Audio Corp
192 Cedar River Rd, Indian Lake, NY 12842
Mailing Address: PO Box 597, Indian Lake, NY 12842-0597
Tel: 518-648-6410 *Fax:* 518-648-6395
E-mail: proinfo@protechaudio.com; prosales@protechaudio.com
Web Site: www.protechaudio.com
Key Personnel
Pres: William Murphy
Founded: 1979
Audio equipment manufacturer.
Catalog(s) available
Membership(s): NSCA

PROTOCOL
16844 Saticoy St, Van Nuys, CA 91406
Tel: 818-782-5705 *Toll Free Tel:* 800-400-5705
Fax: 818-782-5817
E-mail: orders@walkietalkie.com
Web Site: www.walkietalkie.com

Provident-Integrity Distribution
Affiliate of Sony Music Entertainment Inc
741 Cool Springs Blvd, Franklin, TN 37067
Tel: 615-261-6500 *Toll Free Tel:* 800-333-9000
Fax: 615-261-5904 *Toll Free Fax:* 800-333-9408
E-mail: info@providentmusicgroup.com
Key Personnel
Dir, Mktg: Carol Roundtree
Spiritual music distributor.
Online catalog(s) available
Membership(s): CBA: The Association for Christian Retail

ProVideo
2302 W Badger Rd, Madison, WI 53713-2322
Tel: 608-271-1226 *Toll Free Tel:* 800-569-6810
Fax: 608-271-2737
E-mail: info@provideo.com
Web Site: www.provideo.com
Key Personnel
Pres: Jim Stiener
Prodn Coord: Justin Johnson
Founded: 1986
Full service production company.
Membership(s): Madison Ad Federation; MCA-I

ProVision Video Sales & Rentals Inc
143 W Third Ave, Vancouver, BC V5Y 1E6, Canada
Tel: 604-876-0940 *Toll Free Tel:* 877-337-0940
Fax: 604-876-8269
E-mail: sales@provisionvideo.com; rentals@provisionvideo.com
Web Site: www.provisionvideo.com
Key Personnel
Owner, Opers & Rental Mgr: Steven Fuzessery
Sales Mgr: Chris Hopkins
Founded: 2004
Sales & rentals of video production equipment.

PSAV® Presentation Services
111 W Ocean Blvd, Suite 1110, Long Beach, CA 90802-4688
Tel: 562-366-0620 *Toll Free Tel:* 877-430-7728
Fax: 562-366-0628
Web Site: www.psav.com
Key Personnel
CEO & Pres: J Michael McIlwain
COO: Sky Cunningham
CFO & EVP: Dan Bauman
CIO: Pat Enright
SVP & Gen Mgr: Arthur A Clyne, Jr

SVP, Global Sales & Mktg: Greg Van Dyke
Founded: 1967
Branch Office(s)
16320 Arthur St, Cerritos, CA 90703, Br Dir: Jeff Symes *Tel:* 562-991-6050 *Web Site:* www.psav.com/losangeles
1725 Corporate Dr, Suite 300, Norcross, GA 30093, Br Dir: Peter Graves *Tel:* 404-352-1418 *Web Site:* www.psav.com/atlanta
2826 Ualena St, Honolulu, HI 96819, Regl VP: Steven C Osborne *Tel:* 808-877-9400 *Web Site:* www.psav.com/hawaii
50 Rawls Rd, Des Plaines, IL 60018, Dir, Sales: Nick Vitogiannes *Tel:* 847-759-8321 *Web Site:* www.psav.com/chicago
45 Fourth Ave, Needham, MA 02494, Dir, Sales & Opers: Scott Queipo *Tel:* 339-225-3199 *Web Site:* www.psav.com/boston
99 Fifth Ave NW, Suite 500, New Brighton, MN 55112, Br Dir: Nick Madsen *Tel:* 847-759-8321 *Web Site:* www.psav.com/minneapolis
4375 S Valley View, Suite D, Las Vegas, NV 89103, Dir, Sales: Jay Jurgensen *Tel:* 702-891-0953 *Web Site:* www.psav.com/vegas
409 Elk Park Dr, Asheville, NC 28804, Contact: Jay Kirk *Tel:* 828-236-0924 *Web Site:* www.psav.com/asheville
3421 St Vardell Lane, Suite G, Charlotte, NC 28217, Dir, Sales & Opers: Scott Stinson *Tel:* 704-525-2380 ext 204 *Web Site:* www.psav.com/charlotte
1341 N Delaware Ave, Suite 103, Philadelphia, PA 19125, Br Dir: Bonnie Santanna *Tel:* 215-425-5206 *Web Site:* partner.psav.com/philadelphia
517 Meeting St, Charleston, SC 29403, Br Dir: Frank Richardson *Tel:* 843-577-9185 *Web Site:* www.psav.com/charleston
18 Hunter Rd, Hilton Head, SC 29926, Br Dir: David A Delaney *Tel:* 843-681-2034 *Web Site:* partner.psav.com/hiltonheadisland
925 Freeport Pkwy, Suite 100, Coppell, TX 75019, Br Dir: B J Hammer *Tel:* 214-210-8061 *Web Site:* www.psav.com/dallas
2055 Silber Rd, Suite 130, Houston, TX 77055, Br Dir: Dexter Oliver *Tel:* 713-680-8360 *Web Site:* www.psav.com/houston
600 Hemisphere Park, Bldg 277, Suite 113-B, San Antonio, TX 78202, Contact: Ray Ramirez *Tel:* 210-308-0182 *Web Site:* www.psav.com/sanantonio
Membership(s): ASAE; InfoComm International®; MPI; NACE; Professional Convention Management Association

PSAV® Presentation Services (Hotel Services Division)
1700 E Golf Rd, Suite 400, Schaumburg, IL 60173-5820
Tel: 847-222-9800 *Toll Free Tel:* 800-486-9509
E-mail: info@psav.com
Web Site: www.psav.com
Key Personnel
CEO & Pres: J Michael McIlwain
COO: Sky Cunningham
AV presentation professionals.
Catalog(s) available
Membership(s): InfoComm International®; MCA-I; NAPTE

PSB Speakers International
Division of Lenbrook Industries Ltd
633 Granite Ct, Pickering, ON L1W 3K1, Canada
Tel: 905-831-6555 *Toll Free Tel:* 800-263-4641 (cust serv) *Fax:* 905-837-6357
E-mail: info@psbspeakers.com
Web Site: www.psbspeakers.com
Key Personnel
Founder & Chief Design: Paul Barton
Pres, A/V Canada: Pat McKeever
Mktg Mgr, PSB Speaker: Denise Babin
Founded: 1972
Catalog(s) available

PSI Inc
15375 Barranca Pkwy, Suite A 208, Irvine, CA 92618
Tel: 949-261-6119
E-mail: psiinfo@psivideoinc.com
Web Site: www.psivideoinc.com
Key Personnel
Owner & CEO: Timothy Loftus *E-mail:* tim@psivideoinc.com
Founded: 1972
Digital video production - CD/DVD, Event Staging-Duplication.

PsiTech Inc
18368 Bandilier Circle, Fountain Valley, CA 92708
Tel: 714-964-7818 *Toll Free Tel:* 800-872-7385 *Fax:* 714-968-7884
E-mail: info@psitech.com; sales@psitech.com
Web Site: www.psitech.com
Key Personnel
Pres: John Kerr
VP, Sales & Mktg: Rob Mathuny
Founded: 1981
Manufacturer of hardware & software products.
Data sheet(s) available
Branch Office(s)
25-211 Beiqu, Xinhualianjiayuan, Tongzhou, Beijing 101101, China, Dir, Busn Devt: Richard Zhou *Tel:* (010) 5166-7109 *E-mail:* richard.zhou@psitech.com

PSSI
7030 Hayvenhurst Ave, Van Nuys, CA 91406
Tel: 310-575-4400 *Toll Free Tel:* 800-SAT-LINK (728-5465) *Fax:* 310-575-4451
E-mail: operations@pssiglobal.com
Web Site: www.pssiglobal.com
Key Personnel
CEO: Robert Lamb *E-mail:* rlamb@pssiglobal.com
Pres: Matt Bridges *E-mail:* mbridges@pssiglobal.com
Founded: 1979
Provider of mobile satellite transmission services.
Brochure(s) available
Branch Office(s)
4415 Wagon Trail Ave, Las Vegas, NV 89118 *Tel:* 702-458-0876
Membership(s): SSPI

Psych Soft Inc
PO Box 232, North Quincy, MA 02171
Tel: 617-471-8733
E-mail: psoft@psych-soft.com
Web Site: www.psych-soft.com
Founded: 1987
Computer & workstation manufacturer.

Psychological Assessment Resources Inc (PAR)
16204 N Florida Ave, Lutz, FL 33549
Tel: 813-968-3003; 813-449-4065 (cust serv) *Toll Free Tel:* 800-331-8378 (tech support) *Fax:* 813-968-2598 *Toll Free Fax:* 800-727-9329
Web Site: www4.parinc.com
Key Personnel
Chmn: R Bob Smith, III
COO & Pres: Kay Cunningham
Founded: 1978
Leading publisher of assessment tools.
Catalog(s) available
Shipping Address: 16130 N Florida Ave, Lutz, FL 33549
Membership(s): Association of Test Publishers

PTL Cable Service Inc, see PTL Test Equipment Inc

PTL Test Equipment Inc
612 N Orange Ave, Suite D-10, Jupiter, FL 33458
Tel: 561-747-3647 *Fax:* 561-575-4635
E-mail: ptltest@bellsouth.net
Web Site: www.ptltest.com
Key Personnel
Pres: Paul T Legris *E-mail:* ptlte@bellsouth.net
Founded: 1979
New & reconditioned test equipment.
Brochure(s), free
Information sheet(s), free, inventory list available

Public Eye Productions
409 Meeker St, South Orange, NJ 07079
Tel: 917-446-8977
Web Site: www.publiceyeproductions.com
Key Personnel
Owner, Prodr & Dir: Scott Sinkler *E-mail:* scott@publiceyeproductions.com
Founded: 1994
Video production.

Publishers Group West Inc
1700 Fourth St, Berkeley, CA 94710
Tel: 510-809-3700 *Toll Free Tel:* 800-788-3123 (cust serv) *Fax:* 510-809-3777
E-mail: info@pgw.com
Web Site: www.pgw.com
Key Personnel
VP, Field Sales: Elise Cannon
EVP & Dir, Natl Accts: Kimberly Wylie
Educational programming.
Catalog(s) available
Branch Office(s)
154 W 14 St, 12th fl, New York, NY 10011 *Tel:* 212-614-7888 *Fax:* 212-614-7866

Jai Pulnix
625 River Oaks Pkwy, San Jose, CA 95134
Tel: 408-383-0300 *Toll Free Tel:* 800-445-5444 *Fax:* 408-383-0301
E-mail: camerasales.americas@jai.com
Web Site: www.jai.com
Key Personnel
Mktg Communs Mgr: Rich Dickerson
Video camera equipment manufacturer.

Pumpkin Recording Studio Inc
8453 Rob Roy Dr, Orland Park, IL 60462
Tel: 708-349-1485
E-mail: pumpkin1@flash.net
Key Personnel
Pres: Gary Loizzo
Analog/digital 24 track professional tools.

Purefire Communications Inc
200 Evans Ave, Unit 3, Toronto, ON M8Z 1J7, Canada
Tel: 416-503-2323
E-mail: info@purefire.ca
Web Site: www.purefire.ca
Key Personnel
Pres: Tony Patafio *E-mail:* tony@purefire.ca
Founded: 2001
Multimedia solutions company.

Pyramid Media
Division of Pyramid Films Corp
3200 Airport Ave, No 19, Santa Monica, CA 90405
Mailing Address: PO Box 1048, Santa Monica, CA 90406-1048
Tel: 310-398-6149 *Toll Free Tel:* 800-421-2304 *Fax:* 310-398-7869
E-mail: info@pyramidmedia.com; sales@pyramidmedia.com
Web Site: www.pyramidmedia.com
Key Personnel
Pres: Randolph Wright *E-mail:* rwright@pyramidmedia.com
VP & Gen Mgr: Denise Adams

Founded: 1960
Catalog(s) available

Pyramind Studios
Subsidiary of Music Production & Sound Design Training & Services
880 Folsom St, San Francisco, CA 94107
Tel: 415-896-9800 *Toll Free Tel:* 888-378-6463 *Fax:* 415-896-5943
E-mail: news@pyramind.com
Web Site: www.pyramind.com
Key Personnel
Founder & CEO: Gregory Gordon *E-mail:* greg@pyramind.com
Founded: 1987
Music production & training facility.
Online catalog(s) available
Membership(s): The Game Audio Network Guild; The Recording Academy

Pyro Spectaculars
3196 N Locust Ave, Rialto, CA 92377
Mailing Address: PO Box 2329, Rialto, CA 92377-2329
Tel: 909-355-8120 *Toll Free Tel:* 888-477-7976 *Fax:* 909-355-9813
E-mail: info@pyrospectaculars.com
Web Site: www.pyrospectaculars.com
Key Personnel
Pres: James Souza
Founded: 1979
Special effects displays.

Pyrotek Special Effects Inc
7676 Woodbine Ave, Suites 7 & 8, Markham, ON L3R 2N2, Canada
Tel: 905-479-9991 *Toll Free Tel:* 800-481-9910 *Fax:* 905-479-3515
E-mail: info@pyrotekfx.com
Web Site: www.pyrotekfx.com
Key Personnel
CFO: Bruce Baum
Pres & Owner: Doug Adams *E-mail:* doug@pyrotekfx.com
Catalog(s) available
Branch Office(s)
4347 W Sunset, Las Vegas, NV 89118 *Tel:* 702-450-7976 *Fax:* 702-407-0853

Pyxis Industries Inc
25695 Jefferson Ave, Suite 8, Murrieta, CA 92562
Tel: 951-526-1999 *Toll Free Tel:* 888-799-4728 *Fax:* 951-253-9290
Web Site: pyxisindustries.com
Key Personnel
Owner & Pres: Chad Costanzo *Tel:* 951-526-1999 ext 1201 *E-mail:* chad@pyxisindustries.com
Mgr: Kelly Costanzo *Tel:* 951-526-1999 ext 1205 *E-mail:* kelly@pyxisindustries.com
Full service audio, lighting & video event production & sales company.

Q-Prompt Inc
5356 Vail Ct, Mississauga, ON L5M 6G9, Canada
Tel: 905-601-3826 *Toll Free Tel:* 888-848-4134 *Fax:* 905-567-5665
E-mail: info@qprompt.com
Web Site: www.qprompt.com
Key Personnel
Owner: Christian Quilliam *E-mail:* chris@qprompt.com
Founded: 1994

QCA
2832 Spring Grove Ave, Cincinnati, OH 45225
Tel: 513-681-8400 *Toll Free Tel:* 800-859-8401
E-mail: info@go-qca.com
Web Site: www.go-qca.com
Key Personnel
CFO: Andrea Winterhalter *Tel:* 513-681-8400 ext 103 *E-mail:* andrea@go-qca.com
Pres: Jim Bosken *Tel:* 513-681-8400 ext 102 *E-mail:* jim@go-qca.com
Catalog(s) available

QCI International
PO Box 1769, Chico, CA 95927-1769
Tel: 530-893-4095 *Fax:* 530-893-0395
E-mail: info@qci-intl.com
Web Site: www.qualitydigest.com
Key Personnel
Pres: Jeff Dewar
Founded: 1978
Consulting & training videos.
Catalog(s) available
Membership(s): American Society for Quality; Association for Quality & Participation

Qioptiq
Member of Qioptiq Group
78 Shuyler Baldwin, Fairport, NY 14450
Tel: 585-223-2370 *Toll Free Tel:* 800-429-0257 *Fax:* 585-223-1999
E-mail: info@qioptiqlinos.com
Web Site: www.qioptiqlinos.com
Key Personnel
Non-Exec Chmn: Fredrik Arp
CEO: David Marks
CFO: Richard Ivimey-Cook
Supply industrial lenses & accessories for OEM applications. Standard & custom products include photo/electronic imaging optics, laser optics & medical/bio-imaging lenses.
Catalog(s) available

QRS Software Services
11879 Woodbury Rd, Garden Grove, CA 92843
Tel: 714-537-5100 *Toll Free Tel:* 800-228-9699 *Fax:* 714-539-9448
E-mail: qrs@qrssoftware.com; sales@qrssoftware.com
Web Site: www.qrssoftware.com
Key Personnel
VP, Sales & Mktg: Kelly Joseph *Tel:* 714-537-5100 ext 223 *E-mail:* joseph@qrssoftware.com
Founded: 1994
Software manufacturer & distributor.
Catalog(s) available

QSC Audio Products LLC
1675 MacArthur Blvd, Costa Mesa, CA 92626
Tel: 714-754-6175 *Toll Free Tel:* 800-854-4079 *Fax:* 714-754-6174
E-mail: info@qscaudio.com
Web Site: www.qsc.com
Key Personnel
CEO & Pres: Joe Pham
COO & EVP: Jatan Shah
VP, Mktg: Gerry Pschetter
Professional audio sound system manufacturer.
Catalog(s) available
Foreign Office(s): Hoi Shing Rd, No 9, Unit 7A, 28th fl, Tsuen Wan New Territories, Hong Kong *Tel:* 3752 8300
Membership(s): AES; International Technology and Engineering Educators Association; NAMM, the National Association of Music Merchants; NSCA

QSound Labs Inc
2816 11 St NE, Suite 102, Calgary, AB T2E 7S7, Canada
Tel: 403-291-2492 *Fax:* 403-250-1521
E-mail: info@qsound.com; sales@qsound.com
Web Site: www.qsound.com
Key Personnel
CEO & Pres: David Gallagher
Founded: 1986
Catalog(s) available

QTV
Division of Autocue Inc
124 W 30 St, Suite 312, New York, NY 10001
Tel: 212-929-7755 *Fax:* 212-929-2105
E-mail: info@qtv.com
Web Site: www.autocue.com/teleprompter
Founded: 1955
Leader supplier of teleprompting hardware & software for purchase & rentals.
Membership(s): Production Equipment Rental Association

Quabbin Wire & Cable Co Inc
10 Maple St, Ware, MA 01082-1597
Tel: 413-967-6281 *Toll Free Tel:* 800-368-3311 *Fax:* 413-967-7564
E-mail: sales@quabbin.com
Web Site: www.quabbin.com
Key Personnel
Pres: Paul Engel
EVP: Debi Engel
Mktg Coord: Jacqui Jamieson *Tel:* 413-967-6281 ext 343 *E-mail:* jacquij@quabbin.com
Founded: 1975
Manufacture wire & cable.
Catalog(s), free
CD-ROM catalog(s), free

Quad Recording Studios
346 Jersey Ave, Greenwood Lake, NY 10925
Mailing Address: PO Box 1175, Greenwood Lake, NY 10925
Tel: 845-477-0338
Web Site: www.quadstudios.com
Key Personnel
Studio Mgr: Lou Gonzalez *E-mail:* quadlou@aol.com
Founded: 1970
Recording studio.
Branch Office(s)
1802 Grand Ave, Nashville, TN 37212, Studio Mgr: Mark Greenwood *Tel:* 615-321-9500 *Fax:* 615-321-0046 *E-mail:* markquadnash@aol.com *Web Site:* www.quadstudiosnashville.com

Qualiton Imports Ltd
24-02 40 Ave, Long Island City, NY 11101
Tel: 718-937-8515 *Fax:* 718-729-3239
E-mail: qualiton@qualiton.com; steve@qualiton.com
Web Site: www.qualiton.com
Catalog(s) available

Quality Audio Visual Service Inc
6938 Boulevard 26, Fort Worth, TX 76180-8808
Tel: 817-284-3192 *Toll Free Tel:* 800-371-6741 *Fax:* 817-595-2942
E-mail: info@qualityaudiovisual.com
Web Site: www.qualityaudiovisual.com
Key Personnel
Pres: John W Pierce *E-mail:* john@qualityaudiovisual.com
Founded: 1980
Catalog(s) available

Quality Clones
3940 Laurel Canyon Blvd, Suite 405, Studio City, CA 91604
Tel: 323-464-5853
E-mail: info@qualityclones.com
Web Site: www.qualityclones.com
Key Personnel
Pres: Jerry Zampas

Quality Film & Video
3321 Main St, Suite B-1, Manchester, MD 21102
Tel: 410-785-1920
E-mail: quality3321@comcast.net
Web Site: www.qualityfilmvideo.com
Key Personnel
Pres: Peter A Garey

VP: Guy G Garey
Founded: 1958
Catalog(s) available

Quantel Inc
Subsidiary of Quantel Ltd (UK)
25 W 43 St, Suite 1118, New York, NY 10036-7406
Tel: 212-944-6820 *Toll Free Tel:* 800-331-8327 (cust serv) *Fax:* 212-944-6813
Web Site: www.quantel.com
Key Personnel
VP, Prod Support: Mark Toms *E-mail:* mark.toms@quantel.com
VP, Sales, Eastern Region: Brad Wensley *E-mail:* brad.wensley@quantel.com
Founded: 1973
Offices also in Italy, The Netherlands & Singapore.
Catalog(s) available
Branch Office(s)
3800 Barham Blvd, Suite 315, Los Angeles, CA 90068, VP, Sales: Eric Thorne *Tel:* 323-436-7600 *Fax:* 323-878-2596 *E-mail:* eric.thorne@quantel.com
One Yonge St, Suite 1008, Toronto, ON M5E 1E5, Canada, VP, Sales: Mark Northeast *Tel:* 416-362-9522 *Fax:* 416-362-9215 *E-mail:* mark.northeast@quantel.com
Foreign Office(s): Quantel Pty Ltd, 60 Frenchs Rd, Willoughby, Sydney NSW 2068, Australia, Mng Dir: Julien James *Tel:* (02) 9967 0655 *Fax:* (02) 9967 0677 *E-mail:* julien.james@quantel.com
Quantel Ltd, China World Trade Ctr, 1608 Office One, No 1, Jian Guo Men Wai Dajie, Chao Ying District, Beijing 100004, China, Gen Mgr: Johnsen Yue *Tel:* (010) 6505 7178 *Fax:* (010) 6505 3732 *E-mail:* johnsen.yue@quantel.com
Quantel Micro Consultants SAS, 56 rue de Paris, 92100 Boulogne Billancourt, France, Regl Sales Mgr, Broadcast: Jean-Luc Wolff *Tel:* 01 46 99 92 00 *Fax:* 01 46 99 05 10 *E-mail:* jean-luc.wolff@quantel.com
Quantel GmbH, Mottmannstr 4 A, 53842 Troisdorf, Germany, Dir, Sales: Thomas Birner *Tel:* (02241) 49 80 *Fax:* (02241) 49 81 60 *E-mail:* thomas.birner@quantel.com *Web Site:* germany.quantel.co.uk
Quantel Asia Pacific Ltd, 35/F Central Plaza, 18 Harbour Rd, Hong Kong, Hong Kong, Contact: Evita Won *Tel:* 2366 1321 *Fax:* 2369 6678 *E-mail:* evita.won@quantel.com
Quantel KK, 6-5-55 Minami-Aoyama, Minato-Ku, Tokyo 107-0062, Japan, Sales Mgr: Shoji Mori *Tel:* (03) 3400 5711 *Fax:* (03) 3400 5712 *E-mail:* shoji.mori@quantel.com *Web Site:* japan.quantel.co.uk
QAC, A-309 Hanwha Bizmetro, 449-17 Gayang-dong, Gangseo-gu, Seoul 157-804, South Korea, Sales Mgr: Hokeun Lee *Tel:* (02) 780 0950 *Fax:* (02) 7836 0070 *E-mail:* hk.lee@quantel.com
Quantel Espana SA, Edificio Ginebra, Avda de Europa 2, Parque Empresarial la Moraleja, 28108 Madrid, Spain, Sales Mgr: Rafael Zapardiel *Tel:* 607 432 693 *E-mail:* rafael.zapardiel@quantel.com
Quantel Ltd, 31 Turnpike Rd, Newbury, Berkshire RG14 2NX, United Kingdom *Tel:* (01635) 48222 *Fax:* (01635) 815815 (head office)
Membership(s): ISBE; MCA-I; NAB; PromaxBDA; SMPTE

Quantum Data Inc
2111 Big Timber Rd, Elgin, IL 60123-1100
Tel: 847-888-0450 *Toll Free Tel:* 888-252-6133 (tech support) *Fax:* 847-888-2802
E-mail: sales@quantumdata.com
Web Site: www.quantumdata.com
Key Personnel
Founder & Pres: Allen Jorgensen
VP, Sales: Chuck Evans *Tel:* 847-888-0450 ext 117 *E-mail:* cevans@quantumdata.com
Founded: 1979
Video signal generator manufacturing.
Catalog(s) available
Membership(s): SID; VESA

Quantum Instruments Inc
Division of PromarkBRANDS
1268 Humbracht Circle, Bartlett, IL 60103-1631
Tel: 631-656-7400 *Fax:* 631-656-7410
E-mail: quantumhelp@qtm.com
Web Site: www.qtm.com
Key Personnel
Pres: Ken Orlando; Richard Shaper
Founded: 1975
Catalog(s) available
Membership(s): Photo Marketing Association

Quartet Manufacturing Co
Division of ACCO Brands Corp
4 Corporate Dr, Lake Zurich, IL 60047-8997
Toll Free Tel: 800-541-0094 *Toll Free Fax:* 800-247-1317
Web Site: www.quartet.com; www.gbc.com; www.accobrands.com
Founded: 1954
Catalog(s) available
Membership(s): Education Market Association; National Art Education Association; National Art Materials Trade Association; NOPA

Quatrefoil Associates Inc
29 "C" St, Laurel, MD 20707
Tel: 301-470-4748 *Fax:* 301-470-4749
E-mail: info@quatrefoil.com
Web Site: www.quatrefoil.com
Key Personnel
Founding Partner & VP: Paula Schuman
COO: Paul De Camp
Design Dir: Michael Burns; Abbie Chessler *E-mail:* abbie@quatrefoil.com
Technol Dir: Ernie Falcone
Museum exhibit design & fabrication.

Questar Corp
6204 Ingham Rd, New Hope, PA 18938
Tel: 215-862-5277 *Toll Free Tel:* 800-247-9607 *Fax:* 215-862-0512
E-mail: questar@erols.com
Web Site: www.questarcorporation.com
Key Personnel
VP, Opers: James A Perkins
Founded: 1950
Catalog(s) available
Membership(s): The Optical Society

Questar Inc
307 N Michigan Ave, 5th fl, Chicago, IL 60601-5305
Tel: 312-266-9400 *Toll Free Tel:* 800-544-8422 (cust serv) *Fax:* 312-266-9523
E-mail: info@questar1.com
Web Site: questarentertainment.com
Distribute features video.
Branch Office(s)
1413 1/2 Kenneth Rd, Suite 240, Glendale, CA 91201 *Tel:* 818-953-4154 *Fax:* 818-953-4157
Membership(s): Entertainment Merchants Association

Quickbeam Systems Inc (QSI)
4411 McLeod Rd NE, Suite E, Albuquerque, NM 87109
Tel: 505-345-9230 *Fax:* 505-345-4604
E-mail: sales@quickbeam.com
Web Site: www.quickbeam.com
Key Personnel
Co-Founder: Kurt Jaeckel *Tel:* 505-345-9230 ext 17 *E-mail:* kurtj@quickbeam.com; Gary Mathews *Tel:* 505-345-9230 ext 15 *E-mail:* garym@quickbeam.com
Founded: 1977
Stage lighting, video, audio.

QuickSet International Inc
Subsidiary of MOOG Inc
3650 Woodhead Dr, Northbrook, IL 60062-1895
Tel: 847-498-0700 *Toll Free Tel:* 800-247-6563 *Fax:* 847-498-1258
E-mail: info@quickset.com
Web Site: www.quickset.com
Key Personnel
Contact: Trish Logue
Founded: 1933
Elevation control mounts & tripods.
Catalog(s) available
Membership(s): NAB

Quiet Planet LLC
PO Box 900, Indianola, WA 98342
Tel: 360-477-9588
Web Site: www.quietplanet.com
Key Personnel
Founder & Publr: Gordon W Hempton *E-mail:* gordon@soundtracker.com
Nature sound library for independent producers.

Quilt in a Day
1955 Diamond St, San Marcos, CA 92078
Tel: 760-591-0082 *Toll Free Tel:* 800-777-4852 *Fax:* 760-591-4424
E-mail: customerservice@quiltinaday.com
Web Site: www.quiltinaday.com
Key Personnel
Owner: Eleanor Burns
Founded: 1978
Quilting videos.
Catalog(s) available
Branch Office(s)
119 N Fourth St, Paducah, KY 42001 *Tel:* 270-442-2155

Quince Imaging Inc
2810 Towerview Rd, Herndon, VA 20171-3206
Tel: 703-742-7520 *Toll Free Tel:* 888-252-4960 *Fax:* 703-742-7586
E-mail: info@quinceimaging.com; sales@quinceimaging.com; operations@quinceimaging.com
Web Site: www.quinceimaging.com
Key Personnel
CEO: Ron Currier
CFO: Scott Williams *E-mail:* scott@quinceimaging.com
Founded: 1997
Staging equipment sales & rentals.
Catalog(s) available

Bill Quinn Productions
PO Box 213, Ocean Gate, NJ 08740
Tel: 732-237-0525
Key Personnel
Pres: Bill Quinn *E-mail:* billquinn1952@hotmail.com
Prodn Dir: Chris Quinn
Dir, Photog: John Sosenko
Founded: 1982
Commercial production 35mm.
Catalog(s) available
Membership(s): AAPA; HOG

Quintessence Audio Ltd
5701 W Dempster St, Morton Grove, IL 60053
Tel: 847-966-4434 *Fax:* 847-966-0932
E-mail: info@quintessenceaudio.com
Web Site: www.quintessenceaudio.com
Founded: 1977

R & R Cases & Cabinets
Division of R & R Holdings Inc
1217 Rand Rd, Des Plaines, IL 60016

Tel: 847-299-8100 *Fax:* 847-299-8110
E-mail: sales@rrcases.com
Web Site: www.rrcases.com
Key Personnel
VP, Sales & Mktg: Mike Krutsch *Tel:* 847-299-8100 ext 12 *E-mail:* mike@rrcases.com
Contact: Jim Price *Tel:* 847-299-8100 ext 15
Founded: 1974
Manufacturer of carrying cases.
Online catalog(s) available

R & R Lighting Co Inc, see Shadowstone R & R™

R/GA
350 W 39 St, New York, NY 10018
Tel: 212-946-4000 *Fax:* 212-946-4010
E-mail: web@rga.com
Web Site: www.rga.com
Key Personnel
CEO: Bob Greenberg
Creative design.
Catalog(s) available
Branch Office(s)
35 S Park St, San Francisco, CA 94107 *Tel:* 415-624-2000 *Fax:* 415-634-2010
820 Broadway, Suite 350, Santa Monica, CA 90401 *Tel:* 310-496-4239
217 N Jefferson, 5th fl, Chicago, IL 60661 *Tel:* 312-276-5300
106 E Sixth St, Suite 900, Austin, TX 78701 *Tel:* 512-322-3968
Foreign Office(s): Uriarte 1572, C1414DAP Buenos Aires, Argentina *Tel:* (011) 5984 0500
32 Grosvenor St, Sydney, NSW 2000, Australia *Tel:* (02) 9994 4000
Rua Estados Unidos 136, 01427-000 Sao Paulo-SP, Brazil *Tel:* (011) 3958-0900
Str Buzesti 50-52, Et 2, Sector 1, 011015 Bucharest, Romania *Tel:* (021) 302 16 14
The MacDonald House, No 05-01, 40-A Orchard Rd, Singapore 238838, Singapore *Tel:* 6737 7472
Oxtorgsgrand 2-4, 111 57 Stockholm, Sweden *Tel:* (08) 509 0723 0
151 Rosebery Ave, London EC1R 4AB, United Kingdom *Tel:* (020) 7071 3330
Membership(s): AICP; AIGA, the professional association for design; AMPAS; SMPTE

Radial Engineering Ltd
1588 Kebet Way, Port Coquitlam, BC V3C 5M5, Canada
Tel: 604-942-1001 *Toll Free Tel:* 800-939-1001 (orders) *Fax:* 604-942-1010
E-mail: info@radialeng.com
Web Site: www.radialeng.com
Key Personnel
CEO & Pres: Peter Janis *Tel:* 604-942-1001 ext 250 *E-mail:* peterj@radialeng.com
Founded: 1991
Professional audio interface equipment.
Catalog(s) available
Membership(s): AES; NSCA

Radian Audio Engineering Inc
600 N Batavia St, Orange, CA 92868
Tel: 714-288-8900 *Fax:* 714-288-1133
E-mail: info@radianaudio.com
Web Site: www.radianaudio.com
Key Personnel
Pres: Dr Richard Kontrimas
Founded: 1988
High performance audio systems.
Catalog(s) available

Radiant Images
4125 W Jefferson Blvd, Los Angeles, CA 90016
Tel: 323-737-1314 *Fax:* 310-861-0163
E-mail: info@radiantimages.com
Web Site: www.radiantimages.com
Key Personnel
Founder: Michael Mansouri; Gianna Wolfe
Gen Mgr: Syrous Nabatian
Rental Mgr: Art Cristie *Tel:* 323-642-1350 *E-mail:* art@radiantimages.com
Rental Agent: Ric Halpern *Tel:* 323-642-1351 *E-mail:* ric@radiantimages.com
Founded: 2005
Provides 2D & 3D digital cinema solutions, support & high-end cameras & equipment to the film & entertainment industry.

Radio Design Labs (RDL)
659 N Sixth St, Prescott, AZ 86301
Tel: 928-443-9391 (sales); 928-778-3554 (cust serv) *Toll Free Tel:* 800-281-2683 (sales); 800-933-1780 (cust serv) *Fax:* 928-443-9392 (sales); 928-778-3506 (cust serv) *Toll Free Fax:* 800-289-7338 (sales)
E-mail: sales@rdlnet.com; service@rdlnet.com; exportsales@rdlnet.com (Latin America & Asia/Pacific sales)
Web Site: www.rdlnet.com
Manufacture professional audio, video & control modules & equipment.
Catalog(s) available
Foreign Office(s): RDL Europe, BV, Gebouw Y-Tech, Van Diemenstr 36, 1013 NH Amsterdam, Netherlands *Tel:* (020) 6238 983 *Fax:* (020) 6225 287 *E-mail:* eurosale@rdlnet.com
Membership(s): AES; Custom Electronic Design & Installation Association; InfoComm International®; NAB; NSCA

Radio Systems Inc
601 Heron Dr, Logan Township, NJ 08085
Tel: 856-467-8000 *Fax:* 856-467-3044
E-mail: sales@radiosystems.com; tech@radiosystems.com
Web Site: www.radiosystems.com
Key Personnel
Founder & Pres: Dan Braverman *E-mail:* dan@radiosystems.com
Sales Mgr, US: Jo Ann Dunn *E-mail:* jo-ann@radiosystems.com
Founded: 1976
Audio equipment manufacturer.
Catalog(s) available

Radio Vision Inc
531 W Main St, Denison, TX 75020
Tel: 903-337-4200 *Toll Free Tel:* 800-326-3198 *Fax:* 903-337-4296
E-mail: info@radiovisioninc.com
Web Site: www.radiovisioninc.com
Founded: 2005
Radio & TV commercial production facility.

Radio Visions
PO Box 4732, Toms River, NJ 08754-4732
Tel: 732-240-3119
E-mail: sales@radiovisions.com
Web Site: www.radiovisions.com
Key Personnel
Owner: Walt Gradzki
Founded: 1994
A full range of broadcast & non-broadcast technical services.

RadioArt/Bob & Ray CDs & MP3 Files
Division of Radio Foundation Inc
PO Box 519, Plantarium Sta, New York, NY 10024-0519
Tel: 212-595-1837
E-mail: reply@bobandray.com
Web Site: www.bobandray.com
Key Personnel
Pres: Larry Josephson *E-mail:* larryjo@radioart.org
Not-for-profit radio production company.
Online catalog(s) available

RadioShack Corp
Riverfront Campus, 300 RadioShack Circle, Fort Worth, TX 76102-1964
Tel: 817-415-3700; 817-415-3011
E-mail: media.relations@radioshack.com; radioshack.customer.care@radioshack.com
Web Site: www.radioshackcorporation.com
Founded: 1919
Catalog(s) available

Radiotechniques Engineering LLC
Affiliate of Radiotechniques Manufacturing LLC
402 Tenth Ave, Haddon Heights, NJ 08035-1838
Mailing Address: PO Box 367, Haddon Heights, NJ 08035-0367
Tel: 856-546-8008 *Fax:* 856-546-1841
E-mail: sales@radiotechniques.com
Web Site: www.radiotechniques.com
Key Personnel
Pres & Engr: Edward A Schober *Tel:* 856-546-8008 ext 111
Founded: 1979
Primarily provide design services for radio stations.
Membership(s): AES; Association of Federal Communications Consulting Engineers; IEEE; NAB; SBE

Radius® Display Products Inc
800 Fabric X-Press Way, Dallas, TX 75234
Tel: 972-406-1221 *Toll Free Tel:* 800-FABRIC-X (322-7429); 866-966-4066 (sales); 866-966-8266 (hospitality) *Fax:* 972-406-1321 *Toll Free Fax:* 888-322-7429
Web Site: www.radiusdp.com
Key Personnel
Pres: Tim Lightfoot
VP, Sales & Mktg: Tim Bookout
Mktg Coord: Zach Jobin
Founded: 1977 (as Display Products)
AV draping for projection screens, tripod screens & AV carts.
Catalog(s) available
Membership(s): EDPA; InfoComm International®; Promotional Products Association International

RADMAR Inc
PO Box 425, Northbrook, IL 60065-0425
Tel: 847-298-7980
E-mail: radmarinc@gmail.com
Web Site: www.radmarinc.com
Key Personnel
Pres: Richard M Davidson
Founded: 1971
Also publish print & digital books.
Catalog(s), see web site or send e-mail inquiry

Rafik
812 Broadway, Suite 4, New York, NY 10003
Tel: 212-475-7884
E-mail: info@rafikvideo.com; sales@rafikvideo.com
Web Site: www.rafikvideo.com
Key Personnel
CEO & Dir: Mindy Wyatt *E-mail:* mindy@rafikvideo.com
Busn Devt: Lou Sagar *E-mail:* lousager@rafikvideo.com
Sales: Beth Debeer

Rahlic Publishing Co
301 Keithwood Rd, Wynnewood, PA 19096
Tel: 610-649-0982
Key Personnel
Owner & Pres: Alicia M Boyd
Brochure(s) available

Rainbow International Inc/Rainbow Productions Inc
1103 Canyon Rd, Santa Fe, NM 87501

Tel: 773-505-6264 *Fax:* 773-525-6278
Web Site: www.rainbowplace.com
Key Personnel
Dir & Writer: Dirk Wales *E-mail:* dirk@rainbowplace.com
Prodr: Stacey Evenson
Media & communications consulting.
Membership(s): CAPA; MCA-I

Rainbow Media Taos
27 Valencia Rd, Taos, NM 87571
Mailing Address: PO Box 472, Taos, NM 87571-0472
Tel: 575-776-2268 *Toll Free Tel:* 800-748-1540 *Fax:* 575-776-2804
Key Personnel
Pres: Tony Isaacs

Rainbow Rentals
6705-A Electronic Dr, Springfield, VA 22151
Tel: 703-916-0800 *Fax:* 703-916-8013
E-mail: party@rainbow-rental.com
Web Site: www.rainbow-rental.com
Key Personnel
Owner: David T Pell
Founded: 1989
Catalog(s) available

Rainbow Video Productions Inc
23803 S 162 St, Adams, NE 68301
Tel: 402-430-7343
Web Site: www.rainbowvideo.com
Key Personnel
Pres: Phil Troupe *E-mail:* ptroupe@rainbowvideo.com
Industrial video & multimedia products.

Raincoast Books
Division of Raincoast Book Distribution Ltd
2440 Viking Way, Richmond, BC V6V 1N2, Canada
Tel: 604-323-7100 *Toll Free Tel:* 800-663-5714 (cust serv & book orders) *Fax:* 604-270-7161 *Toll Free Fax:* 800-565-3770 (cust serv & book orders)
E-mail: info@raincoast.com; customerservice@raincoast.com
Web Site: www.raincoast.com
Key Personnel
CEO: John Sawyer *E-mail:* johns@raincoast.com
EVP, Sales & Mktg: Paddy Laidley *E-mail:* paddy@raincoast.com
Mktg Coord: Alisha Whitley *E-mail:* alisha@raincoast.com
Founded: 1979
Publisher, distributor & wholesaler.
Catalog(s) available

RAM Systems LLC
27992 W Rte 120, Unit 138, Lakemoor, IL 60051
Tel: 847-487-7575 *Fax:* 847-487-2440
E-mail: sales@ramsyscom.com
Web Site: www.ramsyscom.com
Key Personnel
CEO & Pres: Ron Mitchell
Studio design & installation company.
Catalog(s) available
Branch Office(s)
RAM Broadcast Systems Ltd, 92 Caplan Ave, Suite 255, Barrie, ON L4N 0Z7, Canada *Tel:* 705-487-2915
Membership(s): NAB

Rand McNally Education
9855 Woods Dr, Skokie, IL 60077
Mailing Address: PO Box 7600, Skokie, IL 60680-7600
Toll Free Tel: 800-333-0136
Web Site: www.randmcnally.com
Teacher resources.
Catalog(s) available

Randall House Publications
114 Bush Rd, Nashville, TN 37217
Mailing Address: PO Box 17306, Nashville, TN 37217-0306
Tel: 615-361-1221 *Toll Free Tel:* 800-877-7030 *Fax:* 615-367-0535
Web Site: www.randallhouse.com
Key Personnel
CEO & Exec Dir: Ron Hunter
Christian publications.
Catalog(s) available

R&B Communications Inc
2397 Somrack Dr, Willoughby Hills, OH 44094
Tel: 440-946-9511
Web Site: www.rbcommunications.net
Key Personnel
Owner & Pres: Robert Matzen *Tel:* 440-479-8771 (cell) *E-mail:* bob@rbcommunications.net
Founded: 1982
Full service media production from script to screen. Extensive location production equipment for broadcast quality video. Full post-production facilities, editing, graphics & audio. Complete script to screen video & audio production services.
Membership(s): IABC; MCA-I; NATAS

R&O Studios
5805 N 39 St, McAllen, TX 78504
Tel: 956-203-0520
E-mail: rostudiosrgv@gmail.com
Web Site: www.randostudios.com
Key Personnel
Partner: Arianna Ontiveros; Stephen Ramirez
Web video advertising, corporate/training videos, music videos, video editing, visual effects, VHS to DVD conversion.

Randolf Productions Inc
17935 Skypark Circle, Suite K, Irvine, CA 92614
Tel: 949-794-9109 *Toll Free Tel:* 800-266-7741 *Fax:* 949-794-9117
E-mail: sales@go2rpi.com
Web Site: www.go2rpi.com
Key Personnel
Pres: Randy Ray *E-mail:* randy@go2rpi.com
Opers Mgr: David Duncan
Founded: 1984
Christian music & video products & books.
Catalog(s) available

Random House Audio Publishing Group
Division of Random House Inc
1745 Broadway, New York, NY 10019
Tel: 212-782-9205 *Toll Free Tel:* 800-733-3000
E-mail: customerservice@randomhouse.com; audio@randomhouse.com
Web Site: www.randomhouse.com/audio
Audio publishing for adults & children.
Catalog(s) available

Random House Children's Books
Division of Random House Inc
1745 Broadway, 10th fl, New York, NY 10019
Tel: 212-782-9000
Web Site: www.randomhousekids.com
Key Personnel
Pres & Publr: Barbara Marcus
Publr: Chip Gibson
Literature for pre-school aged children through young adult readers in all formats.
Catalog(s) available
Membership(s): Association of American Publishers

Random House of Canada Limited
One Toronto St, Unit 300, Toronto, ON M5C 2V6, Canada
Tel: 416-364-4449 *Fax:* 416-364-6863
Web Site: www.randomhouse.ca
Key Personnel
CEO: Brad Martin
SVP & Dir, HR: Trish Moore
Sr Ed: Craig Pyette
Founded: 1944
Shipping Address: 2775 Matheson Blvd E, Mississauga, ON L4W 4P7, Canada

Rane
10802 47 Ave W, Mukilteo, WA 98275-5000
Tel: 425-355-6000
E-mail: info@rane.com
Web Site: www.rane.com
Key Personnel
Dir, Cust Serv: Ellen Allhands *Tel:* 425-551-1810 *E-mail:* ellena@rane.com
Dir, Sales: Dean Standing *Tel:* 425-551-1820 *E-mail:* deans@rane.com
Natl Sales Mgr, Contractor/Pro Audio Prods: Jon Bosaw *Tel:* 425-551-1835 *E-mail:* jonb@rane.com
Natl Sales Mgr, Retail/DJ Prods: Mike May *Tel:* 425-551-1819 *E-mail:* mikem@rane.com
Founded: 1982
Catalog(s) available
Membership(s): AES; InfoComm International®; NAMM, the National Association of Music Merchants; NSCA; Synergetic Audio Concepts

The RapcoHorizon Co
3581 Larch Lane, Jackson, MO 63755
Tel: 573-243-1433 *Toll Free Tel:* 800-325-0266 *Fax:* 573-243-4913
E-mail: info@rapcohorizon.com
Web Site: www.rapcohorizon.com
Key Personnel
Pres: Lisa Williams
VP, Mktg: Darius Seabaugh

David Rapkin Audio Production
473 West End Ave, Unit 6A, New York, NY 10024
Tel: 212-362-7236
E-mail: drapco@aol.com
Key Personnel
Owner & Prodr: David Rapkin
Audio production company.

Rauland-Borg Corp
1802 W Central Rd, Mount Prospect, IL 60056
Tel: 847-590-7100 *Toll Free Tel:* 800-752-7725
Web Site: www.rauland.com
Key Personnel
CEO & Pres: Norman Kidder *Tel:* 847-590-7100 ext 252 *E-mail:* norm.kidder@rauland.com
CFO & VP: Rick Stalkfleet *Tel:* 847-590-7100 ext 202 *E-mail:* rick.stalkfleet@rauland.com
VP, Sales & Mktg: Maureen Pajerski *Tel:* 847-590-7100 ext 220 *E-mail:* maureen.pajerski@rauland.com
Founded: 1941
Manufacturer of life-safety equipment.
Catalog(s) available
Membership(s): American Electronics Association

RAVA Films
67 West St, Suite 604, Brooklyn, NY 11222
Web Site: www.ravafilms.com
Key Personnel
Dir & Prodr: Ava Wiland *E-mail:* ava@ravafilms.com
Dir & Ed: Rafael Salazar *E-mail:* rafa@ravafilms.com
Founded: 2011
Create documentaries, films & branded content.

Raven Rental
2617 Peach St, Erie, PA 16508
Tel: 814-456-0331 *Fax:* 814-451-0557
Web Site: www.ravensound.com

Key Personnel
Owner: Phil Papotnik *E-mail:* phil@ravensound.com
Founded: 1971
Professional sound & lighting, sales & rental.

Raven Screen Corp
PO Box 691, Harriman, NY 10926
Tel: 845-782-1844 *Toll Free Tel:* 800-847-6906 *Fax:* 845-782-1840
E-mail: info@ravenscreen.com
Web Site: www.ravenscreen.com
Key Personnel
Pres: Martin Soss
Projection screens & display boards.

Ray Supply Inc
871 Rte 9, Queensbury, NY 12804
Tel: 518-792-5848 *Toll Free Tel:* 800-347-5851 (orders) *Fax:* 518-792-1727
E-mail: sales@raysupply.com
Web Site: www.raysupply.com
Key Personnel
Pres: Keith Zoll
Founded: 1937
AV equipment sales, rentals & repair.
Catalog(s) available

Raymond Entertainment Direct (RED)
3450 Cahuenga Blvd W, Suite 410, Los Angeles, CA 90068
Tel: 323-785-4700 *Fax:* 323-785-4701
E-mail: info@raymondentertainment.com
Web Site: www.raymondentertainment.com
Key Personnel
Founder & CEO: Patrick Raymond *E-mail:* patrick@raymondentertainment.com
VP, Prodn: Andrew D Stum *E-mail:* andrews@raymondentertainment.com
VP, Strategic Mktg & Branding: Megan Brown *E-mail:* megan@raymondentertainment.com
Founded: 1998
Production & post-production services.

Rayven Inc
431 Griggs St N, St Paul, MN 55104
Tel: 651-642-1112 *Toll Free Tel:* 800-878-3776 *Fax:* 651-642-9497
E-mail: info@rayven.com
Web Site: www.rayven.com
Key Personnel
Cont: Mary Dehmer *E-mail:* mdehmer@rayven.com
Pres: Joe Heinemann *E-mail:* jheinemann@rayven.com
VP, HR: Jayna Heinemann *E-mail:* jayna@rayven.com
VP, Sales: Rick Mercado *E-mail:* rmercado@rayven.com
Founded: 1954
Coating & laminating products.
Membership(s): Business Technology Association

RB Productions
3-4191 Longmoor Dr, Burlington, ON L7L 5J9, Canada
Tel: 905-633-7474 *Toll Free Tel:* 866-633-7474
E-mail: sales@radicalbob.com
Web Site: www.rbproductionz.com
Key Personnel
Creative Dir & Media Prodr: Robert Diltz *E-mail:* rob@radicalbob.com
Founded: 1999
Full service media facility for video production, multimedia animation, web application construction & graphic design.
Membership(s): CCTA

RBR Productions
117 W Rockland Rd, Libertyville, IL 60048
Tel: 847-362-4060 *Toll Free Tel:* 888-278-0558
E-mail: info@rbrproductions.com
Web Site: www.rbrproductions.com
Key Personnel
VP & Gen Mgr: Rick Johnson *E-mail:* rick@rbrproductions.com
Digital media, content development & web development.
Catalog(s) available

RC Communications
Division of Rent Com Inc
3900 N River Rd, Schiller Park, IL 60176-2345
Tel: 847-678-7000 *Fax:* 847-678-9378
E-mail: rccsales@rentcom.com; rent@rentcom.com
Web Site: www.rentcom.com; www.rc-communications.com
Key Personnel
Owner: Ron Steinberg *Tel:* 847-678-7000 ext 126
Audio video systems for corporate communications.
Catalog(s) available
Membership(s): InfoComm International®; MCA-I

RCA Records
Division of Sony Music Entertainment
550 Madison Ave, New York, NY 10022
Tel: 212-833-8000
E-mail: info@rcarecords.com
Web Site: www.rcarecords.com; www.sonymusic.com
Key Personnel
SVP, Digital Mktg: Jennifer Fowler
SVP, Promo: Adrian Moreira
Founded: 1929

RCI Custom Products
801 N East St, Suite 2-A, Frederick, MD 21701
Tel: 301-620-9130 *Toll Free Tel:* 800-546-4724 *Fax:* 301-620-9103 *Toll Free Fax:* 800-546-6175
E-mail: info@rcicustom.com
Web Site: www.rcicustom.com
Key Personnel
Pres: Doug Macuch *Tel:* 301-620-9130 ext 221 *E-mail:* dmacuch@rcicustom.com
Off Mgr: Nancy Cox *Tel:* 301-620-9130 ext 222 *E-mail:* nancyc@rcicustom.com
Leading manufacturer of premium quality audio & video control & connector plates, rack panels & custom devices.
Catalog(s) available
Membership(s): InfoComm International®; NSCA

RCS Enterprises
Division of RCS Inc
445 Hamilton Ave, 7th fl, White Plains, NY 10601
Tel: 914-428-4600 *Fax:* 914-428-5922
E-mail: info@rcsworks.com
Web Site: www.rcsworks.com
Key Personnel
VP, Sales: Neal Perchuk
Founded: 1979
Provide broadcast software, also develop real-time audio recognition technology & creates strategic audio programming content for Internet, corporate sites & broadcast sites.
Branch Office(s)
RCS West, 220 Roslyn St, Denver, CO 80230, Contact: Bob Adler *Toll Free Tel:* 877-774-1018
RCS Latin America, 1720 Melrose Ave, Unit 7, Chula Vista, FL 91911, Contact: Horacio Gonzales *Tel:* 619-428-7729 *Fax:* 619-428-7729 *Web Site:* www.rcslatinamerica.com
RCA Southeast, 5046 Highpoint Dr, PO Box 9208, Pensacola, FL 32505, Contact: Jim Colley *Toll Free Tel:* 877-774-1008 *Toll Free Fax:* 877-774-1009
RCS Midwest, 214 N Spruce St, PO Box 887, Ogallala, NE 69153, Contact: Carolyn Bell *Toll Free Tel:* 877-774-1038 *Toll Free Fax:* 877-774-1092
Foreign Office(s): 19/21 Ave George V, 75008 Paris, France, Mgr: Lionel Guiffante *Tel:* 01 53 27 36 36 *Fax:* 01 53 27 36 30

Jimmy Rea Electronics Inc
540 W Broad St, Columbus, OH 43215
Tel: 614-221-5170 *Fax:* 614-221-8898
Web Site: www.jimmyrea.com
Key Personnel
Pres: Jimmy Rea *E-mail:* jimmy@jimmyrea.com
Commercial AV services.

Reading Plus®, see Taylor Associates

Real Cool TV Productions
800 S Main St, Suite 203, Mansfield, MA 02048
Tel: 508-337-8520
E-mail: info@realcooltv.com
Web Site: www.realcooltv.com
Key Personnel
CEO: James Ringrose
COO & VP, Sales: Pia Proal
Busn Devt Mgr: Arlene Simon
Prodn Mgr: Tom Ribeiro
Founded: 2009
Movie, video & advertisement production services, digital photography & voice overs.

Real to Reel Studios Inc
4141 Office Pkwy, Dallas, TX 75204
Mailing Address: 14 Canyon Ridge Dr, Rockwall, TX 75087
Tel: 214-528-4242
Web Site: www.rtrstudios.com
Key Personnel
Owner: Ron Morgan
VP & Mgr: Beth Morgan *E-mail:* beth@rtrstudios.com
Founded: 1975
Specialize in commercial digital recording, editing, file format conversions, audio for radio/TV, industrials, audio books, phone prompts & Internet web sites. Also offer phone patch, music/sound FX libraries & Internet audio delivery.

Reality Check Systems
726 S Flower St, Burbank, CA 91502
Tel: 323-465-3900 *Fax:* 323-465-3600
E-mail: info@realitychecksystems.com
Web Site: www.realityx.com
Key Personnel
Partner: Andrew Heimbold *E-mail:* a.heimbold@realitychecksystems.com; Steven Heimbold *E-mail:* s.heimbold@realitychecksystems.com
Founded: 1997
Animation & computer graphics for broadcast & film.

Really Good Stuff
448 Pepper St, Monroe, CT 06468
Tel: 203-261-1920 *Toll Free Tel:* 800-366-1920 (orders); 877-867-1920 (cust serv) *Fax:* 203-268-1796
Web Site: www.reallygoodstuff.com
Key Personnel
Owner: Jon Sonneborn *E-mail:* jsonneborn@reallygoodstuff.com
Founded: 1992
Videos for elementary schools.
Catalog(s) available

RealNetworks Inc
1501 First Ave S, Suite 600, Seattle, WA 98134
Mailing Address: PO Box 91123, Seattle, WA 98111-9223
Tel: 206-674-2700 *Toll Free Tel:* 800-444-8011 *Fax:* 206-674-2696

Web Site: www.real.com; www.realnetworks.com; service.real.com/localized (cust serv); service.real.com (tech support)
Founded: 1995
Delivers digital entertainment to consumers directly & indirectly through business relationships with mobile operators & other businesses around the world.
Branch Office(s)
462 Seventh Ave, 3rd fl, New York, NY 10018 *Tel:* 212-391-6668 *Fax:* 212-391-9566
11600 Sunrise Valley Dr, Suite 200, Reston, VA 20191 *Tel:* 703-437-4422 *Fax:* 703-437-6515

Rebel Records
PO Box 7405, Charlottesville, VA 22906-7405
Tel: 434-973-5151
E-mail: questions@rebelrecords.com
Web Site: rebelrecords.com
Key Personnel
Owner: David Freeman *E-mail:* dfreeman@rebelrecords.com
Pres: Mark Freeman *E-mail:* mfreeman@rebelrecords.com
Founded: 1959
Produce & distribute bluegrass recordings.
Catalog(s) available
Membership(s): IBMA

Rebirth/Wenha Records
81 Chandler St, Detroit, MI 48202
Tel: 313-875-0289
Key Personnel
Owner: Pamela Wise
Exec Dir: Wendell Harrison
Jazz AV recordings.
Catalog(s) available

Record Plant Remote
1170 Greenwood Lake Tpke, Ringwood, NJ 07456
Tel: 973-728-8114 *Fax:* 973-728-8761
E-mail: info@recordplantremote.com
Web Site: www.recordplantremote.com
Key Personnel
Owner & Chief, Engg: Robert "Kooster" McAllister *E-mail:* kooster@recordplantremote.com
Established as the industry leader in remote audio over twenty years ago, the legendary Record Plant Remote Truck has forged the direction of live music as we know it today. Live album projects, handling audio for live broadcasts & recording in secluded locations.

Recorded Books LLC
270 Skipjack Rd, Prince Frederick, MD 20678
Tel: 410-535-5590 *Toll Free Tel:* 800-638-1304 *Fax:* 410-535-5499
E-mail: customerservice@recordedbooks.com
Web Site: www.recordedbooks.com
Key Personnel
CEO & Pres: Richard Freese
Founded: 1979
Audiobook publisher, educational & library resources.
Catalog(s) available

Recordex USA Inc
10-50 46 Ave, Long Island City, NY 11101
Tel: 718-392-5380 *Fax:* 718-392-5485
E-mail: sales@recordexusa.com; support@recordexusa.com
Web Site: www.recordexmfg.com
Founded: 1969
Digital CD & DVD duplicators.
Catalog(s) available

Recording Media & Equipment Inc (RM&E)
3736 SW 30 Ave, Fort Lauderdale, FL 33312
Tel: 954-791-9797 *Toll Free Tel:* 800-541-9797 *Fax:* 954-791-6662
E-mail: info@rmeinc.com
Web Site: www.rmeinc.com
Key Personnel
Pres: Lutz Meyer
VP & Treas: Mary Meyer
Founded: 1985
Catalog(s) available

Recortec Inc
3329 Kifer Rd, Santa Clara, CA 95051-0719
Tel: 408-928-1480 *Toll Free Tel:* 800-729-7654 *Fax:* 408-928-1489
E-mail: info@recortec.com; support@recortec.com; sales@recortec.com
Web Site: www.recortec.com
Key Personnel
CEO & Pres: Dr Lester Lee
VP: George Wussow
Founded: 1969
Quality rack mount products.

The Recruiters Library
Subsidiary of The Best College Recruiter
14728 Shirley St, Omaha, NE 68144
Tel: 402-334-1676 *Toll Free Tel:* 800-293-1676 *Fax:* 402-334-4437
Web Site: www.thebestcollegerecruiter.com
Key Personnel
Pres: Stephen J Brennan, PhD *E-mail:* brennan160@cox.net
DVD, CD, audio & video resources for college athletic recruiters.
Online catalog(s) available

Red Fox Enterprises
Rte 209 E, Elizabethville, PA 17023
Mailing Address: PO Box 889, Elizabethville, PA 17023-0108
Tel: 717-362-3391 *Fax:* 717-362-8577
E-mail: redfox1@pa.net
Key Personnel
Pres: Ronald Knorr
Off Mgr: Ruth Knorr
Children's programming.

Red Hill Corp
1540 Biglerville Rd, Gettysburg, PA 17325
Mailing Address: PO Box 4234, Gettysburg, PA 17325-4234
Tel: 717-337-3038 *Toll Free Tel:* 800-822-4003 *Fax:* 717-337-0732
E-mail: customerservice@supergrit.com
Web Site: www.supergrit.com
Key Personnel
Pres: Arturo M Ottolenghi
Founded: 1978
Mail order abrasives & refinishing products.
Catalog(s), free, 48 page color

Red Onion Records
PO Box 366, Dayton, OH 45401-0366
Tel: 937-277-3079 *Toll Free Tel:* 800-876-4467 *Fax:* 513-672-0213
Web Site: www.landofjazz.com
Key Personnel
Owner & Pres: Gene Mayl *E-mail:* gene@landofjazz.com
Founded: 1962
Jazz, DVDs, LPs, videos, CDs, 78s & books.
Catalog(s), quarterly, free

Red Sky Studios
184 Everett St, Allston, MA 02134
Tel: 617-903-3373
E-mail: mail@redsky-studios.com
Web Site: redsky-studios.com
Key Personnel
CFO: Dave Cambria
Pres: Frans Weterrings
Studio Prodn Mgr: Tiffany Kinder
Sound stage & equipment rental, short-term office pre-production & production office rental, event hosting.

RED Studios Hollywood
846 N Cahuenga Blvd, Los Angeles, CA 90038
Tel: 323-463-0808
Web Site: www.redstudio.com
Founded: 2007 (as Red Digital Cinema)
Working studio lot with 8 soundstages, host to television, motion picture, music video & commercial filming. Home & headquarters for RED Digital Cinema.

Redco Audio Inc
1701 Stratford Ave, Stratford, CT 06615
Tel: 203-502-7600 *Toll Free Tel:* 800-572-7280 *Fax:* 203-502-7610
E-mail: orders@redco.com
Web Site: www.redco.com
Key Personnel
Sales Mgr: Chris Stubbs *E-mail:* chris@redco.com
Manufacture panels & patch bay.
Catalog(s) available
Membership(s): AES; NAMM, the National Association of Music Merchants

Rediscover Music
705 S Washington St, Suite 3, Naperville, IL 60540
Tel: 630-305-0770 *Toll Free Tel:* 800-232-7328 (orders) *Fax:* 630-305-0782
E-mail: rediscovermusic@rediscovermusic.com
Web Site: www.rediscovermusic.com
Key Personnel
Pres: Allan Shaw *E-mail:* allan@folkera.com
Catalog(s) available
Membership(s): International Bluegrass Music Association; The Recording Academy

Redman Movies & Stories
1075 S 700 W, Salt Lake City, UT 84104
Tel: 801-978-9292 *Fax:* 801-978-2299
E-mail: info@redmanmovies.com
Web Site: www.redmanmovies.com
Key Personnel
Pres: Bryan Clifton
Grip/electric rental house.

Redwood Audiobooks
10375 Nichols Lane, Mendocino, CA 95460
Mailing Address: PO Box 1456, Mendocino, CA 95460-1456
Tel: 707-937-1225
E-mail: audiobks@mcn.org
Web Site: www.universitypressaudiobooks.com
Key Personnel
COO & Pres: Margy Bauman *E-mail:* margy@redwoodaudiobooks.com
Founded: 1990
Catalog(s) available

Reed Presentations Inc (RPI)
17 Water St, Lebanon, NJ 08833
Tel: 908-753-8800 *Fax:* 908-753-8823
E-mail: info@reedpresentations.com
Web Site: www.reedpresentations.com
Key Personnel
Founder, CEO & Pres: Barry A Reed *Tel:* 908-753-8800 ext 101 *E-mail:* barryreed@reedpresentations.com
VP, Fin: Alene Reed
Founded: 1990
Catalog(s) available
Membership(s): AGC; ATD; NJCAMA; NJPMA

Reef Photo & Video
2303 N Andrews Ave, Fort Lauderdale, FL 33311
Tel: 954-537-0644 *Toll Free Tel:* 877-453-8927 *Fax:* 954-537-0645

Web Site: reefphoto.com
Offers underwater photography & videography cameras & equipment.

Reel Men Rentals Inc
2225 E McDowell Rd, Phoenix, AZ 85006
Tel: 602-286-6800 *Fax:* 602-286-0080
E-mail: rentals@reelmen.com
Web Site: www.reelmen.com
Full service provider of rental equipment to the film, video & still photography industry.

Reel Picture
5330 Eastgate Mall, San Diego, CA 92121
Tel: 858-587-0301 *Toll Free Tel:* 866 502-3472 (US & CN) *Fax:* 858-587-8838
Web Site: www.reelpicture.com
Key Personnel
VP, Sales & Mktg: Keith Wright *Tel:* 858-888-7999 *E-mail:* keith@reelpicture.com
Founded: 1983
Full service video/DVD/CD duplicator & replicator & authoring lab.
Membership(s): MCA-I

Reelsound Recording Co
701 Southern Dr, Buda, TX 78610
Tel: 512-312-1610; 512-422-7098 (cell)
Web Site: www.reelsound-usa.com
Key Personnel
Owner & Pres: Malcolm H Harper, Jr *E-mail:* malcolmh@austin.rr.com
Founded: 1969
Mobile audio production truck studio.
Membership(s): AES; Latin Recording Academy; The Recording Academy

Rees Associates
Rees Plaza at East Wharf, Suite 300, 9211 Lake Hefner Pkwy, Oklahoma City, OK 73120
Tel: 405-942-7337 *Fax:* 405-948-1261
E-mail: rees@rees-associates.com
Web Site: www.rees.com
Key Personnel
CEO: Allen R Parr
VP & Dir, Opers OK: Jay W Tullis
VP & Client Devt Leader: Stephen E Lawson
Founded: 1975
Architectural firm that works on broadcast facilities.
Branch Office(s)
Inner Harbor Ctr, 400 E Pratt St, 8th fl, Baltimore, MD 21202 *Tel:* 410-821-7337 *Fax:* 214-522-0444
800 Town & Country Blvd, Suite 300, Houston, TX 77024 *Tel:* 713-988-7337 *Fax:* 214-522-0444
9901 IH-10 W, Suite 800, San Antonio, TX 78230 *Tel:* 210-227-7337 *Fax:* 214-522-0444
Foreign Office(s): Kelvin 10 5to Piso, 11590 Colonia Anzures, Mexico *Tel:* (0155) 5250-5354 *Fax:* (0155) 5250-5355

Reference Recordings
PO Box 77225, San Francisco, CA 94107
Tel: 650-355-1845 *Toll Free Tel:* 800-336-8866 *Fax:* 650-355-1949
E-mail: referencerecordings@gmail.com
Web Site: www.referencerecordings.com
Key Personnel
Partner, Chief Engr & Tech Dir: Keith O Johnson
Exec Dir: Marcia Martin
Sales & Mktg: Janice Mancuso
Founded: 1976
Classics, jazz & blues record label.
Catalog(s) available
Membership(s): The Recording Academy

Refinery
16 W 46 St, 12th fl, New York, NY 10036
Tel: 212-391-8166 *Fax:* 212-391-8783
Web Site: refinerynyc.com
Key Personnel
Exec Prodr: Alan Eisenberg *E-mail:* alan@refinerynyc.com
Prodr & Busn Mgr: Darria Tucker *E-mail:* dtucker@refinerynyc.com
Dir: Jacob Williams *E-mail:* jacob@refinerynyc.com
Post-production.
Membership(s): AICE

Regal Photo Products Inc/Arkay Corp
2769 S 34 St, Milwaukee, WI 53215-3541
Tel: 414-645-2050 *Toll Free Tel:* 800-695-2055 (sales) *Fax:* 414-645-9515
Key Personnel
Off Mgr: Donna Swanson
Catalog(s) available
Membership(s): Photo Marketing Association

Regent Press Publishers & Printers
2747 Regent St, Berkeley, CA 94705
Tel: 510-845-1196
E-mail: regentpress@mindspring.com
Web Site: www.regentpress.net
Key Personnel
Owner, Publr & Mng Ed: Mark Weiman
Publishers of books, videos & audio.
Catalog(s) available

Register Data Systems
Subsidiary of Register Communications Inc
1691 Forsyth St, Macon, GA 31201
Tel: 478-745-5500 *Toll Free Tel:* 800-521-5222 *Fax:* 478-745-0500
E-mail: sales@registerdata.com
Key Personnel
Owner: Lowell Register
Manufacture automation, traffic & billing software & program delay systems designed for radio stations.
Membership(s): Georgia Association of Broadcasters; NAB

REI - Radio Engineering Industries
6534 "L" St, Omaha, NE 68117
Tel: 402-339-2200 *Toll Free Tel:* 800-228-9275 (sales); 877-726-4617 (tech support) *Fax:* 402-339-1704
E-mail: info@radioeng.com; orderdesk@radioeng.com
Web Site: www.radioeng.com
Key Personnel
CEO: Terri Jukes *E-mail:* tjukes@radioeng.com
CFO: Kevin Hermann *E-mail:* khermann@radioeng.com
EVP: Scott Hays *E-mail:* shays@radioeng.com
Founded: 1938
Design & manufacture AV products for the commercial vehicle market (radios, speakers, monitors, amps, PAs, microphones).

Reider Photography & Video Productions
2174 Morris Ave, Union, NJ 07083
Tel: 908-688-8808
E-mail: info@njphotographer.com
Web Site: www.njphotographer.com
Key Personnel
Owner: Allan Reider *E-mail:* allanreider@aol.com

Reinhardt Productions Inc
242-17 Van Zandt Ave, Douglaston, NY 11362
Tel: 718-225-4163 *Fax:* 212-338-0505
Key Personnel
Pres: Bob Reinhardt

Richard Reiter Productions Inc
36 Catherine Ct, Cedar Grove, NJ 07009
Tel: 973-857-2935; 973-857-2557 *Fax:* 973-857-2935
E-mail: reiterjazz@gmail.com; reiterjazz@yahoo.com; reiterjazz@optonline.net
Web Site: www.richardreiter.com
Key Personnel
Pres: Richard Reiter
Founded: 1978
Original music for films, TV, radio, commercials, theater & dance.

Dick Reizner Film & Video
7179 Via Maria, San Jose, CA 95139
Tel: 408-226-6339
Web Site: www.reizner.com
Key Personnel
Owner: Dick Reizner *Tel:* 408-828-3555 (cell) *E-mail:* dick@reizner.com
Founded: 1972
Membership(s): American Society of Lighting Designers; LEVA; MCA-I; NFVA; SMPTE

Related Visual Inc
2941 E Miraloma Ave, Suite 3, Anaheim, CA 92806
Tel: 714-535-1414 *Toll Free Tel:* 800-733-1415 *Fax:* 714-630-3518
E-mail: relatedvis@aol.com
Web Site: www.relatedvisual.com
Key Personnel
Pres: William W Mathy
Sales Mgr: Kevin Mathy
Founded: 1985
Distribute & rent LCD projectors & AV presentation equipment.
Catalog(s), annual
Membership(s): InfoComm International®

Remote Audio Products
220 Great Circle Rd, Suite 114, Nashville, TN 37228-1737
Tel: 615-256-3513 *Fax:* 615-634-2277
E-mail: info@remoteaudio.com
Web Site: www.remoteaudio.com

Renaissance Media
909 Logan St, Suite 11F, Denver, CO 80204
Tel: 303-892-1415
Web Site: www.renaissancemedia.com
Key Personnel
Founder & Pres: Tom Dudzinski *E-mail:* tomd@renaissancemedia.com
Produce HD broadcast television, streaming media & DVDs.

Renegade Animation
111 E Broadway, Suite 208, Glendale, CA 91205
Tel: 818-551-2351 *Fax:* 818-551-2350
Web Site: www.renegadeanimation.com
Key Personnel
Supervising Dir: Darrell Van Citters
Exec Prodr: Ashley Postlewaite
Exec Asst: Heidi Ewart *E-mail:* heidi.ewart@renegadeanimation.com
Founded: 1992
Animation production & post-production services.

Renkus-Heinz Inc
19201 Cook St, Foothill Ranch, CA 92610-3501
Tel: 949-588-9997 *Fax:* 949-588-9514
E-mail: sales@renkus-heinz.com
Web Site: www.renkus-heinz.com
Key Personnel
Chmn: Harro K Heinz *E-mail:* harro@renkus-heinz.com
SVP: Ralph Heinz *E-mail:* ralph@renkus-heinz.com
VP, Sales & Mktg: Rik Kirby *Tel:* 949-588-9997 ext 111 *E-mail:* rik@renkus-heinz.com
Mktg Mgr: Margie Ulm *Tel:* 949-588-9997 ext 149 *E-mail:* margie@renkus-heinz.com
Prodn Mgr: Teresa Urena

Engineers & manufactures integrated sound reinforcement systems, loud speakers, power amplifiers, signal processors & control networks.
Catalog(s) available
Membership(s): NAMM, the National Association of Music Merchants; NSCA

RentACamera.com
Division of The Video Co
1805 Hayes St, Nashville, TN 37203
Tel: 615-320-3200 *Toll Free Tel:* 855-588-2882
E-mail: info@tvcnashville.com
Web Site: www.rentacamera.com
Key Personnel
Owner: Adam Rector
Rents professional, state-of-the-art, broadcast, prosumer & industrial quality video, photography, audio, support, grip, lighting equipment, as well as crewing to the professional photo, video, television & film production industries.

Replicopy Digital Media Center
2101 Midway Rd, Suite 200, Carrollton, TX 75006
Tel: 972-702-8388 *Fax:* 972-387-DUBS (387-3827)
E-mail: replicopy@replicopy.com
Web Site: www.replicopy.com
Key Personnel
Owner & Pres: Daniel L Redd
VP: Jason Ross
Mgr: Robert Redd
Cust Serv: Meagan Holley
Founded: 1984
Offer full line of services including CD, DVD & Blu-ray duplication or replication, mini CDs & DVDs, CD mastering, DVD authoring, video production & video editing.
Membership(s): American Independent Media Manufacturers Association; International Disc Duplicating Association

Reprise Records Burbank
Subsidiary of Warner Bros Records
3300 Warner Blvd, Burbank, CA 91505
Tel: 818-846-9090
E-mail: reprise@wbr.com
Web Site: www.warnerbrosrecords.com
Branch Office(s)
75 Rockefeller Plaza, 21st fl, New York, NY 10019

Research Press Co
2612 N Mattis Ave, Champaign, IL 61822
Mailing Address: Dept 13W, PO Box 7866, Champaign, IL 61826
Tel: 217-352-3273 *Toll Free Tel:* 800-519-2707 *Fax:* 217-352-1221
E-mail: orders@researchpress.com
Web Site: www.researchpress.com
Key Personnel
Pres: Judy Parkinson *E-mail:* jparkinson@researchpress.com
Founded: 1968
Catalog(s) available

Research Technology International (RTI)
4700 Chase Ave, Lincolnwood, IL 60712-1689
Tel: 847-677-3000 *Toll Free Tel:* 800-323-7520 *Fax:* 847-677-1311 *Toll Free Fax:* 800-784-6733
E-mail: sales@rtico.com
Web Site: www.rtico.com
Key Personnel
CEO & Pres: Ray Short
CFO: Matthew Malone
SVP, Sales: Tom Boyle
VP, Sales: Bill Wolavka
Sales & Ad: Sherwin Berger
Founded: 1970
Distribute & manufacture CD, DVD & videotape test & cleaning equipment.
Online catalog(s) available
Foreign Office(s): RTI-UK Ltd, 6 Swan Wharf, Waterloo Rd, Uxbridge UB8 2RA, United Kingdom *Tel:* (01895) 252191 *Fax:* (01895) 274692 *E-mail:* rti-inbox@rtiuk.co.uk
Membership(s): AECT; AIIM; British Kinematograph Sound & Television Society; Consortium of College & University Media Centers; ICVM; InfoComm International®; NAB; National Association of Media & Technology Centers; SMPTE

The Resource Centre
Box 190, Waterloo, ON N2J 3Z9, Canada
Tel: 519-885-0826 *Toll Free Tel:* 800-923-0330 *Fax:* 519-747-5629
E-mail: sales@theresourcecentre.com
Key Personnel
Pres: Neal Gridgeman
Founded: 1981
Catalog(s), annual

Resource Development Co LLC
280 Daines St, Suite 200, Birmingham, MI 48009
Tel: 248-646-2300 *Toll Free Tel:* 800-360-7222 *Fax:* 248-646-0789
E-mail: inquiries@resourcedev.com
Web Site: www.resourcedev.com
Key Personnel
Pres: Thomas Connaughton
Mktg Coord: Lori Koran *E-mail:* lkoran@rdc.us.com
Web-based learning modules.
Catalog(s) available

RetinaVision Productions
19 Barker Ave, Fairfax, CA 94930
Tel: 415-459-3926 *Toll Free Tel:* 877-738-4628
Key Personnel
Pres: Clark Higgins
Founded: 1975
Video assisted film production systems, production engineering, aerial photography & video.
Membership(s): AES; International Alliance of Theatrical Stage Employees; SMPTE

Rev Up Transmedia
20929 Ventura Blvd, Suite 47-212, Woodland Hills, CA 91364
Tel: 818-995-1719 *Toll Free Tel:* 877-372-0005 *Fax:* 818-979-9599
E-mail: info@revuptransmedia.com
Web Site: revuptransmedia.com
Key Personnel
Owner: Diana Weynand
Authorized Apple training center, final cut pro & shake after effects. HD cameras & videotape theory.
Catalog(s) available

Revelli
PO Box 150098, San Rafael, CA 94915
Tel: 415-460-9898
E-mail: colorstyledesign@aol.com
Key Personnel
Owner: Clare Revelli
Catalog(s) available

Revels Records
Division of Revels Inc
80 Mount Auburn St, Watertown, MA 02472
Tel: 617-972-8300
E-mail: info@revels.org
Web Site: www.revels.org
Key Personnel
Exec Dir: Steve Smith *Tel:* 617-972-8300 ext 25 *E-mail:* ssmith@revels.org
Mktg & PR: Alan Casso *Tel:* 617-972-8300 ext 22 *E-mail:* acasso@revels.org
Founded: 1971 (as a nonprofit cultural organization)
Producer of music CDs, songbooks & educational material focusing on traditional music, dance, customs & rituals from around the world.
Catalog(s), semiannual, free
Online catalog(s) available

Revolt Pro Media Inc
7625 Hayvenhurst Ave, Suite 27, Van Nuys, CA 91406
Tel: 818-904-0001 *Fax:* 819-904-0005
E-mail: info@revoltpromedia.com
Web Site: www.revoltpromedia.com
Sells pro media & hardware. Rents broadcast decks & video cameras. Printing, duplicating & packaging of CDs & DVDs. Provides technical post-production services.

Revolution Cinema Rentals
1102 Arroyo St, Unit A, San Fernando, CA 91340
Tel: 818-837-5981 *Fax:* 818-837-5986
E-mail: info@revolutioncinemarentals.com
Web Site: revolutioncinemarentals.com
Boutique rental house for small digital cameras & accessories for video & filmmaking.

Revolution Lighting Technologies Inc
177 Broad St, 12th fl, Stamford, CT 06901
Tel: 203-504-1111 *Fax:* 203-504-1150
Web Site: www.rvlti.com
Key Personnel
CEO & Pres: Charles Schafer
Founded: 1991 (as Super Vision International)
LED & fiber optic lighting manufacturer.
Catalog(s), free to AV production cos & producers
Branch Office(s)
Lumificient Corp, 8752 Monticello Lane N, Maple Grove, MN 55369 *Tel:* 763-424-3702 *Toll Free Tel:* 877-383-4032 *Fax:* 763-390-3135 (signage lighting div)

Rex
Division of Sunny Day Productions Inc
610 SW 17 Ave, Portland, OR 97205
Tel: 503-238-4525
E-mail: info@rexpost.com
Web Site: www.rexpost.com
Key Personnel
Gen Mgr & Chief Audio Engr: Russell Gorsline
Audio, video & design for production & post-production. Experience in consumer & marketing communications segments.
Membership(s): Oregon Media Production Association

RF Industries
7610 Miramar Rd, San Diego, CA 92126
Tel: 858-549-6340 *Toll Free Tel:* 800-233-1728 *Fax:* 858-549-6345
E-mail: rfi@rfindustries.com
Web Site: www.rfindustries.com
Key Personnel
CEO & Pres: Howard Hill
VP, Mktg: Manny Gutsche
Founded: 1979
Design, manufacture & distribute coaxial connectors, cable assemblies, kits & crimp tools as well as signal processing equipment.
Catalog(s), biennial, free

RF Specialties of California Inc
PO Box 16655, San Diego, CA 92176
Tel: 619-501-3936 *Fax:* 619-342-8511
Web Site: www.rfspec.com
Key Personnel
Pres: Steve Moreen *E-mail:* steve@rfsca.com
Sales Engr: Mike Uhl *E-mail:* mike@rfsca.com
An alliance of independent broadcast suppliers.
Catalog(s) available

RF Specialties of Texas LLC
PO Box 1010, Newark, TX 76071-1010
Tel: 214-697-3477 (cell); 817-489-2730
Toll Free Tel: 800-537-1801 (Newark)
E-mail: rfstx@swbell.net
Web Site: www.rfspecialties.com
Key Personnel
Gen Mgr: Dan Sessler
Off Mgr: Tara Littlejohn
Distribute everything to do with radio & TV products.
Catalog(s) available
Branch Office(s)
3528 Fairfax Ave, Forth Worth, TX 76119
Tel: 817-535-0784 *Toll Free Tel:* 888-839-7373 *Fax:* 817-535-1979 *E-mail:* rfstxftw@charter.net

RGB Spectrum
950 Marina Village Pkwy, Alameda, CA 94501
Tel: 510-814-7000 *Fax:* 510-814-7026
E-mail: sales@rgb.com
Web Site: www.rgb.com
Key Personnel
CEO & Pres: Robert Marcus
Cont & VP, Fin: Iana Zemniakova
VP, Intl Sales: Denis Carte
VP, Mktg: Jed Deame
VP, Sales: Tony Spica
Communs Mgr: Carol Marcus *E-mail:* carol@rgb.com
Founded: 1987
Manufacturer of multiview processors, videowall processors, scan converters, fiber optic cables, digital video routers & transmission equipment. Additional offices in Los Angeles, CA; Hartford, CT; Washington, DC; Atlanta, GA; Cincinnati, OH; Dallas, TX; Shanghai, China.
Foreign Office(s): 14F Cimic Tower, 800 Shangcheng Rd, Pudong District, Shanghai, China *Tel:* 212215 7482 *E-mail:* asiasales@rgb.com
Dragonder 20A, 5554 GM Valkenswaard, Netherlands *Tel:* 11 515600 *Fax:* 11 515601 *E-mail:* europesales@rgb.com
Yes Business Ctr, Suite 302, 14B St, Al Mafraq Rd, Al Barsha 1, Dubai, United Arab Emirates *Tel:* 44 46 84 16 *E-mail:* middleeastsales@rgb.com
Membership(s): Custom Electronic Design & Installation Association; InfoComm International®

RGB Technology Inc
590 Herndon Pkwy, Suite 500, Herndon, VA 20170-5267
Tel: 703-834-1500 *Fax:* 703-834-1506
Web Site: www.rgbtec.com
Key Personnel
Pres: S David Warman *E-mail:* sdwarman@rgbtec.com
Treas: David W Chen *E-mail:* dchen@rgbtec.com
Dir, A/V Systems: Victor Blatnik *E-mail:* vblatnik@rgbtec.com
Dir, IT: Kevin Wiott *E-mail:* klwiott@fgbtec.com
Founded: 1987
Systems integration of data, network, audio & video products & services.
Membership(s): InfoComm International®

RGH Lighting LLC
546 W 48 St, New York, NY 10036
Tel: 212-244-8300 *Fax:* 212-244-8769
E-mail: info@scheimpflug.net
Web Site: www.scheimpflug.net
Key Personnel
Owner: John Engstrom
Founded: 1982
Lighting & equipment rentals.

Rhino Home Video
Division of Rhino Entertainment Co Inc
3400 W Olive Ave, Burbank, CA 91505
Tel: 818-238-6100; 410-568-3713 (intl)
Toll Free Tel: 877-RHINO-51 (744-6651 - cust serv)
E-mail: customerservice@rhino.com
Web Site: www.rhino.com
Key Personnel
VP, Media Rel: Lellie Capwell *E-mail:* lellie.capwell@rhino.com
Founded: 1985
Catalog(s) available
Membership(s): Entertainment Merchants Association; Music Business Association

Rhythm & Hues
2100 E Grand Ave, Suite A, El Segundo, CA 90245-5024
Tel: 310-448-7500 *Fax:* 310-448-7600
E-mail: info-la@rhythm.com
Web Site: www.rhythm.com
Key Personnel
Founder & VP, Devt: Pauline Ts'o *E-mail:* tso@rhythm.com
Co-Pres: Lee Berger *Tel:* 310-448-7727 *E-mail:* lee@rhythm.com; Erika Burton *E-mail:* ewb@rhythm.com
VP, Film: Heather Jennings *Tel:* 310-448-7633 *E-mail:* jennings@rhythm.com
Founded: 1987
Character animation & visual effects for entertainment & advertising.
Branch Office(s)
401 W Georgia St, Suite 500 & 600, Vancouver, BC V6B 5A1, Canada *Tel:* 604-288-8745 *E-mail:* info-van@rhythm.com
Foreign Office(s): Rhythm & Hues Studios India Pvt Ltd, The V, Vega Block, 11th fl, Left Wing, Plot No 17, Software Units Layout, HITEC City, Madhapur, Hyderabad 500 081, India *Tel:* (040) 40334567
Rhythm & Hues Studios India Pvt Ltd, Prism Tower, A-Wing, 3rd fl, Goregaon-Malad Link Rd, Goregaon (West), Mumbai 400 062, India *Tel:* (022) 40388888
Rhythm & Hues Studios Taiwan Co Ltd, No 7, Juejiang St, Yancheng District, Kaohsiung City 80344, Taiwan *Tel:* (07) 532-2777 *E-mail:* info-tw@rhythm.com

Rhythmic Medicine
10425 W 177 Terr, Olathe, KS 66062
Tel: 913-851-5100 *Fax:* 913-402-8510
E-mail: music@rhythmicmedicine.com
Web Site: www.rhythmicmedicine.com
Key Personnel
Founder & Owner: Janalea Hoffman
Dir: Marilyn Miller
Therapeutic music on CD & DVD.
Catalog(s) available

Rhythms Productions (Tom Thumb Music)
PO Box 786, Malibu, CA 90265-0786
Tel: 310-836-4678
Key Personnel
Pres: Ruth S White
VP: L Cherin
Founded: 1955
Interactive DVDs.
Catalog(s) available
Membership(s): AES; AFM; ASCAP; Education Market Association; The Recording Academy

RIA Corp
1615 W 2200 S, Suite B, Salt Lake City, UT 84119
Tel: 801-486-8822 *Fax:* 801-486-2741
E-mail: sales@riacorp.com
Web Site: www.riacorp.com
Key Personnel
Pres: Mike Hodges
VP, Sales: Jeff Wade
Opers Mgr: Jill Jakubowski
Founded: 1973
Line sheet(s) available

Rich-Heape Films Inc
5952 Royal Lane, Suite 254, Dallas, TX 75230
Tel: 214-696-6916 *Toll Free Tel:* 888-600-2922 *Fax:* 214-696-6306
Web Site: www.richheape.com
Key Personnel
Pres & Exec Prodr: Steven R Heape *E-mail:* heape@richheape.com
Dir: Chip Richie *E-mail:* chip@richheape.com
Founded: 1994

Lynda Richardson Photography
7239 Lookout Dr, Richmond, VA 23225
Tel: 804-347-9668
E-mail: lynda@lyndarichardsonphotography.com
Web Site: www.lyndarichardsonphotography.com
Key Personnel
Owner: Lynda Richardson
Photographic services.
Stock list(s) available
Membership(s): ASMP; North American Nature Photography Association

Richie Media Productions LLC
2035 Royal Lane, Suite 203, Dallas, TX 75229
Tel: 214-696-9040
Web Site: www.richiemedia.com
Key Personnel
Prodr & Dir: Chip Richie *E-mail:* chip@richiemedia.com
Founded: 1939
Turnkey production, FCP suite, stock footage, HD cameras.

Richmond Sound Design Ltd
5264 Ross St, Vancouver, BC V5W 3K7, Canada
Web Site: www.richmondsounddesign.com
Key Personnel
Pres: Charlie Richmond *E-mail:* charlie.rsd@gmail.com
Proj Mgr: Marilyn Williams *E-mail:* will.rsd@gmail.com
Founded: 1972
Theatre sound design, show control & virtual sound system software.
Catalog(s) available

Richter Productions Inc
521 E 14 St, Suite 4F, New York, NY 10009
Tel: 917-608-7427
E-mail: rrprod@aol.com; richter330@aol.com
Web Site: www.richtervideos.com
Key Personnel
Pres & Prodr: Robert Richter
Founded: 1968
Produce & distribute documentaries.
Online catalog(s), updated regularly
Membership(s): New Day Film Distribution Cooperative

Richter Studios
1143 W Rundell Place, Chicago, IL 60607
Tel: 312-861-9999 *Fax:* 312-997-2387
E-mail: info@richterstudios.com
Web Site: www.richterstudios.com
Key Personnel
Co-Founder & CEO: David Richter *E-mail:* drichter@richterstudios.com
Co-Founder & Pres: Jeremy Richter
VP, New Busn Devt: Eric Schmidt
Founded: 1997
Video, multimedia & interactive company.

Riggs Production Associates Inc
6532 Wahl Rd, Freeland, WA 98249
Tel: 360-331-5155 *Fax:* 360-331-4558
E-mail: sales@riggspfx.com
Web Site: www.riggspfx.com

Founded: 1983
Provides special effects rental equipment & expendables along with full shop capabilities for design & fabrication. Stocking distributors for ULTRATEC, LOOK, CITC & more.

Right Coast Recording Inc
349 Chestnut St, Columbia, PA 17512-1259
Tel: 717-681-9801 *Fax:* 717-681-9801
E-mail: rightcoastrecording@gmail.com
Web Site: www.rightcoastrecording.com
Key Personnel
Owner & Prodr: Dave Natale *E-mail:* daven@rightcoastrecording.com
Owner & Chief Engr: Dave Wilkerson *E-mail:* davew@rightcoastrecording.com
Engr & Prodr: Bob Gentilo *E-mail:* bob@rightcoastrecording.com
Founded: 1990
State of the art vintage recording equipment.

Right Stuf Inc
512 NE Main St, Grimes, IA 50111-0680
Tel: 515-986-1028 *Toll Free Tel:* 800-338-6827 *Fax:* 515-986-1129
E-mail: info@rightstuf.com
Web Site: www.rightstuf.com
Key Personnel
CEO & Pres: Shawne Kleckner
Asst Prodr: David Olsen *E-mail:* davido@rightstuf.com
Founded: 1987
Anime publisher, distributor & retailer.
Catalog(s) available

RingSide Creative
13320 Northend, Suite 3000, Oak Park, MI 48237
Tel: 248-548-2500
E-mail: info@ringsidecreative.com; newbiz@ringsidecreative.com
Web Site: www.ringsidecreative.com
Key Personnel
Founder: Doug Cheek
CEO: Steve Wild
CFO: Brian Efrusy
VP, Opers: John Mroz
Exec Prodr: Robin Tracey
Proj Mgr: Sara Smith
Integrated media studio.
Catalog(s) available

Rink Rat Productions Inc
2 Monk Lane, St John's, NL A1E 1M8, Canada
Mailing Address: 3 Monk Lane, St John's, NL A1E 1M8, Canada
Tel: 709-739-9055 *Fax:* 709-739-9065
E-mail: info@rinkratproductions.com
Web Site: www.rinkratproductions.com
Key Personnel
Prodr: Mary Sexton *E-mail:* msexton@rinkratproductions.com
Founded: 1994
TV & film production.

The Rip-Tie Co
883 San Leandro Blvd, San Leandro, CA 94577
Mailing Address: PO Box 549, San Leandro, CA 94577-0549
Tel: 510-577-0200 *Toll Free Tel:* 800-7-RIPTIE (774-7843) *Fax:* 510-553-0160
E-mail: info@riptie.com
Web Site: www.riptie.com
Key Personnel
Pres: Michael Paul Fennell
Manufacture cable management straps & sell bulk velcro.
Brochure(s) available

Risk International & Associates Inc
8803 W Ontario Ave, Littleton, CO 80128
Tel: 720-922-0707 *Fax:* 720-922-0707
E-mail: info@riskit.com
Web Site: www.riskit.com
Key Personnel
Founder & Pres: Dr Randall WA Davidson *E-mail:* rdavidson@globalhealthandsafety.net
Risk management, health, safety & environmental programs/audits, publications & master classes.

Ritchie's Perfect Press
Division of Emeralda Works
500 Aloha, Suite 105, Seattle, WA 98109
Tel: 206-498-9208 (cell)
Web Site: www.emeralda.com
Key Personnel
Founder: Bill H Ritchie, Jr *E-mail:* ritchie@emeralda.com
Produce prints, books, ephemera & software for the printmaking world.
Catalog(s) available

Ritz Camera & Image
6900 Virginia Manor Rd, Suite 113, Beltsville, MD 20705
Toll Free Tel: 866-849-3045
E-mail: ritzpix@ritzcamera.com
Web Site: www.ritzcamera.com
Founded: 1918
Membership(s): Photo Marketing Association

River Road Recorders (RRR)
122 Crislaur Ave, Harahan, LA 70123-5025
Tel: 504-737-9880 *Fax:* 504-324-1920
E-mail: info@rivrd.com
Key Personnel
Owner: Michael Lea *E-mail:* michaellea@cox.net
Founded: 1985
Full service audio studio specializing in radio & television production, voiceover & ADR.

RJ Video Productions
15585 Tilden St, San Leandro, CA 94579-2316
Tel: 510-357-6535 *Fax:* 510-357-6535
E-mail: tuffnut56@att.net
Key Personnel
Owner & Prodr: Robert J Smart
Founded: 1987
Price list(s), folder
Video(s), folder

RJS Productions
Division of Gilro Associates Inc
PO Box 739, Westminster, MD 21158
Tel: 410-876-6300 *Fax:* 410-857-0608
Key Personnel
Exec Prodr: Richard J Slechter, Sr *E-mail:* slechter@qis.net
Full production facility for industrial/commercial videos, TV, promotionals, commercials & full length programs. Post on media 100-XS facility. Full service from scripting to final product.

RKO Pictures Inc
2034 Broadway, Santa Monica, CA 90404
Tel: 310-277-0707 *Fax:* 310-566-8940
E-mail: info@rko.com
Web Site: www.rko.com
Key Personnel
Chmn & CEO: Ted Hartley
VChmn: Dina Merrill
Pres: Andrew Matthews
EVP, Prodn & Devt: Vanessa Coifman
Founded: 1929
Branch Office(s)
750 Lexington Ave, Suite 2200, New York, NY 10022 *Tel:* 212-644-0600 *Fax:* 212-644-0384
Membership(s): Independent Film & Television Alliance®

RLJ Entertainment Inc
8515 Georgia Ave, Suite 650, Silver Spring, MD 20910
Tel: 301-608-2115 *Toll Free Tel:* 800-999-0212 *Fax:* 301-608-9312
E-mail: inquiries@rljentertainment.com
Web Site: www.us.rljentertainment.com
Key Personnel
CEO: Miguel Penella
Pres, Acorn Brands: Mark Stevens
Catalog(s) available
Branch Office(s)
232 N Main St, Stillwater, MN 55082 *Tel:* 651-351-3990 *E-mail:* customerservice@acornonline.com *Web Site:* www.acornonline.com
Foreign Office(s): 4-14 Buckingham St, Studio 203, Surry Hills, NSW 2010, Australia, Mng Dir: Lesley Fromant *Tel:* (02) 9310 7333 *Fax:* (02) 8221 9743 *E-mail:* customerservice@acornmediaau.com
Acorn Media UK Ltd, 16 Welmar Mews Ivy Works, 154 Clapham Park Rd, London SW4 7DD, United Kingdom, Mng Dir: Paul Holland *Tel:* (020) 7627 7200 *Fax:* (020) 7627 2501 *E-mail:* info@acornmediauk.com
Membership(s): Entertainment Merchants Association; Reading Recovery Council of North America

RLX Media LLC
720 SW 12 Ave, Pompano Beach, FL 33069
Tel: 954-946-7575 *Toll Free Tel:* 800-555-9704 *Fax:* 954-946-7576
E-mail: info@rlxmedia.com
Web Site: www.rlxmedia.com; www.rlxvideo.net
Key Personnel
Owner & Pres: Mike Horsley *E-mail:* mikehorsley@rlxmedia.com
Supplier of quality duplication & printing services to the multimedia industry.
Membership(s): Entertainment Merchants Association

RM Films International
PO Box 3748, Hollywood, CA 90078-3748
Tel: 323-466-7791 *Fax:* 323-461-4152
E-mail: rmf@rmfilms.com
Web Site: www.rmfilms.com; www.russmeyer.com
Key Personnel
Trustee & Pres: Janice Cowart
Dir, Opers: Julio Dottavio
Vintage & cult Russ Meyer movies.
Catalog(s), free

RNJ Electronics
202 New Hwy, Amityville, NY 11701
Mailing Address: PO Box 667, Amityville, NY 11701-0667
Tel: 631-226-2700 *Toll Free Tel:* 800-645-5833 *Fax:* 631-226-2770 *Toll Free Fax:* 800-765-3291
E-mail: sales@rnjelectronics.com
Web Site: www.rnjelectronics.com
Key Personnel
Pres: Jeff Mutterperl *E-mail:* jeff@rnjelectronics.com
Founded: 1981
Distribute security, commercial & pro sound, datacom, home theater, tools & educational supplies.
Catalog(s) available

Road Pictures
5420 N College Ave, Suite 201, Indianapolis, IN 46220
Tel: 317-267-9590 *Toll Free Tel:* 800-267-9590 *Fax:* 317-267-9677
Web Site: www.roadpictures.com
Key Personnel
Owner & Pres: Greg Malone *E-mail:* gmalone@roadpictures.com
Exec Prodr & Sales: Kim Cline *E-mail:* kcline@roadpictures.com
Founded: 1994

Film & video production company. Television commercials, Internet films & corporate films. Final cut pro-edit suite. Production management for out-of-town & foreign producers.
Membership(s): AICP

Roadworthy Image Magnification
Division of Golan Studios/Atomic Imaging Inc
1501 N Magnolia Ave, Chicago, IL 60642
Tel: 312-649-1800 *Toll Free Tel:* 800-C-DA SHOW (232-7469) *Fax:* 312-642-7441
E-mail: imag@atomicimaging.com
Web Site: www.atomicimaging.com; www.golan.tv/roadworthy/index.html
Key Personnel
Film & Video Prodn: Aigar Dombrovskis *Tel:* 312-649-1800 ext 5720 *E-mail:* aigar@atomicimaging.com

Robbins Media Inc
375 Greenwich St, New York, NY 10013
Tel: 212-661-7670 *Fax:* 212-656-1997
E-mail: info@robbinsmedia.com
Web Site: www.robbinsmedia.com
Key Personnel
Pres & Prodr: Shawn Robbins *E-mail:* sr@robbinsmedia.com
Production company.

Robertson Worldwide
13611 Thornton Rd, Blue Island, IL 60406
Toll Free Tel: 800-323-5633 *Toll Free Fax:* 877-388-2420
E-mail: info@robertsonww.com
Web Site: www.robertsonww.com
Key Personnel
Pres: Sandy Bryant
VP, Mktg & Tech Sales: Robert Pelino
Industrial B2B Sales Acct Mgr: Brian Katzberger *Tel:* 800-323-5633 ext 150 *E-mail:* bkatzberger@robertsonww.com
Founded: 1950
Manufacturer of electronic & magnetic ballasts & transformers for fluorescent HID & low-voltage lamps.
Catalog(s), product family specific

Robertstock.com
4203 Locust St, Philadelphia, PA 19104
Tel: 215-386-6300 *Toll Free Tel:* 800-786-6300 *Toll Free Fax:* 800-786-1920
E-mail: info@robertstock.com
Web Site: www.robertstock.com
Key Personnel
Pres: H Armstrong Roberts, III
VP, Sales: John B Fitzpatrick
Stock photography; contemporary, retro, vintage, historical; color & black/white.
Catalog(s) available
Membership(s): ASMP; Picture Agency Council of America

Rockeffects Canada Inc/KABUKI
42 Calder St, Shediac, NB E4P 1K8, Canada
Tel: 506-577-6326 *Toll Free Tel:* 800-461-7625 *Fax:* 506-577-2832 *Toll Free Fax:* 800-461-4329
E-mail: info@kabuki.com
Web Site: www.kabuki.com
Founded: 1990
Manufacturer.
Catalog(s) available

Rocking Horse Studio
1380 Upper City Rd, Pittsfield, NH 03263
Tel: 603-512-5347
E-mail: info@rockinghorsestudio.com
Web Site: www.rockinghorsestudio.com
Key Personnel
Prodr & Engr: Brian Coombes
Founded: 2008
Commercial recording studio for hire.

Rockland Colloid LLC
PO Box 3120, Oregon City, OR 97045-0306
Tel: 503-655-4152 (sales); 914-413-3000 (tech) *Toll Free Fax:* 866-737-0174
E-mail: info@rockaloid.com; orders@rockaloid.com
Web Site: www.rockaloid.com
Key Personnel
Owner & Gen Mgr: Robert Cone
Founded: 1965
Manufacture photographic emulsions, toners, etc.
Online catalog(s) available
Membership(s): IS&T

Rocktown Media
1361 Lincolnshire Dr, Harrisonburg, VA 22802
Tel: 540-433-7700 *Toll Free Tel:* 888-433-8700
E-mail: info@rocktown.tv
Web Site: www.rocktown.tv
Key Personnel
Owner & Prodr: Richard Hiett
Founded: 1996
Complete production service company.
Membership(s): CCM

Rockwell Communications Inc
321 Burnham St, East Hartford, CT 06108
Tel: 860-528-9091 *Toll Free Tel:* 800-566-6681 *Fax:* 860-289-2334
E-mail: rockwellservice@aol.com
Web Site: www.rockwellcommunications.com
Key Personnel
Pres: Richard D Carlson *E-mail:* rdc@rockwellcommunications.com
Off Mgr: Barbara Petersen *E-mail:* petersen@rockwellcommunications.com
Serv Mgr: Ray Nunez *E-mail:* r.nunez@rockwellcommunications.com
Founded: 1947 (as Rockwell Films)
Catalog(s) available
Membership(s): InfoComm International®

Rocky Mountain Audio/Video Productions Inc
7950 S Lincoln St, Littleton, CO 80122
Tel: 303-730-1100 *Toll Free Tel:* 877-856-4644 *Fax:* 303-468-9811
E-mail: sales@rmavp.com
Web Site: www.rmavp.com
Key Personnel
Pres: Terry Talley *E-mail:* terryt@rmavp.com
Founded: 1982
Full service audio video production company.
Catalog(s) available
Membership(s): Colorado Film & Video Association; MCA-I

Roconex Corp
20 Marybill Dr S, Troy, OH 45373
Tel: 937-339-2616 *Fax:* 937-339-1470
E-mail: info@roconex.com
Web Site: www.roconex.com
Key Personnel
Pres: Ty Spear *E-mail:* tyspear@roconex.com
Job shop manufacturing.
Catalog(s) available

Rodeo Video Inc
412 S Main, Snowflake, AZ 85937
Tel: 928-536-7111 *Toll Free Tel:* 800-331-1269 *Fax:* 928-536-7120
E-mail: info@rodeovideo.com
Web Site: www.rodeovideo.com
Key Personnel
Owner & Pres: Keith Flake *E-mail:* kflake@rodeovideo.com
Rodeo videotapes-from bloopers to training & events.
Catalog(s) available

The Fred Rogers Co
2100 Wharton St, Suite 700, Pittsburgh, PA 15203
Tel: 412-687-2990 *Fax:* 412-687-1226
Web Site: www.fredrogers.org
Key Personnel
Dir, PR: David Newell *E-mail:* newell@fredrogers.org
Founded: 1971
Producers of products based on the Mister Rogers' Neighborhood tv series. Also producers of the series prior to the passing of Fred Rogers. Co-producer of a new children's program Daniel Tiger's Neighborhood seen daily on PBS. Distributor of new childrens program, Reg & Cat, seen daily on PBS.
Online catalog(s) available

Rohde & Schwarz Inc
Subsidiary of Rohde & Schwarz GmbH & Co KG
6821 Benjamin Franklin Dr, Columbia, MD 21046
Tel: 410-910-7800 *Toll Free Tel:* 888-837-8772 *Fax:* 410-910-7801
E-mail: info@rsa.rohde-schwarz.com
Web Site: www.rohde-schwarz.us
Manufacture test & measurement equipment for mobile radios & radio communications.
Catalog(s), free
Branch Office(s)
Rohde & Schwarz Federal Systems Inc, 302 Sentinel Dr, Suite 105, Annapolis Junction, MD 20701 *Tel:* 301-957-3490 *Fax:* 301-725-2603 *E-mail:* info@rsfederal.com
7700 Irvine Center Dr, Suite 100, Irvine, CA 92618 *Tel:* 949-885-7000 *Fax:* 949-885-7001
9255 SW Nimbus Ave, Beaverton, OR 97008 *Tel:* 503-403-4700 *Fax:* 503-403-4701
1500 Lakeside Pkwy, Suite 100, Flower Mound, TX 75028 *Tel:* 469-713-5300 *Fax:* 469-713-5301
Rohde & Schwarz Canada Inc, 750 Palladium Dr, Suite 102, Ottawa, ON K2V 1C7, Canada *Tel:* 613-592-8000 *Toll Free Tel:* 877-438-2880 *Fax:* 613-592-8009 *Web Site:* www.rohde-schwarz.ca

Roland Corp US
5100 S Eastern Ave, Los Angeles, CA 90040-2938
Tel: 323-890-3700 *Fax:* 323-721-4875
Web Site: www.rolandus.com
Key Personnel
VP, Sales: Brian Alli
Dir, HR: Debbie Parmenter
Mktg Communs Mgr: Rebecca Eaddy
Catalog(s) available

Glenn Roland Films
10711 Wellworth Ave, Los Angeles, CA 90024
Mailing Address: PO Box 24035, Los Angeles, CA 90024
Tel: 310-475-0937 *Fax:* 310-475-0939
Key Personnel
Dir & Exec Prodr: Glenn Roland
Motion picture & television production, cinematography & production services, lighting & grip equipment, dolly with track packages, studio, director +/or director of photography services, mobile production unit, Super 35mm HD cinematography.

Rollin Studios
199 Green St, Brooklyn, NY 11222
E-mail: more@rollin-studios.com
Web Site: www.rollin-studios.com
Key Personnel
Asst Dir & Prodn Mgr: Satti Ombao
Prodr: Anthony Argento

Founded: 2010
Movie, music & media production services. Location & equipment rentals. Film & TV production services, narrative & commercial.

Rolls Corp
5968 S 350 W, Murray, UT 84107
Tel: 801-263-9053 *Fax:* 801-263-9068
E-mail: info@rolls.com
Web Site: www.rolls.com
Founded: 1989
Audio electronics manufacturing.
Catalog(s) available
Membership(s): InfoComm International®; NAMM, the National Association of Music Merchants; NSCA

Romar Learning
6700 Woodlands Pkwy, Suite 230-292, Woodlands, TX 77382
Tel: 281-292-5508 *Fax:* 281-363-2309
E-mail: info@romarlearning.com
Web Site: www.romarlearning.com
Key Personnel
Owner & Pres: David A Davis
VP: Kaye Leavelle
Tech Dir: Theresa Teltschik
Founded: 1986
Membership(s): ASTO; HeSCA; MCA-I

Ron Rose Productions Inc, see Mach 1 Productions

Rosco Laboratories Inc
52 Harbor View, Stamford, CT 06902
Tel: 203-708-8900 *Toll Free Tel:* 800-ROSCO NY (767-2669) *Fax:* 203-708-8919
E-mail: info@rosco.com
Web Site: www.rosco.com
Key Personnel
Chmn of the Bd: Stan Miller *E-mail:* stan.miller@rosco.com
CEO: Mark Engel *E-mail:* mark.engel@rosco.com
CFO: Rich Luce *E-mail:* rich.luce@rosco.com
Pres, North America: Ed Donhue *E-mail:* ed.donohue@rosco.com
EVP: Stan Schwartz *E-mail:* stan.schwartz@rosco.com
Creative Dir: Donna Nicol *E-mail:* donna.nicol@rosco.com
Dir, Global Mktg: Joshua Alemany *E-mail:* josh.alemany@rosco.com
Dir, Opers: Tracey Cosgrove *E-mail:* tracey.cosgrove@rosco.com
Exec Asst: Dawn T Zacchi *E-mail:* dawn.zacchi@rosco.com
Founded: 1910
Filters for entertainment lighting, gobos, fog & haze machines, dance floors, scenic paint & paint drops & lighting equipment products.
Catalog(s) available
Branch Office(s)
9420 Chivers Ave, Sun Valley, CA 91352, Intl Busn Dir, Asia & Latin America: Jim Meyer *Tel:* 818-543-6700 *Toll Free Tel:* 800-ROSCO LA (767-2652) *Fax:* 818-662-9470 *E-mail:* jim.meyer@rosco.com
1600 Chisholm Trail, Round Rock, TX, Gen Mgr: John Hunter *Tel:* 512-388-5299 *Toll Free Tel:* 866-228-2256 *Fax:* 512-388-0196
Rosco Canada, 3855 Henning Dr, No 107, Burnaby, BC V5C 6N3, Canada, Acct Rep: Jennifer Steer *Tel:* 604-298-7350 *Fax:* 604-298-7360 *E-mail:* jennifer.steer@rosco.com
Rosco Canada, 1241 Denison St, No 44, Markham, ON L3R 4B4, Canada, Global Mkt Devt: Tom Swartz *Tel:* 905-475-1400 *Toll Free Tel:* 888-ROSCO TO (767-2686) *Fax:* 905-475-3351 *E-mail:* tom.swartz@rosco.com (Canadian head off)
Foreign Office(s): Rosco Australia Pty Ltd, 42 Sawyer Lane, Artarmon, NSW 2064, Australia, Dir: Adam P Smith *Tel:* (02) 9906 6262 *Fax:* (02) 9906 3430 *E-mail:* roscoaus@rosco.com.au
Rosco do Brasil, R Visconde de Itaborai, 141, Tatuape, 03308-050 Sao Paulo SP, Brazil, Sales & Info: Mauro Nakada *Tel:* (011) 2098 2865 *Fax:* (011) 2098 0193 *E-mail:* vendas@rosco.com
Gobos Factory Sarl, 2 rue de Vienne, 75008 Paris, France *E-mail:* france@rosco.com
Gorlitzerstr 2, 33758 Schloss Holte-Stukenbrock, Germany *Tel:* (05207) 995989 *Fax:* (05207) 925989 *E-mail:* germany@rosco.com
101-17 Minaminakajima-machi, Ruygasaki-City, Ibaraki 301-0047, Japan, Contact: Koichi Katagiri *E-mail:* katagiri@rosco.com
Estudios Churubusco Azteca, Edificio Luis Bunuel, 304 A, Atletas, 2 Col Country Club, Del Coyuacan, 04220 Mexico, DF, Mexico, Ricardo Ortiz *Tel:* (0155) 5544 3440 *Fax:* (0155) 5544 3440
Claus Stuterweg 125/1b, 2012 WS Haarlem, Netherlands, VP, Europe: Kees Frijters *Tel:* (023) 5288 257 *E-mail:* kees.frijters@rosco.com
Rosco Iberica SA, C/Oro, 76 Poligano Industrial Sur, 28870 Colmenar Viejo, Madrid, Spain, Gen Mgr: Leon Felipe Palomina *Tel:* 918 473 900 *Fax:* 918 463 634 *E-mail:* felipe.palomino@rosco.com
Roscolab Ltd, Kangley Bridge Rd, Sydenham, London SE26 5AQ, United Kingdom, Gen Mgr: Gordon Tomkins *Tel:* (020) 8659 2300 *Fax:* (020) 8659 3153 *E-mail:* gordon.tomkins@rosco.com

Rose Brand
4 Emerson Lane, Secaucus, NJ 07094
Tel: 201-809-1730 *Toll Free Tel:* 800-223-1624 *Fax:* 201-809-1851
E-mail: info@rosebrand.com
Web Site: www.rosebrand.com
Key Personnel
VP, Outside Sales: Roger Claman *Tel:* 201-809-1730 ext 125
Founded: 1921
Theatrical fabric & fabrication company.
Catalog(s) available
Branch Office(s)
10616 Lanark St, Sun Valley, CA 91352, Gen Mgr: Tina Wright *Tel:* 818-505-6290 *Toll Free Tel:* 800-360-5056 *Fax:* 818-505-6293
Membership(s): Professional Lighting & Sound Association; USITT

Rose City Sound
4811 SE 16 Ave, Portland, OR 97202
Tel: 503-238-6330 *Toll Free Tel:* 877-503-7673 *Fax:* 503-238-9872
E-mail: sales@rosecitysound.com
Web Site: www.rosecitysound.com
Key Personnel
AV Sales: Eric Iverson *E-mail:* eric@rosecitysound.com
Founded: 1938
Sound, lighting & AV sales, rentals, production, designs & installations.
Membership(s): InfoComm International®; MCA-I

Rose Packaging & Design Inc
4000 Sopris Mountain Rd, Basalt, CO 81621-9179
Mailing Address: PO Box 3316, Basalt, CO 81621-3316
Tel: 970-927-6515 *Toll Free Tel:* 800-308-1003 *Fax:* 970-927-6514
E-mail: sales@rosepkg.com
Web Site: www.rosepkg.com
Key Personnel
Owner, VP & Mktg Mgr: Robert Rose
E-mail: robrose@rosepkg.com
Catalog(s) available

Judson Rosebush Co Inc
630 Ninth Ave, Suite 507, New York, NY 10036
Tel: 212-581-3000
E-mail: judson@rosebush.com
Web Site: www.rosebush.com
Key Personnel
Owner & Prodr: Judson Rosebush
Creates interactive multimedia Internet products from start to finish. Expert witness in litigation for film, video & digital issues.
Catalog(s) available

Peter Rosen Productions Inc
9 E 78 St, Suite 5-A, New York, NY 10075
Tel: 212-535-8927 *Fax:* 212-517-5337
E-mail: rosenprod@aol.com
Web Site: www.peterrosenproductions.com
Key Personnel
Pres & Prodr: Peter Rosen
Founded: 1970
Film & television production.
Membership(s): BAFTA; DGA; NATAS; Television Academy

The Rosenthal Group
10625 Cohasset St, Sun Valley, CA 91352
Tel: 818-252-1010 *Fax:* 818-252-1070
Web Site: www.therosenthalgroup.com
Key Personnel
Owner: Jim Rosenthal *E-mail:* jim@therosenthalgroup.com
Motion picture & video lighting, rental & design.
Online catalog(s) available

Mary Riepma Ross Media Arts Center
University of Nebraska-Lincoln, 313 N 13 St, Lincoln, NE 68588
Mailing Address: PO Box 880253, Lincoln, NE 68588-0253
Tel: 402-472-9100; 402-472-5353 *Fax:* 402-472-2576
Web Site: www.theross.org
Key Personnel
Dir: Danny Lee Ladely
Busn Mgr: Kassandra Hill
Film-video exhibition programs.
Membership(s): National Alliance for Media Arts & Culture

Ross Video Ltd
8 John St, Iroquois, ON K0E 1K0, Canada
Mailing Address: PO Box 220, Iroquois, ON K0E 1K0, Canada
Tel: 613-652-4886 *Fax:* 613-652-4425
E-mail: solutions@rossvideo.com
Web Site: www.rossvideo.com
Key Personnel
CEO: David Ross *E-mail:* dross@rossvideo.com
EVP & Chief Mktg Offr: Jeff Moore *Tel:* 613-228-0688 *Fax:* 613-228-0464 *E-mail:* jmoore@rossvideo.com
SVP, Worldwide Sales: Darren Budrow *E-mail:* dbudrow@rossvideo.com
Dir, Mktg & Communs: Jan Mills *E-mail:* jmills@rossvideo.com
Founded: 1974
Designs, markets, manufactures & supports innovative products for use in broadcast, distribution, live event & production applications.
Branch Office(s)
64 Auriga Dr, Ottawa, ON K2E 1B8, Canada *Tel:* 613-228-0688 *Fax:* 613-228-0464
Foreign Office(s): 24/49 Corporate Blvd, Bayswater, Victoria 3153, Australia *Tel:* (03) 9721 3200 *Fax:* (03) 9720 7662
Rue des Veterinaires 42, 1070 Brussels, Belgium *Tel:* (02) 331 27 69 *Fax:* (02) 332 12 73

Rossman Audio LLC
597 W Hillside Ave, Suite 100, State College, PA 16803-1509
Tel: 814-234-2044 *Fax:* 814-689-1036
E-mail: info@rossmanaudio.com
Web Site: www.rossmanaudio.com
Key Personnel
Pres: Russ Rossman, Jr
Founded: 1978
Manufacturer of multimedia switching & audio control equipment.

Rough House
550 Bryant St, San Francisco, CA 94107-1217
Tel: 415-561-4544 *Fax:* 415-543-8390
E-mail: info@roughhouse.com
Web Site: www.roughhouse.com
Key Personnel
Exec Prodr: Todd Lindo
Prodn Coord: Karen Stillwell
Founded: 1988
HD digital production & post-production.

Roundabout Entertainment Inc
217 S Lake St, Burbank, CA 91502
Tel: 818-842-9300 *Fax:* 818-842-9301
E-mail: info@roundabout.com
Web Site: www.roundabout.com
Key Personnel
Off Mgr: Kellie Spencer
Founded: 1992
Comprehensive post solutions for television & film.

Rounder Records
Member of Concord Music Group Inc
1209 Pine St, Suite 100, Nashville, TN 37203
Web Site: www.rounder.com
Key Personnel
Founder: Ken Irwin; Marian Leighton-Levy; Bill Nowlin
Pres: John Virant
Founded: 1970

Rovi Corp
2830 De La Cruz Blvd, Santa Clara, CA 95050
Tel: 408-562-8400 *Fax:* 408-567-1800
Web Site: www.rovicorp.com
Key Personnel
CEO & Pres: Tom Carson
CFO: Peter Halt
EVP, HR: Dustin Finer
EVP, Worldwide Sales & Mktg: Matt Milne
Software publishers.
Literature available
Branch Office(s)
2233 N Ontario St, Burbank, CA 91504 *Tel:* 818-295-6650 *Fax:* 818-295-6797
1281 W Bluff Creek Dr, Playa Vista, CA 90094 *Tel:* 310-314-3000
4780 Eastgate Mall, San Diego, CA 92121 *Tel:* 858-882-0600
500 Golden Ridge Rd, Suite 100, Golden, CO 80401 *Tel:* 303-273-7800 *Fax:* 303-273-7880
10 N Martingale Rd, Suite 610, Shaumburg, IL 60173
161 First St, Suite 4B, Cambridge, MA 02142
955 Massachusetts Ave, Cambridge, MA 02139 *Tel:* 781-276-3650
1168 Oak Valley Dr, Ann Arbor, MI 48108 *Tel:* 734-887-5600 *Fax:* 734-827-2492
304 Hudson St, 8th fl, New York, NY 10013-1015 *Tel:* 212-824-0300 *Fax:* 212-741-1246
7140 S Lewis Ave, Tulsa, OK 74136 *Tel:* 918-488-4000 *Fax:* 915-488-4860
4 Radnor Corporate Ctr, 100 Matsonford Rd, Radnor, PA 19088 *Tel:* 610-293-8500 *Fax:* 610-293-6230
Membership(s): Content Delivery & Storage Association; Entertainment Merchants Association; MCA-I

Ron Roy Productions/Moodtapes
2219 W Olive, Suite 312, Burbank, CA 91506
E-mail: info@moodtapes.com
Web Site: www.moodtapes.com
Key Personnel
Pres: Ron Roy

RPG Diffusor Systems Inc
651-C Commerce Dr, Upper Marlboro, MD 20774
Tel: 301-249-0044 *Fax:* 301-390-3602
E-mail: info@rpginc.com
Web Site: www.rpginc.com
Key Personnel
CEO: Dr Peter D'Antonio
EVP: Jeff Madison *Tel:* 304-249-0044 ext 104 *E-mail:* jmadison@rpginc.com
Founded: 1984
Acoustical materials.
Catalog(s) available
Membership(s): AES; ASA; NAB; NSCA

RPM-PSI
8750 Shirley Ave, Northridge, CA 91324
Tel: 818-349-8680 *Fax:* 818-772-7577
E-mail: info@rpm-psi.com
Web Site: www.rpm-psi.com
Key Personnel
VP, Mktg: Mark Mathews
Founded: 1975
Catalog(s) available

RSS Distributors
7930 Old Auction Rd, Manheim, PA 17545
Toll Free Tel: 800-233-0175
E-mail: orders@rssd.com
Web Site: www.rssd.com
Key Personnel
Owner: Jim Miller
Distributes AV equipment for the special events industry.
Catalog(s) available

RSVP, see Russ Sturgeon Productions/RSVP

RTS Inc
40-11 Burt Dr, Deer Park, NY 11729
Tel: 631-242-6801 *Fax:* 631-242-6808
E-mail: rtsinc@rcn.com
Web Site: www.rtsphoto.com
Key Personnel
Mktg Dir: Mike Stango
Distributes Billingham camera bags, Rotolight LED lighting, EWA-marine underwater camera housings, Cullmann tripods, Copal shutters, Graf/Studio ball, Hahnel Battery, charger & camera remotes, Copal shutters.
Catalog(s) available

RTZ Audio Visual
6725 Santa Barbara Ct, Suite 103, Elkridge, MD 21075
Tel: 443-757-0480 *Toll Free Tel:* 800-543-0582 *Fax:* 443-757-0487
E-mail: sales@rtzav.com
Web Site: www.rtzav.com
Key Personnel
Owner: Gary Lunsford
Founded: 1988
Catalog(s) available

Rucinski & Reetz Communications LLC
2155 Terrebonne, Mosinee, WI 54455
Tel: 715-355-9159; 715-241-7316
Web Site: www.rucinskireetz.com
Key Personnel
Owner & Prodr: Susan Reetz *E-mail:* reetz@rucinskireetz.com; Pamela Rucinski *E-mail:* rucinski@rucinskireetz.com
Research, writing, directing & project managing for government, nonprofit & corporate client film, video & multimedia projects.
Membership(s): MCA-I

Ben Rudnick & Friends
Subsidiary of Bartlett Ave Productions Inc
PO Box 1426, Arlington, MA 02474
Tel: 781-643-5137
Web Site: www.benrudnick.com
Key Personnel
CEO: Ben Rudnick *E-mail:* ben@benrudnick.com
Founded: 2000
Creative multiple award-winning musical recordings targeted to the family audience. Live band specializing in adventurously played family music to audiences small to very large. Recordings have won every Parenting Award including six Parents Choice Awards. Recordings include "A Frog Named Sam" (2009), "The Challenger Baseball Song & Other Hits" (2007), "Grace's Bell" (2007), "Live at WERS" (2006), "Blast off" (2004), "Fun & Games" (2002) & "Emily Songs" (2000). In Nov 2010, the band released "It's Santa Claus!", a CD of holiday originals & classics. "Live in Lexington" (2011). "Love is a Superpower" (2012).
Membership(s): BMI

RuffHouse LLC
2823 Lariat Trail, Austin, TX 78734
Tel: 512-965-2957
E-mail: info@ruffhousin.com
Web Site: www.ruffhousin.com
Key Personnel
Dir, Prodr & Writer: Charles Wiedman *E-mail:* charlie@ruffhousin.com
Prodr: David Christopher; Katherine Willis *E-mail:* katherine@ruffhousin.com
Founded: 2003

Rule Broadcast Systems
1284 Soldier's Field Rd, Boston, MA 02135
Tel: 617-277-2200 *Toll Free Tel:* 800-785-3266 *Fax:* 617-277-6800
E-mail: answers@rule.com
Web Site: www.rule.com
Key Personnel
Pres: John Rule *Tel:* 617-277-2200 ext 101 *E-mail:* j.rule@rule.com
Sr Acct Mgr, Sales: Mike Sutton *Tel:* 617-277-2200 ext 206 *E-mail:* sutton@rule.com
Gen Mgr: Brian Malcolm *Tel:* 617-277-2200 ext 102 *E-mail:* malcolm@rule.com
Founded: 1978
Distribute AV equipment & professional video equipment.
Line card(s), online with links
Online catalog(s) available
Membership(s): InfoComm International®; MAB; Northern New England Broadcasters Association; SBE; WEVA

Rum Jungle Media
5295 Eden Rd, Mound, MN 55364
Tel: 952-472-5525
E-mail: rumjungle@rumjungle.com
Web Site: www.rumjungle.com
Key Personnel
Prodn Mgr: Robin Mahle *E-mail:* rmahle@rumjungle.com
Founded: 1991
Television production. Services include camera crews, satellite truck, live event production, HD video production, web streaming, web casts, ENG camera crews, EFP camera crews, satellite services, Ku digital transmissions, location sound, video & lighting, live broadcasts, satellite uplinks & downlinks, tape feeds & fiber.

Running Pony Productions LLC
1770 Kirby Pkwy, Suite 118, Memphis, TN 38138

Tel: 901-683-6693 *Toll Free Tel:* 877-891-7669 *Fax:* 901-683-3093
E-mail: info@runningpony.com
Web Site: www.runningpony.com
Key Personnel
Principal: Rod Starns *E-mail:* rstarns@runningpony.com
Membership(s): NATAS

Russ Bassett Corp
8189 Byron Rd, Whittier, CA 90606-2615
Tel: 562-945-2445 *Toll Free Tel:* 800-350-2445 *Fax:* 562-698-8972
E-mail: info@russbassett.com
Web Site: www.russbassett.com
Key Personnel
CEO & Pres: Mike Dressendorfer
Founded: 1960
Tape & media storage.
Catalog(s) available

Russ InVision Co/AbridgeClub.com
3219 Conquista Ave, Long Beach, CA 90808
Tel: 562-421-1836 *Toll Free Tel:* 888-421-7488 *Fax:* 562-420-9101
E-mail: info@abridgeclub.com
Web Site: abridgeclub.com
Key Personnel
Owner: Angela Russ-Ayon
Music & movement for young children.

Russ Meyer Charitable Trust, see RM Films International

Russell Industries Inc
40 Horton Ave, Lynbrook, NY 11563
Tel: 516-536-5000 *Toll Free Tel:* 800-645-2202 *Fax:* 516-764-5747 *Toll Free Fax:* 800-645-2200
E-mail: sales@russellind.com
Web Site: www.russellind.com
Key Personnel
Pres: Adam Russell
Sales Mgr: Neil Eiger
Distributor of rubber belts, phono needles & cartridges, fuses, bumpers & grommets, heat shrink tubing, velcro wire ties, cable clamps, split loom tubing & flyback transformers.
Catalog(s), free

Norman Russell Design
Member of The Sextant Group
5266 Hollister Ave, Suite 233, Santa Barbara, CA 93111
Tel: 805-964-9375 *Fax:* 805-964-9386
E-mail: normruss@normanrusselldesign.com
Web Site: www.normanrusselldesign.com
Key Personnel
Contact: Norman Russell *E-mail:* nrussell@thesextantgroup.com
Founded: 1978
Lighting consultation & design, fixtures & control equipment.

Russound
5 Forbes Rd, Newmarket, NH 03857
Tel: 603-659-5170 *Toll Free Tel:* 800-638-8055 (US) *Fax:* 603-659-5388
E-mail: sales@russound.com; tech@russound.com
Web Site: www.russound.com
Key Personnel
Owner: Maureen Baldwin
CEO: Charlie Porritt
Dir: Joe Brouillet
Intl Acct Mgr: Steve Dube *E-mail:* steved@russound.com
Founded: 1967
Membership(s): Consumer Electronics Association; Custom Electronic Design & Installation Association

RWD Productions Inc, see Video Advantage

S I Video Sales Group
1318 S Carlisle St, Philadelphia, PA 19146
Tel: 267-519-2222
Web Site: www.sivideo.com; www.capclassics.com; takinglasvegas.com
Key Personnel
Pres: Stan Nicotera *E-mail:* stann@sivideo.com
Produce & distribute educational programs as well as captioned classic movies, children's & sports programs.
Catalog(s) available
Membership(s): Music Business Association; NATPE

Saah Video
12221 Parklawn Dr, Rockville, MD 20852
Tel: 301-770-6699 *Toll Free Tel:* 800-225-9690 *Fax:* 301-770-3250
Web Site: www.saahvideo.com
Key Personnel
Owner: Richard Saah *E-mail:* richard@saahvideo.com
Catalog(s) available

Sabine® Inc
13301 US Hwy 441, Alachua, FL 32615-8544
Tel: 386-418-2000 *Toll Free Tel:* 800-626-7394 *Fax:* 386-418-2001
E-mail: sabine@sabine.com
Web Site: www.sabine.com
Key Personnel
Founder & Pres: Doran Oster
Dir, Mfg: Thomas Phelps
Founded: 1971
Manufacturer of professional audio DSP equipment.
CD-ROM catalog(s), biennial, upon request
Membership(s): AES; NAMM, the National Association of Music Merchants; NSCA

Sacramento Theatrical Lighting Ltd (STL)
950 Richards Blvd, Sacramento, CA 95811
Tel: 916-447-3258 *Toll Free Tel:* 800-283-2785 *Fax:* 916-447-5012
E-mail: info@stlltd.com
Web Site: www.stlltd.com
Key Personnel
Pres: John Cox
Sr Projs Mgr: Steve Odehnal *E-mail:* steveo@stlltd.com
Rentals: Marcus Daniel
Catalog(s) available
Membership(s): MCA-I; MPI; Professional Lighting & Sound Association; USITT

SADiE Inc
Division of Prism Media Products Inc
21 Pine St, Rockaway, NJ 07866
Tel: 973-983-9577 *Fax:* 973-983-9588
E-mail: sales@prismmpi.com
Web Site: www.sadie.com
Key Personnel
US Sales Mgr: Janice Norton *E-mail:* janice@prismmpi.com
CD Mastering & digital audio work stations.
Membership(s): AES; NAB

Safe Harbor Computers
530 W Oklahoma Ave, Suite 500, Milwaukee, WI 53207
Tel: 414-615-4560 *Toll Free Tel:* 800-544-6599 *Fax:* 414-615-4567
E-mail: sales@sharbor.com
Web Site: www.sharbor.com
Key Personnel
Mktg Coord: Marc Leitner *E-mail:* marc@sharbor.com
Founded: 1987
Computer hardware & software for video editing, post-production & animation. Custom TSUNAMI workstations. Authorized reseller for major brands including Apple, Avid, Adobe, AJA, Sony & more.

Safesongs 4 Kids, see SOS Worldwide Productions Inc

Sagebrush Video Productions
2304 County Rd 370, Otis, KS 67565
Tel: 785-222-3313 *Toll Free Tel:* 800-457-3453
Web Site: www.sagebrushvideo.com
Key Personnel
Owner: Rachel Harmon *E-mail:* rachel@sagebrushvideo.com
Founded: 1991

Sahara Records & Filmworks Entertainment Co
Division of The Edward De Miles Co
10573 W Pico Blvd, Suite 352, Los Angeles, CA 90064-2348
Tel: 310-948-9652
E-mail: info@edmsahara.com
Web Site: www.edmsahara.com
Key Personnel
CEO & Pres: Edward De Miles
Founded: 1984
Entertainment productions & services for film, television, radio & recording.

St Bede's Publications
Subsidiary of St Scholastica Priory Inc
271 N Main St, Petersham, MA 01366-9503
Mailing Address: PO Box 606, Petersham, MA 01366-0606
Tel: 978-724-3213
Key Personnel
Pres: Sister Mary Clare Vincent
Catalog(s), semiannual
Sales Office(s): Fordham University Press, University Box L, Bronx, NY 10458-5172, Contact: Margaret Noonan *Tel:* 718-817-4780 *Fax:* 718-817-4785 *Web Site:* www.fordhampress.com (sole distributor)
Shipping Address: New York University Press - NYUP, 838 Broadway, 3rd fl, New York, NY 10003 *Toll Free Tel:* 800-996-6987 *Fax:* 212-995-3833

Saint Elmo Soundstage
415 E St Elmo, Austin, TX 78745
Tel: 512-535-5113
E-mail: contact@saintelmo.info
Web Site: saintelmo.info
Soundstage for film, video, photography & music production.

Salesmaker Carts
403 Roberts Ave, Louisville, KY 40214
Toll Free Tel: 800-281-2278 *Toll Free Fax:* 800-418-2525
Web Site: www.salesmakercarts.com
Key Personnel
CEO: Nathan McKay *E-mail:* nathanm@salesmakercarts.com
Manufacture carts allowing one person to transport heavy or bulky equipment by vehicle.
Catalog(s) available

Charles M Salter Associates Inc
130 Sutter St, Suite 500, San Francisco, CA 94104
Tel: 415-397-0442 *Fax:* 415-397-0454
E-mail: info@cmsalter.com
Web Site: www.cmsalter.com
Key Personnel
Pres: Charles M Salter
SVP: Eric L Broadhurst; Philip N Sanders; Thomas Schindler; David R Schwind
VP: Anthony Nash

Principal Consultant: Thomas Corbett
Founded: 1975
Branch Office(s)
100 W San Fernando, Suite 430, San Jose, CA 95113 *Tel:* 408-295-4944 *Fax:* 408-295-4949
Membership(s): AES; Audio Publishers Association; NSCA; SMPTE

Steven Samler Music & Sound
1298 Green Knolls Dr, Buffalo Grove, IL 60089
Tel: 847-400-5080 *Fax:* 815-366-8227
Web Site: www.stevensamler.com
Key Personnel
Pres: Steven Samler *E-mail:* steve@stevensamler.com
Customization of music libraries & sound design.

Samson Technologies Corp
45 Gilpin Ave, Hauppauge, NY 11788-4723
Tel: 631-784-2200 *Fax:* 631-784-2201
E-mail: info@samsontech.com
Web Site: www.samsontech.com
Key Personnel
Pres: Scott Goodman
Dir, Mktg: Mark Menghi
Mktg Coord: Evan Hay
Founded: 1980
Catalog(s) available

Samsung Electronics America
Subsidiary of Samsung Electronics Co
85 Challenger Rd, Ridgefield Park, NJ 07660
Toll Free Tel: 800-SAMSUNG (726-7864) *Fax:* 864-752-1632
Web Site: www.samsung.com

The Samuels Co
Box 770874, Houston, TX 77215-0874
Tel: 281-564-1055 *Fax:* 530-420-4631
E-mail: staff@thesamuelsco.com
Web Site: www.thesamuelsco.com
Key Personnel
Pres: Ron Samuels *E-mail:* ron@samuels.net
Founded: 1985
Catalog(s) available

Samy's Camera
431 S Fairfax Ave, Los Angeles, CA 90036
Tel: 323-938-4400 *Toll Free Tel:* 800-321-4726 *Fax:* 323-937-2919
E-mail: lacamera@samys.com
Web Site: www.samys.com
Key Personnel
Owner: Samy Kamienowicz
VP: Hedy Kamienowicz
Mgr: Walter Erbe
Founded: 1976
Catalog(s) available
Branch Office(s)
12636 Beatrice St, Los Angeles, CA 90066 *Tel:* 310-450-7062
41 E Walnut St, Pasadena, CA 91103 *Tel:* 626-796-3300 *E-mail:* pasadena@samys.com
3309-B S Bristol St, Santa Ana, CA 92704, Mgr: Alan Bridgewater *Tel:* 714-557-9400 *E-mail:* infosa@samys.com
614 Chapala St, Santa Barbara, CA 93101 *Tel:* 805-963-7269 *Fax:* 805-963-4100 *E-mail:* infosb@samys.com
Membership(s): AICP

San Diego Stage & Lighting Supply Inc
2203 Verus St, San Diego, CA 92154
Tel: 619-299-2300 *Fax:* 619-299-0058
E-mail: info@sdstagelighting.com
Web Site: www.sdstagelighting.com
Key Personnel
Pres: Denise Doyle *E-mail:* denise@sdstagelighting.com
Founded: 1974

San Juan School District Heritage Language Resource Center
28 W 200 N, Blanding, UT 84511
Tel: 435-678-1230; 435-678-1229 *Fax:* 435-678-1283
Web Site: media.sjsd.org
Key Personnel
Media Center Coord: Rebecca Stoneman *E-mail:* rstoneman@sjsd.org
Sell Navajo & Ute language & culture curriculum materials.
Catalog(s) available

Sanako Inc
500 Linden Oaks, Rochester, NY 14625
Toll Free Tel: 888-611-4785 *Toll Free Fax:* 888-389-3858
E-mail: info@sanako.com
Web Site: www.sanako.com
Key Personnel
Busn Mgr: Paul Redhead
Mktg Mgr: Sylvie Hall *E-mail:* sylvie.hall@sanako.com
Multimedia labs, web based language labs & web based online learning.
Catalog(s) available
Branch Office(s)
18662 MacArthur Blvd, Suite 200, Irvine, CA 92612
Membership(s): AECT; AES; InfoComm International®; NAB

Sand Box Studio
555 Minnesota St, San Francisco, CA 94107
Tel: 415-550-8732
E-mail: inquiries@sandboxstudio.com
Web Site: www.sandboxstudio.com
Key Personnel
CEO & Mng Partner: Joe Barrett
COO: Kaly Minh-Nguyen Girot
Mng Partner: Matt Kwan; Charlie Maier; Tom Strollo
Founded: 1992
Facility rentals for photo or video production, consulting & post-production services.
Branch Office(s)
10016 Pioneer Blvd, No 106, Santa Fe Springs, CA 90670 *Tel:* 562-345-5335
250 Hudson St, 11th fl, New York, NY 10013 *Tel:* 212-924-4410
420 NE Ninth Ave, Portland, OR 97232 *Tel:* 503-501-5870

Sandusky Lee Corp
PO Box 6, Littlestown, PA 17340
Toll Free Tel: 800-233-7076 *Fax:* 717-359-4414
E-mail: customerserv@sanduskycabinets.com
Web Site: www.sanduskylee.com
Founded: 2003
Catalog(s) available
Branch Office(s)
PO Box 517, Arvin, CA 93203 *Tel:* 661-854-5551 *Toll Free Tel:* 800-336-0674 *Fax:* 661-854-2003
PO Box 125, Millington, TN 38053 *Tel:* 901-872-0188 *Toll Free Tel:* 800-264-3453 *Fax:* 901-873-1239
Sales Office(s): PO Box 1040, Sandusky, OH 44870 *Tel:* 419-626-5465 *Toll Free Tel:* 800-336-0671 *Fax:* 419-626-3308 *E-mail:* sales@sanduskycabinets.com

Sano Videos
Columbia Plaza, 2450 Virginia Ave NW, Suite E 322, Washington, DC 20037
Tel: 202-293-0454
Key Personnel
Owner: Louise Bedichek *E-mail:* lbedichek@gmail.com
Founded: 1991
Cultural Exchange Consultants.
Membership(s): American Foreign Service Association

Santa Barbara Location Services
403 Orilla del Mar, Unit 2, Santa Barbara, CA 93108
Tel: 805-969-5555; 805-565-1562 *Fax:* 805-969-9595
E-mail: production@sblsonline.com
Web Site: www.santabarbara-locations.com
Key Personnel
Owner & Creative Dir: Ronnie Haran Mellen
Founded: 1983
One stop preproduction services: scouting, management, permits, crew, locations, casting, production vans, catering & more.

Santa Clarita Studios
25135 Anza Dr, Santa Clarita, CA 91355
Tel: 661-294-2000 *Fax:* 661-294-2020
E-mail: mike@sc-studios.com
Web Site: www.santaclaritastudios.com
Full service independent studio with 10 sound stages.

SANYO Fisher Co
Division of SANYO North America Corp
2055 Sanyo Ave, San Diego, CA 92154
Tel: 619-661-1134 *Fax:* 619-661-6795
Web Site: us.sanyo.com; www.fisherav.com
Key Personnel
Credit Analyst: Jodi Slepicoff
Commercial Credit Supv: Carolyn Woo
Founded: 1937
Plasma & LCD screens.
Catalog(s) available
Membership(s): CEMA

SAPSIS Rigging Inc
233 N Lansdowne Ave, Lansdowne, PA 19050
Tel: 215-228-0888 *Toll Free Tel:* 800-SAPSIS-1 (727-7471) *Fax:* 215-228-1786
E-mail: sales@sapsis-rigging.com
Web Site: www.sapsis-rigging.com
Key Personnel
Owner & Pres: Bill Sapsis *E-mail:* bill@sapsis-rigging.com
Catalog(s) available
Branch Office(s)
3883 Ridge Ave, Philadelphia, PA 19132
Membership(s): ABTT; ETA; League of Historical American Theatres; Opera America; Professional Lighting & Sound Association; USITT

Sargent-Welch
Division of VWR International LLC
5100 W Henrietta Rd, Rochester, NY 14692-9012
Toll Free Tel: 800-727-4368 *Toll Free Fax:* 800-676-2540
E-mail: sargentwelchcs@vwr.com
Web Site: www.sargentwelch.com
Branch Office(s)
285 Garyray Dr, Toronto, ON M9L 1P3, Canada
Membership(s): Scientific Apparatus Makers Association

SAS Institute Inc
100 SAS Campus Dr, Cary, NC 27513-2414
Tel: 919-677-8000 *Toll Free Tel:* 800-727-0025 *Fax:* 919-677-4444
Web Site: www.sas.com
Key Personnel
CEO: Jim Goodnight
EVP: John Sall
EVP, SAS Americas: Carl Farrell
EVP, EMEA & AP: Mikael Hagstrom
SVP & Chief Mktg Offr: Jim Davis
SVP & CFO: Don Parker
SVP & CIO: Keith Collins

SVP, Chief Legal Offr & Corp Secy: John Boswell
VP, HR: Jennifer Mann
Founded: 1976
International offices throughout Africa, Asia/Pacific, Europe, Latin America, the Caribbean & the Middle East.
Branch Office(s)
Interstate Tower, Suite 2200, 121 W Trade St, Charlotte, NC 28202-5399 *Tel:* 704-831-5595 *Fax:* 704-831-5594
Jamboree Ctr, Suite 900, 5 Park Plaza, Irvine, CA 92614 *Tel:* 949-852-8550 *Fax:* 949-852-5277 (serves CA & OR)
6700 Koll Center Pkwy, Suite 120, Pleasanton, CA 94566-7032 *Tel:* 925-461-9490 *Fax:* 925-461-0925
Seaview Corporate Ctr, Suite 200, 10188 Telesis Ct, San Diego, CA 92121 *Tel:* 858-526-1502 *Fax:* 858-526-1579 (serves San Diego county)
Post Montgomery Ctr, 34th fl, One Montgomery St, San Francisco, CA 94104 *Tel:* 415-421-2227 *Fax:* 415-421-1213 (bldg entrance 120 Kearny St, serves northern CA)
95 Glastonbury Blvd, Suite 301, Glastonbury, CT 06033-4453 *Tel:* 860-633-4119 *Fax:* 860-633-4064
Southeast Financial Ctr, Suite 2900, 200 S Biscayne Blvd, Miami, FL 33131-2325 *Tel:* 305-381-9980 *Fax:* 305-381-8583
Atlanta Plaza, Suite 3200, 950 E Paces Ferry Rd NE, Atlanta, GA 30326 *Tel:* 404-814-2560 *Fax:* 404-814-2566 (serves GA)
2 Prudential Plaza, Suite 1600, 180 N Stetson St, Chicago, IL 60601 *Tel:* 312-819-6800 *Fax:* 312-240-0342 (serves IL, IN, IA & WI)
9401 Indian Creek Pkwy, Suite 600, Overland Park, KS 66210 *Tel:* 913-491-1166 *Fax:* 913-491-4194 (serves KS & Kansas City, MO)
111 Rockville Pike, Suite 1100, Rockville, MD 20850 *Tel:* 301-838-7030 *Fax:* 301-838-7410
Prudential Tower, Suite 2200, 800 Boylston St, Boston, MA 02199 *Tel:* 617-262-4201 *Fax:* 617-262-4253
Teragram Corp, a SAS company, 10 Fawcett St, Cambridge, MA 02138 *Tel:* 617-576-6800 ext 0 *Fax:* 617-576-6888
35 Village Rd, Suite 800, Middleton, MA 01949 *Tel:* 978-646-8100 *Fax:* 978-646-8110
IDeaS, a SAS company, 8500 Normandale Lake Blvd, Suite 1200, Bloomington, MN 55437 *Tel:* 952-698-4200 *Fax:* 952-698-4299
US Bancorp Ctr, Suite 2800, 800 Nicollet Mall, Minneapolis, MN 55402 *Tel:* 612-349-9023 *Fax:* 612-349-9349
787 Seventh Ave, 47th fl, New York, NY 10019 *Tel:* 212-757-3826 *Fax:* 212-757-4086
1550 Liberty Ridge Dr, Suite 110, Chesterbrook, PA 19087 *Tel:* 610-640-0940 *Fax:* 610-640-1488
One PPG Place, Suite 2950, Pittsburgh, PA 15222 *Tel:* 412-227-6446 *Fax:* 412-227-6596
Millennium I, 15455 N Dallas Pkwy, Suite 1300, Addison, TX 75001 *Tel:* 214-977-3916 *Fax:* 214-977-3921
11920 Wilson Parke Ave, Austin, TX 78726 *Tel:* 512-258-5171 *Fax:* 512-258-3906 (serves TX, LA, NM & OK)
1530 Wilson Blvd, Suite 800-900, Arlington, VA 22209 *Tel:* 571-227-7000 *Fax:* 571-227-7010
517-10 Ave SW, Suite 850, Calgary, AB T2R 0A8, Canada *Tel:* 403-265-5177 *Fax:* 403-265-5410
666 Burrard St, Suite 500, Vancouver, BC V6C 3P6, Canada *Tel:* 604-642-6136 *Fax:* 604-682-1347
Constitution Sq, Suite 1600, 360 Albert St, Ottawa, ON K1R 7X7, Canada *Tel:* 613-231-8503 *Fax:* 613-231-8526
SAS Institute (Canada) Inc, 280 King St E, Suite 500, Toronto, ON M5A 1K7, Canada *Tel:* 416-363-4424 *Fax:* 416-363-5399 (Canadian headquarters)
2001 McGill College Ave, Suite 1800, Montreal, QC H3A 1G1, Canada *Tel:* 514-395-8922 *Fax:* 514-395-8962
70, rue St-Pierre, Quebec, QC G1K 3Z9, Canada *Tel:* 418-380-8791 *Fax:* 418-694-0643

Sascom Marketing Group Inc
34 Nelson St, Oakville, ON L6L 3H6, Canada
Tel: 905-469-8080 *Fax:* 647-439-1510
Web Site: www.sascom.com
Key Personnel
Owner & Pres: Curt Smith *E-mail:* curtsmith.sascom@gmail.com
Founded: 1991
Catalog(s) available
Membership(s): AES; NAMM, the National Association of Music Merchants; SPARS

Satellite Center
2535 Williams Blvd, Kenner, LA 70062
Tel: 504-466-3474 *Toll Free Tel:* 800-256-4010
Web Site: satctr.com
Key Personnel
Pres: Dan Teachworth
Video Prodn: Tom Fitzgerald
Founded: 1984
Specialize in satellite reception systems for TV & radio stations.

Satellite Digital Teleproductions (SDTV)
4004 La Salle St, San Diego, CA 92110-5124
Tel: 619-293-7777 *Toll Free Tel:* 800-SKY-PROD (759-7763 US) *Fax:* 619-223-3626
E-mail: info@sdtv.com
Web Site: www.sdtv.com
Key Personnel
Pres: Mark Yancey

Satellite Media Production
8379 Inspiration Ave, Walkersville, MD 21793
Tel: 301-845-2737 *Toll Free Tel:* 800-747-0856
Web Site: www.satellitemediaproduction.com; www.oldietv.com
Key Personnel
Owner: Ellen Berney
Owner/Video Prodr: Fred Berney *E-mail:* fsberney@verizon.net
Founded: 1956
Video post-production. Reel-to-reel decks, DAT recorders, 16 inch turntable for transcription transfers, mini disc, CD, location recording, microphones & mixers, film, video & slide transfer to DVD, DVD duplicating, reel-to-reel tapes & audiocassette transfers to CD, digital recording.

Satellite Technology Systems Inc
4702 State Rte 176, Unit F, Crystal Lake, IL 60014
Tel: 815-482-0224 *Toll Free Tel:* 800-838-1472 *Fax:* 815-568-8478
E-mail: sts@mc.net
Web Site: www.satellitetechsys.com
Key Personnel
Owner: Charles Spoto *Tel:* 815-482-0224 (cell)
Founded: 1988
Satellite media tours, video production, global video conferencing, video news releases, uplink trucks, event photos.

Saturn Productions Inc
305 E 86 St, Suite 14-JW, New York, NY 10028
Tel: 212-348-7300 *Fax:* 212-426-7907
E-mail: saturnnyc@aol.com
Key Personnel
Pres: Tom Ward
Catalog(s) available

Saturn Studios
Subsidiary of Rock Dog Records
PO Box 3687, Hollywood, CA 90078-3687
Tel: 323-871-4134
Web Site: rollingplanet.com
Key Personnel
CEO: Patt Connolly *E-mail:* mrpatt2@yahoo.com
VP & Prodn Mgr: Gerald North Cannizzaro *E-mail:* gerry.cannizzaro@att.net
Founded: 1986
Audio & video recording, editing & mastering, CD-R & DVD-R recording & mastering equipment.
Online catalog(s) available
Branch Office(s)
Rock Dog Records/Saturn Studios East Coast Div, PO Box 884, Syosset, NY 11791-0884, Contact: Maria Cuccia *Tel:* 631-544-9596
Membership(s): Network of Alternatives for Publishers, Retailers & Artists Inc

Alwin Sauers Audio Productions (ASAP)
PO Box 50957, Oxnard, CA 93031
Tel: 206-484-6144
E-mail: alwinaudio@yahoo.com
Key Personnel
Owner & Engr: Alwin Sauers

Savage Universal Corp
550 E Elliot Rd, Chandler, AZ 85225
Tel: 480-632-1320 *Toll Free Tel:* 800-624-8891 *Fax:* 480-632-1322
Web Site: savageuniversal.com
Key Personnel
COO: Rich Reiser
Pres: Sylvester Hank
VP, Sales: Rich Memoli
Founded: 1937
Catalog(s) available
Membership(s): Photo Marketing Association

Savant Systems LLC
45 Perseverance Way, Hyannis, MA 02601
Tel: 508-683-2500 *Fax:* 508-683-2600
Web Site: www.savantsystems.com
Manufacture residential & commercial lighting control & automation systems.

Save the Children Federation Inc
54 Wilton Rd, Westport, CT 06880
Tel: 203-221-4030 *Toll Free Tel:* 800-728-3843
E-mail: twebster@savechildren.org
Web Site: www.savethechildren.org
Catalog(s) available
Branch Office(s)
2000 "L" St NW, Suite 500, Washington, DC 20036 *Tel:* 202-640-6600

SBS Productions
1646 Livonia Ave, Los Angeles, CA 90035
Tel: 310-557-1545
E-mail: eindigo2@pacbell.net
Key Personnel
SVP: Bunny Yates
Creative Dir: Jerry Rosenbloom
Catalog(s) available

SC Media Canada
2100 Onesime-Gagnon, Lachine, QC H8T 3M8, Canada
Tel: 514-780-0808 *Toll Free Tel:* 888-595-3966 *Fax:* 514-780-1604 *Toll Free Fax:* 800-790-2000
E-mail: information@scmediacanada.com
Web Site: www.scmediacanada.com
Key Personnel
VP, Sales & Mktg: Sami Midani
Founded: 1983
Distributor of professional audio, lighting & video products.

Scala Inc
350 Eagleview Blvd, Suite 350, Exton, PA 19341
Tel: 610-363-3350 *Toll Free Tel:* 888-SCALA-96 (722-5296) *Fax:* 610-363-4010

E-mail: marketing@scala.com
Web Site: scala.com
Key Personnel
CEO: Tom Nix
CFO: Jen Douglas
VP, Global Mktg: Harry Horn
Founded: 1987 (as Digital Vision AS)
Manufacture multimedia software.
Branch Office(s)
21800 Burbank Blvd, Suite 205, Woodland Hills, CA 91367 *Fax:* 818-878-6959
Foreign Office(s): Scala Digital Signage Services India Pvt Ltd, Navigator Bldg, Unit 1, Level 5, International Tech Park, Bangalore, Karnataka 560 066, India *Tel:* (080) 40806666
Scala KK, Gotanda Alpha Bldg, 10th fl, 2-29-9 Nishi-Gotanda, Shinagawa-ku, Tokyo 141-0031, Japan *Tel:* (03) 6417 9645 *Fax:* (03) 6417 9646
Amerikalaan 70B, Maastricht Airport, 6199 AE Maastricht, Netherlands *Tel:* (043) 35 88 300 *Fax:* (043) 35 88 301 *Web Site:* scala.nl
Scala Nordic AS, Vollsveien 13C, 1366 Lysaker, Norway *Tel:* 23 13 30 90 *Fax:* 23 13 30 91 *Web Site:* scala.com/no
Membership(s): InfoComm International®; NSCA; POPAI

Sceno Plus
5423 ave de Lorimier, Montreal, QC H2H 2C3, Canada
Tel: 514-529-4364 *Fax:* 514-529-9164
E-mail: project@sceno-plus.com
Web Site: www.sceno-plus.com
Key Personnel
COO: Lorraine Berthiaume
Pres: Patrick Berge
Founded: 1985
Performing arts & entertainment venue designer. Integration of specialized equipments & other scenic technology such as lighting & rigging design.
Membership(s): CITT; Professional Lighting & Sound Association; USITT

Schafer World Communications Corp
PO Box 1047, Marion, VA 24354-1047
Tel: 276-783-2000
Key Personnel
Pres: Bob Dix

Scheimpflug Digital
546 W 48 St, New York, NY 10036
Tel: 212-244-8300 *Fax:* 212-244-8769
E-mail: info@scheimpflug.net
Web Site: www.scheimpflug.net
Founded: 2004
Equipment rentals, digital services & trucks for independent filmmakers, commercials & still photographers.

Randall Schiller Productions
1207 Fifth Ave, San Francisco, CA 94122
Tel: 415-661-7553 *Fax:* 415-566-6238
E-mail: rsp7@pacbell.net
Web Site: www.randallschillerproductions.com
Key Personnel
Owner: Randy Schiller

Schiller's Audio-Visual
9240 Manchester Rd, St Louis, MO 63144-2636
Tel: 314-968-3650 *Toll Free Tel:* 800-366-7244 *Fax:* 314-968-1184
E-mail: sales@schillers.com; av@schillers.com
Web Site: www.schillersav.com
Key Personnel
Presentation Sales Mgr: David Wyne *Tel:* 314-968-3650 ext 110 *E-mail:* dwyne@schillers.com
Catalog(s) available
Branch Office(s)
10514 W 121 St, Overland Park, KS 66213 *Tel:* 913-814-0501 *Toll Free Tel:* 866-652-0501 *Fax:* 913-814-0027
Pilot Grove, MO *Tel:* 573-864-9092 *Toll Free Tel:* 877-536-4859 *Fax:* 660-834-6226
Sales Office(s): 1651 E Swallow St, Springfield, MO 65804 *Tel:* 417-890-0333 *Toll Free Tel:* 866-225-5779 *Fax:* 417-890-1101
Membership(s): InfoComm International®; MCA-I; Photo Marketing Association

Peter Schleger Co
200 Central Park S, Suite 27B, New York, NY 10019-1415
Tel: 212-245-4973
E-mail: schleger@nyc.rr.com

Schlessinger Media
Division of Library Video Co
PO Box 580, Wynnewood, PA 19096-0580
Tel: 610-645-4000 *Toll Free Tel:* 800-843-3620 *Fax:* 610-645-4040
E-mail: comments@libraryvideo.com
Web Site: www.libraryvideo.com
Key Personnel
Founder & CEO: Andrew Schlessinger
Founded: 1985
Catalog(s) available
Membership(s): ALA; Entertainment Merchants Association

Schneider Optics Inc
Subsidiary of Schneider-Kreuznach
285 Oser Ave, Hauppauge, NY 11788
Tel: 631-761-5000 *Toll Free Tel:* 800-645-7239 *Fax:* 631-761-5090
E-mail: info@schneideroptics.com
Web Site: www.schneideroptics.com
Key Personnel
CEO: Dwight Lindsey
Dir, Sales & Mktg: Barry Rubin
Sales Admin: Henry Greese *E-mail:* hgreese@schneideroptics.com
Founded: 1972
Manufacturer of high quality film lenses, video lenses & filters.
Brochure(s) available
Branch Office(s)
7701 Haskill Ave, Van Nuys, CA 91406-1906 *Tel:* 818-766-3715 *Toll Free Tel:* 800-228-1254 *Fax:* 818-505-9865
Membership(s): NAB; SMPTE

Schoeps, see Posthorn Recordings

Scholastic Canada Ltd
Subsidiary of Scholastic Inc
175 Hillmount Rd, Markham, ON L6C 1Z7, Canada
Tel: 905-887-7323 *Toll Free Tel:* 800-268-3860 *Fax:* 905-887-1131 *Toll Free Fax:* 800-387-4944
E-mail: custserv@scholastic.ca
Web Site: www.scholastic.ca
Key Personnel
Co-Pres: Linda Gosnell
Founded: 1957
Catalog(s) available

Scholastic Library Publishing
Division of Scholastic Inc
90 Sherman Tpke, Danbury, CT 06816
Toll Free Tel: 800-621-1115 (cust serv) *Toll Free Fax:* 866-783-4361
Web Site: www.scholastic.com/aboutscholastic/librarypublishing.htm
Key Personnel
Pres, Scholastic Classroom & Community Group: Greg Worrell
VP, Digital Initiatives: Evan St Lifer
Publishers of children's nonfiction & reference materials in print & online.
Catalog(s) available
Online catalog(s) available

Scholastic Media
Division of Scholastic Inc
557 Broadway, New York, NY 10012
Fax: 212-343-7592
Web Site: www.scholastic.com/aboutscholastic/librarypublishing.htm
Key Personnel
Pres: Deborah A Forte
Dir, Cust Care: Keith Bowles *Tel:* 212-343-7641
Catalog(s) available

School Media Associates LLC
5815 Live Oak Pkwy, Suite 2-B, Norcross, GA 30093-1700
Tel: 770-441-0600 *Toll Free Tel:* 800-451-5226 (orders) *Fax:* 770-441-8529
E-mail: info@smavideo.net
Web Site: www.smavideo.net
Key Personnel
Pres: Randy Kenworthy *E-mail:* rkenworthy@smavideo.net
Distributor of multimedia educational programming.
Catalog(s) available

School Specialty Inc
W6316 Design Dr, Greenville, WI 54942
Mailing Address: PO Box 1579, Appleton, WI 54912-1579
Tel: 419-589-1425 *Toll Free Tel:* 888-388-3224 *Fax:* 419-589-1600 *Toll Free Fax:* 888-388-6344
E-mail: internationalorders@schoolspecialty.com
Web Site: www.schoolspecialty.com
Key Personnel
VP, Mktg: Deb Burns
Distributor of educational AV needs.
Catalog(s) available
Branch Office(s)
School Specialty Canada, 20230 64 Ave, Unit 103, Langley, BC V2Y 1N3, Canada *Toll Free Tel:* 866-519-2816 *Toll Free Fax:* 800-775-0353 *E-mail:* info@schoolspecialty.ca *Web Site:* www.schoolspecialty.ca
Membership(s): Education Market Association; InfoComm International®

Schoolhouse Audio Visual
Division of Instructional Media Inc
1000 20 St, Plano, TX 75074
Tel: 972-423-5874 *Toll Free Tel:* 800-338-8116 *Fax:* 972-424-3501
E-mail: sav@schoolhouseav.com
Web Site: www.schoolhouseav.com
Key Personnel
Owner & Pres: D R Betts
Founded: 1974
Full service audio & visual distributor.
Catalog(s) available
Membership(s): InfoComm International®; NSCA

Schroder Music Co
PO Box 2067, Berkeley, CA 94702-0067
Tel: 510-843-0533 *Fax:* 510-834-5201
Web Site: www.sisterschoice.com
Key Personnel
Mgr: Ruth Pohlman
Contact: Nancy Schimmel *E-mail:* nancy@sisterschoice.com
Catalog(s) available

SCI Television Productions LLC
160 E Grand Ave, Suite 5W, Chicago, IL 60611
Tel: 312-643-2080
E-mail: info@scitvproductions.com
Web Site: www.scitvproductions.com

Key Personnel
Exec Prodr & Dir: Mark Traverso
E-mail: markt@scitvproductions.com
Prodn Coord: Valerie Kennedy
Founded: 1988
Membership(s): NATPE; Television Academy

Science First/STARLAB™
86475 Gene Lasserre Blvd, Yulee, FL 32097
Tel: 904-225-5558 *Toll Free Tel:* 800-875-3214
Fax: 904-225-2228
E-mail: starlab@starlab.com; info@starlab.com
Web Site: starlab.com
Founded: 2008
Portable planetariums.
Catalog(s) available
Membership(s): ASTC; IPS; MAPS; National Science Teachers Association

Science for Kids
1941 Brooke Dr, New Hope, PA 18938
Tel: 215-794-7718 *Fax:* 215-794-7718
Key Personnel
EVP: Charles Moyer
Founded: 1990
Catalog(s) available

Science Museum of Minnesota
120 W Kellogg Blvd, St Paul, MN 55102
Tel: 651-221-9444 *Toll Free Tel:* 800-221-9444
Fax: 651-221-4533
E-mail: info@smm.org
Web Site: www.smm.org
Key Personnel
Pres: Eric J Jolly, PhD
SVP, HR: Sarah Olson-Scovill
Producers & distributors of educational programs.

Science Seeking
705 Gurley Ave, Gallup, NM 87301
Tel: 505-863-7647
Web Site: fs.gallup.unm.edu
Online catalog(s) available
Branch Office(s)
Bell & Howell Co, 300 N Zeeb Rd, PO Box 1346, Ann Arbor, MI 48103-1553 *Toll Free Tel:* 800-521-0600 (book orders)
Foreign Office(s): University of Craiova, 13 Al I Cuza str, Craiova, Romania, Contact: Lon Patrascu

Science Television Co
460 W 24 St, Unit 3A, New York, NY 10011
Tel: 917-593-2537
E-mail: admin@scitv.com
Web Site: www.scitv.com
Key Personnel
Pres: Gary Welz
Producers & distributors of educational videos.
Catalog(s) available

Score Productions Inc
219 E 49 St, New York, NY 10017
Tel: 212-751-2510 *Fax:* 212-754-6305
E-mail: score@scoreproductions.com
Web Site: www.artgraphica.com/preview/ScoreProductions/index.html
Key Personnel
Pres: Robert Israel
EVP: Gary Anderson
Founded: 1963
Musical scoring company.
Branch Office(s)
9601 Wilshire Blvd, Suite 850, Los Angeles, CA 90210 *Tel:* 310-278-6188 *Fax:* 310-278-6055

Scott Resources Inc
Division of American Educational Products LLC
401 Hickory St, Fort Collins, CO 80524-1125
Mailing Address: PO Box 2121, Fort Collins, CO 80522-2121
Tel: 970-484-7445 *Toll Free Tel:* 800-289-9299
Fax: 970-484-1198
E-mail: custserv@amep.com
Web Site: amep.com
Key Personnel
Pres: Michael Warring
Natl Sales & Mktg Mgr: Candace Coffman
Sales Mgr: Katie Dugan
Producers of educational mathematics programs.
Catalog(s) available

Ron Scott Inc
2020 Colquitt St, Houston, TX 77098
Web Site: www.ronscott.com; www.qfx.com
Key Personnel
Pres: Ron Scott *E-mail:* ron@ronscott.com
Image editing software: QFX & commercial photography.

Screen Door Entertainment Inc
PO Box 1002, Agoura Hills, CA 91376
Tel: 818-781-5600
E-mail: info@sdetv.com
Web Site: www.sdetv.com
Key Personnel
Pres & Exec Prodr: Joel Rizor
Founded: 2001
TV & video production company. Full service production & post-production with all broadcast & non-broadcast video production.

The Screen Works®
2201 W Fulton St, Chicago, IL 60612
Tel: 312-243-8265 *Toll Free Tel:* 800-294-8111
Fax: 312-243-8290
E-mail: screens@thescreenworks.com
Web Site: www.thescreenworks.com
Key Personnel
Sales Mgr: David Hull *E-mail:* davidh@thescreenworks.com
Founded: 1959
Manufactures, sells, rents & distributes presentation products & AV equipment. Products include portable projection screens, wide screen & HDTV surface. Accessories include pipe & drape, trim kits, screen surface cleaning, frame repair & modular scenic systems. Custom screens available.
Catalog(s) available
Branch Office(s)
5280 S Valley View Blvd, Suite K, Las Vegas, NV 89118 *Tel:* 702-483-7758
E-mail: swregion@thescreenworks.com
Membership(s): InfoComm International®

Scripps Networks
Division of Scripps Networks Interactive
9721 Sherrill Blvd, Knoxville, TN 37932
Mailing Address: PO Box 51850, Knoxville, TN 37950
Tel: 865-694-2700 *Fax:* 865-693-6576
Web Site: www.scrippsnetworks.com
Key Personnel
Pub Aff Mgr: Stephanie Halouma
E-mail: publicaffairs@scrippsnetwork.com
Television production company.
Membership(s): MCA-I

Scriptware
100 Technology Dr, Suite 315C, Broomfield, CO 80021
Tel: 303-786-7899 *Toll Free Tel:* 800-788-7090 (orders) *Fax:* 303-786-9292
E-mail: info@scriptware.com
Web Site: www.scriptware.com
Key Personnel
CEO & Pres: Steven Sashen
Founded: 1992
Brochure(s) available

Roger Scruggs Films
PO Box 321054, Cocoa Beach, FL 32932-1054
Tel: 321-783-6545 (off); 321-795-6545 (cell)
Web Site: www.tvphotog.com
Key Personnel
Owner: Roger Scruggs *E-mail:* scruggs@tvphotog.com
Videography, photography & cinematography services.
Belongs to both the Brevard Aviation Association & the Experimental Aircrafts Association.
Brochure(s) available
Online catalog(s) available
Membership(s): International Alliance of Theatrical Stage Employees

SDI Technologies Inc
1299 Main St, Rahway, NJ 07065
Tel: 732-574-9000 *Toll Free Tel:* 800-333-3092; 800-888-4491 (cust serv)
Web Site: www.sditechnologies.com; www.ihomeaudio.com
Key Personnel
VP, Mktg: Evan Stein
Founded: 1956
Manufacture & distribute CD players, clock radios, ipod accessories & speaker systems.

Sea Studios Foundation
PO Box 267, Carmel Valley, CA 93924
E-mail: info@seastudios.org; jete@seastudios.org
Web Site: www.seastudios.org
Key Personnel
Exec Prodr: Mark Shelley
Developers of educational television programs.
Catalog(s) available

SeaChange International Inc
50 Nagog Park, Acton, MA 01720
Tel: 978-897-0100 *Fax:* 978-897-0132
Web Site: www.schange.com
Key Personnel
CEO: Raghu Rau
Communs & PR: Jim Sheehan *Tel:* 978-889-3064
E-mail: jim.sheehan@schange.com
Digital multimedia distributing & manufacturing.
Catalog(s) available
Branch Office(s)
890 Hillview Ct, Suite 300, Milpitas, CA 95035
Tel: 408-519-2900 *Fax:* 408-519-2901
1200 NW Naito Pkwy, Suite 210, Portland, OR 97209 *Tel:* 503-228-1140 *Fax:* 503-228-1105
1075 Virginia Dr, Suite 300, Fort Washington, PA 19034 *Tel:* 215-654-8600 *Fax:* 215-654-8698
Membership(s): Interactive Multimedia Association

Seaport Graphics
12 Channel St, Suite 802, Boston, MA 02210
Tel: 617-330-1200 *Fax:* 617-330-1222
E-mail: jobs@seaportgraphics.com
Web Site: www.seaportgraphics.com
Key Personnel
Owner & Pres: Michael Labadie
Sales Mgr: Beth Alvarez
Founded: 1982
Graphic design company.
Brochure(s) available

Sear Sound
353 W 48 St, 6th fl, New York, NY 10036
Tel: 212-582-5380 *Fax:* 212-581-2731
E-mail: waltersear@aol.com
Web Site: www.searsound.com
Key Personnel
Mgr: Roberta Findlay
Chief Engr: Chris Allen *E-mail:* chris@searsound.com
Engr: Ted Tuthill
Founded: 1963
Recording studios - digital & analog. Garritan sound library.

Catalog(s) available
Membership(s): AES; SPARS

2nd Cine
1035 Donna Dr, Belvidere, IL 61008
Tel: 773-398-1452
E-mail: info@2ndcine.com
Web Site: www.2ndcine.com
Key Personnel
Owner: Thomas S Ciciura
Specialize in providing camera & lighting production services for small to medium independent commercial productions for TV or web.

Second Line Stages
800 Richard St, New Orleans, LA 70130
Tel: 504-528-3050
E-mail: info@secondlinestages.com
Web Site: secondlinestages.com
Founded: 2009
Rental of soundstages where operations are designed to enable cleaner, smarter, more responsible physical production practices. Built to comply with the US Green Building Council's LEED Silver Certification standard.

See Factor Industry Inc
37-11 30 St, Long Island City, NY 11101
Tel: 718-784-4200 *Fax:* 718-784-0617
Web Site: www.seefactor.com
Key Personnel
CFO & Pres: Robert See *E-mail:* bobsee@seefactor.com
EVP: Mark Friedman *E-mail:* mfriedman@seefactor.com
Lighting, sound & production company.

See Production Services
3330 Cobb Pkwy, Suite 17-327, Acworth, GA 30101
Tel: 404-474-4416
E-mail: info@seeproductionservices.com
Web Site: seeproductionservices.com
Key Personnel
Owner: Eason Duncan *E-mail:* eason@seeproductionservices.com
Offers full service teleprompting, video assist & camera equipment rental.

SEK'D™ America
1155 N La Brea Ave, West Hollywood, CA 90038
Tel: 323-845-1171 *Toll Free Tel:* 800-330-7753 (orders) *Fax:* 323-845-1170
E-mail: sales@plus24.net
Web Site: www.sekd.com
Founded: 1992
Catalog(s) available

Sekonic
Division of MAC Group
75 Virginia Rd, North White Plains, NY 10603
Tel: 914-347-3300 *Fax:* 914-347-3309
E-mail: info@macgroupus.com
Web Site: www.sekonic.com; www.macgroupus.com
Key Personnel
Pres: Mr Jan Lederman *E-mail:* janl@macgroupus.com
Catalog(s) available

Selco Products Co
Division of Sel Sales Inc
8780 Technology Way, Reno, NV 89521-5908
Toll Free Tel: 877-807-5426 *Fax:* 775-674-5111
E-mail: sales@selcoproducts.com
Web Site: www.selcoproducts.com
Key Personnel
CEO: Timothy Wilkinson
COO & Pres: James Reed
Founded: 1958
Catalog(s) available

Selden Associates
150 S Mountain Ave, Montclair, NJ 07042
Tel: 973-746-0421 *Fax:* 973-509-1498
Key Personnel
CEO: Charles J Selden *E-mail:* charles.selden@mac.com
Freelance writing & scripting services.

Select Media Inc
333 Hudson St, 4th fl, New York, NY 10013
Tel: 212-925-9101 *Toll Free Tel:* 800-707-6334 *Fax:* 212-925-9102
E-mail: info@selectmedia.org
Web Site: www.selectmedia.org
Key Personnel
Proj Mgr: Mika Keegstra *E-mail:* mika@selectmedia.org
Distributors of health education media for youth.
Catalog(s) available

Semiconductor Services
2269 Chestnut St, No 735, San Francisco, CA 94123
Tel: 650-369-7890 *Fax:* 415-346-8099
E-mail: moreinfo@semiconductorservices.com
Web Site: www.semiconductorservices.com
Key Personnel
Pres: Anne Miller *E-mail:* amiller@semiconductorservices.com
Cust Serv: Robinie Lhyne
Founded: 1981
Training resource company.
Catalog(s) available

Semtech
Division of Semtech Corp
4281 Harvester Rd, Burlington, ON L7L 5M4, Canada
Mailing Address: PO Box 489, Sta A, Burlington, ON L7R 3Y3, Canada
Tel: 905-632-2996 *Fax:* 905-632-2055
E-mail: corporate@gennum.com
Web Site: www.semtech.com
Design analog, optical & mixed signal semiconductors for use with video broadcasts, data communications & consumer connecting products.
Catalog(s) available
Branch Office(s)
Snowbush IP, 439 University Ave, Suite 1700, Toronto, ON M5G 1Y8, Canada *Tel:* 416-925-5643 *Web Site:* www.snowbush.com
Foreign Office(s): Nirmala Plaza, No 208-A, Airport Rd, Forest Park Sq, Bhubaneswar 751009, India *Tel:* (0674) 653-4815 *Fax:* (0674) 259-5733
Shinjuku Green Tower Bldg 27-F, 6-14-1, Nishi Shinjuku, Shinjuku-ku Tokyo 160-0023, Japan *Tel:* (03) 3349-5501 *Fax:* (03) 3349-5505 *E-mail:* gennum-japan@gennum.com *Web Site:* www.gennum.co.jp
2 West Point Ct, Great Park Rd, Bradley Stoke, Bristol BS32 4PY, United Kingdom *Tel:* (01454) 462200 *Fax:* (01454) 462201
Shipping Address: 3150 Harvester Rd, Burlington, ON L7N 3W8, Canada
Membership(s): NAB; SMPTE

Sencore Inc
3200 Sencore Dr, Sioux Falls, SD 57107
Tel: 605-978-4600 *Toll Free Tel:* 800-SENCORE (736-2673) *Fax:* 605-335-6379
E-mail: info@sencore.com
Web Site: www.sencore.com
Key Personnel
CFO: Joe Radzak
Pres: Thomas Stingley
Founded: 1951
Designers & manufacturers of innovative electronic test equipment.
CD-ROM catalog(s), free
Branch Office(s)
10333 E Dry Creek Rd, Suite 270, Englewood, CO 80112 *Tel:* 303-790-9589
Membership(s): ATSC; Custom Electronic Design & Installation Association; NAB; NESDA; SCTE

The Mack Sennett Studios
1215 Bates Ave, Los Angeles, CA 90029
Tel: 323-660-8466
E-mail: info@macksennettstage.com
Web Site: www.macksennettstage.com
Key Personnel
Pres & Prodr: Jesse Rogg *E-mail:* jesse@macksennettstudios.net
Founded: 1916

Sennheiser (Canada) Inc
221 ave Labrosse, Pointe Claire, QC H9R 1A3, Canada
Tel: 514-426-3013 *Toll Free Tel:* 800-463-1006 *Fax:* 514-426-3953 *Toll Free Fax:* 800-463-3013
E-mail: info@sennheiser.ca
Web Site: www.sennheiser.ca
Key Personnel
Pres: Jean Langlais
Busn Dir, Consumer Div: Nadine Girard
Busn Dir, Music Prods, Neuman Prods: Nick Mandilaras *Tel:* 514-426-3013 ext 2200
Busn Dir, Pro Audio & Conference Systems Prods: Frederick Girard *Tel:* 514-426-3013 ext 2100
Mktg Dir: Roseline Boire
Mktg Coord: Linda Bisson; Charles Boisvert
Admin Asst, HR: Colette Groleau *E-mail:* groleauc@sennheiser.ca

Sennheiser Electronic Corp
Subsidiary of Sennheiser (Canada) Inc
One Enterprise Dr, Old Lyme, CT 06371
Tel: 860-434-9190 *Toll Free Tel:* 877-SENNHEISER (736-6434) *Fax:* 860-434-1759
E-mail: info@sennheiserusa.com
Web Site: en-us.sennheiser.com
Key Personnel
Pres: Greg Beebe
Media & Campaign, Proj Mgr: Rachel Smolin
Founded: 1945 (as Laboratorium Wennebostel)
Distribute microphones, headphones, recording media, loudspeakers, conferencing systems, assisted listening devices, audio-tour equipment & software.
Catalog(s) available

Sensaphone
901 Tryens Rd, Aston, PA 19014
Tel: 610-558-2700 *Toll Free Tel:* 877-373-2700 *Fax:* 610-558-0222
E-mail: sales@sensaphone.com
Web Site: www.sensaphone.com
Catalog(s) available

Sensormatic®
Division of Tyco
6600 Congress Ave, Boca Raton, FL 33487
Tel: 561-912-6000 *Toll Free Tel:* 800-507-6268
Web Site: www.tyco.com; www.sensormatic.com
Key Personnel
Off Mgr: Cheryl Madison
Design, manufacture & service electronic article surveillance systems.
Catalog(s) available
Membership(s): American Society for Industrial Security

Sensory Technologies LLC
Division of Markey's Audio Visual
6951 Corporate Circle, Indianapolis, IN 46278

Tel: 317-347-5252 *Toll Free Tel:* 800-488-4336 (help desk) *Fax:* 317-347-5262
E-mail: sales@sensorytechnologies.com
Web Site: sensorytechnologies.com
Key Personnel
Mng Principal: Anne Sellers
Principal: Kevin Markey; Derek Paquin *E-mail:* dpaquin@sensorytechnologies.com; Andrew Sellers *E-mail:* asellers@sensorytechnologies.com
Founded: 1999
AV & videoconference solutions provider. Design, sales, installation & support of AV systems.
Online catalog(s) available
Branch Office(s)
1811 Production Rd, Fort Wayne, IN 46808 *Tel:* 260-483-3023
1890 S Elmhurst Rd, Mount Prospect, IL 60056 *Tel:* 847-258-4165 *Fax:* 847-480-7364
5335 Springboro Pike, Suite E, Dayton, OH 45439 *Tel:* 937-746-4670
Membership(s): InfoComm International®; NSCA

Sentry Industries Inc
One Bridge St, Hillburn, NY 10931-0885
Mailing Address: PO Box 885, Hillburn, NY 10931-0885
Tel: 845-753-2910 *Fax:* 845-753-2920
E-mail: techsupport@sentryindustries.com
Web Site: www.sentryindustries.com
Key Personnel
Owner: Daniel Rosen
Sales Mgr: James Staropoli *E-mail:* jstaropoli@sentryindustries.com
Founded: 1963
Manufacturer & distributor of audio equipment.
Catalog(s) available

Serendipity Recordings
511 Slab City Rd, Lincolnville, ME 04849
Tel: 207-763-3677
Key Personnel
Owner: Michael Paul Lund
Founded: 1972
Nostalgia of all kinds in CD, record & DVD formats. Voice overs for radio/TV. Service radio & television stations as well as general public.
Catalog(s) available

Service Quality Institute
9201 E Bloomington Fwy, Minneapolis, MN 55420-3437
Tel: 952-884-3311 *Toll Free Tel:* 800-548-0538 *Fax:* 952-884-8901
E-mail: quality@servicequality.com
Web Site: www.customer-service.com
Key Personnel
Pres: John Tschohl
Founded: 1972
Design & produce customer service video training programs.
Catalog(s) available
Membership(s): NSA

Servoreeler Systems
Unit of Xedit Corp
218-31 97 Ave, Queens Village, NY 11429
Tel: 718-464-9400 *Toll Free Tel:* 800-431-8900
E-mail: srsystems@servoreelers.com
Web Site: www.servoreelers.com
Key Personnel
Pres: Claude M Karczmer
Dir, Sales: Eileen Karczmer
Suspended microphones cable reelers.

SES World Skies
Division of SES SA
4 Research Way, Princeton, NJ 08540
Tel: 609-987-4000; 609-987-4200 *Fax:* 609-987-4517
E-mail: info@ses.com
Web Site: www.ses.com
Key Personnel
CEO & Pres: Romain Bausch
CFO: Andrew Browne
CTO: Padraig McCarthy
Chief Commercial Offr: Ferdinand Kayser
Chief Devt Offr: Gerson Souto
Founded: 1997
Global provider of end-to-end managed network solutions via fiber & satellite. Verestar provides reliable & flexible transport options for the distribution of video content. Video, data & voice communications. Broadcast services include full-time & occasional-use services, videoconferencing & business TV support, tape playback & record, video standards conversion & encryption & encoding.
Catalog(s) available
Branch Office(s)
1129 20 St NW, Suite 100, Washington, DC 20036 *Tel:* 202-478-7100
Membership(s): NAB; World Teleport Association

Sescom Inc
PO Box 720, Mount Marion, NY 12456
Tel: 845-246-1915 *Fax:* 845-246-0626
E-mail: info@sescom.com
Web Site: www.sescom.com
Key Personnel
Dir: Jon Fitzer *E-mail:* jon@sescom.com
Founded: 1975
Manufacturer of high quality audio products & enclosures.

The Set Shop
Subsidiary of Lidderdale Enterprises Inc
428 Colyton St, Los Angeles, CA 90013
Tel: 213-680-1668 *Fax:* 213-680-4269
Web Site: www.thesetshop.tv
Key Personnel
Owner: William Lidderdale *Tel:* 310-486-1741 (cell) *E-mail:* wlidderdale@altrionet.com
Founded: 1999
Entertainment construction (sets & props), art department, set & prop construction, installation, filming location/studio.

Set To Go Studios
86 Lackawana Ave, Suite 235, Woodland Park, NJ 07424
Tel: 973-638-1646
E-mail: settogostudio@gmail.com
Web Site: www.settogostudio.com
Key Personnel
Pres: Dale Kolarek
Professional shooting stage with 30+ beautifully furnished, ready-to-shoot sets for video, film & still photography.

Setcom Corp™
3019 Alvin De Vane Blvd, Suite 560, Austin, TX 78741
Tel: 650-965-8020 *Fax:* 650-965-1193
E-mail: info@setcomcorp.com; sales@setcomcorp.com
Web Site: www.setcomcorp.com
Key Personnel
Mktg Mgr: Ryan Giroir *E-mail:* rg@setcomcorp.com
Founded: 1970
Manufacturer of headphones, headsets & radio equipment.
Catalog(s) available

SevenStar Communications
13315 W Washington Blvd, Suite 200, Los Angeles, CA 90066
Toll Free Tel: 800-578-9526 (orders) *Fax:* 310-302-1208
E-mail: info@taostar.com
Web Site: www.taostar.com
Key Personnel
Publr: Dr Mao Shing Ni
Producers & distributors of educational programs.
Catalog(s) available

SF Global Sourcing
1000 Sansome St, Suite 280, San Francisco, CA 94111
Tel: 415-288-9400 *Toll Free Tel:* 855-SF-GLOBAL (734-5622) *Fax:* 415-288-9410
E-mail: info@sfglobalsourcing.com
Web Site: www.sfglobalsourcing.com
Key Personnel
CEO: Steven Feinberg *E-mail:* steven@sfglobalsourcing.com
EVP: Michael Brandon *E-mail:* michael@sfglobalsourcing.com
VP: Stan Feinberg *E-mail:* stan@sfglobalsourcing.com
Sr Acct Mgr: Sue Coakley *E-mail:* sue@sfglobalsourcing.com
Founded: 1990
Product sourcing experts committed to creating the greatest perceived value with the lowest cost of goods. Specialize in large volume DVD, CD & Blu-ray replication, media replication printing, packaging & fulfillment as well as the ability to source all ancillary products to round out an offer. Global manufacturing capabilities include the US, China & Europe.
Foreign Office(s): 668 Huai An Rd, Suite 5E, Shanghai 200041, China
Membership(s): Direct Marketing Association; Electronic Retailing Association; Northern California Production Community

SGW Teleprompter Solutions Inc
844 Eighth Ave, La Grange, IL 60525-2949
Tel: 773-402-0105 *Fax:* 708-482-9159
E-mail: teleprompter@sbcglobal.net
Web Site: teleprompter solutions.com
Key Personnel
Pres: Sean Graham-White
Teleprompter rental. Camera mount & executive speech teleprompters. Exclusive Stroll & Scroll teleprompter for hand-held camera & steadicam use. Interatron.
Membership(s): International Alliance of Theatrical Stage Employees

Shadow Pictures Inc
319 Sixth Ave, No 4-F, New York, NY 10014
Tel: 212-929-8906; 917-545-9870
E-mail: info@shadowpictures.com
Web Site: www.shadowpictures.com; laurabelsey.com
Key Personnel
Dir: Laura Belsey
Film & commercial production & post-production.

Shadow Play Records & Video
Division of Educational Graphics Press Inc
8127 Mesa Dr, Suite B206-277, Austin, TX 78759
Mailing Address: PO Box 180476, Austin, TX 78718-0476
Tel: 512-349-9962 *Toll Free Tel:* 800-274-8804 *Fax:* 512-345-9515
Web Site: www.hellojoe.com
Key Personnel
Pres: Peter Markham *E-mail:* pete@hellojoe.com
Catalog(s) available

Shadowbox Video Productions
304 Westfield Dr, North Little Rock, AR 72118
Tel: 501-374-3322
E-mail: info@shadowboxvideo.com
Web Site: shadowboxvideo.com
Key Personnel
Owner: James L Linsley *E-mail:* jim@shadowboxvideo.com

Founded: 1995
Full service video/feature film production.

Shadowstone R & R™
813 Silver Spring Ave, Silver Spring, MD 20910
Tel: 301-589-4997 *Fax:* 301-565-5156
Web Site: www.shadowstone.com
Key Personnel
CEO: Frank Marsico *E-mail:* frank@shadowstone.com
Off Mgr: Bill Robertson
Professional lighting equipment rental & sales.
Catalog(s) available

Shaker Microphones & Promotions Inc
PO Box 1070, Diamond City, AR 72630-1070
Tel: 870-422-2988
E-mail: shakermicrophone@shakermicrophone.net
Web Site: www.shakermicrophone.net
Key Personnel
Owner: Joe Harless
Founded: 1992
Build microphones for harmonica players (dynamic & crystal types) as well as recording microphones for resonator guitars.

Shakticom
Division of Satchidananda Ashram-Yogaville
108 Yogaville Way, Buckingham, VA 23921
Tel: 434-969-1347 *Toll Free Tel:* 800-476-1347 (orders)
E-mail: shop@shakticom.org
Web Site: www.shakticom.org
Key Personnel
Owner: Satchidananda Ashram
Yoga AV production.
Catalog(s) available

Shambhala Publications
Horticultural Hall, 300 Massachusetts Ave, Boston, MA 02115
Tel: 617-424-0030; 978-829-2599 (intl orders) *Toll Free Tel:* 888-424-2329 (orders & cust serv) *Fax:* 617-236-1563
E-mail: editors@shambhala.com
Web Site: www.shambhala.com
Founded: 1969
Premier publisher of books on Buddhism & classics of the wisdom traditions.

Shamrock Communications
200 Tornillo Way, Suite 110, Tinton Falls, NJ 07712
Tel: 732-686-1140 *Fax:* 732-686-1148
E-mail: info@shamrockcommunications.com
Web Site: www.shamrockcommunications.com
Key Personnel
Pres: Mr Pat Scanlon
Dir, Fin: Jamye Scanlon
Prodn Coord & Staff Ed: Janet Malik Dorgan
Busn Devt: Noreen Miller
Video production studio rental. Web site, business & corporate video production services.

Shanachie Entertainment Corp
37 E Clinton St, Newton, NJ 07860
Tel: 973-579-7763
Web Site: shanachie.com
Key Personnel
Founder & Pres: Richard Nevins
VP, Publicity: Monifa Brown
Gen Mgr: Randall Grass
Prodn Mgr: Linda Cilurso
Founded: 1975
Music label production company.
Catalog(s) available
Membership(s): Entertainment Merchants Association; Music Business Association; SNA

Shanix Inc
40 Worthington Rd, Cranston, RI 02920
Tel: 401-941-4222 *Toll Free Tel:* 800-783-2067 *Fax:* 401-941-4333
E-mail: info@shanix.com
Web Site: www.shanix.com
Key Personnel
VP: Mustapha Gharaee
Proj Mgr: Jeff Budzinski
AV systems integrators.

Shapeshifter
3405 Cahuenga Blvd W, Los Angeles, CA 90068
Tel: 323-876-3444 *Fax:* 323-876-1444
E-mail: sales@shapeshifterpost.com
Web Site: www.shapeshifterpost.com
Key Personnel
Pres: Russo Anastasio
Founded: 1999
Post-production for TV, DVDs & films. HD & audio mixing.

Steve Shapiro Music
7777 Skyline Blvd, Oakland, CA 94611
Tel: 510-339-7930
Web Site: www.stevemusic.com
Key Personnel
Owner: Steve Shapiro *E-mail:* steve@stevemusic.com
Founded: 1980

Sharp Electronics Corp, Professional Display Division
Subsidiary of Sharp Corp (Osaka, Japan)
One Sharp Plaza, Mahwah, NJ 07495-1163
Tel: 201-529-8200 *Fax:* 201-529-8425
E-mail: prolcd@sharpsec.com
Web Site: www.sharpusa.com
Key Personnel
Dir, B2B Channel Mktg & CRM: Dan Wynne
Dir, Prod Mgmt: Shane Coffey
Founded: 1962
Catalog(s) available
Membership(s): InfoComm International®

Sharp's Audio-Visual Ltd
3636 Seventh St SE, Calgary, AB T2G 2Y8, Canada
Tel: 403-255-4123 *Toll Free Tel:* 800-491-1121 *Fax:* 403-255-3478
E-mail: sales@sharpsav.com
Web Site: www.sharpsav.com
Key Personnel
CEO & Pres: Jeff Faber
EVP, Sales & Mktg: Tim St Louis
HR Mgr: Judy Iwacha
Founded: 1923
Produce digital signage.
Catalog(s) available
Branch Office(s)
10548 106 St NW, Edmonton, AB T5H 2X6, Canada *Tel:* 780-944-0815 *Fax:* 780-944-9929
3830 First Ave, Burnaby, BC V5C 3W1, Canada *Tel:* 604-877-1400 *Fax:* 604-877-0640
1950 Government St, Suite 12, Victoria, BC V8T 4N8, Canada *Tel:* 250-385-3458 *Fax:* 250-381-2626
201 Brownlow Ave, Unit 58, Halifax, NS B3B 1W2, Canada *Tel:* 902-492-7661 *Fax:* 902-492-1913
500 Cochrane Dr, Unit 1, Markham, ON L3R 8E2, Canada *Tel:* 905-415-1333 *Fax:* 905-737-8109
4145 Autoroute des Laurentides, Laval, QC H7L 5W5, Canada *Tel:* 450-686-4583 *Fax:* 450-686-4584
405 Circle Dr E, Suite 11, Saskatoon, SK S7K 4B4, Canada *Tel:* 306-244-2166 *Fax:* 306-244-2133
Membership(s): InfoComm International®; NSCA

Brad Shaw Productions Inc
9950 Roan Meadows Dr, Boise, ID 83709
Tel: 208-362-5500
Web Site: bradshawproductions.com
Key Personnel
Pres: Brad W Shaw *E-mail:* brad@bradshawproductions.com
Founded: 1993
Film & video production & services to promote, train & inform.
Brochure(s) available
Membership(s): Idaho Film & Video Association

Shaw Street Productions
51 Halton St, Unit 127, Toronto, ON M6J 1R5, Canada
Tel: 416-588-9443
E-mail: info@shawstreetpro.com
Web Site: www.shawstreetpro.com
Key Personnel
Pres: Philip Pellat *E-mail:* ppellat@shawstreetpro.com

The Fulton J Sheen Co Inc
73 State St, Rochester, NY 14614
Tel: 585-232-1150 *Toll Free Tel:* 866-357-4336
Web Site: www.bishopsheen.com
Catalog(s) available

Sheffield Audio/Video Productions
Subsidiary of The Sheffield Institute for the Recording Arts
13816 Sunnybrook Rd, Phoenix, MD 21131
Tel: 410-628-7260 *Toll Free Tel:* 800-355-6613 *Fax:* 410-628-1977
E-mail: info@sheffieldav.com
Web Site: www.sheffieldav.com/production
Key Personnel
Owner: John Ariosa *E-mail:* john@sheffieldav.com
Pres: Richard "Vance" Van Horne *E-mail:* vance@sheffieldav.com
Founded: 1968
Full service AV production company.

Shelburne Films
54545 SR 681, Reedsville, OH 45772
Mailing Address: PO Box 6, Reedsville, OH 45772-0006
Tel: 740-378-6297
E-mail: info@shelburnefilms.com
Web Site: www.shelburnefilms.com
Key Personnel
Pres: David Shelburne
VP & Mktg Dir: Ellen Shelburne *E-mail:* ellen@shelburnefilms.com
Film & video producers & distributors.
Catalog(s) available
Membership(s): MCA-I

Shen Milsom & Wilke LLC
417 Fifth Ave, New York, NY 10016
Tel: 212-725-6800 *Fax:* 212-725-0864
E-mail: info@smwllc.com
Web Site: www.smwllc.com
Key Personnel
Partner, NY: Steve Emspak
CEO & Pres, NY: Fred Shen
Global Dir, Mktg, NY: Meredith Lovejoy
Founded: 1986
Technology consulting firm.
Branch Office(s)
33 New Montgomery St, 10th fl, San Francisco, CA 94105, Assoc Principal: Kevin Eldridge *Tel:* 415-391-7610 *Fax:* 415-391-0171
1822 Blacke St, Suite 2A, Denver, CO 80202, Assoc Principal: Jerome Smith *Tel:* 720-482-0770 *Fax:* 720-482-0450
2 N Riverside Plaza, Suite 1460, Chicago, IL 60606, Partner: Randy Tritz *Tel:* 312-559-4585 *Fax:* 312-559-5393
44 Princeton Highstown Rd, Princeton Junction, NJ 08550, Partner: James Merrill *Tel:* 609-716-1900 *Fax:* 609-716-6464

531 Plymouth Rd, Suite 527, Plymouth Meeting, PA 19462, Partner: Kevin Klasic *Tel:* 610-940-4310
712 Main St, Suite 730, Houston, TX 77002, Mgr: Tyson Leonard *Tel:* 713-278-8228 *Fax:* 713-278-8235
1220 N Fillmore St, Suite 360, Arlington, VA 22201, Partner: Richard Derbyshire *Tel:* 703-243-6301 *Fax:* 703-243-6304
Foreign Office(s): Rm F, 19th fl, Bldg D, Oriental Kenzo, No 48 Dongzhimenwai Ave, Dongcheng District, Beijing 100027, China, Dir: Zane Au *Tel:* (010) 8454 9320
Bldg 2, Xin Mei Spring Garden, No 721 Xinhua Rd, Changing District, Shanghai 200052, China, Mgr: Kevin Chen *Tel:* (021) 6208 3337 *Fax:* (021) 5212 5032
16/F Greenwich Ctr, 260 King's Rd, North Point, Hong Kong, Dir: Zane Au *Tel:* 2851 1086 *Fax:* 2544 4266
291 Beach Rd, Suite 02-01, Singapore, Singapore, Dir: Ralph Stefanelli *Tel:* 6292 4101 *Fax:* 6292 3868
Bldg 9, Suite 237, PO Box 502387, Dubai Media City, Dubai, United Arab Emirates, Dir: Russell Wood *Tel:* (04) 3902476 *Fax:* (04) 3908246
Abbey House, 3rd fl, 74-76 Saint John St, London, United Kingdom, Mng Dir: Anders Hall *Tel:* (020) 7014 1441 *Fax:* (020) 7014 1440
Membership(s): AES; American Institute of Architects; ASA; IACC; InfoComm International®; National Council of Acoustical Consultants; NSCA

Sherwood America Inc
6120 Valley View Ave, Buena Park, CA 90620
Tel: 714-739-2000 *Toll Free Tel:* 800-962-3203 *Fax:* 714-739-2009
E-mail: sales@sherwoodamerica.com
Web Site: www.sherwoodamerica.com
Founded: 1953
Car audio systems.
Catalog(s) available
Membership(s): Canadian Export Association; Consumer Electronics Association

ShiftFocus Productions
5126 N Ravenswood Ave, Chicago, IL 60640
Tel: 773-231-2000
Web Site: www.shiftfocusproductions.com
Video production & motion graphics services. Production facility include soundstages, audio production suite, editing, client services & production offices.

Shimad Corp
45 Parsons Way, Los Altos, CA 94022
Tel: 650-962-1234 (Outside USA) *Toll Free Tel:* 888-474-4623 *Fax:* 650-948-3378
E-mail: sales@shimad.com
Web Site: www.shimad.com
Key Personnel
Pres: Adel Elshimi
CD replication services & distribution of CD duplication equipment.

Shokus Video
PO Box 3125, Chatsworth, CA 91313-3125
Tel: 818-538-9985 *Toll Free Tel:* 800-SHOKUS-1 (746-5871 - orders) *Fax:* 818-701-0560
E-mail: info@shokus.com
Web Site: www.shokus.com
Key Personnel
Pres & Owner: Stuart Shostak *E-mail:* stuart@shokus.com
Catalog(s), $3

Stan Sholik Photography
1946 E Blair Ave, Santa Ana, CA 92705
Tel: 949-250-9275 *Fax:* 949-756-2623
E-mail: stan@stansholik.com
Web Site: www.stansholik.com
Founded: 1973
Commercial & advertising photo studio.

Shook Mobile Technology LP
7451 FM 3009, Schertz, TX 78154
Tel: 210-651-5700 *Toll Free Tel:* 888-651-5775 *Fax:* 210-651-5220
E-mail: shook@shook-usa.com
Web Site: www.shook-usa.com
Key Personnel
CEO: John P Heaney
Founded: 1977
Manufacturer of hi-technology mobile vehicles.
Catalog(s) available
Membership(s): NAB; RTDNA; SBE; SMPTE; TAB

Shooting Star Video
256 Shearwater Isle, Foster City, CA 94404
Tel: 650-345-0919 *Fax:* 650-573-6615
E-mail: rent@ssv.com
Web Site: www.ssv.com
Key Personnel
Owner: Jeff Regan
Video equipment rentals & service. Single & multi-camera packages & expert consultation for broadcast, cable, corporate & independent productions.

Shooting Stars Post Inc
3106 W North "A" St, Tampa, FL 33609
Tel: 813-873-0100
Web Site: www.sspmedia.com
Key Personnel
Owner & Pres: John Samaha
Founded: 1987
Full service multimedia company. Digital non-linear & linear edit suites - graphic suites, 4,000 sq ft studio with corner cyc, film & video production.

Shopware
Division of Infobase Learning
c/o Films Media Group, 132 W 31 St, 17th fl, New York, NY 10001
Toll Free Tel: 800-322-8755 *Toll Free Fax:* 800-678-3633
E-mail: custserv@films.com
Web Site: shopware.films.com
Key Personnel
CEO & Pres, Infobase Learning: Mark McDonnell
Founded: 1959
Provider of skills-based, technology driven educational media. Develop content that thoroughly addresses specific vocational & technical skills such as building trades, vehicle maintenance & technology. Assist educators in preparing students to enter the workforce & facilitate professional development programs with videos, interactive media & posters.
Catalog(s), weekly, free, over 100 unique catalogs mailed throughout the year

Shore Manufacturing Co
222 Beade St, Plymouth, PA 18651
Mailing Address: PO Box 214, Manasquan, NJ 08736-0214
Tel: 570-779-4042 *Toll Free Tel:* 800-321-5153 (orders) *Fax:* 570-779-7607 *Toll Free Fax:* 800-272-4334
E-mail: shoremfg@att.net
Web Site: shoremfg.com
Key Personnel
VP, Opers: William Loughran, Jr
Manufacturer of special effects generators.

Shotmaker Co
Division of Moving Vehicular Platforms Inc
10909 Vanowen St, North Hollywood, CA 91605-6408
Tel: 818-219-2043
E-mail: info@shotmaker.com; info@bigshot.tv
Web Site: www.shotmaker.com
Key Personnel
Owner: Brian Gaetke
Distribution & rentals of camera cars & cranes.
Catalog(s) available
Membership(s): AICP; NAB; Production Equipment Rental Association; SMPTE

Shoulder High Productions
50 Elsie St, San Francisco, CA 94110
Tel: 415-235-1984 *Fax:* 415-357-9747
E-mail: info@shoulderhigh.com
Web Site: shoulderhigh.com
Founded: 1998
Full service, content neutral, media production company.

Show Canada Industries Inc
5555 Maurice-Cullen, Laval, QC H7C 2T8, Canada
Tel: 450-664-5155 *Toll Free Tel:* 888-329-5556 *Fax:* 450-664-0852
E-mail: info@show-canada.ca
Web Site: www.show-canada.com
Key Personnel
CEO & Pres: Jean Labadie
HR Mgr: Nicole Gagnon
Founded: 1999
Manufacturer of stage lift & winch.
Foreign Office(s): 7 Xingguang St, Xihongmen, Daxing District, Beijing 100162, China
15 Kubanskaya St, No 14, 2nd fl, Central District, Sochi, Krasdonar, Russia
PO Box 6201, Al Mamoura, Doha, Qatar *Tel:* 5528 2179 (cell)

Show Department Inc
2201 W Fulton St, Chicago, IL 60612
Tel: 312-243-8215 *Toll Free Tel:* 800-294-4111 *Fax:* 312-243-8236
E-mail: info@showdepartment.com
Web Site: www.showdepartment.com
Key Personnel
CEO: Lee Facklis
COO: Jeff Facklis
Founded: 1983
Meeting & event staging, audio, video, lighting, scenic & show management.
Catalog(s) available
Membership(s): InfoComm International®; MPI; Professional Lighting & Sound Association

Show-Me Audio-Visual
Corporate Ridge, 4501 Blue Ridge Cutoff, Kansas City, MO 64133
Tel: 816-358-8700 *Toll Free Tel:* 800-2-SHOWME (274-6963) *Fax:* 816-358-8701
E-mail: info@showmeav.com
Web Site: www.showmeav.com
Key Personnel
Owner & Pres: Ron Dake
Rental Mgr: Nick Baker
AV equipment rentals.

ShowBiz Studios
15521 Lanark St, Van Nuys, CA 91406
Tel: 818-989-7007 *Fax:* 818-989-8272
Web Site: www.showbizstudios.com
Key Personnel
Owner: Scott Webley
Stage rentals for commercials, films, music videos & television.

Showcase Photo & Video
Division of Showcase Inc
2323 Cheshire Bridge Rd, Atlanta, GA 30324
Tel: 404-325-7676 *Toll Free Tel:* 800-886-1976 *Fax:* 404-321-3636

E-mail: sales@showcaseinc.com
Web Site: www.showcaseinc.com
Key Personnel
Video Prodn Mgr: Eric Shipley *Tel:* 404-965-2231 *E-mail:* erics@showcaseinc.com
Provider of professional photographic & video equipment.

Showman Fabricators Inc
47-22 Pearson Place, Long Island City, NY 11101
Tel: 718-935-9899 *Fax:* 718-855-9823
E-mail: info@showfab.com
Web Site: www.showfab.com
Key Personnel
Pres: Bob Usdin *Tel:* 718-935-9899 ext 304 *E-mail:* rusdin@showfab.com
VP: Mark Viola *Tel:* 718-935-9899 ext 335 *E-mail:* mviola@showfab.com
Sr Proj Mgr: Elliot Bertoni *Tel:* 718-935-9899 ext 336 *E-mail:* ebertoni@showfab.com; Chris Hayes *Tel:* 718-935-9899 ext 334 *E-mail:* chayes@showfab.com; Justin Kurtz *Tel:* 718-935-9899 ext 302 *E-mail:* jkurtz@showfab.com
Founded: 1986
Manufacturer & distributor of props, drapes & blinds.
Catalog(s) available

Showorks Audio Visual Inc
100 Naamans Rd, Suite 1-C, Claymont, DE 19703
Tel: 302-798-7999 *Toll Free Tel:* 800-942-7469 *Fax:* 302-798-9705
E-mail: info@showorksav.com
Web Site: showorksav.com
Key Personnel
Pres: Jesse Logan
Founded: 1988
Catalog(s) available
Membership(s): InfoComm International®

Showreel International Inc
1021 N McCadden Place, Hollywood, CA 90038
Tel: 323-464-5111
E-mail: information@showreel.com
Web Site: www.showreel.com
Key Personnel
Partner, CEO, Pres & Exec Prodr: Lynne B Jackson *E-mail:* lynne@showreel.com
Partner & Sr Dir: Eric Jackson *E-mail:* eric@showreel.com
Founded: 1985
Full service film & video production; specializing in HD long format corporate & government messaging for DVD, broadcast & interactive full service production.

Showtime Networks Inc
Subsidiary of CBS Corporation
1633 Broadway, 9th fl, New York, NY 10019
Tel: 212-708-1600 *Fax:* 212-708-1217
Web Site: www.sho.com
Key Personnel
Chmn & CEO: Matthew C Blank
Pres, Entertainment: David Nevins
Owns & operates premium television networks Showtime®, The Movie Channel™, FLIX® & more.
Branch Office(s)
980 Hammond Dr NE, Suite 725, Atlanta, GA 30328 *Tel:* 770-396-1333 *Fax:* 770-396-7946

SHP Electronics
1225 Hulman St, Terre Haute, IN 47802
Tel: 812-232-1003 *Fax:* 812-232-3170
Web Site: www.shpelectronics.com
Key Personnel
Pres: George S Petit *E-mail:* george@shpelectronics.com
Founded: 1978
Electronics systems design, installation, integration & service.

Shure Inc
5800 W Touhy Ave, Niles, IL 60714-4608
Tel: 847-600-2000; 847-600-8440 (tech support); 847-600-8699 (cust serv) *Toll Free Tel:* 800-25-SHURE (257-4873); 800-516-2525 (cust serv) *Fax:* 847-600-1212; 847-600-8444 (tech support); 847-600-8686 (cust serv); 847-600-8688 (parts)
E-mail: info@shure.com; support@shure.com (tech support); service@shure.com (cust serv)
Web Site: www.shure.com
Key Personnel
CEO & Pres: Santo "Sandy" La Mantia
Founded: 1925
Designers & manufacturer of audio products-microphones, wireless systems, earphones & related audio products.
Catalog(s) available
Foreign Office(s): Suzhou Shure Trading Co Ltd, 18/A E Ocean Ctr, 618 Yan An Rd E, Shanghai 200001, China *E-mail:* info@shure.com.cn
Shure Europe GmbH, Jakob-Dieffenbacherstr 12, 75031 Eppingen, Germany *Tel:* (07262) 9249-107 *Fax:* (07262) 9249-114 *E-mail:* info@shure.de
Shure Asia Ltd, 22/F, 625 King's Rd, North Point, Island East, Hong Kong *Tel:* 2893 4290 *Fax:* 2393 4055 *E-mail:* info@shure.com.hk
Shure Japan Ltd, 16F NBF Hibiya Bldg, 1-1-7 Uchisaiwaicho, Chiyoda-ku, Tokyo 100-0011, Japan *E-mail:* info@shure.co.jp

Shure Manufacturing Corp
1901 W Main St, Washington, MO 63090
Tel: 636-390-7100 *Toll Free Tel:* 800-227-4873 *Fax:* 636-390-7171
E-mail: sales@shureusa.com
Web Site: www.shureusa.com
Key Personnel
CEO: Andrew T Richardson
Mktg Mgr: Brad E Smith
Manufacturers of storage cabinets.
Catalog(s) available

Side Door Studio Inc
69 Albe Dr, Newark, DE 19702
Tel: 302-738-8777 *Fax:* 302-731-7601
E-mail: sdseng@sidedoorstudioinc.com
Key Personnel
Chief Engr: Glenn Miller
Founded: 1995
Recording studio.

Side 3 Studios
725 Mariposa St, Denver, CO 80204
Tel: 720-515-2649
E-mail: info@side3.com
Web Site: www.side3.com
Key Personnel
CEO: Adelio Lombardi *E-mail:* adelio@side3.com
Studio Mgr: Tyler Soifer *E-mail:* tyler@side3.com
Recording studio & multimedia facility. Offers both audio recording/engineering & full service video production for broadcast television & original programming.

Sierra Automated Systems
2821 Burton Ave, Burbank, CA 91504
Tel: 818-840-6749 *Fax:* 818-840-6751
E-mail: sales@sasaudio.com; marketing@sasaudio.com
Web Site: www.sasaudio.com
Key Personnel
Pres: Ed Fritz *E-mail:* ed@sasaudio.com
VP: Al Salci *E-mail:* al@sasaudio.com
Sales Support: Emilio Gomez *E-mail:* emilio@sasaudio.com
Founded: 1988
Digital audio network routing, mixing, console control & integrated intercom & talkback systems.
Catalog(s) available
Membership(s): AES; IEEE; SMPTE

Sight & Sound Production Services Inc
1143 Boland Place, St Louis, MO 63117-1411
Tel: 314-647-0665
Web Site: www.sspsinc.com
Key Personnel
Owner: David Houlle *Tel:* 314-374-4314 (cell) *E-mail:* sspshoulle@sbcglobal.net
Founded: 1983
Rental of grip electrical lighting & audio equipment, 3 & 5 ton grip electrical & lighting trucks.

Sight & Sound Productions
11193 Saint Johns Industrial Pkwy N, Jacksonville, FL 32246
Tel: 904-645-7880 *Toll Free Tel:* 800-339-0846 *Fax:* 904-645-7787
E-mail: info@ssav.net
Web Site: www.ssav.net
Key Personnel
Owner & CEO: Jon Davis *Tel:* 904-361-3300 *E-mail:* jdavis@ssav.net
VP, Sales: Alfredo Garcia *Tel:* 904-361-3315 *E-mail:* agarcia@ssav.net
Mktg Mgr: Victor Rosenblum *Tel:* 904-361-3309 *E-mail:* vrosenblum@ssav.net
Founded: 1987
Event & production company.
Catalog(s) available
Membership(s): InfoComm International®; MPI

Sight & Sound Studios
66 Queen St, Suite 1705, Honolulu, HI 96813
Tel: 808-599-7600 *Fax:* 808-599-7601
Web Site: www.sightandsoundhawaii.com
Key Personnel
Owner & Pres: William Maheras *Tel:* 808-754-0080 *E-mail:* bill@sightandsoundhawaii.com
Catalog(s) available
Membership(s): International Alliance of Theatrical Stage Employees

Sight Creative
400 First Ave N, Suite 100, Minneapolis, MN 55401
Tel: 651-646-2442 *Fax:* 651-646-1461
E-mail: info@sightcreative.com
Web Site: www.sightcreative.com
Key Personnel
CEO & Mng Partner: Peter Hager
Experience in marketing communications, creative services, web & interactive technology, multimedia, print & technology solutions.
Catalog(s) available

Sigma Corp of America
Subsidiary of Sigma Corp
15 Fleetwood Ct, Ronkonkoma, NY 11779
Tel: 631-585-1144 *Toll Free Tel:* 800-896-6858 (cust serv) *Fax:* 631-585-1895
E-mail: info@sigmaphoto.com
Web Site: www.sigmaphoto.com
Key Personnel
Pres: Mark Amir-Hamzeh
Dir, Mktg: Christine Moossmann *Tel:* 631-227-2017 *E-mail:* cmoossmann@sigmaphoto.com
Founded: 1985
Import sales, wholesale distribution & service of Sigma products.
Catalog(s) available
Membership(s): Photo Marketing Association

Sign Media Inc
4020 Blackburn Lane, Burtonsville, MD 20866-1167
Tel: 301-421-0268 *Toll Free Tel:* 800-475-4756 *Fax:* 301-421-0270
E-mail: info@signmedia.com
Web Site: www.signmedia.com
Key Personnel
Owner: Verden A Ness
Founded: 1979
Producers of videotaped text material on American Sign Language.
Catalog(s) available
Membership(s): MCA-I

Signal Transport
Division of SigT Inc
PO Box 1028, Lake Forest, CA 92609-1028
Tel: 714-641-5665 *Fax:* 714-641-5664
E-mail: sales@sigt.com; sales@smcpanels.com
Web Site: www.sigt.com; www.smcpanels.com
Key Personnel
Sales Mgr: Jorgen Ravn
Founded: 1998
Source for connector interfaces & control panels.

Signature Entertainment
8306 Wilshire Blvd, Suite 791, Beverly Hills, CA 90211
Tel: 310-498-1805 *Fax:* 310-276-2521
Web Site: www.signature-ent.com
Key Personnel
Owner: Kelly Andrea Rubin *E-mail:* kellyarubin@signature-ent.com
Film producer, line producer & production company.

Silent Source
58 Nonotuck St, Northampton, MA 01062
Tel: 413-584-7944 *Toll Free Tel:* 800-583-7174 (orders) *Fax:* 413-584-2377
E-mail: info@silentsource.com
Web Site: www.silentsource.com
Key Personnel
Pres: W Ridabock
Founded: 1992
Interior acoustical products. Silent source is your one-stop-shop for interior acoustic treatment & soundproofing needs.
Catalog(s) available

Silvestri California
8125 Beach St, Los Angeles, CA 90001
Tel: 323-277-4420 *Toll Free Tel:* 800-647-8874 *Fax:* 323-585-0861
E-mail: info@silvestricalifornia.com
Web Site: www.silvestricalifornia.com
Key Personnel
VP, Mktg & Design: Fidel Argomaniz
Founded: 1934
Manufacturer of products fabricated in fiberglass, urethane, wood & metal.
Catalog(s) available
Membership(s): National Association of Display Industries

SIM Digital
Member of SIM Group
One Atlantic Ave, Suite 110, Toronto, ON M6K 3E7, Canada
Tel: 416-979-9958 *Fax:* 416-979-7770
E-mail: info@simdigital.com
Web Site: www.simdigital.com
Key Personnel
Pres: Rob Sim
Rentals: Jason Kennedy *Tel:* 416-583-3677 *E-mail:* jasonkennedy@simdigital.com; Craig Milne *Tel:* 416-583-3681 *E-mail:* craigmilne@simdigital.com
Founded: 1982
Provides film & broadcast producers with the latest in video equipment rentals.
Branch Office(s)
5258 Lougheed Hwy, Burnaby, BC V5B 2Z8, Canada *Tel:* 604-298-5258 *Fax:* 604-298-4336
1096 Marginal Rd, Halifax, NS B3H 4N4, Canada *Tel:* 902-422-6090 *Fax:* 902-423-1523
738 N Cahuenga Blvd, Hollywood, CA 90038 *Tel:* 323-978-9000 *Fax:* 323-978-9018
1879 Chattahoochee Ave NW, Atlanta, GA 30318 *Tel:* 404-355-8000 *Fax:* 404-355-8005

Sima Products Corp
Division of Arista Group
125 Commerce Dr, Hauppauge, NY 11788
Tel: 631-435-0200 *Toll Free Tel:* 800-345-7462; 800-274-7824 *Fax:* 631-435-4545 *Toll Free Fax:* 800-274-7828
E-mail: info@simacorp.com; custserv@simacorp.com; customerservice@aristagroup.com
Web Site: www.aristagroup.com
Key Personnel
Pres: Robert Leifert
Mktg Mgr: Michael Fredonchick *E-mail:* michael.fredonchick@aristagroup.com
Catalog(s) available
Membership(s): CEMA; Consumer Electronics Association; Custom Electronic Design & Installation Association; Photo Marketing Association

Simco-Ion
Division of Illinois Tool Works
2257 N Penn Rd, Hatfield, PA 19440
Tel: 215-822-6401 *Toll Free Tel:* 800-203-3419 *Fax:* 215-822-3795
E-mail: customerservice@simco-ion.com
Web Site: www.simco-ion.com
Key Personnel
US Industrial Busn Unit Mgr: Jay Perry
Mktg Mgr: Kim West
Mktg Asst: Susan Valent
Founded: 1936
Manufacturer of static bar systems, static charging systems, web & sheet cleaning systems.
Catalog(s) available
Foreign Office(s): Simco-Ion Japan Inc, 1-2-4, Minatojima Nakamachi, Chuo-ku, Kobe City 650-0046, Japan *Tel:* (078) 303-4651 *Fax:* (078) 303-4655 *E-mail:* info@simcoion.jp *Web Site:* www.simcoion.jp
Simco-Ion Europe, Postbus 71, Lochem 7240 AB, Netherlands *Tel:* (0573) 288333 *Fax:* (0573) 257319 *E-mail:* general@simco-ion.nl *Web Site:* www.simco-ion.nl

Simkar Corporation
700 Ramona Ave, Philadelphia, PA 19120-4691
Tel: 215-831-7700 *Toll Free Tel:* 800-523-3602 *Fax:* 215-831-7703
E-mail: lighting@simkar.com
Web Site: www.simkar.com
Key Personnel
VP, Sales: Ken Bopf
Founded: 1952
Lighting equipment manufacturer & distributor.
Catalog(s) available
Membership(s): Illuminating Engineering Society; NAED; NAILD; National Electrical Manufacturers Association; NEMRA-Manufacturers Group

Simon & Schuster, Inc
Division of CBS Corporation
1230 Avenue of the Americas, New York, NY 10020
Tel: 212-698-7000 *Toll Free Tel:* 800-223-2348 (cust serv) *Toll Free Fax:* 800-943-9831
E-mail: customer.service@simonandschuster.net
Web Site: www.simonandschuster.net; www.simonandschuster.biz
Key Personnel
CEO & Pres: Carolyn Reidy
Founded: 1924
Resources of school or library, grades kindergarten through college.
Catalog(s) available

D S Simon Productions
229 W 36 St, 9th fl, New York, NY 10018
Tel: 212-736-2727 *Toll Free Tel:* 800-377-4666 *Fax:* 212-736-7040
E-mail: news@dssimon.com
Web Site: dssimon.com
Key Personnel
CEO & Pres: Douglas Simon *E-mail:* doug@dssimon.com
Media & business communications. Specialize in satellite media tours, Internet media tours, B-roll production & distribution, corporate & web video, video players, ground tours, co-op tours & radio tours.

Simon - Kaloi Engineering
31192 La Baya Dr, Unit G, Westlake Village, CA 91362
Tel: 818-707-8400 *Fax:* 818-707-8401
Key Personnel
CFO: Richard A Simon
Pres: Dennis Kaloi
Catalog(s) available

Simplex Grinnell LP
Division of Tyco
50 Technology Dr, Westminster, MA 01441
Tel: 978-731-2500
Web Site: www.simplexgrinnell.com
Sales & design of professional audio systems for performance applications & sound masking.
Branch Office(s)
2400 Skymark Ave, Mississauga, ON L4W 5K5, Canada *Tel:* 905-212-4600
Membership(s): AES; InfoComm International®; NSCA; The Recording Academy

Simply Audiobooks
935 Sheldon Ct, Burlington, ON L7L 5K6, Canada
Tel: 905-634-3035 *Toll Free Tel:* 877-554-4332
E-mail: customerservice@simplyaudiobooks.com
Web Site: www.simplyaudiobooks.com
Founded: 2003
Unlimited audiobooks delivered to your door.
Branch Office(s)
2225 Kenmore Ave, Suite 122, Buffalo, NY 14207-1359

Simpson Electric Co
520 Simpson Ave, Lac du Flambeau, WI 54538
Mailing Address: PO Box 99, Lac du Flambeau, WI 54538-0099
Tel: 715-588-3947 (cust serv); 715-588-3311 *Fax:* 715-588-1248 (cust serv); 715-588-3326
E-mail: cservice@simpsonelectric.com
Web Site: www.simpsonelectric.com
Founded: 1934
Manufacturer of panel instrumentation & test equipment.
Catalog(s) available

Simtrol Inc
Northwinds 600 Bldg, Suite 250, 11675 Rainwater Dr, Alpharetta, GA 30009
Tel: 678-365-2315 *Fax:* 678-365-2315
Web Site: www.simtrol.com
Powers enterprise-class software solutions.

Sinauer Associates Inc
23 Plumtree Rd, Sunderland, MA 01375
Mailing Address: PO Box 407, Sunderland, MA 01375-0407
Tel: 413-549-4300 *Fax:* 413-549-1118

E-mail: orders@sinauer.com (orders); custserv@sinauer.com (cust serv); publish@sinauer.com (general edit correspondence)
Web Site: www.sinauer.com
Key Personnel
Pres & Ed: Andrew D Sinauer
VP: Dean H Scudder
Mgr: Jason Dirks
Mktg Coord: Marie A Scavotto
Founded: 1969
Publisher of college-level textbooks & educational multimedia products.

Sinclair Institute
402 Millstone Dr, Hillsborough, NC 27278
Tel: 919-732-6005 *Toll Free Tel:* 888-736-2247 *Fax:* 919-732-6146
E-mail: sales@sinclairwholesale.com
Web Site: www.sinclairwholesale.com; www.bettersex.com
Key Personnel
Chmn: Dr Eli Coleman
Media Mgr: Alan Julich
Founded: 1991
Producer & distributor of educational & medical programs.
Catalog(s) available

Barbara Singer Productions
319 E 24 St, No 3-A, New York, NY 10010
Tel: 212-689-0395 *Fax:* 212-686-4890
E-mail: barbara@barbarasinger.com
Web Site: www.barbarasinger.com
Key Personnel
Owner: Barbara Singer
Founded: 1983
Commercial & fine art photography. Barbara has also been an actor & model, doing commercials, film, theatre, voice-overs & print since 2007. She is also the author of *The Impossible Landscapes of Nat Herz & Kurt Seligmann*, 1999.

SintecMedia
425 Madison Ave, Suite 1602, New York, NY 10017
Tel: 917-606-5310 *Fax:* 917-606-5311
E-mail: sales@sintecmedia.com
Web Site: www.sintecmedia.com
Key Personnel
Pres: Chanan Weiss
EVP, Enterprise Sales: Amir Lavi
Founded: 2000
Broadcast management systems, air time sales & traffic.
Branch Office(s)
1580 Lincoln St, Suite 560, Denver, CO 80203 *Tel:* 303-830-0600 *Fax:* 303-830-0601
2964 Peachtree Rd, Suite 400, Atlanta, GA 30305, COO: Eric Levitan *Tel:* 404-869-4575 *Fax:* 404-844-9009
1355 W Towne Square Rd, Mequon, WI 53092, CTO: Toufic Moubarak *Tel:* 262-241-9005 *Fax:* 262-241-9036
Foreign Office(s): 8 Am Ve 'Olamo St, POB 34406, 91342 Jerusalem, Israel, CEO: Amotz Yarden *Tel:* (02) 651 5122 *Fax:* (02) 651 5133 (headquarters)
Fourth Maria Tanase St, Croiova, Dolj, Romania *Tel:* (0351) 801 800

Sirius Images Corp dba WaveGuide Studios
2062 Weems Rd, Tucker, GA 30084
Tel: 770-939-2004 *Toll Free Tel:* 800-578-2004
E-mail: info@waveguidestudios.com
Web Site: www.waveguidestudios.com
Key Personnel
Gen Mgr: Stephanie Phillips
Film production services.

SirsiDynix
3300 N Ashton Blvd, Suite 500, Lehi, UT 84043-5340
Tel: 801-223-5200 *Toll Free Tel:* 800-288-8020 *Fax:* 801-223-5202
E-mail: info@sirsidynix.com; sales@sirsidynix.com
Web Site: www.sirsidynix.com
Key Personnel
CEO: Bill Davison
Chief Sales & Mktg Offr: Keith Sturges
Integrated library automation package for K-12 school libraries combining functionality, support & flexibility.
Branch Office(s)
55 King St W, 7th fl, Kitchener, ON N2G 4W1, Canada
Foreign Office(s): Level 28, 303 Collins St, PO Box 3423, Melbourne, VIC 3000, Australia *Tel:* (03) 9678 9112 *Fax:* (03) 9678 9163
Ave Vitacura 2939 Piso 10, 755001 Santiago, Chile *Tel:* (02) 431-5000
10/F, Central Plaza, 381 Huai Hai Zhong Rd, Shanghai 200020, China *Tel:* (021) 63915210 *Fax:* (021) 63915970
13 rue Camille Desmoulins, 92441 Issy-les-Moulineaux, Cedex, France, Dir: Eric Bazoin *Tel:* 01 58 04 26 65 *Fax:* 01 58 04 23 81 *E-mail:* eric.bazoin@sirsidynix.com
Novabase Edificio Olympus II, Sala 1 e 3 Av D Alfonso, Henriques 1462, 4450-013 Matosinhos, Portugal *Tel:* 22 6085100
Arabian Advanced Systems, 11455 Old Akaria Bldg, 3rd fl, Off 304 Sitteen St, Malaz, Saudi Arabia *Tel:* (01) 4770477
Universal Knowledge Software, PO Box 31186, Braamfontain 2017, South Africa *Tel:* (011) 712 1750 *Fax:* (011) 403 9436
Calle Lopez de Hoyos, 35 - 1º, 28002 Madrid, Spain *Tel:* 91 745 99 00 *Fax:* 91 745 99 995
22 F-3, 91, Section 2, Roosevelt Rd, Taipei, Taiwan *Tel:* (02) 2369 0072
Informascope, Hacettepe Teknokent Beytepe, Kampusu 4, Arge Binasi No 12, Beytepe, 06800 Ankara, Turkey *Tel:* (0312) 446 7792 *Fax:* (0312) 446 7793 *E-mail:* info@informascope.com *Web Site:* www.informascope.com
54 Clarendon Rd, Watford WD17 1DU, United Kingdom *Tel:* (01923) 202900 *Fax:* (01923) 431847

Sisters' Choice Press
PO Box 2067, Berkeley, CA 94702-0067
Tel: 510-843-0533 *Fax:* 510-834-5201
Web Site: www.sisterschoice.com
Key Personnel
Mgr: Ruth Pohlman
Contact: Nancy Schimmel *E-mail:* nancy@sisterschoice.com
Catalog(s) available
Membership(s): The Association of Publishers for Special Sales; IBPA, the Independent Book Publishers Association

SISU Home Entertainment Inc
340 W 39 St, 6th fl, New York, NY 10018
Tel: 212-947-7888 *Toll Free Tel:* 800-223-7478 *Fax:* 212-947-8388 *Toll Free Fax:* 888-221-7478
E-mail: sisu@sisuent.com
Web Site: www.sisuent.com
Key Personnel
Pres: Haim Scheininger
Founded: 1988
Distributor, producer & co-producer of DVDs, videos, films, TV programs & CDs.
Catalog(s) available
Membership(s): Entertainment Merchants Association; Music Business Association; National Media Market; NATPE

Frank Siteman Photography
136 Pond St, Winchester, MA 01890
Tel: 781-729-3747 *Fax:* 781-729-2549
Web Site: www.franksiteman.com
Key Personnel
Pres: Frank Siteman *E-mail:* frank@franksiteman.com
Photography for print company.
Membership(s): American Society of Picture Professionals; ASMP

Sitler's Supplies Inc
702 E Washington St, Washington, IA 52353
Mailing Address: PO Box 10, Washington, IA 52353-0010
Tel: 319-653-2123 *Toll Free Tel:* 800-426-3938 *Fax:* 319-653-3198
E-mail: info@sitlersupplies.com
Web Site: www.sitlersupplies.com
Key Personnel
Pres: Jason Prochaska *E-mail:* jason@sitlersupplies.com
Distributor of projectors, stage lights & related equipment.
Catalog(s) available

63588 Manitoba Ltd, see Big Deal Custom Casings

16 x 9 Inc
28314 Constellation Rd, Valencia, CA 91355
Tel: 661-295-3313 *Toll Free Tel:* 866-800-1699 *Fax:* 661-295-3314
E-mail: info@16x9inc.com
Web Site: www.16x9inc.com
Key Personnel
Mktg Mgr & Intl Sales: Michael Ibanez *E-mail:* michael@16x9inc.com
Tech Support Mgr, Sales: James Lee *E-mail:* james@16x9inc.com
Founded: 2000

SKC Communication Products Inc
8320 Hedge Lane Terr, Shawnee Mission, KS 66227
Tel: 913-422-4222 *Toll Free Tel:* 800-882-7779 *Toll Free Fax:* 800-454-4752
E-mail: contact.us@skccom.com
Web Site: www.skccom.com
Key Personnel
CEO & Pres: Tray Vedock
COO & VP: Charlie Ammeen
Chief Mktg Offr & VP: Jill Phillips
Founded: 1986
Voice, AV & video conferencing products, solutions & services.
Branch Office(s)
8710 "F" St, Suite 112, Omaha, NE 68127
274 Museum Rd, Rock Hill, SC 29732
1910 Firman Dr, Richardson, TX 75018
11370 Theo Trecker Way, West Allis, WI 53214
Shipping Address: 14401 W 106 St, Lenexa, KS 66215 (warehouse)

Skjonberg Controls Inc
1363 Donlon St, Suite 6, Ventura, CA 93003
Tel: 805-650-0877 *Toll Free Fax:* 800-650-0360
E-mail: sales@skjonberg.com
Web Site: www.skjonberg.com
Key Personnel
Mktg: Carolyn Meyer *Tel:* 805-650-0877 ext 103
Tech Sales & Engg: Knut Skjonberg *Tel:* 805-650-0877 ext 104
Founded: 1983
Manufacturer & distributor of control systems.

Skotel Corp
118-6185 boul Teschereau, Suite 144, Brossard, QC J4Z 0E4, Canada
Tel: 514-806-2340
E-mail: skotel@videotron.ca

Key Personnel
Pres: Stephen Scott
Catalog(s) available
Membership(s): SMPTE

Sky-View Co
2800 NE Loop 410, San Antonio, TX 78218
Tel: 210-590-8100 *Toll Free Tel:* 800-562-8439 (US & CN) *Fax:* 210-967-8787
E-mail: sales@sky-view.com
Web Site: www.sky-view.com
Key Personnel
Pres: Dave Key
Natl Sales Mgr: Chris Purtee
Founded: 1983
Manufacture, distribute & rent advertising balloons & search lights.
Catalog(s) available

Skyfire Video
PO Box 2266, Sparks, NV 89432
Tel: 775-323-0965 *Toll Free Tel:* 800-852-2330
Web Site: www.skyfirevideo.com
Key Personnel
CEO/Prodr: Jim Mitchell
Video production company.

Skyhoundz
Subsidiary of PRB & Associates Inc
660 Hembree Pkwy, Suite 110, Roswell, GA 30076
Tel: 770-751-3882 *Fax:* 770-740-1665
E-mail: info@skyhoundz.com
Web Site: www.skyhoundz.com
Key Personnel
Dir: Peter Bloeme
Founded: 1998
Disc Dog videos, books & apparel distribution.
Catalog(s) available

Skyline Broadcast
30 Skyline Dr, Lake Mary, FL 32771
Tel: 407-484-1089 *Fax:* 518-684-2593
E-mail: sales@skylinebroadcast.com
Web Site: www.skylinebroadcast.com
Dealer of refurbished professional broadcast equipment.

Skyriver Films
Division of You Don't Know Jack Inc
6251 Tuttle Place, Suite 102, Anchorage, AK 99507-2099
Tel: 907-243-3332; 907-248-9999 *Toll Free Tel:* 888-660-2257 *Fax:* 907-243-2044
E-mail: info@alaskajacks.com
Web Site: www.alaskajacks.com; www.skyriver.com
Key Personnel
Pres: Starr Horton
Founded: 1990
Distributes documentaries, educational programs & travelogs on DVD.
Catalog(s) available
Membership(s): AICP; Entertainment Merchants Association; SIVA

Skystorm Productions
103 Commerce St, Suite 100, Lake Mary, FL 32746
Tel: 407-328-4747 *Toll Free Tel:* 800-783-8508 *Fax:* 407-328-4479
E-mail: info@skystorm.com
Web Site: www.skystorm.com
Founded: 1998
Video production company. HD mobile production vehicle.

Skyviews Survey Inc
32 Highline Trail, Stamford, CT 06902
Tel: 203-359-3754 *Fax:* 203-359-3791
Web Site: www.skyviewsurvey.com
Key Personnel
Pres: David Margolis *E-mail:* dmar2@optonline.com
Founded: 1946
Aerial photography/videography production service company. Manufacture & rent stabilization platforms for aerial video.

Slate Media Group
1111 S Victory Blvd, Burbank, CA 91502
Tel: 818-569-6500 *Fax:* 818-846-9399
Web Site: www.slatemediagroup.com
Key Personnel
Chmn & CEO: David Rosen
Video equipment rental company.
Catalog(s) available

SLD Lighting
36-05 Broadway, Fair Lawn, NJ 07410
Tel: 201-373-2700 *Toll Free Tel:* 800-245-6630 *Fax:* 201-793-7618
E-mail: sales@sldlighting.com
Web Site: www.sldlighting.com
Key Personnel
Owner: Bob Hilzen
VP, Opers: Glenn D Hilzen *E-mail:* glenn@sldlighting.com
Gen Mgr: Howard Weinrich
Founded: 1976
Provide specification grade lighting/sound equipment for visual/entertainment industries.
Catalog(s) available

SLI Manufacturing Inc
550 McNicholl Ave, Toronto, ON M2H 2E1, Canada
Tel: 416-493-8900 *Toll Free Tel:* 888-216-2382 *Fax:* 416-493-8901
E-mail: salesinfo@slicanada.com
Web Site: www.slicanada.com
Key Personnel
Pres: Andy Sin
Founded: 1993
Full service software duplication & packaging company specializing in CD & DVD manufacturing, custom packaging & fulfillment services.

Slim Goodbody Corp
161 Narrows Rd, Lincolnville, ME 04850
Mailing Address: PO Box 242, Lincolnville Center, ME 04850
Tel: 207-763-2820 *Toll Free Tel:* 800-962-7546 *Fax:* 207-763-4804
E-mail: info@slimgoodbody.com
Web Site: www.slimgoodbody.com
Key Personnel
Founder & Pres: John Burstein
Founded: 1975
Live performances, TV broadcasting & teaching resources on topics including health, fitness, math, reading, science & other core curriculums.
Catalog(s) available

Slow Motion Film & Digital Inc
7211 Clybourn Ave, Los Angeles, CA 91352
Tel: 818-982-4400 *Fax:* 818-982-8500
Web Site: www.slowmotioninc.com
Founded: 1992
Sales, rental & service of digital/video equipment & accessories.

SLR Enterprises LLC
Formerly Primary Connections
PO Box 1111, Orleans, MA 02653
Tel: 508-737-7788 *Fax:* 508-240-6878
E-mail: stephenroth@c4.net
Key Personnel
Pres: Stephen Roth
Founded: 1998
Broker & distributor of wire, cable, fiber optics, assemblies & hardware, velcro, screws & IRF connection cable ties.

SmackDab Media
1033 Third Ave S, Nashville, TN 37210
Toll Free Tel: 888-248-8197
Web Site: smackdabmedia.com
Key Personnel
Owner: John Fucile
Post Prodn Supv: Lisa DeAngelo
Prodn Coord: Liz Taylor
Film & video stage/studio for rehearsal & shooting. Full production & post-production services.

Small Planet Communications Inc
15 Union St, Lawrence, MA 01840
Tel: 978-794-2201
E-mail: planet@smplanet.com
Web Site: www.smplanet.com
Develop print & multimedia materials.

Small Press Distribution Inc
1341 Seventh St, Berkeley, CA 94710-1409
Tel: 510-524-1668 *Toll Free Tel:* 800-869-7553 *Fax:* 510-524-0852
E-mail: spd@spdbooks.org
Web Site: www.spdbooks.org
Key Personnel
Opers Dir: Brent Cunningham *Tel:* 510-524-1668 ext 308 *E-mail:* brent@spdbooks.org
Founded: 1969
Nonprofit literary arts organization dedicated to independently published literature. Offer literary videos & spoken word cassettes/CDs.
Catalog(s) available

Small World Productions Inc
140 Lakeside Ave, Suite 200, Seattle, WA 98122
Mailing Address: PO Box 28369, Seattle, WA 98118-8369
Tel: 206-329-7167 *Toll Free Tel:* 800-866-7425 (orders)
E-mail: info@travelsmallworld.com
Web Site: www.smarttravels.tv
Key Personnel
Partner: John Givens; Patricia Larsen; Sandra Nisbet
Off Mgr: Ann Conroy *E-mail:* annconroy@travelsmallworld.com
Travel video producers.
Catalog(s) available
Membership(s): NATAS

Smart Concepts Ltd
4525 S Jamestown, Tulsa, OK 74135
Tel: 918-636-2376
Web Site: www.smartconceptsinc.com
Key Personnel
Owner: Stephen D Sembritzky *E-mail:* steve@smartconceptsinc.com
Video production company.

SMART Technologies Inc
3636 Research Rd NW, Calgary, AB T2L 1Y1, Canada
Tel: 403-245-0333 *Toll Free Tel:* 888-42-SMART (427-6278 US & Canada) *Fax:* 403-228-2500
E-mail: info@smarttech.com
Web Site: www.smarttech.com
Key Personnel
CEO: Neil Gaydon
Founded: 1987
Manufacturer & distributor of AV equipment.
Sales Office(s): 200 Lexington Ave, Suite 1115, New York, NY 10016 *Tel:* 212-696-9762 *E-mail:* ny.info@smarttech.com
1655 N Fort Myer Dr, Suite 1120, Arlington, VA 22209 *Tel:* 703-516-7627 *Toll Free Tel:* 866-766-6927 *E-mail:* dc.info@smarttech.com

SmartPros Ltd
12 Skyline Dr, Hawthorne, NY 10532-2133
Tel: 914-345-2620 *Fax:* 914-345-2603
E-mail: admin@smartpros.com
Web Site: www.smartpros.com
Key Personnel
Pres & Dir: Jack Fingerhut
VP & Corp Secy: Karen Stolzar
VP, Opers: Jay D Gregory
Founded: 1981
Educational products & duplication services.
Catalog(s) available
Membership(s): ATD

SmartSource Computer & AV Rentals
265 Oser Ave, Hauppauge, NY 11788
Tel: 631-273-8888 *Toll Free Tel:* 800-888-8686 *Fax:* 631-273-8889
E-mail: info@smartsourcerentals.com; longisland@smartsourcerentals.com
Web Site: www.smartsourcerentals.com
Key Personnel
SVP: Steve Shatsoff *E-mail:* sshatsoff@smartsourcerentals.com
Mktg Coord: Debbie Church *E-mail:* dchurch@smartsourcerentals.com
Founded: 1984
High quality computer & AV equipment rental.
Sales Office(s): 4630 E Elwood St, Suite 14, Phoenix, AZ 85040-1962 *Tel:* 480-829-6336 *Fax:* 480-829-6515 *E-mail:* phoenix@smartsourcerentals.com
10391 Jefferson Blvd, Culver City, CA 90232 *Tel:* 310-237-5324 *Fax:* 310-237-5327 *E-mail:* culvercity@smartsourcerentals.com
7243 Engineer Rd, Suite E, San Diego, CA 92111-1017 *Tel:* 858-278-9666 *Fax:* 858-278-9874 *E-mail:* sandiego@smartsourcerentals.com
408 N Canal St, Suite D, South San Francisco, CA 94080 *Tel:* 650-583-5340 *Fax:* 650-588-5591 *E-mail:* sanfrancisco@smartsourcerentals.com
3402 SW 26 Terr, Suite B-1, Fort Lauderdale, FL 33312 *Tel:* 954-316-4489 *Fax:* 954-316-4495 *E-mail:* ftlauderdale@smartsourcerentals.com
2416 Lake Orange Dr, Suite 190, Orlando, FL 32837 *Tel:* 407-582-9807 *Fax:* 407-582-9806 *E-mail:* orlando@smartsourcerentals.com
1850 MacArthur Blvd NW, Suite A, Atlanta, GA 30318 *Tel:* 404-352-0900 *Fax:* 404-352-8240 *E-mail:* atlanta@smartsourcerentals.com
2025 Glen Ellyn Rd, Glendale Heights, IL 60139 *Tel:* 630-588-0200 *Fax:* 630-622-0370 *E-mail:* chicago@smartsourcerentals.com
37 Southwest Park, Westwood, MA 02090 *Tel:* 781-320-6200 *Fax:* 781-326-3454 *E-mail:* boston@smartsourcerentals.com
3915 W Hacienda Ave, Suite A-101, Las Vegas, NV 89118 *Tel:* 702-791-2500 *Fax:* 702-791-2505 *E-mail:* lasvegas@smartsourcerentals.com
490 S Dean St, Englewood, NJ 07631 *Tel:* 201-568-6555 *Toll Free Tel:* 800-927-6555 *Fax:* 201-568-4448 *E-mail:* newyork@smartsourcerentals.com
4110 Butler Pike, Suite 100, Plymouth Meeting, PA 19462 *Tel:* 610-940-9500 *Fax:* 610-940-9501 *E-mail:* philadelphia@smartsourcerentals.com
2101 Midway Rd, Suite 100, Carrollton, TX 75006 *Tel:* 972-960-9888 *Fax:* 972-960-9891 *E-mail:* dallas@smartsourcerentals.com
5610-D Sandy Lewis Dr, Fairfax, VA 22032 *Tel:* 703-978-2321 *Fax:* 703-978-5735 *E-mail:* dc@smartsourcerentals.com
2715 152 Ave NE, No 6, Redmond, WA 98052-5552 *Tel:* 425-881-5353 *Fax:* 425-883-1218 *E-mail:* seattle@smartsourcerentals.com
Membership(s): International Technology Rental Association

SMI Inc
PO Box 7216, Waco, TX 76714-7216
Tel: 254-717-8917 *Fax:* 254-776-1230
E-mail: dmcminn@lmi-inc.com
Web Site: www.success-motivation.com
Key Personnel
EVP: Ian G Dawson *E-mail:* idawson@success-motivation.com

Smith Audio-Visual Inc
310 SW Sixth Ave, Topeka, KS 66603-3109
Tel: 785-235-3481 *Fax:* 785-235-3485
E-mail: sales@smithav.com
Web Site: www.smithav.com
Key Personnel
Pres & Sales Mgr: Larry Heilman *E-mail:* larry@smithav.com
Opers Mgr: Valerie Walker Heilman *E-mail:* valerie@smithav.com
Professional sound installation, presentation, digital surveillance, controlled access & home theater.
Catalog(s) available

Smith System Inc
1714 E 14 St, Plano, TX 75074
Mailing Address: PO Box 860415, Plano, TX 75086
Toll Free Tel: 800-328-1061 *Fax:* 972-398-4051
E-mail: furniture@smithsystem.com
Web Site: www.smithsystem.com
Key Personnel
CEO: Charlie Risdall *E-mail:* charlier@smithsystem.com
Founded: 1905
School furniture manufacturer.
Catalog(s) available
Membership(s): Education Market Association

Smith-Victor Corp
Division of Promark International Inc
1268 Humbracht Circle, Bartlett, IL 60103-1631
Tel: 630-830-9200 *Toll Free Tel:* 800-348-9862 *Fax:* 630-830-9201 *Toll Free Fax:* 800-352-0490
E-mail: sales@smithvictor.com
Key Personnel
Pres: Kenneth Orlando
Founded: 1874
Catalog(s) available
Membership(s): Education Market Association; InfoComm International®; Photo Marketing Association

Smithall Electronics Inc
2001 Vine St, Cincinnati, OH 45202
Tel: 513-381-2828 *Fax:* 513-381-5160
Web Site: www.smithall.com
Key Personnel
Pres: George C Smith
Founded: 1967

Smithsonian Folkways Recordings
Division of Smithsonian Institution
600 Maryland Ave SW, Suite 2001, Washington, DC 20024
Mailing Address: PO Box 37012, MRC 520, Washington, DC 20013-7012
Tel: 202-633-6450 *Toll Free Tel:* 888-FOLKWAYS (365-5929) *Fax:* 202-633-6477
E-mail: smithsonianfolkways@si.edu
Web Site: www.folkways.si.edu
Key Personnel
Dir, Mktg, Sales & Licensing: Richard Burgess *Tel:* 202-633-6452 *E-mail:* burgessr@si.edu
Produce traditional music from around the world. Physical goods, digital downloads, streaming audio & licensing.

Smithsonian National Museum of the American Indian
Affiliate of Film & Video Center for the Smithsonian Institution
c/o Film & Video Ctr, Natl Museum of the American Indian, One Bowling Green, New York, NY 10004-1415
Tel: 212-514-3700 *Fax:* 212-514-3725
E-mail: fvc@si.edu
Web Site: www.nmai.si.edu
Key Personnel
Dir, Film & Video Ctr: Elizabeth Weatherford
Asst Curator: Emelia Seubert
Founded: 1994
Film & video library.

Smolian Sound Studios
One Worman's Mill Ct, Frederick, MD 21701
Tel: 301-694-5134
E-mail: smolians@erols.com
Web Site: www.soundsaver.com
Key Personnel
Owner: Steven Smolian
Founded: 1962
Audio preservation for reel-to-reel tapes, audio cassette tapes, acetate discs, dictation formats. Sound restoration & preservation suites.
Online catalog(s) available
Membership(s): Association for Recorded Sound Collections; Music Library Association

SMP Digital Graphics
163 W 22 St, New York, NY 10011
Tel: 212-691-6766
E-mail: info@smpdigitalgraphics.com
Web Site: www.smpdigitalgraphics.com
Key Personnel
Pres: Stuart Penny
Full service graphics company.
Catalog(s) available

SMPTE, see Society of Motion Picture & Television Engineers (SMPTE)

SNAP
18653 Ventura, Suite 295, Tarzana, CA 91356
Tel: 818-340-0283
E-mail: hdcine@gmail.com
Web Site: www.facebook.com/barry.seybert
Key Personnel
Owner: Barry Seybert
Founded: 1979
Complete production & post-production company & equipment supplier.
Membership(s): Digital Cinema Society; STE

Snell
3519 Pacific Ave, Burbank, CA 91505
Tel: 818-556-2616 *Fax:* 818-556-2626
E-mail: americas@snellgroup.com
Web Site: www.snellgroup.com
Key Personnel
Pres, Americas: Jonathan Goldstein
Mng Dir: Paul Martin
Provides solutions for creation, management & distribution of content as well providing the tools necessary to transition to digital, HDTV & beyond.
Catalog(s) available
Membership(s): SMPTE

SNL Kagan Media & Communications
One SNL Plaza, 212 Seventh St NE, Charlottesville, VA 22902
Tel: 434-977-1600 *Toll Free Tel:* 866-296-3743 *Fax:* 434-977-4466
E-mail: snlkagansales@snl.com
Web Site: www.snl.com
Key Personnel
CEO & Pres: Mike Chinn
Chief Admin Offr: Tom Corbitt
COO: Nick Cafferillo
CFO: Adam Hall
CTO: Galen Warren
Mng Dir, Content: Nate Haskins

Mng Dir, Prod R&D: James Record
Mng Dir, Sales: Will Pappas
Founded: 1969
Worldwide analyses of the media & communications industry sectors, including Broadcast, TV Networks, Wireless & Wireline, US Multichannel, Global Multichannel, TV Programming, Filmed Entertainment & Internet Media.
Catalog(s) available

So Smart Productions
701 Sharpley Rd, Wilmington, DE 19803
Tel: 484-753-1520
E-mail: info@sosmart.com
Web Site: store.sosmart.com
Key Personnel
Founder, CEO & Pres: Alexandra Tornek; Scott Tornek *E-mail:* scott@sosmart.com
Founded: 1997
Producers of award winning "So Smart!" & "King Otis" learning videos & music for babies, toddlers & preschoolers. Distribute & produce DVDs, video/CD-ROMs, computer multimedia & DVD interactive.
Catalog(s) available

Social Studies School Service
10200 Jefferson Blvd, Culver City, CA 90232
Mailing Address: PO Box 802, Culver City, CA 90232-0802
Tel: 310-839-2436 *Toll Free Tel:* 800-421-4246
Fax: 310-839-2249 *Toll Free Fax:* 800-944-5432
E-mail: access@socialstudies.com
Web Site: www.socialstudies.com
Key Personnel
CEO: David Weiner
Founded: 1965
Educational resources-supplementary learning materials including books, CD-ROMs, videos, DVDs, software, charts & posters.
Catalog(s) available

Society of Manufacturing Engineers (SME)
One SME Dr, Dearborn, MI 48128
Tel: 313-425-3000 *Toll Free Tel:* 800-733-4763
E-mail: service@sme.org (cust care)
Web Site: www.sme.org
Key Personnel
Interim CEO: Dennis S Bray
Pres: Michael F Molnar
Founded: 1932
Professional society supporting lifelong manufacturing education.
Catalog(s) available
Branch Office(s)
7100 Woodbine Ave, Suite 312, Markham, ON L3R 5J2, Canada *Tel:* 905-752-4415 *Toll Free Tel:* 888-322-7333 *Fax:* 905-479-0113 *E-mail:* canadasales@sme.org

Society of Motion Picture & Television Engineers (SMPTE)
3 Barker Ave, 5th fl, White Plains, NY 10601
Tel: 914-761-1100 *Fax:* 914-761-3115
E-mail: smpte@smpte.org
Web Site: www.smpte.org
Key Personnel
Exec Dir: Barbara Lange *Tel:* 914-205-2370 *E-mail:* blange@smpte.org
Dir, Opers: Sally-Ann D'Amato *Tel:* 914-205-2375 *E-mail:* sdamato@smpte.org
Mktg & Communs: Aimee Ricca *Tel:* 914-205-2381
Founded: 1916
Technical society for the motion imaging industry - advance engineering & technical aspects of movies, television, arts & sciences.

Sodanceabit
11372 Kelly Lane, Los Alamitos, CA 90720
Tel: 562-799-4340 *Toll Free Tel:* 800-64-DANCE (643-2623)
E-mail: sodanceabit@live.com
Web Site: www.sodanceabit.com
Key Personnel
Owner: Phil Martin
Produce & distribute audios & videos on how to dance & keep fit.
Catalog(s), free

Sofradir EC
373 Rte 46 W, Fairfield, NJ 07004-2442
Tel: 973-882-0211 *Toll Free Tel:* 800-759-9577
Fax: 973-882-0997
E-mail: info@sofradir-ec.com
Web Site: www.nightvisioncameras.com
Founded: 1969
Manufacture night vision modules for ENG cameras, digital & film cameras & camcorders.
Catalog(s) available

SoftWright LLC
PO Box 7205, Charlotte, VA 22906
Tel: 303-344-5486 *Toll Free Tel:* 800-728-4033
Fax: 303-265-9399
E-mail: sales@softwright.com
Web Site: www.softwright.com
Key Personnel
CEO & Pres: Jason O Burkholder, PhD *E-mail:* jason.burkholder@softwright.com
Dir, Prod Devt: John J Reilly
Dir, R&D: Todd A Summers, PhD
Global Sales: Curt Alway
Microcomputer software manufacturer.

Elliot Sokolov Music
Division of User Friendly Music (BMI)
149 Mountainview Rd, Patterson, NY 12563
Tel: 917-690-5487
E-mail: elliotsoko@aol.com
Web Site: www.elliotsokolov.com
Key Personnel
Owner & Prodr: Elliot Sokolov
Music producer, including MP3. User friendly music library.

Solar Studios
1601 S Central Ave, Glendale, CA 91204
Tel: 818-240-1893 *Fax:* 818-240-4187
Web Site: www.solarstudios.com
Key Personnel
Contact: Peter Cohn *E-mail:* peter@solarstudios.com
Studio & soundstage rental for filming, commercial shoots, green screen work, music video, still photo shoots & special events.

Solid Sound Recording Studio
2400 Hassell Rd, Suite 430, Hoffman Estates, IL 60169
Tel: 847-490-2101
E-mail: solidsoundrecordingstudios@gmail.com
Key Personnel
Studio Mgr: John Towner
Founded: 1979

Solid State Logic Inc
320 W 46 St, 2nd fl, New York, NY 10036-8398
Tel: 212-315-1111
E-mail: sales@solidstatelogic.com
Web Site: www.solid-state-logic.com
Key Personnel
SVP: Don Wershba
Designer of audio mixing consoles.
Catalog(s) available
Membership(s): AES; Florida Motion Picture & Television Association; NAB; National Endowment for the Arts; SMPTE; SPARS

Solutek Corp
94 Shirley St, Boston, MA 02119
Tel: 617-445-5335 *Toll Free Tel:* 800-403-0770
Fax: 617-445-9623
E-mail: bflanagan@solutek.com
Web Site: www.solutekphotochemicals.com
Key Personnel
Pres: M A Sigal
Catalog(s) available

Solution Tree
555 N Morton St, Bloomington, IN 47404-3730
Tel: 812-336-7700 *Toll Free Tel:* 800-733-6786
Fax: 812-336-7790
E-mail: info@solution-tree.com
Web Site: www.solution-tree.com
Key Personnel
CEO: Jeff Jones

SoLux, see EiKO Ltd

SOM Publishing Co
Division of School of Metaphysics
163 Moon Valley Rd, Windyville, MO 65783
Tel: 417-345-8411
E-mail: som@som.org
Web Site: www.som.org
Key Personnel
CEO & Dir, Prodn: Barbara O'Guinn Condron
Pres: Laurel Clark
Secy: Brian Kraichley
Asst Dir, Prodn & Intl Secy: Karen Mosby
Master Prodn Engr: Paul Madar
Catalog(s) available

Sonalysts Media
215 Parkway N, Waterford, CT 06385
Mailing Address: PO Box 280, Waterford, CT 06385
Tel: 860-326-3848 *Toll Free Tel:* 800-526-8091 (ext 3848)
E-mail: tour_rehearsals@sonalysts.com
Web Site: www.sonalystsmedia.com
Soundstage rentals. Offers a full suite of integrated media services. Provides services in the areas of animation, audio production, exhibits & events, graphic communications, video production & post-production, web site development & new media.

Sonance
Formerly Sound Advance Systems Inc
212 Avenida Fabricante, San Clemente, CA 92672-7531
Tel: 949-492-7777 *Toll Free Tel:* 800-592-4644; 800-582-0772 (tech support); 800-582-7777
Toll Free Fax: 800-538-5151
E-mail: customerservice@sonance.com
Web Site: www.sonance.com
Key Personnel
Founder: Geoff Spencer; Scott Struthers
Founded: 1982
Manufacture sound systems.
Catalog(s) available
Membership(s): ASID; CES; Custom Electronic Design & Installation Association; NSCA

Sonar Radio Corp
3000 Stirling Rd, Hollywood, FL 33021-2039
Tel: 954-981-8800 *Fax:* 954-981-8800
Key Personnel
Pres: Bernard E Klein
Engineering & licensing company distributing video recording accessories.
Catalog(s) available

Sonic Gravy
2515 Laurel Path, Los Angeles, CA 90046
Tel: 323-650-2751 *Fax:* 323-822-1003
Web Site: www.johnswihart.tumblr.com
Key Personnel
Composer: John Swihart *E-mail:* john@sonicgravy.com
Original music.

Sonic Science Inc
79 Denlow Blvd, Toronto, ON M3B 1P8, Canada
Tel: 416-383-0260 *Toll Free Tel:* 800-267-6642 *Fax:* 416-383-0261
E-mail: sales@sonicscience.com
Web Site: www.sonicscience.com
Key Personnel
Pres: Martin Yale *E-mail:* martin@sonicscience.com
Founded: 1980
Developer of sound retrieval & media mangement systems.

SonicPool
6860 Lexington Ave, Hollywood, CA 90038
Tel: 323-460-4649 *Toll Free Tel:* 866-203-7213 *Fax:* 323-460-6063
E-mail: production@sonicpool.com
Web Site: www.sonicpool.com
Key Personnel
Founder & Pres: Patrick Bird
Founder: John Frost
Founded: 2001
Post-production picture & sound, VFX, titles, deliverables, DVD/Blu-ray creation, authoring & rental. 20,000 sq ft secure access facility.

SoNo Studios
18 Leonard St, Norwalk, CT 06850
Tel: 203-354-4002 *Fax:* 203-354-7018
E-mail: info@sonostudios.com
Web Site: www.sonostudios.com
Full service soundstage rental.

Sonoma Valley Chamber of Commerce
651-A Broadway, Sonoma, CA 95476-7041
Tel: 707-996-1033 *Fax:* 707-996-9402
E-mail: info@sonomachamber.com
Web Site: sonomachamber.org
Key Personnel
CEO: Jennifer Yankovich
Exec Membership & Admin Asst: Angela Beran
Founded: 1909
Distributor of local business video programs.

Sonora Recorders
3222 Los Feliz Blvd, Los Angeles, CA 90039
Tel: 323-663-2500
E-mail: ductape@aol.com
Web Site: www.sonorarecorders.com
Key Personnel
Owner & Engr: Richard Barron
Founded: 1992
Audio recording & mixing.
Online catalog(s) available

Sonoton Music Library
Division of Associated Production Music LLC
6255 Sunset Blvd, Suite 820, Hollywood, CA 90028
Tel: 323-461-3211 *Toll Free Tel:* 800-543-4276 *Fax:* 323-461-9102
Web Site: www.apmmusic.com
Key Personnel
US Mktg Dir: Elisabeth Oei *Tel:* 818-888-6523
Catalog(s) available

Sony Electronics Inc
Division of Sony Corp of America
16530 Via Esprillo, San Diego, CA 92127
Tel: 858-942-2400
Web Site: www.sony.com
Key Personnel
VP, Corp Communs: John Dolak *Tel:* 858-942-2905 *E-mail:* john.dolak@am.sony.com
Manufacture electronics.
Catalog(s) available

Sony Music Custom Marketing
Division of Sony Music
550 Madison Ave, New York, NY 10022
Tel: 212-833-8000
Web Site: www.sonymusic.com
Music production.

Sony Music Entertainment
Division of Sony Music
550 Madison Ave, New York, NY 10022
Tel: 212-833-8000 *Fax:* 212-833-8336
Web Site: www.sonymusic.com
Key Personnel
CFO & EVP: Kevin Kelleher
Membership(s): AES; The Recording Academy; RIAA; SPARS

Sony Pictures Entertainment
Subsidiary of Sony Corp of America
10202 W Washington Blvd, Culver City, CA 90232
Tel: 310-244-4000
Web Site: www.sonypictures.com
Key Personnel
Co-Chmn & CEO: Michael Lynton
Co-Chmn: Amy Pascal
VChmn: Jeff Blake
Film & video producer & distributor.

Sony Pictures Home Entertainment
10202 W Washington Blvd, Culver City, CA 90232-3119
Tel: 310-244-4000 *Fax:* 310-244-2485
Web Site: www.sonypictures.com
Key Personnel
Pres: David Bishop
SVP, Worldwide Publicity: Fritz Friedman
Catalog(s) available
Membership(s): Entertainment Merchants Association

Sony Pro Audio (Broadcast & Professional Systems Division)
Division of Sony Electronics Inc
One Sony Dr, Park Ridge, NJ 07656
Tel: 201-930-1000
Web Site: pro.sony.com/bbsc/ssr/home.do
Key Personnel
Assoc Prod Mktg Specialist: Gina Voigt
Manufacture electronics such as digital recorders & players.
Catalog(s) available
Membership(s): AES; NAMM, the National Association of Music Merchants; NSCA; Professional Audio Manufacturers Alliance

SOS Film Works (Space Ordnance Systems)
Subsidiary of Agua Dulce Movie Ranch Inc
34855 Petersen Rd, Agua Dulce, CA 91390
Tel: 661-251-2365 *Fax:* 661-268-7680
Web Site: www.sosfilmworks.com
Key Personnel
Pres: William Fix *E-mail:* williamfix@sosfilmworks.com
Founded: 1991
Location(s) for feature film, television, commercials & music videos.

SOS Worldwide Productions Inc
2000 Towerside Terr, Suite 607, Miami, FL 33138
Tel: 305-891-9133; 305-653-5321 (cell) *Fax:* 305-603-8111
E-mail: info@safesongs.com; info@safesongs4kids.com
Web Site: www.safesongs.com; www.safesongs4kids.com; www.safesongsforkids.com
Key Personnel
Pres & Creator: Sylvia Ozner Segal
Founded: 1988
Creates music & lyrics of all genres: motivational, educational, inspirational, sports, advertising, back-up music for films, radio & retail. Videos are available on YouTube under AMusicalBuffet.
Brochure(s), as ordered, assorted per pkg, per item. available online
Membership(s): ASCAP; Florida Crime Prevention Association; Grammy Foundation; The Recording Academy; Songwriters Guild of America

SOTA Sales & Service Center
10830 S Nagle Ave, Worth, IL 60482
Mailing Address: PO Box 247, Worth, IL 60482-0247
Tel: 608-538-3500 *Toll Free Tel:* 800-772-7682 *Fax:* 608-538-3502
E-mail: sotaturntables@kwom.com
Web Site: www.sotaturntables.com
Key Personnel
Founder: Donna Bodinet; Kirk Bodinet
Founded: 1997
Manufacture & service turntables & turntable accessories.
Catalog(s) available

Soularium Recording Studios
702 S Alpine Hwy, Alpine, UT 84004
Tel: 801-492-0505
E-mail: solariumstudios@gmail.com
Web Site: www.soulariumstudios.com
Key Personnel
Owner: Dan Carlisle *E-mail:* danc@soulariumstudios.com
Founded: 1996
Music recording/mixing & all audio post-production.

Sound Advance Systems Inc, see Sonance

Sound Advantage
93 Shaw Rd, Little Compton, RI 02837
Tel: 508-653-1644
E-mail: soundadvantage@mac.com
Key Personnel
Pres: Greg Fitzgerald

Sound & Images Inc
104 Corporate Blvd, Suite 411, West Columbia, SC 29169
Mailing Address: PO Box 2102, West Columbia, SC 29171-2102
Tel: 803-791-3925
E-mail: marketing@s-and-i.com
Web Site: www.s-and-i.com
Key Personnel
Founder & CEO: Eddie Wright *E-mail:* ceo@s-and-i.com
Dir, Mktg & Events: Rob Nelson
Founded: 1981
Corporate audio, video & lighting company that rents, sells & installs.

Sound & Video Creations Inc
2408 Felts Ave, Nashville, TN 37211
Tel: 615-460-7330 *Fax:* 615-460-7331
Web Site: www.clickeffects.com
Key Personnel
Pres: Fran Kowalski *E-mail:* fkowalski@clickeffects.com
Founded: 1985
Makers of click effects systems & original music production.
Membership(s): International Association of Assembly Managers; NAMM, the National Association of Music Merchants

Sound & Vision Communications Inc
4601 N "A" St, Tampa, FL 33609-1909
Tel: 813-642-4706
Web Site: www.gosvc.com
Key Personnel
CEO & Creative Dir: Suzanne Harrell

Pres: Ian Cuthbertson *E-mail:* ian@gosvc.com
Sr Conference Prodr & Head, European Opers: Amy Burns
Founded: 1982
Full service meeting, event & video production.

Sound & Vision Media
372 Squire Rd, Revere, MA 02151
Tel: 781-284-9707
Web Site: www.soundandvisionmedia.com
Key Personnel
Mng Partner: Howard Cook; Mark Helms
Gen Mgr: Charles Vitale
Founded: 1972
In-house corporate & commercial video, radio & web production.

Sound Arts Recording Studio
8377 Westview Dr, Houston, TX 77055-5737
Tel: 713-464-4653
Web Site: www.soundartsrecording.com
Key Personnel
Engr, Mixer & Prodr: Brian Baker *E-mail:* brianbaker@soundartsrecording.com
Music recording studio.
Brochure(s) available
Membership(s): ASCAP; BMI

Sound Associates Inc
424 W 45 St, New York, NY 10036
Tel: 212-757-5679 *Toll Free Tel:* 888-772-7686 *Fax:* 212-265-1250
E-mail: newyork@soundassociates.com
Web Site: www.soundassociates.com
Key Personnel
CEO: Richard Fitzgerald *Tel:* 914-963-3452
Founded: 1946
Manufacturer & distributor of hearing assistance systems as well as professional audio & video systems.
Branch Office(s)
979 Saw Mill River Rd, Yonkers, NY 10710 *Tel:* 914-963-3452 *Fax:* 914-963-4236 *E-mail:* info@soundassociates.com
560-F Amsterdam Ave NE, Atlanta, GA 30306, Acct Mgr: Amy Edelkind *Tel:* 404-724-9050 *Fax:* 404-724-9891 *E-mail:* atlanta@soundassociates.com (prodn servs)

Sound by Fitch
Division of Fitch Electronics Inc
1134 Ridge Rd, Pottstown, PA 19465
Tel: 610-469-6082 *Fax:* 610-469-0559
Key Personnel
Pres: William Fitch
Audio equipment distributor.
Membership(s): AES; ARCA

Sound by Singer Ltd
242 W 27 St, 2nd fl, New York, NY 10001
Tel: 212-924-8600 *Fax:* 212-366-6351
E-mail: info@soundbysinger.com
Web Site: www.soundbysinger.com
Key Personnel
Pres: Andrew Singer
Full service AV dealer.

Sound Control Technologies Inc
28 Knight St, Norwalk, CT 06851
Tel: 203-854-5701 *Fax:* 203-854-5702
E-mail: sales@soundcontrol.net
Web Site: www.soundcontrol.net
Key Personnel
Co-Founder & Pres: Adolph Neaderland *E-mail:* aneaderland@soundcontrol.net
Co-Founder & VP: David Neaderland *E-mail:* dneaderland@soundcontrol.net
Founded: 1987
Manufacturer of electronic components for conference & training rooms.

Catalog(s) available
Membership(s): IMFA; InfoComm International®; NSCA

Sound-Craft Systems Inc
1584 Petit Jean Mountain Rd, Morrilton, AR 72110
Tel: 501-727-5476 *Toll Free Tel:* 800-643-8747 *Fax:* 501-727-5402
E-mail: sales@sound-craft.com
Web Site: www.sound-craft.com
Key Personnel
Sales Mgr: Jeffery Zimmerman *E-mail:* jeffz@sound-craft.com
Founded: 1947
Manufacturer of presentation equipment & furniture.
Catalog(s) available
Membership(s): ARA; InfoComm International®

Sound Feelings Records
18375 Ventura Blvd, No 8000, Tarzana, CA 91356
Tel: 818-757-0600
Web Site: www.soundfeelings.com
Key Personnel
Pres: Howard Richman
Founded: 1984
Music for transformation including MP3.
Catalog(s) available

Sound-FX-Design
Subsidiary of Shortwave Recording Co Inc
PO Box 3541, Newport, RI 02840
Tel: 401-952-1186
E-mail: info@sound-fx-design.com
Web Site: www.sound-fx-design.com
Key Personnel
Owner & Pres: Steve Cerilli
Founded: 2000
Sound design, audio & video post-production for 3D animation & TV, production sound & location sound for film.

Sound Ideas
105 W Beaver Creek Rd, Suite 4, Richmond Hill, ON L4B 1C6, Canada
Tel: 905-886-5000 *Toll Free Tel:* 800-387-3030 *Fax:* 905-886-6800
E-mail: info@sound-ideas.com
Web Site: www.sound-ideas.com
Key Personnel
Pres: Brian Nimens
Sound effects & production music for broadcast, film & multimedia.
Catalog(s) available
Membership(s): AES; NAB; SMPTE

The Sound Lab Inc
3355 Bee Cave Rd, Bldg 7, Suite 705, Austin, TX 78746
Tel: 512-476-2122 *Fax:* 512-476-2127
E-mail: info@thesoundlabinc.com
Web Site: www.thesoundlabinc.com
Key Personnel
Owner: Steve Metz *E-mail:* steve@thesoundlabinc.com
Owner & Pres: Phil Mezzetti *E-mail:* phil@thesoundlabinc.com
Founded: 2002
Recording studio; pro tools digital editing, ISDN digital phone patch, ADR, large cutting room; music & sound effects libraries. Radio & TV audio production, audio for film, animation & gaming.

Sound*Light
5438 Tennessee Ave, New Port Richey, FL 34652
Tel: 727-842-6788 *Fax:* 727-842-6788
Web Site: www.awakening-healing.com; www.soundlight.org

Key Personnel
Master of Light: Keth Luke *Tel:* 727-457-1229 (cell) *E-mail:* keth@soundlight.org
Astrologer Consultant: Jan Carter
Founded: 1974
Light photographic, AV services & support.
Brochure(s) available
Branch Office(s)
2140 Bonny Castle, Louisville, KY 40205
Membership(s): NATAS

Sound of Birmingham Productions
3625 Fifth Ave S, Birmingham, AL 35222
Tel: 205-595-8497 *Fax:* 205-595-5220
Web Site: www.soundofbirmingham.com
Key Personnel
Owner: Don Mosley *E-mail:* don@soundofbirmingham.com
Founded: 1975
All types of audio recording. Three studios with DeWolfe, AMC & Custom music libraries.

Sound Physics Labs Inc
PO Box 319, Glenview, IL 60025
Tel: 847-380-9390
E-mail: sales@soundphysics.com; info@soundphysics.com
Web Site: www.soundphysics.com
Key Personnel
Busn Mgr: Kelly McTigue
Sales Mgr: B Skuranskis
Founded: 1996
Manufacturer of audio sound systems & mechanical subwoofers, fixed installation.
Membership(s): NSCA

Sound Service Co
6630 Morella Ave, North Hollywood, CA 91606-1651
Tel: 818-503-4440
Key Personnel
Owner & Sr Systems Engr: Joel Thames *E-mail:* jetames@sbcglobal.net

Sound Sound/Savage Fruitarian Productions
843 Hiawatha Place S, Unit 304, Seattle, WA 98144
Tel: 206-322-6866
Web Site: www.soundsound.com
Key Personnel
Owner & CEO: Tom Fallat *E-mail:* tomss@soundsound.com
Founded: 1990
Audio recording & production facility.
Catalog(s) available
Shipping Address: 2515-B E Union St, Seattle, WA 98122-0999

Sound Strations Audio Productions Inc
3120 South Ave, La Crosse, WI 54601
Tel: 608-787-8133 *Fax:* 608-787-0012
Web Site: soundstrations.com
Key Personnel
Founder: Brett Huus *E-mail:* bhuus@soundstrations.com
Founded: 1993
Full service digital recording studio for marketing, communication & music professionals.

The Sound Tracker®, see Quiet Planet LLC

Sound Venture International
441 MacLaren St, Suite 401, Ottawa, ON K2P 2H3, Canada
Tel: 613-241-5111 *Fax:* 613-241-5010
E-mail: info@soundventure.com
Web Site: www.soundventure.com
Key Personnel
Founder & Pres: Neil Bregman *Tel:* 613-241-5111 ext 250 *E-mail:* neil@soundventure.com
VP & Prodr: Tim Joyce

VP & Dir: Katherine Jeans *Tel:* 613-241-5111 ext 268
Founded: 1980
Produce performing arts, documentary, cultural & children's programming. Film & TV drama production. Audio, video & graphic design services.

Sound/Video Impressions Inc
110 S River Rd, Des Plaines, IL 60016
Tel: 847-297-4360 *Fax:* 847-297-6870
E-mail: info@soundvideoimpressions.com
Web Site: www.soundvideoimpressions.com
Key Personnel
Pres: Bill Holtane
VP, Opers: Paul Snead
Studio Mgr: Kathy Dunaj
Sales: Jerry Jacobs *E-mail:* jerry@soundvideoimpressions.com
Video & audio production & post-production, interactive programming for web, CD-ROM, DVD, video web casts & web sites.
Catalog(s) available

Sound Vision Inc
1450 Davis Rd, Elgin, IL 60123
Tel: 847-742-6000 *Fax:* 847-742-7585
E-mail: info@svi-avsystems.com
Web Site: www.svi-avsystems.com
Key Personnel
VP: James Kaiser
Founded: 1992
Engineer, install, program & maintain AV systems.
Membership(s): National Electrical Contractors Association; National Systems Contractors Association

Sound Works
7110 Gary St, Houston, TX 77055
Tel: 713-960-8222 (ext 1) *Fax:* 713-960-0122
E-mail: w3@soundworks.com; sworks@soundworks.com
Web Site: www.soundworks.com
Key Personnel
Founder & Owner: Dwight Cook *Tel:* 713-960-8222 ext 2 *E-mail:* dcook@soundworks.com
Premier media production company.
Membership(s): AAF; SPARS

SoundByte Productions Inc
353 W 48 St, 6th fl, New York, NY 10036
Tel: 212-675-0600 *Fax:* 212-675-3724
E-mail: info@soundbyte.com
Web Site: www.soundbyte.com
Key Personnel
Owner: Nelson Wong
Owner & Chief Engr: Paul Zinman
Independent audio services company offering production, post-production & location recording services.
Catalog(s) available

Soundcraft USA
Subsidiary of Harman Pro North America
8500 Balboa Blvd, North Ridge, CA 91329
Tel: 818-920-3212 *Fax:* 818-920-3209
E-mail: soundcraft-usa@harman.com
Web Site: usa.soundcraft.com
Key Personnel
Sales: Tom Der *E-mail:* tder@harman.com
Sales & Mktg: Katy Templeman-Holmes
Founded: 1973
Design & manufacture professional audio mixing consoles.
Catalog(s) available
Membership(s): AES; NSCA

Soundfold International
9200 N State Rte 48, Centerville, OH 45458
Tel: 937-885-5100 *Toll Free Tel:* 800-782-8018 *Fax:* 937-885-5115
Web Site: www.soundfold.com
Key Personnel
Pres: Tony Sickels *E-mail:* tsickels@soundfold.com
Founded: 1967
Manufacturer of acoustical wall coverings, wall carpets & surround mounts.
Catalog(s) available

Soundmaster Group
89 Barford Rd, Toronto, ON M9W 4H8, Canada
Tel: 416-741-7057 *Fax:* 416-410-7057
E-mail: mail@soundmaster.com
Web Site: www.soundmaster.com
Key Personnel
Chmn & CEO: Robert Predovich
Developer of the award-winning ION® Operating Environment.

Sounds Interesting Studios
112 Fuller St, Middleboro, MA 02346
Mailing Address: PO Box 465, Middleboro, MA 02346-0465
Tel: 508-947-7387
Web Site: www.soundsinterestingstudio.com
Key Personnel
Owner & Pres: Erik Lindgren *E-mail:* erik@arfarfrecords.com
Engr: Brian Cass *Tel:* 508-264-7727 *E-mail:* brian@overclockinc.com
Acoustically designed professional recording studio.

Sounds Unique
1721-A Little Orchard St, San Jose, CA 95125
Tel: 408-287-3002
Web Site: www.soundsunique.com
Key Personnel
Owner: Michael Steiner *E-mail:* micky@soundsunique.com
Founded: 1972
High-end speaker systems, electronics & media products wholesale to the public.

SoundSpace Inc
845 Dayton St, Yellow Springs, OH 45387
Tel: 937-767-7353 *Fax:* 937-767-7348
E-mail: soundspace@sbcglobal.net
Key Personnel
Pres: Chris Hertzler
Audio production service company & video editing.
Catalog(s) available

Soundsphere
Division of Sonic Systems Inc
10 Research Dr, Stratford, CT 06615
Tel: 203-386-9200 *Fax:* 203-386-0773
E-mail: info@soundsphere.com
Web Site: www.soundsphere.com
Key Personnel
Pres: Peter Hamilton
Sales Mgr: Scott Gronsbell
Founded: 1976
Manufacture Soundsphere omnidirectional loudspeakers.
Catalog(s) available
Membership(s): InfoComm International®

SoundTech
Division of US Music Corp
1000 Corporate Grove Dr, Buffalo Grove, IL 60089
Tel: 847-949-0444 *Toll Free Tel:* 800-US-SOUND (877-6863) *Fax:* 847-949-8444; 775-898-4891
E-mail: soundtech@soundtech.com
Web Site: www.usmusiccorp.com; www.soundtech.com
Key Personnel
Mktg Mgr: Chris Walker *E-mail:* cwalker@usmusiccorp.com
Recording cables.
Catalog(s) available

Soundtrack Recording Studios
162 Columbus Ave, Boston, MA 02116
Tel: 617-303-7500 *Fax:* 617-303-7555
Web Site: www.soundtrackboston.com
Key Personnel
COO: Amy Blankenship *E-mail:* ablankenship@soundtrackboston.com
Production & post-production space & services.
Branch Office(s)
936 Broadway, New York, NY 10010, DOO: Maegan Hayward *Tel:* 212-420-6010 ext 271 *Fax:* 212-777-6403 *E-mail:* maegan.hayward@soundtrackny.com

Soundtracks Production Services LLC
22 N Central Ave, Sicklerville, NJ 08081
Tel: 856-728-8112 *Fax:* 856-728-8075
E-mail: info@soundtracksnj.com
Web Site: www.soundtracksnj.com
Founded: 1985
Production equipment rentals, including speakers, amplifiers, signal processing equipment, microphones, lighting fixtures, special effects generators, projectors, screens & stages.

Soundtrax Optical Sound Recording
8116 Brucar Ct, Gaithersburg, MD 20877
Tel: 301-948-4288 *Fax:* 301-869-9061
Key Personnel
Pres: Leonard Schmitz *Tel:* 240-401-9555 (cell)
Audio equipment rental & location sound recording.

SoundTube Entertainment
Subsidiary of Multi Service Electronics
6430 N Business Park Loop, Park City, UT 84098
Tel: 435-647-9555 *Toll Free Tel:* 800-647-TUBE (647-8823) *Fax:* 435-647-9666
E-mail: sales@soundtube.com
Web Site: www.soundtube.com
Key Personnel
VP, Sales: Duke Ducoff *E-mail:* dducoff@soundtube.com
World leader in speaker innovation.
Membership(s): InfoComm International®

SoundView Services Inc
One Phillips Dr NW, Leesburg, VA 20176
Tel: 703-777-9570 *Toll Free Tel:* 866-680-8189
E-mail: info@soundviewservices.com
Web Site: www.soundviewservices.com
Key Personnel
Prodr: David Mercado *E-mail:* david@soundviewservices.com
Founded: 2001
CD & DVD duplications, video editing, script writing, AV services, video & audio production.

Source Film Studio
1111 N Beachwood Dr, Hollywood, CA 90038
Tel: 323-463-5555
E-mail: info@sourcefilmstudio.com
Web Site: www.sourcefilmstudio.com
Key Personnel
Contact: Juan Hernandez *Tel:* 323-463-5555 ext 3 *E-mail:* juan@sourcefilmstudio.com; Bobby Naidu *Tel:* 323-463-5555 ext 4 *Fax:* 323-463-5556 *E-mail:* bobby@sourcefilmstudio.com
Studio rentals with an extensive inventory of lighting equipment, grip equipment & production supplies.

Source School of Tantra Yoga Inc
PO Box 368, Kahului, HI 96733
Tel: 808-572-8364 *Toll Free Tel:* 888-6-TANTRA (682-6872) *Fax:* 831-703-4221
E-mail: school@sourcetantra.com
Web Site: www.sourcetantra.com
Key Personnel
Founder: Charles Muir
Founded: 1978
Seminars, appearances, books & products on Tantra Yoga.
Catalog(s) available

The Source Stock Footage Library Inc
Subsidiary of The Source Films
140 S Camino Seco, Suite 308, Tucson, AZ 85710
Tel: 520-298-4810 *Fax:* 520-290-4376
E-mail: requests@sourcefootage.com
Web Site: www.sourcefootage.com
Key Personnel
Pres: Rick De Croix *Tel:* 212-925-2547
Lib Mgr: Don E French
Founded: 1982
Stock footage library, assorted film & video originated images transferred to video.
Demo reel(s), VHS demo copy available, no charge to video professionals
Online catalog(s) available
Membership(s): International Quorum of Motion Picture Producers

South Coast Film & Video
5234 Elm St, Houston, TX 77081
Tel: 713-661-3550 *Toll Free Tel:* 800-229-3550 *Fax:* 713-661-4357
E-mail: info@scfilmvideo.com
Web Site: www.scfilmvideo.com
Key Personnel
Pres & Dir: Everett Gorel
Prod Mgr & Audio Engr: Steve Goyette
Sr Ed: Marco DuBose
Founded: 1980
Full service production & post-production company.
Catalog(s) available
Membership(s): NABET-CWA; Texas Association of Motion Media Professionals

South Florida Rehearsal Studios
1885 NE 149 St, Suite 100, North Miami, FL 33181
Tel: 305-949-5303 *Fax:* 305-947-3030
E-mail: sfrsmusic@gmail.com
Web Site: www.sfrs.net
Founded: 1996
Full service production recording facility with five acoustically designed rehearsal studios equipped with professional rehearsal equipment & audio gear.

South Trunk Studios
825 S Trunk Ave, Dallas, TX 75210
Tel: 214-826-2513
E-mail: southtrunk@earthlink.net
Web Site: www.southtrunk.com
Key Personnel
Owner: Randy Murphy
Photography, studio & location; specialty props.

South-Western Publishing Co
Subsidiary of Cengage Learning
5191 Natorp Blvd, Mason, OH 45040
Tel: 513-229-1000 *Toll Free Tel:* 800-543-0487 *Fax:* 513-229-1020
E-mail: esales@cengage.com
Web Site: www.cengage.com
Key Personnel
Admin Asst: Linda Chaffee
Educational programming.
Catalog(s) available
Membership(s): AECT

Southern Audio Visual
11700 NW 102 Rd, Suite 15, Miami, FL 33178
Tel: 305-591-3888 *Fax:* 305-591-7105
Web Site: www.southernav.com
Key Personnel
Owner & CEO: David Brodie *E-mail:* dbrodie@southernav.com
Pres: Paul Lowenthal *E-mail:* plowenthal@southernav.com
Founded: 1947
Exclusive AV provider for hotels & business centers.

Southern California Sound Image Inc
2415 Auto Park Way, Escondido, CA 92029-1222
Tel: 760-737-3900 *Fax:* 760-737-3929
Web Site: www.sound-image.com
Key Personnel
Pres: Dave Shadoan
Sr Estimator: Jason Schmidlapp *E-mail:* jschmidlapp@sound-image.com
Founded: 1971
Audio, video & control integration.
Branch Office(s)
1545 W University Dr, Tempe, AZ 85281 *Tel:* 480-483-6422 *Fax:* 480-483-6428
7127 Cockrill Bend Blvd, Nashville, TN 37209 *Tel:* 615-256-0528 *Fax:* 615-256-9945

Southern Illinois University
605 Agriculture Dr, Mailcode 6632, Carbondale, IL 62901
Tel: 618-453-2258 *Fax:* 618-453-3010
Web Site: www.lib.siu.edu/departments/iss
Key Personnel
Mgr, Instrl Support Servs: Howard Carter *Tel:* 618-453-2522 *E-mail:* hcarter@lib.siu.edu
Video & audio support services.
Catalog(s) available

Southwest Audio-Visual Inc
3058 E Cairo, Springfield, MO 65802
Tel: 417-887-4900 *Fax:* 417-866-6500
E-mail: info@southwestav.com
Web Site: www.southwestav.com
Key Personnel
Pres: Kevin Lines
Founded: 1996
Full service AV provider.

Southwest Binding & Laminating
109 Millwell Ct, Maryland Heights, MO 63043-2509
Mailing Address: PO Box 150, Maryland Heights, MO 63043-9150
Tel: 314-739-4400 *Toll Free Tel:* 800-325-3628 *Toll Free Fax:* 800-942-2010
E-mail: orders@swbindinglaminating.com
Web Site: swbindinglaminating.com
Key Personnel
Pres: Mark Mercer
Founded: 1966
Binding, laminating & presentation supplies & equipment.
Membership(s): VAC

SouthWest Organizing Project (SWOP)
211 Tenth St SW, Albuquerque, NM 87102-2919
Tel: 505-247-8832 *Fax:* 505-247-9972
E-mail: swop@swop.net
Web Site: www.swop.net
Key Personnel
Dir: Marjorie Childress; Monica Cordova
Off Mgr: Robert Roibal *E-mail:* roberto@swop.net
Founded: 1980
A statewide multi-racial, community based membership organization.

Southwest Sound & Electronics Inc
2323 Loop 410 NW, San Antonio, TX 78230-5348
Tel: 210-341-4411 *Fax:* 210-349-8300
Web Site: www.swsoundinc.com
Key Personnel
Pres & Gen Mgr: Stephen Simpson *E-mail:* ssimpson@swsoundinc.com
Founded: 1986
Commercial sound, professional audio contractor.
Membership(s): InfoComm International®; NSCA

Sovfoto/Eastfoto Inc
263 W 20 St, Suite 3, New York, NY 10011
Tel: 212-727-8170 *Fax:* 212-727-8228
E-mail: info@sovfoto.com
Web Site: www.sovfoto.com
Key Personnel
Dir: Mr Vanya Edwards
Founded: 1932
Stock photo agency.
Brochure(s) available

SpaceCam
31111 Via Colinas, Suite 202, Westlake Village, CA 91362
Tel: 818-889-6060 *Fax:* 818-889-6062
E-mail: rentals@spacecam.com
Web Site: spacecam.com
Key Personnel
CEO & Pres: Ron Goodman
VP, Mktg: Sandra Crawford *E-mail:* sandy@spacecam.com
Opers Mgr: Joanne Adalid *E-mail:* joanne@spacecam.com
Inventory Mgr: Ron C Tatham *E-mail:* rtatham@spacecam.com
Camera system rentals for aerial film production.

Sparkfactor
1644 N Honore St, Suite 100, Chicago, IL 60622
Tel: 773-292-8000
E-mail: info@sparkfactor.com
Web Site: www.sparkfactor.com
Key Personnel
Pres: George F Lowe
Founded: 2000
Full service digital agency.

Sparkworks Media
325 W Republican St, Seattle, WA 98119
Tel: 206-284-5500 *Fax:* 206-284-6611
E-mail: info@sparkworksmedia.com
Web Site: sparkworksmedia.com
Key Personnel
Owner & Pres: Michel Hansmire *E-mail:* michel@sparkworksmedia.com
Founded: 2004
Video production & motion media agency.
Catalog(s) available

Sparrow Sound Design
3501 N Southport, 2nd fl, Chicago, IL 60657-1435
Tel: 773-281-8510 *Fax:* 773-472-4330
E-mail: studio@chicagosound.com; southport@chicagosound.com
Web Site: www.chicagosound.com
Key Personnel
Owner: Joanie Pallatto *E-mail:* joanie@chicagosound.com; Bradley Parker-Sparrow *E-mail:* sparrow@chicagosound.com
Recording studio & CD production company.
Catalog(s) available

SPEAK HOUSE Audio™
Division of A Jim-N-I Recording LLC
1844 E Montecito Ave, Phoenix, AZ 85016
Tel: 602-279-0900 *Fax:* 602-279-0980
Web Site: www.speakhouseaudio.com

Key Personnel
Owner: Susan Bolin *E-mail:* susan@lambchops.com
Owner & Pres: Jim Sherry *E-mail:* jim@lambchops.com
Founded: 1977
Audio production, duplication & distribution.

Speakeasy Productions
3616-B Falls Rd, Baltimore, MD 21211
Mailing Address: PO Box 50147, Baltimore, MD 21211-4147
Tel: 410-889-0374
Web Site: www.voiceover.com
Key Personnel
Pres: Kurt Kolb
Founded: 1994
Audio production, voiceovers & audio post. Can deliver audio & voiceovers real-time via ISDN Codec.

Speakers Unlimited
5565 Woodridge Dr, Columbus, OH 43213
Tel: 614-864-3703 *Fax:* 614-864-3876
E-mail: prospeak@aol.com
Web Site: www.speakersunlimited.com
Key Personnel
Owner: Mike Frank
Founded: 1971
Full service speaker bureau.
Catalog(s) available
Membership(s): National Speakers Association

Special Archives Division, Motion Picture Branch
Affiliate of National Archives & Records Administration
8601 Adelphi Rd, College Park, MD 20740-6001
Tel: 301-837-2000 *Toll Free Tel:* 866-272-6272 (cust serv) *Fax:* 301-837-0483
E-mail: mopix@nara.gov
Web Site: www.archives.gov
Key Personnel
Dir & Chief, Motion Pictures: Daniel Rooney *Tel:* 301-837-0526
Distribution center for documentaries & government programs.

Special Effects Systems Inc
6130 Edgewater Dr, Suite A, Orlando, FL 32810
Mailing Address: PO Box 607141, Orlando, FL 32860-7141
Tel: 407-297-6520 *Toll Free Tel:* 877-297-1900 *Fax:* 407-297-4041
E-mail: sales@spfx.com; confetti.info@spfx.com
Web Site: www.spfx.com
Key Personnel
Pres: Randy Buchanan
Founded: 1995
Distributor of confetti launchers & products.
Catalog(s) available

Special Effects Unlimited Inc
1005 N Lillian Way, Hollywood, CA 90038
Tel: 323-466-3361 *Fax:* 323-466-5712
E-mail: seuefx@aol.com
Web Site: www.specialefxunltd.com
Key Personnel
Spec Effects Coord: Allen Hall
Founded: 1962
Supplier of specialized rental equipment & materials to the film industry as well as special effects service supplier to the commercial & music industries.

Special Event Services
3135 Indiana Ave, Winston-Salem, NC 27105
Tel: 336-725-7799 *Toll Free Tel:* 800-423-3996 *Fax:* 336-725-0019
Web Site: www.specialeventservices.com
Key Personnel
Pres: Jim Brammer *E-mail:* jbrammer@specialeventservices.com
Full service technical production company.

Special Projects
345 Glen Iris Dr NE, Atlanta, GA 30312-1445
Tel: 404-588-2800 *Toll Free Tel:* 888-588-2800 *Fax:* 678-904-6629
E-mail: info@specialprojects.tv
Web Site: www.specialprojects.tv
Key Personnel
Pres: Guy H Tuttle *Tel:* gtuttle@specialprojects.tv
Founded: 1980
Set/production design, scenic services, backdrop & set rentals, custom digital printing (construction & rental).
Membership(s): NATAS; USITT

Speciality Bulb Products Inc
20010-100A Ave, Unit 2, Langley, BC V1M 3G4, Canada
Tel: 604-513-8500 *Toll Free Tel:* 800-663-1120 *Fax:* 604-513-8200
E-mail: info@specialtybulb.com; bulbexpert@specialtybulb.com
Web Site: www.specialtybulb.com
Key Personnel
Pres: Peter Janzen
Mktg Assoc: Herb Ens
Founded: 1985
Distributor of projection & photographic equipment.
Catalog(s) available
Membership(s): IPPD

Specialized Audio-Visual Inc
14 Solar Dr, Clifton Park, NY 12065
Tel: 518-383-6501 *Fax:* 518-383-6506
E-mail: info@saviusa.com; sales@saviusa.com
Web Site: www.saviusa.com
Key Personnel
Pres: Michael Cusick
Founded: 1986
AV equipment rentals.
Catalog(s) available
Membership(s): AES; InfoComm International®

Specialized Products Co
1100 S Kimball Ave, Southlake, TX 76092
Tel: 817-329-6647 *Toll Free Tel:* 800-866-5353 *Fax:* 817-329-6195 *Toll Free Fax:* 800-234-8286
E-mail: info@specialized.net
Web Site: www.specialized.net
Key Personnel
Pres: Pete Smith
Tool kits, cases & test equipment.
Catalog(s), 400+ pages
Membership(s): Consumer Electronics Association; InfoComm International®

Specialty Bulb Co Inc
80 Orville Dr, Bohemia, NY 11716
Mailing Address: PO Box 231, Bohemia, NY 11716-0231
Tel: 631-589-3393 *Toll Free Tel:* 800-331-BULB (331-2852) *Fax:* 631-563-3089
E-mail: info@bulbspecialists.com
Web Site: www.bulbspecialists.com
Key Personnel
Pres: Caden Zollo
Founded: 1984
Distributor of lamps.

Specialty Tapes LLC
4221 Courtney Rd, Franksville, WI 53126
Tel: 262-835-0748 *Toll Free Tel:* 800-545-8273 *Fax:* 262-835-0749
E-mail: sales@specialtytapes.net
Web Site: www.specialtytapes.net
Key Personnel
Sales: Tammy Rainer
Founded: 1977
Manufacture pressure sensitive tapes used to hold cables, wires & cords in place. Used for photo, motion pictures, TV studios, convention halls & AU applications; dry mounting & laminating equipment & supplies & slide bindings/mounting supplies.
Online catalog(s) available

Speco/Systems & Products Engineering Co
709 N Sixth St, Kansas City, KS 66101
Tel: 913-321-3978 *Toll Free Tel:* 800-633-5913 *Fax:* 913-321-7439
Key Personnel
Pres: George W Higgenbotham
Manufacturer of projection systems.
Catalog(s) available

Spectra Cine Inc
3607 W Magnolia Blvd, Burbank, CA 91505
Tel: 818-954-9222 *Fax:* 818-954-0016
E-mail: info@spectracine.com
Web Site: www.spectracine.com
Key Personnel
Pres: Nasir Zaidi
EVP: Bernadette Perez

Spectra Film & Video
5626 Vineland Ave, North Hollywood, CA 91601
Tel: 818-762-4545 *Fax:* 818-762-5454
E-mail: sales@spectrafilmandvideo.com
Web Site: www.spectrafilmandvideo.com
Key Personnel
Pres: Douglas Thomas
VP: Gerry Luca
Film processing & telecine services.
Catalog(s) available
Membership(s): AIE™; Photo Marketing Association; PPA

Spectra Sonics Applied Technology Inc
860 W Riverdale Rd, Unit D6, Riverdale, UT 84405
Tel: 801-605-8849 *Fax:* 801-689-2967
Web Site: www.spectra-sonics.com
Key Personnel
Pres: Bill Cheney *E-mail:* billcheney@spectra-sonics.com
Recording equipment sales & manufacturer.
Catalog(s) available

Spectra Video Productions Ltd
309 Wardlaw Ave, Winnipeg, MB R3L 0L5, Canada
Tel: 204-452-9832
Web Site: www.spectra-productions.com
Key Personnel
Owner & Pres: Byrnes Benoit *E-mail:* byrnes@spectra-productions.com
Founded: 1979
Video production company.

Spectrum Audio Visual Services
351 W 45 Ave, Denver, CO 80216
Tel: 303-477-4456 *Toll Free Tel:* 800-477-4752 *Fax:* 303-477-0114
E-mail: info@spectrumav.com
Web Site: www.spectrumav.com
Key Personnel
SVP & Gen Mgr: Bill MacDonald *E-mail:* bmacdonald@spectrumav.com
Dir, Sales-Hotel Div: Pete Yurish *E-mail:* pyurish@spectrumav.com
Natl Sales Mgr, Rental & Staging: Gail Brienza *E-mail:* gbrienza@spectrumav.com
Full service AV distributor.
Catalog(s) available
Membership(s): MCA-I; SMPTE

Spectrum Engineers
324 S State St, Suite 400, Salt Lake City, UT 84111
Tel: 801-328-5151 *Toll Free Tel:* 800-678-7077 *Fax:* 801-328-5155
E-mail: info@spectrum-engineers.com
Web Site: www.spectrum-engineers.com
Key Personnel
Principal & Corp Communs Dir: Jackie McGill *E-mail:* jxm@spectrum-engineers.com
Founded: 1982
AV systems design, acoustical engineering & lighting design. Have branch offices in Phoenix, AZ & St George, UT.
Branch Office(s)
1501 W Fountainhead Pkwy, Suite 330, Tempe, AZ 85282 *Tel:* 480-621-3444
1501 Martingale Ct, Belleville, IL 62226
7033 Cradlerock Farm, Suite 100, Columbia, MD 21045
Membership(s): AES; ASA; IALD; Illuminating Engineering Society; INCE; National Council on Qualifications for the Lighting Professions; Synergetic Audio Concepts; USITT

Spectrum Industries Inc
925 First Ave, Chippewa Falls, WI 54729
Mailing Address: PO Box 400, Chippewa Falls, WI 54729
Tel: 715-723-6750 *Toll Free Tel:* 800-235-1262 *Toll Free Fax:* 800-335-0473
E-mail: info@spectrumfurniture.com
Web Site: www.spectrumfurniture.com
Key Personnel
CEO & Pres: Dave Hancock *E-mail:* dhancock@spectrumfurniture.com
EVP, Sales & Mktg: Scott Dorn *E-mail:* sdorn@spectrumfurniture.com
VP, Sales: Robert Kensinger *E-mail:* rkensinger@spectrumfurniture.com
Mktg & PR: Tony Nelson *E-mail:* tnelson@spectrumfurniture.com
Founded: 1968
Manufacturer of computer, training, laptop & multimedia furniture as well as integrated technology lecterns & instructional stations.
Catalog(s) available
Membership(s): InfoComm International®; NSCA

Spectrum Productions
565 Pinedale Dr, Annapolis, MD 21401
Web Site: www.markgoldberg.com
Key Personnel
Pres: Mark Goldberg *Tel:* 410-212-6879 (cell) *E-mail:* mark@markgoldberg.com
Founded: 1978
Video production & photography.
Membership(s): WEVA

Spectrum Sound Inc
1040 Acorn Dr, Suite C, Nashville, TN 37210
Tel: 615-391-3700
Web Site: www.spectrumsound.net
Key Personnel
Founder, CEO & Pres: Ken Porter
Retail Sales Mgr: Barry Sanders *E-mail:* barry@spectrumsound.net
Live Sound Sales Mgr: Kyle Shepherd
System Integration Sales Mgr: Ken DeBelius *E-mail:* kendeb@spectrumsound.net
Founded: 1979
Professional audio equipment & services.

Spectrum Systems Design
937 SW 14 Ave, Suite 101, Portland, OR 97205
Tel: 503-248-0248 *Toll Free Tel:* 800-288-3492 *Fax:* 503-274-7684
Web Site: www.spectrumsd.com
Key Personnel
Pres: Lindsey L McGill
AV consultation & installation firm.

Speedotron Corp
Division of PromarkBRANDS
1268 Humbracht Circle, Bartlett, IL 60103-1631
Tel: 630-246-5001 *Fax:* 630-830-2525
E-mail: support@speedotron.com
Web Site: www.speedotron.com
Key Personnel
Pres: Ken Orlando *E-mail:* ken.orlando@promarkbrands.com
Founded: 1939
Professional lighting systems for still photography.
Catalog(s) available

Spence-Thomas Audio Post
70 Richmond St E, Suite 300, Toronto, ON M5C 1N8, Canada
Tel: 416-361-6383 *Toll Free Tel:* 866-547-2617 *Fax:* 416-361-2970
E-mail: info@spence-thomas.com; bookings@spence-thomas.com
Web Site: www.spence-thomas.com
Key Personnel
Gen Mgr & Chief Engr: Richard Spence-Thomas *E-mail:* richard@spence-thomas.com
Off Mgr: Marilyn A Serr
Founded: 1967
Sound recordings & video production.

Spider Support Systems
11654 Plaza America Dr, Suite 180, Reston, VA 20190
Tel: 703-758-0699 *Fax:* 703-935-8899
Web Site: www.spidersupport.com
Key Personnel
Pres: Charlie Kendall *E-mail:* ckendall@spidersupport.com
Support equipment for the professional video & photography industry.

Spina Bifida Association
4590 MacArthur Blvd NW, Suite 250, Washington, DC 20007
Tel: 202-944-3285 *Toll Free Tel:* 800-621-3141 (outside DC) *Fax:* 202-944-3295
E-mail: sbaa@sbaa.org
Web Site: www.sbaa.org
Key Personnel
Interim Pres & CEO: Sara Struwe *Tel:* 202-618-4747 *E-mail:* sstruwe@sbaa.org
Produce educational videos regarding spina bifida.
Catalog(s) available

Spire Audio Visual Co Inc
12170 SW 128 Ct, Unit 105, Miami, FL 33186
Tel: 305-378-5334; 786-367-3408 (cell) *Fax:* 786-397-7462
Web Site: www.spireav.com
Key Personnel
Partner: Joanne Spire; John Spire *E-mail:* john@spireav.com
Founded: 1946
AV equipment sales & rental.

Spirig Advanced Technologies Inc (SAT)
Subsidiary of Spirig Ernest Dipl Ing
144 Oakland St, Springfield, MA 01108
Tel: 413-788-6191 *Toll Free Tel:* 866-977-4744 *Fax:* 413-788-0490
E-mail: sat@spirig.com; order@spirig.com
Web Site: www.spirig.com
Key Personnel
Gen Mgr: Lori Topjian
Founded: 1979
Catalog(s) available
Foreign Office(s): Hohlweg 1, PO Box 1140, 8640 Rapperswil, Switzerland *Tel:* (055) 222 6900 *Fax:* (055) 222 6969 *E-mail:* info@spirig.com

Spirit Media
12042 SE Sunnyside Rd, Suite 700, Happy Valley, OR 97015
Tel: 503-698-5540 *Fax:* 503-698-8408
E-mail: info@spiritmedia.com
Web Site: www.spiritmedia.com
Key Personnel
Pres & Strategic Dir: Bill Dolan
Creative Servs Dir: Anne DeRock
Mktg Coord: Suzanne Shelley
Prodn & Events Coord: Jean Klewitz
Founded: 1989
Creative agency serving for profit & nonprofit organizations in the development & delivery of marketing communications.
Membership(s): American Marketing Association; NATAS; NRB; Printing Brokerage Association

Spizzirri Press Inc
PO Box 9397, Rapid City, SD 57709-9397
Tel: 605-348-2749 *Toll Free Tel:* 800-325-9819 *Fax:* 605-348-6251 *Toll Free Fax:* 800-322-9819
E-mail: spizzpub@aol.com
Web Site: www.spizzirri.com
Key Personnel
Co-Founder & Partner: Linda Spizzirri; Peter Spizzirri
Children's programming.
Catalog(s) available
Shipping Address: 15 E Chicago St, Rapid City, SD 57701

Split Image Productions
4134 243 St, Flushing, NY 11363-1658
Tel: 718-428-1438 *Fax:* 718-428-1438
Key Personnel
Pres: Stuart Hersh
Small production company.
Membership(s): AFI; InfoComm International®; NATAS

Spoken Arts Inc
195 S White Rock Rd, Holmes, NY 12531
Tel: 845-878-9600 *Toll Free Tel:* 800-326-4090 *Fax:* 845-878-9009
E-mail: sales@spokenartsmedia.com
Web Site: www.spokenartsmedia.com
Key Personnel
Owner: Daniel M Welsh
Cust Serv: Susan Welsh
Founded: 1956
Producing audio & video for K-6 school & library market.
Catalog(s), biannual (Jan & Sept)
Membership(s): ALA; Audio Publishers Association

Spoken Language Services Inc
PO Box 17113, Urbana, IL 61803
Tel: 217-328-0173 *Fax:* 217-328-0177
E-mail: orders@spokenlanguage.com
Key Personnel
Owner: Mark Cowan
Self instructional language learning materials.
Catalog(s) available

Sports Cinematography Group
Division of Sonic Film Inc
73 Market St, Venice, CA 90291-3606
Tel: 310-785-9100 *Fax:* 310-564-7500
E-mail: sportscinema@earthlink.net
Web Site: www.sportscinematographygroup.com
Key Personnel
Pres & Exec Prodr: David Stoltz
Founded: 1987
Stock footage & production company.
Catalog(s) available

Sportsmen on Film Inc
231 Earl Garrett, Suite 300, Kerrville, TX 78028

Tel: 830-792-4200 *Toll Free Tel:* 800-910-HUNT (910-4868) *Fax:* 830-792-4224
Web Site: www.sportsmenonfilm.com
Key Personnel
Pres & Video Prodr: Ken Wilson
E-mail: kwilson@sportsmenonfilm.com
Hunting & "how to" video production.
Catalog(s) available

Spot Media Production Group
2745 Locust St, St Louis, MO 63103
Tel: 314-667-5915
E-mail: info@spotmpg.com
Web Site: www.spotmpg.com
Key Personnel
Partner: Lynn Hensel; Rick Hensel; Don Rockwell
Exec Prodr: Aleta Harris
Busn Mgr: Mary Smith
Founded: 2003
Video production, post-production, satellite uplink & live streaming.

Sprayway Inc
1005 S Westgate Ave, Addison, IL 60101
Tel: 630-628-3000 *Toll Free Tel:* 800-332-9000 *Fax:* 630-543-7797
E-mail: info@spraywayinc.com
Web Site: www.spraywayinc.com
Key Personnel
VP & Gen Mgr: James Bright
Founded: 1947
Manufacturer of aerosol products.
Catalog(s) available
Membership(s): National Association of Printers & Lithographers

Spring Arbor Distributors
Unit of Ingram Content Group Inc
One Ingram Blvd, LaVergne, TN 37086-1986
Tel: 615-793-5000 (Ingram) *Toll Free Tel:* 800-395-4340 (Christian); 800-395-5599 (sales); 800-234-6737 (electronic ordering); 877-846-6989 (software support); 800-395-7234 (cust serv) *Fax:* 615-213-5192
E-mail: custserv@springarbor.com; orders@springarbor.com
Web Site: www.ingramcontent.com
Key Personnel
Christian Sales Rep: Mary Lou Alexander *Tel:* 800-395-4340 ext 33319 *E-mail:* marylou.alexander@springarbor.com
Distribution services for Christian booksellers.
Catalog(s) available
Membership(s): Entertainment Merchants Association; ICVM

Sprocket Digital
PO Box 1420, Claremont, CA 91711
Tel: 909-946-2364 *Fax:* 909-946-2631
E-mail: sdsales@sprocketdigital.com
Web Site: www.sprocketdigital.com
Key Personnel
Pres: Jeff Des Combes
Manufactures professional audio & video equipment & provides design services for the film & television production & post production industries.

SSL Industries Inc
4935 Anne Louise Lane, Suite 2, Placerville, CA 95667
Mailing Address: PO Box 3113, Diamond Springs, CA 95619-3113
Tel: 530-644-0233
E-mail: sslind@starband.net
Web Site: www.sslinc.net
Key Personnel
Pres: John C Russ
Catalog(s) available

Branch Office(s)
PO Box 190, Scotts Mills, OR 97375 *Tel:* 503-873-7127
Membership(s): AES; SMPTE

ST Productions
Division of Sarkes Tarzian Inc
900 Whitehall Rd, Chattanooga, TN 37405
Tel: 423-267-5412 *Fax:* 423-267-6840
E-mail: stps@wrcbtv.com
Web Site: www.wrcbtv.com
Key Personnel
Prodn Mgr: Doug Loveridge *E-mail:* dlove@wrcbtv.com
Television programming.

Tom Stack & Associates Inc
154 Tequesta St, Tavernier, FL 33070
Tel: 305-852-5520
E-mail: tomstack@earthlink.net
Web Site: tomstackassociates.photoshelter.com
Key Personnel
Pres: Therisa Stack
VP: Tom Stack
Image library of 100,000 images. Creative digital imaging, composite. 25 years experience.

Staco Energy Products Co
301 Gaddis Blvd, Dayton, OH 45403
Tel: 937-253-1191 *Toll Free Tel:* 866-261-1191 *Fax:* 937-253-1723
E-mail: sales@stacoenergy.com; service@stacoenergy.com
Web Site: www.stacoenergy.com
Key Personnel
Busn Devt Mgr & Sales Opers Mgr: Paul Hailigenberg *Tel:* 937-253-1191 ext 128 *E-mail:* hailigenbergp@stacoenergy.com
Founded: 1937
Manufacture power quality & voltage control equipment.
Catalog(s), free

Staedtler-Mars Ltd
5725 McLaughlin Rd, Mississauga, ON L5R 3K5, Canada
Tel: 905-501-9008 *Toll Free Tel:* 800-776-5544; 800-387-5872 *Fax:* 905-501-9117 *Toll Free Fax:* 800-675-8249
E-mail: info@staedtler.ca
Web Site: www.staedtler.ca
Key Personnel
Pres: Axel Huelsmann
Mktg: Diane S Brasil
OHP marker manufacturer (Lumocolor®).
Catalog(s) available
Branch Office(s)
4664 Lougheed Hwy, Suite 177, Burnaby, BC V5C 5T5, Canada *Tel:* 604-299-1001 *Toll Free Tel:* 800-661-6144 (US) *Fax:* 604-291-8884 *Toll Free Fax:* 877-318-6502 (US)
204 boul de Montarville, bureau 130, Boucherville, QC J4B 6S2, Canada *Tel:* 450-449-7460 *Fax:* 450-449-2865

Stage America LLC
4001 S Decatur 37, Suite 532, Las Vegas, NV 89103
Tel: 702-879-8177 *Toll Free Fax:* 877-488-6663
E-mail: info@stageamerica.com
Web Site: www.stageamerica.com
Key Personnel
Pres & Prodn Dir: Raymond W Franklin *E-mail:* rfranklin@stageamerica.com
Prodn Mgr: Mike Benson *E-mail:* mbenson@stageamerica.com
Founded: 1982
Production management for corporate & special events.
Online catalog(s) available
Membership(s): Meeting Professionals International; RTDNA; SMPTE

Stage Crew Audiovisual Inc
PO Box 6097, San Juan, PR 00914-6097
Tel: 787-723-6398 *Fax:* 787-721-1410
E-mail: scav@stagecrewav.com
Web Site: www.stagecrewav.com
Key Personnel
Pres: Hamid Azize *E-mail:* hamid.azize@stagecrewav.com
Dir, Show Servs: Ivan Nieves *E-mail:* ivan.nieves@stagecrewav.com
Membership(s): InfoComm International®; NSCA

Stage Directions
8311 Hempstead Rd, Houston, TX 77008
Tel: 713-863-7469 *Fax:* 713-863-9418
E-mail: sales@stagedirections.com
Web Site: www.stagedirections.com
Key Personnel
Owner & Pres: Richard Hoggatt, Jr *E-mail:* richard@stagedirections.com
Founded: 1987
Media production services, staging services, AV equipment rentals & sales, studio facility.

Stage Equipment & Lighting Inc
4600 SW 36 St, Orlando, FL 32811
Tel: 407-425-2010 *Fax:* 407-648-2604
E-mail: mail@seal-fla.com
Web Site: www.seal-fla.com
Key Personnel
Branch Mgr & Tech Consultant, Sales: Curt Contrata *E-mail:* ccontrata@seal-fla.com
Lighting production equipment for rentals & production services.
Catalog(s) available
Branch Office(s)
12250 NE 13 Ct, Miami, FL 33161 *Tel:* 305-891-2010 *Fax:* 305-893-2828

Stage Front Presentation Systems
6 Southern Oaks Dr, Savannah, GA 31405
Tel: 912-236-1345 *Toll Free Tel:* 800-736-9242 *Fax:* 912-233-5350
Web Site: www.sfps.net; www.stagefrontproductions.com
Key Personnel
Cust Serv Mgr: Dave Mueller *Tel:* 800-736-9242 ext 5704 *E-mail:* davem@sfps.net
Founded: 1978
Performance & presentation systems.
Catalog(s) available
Branch Office(s)
11460 Maxwell Rd, Suite C, Alpharetta, GA 30009 (sales & serv)
4465 Tile Dr, North Charleston, SC 29405 *Tel:* 843-329-0565 (event prodn)
Membership(s): InfoComm International®

Stage Post
255 French Landing Dr, Nashville, TN 37228
Tel: 615-248-1978 *Toll Free Tel:* 877-250-1839 *Fax:* 615-242-8861
E-mail: mail@stagepost.com
Web Site: www.stagepost.com
Key Personnel
Owner & Pres: Lynn Bennett *E-mail:* l.bennett@stagepost.com
Dir, Busn & Opers: Valerie Main *E-mail:* v.main@stagepost.com
Dir, Tech Devt & Prodn Mgr: Martin Olsson *E-mail:* m.olsson@stagepost.com
Sr Prodr: Richard Van Syckle *E-mail:* r.vansyckle@stagepost.com
Assoc Prodr: Caitlin Fryer *E-mail:* c.fryer@stagepost.com
Video production company.

Stage 3 Productions
27500 Donald Ct, Warren, MI 48092
Tel: 586-576-0625 *Toll Free Tel:* 888-330-5179
Web Site: www.stage3.com

Key Personnel
Agent: Andre LaRoche *Tel:* 248-755-0964
E-mail: andre@stage3.com
Provides photography, computer generated imagery, graphic design, retouching, video, print & broadcast production services.

Stageline Mobile Stage Inc
700 Marsolais St, L'Assomption, QC J5W 2G9, Canada
Tel: 450-589-1063 *Toll Free Tel:* 800-26-STAGE (267-8243) *Fax:* 450-589-1711
E-mail: info@stageline.com
Web Site: www.stageline.com
Key Personnel
Mktg & Communs Coord: Maryanne Miron
E-mail: mmiron@stageline.com
Founded: 1987
Distributor & manufacturer of mobile hydraulic stages.
Branch Office(s)
827 L'Ange-Gardien Blvd, L'Assomption, QC J5W 1T3, Canada
Membership(s): IFEA

Stageright Corp
495 Pioneer Pkwy, Clare, MI 48617
Toll Free Tel: 800-438-4499; 888-577-8243 (sales) *Fax:* 989-386-7393
E-mail: info@stageright.com
Web Site: www.stageright.com
Key Personnel
Pres: O David Rogers
Founded: 1984
Manufacturer of portable staging & equipment.

Stages Video Productions
514 29 Ave N, Myrtle Beach, SC 29577
Tel: 843-626-7466
E-mail: info@stagesvideo.com
Web Site: www.stagesvideo.com
Key Personnel
Founder: Chuck Stokes *E-mail:* chuck@stagesvideo.com; Diane De Vaughn-Stokes
E-mail: diane@stagesvideo.com
Founded: 1989
Full service video production company. Specialize in marketing/training videos & television commercial production.

StageSound
2240 Shenandoah Ave NW, Roanoke, VA 24017
Tel: 540-342-2040 *Toll Free Tel:* 800-778-9839
Fax: 540-345-5158
Web Site: stagesound.com
Key Personnel
Gen Mgr & VP, Sales: Jeff Moore *Tel:* 540-342-2040 ext 120
Sales & Mktg: Doug Thurman *Tel:* 540-342-2040 ext 121
Sales of pro audio, lighting & video products. Design & installation of commercial sound, lighting & video systems. Audio, lighting & video production services for corporate & concert events. Pro audio & lighting electronic repair services.

Stagestep Inc
4701 Bath St, No 46, Philadelphia, PA 19137
Tel: 215-636-9000 *Toll Free Tel:* 800-523-0960 (US & CN) *Fax:* 267-672-2912
E-mail: stagestep@stagestep.com; info@stagestep.com
Web Site: www.stagestep.com
Key Personnel
Founder & Pres: Randy Swartz *Tel:* 215-636-9000 ext 105 *E-mail:* randy@stagestep.com
Founded: 1979
Manufacture stage flooring & studio flooring for dances, theatre, health & fitness. Books, CDs, videos & gifts.
Online catalog(s) available

Staging Concepts
7008 Northland Dr N, Suite 150, Minneapolis, MN 55428
Tel: 763-533-2094 *Toll Free Tel:* 800-337-5339
E-mail: info@stagingconcepts.com
Web Site: www.stagingconcepts.com
Key Personnel
CEO: John Lewis
Founded: 1990
Manufacturer of portable staging equipment.
Catalog(s), free
Online catalog(s) available

Staging Directions Inc
1327 Northbrook Pkwy, Suite 440, Suwanee, GA 30024
Tel: 770-409-9909 *Toll Free Tel:* 800-782-4322
Fax: 770-409-0277
E-mail: info@teamsdi.net; sales@teamsdi.net
Web Site: www.stagingdirections.com
Key Personnel
CEO & Pres: Nick D'Allen *E-mail:* nick.allen@teamsdi.net
VP: Kevin Miller *E-mail:* kevin.miller@teamsdi.net
VP, Opers: Richard Palm *E-mail:* richard.palm@teamsdi.net
VP, Sales & Mktg: Kevin McGarty *E-mail:* kevin.mcgarty@teamsdi.net
Stage equipment rentals.

Staging Resources Inc
257 E Helen Rd, Palatine, IL 60067
Tel: 847-963-6600 *Toll Free Tel:* 877-963-6600
Fax: 847-963-6601
E-mail: info@stagingresources.com
Web Site: www.stagingresources.com
Key Personnel
Pres: Jeff Thommes *E-mail:* jt@stagingresources.com
Mgr: Josh Heidenreich *E-mail:* josh@stagingresources.com
Founded: 1987
Provides rental of soundstages, audio equipment, lighting, cameras & projectors.

Stampede Presentation Products Inc
55 Woodridge Dr, Amherst, NY 14228
Tel: 716-635-9474 *Toll Free Tel:* 800-398-5652
Fax: 716-635-9484
E-mail: stampedenews@stampedeglobal.com
Web Site: www.stampede-us.com
Key Personnel
Owner, COO & Pres: Kevin Kelly
Worldwide distributor of presentation & home theatre productions.
Branch Office(s)
165 Matheson Blvd E, Unit 11 & 12, Mississauga, ON L4Z 3K2, Canada *Tel:* 905-602-0888 *Toll Free Tel:* 888-459-9181
Membership(s): Consumer Electronics Association; Custom Electronic Design & Installation Association; InfoComm International®; NSCA

Stanco Sales LLC
1529 S Terry St, Longmont, CO 80501
Tel: 303-776-3770
E-mail: stancosales@comcast.net
Key Personnel
Pres: Burton Moquist
AV equipment manufacturer & distributor.
Catalog(s) available

James Stanfield Co Inc
129 S Quarantina St, Santa Barbara, CA 93103
Mailing Address: PO Box 41058, Santa Barbara, CA 93140
Tel: 805-897-1185 *Toll Free Tel:* 800-421-6534
Fax: 805-897-1187
E-mail: maindesk@stanfield.com
Web Site: www.stanfield.com
Key Personnel
Founder: James Stanfield, EdD
Founded: 1976
Special education & school to life transitions, educational videos, slides & curriculum.
Catalog(s), free

Stanford Research Systems Inc
1290-D Reamwood Ave, Sunnyvale, CA 94089
Tel: 408-744-9040 *Fax:* 408-744-9049
E-mail: info@thinksrs.com
Web Site: www.thinksrs.com
Key Personnel
Sales & Mktg Mgr: David Ames
Founded: 1980
Catalog(s) available

Stanislaus Audio Video Inc
1431 Kansas Ave, Modesto, CA 95351
Tel: 209-529-2700 *Fax:* 209-529-7355
E-mail: info@stanav.com
Web Site: www.stanav.com
Key Personnel
CFO: Carolyn A Turner *E-mail:* cturner@stanav.com
Pres: George E Turner
Founded: 1972
Membership(s): NSCA

Jay S Stanley & Associates Inc
5313 McClanahan Dr, Suite G-5, North Little Rock, AR 72116
Tel: 501-758-8029 *Toll Free Tel:* 888-758-4728
Fax: 501-758-8037
E-mail: info@jaystanley.com
Web Site: www.jaystanley.com
Key Personnel
Pres: Jay S Stanley *E-mail:* jay.stanley@jaystanley.com
Founded: 1935
Full AV equipment distributor.

Stanley Supply & Services Inc
335 Willow St, North Andover, MA 01845-5995
Tel: 978-682-9844 *Toll Free Tel:* 800-225-5370 (sales) *Toll Free Fax:* 800-743-8141
E-mail: sales@stanleyworks.com
Web Site: www.stanleysupplyservices.com
Key Personnel
Multimedia Mgr: Julie Giordano
Founded: 1963
Supplier of products & services for assembling, repairing & testing electronic equipment.
Catalog(s) available

Stanton DJ, see Stanton Magnetics

Stanton Magnetics
Division of Gibson Pro Audio
c/o Gibson Pro Audio, 309 Plus Park Blvd, Nashville, TN 37217
Toll Free Tel: 800-4GIBSON (444-2766)
Web Site: stantondj.com
Founded: 1946
Makers of the SCS (Stanton Control System), professional DJ equipment & accessories.
Catalog(s) available

Star Case Manufacturing Co Inc
648 Superior Ave, Munster, IN 46321
Tel: 219-922-4440 *Toll Free Tel:* 800-822-STAR (822-7827); 800-782-CASE (782-2273)
Fax: 219-922-4442
E-mail: star@starcase.com
Web Site: www.starcase.com
Key Personnel
Pres: Darren Eason
VP, Sales & Mktg: Ralph Hoopes
Founded: 1975
Manufacturer of custom cases.

Catalog(s) available
Membership(s): AES; InfoComm International®; NAB; NAMM, the National Association of Music Merchants; NSCA; SMPTE

Star Video Duplicating
6910 E Fifth Ave, Scottsdale, AZ 85251
Tel: 480-946-3699 *Toll Free Tel:* 800-238-7827 *Fax:* 480-946-4722
Web Site: www.starvideo.com
Key Personnel
Owner & Pres: Paul Brown *E-mail:* paul@starvideo.com
Full duplicating & editing services.

Starburns Industries
1700 W Burbank Blvd, Burbank, CA 91506
Tel: 818-433-3300 *Fax:* 818-433-3383
Web Site: www.starburnsindustries.com
Key Personnel
CEO & Exec Prodr: Joe Russo, II
Exec Prodr: James A Fino; Dan Harmon; Dino Stamatopoulos
Founded: 2010
Provides services for stop-motion animation, 2D animation, post-production & audio recording.
Branch Office(s)
1101 W Isabel St, Burbank, CA 91506 *Tel:* 818-955-8977

Starline Costume
1286 Bandera Rd, San Antonio, TX 78228
Tel: 210-435-3535 *Fax:* 210-435-9425
Web Site: starlinecostumes.com
Key Personnel
Gen Mgr: Julie Moore Kech *E-mail:* julie@starlinecostumes.com
Costume & prop distributor & rental company.
Membership(s): National Costumers Association

Starlite Productions
Subsidiary of Starlite Productions International Inc
9 Whittendale Dr, Moorestown, NJ 08057
Tel: 856-780-8000 *Toll Free Tel:* 800-738-7400 *Fax:* 856-780-8001
E-mail: info@starlite.com
Web Site: www.starlite.com
Key Personnel
CEO & Pres: Dean Danowitz *Tel:* 856-780-8000 ext 221 *E-mail:* dean_d@starlite.com
Gen Mgr: Donna Gomez *E-mail:* donna_g@starlite.com
Dir, Opers: Joe Masciangelo *E-mail:* joe_m@starlite.com
AV Systems Group Mgr: Gus Gomez *Tel:* 856-780-8000 ext 230 *E-mail:* gus_g@starlite.com
Lighting Sales Mgr: Bob Wolfe *Tel:* 856-780-8000 ext 231 *E-mail:* bob_w@starlite.com
Show Technol Group Mgr: Jason Danowitz *Tel:* 856-780-8000 ext 233 *E-mail:* jason_d@starlite.com
Founded: 1983
Design & consultations, 53,000 sq ft corporate office plus wholesale audio, lighting, video & special effects equipment. Retail & wholesale sales, system integration plus installation complete show production services, long & short term rentals, factory authorized repair service.
Membership(s): InfoComm International®; International Special Events Society; NSCA; Professional Lighting & Sound Association

StarTrak Studios Inc
36 Vermont Ave, Unit 1, Warwick, RI 02888
Tel: 401-732-1880
E-mail: info@startrakstudios.com
Web Site: www.startrakstudios.com
Key Personnel
Pres: Jack Rametta
Founded: 1981
ADR, sound design for radio & TV, ISDN casting, corporate & web creative & production services.

Starwest Productions
8760 W 68 Place, Arvada, CO 80004
Tel: 303-295-2222
E-mail: info@starwest.com
Key Personnel
Pres: Steven Pettit
Full service production company.

State of the Art Acoustik Inc
43-1010 Polytek St, Ottawa, ON K1J 9J3, Canada
Tel: 613-745-2003 *Fax:* 613-745-9687
E-mail: sota@sota.ca
Web Site: www.sota.ca
Key Personnel
Principal: Dr Claude Fortier *E-mail:* cfortier@sota.ca
Pres: Kathryn Savage *E-mail:* ksavage@sota.ca
Founded: 1987
Acoustic design & testing services for performance spaces.
Catalog(s) available
Membership(s): ASA; CAA; INCE; NCAC

Staylor-Made Communications Inc
11835 Carmel Mountain Rd, Suite 1304-365, San Diego, CA 92128-4609
Tel: 858-779-4266 *Toll Free Tel:* 800-711-6699
E-mail: info@staylor-made.com
Web Site: staylor-made.com
Key Personnel
Pres & Exec Prodr: Jim Staylor *E-mail:* jim@staylor-made.com
VP: Anne Farrell Staylor *E-mail:* anne@staylor-made.com
Creative Dir: Dennis McNabb *E-mail:* dennis@staylor-made.com
Founded: 1992
Video production & communication services for training, marketing & entertainment.
Branch Office(s)
1726 Conifer Terr, Lake Oswego, OR 97024 *Tel:* 503-490-8250

Stedman Corp
4167 Stedman Dr, Richland, MI 49083
Tel: 269-629-5930 *Toll Free Tel:* 888-629-5960
E-mail: info@stedmancorp.com
Web Site: www.stedmancorp.com
Key Personnel
Owner: William "Bill" Hannapel
Founded: 1992
Manufacturer of the Proscreen™ XL, PS101 & PS100 metal pop filters, SHH Studio Headphone Hanger™ & PC-1 Proclip™ sheet music holder.
Catalog(s) available

Steeldeck® Inc
3339 Exposition Place, Los Angeles, CA 90018-4034
Tel: 323-290-2100 *Toll Free Tel:* 800-50STAGE (507-8243) *Fax:* 323-290-9600
E-mail: sales@steeldeck.com; rentals@steeldeck.com
Web Site: www.steeldeck.com
Key Personnel
VP: Adrian Funnell *E-mail:* adrian@steeldeck.com
Founded: 1993
Manufacture, sales & rentals of platforms & risers, steeldeck, stagebase, nivoflex, ultralight, mirage & platform design.
Branch Office(s)
143-145 Banker St, Brooklyn, NY 11222-3147, VP: Gail Moorecroft *Tel:* 718-599-3700 *Fax:* 718-599-3800 *E-mail:* gail@steeldeckny.com

Steiner Studios
15 Washington Ave, Brooklyn Navy Yard, Brooklyn, NY 11205
Tel: 718-858-1600
Web Site: www.steinerstudios.com
Founded: 2004
Hollywood-style production & support facility equipped for start-to-finish production of major motion pictures, independent films, television, broadcast commercials, photo shoots & music videos.

Stereo Sales Inc
1530 S Monroe St, Tallahassee, FL 32301
Tel: 850-224-2635 *Fax:* 850-224-0950
E-mail: sales@stereosales.net
Web Site: www.stereosales.org; www.stereosales.net
Key Personnel
Pres: Richard W Menasco
Mgr: Steve Merchant
Founded: 1966
Car & professional stereo equipment sales.
Membership(s): AES

StereoScope International
727 N Victory Blvd, Burbank, CA 91502
Tel: 818-919-6253
E-mail: stereoscope3d@gmail.com
Key Personnel
Stereoscopic Imaging Consultant: John A Rupkalvis
Founded: 1972
Stereoscopic (True 3D) imaging consultation, acquisition & display systems for film, video, computer, industry, education, medical, commercial & entertainment. Stereoscopic virtual reality, stereoscopic robot vision systems, stereoscopic film & video optics. Stereoscopic viewing systems with 3D glasses & autostereoscopic systems for free vision. Catalog available on pdf file upon request via e-mail plus 2D to 3D conversion & stereoscopic titles.
Catalog(s), PDF file available upon e-mail request
Membership(s): Digital Cinema Society; ISU; National Stereoscopic Association; SCSC; SMPTE; SPIE

Stevens Design & Animation LLC
3405 Calle Cuervo NW, Unit 912, Albuquerque, NM 87114
Mailing Address: PO Box 2893, Corrales, NM 87048
Tel: 505-200-2042
Web Site: stevensanimation.com
Key Personnel
Directing Animator: Tim Stevens *E-mail:* tstevens@stevensanimation.com
Full service animation & production house specializing in all things character.

Kris Stevens Enterprises
22362 Dardenne St, Calabasas, CA 91302
Tel: 818-225-7585
E-mail: inquiry@kriserikstevens.com
Web Site: www.kriserikstevens.com
Key Personnel
Pres: Kris Erik Stevens *E-mail:* kris@kriserikstevens.com
Exec Prodr: Bruce Barker
Admin: Lauren Parrent
Founded: 1975
Audio recording & mix, voice-over talent, ISDN connection & sound recording studios.
Membership(s): PromaxBDA; SAG-AFTRA

Stevenson Photography
Division of AZP Worldwide
530 E Erie Dr, Tempe, AZ 85282
Tel: 480-967-6312
E-mail: info@stevensonphotography.com
Web Site: www.stevensonphotography.com

Key Personnel
Founder & Mng Dir: Don B Stevenson
Partner & Lead Photog: Ryan Stevenson
Partner: Cameron Stevenson
Founded: 1985
Photography studio.
Catalog(s) available
Branch Office(s)
AZP Worldwide, 12360 Copeland Lane, Flagstaff, AZ 86004 *Tel:* 928-527-0267
Membership(s): ASMP

Stewart Acoustical Consultants
7330 Chapel Hill Rd, Suite 101, Raleigh, NC 27607
Tel: 919-858-0899 *Fax:* 919-858-0878
Web Site: www.sacnc.com
Key Personnel
Pres & Principal Consultant: Noral D Stewart, PhD *Tel:* 919-858-0899 ext 1 *E-mail:* noral@sacnc.com
Founded: 1979
Acoustics & noise control - room acoustics, isolation between rooms & HVAC Noise.
Membership(s): National Council of Acoustical Consultants

Stewart Audio
14397 Cuesta Ct, Suite D1, Sonora, CA 95370
Tel: 209-588-8111 *Fax:* 209-588-8113
E-mail: sales@stewartaudio.com; support@stewartaudio.com
Web Site: www.stewartaudio.com
Key Personnel
Chief Mktg Offr: Brian McCormick
Gen Mgr: Kevin Stone
Founded: 1982
Manufacturer of Audio Power Amplifiers.

Stewart Filmscreen Corp
1161 Sepulveda Blvd, Torrance, CA 90502-2754
Tel: 310-784-5300 *Toll Free Tel:* 800-762-4999 (North America only) *Fax:* 310-326-6870
E-mail: request@stewartfilmscreen.com
Web Site: www.stewartfilmscreen.com
Key Personnel
Pres: Grant Stewart
Founded: 1947
Catalog(s) available
Branch Office(s)
3919 Bach-Buxton Rd, Amelia, OH 45102-1013 *Tel:* 513-753-0800 *Fax:* 513-753-0854
Foreign Office(s): Mileparken 29, 2730 Herlev, Denmark *Tel:* 3648 2204 *Fax:* 3648 2299 *E-mail:* info@stewartfilm-europe.com
No 07-02 Midland House, 112 Middle Rd, Singapore 188970, Singapore *Tel:* 6747 0555 *Fax:* 6747 2221 *E-mail:* stewart@stewartfilm.com.sg
Membership(s): SMPTE

STIL Casing Solution
76 Saint Paul, Suite 301, Quebec City, QC G1K 3V9, Canada
Tel: 418-694-0449 (ext 10); 418-694-0449 (ext 11, sales & cust serv); 418-694-0449 (ext 12, admin) *Toll Free Tel:* 888-414-0449 (CN & US) *Fax:* 418-694-1621
E-mail: info@stilcasing.com; sales@stilcasing.com; admin@stilcasing.com
Web Site: www.stilcasing.com
Key Personnel
CEO: Frederic Lapointe *E-mail:* frederic.lapoint@stilcasing.com
Sales Asst: Melanie Simard *Tel:* 418-694-0449 ext 11 *E-mail:* melanie.simard@stilcasing.com
Founded: 1997
Manufactures, markets & distributes film containers made of plastic to archivists, museums, film laboratories, studios & any other private or public enterprises involved in film conservation or transport may use our products.

Still N'Motion
1727 Little Orchard St, Suite A, San Jose, CA 95125
Tel: 408-292-9982 *Fax:* 408-292-9987
E-mail: info1@stillnmotion.com
Web Site: www.stillnmotion.com
Founded: 1982
Video production & digital media.

Stockfootage.com
Formerly Stockhdvideo.com
231 S Mountain Way Dr, Orem, UT 84058
Tel: 801-221-9570; 801-361-0012 (cell)
E-mail: sales@stockfootage.com
Web Site: www.stockfootage.com
Key Personnel
Owner & CEO: Chris Dortch
Owner: John Farr
Royalty free stock motion footage.

Stockhdvideo.com, see Stockfootage.com

StockMusic.com
Division of Sound Ideas
105 W Beaver Creek Rd, Suite 4, Richmond Hill, ON L4B 1C6, Canada
Tel: 905-886-0077 *Fax:* 905-886-6800
E-mail: info@stockmusic.com
Web Site: www.stockmusic.com
Key Personnel
CEO: Brian Nimens
Exec Coord: Martha Lonsdale *E-mail:* martha@stockmusic.com
Production music & sound effects via online downloads.
Catalog(s) available

Stockyard Photos/Jim Olive Photography
Division of Photolive Inc
1520 Center St, Studio 2, Houston, TX 77007
Tel: 713-520-0898 *Fax:* 713-820-6965
Web Site: www.stockyard.com
Key Personnel
Owner & Photog: James "Jim" Lee Olive *E-mail:* jim@stockyard.com
Photography & stock photography.
Online catalog(s) available
Membership(s): North American Nature Photography Association

Stoney-Wolf Productions Inc
130 W Columbia Ct, Chaska, MN 55318-2304
Tel: 952-556-0075 *Toll Free Tel:* 800-237-7583 *Fax:* 952-361-4217
E-mail: sales@stoneywolf.com
Web Site: www.stoneywolf.com
Key Personnel
Partner & Pres: David Franey
Partner: Patrick Kirsch; Tony Kirsch
Founded: 1984
Outdoor media distributor.
Catalog(s) available
Membership(s): Outdoor Writers Association of America

StoryTrack
212 S Bemiston, St Louis, MO 63105
Tel: 314-725-3003
Web Site: www.storytrack.com
Key Personnel
VP, Opers: Lisa Constance
Exec Prodr: Lori Dowd
Prodr: Mike Larson
Dir, Cinematography: Brant Hadfield
Dir & Story Ed: Frank Popper
Video production & digital marketing services.
Branch Office(s)
2320 N Damen Ave, Suite 2B, Chicago, IL 60647 *Tel:* 847-754-7550

Stouffer Graphic Arts
922 S Cleveland St, Mishawaka, IN 46544
Tel: 574-252-5772 *Fax:* 574-252-5776
E-mail: info@stouffer.net
Web Site: www.stouffer.net
Founded: 1929
Quality control devices for photosensitive systems.
Brochure(s) available
Price list(s) available

Stouffer Industries, see Stouffer Graphic Arts

Straight Shoot'r Cranes Inc
18434 Oxnard St, Unit H, Tarzana, CA 91356
Tel: 818-609-8310 *Fax:* 818-609-8311
Web Site: www.straightshootr.com
Key Personnel
Owner: Andy Coradeschi *E-mail:* andy@straightshootr.com
Founded: 1993
Equipment rental-motion picture crane/jib-arm combined with a proprietary linear sliding camera mount.

Straight Wire Inc
2032 Scott St, Hollywood, FL 33020
Tel: 954-925-2470 *Toll Free Tel:* 800-683-4434 *Fax:* 954-925-7253
E-mail: info@straightwire.com
Web Site: www.straightwire.com
Key Personnel
Owner & Pres: Steven Hill
Founded: 1985
Distribute & manufacture audio cables, interconnects & speaker cables.
Catalog(s) available

Strand Lighting Inc
Division of Philips Entertainment Group
10911 Petal St, Dallas, TX 75238
Tel: 214-647-7880 *Fax:* 214-647-8031
E-mail: sales@strandlighting.com
Web Site: www.strandlighting.com
Key Personnel
Dir, Cust Servs: Julie Smith *Tel:* 214-647-7987 *E-mail:* julie.smith@philips.com
Founded: 1914
Television, motion picture, stage & architectural lighting services. Serving North America, Europe, Middle East, Africa & the Asia/Pacific region.
Catalog(s) available
Foreign Office(s): Philips Entertainment Asia Ltd, Roxy Industrial Ctr, Unit C, 14/F, 41-49 Kwai Cheung Rd, Kwai Chung, NT, Hong Kong *Tel:* 2796 9786 *Fax:* 2798 6545
Rondweg zuid 85, Winterswijk 7102 JD, Netherlands *Tel:* (0543) 542513 *E-mail:* entertainment.europe@phillips.com
Philips-Selecon Lighting, 19-21 Kawana St, Auckland 0627, New Zealand *Tel:* (09) 481 0100 *Fax:* (09) 481 0101 *Web Site:* www.seleconlight.com
Membership(s): American Society of Lighting Directors; LDI; NAB; Professional Film & Video Equipment Association; SMPTE; USITT

Strata™
3013 Santa Clara Dr, Santa Clara, UT 84765
Tel: 435-628-5218 *Toll Free Tel:* 800-STRATA-3D (787-2823); 800-6-STRATA (678-7282) *Fax:* 435-628-9756
E-mail: sales@strata.com
Web Site: www.strata.com
Key Personnel
Off Mgr: Rebecca Taylor *E-mail:* rebeccat@strata.com
Founded: 1988
Computer software package; 3D modeling, rendering & animation & digital video software.

Strategic Connections
2721 Spring Forest Rd, Raleigh, NC 27616
Tel: 919-878-0550 *Fax:* 919-875-8712
E-mail: info@strategicmail.net
Web Site: www.strategicconnections.net
Key Personnel
CEO & Pres: Scott McLaughlin
Raleigh AV Div Mgr: Mike Thompson *E-mail:* miket@strategicmail.net
Dir, Sales AVSL Group: Michael Eickeneier *E-mail:* michaele@strategicmail.net
Founded: 1998
Branch Office(s)
8349-R Arrowridge Blvd, Charlotte, NC 28273 *Toll Free Tel:* 800-255-5664 *Fax:* 704-583-9028
961 Burke St, Winston-Salem, NC 27101 *Tel:* 336-725-2306 *Fax:* 336-777-8304
1335 Enterprise Ave, Suite A, Myrtle Beach, SC 29577 *Tel:* 846-626-2100 *Fax:* 846-626-2267
Membership(s): InfoComm International®; MCA-I; SMPTE

Strauss Photo Technical Service Inc
4574 Beech Rd, Temple Hills, MD 20748
Tel: 202-529-3200 *Fax:* 202-526-6465
E-mail: info@straussphototech.com
Web Site: www.straussphototech.com
Key Personnel
Mgr, Serv Opers: Christine Balcharan; Jeremy Balcharan
Founded: 1949
AV equipment repair.
Catalog(s) available
Membership(s): NAPET; NESDA; North American Retail Dealers Association; Photo Marketing Association

Stray Angel Films
2236 S Barrington Ave, Los Angeles, CA 90064
Tel: 310-277-6900 *Fax:* 801-438-5009
E-mail: rentals@strayangel.com
Web Site: www.strayangel.com
Key Personnel
Founder & CEO: Suren M Seron *E-mail:* suren@strayangel.com
COO: Josh Burrows *E-mail:* josh@strayangel.com
VP, Rental Opers: Billy Civitella *E-mail:* billy@strayangel.com
Exec Dir: Howard Asher *E-mail:* howard@strayangel.com
Dir, Mktg: Jessica Pinney *E-mail:* jessica@strayangel.com
Founded: 2003
Digital motion picture rental, production & production services company.

Stretching Inc
PO Box 767, Palmer Lake, CO 80133-0767
Tel: 719-481-3928 *Toll Free Tel:* 800-333-1307 *Fax:* 719-481-9058
E-mail: office@stretching.com
Web Site: www.stretching.com
Key Personnel
Founder: Bob Anderson; Jean E Anderson
Mail-order & publishing. Produce & distribute videos, DVDs, books, software & posters; fitness related.
Online catalog(s), updated as needed

Stricker Books
8 Main St N, Unit C, Acton, ON L7J 1W1, Canada
Tel: 519-853-2780 *Toll Free Tel:* 800-924-3966 *Fax:* 519-853-2847
E-mail: stricker@strickerbooks.com
Web Site: www.strickerbooks.com
Key Personnel
Pres: Joseph Stricker
VP: Diane Stricker
Dir, Opers: Sue Stricker
Warehouse Mgr: Liz Saliba
Large print & audio books.

Strong Cinema Products
Division of Ballantyne Strong Inc
13710 FNB Pkwy, Suite 400, Omaha, NE 68145
Tel: 402-453-4444 *Toll Free Tel:* 800-424-1215 *Fax:* 402-453-7238
E-mail: info@btn-inc.com
Web Site: www.strong-world.com
Key Personnel
VP, Projection & Display: Ray F Boegner
Cinema Prods Mgr: Troy James *E-mail:* troy.james@btn-inc.com
Manufacture 35mm & digital projection systems & entertainment lighting products.

Strong Entertainment Lighting
Division of Ballantyne Strong Inc
13710 FNB Pkwy, Suite 400, Omaha, NE 68154
Tel: 402-453-4444 *Toll Free Tel:* 800-424-1215 *Fax:* 402-453-7238
E-mail: info@btn-inc.com
Web Site: www.strong-world.com
Key Personnel
Dir, Lighting: Glen Thor *E-mail:* glen.thor@btn-inc.com
Founded: 1948
Full service lighting company.
Catalog(s) available
Membership(s): International Association of Assembly Managers; Professional Lighting & Sound Association; Theatre Equipment Association; USITT

Strong Screen Systems
Division of Ballantyne Strong Inc
1440 Raoul-Charrette, Joliette, QC J6E 8S7, Canada
Tel: 450-755-3795 *Toll Free Tel:* 877-755-3795 *Fax:* 450-755-3122
E-mail: sales@strong-mdicinema.com
Web Site: www.strong-world.com; www.mdicinema.com
Key Personnel
Gen Mgr: Francois Barrette *E-mail:* francois.barrette@strong-mdicinema.com
Founded: 1968 (as Marcel Desrochers Inc)
Manufacturer of screen systems.
Brochure(s) available
Membership(s): Custom Electronic Design & Installation Association; Theatre Equipment Association

Joseph Struhl Co Inc
195 Atlantic Ave, Garden City Park, NY 11040
Mailing Address: PO Box N, Garden City Park, NY 11040
Tel: 516-741-3660 *Toll Free Tel:* 800-552-0023 *Fax:* 516-742-3617
E-mail: info@magicmaster.com; orders@magicmaster.com
Web Site: www.magicmaster.com
Founded: 1948
Manufacturer of display equipment.
Catalog(s) available

Studio A Recording Inc
5619 N Beech Daly, Dearborn Heights, MI 48127-3927
Tel: 313-561-7489 *Fax:* 313-561-6736
Web Site: www.studioarecording.com
Key Personnel
Founder & CFO: Marilyn Morgeson *E-mail:* marilyn@studioarecording.com
Founder & Prodr: Eric Morgeson *E-mail:* eric@studioarecording.com
Founded: 1980
Digidesign authorized pro tools training facility.

Studio B Mastering
821 Louise Ave, Charlotte, NC 28204
Tel: 704-372-9661
Web Site: www.studiobmastering.com
Key Personnel
Owner & Chief Mastering Engr: Dave Harris *E-mail:* dave@studiobmastering.com
Founded: 1990
Full service mastering.
Membership(s): AES; The Recording Academy

The Studio Center
915 Fee Dr, Sacramento, CA 95815
Tel: 916-564-9333
E-mail: info@thestudiocenter.com
Web Site: www.thestudiocenter.com
Key Personnel
Owner & Filmmaker: Frank Casanova *E-mail:* frank@thestudiocenter.com
Film & video production center.

Studio Center Corp
161 Business Park Dr, Virginia Beach, VA 23462
Tel: 757-286-3080 (24 hour cell) *Toll Free Tel:* 866-515-2111 *Fax:* 757-622-0583 (acctg)
Web Site: www.studiocenter.com
Key Personnel
Owner & CEO: William "Woody" Prettyman *E-mail:* william@studiocenter.com
VP: Robin Russ *Tel:* 757-622-2111 *E-mail:* robin@studiocenter.com
Founded: 1966
Creator, recorder & producer of commercial media for television & radio.
Catalog(s) available
Branch Office(s)
1707 Summit Ave, Richmond, VA 23230 *Tel:* 804-359-2111
1548 Ninth St, Santa Monica, CA 90401 *Tel:* 310-230-9839
3875 S Jones Blvd, Las Vegas, NV 89103 *Tel:* 702-248-2111
315 Madison Ave, 11th fl, New York, NY 10017 *Tel:* 212-986-1929

Studio Charleston
620 Dobbin Rd, Charleston, SC 29414
Tel: 843-376-1190 *Fax:* 843-737-4282
E-mail: info@studiocharleston.com
Web Site: www.studiocharleston.com
Film/TV productions, music-video productions, commercial video & photo shoots. Services include studio space rental, production services, production design, set construction, equipment rental & supplies, craft services & catering.

Studio Consulting & Construction Inc
2805 Oakview Dr, Dryden, MI 48428-9740
Tel: 810-796-3235; 248-496-9000
E-mail: scc@hdakers.com
Web Site: www.hdakers.com
Key Personnel
Pres: Harry D Akers *E-mail:* hdakers@hdakers.com
Video(s) available

Studio Dynamics
7703 Alondra Blvd, Paramount, CA 90723
Tel: 562-531-6700 *Toll Free Tel:* 800-595-4273 *Fax:* 562-531-6769
E-mail: sales@studiodynamics.com
Web Site: www.studiodynamics.com
Key Personnel
Founder & Pres: Robert Potier *E-mail:* bob@studiodynamics.com
VP: Thomas O'Hare *E-mail:* thomas@studiodynamics.com
Founded: 1984
Backdrops.
Catalog(s) available

Studio 1444
1444 N Highland Ave, Hollywood, CA 90028
Tel: 323-482-1004

E-mail: info@studio1444.com
Web Site: www.studio1444.com
Key Personnel
Owner: Alen Lin
Founded: 2008
Photo, film & video production facility. Provider of grip & lighting equipment.

Studio Instrument Rentals (SIR)
475 Tenth Ave, 2nd fl, New York, NY 10018
Tel: 212-627-4900 *Fax:* 212-627-7079
E-mail: nyinfo@sir-usa.com
Web Site: www.sir-usa.com
Key Personnel
Partner: Robert N Holst *E-mail:* bo@sirny.com
Prodn Mgr: Ralph Petrosino *E-mail:* ralph@sir-usa.com
Founded: 1967
Musical equipment rentals, sound systems & rehearsal studios.
Branch Office(s)
3541 E Broadway Rd, Phoenix, AZ 85040 *Tel:* 480-966-7800 *Fax:* 480-966-7801 *E-mail:* azinfo@sir-usa.com
6465 Sunset Blvd, Los Angeles, CA 90028 *Tel:* 323-957-5460 *Fax:* 323-957-5472 *E-mail:* lainfo@sir-usa.com
74830 Velie Way, Suite E, Palm Desert, CA 92260 *Tel:* 760-340-4864 *Fax:* 760-836-0252 *E-mail:* psinfo@sir-usa.com
4620 Santa Fe St, San Diego, CA 92109 *Tel:* 858-274-1384 *Fax:* 858-274-1906 *E-mail:* sdinfo@sir-usa.com
520 Townsend St, Bldg B, San Francisco, CA 94103 *Tel:* 415-957-9400 *Fax:* 415-957-9470 *E-mail:* sfinfo@sir-usa.com
12200 NE 14th Ave, North Miami, FL 33161 *Tel:* 305-891-3350 *Fax:* 305-891-3530 *E-mail:* miinfo@sir-usa.com
3400 Rio Vista Ave, Orlando, FL 32805 *Tel:* 305-891-3350 *Fax:* 305-891-3530 *E-mail:* orlinfo@sir-usa.com
2835 N Kedzie Ave, Chicago, IL 60618, Gen Mgr: Cesar Lavin *Tel:* 773-478-8500 *Fax:* 773-478-8555 *E-mail:* chinfo@sir-usa.com
4545 Cameron St, Bldg A, Las Vegas, NV 89103 *Tel:* 702-382-9147 *Fax:* 702-384-5638 *E-mail:* lvinfo@sir-usa.com
2310 NE 82 Ave, Portland, OR 97220 *Tel:* 503-282-5583 *Fax:* 503-282-5584 *E-mail:* orinfo@sir-usa.com
1101 Cherry Ave, Nashville, TN 37203 *Tel:* 612-255-4500 *Fax:* 615-255-4511 *E-mail:* tninfo@sir-usa.com
3631 Interlake Ave N, Seattle, WA 98103 *Tel:* 206-782-6800 *Fax:* 206-782-6862 *E-mail:* wainfo@sir-usa.com
Shipping Address: 501 W 36 St, 2nd fl, New York, NY 10018-1100

The Studio of David Inocencio/Minette Siegel
41 Fairlawn Ave, Daly City, CA 94015
Tel: 415-716-2791 *Fax:* 415-716-2796
Web Site: www.ino-sieg.com
Key Personnel
Partner: David Inocencio *E-mail:* david@sbcglobal.net; Minette Siegel *E-mail:* minettel@sbcglobal.net
Multimedia production studio. Services also include: digital production (video, PowerPoint, Keynote), web site art direction & production, photography (corporate portraits & events) & AV technical direction of events.
Catalog(s) available

Studio 1 Productions™ Inc
1700 Destino Ct, Port Orange, FL 32128
Tel: 386-788-6075 *Fax:* 386-760-5474
E-mail: studio1@studio1productions.com
Web Site: www.studio1productions.com
Key Personnel
Owner & Pres: David Knarr
Founded: 1993
Provide royalty free animation, music & stock footage to the video & film industries.
Online catalog(s) available

Studio 132
6802 Gunn Dr, Oakland, CA 94611-1443
Tel: 510-338-1240
E-mail: info@studio132.com
Web Site: www.studio132.com
Key Personnel
Founder & Owner: B Z Lewis
Founded: 1996
Commercial recording studio. Protools HDX, drum room, vocal booth & control room. Winner of six Emmy Awards.
Membership(s): ASCAP; NATAS; The Recording Academy

Studio 6429
6429 Independence Ave, Woodland Hills, CA 91367
Tel: 818-710-0016
E-mail: paulformanek@studio6429.tv
Web Site: studio6429.tv
Full service post-production studio with editing services, screening room & soundstage.

Studio 637
637 Cypress Ave, Hermosa Beach, CA 90254
Tel: 310-372-8218
Web Site: studio-637.com
Key Personnel
Founder & Prodr: Chuck Wilson *E-mail:* chuck@studio-637.com
Chief Audio Engr: Kevin Yamada
Founded: 2013
Full service audio & video production house.

Studio South
4912 Old Pineville Rd, Charlotte, NC 28217
Tel: 704-525-0296 *Fax:* 704-525-0136
E-mail: studiosouthvideo@earthlink.net
Web Site: www.studiosouthmedia.com
Key Personnel
Owner & Pres: William J Schinman
Video production company providing location video, film transfer, standards conversions & more.

Studio Space Atlanta
3080 McCall Dr, Suite 2, Atlanta, GA 30340
Tel: 404-630-0508
E-mail: info@studiospaceatl.com
Web Site: www.studiospaceatl.com
Key Personnel
Owner: Daniel Minchew
Video, film, photography & production rental studio. Production equipment rentals.

Studio Technologies Inc
5520 W Touhy Ave, Skokie, IL 60077
Tel: 847-676-9177 *Fax:* 847-982-0747
E-mail: stisales-2014@studio-tech.com
Web Site: www.studio-tech.com
Key Personnel
Owner & Pres: Gordon Kapes
Communs Mgr: Carrie Gage *Tel:* 847-676-9177 ext 239
Founded: 1978
Manufacture microphone mixers, intercom & IFB products, loud speaker monitoring management systems & fiber optic transport systems.
Catalog(s) available
Membership(s): NAB

Studio Worx Inc
8252 Brentwood Industrial Dr, Brentwood, MO 63144
Tel: 314-968-2626 *Fax:* 314-968-9866
E-mail: studioworxinc@studioworxinc.com
Web Site: www.studioworxinc.com
Founded: 1986
Full video production services: in-studio, on location, broadcast & production crews. Audio services: recording, editing, mastering & restoration. CD & DVD services: duplication, replication, conversion, authoring & packaging.

Studio14DC
1121 14 St, 5th fl, Washington, DC 20005
Tel: 202-216-8944
E-mail: info@studio14dc.com
Web Site: studio14dc.com
Fully equipped broadcast production facility.

The Studios at Paramount
5555 Melrose Ave, Hollywood, CA 90038
Tel: 323-956-5000
Web Site: www.paramountstudios.com
Key Personnel
Pres, Paramount Studio Group: Randall Baumberger

Stunt Wings Adventure Sports Talent & Equipment
Division of Windsports International Inc
12623 Gridley St, Sylmar, CA 91342
Tel: 818-367-2430; 818-353-5580 (home); 818-266-0874 (cell) *Fax:* 818-367-5363
E-mail: stuntwings@me.com
Web Site: www.stuntwings.com
Key Personnel
Pres: Joe Greblo
Founded: 1974
Sports talent equipment rentals for production needs.
Catalog(s) available
Membership(s): SAG-AFTRA

Russ Sturgeon Productions/RSVP
916 Third Ave S, Nashville, TN 37210
Tel: 615-255-7787 *Fax:* 615-254-7788
Web Site: www.rsvpnashville.com
Key Personnel
Owner: Russ Sturgeon *E-mail:* russ@rsvpnashville.com
Founded: 1972
Full service production company.

Style-City Music Inc
7826 Rhodes Rd, Suite 6, Hudson, FL 34667
Tel: 727-520-2336
E-mail: mail@stylecitymusic.com; stylecitymusic@yahoo.com
Web Site: www.stylecitymusic.com
Key Personnel
Owner: Steven Barry
Founded: 1991
Recording studio & video production.

Substation K
3947 State Line Rd, Kansas City, MO 64111
Tel: 816-531-3838 *Fax:* 816-531-3839
Web Site: www.substationk.com
Key Personnel
Pres & Exec Prodr: Mark McCone *E-mail:* markmccone@substationk.com
Gen Mgr: Lori Christiansen *E-mail:* lorichristiansen@substationk.com
Founded: 1993
Video editing.

Success Motivation International Inc, see SMI Inc

Suede Interactive
693 Main St, Hackensack, NJ 07601-4713
Tel: 201-646-0416
E-mail: suede@suede.tv
Web Site: www.suede.tv

Key Personnel
Owner: Bob Suede
Founded: 1971
Video editing & recording studios.
Catalog(s) available

Sugar Mountain PR
Subsidiary of AV Publicity Services
5505 SW Illinois St, Portland, OR 97221-1643
Tel: 503-293-9498
E-mail: sugarmountainnews@msn.com
Web Site: www.sugarmountainpr.com
Key Personnel
Founder: Beth Blenz-Clucas *E-mail:* bethpr@msn.com
Public relations company specializing in children's & family-friendly music & other media.
Membership(s): Children's Music Network; Coalition for Quality Children's Media; Grammy Foundation

Suggs Media Productions Inc
156 W 44 St, New York, NY 10036
Tel: 212-398-4200 *Fax:* 212-382-0922
Key Personnel
Pres: Jeanne Suggs *E-mail:* jeanne@suggsmedia.com
Full service production company.

Sullivan Home Entertainment
110 Davenport Rd, Toronto, ON M5R 3R3, Canada
Tel: 416-921-7177 *Fax:* 416-921-7538
E-mail: inquire@sullivan-ent.com
Web Site: www.sullivanmovies.com
Key Personnel
Pres & Exec Prodr: Trudy Grant *E-mail:* tgrant@sullivan-ent.com
Pres, Dir & Exec Prodr: Kevin Sullivan *E-mail:* ksullivan@sullivan-ent.com
Studio Mgr & Head, Post Prodn: Dan Matthews *E-mail:* dmatthews@sullivan-ent.com
Founded: 1981
Educational programming distributor.
Catalog(s) available

Sumiko Inc
Subsidiary of Fine Sounds Group
2431 Fifth St, Berkeley, CA 94710
Tel: 510-843-4500 *Toll Free Tel:* 800-301-0799 *Fax:* 510-843-7120
E-mail: mail@sumikoaudio.net
Web Site: www.sumikoaudio.net
Manufacturer & distributor of audio equipment.

Summit Audio Inc
Unit of Blue Microphones
5706 Corsa Ave, Suite 102, Westlake Village, CA 91362
Tel: 775-782-8838 *Fax:* 775-782-8350
E-mail: sound@summitaudio.com
Web Site: www.summitaudio.com
Founded: 1979
Manufacture pre-amplifiers.

Summit Electronics Corp
1060 Holland Dr, Suite M, Boca Raton, FL 33487
Tel: 561-226-8500 *Toll Free Tel:* 800-226-6960 *Fax:* 561-226-8523
E-mail: sales@summitelectronics.com
Web Site: www.summitelectronics.com; www.partsprocurement.com; bocasemi.com
Key Personnel
CEO: Richard Rosenstein *E-mail:* richard@summitelectronics.com
Pres: Scott Rosenstein
Gen Mgr: Sam Rosenstein *E-mail:* sam@summitelectronics.com
Founded: 1998
Sell semiconductors & hard-to-find electronic component parts.
Catalog(s) available

Sun Entertainment Corp
3106 Belmont Blvd, Nashville, TN 37212
Tel: 615-385-1960
E-mail: info@sunrecords.com
Web Site: www.sunrecords.com
Key Personnel
Pres & Dir: John A Singleton *E-mail:* john@sunrecords.com
SVP: Sidney S Singleton
VP, Dir & Gen Mgr: Paul A Martin
VP, Licensing & Admin: Collin L Brace
Dir: Terry O Lashman; Gary G Liu
Founded: 1952
Leasing record masters to other companies.
Catalog(s) available

Sunburst Digital
3150 W Higgins Rd, Suite 140, Hoffman Estates, IL 60619
Toll Free Tel: 800-321-7511
E-mail: service@sunburst.com; sales@sunburst.com
Web Site: sunburst.com
Founded: 1972
Software & video producers.
Catalog(s) available

Sunburst Recording
10313 Jefferson Blvd, Culver City, CA 90232
Tel: 310-204-2222
E-mail: info@sunburstrecording.com
Web Site: sunburstrecording.com
Key Personnel
Dir & Archive Specialist: Robert C Wayne *E-mail:* bob@sunburstrecording.com
Founded: 1977
Audio production services includes 5.1 DVD surround. Audio education private classes.
Catalog(s) available
Membership(s): ASCAP; The Recording Academy

Sundance Systems, Fibox Products Division
Subsidiary of Sundance Systems
7411 Hines Place, Suite 123, Dallas, TX 75235
Mailing Address: PO Box 459, Rio Vista, TX 76093
Tel: 214-920-9190 (Dallas) *Toll Free Tel:* 800-525-3443 *Fax:* 214-920-9339
E-mail: info@sundancesys.com
Web Site: www.sundancesys.com
Key Personnel
SVP: Hamilton Johnson *E-mail:* hsjohnson@sundancesys.com
Catalog(s), PDF

Sunfire Communications Inc
7751 Kingspointe Pkwy, Suite 105, Orlando, FL 32819
Tel: 407-226-8226 *Fax:* 407-226-1660
E-mail: info@sunfirecommunications.com
Web Site: www.sunfirecommunications.com
Key Personnel
Pres & Prodr: Ron Gehring *E-mail:* ron@sunfirecommunications.com
Prodr & Dir: Joe Izquierdo
Founded: 1994
Catalog(s) available

Sunnex Inc
9319 Forsyth Park Dr, Charlotte, NC 28273
Toll Free Tel: 800-445-7869 *Fax:* 508-651-0099
E-mail: sunnex@sunnex.com; info@sunnex.com
Web Site: www.sunnexonline.com
Key Personnel
Pres: Gunnar Lofgren
Lighting manufacturer.
Catalog(s) available

Sunnyside Communications Inc
348 W 38 St, Suite 12-B, New York, NY 10018
Tel: 212-564-4606 *Fax:* 212-967-2968
Web Site: www.sunnysiderecords.com
Key Personnel
Founder & Pres: Francois Zalacain *E-mail:* francois@sunnysiderecords.com
Founded: 1982
CD producers.

Sunrise Media LLC
200 Central Park S, Suite 12F, New York, NY 10019
Tel: 212-221-6310 *Fax:* 212-302-1854
E-mail: info@ipfmedia.org
Web Site: www.ipfmedia.org/vetc.htm
Key Personnel
Dir: Alvin H Perlmutter *E-mail:* ahp@ipfmedia.org
Prodn Supv: Joseph Schroeder *E-mail:* joe@ipfmedia.org
Prodn Coord: Ooana Trien *E-mail:* ooana@ipfmedia.org
Production company.

Sunrise Packaging Inc
9937 Goodhue St NE, Blaine, MN 55449-4433
Tel: 763-785-2505 *Toll Free Tel:* 800-634-8160 *Fax:* 763-785-2210
E-mail: customerservice@sunpack.com
Web Site: www.sunpack.com
Key Personnel
Acct Exec: Nick Rude *Tel:* 763-398-8631 *E-mail:* nrude@sunpack.com
Founded: 1982
Catalog(s) available

Sunrise Studios
1471 SW 96 Terr, Davie, FL 33324
Tel: 954-581-0026 *Fax:* 954-581-0204
E-mail: info@dvdcopypros.com
Web Site: www.dvdcopypros.com
Key Personnel
Owner: Robert Pianka *E-mail:* bob@sunrisestudios.tv
Founded: 1999
Video production company.

Sunset Bronson Studios
1438 N Gower St, Box 88, Hollywood, CA 90028
Tel: 323-460-5858 *Fax:* 323-460-3844
E-mail: sbs.reception@sgsandsbs.com
Web Site: sgsandsbs.com
Key Personnel
Opers Mgr: Jeremy Jacobs *Tel:* 323-460-5263 *E-mail:* jeremy.jacobs@sgsandsbs.com
Dir, Sales: Beth Talbert *E-mail:* beth.talbert@sgsandsbs.com
Ten stages available for television & film productions in addition to office & support space.

Sunset Gower Studios
1438 N Gower St, Box 21, Hollywood, CA 90028
Tel: 323-467-1001 *Fax:* 323-467-2717
E-mail: sgsreception@sgsandsbs.com
Web Site: sgsandsbs.com
Key Personnel
Opers Mgr: Tammy McCann *Tel:* 323-447-8388 *E-mail:* tammy.mccann@sgsandsbs.com
Dir, Sales & Mktg: Mike Mosallam *E-mail:* mike.mosallam@sgsandsbs.com
Office, support, stage space, practical locations, sound-editing facilities & post-production facility for television series, features & commercials.

Supercircuits
11000 N Mopac Expwy, Bldg 300, Austin, TX 78759
Toll Free Tel: 877-995-2288
E-mail: operations@supercircuits.com; customercare@supercircuits.com
Web Site: www.supercircuits.com
Key Personnel
Pres & CEO: Brian Wood
VP, Mktg: George Farley
VP, Sales: Mike Compton
VP, Technol: Jake Lahmann
Founded: 1989
Micro video cameras, transmitters & VCRs/CCTV.
Catalog(s) available
Membership(s): National Retail Federation; Retail Industry Leaders Association

SuperDigital Ltd
1150 NW 17 Ave, Portland, OR 97209-2403
Tel: 503-228-2222 *Toll Free Tel:* 888-79AUDIO (792-8346) *Fax:* 503-228-6819
E-mail: audiosales@superdigital.com
Web Site: www.superdigital.com
Key Personnel
Owner: Rick McMillen
Founded: 1987
Audio equipment distributor & duplication services.

Supergrit® Abrasives, see Red Hill Corp

Superior Electric
Division of Danaher Corp
One Cowles Rd, Plainville, CT 06062
Tel: 860-507-2025 *Toll Free Tel:* 800-787-3532 *Fax:* 860-507-2050 *Toll Free Fax:* 800-821-1369
E-mail: info@superiorelectric.com
Web Site: www.superiorelectric.com
Key Personnel
Dir of Sales: Mike Miga *E-mail:* mike.miga@superiorelectric.com
Manufacturer of voltage control components & power quality solutions.
Catalog(s) available
Membership(s): NAB; SBE

Superior Graphics
10440 Brockwood Rd, Dallas, TX 75238
Tel: 972-437-0542 *Toll Free Tel:* 800-969-8228 *Fax:* 972-690-6029
E-mail: info@superiorgraphics.com
Web Site: www.superiorgraphics.com
Key Personnel
Pres: John Ehrenberger *E-mail:* johne@superiorgraphics.com
Digital printing (large or small format) on paper, vinyl & fabric. Mounting & laminating, binding & finishing on printed items.
Catalog(s) available

Superscope Technologies Inc
1508 Batavia Ave, Geneva, IL 60134-3302
Tel: 630-232-8900 *Toll Free Tel:* 800-374-4118 *Fax:* 630-232-8905
Web Site: www.superscopetechnologies.com
Key Personnel
Sales & Mktg Coord: Jeff Anderson
Founded: 1993
Manufacturer of audio equipment.
Catalog(s) available

SuperStock Inc
6622 Southpoint Dr S, Suite 240, Jacksonville, FL 32216
Tel: 904-565-0066 *Toll Free Tel:* 800-828-4545 *Fax:* 904-565-1620
E-mail: yourfriends@superstock.com
Web Site: www.superstock.com
Key Personnel
Gen Mgr: Carolyn Nolte
Contemporary photography, fine art & vintage images.
Catalog(s) available
CD-ROM catalog(s) available
Foreign Office(s): Abbey House, 74-76 Saint John St, 1st fl, London EC1M 4DZ, United Kingdom *Tel:* (020) 7036-1800 *Fax:* (020) 3384-1911 *E-mail:* info@superstock.co.uk

Supertack® Hot Melt Glue Sticks & Glue Guns, see Red Hill Corp

SuperVision
Division of Sunrise Communications Inc
Pacific Design Ctr, Suite B-120, 8687 Melrose Ave, Los Angeles, CA 90069
Tel: 310-652-9510 *Toll Free Tel:* 877-287-9783 *Fax:* 310-652-9516
E-mail: mail@supervisionav.com
Web Site: www.supervisionav.com
Key Personnel
Pres: Greg Pass
Founded: 1977
Audio equipment distributor.
Membership(s): Custom Electronic Design & Installation Association

Sure Shot Transmissions Inc
10314 Main St, New Middletown, OH 44442
Mailing Address: PO Box 489, New Middletown, OH 44442-0489
Tel: 330-542-0900 *Fax:* 330-542-1020
Web Site: www.sureshotsat.com
Key Personnel
Pres: Dennis Kunce *E-mail:* dkunce@sureshotsat.com
VP, Opers: Paul Day *Tel:* 817-283-8203 *E-mail:* pday@sureshotsat.com
VP, Sales: John McLaughlin *Tel:* 631-261-3409 *E-mail:* jmclaughlin@sureshotsat.com
Chief Engr: Scott Tucker *E-mail:* tvdr.scott@gmail.com
Dir, Fin: Carolyn Blasko *E-mail:* cblasko@sureshotsat.com
Dir, Opers: Tami Anglin *E-mail:* tanglin@sureshotsat.com
Founded: 1987
Remote broadcasting. Sales offices in New York & Dallas.

SurgeX
Division of Electronic Systems Protection Inc
800 Knightdale Blvd, Suite 121, Knightdale, NC 27545
Toll Free Tel: 800-645-9721 (tech & cust support) *Fax:* 919-269-0454
Web Site: www.surgex.com
Key Personnel
CEO & Pres: Stephen F Galloway *Tel:* 919-823-0370 *E-mail:* sgalloway@espei.com
CFO: Rob Wood *Tel:* 919-823-0388 *E-mail:* rwood@espei.com
Pres, Sales: Shannon Townley *Tel:* 919-823-0381 *E-mail:* stownley@surgex.com
VP, Opers: David Perrotta *Tel:* 919-269-6968 *E-mail:* dperrota@espei.com
Dir, Mktg: Tanya Flores *Tel:* 919-823-0374 *E-mail:* tflores@espei.com
Manufacturer of premium AC power conditioning products for the professional & residential audio, video & multimedia marketplace.

SVAT Electronics
4080 Montrose Rd, Niagara Falls, ON L2H 1J9, Canada
Tel: 905-353-0732 *Toll Free Tel:* 866-946-7828 *Fax:* 905-353-1701 *Toll Free Fax:* 888-771-1701
E-mail: sales@svat.com
Web Site: www.svat.com
Key Personnel
Founder & Mng Dir: Raj Jain *E-mail:* rj@svat.com
Mng Dir: Deepak Jain
Develop, manufacture & market do-it-yourself video surveillance & lifestyle improving consumer electronics.
Branch Office(s)
60 Industrial Pkwy, Suite Z64, Cheektowaga, NY 14227
Membership(s): Consumer Electronics Association; Juvenile Products Manufacturers Association

SVS Inc
2513 Jenks Ave, Panama City, FL 32405
Tel: 850-522-4747 *Fax:* 850-522-4739
E-mail: sales@svslifts.com
Web Site: www.svslifts.com
Key Personnel
Pres: Tammy Huffman
Sales & Mktg Mgr: Patricia Palmer *E-mail:* patriciap@svslifts.com
Sales: Dan Boone
Founded: 1989
Projector equipment manufacturers.
Catalog(s) available
Membership(s): Custom Electronic Design & Installation Association; InfoComm International®; National Foundation of Independent Businesses

Swallow
Division of Swallow Publications Inc
238 E Main St, Drawer 10, Ville Platte, LA 70586
Tel: 337-363-2177 *Fax:* 337-363-2094
E-mail: info@flattownmusic.com
Web Site: www.flattownmusic.com
Key Personnel
Pres: Floyd Soileau
Founded: 1957
Catalog(s) available

Swank Audio Visuals
639-E Gravois Bluffs, St Louis, MO 63026
Tel: 636-680-9000 *Toll Free Tel:* 877-792-6528 *Fax:* 636-680-2853
Web Site: www.swankav.com
Key Personnel
CEO & Pres: Gregory R Diekemper
CFO & EVP: Dan Bauman
CIO: Mark White
SVP & Gen Mgr: Arthur A Clyne, Jr
VP: Mike Stengel
Dir, Mktg: Andee Oleno
Founded: 1937
Catalog(s) available
Membership(s): InfoComm International®

Sweetsong Productions
193 Meadsville Rd, Parkersburg, WV 26104
Tel: 304-428-7773
E-mail: sweetsonginfo@sweetsong.com
Web Site: www.sweetsong.com
Key Personnel
Owner: Roger Hoover
Founded: 1976

Sweetwater Sound Inc
5501 US Hwy 30 W, Fort Wayne, IN 46818
Tel: 260-432-8176 *Toll Free Tel:* 800-222-4700 *Fax:* 260-432-1758
Web Site: www.sweetwater.com
Key Personnel
Founder & Pres: Chuck Surack
Edit Dir: Mitch Gallagher
Founded: 1979
Retailer of music technology & music instruments.
Catalog(s), 3 issues/yr, free, industry standard

Online catalog(s) available
Membership(s): NAMM, the National Association of Music Merchants

Switch
6600 Manchester Ave, St Louis, MO 63139
Tel: 314-206-7700 *Toll Free Tel:* 800-445-0633 *Fax:* 314-206-4570
E-mail: switch@theswitch.us
Web Site: www.liberateyourbrand.com
Key Personnel
CEO: Michael O'Neill
Pres: John Nickel
EVP: Kevin Quigley
Founded: 1980
Integrated marketing firm.

Switchcraft® Inc
Division of HEICO Corp
5555 N Elston Ave, Chicago, IL 60630
Tel: 773-792-2700 *Fax:* 773-792-2129
E-mail: sales@switchcraft.com
Web Site: www.switchcraft.com
Key Personnel
CEO & Pres: Keith A Bandolik
EVP: Dave Dunmead
Founded: 1946
Switchcraft offers a wide variety of connectors, adapters, audio & video jacks, plugs, audio & video patchbays & patch cords.
Catalog(s) available
Branch Office(s)
c/o Conxall, 601 E Wildwood, Villa Park, IL 60181 *Tel:* 630-834-7504 *Fax:* 630-834-8540 *E-mail:* sales@conxall.com
Membership(s): Electronic Components Industry Association; NAB; NAMM, the National Association of Music Merchants; NSCA

Swivelier
600 Bradley Hill Rd, Blauvelt, NY 10913
Tel: 845-353-1455 *Fax:* 845-353-1512
E-mail: info@swivelier.com
Web Site: www.swivelier.com
Key Personnel
Pres: Michael Schwartz *Tel:* 845-353-1455 ext 231
Founded: 1947
Manufacture adjustable lighting fixtures, display equipment & accessories for stores, exhibits, convention centers, malls & specialty applications.

Symbolic Sound Corp
PO Box 2549, Champaign, IL 61825-2549
Tel: 217-355-6273 *Fax:* 217-355-6562
E-mail: info-kyma@symbolicsound.com
Web Site: www.symbolicsound.com
Key Personnel
Pres: Carla Scaletti
VP: Kurt Hebel
Founded: 1989
Audio equipment manufacturer.
Catalog(s) available
Membership(s): AES; Association for Computing Machinery; ICMA; IEEE; SEAMUS

SYMCO Inc
29 Poplar Dr, Stirling, NJ 07980
Tel: 908-647-6262 *Fax:* 908-647-4904
E-mail: orders@symcoinc.com
Web Site: www.symcoinc.com
Key Personnel
Pres: Frank Michael Culotta *E-mail:* fmculotta@symcoinc.com
Busn Devt: Chuck Motta *E-mail:* cmotta@symcoinc.com
Acct Mgr: Ruth Walter *E-mail:* rwalter@symcoinc.com
Cust Support Mgr: Kathy Funk *E-mail:* kfunk@symcoinc.com
Off Mgr: Marie DiCanto *E-mail:* mdicanto@symcoinc.com
Audio & Technol Specialist: Jim Zagryn *E-mail:* jzagryn@symcoinc.com
Mktg & Cust Support Specialist: Daniel Pilar *E-mail:* dpilar@symcoinc.com
New Busn Devt, IT Channel: Doug Cook *E-mail:* dcook@symcoinc.com
Founded: 1972
AV equipment distributor. Field offices located in Middletown, CT, Columbus, MD, Mahwah & Ridgefield Park, NJ, Duncannon, PA, Coventry, RI.
Membership(s): ASIS; Computer Technology Industry Association; Consumer Electronics Association; InfoComm International®; NSCA

Symetrix Inc
6408 216 St SW, Mountlake Terrace, WA 98043-2093
Tel: 425-778-7728
E-mail: support@symetrix.co; sales@symetrix.co
Web Site: www.symetrix.co
Key Personnel
Founder & CEO: Dane Butcher
Western Regl Sales Mgr: Tim Murray *Tel:* 310-433-1348 *E-mail:* tmurray@symetrix.co
Manufacturer of amplifiers.
Catalog(s) available

Symmes Systems
3977 Briarcliff Rd NE, Atlanta, GA 30345
Tel: 404-320-1012 *Fax:* 404-320-3465
Key Personnel
Mgr: Ed Symmes
Small production company.
Membership(s): ASMP

Symmetricom Inc, see Microsemi

Synaptic Digital
79 Fifth Ave, 14th fl, New York, NY 10003
Tel: 212-682-8300 *Toll Free Tel:* 800-843-0677 *Fax:* 212-682-5260
E-mail: learnmore@synapticdigital.com
Web Site: www.synapticdigital.com
Key Personnel
CTO: Krish Menon
VP, Fin: Richard Kellner
VP, Sales & Busn Devt: Laura Pair
VP, Strategic Client Devt: Neil Steinberg
Global leader in providing comprehensive multimedia solutions. Also has branch office in Atlanta, GA.
Branch Office(s)
6404 Wilshire Blvd, Suite 1121, Los Angeles, CA 90048 *Tel:* 323-370-6693 *Fax:* 323-944-0056
8 California St, San Francisco, CA 94111 *Tel:* 415-912-1650
National Press Bldg, 529 14 St NW, Suite 941, Washington, DC 20045 *Tel:* 202-662-8933 *Fax:* 202-623-2377
Foreign Office(s): 7-1-102 Jianguomenwai, Diplomatic Residence Compound No 1, Xiushui Jie, Chaoyang District, Beijing, China *Tel:* (010) 8532 4035
Waldhornstr 4, Munich 80997, Germany *Tel:* (089) 811 46 19
909 Venus Atlantis, Prahladnagar Rd, Satellite, Ahmedabad 380 015, India *Tel:* (079) 2909 6531
10-11 Percy St, London W1T 1DN, United Kingdom *Tel:* (020) 7580 8330

SynAudCon
8780 Rufing Rd, Greenville, IN 47124
Tel: 812-923-0174 *Toll Free Fax:* 800-547-0298
Web Site: www.synaudcon.com
Key Personnel
Owner & Corp Secy: Brenda Brown *E-mail:* bbrown@synaudcon.com
Founded: 1973
Programming by type (audio) & also produce educational seminars-both online & in-person training.

Synergem
2323 Randolph Ave, Avenel, NJ 07001
Tel: 732-225-0001 *Fax:* 732-225-7555
E-mail: info@synergem.com
Web Site: www.synergem.com
Key Personnel
Pres: Thomas De Maeyer *Tel:* 732-692-6305
Founded: 1985
Packaging & media content delivery. Duplication & manufacturing of USBs.
Catalog(s) available
Membership(s): American Independent Media Manufacturers Association

Synergetic Audio Concepts Inc, see SynAudCon

Synergistic Batteries Inc
5975 Providence Lane, Cumming, GA 30040
Tel: 770-886-6621 *Toll Free Tel:* 800-634-6000 *Fax:* 770-886-6522
E-mail: sbicas@synbat.com
Web Site: www.synergisticbatteries.com
Key Personnel
CEO: W B Caspari
Founded: 1975
Custom battery assembler.

Synergy Group Inc
Affiliate of Jeff Cooper Architects/Synergetics Inc
23930 Craftsman Rd, Calabasas, CA 91302-1437
Tel: 818-223-9009 *Fax:* 818-223-8999
Web Site: www.jeffcooper.com
Key Personnel
Owner: Jeff Cooper *E-mail:* jeff@jeffcooper.com
Design, build & equip post-production facilities, theatres, home theatres & recording studios.

Synsor Corp
1920 Merrill Creek Pkwy, Everett, WA 98203-5859
Tel: 425-551-1300 *Toll Free Tel:* 800-426-0193 *Fax:* 425-551-1313
E-mail: info@synsor.com
Web Site: www.synsor.com
Key Personnel
Pres & COO: Gary Bullock
Chmn: Edward Kramer
Founded: 1971
Manufacturer of multimedia workstations.
Catalog(s) available

Synthesizer Rental Service
Division of Schafer Digital Inc
2268 Ben Lomond Dr, Los Angeles, CA 90027-2905
Tel: 323-660-4065 *Fax:* 323-660-4597
E-mail: info@2srs.com
Web Site: synthesizerrentalservice.com
Key Personnel
Pres: Michael Boddicker
Founded: 1988
Rent synthesizers & Pro Tools™ Systems.
Catalog(s) available

Synthesizer Systems Technologies (SST)
10907 Magnolia Blvd, Suite 425, North Hollywood, CA 91601
Tel: 818-907-7780
E-mail: sst.shop@yahoo.com
Key Personnel
Owner: Michael Boddicker
Branch Office(s)
2512 Winford Ave, Nashville, TN 37211 *Tel:* 615-327-3500 *Fax:* 615-256-3106 *E-mail:* sstmusiccity@gmail.com

Syracuse Scenery & Stage Lighting Co Inc
101 Monarch Dr, Liverpool, NY 13088-4514
Tel: 315-453-8096 *Toll Free Tel:* 800-453-7775
Fax: 315-453-7897
E-mail: info@syracusescenery.com
Web Site: www.syracusescenery.com
Key Personnel
Sales & Rentals: Steven Le Porte
E-mail: sleporte@syracusescenery.com
Founded: 1922
Catalog(s), annual, free
Membership(s): Professional Lighting & Sound Association; USITT

Systems Impact Inc
3515 Woodley Rd NW, Washington, DC 20016
Toll Free Tel: 888-568-6284
E-mail: support@mathmastery.com
Web Site: mathmastery.com
Educational video producers.

Mark Szczerba, see D A Sound

T & M Digital Services
54 Flint Ridge Rd, Monroe, CT 06468
Mailing Address: PO Box 873, Monroe, CT 06468-0873
Tel: 203-268-5290 *Fax:* 203-268-5290
Key Personnel
Mng Partner: Richard Kraus
Chief Engr: Mark Smith

T-stop Inc
957 Cole Ave, Hollywood, CA 90038
Tel: 323-544-1000 *Fax:* 323-544-4970
E-mail: info@t-stopinc.com
Web Site: www.t-stopinc.com
Founded: 2004
High-end film equipment rentals, including cutting-edge digital cameras, lenses & support.

TAI Audio
5828 Old Winter Garden Rd, Orlando, FL 32835
Tel: 407-296-9959 *Toll Free Tel:* 800-486-6444
Fax: 407-648-1352
E-mail: sales@taiaudio.com
Web Site: www.taiaudio.com
Key Personnel
Pres: Joseph Guzzi
Founded: 1988
Production audio equipment distributor.
Catalog(s) available

Take 1 Media Services
31335 Center Ridge Rd, Cleveland, OH 44145
Tel: 440-899-0101
Web Site: www.take1media.com
Key Personnel
Pres: Jeff Kassouf *E-mail:* jeffk@take1media.com
Founded: 1983
Award winning video, film & multimedia productions.

Take One Productions Ltd
11010 Lake Grove Blvd, Suite 100, Morrisville, NC 27560
Tel: 919-481-0000 *Fax:* 919-460-8809
E-mail: marketing@takeonepro.com
Web Site: www.takeonepro.com
Key Personnel
Owner: Jim Cando *E-mail:* jim@takeonepro.com
Founded: 1972

Talas
Division of Technical Library Service Inc
330 Morgan Ave, Brooklyn, NY 11211
Tel: 212-219-0770 *Fax:* 212-219-0735
E-mail: info@talasonline.com
Web Site: www.talasonline.com
Key Personnel
Pres: Marjorie Salik
VP: Jake Salik
Founded: 1962
Archival & conservation supply company.
Catalog(s), free
Membership(s): AIC; ALA; IIC; SLA

Talk-A-Phone Co
7530 N Natchez Ave, Niles, IL 60714
Tel: 773-539-1100 *Fax:* 773-539-1241
E-mail: info@talkaphone.com
Web Site: www.talkaphone.com
Key Personnel
VP, Sales: Bob Shanes *E-mail:* rshanes@talkaphone.com
Eastern Regl Sales Mgr: Erez Sharoni *Tel:* 773-633-5980 *E-mail:* esharoni@talkaphone.com
Founded: 1937
Manufacturer of intercom systems.
Catalog(s) available

Tallahassee Audio Visual
2880 Apalachee Pkwy, Tallahassee, FL 32301
Tel: 850-877-1152 (photo); 850-877-1154 (AV)
Toll Free Tel: 800-356-9631 *Fax:* 850-878-4026; 850-656-1384
E-mail: info@talcam.com
Web Site: www.talcam.com
Key Personnel
Pres & Mgr: Michael Fraser *E-mail:* mike@talcam.com
Contact: Brendan Fraser *E-mail:* mfraser@talcam.com
Founded: 1941
Professional photofinishing, photographic & AV goods & services.
Membership(s): InfoComm International®; Photo Marketing Association

Tally Display Corp
19 Gardner Rd, Fairfield, NJ 07004
Tel: 973-777-7760 *Toll Free Tel:* 800-758-2559
Fax: 973-777-6220
E-mail: info@tallydisplay.com
Web Site: www.tallydisplay.com
Key Personnel
CEO & Pres: Steven Rose
Founded: 1991
Electronic signage - full color, indoor/outdoor, LED signs, displays & tickers.
CD-ROM catalog(s) available
Membership(s): International Sign Association; NAB; NSA; United States Sign Council

Tam Communications Inc
5610 Scotts Valley Dr, Suite B552, Scotts Valley, CA 95066
Tel: 831-439-1500 *Toll Free Fax:* 866-390-1218
E-mail: info@tamcom.com
Web Site: www.tamcom.com
Key Personnel
Founder & Pres: Susan O'Connor Fraser
Founder: Tam O'Connor Fraser
Founded: 1979
Full service production company.

Tamrac® Inc
9240 Jordan Ave, Chatsworth, CA 91311
Tel: 818-407-9500 *Toll Free Tel:* 800-662-0717
Fax: 818-407-9501
Web Site: www.tamrac.com
Founded: 1977
Manufacture video bags & accessories.
Catalog(s) available
Membership(s): Photo Marketing Association

Tamron USA Inc
Subsidiary of Tamron Co Ltd
10 Austin Blvd, Commack, NY 11725
Tel: 631-858-8400 *Toll Free Tel:* 800-827-8880
Fax: 631-543-5666
E-mail: custserv@tamron.com
Web Site: www.tamron-usa.com
Key Personnel
CEO & Pres: Tak Inoue
VP & Gen Mgr, Photo Div: Bert Krank *Tel:* 631-858-8400 ext 404 *E-mail:* bkrank@aol.com
Chief Mktg Offr: Stacie Errera *Tel:* 631-858-8400 ext 408 *E-mail:* errera@tamron.com
Founded: 1979
Catalog(s) available
Foreign Office(s): 1385, Hasunuma, Minuma-ku, Saitama-shi, Saitama 337-8556, Japan *Tel:* (048) 684-9111 *Fax:* (048) 683-8289 *Web Site:* www.tamron.co.jp (headquarters)

Tanglewood Productions
125 Brinkby Ave, Reno, NV 89509
Tel: 775-688-6282 *Toll Free Tel:* 877-671-8933
E-mail: info@tanglewoodproductions.com
Web Site: www.tanglewoodproductions.com
Key Personnel
Founder & Pres: Michael Eardley
Founded: 1983
Produce award-winning audios & have a talent pool of top voice talents from literally all over the globe. Very efficient studios & producers make sure your project is completed in short order; on time & within budget. Can preview any of our talent's demos on our web site at TanglewoodProductions.com. If you need a particular talent to do a test read on a script, that's no problem. We'll cut the sample & drop it right onto your desktop as an MP3 file. We offer a downloads page on our web site. When it's time for delivery of your spot, we post it on our web site & you or any of your radio or TV stations can download the file with no additional charges.

Tannoy North America Inc
Division of TC Group Americas
335 Gage Ave, Suite 1, Kitchener, ON N2M 5E1, Canada
Tel: 519-745-1158 *Fax:* 519-745-2364
E-mail: info@tcgroup-americas.com
Web Site: www.tannoy.com
Key Personnel
CEO: Marc Bertrand
A leading innovator of premium audio solutions utilizing cutting edge acoustic, electronic & digital expertise.
Catalog(s) available
Foreign Office(s): Coatbridge, Scotland, North Lanarkshire ML5 4TF, United Kingdom *Tel:* (01236) 420199 *Fax:* (01236) 428230

Tantor Media Inc
2 Business Park Rd, Unit 2, Old Saybrook, CT 06475
Tel: 860-395-1155 *Toll Free Tel:* 877-7-TANTOR (782-6867) *Toll Free Fax:* 888-782-7821
E-mail: orders@tantor.com; service@tantor.com
Web Site: www.tantor.com
Key Personnel
CEO: Kevin Colebank
Founded: 2000
Audiobooks.
Catalog(s) available

Tape Resources
845 N Church St, Elmhurst, IL 60126
Tel: 630-993-4673 *Toll Free Tel:* 800-827-3462; 888-496-3282 (sales) *Toll Free Fax:* 888-827-3329
Web Site: www.taperesources.com
Supplier of professional tape & recording media products.

Tape World
309 Wagner Ave, Butler, PA 16001

Tel: 724-283-8621 *Toll Free Tel:* 800-245-6000; 800-322-8273 *Fax:* 724-283-8298 *Toll Free Fax:* 800-322-8273
E-mail: info@tapeworld.com
Web Site: www.tapeworld.com
Key Personnel
Owner: David Grenci
Catalog(s) available

Tapemaker
48 Urban Ave, Westbury, NY 11590
Tel: 516-333-2700 *Fax:* 516-333-0643
E-mail: tapemaker@aol.com
Key Personnel
Pres: Mordy Brandwein
Laser labels, audio & video, audio leader tape-paper, polyester & timing tape, thermal labels & audio & video splicing tape. Film splicing tape & tabs 16mm & 35mm. Shrink tubing by Sumitomo, custom imprinting of shrink tubing in colors, CD laser & inkjet labels, compatible Avery, ACE, Necito designs, Ink Jet photo quality papers, glossy & matte silver & gold laser labels.
Catalog(s) available
Shipping Address: 47 Kinkel St, Westbury, NY 11590

Taperwire
Division of Fuller Manufacturing
c/o Fuller Manufacturing, 523 S Flower St, Burbank, CA 91502
Tel: 818-238-9911 *Fax:* 818-238-9959
E-mail: taperwire@taperwire.com
Web Site: www.taperwire.com
Key Personnel
Engg Mgr: Ronald Fuller
Founded: 1991
Manufacture flat cable suitable for under carpeting.
Catalog(s) available

TapeStockOnline.com
602 N Cypress St, Orange, CA 92867
Tel: 310-352-4230 *Toll Free Tel:* 888-322-TAPE (322-8273) *Fax:* 310-352-4233
E-mail: sales@tapestockonline.com
Web Site: www.tapestockonline.com
Key Personnel
Dir, Mktg: Jim Gibioterra

TapeWorks Texas Inc
4930-B Dacoma, Houston, TX 77092
Tel: 713-688-0696 *Toll Free Tel:* 866-827-3489 *Fax:* 713-688-2509
E-mail: sales@tapeworkstexas.com
Web Site: www.tapeworkstexas.com
Key Personnel
Contact: Curt Hall
Founded: 1997
Distributor of professional broadcast video equipment & accessories.

TAPPI
15 Technology Pkwy S, Norcross, GA 30092
Tel: 770-446-1400 *Toll Free Tel:* 800-332-8686 (US); 800-446-9431 (CN) *Fax:* 770-446-6947
E-mail: memberconnection@tappi.org
Web Site: www.tappi.org
Key Personnel
CEO & Pres: Larry N Montague *E-mail:* lmontague@tappi.org
CFO: Chuck Fiveash *Tel:* 770-729-9980 ext 24 *E-mail:* chuck@ffcpa.net
Cont: Dennis Thompson *Tel:* 770-209-7245 *E-mail:* dthompson@tappi.org
VP, Opers: Eric Fletty *Tel:* 770-209-7535 *E-mail:* efletty@tappi.org
Dir, Mktg: Simona Marcellus *Tel:* 770-209-7293 *E-mail:* smarcellus@tappi.org
Founded: 1915
Leading technical association for the pulp, paper & converting industry.
Catalog(s) available

TARA Labs
1020 Benson Way, Ashland, OR 97520
Tel: 541-488-6465 *Fax:* 541-488-6463
E-mail: sales@taralabs.com
Web Site: www.taralabs.com
Key Personnel
Pres: M J Bergs
Founded: 1986
Manufacturer & distributor of AV cables.

Tarpley Media Systems
Subsidiary of Tarpley Music Co Inc
3737 50 St, Lubbock, TX 79413
Tel: 806-797-5833 *Toll Free Tel:* 800-600-5833 *Fax:* 806-797-5139
E-mail: tms@tarpleymedia.com
Web Site: www.tarpleymedia.com
Key Personnel
VP: David Tarpley
Mgr & Consultant: Jonathan Smither
Sr Consultant: Casey McGrew
Founded: 1927
AV integrator.
Membership(s): AES; InfoComm International®; NAMM, the National Association of Music Merchants

TASCAM
Division of TEAC America Inc
7733 Telegraph Rd, Montebello, CA 90640
Tel: 323-726-0303; 323-727-7617 (support) *Toll Free Tel:* 800-447-8322 *Fax:* 323-727-4805
E-mail: tascamrepair@teac.com
Web Site: www.tascam.com
Key Personnel
Mktg Mgr: Jeff Laity
Founded: 1953
Audio equipment manufacturer.

Tasman Group Pacific Rim
4850 Gregg Rd, Pico Rivera, CA 90660
Tel: 562-695-8877 *Toll Free Tel:* 888-355-8889 *Fax:* 562-908-3912
Web Site: www.tasmangrouppr.com
Key Personnel
Acct Mgr: Kristine Goli
Manufacturing displays & store equipment.
Online catalog(s) available

Tatum Video
Division of Tatum Communications Inc
103 S Davis St, Telluride, CO 81435
Mailing Address: PO Box 944, Telluride, CO 81435-0944
Tel: 213-999-5970 (cell); 970-728-4892 *Fax:* 970-728-4892
E-mail: utemtn@aol.com
Key Personnel
Pres & Prodr: Tom Tatum
Prodn Coord: Kathryn Vinson
Asst to Prodr: Robin Streichler
Dist: Jim Rokas Tomwil *Tel:* 818-769-0883
Founded: 1981
A video & film production company specializing in outdoor extreme sports adventure programs.
Catalog(s) available
Branch Office(s)
87 Vista del Ocaso, Ranchos de Taos, NM 87557

Tatung Co of America Inc
Subsidiary of Tatung Co
2850 El Presidio St, Long Beach, CA 90810
Tel: 310-637-2105 *Toll Free Tel:* 800-827-2850
E-mail: tus@tatungusa.com
Web Site: www.tatungusa.com
Key Personnel
EVP: Edward Chen *Tel:* 800-827-2850 ext 116 *E-mail:* echen@tatungusa.com
Founded: 1972
Worldwide provider of technologically advanced products, customer solutions & manufacturing services.

Carl Tatz Design
6666 Brookmont Terr, Suite 1109, Nashville, TN 37205
Tel: 615-354-6242 *Fax:* 615-356-4791
E-mail: carl@carltatzdesign.com
Web Site: www.carltatzdesign.com
Key Personnel
Pres: Carl Tatz *Tel:* 615-400-5479 (cell)
Acoustic design, analysis & implementation.

The Taunton Press Inc
63 S Main St, Newtown, CT 06470
Mailing Address: PO Box 5506, Newtown, CT 06470-5506
Tel: 203-426-8171 *Toll Free Tel:* 800-926-8776 (ext 3893 - PR); 800-888-8286 (orders) *Fax:* 203-426-3434
Web Site: www.taunton.com
Key Personnel
CEO & Pres: Tim Rahr
Dir, HR: Carol Marotti
Catalog(s) available

Taylor Associates
110 W Canal St, Suite 301, Winooski, VT 05404
Tel: 802-735-1942 *Toll Free Tel:* 800-READ-PLUS (732-3758) *Fax:* 802-419-4786
E-mail: info@readingplus.com
Web Site: www.readingplus.com
Key Personnel
Owner: Stanford E Taylor
CEO: Mark Taylor
COO: Kelly Scanell
Chief Academic Offr: Karen Feller
CIO: Rick Cusick
Dir, Res: Alexandra Spichtig
Nat Sales Dir: Karl Hummel
Educational computer software publisher (reading). Visigraph (hardware & software) & other products available online only.
Membership(s): International Reading Association

Chip Taylor Communications LLC
2 East View Dr, Derry, NH 03038
Tel: 603-434-9262 *Toll Free Tel:* 800-876-CHIP (876-2447) *Fax:* 603-432-2723
E-mail: chip.taylor@chiptaylor.com
Web Site: www.chiptaylor.com
Key Personnel
Pres: Chip Taylor
Founded: 1985
Produce & distribute over 4,000 programs for broadcast, streaming & DVD markets.
Catalog(s) available
Membership(s): ACA; AECT; AIME; ALA; ASCO; Consortium of College & University Media Centers; MCA-I; Music Business Association; National Association of Media & Technology Centers; PAECT

TBA Global Events
220 W 42 St, 10th fl, New York, NY 10036
Tel: 646-445-7000 *Fax:* 646-445-7001
E-mail: newyorkinfo@tbaglobal.com
Web Site: www.tbaglobal.com
Founded: 1994
Creating, producing & marketing events.
Branch Office(s)
TBA San Diego/Southern California, 11455 El Camino Real, Suite 120, San Diego, CA 92130 *Tel:* 858-461-6500 *Fax:* 858-461-6501
TBA San Francisco, 201 Spear St, Suite 100, San Francisco, CA 94105 *Tel:* 415-992-3260 *Fax:* 415-992-3261

535 N Brand Blvd, Suite 800, Glendale, CA 91203 *Tel:* 818-226-2800 *Fax:* 818-226-2801 (acctg off)
TBA Chicago, 200 S Whacker Dr, Suite 3100, Chicago, IL 60606, Contact: Judi Lorek *Tel:* 312-335-9595 *Fax:* 312-335-0790
TBA Detroit, 1000 Town Ctr, Suite 570, Southfield, MI 48075 *Tel:* 248-204-4700 *Fax:* 248-353-3472
113 Seaboard Lane, Suite A105, Franklin, TN 37067 *Tel:* 615-986-7100 *Fax:* 615-986-7101
TBA Banff, AB, 414 Second St, Canmore, AB T1W 2K4, Canada *Tel:* 403-678-6836 *Fax:* 403-678-6874 *E-mail:* canada@tbaglobal.com
TBA Vancouver, BC, 425 Carrall St, Suite 320, Vancouver, BC V6B 6E3, Canada *Tel:* 604-689-3448 *Fax:* 604-633-5054 *E-mail:* vancouver@tbaglobal.com
Membership(s): ASAE; MPI

TBC Consoles Inc
170 Rodeo Dr, Edgewood, NY 11717
Tel: 631-293-4068 *Toll Free Tel:* 888-CONSOLE (266-7653) *Fax:* 631-293-4075
E-mail: info@tbcconsoles.com; sales@tbcconsoles.com; support@tbcconsoles.com
Web Site: www.tbcconsoles.com
Key Personnel
CFO: Diana Lukasik *Tel:* 631-293-4068 ext 103 *E-mail:* dlukasik@tbcconsoles.com
CTO: Peter Pedisich *Tel:* 631-293-4068 ext 111 *E-mail:* ppedisich@tbcconsoles.com
Pres: Jerry Hahn *Tel:* 631-293-4068 ext 102 *E-mail:* jhahn@tbcconsoles.com
Sr Acct Mgr: Steve Struhs *Tel:* 631-293-4068 ext 104 *E-mail:* sstruhs@tbcconsoles.com
Opers Mgr: Jansen Hahn *Tel:* 631-293-4068 ext 121 *E-mail:* jansen@tbcconsoles.com
Founded: 1988
Design & manufacture video production consoles & equipment cabinetry.
Catalog(s) available
Membership(s): ACCP; BCNYS; NAB; SMPTE

TBC Studios
10201 W Appleton Ave, Milwaukee, WI 53225
Tel: 414-536-7337
E-mail: info@tbcstudios.com
Web Site: www.tbcstudios.com
HD video production & digital audio recording facility.

TEA, see Television Equipment Associates Inc (TEA)

TEAC America Inc
Subsidiary of TEAC Corp
7733 Telegraph Rd, Montebello, CA 90640
Tel: 323-726-0303 *Fax:* 323-727-7656
E-mail: custser@teac.com
Web Site: www.teac.com
Founded: 1953
Manufacturer of data recording equipment.

Teach America Corp
121 N Love St, Quincy, FL 32351-2440
Tel: 850-875-0491
Web Site: teachamerica.com; www.accessmanagement.info
Key Personnel
Pres: Frank Broen *E-mail:* fbroen@teachamerica.com
Founded: 1979
Explaining transportation planning issues. Produces interactive visualizations, video/flash programs & multimedia communications.
Catalog(s) available
Membership(s): ATD; ITE

TeachLogic Inc
1688 Ord Way, Oceanside, CA 92056
Tel: 760-631-7800 *Toll Free Tel:* 800-588-0018 *Fax:* 760-631-1283
E-mail: sales@teachlogic.com; info@teachlogic.com
Web Site: www.teachlogic.com
Key Personnel
Pres: Brian Van Waay *E-mail:* bvanwaay@teachlogic.com
VP, Sales & Mktg: Jerry Hogerson *E-mail:* jhogerson@teachlogic.com
Founded: 1992
Manufacture sound field systems & wireless microphones.

Teatown Communications Group
1560 Broadway, New York, NY 10036
Tel: 212-302-0722
E-mail: info@teatown.tv
Web Site: www.teatown.tv
Key Personnel
Pres: Marlen Hecht
Founded: 1980
Editing services/post-production.
Catalog(s) available
Membership(s): AFI; IFP

TEC/West USA Inc
3050 E Victoria St, Rancho Dominguez, CA 90221
Tel: 310-961-3491 *Toll Free Tel:* 800-421-7215 *Fax:* 310-464-9210
E-mail: info@tecwest.com
Web Site: www.tecwest.com
Key Personnel
Natl Sales: Frances Doiuchi
Founded: 1973
Catalog(s) available

Tecfilms Inc
6310 Lemmon Ave, Suite 210, Dallas, TX 75209-5850
Tel: 214-904-0414
E-mail: mail@tecfilms.com
Web Site: www.tecfilms.com
Key Personnel
Owner: Peter S Jordan *E-mail:* peter@tecfilms.com
VP: Sharon Bunyard
Video production for the aerospace industry.
Catalog(s) available

Tech Rentals Inc, see ON Event Services

Tech 21 USA Inc
790 Bloomfield Ave, Clifton, NJ 07012
Tel: 973-777-6996 *Fax:* 973-777-9899
E-mail: info@tech21nyc.com
Web Site: www.tech21nyc.com
Key Personnel
Pres: B Andrew Barta
VP: Dale Krevens *E-mail:* dale@tech21nyc.com
Dir, Sales: Tyme Rogers *E-mail:* tyme@tech21nyc.com
Founded: 1989
Manufacture signal processing equipment, bass & guitar amplifiers & effects.

Techflex Inc
Division of Dermody Associates Inc
29 Brookfield Dr, Sparta, NJ 07871
Tel: 973-300-9242 *Toll Free Tel:* 800-323-5140 *Fax:* 973-300-9409
E-mail: techflex@techflex.com
Web Site: www.techflex.com
Key Personnel
Pres: William Dermody, III
Founded: 1965
Sleeving for wires & cables, bundling & protection, Flexo Brand.

Catalog(s) available
Branch Office(s)
300 E 16 St, Greeley, CO 80631 *Tel:* 970-352-2355 *Fax:* 970-352-3828
Membership(s): NAB

Technet® Systems Group
Division of Steve Vanni Associates Inc
PO Box 422, Auburn, NH 03032-0422
Tel: 603-483-5365 *Toll Free Tel:* 888-TECHNET (832-4638) *Fax:* 603-483-0512
E-mail: sales@technetsystems.com
Web Site: www.technetsystems.com
Key Personnel
Pres: Steve Vanni *E-mail:* svanni@technetsystems.com
Founded: 1982
Broadcast equipment supplies & turn-keyed systems.

Techni-Lux Inc
10900 Palmbay Dr, Orlando, FL 32824
Tel: 407-857-8770 *Fax:* 407-857-8771
E-mail: sales@techni-lux.com
Web Site: www.techni-lux.com
Key Personnel
VP: Alex Gonzalez
Sales Exec: Felix Gallardo
Founded: 1991
Online catalog(s) available

Techni-Tool Inc
1547 N Trooper Rd, Worcester, PA 19490
Mailing Address: PO Box 1117, Worcester, PA 19490-1117
Tel: 610-941-2400 *Toll Free Tel:* 800-832-4866 *Fax:* 610-828-5623 *Toll Free Fax:* 800-854-8665
E-mail: sales@techni-tool.com
Web Site: www.techni-tool.com
Key Personnel
Pres: Paul Weiss
VP, Fin: Dave Deputy
VP, Opers - DC: William Kushner
VP, Sales: Michael Ryan
Gen Mgr: Steve Porter
Founded: 1959
Video repair tools & test equipment.
Catalog(s), quarterly
Branch Office(s)
775 E Baseline Rd, Gilbert, AZ 85233 *Tel:* 480-829-1200 *Toll Free Tel:* 800-434-8665 *Fax:* 480-829-7002 *Toll Free Fax:* 877-854-8665

Technical Audio Devices (TAD)™
Subsidiary of Pioneer Electronics (USA) Inc
1925 E Dominguez St, Long Beach, CA 90810
Tel: 213-746-6337 (cust support) *Toll Free Tel:* 800-421-1404 *Fax:* 310-952-2821
E-mail: tadpioneer@pioneerservice.com
Web Site: www.pioneerelectronics.com/pusa

Technical Exhibits Corp
Subsidiary of Model Builders Inc
6155 S Oak Park Ave, Chicago, IL 60638
Tel: 773-586-3377 *Fax:* 773-586-6575
Web Site: www.technicalexhibits.net
Key Personnel
Pres: Hal Chaffee *E-mail:* hchaffee@sbcglobal.net
Founded: 1960
Exhibit products including telephone handsets & the "Hearphone" hand-held exhibit speaker.
Catalog(s) available

Technical Innovation
2975 Northwoods Pkwy, Norcross, GA 30071
Tel: 770-447-1001 *Toll Free Tel:* 866-447-1004 *Fax:* 770-441-5285
Web Site: www.technical-innovation.com

Key Personnel
CEO: Michael Landrum
CFO: David Sharp
Pres: Kevin Powers
VP, IT: Fred Innes
Mktg Dir: Lisa Matthews
Founded: 1937
Catalog(s) available
Branch Office(s)
140 Business Center Dr, Birmingham, AL 35244, Regl Dir: Danny Grant *Tel:* 205-985-2297 *Fax:* 205-985-4756
10130 Mallard Creek Rd, Suite 300, Charlotte, NC 28262, Proj Devt: Paul Patrick *Tel:* 704-944-3115
10404 Chapel Hill Rd, Suite 107, Morrisville, NC 27560, Regl Dir: Dan Lumsden *Tel:* 919-462-9300 *Fax:* 919-462-9455
1680 Century Ctr Pkwy, Bldg D-10, Memphis, TN 38134, Regl Dir: David Berndt *Tel:* 901-345-5971 *Fax:* 901-969-0170
1449 Donelson Pike, Nashville, TN 37217, Regl Dir: David Berndt *Tel:* 615-244-3933 *Fax:* 615-244-1031
1577 Spring Hill Rd, Suite 450, Tysons Corner, VA 22182
Membership(s): IMCCA; InfoComm International®; MCA-I; NSCA; SBE; SMPTE

Technical Services
10567 Oak Creek Dr, Lakeside, CA 92040
Tel: 619-561-4410
Web Site: www.widcoinc.com
Key Personnel
CEO: Michael D Bell *E-mail:* michael@widcoinc.com

Technical Services
2480 Southwell Rd, Dallas, TX 75229
Tel: 972-421-4230 *Fax:* 972-421-4231
Key Personnel
Mgr: John Eldridge *E-mail:* john@tecserv.biz

Technical Support Systems LLC
2232 Central Ave, Memphis, TN 38104
Tel: 901-398-5908 *Fax:* 901-398-5914
Web Site: www.techsupportsys.com
Key Personnel
Owner: Chip Benson *E-mail:* chip@techsupportsys.com
Founded: 1984
Membership(s): InfoComm International®; NSCA

Technicolor
Division of Thomson Multimedia
3233 E Mission Oaks Blvd, Camarillo, CA 93012
Tel: 805-445-1122 *Fax:* 805-445-4340
E-mail: info@technicolor.com
Web Site: www.technicolor.com
Key Personnel
CEO: Frederic Rose
SVP, Sales: Rich Cusolito
Founded: 1915
Branch Office(s)
2233 N Ontario St, Suite 300, Burbank, CA 91504, Contact: Jim Mann *Tel:* 818-260-4980 *E-mail:* jim.mann@technicolor.com (digital cinema & content services)
2255 N Ontario St, Suite 350, Burbank, CA 91504, Contact: Rob Anker *Tel:* 818-260-2615 *E-mail:* rob.anker@technicolor.net (content & sound services)
5555 Melrose Ave, PPB Rm 3210, Hollywood, CA 90028, Contact: Mark Kaplan *Tel:* 323-956-7010 *E-mail:* mark.kaplan@technicolor.com (sound services)
6040 Sunset Blvd, Hollywood, CA 90028, Contact: Sue Kanarian *Tel:* 323-817-6600 *E-mail:* sue.kanarian@thomson.net (content services)
2 Independence Way, Princeton, NJ 08540
3418 Progress Way, Wilmington, OH 45177, Contact: Tony Butcher *Tel:* 937-383-6014 *Fax:* 937-283-6139 *E-mail:* tony.butcher@technicolor.com (cinema distribution)
2400 Boundary Rd, Unit 130, Burnaby, BC V5M 3Z3, Canada, Gen Mgr: Steve Goetz *Tel:* 604-689-1090 *Fax:* 604-689-1003 *E-mail:* steve.goetz@technicolor.com (content services)
49 Ontario St, Toronto, ON M5A 2V1, Canada, VP, Post Prodn: Louis Major *Tel:* 416-585-9995 *Fax:* 416-364-1585 *E-mail:* louis.major@technicolor.com (content services)
2555 Dollard Ave, Bldg 2, LaSalle, QC H8N 3A9, Canada, Contact: Marie-Claude Boudreau *Tel:* 514-931-6212 *Fax:* 514-931-4588 *E-mail:* marie-claude.boudreau@technicolor.com (cinema distribution)
2101 St Catherine W, Suite 300, Montreal, QC H3H 1M6, Canada *Tel:* 514-939-5060 *Fax:* 514-939-5070 (sound/film/content services)
Foreign Office(s): 134-138 Euston Rd, Alexandria, NSW 2015, Australia, Contact: Simon Hibbins *Tel:* (029) 519 2677 *E-mail:* simon.hibbins@technicolor.com (home entertainment services)
8/F, A, Technology Fortune Ctr, 8 Xue Qing Rd, Hai Dian District, Beijing, China *Tel:* (010) 5883-7222 *Fax:* (010) 8273-0806
221 bis bd Jean-Jaures, 92100 Boulogne Billancourt, France *Tel:* 01 41 04 31 00
One rue Jeanne d'Arc, Issy-les-Moulineaux Cedex, 92443 Paris, France, Contact: Manuel Rodriguez *Tel:* 01 41 86 50 00 (home entertainment services)
975 Ave des Champs Blancs, Cesson Sevigne Cedex, 35576 Rennes, France *Tel:* 02 99 27 30 00
Level 9, Navigator Block, ITPL, Whitefield Rd, Bangalore 560 066, India *Tel:* (080) 4046 1234
Via Tiburtina 1138, 00156 Rome RM, Italy, Contact: Ludovico De Cesare *Tel:* (06) 418 882 56 *Fax:* (06) 411 1694 *E-mail:* ludovico.decesare@technicolor.com (lab/content services)
Via Tiburtina 1138, Via Urbana 172, 00184 Rome RM, Italy, Contact: Marco Ridolf *Tel:* (06) 41 888 238 *Fax:* (06) 474 5246 *E-mail:* marco.ridolfi@technicolor.com (sound services)
Technicolor Mexicana, Avenida Labna 1781, Jardines del Sol, 45050 Zapopan, Jalisco, Mexico, Contact: Guillermo Escutia *Tel:* (33) 3134 4212 *Fax:* (33) 3134 4245 *E-mail:* guillermo.escutia@technicolor.com (home entertainment services)
Ave Galaxia, No 2099, Parque Industrial Mexicali, 21210 Mexicali, Mexico, Contact: Alejandro Monge *Tel:* (686) 9055402 *Fax:* (65) 566 6970 *E-mail:* alejandro.monge@technicolor.com (home entertainment services)
Energieweg 6, 5804 CE Venray, Netherlands, Contact: Godart Spruit *E-mail:* godart.spruit@technicolor.com (home entertainment services)
Technicolor Polska Sp z, Julianowska 65A, 05-500 Piaseczno, Poland, Contact: Robert Wilczynski *Tel:* (022) 7027530 *E-mail:* robert.wilczynski@technicolor.com (home entertainment services)
30 Loyang Way, No 05-23, Loyang Industrial Estate, Singapore 508769, Singapore, Contact: Joe Ng *Tel:* (065) 6546 2867 *Fax:* (065) 6546 2865 *E-mail:* joe.ng@technicolor.com (content services)
Edificio Zye, C/Punto, Net 4, 28805 Alcala de Henares, Spain, Contact: Silvia Aranda *Tel:* (091) 830 5906 *Fax:* (091) 879 76 11 *E-mail:* silvia.aranda@technicolor.com (home entertainment services)
40/19 Soi Amornphunnives 4, Vipavadee Rangsit Rd, Ladyao, Jatujak, Bangkok 10900, Thailand *Tel:* 08-622-9762 (film/content services)
566 Chiswick High Rd, London W4 5AN, United Kingdom *Tel:* (020) 8100 1000 *Fax:* (020) 8100 1001
28-32 Lexington St Soho, London W1F 0LF, United Kingdom, Contact: Matt Adams *Tel:* (0207) 319 4900 *E-mail:* matt.adams@technicolor.com
Perivale Park, Horsenden Lane S, Middx UB6 7RL, United Kingdom, Contact: George Kilpatrick *Tel:* (0208) 799 0503 *E-mail:* george.kilpatrick@technicolor.com (anvil sound & content services)
Cosford Lane, Swift Valley Industrial Estate, Rugby, Warwicks CV21 1QN, United Kingdom, Contact: Simon Miller *Tel:* (01179) 240 494 *E-mail:* simon.miller@technicolor.com (home entertainment services)

Technicolor - PostWorks, see PostWorks

Technicolor SA
Formerly Thomson
10330 N Meridian St, Indianapolis, IN 46290
Tel: 317-587-3000 *Fax:* 317-587-6763
Web Site: www.thomsonconsumer.com
Catalog(s) available
Branch Office(s)
6040 Sunset Blvd, Hollywood, CA 90028
2 Independence Way, Princeton, NJ 08540

Technics
Division of Panasonic Corp of North America
One Panasonic Way, Secaucus, NJ 07094
Tel: 201-348-7000 *Toll Free Tel:* 800-211-7262 (support); 800-405-0652 (orders)
Web Site: www.panasonic.com
Manufacturer of audio components.

Technisphere Corp
134 W 26 St, Ground fl, New York, NY 10001
Tel: 212-777-5100 *Toll Free Tel:* 800-343-9500
E-mail: info@technisphere.com
Web Site: www.technispherecorp.com
Key Personnel
Pres: Jack Goldman
Founded: 1971
AV equipment sales & rentals.
Catalog(s) available

Technologies at Excelitas
200 West St, Waltham, MA 02451
Toll Free Tel: 800-775-OPTO (775-6786); 855-382-2677 *Fax:* 781-290-4702
Web Site: www.excelitas.com
Key Personnel
Sales: Joanne Bakerville *E-mail:* joanne.bakerville@excelitas.com
Founded: 1947
Projection equipment.
Catalog(s) available
Branch Office(s)
1330 E Cypress St, Covina, CA 91724 *Tel:* 626-967-6021 *Toll Free Tel:* 800-363-2095 *Fax:* 626-967-3151 (power supplies)
44370 Christy St, Fremont, CA 94538-3180 *Tel:* 510-979-6500 *Fax:* 510-687-1140
Opto Technology, 160 E Marquardt Dr, Wheeling, IL 60090 *Tel:* 847-537-4277 *Fax:* 847-537-4785 (LED solutions)
35 Congress St, Suite 2021, Salem, MA 01970 *Toll Free Tel:* 800-950-3441 *Fax:* 978-745-0894 (analytical sub-systems, MVS, high energy switches, energetic systems, Rubidium standards)
1100 Vanguard Blvd, Miamisburg, OH 45342 *Tel:* 937-865-4621 *Toll Free Tel:* 866-539-5916 *Fax:* 937-865-5170 (energetic components & systems)
22001 Dumberry, Vaudreuil, QC J7V 8P7, Canada *Tel:* 450-424-3300 *Fax:* 450-424-3345 (sensors)
Membership(s): AEA; OSA; SEMI; SID; SPIE

Technology Learning Services
Affiliate of Madonna University
36600 Schoolcraft Rd, Livonia, MI 48150-1173
Tel: 734-432-5800 *Toll Free Tel:* 800-852-4951
Web Site: ww3.madonna.edu/tls
Key Personnel
Dir: Patricia A Derry *Tel:* 734-432-5574
E-mail: pderry@madonna.edu
TV Opers & Prodn Mgr: Sue Boyd *Tel:* 734-432-5578 *E-mail:* sboyd@madonna.edu
Systs Engr: Dan Boyd *Tel:* 734-432-5575
E-mail: dboyd@madonna.edu
Membership(s): MCA-I; NATAS; SMPTE

Technomad™ Inc
PO Box 273, South Deerfield, MA 01373
Tel: 617-275-8898 *Toll Free Tel:* 800-464-7757
Fax: 617-535-9712
E-mail: sales@technomad.com; customercare@technomad.com
Web Site: www.technomad.com
Founded: 1994
Speaker manufacturer.
Catalog(s) available
Shipping Address: No 5 Tina Dr, South Deerfield, MA 01373
Membership(s): InfoComm International®; NSCA

Technomedia Solutions
4545 36 St, Orlando, FL 32811
Tel: 407-351-0909 *Fax:* 407-248-9484
E-mail: sales@gotechnomedia.com
Web Site: www.gotechnomedia.com
Key Personnel
CFO & EVP: Joni McElwee
Pres: John Miceli
Dir, Engg: Jason Ford
Programmer: John Stancil
Founded: 2001
AV system design & integration blended with custom media creative services for a turn key entertainment solutions offering.
Branch Office(s)
1337 Ocean Ave, Suite B2, Santa Monica, CA 90401 *Tel:* 818-825-9858
5725 S Valley View, Suite 9, Las Vegas, NV 89118 *Tel:* 702-262-7801 *Fax:* 702-644-9154
75 Rockefeller Plaza, 26th fl, New York, NY 10019 *Tel:* 212-452-1100 *Fax:* 212-397-7051
Foreign Office(s): 146 Nassau St, PO Box N-8483, Nassau, The Bahamas
PO Box 116618, Dubai, United Arab Emirates *Tel:* (050) 101 4259
Membership(s): AES; IAAPA; NSCA; SMPTE; Themed Entertainment Association

Technovision® Interactive Inc
1845 Sandstone Manor, Unit 2, Pickering, ON L1W 3X9, Canada
Tel: 905-420-5153
E-mail: sales@technovision.com
Web Site: www.technovision.com
Manufacturer, integrator & supplier of a full range of interfaces, control devices & computer-based systems for a multitude of applications. More than 45,000 of our proprietary laserdisc, DVD & other controllers, merchandising solutions, music samplers & computer-based applications have been placed around the world.
Catalog(s) available

TecNec Distributing
Division of Tower Products Inc
812 Kings Hwy, Saugerties, NY 12477
Mailing Address: PO Box 397, Saugerties, NY 12477
Tel: 845-246-0428 *Toll Free Tel:* 800-543-0909
Fax: 845-246-0626
E-mail: sales@tecnec.com
Web Site: www.tecnec.com
Key Personnel
VP, Sales: Andy Barth *Tel:* 845-246-0428 ext 7311
Catalog(s) available

Tecplot Inc
3535 Factoria Blvd SE, Suite 550, Bellevue, WA 98006
Mailing Address: PO Box 52708, Bellevue, WA 98015-2708
Tel: 425-653-1200; 425-653-9393 (tech support)
Toll Free Tel: 800-763-7005 (orders)
E-mail: info@tecplot.com; sales@tecplot.com
Web Site: www.tecplot.com
Key Personnel
Co-Founder & Chmn: Mike Peery
Co-Founder & Pres: Don Roberts
CTO: Dr Scott Imlay
VP, Cust Devt: Tom Chan
VP, Prod Mgmt: Durrell Rittenberg
VP, Software Devt: Dan Delapp
Gen Mgr: Lisa Greenlee
Mktg Communs Coord: Margaret Connelly
Founded: 1981
Software solutions for scientists & engineers to discover, analyze & communicate results.

Tectonics Industries Inc
Division of Quantum Digital Ventures LLC
24680 Mound Rd, Warren, MI 48091
Tel: 586-755-6522 *Toll Free Tel:* 888-638-3671
Fax: 586-755-6562
E-mail: info@techtonicsindustries.com
Web Site: www.techtonicsindustries.com
Key Personnel
Sales Mgr: Pat Fleming *E-mail:* info@techtonicsindustries.com
Founded: 1933
Full service graphics & digital imaging company.
Catalog(s) available
Membership(s): InfoComm International®

Ted The Fiddler Music
103 S Main St, Spring City, PA 19475-1820
Tel: 610-948-0345
Web Site: www.tfiddler.com
Key Personnel
Owner: Ted Wilby *E-mail:* tw@tfiddler.com

Tek Data Systems Co
1111 W Park Ave, Libertyville, IL 60048
Tel: 847-367-8800 *Fax:* 847-367-0235
E-mail: tekdata@tekdata.com; sales@tekdata.com
Web Site: www.tekdata.com
Key Personnel
Sales Mgr: Randy Kick
Proprietary computer software & media management systems.
Literature available
Membership(s): AECT; ALA; Consortium of College & University Media Centers; National Association of Media & Technology Centers

Tek Gear
938 Corydon Ave, Winnipeg, MB R3M 0Y5, Canada
Tel: 204-988-3001 *Fax:* 204-988-3050
E-mail: sales@tekgear.com
Web Site: tekgear.com
Key Personnel
Pres: Tony Havelka *E-mail:* tonyh@tekgear.com
Sales Mgr: Eric Austman *E-mail:* eric@tekgear.com
Founded: 1993
Branch Office(s)
572 S Fifth St, Pembina, ND 58271

TEK Media Group
711 S Victory Blvd, Burbank, CA 91502
Tel: 818-244-4440; 818-255-5045
Toll Free Tel: 800-255-5045 (support)
Fax: 818-855-8762
E-mail: mshank@tekmg.com
Web Site: www.tekmg.com
Professional audio/video broadcast equipment & industrial electronics repair.

Tekskil Industries Inc
102-998 Harbourside Dr, North Vancouver, BC V7P 3T2, Canada
Tel: 604-985-2250 *Toll Free Tel:* 877-835-7545
Toll Free Fax: 877-576-8361
E-mail: tekskilprompters2012@tekskil.com
Web Site: www.tekskil.com
Key Personnel
Pres: John Veenstra
Opers & Tech Support: Rick Anselmo
E-mail: rick@tekskil.com
Founded: 1981

Tel-Air Interests Inc
2040 Sherman St, Hollywood, FL 33020
Tel: 954-924-4949 *Fax:* 954-924-4980
E-mail: telair@aol.com
Web Site: www.telairint.com
Key Personnel
Pres: Grant H Gravitt, Jr
Prodr: Mary Lou Gravitt
Founded: 1960
Full service production company.

TeL Systems
7235 Jackson Rd, Ann Arbor, MI 48103
Tel: 734-761-4506 *Toll Free Tel:* 800-686-7235
Fax: 734-761-9776
E-mail: sales@telsystemsusa.com
Web Site: www.telsystemsusa.com
Key Personnel
CEO & Pres: Karl Couyoumjian *E-mail:* karlc@telsystemsusa.com
VP: Paul Eiswerth *E-mail:* peiswerth@telsystemsusa.com
Founded: 1965
AV sales & rentals.
Membership(s): InfoComm International®

Tel-Test
Division of Corporate One Hundred Inc
605 NW 53 Ave, Suite A-17, Gainesville, FL 32609
Tel: 352-335-0901 *Fax:* 352-376-3260
Key Personnel
Pres: Zeke Zetien *E-mail:* zekezetien@aol.com
Catalog(s) available
Membership(s): NAB

Telarc International Corp
Division of Concord Music Group Inc
23412 Commerce Park Rd, Cleveland, OH 44122
Tel: 216-464-2313 *Fax:* 216-360-9663
Web Site: www.concordmusicgroup.com/labels/Telarc/; www.concordmusicgroup.com
Key Personnel
Pres, Concord Music Group: Glen Barros
VP, Mktg: Jason Linder *E-mail:* jason.linder@concordmusicgroup.com
Founded: 1977
Classical music recording company.
Newsletter(s), monthly, electronic

Tele-Measurements Inc
145 Main Ave, Clifton, NJ 07014
Mailing Address: PO Box 1078, Clifton, NJ 07014-1078
Tel: 973-473-8822 *Toll Free Tel:* 800-223-0052 (ext 207) *Fax:* 973-473-0521
E-mail: contact@tele-measurements.com
Web Site: www.tele-measurements.com
Key Personnel
CEO: William E Endres

Pres: W Chris Endres
VP, Sales: Gary Gorski *Tel:* 973-473-8822 ext 207 *E-mail:* ggorski@tele-measurements.com
Founded: 1959
Catalog(s) available

Tele-Time Systems
313 Parkway Dr, Cary, IL 60013
Tel: 847-640-1420
E-mail: teletimesystems@netzero.com
Web Site: www.teletimesystems.com
Key Personnel
Owner & Mgr: Curtis A Bendell
Catalog(s) available

Tele-Video Production Services (TVPS)
3655 Grand Ave, 2nd fl, Oakland, CA 94610-2009
Tel: 510-893-0555 *Toll Free Tel:* 800-893-0555 *Fax:* 510-893-0552
E-mail: tvps893@yahoo.com
Web Site: www.tvpsonline.com
Key Personnel
Pres & Exec Prodr: Jim Partridge
Founded: 1979
Full service production company.

Telect Inc
23321 E Knox Ave, Liberty Lake, WA 99019
Tel: 509-926-6000 *Toll Free Tel:* 800-551-4567
E-mail: getinfo@telect.com
Web Site: www.telect.com
Key Personnel
CEO & Pres: Wayne E Williams
CFO & EVP: Stan Hilbert

Teledac Inc
635, rue De La Noue IDS, Verdun, QC H3E 1W1, Canada
Tel: 514-362-6362 *Toll Free Tel:* 888-659-6362
E-mail: general@teledac.com
Web Site: www.teledac.com
Key Personnel
Pres: Martin Chouinard
Founded: 1978
Video billboards & message generators for cable TV systems & information in public buildings.
Catalog(s) available

Teledyne DALSA Inc
Subsidiary of Teledyne Technologies
605 McMurray Rd, Waterloo, ON N2V 2E9, Canada
Tel: 519-886-6000 *Fax:* 519-886-8023
E-mail: sales.americas@teledynedalsa.com
Web Site: www.teledynedalsa.com
Key Personnel
CEO: Brian Doody
EVP, Fin: Silvio Favrin
VP, Busn Devt & Communs: Patrick Myles
Founded: 1980
Manufacture, design, research & development of high performance solid-state image sensors & modular expandable cameras; large format sensor & camera technology; line scan & area scan technology; Time Delay & Integration (TDI) line scan technology for high sensitivity & low noise operation under low light level conditions.
Catalog(s) available

Teledyne Energy Systems Inc
Subsidiary of Teledyne Technologies Inc
10707 Gilroy Rd, Hunt Valley, MD 21031
Tel: 410-771-8600 *Fax:* 410-771-8620
E-mail: energy.systems@teledynees.com
Web Site: www.teledynees.com
Key Personnel
Chmn, CEO & Pres, Teledyne Technologies Inc: Dr Robert Mehrabian
CFO: Jan Hess

Pres: Chris Kuehn
Catalog(s) available

Telemanagement Resources International Inc (TRI)
124 Thomas Lane, Manahawkin, NJ 08050
Tel: 609-597-6334
Web Site: www.triinc.com
Key Personnel
Pres: Dr S Ann Earon *E-mail:* annearon@aol.com
Opers Mgr: Tracey O'Hearen
Sr Consultant: Spencer Freund
Founded: 1982
Catalog(s) available
Membership(s): IMCCA

Telemetrics Inc
6 Leighton Place, Mahwah, NJ 07430
Tel: 201-848-9818 *Fax:* 201-848-9819
E-mail: info@telemetricsinc.com
Web Site: www.telemetricsinc.com
Key Personnel
Pres: Anthony E Cuomo *E-mail:* aec@telemetricsinc.com
Founded: 1973
Catalog(s) available
Membership(s): MCA-I; NAB; SMPTE

Telemotions LLC
405 E 54 St, Suite 3-N, New York, NY 10022
Tel: 212-486-3010
Web Site: www.telemotions.net
Key Personnel
Exec Prodr: Tom Hayes *E-mail:* tomhay972@aol.com
Sr Prodr: Sabine Beckert
Full service production company for TV & film projects.

Teleometrics International
Division of Leadership Management Inc
4567 Lake Shore Dr, Waco, TX 76710
Mailing Address: PO Box 9126, Waco, TX 76714-9126
Tel: 254-776-2060 *Toll Free Tel:* 800-876-2389 *Fax:* 254-772-9588
E-mail: teleocsrv@teleometrics.com
Web Site: www.teleometrics.com
Founded: 1967
Producer of training materials.
Catalog(s) available
Membership(s): ATD

Telepro Video Inc
14730 Adams Circle, Omaha, NE 68137
Tel: 402-593-0999; 402-690-2198 *Fax:* 402-593-6117
E-mail: tmtelepro@aol.com
Web Site: www.teleprovideo.com
Key Personnel
Pres: Theo Mercer
Founded: 1984
AV production facility.
Catalog(s) available

Telequest Inc
66 Witherspoon St, Suite 383, Princeton, NJ 08542
Tel: 609-430-3004
E-mail: contact@telequestinc.com
Web Site: www.telequestinc.com
Key Personnel
Partner: Richard S Blofson; Scott Nielsen; Dan Preston
Founded: 1978

Telescript International
55 Walnut St, Norwood, NJ 07648
Tel: 201-767-6733 *Toll Free Tel:* 888-767-6713 *Fax:* 201-784-0323
E-mail: info@telescript.com
Web Site: telescript.com
Key Personnel
Mng Dir: Chris O'Brien *E-mail:* chris@telescript.com
Professional teleprompting solutions.
Catalog(s) available
Membership(s): NAB; NAMM, the National Association of Music Merchants

Telestream Inc
848 Gold Flat Rd, Nevada City, CA 95959
Tel: 530-470-1300 *Toll Free Tel:* 877-257-6245 *Fax:* 530-470-1301
E-mail: info@telestream.net
Web Site: www.telestream.net
Key Personnel
CEO & Pres: Dan Castles *E-mail:* danc@telestream.net
CFO: Mark Cuny
CTO: Shawn Carnahan *E-mail:* shawnc@telestream.net
VP, Desktop Busn & Corp Mktg: Barbara DeHart *E-mail:* barbd@telestream.net
VP, Engg: Steve Tilly
Mktg Communs Mgr: Janet Swift *E-mail:* janet_swift@telestream.net
Founded: 1998
Video/audio encoding & transcoding workflow automation software & hardware supplier.
Branch Office(s)
2200 Powell St, Suite 210, Emeryville, CA 94608
21351 Ridgetop Circle, Suite 120, Sterling, VA 21351 *Tel:* 703-964-8089 *Fax:* 703-964-8090
Foreign Office(s): Telestream GmbH, Dietkirchenstr 30, 53111 Bonn, Germany
Membership(s): IABM

Teletech Inc
38235 Executive Dr, Westland, MI 48185
Tel: 734-641-2300
Key Personnel
Mktg: Mark Dobronski
Membership(s): IEEE; NAB; National Association of Radio & Telecommunications Engineers

TeleTime Productions
100 Atlantic Ave, Lynbrook, NY 11563
Tel: 516-255-8383
E-mail: info@teletimevideo.com
Web Site: www.teletimevideo.com
Key Personnel
Founder & Pres: Nan Givner-Klein
Founder: Harold Klein
Founded: 1976

Televersions
747 N May St, Chicago, IL 60642
Tel: 312-642-9488 *Toll Free Tel:* 800-942-9488 *Fax:* 312-642-9491
E-mail: convert@televersions.com
Web Site: www.televersions.com
Key Personnel
Pres: Walter Szepesi
Founded: 1996
All formats of HD video services.

TeleVideos
1566 Dola St, Eugene, OR 97402
Toll Free Tel: 800-2-VIDEOS (284-3367)
E-mail: televideos@msn.com
Web Site: televideos.com
Key Personnel
Owner: Barry Hood
Brochure(s) available

Television Equipment Associates Inc (TEA)
16 Mount Ebo Rd S, Suite 6, Brewster, NY 10509
Mailing Address: PO Box 404, Brewster, NY 10509-0404
Tel: 845-278-0960 *Fax:* 845-278-0964
E-mail: info@swatheadsets.com

Web Site: www.swatheadsets.com
Key Personnel
Pres: Steve Tocidlowski
Founded: 1969
Catalog(s) available
Membership(s): NAB; SMPTE

Telex Communications Inc
Unit of Bosch Security Systems
12000 Portland Ave, Burnsville, MN 55337-1522
Tel: 952-884-4051 *Toll Free Tel:* 877-863-4166
Fax: 952-884-0043
E-mail: info@telex.com
Web Site: www.telex.com
Catalog(s) available
Membership(s): InfoComm International®; NAB

Telex EVI
Subsidiary of Telex Communications Inc
12000 Portland Ave S, Burnsville, MN 55337-1522
Tel: 952-884-4051 *Toll Free Tel:* 877-863-4166
Fax: 952-884-0043; 952-887-5585
E-mail: info@telex.com
Web Site: www.telex.com
Catalog(s) available
Membership(s): AES; NAB; NAMM, the National Association of Music Merchants

Tellabs Inc
One Tellabs Ctr, 1415 W Diehl Rd, Naperville, IL 60563
Tel: 630-798-8800 *Fax:* 630-798-2000
Web Site: www.tellabs.com
Key Personnel
Chmn of the Bd: Robert Leggett
CEO: Patrick DiPietro
COO & Pres: Herbert Merz
Branch Office(s)
4555 Great America Pkwy, Suite 601, Santa Clara, CA 95054 *Tel:* 408-970-2400 *Fax:* 408-970-2405
18583 N Dallas Pkwy, Dallas, TX 75287
Tel: 972-588-7000
Foreign Office(s): Xin DongAn Bldg, 915 Tower 2, No 138 Wang Fu Jing St, Dong Cheng District, Beijing 100006, China *Tel:* (010) 6526 3009 *Fax:* (010) 6526 0421
232 Liangjing Rd, Rm 101-102, 2th-4th fl, Zhang Jiang Hi-Tech Park, Pudong New Area, Shanghai 201203, China *Tel:* (021) 2030 3000
Fax: (021) 2030 3111
Lyskaer 3 CD, 2730 Herlev, Denmark *Tel:* 4484 5000
Sinikalliontie 7, 02630 Espoo, Finland *Tel:* (09) 4131 21 *Fax:* (09) 4131 2815
77-A, Sector 18, IFFCO Rd, Guragaon, Haryana 122001, India *Tel:* (012) 4411 2227; (012) 4411 2228; (012) 4411 2229 *Fax:* (012) 4401 2933

Tellens Inc
770 W Landoran Lane, Tucson, AZ 85737
Tel: 520-742-0649 *Fax:* 520-742-0652
E-mail: infotellens@aol.com
Web Site: www.tellens.com
Key Personnel
Pres: Pat Barey *E-mail:* pbarey@aol.com
Founded: 1982
Media production.
Branch Office(s)
2624 Prairie Ave, Suite A, Evanston, IL 60201, Contact: Terry Burson

Telos Systems
1241 Superior Ave E, Cleveland, OH 44114
Tel: 216-241-7225 *Fax:* 216-241-4103
E-mail: inquiry@telos-systems.com
Web Site: www.telos-systems.com
Key Personnel
Mng Dir: Denny Sanders
Mktg Coord: Angi Roberson *E-mail:* angi@telos-systems.com
Catalog(s) available
Foreign Office(s): General-von-Nagelstr 21, 85354 Freising, Germany *Tel:* (08161) 424-67 *Fax:* (08161) 424-02 *E-mail:* europe-info@telos-systems.com
Membership(s): NAB

Tempe Camera
606 W University, Tempe, AZ 85281
Tel: 480-966-6954 *Toll Free Tel:* 800-836-7374
E-mail: rent@tempecamera.com; sales@tempecamera.com
Web Site: www.tempecamera.biz
Key Personnel
Founder & Owner: Joe Wojcich
Founded: 1972
New & used equipment sales, including cameras, lenses, lighting, supplies & darkroom gear. Rent lenses, digital & film cameras & accessories, computer projectors, lighting & grip equipment. Repair services for all items sold.

Tempe Tape & Disc
2737 W Baseline Rd, Suite 21, Tempe, AZ 85283
Tel: 602-453-9663
Web Site: www.tempetape.com
Key Personnel
Owner: Andy Baade *E-mail:* andy@tempetape.com
Founded: 1984
CD & DVD replication & duplication services.

1013 Integrated
1013 Kawaiahao St, Honolulu, HI 96814
Tel: 808-593-8848 *Fax:* 808-593-9427
E-mail: info@1013integrated.com
Web Site: www.1013i.com
Key Personnel
Pres: Jason Suapaia
Founded: 1976
Fully integrated branding & production company.
Catalog(s) available
Membership(s): AICP

10-20 Productions
11120 Indian Oaks Dr, Tampa, FL 33625
Tel: 813-300-4221
Web Site: 1020tv.com
Location video production, providing HD camera packages with lighting & audio as well as teleprompter services.

Tenba
Division of MAC Group
75 Virginia Rd, North White Plains, NY 10603
Tel: 914-347-3300 *Fax:* 914-347-3309
E-mail: info@tenba.com
Web Site: www.tenba.com
Key Personnel
Pres, MAC Group: Mr Jan Lederman
Manufactures shipping & carrying cases for LCD projector cases, photo & computer equipment.
Catalog(s) available

Tennessee Prompters
Division of MediaMan® Productions
727 Wildview Dr, Nashville, TN 37211-1142
Tel: 615-834-9655 *Fax:* 615-834-1086
E-mail: info@tennesseeprompters.com
Web Site: www.tennesseeprompters.com
Key Personnel
Owner: Will Reynolds
Founded: 1991
Complete teleprompter equipment & service company. Podium, stage & through-the-lens prompter systems & operators.

Tennessee Visual Service Co
912 Main St, Nashville, TN 37206
Mailing Address: PO Box 60525, Nashville, TN 37206-0525
Tel: 615-226-0162 *Toll Free Tel:* 800-359-6132
Fax: 615-228-1876
E-mail: sales@tennvisual.com
Web Site: www.tennvisual.com
Key Personnel
CEO & Sales Mgr: Bob Davis, Jr *E-mail:* bob@tennvisual.com
Off Mgr, Acctg & Fin: R Christopher Davis
E-mail: chris@tennvisual.com
Founded: 1946
AV equipment, sales, rentals & service.
Catalog(s) available

Tepco Corp
2603 Bridgeview Dr, Rapid City, SD 57701-5801
Tel: 605-343-7200 *Fax:* 605-343-7240
E-mail: tepco@rapidnet.com
Web Site: www.rapidnet.com/~tepco
Key Personnel
Sales Mgr: Don Le Fever
FM translators.
Catalog(s) available

Terra Nova Films Inc
9848 S Winchester Ave, Chicago, IL 60643
Tel: 773-881-8491 *Toll Free Tel:* 800-779-8491
Fax: 773-881-3368
E-mail: tnf@terranova.org
Web Site: www.terranova.org
Key Personnel
Exec Dir: James Vanden Bosch
Off Mgr: Ginny Priestman *E-mail:* ginny@terranova.org
Founded: 1981
Producer & distributor of videos dealing with aging.
Online catalog(s) available

Terra Productions LLC
2017 Fairview Ave E, Suite G, Seattle, WA 98102
Tel: 206-328-3080
Web Site: www.terraproductions.com
Key Personnel
Prodr: Blair Robbins *E-mail:* blair@terraproductions.com
Founded: 1989
Catalog(s) available

Tetrahedron LLC
5348 Las Vegas Dr, Suite 353, Las Vegas, NV 89108
Tel: 208-265-8065 *Toll Free Tel:* 888-923-9936
E-mail: tetra@tetrahedron.org
Web Site: www.tetrahedron.org
Key Personnel
Founder & Pres: Dr Leonard G Horowitz
Founded: 1978
Educational programming.
Catalog(s), 3 times/yr, free

Texas Heart Institute Visual Communication Services
Denton A Cooley Bldg, Suite C530, 6770 Bertner Ave, Houston, TX 77030
Tel: 832-355-9558 *Fax:* 832-355-9511
Web Site: www.texasheartinstitute.org
Key Personnel
Mgr: Ken Hoge *E-mail:* khoge@heart.thi.tmc.edu
Catalog(s) available

Texas Rebel Radio Network
210 Woodcrest, Fredericksburg, TX 78624
Mailing Address: PO Box 311, Fredericksburg, TX 78624-0311
Tel: 830-997-2197 *Fax:* 830-997-2198
E-mail: txradio@ktc.net
Web Site: www.kfanfmradio.com
Key Personnel
Gen Mgr: Jayson Fritz
Production & programming services.

Texas Wesleyan University
Affiliate of Information Technology Media Services Multimedia
1201 Wesleyan St, Fort Worth, TX 76105
Tel: 817-531-5850
Web Site: www.txwes.edu
Key Personnel
Serv Desk Mgr: George Blackwell *Tel:* 817-333-1252 *E-mail:* gblackwell@txwes.edu
Founded: 1890
Provide support to students, faculty & staff in the effective use of multimedia & information technology.

Texcam Inc
1323 N First St, Bellaire, TX 77401
Tel: 713-524-2774 *Toll Free Tel:* 800-735-2774 *Fax:* 713-524-2779
E-mail: info@texcam.com
Web Site: www.texcam.com
Key Personnel
CEO & Pres: Bob Poimbeauf
Founded: 1985
Motion picture & video equipment rental.
Membership(s): Production Equipment Rental Association; SMPTE; Texas Association of Motion Media Professionals

Texscan MSI, see Outsource Engineering & Manufacturing Inc dba Texscan MSI

TFT Inc
105 Bonaventura Dr, San Jose, CA 95134
Tel: 408-943-9323 *Fax:* 408-432-9218; 408-432-9219
E-mail: info@tftinc.com
Web Site: www.tftinc.com
Key Personnel
SVP: Darryl E Parker *E-mail:* dparker@tftinc.com
Catalog(s), CDs
Membership(s): NAB; SBE; SMPTE

TGA Recording Co
295 Urbandale Ave, Benton Harbor, MI 49022
Tel: 269-926-7581 *Fax:* 269-926-7589
E-mail: tgarecording@sbcglobal.net
Web Site: www.tgarecording.com
Key Personnel
Owner: Thomas Alti
Pres: Larry Coyle
Founded: 1970
Services include webcasting & RC aerial video.

Thales Angenieux, see Angenieux

Thayer Birding Software
12650 Colliers Reserve Dr, Naples, FL 34110
Tel: 239-596-1637 *Toll Free Tel:* 800-865-2473 *Fax:* 239-596-0232
Web Site: www.thayerbirding.com
Key Personnel
Pres: Peter W Thayer *E-mail:* pete@thayerbirding.com
Off Mgr: Kara Scofield *E-mail:* kara@thayerbirding.com
Founded: 1994
Online catalog(s) available

Theatre Arts Video Library
174 Andrew Ave, Leucadia, CA 92024
Tel: 760-632-6355 *Toll Free Tel:* 800-456-8285 *Fax:* 760-632-6859
E-mail: admin@theatreartsvideo.com
Web Site: www.theatreartsvideo.com
Key Personnel
Owner: Ron Ranson
Contact: Nicola Broad
Founded: 1988
Video programs for theatre training.
Catalog(s), annual
Membership(s): USITT

Theatre Effects
1810 Airport Exchange Blvd, Suite 400, Erlanger, KY 41018-3184
Tel: 513-772-7646 (intl) *Toll Free Tel:* 800-791-7646 *Fax:* 513-772-3579
E-mail: service@theatrefx.com
Web Site: www.theatrefx.com
Key Personnel
Owner: Doug Weber *E-mail:* doug@theatrefx.com
Sales Mgr: Chris Wyllie *E-mail:* chris@theatrefx.com
Founded: 1976
Online catalog(s) available
Spec sheet(s) available
Membership(s): Professional Lighting & Sound Association

Theatre House Inc
400 W Third St, Covington, KY 41011-1306
Tel: 859-431-2414 *Toll Free Tel:* 800-827-2414 *Fax:* 859-431-1837
E-mail: theatreh@one.net; info@theatrehouse.com
Web Site: www.theatrehouse.com
Key Personnel
Mgr: Rick Gaukel
Founded: 1955
Theatrical equipment sales.
Catalog(s), $2

Theatre Service & Supply Corp
1792 Union Ave, Baltimore, MD 21211
Tel: 410-467-1225 *Fax:* 410-467-1289
E-mail: sales@stage-n-studio.com
Web Site: www.stage-n-studio.com
Key Personnel
Mgr: Jackie Keleman
Catalog(s) available
Membership(s): Professional Lighting & Sound Association

Theatrical Services & Supplies Inc
415Q Oser Ave, Hauppauge, NY 11788
Tel: 631-873-4790 *Fax:* 631-873-4795
E-mail: sales@gotheatrical.com
Web Site: www.gotheatrical.com
Key Personnel
Owner: Robert F Bayer
Founded: 1969
Theatre system integrator - AV, lighting, rigging, dimming.

Theatrical Services Inc
128 S Washington St, Wichita, KS 67202
Tel: 316-263-4415 *Toll Free Tel:* 888-874-2649 *Fax:* 316-263-9927
Web Site: www.theatricalservices.com
Key Personnel
Pres: Steve Wolf
VP: Tom Johnson
Sales & Rental Mgmt: Josh Jones
Sales: Sean Roberson
Founded: 1976
Catalog(s) available
Membership(s): Professional Lighting & Sound Association

Theatrical Technicians Inc (TTI)
2700 Connecticut Ave NW, Suite 109, Washington, DC 20008-5308
Tel: 202-332-4907 *Fax:* 202-332-4907
E-mail: info@perfect-pickup.com
Web Site: www.perfect-pickup.com
Key Personnel
CEO, Owner & Pres: Bert Morris
Founded: 1980
Theatrical manufacturer & trade publisher for follow spotlight craft training.
Catalog(s) available
Membership(s): ECTC; International Alliance of Theatrical Stage Employees; USITT

Theosophical Publishing House
Division of The Theosophical Society in America
306 W Geneva Rd, Wheaton, IL 60187
Mailing Address: PO Box 270, Wheaton, IL 60189-0270
Tel: 630-665-0130 *Toll Free Tel:* 800-669-9425 *Fax:* 630-665-8791
Web Site: www.questbooks.net
Key Personnel
Opers Mgr: Pat Griebeler *Tel:* 630-668-1571 ext 307 *E-mail:* operations@questbooks.net
Publg Mgr: Sharron Dorr *Tel:* 630-665-0130 ext 356 *E-mail:* sdorr@questbooks.net
Founded: 1875
Religious, educational video producer.
Catalog(s) available
Membership(s): Network of Alternatives for Publishers, Retailers & Artists Inc; Reading Recovery Council of North America

Thermodyne Cases
1841 Business Pkwy, Ontario, CA 91761
Tel: 909-923-9945 *Toll Free Tel:* 877-307-8425 *Fax:* 909-923-7505
E-mail: request@thermodyne-online.com
Web Site: www.thermodyne-online.com
Key Personnel
Pres: Gary S Ackerman
Founded: 1958
Catalog(s) available
CD-ROM catalog(s), free

Thin-Lite Corp
530 Constitution Ave, Camarillo, CA 93012
Tel: 805-987-5021 *Fax:* 805-388-0921
E-mail: thinlite@thinlite.com; thinlitesales@thinlite.com
Web Site: www.thinlite.com
Founded: 1969
Manufacturer of low volt light fixtures & ballasts.

Think 3-D.com
180 Cross Hwy, Westport, CT 06880
Tel: 646-732-9197
Web Site: www.think3-d.com
Key Personnel
Owner & Pres: Mark Yurkiw *E-mail:* mark@think3-d.com
3D art & special effects for film & video.
Cassette catalog(s) available

Thinking Allowed Productions
5966 Zinn Dr, Oakland, CA 94611
Tel: 510-339-8004 *Toll Free Tel:* 800-999-4415
E-mail: thinking@thinkingallowed.com
Web Site: www.thinkingallowed.com
Key Personnel
Pres: Arthur Bloch
Founded: 1986
Independent public television series.
Catalog(s) available

Thinking Maps Inc
401 Cascade Pointe Lane, Cary, NC 27513-5780
Tel: 919-678-8778 *Toll Free Tel:* 800-243-9169 *Fax:* 919-678-8782
E-mail: office@thinkingmaps.com
Web Site: thinkingmaps.com
Key Personnel
Pres: Sherwin Suddreth
Distribute educational programs.
Brochure(s) available

Third Ear Sound Co
30965 San Benito St, Hayward, CA 94544
Tel: 510-429-1000 *Toll Free Tel:* 800-587-1115 *Fax:* 510-429-1001

E-mail: raul@thirdearsound.com
Web Site: www.thirdearsound.com
Key Personnel
Partner: Don Albonico
Mktg Dir: Raul Suarez
Audio equipment rentals.

Third World Newsreel/Camera News Inc
545 Eighth Ave, Suite 550, New York, NY 10018
Tel: 212-947-9277 *Fax:* 212-594-6417
E-mail: twn@twn.org
Web Site: www.twn.org
Key Personnel
Exec Dir: Dorothy Thigpen
Dist & Mktg Dir: Roselly Torres Rojas
Founded: 1968
Educational social issue media.
Catalog(s) available

ThirdWave Learning Inc
120 E Oakland Park Blvd, Suite 105-623, Fort Lauderdale, FL 33334
Toll Free Tel: 888-630-9555 *Fax:* 954-630-9050
Web Site: www.thirdwavelearning.com
Key Personnel
Pres: Geri Michelsen
Training software for ESL curriculum.
Catalog(s) available

31st Street Studios
77 31 St, Pittsburgh, PA 15201
Tel: 412-228-0231
E-mail: info@31ststreetstudios.com
Web Site: www.31ststreetstudios.com
Key Personnel
Owner: Chris Breakwell
Production services, studio development & management.

30 Second Films
3019 Pico Blvd, Santa Monica, CA 90405
Tel: 310-315-1750 *Fax:* 310-315-1757
E-mail: sales@30secondfilms.com
Web Site: www.30secondfilms.com
Key Personnel
Dir & Dir, Photog: Bob Kronovet *E-mail:* bob@30secondfilms.com
Exec Prodr & Ed: Alan Stamm *E-mail:* alan@30secondfilms.com
Founded: 1987
Full service film & video production & post-production for TV, film, commercial & corporate.

30 Second Street Ltd
1209 Mountain Road Place NE, Albuquerque, NM 87110
Tel: 505-265-0224
E-mail: info@thirtysecst.com
Web Site: www.thirtysecst.com
Key Personnel
Gen Mgr: Colleen Burns
Creative Dir: Kelly Lujan
Sr Ed: Clark Morris
Opers Coord: Jade Norris
Video post-production service company.
Membership(s): MCA-I

THK Photo Products Inc
7642 Woodwind Dr, Huntington Beach, CA 92647
Tel: 714-849-5700 *Toll Free Tel:* 800-421-1141 *Fax:* 714-849-5677
E-mail: support@thkphoto.com
Web Site: www.thkphoto.com
Key Personnel
Pres: Yasu Suga

Thomas & Betts Power Solutions
5900 Eastport Blvd, Bldg V, Richmond, VA 23231-4453
Tel: 804-236-3300 *Toll Free Tel:* 800-238-5000; 800-CYBEREX (292-3739) *Fax:* 804-236-4040; 804-236-4841
Web Site: www.tnbpowersolutions.com
Key Personnel
Mktg Communs Mgr: Susan Hughson
Uninterrupted power sources.
Catalog(s) available

Thomas Reprographics
801 Second Ave N, Minneapolis, MN 55405
Tel: 612-374-1120 *Toll Free Tel:* 800-328-7154 *Fax:* 612-374-1129
E-mail: orders501@thomasrepro.com
Web Site: thomasrepro.com
Key Personnel
CEO & Pres: Bryan Thomas
District Mgr: Kent Long *E-mail:* kent.long@thomasrepro.com
Sales Mgr: Doug Cornelsen *E-mail:* doug.cornelsen@thomasrepro.com
Online catalog(s) available
Branch Office(s)
8025 Glen Lane, Eden Prairie, MN 55344, Store Mgr: David Butler *Tel:* 952-835-2141 *Fax:* 952-835-2383 *E-mail:* edenprairie@thomasrepro.com
3345 W Saint Germain St, St Cloud, MN 56301, Store Mgr: Bev Hoeft *Tel:* 320-656-1300 *Fax:* 320-656-1302 *E-mail:* stcloud@thomasrepro.com
Membership(s): AIE™; Photo Marketing Association

Thomega Entertainment Inc
3027 Miller Ave, Bay D, Saskatoon, SK S7K 6G5, Canada
Mailing Address: PO Box 25104, RPO River Heights, Saskatoon, SK S7K 8B7, Canada
Tel: 306-373-3765 *Fax:* 306-242-5845
E-mail: thomega@sasktel.net
Web Site: www.thomega.com
Key Personnel
Pres: Anthony J Towstego
Founded: 1988
Film & TV production.
Membership(s): Canadian Film & Television Production Association; Saskatchewan Chamber of Commerce; Saskatchewan Film & Television Producers Association

Thompson-Mitchell & Associates Inc
1205 Johnson Ferry Rd, No 136, Marietta, GA 30068
Tel: 404-233-5435 *Toll Free Tel:* 800-554-1389 *Fax:* 404-521-4643
Key Personnel
Pres: Harry H Thompson, III
Founded: 1969
Catalog(s), quarterly, can be e-mailed
Newsletter(s), quarterly, can be e-mailed

Thompson Rivers University Open Learning
BC Centre for Open Learning, 4th fl, 900 McGill Rd, Kamloops, BC V2C 0C8, Canada
Tel: 250-852-7000 *Toll Free Tel:* 800-663-9711
E-mail: student@tru.ca; olmarketing@tru.ca
Web Site: www.tru.ca/distance
Key Personnel
Dir, Mktg & Communs: Jennifer Read *E-mail:* jread@tru.ca
Mktg Coord: Corey Wiwchar *E-mail:* cwiwchar@tru.ca
Ed: Elise Desjardine *E-mail:* edesjardine@tru.ca
Distance learning audio & video programs.
Catalog(s) available
Branch Office(s)
1030 W Georgia St, No 233, Vancouver, BC V6E 2Y3, Canada *Tel:* 604-568-6438 (in Vancouver); 250-852-7980 (outside Vancouver) *Fax:* 604-568-6439

Thomson, see Technicolor SA

Thorburn Associates, Acoustic, Technology, Lighting Design
20880 Baker St, Castro Valley, CA 94546
Mailing Address: PO Box 20399, Castro Valley, CA 94546-8399
Tel: 510-886-7826 *Fax:* 510-886-7828
E-mail: ta@ta-inc.com
Web Site: www.ta-inc.com
Key Personnel
Principal & Pres: Lisa A Thorburn
Principal: Steven J Thorburn
Acoustics, AV, telecom & lighting design.
Brochure(s) available
Branch Office(s)
1317 N San Fernando Blvd, Suite 212, Burbank, CA 91504 *Tel:* 818-569-0234 *Fax:* 818-569-0233
2500 Gateway Centre Blvd, Suite 800, Morrisville, NC 27560 *Tel:* 919-463-9995 *Fax:* 919-463-9973
Membership(s): AES; ASA; IEEE; InfoComm International®; NSPE

Thread Marketing Group
4635 W Alexis Rd, Toledo, OH 43623-1005
Tel: 419-887-6801 *Toll Free Tel:* 800-397-0126 *Fax:* 419-887-6802
E-mail: contact@experiencethread.com
Web Site: www.experiencethread.com
Key Personnel
CEO: Joe Sharp *Tel:* 419-887-6820 *E-mail:* joe.sharp@experiencethread.com
Pres: Judy McFarland *Tel:* 419-887-6858 *E-mail:* judy.mcfarland@experiencethread.com
EVP: Holly Goldstein *Tel:* 419-887-6803 *E-mail:* holly.goldstein@experiencethread.com
VP: Michael Dempsey *Tel:* 419-887-6810; Tara Linker *Tel:* 419-887-6805
Creative Dir: Jacqueline Barchick *Tel:* 419-887-6809
Founded: 1986
Integrated multimedia solutions.

Three D Graphics Inc
11340 W Olympic Blvd, Suite 352, Los Angeles, CA 90064-1613
Tel: 310-231-3330 *Toll Free Tel:* 800-913-0008 *Fax:* 310-231-3303
E-mail: info@threedgraphics.com
Web Site: www.threedgraphics.com
Key Personnel
Pres: Elmer Easton
Dir, Mktg: Remi Gagne
Dir, Devt: Daniel Weingart *Tel:* 310-231-3330 ext 307
Founded: 1986

360 Systems
3281 Grande Vista Dr, Newbury Park, CA 91320-1193
Tel: 818-991-0360 *Fax:* 818-991-1360
E-mail: info@360systems.com; sales@360systems.com
Web Site: www.360systems.com
Key Personnel
Pres: Robert Easton *E-mail:* robert.easton@360systems.com
Sales Mgr, Prof Video Prods: Robert Nilo *Tel:* 617-823-2051 *E-mail:* robert.nilo@360systems.com
Sales Administrator, Prof Audio Prods: Roxanna Veltze *E-mail:* roxanna.veltze@360systems.com
Founded: 1972
Brochure(s) available

3M Touch Systems
Unit of 3M Electro & Communications Business
501 Griffin Book Park Dr, Methuen, MA 01844
Tel: 978-659-9000 *Toll Free Tel:* 888-659-1080

Web Site: www.3mtouch.com; www.3m.com/touch
Catalog(s) available

Three Pillars Media
140 N Eighth St, Suite 440, Lincoln, NE 68508
Tel: 402-937-0984
E-mail: contact@threepillarsmedia.com
Web Site: www.threepillarsmedia.com
Key Personnel
Owner: Ryan Cole
Pres: Matt Sherman
Founded: 2003
Video production & photography studio.

Three Rivers Publishing Co
Subsidiary of Kurt House Enterprises Inc
218 Country Wood, San Antonio, TX 78216
Tel: 210-490-2433
E-mail: cowboyhouse@aol.com
Web Site: www.kurthouse.com
Key Personnel
Pres: Kurt D House
Founded: 1980
Publishing books & videos on western collectibles & electric fans.
Flyer(s), 1 page

3008
3008 Ross Ave, Suite 100, Dallas, TX 75204
Tel: 214-922-9232 *Fax:* 214-922-8861
Web Site: www.3008.com
Key Personnel
Partner & Pres: Ken Skaggs *E-mail:* ken@3008.com
Partner & Ed: Brent Herrington *E-mail:* brent@3008.com
Exec Prodr: Anne Strock *E-mail:* anne@3008.com
Post-production services for film & video.

Leo Ticheli Productions
2801 University Blvd, Suite 101, Birmingham, AL 35233
Tel: 205-930-0500 *Fax:* 205-930-0505
Web Site: www.ltpro.com
Key Personnel
Pres: Don McNutt
Audio Engr: Clint Jones
Full service production company.

Tickets.com
555 Anton Blvd, Costa Mesa, CA 92626
Tel: 714-327-5400 *Toll Free Tel:* 800-352-0212 (cust serv) *Fax:* 714-327-5410
E-mail: sales@tickets.com
Web Site: www.tickets.com
Key Personnel
CEO: John Walker
Ticket sellers.

Tierney Brothers Inc
3300 University Ave SE, Minneapolis, MN 55414-3326
Tel: 612-331-5500 *Toll Free Tel:* 866-557-6062 *Fax:* 612-331-3424
E-mail: contactform@tierneybrothers.com
Web Site: www.tierneybrothers.com
Key Personnel
Chmn & Pres: Tom Tierney
CEO: Jim Tierney
Contact: Paula Tierney
Founded: 1977
Provider of LCD projectors, systems integration, large format printers, graphic & engineering supplies & audio & visual communication solutions. Also, design & install conference, training & boardrooms. Offers 24/7 technical service, along with complete rental & image departments.
Branch Office(s)
405 Forest St, Oconomowoc, WI 53066

The Tiffen Co LLC
90 Oser Ave, Hauppauge, NY 11788-3886
Tel: 631-273-2500 *Toll Free Tel:* 800-989-6013; 800-645-8500; 800-645-2522 *Fax:* 631-273-2557
E-mail: techsupport@tiffen.com
Web Site: www.tiffen.com
Key Personnel
CEO & Pres: Steven Tiffen
VP, Mktg: Hilary Araujo *Tel:* 631-273-2500 ext 3216 *E-mail:* haraujo@tiffen.com
Founded: 1938
Manufacturer of glass filters.
Online catalog(s) available
Branch Office(s)
Tiffen-Steadicam, 2815 Winona Ave, Burbank, CA 91504 *Tel:* 818-843-4600 *Fax:* 818-843-8321
Foreign Office(s): Tiffen International Ltd, Avonbury Business Park, Howes Lane, Bicester OX26 2UA, United Kingdom *Tel:* (0870) 100 1220 *Fax:* (01869) 32 1766
Membership(s): ASMP; National Press Photographers Association

Tigar Hare Studios
4485 Matilija Ave, Sherman Oaks, CA 91423
Tel: 818-907-6663 *Fax:* 818-907-0693
E-mail: info@tigarhare.com
Web Site: www.tigarhare.com
Key Personnel
Tech & Creative Dir: Dave Hare
Visual Effects Supvr & Creative Dir: Michael Tigar
Founded: 1997
Full service computer animation, graphics, visual effects, motion capture stage & final cut pro HD editing suite.

Tight Line Productions
1902 Oak St, Melbourne, FL 32901
Tel: 321-725-4668 *Fax:* 321-768-6528
E-mail: info@tightlinetv.com
Web Site: www.tightlinetv.com
Key Personnel
Pres: Mark Lewis *E-mail:* mlewis@tightlinetv.com
Founded: 1995

Tiki Recording Studios Inc
30-A Glen St, Suite 204, Glen Cove, NY 11542
Tel: 516-671-4300 (ext 101) *Fax:* 516-671-8754
Web Site: www.tikirecording.com
Key Personnel
Owner & Engr: Fred Guarino *Tel:* 516-924-3296 (cell) *E-mail:* fred@tikirecording.com
Founded: 1978
Recording studio.
Promo package(s), free
Membership(s): The Recording Academy; SPARS

Time Warner Cable
Subsidiary of Time Warner Inc
60 Columbus Circle, 17th fl, New York, NY 10023
Tel: 212-364-8200
Web Site: www.timewarnercable.com
Key Personnel
Chmn & CEO: Robert D Marcus
COO: Dinesh C Jain
CFO & EVP: Arthur T Minson, Jr
EVP & Chief Communs Offr: Ellen M East
EVP & COO, Media Servs: Joan Hogan Gillman
EVP, Architecture, Devt & Engg: Michael T Hayashi
EVP & Chief Mktg & Sales Offr, Residential Servs: Jeffrey A Hirsch
EVP, Residential Opers: John H Keib
EVP & Chief Technol & Network Opers Offr: Michael L LaJoie
EVP, Gen Coun & Secy: Marc Lawrence Apfelbaum
EVP, Corp Strategy: Kevin J Leddy
EVP & Chief Govt Rel Offr: Gail G MacKinnon
EVP & COO, Busn Servs: Philip G Meeks
EVP & Chief Prod, People & Strategy Offr: Peter C Stern
EVP & Chief Video & Content Offr: Melinda C Witmer

Time Warner Cable Business Class
120 E 23 St, 8th fl, New York, NY 10010
Tel: 212-379-5826
Web Site: www.twcbc.com/nyc
Key Personnel
Dir, Mktg: David A Fitts *E-mail:* david.fitts@twcable.com
Catalog(s) available

Timecode Multimedia
12340 Santa Monica Blvd, Suite 230, West Los Angeles, CA 90025
Tel: 310-826-9199
E-mail: info@timecodemedia.com
Web Site: www.timecodemultimedia.com
Key Personnel
Pres: Stuart Ferreyra
Founded: 1999
Post-production & digital media services.

Timed Exposures Films
122 Old Rd, Germantown, NY 12526-6014
Tel: 518-537-2012
E-mail: info@timedexposures.com
Web Site: www.timedexposures.com
Key Personnel
Pres, Prodr & Dir: Ralph Arlyck *E-mail:* ralph@timedexposures.com
Busn Mgr: Mechelle Nobiletti *E-mail:* mechelle@timedexposures.com
Film & video production.
Catalog(s) available

Timeless Books
Division of Association for the Development of Human Potential
Box 9, Kootenay Bay, BC V0B 1X0, Canada
Tel: 250-227-9224 *Toll Free Tel:* 800-661-8711 *Fax:* 250-227-9494
E-mail: contact@timeless.org
Web Site: www.timeless.org
Key Personnel
Gen Mgr: Maureen Wetsch
Founded: 1978
Catalog(s) available
Branch Office(s)
PO Box 3543, Spokane, WA 99220-3543 *Toll Free Tel:* 800-251-9273 *Fax:* 509-838-6652 *E-mail:* info@timeless.org

Timeless Productions
5050 Traverse Creek Rd, Garden Valley, CA 95633
Tel: 530-333-1335 *Toll Free Tel:* 800-729-1325
E-mail: 4info@timelessproductions.com
Web Site: www.timelessproductions.com
Key Personnel
Owner: David Blonski
Music distributor.
Catalog(s) available

TimeLogic Corp
Division of Active Motif Inc
1914 Palomar Oaks Way, Suite 150, Carlsbad, CA 92008

Tel: 760-431-1263 *Toll Free Tel:* 877-222-9543 *Fax:* 760-431-1351
Web Site: www.timelogic.com
Key Personnel
Mktg & Busn Devt: Eric Simon *Tel:* 877-222-9543 ext 350 *E-mail:* simon@activemotif.com
Brochure(s) available

Times-Square Fantasy Theatre
Subsidiary of Cude & Pickens Productions
519 N Halifax Ave, Daytona Beach, FL 32118
Tel: 386-252-0381 *Fax:* 386-252-0381
E-mail: timessquare@bellsouth.net
Web Site: www.timessquarefantasytheatre.com; www.broadwaymusicdownload.com
Key Personnel
Owner & CEO: Bobby Lee Cude
Online catalog(s) available
Membership(s): Alliance of Artists & Recording Companies; BMI; National Music Publishers' Association; The Recording Academy

TimeSteps Productions Inc
2 Glenside Dr, West Orange, NJ 07052
Tel: 973-669-1930 *Fax:* 973-731-8546
E-mail: info@timesteps.com
Web Site: timesteps.com
Key Personnel
Pres: Marilyn Petrokubi
Founded: 1987
Membership(s): New York Women in Film & Television

Timestream Video
11821 N Circle Dr, Whittier, CA 90601-2338
Tel: 562-699-8797 *Fax:* 562-695-0252
Web Site: www.timestreamvideo.com
Key Personnel
Owner & Prodr: Larry Scher *E-mail:* lscher.tv@verizon.net
Designer: J F Podevin
Membership(s): SMPTE

Rik Tinory Productions
PO Box 311, Cohasset, MA 02025-0311
Tel: 781-383-9494
E-mail: riktinory@aol.com

Tisch School of the Arts
Division of New York University
721 Broadway, 10th & 11th fl, New York, NY 10003
Tel: 212-998-1700; 212-998-1780 *Fax:* 212-995-4063; 212-995-4062
Web Site: www.tisch.nyu.edu
Key Personnel
Assoc Dean: Sheril Antonio
Catalog(s) available
Membership(s): Consortium of College & University Media Centers

Titus Technological Laboratories (TTL)
77 Kreiger Lane, Glastonbury, CT 06033
Tel: 860-633-5472 *Toll Free Tel:* 800-806-TTL1 (806-8851) *Fax:* 860-633-8244
E-mail: sales1@tituslabs.com
Web Site: www.tituslabs.com
Key Personnel
Owner & Pres: Lawrence Titus
Founded: 1971
Manufacturer of radio, television & satellite broadcast equipment.
Catalog(s) available

TKH Security Solutions USA Inc
Member of TKH Group NV
12920 Cloverleaf Center Dr, Germantown, MD 20874
Tel: 301-444-2200 *Toll Free Tel:* 800-BY-FIBER (293-4237) *Fax:* 301-444-2299 *Toll Free Fax:* 800-293-4237
E-mail: sales.us@tkhsecurity.com
Web Site: www.tkhsecurity.com
Key Personnel
Sales Dir: Chuck Queri *Tel:* 301-444-2218 *E-mail:* c.queri@tkhsecurity.com
Founded: 1972
Catalog(s) available

TM Studios Inc
Subsidiary of Triton Medial/Dial-Global
2002 Academy Lane, Suite 110, Dallas, TX 75234
Tel: 972-406-6800 *Fax:* 972-406-6890
E-mail: info@tmstudios.com; tmcustomerservice@tmstudios.com
Web Site: www.tmstudios.com
Key Personnel
VP & Gen Mgr: Greg Clancy *Tel:* 972-406-6847 *E-mail:* clancy@tmstudios.com
Dir, Mktg & Web Devt: Ryan Lambert *Tel:* 972-406-6869 *E-mail:* rlambert@tmstudios.com
Acctg: Jonita Jones *Tel:* 972-406-6859 *E-mail:* jjones@tmstudios.com
Catalog(s) available
Membership(s): NAB; Texas Association of Broadcasters

TMW Media Group
2321 Abbot Kinney Blvd, Suite 101, Venice, CA 90291
Tel: 310-577-8581 *Toll Free Tel:* 800-262-8862 *Fax:* 310-574-0886
E-mail: sale@tmwmedia.com
Web Site: www.tmwmedia.com
Key Personnel
Pres: Michael Bennett
VP, Sales: Leslie Collins
Dir, Mktg: Elaine Dochard
Founded: 1989
K-12 educational programming.
Catalog(s) available

TNA Records & Studios, see Trod Nossel Productions & Recording Studios

TOA Electronics Inc
Subsidiary of TOA Corp (Japan)
1350 Bayshore Hwy, Suite 270, Burlingame, CA 94010
Toll Free Tel: 800-733-7088 (cust serv); 800-733-4750 (main) *Fax:* 650-588-3349 *Toll Free Fax:* 800-733-9766
E-mail: info@toaelectronics.com
Web Site: www.toaelectronics.com
Key Personnel
Pres: Atsuo Honda
VP: Toshio Sakatia
Dir, Sales: Allan Lamberti
Catalog(s) available
CD-ROM catalog(s) available
Foreign Office(s): 7-2-1 Minatojima-Nakamachi, Chuo-ku, Kobe 650-0046, Japan *Tel:* (078) 303 5620 *Fax:* (078) 303 4634
Membership(s): AES; IBMA; IPMA; NAMM, the National Association of Music Merchants; NSCA

Tobias Associates Inc
50 Industrial Dr, Warminster, PA 18974-1433
Mailing Address: PO Box 2699, Warminster, PA 18974-0347
Tel: 215-322-1500 *Toll Free Tel:* 800-877-3367 *Fax:* 215-322-1504
E-mail: sales@tobiasinc.com
Web Site: www.densitometers.net
Key Personnel
VP: Eric M Tobias
Sales Mgr: William Bender
Founded: 1959
Catalog(s) available

Tobin Cinema Systems Inc
6116 N Ormond Rd, Otis Orchards, WA 99027
Mailing Address: 17128 E Baldwin Ave, Spokane Valley, WA 99016
Tel: 509-621-0323
E-mail: filmstodvd@comcast.net
Web Site: www.tobincinemasystems.com
Key Personnel
Pres: Clive Tobin *E-mail:* clivetobin@comcast.net
Founded: 1975
Online catalog(s) available

Tobin Productions Inc
630 Ninth Ave, Suite 215, New York, NY 10036
Tel: 212-727-1500 *Toll Free Tel:* 800-877-8273 *Fax:* 212-727-1766
E-mail: info@tobinproductions.com
Web Site: www.tobinproductions.com
Key Personnel
CEO & Pres: Dwight B Tobin *E-mail:* dwight@tobinproductions.com
Opers Mgr: Tom Mortensen *E-mail:* morty@tobinproductions.com
Sr Ed: Tim Kondrat *E-mail:* tim@tobinproductions.com
DVD Author & Compression: Tom Amici *E-mail:* tom@tobinproductions.com
Founded: 1985

Tobins Lake Sales
11035 Hi Tech Dr, Whitmore Lake, MI 48189
Tel: 734-449-9810 *Toll Free Tel:* 888-525-3753 *Fax:* 734-449-9812
Web Site: www.tobinslakesales.com
Key Personnel
Owner & Pres: William Ebeling *E-mail:* bill@tobinslakesales.com
Catalog(s) available
Membership(s): Professional Lighting & Sound Association; USITT

Dorothy Tod Films
41 Hazel Brown Rd, Warren, VT 05674
Tel: 802-496-5280 *Fax:* 802-496-5280
Key Personnel
Pres: Dorothy Tod *E-mail:* dorothy.tod@gmail.com
Catalog(s) available

Todd-AO Studios
900 N Seward St, Hollywood, CA 90038
Tel: 323-962-4000 *Fax:* 323-466-4062
Web Site: www.toddao.com
Founded: 1953
Recording studio.
Catalog(s) available
Branch Office(s)
2901 W Alameda Ave, Burbank, CA 91505 *Tel:* 818-295-5300
3000 Olympic Blvd, Santa Monica, CA 90404 *Tel:* 310-315-5000
Membership(s): SMPTE

Toko America Inc
Subsidiary of Toko Inc
1250 Feehanville Dr, Mount Prospect, IL 60056
Tel: 847-297-0070 *Toll Free Tel:* 800-PIK-TOKO (745-8656) *Fax:* 847-699-7864
E-mail: info@tokoam.com
Web Site: www.tokoam.com
Founded: 1955
Manufacturer of leading edge electronic components.
Membership(s): GSA

Tom Thumb Music, see Rhythms Productions (Tom Thumb Music)

TOMCAT USA Inc
5427 N National Dr, Knoxville, TN 37914

Mailing Address: PO Box 9187, Knoxville, TX 37940
Tel: 865-219-3700 *Fax:* 865-673-5818
E-mail: info@tomcatusa.com; sales@tomcatusa.com
Web Site: www.tomcatglobal.com
Key Personnel
CEO & Pres: Scott Johnson *Tel:* 865-219-3720
Prodn Mgr: Adam Gross
Fabrication of aluminum structural components for the entertainment & leisure industries, as well as providing related products such as theatrical chain hoists, custom electric assemblies, lighting products & rigging hardware.
Catalog(s) available
Membership(s): Professional Lighting & Sound Association

Tommy Boy Entertainment LLC
902 Broadway, No 14, New York, NY 10010
Tel: 212-388-8300 *Fax:* 212-388-8431
E-mail: info@tommyboy.com
Web Site: shop.tommyboy.com
Key Personnel
Pres: Rosie Lopez
Founded: 1981
Online catalog(s) available

Tomorrow River Music
PO Box 245, Cambridge, WI 53523
Tel: 608-217-5039
Web Site: www.robbieclement.com
Key Personnel
Owner: Robbie Clement *E-mail:* robbieclement@yahoo.com
Catalog(s) available

Tone Zone Recording
1316 N Clybourn, Chicago, IL 60610-1710
Tel: 312-664-5353 *Fax:* 312-664-6560
E-mail: tonezonerecording@sbcglobal.net
Key Personnel
Mgr: Roger Heiss

Toon Makers
17333 Ludlow St, Granada Hills, CA 91344
Tel: 818-832-8666
E-mail: info@toonmakers.com
Web Site: toonmakers.com
Key Personnel
CEO: Rocky Solotoff
Founded: 1991
2D & 3D animation & production for film, DVD, video, TV & commercials.

Top Hat Productions
6615 Boynton Beach Blvd, Suite 310, Boynton Beach, FL 33437
Tel: 561-963-6442 *Toll Free Tel:* 888-794-0528 *Fax:* 561-880-6988
E-mail: info@tophatproductions.net
Web Site: www.tophatproductions.net
Key Personnel
Pres: Keith Carson
Founded: 1997
Creative audio solutions.
Membership(s): Advertising Federation of the Greater Palm Beaches; American Advertising Federation

TopCat Records LLC
PO Box 670234, Dallas, TX 75367-0234
Tel: 972-484-4141
E-mail: info@topcatrecords.com
Web Site: topcatrecords.com
Key Personnel
Pres: Richard Chalk
Production & distribution of blues, jazz & outlaw country music CDs, DVDs & record label. Branch office in Rio de Janeiro, Brazil.
Online catalog(s) available

Torpey Time
Subsidiary of Dixon Systems
580 Danforth Rd, Toronto, ON M1K 1E3, Canada
Tel: 416-261-3773
E-mail: helpdesk@dixonsystems.com; technicalsupport@dixonsystems.com
Web Site: www.dixonsystems.com
Key Personnel
Owner: Brian Dixon
Founded: 1975
Flyer(s) available

Toshiba America Information Systems Inc
Subsidiary of Toshiba Corp
9740 Irvine Blvd, Irvine, CA 92618
Tel: 949-583-3000 *Fax:* 949-583-3437
Web Site: www.toshiba.com

Tosoh USA Inc
Subsidiary of Tosoh Corp
3600 Gantz Rd, Grove City, OH 43123
Tel: 614-277-4348 *Toll Free Tel:* 866-844-6953 *Fax:* 614-875-8086
E-mail: info.tusa@tosoh.com
Web Site: www.tosohusa.com
Founded: 1964
Branch Office(s)
Tosoh Bioscience Inc, 6000 Shoreline Ct, Suite 101, South San Francisco, CA 94080 *Tel:* 650-615-4970 *Toll Free Tel:* 800-248-6764 *E-mail:* info.diag.am@tosoh.com *Web Site:* www.tosohbioscience.com
Tosoh Quartz Inc, 14380 NW Science Park Dr, Portland, OR 97229 *Tel:* 503-605-5600 *Fax:* 503-605-5688 *Web Site:* www.tosohquartz.com

Total AV Systems
923 Sligo Ave, Silver Spring, MD 20910
Tel: 301-589-3337 *Toll Free Tel:* 800-447-7632 *Fax:* 301-494-4770
E-mail: info@total-av.com
Web Site: total-av.com
Key Personnel
Pres: Han S Jan
VP: Josephine Jan
Systems Integrator: Kenneth Jan
Founded: 1978
Professional AV equipment sales, design-integration, service, engineering & installation.
Catalog(s) available
Branch Office(s)
444 "K" St NW, Washington, DC 20001, Branch Mgr: Russell Grigsby *Tel:* 202-737-3900 *Fax:* 202-737-3906 *E-mail:* russell@total-av.com
8 Spruce Lane, Annapolis, MD 21401, Branch Mgr: Jamison Orsetti *Tel:* 410-266-0022 *Fax:* 416-266-0024 *E-mail:* jamison@total-av.com
1011 W Barre St, Baltimore, MD 21230, Branch Mgr: Troy Cates *Tel:* 410-625-4700 *Fax:* 410-625-4704 *E-mail:* troyc@total-av.com
8480 Tyco Rd, Vienna, VA 22182, Branch Mgr: Steve Schirtzinger *Tel:* 703-790-5950 *Fax:* 703-790-5964 *E-mail:* steve@total-av.com
Membership(s): MCA-I

Total Concept Sales
2505 Foothill Blvd, Suite G, La Crescentia, CA 91214
Tel: 818-236-3966 *Toll Free Tel:* 800-488-0589 *Fax:* 818-236-3969
E-mail: info@smartups.com
Web Site: www.smartups.com
Key Personnel
Data Mgr: Alfred Derohanessian
Catalog(s) available

Total Impact Multimedia Group Ltd
1475 Pea Pond Rd, North Bellmore, NY 11710
Tel: 516-783-8800
E-mail: info@totalimpactltd.com
Web Site: www.totalimpactltd.com
Key Personnel
Pres: Kenneth Book
3D rendering & animation, 4D presentations, proposal support, brochures & print advertising, photography, video production & web development.

Total Media
2 N Corporate Dr, 2nd fl, Riverdale, NJ 07457
Tel: 973-248-9700 *Toll Free Tel:* 800-355-4400 *Fax:* 973-248-9707
E-mail: info@totalmedia.com
Web Site: www.totalmedia.com
Founded: 1989
Supplier of professional & commercial blank recording media.

Total Media Group
432 N Canal St, Suite 12, South San Francisco, CA 94080
Tel: 650-583-8236 *Fax:* 650-583-4708
E-mail: info@mediagroup.com
Web Site: www.totalmediagroup.com
Key Personnel
Pres: Megan McKenna
Founded: 1979
Brochure(s) available
Membership(s): Bay Area Video Coalition; Northern California Production Community

Total Video Products Inc
414 Southgate Ct, Mickleton, NJ 08056
Tel: 856-423-7400 *Toll Free Tel:* 800-447-0920 *Fax:* 856-423-4747
E-mail: info@totalvideoproducts.com
Web Site: www.totalvideoproducts.com
Key Personnel
Pres: Larry Gallner *E-mail:* lgallner@totalvideoproducts.com
Founded: 1976
AV & digital media integrator.
Catalog(s), annual, free
Membership(s): American Institute of Architects; Consortium of College & University Media Centers; CSI; InfoComm International®; International Facilities Management Association; NSCA; Philadelphia Advertising Club

ToteVision
1319 Dexter Ave N, Suite 020, Seattle, WA 98109
Tel: 206-623-6000 *Fax:* 206-623-6609
E-mail: info@totevision.com
Web Site: www.totevision.com
Key Personnel
VP: Mark Lakefish *E-mail:* mlakefish@totevision.com
Founded: 1980
Our brightest technology, finest engineering & responsive customer service makes ToteVision your best partner for LCD monitors in sizes from 4 inches to 42 inches. Provide customer-focused solutions by customizing products according to need & demand.
Catalog(s), annual, free, on request
Online catalog(s) available

TouchStar Productions Inc
522 Jackson Park Dr, Meadville, PA 16335
Tel: 814-337-8192 *Toll Free Tel:* 800-759-1294 *Fax:* 814-337-0699
E-mail: doctorb@touchstarpro.com
Web Site: www.touchstarpro.com
Key Personnel
Dir, Mktg: Karen Bittman *E-mail:* keb@touchstarpro.com
Founded: 1995

Medical programming.
Catalog(s) available

Touchstone Center Publications
Subsidiary of The Touchstone Center for Children Inc
141 E 88 St, New York, NY 10128
Tel: 212-831-7717
Web Site: www.touchstonecenter.net
Key Personnel
Dir: Richard Lewis *E-mail:* rlewis212@aol.com
Founded: 1969
A series of audio visual tapes by Geoffry Jones interpreting recent books by Richard Lewis. Including: *The Bird of Imagining*; *Each Sky Has it's Words & Cave*; & *Evocation of the Beginnings of Art*; as well as a variety of documentary tapes on the work of The Touchstone Center in schools & classrooms encouraging the use of the imaginative & poetic process in learning.
Catalog(s) available

Towards 2000 Inc
215 W Palm Ave, Suite 101, Burbank, CA 91502
Tel: 818-557-0903 *Toll Free Fax:* 866-836-5725
E-mail: info@t2k.com
Web Site: www.t2k.com
Key Personnel
Pres: Mark Rowlands
Founded: 1978
Catalog(s) available

Toys From The Attic
Affiliate of Dream Theatre
203 Mamaroneck Ave, Suite 2, White Plains, NY 10601
Tel: 914-421-0069 *Fax:* 914-328-3852
E-mail: info@tfta.com
Web Site: tfta.com
Key Personnel
Owner & Pres: Mario A Campa
Founded: 1995
Retail & custom electronic installations. Hi-end AV retail & installation, vintage & collectible guitars & basses, mechanical watches & accessories.

TPR Enterprises Ltd
644 Fayette Ave, Mamaroneck, NY 10543
Tel: 914-698-1141 *Fax:* 914-698-9419
E-mail: info@tprlights.com
Web Site: www.tprlights.com
Key Personnel
Pres: Thomas Fay *E-mail:* tfay@tprlights.com
Commercial Sales Mgr: Paul Benton *Tel:* 320-266-8996 *E-mail:* pbenton@tprlights.com
Off Mgr: Lisa MacFadden *E-mail:* lmacfadden@tprlights.com
Founded: 1980
Lighting fixture, control equipment, fiber optic lighting & LED lighting.

TR Productions
2 13 St, 3rd fl, Charlestown, MA 02129
Tel: 617-241-5500
E-mail: info@trprod.com
Web Site: www.trprod.com
Key Personnel
Pres: Cary M Benjamin
Business communication & production company.

Trac Record Co & Recording Studio
180 E Warner Ave, Fresno, CA 93710
Tel: 559-448-8722
E-mail: tracsell@sbcglobal.net
Key Personnel
Owner: Stan Anderson
Founded: 1972
Recording studio & artist development. Equipment includes MCI console & tape recorder 24 track.

Trafalgar Square Books
388 Howe Hill Rd, North Pomfret, VT 05053
Mailing Address: PO Box 257, North Pomfret, VT 05053-0257
Tel: 802-457-1911 *Toll Free Tel:* 800-423-4525 *Fax:* 802-457-1913
E-mail: info@horseandriderbooks.com
Web Site: www.horseandriderbooks.com
Key Personnel
Publr: Caroline Robbins
Mng Dir: Martha Cook *Tel:* 802-457-1911 ext 109
Mktg Dir & Craft Ed: Kim Cook
Promos Dir: Julie Beaulieu
Sr Ed & Graphic Designer: Rebecca Didier
Founded: 1985
Publish craft & equestrian books.
Catalog(s), biannual, free

Trailblazer Studios®
1610 Midtown Place, Raleigh, NC 27609
Tel: 919-645-6600 *Fax:* 919-645-6601
Web Site: www.trailblazerstudios.com
Key Personnel
CEO: Tom Waring
VP, Original Programming: Jeff Lanter *Tel:* 919-645-6633 *E-mail:* jeff@trailblazerstudios.com
Exec Prodr, Music & Sound: Eric Johnson *Tel:* 919-645-6622 *E-mail:* eric@trailblazerstudios.com
Exec Prodr, Post Prodn: Leah Welsh *Tel:* 919-645-6657 *E-mail:* leah@trailblazerstudios.com
Exec Prodr, Prodn: Katye Rone *Tel:* 919-645-6615 *E-mail:* katye@trailblazerstudios.com
Catalog(s) available

Trance Formations Unlimited
1425 Steele St, Laramie, WY 82070
Tel: 307-745-7897
Key Personnel
Pres: R Leo Sprinkle
Secy & Treas: Marilyn J Sprinkle
Brochure(s) available

Tranquil Technology Music
PO Box 20463, Oakland, CA 94620-0463
Tel: 510-658-2560
Web Site: michaelmantra.com
Key Personnel
Pres: Michael Stoffan *E-mail:* michaelstoffan@yahoo.com
Catalog(s) available
Membership(s): ASCAP

Trans-Lux Multimedia Corp
Subsidiary of Trans-Lux Corp
950 Third Ave, Suite 2804, New York, NY 10022
Tel: 203-853-4321 *Toll Free Tel:* 800-243-5544; 800-462-2716 *Fax:* 203-229-0691
Web Site: www.trans-lux.com
Key Personnel
CEO & Pres: Jean-Marc L Allain
CFO, Compt & VP: Todd Dupree
VP: Craig Katt; Christopher Stark
Designers of real-time programmable display systems.
Brochure(s) available
Branch Office(s)
3228 S Service Rd, Suite 109, Burlington, ON L7N 3H8, Canada *Toll Free Tel:* 800-268-0491

The Transfer Zone®
4301 Orchard Lake Rd, Suite 180-191, West Bloomfield, MI 48323
Tel: 248-225-0477
Key Personnel
Mktg Dir: Roxane B Newhouse *E-mail:* rpida1@yahoo.com
Founded: 1976
Video post-production facility.
Membership(s): The Adcraft Club of Detroit

Transformational Education Initiatives
PO Box 344, Phoenicia, NY 12464
Tel: 310-795-4910
E-mail: lioneltv@aol.com
Web Site: transformationaledu.org
Key Personnel
Chmn: David Lionel
Founded: 2000
Educational DVD distribution.

Transistor Devices Inc
36 Newburgh Rd, Hackettstown, NJ 07840
Tel: 908-850-5088 *Fax:* 908-850-1607
E-mail: info@tdipower.com
Web Site: www.tdipower.com
Key Personnel
Pres: Jim Feely
VP, Mktg & Sales: Joseph DeLuca *Tel:* 908-850-5088 ext 1480 *E-mail:* joseph.deluca@tdipower.com
Dir, Intl Sales: Declan Walsh *E-mail:* declan.walsh@tdipower.com
Dir, US Natl Sales: Kelly Atkinson *Tel:* 908-850-5088 ext 1796 *E-mail:* kelly.atkinson@tdipower.com
Regl Sales Dir: James Barbero *Tel:* 908-850-5088 ext 1805 *E-mail:* james.barbero@tdipower.com
Catalog(s) available
Branch Office(s)
87 Raynor Ave, Unit 2, Ronkonkoma, NY 11779-6649 *Tel:* 631-471-7492
Foreign Office(s): Jiangmao Gongmao Warehouse, Bldg 19, fl 2-5, Taohua Rd, Futian District, Fuitian Trade Free Zone, China

Transparent Office Products LLC
2550 Haddonfield Rd, Pennsauken, NJ 08110
Tel: 856-488-5455 *Fax:* 856-488-5411
E-mail: sales@transoffprod.biz
Web Site: www.transoffprod.biz
Key Personnel
Opers Mgr: Rick Brown
Archival storage pages.
Catalog(s) available

Transtar Entertainment Co Inc
10650 E Bethany Dr, Suite E, Aurora, CO 80014
Tel: 303-695-4207
Web Site: www.transtarfilm.com
Key Personnel
Pres, Exec Prodr, Dir & Ed: Doug Hanes *E-mail:* doug@transtarfilm.com
Prodr & Dir: Nick Connell
Founded: 1982
Full service production company.
Catalog(s) available
Membership(s): Colorado Film & Video Association; DAF; MCA-I

Transtector Systems Inc
Subsidiary of Smiths Industries
10701 N Airport Dr, Hayden Lake, ID 83835
Tel: 208-772-8515 *Toll Free Tel:* 800-882-9110 *Fax:* 208-762-6133
E-mail: sales@transtector.com
Web Site: www.transtector.com
Key Personnel
Pres: Tom Kritzell
Dir, Engg: Mark Hendricks
Dir, Sales: Mark Norrie
Manufactures surge suppression equipment.
Catalog(s) available
Foreign Office(s): 36-38 Waterloo Rd, London NW2 7UH, United Kingdom *Tel:* (020) 8830 5039 *Fax:* (020) 8830 5075

Transvideo International
11712 Moorpark St, Suite 112-B, North Hollywood, CA 91604
Tel: 818-985-4903 *Fax:* 818-985-4921
Web Site: www.transvideointl.com
Key Personnel
Owner & Pres: Marianne Exbrayat
E-mail: marianne@transvideointl.com
Sales Assoc & Tech Support: Noel Ilaw
Founded: 1999
Design & manufacture professional flat panel monitors, HD & SD wireless video systems & other film & video accessories. Manufacture, sell & repair monitors, format converters, Frameline Generators, Electronic Horizon & lightweight prompters.
Membership(s): NAB

TRC Interactive Inc
4200 Crums Mill Rd, Harrisburg, PA 17112
Mailing Address: PO Box 6685, Harrisburg, PA 17112
Tel: 717-652-3100 *Toll Free Tel:* 800-222-9909 *Fax:* 717-652-8281
E-mail: customerservicetrc01@trcinteractive.com; info@trcinteractive.com
Web Site: www.trcinteractive.com
Key Personnel
CEO & Pres: Jay B Bowden
Founded: 1973
Interactive training systems.
Catalog(s) available

Trebas Institute
550 Sherbrooke St W, Suite 600, Montreal, QC H3A 1B9, Canada
Tel: 514-845-4141 *Toll Free Tel:* 866-5TREBAS (587-3227) *Fax:* 514-845-2581
E-mail: infomtl@trebas.com
Web Site: www.trebas.com
Key Personnel
Founder & CEO: David P Leonard
Founded: 1979
Digital media design & training including film, television & audio production.
Branch Office(s)
2340 Dundas St W, 2nd fl, Toronto, ON M6P 4A9, Canada *Tel:* 416-966-3066 *E-mail:* info@trebas.com
Membership(s): AES; Canadian Academy of Recording Arts & Sciences; MEIEA; The Recording Academy; SMPTE

Treehaus Communications Inc
906 W Loveland Ave, Loveland, OH 45140-2150
Mailing Address: PO Box 249, Loveland, OH 45140-0249
Tel: 513-683-5716 *Toll Free Tel:* 800-638-4287 *Fax:* 513-683-2882
E-mail: treehaus@treehaus1.com
Web Site: www.treehaus1.com
Key Personnel
Pres: Gerard A Pottebaum
Catalog(s) available

Tremetrics Inc Industrial Instruments Division
Division of Diagnostic Group LLC
7625 Golden Triangle Dr, Eden Prairie, MN 55344
Toll Free Tel: 800-825-0121 *Fax:* 952-903-4100
E-mail: info@tremetrics.com
Web Site: www.tremetrics.com
Key Personnel
Prod Line Mgr: Jack Foreman *Tel:* 800-825-0121 ext 4476 *E-mail:* jackf@tremetrics.com
Test equipment manufacturer.
Catalog(s) available

Trendy Studio LLC
196 NW 24 St, Miami, FL 33127
Tel: 305-438-4244 *Fax:* 305-438-4243
E-mail: studio@trendygroup.com
Web Site: trendystudio.net
Full service production company managing productions either in studio or on location. Services include: still & video production coordination; budget management; equipment rental; location scouting; studio rental; casting & talent booking; creative crew booking; wardrobe & styling; props & set building; travel arrangements; permits & insurance; security; local transportation & production vehicles; catering & behind the scenes.

Trew Audio Inc
220 Great Circle Rd, Suite 116, Nashville, TN 37228
Tel: 615-256-3542 *Toll Free Tel:* 800-241-8994 *Fax:* 615-259-2699
E-mail: info@trewaudio.com; sales@trewaudio.com
Web Site: www.trewaudio.com
Key Personnel
EVP & CFO: Richard Rosing *E-mail:* richard@trewaudio.com
Founded: 1994
Sales, rentals & service of audio & communications equipment for film & TV production.
Catalog(s) available
Branch Office(s)
Coffey Sound: A Trew Audio Co, 3325 Cahuenga Blvd W, Los Angeles, CA 90068 *Tel:* 323-876-7525 *Toll Free Tel:* 888-293-3030
3737 Napier St, Burnaby, BC V5C 4Z5, Canada *Tel:* 604-299-9122 *Toll Free Tel:* 877-333-9122 *Fax:* 604-299-9127 *Web Site:* www.trewaudio.ca
Trew Audio Canada, 17 Carlow Ave, Unit 4, Toronto, ON M4M 2R6, Canada *Tel:* 416-778-0656 *Toll Free Tel:* 866-778-8739 *E-mail:* sales@trewaudio.ca *Web Site:* www.trewaudio.ca
Membership(s): CAS

TRF Production Music Libraries
Subsidiary of TRF Music Inc
106 Apple St, Suite 302, Tinton Falls, NJ 07724
Tel: 201-335-0005 *Toll Free Tel:* 800-899-MUSIC (899-6874) *Fax:* 201-335-0004
E-mail: info@trfmusic.com
Web Site: www.trfmusic.com
Key Personnel
CEO & Pres: Michael Nurko
Creative Dir: Eric Nurko
Promos Mgr: Anne Marie Russo
E-mail: annemarie@trfmusic.com
Largest collection of contemporary, retro & traditional production music. Every category available including all types of ethnic & specialty music. Well-known TRF libraries include Arcadia, Bravo, Pyramid, Dennis, Stock library & the authentic international ethnic library, PAN.
Catalog(s), free
Membership(s): ASCAP; BMI; National Music Publishers' Association; Production Music Association

Tri-Color
4303 Normandy Ct, Royal Oak, MI 48073-2266
Tel: 248-549-0150 *Toll Free Tel:* 800-886-5661 *Fax:* 248-549-5270
Web Site: www.tricolorphoto.com
Key Personnel
Pres: Don Kirkland
Full service photo & digital imaging lab specializing in direct to board printing, digital die cutting, full color grand format printing on cloth, mesh canvas & vinyl - used for curtains, wallcoverings, backdrops & props.
Catalog(s) available
Membership(s): AIE™; PMA International

Tri-Digital Software Inc
8424 154 Ave NE, Redmond, WA 98052
Tel: 425-284-3888 *Toll Free Tel:* 800-206-2547 *Fax:* 425-883-3887
E-mail: tdp@tri-digital.com
Web Site: www.tri-digital.com
Key Personnel
Pres: Mark Monrean
CTO: Roger Swearingen
Multimedia service bureau video compression & CD-ROM title developer.
Catalog(s) available
Membership(s): Washington Software Association

Tri-Ed
3625 Cincinnati Ave, Rocklin, CA 95765
Tel: 916-543-4000 *Toll Free Tel:* 800-366-4472 *Fax:* 916-543-4020
E-mail: info@northernvideo.com
Web Site: www.tri-ed.com
Key Personnel
CEO: Steve Roth
COO & Pres: Pat Comunale
EVP, Sales & Mktg: James Rothstein
Founded: 1986
Catalog(s) available
Membership(s): MCA-I

Tri-State Audio Visual Co
2901 Glendora Ave, Cincinnati, OH 45219
Tel: 513-281-7500 *Toll Free Tel:* 800-348-8728 *Fax:* 513-281-7539
E-mail: sales@tristateav.com
Web Site: www.tristateav.com
Key Personnel
Pres: Bruce A Bock *E-mail:* bruce.bock@tristateav.com
Founded: 1984
Sell, install, repair video & sound systems.
Catalog(s), annual, free
Membership(s): InfoComm International®

Tri-State Loudspeaker
650 Franklin Ave, Aliquippa, PA 15001
Tel: 724-375-9203
Key Personnel
Owner: Dante Maruca
Founded: 1987
Speaker re-coning & refoaming services. For additional services see web site.
Catalog(s), wholesale & retail; factory authorized all brands
Price list(s), wholesale & retail
Membership(s): AES; ETA; IEEE

Tri-State Visual Products
885 Ohio Pike, Suite C, Cincinnati, OH 45245
Tel: 513-471-7111 *Toll Free Tel:* 800-473-4474 *Fax:* 513-471-7140
E-mail: info@trivisual.com
Web Site: www.trivisual.com
Key Personnel
Pres: Greg Games
Founded: 1990
Sales, service, rental & installation of multimedia projectors (In Focus, Proxima & Sanyo). Full service AV dealer.

Triad Communications Ltd
2751 Oxford St, Vancouver, BC V5K 1N5, Canada
Tel: 604-253-5351; 604-253-3990
E-mail: triadc@comwave.com
Web Site: www.triadcommunications.ca
Key Personnel
Owner: Roland Loughhead; Gay Ludlow
Founded: 1973

Tricycle Studios
1905 E Seventh Ave, Tampa, FL 33605
Tel: 813-258-6867 *Fax:* 813-258-8595

E-mail: hi@tricyclestudios.com
Web Site: www.tricyclestudios.com
Key Personnel
Co-owner: Tona Bell; Randy Rosenthal
Founded: 1995
Tricyle Studios is a marketing communications company that uses technology based media to achieve high impact results.

The Trinity Recording Studio
PO Box 1417, Corpus Christi, TX 78403
Tel: 361-854-7464
E-mail: info@trinitystudio.com
Web Site: www.trinitystudio.com
Key Personnel
Owner: Jim Wilken; Rachel Whitefield Wilken
Founded: 1988
Full service recording studio. Spirit Digital 328 Mixer, Sonar X2, Adobe Audition, Sony Vegas Pro.
Membership(s): Coastal Bend Gospel Music Association; The Recording Academy

Trio Video
Division of NEP Group Inc
915 Sherwood Dr, Lake Bluff, IL 60044
Tel: 312-421-7060 *Fax:* 312-421-0361
Web Site: www.triovideo.com
Key Personnel
Prodn: Phil Wolf

Tripp Lite
1111 W 35 St, Chicago, IL 60609
Tel: 773-869-1111; 773-869-1234 *Fax:* 773-869-1935
E-mail: av@tripplite.com
Web Site: www.tripplite.com
Key Personnel
Media & PR Mgr: Gloria Wong
Founded: 1922
Catalog(s) available

Tritech Communications
625 Locust St, Suite 300, Garden City, NY 11530
Tel: 631-254-4500 *Fax:* 631-254-4499
E-mail: sales@tritechcomm.com
Web Site: www.tritechcomm.com
Key Personnel
Chmn & CEO: Matthew P O'Reilly
Pres A/V Div: Joseph Melfa
Pres, Communs & Security Div: Edward Dougherty
VP, Fin & Admin: Christian Schachinger
VP, Sales & Mktg: Cliff Alberti
Founded: 2002
AV solutions provider: systems integration, service & maintenance.
Branch Office(s)
4200 Forbes Blvd, Suite 105, Lanham, MD 20706 *Tel:* 301-577-7610 *Fax:* 301-459-3194
225 Franklin St, 26th fl, Boston, MA 02110 *Tel:* 617-217-2540 *Fax:* 617-217-2001
555 Eighth Ave, Suite 202, New York, NY 10018 *Tel:* 212-292-1500 *Fax:* 212-292-1505
Membership(s): InfoComm International®; NSCA

Triumph Learning LLC
Division of Haights Cross Communications®
PO Box 1270, Littleton, MA 01460-4270
Toll Free Tel: 800-338-6519 *Toll Free Fax:* 866-805-5723
E-mail: customerservice@triumphlearning.com
Web Site: www.triumphlearning.com
Educational programming.
Catalog(s) available

Triune Arts
RR 5, 1804 Bedell Rd, Kemptville, ON K0G 1J0, Canada
E-mail: triune@triune.ca
Web Site: www.triune.ca
Founded: 1981

Trod Nossel Productions & Recording Studios
10 George St, Wallingford, CT 06492
Mailing Address: PO Box 57, Wallingford, CT 06492-4008
Tel: 203-269-4465 *Toll Free Tel:* 800-800-HITS (800-4487) *Fax:* 203-294-1745
E-mail: info@trodnossel.com
Web Site: www.trodnossel.com
Key Personnel
Pres: Rob Cavalier
VP: Tom Cavalier
Engr: Kevin Boettger; Derek Mocarski; Justin Watson
Founded: 1966
Founded by the late Thomas "Doc" Cavalier.
Catalog(s) available

Troll Touch
33302 Santiago Rd, Suite C, Acton, CA 93510
Tel: 661-257-1160 *Fax:* 661-257-1161
Web Site: www.trolltouch.com
Key Personnel
VP: Vincent Durso
Founded: 1987
Monitor sales.
Catalog(s) available

Trompeter Electronics Inc
Division of Emerson Network Power Connectivity Solutions Inc
299 Johnson Ave, Suite 100, Waseca, MN 56093
Tel: 507-833-8822 *Fax:* 507-833-6287
E-mail: connectivityinfo@emerson.com; connectivitysales@emerson.com
Web Site: emersonconnectivity.com
Founded: 1960
Manufacturer of RF coax, triax & twinax transmission line connectors & the tools required for assembly. Trompeter specializes in broadcast patching coaxial connectors for studio grade applications.
Catalog(s) available

Tropical Visions Video Inc
62 Halaulani Place, Hilo, HI 96720
Tel: 808-935-5557 *Fax:* 808-935-0066
E-mail: redhotlava@hawaii.rr.com
Web Site: www.volcanoscapes.com
Key Personnel
Pres & Mgr: Mick Kalber
Treas & Secy: Ann Kalber *E-mail:* annthen@hawaii.rr.com
Stock footage & programming/production. HD DVD/Cable/Broadcast TV.
Catalog(s), periodically, free
Membership(s): Film & Video Association at Hawaii

Tropikal Productions
137 Sequoia Rd, Rockwall, TX 75032
Tel: 972-771-3797 *Fax:* 972-771-0853
E-mail: tropikalproductions@gmail.com
Web Site: www.tropikalproductions.com
Key Personnel
Owner & Prodr: Jimi Towry *Tel:* 469-338-9237 (cell)
Engr: Arik Miles
Founded: 1990
Music production, recording, sequencing, arranging, label & booking agency. 24 tracks ADAT, Mac running Opcode Vision. Office in Jaco, Costa Rica.
CD-ROM catalog(s), price varies
Membership(s): BMI; Raggae Ambassadors Worldwide

The Troupe
Subsidiary of Orth-Tec Corp
3 Industrial Dr, Windham, NH 03087
Tel: 603-893-4554 *Fax:* 603-893-9717
E-mail: info@thetroupe.com
Web Site: www.thetroupe.com
Key Personnel
COO: John Connors *E-mail:* john@thetroupe.com
Gen Mgr: Fred Connors, Jr *E-mail:* fred@thetroupe.com
Full service production facility.
Catalog(s) available

Troxell Communications Inc
4830 S 38 St, Phoenix, AZ 85040
Tel: 602-437-7240 *Toll Free Tel:* 800-578-8858 *Fax:* 602-437-7265 *Toll Free Fax:* 800-589-5939
Web Site: www.trox.com
Key Personnel
VP, Opers: Charlotte Crochet *Tel:* 602-437-7240 ext 1002 *E-mail:* charlotte.crochet@trox.com
HR Mgr: Dorri Carpenter
Bid Dept Head: Paul Champion
Info Servs Mgr: Craig Schramm
Founded: 1983
Large AV equipment distributor.
Catalog(s), annual, free, 4-color
Online catalog(s) available

True Audio
387 Duncan Lane, Andersonville, TN 37705
Tel: 865-494-3388 *Toll Free Tel:* 800-621-4411 *Fax:* 865-494-3388
E-mail: sales@trueaudio.com
Web Site: www.trueaudio.com
Key Personnel
Mktg Dir: Sharon Alsup *E-mail:* sharon.alsup@trueaudio.com
Founded: 1990
Software publisher, audio products.

TRUMATCH Inc
PO Box 501, Water Mill, NY 11976-0501
Tel: 631-204-9100 *Toll Free Tel:* 800-TRU-9100 (878-9100) *Fax:* 631-204-0002
E-mail: info@trumatch.com
Web Site: www.trumatch.com
Key Personnel
Pres: Steve Abramson
Founded: 1990
Established the digital 4-color standard (palette) for desktop publishing that makes selecting & matching colors easy & accurate. The TRUMATCH® System was developed for design & illustration software & for output, exclusively, by electronic imagesetters, printers & copiers.
Catalog(s), $85, TRUMATCH Colorfinder Coated Paper (fanguide)
Catalog(s), $85, TRUMATCH Colorfinder Unoated Paper (fanguide)
Membership(s): Printing Industries of America

Trusty Tuneshop Recording Studios
8771 Rose Creek Rd, Nebo, KY 42441
Tel: 270-249-3194
E-mail: etrusty@vci.net
Web Site: trustytuneshop.com
Key Personnel
Owner & Mgr: Elsie Childers
Engr: Mike Cain
Founded: 1979
One-off CDs from DAT tapes - commercial world class 24-TR recording studio.
Brochure(s), request by e-mail/phone or visit web site
Membership(s): Country Music Association

Truth Consciousness Publications
Subsidiary of Truth Consciousness Inc
Desert Ashram, 3403 W Sweetwater Dr, Tucson, AZ 85745-9301
Tel: 520-743-8821 *Fax:* 520-743-3394
E-mail: info@truthconsciousness.org
Web Site: truthconsciousness.org

Key Personnel
Agent: Marianne Martin
Founded: 1974
Spiritual publications including audio Satsangs of Swami Amar Jyoti.
Online catalog(s) available

TSG Publishing Foundation Inc USA
28641 N 63 Place, Cave Creek, AZ 85331
Mailing Address: PO Box 7068, Cave Creek, AZ 85327-7068
Tel: 480-502-1909 *Fax:* 480-502-0713
E-mail: info@tsgfoundation.org
Web Site: www.tsgfoundation.org
Key Personnel
Pres: Gita Saraydarian
Catalog(s), by request
Online catalog(s) available
Foreign Office(s): TSG (UK) Ltd, 4 The Wilderness, East Molesey, Surrey KT8 0JT, United Kingdom, Contact: Catriona Nason *Tel:* (020) 8979 8444 *Fax:* (020) 8979 8473 *E-mail:* info@tsg-uk.org *Web Site:* www.tsg-uk.org

TSR/Baja Damabi Records
18653 Ventura Blvd, Suite 513, Tarzana, CA 91356
Tel: 818-702-9902
Key Personnel
Pres: Tom Hayden

T3Media
1530 16 St, 6th fl, Denver, CO 80202
Tel: 720-382-2869 *Toll Free Tel:* 866-815-6599 *Fax:* 720-382-2719
E-mail: content@t3media.com
Web Site: www.t3licensing.com
Key Personnel
CEO: Bob Pinkerton
CTO: Mark Lemmons
Gen Mgr, Licensing: Mike Emerson
Video research, footage consulting & project management.

Tubeworks Video Productions
1626 Wilcox Ave, Los Angeles, CA 90028
Tel: 323-469-6003
Web Site: www.tubeworksvideo.com
Key Personnel
Owner: Arthur Pritz
Founded: 1978
Digital video services for corporate & event productions.
Membership(s): WEVA

Tufnut Theft Protection
2910 San Isidro Ct, Santa Fe, NM 87501
Mailing Address: PO Box 39, Tesuque, NM 87574-0039
Tel: 505-424-1954 *Toll Free Tel:* 800-227-0949 *Fax:* 505-424-1956
E-mail: tufnut@tufnut.com
Web Site: www.tufnut.com
Key Personnel
Pres: Roland C Zinn
Founded: 1977
Security systems to prevent theft of video & computer systems.
Catalog(s) available

Turner Broadcasting System Inc
One CNN Ctr, Atlanta, GA 30303
Tel: 404-827-1700
Web Site: www.turner.com
Key Personnel
Chmn: Phil Kent
CEO: John Martin
CFO & EVP: John E Kampfe
CTO & EVP: Scott Teissler
EVP: Kelly Regal
VP, Community Rel & Govt Aff: Steve Smith
VP & Gen Coun: Louise Sams

Turner Engineering Inc
14 Morris Ave, Mountain Lakes, NJ 07046-1433
Tel: 973-263-1000 *Fax:* 973-334-1620
E-mail: adair@turnereng.com
Web Site: www.turnereng.com
Key Personnel
Principal & Owner: John J Turner, Jr
Founded: 1967
Membership(s): MCA-I; NAB; SMPTE

TV Crews
2135-B Defoor Hills Rd, Atlanta, GA 30318
Tel: 404-351-8898 *Toll Free Tel:* 800-TV-CREWS (882-7397) *Fax:* 404-351-8893
E-mail: info@tvcrews.com
Web Site: www.tvcrews.com
Key Personnel
Pres: James Jernigan
Catalog(s) available
Membership(s): MCA-I; NAB

TV Juice Productions Inc
PO Box 843, Kilauea, HI 96754-0843
Tel: 808-828-0101; 808-828-0434
E-mail: fido@tvjuice.com
Web Site: www.tvjuice.com
Key Personnel
Pres: Susan LeHoven
Contact: Tony LeHoven
Audio & video production company.

TV One Multimedia Solutions
2791 Circleport Dr, Erlanger, KY 41018
Tel: 859-282-7303 *Toll Free Tel:* 800-721-4044 *Fax:* 859-282-8225
E-mail: sales@tvone.com; info@tvone.com
Web Site: www.tvone.com
Key Personnel
VP: Daniel D Gibson *E-mail:* dan.gibson@tvone.com
Manufacturer of video components.
Catalog(s) available
Branch Office(s)
6991 NW 82 Ave, No 8, Miami, FL 33166 *E-mail:* sales.latinoamerica@tvone.com *Web Site:* www.tvonela.com
Foreign Office(s): TV One China Beijing, Zhucheng Bldg, Rm 1902, No 6, Zhongguancun South St, Haidan District, Beijing 100081, China *Tel:* (010) 5158-2163 *Fax:* (010) 5158-2215 *E-mail:* sales.china@tvone.com *Web Site:* www.tvonechina.com
TV One China Shanghai, Golden Peach Bldg, Rm 1007, No 1900 Shangcheng Rd, Pudong, Shanghai 200120, China *Tel:* (021) 5830-2960 *Fax:* (021) 5851-7949 *E-mail:* sales.china@tvone.com *Web Site:* www.tvonechina.com
TV One China Shenzhen, Hangtian Liye Huating, Rm 2501, Zhenhua Rd, Futian District, Shenzhen 518031, China *Tel:* (0755) 83266685 *Fax:* (0755) 83266685 *E-mail:* sales.china@tvone.com *Web Site:* www.tvonechina.com
TV One Asia, 16F-4, No 75 Sec 1, Xintai Fifth Rd, Xizhi District, New Taipei City 22101, Taiwan *Tel:* (02) 2698-2296 *Fax:* (02) 2698-2297 *E-mail:* sales.asia@tvone.com *Web Site:* www.tvoneasia.com
Arcadia House, 1st fl, 15 Forlease Rd, Maidenhead, Berks SL6 1RX, United Kingdom *Tel:* (01628) 566820 *Fax:* (01628) 566821 *E-mail:* info.europe@tvone.com *Web Site:* www.tvone.eu
Membership(s): ICTA; InfoComm International®; NAB

TV Pro Gear
1630 Flower St, Glendale, CA 91201
Tel: 818-246-7100 *Fax:* 818-246-1945
Web Site: www.tvprogear.com
Key Personnel
CEO & Pres: Andrew Maisner *E-mail:* andy@tvprogear.com
Founded: 1998
Build TV & production studios & video trucks. Sell professional TV equipment.

TV Specialists Inc
180 E 2100 S, Salt Lake City, UT 84115
Tel: 801-486-5757 *Toll Free Tel:* 888-486-5757 *Fax:* 801-486-7566
E-mail: info@tvspecialists.com
Web Site: www.tvspecialists.com
Key Personnel
VP, Sales: Ted Bollinger *E-mail:* tedb@tvspecilists.com
Founded: 1953
Sales, rentals & service of professional production video & display technology including Sony, JVC & Panasonic broadcast products.
Catalog(s) available

TVA Productions
Subsidiary of The Video Agency Inc
3950 Vantage Ave, Studio City, CA 91604
Tel: 818-505-8300 *Toll Free Tel:* 888-322-4296
E-mail: info@tvaproductions.com
Web Site: www.tvaproductions.com
Key Personnel
CEO & Founder: Jeffery Goddard
CFO & Partner: Laura Tu
Sr Dir & Ed: Mark Mannschreck
Founded: 1987
Syndicated programming.
Membership(s): Television Academy

TVN-The Video Network
31 Cutler Dr, Ashland, MA 01721-1210
Tel: 508-881-1800
E-mail: info@tvnvideo.com
Web Site: www.tvnvideo.com
Key Personnel
CEO: Gregg C McAllister
Founded: 1987
Full service production.
Catalog(s) available

TVO/Ontario Educational Communications Authority (OECA)
2180 Yonge St, Toronto, ON M4S 2B9, Canada
Mailing Address: Box 200, Sta Q, Toronto, ON M4T 2T1, Canada
Tel: 416-484-2600; 416-484-2665 (cust rel) *Toll Free Tel:* 800-613-0513; 800-INFO-TVO (463-6886)
E-mail: asktvo@tvo.org
Web Site: tvo.org
Key Personnel
CEO: Lisa de Wilde
CFO & VP, Busn Devt: Paul Dancy
CTO: Todd Slivinskas
VP, Communs & Mktg: Andrew Steele
VP, Talent: Clara Arnold
Mng Dir, Content & Programming: Nancy Chapelle
Digital media organization specializing in educational media.
Catalog(s) available

Twentieth Century Fox Film Corp
Subsidiary of Fox Inc
10201 W Pico Blvd, Bldg 88, Rm 311, Los Angeles, CA 90035
Mailing Address: PO Box 900, Beverly Hills, CA 90213
Tel: 310-369-1000 *Fax:* 310-369-8825
Web Site: www.foxmovies.com
Key Personnel
EVP, Corp Commun: Chris Petrikin
Founded: 1935
One of the world's largest producers & distributors of motion picture entertainment.

21st Century Video Productions
890 S Higley Rd, Pahrump, NV 89048
Mailing Address: PO Box 2075, Pahrump, NV 89041
Tel: 775-727-9400 *Fax:* 775-727-8750
Web Site: www.kpvm.tv
Key Personnel
CEO & Pres: Vernon Van Winkle *E-mail:* videovern@kpvm.tv
Founded: 1986
Television station & production house.

24 Frames Film & Video
Division of Super Suite Digital Post & Transfer
15 Fourth Ave E, Vancouver, BC V5T 1E9, Canada
Tel: 604-877-2299 *Fax:* 604-877-2298
E-mail: info@24frames.ca
Web Site: www.24frames.ca
Key Personnel
CEO: Andy Nathani
Pres: Geoffrey Anthony

Twenty-Third Publications/Bayard
Division of Bayard Canada
One Montauk Ave, Suite 200, New London, CT 06320
Tel: 860-437-3012 *Toll Free Tel:* 800-321-0411; 877-944-5844 (subns) *Toll Free Fax:* 800-572-0788
E-mail: resources@pastoralplanning.com
Web Site: www.23rdpublications.com
Founded: 1967
Distribute & produce VHS, DVD & CDs. Produce adult & catechetical programming.
Catalog(s), annual, free

20/20 Communications Inc
10112 Voss Rd, Marengo, IL 60152
Tel: 847-364-7666 *Fax:* 847-364-7672
Web Site: www.2020communications.com
Key Personnel
Opers Mgr: Leona Haba *E-mail:* leona@2020communications.com
Founded: 1988
Full service producer & duplicator of sales, training, corporate & industrial videos, CD-ROMs & DVDs.

20k
3535 Blvd Ste-Anne, Suite 300, Quebec, QC G1E 3L6, Canada
Tel: 418-694-2220 *Toll Free Tel:* 855-933-2220
E-mail: info@20k.ca
Web Site: www.20k.ca
Consulting specialists in the field of arts & entertainment.

Twin Peaks Creative
445 W Seventh St, San Pedro, CA 90731
Tel: 310-832-3303
E-mail: postmaster@bestmedia.com
Web Site: www.twinpeakscreative.com
Key Personnel
Owner: Mary Jo Masters; Robert Masters *E-mail:* robert@bestmedia.com
Founded: 1983
Office also in Maui, HI.

Twin Sisters Productions LLC
4710 Hudson Dr, Stow, OH 44224
Toll Free Tel: 800-248-TWIN (248-8946) *Toll Free Fax:* 800-480-TWIN (480-8946)
E-mail: twinsisters@twinsisters.com
Web Site: www.twinsisters.com
Key Personnel
CEO: Karen Mitzo Hilderbrand
Pres: Kim Mitzo Thompson
SVP: Vince Douglas
Mktg Dir: Ken Carder *Tel:* 330-631-0362 *E-mail:* ken.carder@twinsisters.com
Founded: 1987
Children's educational company.
Catalog(s), annual, wholesale

Twisted Media Inc
1341 W Granville, Suite 1, Chicago, IL 60660
Tel: 773-856-6586
E-mail: info@twistedtracks.com
Web Site: www.twistedtracks.com
Key Personnel
Pres: Derek Frederickson *E-mail:* derek@twistedmedia.com
Founded: 2000
Professionally produced music.
Membership(s): ASCAP; BMI

Twistedtracks.com, see Twisted Media Inc

Two Animators LLP
PO Box 3174, Mercerville, NJ 08619
Tel: 609-532-6138
E-mail: cartoons@twoanimators.com
Web Site: www.twoanimators.com
Key Personnel
Creative Dir & Partner: Tom Costantini
Animation Dir & Partner: Joe Costantini
Founded: 2001
Animation production studio.

2BruceStudio
2 Wall St, Suite 119, Asheville, NC 28801
Tel: 828-255-2700
E-mail: info@2brucestudio.com
Web Site: 2brucestudio.com
Key Personnel
Owner: Bruce Sales
Founded: 2007
Twenty years of New York experience in the media & entertainment industries, specializing in original music composition, sound design & audio post for film, TV & all media.
Membership(s): ASCAP

Two Door Productions
416 N Harper Ave, Los Angeles, CA 90048
E-mail: shoot@usphotograph.com
Web Site: www.twodoorfx.com
Key Personnel
Dir: Diego Torroija
Writer/Prodr: Holly Payberg-Torroija
Line Prodr: Kathryn Claypool
Founded: 2002
Digital production company specializing in finding hi-tech visual solutions to suit all budgetary needs. Our goal is to offer creative options to communicate "Your Story" in an uncompromised way.

2BK9 Acting Animals
1470 Catherine Ave, Winnipeg, MB R3E 1V8, Canada
Tel: 204-338-1474; 204-997-9247 (cell)
Key Personnel
Animal Coord & Trainer: Jordan Fines
Provides quality animal talent & trainers.

Tyler Camera Systems
14218 Aetna St, Van Nuys, CA 91401
Tel: 818-989-4420 *Toll Free Tel:* 800-390-6070 *Fax:* 818-989-0423
E-mail: info@tylermount.com
Web Site: www.tylermount.com
Key Personnel
Owner: Liz Ziegler
Photography equipment.
Catalog(s) available

U-Direct Productions
10 White St, 1st fl, New York, NY 10013
Tel: 212-647-9200 *Fax:* 212-625-9400
E-mail: udirect@udirectnyc.com
Web Site: www.udirectnyc.com
Key Personnel
Founder & Dir: Daniel Miller *E-mail:* daniel@udirect.com
Founded: 1993
Independent film/video production company. Specialize Media 100, Digj-Beta, Beta, After Effects. Pre-production through post-production, on-air commercials & industrials.

U-Edit Video
1002 N Central Expwy, Suite 555, Richardson, TX 75080
Tel: 972-690-EDIT (690-3348) *Fax:* 214-884-3687
Web Site: www.ueditvideo.com
Key Personnel
Pres: Owen Benatar *E-mail:* owen@ueditvideo.com
Founded: 1973
Turnkey production from recording or mastering to final packaging.

Ultimate Presentation Systems Inc
901 S Hohokam Dr, Tempe, AZ 85281
Tel: 480-966-2000 *Toll Free Tel:* 800-866-4066 *Fax:* 480-968-3009
E-mail: sales@ult.com
Web Site: www.ult.com
Key Personnel
Pres: Diane Reese
VP: Michael Reese *E-mail:* mreese@ult.com
Professional AV sales & systems integration.
Catalog(s) available

Ultimate Support Systems Inc
5836 Wright Dr, Loveland, CO 80538
Toll Free Tel: 800-525-5628 *Fax:* 970-776-1941
E-mail: info@ultimatesupport.com
Web Site: www.ultimatesupport.com
Key Personnel
Dir, Mktg: Dan Hoeye *E-mail:* dan.hoeye@ultimatesupport.com
Founded: 1977
Invent, design & manufacture support solutions & music accessories for the music industry.
Catalog(s) available

Ultimatte Corp
20945 Plummer St, Chatsworth, CA 91311
Tel: 818-993-8007 *Fax:* 818-993-3762
E-mail: sales@ultimatte.com
Web Site: www.ultimatte.com
Key Personnel
CEO: Paul Vlahos
Pres: Lynne Sauve *E-mail:* lsauve@ultimatte.com
Brochure(s) available
Foreign Office(s): 1431 WL Aalsmeer, Netherlands *Tel:* (0297) 362 030 *E-mail:* europeansales@ultimatte.com
Membership(s): MCA-I; NAB; RTDNA; SMPTE

Ultralife Corporation
2000 Technology Pkwy, Newark, NY 14513
Tel: 315-332-7100 *Toll Free Tel:* 800-332-5000 (US & CN) *Fax:* 315-331-7800
E-mail: orders@ulbi.com
Web Site: ultralifecorporation.com
Founded: 1991
The Battery & Energy Products Unit provides a wide range of high-energy non-rechargeable & rechargeable power & charging systems for both defense & commercial applications.
The Communications Systems Unit Provides a single source for tactical communications solutions that support the warfighter & homeland security, from RF amplifiers, to power supplies, to antennas & accessory products for mission requirements.
Catalog(s) available

Ulysses Travel Guides Inc
4176 Rue St-Denis, Montreal, QC H2W 2M5, Canada
Tel: 514-843-9882 *Fax:* 514-843-9448
E-mail: info@ulysse.ca; st-denis@ulysse.ca
Web Site: www.ulysse.ca (French); www.ulyssesguides.com (English)
Key Personnel
Dir, Mktg & Sales: Olivier Gougeon
Travel guides in digital format.
Catalog(s) available
Foreign Office(s): Le Guides de Voyage Ulysses Sarl, 127 Rue Amelot, 75011 Paris, France *Tel:* 01 43 38 89 50 *Fax:* 01 43 38 89 52 *E-mail:* voyage@ulysse.ca
Membership(s): Canadian Booksellers Association; Reading Recovery Council of North America

Umbra of Newburgh LLC
9 Scobie Dr, Newburgh, NY 12550
Toll Free Tel: 855-536-6973 *Fax:* 845-569-9063
E-mail: info@umbranewburgh.com
Web Site: www.umbranewburgh.com
Film production facility.

UMCom Productions
Division of United Methodist Communications
810 12 Ave S, Nashville, TN 37203
Mailing Address: PO Box 320, Nashville, TN 37202-0320
Tel: 615-742-5400 *Fax:* 615-742-5469
E-mail: umcom@umcom.org
Web Site: www.umcom.org
Key Personnel
Dir, Prodn Servs: Harry Leake *Tel:* 615-742-5477 *E-mail:* hleake@umcom.org
Catalog(s) available

Uncharted Country Publishing
PO Box 756, Taos, NM 87571
Tel: 575-776-3470 *Toll Free Tel:* 800-488-4940
E-mail: ucp@taichihealth.com
Web Site: www.taichihealth.com
Key Personnel
Owner & Dir: Tricia Yu *E-mail:* tyu@taichihealth.com
Founded: 1999
Mind, body & health resources; Tai Chi & ROM Dance.

UND Television Center
Subsidiary of University of North Dakota Continuing Education
4300 James Ray Dr, Stop 7307, Grand Forks, ND 58202
Tel: 701-777-4346 *Toll Free Tel:* 800-CALL-UND (225-5863) *Fax:* 701-777-4342
E-mail: tv@und.edu
Web Site: www.und.nodak.edu/dept/tvcenter
Key Personnel
Dir, TV: Barry S Brode *E-mail:* barry.brode@und.edu

Ungar Video & Film
1001 Guilford, Medina, OH 44256
Tel: 216-661-5090
E-mail: donungarvideo@yahoo.com
Key Personnel
Pres: Donald Ungar

Uniconn Productions
8485 Valley Circle Blvd, Suite 203, West Hills, CA 91304
Tel: 818-887-9108 *Fax:* 818-348-6544
E-mail: measeburl@aol.com
Web Site: www.uniconnproductions.com
Key Personnel
Owner: Michael P Connelly
Founded: 1988
Stop-motion & CGI animation production company that provides animation for the TV, film & music video industries.

Unifour Productions Inc
25 First Ave NE, Suite 105, Hickory, NC 28601
Tel: 828-324-1314 *Toll Free Tel:* 888-843-8644 *Fax:* 828-324-1318
Web Site: www.uni4.com
Key Personnel
Pres: Ray Gantt *E-mail:* ray@uni4.com
Founded: 1981

Unilux Inc
59 N Fifth St, Saddle Brook, NJ 07663
Tel: 201-712-1266 *Toll Free Tel:* 800-522-0801 (US only) *Fax:* 201-712-1366
Web Site: www.unilux.com
Key Personnel
Mgr: Earl Wallace *E-mail:* earl.wallace@unilux.com
Founded: 1962
Stroboscopic lighting equipment for film & video production.
Foreign Office(s): Unilux China, 1081-1089 Pudong Ave, Apt 10-B, Shanghai 200135, China, Contact: Joe Zhao *Tel:* (021) 68552511 *Fax:* (021) 68552511 *E-mail:* joezhao@unilux.com
Unilux EMEA, Seeweg 20, 40627 Duesseldorf, Germany, Contact: Volker Schlevoigt *Tel:* (0211) 28071171 *Fax:* (0211) 28071177 *E-mail:* vschlevoigt@unilux.com
Unilux Asia, 179/177 Sualai Place, Sukhumvit Soi 39, Bangkok 10110, Thailand, Contact: Kirk Neil *Tel:* (06) 977-1303 *Fax:* (02) 662-0022 *E-mail:* kirk@unilux.com

Union Connector Co Inc
8182 Baymeadow Way W, Jacksonville, FL 32256
Tel: 631-753-9550 *Fax:* 631-753-9560
E-mail: sales@unionconnector.com
Web Site: www.unionconnector.com
Key Personnel
Pres: Raymond Wolpert
Membership(s): International Association of Assembly Managers; International Independent Showman's Federation; Professional Lighting & Sound Association; USITT

Unique Business Systems
1100 Colorado Ave, Santa Monica, CA 90401
Tel: 310-396-3929 *Toll Free Tel:* 800-669-4827 *Fax:* 310-396-6114
E-mail: sales@unibiz.com
Web Site: www.unibiz.com
Key Personnel
Dir, Busn Devt: Victrim Khosla
Founded: 1982

Unique Communications Ltd
2232 Pegasus Way NE, Calgary, AB T2E 8M5, Canada
Tel: 403-250-3763 *Toll Free Tel:* 800-661-8575 *Fax:* 403-250-2604
Web Site: www.uniquecommunications.ca
Key Personnel
Pres: Dave Ruff *E-mail:* daver@uniquecommunications.ca
Founded: 1981
Membership(s): AES; InfoComm International®; NSCA

UniSat, see Universal Satellite Communications Inc

Uniset Co LLC
449 Avenue "A", Rochester, NY 14621
Tel: 585-544-3820 *Fax:* 585-544-1110
E-mail: info@unisetcorp.com
Web Site: www.unisetcorp.com
Key Personnel
Co-Owner & Pres: Sean Martin
Co-Owner: Brian McKinnon
Founded: 1966
Manufacture studio settings/cycloramas/new settings.
Online catalog(s) available
Membership(s): Alliance for Community Media; NAB; RTDNA

United Audio Video Group Inc
6855 Vineland Ave, North Hollywood, CA 91605
Tel: 818-980-6700 *Toll Free Tel:* 800-247-8606 *Fax:* 818-508-8273
Web Site: www.unitedavg.com
Founded: 1972
Catalog(s) available
Membership(s): AES

United Nations Department of Public Information-News & Media Division
405 E 42 St, Rm IN-913B, New York, NY 10017
Tel: 917-367-5007
E-mail: mediapartnerships@un.org
Web Site: www.un.org
Key Personnel
Chief, Partnerships Unit: Ms Fang Chen
Chief, Multimedia Resources Unit: Antonio Carlos de Silva
AV library holds a unique collection of raw audio & video footage which is used by film & video producers who wish to produce documentaries on the work of the United Nations.
Brochure(s) available

United Nations Multimedia Resources Unit
c/o Audio Library, UN Dept of Public Information, Rm S-1046 & S-1083, New York, NY 10017
Tel: 212-963-9268; 212-963-4501 *Fax:* 212-963-4501
E-mail: avlibrary@un.org
Web Site: www.unmultimedia.org
Key Personnel
Acting Chief, Partnerships & Exec Prodr, News & Media Div: Andi Gitow
International organization, produce & promote their own radio & TV programs to broadcasters worldwide.
Catalog(s) available

United Sound & Electronics
525 E Main St, Bridgeport, WV 26330
Tel: 304-842-6030
E-mail: questions@unitedsound.net
Web Site: www.unitedsound.net
Key Personnel
CEO: Rob Harold *E-mail:* rob@unitedsound.net
Event Prodn: Jeremy Harold *E-mail:* jeremy@unitedsound.net
Founded: 1934
Concerts, production stages, lighting & full sound.

United Way Worldwide
701 N Fairfax St, Alexandria, VA 22314-2045
Tel: 703-836-7112 *Fax:* 703-519-0097
Web Site: www.unitedway.org
Key Personnel
CEO & Pres: Brian A Gallagher
CFO & EVP: Robert Berdelle
Chief Mktg Offr: Vicki Lins
Catalog(s) available

Unitron Ltd
73 Mall Dr, Commack, NY 11725
Tel: 631-543-2000 *Fax:* 631-589-6975
E-mail: info@unitronusa.com
Web Site: www.unitronusa.com

Key Personnel
Sales: Peter Indrigo *E-mail:* peterd@unitronusa.com
Mktg Support: Jeane P Miller *E-mail:* jeane@unitronusa.com
Founded: 1952
Online catalog(s) available

Univenture Inc
13311 Industrial Pkwy, Marysville, OH 43040
Tel: 937-645-4600 *Toll Free Tel:* 877-831-9428 *Fax:* 937-645-4700
E-mail: sales@univenture.com; orders@univenture.com
Web Site: www.univenture.com
Key Personnel
Founder & CEO: Ross O Youngs
CFO: Larry George
Cont: Tim O'Brien
Pres: Michele Cole
Dir, IT & E-Commerce: Mike Rader
Founded: 1988
Design & manufacture media packaging for leading companies in the entertainment, software & publishing industries.
Catalog(s), free, Information Management Specialties (IMS)
Catalog(s), free, FlexPak
Catalog(s), free, Resource Guide

Universal Audio Inc
4585 Scotts Valley Dr, Scotts Valley, CA 95066
Tel: 831-466-3737 *Toll Free Tel:* 866-823-1176; 877-698-2834 (tech support) *Fax:* 831-461-1550
E-mail: info@uaudio.com
Web Site: www.uaudio.com
Key Personnel
Mktg Mgr: Dan Fulop
Founded: 1958
Catalog(s) available
Membership(s): AES; NAMM, the National Association of Music Merchants

Universal Images
Subsidiary of GTA Inc
20750 Civic Center Dr, Suite 100, Southfield, MI 48076
Tel: 248-357-4160
Founded: 1984
Membership(s): The Adcraft Club of Detroit

Universal Music Group
2220 Colorado Ave, Santa Monica, CA 90404
Tel: 310-865-5000
Web Site: www.universalmusic.com
Recorded music, music publishing & merchandising.
Branch Office(s)
1755 Broadway, New York, NY 10019 *Tel:* 212-841-8000 *Fax:* 212-840-9390

Universal Radio Inc
6830 Americana Pkwy, Reynoldsburg, OH 43068
Tel: 614-866-4267 *Toll Free Tel:* 800-431-3939 (orders) *Fax:* 614-866-2339
E-mail: dx@universal-radio.com
Web Site: www.universal-radio.com
Key Personnel
Pres: Fred Osterman *E-mail:* osterman@dxing.com
Founded: 1942
Catalog(s), annual

Universal Rehearsal
17 W 20 St, Suite 4-W, New York, NY 10011
Tel: 212-929-3277
E-mail: univ318277@aol.com
Web Site: www.universalrehearsalnyc.com
Key Personnel
Owner & Off Mgr: Heidi Fenster
Founded: 1973
Music rehearsal studio. Rent studio & equipment by the hour.

Universal Satellite Communications Inc
1530 Nandina Ave, Perris, CA 92571
Tel: 562-483-4800; 951-943-4420 (corp off) *Toll Free Tel:* 888-867-6620 *Fax:* 954-943-0263
Web Site: www.unisatmobile.com
Key Personnel
Pres: Juan Renteria *E-mail:* juan@unisatmobile.com
EVP: George L Edwardz *E-mail:* george@unisatmobile.com
Mktg & Client Servs: Julie C Ragozzino *E-mail:* julie@unisatmobile.com
Fully integrated supplier of television logistics, production & transmission services, including satellite uplinks, downlinks, fiber, microwave, digital provisions, full production, editing, ENG packages & logistical planning.
Branch Office(s)
13426 Rosecrans Ave, Unit C, Norwalk, CA 90650

Universal Studios
100 Universal City Plaza, Universal City, CA 91608-1002
Toll Free Tel: 800-892-1979 *Fax:* 818-866-3600
E-mail: studio.operations2@nbcuni.com
Web Site: www.filmmakersdestination.com; www.nbcuni.com
Key Personnel
Pres, Studio Opers: Michael Moore
SVP, Mktg & Publicity: Jeanne Cordova
Founded: 1912
Production & post-production services for film, television & commercials.

Universal Studios Canada Inc
2450 Victoria Park Ave, Willowdale, ON M2J 4A2, Canada
Tel: 416-491-3000
Web Site: www.universalpictures.ca
Key Personnel
EVP: Ron Suter
Catalog(s) available

Universal Studios Florida® Production Group
1000 Universal Studios Plaza, Bldg 22-A, Orlando, FL 32819
Tel: 407-363-8400 *Toll Free Tel:* 877-612-3737 (outside FL) *Fax:* 407-363-8869
E-mail: productiongroup@universalorlando.com
Web Site: www.universalstudios.com/studio/florida
Key Personnel
VP & Gen Mgr: Pamela Tuscany-Wines

Universal Studios Home Entertainment
Division of NBC Universal Studios
10 Universal City Plaza, 4th fl, Universal City, CA 91608
Tel: 818-777-5159 *Fax:* 818-866-3330
Web Site: www.universalstudiosentertainment.com
Catalog(s) available
Branch Office(s)
Universal Music Distribution, 303 N Glenoaks Blvd, Burbank, CA 91502
1755 Broadway, 8th fl, New York, NY 10022, Contact: Bill Hickman *Tel:* 212-841-8000
Membership(s): Content Delivery & Storage Association; Entertainment Merchants Association; Motion Picture Association of America; National Association of Video Distributors; RIAA

Universal Training
736 N Western Ave, Suite 323, Lake Forest, IL 60045
Tel: 847-235-2170
Web Site: www.universaltraining.com
Key Personnel
Pres: John C Doyle
Founded: 1968
Catalog(s) available
Membership(s): ATD; International Society for Performance and Instruction

Universe Kogaku America Inc
116 Audrey Ave, Oyster Bay, NY 11771
Tel: 516-624-2444 *Fax:* 516-624-3109
E-mail: info@universeoptics.com
Web Site: universeoptics.com
Key Personnel
Pres: Mike Ohtsuki
Off Mgr: Mike Caruso
Founded: 1949
UV quartz lenses & lens design for electronic, optics, medical & precision industrial applications.
Catalog(s) available
Foreign Office(s): Universe Optical Industries Co Ltd, 2729 Inatomi, Tatsuno-Machi, Kamiina, Nagano 399-0428, Japan *Tel:* (0266) 41-0262 *Fax:* (0266) 41-2084 *Web Site:* www.universekk.com
Membership(s): AIIM; Photo Marketing Association; SPIE

University Media Services
University of Delaware, 85 E Delaware Ave, Newark, DE 19716
Tel: 302-831-3546; 302-831-3557 *Fax:* 302-831-3642
Web Site: www.ums.udel.edu; www.udel.edu/ums
Key Personnel
Mgr: Jason Atkinson
Catalog(s) available
Membership(s): AMCEE; AMS; National Association for Music Education; NVTN

University of Florida, Warrington College of Business Administration
100 BRY, Gainesville, FL 32611
Mailing Address: PO Box 117150, Gainesville, FL 32611-7150
Tel: 352-392-2397 *Fax:* 352-392-2086
E-mail: ufwcba@warrington.ufl.edu
Web Site: www.cba.ufl.edu
Key Personnel
Video Prodn: Christopher Smith *Tel:* 352-294-7804 *E-mail:* christopher.smith@warrington.ufl.edu

University of Idaho Engineering Outreach
875 Perimeter Dr MS 1014, Moscow, ID 83844-1014
Tel: 208-885-6373 *Toll Free Tel:* 800-824-2889 *Fax:* 208-885-9249
E-mail: outreach@uidaho.edu
Web Site: eo.uidaho.edu
Key Personnel
Assoc Dean: Barry Willis
State university (accredited). Provide online & DVD programming.
Catalog(s) available

University of Maine Audio Visual Services
28 Shibles Hall, Orono, ME 04469
Tel: 207-581-2500; 207-581-2516
Web Site: www.umaine.edu/it/divisions/av
Key Personnel
Mgr: Cliff Fletcher *E-mail:* clifton.fletcher@umit.maine.edu
Exec Dir, IT: John Gregory *Tel:* 207-581-1602 *E-mail:* john.gregory@umaine.edu
Media Servs Technician: Nick Robbins *E-mail:* nicolas.robbins@umit.maine.edu
Membership(s): Consortium of College & University Media Centers

University of Memphis, Music Industry Division
Music Bldg, Rm 123, 3775 Central Ave, Memphis, TN 38152-3160
Tel: 901-678-2559; 901-678-2541
E-mail: music@memphis.edu
Web Site: www.memphis.edu/music/index.php
Key Personnel
Div Head: Jeff Cline *E-mail:* jwcline@memphis.edu
Catalog(s) available
Membership(s): AES; MEIEA; SPARS

University of Michigan, Center for Middle Eastern & North African Studies
1080 S University, Suite 3603, Ann Arbor, MI 48109-1106
Tel: 734-647-4143 *Fax:* 734-936-0996
E-mail: cmenas@umich.edu
Web Site: www.ii.umich.edu/cmenas
Key Personnel
Dir: Juan Cole *E-mail:* jrcole@umich.edu

University of Missouri-Columbia
Film & Video Library, 505 E Stewart Rd, Columbia, MO 65211-2040
Tel: 573-882-3608 *Fax:* 573-882-6110
E-mail: asc@missouri.edu
Web Site: asc.missouri.edu
Key Personnel
Dir: Sue Hollingsworth *Tel:* 573-882-2801 *E-mail:* video@missouri.edu

University of Missouri-Kansas City School of Dentistry
650 E 25 St, Kansas City, MO 64108
Tel: 816-235-2100 *Fax:* 816-235-5001
Web Site: dentistry.umkc.edu

University of Oklahoma Academic Media & Digital Services
Affiliate of Health Sciences Center
1000 Stanton L Young Blvd, Rm 251, Oklahoma City, OK 73117
Tel: 405-271-2318
E-mail: amds@ouohsc.edu
Web Site: www.ouhsc.edu/amds
Lecture capture, videoconferencing, video production, poster printing & AV design/installation services.
Catalog(s) available

University of South Carolina Press
1600 Hampton St, Colimbia, SC 29208
Tel: 803-777-5243 *Toll Free Tel:* 800-768-2500 *Toll Free Fax:* 800-868-0740
Web Site: www.sc.edu/uscpress
Key Personnel
Dir: Jonathan Haupt *Tel:* 803-777-2243 *E-mail:* jhaupt@mailbox.sc.edu
Asst to Dir: Vicki Bates *Tel:* 803-777-5245 *E-mail:* batesvc@mailbox.sc.edu
Founded: 1944
Catalog(s) available
Shipping Address: 718 Devine St, Columbia, SC 29208

University of Southern California
Davidson Continuing Educ Conference Ctr, Rm 103, 3415 S Figueroa St, Los Angeles, CA 90089-0871
Tel: 213-740-5956; 213-740-5679 *Fax:* 213-740-9366
Web Site: hospitality.usc.edu/catering
Key Personnel
Dir, Hospitality: Dirk De Jong
Dir, Mktg & Training: Erika Chesley *E-mail:* erika.chesley@usc.edu
Catalog(s) available

University of Texas at Austin - Petroleum Extension Service
J J Pickle Research Campus, Petroleum Extension Service, Bldg 2, 10100 Burnet Rd, Austin, TX 78758-4445
Mailing Address: One University Sta, R8100, Austin, TX 78712-1100
Tel: 512-471-5940 *Toll Free Tel:* 800-687-4132 *Fax:* 512-471-9410 *Toll Free Fax:* 800-687-7839
E-mail: petex@www.utexas.edu
Web Site: www.utexas.edu/ce/petex
Key Personnel
Dir: Zahid Yoosufani *E-mail:* zahidy@austin.utexas.edu
Sr Fin Analyst: Rick Garza *E-mail:* rgarza64@mail.utexas.edu
Catalog(s) available
Branch Office(s)
The University of Texas, 4702 N Sam Houston Pkwy W, Suite 800, Houston, TX 77086, Dir: Judy Camerano *Tel:* 281-397-2440 *E-mail:* jcamerano@austin.utexas.edu

University of Toronto, Classroom Technology Support
Saint George Campus, McMurrich Bldg, 4th fl, 12 Queen's Park Crescent W, Toronto, ON M5S 1S8, Canada
Tel: 416-978-6544 *Fax:* 416-978-4802
E-mail: avrequests@utoronto.ca
Web Site: www.osm.utoronto.ca
Key Personnel
Traffic Coord: David Carinci
Providing AV support for classroom teaching.
Catalog(s) available

University of Vermont, Instructional Television Dept
Affiliate of Libraries & Learning Resources
234 Rowell Bldg, Burlington, VT 05405
Tel: 802-656-2927 *Fax:* 802-656-8816
E-mail: video@zoo.uvm.edu
Web Site: www.uvm.edu; www.uvm.edu/~video
Key Personnel
Dir: Wes Graff *Tel:* 802-656-2927 ext 64213 *E-mail:* wgraff@zoo.uvm.edu
Videographer: Eric Melton *Tel:* 802-656-2927 ext 68724 *E-mail:* emelton@zoo.uvm.edu
Broadcast Engr: Foster Nye *Tel:* 802-656-2927 ext 60565 *E-mail:* fnye@zoo.uvm.edu
Professional broadcast video production facility.
Catalog(s) available

University of Wisconsin-Oshkosh Radio-TV-Film Dept
Arts & Communications Bldg, W-112, 800 Algoma Blvd, Oshkosh, WI 54901
Tel: 920-424-3131 *Fax:* 920-424-7041
E-mail: rtf@uwosh.edu
Web Site: www.uwosh.edu/rtf
Key Personnel
Dir, Radio Servs: Randall Davidson *E-mail:* davidsor@uwosh.edu
Dir, TV Servs: Justine Stokes *Tel:* 920-424-3133 *E-mail:* stokesj@uwosh.edu
Membership(s): Media Communications Association; National Broadcasting Society

University Products Inc
517 Main St, Holyoke, MA 01040-0073
Mailing Address: PO Box 101, Holyoke, MA 01041-0101
Tel: 413-532-3372 *Toll Free Tel:* 800-628-1912 *Fax:* 413-532-9281 *Toll Free Fax:* 800-532-9281
E-mail: custserv@universityproducts.com; info@universityproducts.com
Web Site: www.universityproducts.com
Key Personnel
Pres & COO: Scott E Magoon
VP & Gen Mgr: John A Dunphy
Founded: 1968
Catalog(s) available
Membership(s): ALA; Education Market Association

UPN 20 WDCA-TV
Division of Fox Television Stations Inc
5151 Wisconsin Ave NW, 2nd fl, Washington, DC 20016
Tel: 202-244-5151
Web Site: www.my20dc.com
Key Personnel
Gen Mgr: Patrick Paolini
Catalog(s) available
Membership(s): Independent Media Producers Association; Independent TV Association

Upstage Video
212 Shoemaker Rd, Pottstown, PA 19464
Tel: 610-323-7200 *Toll Free Tel:* 877-484-3887 *Fax:* 484-727-9056
E-mail: info@upstagevideo.com
Web Site: www.upstagevideo.com
Key Personnel
Pres: Doug Murray
Natl Sales Dir: Brian Tyson
Natl Sales Rep: Vince Kershner
Founded: 2001
Rent LED video screens.
Branch Office(s)
25601 Ave Stanford, Valencia, CA 91355 *Tel:* 818-651-2000 *E-mail:* ed@upstagevideo.com
1350 Pine St, Suite 3, Boulder, CO 80302 *Tel:* 305-742-8095 *E-mail:* dave@upstagevideo.com

Urbanski Film
PO Box 438, Orland Park, IL 60462-0438
Tel: 708-460-9082 *Fax:* 708-460-9099
E-mail: info@urbanskifilm.com
Web Site: www.urbanskifilm.com
Key Personnel
Pres: Larry Urbanski
Online lists available.

US Case Corp
6301 J Richard Dr, Raleigh, NC 27617
Tel: 919-783-6166 *Toll Free Tel:* 800-648-8474 *Fax:* 919-783-0740
E-mail: customersupport@uscase.com
Web Site: www.uscase.com
Key Personnel
VP & Sales Mgr: Jeff Hines *E-mail:* jeffhines@uscase.com
Gen Mgr: Brad Blumeyer *E-mail:* bradblumeyer@uscase.com
Founded: 1988

US Holocaust Memorial Museum
100 Raoul Wallenberg Place SW, Washington, DC 20024-2126
Tel: 202-488-0400 *Fax:* 202-488-2695
E-mail: membership@ushmm.org
Web Site: www.ushmm.org
Key Personnel
Dir, Memberships: Dana Weinstein
Catalog(s) available

USA Studios
253 W 35 St, 2nd fl, New York, NY 10001
Tel: 212-398-6400 *Fax:* 212-398-4145
E-mail: sales@usastudios.tv; info@usastudios.tv
Web Site: www.usastudios.tv
Key Personnel
Owner & Mktg Dir: Kenny Khan
HD duplications & TV commercials.

USAV Group Inc
5485 S Westridge Dr, New Berlin, WI 53151-7948

Tel: 262-814-2000 *Toll Free Tel:* 800-596-USAV (596-8728) *Fax:* 262-814-2006
Web Site: www.usavgroup.com
Key Personnel
Pres: Andy Fields *E-mail:* afields@usavgroup.com
Acct Mgr: Pete Balistrieri *E-mail:* pbalistrieri@usavgroup.com

USCCB Publishing
Division of United States Conference of Catholic Bishops
3211 Fourth St NE, Washington, DC 20017
Tel: 202-541-3090 *Toll Free Tel:* 800-235-8722 (cust serv) *Fax:* 202-722-8709 (cust serv)
E-mail: publications@usccb.org
Web Site: www.usccbpublishing.org
Key Personnel
Dir: Matthew Kilmurry
Assoc Dir, Devt: David Felber
Assoc Dir, Perms: Mary E Sperry
Catalog(s) available

USDA/FSA Aerial Photography Field Office
2222 W 2300 S, Salt Lake City, UT 84119-2020
Tel: 801-844-2922 *Toll Free Fax:* 855-415-2014
E-mail: apfo.sales@slc.usda.gov
Web Site: www.apfo.usda.gov
Key Personnel
Dir: Ronald Nicholls
Mgmt Opers: Denny Skiles
Aerial imagery.

Ushio America Inc
Subsidiary of Ushio Inc (Japan)
5440 Cerritos Ave, Cypress, CA 90630-4567
Tel: 714-236-8600 *Toll Free Tel:* 800-838-7446 (cust serv) *Fax:* 714-229-3180
Toll Free Fax: 800-776-3641 (cust serv)
E-mail: customerservice@ushio.com
Web Site: www.ushio.com
Key Personnel
CEO & Pres: Shingi Kameda
Founded: 1967
Catalog(s) available

USI Inc
98 Fort Path Rd, Suite A, Madison, CT 06443
Tel: 203-245-8586 *Toll Free Tel:* 800-282-9290
Fax: 203-245-8619
E-mail: customers@usi-corp.com
Web Site: www.usi-laminate.com
Key Personnel
Pres: Peter Gianacoplos
Founded: 1975
Catalog(s) available

USMotivation
7840 Roswell Rd, USM Bldg 100, 3rd fl, Atlanta, GA 30350
Tel: 770-290-4700 *Toll Free Tel:* 800-476-0496
Fax: 770-290-4701
E-mail: information@usmotivation.com
Web Site: www.usmotivation.com
Key Personnel
Sales: Scott Siebert

Utah Scientific Inc
4750 Wiley Post Way, Suite 150, Salt Lake City, UT 84116
Tel: 801-575-8801 *Toll Free Tel:* 800-453-8782
Fax: 801-537-3099
E-mail: info@utahscientific.com
Web Site: www.utahscientific.com
Key Personnel
Dir, Mktg: Scott Bosen *Tel:* 801-575-3770
E-mail: sbosen@utahscientific.com
Founded: 1977

Utopia Films
1976 S La Cienega Blvd, No 130, Los Angeles, CA 90034
Tel: 310-338-0580 *Fax:* 313-557-0580
E-mail: reception@utopiafilms.com; utopiafilms2@gmail.com (large e-mails); production@utopiafilms.com (reels)
Web Site: utopiafilms.com
Key Personnel
Exec Prodr: Howard Cohen *E-mail:* hcohen@utopiafilms.com
Intl Prodr: Justin Bird *Tel:* 877-784-2739
E-mail: jbird@utopiafilms.com
Founded: 1997
Commercial, music video, motion picture & photo production services.
Foreign Office(s): Av Princess Isabel 150, Suite 903, 22011-010 Rio de Janeiro-RJ, Brazil
Tel: (021) 2244 2271 *Fax:* (021) 2244 3841
Calle El Servicio Parque Res, Valle Arriba, Santa Fe-Sur Edificio, Campomanes, Suite 2E, Caracas 1060, Venezuela *Tel:* (0212) 720 2197

Vaddio
131 Cheshire Lane, Suite 500, Minnetonka, MN 55305
Tel: 763-971-4400 *Toll Free Tel:* 800-572-2011
Fax: 763-971-4464
E-mail: info@vaddio.com
Web Site: www.vaddio.com
Key Personnel
CEO: Ed Ellett *E-mail:* ellett@vaddio.com
Pres: Rob Sheeley *E-mail:* rsheeley@vaddio.com
VP, Sales: Tim Henry *E-mail:* thenry@vaddio.com
Mktg & Communs: Hailey Klein
E-mail: hklein@vaddio.com
Founded: 2005
Leading designer & OEM distributor of specialty PTZ cameras & high-end camera control systems used in the broadcasting, AV & videoconferencing industries. Headquartered in Minneapolis, MN, we also have operations throughout the Americas as well as sales & support partners throughout the world.
Membership(s): IABM; InfoComm International®; NAB; NSCA

Valencia Studios
26030 Avenue Hall, Studio 5, Valencia, CA 91355
Tel: 661-702-9102
E-mail: info@valenciastudios.com
Web Site: www.valenciastudios.com
Key Personnel
Stage Mgr: Suzanne Burr
Full service independent TV & film production facility offering sound stages & attached production offices.

Valley Media
421 Roanoke Dr, Martinez, CA 94553-6240
Tel: 925-937-5207; 510-612-5215 (cell)
Web Site: www.valleymedia.com
Key Personnel
Prodr & Dir: Bob Briggs *E-mail:* bobriggs@valleymedia.com
Founded: 1979
Producer & director of videos.

Valley of the Sun Publishing Co
Division of The Sutphen Center
PO Box 2053, Sedona, AZ 86339
Tel: 928-554-1333
E-mail: info@dicksutphen.com
Web Site: www.dicksutphen.com
Key Personnel
Owner: Richard Sutphen
Online publisher of spiritual & human-potential self-help meditation & hypnosis programming ebooks, MP3s, CDs & DVDs.
Catalog(s) available
Membership(s): International Hypnosis Federation

Jack Van Impe Ministries International
1718 Northfield Dr, Rochester Hills, MI 48309
Mailing Address: PO Box 7004, Troy, MI 48007-7004
Tel: 248-852-2244; 248-852-5225 (orders)
Fax: 248-852-2692
E-mail: jvimi@jvim.com
Web Site: www.jvim.com
Key Personnel
Pres: Dr Jack Van Impe
Media Prodn Coord: Ken Muehlhoff
Branch Office(s)
PO Box 1717, Postal Sta A, Windsor, ON N9A 6Y1, Canada

Vancouver Film Studios Ltd
Division of The McLean Group
3500 Cornett Rd, Vancouver, BC V5M 2H5, Canada
Tel: 604-453-5000 *Fax:* 604-453-5045
Web Site: www.vancouverfilmstudios.com
Key Personnel
COO & Pres: Pete Mitchell
VP, Opers: Natasha Dickson
VP, Prodn Servs: Gerry Rutherford
VP, Sales & Mktg: Kimberlee Alexander
Production facilities for film & television production, including soundstages & production offices.

Vanguard Documentaries
PO Box 26635, Brooklyn, NY 11202
Tel: 347-725-1677
Web Site: www.vanguarddocumentaries.com
Key Personnel
Founder & Exec Prodr: Charles Hobson
E-mail: charleshobson@gmail.com
Film development & production company. Specialize in arts, cultural affairs & political documentaries.
Catalog(s) available

Vanner Inc
4282 Reynolds Dr, Hilliard, OH 43026
Tel: 614-771-2718 *Toll Free Tel:* 800-ACPOWER (227-6937) *Fax:* 614-771-4904
E-mail: info@vanner.com; pwrsales@vanner.com
Web Site: www.vanner.com
Key Personnel
VP, Sales & Mktg: Bruce Beegle *Tel:* 704-489-9793 *Fax:* 704-489-9216 *E-mail:* bruceb@vanner.com
Inside Sales Mgr: Darlene Dowell
Additional offices in Taylorsville, GA; Denver, NC; Columbus, OH.
Catalog(s) available

Vantage/Legrand
1061 S 800 E, Orem, UT 84097
Tel: 801-229-2800 *Toll Free Tel:* 800-555-9891
Fax: 801-224-0355
E-mail: vantage.info@vantagecontrols.com
Web Site: www.vantagecontrols.com
Designer & manufacturer of home control systems for luxury residences.
Catalog(s) available
Membership(s): Consumer Electronics Association; Continental Automated Buildings Association; Custom Electronic Design & Installation Association; ISO; US Green Building Council

Vantage Point Products Corp
PO Box 2485, Santa Fe Springs, CA 90670
Tel: 562-946-1718 *Toll Free Tel:* 888-886-6868
Fax: 562-946-3898
Web Site: www.thinkvp.com
Key Personnel
Off Mgr: John Silva
Founded: 1988

Manufacturer of stylish, well designed AV support products: TV mounts, LCD mounts, speaker stands, furniture, iPad stands & mounts.

Varese Sarabande Records Inc
9100 Wilshire Blvd, Suite 455E, Beverly Hills, CA 90212
Tel: 310-853-5400 *Toll Free Tel:* 800-827-3734
E-mail: info@varesesarabande.com; orders@varesesarabande.com
Web Site: www.varesesarabande.com
Key Personnel
Sales Mgr: Jeff Safran

Vari-Lite
Subsidiary of Philips Lighting Business Unit-Professional Luminaires North America
10911 Petal St, Dallas, TX 75238
Tel: 214-647-7880 *Toll Free Tel:* 877-VARILITE (877-827-4548) *Fax:* 214-647-8038
E-mail: entertainment.service@philips.com
Web Site: www.vari-lite.com
Key Personnel
North American Sales Mgr: Leonard Miller *E-mail:* leonard.miller@philips.com
Prod Segment Mgr: Brad Schiller *Tel:* 214-647-7980 *E-mail:* brad.schiller@philips.com
Founded: 1981
Designer, manufacturer & distributor of automated lighting products, systems & related products.
Online catalog(s) available
Membership(s): Professional Lighting & Sound Association; USITT

VariQuest Visual Learning Tools, see Varitronics LLC

Varitronic Systems, A Brady Business, see Varitronics LLC

Varitronics LLC
2355 Polaris Lane N, Suite 100, Plymouth, MN 55447
Tel: 763-536-6400 *Toll Free Tel:* 800-328-0585 *Toll Free Fax:* 800-543-8966
Web Site: www.variquest.com
Key Personnel
CEO & Pres: David Grey
Provides education technology solutions & visual support to improve academic progress & classroom engagement.

Varta Microbattery Inc
Subsidiary of Varta GmbH
555 Theodore Fremd Ave, Suite C304, Rye, NY 10580
Tel: 914-592-2500 *Toll Free Tel:* 800-468-2782 *Fax:* 914-345-0488
Web Site: www.varta-microbattery.com; www.varta-microbattery.us
Key Personnel
CEO & Pres: William Flanagan
CFO: James Bremner
Research, development, production & sales of high quality batteries & battery packs for electronic devices.
Catalog(s) available

Varto Technologies
195 Hackensack St, East Rutherford, NJ 07073
Toll Free Tel: 888-656-6233 *Fax:* 201-604-2661
E-mail: sales@vartotechnologies.com
Web Site: www.vartotechnologies.com
Founded: 1984
Design & integrate reliable, cost-effective audio, video, digital media & live broadcast solutions.

Mike Vasilinda Productions Inc
310 N Monroe St, Tallahassee, FL 32301
Mailing Address: PO Box 10004, Tallahassee, FL 32302-2004
Tel: 850-224-5420
Web Site: mvptv.tv
Key Personnel
SVP & Opers Mgr: Andy Bundschuh *E-mail:* andy@mvptv.tv

VCI Entertainment
Division of Blair & Associates Ltd
11333 E 60 Place, Tulsa, OK 74146-6828
Tel: 918-254-6337 *Toll Free Tel:* 800-331-4077 *Fax:* 918-254-6117
E-mail: vci@vcientertainment.com
Web Site: www.vcientertainment.com
Key Personnel
Pres: Robert A Blair *E-mail:* rablair@vcientertainment.com
VP: Don Blair
Catalog(s) available
Membership(s): Entertainment Merchants Association

VCom International Multimedia Corp
80 Little Falls Rd, Fairfield, NJ 07004
Toll Free Tel: 800-572-6373
E-mail: info@vcomimc.com
Web Site: www.vcomimc.com
Key Personnel
Pres: Shelly Goldstein
Founded: 1969
Catalog(s), annual

VCSvideo
2807 Hunterdon Dr, Cinnaminson, NJ 08077
Tel: 856-273-8800 *Toll Free Tel:* 877-VCS-VIDEO (827-8433)
Web Site: www.vcsvideo.com
Key Personnel
Principal & Prodr/Dir/Writer: David Fox
Principal & Prodr/Dir: Frank Siegel
Founded: 1979
Membership(s): MCA-I; NATAS; NATPE

VDO Lab Inc
400 Tarrytown Rd, White Plains, NY 10607-1314
Tel: 914-681-0849; 914-949-1741 *Fax:* 914-949-5743
E-mail: sales@vdolab.net
Web Site: vdolab.net
Key Personnel
Pres: Jeff Hass
Film & video transfer, DVD-CD duplicating & printing & packaging.

VDO Ltd, see GHO Group LLC

Vedanta Press & Catalog
Division of Vedanta Society of Southern California
1946 Vedanta Place, Hollywood, CA 90068
Tel: 323-960-1727 (bookstores); 323-960-1736 (outside US) *Toll Free Tel:* 800-816-2242
E-mail: info@vedanta.com
Web Site: www.vedanta.com
Key Personnel
Mgr: Robert Adjemian *Tel:* 323-960-1728 *E-mail:* bob@vedanta.org
Founded: 1934

Vedanta Society of St Louis
205 S Skinker Blvd, St Louis, MO 63105
Tel: 314-721-5118
Web Site: vedantastl.org
Key Personnel
Mgr: Swami Nirakarananda
Publish materials on Vedanta & comparative religion.
Flyer(s) available

Veetronix Inc
1311 W Pacific St, Lexington, NE 68850
Mailing Address: PO Box 480, Lexington, NE 68850-0480
Tel: 308-324-6661 *Toll Free Tel:* 800-445-0007 *Fax:* 308-324-4985
E-mail: sales@veetronix.com
Web Site: www.veetronix.com
Key Personnel
Sales Mgr: Roger Teeters
Manufacture push-button switches.
Catalog(s) available

Vela Research
5540 Rio Vista Dr, Clearwater, FL 33760-3107
Tel: 727-507-5300 *Fax:* 727-507-5312
E-mail: vela_info@vela.com
Web Site: www.vela.com
Key Personnel
VP, Fin: Kevin Donald
Dir, Intl Sales: Rick Powell *Tel:* 727-507-5367 *E-mail:* rpowell@vela.com
Founded: 1992
Provider of MPEG video encoding & decoding technology & products.
Online catalog(s), available for download
Membership(s): NAB; SCTE; SMPTE

Velodyne Acoustics Inc
345 Digital Dr, Morgan Hill, CA 95037
Tel: 408-465-2800 *Toll Free Tel:* 866-243-0789 *Fax:* 408-779-9227; 408-779-9208 (cust serv); 408-779-9377 (orders)
E-mail: service@velodyne.com; orders@velodyne.com
Web Site: www.velodyne.com
Key Personnel
Founder & CEO: David Hall
Cont: Houshang Vala
Pres: Marta Thoma Hall
EVP & Gen Mgr: George Ross
Founded: 1983
Universally recognized as the leading manufacturer of high performance, low distortion powered subwoofers at all price levels.
Data sheet(s) available

Venice Media Group
101 W Venice Ave, Unit 10, Venice, FL 34285
Tel: 941-485-0699
E-mail: info@venicemediagroup.com
Web Site: www.venicemediagroup.com
Video production services, TV commercials, web advertising, music videos, conversion & duplication services, photography, graphic design, audio recording studio.

Venture Media
902 Harvest Pointe Dr, Fort Mill, SC 29708
Tel: 803-547-3878
E-mail: info@venturemedia.tv
Web Site: www.venturemedia.tv
Key Personnel
CEO & Prodr: Kris Duffy
Pres & Dir: Jim Duffy *E-mail:* jim@venturemedia.tv
Founded: 1979
Provide creative development, writing, film & video production & multimedia services.
Online catalog(s) available

Ver Sales Inc
2509 N Naomi St, Burbank, CA 91504
Tel: 818-567-3000 *Toll Free Tel:* 800-229-0518; 800-300-WIRE (300-9479, CA only) *Fax:* 818-567-3018
E-mail: sales@versales.com
Web Site: www.versales.com
Key Personnel
VP, Opers: Craig Ryan
VP, Sales: Paul Ryan
Inside Sales: Vince Yanes

Founded: 1972
Lighting rental & fall protection safety, rigging & hardware.

VER-Video Equipment Rentals
912 Ruberta Ave, Glendale, CA 91201
Tel: 818-956-1444 *Toll Free Tel:* 800-794-1407 (cust serv); 888-584-TECH (584-8324) *Fax:* 818-241-4519
E-mail: rentals@verrents.com; info@verrents.com
Web Site: www.verrents.com
An equipment rental company with vast inventory in AV, audio, broadcast & computer equipment, creative LED & lighting.
Catalog(s), by request
Branch Office(s)
1655 S Claudina Way, Anaheim, CA 92805 *Tel:* 714-978-8811 *Toll Free Tel:* 866-837-7368 *Fax:* 714-978-8812
1048 Cudahy Place, San Diego, CA 92110 *Tel:* 619-299-8336 *Toll Free Tel:* 866-850-1860 *Fax:* 619-299-3350
410 E Grand Ave, South San Francisco, CA 94080 *Tel:* 650-837-9480 *Toll Free Tel:* 866-680-0250 *Fax:* 650-837-9488
4625 S 32nd St, Phoenix, AZ 85040 *Tel:* 602-268-8000 *Toll Free Tel:* 800-403-9567 *Fax:* 602-268-8014
5000 Dahlia St, Suite D, Denver, CO 80216 *Tel:* 303-355-5001 *Fax:* 303-355-5015
7060 State Rd 84, Suite 11, Davie, FL 33317 *Tel:* 954-723-2828 *Fax:* 954-723-2833
1611 Cypress Lake Dr, Orlando, FL 32837 *Tel:* 407-582-0350 *Toll Free Tel:* 888-582-0350 *Fax:* 407-582-0370
2105 Nancy Hanks Dr, Norcross, GA 30071 *Tel:* 770-300-0401 *Fax:* 770-300-0341
3810 N Carnation St, Franklin Park, IL 60131 *Tel:* 847-671-4966 *Fax:* 847-671-4936
3000 Lausat St, Metairie, LA 70001 *Tel:* 504-831-6966 *Fax:* 504-834-7537
4390 Parliament Place, Suite B, Lanham, MD 20706 *Tel:* 301-731-9560 *Toll Free Tel:* 866-583-7837 *Fax:* 301-731-9570
226 W Cummings Park, Woburn, MA 01801 *Tel:* 781-937-7612 *Toll Free Tel:* 866-255-4837 *Fax:* 781-937-0682
21304 Hilltop St, Southfield, MI 48034 *Tel:* 248-304-9749 *Fax:* 248-304-9926
3855 W Harmon Ave, Las Vegas, NV 89103 *Tel:* 702-895-9777 *Toll Free Tel:* 877-837-8342 *Fax:* 702-895-7377
620 12 Ave, 3rd fl, New York, NY 10036 *Tel:* 212-206-3730 *Toll Free Tel:* 866-483-7692 *Fax:* 212-206-9154
12630 Old Hickory Blvd, Nashville, TN 37013 *Tel:* 615-280-2255 *Fax:* 615-280-2181
455 W 38, Houston, TX 77018 *Tel:* 713-691-1332 *Fax:* 713-691-1378
1775 Hurd Dr, Irving, TX 75038 *Tel:* 214-260-1295 *Toll Free Tel:* 877-920-9020 *Fax:* 214-260-1300
12610 Interurban Ave S, Suite 110, Tukwila, WA 98168 *Tel:* 206-242-3860 *Toll Free Tel:* 866-837-9288 *Fax:* 206-242-3859
6741 Cariboo Rd, Unit 301, Burnaby, Vancouver, BC V3N 4A3, Canada *Tel:* 604-420-3440 *Fax:* 604-420-3446
5925 Tomken Rd, Unit 18-19, Mississauga, ON L4W 4L8, Canada *Tel:* 905-795-8008 *Fax:* 905-795-2769
110 Nordic Ave, Pointe-Claire, QC H9R 3Y2, Canada *Tel:* 514-630-3939 *Fax:* 514-630-0990
Foreign Office(s): Waidstr 207, 63071 Offenbach am Main, Germany *Tel:* (069) 978991300 *Fax:* (069) 978991301
Cessnalaan 55, Schiphol-Rijk, 1119 NK Amsterdam, Netherlands *Tel:* (020) 3160520 *Fax:* (020) 3160521
Downland Close, Units 3-4, London N20 9LB, United Kingdom *Tel:* (020) 8445 0267 *Fax:* (020) 8492 1932

Verilux® - The Healthy Lighting Co
340 Mad River Park, Suite 1, Waitsfield, VT 05673
Tel: 802-496-3101 *Toll Free Tel:* 888-544-4865 (cust support); 800-454-4408 (orders) *Fax:* 802-496-3105 (orders)
E-mail: info@verilux.com
Web Site: www.verilux.com
Key Personnel
Pres: Nicholas Harmon
Sr Sales Acct Mgr: Dawn Tudor *Tel:* 802-496-3101 ext 112 *E-mail:* dtudor@verilux.com
Founded: 1956
Catalog(s), new consumer catalogs every few months, free by request

Veritech Corp
80 Denslow Rd, East Longmeadow, MA 01028
Tel: 413-525-3368 *Toll Free Tel:* 800-525-5912 *Fax:* 413-525-7449
E-mail: info@veritechmedia.com
Web Site: www.veritechmedia.com
Key Personnel
Pres: Steven Graziano *Tel:* 651-379-1012
VP & Gen Mgr: Donald Wesson
VP, Prodn: Jeremy Cole
Founded: 1976
Video & interactive multimedia production company.
Membership(s): AAM; HCEA; NAME

Versatech Industries Inc
14750 S Grant St, Bixby, OK 74008
Tel: 918-366-7400
Key Personnel
Pres: Gene B Randall, Jr
Remote surveillance, closed-circuit TV.
Catalog(s) available

Versatruss
Division of 1859936 Ontario Inc
5028 Hwy 43, Perth, ON K7H 3C7, Canada
Tel: 613-264-0074 *Toll Free Tel:* 888-430-7613 *Fax:* 613-264-0889
E-mail: info@versatruss.com
Web Site: www.versatruss.com
Key Personnel
Acct Exec: Gordon O'Connor
Manufacture aluminum truss systems.
Catalog(s) available

The Verve Music Group
Member of Universal Music Group
134 W 25 St, 5th fl, New York, NY 10001
Tel: 212-494-0078
E-mail: contact@vervemusicgroup.com
Web Site: www.vervemusicgroup.com; www.umusic.com
Key Personnel
VP, A&R: Bud Harner
Founded: 1956
Jazz music distribution.

Vexcel Corp
Subsidiary of Microsoft
5775 Flatiron Pkwy, Suite 220, Boulder, CO 80301
Tel: 303-415-6000 *Fax:* 303-442-2956
E-mail: vexcel@microsoft.com
Web Site: www.vexcel.com
Key Personnel
Mktg Communs Mgr, Microsoft: Jerry Skaw
Founded: 1985
The company offers a range of aerial mapping & remote sensing products & services to government & commercial markets. Areas of specialization include:
i) photogrammetry & mapping hardware & software
ii) GIS products & system solutions
iii) SAR research, exploitation software & services
iv) remote sensing ground systems.

La Vezzi Precision Inc
999 Regency Dr, Glendale Heights, IL 60139-2281
Tel: 630-582-1230 *Toll Free Tel:* 800-323-1772 (outside IL) *Fax:* 630-582-1238 (orders)
E-mail: lpi@lavezzi.com
Web Site: www.lavezzi.com
Key Personnel
Sales & Mktg Mgr: Stephanie La Vezzi *E-mail:* stephlav@lavezzi.com
Founded: 1908
Precision machined components manufacturer.
Catalog(s) available
Membership(s): SMPTE

VFGadgets Inc
22 Elmer Ave, Toronto, ON M4L 3R7, Canada
Tel: 416-686-1452
E-mail: sales@vfgadgets.com; customerservice@vfgadgets.com
Web Site: www.vfgadgets.com
Key Personnel
Prod Devt: David O'Keefe *E-mail:* djokeefe@vfgadgets.com
Founded: 2001
Sells equipment solutions for video & film production.

VGI Productions
Division of Video Genesis Inc
3655 Tolland Rd, Shaker Heights, OH 44122
Tel: 216-464-3635 *Fax:* 216-464-5630
Web Site: www.vgipro.com
Key Personnel
Pres & Gen Mgr: Howard J Schwartz *E-mail:* hs@vgipro.com
Founded: 1978
HD video production facility.

Via Verde Productions
22631 Pacific Coast Hwy, Suite 480, Malibu, CA 90265-5036
Tel: 310-458-3778 *Fax:* 310-496-2992
E-mail: info@viaverdedigital.com
Web Site: www.viaverdedigital.com
Key Personnel
Founder & Dir: Melissa Landini
Full service film & digital production company & post-production studio.

Via-Vision Film & Video Productions
18 College St, Lewiston, ME 04240
Mailing Address: PO Box 217, Lewiston, ME 04243
Tel: 207-783-2550
Web Site: www.viavisionproductions.com
Key Personnel
Exec Dir: Francis Gagnon
Founded: 1989
Film & video production company. Weddings & dance videography, film & video transfers, video projector rentals.
Branch Office(s)
Senter Place, 124 Maine St, Suite 20, Brunswick, ME 04011 *Tel:* 207-729-1001
Membership(s): WEVA

Vicon Industries Inc
131 Heartland Blvd, Edgewood, NY 11717
Tel: 631-952-2288 *Toll Free Tel:* 800-645-9116 *Fax:* 631-951-2288
Web Site: www.vicon-security.com
Key Personnel
CEO: Eric Fullerton
SVP, Fin: John Badke
SVP, Sales & Mktg: Bret McGowan
VP, Opers: Peter Horn

VP, Technol & Devt: Frank Jacovino
Founded: 1967
Design, manufacture & market a broad line of products used in integrated video surveillance systems. Vicon's marketing & development efforts focus on today's leading edge security technologies, including digital recording & IP video solutions, access control, matrix controls, cameras, monitors, mounting accessories, remote positioning devices & fiber optic equipment. Our products are used in a variety of surveillance, security, safety & control applications, in banks, gaming casinos, traffic control, hospitals, retailing, multiple commercial & industrial installations, etc.
Catalog(s) available
Foreign Office(s): Vicon Industries Ltd, Brunel Way, Fareham PO15 5TX, United Kingdom *Tel:* (01489) 566300 *Fax:* (01489) 566322
Membership(s): ASIS; Closed Circuit Television Manufacturers Association; SIA

Victoria Supply Inc/Topbulb.com
5204 Indianapolis Blvd, East Chicago, IN 46312-3838
Tel: 219-398-2362 *Toll Free Tel:* 800-TOP-BULB (867-2852) *Toll Free Fax:* 877-329-2852
E-mail: sales@topbulb.com
Web Site: www.topbulb.com
Distributor of light bulbs, lighting products & accessories.
Catalog(s), free

Victory Cinevideo Battery Corp
10509 Burbank Blvd, N Hollywood, CA 91601
Tel: 818-754-0647 *Toll Free Tel:* 800-292-6565 *Fax:* 818-754-0640
Web Site: www.victorycinevideobattery.com
Supply battery packs & belts; repair service for cinevideo film & video industry.
Catalog(s) available

Victory Studios
2247 15 Ave W, Seattle, WA 98119
Tel: 206-282-1776 *Toll Free Tel:* 888-282-1776 *Fax:* 206-282-3535 *Toll Free Fax:* 888-765-9563
E-mail: info@victorystudios.com
Web Site: www.victorystudios.com
Key Personnel
Owner & CEO: Conrad W Denke *E-mail:* conrad@victorystudios.com
Dir, Engg: Scott Thomas *Tel:* 206-576-3228 *E-mail:* scott@victorystudios.com
Catalog(s) available
Branch Office(s)
10911 Riverside Dr, Suite 100, North Hollywood, CA 91602 *Tel:* 818-769-1776 *Fax:* 818-760-1280
Membership(s): AICP; MCA-I; NATPE; Producers Guild of America

VidCAD by Commsys Design LLC
2010 E Lohman Ave, Suite 2, Las Cruces, NM 88001
Tel: 575-522-0003 *Toll Free Tel:* 800-VIDCAD-6 (843-2236 sales); 888-4-VIDTEC (484-3832 tech support) *Fax:* 575-635-4518
E-mail: sales@vidcad.com
Web Site: www.vidcad.com
Key Personnel
Pres: Janine Sotelo *E-mail:* j9@vidcad.com
Manufacturer of software that automates the design & documentation of television, radio, AV & telecommunications systems. VidCAD ESP (Enterprise-wide in scope), VidCAD Engineer, VidCAD Designer & VidCAD TecXpert.
Brochure(s), by request

VidCan Media Solutions
24133 Del Monte Dr, Unit 204, Valencia, CA 91355
Tel: 818-239-4729; 818-312-5128
Web Site: www.vidcan.com
Key Personnel
Owner: Graham Jones *E-mail:* gjones@vidcan.com
Award winning production & full service post-production, including compositing & DVD authoring & duplication.

Vidcraft Productions Ltd
425 Curling St, Corner Brook, NL A2H 3K4, Canada
Tel: 709-785-1157
E-mail: info@vidcraft.com
Web Site: www.vidcraft.com
Key Personnel
Pres: Ron O'Connell
VP: Paula O'Connell
Founded: 1991
Professional multimedia/broadcast video production.

Vide-O-Go/That's Infotainment!
Subsidiary of That's Infotainment Inc
206 Winding Ridge Dr, Cary, NC 27518-8934
Tel: 919-363-7920
E-mail: videogo@aol.com
Web Site: www.videogo.com
Key Personnel
Pres: Dean W Stevens
Founded: 1989
Distribution of packaged media programs serving the acquisition interests of schools & libraries.
Membership(s): Entertainment Merchants Association

Video Accessory Corp
1243 Sherman Dr, Suite 8, Longmont, CO 80501
Tel: 303-443-1319 *Toll Free Tel:* 800-821-0426 *Fax:* 303-440-8878
E-mail: sales@vac-brick.net
Web Site: www.vac-brick.com
Key Personnel
Owner & CEO: Richard Frey *E-mail:* richard@vac-brick.net
Manufactures video & audio distribution amplifiers, switches, breakouts, black burst generators & other products for video & audio professionals.

Video Advantage
90 Houseman Crescent, Richmond Hill, ON L4C 7S6, Canada
Tel: 905-883-5332
E-mail: info@videoadvantage.ca
Web Site: www.videoadvantage.ca
Key Personnel
Principal & Exec Prodr: Rick Davis
Creative Dir: Michael O'Brien
Founded: 1998
HD video production, from concept to post-production, TV commercials & PSAs, corporate & web video production, TV series & documentaries.

Video Aided Instruction Inc
485-34 S Broadway, Hicksville, NY 11801-5071
Tel: 516-939-0707 *Toll Free Tel:* 800-238-1512 *Toll Free Fax:* 800-588-1419
E-mail: custsvc@videoaidedinstruction.com
Web Site: www.videoaidedinstruction.com
Key Personnel
Pres: Peter Lanzer
VP: Mona E Lanzer
Founded: 1983
Publish multimedia products for the educational market. Provide DVDs to the institutional & consumer markets.
Online catalog(s) available

Video Artists International & VAI Audio
109 Wheeler Ave, Pleasantville, NY 10570
Tel: 914-769-3691 *Toll Free Tel:* 800-477-7146 *Fax:* 914-769-5407
E-mail: orders@vaimusic.com
Web Site: www.vaimusic.com
Key Personnel
Owner: Edward Cardona
Sales Mgr: Foster Grimm
Prodn Coord: Allan Altman
Founded: 1983
Production & distribution of own label, also distribute other related classical labels. Music video, classical, opera, ballet & jazz.
Catalog(s) available
Membership(s): Entertainment Merchants Association

Video Associates Labs Inc
2201 Denton Dr, Suite 109 B, Austin, TX 78758
Tel: 512-491-7091 *Toll Free Tel:* 800-331-0547 *Fax:* 512-491-7619
E-mail: sales@val.com
Web Site: www.val.com
Key Personnel
Pres: Randy Feingersh
Off Mgr: Nancy Nawrocki
Manufacture USB cameras for photo ID applications.

Video Automation Systems Inc
13 Arrow Meadow Rd, New Fairfield, CT 06812
Tel: 203-312-0152 *Fax:* 203-312-0157
Web Site: www.videoautomation.com/videoautomation.html
Key Personnel
Pres & Chief Engr: Thorsten Cook *E-mail:* tpcook@videoautomation.com
Founded: 1976
Manufactures video systems/components cameras, multiplexers & provides video consultants/engineers.
Membership(s): SMPTE

Video Caption Corp
88 Hunns Lake Rd, Stanfordville, NY 12581
Tel: 845-868-1200 *Toll Free Tel:* 800-705-1203 *Fax:* 845-868-1188 *Toll Free Fax:* 800-705-1207
E-mail: mail@vicaps.com
Web Site: www.vicaps.com
Key Personnel
VP, Sales & Mktg: Constance Carlson *E-mail:* ccarlson@vicaps.com
Founded: 1997
Branch Office(s)
300 E Magnolia Blvd, Suite 506, Burbank, CA 91502 *Tel:* 818-736-5446

Video Catalogue Co Inc
105 E 34 St, Suite 105, New York, NY 10016
Toll Free Tel: 866-843-2282
E-mail: info@vidcat.com
Web Site: www.vidcat.com
Key Personnel
Pres & Exec Prodr: Janet Pytowski *E-mail:* janet@vidcat.com
Fashion show videos, DVDs, footage & fashion TV.
Catalog(s) available

Video Communication Productions Inc
446 Salem Dr, Pittsburgh, PA 15243
Tel: 412-915-6776
Web Site: www.pittsburghvideoguy.com
Key Personnel
Prodr & Videographer: Jay D Kuntz *E-mail:* j.vid@verizon.net
Video production services.

Video Communication Services, see VCSvideo

Video Concepts Unlimited
PO Box 577, North Chili, NY 14514
Tel: 585-293-2222 *Toll Free Tel:* 800-930-5411
E-mail: videocu@aol.com
Web Site: www.dvdtransferservices.com
Key Personnel
CEO: Denise Dusinberre
Old home movies, photographs & slides transferred to videos or DVDs. Produce corporate video programs & special event videography.

Video Copy Services Inc
3980 Dekalb Technology Pkwy, Suite 670, Atlanta, GA 30340
Toll Free Tel: 800-553-3616
E-mail: info@video-copy.com
Web Site: www.video-copy.com
Key Personnel
Owner & Pres: George Helms *E-mail:* george@video-copy.com
Dir, Opers: Bob Chirum
Founded: 1984
CD & DVD duplication.
Catalog(s) available
Membership(s): MCA-I; Women in Film

Video Corporation of America (VCA)
7 Veronica Ave, Somerset, NJ 08873
Mailing Address: PO Box 5480, Somerset, NJ 08875-5480
Tel: 732-545-8000 *Fax:* 732-545-5101
E-mail: njsales@vcaglobal.com
Web Site: www.vcaglobal.com
Key Personnel
Pres: David M Berlin
Founded: 1972
AV systems integrator & reseller of professional audio & digital video equipment & AV presentation systems.
Catalog(s) available
Branch Office(s)
370 Seventh Ave, Suite 550, New York, NY 10001 *Tel:* 212-967-4400 *Fax:* 212-967-1585
1004 W Ninth Ave, 2nd fl, King of Prussia, PA 19406, Contact: Rick Gamble *Tel:* 610-265-1001 *Fax:* 610-265-3663
Membership(s): InfoComm International®; MCA-I; NAB; PSNI

Video Design Group
51 Hattertown Rd, Monroe, CT 06468
Tel: 203-261-7995
Web Site: www.videodesigngroup.com
Key Personnel
Prop: Gregory Loehr *E-mail:* greg@videodesigngroup.com
Founded: 1984
Membership(s): PVA

Video Editing Services Inc, see The Media Collaboratory

Video Excellence Productions
94 Breckonwood Crescent, Thornhill, ON L3T 5E8, Canada
Tel: 905-731-4355
Web Site: www.videoexcellence.com
Key Personnel
Owner & Pres: Brian Korson *E-mail:* brian@videoexcellence.com
Founded: 1983
Filming & editing of industrial, promotional & training programs with output to tape, CD, DVD & Internet. Multi-camera filming of events & streaming of video content.
Membership(s): PEO; WEVA

Video Express
Division of Lessard Taylor Communications Inc
181 Newbury St, 5th fl, Boston, MA 02116
Tel: 617-267-7900 *Fax:* 617-267-6306
E-mail: information@evideoexpress.com
Web Site: www.evideoexpress.com
Key Personnel
Pres: Bill Taylor, Jr
Catalog(s) available

Video/Film Associates
3310 W Queen Lane, Philadelphia, PA 19129
Tel: 215-922-3333
Key Personnel
Prodr: Ron Kanter *E-mail:* ronkanter@gmail.com
Creates programs about the arts, education & social issues.

Video Gear Rentals Inc
8969 Kenamar Dr, Suite 104, San Diego, CA 92121
Tel: 858-356-0200 *Fax:* 858-356-0204
Web Site: www.video-gear.com
Key Personnel
Owner: Martin Banks *E-mail:* martin@video-gear.com
Video production equipment for sale or rent.
Membership(s): MCA-I; San Diego Filmmakers

Video I-D Teleproductions Inc
105 Muller Rd, Washington, IL 61571
Tel: 309-444-4323 *Toll Free Tel:* 800-333-9123 *Fax:* 309-444-4333
Web Site: www.videoid.com
Key Personnel
Owner & Pres: Sam B Wagner *E-mail:* sbw@videoid.com
Founded: 1977
Production services include DVD Interactive.

Video Ideas Productions
1501 64 St, North Bergen, NJ 07047
Tel: 201-951-3798 *Fax:* 201-662-4846
Web Site: osoriomedia.com
Key Personnel
Pres: William Osorio
Fully equipped professional video production & post-production house.

Video Impressions
2505 Diehl Rd, Aurora, IL 60502
Tel: 630-851-1663 *Fax:* 630-851-2688
E-mail: office@video-impressions.com
Web Site: www.video-impressions.com
Key Personnel
Founder: Mark W Hislop *E-mail:* mark@video-impressions.com
Founded: 1981

Video In Studios/Video Out Distribution
Affiliate of Vivo Media Arts Centre
2625 Kaslo St, Vancouver, BC V5M 3G9, Canada
Tel: 604-872-8337; 604-872-8449 *Fax:* 604-876-1185
E-mail: info@vivomediaarts.com; info@videoout.ca
Web Site: www.videoinstudios.com; www.videoout.ca
Key Personnel
Gen Mgr: Emma Hendrix *Tel:* 604-872-8337 ext 4
Founded: 1980
An artist-run media arts access center (VIVO) & distributor of media art on video.
Catalog(s) available
Membership(s): Canadian Museums Association; Independent Film & Video Alliance

Video International Development Inc
PO Box 349, Locust Valley, NY 11560
Tel: 516-671-6765 *Fax:* 516-730-5084
E-mail: info@videointernational.org
Web Site: www.videointernational.org
Key Personnel
Dir: Bernd Bressel *E-mail:* bernd@videointernational.org
West Coast Sales Mgr: Stan Paris *E-mail:* stan@videointernational.org
Founded: 1980
Manufacturer & importer/distributor of TV broadcast equipment.
Catalog(s), PDF files
CD-ROM catalog(s) available
Foreign Office(s): Video International Development GmbH, Ulmenweg 11, 30890 Barsinghausen, Germany
Shipping Address: 21 Winans Place, Locust Valley, NY 11560
Membership(s): InfoComm International®; NAB; SMPTE

Video Labs
15237 Display Ct, Rockville, MD 20850
Tel: 301-217-0000 *Toll Free Tel:* 800-800-8240 *Fax:* 301-217-0044
E-mail: sales@videolabs.net
Web Site: www.videolabs.net
Key Personnel
CEO: Michael Weiss
Founded: 1978
Duplication & replication services, multimedia services, printing, packaging & order fulfillment.
Catalog(s) available
Membership(s): American Independent Media Manufacturers Association; MCA-I; Women in Film & Video

Video Learning Library
15838 N 62 St, Scottsdale, AZ 85254-1988
Tel: 480-596-9970 *Toll Free Tel:* 800-383-8811 (orders)
E-mail: videos@videolearning.com
Web Site: www.videolearning.com
Key Personnel
Pres: James R Spencer
Founded: 1987
Rental & sales of how-to, special interest & educational videos.
Catalog(s) available
Membership(s): Entertainment Merchants Association

Video Media Productions (VMP)
Division of Arizona Production Center
175 S Hamilton Place, Gilbert, AZ 85233
Tel: 480-745-2776
E-mail: question@videomediaproductions.com; video@videomediaproductions.com
Web Site: www.videomediaproductions.com
Key Personnel
Mgr, Duplication Div & Videographer: Rob Satterfield
Founded: 1975
Boutique style production center for film, video, audio, post-production & duplication.

The Video Messenger Co
862 Judson Place, Stratford, CT 06615
Tel: 203-358-8842 *Toll Free Tel:* 800-800-7128 *Fax:* 203-547-6216
E-mail: vmc@videomessenger.com
Web Site: www.videomessenger.com
Key Personnel
Pres: Charles P Corsello
Sales: Peter Murphy
Founded: 1989
Also manufacture & distribute networkable video message system, digital signs.
Catalog(s) available

Video Mount Products (VMP)
345 Log Canoe Circle, Stevensville, MD 21666

Tel: 410-643-6390 *Toll Free Tel:* 877-281-2169
Fax: 410-643-6615
E-mail: sales@videomount.com
Web Site: www.videomount.com
Key Personnel
Pres: Keith Fulmer
Founded: 1994
Mounting solutions for AV communications & security.
Catalog(s) available
Membership(s): InfoComm International®

Video Movie Magic
26941 Cabot Rd, Suite 127, Laguna Hills, CA 92653
Tel: 949-582-8596 *Fax:* 949-582-8223
E-mail: sales@videomoviemagic.com
Web Site: www.videomoviemagic.com
Key Personnel
Owner: R Mike Jones
Mgr: Rick Jones
Founded: 1982

Video Perspective
PO Box 591843, Houston, TX 77259-1843
Tel: 281-996-7974 *Toll Free Tel:* 888-996-7974
E-mail: vp@vidper.com
Web Site: www.videoperspective.com
Key Personnel
Dir, Photog: Stephen Henry
Founded: 1990
Full service video production company.
Membership(s): Texas Association of Motion Media Professionals; Texas Film Commission

Video Production Associates Inc
525 Bridgeport Ave, Shelton, CT 06484-1397
Tel: 203-929-8869 *Toll Free Tel:* 800-394-8869
Fax: 203-925-0344
Web Site: www.vpa-inc.com
Key Personnel
Pres: Joseph Sullivano *E-mail:* joe-vpa@snet.net
Founded: 1978
Catalog(s) available

The Video Project
Subsidiary of Specialty Studios
145 Ninth St, Suite 102, San Francisco, CA 94103
Mailing Address: PO Box 411376, San Francisco, CA 94111
Tel: 415-981-9710 *Toll Free Tel:* 800-475-2638
Toll Free Fax: 888-562-9012
E-mail: orders@videoproject.com; support@videoproject.com
Web Site: www.videoproject.com
Key Personnel
Pres: Steve Michelson
Dir, Busn Aff: Craig Malina
Dir, Opers: Lucy Logsdon
Mgmt & Mktg Consultant: Steve Ladd
Acctg: Rebecca Holland
Graphic Designer: Jesse Sotelo
Founded: 1983
Distribute documentary film to educational institutions on the topics of the environment, science & social sciences.
Catalog(s) available

Video Resources Inc
1809 E Dyer Rd, Suite 307, Santa Ana, CA 92705
Tel: 949-261-7266 *Toll Free Tel:* 800-261-7266
Fax: 949-261-5908
E-mail: info@videoresources.com
Web Site: www.videoresources.com
Key Personnel
Gen Mgr: Ecar Oden
Video production, animation, staging, equipment rentals.
Branch Office(s)
110 Campus Dr, Marlborough, MA 01752
Tel: 508-485-8100

Video Service of America Inc (VSA)
6929 Seward Ave, Lincoln, NE 68507
Tel: 402-467-3668 *Toll Free Tel:* 800-888-2140 (orders) *Fax:* 402-325-8033
E-mail: sales@vsa1.com
Web Site: www.vsa1.com
Key Personnel
Credit Mgr: Barb Greene
Founded: 1976
Catalog(s) available

Video Solutions
2121 Eisenhower Ave, Suite 103, Alexandria, VA 22314
Tel: 703-683-5305; 703-628-0702 (cell)
E-mail: inquiries@thevideosolution.com
Web Site: www.thevideosolution.com
Key Personnel
Owner & Pres: Clark Bavin
Founded: 1991
Your video solution in DC. Deliver imaginative, compelling, award-winning results through our creative talent & technical capabilities. Complete HD video & multimedia production. Two HD video edit suites & narraration booth, insert studio & ammenities. We put ideas into motion.

The Video Store Shopper
Division of The Shopper Inc
3987 Heritage Oak Ct, Simi Valley, CA 93063
Tel: 805-583-8500 *Toll Free Tel:* 800-462-9040; 800-325-6867 (cust serv) *Fax:* 805-583-8546
Toll Free Fax: 800-947-2060
E-mail: sales@shopperinc.com; customerservice@shopperinc.com
Web Site: www.thevideostoreshopper.com
Key Personnel
Pres: Bill Bieda
Founded: 1983
Catalog(s) available
Membership(s): Entertainment Merchants Association; National Association of Video Distributors

Video Symphony TV & Film School
266 E Magnolia Blvd, Burbank, CA 91502
Tel: 818-557-7200 *Toll Free Tel:* 800-871-2843
Fax: 818-845-1951
E-mail: info@videosymphony.com
Web Site: www.videosymphony.com
Key Personnel
Pres: Mike Flanagan *E-mail:* mike@vs.edu
Founded: 1994
TV & film college for post-production.
Catalog(s), biannual, courses & programs

Video Techniques Inc
3306 26 St W, Bradenton, FL 34205-3608
Mailing Address: PO Box 9649, Bradenton, FL 34206-9649
Tel: 941-758-3077 *Fax:* 941-301-4696
E-mail: vti1@videotechniques.com
Key Personnel
Pres & Exec Prodr: Bob Lorentzen
E-mail: bob11@videotechniques.com
Founded: 1979

Video Technology Services Inc
5 Ariel Way, Suite 300, Syosset, NY 11791
Tel: 516-937-9700 *Fax:* 516-937-9704
E-mail: vts1@optonline.net
Web Site: www.videotechnologyservices.com
Key Personnel
Pres: Andres Sierra *E-mail:* andressdm@optonline.net
Founded: 1986
Manufacture video communications systems for commercial airlines.

Video Visions Inc
Division of Milanese Associates Inc
3600 Boundbrook Ave, Trevose, PA 19053
Tel: 215-942-6642 *Fax:* 267-684-6819
E-mail: sales@video-visions.com
Web Site: www.video-visions.com
Key Personnel
Pres: Mary Ellen Milanese-Distasio
E-mail: memilanesedistasio@video-visions.com
Founded: 1991
Catalog(s) available
Branch Office(s)
1015 N Bumby Ave, Orlando, FL 32803, Contact: Joe McConahy *Tel:* 407-249-8500 *Fax:* 407-249-1900 *E-mail:* jmcconahy@video-visions.com
Membership(s): InfoComm International®; NAB

Video West Inc
570 W Southern Ave, Tempe, AZ 85282
Tel: 480-222-3180 *Fax:* 480-222-3191
E-mail: info@videowestinc.com
Web Site: www.videowestinc.com
Key Personnel
Pres: Jack Waitkus
Sr Dir, Mktg: Becky Spooner
E-mail: beckyspooner@videowestinc.com
Founded: 1982
Catalog(s) available

Video Wisconsin Inc
18110 W Bluemound Rd, Brookfield, WI 53045
Tel: 262-785-1110 *Fax:* 262-785-9827
Web Site: www.videowisconsin.tv
Key Personnel
VP, Opers: Colleen S Hartley
Video, multimedia production & post-production.

Videobotics
220 N Palisade Dr, Santa Maria, CA 93454
Tel: 805-349-1104
E-mail: videobotics@megagem.com; megagem@megagem.com
Web Site: www.videobotics.com; camrobot.com
Key Personnel
Owner: Daniel Wolf
Founded: 1999
Create computer software to control video equipment (PT/Z cameras, video mixers, VCRs, DVDs), direct from PC or through network or Internet. Applications: TV production, remote observation, multimedia presentation, film production, military, churches, city government, industrial & education. Android tablets & phone apps to control video equipment.
Membership(s): AAAS

Videofashion Network
611 Broadway, Suite 307, New York, NY 10012
Tel: 212-274-1600 *Fax:* 212-219-1969
E-mail: licensing@videofashion.com
Web Site: www.videofashion.com
Key Personnel
Edit Dir: Nick Charney
Mng Ed: Anne V Adami *Tel:* 212-274-1600 ext 25 *E-mail:* aadami@videofashion.com
Founded: 1976
Catalog(s) available
Membership(s): NATPE

Videofax
1750 Cesar Chavez St, Unit G, San Francisco, CA 94124
Tel: 415-641-0100

E-mail: rentals@videofax.com
Web Site: www.videofax.com
Key Personnel
Mng Partner: Leigh Blicher *E-mail:* leigh@videofax.com
Partner: Jim Rolin; Tomas Tucker
Rental Mgr: Mona Marks *E-mail:* mona@videofax.com
Founded: 1987
Rents video equipment & accessories to serve the commercial & motion picture industries as well as corporate, documentary, television & the online media community.

Videofilm Systems Inc
7 Islandbrook Ave, Unit D-1, Bridgeport, CT 06606
Tel: 203-870-6013
Web Site: www.videofilmsystems.com
Key Personnel
Owner: Justin Cihi *E-mail:* justincihi@gmail.com
Mktg Mgr: Giselle Vogel *E-mail:* gvogel@vfstv.com
Founded: 1979
Systems integration & design. Sales & rentals, digital signage & projection.

Videograf
144 W 27 St, 12th fl, New York, NY 10001
Tel: 212-242-7871
E-mail: videograf@verizon.net
Key Personnel
Pres: Michael Frenchman
General video production.

Videografix LLC
2530 Berryessa Rd, Suite 314, San Jose, CA 95132-2903
Tel: 408-499-1280 *Fax:* 408-583-4018
E-mail: info@videografix.com
Web Site: www.videografix.com
Key Personnel
Sr Prodr: Steve Young
Mktg Dir: Dylis Watts
Creative Dir: Bill Rice
Dir, Photog: Dan Agulian
Founded: 1989
Teleprompting & green screen.
Catalog(s) available

Videography Productions
PO Box 653, Amagansett, NY 11930-0653
Tel: 520-907-1900
Web Site: www.dickfisher.net
Key Personnel
Owner & Pres: Dick Fisher *E-mail:* fisherdp@yahoo.com
Founded: 1982
Membership(s): Society of Camera Operators

Videoguys
10-12 Charles St, Glen Cove, NY 11542
Tel: 516-759-1611 *Toll Free Tel:* 800-323-2325 *Fax:* 516-671-3092
E-mail: sales@videoguys.com
Web Site: www.videoguys.com
Key Personnel
Pres: Gary Bettan
Full range of video editing software & hardware.

The Videohouse Inc
975 Greentree Rd, Pittsburgh, PA 15220
Tel: 412-921-7577 *Fax:* 412-921-5535
E-mail: tvirjb@aol.com
Web Site: www.thevideohouse.com
Key Personnel
Founder & Pres: Ron Bruno
Prodn Coord: Dawn Azua *E-mail:* dawn@thevideohouse.com
Founded: 1985

Videolady
PO Box 2276, San Bernardino, CA 92406-2276
Tel: 909-882-4057 *Fax:* 909-882-4057
E-mail: vldy@aol.com
Web Site: videoladystudios.com
Key Personnel
Prop: Shirley Harlan
Camera/Ed: Steve Chandler
Founded: 1970
Full service production & post-production. Beta SP & digital cameras, lighting, etc. Final cut production editing, analog & HD. Transfer film to DVD, DVD duplication.
Price list(s) available
Shipping Address: 3939 Newmark Ave, San Bernardino, CA 92405

VideoLink Inc
1230 Washington St, Newton, MA 02465
Tel: 617-340-4100 *Fax:* 617-340-4101
Web Site: www.videolinktv.com
ReadyCam®, HD live insert studio, HD transmission satellite trucks. Creative services, webcasting, general video production.
Branch Office(s)
10 Liberty Sq, Boston, MA 02109 *Tel:* 617-340-4290 *Toll Free Tel:* 800-990-4995
1619 Massachusetts Ave, Washington, DC 20036
10 N Calvert St, Baltimore, MD 21202 *Tel:* 443-524-8000 *Toll Free Tel:* 800-741-7913 *Fax:* 443-524-1958
5100 Buckeystown Pike, Suite 250, Frederick, MD 21704
11 Saint Anselm Dr, Manchester, NH 03102 *Tel:* 617-340-4100 *Fax:* 617-340-4101
1524 Delancey St, Philadelphia, PA 19102 *Tel:* 215-940-3000 *Toll Free Tel:* 800-990-4995 *Fax:* 215-940-3026
Membership(s): CMAA; IABC; SMEI

Videomagnetics
3970 Clearview Frontage Rd, Colorado Springs, CO 80911
Tel: 719-390-1313 *Toll Free Tel:* 800-432-3887 *Fax:* 719-390-1316
E-mail: vmi@csprings.com
Web Site: www.videomagnetics.com
Key Personnel
Pres: Tony Korte
Cont: Jane Pennie
Catalog(s) available
Membership(s): NAB

Videorama Industries LLC
1119 N Hudson Ave, Hollywood, CA 90038
Tel: 323-466-7232 *Fax:* 323-466-7228
Web Site: www.videorama.com
Key Personnel
Owner & CFO: Howard L Van Emden *E-mail:* howardv@videorama.com
Owner & CTO: R Scott Lawrence *E-mail:* rscott@videorama.com
Rental Mgr: Mike Gibbs *E-mail:* mike@videorama.com
Off Mgr & Rental Asst: Natalie Urick *E-mail:* natalie@videorama.com
Founded: 1995
Video assist equipment & accessory rental for the film industry. Also includes audio (music) playback systems.

Videoscope
7711 NW 46 St, Miami, FL 33166
Tel: 305-436-1684 *Fax:* 305-438-3743
E-mail: info@videoscopeusa.com
Web Site: www.videoscopeusa.com
Founded: 1997
Distribute broadcast audio & video equipment, including camcorders, lighting equipment, tripods, microphones, mixers, switchers, cases, batteries & chargers.

Videosmith Inc
200 Spring Garden St, Suite C, Philadelphia, PA 19123
Tel: 215-238-5070 *Fax:* 215-238-5075
E-mail: info@videosmith.com
Web Site: videosmith.com
Key Personnel
Pres: Steven T Smith
Gen Mgr: Chris Cerasoli
Online catalog(s) available
Membership(s): MCA-I; NATAS

Videotex Systems Inc
10255 Miller Rd, Dallas, TX 75238
Tel: 972-231-9200 *Toll Free Tel:* 800-88-VIDEO (888-4336) *Fax:* 972-231-2420
E-mail: info@videotexsystems.com
Web Site: www.videotexsystems.com
Key Personnel
Pres: Bob Gillman *Tel:* 972-231-9200 ext 102 *E-mail:* gillman@videotexsystems.com
Founded: 1984
AV equipment provider. Specialize in AV integration for schools, churches, corporations & government organizations.
Online catalog(s) available

Videowerks
3435 Ocean Park Blvd, Suite 107, Santa Monica, CA 90405
Tel: 310-393-8754; 310-780-4156 (cell) *Fax:* 310-399-1829
E-mail: videowerks@earthlink.net
Web Site: www.videowerks.com
Key Personnel
Owner: David M Werk
Founded: 1981
Professional video production services.

Videssence
10768 Lower Azusa Rd, El Monte, CA 91731
Tel: 626-579-0943 *Fax:* 626-579-6803
E-mail: contact@videssence.tv
Web Site: www.videssence.tv
Key Personnel
Pres: Lauri Maines
Intl Sales Mgr: Amanda McGinnis *E-mail:* mmcginnis@videssence.tv
Natl Sales Mgr: Gary Thomas *E-mail:* gthomas@videssence.tv
Prod Mgr: Stan Wong *E-mail:* swong@videssence.tv
Founded: 1980
Catalog(s) available

Vidicom Inc
520 Eighth Ave, Suite 2206, New York, NY 10018
Tel: 212-895-8300
E-mail: info@vidicom.com
Web Site: vidicom.com
Key Personnel
CEO: Scott Michaeloff
SVP, Sales: Sebastian Hill
VP, Prodn & Content: Sean Cassels
Dir, Prodn: Jenna Pace
Branded video content, digital distribution & interactive live programming.

Vidox Motion Imagery
204 Winchester Dr, Lafayette, LA 70506
Tel: 337-237-1700 *Fax:* 337-237-1712
Web Site: www.vidox.com
Key Personnel
Owner: Chris Allain *E-mail:* chris@vidox.com
Prodr: Scott Rachal
Founded: 1982
Full service video production company offering HD cinematography & post-production. In addition to turnkey projects, the company regularly tackles complex animation & visual

effects, like lip-synced characters or 3D industrial illustrations. In-house music composition & sound design round out the list of creative & technical services.
Membership(s): Open Studio Association

VIEW Inc (Video International Entertainment World Inc)
11 Reservoir Rd, Saugerties, NY 12477
Mailing Address: PO Box 77, Saugerties, NY 12477
Tel: 845-246-9955 *Toll Free Tel:* 800-843-9843 *Fax:* 845-246-9966
E-mail: viewvid@aol.com
Web Site: www.view.com
Key Personnel
Pres: Bob Karcy *E-mail:* bob@view.com
Mgr: Tom Hoose
Off Mgr: Emily Roberts-Negron
Founded: 1983
International home video production & distribution, licensing & TV syndication of special interest programs in areas of art, jazz, pop music, opera, dance, children's interactive sports & modern lifestyle programs.
Catalog(s) available
Membership(s): Entertainment Merchants Association; IAJE; Music Business Association; NAMM, the National Association of Music Merchants; NATAS; NATPE; The Recording Academy

Viewpoint Production Services Inc
419 Mount Nebo Rd, Pittsburgh, PA 15237
Tel: 412-369-7171 *Toll Free Tel:* 800-820-0402
Web Site: viewpoint.tv
Founded: 1982
Serving the broadcast & video production community. Equipment rental, ENG/EFP shoots, crewing, mobile units, production management, studio facilities & turnkey production.

ViewSonic
381 Brea Canyon Rd, Walnut, CA 91789-0708
Tel: 909-444-8888 *Toll Free Tel:* 800-688-6688; 800-888-8583 *Fax:* 909-468-1240
Web Site: www.viewsonic.com
Founded: 1987
Manufacture desktop virtualization, monitors, projectors & large format displays.

Viking Cases
Division of The Stemler Corp
10480 Oak St NE, St Petersburg, FL 33716
Tel: 727-577-1216 *Toll Free Tel:* 800-237-8560 *Fax:* 727-577-2082
E-mail: sales@vikingcases.com
Web Site: www.vikingcases.com
Key Personnel
CEO: Arthur W Stemler
Pres: Bruce S Stemler *E-mail:* bruce@vikingcases.com
Founded: 1975
Catalog(s) available
Membership(s): InfoComm International®

Vincent Associates
803 Linden Ave, Rochester, NY 14625
Tel: 585-385-5930 *Toll Free Tel:* 800-828-6972 *Fax:* 585-385-6004
E-mail: info@uniblitz.com
Web Site: www.uniblitz.com
Key Personnel
Pres: Kevin Farrell *E-mail:* kfarrell@uniblitz.com
Founded: 1969
Manufacture & distribute UNIBLITZ® electro-programmable shutter systems.
Catalog(s) available

Vincent Lighting Systems
6161 Cochran Rd, Suite D, Solon, OH 44139
Tel: 216-475-7600 *Toll Free Tel:* 800-922-5356 *Fax:* 216-475-6376
E-mail: info@vls.com
Web Site: www.vincentlighting.com
Key Personnel
Pres: Paul Vincent
Mktg Dir: Kim Craigie *E-mail:* kcraigie@vincentlighting.com
Founded: 1978
Catalog(s), annual, free
Branch Office(s)
1420 Jamike Ave, Suite 1, Erlanger, KY 41018 *Tel:* 859-525-2000 *Fax:* 859-525-2050
36500 Ford Rd, Suite 173, Westland, MI 48185-2211, Contact: Drew Franklin *Tel:* 734-660-8959
920 Vista Park Dr, Pittsburgh, PA 15205 *Tel:* 412-788-5250 *Fax:* 412-788-6115
Membership(s): Professional Lighting & Sound Association; USITT

Vineyard Productions
3640 Lovall Valley Rd, Sonoma, CA 95476
Tel: 707-939-3566
Web Site: www.vineyardproductions.com
Key Personnel
Co-Owner & CEO: Paul Martin *E-mail:* paul@vineyardproductions.com
Co-Owner: Patti Kozlovsky
Founded: 1999
Film & video production & post-production.

Vineyard Video & Photography
4193 Concord Ave, Santa Rosa, CA 95407
Tel: 707-591-9999; 707-591-1927 (cell)
Web Site: www.vineyardvideo.com
Key Personnel
Dir, Photog: Stuart Kiehl *E-mail:* stuart@vineyardvideo.com

VIP Presentation Products
69 S Dixie Hwy, Suite A, St Augustine, FL 32084
Tel: 904-824-0824 *Toll Free Tel:* 800-874-0855 *Fax:* 904-829-6903
E-mail: info@vippresentationproducts.com
Web Site: vippresentationproducts.com
Key Personnel
VP & Gen Mgr: Bill Blalock
Manufacture vinyl binders, tabs, specialty pocket folders (including die-cut slits for CDs or DVDs) & other presentation products.

Virtual Research Systems Inc
3824 Vienna Dr, Aptos, CA 95003
Tel: 408-748-8712 *Fax:* 408-748-8714
Web Site: www.virtualresearch.com
Key Personnel
Pres: Evan Yeaman *E-mail:* evan@virtualresearch.com
Founded: 1991
Customized display products for the professional simulation & training markets.
Brochure(s) available

VirtualMix
311 W Third St, Suite 2914, Carson City, NV 89703
Tel: 818-209-6176
E-mail: virtualmixpost@gmail.com
Web Site: www.virtualmix.com
Key Personnel
Sound Designer & Prodn Mixer: Patrick Giraudi *E-mail:* patrick@virtualmix.com
Founded: 2001
Audio post-production for film, television & multimedia.
Branch Office(s)
2607 W Magnolia Blvd, Burbank, CA 91505

Vis-Ed, see Visual Education

Vision Identics Systems Inc
110 Villa Ave, Mamaroneck, NY 10543
Mailing Address: PO Box 193, Mamaroneck, NY 10543
Tel: 914-381-2625 *Toll Free Tel:* 800-750-8840 *Fax:* 914-381-2752
E-mail: inquiry@visionid.com
Web Site: www.visionid.com
Key Personnel
Pres: George Kiriazides *E-mail:* george@visionid.com
Founded: 1990
Catalog(s) available

Vision Maker Media
1800 N 33 St, Lincoln, NE 68503
Tel: 402-472-3522 *Fax:* 402-472-8675
E-mail: visionmaker@unl.edu
Web Site: www.visionmakermedia.org
Key Personnel
Exec Dir: Shirley K Sneve *E-mail:* shirley.sneve@unl.edu
Busn & Projs Mgr: Mary Ann Koehler
To support the creation, promotion & distribution of Native American media.
Catalog(s) available

Vision Quest Productions Inc
PO Box 1896, Wayne, NJ 07470-1896
Tel: 973-686-9400 *Fax:* 973-694-8314
Web Site: vqpi.yolasite.com
Key Personnel
Pres: James Benson *E-mail:* bensonj@earthlink.net
Founded: 1996

Vision Video
2030 Wentz Church Rd, Lansdale, PA 19446
Mailing Address: PO Box 540, Worcester, PA 19490-0540
Tel: 610-584-3500 *Toll Free Tel:* 800-523-0226 *Fax:* 610-584-6643
E-mail: support@visionvideo.com
Web Site: www.visionvideo.com
Key Personnel
Gen Mgr: Bill Curtis *E-mail:* bill@visionvideo.com
Mail order video & DVD distribution.
Catalog(s) available
Membership(s): ICVM

Visionary Solutions Inc
2060 Alameda Padre Serra, Suite 100, Santa Barbara, CA 93103
Tel: 805-845-8900 *Fax:* 805-845-8889
E-mail: info@vsicam.com; sales@vsicam.com
Web Site: www.vsicam.com
Key Personnel
Pres: Jordan Christoff
Founded: 1995
Manufacturer & supplier of IPTV equipment.

Visioneering International Inc
659 Auburn Ave NE, Suite 267, Atlanta, GA 30312
Tel: 404-681-9028 *Fax:* 404-681-5947
E-mail: design@visioneering.com
Web Site: www.visioneering.com
Key Personnel
CEO & Pres: Robert Foah
VP & Creative Dir: Honora Foah
Dir, Fin: H R Fraval
Dir, Lighting & Set Design: Gregg Aukerman

Visions Plus
200 Valley Dr, Suite 5, Brisbane, CA 94005
Tel: 415-467-3300
E-mail: web_inquiry@visionsplus.com
Web Site: visionsplus.com
Key Personnel
Owner: Steven Dung

Founded: 1986
Video production services for businesses & non-profit organizations in the San Francisco Bay Area.

Visionworks Design Services Inc
204 Peach Way, Suite H, Columbia, MO 65203
Tel: 573-449-8567 *Fax:* 573-449-6714
E-mail: info@visionworksgroup.com
Web Site: visionworksgroup.com
Key Personnel
Pres: Lili Vianello

Visix™ Inc
230 Scientific Dr, Suite 80, Norcross, GA 30092
Tel: 770-446-1416 *Toll Free Tel:* 800-572-4935 *Fax:* 770-448-5724
E-mail: info@visix.com
Web Site: www.visix.com
Key Personnel
Chmn: Edward D Matthews, II
CEO & Pres: Sean Matthews
CFO: Christy Gear
COO: Tony Martin
Chief Sales Offr: Trey Hicks
Mktg Communs Mgr: Debbie DeWitt
Founded: 1980
Catalog(s) available
Membership(s): COMMTEX

Vista Color Imaging Inc
2048 Fulton Rd, Cleveland, OH 44113
Tel: 216-651-2830 *Toll Free Tel:* 800-890-0062 *Fax:* 216-651-5004
E-mail: info@vistacolorimaging.com
Web Site: www.vistacolorimaging.com
Key Personnel
CEO: Paul E Gallo *E-mail:* pgallo@vistacolorimaging.com
Pres: Kevin Vesely *E-mail:* kcvesely@vistacolorimaging.com
Founded: 1929
Produce interpretive exhibit & museum graphics. Supplier of graphic solutions.
Catalog(s) available
Membership(s): Specialty Graphic Imaging Association

Vista Group International Inc
25 Van Zant St, Unit 8-D, Norwalk, CT 06855
Tel: 203-852-5557 *Toll Free Tel:* 800-866-2113 *Fax:* 203-852-5559
E-mail: info@vistagroupinternational.com
Web Site: www.vistagroupinternational.com
Key Personnel
Pres: Martha Yaney *E-mail:* martha.yaney@vistagroupinternational.com
Designs, manufacturers & markets SoundStik® audio handsets for museums, tradeshows & tourist attractions. The SoundStik® personal listening device is used with video kiosks & exhibits to deliver clear, crisp sound while maintaining a quiet ambiance. Vista Group also offers custom outdoor listening stations, audio tour systems & services, FM tour guide systems & related products.
Catalog(s) available
Membership(s): American Alliance of Museums; NAME

Vistacom Inc
1902 Vultee St, Allentown, PA 18103-2998
Tel: 610-791-9081 *Toll Free Tel:* 800-747-0459 *Fax:* 610-791-9510
Web Site: www.vistacominc.com
Key Personnel
Pres: James Ferlino
COO: Angela Nolan
Founded: 1954
Commercial AV integration firm.
Membership(s): AES; InfoComm International®; NSCA

Vistamax Productions
9705 Little Pond Way, Tampa, FL 33647
Tel: 813-907-1010 *Fax:* 813-907-1991
E-mail: info@vistamax.com; sales@vistamax.com
Web Site: www.vistamax.com
Key Personnel
Pres: Steve Farkas *E-mail:* steve@vistamax.com
Founded: 1997

Visual Aids Electronics Corp
12900 Cloverleaf Center Dr, Suite C, Germantown, MD 20874
Tel: 301-330-6900 *Fax:* 301-330-6901
Web Site: www.vaecorp.com
Key Personnel
COO: David Martin *E-mail:* dmartin@vaecorp.com
CFO: Fred Dixon *E-mail:* fdixon@vaecorp.com
Staging & rental of AV for conventions & shows (road) & corporate meetings.
Membership(s): InfoComm International®

Visual Aids Electronics of North Carolina Inc
245 Executive Park Blvd, Winston-Salem, NC 27103
Tel: 336-768-5454 *Toll Free Tel:* 855-934-2828 *Fax:* 336-768-5054
E-mail: avrentals@avconnectionsusa.com
Web Site: avconnectionsusa.com
Key Personnel
Owner: Brad Luckhart
Founded: 1985
Branch Office(s)
AV Connections, 1012 Saint Andrews Blvd, Suite C, Charleston, SC 29407, Br Mgr: Jared Luckhart *Tel:* 843-529-1449 *Fax:* 843-529-1446 *E-mail:* avrentals@avconnectionssc.com

Visual Communications Group Inc
5721 Arapahoe Ave, Suite A-2, Boulder, CO 80303
Tel: 303-413-0878 *Fax:* 303-413-0683
E-mail: vcg@visualcomgroup.com
Web Site: www.visualcomgroup.com
Key Personnel
Partner: Fred Hull

Visual Communications - Southern California Asian American Studies Central Inc
120 Judge John Aiso St, Basement Level, Los Angeles, CA 90012
Tel: 213-680-4462 *Fax:* 213-687-4848
E-mail: info@vconline.org
Web Site: www.vconline.org
Key Personnel
Interim Exec Dir: Douglas Aihara *Tel:* 213-680-4462 ext 22 *E-mail:* shinae@vconline.org
Opers Dir: Janet Chen *Tel:* 213-680-4462 ext 38 *E-mail:* janet@vconline.org
Tech Dir: Mark Mangoba *E-mail:* mark@vconline.org
Founded: 1970
Asian Pacific American media arts center. Training & education workshops in film, video & new media.
Membership(s): National Alliance for Media Arts & Culture

Visual Departures Ltd
48 Sheffield Business Park, Ashley Falls, MA 01222
Tel: 413-229-2272 *Toll Free Tel:* 800-628-2003 *Fax:* 413-229-2274
E-mail: sales@visualdepartures.com
Web Site: www.visualdepartures.com
Key Personnel
Pres: Allen Green
Sales Dir: Ross Carswell
Founded: 1982
Catalog(s) available

Visual Education
Division of Graphic Paper Products
PO Box 1666, Springfield, OH 45501-1666
Toll Free Tel: 800-243-7070 *Fax:* 937-324-5697
E-mail: sales@vis-ed.com
Web Site: www.vis-ed.com
Key Personnel
Pres: Jeanne A Lampe
Catalog(s) available
Shipping Address: 300 E Auburn Ave, Springfield, OH 45505
Membership(s): EDSA; National Association of College Stores; Reading Recovery Council of North America

Visual Instrumentation Corp
1110 West Ave L-12, Unit 2, Lancaster, CA 93534-7039
Tel: 661-945-7999 *Fax:* 661-723-5667
E-mail: visinst@earthlink.net
Web Site: www.visinst.com
Key Personnel
Pres: Robert Lewis
Founded: 1970
Manufacturer & distributor of precision accessory products for high-speed digital & film camera applications.
Catalog(s) available
Membership(s): InfoComm International®; SPIE

Visual Products Inc
790 Shiloh Ave, Wellington, OH 44090
Tel: 440-647-4999 *Fax:* 440-647-4998
E-mail: sales@visualproducts.com
Web Site: www.visualproducts.com
Key Personnel
Owner & Pres: Jim Budzilek
Reseller of used motion picture equipment.

Visual Sound Inc
485 Park Way, Broomall, PA 19008
Tel: 610-544-8700 *Toll Free Tel:* 800-523-7525 *Fax:* 610-544-3385
Web Site: www.visualsound.com
Key Personnel
Pres: Karen Bogosian
VP, Educ Sales: Ann Pfister
VP, Sales: Linda Penrod
Founded: 1967
Leading AV systems integrator, service provider & reseller of professional/broadcast audio, video & AV presentation technology. Serves clients in the corporate, education, house of worship & government arenas. For customers planning special events or meetings, Visual Sound's Rental & Staging Division is available to provide on-site production services or as-needed equipment rentals. Certified WBE.
Catalog(s) available
Branch Office(s)
4706 Westport Dr, Suite 1500, Mechanicsburg, PA 17055
1642 Sulphur Springs Rd, Baltimore, MD 21227
Membership(s): InfoComm International®; NSCA; Photo Marketing Association

The Visual Studies Workshop (VSW)
31 Prince St, Rochester, NY 14607
Tel: 585-442-8676 *Fax:* 585-442-1992
E-mail: info@vsw.org
Web Site: www.vsw.org
Key Personnel
Exec Dir: Tate Shaw *Tel:* 585-442-8676 ext 21 *E-mail:* tateshaw@vsw.org
Admin Asst: Melissa Sample *Tel:* 585-442-8676 ext 20 *E-mail:* melissasample@vsw.org
Founded: 1969
Catalog(s) available

Visual Systems
845 Encino Place, Santa Paula, CA 93060
Tel: 805-933-8044 *Fax:* 805-933-9744
E-mail: info@visualsystemsonline.com
Web Site: www.visualsystemsonline.com
New & used digital & analog video equipment, broadcast video equipment & motion picture equipment.

Visual Technologies Corp
Subsidiary of VTC Specialties Inc
1620 Burnet Ave, Syracuse, NY 13206
Tel: 315-423-2000 *Toll Free Tel:* 888-423-0004 *Fax:* 315-423-0004
E-mail: contact@visualtec.com
Web Site: www.visualtec.com; www.vtcspecialties.com
Key Personnel
Pres: David J Foor *Tel:* 315-423-2000 ext 101 *E-mail:* dfoor@visualtec.com
Sales Coord: Michelle Fontaine *Tel:* 315-423-2000 ext 103 *E-mail:* mfontaine@visualtec.com
Founded: 1954
AV/Video rental & sales. Installation company.
Catalog(s), annual, free, upon request
Branch Office(s)
VTC AV Services, Holiday Inn Conference Ctr, Seventh N & Electronics Pkwy, Liverpool, NY 13088, Contact: Tim Allen
Visual Tech/AV Services, Sheraton University Inn & Conference Ctr, 801 University Ave, Syracuse, NY 13210
Membership(s): ATD; InfoComm International®

Visual Word Systems Inc
35 W 36 St, 8th fl, New York, NY 10018
Tel: 212-629-8383 *Fax:* 212-629-8333
Web Site: www.visualword.com
Key Personnel
Pres: Ike Eckstein *E-mail:* ike@visualword.com
Founded: 1981
Membership(s): InfoComm International®

Vital Learning LLC
1675 Larimer St, No 410, Denver, CO 80202
Tel: 402-592-1602 *Toll Free Tel:* 800-243-5858 *Fax:* 402-592-7142
E-mail: sales@vital-learning.com; info@vital-learning.com
Web Site: www.vital-learning.com
Key Personnel
CEO & Pres: Jay Tankersley
Dir, Affiliate Opers: Melodi Szymczak
Prod Mgr: Todd Macey
Cust Support Specialist: Kelly Duden
Produce & distribute training & development courses for businesses & organizations.
Catalog(s) available
Branch Office(s)
10665 Bedford Ave, No 202, Omaha, NE 68134 *Tel:* 402-592-1602
Membership(s): ATD

VITEC Multimedia
931 Benecia, Sunnyvale, CA 94085
Tel: 650-230-2400 *Toll Free Tel:* 800-451-5101 *Fax:* 404-320-3132
E-mail: info@vitec.com
Web Site: www.vitec.com
Key Personnel
Dir, US Opers: Lionel Zajde
VP, Prod Mgmt: Eli Garten
Founded: 1988
Worldwide leading provider of powerful digital video products that support end-to-end media solutions for broadcast, corporate, education, government, industrial, medical, military & Telco customers. By integrating world famous brands including Optibase, Focus, Como & Stradis, VITEC Multimedia now controls the complete video chain with professional-grade products for acquisition, encoding, processing, management & delivery. With over 100 R&D engineers specializing in digital video, we offer innovative & effective hardware & software, advanced technology research & custom product designs for world-class OEMs. VITEC Multimedia is headquartered in Paris, France, with worldwide R&D Sales & System Integration offices.
Branch Office(s)
99, rue Pierre Semard, 92324 Chatillon Cedex, France *Tel:* 01 46 73 06 06 *Fax:* 09 59 85 99 92 (headquarters)

Vitec Videocom Inc
Formerly Camera Dynamics
Division of The Vitec Group
709 Executive Blvd, Valley Cottage, NY 10989
Tel: 845-268-0100 *Fax:* 845-268-0113
E-mail: info-cd-usa@vitecgroup.com
Web Site: www.vitecgroup.com
Key Personnel
Pres: Jay Dishong
Dir, Vinten Radamec Cam Sales: Gary Rotondelli
Northeast Regl Sales Mgr: Bob Jones *E-mail:* bob.jones@vitechgroup.com
Inside Sales Coord: Mara-Lynne Brenner *Tel:* 203-402-7988
Camera support equipment.
Catalog(s) available
Online catalog(s) available
Foreign Office(s): Western Way, Bury St Edmunds, Suffolk IP33 3TB, United Kingdom *Tel:* (01284) 752121 *Fax:* (01284) 750560
Membership(s): NAB; SBE; SMPTE

Vitruvian Entertainment
727 N Victory Blvd, Burbank, CA 91502
Mailing Address: 4712 Admirality Way, Unit 417, Marina Del Ray, CA 90292
Tel: 818-244-3575; 818-720-3250
Web Site: vitruvianent.com
Key Personnel
Pres: Irfan Merchant *E-mail:* merchant@vitruvianent.com
Busn Opers & Prodr: Kalynn Jenkins
Founded: 2011
Virtual production, motion capture, 3D animation, stereo, event, live & post-production services. Specialize in television, commercials, promos, youtube content & corporate productions.

ViVi Co
PO Box 750, Glendale, CA 91209
Tel: 818-500-8889 *Fax:* 818-507-6600
E-mail: zibreathe@aol.com
Web Site: www.theartofbreathing.com
Key Personnel
Pres: Nancy Zi Li
Founded: 1993
Shipping Address: 222 Monterey Rd, Suite 1006, Glendale, CA 91206 *Tel:* 818-500-8084

VMI Inc
211 E Weddell Dr, Sunnyvale, CA 94089
Tel: 408-745-1700 *Fax:* 408-745-6721
E-mail: sales@vmivideo.com
Web Site: www.vmivideo.com
Key Personnel
Mktg Dir: Jennifer Dorsa
Founded: 1975
Catalog(s) available
Branch Office(s)
VMI Inc Broadcast & Professional Video, 11258 Monarch St, Unit A, Garden Grove, CA 92481, Contact: Lew Wilson *Tel:* 714-894-6100

VMI (Video Masters Inc)
PO Box 681100, Kansas City, MO 64168-1100
E-mail: sales@vmi.com
Web Site: www.vmi.com
Key Personnel
VP, Engg: Tom Schulze
Founded: 1976
Acoustic portable broadcast systems. Specialize in tactical loudspeakers, mobile broadcast & electronic systems integration.
Shipping Address: 2604 Industrial Dr, Suite 150, Kansas City, MO 64117-3142 *Tel:* 816-474-3995 *Fax:* 816-474-3975

VMS Inc
805 Airway Dr, Allegan, MI 49101-8516
Tel: 269-673-2200 *Toll Free Tel:* 800-343-6430 *Fax:* 269-673-9509
E-mail: sales@vms-online.com
Web Site: www.vms-online.com
Key Personnel
Pres: Michael S Walsh *E-mail:* mike@vms-online.com
Founded: 1986
Distributor of occupational training books, videos & software to schools.
Online catalog(s), 2 issues/yr, 3,000 titles in 6 major catalogs
Membership(s): Educational Exhibitor's Association

The Vocal Point/Profile Communications Ltd
1196 Habgood St, White Rock, BC V4B 4W9, Canada
Tel: 604-531-6908
Web Site: www.profilecomm.com
Key Personnel
Owner & Pres: Steve Herringer *E-mail:* steve@profilecomm.com
Founded: 1985
Audio, video & film voiceovers.

Voice & Video Rentals
4909 Ruffner St, San Diego, CA 92111
Tel: 858-560-5000 *Toll Free Tel:* 800-638-8878 *Fax:* 858-560-9900
Web Site: www.voiceandvideo.com
Key Personnel
CEO & Pres: Kenneth Gimbel
Founded: 1973
Audio & video rentals.

Volcano Video Productions, see Ka Io Productions Inc

VO2 Mix Studios
116 Spadina Ave, Suite 208, Toronto, ON M5V 2K6, Canada
Tel: 416-603-3954 *Fax:* 416-603-3957
E-mail: info@vo2mix.ca
Web Site: www.vo2mix.ca
Key Personnel
Founder: Euan Hunter *Tel:* 416-603-3954 ext 110 *E-mail:* ehunter@vo2mix.ca; Terry Wedel *Tel:* 416-603-3954 ext 112 *E-mail:* twedel@vo2mix.ca
Founded: 1999
Audio post facility.

Voyager Recordings & Publications
424 35 Ave, Seattle, WA 98122
Tel: 206-323-1112
E-mail: info@voyagerrecords.com
Web Site: www.voyagerrecords.com
Key Personnel
Founder & Owner: Vivian T Williams
Founded: 1967
Independent record label & book publishing company focusing on traditional fiddle & string band music from the Pacific Northwest & throughout North America.
Catalog(s) available

Voyetra Turtle Beach
100 Summit Lake Dr, Suite 100, Valhalla, NY 10595
Tel: 914-345-2255 *Fax:* 914-345-2266
E-mail: sales@turtlebeach.com
Web Site: www.turtlebeach.com
Key Personnel
VP, Opers: Scott Rankin
Audio equipment manufacturer.

VRSim Inc
222 Pitkin St, Suite 119, East Hartford, CT 06108-3220
Tel: 860-893-0080
E-mail: info@vrsim.net
Web Site: www.vrsim.net
Key Personnel
CEO & Pres: Matthew Wallace
CFO: Leslie Solomon
Opers Mgr: David Zboray
Off Mgr: Michele Sharpe
Founded: 2001
Virtual reality systems for industrial training & technical education.

VSA
2700 "F" St NW, Washington, DC 20566
Tel: 202-416-8898 *Fax:* 202-416-4840
E-mail: vsainfo@kennedy-center.org
Web Site: www.vsarts.org
Key Personnel
Dir: Betty Siegel
Founded: 1974
Creating a society for people with disabilities to learn, participate in & enjoy the arts.

VSG Digital Media Solutions
11126 Lindbergh Business Ct, St Louis, MO 63123
Tel: 314-487-8045 *Toll Free Tel:* 800-737-8045 *Fax:* 314-487-9387
Web Site: www.vsginc.net
Key Personnel
Owner: Chris Ramsey *Tel:* 314-487-8045 ext 103; Barry Romine *Tel:* 314-487-8045 ext 104
Pres: Patrick Reagan *Tel:* 314-487-8045 ext 117
Dir, Sales: Mike Gallagher *Tel:* 314-487-8045 ext 123
Founded: 1981
Full service media manufacturing. Facilities also located in Orlando, FL, Raleigh, NC, Nashville, TN & Dallas, TX.
Branch Office(s)
1033 Elm Hill Pike, Nashville, TN 37210, Sales: Greg Shriner *Tel:* 615-248-1010
1870 Crown Dr, Suite 1505, Farmers Branch, TX 75234, Acct Exec: Patrick Spellman *Tel:* 972-830-9400

VTP Inc
2721 W Magnolia Blvd, Burbank, CA 91505
Tel: 818-566-9898 *Toll Free Tel:* 800-422-2444
E-mail: sales@vtpcorp.com
Web Site: www.myvtp.com
Key Personnel
CEO & Pres: John L Palazzola
VP, Sales: Randy Marzec
Founded: 1979
Full line video & audio hardware distributors.
Branch Office(s)
41210 Bridge St, Novi, MI 48375
Membership(s): SMPTE

VTS Video & Media
3121D Fire Rd, Suite 105, Egg Harbor Township, NJ 08234
Toll Free Tel: 877-891-1002
E-mail: info@videotapingservice.com
Web Site: www.videotapingservice.com
Key Personnel
Mktg Dir: Stephanie Shapiro
Founded: 1981
DVD duplication.

Vutec Corp, Video Products Division
11711 W Sample Rd, Coral Springs, FL 33065-3155
Tel: 954-545-9000 *Toll Free Tel:* 800-770-4700 *Fax:* 954-545-9011 *Toll Free Fax:* 800-548-5885
E-mail: info@vutec.com; sales@vutec.com
Web Site: www.vutec.com
Key Personnel
Pres: Howard L Sinkoff
Founded: 1977
Manufacturer of video projection screens, accessories & AV presentation tools.
Brochure(s), biannual, free
Catalog(s), biannual, free
Membership(s): CEMA; Custom Electronic Design & Installation Association; InfoComm International®; NSCA

VWR International LLC
Radnor Corporate Ctr, Bldg 1, 100 Matsonford Rd, Suite 200, Radnor, PA 19087-8660
Mailing Address: PO Box 6660, Radnor, PA 19087-8660
Tel: 610-431-1700 (corp off) *Toll Free Tel:* 800-932-5000 (cust serv)
E-mail: solutions@vwr.com; vwrcustomerservice@vwr.com
Web Site: www.vwr.com; us.vwr.com
Catalog(s) available

WAC Lighting Co
44 Harbor Park Dr, Port Washington, NY 11050
Tel: 516-515-5000 *Toll Free Tel:* 800-526-2588 *Fax:* 516-515-5050 *Toll Free Fax:* 800-526-2585
E-mail: sales@waclighting.com
Web Site: www.waclighting.com
Key Personnel
CEO: Tony Wang
VP, Mktg: Sean Tham
Lighting fixture company.
Catalog(s) available
Branch Office(s)
1750 Archibald Ave, Ontario, CA 91561

Wacom Technology Corp
Affiliate of Wacom Co Ltd (Japan)
1311 SE Cardinal Ct, Vancouver, WA 98683
Tel: 360-896-9833 *Toll Free Tel:* 800-922-6613 *Fax:* 360-896-9734
Web Site: www.wacom.com
Key Personnel
Pres: Joe Deal
Manufacturer of pen tablets, interactive pen displays & digital interface solutions.

Waldom Electronics Corp
1801 Morgan St, Rockford, IL 61102-2690
Tel: 815-968-9661 *Toll Free Tel:* 800-435-2931 (cust serv) *Fax:* 815-968-9029
E-mail: sales@waldom.com; corp@waldom.com
Web Site: www.waldom.com
Key Personnel
Sales Mgr: Alan Conway *E-mail:* alan@waldom.com
Distribute audio equipment.

WalkerVision Interarts
PO Box 22533, San Diego, CA 92192-2533
Tel: 858-458-9038 *Fax:* 858-458-9104
Web Site: www.walkervisioninterarts.com
Key Personnel
Partner: Christopher Walker; Lea Ann Walker; Melissa Walker; Patrick E Walker *E-mail:* pwalker@cts.com
Founded: 1987
Full production services & video events.
Membership(s): PPA

Wallace Creative Inc
1705 NW 25 Ave, Portland, OR 97210
Tel: 503-224-9660
E-mail: info@wallyhood.com
Web Site: www.wallyhood.com
Key Personnel
Pres & Creative Dir: Donald Wallace *E-mail:* donw@wallyhood.com
Design & animation studio & conceptual design.
Membership(s): Oregon Media Production Association

Wallace Film Studios
258 Wallace Ave, Toronto, ON M6P 3N9, Canada
Tel: 416-538-3535
E-mail: info@wallacefilmstudios.ca
Web Site: wallacefilmstudios.ca
Key Personnel
Contact: Lesley Sherman
Three studios available with in-house lighting & grip availability for film, video or photographic production.

Wallach Entertainment
1400 Braeridge Dr, Beverly Hills, CA 90210
Tel: 310-278-4574 *Fax:* 310-273-0548
E-mail: gwallach@roadrunner.com
Key Personnel
Pres: George Wallach
Production company.

Walltalkers
Division of Koroseal Interior Products Group
3875 Embassy Pkwy, Fairlawn, OH 44333
Tel: 330-668-7600 *Toll Free Tel:* 800-820-9255 *Fax:* 330-668-7703
E-mail: customerservice@koroseal.com
Web Site: www.walltalkers.com
Key Personnel
Mgr, Cust Serv: Don Watson
Manufacture dry erase presentation wallcoverings.
Membership(s): ATD; InfoComm International®

The Walt Disney Co
500 S Buena Vista St, Burbank, CA 91521
Tel: 818-560-1000
Web Site: disney.com
Key Personnel
CEO & Pres: Robert W Iger
Founded: 1923

Walt Disney Records Consumer Products Division
Subsidiary of The Walt Disney Co
1201 Flower St, Glendale, AZ 91201
Tel: 818-560-1000
Web Site: disney.com; www.disneyconsumerproducts.com
Key Personnel
Pres: Bob Chapek
Founded: 1929
Catalog(s) available

Walt Disney Studio
500 S Buena Vista St, Burbank, CA 91521
Tel: 818-560-1000
Web Site: studioservices.go.com
Key Personnel
Pres, Disney Consumer Prods: Bob Chapek
Founded: 1923
Disney production & post-production facilities.

Walters-Storyk Design Group Inc (WSDG)
262 Martin Ave, Highland, NY 12528
Tel: 845-691-9300 *Fax:* 845-691-9361
E-mail: info@wsdg.com
Web Site: www.wsdg.com

Key Personnel
Principal & Designer: John Storyk
Principal & Interior Designer: Beth Walters
Full service architectural design & acoustical consulting firm specializing in media facility planning & technical commercial architecture, acoustics, mechanical noise control, sound system design, AV system design.

Walterscheid Productions
PO Box 995, Wichita, KS 67201
Tel: 316-258-1152
E-mail: bobwalter1@aol.com
Web Site: www.wponline.com
Founded: 1968
Create TV commercials & infomercials & business videos.

Wanted! Sound + Picture
409 King St W, Suite 300, Toronto, ON M5V 1K1, Canada
Tel: 416-596-1101 *Fax:* 416-596-0690
E-mail: info@wantedsp.com
Web Site: www.wantedsp.com
Key Personnel
Exec Prodr: Augusta Brook
Dir, Sales & Mktg/New Busn Devt: Bob Johnston
Voice & Music Dir: Earl Torno
Studio Mgr: Karen Murphy
Founded: 1970
Creative/production services for digital media/radio & television advertising. Original music & audio/video post-production for commercials, animation/anime, reality, documentary, corporate & live action.

Ward-Beck Systems Ltd
945 Middlefield Rd, Unit 9, Toronto, ON M1V 5E1, Canada
Tel: 416-335-5999 *Toll Free Tel:* 800-771-2556 *Fax:* 416-335-5202
E-mail: sales@ward-beck.com
Web Site: www.ward-beck.com
Key Personnel
COO: Kevin Lyver *E-mail:* kevinlyver@ward-beck.com
Mng Dir: Eugene L Johnson *E-mail:* eugenejohnson@ward-beck.com
Founded: 1967
Design & manufacture analog & digital broadcast equipment.
Catalog(s) available
Membership(s): NAB; SMPTE

Warner Bros Animation
Division of Warner Bros/Time-Warner
4000 Warner Blvd, Burbank, CA 91522
Tel: 818-954-6000
Web Site: www.warnerbros.com
Key Personnel
Pres: Sam Register
All facets of animation as well as programming.

Warner Bros Entertainment Inc
Division of Time Warner Inc
4000 Warner Blvd, Burbank, CA 91522
Tel: 818-954-3000 *Fax:* 818-954-4918
E-mail: wbsf@warnerbros.com
Web Site: www.warnerbros.com; studiofacilities.warnerbros.com
Key Personnel
CFO & EVP: Edward A Romano
Chief Digital Offr & EVP, Strategy & Busn Devt: Thomas Gewecke
EVP & Gen Coun: John Rogovin
EVP, Intl: Richard J Fox
EVP, Worldwide Corp Communs & Pub Aff: Dee Dee Myers
EVP, Worldwide HR: Kiko Washington
Founded: 1923
Fully integrated, broad-based entertainment company. Feature films to television, home entertainment/DVD, animation, product & brand licensing & interactive entertainment.

Warner Bros Production Sound & Video Services
Division of Time Warner Inc
4000 Warner Blvd, Burbank, CA 91522
Tel: 818-954-2511 *Fax:* 818-954-1037
E-mail: wbsf@warnerbros.com; wbsfproductionsound@warnerbros.com
Web Site: www.wbsf.com; www.wbsoundandvideo.com
Founded: 1955
Supplier of audio & video equipment for single & multi-camera productions, corporate presentations, meetings & special events.
Catalog(s) available

Warner/Chappell Production Music
1030 16 Ave S, Nashville, TN 37212
Toll Free Tel: 888-615-8729 *Fax:* 615-242-2455
E-mail: info@warnerchappellpm.com
Web Site: www.warnerchappellpm.com/615-music
Key Personnel
CEO & Pres, Worldwide: Randy Wachtler *E-mail:* randy.wachtler@warnerchappellpm.com
VP, Prodn: Aaron Gant *Tel:* 615-244-6515 *E-mail:* aaron.gant@warnerchappellpm.com
Prodn Mgr: Jennifer Sprague *E-mail:* jennifer.sprague@warnerchappellpm.com
Founded: 1984
Production music library & custom music production.
Branch Office(s)
10585 Santa Monica Blvd, Los Angeles, CA 90025, Trailer Sales Rep: Dan Epstein
1633 Broadway, 9th fl, New York, NY 10019
Membership(s): Production Music Association

Warner Home Video Inc
Subsidiary of Warner Bros Entertainment Inc
4000 Warner Blvd, Bldg 160, Burbank, CA 91522
Tel: 818-954-6000 *Fax:* 818-954-6480
Web Site: www.warnerbros.com
Key Personnel
Pres: Kim Wuthrich
SVP, New Media Applications: Lewis Ostrover
EVP, Sales: Mike Takac
VP, Dom Sales: Darlene Walters
Mng Dir, CN & Mexico: Schuyler Hollingsworth
Sales Dir: Joe Bakala
BP Sales Communs, Events: Amy Beth Chamberlin
Founded: 1980
Catalog(s) available
Branch Office(s)
3903 W Olive Ave, Suite 3139, Burbank, CA 91505, VP, Sales Communs: Christine Martinez *Tel:* 818-954-7300
3400 W Riverside Dr, Burbank, CA 91505
Shipping Address: 3903 W Olive Ave, Suite 3139, Burbank, CA 91505
Membership(s): Entertainment Merchants Association

WARPed Pictures
2447 Benedict Canyon Dr, Beverly Hills, CA 90210
Tel: 310-777-8828; 310-999-1219 (cell) *Fax:* 310-777-8805
Web Site: www.warpedpictures.com
Key Personnel
Pres: Volker Fleck *E-mail:* v@warpedpictures.com
Founded: 1996
Production service & representation company.

Water Bearer Films Inc
3239 Gateway Circle, Charlottesville, VA 22911
Tel: 434-923-8686 *Toll Free Tel:* 800-551-8304
E-mail: sales@waterbearerfilms.com
Web Site: store.waterbearerfilms.com
Key Personnel
Owner & Pres: Mike Stimler
Founded: 1988
Home viewing entertainment-gay themed films.

Waterworks Acoustics
1038 44 Ave, Oakland, CA 94601
Tel: 510-653-4300 *Fax:* 510-437-9231
E-mail: waterworksacoustics@earthlink.net
Web Site: www.soundpipes.com
Key Personnel
Pres: Tom George
Founded: 1986
High end audio, indoor/outdoor weatherproof speakers.
Catalog(s) available

WATL-TV Inc
Subsidiary of Gannett Broadcasting
One Monroe Place NE, Atlanta, GA 30324
Tel: 404-892-1611 *Fax:* 404-881-3635
Web Site: www.myatltv.com
Key Personnel
Pres & Gen Mgr: John Deushane
Local Sales Mgr: Mike Clifford
TV station.

Watson Desking
26246 Twelve Trees Lane NW, Poulsbo, WA 98370
Tel: 360-394-1300 *Toll Free Tel:* 800-426-1202 *Fax:* 360-394-1322
E-mail: service@watsondesking.com; info@watsondesking.com
Web Site: www.watsonfurniture.com
Key Personnel
CEO: Clif McKenzie
VP, Sales: Steve Hayes *Tel:* 360-394-1300 ext 215
Natl Sales Mgr: Mike Hanson
Manufacture ergonomic furniture/media storage.
Catalog(s) available

Watts Communications Inc
149 N 120 St, Wauwatosa, WI 53226
Tel: 414-727-9505 *Fax:* 414-727-9506
E-mail: sales@wattscom.com
Web Site: www.wattscom.com
Key Personnel
CEO & Founder: Keith Watts
Pres & Prodr: Jeff Watts *E-mail:* jeffw@wattscom.com
Founded: 1991
Full service production company specializing in promotional & training videos, television programming, web site design, CD-ROM & DVD authoring - from concept to completion.
Membership(s): MCA-I; NATAS

WaveGuide Studios, see Sirius Images Corp dba WaveGuide Studios

Waveland Software Inc
1900 W Berwyn Ave, Suite 2, Chicago, IL 60640
Tel: 773-334-0408 *Fax:* 773-334-0408
Key Personnel
Exec Dir: Jim Passin
Founded: 1976
Not for profit corporation.

Wavemaker Media Design
PO Box 226, Duncans Mills, CA 95430
Tel: 707-788-6040 *Fax:* 707-788-6040
E-mail: sales@wavemakermediadesign.com
Web Site: www.wavemakermediadesign.com
Key Personnel
Owner & Prodr: Steve Witte
Full service logo, print, web, video design & production company.

WaxWorks VideoWorks
Subsidiary of WaxWorks Inc
325 E Third St, Owensboro, KY 42303
Tel: 270-926-0008 *Toll Free Tel:* 800-825-8558 *Fax:* 270-663-0737
Web Site: www.waxworksonline.com
Key Personnel
Pres: Terry Woodward
VP, Sales: Clayton Nichols
Wholesale entertainment distributor.
Catalog(s) available

Don Wayne Magic Inc
10907 Magnolia Blvd, Suite 467, North Hollywood, CA 91601
Tel: 818-763-3192
E-mail: info@donwaynemagic.com
Web Site: www.donwaynemagic.com
Key Personnel
Owner & Dir: Don Wayne
Mechanical visual effects; designers of magic illusions.

Wayne State University Media Services
Division of Wayne State University Libraries
Purdy/Kresge Library, 5244 Gullen Mall, Detroit, MI 48202
Tel: 313-577-1980 *Fax:* 313-577-6777
E-mail: mediaservices@wayne.edu
Web Site: library.wayne.edu
Key Personnel
Assoc Dir: Alan Bartlett *Tel:* 313-993-4321 *E-mail:* ab2475@wayne.edu
University media library.
Catalog(s) available
Membership(s): AECT; Consortium of College & University Media Centers; Michigan Association for Media in Education

WCJB TV20
Subsidiary of Diversified Communications (Portland, Maine)
6220 NW 43 St, Gainesville, FL 32653
Tel: 352-416-0623 *Fax:* 352-373-6516
E-mail: comments@divcom.com
Web Site: divcom.com
Key Personnel
Prodn Mgr: Ron Bates
Founded: 1971
Studios, grip lighting truck, camera crew, digital editing, public service programs & commercial programs.

Weapons of Choice™
4075 Browns Valley Rd, Napa, CA 94558-4144
Tel: 707-226-2845
E-mail: info@weaponsofchoice.com
Web Site: weaponsofchoicetheatrical.com
Founded: 1990
Theatrical props distributor.

Webb Audio Visual Communication
3020 S West Temple, Salt Lake City, UT 84115
Tel: 801-484-8567 (installation)
Toll Free Tel: 877-909-8567 *Fax:* 801-484-8589
Web Site: www.webbav.com
Key Personnel
Owner & Pres: Steven M Webb
Owner & VP: Scott T Webb
Founded: 1955
Full service audio visual company.
Membership(s): InfoComm International®

Webster Communications
607 N Avenue 64, Los Angeles, CA 90042
Tel: 323-258-6741
E-mail: info@vanwebster.com
Web Site: www.vanwebster.com
Key Personnel
Founder & Pres: Van Webster
Independent creative presentation company.
Catalog(s) available
Membership(s): AES; The Recording Academy; SMPTE

WEEK TV
Division of Granite Broadcasting
2907 Springfield Rd, East Peoria, IL 61611
Tel: 309-698-2525 *Fax:* 309-698-9335
Web Site: www.week.com
Key Personnel
Pres & Gen Mgr: Mark DeSantis *E-mail:* mdesantis@week.com
Television station.

Wegener Communications
Technology Park, 11350 Technology Circle, Johns Creek, GA 30097
Tel: 770-814-4000; 770-814-4021 (sales); 770-814-4057 (cust serv) *Toll Free Tel:* 800-848-9467 (cust serv) *Fax:* 770-623-0698; 770-232-0621 (cust serv)
E-mail: info@wegener.com; globalsales@wegener.com; service@wegener.com
Web Site: www.wegener.com
Key Personnel
Chmn of the Bd: Robert Placek
CEO: Troy Woodbury
PR: Ken Leffingwell *Tel:* 770-814-4040 *E-mail:* k.leffingwell@wegener.com
Founded: 1978
Full range of customized media distribution solutions.

Weigl Publishers Inc
350 Fifth Ave, 59th fl, New York, NY 10118
Toll Free Tel: 866-649-3445 *Toll Free Fax:* 866-449-3445
Web Site: www.weigl.com
Key Personnel
Pres & Publr: Linda A Weigl *E-mail:* linda@weigl.com
Founded: 1992
Educational programming producer.
Catalog(s) available

Weisman Video Productions Inc, see WVP Boston

Alan Weiss Productions
270 White Plains Rd, Suite 2N, East Chester, NY 10709
Tel: 212-974-0606
E-mail: awpinfo@awptv.com
Web Site: www.awptv.com
Key Personnel
Pres & Exec Prodr: Alan Weiss
VP & Proj Mgr: Marilou Yacoub *Tel:* 212-974-0606 ext 313 *E-mail:* myacoub@alanweissproductions.com
Full service production company.

Welk Music Group
Division of The Welk Group Inc
11400 W Olympic Blvd, Suite 1450, Los Angeles, CA 90064
Tel: 310-829-9355 *Fax:* 310-315-9996
E-mail: info@vanguardrecords.com; order@vanguardrecords.com
Web Site: www.vanguardrecords.com
Key Personnel
SVP & Gen Mgr: Dan Sell
VP, Publicity: Lucy Sabini *Tel:* 310-829-9355 ext 137 *E-mail:* lsabini@vanguardrecords.com
Music distributors.
Catalog(s) available
Membership(s): Music Business Association

The Well-Tempered Music Library
PO Box 465, Middleboro, MA 02346-0465
Tel: 508-947-7387 *Fax:* 508-947-7387
E-mail: info@arfarfrecords.com; page@arfarfrecords.com
Web Site: www.arfarfrecords.com
Key Personnel
Pres: Erik Lindgren *E-mail:* erik@arfarfrecords.com
Buy-out music library consisting of 427 tracks on 7 CDs.
Catalog(s) available

Wells-Gardner Electronics Corp
9500 W 55 St, Suite A, McCook, IL 60525-3605
Tel: 708-290-2100 *Toll Free Tel:* 800-336-6630 *Fax:* 708-290-2200
Web Site: www.wellsgardner.com
Key Personnel
VP, Engg: Ted Panek *E-mail:* tpanek@wellsgardner.com
SVP, Global Sales: Wally Sad *E-mail:* wsad@wellsgardner.com
Founded: 1925
Manufacturer & integrator of LCD panels & touch screens.
Catalog(s), free, call to order

Welocalize
241 E Fourth St, Suite 207, Frederick, MD 21701
Tel: 301-668-0330 *Toll Free Tel:* 800-370-9515 *Fax:* 301-668-0335
E-mail: info@welocalize.com
Web Site: www.welocalize.com
Key Personnel
Co-Founder & CEO: Smith Yewell
Co-Founder: Julia Yewell
CFO: Jeff Ash
CTO: Eugene McGinty
SVP, Technol & Devt: Derek Coffey
VP, Global Mktg & Sales Opers: Jamie Glass
Founded: 1997
Translating & dubbing videos, AV, film & audio tapes into foreign languages.
Membership(s): ATA

WESCAM Inc
Division of L-3 Communications
649 N Service Rd W, Burlington, ON L7P 5B9, Canada
Tel: 905-633-4000 *Toll Free Tel:* 800-668-4355 *Fax:* 905-633-4100
E-mail: sales.wescam@l-3com.com
Web Site: www.wescam.com
Key Personnel
Pres: John Dehne
CFO & VP: Larry Spanier
CTO: Steve Tritchew
VP, Gen Coun & Secy: Bruce Latimer
VP & Gen Mgr: Allan Bignell
VP, Cust Serv: Rod Till
VP, Govt Sales & New Busn Devt: Paul Jennison
VP, HR: Roman Turchyn
VP, Opers: Mario Grande
Electro-optic/infrared laser imaging & targeting sensor sytems to the defense/military, homeland security & airborne law enforcement agencies.
BSI Division supplies wireless on-board camera systems for live television/broadcast sports.

Wespen Audio Visual Co
101 Riverside Dr, Hawthorn, PA 16230
Key Personnel
Pres: J Richard George
VP, Sales & Mktg: John D George
Founded: 1944
AV equipment supplier.
Catalog(s), annually, free
Online catalog(s), e-commerce web site updated weekly
Membership(s): InfoComm International®

West Coast Projections Inc
12463 Rancho Bernardo Rd, No 149, San Diego, CA 92128-2143
Tel: 858-674-7334

E-mail: wcpinfo@westcoastprojections.com
Web Site: westcoastprojections.com
Key Personnel
Pres: David Gibbs
Founded: 1980
Full service production company.

West Eagle Films Inc
800 Lower Ganges Rd, Salt Spring Island, BC V8K 2N5, Canada
Tel: 250-538-1780
E-mail: mailbox@westeaglefilms.com
Web Site: www.westeaglefilms.com
Key Personnel
Writer, Dir & Cinematographer: David Douglas
Prodr: Diane Roberts
Full service production company. Specialize in large format film production, innovative digital film design & multimedia communication exhibits for science centers & museums.

West Penn Wire
2833 W Chestnut St, Washington, PA 15301
Mailing Address: PO Box 762, Washington, PA 15301-0762
Tel: 724-222-7060 *Toll Free Tel:* 800-245-4964 *Fax:* 724-222-6420
E-mail: info@westpenn-wpw.com
Web Site: www.westpenn-wpw.com
Key Personnel
Pres: Scott Harden
VP, Sales: Andy Oswald *E-mail:* aoswald@westpenn-wpw.com
Dir, Engg: Mark Sams *E-mail:* msams@westpenn-wpw.com
Dir, Mktg: Aaron Reighard *E-mail:* areighard@westpenn-wpw.com
Dir, Sales-Eastern Region: Ron Leone *E-mail:* rleone@westpenn-wpw.com
Sr Prod Mgr: Todd Hirt *E-mail:* thirt@westpenn-wpw.com
Founded: 1971
Manufacturer of low voltage electronic wire & cable.
Catalog(s) available
Branch Office(s)
4641 Pell Dr, No 4, Sacramento, CA 95838 *Tel:* 916-922-6877
4606 Elk Ridge Ct, Suite F, Flowery Branch, GA 30542
1355 Bowes Rd, Elgin, IL 60123

Westar Music
105 W Beaver Creek Rd, Suite 4, Richmond Hill, ON L4B 1C6, Canada
Tel: 905-886-3100 *Toll Free Tel:* 800-665-3000 *Fax:* 905-886-6800
E-mail: info@westarmusic.com
Web Site: www.westarmusic.com
Key Personnel
Pres: Brian Nimens
Sales Mgr: Peter Alexander
Stock music library/production music.

Westbrook Technologies Inc
Subsidiary of DocuWare Corp
35 Thorpe Ave, Suite 201, Wallingford, CT 06492
Tel: 203-871-4984 *Fax:* 203-269-0322
E-mail: info@westbrooktech.com
Web Site: www.westbrooktech.com
Key Personnel
CEO: Thomas Schneck
CFO: Paul Remington
Sr Dir, Prod Mgmt & Devt: Jonathan Langdon
Sr Dir, Prof Servs: Brian Love
Dir, Quality Assurance: Daniel Fleischer
Software Support Mgr: Chad Folts
Founded: 1991
Provider of electronic document imaging & management solutions; Fortis, Fortis SE & FortisBlue.
Membership(s): AIIM

Westbury National Show Systems Ltd
772 Warden Ave, Toronto, ON M1L 4T7, Canada
Tel: 416-752-1371 *Fax:* 416-752-1382
E-mail: mail@westbury.com
Web Site: www.westbury.com
Key Personnel
Pres: David Bennett
VP: Frank Gerstein; Rob Sandolowich
Founded: 1971
Professional audio, AV, lighting & staging company. With more than a hundred full time employees at our Toronto headquarters, Westbury offers equipment rentals & production services as well as sound reinforcement, system sales, design, installation & repair services.
Membership(s): AES; InfoComm International®; NSCA

Westcoast Video Productions Inc
14141 Covello St, Suite 9-A, Van Nuys, CA 91405
Tel: 818-785-8033 *Toll Free Tel:* 800-477-8417 *Fax:* 818-785-8035
E-mail: mail@wvpinc.com
Web Site: www.wvpinc.com
Key Personnel
Pres: Larry Chong *E-mail:* larry@wvpinc.com
Founded: 1986
Catalog(s) available

Western Digital Corp
3355 Michelson Dr, Suite 100, Irvine, CA 92612
Tel: 949-672-7000 *Toll Free Tel:* 888-935-8893 *Fax:* 408-717-9282
Web Site: www.wdc.com
Key Personnel
CEO & Pres: Steve Milligan
Manufacturer of network systems.

Western Instructional Television Inc
1438 Gower St, No 18, Los Angeles, CA 90028
Tel: 323-466-8601
Key Personnel
Pres: Donna Matson
Children's educational programming distributor.
Catalog(s), free

Westlake Recording Studios
7265 Santa Monica Blvd, Los Angeles, CA 90046
Tel: 323-851-9800
E-mail: bookings@thelakestudios.com; info@thelakestudios.com
Web Site: www.thelakestudios.com
Key Personnel
Owner & Pres: Steve Burdick
Studio Mgr: Sara Clark
Recording studio for music, film, TV & commercials.

Stuart Westmorland Photography
14128 11 Dr SE, Mill Creek, WA 98012
Tel: 425-225-5733 *Fax:* 425-225-5733
E-mail: info@stuartwestmorland.com
Web Site: stuartwestmorland.com
Key Personnel
Owner: Stuart Westmorland *Tel:* 425-770-3951
Freelance photography & stock photo library with worldwide coverage. Specialties include concepts for advertising, weddings & portraits.
Membership(s): Stock Artists Alliance

Weston Woods Canada
Division of McNabb & Connolly
60 Briarwood Ave, Mississauga, ON L5G 3N6, Canada
Tel: 905-278-0566 *Toll Free Tel:* 866-722-1522 *Fax:* 905-278-2801 *Toll Free Fax:* 866-722-1822
E-mail: info@mcnabbconnolly.ca
Web Site: www.mcnabbconnolly.ca
Key Personnel
Founder: Steve Connolly
Founded: 1986
Canadian supplier of quality educational programming for K-12 schools, post secondary institutions & public libraries.

Weston Woods Studios Inc
Division of Scholastic Inc
90 Old Sherman Tpke, Danbury, CT 06816
Tel: 203-797-3520 *Toll Free Tel:* 800-243-5020 *Fax:* 203-797-3531
E-mail: westonwoodsquestions@scholastic.com
Web Site: www.scholastic.com/westonwoods
Key Personnel
VP & Gen Mgr: Linda Lee *Tel:* 800-243-5020 ext 3523 *E-mail:* llee@scholastic.com
Prodr/Acqs: Melissa Reilly Ellard *Tel:* 800-243-5020 ext 3522 *E-mail:* mreillyellard@scholastic.com
Founded: 1953
Produces public performance DVDs & audios based on outstanding children's books.
Catalog(s), biannual
Membership(s): AECT; ALA

Westworks Studios
4100 E Dry Creek Rd, Littleton, CO 80122
Toll Free Tel: 800-491-1947
E-mail: info@westworksstudios.com
Web Site: westworksstudios.com
Key Personnel
Sr Dir & Gen Mgr: Paul Catterson
Sr Prodn Mgr: Todd Smoots
Mgr, Prodn Engg: Robert Baker
Prodn Coord: Cora Palmer
Full service provider for HD studio production & post-production.

WETA Production Center
Subsidiary of WETA-Channel 26 (PBS)
3620 S 27 St, Arlington, VA 22206
Tel: 703-998-2054 *Fax:* 703-998-2706
Web Site: www.weta.org/tv/productioncenter
Key Personnel
Mgr: Jim Snyder
Video programming, videoconferencing, webcasts, teleconferencing, producer of local programming for the Washington DC area & local PBS station. Also produced & broadcast the Muscular Dystrophy Telethon.
Membership(s): NAB

David Wexler & Co
7807 E Greenway Rd, Suite 8, Scottsdale, AZ 85260-1717
Tel: 480-675-8888 *Fax:* 480-675-8900
E-mail: wexlermusic@aol.com
Web Site: www.wexlermusic.com
Key Personnel
Pres: B R Wexler
Founded: 1920

Wexler Music, see David Wexler & Co

WFRV-TV 5 CBS
1181 E Mason St, Green Bay, WI 54301
Mailing Address: PO Box 19055, Green Bay, WI 54307-9055
Tel: 920-437-5411 *Fax:* 920-437-4576
E-mail: mailbox@wfrv.com
Web Site: www.wfrv.com
Key Personnel
Pres & Gen Mgr: Joe Denk
Mktg Dir: Shawn Connelly
Assignment Ed: Ed Walters

Television station.
Membership(s): NAB; Wisconsin Broadcasters Association

WGBH Production Group
Division of WGBH Educational Foundation
One Guest St, Boston, MA 02135
Tel: 617-300-2200 *Fax:* 617-300-3460
Web Site: www.wgbh.org/productionservices
Key Personnel
Opers Mgr: Terry Quinn *Tel:* 617-300-2349 *E-mail:* terry.quinn@wgbh.org
Prodn Mgr: Kim Neger *Tel:* 617-300-2579 *E-mail:* kim.neger@wgbh.org
Two studios, post-production & tape playouts.

WGBH Stock Sales
Unit of WGBH Educational Foundation
One Guest St, Boston, MA 02135
Tel: 617-300-3939 *Fax:* 617-300-1056
E-mail: stock_sales@wgbh.org
Web Site: www.wgbhstocksales.org
Key Personnel
Lead Sales Supvr: James Auclair *Tel:* 617-300-3901 *E-mail:* james_auclair@wgbh.org
Stock footage from PBS's largest producer: NOVA, Frontline & American Experience.
Membership(s): Association of Commercial Stock Image Licensors

WGME-TV
Division of Sinclair Broadcast Group Inc
81 Northport Dr, Portland, ME 04103
Tel: 207-797-1313 *Fax:* 207-878-7842
E-mail: tvmail@wgme.com
Web Site: www.wgme.com
Key Personnel
Gen Mgr: Tom Humpage *E-mail:* thumpage@sbgtv.com
Television station.
Membership(s): NAB; NATPE

WGVU TV
Division of Grand Valley State University
301 Fulton St W, Grand Rapids, MI 49504-6492
Tel: 616-331-6666 *Toll Free Tel:* 800-442-2771
E-mail: wgvu@gvsu.edu
Web Site: www.wgvu.org
Key Personnel
Gen Mgr: Michael T Walenta
Prog Mgr: Ed Spier
Founded: 1972
Post-production services.
Membership(s): PBS

The Whale Video Co
225 Indian Creek Dr, Mechanicsburg, PA 17050
Tel: 717-763-9507
Web Site: www.whalevideo.com
Key Personnel
Founder & Pres: A Daniel Knaub *E-mail:* danknaub@comcast.net
Founded: 1988
Produce & distribute DVDs & videotapes of whales for education & entertainment.
Brochure(s) available
Membership(s): CSI

Whalley-Abbey Media Holdings Inc
1303 Greene Ave, Suite 300, Westmount, QC H3Z 2A7, Canada
Tel: 514-846-1940 *Fax:* 514-846-1550
Web Site: whalleyabbey.com
Key Personnel
Pres: Hans Rosenstein *E-mail:* hansr@painted-house.com
Founded: 1991
Producer of life-style programming.

Wheatstone Corp
600 Industrial Dr, New Bern, NC 28562
Tel: 252-638-7000 *Fax:* 252-635-1285
E-mail: sales@wheatstone.com
Web Site: www.wheatstone.com
Key Personnel
Dir, Sales: Jay Tyler *E-mail:* jay@wheatstone.com
Manufacture digital audio network infrastructures, digital audio control surfaces, audio network systems, audio network routers & signal processors.
Catalog(s) available

Whirlwind Music Distributors Inc
99 Ling Rd, Rochester, NY 14612
Tel: 585-663-8820 *Toll Free Tel:* 800-733-9473 (US only) *Fax:* 585-865-8930
E-mail: sales@whirlwindusa.com; techsupport@whirlwindusa.com; darylg@whirlwindusa.com (Canadian inquiries)
Web Site: whirlwindusa.com
Key Personnel
Pres: Michael Laiacona *Tel:* 800-733-9473 ext 147 *E-mail:* michael@whirlwindusa.com
Gen Mgr: Al Keltz *Tel:* 800-733-9473 ext 140 *E-mail:* alk@whirlwindusa.com
Mktg Dir/Artist Rel: Will Young *Tel:* 800-733-9473 ext 169 *E-mail:* willy@whirlwindusa.com
Chief Engr: Carl Cornell *Tel:* 800-733-9473 ext 130 *E-mail:* carlc@whirlwindusa.com
Prodn Mgr: Debbie Noble *Tel:* 800-733-9473 ext 142 *E-mail:* debbien@whirlwindusa.com
Online catalog(s) available
Membership(s): AES; NAB; NAMM, the National Association of Music Merchants; NSCA

WhisperRoom™ Inc
116 S Sugar Hollow Rd, Morristown, TN 37813
Tel: 423-585-5827 *Toll Free Tel:* 800-200-8168 *Fax:* 423-585-5831
E-mail: info@whisperroom.com
Web Site: www.whisperroom.com
Key Personnel
VP: Sharon White
Sales Mgr: Debbie Sweany
Founded: 1990
Manufacturer of sound isolation enclosures.
Catalog(s) available

White Buffalo Multimedia
13 Charles Bach Rd, Saugerties, NY 12477
Tel: 845-246-9995
Key Personnel
Creative Dir & Prodr: Shelli Lipton
Educational programming & digital multimedia services.

White Diamond Productions
2267 Hwy 43 S, Harrison, AR 72601
Tel: 870-365-7374
Key Personnel
Projs Mgr: Marty Roberts
Award winning production company.

White Dog Studios
587 Virginia Ave NE, Suite 1, Atlanta, GA 30306
Tel: 404-355-2200
E-mail: info@whitedogstudios.net
Web Site: www.whitedogstudios.net
Key Personnel
Founder & Pres: Curt Bush
Audio post-production facility.

White Lotus Foundation
2500 San Marcos Pass, Santa Barbara, CA 93105
Tel: 805-964-1944 *Fax:* 805-964-9617
E-mail: info@whitelotus.org
Web Site: www.whitelotus.org
Key Personnel
Founder & Pres: Mr Ganga White
Trustee & Dir: Tracey Rich
Yoga educational programming.

White Rain Films Ltd
2009 Dexter Ave N, Seattle, WA 98109
Tel: 206-682-5417 *Toll Free Tel:* 800-816-5244 *Fax:* 206-682-3038
E-mail: info@whiterainfilms.com
Web Site: www.whiterainfilms.com
Key Personnel
Owner & Prodr: Bill Phillips
Dir & Ed: Brad Bolling
Ed: Rick Barbarino
New Media: Chris Auger
Founded: 1991
Full service production company.

White Swan Music Inc
6395 Gunpark Dr, Suite A, Boulder, CO 80301
Tel: 303-527-0770 *Toll Free Tel:* 800-825-8656 *Fax:* 303-527-0771
E-mail: info@whiteswanmusic.com
Web Site: whiteswanmusic.com
Key Personnel
Pres: Parmita Pushman
Distributes a diverse catalog of yoga & world music.
Catalog(s) available
Membership(s): Museum Store Association; Network of Alternatives for Publishers, Retailers & Artists Inc

William F White International Inc
Member of Comweb Group
800 Islington Ave, Toronto, ON M8Z 6A1, Canada
Tel: 416-239-5050 *Toll Free Tel:* 800-465-0160 (CN only); 800-268-2200 *Fax:* 416-207-2777
E-mail: info@cinequipwhite.com
Web Site: www.whites.com
Key Personnel
Chmn & CEO: Paul Bronfman *E-mail:* paul@comwebmail.com
EVP & CFO: Munir Noorbhai *Tel:* 416-207-2766 *E-mail:* mnoorbhai@whites.com
VP, Busn Devt: Rick Perotto *Tel:* 416-207-2051 *E-mail:* rperotto@whites.com
VP, Indus & Govt Rels: David Hardy *Tel:* 416-207-2751 *E-mail:* dhardy@whites.com
Founded: 1963
Motion picture, television & theatrical equipment supply.
Branch Office(s)
Bldg H5-CFB Currie, 4530 Quesnay Wood Dr SW, Calgary, AB T3E 7J3, Canada, Asst Gen Mgr: Sean Toner *Tel:* 403-279-2693 *Fax:* 403-279-8683
8363 Lougheed Hwy, Unit 100, Burnaby, BC V5A 1X3, Canada, COO & EVP, Sales & Mktg: Paul Roscorla *Tel:* 604-253-5050 *Toll Free Tel:* 800-663-1733 *Fax:* 604-253-5055
11-2073 Logan Ave, Winnipeg, MB R2R 0J1, Canada, Gen Mgr: Steve Morrisson *Tel:* 204-799-5434
Tour Tech East, 180 Thornhill Dr, Unit 2, Dartmouth, NS B3B 1V3, Canada *Tel:* 902-450-1284
828 Beatrice Crescent, Sudbury, ON P3A 3E6, Canada, VP, Commercial Prodn Servs: Dan St Armour *Tel:* 705-562-1992; 416-847-8337

The Whitlock Group
12820 West Creek Pkwy, Richmond, VA 23238
Tel: 804-273-9100 *Toll Free Tel:* 800-726-9843 *Fax:* 804-273-9380
E-mail: information@whitlock.com
Web Site: www.whitlock.com
Key Personnel
Founder & Chmn: John Whitlock
CEO: Doug Hall *E-mail:* halld@whitlock.com
COO: Roger Patrick
CFO: Mark Baker
Dir, Mktg & Communs: Cheryl Cox
Broadcast & presentation solutions.

Catalog(s) available
Branch Office(s)
20099 Ashbrook Pl, Suite 105, Ashburn, VA 20147, Contact: Ewan Smith *Tel:* 703-297-8561 *E-mail:* smithe@whitlock.com
230 Clearfield Ave, Suite 103, Virginia Beach, VA 23462, Contact: Rob Krupp *Tel:* 757-671-7478 *Fax:* 757-671-7481 *E-mail:* kruppr@whitlock.com
108 Court Way, Pelham, AL 35124, Contact: John Schnibbe *Tel:* 770-993-1001 *E-mail:* schnibbej@whitlock.com
48017 Fremont Blvd, Fremont, CA 95483, Contact: Tom Govan *Tel:* 510-344-5618 *E-mail:* govant@whitlock.com
6555 S Kenton St, Suite 301, Centennial, CO 80112, Contact: Ken Bayern *Tel:* 303-799-1480 *Fax:* 303-799-8539 *E-mail:* bayernk@whitlock.com
15712 SW 41 St, Suite 11, Davie, FL 33331, Contact: John Schnibbe *Tel:* 954-384-4286 *Fax:* 954-473-0205
5910 Breckenridge Pkwy, Suite H, Tampa, FL 33610, Contact: John Schnibbe *Tel:* 813-886-5252 *Fax:* 813-884-4145 *E-mail:* schnibbej@whitlock.com
1075 Windward Ridge Pkwy, Suite 180, Atlanta, GA 30005, Contact: John Schnibbe *Tel:* 770-993-1001 *Fax:* 770-992-8175 *E-mail:* schnibbej@whitlock.com
1000 E State Pkwy, Suite F, Schaumburg, IL 60173, Contact: John Bagnell *Tel:* 847-380-1007 *E-mail:* bagnellj@whitlock.com
1001 Avenue of the Americas, 11th fl, New York, NY 10018, Contact: John Cerone *Tel:* 212-719-7555 *Fax:* 212-719-7554 *E-mail:* ceronej@whitlock.com
4101 Stuart Andrew Blvd, Suite F, Charlotte, NC 28217, Contact: Nick Lenaeus *Tel:* 704-494-3500 *E-mail:* lenaeusn@whitlock.com
4020 Stirrup Creek Dr, Suite 111, Durham, NC 27703, Contact: Nick Lenaeus *Tel:* 919-806-1009 *Toll Free Tel:* 877-806-1009 *Fax:* 919-806-1016 *E-mail:* lenaeusn@whitlock.com
3600 McClaren Woods Dr, Coraopolis, PA 15108, Contact: John Cerone *Tel:* 610-296-0100 *Fax:* 610-296-2583 *E-mail:* ceronej@whitlock.com
9048 William Penn Hwy, Suite 9, Huntingdon, PA 16652, Contact: John Cerone *Tel:* 610-296-0100 *Fax:* 610-296-2583 *E-mail:* ceronej@whitlock.com
273 Great Valley Pkwy, Malvern, PA 19355, Contact: John Cerone *Tel:* 610-296-0100 *Fax:* 610-296-2583 *E-mail:* ceronej@whitlock.com
11100 Metric Blvd, Suite 200E, Austin, TX 78758, Contact: Jason Carr *Tel:* 512-280-3710 *Fax:* 512-933-0291 *E-mail:* carrj@whitlock.com
9101 Jameel Rd, Suite 160, Houston, TX 77040, Contact: Jason Carr *Tel:* 713-796-0700 *Fax:* 713-796-0701 *E-mail:* carrj@whitlock.com
Gateway Business Ctr, Suite 320, 6005 Commerce Dr, Irving, TX 75063, Contact: Jason Carr *Tel:* 972-465-8888 *Fax:* 972-465-8223 *E-mail:* carrj@whitlock.com
15207 NE 95 St, Redmond, WA 98052, Contact: John Rasanen *Tel:* 425-861-3484 *Fax:* 425-861-3481 *E-mail:* rasanenj@whitlock.com
Membership(s): InfoComm International®

Whole Person Associates Inc
101 W Second St, Suite 203, Duluth, MN 55802-5004
Tel: 218-727-0500 *Toll Free Tel:* 800-247-6789 *Fax:* 218-727-0505
E-mail: books@wholeperson.com
Web Site: www.wholeperson.com
Key Personnel
Publr: Carlene Sippola
Founded: 1980
Distribute & produce AV programs on stress management & wellness promotion.
Catalog(s), quarterly, free

WHYY Inc
Independence Mall West, 150 N Sixth St, Philadelphia, PA 19106
Tel: 215-351-1200 *Fax:* 215-351-0398
E-mail: talkback@whyy.org
Web Site: www.whyy.org
Key Personnel
CEO & Pres: William J Marrazzo *E-mail:* wmarrazzo@whyy.org
COO & EVP: Kyra G McGrath *E-mail:* kmcgrath@whyy.org
CFO & SVP: A William Dana *E-mail:* bdana@whyy.org
CTO & VP: William J Weber *E-mail:* bweber@whyy.org
Radio recording facility.
Branch Office(s)
625 Orange St, Wilmington, DE 19801 *Tel:* 302-888-1200 *Fax:* 302-575-0346

Wide Eye Productions
1018 W Hays St, Boise, ID 83702
Tel: 208-336-0391 *Fax:* 208-336-6644
E-mail: info@wideeye.tv
Web Site: wideeye.tv
Key Personnel
Dir & Photog: Tom Hadzor *Tel:* 208-861-1184 (cell)
Writer & Prodr: Jennifer Isenhart *Tel:* 208-861-6824 (cell)
Founded: 1996
Full service professional & broadcast video production utilizing top of the line P2 Panasonic Vancam, sound, lighting & non-linear editing gear. ENG/EFP. Branch office in Seattle, WA.
Membership(s): NATAS

WIFR-TV
Division of Gray Television Inc
2523 N Meridian Rd, Rockford, IL 61101
Tel: 815-987-5300 *Fax:* 815-965-0981
E-mail: talkto23@wifr.com
Web Site: www.wifr.com
Key Personnel
Gen Mgr: Tim Myers *E-mail:* tim.myers@wifr.com
Opers Mgr: Jeff Clark *E-mail:* jeff.clark@wifr.com
Television programming.

Wild Plum
2128 Narcissus Ct, Venice, CA 90291
Tel: 310-823-7445 *Fax:* 310-578-1445
Web Site: www.wildplum.tv
Key Personnel
Partner & CFO: Alisa Allen *Tel:* 818-802-8886 *E-mail:* alisa@wildplum.tv
Partner & Exec Prodr: Shelby Sexton *Tel:* 310-962-9340 *E-mail:* shelby@wildplum.tv
Creative Dir: Ben Ross *Tel:* 310-923-8159 *E-mail:* ben@wildplum.tv
Founded: 2007

Wild Visions Inc
PO Box 42194, Phoenix, AZ 85080
Tel: 623-512-9810
Web Site: www.wildvisions.net
Key Personnel
Pres: Mike Pellegatti *E-mail:* mike@wildvisions.net
TV & video productions using HD, DVCAM & Beta SP cameras. Final cut & PCO editing.

Wilderness Video
888 Beswick Way, Ashland, OR 97520
Tel: 541-488-9363
Web Site: www.wildernessvideo.com
Key Personnel
Owner: Robert Glusic *E-mail:* bob@wildernessvideo.com
Founded: 1980
Collection of HD stock nature footage & 35mm timelapse.

Wildfire Lighting & Visual Effects
2908 Oregon Ct, Suite G1, Torrance, CA 90503
Tel: 310-755-6780 *Toll Free Tel:* 800-937-8065 *Fax:* 310-755-6781
E-mail: mail@wildfirefx.com; sales@wildfirefx.com
Web Site: www.wildfirefx.com
Key Personnel
Founder & Chmn: Laurence Friedman
CEO & Pres: John Berardi
Founded: 1989
Manufacturer of long-throw UV (blacklight) fixtures, UV fluorescent paints & materials & scenic art.
Catalog(s) available
Membership(s): IAAPA; Themed Entertainment Association

Wildfire Post Production Studios
Division of Digital Ventures Inc
640 S San Vicente Blvd, Los Angeles, CA 90048
Tel: 323-951-1700 *Fax:* 323-951-1710
Web Site: www.wildfirepost.com
Founded: 2007
Staging products.
Branch Office(s)
800 Common St, New Orleans, LA 70112
2505 Jefferson St NE, Albuquerque, NM 87110

John Wiley & Sons Inc
111 River St, Hoboken, NJ 07030
Tel: 201-748-6000 *Toll Free Tel:* 800-225-5945 *Fax:* 201-748-6088
E-mail: info@wiley.com
Web Site: www.wiley.com
Key Personnel
CEO & Pres: Stephen M Smith
CFO & EVP: John Kritzmacher
CTO & EVP: Patrik Dyberg
Chief Mktg Offr & EVP: Clay Stobaugh
EVP & Gen Coun: Gary M Rinck
EVP, Educ: Joseph S Heider
EVP, Global Res: Steven Miron
EVP, HR: MJ O'Leary
EVP, Prof Devt: Mark Allin
SVP & Corp Cont: Edward J Melando
SVP & Treas: Vincent Marzano
SVP, Intl Devt & GR Sales: Reed Elfenbein
SVP, Planning & Devt: John Semel
Corp Secy: Edward J May
Founded: 1807

The Will-Burt Co
169 S Main St, Orrville, OH 44667
Tel: 330-682-7015; 330-684-4000 (cust serv) *Fax:* 330-684-1190
E-mail: contact_us@willburt.com
Web Site: www.willburt.com
Key Personnel
CEO & Pres: Jeff Evans
Dir, Mktg & Busn Devt: Scott Hinterleiter
Mktg Communs Specialist: Dave Kotsmire
Manufacture telescoping masts & portable towers for the broadcast & entertainment industries.
Branch Office(s)
Integrated Tower Systems, 2703 Dawson Rd, Tulsa, OK 74110 *Toll Free Tel:* 800-850-8535 *Fax:* 918-749-8537
Foreign Office(s): GEROH, Fischergasse 25, Waischenfeld, Germany *Tel:* (09202) 18-0 *Fax:* (09202) 18-11 *E-mail:* info@geroh.com *Web Site:* www.geroh.com
One Fullerton Rd, No 02-01, Singapore 049213, Singapore, Contact: Felix Wu *Tel:* 6832 5689 *Fax:* 6722 0664 *E-mail:* xfwu@willburt.com

Morris Business Ctr, Unit P, Morris Farm, Old Holbrook, Horsham, West Sussex RH12 4TW, United Kingdom, Contact: Christie Williams
Tel: (01403) 265532 *Fax:* (01403) 259072
E-mail: cwilliams@willburt.com

Williams Sound Corp
10300 Valley View Rd, Eden Prairie, MN 55344-3446
Tel: 952-943-2252 *Toll Free Tel:* 800-328-6190 *Fax:* 952-943-2174
E-mail: info@williamssound.com
Web Site: www.williamssound.com
Key Personnel
CEO & Pres: Paul Ingebrigtsen *E-mail:* pauli@williamssound.com
CFO & VP, Fin & Admin: Richard Lough
VP, Mktg: Janet Beckman *E-mail:* janetb@williamssound.com
VP, Sales: Anthony Braun *E-mail:* anthony@williamssound.com
Founded: 1976
Manufacturer of large area FM, infrared, loop & digital wireless communication assistive listening devices, wireless intercom, tour guide, language interpretation.
Catalog(s), available separately for commercial sound products, assistive listening products, listening accessories
Membership(s): International Technology and Engineering Educators Association; NSCA

Willoughby's Imaging Center
298 Fifth Ave, New York, NY 10001
Tel: 212-564-1600 *Toll Free Tel:* 800-378-1898 *Fax:* 212-564-1608
E-mail: sales@willoughbys.com; customersupport@willoughbys.com
Web Site: www.willoughbys.com
Key Personnel
Pres: Joseph Douek
Founded: 1898
Catalog(s) available
Membership(s): InfoComm International®

Willow Creek Press Inc
PO Box 147, Minocqua, WI 54548-0147
Tel: 715-358-7010 *Toll Free Tel:* 800-850-9453 *Fax:* 715-358-2807
E-mail: info@willowcreekpress.com
Web Site: www.willowcreekpress.com
Key Personnel
VP, Sales: Jeremy Petrie *E-mail:* jpetrie@willowcreekpress.com
Distribute nature birding & pet videos; publish outdoor, hunting, cooking books, calendars & pet related gift items.
Catalog(s) available
Shipping Address: 9931 Hwy 70 W, Minocqua, WI 54548

Willow Mixed Media Inc
25 Lennox Ave, Glenford, NY 12433
Mailing Address: PO Box 194, Glenford, NY 12433-0194
Tel: 845-657-2914
E-mail: video@hvc.rr.com
Web Site: www.willowmixedmedia.org; www.documentaryworld.com
Key Personnel
Pres: Tobe Carey
Edit DVDs & documentary production.
Online catalog(s) available

Wilmington Camera Services
905 N 23 St, Wilmington, NC 28405
Tel: 910-343-1089 *Fax:* 910-343-0247
E-mail: info@wilmingtoncameraservices.com
Key Personnel
Owner: Joe Dunton
Rental Mgr: Channing Duke
Founded: 1991
Motion picture camera rental & anamorphic lens specialists.

Wilray Audio Visual Corp
615 Jackson Valley Rd, Port Murray, NJ 07865
Tel: 908-689-1300 *Toll Free Tel:* 800-452-9184 *Fax:* 908-689-8839
E-mail: wilray@mindspring.com
Key Personnel
Pres & Gen Mgr: Ray Malejko
AV equipment distributor.

Wilson Case Inc
113 Road 3168, Hastings, NE 68901-9418
Tel: 402-463-5040 *Toll Free Tel:* 800-322-5493 *Fax:* 402-463-5276
E-mail: sales@wilsoncase.com
Web Site: www.wilsoncase.com
Founded: 1976
Custom manufacturer of ATA300 (cat 1) protective cases.
Catalog(s), free
Online catalog(s) available

H Wilson Co
Division of EBSCO Industries Inc
2245 Delany Rd, Waukegan, IL 60087
Tel: 847-244-1800 *Toll Free Tel:* 800-245-7224; 800-323-4656 (sales) *Fax:* 708-210-2069; 847-244-1818 (sales) *Toll Free Fax:* 800-245-8224; 800-327-1698 (sales)
E-mail: sales@hwilson.com; info@wilson.com; customerservice@wilson.com
Web Site: www.hwilson.com
Key Personnel
Mktg & Travel Show Coord: Joanne Townsend *Tel:* 800-323-4656 ext 142 *E-mail:* jbilder@luxorfurn.com
Founded: 1959
Catalog(s) available
Membership(s): AECT; Education Market Association; InfoComm International®; NSCA

Wilson McLeran Inc
41 Corey Hill Rd, Saxtons River, VT 05154
Mailing Address: PO Box 744, Saxtons River, VT 05154-0744
Tel: 802-869-3111 *Toll Free Tel:* 800-562-9646 *Fax:* 802-869-3111
Web Site: www.job-bridge.com
Key Personnel
Pres: Robert F Wilson *E-mail:* rfwilson@job-bridge.com
VP & Secy: Martha Buchanan
Creative Dir: Robert S Tinnon
Founded: 1988
Online catalog(s) available
Membership(s): American Association of Journalists & Authors; The Authors Guild

Wiltronix
16850 Oakmont Ave, Washington Grove, MD 20880
Mailing Address: PO Box 364, Washington Grove, MD 20880-0364
Tel: 301-258-7676 *Toll Free Tel:* 800-848-7870 *Fax:* 301-854-3434
E-mail: equipsales@wiltronix.com
Web Site: www.wiltronix.com
Key Personnel
Pres: Dwight Wilcox
Mktg Mgr: Ellen Packard
Founded: 1970
Distribute scan converters & Internet to HDTV equipment.
Membership(s): IEEE Computer Society; SBE; SMPTE

Win Media Inc
317 N Dodge St, Burlington, WI 53105
Tel: 262-763-6397
E-mail: info@winmediainc.com
Web Site: www.winmediainc.com
Key Personnel
Pres: Shad Branen *Tel:* 262-763-6397 ext 11 *E-mail:* shad@winmediainc.com
Multimedia development services.

Winchester Electronics Corp
68 Water St, Norwalk, CT 06854
Tel: 203-741-5400
E-mail: info@winchesterelectronics.com
Web Site: www.winchesterelectronics.com
Key Personnel
CEO & Pres: Kevin Perhamus
Inside Sales Busn Mgr: Beth Beadle *Tel:* 203-741-5481 *E-mail:* beth_beadle@winchesterelectronics.com
Founded: 1941
Catalog(s) available
Membership(s): EDS; NAB; SMPTE

Wind River Broadcast Center
117 E 11 St, Loveland, CO 80537
Tel: 970-669-3442 *Toll Free Tel:* 800-669-3993 *Fax:* 970-663-6081
Web Site: www.windriverbroadcast.com
Key Personnel
Owner: Jim McDonald *E-mail:* jim@windriverbroadcast.com
Broadcast services.
Product sheet(s) available

Windel International/Weyel
Division of ICA Corp
3714 Illinois Ave, St Charles, IL 60174-2421
Toll Free Tel: 800-395-7093 *Fax:* 630-587-2833
Web Site: www.windel.com
Catalog(s) available
Membership(s): ASTO; CSI

WindTech™ Microphone Windscreens & Accessories
Division of Olsen Audio Group Inc
7845 E Evans Rd, Scottsdale, AZ 85260-2919
Tel: 480-998-7140 *Fax:* 480-998-7192
E-mail: information@olsenaudio.com; webinfo3@olsenaudio.com
Web Site: www.olsenaudio.com; www.windtech.tv
Key Personnel
Pres: Craig N Olsen
Founded: 1976
Catalog(s) available
Membership(s): AES; NAMM, the National Association of Music Merchants

The Wine Appreciation Guild Ltd
360 Swift Ave, Unit 30-40, South San Francisco, CA 94080
Tel: 650-866-3020 *Toll Free Tel:* 800-231-9463 *Fax:* 650-866-3513
E-mail: info@wineappreciation.com
Web Site: www.wineappreciation.com
Key Personnel
Pres: Donna Bottrell *E-mail:* donna@wineappreciation.com
Founded: 1939
Publisher & distributor of wine education materials: audiotapes, videotapes, DVDs, CD-ROMs & multimedia packages.
Catalog(s), annual
Membership(s): American Wine Society; The Wine Institute

Winegard Co
2736 Mt Pleasant St, Suite 140, Burlington, IA 52601
Tel: 319-754-0600 *Toll Free Tel:* 800-288-8094 *Fax:* 319-754-0787 *Toll Free Fax:* 800-247-8221
Web Site: www.winegard.com

Key Personnel
Natl Sales Mgr: Keith Larson *Tel:* 319-754-0628 *E-mail:* klars@winegard.com
Manufacture TV antenna & satellite television products.
Catalog(s) available

Wings Wildlife Production, see Birds & Animals Unlimited

Babe Winkelman Productions Inc
7119 Forthun Rd S, Baxter, MN 56425
Mailing Address: PO Box 407, Brainerd, MN 56401
Tel: 218-822-4424 *Toll Free Tel:* 800-333-0471 *Fax:* 218-822-7436
Web Site: www.winkelman.com
Key Personnel
Pres: Babe Winkelman *E-mail:* babe@winkelman.com
Prodr: Ray Eng
Produce two nationally syndicated outdoor fishing & hunting shows. Panasonic DVC Pro 50 cameras, 2 media cameras, 1000 Avid Editing Systems. DVC Pro 50 Deck, Unity 600 GB digital storage. Other effects, Bryce 3D Graphics, production studio. Custom production commercials, industrial tapes & raw footage sales.

Winsted Corp
10901 Hampshire Ave S, Minneapolis, MN 55438
Tel: 952-944-9050 *Toll Free Tel:* 800-447-2257 *Fax:* 952-944-1546 *Toll Free Fax:* 800-421-3839
E-mail: info@winsted.com
Web Site: www.winsted.com
Key Personnel
CEO: Steve Hoska
Pres: Randy Smith
Natl Sales Mgr: Wayne Cook
Founded: 1963
Manufacture control room consoles, furniture & vertical racks.
Catalog(s), annual
Branch Office(s)
1750 Breckinridge Pkwy, Suite 100, Duluth, GA 30096-7576 *Tel:* 770-840-0880 *Toll Free Tel:* 800-237-5606 *Fax:* 770-840-9685 *E-mail:* info@techinteriors.com *Web Site:* techinteriors.com
Foreign Office(s): Winsted Ltd, Hampton Lovett Industrial Estate, Lovett Rd, Units 7-8, Droitwich WR9 0QG, United Kingdom *Tel:* (0190) 5770276 *Fax:* (0190) 5779791 *E-mail:* info@winsted.co.uk *Web Site:* www.winsted.co.uk
Membership(s): MCA-I; NAB

Winter Productions
10625 S Hoyne, Chicago, IL 60643
E-mail: winterpr@aol.com
Web Site: www.winterproductions.com
Key Personnel
Pres: Don Winter *Tel:* 773-405-3899 (cell)
Full service production company.

Wintergreen Learning Materials
3075 Line 8, RR2, Bradford, ON L3Z 2A5, Canada
Toll Free Tel: 800-268-1268 *Toll Free Fax:* 800-567-8054
E-mail: info@wintergreen.ca
Web Site: www.wintergreen.ca
Key Personnel
CFO: Joe Hayward
Pres: Michael Hayward
Educational programming distributor.

Winterland Studios
5417 Boone Ave N, New Hope, MN 55428
Tel: 763-971-8943 *Fax:* 763-971-8952
E-mail: studio@winterlandstudios.com
Web Site: www.winterlandstudios.com
Key Personnel
Prodr & Engr: Todd Fitzgerald *E-mail:* todd@winterlandstudios.com

Wired 4 Sound Inc
PO Box 683, Clifton, NJ 07012-0683
Tel: 973-773-2565 *Toll Free Fax:* 888-453-8819
E-mail: info@wired4sound.com
Web Site: www.wired4sound.com
Key Personnel
CEO & Pres: Andre Grandinetti *Tel:* 973-773-2565 ext 105 *E-mail:* agrandinetti@wired4sound.com
Founded: 1987
Audio, video design/engineering, consulting & installation services.
Catalog(s) available
Shipping Address: 17 Frances Ct, Cedar Grove, NJ 07009
Membership(s): Custom Electronic Design & Installation Association; NSCA

Wireless Xcessories Group Inc
1840 County Line Rd, Suite 301, Huntingdon Valley, PA 19006
Tel: 215-322-4600 *Toll Free Tel:* 800-233-0013 *Toll Free Fax:* 866-570-7686
E-mail: sales@wirexgroup.com
Web Site: store.wirexgroup.com
Key Personnel
VP: Susan Rade *Tel:* 866-848-0680 *E-mail:* suerade@wirexgroup.com
Manufacturer of pagers & accessories.

Wirestrippers.com
34925 Cherry St, Wildomar, CA 92595
Tel: 951-245-6212 *Toll Free Tel:* 800-490-8520 *Fax:* 951-245-6213
E-mail: wirestrippers@verizon.net
Web Site: www.wirestrippers.com
Key Personnel
Pres: Grant Rupert
Founded: 1952
Wire processing equipment/manufacture (MSC-100 cut & strip machines).
Brochure(s), available online

Wireworks Corp
380 Hillside Ave, Hillside, NJ 07205
Tel: 908-686-7400 *Toll Free Tel:* 800-642-9473 *Fax:* 908-686-0483
E-mail: sales@wireworks.com; info@wireworks.com
Web Site: www.wireworks.com
Key Personnel
Pres: Gerald J Krulewicz *E-mail:* krulewicz@wireworks.com
Treas: Larry J Williams *E-mail:* williams@wireworks.com
Inside Sales Mgr: Richard Chilvers *E-mail:* chilvers@wireworks.com
Founded: 1974
Manufacturer of audio & video cable assemblies.
Membership(s): AES; InfoComm International®; NAB; NSCA

Wisconsin Public Television
Division of University of Wisconsin Extension-Wisconsin Education Communications Board
821 University Ave, Madison, WI 53706
Tel: 608-263-2121 *Toll Free Tel:* 800-422-9707 *Fax:* 608-263-9763
E-mail: comments@wpt.org
Web Site: www.wpt.org
Key Personnel
Dir, Prodn: Kathy Bissen
Dir, Programming: Gary Denny
Dir, Television: James Steinbach *Tel:* 608-263-1232
Exec Prodr, Prodn Servs: Laurie Gorman *Tel:* 608-263-4106 *Fax:* 608-263-0429 *E-mail:* laurie.gorman@wpt.org
Brochure(s) available

Wisconsin Technical College System Foundation Inc
One Foundation Circle, Waunakee, WI 53597-8914
Tel: 608-849-2424; 608-849-2400 *Toll Free Tel:* 800-821-6313 *Fax:* 608-849-2468
E-mail: foundation@wtcsf.tec.wi.us
Web Site: www.wtcsf.tec.wi.us
Key Personnel
Pres: Edward Chin
VP: Robert Sorensen
Secy: James Elliott
Treas: Dan Clancy
Dir: Linda Stewart
Founded: 1977
Catalog(s) available

Wise Audio Video
PO Box 105523, Jefferson City, MO 65110
Tel: 573-761-7888 *Toll Free Tel:* 877-775-7888
Web Site: www.wiseaudiovideo.com
Key Personnel
Pres: John Hickey *E-mail:* johnhickey@wiseaudiovideo.com
Founded: 1999
Specialize in audio, video, lighting, acoustical treatment, teleconferencing, digital signage & security systems.

Witcher Productions, see Marsh Media

WKMG-TV Channel 6
Subsidiary of Graham Media Group
4466 N John Young Pkwy, Orlando, FL 32804
Tel: 407-521-1200 *Fax:* 407-521-1204
Web Site: www.clickorlando.com
Key Personnel
Creative Servs Dir: Kym Peoples
Television station.

WKPT-TV
Subsidiary of Holston Valley Broadcasting Corp
222 Commerce St, Kingsport, TN 37660
Tel: 423-246-9578 *Fax:* 423-246-1863
Web Site: www.abc19.tv
Key Personnel
Pres: George DeVault, Jr *E-mail:* gdevault@hvbcgroup.com
Founded: 1969
Television station.
Membership(s): NAB; Tennessee Association of Broadcasters

WKYT Productions
Subsidiary of Gray Television Inc
2851 Winchester Rd, Lexington, KY 40509
Tel: 859-299-0411; 859-299-2727 (newsroom) *Fax:* 859-299-2494
Web Site: www.wkyt.com
Key Personnel
Pres & Gen Mgr: Chris Mossman *E-mail:* chris.mossman@wkyt.com
VP & Opers Mgr: Mike Kanarek *E-mail:* mike.kanarek@wkyt.com
Video production company.
Membership(s): NAB

WMAR-TV
Subsidiary of Scripps-Howard Broadcasting Co
6400 York Rd, Baltimore, MD 21212
Tel: 410-377-2222
E-mail: newsroom@wmar.com
Web Site: www.abc2news.com
Key Personnel
VP & Gen Mgr: Bill Hooper
News Dir: Kelly Groft
Television station.

WMS Media Inc
555 Bryant St, Suite 361, Palo Alto, CA 94301
Toll Free Tel: 800-487-1073 *Fax:* 510-796-0924
E-mail: info@wmsmedia.com
Web Site: www.wmsmedia.com
Key Personnel
Owner & Pres: Thomas A Wohlmut
E-mail: tom@wmsmedia.com
Founded: 1978
Video, web sites, multimedia & print.
Membership(s): ATD

WNET/NET TELECON
Division of Thirteen/WNET
825 Eighth Ave, New York, NY 10019
Tel: 212-560-1313 *Fax:* 212-560-1314
E-mail: programming@thirteen.org
Web Site: www.thirteen.org; www.wnet.org
Key Personnel
CEO & Pres: Neal Shapiro
Television programming.

Wohler Technologies Inc
31055 Huntwood Ave, Hayward, CA 94544
Tel: 510-870-0810 *Toll Free Tel:* 888-5-WOHLER (596-4537) *Fax:* 510-870-0811
E-mail: sales@wohler.com; info@wohler.com
Web Site: www.wohler.com
Founded: 1983
Audio & video equipment manufacturer.
Catalog(s) available
Foreign Office(s): Wohler APAC, 45/F The Lee Gardens, 33 Hysan Ave, Causeway Bay, Hong Kong *Tel:* 8199 0563 *Fax:* 3180 2299 *E-mail:* salesasia@wohler.com
Wolher Europe, Medaxon House, Suite 3, Mill Mead, Staines TW18 4UQ, United Kingdom *Tel:* (02071) 935507 *E-mail:* salesemea@wohler.com
Membership(s): SMPTE

Wolf Coach, see L-3 ESSCO

WolfVision Inc
1601 Bayshore Hwy, Suite 168, Burlingame, CA 94010
Tel: 650-648-0002 *Toll Free Tel:* 800-356-9653 *Fax:* 650-648-0009
E-mail: sales@wolfvision.us; support@wolfvision.us
Web Site: www.wolfvision.com
Key Personnel
Pres, WolfVision USA: Joseph Wolf
Gen Mgr & VP: Arthur Jenni
Asst VP & Sales Mgr, West: Andrea Mayer
Founded: 1995
Manufacturer of top quality portable, professional & ceiling visualizers used for displaying material in presentations, training, education/teaching, video-conferencing, 3D scanning, telemedicine & broadcasting. Designed to easily & accurately capture any kind of material to be displayed, whether it be written material on paper or transparency, x-rays, 3D objects & even items or people in a room.
Catalog(s) available
Literature available
Branch Office(s)
2055 Sugarloaf Circle, Suite 125, Duluth, GA 30097, VP & Gen Mgr: Arthur Jenni *Tel:* 770-931-6802 *Toll Free Tel:* 877-873-9653
WolfVision Canada Inc, 7-5380 Canotek Rd, Ottawa, ON K1J 1H7, Canada, Sales Mgr: Ben Kislich-Lemyre *Tel:* 613-741-9898 *Toll Free Tel:* 877-513-2002 *Fax:* 613-741-3747 *Toll Free Fax:* 877-513-1993 *E-mail:* wolfvision.canada@wolfvision.com
Foreign Office(s): WolfVision GmbH, Oberes Ried 14, 6833 Klaus, Austria, Dir, Sales: Michael Lisch *Tel:* (05523) 52250 *Fax:* (05523) 52249 *E-mail:* wolfvision@wolfvision.com
WolfVision Co Ltd, TMB Doshomachi Bldg 3F, 2-1-10 Doshomachi, Chuo-ku, Osaka 541-0045, Japan *Tel:* (06) 6222 3221 *Fax:* (06) 6220 0660 *E-mail:* wolfvision.japan@wolfvision.com
WolfVision Co Ltd, Advance Bldg 2F, 8-1-16 Nishi Shinjuku, Shinjuku, Toyko 160-0023, Japan *Tel:* (03) 3360 3231 *Fax:* (03) 3360 3236 *E-mail:* wolfvision.japan@wolfvision.com
WolfVision Pte Ltd, 81 Ubi Ave 4 No 06-27, UB One, 408830 Singapore, Singapore, Local Dir: Martin Low *Tel:* 6636 1268 *Fax:* 6636 1269 *E-mail:* info@wolfvisionasia.com
WolfVision Middle East, Jumeirah Terr, Suite 401, Jumeirah 1, Dubai, United Arab Emirates, Sales Mgr: Hazem Mahdy *Tel:* (04) 354 2233 *Fax:* (04) 354 2244 *E-mail:* middle.east@wolfvision.net
WolfVision UK Ltd, Trident One, Styal Rd, Manchester M2Z 5XB, United Kingdom *Tel:* (0161) 435 6081 *Fax:* (0161) 435 6100 *E-mail:* wolfvision.uk@wolfvision.com
Membership(s): InfoComm International®

Women Make Movies Inc
115 W 29 St, Suite 1200, New York, NY 10001
Tel: 212-925-0606 *Fax:* 212-925-2052
E-mail: info@wmm.com
Web Site: www.wmm.com
Key Personnel
Exec Dir: Debra Zimmerman
E-mail: dzimmerman@wmm.com
Dir, Dist & Sales: Julie Whang *E-mail:* jw@wmm.com
Founded: 1972
Video distributor.
Catalog(s) available

Wonderwomen™ Enterprises
485 Rugby Rd, Brooklyn, NY 11226
Tel: 646-456-3266; 718-693-4322
E-mail: info@wonderwomen.com
Key Personnel
CEO & Pres: Harriet Rita Semegram
Founded: 1961 (restructured & renamed in 1989)
Documentary film production.

WoodenBoat Publications
41 WoodenBoat Lane, Brooklin, ME 04616
Mailing Address: PO Box 78, Brooklin, ME 04616-0078
Tel: 207-359-4651 *Toll Free Tel:* 800-877-5284 (subns); 800-487-2084 (subns) *Fax:* 207-359-8920; 818-487-4550 (subns)
E-mail: woodenboat@woodenboat.com
Web Site: www.woodenboat.com
Key Personnel
Chmn & Ed-in-Chief: Jon Wilson
Pres & Gen Mgr: James E Miller
Publr: Carl Cramer *E-mail:* carl@woodenboat.com
Edit: Matt Murphy *E-mail:* matt@woodenboat.com
Founded: 1974
Boat design, construction & repair videos.
Catalog(s) available
Membership(s): SIVA

Woodside Avenue Music Productions Inc
2906 Central St, No 117, Evanston, IL 60201
Tel: 847-864-6655
E-mail: music@woodsideavenue.com
Web Site: www.woodsideavenue.com
Key Personnel
Prodr: Steve Rashid
Dir: Bea Rashid
Full service production company.

Mark Woollen & Associates
207 Ashland Ave, Santa Monica, CA 90405
Tel: 310-399-2690
E-mail: info@markwoollen.com
Web Site: www.markwoollen.com
Key Personnel
Prodr: Scott Mitsui *E-mail:* scott@markwoollen.com; Sohini Sengupta *E-mail:* sohini@markwoollen.com
Motion picture advertising.

Word Label Group
Division of Warner Bros Entertainment
25 Music Sq W, Nashville, TN 37203
Tel: 615-251-0600 *Fax:* 615-726-7886 (publicity)
E-mail: wbrc.publicity@wbr.com
Web Site: www.wordlabelgroup.com
Key Personnel
CEO & Pres: Rod Riley
Christian recording & music publications.
Catalog(s) available

World Beat Studio
137 Sequoia Rd, Rockwall, TX 75032
Tel: 972-771-3797 *Fax:* 972-771-0853
E-mail: tropikalproductions@gmail.com
Web Site: www.tropikalproductions.com
Key Personnel
Owner & Prodr: Jimi Towry *Tel:* 469-338-9237 (cell)
Engr: Arik Miles
Founded: 1990
Recording/music production studio. Digital recording-MAC with Apple Logic Pro, MIDI keyboards, drums, percussion, bass amp, guitar amp, piano. Office in Playa Bejuco, Costa Rica.
Membership(s): BMI

World Beatnik Records, see World Beat Studio

World Class Learning Materials Inc
PO Box 639, Candler, NC 28715
Toll Free Tel: 800-638-6470 *Toll Free Fax:* 800-638-6499
E-mail: dealers@wclm.com
Web Site: www.wclm.com; learningwelled.com
Key Personnel
Pres: Bruce Brown *E-mail:* bbrown@wclm.com
Manufacturer & publisher of educational materials.
Catalog(s) available
Membership(s): Education Market Association

World Events Productions Ltd
Subsidiary of Koplar Communications Inc
50 Maryland Plaza, Suite 300, St Louis, MO 63108
Tel: 314-345-1060 *Fax:* 314-345-1093
E-mail: wep@wep.com
Web Site: www.wep.com
Key Personnel
CEO & Pres: Edward J Koplar
Mng Dir: Tiffany Ilarde
Founded: 1982

World Media Group Inc
6737 E 30 St, Indianapolis, IN 46219
Tel: 317-549-8484 *Toll Free Tel:* 800-400-4964 *Fax:* 317-549-8480
E-mail: getstarted@worldmediagroup.com
Web Site: www.worldmediagroup.com
Key Personnel
Pres: Jeff Mellentine *Tel:* 317-275-1042
E-mail: jeffm@worldmediagroup.com
VP, Opers: Josh Mellentine *Tel:* 317-275-1058
E-mail: joshm@worldmediagroup.com
VP, Sales: Holly Viering *Tel:* 317-275-1041
E-mail: hollyv@worldmediagroup.com
Graphic design & custom printing on plastic cards, digital mastering & manufacturing of USB flash drives & DVDs.
Online catalog(s) available

Branch Office(s)
555 Eighth Ave, Suite 1803, New York, NY 10018 *Tel:* 212-947-4550 *Fax:* 212-564-8865
Membership(s): Audio Publishers Association

World Video Sales Co Inc
PO Box 117, Boyertown, PA 19512-0117
Tel: 610-754-6800 *Fax:* 610-754-9766
E-mail: sales@mivs.com
Web Site: www.mivs.com
Key Personnel
Pres: John Taylor *E-mail:* jataylor@mivs.com
Catalog(s) available
Shipping Address: 625 Hoffmansville Rd, Suite 3, Bechtelsville, PA 19505

World Wide Pictures Inc
Subsidiary of Billy Graham Evangelistic Association
One Billy Graham Pkwy, Charlotte, NC 28266-8029
Mailing Address: PO Box 668029, Charlotte, NC 28266-8029
Tel: 704-401-2432 *Toll Free Tel:* 800-745-4318 *Fax:* 704-401-3045
Web Site: www.wwp.org
Key Personnel
Video & Film Archives Mgr: David Eades
Catalog(s) available

WorldStage
259 W 30 St, 12th fl, New York, NY 10001-2863
Tel: 212-582-2345 *Fax:* 718-610-1750
E-mail: info@worldstage.com
Web Site: www.worldstage.com
Key Personnel
CEO: Gary Standard
CFO: Stan Jacobs
Pres: Josh Weisberg
AV & lighting equipment, LED lighting & video.

Worldview Entertainment Holdings Inc
1384 Broadway, 25th fl, New York, NY 10018
Tel: 212-431-3090 *Fax:* 212-431-0390
E-mail: info@worldviewent.com
Web Site: www.worldviewent.com
Key Personnel
COO: Molly Conners
Founded: 2007
Motion picture investment & production company focused on well-crafted high production value filmed entertainment.
Catalog(s) available

WorldView Software
76 N Broadway, Suite 2002, Hicksville, NY 11801
Tel: 516-681-1773 *Toll Free Tel:* 800-347-8839 *Fax:* 516-681-1775
E-mail: history@worldviewsoftware.com
Web Site: www.worldviewsoftware.com
Key Personnel
Pres: Jerry Kleinstein
VP: Arnold Kleinstein
Founded: 1990
Produce & distribute educational/social science software programs for grades 7-12.
Catalog(s) available

Worldwide Entertainment Corp
135 S McCarty Dr, Suite 101, Beverly Hills, CA 90212
Tel: 310-858-1272 *Fax:* 310-858-3774
Key Personnel
Pres: Jack H Harris *E-mail:* jackhh@pacbell.net
Founded: 1974
Producing & distribution of classic sci-fi & exploitation films, including *The Blob*.
Brochure(s) available
Catalog(s) available

Worthwhile Films
317 Winona St, Northfield, MN 55057
Toll Free Tel: 877-507-5077
Web Site: worthwhilefilms.org
Key Personnel
Prodr: Steve Braker *E-mail:* steve@worthwhilefilms.org
Founded: 1985
Narration free documentary production with & for virtuous nonprofit organizations, benign government agencies & other worthwhile causes.
Rate sheet(s), on request, call or write for a detailed proposal
Membership(s): IDA; MCA-I

WOUB Public Media
35 S College St, Athens, OH 45701
Tel: 740-593-1771 *Fax:* 740-593-0240
E-mail: woub@woub.org
Web Site: woub.org
Key Personnel
Dir & Gen Mgr: Thomas Hodson *E-mail:* hodson@ohio.edu

The WPA Film Library
Division of MPI Media Group
16101 S 108 Ave, Orland Park, IL 60467
Tel: 708-460-0555 *Toll Free Tel:* 800-323-0442 *Fax:* 708-460-0187
E-mail: sales@wpafilmlibrary.com
Web Site: www.wpafilmlibrary.com
Key Personnel
Gen Mgr: Nicola Goelzhauser
License stock footage.
Foreign Office(s): Library Media Solutions Ltd, 77 Oxford St, W1D 2ES, United Kingdom, Contact: Patrick Smith *Tel:* (020) 7659 2348 *Fax:* (020) 7183 2360 *E-mail:* patrick@librarymediasolutions.com
Membership(s): Association of Moving Image Archivists; Entertainment Merchants Association; The Federation of Commercial Audiovisual Libraries Ltd; MCA-I

WPGH-TV
Subsidiary of Sinclair Broadcast Group Inc
750 Ivory Ave, Pittsburgh, PA 15214
Tel: 412-931-5300 *Fax:* 412-931-4284
Web Site: www.sbgi.net; www.wpgh53.com
Key Personnel
Gen Mgr: Alan Frank
Station Administrator & Dir, HR: Julie Dallas *Tel:* 412-931-8088
TV broadcasting.

WPHL-TV
5001 Wynnefield Ave, Philadelphia, PA 19131
Tel: 215-878-1700 *Fax:* 215-879-7683; 215-877-4912
E-mail: feedback@phl17.com
Web Site: www.phl17.com
Key Personnel
VP & Gen Mgr: Vincent Giannini
Creative Servs Dir: Travis Brower
Gen Sales Mgr: Dave Yost
Founded: 1965

WQED-Multimedia
4802 Fifth Ave, Pittsburgh, PA 15213
Tel: 412-622-1300; 412-622-1370 *Fax:* 412-622-1488
E-mail: wqed@wqed.org
Web Site: www.wqed.org
Key Personnel
CEO & Pres: Deborah L Acklin
CFO: Carole Bailey
Sta Rel: Lisa Przyborski *E-mail:* lprzyborski@wqed.org
Founded: 1954
HD studio & field production, HD non-linear editing, VYUX connectivity (HD), fiber connectivity to Pittsburgh Teleport (HD). Studios available to rent: 35' x 35', 40' x 60' & 80' x 80'. Omni music, studio cutz & sound ideas music libraries.

The Wright Group
Subsidiary of McGraw-Hill Education
860 Taylor Station Rd, Blacklick, OH 43004
Mailing Address: PO Box 182605, Columbus, OH 43218
Toll Free Tel: 800-334-7344
E-mail: customer.service@mheducation.com
Web Site: www.mheonline.com
Educational programming producers.
Catalog(s) available

Writer's AudioShop/Davenport Productions
1316 Overland Stage Rd, Dripping Springs, TX 78620
Tel: 512-476-1616 *Fax:* 512-264-7067
E-mail: wrtaudshop@aol.com
Web Site: www.writersaudio.com
Key Personnel
Owner & Publr: Elaine Davenport
Founded: 1985
Publishes live seminars on how to write - workshops from America's top writers, teaching the ABCs (art, business & craft) of writing. Also, folklore & Texana recordings.
Catalog(s) available
Membership(s): Audio Publishers Association

The Writing Co
Division of Social Studies School Service
10200 Jefferson Blvd, Culver City, CA 90232
Mailing Address: PO Box 802, Culver City, CA 90232-0802
Tel: 310-839-2436 *Toll Free Tel:* 800-421-4246 *Fax:* 310-839-2249 *Toll Free Fax:* 800-944-5432
E-mail: access@writingco.com; access@socialstudies.com
Web Site: www.socialstudies.com; www.writingco.com
Key Personnel
Pres: Irwin Levin; Sanford Weiner
Supplementary curriculum material.
Catalog(s) available

WSAZ-TV 3/WSAZ Productions
Division of Gray Television Inc
645 Fifth Ave, Huntington, WV 25701
Tel: 304-697-4780 *Fax:* 304-690-3061 (sales); 304-690-3065 (news)
E-mail: newschannel3@wsaz.com
Web Site: www.wsaz.com
Key Personnel
Gen Mgr: Matt Jaquint
Satellite uplink facility KU band. Produce & edit short form/long form commercials.
Branch Office(s)
111 Columbia Ave, Charleston, WV 25302, Contact: Jeff Sadler *Tel:* 304-344-3521 *Fax:* 304-340-4649

WSI
Division of The Weather Co
400 Minuteman Rd, Andover, MA 01810
Tel: 978-983-6300 *Fax:* 978-983-6400
Web Site: www.wsi.com
Key Personnel
Pres: Mark Gildersleeve
VP, Media Sales & Mktg: Steve Ward
Mktg Mgr: Kerry McCord-Morelli
World's leading source of professional on-air weather related graphic systems & forecasting tools for television; turning mountains of meteorological information into the country's most popular real-time weather data & forecasting services.
Membership(s): NAB; RTDNA

WTL Productions
345 E 52 St, Suite 1, New York, NY 10022
Tel: 212-355-1893
E-mail: wtlvideo@aol.com
Key Personnel
Prodr: William Whitlock
Funded projects (government, local & private foundations).
Catalog(s) available

WTMJ-TV
Subsidiary of Journal Broadcast Group Inc
720 E Capitol Dr, Milwaukee, WI 53212
Tel: 414-332-9611; 414-967-5444 *Fax:* 414-967-5255
E-mail: tmj4feedback@todaystmj4.com
Web Site: www.jrn.com/tmj4
Key Personnel
VP & Gen Mgr: Joe Poss *E-mail:* jposs@jrn.com

WTVS-Station Enterprises
Subsidiary of WTVS, Detroit Public Television
Riley Broadcast Ctr, One Clover Ct, Wixom, MI 48393-2247
Tel: 248-305-DPTV (305-3788) *Fax:* 248-305-3990
E-mail: email@dptv.org
Web Site: www.dptv.org
Key Personnel
CEO & Pres: Rich Homberg *E-mail:* rhomberg@dptv.org
EVP, Prodn & Opers: Jeff Forster *Tel:* 248-305-3790 *E-mail:* jforster@dptv.org
SVP: Daniel Alpert *Tel:* 248-305-3702 *E-mail:* dalpert@dptv.org
Prodn Mgr: Carlota Almanza-Lumpkin *Tel:* 248-305-3826 *E-mail:* calmanza@dptv.org
Founded: 1955
Studio, field & post-production services with transmission & HD mobile production truck.
Rate card(s) available
Membership(s): DGA; IBEW; Michigan Association of Public Broadcasters; PBS

WVLA-TV
Subsidiary of Knight Broadcasting
10000 Perkins Rd, Baton Rouge, LA 70810
Tel: 225-766-3233 *Fax:* 225-768-9293
Web Site: www.nbc33tv.com
Key Personnel
Gen Mgr: Jim Baronet
Commercial & industrial production & studio rental.
Membership(s): AAF

WVP Boston
Formerly Weisman Video Productions Inc
50 Hunt St, Watertown, MA 02472
Tel: 617-926-2089 *Fax:* 617-926-7965
E-mail: info@wvp.com
Web Site: www.weismanvideo.com
Key Personnel
Prodr & Prodn Mgr: Andy Jablon *E-mail:* andy@wvp.com
Dir, Photog: Jim Petit *E-mail:* jim@wvp.com
Full service video production.

The Wyland Group
Division of Adventist Media Center
101 W Cochran St, Simi Valley, CA 93065
Tel: 805-955-7680 *Fax:* 805-522-1082
Web Site: www.adventistmediacenter.com
Key Personnel
Acct Exec: Chauncey Smith
Founded: 1955

Xantech LLC
Subsidiary of Core Brands LLC
1800 S McDowell Blvd, Petaluma, CA 94954
Tel: 707-283-5900 *Toll Free Tel:* 800-472-5555 *Fax:* 707-283-5901
E-mail: info@xantech.com; customerservice@xantech.com
Web Site: www.xantech.com
Founded: 1969
Manufacturer & marketer of consumer electronics components & AV entertainment systems.
Catalog(s) available
Membership(s): Consumer Electronics Association; Custom Electronic Design & Installation Association; NSCA

Xenon Pictures Inc
Division of Xenon Entertainment Group
3521 Jack Northrop Ave, Hawthorne, CA 90250
Tel: 310-451-5510 *Fax:* 310-395-4058
E-mail: info@xenonpictures.com; sales@xenonpictures.com
Web Site: xenonpictures.com
Key Personnel
Founder, CEO & Pres: Leigh Savidge *E-mail:* lsavidge@xenonpictures.com
COO & EVP: Steve Housden *E-mail:* housden@xenonpictures.com
VP, Sales & Mktg: Kristi Alires *E-mail:* kalires@xenonpictures.com
Consultant: Kent Little
Founded: 1986
Universal music & video distribution.
Catalog(s) available
Membership(s): Entertainment Merchants Association

Xerox Audio Visual Solutions, see The Whitlock Group

Xetron
Division of Northrop Grumman Systems Corp
460 W Crescentville Rd, Cincinnati, OH 45246-1221
Tel: 513-881-3100
Founded: 1916
Catalog(s) available
Membership(s): InfoComm International®; SMPTE

Xintekvideo Inc
56 W Broad St, Stamford, CT 06902
Tel: 203-348-9229
Web Site: www.xintekvideo.com
Key Personnel
Pres: John Rossi *E-mail:* jrossi@xintekvideo.com
Founded: 1986
Manufacture video processing equipment for picture enhancement & video quality restoration.
Brochure(s) available
Membership(s): NAB

X-Rite
4300 44 St SE, Grand Rapids, MI 49512
Tel: 616-803-2100 *Toll Free Tel:* 800-248-9748
E-mail: info@xrite.com
Web Site: www.xrite.com
Key Personnel
CFO: Jeffrey McKee
CTO: Dr Francis Lamy
Color systems & software.
Catalog(s) available
Membership(s): American Manufacturers Association; American Society for Testing Materials

XTA Electronics Ltd
Division of Group One Ltd
70 Sea Lane, Farmingdale, NY 11735
Tel: 516-249-1399 *Fax:* 516-249-8870
E-mail: sales@g1limited.com
Web Site: www.g1limited.com
Key Personnel
Pres: Jack Kelly *Tel:* 516-249-1399 ext 102 *E-mail:* jackk@g1limited.com
Membership(s): AES; NAB; NSCA

Xtech Inc
241 Rock Creek Lane, Suite B, Scarsdale, NY 10583
Mailing Address: PO Box 147, Scarsdale, NY 10583-0147
Tel: 718-543-1222 *Toll Free Fax:* 888-528-6511
E-mail: info@xtechsystems.com
Web Site: www.xtechsystems.com
Key Personnel
Pres: Richard Woolf
Wireless systems infrastructure specialists.
Catalog(s) available
Membership(s): ARA; ASAE

Xytech Systems Corp
15451 San Fernando Mission Blvd, Suite 400, Mission Hills, CA 91345
Tel: 818-698-4900 *Fax:* 818-698-4901
E-mail: sales@xytechsystems.com
Web Site: www.xytechsystems.com
Key Personnel
CEO & Pres: Richard Gallagher
EVP & Co-Principal: Peter Tanke
COO: Greg Dolan
SVP, R&D: Ken Shook
VP, Fin & Admin: Carol Nowlin
VP, Prof Servs: Patrick Bennett
Dir, Mktg: Michelle Gallagher *E-mail:* mgallagher@xytechsystems.com
Founded: 1998
Delivers one-stop shopping for any size facility, from a single user to hundreds of interactive users, with the support infrastructure of consulting, technical assistance, training & systems integration. Installs facilities management systems in commercial teleproduction & corporate industrial facilities, satellite broadcasting corporations & Fortune 500 companies around the globe.
Foreign Office(s): Xytech Systems UK Ltd, 28 Margaret St, 3rd fl, London W1W 8RZ, United Kingdom, Gen Mgr: Daniel Lynch *Tel:* (020) 3478 1450 *Fax:* (020) 3478 1441

Yada/Levine Video Productions
1253 Vine St, Suite 21-A, Hollywood, CA 90038
Tel: 323-461-1616 *Fax:* 323-461-2288
E-mail: video@yadalevine.com
Web Site: www.yadalevine.com
Key Personnel
Pres: Michael Yada
Video production.

Yale Film & Video
Affiliate of Yale Laboratory Inc
25601 Avenue Stanford, Valencia, CA 91355
Tel: 661-295-7170; 661-295-7160
E-mail: info@yalefilmandvideo.com
Web Site: www.yalefilmandvideo.com
Key Personnel
CEO: Keith C Anderson
CFO: Carlos Cruz
Founded: 1946
Motion picture processing & film to video transfers. Transfer film to DVD/hard drive & film processing. Offering HD & 2K Scanning for super 8, regular 8, 16, S16 & 35mm.
Price list(s) available

Yamaha Electronics Corp
Subsidiary of Yamaha Corp of America
6660 Orangethorpe Ave, Buena Park, CA 90620
Tel: 714-522-9105 *Toll Free Tel:* 800-292-2982 (cust support) *Toll Free Fax:* 800-782-8484
Web Site: www.yamaha.com
Key Personnel
COO & Pres: Hogan Osawa
VP, Sales: Steve Caldero
Corp Ad & Promo Mgr: Doan Hoff
Serv Mgr: Curt Sidles
Founded: 1960
Home audio components & systems.

Catalog(s) available
Membership(s): Consumer Electronics Association

Yanchar Design & Consulting Group
26741 Portola Pkwy, Suite 1-E, Foothill Ranch, CA 92610-1763
Tel: 949-770-6601 *Fax:* 949-770-6575
E-mail: info@yanchardesign.com
Web Site: www.yanchardesign.com
Key Personnel
Pres: Carl J Yanchar *E-mail:* carl@yanchardesign.com
Membership(s): AES; ASA; SMPTE

YAP Films
96 Spadina Ave, Suite 205, Toronto, ON M5V 2J6, Canada
Tel: 416-504-3662 *Fax:* 416-504-3667
E-mail: thedog@yapfilms.com
Web Site: www.yapfilms.com
Key Personnel
Exec Prodr & Dir: Elliot Halpern
Cont: Sam Simpson
Dir, Devt: Elizabeth Trojian
In-House Dir: Alex McIntosh
Busn Aff Mgr: Robin Gleadall
In-House Prodn Mgr: Anja Sobkowska
Post-Prodn Supv: Harrison Freedman

Yarn Barn of Kansas
930 Massachusetts St, Lawrence, KS 66044
Tel: 785-842-4333 *Toll Free Tel:* 800-468-0035 *Fax:* 785-842-0794
E-mail: info@yarnbarn-ks.com
Web Site: www.yarnbarn-ks.com
Key Personnel
Pres: Susan Bateman
Founded: 1971
Online catalog(s) available

Yellow Cat Productions Inc
505 11 St SE, Washington, DC 20003
Tel: 202-543-2221
E-mail: yellowcat@yellowcat.com
Web Site: www.yellowcat.com
Key Personnel
Pres & Sr Prodr: Michael Ford
VP: Katie Gates
Founded: 1980
Full service video production.
Catalog(s) available
Membership(s): MCA-I; NABET-CWA; Women in Film & Video

Yellow Moon Press
PO Box 381316, Cambridge, MA 02238-1316
Tel: 617-776-2230 *Toll Free Tel:* 800-497-4385 *Fax:* 617-776-8246
E-mail: story@yellowmoon.com
Web Site: www.yellowmoon.com
Key Personnel
Pres: Robert Smyth
Founded: 1978
Publish material from the various arts of the oral tradition as it pertains to storytelling, poetry & music. It is our goal to make available material that both explores the history of the oral tradition & breathes new life into it.
Catalog(s) available

Yellowknife Films Inc
5021 53 St, Yellowknife, NT X1A 1V5, Canada
Tel: 867-873-8610
E-mail: ykf@theedge.ca
Web Site: www.ykfilms.ca
Key Personnel
Pres & Dir: Alan Booth *E-mail:* alan@theedge.ca
HD video production, editing videography & arctic specialists.

YES Productions
Subsidiary of WYES-TV
916 Navarre Ave, New Orleans, LA 70124
Tel: 504-840-4891 *Toll Free Tel:* 800-736-8812 *Fax:* 504-840-4895
Web Site: www.yesproductions.com
Key Personnel
Gen Mgr: Jim Moriarty *Tel:* 504-616-3999 (cell) *E-mail:* jim@yesproductions.com
Alliance Productions partner.
Brochure(s) available

Yessian
137 Fifth Ave, 3rd fl, New York, NY 10010
Tel: 212-533-3443
E-mail: info-ny@yessian.com
Web Site: www.yessian.com
Key Personnel
Partner & Chief Commercial Offr: Brian Yessian *E-mail:* brian@yessian.com
Partner & Head, Prodn: Michael Yessian *E-mail:* michael@yessian.com
Mng Dir & Exec Prodr: Marlene Bartos *E-mail:* marlene@yessian.com
Full service studio facility. Specialize in original music, sound design, audio engineering & TV & film scores.
Branch Office(s)
Venice, CA 90025, Exec Prodr: David Gold *Tel:* 310-902-5297 *E-mail:* david.gold@yessian.com
33117 Hamilton Ct, Farmington Hills, MI 48334, Exec Prodr: Gerard Smerek *Tel:* 248-553-4044 *Fax:* 248-893-4044 *E-mail:* gerard@yessian.com
Foreign Office(s): Schulterblatt 58, 20357 Hamburg, Germany, Exec Prodr: Ingmar Rehberg *Tel:* (040) 40185159 *E-mail:* ingmar@yessian.com

The Yesterday USA Radio Networks
2001 Plymouth Rock Dr, Richardson, TX 75081-3946
Tel: 972-889-9872 *Fax:* 972-889-2329
Web Site: www.yesterdayusa.com
Key Personnel
Founder: Bill Bragg *E-mail:* bb@yesterdayusa.com
Founded: 1983
Broadcasting old time radio shows & vintage music.

YMAA Publication Center Inc
16 Lehner St, Wolfeboro, NH 03894
Mailing Address: PO Box 480, Wolfeboro, NH 03894
Tel: 603-569-7988 *Toll Free Tel:* 800-669-8892 *Fax:* 603-569-1889
E-mail: info@ymaa.com
Web Site: www.ymaa.com
Key Personnel
Pres & Publr: David Ripianzi *E-mail:* davidr@ymaa.com
Founded: 1982
Production & distribution of martial arts instructional videos, books & DVDs.
Catalog(s), annual
Membership(s): NEBA; PMA International; Reading Recovery Council of North America

Yoga 1 Inc
3128 Carlisle St, Columbia, SC 29205
Tel: 803-254-6121 *Toll Free Tel:* 888-364-1310 (orders)
Web Site: www.yogaone.com
Key Personnel
Owner & Pres: Priscilla Patrick *E-mail:* prisyoga@aol.com
Yoga videos & yoga PBS TV programs.
Membership(s): SIVA

York Telecom
81 Corbett Way, Eatontown, NJ 07724
Tel: 732-413-6000 *Toll Free Tel:* 866-836-8463 *Fax:* 732-413-6060
E-mail: knowmore@yorktel.com
Web Site: yorktel.com
Key Personnel
Founder & Chmn of the Bd: Vork Wang, PhD
CEO: Ron Gaboury
CTO: Bin Guan
CIO: Dr Joe-E Hu
CFO: Judi Pulig
EVP, Busn Mgmt: Karen Paglia
EVP, Opers: Jim DeBlasio
EVP, Sales: Greg Douglas
SVP, Advanced Servs: Joseph M Arena
SVP, Media Servs: Mark Maxey
Founded: 1985
AV & presentation products.
Catalog(s) available
Branch Office(s)
8400 Corporate Dr, Suite 450, Landover, MD 20785 *Tel:* 240-898-2400 *Fax:* 240-898-2405
33 Upton Dr, Wilmington, MA 01887 *Tel:* 978-658-5150 *Toll Free Tel:* 800-868-5150 *Fax:* 978-753-4777
4140 Sheridan Dr, Suite 4, Williamsville, NY 14221 *Tel:* 716-810-9550 *Fax:* 716-810-9553
342 Victory Dr, Herndon, VA 20170 *Tel:* 571-612-8991
Membership(s): InfoComm International®; MCA-I; PSNI

Yorkville Sound Inc
Subsidiary of Yorkville Sound Ltd
4625 Witmer Industrial Estate, Niagara Falls, NY 14305
Tel: 716-297-2920 *Fax:* 716-297-3689
E-mail: usa@yorkville.com
Web Site: www.yorkville.com
Key Personnel
Dir, Sales: Steve Hendee *Tel:* 716-297-2920 ext 29
Catalog(s) available
Branch Office(s)
Yorkville Sound Ltd, 550 Granite Ct, Pickering, ON L1W 3Y8, Canada *Tel:* 905-837-8481 *Fax:* 905-839-5776 *E-mail:* canada@yorkville.com
Membership(s): AES; LDI; NAMM, the National Association of Music Merchants; NSCA

Young Chang America
6000 Phyllis Dr, Cypress, CA 90630
Toll Free Tel: 866-798-6979 *Fax:* 657-200-3477
E-mail: marketing@ycapiano.com
Web Site: www.youngchang.com
Founded: 1982
Specializes in pianos & Kurzweil® brand music systems/synthesizers.
Membership(s): NAMM, the National Association of Music Merchants

Young Minds Inc
1014 E Cooley Dr, Suite H, Colton, CA 92324
Tel: 909-426-4860 *Fax:* 909-426-4866
E-mail: info@ymi.com; sales@ymi.com
Web Site: www.ymi.com
Key Personnel
Chmn: Andrew Young
CEO: David H Cote
Pres: Matthew Hornbeck
Founded: 1989
Provides a complete line of cross-platform CD & DVD recording systems & network-attached data archiving solutions. YMi pioneered CD recording & CD-ROM mass storage in the UNIX market & continues to deliver the innovative solutions that are reliable, cost-effective & easy to use. Andrew Young, Chmn & Co-Founder of the company, authored the Rock Ridge Interchange Protocols, which define

additional functionality for CD & DVD discs used in UNIX environments.
Catalog(s) available

Z-Axis Corp
4600 S Ulster St, Suite 270, Denver, CO 80237
Tel: 303-713-0200 *Toll Free Tel:* 800-827-2947
E-mail: info@zaxis.com
Web Site: www.zaxis.com
Key Personnel
CEO: Alan Treibitz
Pres: Stephanie Kelso
Visual Strategy Consultant/Sr Prodr: Gary Freed
Natl Accts Mgr: Raymond Hauschel *E-mail:* raymond.hauschel@zaxis.com
Founded: 1983
Strategic consulting, visual production services, technology & on-site presentation support for court cases in the US & abroad.
Catalog(s) available

Z-Systems Audio Engineering
1325 NW 53 Ave, Suite B, Gainesville, FL 32609
Tel: 352-371-0990
E-mail: z-sys@z-sys.com
Web Site: www.z-sys.com
Key Personnel
Pres: Glenn Zelnikel
VP, Opers: Richard Auerbach
Founded: 1993
Manufacture professional digital audio equipment. R&D for customer concepts using DSP.

Z-Ville Productions
34710 Lancaster Rd, Gorman, CA 93536
Mailing Address: PO Box 42, Gorman, CA 93243
Tel: 310-422-9590 *Fax:* 310-422-9590
E-mail: info@zvpro.com
Web Site: www.z-ville.com
Key Personnel
Owner: Zander Villayne

Zachry Associates Inc
500 Chestnut St, Suite 2000, Abilene, TX 79602
Tel: 325-677-1342 *Fax:* 325-672-2001
E-mail: info@zachryinc.com
Web Site: zachryinc.com
Key Personnel
Founder & Chmn: H C Zachry
Pres: Paul Fulham *Tel:* 325-677-1342 ext 108 *E-mail:* pfulham@zachryinc.com
VP: Debbie Moran; Bob Nutt *Tel:* 325-677-1342 ext 123 *E-mail:* bnutt@zachryinc.com; Jeff Warr, Jr, PhD *Tel:* 325-668-8476 *E-mail:* jwarr@zachryinc.com
Founded: 1970
Writing, design & production for print, radio & television.
Branch Office(s)
6301 Gaston Ave, Dallas, TX 75214 *Tel:* 325-829-1671

Zack Electronics Inc
1075 Hamilton Rd, Duarte, CA 91010
Tel: 626-303-0655 *Toll Free Tel:* 800-466-0449 *Fax:* 626-303-8694
E-mail: info@zackelectronics.com
Web Site: www.zackelectronics.com
Key Personnel
Pres: Dennis Awad *E-mail:* dawad@zackelectronics.com
Founded: 1931
Specialize in wire, cable, connectors & installation solutions for audio, video, broadcast & datacom professionals.
Catalog(s) available
Membership(s): Direct Marketing Association; NAB; SBE; SMPTE

Zacuto
401 W Ontario Ave, Chicago, IL 60654
Tel: 312-863-3456; 312-863-3453 (rentals) *Toll Free Tel:* 888-294-3456 *Fax:* 312-863-3455; 312-377-3016 (rentals)
E-mail: rentals@zacuto.com
Web Site: www.zacuto.com
Key Personnel
VP, Sales & Mktg: Mandy Rogers *E-mail:* mandy@zacuto.com
Mktg Mgr: Rachel Kenton *E-mail:* kenton@zacuto.com
Founded: 2000
Creates, sells & rents filmmaking accessories & creates original content for the web.

Zamacona Productions
2600 Tenth St, Suite 302, Berkeley, CA 94710
Tel: 510-704-4011 *Fax:* 510-704-4013
E-mail: admin@zamacona-productions.com
Web Site: www.zamacona-productions.com
Key Personnel
Dir & Prodr: Frank Zamacona
Founded: 1983
Director & producer services with emphasis on live & live-on-tape productions.
Membership(s): DGA; NATAS

ZBS Foundation
174 N River Rd, Fort Edward, NY 12828-9713
Tel: 518-695-6406 *Toll Free Tel:* 800-662-3345 *Fax:* 518-695-4041
E-mail: custserv@zbs.org
Web Site: www.zbs.org
Key Personnel
Pres: Thomas Lopez
Founded: 1970
Radio/audio story producers. ZBS Foundation became a 501(c)(3) nonprofit corporation in 1972.
Catalog(s) available

Zebedee Productions
231 SW Fifth Ct, Pompano Beach, FL 33060
Tel: 954-942-0044
E-mail: info@zbd.us
Web Site: zebedeeproductions.com
Key Personnel
Owner: Andrea Arnold; Sandy Arnold
Services include AV rental & production, sound, lighting, video & staging. Specialize in design, fabrication, sales & installation services for complete AV systems, theatrical curtains & acoustical treatments.

Zeitgeist Films Ltd
247 Centre St, 2nd fl, New York, NY 10013
Tel: 212-274-1989 *Fax:* 212-274-1644
E-mail: mail@zeitgeistfilms.com
Web Site: www.zeitgeistfilms.com
Key Personnel
Co-Pres: Nancy Gerstman *E-mail:* nancy@zeitgeistfilms.com; Emily Russo *E-mail:* emily@zeitgeistfilms.com
Design Dir: Adrian Curry
Dir, Home Media Sales & DVD: Ian Stimler
Founded: 1988
Acquires & distributes quality foreign & independent feature films & documentaries.
Catalog(s) available

Zelco Industries Inc
110 Hartford Ave, Mount Vernon, NY 10553
Tel: 914-699-6230 *Toll Free Tel:* 800-431-2486
E-mail: office@zelco.com
Web Site: www.zelco.com
Key Personnel
Admin: Peter Fowler
Founded: 1976
Manufacture & distribute products including book lights, desk lamps, optics, household items & travel accessories.
Catalog(s) available

Zelman Studios Ltd
Division of Zelman Communications
623 Cortelyou Rd, Brooklyn, NY 11218
Tel: 718-941-5500
E-mail: kaforce@yahoo.com
Key Personnel
Pres: Sidney M Zelman
VP: D'vora Zelman
Gen Mgr: Jerry Krone
Video design, production & presentation.

Zelo Productions Inc
3 S Newton St, Denver, CO 80219
Tel: 303-936-8995; 303-898-0911 (cell) *Fax:* 303-936-0799
E-mail: zelo@earthlink.net
Web Site: www.zeloproductions.com
Key Personnel
Pres: V Zorba
Founded: 1990
Film & video production & post-production.

Zenith Electronics LLC
Member of LG Electronics USA Inc
2000 Millbrook Dr, Lincolnshire, IL 60069
Tel: 847-941-8000 *Toll Free Tel:* 877-9-ZENITH (993-6484) *Fax:* 847-941-8177
E-mail: customer.service@zenith.com
Web Site: www.zenith.com
Key Personnel
Dir: Sang Chi
Founded: 1918
Plasma TV, HDTV.

ZERO Manufacturing Inc
500 W 200 N, North Salt Lake, UT 84054
Tel: 801-298-5900 *Toll Free Tel:* 800-500-ZERO (500-9376) *Fax:* 801-299-7389
E-mail: sales@zerocases.com
Web Site: www.zerocases.com
Key Personnel
Dir Sales, Americas: Tom Grezechowiak *E-mail:* tom.g@zerocases.com
Aluminum & molded plastic cases & enclosures.
Catalog(s) available
Membership(s): ADPA; AFCEA; NIPHLE; SPHE

ZGC Inc
264 Morris Ave, Mountain Lakes, NJ 07046
Tel: 973-335-4460 *Fax:* 973-335-4560
E-mail: sales@zgc.com
Web Site: www.zgc.com
Key Personnel
Pres & Head, Prod Sales: Les Zellan *Tel:* 973-335-4460 ext 10 *E-mail:* les@zgc.com
Tech Dir: Guy Genin *Tel:* 973-335-4460 ext 15 *E-mail:* guy@zgc.com
Mktg Coord, Webmaster & Engr: Patti Greene *Tel:* 973-335-4460 ext 21 *E-mail:* patti@zgc.com
Catalog(s) available

Zhone Technologies Inc
7195 Oakport St, Oakland, CA 94621
Tel: 510-777-7000 *Toll Free Tel:* 877-ZHONE-20 (946-6320, US & CN) *Fax:* 510-777-7001
E-mail: info@zhone.com; sales@zhone.com
Web Site: www.zhone.com
Key Personnel
Exec Chmn: Mory Ejabat
CEO: Jim Norrod
COO: Robert Smith
CFO, Corp Treas & Secy: Kirk Misaka
Chief Mktg Offr: Brian Caskey
CTO: Eric Presworsky
SVP, Engg: Bruce Roe
VP, Busn Devt: David Misunas
VP, Enterprise Sales: Monique Apter
VP, US Sales: Michael Fischer
Catalog(s) available
Branch Office(s)
801 Brickell Ave, 9th fl, Miami, FL 33131,

Contact: Antonio Jonusas *Tel:* 305-789-6680 *Fax:* 305-371-0084 *E-mail:* ajonusas@zhone.com
Foreign Office(s): Av Libertador 2442, 3 y 4 piso, B1636DSR Olivos, Buenos Aires, Argentina, Contact: Cristian Herfert *Tel:* (011) 4711 8769 *Fax:* (011) 4711 8201 *E-mail:* cherfert@zhone.com
Zhone Technologies do Brasil, Rua Funchal 573, 9º andar, Cjs 93/94, sala 9, 04551-060 Vila Olimpia-SP, Brazil, Contact: Rony Pedroso *Tel:* (011) 3230 8696 *E-mail:* rpedroso@zhone.com
Zhone Technologies de Colombia Ltda, Cra 18, No 86-A 14, Bogota, Colombia, Contact: Alex Baber *Tel:* (01) 638-6186 *Fax:* (01) 616-3030 *E-mail:* ababer@zhone.com
Zhone Technologies International Inc, 19 El Shahid Helmy El Masry St, 2nd fl, Off No 6-Almaza, Heliopolis, Cairo, Egypt, Contact: Karim Salah *Tel:* (02) 4187273 *Fax:* (02) 4147906 *E-mail:* ksalah@zhone.com
Zhone Technologies GmbH, Lahrer Weg 98, 92318 Neumark/Opf, Germany, Contact: Stefan Knodler *Tel:* (09181) 698 6899 *Fax:* (09181) 698 6890 *E-mail:* sknodler@zhone.com
Zhone Technologies Ltd, Hong Kong, Contact: Raymond Chiu *Tel:* 9422 9990 *Fax:* 3011 5440 *E-mail:* rchiu@zhone.com
Zhone Technologies SRL, Via Alfredo Catalani 5, 20900 Monza MB, Italy, Contact: Slobodan Zlatkovic *Tel:* 335 582 9734 *E-mail:* szlatkovic@zhone.com
Reforma 350 Piso 11 (Torre Angel), Col Juarez, 06600 Mexico, DF, Mexico, Contact: Alex Baber *Tel:* (0155) 9171-1480 *Fax:* (0155) 5209-8499 *E-mail:* ababer@zhone.com
Calle Sol No 310, Old San Juan 00901, Puerto Rico, Contact: Alex Baber *Tel:* 787-723-3217 *Fax:* 786-431-2504 *E-mail:* ababer@zhone.com
Zhone Technologies Pte Ltd, 20 Maxwell Rd, No 10-12 Maxwell House, Singapore 069113, Singapore, Contact: ChongBee Chew *Tel:* 8100 8111 *Fax:* 6415 1148 *E-mail:* cchew@zhone.com
Zhone Technologies AB, Kopmangatan 19, 64130 Katrineholm, Sweden, Contact: Peter Hagelin *Tel:* (0705) 478100 *E-mail:* phagelin@zhone.com
Zhone Technologies International Inc, Dubai Media City, Busn Central Towers, Tower B, Off 2701, PO Box 9456, Dubai, United Arab Emirates, Contact: Hakim Alhusan *Tel:* (04) 449 4017 *Fax:* (04) 449 4018 *E-mail:* halhusan@zhone.com
Zhone Technologies UK, 40 Basepoint Business Ctr, Riverhead Dr, Swindon SN5 7EX, United Kingdom, Contact: Anthony Clarkson *Tel:* (01793) 677676 *Fax:* (01793) 677696 *E-mail:* aclarkson@zhone.com
Membership(s): IEEE; The Optical Society; SMPTE; SPIE

Zim Records
18 Ivy Dr, Jericho, NY 11753
Mailing Address: PO Box 158, Jericho, NY 11753-0158
Tel: 516-681-7102
E-mail: zimrecords@msn.com
Key Personnel
Owner: Arthur Zimmerman
Catalog(s) available

Zion Music Group
Subsidiary of Nashville Teleproductions Co
357 Riverside Dr, Suite 200, Franklin, TN 37064
Mailing Address: 306 Monticello Rd, Franklin, TN 37064
Tel: 615-262-2600 *Toll Free Tel:* 800-883-1772 *Fax:* 615-226-4070
Web Site: www.zionmusic.com
Key Personnel
Pres: Kevin T McManus
VP: Beverly Cohron McManus
Recording engineering & production.

Zippertubing® Co
7150 W Erie St, Chandler, AZ 85226
Tel: 480-285-3900 *Toll Free Tel:* 800-321-8178 *Fax:* 480-285-3997
E-mail: info@zippertubing.com; orders@zippertubing.com
Web Site: www.zippertubing.com
Cable management solutions, wire protection.
Catalog(s) available

Zondervan, A HarperCollins Company
3900 Sparks Dr, Grand Rapids, MI 49546
Tel: 616-698-6900 *Toll Free Tel:* 800-226-1122; 800-727-3480 (retail orders) *Fax:* 616-698-3255 (retail orders)
E-mail: zinfo@zondervan.com
Web Site: www.zondervan.com
Key Personnel
CEO & Pres: Mark Schoenwald
EVP, Sales: Tom Knight
SVP & Publr: Annette Bourland
HR Mgr: Anna Elzinga
Founded: 1931
Religious programming distributor.
Catalog(s) available
Membership(s): Audio Publishers Association; ICVM

ZTV Broadcast Services Inc
1333 Matheson Blvd E, Mississauga, ON L4W 1R1, Canada
Tel: 905-290-4430 *Fax:* 905-290-3370
Web Site: ztvbroadcast.com
Key Personnel
Pres: Steve Zajaczkiwsky *E-mail:* steve@ztvbroadcast.com
Rentals & Tech Support: Henry Pinnock *E-mail:* henry@ztvbroadcast.com
Founded: 1992
Professional video equipment rentals.

Zygote Media Group Inc
1045 S 500 E, Suite 200, American Fork, UT 84003
Tel: 801-765-4141 *Fax:* 801-705-2234
E-mail: customerservices@zygote.com
Web Site: www.zygote.com
Key Personnel
Pres: Roger Clarke
VP, Busn Devt: Dave Dunston
Founded: 1994
3D animation studio specializing in characters & biomedical content as well as vehicles & electronic products. Catalogue of licensable content. Services include modeling, texture mapping, animation, compositing, motion graphics & effects utilizing Maya, XS1, 305Max, after effects & combustion.

Associations

AV trade associations, as well as selected media-related organizations and educational and library groups with an AV interest, are listed in this section.

AAM, see American Alliance of Museums (AAM)

AAUW, see American Association of University Women (AAUW)

AAVIM, see American Association for Vocational Instructional Materials (AAVIM)

The Academy of Motion Picture Arts and Sciences (AMPAS)
8949 Wilshire Blvd, Beverly Hills, CA 90211
Tel: 310-247-3000 *Fax:* 310-859-9619
E-mail: awardsoffice@oscars.org
Web Site: www.oscars.org
Key Personnel
CEO: Dawn Hudson
Mng Dir, Membership & Awards: Kimberly Roush *Tel:* 310-247-3000 ext 1127 *E-mail:* kroush@oscars.org
Founded: 1927
Advance the arts & sciences of motion pictures.
Number of Members: 6,441

Academy of Science Fiction, Fantasy & Horror Films
334 W 54 St, Los Angeles, CA 90037
Tel: 323-752-5811
E-mail: scifiacademy@ca.rr.com
Web Site: www.saturnawards.org
Key Personnel
CEO & Pres: Robert Holguin
VP: Roger Fenton
Dir, Opers: Michael Laster
Founded: 1972
Present awards, screen films, etc.
Number of Members: 3,000
Publication(s): *The Saturn Rings*

Academy of Television Arts & Sciences, see Television Academy

Acoustical Society of America (ASA)
1305 Walt Whitman Rd, Suite 300, Melville, NY 11747-4300
Tel: 516-576-2360 *Fax:* 516-576-2377
E-mail: asa@aip.org
Web Site: www.acousticalsociety.org
Key Personnel
Exec Dir: Susan E Fox
Founded: 1929
Increase & diffuse the knowledge of acoustics & promote its practical applications.
Number of Members: 7,500
2015 Conference(s): 169th Meeting, Wyndham Grand Pittsburgh Downtown Hotel, Pittsburgh, PA, May 18-22, 2015; 170th Meeting, Jacksonville, FL, Nov 2-6, 2015
2016 Conference(s): 171st Meeting, Salt Lake City, UT, May 23-27, 2016
Publication(s): *The Journal of the Acoustical Society of America* (monthly)

AFI, see American Film Institute (AFI)

Agency for Instructional Technology (AIT)
8111 N Lee Paul Rd, Bloomington, IN 47404-7916
Tel: 812-339-2203 *Toll Free Tel:* 800-457-4509 *Fax:* 812-333-4218
E-mail: info@ait.net
Web Site: www.ait.net
Key Personnel
Exec Dir: Charles Wilson *E-mail:* cwilson@ait.net
Founded: 1962
Nonprofit education organization established to develop, acquire & distribute quality technology-based resources including computer interactive videos, CD-ROMs, broadcast & related printed materials.

AHIMA, see American Health Information Management Association (AHIMA)

AIE™, see Association of Imaging Executives™ (AIE™), A PMA Member Association

AIGA, the professional association for design
164 Fifth Ave, New York, NY 10010
Tel: 212-807-1990 *Toll Free Tel:* 800-548-1634 *Fax:* 212-807-1799
E-mail: general@aiga.org
Web Site: www.aiga.org
Key Personnel
CEO: Richard Grefe *Tel:* 212-710-3100
Founded: 1914
Organization for graphic artists involved in book design, illustration, advertising, corporate graphics, promotion & exhibitions.
Number of Members: 22,000
Publication(s): *365: AIGA Year in Design* (annual); *Voice: AIGA Journal of Design* (online)

AIIM, see Association for Information and Image Management (AIIM)

AIME, see Association for Information Media & Equipment

AIT, see Agency for Instructional Technology (AIT)

ALA, see American Library Association (ALA)

Alliance for Community Media (ACM)
4248 Park Glen Rd, Minneapolis, MN 55416
Tel: 952-928-4643
E-mail: info@allcommunitymedia.org
Web Site: www.allcommunitymedia.org
Key Personnel
Contact: Michelle Herr
Founded: 1976
Provide services to people working in community programming & cultivate citizen participation in community access TV.
Number of Members: 387
2015 Conference(s): ACM Annual Conference, Hilton Pasadena, 168 S Los Robles Ave, Pasadena, CA, Aug 12-14, 2015

Alliance for Women in Media/Alliance for Women in Media Foundation
1250 24 St NW, Suite 300, Washington, DC 20037
Tel: 703-506-3290 *Fax:* 202-750-3664
Web Site: www.allwomeninmedia.org
Key Personnel
Pres: Erin M Fuller *E-mail:* efuller@allwomeninmedia.org
Work worldwide to improve the quality of radio & TV; promote the entry, development & advancement of women in radio & TV & their allied fields; serve as a medium for communication & idea exchange.
Publication(s): *AWM* (ezine, weekly, free)

Alliance of Motion Picture & Television Producers (AMPTP)
15301 Ventura Blvd, Bldg E, Sherman Oaks, CA 91403
Tel: 818-995-3600 *Fax:* 818-285-4450
E-mail: info@tw.amptp.org
Web Site: www.amptp.org
Key Personnel
Communs Dir: Jesse Hiestand
Founded: 1982
Trade organization; handle collective bargaining negotiation for the entertainment industry.

Alliance Quebecoise des Techniciens de l'Image et du Son (AQTIS)
533 Ontario St E, Suite 300, Montreal, QC H2L 1N8, Canada
Tel: 514-844-2113 *Toll Free Tel:* 888-647-0681 *Fax:* 514-844-3540
E-mail: info@aqtis.qc.ca
Web Site: www.aqtis.qc.ca
Key Personnel
Gen Mgr: Jean-Claude Rocheleau *E-mail:* jcrocheleau@aqtis.qc.ca
Mgr, Labor Rel: Charles Paradis *E-mail:* cparadis@aqtis.qc.ca
Quebec's film, TV & creative technicians' union.
Number of Members: 3,500

Alma-The International Loudspeaker Association
55 Littleton Rd, Unit 13-B, Ayer, MA 01432
Tel: 978-772-6977 *Fax:* 617-848-9935
E-mail: management@almainternational.org
Web Site: www.almainternational.org
Key Personnel
Exec Dir: Carol Bousquet
Founded: 1964
Not-for-profit trade association of loudspeaker manufacturers, designers & distributors.
Number of Members: 150
Publication(s): *ALMANews* (4 issues/yr)

AMA, see American Management Association®

American Alliance of Museums (AAM)
1575 Eye St NW, Suite 400, Washington, DC 20005
Tel: 202-289-1818 *Fax:* 202-289-6578
Web Site: www.aam-us.org
Key Personnel
COO: Laura Lott *Tel:* 202-289-9112 *E-mail:* llott@aam-us.org
Sr Dir, Leadership Progs: Dean Phelus *Tel:* 202-218-2674 *E-mail:* dphelus@aam-us.org
Founded: 1906
Promote the welfare of museums & museum professionals.
Number of Members: 20,890
2015 Conference(s): Annual Meeting & MuseumExpo, Atlanta, GA, April 26-29, 2015
2016 Conference(s): Annual Meeting & MuseumExpo, Washington, DC, May 26-29, 2016

2017 Conference(s): Annual Meeting & MuseumExpo, St Louis, MO, May 7-10, 2017
Publication(s): *Aviso* (ezine, monthly, free to membs; $40/yr non-membs); *Museum* (magazine, 6 issues/yr, free to membs; $38/yr non-membs)

American Association for Vocational Instructional Materials (AAVIM)
220 Smithonia Rd, Winterville, GA 30683
Tel: 706-742-5355 *Toll Free Tel:* 800-228-4689 *Fax:* 706-742-7005
E-mail: sales@aavim.com
Web Site: www.aavim.com
Key Personnel
Dir: Gary Farmer
Founded: 1949
Develop, produce & distribute training materials for vocational education.
Membership(s): National Association of Agriculture Educators

American Association of School Administrators (AASA)
1615 Duke St, Alexandria, VA 22314
Tel: 703-528-0700 *Fax:* 703-841-1543
E-mail: info@aasa.org
Web Site: www.aasa.org
Key Personnel
Exec Dir: Daniel A Domenech *Tel:* 703-875-0722 *E-mail:* ddomenech@aasa.org
International organization for school administrators.
Number of Members: 14,000
2016 Conference(s): AASA National Conference on Education, Phoenix Convention Center, Phoenix, AZ, Feb 11-13, 2016
Publication(s): *The School Administrator* (11 issues/yr, $10/issue membs; $11/issue non-membs)

American Association of School Librarians (AASL)
Division of American Library Association (ALA)
50 E Huron St, Chicago, IL 60611
Tel: 312-280-4382 *Toll Free Tel:* 800-545-2433 (ext 4382) *Fax:* 312-280-5276
E-mail: aasl@ala.org
Web Site: www.aasl.org
Key Personnel
Exec Dir: Julie A Walker *Tel:* 800-545-2433 ext 4388 *E-mail:* jwalker@ala.org
Founded: 1951
Advocate excellence, facilitate change & develop leaders in the school library media field.
Number of Members: 7,537
Publication(s): *Knowledge Quest* (journal); *School Library Research* (journal)

American Association of University Women (AAUW)
1111 16 St NW, Washington, DC 20036
Tel: 202-785-7700 *Toll Free Tel:* 800-326-AAUW (326-2289) *Fax:* 202-872-1425
E-mail: helpline@aauw.org; connect@aauw.org
Web Site: www.aauw.org
Key Personnel
Pres: Carolyn Garfein
Founded: 1881
Promote education & equity for women & girls.
Number of Members: 100,000
Publication(s): *AAUW Outlook* (magazine, 3 issues/yr, free to membs)

American Center for Children & Media
5400 N Saint Louis Ave, Chicago, IL 60625
Tel: 773-509-5510 *Fax:* 773-509-5303
E-mail: info@centerforchildrenandmedia.org
Web Site: www.centerforchildrenandmedia.org
Key Personnel
Founder: James Fellows
Pres: David W Kleeman *E-mail:* dkleeman@atgonline.org
Founded: 1985
Executive round table that leads the US industry in developing sustainable & kid-friendly solutions to long-standing issues. The center also promotes the exchange of ideas, expertise & information as a means for building quality & looks worldwide for best practices.

American Cinema Editors Inc (ACE)
Verna Fields Bldg 2282, Rm 190, 100 Universal City Plaza, Universal City, CA 91608
Tel: 818-777-2900 *Fax:* 818-733-5023
E-mail: americancinema@editors.com
Web Site: www.ace-filmeditors.org
Key Personnel
Pres: Alan Heim
VP: Randy Roberts
Founded: 1950
To advance the art & science of the editing profession in motion pictures & television. To bring into close alliance those editors who desire to advance the prestige & dignity of the editing profession. It is an honorary professional society apart from the editors guild.
Number of Members: 550
Publication(s): *Cinemaeditor Magazine* (magazine, quarterly, $20/yr; $36/yr intl)

American Educational Research Association (AERA)
1430 "K" St NW, Suite 1200, Washington, DC 20005
Tel: 202-238-3200 *Fax:* 202-238-3250
Web Site: www.aera.net
Key Personnel
Exec Dir: Felice J Levine *Tel:* 202-238-3200 ext 201 *E-mail:* flevine@aera.net
Founded: 1916
Support & disseminate educational research.
Number of Members: 25,000
2015 Conference(s): Annual Meeting, Chicago, IL, April 16-20, 2015
2016 Conference(s): Annual Meeting, Washington, DC, April 8-12, 2016
Publication(s): *American Educational Research Journal* (quarterly, $52); *Educational Evaluation & Policy Analysis* (quarterly, $52); *Educational Researcher* (9 issues/yr, $52); *Journal of Educational & Behavioral Statistics* (quarterly, $66); *Review of Educational Research* (quarterly, $52); *Review of Research in Education* (annual, $52)

American Federation of Musicians of the United States & Canada (AFM)
1501 Broadway, Suite 600, New York, NY 10036
Tel: 212-869-1330 *Fax:* 212-764-6134
Web Site: www.afm.org
Key Personnel
COO: Lew Mancini *E-mail:* lmancini@afm.org
Pres: Ray Hair *E-mail:* presoffice@afm.org
Founded: 1896
Labor union for musicians.
Number of Members: 90,000
Publication(s): *International Musician* (monthly)

American Film Institute (AFI)
Attn: Facilities Off, 2021 N Western Ave, Los Angeles, CA 90027-1657
Tel: 323-856-7600 *Toll Free Tel:* 800-774-4AFI (774-4234 membership) *Fax:* 323-467-4578
E-mail: information@afi.com
Web Site: www.afi.com
Key Personnel
CEO & Pres: Bob Gazzale
COO: Nancy Harris
Founded: 1967
AFI is a national institute providing leadership in screen education & the recognition & celebration of excellence in the art of film, television & digital media.
Number of Members: 12,000

American Foundation for the Blind (AFB)
2 Penn Plaza, Suite 1102, New York, NY 10121
Tel: 212-502-7600; 212-502-7662 (TDD) *Toll Free Tel:* 800-232-5463 *Fax:* 212-502-7777 *Toll Free Fax:* 888-545-8331
E-mail: afbinfo@afb.net
Web Site: www.afb.org
Key Personnel
Pres & CEO: Carl R Augusto
Chief Admin Offr: Kelly Bleach
CFO: Rick Bozeman
Chief Communs & Mktg Offr: Adrianna Montague-Devaud
VP, Progs & Policy: Paul Schroeder
Founded: 1921
A national nonprofit that expands possibilities for people with vision loss. Priorities include broadening access to technology; elevating the quality of information & tools for the professionals who serve people with vision loss; & promoting independent & healthy living for people with vision loss by providing them & their families with relevant & timely resources. In addition, AFB's web site serves as a gateway to a wealth of vision loss information & services. Houses the Helen Keller Archives & honors the over forty years that Helen Keller worked tirelessly with AFB. For more information, visit www.afb.org.
Branch Office(s)
AFB Public Policy Center, 1660 "L" St NW, Suite 513, Washington, DC 20036 *Tel:* 202-469-6831 *Fax:* 646-478-9260
100 Peachtree St, Suite 2145, Atlanta, GA 30303 *Tel:* 404-525-2303 *Fax:* 646-478-9260 *E-mail:* literacy@afb.net
AFB Center on Vision Loss, 11030 Ables Lane, Dallas, TX 75229 *Tel:* 214-352-7222 *Fax:* 646-478-9260 *E-mail:* dallas@afb.net
1000 Fifth Ave, Suite 350, Huntington, WV 25701 *Tel:* 304-523-8651 *Fax:* 646-478-9260
Publication(s): *AccessWorld* (monthly); *Journal of Visual Impairment & Blindness* (monthly)

American Health Information Management Association (AHIMA)
233 N Michigan Ave, 21st fl, Chicago, IL 60601-5809
Tel: 312-233-1100 *Toll Free Tel:* 800-335-5535 *Fax:* 312-233-1090; 312-233-1500 (orders)
E-mail: info@ahima.org
Web Site: www.ahima.org
Key Personnel
CEO: Lynne Thomas Gordon
Founded: 1928
Promote the art & science of medical records administration; aim to improve the quality of comprehensive health information services for the public welfare.
Number of Members: 71,000
2015 Conference(s): AHIMA Convention & Exhibit, New Orleans, LA, Sept 26-30, 2015
Publication(s): *Journal of AHIMA* (journal, 11 issues/yr, free to membs; non-membs: $100/yr US, $110/yr CN, $120/yr other)

American Library Association (ALA)
50 E Huron St, Chicago, IL 60611-2795
Tel: 312-944-6780 *Toll Free Tel:* 800-545-2433 (ext 3223, conference servs) *Fax:* 312-440-9374
E-mail: ala@ala.org
Web Site: www.ala.org
Key Personnel
Exec Dir: Keith Michael Fiels *E-mail:* kfiels@ala.org
Founded: 1876

Promote & improve library service & librarianship.
Number of Members: 60,000
2015 Conference(s): Annual Conference, Moscone Center, San Francisco, CA, June 25-30, 2015
2016 Conference(s): Annual Conference, Orlando, FL, June 23-28, 2016; Midwinter Meeting, Boston, MA, Jan 8-12, 2016
2017 Conference(s): Annual Conference, Chicago, IL, June 22-27, 2017; Midwinter Meeting, Atlanta, GA, Jan 20-24, 2017
2018 Conference(s): Annual Conference, New Orleans, LA, June 21-26, 2018; Midwinter Meeting, Denver, CO, Feb 9-13, 2018
2019 Conference(s): Annual Conference, Washington, DC, June 20-25, 2019; Midwinter Meeting, Seattle, WA, Jan 25-29, 2019
Publication(s): *American Libraries* (6 issues/yr); *Booklist* (22 issues/yr)

American Management Association®
1601 Broadway, New York, NY 10019
Tel: 212-586-8100 *Toll Free Tel:* 877-566-9441 (cust serv) *Fax:* 212-903-8168; 518-891-0368 (cust serv)
E-mail: customerservice@amanet.org
Web Site: www.amanet.org
Key Personnel
CEO & Pres: Edward T Reilly
PR Mgr: Roger Kelleher *Tel:* 212-903-7976 *E-mail:* rkelleher@amanet.org
Founded: 1923
With over 85 years of experience delivering 140+ training seminars throughout the country, AMA has refined their training programs to meet today's challenges. AMA promotes the goals of individuals & organizations through a comprehensive range of solutions, including business seminars, blended learning, Webcasts & podcasts, conferences, books, whitepapers, articles & more.
Number of Members: 100,000

American Optometric Association (AOA)
243 N Lindbergh Blvd, 1st fl, St Louis, MO 63141-7881
Tel: 314-991-4100 *Toll Free Tel:* 800-365-2219 *Fax:* 314-991-4101
Web Site: www.aoa.org
Key Personnel
Dir, Meetings & Conventions: Lori Lee *Tel:* 314-983-4256
Founded: 1898
A federation of state, student & armed forces, optometric associations serving members consisting of optometrists, students of optometry, paraoptomeric assistants & technicians.
Number of Members: 36,000
Branch Office(s)
1505 Prince St, Suite 300, Alexandria, VA 22314, Contact: Debbie Espinoza *Tel:* 703-739-9200 *Fax:* 703-739-9497
2015 Conference(s): Optometry's Meeting®, Washington State Convention Center, Seattle, WA, June 24-28, 2015
2016 Conference(s): Optometry's Meeting®, Boston, MA, June 29-July 2, 2016
2017 Conference(s): Optometry's Meeting®, Washington, DC, June 21-25, 2017
Publication(s): *AOA News* (monthly); *Optometry; Journal of the American Optometric Association* (monthly)

American Photographic Artisans Guild (APAG)
2269 N 400 Rd, Eudora, KS 66025
Tel: 785-883-4166
Web Site: www.apag.net
Key Personnel
Exec Dir: Quinn Hancock
Founded: 1966
An international guild dedicated to the development of each member's skills for service to the photographic industry & the promotion of the role of the photographic artisan as skilled professionals.
Number of Members: 250

The American Society for Photogrammetry & Remote Sensing, see ASPRS: The Imaging and Geospatial Information Society

American Society for Training & Development (ASTD), see Association for Talent Development (ATD)

American Society of Cinematographers
1782 N Orange Dr, Hollywood, CA 90028
Mailing Address: PO Box 2230, Hollywood, CA 90078
Tel: 323-969-4333 *Toll Free Tel:* 800-448-0145 (US only) *Fax:* 323-882-6391
E-mail: office@theasc.com
Web Site: www.theasc.com
Key Personnel
Pres: Richard Crudo *E-mail:* president@theasc.com
Founded: 1919
Private association of motion picture cameramen. Membership is by invitation only.
Number of Members: 500
Publication(s): *American Cinematographer Magazine* (monthly)

American Society of Media Photographers Inc (ASMP)
150 N Second St, Philadelphia, PA 19016
Tel: 215-451-2767 *Fax:* 215-451-0880
E-mail: info@asmp.org
Web Site: www.asmp.org
Key Personnel
Exec Dir: Eugene Mopsik
Gen Mgr: Elena Goertz *Tel:* 215-451-2767 ext 203 *E-mail:* goertz@asmp.org
Founded: 1944
Protect the interests of professional photographers; maintain & promote high professional standards & ethics; cultivate mutual understanding among professional photographers.
Number of Members: 7,000
Publication(s): *ASMP Bulletin* (bulletin, 5 issues/yr); *Professional Business Practices in Photography* ($25 membs; $35 non-membs plus shipping & handling. Available at amazom.com for discount)

American Society of Photographers (ASP)
3120 N Argonne Dr, Milwaukee, WI 53222
Tel: 414-871-6600
Web Site: s17670789.onlinehome-server.com/
Key Personnel
Exec Dir: Jon Allyn *E-mail:* jonallyn@aol.com
Founded: 1937
Professional photographers organization promoting the ideas of photography as an art & science.
Number of Members: 850
Publication(s): *ASP Magazine* (quarterly)

American Society of Safety Engineers (ASSE)
1800 E Oakton St, Des Plaines, IL 60018
Tel: 847-699-2929
E-mail: customerservice@asse.org
Web Site: www.asse.org
Key Personnel
Exec Dir: Fred Fortman *Tel:* 847-768-3450
Dir, Fin/Cont: Bruce Sufranski *Tel:* 847-768-3401
Deputy Exec Dir/COO: Kelly Fanella *Tel:* 847-768-3409
Dir, Prof Devt: Dewey Whitmire *Tel:* 847-768-3418
Ed, Professional Safety Magazine: Sue Trebswether *Tel:* 847-768-3433
Founded: 1911
A nonprofit individual membership society of safety professionals in industry, insurance, government, education & private consulting.
Number of Members: 32,299
2015 Conference(s): Professional Development Conference & Exposition (Safety 2015), The Kay Bailey Hutchison Convention Center, 650 S Griffin St, Dallas, TX, June 7-10, 2015
Publication(s): *Professional Safety Magazine* (monthly, free to membs)

American Sportscasters Association Inc (ASA)
Affiliate of American Sportscasters Hall of Fame Trust
225 Broadway, Suite 2030, New York, NY 10007
Tel: 212-227-8080 *Fax:* 212-571-0556
Web Site: www.americansportscasters.com; www.americansportscastersonline.com
Key Personnel
Chmn of the Bd: Dick Enberg
Pres: Louis O Schwartz *E-mail:* lschwa8918@aol.com
Founded: 1980
Advance the profession of sportscasting, voting for Sportscaster of the Year, Sports Personality, Hall of Fame inductee, Graham McNamee Award, Sports Legend Award, International Sportscaster of the Year.
Number of Members: 500
Publication(s): *Insiders Sports Letter* (quarterly)

AMPAS, see The Academy of Motion Picture Arts and Sciences (AMPAS)

Amusement & Music Operators Association (AMOA)
600 Spring Hill Ring Rd, Suite 111, West Dundee, IL 60118
Tel: 847-428-7699 *Toll Free Tel:* 800-YES-AMOA (937-2662) *Fax:* 847-428-7719
E-mail: amoa@amoa.com
Web Site: www.amoa.com
Key Personnel
EVP: Jack Kelleher
Deputy Dir: Lori Schneider
Founded: 1948
Trade association representing music, amusement & vending industries & coin-operated amusement devices.
Number of Members: 1,400
2016 Conference(s): AAMA/AMOA Amusement Expo, Las Vegas Convention Center, 3150 Paradise Rd, Las Vegas, NV, March 15-17, 2016

AQTIS, see Alliance Quebecoise des Techniciens de l'Image et du Son (AQTIS)

Arizona Production Association
6615 N Scottsdale Rd, Suite 101, Scottsdale, AZ 85250
Tel: 480-345-6464 *Toll Free Tel:* 866-345-6469 *Fax:* 480-941-2557
E-mail: info@azproduction.com
Web Site: www.azproduction.com
Key Personnel
Admin Dir: Julie Lee
Nonprofit trade organization of film, theatre & television professionals.
Number of Members: 350
Publication(s): *Arizona Production Guide (online only); On the Arizona Set* (newsletter, 4-6 issues/yr, $12)

Art Directors Guild (ADG)
11969 Ventura Blvd, 2nd fl, Studio City, CA 91604
Tel: 818-762-9995 *Fax:* 818-762-9997
Web Site: www.adg.org

Key Personnel
Exec Dir: Scott Roth *E-mail:* scott@artdirectors.org
Assoc Exec Dir: John Moffit *E-mail:* john@artdirectors.org
Dir, Opers: Lydia Zimmer *E-mail:* lydia@artdirectors.org
Opers Mgr: Cynthia Paskos *E-mail:* cynthia@artdirectors.org
International union representing employees in the entertainment industry, including art directors, graphic artists, illustrators, matte artists, model makers, scenic artists, set designers & title artists.
Number of Members: 810

ASCD
1703 N Beauregard St, Alexandria, VA 22311-1714
Tel: 703-578-9600 *Toll Free Tel:* 800-933-2723 *Fax:* 703-575-5400
E-mail: exhibits@ascd.org
Web Site: www.ascd.org
Key Personnel
Exec Dir: Judy Seltz
Founded: 1943
ASCD is a membership organization that develops programs, products & services essential to the way educators learn, teach & lead. Advertising opportunities on the web site as well.
Number of Members: 178,000
2016 Conference(s): ASCD Annual Conference & Exhibit Show, Atlanta, GA, April 2-4, 2016
2017 Conference(s): ASCD Annual Conference & Exhibit Show, Anaheim, CA, March 25-27, 2017
2018 Conference(s): ASCD Annual Conference & Exhibit Show, Boston, MA, March 24-26, 2018
2019 Conference(s): ASCD Annual Conference & Exhibit Show, Chicago, IL, March 16-18, 2019
Publication(s): *Educational Leadership* (8 issues/yr)

ASMP, see American Society of Media Photographers Inc (ASMP)

ASPRS: The Imaging and Geospatial Information Society
5410 Grosvenor Lane, Suite 210, Bethesda, MD 20814-2160
Tel: 301-493-0290 *Fax:* 301-493-0208
E-mail: asprs@asprs.org
Web Site: www.asprs.org
Key Personnel
Exec Dir: Michael Hauck *Tel:* 301-493-0290 ext 102 *E-mail:* mhauck@asprs.org
Asst Communs Dir/Meetings-Mktg Mgr: Heather Staverman *Tel:* 301-493-0290 ext 106 *E-mail:* hstaverman@asprs.org
Nonprofit scientific society. Disseminate information on photogrammetry, remote sensing, geographic information systems & satellite imagery.
Number of Members: 6,500
2015 Conference(s): Annual Conference, Tampa Bay Marriott Waterside Hotel, Tampa, FL, May 4-8, 2015
Publication(s): *Photogrammetric Engineering & Remote Sensing* (monthly)

ASSE, see American Society of Safety Engineers (ASSE)

Association for Educational Communications & Technology (AECT)
320 W Eighth St, Suite 101, Bloomington, IN 47404-3745
Tel: 812-335-7675 *Toll Free Tel:* 877-677-AECT (677-2328) *Fax:* 812-335-7678
E-mail: aect@aect.org
Web Site: www.aect.org
Key Personnel
Exec Dir: Phillip Harris *Tel:* 812-335-7675 ext 202 *E-mail:* pharris@aect.org
Dir, Electronic Servs: Larry Vernon *E-mail:* lvernon@aect.org
Founded: 1923
Improve instruction through use of all media & educational technology.
Number of Members: 5,000
Publication(s): *TechTrends*

Association for Information and Image Management (AIIM)
1100 Wayne Ave, Suite 1100, Silver Spring, MD 20910
Tel: 301-587-8202 *Toll Free Tel:* 800-477-2446 *Fax:* 301-587-2711
E-mail: aiim@aiim.org
Web Site: www.aiim.org
Key Personnel
Pres & CEO: John F Mancini
COO: Atle Skjekkeland
CFO: Felicia Dillard
VP & Chief Mktg Offr: Peggy Winton
Founded: 1943
Trade association & professional society representing the document management industry.
Number of Members: 6,800
Publication(s): *Connect* (ezine, weekly); *Get Smart at AIIM* (ezine, biweekly)

Association for Information Media & Equipment
PO Box 9844, Cedar Rapids, IA 52409-9844
Tel: 319-654-0608 *Fax:* 319-654-0609
Web Site: www.aime.org
Key Personnel
Exec Dir: Betty Gorsegner Ehlinger *E-mail:* bettyge@mchsi.com
Founded: 1986
Promote copyright awareness & education for informational motion media.
Number of Members: 150
Publication(s): *AIME News* (quarterly)

Association for Recorded Sound Collections Inc (ARSC)
c/o Knight Library, 1299 University of Oregon, Eugene, OR 97403-1299
Web Site: www.arsc-audio.org
Key Personnel
Exec Dir: Nathan Georgitis *E-mail:* execdir@arsc-audio.org
Founded: 1966
Performs research & studies, publication & information exchange covering all aspects of recordings & recorded sound.
Number of Members: 1,000
2015 Conference(s): ARSC Annual Conference, Westin Convention Center Hotel, Pittsburgh, PA, May 27-30, 2015
Publication(s): *ARSC Journal* (semiannual)

Association for Talent Development (ATD)
Formerly American Society for Training & Development (ASTD)
1640 King St, Alexandria, VA 22314-2743
Tel: 703-683-8100 *Toll Free Tel:* 800-628-2783 *Fax:* 703-299-8723; 703-683-1523 (cust care)
E-mail: customercare@td.org
Web Site: www.td.org; www.astd.org
Key Personnel
Pres & CEO: Tony Bingham
VP: Jennifer Homer
Founded: 1943
Mission: Provides leadership to individual organizations & society. Achieve work related competence performance & fulfillment. Empower professionals to develop knowledge & skills successfully.
Number of Members: 70,000
2015 Conference(s): ATD International Conference & Exposition, Orange County Convention Center, 9990 International Dr, Orlando, FL, May 17-20, 2015
2016 Conference(s): ATD International Conference & Exposition, Denver, CO, May 22-25, 2016
Publication(s): *Info-Line* (monthly); *T&D Magazine* (monthly)

The Association for Women in Communications (AWC)
3337 Duke St, Alexandria, VA 22314
Tel: 703-370-7436 *Fax:* 703-342-4311
E-mail: info@womcom.org
Web Site: www.womcom.org
Key Personnel
Exec Dir: Pamela Valenzuela
Founded: 1909
Champions the advancement of women across all communications disciplines by recognizing excellence, promoting leadership & positioning its members at the forefront of the evolving communications era communication. More than 90 professional & campus chapters worldwide provide the membership with the opportunity for local networking, education & support.
Number of Members: 3,000
2015 Conference(s): AWC National Conference, Kansas City, MO, Oct 8-10, 2015

Association of American Publishers (AAP)
71 Fifth Ave, 2nd fl, New York, NY 10003-3004
Tel: 212-255-0200 *Fax:* 212-255-7007
E-mail: info@publishers.org
Web Site: www.publishers.org
Key Personnel
Pres & CEO: Tom Allen *E-mail:* tallen@publishers.org
VP: Tina Jordan *Tel:* 212-255-0275 *E-mail:* tjordan@publishers.org
VP & Exec Dir, Prof & Scholarly Publg: John Tagler *Tel:* 212-255-1407 *E-mail:* jtagler@publishers.org
Gen Coun & VP, Govt Aff: Allan R Adler *Tel:* 202-220-4544 *E-mail:* adler@publishers.org
Founded: 1970
Monitor & promote the USA publishing industry. Members: those actively engaged in the creation, publication & production of books, journals, electronic media, testing materials & a range of educational materials.
Number of Members: 450
Branch Office(s)
455 Massachusetts Ave NW, Suite 700, Washington, DC 20001-2777, Dir, Communs: Marisa Bluestone *Tel:* 202-347-3375 *Fax:* 202-347-3690 *E-mail:* mbluestone@publishers.org
325 Chestnut St, Suite 1110, Philadelphia, PA 19106-7761 *Tel:* 267-351-4310 *Fax:* 267-351-4317
Publication(s): *AAP Export Sales Report* (annual); *AAP StatShot* (monthly)

Association of Biomedical Communications Directors (ABCD)
State University of New York at Stony Brook, L3 044 Health Science Ctr, Stony Brook, NY 11794-8030
Tel: 631-444-3228 *Fax:* 631-444-3500
Web Site: www.abcdirectors.org
Key Personnel
Secy: Kathleen Gebhart *E-mail:* kgebhart@notes.cc.sunysb.edu
Founded: 1974
The purpose of Association of Biomedical Communications Directors (ABCD) is to promote the establishment, growth & effective use of information, communications & educational technology to meet the growing needs of health education, patient care & biomedical research.

To this end ABCD will serve as a continuing forum for administrators to share expertise, materials & ideas & as a body, will study & act on matters of mutual interest to the membership.
Number of Members: 25
Publication(s): *Journal of Biocommunication* (quarterly)

Association of Catholic TV & Radio Syndicators
518 S Alandele Ave, Los Angeles, CA 90036
Tel: 323-938-4861
Key Personnel
VP: Mary Jane Hopkins
Discuss TV & radio syndication.
Number of Members: 60
Publication(s): *Newsletter* (1 issue/yr)

Association of Federal Communications Consulting Engineers (AFCCE)
PO Box 19333, Washington, DC 20036-0333
E-mail: secretary@afcce.org
Web Site: www.afcce.org
Key Personnel
Pres: Mark D Neuman
VP: David Snavely
Founded: 1948
Registered professional consulting engineers who practice before the FCC.
Number of Members: 242

Association of Imaging Executives™ (AIE™), A PMA Member Association
2282 Springport Rd, Suite F, Jackson, MI 49202
Tel: 517-788-8100 *Toll Free Tel:* 800-762-9287 *Fax:* 517-788-8371
E-mail: aie@pmai.org
Web Site: www.pmai.org/aie
Key Personnel
Exec Dir: Jim Esp
Trade association for the photographic industry.
Number of Members: 700

Association of Independent Commercial Producers (AICP)
3 W 18 St, 5th fl, New York, NY 10011
Tel: 212-929-3000 *Fax:* 212-929-3359
E-mail: info@aicp.com
Web Site: www.aicp.com
Key Personnel
Pres & CEO: Matt Miller *E-mail:* mattm@aicp.com
Founded: 1972
Represents, exclusively, the interests of companies that specialize in producing commercials in various media (film, video & computer) for advertisers & agencies. The association, with national offices in New York & Los Angeles as well as regional chapters across the country, serves as a strong collective voice for this $5.5 billion industry, disseminating information; representing the production industry within the advertising community, in business circles, in labor negotiations & before governmental officials; developing industry standards & tools; providing professional development & marketing American production through the AICP Show: The Art & Technique of the American Television Commercial. The AICP Show is an exhibit of the artistry & expertise of commercial filmmakers in the US.
Number of Members: 500
Branch Office(s)
650 N Bronson Ave, Suite 223B, Los Angeles, CA 90004, Contact: Denise Gilmartin *Tel:* 323-960-4763 *Fax:* 323-960-4766 *E-mail:* deniseg@aicp.com
2015 Conference(s): AICP Week, MoMA, New York, NY, June 2-4, 2015

Association of National Advertisers Inc (ANA)
708 Third Ave, 33rd fl, New York, NY 10017-4270
Tel: 212-697-5950 *Fax:* 212-687-7310
E-mail: info@ana.net
Web Site: www.ana.net
Key Personnel
Pres & CEO: Bob Liodice *Tel:* 212-455-8050 *E-mail:* bliodice@ana.net
COO & CFO: Christine Manna *Tel:* 212-455-8060 *E-mail:* cmanna@ana.net
EVP & CIO: Robert Rothe *Tel:* 212-455-8068 *E-mail:* rrothe@ana.net
EVP & Chief Mktg Offr: Duke Fanelli *Tel:* 212-455-8030 *E-mail:* dfanelli@ana.net
SVP: Andrea Kislan *Tel:* 212-455-8071 *E-mail:* akislan@ana.net
SVP, Memb Rel: Brian Davidson *Tel:* 212-455-8012 *E-mail:* bdavidson@ana.net
Founded: 1910
Advertising trade association, conduct educational seminars, conferences, forums for member companies & others.
Number of Members: 640
Branch Office(s)
2020 "K" St NW, Suite 660, Washington, DC 20006 *Tel:* 202-296-1883 *Fax:* 202-296-1430
2015 Conference(s): ANA Masters of Marketing Conference, Orlando World Center Marriott, 8701 World Center Dr, Orlando, FL, Oct 14-17, 2015
Publication(s): *ANA Magazine* (6 issues/yr)

Association of Progressive Rental Organizations (APRO)
1504 Robin Hood Trail, Austin, TX 78703
Tel: 512-794-0095 *Toll Free Tel:* 800-204-2776 *Fax:* 512-794-0097
Web Site: www.rtohq.org
Key Personnel
Pres: Gary Ferriman *E-mail:* gferriman@showplacerents.com
Exec Dir: William Keese *E-mail:* bkeese@rtohq.org
Founded: 1980
National trade association for the rent-to-own industry.
Number of Members: 2,500
2015 Conference(s): APRO National Cenference & Trade Show, Hilton Daytona Beach Oceanfront Resort/Ocean Center, Daytona Beach, FL, May 18-20, 2015

Association of Public Television Stations (APTS)
2100 Crystal Dr, Suite 700, Arlington, VA 22202
Tel: 202-654-4200 *Fax:* 202-654-4236
Web Site: www.apts.org
Key Personnel
Pres & CEO: Patrick Butler
EVP & COO: Lonna Thompson *E-mail:* lonna@apts.org
Founded: 1980
Trade association; deals with congressional lobbying & research on behalf of America's public broadcasting stations.

ATD, see Association for Talent Development (ATD)

Audio Engineering Society Inc (AES)
60 E 42 St, Rm 2520, New York, NY 10165-2520
Tel: 212-661-8528 *Fax:* 212-682-0477
Web Site: www.aes.org
Key Personnel
Pres: Frank Wells
Exec Dir: Bob Moses
Deputy Dir: Roger K Furness
Founded: 1948
Uniting persons performing professional services in the audio engineering field & its allied arts. Collecting, collating & disseminating scientific knowledge in the field of audio engineering & its allied arts. Advancing such science in both theoretical & practical applications & preparing, publishing & distributing literature & periodicals relative to the foregoing purposes & policies.
Number of Members: 14,000
2015 Conference(s): AES Convention, Jacob K Javits Convention Center, 655 W 43 St, New York, NY, Oct 29-Nov 1, 2015
Publication(s): *Journal of the AES* (10 issues/yr, $50/yr print, online free membs, $290/yr print, $545 online (access to archive), $695/yr both nonmembs)

Austin Film Society (AFS)
1901 E 51 St, Austin, TX 78723
Tel: 512-322-0145 *Fax:* 512-322-5192
E-mail: afs@austinfilm.org
Web Site: www.austinfilm.org
Key Personnel
Exec Dir: Rebecca Campbell *E-mail:* rebecca@austinfilm.org
Founded: 1985
Nonprofit media arts organization & production studio.
Number of Members: 3,000

BAA, see Brand Activation Association

BEA, see Broadcast Education Association (BEA)

BFF, see Black Filmmaker Foundation (BFF)

Black Filmmaker Foundation (BFF)
131 Varick St, Suite 937, New York, NY 10013
Tel: 212-253-1690 *Fax:* 212-255-7575
E-mail: community@dvrepublic.org
Web Site: www.dvrepublic.org
Key Personnel
Founder & Chief: Warrington Hudlin *E-mail:* hudlin@dvrepublic.org
Founded: 1978
Develops the awareness of Black independent film & video as an important artistic movement. Supports emerging filmmakers & builds audiences for their work with a wide variety of programs & services. Created video series "Pass the Torch," about prominent entertainer-activists such as Harry Belafonte, Katherine Dunham, James Mtume & Pam Grier.

Brand Activation Association
650 First Ave, Suite 2-SW, New York, NY 10016
Tel: 212-420-1100 *Fax:* 212-533-7622
Web Site: www.baalink.org
Key Personnel
Pres: Bonnie J Carlson *Tel:* 212-420-1100 ext 180 *E-mail:* bcarlson@baalink.org
Founded: 1911
Trade association for companies in the integrated marketing industry with their roots in promotion.
Number of Members: 600

Broadcast Education Association (BEA)
Affiliate of National Association of Broadcasters (NAB) (in partnership with)
1771 "N" St NW, Washington, DC 20036-2891
Fax: 202-609-9940
E-mail: help@beaweb.org
Web Site: www.beaweb.org
Key Personnel
Exec Dir: Heather Birks *Tel:* 202-602-0584 *E-mail:* heather@beaweb.org
Founded: 1955
Professional development association of professors, students, broadcasters or any individuals interested in electronic communication.
Number of Members: 1,530

2015 Conference(s): BEA15, Westgate Las Vegas Resort & Casino, 3000 Paradise Rd, Las Vegas, NV, April 12-15, 2015
2016 Conference(s): BEA16, Westgate Las Vegas Resort & Casino, 3000 Paradise Rd, Las Vegas, NV, April 17-20, 2016
2017 Conference(s): BEA17, Westgate Las Vegas Resort & Casino, 3000 Paradise Rd, Las Vegas, NV, April 23-26, 2017
Publication(s): *Journal of Broadcasting & Electronic Media (JOBEM)* (quarterly); *Journal of Radio & Audio Media (JRAM)* (semiannual)

Broadcasters Foundation of America
125 W 55 St, 3rd fl, New York, NY 10019-5366
Tel: 212-373-8250 *Fax:* 212-373-8254
E-mail: info@thebfoa.org
Web Site: www.broadcastersfoundation.org
Key Personnel
Pres: Jim Thompson *E-mail:* jim@thebfoa.org
Assisting broadcasters in personal financial need; awards & distinguished notices given.
Number of Members: 5,000

Cable & Telecommunications Association for Marketing (CTAM)
120 Waterfront St, Suite 200, National Harbor, MD 20745
Tel: 301-485-8900 *Fax:* 301-560-4964
E-mail: info@ctam.com
Web Site: www.ctam.com
Key Personnel
CEO & Pres: John Lansing *E-mail:* john@ctam.com
Nonprofit professional association dedicated to helping the cable industry grow.
Number of Members: 3,000
Publication(s): *CTAM SmartBrief*

Canadian Academy of Recording Arts & Sciences (CARAS)
345 Adelaide St W, 2nd fl, Toronto, ON M5V 1R5, Canada
Tel: 416-485-3135 *Toll Free Tel:* 888-440-JUNO (440-5866, CN only) *Fax:* 416-485-4978
E-mail: submissions@junoawards.ca
Web Site: www.carasonline.ca; junoawards.ca
Key Personnel
Pres & CEO: Allan Reid *E-mail:* allan@junoawards.ca
Sr Mgr, Communs: Meghan McCabe *E-mail:* meghan@junoawards.ca
Not-for-profit organization promoting & celebrating Canadian music & artists.
Number of Members: 1,600
Publication(s): *CARAS News* (quarterly)

Canadian Broadcast Standards Council (CBSC)
PO Box 3265, Sta D, Ottawa, ON K1P 6H8, Canada
Tel: 613-233-4607 *Toll Free Tel:* 866-696-4718 (CN only) *Fax:* 613-233-4826
E-mail: info@cbsc.ca
Web Site: www.ccnr.ca
Key Personnel
Natl Chair: Andree I Noel
Exec Dir: John MacNab *Tel:* 613-233-4607 ext 111 *E-mail:* jmacnab@cbsc.ca
Founded: 1990
Number of Members: 790

Catholic Library Association (CLA)
8550 United Plaza Blvd, Suite 1001, Baton Rouge, LA 70809
Tel: 225-408-4417
E-mail: cla2@cathla.org
Web Site: www.cathla.org
Key Personnel
Pres: Sara R Baron *E-mail:* sbaron@regent.edu
Interim Exec Dir: Malachy R McCarthy *E-mail:* mmccarthy@cathla.org
Founded: 1921
Fostering advancement of library services & improvement of library resources through Catholic, ecumenical & interreligious collaboration, publication, education & information.
2015 Conference(s): CLA Convention (held in conjunction with National Catholic Educational Association (NCEA) Convention & Expo), Orange County Convention Center, Orlando, FL, April 7-9, 2015
Publication(s): *Catholic Library World* (quarterly, only with membership)

CBSC, see Canadian Broadcast Standards Council (CBSC)

CCUMC, see Consortium of College & University Media Centers (CCUMC)

Center for Asian American Media (CAAM)
145 Ninth St, Suite 350, San Francisco, CA 94103
Tel: 415-863-0814 *Fax:* 415-863-7428
E-mail: info@caamedia.org
Web Site: www.caamedia.org
Key Personnel
Festival Dir: Masashi Niwano
Festival Mng Dir: Christine Kwon
A nonprofit, educational organization. Support high quality film, video & digital media works produced by & about Asian Americans, encourage greater multi-cultural understanding of the Asian-American experience & promote artistic quality & merit in Asian-American productions.
Number of Members: 600
Conference(s): San Francisco International Asian American Film Festival (SFIAAFF), San Francisco, Berkeley & San Jose, CA, March

Centre for Art Tapes (CFAT)
2238 Maitland St, Halifax, NS B3K 2Z9, Canada
Tel: 902-422-6822 *Fax:* 902-422-6823
E-mail: info@cfat.ca
Web Site: cfat.ca
Key Personnel
Tech Coord: Thomas Elliott *E-mail:* tom@cfat.ca
Communs & Prog Coord: Kristy Depper *E-mail:* kristy@cfat.ca
Founded: 1979

Chicago Film Critics Association
155 E Algonquin Rd, Arlington Heights, IL 60006
Mailing Address: PO Box 280, Arlington Heights, IL 60006-0280
Tel: 847-427-4530 *Fax:* 847-427-1301
E-mail: critics@chicagofilmcritics.org
Web Site: www.chicagofilmcritics.org
Key Personnel
Pres: Dann Gire
Founded: 1990
Critics views at annual awards show; critics roundtable at colleges; critic membership & representation such as issuing statements on artists rights & media issues. Membership fees $50/yr.
Number of Members: 49

City of Boston Office of Cable Communications
43 Hawkins St, Boston, MA 02114
Tel: 617-635-3112 *Fax:* 617-635-4475
E-mail: cable@cityofboston.gov
Web Site: www.cityofboston.gov/cable
Key Personnel
Dir: Michael Lynch
Regulate activities of cable service. Produce & acquire programming for use on municipal channel.

Communications Media Management Association (CMMA)
c/o The Association Source LLC, 20423 State Rd 7, Suite F6-491, Boca Raton, FL 33498
Tel: 561-477-8100
Web Site: www.cmma.org
Key Personnel
Exec Dir: Ricky Atkins *E-mail:* executive.director@cmma.org
Founded: 1946
Dedicated to professional growth of corporate, education & government communications managers.
2015 Conference(s): National Conference, Fall 2015; Professional Development Conference, Marriott Headquarters, Washington, DC, April 26-28, 2015
Publication(s): *e-visions* (3 issues/yr by e-mail to membs, can view past issues on web site)

Consortium of College & University Media Centers (CCUMC)
c/o Indiana University, 306 N Union St, Bloomington, IN 47405-3888
Tel: 812-855-6049 *Fax:* 812-855-2103
E-mail: ccumc@ccumc.org
Web Site: www.ccumc.org
Key Personnel
Exec Dir: Aileen Scales
Prog Coord: Kirsten Phillips
Founded: 1971
To provide leadership & a forum for information exchange to the providers of media content, academic technology & support for quality teaching & learning at institutions of higher education.
Number of Members: 750
2015 Conference(s): Annual Conference, Pittsburgh, PA, Oct 2015
Publication(s): *College & University Media Review* (journal, annual, membs only); *Leader* (newsletter, 3 times/yr, membs only)

Consumer Electronics Association (CEA)
1919 S Eads St, Arlington, VA 22202
Tel: 703-907-7600 *Toll Free Tel:* 866-858-1555 *Fax:* 703-907-7675 *Toll Free Fax:* 866-858-2555
E-mail: cea@ce.org
Web Site: www.ce.org
Key Personnel
Pres & CEO: Gary Shapiro
Represents all facets of electronics manufacturing, including US manufacturers of audio, video, accessories, mobile electronics, communications equipment, information products & multimedia products.
Number of Members: 2,000
2016 Conference(s): International CES (Consumer Electronics Show), Las Vegas, NV, Jan 6-9, 2016
2017 Conference(s): International CES (Consumer Electronics Show), Las Vegas, NV, Jan 5-8, 2017
2018 Conference(s): International CES (Consumer Electronics Show), Las Vegas, NV, Jan 9-12, 2018
2019 Conference(s): International CES (Consumer Electronics Show), Las Vegas, NV, Jan 8-11, 2019
Publication(s): *Vision Magazine*

Corporation for Public Broadcasting (CPB)
401 Ninth St NW, Washington, DC 20004-2129
Tel: 202-879-9600 *Toll Free Tel:* 800-272-2190 (general comments) *Fax:* 202-879-9700

E-mail: comments@cpb.org
Web Site: www.cpb.org
Key Personnel
CEO & Pres: Patricia de Stacy Harrison
Founded: 1967
Private nonprofit corporation; develop noncommercial radio & TV services for the American people.
Publication(s): *CPB Report* (2 issues/month)

Council on International Nontheatrical Events (CINE)
1003 "K" St NW, Suite 208, Washington, DC 20001
Tel: 507-400-CINE (400-2463)
E-mail: info@cine.org
Web Site: www.cine.org
Key Personnel
Exec Dir: Jon Gann *E-mail:* jon@cine.org
Dir, Awards & Opers: Betsy Walters *E-mail:* bwalters@cine.org
Founded: 1957
Coordinate selection & submission of American short & feature-length (non-commercial) nontheatrical films & videos to international film & video festivals.
Number of Members: 15,000

CPB, see Corporation for Public Broadcasting (CPB)

CTAM, see Cable & Telecommunications Association for Marketing (CTAM)

Denver Film Society
1510 York St, 3rd fl, Denver, CO 80206
Tel: 303-595-3456 *Fax:* 303-595-0956
E-mail: info@denverfilm.org
Web Site: www.denverfilm.org
Key Personnel
Exec Dir: Tom Botelho *E-mail:* tom@denverfilm.org
Artistic Dir: Brit Withey *E-mail:* brit@denverfilm.org
Festival Dir: Britta Erickson *E-mail:* britta@denverfilm.org
Founded: 1978
Thirty-one year old nonprofit arts organization, producers of the Starz Denver Film Festival & Film on the Rocks. Year-round operators of the Starz Film Center.
Number of Members: 2,000

DGA, see Directors Guild of America (DGA)

Direct Marketing Association Inc (DMA)
1120 Avenue of the Americas, New York, NY 10036-6700
Tel: 212-768-7277 *Fax:* 212-302-6714
Web Site: thedma.org
Key Personnel
CEO: Thomas J Benton
Pres: Jane Berzan
VP, Conferences & Events: Paul A McDonnough
Founded: 1917
Provides information to its members, the industry & the public; sponsors several major annual conferences; has reference library of more than 2,500 portfolios from its annual ECHO Awards Competitions & a database collection of abstracts on direct marketing, monitors relevant legislative & regulatory matters on Capitol Hill & in state legislatures, sponsors ethics & consumer service programs, research projects, books & monographs on aspects of direct marketing.
Number of Members: 4,500
Branch Office(s)
1615 "L" St NW, Suite 1100, Washington, DC 20036 *Tel:* 202-955-5030 *Fax:* 202-955-0085
2015 Conference(s): DMA2015, Boston Convention & Exhibition Center, Boston, MA, Oct 3-8, 2015
2016 Conference(s): DMA2016, Los Angeles Convention Center, Los Angeles, CA, Oct 15-20, 2016
Publication(s): *Direct Line* (monthly); *Quarterly Business Review* (quarterly); *Washington Report* (monthly)

Directors Guild of America (DGA)
7920 Sunset Blvd, Los Angeles, CA 90046
Tel: 310-289-2000 *Toll Free Tel:* 800-421-4173
Web Site: www.dga.org
Key Personnel
Pres: Paris Barclay
Founded: 1936
Guild & labor union.
Number of Members: 15,000
Branch Office(s)
400 N Michigan Ave, Suite 307, Chicago, IL 60611 *Tel:* 312-644-5050 *Toll Free Tel:* 888-600-6975
110 W 57 St, New York, NY 10019 *Tel:* 212-258-0800 *Toll Free Tel:* 800-356-3754
Publication(s): *DGA Monthly* (free to membs); *DGA Quarterly* (free to membs, $32/yr non-membs)

The Dramatists Guild of America
1501 Broadway, Suite 701, New York, NY 10036
Tel: 212-398-9366 *Fax:* 212-944-0420
E-mail: info@dramatistsguild.com
Web Site: www.dramatistsguild.com
Key Personnel
Exec Dir, Busn Aff: Ralph Sevush *E-mail:* rsevush@dramatistsguild.com
Dir, Pubns: Joey Stocks *E-mail:* jstocks@dramatistsguild.com
Founded: 1919
Professional association of playwrights, composers & lyricists.
Number of Members: 6,000
Publication(s): *The Dramatist* (journal, 6 issues/yr, free to membs, $30/yr non-membs); *Resource Directory Online (RDO)*

The Electronic Document Systems Association®, see Xplor® International

Electronic Service Dealers Association
4925 W Irving Park Rd, Chicago, IL 60641
Tel: 773-282-9400
Key Personnel
Exec Dir: George Weiss
Promote independent electronic service dealers in the Midwest.
Number of Members: 100

Electronics Representatives Association (ERA)
111 N Canal St, Suite 885, Chicago, IL 60606
Tel: 312-559-3050 *Fax:* 312-559-4566
E-mail: info@era.org
Web Site: www.era.org
Key Personnel
CEO & EVP: Thomas J Shanahan *E-mail:* tshanahan@era.org
Founded: 1935
To promote, protect & improve the professional field sales function.
Number of Members: 670
Publication(s): *The Representor*

Electronics Technicians Association International Inc
5 Depot St, Greencastle, IN 46135
Tel: 765-653-8262 *Toll Free Tel:* 800-288-3824 *Fax:* 765-653-4287
E-mail: eta@eta-i.org
Web Site: www.eta-i.org
Key Personnel
Pres: Teresa Maher *E-mail:* tmaher@eta-i.org
Founded: 1978
Education, information, certification of electronics technicians, FCC exams; membership nonprofit professional association; fiber optics certification; telecommunication, industrial, consumer, biomedical electronics.
Number of Members: 3,500
Publication(s): *The High Tech News* (magazine, 6 issues/yr, free to membs, $20 non-membs)

EMA, see The Entertainment Merchants Association (EMA)

The Entertainment Merchants Association (EMA)
16530 Ventura Blvd, Suite 400, Encino, CA 91436-4551
Tel: 818-385-1500 *Fax:* 818-933-0910
E-mail: emaoffice@entmerch.org
Web Site: www.entmerch.org
Key Personnel
EVP: Mark Fisher *Tel:* 818-385-1500 ext 256 *E-mail:* mfisher@entmerch.org
VP, Mktg & Indus Rel: Carrie Dieterich *Tel:* 818-385-1500 ext 227 *E-mail:* cdieterich@entmerch.org
VP, Pub Aff: Sean Bersell *Tel:* 818-531-4362 *E-mail:* sbersell@entmerch.org
Founded: 2006
Nonprofit trade organization representing retailers & distributors of pre-recorded video products & suppliers of products & services relating to the home video industry.
Number of Members: 4,200

ETA® International, see Electronics Technicians Association International Inc

Exemplar Global
Formerly RABQSA International Inc
600 N Plankington Ave, Milwaukee, WI 53201
Mailing Address: PO Box 602, Milwaukee, WI 53201-0602
Tel: 414-272-3937 *Toll Free Tel:* 888-722-2440 *Fax:* 414-765-8661
Web Site: www.exemplarglobal.org
Key Personnel
CEO & Pres: Peter Holtmann *E-mail:* pholtmann@exemplarglobal.org
Mgr, Prod Devt: Monique Inman *E-mail:* minman@exemplarglobal.org
Creates value for you & your customers. Design, develop & deliver personnel & training certification services relevant to your industry.
Number of Members: 16,000

Exhibit & Event Marketers Association (E2MA)
2214 NW Fifth St, Bend, OR 97701
Tel: 541-317-8768 *Fax:* 541-317-8749
Web Site: www.e2ma.org
Key Personnel
Exec Dir: Jim Wurm *E-mail:* jimwurm@e2ma.org
Provide educational programs & networking opportunities to professionals in the exhibit & event marketing industry.
Number of Members: 2,300

Film Florida
c/o Jennifer Parramore, St Petersburg-Clearwater Film Commission, 13805 58 St N, Suite 2-200, Clearwater, FL 33760
E-mail: info@filmflorida.org
Web Site: www.filmflorida.org
Key Personnel
Pres: Leah Sokolowsky *Tel:* 305-642-6255
Offer businesses & individuals the benefits of a statewide trade association to promote the

creation of jobs in the film & entertainment production industries & to promote economic development & tourism.

Film Liaisons In California Statewide (FLICS)
c/o Placer-Lake Tahoe Film Off, 175 Fulweiler Ave, Auburn, CA 95603
Tel: 530-889-4091 *Toll Free Tel:* 877-228-3456 *Fax:* 530-889-4095
Web Site: www.filmcalifornia.com
Key Personnel
Chair: Beverly Lewis
Founded: 2005
Professional association of film commissioners throughout California.
Number of Members: 42
Conference(s): California On Location Awards (COLA), Los Angeles, CA, Annually in Autumn; California Only Show & Reception, Los Angeles, CA, Annually in Spring

FilmL.A., Inc
6255 W Sunset Blvd, 12th fl, Los Angeles, CA 90028
Tel: 213-977-8600 *Fax:* 213-977-8610; 213-977-8601 (permits)
E-mail: info@filmla.com
Web Site: www.filmla.com
Key Personnel
Chair: Leron Gubler
Secy: David Phelps
Founded: 1995 (as Entertainment Industry Development Corp)
Nonprofit film office serving the greater Los Angeles area. Film permits & programs to minimize filming impact on local community.
Membership(s): Association of Film Commissioners International

Filmmakers Alliance (FA)
1317 N San Fernando Blvd, Unit 366, Burbank, CA 91504
Tel: 310-568-0633 *Fax:* 818-301-2257
E-mail: info@filmmakersalliance.org
Web Site: filmmakersalliance.org
Key Personnel
Founder: Diane Gaidry
Founder & Pres: Jacques Thelemaque
Founded: 1993

Foundation for Economic Education
30 S Broadway, Irvington-on-Hudson, NY 10533
Tel: 914-591-7230 *Toll Free Tel:* 800-960-4333
E-mail: editor@fee.org; info@fee.org
Web Site: www.fee.org
Key Personnel
Pres: Lawrence Reed *E-mail:* lreed@fee.org
Founded: 1946
A tax-exempt educational organization, which publishes a monthly journal & other books & pamphlets, conducts seminars & conferences. Goal is to preserve the free market, limited government & private property philosophy.
Number of Members: 12,500
Branch Office(s)
260 Peachtree St NW, Suite 2200, Atlanta, GA 30303
Publication(s): *The Freeman* (monthly)

Giant Screen Cinema Association (GSCA)
624 Holly Springs Rd, Suite 243, Holly Springs, NC 27540
Tel: 919-346-1123 *Fax:* 919-573-9100
E-mail: info@giantscreencinema.com
Web Site: www.giantscreencinema.com
Key Personnel
Exec Dir: Tammy Seldon *E-mail:* tammy@giantscreencinema.com
Communs & Membership Dir: Kelly Germain *Tel:* 651-917-1080 *E-mail:* kelly@giantscreencinema.com
Founded: 1996
Nonprofit 501(c)(3). Membership fees: $250 (indiv), $850 (corp), $75 (student - must be enrolled in an accredited film school).
Number of Members: 300

Graphic Artists Guild
32 Broadway, Suite 1114, New York, NY 10004
Tel: 212-791-3400 *Fax:* 212-791-0333
E-mail: admin@gag.org; sales@gag.org
Web Site: www.graphicartistsguild.org
Key Personnel
Exec Dir: Patricia McKiernan *Tel:* 212-791-3400 ext 15
National advocacy organization representing professional graphic artists, including illustrators, graphic designers & other commercial artists.
Number of Members: 3,000
Publication(s): *Graphic Artists Guild Directory of Illustration* (annual, $33.99 for membs); *Graphic Artists Guild Handbook: Pricing & Ethical Guidelines* (biennial, $39.99, free to membs)

Graphic Arts Technical Foundation, see Printing Industries of America

GSCA, see Giant Screen Cinema Association (GSCA)

Guild of Italian American Actors (GIAA)
Subsidiary of Associated Actors & Artists of America
Canal Street Sta, PO Box 123, New York, NY 10013-0123
Tel: 201-344-3411
E-mail: info@giaa.us
Web Site: www.giaa.us
Key Personnel
Pres: Carlo Fiorletta
1st VP: Carson Ferri-Grant
2nd VP: Debbie Klaar
Secy/Treas: Mara Lesemann *Tel:* 551-200-8112 *E-mail:* maralesemann@yahoo.com
Founded: 1937
Acting union representing actors in Italian language theatre in the US & Canada.
Number of Members: 250

Hollywood Post Alliance
846 S Broadway, Suite 601, Los Angeles, CA 90014
Tel: 213-614-0860 *Fax:* 213-614-0890
Web Site: www.hpaonline.com
Key Personnel
Exec Dir: Eileen Kramer *E-mail:* ekramer@hpaonline.com
Founded: 2001
Trade association for business & professionals in post-production.
Number of Members: 400
Conference(s): HPA Tech Retreat, Annually in Feb

IAAVC (International Association of Audio Visual Communicators)
PO Box 270779, Flower Mound, TX 75027-0779
Tel: 469-464-4180 *Fax:* 469-464-4170
Web Site: www.iaavc.org
Key Personnel
Exec Dir: Phillip N Shuey
Founded: 1957
Promote excellence within the film, video & multimedia industries.
Number of Members: 6,200

IABC, see International Association of Business Communicators (IABC)

IATSE
207 W 25 St, 4th fl, New York, NY 10001
Tel: 212-730-1770 *Fax:* 212-730-7809
Web Site: www.iatse-intl.org
Key Personnel
Intl Pres: Matthew D Loeb
Gen Secy & Treas: James B Wood *Fax:* 212-921-7699
Founded: 1893
Nonprofit union for theatrical & commercial film/tape craft employees.
Number of Members: 110,000
Publication(s): *Official Bulletin* (quarterly)

IBPA, Independent Book Publishers Association
1020 Manhattan Beach Blvd, Suite 204, Manhattan Beach, CA 90266
Tel: 310-546-1818 *Fax:* 310-546-3939
E-mail: info@ibpa-online.org
Web Site: www.ibpa-online.org
Key Personnel
COO: Terry Nathan *E-mail:* terry@ibpa-online.org
Exec Dir: Angela Bole *E-mail:* angela@ibpa-online.org
Asst Dir: Lisa Krebs *E-mail:* lisa@ibpa-online.org
Founded: 1983
Cooperative marketing & education for independent book publishers.
Number of Members: 4,000
Publication(s): *Independent* (newsletter, monthly, $40/yr)

IES, see Illuminating Engineering Society (IES)

IFP, see The Independent Filmmaker Project (IFP)

IIE, see Institute of Industrial Engineers (IIE)

Illuminating Engineering Society (IES)
120 Wall St, 17th fl, New York, NY 10005-4001
Tel: 212-248-5000 *Fax:* 212-248-5017; 212-248-5018
E-mail: ies@ies.org
Web Site: www.ies.org
Key Personnel
Mktg Mgr: Clayton Gordon *Tel:* 212-248-5000 ext 110
Founded: 1906
Technical authority for the illumination field; information on all aspects of lighting practice for individual members, industry & consumers through a variety of programs, publications & services.
Number of Members: 8,000
2015 Conference(s): IES Annual Conference, Cincinnati, OH, Nov 2015
Publication(s): *IES Lighting Handbook* ($350/yr membs, $595/yr nonmembs); *LEUKOS, The Journal of the Illuminating Engineering Society of North America* (quarterly online, end of yr print compilation, free to membs); *Lighting Design + Application* (monthly, free to membs, $48/yr nonmembs)

IMCCA, see Interactive Multimedia & Collaborative Communications Alliance (IMCCA)

In-Plant Printing & Mailing Association
155 S Sam Barr Dr, Suite 203, Kearney, MO 64060
Tel: 816-903-4762
E-mail: ipmainfo@ipma.org
Web Site: www.ipma.org
Key Personnel
Exec Dir: Carma Goin *E-mail:* cgoin@ipma.org
Founded: 1964
Membership association for in-house printing, publishing & mail managers. Provides oppor-

tunities for education & further managerial advancement.
Number of Members: 1,000
Publication(s): *InsideEdge* (e-newsletter)

iNARTE, see Exemplar Global

Independent Film & Television Alliance® (IFTA)
10850 Wilshire Blvd, 9th fl, Los Angeles, CA 90024-4311
Tel: 310-446-1000 *Fax:* 310-446-1600
E-mail: info@ifta-online.org
Web Site: www.ifta-online.org
Key Personnel
CEO & Pres: Jean M Prewitt *Tel:* 310-446-1001 *E-mail:* jprewitt@ifta-online.org
EVP & Mng Dir, American Film Market: Jonathan Wolf *Tel:* 310-446-1010 *E-mail:* jwolf@ifta-online.org
Founded: 1980
Trade association for independent motion picture & TV distributors.
Number of Members: 170
2015 Conference(s): American Film Market, Santa Monica, CA, Nov 4-11, 2015
2016 Conference(s): American Film Market, Santa Monica, CA, Nov 2-9, 2016
2017 Conference(s): American Film Market, Santa Monica, CA, Nov 1-8, 2017

The Independent Filmmaker Project (IFP)
68 Jay St, Rm 425, Brooklyn, NY 11201-8361
Tel: 212-465-8200 *Fax:* 212-465-8525
Web Site: www.ifp.org
Key Personnel
Exec Dir: Joana Vicente
Sr Dir, Programming: Milton Tabbot *E-mail:* mtabbot@ifp.org
Advise, support & promote independent filmmakers through film market, seminars, screenings, publications, etc.
Number of Members: 1,200
Branch Office(s)
7000 E Mayo Blvd, Suite 1059, Phoenix, AZ 85054, Exec Dir: Jason Carney *Tel:* 602-955-6444 *E-mail:* jason@phxfilm.com *Web Site:* www.ifpphx.org
2446 University Ave W, Suite 100, St Paul, MN 55114, Exec Dir: Andrew Peterson *Tel:* 651-644-1912 *Fax:* 651-644-5708 *E-mail:* apeterson@ifpmn.org *Web Site:* www.ifpmn.org
Publication(s): *Filmmaker Magazine* (magazine, quarterly)

InfoComm International®
11242 Waples Mill Rd, Suite 200, Fairfax, VA 22030
Tel: 703-273-7200 *Toll Free Tel:* 800-659-SHOW (659-7469) *Fax:* 703-278-8082
E-mail: customerservice@infocomm.org
Web Site: www.infocomm.org
Key Personnel
Exec Dir & CEO: David Labuskes
Founded: 1939
The trade association for the professional AV communications industry worldwide & founder of InfoComm, the largest exhibition & conference for AV professionals.
Number of Members: 5,000
2015 Conference(s): InfoComm, Orange County Convention Center, West Bldg, Orlando, FL, June 13-19, 2015
2016 Conference(s): InfoComm, Las Vegas Convention Center, North & Central Halls, Las Vegas, NV, June 4-10, 2016
2017 Conference(s): InfoComm, Orange County Convention Center, West Bldg, Orlando, FL, June 10-16, 2017
2018 Conference(s): InfoComm, Las Vegas Convention Center, North & Central Halls, Las Vegas, NV, June 2-8, 2018
2019 Conference(s): InfoComm, Orange County Convention Center, West Bldg, Orlando, FL, June 8-14, 2019

Institute of Industrial Engineers (IIE)
3577 Parkway Lane, Suite 200, Norcross, GA 30092
Tel: 770-449-0460 *Toll Free Tel:* 800-494-0460 *Fax:* 770-441-3295
E-mail: cs@iienet.org
Web Site: www.iienet2.org
Key Personnel
CEO: Don Greene *E-mail:* executiveoffices@iienet.org
Dir, Communs: Monica Elliott
Founded: 1948
Membership service organization.
Number of Members: 30,000
2015 Conference(s): IIE Annual Conference & Expo, Renaissance Nashville Hotel, Nashville, TN, May 30-June 2, 2015
2016 Conference(s): IIE Annual Conference & Expo, Disneyland Resort Hotel, Anaheim, CA, May 21-24, 2016
Publication(s): *Industrial Engineer* (magazine, monthly, free to membs; $176/yr nonmembs US; $219/yr nonmembs foreign)

Interactive Multimedia & Collaborative Communications Alliance (IMCCA)
PO Box 756, Syosset, NY 11791
Web Site: www.imcca.org
Key Personnel
Chmn: Rick Snyder *E-mail:* risnyder@cisco.com
Exec Dir: Carol Zelkin *Tel:* 516-818-8184 *E-mail:* czelkin@imcca.org
Founded: 1998
Educate the public & promote use of collaborative conferencing.
Number of Members: 2,500
Publication(s): *IMCCA Newsletter* (monthly)

International Association of Audio Visual Communicators, see IAAVC (International Association of Audio Visual Communicators)

International Association of Business Communicators (IABC)
601 Montgomery St, Suite 1900, San Francisco, CA 94111
Tel: 415-544-4700 *Toll Free Tel:* 800-776-4222 *Fax:* 415-544-4747
E-mail: member_relations@iabc.com
Web Site: www.iabc.com
Key Personnel
Interim Exec Dir: Ann Lazarus *E-mail:* alazarus@iabc.com
Dir, Communs: Aaron Heinrich *E-mail:* aheinrich@iabc.com
Founded: 1970
Help communicators & organizations worldwide improve their communication with all audiences via publications, conferences & local chapters.
Number of Members: 15,000
2015 Conference(s): IABC World Conference, San Francisco Marriott Marquis, 55 Fourth St, San Francisco, CA, June 14-17, 2015
2016 Conference(s): IABC World Conference, Hilton New Orleans Riverside, 2 Poydras, New Orleans, LA, June 5-8, 2016

International Association of Radio & Telecommunications Engineers Inc, see Exemplar Global

International Cinema Technology Association (ICTA)
770 Broadway, 5th fl, New York, NY 10003-9595
Tel: 212-493-4097; 212-493-4058 *Fax:* 212-257-6428
E-mail: info@itea.com
Web Site: www.internationalcinematechnologyassociation.com
Key Personnel
Exec Dir: Robert H Sunshine *E-mail:* robert.sunshine@nielsen.com
Contact: Edith Malijan *E-mail:* edith.malijan@filmexpos.com
Founded: 1971
Trade association for motion picture theater equipment manufacturers & dealers.
2015 Conference(s): CinemaCon, Caesars Palace, Las Vegas, NV, April 20-23, 2015

International Documentary Association
3470 Wilshire Blvd, Suite 980, Los Angeles, CA 90010
Tel: 213-232-1660 *Fax:* 213-232-1669
E-mail: info@documentary.org
Web Site: www.documentary.org
Key Personnel
Exec Dir: Michael Lumpkin *Tel:* 213-232-1660 ext 201 *E-mail:* michael@documentary.org
Progs & Events Mgr: Amy Jelenko *Tel:* 213-232-1660 ext 208 *E-mail:* amy.j@documentary.org
Founded: 1982
Nonprofit membership organization for documentary filmmakers & friends of the documentary. Promotion of documentary production, exhibition & distribution around the world.
Number of Members: 2,800
Publication(s): *Documentary* (magazine, quarterly, free for membs); *Membership Directory* (online)

International Radio & Television Society Foundation (IRTS)
1697 Broadway, 10th fl, New York, NY 10019
Tel: 212-867-6650
Web Site: irtsfoundation.org
Key Personnel
CEO & Pres: Joyce M Tudryn *Tel:* 212-867-6650 ext 11
Founded: 1939
Place where those interested in electronic communications can exchange ideas, gain professional enrichment & improve the standards of the business.
Number of Members: 1,000

International Society for Performance Improvement® (ISPI)
PO Box 13035, Silver Spring, MD 20910
Tel: 301-587-8570 *Fax:* 301-587-8573
E-mail: info@ispi.org
Web Site: www.ispi.org
Key Personnel
Exec Dir: April Davis *Tel:* 301-587-8570 ext 112 *E-mail:* april@ispi.org
Dir, Pubns & Social Media: Brian Gresham *Tel:* 301-587-8570 ext 106 *E-mail:* briang@ispi.org
Founded: 1962
Dedicated to increasing productivity & competence in the workplace through the application of performance & instructional technologies.
Number of Members: 10,000
2015 Conference(s): THE Performance Improvement Conference, Hyatt Regency San Antonio Riverwalk, San Antonio, TX, April 24-29, 2015
Publication(s): *Performance Improvement Journal* (10 issues/yr, free to membs, $95 nonmembs)

International Storytelling Center
116 W Main St, Jonesborough, TN 37659

Tel: 423-753-2171 *Toll Free Tel:* 800-952-8392 *Fax:* 423-913-8219
E-mail: customerservice@storytellingcenter.net
Web Site: www.storytellingcenter.net
Key Personnel
Exec Dir: Kiran Sirah *E-mail:* kiran@storytellingcenter.net
Dir, Progs: Susan O'Connor *E-mail:* susan@storytellingcenter.net
Nonprofit association open to anyone interested in the preservation & promotion of the storytelling tradition as an educational tool & preserver of folkloric history & its perpetuation as a major art form. Maintain a video & audio archive, produce the National Storytelling Festival & Teller-in-Residence program.
Conference(s): National Storytelling Festival, Jonesborough, TN, Annually in Oct; Teller-in-Residence Series, Jonesborough, TN, May-Oct

International Ticketing Association Inc (INTIX)
2 Meridian Plaza, 10401 N Meridian St, Suite 300, Indianapolis, IN 46290
Tel: 212-629-4036 *Fax:* 212-629-8532
E-mail: info@intix.org
Web Site: www.intix.org
Key Personnel
CEO & Pres: Jena L Hoffman *E-mail:* jhoffman@intix.org
Founded: 1980
Leading the forum for the entertainment ticketing industry.
Number of Members: 1,000
2016 Conference(s): Annual Conference & Exhibition, Disneyland Hotel, Anaheim, CA, Jan 20-22, 2016
Publication(s): *Intix News* (ezine, free to membs)

Iowa Cable & Telecommunications Association (ICTA)
2024 NW 92 Ct, Suite 6, Clive, IA 50325
Tel: 515-276-0006
E-mail: info@iacable.com
Web Site: www.iacable.com
Key Personnel
EVP & Dir: Thomas P Graves
Number of Members: 215
Publication(s): *Iowa Cable News* (monthly, online only)
Membership(s): Association of Cable Television Operators

IPMA, see In-Plant Printing & Mailing Association

IPRO
34157 W 9 Mile Rd, Farmington Hills, MI 48335
Tel: 248-474-0522 *Toll Free Tel:* 800-420-4268
Web Site: www.avreps.org
Key Personnel
Pres: Dave Humphries
Exec Dir: Ray Wright *Tel:* 248-514-4418 *E-mail:* ray@avreps.org
Founded: 1988
Upgrade professional standing in AV & custom installation industry.
Number of Members: 110
Publication(s): *IPRO Newsletter* (free to membs & indus affiliates)

IRTS, see International Radio & Television Society Foundation (IRTS)

Library & Information Technology Association (LITA)
Division of American Library Association (ALA)
c/o American Library Association, 50 E Huron St, Chicago, IL 60611-2795
Toll Free Tel: 800-545-2433 (ext 4270) *Fax:* 312-280-3257
E-mail: lita@ala.org
Web Site: www.ala.org/lita
Key Personnel
Exec Dir: Mary C Taylor *Tel:* 312-280-4267 *E-mail:* mtaylor@ala.org
Progs & Mktg Specialist: Melissa Prentice *Tel:* 312-280-4268 *E-mail:* mprentice@ala.org
Prog Coord: Valerie A Edmonds-Merritt *Tel:* 312-280-4269 *E-mail:* vedmonds@ala.org
Cover library automation, information technology, communications, telecommunications, Internet/web technology & emerging technology.
Number of Members: 3,000
Publication(s): *Information Technology & Libraries* (quarterly)

LITA, see Library & Information Technology Association (LITA)

Media Alliance
1904 Franklin St, Suite 818, Oakland, CA 94612
Tel: 510-832-9000 *Fax:* 510-238-8557
E-mail: information@media-alliance.org
Web Site: www.media-alliance.org
Key Personnel
Exec Dir: Tracy Rosenberg *Tel:* 510-684-6853 (cell) *E-mail:* tracy@media-alliance.org
Founded: 1976
Membership services organization networking media professionals & carrying out media activist work in the Bay Area.
Number of Members: 600
Publication(s): *How-to Media Guidebook* ($15/membs; $20/non-membs); *Media Directory* ($35 Northern & Southern CA); *Media News* (newsletter, electronic, free to membs)

Media Communications Association-International (MCA-I)
PO Box 5135, Madison, WI 53705-0135
Tel: 608-836-0722 *Toll Free Tel:* 888-899-MCAI (899-6224) *Fax:* 608-443-2474; 608-443-2478 *Toll Free Fax:* 888-862-8150
E-mail: info@mca-i.org
Web Site: www.mca-i.org
Key Personnel
Exec Dir: Connie Terwilliger
Founded: 1968
Nonprofit organization for media professionals. For video communication professionals: nonbroadcast, private television for training & other purposes.
Number of Members: 8,000
Publication(s): *ITVA News* (monthly); *Membership Directory* (annual)

Media Financial Management Association (MFM)
550 W Frontage Rd, Suite 3600, Northfield, IL 60093
Tel: 847-716-7000 *Fax:* 847-716-7004
E-mail: info@mediafinance.org
Web Site: www.mediafinance.org
Key Personnel
MFM/BCCA Pres & CEO: Mary M Collins *E-mail:* mary.collins@mediafinance.org
MFM/BCCA Dir of Opers: Jamie L Smith *E-mail:* jamie.smith@mediafinance.org
Founded: 1961
Professional membership organization for financial executives, business managers, credit professionals & related fields for the media industry.
Number of Members: 1,300
2015 Conference(s): Media Finance Focus 2015 (MFM & BCCA Annual Conference), The Arizona Grand Hotel & Spa, 8000 S Arizona Grand Pkwy, Phoenix, AZ, May 18-20, 2015
Publication(s): *The Financial Manager (TFM)* (6 issues/yr, $69)

MEIEA, see Music & Entertainment Industry Educators Association (MEIEA)

Motion Picture Association of America (MPAA)
15301 Ventura Blvd, Bldg E, Sherman Oaks, CA 91403-5885
Tel: 818-995-6600 *Fax:* 818-285-4403
E-mail: contactus@mpaa.org
Web Site: www.mpaa.org
Key Personnel
Chmn & CEO: Christopher J Dodd
Founded: 1922
Serves as the voice & advocate of the American motion picture & television industry.
Branch Office(s)
1600 Eye St NW, Washington, DC 20006 *Tel:* 202-293-1966 *Fax:* 202-296-7410
500 Mamaroneck Ave, Suite 403, Harrison, NY 10528 *Tel:* 914-333-8892 *Fax:* 914-333-7541
1425 Greenway Dr, Suite 270, Irving, TX 75038 *Tel:* 972-756-9078 *Fax:* 972-756-9402
55 Saint Clair Ave W, Suite 210, Toronto, ON M4V 2Y7, Canada *Tel:* 416-961-1888 *Fax:* 416-968-1016 *Web Site:* www.mpa-canada.org

Motion Picture Editors Guild Local 700
Affiliate of IATSE
7715 Sunset Blvd, Suite 200, Hollywood, CA 90046
Tel: 323-876-4770 *Toll Free Tel:* 800-705-8700 *Fax:* 323-876-0861
E-mail: mail@editorsguild.com
Web Site: www.editorsguild.com
Key Personnel
Natl Exec Dir: Ronald Kutak *E-mail:* rkutak@editorsguild.com
Western Exec Dir: Cathy Repola *E-mail:* crepola@editorsguild.com
Dir, Membership Servs: Serena Kung *Tel:* 323-876-4770 ext 247 *E-mail:* skung@editorsguild.com
Number of Members: 7,000
Branch Office(s)
145 Hudson St, Suite 201, New York, NY 10013, Eastern Exec Dir: Paul Moore *Tel:* 212-302-0700 *Fax:* 212-302-1091 *E-mail:* pmoore@editorsguild.com
Publication(s): *Editors Guild Magazine* (6 issues/yr, $45 dom, $25 student)

Music & Entertainment Industry Educators Association (MEIEA)
1900 Belmont Blvd, Nashville, TN 37212-3758
Tel: 615-460-6946
E-mail: office@meiea.org
Web Site: www.meiea.org
Key Personnel
Pres: Serona Elton *E-mail:* selton@miami.edu
VP: Storm Gloor *E-mail:* storm.gloor@ucdenver.edu
Treas: David Schrieber *E-mail:* treasurer@meiea.org
Secy: Catherine Radbill *E-mail:* secretary@meiea.org
Admin Asst: Angela Breedon
Founded: 1979
Establish & maintain standards of music industry education; encourage & facilitate interaction between the education community & the music industry.
Number of Members: 650
Publication(s): *MEIEA Journal* (annual, free to membs, $25/issue for past issues)

Music Business Association (Music Biz)
One Eves Dr, Suite 138, Marlton, NJ 08053
Tel: 856-596-2221 *Fax:* 856-596-7299
Web Site: www.musicbiz.org
Key Personnel
Pres: James Donio *E-mail:* donio@musicbiz.org
Founded: 1958

Number of Members: 350
2015 Conference(s): Music Biz 2015, Sheraton Nashville Downtown Hotel, Nashville, TN, May 12-14, 2015
Publication(s): *Research Briefs* (free to members)

NAB, see National Association of Broadcasters (NAB)

NABA, see North American Broadcasters Association (NABA)

NAMM, the National Association of Music Merchants
5790 Armada Dr, Carlsbad, CA 92008
Tel: 760-438-8001 *Toll Free Tel:* 800-767-6266 (memb hotline) *Fax:* 760-438-7327
E-mail: info@namm.org
Web Site: www.namm.org
Key Personnel
CEO & Pres: Joe Lamond
Dir, IT & Mktg Communs: Shawn Lowery
Founded: 1901
To unify, lead & strengthen the global music products industry & to increase active participation in music.
Number of Members: 9,000
2015 Conference(s): Summer NAMM, Nashville Music City Center, 700 Korean Veterans Blvd, Nashville, TN, July 9-11, 2015
2016 Conference(s): NAMM Show, Anaheim Convention Center, 800 W Katella Ave, Anaheim, CA, Jan 21-24, 2016

NAPET, see National Association of Photo Equipment Technicians (NAPET)

NARAS, see The Recording Academy

NARDA, see North American Retail Dealers Association (NARDA)

NARIP, see National Association of Record Industry Professionals (NARIP)

NARM, see Music Business Association (Music Biz)

NATAS, see The National Academy of Television Arts & Sciences (NATAS)

National Academy of Recording Arts & Sciences Inc, see The Recording Academy

The National Academy of Television Arts & Sciences (NATAS)
1697 Broadway, Suite 1001, New York, NY 10019
Tel: 212-586-8424 *Fax:* 212-246-8129
Web Site: www.emmyonline.org
Key Personnel
CFO & COO: Carolyn Grippi
Chief Admin Offr & Spec Events Dir: Paul Pilliteri
Founded: 1955
Encourage excellence in television.
Number of Members: 14,000
Publication(s): *National Newsletter* (3 issues/yr); *TVQ* (quarterly)

National Association for Music Education (NAfME)
1806 Robert Fulton Dr, Reston, VA 20191
Tel: 703-860-4000 *Toll Free Tel:* 800-336-3768 *Fax:* 703-860-1531
E-mail: memberservices@nafme2.org
Web Site: www.menc.org; www.nafme.org
Key Personnel
Exec Dir & CEO: Michael A Butera
E-mail: michaelb@nafme.org
Deputy Exec Dir & COO: Mike Blakeslee
E-mail: mikeb@nafme.org
Professional association for music educators.
Number of Members: 60,000
2016 Conference(s): NAfME Music Research and Teacher Education National Conference, Atlanta, GA, March 17-19, 2016
Publication(s): *General Music Today* (3 issues/yr, online only); *Journal of Music Teacher Education* (semiannual); *Journal of Research in Music Education* (quarterly); *Music Educators Journal* (quarterly); *Teaching Music* (6 issues/yr); *UPDATE: Applications of Research in Music Education* (semiannual, online only)

National Association of Biology Teachers (NABT)
1313 Dolley Madison Blvd, Suite 402, McLean, VA 22101
Tel: 703-264-9696 *Toll Free Tel:* 888-501-NABT (501-6228) *Fax:* 703-790-2672
Toll Free Fax: 800-883-0698
E-mail: office@nabt.org
Web Site: www.nabt.org
Key Personnel
Exec Dir: Jaclyn Reeves-Pepin
E-mail: jreevespepin@nabt.org
Founded: 1938
Professional education association for life science & biology teachers at all levels.
Number of Members: 8,000
2015 Conference(s): NABT Professional Development Conference, Rhode Island Convention Center, Providence, RI, Nov 11-14, 2015
2016 Conference(s): NABT Professional Development Conference, Denver Sheraton Downtown, Denver, CO, Nov 3-6, 2016
Publication(s): *American Biology Teacher* (9 issues/yr); *News & Views* (weekly, online)

National Association of Black Journalists (NABJ)
1100 Knight Hall, Suite 3100, College Park, MD 20742
Tel: 301-405-0248 *Fax:* 301-314-1714
E-mail: nabj@nabj.org
Web Site: www.nabj.org
Key Personnel
Exec Dir: Maurice Foster *E-mail:* mfoster@nabj.org
Founded: 1975
An organization of journalists, students & media-related professionals that provide quality programs & services & advocates on behalf of Black journalists worldwide.
Number of Members: 3,000
2015 Conference(s): NABJ Annual Convention & Career Fair, Minneapolis Convention Center, 1301 Second Ave S, Minneapolis, MN, Aug 5-9, 2015
Publication(s): *NABJ Journal* (journal, 3 times/yr)

National Association of Broadcasters (NAB)
1771 "N" St NW, Washington, DC 20036
Tel: 202-429-5300 *Fax:* 202-429-4199
E-mail: nab@nab.org
Web Site: www.nab.org
Key Personnel
CEO & Pres: Gordon H Smith
Founded: 1922
Trade association that advocates on behalf of free, local radio & television stations & also broadcast networks before Congress, the Federal Communications Commissions & the Courts.
2015 Conference(s): NAB Show®, Las Vegas Convention Center, Las Vegas, NV, April 11-16, 2015; Radio Show (co-produced with Radio Advertising Bureau), Atlanta Marriott Marquis, Atlanta, GA, Sept 30-Oct 2, 2015
2016 Conference(s): Radio Show (co-produced with Radio Advertising Bureau), Omni Nashville Hotel, Nashville, TN, Sept 21-23, 2016

National Association of Photo Equipment Technicians (NAPET)
2282 Springport Rd, Suite F, Jackson, MI 49202
Tel: 517-788-8100 *Toll Free Tel:* 800-762-9287 *Fax:* 517-788-8371
Web Site: www.pmai.org/napet
Key Personnel
Pres: Raymond J Heinbokel, Jr
Section of the Photo Marketing Association International providing management information for camera & video repair firms.
Number of Members: 230
Publication(s): *NAPET News* (newsletter, quarterly)

National Association of Record Industry Professionals (NARIP)
PO Box 2446, Toluca Lake, CA 91610-2446
Tel: 818-769-7007; 559-271-7900 (Pollstar Live!) *Fax:* 818-769-6191
E-mail: info@narip.com
Web Site: www.narip.com
Key Personnel
Pres: Tess Taylor
Founded: 1998
Created to promote career advancement, continued education & goodwill among record executives.

National Association of Video Distributors (NAVD)
5584 Prestwick Dr, Newburgh, IN 47630
Tel: 270-860-8904
Web Site: www.navdonline.org
Key Personnel
Exec Dir: Bill Burton
Founded: 1982
Association for video distribution specialists.
Number of Members: 20

National Board of Review (of Motion Pictures)
40 W 37 St, Suite 501, New York, NY 10018
Tel: 212-465-9166 *Fax:* 212-465-9168
E-mail: nbr@nbrmp.org
Web Site: www.nationalboardofreview.org
Key Personnel
Mng Dir: Orson Robbins-Pianka *E-mail:* orson@nbrmp.org
Creative Dir: Wendy Smith
Founded: 1909
Dedicates its efforts to the support of film, domestic & foreign, as both art & entertainment. The NBR is a nonprofit, membership organization which promotes commentary on all aspects of film production & history of film with panels, seminars & Q&As at screenings held throughout the year.
Number of Members: 150
Conference(s): NBR Annual Awards Gala, New York, NY, Jan

National Council of Acoustical Consultants (NCAC)
9100 Purdue Rd, Suite 200, Indianapolis, IN 46268
Tel: 317-328-0642 *Fax:* 317-328-4629
E-mail: info@ncac.com
Web Site: www.ncac.com
Key Personnel
Exec Dir: Jackie Williams *E-mail:* jwilliams@ncac.com
Founded: 1962
Dedicated to management & related concerns of professional acoustical consulting firms & to safeguarding the interests of the clients & public which they serve.
Number of Members: 130

2015 Conference(s): NCAC Annual Meeting, Hyatt Regency San Francisco, 5 Embarcadero Center, San Francisco, CA, Aug 7-9, 2015
Publication(s): *NCAC Quarterly Newsletter*

National Council of Teachers of English (NCTE)
1111 W Kenyon Rd, Urbana, IL 61801-1096
Tel: 217-328-3870 *Toll Free Tel:* 877-369-6283 *Fax:* 217-328-9645
Web Site: www.ncte.org
Key Personnel
Exec Dir: Kent Williamson
Founded: 1911
Improve the quality of instruction in English at all education levels; encourage research, experimentation & investigation in teaching English.
Number of Members: 77,000
2015 Conference(s): NCTE Annual Convention, Minneapolis, MN, Nov 19-22, 2015
2016 Conference(s): NCTE Annual Convention, Altanta, GA, Nov 17-20, 2016
2017 Conference(s): NCTE Annual Convention, St Louis, MO, Nov 16-19, 2017
2018 Conference(s): NCTE Annual Convention, Houston, TX, Nov 15-18, 2018
Publication(s): *College Composition & Communication* (quarterly); *College English* (6 issues/yr); *The Council Chronicle Magazine* (quarterly); *English Education* (quarterly); *English Journal* (6 issues/yr); *English Leadership Quarterly* (quarterly); *Inbox Newsletter* (weekly e-mail); *Language Arts* (6 issues/yr); *Research in the Teaching of English* (quarterly); *Talking Points* (semiannual); *Teaching English in the Two-Year College* (quarterly); *Voices From the Middle* (quarterly)

National Freedom of Information Coalition (NFOIC)
Missouri School of Journalism, 101E Reynolds Journalism Institute, Columbia, MO 65211
Tel: 573-882-4856
E-mail: info@nfoic.org
Web Site: www.nfoic.org
Key Personnel
Off Administrator: Denise Meyers
An affiliation of member state FOI groups, academic centers & interested individuals.
Publication(s): *FOI Advocate* (blog); *FOI InSight* (newsletter, online)

National Press Photographers Association (NPPA)
3200 Croasdaile Dr, Suite 306, Durham, NC 27705
Tel: 919-383-7246 *Fax:* 919-383-7261
E-mail: info@nppa.org
Web Site: www.nppa.org
Key Personnel
Prof Servs Coord: Thomas Kenniff *Tel:* 919-383-7246 ext 10
Founded: 1946
Educational advancement of photojournalism.
Number of Members: 9,000
Conference(s): News Video Workshop, Gaylord College of Journalism & Mass Communications, University of Oklahoma, Norman, OK, Annually in March
Publication(s): *News Photographer* (magazine, monthly)

National Public Radio (NPR)
1111 N Capitol St NE, Washington, DC 20002
Tel: 202-513-2000
Web Site: www.npr.org
Key Personnel
CEO & Pres: Paul G Haaga, Jr
CFO & VP, Fin: Deborah A Cowan
Chief Mktg Offr: Emma Carrasco
VP, Dist: Peter Loewenstein
VP, Programming: Eric Nuzum
Leading news, information & arts provider to 975 nonprofit radio station, sirius satellite radio, NPR.org & worldwide.

National Religious Broadcasters (NRB)
9510 Technology Dr, Manassas, VA 20110
Tel: 703-330-7000 *Fax:* 703-330-7100
E-mail: info@nrb.org
Web Site: www.nrb.org
Key Personnel
CEO & Pres: Dr Jerry A Johnson *E-mail:* jjohnson@nrb.org
EVP & COO: Linda W Smith *Tel:* 703-330-7000 ext 507 *E-mail:* lsmith@nrb.org
SVP, Communs & Gen Coun: Craig Parshall
Dir, Conventions & Expositions: Tammy Singleton
Founded: 1944
Number of Members: 1,600
2016 Conference(s): NRB International Christian Media Convention & Exposition, Gaylord Opryland Resort & Convention Center, Nashville, TN, Feb 23-26, 2016
Publication(s): *NRB Today* (newsletter, weekly)

National School Boards Association (NSBA)
1680 Duke St, Alexandria, VA 22314
Tel: 703-838-6722 *Fax:* 703-683-7590
E-mail: info@nsba.org
Web Site: www.nsba.org
Key Personnel
Exec Dir: Thomas Gentzel *Tel:* 703-838-6730 *E-mail:* tgentzel@nsba.org
Founded: 1940
To foster excellence & equity in public education through school board leadership.
Number of Members: 90,000
2016 Conference(s): Annual Conference & Exposition, Boston, MA, April 9-11, 2016
2017 Conference(s): Annual Conference & Exposition, Denver, CO, March 25-27, 2017
2018 Conference(s): Annual Conference & Exposition, San Antonio, TX, April 7-9, 2018

National Systems Contractors Association (NSCA)
3950 River Ridge Dr NE, Cedar Rapids, IA 52402
Tel: 319-366-6722 *Toll Free Tel:* 800-446-6722 *Fax:* 319-366-4164
E-mail: nsca@nsca.org
Web Site: www.nsca.org
Key Personnel
Exec Dir: Chuck Wilson *E-mail:* cwilson@nsca.org
Association of low voltage systems integrators. Represents more than 2,500 companies worldwide & is a leading advocate for the commercial electronic systems industry. The services offered by the NSCA are an invaluable resource for systems integrators, design firms, large & small contracting companies & others in the electronic systems industry from around the globe.
Number of Members: 2,500
Publication(s): *Building Connections* (6 issues/yr, free to membs)

National Telemedia Council Inc
1922 University Ave, Madison, WI 53726
Tel: 608-218-1182
E-mail: ntelemedia@aol.com
Web Site: www.nationaltelemediacouncil.org
Key Personnel
Pres: Karen Ambrosh *E-mail:* kambrosh@wi.rr.com
Exec Dir & Ed: Marieli Rowe
Founded: 1953
Work toward a mediawise society by developing media literacy & critical viewing skills, work with educators, parents & the broadcast industry.
Number of Members: 300
Publication(s): *The Journal of Media Literacy* (up to 3 issues/yr, free to membs)

National Traditional Country Music Association Inc (NTCMA)
PO Box 492, Anita, IA 50020-0492
Tel: 712-762-4363; 712-249-5989 (cell)
E-mail: ruralcountrymusic@gmail.com
Web Site: ntcma.net
Key Personnel
Pres: Bob Everhart *E-mail:* bobeverhart@yahoo.com
Founded: 1976
Music preservation.
Number of Members: 3,000
2015 Conference(s): National Old Time Country Bluegrass & Folk Music Festival, Le Mars, IA, Aug 31-Sept 6, 2015
Publication(s): *Tradition* (magazine)

NCAC, see National Council of Acoustical Consultants (NCAC)

NCTE, see National Council of Teachers of English (NCTE)

Nevada Broadcasters Association
1050 E Flamingo Rd, No 102, Las Vegas, NV 89119
Tel: 702-794-4994
Web Site: www.nevadabroadcasters.org
Key Personnel
Pres: Bob Fisher *E-mail:* rdfnba@aol.com
VP: Adam Sandler *E-mail:* adam@nevadabroadcasters.org
Information resource for Nevada's broadcast radio & television stations. Assists in workforce development.

New York Film/Video Council (NYFVC)
PO Box 1685, New York, NY 10185-1685
Tel: 212-330-0450
E-mail: info@nyfvc.org
Web Site: www.nyfvc.org
Key Personnel
Pres: Marie Regan
VP, Communs: Laura Coxson
VP, Programming: Trilby Schreiber
Treas: David Callahan
Founded: 1946
Nonprofit cultural membership organization of people involved in the production, distribution & study of documentary, industrial & non-theatrical films. Annual schedule of ten monthly meetings/programs on broad range of subjects of interest to members. Hold monthly events from Sept-June.
Number of Members: 250
Publication(s): *NYFC Newsletter* (3-8 issues/yr)

North American Broadcasters Association (NABA)
Canadian Broadcasting Centre, 25 John St, Suite 6C300, Toronto, ON M5V 3G7, Canada
Mailing Address: PO Box 500, Sta A, Toronto, ON M5W 1E6, Canada
Tel: 416-598-9877 *Fax:* 416-598-9774
E-mail: contact@nabanet.com
Web Site: www.nabanet.com
Key Personnel
Dir Gen: Michael McEwen
Dir, Admin: Anh Ngo
Sr Coord: Jason Paris
Founded: 1972
Number of Members: 26
Conference(s): Annual Meeting & Conference
Membership(s): World Broadcasting Unions

North American Retail Dealers Association (NARDA)
222 S Riverside Plaza, Suite 2100, Chicago, IL 60606
Tel: 312-648-0649 *Toll Free Tel:* 800-621-0298 (US only) *Fax:* 312-648-1212
E-mail: nardasvc.@narda.com
Web Site: www.narda.com
Key Personnel
Exec Dir: Otto Papasadero
Founded: 1943
Retail management education & services for independent dealers.
Number of Members: 1,300

Northeast Conference on the Teaching of Foreign Languages (NECTFL)
c/o Dickinson College, PO Box 1773, Carlisle, PA 17013-2896
Tel: 717-245-1977 *Fax:* 717-245-1976
E-mail: nectfl@dickinson.edu
Web Site: www.nectfl.org
Key Personnel
Exec Dir: Rebecca R Kline
Assoc Exec Dir: Susan M Shaffer
Founded: 1954
Foreign language education & professional development for teachers at all levels.
Number of Members: 150
Conference(s): Annual Conference, Spring
Publication(s): *The NECTFL Review* (semiannual)

NPES The Association for Suppliers of Printing, Publishing & Converting Technologies
1899 Preston White Dr, Reston, VA 20191
Tel: 703-264-7200 *Fax:* 703-620-0994
E-mail: npes@npes.org
Web Site: www.npes.org
Key Personnel
Pres: Ralph J Nappi *E-mail:* rnappi@npes.org
VP: William K Smythe, Jr
Founded: 1933 (as The National Printing Equipment Association)
Represent manufacturers of printing, publishing & converting equipment supplies, services, systems & software.
Number of Members: 450
Publication(s): *NPES News* (newsletter, monthly)

NPR, see National Public Radio (NPR)

NSCA, see National Systems Contractors Association (NSCA)

NTCMA, see National Traditional Country Music Association Inc (NTCMA)

NYFVC, see New York Film/Video Council (NYFVC)

PCIA, see Personal Communications Industry Association (PCIA)

Personal Communications Industry Association (PCIA)
500 Montgomery St, Suite 500, Alexandria, VA 22314
Tel: 703-739-0300 *Toll Free Tel:* 800-759-0300 *Fax:* 703-836-1608
Web Site: www.pcia.com
Key Personnel
CEO & Pres: Jonathan S Adelstein
VP, Mktg & External Rel: Tim House *Tel:* 703-535-7409 *E-mail:* houset@pcia.com
Dir, Meetings & Events: Nancy Touhill *Tel:* 703-535-7411 *E-mail:* touhilln@pcia.com
Founded: 1924
Trade group for the wireless infrastructure industry.

Photo Marketing Association International (PMA)
2282 Springport Rd, Suite F, Jackson, MI 49202
Tel: 517-788-8100 *Toll Free Tel:* 800-762-9287 *Fax:* 517-788-8371
Web Site: www.pmai.org
Key Personnel
Exec Dir/Secy: Jim Esp
Founded: 1924
Trade association for the photo industry; serves photo & video retailers, finishers, processors & camera repair firms.
Number of Members: 18,000
Publication(s): *Photo Marketing Magazine* (6 issues/yr)

Photographic Society of America® (PSA®)
3000 United Founders Blvd, Suite 103, Oklahoma City, OK 73112
Tel: 405-843-1437 *Toll Free Tel:* 855-PSA-INFO (772-4636) *Fax:* 405-843-1438
E-mail: hq@psa-photo.org
Web Site: www.psa-photo.org
Key Personnel
Opers Mgr: Kara Goodson
Founded: 1934
Deals with photographic material & its techniques.
2015 Conference(s): PSA Annual Conference, Yellowstone National Park, West Yellowstone, MT, Sept 27-Oct 3, 2015
Publication(s): *PSA Journal* (monthly)

Photoimaging Manufacturers & Distributors Association Inc
7600 Jericho Tpke, Suite 301, Woodbury, NY 11797
Tel: 516-802-0895 *Fax:* 516-364-0140
Web Site: www.pmda.com
Key Personnel
Exec Ed: Jerry Grossman *E-mail:* jerry@pmda.com
Ed: Jackie Augustine *E-mail:* jackie@pmda.com
Administrator: Michelle Tramantano *E-mail:* michellepmda@hotmail.com
Founded: 1939
Promote the welfare of the photographic industry as well as picture-taking to the public. Meetings & symposiums 7-8 times a year.
Number of Members: 88

PMDA, see Photoimaging Manufacturers & Distributors Association Inc

Printing Industries of America
200 Deer Run Rd, Sewickley, PA 15143
Tel: 412-741-6860 *Toll Free Tel:* 800-910-4283 *Fax:* 412-741-2311
E-mail: printing@printing.org
Web Site: www.printing.org
Key Personnel
VP: Julie Schaffer
Printing Industries of America along with its affiliates, delivers products & services that enhance the growth & profitability of its members & the industry through advocacy, education, research & technical information.
Number of Members: 10,900
Branch Office(s)
601 13 St NW, Suite 350S, Washington, DC 20005-3807 *Tel:* 202-730-7970
Publication(s): *Printing Industries of America: The Magazine* (10 issues/yr)

Producers Guild of America Inc (PGA)
8530 Wilshire Blvd, Suite 400, Beverly Hills, CA 90211
Tel: 310-358-9020
E-mail: info@producersguild.org
Web Site: www.producersguild.org
Key Personnel
Natl Exec Dir: Vance Van Petten
Dir of Opers: Jo-Ann West
Founded: 1950
Organization for producers.
Number of Members: 5,000

Professional Photographers of America (PPA)
229 Peachtree St NE, Suite 2200, Atlanta, GA 30303
Tel: 404-522-8600 *Toll Free Tel:* 800-786-6277 *Fax:* 404-614-6400
E-mail: csc@ppa.com
Web Site: www.ppa.com
Key Personnel
Pres: Ralph Romaguera *E-mail:* rromaguera@ppa.com
Dir of Mktg/Communs: Carla Plouin
Founded: 1869
Advance the art & science of professional photography & help professional photographers in their careers.
Number of Members: 24,000
2016 Conference(s): Imaging USA, Georgia World Congress Center, Atlanta, GA, Jan 10-12, 2016
2017 Conference(s): Imaging USA, San Antonio, TX, Jan 8-10, 2017
2018 Conference(s): Imaging USA, Nashville, TN, Jan 14-16, 2018
Publication(s): *Professional Photographer* (monthly, $19.95/yr US; $35.95/yr CN; free for membs)

Professional Photographers of Canada – Ontario (PPOC-ON)
209 Light St, Woodstock, ON N4S 6H6, Canada
Tel: 519-537-2555 *Toll Free Tel:* 888-643-7762 *Toll Free Fax:* 888-831-4036
E-mail: info@ppocontario.com
Web Site: www.ppocontario.com
Key Personnel
Pres: Robert Nowell *Tel:* 905-682-0063 *E-mail:* robertnowell@cogeco.ca
Exec Dir: Tonya Thompson *E-mail:* execdirector@ppocontario.com
Founded: 1890
Membership organization for professional photographers.
Number of Members: 300
Publication(s): *Exposure Ontario*
Membership(s): Professional Photographers of Canada

Professional Women Photographers (PWP)
119 W 72 St, Suite 223, New York, NY 10023
E-mail: info@pwponline.org
Web Site: www.pwponline.org
Key Personnel
Pres: Beth Portnoi Shaw
Founded: 1975
To educate the public & support women photographers; monthly meetings every first Wednesday except July & Aug.
Number of Members: 200
Publication(s): *IMPRINTS* (magazine)

PromaxBDA
1522e Cloverfield Blvd, Santa Monica, CA 90404
Tel: 310-788-7600 *Fax:* 310-788-7616
Web Site: www.promaxbda.org
Key Personnel
SVP & CFO: Randy Smith *Tel:* 310-789-1514 *E-mail:* randy@promaxbda.org
CIO: Lucian Cojescu *Tel:* 310-789-1552 *E-mail:* lucian@promaxbda.org
VP, Bd Rel & Global Awards Devt: Stacy La Cotera *Tel:* 310-789-1503 *E-mail:* stacy@promaxbda.org
Edit Dir, Brief: Paige Albiniak *E-mail:* paige@promaxbda.org

Sr Mgr, Global Awards & Competitions: Eileen Rasnake *Tel:* 310-789-1506 *E-mail:* eileen@promaxbda.org
Mgr, Memb Servs: Anush Payaslyan *Tel:* 310-789-1509 *E-mail:* anush@promaxbda.org
Founded: 1956
Promote professionalism in marketing, advertising & promotion in radio, TV & cable broadcasting.
2015 Conference(s): PromaxBDA: The Conference 2015, JW Marriott Los Angeles LA Live, 900 W Olympic Blvd, Los Angeles, CA, June 9-11, 2015

PSA®, see Photographic Society of America® (PSA®)

PSNI (Professional Systems Network Inc)
1831 E 71 St, Tulsa, OK 74136
Tel: 918-388-1343
Web Site: www.psni.org
Key Personnel
Exec Dir: Chris Miller *E-mail:* cmiller@psni.org
Dir, Mktg Communs: Denise Harrison *E-mail:* dharrison@psni.org
Founded: 1986
Network of independent AV & broadcast communications systems integrators.

Quickdraw Animation Society
351 11 Ave SW, Suite 201, Calgary, AB T2R 0C7, Canada
Tel: 403-261-5767 *Fax:* 403-261-5644
E-mail: info@quickdrawanimation.ca; production@quickdrawanimation.ca; programming@quickdrawanimation.ca
Web Site: quickdrawanimation.ca; www.giraffest.ca
Key Personnel
Exec Dir: Peter Hemminger *E-mail:* peter@quickdrawanimation.ca
Prog Dir: Laura Leif
GIRAF Festival Coord: Jolie Bird *E-mail:* giraf@quickdrawanimation.ca
Prodn Coord: Duncan Kenworthy
Founded: 1984
2015 Conference(s): GIRAF (Giant Incandescent Resonating Animation Festival), Globe Cinema, Calgary, AB, CN, Nov 2015

RAB, see Radio Advertising Bureau (RAB)

RABQSA International Inc, see Exemplar Global

Radio Advertising Bureau (RAB)
125 W 55 St, 5th fl, New York, NY 10019
Tel: 212-681-7200 *Toll Free Tel:* 800-252-7234 *Fax:* 212-681-7223
Web Site: www.rab.com
Key Personnel
CEO & Pres: Erica Farber *E-mail:* efarber@rab.com
CFO & EVP: Van Allen *E-mail:* vallen@rab.com
SVP/Mktg & Communs: Leah Kamon *E-mail:* lkamon@rab.com
Sales & marketing arm for radio industry; provide sales tools & services to radio stations.
Number of Members: 7,000
Branch Office(s)
1320 Greenway Dr, Suite 500, Irving, TX 75038 *Toll Free Tel:* 800-232-3131
2015 Conference(s): Radio Show (co-produced with National Association of Broadcasters), Atlanta, GA, Sept 30-Oct 2, 2015
2016 Conference(s): Radio Show (co-produced with National Association of Broadcasters), Nashville, TN, Sept 21-23, 2016

Radio Television Digital News Association (RTDNA)
The National Press Bldg, 529 14 St NW, Suite 425, Washington, DC 20045
Tel: 202-659-6510 *Fax:* 202-223-4007
Web Site: www.rtdna.org
Key Personnel
Exec Dir: Mike Cavender *Tel:* 770-622-7011 *E-mail:* mikec@rtdna.org
Communs, Mktg & Digital Media Mgr: Derrick Hinds *E-mail:* derrickh@rtdna.org
To foster professionalism in electronic journalism.
Number of Members: 3,500
2015 Conference(s): Excellence in Journalism 2015, Orlando World Center Marriott, 8701 World Center Dr, Orlando, FL, Sept 18-20, 2015
Publication(s): *Communicator* (online, free)

The Recording Academy
3030 Olympic Blvd, Santa Monica, CA 90404
Tel: 310-392-3777 *Fax:* 310-392-2306
E-mail: losangeles@grammy.com
Web Site: www.grammy.org/recording-academy
Key Personnel
CEO & Pres: Neil Portnow
VP: Phil Soussan
Nonprofit Grammy Award association.
Number of Members: 8,000
Publication(s): *GRAMMY Magazine*

Recording Industry Association of America (RIAA)
1025 "F" St NW, 10th fl, Washington, DC 20004
Tel: 202-775-0101
Web Site: www.riaa.com
Key Personnel
Chmn & CEO: Cary Sherman
Sr EVP: Mitch Glazier
Nonprofit trade association for US record companies.
Publication(s): *Inside RIAA* (quarterly, online); *Inside the Recording Industry: A Statistical Overview* (online); *Inside the Recording Industry: Introduction to American Music Business* (online)

RIAA, see Recording Industry Association of America (RIAA)

SAG-AFTRA, see Screen Actors Guild & American Federation of Television & Radio Artists (SAG-AFTRA)

SALT®, see Society for Applied Learning Technology (SALT®)

Satellite Broadcasting & Communications Association
1100 17 St NW, Suite 1150, Washington, DC 20036
Tel: 202-349-3620 *Toll Free Tel:* 800-541-5981 *Fax:* 202-349-3621
E-mail: info@sbca.org
Web Site: www.sbca.com
Key Personnel
Exec Dir: Joseph Widoff *Tel:* 202-349-3656
Founded: 1986
Represent satellite broadcasting communication industry.
Number of Members: 500

Screen Actors Guild & American Federation of Television & Radio Artists (SAG-AFTRA)
5757 Wilshire Blvd, 7th fl, Los Angeles, CA 90036-3600
Tel: 323-954-1600 (former SAG); 323-634-8100 (former AFTRA) *Toll Free Tel:* 855-SAG-AFTRA (724-2387) *Fax:* 323-634-8194
E-mail: sagaftrainfo@sagaftra.org
Web Site: www.sagaftra.org/ny
Key Personnel
CFO: Arianna Ozzanto
Chief Admin Offr & Gen Coun: Duncan Crabtree-Ireland
Natl Exec Dir: David White
Assoc Natl Exec Dir: Mathis Dunn
Founded: 1933
Performers labor union.
Number of Members: 95,000
Branch Office(s)
360 Madison Ave, 12th fl, New York, NY 10017 *Tel:* 212-944-1030 *Fax:* 212-944-6774
Publication(s): *Screen Actor Magazine*

SCTE, see Society of Cable Telecommunications Engineers Inc (SCTE)

SESAC Inc
55 Music Sq E, Nashville, TN 37203
Tel: 615-320-0055 *Fax:* 615-963-3527
Web Site: www.sesac.com
Key Personnel
EVP, Busn Aff: Dennis Lord *E-mail:* dlord@sesac.com
SVP, Writer/Publr Rel: Trevor Gale *E-mail:* tgale@sesac.com
VP, Broadcast & Cable Licensing: Deborah Houghton *E-mail:* dhoughton@sesac.com
VP, Corp Rel: Ellen Bligh Truley *E-mail:* etruley@sesac.com
VP, Writer/Publr Rel NY: Linda Lorence Critelli *E-mail:* llorence@sesac.com
Mgr, Spec Projs: Jocelyn Harms *E-mail:* jharms@sesac.com
Founded: 1930
Performing rights organization.
Branch Office(s)
6100 Wilshire Blvd, Suite 700, Los Angeles, CA 90048 *Tel:* 323-937-3722 *Fax:* 323-937-3733
420 Lincoln Rd, Suite 502, Miami, FL 33139 *Tel:* 305-534-7500
981 Joseph E Lowery Blvd NW, Suite 102, Atlanta, GA 30318 *Tel:* 404-897-1330
152 W 57 St, 57th fl, New York, NY 10019 *Tel:* 212-586-3450 *Fax:* 212-489-5699
Foreign Office(s): SESAC Intl, 67 Upper Berkeley St, London W1H 7QX, United Kingdom *Tel:* (020) 7616 9284 *Fax:* (020) 7563 7029

Sesame Workshop
1900 Broadway, 4th fl, New York, NY 10023
Tel: 212-595-3456 *Fax:* 212-875-6113
Web Site: www.sesameworkshop.org
Key Personnel
CEO: Melvin Ming
Pres: Gary Knell
VP & Supervising Prodr: Nadine Zylstra
Founded: 1968 (as the Children's Television Workshop)
Nonprofit educational organization which develops educational content for TV, radio, books, magazines, interactive media & outreach.
Number of Members: 300
Publication(s): *Sesame Street Magazine*

Set Decorators Society of America (SDSA)
7100 Tujunga Ave, Suite A, North Hollywood, CA 91605
Tel: 818-255-2425 *Fax:* 818-982-8597
E-mail: sdsa@setdecorators.org
Web Site: www.setdecorators.org
Key Personnel
Pres: Shirley Starks
VP: Jan Pascale
Treas: Regina O'Brien
Recording Secy: Halina Siwolop
Exec Dir: Gene Cane
Founded: 1993
Number of Members: 500
Publication(s): *Set Decor* (online)

SIIA, see Software & Information Industry Association (SIIA)

SMPTE, see Society of Motion Picture & Television Engineers (SMPTE)

Societe de developpement des enterprises culturelles, see SODEC

Society for Applied Learning Technology (SALT®)
50 Culpeper St, Warrenton, VA 20186
Tel: 540-347-0055 *Fax:* 540-349-3169
E-mail: info@lti.org
Web Site: www.salt.org
Key Personnel
Exec Dir: John G Fox, II
Conference & Exhibit Mgr: Carrie Vespico *E-mail:* carrie@lti.org
Founded: 1972
Exchange state-of-the-art information in the field of interactive multimedia applications in education & training.
Number of Members: 500
Publication(s): *Journal of Applied Learning Technology (JALT)* (online, quarterly); *Journal of Education Technology Systems (JETS)* (quarterly)

Society for Imaging Science and Technology (IS&T)
7003 Kilworth Lane, Springfield, VA 22151
Tel: 703-642-9090 *Fax:* 703-642-9094
E-mail: info@imaging.org
Web Site: www.imaging.org
Key Personnel
Pres: Alan Hodgson
Exec Dir: Suzanne E Grinnan *E-mail:* sgrinnan@imaging.org
Conference Prog Mgr: Diana Gonzalez *E-mail:* dgonzalez@imaging.org
Exec Asst: Donna Smith *E-mail:* dsmith@imaging.org
Founded: 1947
Disseminate information in the field of imaging science: photo systems, non-impact printing, electronic imaging.
Number of Members: 1,500
2015 Conference(s): Archiving Conference, Los Angeles, CA, May 19-22, 2015; Digital Fabrication Conference, Portland, OR, Sept 27-Oct 1, 2015; NIP: International Conference on Digital Printing Technologies, Portland, OR, Sept 27-Oct 1, 2015
2016 Conference(s): Electronic Imaging Conference, San Francisco, CA, Feb 7-11, 2016
Publication(s): *IS&T Reporter* (6 issues/yr); *Journal of Electronic Imaging (JEI)* ($75); *Journal of Imaging Science & Technology (JIST)* (6 issues/yr)

Society for Information Display (SID)
1475 S Bascom Ave, Suite 114, Campbell, CA 95008-4006
Tel: 408-879-3901 *Fax:* 408-879-3833
E-mail: office@sid.org
Web Site: www.sid.org
Key Personnel
Pres: Brian Berkeley *E-mail:* sid1@theberkeleys.net
Secy: Helge Seetzen
Treas: Yong-Seog Kim
Sr Busn Mgr: Doug Bragdon *E-mail:* doug@sid.org
Founded: 1962
Committed to the presentation, exchange & preservation of the ideas & technologies of information display.
Number of Members: 6,100
2015 Conference(s): Display Week, San Jose Convention Center, San Jose, CA, May 31-June 5, 2015
Publication(s): *Information Display Magazine* (monthly); *SID International Symposium Digest of Technical Papers* (annual)

Society of Broadcast Engineers Inc (SBE)
9102 N Meridian St, Suite 150, Indianapolis, IN 46260
Tel: 317-846-9000
Web Site: www.sbe.org
Key Personnel
Exec Dir: John Poray *E-mail:* jporay@sbe.org
Certification Dir: Megan Clappe *E-mail:* mclappe@sbe.org
Founded: 1964
Society for television & radio broadcast engineers, membership services, education, certification.
Number of Members: 5,500
Publication(s): *The Signal* (newsletter, 6 issues/yr)

Society of Cable Telecommunications Engineers Inc (SCTE)
140 Philips Rd, Exton, PA 19341-1318
Tel: 610-363-6888 *Toll Free Tel:* 800-542-5040 (cust care) *Fax:* 610-363-5898
E-mail: information@scte.org
Web Site: www.scte.org
Key Personnel
Pres & CEO: Mark Dzuban *Fax:* 610-363-7309
Founded: 1969
A nonprofit professional association that provides technical leadership for the telecommunications industry & serves its members through professional development, standards, certification & information. The society serves its diverse membership & the industry by offering a wide variety of educational programs & services.
Number of Members: 14,000
2015 Conference(s): SCTE Cable-Tec Expo®, New Orleans, LA, Oct 13-16, 2015

Society of Camera Operators
PO Box 2006, Toluca Lake, CA 91610-0006
Tel: 818-382-7070
E-mail: info@soc.org
Web Site: www.soc.org
Key Personnel
Pres: Chris Tufty *E-mail:* pres@soc.org
Treas: Douglas Knapp
Founded: 1979

Society of Motion Picture & Television Engineers (SMPTE)
3 Barker Ave, 5th fl, White Plains, NY 10601
Tel: 914-761-1100 *Fax:* 914-761-3115
E-mail: membership@smpte.org
Web Site: www.smpte.org
Key Personnel
Exec Dir: Barbara Lange *Tel:* 914-205-2370 *E-mail:* blange@smpte.org
Dir, Opers: Sally-Ann D'Amato *Tel:* 914-205-2375 *E-mail:* sdamato@smpte.org
Mgr, Memb Rel: Roberta Gorman *Tel:* 914-205-2376 *E-mail:* rgorman@smpte.org
Exec Asst: June Marie Sobrito *Tel:* 914-205-2384 *E-mail:* jsobrito@smpte.org
Founded: 1916
Advance engineering & technical aspects of motion picture, television, the allied arts & sciences.
Number of Members: 5,500
2015 Conference(s): SMPTE Annual Technical Conference & Exhibition, Oct 26-29, 2015
2016 Conference(s): SMPTE Annual Technical Conference & Exhibition, Oct 24-27, 2016
2017 Conference(s): SMPTE Annual Technical Conference & Exhibition, Oct 23-26, 2017
Publication(s): *SMPTE Journal* (8 issues/yr)

The Society of Professional Audio Recording Services (SPARS)
PO Box 606, Palacios, TX 77465
Toll Free Tel: 800-771-7727 *Fax:* 214-722-1442
E-mail: spars@spars.com
Web Site: spars.com
Key Personnel
Exec Dir: Paul Christensen *E-mail:* paul@spars.com
Founded: 1979
Communication between professional audio recording studios & those they service & are serviced by.
Number of Members: 300
Publication(s): *Sound Bytes* (monthly, free)

SODEC
215 rue Saint-Jacques St, Rm 800, Montreal, QC H2Y 1M6, Canada
Tel: 514-841-2200 *Toll Free Tel:* 800-363-0401 (CN only) *Fax:* 514-841-8606
E-mail: info@sodec.gouv.qc.ca
Web Site: www.sodec.gouv.qc.ca
Key Personnel
CEO & Pres: Monique Simard
Film, television, books, records, theater, dance, etc; SODEC is a government agency.
Publication(s): *Annual Report*

Software & Information Industry Association (SIIA)
1090 Vermont Ave NW, 6th fl, Washington, DC 20005-4095
Tel: 202-289-7442 *Fax:* 202-289-7097
Web Site: www.siia.net
Key Personnel
Pres: Kenneth Wasch *Tel:* 202-789-4440
VP, Mktg: Eileen Bramlet
VP, Membership: Eric Fredell *Tel:* 202-789-4464
Mktg Coord: Nadia Hassairi *Tel:* 202-789-4468
Represent corporations interested in the business opportunities associated with the generation, distribution & use of information.
Number of Members: 550

SPARS, see The Society of Professional Audio Recording Services (SPARS)

SPIE
PO Box 10, Bellingham, WA 98227-0010
Tel: 360-676-3290 *Toll Free Tel:* 888-504-8171 *Fax:* 360-647-1445
E-mail: customerservice@spie.org
Web Site: www.spie.org
Key Personnel
AV Mgr: Ben Lockwood
Founded: 1955
Not-for-profit international society dedicated to advancing optics & photonics; organize worldwide science conferences & publish the proceedings.
Publication(s): *Optical Engineering Journal* (monthly, $45/yr online, $240/yr print (membs only))

Television Academy
5220 Lankershim Blvd, North Hollywood, CA 91601-3109
Tel: 818-754-2800 *Fax:* 818-761-2827
Web Site: www.emmys.com
Key Personnel
Pres & COO: Maury McIntyre
CFO & EVP, Busn Opers: Heather Cochran
SVP, Awards: Dr John Leverence
SVP, Media & Brand Mgmt: Susan Spence
VP, Awards: Julie Shore
VP, Mktg: Laurel Whitcomb
Founded: 1946
To further the telecommunications arts & sciences.
Number of Members: 22,000
Publication(s): *Emmy Magazine*

Television Bureau of Advertising Inc (TVB)
120 Wall St, 15th fl, New York, NY 10005-3908
Tel: 212-486-1111 *Fax:* 212-935-5631
E-mail: info@tvb.org

Web Site: www.tvb.org
Key Personnel
CEO & Pres: Steven Lanzano *E-mail:* steve@tvb.org
EVP & Chief Mktg Offr: Abby Auerbach *E-mail:* abby@tvb.org
Marketing trade association for TV industry; represent TV stations, networks, national spot sales representatives & program producer syndicators.
Number of Members: 600

Texas Association of Film & Tape Professionals (TAFTP), see Texas Association of Motion Media Professionals (TAMMP)

Texas Association of Motion Media Professionals (TAMMP)
Formerly Texas Association of Film & Tape Professionals (TAFTP)
9629 Carnegie Dr, Dallas, TX 75228
Tel: 214-766-1924
E-mail: info@taftp.com
Web Site: taftp.com
Founded: 1976
Nonprofit association dedicated to promoting & advancing film & tape production in Texas.
Number of Members: 950

Trade Show Exhibitors Association (TSEA), see Exhibit & Event Marketers Association (E2MA)

United Scenic Artists Local 829
29 W 38 St, 15th fl, New York, NY 10018
Tel: 212-581-0300 *Fax:* 212-977-2011
E-mail: businessoffice@usa829.org
Web Site: www.usa829.org; vfx.usa829.org
Key Personnel
Natl Busn Agent: Cecilia Friederichs *E-mail:* ceciliaf@usa829.org
Pres: Beverly Miller *E-mail:* bev@usa829.org
Busn Rep: Mike Smith *E-mail:* mikes@usa829.org
Founded: 1897
Labor Union representing Art Directors, Scenic, Costume, Lighting, Sound & Projection Designers & Scenic & Computer Artists in motion pictures, television & live performance.
Number of Members: 3,800
Publication(s): *Newsletter* (monthly)

University Film & Video Association (UFVA)
c/o University of Illinois Press, 1325 S Oak St, Champaign, IL 61820
Tel: 217-244-0626 (journals); 217-333-0950 (main) *Toll Free Tel:* 866-244-0626 (journals); 866-647-8382 (main) *Fax:* 217-244-9910
E-mail: ufvahome@gmail.com
Web Site: www.ufva.org
Key Personnel
Pres: Francisco Menendez *E-mail:* francisco.menendez@unlv.edu
Treas: Tom Sanny *E-mail:* tsanny@me.com
Founded: 1947
Foster the development, improvement of film & video studies & production in educational institutions. Serves as liaison with the industry.
Number of Members: 800
2015 Conference(s): UFVA Conference (Media With Impact: Engaging, Enterprising & Experimental), American University, Washington, DC, Aug 4-8, 2015
Publication(s): *The Journal of Film & Video* (quarterly); *UFVA Digest* (newsletter, monthly, online only)

USITT: United States Institute for Theatre Technology Inc
315 S Crouse Ave, Suite 200, Syracuse, NY 13210-1844
Tel: 315-463-6463 *Toll Free Tel:* 800-938-7488 *Fax:* 315-463-6525 *Toll Free Fax:* 866-398-7488
E-mail: info@office.usitt.org
Web Site: www.usitt.org
Key Personnel
Exec Dir: David Grinole *E-mail:* david@usitt.org
Dir, Communs: Barbara E R Lucas *E-mail:* barbara@usitt.org
Dir, Fin & HR: Carol B Carrigan *E-mail:* carol@usitt.org
Dir, Memb Servs: Monica L Merritt *E-mail:* monica@usitt.org
Founded: 1960
Mission is to advance the knowledge & skills of its members who are design, production & technology professionals in the performing arts & entertainment industry.
Number of Members: 3,800
2016 Conference(s): Annual Conference & Stage Expo, Calvin L Rampton Salt Palace Convention Center, Salt Lake City, UT, March 16-19, 2016
Publication(s): *Sightlines* (monthly); *TD&T - Theatre Design & Technology* (quarterly)

Women In Animation
PO Box 17706, Encino, CA 91416-7706
Tel: 818-759-9596
E-mail: wia@womeninanimation.org; info@womeninanimation.org
Web Site: www.womeninanimation.org
Key Personnel
Founder & Pres: Rita Street
Pres: Jan Nagel
Founded: 1994
Professional peer organization for both women & men working in the Act & Industry of Animation.
Number of Members: 400

Women In Film
6100 Wilshire Blvd, Suite 710, Los Angeles, CA 90048-5117
Tel: 323-935-2211 *Fax:* 323-935-2212
E-mail: info@wif.org
Web Site: www.wif.org
Key Personnel
Exec Dir: Gayle Nachlis *Tel:* 323-935-2211 ext 106 *E-mail:* gnachlis@wif.org
Founded: 1973
Film industry networking & support group. Also providing scholarships & grants which promote educational & professional opportunities for women working in the entertainment industry.
Number of Members: 2,000

Women in Film & Television-Florida (WIFT-FL)
PO Box 533541, Orlando, FL 32853-3541
E-mail: info@womeninfilmfl.org
Web Site: womeninfilmfl.org
Key Personnel
Pres: Lyn Henderson
Founded: 1989
Promotes women's roles in film industry.

Writers Anonymous
34225 Acton Canyon Rd, Acton, CA 93510-1309
Tel: 661-269-0260
Key Personnel
Pres: Jack Adams *E-mail:* jackadams@earthlink.net
Support of scriptwriters in creating, developing, marketing & selling scripts to the film & television industry.
Publication(s): *Get an Agent to Sell Your Script*; *Pitch Your Film & Television Projects*; *Top 50 Script Marketing Tips*; *WA Newsletter* (quarterly); *Write to Get Past the Script Reader*; *Writing Personal & Family Histories: Tell & Sell Your Story Well*

Writers Guild of America, West (WGAW)
7000 W Third St, Los Angeles, CA 90048
Tel: 323-951-4000 *Toll Free Tel:* 800-548-4532 *Fax:* 323-782-4800
Web Site: www.wga.org
Key Personnel
Pres: Chris Keyser
VP: Howard A Rodman
Secy & Treas: Carl Gottlieb
Union for writers in TV, screen & radio, film broadcasting & cable industry including writers of entertainment, news, documentaries & informational programming.
Number of Members: 10,000
Publication(s): *Written By: The Magazine of the Writers Guild of America, West* (9 issues/yr)

Xplor® International
24156 State Rd 54, Suite 4, Lutz, FL 33559
Tel: 813-949-6170 *Toll Free Tel:* 800-669-7567 *Fax:* 813-949-9977
E-mail: info@xplor.org
Web Site: www.xplor.org
Key Personnel
CEO & Pres: Skip Henk *E-mail:* skip@xplor.org
Dir, Opers: Lynn B Robins *E-mail:* lynn@xplor.org
Dir, Sales: Deborah Green *Tel:* 770-444-3845 *E-mail:* deborahgreen1@earthlink.net
Mktg Coord: Chad Henk *Tel:* 813-949-6171 *E-mail:* chad@xplor.org
Prog Coord: Jennifer J Smith *E-mail:* jennifer@xplor.org
Founded: 1981
Provides organizations & individuals with learning & networking opportunities which enhance the effective use of electronic document technology to achieve business objectives.
Number of Members: 3,500
Publication(s): *Xplorer* (monthly, online)

Film & Television Commissions

Listed here are state, county and city agencies that are responsible for providing information and services (location scouting, local casting, permits, shelter, etc.) to prospective film, TV and commercial producers. The listings in this section are sorted geographically by state, then city.

ALABAMA

Mobile Film Office
Affiliate of City of Mobile
164 Saint Emanuel St, Mobile, AL 36602
Tel: 251-438-7102 *Fax:* 251-438-7104
Web Site: www.mobilefilmoffice.com
Key Personnel
Dir: Eva H Golson *E-mail:* golson@cityofmobile.org
Film Off & Location Coord: Diane Hall *Tel:* 251-438-7100 *E-mail:* diane.hall@cityofmobile.org
Assisting in finding locations, scouting & permits.

Alabama Film Office
Alabama Center for Commerce, 401 Adams Ave, Suite 170, Montgomery, AL 36104-1430
Tel: 334-242-4195 *Fax:* 334-242-2077
Web Site: www.alabamafilm.org
Key Personnel
Mgr: Kathy Faulk *Tel:* 334-242-7127 *E-mail:* kathy.faulk@film.alabama.gov
Community Liaison: Courtney Murphy *Tel:* 334-242-3989 *E-mail:* courtney.murphy@film.alabama.gov
Assist all legitimate motion picture production companies; location scouting available.

ALASKA

Alaska Film Office
Affiliate of State of Alaska Department of Revenue
550 W Seventh Ave, Suite 500, Anchorage, AK 99501
Tel: 907-269-1018 *Fax:* 907-269-6644
E-mail: alaskafilmoffice@alaska.gov
Web Site: tax.alaska.gov/AlaskaFilmOffice/
Key Personnel
Exec Dir: Kelly Mazzei
Help find locations & provide assistance with permits, accommodations & activity coordination. Production manual available online. Film incentive is up to 44% in transferrable tax credits.

ARIZONA

Apache Junction Chamber of Commerce
567 W Apache Trail, Apache Junction, AZ 85120
Mailing Address: PO Box 1747, Apache Junction, AZ 85117-1747
Tel: 480-982-3141 *Toll Free Tel:* 800-252-3141 *Fax:* 480-982-3234
Web Site: www.ajchamber.com
Key Personnel
VP, Opers: Jan Long *E-mail:* jan@ajchamber.com

Cochise County Arizona
Queen Mine Tour Bldg, 478 Dart Rd, Bisbee, AZ 85603
Mailing Address: PO Box 1642, Bisbee, AZ 85603
Tel: 520-432-3554 *Toll Free Tel:* 866-2BISBEE (224-7233)
E-mail: ilona@discoverbisbee.com
Web Site: www.explorecochise.com
Key Personnel
Film Rep: Ilona Smerekanich
Contact: Gussie Motter *E-mail:* gmotter@cochise.az.gov

Flagstaff Convention & Visitors Bureau
One E Rte 66, Flagstaff, AZ 86001-5303
Tel: 928-213-2910 *Toll Free Tel:* 800-842-7293
E-mail: cvb@flagstaffaz.gov
Web Site: www.flagstaffarizona.org
Key Personnel
Dir: Heidi Hansen *Tel:* 928-213-2921
Admin Specialist: Carrie Nelson *Tel:* 928-213-2919
Assists with location, scouting & permits for film, TV companies & still photography.

Globe/Miami Film Commission
Division of Globe-Miami Regional Chamber of Commerce & Economic Development Corp
1360 N Broad St, US 60, Globe, AZ 85501
Tel: 928-425-4495 *Toll Free Tel:* 800-804-5623 *Fax:* 928-425-3410
E-mail: gmr@cableone.net
Web Site: www.globemiamichamber.com
Key Personnel
Exec Dir: Ellen Kretsch
Provide films on Globe - Miami area culture & history.

Holbrook Film Commission
465 N First Ave, Holbrook, AZ 86025
Mailing Address: PO Box 970, Holbrook, AZ 86025
Tel: 928-524-6227 *Toll Free Tel:* 800-524-2459 *Fax:* 928-524-1719
E-mail: holbrook@gotouraz.com
Web Site: www.gotouraz.com
Key Personnel
Dir: Kathleen Smith
Number of Members: 200

Page-Lake Powell Film Commission
PO Box 1180, Page, AZ 86040
Tel: 928-645-3410 *Toll Free Tel:* 888-261-PAGE (261-7243) *Fax:* 928-645-4250
Web Site: visitpagealakepowell.com
Key Personnel
Tourism Dir: Lee McMichael *E-mail:* lmcmichael@cityofpage.org
Location scouting, production assistants, permits, key people, service directories.

Parker Area Chamber of Commerce
1217 California Ave, Parker, AZ 85344
Tel: 928-669-2174 *Fax:* 928-669-6304
E-mail: info@parkeraz.org
Web Site: www.parkeraz.org
Key Personnel
Exec Dir: Mary Hamilton *E-mail:* director@parkeraz.org
Offer tourism, business & economic development services.

City of Phoenix Film Office
200 W Washington St, 20th fl, Phoenix, AZ 85003
Tel: 602-262-4850
E-mail: filmphx@phoenix.gov
Web Site: www.phoenix.gov/econdev/filming/
Key Personnel
Film Commissioner: Philip Bradstock
Promote Phoenix as the site for filming of motion pictures, feature films, commercials, industrial & educational productions to the film & tape industry.

City of Prescott Film Office
201 S Cortez St, Prescott, AZ 86303
Tel: 928-777-1204 *Fax:* 928-777-1255
Web Site: www.cityofprescott.net/business/film
Key Personnel
Tourism & Economic Devt Coord: Wendy Bridges *E-mail:* wendy.bridges@prescott-az.gov
Membership(s): Association of Film Commissioners International

City of Scottsdale
3939 N Drinkwater Blvd, Scottsdale, AZ 85251
Tel: 480-312-2550; 480-312-3111; 480-312-2500 (permit servs) *Fax:* 480-312-2888
Web Site: www.scottsdaleaz.gov
Key Personnel
Communs & Pub Aff Dir: Kelly Corsette *Tel:* 480-312-2336 *E-mail:* kcorsette@scottsdaleaz.gov
Pub Aff Mgr: Mike Phillips *Tel:* 480-312-7825 *E-mail:* mphillips@scottsdaleaz.gov
Film & TV office.

Sedona Film Office
Division of Sedona Chamber of Commerce
45 Sunset Dr, Sedona, AZ 86336
Mailing Address: PO Box 478, Sedona, AZ 86339-0478
Tel: 928-204-1123 ext 130 *Fax:* 928-204-1064
E-mail: pr@sedonachamber.com
Web Site: www.sedonafilmoffice.com
Key Personnel
CEO & Pres: Jennifer Wesselhoff *E-mail:* jwess@sedonachamber.com
PR & Events Mgr: Kegn Hall *Tel:* 928-204-1123 ext 170 *E-mail:* khall@sedonachamber.com

Tucson Film Office
Division of Metropolitan Tucson Convention & Visitors Bureau
100 S Church Ave, Tucson, AZ 85701
Tel: 520-770-2151 *Fax:* 520-629-0160
Web Site: www.filmtucson.com
Key Personnel
Dir: Shelli Hall *E-mail:* shall@visittucson.org
Prodn Coord: Peter Catalanotte *E-mail:* pcatalanotte@visittucson.org
Scouting; assist with government agencies, clearances & on-site; work with television, film, commercial & still shots. Publish production manual.

Wickenburg Film Commission
216 N Frontier St, Wickenburg, AZ 85390
Tel: 928-684-5479; 928-684-0977 *Toll Free Tel:* 800-942-5242 *Fax:* 928-684-5470
E-mail: info@wickenburgchamber.com
Web Site: www.wickenburgchamber.com/film-commission
Key Personnel
Exec Dir: Julie Brooks

Chmn, Film Commission: Kristi Henson
Local film services, photo library of area & location assistance.

Yuma Film Commission
180 W First St, Suite D, Yuma, AZ 85364
Tel: 928-314-9247 *Fax:* 928-373-0133
Web Site: www.filmyuma.com
Key Personnel
Exec Dir: Linda Morgan *E-mail:* linda@visityuma.com
Event Coord: Adrianne Wagner *E-mail:* adrianne@visityuma.com

ARKANSAS

Eureka Springs Advertising & Promotions Commission
PO Box 522, Eureka Springs, AR 72632-0522
Tel: 479-253-7333 *Toll Free Tel:* 866-566-9387 *Fax:* 479-363-9380
E-mail: info@eurekasprings.org
Web Site: www.eurekasprings.org
Key Personnel
Exec Dir: Mike Maloney *Tel:* 479-253-7333 ext 13
Founded: 1972
Scouting services, location assistance & permits.

Arkansas Film Commission
900 W Capitol Ave, Suite 400, Little Rock, AR 72201
Tel: 501-682-7676 *Fax:* 501-682-7394
Web Site: www.arkansasproduction.com
Key Personnel
Film Commissioner: Christopher Crane
Founded: 1979
Promote location filming in Arkansas.

CALIFORNIA

Humboldt-Del Norte Film Commission
1385 Eighth St, Suite 106, Arcata, CA 95521
Tel: 707-825-7600
Web Site: www.filmhumboldtdelnorte.org
Key Personnel
Film Commissioner: Cassandra Hesseltine *Tel:* 707-825-7600
Locations for movie making in the majestic redwoods & source of permits.

Placer-Lake Tahoe Film Office
Division of Placer County Office of Economic Development
145 Fulweiler Ave, Auburn, CA 95603
Mailing Address: 175 Fulweiler Ave, Auburn, CA 95603
Tel: 530-889-4091 *Toll Free Tel:* 877-228-3456 *Fax:* 530-889-4095
Web Site: www.placer.ca.gov/films
Key Personnel
Dir: Beverly Lewis *E-mail:* blewis@placer.ca.gov
Founded: 1998
Film commission, location assistance (photo library, maps, etc), facilitates county film permits.
Membership(s): Film Liaisons in California Statewide

Catalina Island Film Commission
One Green Pier, Avalon, CA 90704-0217
Mailing Address: PO Box 217, Avalon, CA 90704-0217
Tel: 310-510-7649 *Fax:* 310-510-7607
Web Site: www.catalinachamber.com/mediafilming/contact
Key Personnel
Mktg & Film Liaison: Donna Harris *E-mail:* dharris@catalinachamber.com
Information & coordination for all shooting on Catalina Island.
Membership(s): California Film Commission; Film Liaisons in California Statewide

Kern County Film Commission
2101 Oak St, Bakersfield, CA 93301
Tel: 661-868-KERN (868-5376) *Toll Free Tel:* 800-500-KERN (500-5376) *Fax:* 661-861-2017
E-mail: kerninfo@co.kern.ca.us
Web Site: www.filmkern.com
Key Personnel
Film Commissioner: Joanie Haenelt
Coordinate film location sites & permits. Film location directory available.

Berkeley Film Office
2030 Addison St, Suite 102, Berkeley, CA 94704
Tel: 510-549-7040 *Toll Free Tel:* 800-847-4823 *Fax:* 510-644-2052
E-mail: film@visitberkeley.com
Web Site: www.filmberkeley.com
Key Personnel
Film Commissioner: Barbara Hillman
Founded: 1994
Assist with location referrals & coordination of commercial filming within the city of Berkeley.
Membership(s): Association of Film Commissioners International

Big Bear Chamber of Commerce
630 Bartlett Rd, 1st fl, Big Bear Lake, CA 92315
Mailing Address: PO Box 2860, Big Bear Lake, CA 92315-2860
Tel: 909-866-4607 *Fax:* 909-866-5412
E-mail: contact@bigbearchamber.com
Web Site: www.bigbearchamber.com
Key Personnel
Exec Dir: Pam Scannell *Tel:* 909-866-4607 ext 947 *E-mail:* pscannell@bigbearchamber.com
Dir, Event Resource Off: Rick Bates *Tel:* 909-866-2638 *E-mail:* rickbates@eventsinbigbear.com
Founded: 1947

Bishop Area Chamber of Commerce & Visitors Bureau
690 N Main St, Bishop, CA 93514
Tel: 760-873-8405 *Toll Free Tel:* 888-395-3952 *Fax:* 760-873-6999
Web Site: www.bishopvisitor.com
Key Personnel
Exec Dir: Tawni Thomson *E-mail:* execdir@bishopvisitor.com
Founded: 1913
Please call for specifics.
Number of Members: 300

San Mateo County Film Commission
Seabreeze Plaza, Suite 410, 111 Anza Blvd, Burlingame, CA 94010
Tel: 650-348-7600 *Fax:* 650-348-7687
E-mail: info@filmsanmateocounty.com
Web Site: www.sanmateocountycvb.com
Key Personnel
Film Commissioner: Brena Bailey *Tel:* 650-348-7600 ext 110 *E-mail:* bbailey@smccvb.com
Media Mgr: Stephanie Fermin
Film commission covering 20 cities surrounding San Francisco International Airport, North of Santa Clara County, South of San Francisco.
Membership(s): Association of Film Commissioners International; California Film Commission

Camarillo Chamber of Commerce
2400 E Ventura Blvd, Camarillo, CA 93010
Tel: 805-484-4383 *Fax:* 805-484-1395
E-mail: info@camarillochamber.org
Web Site: www.camarillochamber.org
Key Personnel
Pres/CEO: Gary Cushing *Tel:* 805-484-4383 ext 8 *E-mail:* ceo@camarillochamber.org
Dir, Progs & Events: Sandy Wheat-James *Tel:* 805-484-4383 ext 5 *E-mail:* sandy@camarillochamber.org
Founded: 1940

Chico Chamber of Commerce/Butte County Film Commission
441 Main St, Suite 150, Chico, CA 95928
Mailing Address: PO Box 3300, Chico, CA 95927-3300
Tel: 530-891-5556 *Toll Free Tel:* 800-852-8570 *Fax:* 530-891-3613
E-mail: info@chicochamber.com
Web Site: chicochamber.com
Key Personnel
CEO & Pres: Katie Simmons *Tel:* 530-891-5556 ext 303
Events & Devt Dir: Alice Patterson *Tel:* 530-891-5556 ext 315 *E-mail:* alice@chicochamber.com
Memb Servs Mgr: Heather Ugie *Tel:* 530-891-5556 ext 314
Admin & Spec Projs Coord: Angela Cole *Tel:* 530-891-5556 ext 306
Provide free location & production assistance.

Desert Hot Springs Chamber of Commerce & Visitors Center
11999 Palm Dr, Desert Hot Springs, CA 92240
Tel: 760-329-6403
E-mail: info@deserthotsprings.com
Web Site: www.deserthotsprings.com
Key Personnel
Contact: Heather Coladonato
Founded: 1949
Chamber of Commerce & visitor information.
Number of Members: 300

Fresno County Film Commission
2220 Tulare St, 8th fl, Fresno, CA 93721
Tel: 559-600-4271 *Fax:* 559-600-4549
Web Site: www.filmfresno.com
Key Personnel
Film Commissioner: Gigi Gibbs *E-mail:* ggibbs@co.fresno.ca.us
Assoc Film Commissioner: Kristi Johnson *E-mail:* kgjohnson@co.fresno.ca.us
Location & production services for filming throughout Fresno County, CA.
Membership(s): Film Liaisons in California Statewide

Fresno Film Commission
Division of Creative Fresno
5241 E Townsend Ave, Fresno, CA 93727
Tel: 559-908-0539 *Fax:* 559-354-5980
E-mail: fresnofilm@gmail.com
Web Site: www.fresnofilm.com
Key Personnel
Film Commissioner: Ray Arthur
Founded: 2007
Film commission marketing the city of Fresno, CA.
Membership(s): California Film Commission

Orange County Film Commission
800 N State College Blvd, MH 133, Fullerton, CA 92834-6850
Mailing Address: CSUF, PO Box 6850, Fullerton, CA 92834-6850
Tel: 657-278-7569 *Fax:* 657-278-7521
Web Site: www.filmorangecounty.org
Key Personnel
Orange County Film Commissioner: Janice Arrington *E-mail:* jarrington@filmorangecounty.org
Locations scouting; assistance in obtaining permits, negotiating fees, finding local cast & crew members, products & services; troubleshooting 24 hours a day.

Grass Valley/Nevada County Chamber of Commerce
128 E Main St, Grass Valley, CA 95945
Tel: 530-273-4667 *Toll Free Tel:* 800-655-4667 *Fax:* 530-272-5440
E-mail: info@grassvalleychamber.com
Web Site: www.grassvalleychamber.com
Key Personnel
CEO & Exec Dir: Keith Davies; Robin Galvan-Davies
Provide information for filming in the area, assist with permits & location services.

California Film Commission (CFC)
7080 Hollywood Blvd, Suite 900, Hollywood, CA 90028-6936
Tel: 323-860-2960 (24-hr serv)
Toll Free Tel: 800-858-4749 *Fax:* 323-860-2972
E-mail: filmca@film.ca.gov
Web Site: www.film.ca.gov
Key Personnel
Exec Dir: Amy Lemisch *Tel:* 323-860-2960 ext 102 *E-mail:* alemisch@film.ca.gov
Deputy Dir: Eve Honthaner *Tel:* 323-860-2960 ext 136 *E-mail:* ehonthaner@film.ca.gov
Write permits to film on state-owned & operated property. Location resource library & mediator services. Administers California film & TV techs credit program.

Antelope Valley Film Office-Lancaster
42035 12 St W, Suite 103, Lancaster, CA 93534
Tel: 661-723-6090; 661-510-4231 (cell)
Web Site: antelope-valley-film-office.hollywoodserve.com
Key Personnel
Film Liaison: Pauline East *E-mail:* pauline@filmantelopevalley.org
Provide location scouting & local support services referrals for the entertainment industry (film, television & still production companies).

FilmL.A., Inc
6255 W Sunset Blvd, 12th fl, Los Angeles, CA 90028
Tel: 213-977-8600 *Fax:* 213-977-8610; 213-977-8601 (permits)
E-mail: info@filmla.com
Web Site: www.filmla.com
Key Personnel
Chair: Leron Gubler
Secy: David Phelps
Founded: 1995 (as Entertainment Industry Development Corp)
Nonprofit corporation issuing permits & providing assistance for filming in the county of Los Angeles.

Mammoth Location Services
One Minaret Rd, Mammoth Lakes, CA 93546
Mailing Address: PO Box 24, Mammoth Lakes, CA 93546-0024
Tel: 760-934-0628 *Fax:* 760-924-7026
Key Personnel
Film & Entertainment Mgr: Steve Morrison *E-mail:* smorrison@mammoth-mtn.com
Location scouting & coordination; local casting & crew; equipment rentals.

Merced Visitor Services
California Welcome Ctr, 710 W 16 St, Merced, CA 95340
Tel: 209-724-8104 *Toll Free Tel:* 800-446-5353
E-mail: info@visitmerced.travel
Web Site: www.yosemite-gateway.org
Key Personnel
Exec Dir & Film Commissioner: Karen Baker *E-mail:* bakerk@cityofmerced.org
Tourism promotion & film commission.

Modesto Convention & Visitors Bureau
1150 Ninth St, Suite C, Modesto, CA 95354
Tel: 209-526-5588 *Toll Free Tel:* 888-640-8467 *Fax:* 209-526-5586
E-mail: films@visitmodesto.com; info@visitmodesto.com
Web Site: www.visitmodesto.com
Key Personnel
CEO & Exec Dir: Jennifer Mullen *E-mail:* jennifer@visitmodesto.com
Free preliminary location scouting services, photos & production information available to location scouts & managers upon request.
Membership(s): Association of Film Commissioners International

Modesto/Stanislaus County Film Commission, see Modesto Convention & Visitors Bureau

Monterey County Film Commission
801 Lighthouse Ave, Suite 104, Monterey, CA 93940
Mailing Address: PO Box 111, Monterey, CA 93942-0111
Tel: 831-646-0910 *Fax:* 831-655-9250
E-mail: info@filmmonterey.org
Web Site: www.filmmonterey.org
Key Personnel
Dir, Mktg & Film Prodn: Karen Nordstrand *E-mail:* karen@filmmonterey.org
Off Administrator: Moira LaMountain *E-mail:* moira@filmmonterey.org
Founded: 1987
Provide assistance & information on locations, permits, crew & other production services.
Membership(s): Association of Film Commissioners International

Morro Bay Chamber of Commerce & Business Center
695 Harbor St, Morro Bay, CA 93442
Tel: 805-772-4467 *Toll Free Tel:* 800-231-0592
Web Site: www.morrobay.org
Key Personnel
CEO: Craig Schmidt *E-mail:* craigschmidt@morrobay.org

Calaveras County Film Commission
183 Three "M" Lane, Mountain Ranch, CA 95246
Mailing Address: PO Box 1, Mountain Ranch, CA 95246-0001
Tel: 209-754-3053
Key Personnel
Chmn: Marge Mobley
Assist film, TV & other media in completing location shoots. Specialize in commercials.

Madera County Film Commission
PO Box 3690, Oakhurst, CA 93644
Tel: 559-760-1143 *Fax:* 559-658-2851
Web Site: www.yosemite-sierra.com; www.filmcalifornia.com/yosemite.html
Key Personnel
Film Commissioner: Dave Wolin *E-mail:* davewolin@earthlink.net
Location scouting, permits, security, lodging.

Oakland Film Office
One Frank H Ogawa Plaza, 9th fl, Oakland, CA 94612-1406
Tel: 510-238-4734 *Fax:* 510-238-6149
E-mail: filmoakland@filmoakland.com
Web Site: www.filmoakland.com
Key Personnel
Film Coord: Jim MacIlvaine
Act as a liaison between film companies & city; provide assistance with locations & approval processes.

Ojai Valley Chamber of Commerce
206 N Signal St, Suite P, Ojai, CA 93023
Mailing Address: PO Box 1134, Ojai, CA 93024-1134
Tel: 805-646-8126 *Fax:* 805-646-9762
E-mail: info@ojaichamber.org
Web Site: www.ojaichamber.org
Key Personnel
CEO & Dir: Scott Eicher
Provide tourist info, promote trade.

Palmdale Chamber of Commerce
817 E Avenue Q-9, Palmdale, CA 93550
Tel: 661-273-3232 *Fax:* 661-273-8508
E-mail: chamberstaff@palmdalechamber.org
Web Site: www.palmdalechamber.org
Key Personnel
CEO: Jeff McElfresh *E-mail:* jmcelfresh@palmdalechamber.org
Founded: 1941
To promote, develop & service business, industry & community.
Number of Members: 420

El Dorado Lake Tahoe Film & Media Office
Division of The El Dorado County Chamber of Commerce
542 Main St, Placerville, CA 95667
Tel: 530-626-4400 *Toll Free Tel:* 800-457-6279 *Fax:* 530-642-1624
E-mail: film@eldoradocounty.org
Web Site: filmtahoe.com
Key Personnel
Exec Dir: Kathleen Dodge
Free maps, scouting, location photo library, permits, crew & service referrals; key locations: South Lake Tahoe, Placerville, Apple Hill, Wineries, The American River.
Membership(s): Association of Film Commissioners International; FLIC

Shasta County Film Commission
Subsidiary of Redding Convention & Visitors Bureau
2334 Washington Ave, Suite B, Redding, CA 96001
Tel: 530-225-4103 *Toll Free Tel:* 800-874-7562 *Fax:* 530-225-4354
Web Site: www.visitredding.org/film
Key Personnel
CEO: Laurie Baker *Tel:* 530-225-4485 *E-mail:* laurie@shastacascade.org
Mktg Dir: Krista Buckel *E-mail:* krista@visitredding.com
Founded: 1986
Location scout-resource files & permits.
Membership(s): Association of Film Commissioners International; California Film Commission

Ridgecrest Film Commission
634 N China Lake Blvd, Suite C, Ridgecrest, CA 93555
Mailing Address: PO Box 1838, Ridgecrest, CA 93556
Tel: 760-375-8202 *Toll Free Tel:* 800-847-4830 *Fax:* 760-375-9850
E-mail: racvb@filmdeserts.com
Web Site: www.filmdeserts.com
Key Personnel
Film Commissioner: Doug Lueck
Founded: 1992
Facilitation of film locations; specialize in deserts, small towns, unique geological formations & 360 degrees unobstructed panoramas.

Sacramento Film Commission
1608 "I" St, Sacramento, CA 95814-2042
Tel: 916-808-7777 *Fax:* 916-808-7788
Web Site: www.filmsacramento.com

Key Personnel
Film Commissioner: Lucy Steffens *Tel:* 916-808-5553 *E-mail:* lsteffens@visitsacramento.com
Membership(s): Association of Film Commissioners International; Film Liaisons in California Statewide

Inland Empire Film Commission (IEFC)
Division of Inland Empire Economic Partnership (IEEP)
1601 E Third St, Suite 102, San Bernardino, CA 92408
Fax: 909-382-6060
E-mail: info@filminlandempire.com
Web Site: www.filminlandempire.com
Key Personnel
Dir: Sheri Davis *Tel:* 951-377-7849 (cell) *E-mail:* sheridavis@filminlandempire.com
Deputy Dir: Dan Taylor *Tel:* 951-232-1271 (cell) *E-mail:* dantaylor@filminlandempire.com
Film commission representing Riverside & San Bernardino Counties including the City of Big Bear Lakes & the Palm Spring Desert Resort area. Free scouting, location photos, permit assistance, service/supply directory & information "hot-line" service 24/7. Permits for the unincorporated areas of Riverside & San Bernardino Counties. US Forest Service permits for the San Bernardino Mountains & Bureau of Land Management permits for the Barstow Field Office & permits for US Forest Service in Idyllwild, San Jacinto Mountains & Lytle Creek.
Branch Office(s)
3111 Taquitz Canyon Dr, Suite 140, Palm Springs, CA 92264, Aide: Marc Hlavaty *Tel:* 909-553-6881 *E-mail:* lizard.m@verizon.net *Web Site:* www.palmspringsfilm.com
Membership(s): Film Liaisons in California Statewide

San Francisco Film Commission
City Hall, Rm 473, One Dr Carlton B Goodlett Place, San Francisco, CA 94102-4649
Tel: 415-554-6241 *Fax:* 415-554-6503
E-mail: film@sfgov.org
Web Site: www.filmsf.org
Key Personnel
Pres: Marlene Sharon Saritzky
VP: Denise Bradley
Exec Dir: Susannah Greason Robbins
Filming Coord: Maggie Weiland
Arrange permits for filming on city streets; provide information for local film industry; location photo file.

San Jose Film & Video Commission
c/o San Jose Convention & Visitors Bureau, 408 Almaden Blvd, San Jose, CA 95110
Tel: 408-295-9600 *Toll Free Tel:* 800-SAN-JOSE (726-5673)
Web Site: www.sanjose.org/film
Key Personnel
Dir, Event Opers: Julie Davis-Petit *Tel:* 408-792-4554 *E-mail:* jdavispetit@sanjose.org
Location assistance for production companies, information on permits & services for production in the San Jose/Silicon Valley area.

San Luis Obispo County Film Commission
Affiliate of Visit San Luis Obispo County
811 El Capitan, Suite 200, San Luis Obispo, CA 93401
Tel: 805-541-8000 *Fax:* 805-543-9498
Web Site: www.sanluisobispocounty.com
Key Personnel
Exec Dir: Stacie Jacob *E-mail:* stacie@sanluisobispocounty.com
Event Dir: Faith Wells *E-mail:* faith@sanluisobispocounty.com
Serve as liaison between film & TV companies & the county.

Santa Barbara County Film Commission
500 E Montecito St, Santa Barbara, CA 93103
Tel: 805-966-9222 *Toll Free Tel:* 800-676-1266 *Fax:* 805-966-1728
Web Site: www.filmsantabarbara.com
Key Personnel
County Film Commissioner: Geoff Alexander *Tel:* 805-966-9222 ext 110 *E-mail:* geoff@filmsantabarbara.com
Promotions & referrals to assist film companies filming in the county.

Santa Clarita Film Office
23920 Valencia Blvd, Suite 100, Santa Clarita, CA 91355
Tel: 661-284-1425 *Fax:* 661-286-4001
E-mail: film@santa-clarita.com
Web Site: www.filmsantaclarita.com
Key Personnel
Film Permit Specialist: Jennifer Jzyk

Sonoma County Film Office
Division of Sonoma County Economic Development Board
141 Stony Circle, Suite 110, Santa Rosa, CA 95401-4154
Tel: 707-565-7170 *Fax:* 707-565-7231
E-mail: film@sonoma-county.org
Web Site: www.sonoma-county.org/film
Key Personnel
Dir, Sonoma County Economic Development Board: Ben Stone
Film Liaison: Colette Thomas
Free & prompt film services, including location information, permits, accommodations, recommendations & local industry personnel referrals.
Membership(s): Film Liaisons in California Statewide

Sonoma Valley Chamber of Commerce
651-A Broadway, Sonoma, CA 95476-7041
Tel: 707-996-1033 *Fax:* 707-996-9402
E-mail: info@sonomachamber.com
Web Site: sonomachamber.org
Key Personnel
CEO: Jennifer Yankovich
Exec Membership & Admin Asst: Angela Beran
Founded: 1909
Promote better business in Sonoma Valley. Provide local coordination with the Sonoma County Convention & Visitors Bureau Film/Video Commission.

Tuolumne County Film Commission
542 W Stockton St, Sonora, CA 95370
Tel: 209-533-4420 *Toll Free Tel:* 800-446-1333 *Fax:* 209-532-2502
E-mail: info@tcfilm.org
Web Site: www.tcfilm.org
Key Personnel
Exec Dir: Lisa Mayo
Founded: 1991
Film information & services to the film & television industry; scout locations, film permits.
Membership(s): Association of Film Commissioners International; FLIC

Stockton/San Joaquin Film Liaison
Division of Stockton Convention & Visitors Bureau
125 Bridge Place, Stockton, CA 95202
Mailing Address: PO Box 2336, Stockton, CA 95201
Tel: 209-938-1555 *Toll Free Tel:* 877-778-6258 *Fax:* 209-938-1554
Web Site: visitstockton.org/footer/resources/stockton-film-commission
Key Personnel
CEO: Wes Rhea *E-mail:* wes@visitstockton.org
Location scouting, logistics & casting services offered to film, television & commercial industry.

Santa Monica Mountains NRA
401 W Hillcrest Dr, Thousand Oaks, CA 91360
Tel: 805-370-2301 *Fax:* 805-370-2351
Web Site: www.nps.gov/samo
Founded: 1978
Film permits, locations.

Vallejo/Solano County Film Office
289 Mare Island Way, Vallejo, CA 94590
Tel: 707-642-3653 *Toll Free Tel:* 800-4-VALLEJO (482-5535) *Fax:* 707-644-2206
Web Site: www.visitvallejo.com/film-office
Key Personnel
Communs/Film: Jim Reikowsky *E-mail:* jim@visitvallejo.com
Founded: 1996
Maintain photo library, assist location managers facilitate photo shoots (movies, commercials, still) & facilitate permit issuing.
Membership(s): Association of Film Commissioners International; Film Liaisons in California Statewide

City of West Hollywood Film Office
8300 Santa Monica Blvd, West Hollywood, CA 90069-6216
Tel: 323-848-6489 *Fax:* 323-848-6561
E-mail: wehofilm@weho.org/film
Web Site: www.weho.org/film
Key Personnel
Film Liaison: Eddie Robinson *E-mail:* erobinson@weho.org
Founded: 1985
Film location permitting for West Hollywood.

COLORADO

Boulder County Film Commission
Affiliate of Colorado Film Commission
2440 Pearl St, Boulder, CO 80302
Tel: 303-442-2911; 303-938-2066 *Toll Free Tel:* 800-444-0447 *Fax:* 303-938-2098
Web Site: www.bouldercoloradousa.com/film
Key Personnel
Communs Mgr: Kim Farin *E-mail:* kim.farin@bouldercvb.com
A resource & referral organization for filming in Boulder County & assistance with production companies in finding locations & permits.

Fremont/Custer County Film Commission
403 Royal Gorge Blvd, Canon City, CO 81212
Tel: 719-275-2331 *Toll Free Tel:* 800-876-7922 *Fax:* 719-275-2332
E-mail: chamber@canoncity.com
Web Site: www.canoncitychamber.com
Provide local scouting & production assistance.

Colorado Springs Film Commission
515 S Cascade Ave, Colorado Springs, CO 80903
Tel: 719-685-7637 *Toll Free Tel:* 800-888-4748 (ext 137) *Fax:* 719-635-4968
Web Site: www.filmcoloradosprings.com
Key Personnel
Film Liaison & Mktg Coord: Denise Noble *E-mail:* Denise@VisitCOS.com
Founded: 1989
Location scouting assistance, location photo inventory, reference information for Colorado Springs region film industry resources; permit info/assistance.
Membership(s): Association of Film Commissioners International; Colorado Film & Video Association

Colorado Office of Film, Television & Media
Division of Colorado Office of Economic Development & International Trade

1625 Broadway, Suite 2700, Denver, CO 80202
Tel: 303-892-3840 *Fax:* 303-892-3848
E-mail: info@coloradofilm.org
Web Site: www.coloradofilm.org
Key Personnel
State Film Commissioner: Donald Zuckerman
E-mail: donald.zuckerman@state.co.us
Deputy State Film Commissioner: Lauren Grimshaw Sloan *E-mail:* lauren.sloan@state.co.us
Full service film commission.
Membership(s): Colorado Film & Video Association

The Denver Office of Economic Development
Wellington E Webb Municipal Bldg, 2nd fl, 201 W Colfax Ave, Dept 1005, Denver, CO 80202
Tel: 720-913-1999 *Fax:* 720-913-1802
E-mail: oed@denvergov.org
Web Site: www.milehigh.com
Key Personnel
Exec Dir: Paul Washington
Deputy Dir: John Lucero
Government services.

Estes Park Film Commission
Subsidiary of Visit Estes Park
1200 Graves Ave, Estes Park, CO 80517
Mailing Address: PO Box 4426, Estes Park, CO 80517
Tel: 970-586-0500 *Fax:* 970-586-4036
Key Personnel
Film Commission Rep: Suzy Blackhurst
E-mail: sblackhurst@visitestespark.com
Film liaison to assist producers when looking for commercial, film & still shooting in Estes Park, CO area.
Membership(s): Colorado Film Commission

Greeley/Weld Film Commission
902 Seventh Ave, Greeley, CO 80631
Tel: 970-352-3567 *Toll Free Tel:* 800-449-3866 *Fax:* 970-352-3572
E-mail: info@greeleycvb.com
Web Site: www.greeleychamber.com
Key Personnel
Visit Greeley Dir: LeeAnn Sterling
E-mail: leeann@visitgreeley.org
Respond to inquiries about film production in the Greeley area.

City of Montrose Office of Business & Tourism
107 S Cascade Ave, Montrose, CO 81401
Tel: 970-497-8558 *Toll Free Tel:* 855-497-8558
Web Site: www.visitmontrose.com
Assists in all areas for film making.

Montrose Association of Commerce & Tourism, see City of Montrose Office of Business & Tourism

Northwest Colorado Film Commission
125 Anglers Dr, Steamboat Springs, CO 80487
Mailing Address: PO Box 774408, Steamboat Springs, CO 80477
Tel: 970-879-0880 *Fax:* 970-285-3550
E-mail: info@steamboatchamber.com; media@steamboatchamber.com
Web Site: www.steamboat-chamber.com
Key Personnel
PR Mgr: Michelle Krasilinec *Tel:* 970-875-7009
E-mail: michelle@steamboatchamber.com
Assistance with film locations & support services, talent & crew in Northwest Colorado.

Trinidad Film Commission
136 W Main St, Trinidad, CO 81082
Tel: 719-846-7324 *Toll Free Tel:* 866-480-4750 *Fax:* 719-846-3545
Web Site: www.trinidadchamber.com
Key Personnel
CEO & Exec Dir: Kim Schultz *Tel:* 719-846-9285
Film Liaison & Contact: Joe Tarabino
E-mail: inedludd@gmail.com
Scouting aid, location guide, prop searches, housing & location detailed information.

CONNECTICUT

Connecticut Office of Film, Television & Digital Media
c/o Dept of Economic & Community Development, 505 Hudson St, Hartford, CT 06106
Tel: 860-270-8198
Web Site: www.ctfilm.com
Key Personnel
Dir: George Norfleet *E-mail:* george.norfleet@ct.gov
Location Servs: Mark Dixon *Tel:* 860-270-8218
E-mail: mark.dixon@ct.gov
Film & Tax Credit Admin: Ed Ruggiero *Tel:* 860-270-8211 *E-mail:* ed.ruggiero@ct.gov
Prodn Servs: Ellen Woolf *E-mail:* ellen.woolf@ct.gov
State film & television commission.
Membership(s): Association of Film Commissioners International

Western Connecticut Convention & Visitors Bureau
PO Box 968, Litchfield, CT 06759-0968
Tel: 860-567-4506 *Toll Free Tel:* 800-663-1273 *Fax:* 860-567-5214
E-mail: info@litchfieldhills.com
Web Site: www.visitwesternct.com; www.litchfieldhills.com; www.visitfairfieldcountyct.com
Key Personnel
Co-Exec Dir: Janet Serra *E-mail:* lhcvbnwct@aol.com; Jim Whitney *E-mail:* jim@northwestct.com
Assist with locations in 51 towns of northwest Connecticut.
Number of Members: 500
Branch Office(s)
116 Bank St, Waterbury, CT 06702, Co-Dir: Jim Whitney *Toll Free Tel:* 800-588-2880

City of Stamford
888 Washington Blvd, Stamford, CT 06901
Tel: 203-977-5858 *Fax:* 203-977-5545
Web Site: www.cityofstamford.org
Key Personnel
Supv: Frank Fedeli
All city services.

DELAWARE

Delaware Tourism Office
99 Kings Hwy, Dover, DE 19901
Tel: 302-739-4271 *Toll Free Tel:* 866-284-7483 *Fax:* 302-739-5749
Web Site: www.visitdelaware.com
Key Personnel
Dir, Tourism Off: Linda Parkowski
Mktg Dir: Eric Ruth *Tel:* 302-672-6813
Services arranged on an individual basis. Film services information available.

DISTRICT OF COLUMBIA

District of Columbia Office of Motion Picture & TV Development
200 "I" St SE, Suite 1800, Washington, DC 20003
Tel: 202-727-6608 *Fax:* 202-727-3246
E-mail: film@dc.gov
Web Site: www.film.dc.gov
Key Personnel
Dir: Pierre Bagley
Initiates & manages operations & logistics of film production in the district through permitting, networking, scouting & workforce development.
Number of Members: 6

FLORIDA

Central Florida Visitors & Convention Bureau
2701 Lake Myrtle Park Rd, Auburndale, FL 33823-9360
Tel: 863-551-4750 *Toll Free Tel:* 800-828-7655 *Fax:* 863-551-4740
Web Site: www.visitcentralflorida.org
Key Personnel
Sales & Event Rep: Carol DeHaven *Tel:* 863-551-4709 *E-mail:* carol@visitcentralflorida.org
Provide one-stop permitting, preliminary scouting & liaison services.

Polk County Film Office, see Central Florida Visitors & Convention Bureau

Space Coast Film Commission
430 Brevard Ave, Suite 150, Cocoa Village, FL 32922
Tel: 321-433-4470 *Toll Free Tel:* 877-57-BEACH (572-3224) *Fax:* 321-433-4476
Web Site: www.visitspacecoast.com/space-coast-film-commission
Key Personnel
Film Commissioner: Bonnie King
E-mail: bkingfilm@aol.com
Provide varied locations: beaches, wildlife refuge, unique architecture, lakes & the Kennedy Space Center; Port Canaveral Cruise Ships.

Daytona Beach Area Film Office, see Team Volusia Economic Development Corp

Team Volusia Economic Development Corp
One Daytona Blvd, Suite 240, Daytona Beach, FL 32114
Tel: 386-255-6332
E-mail: dmott@tvedc.com
Web Site: tvedc.com
Conduit for film & motion picture inquiries.

Greater Fort Lauderdale/Broward Office of Film & Entertainment
110 E Broward, Suite 1990, Fort Lauderdale, FL 33301
Tel: 954-524-3113 *Toll Free Tel:* 800-741-1420 *Fax:* 954-524-3167
E-mail: info@browardalliance.org
Web Site: www.browardalliance.org/film; www.sunny.org
Key Personnel
Dir, Film Commission: Noelle Stevenson
Tel: 954-767-2440 *E-mail:* nstevenson@broward.org
Encourage companies to work in the Broward County/Fort Lauderdale area & serve as resource & liaison between production companies & the community.

Emerald Coast Film Commission
PO Box 609, Fort Walton Beach, FL 32549-0609
Tel: 850-651-7644 *Fax:* 850-651-7149
E-mail: emeraldfilm@co.okaloosa.fl.us
Web Site: filmemeraldcoast.com
Founded: 1996
Pre-scouting, on location support, production guide & talent, casting assistance & location library.
Membership(s): Association of Film Commissioners International

Jacksonville Office of Economic Development, Film & Television Office
117 W Duval St, Suite 280, Jacksonville, FL 32202
Tel: 904-630-2522 *Fax:* 904-630-3693
Web Site: www.filmjax.com
Key Personnel
Dir: Todd Roobin *E-mail:* troobin@coj.net
Location scouting, location photos & permits.

Florida Keys & Key West Film Commission
Division of Monroe County Tourist Development Council
1201 White St, Suite 102, Key West, FL 33040
Tel: 305-293-1800 *Toll Free Tel:* 800-FILM-KEYS (345-6539) *Fax:* 305-296-0788
Web Site: www.filmkeys.com
Key Personnel
Film Commissioner: Rita Brown *E-mail:* rita@filmkeys.com
Provide location scouting, permits, assistance in accomodations & any other services that would assist in film production in Monroe County.

St Petersburg/Clearwater Film Commission
8200 Bryan Dairy Rd, Suite 200, Largo, FL 33777
Tel: 727-464-7241 *Toll Free Tel:* 877-352-3224
E-mail: info@filmspc.com
Web Site: www.filmspc.com
Key Personnel
Film Commissioner: Tony Armer *Tel:* 727-464-7240
Marketing Pinellas County, FL to film, television & commercial producers & to provide liaison assistance to local governments & services for companies on location.
Membership(s): Association of Film Commissioners International; Film Florida; Media Professionals of Florida Inc; Women in Film & TV-FL

Miami-Dade Office of Film & Entertainment
111 NW First St, Suite 2200, Miami, FL 33128
Tel: 305-375-3288 *Fax:* 305-375-3266
E-mail: filmoffice@miamigov.com
Web Site: www.filmiami.org
Key Personnel
Film Commissioner: Sandy Lighterman *E-mail:* sandyl@miamidade.gov
Permit Coord & Digital Info Specialist: Dee Belz *E-mail:* dbelz@miamidade.gov
Issue permits for filming or photography. Coordinate use of public properties for film, video, photo use. Provide information on personnel, goods & services available.

The Paradise Coast Film Commission
755 Eighth Ave S, Naples, FL 34102
Tel: 239-659-FILM (659-3456) *Fax:* 239-213-3053
Web Site: www.shootinparadise.com
Key Personnel
Film Commission Dir: Maggie McCarty *E-mail:* maggie@shootinparadise.com
Film liaison for Naples, Collier County. Facilitates permits, free location scouting, sales tax rebate. Sub-tropical climate, white sand beaches on the Florida Gulf Coast. Full service film commission.

Ocala/Marion County Chamber of Commerce
310 SE Third St, Ocala, FL 34471
Tel: 352-629-8051 *Fax:* 352-629-7651
Web Site: www.ocalacc.com
Key Personnel
CEO & Pres: Kevin Sheilley
Founded: 1887

Metro Orlando Film Commission
Division of Metro Orlando Economic Development Commission
301 E Pine St, Suite 900, Orlando, FL 32801
Tel: 407-422-7159 *Fax:* 407-425-6428
E-mail: info@filmorlando.com
Web Site: www.filmorlando.com
Key Personnel
Film Commissioner: Sheena Fowler *E-mail:* sheena@filmorlando.com
Assoc Dir: Amy Nettles *E-mail:* amy@filmorlando.com
Media: Jennifer Wakefield *E-mail:* jennifer.wakefield@orlandoedc.com
Full service film commission; film permitting; location assistance.

Manatee County Film Commission
One Haben Blvd, Palmetto, FL 34221
Mailing Address: PO Box 1000, Bradenton, FL 34206-1000
Tel: 941-729-9177 *Toll Free Tel:* 800-822-2017 *Fax:* 941-729-1820
Web Site: www.bradentongulfislands.com
Key Personnel
Film Commissioner: Debbie Meihls *Tel:* 941-545-4424 *E-mail:* debbie.meihls@bacvb.com
Film Liaison: Kelly Klotz *Tel:* 941-729-9177 ext 233 *E-mail:* kelly.klotz@bacvb.com
Film Asst: Monica Luff *Tel:* 941-729-9177 ext 231 *E-mail:* monica.luff@bacvb.com

Film Liaison of Escambia County
Division of Greater Pensacola Chamber
1401 E Gregory St, Pensacola, FL 32501
Tel: 850-390-3974 *Toll Free Tel:* 800-874-1234
Web Site: filmnorthflorida.com
Key Personnel
Film Liaison: Tom Roush *E-mail:* tom@filmnorthflorida.com
Founded: 1983
Marketing organization for Pensacola, Pensacola Beach, Perdido Key & Gulf Breeze.
Number of Members: 204

City of Port St Lucie Community Relations/Film Office
121 SW Port St Lucie Blvd, Bldg A, 1st fl, Rm 145, Port St Lucie, FL 34984
Tel: 772-871-5219 *Fax:* 772-344-4111
E-mail: info@cityofpsl.com
Web Site: www.cityofpsl.com
Key Personnel
Communs Dir: Edward Cunningham

Sarasota County Film & Entertainment Office
1680 Fruitville Rd, Suite 402, Sarasota, FL 34236
Tel: 941-309-1200 *Fax:* 941-309-1209
E-mail: info@filmsarasota.com
Web Site: www.filmsarasota.com
Key Personnel
Dir: Jeanne Corcoran *E-mail:* jeanne@filmsarasota.com
Liaison between production companies & the community; assist with locations, permitting, talent & technical support; resource guide is available at no cost to production companies.

St Augustine, Ponte Vedra & The Beaches Visitors and Convention Bureau
29 Old Mission Ave, St Augustine, FL 32084
Tel: 904-829-1711 *Toll Free Tel:* 800-653-2489
Web Site: www.floridashistoriccoast.com
Key Personnel
Communs Dir: Kathryn Catron *Tel:* 904-209-4424 *E-mail:* kcatron@floridashistoriccoast.com
Communs Mgr: Barbara Golden *Tel:* 904-209-4425 *E-mail:* bgolden@floridashistoriccoast.com
Founded: 1996
Film liaison office, assists with location & scouting.

The Florida Office of Film & Entertainment
Division of Florida Department of Economic Opportunity
107 E Madison St, MSC 80, Tallahassee, FL 32399
Tel: 850-717-8990; 818-508-7772 *Toll Free Tel:* 877-FLA-FILM (352-3456) *Fax:* 850-410-4770
Web Site: www.filminflorida.com
Key Personnel
Interim State Film Commissioner: Niki Welge *E-mail:* niki.welge@deo.myflorida.com
Communs Coord: Colleen McClure
State of Florida's economic development program for the advancement & expansion of the motion picture, digital media & entertainment industry sectors.

Tampa Bay Film Commission
401 E Jackson St, Suite 2100, Tampa, FL 33602
Tel: 813-223-1111 (ext 4058) *Toll Free Tel:* 800-826-8358 *Fax:* 813-218-3328
Web Site: www.filmtampabay.com
Key Personnel
Film Commission Mgr: Alex Acosta *E-mail:* aacosta@visittampabay.com
One-stop free permitting for location filming; use of location library & production resource crew listings; support throughout entire production schedule; familiarization tours; great working relationship with Governor's office of film; work with local government officials.
Membership(s): Association of Film Commissioners International

Palm Beach County Film & Television Commission
1555 Palm Beach Lakes Blvd, Suite 900, West Palm Beach, FL 33401
Tel: 561-233-1000 *Toll Free Tel:* 800-745-FILM (745-3456) *Fax:* 561-233-3113
Web Site: www.pbfilm.com
Key Personnel
Film Commissioner: Chuck Elderd *E-mail:* celderd@pbfilm.com
Deputy Film Commissioner: Michelle Hillery *E-mail:* mhillery@pbfilm.com
Founded: 1989
Palm Beach County offers an all-inclusive invitation to film in a world-class destination that features a film-friendly community, year-round warm weather, diverse locations & free production space. Take advantage of uncharted hot spots, ambitious crews & a film commission that will go the distance to guarantee your satisfaction. Go beyond your set & explore all that Palm Beach County has to offer.

GEORGIA

Georgia Film, Music & Digital Entertainment Office
75 Fifth St W, Suite 1200, Atlanta, GA 30308
Tel: 404-962-4052 *Toll Free Tel:* 877-SHOOTGA (746-6842) *Fax:* 404-962-4053
E-mail: film@georgia.org
Web Site: www.georgia.org
Key Personnel
Div Dir: Lee Thomas *Tel:* 404-962-4048 *E-mail:* lthomas@georgia.org
Dir, Music Mktg & Devt: Lisa Love *Tel:* 404-962-4051 *E-mail:* llove@georgia.org
Mktg & Budget Proj Mgr: Alison Fibben *Tel:* 404-962-4050 *E-mail:* afibben@georgia.org
Founded: 1973
Location scouting, pre-production & production assistance (including securing housing, crew & transportation needs).

City of Savannah Film Office
One Waring Dr, Savannah, GA 31404

Mailing Address: PO Box 1027, Savannah, GA 31402
Tel: 912-651-2360 *Fax:* 912-651-0982
E-mail: info@savannahfilm.org
Web Site: www.savannahfilm.org
Key Personnel
Film Servs Dir: William P Hammagren
E-mail: whammagren@savannahga.org
Founded: 1994
Full service, professionally staffed & certified film commission. We promote & enable all types of media production in the Savannah area, including permitting, location assistance & assistance in coordinating with local crew & services. The Savannah area boasts a wealth of locations including the nation's largest historical district, an evergreen urban forest & unique coastal & rural settings. The commission will assist those wanting to utilize the natural beauty of Savannah in their next project.

HAWAII

Big Island Film Office
25 Aupuni St, Hilo, HI 96720
Tel: 808-961-8369 *Fax:* 808-935-1205
E-mail: film@filmbigisland.com
Web Site: www.filmbigisland.com
Key Personnel
Film Commissioner: T. Ilihia Gionson
E-mail: film@filmbigisland.com
Founded: 1995
Business commission.

Honolulu Film Office
530 S King St, Rm 306, Honolulu, HI 96813
Tel: 808-768-6108 *Fax:* 808-768-6102
E-mail: info@filmhonolulu.com
Web Site: www.filmhonolulu.com
Key Personnel
Film Commissioner: Walea L Constantinau
Location photographs-free of charge; permit information; islandwide resources information; liaison to city & county agencies including fire department, police department, parks, streets & others in Honolulu & on Oahu.

State of Hawaii Film Office
Affiliate of Department of Business, Economic Development & Tourism
250 S Hotel St, Suite 510-A, Honolulu, HI 96813
Mailing Address: PO Box 2359, Honolulu, HI 96804
Tel: 808-586-2570 *Fax:* 808-586-2572
E-mail: info@hawaiifilmoffice.com
Web Site: www.filmoffice.hawaii.gov
Key Personnel
Chief Offr, Creative Industries Div: Georja Skinner
State Film Commissioner: Donne Dawson
Founded: 1978
Coordinate film permits for filmmakers seeking to use state property; promote local film industry; refer production resources & provide general project assistance to filmmakers.

Maui County Film Office
Off of Economic Devt, One Main Plaza, 2200 S Main St, Suite 305, Wailuku, HI 96793
Tel: 808-270-7710 *Fax:* 808-270-7995
Web Site: www.co.maui.hi.us
Key Personnel
Head: Tracy Bennett *E-mail:* tracy.bennett@mauicounty.gov
Founded: 1993
Permitting, location scouting, production services & accommodations.

IDAHO

Idaho Film Office
Affiliate of Idaho Department of Commerce
700 W State St, Boise, ID 83702
Mailing Address: PO Box 83720, Boise, ID 83720-0093
Tel: 208-334-2470 *Toll Free Tel:* 800-942-8338 *Fax:* 208-334-2631
Web Site: www.filmidaho.com
Key Personnel
Film Mgr: Peg Owens *E-mail:* peg.owens@tourism.idaho.gov
Mgr, Tourism: Diane Norton *E-mail:* diane.norton@tourism.idaho.gov
Provide assistance for location scouting, pre-production & production assistance.

ILLINOIS

Chicago Film Office
Division of City of Chicago Department of Cultural Affairs & Special Events
Chicago Cultural Center, 78 E Washington, Rm 108, Chicago, IL 60602
Tel: 312-744-6415 *Fax:* 312-744-1378
E-mail: filmoffice@cityofchicago.org
Web Site: www.cityofchicago.org/city/en/depts/dca/provdrs/chicago_film_office.html
Key Personnel
Dir: Richard Moskal *E-mail:* rmoskal@cityofchicago.org
Founded: 1980
Coordinates all production for film making in the city; agents & liaisons.

Illinois Film Office
Affiliate of Dept of Commerce & Economic Opportunity
James R Thompson Ctr, Suite 3-400, 100 W Randolph, Chicago, IL 60601
Tel: 312-814-3600 *Fax:* 312-814-8874
E-mail: film@illinois.gov
Web Site: www.illinoisfilm.biz
Key Personnel
Mng Dir: Betsy Steinberg
Services include location scouting; obtaining permits & clearances; acting as liaison between individuals, communities, state & local governments.

INDIANA

Film Indiana
Affiliate of Indiana Economic Development Corp (IEDC)
One N Capitol, Suite 700, Indianapolis, IN 46204-2288
Tel: 317-234-2087 *Fax:* 317-232-4146
E-mail: filminfo@iedc.in.gov
Web Site: www.filmindiana.com
Key Personnel
Dir: Erin Newell Schneider
Scout film locations; establish liaison with film companies & the communities in which they work; help contact local crew & production companies.

IOWA

Quad Cities First
Affiliate of Quad Cities Chamber of Commerce
130 W Second St, Davenport, IA 52801
Tel: 563-326-1005
Web Site: www.quadcitiesfirst.com
Key Personnel
Pres: Bill Martin *Tel:* 563-884-7889
E-mail: bmartin@quadcitiesfirst.com
Founded: 2009 (successor to Quad City Development Group)
Film coalition group, location information, liaisons.

Dubuque Convention & Visitors Bureau
300 Main St, Suite 200, Dubuque, IA 52001
Tel: 563-557-9200 *Fax:* 563-557-1591
E-mail: office@dubuquechamber.com
Web Site: www.dubuquechamber.com
Key Personnel
Pres: Keith Rahe
Develop & implement plans to promote the Dubuque area as a convention & tourist destination.

KANSAS

Lawrence Convention & Visitors Bureau
402 N Second St, Lawrence, KS 66044
Mailing Address: PO Box 526, Lawrence, KS 66044
Tel: 785-856-3040; 785-856-5282 *Fax:* 785-856-5303
E-mail: visinfo@visitlawrence.com
Web Site: www.visitlawrence.com
Key Personnel
Mgr: Debbie McCarthy
Asst Mgr: Keith Manies
Communs Mgr: Christine Metz Howard
Marketing service for convention, convention sales & group tours, help visiting production companies find proper locations.

Manhattan Film Commission
Affiliate of Manhattan CVB
501 Poyntz Ave, Manhattan, KS 66502
Tel: 785-776-8829 *Toll Free Tel:* 800-759-0134 *Fax:* 785-776-0679
E-mail: cvb@manhattan.org
Web Site: www.manhattancvb.org
Key Personnel
Manhattan CVB Dir: Karen Hibbard
E-mail: karen@manhattan.org
Assistance with location & scouting.

Salina Film Commission
120 W Ash St, Salina, KS 67402
Tel: 785-827-9301 *Fax:* 785-827-9758
E-mail: info@salinakansas.org
Web Site: www.salinakansas.org
Key Personnel
SVP: Don Weiser
Dir, Visit Salina: Sylvia Rice *E-mail:* srice@salinakansas.org
Founded: 1911
Supports the state film commission.

Kansas Film Commission
Affiliate of Kansas Dept of Commerce
1000 SW Jackson St, Suite 100, Topeka, KS 66612-1354
Tel: 785-296-2178 *Fax:* 785-296-3490
Web Site: www.filmkansas.com
Key Personnel
Dir: Peter Jasso *E-mail:* pjasso@kansascommerce.com
Offer location scouting assistance, liaison between communities & production companies as well as pre-production & production assistance. Publish *Kansas Production Guide*, listing Kansas crews, companies & important information regarding filming in Kansas.

Visit Topeka Inc
618 S Kansas Ave, Topeka, KS 66603
Tel: 785-234-1030 *Toll Free Tel:* 800-235-1030 *Fax:* 785-234-8282
E-mail: info@visittopeka.com
Web Site: www.visittopeka.com

Key Personnel
CEO & Pres: Terry Cook
Dir, Mktg: Shalyn Murphy
Coordinates with the Kansas Film Commission, film companies & hotels; provides service directory, cast, crews & materials; assists with permits within the city.

Greater Wichita Convention & Visitors Bureau/Wichita Film Commission
515 S Main St, Suite 115, Wichita, KS 67202
Tel: 316-265-2800 *Toll Free Tel:* 800-288-9424 *Fax:* 316-265-0162
Web Site: www.gowichita.com
Key Personnel
VP, Sales & Mktg: Maureen Hofrenning *E-mail:* mhofrenning@gowichita.com
Assists in all areas of film location & production, what to do, where to go, scouting, etc.

Wichita Film Commission, see Greater Wichita Convention & Visitors Bureau/Wichita Film Commission

KENTUCKY

Kentucky Film Office
Affiliate of Kentucky Commerce Cabinet
2200 Capital Plaza Tower, 500 Mero St, Frankfort, KY 40601
Tel: 502-564-3456 *Toll Free Tel:* 800-345-6591 *Fax:* 502-564-5695
E-mail: kentucky.filmoffice@ky.gov
Web Site: filmoffice.ky.gov
Key Personnel
Exec Dir: Mike Cooper *Tel:* 502-564-4930 *E-mail:* mike.cooper@ky.gov
Dir: M Todd Cassidy *Tel:* 502-564-8110 ext 154 *E-mail:* todd.cassidy@ky.gov
Provide free film permits & services during preproduction & production. Refund to film & national TV producers of sales tax spent on location. Location scouting. Low to non-existent location fees; no fees for filming on state property.

LOUISIANA

Louisiana Entertainment
Division of Louisiana Economic Development
Off of Entertainment Indus Devt, Capital Annex Bldg, 1051 N Third St, Baton Rouge, LA 70802
Mailing Address: PO Box 94185, Baton Rouge, LA 70804-9185
Tel: 225-342-5403 *Fax:* 225-342-5554
E-mail: led-entertainment@la.gov
Web Site: louisianaentertainment.gov
Key Personnel
Exec Dir: Christopher Stelly *E-mail:* chris.stelly@la.gov
Administers Louisiana's motion picture incentive program & facilitates filming in our state's communities.
Membership(s): Association of Film Commissioners International; The Broadway League

Jeff Davis Parish Tourist Commission
100 Rue de l'Acadie, Jennings, LA 70546
Tel: 337-821-5521 *Toll Free Tel:* 800-264-5521 *Fax:* 337-821-5536
Web Site: www.jeffdavis.org; www.louisianatravel.com
Key Personnel
Exec Dir: Marion Fox
Scouting & location work.

Monroe-West Monroe Convention & Visitors Bureau
601 Constitution Dr, West Monroe, LA 71292
Mailing Address: PO Box 1436, West Monroe, LA 71294-1436
Tel: 318-387-5691 *Toll Free Tel:* 800-843-1872 *Fax:* 318-324-1752
E-mail: mwmcvb@monroe-westmonroe.org
Web Site: www.monroe-westmonroe.org
Key Personnel
Exec Dir: Alana Cooper *E-mail:* acooper@monroe-westmonroe.org
Communs Dir: Sheila M Snow *E-mail:* ssnow@monroe-westmonroe.org
Responds to requests on film locations.

MAINE

Maine Film Office
Division of Maine Department of Economic & Community Development
59 State House Sta, Augusta, ME 04333
Tel: 207-624-9828 *Fax:* 207-287-8070
E-mail: film@maine.gov
Web Site: www.filminmaine.com
Key Personnel
Dir: Karen Carberry Warhola *E-mail:* karen.carberrywarhola@maine.gov
Founded: 1987
Promote & assist location filming.

MARYLAND

Baltimore Film Office
Division of Baltimore Office of Promotion & the Arts
10 E Baltimore St, 10th fl, Baltimore, MD 21202
Tel: 410-752-8632; 443-263-4313 *Fax:* 410-385-0361
Web Site: www.baltimorefilm.com
Key Personnel
Dir: Debbie Donaldson Dorsey *Tel:* 443-807-2220 (cell) *E-mail:* ddorsey@promotionandarts.com
Logistics Coord: Fran Carmen *Tel:* 443-807-7190 (cell) *E-mail:* fcarmen@promotionandarts.com
Assist production teams in finding locations, act as liaison between city agencies & film companies.

Maryland Film Office
Division of Maryland Department of Business & Economic Development
401 E Pratt St, 14th fl, Baltimore, MD 21202
Tel: 410-767-6340 *Toll Free Tel:* 800-333-6632 *Fax:* 410-333-0044
E-mail: filminfo@marylandfilm.org
Web Site: www.marylandfilm.org
Key Personnel
Dir, Film & Digital Media: Jack Gerbes *Tel:* 410-767-6343
Deputy Dir: Catherine Batavick *Tel:* 410-767-6313
Scout locations, offer information on caterers, hotels, equipment rentals; provide liaison with police, fire, medical, security; arrange 24-hour dailies & technical staff & talent for film, TV, commercial productions & features.

MASSACHUSETTS

Boston Film Bureau
One City Hall Sq, Rm 802, Boston, MA 02201-2029
Tel: 617-635-3911 *Fax:* 617-635-4428
E-mail: filmbureau@cityofboston.gov
Web Site: www.cityofboston.gov/arts/film
Key Personnel
Film Dir: Patricia Papa
Permits, film locations & assistance.

MICHIGAN

Film Detroit
Division of Detroit Metro Convention & Visitors Bureau
211 W Fort St, Suite 1000, Detroit, MI 48226
Tel: 313-202-1990 *Toll Free Tel:* 877-478-7883
Web Site: www.filmdetroit.com
Key Personnel
Dir, Bureau Servs, Detroit Metro Convention & Visitors Bureau: Harriet Carter *E-mail:* hcarter@visitdetroit.com
Natl Mgr: Karla Murray *E-mail:* kmurray@filmdetroit.com
Founded: 1993
Scouting, negotiations of all locations, arrangements for all city services & interface local crews with local producers.

Michigan Film Office
Affiliate of State of Michigan
300 N Washington Sq, 4th fl, Lansing, MI 48913
Tel: 517-373-3456 *Toll Free Tel:* 800-477-FILM (477-3456) *Fax:* 517-241-0867
E-mail: mfo@michigan.org
Web Site: www.michiganfilmoffice.org
Key Personnel
Dir: Margaret O'Riley
Sr Exec Mgmt Asst: Faith Goins *E-mail:* goinsf2@michigan.org
Founded: 1979
Assist & attract incoming production companies; promote the growth of indigenous industry; services include but are not limited to location scouting & photographs, government liaison, assistance with crew, equipment, talent, unions & anything reasonable.
Membership(s): Association of Film Commissioners International

Traverse City Convention & Visitors Bureau
101 W Grandview Pkwy, Traverse City, MI 49684
Tel: 231-947-1120 *Toll Free Tel:* 800-940-1120 *Fax:* 231-947-2621
Web Site: www.visittraversecity.com
Key Personnel
CEO & Pres: Brad Van Dommelen
Good airport accessibility & frequency, variety of accommodations. Site selection assistance; comprehensive proposals & site inspections, promotional materials, registration assistance & more. Media kits, slides.

MINNESOTA

Minneapolis Licenses & Consumer Services
350 S Fifth St, Rm 1C, Minneapolis, MN 55415-1391
Tel: 612-673-2080 *Fax:* 612-673-3399
Web Site: www.minneapolismn.gov/business-licensing
Key Personnel
Film & Video Coord: Craig Eliason *Tel:* 612-673-3370 *E-mail:* craig.eliason@minneapolismn.gov
Permits, information, referrals for filming in the City of Minneapolis.

Minnesota Film & TV
401 N Third St, Suite 245, Minneapolis, MN 55401
Tel: 612-767-0095 *Fax:* 612-767-2425
Web Site: www.mnfilmtv.org
Key Personnel
Exec Dir: Lucinda Winter *E-mail:* lucinda@mnfilmtv.org
Founded: 1981
Minnesota related research; state & local permit assistance; logistical planning; production personnel referrals; casting referrals; transportation arrangements; lodging & catering referrals;

equipment rental & purchase information; location search, photography & touring; publish Minnesota production guide.

Explore Minnesota Tourism
Affiliate of Audio/Visual Dept
Metro Sq, Suite 100, 121 E Seventh Place, St Paul, MN 55101-2112
Tel: 651-757-1870 *Toll Free Tel:* 800-657-3638 *Fax:* 651-296-7095
E-mail: explore@state.mn.us
Web Site: www.exploreminnesota.com
Key Personnel
Communs Mgr: Erica Wacker
Graphic Designer: Leslie Anderson *E-mail:* leslie.anderson@state.mn.us
Lending library of digital photo files.

MISSISSIPPI

Columbus Film Commission
117 Third St S, Columbus, MS 39701
Mailing Address: PO Box 789, Columbus, MS 39703-0789
Tel: 662-329-1191 *Toll Free Tel:* 800-327-2686 *Fax:* 662-329-8969
E-mail: ccvb@columbus-ms.org
Web Site: visitcolumbusms.org
Key Personnel
Exec Dir: Nancy Carpenter
Liaison for city, county & government; provides clearance & location assistance.

Greenwood Convention & Visitors Bureau & Film Commission
111 E Market St, Greenwood, MS 38935
Mailing Address: PO Drawer 739, Greenwood, MS 38935-0739
Tel: 662-453-9197 *Toll Free Tel:* 800-748-9064 *Fax:* 662-453-5526
E-mail: info@gcvb.com
Web Site: www.greenwoodms.org
Key Personnel
Exec Dir: Paige Hunt
Founded: 1989
Location assistance, government liaison.

Mississippi Film Office
501 N West St, Suite B-01, Jackson, MS 39201
Mailing Address: PO Box 849, Jackson, MS 39205-0849
Tel: 601-359-3297 *Fax:* 601-359-5048
Web Site: www.filmmississippi.org
Key Personnel
Mgr: Ward Emling *Tel:* 601-359-3422 *E-mail:* wemling@mississippi.org
Assoc Mgr: Nina Parikh
Off Coord: Betty Black
Founded: 1973
Location scouting & pre-production services, coordination of local casting. Acts as liaison between production & local/state government. New incentive program.
Membership(s): Association of Film Commissioners International

Natchez Film Commission
Division of Natchez Convention & Visitors Bureau
640 S Canal St, Box C, Natchez, MS 39120
Tel: 601-446-6345 *Toll Free Tel:* 800-647-6724 *Fax:* 601-442-0814
E-mail: info@visitnatchez.org
Web Site: www.visitnatchez.org
Key Personnel
Dir of Tourism: Connie Taunton *E-mail:* ctaunton@visitnatchez.com
Publicity & Promos Dir/Media Liaison: Sally Durkin *Tel:* 800-647-6724 ext 11 *E-mail:* sdurkin@visitnatchez.org
Assist film companies in finding locations, personnel & set design needs, work as a liaison between local people & film management.

Oxford Film Commission
415 S Lamar Blvd, Oxford, MS 38655
Tel: 662-232-2477 *Toll Free Tel:* 800-758-9177
E-mail: tourism@visitoxfordms.com
Web Site: visitoxfordms.com
Key Personnel
Dir: Mary-Kathryn Herrington *E-mail:* marykathryn@visitoxfordms.com
Outreach & Opers Mgr: Kinney Ferris *E-mail:* kinney@visitoxfordms.com
Tourism Mgr: Mary Allyn Hedges *E-mail:* maryallyn@visitoxfordms.com
Founded: 1988

Tupelo Film Commission
399 E Main St, Tupelo, MS 38804
Mailing Address: PO Drawer 47, Tupelo, MS 38802-0047
Tel: 662-841-6521 *Toll Free Tel:* 800-533-0611 *Fax:* 662-841-6558
E-mail: visittupelo@tupelo.net
Web Site: www.tupelo.net
Key Personnel
Commissioner: Pat Rasberry *E-mail:* prasberry@tupelo.net
Founded: 1989
Film location service.

MISSOURI

Cape Girardeau Convention & Visitors Bureau
400 Broadway St, Suite 100, Cape Girardeau, MO 63701
Tel: 573-335-1631 *Toll Free Tel:* 800-777-0068 *Fax:* 573-334-6702
E-mail: info@visitcape.com
Web Site: visitcape.com
Key Personnel
Exec Dir: Chuck Martin *E-mail:* cmartin@visitcape.com
PR Dir: Stacy Dohogne Lane *E-mail:* slane@visitcape.com
Sales Dir: Alyssa Lage *E-mail:* alage@visitcape.com
Admin Asst: Betty Roth *E-mail:* broth@visitcape.com
Mktg Asst: Margie Stull *E-mail:* mstull@visitcape.com
Founded: 1984
Help obtain permits needed to film on public property, to close streets +/or traffic control; secure accommodations for scouting & location personnel; provide pre-scouting for any necessary photos & related material; provide help to the production company in the event problems arise during their stay.
Membership(s): Missouri Association of Convention & Visitors Bureaus; Missouri Travel Council

Missouri Film Commission
301 W High St, Suite 720, Jefferson City, MO 65101
Tel: 573-526-3566
E-mail: mofilm@ded.mo.gov
Web Site: www.mofilm.org
Key Personnel
Proj Mgr: Michael Nichols *Tel:* 573-522-1288 *E-mail:* michael.nichols@ded.mo.gov
Film Off Specialist: Andrea Sporcic
Founded: 1983
State film/tape production liaison; all film commission activities.
Membership(s): Association of Film Commissioners International

Film Commission of Greater Kansas City
1906 Wyandotte, Kansas City, MO 64108
Tel: 816-471-2215 *Fax:* 816-471-6500
E-mail: contact@kcfilm.com; greaterkcfilmcommission@gmail.com
Web Site: kcfilm.com
Key Personnel
Film Commission Chair: Heather Laird *Tel:* 877-396-4377
Founded: 1989

MONTANA

Billings Film Liaison Office
815 S 27 St, Billings, MT 59101
Mailing Address: PO Box 31177, Billings, MT 59107-1177
Tel: 406-245-4111 *Toll Free Tel:* 800-711-2630 *Fax:* 406-245-7333
Web Site: www.visitbillings.com
Key Personnel
Exec Dir: Alex Tyson *E-mail:* alex@visitbillings.com
Visit Billings is the tourism bureau for Billings, Montana's Trailhead. The Visit Billings team works closely with the Montana Film Office to help meet the needs of prospective clients. We value the opportunity & confidentiality related to the film industry.

Butte Film Liaison Office, see Butte-Silver Bow Chamber of Commerce

Butte-Silver Bow Chamber of Commerce
1000 George St, Butte, MT 59701
Tel: 406-723-3177 *Toll Free Tel:* 800-735-6814 *Fax:* 406-723-1215
E-mail: chamber@buttechamber.org; marketing@buttechamber.org
Web Site: www.buttechamber.org
Key Personnel
Exec Dir: Marko Lucich *E-mail:* mlucich@buttechamber.org
Assist with filming & scouting when possible (especially arrangements before filming), permissions, hotels, etc.

Montana Film Office
Division of Montana Department of Commerce
301 S Park Ave, Helena, MT 59620
Tel: 406-841-2876 *Toll Free Tel:* 800-553-4563 *Fax:* 406-841-2877
E-mail: montanafilm@mt.gov
Web Site: www.montanafilm.com
Key Personnel
Film Commissioner: Deny Staggs *Tel:* 406-841-2881 *E-mail:* dstaggs@mt.gov
Founded: 1974
State film commission for Montana. Provide location services & assistance with permits, online production guide with searchable location database, extensive photo library, administers film production incentives & Montana Big Sky Film Grant program.
Membership(s): Association of Film Commissioners International

NEBRASKA

Nebraska Film Office
Affiliate of Nebraska Dept of Economic Development
PO Box 98907, Lincoln, NE 68509-8907
Tel: 402-471-3746 *Toll Free Tel:* 800-228-4307
E-mail: info@filmnebraska.org

Web Site: www.filmnebraska.org; www.neded.org/nebraska-film-office-home
Key Personnel
Film Offr: Laurie Richards *Tel:* 402-202-1905
State liaison with film & videotape industry; site location; crews.

Greater Omaha Film Commission
1819 Farnam St, Suite 300, Omaha, NE 68183
Tel: 402-444-5000
Full service film commission.

NEVADA

Nevada Film Office
Division of State of Nevada, Governor's Office of Economic Development
6655 W Sahara, Suite C106, Las Vegas, NV 89146
Tel: 702-486-2711 *Toll Free Tel:* 877-638-3456 *Fax:* 702-486-2712
E-mail: lvnfo@nevadafilm.com
Web Site: www.nevadafilm.com
Key Personnel
Dir: Eric Preiss *E-mail:* epreiss@nevadafilm.com
Resources Coord: Danette Tull *E-mail:* dtull@nevadafilm.com
Film & television production coordination.

Lake Tahoe Visitors Authority (LTVA)
169 Hwy 50, Stateline, NV 89449
Mailing Address: PO Box 5878, Stateline, NV 89449
Tel: 775-588-5900 *Toll Free Tel:* 800-288-2463 (reservations) *Fax:* 775-588-1941
E-mail: info@ltva.org
Web Site: ltva.org
Key Personnel
Exec Dir: Carol Chaplin *Tel:* 775-588-5900 ext 302 *E-mail:* carol@ltva.org
Deputy Dir: Sue Barton *Tel:* 530-544-5050 ext 224 *E-mail:* sue@ltva.org
Founded: 1986
Provide information for filming in the area, assist with permits & location services.

NEW HAMPSHIRE

New Hampshire Film & TV Office
19 Pillsbury St, 1st fl, Concord, NH 03301
Tel: 603-271-2220 *Fax:* 603-271-3584
E-mail: film@nh.gov
Web Site: www.nh.gov/film
Key Personnel
Dir: Matthew W Newton
Founded: 1998
Markets the state of New Hampshire as a filming location & supports New Hampshire filmmakers.
Membership(s): Association of Film Commissioners International

NEW JERSEY

New Jersey Motion Picture & Television Commission
153 Halsey St, 5th fl, Newark, NJ 07102-2807
Mailing Address: PO Box 47023, Newark, NJ 07101-8004
Tel: 973-648-6279 *Fax:* 973-648-7350
E-mail: njfilm@njfilm.org
Web Site: www.njfilm.org
Key Personnel
Exec Dir: Steven Gorelick
Assoc Dir: David W Schoner, Jr
Prodn Coord: Andrew S Graham
Opers Mgr: Charles Ricciardi
Location assistance/liaison with state, county & municipal governments.

NEW MEXICO

Albuquerque Film Office
Economic Development Dept, One Civic Plaza NW, Albuquerque, NM 87102
Mailing Address: PO Box 1293, Albuquerque, NM 87102
Tel: 505-768-3283 *Fax:* 505-768-3280
Web Site: www.cabq.gov/film
Key Personnel
Film Liaison: Ann Lerner *E-mail:* alerner@cabq.gov
Coordination & permit assistance. Serves as a clearing house of information for the public concerning projects currently in the area.
Membership(s): Association of Film Commissioners International

Las Cruces Film Commission
700 N Main St, Las Cruces, NM 88001
Mailing Address: PO Box 20000, Las Cruces, NM 88004
Tel: 575-541-2271
E-mail: econdev@las-cruces.org
Web Site: www.las-cruces-film.org
Location assistance.
Membership(s): Association of Film Commissioners International

New Mexico Film Office
Division of New Mexico Economic Development Dept
Joseph M Montoya Bldg, 1st fl, 1100 St Francis Dr, Suite 1213, Santa Fe, NM 87505
Tel: 505-476-5600 *Toll Free Tel:* 800-545-9871 *Fax:* 505-476-5601
E-mail: info@nmfilm.com
Web Site: www.nmfilm.com
Key Personnel
Dir: Nick Maniatis *Tel:* 505-476-5604
New Mexico continues to offer one of the most competitive incentive packages, which includes a 25% Refundable Tax Credit, Film Investment Loan Program & Film Crew Advancement Program. Post-production services rendered in New Mexico also qualify for the 25% Refundable Tax Credit.

NEW YORK

Suffolk County Film Commission
H Lee Dennison Bldg, 2nd fl, 100 Veterans Memorial Hwy, Hauppauge, NY 11788-0099
Tel: 631-853-4800 *Fax:* 631-853-4888
Web Site: www.suffolkcountyfilmcommission.com
Key Personnel
Commissioner: Robert Beuka
Dir, Film & Cultural Aff: Michelle Isabelle-Stark *E-mail:* michelle.stark@suffolkcountyny.gov
To encourage, participate & assist in the making, promotion, distribution & exhibition of the Suffolk County film community. Staff is available for location & facility information & provides complete production services by coordinating activities between production companies, communities & government agencies. Production, logistics & permits are expedited free of charge. Publishes quarterly newspaper in the spring, summer, fall & winter. Call for more information.
Membership(s): Association of Film Commissioners International; IFP

Nassau County Film Office
Affiliate of Long Island Film/TV Foundation
Executive Bldg, One West St, Mineola, NY 11501
Tel: 516-571-3168 *Fax:* 516-571-6195
Web Site: www.longislandfilm.com
Key Personnel
Dir: Debra Markowitz *E-mail:* dmarkowitz@nassaucountyny.gov
Founded: 1989
Assist in site location, permits & police assistance, film support service brochure, location brochure, photo file. Long Island International Film Expo.
Membership(s): Association of Film Commissioners International

Cayman Islands Department of Tourism
Empire State Bldg, 350 Fifth Ave, Suite 2720, New York, NY 10018
Tel: 212-889-9009 *Toll Free Tel:* 877-4-CAYMAN (422-9626) *Fax:* 212-889-9125
Web Site: www.caymanislands.ky; www.divecayman.ky
Key Personnel
Northeast Mktg Rep: Veronica Torra *Tel:* 732-789-5122
Promotion of Grand Cayman Islands.

New York City Mayor's Office of Film, Theatre & Broadcasting
1697 Broadway, 6th fl, Suite 602, New York, NY 10019
Tel: 212-489-6710 *Fax:* 212-307-6237
E-mail: info@film.nyc.gov
Web Site: www.nyc.gov/film
Key Personnel
Commissioner: Katherine Oliver
Provide shooting permits, police assistance, production assistance, project development assistance, promotion & economic development services.

New York State Governor's Office for Motion Picture & Television Development
633 Third Ave, 33rd fl, New York, NY 10017
Tel: 212-803-2330 *Fax:* 212-803-2339
E-mail: nyfilm@esd.ny.gov
Web Site: www.nylovesfilm.com
Key Personnel
Exec Dir: Gigi Semone
Connection to all the diverse locations in New York State. Peruse the 100,000 images in our location library & take advantage of our extensive network for locations across the state.

Saint Vincent & The Grenadines Tourist Office
801 Second Ave, 1st fl, New York, NY 10017
Tel: 212-687-4981 *Toll Free Tel:* 800-729-1726 *Fax:* 212-949-5946
E-mail: svgtony@aol.com
Web Site: www.discoversvg.com
Key Personnel
Asst Sales Dir: Eleen Ackie

Rochester/Finger Lakes Film & Video Office
Division of Greater Rochesters Visitors Association
45 East Ave, Suite 400, Rochester, NY 14604-2294
Tel: 585-279-8308 *Fax:* 585-232-4822
Web Site: www.filmrochester.org
Key Personnel
Exec Dir: Nora Brown *E-mail:* nbrown@visitrochester.com
Deputy Dir: Karl Goldsmith
Founded: 1990
Film commission.
Membership(s): Association of Film Commissioners International

Capital - Saratoga Film Commission
28 Clinton St, Saratoga Springs, NY 12866
Tel: 518-584-3255 *Fax:* 518-587-0318
E-mail: info@capital-saratogafilm.com
Web Site: www.saratoga.org

Key Personnel
VP, Tourism: Annamaria Bellantoni
Founded: 1980 (expanded 2004)

NORTH CAROLINA

Charlotte Regional Film Commission
500 S College St, Suite 300, Charlotte, NC 28202
Tel: 704-331-2723 *Toll Free Tel:* 800-722-1994 *Fax:* 704-342-3972 *Toll Free Fax:* 800-722-1994
Web Site: www.charlottefilm.com
Key Personnel
Dir, Film Div: Beth Petty *E-mail:* bpetty@charlottefilm.com

Western North Carolina Film Commission
Subsidiary of Program of AdvantageWest Economic Development Group
134 Wright Brothers Way, Fletcher, NC 28732
Tel: 828-687-7234 *Toll Free Tel:* 888-595-7234 *Fax:* 828-687-7552
E-mail: film@awnc.org
Web Site: www.wncfilm.com; www.advantagewest.com
Key Personnel
CEO & Pres: Scott Hamilton
Dir: Amanda Baranski
Founded: 1995
Film commission serving the 23 western counties of North Carolina.

North Carolina's Piedmont Triad Film Commission
416 Gallimore Dairy Rd, Suite M, Greensboro, NC 27409
Tel: 336-393-0001
E-mail: info@piedmontfilm.com
Web Site: www.piedmontfilm.com
Key Personnel
Exec Dir: Rebecca Clark *E-mail:* rebecca@piedmontfilm.com
Mktg & Communs Coord: Sara Hancock *E-mail:* sara@piedmontfilm.com
Founded: 1993
Membership(s): Association of Film Commissioners International

North Carolina Film Office
Affiliate of North Carolina Dept of Commerce
301 N Wilmington St, Raleigh, NC 27601
Mailing Address: 4324 Mail Service Ctr, Raleigh, NC 27699-4324
Tel: 919-733-9900 *Toll Free Tel:* 866-468-2273 *Fax:* 919-715-0151
Web Site: www.ncfilm.com
Key Personnel
Dir: Aaron Syrett *E-mail:* aaron@ncfilm.com
Prodn Servs Exec: Guy Gaster *E-mail:* guy@ncfilm.com
Exec Asst: Cheryl Mauro *E-mail:* cheryl@ncfilm.com
Promote film & television work.

Triangle Regional Film Commission
PO Box 13041, Research Triangle Park, NC 27709-3041
Tel: 919-544-5501
E-mail: triangleregionalfilm@gmail.com
Web Site: www.trianglencfilm.com
Key Personnel
Exec Dir & Film Commissioner: Rob Shoaf
Founded: 2011
Location scouting services for film productions, housing, catering & liaison with Research Triangle Park community service providers.

Wilmington Regional Film Commission Inc
1223 N 23 St, Wilmington, NC 28405
Tel: 910-343-3456 *Fax:* 910-343-3457
E-mail: commish@wilmingtonfilm.com
Web Site: www.wilmingtonfilm.com
Key Personnel
Dir: Johnny Griffin
Founded: 1983
Full service regional film commission. Location scouting, location library, annual production guide, crew/equipment/service information & production clearinghouse.

NORTH DAKOTA

North Dakota Tourism Division/Film Commission
Century Ctr, 1600 E Century Ave, Suite 2, Bismarck, ND 58502-2057
Mailing Address: PO Box 2057, Bismarck, ND 58502-2057
Tel: 701-328-2525 *Toll Free Tel:* 800-435-5663 *Fax:* 701-328-4878
E-mail: tourism@nd.gov
Web Site: www.ndtourism.com
Key Personnel
Tourism Dir: Sara Otte Coleman *E-mail:* socoleman@nd.gov
Mktg Mgr: Heather LeMoine *E-mail:* hlemoine@nd.gov
Outdoor Promos Mgr: Mike Jensen *E-mail:* mjjensen@nd.gov
Coordinate economic development & promotion for North Dakota.

OHIO

Greater Cincinnati & Northern Kentucky Film Commission
602 Main St, Suite 712, Cincinnati, OH 45202
Tel: 513-784-1744 *Fax:* 513-768-8963
E-mail: info@filmcincinnati.com
Web Site: www.filmcincinnati.com
Provide assistance with location scouting, permits, talent, supplies, vehicles, hotels, traffic & props.

Greater Columbus Film Commission
PO Box 12735, Columbus, OH 43212
Tel: 614-450-0264
E-mail: info@columbusfilmcommission.com
Web Site: www.filmcolumbus.com
Key Personnel
Exec Dir: Thomas McClure *E-mail:* tmcclure@columbusfilmcommission.com
Founded: 2006
Location searching & resource for film & video production companies when shooting in Central Ohio.

OKLAHOMA

Oklahoma City Convention & Visitors Bureau
123 Park Ave, Oklahoma City, OK 73102
Tel: 405-297-8912 *Toll Free Tel:* 800-225-5652 *Fax:* 405-297-8888
E-mail: contact@visitokc.com
Web Site: www.visitokc.org
Key Personnel
Dir, Mktg & Communs: Seth Spillman *Tel:* 405-297-8905 *E-mail:* sspillman@visitokc.com
Promotes Oklahoma City as a visitor & convention destination.

Oklahoma Film Commission & Music Office
120 N Robinson, Suite 600, Oklahoma City, OK 73102
Tel: 405-230-8440 *Toll Free Tel:* 800-766-3456 *Fax:* 405-230-8640
Web Site: www.oklahomafilm.org; thebuffalolounge.com
Key Personnel
Dir: Jill Simpson *E-mail:* Jill.Simpson@TravelOK.com
Deputy Dir: Leslie Channell *E-mail:* Leslie.Channell@TravelOK.com
Founded: 1979
Provide liaison with state, county & local governments; assistance with hotel accomodations, props, set dressing & equipment rental; production files available. Free location scouting & set assistance. Few permits required.

OREGON

Eugene, Cascades & Coast-Travel Lane County
754 Olive St, Eugene, OR 97401
Mailing Address: PO Box 10286, Eugene, OR 97440-2286
Tel: 541-484-5307 *Toll Free Tel:* 800-547-5445 *Fax:* 541-343-6335
E-mail: film@eugenecascadescoast.org
Web Site: www.eugenecascadescoast.org
Key Personnel
VP, Tourism Mktg: Natalie Inouye *Tel:* 541-743-8754 *E-mail:* natalie@eugenecascadescoast.org
Tourism Sales Mgr: Meg Trendler *Tel:* 541-484-5307 *E-mail:* meg@eugenecascadescoast.org
Liaison to Oregon Film Commission; advice on permits & scouting.

Travel Lane County, see Eugene, Cascades & Coast-Travel Lane County

Mayor's Office of Film & Video
Division of Bureau of Licenses, City of Portland
222 NW Fifth Ave, Portland, OR 97209-3859
Tel: 503-823-4039 *Fax:* 503-865-3791
Web Site: www.portlandonline.com/filmandvideo; www.pdc.us/film
Key Personnel
Contact: Shelley Midthun *E-mail:* midthuns@pdc.us
Permit coordination.

Oregon Film & Video Office
123 NE Third Ave, Suite 210, Portland, OR 97232
Tel: 503-229-5832 *Fax:* 503-229-6869
E-mail: shoot@oregonfilm.org
Web Site: www.oregonfilm.org
Key Personnel
Exec Dir: Vince Porter *E-mail:* vince@oregonfilm.org
Sr Proj Mgr: Bob Schmaling *E-mail:* bob@oregonfilm.org
Proj Mgr: Jane Ridley *E-mail:* jane@oregonfilm.org
IT & Creative Mgr: Nathan Cherrington *E-mail:* nathan@oregonfilm.org
Founded: 1968
Film commission, logistics & location scouting.

PENNSYLVANIA

Pennsylvania Film Office
Affiliate of Department of Community & Economic Development
Commonwealth Keystone Bldg, 4th fl, 400 North St, Harrisburg, PA 17120-0225
Tel: 717-783-3456 *Fax:* 717-787-6825
E-mail: info@filminpa.com
Web Site: www.filminpa.com
Key Personnel
Locations Mgr & Admin Offr: Maryann P Marsico
Film Off Dir: Janice Collier
Founded: 1977
Work to attract feature films, TV movies & series, commercials & documentaries to Pennsylvania.

Greater Philadelphia Film Office
One Parkway Bldg, 11th fl, 1515 Arch St, Philadelphia, PA 19102
Tel: 215-686-2668 *Fax:* 215-686-3659
E-mail: mail@film.org
Web Site: www.film.org
Key Personnel
Exec Dir: Sharon Pinkenson *E-mail:* sharon@film.org
Dir, Greater Philadelphia Filmmakers: Joan Bressler *E-mail:* joanb@film.org
Dir, Mktg & Multicultural Aff: Nicole Giles *E-mail:* nicoleg@film.org
Dir, Opers & Govt Aff: Nicole Shiner *E-mail:* nicole@film.org
Prodn Coord: Erin Jackson Wagner *E-mail:* erin@film.org
Mktg Asst: Rob Buscher *E-mail:* rob@film.org
Markets Southeastern Pennsylvania area as location to feature film, television, video, commercial, production companies etc. Provides liaison services with city departments. Maintains location photo files & sends out informational packets including *Greater Philadelphia Film & Video Guide*.

Pittsburgh Film Office
The Century Bldg, Suite 202, 130 Seventh St, Pittsburgh, PA 15222
Tel: 412-261-2744 *Toll Free Tel:* 888-744-3456 *Fax:* 412-471-7317
E-mail: info@pghfilm.org
Web Site: www.pghfilm.org
Key Personnel
Dir: Dawn M Keezer
Founded: 1990
Pittsburgh/Western Pennsylvania office for information regarding production locations, crew & resources. Will also assist with location permits & clearances.

RHODE ISLAND

Rhode Island Film & Television Office
Division of Rhode Island State Council on the Arts
One Capitol Hill, 3rd fl, Providence, RI 02908
Tel: 401-222-3456; 401-222-6666 (hotline) *Fax:* 401-222-3018
Web Site: www.film.ri.gov
Key Personnel
Exec Dir: Steven Feinberg *E-mail:* steven.feinberg@arts.ri.gov
One-stop permit office, free location scouting assistance with travel, hotel & catering arrangements; assist with pre-production, on-location & post-production requirements for successful film making. Aggressive tax incentives.
Number of Members: 26
Membership(s): Association of Film Commissioners International

SOUTH CAROLINA

South Carolina Film Commission
Affiliate of South Carolina Department of Parks, Recreation & Tourism
1205 Pendleton St, Rm 225, Columbia, SC 29201-3261
Tel: 803-737-0490 *Fax:* 803-734-0670
E-mail: filmsc@scprt.com
Web Site: www.filmsc.com
Key Personnel
Film Commissioner: Tom Clark *Tel:* 803-737-0498 *E-mail:* tclark@scprt.com
Production incentives are wage & supplier cash rebates. Free location scouting services, for qualified prospects liaison assistance between local communities & the production company, contacts with state & local officials, assistance with accommodations & contacts with local crew & casting assistance.

SOUTH DAKOTA

South Dakota Film Office
Dept of Tourism, 711 E Wells Ave, Pierre, SD 57501-3369
Tel: 605-773-3301 *Toll Free Tel:* 800-952-3625 *Fax:* 605-773-3256
E-mail: filmsd@state.sd.us
Web Site: www.filmsd.com
Key Personnel
Media Rel Rep: Katlyn Richter
Location scouting, lodging, catering, production assistance, hosting; promotional packet available.

Sioux Falls Convention & Visitors Bureau
200 N Phillips Ave, Suite 102, Sioux Falls, SD 57104
Tel: 605-275-6060 *Toll Free Tel:* 800-333-2072 *Fax:* 605-338-0682
E-mail: sfcvb@siouxfalls.com
Web Site: www.siouxfallscvb.com; visitsiouxfalls.com
Key Personnel
Exec Dir: Teri Schmidt
Founded: 1973
Full service convention & visitors bureau.

TENNESSEE

The Memphis & Shelby County Film & TV Commission
496 S Main St, Suite 101, Memphis, TN 38103
Tel: 901-527-8300 (ext 2) *Fax:* 901-527-8326
E-mail: info@memphisfilmcomm.org
Web Site: www.filmmemphis.org
Key Personnel
Film Commissioner: Linn Sitler
Deputy Film Commissioner & Contact: Sharon Fox O'Guin
Founded: 1985
Location scouting & services; free production directory; crew equipment; scout West Tennessee, Eastern Arkansas & Northern Mississippi.
Membership(s): Association of Film Commissioners International

Mayor's Office of Economic & Community Development
Metropolitan Courthouse, Suite 102, One Public Sq, Nashville, TN 37219
Tel: 615-862-4700 *Fax:* 615-862-6025
Web Site: www.nashville.gov
Key Personnel
Dir, Spec Events: Marilyn Edwards *E-mail:* marilyn.edwards@nashville.gov

Tennessee Film, Entertainment & Music Commission
312 Rosa L Parks Ave, 26th fl, Nashville, TN 37243
Tel: 615-741-FILM (741-3456) *Toll Free Tel:* 877-818-FILM (818-3456) *Fax:* 615-741-5554
E-mail: tn.film@tn.gov
Web Site: www.state.tn.us/film
Key Personnel
Exec Dir: Bob Raines *E-mail:* bob.raines@tn.gov
Liaison & assistance to production companies working on location.
Membership(s): Association of Film Commissioners International

TEXAS

Alpine Texas Chamber of Commerce
106 N Third St, Alpine, TX 79830
Tel: 432-837-2326 *Toll Free Tel:* 800-561-3712 *Fax:* 432-837-1259
E-mail: info@alpinetexas.com
Web Site: www.alpinetexas.com
Key Personnel
Exec Dir: Abigail Garza *E-mail:* manager@alpinetexas.com
Assoc Dir: Kirsten Thompson *E-mail:* accounts@alpinetexas.com
Location scouting for feature films, western catalogs & television commercials.

Amarillo Film Commission
Division of Amarillo Convention & Visitors Council
1000 S Polk St, Amarillo, TX 79101
Tel: 806-342-2016 *Toll Free Tel:* 800-692-1338 *Fax:* 806-373-3909
Web Site: www.amarillofilm.org; www.visitamarillotx.com
Key Personnel
Film Commissioner: Eric Miller *E-mail:* eric@visitamarillo.com
Business referral/liaison to the private sector & city government; limited location scouting. Provide free production directory & some location pictures.

Austin Film Commission
301 Congress Ave, Suite 200, Austin, TX 78701
Tel: 512-583-7229 *Toll Free Tel:* 800-926-2282 (ext 7229) *Fax:* 512-583-7281
Web Site: www.austintexas.org/film; www.austinfilmcommission.com
Key Personnel
Dir: Gary Bond *E-mail:* gbond@austintexas.org
Location, scouting & street closures.

Texas Film Commission
1100 San Jacinto, Suite 3.410, Austin, TX 78701
Mailing Address: PO Box 13246, Austin, TX 78711-3246
Tel: 512-463-9200 *Fax:* 512-463-4114
E-mail: film@governor.state.tx.us
Web Site: www.governor.state.tx.us/film
Key Personnel
Off Mgr: Katie Kelly
Founded: 1971
Whether you are an industry professional or new to the business, the Commission is here to help with your film, television, commercial, animation & video game projects. Since 1971, the Commission has supported the media industries of Texas, maintaining the state's competitive position worldwide as a production destination.

Beaumont Convention & Visitors Bureau
505 Willow St, Beaumont, TX 77701
Mailing Address: PO Box 3827, Beaumont, TX 77704-3827
Tel: 409-880-3749 *Toll Free Tel:* 800-392-4401 *Fax:* 409-880-3750
Web Site: www.beaumontcvb.com
Key Personnel
Exec Dir: Dean Conwell *Tel:* 409-880-3165 *E-mail:* dconwell@ci.beaumont.tx.us
Dir, Mktg: Stephanie Molina *Tel:* 409-880-3170 *E-mail:* smolina@ci.beaumont.tx.us
Founded: 1970
Video, photos, location assistance, site visits & resource coordination. Branch office in Houston, TX.
Membership(s): AAF; Destination Marketing Association International; PRSA; Texas Film Commission; Texas Travel & Industry Association

Corpus Christi Convention & Visitors Bureau
101 N Shoreline Blvd, Suite 430, Corpus Christi, TX 78401
Tel: 361-881-1888 *Toll Free Tel:* 800-678-6232 *Fax:* 361-887-9023
Web Site: www.corpuschristicvb.com
Key Personnel
Dir, Spec Events: Heidi Hovda *E-mail:* hhovda@visitcorpuschristitx.org

El Paso Film Commission
Affiliate of El Paso Convention & Visitors Bureau
One Civic Center Plaza, El Paso, TX 79901
Toll Free Tel: 800-351-6024 *Fax:* 915-532-2963
Web Site: www.visitelpaso.com/film
Key Personnel
Film Commissioner & Dir: Susie Gaines *Tel:* 915-534-0698 *E-mail:* sgaines@destinationelpaso.com
Location scouting, liaison in obtaining permits.
Membership(s): Association of Film Commissioners International; Texas Association of Film Commissions

Houston Film Commission
Division of The Greater Houston Convention & Visitors Bureau
4 Houston Ctr, 1331 Lamar St, 7th fl, Houston, TX 77010
Tel: 713-437-5251 *Toll Free Tel:* 800-365-7575 *Fax:* 713-223-3816
E-mail: jmontgomery@ghcvb.org
Web Site: www.houstonfilmcommission.com
Key Personnel
Exec Dir: Rick Ferguson
Founded: 1986
Free location scouting; script breakdown; conduct location survey for production crew, assist as a liaison with city, county & state agencies.

Kerrville Convention & Visitors Bureau
2108 Sidney Baker St, Kerrville, TX 78028
Tel: 830-792-3535 *Toll Free Tel:* 800-221-7958 *Fax:* 830-792-3230
E-mail: info@kerrvilletexascvb.com; kerrcvb@ktc.com
Web Site: www.kerrvilletexascvb.com
Key Personnel
Exec Dir: Carlie McIlvain
Videos & books about Texas.

San Antonio Film Commission
Division of Department for Culture & Creative Development
203 S Saint Mary's St, Suite 360, San Antonio, TX 78205
Mailing Address: PO Box 839966, San Antonio, TX 78283-3966
Tel: 210-207-6730 *Toll Free Tel:* 800-447-3372 *Fax:* 210-207-4526
E-mail: filmsa@filmsanantonio.com
Web Site: www.filmsanantonio.com
Key Personnel
Dir: Drew Mayer-Oakes *E-mail:* drew@filmsanantonio.com
Location Coord: Janet Vasquez *Tel:* 210-207-6777 *E-mail:* janetv@filmsanantonio.com

UTAH

Kanab/Kane County Film Commission
Kane County Utah Off of Tourism, 78 S 100 E, Kanab, UT 84741
Tel: 435-644-5033 *Toll Free Tel:* 800-733-5263 *Fax:* 435-644-5923
E-mail: filmcomm@xpressweb.com
Web Site: www.kaneutah.com
Key Personnel
Film Commissioner: Ken Gotzen-Berg *E-mail:* kengotzenberg@kaneutah.com
Membership(s): Association of Film Commissioners International

Moab to Monument Valley Film Commission
217 E Center St, Moab, UT 84532
Tel: 435-259-4341 *Fax:* 435-259-4135
Web Site: www.filmmoab.com; film.utah.gov
Key Personnel
Dir: Tara S Penner *Tel:* 435-260-1575 (cell) *E-mail:* tara@moabcity.org
Founded: 1949
Location scouting services; liaison for permitting & services.
Membership(s): Association of Film Commissioners International

Park City Film Commission
1910 Prospector Ave, Park City, UT 84060
Mailing Address: PO Box 1630, Park City, UT 84060-1630
Tel: 435-649-6100 *Toll Free Tel:* 800-453-1360 *Fax:* 435-649-4132
Web Site: www.visitparkcity.com/media/park-city-film-commission/
Key Personnel
Dir, Opers: Sue Kapis *E-mail:* sue@visitparkcity.com
Assist crews, provide locating services. Call for a film production kit.

Utah Valley Film Commission
220 W Center St, Suite 100, Provo, UT 84601
Tel: 801-851-2100 *Toll Free Tel:* 800-222-8824 *Fax:* 801-851-2109
E-mail: visitors@utahvalley.com
Web Site: www.utahvalley.com/film
Key Personnel
Film Commissioner & Sales Mgr: Lee Adamson *Tel:* 801-851-2110 *E-mail:* lee@utahvalley.com
Marketing, location & permit assistance; location photo presentations, crew resource guide.

Utah Film Commission
Subsidiary of Utah Governor's Office of Economic Development
Council Hall/Capitol Hill, 300 N State St, Salt Lake City, UT 84114
Tel: 801-538-8740 *Toll Free Tel:* 800-453-8824 *Fax:* 801-538-1397
Web Site: www.film.utah.gov
Key Personnel
Film Commissioner: Virginia Pearce
Founded: 1974
Provide location scouting, photographs of the area, help secure permits, provide information & resource materials, script breakdown. Serves as a liaison between video & filmmakers & all government agencies as well as private industry & local residents.
Membership(s): Association of Film Commissioners International

VIRGINIA

Virginia Film Office
Division of Virginia Tourism Corp
901 E Byrd St, Richmond, VA 23219-4048
Tel: 804-545-5530 *Toll Free Tel:* 800-854-6233 *Fax:* 804-545-5501
E-mail: vafilm@virginia.org
Web Site: www.film.virginia.org
Key Personnel
Dir: Andy Edmunds *Tel:* 804-545-5534 *E-mail:* aedmunds@virginia.org
Deputy Dir: Mary Nelson *Tel:* 804-545-5535 *E-mail:* mnelson@virginia.org
Founded: 1980
Assistance in finding locations for film, television, video & still shoots. Extensive online location library. Custom location packages overnight or by e-mail. Staff will arrange for location scouts with key production personnel. Comprehensive Production Services Directory available. Provide research assistance. Facilitate use of government facilities & services for filming. Virginia has a broad sales & use tax exemption for filmmakers. Call for additional incentive information.
Membership(s): Association of Film Commissioners International; MCA-I; Virginia Production Alliance; Women in Film & Video

WASHINGTON

Seattle Mayor's Office of Film & Music
700 Fifth Ave, Suite 5752, Seattle, WA 98104
Mailing Address: PO Box 94708, Seattle, WA 98124-4708
Tel: 206-684-8090 *Fax:* 206-684-0379
E-mail: filmandmusicoffice@seattle.gov
Web Site: www.seattle.gov/filmandmusic
Key Personnel
Dir: James Keblas *E-mail:* james.keblas@seattle.gov
Film & Special Events Prog Mgr: Chris Swenson *Tel:* 206-733-9245 *E-mail:* chris.swenson@seattle.gov
Creative Industries Busn Devt Mgr: Rachel White Sawyer *Tel:* 206-684-8504 *E-mail:* rachel.white@seattle.gov
Permits, location scouting services & film liaison.

Washington Filmworks
1411 Fourth Ave, Suite 420, Seattle, WA 98101
Tel: 206-264-0667 *Fax:* 206-382-4343
E-mail: info@washingtonfilmworks.org
Web Site: washingtonfilmworks.org
Key Personnel
Exec Dir: Amy Lillard
Dir, Fin & Opers: Julie Daman
Prodn Servs Coord: Krys Karns
Communs Coord: Andrew Espe
Manages Washington state's film & production incentive programs. Free assistance for all pre-production needs, location scouting & support service referral. Free location photos, permitting contact & resources. Resource manual available.

Tacoma-Regional Film Commission
1119 Pacific Ave, Suite 1400, Tacoma, WA 98402
Mailing Address: PO Box 1754, Tacoma, WA 98401-1754
Tel: 253-627-2836 (ext 26) *Fax:* 253-627-8783
Web Site: www.traveltacoma.com/press-room/film-commission
Key Personnel
Dir, Mktg & Communs: Andrea Mensink *Tel:* 253-284-3267 *E-mail:* andrea@traveltacoma.com

WEST VIRGINIA

West Virginia Film Office
Unit of West Virginia Department of Commerce
90 MacCorkle Ave SW, South Charleston, WV 25303
Toll Free Tel: 866-6WV-FILM (698-3456) *Fax:* 304-558-1662
Web Site: wvfilm.wvcommerce.org
Key Personnel
Dir: Pam Haynes *Tel:* 304-957-9382 *E-mail:* pamela.j.haynes@wv.gov
Acts as liaison between production companies & state agencies, municipalities & the private sector to expedite motion picture, television & commercial productions. Provides scouting

assistance in securing locations. Offers a production directory containing a comprehensive listing of in-state personnel & production services; assists with facilitating negotiations for the use of locations.
Membership(s): Association of Film Commissioners International

WISCONSIN

VISIT Milwaukee
648 N Plankinton Ave, Suite 425, Milwaukee, WI 53203-2917
Tel: 414-273-3950 *Toll Free Tel:* 800-554-1448 *Fax:* 414-273-5596
E-mail: info@milwaukee.org
Web Site: www.visitmilwaukee.org
Key Personnel
PR Coord: Margaret Casey
Locations, permits, accommodations, production services, personnel, facilities.

Film Wisconsin Inc
PO Box 93, Waunakee, WI 53597
Tel: 414-333-2366
E-mail: info@filmwisconsin.net
Web Site: www.filmwisconsin.net
Founded: 1987
Public/private film office partnership featuring state incentives program & location & logistical services.
Membership(s): Association of Film Commissioners International

WYOMING

Wyoming Film Office
5611 High Plains Rd, Cheyenne, WY 82007
Tel: 307-777-3400 *Toll Free Tel:* 800-458-6657 *Fax:* 307-777-2877
E-mail: info@filmwyoming.com
Web Site: www.filmwyoming.com
Key Personnel
Film Prodn Sr Coord: Colin Stricklin *E-mail:* colin.stricklin@wyo.gov
Provides location scouting & liaison services to the motion picture industry interested in production in Wyoming.
Membership(s): Association of Film Commissioners International

Jackson Hole Film Commission
112 Center St, Jackson, WY 83001
Mailing Address: PO Box 550, Jackson, WY 83001-0550
Tel: 307-733-3316 (ext 104) *Fax:* 307-733-5585
Web Site: www.jacksonholechamber.com
Key Personnel
Communs Mgr: Kate Foster *E-mail:* kate@jacksonholechamber.com
Founded: 1946
Resource reference center for companies wanting to film in Jackson.
Number of Members: 1,000
Membership(s): Destination Marketing Association International

PUERTO RICO

Puerto Rico Film Commission
Affiliate of Department of Economic Development & Commerce
355 FD Roosevelt Ave, Suite 106, Hato Rey, PR 00918
Mailing Address: PO Box 362350, San Juan, PR 00936-2350
Tel: 787-754-6444 *Fax:* 787-756-5706
E-mail: info@puertoricofilm.pr.gov
Web Site: www.puertoricofilm.com
Key Personnel
Exec Dir: Demetrio Fernandez-Manzano *Tel:* 787-758-4747 ext 2251 *E-mail:* demetrio.fernandez@puertoricofilm.pr.gov
Tax Credit Prog Mgr: Nadia Barbarossa *Tel:* 787-758-4747 ext 2250 *E-mail:* nadia.barbarossa@puertoricofilm.pr.gov
Founded: 1980
Provide assistance to production companies by researching & pre-scouting locations; liaison between local, state & federal authorities; secures permits & clearances & arranges accommodations & itineraries for scouting & location stays. Also process applications for tax credits (40% local residents & 20% actors, producers, directors, screenwriters & qualified personnel).
Membership(s): Association of Film Commissioners International

VIRGIN ISLANDS

US Virgin Islands Film Promotion Office
Affiliate of US Virgin Islands Dept of Tourism
PO Box 6400, St Thomas, VI 00804-6400
Tel: 340-775-1444 (ext 2243) *Fax:* 340-774-4390
E-mail: info@filmusvi.com
Web Site: www.filmusvi.com
Key Personnel
Film Coord: Luana Wheatley *E-mail:* lawheatley@usvitourism.vi
Founded: 1973
Free color location manual, location pictures, maps & videos, scouting assistance, liaison with government agencies & with the private sector, introduction to local production services.
Membership(s): Association of Film Commissioners International; Location Managers Guild of America

ALBERTA

City of Calgary Film Commission
Division of Calgary Economic Development
731 First St SE, Calgary, AB T2G 2G9, Canada
Tel: 403-221-7831 *Toll Free Tel:* 888-222-5855 *Fax:* 403-221-7828
Web Site: www.calgaryeconomicdevelopment.com
Key Personnel
Commissioner, Film, TV & Creative Industries: Luke Azevedo *Tel:* 403-221-7868 *E-mail:* lazevedo@calgaryeconomicdevelopment.com
Logistics Coord, Film, TV & Creative Industries: Lissa Craig *Tel:* 403-221-7829 *E-mail:* lissa@calgaryeconomicdevelopment.com
Development of film industry in Calgary & area, including locations & liaisons with city, media & film industry.
Membership(s): Association of Film Commissioners International

Alberta Film Commission
140 Whitemud Crossing, 4211-106 St, Edmonton, AB T6J 6L7, Canada
Tel: 780-422-8584 *Toll Free Tel:* 888-813-1738 *Fax:* 780-422-8582
E-mail: info@albertafilm.ca
Web Site: www.albertafilm.ca
Key Personnel
Commissioner: Jeff Brinton *E-mail:* jeff.brinton@gov.ab.ca
Founded: 2002
Alberta Film was created to provide an efficient one-window approach to serve local, national & international filmmakers.
Branch Office(s)
Standard Life Bldg, 3rd fl, 639 Fifth Ave SW, Calgary, AB T2P 0M9, Canada, Contact: Marla Touw *Tel:* 403-297-6241 *Fax:* 403-297-6168 *E-mail:* marla.touw@gov.ab.ca
Membership(s): AMPIA; Association of Film Commissioners International

BRITISH COLUMBIA

Burnaby Film Office
6450 Deerlake Ave, Burnaby, BC V5G 2J3, Canada
Tel: 604-294-7314 *Fax:* 604-205-3001
Web Site: www.burnaby.ca
Key Personnel
Film Coord: Susan Rae *E-mail:* susan.rae@burnaby.ca
Film liaison & permits (approvals).
Membership(s): Motion Picture Production Industry Association of British Columbia

Thompson-Nicola Film Commission
300-465 Victoria St, Kamloops, BC V2C 2A9, Canada
Tel: 250-377-8673 *Toll Free Tel:* 877-377-8673 (BC only) *Fax:* 250-372-5048
E-mail: admin@tnrd.bc.ca
Web Site: www.tnrdfilm.com
Key Personnel
Exec Dir, Film: Victoria (Vicci) Weller *Tel:* 250-377-7058 *E-mail:* vweller@tnrd.ca
Full service film commission, scouting, script breakdown services plus location library, brochures & directory of services.

Okanagan Film Commission
1450 KLO Rd, Kelowna, BC V1W 3Z4, Canada
Tel: 250-717-0087 *Fax:* 250-868-0512
E-mail: info@okanaganfilm.com
Web Site: www.okanaganfilm.com
Key Personnel
Film Commissioner: Jon Summerland
Film & New Media Offr: Ashley Ramsay
Founded: 1990
To generate a positive economic impact by enabling the growth of the Okanagan-Similkameen-Boundary region as a film centre. The Okanagan Film Commission will continue to attract & build the film industry in this region through infrastructure development, strategic partnering, marketing & promotion.
Membership(s): Association of Film Commissioners International

British Columbia Film Commission, see Creative BC (CrBC)

Creative BC (CrBC)
Formerly British Columbia Film Commission
2225 W Broadway, Vancouver, BC V6K 2E4, Canada
Tel: 604-730-2732 *Fax:* 604-736-7290
E-mail: info@creativebc.com
Web Site: www.creativebc.com
Key Personnel
Pres & CEO: Richard Brownsey *Tel:* 604-730-2233 *E-mail:* rbrownsey@creativebc.com
VP & Acting Film Commissioner: Robert Wong *Tel:* 604-730-2236 *E-mail:* bwong@creativebc.com
Client Servs Coord: Valyce Carpenter *Tel:* 604-730-2248 *E-mail:* valyce@creativebc.com
Founded: 1978
Worldwide promotion of British Columbia within the film industry as a prime location for film, TV & commercial production. Initial scouting, photographs, maps, budget & production information supplied. Provide information on the availability of local crews, technical facilities & other support services. Acts as a liaison between production companies & other interested parties during & after the production crews work.

Vancouver Film & Special Events Office
Division of City of Vancouver
126 Keefer St, Vancouver, BC V6A 1X4, Canada
Mailing Address: Engineering Servs, Film & Special Events Office, 320-507 W Broadway, Vancouver, BC V5Z 0B4, Canada
Tel: 604-257-8840 *Fax:* 604-257-8859
E-mail: film.office@vancouver.ca
Web Site: www.vancouver.ca/engsvcs/filmandevents
Key Personnel
Mgr: Cael Hopwood *Tel:* 604-257-8848 *E-mail:* cael.hopwood@vancouver.ca
Founded: 1978
Act as liaison with film production companies; coordinate use of city services; authorize use of city streets by film production companies; issue permits as required.

Greater Victoria Film Commission, see Vancouver Island South Film & Media Commission

Vancouver Island South Film & Media Commission
Affiliate of British Columbia Film Commission
100-852 Fort St, Victoria, BC V8W 1H8, Canada
Mailing Address: PO Box 34-794 Fort St, Victoria, BC V8W 1H2, Canada
Tel: 250-386-3976 *Toll Free Tel:* 888-537-3456 *Fax:* 250-386-3967
E-mail: admin@filmvictoria.com
Web Site: www.filmvictoria.com
Key Personnel
Film Commissioner: Kathleen Gilbert
Founded: 1976
Facilitate the growth of the film industry within the greater Victoria region.
Number of Members: 120
Membership(s): Association of Film Commissioners International

MANITOBA

Manitoba Film & Music
410-93 Lombard Ave, Suite 410, Winnipeg, MB R3B 3B1, Canada
Tel: 204-947-2040 *Fax:* 204-956-5261
E-mail: info@mbfilmmusic.ca
Web Site: www.mbfilmmusic.ca
Key Personnel
CEO & Film Commissioner: Carole Vivier *E-mail:* carole@mbfilmmusic.ca
Mgr, Film Progs & Location Servs: Louise O'Brien-Moran *Tel:* 204-947-2040 ext 17 *E-mail:* louise@mbfilmmusic.ca
Founded: 1998
Provide a variety of location services supported by an extensive photo library, full location scouting, script & budget breakdowns, assistance regarding local crews & resources & liaison with all levels of government & private business. On-going production assistance & a comprehensive *Production Guide* that lists local production personnel & services & contains a photo survey of Manitoba locations. Also administers the Manitoba Film & Video Production Tax Credit which is a tax credit of up to 55% (base rate = 45%, plus eligible bonuses). A statutory corporation funded by the Province of Manitoba through the Department of Culture, Heritage & Tourism.
Membership(s): Association of Film Commissioners International

NEW BRUNSWICK

New Brunswick Film (NB Film)
c/o New Brunswick Division of Tourism, Heritage & Culture, Place 2000, 250 King St, Fredericton, NB E3B 9M9, Canada
Tel: 506-453-2909 *Fax:* 506-453-2416
Key Personnel
Prog Consultant: Ghislain Labbe *Tel:* 506-869-6875 *E-mail:* ghislain.labbe@gnb.ca
Location scouts, production assistance, no permits necessary. Film commission for the province.

NEWFOUNDLAND AND LABRADOR

Newfoundland & Labrador Film Development Corp
12 King's Bridge Rd, St John's, NL A1C 3K3, Canada
Tel: 709-738-3456 *Toll Free Tel:* 877-738-3456 (CN) *Fax:* 709-739-1680
E-mail: info@nlfdc.ca
Web Site: www.nlfdc.ca
Key Personnel
Exec Dir & Film Commissioner: Chris Bonnell *E-mail:* chris@nlfdc.ca
Promote the local capabilities & infrastructure that is currently available to the film & video industry in Newfoundland & Labrador.

NORTHWEST TERRITORIES

Northwest Territories Film Commission
Division of Government of the Northwest Territories
PO Box 1320, Yellowknife, NT X1A 2L9, Canada
Tel: 867-920-8793 *Fax:* 867-873-0101 *Toll Free Fax:* 877-445-2787 (ext 6)
E-mail: nwtfilm@gov.nt.ca
Web Site: www.nwtfilm.com
Key Personnel
Assoc Film Commissioner: Camilla MacEachern
Membership(s): Association of Film Commissioners International

NWT Film Commission, see Northwest Territories Film Commission

NOVA SCOTIA

Film & Creative Industries Nova Scotia
Historic Properties, Collins Bank Bldg, 3rd fl, 1883 Upper Water St, Suite 302, Halifax, NS B3J 1S9, Canada
Mailing Address: PO Box 34104, Scotia Sq RPO, Halifax, NS B3J 3S1, Canada
Tel: 902-424-7177 *Toll Free Tel:* 888-360-2111 *Fax:* 902-424-0617
E-mail: filmandcreativens@gov.ns.ca
Web Site: www.filmandcreativens.ca
Key Personnel
CEO & Pres: Lisa Bugden *E-mail:* bugdenlm@gov.ns.ca
Locations Offr: Melanie Solomon *E-mail:* solomomr@gov.ns.ca
Off Administrator: Monette McCue *E-mail:* mccuema@gov.ns.ca
Development agency providing a variety of loans, investments, programs & services. Works to support the growth & development of Nova Scotia's creative enterprises.

ONTARIO

Niagara Region-Economic Development
Campbell East, 3rd fl, 2201 Saint David's Rd, Thorold, ON L2V 4T7, Canada
Mailing Address: PO Box 1042, Thorold, ON L2V 4T7, Canada
Tel: 905-685-4225 *Toll Free Tel:* 800-263-7215 *Fax:* 905-688-5907
E-mail: info@niagaracanada.com
Web Site: www.niagaracanada.com
Key Personnel
Dir, Economic Devt: Diane Simsovic *Tel:* 905-685-4225 ext 3673 *E-mail:* diane.simsovic@niagararegion.ca

Ontario Media Development Corp
South Tower, Suite 501, 175 Bloor St E, Toronto, ON M4W 3R8, Canada
Tel: 416-314-6858 *Fax:* 416-314-6876
E-mail: reception@omdc.on.ca
Web Site: www.omdc.on.ca
Key Personnel
CEO & Pres: Karen Thorne-Stone *Tel:* 416-642-6612
Communs Offr: Sharon Wilson *Tel:* 416-642-6616
Mgr, Film: Donna Zuchlinski *Tel:* 416-642-6628
Encourage producers to make films by offering tax credits, skills development & marketing initiatives, funding specific programs & locations library with photos.

Toronto Film, Television & Digital Media Office
Toronto City Hall, Main fl, Rotunda N, 100 Queen St W, Toronto, ON M5H 2N2, Canada
Tel: 416-338-FILM (338-3456) *Fax:* 416-338-0685
E-mail: filmtoronto@toronto.ca
Web Site: www.toronto.ca/tfto
Key Personnel
Film Commissioner: Randy McLean *Tel:* 416-392-3397 *E-mail:* rmclean@toronto.ca
Free location filming permits & assistance.

University of Toronto Academic & Campus Events
St George Campus, McMurrich Bldg, 4th fl, 12 Queen's Park Crescent W, Toronto, ON M5S 1S8, Canada
Tel: 416-978-2187; 416-978-8613 (film & photo shoot permits) *Fax:* 416-978-4802
E-mail: ace.team@utoronto.ca
Web Site: www.ace.utoronto.ca
Key Personnel
Dir: Steven Bailey

QUEBEC

Montreal Film & TV Commission
Duke Pavilion, 5th fl, 801 Brennan St, Montreal, QC H3C 0G4, Canada
Tel: 514-872-2883 *Fax:* 514-872-3409
E-mail: film.tv@ville.montreal.qc.ca
Web Site: www.montrealfilm.com
Key Personnel
Assoc Dir: Daniel Bissonnette *E-mail:* dbissonnette_2@ville.montreal.qc.ca
Team Leader, Location & Resources: Nicholas Barker *Tel:* 514-872-3102 *E-mail:* nbarker@ville.montreal.qc.ca
Team Leader, Logistics & Permits: Josee Rochefort *Tel:* 514-872-1164 *E-mail:* jrochefort@ville.montreal.qc.ca
Liaison Agent, Location & Resources: Yan Ethier *Tel:* 514-872-1503 *E-mail:* yanethier@ville.montreal.qc.ca
Liaison Agent, Logistics & Permits: Valerie Martel *Tel:* 514-872-1023 *E-mail:* valerie.martel@ville.montreal.qc.ca
Liaison Agent, Info & Resources: Sylvie Lacelle *Tel:* 514-872-1162 *E-mail:* slacelle@ville.montreal.qc.ca
Clerk: Josee Rochon *Tel:* 514-872-4261 *E-mail:* jrochon@ville.montreal.qc.ca
Founded: 1979
One-stop shop to help filmmakers & producers to shoot in Montreal. Offers access to relevant services offered by the City of Montreal, such as permits & authorizations, locations & troubleshooting.

SASKATCHEWAN

City of Regina Film Office
Queen Elizabeth II Ct, 2476 Victoria Ave, Regina, SK S4P 3C8, Canada
Mailing Address: PO Box 1790, Regina, SK S4P 3C8, Canada
Tel: 306-777-7000; 306-777-7529 (scheduling)
Web Site: www.regina.ca/business/filming
Central civic contact when filming in Regina.

YUKON

Yukon Film & Sound Commission (YFSC)
Unit of Yukon Department of Economic Development
Box 2703, Whitehorse, YT Y1A 2C6, Canada
Tel: 867-667-5400; 867-661-0408 (ext 5400, no charge for calls from within Yukon)
Fax: 867-393-7040
E-mail: info@reelyukon.com
Web Site: www.reelyukon.com
Key Personnel
Film & Media Advisor: Iris Merritt *Tel:* 867-667-5678 *E-mail:* iris.merritt@gov.yk.ca
Film Offr: Kevin Hannam *Tel:* 867-667-8285 *E-mail:* kevin.hannam@gov.yk.ca
Founded: 1998
Assists producers who are filming or are contemplating filming in Canada's Yukon Territory. May provide ground transportation & qualified personnel for location scouting. Clearing agency services & communications with all other levels of government. Assistance in obtaining permits & licenses where required. Still photography & location videos of prospective locations; incentive programs available.
Membership(s): Association of Film Commissioners International

Awards & Festivals

Included in this section are selected AV awards and festivals open to professional, student, educational and industrial media producers.

AAAS Kavli Science Journalism Awards
The American Association for the Advancement of Science (AAAS)
1200 New York Ave NW, Washington, DC 20005
Tel: 202-326-6431; 202-326-6440 *Fax:* 202-789-0455
E-mail: media@aaas.org
Web Site: www.aaas.org
Key Personnel
Sr Communs Offr: Earl Lane
Established: 1945
Encourage & recognize outstanding reporting for general audience on science & engineering & its application in a large newspaper, small newspaper, general circulation magazines, TV, radio, online & science news for children. Contest runs July 1-June 30 of the following year.
Other Sponsor(s): The Kavli Foundation
Award: Trip to AAAS Annual Meeting & cash award
Closing Date: Submitted on or before midnight, Aug 1
Entry Fee: None

Academy Awards®
The Academy of Motion Picture Arts and Sciences (AMPAS)
8949 Wilshire Blvd, Beverly Hills, CA 90211
Tel: 310-247-3000 *Fax:* 310-859-9619
E-mail: awardsoffice@oscars.org; publicity@oscars.org
Web Site: www.oscars.org
Key Personnel
CEO: Dawn Hudson
Mng Dir, Membership & Awards: Kimberly Roush *Tel:* 310-247-3000 ext 1127 *E-mail:* kroush@oscars.org
Established: 1929
Categories: Film features, documentaries & shorts
Award: Gold statuettes
Presented: Dolby Theatre, Hollywood, CA, Annually in Feb

AFI FEST
American Film Institute (AFI)
2021 N Western Ave, Los Angeles, CA 90027-1657
Tel: 323-856-7600 *Toll Free Tel:* 866-AFI-FEST (234-3378) *Fax:* 323-467-4578
E-mail: afifest@afi.com; festpublicity@afi.com
Web Site: www.afi.com
Key Personnel
Dir, Festival & Opers: Jacqueline Lyanga *E-mail:* jlyanga@afi.com
Established: 1971
International, documentary & shorts. Submissions on DVD only.
Other Sponsor(s): Audi
Categories: Official Competition, World Cinema, New Directions, Documentary & Short Subject Competition
Award: Cash, trophy
Closing Date: March (applications available), June (early submissions), August (final deadline), see web site for exact dates
Entry Fee: Shorts: $30 early, $55 final deadline; Features (over 30 minutes): $50 early, $75 final deadline
Presented: Nov

AGLIFF-Austin Gay & Lesbian International Film Festival
AGLIFF
2905 San Gabriel St, Suite 300, Austin, TX 78705
Tel: 512-302-9889 *Fax:* 512-302-1088
E-mail: info@agliff.org
Web Site: www.agliff.org
Key Personnel
Film Programming Dir: Jim Brunzell
Established: 1987
Presented: Austin, TX, Sept

Alabama State Council on the Arts Fellowships & Grants
Alabama State Council on the Arts (ASCA)
RSA Tower, Suite 110, 201 Monroe St, Montgomery, AL 36130-1800
Tel: 334-242-4076 *Fax:* 334-240-3269
E-mail: staff@arts.alabama.gov
Web Site: www.arts.alabama.gov
Key Personnel
Prog Mgr, Visual Arts: Elliot Knight, PhD
Two-year residency required.
Award: $5,000
Closing Date: Annually, March 1
Presented: Quarterly Meeting, Montgomery, AL, Annually in June

American Legion Fourth Estate Award
The American Legion National Headquarters
Public Relations Div, 700 N Pennsylvania St, Indianapolis, IN 46204
Tel: 317-630-1253 *Fax:* 317-630-1368
E-mail: pr@legion.org
Web Site: www.legion.org
Key Personnel
Dir, Natl PR: Joseph H March *E-mail:* jmarch@legion.org
PR: Debra Murrell *Tel:* 317-630-1253 ext 253
Media & Communs: John Raughter *Tel:* 317-630-1350 *E-mail:* jraughter@legion.org
Established: 1958
Publications, broadcast organizations & online media eligible.
Categories: TV, radio, newspapers, magazines or books
Award: 15" Pylon Trophy, miniature trophy, $2000 stipend
Closing Date: Jan 31
Entry Fee: None
Presented: National Convention, Aug

Ann Arbor Film Festival
217 N First St, Ann Arbor, MI 48104
Mailing Address: PO Box 8232, Ann Arbor, MI 48107
Tel: 734-995-5356 *Fax:* 734-995-5396
E-mail: info@aafilmfest.org
Web Site: www.aafilmfest.org
Key Personnel
Exec Dir: Leslie Raymond
Prog Dir: David Dinnell
Opers Mgr: Ellie White
Tech Dir: Tom Bray
Established: 1963
Submissions open July 1.
Media: 16mm & 35mm film, DVD, Beta Sp, Super 8mm, all fomats for video, shorts, features
Categories: Afterparty, animation, documentary, experimental, feature length, filmmaker in attendance, films in competition, historic film, midnight movies, music video, narrative, short film, special presentations, themed competition programs
Award: $20,000 in cash prizes
Closing Date: Aug 15 early, Oct 3 standard, Nov 3 late
Entry Fee: $30 early; $40 standard; $50 late. Features: $40 early; $50 standard; $60 late
Presented: The Historic Michigan Theater & various other locations in Ann Arbor, MI, Annually in March

Arizona State University Art Museum Annual Short Film & Video Festival
Arizona State University Art Museum
PO Box 872911, Tempe, AZ 85287-2911
Tel: 480-965-2787 *Toll Free Tel:* 855-278-6060 *Fax:* 480-965-5254
E-mail: asuartmuseum@asu.edu
Web Site: asuartmuseum.asu.edu/filmfest
Key Personnel
Dir: Gordon Knox *E-mail:* gordon.knox@asu.edu
Established: 1997
Outdoor festival celebrating the artistic & creative endeavors of people with different visions & levels of experience. Awards include Juror Choice, LeBlanc Audience Choice, AZ Award.
Other Sponsor(s): Friends of the ASU Art Museum; Star Video Duplicating; Tempe Camera
Media: VHS, NTSC
Award: Title & listing on web site
Closing Date: Feb
Entry Fee: None
Presented: Nelson Fine Arts Center Plaza (behind ASU Art Museum), Tempe, AZ, April

Arkansas Arts Council Fellowships & Grants Program
Arkansas Arts Council (AAC)
323 Center St, Suite 1500, Little Rock, AR 72201-2606
Tel: 501-324-9766 *Fax:* 501-324-9207
E-mail: info@arkansasarts.com
Web Site: www.arkansasarts.org
Key Personnel
Artist Servs Prog Mgr: Robin McClea
Categories: Rotating categories of fellowships; Arkansas residents only
Closing Date: Annually in April
Entry Fee: None
Presented: Annually in Oct

ARSC Awards for Excellence
Association for Recorded Sound Collections Inc (ARSC)
c/o Knight Library, 1299 University of Oregon, Eugene, OR 97403-1299
Tel: 541-346-1852
Web Site: www.arsc-audio.org
Key Personnel
Exec Dir: Nathan Georgitis *E-mail:* execdir@arsc-audio.org
Established: 1991
Published material, sound recordings, discographies.
Categories: Research in recorded classical music, recorded rock, rhythm & blues or soul, recorded general popular music, recorded jazz or blues, recorded country, folk or ethnic music, spoken word recordings, record labels or manufacturers, vintage phonographs & preservation or reproduction of recordings
Award: Certificate, plaque
Closing Date: Annually, Jan 31

Artadia James D Phelan Award in the Visual Arts
The San Francisco Foundation (TSFF)
One Embarcadero Ctr, Suite 1400, San Francisco, CA 94111
Tel: 415-733-8500 *Fax:* 415-477-2783
E-mail: artsinfo@sff.org; info@sff.org
Web Site: www.sff.org
Key Personnel
Arts & Culture Prog Offr: Terezita (Tere) Romo *Tel:* 415-733-8523
Awarded every 2 years in partnership with Artadia.
Media: Film, video
Award: Cash awards
Entry Fee: None

Artist Fellowships
New York Foundation for the Arts
20 Jay St, 7th fl, Suite 740, Brooklyn, NY 11201
Tel: 212-366-6900 *Fax:* 212-366-1778
E-mail: fellowships@nyfa.org
Web Site: nyfa.org
Key Personnel
Exec Dir: Michael L Royce *E-mail:* mroyce@nyfa.org
Dir of Progs/Curator: David C Terry *E-mail:* dterry@nyfa.org
Prog Offr, Artists' Fellowships: Elizabeth Flyntz *E-mail:* eflyntz@nyfa.org
Prog Assoc, Artists' Fellowships: Lauren van Haaften-Schick *E-mail:* laurenvhs@nyfa.org
Established: 1984
Grants are awarded in 15 artistic disciplines with applications accepted in five categories each year. Only NY state residents over age of 18 are eligible, non-students only.
Categories: Architecture/environmental structures, choreography, fiction, music composition, painting, photography, playwriting/screenwriting, video, computer arts, crafts, film, nonfiction literature, performance art/multidisciplinary work, poetry, printmaking/drawing/artists' books, sculpture
Award: $7,000 fellowship
Closing Date: Early Jan
Presented: Spring

Artist Initiative Grant Program
Minnesota State Arts Board
Park Square Ct, Suite 200, 400 Sibley St, St Paul, MN 55101-1928
Tel: 651-215-1600 *Toll Free Tel:* 800-866-2787
E-mail: msab@arts.state.mn.us
Web Site: www.arts.state.mn.us
Established: 2003
Must be Minnesota resident, professional artist.
Media: JPG for images, MP3 for audio, PDF with Vimeo URL for videos
Categories: Performing arts, dance, music, theater
Award: 1/yr $2,000-$10,000
Entry Fee: None

Artist Research and Development Grants
Arizona Commission on the Arts
417 W Roosevelt St, Phoenix, AZ 85003-1326
Tel: 602-771-6501 *Fax:* 602-256-0282
E-mail: info@azarts.gov
Web Site: www.azarts.gov
Key Personnel
Exec Dir: Robert C Booker *Tel:* 602-771-6501 *E-mail:* rbooker@azarts.gov
Deputy Dir: Jamie Dempsey *Tel:* 602-771-6520 *E-mail:* jdempsey@azarts.gov
Grants awarded to individual artists from all disciplines.
Award: Cash
Closing Date: Annually in Sept

Artist Residency Program
Ragdale Foundation
1260 N Green Bay Rd, Lake Forest, IL 60045
Tel: 847-234-1063 *Fax:* 847-234-1063
E-mail: info@ragdale.org
Web Site: www.ragdale.org
Key Personnel
Exec Dir: Jeffrey Meeuwsen *Tel:* 847-234-1063 ext 22
Dir, Residencies & Fellowships: Regin Igloria *Tel:* 847-234-1063 ext 26
Categories: Creative
Award: Residency
Closing Date: Jan 15 (residencies June-1st week of Sept), May 15 (residencies for Sept-Dec), Sept 15 (residencies Jan-May)
Entry Fee: $40; $35/day residency fee if accepted

Artists Fellowships & Grants, see DEC Grants

Arts Create & Arts Respond Grant
Texas Commission on the Arts
E O Thompson Off Bldg, 920 Colorado St, Suite 501, Austin, TX 78701
Mailing Address: PO Box 13406, Austin, TX 78711-3406
Tel: 512-463-5535 *Fax:* 512-475-2699
E-mail: front.desk@arts.state.tx.us
Web Site: www.arts.state.tx.us
Key Personnel
Prog Administrator: Casandra Scholte Jensen *Tel:* 512-936-6563 *E-mail:* casandra@arts.texas.gov
Nonprofits submit application for competitive peer review.
Closing Date: varies

Arts Grants
The Canada Council for the Arts/Conseil des Arts du Canada
350 Albert St, Ottawa, ON K2P 1L4, Canada
Mailing Address: PO Box 1047, Ottawa, ON K1P 5V8, Canada
Tel: 613-566-4414 *Toll Free Tel:* 800-263-5588 *Fax:* 613-566-4390
E-mail: info@canadacouncil.ca
Web Site: www.canadacouncil.ca; www.conseildesarts.ca
Key Personnel
PR Mgr: Genevieve Vallerand *Tel:* 613-566-4414 ext 5145 *E-mail:* genevieve.vallerand@canadacouncil.ca
Established: 1957
Grants & services given to professional Canadian artists (citizens or permanent residents) & arts organizations. Requests must come from Canadian citizens or permanent residents of Canada. Consult web site for various deadlines for different programs.
Categories: Dance, media arts, music, theatre, visual arts, writing & publishing
Award: Varies depending on programs

Asian American International Film Festival (AAIFF)
Asian CineVision Inc (ACV)
115 W 30 St, Suite 708, New York, NY 10001-4068
Tel: 212-989-1422 *Fax:* 212-727-3584
E-mail: festival@asiancinevision.org; info@asiancinevision.org
Web Site: aaiff.org; www.asiancinevision.org
Key Personnel
Exec Dir: John C Woo *E-mail:* john@asiancinevision.org
Prog Mgr: Lesley Yiping Qin *E-mail:* progs@asiancinevision.org
Established: 1978
Media: 16mm & 35mm film, DVD & Beta
Closing Date: Feb
Presented: Various locations throughout New York, NY, Mid-Summer

Atlanta Film Festival (ATLFF)
IMAGE Film & Video Center (Independent Media Artists of Georgia Etc)
25 Park Place NE, Suite 900, Atlanta, GA 30303
Mailing Address: PO Box 5060, Atlanta, GA 30302-5060
Tel: 678-929-8103
E-mail: info@atlantafilmfestival.com
Web Site: atlantafilmfestival.com
Key Personnel
Exec Dir: Christopher Escobar *E-mail:* chris@atlantafilmfestival.com
Artistic Dir: Charles Judson *E-mail:* charles@atlantafilmfestival.com
Established: 1976
Premier screenings of new films & videos, informative seminars about video & film making, panel discussions & guest appearances by filmmakers, video artists & media professionals from around the world. Films selected for competition will compete for over $100,000 in cash & prizes. The short narrative winner will be eligible for Academy Award® competition.
Other Sponsor(s): Eurochannel; Fulton County Arts & Culture; Turner Voices; UBER; XFINITY
Categories: Narrative features, narrative shorts, documentary features, documentary shorts, animated shorts, puppetry shorts, experimental shorts, music videos
Award: Cash & awards
Closing Date: June (early), Oct (regular), Nov (late)
Entry Fee: Features - Withoutabox or student/ATLFF memb $30 early, $40 regular, $50 late; standard $35 early, $45 regular, $55 late. Shorts - Withoutabox or student/ATLFF memb $20 early, $30 regular, $40 late; standard $25 early, $35 regular, $45 late
Presented: Plaza Theatre, Atlanta, GA, March

Austin Film Festival
1801 Salina St, Austin, TX 78702
Tel: 512-478-4795 *Toll Free Tel:* 800-310-FEST (310-3378) *Fax:* 512-478-6205
E-mail: info@austinfilmfestival.com
Web Site: www.austinfilmfestival.com
Key Personnel
Founder & Exec Dir: Barbara Morgan *E-mail:* barb@austinfilmfestival.com
Established: 1993
Presented: Oct 29-Nov 5, 2015

Austin Gay & Lesbian International Film Festival, see AGLIFF-Austin Gay & Lesbian International Film Festival

Avatar Award
Media Financial Management Association (MFM)
550 W Frontage Rd, Suite 3600, Northfield, IL 60093
Tel: 847-716-7000 *Fax:* 847-716-7004
E-mail: info@mediafinance.org
Web Site: www.mediafinance.org
Key Personnel
MFM/BCCA Pres & CEO: Mary M Collins *E-mail:* mary.collins@mediafinance.org
MFM/BCCA Dir of Opers: Jamie L Smith *E-mail:* jamie.smith@mediafinance.org
Categories: Broadcast/Cable industry
Closing Date: Annually, Dec 31
Presented: Annual Conference, Annually in May

Banff Mountain Film & Book Festival
The Banff Centre
107 Tunnel Mountain Dr, Banff, AB T1L 1H5, Canada
Mailing Address: PO Box 1020, Banff, AB T1L 1H5, Canada
Tel: 403-762-6347 *Fax:* 403-762-6277
E-mail: banffmountainfestival@banffcentre.ca
Web Site: www.banffcentre.ca/mountainfestival

Key Personnel
Festival Coord: Christine Thel *Tel:* 403-762-6347
E-mail: christine_thel@banffcentre.ca
Film Coord: Karin Stubenvoll *Tel:* 403-762-6441
Mktg Offr: Nicky Lynch *Tel:* 403-762-6496
E-mail: nicky_lynch@banffcentre.ca
Established: 1976
Festival is presented over 9 days each fall.
Other Sponsor(s): MEC
Media: 35mm & 16mm film, Betacam SP NTSC, Digital Betacam 525, DVD NISC DV NTSC, HD-DS HDTV, HDCAM HDTV
Categories: Best film on climbing, mountain sports, mountain environment or mountain culture
Award: Film Competition: Cash Award $2,000; Grand Prize $4,000
Presented: Fall

Banff World Media Festival
Achilles Media Ltd
102 Boulder Crescent, Suite 202, Canmore, AB T1W 1L2, Canada
Tel: 403-678-1216 *Toll Free Tel:* 888-287-2279 *Fax:* 403-678-3357
E-mail: info@achillesmedia.com
Web Site: banffmediafestival.com
Key Personnel
Administrator: Esme Comfort
Exec Dir: Ferne Cohen
Awards Prodr & Coord: Henry Wong
E-mail: hwong@achillesmedia.com
Established: 1979
Media: International television programs, interactive media
Presented: The Fairmont Banff Springs Hotel, 405 Spray Ave, Banff, AB, CN, Annually in June
Branch Office(s)
21 St Clair Ave E, Suite 700, Toronto, ON M4T 1L9, Canada *Tel:* 416-921-3171 *Fax:* 416-921-9878

The Whitman Bassow Award
Overseas Press Club of America
40 W 45 St, New York, NY 10036
Tel: 212-626-9220 *Fax:* 212-626-9210
Web Site: www.opcofamerica.org
Key Personnel
Exec Dir: Patricia Kranz
Best reporting in any medium on international environmental issues. All entries are submitted online.
Award: Certificate & $1,000 check
Closing Date: Late Jan
Entry Fee: $200 per category
Presented: Hotel Mandarin-Oriental, New York, NY, April

BEA National Scholarships in Broadcasting
Broadcast Education Association (BEA)
Affiliate of National Association of Broadcasters (NAB) (in partnership with)
1771 "N" St NW, Washington, DC 20036-2891
Tel: 202-602-0587 *Fax:* 202-609-9940
E-mail: help@beaweb.org
Web Site: www.beaweb.org
Key Personnel
Exec Dir: Heather Birks *Tel:* 202-602-0584
E-mail: heather@beaweb.org
Award: Scholarships
Closing Date: Oct

Bel-Air Film Festival (BAFF)
Los Angeles Magazine
5900 Wilshire Blvd, 10th fl, Los Angeles, CA 90036
Tel: 323-801-0100
E-mail: info@belairfilmfestival.com
Web Site: www.belairfilmfestival.com
Key Personnel
Pres: Melody Storm
Prodn Coord: Kiah Carr
Established: 2008
Categories: Film screenings include documentaries, animation, short films, student film & comedy
Presented: Throughout Bel-Air & greater Los Angeles, CA, Annually in Nov

The Robert Spiers Benjamin Award
Overseas Press Club of America
40 W 45 St, New York, NY 10036
Tel: 212-626-9220 *Fax:* 212-626-9210
Web Site: www.opcofamerica.org
Key Personnel
Exec Dir: Patricia Kranz
Best reporting in any medium on Latin America. All entries are submitted online.
Other Sponsor(s): Didi Hunter
Award: Certificate & $1,000 check
Closing Date: Late Jan
Entry Fee: $200
Presented: Hotel Mandarin-Oriental, New York, NY, April

Berkeley Video & Film Festival
East Bay Media Center
1939 Addison St, Berkeley, CA 94704
Tel: 510-843-3699 *Fax:* 510-843-3379
E-mail: maketv@aol.com
Web Site: www.berkeleyvideofilmfest.org
Key Personnel
Festival Dir: Mel Vapour
Established: 1990
Media: DVD or Blu-ray, NTSC format
Categories: Student films, documentaries, features, shorts, animation & experimental
Closing Date: June 15
Entry Fee: $40
Presented: East Bay Media Center Performance Space, 1939 Addison St, Berkeley CA, Oct

The Bessies Awards
Television Bureau of Canada
160 Bloor St E, Suite 1005, Toronto, ON M4W 1B9, Canada
Tel: 416-923-8813 *Toll Free Tel:* 800-231-0051 (CN only) *Fax:* 416-413-3879
E-mail: tvb@tvb.ca
Web Site: www.tvb.ca/pages/thebessies.htm; thebessies.ca
Key Personnel
CEO & Pres: Theresa Treutler *E-mail:* ttreutler@tvb.ca
Events Planner: Karine Picard *E-mail:* kpicard@tvb.ca
Established: 1963
Recognize the best in Canadian English language television advertising. Online entry packages are available in mid-Dec.
Closing Date: Feb
Presented: Bessies Gala, Toronto, ON, CN, April

The Best of Photojournalism (BOP)
National Press Photographers Association (NPPA)
3200 Croasdaile Dr, Suite 306, Durham, NC 27705
Tel: 919-383-7246 *Fax:* 919-383-7261
E-mail: info@nppa.org
Web Site: www.nppa.org
Key Personnel
Prof Servs Coord: Thomas Kenniff *Tel:* 919-383-7246 ext 10
Established: 1947
World's leading photojournalism contest. See web site for entry rules & procedures.
Other Sponsor(s): Camera Bits; Canon
Categories: TV news, photography & still news, photo editing, TV photography, web site & TV editing
Award: Certificates & plaques
Closing Date: Jan
Presented: Annual Summit, June

Big Bear Lake International Film Festival
PO Box 1981, Big Bear Lake, CA 92315
Tel: 909-547-4019
E-mail: info@bigbearfilmfestival.com
Web Site: www.bigbearfilmfestival.com
Key Personnel
Exec Dir: Erica Tennyson *E-mail:* erica@bigbearfilmfestival.com
Dir of Programming: Monika Skerbelis
E-mail: monika@bigbearfilmfestival.com
Dir of Screenwriting Competition: Andrew Piggott *E-mail:* screenplaydirector@bigbearfilmfestival.com
Tech Dir: Jeff Underwood *E-mail:* jeff@bigbearfilmfestival.com
Dir of Branding & Communs: Alex Van Mecl
E-mail: alex@bigbearfilmfestival.com
Established: 2000
Jury & audience awards. Mail film submissions on DVD to PO Box 12995, Newport Beach, CA 92658. Screenplay submissions online only. See web site for complete details.
Media: Film, screenplays
Categories: Feature films, short films (narrative & documentary), animation, student films, family films
Award: $1,000 Screenplay Grand Prize
Closing Date: Multiple deadlines (see web site)
Presented: Big Bear Lake, CA

Big Muddy Film Festival
Southern Illinois University at Carbondale, Department of Cinema & Photography
1100 Lincoln Dr, Rm 1101, Carbondale, IL 62901-6610
Tel: 618-453-8301 *Fax:* 618-453-2264
E-mail: info@bigmuddyfilm.com
Web Site: www.bigmuddyfilm.com
Key Personnel
Festival Coord: Elisa Herrmann
Established: 1978
The festival showcases all independent films & while it emphasizes the experimental & documentary filmmaker, the festival also includes narrative & feature length works. The festival provides an opportunity for filmmakers to compete & gain recognition for their work. Among the monetary awards is the newly established John Michaels Memorial Film Award, presented to the best work entered in the Big Muddy Film Festival that promotes human rights, peace & justice topics or environmental issues.
Other Sponsor(s): Illinois Arts Council
Media: 16mm film, DVD, DV, 1/2 inch, 3/4 inch Umatic (all NTSC)
Categories: Animation, documentary, experimental, narrative
Award: $4,000 cash & certificate
Closing Date: Dec
Entry Fee: $35 works under 20 minutes; $40 works 20-50 minutes, $45 works over 50 minutes (all include return shipping)
Presented: Feb

Black Maria Film/Video Festival
Thomas A Edison Media Arts Consortium
c/o New Jersey City University, Dept of Media Arts, 2039 Kennedy Blvd, Jersey City, NJ 07305
Tel: 201-200-2043 *Fax:* 201-200-3490
E-mail: info@blackmariafilmfestival.org
Web Site: www.blackmariafilmfestival.org
Key Personnel
Exec Dir: Jane Steuerwald
Established: 1981
Juror's Choice (1st prize) share $2,500; Juror's Citation (2nd prize) share $2,000; Director's Choice (3rd prize) share $1,000.
Other Sponsor(s): Academy of Motion Picture Arts & Sciences Foundation; Geraldine R Dodge Foundation; New Jersey State Council on the Arts; The Charles Edison Fund; The

Donner Foundation; The National Endowment for the Arts
Media: DVD, 35mm, 16mm, S8mm film. No film prints on cores
Categories: Open competition, no specific categories
Award: Cash & certificate
Closing Date: Dec
Entry Fee: $35 for works up to 20 minutes; $45 for works 21-60 minutes; $15 surcharge for missing fees, bounced check or late entries. Foreign entries must be paid by certified bank check in US dollars
Presented: Festival tours nationally, Late Jan to early June

Blue Water Film Award
Blue Water Film Festival (BWFF)
PO Box 611109, Port Huron, MI 48061
E-mail: bwff@bluewaterfilmfestival.com
Web Site: bluewaterfilmfestival.com
Key Personnel
Exec Dir: Jeremy Stemen *E-mail:* jeremy@bluewaterfilmfestival.com
VP & Film Selection Chpn: Kelly Kennedy *E-mail:* kelly@bluewaterfilmfestival.com
Film Scout: Scott Hall *E-mail:* scott@bluewaterfilmfestival.com
Established: 2009
Other Sponsor(s): Blue Water Arts Committee
Presented: Port Huron, MI, Annually 2nd weekend in Oct

The Brainwash Movie Festival
1675 Seventh St, No 23302, Oakland, CA 94623-6009
Tel: 510-836-3210
Web Site: www.brainwashm.com
Key Personnel
Gen Partner: Dave Krzysik
Festival Dir: Shelby Toland *E-mail:* shelbytoland@yahoo.com
Established: 1995
Shorts are under 13 minutes, Features under 130 minutes. Movies 13-59 minutes are Shorts & 60-129 minutes are Features. For more information, see www.brainwashm.com/entries.
Other Sponsor(s): Adolph Gasser Film & Video; City CarShare; Down Home Music; East Bay Express; Jungle Software; Nimby; OTX
Media: Region 1 or 0 DVD
Award: Gorilla Standard Software (3 prizes) plus certificate & trophy
Closing Date: Dec 31 (extra early), March 15 (early), May 1 (regular), May 10 (late), May 15 (extended)
Entry Fee: Shorts $10, Features $25 (extra early); Shorts $20, Features $50 (early); Shorts $25, Features $65 (regular); Shorts $35, Features $90 (late); Shorts $40, Features $100 (extended)
Presented: Festival Venue, Nimby, Oakland, CA, Annually, July-Sept

Beatrice E Griggs Elementary Administrator's Award
New York Library Association/Section of School Librarians (NYLA/SSL)
6021 State Farm Rd, Guilderland, NY 12084
Tel: 518-432-6952 *Toll Free Tel:* 800-252-6952 *Fax:* 518-427-1697
E-mail: info@nyla.org
Web Site: www.nyla.org
Key Personnel
Exec Dir, NYLA: Jeremy Johannesen *Tel:* 518-432-6952 ext 101 *E-mail:* director@nyla.org
Awards Chair: Dawn Pressimone *E-mail:* dpressimone@wayne.k12.ny.us
To recognize an administrator who has effectively supported the use & improvement of an elementary library media program in a New York State school district during the past 3-5 years.
Award: Plaque
Closing Date: Dec 1

Broadcasters Foundation Awards
Broadcasters Foundation of America
125 W 55 St, 3rd fl, New York, NY 10019-5366
Tel: 212-373-8250 *Fax:* 212-373-8254
E-mail: info@thebfoa.org
Web Site: www.broadcastersfoundation.org
Key Personnel
Pres: Jim Thompson *E-mail:* jim@thebfoa.org
VP: Carl Butrum *E-mail:* carl@thebfoa.org

Bronze Anvil Awards
Public Relations Society of America
33 Maiden Lane, 11th fl, New York, NY 10038-5150
Tel: 212-460-1400 *Toll Free Tel:* 800-350-0111 *Fax:* 212-995-0757
E-mail: awards@prsa.org
Web Site: www.prsa.org
Key Personnel
VP, Spec Events & Progs: Karla Voth *Tel:* 212-460-1446 *E-mail:* karla.voth@prsa.org
Media: 16mm film or video
Categories: Corporate/institutional identity, community relations, internal communications, internal newscasts, public education, product promotion, special public, public service announcements, video news releases
Award: Trophy
Closing Date: Entry form included in *Tactics*
Presented: Winners recognized in *Tactics*

Brooklyn Film Festival (BiFF)
Brooklyn Film Festival Inc
180 S Fourth St, Suite 2-S, Brooklyn, NY 11211
Tel: 718-388-4306 *Fax:* 718-599-5039
E-mail: festival@wbff.org
Web Site: www.brooklynfilmfestival.org
Key Personnel
Exec Dir: Marco Ursino
Dir, Programming: Nathan Kensinger
Dir, Devt: Susan E Mackell
Established: 1998
Best in each category, best of festival & others.
Categories: Short, animation, documentary, experimental, feature
Award: $85,000 in services, products & cash
Closing Date: Nov 30 (early), March 15 (final)
Entry Fee: $40 early; $60 late
Presented: Brooklyn, NY, June

Heywood Broun Award
The Newspaper Guild (CWA)
501 Third St NW, Washington, DC 20001-2706
Tel: 202-434-7177 *Fax:* 202-434-1472
Web Site: www.newsguild.org
Key Personnel
Ed: Janelle Hartman *E-mail:* jhartman@cwa-union.org
Newspaper, magazine articles & broadcast tapes for outstanding journalistic achievement in the spirit of Heywood Broun, a champion of the underdog & the underprivileged. No application. See web site for eligibility & requirements.
Categories: Professional journalism
Award: $5,000 plus two awards of $1,000 for entries of substantial distinction
Closing Date: Annually in Jan
Entry Fee: None

James W Brown Publication Award
Association for Educational Communications & Technology (AECT)
320 W Eighth St, Suite 101, Bloomington, IN 47404-3745
Tel: 812-335-7675 *Toll Free Tel:* 877-677-AECT (677-2328) *Fax:* 812-335-7678
E-mail: aect@aect.org
Web Site: www.aect.org
Key Personnel
Exec Dir: Phillip Harris *Tel:* 812-335-7675 ext 202 *E-mail:* pharris@aect.org
Publication print.
Categories: Educational technology
Award: $500 & plaque of achievement
Closing Date: Annually, July 15
Entry Fee: None
Presented: Hyatt Regency, Jacksonville Waterfront, Jacksonville, FL, Nov

Buffalo Niagara Film Festival (BNFF)
3840 E Robinson Rd, Suite 166, Amherst, NY 14228
Tel: 716-432-1065
E-mail: info@buffaloniagarafilmfestival.com
Web Site: thebnff.com
Key Personnel
Pres & Chmn: Bill Cowell *E-mail:* bcowell@thebnff.com
Festival Dir: Rob Imbs *E-mail:* robi@buffaloniagarafilmfestival.com; Charles Quinniey *E-mail:* charlesq@buffaloniagarafilmfestival.com
Established: 2007
A filmmaker's festival. Hosted by filmmakers & screenwriters for filmmakers & screenwriters.
Media: DVD, 35mm, Blu-ray
Categories: Narrative, shorts, documentaries, screenplays
Award: Trophies & cash
Closing Date: Dec 31
Entry Fee: $45 early; $65 regular; $75 extended
Presented: Buffalo, NY/Niagara Falls, NY, Spring

Calgary International Film Festival
Calgary International Film Festival (CIFF)
214 11 Ave SE, Unit 207, Calgary, AB T2G 0X8, Canada
Tel: 403-283-1490
E-mail: info@calgaryfilm.com
Web Site: www.calgaryfilm.com
Key Personnel
Exec Dir: Steve Schroeder
Established: 1999
Awards presented include Maverick Award; Best Canadian Feature; Best International Feature; Best Documentary Feature; Best Live Action Short Film; Best Animated Short Film; Best Short Documentary; People's Choice Award; Best of Alberta (short film); Youth By Youth Cinema (3 teenager awards).
Media: DVD & Quicktime files
Categories: Genres include animation, art-house, Asian, Black, children, comedy, documentary, drama, experimental, gay & lesbian, historical, humor, independent, Jewish, music video, national, religious, romance, science fiction, short, silent, student, thriller & women
Entry Fee: See web site for various submission fees
Presented: Calgary, AB, CN, Annually end of Sept for 10 days

California Independent Film Festival (CAIFF)
CAIFF Association
350 Park St, Moraga, CA 94566
Tel: 925-388-0752; 310-879-9188 (Los Angeles off)
E-mail: info@caiff.org
Web Site: caiff.org
Key Personnel
Pres & Founder: Derek Zemrak *E-mail:* derek@caiff.org
Exec Dir: Leonard Pirkle *E-mail:* leonard@caiff.org
VP: Joanne Foy *E-mail:* joanne@caiff.org
Established: 1997
Annual festival & premier showcase for independent, foreign & mainstream films. Includes

Slate Award, screenplay competition & Iron Filmmaker contest.
Presented: Multiple theatres

Canadian Screen Awards
Academy of Canadian Cinema & Television (ACCT)
49 Ontario St, Suite 501, Toronto, ON M5A 2V1, Canada
Tel: 416-366-2227 *Toll Free Tel:* 800-644-5194 *Fax:* 416-366-8454
E-mail: academie@acct.ca
Web Site: www.acct.ca/prixgemeaux; www.academy.ca/awards
Key Personnel
CEO: Helga Stephenson *Tel:* 416-366-2227 ext 240 *E-mail:* hstephenson@academy.ca
Dir, Communs: Suzan Ayscough *Tel:* 416-366-2227 ext 231 *E-mail:* sayscough@academy.ca
Dir, Awards & Spec Events: Louis Calabro *Tel:* 416-366-2227 ext 234 *E-mail:* louis@academy.ca
Recognize excellence in Canadian film, television & digital media.
Media: Streaming video & DVDs
Award: Statuette
Entry Fee: Varies for TV/Digital/Film. See www.academy.ca/awards for complete entry fee information

Canadian Student Film Festival
Montreal World Film Festival
1432 de Bleury St, Montreal, QC H3A 2J1, Canada
Tel: 514-848-3883 *Fax:* 514-848-3886
E-mail: info@ffm-montreal.org
Web Site: www.ffm-montreal.org
Key Personnel
Gen Dir: Daniele Cauchard *E-mail:* dcauchard@ffm-montreal.org
Media: 35mm film, video, DVD, Digibeta, Blu-ray or HDCAM
Categories: Fiction, documentary, animation, experimental
Award: Cash, certificate
Closing Date: June 1
Entry Fee: $40; $100 feature
Presented: Montreal, QC, CN

Chester F Carlson Award
Society for Imaging Science and Technology (IS&T)
7003 Kilworth Lane, Springfield, VA 22151
Tel: 703-642-9090 *Fax:* 703-642-9094
E-mail: info@imaging.org
Web Site: www.imaging.org
Key Personnel
Exec Dir: Suzanne E Grinnan *E-mail:* sgrinnan@imaging.org
Exec Asst: Donna Smith *E-mail:* dsmith@imaging.org
Established: 1985
Other Sponsor(s): Xerox Corp
Categories: Electrophotography or related electrostatic imaging systems
Award: $1000 & plaque
Closing Date: Annually, Oct 1

Carolina Film & Video Festival (CFVF)
UNC Greensboro Dept of Media Studies
210 Brown Bldg, UNC Greensboro, Greensboro, NC 27402
Mailing Address: PO Box 26170, UNC Greensboro, Greensboro, NC 27403-6170
Tel: 336-334-5360 *Fax:* 336-334-5039
E-mail: cfvf@uncg.edu
Web Site: cfvf.uncg.edu; www.carolinafilmandvideofestival.org
Key Personnel
Admin Asst: Julie Cullen *E-mail:* jbcullen@uncg.edu
Winners of the UNCG Cellphone Video Competition & the CFVF Trailer Contest will be shown at the festival.
Other Sponsor(s): UNCG Film Union
Media: DVD or .MOV (standard play mode, NTSC)
Categories: Non-categorical, all entries considered
Award: Cash & filmstock
Closing Date: Annually in Jan
Entry Fee: $15 students; $25 non-students; $5 if going to UNC-Greensboro
Presented: Elliott University Center Auditorium, UNC Greensboro, Greensboro, NC, Annually in Feb

Celebration of Service to America Awards
National Association of Broadcasterd Education Foundation (NABEF)
1771 "N" St NW, Washington, DC 20036-2891
Tel: 202-421-3191
E-mail: nabef@nab.org
Web Site: www.nabef.org
Key Personnel
Prog Mgr: Amanda Smith *E-mail:* asmith@nab.org
Mktg & Events Mgr: Isabelle Tilghman *E-mail:* itilghman@nab.org
Established: 1999
Awards for public services presented to US free, local radio & television broadcasters.
Media: Radio & television
Categories: General programming, public service announcements, public service campaigns produced at US television stations
Award: Eagle trophy
Closing Date: March
Presented: Washington, DC, June

Charleston International Film Festival (CIFF)
915 Folly Rd, No 78, Charleston, SC 29412
Tel: 843-817-1617
E-mail: info@charlestoniff.org
Web Site: charlestoniff.org
Key Personnel
Pres/Co-Founder: Summer Peacher
VP/Co-Founder: Brian Peacher
Dir, Festival Opers: Jim Bush
Venue Dir: Jim Gooden
Dir, Logistics: Rob Potter
Dir, VIP Rel: Barbara Yaetes
Dir, Filmmaker Rel: Rob Britt
Dir, Box Off & Volunteers: Deb Britt
Mktg Dir: Genna Shelnutt
Musical Dir: Lee Barbour
Festival Liaison: Gabrielle Schecker
Established: 2007
Categories: Features, documentaries, shorts & animations
Presented: Charleston Music Hall, Downtown Charleston, SC, Nov 4-8, 2015

Chicago International Children's Film Festival
Facets Multi-Media Inc
1517 W Fullerton Ave, Chicago, IL 60614
Tel: 773-281-9075 (ext 3011) *Fax:* 773-929-0266
E-mail: kids@facets.org
Web Site: www.cicff.org; www.facets.org
Key Personnel
Founder & Dir: Nancy Goldenberg
Dir, Mktg: Elizabeth Edwards
Opers Mgr: Kathleen Beckman
Established: 1983
Represents the very best in international children's video, film & television programs.
Other Sponsor(s): Days Inn; NEA; Radio Disney
Media: 35mm & 16mm film & Beta SP
Categories: Children's
Award: Plaque, certificate & cash
Closing Date: May 1 (early), May 31 (late)
Entry Fee: $40 shorts (1-59 minutes); $80 features (60 minutes or longer); $60 shorts, $100 features late entries
Presented: Facets Multi-Media & other Chicago Venues, Chicago, IL, Oct 23-Nov 1, 2015

Chicago International Film Festival
Cinema/Chicago
30 E Adams St, Suite 800, Chicago, IL 60603
Tel: 312-683-0121 *Fax:* 312-683-0122
E-mail: info@chicagofilmfestival.com
Web Site: www.chicagofilmfestival.com
Key Personnel
Founder & Artistic Dir: Michael J Kutza
Mng Dir: Vivian Teng
Media: DVD (NTSC & Pal)
Categories: Feature films, documentaries, short subjects, student films, TV productions & commercials
Award: Gold & silver "Hugos," gold & silver plaques, certificates of merit
Presented: Oct 15-29, 2015

Chicago International REEL Shorts Festival
Project Chicago
428 N Wolcott, Chicago, IL 60622
Web Site: www.projectchicago.com
Key Personnel
Co-Dir: Nels Dahlquist *E-mail:* nels@projectchicago.com; Scott Rudolph *E-mail:* scott@projectchicago.com
Established: 2003
Media: Shorts
Categories: Comedy to sci-fi
Entry Fee: $25 (early), $35 (regular), $40 (late), $50 (extended)
Presented: Chicago, IL, Annually in Sept

Chicago Irish Film Festival (CIFF)
c/o Society for Arts, 1112 N Milwaukee Ave, Chicago, IL 60642
Tel: 773-486-9612 *Fax:* 773-486-9613
Web Site: www.chicagoirishfilmfestival.com
Key Personnel
Festival Dir: Jude Blackburn *E-mail:* jude@chicagoirishfilmfestival.com
Established: 2000
Entries must be submitted online or on DVD. See web site for details.
Other Sponsor(s): Consulate General of Ireland; Film Ireland; IFTN; Irish American News; Irish Film Board; Irish Film Institute; Network Ireland Television; Northern Ireland Screen
Media: Blu-ray Region Free, DCP, Digital Betz NTSC. HDCAM
Categories: Features, shorts, animation, documentaries, Indie, experimental
Entry Fee: Free
Presented: Annually in March

Chicago Latino Film Festival
The International Latino Cultural Center
676 N La Salle Dr, Suite 520, Chicago, IL 60654
Tel: 312-431-1330 *Fax:* 312-786-0126
E-mail: info@latinoculturalcenter.org
Web Site: www.chicagolatinofilmfestival.org
Key Personnel
Founder & Exec Dir: Pepe Vargas
Dir, Devt & Mktg: Sylvia Hevia
Opers Mgr: Berenice Vargas
Established: 1985
Media: Submissions: DVD Region 0 or 1 preferred, Blu-ray (Multi Region or Region A) if DVD backup included; Screening: DCP
Closing Date: Annually in Dec
Entry Fee: $50 per work
Presented: Chicago, IL, Annually in April

Chicago South Asian Film Festival (CSAFF)
Chicago South Asian Arts Council Inc

2909 N Sheridan Rd, Unit 1902, Chicago, IL 60657
Tel: 773-980-9285
E-mail: info@csaff.org
Web Site: www.csaff.org
Key Personnel
Festival Dir: Amit Rana
Established: 2010
Categories: Features, documentaries, shorts & animation
Closing Date: July 15 (regular), Aug 1 (late)
Entry Fee: $50 feature, $35 other (regular); $70 feature, $50 other (late)
Presented: Locations throughout the Chicago, IL area, Sept

Chicago Underground Film Festival
IFP Chicago
2044 W Chicago Ave, PMB 155, Chicago, IL 60622
Tel: 773-341-6727
E-mail: info@cuff.org
Web Site: www.cuff.org
Key Personnel
Festival Dir: Bryan Wendorf *E-mail:* director@cuff.org
Festival Coord: Heather Nichols
Established: 1993
Categories: Student films, nonfiction, comedy, experimental & dramatic
Award: Handmade award by a local artist
Closing Date: Annually in Dec
Entry Fee: Early: Features $25 (students $20); Shorts $30 (students $15). Regular: Features $45 (students $20); Shorts $35 (students $15). Late: Features $55 (students $25); Shorts $40 (students $20)
Presented: Annually in the Spring

The Chris Awards
Columbus International Film + Video Festival
Division of Film Council of Greater Columbus Inc (aka Columbus Film Council)
1021 E Broad St, Columbus, OH 43205-1357
Tel: 614-444-7460
E-mail: info@columbusfilmcouncil.org
Web Site: www.columbusfilmcouncil.org
Key Personnel
Exec Dir: Susan B Halpern
Established: 1952
Annual awards. Now accepting student film & video.
Media: DVD
Award: Chris Award, Bronze Plaque Award, Honorable Mention, Silver Chris for Best of Division, Best of Festival
Closing Date: July 1
Entry Fee: See web site
Presented: Nov

CINE Golden Eagle Awards
Council on International Nontheatrical Events (CINE)
1003 "K" St NW, Suite 208, Washington, DC 20001
Tel: 507-400-CINE (400-2463)
E-mail: info@cine.org
Web Site: www.cine.org
Key Personnel
Dir, Awards & Opers: Betsy Walters *E-mail:* bwalters@cine.org
Established: 1957
Titles are judged based on overall production excellence against criteria that include writing, sound, creativity, insight & effective communication to the intended audience.
Other Sponsor(s): A&E Network; Discovery Communications; Henninger Media Services; National Geographic
Media: Film, video & interactive video, TV, digital, web
Categories: Student, amateur, news, documentary, business, fiction, nonfiction, children's PSAs, science & technology; all lengths; 31 categories total
Award: CINE Golden Eagle Award, CINE Special Jury Award, CINE Masters Series Award, CINE Award of Excellence
Closing Date: Feb/March (spring), Sept/Oct (fall)
Entry Fee: Varies according to length of film/tape from $85 to $175 & up; amateurs $45 & up

Cine Las Americas International Film Festival (CLAIFF)
Cine Las Americas
81 San Marcos St, Austin, TX 78702
Mailing Address: PO Box 1626, Austin, TX 78767-1626
Tel: 512-535-0765 *Fax:* 512-535-6268
E-mail: cine@cinelasamericas.org
Web Site: www.cinelasamericas.org; www.facebook.com/cinelasamericasaustin
Key Personnel
Film Prog Dir: Jean Anne Lauer
Outreach & Opers Mgr: Keeley Steenson
Established: 1998
Best narrative feature, best documentary feature, best short narrative, best documentary short, best youth film, audience, best narrative & documentary features, best film made in Texas (Tami Award). Submissions must be director's first or second feature film. For more information, see web site.
Other Sponsor(s): American Airlines; City of Austin; LatinWorks; Texas Commission on the Arts
Media: Submissions: DVD (NTSC Region 1 or 0); Screening: 35mm, HDCAM 59.94i (excluding SR), DCP, Blu-ray (NTSC Region 1 or 0)
Award: Mention
Entry Fee: $25
Presented: Austin, TX, Annually in April

Cine-World Film Festival
Sarasota Film Society Inc (SFS)
10715 Rodeo Dr, Suite 8, Lakewood Ranch, FL 34202
Tel: 941-364-8478 *Fax:* 941-364-8478
E-mail: mail@filmsociety.org
Web Site: www.filmsociety.org
Key Personnel
Exec Dir: Barbara Caras *Tel:* 941-364-8662 ext 2011 *E-mail:* barbara@filmsociety.org
Mng Dir: Nick Caras *Tel:* 941-364-8662 ext 2006 *E-mail:* nick@filmsociety.org
Artistic & Mktg Dir: Michael Kayatta *E-mail:* mike@filmsociety.org
Established: 2006
Audience Favorite.
Media: 35mm film & DVD
Award: Original sculpture
Closing Date: Sept
Presented: Burns Court Cinemas, Sarasota, FL & Lakewood Ranch Cinemas, Lakewood Ranch, FL, Nov

Cinequest Film Festival (CQFF)
Cinequest
PO Box 720040, San Jose, CA 95172-0040
Tel: 408-295-FEST (295-3378); 408-995-5033 (off) *Fax:* 408-995-5713
E-mail: contact@cinequest.org
Web Site: www.cinequest.org
Key Personnel
Pres & Co-Founder: Katherine Powell
Dir, CEO & Co-Founder: Halfdan Hussey
Programming Dir: Mike Rabehl
Thirteen day event featuring 200 international films.
Media: DCP, HDCAM, DigiBeta, BetaSP, Blu-ray
Categories: Tribute to Maverick Filmmakers, Competitive Independent Films, Asian, Latino Films, Scriptwriting Contest
Closing Date: Shorts: Oct 29, Features: Oct 29, Screenplay: Oct 4 (visit web site for late submission dates)
Entry Fee: Varies
Presented: San Jose, CA, Annually in Feb/March

The Citation of Outstanding Service to the Society Award
Society of Motion Picture & Television Engineers (SMPTE)
3 Barker Ave, 5th fl, White Plains, NY 10601
Tel: 914-761-1100 *Fax:* 914-761-3115
E-mail: smpte@smpte.org
Web Site: www.smpte.org
Key Personnel
Exec Dir: Barbara Lange *Tel:* 914-205-2370 *E-mail:* blange@smpte.org
Dir, Opers: Sally-Ann D'Amato *Tel:* 914-205-2375 *E-mail:* sdamato@smpte.org
Mktg & Communs: Aimee Ricca *Tel:* 914-205-2381
Exec Asst: June Marie Sobrito *Tel:* 914-205-2384 *E-mail:* jsobrito@smpte.org
Recognizes dedicated service to the society over a sustained period of time.
Closing Date: Annually in April
Presented: SMPTE Annual Technical Conference & Exhibition, Loews Hollywood Hotel, Hollywood, CA, Annually in Oct

Clarion Awards
The Association for Women in Communications (AWC)
3337 Duke St, Alexandria, VA 22314
Tel: 703-370-7436 *Fax:* 703-342-4311
E-mail: clarion@womcom.org
Web Site: www.womcom.org
Key Personnel
Exec Dir: Pamela Valenzuela
Membership Coord: Hannah Schmuckler
Established: 1972
Honors excellence in more than 100 categories across all communications disciplines.
Categories: Newspapers, magazines, broadcast, advertising, productions, newsletters, marketing, photography & public relations, book publishing & new media production, International Crystal Clarion for the company that has won the most Clarion Awards
Award: Crystal Awards
Closing Date: March (early-bird), April (final deadline)
Entry Fee: See web site for details
Presented: National Conference & via mail, Annually in Fall

Cleveland International Film Festival
Cleveland Film Society
2510 Market Ave, Cleveland, OH 44113-3434
Tel: 216-623-3456 *Fax:* 216-623-0103
Web Site: www.clevelandfilm.org
Key Personnel
Exec Dir: Marcie Goodman *E-mail:* marcie@clevelandfilm.org
Membership Dir & Off Mgr: Debbie Marshall *E-mail:* marshall@clevelandfilm.org
Established: 1977
Media: DVD
Categories: Narrative, documentary, or animated feature or short
Award: Cash
Closing Date: Annually, Nov 30
Presented: Tower City Cinemas, Cleveland, OH, Annually in March

The Clio Awards
Prometheus Global Media LLC
770 Broadway, 15th fl, New York, NY 10003
Tel: 212-683-4300 *Toll Free Tel:* 800-WIN-CLIO (946-2546) *Fax:* 212-683-4796
Web Site: www.clioawards.com

Key Personnel
Exec Dir: Nicole Purcell
Busn Mgr: Juan Ferreira
Sr Entries & Judging Mgr: Steve Mergaman
Established: 1959
Celebrates creative excellence & innovation in advertising & design.
Categories: TV, radio, print, outdoor, design, interactive, integrated, innovative media, technique, content & contact & student work
Award: Gold, silver & bronze statuettes
Closing Date: Jan
Presented: Annual Clio Awards Festival, May

Communication Arts Design & Advertising Competition
Communication Arts Magazine
Affiliate of Coyne & Blanchard Inc
110 Constitution Dr, Menlo Park, CA 94025-1107
Tel: 650-326-6040 *Fax:* 650-326-1648
E-mail: competition@commarts.com
Web Site: www.commarts.com
Key Personnel
Competition Coord: Lauren Coyne
Established: 1960
Media: AV: submit TV commercials & motion graphics on DVD NTSC (viewable on a standard DVD player) or CD-ROM. Single entries must be on individual cassettes/disks. Computerized formats: Quicktime or Flash should have a maximum screen size of 1024 x 768. Radio Commercials: submitted as WAVE or AIFF files on CD-ROM. Web Based Media: online advertising must be submitted on CD-ROM. If multiple files such as SWFs, embed the project on one HTML document
Categories: Consumer magazine advertising, consumer newspaper advertising, institutional advertising, posters, record jackets, packaging, letterheads, company literature, editorial, books, TV advertising, radio advertising, TV/radio stations IDs, self-promotion, web banners, miscellaneous
Award: Winners will be published in one of our annuals, as well as receiving an Award of Excellence trophy; Design published in Sept; Advertising published in Nov
Closing Date: Annually in May
Entry Fee: $45 single print entry; $90 print series; $110 single video or radio entry; $220 video or radio series

Community Arts Grants Program
Arts & Cultural Council for Greater Rochester
200 Ridge Rd W, Suite 214, Rochester, NY 14615
Tel: 585-473-4000 *Fax:* 585-473-4051
E-mail: artsandculturalcouncil@artsrochester.org
Web Site: www.artsrochester.org
Key Personnel
Grants Coord: Ann C Salter *Tel:* 585-473-4000 ext 208
Grants for public programs taking place the following calendar year. Funds of up to $5,000 are available for nonprofits. Monroe County organizations are eligible to apply to the Decentralization Fund. Arts organizations with budgets under $800,000 & based in Monroe, Wayne, Ontario, Livingston, Genesee & Orleans Counties may apply for Rochester Area Community Foundation Capacity Building Grants. Total amount granted is approximately $100,000.
Other Sponsor(s): Governor Andrew Cuomo; NY State Council on the Arts; NY State Legislature
Closing Date: Typically in the fall for projects taking place during the following year

Creative Arts Film Festival (CAFF)
PO Box 823, Frazer, PA 19355
Tel: 610-889-4928
Web Site: www.creativeartsfilmfestival.com
Key Personnel
Festival Dir: Fel Angel *E-mail:* matterstone@aol.com
Established: 2011
Online international short film festival that promotes filmmakers.
Media: Online link or DVD (NTSC, region 0 or 1) 60 minutes maximum
Categories: Action adventure, animated, documentary, dramatic, experimental, fantasy, horror, science fiction, thriller
Award: Perfect Spirit Film Awards, free promotional listings & cash prizes
Closing Date: March 1-April 15 (early bird), June 15 (regular), July 31 (late), Aug 31 (filmmaker hospitality), Sept 15 (appreciation), Sept 30 (extended)
Entry Fee: $40 (early bird); $50 (regular); $60 (late); $65 (filmmaker hospitality); $70 (appreciation); $90 (extended)
Presented: Annually the entire month of Dec

Creative Impulse Awards (Impies)
Creative Impulse Group
c/o RIIFF, 36 Rhode Island Ave, Newport, RI 02840
Mailing Address: c/o RIIFF, PO Box 162, Newport, RI 02840-0002
Tel: 401-861-4445 *Fax:* 401-490-6735
E-mail: info@film-fesitval.org
Web Site: www.film-festival.org/CreativeIM.php
Key Personnel
Exec Dir/CEO: George T Marshall *E-mail:* georget@film-festival.org
Foil stamped certificate.
Media: Video/Film materials: DVD NTSC; Print materials: no specific requirements, except that an English translation must accompany foreign language entries; Audio entries: CD or DAT; Web site entries: CD or provide URL
Award: Silver & Gold
Closing Date: Annually in May
Entry Fee: $35
Presented: Rhode Island International Film Festival (RIIFF)

CSC Awards
Canadian Society of Cinematographers (CSC)
3007 Kingston Rd, Suite 131, Toronto, ON M1M 1P1, Canada
Tel: 416-266-0591 *Fax:* 416-266-3996
E-mail: admin@csc.ca
Web Site: www.csc.ca
Key Personnel
Exec Offr: Susan Saranchuk
Communs & Pubns: Fanen Chiahemen *Tel:* 647-477-3288 *E-mail:* editor@csc.ca
Awards Chair: Alwyn Kumst csc
Established: 1957
Cinematography competition in 17 categories.
Presented: CSC Awards Dinner, Toronto, ON, CN, Annually in Spring

Cucalorus Film Festival
Jengo's Playhouse, 815 Princess St, Wilmington, NC 28401
Tel: 910-343-5995 *Fax:* 910-343-5227
E-mail: development@cucalorus.org
Web Site: www.cucalorus.org
Key Personnel
Festival Dir: Dan Brawley *E-mail:* dan@cucalorus.org
Established: 1994
Non-competitive.
Other Sponsor(s): Art Works; North Carolina Arts Council; PNC; UNCW
Media: Film & Video
Categories: All genres
Closing Date: Annually in June & July
Presented: Wilmington, NC, Annually in Nov

Dailey & Vincent Land Fest
Denton FarmPark
1072 Cranford Rd, Denton, NC 27239-7930
Tel: 336-859-2755 *Fax:* 336-859-2567
E-mail: manager@threshers.com
Web Site: www.daileyvincentfest.com; www.farmpark.com
Presented: Denton FarmPark, 1072 Cranford Rd, Denton, NC, Annually in Sept

Dallas Video Festival
Video Association of Dallas (VAD)
1405 Woodlawn Ave, Dallas, TX 75208
E-mail: info@videofest.org
Web Site: www.videofest.org
Key Personnel
Founder & Pres, VAD: Bart Weiss
Mng Dir: Raquel Chapa *E-mail:* raquel@videofest.org
Media: DVD or secure online screener
Closing Date: June
Entry Fee: $40

Dance on Camera Festival
Dance Films Association Inc
252 Java St, Suite 333, Brooklyn, NY 11222
Tel: 347-505-8649
E-mail: info@dancefilms.org
Web Site: www.dancefilms.org
Key Personnel
Dir, Communs & Programming: Brighid Greene *E-mail:* brighid@dancefilms.org
Festival Co-Curator: Liz Wolff *E-mail:* liz@dancefilms.org
Established: 1971
Other Sponsor(s): Film Society of Lincoln Center; National Endowment for the Arts (NEA); NYC Dept of Cultural Affairs
Media: Online submission
Categories: Documentary, experimental, narrative, short & feature
Closing Date: Annually, Sept 15
Presented: Film Society of Lincoln Center, New York, NY, Anually in Jan, Feb

Dances With Films
Formosa Bldg, 2nd fl, 1041 N Formosa Ave, West Hollywood, CA 90046
Tel: 323-850-2929
E-mail: info@danceswithfilms.com
Web Site: www.danceswithfilms.com
Key Personnel
Founder: Leslee Scallon; Michael Trent
Established: 1998
Categories: Features, shorts, documentaries & music videos
Presented: Hollywood, CA, Annually

DC Asian Pacific American Film Festival
Asian Pacific American Film Inc
2515 Virginia Ave NW, No 58205, Washington, DC 20037
Tel: 703-507-4375
E-mail: info@apafilm.org; admin@apafilm.org
Web Site: www.apafilm.org
Key Personnel
Exec Dir: Christian Oh *E-mail:* christian@apafilm.org
Event Mgmt Dir: Rose Aruta *E-mail:* rose@apafilm.org
Established: 2000
Devoted to highlighting film & media arts created by +/or about Americans of Asian Pacific Islander descent & other Asian groups worldwide.
Presented: Annually in Oct

DEC Grants
Formerly Artists Fellowships & Grants
Arts Mid-Hudson Inc

696 Dutchess Tpke, Suite F, Poughkeepsie, NY 12603
Tel: 845-454-3222 *Fax:* 845-454-6902
E-mail: info@artsmidhudson.org
Web Site: www.artsmidhudson.org
Key Personnel
Exec Dir: Linda Marston-Reid *E-mail:* lmr@artsmidhudson.org
Dir, Folk Arts Prog: Polly Adema
Dir, Admin: Lisa Fiorese
Dir of Progs & Art Servs: Eve Madalengoitia
Annual award. Some residential restrictions apply. Please see web site for details.
Award: Cash
Entry Fee: None

Detroit Windsor International Film Festival (DWIFF)
15206 Mack Ave, Suite 9, Detroit, MI 48230
Tel: 313-881-0122
E-mail: info@dwiff.org
Web Site: www.dwiff.org
Key Personnel
Festival Dir: John F Kelly
Founder & VP, Community Devt: Scott Paul Dunham
Established: 2008
Other Sponsor(s): Superhouse Media; Wayne State University
Presented: Annually in June

DGA Awards
Directors Guild of America (DGA)
7920 Sunset Blvd, Los Angeles, CA 90046
Tel: 310-289-2038
E-mail: dgaawards@dga.org
Web Site: www.dga.org
Key Personnel
Asst Exec Dir, Communs: Sahar Moridani *Tel:* 310-289-5334 *E-mail:* sahar.moridani@dga.org
Awards Administrator: Elisabeth Jones *E-mail:* ejones@dga.org
To recognize leadership in the film & TV industry.
Presented: Jan

DocMiami International Film Festival
DocMiami International Film Festival Inc
8770 Sunset Dr, No 274, Miami, FL 33173-3512
Tel: 786-493-8308
E-mail: info@docmiami.org
Web Site: www.docmiami.org
Key Personnel
Exec Dir: Monica Rosales *E-mail:* mrosales@docmiami.org
Event Coord: Krystal Oliva
Tech Dir: Nick Toutoungi
Established: 2009
Presented: Annually in May

Dollar Bank Three Rivers Arts Festival
Pittsburgh Cultural Trust
803 Liberty Ave, Pittsburgh, PA 15222
Tel: 412-471-3191
Web Site: www.3riversartsfest.org
Established: 1960
Annual 10 day festival of visual & performing arts.
Other Sponsor(s): Dollar Bank
Presented: Downtown Pittsburgh, Pittsburgh, PA, June 5-14, 2015

DV Awards
6300 N Sagewood Dr, Suite H-383, Park City, UT 84098
E-mail: info@dvawards.com
Web Site: www.dvawards.com
Key Personnel
Pres & Awards Administrator: Martin Rhodes
Established: 2002
Recognizing outstanding achievement in digital video.
Categories: 44 total
Award: Acrylic sculpture
Closing Date: May 1 & Nov 1 (2 sessions)
Entry Fee: $45
Presented: Twice annually, Spring & Fall

East Lansing Film Festival (ELFF)
210 Abbot Rd, Suite 48, East Lansing, MI 48823-4348
Tel: 517-980-5802
Web Site: elff.com
Key Personnel
Dir: Susan W Woods *E-mail:* susanwoods@elff.com
Established: 1997
The Lake Michigan Film Competition (LMFC), consisting of films from the Lake Michigan region, takes place during the festival.
Categories: Features, documentaries & shorts
Closing Date: Aug
Presented: East Lansing, MI, Fall

ELFF, see East Lansing Film Festival (ELFF)

Emmy Awards (Primetime)
Television Academy
5220 Lankershim Blvd, North Hollywood, CA 91601-3109
Tel: 818-754-2800 *Fax:* 818-754-2836
Web Site: www.emmys.com
Key Personnel
SVP, Awards: Dr John Leverence
VP, Awards: Julie Shore
Established: 1949
Presented for program & individual achievement.
Media: DVDs
Award: Statuettes
Closing Date: April
Entry Fee: $300 for program categories; $200 individual achievement entries
Presented: Los Angeles, CA, Aug-Sept

Federico Fellini Award
Tiburon International Film Festival (TIFF)
6 Beach Rd, 544, Tiburon, CA 94920
Tel: 415-251-8433 *Fax:* 633-444-8433
E-mail: info@tiburonfilmfestival.com
Web Site: www.tiburonfilmfestival.com
Given to a first time international filmmaker.
Media: Film & entertainment
Categories: Fiction, documentary, short, experimental, student, children, music video, sports
Award: Trophy & certificate
Closing Date: Dec 1 (early), Jan 15 (late)
Entry Fee: $45 films 50 minutes & over; $35 films under 50 minutes; free for students
Presented: Tiburon, CA, April

Festival du cinema international en Abitibi-Temiscamingue, see International Film Festival in Abitibi-Teiscamingue/Festival du cinema international en Abitibi-Temiscamingue

Festival du Nouveau Cinema-Montreal, see Montreal International Festival of Nouveau Cinema

Film/Video Fellowship Grants
North Carolina Arts Council
Division of North Carolina Department of Cultural Resources
109 E Jones St, Raleigh, NC 27601
Mailing Address: Dept of Cultural Resources, c/o Mail Serv Ctr 4632, Raleigh, NC 27699-4632
Tel: 919-807-6500 (main) *Fax:* 919-807-6532
E-mail: ncarts@ncdcr.gov
Web Site: www.ncarts.org
Key Personnel
Sr Prog Dir for Artists & Communities: Jeff Pettus *Tel:* 919-807-6513 *E-mail:* jeff.pettus@ncdcr.gov
Established: 1996
Fellowship award established 1980, film/video category added 1996.
Categories: North Carolina film & video artists only
Award: $10,000
Closing Date: Biennially, Nov 1 (odd-numbered years)

Robert Flaherty Film Seminar
International Film Seminars
6 E 39 St, 12th fl, New York, NY 10016
Tel: 212-448-0457 *Fax:* 212-448-0458
E-mail: ifs@flahertyseminar.org
Web Site: www.flahertyseminar.org
Key Personnel
Exec Dir: Anita Reher
Annual film/video seminar featuring independent moving-image making. Takes place one week every summer. Open to all interested in pursuing the art of cinema & video. Registration fee & guest filmmakers.
Presented: Colgate University, Hamilton, NY, June

FLICKERS: Rhode Island International Film Festival™ (RIIFF)
Flickers Art Collaborative
83 Park St, Suite 1, Providence, RI 02903
Mailing Address: PO Box 162, Newport, RI 02840-0002
Tel: 401-861-4445 *Fax:* 401-490-6735
E-mail: info@film-festival.org
Web Site: film-festival.org/enteraskidseye.php
Key Personnel
CEO & Exec Dir: George T Marshall *E-mail:* georgetm@film-festival.org
Established: 1996
Media: DVD
Categories: Shorts, documentaries, animation, debut, feature, et al
Award: Trophies, cash, products
Closing Date: May 15 (regular), June 1 (late), June 15 (extended)
Entry Fee: $45 ($10 late fee after regular deadline)
Presented: Venues throughout RI

Florida Film Festival
c/o Enzian, 1300 S Orlando Ave, Maitland, FL 32751
Tel: 407-629-1088 *Fax:* 407-629-6870
E-mail: filmfest@enzian.org
Web Site: www.floridafilmfestival.com; enzian.org
Key Personnel
Mktg & PR Mgr: Jennifer Guhl *Tel:* 407-644-5625 ext 302 *E-mail:* jguhl@enzian.org
Established: 1992
Jury & audience awards. Produced by Enzian.
Other Sponsor(s): Full Sail Real World Education
Media: 35mm video (BetaSp/DigiBeta)
Categories: For American independent films: narrative, documentaries, shorts, plus animation & foreign films, midnight movies, Florida student works
Award: Trophies
Closing Date: Shorts: Oct (early); Nov (late). Features: Nov (early); Dec (late)
Entry Fee: $30 shorts; $50 features
Presented: Enzian Theater, Orlando, FL, April

Frameline Completion Fund
Frameline
145 Ninth St, Suite 300, San Francisco, CA 94103
Tel: 415-703-8650 *Fax:* 415-861-1404
E-mail: info@frameline.org
Web Site: www.frameline.org
Key Personnel
Festival Dir: Frances Wallace *Tel:* 415-703-8650 ext 310 *E-mail:* frances@frameline.org

Established: 1990
Completion of film/video works.
Categories: Lesbian/gay/bisexual/transgender
Award: $1,500-$5,000 grant
Closing Date: Annually in Oct
Entry Fee: None
Presented: Annually in Jan

Freedoms Foundation National Awards
Freedoms Foundation at Valley Forge
1601 Valley Forge Rd, Valley Forge, PA 19482
Mailing Address: PO Box 67, Valley Forge, PA 19481-0067
Tel: 610-933-8825 *Fax:* 610-935-0522
E-mail: info@ffvf.org
Web Site: www.freedomsfoundation.com
Key Personnel
CEO & Pres: Michael Di Yeso *Tel:* 610-933-8825 ext 240 *E-mail:* mdiyeso@ffvf.org
Dir, Educ Progs: Carolyn E Santangelo *Tel:* 610-933-8825 ext 234 *E-mail:* csantangelo@ffvf.org
Established: 1949
To publicly honor & recognize exceptional efforts of individuals, corporations, schools & organizations who promote through words & deeds an understanding of responsible citizenship & the benefits of a free society. Entries should focus on the themes of patriotism, responsible citizenship & community involvement. Send synopsis or script, press release & photos.
Award: George Washington Honor Medal
Closing Date: June 1
Entry Fee: None
Presented: Recipients are notified in the Fall. Presentations vary by Chapter

Fresh Film Northwest (FFNW)
Northwest Film Center
Division of Portland Art Museum
934 SW Salmon St, Portland, OR 97205
Mailing Address: 1219 SW Park Ave, Portland, OR 97205
Tel: 503-221-1156 (ext 10) *Fax:* 503-294-0874
E-mail: info@nwfilm.org
Web Site: www.nwfilm.org
Key Personnel
Dir: Bill Foster *E-mail:* bill@nwfilm.org
Categories: Young filmmakers ages 13-19
Award: Certificate
Closing Date: Aug 1
Presented: Northwest Film Center, Nov

Gabriel Awards
Catholic Academy of Communication Professionals
1645 Brook Lynn Dr, Suite 2, Dayton, OH 45432-1944
Tel: 937-458-0265 *Fax:* 937-458-0263
E-mail: admin@catholicacademy.org
Web Site: www.catholicacademy.org; www.gabrielawards.com
Key Personnel
Off Administrator: Sue West
Established: 1965
Honors works of excellence in film, network, cable television & radio as well as social media.
Media: Upload on the awards web site
Categories: Entertainment, information/education, religion, youth, public service announcements, features, news stories, community awareness campaigns, radio/TV stations of the year & personal achievement
Award: Gabriel statuette & certificate
Closing Date: Jan
Entry Fee: $195 TV; $125 radio; $250 film
Presented: June

Gavel Awards, see Silver Gavel Awards for Media and the Arts

Gemini Awards, see Prix Gemeaux (French language TV)

Gettysburg Bluegrass Festival
3340 Fairfield Rd, Gettysburg, PA 17325
Tel: 717-642-8749
E-mail: bluegrass@granitehillcampingresort.com
Web Site: www.gettysburgbluegrass.com
Key Personnel
Contact: Rich Winkelmann
Established: 1979
Presented: Granite Hill Camping Resort, 3340 Fairfield Rd, Gettysburg, PA, Twice annually in May & Aug

The Global Awards
New York Festivals®
260 W 39 St, 10th fl, New York, NY 10018
Tel: 212-643-4800 *Fax:* 212-643-0170
E-mail: info@newyorkfestivals.com
Web Site: www.theglobalawards.com
Key Personnel
Exec Dir: Rose Anderson *E-mail:* randerson@newyorkfestivals.com
Intl Devt Mgr: Gayle Mandel *E-mail:* gmandel@internationalawardsgroup.com
Established: 1994
The Global Award is given to the highest scoring entry in each competition category. The Global Grand Award is given to the highest scoring Global Award winner in each main competition. Winners are announced in Oct & published on the web site.
Media: U-Matic, CD-ROM, web site, tearsheet, DVD & Beta
Categories: All print, direct mail, radio or TV advertising to the healthcare profession & the consumer; production; craftsmanship, long form film/video & educational programs; public service announcements, newsletters & multimedia
Award: Finalist certificates are also awarded
Closing Date: Aug

Global Peace Film Festival (GPFF)
1000 Universal Studios Plaza, Bldg 22-A, Orlando, FL 32819
Tel: 407-224-6625
E-mail: info@peacefilmfest.org
Web Site: www.peacefilmfest.org
Key Personnel
Exec Dir: Nina Streich *E-mail:* nina@peacefilmfest.org
Tech Dir: Carl Coleman
Established: 2003
Presents films from around the world & global discussions that highlight the power of this extraordinary medium as it relates to new peace issues.
Presented: Annually in Sept

Golden Gate Awards
San Francisco International Film Festival
Division of San Francisco Film Society
c/o San Francisco Film Society, The Presidio, Suite 110, 39 Mesa St, San Francisco, CA 94129-1025
Tel: 415-561-5000 *Fax:* 415-440-1760
E-mail: info@sffs.org
Web Site: festival.sffs.org; www.sffs.org
Key Personnel
Dir, Programming: Rachel Rosen *Tel:* 415-561-5010 *E-mail:* rrosen@sffs.org
Mktg & Communs Mgr: Jaime Galli *Tel:* 415-561-5013 *E-mail:* jgalli@sffs.org
Publicity Mgr: Bill Proctor *Tel:* 415-561-5024 *E-mail:* bproctor@sffs.org
Established: 1957
Other Sponsor(s): California Arts Council; Contributions from Grants for the Arts of the San Francisco Hotel Tax Fund; National Endowment For The Arts
Media: All formats
Categories: Film & video for independently produced short narratives, animation & various documentary genres; TV for current commercial, non-commercial & cable TV productions; New Visions for works that challenge the language of film & video; Bay Area Film & Video for San Francisco Bay Area works that reflect the rich variety of documentaries & shorts. Skyy competition for first narrative features
Award: Cash
Closing Date: Nov (primary), Dec (final)
Entry Fee: $20-$250

Golden Globe Awards
Hollywood Foreign Press Association
646 N Robertson Blvd, West Hollywood, CA 90069
Tel: 310-657-1731 *Fax:* 310-657-5576
E-mail: info@hfpa.org
Web Site: www.hfpa.org
Key Personnel
Pres: Theo Kingma
VP: Lorenzo Soria
Categories: Motion pictures/television
Award: Golden Globe statuettes
Closing Date: Annually in Dec
Presented: Beverly Hilton, Beverly Hills, CA, Annually in Jan

Golden Mike Award
Broadcasters Foundation of America
125 W 55 St, 3rd fl, New York, NY 10019-5366
Tel: 212-373-8250 *Fax:* 212-373-8254
E-mail: info@thebfoa.org
Web Site: www.broadcastersfoundation.org
Key Personnel
Pres: Jim Thompson *E-mail:* jim@thebfoa.org
Awarded annually to individuals for distinguished service in the broadcast area.
Presented: Feb

Golden Reel Award
Tiburon International Film Festival (TIFF)
6 Beach Rd, 544, Tiburon, CA 94920
Tel: 415-251-8433 *Fax:* 633-444-8433
E-mail: info@tiburonfilmfestival.com
Web Site: www.tiburonfilmfestival.com
Established: 2002
Media: Film festival & entertainment
Categories: Fiction, documentary, short, experimental, student, children, music video, sports
Award: Trophy & certificate
Closing Date: Dec 1 (early); Jan 15 (late)
Presented: Tiburon, CA, April

Golden Reel Awards
Motion Picture Sound Editors
10061 Riverside Dr, PMB 751, Toluca Lake, CA 91602-2550
Tel: 818-506-7731 *Fax:* 818-506-7732
E-mail: mail@mpse.org; info@mpse.org
Web Site: www.mpse.org
Key Personnel
Pres: Frank Morrone
VP: Mark Lanza
Established: 1953
Sound editing. See web site for application & presentation information. Only for active members.
Media: Film, television & computer entertainment
Categories: Dialogue/ADR, Sound Effects/ Foley & Music
Award: Golden Reel Award trophies
Presented: Feb

Golden Sheaf Awards
Yorkton Film Festival (YFF)
49 Smith St E, Yorkton, SK S3N 0H4, Canada
Tel: 306-782-7077 *Fax:* 306-782-1550
E-mail: info@yorktonfilm.com
Web Site: yorktonfilm.com/golden-sheaf-awards/

Key Personnel
Exec Dir: Randy Goulden
Established: 1956
Media: DVD
Categories: Aboriginal, animation, children/youth productions, comedy, drama, experimental, multicultural, performing arts & entertainment, arts/culture, biography, history, nature/environment, point of view, science/medicinetechnology, series, short subject, social/political
Award: Plaques, cash, bronze statuette
Closing Date: Annually, Jan 31
Entry Fee: $50 mid-Dec standard early entries; $20 mid-Dec student early entries
Presented: Yorkton Film Festival, Yorkton, SK, CN, Annually in May

Golden Space Needle Awards
Seattle International Film Festival
305 Harrison St, Seattle, WA 98109
Tel: 206-464-5830 *Fax:* 206-264-7919
E-mail: info@siff.net
Web Site: www.siff.net
Key Personnel
Mng Dir: Mary Bacarella *E-mail:* mary.b@siff.net
Artistic Dir: Carl Spence *E-mail:* carl@siff.net
Dir, Opers: Jodie Levey *E-mail:* jodie.levey@siff.net
Programming Mgr: Beth Barrett *E-mail:* beth@siff.net
Established: 1976
Audience voted awards including best film, actor, actress, director, best short film & best documentary (Golden Space Needle Award), juried awards include New Directors Competition, Documentary Feature Competition & Short Film: Live Action, Animation & Documentary.
Media: Submissions: DVD NTSC (Region 1) is preferred, PAL accepted; Screening: DCP & HDCAM preferred
Award: Cash prizes for juried awards
Closing Date: Oct (early), Nov (regular), Jan (final)
Entry Fee: $35-$70 (30 minutes or less); $50-$100 (31 minutes or more)
Presented: Seattle, WA

The Gracies®
Alliance for Women in Media/Alliance for Women in Media Foundation
1250 24 St NW, Suite 300, Washington, DC 20037
Tel: 202-750-3664 *Fax:* 202-750-3664
Web Site: www.allwomeninmedia.org; www.thegracies.org
Key Personnel
Pres: Erin M Fuller *E-mail:* efuller@allwomeninmedia.org
National winners honored at the Gracies Gala in CA, awards for excellence in local, online, public & student markets presented in NY.
Media: CD, DVD, digital media online
Categories: Over 50 categories
Award: Statue
Closing Date: Annually in Jan
Entry Fee: Varies according to category

Grammy Awards
The Recording Academy
3030 Olympic Blvd, Santa Monica, CA 90404
Tel: 310-392-3777 *Fax:* 310-392-2306
Web Site: www.grammy.org; www.grammy.com
Key Personnel
Pres/CEO: Neil Portnow
Established: 1959
Award: Statuette
Presented: Staples Center, Los Angeles, CA, Winter

Grants for Arts & Cultural Activities, see DEC Grants

Guerrilla Film Fest
1421 Massachusetts Ave NW, Suite 202, Washington, DC 20005
Tel: 202-234-2889
E-mail: gfilmfest@yahoo.com
Web Site: www.gfilmfest.com
Key Personnel
Dir: John Hanshaw *E-mail:* john@gfilmfest.com
Dir, Opers: Mike Tibodeau
Established to provide an alternative venue for independent & foreign filmmakers who work outside the Hollywood system.

The Hamptons International Film Festival
47 Newtown Lane, East Hampton, NY 11937
Tel: 631-324-4600; 631-747-7978 *Fax:* 631-324-1558
E-mail: info@hamptonsfilmfest.org
Web Site: www.hamptonsfilmfest.org
Key Personnel
Exec Dir: Anne Chaisson
Established: 1993
Forum for independent filmmakers from around the world.
Categories: Independent film - long, short, fiction & documentary
Award: Awards package worth over $200,000
Presented: 5 days in mid-Oct annually

Havana Film Festival New York (HFFNY)
American Friends of the Ludwig Federation of Cuba
4 W 43 St, Suite 304, New York, NY 10036
Tel: 212-687-2146 *Fax:* 212-681-8037
E-mail: info@hffny.com; info@aflfc.org
Web Site: www.hffny.com
Key Personnel
Pres: Carole Rosenberg *E-mail:* cr@aflfc.org
Exec Dir: Ines Aslan *E-mail:* ines@aflfc.org
Artistic Dir: Diana Vargas *E-mail:* vargasher2@gmail.com
Established: 1999
Other Sponsor(s): El Diario La Prensa; NBC/Telemundo; NYC Dept of Cultural Affairs; NYS Council on the Arts
Award: Best Feature, Best Director, Best Screenplay, Best Documentary, Best Actor, Best Actress
Presented: Quad Cinema, King Juan Carlos I of Spain Center at New York University, Bronx Museum of the Arts, Annually in April

Hawaii International Film Festival
680 Iwilei Rd, Suite 100, Honolulu, HI 96817
Tel: 808-792-1577 *Fax:* 808-749-7783
E-mail: info@hiff.org
Web Site: www.hiff.org
Key Personnel
Exec Dir: Chuck Boller *E-mail:* boller@hiff.org
Dir, Programming: Anderson Le *E-mail:* ale@hiff.org
Festival Dir: Joshua Nye *E-mail:* josh@hiff.org
Other Sponsor(s): Aloha Airlines; City & County of Honolulu; County of Maui State Foundation on Culture & the Arts; Hawaii Community Foundation; Hollywood Foreign Press Association; Louis Vuitton; Oceanic Cablevision; Sheraton Hotels in Waikiki
Media: 35mm, 16mm film, video
Categories: All categories
Award: Jury Award, Audience Award & NETPAC Award
Closing Date: June
Entry Fee: $35
Presented: Oct

Heartland Film Festival
Heartland Truly Moving Pictures™
1043 Virginia Ave, Suite 2, Indianapolis, IN 46203
Tel: 317-464-9405
Web Site: www.heartlandfilmfestival.org
Key Personnel
Dir, Opers: Adam Howell
Artistic Dir: Tim Irwin
Established: 1991
Other Sponsor(s): AMC Independent; Business Furniture; Innovative
Categories: Narrative, documentary & animation feature length & short films
Presented: Indianapolis, IN, Annually 10 days in Oct

Hillman Prizes in Journalism
The Sidney Hillman Foundation Inc
12 W 31 St, 12th fl, New York, NY 10001
Tel: 646-448-6413
Web Site: www.hillmanfoundation.org
Key Personnel
Exec Dir: Alexandra Lescaze *E-mail:* alex@hillmanfoundation.org
Established: 1950
Presented for a piece of outstanding socially-conscious journalism.
Media: Books, magazine & newspaper articles, television, radio. Published material only
Award: $5,000 & certificate
Closing Date: Jan 31
Entry Fee: None
Presented: The New York Times Center, Annually

Hot Springs Documentary Film Festival
Hot Springs Documentary Film Institute
659 Ouchita Ave, Hot Springs, AR 71901
Tel: 501-538-2290
Web Site: www.hsdfi.org
Key Personnel
Exec Dir: Courtney Pledger
Assoc Dir & Opers Mgr: Megan Baker
Established: 1992

Houston International Film & Video Festival, see WorldFest-Houston

Humboldt International Film Festival
Humboldt State University
Dept Theatre, Film & Dance, One Harpst St, Arcata, CA 95521
Tel: 707-826-4113 *Fax:* 707-826-4112
E-mail: filmfest@humboldt.edu
Web Site: hsufilmfestival.com
Key Personnel
Faculty Advisor: Susan M Abbey *E-mail:* sa45@humboldt.edu
Established: 1967
Oldest continuous student-run film festival in the world.
Other Sponsor(s): Associated Students at HSU
Media: DVD/Blu-ray or DCP
Categories: Narrative, documentary, experimental, animation; focus on independent work of 1-30 minutes
Award: Cash & prizes
Closing Date: Jan
Entry Fee: Varies, check web site
Presented: Screening at Humboldt State University, Minor Theatre, Arcata, CA

IDA Documentary Awards
International Documentary Association
3470 Wilshire Blvd, Suite 980, Los Angeles, CA 90010
Tel: 213-232-1660 *Fax:* 213-232-1669
E-mail: info@documentary.org
Web Site: www.documentary.org
Key Personnel
Exec Dir: Michael Lumpkin *Tel:* 213-232-1660 ext 201 *E-mail:* michael@documentary.org
Progs & Events Mgr: Amy Jelenko *Tel:* 213-232-1660 ext 208 *E-mail:* amy.j@documentary.org
Open submission. Membership organization for documentary filmmakers & friends of the documentary. Promotion of documentary production, exhibition & distribution around the world.

Winners are screened at IDA's DocuDay. David L Wolper Student Documentary Awards open to university level students.
Media: DVD (NTSC Region 1 or 0), streaming video link
Categories: Documentary
Award: Statuette for IDA Awards; $1,000 cash prize for David L Wolper Student Awards competition
Closing Date: June
Presented: Dec

Independent Film Week
The Independent Filmmaker Project (IFP)
68 Jay St, Rm 425, Brooklyn, NY 11201-8361
Tel: 212-465-8200 *Fax:* 212-465-8525
Web Site: www.ifp.org/programs/independent-film-week
Key Personnel
Exec Dir: Joana Vicente
Sr Dir, Programming: Milton Tabbot
E-mail: mtabbot@ifp.org
Categories: Emerging Storytellers, No Borders International Co-production Market, Independent Filmmaker Labs, Spotlight on Documentaries
Award: Sculpture
Closing Date: March-May
Presented: New York, NY, Sept

Indianapolis International Film Festival
PO Box 1917, Indianapolis, IN 46206
Tel: 317-560-4433
E-mail: info@indyfilmfest.org
Web Site: indyfilmfest.org
Key Personnel
COO & Pres: Craig Mince
VP & VP, Mktg: Jason Roemer
Established: 2004
Categories: American Spectrum, Hoosier Lens, World Cinema & Matter of Fact
Closing Date: Dec 31 (early), Feb 28 (regular), April 15 (late), April 30 (Withoutabox extended)
Entry Fee: $25 early, $30 regular, $40 late; Withoutabox membs $15 early, $20 regular, $30 late
Presented: Annually in July

Individual Artist Fellowship
Delaware Division of the Arts
Carvel State Off Bldg, 4th fl, 820 N French St, Wilmington, DE 19801
Tel: 302-577-8278 *Fax:* 302-577-6561
E-mail: delarts@state.de.us
Web Site: www.artsdel.org
Key Personnel
Deputy Dir: Kristin Pleasanton *Tel:* 302-577-8284 *E-mail:* kristin.pleasanton@state.de.us
Awarded to emerging & established professionals. Delaware residents (at least 1 year) only age 18 or older. See web site for complete details.
Other Sponsor(s): Delaware State Legislature; National Endowment for the Arts (NEA)
Categories: Dance, folk arts, literature, media arts, music & visual arts
Award: $3,000 cash emerging professionals, $6,000 cash established professionals
Closing Date: Aug
Presented: Annually in Jan

Individual Artist Fellowship Program
Maine Arts Commission
193 State St, 25 State House Sta, Augusta, ME 04330-0025
Tel: 207-287-2724 *Fax:* 207-287-2725
E-mail: mainearts.info@maine.gov
Web Site: mainearts.maine.gov/Pages/Grants/Individual-Artist-Fellowships
Key Personnel
Exec Dir: Julie Richard *Tel:* 207-287-2710 *E-mail:* julie.richard@maine.gov
Established: 1988
Award to honor artistic excellence in all artistic disciplines for current work (within past 3 years). Maine artists only.
Media: Text files are preferred in PDF, but DOC or RTF files allowed. Work samples should be submitted as follows - Mss: PDF or WORD; IMages: JPEG or PDF; Audio: MP3, WAV or AIFF; Video: MPEG-4, MOV or AVI; Web: URL address in PDF or WORD
Categories: Functional craft, literary arts, performing/media arts, traditional arts, visual arts
Award: $5,000 grant
Closing Date: May 5, 2015 for all genres
Entry Fee: None
Presented: Fall

Indy Film Fest, see Indianapolis International Film Festival

INTERCOM
Cinema/Chicago
30 E Adams St, Suite 800, Chicago, IL 60603
Tel: 312-683-0121 *Fax:* 312-683-0122
E-mail: info@chicagofilmfestival.com
Web Site: www.chicagofilmfestival.com
Key Personnel
Founder & Artistic Dir: Michael J Kutza
Mng Dir: Vivian Teng
Competitions Coord/Programmer: Alex Kopecky
Established: 1964
International competition recognizing creativity in the non-theatrical dimensions of filmmaking.
Media: DVD (NTSC & Pal)
Categories: Educational, business, industrial, film & video, corporate
Award: Gold & silver "Hugos," gold & silver plaques, certificates of merit
Closing Date: Aug
Presented: Chicago International Film Festival Awards Night Gala

International CINDY Competitions
IAAVC (International Association of Audio Visual Communicators)
PO Box 270779, Flower Mound, TX 75027-0779
Tel: 469-464-4180 *Fax:* 469-464-4170
E-mail: cindy@cindys.com
Web Site: www.cindys.com
Key Personnel
Exec Dir: Phillip N Shuey
Established: 1959
International web site, videotapes, DVDs, CD-ROMs, computer disks, audiocassettes, films & video walls. Podcast to broadcast. Offered twice a year.
Other Sponsor(s): Apple Computer Inc; Video Placement Worldwide
Categories: Theatrical, Broadcast, Non-Broadcast
Award: Plaques, cash, goods, services & certificates
Closing Date: See web site for deadlines by region
Entry Fee: Varies according to format. See web site

International Communications Media Competition, see INTERCOM

International Emmy® Awards
The International Academy of Television Arts & Sciences
25 W 52 St, New York, NY 10019
Tel: 212-489-6969 *Fax:* 212-489-6557
E-mail: iemmys@iemmys.tv; awardsdept@iemmys.tv
Web Site: www.iemmys.tv
Key Personnel
SVP & Exec Dir: Camille Bidermann-Roizen
Established: 1969
Best television programs produced & initially aired outside the US.
Categories: Arts Programming; Best Performance by an Actor; Best Performance by an Actress; Comedy; Current Affairs; Digital Program: Children & Young People; Digital Program: Fiction; Digital Program: Nonfiction; Documentary; Drama Series; Kids: Preschool; Kids: Animation; Kids: Factual; Kids: Non-Scripted Entertainment; Kids: Series; Kids: TV Movie/Mini-Series; News; Non-Scripted Entertainment; Telenovela; TV Movie/Mini-Series
Award: Statuette
Entry Fee: $350 (non-English); $400 (English)

International Film Festival in Abitibi-Teiscamingue/Festival du cinema international en Abitibi-Temiscamingue
215 Ave Mercier, Rouyn-Noranda, QC J9X 5W8, Canada
Tel: 819-762-6212 *Fax:* 819-762-6762
E-mail: info@festivalcinema.ca
Web Site: www.festivalcinema.ca
Key Personnel
Coord: Stephanie Thuot *E-mail:* sthuot@festivalcinema.ca
Off Mgr: Milene Poirier
Established: 1982
Media: DCP, 35mm or Betacam
Categories: Short, animated films & long feature
Award: Cash prize to the best short or medium-length feature
Closing Date: June 15
Entry Fee: $12.25-$38
Presented: Rouyn-Noranda, QC, CN, Last Sat in Oct through the following Thurs (6 days)

International Wildlife Film Festival
International Wildlife Media Center & Film Festival
Roxy Theater, 718 S Higgins Ave, Missoula, MT 59801
Tel: 406-728-9380 *Fax:* 406-728-2881
E-mail: iwff@wildlifefilms.org
Web Site: www.wildlifefilms.org
Key Personnel
Coord: Chris Sand *E-mail:* coordinator@wildlifefilms.org
Established: 1977
Multiple glass engraved awards; occasional cash awards for Best of Categories & Special Jury Prize.
Other Sponsor(s): Animal Planet; BBC; Center for Environmental Filmmaking; Discovery; Montana Film Office; Montana State University Graduate Program in Science & Natural History Filmmaking; National Geographic; Nature; Panasonic; University of Montana
Award: Engraved glass & certificates
Closing Date: Jan 31, late deadline Feb 9
Entry Fee: Contingent on categories
Presented: Missoula, MT, Annually in April/May

IRE Annual Awards for Investigative Reporting
Investigative Reporters & Editors (IRE)
Missouri School of Journalism, 141 Neff Annex, Columbia, MO 65211
Tel: 573-882-2042 *Fax:* 573-882-5431
E-mail: rescntr@ire.org; info@ire.org
Web Site: www.ire.org/awards
Key Personnel
Resource Ctr Dir: Lauren Grandestaff *Tel:* 573-882-6668 *E-mail:* lauren@ire.org
Recognizes top investigative work in print, broadcast & online media.
Media: Print, audio, video & online
Categories: Print/online-large, medium, small; Broadcast/video-large, medium, small; Multiplatform-large, medium, small; Radio/audio-all sizes; Book-all sizes. Special categories: Tom Renner Award, IRE FOI Award, Investigations Triggered by Breaking News,

Student Work, Gannett Award for Innovation in Watchdog Journalism
Award: Plaque, certificate, cash
Closing Date: Beginning of Jan
Entry Fee: $55 per entry (IRE membs); $125 per entry (nonmembs); $25 per entry (nonmemb students)
Presented: April

Israel Film Festival
IsraFest Foundation Inc
324 S Beverly Dr, No 424, Beverly Hills, CA 90212
Tel: 323-966-4166
E-mail: info@israelfilmfestival.org
Web Site: www.israelfilmfestival.com
Key Personnel
Founder & Exec Dir: Meir Fenigstein
Established: 1982
Audience Choice awards presented for best feature film & best documentary. Held alternately in Los Angeles, New York & Miami.
Media: DVD
Categories: Feature films, documentaries

The Journal Award & SMPTE Journal Certificate of Merit
Society of Motion Picture & Television Engineers (SMPTE)
3 Barker Ave, 5th fl, White Plains, NY 10601
Tel: 914-761-1100 *Fax:* 914-761-3115
E-mail: smpte@smpte.org
Web Site: www.smpte.org
Key Personnel
Exec Dir: Barbara Lange *Tel:* 914-205-2370 *E-mail:* blange@smpte.org
Dir, Opers: Sally-Ann D'Amato *Tel:* 914-205-2375 *E-mail:* sdamato@smpte.org
Mktg & Communs: Aimee Ricca *Tel:* 914-205-2381
Exec Asst: June Marie Sobrito *Tel:* 914-205-2384 *E-mail:* jsobrito@smpte.org
The Journal Award recognizes the outstanding paper originally published in the journal of the society during preceding calendar years, either in the field of motion pictures or in the field of television. SMPTE Journal Certificate of Merit: presented to the authors of the paper(s) receiving the next highest score (up to two may be presented).
Closing Date: Annually in April
Presented: SMPTE Annual Technical Conference & Exhibition, Loews Hollywood Hotel, Hollywood, CA, Annually in Oct

Juno Awards
Canadian Academy of Recording Arts & Sciences (CARAS)
345 Adelaide St W, 2nd fl, Toronto, ON M5V 1R5, Canada
Tel: 416-485-3135 *Toll Free Tel:* 888-440-JUNO (440-5866, CN only) *Fax:* 416-485-4978
E-mail: info@junoawards.ca; info@carasonline.ca; submissions@junoawards.ca
Web Site: junoawards.ca; www.facebook.com/theJunoAwards
Key Personnel
Pres & CEO: Allan Reid *E-mail:* allan@junoawards.ca
Sr Mgr, Communs: Meghan McCabe *E-mail:* meghan@junoawards.ca
Sr Mgr, Awards & Spec Events: Laura Bryan *E-mail:* laura@junoawards.com
Promotes & celebrates Canadian music & artists.
Categories: 42 categories for professionals from "Album of the Year" to "Recording Engineer of the Year"
Award: Statuette
Entry Fee: $30-$80 per submission
Presented: Annually during Juno Week

KahBang Festival
KahBang Arts
84 Harlow St, Suite 1, Bangor, ME 04401
E-mail: info@kahbang.com; press@kahbang.com
Web Site: www.kahbang.com
Key Personnel
Festival Founder: Chas Bruns; Timothy Lo
Established: 2009
Annual event of independent artists in music, art & film.
Presented: Bangor, ME, Aug

Kansas City FilmFest
4741 Central, Suite 306, Kansas City, MO 64112
Tel: 816-286-4777
E-mail: contact@jubilee.org
Web Site: kcfilmfest.org
Key Personnel
Founder: Fred G Andrews
Exec Dir: Veronica Elliott Loncar *E-mail:* veronica@kcfilmfest.org
Established: 1996
Other Sponsor(s): Bauhaus; Fuji Film; Kodak; NewTek; Time Warner Cable
Media: DVD, Blu-ray & Digital
Categories: US/International Short Narrative (fiction) (Drama/Comedy), US/International Short Documentary, US/International Feature Narrative (fiction) (Drama/Comedy), US/International Feature Documentary, Animation, Heartland Short Narrative (fiction) (Drama/Comedy), Heartland Short Documentary, Heartland Feature Narrative (fiction) (Drama/Comedy), Heartland Feature Documentary, Heartland Student Short, KCWIFT Short Screenplay Contest, Experimental, Web Series-Heartland
Award: $500-$1,000
Closing Date: Oct 18 (early), Nov 22 (regular), Dec 31 (late), Jan 15 (Withoutabox extended)
Entry Fee: Varies by category
Presented: Festival Awards Gala, Annually in April

The David Kaplan Award
Overseas Press Club of America
40 W 45 St, New York, NY 10036
Tel: 212-626-9220 *Fax:* 212-626-9210
Web Site: www.opcofamerica.org
Key Personnel
Exec Dir: Patricia Kranz
Best TV spot news reporting from abroad. All entries are submitted online.
Other Sponsor(s): Ben & Karen Sherwood
Categories: Best TV spot news reporting from abroad
Award: Certificate & $1,000 check
Closing Date: Late Jan
Entry Fee: $200 per category
Presented: Hotel Mandarin-Oriental, New York, NY, April

Robert F Kennedy Journalism Awards
Robert F Kennedy Center for Justice & Human Rights
1300 19 St NW, Suite 750, Washington, DC 20036
Tel: 202-463-7575
E-mail: info@rfkcenter.org
Web Site: www.rfkcenter.org
Key Personnel
Pres: Kerry Kennedy
Exec Dir: Lynn Delaney
Established: 1968
Categories: Print, photojournalism & broadcasting (domestic & international), editorial cartoons & college
Award: Cash award
Closing Date: Jan 30
Entry Fee: $75 for all categories except college
Presented: Washington, DC, Early May

KidFilm®
USA Film Festival
6116 N Central Expwy, Suite 105, Dallas, TX 75206
Tel: 214-821-6300; 214-821-FILM (821-3456) *Fax:* 214-821-6364
E-mail: usafilmfestival@aol.com
Web Site: www.usafilmfestival.com
Key Personnel
Mng Dir: Ann Alexander
Established: 1985
Oldest & largest children's film festival in the US. No entry fee. Send with synopsis & contact info addressed to Program Coordinator. No Withoutabox submissions.
Media: DVD screener (NTSC only)
Categories: Shorts & feature length
Presented: Angelika Film Center (in Mockingbird Station), 5321 E Mockingbird Lane, Dallas, TX, Annually in Jan

KidsEye™ International Film Festival
Flickers Art Collaborative
83 Park St, Suite 1, Providence, RI 02903
Mailing Address: PO Box 162, Newport, RI 02840-0002
Tel: 401-861-4445 *Fax:* 401-490-6735
E-mail: info@film-festival.org
Web Site: film-festival.org/enteraskidseye.php
Key Personnel
CEO & Exec Dir: George T Marshall *E-mail:* georgetm@film-festival.org
Takes place during the main FLICKERS: Rhode Island International Film Festival™. Prizes given for best feature, best short & best animation.
Media: DVD or Blu-ray
Categories: Feature, short, animation; eligible age: 8-17
Award: Trophy, passes & an opportunity to have work screened during our best of fest week after the main festival
Entry Fee: $45 adults; films by kids (8-17) $15; films for kids (prof) $45
Presented: Aug 4-9, 2015

LA Femme International Film Festival
Subsidiary of La Femme Inc
324 S Beverly Dr, Suite 436, Beverly Hills, CA 90212
Tel: 310-441-1645 *Fax:* 310-475-8213
Web Site: www.lafemme.org
Key Personnel
Pres & Festival Dir: Leslie La Page *E-mail:* llapage@lafemme.org
Established: 2005
3,000 awards & prizes in each category. Focus on women filmmakers platforming their commercial films for the worldwide audience.
Other Sponsor(s): SAG; WGA
Media: All filmed or digital media
Categories: Screenplay, features, documentary, shorts, music video commercials
Award: Crystal award plus in-kind services & product
Entry Fee: $45-$100 depending on entry date
Presented: LA LIVE Regal Theatre Stadium 14, Los Angeles, CA, Annually in Oct

The Livingston Awards for Young Journalists
University of Michigan
Wallace House, 620 Oxford Rd, Ann Arbor, MI 48104
Tel: 734-998-7575 *Fax:* 734-998-7979
E-mail: livawards@umich.edu
Web Site: www.livawards.org
Key Personnel
Dir: Charles R Eisendrath
Prog Administrator: Melissa Riley
Established: 1981

Annual award recognizing an exceptional professional under the age of 35 for their excellence in print, online or broadcast journalism.
Other Sponsor(s): Knight Foundation
Media: Print, online, broadcast
Categories: Local, national & international reporting
Award: $10,000
Closing Date: Feb 1
Entry Fee: None
Presented: New York City, June

The Los Angeles Asian Pacific Film Festival
Visual Communications
120 Judge John Aiso St, Basement Level, Los Angeles, CA 90012-3805
Tel: 213-680-4462 *Fax:* 213-687-4848
E-mail: festival@vconline.org
Web Site: asianfilmfestla.org
Key Personnel
Dir of Exhibitions: Abraham Ferrer *Tel:* 213-680-4462 ext 25 *E-mail:* abe@vconline.org
Festival Co-Prodr: David Magdael *Tel:* 213-624-7827 *E-mail:* dmagdael@tcdm-associates.com
Established: 1983
Grand Jury Awards (Narrative Feature; Documentary Feature); Festival Gold Reel Award (excellence in short film); Linda Mabalot New Directors/New Visions Award (innovation in short film); Festival Audience Award (Favorite Narrative Feature; Favorite Documentary Feature).
Media: Film: 16mm, 35mm; Video: DigiBeta, digital file
Categories: Experimental, documentary, narrative, graphic/animation
Award: Cash, certificate, product
Closing Date: Nov (early), Dec (final)
Entry Fee: $25 (early); $35 (final)
Presented: Directors Guild of America, Japan America Theatre, Los Angeles, CA

Los Angeles Film Festival
Film Independent
9911 W Pico Blvd, Suite 1100, Los Angeles, CA 90035
Toll Free Tel: 866-345-6337
E-mail: lafilmfest@filmindependent.org
Web Site: www.lafilmfest.com
Key Personnel
Festival Dir: Stephanie Allain
Artistic Dir: David Ansen
Established: 1995
Juried & audience awards.
Closing Date: Jan
Entry Fee: $20-$70
Presented: June

Los Angeles Latino International Film Festival (LALIFF)
Latino International Film Institute
453 S Spring St, Suite 1030, Los Angeles, CA 90013
Mailing Address: PO Box 149, Hollywood, CA 90078
Tel: 323-446-2770 *Fax:* 323-446-2770
E-mail: info@latinofilm.org
Web Site: latinofilm.org
Key Personnel
Exec Dir: Marlene Dermer *E-mail:* director@latinofilm.org
Festival Mgr: Rafael Agustin *E-mail:* festivalmanager@latinofilm.org
Established: 1997
Competitive festival with prizes, serving as a venue where Latino filmmakers come together with industry buyers & distributors.
Entry Fee: $50 feature films; $40 documentaries & short films
Presented: Annually in Oct

Love Your Shorts Film Festival
608 S Elm Ave, Sanford, FL 32771
E-mail: contact@loveyourshorts.com
Web Site: www.loveyourshorts.com
Key Personnel
Chair, Bd of Dirs & Festival Dir: Nelson D Beverly
Vice Chair, Bd of Dirs: Debra Martin
Treas: Rachel Delinski
Secy: Gene Kruckemyer
Established: 2011
Welcomes short films (30 minutes or less) in all genres. Open to amateur & professional filmmakers in all categories.
Categories: Animation & comedy
Award: Monroe Award: Metal artwork designed by Julie Kessler
Presented: Sanford, FL, Feb

Carl F & Viola V Mahnke Multimedia Award
Association for Educational Communications & Technology (AECT)
320 W Eighth St, Suite 101, Bloomington, IN 47404-3745
Tel: 812-335-7675 *Toll Free Tel:* 877-677-AECT (677-2328) *Fax:* 812-335-7678
E-mail: aect@aect.org
Web Site: www.aect.org
Key Personnel
Exec Dir: Phillip Harris *Tel:* 812-335-7675 ext 202 *E-mail:* pharris@aect.org
Media: Multimedia
Categories: K-12 & higher education
Award: Plaque
Presented: Hyatt Regency, Jacksonville Riverfront, Jacksonville, FL, Nov

Maine Student Film & Video Festival
Maine Alliance of Media Arts
103 Montrose Ave, Portland, ME 04103
Tel: 207-415-7154
E-mail: info@msfvf.com
Web Site: www.msfvf.com
Award for Maine residents & students 19 years of age or younger. All genres accepted.
Media: All video formats & DVD
Categories: Pre-teen grades (K-6), Junior (grades 7-8), Senior (grades 9-12)
Award: $2,500 scholarship to Young Filmmakers Prog
Closing Date: Annually in June
Entry Fee: $10
Presented: Maine International Film Festival, Waterville Opera House, Waterville, ME, Annually in July

The Martha's Vineyard Film Festival (MVFF)
PO Box 592, 9 State Rd, Chilmark, MA 02535
Tel: 508-645-9599 *Fax:* 508-645-9893
Web Site: www.tmvff.org
Key Personnel
Founder, Prodr & Creative Dir: Thomas Bena
Mng Dir: Brian Ditchfield
Established: 2001
Presented: Chilmark Community Center, 560 South Rd, Chilmark, MA, Annually 3 days in mid-March

Martha's Vineyard International Film Festival
Martha's Vineyard Film Society Inc
PO Box 4423, Vineyard Haven, MA 02568
Tel: 508-696-9369
E-mail: info@mvfilmsociety.com
Web Site: www.mvfilmfest.com
Key Personnel
Founder, Pres & Festival Dir: Richard Paradise *E-mail:* rich@mvfilmsociety.com
Established: 2006
Presented: Martha's Vineyard Film Center, Tisbury Marketplace, 79 Beach Rd, Vineyard Haven, MA, Sept 8-13, 2015

Maverick Awards
Woodstock Film Festival
13 Rock City Rd, Woodstock, NY 12498
Mailing Address: PO Box 1406, Woodstock, NY 12498-8406
Tel: 845-679-4265; 845-810-0131 *Fax:* 509-479-5414
E-mail: info@woodstockfilmfestival.com
Web Site: www.woodstockfilmfestival.com
Key Personnel
Co-Founder & Festival Dir: Meira Blaustein *E-mail:* meira@woodstockfilmfestival.com
Co-Founder & Dir, Devt: Laurent Rejto *E-mail:* laurent@woodstockfilmfestival.com
Established: 2000
Cash, prizes +/or services are given out in most categories. Audience awards are also presented for best feature & best documentary.
Categories: Feature, documentary, short documentary short film, student film, cinematography, editing & animation
Closing Date: June
Entry Fee: $25-$50
Presented: Woodstock, NY, Oct

Annual MCA-I Media Festival
Media Communications Association-International (MCA-I)
PO Box 5135, Madison, WI 53705-0135
Tel: 608-836-0722 *Toll Free Tel:* 888-899-MCAI (899-6224) *Toll Free Fax:* 888-862-8150
E-mail: info@mca-i.org; mcaimediafestival@gmail.com
Web Site: www.mca-i.org
Key Personnel
Exec Dir: Connie Terwilliger
Media: Online
Categories: Training, information, sales & marketing, internal & external communications, interactive video, videoconferencing, public service announcement & student, budget production, training/educational, writing, graphic/animation
Award: Plaque
Entry Fee: $80 membs, $100 non-membs, student membs $25, student non-membs $40

Media Arts Grants
Jerome Foundation
400 Sibley St, Suite 125, St Paul, MN 55101
Tel: 651-224-9431 *Toll Free Tel:* 800-995-3766 *Fax:* 651-224-3439
E-mail: info@jeromefdn.org
Web Site: www.jeromefdn.org
Key Personnel
Prog Dir: Robert Byrd *E-mail:* rbyrd@jeromefdn.org
Grants to emerging filmmakers who reside in Minnesota or New York City.
Other Sponsor(s): Jerome Foundation
Media: Film & Video
Categories: Documentary, narrative, experimental, animation
Award: Up to $30,000
Closing Date: Ongoing

Melbourne Independent Filmmakers Festival (MIFF)
3 Boys Productions
1399 S Harbor City Blvd, Melbourne, FL 32901
Tel: 321-726-1711 *Fax:* 321-726-1715
Web Site: www.3boysproductions.com
Key Personnel
Prog Chmn: Terry Cronin *E-mail:* tcronin2@aol.com
Established: 1999
Audience Award, Peer Award.
Categories: Features, shorts, documentaries, animation, horror, science fiction, drama, comedy
Closing Date: May 1
Entry Fee: None; $10 after deadline

Miami International Film Festival
Miami Film Society

300 NE Second Ave, Miami, FL 33132
Tel: 305-237-FILM (237-3456) *Fax:* 305-237-7344
E-mail: info@miamifilmfestival.com
Web Site: miamifilmfestival.com
Key Personnel
Exec Dir: Jaie Laplante
Established: 1984
Grand Jury Prizes & Audience Awards are presented in 3 categories: Dramatic Features—World Cinema Competition, Dramatic Features—Ibero-American Cinema Competition & Documentary Features—World & Ibero-American Cinema Competition. FIPRESCI Prize is presented by the International Federation of Film Critics to a film in the Dramatic Features—World Cinema Competition category.
Media: Submissions: Secure online screener; Screening: DCP
Categories: Knight Competition, Knight Documentary Competition, Ibero-American Opera Prima Competition, Cinema 360, Doc-You-Up, Florida Focus, Lee Brian Schrager's Culinary Cinema, Shorts Competition, Reel Music Scene, America the Beautiful, Visions, Mayhem, Veo Miami Digital Market, Veo Voir Canada, Miami-Shanghai CinemaSlam
Award: Cash

Miami short Film Festival (MsFF)
247 SW Eighth St, Suite 44, Miami, FL 33130
E-mail: info@miamishortfilmfestival.com
Web Site: www.miamishortfilmfestival.com
Key Personnel
Founder & Festival Dir: William Vela
E-mail: william@miamishortfilmfestival.com
Mktg/PR & Coord: Melany Carcamo-Birchenall
E-mail: melany@miamishortfilmfestival.com
Dir, Opers: Paola Celpa *E-mail:* paola@miamishortfilmfestival.com
Established: 2002
Short films of 20 minutes or less. See web site for full list of eligibility requirements.
Media: 35mm, 16mm, 8mm, HD, Video
Categories: Best of Fest, Best Foreign Film, Best Animation, Best Experimental, Best Documentary, Best Narrative, Best Environmental, Best Local, Best Music Video, Best Cell or Mobile Short, Best Extreme Sport Video
Closing Date: Multiple deadlines, see web site for details
Entry Fee: $35-$90
Presented: Dec 4-11, 2015

MIFF, see Melbourne Independent Filmmakers Festival (MIFF)

Mill Valley Film Festival
California Film Institute
Affiliate of Christopher B Smith Rafael Film Center
1001 Lootens Place, Suite 220, San Rafael, CA 94901
Tel: 415-383-5256 *Fax:* 415-383-8606
E-mail: mvff@cafilm.org; info@cafilm.org
Web Site: www.mvff.com; www.cafilm.org
Key Personnel
Founder/Dir: Mark Fishkin
Dir of Programming: Zoe Elton
Established: 1977
Non-competitive, invitational festival; call for entry & institute requests.
Other Sponsor(s): Academy of Motion Pictures Arts & Sciences; American Airlines; Fireman's Fund; Marin Community Foundation; Maroevich, O'Shea & Coghlan; Piper Jaffray
Media: Submissions: DVD (NTSC Region 1 or 0); Exhibition: 35mm, HDCAM, Blu-ray & other digital formats
Categories: Animated, narrative, features & shorts, documentary, video art, experimental
Closing Date: May 17 (early); June 14 (final); check in Spring for update
Entry Fee: $30 postmarked May 17; $40 after May 17; check in Spring for update
Presented: Sequoia Twin Theatres, Mill Valley, CA & Smith Rafael Film Center, San Rafael, CA, 1st Thursday in Oct, 11 day festival

Minneapolis St Paul International Film Festival (MSPIFF)
The Film Society of Minneapolis St Paul
125 SE Main St, Suite 125A, Minneapolis, MN 55414
Tel: 612-331-7563 *Fax:* 612-378-7750
E-mail: info@mspfilmsociety.org; submissions@mspfilmsociety.org
Web Site: www.mspfilmsociety.org
Key Personnel
Artistic Dir: Al Milgrom
Established: 1981
Emerging Filmmaker, Best Documentary, Minnesota Made, Audience choice.
Media: DVD, DCP, HDcam, Blu-ray (feature); ProRes, H.264 or similar (shorts)
Categories: Narrative feature, documentary feature, narrative short, documentary short, emerging filmmaker, Minnesota made
Closing Date: Oct (early), Nov (regular), Dec (late), Jan (extended)
Entry Fee: Early: $30 (shorts), $45 (features); Regular: $45 (shorts), $60 (features); Late: $60 (shorts), $75 (features); Extended: $75 (shorts), $90 (features), $30 (Minnesota Made); Withoutabox Extended: $85 (shorts), $100 (features), $45 (Minnesota Made). No submission fees required for early
Presented: April

Missouri Honor Medal for Distinguished Service in Journalism
Missouri School of Journalism
School of Journalism, 120 Neff Hall, Columbia, MO 65211-1200
Tel: 573-882-4821 *Fax:* 573-884-5400
E-mail: journalism@missouri.edu
Web Site: journalism.missouri.edu
Key Personnel
Exec Dir, Advancement: Colin Kilpatrick
Tel: 573-884-4803 *E-mail:* kilpatrickc@missouri.edu
Established: 1930
Missouri Honor Medal for Distinguished Service in Journalism.
Award: Certificate & medal
Presented: Columbia, MO

The Mobius Advertising Awards
The United States Festivals Association
713 S Pacific Coast Hwy, Suite A, Redondo Beach, CA 90277-4233
Tel: 310-540-0959 *Fax:* 310-316-8905
E-mail: mobiusinfo@mobiusawards.com
Web Site: www.mobiusawards.com
Key Personnel
Chmn: Lee W Gluckman, Jr
E-mail: leegluckman@mobiusawards.com
Exec Dir: Kristen Gluckman
E-mail: kristengluckman@mobiusawards.com
Established: 1971
Categories: Automotive, children's products, clothing, commercial products, food, home care products, home furnishings, personal products, personal articles & gift items, pet products, pharmaceuticals, recreation, services, miscellaneous, production techniques, including art animation, copywriting, direction, editing, etc
Award: Mobius statuettes & certificates & special industry sponsored awards
Closing Date: Annually, Oct 1
Entry Fee: None
Presented: Annually, early Feb

Montreal International Festival of Films on Art
2130 Crescent St, Montreal, QC H3G 2B8, Canada
Tel: 514-874-1637 *Fax:* 514-874-9929
E-mail: info@artfifa.com
Web Site: www.artfifa.com
Key Personnel
Founder & Dir: Rene Rozon
Programming Asst: Karen Archambault
Established: 1981
Media: Preselection process: DVD or CD; Festival screening: HDCAM, HDCAM SR, DigiBeta, 35mm film, NTSC or PAL, .MOV digital files
Categories: Competition, tributes, horizons, media arts, focus on the 7th art, time recaptured
Award: A dozen honorary awards, some with cash grants
Closing Date: Oct
Entry Fee: $50 US or CN per film & video title submitted, $40 US or CN if submitted no later than early Sept
Presented: Montreal, QC, CN, March

Montreal International Festival of Nouveau Cinema
3805 Blvd Ste-Laurent, Montreal, QC H2W 1X9, Canada
Tel: 514-282-0004 *Fax:* 514-282-6664
E-mail: info@nouveaucinema.ca
Web Site: www.nouveaucinema.ca
Key Personnel
Exec Dir: Nicolas Girard Deltruc
Dir, Programming: Claude Chamberlan
Established: 1971
Golden shewolf-Quebecor ($15,000).
Media: 16mm & 35mm film, HD, new media, beta, 3D
Categories: Feature, documentary, short, new media works, experimental, music
Award: Prize
Closing Date: July 1
Entry Fee: $35 CN
Presented: Montreal, QC, CN, Mid-Oct

Montreal World Film Festival
1432 de Bleury St, Montreal, QC H3A 2J1, Canada
Tel: 514-848-3883 *Fax:* 514-848-3886
E-mail: info@ffm-montreal.org
Web Site: www.ffm-montreal.org
Key Personnel
Pres: Serge Losique
Media: DCP, HDCAM, 3D
Categories: World Competition, First Films World Competition, Hors Concours (World Greats, out of competition), Focus on World Cinema (Americas, Europe, Asia, Africa, Oceania), Documentaries of the World, Tributes, Our Cinema, Cinema Under the Stars, Student Film Festival
Award: Trophy
Closing Date: Jan 1-July 1 features; Jan 1-June 10 shorts
Entry Fee: $100 features; $40 short
Presented: Montreal, QC, CN, Aug 27-Sept 7, 2015

Moondance International Film Festival
Mermaid7seas Productions
970 Ninth St, Boulder, CO 80302-7226
Tel: 303-545-0202
Web Site: moondancefilmfestival.com
Key Personnel
Founder, Exec Dir & Creative Dir: Elizabeth English *E-mail:* director@moondancefilmfestival.com
Established: 1999
Spirit of Moondance Award (women), Seahorse Award (men), Dolphin Award (18 years & under), Neptune Award (75 years & over), Sand

Castle Award (male-female team), Calypso Award (environmental protection), Gaia (inspirational), Columbine (non-violent conflict resolution), Atlantis Award (foreign), Starfish Award (comedy), Living Legend (women), Angel Award (men & women), Cinema Pioneer Award (men & women), DGA Director's Award (men & women), Abyss Award (meaningful thriller, horror & supernatural), Colorado Ocean Award (CO residents), Seven Seas Award (promote cross-cultural knowledge & awareness), Mermaid's Pearl Award (contributing women in film industry), Legacy Award (women who helped others achieve success in film), Better World Award (important contribution about vital humanitarian or environmental issues).
Categories: Features: animation, documentary, narrative, films for kids, multimedia, music; Music: film score, libretto, music video; TV: original mini-series (1 hour), movie of the week, episodic (1/2 hour & 1 hour), filmed pilot, pilot script, pilot for kids; Short Film: animation, documentary, film by kids 18 & under, film for kids, multimedia; Radio: play (comedy or drama), documentary; Web: web series webisode
Closing Date: Dec 1-Dec 31 (early), Jan 1-June 30 (regular), July 1-31 (final)
Entry Fee: $50 early; $75 regular; $100 final

Mountainfilm in Telluride
109 E Colorado Ave, Suite 1, Telluride, CO 81435
Mailing Address: PO Box 1088, Telluride, CO 81435-1088
Tel: 970-728-4123 *Fax:* 970-728-6458
E-mail: contact@mountainfilm.org
Web Site: www.mountainfilm.org
Key Personnel
Exec Dir: Peter Kenworthy
Festival Dir: David Holbrooke *Tel:* 970-728-4123 ext 14
Festival Prodr: Stash Wislocki
Established: 1979
Other Sponsor(s): Eddie Bauer; Horny Toad Activewear; Jansport; Original Productions; Osprey; Outside Magazine; Outside Television; Raynier Foundation; Shady Acres; Telluride Foundation; Telluride Ski Resort; Town of Telluride
Media: Submissions: DVD or online screener; Screening: DCP, HDCAM
Categories: Norman Vaughan Indomitable Spirit Award, Moving Mountains Prize, Student Award, Audience Award, Charlie Fowler Award, Cinematography Award, Festival Director's Award
Award: $3,000 (grand prize)
Closing Date: Dec (early), Jan (regular), Feb (late)
Entry Fee: Early: $60 (features), $30 (shorts); Regular: $80 (features), $40 (shorts); Late: $100 (features); $50 (shorts)
Presented: Telluride, CO, May

The Edward R Murrow Award
Overseas Press Club of America
40 W 45 St, New York, NY 10036
Tel: 212-626-9220 *Fax:* 212-626-9210
Web Site: www.opcofamerica.org
Key Personnel
Exec Dir: Patricia Kranz
Best TV interpretation or documentary on international affairs. All entries are submitted online.
Other Sponsor(s): CBS
Award: Certificate & $1,000 check
Closing Date: Annually in late Jan
Entry Fee: $200 per category
Presented: Hotel Mandarin-Oriental, New York, NY, Annually in April

Edward R Murrow Award
Corporation for Public Broadcasting (CPB)
401 Ninth St NW, Washington, DC 20004-2129
Tel: 202-879-9600 *Toll Free Tel:* 800-272-2190 *Fax:* 202-879-9700
E-mail: comments@cpb.org
Web Site: www.cpb.org
Key Personnel
SVP, Journalism & Radio: Bruce Theriult *Tel:* 202-879-9801
Established: 1977
Public Radio.
Media: Radio
Categories: Award given to person for outstanding contribution to public radio
Award: Plaque
Closing Date: Varies
Entry Fee: None
Presented: Public Radio Program Conference, Washington, DC, Varies

NAB Distinguished Service Award
National Association of Broadcasters (NAB)
1771 "N" St NW, Washington, DC 20036
Tel: 202-429-5300 *Fax:* 202-775-3516
E-mail: nab@nab.org
Web Site: www.nab.org
Key Personnel
VP, NAB Television: Carolyn Wilkins
Established: 1953
Awarded annually to a distinguished member of the broadcast industry.
Award: Sculpture
Presented: The NAB Show, Las Vegas Convention Center, Las Vegas, NV, April

Nantucket Film Festival (NFF)
68 Jay St, Suite 319, Brooklyn, NY 11201
Tel: 646-480-1900; 508-325-6274 *Fax:* 646-365-3367
E-mail: info@nantucketfilmfestival.org
Web Site: www.nantucketfilmfestival.org
Key Personnel
Exec Dir: Colin Stanfield
Festival Dir: Mystelle Brabbee *E-mail:* mystelle@nantucketfilmfestival.org
Festival Prodr: Bill Curran
Established: 1996
Categories: Feature films, short films, feature screenplay, hour-long TV pilot, half-hour TV pilot, short screenplay
Closing Date: See web site for submisison guidelines
Presented: Various venues, Nantucket, MA, June 24-29, 2015

National Headliner Awards
Press Club of Atlantic City
PO Box 239, Northfield, NJ 08225-0239
Tel: 609-601-2116
E-mail: info@headlinerawards.org
Web Site: www.headlinerawards.org
Key Personnel
Admin Asst: Erika Melhorn
Established: 1935
Journalism awards, excellence in reporting radio & TV.
Media: DVD
Categories: Print, radio, TV & Internet
Award: Plaques & certificates, cash prizes for each division of Grand Award
Closing Date: Jan
Entry Fee: $75

National Old Time Country Bluegrass & Folk Music Festival
National Traditional Country Music Association Inc (NTCMA)
PO Box 492, Anita, IA 50020
Tel: 712-762-4363
Web Site: ntcma.net
Key Personnel
Contact: Bob Everhart *E-mail:* bobeverhart@yahoo.com
Presented: Le Mars, IA, Aug 31-Sept 6, 2015

National Short Film & Video Competition
USA Film Festival
6116 N Central Expwy, Suite 105, Dallas, TX 75206
Tel: 214-821-6300; 214-821-FILM (821-3456) *Fax:* 214-821-6364
E-mail: usafilmfestival@aol.com
Web Site: www.usafilmfestival.com
Key Personnel
Mng Dir: Ann Alexander
Established: 1979
Media: Submissions: DVD screener; Finished formats: 16mm, 35mm & 70mm film, IMAX, HDCAM, DVCAM, DCI, BetaSP, DigiBeta, Blu-ray, DCP, DVD
Categories: Fiction, nonfiction, experimental, animated, family, student, Texas-produced
Award: $1,000 cash for fiction, nonfiction, experimental & animated, student & Texas-produced. $250 Special Jury awards
Closing Date: Feb 1 or March 1 (final)
Entry Fee: $60 by Feb 1, $65 by March 1
Presented: Annually, late April

National Storytelling Festival
International Storytelling Center
Affiliate of Smithsonian Institution
116 W Main St, Jonesborough, TN 37659
Tel: 423-753-2171 *Toll Free Tel:* 800-952-8392 *Fax:* 423-913-8219
E-mail: customerservice@storytellingcenter.net
Web Site: www.storytellingfestival.net; www.storytellingcenter.net
Key Personnel
Exec Dir: Kiran Sirah *E-mail:* kiran@storytellingcenter.net
Dir, Progs: Susan O'Connor *E-mail:* susan@storytellingcenter.net
Established: 1973
Premier storytelling event.
Presented: Jonesborough, TN, Annually, first full weekend in Oct

National Student Production Awards
College Broadcasters Inc (CBI)
Hershey Square Ctr, 1152 Mae St, Hummelstown, PA 17036
Toll Free Tel: 855-ASK-4CBI (275-4224)
Web Site: www.askcbi.org
Key Personnel
Pres: Greg Weston
VP: Herbert Dunmore
Treas: Lisa Marshall
Awards Coord: Steven Hames *Tel:* 706-368-6963 *E-mail:* shames@berry.edu
For excellence in AV production by students.
Media: Audio: MP3; Video: MP4 or MOV
Categories: News, documentary, comedy, drama, DJ, production, sports & more
Award: Certificate & trophy
Closing Date: Annually in May
Entry Fee: free to CBI memb stations, $65 nonmembs
Presented: Annually in Oct/Nov

National Undergraduate Student Electronic Media Competition
National Broadcasting Society-Alpha Epsilon Rho (NBS-AERho)
PO Box 4206, Chesterfield, MO 63006
Tel: 636-536-1943 *Fax:* 636-898-6920
E-mail: national-office@nbs-aerho.org
Web Site: www.nbs-aerho.org
Key Personnel
Exec Dir: Jim Wilson
Established: 1962

For excellence in audio & video production, scriptwriting & web design by students. See web site for entry fee information.
Media: Electronic
Categories: 60 electronic media categories
Award: Certificate & trophy
Closing Date: Dec 6
Presented: NBS-AERho Annual National Convention, March 15

New Jersey Film Festival
Rutgers Film Co-op/NJ Media Arts Center Inc
Admin Off, 30 Bedford Rd, Somerset, NJ 08873
Mailing Address: Rutgers University, 018 Loree Hall, 72 Lipman Dr, New Brunswick, NJ 08901-8525
Tel: 848-932-8482 *Fax:* 732-932-1935
E-mail: njmac@aol.com
Web Site: www.njfilmfest.com
Key Personnel
CEO & Curator: Albert Gabriel Nigrin
Established: 1982
Competitive.
Other Sponsor(s): Johnson & Johnson; Jungle Software; Over 20 Foundations & Corporations; Rutgers University Program in Cinema Studies
Media: DVD, Blu-ray
Categories: Independent/international features, documentary, experimental, animation
Award: Varies
Closing Date: On-going fall/spring seasons
Presented: Rutgers University, New Brunswick, NJ, Spring: Jan-May; Fall: Sept-Nov

New Jersey International Film Festival
Rutgers Film Co-op/NJ Media Arts Center Inc
Admin Off, 30 Bedford Rd, Somerset, NJ 08873
Mailing Address: Rutgers University, 018 Loree Hall, 72 Lipman Dr, New Brunswick, NJ 08901-8525
Tel: 848-932-8482 *Fax:* 732-932-1935
E-mail: njmac@aol.com
Web Site: www.njfilmfest.com
Key Personnel
CEO & Curator: Albert Gabriel Nigrin
Other Sponsor(s): Johnson & Johnson; Jungle Software; New Brunswick City Market; Rutgers University Program in Cinema Studies
Media: Blu-ray, DVD
Categories: Independent/international features, documentary, experimental, animation
Award: Competitive Service & Certificates Awards
Closing Date: Annually, April 1
Entry Fee: Varies
Presented: Rutgers University, New Brunswick, NJ, Annually in June

New Orleans Film Festival
New Orleans Film Society
900 Camp St, New Orleans, LA 70130
Tel: 504-309-6633 *Fax:* 504-309-0923
E-mail: info@neworleansfilmfest.com
Web Site: www.neworleansfilmsociety.org
Key Personnel
Exec Dir: Jolene Pinder
Artistic Dir: John Desplas *E-mail:* johndesplas@aol.com
Prog Dir: Clint Bowie *E-mail:* clintbowie@neworleansfilmfest.com
Participate in workshops, seminars, film festivals & film competition.
Media: 16mm, 35mm film, 3/4 inch videocassettes
Presented: Oct

New York Emmy Awards
New York Chapter, The National Academy of Television Arts & Sciences (NY/NATAS)
Division of The National Academy of Television Arts & Sciences
1375 Broadway, Suite 2103, New York, NY 10018
Tel: 212-459-3630 *Fax:* 212-459-9772
Web Site: www.nyemmys.org
Key Personnel
Exec Dir: Jacqueline Gonzalez *Tel:* 212-459-3630 ext 203 *E-mail:* jgonzalez@nyemmys.org
Established: 1953
Honoring outstanding achievement in local television.
Media: DVD only
Categories: News & programming, creative crafts
Award: Statuette
Closing Date: Varies, see web site
Entry Fee: $125 (NATAS membs); $175 (non-membs)
Presented: New York, NY, April

New York Festivals®-International Advertising Awards
New York Festivals®
260 W 39 St, 10th fl, New York, NY 10018
Tel: 212-643-4800 *Fax:* 212-643-0170
E-mail: info@newyorkfestivals.com
Web Site: www.newyorkfestivals.com
Key Personnel
Exec Dir: Michael Demetriades *E-mail:* mdemetriades@newyorkfestivals.com
Media: All media
Award: First, Second, Third Prize, Grand Awards for Best of Show. Finalists in public service advertising categories are eligible for the United Nations Department of Public Information (UNDPI) Awards for advertising that best exemplifies the goals & ideals of the United Nations
Closing Date: March
Entry Fee: Various
Presented: Frederick P Rose Hall, Jazz at Lincoln Center, New York City, Official notification in May

New York Festivals®-International Radio Program Awards
New York Festivals®
260 W 39 St, 10th fl, New York, NY 10018
Tel: 212-643-4800 *Fax:* 212-643-0170
E-mail: info@newyorkfestivals.com
Web Site: www.newyorkfestivals.com
Key Personnel
Exec Dir: Rose Anderson *E-mail:* randerson@newyorkfestivals.com
Media: MP3
Categories: All professional radio news, documentary, entertainment & music programs, features & spots first broadcast after Jan 1 the year prior to the presentation. Productions not in English must be accompanied by detailed script or synopsis in English
Award: Gold, Silver & Bronze World Medals & Grand Awards for Best of Show will be presented to the winning entries. Finalist certificates also awarded. Finalists are eligible for the United Nations Department of Public Information (UNDPI) Awards
Closing Date: March
Entry Fee: Various
Presented: New York, NY, June 22, 2015

New York Festivals®-International TV & Film Awards
New York Festivals®
260 W 39 St, 10th fl, New York, NY 10018
Tel: 212-643-4800 *Fax:* 212-643-0170
E-mail: info@newyorkfestivals.com
Web Site: www.newyorkfestivals.com
Key Personnel
Exec Dir: Rose Anderson *E-mail:* randerson@newyorkfestivals.com
Media: H.264.mov files
Categories: Feature & corporate films, all TV programs including news, documentary, entertainment, sports, promotions spots & station IDs. Entries in language other than English must have subtitles, voice overs or be accompanied by translation. Campaign entries should feature no more than three spots
Award: Gold, Silver & Bronze World Medals & Grand Awards for Best of Show; finalist certificates also awarded; special presentations are made of the United Nations Department of Information (UNDPI) Awards for programming that best exemplifies the goals & ideals of the United Nations
Closing Date: Nov
Entry Fee: Various
Presented: NAB Show, Las Vegas, NV, April 14, 2015

Newark Black Film Festival (NBFF)
Newark Museum
49 Washington St, Newark, NJ 07102-3176
Tel: 973-596-6550 *Fax:* 973-642-0459
E-mail: nbff@newarkmuseum.org
Web Site: www.newarkmuseum.org/nbff
Key Personnel
NBFF Coord: Pat Faison *Tel:* 973-596-6635 *E-mail:* pfaison@newarkmuseum.org
Established: 1974
Other Sponsor(s): Bank of America
Categories: Films related to the African-American experience
Closing Date: March
Presented: Newark, NJ, Summer

Nicholl Fellowships in Screenwriting
The Academy of Motion Picture Arts and Sciences (AMPAS)
8949 Wilshire Blvd, Beverly Hills, CA 90211
Tel: 310-247-3010
E-mail: nicholl@oscars.org
Web Site: www.oscars.org
Key Personnel
Dir: Greg Beal
Categories: Original feature film screenplays, unproduced screenwriters
Award: $35,000 fellowship
Closing Date: Annually, May 1
Entry Fee: $35 early; $52 regular

Nikon Small World
Nikon Instruments Inc
1300 Walt Whitman Rd, Melville, NY 11747
Tel: 631-547-8500 *Toll Free Tel:* 800-52-NIKON (526-4566 - US only) *Fax:* 631-547-0306
E-mail: info@nikonsmallworld.com
Web Site: www.nikonsmallworld.com; www.nikoninstruments.com
Key Personnel
Communs Mgr: Eric Flem
Established: 1975
Photo & video competitions.
Media: Color slides, digital files
Categories: Any subject & technique employing a microscope. Open to scientific photographers
Award: Nikon equipment
Closing Date: April 30
Presented: New York, NY, Early Oct

Northwest Filmmakers' Festival
Northwest Film Center
Subsidiary of Portland Art Museum
934 SW Salmon St, Portland, OR 97205
Mailing Address: 1219 SW Park Ave, Portland, OR 97205
Tel: 503-221-1156 (ext 10) *Fax:* 503-294-0874
E-mail: info@nwfilm.org
Web Site: www.nwfilm.org
Key Personnel
Regl Servs Mgr: Thomas Phillipson *Tel:* 503-221-1156 ext 13 *E-mail:* thomas@nwfilm.org
Established: 1973
Media: 35mm, 16mm, 1/2 inch, Mini-DV, DVCAM, Beta SP, DVD, Blu-ray, MOV file

Categories: Any length or genre released since Aug 1, two years prior & not previously entered in the festival. Open to permanent residents of AK, BC, ID, MT, OR & WA. Student entries (college & university only) must be from a school located in the Northwest
Award: Selected works will be assembled for the Best of Northwest Touring Program that will circulate througout the region in the following year. Participants will share in approximately $15,000 in lab service awards & tour honoraria
Closing Date: Aug 1
Entry Fee: None
Presented: The Northwest Film Center, Portland, OR, Nov

NWT Arts Council
Education Culture & Employment
Box 1320, Govt NW Territories, Yellowknife, NT X1A 2L9, Canada
Tel: 867-920-6370 *Fax:* 867-873-0205
Web Site: www.pwnhc.ca; www.pwnhc.ca/artscouncil
Key Personnel
Mgr, Community Progs: Boris Atamanenko *E-mail:* boris_atamanenko@govt.nt.ca
Established: 1985
Contributions given annually.
Categories: Open to residents of the Northwest Territories only
Closing Date: Feb 28

Ohio Independent Film Festival
Independent Pictures (IP)
6516 Detroit Ave, Suite 3, Cleveland, OH 44102-3057
Tel: 216-926-6166
E-mail: ohiofilms@yahoo.com
Web Site: www.ohiofilms.com
Key Personnel
Artistic Dir: Bernadette Gillota
Established: 1993
Audience award.
Other Sponsor(s): Cuyahoga Arts & Culture; Ohio Arts Council
Media: DVD
Closing Date: Sept
Entry Fee: $35 under 15 minutes; $50 15 minutes & over (double for late entry)
Presented: Atlas Cinemas Lakeshore 7, Euclid, OH, Nov 5-8, 2015

Ohio Independent Screenplay Awards
Independent Pictures (IP)
6516 Detroit Ave, Suite 3, Cleveland, OH 44102-3057
Tel: 216-926-6166
E-mail: ohiofilms@yahoo.com
Web Site: www.ohiofilms.com
Key Personnel
Artistic Dir: Bernadette Gillota
Categories: Best screenplay, best north coast screenplay, best voice of color screenplay
Award: Cash
Closing Date: Sept
Entry Fee: $65 (early); $85 (late)

OIAF, see Ottawa International Animation Festival

168 Film Festival
168 Film Project
100 E Cedar, Burbank, CA 91502
Mailing Address: 145 S Glenoaks Blvd, No 159, Burbank, CA 91502
Tel: 818-557-8507 *Fax:* 818-942-6076
E-mail: info@168project.com
Web Site: www.168project.com
Key Personnel
Founder & Pres: John David Ware
Prog Dir: Peter Robinson
Established: 2003
Entry Fee: See web site for information
Presented: Annually in Summer

Orson Welles Award
Tiburon International Film Festival (TIFF)
6 Beach Rd, 544, Tiburon, CA 94920
Tel: 415-251-8433 *Fax:* 633-444-8433
E-mail: info@tiburonfilmfestival.com
Web Site: www.tiburonfilmfestival.com
Given to a first time American filmmaker.
Media: Film festival & entertainment
Categories: Fiction, documentary, short, experimental, student, children, music video, sports
Award: Trophy & certificate
Closing Date: Annually, Dec 1
Entry Fee: $40 films 50 minutes & over; $35 films under 50 minutes, free for students (postmarked by Nov 17); $55 feature film, $45 short, $35 student (postmarked by Dec 15)
Presented: Tiburon, CA, Annually in April

Ottawa International Animation Festival
Canadian Film Institute
2 Daly Ave, Suite 120, Ottawa, ON K1N 6E2, Canada
Tel: 613-232-8769 *Fax:* 613-232-6315
E-mail: info@animationfestival.ca
Web Site: www.animationfestival.ca
Key Personnel
Mng Dir: Kelly Neall *E-mail:* kelly@animationfestival.ca
Artistic Dir: Chris Robinson *E-mail:* chris@animationfestival.ca
Dir, The Animation Conference (TAC) & Prof Devt: Azarin Sohrabkani *E-mail:* azarin@animationfestival.ca
Established: 1976
Presented: Multiple venues throughout Ottawa, ON, CN, Sept 16-20, 2015

Outfest
Outfest: The Los Angeles Gay & Lesbian Film Festival
3470 Wilshire Blvd, Suite 935, Los Angeles, CA 90010
Tel: 213-480-7088 *Fax:* 213-480-7099
E-mail: outfest@outfest.org
Web Site: www.outfest.org
Key Personnel
Exec Dir: Kirsten Schaffer
Sr Dir, External Aff: Kerri Stoughton-Jackson
Established: 1982
Media: 35mm, 16mm film, 3/4 inch video, 1/2 inch video, DVD
Categories: Gay & Lesbian, Bisexual & Transgender
Award: 15 audience & juried awards
Closing Date: Jan (early), March (final)
Entry Fee: $15-$35
Presented: Directors Guild of America, Orpheum Theater, Los Angeles, CA, John Anson Ford Theatres, Hollywood, CA & Village at Ed Gould Plaza, Los Angeles, CA, July

Palm Beach International Film Festival (PBIFF)
2101 S Congress Ave, Delray Beach, FL 33445
Tel: 561-362-0003
E-mail: info@pbifilmfest.org; submissions@pbifilmfest.org
Web Site: www.pbifilmfest.org
Key Personnel
Exec Dir: Randi Emerman
Media: Film
Categories: Jury selection: best feature, best short, best documentary. Audience favorites: feature, short, documentary
Closing Date: Nov 15 (early), Jan 10 (late)
Entry Fee: $15-$75
Presented: Palm Beach, FL, Early Spring

Palm Springs International Film Festival
Palm Springs International Film Society
1700 E Tahquitz Canyon Way, Suite 3, Palm Springs, CA 92262
Tel: 760-322-2930 *Toll Free Tel:* 800-898-7256
Fax: 760-322-4087
E-mail: info@psfilmfest.org
Web Site: www.psfilmfest.org
Key Personnel
Festival Dir: Darryl Macdonald *E-mail:* darryl@psfilmfest.org
Established: 1990
Black Tie Gala Film Awards includes Career Achievement, International Director, Desert Palm Achievement, Rising Star & Frederick Loewe Award.
Other Sponsor(s): Cartier
Media: Film
Closing Date: Oct
Presented: Palm Springs Convention Center, Palm Springs, CA, Jan

Pan African Film & Arts Festival
Pan African Film Festival (PAFF)
6820 La Tijera Blvd, Suite 200, Los Angeles, CA 90045
Tel: 310-337-4737 *Fax:* 310-337-4736
E-mail: info@paff.org
Web Site: www.paff.org
Key Personnel
Exec Dir: Ayuko Babu *E-mail:* babu@paff.org
Dir, Res Filmmaker Liaison: Mike Goral
Dir, Art Show: Allohn Agbenya
Established: 1992
Best Feature, Best Short, Best Documentary Feature, Best Documentary Short, Best First Feature Director, Audience Favorite, Festival Board Award, Jury Award.
Closing Date: Oct 31
Entry Fee: $40
Presented: Feb

George Foster Peabody Awards
Grady College of Journalism & Mass Communication
c/o University of Georgia, Grady College of Journalism & Mass Communication, 120 Hooper St, Athens, GA 30602-3018
Tel: 706-542-3787 *Fax:* 706-542-9273
E-mail: peabody@uga.edu
Web Site: www.peabodyawards.com
Key Personnel
Dir: Dr Jeff Jones *E-mail:* jpjones7@uga.edu
Established: 1940
Media: Beta-SPX2 also radio, audiocassette, CDX2 videocassettes, 1/2 inch VHS, DVD
Categories: Radio & broadcast television, cableX2 InternetX2 news, entertainment, education, programs for children, documentary, public service, other
Award: Statuette
Closing Date: Annually in Jan
Entry Fee: $300 TV & web; $175 radio
Presented: New York, NY, Annually in late May or early June

Philadelphia Film Festival
Philadelphia Film Society
1600 N Fifth St, Philadelphia, PA 19122
Tel: 267-239-2941
E-mail: info@filmadelphia.org
Web Site: www.filmadelphia.org
Key Personnel
Exec Dir: Andrew Greenblatt *E-mail:* agreenblatt@filmadelphia.org
Mng Dir: Parinda Patel
Established: 1991
Presented: Philadelphia, PA, Annually in Oct

Philadelphia International Film Festival & Market
International Association of Motion Picture & Television Producers Inc

PO Box 48134, Philadelphia, PA 19144
Tel: 215-849-2716 (festival) *Toll Free Tel:* 877-347-FILM (347-3456)
E-mail: info@philafilm.org
Web Site: www.philafilm.org
Key Personnel
Festival Dir: Lawrence L Smallwood, Jr
E-mail: lsmall1@yahoo.com
Gen Mgr: Chris Johnson
Established: 1977
Other Sponsor(s): African-American Museum in Philadelphia; I A Capital Fund, LLC; International Assoc of Motion Picture & Television Producers Inc; Philadelphia Corp for Aging; WPVI-TV 6, Philadelphia, PA
Media: 35mm, 16mm, DVD
Categories: Professional & Independent film/television producers, directors, writers
Award: Trophies, Certificates, Product Prizes
Entry Fee: $20-$100 (based upon entry category)
Presented: Varied Center City locales, Philadelphia, PA

Philafilm, see Philadelphia International Film Festival & Market

George Polk Awards in Journalism
Long Island University
Journalism Dept, One University Plaza, Brooklyn, NY 11201-5372
Tel: 718-488-1009 *Fax:* 718-780-4046
Web Site: www.liu.edu/polk
Key Personnel
Curator: John Darnton
Faculty Coord: Ralph Engelman
Established: 1949
Investigative journalism (print & electronic).
Media: Audio, video or digital recordings, DVD
Categories: Media
Award: Plaque
Closing Date: Jan
Presented: The Roosevelt Hotel, New York, NY, April

Premio Mesquite
San Antonio CineFestival
Subsidiary of Guadalupe Cultural Arts Center
723 S Brazos St, San Antonio, TX 78207
Tel: 210-271-3151 (ext 232) *Fax:* 210-271-3480
E-mail: cine@guadalupeculturalarts.org
Web Site: www.guadalupeculturalarts.org
Key Personnel
CineFestival Curator: Patty Ortiz *E-mail:* pattyo@guadalupeculturalarts.org
Recognizes excellence in Chicano/Latino film & video production.
Media: 35mm film, HDCAM, Blu-ray, DVD, Digi-Beta; English subtitles strongly recommended
Categories: Feature, documentary, short, emerging artist/first film, special jury award
Closing Date: Oct (early), Nov (late)
Entry Fee: Early: $25, $15 student; Late: $35, $25 student
Presented: San Antonio, TX, Feb

The Presidential Proclamation Award
Society of Motion Picture & Television Engineers (SMPTE)
3 Barker Ave, 5th fl, White Plains, NY 10601
Tel: 914-761-1100 *Fax:* 914-761-3115
E-mail: smpte@smpte.org
Web Site: www.smpte.org
Key Personnel
Exec Dir: Barbara Lange *Tel:* 914-205-2370
E-mail: blange@smpte.org
Dir, Opers: Sally-Ann D'Amato *Tel:* 914-205-2375 *E-mail:* sdamato@smpte.org
Mktg & Communs: Aimee Ricca *Tel:* 914-205-2381
Exec Asst: June Marie Sobrito *Tel:* 914-205-2384
E-mail: jsobrito@smpte.org
Recognizes an individual of established outstanding status & reputation in motion picture & television industry worldwide.
Closing Date: Annually in April
Presented: SMPTE Annual Technical Conference & Exhibition, Loews Hollywood Hotel, Hollywood, CA, Annually in Oct

Prix Gemeaux (French language TV)
Academy of Canadian Cinema & Television (ACCT)
225 rue Roy E, bureau 106, Montreal, QC H2W 1M5, Canada
Tel: 514-849-7448 *Fax:* 514-849-5069
E-mail: academie@acct.ca
Web Site: www.acct.ca/prixgemeaux; www.acct.ca; www.academy.ca
Key Personnel
Exec Dir: Patrice Lachance *Tel:* 514-849-7448 ext 21 *E-mail:* plachance@acct.ca
Award Coord: Samuel Belisle *Tel:* 514-849-7448 ext 28 *E-mail:* sbelisle@acct.ca
Media: DVD
Categories: TV & digital media
Award: Statuette
Presented: Montreal, QC, CN, Fall

The Progress Medal Award
Society of Motion Picture & Television Engineers (SMPTE)
3 Barker Ave, 5th fl, White Plains, NY 10601
Tel: 914-761-1100 *Fax:* 914-761-3115
E-mail: smpte@smpte.org
Web Site: www.smpte.org
Key Personnel
Exec Dir: Barbara Lange *Tel:* 914-205-2370
E-mail: blange@smpte.org
Dir, Opers: Sally-Ann D'Amato *Tel:* 914-205-2375 *E-mail:* sdamato@smpte.org
Mktg & Communs: Aimee Ricca *Tel:* 914-205-2381
Exec Asst: June Marie Sobrito *Tel:* 914-205-2384
E-mail: jsobrito@smpte.org
Recognizes outstanding technical contributions to the progress of engineering phases of motion picture television or motion imaging industries.
Closing Date: Annually in April
Presented: SMPTE Annual Technical Conference & Exhibition, Loews Hollywood Hotel, Hollywood, CA, Annually in Oct

PromaxBDA Design Awards
PromaxBDA
1522e Cloverfield Blvd, Santa Monica, CA 90404
Tel: 310-788-7600 *Fax:* 310-788-7616
Web Site: www.promaxbda.org
Key Personnel
Sr Mgr, Global Awards & Competitions: Eileen Rasnake *Tel:* 310-789-1506 *E-mail:* eileen@promaxbda.org
Computer design, TV, film. Acknowledge & reward outstanding individuals for design contribution in the electronic media, thereby promoting & encouraging creative integrity & excellence within the media.
Award: Gold & silver awards

Providence Underground Film Festival
Flickers Art Collaborative
83 Park St, Suite 1, Providence, RI 02903
Mailing Address: PO Box 162, Newport, RI 02840-0002
Tel: 401-861-4445 *Fax:* 401-490-6735
E-mail: info@film-festival.org
Web Site: www.film-festival.org/Prov.Underground.php
Key Personnel
CEO & Exec Dir: George T Marshall
E-mail: georgetm@film-festival.org
Established: 1998
Media: DVD
Categories: Short, feature
Award: Trophies
Entry Fee: $45 ($10 late fee after regular deadline)
Presented: Providence, RI

PXL This Video Festival
2427 1/2 Glyndon Ave, Venice, CA 90291
Tel: 310-306-7330
E-mail: pfsuzy@aol.com
Web Site: laughtears.com
Key Personnel
Dir & Curator: Gerry Fialka
Established: 1991
Award to support independent video-makers. The 2 hour program features entries from across North America spanning many genres including documentary, poetry, experimental, drama, comedy & music. Submissions must be shot with the PXL 2000 camera, but not exclusively & entered on DVD. Also include a synopsis & three first-class postage stamps with each entry. Do not send originals; no returns. All categories accepted.
Media: Videos made with PXL 2000, toy video camera
Categories: All categories accepted
Closing Date: Annually in Oct
Presented: Publicly in Los Angeles, CA & tours in US, Dec & May

Radio & TV Engineering Achievement Awards
National Association of Broadcasters (NAB)
1771 "N" St NW, Washington, DC 20036
Tel: 202-429-5300 *Fax:* 202-429-4199
E-mail: nab@nab.org
Web Site: www.nab.org
Key Personnel
VP, Technol Opers: Janet Elliott
Established: 1959
Recognized annually on basis of single significant contribution or contributions made over a period of time, which significantly advance the state of the art of broadcast engineering.
Award: Plaque
Presented: NAB Technology Luncheon, Las Vegas Convention Center, Las Vegas, NV

Real to Reel International Film Festival
Subsidiary of Cleveland County Arts Council
111 S Washington St, Shelby, NC 28150
Tel: 704-484-2787 *Fax:* 704-481-1822
E-mail: info@ccartscouncil.org
Web Site: www.ccartscouncil.org/realtoreel
Key Personnel
Mktg Dir: Violet Arth *E-mail:* violet.arth@ccartscouncil.org
Established: 2000
Showcase thought-provoking films.
Media: Original formats can be shot on 8mm, 16mm, 35mm, all formats of video as well as all formats digital & computer multimedia. All formats must be on DVD
Categories: Feature short, documentary, animation
Award: Cash award for top winners, $300-$1,000
Closing Date: Jan (early bird), Feb (regular), March (late)
Entry Fee: $40 early bird, $50 regular, $55 late (professional). $20 early bird, $25 regular, $30 late (student/amateur)
Presented: Joy Performance Theater, Kings Mountain, NC, July

Reelout Queer Film + Video Festival
Reelout Arts Project Inc
82 Sydenham St, Kingston, ON K7L 3H4, Canada
Tel: 613-549-REEL (549-7335)
Web Site: www.reelout.com
Key Personnel
Festival Dir: Matt Salton *E-mail:* director@reelout.com
Established: 1999

Showcase for independent GLBTT films & videos. Audience awards for Best Feature, Best Documentary, Best Canadian Short Film.
Categories: Film, Video
Closing Date: Annually, Sept 30
Entry Fee: None

ReelWorld Film Festival
ReelWorld Foundation
438 Parliament St, Suite 300, Toronto, ON M5A 3A2, Canada
Tel: 416-598-7933
E-mail: info@reelworld.ca; events@reelworld.ca
Web Site: www.reelworld.ca
Key Personnel
Founder, Exec Dir & Head, Programming: Tonya Lee Williams *E-mail:* tonya@reelworld.ca
Fin Mgr: Rodrigo Diaz Varela
Festival Coord: Stacey Agard; Yash Brar
Established: 2001
Screen Canadian & international films that reflect positive images from Aboriginal, Asian, Black, Latino, Middle Eastern, South Asian & other multi-racial communities.

Regional Artist Project Grants Program
Arts & Science Council Charlotte/Mecklenburg
227 W Trade St, Suite 250, Charlotte, NC 28202
Tel: 704-333-2272 *Fax:* 704-333-2720
E-mail: asc@artsandscience.org
Web Site: www.artsandscience.org
Key Personnel
VP, Cultural & Community Investment: Ryan Deal
Grant awarded to all disciplines. Recipients notified by mail/e-mail.
Other Sponsor(s): Cabarrus Arts Council; Cleveland Arts Council; Gaston Arts Council; Iredell Arts Council; North Carolina Arts Council; Rowan Arts Council; Rutherford Arts Council; Union County Arts Council; York (SC) Arts Council
Categories: All disciplines
Award: Up to $2,000 cash grant
Closing Date: Annually in Sept

Residency Fellowship
Virginia Center for the Creative Arts (VCCA) Fellowship Programs
154 San Angelo Dr, Amherst, VA 24521
Tel: 434-946-7236 *Fax:* 434-946-7239
E-mail: vcca@vcca.com
Web Site: www.vcca.com
Key Personnel
Exec Dir: Gregory Allgire Smith
Artists Serv Dir: Sheila Gulley Pleasants
Off Mgr: Beatrice Booker
Established: 1971
Residential fellowships for writers, visual artists & composers.
Closing Date: Annually, Jan 15, May 15 & Sept 15
Entry Fee: $40 application fee (waived in cases of financial need). Artists are accepted to VCCA without regard for their financial situation. A suggested daily contribution, if possible, is $45

Rhode Island International Film Festival™ (RIIFF), see FLICKERS: Rhode Island International Film Festival™ (RIIFF)

Rhode Island State Council on the Arts Fellowships & Grants Program
Division of The State of Rhode Island
One Capitol Hill, 3rd fl, Providence, RI 02908
Tel: 401-222-3880 *Fax:* 401-222-3018
E-mail: info@arts.ri.gov
Web Site: www.arts.ri.gov
Key Personnel
Dir, Indiv Artists Progs: Cristina M Di Chiera *Tel:* 401-222-3881 *E-mail:* cristina.dichiera@arts.ri.gov
Established: 1967
Grants for Rhode Island resident artists, nonprofit organizations, schools & arts educators.
Other Sponsor(s): National Endowment for the Arts
Categories: April 1st deadline for fellowships in fiction, poetry, playwriting/screenwriting, crafts, film & video, folk art, photography & 3D art; Oct 1st deadline for choreography, drawing & printmaking, music composition, new genres & painting. Project grants accepted from individuals & organizations also on these deadlines in all disciplines
Award: Cash
Closing Date: Annually, April 1 & Oct 1
Entry Fee: None
Presented: Annually, 4 months after closing date

The RIAA® Gold® & Platinum® Awards
Recording Industry Association of America (RIAA)
1025 "F" St NW, 10th fl, Washington, DC 20004
Tel: 202-775-0101
Web Site: www.riaa.com
Key Personnel
Chmn & CEO: Cary Sherman
Sr EVP: Mitch Glazier
Established: 1958
Gold® album award for the sale of 500,000 copies. Platinum® album award for the sale of 1,000,000 copies.
Media: CDs, digital tracks, digital albums, ringtones
Categories: Record industry
Award: Plaque containing RIAA® holographic seal

The Bart Richards Award for Media Criticism
Penn State College of Communications
302 James Bldg, University Park, PA 16801-3867
Tel: 814-865-8801 *Fax:* 814-863-6134
Web Site: comm.psu.edu/news-events/awards/bart-richards-award-for-media-criticism
Key Personnel
Dir of Strategic Communs: Steve Sampsell *E-mail:* steves@psu.edu
Established: 1994
Improving print & broadcast journalism through responsible evaluation or critical evaluation.
Media: DVD (with final script or summaries)
Award: $1,000
Closing Date: Jan 31
Entry Fee: None
Presented: National Press Club, Washington, DC, Annually in May

The Ridenhour Documentary Film Prize
The Nation Institute
116 E 16 St, 8th fl, New York, NY 10003
Tel: 212-822-0250 *Fax:* 212-253-5356
E-mail: ridenhour@nationinstitute.org
Web Site: www.ridenhour.org
Key Personnel
CEO & Exec Dir: Taya Kitman *Tel:* 212-822-0252 *E-mail:* taya@nationinstitute.org
Given to a documentary film that in the view of the judges best reflects the legacy of Ron Ridenhour-journalist, whistleblower, truth-teller & social activist. The prize seeks to recognize a documentary that defends the public interest, advances or promotes social justice, or illuminates a more just vision of society.
Other Sponsor(s): The Fertel Foundation
Award: $10,000 stipend

Paul Robeson Awards
Newark Museum
49 Washington St, Newark, NJ 07102-3176
Tel: 973-596-6550 *Fax:* 973-642-0459
E-mail: nbff@newarkmuseum.org
Web Site: www.newarkmuseum.org/nbff
Key Personnel
NBFF Coord: Pat Faison *Tel:* 973-596-6635 *E-mail:* pfaison@newarkmuseum.org
Established: 1985
Biennial film competition featured during the Newark Black Film Festival in even numbered years.
Media: DVD (NTSC)
Categories: Films related to the African-American experience
Award: Cash
Closing Date: Feb
Entry Fee: $40
Presented: Newark & Trenton, NJ, Summer

Rochester International Film Festival
Movies on a Shoestring Inc
PO Box 17746, Rochester, NY 14617
Tel: 585-234-7411 (voice mail)
E-mail: president@rochesterfilmfest.org (use MOAS on subject)
Web Site: www.rochesterfilmfest.org
Key Personnel
Pres: Al Figler
Established: 1959
Media: Submissions: DVD (region 1 or region free) format; Screening: Quicktime (.MOV), 16mm, 35mm
Categories: Shorts under 30 minutes, all genre
Award: Trophy
Closing Date: Feb 1
Entry Fee: $50 ($35 before Dec 1)
Presented: Dryden Theatre, George Eastman House, 900 East Ave, Rochester, NY, Annually in Spring

Rockie Awards
Achilles Media Ltd
21 St Clair Ave E, Suite 700, Toronto, ON M4T 1L9, Canada
Tel: 416-921-3171
E-mail: info@achillesmedia.com
Web Site: www.banffmediafestival.com
Key Personnel
Awards Prodr & Coord: Henry Wong *E-mail:* hwong@achillesmedia.com
International awards program for television & digital properties from around the world.
Categories: Drama, factual, kids & animation, entertainment, interactive
Award: Trophy
Closing Date: Dec (early bird), March (final), see web site for exact dates
Presented: Banff World Media Festival, Banff, AB, CN, June 7-10, 2015

The Madeline Dane Ross Award
Overseas Press Club of America
40 W 45 St, New York, NY 10036
Tel: 212-626-9220 *Fax:* 212-626-9210
Web Site: www.opcofamerica.org
Key Personnel
Exec Dir: Patricia Kranz
Given to a correspondent in print medium or online for the best international reporting showing a concern for human condition. All entries are submitted online.
Other Sponsor(s): Linda Fasulo
Media: Print & online
Award: Certificate & $1,000 check
Closing Date: Annually in late Jan
Entry Fee: $200
Presented: Hotel Mandarin-Oriental, New York, NY, Annually in April

RTDNA Edward R Murrow Awards
Radio Television Digital News Association (RTDNA)
The National Press Bldg, 529 14 St NW, Suite 425, Washington, DC 20045
Tel: 202-659-6510 *Fax:* 202-223-4007
E-mail: awards@rtdna.org

Web Site: www.rtdna.org
Key Personnel
Exec Dir: Mike Cavender *Tel:* 770-622-7011 *E-mail:* mikec@rtdna.org
Progs, Awards & Membership Mgr: Katie Switchenko *Tel:* 202-725-8318 *E-mail:* katies@rtdna.org
Established: 1971
Outstanding achievements in electronic journalism.
Categories: Radio & television stations only
Award: National Murrow winner receives a crystal trophy. All others receive a plaque
Closing Date: Feb
Entry Fee: $70-$250; see web site for rates per category
Presented: RTDNA Awards Dinner, New York Marriott Marquis, New York, NY, Columbus Day

St Barth Film Festival
410 W 24 St, New York, NY 10011
Tel: 212-989-8004 *Fax:* 212-727-1774
E-mail: staff@stbarthff.org
Web Site: www.stbarthff.org
Key Personnel
Dir: Joshua Harrison; Ellen Lampert-Greaux *E-mail:* elgreaux@wanadoo.fr
Established: 1996
Media: 35mm, DVD, Blu-ray
Categories: Narrative/Documentary
Closing Date: Annually, March 1
Entry Fee: Sliding scale
Presented: L'Orient, St Barth, Annually in April

St John's International Women's Film Festival
28 Cochrane St, Suite 101, St John's, NL A1C 3L3, Canada
Mailing Address: PO Box 984, Sta C, St John's, NL A1C 5M3, Canada
Tel: 709-754-3141
E-mail: info@womensfilmfestival.com
Web Site: www.womensfilmfestival.com
Key Personnel
Exec Dir: Kelly Davis *E-mail:* kelly@womensfilmfestival.com
Established: 1989
Non-competitive.
Other Sponsor(s): CBC; Government of Canada
Media: Film (mainly Beta SP, Digibeta & 16mm - 35mm very limited) & DVD
Categories: Dramatic features, dramatic shorts, animated shorts, documentary features, documentary shorts & experimental films
Closing Date: Annually, March 18 (early), April 15 (regular), May 20 (late), May 27 (Withoutabox extended deadline)
Entry Fee: $10 early; $20 regular; $35 late; $50 Withoutabox extended deadline
Presented: St John's Arts & Culture Centre, LSPU Hall, Holy Heart Theater & Masonic Temple, St Johns', NL, CN, Annually in Oct-Nov

Sally Mountain Park Bluegrass Festival
Sally Mountain Show
Rte 2, Box 15, Greentop, MO 63546
Tel: 660-949-2345
E-mail: festival@marktwain.net
Web Site: www.sallymountainshow.com
Key Personnel
Contact: Carolyn Vincent; Johnny Vincent
Presented: Queen City, MO, July 1-5, 2015

San Antonio Film Festival
1633 Babcock Rd, Suite 111, San Antonio, TX 78229
Tel: 210-885-5888
E-mail: safilm@gmail.com
Web Site: www.safilm.com
Key Personnel
Dir: Adam Rocha *E-mail:* adam@safilm.com
Mktg Dir: Kacie LaCombe *E-mail:* kacie@safilm.com
Festival Prodr: Susan Ranjel *E-mail:* susan@safilm.com
Closing Date: Annually in March
Entry Fee: $40, $60 (late)
Presented: San Antonio, TX, Annually in June

San Diego Film Festival
San Diego Film Foundation
2683 Via de la Valle, Suite G210, Del Mar, CA 92014
Tel: 619-818-2221
E-mail: info@sdff.org
Web Site: www.sdfilmfest.com
Key Personnel
Exec Dir & Founder: Robin Laatz
Established: 2001
Closing Date: Annually, June 15
Presented: Annually in Sept

San Francisco Black Film Festival
PO Box 15490, San Francisco, CA 94115
Tel: 415-400-4602 *Fax:* 415-346-9046
E-mail: sfbff@sfbff.org
Web Site: www.sfbff.org
Key Personnel
Festival Registrar: Katera Crossley *E-mail:* katera@sfbff.org
Established: 1998
Other Sponsor(s): San Francisco Arts Commission; San Francisco Grants for the Arts
Entry Fee: $40 early; $45 late
Presented: June

San Francisco International Film Festival
Division of San Francisco Film Society
39 Mesa St, Suite 110, The Presidio, San Francisco, CA 94129-1025
Tel: 415-561-5000 *Fax:* 415-440-1760
E-mail: info@sffs.org
Web Site: festival.sffs.org; www.sffs.org; www.sf360.org
Key Personnel
Dir, Programming: Rachel Rosen *Tel:* 415-561-5010 *E-mail:* rrosen@sffs.org
Mktg & Communs Mgr: Jaime Galli *Tel:* 415-561-5013 *E-mail:* jgalli@sffs.org
Publicity Mgr: Bill Proctor *Tel:* 415-561-5024 *E-mail:* bproctor@sffs.org
Established: 1957
The festival highlights current trends in international film & video production with an emphasis on work that has not yet secured US distribution. Also invites recent feature length narratives & documentaries & archival presentations from around the globe, special awards & tributes recognizing individual achievement.
Closing Date: Oct-Dec for following year's festival
Entry Fee: Varies

San Francisco International LGBT Film Festival
Frameline
145 Ninth St, Suite 300, San Francisco, CA 94103
Tel: 415-703-8650 *Fax:* 415-861-1404
E-mail: info@frameline.org
Web Site: www.frameline.org
Key Personnel
Exec Dir: K C Price *Tel:* 415-703-8650 ext 302 *E-mail:* kcprice@frameline.org
Festival Dir: Frances Wallace *Tel:* 415-703-8650 ext 310 *E-mail:* frances@frameline.org
Established: 1977
Media: All formats, film & video, by, about or of interest to lesbian, gay, bisexual & transgender people
Categories: All categories
Award: Cash prizes for filmmakers: $7,500 for First Feature Award. Festival Audience Cash Awards: $2,500
Closing Date: Annually, Dec (early), Feb (late)
Presented: Annually in June

San Francisco Jewish Film Festival
145 Ninth St, Suite 200, San Francisco, CA 94103
Tel: 415-621-0556 *Fax:* 415-621-0568
E-mail: jewishfilm@sfjff.org
Web Site: www.sfjff.org
Key Personnel
Exec Dir: Lexi Leban *E-mail:* lleban@sfjff.org
Prog Dir: Jay Rosenblatt *E-mail:* rosenblatt@sfjff.org
Established: 1980
Annually presents best of independent Jewish-themed film. All genres & subject matter welcome.
Media: Film, video, digital video
Closing Date: Feb
Entry Fee: $20, $30 (feature films)
Presented: Four Bay Area cities, CA, Summer

Santa Barbara International Film Festival
1528 Chapala St, Suite 203, Santa Barbara, CA 93101
Tel: 805-963-0023 *Fax:* 805-962-2524
E-mail: generalinfo@sbfilmfestival.org
Web Site: sbiff.org
Key Personnel
Exec Dir: Roger Durling
Dir, Devt: Michael Wiesbrock *E-mail:* michael@sbfilmfestival.org
Dir, Opers: Sean Pratt *E-mail:* sean@sbfilmfestival.org
Established: 1985
Media: Submissions: DVD (NTSC Region 0 or 1); Exhibition: 35mm, HDCAM 23.98P & 60i(59.94) (stereo), DigitBeta 29.97fps (stereo), DCP
Categories: Independent features, documentaries, live action shorts, animated shorts, world cinema, local films
Award: Certificate, plaque & cash prizes
Closing Date: Annually in Sept, late entries by special request
Entry Fee: Varies by date submitted
Presented: Santa Barbara, CA

Saturn Awards
Academy of Science Fiction, Fantasy & Horror Films
334 W 54 St, Los Angeles, CA 90037
Tel: 323-752-5811
Web Site: www.saturnawards.org
Key Personnel
CEO & Pres: Robert Holguin
Exec Adminstrator: David Bilbrey
Dir, Opers: Michael Laster
Prodr: Aaron Griffin
Categories: Film, television, home entertainment & live stage theatre
Award: Saturn gold color award statue
Presented: May or June

Screamfest® Horror Film Festival & Screenplay Competition
8840 Wilshire Blvd, 3rd fl, Beverly Hills, CA 90211
Tel: 310-358-3273 *Fax:* 310-358-3272
E-mail: info@screamfestla.com
Web Site: www.screamfestla.com
Key Personnel
Founder & Festival Dir: Rachel Belofsky
Established: 2001
Eligible films must have been completed after Jan of the year prior to the festival & not have been released on DVD. Feature film script length should be at least 75 pages & not over 130.

Media: Submissions: Online screener or DVD (NTSC or All Region); Screening: DCP, HDCAM, 35mm, Digibeta
Categories: Feature, shorts, super shorts, documentary, animation, student horror film
Award: Cash, software, statue, film
Closing Date: Film: April 15 (early), July 15 (regular), Aug 1 (final). Screenplay: Jan 15 (early), March 15 (regular), June 2 (final)
Entry Fee: Feature: $40 early, $45 regular, $60 final; Short: $30 early, $35 regular, $50 final; Super short: $25 early, $30 regular, $40 final; Screenplay: $35 early, $50 regular, $60 final
Presented: Los Angeles, CA, Oct

Seattle International Film Festival (SIFF)
305 Harrison St, Seattle, WA 98109
Tel: 206-464-5830 *Fax:* 206-264-7919
E-mail: info@siff.net
Web Site: www.siff.net
Key Personnel
Mng Dir: Mary Bacarella *E-mail:* mary.b@siff.net
Artistic Dir: Carl Spence *E-mail:* carl@siff.net
Dir, Programming: Beth Barrett *E-mail:* beth@siff.net
Mktg Mgr: Maria Rodriguez Abad *E-mail:* maria.rodriguezabad@siff.net
Established: 1976
Categories: Audience voted awards: The Golden Space Needle. Jury awards: The New Director's Competition Documentary Feature Competition & Short Film: Live Action, Animation & Documentary
Closing Date: Jan
Presented: Seattle, WA, Spring

Seattle Jewish Film Festival (SJFF)
Stroum Jewish Community Center
3801 E Mercer Way, Mercer Island, WA 98040
Tel: 206-232-7115 *Fax:* 206-232-7119
E-mail: sjff@sjcc.org
Web Site: www.seattlejewishfilmfestival.org
Key Personnel
Festival Dir: Pamela Lavitt *Tel:* 206-388-0832
Established: 1995
Audience Choice Award for best picture, best documentary & best short films. Also Rell Difference Award for extraordinary human rights, civil rights or profound impact on the community.
American Jewish Committee (AJC) is a founding partner of this 10 day annual event.
Media: Film & digital
Presented: Venues in downtown Seattle, WA & the Stroum Jewish Community Center, Mercer Island, WA, March
Branch Office(s)
2618 NE 80 St, Seattle, WA 98115 *Tel:* 206-526-8073 *Fax:* 206-526-9958

Sigma Delta Chi Awards in Journalism
Society of Professional Journalists
Eugene S Pulliam National Journalism Ctr, 3909 N Meridian St, Indianapolis, IN 46208
Tel: 317-927-8000 *Fax:* 317-920-4789
E-mail: awards@spj.org
Web Site: www.spj.org
Key Personnel
Exec Dir: Joe Skeel *Tel:* 317-927-8000 ext 216 *E-mail:* jskeel@spj.org
Assoc Exec Dir: Chris Vachon *Tel:* 317-927-8000 ext 207 *E-mail:* cvachon@spj.org
Awards Coord: Chad Hosier *Tel:* 317-927-8000 ext 210 *E-mail:* chosier@spj.org
Established: 1932
Media: PDF or URL
Categories: Various journalism
Award: Plaque with medallion
Closing Date: Annually in Feb
Entry Fee: $60 for membs, $85 after deadline; $100 for non-membs, $120 after deadline
Presented: SPJ National Press Club, Washington, DC

Silver Anvil Awards
Public Relations Society of America
33 Maiden Lane, 11th fl, New York, NY 10038-5150
Tel: 212-460-1400 *Toll Free Tel:* 800-350-0111 *Fax:* 212-995-0757
E-mail: awards@prsa.org
Web Site: www.prsa.org
Key Personnel
VP, Spec Events & Progs: Karla Voth *Tel:* 212-460-1446 *E-mail:* karla.voth@prsa.org
Public relations program.
Categories: Community relations, institutional programs, special events & observances (7 days or less), special events & observances (more than 7 days), public service, public affairs, marketing communications, international public relations, crisis communications, internal communications, investor relations
Award: Trophy
Closing Date: Feb

Silver Gavel Awards for Media and the Arts
Formerly Gavel Awards
American Bar Association
Div for Public Education, 321 N Clark St, Chicago, IL 60654
Tel: 312-988-5733 *Toll Free Tel:* 800-285-2221 *Fax:* 312-988-5494 (Attn: Gavel Awards)
E-mail: publiceducation@americanbar.org
Web Site: www.americanbar.org
Key Personnel
Div Dir: Mabel McKinney-Browning *Tel:* 312-988-5731 *E-mail:* mabel.mckinneybrowning@americanbar.org
Dir: Howard Kaplan *Tel:* 312-988-5738 *E-mail:* howard.kaplan@americanbar.org
Media: CDs, DVDs
Categories: Categories: Books, magazines, newspapers, commentary, drama & literature, documentaries, TV, radio & other media
Award: Silver gavel & wooden plaques for honorable mentions
Closing Date: Annually in Jan
Entry Fee: $125 television; $75 for other entries
Presented: National Press Club, Washington, DC, July

Slamdance Film Festival
5634 Melrose Ave, Los Angeles, CA 90038
Tel: 323-466-1786 *Fax:* 323-466-1784
E-mail: submissions@slamdance.com
Web Site: www.slamdance.com
Key Personnel
Founder & Pres: Peter Baxter
Founder: Jon Fitzgerald; Shane Kuhn; Dan Mirvish
Devt Mgr/Sponsorship: Nandy Wilson
Established: 1995
Independent filmmakers festival.
Other Sponsor(s): Directors Guild of America (DGA); Kodak
Media: Film & video
Categories: New filmmakers, special screenings
Award: $90,000 in goods & services
Closing Date: Oct
Entry Fee: $30-$75
Presented: Park City, UT, Jan

Stanley Film Festival
Denver Film Society
1510 York St, 3rd fl, Denver, CO 80206
Tel: 970-577-4111
E-mail: stanley@denverfilm.org
Web Site: www.stanleyfilmfest.com
Key Personnel
Volunteer Mgr: Kristy King
Press: Joanna Cintron *E-mail:* joanna@denverfilm.org
Programming/Submission Inquiries: Matthew Campbell *E-mail:* matt@denverfilm.org
Sponsorships: Ryan Gaterman *E-mail:* rgaterman@stanleyfilmfest.com
Established: 2013
Showcases classic & contemporary independent horror cinema.
Other Sponsor(s): Chiller; Estes Park, Colorado; Reel Mountain Theater; The Stanley Hotel
Media: Submissions: Online screener; Screening: Blu-ray, digital file & DCP
Categories: Features, Shorts, Stanley Dean's Cup Student Competition
Entry Fee: Features: $35/$25 student (early), $45/$30 student (regular), $60/$30 student (late); Shorts: $35/$25 student (early), $45/$25 student (regular), $60/$30 student (late); Stanley Dean's Cup Student Short Films: $25 (early & regular), $30 (late)
Presented: The Stanley Hotel, Estes Park, CO, April 30-May 3, 2015

Starz Denver Film Festival
Denver Film Society
1510 York St, 3rd fl, Denver, CO 80206
Tel: 303-595-3456 *Fax:* 303-595-0956
E-mail: info@denverfilm.org
Web Site: www.denverfilm.org/festival
Key Personnel
Exec Dir: Tom Botelho *E-mail:* tom@denverfilm.org
Festival Dir: Britta Erickson *E-mail:* britta@denverfilm.org
Artistic Dir: Brit Withey *E-mail:* brit@denverfilm.org
Established: 1978
Three non-competitive awards sponsored by Starz: Mayor's Lifetime Achievement Award, John Cassavetes Award & Stan Brakhage Vision Award.
Media: Submissions: DVD screener; Screening: 35mm, HDCAM, Blu-ray & some DCP
Categories: Contemporary World Cinema, New Directors Showcase, documentary & short subjects
Entry Fee: June 1 $30/$20 student/Withoutabox $25/$15; July 15 $35/$20 student/Withoutabox $30/$15; Aug 1 $45/$25 student/Withoutabox $40/$20; Aug 10 $55/35 student/Withoutabox $40/$25
Presented: Sie Film Center, 2510 E Colfax, Denver, CO, Nov

Student Academy Awards Competition
The Academy of Motion Picture Arts and Sciences (AMPAS)
8949 Wilshire Blvd, Beverly Hills, CA 90211
Tel: 310-247-3000 *Fax:* 310-859-9619
E-mail: SAA@oscars.org
Web Site: www.oscars.org/saa
Key Personnel
CEO: Dawn Hudson
Mgr, Student Academy Awards: Shawn Guthrie *Tel:* 310-247-3000 ext 3306 *E-mail:* sguthrie@oscars.org
Established: 1972
College & university students only. First submit entry online; if advances, submit a copy on film (16mm or 35mm), as a DCP or as a digital ProRes file within 7 days notice.
Media: Submissions: digital upload; Screening: 16mm, 35mm, DCP, ProRes Digital file
Categories: Animation, documentary, narrative, alternative
Award: Trophy, cash: $5,000 (gold), $3,000 (silver) & $2,000 (bronze)
Closing Date: June 1
Entry Fee: None
Presented: Academy's Samuel Goldwyn Theater, 8949 Wilshire Blvd, Beverly Hills, CA

Sundance Film Festival
Sundance Institute
1825 Three Kings Dr, Park City, UT 84060

Mailing Address: PO Box 684429, Park City, UT 84068
Tel: 435-658-3456 *Fax:* 435-658-3457
E-mail: customerservice@sundance.org; press@sundance.org; institute@sundance.org
Web Site: www.sundance.org/festival/
Key Personnel
Dir: John Cooper
Co-Mng Dir, Opers & Utah Community Rel: Sara Pearce
Dir, Programming: Trevor Groth
Mgr, Festival Opers: Meredith Potter
Mgr, Media Rel: Elizabeth Latenser
Established: 1985
Other Sponsor(s): Acura Advance; Chase Sapphire; Entertainment Weekly; HP; Sundance Channel
Presented: Park City, UT, Annually in Jan

Technicolor-Herbert T Kalmus Gold Medal Award
Society of Motion Picture & Television Engineers (SMPTE)
3 Barker Ave, 5th fl, White Plains, NY 10601
Tel: 914-761-1100 *Fax:* 914-761-3115
E-mail: smpte@smpte.org
Web Site: www.smpte.org
Key Personnel
Exec Dir: Barbara Lange *Tel:* 914-205-2370 *E-mail:* blange@smpte.org
Dir, Opers: Sally-Ann D'Amato *Tel:* 914-205-2375 *E-mail:* sdamato@smpte.org
Mktg & Communs: Aimee Ricca *Tel:* 914-205-2381
Exec Asst: June Marie Sobrito *Tel:* 914-205-2384 *E-mail:* jsobrito@smpte.org
Honors an individual who has made outstanding contributions that reflect a commitment to the highest standards of quality & innovation in motion picture post-production & distribution services.
Closing Date: Annually in April
Presented: SMPTE Annual Technical Conference & Exhibition, Loews Hollywood Hotel, Hollywood, CA, Annually in Oct

Technology and Engineering Emmy Awards
The National Academy of Television Arts & Sciences (NATAS)
1697 Broadway, Suite 1001, New York, NY 10019
Tel: 212-586-8424 *Fax:* 212-246-8129
E-mail: techemmys@emmyonline.tv
Web Site: www.emmyonline.org
Key Personnel
Chief Admin Offr & Spec Events Dir: Paul Pillitteri
Established: 1948
Media: TV
Award: Gold statuette
Presented: Las Vegas, NV, Jan

Telluride Film Festival
National Film Preserve Ltd
800 Jones St, Berkeley, CA 94710
Tel: 510-665-9494 *Fax:* 510-665-9589
E-mail: mail@telluridefilmfestival.org
Web Site: www.telluridefilmfestival.org
Key Personnel
Dir: Julie Huntsinger; Tom Luddy; Gary Meyer
Media: 35mm film, Digital Beta NTSC or HD-CAM 1080, 24p or 30i
Closing Date: Annually in July
Entry Fee: $35-$95
Presented: Telluride, CO, Sept 4-7, 2015

The Lowell Thomas Award
Overseas Press Club of America
40 W 45 St, New York, NY 10036
Tel: 212-626-9220 *Fax:* 212-626-9210
Web Site: www.opcofamerica.org
Key Personnel
Exec Dir: Patricia Kranz
Best radio news or interpretation of international affairs. All entries are submitted online.
Award: Certificate & $1,000 check
Closing Date: Annually in late Jan
Entry Fee: $200 per category
Presented: Hotel Mandarin-Oriental, New York, NY, Annually in April

Three Rivers Arts Festival, see Dollar Bank Three Rivers Arts Festival

Tiburon International Film Festival (TIFF)
6 Beach Rd, 544, Tiburon, CA 94920
Tel: 415-251-8433 *Fax:* 633-444-8433
E-mail: info@tiburonfilmfestival.com
Web Site: www.tiburonfilmfestival.com
Established: 2002
Golden Reel Award.
Media: Film
Categories: Fiction, documentary, short, animation, children & music video
Award: Certificate of Excellence
Closing Date: Annually, Dec 1
Entry Fee: $45 films 50 minutes & over; $35 films under 50 minutes
Presented: Tiburon, CA, Annually in April

Toronto Reel Asian International Film Festival
401 Richmond St W, Suite 309, Toronto, ON M5V 3A8, Canada
Tel: 416-703-9333 *Fax:* 416-703-9986
E-mail: info@reelasian.com; programming@reelasian.com
Web Site: www.reelasian.com
Key Personnel
Exec Dir: Sonia Sakamoto-Jog *E-mail:* sonia@reelasian.org
Opers Mgr: Chris Chin *E-mail:* chris@reelasian.com
Established: 1997
Entry Fee: Free up to early deadline
Presented: Toronto, ON, CN, Annually in Nov

Tribeca Film Festival
Tribeca Enterprises
375 Greenwich St, New York, NY 10013
Tel: 212-941-2400 *Fax:* 212-941-3939
E-mail: festival@tribecafilmfestival.org
Web Site: tribecafilm.com/festival/; tribecafilmfestival.org/festival
Key Personnel
Mng Dir: Casey Baltes
Mgr, Event Prodns: Ryan Littman
VP, Commun & Media: Tammie Rosen *E-mail:* trosen@tribecaenterprises.com
Established: 2002
Annual, well known, diverse international film festival.
Other Sponsor(s): AT&T
Media: Film (full length & shorts) & transmedia
Categories: Narrative & documentary
Closing Date: Multiple deadlines, see web site for details
Presented: New York, NY, April

TVB Retail Commercial Awards (RCA), see The Bessies Awards

United States Super 8mm Film & Digital Video Festival
Rutgers Film Co-op/NJ Media Arts Center Inc
Admin Off, 30 Bedford Rd, Somerset, NJ 08873
Mailing Address: Rutgers University, 018 Loree Hall, 72 Lipman Dr, New Brunswick, NJ 08901-8525
Tel: 848-932-8482 *Fax:* 732-932-1935
E-mail: njmac@aol.com
Web Site: www.njfilmfest.com
Key Personnel
CEO & Curator: Albert Gabriel Nigrin
Other Sponsor(s): Jungle Software; Middlesex County Cultural & Heritage Commission; NAMAC & NEA; New Jersey Media Arts; New Jersey State Council on the Arts Center; Pro 8mm; Rutgers University
Media: Super 8, 16mm, DVD, Blu-ray, must predominantly (50%) originate on 8/S8 film or 8mm video or digital video
Categories: Amateur, business/industry; experimental, personal, documentary, narrative, etc
Award: $3,000-$5,000
Closing Date: Annually in Jan
Entry Fee: $45 for works under 20 minutes, $55 for works 20-50 minutes, $75 for works over 50 minutes
Presented: Rutgers University, New Brunswick, NJ, Annually in Feb

US International Film & Video Festival Awards
The United States Festivals Association
713 S Pacific Coast Hwy, Suite A, Redondo Beach, CA 90277-4233
Tel: 310-540-0959 *Fax:* 310-316-8905
E-mail: filmfestinfo@filmfestawards.com
Web Site: www.filmfestawards.com
Key Personnel
Chmn: Lee W Gluckman, Jr *E-mail:* leegluckman@mobiusawards.com
Exec Dir: Kristen Gluckman *E-mail:* kristengluckman@mobiusawards.com
Media Rel: Sandra B Kelly *E-mail:* mediarelations@filmfestawards.com
Established: 1967
For productions produced or released within the 18 months preceding the annual March 1st entry deadline. Offer categories covering all subjects & production techniques.
Media: Entry may be made on DVD. Tapes can be in NTSC or PAL standards. See web site for details
Categories: Advertising, sales, promotion; agriculture; art, culture; children's programming; community development; corporate communications; documentary; education; entertainment & short subjects; environmental concerns, energy; fund raising; history, biography; manufacturing, industrial, technical processes; medicine, health; nature, wildlife; oceanography, politics, government, citizenship, world relations; public relations; recreation, sports, hobbies, crafts; religion, ethics, humanities; safety, welfare, insurance; sciences, research, exploration; social issues; television programming; training; travel, geography; plus production technique categories such as editing, photography, etc
Award: Gold Camera Statuette (1st place), Silver Screen Statuette (2nd place), certificate for creativity (3rd place), lifetime achievement & best show award
Closing Date: Annually in March
Presented: Los Angeles, CA, Annually in June

USA Film Festival
6116 N Central Expwy, Suite 105, Dallas, TX 75206
Tel: 214-821-6300 *Fax:* 214-821-6364
E-mail: usafilmfestival@aol.com
Web Site: www.usafilmfestival.com
Key Personnel
Mng Dir: Ann Alexander
Established: 1971
Media: Submissions: DVD screener (NTSC); Finished formats: 16mm, 35mm & 70mm film, IMAX, HDCAM, DV/DVCAM, DVD, BetaSP, DigiBeta, Blu-ray
Award: Short Film Awards
Closing Date: March 1
Entry Fee: Visit www.usafilmfestival.com
Presented: April

Vancouver International Film Festival
Vancouver International Film Centre, 1181 Seymour St, Vancouver, BC V6B 3M7, Canada
Tel: 604-685-0260 *Fax:* 604-688-8221
E-mail: viff@viff.org
Web Site: www.viff.org
Key Personnel
Exec Dir: Jacqueline Dupuis
Dir, Programming: Alan Franey
Sr Programmer: PoChu AuYeung
VIFF Indus Prodr: Fran Bergin
Established: 1982
One of the largest film festivals in North America, VIFF features approximately 320 films (220 features/100 shorts) from over 70 countries at 9 theatres to an expected audience of 140,000. VIFF is officially "non-competitive" but does offer several adjudicated cash prizes & audience awards. To find out more about our event, please visit our web site at www.viff.org.
Media: DCP, 16mm & 35mm film or on most video formats (NTSC or PAL) including BetaSP, DigiBeta, HDCAM
Categories: Shorts, documentaries & narrative feature films
Closing Date: June 17 CN, July 1 Intl (tentative)
Entry Fee: $40 US; $20 CN (less than 20 mins); $40 CN (20 mins or longer); $60 Intl (features), $40 (shorts)
Presented: Vancouver, BC, CN

VC Filmfest, see The Los Angeles Asian Pacific Film Festival

Vermont International Film Festival
230 College St, Burlington, VT 05401
Mailing Address: PO Box 483, Burlington, VT 05402-0483
Tel: 802-660-2600 *Fax:* 802-860-9555
E-mail: info@vtiff.org
Web Site: www.vtiff.org
Key Personnel
Pres: Lorna-Kay Peal
Exec Dir: Orly Yadin
Established: 1985
International festival of independent films.
Media: Blu-ray
Categories: Independent films of all genres. The festival also invites out of competition from Vermont filmmakers
Award: Cash, plaque & certificate
Presented: Several locations in Burlington, VT, Oct

The Virginia Film Festival
University of Virginia
617 W Main St, 2nd fl, Charlottesville, VA 22903
Mailing Address: PO Box 400869, Charlottesville, VA 22904
Tel: 434-982-5277 *Fax:* 434-924-3374
E-mail: info@virginiafilmfestival.org
Web Site: www.virginiafilmfestival.org
Key Personnel
Dir: Jody Kielbasa
Mng Dir: Jenny Mays
Media: Submissions: DVD (NTSC Region 0 or 1) or online screener; Screening: 16mm, 35mm & 3/4 inch film
Categories: Independent filmmakers, classics, major releases
Entry Fee: $30
Presented: Annually in the Fall

Voice of Democracy Scholarship Program
Veterans of Foreign Wars of the United States
406 W 34 St, Kansas City, MO 64111
Tel: 816-968-1117 *Fax:* 816-968-1149
Web Site: www.vfw.org
Key Personnel
Prog Coord: Kris Harmer *E-mail:* kharmer@vfw.org
Established: 1947
National audio essay competition for high school students in grades 9-12; one contestant from each state who voices their opinion on their responsibility to our country via audiocassette tape recording or CD. Information about the winners can be found on our web site www.vfw.org/VOD.
Media: Audio CD
Categories: Audio essay
Award: $30,000 scholarship (1st place); $152,000 in national awards; state winners receive an all-expense paid trip to Washington, DC
Closing Date: Nov 1
Entry Fee: None
Presented: National Finals, Washington, DC, March

The Samuel L Warner Memorial Award
Society of Motion Picture & Television Engineers (SMPTE)
3 Barker Ave, 5th fl, White Plains, NY 10601
Tel: 914-761-1100 *Fax:* 914-761-3115
E-mail: smpte@smpte.org
Web Site: www.smpte.org
Key Personnel
Exec Dir: Barbara Lange *Tel:* 914-205-2370 *E-mail:* blange@smpte.org
Dir, Opers: Sally-Ann D'Amato *Tel:* 914-205-2375 *E-mail:* sdamato@smpte.org
Mktg & Communs: Aimee Ricca *Tel:* 914-205-2381
Exec Asst: June Marie Sobrito *Tel:* 914-205-2384 *E-mail:* jsobrito@smpte.org
Honors an individual who has made outstanding contributions to the design & development of new & improved methods +/or apparatus for sound-on film motion pictures including any steps in the process.
Closing Date: Annually in April
Presented: SMPTE Annual Technical Conference & Exhibition, Loews Hollywood Hotel, Hollywood, CA, Annually in Oct

Washington DC International Film Festival
PO Box 21396, Washington, DC 20009-0896
Tel: 202-274-5782 *Fax:* 202-274-6690
E-mail: filmfestdc@filmfestdc.org
Web Site: www.filmfestdc.org
Key Personnel
Dir: Anthony Gittens
Awards presented: Audience Award, Circle Award & Justice Matters Award.
Media: 35mm, digital
Categories: All
Entry Fee: $15 under 30 minutes; $30 over 30 minutes

Waterfront Film Festival (WFF)
PO Box 387, Saugatuck, MI 49453-0387
Tel: 269-857-8351 *Fax:* 269-857-1072
E-mail: info@waterfrontfilm.org
Web Site: www.waterfrontfilm.org
Key Personnel
Founder: Dana DePree-Minter; Dori DePree; Hopwood DePree; Kori Eldean; Judy Smith
Established: 1999
Media: Online screener or DVD
Categories: Films (any genre)
Closing Date: Feb
Presented: Multiple venues throughout South Haven, MI, Annually in June

Welles, Orson Award, see Orson Welles Award

Western Heritage Awards
National Cowboy & Western Heritage Museum
1700 NE 63 St, Oklahoma City, OK 73111
Tel: 405-478-2250 *Fax:* 405-478-4714
Web Site: nationalcowboymuseum.org
Key Personnel
Dir, PR & Museum Events: Catherine Page *Tel:* 405-478-2250 ext 221 *E-mail:* cpage@nationalcowboymuseum.org
Established: 1961
Application online.
Media: VHS, DVD, CD, Books
Categories: Western music new artist, Western music original composition, Traditional western music album. All western genre, theatrical motion picture, television feature film, docudrama, documentary, television news feature, fictional drama, Western novel, Western nonfiction book, Western art book, Western photography book, Western juvenile book, Western magazine article, Western poetry book
Award: "The Wrangler" - bronze sculpture of a cowboy on horseback
Closing Date: Nov 30 (literature), Dec 31 (film & music)
Entry Fee: $50 per entry per category
Presented: National Cowboy & Western Heritage Museum, Oklahoma City, OK, April

Winter Film Awards
419 Lafayette St, New York, NY 10003
Tel: 646-355-4371
E-mail: info@winterfilmawards.com
Web Site: www.winterfilmawards.com
Key Personnel
Exec Dir: Steffanie L Finn
CFO & Treas: Mobasher Ahmed
Celebrates the diversity of local & international filmmaking, hosting 4-6 events annually in addition to the annual Independent Film Festival in New York City.

Winter Film Awards Independent Film Festival
Winter Film Awards
419 Lafayette St, New York, NY 10003
Tel: 646-355-4371
E-mail: info@winterfilmawards.com; submissions@winterfilmawards.com
Web Site: www.winterfilmawards.com
Key Personnel
Exec Dir: Steffanie L Finn
CFO & Treas: Mobasher Ahmed
Submission categories include: Narrative Feature, Foreign Language, Short, Documentary, Animation, Music Video & Horror.
Presented: Annually in Feb

Women in Film Foundation Film Finishing Fund
Women in Film Foundation
6100 Wilshire Blvd, Suite 710, Los Angeles, CA 90048
Tel: 323-935-2211 *Fax:* 323-935-2212
E-mail: info@wif.org
Web Site: www.wif.org
Key Personnel
Exec Dir: Gayle Nachlis *Tel:* 323-935-2211 ext 106 *E-mail:* gnachlis@wif.org
Foundation Coord: Morgan Green *Tel:* 323-935-2211 ext 109 *E-mail:* foundation@wif.org
Established: 1985
Awarded for films made by, for or about women. The number of grants given vary from year to year. Student projects are not eligible.
Media: DVD (NTSC Region 1 or 0)
Categories: Narrative, documentary, educational, animated & experimental (long or short format)
Award: Cash & in-kind services
Closing Date: See web site
Entry Fee: $75

WorldFest-Houston
WorldFest
9898 Bissonnet St, Suite 650, Houston, TX 77036
Mailing Address: PO Box 56566, Houston, TX 77256-6566
Tel: 713-965-9955 *Toll Free Tel:* 866-965-9955 *Fax:* 713-965-9960
E-mail: mail@worldfest.org; entry@worldfest.org
Web Site: www.worldfest.org

Key Personnel
Chmn & Founding Dir: Hunter Todd
Prog & Artistic Dir: Kathleen Haney
Entry Dir: Lauren Calderon
Other Sponsor(s): Action Motors & Limousines; AMC Independent; Arcodoro® Houston; Art Works; Avis Budget; Becker Vineyards; Boxer Property®; City of Houston, TX; Film Freeway; Harris County, TX; HBU Bradshaw Fitness Center; Houston Arts Alliance; Houston Film Commission; Houston Yacht Club; InkTip; Regent University; Space Center Houston; Texas Commission for the Arts; Texas Film Commission; The Homestead 1766; Tippit & Moo; Wagner Media
Media: DVD, Blu-ray or Beta-SP
Categories: Short, documentary, feature, experimental, interactive, TV, student, music video, new media & screenplays
Award: Statuette, Gold Bowl, Gold Lone Star, Cash Grants (winners are part of the WorldFest "Discovery Program" & are entered into more than 200 top international film festivals)
Closing Date: Dec 15
Entry Fee: $40-$150, depending on length
Presented: Houston, TX, April

Yorkton Film Festival (YFF)
49 Smith St E, Yorkton, SK S3N 0H4, Canada
Tel: 306-782-7077 *Fax:* 306-782-1550
E-mail: info@yorktonfilm.com
Web Site: yorktonfilm.com
Key Personnel
Exec Dir: Randy Goulden
Festival Coord: Scott Stelmaschuk
Established: 1947
Best in Canadian short media content. Golden Sheaf Awards presented during the festival.
Presented: Yorkton, SK, CN, May 21-24, 2015

Calendar of Events—Alphabetical Index of Sponsors

Calendar of Events—Alphabetical Index of Events

Calendar of Events

AV-related trade shows, meetings and conventions scheduled (at press time) from early 2015 through 2019 are listed chronologically by year and month, and then alphabetically by the event name. Preceding this section are two indexes: the Sponsor Index is an alphabetical list of event sponsors and includes the names and dates of the events they sponsor; the Event Index is an alphabetical list of events along with the dates on which they are held.

2015

APRIL

AAM Annual Meeting & MuseumExpo
Sponsored by American Alliance of Museums (AAM)
1575 Eye St NW, Suite 400, Washington, DC 20005
Tel: 202-289-1818 *Fax:* 202-289-6578
Web Site: www.aam-us.org
Key Personnel
Dir, Meetings & Events: Andrea Streat *Tel:* 202-218-7678 *E-mail:* astreat@aam-us.org
Sr Mgr, Meetings & Events: Lisa McBride *Tel:* 202-218-7676 *E-mail:* smcbride@aam-us.org
Sr Meeting & Events Mgr: Stephanie Szurek *Tel:* 202-218-7708 *E-mail:* sszurek@aam-us.org
Location: Atlanta, GA
April 26-29, 2015

AERA Annual Meeting
Sponsored by American Educational Research Association (AERA)
1430 "K" St NW, Suite 1200, Washington, DC 20005
Tel: 202-238-3200 *Fax:* 202-238-3250
E-mail: annualmtg@aera.net
Web Site: www.aera.net
Key Personnel
Meetings Dir: Laurie Cipriano *Tel:* 202-238-3200 ext 210 *E-mail:* lcipriano@aera.net
Meetings Mgr: Samara Fetner *Tel:* 202-238-3200 ext 212 *E-mail:* sfetner@aera.net
Meetings Assoc: Kimberly Ricks *Tel:* 202-238-3200 ext 211 *E-mail:* kricks@aera.net
Meetings Asst: Brittany Salzman *Tel:* 202-238-3200 ext 213 *E-mail:* bsalzman@aera.net
Location: Chicago, IL
April 16-20, 2015

BEA2015
Sponsored by Broadcast Education Association (BEA)
Affiliate of National Association of Broadcasters (NAB) (in partnership with)
1771 "N" St NW, Washington, DC 20036-2891
Fax: 202-609-9940
E-mail: help@beaweb.org
Web Site: www.beaweb.org/2015/bea2015.html; www.beaweb.org
Key Personnel
Exec Dir: Heather Birks *Tel:* 202-602-0584 *E-mail:* heather@beaweb.org
Dir of Sales & Mktg: J-D Boyle *Tel:* 202-602-0586 *E-mail:* jd@beaweb.org
Annual convention co-located next to NAB Show.
Location: Westgate Las Vegas Resort & Casino, Las Vegas, NV
April 12-15, 2015

CLA Annual Convention
Sponsored by Catholic Library Association (CLA)
8550 United Plaza Blvd, Suite 1001, Baton Rouge, LA 70809
Tel: 225-408-4417 *Toll Free Tel:* 855-739-1776 *Fax:* 312-739-1778
Web Site: www.cathla.org
Key Personnel
Interim Exec Dir: Malachy R McCarthy *E-mail:* mmccarthy@cathla.org
Held in conjunction with National Catholic Educational Association (NCEA) Convention & Expo.
Location: Orange County Convention Center, Orlando, FL
April 7-9, 2015

CMMA Professional Development Conference
Sponsored by Communications Media Management Association (CMMA)
c/o The Association Source LLC, 20423 State Rd 7, Suite F6-491, Boca Raton, FL 33498
Tel: 561-477-8100
Web Site: www.cmma.org
Key Personnel
Exec Dir: Ricky Atkins *E-mail:* executive.director@cmma.org
Location: Marriott Headquarters, Washington, DC
April 26-28, 2015

Computers in Libraries (CIL)
Sponsored by Information Today, Inc
143 Old Marlton Pike, Medford, NJ 08055-8750
Tel: 609-654-6266 *Toll Free Tel:* 800-300-9868 (cust serv) *Fax:* 609-654-4309
E-mail: custserv@infotoday.com
Web Site: www.infotoday.com/cil2015/; www.facebook.com/ComputersInLibraries
Key Personnel
Pres & CEO: Thomas H Hogan
Dir, Meeting Planning: Stacey Hogan
Conference & exhibition focusing on all aspects of library & information delivery technology.
Location: Hilton Washington, Washington, DC
April 27-29, 2015

Interop Las Vegas
Sponsored by UBM Tech
Suite 900, 9th fl, South Tower, 303 Second St, San Francisco, CA 94107
Tel: 415-947-6916 (registration dept) *Toll Free Tel:* 866-535-8992 (registration dept) *Fax:* 415-947-6011 (completed registration form)
E-mail: interoplvregistration@ubm.com; interoplv@ubm.com (exhibitor servs)
Web Site: www.interop.com/lasvegas
Key Personnel
Gen Mgr, Interop: Jennifer Jessup *E-mail:* jennifer.jessup@ubm.com
Co-located with InformationWeek Conference & Cloud Connect.
Location: Mandalay Bay Convention Center, Las Vegas, NV
April 27-May 1, 2015

NAB Show®
Sponsored by National Association of Broadcasters (NAB)
1771 "N" St NW, Washington, DC 20036
Tel: 202-429-5300 *Toll Free Tel:* 800-342-2460 (registration); 800-NAB-EXPO (622-3976, exhibit sales)
E-mail: nab@nab.org
Web Site: www.nabshow.com; www.facebook.com/pages/NAB-Show/195269533220; twitter.com/NABShow; www.nab.org
Key Personnel
CEO & Pres: Gordon H Smith
EVP, Conventions & Busn Opers: Mr Chris Brown
SVP, Communs: Ann Marie Cumming *Tel:* 202-429-5307 *E-mail:* amcumming@nab.org
The NAB Show® delivers the most comprehensive showcase of digital communications technologies including every element of television & radio broadcasting, film/video production & post-production, audio production, multimedia, the Internet, satellite & telecommunications.
Location: Las Vegas Convention Center, Las Vegas, NV
April 11-16, 2015

NCEA Convention & Expo
Sponsored by National Catholic Educational Association (NCEA)
1005 N Glebe Rd, Suite 525, Arlington, VA 22201
Toll Free Tel: 800-711-NCEA (711-6232) *Fax:* 703-243-0025
Web Site: www.ncea.org/convention; www.ncea.org
Key Personnel
Dir of Events: Amy Durkin *Tel:* 571-257-0013 *E-mail:* adurkin@ncea.org
Annual meeting for all working in Catholic education, Pre-K through college.
Location: Orange County Convention Center, Orlando, FL
April 7-9, 2015

THE Performance Improvement Conference
Sponsored by International Society for Performance Improvement® (ISPI)
PO Box 13035, Silver Spring, MD 20910
Tel: 301-587-8570 *Fax:* 301-587-8573
E-mail: info@ispi.org
Web Site: www.ispi.org
Key Personnel
Exec Dir: April Davis *Tel:* 301-587-8570 ext 112 *E-mail:* april@ispi.org
Location: Hyatt Regency San Antonio Riverwalk, San Antonio, TX
April 24-29, 2015

MAY

ASPRS Annual Conference
Sponsored by ASPRS: The Imaging and Geospatial Information Society
5410 Grosvenor Lane, Suite 210, Bethesda, MD 20814-2160
Tel: 301-493-0290 *Fax:* 301-493-0208
E-mail: asprs@asprs.org
Web Site: www.asprs.org
Key Personnel
Asst Communs Dir/Meetings-Mktg Mgr: Heather Staverman *Tel:* 301-493-0290 ext 106 *E-mail:* hstaverman@asprs.org
Location: Tampa Bay Marriott Waterside Hotel, Tampa, FL
May 4-8, 2015

ATD International Conference & Exposition
Sponsored by Association for Talent Development (ATD)
1640 King St, Alexandria, VA 22314-2743
Tel: 703-683-8100 *Toll Free Tel:* 800-628-2783; 866-238-2146 (cust care) *Fax:* 703-299-8723; 703-683-1523 (cust care)
E-mail: customercare@td.org
Web Site: www.atdconference.org; www.td.org
Location: Orange County Convention Center, 9990 International Dr, Orlando, FL
May 17-20, 2015

BookExpo America (BEA)
Sponsored by Reed Exhibitions USA
Division of Reed Elsevier plc
383 Main Ave, Norwalk, CT 06851
Tel: 203-840-4800 *Toll Free Tel:* 800-840-5614 *Fax:* 203-840-5805
E-mail: inquiry@bookexpoamerica.com
Web Site: bookexpoamerica.com
Key Personnel
Event Dir: Steve Rosato *Tel:* 203-840-5463 *Fax:* 203-840-9463 *E-mail:* srosato@reedexpo.com
Dir of Mktg: Kimberlie I Leon *Tel:* 203-840-5653 *Fax:* 203-840-9653 *E-mail:* kleon@reedexpo.com
Produced & managed by Reed Exhibitions USA, BEA is sponsored by the American Booksellers Association (ABA), the Association of American Publishers Inc (AAP) & the Association of Authors' Representatives Inc (AAR).
Location: Jacob K Javits Convention Center, 655 W 43 St, New York, NY
May 27-29, 2015

Display Week
Sponsored by Society for Information Display (SID)
1475 S Bascom Ave, Suite 114, Campbell, CA 95008-4006
Tel: 408-879-3901 *Fax:* 408-879-3833
E-mail: office@sid.org
Web Site: www.displayweek.org; www.sid.org
Key Personnel
Sr Busn Mgr: Doug Bragdon *E-mail:* doug@sid.org
Conference Coord: Mark Goldfarb *Tel:* 212-460-8090 ext 202 *E-mail:* mark@sid.org
Premier showcase of the display industry.
Location: San Jose Convention Center, San Jose, CA
May 31-June 5, 2015

INTX: The Internet & Television Expo
Formerly The Cable Show
Sponsored by National Cable & Telecommunications Association (NCTA)
Industry Affairs Dept, 25 Massachusetts Ave NW, Suite 100, Washington, DC 20001
Tel: 202-222-2430; 202-463-7905 (exhibitor inquiries) *Fax:* 202-222-2431
E-mail: infointx@ncta.com; exhibitinfo@ncta.com
Web Site: www.ncta.com; intx.ncta.com
Location: McCormick Place Convention Center (West Bldg), 2301 S Lake Shore Dr, Chicago, IL
May 5-7, 2015

IS&T Archiving Conference
Sponsored by Society for Imaging Science and Technology (IS&T)
7003 Kilworth Lane, Springfield, VA 22151
Tel: 703-642-9090 *Fax:* 703-642-9094
E-mail: info@imaging.com
Web Site: www.imaging.org/ist/conferences/archiving; www.imaging.org
Key Personnel
Exec Dir: Suzanne E Grinnan *E-mail:* sgrinnan@imaging.org
Exec Asst: Donna Smith *E-mail:* dsmith@imaging.org
Conference Prog Mgr: Diana Gonzalez *E-mail:* dgonzalez@imaging.org
Annual conference located alternately in North America (odd numbered years) & Europe (even numbered years). Digital preservation & stewardship of hardcopy, audio & video is the focus.
Location: Getty Center, Los Angeles, CA
May 19-22, 2015

Media Finance Focus 2015
Sponsored by Media Financial Management Association (MFM)
550 W Frontage Rd, Suite 3600, Northfield, IL 60093
Tel: 847-716-7000 *Fax:* 847-716-7004
E-mail: info@mediafinance.org
Web Site: www.mediafinance.org
Key Personnel
MFM/BCCA Dir of Opers: Jamie L Smith *E-mail:* jamie.smith@mediafinance.org
Fin Consultant & Conference Coord: Charlie Warner *E-mail:* charlie.warner@mediafinance.org
Co-sponsored by the Broadcast Cable Credit Association (BCCA).
Location: The Arizona Grand Hotel & Spa, 8000 S Arizona Grand Pkwy, Phoenix, AZ
May 18-20, 2015

PMBA Annual Conference
Sponsored by Public Media Business Association (PMBA)
7918 Jones Branch Dr, Suite 300, McLean, VA 22102
Tel: 703-506-3292 *Fax:* 703-506-3266
Web Site: www.pbma.org
Key Personnel
Sr Events Mgr: Pamela Vail *E-mail:* pvail@pmbaonline.org
Location: Washington Marriott Georgetown, Washington, DC
May 26-29, 2015

Streaming Media East
Sponsored by Information Today, Inc
143 Old Marlton Pike, Medford, NJ 08055-8750
Tel: 609-654-6266 *Toll Free Tel:* 800-300-9868 (cust serv) *Fax:* 609-654-4309
E-mail: custserv@infotoday.com
Web Site: www.streamingmedia.com/conferences/East
Key Personnel
Pres & CEO: Thomas H Hogan
Dir, Meeting Planning: Stacey Hogan
Held in conjunction with Data Summit.
Location: New York Hilton Midtown, 1335 Avenue of the Americas, New York, NY
May 12-13, 2015

JUNE

AICP Week
Sponsored by Association of Independent Commercial Producers (AICP)
3 W 18 St, 5th fl, New York, NY 10011
Tel: 212-929-3000 *Fax:* 212-929-3359
E-mail: info@aicp.com
Web Site: www.aicp.com
Key Personnel
Pres & CEO: Matt Miller *E-mail:* mattm@aicp.com
Dir of Events: Ileana Montalvo *E-mail:* ileanam@aicp.com
The show is produced in partnership with MoMA & the work that will be honored by inclusion in the show is given further tribute by becoming part of the film collection of MoMA's Department of Film.
In the months following the main event, the show travels to several locations around the country.
Location: MoMA, New York, NY
June 2-4, 2015

ALA Annual Conference
Sponsored by American Library Association (ALA)
50 E Huron St, Chicago, IL 60611-2795
Tel: 312-944-6780 *Toll Free Tel:* 800-545-2433 (ext 3223, conference servs) *Fax:* 312-440-9374
E-mail: ala@ala.org
Web Site: www.ala.org
Key Personnel
Conference Dir: Paul Graller *E-mail:* pgraller@ala.org
Conference Mgr: Amy R McGuigan *Tel:* 800-545-2433 ext 3226 *E-mail:* amcguigan@ala.org
Registration & Housing Specialist: Alicia Babcock *Tel:* 800-545-2433 ext 3229 *E-mail:* ababcock@ala.org
Meeting, AV & Catering Coord: Yvonne A McLean *Tel:* 800-545-2433 ext 3222 *E-mail:* ymclean@ala.org
Conference Coord: Lindsay Rosales *E-mail:* lrosales@ala.org
Meetings Coord: Alicia (Alee) Navarro *E-mail:* anavarro@ala.org
Location: Moscone Center, San Francisco, CA
June 25-30, 2015

ASSE Professional Development Conference & Exposition
Sponsored by American Society of Safety Engineers (ASSE)
1800 E Oakton St, Des Plaines, IL 60018
Tel: 847-699-2929
E-mail: customerservice@asse.org
Web Site: www.safety2015.org; www.asse.org
Key Personnel
Exec Dir: Fred Fortman *Tel:* 847-768-3450
Dir, Prof Devt: Dewey Whitmire *Tel:* 847-768-3418
Mgr, Conferences & Meetings: Stephanie Rennie-Sanchez *Tel:* 847-768-3417
Sr Coord, Conferences & Meetings: Bonnie Lipinski *Tel:* 847-768-3467; Cindy Milner *Tel:* 847-769-3448
Location: The Kay Bailey Hutchison Convention Center, 650 S Griffin St, Dallas, TX
June 7-10, 2015

Design Automation Conference (DAC)
Sponsored by MP Associates Inc
1721 Boxelder St, Suite 107, Louisville, CO 80027
Tel: 303-530-4333; 303-530-4562 *Toll Free Tel:* 800-321-4573 *Fax:* 303-530-4334
Web Site: www.dac.com
Key Personnel
Co-Pres: Kevin Lepine *Tel:* 303-530-4562 ext 111 *E-mail:* kevin@mpassociates.com; Lee Wood *Tel:* 303-530-4562 ext 112 *E-mail:* lee@mpassociates.com
Dir of Exhibit Opers: Susie Horn *Tel:* 303-530-4562 ext 125 *E-mail:* susie@mpassociates.com
Exhibit Coord: Candi Wooldridge *Tel:* 303-530-4562 ext 222; Stacy DiLallo *Tel:* 303-530-4562 ext 115
Dir of Sales & Busn Devt: Karen Popp *Tel:* 303-530-4562 ext 133
Event for the design of electronic circuits & systems, embedded systems & software & electronic design automation.
Sponsored by the Association of Computing Machinery, Electronic Design Automation Consortium & Institute of Electrical & Electronics Engineers.

Location: Moscone Center, San Francisco, CA
June 7-11, 2015

EastPack®
Sponsored by UBM Canon LLC
2901 28 St, Suite 100, Santa Monica, CA 90405
Tel: 310-445-4200
E-mail: packaginginfo@ubm.com; ubmcanonconferences@ubm.com
Web Site: www.canontradeshows.com; ubmcanon.com
Location: Jacob K Javits Convention Center, 655 W 43 St, New York, NY
June 9-11, 2015

IABC World Conference
Sponsored by International Association of Business Communicators (IABC)
601 Montgomery St, Suite 1900, San Francisco, CA 94111
Tel: 415-544-4700 *Toll Free Tel:* 800-776-4222 *Fax:* 415-544-4747
E-mail: conference@iabc.com; member_relations@iabc.com
Web Site: wc.iabc.com; www.iabc.com
Key Personnel
Dir, Conferences & Events: Charles Herrick *Tel:* 415-544-4745 *E-mail:* cherrick@iabc.com
Location: San Francisco Marriott Marquis, 55 Fourth St, San Francisco, CA
June 14-17, 2015

InfoComm
Sponsored by InfoComm International®
11242 Waples Mill Rd, Suite 200, Fairfax, VA 22030
Tel: 703-273-7200 *Toll Free Tel:* 800-659-SHOW (659-7469) *Fax:* 703-273-5924
E-mail: customerservice@infocomm.org
Web Site: www.infocommshow.org; www.infocomm.org
Key Personnel
Exec Dir & CEO: David Labuskes
SVP, Expositions: Jason McGraw *Tel:* 703-279-6361 *E-mail:* jmcgraw@infocomm.org
Dir, Exposition Opers: Kurt St Clair *Tel:* 703-279-6365 *E-mail:* kstclair@infocomm.org
Expositions Opers Mgr: Laura Reed *Tel:* 703-279-2167 *E-mail:* lreed@infocomm.org; Allison Konczyk *Tel:* 703-279-2165 *E-mail:* akonczyk@infocomm.org
Expositions Opers Coord: Debbie Clisham *Tel:* 703-279-9933 *E-mail:* dclisham@infocomm.org
Location: Orange County Convention Center, West Bldg, Orlando, FL
June 13-19, 2015

ISTE® 2015
Sponsored by International Society for Technology in Education (ISTE®)
180 W Eighth Ave, Suite 300, Eugene, OR 97401-2916
Tel: 541-302-3777 *Toll Free Tel:* 800-336-5191 (US & CN) *Fax:* 541-302-3778
E-mail: iste@iste.org
Web Site: www.isteconference.org; www.iste.org
Key Personnel
Sr Dir, Conference & Memb Progs: Jennifer Ragan-Fore *Tel:* 541-434-8938 *E-mail:* jraganfore@iste.org
Dir of Logistics: Vincent Barnett *Tel:* 541-434-9591 *E-mail:* vbarnett@iste.org
Location: Philadelphia, PA
June 28-July 1, 2015

NAESP 2015 Best Practices for Better Schools™ Conference
Sponsored by National Association of Elementary School Principals (NAESP)
1615 Duke St, Alexandria, VA 22314
Tel: 703-684-3345 *Toll Free Tel:* 800-386-2377 *Fax:* 703-549-5568 *Toll Free Fax:* 800-396-2377
E-mail: conference@naesp.org; naesp@naesp.org
Web Site: www.naesp.org
Key Personnel
Asst Exec Dir, Conferences & Exhibits: Deborah M Young *Tel:* 703-684-3345 ext 296 *E-mail:* dyoung@naesp.org
Location: Long Beach Convention & Entertainment Center, 300 E Ocean Blvd, Long Beach, CA
June 30-July 2, 2015

Optometry's Meeting®
Sponsored by American Optometric Association (AOA)
243 N Lindbergh Blvd, 1st fl, St Louis, MO 63141-7881
Tel: 314-991-4100 *Toll Free Tel:* 800-386-6825 (meetings hotline) *Fax:* 314-991-4101
Web Site: www.optometrysmeeting.org; www.exhibitsom.org; www.aoa.org
Key Personnel
Dir, Meetings & Conventions: Lori Lee *Tel:* 314-983-4256
Annual meeting of the American Optometric Association & the American Optometric Student Association.
Location: Washington State Convention Center, Seattle, WA
June 24-28, 2015

PromaxBDA: The Conference 2015
Sponsored by PromaxBDA
1522e Cloverfield Blvd, Santa Monica, CA 90404
Tel: 310-788-7600 *Fax:* 310-788-7616
Web Site: www.promaxbda.org
Key Personnel
VP, Events & Prodn: Tripp Mahan *Tel:* 310-789-1530 *E-mail:* tripp@promaxbda.org
Sr Mgr, Events & Prodn: Christina Woodward *Tel:* 310-789-1532 *E-mail:* christinaw@promaxbda.org
Mgr, Events & Prodn: Anna Lyn Arboleda *Tel:* 310-789-1512 *E-mail:* annalyn@promaxbda.org
Location: JW Marriott Los Angeles LA Live, 900 W Olympic Blvd, Los Angeles, CA
June 9-11, 2015

SLA Annual Conference & INFO-EXPO
Sponsored by Special Libraries Association (SLA)
331 S Patrick St, Alexandria, VA 22314-3501
Tel: 703-647-4900 *Fax:* 703-647-4901
E-mail: events@sla.org
Web Site: www.sla.org
Key Personnel
CEO: Janice R Lachance *Tel:* 703-647-4933 *E-mail:* janice@sla.org
Dir, Events: Caroline Hamilton (Rives) *Tel:* 703-647-4949 *E-mail:* chamilton@sla.org
Dir, Mktg & Exhibits: Jeff Leach *Tel:* 703-647-4922 *E-mail:* jleach@sla.org
Location: Boston Convention & Exposition Center, 415 Summer St, Boston, MA
June 14-16, 2015

UPAA Annual Technical Symposium
Sponsored by University Photographers' Association of America (UPAA)
c/o Moraine Valley Community College, 9000 W College Pkwy, Palos Hills, IL 60465
Tel: 708-974-5495
Web Site: www.upaa.org
Key Personnel
Pres: Glenn Carpenter *E-mail:* carpenter@morainevalley.edu
Location: University of Michigan, Ann Arbor, MI
June 7-11, 2015

JULY

Summer NAMM
Sponsored by NAMM, the National Association of Music Merchants
5790 Armada Dr, Carlsbad, CA 92008
Tel: 760-438-8001 *Toll Free Tel:* 800-767-6266 (memb hotline) *Fax:* 760-438-7327
E-mail: info@namm.org
Web Site: www.namm.org; www.facebook.com/nammshow; twitter.com/nammshow
Key Personnel
Dir, Trade Show Sales: Dan Moylan *Tel:* 760-438-8007 ext 114 *E-mail:* danielm@namm.org
Assoc Dir, Trade Show Sales: Dominique Agnew *Tel:* 760-438-8007 ext 123 *E-mail:* dominiquea@namm.org
Location: Nashville Music City Center, 700 Korean Veterans Blvd, Nashville, TN
July 9-11, 2015

AUGUST

ACM Annual Conference
Sponsored by Alliance for Community Media (ACM)
4248 Park Glen Rd, Minneapolis, MN 55416
Tel: 952-928-4643
E-mail: info@allcommunitymedia.org
Web Site: www.allcommunitymedia.org
Key Personnel
Contact: Michelle Herr
Held jointly with National Alliance for Media Arts and Culture (NAMAC).
Location: Hilton Pasadena, 168 S Los Robles Ave, Pasadena, CA
Aug 12-14, 2015

MAB & MABF's Summer Celebration & Annual Meeting
Sponsored by Michigan Association of Broadcasters (MAB)
819 N Washington Ave, Lansing, MI 48906-5815
Tel: 517-484-7444 *Toll Free Tel:* 800-YOUR-MAB (968-7622) *Fax:* 517-484-5810
E-mail: mab@michmab.com
Web Site: www.michmab.com
Key Personnel
VP, Progs: Jennifer Preslar *E-mail:* preslar@michmab.com
Sponsored jointly with MAB Foundation.
Location: Shanty Creek Resorts, 5780 Shanty Creek Rd, Bellaire, MI
Aug 17-19, 2015

SIGGRAPH 2015
Sponsored by Association for Computing Machinery (ACM)
2 Penn Plaza, Suite 701, New York, NY 10121-0701
Tel: 212-626-0500 *Toll Free Tel:* 800-342-6626 (US & CN) *Fax:* 212-944-1318
E-mail: acmhelp@acm.org (memb servs)
Web Site: s2015.siggraph.org; www.siggraph.org; www.acm.org
Key Personnel
Asst Dir, Off of SIG Servs: Ashley Cozzi *Tel:* 212-626-0614 *E-mail:* acozzi@hq.acm.org
Prog Coord: Farrah Khan *Tel:* 212-626-0601 *E-mail:* farrah.khan@hq.acm.org
Location: Los Angeles Convention Center, Los Angeles, CA
Aug 9-13, 2015

VenueConnect
Sponsored by International Association of Venue Managers (IAVM)
635 Fritz Dr, Suite 100, Coppell, TX 75019-4442
Tel: 972-906-7441 *Toll Free Tel:* 800-935-4226 *Fax:* 972-906-7418
Web Site: www.iavm.org
Key Personnel
Pres & CEO: Vicki Hawarden *E-mail:* vicki.hawarden@iavm.org
Meetings Mgr: Bill Jenkins *Tel:* 972-538-1019 *E-mail:* Bill.Jenkins@iavm.org
Location: Baltimore Convention Center, Baltimore, MD
Aug 1-4, 2015

AUTUMN

CMMA National Conference
Sponsored by Communications Media Management Association (CMMA)
c/o The Association Source LLC, 20423 State Rd 7, Suite F6-491, Boca Raton, FL 33498
Tel: 561-477-8100
Web Site: www.cmma.org
Key Personnel
Exec Dir: Ricky Atkins *E-mail:* executive.director@cmma.org
Fall 2015

MAME Annual Conference
Sponsored by Michigan Association for Media in Education (MAME)
1407 Rensen St, Lansing, MI 48910
Tel: 517-394-2808 *Fax:* 517-492-3878
E-mail: mame@mimame.org
Web Site: www.mimame.org/our-annual-conference.html; www.mimame.org
Key Personnel
Pres: Katherine Lester *E-mail:* kathyl@mimame.org
Pres-Elect: Gwenn Marchesano *E-mail:* gmarchesano@mimame.org
Annual conference for Michigan School Librarians. Affiliate of American Association of School Librarians, International Society for Technology in Education.
Autumn 2015

Plant Management & Design Engineering Show (PMDS)
Sponsored by Society of Manufacturing Engineers Canada (SME Canada)
7100 Woodbine Ave, Suite 312, Markham, ON L3R 5J2, Canada
Tel: 905-752-4415 *Toll Free Tel:* 888-322-7333 *Fax:* 905-479-0113
E-mail: exposales@sme.org
Web Site: www.pmds.ca; www.sme.org/smecanada
Held every 2 years, PMDS is the only show of its kind serving Quebec's electronics manufacturing industry.
Location: Montreal, QC, CN
Fall 2015

SEPTEMBER

Digital Fabrication Conference
Sponsored by Society for Imaging Science and Technology (IS&T)
7003 Kilworth Lane, Springfield, VA 22151
Tel: 703-642-9090 *Fax:* 703-642-9094
E-mail: info@imaging.org
Web Site: www.imaging.org/ist/conferences/df; www.imaging.org
Key Personnel
Exec Dir: Suzanne E Grinnan *E-mail:* sgrinnan@imaging.org
Exec Asst: Donna Smith *E-mail:* dsmith@imaging.org
Conference Prog Mgr: Diana Gonzalez *E-mail:* dgonzalez@imaging.org
Co-located with NIP: International Conference on Digital Printing Technologies.
Location: Portland, OR
Sept 27-Oct 1, 2015

Graph Expo®
Sponsored by Graphic Arts Show Company (GASC)
1899 Preston White Dr, Reston, VA 20191-5468
Tel: 703-264-7200 *Fax:* 703-620-9187
E-mail: info@gasc.org
Web Site: www.graphexpo.com; www.gasc.org
Key Personnel
VP: Chris Price *Tel:* 703-264-7200 ext 221 *E-mail:* cprice@gasc.org
Dir of Opers: Kelly E Kilga *Tel:* 703-264-7200 ext 213 *E-mail:* kkilga@gasc.org
Dir of Communs: Deborah Vieder *Tel:* 703-264-7200 ext 222
Conference Mgr: Lilly Kinney *Tel:* 703-264-7200 ext 255 *E-mail:* lkinney@gasc.org
Location: McCormick Place, 2301 S Lake Shore Dr, Chicago, IL
Sept 13-16, 2015

NIP: International Conference on Digital Printing Technologies
Sponsored by Society for Imaging Science and Technology (IS&T)
7003 Kilworth Lane, Springfield, VA 22151
Tel: 703-642-9090 *Fax:* 703-642-9094
E-mail: info@imaging.org
Web Site: www.imaging.org/ist/conferences/nip; www.imaging.org
Key Personnel
Exec Dir: Suzanne E Grinnan *E-mail:* sgrinnan@imaging.org
Exec Asst: Donna Smith *E-mail:* dsmith@imaging.org
Conference Prog Mgr: Diana Gonzalez *E-mail:* dgonzalez@imaging.org
Co-located with the Digitial Fabrication Conference.
Location: Portland, OR
Sept 27-Oct 1, 2015

Radio Show
Sponsored by National Association of Broadcasters (NAB)
1771 "N" St NW, Washington, DC 20036
Tel: 202-429-5300 *Toll Free Tel:* 800-342-2460 (registration); 800-NAB-EXPO (622-3976, exhibit sales)
E-mail: nab@nab.org
Web Site: www.radioshowweb.com; www.facebook.com/radioshowweb; twitter.com/RadioShowWeb; www.nab.org
Key Personnel
CEO & Pres: Gordon H Smith
EVP, Conventions & Busn Opers: Mr Chris Brown
SVP, Communs: Ann Marie Cumming *Tel:* 202-429-5307 *E-mail:* amcumming@nab.org
Co-produced with Radio Advertising Bureau (RAB).
Location: Atlanta, GA
Sept 30-Oct 2, 2015

WebSearch University
Sponsored by Information Today, Inc
143 Old Marlton Pike, Medford, NJ 08055-8750
Tel: 609-654-6266 *Toll Free Tel:* 800-300-9868 (cust serv) *Fax:* 609-654-4309
E-mail: custserv@infotoday.com
Web Site: www.websearchu.com
Key Personnel
Pres & CEO: Thomas H Hogan
Dir, Meeting Planning: Stacey Hogan
Location: DoubleTree by Hilton Crystal City, 300 Army Navy Dr, Arlington, VA
Sept 17-18, 2015

OCTOBER

AES Convention
Sponsored by Audio Engineering Society Inc (AES)
60 E 42 St, Rm 2520, New York, NY 10165-2520
Tel: 212-661-8528 *Fax:* 212-682-0477
Web Site: www.aes.org
Key Personnel
Exec Dir: Bob Moses
Location: Jacob K Javits Convention Center, 655 W 43 St, New York, NY
Oct 29-Nov 1, 2015

ANA Masters of Marketing Conference
Sponsored by Association of National Advertisers Inc (ANA)
708 Third Ave, 33rd fl, New York, NY 10017-4270
Tel: 212-697-5950 *Fax:* 212-687-7310
E-mail: info@ana.net
Web Site: www.ana.net
Key Personnel
VP, Conferences: Kristen McDonough *Tel:* 212-455-8056 *E-mail:* kmcdonough@ana.net
Mgr, Conferences: Leigh Walczak *Tel:* 212-455-8025 *E-mail:* lwalczak@ana.net
Location: Orlando World Center Marriott, 8701 World Center Dr, Orlando, FL
Oct 14-17, 2015

ASTC Annual Conference
Sponsored by Association of Science-Technology Centers (ASTC)
818 Connecticut Ave NW, 7th fl, Washington, DC 20006-2734
Tel: 202-783-7200 *Fax:* 202-783-7207
E-mail: conference@astc.org; info@astc.org
Web Site: conference.astc.org; www.astc.org
Key Personnel
Conference Dir: David Corson *Tel:* 202-783-7200 ext 121
Coord, Meetings & Conferences: Nina Humes *Tel:* 202-783-7200 ext 133
Location: Montreal Science Centre, Montreal, QC, CN
Oct 17-20, 2015

AWC National Conference
Sponsored by The Association for Women in Communications (AWC)
3337 Duke St, Alexandria, VA 22314
Tel: 703-370-7436 *Fax:* 703-342-4311
E-mail: info@womcom.org
Web Site: www.womcom.org
Key Personnel
Exec Dir: Pamela Valenzuela
Held biennially.
Location: Kansas City, MO
Oct 8-10, 2015

CCUMC Annual Conference
Sponsored by Consortium of College & University Media Centers (CCUMC)
c/o Indiana University, 306 N Union St, Bloomington, IN 47405-3888
Tel: 812-855-6049
E-mail: ccumc@ccumc.org
Web Site: www.ccumc.org
Key Personnel
Exec Dir: Aileen Scales

Prog Coord: Kirsten Phillips
Location: Pittsburgh, PA
Oct 2015

FiO/LS
Sponsored by The Optical Society® (OSA)
2010 Massachusetts Ave NW, Washington, DC 20036
Tel: 202-416-1972; 202-416-1953; 202-416-1907 (cust serv) *Fax:* 202-223-1096; 202-416-6140 (cust serv)
E-mail: exhibits@osa.org; custserv@osa.org; info@osa.org
Web Site: www.frontiersinoptics.com; www.osa.org
Key Personnel
Dir, Exhibits: David Coray
Exhibit Coord: Kathy O'Driscoll
Co-sponsored by American Physical Society/Division of Laser Science.
Location: Fairmont San Jose & The St Claire Hotel, San Jose, CA
Oct 18-22, 2015

Live Design International (LDI)
Sponsored by Penton
1166 Avenue of the Americas, 10th fl, New York, NY 10036
Tel: 212-204-4200
Web Site: www.ldishow.com
Key Personnel
Exhibitor Serv Rep: Robert Eldridge *Tel:* 303-998-9528 *Fax:* 913-981-6153 *E-mail:* robert.eldridge@penton.com
Creative Dir, Studio Live Design: Ellen Lampert-Greaux *Tel:* 917-725-5043 *E-mail:* elgreaux@livedesignonline.com
Location: Las Vegas Convention Center, North Hall, Las Vegas, NV
Oct 23-25, 2015

PDN PhotoPlus International Conference + Expo
Sponsored by Emerald Expositions Inc
85 Broad St, 11th fl, New York, NY 10004
Tel: 646-688-3700; 240-439-2985 (intl registration) *Toll Free Tel:* 877-699-5410 (US registration)
E-mail: info@emeraldexpo.com; photoplus@experient-inc.com (registration)
Web Site: www.photoplusexpo.com; emeraldexpositions.com
Key Personnel
Conference Mgr: Laura Caskey *E-mail:* laura.caskey@emeraldexpo.com
Educ Coord: Jodi Rosenblum *Tel:* 646-688-3754 *E-mail:* jodi.rosenblum@emeraldexpo.com
Location: Jacob K Javits Convention Center, 655 W 34 St, New York, NY
Oct 2015

SCTE Cable-Tec Expo®
Sponsored by Society of Cable Telecommunications Engineers Inc (SCTE)
140 Philips Rd, Exton, PA 19341-1318
Tel: 610-363-6888 *Toll Free Tel:* 800-542-5040 (cust care) *Fax:* 610-363-5898
E-mail: expo@scte.org
Web Site: expo.scte.org; www.scte.org
SCTE's Cable-Tec Expo® - the industry's engineering show of the year - hosts thousands of annual attendees & provides the opportunity to discover & learn first-hand about the latest in cable telecommunications technology, products & services in one cost-effective setting.
Location: New Orleans, LA
Oct 13-16, 2015

SMPTE Annual Technical Conference & Exhibition
Sponsored by Society of Motion Picture & Television Engineers (SMPTE)
3 Barker Ave, 5th fl, White Plains, NY 10601
Tel: 914-761-1100 *Fax:* 914-761-3115
Web Site: www.smpte.org
Key Personnel
Dir, Opers: Sally-Ann D'Amato *Tel:* 914-205-2375 *E-mail:* sdamato@smpte.org
Location: Loews Hollywood Hotel, Hollywood, CA
Oct 26-29, 2015

NOVEMBER

American Film Market® & Conferences
Sponsored by Independent Film & Television Alliance® (IFTA)
10850 Wilshire Blvd, 9th fl, Los Angeles, CA 90024-4311
Tel: 310-446-1000 *Fax:* 310-446-1600
E-mail: afm@ifta-online.org
Web Site: www.americanfilmmarket.com; www.ifta-online.org
Key Personnel
EVP & Mng Dir, American Film Market: Jonathan Wolf *Tel:* 310-446-1010 *E-mail:* jwolf@ifta-online.org
VP, Mktg & Membership: Robin Burt *Tel:* 310-446-1020 *E-mail:* rburt@ifta-online.org
Dir, AFM Attendee Servs: Wendy Arroyo *Tel:* 310-446-1088 *E-mail:* warroyo@ifta-online.org
Dir, AFM Exhibitor Servs: Andrea Contarino *Tel:* 310-446-1026 *E-mail:* acontarino@ifta-online.org
Event offering producers & distributors the opportunity to license films. Screenings take place at theaters throughout Santa Monica. Conferences are held at the Fairmont Miramar Hotel in Santa Monica.
Location: Santa Monica, CA
Nov 4-11, 2015

IES Annual Conference
Sponsored by Illuminating Engineering Society (IES)
120 Wall St, 17th fl, New York, NY 10005-4001
Tel: 212-248-5000 *Fax:* 212-248-5017; 212-248-5018
E-mail: ies@ies.org
Web Site: www.ies.org/ac; www.ies.org
Key Personnel
Dir, Memb Servs & Conference Mgr: Valerie Landers *Tel:* 212-248-5000 ext 117
Location: Cincinnati, OH
Nov 2015

KMWorld
Sponsored by Information Today, Inc
143 Old Marlton Pike, Medford, NJ 08055-8750
Tel: 609-654-6266 *Toll Free Tel:* 800-300-9868 (cust serv) *Fax:* 203-761-1444
E-mail: custserv@infotoday.com
Web Site: www.kmworld.com/Conference
Key Personnel
Pres & CEO: Thomas H Hogan
Dir, Meeting Planning: Stacey Hogan
Enterprise Search & Discovery; SharePoint Symposium & Taxonomy Boot Camp held in conjunction with KMWorld.
Location: JW Marriott, 1331 Pennsylvania Ave NW, Washington, DC
Nov 3-5, 2015

NABT Professional Development Conference
Sponsored by National Association of Biology Teachers (NABT)
1313 Dolley Madison Blvd, Suite 402, McLean, VA 22101
Tel: 703-264-9696 *Toll Free Tel:* 888-501-NABT (501-6228) *Fax:* 703-790-2672
E-mail: conference@nabt.org; office@nabt.org
Web Site: www.nabt.org
Key Personnel
Exec Dir: Jaclyn Reeves-Pepin *E-mail:* jreevespepin@nabt.org
Location: Rhode Island Convention Center, Providence, RI
Nov 11-14, 2015

NCTE Annual Convention
Sponsored by National Council of Teachers of English (NCTE)
1111 W Kenyon Rd, Urbana, IL 61801-1096
Tel: 217-328-3870 *Toll Free Tel:* 877-369-6283 *Fax:* 217-328-9645
E-mail: conventionquestions@ncte.org
Web Site: www.ncte.org
Key Personnel
Convention Mgr: Eileen Maley
Location: Minneapolis, MN
Nov 19-22, 2015

SouthPack®
Sponsored by UBM Canon LLC
2901 28 St, Suite 100, Santa Monica, CA 90405
Tel: 310-445-4200
E-mail: packaginginfo@ubm.com; ubmcanonconferences@ubm.com
Web Site: www.canontradeshows.com; ubmcanon.com
Location: Orange County Convention Center, Orlando, FL
Nov 18-19, 2015

Streaming Media West
Sponsored by Information Today, Inc
143 Old Marlton Pike, Medford, NJ 08055-8750
Tel: 609-654-6266 *Toll Free Tel:* 800-300-9868 (cust serv) *Fax:* 609-654-4309
E-mail: custserv@infotoday.com
Web Site: www.streamingmedia.com/Conferences/West
Key Personnel
Pres & CEO: Thomas H Hogan
Dir, Meeting Planning: Stacey Hogan
Location: Hyatt Regency Huntington Beach, 21500 Pacific Coast Hwy, Huntington Beach, CA
Nov 17-18, 2015

TechNet Asia-Pacific
Sponsored by AFCEA International
4400 Fair Lakes Ct, Fairfax, VA 22033-3899
Tel: 703-631-6100 *Toll Free Tel:* 800-336-4583 *Fax:* 703-631-6169
E-mail: events@afcea.org
Web Site: www.afcea.org/events/asiapacific; www.afcea.org
Key Personnel
Dir of Events: Pat Holmes *Tel:* 703-631-6130 *E-mail:* pholmes@afcea.org
Co-sponsored by AFCEA Hawaii & managed by J Spargo & Associates Inc.
Location: Hilton Hawaiian Village, Honolulu, HI
Nov 17-19, 2015

2016

JANUARY

Imaging USA
Sponsored by Professional Photographers of America (PPA)
229 Peachtree St NE, Suite 2200, Atlanta, GA 30303

Tel: 404-522-8600 *Toll Free Tel:* 800-786-6277 *Fax:* 404-614-6400
E-mail: info@imagingusa.org
Web Site: www.imagingusa.org; www.ppa.com
Key Personnel
Dir of Events: Fiona Hendricks *E-mail:* fhendricks@ppa.com
Events Mgr: Sharon Palmer *E-mail:* spalmer@ppa.com
Location: Georgia World Congress Center, Atlanta, GA
Jan 10-12, 2016

International CES
Sponsored by Consumer Electronics Association (CEA)
1919 S Eads St, Arlington, VA 22202
Tel: 703-907-7600 *Toll Free Tel:* 866-233-7968 (cust serv) *Fax:* 703-907-7030
E-mail: cesinfo@ce.org; events@ce.org
Web Site: www.cesweb.org; www.ce.org
Key Personnel
Sr Dir, Strategic Partnerships & Conferences: Kara Dickerson
Dir of Mktg, Strategic Partnerships & Events: Nicole Vidovich-Parker *E-mail:* nparker@ce.org
Dir, CES Conferences: Amanda Whipkey McMaster
Location: Las Vegas, NV
Jan 6-9, 2016

The NAMM Show
Sponsored by NAMM, the National Association of Music Merchants
5790 Armada Dr, Carlsbad, CA 92008
Tel: 760-438-8001 *Toll Free Tel:* 800-767-6266 (memb hotline) *Fax:* 760-438-7327
E-mail: info@namm.org
Web Site: www.namm.org; www.facebook.com/nammshow; twitter.com/nammshow
Key Personnel
Dir, Trade Show Sales: Dan Moylan *Tel:* 760-438-8007 ext 114 *E-mail:* danielm@namm.org
Assoc Dir, Trade Show Sales: Dominique Agnew *Tel:* 760-438-8007 ext 123 *E-mail:* dominiquea@namm.org
Location: Anaheim Convention Center, 800 W Katella Ave, Anaheim, CA
Jan 21-24, 2016

PTC Conference
Sponsored by Pacific Telecommunications Council (PTC)
914 Coolidge St, Honolulu, HI 96826-3085
Tel: 808-941-3789 *Fax:* 808-944-4874
E-mail: info@ptc.org
Web Site: www.ptc.org
Key Personnel
CEO: Sharon Nakama *Tel:* 808-941-3789 ext 110 *E-mail:* snakama@ptc.org
Lead Conference & HR Coord: Lori Takeuchi *Tel:* 808-941-3789 ext 111 *E-mail:* lori@ptc.org
Conference Coord: Jamie Wan-Lopaz *Tel:* 808-941-3789 ext 124 *E-mail:* jamie@ptc.org
Exec Asst: Colleen Shishido *Tel:* 808-941-3789 ext 104 *E-mail:* colleen@ptc.org
Location: Hilton Hawaiian Village Beach Resort & Spa, Honolulu, HI
Jan 17-20, 2016

FEBRUARY

AACTE Annual Meeting
Sponsored by American Association of Colleges for Teacher Education (AACTE)
1307 New York Ave NW, Suite 300, Washington, DC 20005
Tel: 202-293-2450 *Fax:* 202-457-8095
E-mail: aacte@aacte.org
Web Site: www.aacte.org
Key Personnel
VP, Events & Strategic Initiatives: Gail M Bozeman *Tel:* 202-478-4512 *E-mail:* gbozeman@aacte.org
Dir of Meetings, Events & Spec Projs: Matthew J Wales *Tel:* 202-478-4597 *E-mail:* mwales@aacte.org
Meetings & Events Coord: Christine Tambini *Tel:* 202-478-4591 *E-mail:* ctambini@aacte.org
Location: The Mirage, Las Vegas, NV
Feb 23-25, 2016

AASA National Conference on Education
Sponsored by American Association of School Administrators (AASA)
1615 Duke St, Alexandria, VA 22314
Tel: 703-528-0700 *Fax:* 703-841-1543
E-mail: nce@aasa.org; info@aasa.org
Web Site: www.aasa.org
Key Personnel
Assoc Exec Dir, Leadership, Meetings & Partnerships: Dennis Deardon *Tel:* 703-875-0731 *E-mail:* ddeardon@aasa.org
Dir, Meetings: Christopher Daw *Tel:* 703-875-0713 *E-mail:* cdaw@aasa.org
Asst Dir, Meetings: Jennifer Rooney *Tel:* 703-875-0778 *E-mail:* jrooney@aasa.org
Location: Phoenix Convention Center, Phoenix, AZ
Feb 11-13, 2016

Electronic Imaging Conference
Sponsored by Society for Imaging Science and Technology (IS&T)
7003 Kilworth Lane, Springfield, VA 22151
Tel: 703-642-9090 *Fax:* 703-642-9094
E-mail: info@imaging.org
Web Site: www.imaging.org/ist/conferences/ei; spie.org/electronic-imaging.xml; www.imaging.org
Key Personnel
Exec Dir: Suzanne E Grinnan *E-mail:* sgrinnan@imaging.org
Exec Asst: Donna Smith *E-mail:* dsmith@imaging.org
Conference Prog Mgr: Diana Gonzalez *E-mail:* dgonzalez@imaging.org
Co-sponsored by SPIE, the international society for optics and photonics.
Location: San Francisco, CA
Feb 7-11, 2016

NRB International Christian Media Convention & Exposition
Sponsored by National Religious Broadcasters Inc (NRB)
9510 Technology Dr, Manassas, VA 20110
Tel: 703-330-7000 *Fax:* 703-330-7100
E-mail: info@nrb.org
Web Site: www.nrbconvention.org; www.nrb.org; facebook.com/nrbconvention; twitter.com/nrbconvention
Key Personnel
Dir, Mktg: Steve Cross *Tel:* 703-331-4518 *E-mail:* scross@nrb.org
Dir, Conventions & Expositions: Beth Wakefield *Tel:* 615-663-0099 *E-mail:* bwakefield@nrb.org
Convention Registrar & Admin Asst: Patsy Smith *Tel:* 703-331-4503 *E-mail:* psmith@nrb.org
Location: Gaylord Opryland Resort & Convention Center, Nashville, TN
Feb 23-26, 2016

WestPack®
Sponsored by UBM Canon LLC
2901 28 St, Suite 100, Santa Monica, CA 90405
Tel: 310-445-4200
E-mail: packaginginfo@ubm.com; ubmcanonconferences@ubm.com
Web Site: www.canontradeshows.com; ubmcanon.com
Location: Anaheim Convention Center, 800 W Katella Ave, Anaheim, CA
Feb 2016

MARCH

AAMA/AMOA Amusement Expo
Sponsored by Amusement & Music Operators Association (AMOA)
600 Spring Hill Ring Rd, Suite 111, West Dundee, IL 60118
Tel: 847-428-7699 *Toll Free Tel:* 800-YES-AMOA (937-2662) *Fax:* 847-428-7719
E-mail: amoa@amoa.com
Web Site: www.amusementexpo.org; www.amoa.com
Key Personnel
EVP: Jack Kelleher
Deputy Dir: Lori Schneider
Sponsored jointly by American Amusement Machine Association (AAMA).
Location: Las Vegas Convention Center, 3150 Paradise Rd, Las Vegas, NV
March 15-17, 2016

American Council on Education Annual Meeting
Sponsored by American Council on Education (ACE)
One Dupont Circle NW, Washington, DC 20036
Tel: 202-939-9444; 202-939-9300
E-mail: annualmeeting@acenet.edu
Web Site: www.aceannualmeeting.org; www.acenet.edu
Key Personnel
Exec Admin Specialist: Cameron Carswell
Location: San Francisco, CA
March 12-15, 2016

Great Lakes Broadcasting Conference (GLBC)
Sponsored by Michigan Association of Broadcasters (MAB)
819 N Washington Ave, Lansing, MI 48906-5815
Tel: 517-484-7444 *Toll Free Tel:* 800-YOUR-MAB (968-7622) *Fax:* 517-484-5810
E-mail: mab@michmab.com
Web Site: www.michmab.com
Key Personnel
VP, Progs: Jennifer Preslar *E-mail:* preslar@michmab.com
Location: The Lansing Center, Lansing, MI
March 8-9, 2016

ITEEA's Annual Conference
Sponsored by International Technology and Engineering Educators Association (ITEEA)
1914 Association Dr, Suite 201, Reston, VA 20191-1539
Tel: 703-860-2100 *Fax:* 703-860-0353
E-mail: iteea@iteea.org
Web Site: www.iteea.org
Key Personnel
Exec Dir: Steven A Barbato *E-mail:* sbarbato@iteea.org
Mktg Dir: Christine Maggio *Tel:* 703-860-5028 *E-mail:* cmaggio@iteea.org
Location: National Harbor, Washington, DC
March 2-4, 2016

NAfME Music Research and Teacher Education National Conference
Sponsored by National Association for Music Education (NAfME)
1806 Robert Fulton Dr, Reston, VA 20191

Tel: 703-860-4000 *Toll Free Tel:* 800-336-3768
Fax: 703-860-1531
E-mail: memberservices@nafme2.org
Web Site: www.nafme.org
Key Personnel
Exec Dir & CEO: Michael A Butera
E-mail: michaelb@nafme.org
Deputy Exec Dir & COO: Mike Blakeslee
E-mail: mikeb@nafme.org
Mktg & Events Coord: Brendan McAloon
E-mail: brendanm@nafme.org
Location: Atlanta, GA
March 17-19, 2016

NCEA Convention & Expo
Sponsored by National Catholic Educational Association (NCEA)
1005 N Glebe Rd, Suite 525, Arlington, VA 22201
Toll Free Tel: 800-711-NCEA (711-6232)
Fax: 703-243-0025
Web Site: www.ncea.org/convention; www.ncea.org
Key Personnel
Dir of Events: Amy Durkin *Tel:* 571-257-0013
E-mail: adurkin@ncea.org
Annual meeting for all working in Catholic education, Pre-K through college.
Location: San Diego, CA
March 29-31, 2016

USITT Annual Conference & Stage Expo
Sponsored by United States Institute for Theatre Technology Inc (USITT)
315 S Crouse Ave, Suite 200, Syracuse, NY 13210-1844
Tel: 315-463-6463 *Toll Free Tel:* 800-938-7488
Fax: 315-463-6525 *Toll Free Fax:* 866-398-7488
E-mail: info@usitt.org
Web Site: www.usitt.org
Key Personnel
Dir of Communs: Barbara E R Lucas *Tel:* 800-938-7488 ext 103 *E-mail:* barbara@usitt.org
Dir of Memb Servs: Monica L Merritt *Tel:* 800-938-7488 ext 104 *E-mail:* monica@usitt.org
Stage Expo Mgr & Spec Events Coord: Ron Procopio *Tel:* 800-938-7488 ext 107 *E-mail:* ron@usitt.org
Location: Calvin L Rampton Salt Palace Convention Center, Salt Lake City, UT
March 16-19, 2016

APRIL

AERA Annual Meeting
Sponsored by American Educational Research Association (AERA)
1430 "K" St NW, Suite 1200, Washington, DC 20005
Tel: 202-238-3200 *Fax:* 202-238-3250
E-mail: annualmtg@aera.net
Web Site: www.aera.net
Key Personnel
Meetings Dir: Laurie Cipriano *Tel:* 202-238-3200 ext 210 *E-mail:* lcipriano@aera.net
Meetings Mgr: Samara Fetner *Tel:* 202-238-3200 ext 212 *E-mail:* sfetner@aera.net
Meetings Assoc: Kimberly Ricks *Tel:* 202-238-3200 ext 211 *E-mail:* kricks@aera.net
Meetings Asst: Brittany Salzman *Tel:* 202-238-3200 ext 213 *E-mail:* bsalzman@aera.net
Location: Washington, DC
April 8-12, 2016

ASCD Annual Conference & Exhibit Show
Sponsored by ASCD
1703 N Beauregard St, Alexandria, VA 22311-1714
Tel: 703-578-9600 *Toll Free Tel:* 800-933-2723
Fax: 703-575-5400
Web Site: annualconference.ascd.org; www.ascd.org
Key Personnel
Exec Dir: Judy Seltz
Communs Mgr: Katie Test *Tel:* 703-575-5608
Location: Atlanta, GA
April 2-4, 2016

BEA2016
Sponsored by Broadcast Education Association (BEA)
Affiliate of National Association of Broadcasters (NAB) (in partnership with)
1771 "N" St NW, Washington, DC 20036-2891
Fax: 202-609-9940
E-mail: help@beaweb.org
Web Site: www.beaweb.org
Key Personnel
Exec Dir: Heather Birks *Tel:* 202-602-0584
E-mail: heather@beaweb.org
Dir of Sales & Mktg: J-D Boyle *Tel:* 202-602-0586 *E-mail:* jd@beaweb.org
Annual convention co-located next to NAB Show.
Location: Westgate Las Vegas Resort & Casino, Las Vegas, NV
April 17-20, 2016

NSBA Annual Conference & Exposition
Sponsored by National School Boards Association (NSBA)
1680 Duke St, Alexandria, VA 22314
Tel: 703-838-6722 *Toll Free Tel:* 800-950-6722 (conference registration) *Fax:* 703-683-7590
E-mail: conference@nsba.org; info@nsba.org
Web Site: www.nsba.org/conference; www.nsba.org
Key Personnel
Dir, Exhibits: Karen Miller *Tel:* 703-535-1616
E-mail: kmiller@nsba.org
Mgr, Meetings Servs: Heather Eggleston
Tel: 703-838-6786 *E-mail:* heggleston@nsba.org
Conferences Mgr: Sandra Folks *Tel:* 703-838-6787 *E-mail:* sfolks@nsba.org
Exhibit Sales Assoc: Susan Clubb *Tel:* 703-838-6167 *E-mail:* sclubb@nsba.org
Location: Boston, MA
April 9-11, 2016

MAY

AAM Annual Meeting & MuseumExpo
Sponsored by American Alliance of Museums (AAM)
1575 Eye St NW, Suite 400, Washington, DC 20005
Tel: 202-289-1818 *Fax:* 202-289-6578
Web Site: www.aam-us.org
Key Personnel
Dir, Meetings & Events: Andrea Streat *Tel:* 202-218-7678 *E-mail:* astreat@aam-us.org
Sr Mgr, Meetings & Events: Lisa McBride
Tel: 202-218-7676 *E-mail:* smcbride@aam-us.org
Sr Meeting & Events Mgr: Stephanie Szurek
Tel: 202-218-7708 *E-mail:* sszurek@aam-us.org
Location: Washington, DC
May 26-29, 2016

ATD International Conference & Exposition
Sponsored by Association for Talent Development (ATD)
1640 King St, Alexandria, VA 22314-2743
Tel: 703-683-8100 *Toll Free Tel:* 800-628-2783; 866-238-2146 (cust care) *Fax:* 703-299-8723; 703-683-1523 (cust care)
E-mail: customercare@td.org
Web Site: www.atdconference.org; www.td.org
Location: Denver, CO
May 22-25, 2016

BookExpo America (BEA)
Sponsored by Reed Exhibitions USA
Division of Reed Elsevier plc
383 Main Ave, Norwalk, CT 06851
Tel: 203-840-4800 *Toll Free Tel:* 800-840-5614
Fax: 203-840-5805
E-mail: inquiry@bookexpoamerica.com
Web Site: bookexpoamerica.com
Key Personnel
Event Dir: Steve Rosato *Tel:* 203-840-5463
Fax: 203-840-9463 *E-mail:* srosato@reedexpo.com
Dir of Mktg: Kimberlie I Leon *Tel:* 203-840-5653
Fax: 203-840-9653 *E-mail:* kleon@reedexpo.com
Produced & managed by Reed Exhibitions USA, BEA is sponsored by the American Booksellers Association (ABA), the Association of American Publishers Inc (AAP) & the Association of Authors' Representatives Inc (AAR).
Location: Chicago, IL
May 12-14, 2016

JUNE

ALA Annual Conference
Sponsored by American Library Association (ALA)
50 E Huron St, Chicago, IL 60611-2795
Tel: 312-944-6780 *Toll Free Tel:* 800-545-2433 (ext 3223, conference servs) *Fax:* 312-440-9374
E-mail: ala@ala.org
Web Site: www.ala.org
Key Personnel
Conference Dir: Paul Graller *E-mail:* pgraller@ala.org
Conference Mgr: Amy R McGuigan *Tel:* 800-545-2433 ext 3226 *E-mail:* amcguigan@ala.org
Registration & Housing Specialist: Alicia Babcock *Tel:* 800-545-2433 ext 3229
E-mail: ababcock@ala.org
Meeting, AV & Catering Coord: Yvonne A McLean *Tel:* 800-545-2433 ext 3222
E-mail: ymclean@ala.org
Conference Coord: Lindsay Rosales
E-mail: lrosales@ala.org
Meetings Coord: Alicia (Alee) Navarro
E-mail: anavarro@ala.org
Location: Orlando, FL
June 23-28, 2016

Design Automation Conference (DAC)
Sponsored by MP Associates Inc
1721 Boxelder St, Suite 107, Louisville, CO 80027
Tel: 303-530-4333; 303-530-4562
Toll Free Tel: 800-321-4573 *Fax:* 303-530-4334
Web Site: www.dac.com
Key Personnel
Co-Pres: Kevin Lepine *Tel:* 303-530-4562 ext 111
E-mail: kevin@mpassociates.com; Lee Wood
Tel: 303-530-4562 ext 112 *E-mail:* lee@mpassociates.com
Dir of Exhibit Opers: Susie Horn *Tel:* 303-530-4562 ext 125 *E-mail:* susie@mpassociates.com
Exhibit Coord: Candi Wooldridge *Tel:* 303-530-4562 ext 222; Stacy DiLallo *Tel:* 303-530-4562 ext 115
Dir of Sales & Busn Devt: Karen Popp *Tel:* 303-530-4562 ext 133

Event for the design of electronic circuits & systems, embedded systems & software & electronic design automation.
Sponsored by the Association of Computing Machinery, Electronic Design Automation Consortium & Institute of Electrical & Electronics Engineers.
Location: Austin Convention Center, Austin, TX
June 5-9, 2016

IABC World Conference
Sponsored by International Association of Business Communicators (IABC)
601 Montgomery St, Suite 1900, San Francisco, CA 94111
Tel: 415-544-4700 *Toll Free Tel:* 800-776-4222 *Fax:* 415-544-4747
E-mail: conference@iabc.com; member_relations@iabc.com
Web Site: wc.iabc.com; www.iabc.com
Key Personnel
Dir, Conferences & Events: Charles Herrick *Tel:* 415-544-4745 *E-mail:* cherrick@iabc.com
Location: Hilton New Orleans Riverside, 2 Poydras, New Orleans, LA
June 5-8, 2016

InfoComm
Sponsored by InfoComm International®
11242 Waples Mill Rd, Suite 200, Fairfax, VA 22030
Tel: 703-273-7200 *Toll Free Tel:* 800-659-SHOW (659-7469) *Fax:* 703-273-5924
E-mail: customerservice@infocomm.org
Web Site: www.infocommshow.org; www.infocomm.org
Key Personnel
Exec Dir & CEO: David Labuskes
SVP, Expositions: Jason McGraw *Tel:* 703-279-6361 *E-mail:* jmcgraw@infocomm.org
Dir, Exposition Opers: Kurt St Clair *Tel:* 703-279-6365 *E-mail:* kstclair@infocomm.org
Expositions Opers Mgr: Laura Reed *Tel:* 703-279-2167 *E-mail:* lreed@infocomm.org; Allison Konczyk *Tel:* 703-279-2165 *E-mail:* akonczyk@infocomm.org
Expositions Opers Coord: Debbie Clisham *Tel:* 703-279-9933 *E-mail:* dclisham@infocomm.org
Location: Las Vegas Convention Center, North & Central Halls, Las Vegas, NV
June 4-10, 2016

ISTE® 2016
Sponsored by International Society for Technology in Education (ISTE®)
180 W Eighth Ave, Suite 300, Eugene, OR 97401-2916
Tel: 541-302-3777 *Toll Free Tel:* 800-336-5191 (US & CN) *Fax:* 541-302-3778
E-mail: iste@iste.org
Web Site: www.isteconference.org; www.iste.org
Key Personnel
Sr Dir, Conference & Memb Progs: Jennifer Ragan-Fore *Tel:* 541-434-8938 *E-mail:* jraganfore@iste.org
Dir of Logistics: Vincent Barnett *Tel:* 541-434-9591 *E-mail:* vbarnett@iste.org
Location: Denver, CO
June 26-29, 2016

Optometry's Meeting®
Sponsored by American Optometric Association (AOA)
243 N Lindbergh Blvd, 1st fl, St Louis, MO 63141-7881
Tel: 314-991-4100 *Toll Free Tel:* 800-386-6825 (meetings hotline) *Fax:* 314-991-4101
Web Site: www.optometrysmeeting.org; www.exhibitsom.org; www.aoa.org
Key Personnel
Dir, Meetings & Conventions: Lori Lee *Tel:* 314-983-4256
Annual meeting of the American Optometric Association & the American Optometric Student Association.
Location: Boston, MA
June 29-July 2, 2016

SLA Annual Conference & INFO-EXPO
Sponsored by Special Libraries Association (SLA)
331 S Patrick St, Alexandria, VA 22314-3501
Tel: 703-647-4900 *Fax:* 703-647-4901
E-mail: events@sla.org
Web Site: www.sla.org
Key Personnel
CEO: Janice R Lachance *Tel:* 703-647-4933 *E-mail:* janice@sla.org
Dir, Events: Caroline Hamilton (Rives) *Tel:* 703-647-4949 *E-mail:* chamilton@sla.org
Dir, Mktg & Exhibits: Jeff Leach *Tel:* 703-647-4922 *E-mail:* jleach@sla.org
Location: Philadelphia Convention Center, Philadelphia, PA
June 12-14, 2016

JULY

VenueConnect
Sponsored by International Association of Venue Managers (IAVM)
635 Fritz Dr, Suite 100, Coppell, TX 75019-4442
Tel: 972-906-7441 *Toll Free Tel:* 800-935-4226 *Fax:* 972-906-7418
Web Site: www.iavm.org
Key Personnel
Pres & CEO: Vicki Hawarden *E-mail:* vicki.hawarden@iavm.org
Meetings Mgr: Bill Jenkins *Tel:* 972-538-1019 *E-mail:* Bill.Jenkins@iavm.org
Location: Minneapolis Convention Center, Minneapolis , MN
July 23-26, 2016

SEPTEMBER

ASTC Annual Conference
Sponsored by Association of Science-Technology Centers (ASTC)
818 Connecticut Ave NW, 7th fl, Washington, DC 20006-2734
Tel: 202-783-7200 *Fax:* 202-783-7207
E-mail: conference@astc.org; info@astc.org
Web Site: conference.astc.org; www.astc.org
Key Personnel
Conference Dir: David Corson *Tel:* 202-783-7200 ext 121
Coord, Meetings & Conferences: Nina Humes *Tel:* 202-783-7200 ext 133
Location: Museum of Science and Industry (MOSI), Tampa, FL
Sept 24-27, 2016

OCTOBER

FiO/LS
Sponsored by The Optical Society® (OSA)
2010 Massachusetts Ave NW, Washington, DC 20036
Tel: 202-416-1972; 202-416-1953; 202-416-1907 (cust serv) *Fax:* 202-223-1096; 202-416-6140 (cust serv)
E-mail: exhibits@osa.org; custserv@osa.org; info@osa.org
Web Site: www.frontiersinoptics.com; www.osa.org
Key Personnel
Dir, Exhibits: David Coray
Exhibit Coord: Kathy O'Driscoll
Co-sponsored by American Physical Society/Division of Laser Science.
Location: Rochester Riverside Convention Center, Rochester, NY
Oct 16-20, 2016

Graph Expo®
Sponsored by Graphic Arts Show Company (GASC)
1899 Preston White Dr, Reston, VA 20191-5468
Tel: 703-264-7200 *Fax:* 703-620-9187
E-mail: info@gasc.org
Web Site: www.graphexpo.com; www.gasc.org
Key Personnel
VP: Chris Price *Tel:* 703-264-7200 ext 221 *E-mail:* cprice@gasc.org
Dir of Opers: Kelly E Kilga *Tel:* 703-264-7200 ext 213 *E-mail:* kkilga@gasc.org
Dir of Communs: Deborah Vieder *Tel:* 703-264-7200 ext 222
Conference Mgr: Lilly Kinney *Tel:* 703-264-7200 ext 255 *E-mail:* lkinney@gasc.org
Location: McCormick Place, 2301 S Lake Shore Dr, Chicago, IL
Oct 2-5, 2016

PDN PhotoPlus International Conference + Expo
Sponsored by Emerald Expositions Inc
85 Broad St, 11th fl, New York, NY 10004
Tel: 646-688-3700; 240-439-2985 (intl registration) *Toll Free Tel:* 877-699-5410 (US registration)
E-mail: info@emeraldexpo.com; photoplus@experient-inc.com (registration)
Web Site: www.photoplusexpo.com; emeraldexpositions.com
Key Personnel
Conference Mgr: Laura Caskey *E-mail:* laura.caskey@emeraldexpo.com
Educ Coord: Jodi Rosenblum *Tel:* 646-688-3754 *E-mail:* jodi.rosenblum@emeraldexpo.com
Location: Jacob K Javits Convention Center, 655 W 34 St, New York, NY
Oct 2016

SMPTE Annual Technical Conference & Exhibition
Sponsored by Society of Motion Picture & Television Engineers (SMPTE)
3 Barker Ave, 5th fl, White Plains, NY 10601
Tel: 914-761-1100 *Fax:* 914-761-3115
Web Site: www.smpte.org
Key Personnel
Dir, Opers: Sally-Ann D'Amato *Tel:* 914-205-2375 *E-mail:* sdamato@smpte.org
Location: Loews Hollywood Hotel, Hollywood, CA
Oct 24-27, 2016

NOVEMBER

American Film Market® & Conferences
Sponsored by Independent Film & Television Alliance® (IFTA)
10850 Wilshire Blvd, 9th fl, Los Angeles, CA 90024-4311
Tel: 310-446-1000 *Fax:* 310-446-1600

E-mail: afm@ifta-online.org
Web Site: www.americanfilmmarket.com; www.ifta-online.org
Key Personnel
EVP & Mng Dir, American Film Market: Jonathan Wolf *Tel:* 310-446-1010 *E-mail:* jwolf@ifta-online.org
VP, Mktg & Membership: Robin Burt *Tel:* 310-446-1020 *E-mail:* rburt@ifta-online.org
Dir, AFM Attendee Servs: Wendy Arroyo *Tel:* 310-446-1088 *E-mail:* warroyo@ifta-online.org
Dir, AFM Exhibitor Servs: Andrea Contarino *Tel:* 310-446-1026 *E-mail:* acontarino@ifta-online.org
Event offering producers & distributors the opportunity to license films. Screenings take place at theaters throughout Santa Monica. Conferences are held at the Fairmont Miramar Hotel in Santa Monica.
Location: Santa Monica, CA
Nov 2-9, 2016

NABT Professional Development Conference
Sponsored by National Association of Biology Teachers (NABT)
1313 Dolley Madison Blvd, Suite 402, McLean, VA 22101
Tel: 703-264-9696 *Toll Free Tel:* 888-501-NABT (501-6228) *Fax:* 703-790-2672
E-mail: conference@nabt.org; office@nabt.org
Web Site: www.nabt.org
Key Personnel
Exec Dir: Jaclyn Reeves-Pepin *E-mail:* jreevespepin@nabt.org
Location: Denver Sheraton Downtown, Denver, CO
Nov 3-6, 2016

NCTE Annual Convention
Sponsored by National Council of Teachers of English (NCTE)
1111 W Kenyon Rd, Urbana, IL 61801-1096
Tel: 217-328-3870 *Toll Free Tel:* 877-369-6283 *Fax:* 217-328-9645
E-mail: conventionquestions@ncte.org
Web Site: www.ncte.org
Key Personnel
Convention Mgr: Eileen Maley
Location: Atlanta, GA
Nov 17-20, 2016

2017

JANUARY

Imaging USA
Sponsored by Professional Photographers of America (PPA)
229 Peachtree St NE, Suite 2200, Atlanta, GA 30303
Tel: 404-522-8600 *Toll Free Tel:* 800-786-6277 *Fax:* 404-614-6400
E-mail: info@imagingusa.org
Web Site: www.imagingusa.org; www.ppa.com
Key Personnel
Dir of Events: Fiona Hendricks *E-mail:* fhendricks@ppa.com
Events Mgr: Sharon Palmer *E-mail:* spalmer@ppa.com
Location: San Antonio, TX
Jan 8-10, 2017

International CES
Sponsored by Consumer Electronics Association (CEA)
1919 S Eads St, Arlington, VA 22202
Tel: 703-907-7600 *Toll Free Tel:* 866-233-7968 (cust serv) *Fax:* 703-907-7030
E-mail: cesinfo@ce.org; events@ce.org
Web Site: www.cesweb.org; www.ce.org
Key Personnel
Sr Dir, Strategic Partnerships & Conferences: Kara Dickerson
Dir of Mktg, Strategic Partnerships & Events: Nicole Vidovich-Parker *E-mail:* nparker@ce.org
Dir, CES Conferences: Amanda Whipkey McMaster
Location: Las Vegas, NV
Jan 5-8, 2017

MARCH

AACTE Annual Meeting
Sponsored by American Association of Colleges for Teacher Education (AACTE)
1307 New York Ave NW, Suite 300, Washington, DC 20005
Tel: 202-293-2450 *Fax:* 202-457-8095
E-mail: aacte@aacte.org
Web Site: www.aacte.org
Key Personnel
VP, Events & Strategic Initiatives: Gail M Bozeman *Tel:* 202-478-4512 *E-mail:* gbozeman@aacte.org
Dir of Meetings, Events & Spec Projs: Matthew J Wales *Tel:* 202-478-4597 *E-mail:* mwales@aacte.org
Meetings & Events Coord: Christine Tambini *Tel:* 202-478-4591 *E-mail:* ctambini@aacte.org
Location: Tampa Convention Center, Tampa, FL
March 2-4, 2017

ASCD Annual Conference & Exhibit Show
Sponsored by ASCD
1703 N Beauregard St, Alexandria, VA 22311-1714
Tel: 703-578-9600 *Toll Free Tel:* 800-933-2723 *Fax:* 703-575-5400
Web Site: annualconference.ascd.org; www.ascd.org
Key Personnel
Exec Dir: Judy Seltz
Communs Mgr: Katie Test *Tel:* 703-575-5608
Location: Anaheim, CA
March 25-27, 2017

NSBA Annual Conference & Exposition
Sponsored by National School Boards Association (NSBA)
1680 Duke St, Alexandria, VA 22314
Tel: 703-838-6722 *Toll Free Tel:* 800-950-6722 (conference registration) *Fax:* 703-683-7590
E-mail: conference@nsba.org; info@nsba.org
Web Site: www.nsba.org/conference; www.nsba.org
Key Personnel
Dir, Exhibits: Karen Miller *Tel:* 703-535-1616 *E-mail:* kmiller@nsba.org
Mgr, Meetings Servs: Heather Eggleston *Tel:* 703-838-6786 *E-mail:* heggleston@nsba.org
Conferences Mgr: Sandra Folks *Tel:* 703-838-6787 *E-mail:* sfolks@nsba.org
Exhibit Sales Assoc: Susan Clubb *Tel:* 703-838-6167 *E-mail:* sclubb@nsba.org
Location: Denver, CO
March 25-27, 2017

APRIL

BEA2017
Sponsored by Broadcast Education Association (BEA)
Affiliate of National Association of Broadcasters (NAB) (in partnership with)
1771 "N" St NW, Washington, DC 20036-2891
Fax: 202-609-9940
E-mail: help@beaweb.org
Web Site: www.beaweb.org
Key Personnel
Exec Dir: Heather Birks *Tel:* 202-602-0584 *E-mail:* heather@beaweb.org
Dir of Sales & Mktg: J-D Boyle *Tel:* 202-602-0586 *E-mail:* jd@beaweb.org
Annual convention co-located next to NAB Show.
Location: Westgate Las Vegas Resort & Casino, Las Vegas, NV
April 23-26, 2017

MAY

AAM Annual Meeting & MuseumExpo
Sponsored by American Alliance of Museums (AAM)
1575 Eye St NW, Suite 400, Washington, DC 20005
Tel: 202-289-1818 *Fax:* 202-289-6578
Web Site: www.aam-us.org
Key Personnel
Dir, Meetings & Events: Andrea Streat *Tel:* 202-218-7678 *E-mail:* astreat@aam-us.org
Sr Mgr, Meetings & Events: Lisa McBride *Tel:* 202-218-7676 *E-mail:* smcbride@aam-us.org
Sr Meeting & Events Mgr: Stephanie Szurek *Tel:* 202-218-7708 *E-mail:* sszurek@aam-us.org
Location: St Louis, MO
May 7-10, 2017

JUNE

ALA Annual Conference
Sponsored by American Library Association (ALA)
50 E Huron St, Chicago, IL 60611-2795
Tel: 312-944-6780 *Toll Free Tel:* 800-545-2433 (ext 3223, conference servs) *Fax:* 312-440-9374
E-mail: ala@ala.org
Web Site: www.ala.org
Key Personnel
Conference Dir: Paul Graller *E-mail:* pgraller@ala.org
Conference Mgr: Amy R McGuigan *Tel:* 800-545-2433 ext 3226 *E-mail:* amcguigan@ala.org
Registration & Housing Specialist: Alicia Babcock *Tel:* 800-545-2433 ext 3229 *E-mail:* ababcock@ala.org
Meeting, AV & Catering Coord: Yvonne A McLean *Tel:* 800-545-2433 ext 3222 *E-mail:* ymclean@ala.org
Conference Coord: Lindsay Rosales *E-mail:* lrosales@ala.org
Meetings Coord: Alicia (Alee) Navarro *E-mail:* anavarro@ala.org
Location: Chicago, IL
June 22-27, 2017

Design Automation Conference (DAC)
Sponsored by MP Associates Inc
1721 Boxelder St, Suite 107, Louisville, CO 80027

Tel: 303-530-4333; 303-530-4562
Toll Free Tel: 800-321-4573 *Fax:* 303-530-4334
Web Site: www.dac.com
Key Personnel
Co-Pres: Kevin Lepine *Tel:* 303-530-4562 ext 111 *E-mail:* kevin@mpassociates.com; Lee Wood *Tel:* 303-530-4562 ext 112 *E-mail:* lee@mpassociates.com
Dir of Exhibit Opers: Susie Horn *Tel:* 303-530-4562 ext 125 *E-mail:* susie@mpassociates.com
Exhibit Coord: Candi Wooldridge *Tel:* 303-530-4562 ext 222; Stacy DiLallo *Tel:* 303-530-4562 ext 115
Dir of Sales & Busn Devt: Karen Popp *Tel:* 303-530-4562 ext 133
Event for the design of electronic circuits & systems, embedded systems & software & electronic design automation.
Sponsored by the Association of Computing Machinery, Electronic Design Automation Consortium & Institute of Electrical & Electronics Engineers.
Location: Moscone Center, San Francisco, CA
June 18-22, 2017

InfoComm
Sponsored by InfoComm International®
11242 Waples Mill Rd, Suite 200, Fairfax, VA 22030
Tel: 703-273-7200 *Toll Free Tel:* 800-659-SHOW (659-7469) *Fax:* 703-273-5924
E-mail: customerservice@infocomm.org
Web Site: www.infocommshow.org; www.infocomm.org
Key Personnel
Exec Dir & CEO: David Labuskes
SVP, Expositions: Jason McGraw *Tel:* 703-279-6361 *E-mail:* jmcgraw@infocomm.org
Dir, Exposition Opers: Kurt St Clair *Tel:* 703-279-6365 *E-mail:* kstclair@infocomm.org
Expositions Opers Mgr: Laura Reed *Tel:* 703-279-2167 *E-mail:* lreed@infocomm.org; Allison Konczyk *Tel:* 703-279-2165 *E-mail:* akonczyk@infocomm.org
Expositions Opers Coord: Debbie Clisham *Tel:* 703-279-9933 *E-mail:* dclisham@infocomm.org
Location: Orange County Convention Center, West Bldg, Orlando, FL
June 10-16, 2017

ISTE® 2017
Sponsored by International Society for Technology in Education (ISTE®)
180 W Eighth Ave, Suite 300, Eugene, OR 97401-2916
Tel: 541-302-3777 *Toll Free Tel:* 800-336-5191 (US & CN) *Fax:* 541-302-3778
E-mail: iste@iste.org
Web Site: www.isteconference.org; www.iste.org
Key Personnel
Sr Dir, Conference & Memb Progs: Jennifer Ragan-Fore *Tel:* 541-434-8938 *E-mail:* jraganfore@iste.org
Dir of Logistics: Vincent Barnett *Tel:* 541-434-9591 *E-mail:* vbarnett@iste.org
Location: San Antonio, TX
June 26-29, 2017

Optometry's Meeting®
Sponsored by American Optometric Association (AOA)
243 N Lindbergh Blvd, 1st fl, St Louis, MO 63141-7881
Tel: 314-991-4100 *Toll Free Tel:* 800-386-6825 (meetings hotline) *Fax:* 314-991-4101
Web Site: www.optometrysmeeting.org; www.exhibitsom.org; www.aoa.org
Key Personnel
Dir, Meetings & Conventions: Lori Lee *Tel:* 314-983-4256
Annual meeting of the American Optometric Association & the American Optometric Student Association.
Location: Washington, DC
June 21-25, 2017

SEPTEMBER

PRINT®
Sponsored by Graphic Arts Show Company (GASC)
1899 Preston White Dr, Reston, VA 20191-5468
Tel: 703-264-7200 *Fax:* 703-620-9187
E-mail: info@gasc.org
Web Site: www.gasc.org
Key Personnel
VP: Chris Price *Tel:* 703-264-7200 ext 221 *E-mail:* cprice@gasc.org
Dir of Opers: Kelly E Kilga *Tel:* 703-264-7200 ext 213 *E-mail:* kkilga@gasc.org
Dir of Communs: Deborah Vieder *Tel:* 703-264-7200 ext 222
Conference Mgr: Lilly Kinney *Tel:* 703-264-7200 ext 255 *E-mail:* lkinney@gasc.org
Graphic communications exposition held every four years.
Location: McCormick Place, 2301 S Lake Shore Dr, Chicago, IL
Sept 10-14, 2017

OCTOBER

ASTC Annual Conference
Sponsored by Association of Science-Technology Centers (ASTC)
818 Connecticut Ave NW, 7th fl, Washington, DC 20006-2734
Tel: 202-783-7200 *Fax:* 202-783-7207
E-mail: conference@astc.org; info@astc.org
Web Site: conference.astc.org; www.astc.org
Key Personnel
Conference Dir: David Corson *Tel:* 202-783-7200 ext 121
Coord, Meetings & Conferences: Nina Humes *Tel:* 202-783-7200 ext 133
Location: The Tech Museum of Innovation, San Jose, CA
Oct 21-24, 2017

SMPTE Annual Technical Conference & Exhibition
Sponsored by Society of Motion Picture & Television Engineers (SMPTE)
3 Barker Ave, 5th fl, White Plains, NY 10601
Tel: 914-761-1100 *Fax:* 914-761-3115
Web Site: www.smpte.org
Key Personnel
Dir, Opers: Sally-Ann D'Amato *Tel:* 914-205-2375 *E-mail:* sdamato@smpte.org
Location: Loews Hollywood Hotel, Hollywood, CA
Oct 23-26, 2017

NOVEMBER

American Film Market® & Conferences
Sponsored by Independent Film & Television Alliance® (IFTA)
10850 Wilshire Blvd, 9th fl, Los Angeles, CA 90024-4311
Tel: 310-446-1000 *Fax:* 310-446-1600
E-mail: afm@ifta-online.org
Web Site: www.americanfilmmarket.com; www.ifta-online.org
Key Personnel
EVP & Mng Dir, American Film Market: Jonathan Wolf *Tel:* 310-446-1010 *E-mail:* jwolf@ifta-online.org
VP, Mktg & Membership: Robin Burt *Tel:* 310-446-1020 *E-mail:* rburt@ifta-online.org
Dir, AFM Attendee Servs: Wendy Arroyo *Tel:* 310-446-1088 *E-mail:* warroyo@ifta-online.org
Dir, AFM Exhibitor Servs: Andrea Contarino *Tel:* 310-446-1026 *E-mail:* acontarino@ifta-online.org
Event offering producers & distributors the opportunity to license films. Screenings take place at theaters throughout Santa Monica. Conferences are held at the Fairmont Miramar Hotel in Santa Monica.
Location: Santa Monica, CA
Nov 1-8, 2017

NCTE Annual Convention
Sponsored by National Council of Teachers of English (NCTE)
1111 W Kenyon Rd, Urbana, IL 61801-1096
Tel: 217-328-3870 *Toll Free Tel:* 877-369-6283 *Fax:* 217-328-9645
E-mail: conventionquestions@ncte.org
Web Site: www.ncte.org
Key Personnel
Convention Mgr: Eileen Maley
Location: St Louis, MO
Nov 16-19, 2017

2018

JANUARY

Imaging USA
Sponsored by Professional Photographers of America (PPA)
229 Peachtree St NE, Suite 2200, Atlanta, GA 30303
Tel: 404-522-8600 *Toll Free Tel:* 800-786-6277 *Fax:* 404-614-6400
E-mail: info@imagingusa.org
Web Site: www.imagingusa.org; www.ppa.com
Key Personnel
Dir of Events: Fiona Hendricks *E-mail:* fhendricks@ppa.com
Events Mgr: Sharon Palmer *E-mail:* spalmer@ppa.com
Location: Nashville, TN
Jan 14-16, 2018

International CES
Sponsored by Consumer Electronics Association (CEA)
1919 S Eads St, Arlington, VA 22202
Tel: 703-907-7600 *Toll Free Tel:* 866-233-7968 (cust serv) *Fax:* 703-907-7030
E-mail: cesinfo@ce.org; events@ce.org
Web Site: www.cesweb.org; www.ce.org
Key Personnel
Sr Dir, Strategic Partnerships & Conferences: Kara Dickerson
Dir of Mktg, Strategic Partnerships & Events: Nicole Vidovich-Parker *E-mail:* nparker@ce.org
Dir, CES Conferences: Amanda Whipkey McMaster
Location: Las Vegas, NV
Jan 9-12, 2018

MARCH

AACTE Annual Meeting
Sponsored by American Association of Colleges for Teacher Education (AACTE)
1307 New York Ave NW, Suite 300, Washington, DC 20005
Tel: 202-293-2450 *Fax:* 202-457-8095
E-mail: aacte@aacte.org
Web Site: www.aacte.org
Key Personnel
VP, Events & Strategic Initiatives: Gail M Bozeman *Tel:* 202-478-4512 *E-mail:* gbozeman@aacte.org
Dir of Meetings, Events & Spec Projs: Matthew J Wales *Tel:* 202-478-4597 *E-mail:* mwales@aacte.org
Meetings & Events Coord: Christine Tambini *Tel:* 202-478-4591 *E-mail:* ctambini@aacte.org
Location: Baltimore Convention Center, Baltimore, MD
March 1-3, 2018

ASCD Annual Conference & Exhibit Show
Sponsored by ASCD
1703 N Beauregard St, Alexandria, VA 22311-1714
Tel: 703-578-9600 *Toll Free Tel:* 800-933-2723 *Fax:* 703-575-5400
Web Site: annualconference.ascd.org; www.ascd.org
Key Personnel
Exec Dir: Judy Seltz
Communs Mgr: Katie Test *Tel:* 703-575-5608
Location: Boston, MA
March 24-26, 2018

APRIL

NSBA Annual Conference & Exposition
Sponsored by National School Boards Association (NSBA)
1680 Duke St, Alexandria, VA 22314
Tel: 703-838-6722 *Toll Free Tel:* 800-950-6722 (conference registration) *Fax:* 703-683-7590
E-mail: conference@nsba.org; info@nsba.org
Web Site: www.nsba.org/conference; www.nsba.org
Key Personnel
Dir, Exhibits: Karen Miller *Tel:* 703-535-1616 *E-mail:* kmiller@nsba.org
Mgr, Meetings Servs: Heather Eggleston *Tel:* 703-838-6786 *E-mail:* heggleston@nsba.org
Conferences Mgr: Sandra Folks *Tel:* 703-838-6787 *E-mail:* sfolks@nsba.org
Exhibit Sales Assoc: Susan Clubb *Tel:* 703-838-6167 *E-mail:* sclubb@nsba.org
Location: San Antonio, TX
Aprl 7-9, 2018

JUNE

ALA Annual Conference
Sponsored by American Library Association (ALA)
50 E Huron St, Chicago, IL 60611-2795
Tel: 312-944-6780 *Toll Free Tel:* 800-545-2433 (ext 3223, conference servs) *Fax:* 312-440-9374
E-mail: ala@ala.org
Web Site: www.ala.org
Key Personnel
Conference Dir: Paul Graller *E-mail:* pgraller@ala.org
Conference Mgr: Amy R McGuigan *Tel:* 800-545-2433 ext 3226 *E-mail:* amcguigan@ala.org
Registration & Housing Specialist: Alicia Babcock *Tel:* 800-545-2433 ext 3229 *E-mail:* ababcock@ala.org
Meeting, AV & Catering Coord: Yvonne A McLean *Tel:* 800-545-2433 ext 3222 *E-mail:* ymclean@ala.org
Conference Coord: Lindsay Rosales *E-mail:* lrosales@ala.org
Meetings Coord: Alicia (Alee) Navarro *E-mail:* anavarro@ala.org
Location: New Orleans, LA
June 21-26, 2018

InfoComm
Sponsored by InfoComm International®
11242 Waples Mill Rd, Suite 200, Fairfax, VA 22030
Tel: 703-273-7200 *Toll Free Tel:* 800-659-SHOW (659-7469) *Fax:* 703-273-5924
E-mail: customerservice@infocomm.org
Web Site: www.infocommshow.org; www.infocomm.org
Key Personnel
Exec Dir & CEO: David Labuskes
SVP, Expositions: Jason McGraw *Tel:* 703-279-6361 *E-mail:* jmcgraw@infocomm.org
Dir, Exposition Opers: Kurt St Clair *Tel:* 703-279-6365 *E-mail:* kstclair@infocomm.org
Expositions Opers Mgr: Laura Reed *Tel:* 703-279-2167 *E-mail:* lreed@infocomm.org; Allison Konczyk *Tel:* 703-279-2165 *E-mail:* akonczyk@infocomm.org
Expositions Opers Coord: Debbie Clisham *Tel:* 703-279-9933 *E-mail:* dclisham@infocomm.org
Location: Las Vegas Convention Center, North & Central Halls, Las Vegas, NV
June 2-8, 2018

OCTOBER

ASTC Annual Conference
Sponsored by Association of Science-Technology Centers (ASTC)
818 Connecticut Ave NW, 7th fl, Washington, DC 20006-2734
Tel: 202-783-7200 *Fax:* 202-783-7207
E-mail: conference@astc.org; info@astc.org
Web Site: conference.astc.org; www.astc.org
Key Personnel
Conference Dir: David Corson *Tel:* 202-783-7200 ext 121
Coord, Meetings & Conferences: Nina Humes *Tel:* 202-783-7200 ext 133
Location: Connecticut Science Center, Hartford, CT
Sept 29-Oct 2, 2018

NOVEMBER

NCTE Annual Convention
Sponsored by National Council of Teachers of English (NCTE)
1111 W Kenyon Rd, Urbana, IL 61801-1096
Tel: 217-328-3870 *Toll Free Tel:* 877-369-6283 *Fax:* 217-328-9645
E-mail: conventionquestions@ncte.org
Web Site: www.ncte.org
Key Personnel
Convention Mgr: Eileen Maley
Location: Houston, TX
Nov 15-18, 2018

2019

JANUARY

International CES
Sponsored by Consumer Electronics Association (CEA)
1919 S Eads St, Arlington, VA 22202
Tel: 703-907-7600 *Toll Free Tel:* 866-233-7968 (cust serv) *Fax:* 703-907-7030
E-mail: cesinfo@ce.org; events@ce.org
Web Site: www.cesweb.org; www.ce.org
Key Personnel
Sr Dir, Strategic Partnerships & Conferences: Kara Dickerson
Dir of Mktg, Strategic Partnerships & Events: Nicole Vidovich-Parker *E-mail:* nparker@ce.org
Dir, CES Conferences: Amanda Whipkey McMaster
Location: Las Vegas, NV
Jan 8-11, 2019

MARCH

ASCD Annual Conference & Exhibit Show
Sponsored by ASCD
1703 N Beauregard St, Alexandria, VA 22311-1714
Tel: 703-578-9600 *Toll Free Tel:* 800-933-2723 *Fax:* 703-575-5400
Web Site: annualconference.ascd.org; www.ascd.org
Key Personnel
Exec Dir: Judy Seltz
Communs Mgr: Katie Test *Tel:* 703-575-5608
Location: Chicago, IL
March 16-18, 2019

JUNE

ALA Annual Conference
Sponsored by American Library Association (ALA)
50 E Huron St, Chicago, IL 60611-2795
Tel: 312-944-6780 *Toll Free Tel:* 800-545-2433 (ext 3223, conference servs) *Fax:* 312-440-9374
E-mail: ala@ala.org
Web Site: www.ala.org
Key Personnel
Conference Dir: Paul Graller *E-mail:* pgraller@ala.org
Conference Mgr: Amy R McGuigan *Tel:* 800-545-2433 ext 3226 *E-mail:* amcguigan@ala.org
Registration & Housing Specialist: Alicia Babcock *Tel:* 800-545-2433 ext 3229 *E-mail:* ababcock@ala.org
Meeting, AV & Catering Coord: Yvonne A McLean *Tel:* 800-545-2433 ext 3222 *E-mail:* ymclean@ala.org
Conference Coord: Lindsay Rosales *E-mail:* lrosales@ala.org
Meetings Coord: Alicia (Alee) Navarro *E-mail:* anavarro@ala.org
Location: Washington, DC
June 20-25, 2019

InfoComm
Sponsored by InfoComm International®
11242 Waples Mill Rd, Suite 200, Fairfax, VA 22030
Tel: 703-273-7200 *Toll Free Tel:* 800-659-SHOW (659-7469) *Fax:* 703-273-5924
E-mail: customerservice@infocomm.org
Web Site: www.infocommshow.org; www.infocomm.org

Key Personnel
Exec Dir & CEO: David Labuskes
SVP, Expositions: Jason McGraw *Tel:* 703-279-6361 *E-mail:* jmcgraw@infocomm.org
Dir, Exposition Opers: Kurt St Clair *Tel:* 703-279-6365 *E-mail:* kstclair@infocomm.org
Expositions Opers Mgr: Laura Reed *Tel:* 703-279-2167 *E-mail:* lreed@infocomm.org;
Allison Konczyk *Tel:* 703-279-2165 *E-mail:* akonczyk@infocomm.org
Expositions Opers Coord: Debbie Clisham *Tel:* 703-279-9933 *E-mail:* dclisham@infocomm.org
Location: Orange County Convention Center, West Bldg, Orlando, FL
June 8-14, 2019

Periodicals for the Trade

The majority of the publications listed in this section are specifically media-oriented. Others have been included because they contain important AV-related information, such as software reviews, equipment appraisals or guidelines on AV instruction.

Advertising Age
Published by Crain Communications Inc
711 Third Ave, New York, NY 10017-4036
Tel: 212-210-0100 *Toll Free Tel:* 877-320-1721 *Fax:* 212-210-0200; 212-210-0111
E-mail: adageeditor@adage.com
Web Site: www.adage.com
Subscription Address: 1155 Gratiot Ave, Detroit, MI 48207-2912 *Tel:* 313-446-0450 *Fax:* 313-446-6777
Key Personnel
Ed-in-Chief: Rance Crain *E-mail:* rcrain@crain.com
VP & Publr: Allison P Arden *E-mail:* aarden@adage.com
VP, Publg & Edit Dir: David Klein *E-mail:* dklein@crain.com
Assoc Publr: Jackie Ghedine *E-mail:* jghedine@adage.com
News of advertising & marketing for advertising & marketing professionals.
First published 1930
Media Reviewed: Advertising, Commercials
Frequency: Weekly
Circulation: 60,508
$109/yr US, $239/yr CN & Mexico, $429/yr other (45 print issues, unlimited access to adage.com & weekly digital editions)
ISSN: 0001-8899
Trim Size: 10 x 13
Ad Rates: B&W page $26,530, 4-color page $34,500
Ad Closing Date(s): ROP, 11 days prior to issue date

AES-Journal of the Audio Engineering Society
Published by Audio Engineering Society Inc (AES)
60 E 42 St, Rm 2520, New York, NY 10165-2520
Tel: 212-661-8528 *Fax:* 212-682-0477
E-mail: hq@aes.org
Web Site: www.aes.org
Key Personnel
Pres: Frank Wells
Exec Dir: Bob Moses
Deputy Dir: Roger K Furness
Mng Ed: Bill McQuaide *Tel:* 212-661-8528 ext 22
First published 1953
Frequency: 10 issues/yr
Number of pages: 110
Circulation: 14,000
$50/yr print, online free membs, $290/yr print, $545 online (includes archived), $695/yr both nonmembs
ISSN: 1549-4950
Trim Size: 8 1/4 x 11
Ad Rates: $1,150 page, $958 2/3 page, $863 1/2 page island, $767 1/2 page, $671 1/3 page island, $575 1/3 page, $345 1/6 page, bleed charge $95 per page, $500 extra/standard color, $550 extra/matched color, $1,850 extra/page or fraction
Ad Closing Date(s): 60 days prior to publication month, 75 days prior to combined issues Jan/Feb & July/Aug

Afterimage: The Journal of Media Arts & Cultural Criticism
Published by The Visual Studies Workshop (VSW)
31 Prince St, Rochester, NY 14607
Tel: 585-442-8676 (ext 26) *Fax:* 585-442-1992
E-mail: afterimage@vsw.org
Web Site: www.vsw.org/ai
Key Personnel
Ed: Karen vanMeenen *E-mail:* afterimageeditor@yahoo.com
Assoc Ed: Lucia Sommer
Feature articles, books & exhibition reviews, essay & news about the visual arts, photography, independent film & video, new media & alternative publishing.
First published 1972
Media Reviewed: Alternative Publishing, Artists Books, Books, Hypermedia, Independent Films, Mixed Media, Photography, Videotapes
Frequency: 6 issues/yr
Circulation: 10,000
Indivs: $33/yr US, $45/yr CN, $20/yr student, $90/yr foreign; Instns: $100/yr US, $120/yr CN, $165/yr foreign
ISSN: 0300-7472
Trim Size: 7 1/2 x 9 3/4
Ad Rates: B&W $300 1/2 page, $500 full page
Ad Closing Date(s): 4 weeks prior to publication date

American Cinematographer
Published by American Society of Cinematographers
1782 N Orange Dr, Hollywood, CA 90028
Mailing Address: PO Box 2230, Hollywood, CA 90078
Tel: 323-969-4333 *Toll Free Tel:* 800-448-0145 (US only) *Fax:* 323-876-4973
E-mail: publisher@ascmag.com
Web Site: www.theasc.com
Key Personnel
Publr: Martha Winterhalter *E-mail:* martha@ascmag.com
Exec Ed: Stephen Pizzello
International journal of motion imaging.
First published 1920
Media Reviewed: Books, Commercials, Films, TV
Frequency: Monthly
Circulation: 35,000 print
$29.95/yr US, $49.95/yr CN & Mexico, $69.95/yr other, $29.95/yr digital
ISSN: 0002-7928
Trim Size: 8 1/8 x 10 1/2
Ad Rates: B&W page $4,532, 4-color page $5,701 (one time)
Ad Closing Date(s): 2 months in advance, artwork 2nd week of month, 2 months in advance

American Libraries
Published by American Library Association (ALA)
50 E Huron St, Chicago, IL 60611-2795
Tel: 312-944-6780 *Toll Free Tel:* 800-545-2433 (ext 3223, conference servs) *Fax:* 312-440-9374
E-mail: americanlibraries@ala.org
Web Site: www.americanlibrariesmagazine.org
Key Personnel
Publr & Ed: Laurie D Borman *Tel:* 800-545-2433 ext 4213 *E-mail:* lborman@ala.org
Mng Ed: Sanhita SinhaRoy *Tel:* 800-545-2433 ext 4219 *E-mail:* ssinharoy@ala.org
Ad & Mktg Specialist: Katie Bane *Tel:* 800-545-2433 ext 5105 *E-mail:* kbane@ala.org
News & trends for the library community.
First published 1907
Media Reviewed: CD-ROMs, DVDs, Library Software
Frequency: 6 issues/yr
Circulation: 58,000
$70/yr North American & Mexican, $80/yr foreign instns
ISSN: 0002-9769
Trim Size: 7 7/8 x 10 1/2
Ad Rates: B&W page $5,130, 4-color page $8,065
Ad Closing Date(s): Approximately 4 weeks prior to cover date. See media kit for additional info

American Record Guide
Published by Record Guide Productions
4412 Braddock St, Cincinnati, OH 45204
Tel: 513-941-1116 *Toll Free Tel:* 888-658-1907
E-mail: subs@americanrecordguide.com
Web Site: www.americanrecordguide.com
Key Personnel
Ed: Donald R Vroon *E-mail:* don@americanrecordguide.com
Art & Circ: Ray Hassard
Classical music reviews. No unsol mss, query first.
First published 1935
Media Reviewed: CDs, Concerts, DVDs, Operas
Frequency: 6 issues/yr
Number of pages: 300
Circulation: 3,400
$7.99/issue, $45/yr, $55/yr instns
ISSN: 0003-0716
Trim Size: 6 x 9
Ad Rates: B&W page $1,000, 1/2 page $550, 1/3 page $375, 1/4 page $280; 4-color cover $1,500
Ad Closing Date(s): 6 weeks before issue date

The AMSAT Journal
Published by Radio Amateur Satellite Corp (AMSAT)
850 Sligo Ave, Suite 600, Silver Spring, MD 20910
Tel: 301-589-6062 *Toll Free Tel:* 888-322-6728 (US only) *Fax:* 301-608-3410
E-mail: journal@amsat.org
Web Site: www.amsat.org/amsat-new/journal
Key Personnel
Pres: Barry Baines
First published 1989
Frequency: 6 issues/yr
Circulation: 7,000
Free to membs
ISSN: 1047-3076

Animation Magazine
Published by Animation Magazine Inc
26500 W Agoura Rd, Suite 102-651, Calabasas, CA 91302
Tel: 818-883-2884 *Fax:* 818-883-3773
E-mail: info@animationmagazine.net; sales@animationmagazine.net
Web Site: www.animationmagazine.net
Key Personnel
Pres & Publr: Jean Thoren *E-mail:* jthoren@animationmagazine.net
Ed-in-Chief: Ramin Zahed *E-mail:* rzahed@animationmagazine.net

Publication dedicated to the business, technology & art of animation & VFX.
First published 1987
Media Reviewed: Records
Frequency: 9 issues/yr (plus supplements), calendar, school guide & show guides
Circulation: 20,824
$55/yr US, $70/yr CN & Mexico, $85/yr elsewhere; $36/yr digital
ISSN: 1041-617X
Trim Size: 8 3/8 x 10 7/8

ARSC Journal
Published by Association for Recorded Sound Collections Inc (ARSC)
c/o Knight Library, 1299 University of Oregon, Eugene, OR 97403-1299
Tel: 541-346-1852 *Fax:* 410-349-0175
Web Site: www.arsc-audio.org
Key Personnel
Exec Dir: Nathan Georgitis *E-mail:* execdir@arsc-audio.org
Ed: Barry R Ashpole *E-mail:* barryashpole@belnet.ca
Ad Ed: David Lewis *E-mail:* dlewis@gmail.com
Book Reviews Ed: Jim Farrington *E-mail:* jfarrington@esm.rochester.edu
Devoted to the results of major research, technical developments, unusual discoveries, discographies & articles of general interest in the field; carries reviews of special interest to the collector & archivist as well as comprehensive index of such articles appearing in other publications; annual awards for excellence in recorded sound research.
First published 1967
Media Reviewed: Books, Records
Frequency: Semiannual
Circulation: 1,100
$75 membership fee for instns includes 1 yr subn, $45 indiv membership fee includes 1 yr subn, foreign postage extra (Mexico & CN $15, $30 air delivery)
ISSN: 0004-5438
Trim Size: 6 x 9
Ad Rates: Covers (not newsletter) $350, full page $200, 1/2 page vertical or horizontal $150, 1/4 page $100
Ad Closing Date(s): Feb 1 for spring issue, Sept 1 for fall issue

Arts & Activities
Published by Publishers Development Corp
12345 World Trade Dr, San Diego, CA 92128
Tel: 858-605-0242 (edit) *Fax:* 858-605-0247
Web Site: artsandactivities.com
Key Personnel
Ed-in-Chief: Maryellen Bridge *E-mail:* ed@artsandactivities.com
Art education & instruction for teachers at all levels.
First published 1932
Media Reviewed: CD-ROMs, DVDs, Filmstrips, Software, Videotapes
Frequency: Monthly (exc July & Aug)
Number of pages: 52
Circulation: 18,000
$40/yr US, $90/yr other
ISSN: 0004-3931
Trim Size: 7 x 10
Ad Rates: B&W page $2,324, 4-color page $2,979
Ad Closing Date(s): 1st or 2nd week of the month, 2 months prior to cover date

ATM Telecommunications Newsletter
Published by Information Gatekeepers Inc
1340 Soldiers Field Rd, Suite 2, Boston, MA 02135
Tel: 617-782-5033 *Fax:* 617-507-8338
E-mail: info@igigroup.com
Web Site: www.igigroup.com
Key Personnel
CEO & Pres: Paul Polishuk, PhD
Ed-in-Chief & Chief Analyst: Dr Hui Pan *E-mail:* hpan@igigroup.com
Technology, markets, industry events & international developments.
First published 1989
Frequency: Monthly
Circulation: 1,000
$695/yr US & CN, $745/yr other print, $695 PDF (1 user)
ISSN: 1051-1903
Trim Size: 8 1/2 x 11

AudioFile® Magazine
Published by AudioFile® Publications
37 Silver St, Portland, ME 04101
Mailing Address: PO Box 109, Portland, ME 04112-0109
Tel: 207-774-7563 *Toll Free Tel:* 800-506-1212 *Fax:* 207-775-3744
E-mail: info@audiofilemagazine.com
Web Site: www.audiofilemagazine.com
Key Personnel
Ed & Publr: Robin F Whitten *E-mail:* robin@audiofilemagazine.com
Audiobook & spoken audio reviews & articles.
First published 1992
Media Reviewed: Audiobooks
Frequency: 6 issues/yr
Circulation: 20,000 print, 120,000 digital ed
Digital; full online access including PDF ed $2.95/month, Basic Listener; Print ed & online access $36/yr, Audio File Plus; print, online access including Archive of Reviews, the Audiobook Reference Guide, Real Time Reviews & Library Listeners $60/yr
ISSN: 1063-0244
Trim Size: 8 3/8 x 10 7/8
Ad Rates: 4-color page $3,100
Ad Closing Date(s): 8 weeks prior to cover date

Audiotex Update
Published by Worldwide Videotex
PO Box 3273, Boynton Beach, FL 33424-3273
Tel: 561-738-2276
Key Personnel
Publr & Ed: Linda Bara
Providing the latest news & information on the audiotex industry.
First published 1981
Frequency: Monthly
$165/yr North America print & $180/yr intl print
ISSN: 1045-5795

Billboard: The International Newsweekly of Music, Video & Home Entertainment
Published by Prometheus Global Media LLC
770 Broadway, 15th fl, New York, NY 10003
Tel: 212-493-4100
Web Site: www.billboard.biz; www.billboard.com (online ed)
Key Personnel
Edit Dir: Bill Werde
Prodn Dir: Terrence C Sanders
Print & online magazine covering retailing & programming news for the music & home entertainment industries.
Bureaus in Los Angeles, Miami & London with editorial correspondents worldwide.
First published 1894
Media Reviewed: CDs, Home Video, Records, Tapes, Video Games
Frequency: Weekly
Circulation: 16,327
$14.99/mo (print & iPad or iPad & online), $24.99/mo, $249/yr (print, iPad & online) US, $14.99/mo (iPad & online), $29.99/mo, $299/yr (print, iPad & online) foreign
ISSN: 0006-2510
Trim Size: 10 7/8 x 13 1/2

BMI: MusicWorld®
Published by Broadcast Music Inc
7 World Trade Ctr, 250 Greenwich St, New York, NY 10007-0030
Tel: 212-220-3000
E-mail: newyork@bmi.com
Web Site: www.bmi.com/musicworld
Key Personnel
Pres: Del R Bryant
Online publication that feature advice & career strategies for song writers, awards show coverage & more.
First published 1962
Frequency: Monthly
Circulation: 55,000
Free
ISSN: 0045-317X

Booklist
Published by American Library Association (ALA)
50 E Huron St, Chicago, IL 60611-2795
Tel: 312-944-6780 *Toll Free Tel:* 800-545-2433 (ext 3223, conference servs) *Fax:* 312-440-9374
E-mail: info@booklistonline.com
Web Site: www.booklistonline.com
Key Personnel
Publr & Ed: Bill Ott *Tel:* 800-545-2433 ext 5717 *E-mail:* bott@ala.org
Mktg Mgr: Katharine Fronk *Tel:* 800-545-2433 ext 5713 *E-mail:* kfronk@ala.org
Ed, Adult Books: Brad Hooper *Tel:* 800-545-2433 ext 5757 *E-mail:* bhopper@ala.org
Ed, Booklist Online: Keir Graff *Tel:* 800-545-2433 ext 5728
Ed, Books for Youth: Gillian Engberg *Tel:* 800-545-2433 ext 5711 *E-mail:* gengberg@ala.org
Video Ed: Sue-Ellen Beauregard
Reviews of adult fiction & nonfiction; children's & young adult books; multivolume encyclopedias, dictionaries & atlases; foreign language materials; AV materials.
First published 1905
Media Reviewed: Audiobooks, CD-ROMs, Children's Recordings
Frequency: 22 issues/yr (semimonthly Sept-June, monthly July-Aug)
Circulation: 15,000
$147.50/yr
ISSN: 0006-7385
Trim Size: 7 7/8 x 10 1/2
Ad Rates: B&W page $6,545, 4-color page $9,045
Ad Closing Date(s): Approximately 5-6 weeks prior to cover date. See media kit for additional info

Boxoffice Magazine
Published by Boxoffice Media LLC
9107 Wilshire Blvd, Suite 450, Beverly Hills, CA 90210
Tel: 310-876-9090
E-mail: help@boxoffice.com
Web Site: www.boxoffice.com
Key Personnel
Publr: Peter Cane *E-mail:* peter@boxoffice.com
VP, Ad: Susan Uhrlass *E-mail:* susan@boxoffice.com
Ed: Phil Contrino *E-mail:* phil@boxoffice.com
Articles of interest to the motion picture & movie theatre industry.
First published 1920
Media Reviewed: Books (film related), DVDs (on web site only), Films, Software (movie theatre industry related), Trailers
Frequency: Monthly
Circulation: 10,000
$59.95/yr US, $89.95/2 yrs US, $109.95/3 yrs US, $74.95/yr CN & Mexico, $135/yr elsewhere
ISSN: 0006-8527
Trim Size: 8 1/8 x 10 7/8

Ad Rates: 4-color page $3,681; for other rates, contact publr
Ad Closing Date(s): 6 weeks prior to issue

Broadband Newsletter
Published by Information Gatekeepers Inc
1340 Soldiers Field Rd, Suite 2, Boston, MA 02135
Tel: 617-782-5033 *Fax:* 617-507-8338
E-mail: info@igigroup.com
Web Site: www.igigroup.com
Key Personnel
CEO & Pres: Paul Polishuk, PhD
Ed-in-Chief & Chief Analyst: Dr Hui Pan *E-mail:* hpan@igigroup.com
Provides information on technology, applications & products for broadband. International development.
Frequency: Monthly
Circulation: 1,000
$695/yr (PDF, 1 user)
ISSN: 1078-1005
Trim Size: 8 1/2 x 11

Broadcast Engineering
Published by Penton
9800 Metcalf Ave, Overland Park, KS 66212
Web Site: broadcastengineering.com
Subscription Address: PO Box 2100, Skokie, IL 60076-7800 *Tel:* 847-763-9504 *Toll Free Tel:* 866-505-7173 *Fax:* 847-763-9682 *E-mail:* broadcastengineering@pbinews.com
Key Personnel
Edit Dir & Ed: Brad Dick *Tel:* 913-967-1737 *Fax:* 913-967-1905 *E-mail:* brad.dick@penton.com
For corporate managers, engineers, technicians & other station management personnel at TV stations, cable & telephone companies, teleproduction & post-production facilities, recording studios & government agencies. Also available in a Spanish edition.
First published 1959
Frequency: Monthly
Circulation: 45,000
Free to qualified US & CN residents
ISSN: 0007-1994
Trim Size: 7 3/4 x 10 3/4
Ad Rates: B&W page $9,837, contact for color rates
Ad Closing Date(s): Approximately 2-4 weeks prior to issue month

Broadcaster Magazine
Published by Business Information Group
Division of Glacier BIG Holdings Co Ltd
80 Valleybrook Dr, Toronto, ON M3B 2S9, Canada
Tel: 416-442-5600 *Toll Free Tel:* 800-268-7742 (CN); 800-387-0273 (US)
Web Site: www.broadcastermagazine.com
Key Personnel
CEO & Pres: Bruce Creighton
EVP: Alex Papanou
Sr Publr: James Cook *Tel:* 416-510-6871 *Fax:* 416-510-5134 *E-mail:* jcook@broadcastermagazine.com
Ed: Lee Rickwood *Tel:* 416-510-6865 *Fax:* 416-510-5134 *E-mail:* editor@mediacastermagazine.com
Articles on the Canadian communications industry.
First published 1942
Frequency: 8 issues/yr
Circulation: See online media kit or by request
$50.95/yr (US dollars) CN, $63.95/yr (US dollars) US & other, includes Broadcaster Directory (annual); free to qualified personnel
ISSN: 0008-3038 (print); 1923-340X (online)
Ad Rates: See online media kit or by request
Ad Closing Date(s): See online media kit or by request

Broadcasting & Cable
Published by NewBay Media LLC
28 E 28 St, 12th fl, New York, NY 10016
Tel: 212-378-0400; 515-247-2984 (cust serv outside the US) *Toll Free Tel:* 800-554-5729 (cust serv within US) *Fax:* 212-378-0470
E-mail: BCBcustserv@cdsfulfillment.com
Web Site: www.broadcastingcable.com
Key Personnel
VP, Group Publr & Assoc Publr: Louis Hillelson *Tel:* 917-281-4730 *E-mail:* lhillelson@nbmedia.com
Mng Ed: Brian Moran *Tel:* 917-281-4708 *E-mail:* bmoran@nbmedia.com
Publication covers the business of television.
First published 1931
Frequency: 47 issues/yr
$249/yr print & digital
ISSN: 1068-6827
Trim Size: 9 x 10 7/8
Ad Closing Date(s): 12 days prior to issue date

Cable & TV Station Coverage Atlas
Published by Warren Communications News Inc
2115 Ward Ct NW, Washington, DC 20037
Tel: 202-872-9200 *Toll Free Tel:* 800-771-9202 (cust serv) *Fax:* 202-318-8350
E-mail: info@warren-news.com
Web Site: www.warren-news.com/atlas.htm
Key Personnel
Chmn & Publr: Paul Warren *E-mail:* pwarrendc@warren-news.com
Pres & Ed: Daniel Warren *E-mail:* dwarrendc@warren-news.com
Mng Ed & Asst Publr, Directories: Michael C Taliaferro *E-mail:* mtaliaferrodc@warren-news.com
Dir, Sales: William R Benton *E-mail:* wbentondc@warren-news.com
Provides maps of cable systems relative to television signals. Also lists cable systems county by county & state by state, television 35 & 55-mile zone maps for every market. Available on CD-ROM only.
First published 1966
Media Reviewed: CD-ROMs
Frequency: Annual
$695, $295 2nd copy, $195 additional copies
ISSN: 1047-9902

CableFAX: The Magazine
Published by Access Intelligence LLC
4 Choke Cherry Rd, 2nd fl, Rockville, MD 20850
Tel: 301-354-2000
E-mail: clientservices@accessintel.com
Web Site: www.cablefax.com
Key Personnel
Publr: Debbie Vodenos *Tel:* 301-354-1695 *E-mail:* dvodenos@accessintel.com
Exec Ed, Cable Fax Group: Michael Grebb *Tel:* 301-354-1790 *E-mail:* mgrebb@accessintel.com
Sr Community Ed: Kaylee Hultgren *E-mail:* khultgren@accessintel.com
Mng Contrib Ed: Catherine Applefeld Olson *E-mail:* catholson@aol.com
Columnist: Stephen R Effros *E-mail:* steve@effros.com
Magazine highlighting the people, programs, companies & technologies in the cable television industry.
First published 1989
Frequency: 4 issues/yr
Circulation: 12,000 print, 40,000 e-media

Camera Obscura: A Journal of Feminism & Film Theory
Published by Duke University Press
905 W Main St, Suite 18B, Durham, NC 27701
SAN: 201-3436
Tel: 919-688-5134 *Toll Free Tel:* 888-651-0122 *Fax:* 919-688-2615 *Toll Free Fax:* 888-651-0124
E-mail: customerservice@dukeupress.edu
Web Site: cameraobscura.dukejournals.org
Key Personnel
Edit & Admin Mgr: Rob Dilworth
Acqs Ed, Journals: Erich Staib *Tel:* 919-687-3664
Provide a forum for scholarship & debate on feminism, culture & media studies. Encourage contributions in areas such as the conjuctions of gender, race, class & sexuality with audiovisual culture; new histories & theories of film, television, video & digital media & politically engaged approaches to a range of media practices.
First published 1976
Frequency: 3 issues/yr
Circulation: 630
$30/yr indivs, $20/yr students, $176/yr instns print, $148/yr instns electronic, $188/yr instns both
ISSN: 0270-5346 (print); 1529-1510 (online)
Trim Size: Full page 3 3/4 x 6 3/4, 1/2 page 3 3/4 x 3 1/2
Ad Rates: B&W page $250, 1/2 page $200, banner-call for availability & pricing
Ad Closing Date(s): Annually in March (Spring), July (Summer), Oct (Fall)

Canadian Journal of Communication
c/o Simon Fraser University, 515 W Hastings St, Vancouver, BC V6B 5K3, Canada
Tel: 604-897-5240 (subns) *Fax:* 778-782-5239 (subns)
E-mail: subscriptions@cjc-online.ca
Web Site: www.cjc-online.ca
Key Personnel
Publr: Richard Smith *E-mail:* publisher@cjc-online.ca
Ed: Michael Dorland *E-mail:* editor@cjc-online.ca
Mng Ed: Marilyn Bittman *E-mail:* managing_editor@cjc-online.ca
Online Ed: Michael Felczak *E-mail:* online_editor@cjc-online.ca
A journal for academics, media practitioners & government personnel about communications & journalism research.
First published 1974
Media Reviewed: Cable TV, CD-ROMs, Films, Radio, TV, Videotapes
Frequency: Quarterly
Circulation: 425
$35/yr CN & US student print & online; $60/yr CN & US indiv print & online; $170/yr CN & US instns print & online, $100/yr online only, $145/yr print only
ISSN: 0705-3657 (print); 1499-6642 (electronic)
Trim Size: 4 1/2 x 7

CED Magazine
Published by Advantage Business Media
100 Enterprise Dr, Suite 600, Rockaway, NJ 07866
Tel: 973-920-7000 *Fax:* 717-505-9701 (reprints)
Web Site: www.cedmagazine.com
Key Personnel
Publr: Rhonda Rhodes *Tel:* 303-408-3267 *E-mail:* rhonda.rhodes@advantagemedia.com
Ed-in-Chief: Brian Santo *Tel:* 503-788-7252 *E-mail:* brian.santo@advantagemedia.com
Sr Ed: Mike Robuck *Tel:* 970-964-4060 *E-mail:* michael.robuck@advantagemedia.com
For upper management - engineering & design of cable hardware, telecommunications & data products.
First published 1975
Frequency: 6 issues/yr
Circulation: 20,873
Free to qualified personnel, others: $64/yr US, $85/yr CN, $92/yr intl
ISSN: 1044-2871

Trim Size: 8 3/8 x 10 7/8
Ad Rates: B&W page $6,325, 4-color page $8,305
Ad Closing Date(s): Annually in Dec, Feb, April, June, Aug & Oct

CHOICE
Published by Association of College & Research Libraries
Division of American Library Association
575 Main St, Suite 300, Middletown, CT 06457
Tel: 860-347-6933 (ad) *Fax:* 860-346-8586 (edit)
E-mail: choiceonline@ala-choice.org
Web Site: www.ala.org/acrl/choice; www.cro2.org
Subscription Address: PO Box 141, Annapolis Junction, MD 20701
Tel: 240-646-7027 *Fax:* 240-757-7223
E-mail: choicesubscriptions@brightkey.com
Key Personnel
Publr & Ed: Mark Cummings
E-mail: mcummings@ala-choice.org
Edit Dir: Francine Graf *E-mail:* fgraf@ala-choice.org
Ad Sales Mgr: Pam Marino *E-mail:* pmarino@ala-choice.org
Review books, software, Internet resources, CD-ROM & online databases.
First published 1963
Media Reviewed: Books, CD-ROMs, Microcomputer Software, Online Databases, Web Sites
Frequency: Monthly
Circulation: 1,907
$30/issue, $415/yr, $465/yr CN & Mexico, $535/yr other
ISSN: 0009-4978
Trim Size: 8 1/2 x 11
Ad Rates: B&W page $2,650, 4-color page $3,825
Ad Closing Date(s): 8 weeks prior to issue date

Cineaste
Published by Cineaste Publishers Inc
708 Third Ave, 5th fl, New York, NY 10017-4201
E-mail: cineaste@cineaste.com
Web Site: www.cineaste.com
Subscription Address: PO Box 2242, New York, NY 10009-8917
Key Personnel
Founder & Ed-in-Chief: Gary Crowdus
Book Review Ed: Richard Porton
Ad Mgr: Barbara Saltz
Focus on both the art & politics of the cinema. Accept unsol mss.
First published 1967
Media Reviewed: Films, Home Video
Frequency: Quarterly
Circulation: 10,000
$22/yr US, $27/yr CN & Mexico, $40/yr other
ISSN: 0009-7004
Trim Size: 8 1/4 x 10 7/8
Ad Rates: B&W page $500, 4-color page $750
Ad Closing Date(s): 5 weeks prior to publication

Cinema Journal
Published by Society for Cinema & Media Studies
Affiliate of University of Texas Press
2100 Comal St, Austin, TX 78722
Mailing Address: Journals Div, PO Box 7819, Austin, TX 78713-7819
Tel: 512-232-7621; 512-471-7233
Toll Free Tel: 800-252-3206 (orders) *Fax:* 512-232-7178 *Toll Free Fax:* 800-687-6046 (orders)
E-mail: journals@utpress.utexas.edu
Web Site: utpress.utexas.edu/index.php/journals/cinema-journal
Key Personnel
Ed: Will Brooker
Film & TV criticism, history, theory for students & teachers.
First published 1961
Frequency: Quarterly
Number of pages: 192
Circulation: 3,800
$22/issue, $55/yr, $183/yr instns; $33/issue CN, $85/yr CN, $213/yr CN instns; $38/issue foreign, $99/yr foreign, $227/yr foreign instns
ISSN: 0009-7101
Trim Size: 6 x 9
Ad Rates: B&W page $400, 1/2 pg $300
Ad Closing Date(s): 2 months prior to issue date

CineVue
Published by Asian CineVision Inc (ACV)
115 W 30 St, Suite 708, New York, NY 10001
Tel: 212-989-1422 *Fax:* 212-727-3584
E-mail: cinevue@asiancinevision.org
Web Site: www.asiancinevision.org/cinevue
Key Personnel
Prodn Coord: Ellen Sea *E-mail:* ellen@asiancinevision.org
Prog Assoc: Lesley Qin
Online journal that showcases media content produced by, for & about the Asian Pacific American experience including profiles, features, interviews, critiques, essays, commentary & original content.
First published 1986
Circulation: 2,000,000
ISSN: 0895-805X

Classic Images
Published by Muscatine Journal
Subsidiary of Lee Enterprises Inc
301 E Third St, Muscatine, IA 52761
Tel: 563-262-0537 *Toll Free Tel:* 800-383-3198
Fax: 563-262-8042
E-mail: classicimages@classicimages.com
Web Site: www.classicimages.com
Key Personnel
Gen Mgr & Ed: Bob King *Tel:* 563-262-0538
Articles, features & reviews of classic movies; news of home entertainment industry; information & reviews of classic films, videotapes & videodiscs; technical articles on equipment; biographies & career articles on film people; film industry obits.
First published 1962
Media Reviewed: DVDs, VHS Tapes, Videotapes
Frequency: Monthly
Circulation: 5,500
$36/yr, $108/yr foreign
ISSN: 0275-8423
Trim Size: 9 1/2 x 9 4/5
Ad Rates: B&W page $220, 4-color page $460
Ad Closing Date(s): 10th of the month prior to issue

Communication Abstracts
Published by EBSCOhost®
10 Estes St, Ipswich, MA 01938
Tel: 978-356-6500 *Toll Free Tel:* 800-653-2726
Fax: 978-356-6565
E-mail: information@ebsco.com
Web Site: www.ebscohost.com
Key Personnel
VP, Sales E-Books & Audiobooks: Scott Wasinger *E-mail:* swasinger@ebsco.com
Dir, E-Book Prods: Ken Breen *E-mail:* kbreen@ebsco.com
Dir, E-Books & PR: Paige Larkin
E-mail: plarkin@ebsco.com
Provide coverage of recent literature in all areas of communication studies (both mass & interpersonal). Includes expanded coverage of new communication technologies; no unsol mss.
First published 1978
Media Reviewed: Books (journal articles), Journals
Circulation: 1,250
$353/yr indivs, $1,749/yr instns
ISSN: 0162-2811
Trim Size: 6 x 9

Communication Arts
Published by Coyne & Blanchard Inc
110 Constitution Dr, Menlo Park, CA 94025
Tel: 650-326-6040 *Fax:* 650-326-1648
E-mail: editorial@commarts.com
Web Site: www.commarts.com
Key Personnel
Ed & Designer: Patrick S Coyne
Exec Ed: Jean A Coyne
Mng Ed: Robin Alyse Doyle
Print & online magazine that covers creativity in design & advertising. Features six juried competitions that cover the entire field of visual communications.
First published 1959
Frequency: 6 issues/yr
Circulation: 41,500 paid
$53/yr US, $70/yr CN, $110/yr other print & digital; $30/yr digital
ISSN: 0010-3519
Trim Size: 8 5/8 x 10 7/8
Ad Rates: B&W page $7,535, 4-color page $10,035
Ad Closing Date(s): Approximately 2 months prior to cover date. See media kit for additional info

Communication Research
Published by Sage Publications Inc
2455 Teller Rd, Thousand Oaks, CA 91320
Tel: 805-499-9774 *Toll Free Tel:* 800-818-7243
Fax: 805-499-0871 *Toll Free Fax:* 800-583-2665
E-mail: journals@sagepub.com
Web Site: www.sagepub.com
Key Personnel
Ed: Michael E Roloff; Pamela Shoemaker
Provide an interdisciplinary forum for scholars & professionals to present new research in communication. Encourages rigorous empirical studies of mass & interpersonal communications.
First published 1974
Frequency: 6 issues/yr
Circulation: 700
$176/yr indivs, $1,251/yr instns
ISSN: 0093-6502
Trim Size: 7 x 10
Ad Rates: B&W page $605, 4-color page $1,685
Ad Closing Date(s): First of the month, 2 months prior to publication month

Communications Daily
Published by Warren Communications News Inc
2115 Ward Ct NW, Washington, DC 20037
Tel: 202-872-9200 *Toll Free Tel:* 800-771-9202 (cust serv) *Fax:* 202-318-8350
E-mail: info@warren-news.com
Web Site: www.warren-news.com
Key Personnel
Chmn & Publr: Paul Warren *E-mail:* pwarrendc@warren-news.com
Pres & Ed: Daniel Warren *E-mail:* dwarrendc@warren-news.com
Exec Sr Ed: Howard Buskirk
E-mail: hbuskirkdc@warren-news.com
Exec Ed: R Michael Feazel *E-mail:* mfeazeldc@warren-news.com
Mng Ed: Jonathan Make *E-mail:* jmakedc@warren-news.com
Dir, Sales: William R Benton
E-mail: wbentondc@warren-news.com
Covers electronic communications including broadcasting, cable, telephone & data communications, electronic information distribution, satellites, electronic mail, consumer electronics, home video & mobile radio. No unsol mss.
First published 1981
Frequency: Daily (weekdays)
$5,495 (electronic or print)
ISSN: 0277-0679
Trim Size: 7 1/2 x 9 1/2

Ad Rates: See www.warren-news.com/advertising-CommDaily.htm
Ad Closing Date(s): By 2:00 pm 2 business days prior to publication

Creative
Published by Magazines/Creative Inc
31 Merrick Ave, Merrick, NY 11566
Tel: 516-378-0800
E-mail: info@creativemag.com
Web Site: creativemag.com
Key Personnel
Publr & Ed: David Flasterstein
AV & marketing news & ideas for advertising, sales promotion & marketing managers.
First published 1966
Frequency: 6 issues/yr
Circulation: 15,000
$4/issue, $30/yr, $50/yr foreign, $20 annual illustrated guide
ISSN: 0737-5883
Trim Size: 8 1/4 x 11 1/4
Ad Rates: B&W page $1,960, 4-color page $2,560

Digital Video
Published by NewBay Media
28 E 28 St, 12th fl, New York, NY 10016
Tel: 212-378-0400
Web Site: www.newbaymedia.com
Key Personnel
Publr: Eric Trabb *Tel:* 212-378-0400 ext 532 *E-mail:* etrabb@nbmedia.com
Edit Dir: Cristina Clapp *Tel:* 310-429-8484 *E-mail:* cclapp@nbmedia.com
First published 2011
Frequency: Monthly
ISSN: 2164-0963
Ad Rates: 4-color page $6,700

District Administration
Published by Professional Media Group LLC
488 Main Ave, Norwalk, CT 06851
Tel: 203-663-0100 *Fax:* 203-663-0149; 203-663-0148 (edit)
Web Site: www.districtadministration.com
Key Personnel
Publr: Daniel A Kinnaman *E-mail:* dkinnaman@promediagrp.com
Assoc Publr & East Coast Sales Mgr: George Halo *E-mail:* ghalo@districtadministration.com
Edit Dir: J D Solomon *E-mail:* jdsolomon@promediagrp.com
Mng Ed: Angela Pascopella *E-mail:* apascopella@promediagrp.com
Sr Assoc Ed: Matt Zalaznick *E-mail:* mzalaznick@promediagrp.com
Asst Ed: Lauren Williams *E-mail:* lwilliams@promediagrp.com
Includes descriptions of new products; for school administrators & personnel at district level, administrators K-12.
First published 1986
Media Reviewed: Educational Media
Frequency: Monthly
Free
Trim Size: 8 x 11
Ad Closing Date(s): Approximately 4-5 weeks prior to issue month

Documentary
Published by International Documentary Association
3470 Wilshire Blvd, Suite 980, Los Angeles, CA 90010
Tel: 213-232-1660 *Fax:* 213-232-1669
E-mail: info@documentary.org; subscriptions@documentary.org
Web Site: www.documentary.org
Key Personnel
Exec Dir: Michael Lumpkin *Tel:* 213-232-1660 ext 201 *E-mail:* michael@documentary.org
Ed: Thomas White *Tel:* 213-232-1600 ext 214 *E-mail:* tom@documentary.org
First published 1982
Media Reviewed: Books
Frequency: Quarterly
Circulation: 5,500
$6/issue instns, $45/yr US libs & instns, $55/yr foreign libs & instns
ISSN: 1559-1034
Trim Size: 8 3/8 x 10 7/8
Ad Closing Date(s): Dec 25 for Spring issue, March 25 for Summer issue, Aug 7 for Fall issue, Nov 13 for Winter issue

Educational Dealer
Published by Fahy-Williams Publishing Inc
171 Reed St, Geneva, NY 14456
Mailing Address: PO Box 1080, Geneva, NY 14456
Tel: 315-789-0458 *Toll Free Tel:* 800-344-0559 *Fax:* 315-789-4263
Web Site: www.fwpi.com; www.eddealermagazine.com
Key Personnel
Dir, Ad: Tim Braden *E-mail:* tbraden@fwpi.com
Edit Dir: Tina Manzer *E-mail:* tmanzer@fwpi.com
Publr: J Kevin Fahy *E-mail:* kfahy@fwpi.com
Features, departments & new product announcements for dealers & producers of educational materials.
First published 1976
Frequency: 5 issues/yr
Circulation: 5,793
Free
ISSN: 0193-1067
Trim Size: 8 3/8 x 11 1/8
Ad Rates: B&W page $1,390, 4-color page $1,985
Ad Closing Date(s): 36 days prior to issue date

Educational Technology Research & Development (ETR&D)
Published by Association for Educational Communications & Technology (AECT)
320 W Eighth St, Suite 101, Bloomington, IN 47404-3745
Tel: 812-335-7675 *Toll Free Tel:* 877-677-AECT (677-2328) *Fax:* 812-335-7678
E-mail: aect@aect.org
Web Site: www.aect.org
Key Personnel
Exec Dir: Phillip Harris *Tel:* 812-335-7675 ext 202 *E-mail:* pharris@aect.org
Co-Ed-in-Chief: Michael Hannafin *E-mail:* hannafin@uga.edu; Michael Spector *E-mail:* mspector@uga.edu
Offers controversial, well-documented articles on research & applied theory in educational technology & development.
First published 1953
Media Reviewed: CD-ROMs, Software
Frequency: 6 issues/yr
Circulation: 7,500
$35/yr membs
ISSN: 1042-1629

Educational Technology: The Magazine for Managers of Change in Education
Published by Educational Technology Publications Inc
700 Palisade Ave, Englewood Cliffs, NJ 07632-0564
Tel: 201-871-4007 *Toll Free Tel:* 800-952-2665 (orders) *Fax:* 201-871-4009
E-mail: edtecpubs@aol.com
Web Site: bookstoread.com/etp
Key Personnel
Publr & Sr Ed: Lawrence Lipsitz
For educators & trainers.
First published 1961
Media Reviewed: Communications Media, Hypermedia, Microcomputer Software, Records, 16mm Films, Videodiscs, Videotapes
Frequency: 6 issues/yr
Number of pages: 68
Circulation: 2,500
$259/yr, $289/yr foreign
ISSN: 0013-1962
Trim Size: 8 1/2 x 11

Electronic Musician
Published by NewBay Media LLC
28 E 28 St, 12th fl, New York, NY 10016
Tel: 212-378-0400 *Fax:* 212-378-0470
Web Site: www.emusician.com
Key Personnel
Publr: Joe Perry *Tel:* 770-343-9978 *E-mail:* jperry@musicplayer.com
Ed: Sarah Jones *Tel:* 650-238-0330 *E-mail:* sjones@musicplayer.com
Project recording & sound techniques for the professional audio market. Digital version also available.
First published 1990
Frequency: Monthly
Circulation: 500,000 paid
$23.97/yr US, $30/yr CN, $50/yr intl (print); $23.96/yr (digital); $29.97/yr US, $36/yr CN, $56/yr intl (print & digital)
ISSN: 1050-7868
Trim Size: 9 x 10 7/8
Ad Rates: 4-color page $5,945
Ad Closing Date(s): 8-9 weeks prior to issue date

ETR&D, see Educational Technology Research & Development (ETR&D)

exposure
Published by Society for Photographic Education
2530 Superior Ave, Suite 403, Cleveland, OH 44114
Tel: 216-622-2733 *Fax:* 216-622-2712
E-mail: exposure@spenational.org
Web Site: www.spenational.org
Key Personnel
Exec Dir: Virginia Morrison *E-mail:* vmorrison@spenational.org
Ed: Stacey McCarroll Cutshaw
Events & Pubns Coord: Ginenne Clark
Registrar: Meghan Borato
Photographic educators, artists, professionals & students.
First published 1973
Media Reviewed: Films, Photography, Videotapes
Frequency: Semiannual
Circulation: 2,500
$225/yr sustaining, $125/yr regular, $90/yr adjunct, $55/yr student, $75/yr senior
ISSN: 0098-8863
Trim Size: 7 3/8 x 9 1/2
Ad Rates: $1,500 outside back cover, $1,000 inside front & back covers, $600 full page, $400 1/2 page, $300 1/4 page
Ad Closing Date(s): May 15 fall issue, Nov 15 spring issue

Fiber Optics Weekly Update
Published by Information Gatekeepers Inc
1340 Soldiers Field Rd, Suite 2, Boston, MA 02135
Tel: 617-782-5033 *Fax:* 617-507-8338
E-mail: info@igigroup.com
Web Site: www.igigroup.com
Key Personnel
CEO & Pres: Paul Polishuk, PhD
Ed-in-Chief & Chief Analyst: Dr Hui Pan *E-mail:* hpan@igigroup.com
Provides information on technology, markets, applications & products for fiber optics.
First published 1978
Frequency: Weekly
$695/yr US & CN, $745/yr other (PDF, 1 user)

ISSN: 1051-189X
Trim Size: 8 1/2 x 11

Film & History: An Interdisciplinary Journal
Published by Historians Film Committee
Lawrence University, Memorial Hall B5, 711 E Boldt Way, Appleton, WI 54911
Tel: 920-832-6649
E-mail: center@filmandhistory.org
Web Site: www.uwosh.edu/filmandhistory
Key Personnel
Ed-in-Chief: Loren PQ Baybrook *E-mail:* editor@filmandhistory.org
Articles by historical scholars involving the use of film & television in their research, teaching & production.
First published 1971
Media Reviewed: Books, CD-ROMs, Films
Frequency: Semiannual
Circulation: 3,500
$55/yr indiv, $90/yr instn
ISSN: 0360-3695
Trim Size: 8 1/2 x 11
Ad Rates: $500/issue ad or insert
Ad Closing Date(s): March 1 Spring issue, Sept 1 Fall issue

Film Comment
Published by Film Society of Lincoln Center
70 Lincoln Center Plaza, New York, NY 10023
Tel: 212-875-5610 *Toll Free Tel:* 800-783-4903 (cust serv); 888-313-6085 *Fax:* 212-875-5636
E-mail: editor@filmlinc.com; info@filmlinc.com
Web Site: www.filmlinc.com; www.filmcomment.com
Key Personnel
Mng Ed: Laura Kern *E-mail:* lkern@filmlinc.com
Sr Ed: Nicolas Rapold
Ed: Gavin Smith
Feature reviews & analysis of mainstream, art-house & avant-garde filmmaking from around the world.
First published 1962
Media Reviewed: Books, Films, TV
Frequency: 6 issues/yr
Circulation: 40,000
$5.95/issue, $29.95/yr, $40/yr Mexico & CN, $60/yr elsewhere
ISSN: 0015-119X
Trim Size: 7 1/2 x 10 3/8
Ad Rates: B&W page $2,650, 4-color page $3,750
Ad Closing Date(s): Approximately 7 weeks prior to cover date. See media kit for additional info

Film Quarterly
Published by University of California Press, Journals Division
2000 Center St, Suite 303, Berkeley, CA 94704-1223
Tel: 510-643-7154 (cust serv) *Fax:* 510-642-9917
E-mail: journals@ucpress.edu; customerservice@ucpress.edu
Web Site: www.ucpressjournals.com; www.filmquarterly.org
Key Personnel
Ed: B Ruby Rich
Consulting Ed: Ann Martin *E-mail:* ann.martin@ucpress.edu
Book Review Ed: Noah Isenberg *E-mail:* isenbern@newschool.edu
Scholarly film criticism, theory & history.
First published 1958
Media Reviewed: Films
Frequency: Quarterly
Number of pages: 96
Circulation: 6,500
$12/issue, $51/yr indivs, $26/yr students & retired, e-only $142/yr instns, e-only indivs $20/yr
ISSN: 0015-1386
Trim Size: 8 1/2 x 11
Ad Rates: B&W page $660, 1/2 page $465, 1/4 page $230
Ad Closing Date(s): Jan 15, April 15, July 15, Oct 15

Filmmaker: The Magazine of Independent Film
Published by The Independent Filmmaker Project (IFP)
68 Jay St, Rm 425, Brooklyn, NY 11201-8361
Tel: 212-465-8200 (ext 206) *Fax:* 212-465-8525
Web Site: www.filmmakermagazine.com; www.ifp.org
Key Personnel
Natl Sales Dir: Kari Fields *E-mail:* kfields@ifp.org
Ed-in-Chief: Scott Macaulay *E-mail:* scott@filmmakermagazine.com
Mng Ed: Nick Dawson *E-mail:* nick@filmmakermagazine.com
Sr Ed: Peter Bowen *E-mail:* peter@filmmakermagazine.com
First published 1992
Frequency: Quarterly
Number of pages: 112
Circulation: 32,000
$18/yr, $30/2 yrs includes digital, $10/yr digital includes 4 print issues
ISSN: 1063-8954
Trim Size: 8 3/8 x 10 7/8
Ad Rates: B&W page $2,420, 4-color page $4,000
Ad Closing Date(s): 3 weeks prior to issue date (Spring, Summer & Fall); 5 weeks prior to issue date (Winter)

Government Video
Published by NewBay Media LLC
28 E 28 St, 12th fl, New York, NY 10016
Tel: 212-378-0400 *Fax:* 212-378-0470
Web Site: www.governmentvideo.com
Key Personnel
VP & Group Publr: Eric Trabb *Tel:* 212-378-0400 ext 532 *Fax:* 732-588-0834 *E-mail:* etrabb@nbmedia.com
Resource for state, federal & government video professionals.
First published 1989
Frequency: Monthly
Circulation: 15,000
$54/yr US, $92/yr CN, $106/yr other, free to qualified US residents
ISSN: 1087-917X
Trim Size: 8 x 10 3/4
Ad Rates: 4-color page $4,870, 1/2 page $3,400, 1/4 page $2,530, see web site for additional rates
Ad Closing Date(s): Up to 2 weeks preceding issue month

Home Media Magazine
Published by Questex Media Group Inc
201 Sandpointe Ave, Suite 500, Santa Ana, CA 92707
Mailing Address: PO Box 1270, Skokie, IL 60076-8270
Tel: 714-759-HMM1 (759-4661, edit); 949-413-9311 (sales)
E-mail: homemediamagazine@questex.com; homemedia@halldata.com
Web Site: www.questex.com; www.homemediamagazine.com
Key Personnel
Exec Ed: Angelique Flores *E-mail:* aflores@questex.com
Ed-in-Chief & Assoc Ed: Stephanie Prange *E-mail:* sprange@questex.com
Publr & Edit Dir: Thomas K Arnold *E-mail:* tarnold@questex.com
Ad Sales Rep: Julie Savant *E-mail:* jsavant@questex.com
For home entertainment specialty retailers, online retailers & merchants of DVD software, hardware & accessories.
First published 1978
Media Reviewed: DVDs, VHS Tapes
Frequency: Weekly
Circulation: 25,500
$49.99/yr US; $79.99/yr CN & Mexico; $99.99/yr other
ISSN: 1934-9882
Trim Size: 10 1/2 x 14

ICG Magazine
Published by International Cinematographers Guild
7755 Sunset Blvd, Hollywood, CA 90046
Tel: 323-876-0160 *Fax:* 323-876-6383
E-mail: info@icgmagazine.com
Web Site: icgmagazine.com; www.cameraguild.com
Key Personnel
Exec Ed: David Geffner *Tel:* 323-969-2715 *E-mail:* davidgeffner@icgmagazine.com
Assoc Publr: Teresa M Munoz *Tel:* 323-969-2714 *Fax:* 323-878-1180 *E-mail:* teresa@icgmagazine.com
Professional film & video/digital techniques magazine.
First published 1929
Frequency: Monthly
Number of pages: 75
Circulation: 12,000
$48/yr, $36/yr student, $82/yr foreign (surface mail), $117/yr foreign (air mail)
ISSN: 0020-8299
Trim Size: 8 1/2 x 11
Ad Rates: B&W page $2,275, 4-color page $3,435
Ad Closing Date(s): Approximately 5-6 wks prior to cover date

IEEE Journal on Selected Areas in Communications
Published by Institute of Electrical & Electronics Engineers Inc (IEEE)
445 Hoes Lane, Piscataway, NJ 08854-4141
Tel: 732-981-0060 *Toll Free Tel:* 800-678-4333 (contact ctr) *Fax:* 732-981-9511 (media contacts); 732-562-6380 (contact ctr)
E-mail: customer.service@ieee.org
Web Site: www.ieee.org; ieeexplore.ieee.org
Key Personnel
Ed-in-Chief: Martha Steenstrup *E-mail:* steenie@rcn.com
Articles on theory & technology of telecommunications; each issue covers a specific topic. No advertising included.
First published 1983
Frequency: Monthly
$1,700/yr print, $1,495/yr online, $2,040/yr print & online, $45 S&H, $55 air freight
ISSN: 0733-8716
Trim Size: 8 1/2 x 11

IEEE Spectrum Magazine
Published by Institute of Electrical & Electronics Engineers Inc (IEEE)
3 Park Ave, 17th fl, New York, NY 10016
Tel: 212-419-7555 *Fax:* 212-419-7570
E-mail: ieeespectrum@ieee.org
Web Site: www.spectrum.ieee.org
Key Personnel
Ed-in-Chief: Susan Hassler *E-mail:* s.hassler@ieee.org
Frequency: Monthly
Circulation: 408,000
$299/yr print, $200/yr online, $229/yr print & online, $45 S&H, free with membership
ISSN: 0018-9235

IEEE Transactions on Broadcasting
Published by Institute of Electrical & Electronics Engineers Inc (IEEE)
445 Hoes Lane, Piscataway, NJ 08854-4141
Tel: 732-562-6061 *Toll Free Tel:* 800-678-4333 (contact ctr) *Fax:* 732-981-1769
E-mail: bts@ieee.org
Web Site: bts.ieee.org; www.ieee.org
Key Personnel
Ed-in-Chief: Yiyan Wu *Tel:* 613-998-2870 *E-mail:* yiyan.wu@crc.ca
Contains information on broadcast transmission systems engineering, including the design & utilization of broadcast equipment. No advertising included.
First published 1955
Frequency: Quarterly
Circulation: 3,800
$180/yr print, $155/yr online, $215/yr print & online, $45 S&H, $55 air freight
ISSN: 0018-9316
Trim Size: 8 1/2 x 11

IEEE Transactions on Communications
Published by Institute of Electrical & Electronics Engineers Inc (IEEE)
445 Hoes Lane, Piscataway, NJ 08854-4141
Tel: 732-981-0060 *Toll Free Tel:* 800-678-4333 (contact ctr) *Fax:* 732-981-0624 (pubns)
E-mail: publishing-operations@ieee.org
Web Site: www.ieee.org; ieeexplore.ieee.org
Key Personnel
Ed-in-Chief: Robert Schober *E-mail:* eic-tcom@dei.unipd.it
Articles on theory & technology of telecommunications for professionals in the field.
First published 1953
Frequency: Monthly
$1,795/yr print, $1,595 online, $2,150 print & online, $45 S&H, $55 air freight
ISSN: 0090-6778
Trim Size: 8 1/2 x 11

Image
Published by George Eastman House International Museum of Photography & Film
900 East Ave, Rochester, NY 14607
Tel: 585-271-3361 *Fax:* 585-271-3970
Web Site: www.eastmanhouse.org
Key Personnel
Dir, Museum: Dr Bruce Barnes
Mng Ed: Amy Schelemanow
Members magazine.
First published 1952
Media Reviewed: Motion Pictures, Photography
Frequency: Semiannual
Circulation: 3,000
$60/yr membs, $70/yr foreign membs
ISSN: 0536-5465
Trim Size: 7 1/2 x 12

Information Technology & Libraries
Published by Library & Information Technology Association (LITA)
Division of American Library Association (ALA)
c/o American Library Association, 50 E Huron St, Chicago, IL 60611-2795
Toll Free Tel: 800-545-2433 (ext 4270) *Fax:* 312-280-3257
E-mail: lita@ala.org
Web Site: www.ala.org/lita
Key Personnel
Exec Dir: Mary C Taylor *Tel:* 312-280-4267 *E-mail:* mtaylor@ala.org
Ed: Bob Gerrity *E-mail:* r.gerrity@uq.edu.au
Covers digital libraries, general library & information technology, electronic publishing & library automation. Available online only.
First published 1968
Media Reviewed: Books, Periodicals, Software
Frequency: Quarterly
ISSN: 2163-5226

Information Today
Published by Information Today, Inc
143 Old Marlton Pike, Medford, NJ 08055-8750
Tel: 609-654-6266 *Toll Free Tel:* 800-300-9868 (cust serv) *Fax:* 609-654-4309
E-mail: custserv@infotoday.com
Web Site: www.infotoday.com/IT/default.asp
Key Personnel
Publr/Pres & CEO: Thomas H Hogan
Ed: Donovan Griffin *E-mail:* dgriffin@infotoday.com
Electronic information delivery for users & providers of information services. Includes editorial focus on news: new services, databases, information companies, technology trends, controversial issues. Also includes a comprehensive events calendar listing pertinent conferences, exhibitions & other industry meetings.
First published 1983
Frequency: 10 issues/yr
Number of pages: 32
Circulation: 8,000
$96.95/yr, $183/2 yrs, $280/3 yrs US; $125/yr, $235/2 yrs, $360/3 yrs CN & Mexico; $140 yr, $265/2 yrs, $403/3 yrs other; agencies $2 less
ISSN: 8755-6286
Trim Size: 9 1/2 x 11 3/4
Ad Rates: See web site for complete details

Instant Replay
6020 Lower Mountain Rd, New Hope, PA 18938
Tel: 215-794-3616 *Fax:* 215-794-5279
Web Site: www.irvm.com
Key Personnel
Pres & Ed-in-Chief: Chuck Azar *E-mail:* cazar@irvm.com
Consumer DVD magazine; videotape library, videotape, DVD & online. Industry newsletter.
First published 1977
Media Reviewed: CDs, DVDs, Music, Videotapes
Frequency: Quarterly
Circulation: 5,000
$29.95/issue, $99/yr
Ad Rates: B&W page $2,000

Instructor
Published by Scholastic Inc
557 Broadway, New York, NY 10012-3999
Toll Free Tel: 866-436-2455 (subns)
E-mail: info@scholastic.com; instructor@emailcustomerservice.com
Web Site: www.scholastic.com/instructor
Key Personnel
Group Publr: Michele Robinson *Tel:* 212-343-6455 *E-mail:* mrobinson@scholastic.com
Exec Ed: Wayne D'Orio *Tel:* 212-343-4914 *E-mail:* wdorio@scholastic.com
Sr Sales & Mktg Assoc: Jenna Bryerman *Tel:* 212-343-6205 *E-mail:* jbryerman@scholastic.com
The leading professional magazine for educators of children, kindergarten through 8th grade. Features professional articles, hands-on activities, best practices, reproducibles & more.
First published 1891
Media Reviewed: Art Supplies, Audiotapes, CD-ROMs, Children's Books, DVDs, Educational Media, Music Books, Professional Books, Software, Video Games, Videotapes
Frequency: 8 issues/yr (monthly March, April, Aug, Sept & Oct; bimonthly Jan/Feb, May/June, Nov/Dec)
Circulation: 525,000
$14/yr, $28/2 yrs, $26/yr CN, $32/yr foreign
ISSN: 1049-5851
Trim Size: 7 7/8 x 10 1/2
Ad Rates: 4-color page $11,800
Ad Closing Date(s): Jan 14 for March issue, etc

International Journal of Instructional Media
Published by Westwood Press Inc
118 Five Mile River Rd, Darien, CT 06820
Tel: 203-656-8680
Web Site: www.adprima.com/ijim.htm
Key Personnel
Exec Ed: Dr Phillip J Sleeman *Tel:* 860-875-5484 *E-mail:* PLSleeman@aol.com
Assoc Ed: Linda B Sleeman
Internet & Web Reviews: Dr Robert Kizlik
Media Reviews: Dr John G Flores
Papers on the most advantageous applications & deployment of instructional media; for scholars & educators.
First published 1970
Frequency: Quarterly
Circulation: 500 dom, 200 foreign
$225/yr plus $20/yr dom postage, $40/yr foreign postage
ISSN: 0892-1815
Trim Size: 6 x 9

Journal of Applied Communication Research
Published by Routledge Journals
Member of Taylor & Francis Group
711 Third Ave, New York, NY 10017
Tel: 212-216-7800 *Fax:* 212-564-7854
Web Site: www.routledge.com
Key Personnel
Mng Ed: Katherine De Blanger
For applied communication practitioners & scholars.
First published 1973
Frequency: Quarterly
Circulation: 2,000
$375 instn (online); $429/yr instn (print & online); $110 indiv (print)
ISSN: 0090-9882 (print); 1479-5752 (online)

Journal of Broadcasting & Electronic Media (JOBEM)
Published by Broadcast Education Association (BEA)
Affiliate of National Association of Broadcasters (NAB) (in partnership with)
1771 "N" St NW, Washington, DC 20036-2891
Tel: 202-429-3935 *Fax:* 202-609-9940
Web Site: www.beaweb.org
Key Personnel
Exec Dir: Heather Birks *Tel:* 202-602-0584 *E-mail:* heather@beaweb.org
Ed: Zizi Papacharissi *Tel:* 312-996-3188 *E-mail:* zizi@uic.edu
First published 1956
Frequency: Quarterly
Circulation: 2,400
ISSN: 0883-8151
Trim Size: 6 x 9

Journal of Communication
Published by Wiley-Blackwell
111 River St, Hoboken, NJ 07030
Tel: 201-748-6000 *Fax:* 201-748-6088
E-mail: info@wiley.com; onlinelibrarysales@wiley.com
Web Site: www.wiley.com
Key Personnel
Ed: Malcolm Parks
Ad Sales Rep: Kristen McCarthy *E-mail:* kmccarthy@wiley.com
Covers communication theory, research, history, policy & practice.
First published 1951
Media Reviewed: Books
Frequency: 6 issues/yr
Circulation: 6,200
$71/yr student (print & online), $107/yr indivs (print & online)
ISSN: 1460-2466 (online); 0021-9916 (print)
Trim Size: 6 7/8 x 9 3/4
Ad Rates: B&W page $556, 1/2 page $386

Journal of Educational Technology Systems
Published by Baywood Publishing Co Inc
26 Austin Ave, Amityville, NY 11701

Mailing Address: PO Box 337, Amityville, NY 11701
Tel: 631-691-1270 *Toll Free Tel:* 800-638-7819 (orders only) *Fax:* 631-691-1770
E-mail: info@baywood.com
Web Site: baywood.com
Key Personnel
Exec Ed: Dr Thomas T Liao; Dr Lori L Scarlatos
Reports on the application of technology to the teaching process with emphasis on the use of computers as an integral component of educational systems & teacher-oriented curricula.
First published 1972
Media Reviewed: Floppy Discs, Videodiscs, Videotapes
Frequency: Quarterly
$486 instns (print & online), $462 (online only)
ISSN: 0047-2395 (print); 1541-3810 (online)
Trim Size: 6 x 9

Journal of Film and Video
Published by University Film & Video Association
Ithaca College, James B Pendleton Ctr, Suite 305, 3800 Barham Blvd, Los Angeles, CA 90068
Tel: 323-851-6199 *Toll Free Tel:* 800-280-7709; 866-647-8382 *Fax:* 323-851-6748
E-mail: journaloffilmandvideo@gmail.com
Web Site: www.ufva.org/journal
Key Personnel
Pres: Norman Hollyn *E-mail:* nhollyn@cinema.usc.edu
Ed: Stephen Tropiano
Scholarly articles on film & video; teachers & professionals. Individual subscribers must join the University Film & Video Association ($75 membership fee).
First published 1947
Media Reviewed: Books, Films, Videotapes
Frequency: Quarterly
Circulation: 1,300
Free to indiv membs; $20 single issue; Insts: $75/yr print or electronic, $95/yr print & electronic; $10 non-US postage (CN & Mexico), $35 (other non-US locations)
ISSN: 0742-4671
Trim Size: Full page 4 3/8 x 7 1/4, half page 4 3/8 x 3 5/8
Ad Rates: Full page $250, 1/2 page $185
Ad Closing Date(s): 1 month prior to publication date

Journal of Imaging Science & Technology (JIST)
Published by Society for Imaging Science and Technology (IS&T)
7003 Kilworth Lane, Springfield, VA 22151
Tel: 703-642-9090 *Fax:* 703-642-9094
E-mail: info@imaging.org
Web Site: www.imaging.org
Key Personnel
Ed: Dr George TC Chiu
Articles on photochemistry, photophysics, silver halide material, organic light sensitive systems, electrophotography & associated areas. Imaging applications for scientists & engineers.
First published 1950
Frequency: 6 issues/yr
Circulation: 7,000
Insts: Hardcopy $295 US, $325 foreign, online only $385, hardcopy & online $560 US, $595 foreign; Indivs: Free online subn with membership, add hardcopy $55 US, $70 foreign
ISSN: 1062-3701
Trim Size: 8 1/4 x 11 1/4

Journal of Popular Film & Television
Published by Taylor & Francis Inc
c/o Taylor & Francis, 325 Chestnut St, Suite 800, Philadelphia, PA 19106
Mailing Address: PO Box 32794, Hartford, CT 06150
Tel: 215-625-8900 *Toll Free Tel:* 800-354-1420
E-mail: customerservice@taylorandfrancis.com
Web Site: www.taylorandfrancis.com; www.tandfonline.com
Key Personnel
Ad Sales Coord: Patrick Dunn *Tel:* 215-606-4322 *E-mail:* patrick.dunn@taylorandfrancis.com
Reflects interest in popular culture studies; examines commercial films & television from a socio-cultural perspective.
First published 1971
Frequency: Quarterly
Circulation: 817
$70/yr print & online, $210/yr print & online instns, $184/yr online instns
ISSN: 0195-6051 (print); 1930-6458 (online)
Trim Size: 8 1/2 x 11
Ad Rates: B&W page $350, 1/2 page $175; contact for additional rates
Ad Closing Date(s): Aug 25 (Fall), Oct 25 (Winter), Feb 25 (Spring), April 25 (Summer), contact us for other closing dates

Jump Cut: A Review of Contemporary Media
Published by Jump Cut Associates
465 65 St, Oakland, CA 94609-1101
Tel: 510-658-7721
Web Site: www.ejumpcut.org
Key Personnel
Ed: John Hess *E-mail:* johndavidhess@gmail.com; Chuck Kleinhans *E-mail:* chuckkle@northwestern.edu; Julia Lesage *E-mail:* jlesage@uoregon.edu
Online reviews & articles on all aspects of film & video; for teachers, students & producers.
First published 1974
Media Reviewed: Books, 16mm Films, Slides, TV, 35mm Films, Videotapes
Frequency: Irregular (1-2 issues/yr)
Free
ISSN: 0146-5546

Library Journal
Published by Media Source Inc
160 Varick St, 11th fl, New York, NY 10013
Tel: 646-380-0700 *Fax:* 646-380-0756
E-mail: ljinfo@mediasourceinc.com; ljcustserv@cdsfulfillment.com
Web Site: lj.libraryjournal.com
Subscription Address: PO Box 5881, Harlan, IA 51593 *Tel:* 515-247-2984 *Toll Free Tel:* 800-588-1030 subns *E-mail:* ljlcustserv@cdsfulfilment.com
Key Personnel
Publr: Ian Singer *Tel:* 646-380-0747 *E-mail:* isinger@mediasourceinc.com
Ed-in-Chief: John N Berry, III *Tel:* 646-380-0760 *E-mail:* jberry@mediasourceinc.com
News; features; book, magazine, AV & CD-ROM reviews; new product information for academic, public & special librarians. Also available online.
First published 1876
Media Reviewed: Audiobooks, Books (& ebooks), DVDs, Videotapes, Web Sites (& databases/systems)
Frequency: Semimonthly (exc monthly during Jan, July, Aug & Dec)
Number of pages: 150
Circulation: 16,971
$157.99/yr US, $199.99/yr CN; $259.99/yr other
ISSN: 0363-0277
Trim Size: 10 1/2 x 7 7/8

Lightwave
Published by PennWell Corp
98 Spit Brook Rd, Nashua, NH 03062
Tel: 603-891-0123 *Fax:* 603-891-0587
Web Site: www.lightwaveonline.com
Key Personnel
Edit Dir & Assoc Publr: Stephen M Hardy *Tel:* 603-891-9454 *E-mail:* stephenh@penwell.com
Group Publr: Ernesto Burden
For professionals-fiber optics technology & applications.
First published 1984
Frequency: Monthly
Circulation: 31,000
$150/yr US, $170/yr CN, $207/yr other
ISSN: 0741-5834
Trim Size: 11 x 14 1/4, Bleed 11 3/8 x 14 3/4
Ad Rates: See web site for regional sales contact
Ad Closing Date(s): 1st of month prior to cover date

Literature/Film Quarterly
Published by Salisbury University
1101 Camden Ave, Salisbury, MD 21801-6860
Tel: 410-677-5357 *Fax:* 410-543-6203
E-mail: litfilmquart@salisbury.edu
Web Site: www.salisbury.edu/lfq
Key Personnel
Busn Mgr & Copy Ed: Brenda J Grodzicki
Ed: David T Johnson; Elsie M Walker
Articles on literary & dramatic adaptations, interviews, book reviews, film reviews.
First published 1973
Frequency: Quarterly
Number of pages: 80
Circulation: 800
$15/issue indivs & instns, $40/yr indivs, $90/yr instns & US libs, $100/yr foreign instns & indivs, $10/back issue
ISSN: 0090-4260
Trim Size: 6 x 9
Ad Rates: Full page inside back cover $250, full page $200, 1/2 page $100, 1/4 page $75
Ad Closing Date(s): Jan 1, April 1, July 1, Oct 1

Markee 2.0
Published by Lionheart Publishing Inc
506 Roswell St, Suite 220, Marietta, GA 30060
Tel: 770-431-0867 *Toll Free Tel:* 888-303-5639 *Fax:* 770-432-6969
E-mail: lpi@lionhrtpub.com
Web Site: www.markeemagazine.com
Key Personnel
Pres: John Llewellyn *Tel:* 770-431-0867 *E-mail:* llewellyn@lionhrtpub.com
First published 1985
Frequency: 6 issues/yr
Circulation: 20,000
$8/issue, $34/yr US, $60/yr CN & Mexico, $120/yr other
ISSN: 1073-8924
Trim Size: 8 3/8 x 10 7/8

Mediacaster Magazine
Published by Business Information Group
Division of Glacier BIG Holdings Co Ltd
80 Valleybrook Dr, Toronto, ON M3B 2S9, Canada
Tel: 416-442-5600 *Toll Free Tel:* 800-268-7742 (CN); 800-387-0273 (US)
Web Site: www.mediacastermagazine.com
Key Personnel
CEO & Pres: Bruce Creighton
EVP: Alex Papanou
Sr Publr: James Cook *Tel:* 416-510-6871 *Fax:* 416-510-5134 *E-mail:* jcook@broadcastermagazine.com
Ed: Lee Rickwood *Tel:* 416-510-6865 *Fax:* 416-510-5134 *E-mail:* lrickwood@mediacastermagazine.com
Canadian broadband & content trade magazine industry.
First published 2006
Frequency: Quarterly
$39.95/yr CN, $45.95/yr US, $50.95/yr other, subn includes Mediacaster Directory (2 issues/yr); free to qualified personnel
ISSN: 1914-217X (print); 1923-3493 (online)

Mix Magazine
Published by NewBay Media LLC
28 E 28 St, 12th fl, New York, NY 10016
Tel: 212-378-0400 *Fax:* 212-378-0470
Web Site: mixonline.com
Key Personnel
EVP & Group Publr: Adam Goldstein
E-mail: agoldstein@nbmedia.com
Ed: Tom Kenny *Tel:* 650-238-0345
E-mail: tkenny@nbmedia.com
Tech Ed: Kevin Becka *E-mail:* kbecka@earthlink.com
Leading industry magazine covering the full spectrum of professional audio & music production, including AV post-production & live performance. Available in print & online.
First published 1977
Media Reviewed: Concerts, Music
Frequency: Monthly
$23.97/yr US, $40/yr CN, $50/yr other print; $35.97/yr US, $46/yr CN, $56/yr other print & digital
ISSN: 0164-9957
Trim Size: 9 x 10 7/8
Ad Rates: 4-color page $6,685
Ad Closing Date(s): Approximately 3-4 weeks prior to issue month. See media kit for additional info

Motion Picture, TV & Theatre Directory
Published by Motion Picture Enterprises Publications Inc
PO Box 276, Tarrytown, NY 10591-0276
Tel: 212-245-0969 *Fax:* 212-245-0974
E-mail: publications@mpe.net
Web Site: www.mpe.net
Key Personnel
Publr: Neal R Pilzer
Classified directory listing companies in the motion picture, television & video industry for products & services.
First published 1960
Frequency: Semiannual
Circulation: 82,500
$22.53/issue within NY; $20.79/issue outside NY
ISSN: 0580-0412
Trim Size: 8 1/2 x 4
Ad Rates: Single line $116.40, B&W 1/3 page $809, 1/2 page $1,198.60, full page $2,061.10
Ad Closing Date(s): Jan 20 for March issue, July 26 for Sept issue

Multichannel News
Published by NewBay Media LLC
28 E 28 St, 12th fl, New York, NY 10016
Tel: 212-378-0400; 515-247-2984 (cust serv outside the US) *Toll Free Tel:* 800-554-5729 (cust serv within US) *Fax:* 212-378-0470
E-mail: MULcustserv@cdsfulfillment.com (cust serv)
Web Site: www.multichannel.com
Key Personnel
VP, Group Publr & Assoc Publr: Louis Hillelson *Tel:* 917-281-4730 *E-mail:* lhillelson@nbmedia.com
Ed-in-Chief: Mark Robichaux *Tel:* 917-281-4750
E-mail: mrobichaux@nbmedia.com
Exec Ed: Kent Gibbons *Tel:* 917-281-4722
E-mail: kgibbons@nbmedia.com
Mng Ed: Michael Demenchuk *Tel:* 971-281-4712
E-mail: mdemenchuk@nbmedia.com
National & international cable TV, pay TV, pay-per-view, multipoint distribution service, cable TV contractors, consulting firms & investors, DBS.
First published 1980
Media Reviewed: Cable TV
Frequency: 47 issues/yr
$249/yr print & digital
ISSN: 0276-8593
Trim Size: 10 1/2 x 13 1/2
Ad Closing Date(s): 12 days prior to issue date

Multimedia Publisher
Published by Worldwide Videotex
PO Box 3273, Boynton Beach, FL 33424-3273
Tel: 561-738-2276
Key Personnel
Ed-in-Chief: Linda Bara
Multimedia vendors, users, publishers.
First published 1990
Frequency: Monthly
$165/yr, $180/yr foreign

The Music & Sound Retailer
Published by Testa Communications
25 Willowdale Ave, Port Washington, NY 11050-3779
Tel: 516-767-2500 *Toll Free Tel:* 800-937-7678 *Fax:* 516-767-9335 (sales & editorial)
E-mail: msrorders@testa.com (subns)
Web Site: www.testa.com; www.msretailer.com
Key Personnel
Pres & Publr: Vincent P Testa
Prodn Mgr: Steve Thorakos *E-mail:* sthorakos@testa.com
Ed: Dan Ferrisi *Tel:* 516-767-2500 ext 704
E-mail: dferrisi@testa.com
Monthly trade magazine serving musical instrument dealers & professional audio shops.
First published 1996
Frequency: Monthly
$18/yr, free to qualified industry professionals
Ad Rates: $4,845 4-color tabloid page, $3,180 1/2 tabloid page
Ad Closing Date(s): 1st of month

Music Connection Magazine
14654 Victory Blvd, Van Nuys, CA 91411
Tel: 818-995-0101 *Fax:* 818-995-9235
E-mail: contactmc@musicconnection.com
Web Site: musicconnection.com
Key Personnel
Publr & Ad Dir: Eric Bettelli *E-mail:* ericb@musicconnection.com
Assoc Publr & Sr Ed: Mark Nardone
E-mail: markn@musicconnection.com
Mktg & Ad Mgr: Hillorie Rudolph
E-mail: hillorier@musicconnection.com
Opers Mgr & Directories Ed: Denise Coso
E-mail: denisec@musicconnection.com
Music industry trade publication.
First published 1977
Frequency: Monthly
Number of pages: 80
$3.95/issue, $35/yr US, $60 foreign
ISSN: 1091-9791
Trim Size: 8 3/8 x 10 7/8
Ad Rates: B&W full page $1,980, 4-color full page $2,700
Ad Closing Date(s): Approximately 2-3 weeks prior to cover date

Optical Networks/WDM Newsletter
Published by Information Gatekeepers Inc
1340 Soldiers Field Rd, Suite 2, Boston, MA 02135
Tel: 617-782-5033 *Fax:* 617-507-8338
E-mail: info@igigroup.com
Web Site: www.igigroup.com
Key Personnel
CEO & Pres: Paul Polishuk, PhD
Ed-in-Chief & Chief Analyst: Dr Hui Pan
E-mail: hpan@igigroup.com
Technology, international developments & market trends.
First published 1990
Frequency: Monthly
Circulation: 1,000
$695/yr US & CN, $745/yr other print, $695 PDF (1 user)
ISSN: 1057-5383
Trim Size: 8 1/2 x 11

Photo Solution Magazine
Published by Apex Publications Inc
185 rue Saint Paul, Quebec, QC G1K 3W2, Canada
Tel: 418-692-2110 *Toll Free Tel:* 800-905-7468 *Fax:* 418-692-3392 *Toll Free Fax:* 800-664-2739
E-mail: art@photosolution.ca; redaction@photosolution.ca
Web Site: www.photosolution.ca
Key Personnel
Exec Ed: Valerie Racine
Art Dir & Broadcast: Guy Langevin
Ed & Dir, Sales: Guy J Poirier *Tel:* 418-692-2110 ext 101 *E-mail:* gpoirier@photosolution.ca
Photography-portfolios & technical.
First published 1981
Media Reviewed: CDs, Photography Equipment
Frequency: 6 issues/yr
Circulation: 7,700
$27/yr plus $10 postage US, $27/yr CN, $27/yr plus $90 postage elsewhere, includes digital
ISSN: 1916-100X
Trim Size: 8 1/4 x 10 7/8
Ad Rates: 4-color page $4,525 (1x rate), 4-color page $4,070 (6 issues/yr)
Ad Closing Date(s): 60 days before publication date

PhotoDaily
Published by PhotoSource International
Pine Lake Farm, 1910 35 Rd, Osceola, WI 54020-5602
Tel: 715-248-3800 *Toll Free Tel:* 800-624-0266 *Fax:* 715-248-7394 *Toll Free Fax:* 800-624-0266
E-mail: info@photosource.com; psi2@photosource.com
Web Site: www.photosource.com
Key Personnel
Edit Dir: Jeri Engh *E-mail:* jeri@photosource.com
Intl Dir & Publr: Rohn Engh
Ed: Lela La Bree *E-mail:* eds@photosource.com
First published 1985
Media Reviewed: Books, CD-ROMs, Videotapes
Frequency: Daily & Weekly
Circulation: 355
$35/mo, $195/6 mos, $375/yr, $563/2 yrs
ISSN: 0885-4270
Trim Size: 8 1/2 x 11

PhotoStockNotes
Published by PhotoSource International
Pine Lake Farm, 1910 35 Rd, Osceola, WI 54020-5602
Tel: 715-248-3800 *Toll Free Tel:* 800-624-0266 *Fax:* 715-248-7394 *Toll Free Fax:* 800-746-6329
E-mail: info@photosource.com
Web Site: www.photosource.com
Key Personnel
Edit Dir: Jeri Engh *E-mail:* jeri@photosource.com
Intl Dir & Publr: Rohn Engh
Online newsletter; pairs picture buyers with freelance photographers.
First published 1984
Media Reviewed: Books, CD-ROMs, Print
Frequency: Weekly
Circulation: 2,059
$3.50/mo, $35/yr, $62/2 yrs
ISSN: 0190-1400
Trim Size: 8 1/2 x 11
Ad Rates: B&W page $138

Playback
Published by Brunico Communications Ltd
366 Adelaide St W, Suite 100, Toronto, ON M5V 1R9, Canada
Tel: 416-408-2300 *Toll Free Tel:* 888-BRUNICO (278-6426) *Fax:* 416-408-0870
E-mail: customersupport-playback@brunico.com

Web Site: www.playbackonline.ca; www.brunico.com
Key Personnel
VP, Publr & Edit Dir: Mary Maddever
E-mail: mmaddever@brunico.com
Ed & Content Dir: Katie Bailey
E-mail: kbailey@brunico.com
Online publication dealing with broadcasting & production in Canada.
First published 1986
Frequency: Monthly
Circulation: 13,250 controlled
$12.95/mo, $129.50/yr
ISSN: 0836-2114

PMA Magazine
Published by Photo Marketing Association International
2282 Springport Rd, Suite F, Jackson, MI 49202
Tel: 517-788-8100 *Toll Free Tel:* 800-762-9287
Fax: 517-788-8371
Web Site: www.pmai.org/magazine
Key Personnel
Publr: Jennifer Kruger *Tel:* 517-788-8100 ext 104
E-mail: jkruger@pmai.org
Trade publication for photo imaging professional, targeted toward retailers, photofinishers & digital imagers.
First published 1924
Frequency: 6 issues/yr
Circulation: 19,500
$5/issue; CN funds plus GST: $50/yr US (with Newsline $85), $90/2 yrs US (with Newsline $150), $55/yr CN (with Newsline $90), $100/2 yrs CN (with Newsline $160); US funds: $70/yr intl (with Newsline $105), $130/2 yrs intl (with Newsline $190)
ISSN: 0031-8531
Trim Size: 8 1/8 x 10 3/4
Ad Rates: 4-color page $2,000, 1/2 page $1,530
Ad Closing Date(s): 1st or 2nd of month preceding publication month

PopPhoto, see Popular Photography Magazine

Popular Communications
Published by CQ Communications Inc
25 Newbridge Rd, Hicksville, NY 11801
Tel: 516-681-2922 *Toll Free Tel:* 800-853-9797
Fax: 516-681-2926
E-mail: pcmagazine@popular-communications.com
Web Site: www.popular-communications.com
Key Personnel
Pres & Publr: Richard Ross
Dir, Ad & Mktg: Jon Kummer
Ed: Richard Fisher *E-mail:* ki6sn@aol.com
Monthly magazine for shortwave listening & scanner monitoring.
First published 1982
Frequency: Monthly
$34.95/yr US, $44/yr CN & Mexico, $54/yr other; $24/yr digital
ISSN: 0733-3315
Trim Size: 8 1/8 x 10 3/4
Ad Rates: B&W page $2,420, 4-color page $2,970
Ad Closing Date(s): Approximately 2 months prior to publication

Popular Photography Magazine
Published by Bonnier Corp
2 Park Ave, New York, NY 10016
Tel: 212-779-5000
E-mail: contact@popphoto.com
Web Site: www.popphoto.com
Key Personnel
Assoc Publr: Anthony Ruotolo *Tel:* 212-779-5481
E-mail: anthony.ruotolo@bonniercorp.com
Ed-in-Chief: Miriam Leuchter
Art Dir: Jason Beckstead
Consumer magazine of photography including how-to stories, photographer's portfolios, equipment tests & reviews, coverage of new products, photo essays, book reviews, nature, travel, digital imaging.
First published 1937
Media Reviewed: Photography Books, VHS Tapes
Frequency: Monthly
Circulation: 454,741
$14/yr US, $24/2 yrs US, $22/yr CN, $31.93/yr other, $59.86/2 yrs other
ISSN: 1542-0337
Trim Size: 7 7/8 x 10 1/2
Ad Rates: B&W page $53,800, 4-color page $69,300
Ad Closing Date(s): 6 weeks prior to issue date

Post Magazine
Published by COP Communications Inc
620 W Elk Ave, Glendale, CA 91204
Tel: 818-291-1100 (subns) *Fax:* 818-547-4607
Web Site: www.postmagazine.com
Key Personnel
Dir, Sales: Mari Kohn *Tel:* 818-291-1153
E-mail: mkohn@copcomm.com
Sr Ed: Marc Loftus *Tel:* 516-376-1087
E-mail: mloftus@postmagazine.com
Focus on all aspects of post-production for TV, feature films, commercials, etc. News & features on creative technology in audio, video & films.
First published 1986
Media Reviewed: DVDs, Videotapes
Frequency: Monthly
Circulation: 26,000
Print +/or digital free for qualified subscribers, intl free digital only
Trim Size: 10 x 12
Ad Rates: 4-color page $8,630
Ad Closing Date(s): 2 months prior to issue date

Pro Sound News
Published by NewBay Media LLC
28 E 28 St, 12th fl, New York, NY 10016
Tel: 212-378-0400 *Fax:* 212-378-0470
Web Site: www.prosoundnetwork.com
Key Personnel
Edit Dir: Frank Wells *Tel:* 212-378-0400 ext 535
E-mail: fwells@nbmedia.com
Mng Ed: Fred Goodman *Tel:* 212-378-0423
E-mail: fgoodman@nbmedia.com
Professional sound production industry, digital edition available.
First published 1978
Frequency: Monthly
Circulation: 24,500
$24.95/yr US, $50/yr foreign, free to qualified US residents
ISSN: 0164-6338
Trim Size: 10 7/8 x 14 1/2
Ad Rates: 4-color tab $8,295, see web site for additional rates

Professional Photographer
Published by PPA Publications & Events Inc
International Tower, Suite 2200, 229 Peachtree St NE, Atlanta, GA 30303
Tel: 404-522-8600 *Toll Free Tel:* 800-786-6277; 800-742-7468 (circ) *Fax:* 404-614-6406
E-mail: csc@ppa.com
Web Site: www.ppmag.com
Key Personnel
Sr Ed: Joan Sherwood
Features Ed: Leslie Hunt
Marketing & photographic technique for professional photographers.
First published 1907
Media Reviewed: Books
Frequency: Monthly
Circulation: 54,074
$19.95/yr US, $35.95/yr CN
ISSN: 1528-5286
Trim Size: 7 1/2 x 10
Ad Closing Date(s): Approximately 6 weeks prior to issue month. See media kit for additional info

PSA Journal
Published by Photographic Society of America Inc
3000 United Founders Blvd, Suite 103, Oklahoma City, OK 73112
Tel: 405-843-1437 *Toll Free Tel:* 855-772-4636
Fax: 405-843-1438
E-mail: hq@psa-photo.org
Web Site: www.psa-photo.org
Key Personnel
Ed: Donna Brennan *E-mail:* editor@psa-photo.org
Monthly magazine for PSA members containing how-to articles for advanced amateur photographers. Also available online.
First published 1934
Media Reviewed: Photography Books, Videotapes
Frequency: Monthly
Circulation: 5,600
$60/yr US membs & CN, $100/yr other
ISSN: 0030-8277
Trim Size: 7 1/2 x 10
Ad Rates: B&W page $1,336, 4-color page $2,464
Ad Closing Date(s): 1st day of month, 2 months prior to issue month

P3 Update Magazine
Published by Location Update Inc
PO Box 941978, Simi Valley, CA 93094
Tel: 323-786-0340 *Fax:* 323-395-5954
E-mail: contact-p3@p3update.com
Web Site: www.p3update.com
Key Personnel
Publr: James Thompson *E-mail:* jt@p3update.com
Ed: Dyana Carmella
Film, video & digital production digital trade publication.
First published 1985
Frequency: Quarterly
Free
ISSN: 1058-3238

Publishers Weekly
Published by PWxyz LLC
71 W 23 St, Suite 1608, New York, NY 10010
Tel: 212-377-5500 *Fax:* 212-377-2733
Web Site: www.publishersweekly.com
Subscription Address: PO Box 16957, North Hollywood, CA 91615-6957 *Tel:* 818-487-2069
Toll Free Tel: 800-278-2991 *Fax:* 818-487-4550
E-mail: pw@pubservice.com
Key Personnel
Pres: George Slowik, Jr *E-mail:* george@publishersweekly.com
Publr: Cevin Bryerman *Tel:* 212-377-5703
E-mail: cbryerman@publishersweekly.com
Art Dir: Clive Chiu *E-mail:* cchiu@publishersweekly.com
Dir, Digital Opers: Craig Teicher
E-mail: cteicher@publishersweekly.com
Edit Dir: Michael Coffey *E-mail:* mcoffey@publishersweekly.com; Jim Milliot *Tel:* 212-377-5705 *E-mail:* jmilliot@publishersweekly.com
Reviews Dir: Louisa A Ermelino
E-mail: lermelino@publishersweekly.com
Sr Ed: Mark Rotella *E-mail:* mrotella@publishersweekly.com
Sr Ed, Children's Books: Diane Roback
E-mail: roback@publishersweekly.com
Sr Ed, Digital: Jonathan Segura *E-mail:* jsegura@publishersweekly.com
Sr News Ed: Rachel Deahl *E-mail:* rdeahl@publishersweekly.com; Calvin Reid
E-mail: creid@publishersweekly.com

Sr Religion Ed: Lynn Garrett *E-mail:* lgarrett@publishersweekly.com
Sr Reviews Ed: Peter Cannon *E-mail:* pcannon@publishersweekly.com
Deputy Reviews Ed: Mike Harvkey
Ed, PW Select & Audio: Adam Boretz *E-mail:* aboretz@publishersweekly.com
Reviews Ed: Rose Fox *E-mail:* rfox@publishersweekly.com
Sr Writer: Andrew R Albanese *E-mail:* aalbanese@publishersweekly.com
Mktg Mgr: Bryan Kinney *E-mail:* bkinney@publishersweekly.com
News for the book trade including reviews, excerpts, features & statistics.
First published 1872
Frequency: 51 issues/yr
Number of pages: 112
Circulation: 25,302
$249.99/yr print & digital US, $209/yr digital US, $12.50/back issue
ISSN: 0000-0019 (print); 2150-4000 (digital)

Radio Ink
Published by Streamline Publishing Inc
1901 S Congress Ave, Suite 118, Boynton Beach, FL 33426-6549
Tel: 561-655-8778 *Toll Free Tel:* 800-610-5771
Web Site: www.radioink.com
Key Personnel
CEO & Publr: B Eric Rhoads *E-mail:* bericrhoads@gmail.com
EVP, Radio: Deborah Parenti *Tel:* 610-321-0281 *E-mail:* parenti@aol.com
Art Dir: Ken Whitney *E-mail:* kenneth.whitney@gmail.com
Ed-in-Chief: Ed Ryan *E-mail:* edryantheeditor@gmail.com
Mng Ed: Brida Connolly *E-mail:* bridaconnolly@gmail.com
Ad & Mktg Consultant: Jake Russell *E-mail:* jakerussell48@gmail.com
Mktg Consultant: Evelyn Yaus *E-mail:* evelynyaus1@gmail.com
Premier radio management & marketing magazine; includes news, interviews, features, book reviews, illustrations & advertising.
First published 1986
Frequency: 20 issues/yr
$147/yr, $247/2 yrs domestic; $249/yr, $398/2 yrs intl

Radio Magazine
Published by NewBay Media LLC
28 E 28 St, 12th fl, New York, NY 10016
Tel: 212-378-0400 *Fax:* 212-378-0470
Web Site: www.radiomagonline.com
Key Personnel
Ed: Chriss Scherer *Tel:* 212-378-0400 ext 531 *E-mail:* cscherer@radiomagonline.com
Sr Assoc Ed: Erin Shipps *Tel:* 212-378-0400 ext 539 *E-mail:* eshipps@radiomagonline.com
Assoc Publr: Steven Bell *Tel:* 212-378-0400 ext 519 *E-mail:* sbell@radiomagonline.com
Radio technology.
First published 1994
Frequency: Monthly
Circulation: 9,000
$66/yr US, $86/yr CN, $106/yr other, free to qualified personnel
ISSN: 1542-0620
Trim Size: 9 x 10 7/8
Ad Rates: 4-color page $4,738
Ad Closing Date(s): Approximately 2-3 weeks prior to issue month. See media kit for additional info

Rangefinder Magazine
Published by Emerald Expositions Inc
85 Broad St, 20th fl, New York, NY 10004
Tel: 847-763-9546 (subns/cust serv) *Toll Free Tel:* 866-249-6122 (subns/cust serv) *Fax:* 656-654-5813
Web Site: www.rangefinderonline.com
Key Personnel
VP, Emerald Expositions Photo Group: Lauren Wendle *Tel:* 646-654-5811 *E-mail:* lauren.wendle@emeraldexpo.com
Ed-in-Chief: Jacqueline Tobin *Tel:* 646-654-5803 *E-mail:* jacqueline.tobin@emeraldexpo.com
Mng Ed: Jessica Gordon
Sr Tech Ed: Dan Havlik
Contrib Ed: John Rettie
Mktg Dir: Michael Zorich
Prodn Mgr: Gennie Kiuchi
Technical, business & profile features; also several columns & departments geared specifically to professional photographers.
First published 1952
Media Reviewed: Books, New Products, Videotapes
Frequency: Monthly
Circulation: 61,000
$5/issue, free to qualified subscribers
ISSN: 0033-9202
Trim Size: 8 3/8 x 10 7/8
Ad Rates: Full page $8,663, 1/2 page $5,634
Ad Closing Date(s): Approximately 6-7 weeks prior to issue month

Recording
Published by Music Maker Publications Inc
5408 Idylwild Trail, Boulder, CO 80301
Tel: 303-516-9118 *Toll Free Tel:* 800-582-8326 (subns)
E-mail: info@recordingmag.com
Web Site: www.recordingmag.com
Key Personnel
Pres & Publr: Tom Hawley *E-mail:* tom@recordingmag.com
VP & Assoc Publr: Brent Heintz *E-mail:* brent@recordingmag.com
Ed: Lorenz Rychner *E-mail:* lorenz@recordingmag.com
Assoc Ed: Mike Metlay, PhD *E-mail:* mike@recordingmag.com
Recording musicians - geared toward use with music equipment.
First published 1987
Media Reviewed: Recording Equipment
Frequency: Monthly
Number of pages: 112
Circulation: 30,000
$5.95/issue, $19.95/yr US, $5.95/issue CN, $34.95/yr CN & Mexico, $64.95/yr other
ISSN: 1078-8352

The Reel Directory
PO Box 1910, Boyes Hot Springs, CA 95416
Tel: 415-531-9760 *Fax:* 707-581-1725
E-mail: ivisual@aol.com; info@reeldirectory.com
Web Site: www.reeldirectory.com
Key Personnel
Publr: Lynetta Freeman
Art Dir: Keith Marsalis *E-mail:* keith@reeldirectory.com
Dir, Mktg & Promos: Katie Carney *E-mail:* katie@reeldirectory.com
Dir, Sales & Mktg: Ami Zins *E-mail:* ami@reeldirectory.com
Resource guide for film, video & multimedia in Northern California. Also offer iVisual, The Art Dawgs Guide, a supplement printed & distributed along with the Reel Directory.
Frequency: Annual
Number of pages: 680
Circulation: 5,000
$30
Trim Size: 8 1/2 x 11
Ad Rates: B&W page $1,500 ($1,350 if received by Feb 1), 4-color page $2,200 ($2,050 if received by Feb 1)
Ad Closing Date(s): March 15

SB&F, see Science Books & Films

Science Books & Films
Published by American Association for the Advancement of Science
1200 New York Ave NW, Washington, DC 20005
Tel: 202-326-6417 (order); 202-326-6500 (edit ctr) *Toll Free Tel:* 866-434-2227 *Fax:* 202-842-1065 (order); 202-289-7562 (edit ctr)
E-mail: sbfeditors@gmail.com
Web Site: www.aaas.org; www.sbfonline.com
Key Personnel
Ed-in-Chief: Maria Sosa *Tel:* 202-326-6453 *E-mail:* msosa@aaas.org
Online publication including short reviews of books, AV materials & software in all the sciences for all ages; for librarians, media specialists, educators.
First published 1965
Media Reviewed: Books, DVDs, Microcomputer Software
Frequency: Monthly
Circulation: 2,000
$45/yr

Sensible Sound
Published by Sensible Sound Inc
403 Darwin Dr, Snyder, NY 14226
Tel: 716-698-8086
E-mail: texbook@hotmail.com
Key Personnel
Publr & Ed: John A Horan
Music Ed: Karl A Nehring
Audio equipment & music recording reviews, helping audiophiles & music lovers to spend less & get more.
First published 1977
Media Reviewed: Audio Equipment, CDs, DVDs
Frequency: 6 issues/yr
Number of pages: 84
Circulation: 14,300
$7 at newsstand, $29/yr, $54/2 yrs, $78/3 yrs
ISSN: 0199-4654
Trim Size: 7 3/5 x 10 1/2
Ad Rates: B&W page $500, 4-color page $1,000, multiple placement discounts

SHOOT
Published by DCA Business Media LLC
256 Post Rd E, Suite 206, Westport, CT 06880
Tel: 203-227-1699 *Fax:* 203-227-2787
E-mail: info@shootonline.com
Web Site: www.shootonline.com
Key Personnel
Publr & Edit Dir: Roberta Griefer *Tel:* 203-227-1699 ext 13 *E-mail:* rgriefer@shootonline.com
Ed: Robert Goldrich *Tel:* 323-445-6818 *E-mail:* rgoldrich@shootonline.com
Print & online publication for professionals in the commercial production industry.
West Coast Office: 650 N Bronson Ave, Suite B140, Los Angeles, CA 90004. *Tel:* 323-445-6818.
First published 1960
Frequency: 11 issues/yr
Circulation: 28,000
Free for industry personnel, $75/yr US, $115/yr CN, $145/yr other
ISSN: 1055-9825
Trim Size: 9 x 10 7/8
Ad Rates: B&W page $2,500, 4-color page $3,800
Ad Closing Date(s): 7 days prior to issue date

SMPTE Motion Imaging Journal
Published by Society of Motion Picture & Television Engineers (SMPTE)
3 Barker Ave, 5th fl, White Plains, NY 10601
Tel: 914-761-1100 *Fax:* 914-761-3115
E-mail: smptepress@allenpress.com
Web Site: www.smpte.org
Subscription Address: PO Box 7065, Lawrence, KS 66044-7065

Key Personnel
Exec Dir: Barbara Lange *Tel:* 914-205-2370
E-mail: blange@smpte.org
Educ VP: Pat Griffis
Chair, Bd of Eds: Glen Pensinger
Mng Ed: Dianne Purrier *Tel:* 914-205-2377
E-mail: dpurrier@smpte.org
Articles on TV & motion picture technology, computer imaging, multimedia.
First published 1916
Media Reviewed: Technical Books, Television Systems
Frequency: 8 issues/yr
Circulation: 10,500
$165 US & CN, $180 elsewhere
ISSN: 0036-1682
Trim Size: 8 1/8 x 10 7/8
Ad Rates: Full page (8 issues) $3,600, 1/2 page $2,200

Sound & Communications
Published by Testa Communications
25 Willowdale Ave, Port Washington, NY 11050-3779
Tel: 516-767-2500 *Fax:* 516-767-9335 (sales & editorial)
Web Site: www.soundandcommunications.com
Key Personnel
Pres & Publr: Vincent P Testa
Assoc Publr: John Carr *Tel:* 516-767-2500 ext 509 *E-mail:* jcarr@testa.com
Prodn Mgr: Steve Thorakos *E-mail:* sthorakos@testa.com
Ed: David Silverman *Tel:* 516-767-2500 ext 710
E-mail: dsilverman@testa.com
Business, product & technical journal for audio & video display installation contractors, consultants & systems engineers.
First published 1955
Media Reviewed: AV Products (commercial), Books, Engineered Sound Products, Test Equipment
Frequency: Monthly + annual directory
Number of pages: 120
Circulation: 25,500
Free to qualified recipients, $25/yr US, $35/yr CN & Mexico, $65/yr other
ISSN: 0038-1845
Trim Size: 8 1/2 x 10 7/8
Ad Rates: 4-color full page $6,610
Ad Closing Date(s): 14th of the month prior to cover date

Sound & Video Contractor
Published by NewBay Media LLC
28 E 28 St, 12th fl, New York, NY 10016
Tel: 212-378-0400 *Fax:* 212-378-0470
Web Site: www.svconline.com
Key Personnel
EVP & Group Publr: Adam Goldstein
E-mail: agoldstein@nbmedia.com
Mng Ed: Jessaca Gutierrez *Tel:* 212-378-0400 ext 527 *E-mail:* jgutierrez@nbmedia.com
Ed: Cynthia Wisehart *Tel:* 212-378-0400 ext 526
E-mail: cwisehart@nbmedia.com
For professionals, involves various aspects of engineering, contracting, design on construction in the sound & video fields.
First published 1983
Media Reviewed: Books
Frequency: Monthly
Circulation: 22,000
$39/yr US, $59/yr CN, $79/yr other, free to qualified US residents
ISSN: 0741-1715
Trim Size: 9 x 10 7/8
Ad Rates: 4-color page $7,045
Ad Closing Date(s): Approximately 1-2 weeks prior to issue month. See media kit for additional info

Sound & Vision
Published by Source Interlink Media
261 Madison Ave, New York, NY 10006
Toll Free Tel: 800-264-9872 (subn) *Fax:* 212-915-4167
Web Site: www.soundandvisionmag.com; www.circsource.com
Key Personnel
Publr: Keith Pray *Tel:* 212-915-4157
E-mail: keith.pray@sorc.com
Ed: Rob Sarin *E-mail:* rob.sarin@sorc.com
Assoc Ed: Ed DiBenedetto *Tel:* 212-915-4153
E-mail: ed.dibenedetto@sorc.com
Analysis on the latest in cutting edge AV & hands-on guides including HDTV, 3DTV & front projection audio receivers, speakers & sound bars; Blu-ray players & the best new movie software & more.
First published 1958
Media Reviewed: CDs, DVDs
Frequency: 10 issues/yr with Feb/March & July/Aug being combined issues
Circulation: 105,000
$12.97/yr, $22.97/yr CN, $32.97/yr other
ISSN: 1537-5838
Trim Size: 8 1/4 x 10 7/8
Ad Rates: B&W page $13,945, 4-color page $18,360
Ad Closing Date(s): 7 weeks prior to issue date

Strategy
Published by Brunico Communications Ltd
366 Adelaide St W, Suite 100, Toronto, ON M5V 1R9, Canada
Tel: 416-408-2300 *Fax:* 416-408-0870
E-mail: strategycustomercare@brunico.com
Web Site: strategyonline.ca; www.brunico.com
Key Personnel
VP, Publr & Edit Dir: Mary Maddever
E-mail: mmaddever@brunico.com
Online magazine about marketing & advertising in Canada.
First published 1989
Frequency: 10 times/yr
Circulation: 13,152
$6.95/issue; $80/yr, $144/2 yrs CN; $108/yr, $194/2 yrs US; $214/yr, $385/2 yrs other

StudioDaily
Published by Access Intelligence LLC
88 Pine St, Suite 510, New York, NY 10005
Tel: 212-621-4900 *Fax:* 212-621-4635
E-mail: clientservices@accessintel.com
Web Site: www.studiodaily.com
Key Personnel
Ed-in-Chief: Beth Marchant *Tel:* 212-621-4645
E-mail: bmarchant@accessintel.com
SVP & Group Publr: Diane Schwartz *Tel:* 212-621-4964 *E-mail:* dschwartz@accessintel.com
HR & Corp Comm: Mary Fecto *Tel:* 301-354-1550 *E-mail:* mfecto@accessintel.com
Online publication for news, features, tips & techniques, applications, software & equipment reviews of products & services used in the production of video, audio, 3D/animation, digital video & interactive media. Audience includes producers & managers of professional video productions, media managers & independent producers.
First published 1996
Frequency: Online 24/7; part of StudioDaily.com online network of sites
ISSN: 1554-3412

Systems Contractor News
Published by NewBay Media LLC
28 E 28 St, 12th fl, New York, NY 10016
Tel: 212-378-0400 *Fax:* 212-378-0470
Web Site: www.avnetwork.com/scn
Key Personnel
EVP & Group Publr: Adam Goldstein
E-mail: agoldstein@nbmedia.com
Mng Ed: Chuck Ansbacher *Tel:* 212-378-0486
E-mail: cansbacher@nbmedia.com
Ed: Kirsten Nelson *Tel:* 212-378-0400 ext 522
E-mail: knelson@nbmedia.com
Asst Ed: Lindsey Adler *Tel:* 917-281-4713
E-mail: ladler@nbmedia.com
First published 1994
Frequency: Monthly + 2 special issues & 1 product guide
Circulation: 18,000
$59/yr US, $109/yr CN, $169/yr other, free to qualified US residents
ISSN: 1078-4993
Trim Size: 10 3/8 x 14 1/4
Ad Rates: B&W tab $5,400, 4-color tab $6,906; see web site for additional rates
Ad Closing Date(s): Approximately 2-4 weeks prior to cover date

TechTrends: For Leaders in Education & Training
Published by Association for Educational Communications & Technology (AECT)
320 W Eighth St, Suite 101, Bloomington, IN 47404-3745
Tel: 812-335-7675 *Toll Free Tel:* 877-677-AECT (677-2328) *Fax:* 812-335-7678
E-mail: aect@aect.org
Web Site: www.aect.org
Key Personnel
Exec Dir: Phillip Harris *Tel:* 812-335-7675 ext 202 *E-mail:* pharris@aect.org
Ed-in-Chief: Daniel Surry
Designed for educators who use technology to enhance the learning process.
First published 1956
Media Reviewed: Books, CD-ROMs, Computer Hardware, Educational Media, Laser Discs, Software
Frequency: 6 issues/yr
Circulation: 3,000
$20/yr membs
ISSN: 8756-3894 (print); 1559-7075 (electronic)
Trim Size: 8 1/2 x 11
Ad Rates: B&W page $1,300, 4-color page $2,100
Ad Closing Date(s): 15th of month, 2 months prior to publication date

Television y Video
Published by Latin Press
2455 SW 27 Ave, Suite 200, Miami, FL 33145
Tel: 305-285-3133
E-mail: editorial@tvyvideo.com
Web Site: www.tvyvideo.com
Key Personnel
Group Publr, Latin Press: Sebastian Fernandez
Tel: 305-285-3133 ext 71 *E-mail:* sfernandez@tvyvideo.com
Proj Dir, AV/Security Systems: Viviane Torres
E-mail: vtorres@tvyvideo.com
A multimedia publication dedicated to serving the information needs of over 10,000 television industry & video professionals throughout all of Latin America, with BPA-qualified subscribers. Directed to engineering & management in TV stations, cable companies, satellite operators, pre & post-production agencies & other companies engaged in the production or broadcasting of television. Also, features product & industry news & technical articles dealing with all facets of the TV production process. Text in Spanish, Portuguese & English.
First published 1994
Frequency: 6 issues/yr
Circulation: 10,250
ISSN: 0121-9235

TV Guide
Published by CBS Interactive Inc
PO Box 37360, Boone, IA 50099
Tel: 212-852-7500 *Toll Free Tel:* 800-866-1400 (cust serv) *Fax:* 212-852-7323
Web Site: www.tvguidemagazine.com

Key Personnel
CEO: Jack Kliger
Pres & Ed-in-Chief: Debra Birnbaum
Publr: Lori O'Connor *E-mail:* lori.oconnor@tvguidemagazine.com
Ad Dir: Bob Mattone *E-mail:* bob.mattone@tvguidemagazine.com
PR Dir: Jessica Ricci *E-mail:* jessica.ricci@tvguidemagazine.com
Also published online.
First published 1953
Media Reviewed: Books, Films, TV, Video Games
Frequency: Weekly
Circulation: 13,000,000
$3.99 newsstand, $16.50 online (56 issues)
ISSN: 0039-8543
Trim Size: 7 3/8 x 10 1/2
Ad Rates: B&W page $137,800, 4-color page $168,100
Ad Closing Date(s): 18 days prior to issue date

TV Technology
Published by NewBay Media LLC
28 E 28 St, 12th fl, New York, NY 10016
Tel: 212-378-0400 *Fax:* 212-378-0470; 703-852-4582
Web Site: www.tvtechnology.com
Key Personnel
Ed-in-Chief: Tom Butts *Tel:* 703-852-4631 *E-mail:* tbutts@nbmedia.com
Exec Ed: Deborah McAdams *Tel:* 310-498-1587 *E-mail:* dmcadams@nbmedia.com
Technol Ed: James O'Neal *Tel:* 703-852-4632 *E-mail:* joneal@nbmedia.com
Mng Ed: Terry Hanley *Tel:* 703-852-4636 *E-mail:* thanley@nbmedia.com
Hands-on applications oriented tabloid technical trade publication serving the professional video industry.
First published 1983
Media Reviewed: Publications
Frequency: 26 issues/yr
Circulation: 30,000
$39.95/yr, $74.95/2 yrs US; $125/yr, $250/2 yrs foreign; free to qualified US residents
ISSN: 0887-1701
Trim Size: 10 5/8 x 13
Ad Rates: 4-color tabloid page $7,555, standard page $6,800
Ad Closing Date(s): 26 days prior ti issue date

2.5-4G Newsletter
Published by Information Gatekeepers Inc
1340 Soldiers Field Rd, Suite 2, Boston, MA 02135
Tel: 617-782-5033 *Fax:* 617-507-8338
E-mail: info@igigroup.com
Web Site: www.igigroup.com
Key Personnel
CEO & Pres: Paul Polishuk, PhD
Ed-in-Chief & Chief Analyst: Dr Hui Pan *E-mail:* hpan@igigroup.com
Technology, markets & industry activities.
Frequency: Monthly
Circulation: 1,000
$695/yr US & CN, $745/yr other (PDF, 1 user)
ISSN: 1058-6725
Trim Size: 8 1/2 x 11

Variety
Published by Penske Media Group
Subsidiary of Penske Business Media
5900 Wilshire Blvd, Suite 3100, Los Angeles, CA 90036
Tel: 323-617-9100
E-mail: news@variety.com; community@variety.com
Web Site: www.variety.com
Key Personnel
Founder, Chmn & CEO: Jay Penske
VP & Exec Dir: Steven Gaydos
VP & Mng Ed: Kirstin Wilder
Publr: Michelle Sobrino-Sterns
Ed-at-Large: Peter Bart
Ed-in-Chief, Digital: Andrew Wallenstein
Ed-in-Chief, Film: Claudia Eller
Ed-in-Chief, Television: Cynthia Littleton
Awards Ed: Timothy M Gray
Business to business publication for the entertainment industry.
First published 1905
Media Reviewed: Concerts, Films, Music, Nightclubs, TV, Videotapes
Frequency: 48 issues/yr
Circulation: 60,000
$199/yr, $339/2 yrs, $449/3 yrs
ISSN: 0042-2738
Trim Size: 10 1/2 x 13 1/2
Ad Closing Date(s): 6 days prior to issue

Video Age International
Published by TV Trade Media Inc
216 E 75 St, Suite PW, New York, NY 10021
Tel: 212-288-3933 *Fax:* 212-288-3424
E-mail: admin@videoageinternational.com
Web Site: www.videoageinternational.com
Key Personnel
Publr: Dom Serafini *E-mail:* dsvideoag@aol.com
Ed & Mktg Supv: Monica Gorghetto
First published 1981
Media Reviewed: Books, Films, Satellite, TV
Frequency: 7 issues/yr
Circulation: 12,000
$5.50/issue, $30/yr US & CN, $45/yr other
ISSN: 0278-5013
Trim Size: 10.63 x 14.173
Ad Rates: B&W or 4-color page $3,500

Video Librarian
3435 NE Nine Boulder Dr, Poulsbo, WA 98370
Tel: 360-626-1259 *Toll Free Tel:* 800-265-7965 (adv); 800-692-2270 (subns) *Fax:* 360-626-1260
E-mail: vidlib@videolibrarian.com
Web Site: www.videolibrarian.com
Key Personnel
Publr & Ed: Randy Pitman
Assoc Ed: Jazza Williams-Wood *E-mail:* jazza@videolibrarian.com
Mktg Dir: Anne Williams *E-mail:* anne@videolibrarian.com
Over 200 reviews per issue of special-interest, documentary & theatrical video releases, as well as product announcements & video news.
First published 1986
Media Reviewed: DVDs, Videotapes
Frequency: 6 issues/yr
Circulation: 2,000
$11/issue, $64/yr domestic, $69/yr CN, $86/yr elsewhere (print only), $99/yr domestic, $104/yr CN, $121/yr elsewhere (print & online)
ISSN: 0887-6851
Trim Size: 8 1/2 x 11
Ad Rates: B&W full page $950, 4-color full page $1,300
Ad Closing Date(s): Approximately 1 month prior to publication

Video Watchdog
PO Box 5283, Cincinnati, OH 45205-0283
Tel: 513-297-1855 *Fax:* 206-333-1405
E-mail: orders@videowatchdog.com
Web Site: www.videowatchdog.com
Key Personnel
Publr: Donna Lucas
Ed: Tim Lucas *E-mail:* tim@videowatchdog.com
The original ultimate monthly review of horror, sci-fi & cult films on DVD, with serious in-depth reviews & articles on domestic & import releases by the best writers in the field. All-new, all-color format.
First published 1990
Media Reviewed: Books, CDs, DVDs
Frequency: 6 issues/yr
Number of pages: 80
Circulation: 10,000
$8.95/copy, $54/yr US, $76/yr outside US
ISSN: 1070-9991
Trim Size: 6 x 8 1/4
Ad Rates: Call
Ad Closing Date(s): Call for schedule

Videomaker
Published by York Publishing
1350 E Ninth St, Chico, CA 95928-5932
Mailing Address: PO Box 4591, Chico, CA 95927-4591
Tel: 530-891-8410 *Toll Free Tel:* 800-284-3226 *Fax:* 530-891-8443
E-mail: customerservice@videomaker.com
Web Site: www.videomaker.com
Subscription Address: PO Box 3780, Chico, CA 95927
Key Personnel
Publr: Matt York *E-mail:* myork@videomaker.com
Exec Ed: Mike Wilhelm *E-mail:* mwilhelm@videomaker.com
Mng Ed: Jennifer O'Rourke *E-mail:* jorourke@videomaker.com
Assoc Tech Ed: Jackson Wong *E-mail:* jwong@videomaker.com
Coverage of video production tools, tips & techniques information for hobbyists & professionals involved with video production as a hobby, in business, or in education; "how to" source for video production products & services, trends & potentials. Includes thorough coverage of computer-based video editing systems. No unsol mss, query first.
First published 1985
Media Reviewed: Books (video production related only), DVDs (video production related only)
Frequency: Monthly
Number of pages: 64
Circulation: 60,060 paid
$5.99/issue, $19.97/yr
ISSN: 0889-4973
Trim Size: 7 3/4 x 10 1/2
Ad Rates: B&W page $5,568, 4-color page $7,072 (1x rates)
Ad Closing Date(s): Reserve space Wednesday of 2nd week of month, material due following Friday 3 months in advance of cover date

Weekly Variety, see Variety

Wireless Lan
Published by Information Gatekeepers Inc
1340 Soldiers Field Rd, Suite 2, Boston, MA 02135
Tel: 617-782-5033 *Fax:* 617-507-8338
E-mail: info@igigroup.com
Web Site: www.igigroup.com
Key Personnel
CEO & Pres: Paul Polishuk, PhD
Ed-in-Chief & Chief Analyst: Dr Hui Pan *E-mail:* hpan@igigroup.com
Technology, market trends & international developments.
First published 1991
Frequency: Monthly
$695/yr US & CN, $745/yr other print, $695/yr PDF (1 user)
ISSN: 1057-5391

Wireless Satellite & Broadcasting
Published by Information Gatekeepers Inc
1340 Soldiers Field Rd, Suite 2, Boston, MA 02135
Tel: 617-782-5033 *Fax:* 617-507-8338
E-mail: info@igigroup.com
Web Site: www.igigroup.com
Key Personnel
CEO & Pres: Paul Polishuk, PhD

Ed-in-Chief & Chief Analyst: Dr Hui Pan
E-mail: hpan@igigroup.com
Markets, technology, applications, standard regulatory & systematical.
First published 1991
Frequency: Monthly
Circulation: 1,000
$695/yr US & CN, $745/yr other print, $695 PDF (1 user)
ISSN: 1058-6695
Trim Size: 8 1/2 x 11

Reference Books for the Trade

The books listed below represent a selected list of major audio visual reference materials that deal with such topics as AV production techniques, multimedia education and AV hardware, software and review sources.

Advanced Techniques in Multimedia Watermarking: Image, Video and Audio Applications
Published by IGI Global
701 E Chocolate Ave, Hershey, PA 17033-1240
Tel: 717-533-8845 (ext 100) *Toll Free Tel:* 866-342-6657 *Fax:* 717-533-8661
E-mail: cust@igi-global.com
Web Site: www.igi-global.com
Covers new advancements in digital image watermarking to prevent illegal & malicious copying & distribution of digital media.
2010: 566 pp, $180
ISBN(s): 978-1-61520-903-3; 978-1-61520-904-0 (ebook)

Announcing: Broadcast Communicating Today
Published by Wadsworth Publishing Group
Division of Cengage Learning™
20 Davis Dr, Belmont, CA 94002
Tel: 650-595-2350 *Toll Free Tel:* 800-354-9706 *Fax:* 650-592-3022 *Toll Free Fax:* 800-487-8488
E-mail: esales@cengage.com
Web Site: www.cengage.com/highered; www.cengage.com
Key Personnel
Author: Philip Benoit; Carl Hausman; Frank Messere; Lewis B O'Donnell
Coord, Prof Sales: Joyce Leibach *Tel:* 518-348-2556 *E-mail:* joyce.leibach@cengage.com
Focuses on the role of announcer as communicator, offering principles & techniques for communicating effectively in all types of broadcast situations.
5th ed, 2004: 480 pp, $206.99 casebound
Shipping Address: 10650 Toebben Dr, Independence, KY 41051 *Tel:* 859-525-2230 *Toll Free Tel:* 800-544-0550 *Fax:* 859-282-5700; 859-647-4599 *E-mail:* claimscs@cengage.com
ISBN(s): 978-0-534-56310-3

Art of Digital Audio
Published by Focal Press
7625 Empire Dr, Florence, KY 41042
Toll Free Tel: 800-634-7064 *Toll Free Fax:* 800-248-4724
E-mail: orders@taylorandfrancis.com
Web Site: www.focalpress.com
Key Personnel
Author: John Watkinson
Basic concepts, theory, advanced topics & practical implementation of digital audio.
3rd ed, Dec 2000; ebook April 2013: 752 pp, $136
ISBN(s): 978-0-080-49936-9 (ebook); 978-0-240-51587-8 (hardcover)

ASMP Professional Business Practices in Photography
Published by American Society of Media Photographers Inc (ASMP)
150 N Second St, Philadelphia, PA 19016
Tel: 215-451-2767 *Fax:* 215-451-0880
E-mail: info@asmp.org
Web Site: www.asmp.org
Key Personnel
Gen Mgr: Elena Goertz *Tel:* 215-451-2767 ext 203 *E-mail:* goertz@asmp.org
Contains more than 400 pages on subjects ranging from assignment, stock, pricing & estimating, negotiating fees & agreements, rights & value in traditional & electronic media, formalizing agreements (with a range of forms & appropriate language for terms & conditions), releases, copyright, electronic technology, business & marketing strategies, book publishing & professional services. Also includes a comprehensive bibliography of software, web sites, directories & professional organizations which can help photographers.
7th ed, 2008: 400 pp, $35 nonmembs
ISBN(s): 978-1-58115-497-9

Audio in Media
Published by Wadsworth Publishing Group
Division of Cengage Learning™
20 Davis Dr, Belmont, CA 94002
Tel: 650-595-2350 *Toll Free Tel:* 800-354-9706 *Fax:* 650-592-3022 *Toll Free Fax:* 800-487-8488
E-mail: esales@cengage.com
Web Site: www.cengage.com/highered; www.cengage.com
Key Personnel
Author: Stanley R Alten
Coord, Prof Sales: Joyce Leibach *Tel:* 518-348-2556 *E-mail:* joyce.leibach@cengage.com
Broad practical approach to audio in various media; emphasis on principles & generic equipment, covering basic theory & aesthetics; organization based preproduction, production, postproduction process. Also available as ebook.
Triennial.
10th ed, 2014: 624 pp, $202.99 hardcover
Shipping Address: 10650 Toebben Dr, Independence, KY 41051 *Tel:* 859-525-2230 *Toll Free Tel:* 800-544-0550 *Fax:* 859-282-5700; 859-647-4599 *E-mail:* claimscs@cengage.com
ISBN(s): 978-1-133-30723-5

Audio Post-Production for Television & Film: An Introduction to Technology & Techniques
Published by Focal Press
7625 Empire Dr, Florence, KY 41042
Toll Free Tel: 800-634-7064 *Toll Free Fax:* 800-248-4724
E-mail: orders@taylorandfrancis.com
Web Site: www.focalpress.com
Key Personnel
Author: Tim Amyes; Hilary Wyatt
Provides a thorough overview of audio post-production theory & technique.
3rd ed, Oct 2004; ebook July 2013: 304 pp, $49.95
ISBN(s): 978-0-080-47045-0 (ebook); 978-0-240-51947-0 (paper)

Audio-Tutorial System
Published by Educational Technology Publications Inc
700 Palisade Ave, Englewood Cliffs, NJ 07632-0564
Tel: 201-871-4007 *Toll Free Tel:* 800-952-2665 (orders) *Fax:* 201-871-4009
E-mail: edtecpubs@aol.com
Web Site: bookstoread.com/etp
Key Personnel
Pres & Ed: Lawrence Lipsitz
Author: James D Russell
Ed: Danny G Langdon
Vol 3 in the Instructional Design Library series.
1978: 80 pp, $27.95
ISBN(s): 978-0-87778-107-3

Audio-Visual Aid Technician
Published by National Learning Corp
212 Michael Dr, Syosset, NY 11791
Tel: 516-921-8888 *Toll Free Tel:* 800-645-6337 (outside NY); 800-632-8888 *Fax:* 516-921-8743
E-mail: info@passbooks.com
Web Site: www.passbooks.com
Key Personnel
Author: Jack Rudman
Study guide.
2012, $34.95 paper, $54.95 hardcover
ISBN(s): 978-0-8373-0058-0

Audio-Visual Aide
Published by National Learning Corp
212 Michael Dr, Syosset, NY 11791
Tel: 516-921-8888 *Toll Free Tel:* 800-645-6337 (outside NY); 800-632-8888 *Fax:* 516-921-8743
E-mail: info@passbooks.com
Web Site: www.passbooks.com
Key Personnel
Author: Jack Rudman
Study guide.
2000, $29.95 paper, $49.95 hardcover
ISBN(s): 978-0-8373-2903-1

Audio-Visual Programs Specialist
Published by National Learning Corp
212 Michael Dr, Syosset, NY 11791
Tel: 516-921-8888 *Toll Free Tel:* 800-645-6337 (outside NY); 800-632-8888 *Fax:* 516-921-8743
E-mail: info@passbooks.com
Web Site: www.passbooks.com
Key Personnel
Author: Jack Rudman
Study guide.
2011, $34.95 paper, $54.95 hardcover
ISBN(s): 978-0-8373-3209-3

Audio-Visual Specialist
Published by National Learning Corp
212 Michael Dr, Syosset, NY 11791
Tel: 516-921-8888 *Toll Free Tel:* 800-645-6337 (outside NY); 800-632-8888 *Fax:* 516-921-8743
E-mail: info@passbooks.com
Web Site: www.passbooks.com
Key Personnel
Author: Jack Rudman
Study guide.
2009, $34.95 paper, $54.95 hardcover
ISBN(s): 978-0-8373-1826-4

Audio-Visual Technician
Published by National Learning Corp
212 Michael Dr, Syosset, NY 11791
Tel: 516-921-8888 *Toll Free Tel:* 800-645-6337 (outside NY); 800-632-8888 *Fax:* 516-921-8743
E-mail: info@passbooks.com
Web Site: www.passbooks.com
Key Personnel
Author: Jack Rudman

Study guide.
2004, $34.95 paper, $54.95 hardcover
ISBN(s): 978-0-8373-1894-3

Audio-Visual Training Modules
Published by Educational Technology Publications Inc
700 Palisade Ave, Englewood Cliffs, NJ 07632-0564
Tel: 201-871-4007 *Toll Free Tel:* 800-952-2665 (orders) *Fax:* 201-871-4009
E-mail: edtecpubs@aol.com
Web Site: bookstoread.com/etp
Key Personnel
Pres & Ed: Lawrence Lipsitz
Author: Harold D Stolovitch
Ed: Danny G Langdon
Vol 4 in the Instructional Design Library series.
1978: 104 pp, $27.95
ISBN(s): 978-0-87778-108-0

Audio-Workbook
Published by Educational Technology Publications Inc
700 Palisade Ave, Englewood Cliffs, NJ 07632-0564
Tel: 201-871-4007 *Toll Free Tel:* 800-952-2665 (orders) *Fax:* 201-871-4009
E-mail: edtecpubs@aol.com
Web Site: bookstoread.com/etp
Key Personnel
Pres & Ed: Lawrence Lipsitz
Ed & Author: Danny G Langdon
Vol 5 in the Instructional Design Library series.
1978: 80 pp, $27.95
ISBN(s): 978-0-87778-109-7

AV Market Place (AVMP)
Published by Information Today, Inc
630 Central Ave, New Providence, NJ 07974
Toll Free Tel: 800-409-4929; 800-300-9868 (cust serv) *Fax:* 908-219-0192
E-mail: custserv@infotoday.com
Web Site: www.infotoday.com
A complete directory of the AV Market, listing the activities of almost 5,100 manufacturers, distributors & production service companies. Heavily indexed. Also contains information on related associations, state & local film & TV commissions, awards & festivals, periodicals, reference books & AV oriented conferences & exhibits.
Annual (Feb).
43rd ed, 2015: 1,450 pp, $329.50 paper
ISBN(s): 978-1-57387-502-8

The Avid Handbook: Advanced Techniques, Strategies & Survival Information for Avid Editing Systems
Published by Focal Press
7625 Empire Dr, Florence, KY 41042
Toll Free Tel: 800-634-7064 *Toll Free Fax:* 800-248-4724
E-mail: orders@taylorandfrancis.com
Web Site: www.focalpress.com
Key Personnel
Author: Steve Bayes; Greg Staten
5th ed, Sept 2009: 368 pp, $49.95 paper
ISBN(s): 978-0-240-81081-2

Bacon's Radio/TV/Cable Directory, see Cision Media Database

Basics of Video Lighting
Published by Focal Press
7625 Empire Dr, Florence, KY 41042
Toll Free Tel: 800-634-7064 *Toll Free Fax:* 800-248-4724
E-mail: orders@taylorandfrancis.com
Web Site: www.focalpress.com
Key Personnel
Author: Des Lyver; Graham Swainson
What you need to know about the planning, selecting & positioning of lights. Covers the fundamentals of lighting, including comprehensive details on various types of equipment.
2nd ed, May 1999; ebook Dec 2012: 149 pp, $35.95
ISBN(s): 978-0-080-49992-5 (ebook); 978-0-240-51559-5 (paper)

Basics of Video Production Diary
Published by Focal Press
7625 Empire Dr, Florence, KY 41042
Toll Free Tel: 800-634-7064 *Toll Free Fax:* 800-248-4724
E-mail: orders@taylorandfrancis.com
Web Site: www.focalpress.com
Key Personnel
Author: Des Lyver; Graham Swainson
July 2001; ebook Jan 2013: 224 pp, $37.95
ISBN(s): 978-0-080-49052-6 (ebook); 978-0-240-51658-5 (paper)

Bowker's Complete Video Directory™
Published by Grey House Publishing Inc™
2 University Plaza, Suite 310, Hackensack, NJ 07601
SAN: 208-838X
Mailing Address: PO Box 56, Amenia, NY 12501-0056
Tel: 518-789-8700 *Toll Free Tel:* 800-562-2139 *Fax:* 518-789-0556
E-mail: books@greyhouse.com
Web Site: www.greyhouse.com
Key Personnel
Edit Dir: Laura Mars *E-mail:* lmars@greyhouse.com
Vols 1 & 2 (Entertainment) offer descriptive listings for feature films, other performing arts & entertainment events. Contains more than 73,000 entries in an Awards index & as well as a Genre index covering up to 364 entertainment genres. Cast/director, Spanish Language, Laser Videodisc & Closed Captioned indexes are also provided.
Vols 3 & 4 (Education/Special Interest) offer information on more than 186,000 educational & special interest videos. Complete information for documentaries, religion & other videos directed towards specialized audiences. A Subject index covers over 500 categories as diverse as anthropology, word processing & yoga. Manufacturers & Distributors name indexes save time in the ordering process.
Annual.
2015: 7,900 pp, $720/4 vol set
ISBN(s): 978-1-61925-631-6 (4 vol set)

Broadband & Cable Industry Law
Published by Practising Law Institute
1177 Avenue of the Americas, 2nd fl, New York, NY 10036
Tel: 212-824-5700 *Toll Free Tel:* 800-260-4PLI (260-4754, cust serv) *Toll Free Fax:* 800-321-0093 (cust serv)
E-mail: info@pli.edu (cust serv); media@pli.edu (press requests)
Web Site: www.pli.edu
Key Personnel
VP, Publg: William C Cubberley
Course handbook.
Annual.
2014: 1,767 pp, $240/2 vol set
ISBN(s): 978-1-4024-2148-8 (2 vol set)

The Broadcast Century & Beyond: A Biography of American Broadcasting
Published by Focal Press
7625 Empire Dr, Florence, KY 41042
Toll Free Tel: 800-634-7064 *Toll Free Fax:* 800-248-4724
E-mail: orders@taylorandfrancis.com
Web Site: www.focalpress.com
Key Personnel
Author: Robert L Hilliard; Michael C Keith
The story of broadcasting told in a direct & informal style, blending personal insight & authoritative scholarship to fully capture the many facets of this dynamic industry.
5th ed, March 2010: 377 pp, $59.95 paper
ISBN(s): 978-0-240-81236-6

The Broadcast Communications Dictionary
Published by ABC-CLIO
130 Cremona Dr, Santa Barbara, CA 93117
Mailing Address: PO Box 1911, Santa Barbara, CA 93116-1911
Tel: 805-968-1911 *Toll Free Tel:* 800-368-6868 *Fax:* 805-685-9685 *Toll Free Fax:* 866-270-3856
E-mail: customerservice@abc-clio.com
Web Site: www.abc-clio.com
Key Personnel
Author: Lincoln Diamant
Digital Prods & Natl Accts: Joyce Fryer *Tel:* 805-968-1911 ext 154
Dictionary of technical, common & slang language used in the field of broadcasting.
Printed on demand.
3rd ed, 1989: 266 pp, $76.95
ISBN(s): 978-0-313-26502-0

CAI Author-Instructor: An Introduction and Guide to the Independent Preparation of Computer-Assisted Instruction Materials
Published by Educational Technology Publications Inc
700 Palisade Ave, Englewood Cliffs, NJ 07632-0564
Tel: 201-871-4007 *Toll Free Tel:* 800-952-2665 (orders) *Fax:* 201-871-4009
E-mail: edtecpubs@aol.com
Web Site: bookstoread.com/etp
Key Personnel
Pres & Ed: Lawrence Lipsitz
Author: Joseph C Meredith
How to design instruction programs for the computer.
1971: 144 pp, $29.95
ISBN(s): 978-0-87778-014-4

Career Opportunities in the Film Industry
Published by Ferguson Publishing
Division of Infobase Learning
132 W 31 St, 17th fl, New York, NY 10001
Tel: 212-967-8800 *Toll Free Tel:* 800-322-8755 *Toll Free Fax:* 800-678-3633
E-mail: custserv@factsonfile.com
Web Site: www.infobasepublishing.com
Key Personnel
Author: Fred Yager; Jan Yager
Edit Dir, Facts on File: Laurie Likoff
A complete guide to career opportunities in the film industry. Includes career profiles & career ladders for more than 80 specific job titles in areas of development, financing, cinematography, sound, editing, casting, distribution & marketing. Also contains listings of degree & non-degree programs, unions, associations & important publications.
2nd ed: 296 pp, $49.50 hardcover
ISBN(s): 978-0-8160-7352-8; 978-1-4381-2064-5 (ebook)

Cataloging Sound Recordings: A Manual With Examples
Published by Routledge/Taylor & Francis
Member of Taylor & Francis Group
711 Third Ave, 8th fl, New York, NY 10017
SAN: 213-196X
Tel: 212-216-7800 *Fax:* 212-564-7854
Web Site: www.routledge.com; www.taylorandfrancis.com

Key Personnel
Author: Deanne Holzberlein; Ruth C Carter
A manual that takes the chore out of cataloging sound recordings. The author clarifies the AACR2 rules in the thought process used in cataloging a sound recording. All the examples of catalog cards presented range from 20th century music to spoken records & compact discs. The appendixes include order & content of cataloging notes, order of parts in a uniform title, a glossary of musical terms & acronyms, a list of basic reference books & thematic indexes, a complete set of catalog cards & the Library of Congress rule interpretations for sound recordings.
1st ed, 1988: 300 pp, $125 hardcover
ISBN(s): 978-0-86656-790-9

Cision Media Database
Published by Cision US Inc
Division of Cision
332 S Michigan Ave, Suite 900, Chicago, IL 60604
Tel: 312-922-2400 *Toll Free Tel:* 877-922-2400; 866-639-5087 *Fax:* 312-922-3127 *Toll Free Fax:* 800-922-2477
E-mail: info.us@cision.com
Web Site: www.cision.com
Database containing traditional & social media contacts. Inquire about pricing & subscription options through web site.

Collection Development Policies & Procedures
Published by ABC-CLIO
130 Cremona Dr, Santa Barbara, CA 93117
Mailing Address: PO Box 1911, Santa Barbara, CA 93116-1911
Tel: 805-968-1911 *Toll Free Tel:* 800-368-6868 *Fax:* 805-685-9685 *Toll Free Fax:* 866-270-3856
E-mail: customerservice@abc-clio.com
Web Site: www.abc-clio.com
Key Personnel
Author: Elizabeth Futas
Digital Prods & Natl Accts: Joyce Fryer *Tel:* 805-968-1911 ext 154
Printed on demand.
3rd ed, 1994: 360 pp, $57.95
ISBN(s): 978-0-89774-797-4

Communication Technology Update & Fundamentals
Published by Focal Press
7625 Empire Dr, Florence, KY 41042
Toll Free Tel: 800-634-7064 *Toll Free Fax:* 800-248-4724
E-mail: orders@taylorandfrancis.com
Web Site: www.focalpress.com
Key Personnel
Ed: August E Grant; Jennifer H Meadows
Latest developments, trends & issues in communication technology. Has become an indispensable information resource for business, government & academia. As always, every chapter has been completely rewritten to reflect the latest developments & market statistics. Also available as ebook.
14th ed, 2014: 326 pp, $49.95 paper
ISBN(s): 978-0-415-73295-6

Communications Law in the Digital Age
Published by Practising Law Institute
1177 Avenue of the Americas, 2nd fl, New York, NY 10036
Tel: 212-824-5700 *Toll Free Tel:* 800-260-4PLI (260-4754, cust serv) *Toll Free Fax:* 800-321-0093 (cust serv)
E-mail: info@pli.edu (cust serv); media@pli.edu (press requests)
Web Site: www.pli.edu
Key Personnel
Dir, Publg, Technol & Prodn: James E Gaskin
Course handbook.
Annual.
2014: 3,378 pp, $330/3 vol set
ISBN(s): 978-1-4024-2331-4

Computer-Based Integrated Learning Systems
Published by Educational Technology Publications Inc
700 Palisade Ave, Englewood Cliffs, NJ 07632-0564
Tel: 201-871-4007 *Toll Free Tel:* 800-952-2665 (orders) *Fax:* 201-871-4009
E-mail: edtecpubs@aol.com
Web Site: bookstoread.com/etp
Key Personnel
Pres & Ed: Lawrence Lipsitz
Ed: Gerald D Bailey
1993: 184 pp, $34.95
ISBN(s): 978-0-87778-256-8

Computer Managed Instruction: Theory and Practice
Published by Educational Technology Publications Inc
700 Palisade Ave, Englewood Cliffs, NJ 07632-0564
Tel: 201-871-4007 *Toll Free Tel:* 800-952-2665 (orders) *Fax:* 201-871-4009
E-mail: edtecpubs@aol.com
Web Site: bookstoread.com/etp
Key Personnel
Pres & Ed: Lawrence Lipsitz
Author: Frank B Baker
Describes & shows detailed examples of how to manage instruction using a computer.
1978: 440 pp, $44.95
ISBN(s): 978-0-87778-099-1

Copywriting for the Electronic Media: A Practical Guide
Published by Wadsworth Publishing Group
Division of Cengage Learning™
20 Davis Dr, Belmont, CA 94002
Tel: 650-595-2350 *Toll Free Tel:* 800-354-9706 *Fax:* 650-592-3022 *Toll Free Fax:* 800-487-8488
E-mail: esales@cengage.com
Web Site: www.cengage.com/highered; www.cengage.com
Key Personnel
Author: Milan D Meeske
Coord, Prof Sales: Joyce Leibach *Tel:* 518-348-2556 *E-mail:* joyce.leibach@cengage.com
Offers basic principles & techniques for writing effective commercials for radio, television & cable.
6th ed, 2009: 336 pp, $165.49 paper
Shipping Address: 10650 Toebben Dr, Independence, KY 41051 *Tel:* 859-525-2230 *Toll Free Tel:* 800-544-0550 *Fax:* 859-282-5700; 859-647-4599 *E-mail:* claimscs@cengage.com
ISBN(s): 978-0-495-41117-8

Counseling Clients in the Entertainment Industry
Published by Practising Law Institute
1177 Avenue of the Americas, 2nd fl, New York, NY 10036
Tel: 212-824-5700 *Toll Free Tel:* 800-260-4PLI (260-4754, cust serv) *Toll Free Fax:* 800-321-0093 (cust serv)
E-mail: info@pli.edu (cust serv); media@pli.edu (press requests)
Web Site: www.pli.edu
Key Personnel
VP, Publg: William C Cubberley
Course handbook.
Annual.
2014: 2,292 pp, $240/2 vol set
ISBN(s): 978-1-4024-2174-7

Creating Special Effects for TV & Video
Published by Focal Press
7625 Empire Dr, Florence, KY 41042
Toll Free Tel: 800-634-7064 *Toll Free Fax:* 800-248-4724
E-mail: orders@taylorandfrancis.com
Web Site: www.focalpress.com
Key Personnel
Author: Bernard Wilkie
3rd ed, Nov 1996: 224 pp, $54.95 paper
ISBN(s): 978-0-240-51474-1

Criteria for the Selection and Use of Visuals for Instruction
Published by Educational Technology Publications Inc
700 Palisade Ave, Englewood Cliffs, NJ 07632-0564
Tel: 201-871-4007 *Toll Free Tel:* 800-952-2665 (orders) *Fax:* 201-871-4009
E-mail: edtecpubs@aol.com
Web Site: bookstoread.com/etp
Key Personnel
Pres & Ed: Lawrence Lipsitz
Author: George L Gropper
How to select visuals to achieve specific instructional objectives. Includes workbook.
1971: 971 pp, $59.95 paper
ISBN(s): 978-0-87778-021-2

Digital Audio Technology: A Guide to CD, MiniDisc, SACD, DVD(A), MP3 & DAT
Published by Focal Press
7625 Empire Dr, Florence, KY 41042
Toll Free Tel: 800-634-7064 *Toll Free Fax:* 800-248-4724
E-mail: orders@taylorandfrancis.com
Web Site: www.focalpress.com
Key Personnel
Ed: Jan Maes; Marc Vercammen
An expert team from SONY Europe explains the technology behind today's major digital audio consumer products, including the Compact Disc, MiniDisc Super Audio CD, DVD-Audio, MP3 & Digital Audio Tape.
4th ed, Oct 2001: 360 pp, $84.95
ISBN(s): 978-0-080-49453-1 (ebook); 978-0-240-51654-7 (hardcover)

Digital AudioCraft: An Introduction to the Tools & Techniques of Digital Audio Production
Published by The National Federation of Community Broadcasters (NFCB)
2751 Hennepin Ave S, Unit 41, Minneapolis, MN 55408
Tel: 612-998-9619
E-mail: officemanager@nfcb.org
Web Site: www.nfcb.org
Key Personnel
Author: Mike Freitas; Gregg McVicar; Randy Thom
Basic concepts of sound to full scale documentaries & concert recordings. Covers all aspects of digital production. Includes CD-ROM.
2nd ed: 200 pp, $40 membs, $55 nonmembs, plus shipping & handling
ISBN(s): 978-0-941209-02-4

Digital Moviemaking
Published by Wadsworth Publishing Group
Division of Cengage Learning™
20 Davis Dr, Belmont, CA 94002
Tel: 650-595-2350 *Toll Free Tel:* 800-354-9706 *Fax:* 650-592-3022 *Toll Free Fax:* 800-487-8488
E-mail: esales@cengage.com
Web Site: www.cengage.com/highered; www.cengage.com
Key Personnel
Author: Lynne S Gross
Coord, Prof Sales: Joyce Leibach *Tel:* 518-348-2556 *E-mail:* joyce.leibach@cengage.com

Emphasizes use of single-camera video equipment, in conjunction with traditional film techniques, to produce narratives & documentaries.
7th ed, 2009: 304 pp, $171.49 paper
Shipping Address: 10650 Toebben Dr, Independence, KY 41051 *Tel:* 859-525-2230 *Toll Free Tel:* 800-544-0550 *Fax:* 859-282-5700; 859-647-4599 *E-mail:* claimscs@cengage.com
ISBN(s): 978-0-495-57050-9

Digital TV Over Broadband: Harvesting Bandwith
Published by Focal Press
7625 Empire Dr, Florence, KY 41042
Toll Free Tel: 800-634-7064 *Toll Free Fax:* 800-248-4724
E-mail: orders@taylorandfrancis.com
Web Site: www.focalpress.com
Key Personnel
Author: Joan Van Tassel
2nd ed, Jan 2001: 608 pp, $75.95 paper
ISBN(s): 978-0-240-80357-9

Directing the Documentary
Published by Focal Press
7625 Empire Dr, Florence, KY 41042
Toll Free Tel: 800-634-7064 *Toll Free Fax:* 800-248-4724
E-mail: orders@taylorandfrancis.com
Web Site: www.focalpress.com
Key Personnel
Author: Michael Rabiger
Definitive guide to making a documentary.
6th ed, Aug 2014: 672 pp, $49.95 paper
ISBN(s): 978-0-451-71930-8

Educational Computing: Principals and Applications
Published by Educational Technology Publications Inc
700 Palisade Ave, Englewood Cliffs, NJ 07632-0564
Tel: 201-871-4007 *Toll Free Tel:* 800-952-2665 (orders) *Fax:* 201-871-4009
E-mail: edtecpubs@aol.com
Web Site: bookstoread.com/etp
Key Personnel
Pres & Ed: Lawrence Lipsitz
Author: Reza Azarmsa
1991: 230 pp, $24.95 paper
ISBN(s): 978-0-87778-222-3

Educational Media and Technology Yearbook
Published by Libraries Unlimited
130 Cremona Dr, Santa Barbara, CA 93117
Mailing Address: PO Box 1911, Santa Barbara, CA 93116-1911
Tel: 805-968-1911 *Toll Free Tel:* 800-368-6868 *Toll Free Fax:* 866-270-3856
E-mail: orders@abc-clio.com; customerservice@abc-clio.com
Web Site: www.abc-clio.com
Up-to-date source of significant information about educational media & instructional technology.
Vol 33, April 2008: 368 pp, $80 hardcover
ISBN(s): 978-0-313-36374-0 (ebook); 978-1-59158-647-0

Educational Technology: Leadership Perspectives
Published by Educational Technology Publications Inc
700 Palisade Ave, Englewood Cliffs, NJ 07632-0564
Tel: 201-871-4007 *Toll Free Tel:* 800-952-2665 (orders) *Fax:* 201-871-4009
E-mail: edtecpubs@aol.com
Web Site: bookstoread.com/etp
Key Personnel
Pres & Ed: Lawrence Lipsitz
Ed: Greg Kearsley; William Lynch
1994: 218 pp, $34.95 cloth
ISBN(s): 978-0-87778-265-0

Educational Technology Telecommunications Dictionary with Acronyms
Published by Educational Technology Publications Inc
700 Palisade Ave, Englewood Cliffs, NJ 07632-0564
Tel: 201-871-4007 *Toll Free Tel:* 800-952-2665 (orders) *Fax:* 201-871-4009
E-mail: edtecpubs@aol.com
Web Site: bookstoread.com/etp
Key Personnel
Pres & Ed: Lawrence Lipsitz
Author: Douglas E Hansen
1991: 60 pp, $24.95 paper
ISBN(s): 978-0-87778-232-2

Educators Guide to Free Films, Filmstrips & Slides
Published by Educators Progress Service Inc
214 Center St, Randolph, WI 53956-1497
Tel: 920-326-3126 *Toll Free Tel:* 888-951-4469 *Fax:* 920-326-3127
E-mail: questions@freeteachingaids.com
Web Site: www.freeteachingaids.com
Key Personnel
Pres: Kathleen Nehmer
Lists approximately 528 free-loan films, filmstrips, slides & audiotapes.
74th ed, 2014-2015, $42.95 paper (plus $6.50 postage & handling)
ISBN(s): 978-0-87708-567-6

Educators Guide to Free Internet Resources—Elementary/Middle School Edition
Published by Educators Progress Service Inc
214 Center St, Randolph, WI 53956-1497
Tel: 920-326-3126 *Toll Free Tel:* 888-951-4469 *Fax:* 920-326-3127
E-mail: questions@freeteachingaids.com
Web Site: www.freeteachingaids.com
Key Personnel
Pres: Kathleen Nehmer
Free disks, pamphlets, booklets, magazines, downloadable programs, articles & more for elementary & middle schools.
14th ed, 2014-2015: 183 pp, $42.95 (plus $6.50 postage & handling)
ISBN(s): 978-0-87708-568-3

Educators Guide to Free Internet Resources—Secondary Edition
Published by Educators Progress Service Inc
214 Center St, Randolph, WI 53956-1497
Tel: 920-326-3126 *Toll Free Tel:* 888-951-4469 *Fax:* 920-326-3127
E-mail: questions@freeteachingaids.com
Web Site: www.freeteachingaids.com
Key Personnel
Pres: Kathleen Nehmer
Free disks, pamphlets, booklets, magazines, downloadable programs, articles & more for secondary schools.
32nd ed, 2014-2015: 179 pp, $42.95 (plus $6.50 postage & handling)
ISBN(s): 978-0-87708-576-8

Educators Guide to Free Videos—Elementary/Middle School Edition
Published by Educators Progress Service Inc
214 Center St, Randolph, WI 53956-1497
Tel: 920-326-3126 *Toll Free Tel:* 888-951-4469 *Fax:* 920-326-3127
E-mail: questions@freeteachingaids.com
Web Site: www.freeteachingaids.com
Key Personnel
Pres: Kathleen Nehmer
15th ed, 2014-2015: 247 pp, $42.95 (plus $6.50 postage & handling)
ISBN(s): 978-0-87708-581-2

Educators Guide to Free Videos—Secondary Edition
Published by Educators Progress Service Inc
214 Center St, Randolph, WI 53956-1497
Tel: 920-326-3126 *Toll Free Tel:* 888-951-4469 *Fax:* 920-326-3127
E-mail: questions@freeteachingaids.com
Web Site: www.freeteachingaids.com
Key Personnel
Pres: Kathleen Nehmer
61st ed, 2014-2015: 263 pp, $42.95 (plus $6.50 postage & handling)
ISBN(s): 978-0-87708-571-3

Educator's Survival Guide to TV Production and Activities
Published by Libraries Unlimited
130 Cremona Dr, Santa Barbara, CA 93117
Mailing Address: PO Box 1911, Santa Barbara, CA 93116-1911
Tel: 805-968-1911 *Toll Free Tel:* 800-368-6868 *Toll Free Fax:* 866-270-3856
E-mail: customerservice@abc-clio.com
Web Site: www.abc-clio.com
Key Personnel
Edit Dir, Electronic: Judy Fay
Author: Christopher Curchy; Keith Kyker
How to set up & maintain a TV production studio. Designed for educators, the book helps you select, connect & use AV production equipment in the school. A practical & complete guide for educators that will also be appreciated by public librarians working with AV production. Grades K-12.
2nd ed, May 2003: 288 pp, $35 paper
ISBN(s): 978-0-313-05977-3 (ebook); 978-1-56308-983-1

Effective TV Production
Published by Focal Press
7625 Empire Dr, Florence, KY 41042
Toll Free Tel: 800-634-7064 *Toll Free Fax:* 800-248-4724
E-mail: orders@taylorandfrancis.com
Web Site: www.focalpress.com
Key Personnel
Author: Gerald Millerson
3rd ed, April 1993: 224 pp, $50.95 hardcover
ISBN(s): 978-0-240-51324-9

Electronic Text: Learning to Write, Read, and Reason with Computers
Published by Educational Technology Publications Inc
700 Palisade Ave, Englewood Cliffs, NJ 07632-0564
Tel: 201-871-4007 *Toll Free Tel:* 800-952-2665 (orders) *Fax:* 201-871-4009
E-mail: edtecpubs@aol.com
Web Site: bookstoread.com/etp
Key Personnel
Pres & Ed: Lawrence Lipsitz
Author: William V Costanzo
1989: 320 pp, $39.95 cloth
ISBN(s): 978-0-87778-208-7

Empowering Networks: Computer Conferencing in Education
Published by Educational Technology Publications Inc
700 Palisade Ave, Englewood Cliffs, NJ 07632-0564
Tel: 201-871-4007 *Toll Free Tel:* 800-952-2665 (orders) *Fax:* 201-871-4009
E-mail: edtecpubs@aol.com
Web Site: bookstoread.com/etp
Key Personnel
Pres & Ed: Lawrence Lipsitz
Ed: Michael D Waggoner
1992: 263 pp, $39.95 cloth
ISBN(s): 978-0-87778-238-4

Exploring Multimodal Composition and Digital Writing
Published by IGI Global
701 E Chocolate Ave, Hershey, PA 17033-1240
Tel: 717-533-8845 (ext 100) *Toll Free Tel:* 866-342-6657 *Fax:* 717-533-8661
E-mail: cust@igi-global.com
Web Site: www.igi-global.com
Investigates the use of digital technologies to create multimedia documents that utilize video, audio & web-based elements to further written communication.
2014: 352 pp, $175
ISBN(s): 978-1-4666-4345-1; 978-1-4666-4346-8 (ebook)

Film Plots: Scene-by-Scene Narrative Outlines for Feature Film Study
Published by Pierian Press
3196 Maple Dr, Ypsilanti, MI 48197
Tel: 734-434-5530; 734-434-4074 (orders) *Toll Free Tel:* 800-678-2435 *Fax:* 734-434-5582
E-mail: mew_42strat@yahoo.com
Web Site: www.pierianpress.com
Key Personnel
Author: Leonard J Leff
Contact: C Edward Wall *E-mail:* cewall@pierianpress.com
Provides scene-by-scene analysis of classic & modern films.
Vol 1: 1983 (67 films, 402 pp), Vol 2: 1988 (50 films, 483 pp): 885 pp, $65/vol hardcover plus $5 shipping
ISBN(s): 978-0-87650-149-8 (vol 1); 978-0-87650-241-9 (vol 2)

Filmstrips
Published by Educational Technology Publications Inc
700 Palisade Ave, Englewood Cliffs, NJ 07632-0564
Tel: 201-871-4007 *Toll Free Tel:* 800-952-2665 (orders) *Fax:* 201-871-4009
E-mail: edtecpubs@aol.com
Web Site: bookstoread.com/etp
Key Personnel
Pres & Ed: Lawrence Lipsitz
Author: LaMond F Beatty
Ed: James E Duane
Vol 4 in the Instructional Media Library series.
1981: 104 pp, $27.95
ISBN(s): 978-0-87778-164-6

The Focal Encyclopedia of Photography
Published by Focal Press
7625 Empire Dr, Florence, KY 41042
Toll Free Tel: 800-634-7064 *Toll Free Fax:* 800-248-4724
E-mail: orders@taylorandfrancis.com
Web Site: www.focalpress.com
Key Personnel
Ed-in-Chief & Author: Michael Peres
4th ed, April 2007: 880 pp, $99.95
ISBN(s): 978-0-080-47784-8 (ebook); 978-0-240-80740-9 (hardcover)

Guide to Reference Materials for School Library Media Centers
Published by Libraries Unlimited
130 Cremona Dr, Santa Barbara, CA 93117
Mailing Address: PO Box 1911, Santa Barbara, CA 93116-1911
Tel: 805-968-1911 *Toll Free Tel:* 800-368-6868 *Toll Free Fax:* 866-270-3856
E-mail: customerservice@abc-clio.com
Web Site: www.abc-clio.com
Key Personnel
Author: Barbara Ripp Safford
Annotates nearly 2,000 basic reference materials recommended for elementary & secondary school media centers.
6th ed, 2010: 236 pp, $60 hardcover
ISBN(s): 978-1-59158-277-9

Haven't I Seen You Somewhere Before? Remakes, Sequels & Series in Motion Pictures, Videos & Television, 1896-1990
Published by Pierian Press
3196 Maple Dr, Ypsilanti, MI 48197
Tel: 734-434-5530; 734-434-4074 (orders) *Toll Free Tel:* 800-678-2435 *Fax:* 734-434-5582
E-mail: mew_42strat@yahoo.com
Web Site: www.pierianpress.com
Key Personnel
Author: James L Limbacher
Contact: C Edward Wall *E-mail:* cewall@pierianpress.org
Covers film remakes (including those remade for television), film sequels & film series. Contains information on producer, year of production, original source & pertinent notes.
2nd ed, 1991: 440 pp, $65 hardcover plus $5 shipping
ISBN(s): 978-0-87650-244-0

Hawaii Production Index
Published by Media Index Publishing Group
14240 Interurban Ave S, Suite 190, Tukwila, WA 98168
Mailing Address: PO Box 24365, Seattle, WA 98124-0365
Tel: 206-382-9220 *Toll Free Tel:* 800-332-1736 *Fax:* 206-382-9437
E-mail: media@media-inc.com
Web Site: hawaiifilm.com; www.mediaindexpublishing.com
Key Personnel
Pres: James Baker *E-mail:* jbaker@media-inc.com
Assoc Ed/Res Dir: Katie Sauro *E-mail:* ksauro@media-inc.com
Publication listing almost 1,000 production resource companies in Hawaii. Available in print & online.

Human-Computer Interaction: A Design Guide
Published by Educational Technology Publications Inc
700 Palisade Ave, Englewood Cliffs, NJ 07632-0564
Tel: 201-871-4007 *Toll Free Tel:* 800-952-2665 (orders) *Fax:* 201-871-4009
E-mail: edtecpubs@aol.com
Web Site: bookstoread.com/etp
Key Personnel
Pres & Ed: Lawrence Lipsitz
Author: Mark K Jones
1989: 160 pp, $24.95 paper
ISBN(s): 978-0-87778-207-0

Impact of Technology on Resource Sharing: Experimentation & Maturity
Published by CRC Press LLC
Subsidiary of Taylor & Francis
6000 Broken Sound Pkwy NW, Suite 300, Boca Raton, FL 33487
Tel: 561-994-0555 *Toll Free Tel:* 800-272-7737 *Fax:* 561-989-9732 (intl orders) *Toll Free Fax:* 800-374-3401 (US orders)
E-mail: orders@crcpress.com (cust serv); orders@taylorandfrancis.com
Web Site: www.crcpress.com
Key Personnel
Pres: Emmett Dages
Author: Thomas C Wilson
Critical analysis of the impact ground-breaking technologies, new & established, have had on resource sharing in the information industry.
1993: 196 pp, $91.95 hardcover
ISBN(s): 978-1-56024-391-5

Instructional Materials Centers
Published by Educational Technology Publications Inc
700 Palisade Ave, Englewood Cliffs, NJ 07632-0564
Tel: 201-871-4007 *Toll Free Tel:* 800-952-2665 (orders) *Fax:* 201-871-4009
E-mail: edtecpubs@aol.com
Web Site: bookstoread.com/etp
Key Personnel
Pres & Ed: Lawrence Lipsitz
Author: LaMond F Beatty
Ed: James E Duane
Vol 5 in the Instructional Media Library series.
1981: 104 pp, $27.95 cloth
ISBN(s): 978-0-87778-165-3

Instructional Systems Development in Large Organizations
Published by Educational Technology Publications Inc
700 Palisade Ave, Englewood Cliffs, NJ 07632-0564
Tel: 201-871-4007 *Toll Free Tel:* 800-952-2665 (orders) *Fax:* 201-871-4009
E-mail: edtecpubs@aol.com
Web Site: bookstoread.com/etp
Key Personnel
Pres & Ed: Lawrence Lipsitz
Author: Wallace J Hannum; Carol Hansen
1989: 328 pp, $44.95 cloth
ISBN(s): 978-0-87778-204-9

Interactive Multimedia Instruction
Published by Educational Technology Publications Inc
700 Palisade Ave, Englewood Cliffs, NJ 07632-0564
Tel: 201-871-4007 *Toll Free Tel:* 800-952-2665 (orders) *Fax:* 201-871-4009
E-mail: edtecpubs@aol.com
Web Site: bookstoread.com/etp
Key Personnel
Pres & Ed: Lawrence Lipsitz
Author: Richard A Schwier; Earl R Misanchuk
1993: 392 pp, $44.95 cloth
ISBN(s): 978-0-87778-251-3

Interactive Television and Instruction: A Guide to Technology, Technique, Facilities Design, and Classroom Management
Published by Educational Technology Publications Inc
700 Palisade Ave, Englewood Cliffs, NJ 07632-0564
Tel: 201-871-4007 *Toll Free Tel:* 800-952-2665 (orders) *Fax:* 201-871-4009
E-mail: edtecpubs@aol.com
Web Site: bookstoread.com/etp
Key Personnel
Pres & Ed: Lawrence Lipsitz
Author: Robert H Lochte
1993: 160 pp, $32.95 cloth
ISBN(s): 978-0-87778-252-0

Interactive Video
Published by Educational Technology Publications Inc
700 Palisade Ave, Englewood Cliffs, NJ 07632-0564
Tel: 201-871-4007 *Toll Free Tel:* 800-952-2665 (orders) *Fax:* 201-871-4009
E-mail: edtecpubs@aol.com
Web Site: bookstoread.com/etp
Key Personnel
Pres & Ed: Lawrence Lipsitz
Author: Richard A Schwier
1987: 202 pp, $34.95 cloth
ISBN(s): 978-0-87778-206-3

Interactive Video Management and Production
Published by Educational Technology Publications Inc
700 Palisade Ave, Englewood Cliffs, NJ 07632-0564

Tel: 201-871-4007 *Toll Free Tel:* 800-952-2665 (orders) *Fax:* 201-871-4009
E-mail: edtecpubs@aol.com
Web Site: bookstoread.com/etp
Key Personnel
Pres & Ed: Lawrence Lipsitz
Author: Steven Imke
1991: 176 pp, $24.95 paper
ISBN(s): 978-0-87778-233-9

International Motion Picture Almanac
Published by Quigley Publishing Co
Division of QP Media Inc
64 Wintergreen Lane, Groton, MA 01450
Tel: 978-448-0272 (corp); 347-442-1318 (sales) *Fax:* 978-448-9325 (corp); 347-442-1319 (sales)
E-mail: quigleypub@quigleypublishing.com
Web Site: www.quigleypublishing.com
Key Personnel
Pres: William J Quigley
Ed: Jayme Kulesz
Annual.
85th ed, 2014: 1,121 pp, $275
First published 1930
ISBN(s): 978-0-900610-94-3

International Television & Video Almanac
Published by Quigley Publishing Co
Division of QP Media Inc
64 Wintergreen Lane, Groton, MA 01450
Tel: 978-448-0272 (corp); 347-442-1318 (sales) *Fax:* 978-448-9325 (corp); 347-442-1319 (sales)
E-mail: quigleypub@quigleypublishing.com
Web Site: www.quigleypublishing.com
Key Personnel
Pres: William J Quigley
Ed: Jayme Kulesz
Comprehensive TV, cable & home video trade reference book.
Annual.
59th ed, 2014: 1,056 pp, $275
First published 1955
ISBN(s): 978-0-900610-95-0

Library Media Specialist, see Media Specialist—Library & Audio-Visual Services

Lighting for Film & Digital Cinematography
Published by Wadsworth Publishing Group
Division of Cengage Learning™
20 Davis Dr, Belmont, CA 94002
Tel: 650-595-2350 *Toll Free Tel:* 800-354-9706 *Fax:* 650-592-3022 *Toll Free Fax:* 800-487-8488
E-mail: esales@cengage.com
Web Site: www.cengage.com/highered; www.cengage.com
Key Personnel
Author: Dave Viera; Maria Viera
Coord, Prof Sales: Joyce Leibach *Tel:* 518-348-2556 *E-mail:* joyce.leibach@cengage.com
Offers basic principles for designing & implementing lighting setups; analyzes numerous visual examples for films, videos & photography.
2nd ed, 2005: 288 pp, $166.99 paper
Shipping Address: 10650 Toebben Dr, Independence, KY 41051 *Tel:* 859-525-2230 *Toll Free Tel:* 800-544-0550 *Fax:* 859-282-5700; 859-647-4599 *E-mail:* claimscs@cengage.com
ISBN(s): 978-0-534-26498-7

Lighting for TV & Film
Published by Focal Press
7625 Empire Dr, Florence, KY 41042
Toll Free Tel: 800-634-7064 *Toll Free Fax:* 800-248-4724
E-mail: orders@taylorandfrancis.com
Web Site: www.focalpress.com
Key Personnel
Author: Gerald Millerson
3rd ed, June 1999; ebook Aug 2013: 472 pp, $81.95
ISBN(s): 978-0-080-57349-6 (ebook); 978-0-240-51582-3 (paper)

Lighting for Video
Published by Focal Press
7625 Empire Dr, Florence, KY 41042
Toll Free Tel: 800-634-7064 *Toll Free Fax:* 800-248-4724
E-mail: orders@taylorandfrancis.com
Web Site: www.focalpress.com
Key Personnel
Author: Gerald Millerson
A practical guide to lighting for anyone using a video camera.
3rd ed, Aug 1991: 156 pp, $42.95 paper
ISBN(s): 978-0-240-51303-4

Loudspeaker & Headphone Handbook
Published by Focal Press
7625 Empire Dr, Florence, KY 41042
Toll Free Tel: 800-634-7064 *Toll Free Fax:* 800-248-4724
E-mail: orders@taylorandfrancis.com
Web Site: www.focalpress.com
Key Personnel
Ed: John Borwick
Newly revised, covers all the latest aspects of digital signal processing & loudspeaker enclosures. Brings together in a single volume every aspect of loudspeaker & headphone theory & practice in sufficient depth to equip readers with a solid working knowledge of the subject. Provides a detailed & up-to-date technical reference of all aspects of loudspeakers & headphones.
3rd ed, March 2001: 736 pp, $225 hardcover
ISBN(s): 978-0-240-51578-6

Magnetic Tape Librarian
Published by National Learning Corp
212 Michael Dr, Syosset, NY 11791
Tel: 516-921-8888 *Toll Free Tel:* 800-645-6337 (outside NY); 800-632-8888 *Fax:* 516-921-8743
E-mail: info@passbooks.com
Web Site: www.passbooks.com
Key Personnel
Author: Jack Rudman
Study guide.
2005, $29.95 paper, $49.95 hardcover
ISBN(s): 978-0-8373-2872-0

Managing Interactive Video/Multimedia Projects
Published by Educational Technology Publications Inc
700 Palisade Ave, Englewood Cliffs, NJ 07632-0564
Tel: 201-871-4007 *Toll Free Tel:* 800-952-2665 (orders) *Fax:* 201-871-4009
E-mail: edtecpubs@aol.com
Web Site: bookstoread.com/etp
Key Personnel
Pres & Ed: Lawrence Lipsitz
Author: Robert E Bergman; Thomas V Moore
1990: 240 pp, $44.95 paper
ISBN(s): 978-0-87778-209-4

Mass Media Research: An Introduction
Published by Wadsworth Publishing Group
Division of Cengage Learning™
20 Davis Dr, Belmont, CA 94002
Tel: 650-595-2350 *Toll Free Tel:* 800-354-9706 *Fax:* 650-592-3022 *Toll Free Fax:* 800-487-8488
E-mail: esales@cengage.com
Web Site: www.cengage.com/highered; www.cengage.com
Key Personnel
Author: Joseph R Dominick; Roger D Wimmer
Coord, Prof Sales: Joyce Leibach *Tel:* 518-348-2556 *E-mail:* joyce.leibach@cengage.com
Covers practical research techniques for media, including radio & television; concentrates on solutions rather than intricacies of theory. Also available as ebook.
10th ed, 2014: 496 pp, $146.99 paper
Shipping Address: 10650 Toebben Dr, Independence, KY 41051 *Tel:* 859-525-2230 *Toll Free Tel:* 800-544-0550 *Fax:* 859-282-5700; 859-647-4599 *E-mail:* claimscs@cengage.com
ISBN(s): 978-1-133-30733-4

Media About Media: An Annotated Listing of Media Software
Published by Educational Technology Publications Inc
700 Palisade Ave, Englewood Cliffs, NJ 07632-0564
Tel: 201-871-4007 *Toll Free Tel:* 800-952-2665 (orders) *Fax:* 201-871-4009
E-mail: edtecpubs@aol.com
Web Site: bookstoread.com/etp
Key Personnel
Pres & Ed: Lawrence Lipsitz
Author: James E Duane
Vol 6 of the Instructional Media Library series.
1981: 232 pp, $27.95 hardcover
ISBN(s): 978-0-87778-166-0

Media and You: An Elementary Media Literacy Curriculum
Published by Educational Technology Publications Inc
700 Palisade Ave, Englewood Cliffs, NJ 07632-0564
Tel: 201-871-4007 *Toll Free Tel:* 800-952-2665 (orders) *Fax:* 201-871-4009
E-mail: edtecpubs@aol.com
Web Site: bookstoread.com/etp
Key Personnel
Pres & Ed: Lawrence Lipsitz
Author: Donna Lloyd-Kolkin; Kathleen R Tyner
1991: 170 pp, $34.95 paper
ISBN(s): 978-0-87778-226-1

Media Law for Producers
Published by Focal Press
7625 Empire Dr, Florence, KY 41042
Toll Free Tel: 800-634-7064 *Toll Free Fax:* 800-248-4724
E-mail: orders@taylorandfrancis.com
Web Site: www.focalpress.com
Key Personnel
Author: Philip Miller
Helps the media producer protect him/herself from lawsuits & legal entanglements & shows what steps are necessary to protect one's work.
4th ed, 2002; ebook Feb 2013: 424 pp, $52.95
ISBN(s): 978-0-080-49181-3 (ebook); 978-0-240-80478-1 (paper)

Media Programming: Strategies & Practices
Published by Wadsworth Publishing Group
Division of Cengage Learning™
20 Davis Dr, Belmont, CA 94002
Tel: 650-595-2350 *Toll Free Tel:* 800-354-9706 *Fax:* 650-592-3022 *Toll Free Fax:* 800-487-8488
E-mail: esales@cengage.com
Web Site: www.cengage.com/highered; www.cengage.com
Key Personnel
Author: Susan Tyler Eastman; Douglas A Ferguson
Coord, Prof Sales: Joyce Leibach *Tel:* 518-348-2556 *E-mail:* joyce.leibach@cengage.com

Treats decision making in broadcast programming, both day-to-day & long range strategies. Also available as ebook.
9th ed, 2013: 496 pp, $157.49 paper
Shipping Address: 10650 Toebben Dr, Independence, KY 41051 *Tel:* 859-525-2230 *Toll Free Tel:* 800-544-0550 *Fax:* 859-282-5700; 859-647-4599 *E-mail:* claimscs@cengage.com
ISBN(s): 978-1-111-34447-4

Media Specialist—Library & Audio-Visual Services
Published by National Learning Corp
212 Michael Dr, Syosset, NY 11791
Tel: 516-921-8888 *Toll Free Tel:* 800-645-6337 (outside NY); 800-632-8888 *Fax:* 516-921-8743
E-mail: info@passbooks.com
Web Site: www.passbooks.com
Key Personnel
Author: Jack Rudman
Study guide.
2010, $23.95 paper, $43.95 hardcover
ISBN(s): 978-0-8373-8439-9

Memphis & Shelby County Production Directory
Published by The Memphis & Shelby County Film & TV Commission
496 S Main St, Suite 101, Memphis, TN 38103
Tel: 901-527-8300 (ext 2) *Fax:* 901-527-8326
E-mail: info@memphisfilmcomm.org
Web Site: www.filmmemphis.org
Key Personnel
Film Commissioner: Linn Sitler
Deputy Film Commissioner & Contact: Sharon Fox O'Guin
Production directory in digital format of Memphis area services; location scouting services; free production directory; crew/equipment information; scout West Tennessee, Eastern Arkansas & Northern Mississippi.
Annual.
202 pp, $44.95

Messages That Work: A Guide to Communication Design
Published by Educational Technology Publications Inc
700 Palisade Ave, Englewood Cliffs, NJ 07632-0564
Tel: 201-871-4007 *Toll Free Tel:* 800-952-2665 (orders) *Fax:* 201-871-4009
E-mail: edtecpubs@aol.com
Web Site: bookstoread.com/etp
Key Personnel
Pres & Ed: Lawrence Lipsitz
Author: Patrick D Marsh
1983: 460 pp, $49.95
ISBN(s): 978-0-87778-184-4

Microcomputer/Audio-Visual Repair Supervisor
Published by National Learning Corp
212 Michael Dr, Syosset, NY 11791
Tel: 516-921-8888 *Toll Free Tel:* 800-645-6337 (outside NY); 800-632-8888 *Fax:* 516-921-8743
E-mail: info@passbooks.com
Web Site: www.passbooks.com
Key Personnel
Author: Jack Rudman
Study guide.
2011, $39.95 paper, $59.95 hardcover
ISBN(s): 978-0-8373-3732-6

The MIDI Manual: A Practical Guide to MIDI in the Project Studio
Published by Focal Press
7625 Empire Dr, Florence, KY 41042
Toll Free Tel: 800-634-7064 *Toll Free Fax:* 800-248-4724
E-mail: orders@taylorandfrancis.com
Web Site: www.focalpress.com
Key Personnel
Author: David Miles Huber
For music students, professional musicians & audio engineers. Comprehensive guide to the musical instrument digital interface.
3rd ed, March 2007: 384 pp, $36.95 paper
ISBN(s): 978-0-240-80798-0

Modern Radio Production: Production Programming & Performance
Published by Wadsworth Publishing Group
Division of Cengage Learning™
20 Davis Dr, Belmont, CA 94002
Tel: 650-595-2350 *Toll Free Tel:* 800-354-9706 *Fax:* 650-592-3022 *Toll Free Fax:* 800-487-8488
E-mail: esales@cengage.com
Web Site: www.cengage.com/highered; www.cengage.com
Key Personnel
Author: Philip Benoit; Carl Hausman; Frank Messere; Lewis B O'Donnell
Coord, Prof Sales: Joyce Leibach *Tel:* 518-348-2556 *E-mail:* joyce.leibach@cengage.com
Guide to current radio production techniques & to their application for producing good news coverage, commercials & live on-air programs. Also available as ebook.
Triennial.
9th ed, 2013: 464 pp, $137.49
Shipping Address: 10650 Toebben Dr, Independence, KY 41051 *Tel:* 859-525-2230 *Toll Free Tel:* 800-544-0550 *Fax:* 859-282-5700; 859-647-4599 *E-mail:* claimscs@cengage.com
ISBN(s): 978-1-111-34439-9

Modern Recording Techniques
Published by Focal Press
7625 Empire Dr, Florence, KY 41042
Toll Free Tel: 800-634-7064 *Toll Free Fax:* 800-248-4724
E-mail: orders@taylorandfrancis.com
Web Site: www.focalpress.com
Key Personnel
Author: David Miles Huber; Robert E Runstein
Addresses the rapidly growing market of project studio recording, the large base of home music production using multitrack, hard-disk & MIDI technologies. It provides anyone wishing to learn professional recording with everything they need to fully understand the tools & day-to-day practices of music recording & production.
8th ed, Aug 2013: 672 pp, $49.95
ISBN(s): 978-0-240-82157-3 (paper); 978-0-240-82464-2 (ebook)

Motion Picture Operator
Published by National Learning Corp
212 Michael Dr, Syosset, NY 11791
Tel: 516-921-8888 *Toll Free Tel:* 800-645-6337 (outside NY); 800-632-8888 *Fax:* 516-921-8743
E-mail: info@passbooks.com
Web Site: www.passbooks.com
Key Personnel
Author: Jack Rudman
Study guide.
2000, $29.95 paper, $49.95 hardcover
ISBN(s): 978-0-8373-0501-1

Motion Picture TV & Theatre Directory
Published by Motion Picture Enterprises Inc
PO Box 276, Tarrytown, NY 10591-0276
Tel: 212-245-0969 *Fax:* 212-245-0974
E-mail: publications@mpe.net
Web Site: www.mpenyc.com
Key Personnel
Publr: Neal R Pilzer
Directory of products & services in film, television & theatrical production.
$22.53 (within NY), $20.79 (outside NY)
First published 1960

Movies Unlimited Catalog
Published by Movies Unlimited
3015 Darnell Rd, Philadelphia, PA 19154
Tel: 215-637-4444 *Toll Free Tel:* 800-4-MOVIES (466-8437)
E-mail: movies@moviesunlimited.com
Web Site: www.moviesunlimited.com
Key Personnel
Pres: Jerry Frebowitz
Gen Mgr: Ed Weiss
Pre-recorded video (DVD) titles.
Annual.
2015: 800 pp, $9.95 (plus shipping $5 US, $15 CN, $30 other)

MPEG Handbook
Published by Focal Press
7625 Empire Dr, Florence, KY 41042
Toll Free Tel: 800-634-7064 *Toll Free Fax:* 800-248-4724
E-mail: orders@taylorandfrancis.com
Web Site: www.focalpress.com
Key Personnel
Author: John Watkinson
A complete professional "bible" on all aspects of audio & video compression using MPEG technology. Fundamental knowledge is provided alongside practical guidance eg: how to avoid quality loss or the creating of MPEG elementary streams & their multiplexing into transport streams (including the problems involved in synchronizing all of the signals in a multiplex). The clarity of explanation & depth of technical detail combine to make this book an essential & definitive reference work. Gives a comprehensive treatment of significant extensions made available by MPEG4, such as object coding, mesh coding & animation.
2nd ed, Nov 2004: 470 pp, $84.95 hardcover
ISBN(s): 978-0-240-80578-8

Multimedia for Learning: Development, Application, Evaluation
Published by Educational Technology Publications Inc
700 Palisade Ave, Englewood Cliffs, NJ 07632-0564
Tel: 201-871-4007 *Toll Free Tel:* 800-952-2665 (orders) *Fax:* 201-871-4009
E-mail: edtecpubs@aol.com
Web Site: bookstoread.com/etp
Key Personnel
Pres & Ed: Lawrence Lipsitz
Ed: Diane M Gayeski
1993: 184 pp, $34.95 hardcover
ISBN(s): 978-0-87778-250-6

Music Directory Canada
Published by Norris-Whitney Communications
4056 Dorchester Rd, Suite 202, Niagara Falls, ON L2E 6M9, Canada
Tel: 905-374-9849 *Toll Free Tel:* 800-265-8481 (cust serv) *Toll Free Fax:* 888-665-1307
E-mail: mdc@nor.com; order@nor.com
Web Site: www.musicdirectorycanada.com; www.musicbooksplus.com
Key Personnel
Consumer Serv Dir: Maureen Jack
E-mail: mjack@nor.com
Organizations, companies, individuals in the Canadian music business. Go to musicbooksplus.com for ordering information.
9th ed, $44.95
ISBN(s): 978-0-9691272-9-1

Northwest Production Index
Published by Media Index Publishing Group
14240 Interurban Ave S, Suite 190, Tukwila, WA 98168
Mailing Address: PO Box 24365, Seattle, WA 98124-0365
Tel: 206-382-9220 *Toll Free Tel:* 800-332-1736 *Fax:* 206-382-9437
E-mail: media@media-inc.com
Web Site: nwfilm.com; www.mediaindexpublishing.com
Key Personnel
Pres: James Baker *E-mail:* jbaker@media-inc.com
Assoc Ed/Res Dir: Katie Sauro *E-mail:* ksauro@media-inc.com
Comprehensive guide to northwest production, post-production, equipment & support resources for the film, video & audio industries. Also available online.

Orion Blue Book: Audio
Published by Orion Research Corp
14555 N Scottsdale Rd, Suite 330, Scottsdale, AZ 85254
Tel: 480-951-1114 *Toll Free Tel:* 800-844-0759 *Fax:* 480-951-1117
E-mail: sales@usedprice.com
Web Site: www.usedprice.com
Key Personnel
Owner: Mark Rohrs; Rob Rohrs
Sales: Trish Thatcher *Tel:* 480-951-1114 ext 206 *E-mail:* trish@usedprice.com
Audio equipment used prices.
$150/yr online only

Orion Blue Book: Video & Television
Published by Orion Research Corp
14555 N Scottsdale Rd, Suite 330, Scottsdale, AZ 85254
Tel: 480-951-1114 *Toll Free Tel:* 800-844-0759 *Fax:* 480-951-1117
E-mail: sales@usedprice.com
Web Site: www.usedprice.com
Key Personnel
Owner: Mark Rohrs; Rob Rohrs
Sales: Trish Thatcher *Tel:* 480-951-1114 ext 206 *E-mail:* trish@usedprice.com
Describes features of all types of video equipment; computer disk also available (DOS & Windows), Web books.
$130/yr online only

Photographer's Market
Published by F+W, A Content + eCommerce Company
10151 Carver Rd, Suite 200, Blue Ash, OH 45242
Tel: 513-531-2690 *Toll Free Tel:* 855-842-5267 (cust serv) *Fax:* 513-891-7153
E-mail: photomarket@fwmedia.com
Web Site: www.artistsmarketonline.com
Key Personnel
Sr Content Developer: Mary Burzlaff Bostic
More than 1,500 listings of photo buyers with complete contact information; for freelance & stock photographers.
38th ed, 2015: 688 pp, $34.99 includes 1 yr subn to artistmarketonline.com
ISBN(s): 978-1-4403-3567-9

Photography
Published by Educational Technology Publications Inc
700 Palisade Ave, Englewood Cliffs, NJ 07632-0564
Tel: 201-871-4007 *Toll Free Tel:* 800-952-2665 (orders) *Fax:* 201-871-4009
E-mail: edtecpubs@aol.com
Web Site: bookstoread.com/etp
Key Personnel
Pres & Ed: Lawrence Lipsitz
Author: Robert V Bullough
Ed: James E Duane
Vol 11 in the Instructional Media Library series.
1981: 104 pp, $27.95 cloth
ISBN(s): 978-0-87778-171-4

Placing Shadows: Lighting Techniques for Video Production
Published by Focal Press
7625 Empire Dr, Florence, KY 41042
Toll Free Tel: 800-634-7064 *Toll Free Fax:* 800-248-4724
E-mail: orders@taylorandfrancis.com
Web Site: www.focalpress.com
Key Personnel
Author: Chuck Gloman; Tom Le Tourneau
Instructs the student & professional in the physical properties of light & the selection of proper instruments & placements to convey moods. Numerous illustrations, examples & checklists reinforce the professional techniques described.
3rd ed, Feb 2005: 320 pp, $46.95 paper
ISBN(s): 978-0-240-80661-7

Portable Video: ENG & EFP
Published by Focal Press
7625 Empire Dr, Florence, KY 41042
Toll Free Tel: 800-634-7064 *Toll Free Fax:* 800-248-4724
E-mail: orders@taylorandfrancis.com
Web Site: www.focalpress.com
Key Personnel
Author: Edward J Fink; Norman J Medoff
Focuses on technique & technology for single camera electronic news gathering & electronic field production. Covering everything from basic creative & technical editing techniques to budgets & copyright issues, it is accessible to the home videomaker or amateur & to the professional seeking information on the newest advances in technique & equipment.
6th ed, March 2012; ebook Sept 2012: 392 pp, $51.95 paper, $49.95 ebook
ISBN(s): 978-0-240-81499-5 (paper); 978-0-240-81500-8 (ebook)

Preparing Instructional Text: Document Design Using Desktop Publishing
Published by Educational Technology Publications Inc
700 Palisade Ave, Englewood Cliffs, NJ 07632-0564
Tel: 201-871-4007 *Toll Free Tel:* 800-952-2665 (orders) *Fax:* 201-871-4009
E-mail: edtecpubs@aol.com
Web Site: bookstoread.com/etp
Key Personnel
Pres & Ed: Lawrence Lipsitz
Author: Earl R Misanchuk
1992: 327 pp, $39.95 paper
ISBN(s): 978-0-87778-241-4

Principles of Digital Audio
Published by The McGraw-Hill Companies Inc
Division of McGraw-Hill Professional Book Group
2 Penn Plaza, 20th fl, New York, NY 10121-2298
Tel: 212-904-2000 *Toll Free Tel:* 800-262-4729 (book clubs)
E-mail: customer.service@mcgraw-hill.com
Web Site: www.mhprofessional.com
Key Personnel
Author: Ken Pohlmann
6th ed, 2010: 816 pp, $55 paper
ISBN(s): 978-0-07-166346-5

Producers Masterguide®
Published by Producers Masterguide
60 E Eighth St, 34th fl, New York, NY 10003-6514
Tel: 212-777-4002; 212-995-5555 *Fax:* 212-777-4101
Web Site: www.producers.masterguide.com
International film production directory & guide for motion pictures, broadcast television, feature films, commercials, cable, satellite, digital, videotape & Internet industries, covering all states in the USA, all Canadian provinces, Mexico, the Caribbean Islands, Australia, New Zealand, the United Kingdom, Europe, Israel, Morocco, South Africa, the Far East & South America.
20th ed, 2008: 500 pp, $175 US, $185 USD CN, $205 USD elsewhere (paperback)
ISBN(s): 978-0-935744-19-4

The Radio Book
Published by Inside Radio
PO Box 567925, Atlanta, GA 31156
Toll Free Tel: 800-248-4242 *Fax:* 404-965-4131
E-mail: info@insideradio.com
Web Site: www.theradiobook.com; www.insideradio.com
Key Personnel
Gen Mgr & Publr: Gene McKay *Tel:* 800-248-4242 ext 711 *E-mail:* genemckay@insideradio.com
Directory of US & Canadian radio stations & networks. The 19th ed is the last print edition offered but it is now available exclusively online & updated twice a year.
$89.95 ebook

Real Objects and Media
Published by Educational Technology Publications Inc
700 Palisade Ave, Englewood Cliffs, NJ 07632-0564
Tel: 201-871-4007 *Toll Free Tel:* 800-952-2665 (orders) *Fax:* 201-871-4009
E-mail: edtecpubs@aol.com
Web Site: bookstoread.com/etp
Key Personnel
Pres & Ed: Lawrence Lipsitz
Author: J Steven Soulier
Ed: James E Duane
Vol 12 in the Instructional Media Library series.
1981: 96 pp, $27.95 cloth
ISBN(s): 978-0-87778-172-1

Satellite Industry Directory
Published by Access Intelligence LLC
4 Choke Cherry Rd, 2nd fl, Rockville, MD 20850
Tel: 301-354-2000; 301-354-2101 *Toll Free Tel:* 800-777-5006
E-mail: clientservices@accessintel.com
Web Site: www.satellitetoday.com/sid/
Key Personnel
VP: Joe Rosone
Ad: Daniel Chase *Tel:* 301-354-1673
Online directory of satellite-related services, products & governmental agencies both national & international, including satellite coverage maps.
$497/yr
First published 1979

School District Instructional Computer-Use Evaluation Manual
Published by Educational Technology Publications Inc
700 Palisade Ave, Englewood Cliffs, NJ 07632-0564
Tel: 201-871-4007 *Toll Free Tel:* 800-952-2665 (orders) *Fax:* 201-871-4009
E-mail: edtecpubs@aol.com
Web Site: bookstoread.com/etp
Key Personnel
Pres & Ed: Lawrence Lipsitz
Author: Chris Morton; Don Beverly
1989: 61 pp, $24.95 paper
ISBN(s): 978-0-87778-214-8

Senior Audio-Visual Aid Technician
Published by National Learning Corp
212 Michael Dr, Syosset, NY 11791

Tel: 516-921-8888 *Toll Free Tel:* 800-645-6337 (outside NY); 800-632-8888 *Fax:* 516-921-8743
E-mail: info@passbooks.com
Web Site: www.passbooks.com
Key Personnel
Author: Jack Rudman
Study guide.
2009, $34.95 paper, $54.95 hardcover
ISBN(s): 978-0-8373-1471-6

The SHOOT Directory
Published by DCA Business Media LLC
256 Post Rd E, Suite 206, Westport, CT 06880
Tel: 203-227-1699 *Fax:* 203-227-2787
E-mail: info@shootonline.com
Web Site: www.shootonline.com
Key Personnel
Publr & Edit Dir: Roberta Griefer *Tel:* 203-227-1699 ext 13 *E-mail:* rgriefer@shootonline.com
Ed: Robert Goldrich *Tel:* 323-445-6818 *E-mail:* rgoldrich@shootonline.com
Online directory of commercial production & postproduction companies, advertising agencies as well as related fields, such as stock footage, interactive, animation, music, film labs, film commissions, etc.
Free to subscribers of *SHOOT* Magazine

A Short History of the Movies
Published by Pearson
Division of Pearson Education
One Lake St, Upper Saddle River, NJ 07458
Tel: 201-236-7000
Web Site: www.pearsonhighered.com; www.mypearsonstore.com
Key Personnel
Author: Bruce F Kawin; Gerald Mast
11th ed, 2010: 784 pp, $125.80 paper
ISBN(s): 978-0-205-75557-8

Sight, Sound, Motion: Applied Media Aesthetics
Published by Wadsworth Publishing Group
Division of Cengage Learning™
20 Davis Dr, Belmont, CA 94002
Tel: 650-595-2350 *Toll Free Tel:* 800-354-9706 *Fax:* 650-592-3022 *Toll Free Fax:* 800-487-8488
E-mail: esales@cengage.com
Web Site: www.cengage.com/highered; www.cengage.com
Key Personnel
Author: Herbert Zettl
Coord, Prof Sales: Joyce Leibach *Tel:* 518-348-2556 *E-mail:* joyce.leibach@cengage.com
Analyzes television & film in terms of light, space, time-motion & sound & demonstrates how to apply these to create clarity & impact. Also available as ebook.
Triennial.
7th ed, 2014: 464 pp, $205.49 hardcover
Shipping Address: 10650 Toebben Dr, Independence, KY 41051 *Tel:* 859-525-2230 *Toll Free Tel:* 800-544-0550 *Fax:* 859-282-5700; 859-647-4599 *E-mail:* claimscs@cengage.com
ISBN(s): 978-1-133-30735-8

Slides
Published by Educational Technology Publications Inc
700 Palisade Ave, Englewood Cliffs, NJ 07632-0564
Tel: 201-871-4007 *Toll Free Tel:* 800-952-2665 (orders) *Fax:* 201-871-4009
E-mail: edtecpubs@aol.com
Web Site: bookstoread.com/etp
Key Personnel
Pres & Ed: Lawrence Lipsitz
Author: Roger A Kueter; Janeen Miller
Ed: James E Duane
Vol 13 in the Instructional Media Library series.
1981: 112 pp, $27.95 cloth
ISBN(s): 978-0-87778-173-8

Sound & Recording
Published by Focal Press
7625 Empire Dr, Florence, KY 41042
Toll Free Tel: 800-634-7064 *Toll Free Fax:* 800-248-4724
E-mail: orders@taylorandfrancis.com
Web Site: www.focalpress.com
Key Personnel
Author: Tim McCormick; Francis Rumsey
Introduces the principles of sound, perception, audio technology & systems. It offers vital reading for trainee engineers entering music recording, broadcasting & associated industries.
6th ed, Oct 2009: 652 pp, $57.95 paper
ISBN(s): 978-0-240-52163-3

Sound Studio: Audio Techniques for Radio, Television, Film & Recording
Published by Focal Press
7625 Empire Dr, Florence, KY 41042
Toll Free Tel: 800-634-7064 *Toll Free Fax:* 800-248-4724
E-mail: orders@taylorandfrancis.com
Web Site: www.focalpress.com
Key Personnel
Author: Alec Nisbett
Intended for use by directors, writers & performers who have a creative interest in sound & for those more directly involved with the technical aspects of sound.
7th ed, 2004: 400 pp, $74.95 paper
ISBN(s): 978-0-240-51911-1

Still Pictures
Published by Educational Technology Publications Inc
700 Palisade Ave, Englewood Cliffs, NJ 07632-0564
Tel: 201-871-4007 *Toll Free Tel:* 800-952-2665 (orders) *Fax:* 201-871-4009
E-mail: edtecpubs@aol.com
Web Site: bookstoread.com/etp
Key Personnel
Pres & Ed: Lawrence Lipsitz
Author: LaMond F Beatty
Ed: James E Duane
Vol 14 in the Instructional Media Library series.
1981: 112 pp, $27.95 cloth
ISBN(s): 978-0-87778-174-5

Subject Access to Visual Resources Collections: A Model for the Computer Construction of Thematic Catalogs
Published by ABC-CLIO
130 Cremona Dr, Santa Barbara, CA 93117
Mailing Address: PO Box 1911, Santa Barbara, CA 93116-1911
Tel: 805-968-1911 *Toll Free Tel:* 800-368-6868 *Fax:* 805-685-9685 *Toll Free Fax:* 866-270-3856
E-mail: customerservice@abc-clio.com
Web Site: www.abc-clio.com
Key Personnel
Author: Karen Markey
Digital Prods & Natl Accts: Joyce Fryer *Tel:* 805-968-1911 ext 154
1986: 209 pp, $112.95
ISBN(s): 978-0-313-24031-7

Taxonomy of Communication Media
Published by Educational Technology Publications Inc
700 Palisade Ave, Englewood Cliffs, NJ 07632-0564
Tel: 201-871-4007 *Toll Free Tel:* 800-952-2665 (orders) *Fax:* 201-871-4009
E-mail: edtecpubs@aol.com
Web Site: bookstoread.com/etp
Key Personnel
Pres & Ed: Lawrence Lipsitz
Author: Rudy Bretz
Description of the various categories of AV media.
1971: 192 pp, $34.95 cloth
ISBN(s): 978-0-87778-012-0

Techniques and Principles in Three-Dimensional Imaging: An Introductory Approach
Published by IGI Global
701 E Chocolate Ave, Hershey, PA 17033-1240
Tel: 717-533-8845 (ext 100) *Toll Free Tel:* 866-342-6657 *Fax:* 717-533-8661
E-mail: cust@igi-global.com
Web Site: www.igi-global.com
Provides the reader with a concrete understanding of basic principles & pitfalls for 3D capturing.
2014: 324 pp, $200
ISBN(s): 978-1-4666-4932-3; 978-1-4666-4933-0 (ebook)

Technologies for Education: A Practical Guide
Published by Libraries Unlimited
130 Cremona Dr, Santa Barbara, CA 93117
Mailing Address: PO Box 1911, Santa Barbara, CA 93116-1911
Tel: 805-968-1911 *Toll Free Tel:* 800-368-6868 *Toll Free Fax:* 866-270-3856
E-mail: customerservice@abc-clio.com
Web Site: www.abc-clio.com
Key Personnel
Author: Ann E Barron; Karen S Ivers; Nick Lilavois; Julie A Wells
Designed for all educators who are interested in the instructional applications of technology, it provides an overview of teaching with technology; computer graphics; advanced computer graphics: animation, 3D graphics & virtual reality; digital audio; digital video; telecommunications; distance learning & assistive technologies in the classroom. The advantages, disadvantages & educational applications of each technology are presented, along with detailed graphics & glossaries. Each chapter also provides a scenario to illustrate implementation techniques, a copy-ready brochure for in-service training workshops & abundant resource information.
5th ed, July 2006: 204 pp, $55 paper
First published 1997
ISBN(s): 978-1-59158-250-2

Telecommunications Directory
Published by Gale
Division of Cengage Learning
27500 Drake Rd, Farmington Hills, MI 48331-3535
Tel: 248-699-4253 *Toll Free Fax:* 877-363-4253
E-mail: galeord@gale.cengage.com
Web Site: www.cengage.com
Descriptive guide to over 10,000 telecommunications organizations, systems & services covering voice & data communications, audiotex services, cellular radio, electronic mail/message, facsimile, local area networks, microwave networks, satellite services, shared-tenant services, teleconferencing, telegram, telex, transactional services, voicemail, videotex & teletext, telecommunications-related associations, consultants, law firms & financial organizations, marketing & advertising companies, publishers & information services, regulatory & standards bodies, research organizations, seminar & conference providers & training organizations & Internet access users.
Annual.
25th ed, 2014: 2,500 pp, $1,038/4 vol set
Shipping Address: PO Box 9187, Farmington Hills, MI 48333-9187
ISBN(s): 978-1-4144-7993-4 (4 vol set)

Telecommunications for Learning
Published by Educational Technology Publications Inc
700 Palisade Ave, Englewood Cliffs, NJ 07632-0564
Tel: 201-871-4007 *Toll Free Tel:* 800-952-2665 (orders) *Fax:* 201-871-4009
E-mail: edtecpubs@aol.com
Web Site: bookstoread.com/etp
Key Personnel
Pres & Ed: Lawrence Lipsitz
Vol 3 of the Educational Technology Anthology Series.
1991: 202 pp, $34.95
ISBN(s): 978-0-87778-225-4

Telecommunications Policy & Regulation Institute
Published by Practising Law Institute
1177 Avenue of the Americas, 2nd fl, New York, NY 10036
Tel: 212-824-5700 *Toll Free Tel:* 800-260-4PLI (260-4754, cust serv) *Toll Free Fax:* 800-321-0093 (cust serv)
E-mail: info@pli.edu (cust serv); media@pli.edu (press requests)
Web Site: www.pli.edu
Key Personnel
Dir, Publg, Technol & Prodn: James E Gaskin
Course handbook.
Annual.
32nd ed, 2014: 420 pp, $220
ISBN(s): 978-1-4024-2343-7

Television & Cable Factbook
Published by Warren Communications News Inc
2115 Ward Ct NW, Washington, DC 20037
Tel: 202-872-9200 *Toll Free Tel:* 800-771-9202 (cust serv)
E-mail: info@warren-news.com
Web Site: www.tvcablefactbook.com; www.warren-news.com
Key Personnel
Chmn & Publr: Paul Warren *E-mail:* pwarrendc@warren-news.com
Pres & Ed: Daniel Warren *E-mail:* dwarrendc@warren-news.com
Dir, Sales: William R Benton
E-mail: wbentondc@warren-news.com
Mng Ed & Asst Publr, Directories: Michael C Taliaferro *E-mail:* mtaliaferrodc@warren-news.com
Complete compilation of TV stations, cable systems, services they provide, markets served, equipment, key personnel, manufacturers & suppliers, associations, consultants, etc. Over 930,000 detailed records.
Vols 1 & 2: *Stations*
Vols 3 & 4: *Cable Systems*.
Annual.
2015, $1,135 print, $995 online
First published 1945
ISBN(s): 978-1-57696-008-0

Television Production
Published by Focal Press
7625 Empire Dr, Florence, KY 41042
Toll Free Tel: 800-634-7064 *Toll Free Fax:* 800-248-4724
E-mail: orders@taylorandfrancis.com
Web Site: www.focalpress.com
Key Personnel
Author: Gerald Millerson; Jim Owens
Covers each facet of studio operation: camera work, lighting, scenic design, etc.
15th ed, March 2012; ebook Aug 2012: 442 pp, $64.95
ISBN(s): 978-0-240-52257-9 (paper); 978-0-240-52258-6 (ebook)

Television Production
Published by Educational Technology Publications Inc
700 Palisade Ave, Englewood Cliffs, NJ 07632-0564
Tel: 201-871-4007 *Toll Free Tel:* 800-952-2665 (orders) *Fax:* 201-871-4009
E-mail: edtecpubs@aol.com
Web Site: bookstoread.com/etp
Key Personnel
Pres & Ed: Lawrence Lipsitz
Author: Dan Baker; Bill Weisgerber
Ed: James E Duane
Volume 15 in the Instructional Media Library series.
1981: 112 pp, $27.95 cloth
ISBN(s): 978-0-87778-175-2

Television Production: A Classroom Approach
Published by Libraries Unlimited
130 Cremona Dr, Santa Barbara, CA 93117
Mailing Address: PO Box 1911, Santa Barbara, CA 93116-1911
Tel: 805-968-1911 *Toll Free Tel:* 800-368-6868 *Toll Free Fax:* 866-270-3856
E-mail: customerservice@abc-clio.com
Web Site: www.abc-clio.com
Key Personnel
Author: Christopher Curchy; Keith Kyker
Hands on approach offers students the opportunity to learn about topics ranging from TV studio design, scripting & camera work to creating a dramatic video production. Grades 7-12.
2nd ed, Sept 2004: 256 pp, $55 paper
ISBN(s): 978-0-89789-967-3 (ebook); 978-1-56308-774-5

Television Production for Elementary and Middle Schools
Published by Libraries Unlimited
130 Cremona Dr, Santa Barbara, CA 93117
Mailing Address: PO Box 1911, Santa Barbara, CA 93116-1911
Tel: 805-968-1911 *Toll Free Tel:* 800-368-6868 *Toll Free Fax:* 866-270-3856
E-mail: customerservice@abc-clio.com
Web Site: www.abc-clio.com
Key Personnel
Author: Christopher Curchy; Keith Kyker
Contains practical information on subjects that range from equipment, copyright considerations, news show production & videotaping school functions to using video to teach media skills & lessons on concepts & careers in television production. Reproducible student handouts & questions, notes to the teacher & enrichment activities accompany the lessons. Grades K-8.
Aug 1994: 211 pp, $45 paper
ISBN(s): 978-0-313-07912-2 (ebook); 978-1-56308-186-6

Television Production Handbook
Published by Wadsworth Publishing Group
Division of Cengage Learning™
20 Davis Dr, Belmont, CA 94002
Tel: 650-595-2350 *Toll Free Tel:* 800-354-9706 *Fax:* 650-592-3022 *Toll Free Fax:* 800-487-8488
E-mail: esales@cengage.com
Web Site: www.cengage.com/highered; www.cengage.com
Key Personnel
Author: Herbert Zettl
Coord, Prof Sales: Joyce Leibach *Tel:* 518-348-2556 *E-mail:* joyce.leibach@cengage.com
Practical guide to major elements & techniques of TV production.
Triennial.
12th ed, 2014: 544 pp, $295.95
Shipping Address: 10650 Toebben Dr, Independence, KY 41051 *Tel:* 859-525-2230 *Toll Free Tel:* 800-544-0550 *Fax:* 859-282-5700; 859-647-4599 *E-mail:* claimscs@cengage.com
ISBN(s): 978-1-285-05267-0

TV Scenic Design
Published by Focal Press
7625 Empire Dr, Florence, KY 41042
Toll Free Tel: 800-634-7064 *Toll Free Fax:* 800-248-4724
E-mail: orders@taylorandfrancis.com
Web Site: www.focalpress.com
Key Personnel
Author: Gerald Millerson
2nd ed, Aug 1997; ebook Aug 2013: 280 pp, $79.95
ISBN(s): 978-0-080-51981-4 (ebook); 978-0-240-51493-2 (paper)

Using Video: Interactive and Linear Designs
Published by Educational Technology Publications Inc
700 Palisade Ave, Englewood Cliffs, NJ 07632-0564
Tel: 201-871-4007 *Toll Free Tel:* 800-952-2665 (orders) *Fax:* 201-871-4009
E-mail: edtecpubs@aol.com
Web Site: bookstoread.com/etp
Key Personnel
Pres & Ed: Lawrence Lipsitz
Author: Joseph W Arwady; Diane M Gayeski
Part of the Techniques in Training & Performance Development Series.
1989: 190 pp, $39.95 cloth
ISBN(s): 978-0-87778-199-8

Video Camera Techniques
Published by Focal Press
7625 Empire Dr, Florence, KY 41042
Toll Free Tel: 800-634-7064 *Toll Free Fax:* 800-248-4724
E-mail: orders@taylorandfrancis.com
Web Site: www.focalpress.com
Key Personnel
Author: Gerald Millerson
2nd ed, Oct 1994: 160 pp, $45.95 hardcover
ISBN(s): 973-0-240-51376-8

Video Production Handbook
Published by Focal Press
7625 Empire Dr, Florence, KY 41042
Toll Free Tel: 800-634-7064 *Toll Free Fax:* 800-248-4724
E-mail: orders@taylorandfrancis.com
Web Site: www.focalpress.com
Key Personnel
Author: Gerald Millerson; Jim Owens
At-a-glance guide to quality video program-making on a modest budget. Emphasis throughout is on excellence with economy; whether you are working alone or with a small multi-camera group. The well-tried techniques detailed here will steer you through the hazards of production, helping you to avoid those frustrating, time-wasting problems & to create an effective video program. Also available as ebook.
5th ed, 2012: 394 pp, $49.95 paper
ISBN(s): 978-0-240-52220-3; 978-0-240-52221-0 (ebook)

The Video Source Book
Published by Gale
Division of Cengage Learning
27500 Drake Rd, Farmington Hills, MI 48331-3535
Tel: 248-699-4253 *Toll Free Tel:* 800-877-4253 *Fax:* 248-699-8049 (tech support) *Toll Free Fax:* 877-363-4253
E-mail: galeord@gale.cengage.com
Web Site: www.cengage.com

Key Personnel
Ed: Jim Craddock
Over 120,000 entries in two volumes describe 160,000 video titles currently available on tape & disc. Entries include information about availability, running time, audience rating, intended use, price, credits, distributor, etc. Includes Subject Index, Credits Index, Special Formats Index, Alternate Title Index, Awards Index & Program Distributors.
51st ed, 2013, $866/9 vol set
Shipping Address: PO Box 9187, Farmington Hills, MI 48333-9187
ISBN(s): 978-1-4144-8114-2 (9 vol set)

Video Surveillance Techniques and Technologies
Published by IGI Global
701 E Chocolate Ave, Hershey, PA 17033-1240
Tel: 717-533-8845 (ext 100) *Toll Free Tel:* 866-342-6657 *Fax:* 717-533-8661
E-mail: cust@igi-global.com
Web Site: www.igi-global.com
Presents empirical research & acquired experience on the original solutions & mathematical algorithms for motion detection & object identification problems.
2014: 369 pp, $215
ISBN(s): 978-1-4666-4896-8; 978-1-4666-4897-5 (ebook)

Videocassette Technology in American Education
Published by Educational Technology Publications Inc
700 Palisade Ave, Englewood Cliffs, NJ 07632-0564
Tel: 201-871-4007 *Toll Free Tel:* 800-952-2665 (orders) *Fax:* 201-871-4009
E-mail: edtecpubs@aol.com
Web Site: bookstoread.com/etp
Key Personnel
Pres & Ed: Lawrence Lipsitz
Author: George N Gordon; Irving A Falk
Analysis of potential uses for videocassettes in the nation's schools.
1972: 176 pp, $34.95 cloth
ISBN(s): 978-0-87778-035-9

Videodisc/Microcomputer Courseware Design
Published by Educational Technology Publications Inc
700 Palisade Ave, Englewood Cliffs, NJ 07632-0564
Tel: 201-871-4007 *Toll Free Tel:* 800-952-2665 (orders) *Fax:* 201-871-4009
E-mail: edtecpubs@aol.com
Web Site: bookstoread.com/etp
Key Personnel
Pres & Ed: Lawrence Lipsitz
Ed: Michael L DeBloois
Describes how-to design materials for videodisc/microcomputer presentations.
1982: 192 pp, $37.95 cloth
ISBN(s): 978-0-87778-183-7

Videodiscs
Published by Educational Technology Publications Inc
700 Palisade Ave, Englewood Cliffs, NJ 07632-0564
Tel: 201-871-4007 *Toll Free Tel:* 800-952-2665 (orders) *Fax:* 201-871-4009
E-mail: edtecpubs@aol.com
Web Site: bookstoread.com/etp
Key Personnel
Pres & Ed: Lawrence Lipsitz
Author: Edward W Schneider; Junius L Bennion
Ed: James E Duane
Vol 16 in the Instructional Media Library series.
1981: 128 pp, $27.95 cloth
ISBN(s): 978-0-87778-176-9

Visual Communicating
Published by Educational Technology Publications Inc
700 Palisade Ave, Englewood Cliffs, NJ 07632-0564
Tel: 201-871-4007 *Toll Free Tel:* 800-952-2665 (orders) *Fax:* 201-871-4009
E-mail: edtecpubs@aol.com
Web Site: bookstoread.com/etp
Key Personnel
Pres & Ed: Lawrence Lipsitz
Author: Ralph E Wileman
1993: 160 pp, $37.95
ISBN(s): 978-0-87778-248-3

Visual Information
Published by Educational Technology Publications Inc
700 Palisade Ave, Englewood Cliffs, NJ 07632-0564
Tel: 201-871-4007 *Toll Free Tel:* 800-952-2665 (orders) *Fax:* 201-871-4009
E-mail: edtecpubs@aol.com
Web Site: bookstoread.com/etp
Key Personnel
Pres & Ed: Lawrence Lipsitz
Author: Rune Pettersson
2nd ed, 1993: 400 pp, $59.95
ISBN(s): 978-0-87778-262-9

When Words Collide: A Media Writer's Guide to Grammar & Style
Published by Wadsworth Publishing Group
Division of Cengage Learning™
20 Davis Dr, Belmont, CA 94002
Tel: 650-595-2350 *Toll Free Tel:* 800-354-9706 *Fax:* 650-592-3022 *Toll Free Fax:* 800-487-8488
E-mail: esales@cengage.com
Web Site: www.cengage.com/highered; www.cengage.com
Key Personnel
Author: Lauren Kessler; Duncan McDonald
Coord, Prof Sales: Joyce Leibach *Tel:* 518-348-2556 *E-mail:* joyce.leibach@cengage.com
Shows how to use language in writing for the media that is direct & correct & that sparks & creates energy. Also available as ebook.
Quadrennial.
8th ed, 2012: 264 pp, $97.99 spiralbound
Shipping Address: 10650 Toebben Dr, Independence, KY 41051 *Tel:* 859-525-2230 *Toll Free Tel:* 800-544-0550 *Fax:* 859-282-5700; 859-647-4599 *E-mail:* claimscs@cengage.com
ISBN(s): 978-0-495-57240-4

Writing for Television, Radio & New Media
Published by Wadsworth Publishing Group
Division of Cengage Learning™
20 Davis Dr, Belmont, CA 94002
Tel: 650-595-2350 *Toll Free Tel:* 800-354-9706 *Fax:* 650-592-3022 *Toll Free Fax:* 800-487-8488
E-mail: esales@cengage.com
Web Site: www.cengage.com/highered; www.cengage.com
Key Personnel
Author: Robert L Hilliard
Coord, Prof Sales: Joyce Leibach *Tel:* 518-348-2556 *E-mail:* joyce.leibach@cengage.com
Training in principles, forms & techniques of various kinds of writing, including drama news, sports, features, talk shows & educational programs.
11th ed, 2014: 528 pp, $160.49 paper
Shipping Address: 10650 Toebben Dr, Independence, KY 41051 *Tel:* 859-525-2230 *Toll Free Tel:* 800-544-0550 *Fax:* 859-282-5700; 859-647-4599 *E-mail:* claimscs@cengage.com
ISBN(s): 978-1-285-46507-4

Company Index

Included in this index are the names, addresses, telecommunication numbers and electronic addresses of the organizations included in *AVMP*. Entries also include the page number(s) on which the listings appear.

Sections not represented in this index are **Calendar of Events; Periodicals for the Trade** and **Reference Books for the Trade.**

A & J Cases, 11121 Hindry Ave, Los Angeles, CA 90045 *Tel:* 310-216-2170 *Toll Free Tel:* 800-537-4000 *Fax:* 310-216-2694 *Web Site:* www.ajcases.com, pg 771

A Cut Above Video Productions Inc, 4450 W Eau Gallie Blvd, Suite 220, Melbourne, FL 32934 *Tel:* 321-253-5677 *Fax:* 321-253-5611 *Web Site:* www.acutabovevideo.com, pg 771

A Go Go Films, 4324 Via Marina, Marina Del Rey, CA 90292 *Tel:* 310-576-4992 *E-mail:* art@agogofilms.com *Web Site:* www.agogofilms.com, pg 771

A KTVA Production LLC, 9818 SE 17 Ave, Suite B, Milwaukie, OR 97222 *Tel:* 503-659-4417 *Toll Free Tel:* 800-282-KTVA (282-5882, OR & WA only) *E-mail:* mail@ktvavideo.com *Web Site:* www.ktvavideo.com, pg 771

A M Graphics Products, dba Affton Graphics Inc, 2500 Third Ave, Bronx, NY 10454 *Tel:* 718-401-4040 *Toll Free Tel:* 800-777-0539 *Fax:* 718-401-3322 *E-mail:* amproducts@aol.com *Web Site:* www.amdba.com, pg 771

A/S Custom Furniture, 364-C Valley Rd, Warrington, PA 18976 *Tel:* 215-491-3100 *Fax:* 215-491-3107 *E-mail:* sales@ascustom.com *Web Site:* www.ascustom.com, pg 771

A T Products Inc, 1600 S Division St, Harvard, IL 60033 *Tel:* 815-943-3590 *Toll Free Tel:* 800-848-2205 *Fax:* 815-943-3604 *E-mail:* atprod@mc.net *Web Site:* atproducts.com, pg 771

A to Z Theatrical Supply & Service, 307 W 80 St, Kansas City, MO 64114-2376 *Tel:* 816-523-1655 *Toll Free Tel:* 800-732-8252 *Fax:* 816-523-1690 *E-mail:* atoz@atoztheatrical.com *Web Site:* www.atoztheatrical.com, pg 771

A-V Services Inc, 99 Fairfield Rd, Fairfield, NJ 07004 *Tel:* 973-575-5222 *Fax:* 973-575-0857 *E-mail:* sales@avservices.net *Web Site:* www.avservices.net, pg 771

A-Ware Software Inc, 330 S Executive Dr, Suite 205, Brookfield, WI 53005-4215 *Tel:* 262-717-2220 *Toll Free Tel:* 800-326-2609 *Fax:* 262-717-2230 *E-mail:* info@musicmaster.com; sales@musicmaster.com *Web Site:* www.a-ware.com, pg 771

AAAS Kavli Science Journalism Awards, 1200 New York Ave NW, Washington, DC 20005 *Tel:* 202-326-6431; 202-326-6440 *Fax:* 202-789-0455 *E-mail:* media@aaas.org *Web Site:* www.aaas.org, pg 1107

A&E Home Video, 235 E 45 St, New York, NY 10017 *Tel:* 212-210-1400 *Toll Free Tel:* 877-447-4253 *Fax:* 212-907-9418 *Web Site:* www.aetv.com, pg 771

A&E Television Networks LLC, 235 E 45 St, New York, NY 10017 *Tel:* 212-210-1400 *Web Site:* www.aetv.com, pg 771

A&I, 257 S Lake St, Burbank, CA 91502 *Tel:* 323-856-5280; 818-848-9001 *Fax:* 323-856-5110 *E-mail:* mail@aandi.com *Web Site:* www.aandi.com, pg 771

A&M Productions, 86 Weybosset St, 5th fl, Providence, RI 02903 *Tel:* 401-453-6161 *Fax:* 401-421-6443 *E-mail:* info@a-mproductions.com *Web Site:* www.a-mproductions.com, pg 771

A&S Case Co Inc, 5260 Vineland Ave, North Hollywood, CA 91601 *Tel:* 818-509-5920 *Toll Free Tel:* 800-394-6181 *Fax:* 818-509-1397 *E-mail:* info@ascase.com *Web Site:* www.ascase.com, pg 771

A&V Company, 4238 Piedmont Pkwy, Greensboro, NC 27410-8111 *Tel:* 336-292-9700 *Toll Free Tel:* 800-292-9700 *Fax:* 336-854-5282 *E-mail:* info@avcompany.com *Web Site:* www.avcompany.com, pg 772

Aardvark Productions LLC, 6738 S La Rosa Dr, Tempe, AZ 85283-3737 *Tel:* 480-775-8237 *Fax:* 480-775-8237 *E-mail:* aardvarkproductions@cox.net *Web Site:* www.aardvarkproductionsllc.com, pg 772

Aardvark Video & Media Productions, 17 Winding Rd, Henderson, NV 89052 *Tel:* 702-897-4477 *Toll Free Tel:* 800-692-4445 *E-mail:* creators@computer.net *Web Site:* aardvarkvideolasvegas.com, pg 772

Aarmor Case Co, 2100 Lapo Rd, Lake Odessa, MI 48849 *Toll Free Tel:* 800-722-5763 *E-mail:* scat@sell104.com, pg 772

Aaron & Le Duc, 2210 Third St, No 316, Santa Monica, CA 90405 *Tel:* 310-452-2034, pg 772

Aaron Marcus & Associates Inc, 1196 Euclid Ave, Suite 1-F, Berkeley, CA 94708-1640 *Tel:* 510-601-0994 *Fax:* 510-527-1994 *Web Site:* www.amanda.com, pg 772

AB Audio Visual Entertainment Inc, PO Box 8020, Long Beach, CA 90808 *Tel:* 562-429-1042 *Toll Free Tel:* 877-222-8346 *Fax:* 562-429-2401 *E-mail:* media@abaudio.com *Web Site:* www.abaudio.com, pg 772

AB Systems Amplifiers, 6120 Brace Rd, Loomis, CA 95650 *Tel:* 916-223-1133 *E-mail:* absales@abamps.com *Web Site:* www.abamps.net, pg 772

Abacus Group of Saint Louis LLC, No 11 Tower, Glen Carbon, IL 62034 *Tel:* 314-583-3747 *E-mail:* abacusgroup@agstl.com *Web Site:* www.agstl.com, pg 772

Abel Cine Tech Los Angeles, 801 S Main St, Suite 104, Burbank, CA 91506 *Tel:* 818-972-9078 *Toll Free Tel:* 888-700-4416 *Fax:* 818-972-2673 *E-mail:* orders@abelcine.com *Web Site:* www.abelcine.com, pg 772

Aberdeen Broadcast Services, 22362 Gilberto, Suite 120, Rancho Santa Margarita, CA 92688 *Tel:* 949-858-4463 *Toll Free Tel:* 800-688-6621 *Fax:* 949-420-2431 *E-mail:* info@abercap.com *Web Site:* www.abercap.com, pg 772

Abingdon Press, 201 Eighth Ave S, Nashville, TN 37203 *Tel:* 615-749-6000 *Toll Free Tel:* 800-251-3320 *Fax:* 615-749-6061 *E-mail:* orders@abingdonpress.com *Web Site:* www.abingdonpress.com, pg 772

ABS Enterprises, PO Box 5127, Evanston, IL 60204-5127 *Tel:* 847-982-1414, pg 772

ABSA Productions Inc, 125 N Halsted St, Chicago, IL 60661 *Tel:* 312-382-1029 *Web Site:* www.absaproductions.com, pg 772

Absolute Hollywood, 10232 Harvest Fields Dr, Woodstock, MD 21163 *Tel:* 443-341-6424 *E-mail:* events@absolutehollywood.com *Web Site:* www.absolutehollywood.com, pg 772

Absolute Rentals, 2633 N San Fernando Blvd, Burbank, CA 91504 *Tel:* 818-842-2828 *Web Site:* www.absoluterentals.com, pg 772

Ac-cetera Inc, 5049 Center Dr, Bldg D-1, Latrobe, PA 15650 *Tel:* 724-532-3363 *Fax:* 724-532-3364 *E-mail:* contact@ez-clamp.net *Web Site:* www.ac-cetera.com, pg 772

AC Lighting Inc, 88 Horner Ave, Toronto, ON M8Z 5Y3, Canada *Tel:* 416-255-9494 *Fax:* 416-255-3514 *E-mail:* northamerica@aclighting.com *Web Site:* www.aclighting.com, pg 772

Academic & Campus Technology Services, 37 Dewey Field Rd, Hanover, NH 03755 *Tel:* 603-646-2999 *Fax:* 603-646-1343 *Web Site:* dartmouth.edu, pg 773

Academy Awards®, 8949 Wilshire Blvd, Beverly Hills, CA 90211 *Tel:* 310-247-3000 *Fax:* 310-859-9619 *E-mail:* awardsoffice@oscars.org; publicity@oscars.org *Web Site:* www.oscars.org, pg 1107

The Academy of Motion Picture Arts and Sciences (AMPAS), 8949 Wilshire Blvd, Beverly Hills, CA 90211 *Tel:* 310-247-3000 *Fax:* 310-859-9619 *E-mail:* awardsoffice@oscars.org *Web Site:* www.oscars.org, pg 1075

Academy of Science Fiction, Fantasy & Horror Films, 334 W 54 St, Los Angeles, CA 90037 *Tel:* 323-752-5811 *E-mail:* scifiacademy@ca.rr.com *Web Site:* www.saturnawards.org, pg 1075

Academy Savant, 524 W Commonwealth Ave, Suite E, Fullerton, CA 92832 *Tel:* 714-870-7880 *Toll Free Tel:* 800-472-8268 *Fax:* 714-526-7400 *E-mail:* info@academysavant.com *Web Site:* www.academysavant.com, pg 773

Accel Video Productions, 14056 Golden Eagle Dr, Jacksonville, FL 32226 *Tel:* 904-677-9063; 848-467-6299 *E-mail:* accelv@yahoo.com *Web Site:* www.accelvideo.com, pg 773

Accelerated Learning Foundation, 118 N Court St, Fairfield, IA 52556 *Tel:* 641-954-5443 *Toll Free Tel:* 800-289-2377 *Fax:* 641-954-5851 *E-mail:* info@gamesforthinkers.org *Web Site:* gamesforthinkers.org, pg 773

Accenture, 161 N Clark St, Chicago, IL 60601 *Tel:* 312-693-0161 *Toll Free Tel:* 877-889-9009 *Fax:* 312-693-0507 *Web Site:* www.accenture.com, pg 773

Access Media Group, 4250 114 Terr N, Clearwater, FL 33762 *Tel:* 727-573-9600 *Toll Free Tel:* 888-354-2510 *Fax:* 727-573-9606 *E-mail:* hitech@videoequipment.com *Web Site:* www.videoequipment.com, pg 773

Access Video in Berkeley, 1442 A Walnut St, Berkeley, CA 94709 *Tel:* 510-528-6044 *E-mail:* accessvideo@hotmail.com *Web Site:* www.accessvideoproductions.com, pg 773

ACCO Brands Corp, 4 Corporate Dr, Lake Zurick, IL 60047-8997 *Toll Free Tel:* 800-541-0094 *Toll Free Fax:* 800-941-4463 *E-mail:* contactus@gbc.com *Web Site:* www.accobrands.com, pg 773

Accord Productions, 2140 S Dixie Hwy, Suite 301, Miami, FL 33133 *Tel:* 305-856-1245 *Toll Free Tel:* 800-833-1245 *Fax:* 305-856-9101 *Web Site:* www.accordvideo.com, pg 773

Accu-Tech, 11350 Old Roswell Rd, Suite 100, Roswell, GA 30009 *Tel:* 770-740-2240 *Toll Free Tel:* 800-221-4767; 888-222-8832 *Fax:* 770-740-2260 *Web Site:* www.accu-tech.com, pg 773

Accusoft, 4001 N Riverside Dr, Tampa, FL 33603 *Tel:* 813-875-7575 *Toll Free Tel:* 800-875-7009 *Fax:* 813-875-7705 *E-mail:* sales@accusoft.com *Web Site:* www.accusoft.com, pg 774

AccuWeather Inc, 385 Science Park Rd, State College, PA 16803 *Tel:* 814-235-8600 *Toll Free Tel:* 800-566-6606 *Fax:* 814-235-8609 *E-mail:* sales@accuweather.com *Web Site:* www.accuweather.com, pg 774

ACDC Audio CD & Cassette, 606 Alamo Pintado Rd, Suite 3-281, Solvang, CA 93463 *Tel:* 818-762-ACDC (762-2232) *Web Site:* www.acdc-cdr.com, pg 774

Ace Video, 178 Columbus Ave, No 237072, New York, NY 10023 *Tel:* 212-727-7969 *Toll Free Fax:* 888-315-9596 *E-mail:* acevideonyc@gmail.com *Web Site:* www.acevideonyc.com, pg 774

ACE Video Resources Software, 11767 S Dixie Hwy, Suite 222, Miami, FL 33156 *Tel:* 305-596-6908 *Toll Free Tel:* 888-223-6284 *Fax:* 305-256-0467 *E-mail:* mailroom@tutorace.com *Web Site:* www.tutorace.com, pg 774

Acey Decy Lighting, 200 Parkside Dr, San Fernando, CA 91340 *Tel:* 818-408-4444 *Fax:* 818-408-2777 *E-mail:* rcarranza@aceydecy.com *Web Site:* www.aceydecy.com; www.lighttrader.com, pg 774

ACM Productions Ltd, 38 Bob Hill Rd, Ridgefield, CT 06877 *Tel:* 203-431-9575 *E-mail:* info@acmproductions.tv *Web Site:* www.acmproductions.tv, pg 774

Acme Filmworks, 3347 Motor Ave, Suite 100, Los Angeles, CA 90034 *Tel:* 323-464-7805 *Fax:* 323-464-6614 *Web Site:* www.acmefilmworks.com, pg 774

Acme Recording Studios Inc, 112 W Boston Post Rd, Mamaroneck, NY 10543 *Tel:* 914-381-4141 *Web Site:* www.acmerec.com, pg 774

ACO Pacific Inc, 2604 Read Ave, Belmont, CA 94002 *Tel:* 650-595-8588 *Fax:* 650-591-2891 *E-mail:* sales@acopacific.com; info@acopacific.com; support@acopacific.com *Web Site:* www.acopacific.com, pg 774

Acorn Productions, 620 Homewood Dr, Plano, TX 75025 *Tel:* 972-385-9977 *Fax:* 972-385-9944 *E-mail:* acornprod@aol.com, pg 774

Acoustic Systems, 1301 Arrow Point Dr, Cedar Park, TX 78613 *Tel:* 512-531-6400 *Toll Free Tel:* 800-749-1460 *Fax:* 512-531-6500 *E-mail:* sales@ets-lindgren.com *Web Site:* www.ets-lindgren.com, pg 774

Acoustical Society of America (ASA), 1305 Walt Whitman Rd, Suite 300, Melville, NY 11747-4300 *Tel:* 516-576-2360 *Fax:* 516-576-2377 *E-mail:* asa@aip.org *Web Site:* www.acousticalsociety.org, pg 1075

Acoustical Solutions Inc, 2420 Grenoble Rd, Richmond, VA 23294 *Tel:* 804-346-8350 *Toll Free Tel:* 800-782-5742 *Fax:* 804-346-8808 *E-mail:* info@acousticalsolutions.com *Web Site:* www.acousticalsolutions.com, pg 774

Acoustics First Corp, 2247 Tomlyn St, Richmond, VA 23230-3334 *Tel:* 804-342-2900 *Toll Free Tel:* 888-765-2900 *Fax:* 804-342-1107 *E-mail:* info@acousticsfirst.com *Web Site:* www.acousticsfirst.com, pg 775

Acoustone Corp, 140 58 St, Unit 9 W, Bldg A, Brooklyn, NY 11220 *Tel:* 718-782-5560 *Fax:* 718-782-7367 *E-mail:* acoustone@newcastlefabrics.com *Web Site:* www.acoustonegrillecloth.com, pg 775

ACS Technologies, 180 N Dunbarton Dr, Florence, SC 29501 *Tel:* 843-662-1681 *Toll Free Tel:* 800-736-7425 *Fax:* 843-669-3198 *E-mail:* info@acstechnologies.com *Web Site:* www.acstechnologies.com, pg 775

Act One Video, PO Box 342076, Kailua, HI 96734-8997 *Tel:* 808-220-3625 *E-mail:* info@actonevideo.tv *Web Site:* www.actonevideo.tv, pg 775

ACT Productions, 407 Lincoln Rd, Suite 302, Miami Beach, FL 33139 *Tel:* 305-538-3809 *Fax:* 305-538-3814 *E-mail:* info@actproductions.com *Web Site:* www.actproductions.com, pg 775

ACTA Publications, 4848 N Clark St, Chicago, IL 60640 *Tel:* 773-271-1030 *Toll Free Tel:* 800-397-2282 *Fax:* 773-271-7399 *Toll Free Fax:* 800-397-0079 *Web Site:* www.actapublications.com, pg 775

Action Audio & Visual, 10834 Burbank Blvd, Suite A-100, North Hollywood, CA 91601 *Tel:* 818-760-2585 *Toll Free Tel:* 888-406-8164 *Fax:* 818-760-2175 *E-mail:* info@actionaudioandvisual.com *Web Site:* www.actionaudioandvisual.com, pg 775

Action Photo Service Inc, 1741 Clayton Rd, Concord, CA 94520 *Tel:* 925-676-7777 *Fax:* 925-676-9275 *E-mail:* actionps@sbcglobal.net *Web Site:* www.actionphotoservice.com, pg 775

Action Sports/All Stock, PO Box 301, Malibu, CA 90265-0301 *Tel:* 310-459-2526 *Fax:* 310-456-1743 *E-mail:* info@sdfilms.com *Web Site:* www.actionsportsstockfootage.com, pg 775

Action Video, 2373 Walnut Blvd, Walnut Creek, CA 94597 *Tel:* 925-934-4366 *E-mail:* actvid@aol.com *Web Site:* actionvideo.biz, pg 775

Activu Corp, 301 Roundhill Dr, Rockaway, NJ 07866 *Tel:* 973-366-5550 *Toll Free Tel:* 888-ACTIVU1 (228-4881) *Fax:* 973-625-7775 *E-mail:* info@activu.com *Web Site:* www.activu.com, pg 775

Actors Attic, 540 Otis Dr, Dover, DE 19901 *Tel:* 302-734-8214 *Fax:* 302-734-8207 *E-mail:* sales@actorsattic.com *Web Site:* www.actorsattic.com, pg 775

ADAM Inc, 5 Concourse Pkwy, Suite 3200, Atlanta, GA 30328 *Tel:* 404-604-2757 *Toll Free Tel:* 800-755-ADAM (755-2326) *E-mail:* editorialdirector@adamcorp.com *Web Site:* www.adam.com, pg 775

Adams Creative & Production Services, PO Box 98636, Des Moines, WA 98198-0636 *Tel:* 206-824-6970 *Fax:* 206-824-7036 *E-mail:* adamscreative@isomedia.com *Web Site:* www.adamscreative.net, pg 775

D L Adams Associates Inc, 1536 Augden St, Denver, CO 80218 *Tel:* 303-455-1900 *Fax:* 303-455-9187 *E-mail:* denver@dlaa.com *Web Site:* www.dlaa.com, pg 775

DL Adams Associates Ltd, 970 N Kalaheo Ave, Suite A-311, Kailua, HI 96734 *Tel:* 808-254-3318 *Fax:* 808-254-5295 *E-mail:* infohawaii@dlaa.com *Web Site:* www.dlaa.com, pg 775

Adams Evidence Grade Technology Inc, 4123 N Little Creek Rd, Utopia, TX 78884 *Tel:* 830-966-4210 *Toll Free Tel:* 877-643-4900 *Fax:* 830-966-4214 *E-mail:* info1@evidencegrade.com; customerservice@evidencegrade.com *Web Site:* www.evidencegrade.com, pg 775

Adaptive Video Walls & Displays, 1635 E Burnett St, Signal Hill, CA 90755 *Tel:* 562-424-1100 *Fax:* 562-424-3520 *E-mail:* info@adapttechgroup.com *Web Site:* www.adapttechgroup.com, pg 775

Adcom LLC, PO Box 54096, Phoenix, AZ 85078 *Tel:* 480-607-2277 *Fax:* 623-505-9523 *E-mail:* sales@adcom-usa.com *Web Site:* www.adcom-usa.com, pg 776

ADD Plus, 488 Glacier Way S, Monmouth, OR 97361 *Toll Free Tel:* 800-847-1233 *Fax:* 503-838-1608 *Web Site:* www.add-plus.com, pg 776

Addlogix, 47 Peters Canyon Rd, Irvine, CA 92606 *Tel:* 949-341-0888 *Toll Free Tel:* 800-344-6921 *Fax:* 949-341-0669 *E-mail:* sales@addlogix.com *Web Site:* www.addlogix.com, pg 776

Adelphi Records Inc, PO Box 7688, Silver Spring, MD 20907-7688 *Tel:* 301-434-6958 *Fax:* 301-434-3056 *E-mail:* adelphi@adelphirecords.com *Web Site:* www.adelphirecords.com, pg 776

ADI Systems Inc, 3144 Thunderbird Crescent, Burnaby, BC V5A 3G4, Canada *Tel:* 604-291-1839 *Toll Free Tel:* 800-663-1042 *Fax:* 604-294-5782 *E-mail:* burnaby.ca@adiglobal.com *Web Site:* www.adiglobal.ca, pg 776

Adobe Systems Inc, 345 Park Ave, San Jose, CA 95110-2704 *Tel:* 408-536-6000 *Fax:* 408-537-6000 *Web Site:* www.adobe.com, pg 776

Adolph Gasser Inc, 181 Second St, San Francisco, CA 94105 *Tel:* 415-495-3852 *Toll Free Tel:* 800-994-2773 *Fax:* 415-543-8510 *E-mail:* agivideo@yahoo.com *Web Site:* www.gasserphoto.com, pg 776

Adorama Rental Co, 42 W 18 St, 6th fl, New York, NY 10011 *Tel:* 212-627-8487 *E-mail:* rent@adorama.com *Web Site:* www.adoramarentals.com, pg 776

Adrenaline Films, 5224 S Orange Ave, Orlando, FL 32809 *Tel:* 407-850-0711 *Fax:* 407-859-6527 *E-mail:* contact@adrenalinefilms.com *Web Site:* www.adrenalinefilms.com, pg 777

Adrienne Electronics Corp (AEC), 901 American Pacific Dr, Suite 170, Henderson, NV 89014 *Tel:* 702-896-1858 *Toll Free Tel:* 800-782-2321 *Fax:* 702-896-3034 *E-mail:* info@adrielec.com; orders@adrielec.com; support@adrielec.com *Web Site:* www.adrielec.com, pg 777

The ADS Group, 2155 Niagara Lane N, Suite 120, Plymouth, MN 55447 *Tel:* 763-449-5500 *Toll Free Tel:* 800-759-0992 *Fax:* 763-449-5555 *E-mail:* sales@theadsgroup.com *Web Site:* www.theadsgroup.com, pg 777

ADS Media, 620 Trinity Church Rd, Hamilton, ON L0R 1P0, Canada *Tel:* 905-692-2960 *Fax:* 905-692-2961 *E-mail:* info@adsmedia.ca *Web Site:* www.adsmedia.ca, pg 777

ADS Technologies, 160 Commerce Way, Walnut, CA 91789 *Tel:* 909-839-2929 *Fax:* 909-839-2930 *E-mail:* sales@adesso.com *Web Site:* www.adesso.com, pg 777

Adtec Digital Inc, 408 Russell St, Nashville, TN 37206 *Tel:* 615-256-6619 *Fax:* 615-256-6593 *E-mail:* sales@adtecinc.com *Web Site:* www.adtecinc.com, pg 777

Advance Audiovisual Presentation Ltd, 5 Rothschild Ct, Gaithersburg, MD 20878 *Tel:* 301-937-0900 *Fax:* 301-330-2937 *E-mail:* aaplav@outlook.com *Web Site:* aaplav.com, pg 777

Advance Concepts Inc, 8453 Tyco Rd, Suite N, Vienna, VA 22182-2623 *Tel:* 703-448-0445 *Fax:* 703-893-8049 *Web Site:* www.advanceconcepts.com, pg 777

Advance Pro, 1300 Portage Ave, Winnipeg, MB R3G 0V1, Canada *Tel:* 204-772-0386 *Toll Free Tel:* 800-392-1295 *Fax:* 204-783-2177 *E-mail:* ap@advance.mb.ca *Web Site:* www.advance-pro.com, pg 777

Advanced Audio Technology, 200 Easy St, Carol Stream, IL 60188 *Tel:* 630-665-3344 *Fax:* 630-665-3347 *E-mail:* info@advancedaudio.net *Web Site:* www.advancedaudio.net, pg 777

Advanced Audio-Visual Inc, 11978 Riverwood Dr, Burnsville, MN 55337 *Tel:* 952-881-4500 *Web Site:* www.aavmn.com, pg 777

Advanced AV, 208 Carter Dr, Suite 7, West Chester, PA 19382 *Toll Free Tel:* 877-696-7700 *Fax:* 610-692-8421 *E-mail:* sales@advancedav.com *Web Site:* www.advancedav.com, pg 777

Advanced Battery Systems Inc, 516 Bedford St, East Bridgewater, MA 02333 *Tel:* 508-378-2284 *Toll Free Tel:* 800-634-8132 *E-mail:* abs@batteryprice.com *Web Site:* www.batteryprice.com, pg 777

Advanced Designs Corp, 1169 W Second St, Bloomington, IN 47403 *Tel:* 812-333-1922 *Fax:* 812-333-2030 *Web Site:* www.doprad.com, pg 777

Advanced Imaging Concepts Inc, 301 N Harrison St, Bldg B, Suite 266, Princeton, NJ 08540 *Tel:* 609-921-3629; 609-529-9200 *Fax:* 609-924-3010 *E-mail:* info@aic-imagecentral.com; sales@aic-imagecentral.com *Web Site:* www.aic-imagecentral.com, pg 777

Advanced Lighting & Production Services Inc (ALPS), 65 Teed Dr, Randolph, MA 02368 *Tel:* 781-961-3066 *Toll Free Tel:* 866-961-3066 *Fax:* 781-961-3256 *E-mail:* info@alpsweb.com *Web Site:* www.alpsweb.com, pg 777

Advanced Media Integration, 2300 Meyer Rd, Fort Wayne, IN 46805 *Tel:* 260-428-2698 *Toll Free Tel:* 877-428-2610 *Fax:* 260-428-2699 *E-mail:* info@advancedmediaintegration.com *Web Site:* www.advancedmediaintegration.com, pg 777

Advanced Media LLC, 369 N Fairfax Ave, Suite A, Los Angeles, CA 90036 *Tel:* 323-469-0707 *Fax:* 323-461-3715 *E-mail:* info@advancedmediallc.com *Web Site:* www.advancedmediallc.com, pg 778

Advanced Sound, 4611 Central Ave Pike, Suite F, Knoxville, TN 37912 *Tel:* 865-661-5961 *Fax:* 865-637-6694 *Web Site:* www.advancedsound.com, pg 778

Advanced Systems Group LLC, 1226 Powell St, Emeryville, CA 94608-2618 *Tel:* 510-654-8300 *Fax:* 510-654-8370 *Web Site:* www.asgllc.com, pg 778

Advent Media Inc, 5629 Fraley Ct, Columbus, OH 43235 *Tel:* 614-538-1622 *Toll Free Tel:* 877-538-1622 *Fax:* 614-538-1621 *Web Site:* www.adventmediainc.com, pg 778

AdventSource, 5120 Prescott Ave, Lincoln, NE 68506 *Tel:* 402-486-8800 *Toll Free Tel:* 800-328-0525 *Fax:* 402-486-8819 *E-mail:* service@adventsource.org *Web Site:* www.adventsource.org, pg 778

Adventure Productions LLC, 5910 York Rd, Lower Level, Baltimore, MD 21212 *Tel:* 410-878-1261; 410-961-5942 (cell) *Fax:* 410-878-1263 *Web Site:* www.adventureproductions.com, pg 778

Adwar Video, 125 Gazza Blvd, Farmingdale, NY 11735 *Tel:* 631-777-7070 *Toll Free Tel:* 877-GOADWAR (462-3927) *Fax:* 631-777-7011 *E-mail:* sales@adwarvideo.com *Web Site:* adwarvideo.com, pg 778

AEMC Instruments, 200 Foxborough Blvd, Foxborough, MA 02035 *Tel:* 508-698-2115 *Toll Free Tel:* 800-343-1391 *Fax:* 508-698-2118 *E-mail:* sales@aemc.com *Web Site:* www.aemc.com, pg 778

AEON Communications Inc, PO Box 96, Mountlake Terrace, WA 98043 *Tel:* 425-672-8222 *E-mail:* winningcolors@mindspring.com *Web Site:* winningcolors.com, pg 778

Aerial Imaging Productions, 12001 E 33 Ave, Unit R, Aurora, CO 80010 *Tel:* 720-255-1195 *E-mail:* info@aerialimagingproductions.com *Web Site:* www.aerialimagingproductions.com, pg 778

Aerial Video Systems, 712 S Main St, Burbank, CA 91506 *Tel:* 818-954-8842 *Fax:* 818-954-8842 *Web Site:* aerialvideo.com, pg 778

Aero-Tech Light Bulb Co Inc, 534 Pratt Ave N, Schaumburg, IL 60193 *Tel:* 847-352-4900 *Toll Free Tel:* 800-955-2376 *Fax:* 847-352-4999 *E-mail:* info@aerolights.com *Web Site:* www.aerolights.com, pg 778

AFI FEST, 2021 N Western Ave, Los Angeles, CA 90027-1657 *Tel:* 323-856-7600 *Toll Free Tel:* 866-AFI-FEST (234-3378) *Fax:* 323-467-4578 *E-mail:* afifest@afi.com; festpublicity@afi.com *Web Site:* www.afi.com, pg 1107

African American Images, PO Box 1799, Chicago Heights, IL 60412 *Tel:* 708-672-4909 *Toll Free Tel:* 800-552-1991 *Fax:* 708-672-0466 *E-mail:* customersvc@africanamericanimages.com *Web Site:* www.africanamericanimages.com, pg 778

Agency for Instructional Technology (AIT), 8111 N Lee Paul Rd, Bloomington, IN 47404-7916 *Tel:* 812-339-2203 *Toll Free Tel:* 800-457-4509 *Fax:* 812-333-4218 *E-mail:* info@ait.net *Web Site:* www.ait.net, pg 778, 1075

AGF Media Services, 14932 Delano St, Van Nuys, CA 91411-2122 *Tel:* 818-780-7400; 818-780-8085 (24 hours) *Fax:* 818-904-9905 *E-mail:* info@agfmedia.com *Web Site:* www.agfmedia.com, pg 778

Agfa Graphics, 611 River Dr, Ctr 3, Elmwood Park, NJ 07407 *Tel:* 201-440-2500 *Toll Free Tel:* 800-540-2432 *Web Site:* www.agfagraphics.com; www.agfa.com, pg 778

Aggressive Records Audio Duplication LLC, 1951 University Ave W, Suite 107, St Paul, MN 55104 *Tel:* 651-645-7805 *E-mail:* sales@aggressiverecords.com *Web Site:* www.aggressiverecords.com, pg 778

AGLIFF-Austin Gay & Lesbian International Film Festival, 2905 San Gabriel St, Suite 300, Austin, TX 78705 *Tel:* 512-302-9889 *Fax:* 512-302-1088 *E-mail:* info@agliff.org *Web Site:* www.agliff.org, pg 1107

Agrama Film Enterprises Inc, 7655 Sunset Blvd, Los Angeles, CA 90046 *Tel:* 323-851-4900 *Fax:* 323-851-5599 *E-mail:* sales@harmonygold.com *Web Site:* harmonygold.com, pg 778

Ahead Stereo Inc, 7428 Beverly Blvd, Los Angeles, CA 90036 *Tel:* 323-931-8873 *Fax:* 323-937-7285 *E-mail:* mrstereo@pacbell.net *Web Site:* www.aheadstereo.com, pg 778

AheadTeK, 6410 Via Del Oro, San Jose, CA 95119 *Tel:* 408-226-9800; 408-226-9991 *Toll Free Tel:* 800-971-9191 *Fax:* 408-226-9195 *Web Site:* www.aheadtek.com, pg 778

The Ahern Group, 3701 Malden Ave, Unit A, Baltimore, MD 21211 *Tel:* 410-367-9660 *Fax:* 410-367-9661 *E-mail:* videoahern@aol.com *Web Site:* www.theaherngroup.com, pg 779

The Charles Aidikoff Screening Room, 150 S Rodeo Dr, Suite 140, Beverly Hills, CA 90212 *Tel:* 310-274-0866 *Fax:* 310-550-1794 *E-mail:* info@aidikoff.com *Web Site:* www.aidikoff.tv, pg 779

AIGA, the professional association for design, 164 Fifth Ave, New York, NY 10010 *Tel:* 212-807-1990 *Toll Free Tel:* 800-548-1634 *Fax:* 212-807-1799 *E-mail:* general@aiga.org *Web Site:* www.aiga.org, pg 1075

AiH Group Inc, 709 S Aiken Ave, Pittsburgh, PA 15232 *Tel:* 412-687-5700 *E-mail:* aih@aihgroup.com *Web Site:* www.aihgroup.com, pg 779

Aiphone Corp, 1700 130 Ave NE, Bellevue, WA 98005 *Tel:* 425-455-0510 *Toll Free Tel:* 800-692-0200 *Fax:* 425-455-0516 (sales); 425-455-0071 *Toll Free Fax:* 800-525-3372 (cust serv) *E-mail:* info@aiphone.com; cs@aiphone.com *Web Site:* www.aiphone.com, pg 779

Air Sea Land Productions Inc (ASL), 19-69 Steinway St, Astoria, NY 11105-1108 *Tel:* 718-626-2646 *Toll Free Tel:* 888-ASL-LENS (275-5367) *Fax:* 718-626-1493 *E-mail:* sales@airsealand.com *Web Site:* www.airsealand.com, pg 779

AirBrands Event & Marketing Group, 6470 Wyoming St, Dearborn, MI 48126 *Tel:* 519-254-9563 *Toll Free Tel:* 800-411-6200 (ext 26) *E-mail:* service@airbrandsmarketing.com *Web Site:* www.airbrandsmarketing.com, pg 779

AirCraft Production Libraries, 162 Columbus Ave, Boston, MA 02116-5222 *Tel:* 617-303-7600 *Toll Free Tel:* 800-343-2514 *Fax:* 617-303-7666 *E-mail:* info@aircraftmusiclibrary.com; acsales@aircraftmusiclibrary.com *Web Site:* www.aircraftmusiclibrary.com, pg 779

Airshow Mastering, 3063 Sterling Circle, Suite 3, Boulder, CO 80301 *Tel:* 303-247-9035 *Toll Free Tel:* 888-545-9035 *Toll Free Fax:* 888-545-9035 *E-mail:* studio@airshowmastering.com *Web Site:* www.airshowmastering.com, pg 779

Airwave Recording Studio, 5176 Hollow Log Lane, Birmingham, AL 35244 *Tel:* 205-427-4675, pg 779

Airways Digital Media, 4055 W Peterson Ave, Chicago, IL 60646 *Tel:* 773-539-8400 *E-mail:* info@airwaysdigital.com *Web Site:* www.airwaysdigital.com, pg 779

AITech International, 1288 Kifer Rd, Suite 203, Sunnyvale, CA 94086 *Tel:* 408-991-9699 *Fax:* 408-991-9691 *E-mail:* info@aitech.com; aitechproducts@aitech.com *Web Site:* www.aitech.com, pg 779

AJA Video Systems Inc, 180 Litton Dr, Grass Valley, CA 95945 *Tel:* 530-274-2048 *Fax:* 530-274-9442 *E-mail:* sales@aja.com *Web Site:* www.aja.com, pg 779

Akai Professional, 200 Scenic View Dr, Suite 201, Cumberland, RI 02864 *Tel:* 401-658-4032 *E-mail:* info@akaipro.com *Web Site:* www.akaipro.com, pg 779

AKG Acoustics US, 8500 Balboa Blvd, Northridge, CA 91329 *Tel:* 818-920-3212 *Fax:* 818-920-3208 *E-mail:* akgusa@harman.com *Web Site:* www.akg.com/us, pg 779

Alabama Film Office, Alabama Center for Commerce, 401 Adams Ave, Suite 170, Montgomery, AL 36104-1430 *Tel:* 334-242-4195 *Fax:* 334-242-2077 *Web Site:* www.alabamafilm.org, pg 1091

Alabama State Council on the Arts Fellowships & Grants, RSA Tower, Suite 110, 201 Monroe St, Montgomery, AL 36130-1800 *Tel:* 334-242-4076 *Fax:* 334-240-3269 *E-mail:* staff@arts.alabama.gov *Web Site:* www.arts.alabama.gov, pg 1107

Alarmco Intelligent Message Repeaters, One Bailey Dr, Guilford, CT 06437 *Tel:* 203-458-2646 *Toll Free Tel:* 800-824-5006 *E-mail:* info@messagerepeaters.com *Web Site:* www.messagerepeaters.com, pg 779

Alaska Film Office, 550 W Seventh Ave, Suite 500, Anchorage, AK 99501 *Tel:* 907-269-1018 *Fax:* 907-269-6644 *E-mail:* alaskafilmoffice@alaska.gov *Web Site:* tax.alaska.gov/AlaskaFilmOffice/, pg 1091

Alaska Film Services Inc, 11050 Cange St, Anchorage, AK 99516 *Tel:* 907-230-6870 *Fax:* 907-272-6778 *E-mail:* filmservices@alaska.net *Web Site:* www.alaskafilmservices.com, pg 779

Alaska Video Postcards Inc, PO Box 112808, Anchorage, AK 99511-2808 *Tel:* 907-349-8002 *Toll Free Tel:* 800-248-2624 *E-mail:* mail@akvideo.com *Web Site:* www.akvideo.com, pg 779

Albany Theatre Supply Co Inc, 445 N Pearl St, Albany, NY 12204 *Tel:* 518-465-8895 *Fax:* 518-465-8908 *E-mail:* sales@albanytheatresupply.com *Web Site:* www.albanytheatresupply.com, pg 780

Alberta Film Commission, 140 Whitemud Crossing, 4211-106 St, Edmonton, AB T6J 6L7, Canada *Tel:* 780-422-8584 *Toll Free Tel:* 888-813-1738 *Fax:* 780-422-8582 *E-mail:* info@albertafilm.ca *Web Site:* www.albertafilm.ca, pg 1104

Albumx Corp, 21 Grace Church St, Port Chester, NY 10573 *Tel:* 914-939-6878 *Toll Free Tel:* 800-961-6710 *Fax:* 914-939-8047 *E-mail:* info@renaissancealbums.com *Web Site:* www.renaissancealbums.com, pg 780

Albuquerque Film Office, Economic Development Dept, One Civic Plaza NW, Albuquerque, NM 87102 *Tel:* 505-768-3283 *Fax:* 505-768-3280 *Web Site:* www.cabq.gov/film, pg 1100

ALC (Auernheimer Labs & Co), 4561 E Florence Ave, Fresno, CA 93725 *Tel:* 559-442-1048, pg 780

Alcorn McBride Inc, 3300 S Hiawassee Rd, Bldg 105, Orlando, FL 32835 *Tel:* 407-296-5800 *Fax:* 407-296-5801 *E-mail:* info@alcorn.com; sales@alcorn.com *Web Site:* www.alcorn.com, pg 780

Alden Films, PO Box 449, Clarksburg, NJ 08510-0449 *Tel:* 732-462-3522 *Toll Free Tel:* 800-832-0980 *Fax:* 732-294-0330 *E-mail:* info@aldenfilms.com *Web Site:* www.aldenfilms.com, pg 780

Alegra House Publishers, PO Box 1443, Warren, OH 44482-1443 *Tel:* 330-372-2951 *Fax:* 330-399-1619, pg 780

Alexander Media Productions, 1901 Diamond Ridge Dr, Carrollton, TX 75010 *Tel:* 214-274-3456 *Web Site:* www.heatheralexander.net, pg 780

Alexander Street Press, 3212 Duke St, Alexandria, VA 22314 *Tel:* 703-212-8520 *E-mail:* sales@alexanderstreet.com *Web Site:* academicvideostore.com, pg 780

Alford Media Services, 296 Freeport Pkwy, Coppell, TX 75019 *Tel:* 972-538-9400 *Toll Free Tel:* 800-554-9144 *Fax:* 972-538-0800 *E-mail:* info@alfordmedia.com; sales@alfordmedia.com *Web Site:* www.alfordmedia.com, pg 780

Alien Skin Software LLC, 1111 Haynes St, Suite 113, Raleigh, NC 27604 *Tel:* 919-832-4124 *Toll Free Tel:* 888-921-7546 *Fax:* 919-832-4065 *E-mail:* sales@alienskin.com *Web Site:* www.alienskin.com, pg 780

Aliso Creek Productions Inc, 4106 W Burbank Blvd, Burbank, CA 91510 *Tel:* 818-954-9931 *Web Site:* www.alisocreek.net, pg 780

All Access Staging & Productions, 1320 Storm Pkwy, Torrance, CA 90501 *Tel:* 310-784-2464 *Toll Free Tel:* 877-784-2464 *Fax:* 310-517-0899 *E-mail:* usinfo@allaccessinc.com *Web Site:* www.allaccessinc.com, pg 780

All Communications Rentals Inc (ALLCOMM), 1402 SW 13 Ct, Pompano Beach, FL 33069 *Tel:* 954-788-9555 *Web Site:* www.allcommrentals.com, pg 780

All Jersey Studios, 222 Cavour St, Colonia, NJ 07067 *Tel:* 732-382-2333 *E-mail:* info@alljerseystudios.com *Web Site:* www.alljerseystudios.com, pg 780

All Mobile Video Inc, 221 W 26 St, New York, NY 10001 *Tel:* 212-727-1234 *Fax:* 212-255-6644 *E-mail:* contact@amvchelsea.com *Web Site:* allmobilevideo.com, pg 780

All Pro Media Inc, 422 S Spring St, Burlington, NC 27216 *Tel:* 336-229-7700 *Toll Free Tel:* 800-270-2207 *Fax:* 336-229-7778 *Web Site:* www.allpromedia.com, pg 780

All Service Musical Electronics Repair, 617 SE Morrison St, Portland, OR 97214 *Tel:* 503-231-6552 *Fax:* 503-239-7157 *E-mail:* service@asmusic.org *Web Site:* www.all-service-musical.com, pg 780

All Terrain Power Co Inc, PO Box 18, Bellport, NY 11713 *Tel:* 718-852-4922 *Fax:* 718-267-0002 *Web Site:* www.allterrainpower.com, pg 781

All Video Productions, 726 Santa Monica Blvd, Suite 212, Santa Monica, CA 90401 *Tel:* 310-666-5606 *Fax:* 310-656-1155 *E-mail:* info@allvideoproductions.com *Web Site:* www.allvideoproductions.com, pg 781

Allegro Corp/Allegro Entertainment Canada Ltd, 20048 NE San Rafael St, Portland, OR 97230-7459 *Tel:* 503-491-8480 *Toll Free Tel:* 800-288-2007 (ext 2500, cust serv) *Fax:* 503-491-8488 *E-mail:* mailcs@allegro-music.com (cust serv) *Web Site:* www.allegromediagroup.com, pg 781

Allegro Productions Inc, 1000 Clint Moore Rd, Suite 108, Boca Raton, FL 33487 *Tel:* 561-994-9111 *Toll Free Tel:* 800-232-2133 (ext 201) *Fax:* 561-241-0707 *Web Site:* www.allegrovideo.com, pg 781

Allen Avionics Inc, 255 E Second St, Mineola, NY 11501 *Tel:* 516-248-8080 *Fax:* 516-747-6724 *E-mail:* info@allenavionics.com *Web Site:* www.allenavionics.com, pg 781

John E Allen Inc, PO Box 452, Newfoundland, PA 18445 *Tel:* 570-676-4152 *Fax:* 570-676-9194 *E-mail:* jeainc@gmail.com *Web Site:* www.allenarchive.com/wordpress, pg 781

Allen Products Co Inc, 1635 E Burnett St, Signal Hill, CA 90755 *Tel:* 562-424-1100 *Fax:* 562-424-3520 *E-mail:* info@adapttechgroup.com *Web Site:* www.adapttechgroup.com, pg 781

Allen Visual Systems Inc, 1405 Busch Pkwy, Buffalo Grove, IL 60089 *Tel:* 847-520-4960 *Fax:* 847-520-7370 *E-mail:* sales@allenvisual.com *Web Site:* www.allenvisual.com, pg 781

Alliance Entertainment Corp (AEC) LLC, 4250 Coral Ridge Dr, Coral Springs, FL 33065 *Tel:* 954-346-4024 *Toll Free Tel:* 800-356-2049 (ext 4600) *Web Site:* www.aent.com, pg 781

The Alliance for Christian Media, 2715 Peachtree Rd NE, Atlanta, GA 30305 *Tel:* 404-815-0640 *Toll Free Tel:* 800-229-3788 *E-mail:* contact@allianceforchristianmedia.org *Web Site:* www.allianceforchristianmedia.org, pg 781

Alliance for Community Media (ACM), 4248 Park Glen Rd, Minneapolis, MN 55416 *Tel:* 952-928-4643 *E-mail:* info@allcommunitymedia.org *Web Site:* www.allcommunitymedia.org, pg 1075

Alliance for Women in Media/Alliance for Women in Media Foundation, 1250 24 St NW, Suite 300, Washington, DC 20037 *Tel:* 703-506-3290 *Fax:* 202-750-3664 *Web Site:* www.allwomeninmedia.org, pg 1075

Alliance of Motion Picture & Television Producers (AMPTP), 15301 Ventura Blvd, Bldg E, Sherman Oaks, CA 91403 *Tel:* 818-995-3600 *Fax:* 818-285-4450 *E-mail:* info@tw.amptp.org *Web Site:* www.amptp.org, pg 1075

Alliance Publications Inc (API)/Sinsinawa Studios Productions, 585 County Rd Z, Sinsinawa, WI 53824-0157 *Tel:* 608-748-4411 (ext 124) *Fax:* 608-748-4491 *E-mail:* api@apimusic.org *Web Site:* www.apimusic.org, pg 781

Alliance Quebecoise des Techniciens de l'Image et du Son (AQTIS), 533 Ontario St E, Suite 300, Montreal, QC H2L 1N8, Canada *Tel:* 514-844-2113 *Toll Free Tel:* 888-647-0681 *Fax:* 514-844-3540 *E-mail:* info@aqtis.qc.ca *Web Site:* www.aqtis.qc.ca, pg 1075

Alliant Event Services, 196 University Pkwy, Pomona, CA 91768 *Tel:* 909-622-3306 *Toll Free Tel:* 800-851-5415 *Fax:* 909-622-3917 *E-mail:* marketing@alliantevents.com *Web Site:* www.alliantevents.com, pg 781

Allied Artists International Inc, Production Services Ctr, 15810 E Gale Ave, Suite 133, Hacienda Heights, CA 91745 *Tel:* 626-330-0600 *Fax:* 626-961-0411 *E-mail:* info@alliedartists.net *Web Site:* us.alliedartists.com, pg 781

Allied Media Corp, 5252 Cherokee Ave, Suite 200, Alexandria, VA 22312 *Tel:* 703-333-2008 *Fax:* 703-997-7539 *Toll Free Fax:* 888-747-0957 *E-mail:* info@allied-media.com; contact@allied-media.com *Web Site:* www.allied-media.com, pg 781

Allied Photo Color Co, 4221 Forest Park Ave, St Louis, MO 63108 *Tel:* 314-652-4000 *Fax:* 314-652-8203 *Web Site:* alliedphotocolor.com, pg 781

Alligator Records & Artist Management Inc, 1441 W Devon Ave, Chicago, IL 60660 *Tel:* 773-973-7736 *Fax:* 773-973-2088 *E-mail:* info@allig.com *Web Site:* www.alligator.com, pg 781

Allsop Inc, PO Box 23, Bellingham, WA 98227-0023 *Tel:* 360-734-9090 *Toll Free Tel:* 800-426-4303 *Fax:* 360-734-9858 (sales); 360-733-4302 (corp) *E-mail:* info@allsop.com *Web Site:* www.allsop.com, pg 781

Allstar Audio Systems Inc, PO Box 541964, Merritt Island, FL 32954-1964 *Tel:* 321-455-2202 *Fax:* 321-455-2224 *E-mail:* info@allstaraudio.com *Web Site:* www.allstaraudio.com; allstarsystems.net, pg 782

Allstar Show Industries Inc, 10331 176 St, Edmonton, AB T5S 2E4, Canada *Tel:* 780-486-4000 *Toll Free Tel:* 800-663-4063 (CN & US) *Fax:* 780-414-5724 *E-mail:* allsales@allstar-show.com *Web Site:* www.allstar-show.com, pg 782

Alltec Stores, a Vcom IMC Company, 80 Little Falls Rd, Fairfield, NJ 07004 *Toll Free Tel:* 800-637-3181 *Toll Free Fax:* 800-965-7836 *E-mail:* sales@alltecstores.com *Web Site:* www.alltecstores.com, pg 782

Allusion Studios & Pure Wave Audio, 248 W Elm St, Tucson, AZ 85705 *Tel:* 520-622-3895 *Fax:* 520-622-3895 *E-mail:* contact@allusionstudios.com *Web Site:* www.allusionstudios.com; www.purewaveaudio.com, pg 782

Alma-The International Loudspeaker Association, 55 Littleton Rd, Unit 13-B, Ayer, MA 01432 *Tel:* 978-772-6977 *Fax:* 617-848-9935 *E-mail:* management@almainternational.org *Web Site:* www.almainternational.org, pg 1075

ALOM Technologies Corp, 48105 Warm Springs Blvd, Fremont, CA 94539-7498 *Tel:* 510-360-3600 *Toll Free Tel:* 800-500-9991 *Fax:* 510-226-7617 *E-mail:* customerservice@alom.com *Web Site:* www.alom.com, pg 782

Alpec®, 1231 Midas Way, Sunnyvale, CA 94085 *Tel:* 408-735-6180 *Toll Free Tel:* 800-854-6686 *Fax:* 408-735-6190 *Web Site:* www.alpec.com, pg 782

Alpha & Omega Recording, 150 Bellam Blvd, Suite 255, San Rafael, CA 94901, pg 782

Alpha Source Inc, 6619 W Calumet Rd, Milwaukee, WI 53223-4186 *Tel:* 414-760-2222 *Toll Free Tel:* 800-654-9845 *Fax:* 414-760-2070 *Toll Free Fax:* 888-654-9840 *E-mail:* customer.service@alphasource.com; info@alphasource.com *Web Site:* www.alphasource.com, pg 782

Alpha Technologies, 3767 Alpha Way, Bellingham, WA 98226 *Tel:* 360-647-2360 *Fax:* 360-671-4936 *E-mail:* alpha@alpha.com *Web Site:* www.alpha.com, pg 782

Alpha Video & Audio Inc, 7711 Computer Ave, Edina, MN 55435 *Tel:* 952-896-9898 *Toll Free Tel:* 800-388-0008 *Fax:* 952-896-9899 *E-mail:* info@alphavideo.com *Web Site:* www.alphavideo.com, pg 782

Alpha Video Productions, 441 Biscay Dr, Garland, TX 75043 *Tel:* 972-497-9959 *E-mail:* alphaghb@sbcglobal.net *Web Site:* www.alphavideo.net, pg 782

Alpha Wire Co, 711 Lidgerwood Ave, Elizabeth, NJ 07207-0711 *Tel:* 908-925-8000 *Toll Free Tel:* 800-52-ALPHA (522-5742) *Fax:* 908-925-6923 *E-mail:* info@alphawire.com *Web Site:* www.alphawire.com, pg 782

AlphaDogs Inc, 1612 W Olive Ave, Suite 200, Burbank, CA 91506-2462 *Tel:* 818-729-9262 *Fax:* 818-729-8537 *Web Site:* www.alphadogs.tv, pg 782

Alpine Media, 1644 Conestoga St, Suite 3, Boulder, CO 80301 *Tel:* 303-444-1257 *Toll Free Tel:* 800-475-0872 *E-mail:* info@alpinemedia.com; production@alpinemedia.com; av@alpinemedia.com *Web Site:* www.alpinemedia.com, pg 782

Alpine Optics Inc, 150 View Rd, Brevard, NC 28712 *Tel:* 828-884-5822 *Fax:* 828-884-5884 *E-mail:* toalpine_optics@citcom.net, pg 783

Alpine Texas Chamber of Commerce, 106 N Third St, Alpine, TX 79830 *Tel:* 432-837-2326 *Toll Free Tel:* 800-561-3712 *Fax:* 432-837-1259 *E-mail:* info@alpinetexas.com *Web Site:* www.alpinetexas.com, pg 1102

ALTEL Systems Inc, 601 N Main St, Brewster, NY 10509 *Tel:* 845-278-4400 *Toll Free Tel:* 800-88ALTEL (882-5835) *Fax:* 845-278-2824 *E-mail:* info@altel-av.com *Web Site:* www.altel-av.com, pg 783

Alternative Rentals, 5805 W Jefferson Blvd, Los Angeles, CA 90016 *Tel:* 310-204-3388 *Fax:* 310-204-3384 *E-mail:* info@alternativerentals.com *Web Site:* www.alternativerentals.com, pg 783

ALTINEX Inc, 592 Apollo St, Brea, CA 92821 *Tel:* 714-990-2300 *Toll Free Tel:* 800-ALTINEX (258-4639) *Fax:* 714-990-3303 *E-mail:* sales@altinex.com *Web Site:* www.altinex.com, pg 783

Altruist Media LLC, 1023 Williamsport Pike, Martinsburg, WV 25404 *Tel:* 703-812-8813 *Fax:* 703-812-9710 *E-mail:* frank@altruistmedia.com *Web Site:* www.altruistmedia.com, pg 783

AM Productions, 1141 S Pasadena Ave, Pasadena, CA 91105 *Tel:* 626-403-0258 *Fax:* 626-403-0138, pg 783

AM Stock-Cameo Film Library, 1663 Sawtelle Blvd, Suite 305, Los Angeles, CA 90025 *Tel:* 310-479-4800 *Fax:* 310-933-6979 *E-mail:* researcher@amstockcameo.com *Web Site:* www.amstockcameo.com, pg 783

AMA Nystrom Printing/Finishing, 920 N Valley Mills Dr, Waco, TX 76710 *Tel:* 254-776-8860 *Toll Free Tel:* 800-369-9226 *Fax:* 254-751-2127 *E-mail:* info@amanystrom.com *Web Site:* www.amanystrom.com, pg 783

Amarillo Film Commission, 1000 S Polk St, Amarillo, TX 79101 *Tel:* 806-342-2016 *Toll Free Tel:* 800-692-1338 *Fax:* 806-373-3909 *Web Site:* www.amarillofilm.org; www.visitamarillotx.com, pg 1102

Ambrose Video Publishing Inc, 145 W 45 St, Suite 1115, New York, NY 10036 *Tel:* 212-768-7373 *Toll Free Tel:* 800-526-4663 *Fax:* 212-768-9282 *E-mail:* customerservice@ambrosevideo.com *Web Site:* www.ambrosevideo.com, pg 783

America By Air Stock Footage Library, 154 Euclid Blvd, Lantana, FL 33462 *Toll Free Tel:* 800-488-6359 *Fax:* 413-235-1462 *E-mail:* footage@americabyair.com *Web Site:* www.americabyair.com; www.hdfootage.com, pg 783

American Alliance of Museums (AAM), 1575 Eye St NW, Suite 400, Washington, DC 20005 *Tel:* 202-289-1818 *Fax:* 202-289-6578 *Web Site:* www.aam-us.org, pg 1075

American Artist Studio, 1114 W 26 St, Erie, PA 16508-1518 *Tel:* 814-455-4796 *Toll Free Tel:* 888-462-7813 *Web Site:* americanartiststudio.com, pg 783

American Artists Representatives Inc, 4700 Mamaroneck Ave, White Plains, NY 10605 *Tel:* 212-682-2462; 646-286-5633 (cell) *E-mail:* info@aareps.com *Web Site:* www.aareps.com, pg 783

American Association for Vocational Instructional Materials (AAVIM), 220 Smithonia Rd, Winterville, GA 30683 *Tel:* 706-742-5355 *Fax:* 706-742-7005 *E-mail:* sales@aavim.com *Web Site:* www.aavim.com, pg 783

American Association for Vocational Instructional Materials (AAVIM), 220 Smithonia Rd, Winterville, GA 30683 *Tel:* 706-742-5355 *Toll Free Tel:* 800-228-4689 *Fax:* 706-742-7005 *E-mail:* sales@aavim.com *Web Site:* www.aavim.com, pg 1076

American Association of School Administrators (AASA), 1615 Duke St, Alexandria, VA 22314 *Tel:* 703-528-0700 *Fax:* 703-841-1543 *E-mail:* info@aasa.org *Web Site:* www.aasa.org, pg 1076

American Association of School Librarians (AASL), 50 E Huron St, Chicago, IL 60611 *Tel:* 312-280-4382 *Toll Free Tel:* 800-545-2433 (ext 4382) *Fax:* 312-280-5276 *E-mail:* aasl@ala.org *Web Site:* www.aasl.org, pg 1076

American Association of University Women (AAUW), 1111 16 St NW, Washington, DC 20036 *Tel:* 202-785-7700 *Toll Free Tel:* 800-326-AAUW (326-2289) *Fax:* 202-872-1425 *E-mail:* helpline@aauw.org; connect@aauw.org *Web Site:* www.aauw.org, pg 1076

American Audio Prose Library Inc (AAPL), 600 Crestland Ave, Columbia, MO 65203 *Tel:* 573-443-0361 *Fax:* 573-499-0579 *E-mail:* aaplinc@centurytel.net *Web Site:* www.americanaudioprose.org, pg 783

American Audio Visual Center, 7434 E Monte Cristo Ave, Scottsdale, AZ 85260 *Tel:* 480-596-9880 *Fax:* 480-596-0942 *Web Site:* www.americanavc.com, pg 783

American AV, 2862 Hartland Rd, Falls Church, VA 22043 *Tel:* 703-573-6910 *Fax:* 703-573-3539 *E-mail:* sales@aavevents.com *Web Site:* www.aavevents.com, pg 783

American Blackguard Inc, PO Box 680686, Franklin, TN 37068-0686 *Tel:* 615-599-4032 *E-mail:* contact@americanblackguard.com *Web Site:* www.americanblackguard.com, pg 784

American Center for Children & Media, 5400 N Saint Louis Ave, Chicago, IL 60625 *Tel:* 773-509-5510 *Fax:* 773-509-5303 *E-mail:* info@centerforchildrenandmedia.org *Web Site:* www.centerforchildrenandmedia.org, pg 1076

American Chemical Society (ACS), Dept of Professional Education, 1155 16 St NW, Washington, DC 20036 *Tel:* 202-872-4508 *Toll Free Tel:* 800-ACS-5558 (227-5558 ext 4508) *Fax:* 202-872-6336 *E-mail:* proed@acs.org *Web Site:* proed.acs.org, pg 784

American Choral Catalog Ltd, 205 S Water St, Northfield, MN 55057 *Tel:* 507-645-4695 *Toll Free Tel:* 800-246-7257 *Fax:* 507-645-2474 *E-mail:* info@americanchoral.com *Web Site:* www.americanchoral.com, pg 784

American Cinema Editors Inc (ACE), Verna Fields Bldg 2282, Rm 190, 100 Universal City Plaza, Universal City, CA 91608 *Tel:* 818-777-2900 *Fax:* 818-733-5023 *E-mail:* americancinema@editors.com *Web Site:* www.ace-filmeditors.org, pg 1076

The American Classical League, Miami University, 422 Wells Mill Dr, Oxford, OH 45056 *Tel:* 513-529-7741 *Fax:* 513-529-7742 *E-mail:* info@aclclassics.org *Web Site:* www.aclclassics.org, pg 784

American Color Imaging (ACI), 715 E 18 St, Cedar Falls, IA 50613 *Tel:* 319-277-3655 *Toll Free Tel:* 800-728-2722 *Fax:* 319-277-6522 *E-mail:* sales@acilab.com *Web Site:* www.acilab.com, pg 784

American Counseling Association, 6101 Stevenson Ave, Alexandria, VA 22304 *Tel:* 703-823-9800 (ext 222) *Toll Free Tel:* 800-422-2648 (ext 222) *Fax:* 703-370-4833 *Toll Free Fax:* 800-473-2329 *E-mail:* membership@counseling.org *Web Site:* www.counseling.org, pg 784

American Educational Research Association (AERA), 1430 "K" St NW, Suite 1200, Washington, DC 20005 *Tel:* 202-238-3200 *Fax:* 202-238-3250 *Web Site:* www.aera.net, pg 1076

American Federation of Musicians of the United States & Canada (AFM), 1501 Broadway, Suite 600, New York, NY 10036 *Tel:* 212-869-1330 *Fax:* 212-764-6134 *Web Site:* www.afm.org, pg 1076

American Fibertek Inc, 120 Belmont Dr, Somerset, NJ 08873-4243 *Tel:* 732-302-0660 *Toll Free Tel:* 877-234-7200 *Fax:* 732-302-0667 *E-mail:* sales@americanfibertek.com; techinfo@americanfibertek.com *Web Site:* www.americanfibertek.com, pg 784

American Film Institute (AFI), Attn: Facilities Off, 2021 N Western Ave, Los Angeles, CA 90027-1657 *Tel:* 323-856-7600 *Toll Free Tel:* 800-774-4AFI (774-4234 membership) *Fax:* 323-467-4578 *E-mail:* information@afi.com *Web Site:* www.afi.com, pg 1076

American Foundation for the Blind (AFB), 2 Penn Plaza, Suite 1102, New York, NY 10121 *Tel:* 212-502-7600; 212-502-7662 (TDD) *Toll Free Tel:* 800-232-5463 *Fax:* 212-502-7777 *Toll Free Fax:* 888-545-8331 *E-mail:* afbinfo@afb.net *Web Site:* www.afb.org, pg 1076

American Gramaphone LLC, 9130 Mormon Bridge Rd, Omaha, NE 68152 *Tel:* 402-457-4341 *Fax:* 402-457-4332 *E-mail:* mailbox@mannheimsteamroller.com *Web Site:* www.mannheimsteamroller.com, pg 784

American Harlequin Corp, 1531 Glen Ave, Moorestown, NJ 08057 *Tel:* 856-234-5505 *Toll Free Tel:* 800-642-6440 *Fax:* 856-231-4403 *E-mail:* dance@harlequinfloors.com *Web Site:* www.harlequinfloors.com, pg 784

American Health Information Management Association (AHIMA), 233 N Michigan Ave, 21st fl, Chicago, IL 60601-5809 *Tel:* 312-233-1100 *Toll Free Tel:* 800-335-5535 *Fax:* 312-233-1090; 312-233-1500 (orders) *E-mail:* info@ahima.org *Web Site:* www.ahima.org, pg 1076

American History Workshop (NY) Inc, 588 Seventh St, Brooklyn, NY 11215-3707 *Tel:* 718-499-6500 *E-mail:* info@americanhistoryworkshop.com *Web Site:* www.americanhistoryworkshop.com, pg 784

American Hospital Association, 155 N Wacker Dr, Suite 400, Chicago, IL 60606-1725 *Tel:* 312-422-3000 *Fax:* 312-422-4700 *Web Site:* www.aha.org, pg 784

American Law Institute Continuing Legal Education (ALICLE), 4025 Chestnut St, Philadelphia, PA 19104-3099 *Toll Free Tel:* 800-253-6397 *Fax:* 215-243-1664 *Web Site:* www.ali-cle.org, pg 784

American Legion Fourth Estate Award, Public Relations Div, 700 N Pennsylvania St, Indianapolis, IN 46204 *Tel:* 317-630-1253 *Fax:* 317-630-1368 *E-mail:* pr@legion.org *Web Site:* www.legion.org, pg 1107

American Library Association (ALA), 50 E Huron St, Chicago, IL 60611-2795 *Tel:* 312-944-6780 *Toll Free Tel:* 800-545-2433 (ext 3223, conference servs) *Fax:* 312-440-9374 *E-mail:* ala@ala.org *Web Site:* www.ala.org, pg 1076

American Management Association®, 1601 Broadway, New York, NY 10019 *Tel:* 212-586-8100 *Toll Free Tel:* 877-566-9441 (cust serv) *Fax:* 212-903-8168; 518-891-0368 (cust serv) *E-mail:* customerservice@amanet.org *Web Site:* www.amanet.org, pg 784, 1077

American Management Association International, 600 AMA Way, Saranac Lake, NY 12983 *Tel:* 518-891-1500 (ext 300) *Toll Free Tel:* 877-566-9441 (cust serv) *Fax:* 518-891-0368 *E-mail:* customerservice@amanet.org *Web Site:* www.amanet.org, pg 784

American Melody, PO Box 270, Guilford, CT 06437-0270 *Tel:* 203-457-0881 *Web Site:* www.americanmelody.com, pg 784

American Montage Inc, PO Box 1042, New York, NY 10003 *Tel:* 212-334-8283 *Web Site:* americanmontage.com, pg 784

American Museum of Natural History (AMNH), c/o Moving Image Collection, Library Services Dept, Central Park W & 79 St, New York, NY 10024-5192 *Tel:* 212-769-5420 *Fax:* 212-769-5009 *E-mail:* speccol@amnh.org *Web Site:* www.amnh.org, pg 784

American Music & Sound (AM&S), 925 Broadbeck Dr, No 220, Newbury Park, CA 91320 *Toll Free Tel:* 800-431-2609 *Toll Free Fax:* 866-707-0717 *E-mail:* info@americanmusicandsound.com *Web Site:* www.americanmusicandsound.com, pg 785

American Music Environments Inc (AME), 1133 W Long Lake Rd, Suite 200, Bloomfield Hills, MI 48302 *Tel:* 248-646-2020 *Toll Free Tel:* 888-AME-5005 (263-5005) *Toll Free Fax:* 888-AME-6006 (263-6006) *E-mail:* info@amemusic.com *Web Site:* www.amemusic.com, pg 785

American Optometric Association (AOA), 243 N Lindbergh Blvd, 1st fl, St Louis, MO 63141-7881 *Tel:* 314-991-4100 *Toll Free Tel:* 800-365-2219 *Fax:* 314-991-4101 *Web Site:* www.aoa.org, pg 785, 1077

American Photographic Artisans Guild (APAG), 2269 N 400 Rd, Eudora, KS 66025 *Tel:* 785-883-4166 *Web Site:* www.apag.net, pg 1077

American Playback Images, 27748 Caraway Lane, Santa Clarita, CA 91350 *Tel:* 818-427-8292 *Fax:* 661-263-2387 *E-mail:* americanplayback@aol.com, pg 785

American Production Services LLC, 150 Nims Spring Dr, Fort Mill, SC 29715 *Tel:* 803-548-2290 *Toll Free Tel:* 888-506-2400 *Fax:* 803-548-3406 *Web Site:* www.apsvideo.com, pg 785

American Recordable Media, 110 Dewey Dr, Suite A, Nicholasville, KY 40356 *Toll Free Tel:* 800-598-8273 *E-mail:* info@americanrecordablemedia.com *Web Site:* www.americanrecordablemedia.com, pg 785

American Society of Cinematographers, 1782 N Orange Dr, Hollywood, CA 90028 *Tel:* 323-969-4333 *Toll Free Tel:* 800-448-0145 (US only) *Fax:* 323-882-6391 *E-mail:* office@theasc.com *Web Site:* www.theasc.com, pg 1077

American Society of Media Photographers Inc (ASMP), 150 N Second St, Philadelphia, PA 19016 *Tel:* 215-451-2767 *Fax:* 215-451-0880 *E-mail:* info@asmp.org *Web Site:* www.asmp.org, pg 1077

American Society of Photographers (ASP), 3120 N Argonne Dr, Milwaukee, WI 53222 *Tel:* 414-871-6600 *Web Site:* s17670789.onlinehome-server.com/, pg 1077

American Society of Safety Engineers (ASSE), 1800 E Oakton St, Des Plaines, IL 60018 *Tel:* 847-699-2929 *E-mail:* customerservice@asse.org *Web Site:* www.asse.org, pg 1077

American Sportscasters Association Inc (ASA), 225 Broadway, Suite 2030, New York, NY 10007 *Tel:* 212-227-8080 *Fax:* 212-571-0556 *Web Site:* www.americansportscasters.com; www.americansportscastersonline.com, pg 1077

American Thermoplastic Co, 106 Gamma Dr, Pittsburgh, PA 15238 *Tel:* 412-967-0900 *Toll Free Tel:* 800-245-6600 *Fax:* 412-967-9990 *E-mail:* atc@binders.com *Web Site:* www.binders.com, pg 785

The American University, Dept of Performing Arts, 4400 Massachusetts Ave NW, Washington, DC 20016-8053 *Tel:* 202-885-2746 *Fax:* 202-885-1092 *E-mail:* audiotech@american.edu *Web Site:* www.american.edu, pg 785

American Video Inc, 780 Third Ave, 5th fl, New York, NY 10017-2024 *Tel:* 212-527-9000 *Toll Free Tel:* 800-582-4184 *E-mail:* sales@accnewyork.com *Web Site:* www.americanvideo.com, pg 785

American Visions, One Deerfield Lane, Cedar Rapids, IA 52403 *Tel:* 319-360-3211 *E-mail:* info@americanvisions.org *Web Site:* www.americanvisions.org, pg 785

Amerinex Applied Imaging Inc, PO Box 6473, Monroe Township, NJ 08831-6473 *Tel:* 609-944-8855 *Toll Free Tel:* 877-664-8772 *Fax:* 609-944-8855 *E-mail:* info@amerineximaging.com *Web Site:* www.amerineximaging.com, pg 785

Ames Recording Studios, 840 Danit St, Prescott, AZ 86301 *Tel:* 928-830-2313 *Web Site:* www.amesrecordingstudios.com, pg 785

Ametek Programmable Power, 9250 Brown Deer Rd, San Diego, CA 92121 *Tel:* 858-450-0085 *Toll Free Tel:* 800-733-5427 *Fax:* 858-458-0267 *E-mail:* sales.ppd@amtek.com *Web Site:* programmablepower.com, pg 785

Ametron Audio/Video, 1546 N Argyle Ave, Hollywood, CA 90028-6410 *Tel:* 323-466-4321 *Fax:* 323-871-0127 *E-mail:* info@ametron.com *Web Site:* www.ametron.com, pg 785

AMG Studios-Los Angeles, 2225 E 28 St, Suite 511, Signal Hill, CA 90755 *Tel:* 562-424-0824 *Web Site:* www.amgstudiosla.com, pg 785

Amherst Records Inc, 1762 Main St, Suite A, Buffalo, NY 14208 *Tel:* 716-883-9520 *Toll Free Tel:* 800-836-0751 *Fax:* 716-884-1432 *E-mail:* info@amherstrecords.com *Web Site:* www.amherstrecords.com, pg 785

AMP Services Inc, 3111 Fortune Way, Suite B-18, West Palm Beach, FL 33414 *Tel:* 561-333-0335 *Fax:* 561-333-0370 *Web Site:* www.audiomagnetics.com, pg 785

Ampex Data Systems Corp, 500 Broadway, Redwood City, CA 94063 *Tel:* 650-367-2011 *Fax:* 650-367-2444 *E-mail:* info@ampex.com *Web Site:* www.ampex.com, pg 785

Amplifier Technologies Inc (ATI), 1749 Chapin Rd, Montebello, CA 90640 *Tel:* 323-278-0001 *Fax:* 323-278-0083 *E-mail:* sales@ati-amp.com *Web Site:* www.ati-amp.com, pg 785

AmpliVox Portable Sound Systems, 650 Anthony Trail, Suite D, Northbrook, IL 60062-2512 *Tel:* 847-498-9000 *Toll Free Tel:* 800-267-5486 *Toll Free Fax:* 800-267-5489 *E-mail:* info@ampli.com *Web Site:* www.ampli.com, pg 785

AMPLUS Productions, 1484 Liveoak Dr, Mississauga, ON L5E 2X1, Canada *Tel:* 416-889-7664 *Fax:* 905-274-7687 *Web Site:* www.amplusproductions.com, pg 786

AMS Pictures, 16986 N Dallas Pkwy, Dallas, TX 75248 *Tel:* 972-818-7400 *Toll Free Tel:* 866-691-3660 *Fax:* 972-818-1257 *Web Site:* www.amspictures.com, pg 786

Amusement & Music Operators Association (AMOA), 600 Spring Hill Ring Rd, Suite 111, West Dundee, IL 60118 *Tel:* 847-428-7699 *Toll Free Tel:* 800-YES-AMOA (937-2662) *Fax:* 847-428-7719 *E-mail:* amoa@amoa.com *Web Site:* www.amoa.com, pg 1077

AMV/Unitel, 515 W 57 St, New York, NY 10019 *Tel:* 212-265-3600 (studios); 212-586-8616 (sales) *Fax:* 212-246-5059 *E-mail:* hdsales@allmobilevideo.com *Web Site:* www.allmobilevideo.com, pg 786

AMX, 3000 Research Dr, Richardson, TX 75082 *Tel:* 469-624-8000 *Toll Free Tel:* 800-222-0193 *Fax:* 469-624-7153 *E-mail:* service@amx.com *Web Site:* www.amx.com, pg 786

Analog Free Media, 111 E Ninth St, Lockport, IL 60441 *Tel:* 815-588-5000 *Toll Free Tel:* 877-4MYVIDEO (469-8433) *E-mail:* analogfreemedia@yahoo.com *Web Site:* www.analogfreemedia.com, pg 786

Analog Man Recording Studio, PO Box 70245, Nashville, TN 37207 *Tel:* 615-242-2908, pg 786

Analog Way Inc, 299 Broadway, Suite 1620, New York, NY 10007 *Tel:* 212-269-1902 *Fax:* 212-269-1943 *E-mail:* salesusa@analogway.com *Web Site:* www.analogway.com, pg 786

Anchor Audio Inc, 5931 Darwin Ct, Carlsbad, CA 92008 *Tel:* 760-827-7100 *Toll Free Tel:* 800-262-4671 *Fax:* 760-827-7105 *E-mail:* sales@anchoraudio.com *Web Site:* www.anchoraudio.com, pg 786

Anchor Bay Entertainment LLC, 9242 Beverly Blvd, Suite 201, Beverly Hills, CA 90210 *Tel:* 424-204-4166 *E-mail:* questions@anchorbayent.com *Web Site:* www.anchorbayentertainment.com, pg 786

Anchor Distributors, 1030 Hunt Valley Circle, New Kensington, PA 15068 *Tel:* 724-334-7000 *Toll Free Tel:* 800-444-4484 *Fax:* 724-334-1200 *Toll Free Fax:* 800-765-1960 *E-mail:* marketing@anchordistributors.com *Web Site:* www.anchordistributors.com; www.whitakerhouse.com, pg 786

Ancient Future, PO Box 264, Kentfield, CA 94914-0264 *Tel:* 415-459-1892 *E-mail:* info@ancient-future.com *Web Site:* www.ancient-future.com, pg 786

Olson Anderson Co, 3124 Kochville Rd, Suite 121, Saginaw, MI 48604-9305 *Tel:* 989-399-3024 *E-mail:* oac100@aol.com *Web Site:* www.olsonanderson.com, pg 786

Paul L Anderson Productions Inc, 2107 Constitution Ave, Fort Collins, CO 80526 *Web Site:* www.paulanderson.com, pg 786

Angenieux, 40-G Commerce Way, Totowa, NJ 07512 *Tel:* 973-812-3858 *Fax:* 973-812-9049 *E-mail:* angenieux@tccus.com *Web Site:* www.angenieux.com, pg 786

Angstrom Lighting, 837 N Cahuenga Blvd, Hollywood, CA 90038 *Tel:* 323-462-4246 *Fax:* 323-462-8190 *Web Site:* www.angstromlighting.com, pg 786

Animated Software Co, PO Box 1936, Carlsbad, CA 92018-1936 *Tel:* 760-720-7261 *Toll Free Tel:* 800-551-2726 *Web Site:* www.animatedsoftware.com, pg 786

Animax, 6627 Valjean Ave, Van Nuys, CA 91406 *Tel:* 818-787-4444 *E-mail:* hello@animaxent.com *Web Site:* www.animaxent.com, pg 787

Animotion Inc, 501 W Fayette St, Syracuse, NY 13204 *Tel:* 315-471-3533 *Fax:* 315-471-2730 *E-mail:* info@animotioninc.com *Web Site:* animotioninc.com, pg 787

Anixter Inc, 2301 Patriot Blvd, Glenview, IL 60026 *Tel:* 224-521-8000 *Toll Free Tel:* 800-323-8167 *Fax:* 224-521-8100 *Web Site:* www.anixter.com, pg 787

Ann Arbor Film Festival, 217 N First St, Ann Arbor, MI 48104 *Tel:* 734-995-5356 *Fax:* 734-995-5396 *E-mail:* info@aafilmfest.org *Web Site:* www.aafilmfest.org, pg 1107

Annenberg Learner, PO Box 26983, St Louis, MO 63118 *Tel:* 202-783-0500 (outside US) *Toll Free Tel:* 800-LEARNER (532-7637) *Fax:* 202-783-0333 *E-mail:* order@learner.org *Web Site:* www.learner.org, pg 787

The Annex, PO Box 2390, Los Gatos, CA 95031 *Tel:* 650-328-8338 *E-mail:* info@theannex.us *Web Site:* theannexstudios.com, pg 787

R B Annis Instruments Inc, 117 W Franklin St, Greencastle, IN 46135-1223 *Tel:* 765-848-1621 *Fax:* 765-848-1625 *E-mail:* info@rbannis.com *Web Site:* www.rbannis.com, pg 787

Anode Inc, 926 Main St, Nashville, TN 37206 *Tel:* 615-742-1490 *Toll Free Tel:* 866-802-2436 *Fax:* 615-742-1487 *E-mail:* inquiry@anode.com *Web Site:* www.anode.com, pg 787

Ansonia Prompting Inc, 251 W 30 St, Suite 11-FE, New York, NY 10001 *Tel:* 212-594-0500 *Fax:* 212-202-4925 *E-mail:* info@ansoniaprompting.com *Web Site:* www.ansoniaprompting.com, pg 787

AnswersMedia, 30 N Racine Ave, Suite 300, Chicago, IL 60607 *Tel:* 312-421-0113 *Fax:* 312-421-1457 *E-mail:* contactus@answersmediainc.com *Web Site:* www.answersmediainc.com, pg 787

Antelope Valley Film Office-Lancaster, 42035 12 St W, Suite 103, Lancaster, CA 93534 *Tel:* 661-723-6090; 661-510-4231 (cell) *Web Site:* antelope-valley-film-office.hollywoodserve.com, pg 1093

Antelope Valley Locations & Production Services, 42848 150 St E, Lancaster, CA 93535 *Tel:* 661-946-1515 *Fax:* 661-946-0454 *E-mail:* clubed@avlocations.com *Web Site:* www.avlocations.com, pg 787

Antenna International, 383 Main Ave, Norwalk, CT 06851 *Tel:* 203-523-0320 *Fax:* 203-354-5519 *E-mail:* inquiry@antennainternational.com *Web Site:* www.antennainternational.com, pg 787

Antex Electronics Corp, 19160 Van Ness Ave, Torrance, CA 90501 *Tel:* 310-532-3092 *Toll Free Tel:* 800-338-4231 *Fax:* 310-532-8509 *E-mail:* ainfo@antex.com; asales@antex.com *Web Site:* www.antex.com, pg 787

Anthro Corp, 10450 SW Manhasset Dr, Tualatin, OR 97062 *Tel:* 503-691-2556 *Toll Free Tel:* 800-325-3841 (cust serv) *Fax:* 503-691-2409 *Toll Free Fax:* 800-325-0045 *E-mail:* sales@anthro.com *Web Site:* www.anthro.com, pg 787

Anton/Bauer Inc, 14 Progress Dr, Shelton, CT 06484 *Tel:* 203-929-1100 *Toll Free Tel:* 800-422-3473 *Fax:* 203-929-9935 *E-mail:* sales@antonbauer.com; americas@antonbauer.com *Web Site:* www.antonbauer.com, pg 787

Antronics Inc, 25 Summer Ave, Waltham, MA 02452-5634 *Tel:* 781-891-7525 *Fax:* 781-647-3667 *E-mail:* info@antronics.net *Web Site:* www.antronics.net, pg 787

Anvil Cases, 15730 Salt Lake Ave, City of Industry, CA 91745 *Tel:* 626-968-4100 *Toll Free Tel:* 800-359-2684 *Fax:* 626-968-1703 *E-mail:* web.sales@anvilcase.com *Web Site:* www.anvilcase.com, pg 787

Aon Hewitt, 1100 Reynolds Blvd, Winston-Salem, NC 27105-3400 *Tel:* 336-748-1120 *Fax:* 847-953-4854 *Web Site:* www.aon.com, pg 787

AP/Images, 450 W 33 St, 15th fl, New York, NY 10001 *Tel:* 212-621-1930 *Fax:* 212-621-1955 *Web Site:* www.apimages.com, pg 788

Apache Junction Chamber of Commerce, 567 W Apache Trail, Apache Junction, AZ 85120 *Tel:* 480-982-3141 *Toll Free Tel:* 800-252-3141 *Fax:* 480-982-3234 *Web Site:* www.ajchamber.com, pg 1091

APC by Schneider Electric, 132 Fairgrounds Rd, West Kingston, RI 02892 *Tel:* 401-789-5735 *Toll Free Tel:* 800-788-2208 *Fax:* 401-789-3710 *Web Site:* www.apc.com, pg 788

Apertura, 535 Main St, Orford, NH 03777 *Tel:* 603-353-9067 *Fax:* 603-353-4646 *Web Site:* www.apertura.org, pg 788

Aperture Studios Miami, 385 NE 59 St, Miami, FL 33137 *Tel:* 305-759-4327 *Fax:* 305-757-1198 *E-mail:* rental@aperturepro.com *Web Site:* aperturepro.com, pg 788

Apex Jr, 1450 W 228 St, Unit 4, Torrance, CA 90501 *Tel:* 818-248-0416 *Fax:* 424-263-4614 *E-mail:* steve.apexjr@prodigy.net *Web Site:* www.apexjr.com, pg 788

Apex Machine Co, 3000 NE 12 Terr, Fort Lauderdale, FL 33334 *Tel:* 954-566-1572 *Fax:* 954-563-2844 *E-mail:* email@apexmachine.com *Web Site:* www.apexmachine.com, pg 788

Aphex LLC, PO Box 711674, Salt Lake City, UT 84171 *Tel:* 818-767-2929 *E-mail:* sales@aphex.com *Web Site:* www.aphex.com, pg 788

API, 8301 Patuxent Range Rd, Jessup, MD 20794 *Tel:* 301-776-7879 *Fax:* 301-776-8117 *E-mail:* service@apiaudio.com *Web Site:* www.apiaudio.com, pg 788

Apogee Communications Group, 159 Alpine Way, Boulder, CO 80304 *Tel:* 303-443-8473 *Toll Free Tel:* 800-210-5700 *Fax:* 303-443-0500 *E-mail:* sales@apogeevideo.com; orders@apogeevideo.com *Web Site:* www.apogeevideo.com, pg 788

Apogee Electronics Corp, 1715 Berkeley St, Santa Monica, CA 90404 *Tel:* 310-584-9394 *Fax:* 310-584-9385 *Web Site:* www.apogeedigital.com, pg 788

Apogee Sound International LLC, 50 Spring St, Ramsey, NJ 07446 *Toll Free Tel:* 800-443-3979 *Toll Free Fax:* 800-999-9016 *E-mail:* info@apogee-sound.com *Web Site:* www.apogee-sound.com, pg 788

Apollo Design Technology Inc, 4130 Fourier Dr, Fort Wayne, IN 46818 *Tel:* 260-497-9191 *Toll Free Tel:* 800-288-4626 *Fax:* 260-497-9192 *E-mail:* sales@apollodesign.net *Web Site:* www.apollodesign.net, pg 788

Applause Learning Resources, 85 Fernwood Lane, Roslyn, NY 11576 *Tel:* 516-625-1145 *Toll Free Tel:* 800-277-5287 *Toll Free Fax:* 877-365-7484 *E-mail:* info@applauselearning.com *Web Site:* www.applauselearning.com, pg 788

Applause Productions & Publications, PO Box 820024, Dallas, TX 75382-0024 *Tel:* 214-652-4300 *Fax:* 214-652-4075 *E-mail:* info@applauseproductions.com *Web Site:* applauseproductions.com, pg 788

Apple Inc, One Infinite Loop, Cupertino, CA 95014 *Tel:* 408-996-1010 *Web Site:* www.apple.com, pg 788

Applebox Studio, 48 Kingswood Dr, Bethel, CT 06801 *Tel:* 203-762-7333 *Toll Free Fax:* 888-624-2829 *E-mail:* info@appleboxstudio.com; info@appleboxvideo.com *Web Site:* www.appleboxstudio.com, pg 788

Pat Appleson Studios Inc, 2359 Hwy 70 SE, Suite 102, Hickory, NC 28602 *Tel:* 828-994-4361; 828-461-3003 (cell) *Web Site:* www.appleson.com, pg 788

Applied Electronics, 722 Blue Crab Rd, Newport News, VA 23606 *Tel:* 757-591-9371 *Toll Free Tel:* 800-883-0008 *Fax:* 757-591-9514 *E-mail:* sales@appliednn.com *Web Site:* www.appliednn.com, pg 788

Applied Electronics Ltd, 1260 Kamato Rd, Mississauga, ON L4W 1Y1, Canada *Tel:* 905-625-4321 *Fax:* 905-625-4333 *E-mail:* ael.toronto@appliedelectronics.com *Web Site:* www.appliedelectronics.com, pg 788

Applied Integration Corp, 3930 W New York Dr, Tucson, AZ 85745 *Tel:* 520-743-3095 *E-mail:* info@appliedi.com *Web Site:* www.appliedi.com, pg 789

APS Lighting-Sound-AV, 901 Columbia Circle, Merrimack, NH 03054 *Tel:* 603-424-9198 *Toll Free Tel:* 800-837-0005 *Fax:* 603-423-9816 *E-mail:* info@apslightingnh.com *Web Site:* www.apslightingnh.com, pg 789

APTE Inc, 1424 Wesley Ave, Suite A, Evanston, IL 60201 *Tel:* 847-866-1872 *Fax:* 847-866-1873 *E-mail:* mail@apte.com *Web Site:* www.apte.com, pg 789

ARC Document Solutions, 1981 N Broadway, Suite 385, Walnut Creek, CA 94596 *Tel:* 925-949-5100 *Fax:* 925-949-5101 *E-mail:* info@e-arc.com *Web Site:* www.e-arc.com, pg 789

Arc Light Efx Inc, 9338 San Fernando Rd, Sun Valley, CA 91352 *Tel:* 818-394-6330 *Fax:* 818-252-3486 *E-mail:* gaslights@arclightefx.com *Web Site:* www.arclightefx.com, pg 789

Archai Media, 31E Patrick St, Frederick, MD 21701 *Tel:* 301-401-8117 *E-mail:* rentals@archaimedia.com *Web Site:* archaimedia.com, pg 789

Arcor Electronics Co, 5689 W Howard St, Niles, IL 60714 *Tel:* 847-588-0088 *Fax:* 847-588-0080 *E-mail:* sales@arcorelectronics.com *Web Site:* www.arcorelectronics.com, pg 789

Arctek Studios, 140 E Chestnut Ave, Monrovia, CA 91016 *Tel:* 626-509-2123 *E-mail:* info@arctekstudios.com *Web Site:* arctekstudios.com, pg 789

Arcube Multimedia Inc, 959 E Collins Blvd, Suite 123, Richardson, TX 75081 *Tel:* 972-267-1800 *Toll Free Tel:* 877-677-9582 *Fax:* 972-267-1922 *E-mail:* sales@arcube.com *Web Site:* www.arcube.com, pg 789

Ardent Music LLC, 2000 Madison Ave, Memphis, TN 38104 *Tel:* 901-725-0855 *Fax:* 901-725-7011 *E-mail:* info@ardentmusic.com *Web Site:* www.ardentmusic.com, pg 789

Ardent Studios Inc, 2000 Madison Ave, Memphis, TN 38104 *Tel:* 901-725-0855 *Fax:* 901-725-7011 *E-mail:* info@ardentstudios.com *Web Site:* www.ardentstudios.com, pg 789

Area 19, 24562 County Rd 75, St Augusta, MN 56301 *Tel:* 320-253-9493 *Toll Free Tel:* 888-334-4825 *Fax:* 320-257-8788 *E-mail:* info@areanineteen.com *Web Site:* www.areanineteen.com, pg 789

ARF!ARF!, PO Box 465, Middleboro, MA 02346-0465 *Tel:* 508-947-7387 *Fax:* 508-947-7387 *E-mail:* page@arfarfrecords.com *Web Site:* www.arfarfrecords.com, pg 789

Argentine Productions Inc, 603 Washington Rd, Suite 501, Pittsburgh, PA 15228 *Tel:* 412-341-6448 *E-mail:* info@argentineproductions.com *Web Site:* www.argentineproductions.com, pg 789

Argraph Corp, 111 Asia Place, Carlstadt, NJ 07072 *Tel:* 201-939-7722 *Toll Free Tel:* 800-526-6290 *Fax:* 201-939-7782 *E-mail:* info@argraph.com; sales@argraph.com *Web Site:* www.argraph.com, pg 789

Argyle Post, 2633 N San Fernando Blvd, Burbank, CA 91504 *Tel:* 818-845-5555; 310-560-2373 *Fax:* 818-842-8115 *E-mail:* info@argylepost.com *Web Site:* www.argylepost.com, pg 789

Arhoolie Productions Inc (aka Arhoolie Records), 10341 San Pablo Ave, El Cerrito, CA 94530 *Tel:* 510-525-7471 *Fax:* 510-525-1204 *E-mail:* info@arhoolie.com *Web Site:* www.arhoolie.com, pg 789

Aries Productions, 1110 Avenue "H" E, Suite 200, Arlington, TX 76011 *Tel:* 817-640-9955; 817-300-5255 (cell) *Fax:* 817-649-2529 *E-mail:* inform@aries-prods.com *Web Site:* www.aries-prods.com, pg 789

Arizona Cine Equipment, 2125 E 20 St, Tucson, AZ 85719 *Tel:* 520-623-8268 *Fax:* 520-623-1092 *Web Site:* www.azcine.com, pg 789

Arizona Production Association, 6615 N Scottsdale Rd, Suite 101, Scottsdale, AZ 85250 *Tel:* 480-345-6464 *Toll Free Tel:* 866-345-6469 *Fax:* 480-941-2557 *E-mail:* info@azproduction.com *Web Site:* www.azproduction.com, pg 1077

Arizona Public Media, 1423 E University, MLB67, Rm 223, Tucson, AZ 85719 *Tel:* 520-621-5828; 520-621-5836 (sales) *Fax:* 520-621-3360 *Web Site:* www.azpm.org, pg 790

Arizona State University Art Museum Annual Short Film & Video Festival, PO Box 872911, Tempe, AZ 85287-2911 *Tel:* 480-965-2787 *Toll Free Tel:* 855-278-6060 *Fax:* 480-965-5254 *E-mail:* asuartmuseum@asu.edu *Web Site:* asuartmuseum.asu.edu/filmfest, pg 1107

Arizona Virtual Studios, 4614 E McDowell Rd, Phoenix, AZ 85008 *Tel:* 602-275-9100 *E-mail:* john@azvirtualstudios.com *Web Site:* azvirtualstudios.com, pg 790

Ariztical Entertainment Inc, 12400 Ventura Blvd, Suite 686, Studio City, CA 91604-2406 *Tel:* 818-760-3739 *Fax:* 818-760-3581 *E-mail:* info@ariztical.com *Web Site:* www.ariztical.com, pg 790

Ark Media Group Ltd, PO Box 410685, San Francisco, CA 94141-0685 *Tel:* 415-863-7200 *Fax:* 415-864-5437 *E-mail:* sales@arkmedia.com *Web Site:* www.arkmedia.com, pg 790

Arkansas Arts Council Fellowships & Grants Program, 323 Center St, Suite 1500, Little Rock, AR 72201-2606 *Tel:* 501-324-9766 *Fax:* 501-324-9207 *E-mail:* info@arkansasarts.com *Web Site:* www.arkansasarts.org, pg 1107

Arkansas Film Commission, 900 W Capitol Ave, Suite 400, Little Rock, AR 72201 *Tel:* 501-682-7676 *Fax:* 501-682-7394 *Web Site:* www.arkansasproduction.com, pg 1092

Arkon Resources Inc, 20 La Porte St, Arcadia, CA 91006 *Tel:* 626-254-9005 *Toll Free Tel:* 800-841-0884 *Fax:* 626-254-9266 *E-mail:* arkon5@arkon.com *Web Site:* www.arkon.com, pg 790

Arkwright Advanced Coating Inc, 538 Main St, Fiskeville, RI 02823 *Tel:* 401-821-1000 *Toll Free Tel:* 800-556-6866 *Web Site:* www.sihlusa.com, pg 790

Arms Communications, 1517 Maurice Dr, Woodbridge, VA 22191 *Tel:* 703-690-3338 *Fax:* 703-490-3810 (call first) *E-mail:* info@armscomm.com *Web Site:* www.armscomm.com, pg 790

J Arnold Productions Inc, 147 Cove Creek Rd, Mooresville, NC 28117-8910 *Tel:* 704-663-4444 *Web Site:* www.jarnoldproductions.com, pg 790

Arrakis Systems, 6604 Powell St, Loveland, CO 80538 *Tel:* 970-461-0730 *Fax:* 970-663-1010 *E-mail:* support@arrakis-systems.com *Web Site:* www.arrakis-systems.com, pg 790

ARRI Inc, 600 N Victory Blvd, Burbank, CA 91502-1639 *Tel:* 818-841-7070 *Fax:* 818-848-4028 *E-mail:* info@arri.com *Web Site:* www.arri.com, pg 790

ARRIS Group Inc, 3871 Lakefield Dr, Suwanee, GA 30024 *Tel:* 678-473-2907 *Toll Free Tel:* 866-36-ARRIS (362-7747) *Fax:* 678-473-8470 *Web Site:* www.arrisi.com, pg 790

ARS Electronics, 7110 DeCelis Place, Van Nuys, CA 91406 *Tel:* 818-997-6279 *Fax:* 818-997-6158 *E-mail:* info@arselectronics.com *Web Site:* www.arselectronics.com, pg 791

ARSC Awards for Excellence, c/o Knight Library, 1299 University of Oregon, Eugene, OR 97403-1299 *Tel:* 541-346-1852 *Web Site:* www.arsc-audio.org, pg 1107

ART (Applied Research & Technology Inc), 4625 Witmer Industrial Estate, Niagara Falls, NY 14305 *Tel:* 716-297-2920 *Fax:* 716-297-3689 *E-mail:* usa@yorkville.com *Web Site:* www.artproaudio.com; www.yorkville.com, pg 791

Art Directors Guild (ADG), 11969 Ventura Blvd, 2nd fl, Studio City, CA 91604 *Tel:* 818-762-9995 *Fax:* 818-762-9997 *Web Site:* www.adg.org, pg 1077

Art Gallery of Ontario, 317 Dundas St W, Toronto, ON M5T 1G4, Canada *Tel:* 416-979-6660 *Toll Free Tel:* 877-225-4246 *Fax:* 416-979-6674 *E-mail:* danny_winchester@ago.net *Web Site:* www.ago.net, pg 791

Art Museum of the Americas, 201 18 St, Washington, DC 20006 *Tel:* 202-370-0147 *E-mail:* artmus@oas.org *Web Site:* www.amamuseum.org, pg 791

Art Resource, 536 Broadway, 5th fl, New York, NY 10012 *Tel:* 212-505-8700 *Fax:* 212-505-2053 *E-mail:* requests@artres.com *Web Site:* www.artres.com, pg 791

Artadia James D Phelan Award in the Visual Arts, One Embarcadero Ctr, Suite 1400, San Francisco, CA 94111 *Tel:* 415-733-8500 *Fax:* 415-477-2783 *E-mail:* artsinfo@sff.org; info@sff.org *Web Site:* www.sff.org, pg 1108

Artaflex Inc, 96 Steelcase Rd W, Markham, ON L3R 1B5, Canada *Tel:* 905-470-0109 *Toll Free Tel:* 866-502-3378 *Fax:* 905-470-0621 *Web Site:* www.artaflex.com, pg 791

Artbeats, 1405 N Myrtle Rd, Myrtle Creek, OR 97457 *Tel:* 541-863-4429 *Toll Free Tel:* 800-444-9392 *Fax:* 541-863-4547 *E-mail:* info@artbeats.com *Web Site:* www.artbeats.com, pg 791

Artech Electronics Ltd, PO Box 1547, Williston, VT 05495-1547 *Toll Free Tel:* 800-631-6448 *Toll Free Fax:* 800-934-7166 *E-mail:* info@artech-electronics.com *Web Site:* www.artech-electronics.com, pg 791

Artel Video Systems, 5B Lyberty Way, Westford, MA 01886 *Tel:* 978-263-5775 *Toll Free Tel:* 800-225-0228 *Fax:* 978-263-9755 *E-mail:* sales@artel.com *Web Site:* www.artel.com, pg 791

Artichoke Productions, 4114 Linden St, Oakland, CA 94608 *Tel:* 510-655-1283 *Web Site:* www.artichokepro.com, pg 791

Artist Fellowships, 20 Jay St, 7th fl, Suite 740, Brooklyn, NY 11201 *Tel:* 212-366-6900 *Fax:* 212-366-1778 *E-mail:* fellowships@nyfa.org *Web Site:* nyfa.org, pg 1108

Artist Initiative Grant Program, Park Square Ct, Suite 200, 400 Sibley St, St Paul, MN 55101-1928 *Tel:* 651-215-1600 *Toll Free Tel:* 800-866-2787 *E-mail:* msab@arts.state.mn.us *Web Site:* www.arts.state.mn.us, pg 1108

Artist Research and Development Grants, 417 W Roosevelt St, Phoenix, AZ 85003-1326 *Tel:* 602-771-6501 *Fax:* 602-256-0282 *E-mail:* info@azarts.gov *Web Site:* www.azarts.gov, pg 1108

Artist Residency Program, 1260 N Green Bay Rd, Lake Forest, IL 60045 *Tel:* 847-234-1063 *Fax:* 847-234-1063 *E-mail:* info@ragdale.org *Web Site:* www.ragdale.org, pg 1108

Artistic Video, 87 Tyler Ave, Dept V, Sound Beach, NY 11789 *Tel:* 631-744-5999 *Toll Free Tel:* 888-982-4244 *Fax:* 631-744-5993 *E-mail:* info@movementsofmagic.com *Web Site:* www.movementsofmagic.com, pg 791

Artograph Inc, 525 Ninth St S, Delano, MN 55328-8624 *Tel:* 763-553-1112 *Toll Free Tel:* 888-975-9555 *Fax:* 763-553-1262 *E-mail:* sales@artograph.com; info@artograph.com *Web Site:* www.artograph.com, pg 791

Arts Create & Arts Respond Grant, E O Thompson Off Bldg, 920 Colorado St, Suite 501, Austin, TX 78701 *Tel:* 512-463-5535 *Fax:* 512-475-2699 *E-mail:* front.desk@arts.state.tx.us *Web Site:* www.arts.state.tx.us, pg 1108

Arts Grants, 350 Albert St, Ottawa, ON K2P 1L4, Canada *Tel:* 613-566-4414 *Toll Free Tel:* 800-263-5588 *Fax:* 613-566-4390 *E-mail:* info@canadacouncil.ca *Web Site:* www.canadacouncil.ca; www.conseildesarts.ca, pg 1108

ASACA/ShibaSoku Corp of America, 33 Boston Post Rd W, Suite 130, Marlborough, MA 01752 *Tel:* 508-229-0107 *Toll Free Tel:* 800-423-6347 *Fax:* 508-229-0721, pg 791

ASC Systems, Mack Place, 566, St Clair Shores, MI 48080-0566 *Tel:* 313-882-1133 *E-mail:* ascsystems@live.com *Web Site:* www.airi.com, pg 791

ASC-Tube Trap, 4275 W Fifth Ave, Eugene, OR 97402 *Tel:* 541-343-9727 *Toll Free Tel:* 800-272-8823 *Fax:* 541-343-9245 *E-mail:* info@acousticsciences.com *Web Site:* www.acousticsciences.com, pg 791

ASCD, 1703 N Beauregard St, Alexandria, VA 22311-1714 *Tel:* 703-578-9600 *Toll Free Tel:* 800-933-2723 *Fax:* 703-575-5400 *E-mail:* exhibits@ascd.org *Web Site:* www.ascd.org, pg 1078

Ascom Communications Contractors, 11952 James St, Holland, MI 49424 *Tel:* 616-820-1289 *Toll Free Tel:* 800-968-2444 *Fax:* 616-538-4311 *E-mail:* info@ascominc.com *Web Site:* www.ascomllc.com, pg 791

Asentria Corp, 1200 N 96 St, Seattle, WA 98103 *Tel:* 206-344-8800 *Fax:* 206-344-2116 *E-mail:* sales@asentria.com *Web Site:* www.asentria.com, pg 792

ASET - The Neurodiagnostic Society, 402 E Bannister Rd, Suite A, Kansas City, MO 64131-3019 *Tel:* 816-931-1120 *Fax:* 816-931-1145 *E-mail:* info@aset.org *Web Site:* www.aset.org, pg 792

Ashgate Publishing Co, 110 Cherry St, Suite 3-1, Burlington, VT 05401-3818 *Tel:* 802-865-7641 *Toll Free Tel:* 800-535-9544 (distribution) *Fax:* 802-865-7847 *E-mail:* info@ashgate.com *Web Site:* www.ashgate.com, pg 792

Ashly Audio Inc, 847 Holt Rd, Webster, NY 14580-9103 *Tel:* 585-872-0010 *Toll Free Tel:* 800-828-6308 *Fax:* 585-872-0739 *E-mail:* info@ashly.com; sales@ashly.com *Web Site:* www.ashly.com, pg 792

Asia Society, 725 Park Ave, New York, NY 10021 *Tel:* 212-288-6400 *Fax:* 212-517-8315 *E-mail:* pr@asiasociety.org *Web Site:* www.asiasociety.org; www.asiasociety.org/video, pg 792

Asian American International Film Festival (AAIFF), 115 W 30 St, Suite 708, New York, NY 10001-4068 *Tel:* 212-989-1422 *Fax:* 212-727-3584 *E-mail:* festival@asiancinevision.org; info@asiancinevision.org *Web Site:* aaiff.org; www.asiancinevision.org, pg 1108

Aspen Systems Inc, 3900 Youngfield St, Wheat Ridge, CO 80033-3865 *Tel:* 303-431-4606 *Toll Free Tel:* 800-992-9242 *Fax:* 303-431-7196 *E-mail:* sales@aspsys.com *Web Site:* www.aspsys.com, pg 792

ASPRS: The Imaging and Geospatial Information Society, 5410 Grosvenor Lane, Suite 210, Bethesda, MD 20814-2160 *Tel:* 301-493-0290 *Fax:* 301-493-0208 *E-mail:* asprs@asprs.org *Web Site:* www.asprs.org, pg 1078

Assignment Desk, 820 N Orleans St, Suite 205, Chicago, IL 60610 *Tel:* 312-464-8600 *Toll Free Tel:* 800-959-DESK (959-3375) *Fax:* 312-464-8605 *E-mail:* crew@assignmentdesk.com *Web Site:* www.assignmentdesk.com, pg 792

Associated Bag Co, 400 W Boden St, Milwaukee, WI 53207 *Tel:* 414-769-1000 *Toll Free Tel:* 800-926-6100 *Fax:* 414-769-6530 *Toll Free Fax:* 800-926-4610 *E-mail:* customerservice@associatedbag.com *Web Site:* www.associatedbag.com, pg 792

Associated Press Television News, 450 W 33 St, New York, NY 10001 *Tel:* 212-621-1500 *Fax:* 212-621-7419 *Web Site:* www.aptn.com, pg 792

Associated Producers Ltd, 18 Dupont St, Toronto, ON M5R 1V2, Canada *Tel:* 416-504-6662 *Fax:* 416-504-6667 *E-mail:* general@apltd.ca *Web Site:* www.apltd.ca, pg 792

Associated Production Music LLC, 6255 Sunset Blvd, Suite 900, Hollywood, CA 90028 *Tel:* 323-461-3211 *Fax:* 323-461-9102 *E-mail:* info@apmmusic.com *Web Site:* www.apmmusic.com, pg 792

Associated Sound, 1417 Del Paso Blvd, Sacramento, CA 95815 *Tel:* 916-649-8040 *Toll Free Tel:* 800-492-6800 *Fax:* 916-649-0243 *E-mail:* sales@associatedsound.com *Web Site:* www.associatedsound.com, pg 792

Associated Video, 2542 MacLaren Circle, Atlanta, GA 30360 *Tel:* 404-873-6411, pg 792

Association for Educational Communications & Technology (AECT), 320 W Eighth St, Suite 101, Bloomington, IN 47404-3745 *Tel:* 812-335-7675 *Toll Free Tel:* 877-677-AECT (677-2328) *Fax:* 812-335-7678 *E-mail:* aect@aect.org *Web Site:* www.aect.org, pg 1078

Association for Information and Image Management (AIIM), 1100 Wayne Ave, Suite 1100, Silver Spring, MD 20910 *Tel:* 301-587-8202 *Toll Free Tel:* 800-477-2446 *Fax:* 301-587-2711 *E-mail:* aiim@aiim.org *Web Site:* www.aiim.org, pg 1078

Association for Information Media & Equipment, PO Box 9844, Cedar Rapids, IA 52409-9844 *Tel:* 319-654-0608 *Fax:* 319-654-0609 *Web Site:* www.aime.org, pg 1078

Association for Recorded Sound Collections Inc (ARSC), c/o Knight Library, 1299 University of Oregon, Eugene, OR 97403-1299 *Web Site:* www.arsc-audio.org, pg 1078

Association for Talent Development (ATD), 1640 King St, Alexandria, VA 22314-2743 *Tel:* 703-683-8100 *Toll Free Tel:* 800-628-2783 *Fax:* 703-299-8723; 703-683-1523 (cust care) *E-mail:* customercare@td.org *Web Site:* www.td.org; www.astd.org, pg 1078

The Association for Women in Communications (AWC), 3337 Duke St, Alexandria, VA 22314 *Tel:* 703-370-7436 *Fax:* 703-342-4311 *E-mail:* info@womcom.org *Web Site:* www.womcom.org, pg 1078

Association of American Publishers (AAP), 71 Fifth Ave, 2nd fl, New York, NY 10003-3004 *Tel:* 212-255-0200 *Fax:* 212-255-7007 *E-mail:* info@publishers.org *Web Site:* www.publishers.org, pg 1078

Association of Biomedical Communications Directors (ABCD), State University of New York at Stony Brook, L3 044 Health Science Ctr, Stony Brook, NY 11794-8030 *Tel:* 631-444-3228 *Fax:* 631-444-3500 *Web Site:* www.abcdirectors.org, pg 1078

Association of Catholic TV & Radio Syndicators, 518 S Alandele Ave, Los Angeles, CA 90036 *Tel:* 323-938-4861, pg 1079

Association of Federal Communications Consulting Engineers (AFCCE), PO Box 19333, Washington, DC 20036-0333 *E-mail:* secretary@afcce.org *Web Site:* www.afcce.org, pg 1079

Association of Imaging Executives™ (AIE™), A PMA Member Association, 2282 Springport Rd, Suite F, Jackson, MI 49202 *Tel:* 517-788-8100 *Toll Free Tel:* 800-762-9287 *Fax:* 517-788-8371 *E-mail:* aie@pmai.org *Web Site:* www.pmai.org/aie, pg 1079

Association of Independent Commercial Producers (AICP), 3 W 18 St, 5th fl, New York, NY 10011 *Tel:* 212-929-3000 *Fax:* 212-929-3359 *E-mail:* info@aicp.com *Web Site:* www.aicp.com, pg 1079

Association of National Advertisers Inc (ANA), 708 Third Ave, 33rd fl, New York, NY 10017-4270 *Tel:* 212-697-5950 *Fax:* 212-687-7310 *E-mail:* info@ana.net *Web Site:* www.ana.net, pg 1079

Association of Progressive Rental Organizations (APRO), 1504 Robin Hood Trail, Austin, TX 78703 *Tel:* 512-794-0095 *Toll Free Tel:* 800-204-2776 *Fax:* 512-794-0097 *Web Site:* www.rtohq.org, pg 1079

Association of Public Television Stations (APTS), 2100 Crystal Dr, Suite 700, Arlington, VA 22202 *Tel:* 202-654-4200 *Fax:* 202-654-4236 *Web Site:* www.apts.org, pg 1079

Astoria Communications Inc, 12054 Miramar Pkwy, Miami, FL 33025 *Tel:* 305-728-4280 *Toll Free Tel:* 877-GETMEAV (438-6328) *Fax:* 305-728-4285 *Web Site:* www.getmeav.com, pg 792

Astro Audio Visual, 1336 W Clay St, Houston, TX 77019 *Tel:* 713-528-7119 *Fax:* 713-526-0607, pg 792

Astronomical Society of the Pacific, 390 Ashton Ave, San Francisco, CA 94112 *Tel:* 415-337-1100 *Toll Free Tel:* 800-335-2624 *Fax:* 415-337-5205 *E-mail:* service@astrosociety.org *Web Site:* astrosociety.org, pg 792

ATA Trading Corp/Favorite TV Inc, 877 Oceanfront, Long Beach, NY 11561-1542 *Tel:* 516-431-2302 *Fax:* 516-431-2302 *E-mail:* atat@verizon.net, pg 792

ATCi (Antenna Technology Communication Solutions Inc), 450 N McKemy Ave, Chandler, AZ 85226 *Tel:* 480-844-8501 *Fax:* 480-898-7667 *Web Site:* www.atci.com, pg 793

ATD Northwest Inc, 17 N 100 W, Lehi, UT 84043 *Tel:* 801-407-8310 *Toll Free Fax:* 866-870-3697 *E-mail:* sales@atdnw.com *Web Site:* www.atdnw.com; www.atdnorthwest.com, pg 793

ATI Audio, 154 Cooper Rd, Bldg 902, West Berlin, NJ 08091 *Tel:* 856-719-9900 *E-mail:* info@daysequerra.com; sales@daysequerra.com *Web Site:* www.atiaudio.com, pg 793

Atlanta Film Festival (ATLFF), 25 Park Place NE, Suite 900, Atlanta, GA 30303 *Tel:* 678-929-8103 *E-mail:* info@atlantafilmfestival.com *Web Site:* atlantafilmfestival.com, pg 1108

Atlanta Filmworks, 4280 Northeast Expwy, Atlanta, GA 30340 *E-mail:* info@atlantafilmworks.com *Web Site:* atlantafilmworks.com, pg 793

Atlantic Illumination Entertainment Lighting, 80 Fairbanks St, Dartmouth, NS B3A 1C4, Canada *Tel:* 902-463-7418 *E-mail:* aiel@chebucto.biz *Web Site:* aiel.chebucto.biz/, pg 793

Atlas Sound, 4545 E Baseline Rd, Phoenix, AZ 85042 *Toll Free Tel:* 800-876-3333 *Toll Free Fax:* 800-765-3435 *Web Site:* www.atlassound.com, pg 793

ATM Fly-Ware, 1635 E Burnett St, Signal Hill, CA 90755 *Tel:* 562-424-1100 *Fax:* 562-424-3520 *E-mail:* info@adapttechgroup.com; marketing@adapttechgroup.com *Web Site:* www.adapttechgroup.com/atmflyware.html, pg 793

Atma-Sphere Music Systems Inc, 1742 Selby Ave, St Paul, MN 55104 *Tel:* 651-690-2246 *Web Site:* www.atma-sphere.com, pg 793

ATS Cases Inc, 172 Otis St, Northborough, MA 01532 *Tel:* 508-393-9110 *Toll Free Tel:* 800-451-4242; 800-519-2771 *Fax:* 508-393-9508 *E-mail:* casemakers@mac.com *Web Site:* atscases.com, pg 793

Attainment Co Inc, 504 Commerce Pkwy, Verona, WI 53593 *Tel:* 608-845-7880 *Toll Free Tel:* 800-327-4269 *Fax:* 608-845-8040 *Toll Free Fax:* 800-942-3865 *E-mail:* customerservice@attainmentcompany.com; international@attainmentcompany.com *Web Site:* www.attainmentcompany.com, pg 793

ATTCO Inc, 825 Ilaniwai St, Honolulu, HI 96813 *Tel:* 808-836-1191 *Fax:* 808-834-1046 *E-mail:* information@attcoinc.com *Web Site:* www.attcoinc.com, pg 793

ATTO Technology Inc, 155 CrossPoint Pkwy, Amherst, NY 14068 *Tel:* 716-691-1999 *Fax:* 716-691-9353 *Web Site:* www.attotech.com, pg 793

ATV Research Inc, 1301 Broadway, Dakota City, NE 68731 *Tel:* 402-987-3771 *Toll Free Tel:* 800-392-3922 *Fax:* 402-987-3709 *E-mail:* sales@atvresearch.com *Web Site:* www.atvresearch.com, pg 793

ATV Video Center Inc, 2424 Glendale Lane, Sacramento, CA 95825 *Tel:* 916-973-9100 *Toll Free Tel:* 800-635-1266 *Fax:* 916-973-8100 *E-mail:* info@atv.net *Web Site:* www.atv.net, pg 793

A2D Solutions Inc, 20200 NW Second Ave, Suite 403, Miami Gardens, FL 33169 *Tel:* 305-895-5888 *Toll Free Tel:* 866-223-7253 *E-mail:* sales@a2dsolutions.com *Web Site:* a2dsolutions.com, pg 793

Audacity Creative, 2734 Polk St, Suite B, Hollywood, FL 33020 *Tel:* 954-920-4418 *Toll Free Fax:* 877-229-6298 *E-mail:* info@audacitycreative.com; audacityrecording@mac.com *Web Site:* audacitycreative.com; audacityrecording.com, pg 793

Audience Response Systems Inc, 5611-C E Morgan Ave, Evansville, IN 47715 *Tel:* 812-479-7507 *Toll Free Tel:* 800-INVOLVE (468-6583) *Fax:* 812-479-1057 *Web Site:* www.audienceresponse.com, pg 794

Audio Accessories Inc, 25 Mill St, Marlow, NH 03456 *Tel:* 603-446-3335 *Fax:* 603-446-7543 *E-mail:* audioacc@patchbays.com *Web Site:* www.patchbays.com, pg 794

Audio & Light, 2209 Randleman Rd, Greensboro, NC 27406 *Tel:* 336-274-1234 *Fax:* 336-274-4022 *E-mail:* info@audio-light.com *Web Site:* www.audio-light.com, pg 794

Audio Art, 124 Forsythe Dr, Chapel Hill, NC 27517 *Tel:* 919-260-1507, pg 794

Audio Book Contractors LLC, PO Box 96, Riverdale, MD 20738-0096 *Tel:* 301-439-5830 *Fax:* 301-439-5830 *E-mail:* info@audiobookcontractors.com *Web Site:* www.audiobookcontractors.com, pg 794

Audio Consultant Services Inc, 2133 S Bellair, Suite 5, Denver, CO 80222 *Tel:* 303-296-1885 *Web Site:* www.audio-consultants.com, pg 794

The Audio Department Inc, 119 W 57 St, Suite 400, New York, NY 10019 *Tel:* 212-586-3503 *Fax:* 212-245-1675 *E-mail:* scheduling@theaudiodepartment.com *Web Site:* www.theaudiodepartment.com, pg 794

Audio Editions Books-On-Cassette & CD, 131 E Placer St, Auburn, CA 95603 *Tel:* 530-888-7801 *Toll Free Tel:* 800-231-4261 *Toll Free Fax:* 800-882-1840 *E-mail:* info@audioeditions.com *Web Site:* audioeditions.com; audioeditionslibrary.com, pg 794

Audio Engineering Society Inc (AES), 60 E 42 St, Rm 2520, New York, NY 10165-2520 *Tel:* 212-661-8528 *Fax:* 212-682-0477 *Web Site:* www.aes.org, pg 1079

Audio Graphic Services, 1516 Ferris Ave, Royal Oak, MI 48067 *Tel:* 248-544-1793 *E-mail:* netmail@audiographicservices.com *Web Site:* www.audiographicservices.com, pg 794

Audio Images Corp, 701 Bryant St, 2nd fl, San Francisco, CA 94107 *Tel:* 415-957-9131 *Fax:* 415-957-1531 *Web Site:* www.audioimages.com, pg 794

Audio Mechanics, 1200 W Magnolia Blvd, Burbank, CA 91506 *Tel:* 818-846-5525 *Fax:* 818-846-5501 *E-mail:* info@audiomechanics.com *Web Site:* audiomechanics.com, pg 794

Audio Media Productions, 6739 Kirby Trace Cove, Memphis, TN 38119 *Tel:* 901-751-2363 *E-mail:* ampman@aol.com *Web Site:* www.audiomediaprod.com, pg 794

Audio Network US Inc, 48 W 25 St, 10th fl, New York, NY 10010 *Tel:* 646-688-4320 *E-mail:* nyoffice@audionetwork.com *Web Site:* us.audionetwork.com, pg 794

Audio Precision, 5750 SW Arctic Dr, Beaverton, OR 97005 *Tel:* 503-627-0832 *Toll Free Tel:* 800-231-7350 *Fax:* 503-469-0336 *E-mail:* sales@ap.com *Web Site:* www.ap.com, pg 794

Audio Producers Group, 200 N Dearborn St, Suite 2705, Chicago, IL 60601 *Tel:* 312-977-9400 *Fax:* 312-977-9494 *E-mail:* info@apgaudio.com *Web Site:* www.audioproducersgroup.com, pg 794

Audio Rents, 1541 N Wilcox Ave, Hollywood, CA 90028 *Tel:* 323-874-1000 *Fax:* 323-460-2676 *E-mail:* info@audiorents.com *Web Site:* www.audiorents.com, pg 794

Audio Resource Honolulu, 1750 Kalakaua Ave, Suite 201, Honolulu, HI 96826 *Tel:* 808-944-9400 *Toll Free Fax:* 866-774-4184 *E-mail:* information@audioresourcehonolulu.com *Web Site:* www.audioresourcehonolulu.com, pg 794

Audio-Technica US Inc, 1221 Commerce Dr, Stow, OH 44224 *Tel:* 330-686-2600 *Fax:* 330-686-0719 *E-mail:* pro@atus.com *Web Site:* www.audio-technica.com, pg 794

Audio Upgrades, 6982 Mimosa Dr, Carlsbad, CA 92011 *Tel:* 818-780-1222 *Web Site:* www.audioupgrades.com, pg 795

Audio-Video Corp, 213 Broadway, Albany, NY 12204 *Tel:* 518-449-7213 *Fax:* 518-449-1205 *E-mail:* info@audiovideocorp.com; sales@audiovideocorp.com *Web Site:* www.audiovideocorp.com, pg 795

Audio Video Resources, 4323 E Cotton Center Blvd, Phoenix, AZ 85040 *Tel:* 602-643-4200; 602-643-4300 (rentals) *Toll Free Tel:* 877-643-4204 *Fax:* 602-643-4270 *E-mail:* sales@avrinc.com; rentals@avrinc.com *Web Site:* www.avrinc.com, pg 795

Audio-Video Resources Inc, 1043 Adams Ave, Montgomery, AL 36104 *Tel:* 334-262-4806 *Fax:* 334-240-0000 *E-mail:* avrinc@bellsouth.net, pg 795

Audio/Video Supply Inc, 4575 Ruffner St, San Diego, CA 92111 *Tel:* 858-565-1101 *Toll Free Tel:* 800-284-2288 *Fax:* 858-565-7845 *E-mail:* sales@avsupply.com *Web Site:* www.avsupply.com, pg 795

Audio-VideoGraphics Inc, 17501 E 40 Hwy, Suite 219, Independence, MO 64055 *Tel:* 816-350-0800 *Toll Free Tel:* 800-322-2832 *Fax:* 816-350-0804 *E-mail:* mail@avginc.com *Web Site:* www.avginc.com, pg 795

Audio Visions Inc, 1501 N George St, York, PA 17404 *Tel:* 717-843-1561 *Fax:* 717-848-3289 *Web Site:* www.audiovisionsinc.com, pg 795

Audio Vistas LLC, 170 N Woods Dr, South Orange, NJ 07079 *Tel:* 212-586-2177 *E-mail:* info@audiovistas.com *Web Site:* www.audiovistas.com, pg 795

Audio Visual Actions Inc (AVA), 5641-C General Washington Dr, Alexandria, VA 22312 *Tel:* 703-750-0950 *Toll Free Tel:* 866-893-5382 *Fax:* 703-750-0954 *E-mail:* info@avactions.com *Web Site:* avactions.com, pg 795

Audio Visual Associates, One Stewart Ct, Denville, NJ 07834 *Toll Free Tel:* 888-435-6678 *Fax:* 973-442-0888 *E-mail:* sales@avaonline.com; info@avaonline.com *Web Site:* www.avaonline.com, pg 795

Audio Visual Communications Inc, 1336 Cherry St, Boothwyn, PA 19061 *Tel:* 610-272-8500 *E-mail:* audiovc@verizon.net *Web Site:* www.audiovc.com, pg 795

The Audio Visual Co (AVCO), 98-810 Moanalua Rd, Aiea, HI 96701 *Tel:* 808-485-3200 *Fax:* 808-487-0733 *Web Site:* www.theavco.com, pg 795

Audio Visual Concepts Inc, PO Box 3915, Guaynabo, PR 00970-3915 *Tel:* 787-753-7700 *Fax:* 787-766-7712 *Web Site:* www.mig-avc.com, pg 795

Audio Visual Consultants, 3640 Grand Ave, Suite 105, Oakland, CA 94610 *Tel:* 510-839-2020 *Fax:* 510-839-6464 *E-mail:* info@avconsultants.com *Web Site:* www.avconsultants.com, pg 795

Audio Visual Dynamics®, 8 Budd St, Morristown, NJ 07960 *Tel:* 973-993-8500 *Fax:* 973-984-0644 *Web Site:* www.avdusa.com, pg 795

Audio Visual Dynamics Ltd, 2360 23 Ave, Lachine, QC H8T 0A3, Canada *Tel:* 514-332-6440 *Fax:* 514-332-2009 *E-mail:* service@avd.ca *Web Site:* www.avd.ca, pg 795

Audio Visual Imagineering Inc, 6565 Hazeltine National Dr, Suite 2, Orlando, FL 32822 *Tel:* 407-859-8166 *Fax:* 407-859-8254 *Web Site:* www.av-imagineering.com, pg 795

Audio Visual Media, 1141 Lexington Ave, Mansfield, OH 44907 *Tel:* 419-756-2698 *Fax:* 419-756-1560 *E-mail:* avm2698@aol.com *Web Site:* audiovisualmedia.net, pg 795

Audio Visual of Milwaukee Inc, 285 N Janacek Rd, Brookfield, WI 53045 *Tel:* 262-432-1077 *Toll Free Tel:* 800-236-6909 *Fax:* 262-432-1078 *E-mail:* avm@avmonline.com *Web Site:* www.avmonline.com, pg 795

Audio Visual Resources Inc, 3932 Ogeechee Rd, Savannah, GA 31405 *Tel:* 912-447-5656 *Fax:* 912-447-5655 *E-mail:* aaavr@aol.com *Web Site:* www.avrsav.com, pg 795

Audio Visual Resources LLC, 1000 N Division St, Suite 2F, Peekskill, NY 10566 *Tel:* 914-526-2698 *Fax:* 914-526-3060 *E-mail:* info@avrny.com *Web Site:* www.avrny.com, pg 795

Audio Visual Sales & Service Inc, 2601 Curry Rd, Schenectady, NY 12303 *Tel:* 518-688-0640 *Fax:* 518-688-0634 *E-mail:* info@avssi.com, pg 796

Audio Visual Services Corp, 1700 E Golf Rd, Suite 400, Schaumburg, IL 60173 *Tel:* 847-222-9800 *Toll Free Tel:* 800-486-9509 *Fax:* 847-222-1600 *Web Site:* www.psav.com, pg 796

Audio Visual Systems Rental Centres, Pennjerdel House, 449 High St, Burlington, NJ 08016-4514 *Tel:* 609-387-3636 *Toll Free Tel:* 800-416-3636 *Fax:* 609-871-3636 *Web Site:* www.avsgroup.com, pg 796

Audio Visual Techniques Inc, 1489 Leestown Rd, Lexington, KY 40511 *Tel:* 859-254-8954 *Fax:* 859-233-4754 *E-mail:* info@avtav.com *Web Site:* avtav.com, pg 796

Audio Visual Technologies Group, 12502 Exchange Dr, Stafford, TX 77477 *Tel:* 281-240-2100 *Toll Free Tel:* 800-522-3687 *E-mail:* avtginfo@avtg.com *Web Site:* www.avtg.com, pg 796

Audioarts Engineering, 600 Industrial Dr, New Bern, NC 28562 *Tel:* 252-638-7000 *Fax:* 252-637-1285; 252-635-4857 (sales) *E-mail:* sales@wheatstone.com *Web Site:* www.wheatstone.com, pg 796

AudioControl®, 22410 70 Ave W, Mountlake Terrace, WA 98043 *Tel:* 425-775-8461 *Fax:* 425-778-3166 *E-mail:* sound.better@audiocontrol.com; superio.sound@audiocontrol.com *Web Site:* www.audiocontrol.com, pg 796

AudioImage Recording, 110 N Jefferson St, Richmond, VA 23220-5022 *Tel:* 804-644-7700 *Fax:* 804-644-8801 *E-mail:* info@audioimagerecording.com *Web Site:* www.audioimagerecording.com, pg 796

Audiomoxie®, PO Box 304, Georgetown, TX 78627 *E-mail:* info@audiomoxie.com *Web Site:* www.audiomoxie.com, pg 796

AudioTransitions, 6429 N Talman Ave, Chicago, IL 60645 *Tel:* 773-338-8813 *Fax:* 773-338-8813 *Web Site:* www.judithwest.com, pg 796

Audiovox, 180 Marcus Blvd, Hauppauge, NY 11788 *Tel:* 631-231-7750 *Toll Free Tel:* 800-645-4994 *Fax:* 631-231-4006 *Web Site:* www.voxxelectronics.com; www.voxxintl.com, pg 796

Audix Corp, 9400 SW Barber St, Wilsonville, OR 97070 *Tel:* 503-682-6933 *Toll Free Tel:* 800-966-8261 *Fax:* 503-682-7114 *E-mail:* info@audixusa.com *Web Site:* www.audixusa.com, pg 796

Augsburg Fortress Publishers, 100 S Fifth St, Suite 600, Minneapolis, MN 55402 *Tel:* 612-330-3300 *Toll Free Tel:* 800-328-4648 *Fax:* 612-330-3455 *Toll Free Fax:* 800-722-7766 *E-mail:* info@augsburgfortress.org *Web Site:* www.augsburgfortress.org, pg 796

August House Audio, 3500 Piedmont Rd NE, Suite 310, Atlanta, GA 30305 *Tel:* 404-442-4420 *Toll Free Tel:* 800-284-8784 *Fax:* 404-442-4435 *E-mail:* ahinfo@augusthouse.com *Web Site:* www.augusthouse.com, pg 796

Aura Sonic Ltd, PO Box 520791, Flushing, NY 11352-0791 *Tel:* 718-886-6500 *E-mail:* somebody@aurasonic.com *Web Site:* www.aurasonicltd.com, pg 796

Aural Gratification Inc, 32 Nissen Lane, West Hurley, NY 12491-5903 *Tel:* 845-679-5674 *E-mail:* auralg@gmail.com, pg 796

Auralex Acoustics Inc, 9955 Westpoint Dr, Suite 101, Indianapolis, IN 46256 *Tel:* 317-842-2600 *Toll Free Tel:* 800-95-WEDGE (959-3343, orders) *Fax:* 317-842-2760 *E-mail:* info@auralex.com *Web Site:* www.auralex.com, pg 796

Auratron Systems, 3716 N Broadway, Knoxville, TN 37917-3120 *Tel:* 865-687-6060; 865-687-6006 *Fax:* 865-687-6020 *Web Site:* www.auratronsystems.com, pg 796

Auriga Productions Ltd, 2856 rue du Comtois, Ste-Lazare, QC J7T 0E7, Canada *Tel:* 514-984-4202 *E-mail:* aurigapix@gmail.com *Web Site:* www.aurigapix.com, pg 797

Aurora Films, 324 E Dowling Rd, Suite 4, Anchorage, AK 99518 *Tel:* 907-258-4686 *Fax:* 907-561-6622 *E-mail:* aurorafilms@acsalaska.net, pg 797

aurora productions, 315 Walt Whitman Rd, Suite 210, Huntington Station, NY 11746-4112 *Tel:* 631-549-8933 *E-mail:* info@auroraproductions.tv *Web Site:* www.auroraproductions.tv, pg 797

Auslender Productions/Celestial Images, 6036 Comey Ave, Los Angeles, CA 90034-2204 *Tel:* 323-931-3277 *Fax:* 323-937-1720 *Web Site:* celestial-images.net; auslender.com, pg 797

Austin Film Commission, 301 Congress Ave, Suite 200, Austin, TX 78701 *Tel:* 512-583-7229 *Toll Free Tel:* 800-926-2282 (ext 7229) *Fax:* 512-583-7281 *Web Site:* www.austintexas.org/film; www.austinfilmcommission.com, pg 1102

Austin Film Festival, 1801 Salina St, Austin, TX 78702 *Tel:* 512-478-4795 *Toll Free Tel:* 800-310-FEST (310-3378) *Fax:* 512-478-6205 *E-mail:* info@austinfilmfestival.com *Web Site:* www.austinfilmfestival.com, pg 1108

Austin Film Society (AFS), 1901 E 51 St, Austin, TX 78723 *Tel:* 512-322-0145 *Fax:* 512-322-5192 *E-mail:* afs@austinfilm.org *Web Site:* www.austinfilm.org, pg 1079

Autodesk Inc, 111 McInnis Pkwy, San Rafael, CA 94903 *Tel:* 415-507-5000 *Fax:* 415-507-5100 *Web Site:* www.autodesk.com, pg 797

AutoDesSys Inc, 3518 Riverside Dr, Suite 102, Columbus, OH 43221 *Tel:* 614-488-8838 *Fax:* 614-488-0848 *E-mail:* formz@formz.com; sales@formz.com; sales@autodessys.com *Web Site:* www.formz.com, pg 797

Autogram/Crl, 920 Edison Ave, Suite 4, Benton, AR 72015 *Tel:* 480-893-7080 *Fax:* 501-776-0357 *Web Site:* www.orban.com, pg 797

Automated Entertainment, PO Box 1079, Little Rock, CA 95343-1079 *Tel:* 661-944-2299 *Toll Free Tel:* 800-880-6567 (orders) *Fax:* 661-944-2348 *E-mail:* questions@automatedhd.com *Web Site:* www.automatedhd.com, pg 797

Automatic Devices Co, 2121 S 12 St, Allentown, PA 18103 *Tel:* 610-797-6000 *Toll Free Tel:* 800-360-2321 *Fax:* 610-797-4088 *E-mail:* info@automaticdevices.com *Web Site:* www.automaticdevices.com, pg 797

Automobile Film Club of America Inc, 10 Cross St, Staten Island, NY 10304 *Tel:* 718-447-2255 *Fax:* 718-447-2289 *E-mail:* autofilm@aol.com *Web Site:* www.autofilmclub.com, pg 797

Auton Motorized Systems, 29102 Hancock Pkwy, Valencia, CA 91355 *Tel:* 661-257-9282 *Fax:* 661-295-5638 *E-mail:* tvlifts@auton.com *Web Site:* www.auton.com, pg 797

AV Bluebook, 80 Little Falls Rd, Fairfield, NJ 07004 *Toll Free Tel:* 800-631-7791 *Toll Free Fax:* 800-332-5871 *E-mail:* info@avbluebook.com *Web Site:* www.avbluebook.com, pg 797

AV Chicago Inc, 619 W Taylor St, Chicago, IL 60607 *Tel:* 312-229-4100 *Toll Free Tel:* 888-709-9599 *Web Site:* www.avchicago.com, pg 797

AV Concepts, 1917 W First St, Tempe, AZ 85281 *Tel:* 480-557-6000 *Toll Free Tel:* 866-927-7590 *Fax:* 480-894-8376 *E-mail:* info@avconcepts.com *Web Site:* www.avconcepts.com, pg 797

AV Conferencing, PO Box 21606, Concord, CA 94521 *Tel:* 925-216-6319 *Fax:* 801-382-5573 *E-mail:* sales@avconferencing.com *Web Site:* www.avconferencing.com, pg 797

A/V Davey, 71 Clifton Place, Bridgeport, CT 06606 *Tel:* 203-372-3286 *Toll Free Tel:* 877-AVDAVEY (283-2839) *Fax:* 203-372-3307 *Web Site:* avdavey.com, pg 797

AV Guys, 1641 Pacific Rim Ct, Suite AB, San Diego, CA 92154 *Tel:* 619-474-5050 *Fax:* 619-474-5454 *Web Site:* www.avguys.com, pg 797

AV Metro Inc, 5401 Etta Burke Ct, Raleigh, NC 27606 *Tel:* 919-233-1901 *Fax:* 919-233-1804 *E-mail:* info@avmetro.com *Web Site:* www.avmetro.com, pg 797

A/V Presentations Inc, 104 Otis St, Suite 30, Northborough, MA 01532 *Tel:* 508-393-9767 *Toll Free Tel:* 800-648-7176 *Fax:* 508-393-6698 *Web Site:* www.avpresentations.com, pg 797

AV Toolbox, 2791 Circleport Dr, Erlanger, KY 41018 *Tel:* 859-282-7303 *Toll Free Tel:* 800-235-3280; 800-721-4044 *E-mail:* sales@avtoolbox.com *Web Site:* www.avtoolbox.com, pg 797

AV Workshop, 500 W 37 St, 3rd fl, New York, NY 10018 *Tel:* 212-643-0040 *Fax:* 212-564-5277 *E-mail:* sales@avworkshop.com *Web Site:* avworkshop.com, pg 797

AVA Electronics Corp, 4000 Bridge St, Drexel Hill, PA 19026 *Tel:* 610-284-2500 *Fax:* 610-259-8379, pg 798

AVA Productions, 4760 E 65 St, Indianapolis, IN 46220 *Tel:* 317-255-6457 *E-mail:* avaprods@comcast.net *Web Site:* www.avavideoproductions.com, pg 798

Available Light, 29-20 37 Ave, Long Island City, NY 11101 *Tel:* 718-707-9670; 718-707-9671 *Fax:* 718-707-9693 *E-mail:* info@alny.net *Web Site:* www.alny.net, pg 798

Available Light, 5251 Dixon Rd, Oceanside, CA 92056-2319 *Tel:* 760-505-1605; 760-505-1600 *E-mail:* availablelight@jtservices.com *Web Site:* www.jtservices.com, pg 798

Available Lighting & Motion Picture Services Inc, 826 Jefferson Hwy, New Orleans, LA 70120 *Tel:* 504-831-5214 *Fax:* 504-831-5361 *E-mail:* avlight@bellsouth.net *Web Site:* www.availablelighting.com, pg 798

Avalon Acoustics, 2800 Wilderness Place, Boulder, CO 80301 *Tel:* 303-440-0422 *Fax:* 303-440-4396 *E-mail:* sales@avalonacoustics.com *Web Site:* www.avalonacoustics.com, pg 798

Avast! Recording Co, 601 NW 80 St, Seattle, WA 98117 *Tel:* 206-633-3926 *Fax:* 206-789-7569 *E-mail:* avast@comcast.net *Web Site:* www.avastrecording.com, pg 798

Avatar Award, 550 W Frontage Rd, Suite 3600, Northfield, IL 60093 *Tel:* 847-716-7000 *Fax:* 847-716-7004 *E-mail:* info@mediafinance.org *Web Site:* www.mediafinance.org, pg 1108

Avatar Studios, 2675 Scott Ave, Suite G, St Louis, MO 63103 *Tel:* 314-533-2242 *Fax:* 314-533-3349 *Web Site:* www.avatar-studios.com, pg 798

Avaya Inc, 211 Mount Airy Rd, Basking Ridge, NJ 07920 *Tel:* 908-953-6000 *Toll Free Tel:* 866-GO-AVAYA (462-8292 US & CN) *Web Site:* www.avaya.com, pg 798

Avekta Productions Inc, One Rock Place, Yonkers, NY 10705 *Tel:* 914-378-8000 *Web Site:* avekta.com, pg 798

AVerMedia Technologies Inc, 47358 Fremont Blvd, Fremont, CA 94538 *Tel:* 510-403-0006 (sales) *Fax:* 510-403-0022 *E-mail:* avtsales.usa@avermedia.com; avt.pmk@avermedia.com *Web Site:* www.avermedia-usa.com, pg 798

AVES Audio Visual Systems Inc, PO Box 500, Sugar Land, TX 77487-0500 *Tel:* 281-295-1300 *Toll Free Tel:* 800-365-AVES (365-2837) *Fax:* 281-295-1310 *E-mail:* sales@avesav.com *Web Site:* www.avesav.com, pg 798

AVForSale, 1222 Logan Cir, Atlanta, GA 30318 *Tel:* 404-355-6147 *Toll Free Tel:* 866-634-5296 *Fax:* 404-355-7462 *E-mail:* customerservice@avforsale.com *Web Site:* www.avforsale.com, pg 798

AVFX Inc, 96 Holton St, Boston, MA 02135 *Tel:* 617-254-0770 *Toll Free Tel:* 888-254-0770 *E-mail:* info@avfx.com *Web Site:* www.avfx.com, pg 798

AVI-SPL, 6301 Benjamin Rd, Suite 101, Tampa, FL 33634 *Tel:* 813-884-7168 *Toll Free Tel:* 866-708-5034; 800-282-6733; 866-925-8298 (cust serv); 866-559-8197 (sales) *Fax:* 813-882-9508 *E-mail:* questions@avispl.com; sales@avispl.com; customerservice@avispl.com *Web Site:* www.avispl.com, pg 798

AVI Systems, 9675 W 76 St, Suite 200, Eden Prairie, MN 55344 *Tel:* 952-949-3700 *Toll Free Tel:* 800-488-4954 *Fax:* 952-949-6000 *E-mail:* info@avisystems.com *Web Site:* www.avisystems.com, pg 799

Avid Technology Inc, 65-75 Network Dr, Burlington, MA 01830 *Tel:* 978-640-6789 *Fax:* 978-640-3366 *Web Site:* www.avid.com, pg 799

Avidex Inc, 13555 Bel-Red Rd, Suite 226, Bellevue, MA 98005 *Tel:* 425-643-0330 *Fax:* 425-274-7091 *E-mail:* info@avidexav.com *Web Site:* www.avidexav.com, pg 799

Aviom Inc, 1157 Phoenixville Pike, Suite 201, West Chester, PA 19380-4254 *Tel:* 610-738-9005 *Fax:* 610-738-9950 *E-mail:* info@aviom.com *Web Site:* www.aviom.com, pg 799

Avitecture Inc, One Export Dr, Sterling, VA 20164-4421 *Tel:* 703-404-8900 *Fax:* 703-404-8940 *E-mail:* info@avitecture.com *Web Site:* www.avitecture.com, pg 799

AVL Systems Design LLC, 14901 Bristol Park Blvd, Edmond, OK 73013 *Tel:* 405-749-1866 *Fax:* 405-749-1851 *E-mail:* dnix@avl1.com *Web Site:* www.avl1.com, pg 800

AVP Mfg & Supply Inc, 2288-B7 Dumfries Rd RR2, Cambridge, ON N1R 5S3, Canada *Tel:* 519-740-7966 *Toll Free Tel:* 800-481-2493 *Fax:* 519-740-0131 *E-mail:* sales@jackfields.com *Web Site:* www.jackfields.com, pg 800

AVS Group, 3120 South Ave, La Crosse, WI 54601 *Tel:* 608-787-1010 *Fax:* 608-787-0012 *E-mail:* info@avsgroup.com *Web Site:* www.avsgroup.com, pg 800

AVS Media Group, 11193 Old Hwy 31, Suite 1, Spanish Fort, AL 36527 *Tel:* 251-621-1200 *E-mail:* info@avsmediagroup.com *Web Site:* www.avsmediagroup.com, pg 800

AVS Technologies Inc, 2100 Place Transcanadienne, Dorval, QC H4R 2B7, Canada *Tel:* 514-683-1771, pg 800

Avtech Systems Inc, 7-01 Bellair Ave, Fairlawn, NJ 07410 *Tel:* 201-833-8777 *Fax:* 201-833-4995 *E-mail:* sales@avtechsystems.com *Web Site:* www.avtechsystems.com, pg 800

AVW-TELAV Audio Visual Solutions, a Freeman Company, 2056 32 Ave, Montreal, QC H8T 3H7, Canada *Tel:* 514-631-1821 *Toll Free Tel:* 800-868-6886 *Web Site:* freemanav-ca.com, pg 800

Award Productions, 164 Great Rd, Acton, MA 01720 *Tel:* 978-667-3335 *E-mail:* web@awardproductions.com *Web Site:* www.awardproductions.com, pg 800

Norman N Axelrod Associates, 445 E 86 St, New York, NY 10028 *Tel:* 212-741-6302 *E-mail:* naxelrod@axelrodassociates.com *Web Site:* www.axelrodassociates.com, pg 800

Axis Films, 3138 Cumberland Rd, Berkley, MI 48072 *Tel:* 248-722-1734 *Web Site:* www.axisfilms.tv, pg 800

Axxis Inc, 845 S Ninth St, Louisville, KY 40203 *Tel:* 502-568-6030 *Fax:* 502-568-6204 *E-mail:* info@axxisinc.com *Web Site:* www.axxisinc.com, pg 800

Aydin Displays Inc, One Riga Lane, Birdsboro, PA 19508 *Tel:* 610-404-7400; 610-404-5353 (sales) *Toll Free Tel:* 866-367-2934 *Fax:* 610-404-8190

E-mail: sales1@aydindisplays.com; orders@aydindisplays.com *Web Site:* www.aydindisplays.com, pg 800

Cliff Ayers Enterprises, American Big Band Hall of Fame, 608 SW 75 Terr, North Lauderdale, FL 33068 *Tel:* 615-361-7902 *Fax:* 615-336-2480 *E-mail:* info@entertainernet.net *Web Site:* www.entertainernet.net, pg 800

Aylmer Press, PO Box 2302, Madison, WI 53701-2302 *Tel:* 608-441-5277 *Fax:* 608-251-0890 *Web Site:* www.signit2.com, pg 801

AZ Spectrum, 53-53 62 St, Maspeth, NY 11378 *Tel:* 718-779-1892 *Fax:* 718-779-1892 *E-mail:* az@az-spectrum.com; azspectrum@aol.com *Web Site:* www.az-spectrum.com, pg 801

Aztec Video Productions, 2967 Montana Ave, Cincinnati, OH 45211 *Tel:* 513-481-5004 *E-mail:* aztec@fuse.net *Web Site:* www.aztecvideo.com, pg 801

Aztech Productions LLC, 400 Bethlehem Pike, Erdenheim, PA 19038 *Tel:* 215-836-5490 *Fax:* 215-836-0577 *Web Site:* aztechproductions.com, pg 801

Aztek Inc, 13765-F Alton Pkwy, Irvine, CA 92618 *Tel:* 949-770-8787 *Toll Free Tel:* 800-GRAPH-55 (472-7455) *Fax:* 949-770-4986 *E-mail:* mail@aztek.com *Web Site:* www.aztek.com, pg 801

B & B Video Productions Inc, 233 N Main St, West Point, NE 68788 *Tel:* 402-372-2628 *E-mail:* info@bandbvideo.com *Web Site:* www.bandbvideo.com, pg 801

B-K Lighting, 40429 Brickyard Dr, Madera, CA 93636 *Tel:* 559-438-5800 *Fax:* 559-438-5900 *E-mail:* info@bklighting.com *Web Site:* www.bklighting.com, pg 801

Back to the Bible, 6400 Cornhusker Hwy, Lincoln, NE 68507 *Tel:* 402-464-7200 *Toll Free Tel:* 800-759-6655 (inquires); 800-759-2425 (orders) *Fax:* 402-464-7474 *E-mail:* info@backtothebible.org *Web Site:* www.backtothebible.org, pg 801

Backdrop Outlet, 3540 Seagate Way, Oceanside, CA 92056 *Tel:* 760-547-2900 *Toll Free Tel:* 800-466-1755 *Fax:* 760-547-2899 *E-mail:* cs@backdropoutlet.com *Web Site:* www.backdropoutlet.com, pg 801

Backstage Equipment Inc, 8052 Lankershim Blvd, North Hollywood, CA 91605 *Tel:* 818-504-6026 *Toll Free Tel:* 800-692-2787 *Fax:* 818-504-6180 *E-mail:* info@backstageweb.com *Web Site:* www.backstageweb.com, pg 801

Backstage Pass Entertainment Inc, 7438 Shoshone Ave, Lake Balboa, CA 91406-2340 *Tel:* 818-881-9888 *Toll Free Tel:* 800-664-6555 *Fax:* 818-881-0555 *E-mail:* blowinsmokeband@ktb.net, pg 801

Backstar Creative Media Inc, 676 N La Salle Dr, Suite 424, Chicago, IL 60654 *Tel:* 312-467-0425 *Toll Free Tel:* 800-955-8900 *E-mail:* solutions@backstar.com *Web Site:* www.backstar.com, pg 801

Badiyan Inc, 720 W 94 St, Bloomington, MN 55420 *Tel:* 952-888-5507 *Fax:* 952-888-0360 *E-mail:* info@badiyan.com *Web Site:* www.badiyan.com, pg 801

Bag End Loudspeakers, 1201 Armstrong St, Algonquin, IL 60102 *Tel:* 847-658-8888 *Fax:* 847-658-5008 *E-mail:* info@bagend.com; usedcars@bagend.com (sales) *Web Site:* www.bagend.com, pg 801

Baha'i Distribution Service (BDS), 401 Greenleaf Ave, Wilmette, IL 60091 *Tel:* 847-425-7950 *Toll Free Tel:* 800-999-9019 *Fax:* 847-425-7951 *E-mail:* bds@usbnc.org *Web Site:* www.bahaibookstore.com, pg 801

BAI Distributors Inc, 2312 NE 29 Ave, Ocala, FL 34470-3999 *Tel:* 352-732-7009 *Toll Free Tel:* 888-224-3446 *Fax:* 352-732-1616 *E-mail:* sales@baionline.com *Web Site:* www.baionline.com, pg 801

Baker & Taylor Inc, 2550 W Tyvola Rd, Suite 300, Charlotte, NC 28217 *Tel:* 704-998-3100 *Toll Free Tel:* 800-775-1800 *E-mail:* btinfo@baker-taylor.com *Web Site:* www.btol.com, pg 801

Baker Audio Inc, 2195 N Norcross Tucker Rd, Norcross, GA 30071 *Tel:* 770-441-2000 *Toll Free Tel:* 800-847-3523 *Fax:* 770-449-7719 *E-mail:* sales@bakeraudiovisual.com *Web Site:* www.bakeraudiovisual.com, pg 801

Balboa Capital Corp, 2010 Main St, Suite 1100, Irvine, CA 92614 *Tel:* 949-756-0800 *Toll Free Tel:* 888-BALBOA1 (225-2621) *Fax:* 949-756-2565 *E-mail:* customerservice@balboacapital.com *Web Site:* www.balboacapital.com, pg 802

Baldwin Productions, 160 Tioga Lane, Greenbrae, CA 94904 *Tel:* 415-925-9262 *Fax:* 415-925-1040 *Web Site:* www.baldwinproductions.com, pg 802

Ballantyne Strong Inc, 13710 FNB Pkwy, Suite 400, Omaha, NE 68154 *Tel:* 402-453-4444 *Toll Free Tel:* 800-424-1215 *Fax:* 402-453-7238 *E-mail:* info@btn-inc.com *Web Site:* ballantynestrong.com, pg 802

Baltimore Film Office, 10 E Baltimore St, 10th fl, Baltimore, MD 21202 *Tel:* 410-752-8632; 443-263-4313 *Fax:* 410-385-0361 *Web Site:* www.baltimorefilm.com, pg 1098

Band Pro Film & Digital Inc, 3403 W Pacific Ave, Burbank, CA 91505 *Tel:* 818-841-9655 *Toll Free Tel:* 888-BANDPRO (226-3776) *Fax:* 818-841-7649 *Web Site:* www.bandpro.com, pg 802

B&B Electronics Manufacturing Co, 707 Dayton Rd, Ottawa, IL 61350 *Tel:* 815-433-5100 *Toll Free Tel:* 800-346-3119 *Fax:* 815-433-5109 *E-mail:* info@bb-elec.com; orders@bb-elec.com *Web Site:* www.bb-elec.com, pg 802

B&H Photo & Video Pro Audio, 420 Ninth Ave, New York, NY 10001 *Tel:* 212-444-5000; 212-444-6615 *Toll Free Tel:* 800-606-6969 *Fax:* 212-239-7770 *Toll Free Fax:* 800-947-7008 *Web Site:* www.bhphotovideo.com, pg 802

B&H Publishing Group, One Lifeway Plaza, Nashville, TN 37234 *Toll Free Tel:* 800-251-3225 (retailers); 800-448-8032 (consumers); 800-458-2772 (churches) *Fax:* 615-251-3914 (consumers); 615-251-5933 (churches) *Toll Free Fax:* 800-296-4036 (retailers) *Web Site:* www.bhpublishinggroup.com, pg 802

B&K Components Ltd, 1749 Chapin Rd, Montebello, CA 90640 *Tel:* 323-278-0001 *Fax:* 323-278-0083 *Web Site:* www.bkcomp.com, pg 802

Banff Mountain Film & Book Festival, 107 Tunnel Mountain Dr, Banff, AB T1L 1H5, Canada *Tel:* 403-762-6347 *Fax:* 403-762-6277 *E-mail:* banffmountainfestival@banffcentre.ca *Web Site:* www.banffcentre.ca/mountainfestival, pg 1108

Banff World Media Festival, 102 Boulder Crescent, Suite 202, Canmore, AB T1W 1L2, Canada *Tel:* 403-678-1216 *Toll Free Tel:* 888-287-2279 *Fax:* 403-678-3357 *E-mail:* info@achillesmedia.com *Web Site:* banffmediafestival.com, pg 1109

Bang Pictures, 78 Graterford Rd, Schwenksville, PA 19473 *Tel:* 610-357-1015 *Web Site:* www.bangpictures.com, pg 802

The Banquet Sound Studios, 5870 McFarland Rd, Sebastopol, CA 95472 *Tel:* 707-823-3500 *E-mail:* info@banquetstudios.com *Web Site:* www.banquetstudios.com, pg 802

Bantam Doubleday Dell Audio Publishing, 1745 Broadway, New York, NY 10019 *Tel:* 212-782-9000 *E-mail:* audio@randomhouse.com *Web Site:* www.randomhouse.com; bantam-dell.atrandom.com, pg 802

Barber Tech Video Products, 205 E Anaheim St, Long Beach, CA 90813 *Tel:* 818-982-7775 *Toll Free Tel:* 877-887-6388 *E-mail:* info@barbertvp.com *Web Site:* www.barbertvp.com, pg 802

Barbizon Electric Co Inc, 456 W 55 St, New York, NY 10019-4403 *Tel:* 212-586-1620 *Toll Free Tel:* 800-582-9941 *Fax:* 212-247-8818 *E-mail:* benysales@barbizon.com *Web Site:* www.barbizon.com, pg 802

Barbosa Video Services, 11 Plaza, Suite E, Patterson, CA 95363 *Tel:* 209-324-5327 *Web Site:* barbosavideo.com, pg 802

Barco Inc, 3059 Premiere Pkwy, Suite 400, Duluth, GA 30097 *Tel:* 916-859-2500; 678-475-8000 *Toll Free Tel:* 888-414-7226 *E-mail:* sales.events.us@barco.com *Web Site:* www.barco.com, pg 803

Bardes Products Inc, 5245 W Clinton Ave, Milwaukee, WI 53223 *Tel:* 414-354-9000 *Toll Free Tel:* 800-223-1357 *Fax:* 414-354-1921 *E-mail:* sales@bardes.com *Web Site:* www.bardes.com, pg 803

Barger-Lite, PO Box 90294, Venice, CA 90294 *Tel:* 310-401-0633 *Fax:* 310-392-6791 *Web Site:* www.bargerlite.com, pg 803

Jake Barner Studio, 120 S Barner Dr, Centralia, WA 98531 *Tel:* 360-736-1764, pg 803

Bill Barnes Video Productions LLC, 14238 Honeysuckle Ridge, Matthews, NC 28105-6403 *Tel:* 704-847-8685 *Toll Free Tel:* 888-893-7331 *Fax:* 704-847-7279 *E-mail:* bill@bbvp.tv *Web Site:* bbvp.tv, pg 803

Baron Stage Curtain & Equipment Co Inc, 3218 Noble St, Baltimore, MD 21224 *Tel:* 410-327-6962 *Fax:* 410-327-7077 *E-mail:* curtains@baronstage.com *Web Site:* www.baronstage.com, pg 803

Barron's Educational Series Inc, 250 Wireless Blvd, Hauppauge, NY 11788 *Tel:* 631-434-3311 *Toll Free Tel:* 800-645-3476 *Fax:* 631-434-3723 *E-mail:* barrons@barronseduc.com *Web Site:* www.barronseduc.com, pg 803

Ben Barry & Associates Inc, 10246 Briarwood Dr, Los Angeles, CA 90077 *Tel:* 310-274-1523 *Fax:* 310-274-1523 *E-mail:* benbarryfilms@sbcglobal.net, pg 803

Carl Barth Images, PO Box 5325, Santa Barbara, CA 93150-5325 *Tel:* 805-637-0881 *E-mail:* carlbarthimages@cox.net, pg 803

Bartha, 600 N Cassady Ave, Columbus, OH 43219 *Tel:* 614-252-7455 *Toll Free Tel:* 800-363-2698 *Fax:* 614-252-7641 *E-mail:* info@bartha.com *Web Site:* www.bartha.com, pg 803

Bartok Records & Publications, PO Box 399, Homosassa, FL 34487 *Tel:* 352-382-2015 *Fax:* 352-382-0341 *E-mail:* bartok@atlantic.net *Web Site:* www.bartokrecords.com, pg 803

The Whitman Bassow Award, 40 W 45 St, New York, NY 10036 *Tel:* 212-626-9220 *Fax:* 212-626-9210 *Web Site:* www.opcofamerica.org, pg 1109

Bay Photo Lab, 920 Disc Dr, Scotts Valley, CA 95066 *Tel:* 831-475-6686 *Toll Free Tel:* 800-435-6686 *Fax:* 831-475-5275 *E-mail:* support@bayphoto.com (cust serv) *Web Site:* www.bayphoto.com, pg 803

Bay Records, 3365 S Lucille Lane, Lafayette, LA 94549 *Tel:* 925-284-7797 *Web Site:* www.bayrec.com, pg 803

Bay Stage Lighting Co Inc, 4008 W Alva St, Tampa, FL 33614 *Tel:* 813-877-1089 *Fax:* 813-875-8837 *Web Site:* www.baystagelighting.com, pg 803

BBC Worldwide Canada Ltd, 409 King St W, 5th fl, Toronto, ON M5V 1K1, Canada *Tel:* 416-204-0500 *Web Site:* www.bbcworldwide.com, pg 803

BBC Worldwide Learning, 1120 Avenue of the Americas, 5th fl, New York, NY 10036 *Tel:* 212-339-1700 *Fax:* 212-705-9530 *E-mail:* education.us@bbc.com *Web Site:* www.bbcworldwidelearning.com, pg 803

BBE Sound Inc, 2548 Fender Ave, Fullerton, CA 92831 *Tel:* 714-897-6766 *Toll Free Tel:* 800-233-8346 *Fax:* 714-895-6728 *Web Site:* www.bbesound.com, pg 803

BC Video Inc, 152 W 25 St, 2nd fl, New York, NY 10001 *Tel:* 212-242-4065 *Toll Free Tel:* 800-846-9682 *Fax:* 212-242-4190 *Web Site:* www.bcvideo.com, pg 803

BCD Associates Inc, 2800 NW 36 St, Suite 220, Oklahoma City, OK 73112 *Tel:* 405-702-6888 *Toll Free Tel:* 800-223-6734 *E-mail:* salesweb@bcdusa.com; sales@bcdusa.com *Web Site:* www.bcdusa.com, pg 803

The BD Co, PO Box 2048, Chandler, AZ 85225-2048 *Tel:* 480-632-1160 *Toll Free Tel:* 800-704-3072 *Fax:* 480-632-1163 *E-mail:* info@bdcompany.com *Web Site:* www.bdcompany.com, pg 804

Be Media, 9729 Lurline Ave, Chatsworth, CA 91311 *Tel:* 310-725-8500 *Toll Free Tel:* 877-210-7664 *Fax:* 310-725-9500 *Web Site:* www.bemedia.com, pg 804

BEA National Scholarships in Broadcasting, 1771 "N" St NW, Washington, DC 20036-2891 *Tel:* 202-602-0587 *Fax:* 202-609-9940 *E-mail:* help@beaweb.org *Web Site:* www.beaweb.org, pg 1109

BeachTek Inc, 480 Osprey Ave, Kelowna, BC V1Y 5A5, Canada *Tel:* 416-690-9457 *E-mail:* info@beachtek.com *Web Site:* www.beachtek.com, pg 804

BeachWare Inc, 4980 N Campbell Ave, Tucson, AZ 85718 *Tel:* 520-577-8945 *Fax:* 520-577-8945 *Web Site:* www.beachware.com, pg 804

Beachwood Productions, 1500 Mill Creek Ct SW, Marietta, GA 30008 *Tel:* 770-432-6563; 404-324-7271 (cell) *Web Site:* www.beachwoodproductions.com, pg 804

Bear Creek Studio & Music Production Inc, 6313 Maltby Rd, Woodinville, WA 98072 *Tel:* 425-481-4100 *Fax:* 425-486-2718 *E-mail:* bearcreek@seanet.com *Web Site:* bearcreekstudio.com, pg 804

Beast Atlanta, 3399 Peachtree Rd NE, Suite 200, Atlanta, GA 30326-1149 *Tel:* 404-237-9977 *Fax:* 404-237-3923 *E-mail:* info@riotatlanta.com *Web Site:* www.beast.tv, pg 804

Beatty TeleVisual Productions, 1287 Wabash Ave, Springfield, IL 62704 *Tel:* 217-787-4747 *Toll Free Tel:* 800-777-2043 *Fax:* 217-787-4857 *E-mail:* bargins@beattytelevisual.com *Web Site:* www.beattytelevisual.com, pg 804

Beaumont Convention & Visitors Bureau, 505 Willow St, Beaumont, TX 77701 *Tel:* 409-880-3749 *Toll Free Tel:* 800-392-4401 *Fax:* 409-880-3750 *Web Site:* www.beaumontcvb.com, pg 1102

Russ Beckner Pictures, 2100 Heatherwood Ct, Middletown, OH 45042 *Tel:* 513-422-9552 *Web Site:* www.russbecknerpictures.com, pg 804

Beekman Books Inc, 300 Old All Angels Hill Rd, Wappingers Falls, NY 12590 *Tel:* 845-297-2690 *Fax:* 845-297-1002 *E-mail:* manager@beekmanbooks.com *Web Site:* www.beekmanbooks.com, pg 804

Beholder Productions Inc, 1515 Market St, Suite 1200, Philadelphia, PA 19102 *Toll Free Tel:* 844-BEHOLD-R (234-6537) *E-mail:* info@beholderproductions.com *Web Site:* www.beholderproductions.com, pg 804

Lawrence Behr Associates Inc, 3400 Tupper Dr, Greenville, NC 27834 *Tel:* 252-757-0279 *Toll Free Tel:* 800-522-4464 *Fax:* 252-752-9155 *E-mail:* lbassc@lbagroup.com *Web Site:* www.lbagroup.com/associates, pg 804

Bel-Air Film Festival (BAFF), 5900 Wilshire Blvd, 10th fl, Los Angeles, CA 90036 *Tel:* 323-801-0100 *E-mail:* info@belairfilmfestival.com *Web Site:* www.belairfilmfestival.com, pg 1109

Belar Electronics Laboratory Inc, 1140 McDermott Dr, Suite 105, West Chester, PA 19380-4043 *Tel:* 610-687-5550 *Fax:* 610-687-2686 *E-mail:* sales@belar.com *Web Site:* www.belar.com, pg 804

Belden, 401 Pennsylvania Pkwy, Suite 200, Indianapolis, IN 46280 *Tel:* 317-818-6300 (ext 6334) *Toll Free Tel:* 800-235-3362; 800-BELDEN-1 (235-3361) *Fax:* 317-818-6365 *E-mail:* info@belden.com *Web Site:* www.belden.com, pg 804

Belew Enterprises, 524 Vance Dr, Bristol, TN 37620 *Tel:* 423-764-4116 *E-mail:* bsv@tricon.net, pg 804

Bell & Howell LLC, 760 S Wolf Rd, Wheeling, IL 60090 *Tel:* 847-675-7600 *Toll Free Tel:* 800-220-3030 (cust serv) *E-mail:* marketing@bhemail.com *Web Site:* www.bellhowell.net, pg 804

Bella Faccia Inc, 6521 Chillum Place NW, Washington, DC 20012 *Tel:* 202-291-1932 *Fax:* 202-301-7716 *E-mail:* contact@bellafaccia.net *Web Site:* www.bellafaccia.net, pg 804

Bellin Productions, 812 Hickory Grove Dr, Larchmont, NY 10538 *Tel:* 914-834-5520 *Fax:* 914-834-5477 *E-mail:* info@bellinproductions.com *Web Site:* www.bellinproductions.com, pg 805

Ben Nye Makeup, 3655 Lenawee Ave, Los Angeles, CA 90016 *Tel:* 310-839-1984 *Fax:* 310-839-2640 *E-mail:* sales1@bennyemakeup.com *Web Site:* www.bennye.com, pg 805

Benchmark Media, 72 N State Rd, Suite 415, Briarcliff Manor, NY 10510 *Tel:* 914-762-3838 *Fax:* 914-762-3895 *E-mail:* benchmarkmedia.info@gmail.com *Web Site:* www.benchmarkmedia.info, pg 805

Benchmark Media Systems Inc, 203 E Hampton Place, Suite 2, Syracuse, NY 13206 *Tel:* 315-437-6300 *Toll Free Tel:* 800-262-4675 *Fax:* 315-437-5119 *E-mail:* info@benchmarkmedia.com *Web Site:* www.benchmarkmedia.com, pg 805

Robert Benedetto, 10 Mall Terr, Suite A, Savannah, GA 31406 *Tel:* 912-692-1400 *Fax:* 912-692-1403 *Web Site:* www.benedettoguitars.com, pg 805

Benjamin Creative Productions, 577 Lakeside Dr, Waterford, MI 48328 *Tel:* 248-682-6566 *Fax:* 248-682-0508 *Web Site:* www.benjaminvideo.com, pg 805

The Robert Spiers Benjamin Award, 40 W 45 St, New York, NY 10036 *Tel:* 212-626-9220 *Fax:* 212-626-9210 *Web Site:* www.opcofamerica.org, pg 1109

Bennett Media Corp, 2321 Abbot Kinney Blvd, Venice, CA 90291 *Tel:* 310-827-8064 *Toll Free Tel:* 800-733-8862 *Fax:* 310-827-8074 *E-mail:* sale@bennettmarine.com *Web Site:* www.bennettmarine.com, pg 805

Bennett-Watt HD Productions Inc, 13021 244 Ave SE, Issaquah, WA 98027 *Tel:* 425-392-3935 *Toll Free Tel:* 800-327-2893 *Fax:* 425-526-5851 *E-mail:* info@bennett-watt.com *Web Site:* www.bennett-watt.com, pg 805

Benro, 75 Virginia Rd, Suite 1, North White Plains, NY 10603 *Tel:* 914-347-3300 *Fax:* 914-347-3309 *E-mail:* info@benrousa.com *Web Site:* www.benrousa.com, pg 805

The Bergman Collection of Medical/Technical/Scientific Stock Images, 134 Leabrook Lane, Princeton, NJ 08540-3622 *Tel:* 609-921-0749 *E-mail:* information@pmiprinceton.com *Web Site:* pmiprinceton.com, pg 805

Bergwall Productions Inc, 120 N Church St, Suite 106, West Chester, PA 19380 *Tel:* 610-436-4017 *Toll Free Tel:* 800-934-8696 *Fax:* 610-436-4018 *Web Site:* www.bergwall.com, pg 805

Berke Creative Inc, 50 Mendell St, Suite 11, San Francisco, CA 94124 *Tel:* 415-285-8800 *Fax:* 415-285-8847 *Web Site:* www.berkesound.com, pg 805

Berkeley Film Office, 2030 Addison St, Suite 102, Berkeley, CA 94704 *Tel:* 510-549-7040 *Toll Free Tel:* 800-847-4823 *Fax:* 510-644-2052 *E-mail:* film@visitberkeley.com *Web Site:* www.filmberkeley.com, pg 1092

Berkeley Sound Artists Inc, 2600 Tenth St, Suite 312, Berkeley, CA 94710 *Tel:* 510-486-2290 *Fax:* 510-549-0287 *E-mail:* info@berkeleysoundartists.com *Web Site:* www.berkeleysoundartists.com, pg 805

Berkeley Video & Film Festival, 1939 Addison St, Berkeley, CA 94704 *Tel:* 510-843-3699 *Fax:* 510-843-3379 *E-mail:* maketv@aol.com *Web Site:* www.berkeleyvideofilmfest.org, pg 1109

Bernie's Photo Center, 525 E Ohio St, Pittsburgh, PA 15212 *Tel:* 412-231-1717 *Toll Free Tel:* 800-346-8884 *Fax:* 412-231-1217 *E-mail:* info@berniesphoto.com *Web Site:* www.berniesphoto.com, pg 805

Berry & Homer, 2035 Richmond St, Philadelphia, PA 19125 *Tel:* 215-425-0888 *Fax:* 215-425-2701 *E-mail:* info@berryandhomer.com *Web Site:* www.berryandhomer.com, pg 805

BES Studios, 6829 Atmore Dr, Suite E, Richmond, VA 23225 *Tel:* 804-276-0806 *Toll Free Tel:* 800-995-2371 *E-mail:* info@besstudios.com *Web Site:* www.besstudios.com, pg 805

Beseler Photo, 2018 W Main St, Stroudsburg, PA 18360 *Toll Free Tel:* 800-237-3537 *Toll Free Fax:* 800-966-4515 *Web Site:* www.beselerphoto.com, pg 805

The Bessies Awards, 160 Bloor St E, Suite 1005, Toronto, ON M4W 1B9, Canada *Tel:* 416-923-8813 *Toll Free Tel:* 800-231-0051 (CN only) *Fax:* 416-413-3879 *E-mail:* tvb@tvb.ca *Web Site:* www.tvb.ca/pages/thebessies.htm; thebessies.ca, pg 1109

Best Bet Camera Rentals, 5247 Agnes Ave, Unit 5, Valley Village, CA 91607 *Tel:* 818-508-9249 *E-mail:* info@bestbetcamera.com *Web Site:* www.bestbetcamera.com, pg 805

Best Film & Video, 3913 Fall Wheat Dr, Plano, TX 75075 *Tel:* 214-395-4070 *Web Site:* www.bestfilmandvideo.com, pg 805

The Best of Photojournalism (BOP), 3200 Croasdaile Dr, Suite 306, Durham, NC 27705 *Tel:* 919-383-7246 *Fax:* 919-383-7261 *E-mail:* info@nppa.org *Web Site:* www.nppa.org, pg 1109

Best Shot, 4301 W Cayuga St, Tampa, FL 33614 *Tel:* 813-454-5768 *E-mail:* request@bestshotfootage.com *Web Site:* www.bestshotfootage.com, pg 806

Bestek Lighting & Staging, 98 Mahan St, West Babylon, NY 11704 *Tel:* 631-643-0707 *Fax:* 631-643-0764 *E-mail:* production@bestek.com *Web Site:* www.bestek.com, pg 806

Bestwell Optical Instrument Corp, 46 Henry St, Merrick, NY 11566 *Tel:* 516-379-2280 *Fax:* 516-706-1744 *Web Site:* www.bestwelloptical.com, pg 806

Beta Electronics Inc, 130 S Barranca St, Apt 314, West Covina, CA 91791-2279 *Tel:* 614-538-8207 *Toll Free Tel:* 800-546-2382 *Fax:* 614-538-8209 *Toll Free Fax:* 888-329-2382 *E-mail:* sales@betalaser.com *Web Site:* www.betalaser.com, pg 806

Bethesda Softworks LLC, 1370 Piccard Dr, Suite 120, Rockville, MD 20850 *Tel:* 301-926-8300 *E-mail:* info@bethsoft.com *Web Site:* www.bethsoft.com, pg 806

Bevilacqua Studios, 202 E 42 St, New York, NY 10017 *Tel:* 212-490-0355 *Fax:* 212-490-0355, pg 806

Bexel Corp, 2701 N Ontario St, Burbank, CA 91504 *Tel:* 818-565-4322 *Toll Free Tel:* 800-225-6185 (tech support) *E-mail:* rentals@bexel.com *Web Site:* www.bexel.com, pg 806

Bext Inc, 1045 Tenth Ave, San Diego, CA 92101 *Tel:* 619-BEXTINC (239-8462) *Toll Free Tel:* 888-BEXTINC (239-8462) *Fax:* 619-239-8474 *E-mail:* bext@bext.com *Web Site:* www.bext.com, pg 806

beyerdynamic Inc, 56 Central Ave, Farmingdale, NY 11735 *Tel:* 631-293-3200 *Toll Free Tel:* 800-293-4463 *Fax:* 631-293-3288 *E-mail:* info@beyerdynamic-usa.com *Web Site:* north-america.beyerdynamic.com, pg 806

Beyers Sound & Essay Audio, PO Box 120442, St Paul, MN 55112-0018 *Tel:* 651-633-3933 *E-mail:* info@essayaudio.com *Web Site:* www.essayaudio.com, pg 806

BFS Entertainment & Multimedia Limited, 360 Newkirk Rd, Richmond Hill, ON L4C 3G7, Canada *Tel:* 905-884-2323 *Fax:* 905-884-8292 *E-mail:* info@bfsent.com; contact@bfsent.com *Web Site:* www.bfsent.com, pg 806

BGW Systems, an Amplifier Technologies Inc Company, 1749 Chapin Rd, Montebello, CA 90640 *Tel:* 323-278-0001 *Fax:* 323-278-0083 *E-mail:* sales@bgw.com; info@bgw.com *Web Site:* www.bgw.com, pg 806

BIAMP Systems, 9300 SW Gemini Dr, Beaverton, OR 97008 *Tel:* 503-641-7287 *Toll Free Tel:* 800-826-1457 (US & CN) *Fax:* 503-626-0281 *E-mail:* biampinfo@biamp.com; salesteam@biamp.com *Web Site:* www.biamp.com, pg 806

Bias Studios, 5400 Carolina Place, Springfield, VA 22151 *Tel:* 703-941-3333 *E-mail:* info@biasstudios.com *Web Site:* www.biasstudios.com, pg 806

Biblical Archaeology Society (BAS), 4710 41 St NW, Washington, DC 20016 *Tel:* 202-364-3300 *Toll Free Tel:* 800-221-4644 *Fax:* 202-364-2636 *E-mail:* bas@bib-arch.org; merchandise@bib-arch.org *Web Site:* www.biblicalarchaeology.org, pg 806

Big Apple Films, 636 W 28 St, New York, NY 10001 *Tel:* 212-368-1111 *Fax:* 347-689-1604 *Web Site:* www.bigapplefilms.com, pg 806

Big Bear Chamber of Commerce, 630 Bartlett Rd, 1st fl, Big Bear Lake, CA 92315 *Tel:* 909-866-4607 *Fax:* 909-866-5412 *E-mail:* contact@bigbearchamber.com *Web Site:* www.bigbearchamber.com, pg 1092

Big Bear Lake International Film Festival, PO Box 1981, Big Bear Lake, CA 92315 *Tel:* 909-547-4019 *E-mail:* info@bigbearfilmfestival.com *Web Site:* www.bigbearfilmfestival.com, pg 1109

Big Byte Video Productions, 223 Washington Blvd, Lake Placid, FL 33852 *Tel:* 863-699-6229 *Fax:* 863-699-0145 *E-mail:* bigbytevideo@yahoo.com *Web Site:* www.bigbytevideo.us, pg 806

Big Deal Custom Casings, 100 Durand Rd, Winnipeg, MB R2J 3T2, Canada *Tel:* 204-663-4870 *Toll Free Tel:* 800-337-3325 *Fax:* 204-668-7404 *E-mail:* info@bigdealcases.com *Web Site:* bigdealcases.ca, pg 807

Big Door, 114 Sheldon St, El Segundo, CA 90245 *Tel:* 310-546-6100 *Fax:* 310-906-4585 *E-mail:* sales@bigdoor.tv *Web Site:* www.bigdoor.tv; www.bigdoorstudio.tv, pg 807

Big Event Productions LLC, 77 13 Ave NE, Studio 101, Minneapolis, MN 55413 *Tel:* 612-623-7800 *Fax:* 612-455-0450 *Web Site:* www.bigeventpros.com, pg 807

Big Film Design, 375 S End Ave, No 9S, New York, NY 10280 *Tel:* 212-627-3430 *E-mail:* info@bigfilmdesign.com *Web Site:* www.bigfilmdesign.com, pg 807

Big Fish Productions Inc, PO Box 782, Bronx, NY 10462-0782 *Tel:* 212-860-3639 *Web Site:* www.bigfishproductioninc.com, pg 807

Big Foot Productions Inc, 37-09 36 Ave, Long Island City, NY 11101 *Tel:* 718-729-1900 *Fax:* 718-729-8638 *E-mail:* info@bigfootnyc.com *Web Site:* www.bigfootnyc.com, pg 807

The Big House Group, 17 Waller Ave, Ossining, NY 10562 *Tel:* 914-944-4011 *Fax:* 914-944-8044 *Web Site:* www.bighousetv.com, pg 807

Big House Sound Inc, 4001 Drossett Dr, Austin, TX 78744 *Tel:* 512-443-0019 *Fax:* 512-443-0916 *Web Site:* www.bighousesound.com, pg 807

Big Island Film Office, 25 Aupuni St, Hilo, HI 96720 *Tel:* 808-961-8369 *Fax:* 808-935-1205 *E-mail:* film@filmbigisland.com *Web Site:* www.filmbigisland.com, pg 1097

Big Kids Productions Inc, 2620 Barton Hills Dr, Austin, TX 78704 *Tel:* 512-441-0737 *Toll Free Tel:* 800-477-7811 *Fax:* 512-441-0339 *E-mail:* customerservice@bigkids.com *Web Site:* bigkids.com, pg 807

Big Muddy Film Festival, 1100 Lincoln Dr, Rm 1101, Carbondale, IL 62901-6610 *Tel:* 618-453-8301 *Fax:* 618-453-2264 *E-mail:* info@bigmuddyfilm.com *Web Site:* www.bigmuddyfilm.com, pg 1109

Big Shoulders Digital Video Productions, 875 N Michigan Ave, Suite 3750, Chicago, IL 60611 *Tel:* 312-540-5400 *E-mail:* info@bigshoulders.com; sales@bigshoulders.com *Web Site:* www.bigshoulders.com, pg 807

Big Time Picture Company Inc, 12210 1/2 Nebraska Ave, Los Angeles, CA 90025 *Tel:* 310-207-0921 *Fax:* 310-826-0071 *E-mail:* info@bigtimepic.com *Web Site:* www.bigtimepic.com, pg 807

Bil-Jax Inc, 125 Taylor Pkwy, Archbold, OH 43502 *Tel:* 419-445-8915 *Toll Free Tel:* 800-537-0540 *Fax:* 419-445-0367 *E-mail:* sales@biljax.com *Web Site:* www.biljax.com, pg 807

Bill Bachmann Studios, PO Box 950833, Lake Mary, FL 32795 *Tel:* 407-333-9988 *Web Site:* www.billbachmann.com, pg 807

Billings Film Liaison Office, 815 S 27 St, Billings, MT 59101 *Tel:* 406-245-4111 *Toll Free Tel:* 800-711-2630 *Fax:* 406-245-7333 *Web Site:* www.visitbillings.com, pg 1099

BingoLewis, 203 NE Weidler St, Portland, OR 97232 *Tel:* 503-223-2224 *E-mail:* info@bingolewis.com *Web Site:* www.bingolewis.com, pg 807

BioMedia Inc, PO Box 918, Franklin, NY 13775 *Tel:* 917-754-3274 (cell) *E-mail:* andy@bio-media.com *Web Site:* bio-media.com, pg 807

Biomedical Media Communications Dept, 263 Farmington Ave, Farmington, CT 06030-2910 *Tel:* 860-679-2119; 860-679-2433 *Fax:* 860-679-4034 *Web Site:* video.uchc.edu, pg 807

Biomorph Desks, 11 Broadway, Rm 905, New York, NY 10004 *Tel:* 212-809-4323 *Toll Free Tel:* 888-302-DESK (302-3375) *Toll Free Fax:* 888-652-7137 *E-mail:* info@biomorphdesk.com *Web Site:* www.biomorphdesk.com, pg 807

Birds & Animals Unlimited, 34145 Pacific Coast Hwy, No 761, Dana Point, CA 92629 *Tel:* 661-269-0148 *Toll Free Tel:* 877-542-1355 *Toll Free Fax:* 866-212-7899 *E-mail:* california@birdsandanimals.com *Web Site:* www.birdsandanimals.com, pg 808

Birns & Sawyer Inc, 5275 Craner Ave, North Hollywood, CA 91601 *Tel:* 323-466-8211 *Fax:* 323-466-1868; 818-358-4395 (rental) *E-mail:* info@birnsandsawyer.com *Web Site:* www.birnsandsawyer.com, pg 808

Bishop Area Chamber of Commerce & Visitors Bureau, 690 N Main St, Bishop, CA 93514 *Tel:* 760-873-8405 *Toll Free Tel:* 888-395-3952 *Fax:* 760-873-6999 *Web Site:* www.bishopvisitor.com, pg 1092

Bisk Education, 9417 Princess Palm Ave, Tampa, FL 33619 *Toll Free Tel:* 800-280-9718 *E-mail:* customerservice@bisk.com *Web Site:* www.bisk.com, pg 808

Bismeaux Studio, PO Box 463, Austin, TX 78767-0463 *Tel:* 512-444-9885 *Fax:* 512-444-4699 *Web Site:* www.bismeauxstudio.com, pg 808

Bitcentral Inc, 4340 Von Karman Ave, Suite 400, Newport Beach, CA 92660 *Tel:* 949-253-9000 *E-mail:* sales@bitcentral.com; support@bitcentral.com *Web Site:* www.bitcentral.com, pg 808

BitFlow Inc, 400 W Cummings Park, Suite 5050, Woburn, MA 01801 *Tel:* 781-932-2900 *Fax:* 781-933-9965 *E-mail:* sales@bitflow.com *Web Site:* www.bitflow.com, pg 808

Biway Media, 5803 Sovereign, Suite 204, Houston, TX 77036 *Tel:* 713-271-4036 *Toll Free Tel:* 877-BIWAY DV (249-2938) *Fax:* 713-271-4240 *E-mail:* info@biwaymedia.com; sales@biwaymedia.com; audiosales@biwaymedia.com *Web Site:* www.biwaymedia.com, pg 808

BJU Press, 1700 Wade Hampton Blvd, Greenville, SC 29614 *Tel:* 864-770-1317 *Toll Free Tel:* 800-845-5731 *Fax:* 864-271-8151 *Toll Free Fax:* 800-525-8398 *E-mail:* bjupinfo@bjupress.com *Web Site:* www.bjupress.com; www.bjupresshomeschool.com, pg 808

The Black Academy of Arts & Letters Inc, Dallas Convention Ctr Theater Complex, 1309 Canton St, Dallas, TX 75201 *Tel:* 214-743-2440 *Fax:* 214-743-2451 *E-mail:* info@tbaal.org *Web Site:* www.tbaal.org, pg 808

Black Film Center Archive, Indiana University, Wells Library, Rm 044, 1320 E Tenth St, Bloomington, IN 47405 *Tel:* 812-855-6041 *Fax:* 812-856-5832 *E-mail:* bfca@indiana.edu *Web Site:* www.indiana.edu/~bfca, pg 808

Black Filmmaker Foundation (BFF), 131 Varick St, Suite 937, New York, NY 10013 *Tel:* 212-253-1690 *Fax:* 212-255-7575 *E-mail:* community@dvrepublic.org *Web Site:* www.dvrepublic.org, pg 1079

Black Maria Film/Video Festival, c/o New Jersey City University, Dept of Media Arts, 2039 Kennedy Blvd, Jersey City, NJ 07305 *Tel:* 201-200-2043 *Fax:* 201-200-3490 *E-mail:* info@blackmariafilmfestival.org *Web Site:* www.blackmariafilmfestival.org, pg 1109

Black Media Works, 534 21 Ave SW, Calgary, AB T2S 0H1, Canada *Tel:* 403-802-0010 *E-mail:* info@blackmediaworks.com *Web Site:* www.blackmediaworks.com, pg 808

Black Star Publishing Co Inc, 333 Mamaroneck Ave, PMB 175, White Plains, NY 10605 *Tel:* 212-679-3288 *Fax:* 212-889-2052 *Web Site:* www.blackstar.com, pg 808

Blackburst Entertainment, 1830 Longwood Lake Mary Rd, No 1024, Longwood, FL 32750 *Tel:* 407-599-5353 *E-mail:* info@blackburst.net *Web Site:* www.blackburstentertainment.com, pg 808

Blackstone Audio Inc, 31 Mistletoe Rd, Ashland, OR 97520 *Toll Free Tel:* 800-621-0182 *Toll Free Fax:* 877-492-0793 *E-mail:* libraryservices@blackstoneaudio.com *Web Site:* www.blackstoneaudio.com; www.blackstonelibrary.com, pg 808

Blackstone Magik Enterprises Inc, 12800 Puesta Del Sol, Redlands, CA 92373 *Tel:* 909-792-1227 *Fax:* 909-794-2737 *E-mail:* magik@blackstonemagic.com *Web Site:* www.blackstonemagic.com, pg 808

Blackwater Video Productions, PO Box 909, Morgantown, WV 26507 *Tel:* 304-296-4048 *E-mail:* blackwatervideo@hotmail.com *Web Site:* www.blackwatervideo.com, pg 808

Michael Blackwood Productions Inc, 6 W 18 St, Suite 2B, New York, NY 10011 *Tel:* 212-242-1805 *Fax:* 212-242-1671 *E-mail:* blackwoodfilm@aol.com *Web Site:* www.michaelblackwoodproductions.com, pg 808

Blair Inc, 7001 Loisdale Rd, Springfield, VA 22150 *Tel:* 703-922-0200 *Fax:* 703-924-0765 *E-mail:* info@blairinc.com *Web Site:* www.blairinc.com, pg 809

Blair Packaging, 1515 Independence St, Cape Girardeau, MO 63703 *Tel:* 573-264-2146 *Toll Free Tel:* 800-624-3150 *Fax:* 573-264-3730 *E-mail:* info@blairpkg.com *Web Site:* www.blairpkg.com, pg 809

Blaise Media, 3400 "J" St, Sacramento, CA 95816 *Tel:* 916-446-3126 *Fax:* 916-446-8089 *Web Site:* blaisemedia.com, pg 809

Les Blank Films Inc, 10341 San Pablo Ave, El Cerrito, CA 94530-3123 *Tel:* 510-525-0942 *Toll Free Tel:* 800-572-7618 *Fax:* 510-525-1204 *E-mail:* lesblankfilmsinc@gmail.com, pg 809

Blind, 1702 Olympic Blvd, Santa Monica, CA 90404 *Tel:* 310-314-1618 *Fax:* 310-314-1718 *Web Site:* www.blind.com, pg 809

Blind Pig Records, PO Box 2344, San Francisco, CA 94126 *Tel:* 415-550-6484 *Toll Free Tel:* 888-474-4736 *Fax:* 415-550-6485 *E-mail:* info@blindpigrecords.com *Web Site:* www.blindpigrecords.com, pg 809

Blonder Tongue Laboratories Inc, One Jake Brown Rd, Old Bridge, NJ 08857 *Tel:* 732-679-4000 *Toll Free Tel:* 800-523-6049 *Fax:* 732-679-4353 *E-mail:* custsvc@blondertongue.com; btglobalsales@blondertongue.com (other than US & CN) *Web Site:* www.blondertongue.com, pg 809

Blood-Horse Publications, 3101 Beaumont Centre Circle, Lexington, KY 40513 *Toll Free Tel:* 800-866-2361; 800-582-5604 *E-mail:* customerservice@bloodhorse.com; advertise@bloodhorse.com *Web Site:* www.bloodhorse.com, pg 809

Blue Barn Pictures Inc, 68 Jay St, Suite 311, Brooklyn, NY 11201 *Tel:* 718-852-1403 *Web Site:* www.bluebarnpictures.com, pg 809

Blue Dolphin Multimedia, 13340-D Grass Valley Ave, Grass Valley, CA 95945 *Tel:* 530-477-1503 *Toll Free Tel:* 800-643-0765 (orders) *Fax:* 530-477-8342 *E-mail:* bdolphin@bluedolphinpublishing.com *Web Site:* www.bluedolphinpublishing.com, pg 809

Blue Earth Pictures, 5532 Code Ave, Minneapolis, MN 55436 *Tel:* 612-619-5909 *E-mail:* missioncontrol@blueearthpictures.com *Web Site:* www.blueearthpictures.com, pg 809

Blue Lotus Temple Studio, PO Box 888, Boulder Creek, CA 95006 *Tel:* 831-338-2544 *E-mail:* info@bluelotustemple.com *Web Site:* www.bluelotustemple.com, pg 809

Blue Media Supply Inc, 3511 Church St, Suite F, Atlanta, GA 30021 *Tel:* 404-622-6709 *Toll Free Tel:* 866-717-6334 *Fax:* 404-622-1008 *E-mail:* sales@bluemediasupply.com *Web Site:* www.bluemediasupply.com, pg 809

Blue Mouse Studio, 26829 37 St, Gobles, MI 49055 *Tel:* 269-628-5160 *E-mail:* frogville@earthlink.net; mwivi@earthlink.net, pg 809

blue onion, 940 Wadsworth Blvd, 3rd fl, Lakewood, CO 80214 *Tel:* 303-232-1100 *Fax:* 303-232-2241 *E-mail:* info@digourideas.com *Web Site:* www.digourideas.com, pg 810

Blue River Productions, PO Box 1535, Breckenridge, CO 80424-1535 *Tel:* 970-390-8568 *E-mail:* filmbreckenridge@gmail.com *Web Site:* www.filmcolorado.com, pg 810

Blue Room Post, MBS Raleigh Studios, Bldg 5-A, Suite 100, 1600 Rosecrans Ave, Manhattan Beach, CA 90266 *Tel:* 310-727-2600 *Web Site:* www.blueroompost.com, pg 810

Blue 60 Pictures, 555 First Ave NE, Suite 200, Minneapolis, MN 55413 *Tel:* 612-871-6800 *E-mail:* info@blue-60.com *Web Site:* www.blue-60.com, pg 810

Blue Sky Stock Footage, PO Box 177, Santa Fe, NM 87504-0177 *Tel:* 310-859-4709 *Toll Free Tel:* 877-992-5477 *Fax:* 310-823-0924 *E-mail:* sales@blueskyfootage.com *Web Site:* www.blueskyfootage.com, pg 810

Blue Water Film Award, PO Box 611109, Port Huron, MI 48061 *E-mail:* bwff@bluewaterfilmfestival.com *Web Site:* bluewaterfilmfestival.com, pg 1110

Blue Wave Records, 3221 Perryville Rd, Baldwinsville, NY 13027 *Tel:* 315-638-4286 *Fax:* 315-635-4757 *E-mail:* bluewave@localnet.com *Web Site:* www.bluewaverecords.com, pg 810

Blueyed Pictures Inc, 8950 W Olympic Blvd, Suite 324, Beverly Hills, CA 90211 *Tel:* 310-295-0848 *Fax:* 310-295-0260 *E-mail:* la@blueyedpictures.com *Web Site:* www.blueyedpictures.com, pg 810

BMI Supply, 571 Queensbury Ave, Queensbury, NY 12804 *Tel:* 518-793-6706 *Toll Free Tel:* 800-836-0524 *Fax:* 518-793-6181 *E-mail:* bminy@bmisupply.com *Web Site:* www.bmisupply.com, pg 810

Boeckeler Instruments Inc, 4650 S Butterfield Dr, Tucson, AZ 85714 *Tel:* 520-745-0001 *Toll Free Tel:* 800-552-2262 *Fax:* 520-745-0004 *E-mail:* support@pointmaker.com *Web Site:* www.boeckeler.com, pg 810

Bogen Communications Inc, 50 Spring St, Ramsey, NJ 07446 *Tel:* 201-934-8500 *Fax:* 201-934-9832 *E-mail:* info@bogen.com *Web Site:* www.bogen.com, pg 810

Boitnott Visual Communications Corp (BVC), 14201 Justice Rd, Midlothian, VA 23113 *Tel:* 804-379-9400 *Fax:* 804-379-9413 *Web Site:* www.boitnottvisual.com, pg 810

Boland Communications, 16 Rancho Circle, Lake Forest, CA 92630 *Tel:* 949-465-9911 *Toll Free Tel:* 800-918-9090 *Fax:* 949-465-9944 *E-mail:* sales@bolandcom.com *Web Site:* www.bolandcom.com, pg 810

Bolchazy - Carducci Publishers Inc, 1570 Baskin Rd, Mundelein, IL 60060 *Tel:* 847-526-4344 *Toll Free Tel:* 800-392-6453 *Fax:* 847-526-2867 *E-mail:* info@bolchazy.com *Web Site:* www.bolchazy.com, pg 810

Bond Street Studio, 235 Bond St, Brooklyn, NY 11217 *Tel:* 718-858-2238 *Fax:* 718-858-2239 *E-mail:* info@bondstreetstudio.com *Web Site:* www.bondstreetstudio.com, pg 810

Bonnin Electronics Inc, 617 Hipodromo St, San Juan, PR 00909 *Tel:* 787-725-4765 *Fax:* 787-725-0840 *Web Site:* www.bonninelectronics.com, pg 810

Book Marketing Works LLC, 50 Lovely St, Avon, CT 06001 *Tel:* 860-675-1344 *Web Site:* www.bookmarketingworks.com, pg 810

Books In Motion, 9922 E Montgomery Dr, Suite 31, Spokane Valley, WA 99206 *Tel:* 509-922-1646 *Toll Free Tel:* 800-752-3199 *Fax:* 509-922-1445 *E-mail:* sales@booksinmotion.com *Web Site:* www.booksinmotion.com, pg 811

Books on Tape®, c/o Library & School Servs, 400 Hahn Rd, Westminster, MD 21157 *Toll Free Tel:* 800-733-3000 *Toll Free Fax:* 800-940-7046 *E-mail:* csbot@randomhouse.com *Web Site:* www.booksontape.com, pg 811

Boonton Electronics, 25 Eastmans Rd, Parsippany, NJ 07054 *Tel:* 973-386-9696 *Fax:* 973-386-9191 *E-mail:* info@boonton.com *Web Site:* www.boonton.com, pg 811

Bosch Security Systems North America, 130 Perinton Pkwy, Fairport, NY 14450 *Tel:* 585-223-4060 *Toll Free Tel:* 800-289-0096 *Fax:* 585-223-9180 *Web Site:* us.boschsecurity.com, pg 811

Bose Corp, The Mountain, MS 2C3, Framingham, MA 01701-8863 *Tel:* 508-879-7330; 508-766-1099 (sales outside US) *Toll Free Tel:* 800-999-2673; 800-869-1855 (sales) *Fax:* 508-820-3465 *E-mail:* support@bose.com *Web Site:* www.bose.com, pg 811

Boston Acoustics, 7 Constitution Way, Woburn, MA 01801 *Tel:* 201-762-6429 *Fax:* 978-538-6237 *E-mail:* weborders@bostonacoustics.com *Web Site:* www.bostonacoustics.com, pg 811

The Boston Connection Inc, PO Box 1835, Cotuit, MA 02635 *Tel:* 617-908-6258 *Fax:* 508-428-2036 *E-mail:* bconnect@cutfilm.com *Web Site:* www.cutfilm.com, pg 811

Boston Film Bureau, One City Hall Sq, Rm 802, Boston, MA 02201-2029 *Tel:* 617-635-3911 *Fax:* 617-635-4428 *E-mail:* filmbureau@cityofboston.gov *Web Site:* www.cityofboston.gov/arts/film, pg 1098

Boston Light & Sound Inc, 290 N Beacon St, Boston, MA 02135-1990 *Tel:* 617-787-3131 *Fax:* 617-787-4257 *E-mail:* info@blsi.com *Web Site:* www.blsi.com, pg 811

Boston Productions Inc, 290 Vanderbilt Ave, Suite 1, Norwood, MA 02062 *Tel:* 781-255-1555 *E-mail:* imagine@bostonproductions.com *Web Site:* www.bostonproductions.com, pg 811

Boulder County Film Commission, 2440 Pearl St, Boulder, CO 80302 *Tel:* 303-442-2911; 303-938-2066 *Toll Free Tel:* 800-444-0447 *Fax:* 303-938-2098 *Web Site:* www.bouldercoloradousa.com/film, pg 1094

Bowens USA, 75 Virginia Rd, North White Plains, NY 10603 *Tel:* 914-347-3300 *Fax:* 914-347-3309 *Web Site:* www.bowensusa.com, pg 811

Bowers Media Group Inc, 6035 Florence Ave, Suite 100, Charlotte, NC 28212 *Tel:* 704-542-8754 *Fax:* 704-532-1058 *Web Site:* www.bowersmediagroup.com, pg 811

Bowie Audio Visual Enterprises Inc, 290 Highpoint Dr, Ridgeland, MS 39157 *Tel:* 601-957-6566 *Toll Free Tel:* 800-748-9030 *Fax:* 601-957-7042 *E-mail:* sales@bowieav.com *Web Site:* www.bowieav.com, pg 811

Boxcar Studio, 1444 Dupont St W, Bldg C, Suite 21, Toronto, ON M6P 4H3, Canada *Tel:* 416-465-8094 *E-mail:* info@boxcarstudio.ca *Web Site:* www.boxcarstudio.ca, pg 811

Boxlight Inc, NE 151 Hwy 300, Suite A, Belfair, WA 98528 *Tel:* 360-464-2119 *Fax:* 360-282-6141 *E-mail:* sales@boxlight.com *Web Site:* www.boxlight.com, pg 811

Boyce Nemec Designs, PO Box 566, Norfolk, CT 06058-0566 *Tel:* 860-542-5937 *Web Site:* www.boycenemec.com, pg 811

Bradley Broadcast & Pro Audio, PO Box 756, New Market, MD 21774 *Tel:* 301-682-8700 *Toll Free Tel:* 800-732-7665 *Fax:* 301-263-7042 *E-mail:* beburg@bradleybroadcast.com *Web Site:* www.bradleybroadcast.com, pg 811

Brady Corp, 6555 W Good Hope Rd, Milwaukee, WI 53201-0571 *Tel:* 414-358-6600 *Toll Free Tel:* 800-541-1686 *Toll Free Fax:* 800-292-2289 *Web Site:* www.bradycorp.com, pg 811

The Brainwash Movie Festival, 1675 Seventh St, No 23302, Oakland, CA 94623-6009 *Tel:* 510-836-3210 *Web Site:* www.brainwashm.com, pg 1110

Branam Enterprises Inc, 9152 Independence Ave, Chatsworth, CA 91311 *Tel:* 818-885-6474 *Toll Free Tel:* 877-295-3390 *Fax:* 818-885-6475 *E-mail:* info@branament.com *Web Site:* www.branament.com, pg 811

Brand Activation Association, 650 First Ave, Suite 2-SW, New York, NY 10016 *Tel:* 212-420-1100 *Fax:* 212-533-7622 *Web Site:* www.baalink.org, pg 1079

The Brand Gallery, 701 W Putnam Ave, Greenwich, CT 06830 *Tel:* 203-422-3900 *Fax:* 203-531-1394 *Web Site:* www.thebrandgallery.com, pg 812

Brantley Sound Associates Inc, 115 Duluth Ave, Nashville, TN 37209-1207 *Tel:* 615-256-6260 *E-mail:* ccussick@brantleysound.com *Web Site:* www.brantleysound.com, pg 812

Bravo Studios, 40 W 27 St, 2nd fl, New York, NY 10001 *Tel:* 212-563-0054 *E-mail:* info@newyorkgreenscreen.com *Web Site:* www.newyorkgreenscreen.com, pg 812

BRB Audiovisual Productions, 135 Punkup Rd, Oxford, CT 06478-1747 *Tel:* 203-881-3577 *Toll Free Tel:* 800-587-7521 *E-mail:* services@brbaudiovisual.com *Web Site:* brbaudiovisual.com, pg 812

Breeze Productions Inc, 1660 Edgewood Rd, Highland Park, IL 60035 *Tel:* 312-860-1710 *Web Site:* www.breezeprod.com, pg 812

Bretford Manufacturing Inc, 11000 Seymour Ave, Franklin Park, IL 60131 *Tel:* 847-678-2545 *Toll Free Tel:* 800-521-9614 *Fax:* 847-678-0852 *Toll Free Fax:* 800-343-1779 *E-mail:* customerservice@bretford.com *Web Site:* bretford.com, pg 812

BRg Music Works, 111 Presidential Blvd, Suite 100, Bala Cynwyd, PA 19004 *Tel:* 610-971-9490 *Web Site:* brg.sourceaudio.com, pg 812

Brian Film Productions LLC, 254 W 25 St, Suite 6-A, New York, NY 10001-7325 *Tel:* 212-645-8795, pg 812

The Brick Studio, 414 Raymond Blvd, Studio 5, Newark, NJ 07105 *Tel:* 646-801-4449 *E-mail:* info@thebrickstudio.com *Web Site:* www.thebrickstudio.com, pg 812

Bridge Publications Inc, 5600 E Olympic Blvd, Los Angeles, CA 90022 *Tel:* 323-953-3320; 323-888-6200 *Toll Free Tel:* 800-722-1733 *Fax:* 323-888-6202 *E-mail:* info@bridgepub.com *Web Site:* www.bridgepub.com, pg 812

Bridge Records Inc, 200 Clinton Ave, New Rochelle, NY 10801 *Tel:* 914-654-9270 *E-mail:* bridgerec@bridgerecords.com *Web Site:* www.bridgerecords.com, pg 812

Bridger Productions Inc, 4150 Glory View Lane, Jackson, WY 83001 *Tel:* 307-733-7871 *Fax:* 307-734-1947 *E-mail:* info@bridgerproductions.com *Web Site:* www.bridgerproductions.com, pg 812

Beatrice E Griggs Elementary Administrator's Award, 6021 State Farm Rd, Guilderland, NY 12084 *Tel:* 518-432-6952 *Toll Free Tel:* 800-252-6952 *Fax:* 518-427-1697 *E-mail:* info@nyla.org *Web Site:* www.nyla.org, pg 1110

Bright Giant Creative Group, 7600 Burnet Rd, Suite 180, Austin, TX 78757 *Tel:* 512-535-7855 *E-mail:* info@brightgiantstudios.com *Web Site:* brightgiantcg.com, pg 812

Bright Ideas Creative Services, 107 W Maple St, Suite 206, Jeffersonville, IN 47130 *Tel:* 812-282-9900; 502-693-9900 (cell) *Toll Free Fax:* 866-593-5753 *Web Site:* www.brightideascreative.com, pg 812

Bright Star Productions Inc, 2420 Center St, Houston, TX 77007 *Tel:* 713-529-2757 *Fax:* 713-529-2329 *Web Site:* www.brightstarproductions.com, pg 812

Brightline LP, 580 Mayer St, Bldg 7, Bridgeville, PA 15017 *Tel:* 412-206-0106 *Fax:* 412-206-0146 *E-mail:* information@brightlines.com *Web Site:* www.brightlines.com, pg 812

Brilliance Audio, 1704 Eaton Dr, Grand Haven, MI 49417 *Tel:* 616-846-5256 *Toll Free Tel:* 800-648-2312 (orders) *Fax:* 616-846-0630 *E-mail:* customerservice@brillianceaudio.com *Web Site:* www.brillianceaudio.com, pg 812

Brim Electronics, 120 Home Place, Lodi, NJ 07644 *Tel:* 201-796-2886 *Fax:* 973-778-2792 *E-mail:* info@brimelectronics.com *Web Site:* www.brimelectronics.com, pg 812

Britannica Film & Video, 331 N LaSalle St, Chicago, IL 60654 *Toll Free Tel:* 800-621-3900 *Toll Free Fax:* 800-344-9624 *E-mail:* contact@eb.com *Web Site:* info.eb.com, pg 812

Broad Street Inc, 242 W 30 St, 2nd fl, New York, NY 10001 *Tel:* 212-780-5700 *E-mail:* newyork@broadstreet.com *Web Site:* www.broadstreet.com, pg 812

Broadcast Center Studios, 700 Millbridge Gardens, Clementon, NJ 08021 *Tel:* 856-751-3500 *Web Site:* www.broadcastcenterstudios.com, pg 813

Broadcast Devices Inc, Westchester Industrial Complex, 3199 Albany Post Rd, Suite 122, Buchanan, NY 10511-1639 *Tel:* 914-737-5032 *Fax:* 914-736-6916 *E-mail:* sales@broadcast-devices.com *Web Site:* www.broadcast-devices.com, pg 813

Broadcast Education Association (BEA), 1771 "N" St NW, Washington, DC 20036-2891 *Fax:* 202-609-9940 *E-mail:* help@beaweb.org *Web Site:* www.beaweb.org, pg 1079

Broadcast Electronics, 4100 N 24 St, Quincy, IL 62305 *Tel:* 217-224-9600 *Fax:* 217-224-9607 *E-mail:* bdcast@bdcast.com *Web Site:* www.bdcast.com, pg 813

Broadcast Management Group, 1625 Eye St NW, Suite 620, Washington, DC 20006 *Tel:* 202-609-7757 *E-mail:* info@broadcastmgmt.com *Web Site:* www.broadcastmgmt.com, pg 813

Broadcast Microwave Services (BMS), 12367 Crosthwaite Circle, Poway, CA 92064 *Tel:* 858-391-3050 *Toll Free Tel:* 800-669-9667 *Fax:* 858-391-3049 *E-mail:* sales@bms-inc.com *Web Site:* www.bms-inc.com, pg 813

Broadcast Rentals, 2343 W University Dr, Suite 101, Tempe, AZ 85281 *Tel:* 480-894-1456 *Toll Free Tel:* 888-686-7368 *Fax:* 480-894-1023 *E-mail:* rent@broadcastrentals.com *Web Site:* www.broadcastrentals.com, pg 813

Broadcast Supply World Wide, 2237 S 19 St, Tacoma, WA 98405 *Tel:* 253-565-2301 (intl) *Toll Free Tel:* 800-426-8434 *Fax:* 253-565-8114 (intl) *Toll Free Fax:* 800-231-7055 *E-mail:* sales@bswusa.com; info@bswusa.com; customersupport@bswusa.com *Web Site:* www.bswusa.com, pg 813

Broadcast Video Productions LLC, 61 Briarwood Dr, Old Saybrook, CT 06475 *Tel:* 860-575-7247 *Fax:* 860-395-2036 *E-mail:* bvpusa@comcast.net, pg 813

Broadcast Video Systems Corp, 25 Forest Ridge Rd, Richmond Hill, ON L4E 3L8, Canada *E-mail:* broadcastvideosystems@gmail.com *Web Site:* www.bvs.ca, pg 813

Broadcasters Foundation Awards, 125 W 55 St, 3rd fl, New York, NY 10019-5366 *Tel:* 212-373-8250 *Fax:* 212-373-8254 *E-mail:* info@thebfoa.org *Web Site:* www.broadcastersfoundation.org, pg 1110

Broadcasters Foundation of America, 125 W 55 St, 3rd fl, New York, NY 10019-5366 *Tel:* 212-373-8250 *Fax:* 212-373-8254 *E-mail:* info@thebfoa.org *Web Site:* www.broadcastersfoundation.org, pg 1080

Broadcasters General Store Inc, 2480 SE 52 St, Ocala, FL 34480 *Tel:* 352-622-7700 *Fax:* 352-629-7000 *E-mail:* sales@bgs.cc (orders) *Web Site:* www.bgs.cc, pg 813

BroadcastStore.com, 9420 Lurline Ave, Unit C, Chatsworth, CA 91311 *Tel:* 818-998-9100 *Fax:* 818-998-9106 *E-mail:* sales@broadcaststore.com *Web Site:* www.broadcaststore.com, pg 813

Broadview Media, 4455 W 77 St, Minneapolis, MN 55435 *Tel:* 952-835-4455; 612-280-6947 *Fax:* 952-835-0971 *E-mail:* sales@broadviewmedia.com; corporate@broadviewmedia.com *Web Site:* www.broadviewmedia.com, pg 813

Broadview Software Inc, 110 Adelaide St E, Toronto, ON M5C 1K9, Canada *Tel:* 416-778-0623 *Fax:* 416-778-0648 *E-mail:* sales@broadviewsoftware.com *Web Site:* www.broadviewsoftware.com, pg 813

Broadway Costumes Inc, 1100 W Cermak Rd, 2nd fl, Chicago, IL 60608 *Tel:* 312-829-6400 *Toll Free Tel:* 800-397-3316 *Fax:* 312-829-8621 *E-mail:* rentals@broadwaycostumes.com *Web Site:* www.broadwaycostumes.com, pg 813

Broadway Digital, 1014 E Broadway, Louisville, KY 40204 *Tel:* 502-540-5301 *Fax:* 502-540-5565 *E-mail:* msworkscm@mindspring.com *Web Site:* www.broadwaydigital.us, pg 813

Brodart Co, 500 Arch St, Williamsport, PA 17701 *Tel:* 570-769-3265 *Toll Free Tel:* 888-820-4377 *Toll Free Fax:* 800-283-6087 *E-mail:* supplies.customerservice@brodart.com *Web Site:* www.shopbrodart.com, pg 813

Brodsky & Treadway, 69 Warehouse Lane, Rowley, MA 01969 *Tel:* 978-948-7985 *Web Site:* www.LittleFilm.com, pg 813

Bromwell Marketing, 3 Allegheny Ctr, Suite 111, Pittsburgh, PA 15212 *Tel:* 412-321-4118 *E-mail:* bromwell@earthlink.net *Web Site:* www.bromwellmarketing.com, pg 813

Bronze Anvil Awards, 33 Maiden Lane, 11th fl, New York, NY 10038-5150 *Tel:* 212-460-1400 *Toll Free Tel:* 800-350-0111 *Fax:* 212-995-0757 *E-mail:* awards@prsa.org *Web Site:* www.prsa.org, pg 1110

Paul H Brookes Publishing Co, PO Box 10624, Baltimore, MD 21285-0624 *Tel:* 410-337-9580 *Toll Free Tel:* 800-638-3775 (cust serv) *Fax:* 410-337-8539 *E-mail:* custserv@brookespublishing.com *Web Site:* www.brookespublishing.com, pg 814

Brookline Books, 8 Trumbull Rd, Suite B-001, Northampton, MA 01060 *Tel:* 413-584-0184; 603-669-7032 (orders) *Toll Free Tel:* 800-666-BOOK (666-2665 cust serv) *Fax:* 413-584-6184 *E-mail:* brbooks@yahoo.com *Web Site:* www.brooklinebooks.com, pg 814

Brooklyn Botanic Garden, 1000 Washington Ave, Brooklyn, NY 11225 *Tel:* 718-623-7200 *E-mail:* feedback@bbg.org *Web Site:* www.bbg.org, pg 814

Brooklyn College Television Center, Whitehead Hall, 2900 Bedford Ave, Rm 018-A, Brooklyn, NY 11210-2889 *Tel:* 718-951-5585 *Fax:* 718-951-5558 *Web Site:* www.bctvr.org/tvcenter_base.php, pg 814

Brooklyn Film Festival (BiFF), 180 S Fourth St, Suite 2-S, Brooklyn, NY 11211 *Tel:* 718-388-4306 *Fax:* 718-599-5039 *E-mail:* festival@wbff.org *Web Site:* www.brooklynfilmfestival.org, pg 1110

Brooklyn Films, PO Box 20412, New York, NY 10021-0066 *Tel:* 212-744-2845 *E-mail:* inquiries@brooklynfilms.com *Web Site:* www.brooklynfilms.com, pg 814

Brooklyn Fire Proof, 119 Ingraham St, Brooklyn, NY 11237 *Tel:* 718-456-7570 *E-mail:* hello@brooklynfireproof.com *Web Site:* www.brooklynfireproof.com, pg 814

Brooklyn Studios, 211 Meserole Ave, 2nd fl, Brooklyn, NY 11222 *Tel:* 718-392-1007 *Fax:* 718-392-1008 *E-mail:* brooklynstudios@verizon.net *Web Site:* www.brooklynstudios.net, pg 814

The Brookwood Studio Inc, 6870 N Territorial Rd, Plymouth, MI 48170 *Tel:* 734-358-6071 *E-mail:* info@brookwoodstudio.com *Web Site:* www.brookwoodstudio.com, pg 814

Broughton's Church Supplies, Religious Books & Gifts, 322 Consumers Rd, North York, ON M2J 1P8, Canada *Tel:* 416-690-4777 *Toll Free Tel:* 800-268-4449 *Fax:* 416-690-5357 *E-mail:* sales@bbroughton.com *Web Site:* www.bbroughton.com, pg 814

Heywood Broun Award, 501 Third St NW, Washington, DC 20001-2706 *Tel:* 202-434-7177 *Fax:* 202-434-1472 *Web Site:* www.newsguild.org, pg 1110

Brown Bag Imaging, 111 Presidential Blvd, Suite 100, Bala Cynwyd, PA 19004 *Toll Free Tel:* 800-533-8686 *E-mail:* sales@brownbagimaging.com *Web Site:* brownbag.sourceaudio.com, pg 814

James W Brown Publication Award, 320 W Eighth St, Suite 101, Bloomington, IN 47404-3745 *Tel:* 812-335-7675 *Toll Free Tel:* 877-677-AECT (677-2328) *Fax:* 812-335-7678 *E-mail:* aect@aect.org *Web Site:* www.aect.org, pg 1110

Brown United, PO Box 362, Monrovia, CA 91017-0362 *Tel:* 626-357-1161 *Toll Free Tel:* 800-44-BROWN (442-7696) *Fax:* 626-358-3064 *Toll Free Fax:* 800-26-BROWN (262-7696) *E-mail:* info@brownunited.com *Web Site:* www.brownunited.com, pg 814

Brush Industries Inc, 301 Reagan St, Sunbury, PA 17801 *Tel:* 570-286-5611 *Fax:* 570-286-2649 *E-mail:* info@brushindustries.com *Web Site:* www.brushindustries.com, pg 814

Bryce Corp, 4505 Old Lamar Ave, Memphis, TN 38118 *Tel:* 901-369-4400 *Toll Free Tel:* 800-238-7277 *Web Site:* www.brycecorp.com, pg 814

Bryston Ltd, 677 Neal Dr, Peterborough, ON K9J 6X7, Canada *Tel:* 705-742-5325 *Fax:* 705-742-0882 *Web Site:* bryston.com, pg 814

BSW Records, PO Box 2297, Universal City, TX 78148-1297 *Tel:* 210-653-3989 *Fax:* 210-653-3989 *E-mail:* bswr18@att.net *Web Site:* www.bsw-records.com, pg 814

BTX Technologies, 5 Skyline Dr, Hawthorne, NY 10532 *Tel:* 914-592-1800 *Toll Free Tel:* 800-666-0996 *Toll Free Fax:* 800-569-4244 *E-mail:* info@btx.com *Web Site:* www.btx.com, pg 814

Bud Industries, 4605 E 355 St, Willoughby, OH 44094 *Tel:* 440-946-3200 *Fax:* 440-951-4015 *E-mail:* saleseast@budind.com *Web Site:* www.budind.com, pg 814

Billy Budd Films Inc, 235 E 57 St, New York, NY 10022 *Tel:* 212-755-3968 *E-mail:* info@billybuddfilms.com *Web Site:* www.billybuddfilms.com, pg 814

Budget Films Stock Footage Inc, 706 N Vendome St, Suite 6, Los Angeles, CA 90026 *Tel:* 323-660-0187 *Fax:* 323-660-5571 *E-mail:* filmclip@aol.com; info@budgetfilms.com *Web Site:* www.budgetfilms.com, pg 814

Budget Video Rentals, 1825 NE 149 St, Miami, FL 33181 *Tel:* 305-945-8888 *Toll Free Tel:* 800-772-1111 *Fax:* 305-945-0300 *E-mail:* rentals@budgetvideo.com *Web Site:* budgetvideo.com, pg 815

BUF Technology, 12335 World Trade Dr, Suite 11, San Diego, CA 92128 *Tel:* 858-451-1350 *Fax:* 858-451-6589 *E-mail:* info@buftek.com *Web Site:* www.buftek.com, pg 815

Buffalo Niagara Film Festival (BNFF), 3840 E Robinson Rd, Suite 166, Amherst, NY 14228 *Tel:* 716-432-1065 *E-mail:* info@buffaloniagarafilmfestival.com *Web Site:* thebnff.com, pg 1110

Bulb Direct, 7911 Rae Blvd, Victor, NY 14564 *Tel:* 585-385-3540 *Toll Free Tel:* 800-772-5267 *Fax:* 585-385-4976 *Toll Free Fax:* 800-257-0760 *E-mail:* info@bulbdirect.com *Web Site:* www.bulbdirect.com, pg 815

Bulbman Inc, 630 Sunshine Lane, Reno, NV 89502 *Tel:* 775-788-5661 *Toll Free Tel:* 800-648-1163 *Fax:* 775-329-6599 *Toll Free Fax:* 800-548-6216 *E-mail:* service@bulbman.com *Web Site:* www.bulbman.com, pg 815

Bulbtronics Inc, 45 Banfi Plaza N, Farmingdale, NY 11735 *Tel:* 631-249-2272 *Toll Free Tel:* 800-654-8542 (sales); 800-588-2852 *Fax:* 631-249-6066 *E-mail:* marketing@bulbtronics.com *Web Site:* www.bulbtronics.com, pg 815

Bullfrog Films Inc, PO Box 149, Oley, PA 19547-0149 *Tel:* 610-779-8226 *Toll Free Tel:* 800-543-3764 *Fax:* 610-370-1978 *E-mail:* video@bullfrogfilms.com *Web Site:* www.bullfrogfilms.com, pg 815

Richard W Burden Associates, 20944 Sherman Way, Canoga Park, CA 91303 *Tel:* 818-340-4590, pg 815

The Bureau for At-Risk Youth, PO Box 170, Farmingdale, NY 11738 *Toll Free Tel:* 800-99-YOUTH (999-6884) *Toll Free Fax:* 800-262-1886 *Web Site:* www.at-risk.com; www.guidance-group.com, pg 815

Burk Technology Inc, 7 Beaver Brook Rd, Littleton, MA 01460 *Tel:* 978-486-0086 *Toll Free Tel:* 800-255-8090 *Fax:* 978-486-0081 *E-mail:* sales@burk.com; orders@burk.com *Web Site:* www.burk.com, pg 815

Burlington A/V Recording Media, 106 Mott St, Oceanside, NY 11572 *Tel:* 516-678-4414 *Toll Free Tel:* 800-331-3191 *Fax:* 516-678-8959 *E-mail:* burlington@optonline.net *Web Site:* www.recordingstore.com, pg 815

Burnaby Film Office, 6450 Deerlake Ave, Burnaby, BC V5G 2J3, Canada *Tel:* 604-294-7314 *Fax:* 604-205-3001 *Web Site:* www.burnaby.ca, pg 1104

Larry Burr, 602 Via Casitas, Greenbrae, CA 94904 *Tel:* 415-925-0822 *E-mail:* jabarni@yahoo.com, pg 815

Burrud Productions Inc, 468 N Camden Dr, 2nd fl, Beverly Hills, CA 90210 *Tel:* 310-860-5158 *Fax:* 562-595-5986 *E-mail:* info@burrud.com *Web Site:* www.burrud.com, pg 815

Burst Electronics Inc, PO Box 65947, Albuquerque, NM 87193 *Tel:* 505-898-1455 *E-mail:* sales@burstelectronics.com *Web Site:* www.burstelectronics.com, pg 815

Burst Video/Film Inc, PO Box 5354, Atlanta, GA 31107-0354, pg 815

Business & Legal Reports Inc, 141 Mill Rock Rd E, Old Saybrook, CT 06475 *Tel:* 860-510-0100 *Toll Free Tel:* 800-727-5257 *Fax:* 860-510-7224 *E-mail:* service@blr.com *Web Site:* www.blr.com, pg 815

Business Education Films, PO Box 449, Clarksburg, NJ 08510-0449 *Tel:* 732-462-3522 *Fax:* 732-294-0330 *E-mail:* info@aldenfilms.com *Web Site:* www.aldenfilms.com, pg 815

Butler Films Inc, 108 Old Solomons Island Rd, Suite L-10, Annapolis, MD 21401 *Tel:* 410-280-1160 *Fax:* 443-458-5315 *E-mail:* info@butlerfilm.com *Web Site:* www.butlerfilm.com, pg 815

Butte-Silver Bow Chamber of Commerce, 1000 George St, Butte, MT 59701 *Tel:* 406-723-3177 *Toll Free Tel:* 800-735-6814 *Fax:* 406-723-1215 *E-mail:* chamber@buttechamber.org; marketing@buttechamber.org *Web Site:* www.buttechamber.org, pg 1099

Butter Tree Studio, 32 Merry Lane, East Hanover, NJ 07936 *Tel:* 973-585-7632 *Fax:* 973-585-7633 *Web Site:* www.buttertreestudios.com, pg 816

Buttercup Pictures, 2415 Michigan Ave, Bldg H, Santa Monica, CA 90404 *Tel:* 323-692-0909 *E-mail:* info@buttercuppictures.com *Web Site:* buttercuppictures.com, pg 816

Buzzco Associates Inc, 33 Bleecker St, New York, NY 10012 *Tel:* 212-473-8800 *Fax:* 212-473-8891 *E-mail:* info@buzzzco.com *Web Site:* www.buzzzco.com, pg 816

BZ/Rights & Permissions Inc, 145 W 86 St, New York, NY 10024 *Tel:* 212-924-3000 *Fax:* 212-924-2525 *E-mail:* info@bzrights.com *Web Site:* www.bzrights.com; www.thepublicdomainsite.com, pg 816

C & M Publishing Co, 1076 Torrey Pines Rd, Chula Vista, CA 91915 *Tel:* 619-656-6462, pg 816

C-Ducer/C T Audio, 54 Old Lakeside Rd S, Hewitt, NJ 07421 *Tel:* 973-728-1743 *Toll Free Tel:* 800-282-8346 *Toll Free Fax:* 866-548-7683 *E-mail:* meow54@rocketmail.com *Web Site:* www.c-ducer.com, pg 816

C Vision Productions, 5533 144 Ave NW, Ramsey, MN 55303-5646 *Tel:* 763-577-1358 *Toll Free Tel:* 888-827-3287 *Fax:* 763-577-1359 *Web Site:* www.cvisionproductions.com, pg 816

CA Technologies, 520 Madison Ave, 22nd fl, New York, NY 10022 *Toll Free Tel:* 800-225-5224 *Web Site:* www.ca.com, pg 816

Cabbage Cases Inc, 1166-C Steelwood Rd, Columbus, OH 43212-1356 *Tel:* 614-486-2495 *Toll Free Tel:* 800-888-2495 *Fax:* 614-486-2788 *E-mail:* sales@cabbagecases.com *Web Site:* www.cabbagecases.com, pg 816

Cable & Telecommunications Association for Marketing (CTAM), 120 Waterfront St, Suite 200, National Harbor, MD 20745 *Tel:* 301-485-8900 *Fax:* 301-560-4964 *E-mail:* info@ctam.com *Web Site:* www.ctam.com, pg 1080

Cable Films & Video, PO Box 7171, Country Club Sta, Kansas City, MO 64113-0171 *Tel:* 913-362-2804 *Toll Free Tel:* 800-514-2804 *Fax:* 913-362-2804 *E-mail:* cablefilms@kc.rr.com, pg 816

CACI Productions Group, 14370 Newbrook Dr, Chantilly, VA 20151 *Tel:* 703-679-3100 *Web Site:* www.caci.com, pg 816

CAD Audio, 6573 Cochran Rd, Bldg I, Solon, OH 44139 *Tel:* 440-349-4900 *Toll Free Tel:* 800-762-9266 (ext 211) *Fax:* 440-248-4902 *E-mail:* sales@cadaudio.com *Web Site:* www.cadaudio.com, pg 816

Cadence Jazz Records, Cadence Bldg, Redwood, NY 13679 *Tel:* 315-287-2852 *Fax:* 315-287-2860 *E-mail:* cjr@cadencebuilding.com; cadence@cadencebuilding.com; info@cadencemagazine.com *Web Site:* www.cadencebuilding.com, pg 816

Cadex Electronics Inc, 22000 Fraserwood Way, Richmond, BC V6W 1J6, Canada *Tel:* 604-231-7777 *Toll Free Tel:* 800-565-5228 *Fax:* 604-231-7755 *E-mail:* info@cadex.com *Web Site:* www.cadex.com, pg 816

CADint, 10517 W Bellarose Dr, Sun City, AZ 85351-2241 *Tel:* 303-520-0907 *Toll Free Tel:* 800-553-1177 (ext 12) *Fax:* 707-924-0907 *E-mail:* info@cadint.com; sales@cadint.com *Web Site:* www.cadint.com, pg 816

Cahokia Mounds Museum Society, 30 Ramey Dr, Collinsville, IL 62234 *Tel:* 618-344-7316 *Fax:* 618-346-5162 *E-mail:* museumsociety@cahokiamounds.org *Web Site:* www.cahokiamounds.org, pg 816

Calaveras County Film Commission, 183 Three "M" Lane, Mountain Ranch, CA 95246 *Tel:* 209-754-3053, pg 1093

Calbor Enterprises Two Inc, 10646 Chiquita St, Toluca Lake, CA 91602 *Tel:* 818-760-3222 *E-mail:* pyro-fx@sbcglobal.net *Web Site:* www.pyro-fx.net, pg 816

Calculated Industries Inc, 4840 Hytech Dr, Carson City, NV 89706 *Tel:* 775-885-4900 *Toll Free Tel:* 800-854-8075 *Fax:* 775-885-4949 *E-mail:* info@calculated.com *Web Site:* www.calculated.com, pg 816

Calgary International Film Festival, 214 11 Ave SE, Unit 207, Calgary, AB T2G 0X8, Canada *Tel:* 403-283-1490 *E-mail:* info@calgaryfilm.com *Web Site:* www.calgaryfilm.com, pg 1110

Calger Lighting Inc, 200 Lexington Ave, Suite 434, New York, NY 10016 *Tel:* 212-689-9511 *Fax:* 212-779-0721 *E-mail:* sales@calgerlighting.com *Web Site:* www.calgerlighting.com, pg 816

CALIBRE, Metro Park, 6354 Walker Lane, Alexandria, VA 22310-3252 *Tel:* 703-797-8500 *Toll Free Tel:* 888-CALIBRE (225-4273) *Fax:* 703-797-8501 *E-mail:* info@calibresys.com *Web Site:* www.calibresys.com, pg 816

Califone International Inc, 1145 Arroyo Ave, No A, San Fernando, CA 91340 *Tel:* 818-407-2400 *Toll Free Tel:* 800-722-0500 *Fax:* 818-407-2405 *Toll Free Fax:* 877-402-2248 *Web Site:* www.califone.com, pg 817

California Film Commission (CFC), 7080 Hollywood Blvd, Suite 900, Hollywood, CA 90028-6936 *Tel:* 323-860-2960 (24-hr serv) *Toll Free Tel:* 800-858-4749 *Fax:* 323-860-2972 *E-mail:* filmca@film.ca.gov *Web Site:* www.film.ca.gov, pg 1093

California Independent Film Festival (CAIFF), 350 Park St, Moraga, CA 94566 *Tel:* 925-388-0752; 310-879-9188 (Los Angeles off) *E-mail:* info@caiff.org *Web Site:* caiff.org, pg 1110

California/International Arts Foundation, 2737 Outpost Dr, Los Angeles, CA 90068 *Tel:* 323-874-4107 *Fax:* 323-874-8195, pg 817

California Language Laboratories, 6170 Palmero Circle, Cameron Park, CA 95682 *Toll Free Tel:* 800-327-1147 *Fax:* 530-350-8072 *E-mail:* info@esltapes.com *Web Site:* www.esltapes.com, pg 817

California Newsreel, 44 Gough St, Suite 303, San Francisco, CA 94103 *Tel:* 415-284-7800 *Fax:* 415-284-7801 *E-mail:* contact@newsreel.org *Web Site:* www.newsreel.org, pg 817

California Stage & Lighting, 3601 W Garry Ave, Santa Ana, CA 92704 *Tel:* 714-966-1852 *Fax:* 714-966-0104 *E-mail:* sales@calstage.com *Web Site:* www.calstage.com, pg 817

California Stainless Manufacturing Inc, 32 N Wood Rd, Camarillo, CA 93010 *Tel:* 805-484-1038 *Toll Free Tel:* 888-712-7035 *Fax:* 805-484-1030 *E-mail:* contact@calstainless.com *Web Site:* www.calstainless.com, pg 817

California Tape Products Inc, PO Box 177, Forest Falls, CA 92339-0177 *Tel:* 909-794-6524 *E-mail:* info@caltape.com *Web Site:* www.caltape.com, pg 817

California Teleprompter, PO Box 13024, La Jolla, CA 92039-3024 *Tel:* 858-945-2076 *E-mail:* caprompter@aol.com *Web Site:* www.sandiegoteleprompter.com, pg 817

Callen Photo Mount, 185 Sixth Ave, Paterson, NJ 07524 *Tel:* 973-925-2390 *Toll Free Tel:* 800-225-5360 *Fax:* 973-925-9615 *Web Site:* www.callencorp.com, pg 817

Calrad Electronics, 819 N Highland Ave, Los Angeles, CA 90038 *Tel:* 323-465-2131 *Toll Free Tel:* 800-821-8536 *Fax:* 323-465-3504 *E-mail:* calradelectronics@calrad.com *Web Site:* www.calrad.com, pg 817

Calumet Carton Co, 16920 State St, South Holland, IL 60473 *Tel:* 708-333-6521 *Fax:* 708-333-8540 *E-mail:* info@calumetcarton.com *Web Site:* www.calumetcarton.com, pg 817

Calumet College of Saint Joseph, 2400 New York Ave, Whiting, IN 46394 *Tel:* 219-473-7770 *Fax:* 219-473-4259 *Web Site:* www.ccsj.edu, pg 817

Calzone Anvil Case Co, 225 Black Rock Ave, Bridgeport, CT 06605 *Tel:* 203-367-5766 *Toll Free Tel:* 800-243-5152 *Fax:* 203-336-4406 *E-mail:* info@calzonecase.com *Web Site:* www.calzonecase.com, pg 817

CAM Audio Inc, 2210 Executive Dr, Garland, TX 75041 *Tel:* 972-271-2800 *Toll Free Tel:* 800-527-3458 *Fax:* 972-271-1555 *E-mail:* sales@camaudio.com *Web Site:* www.camaudio.com, pg 817

Camarillo Chamber of Commerce, 2400 E Ventura Blvd, Camarillo, CA 93010 *Tel:* 805-484-4383 *Fax:* 805-484-1395 *E-mail:* info@camarillochamber.org *Web Site:* www.camarillochamber.org, pg 1092

Camart, 6 W 20 St, New York, NY 10011 *Tel:* 212-691-8840 *E-mail:* rentals@camart.com *Web Site:* www.camart.com, pg 817

Cambium Catalyst International (CCI), 18 Dupont St, Toronto, ON M5R 1V2, Canada *Tel:* 416-964-8750 *Fax:* 416-964-1980 *E-mail:* info@ccientertainment.com *Web Site:* www.ccientertainment.com, pg 817

Cambridge Documentary Films Inc, 3099 Hidden Valley Lane, Santa Barbara, CA 93108 *Tel:* 617-484-3993 *E-mail:* info@cambridgedocumentaryfilms.org *Web Site:* www.cambridgedocumentaryfilms.org, pg 818

Cambridge University Press, 32 Avenue of the Americas, New York, NY 10013-2473 *Tel:* 212-337-5000 *Toll Free Tel:* 800-221-4512 *Fax:* 212-691-3239 *E-mail:* information@cambridge.org; newyork@cambridge.org *Web Site:* www.cambridge.org, pg 818

Camcor Inc, 2273 S Church St, Burlington, NC 27215 *Tel:* 336-228-0251 *Toll Free Tel:* 800-868-2462 *Fax:* 336-222-8011 *Toll Free Fax:* 800-298-1181 *E-mail:* info@camcor.com *Web Site:* www.camcor.com, pg 818

Camera Co Inc/Broadcast Divison, 858 Boston-Providence Tpke, Norwood, MA 02062 *Tel:* 781-769-7810 *Toll Free Tel:* 866-769-0210 *Fax:* 781-769-5750 *Web Site:* www.cameraco.com, pg 818

Camera Corner Connecting Point, PO Box 248, Green Bay, WI 54305-0248 *Tel:* 920-435-5353 *Toll Free Tel:* 800-236-4950 (orders) *Fax:* 920-435-6984 *E-mail:* contactus@cccp.com; salessupport@cccp.com *Web Site:* www.cccp.com, pg 818

Camera Essentials, 91 N Daisy Ave, Pasadena, CA 91107-3705 *Tel:* 626-844-3722 *Fax:* 323-686-5830 *E-mail:* info@cameraessentials.com *Web Site:* www.cameraessentials.com, pg 818

CamMate Systems, 425 E Comstock, Chandler, AZ 85225 *Tel:* 480-813-9500 *Fax:* 480-813-9292 *E-mail:* cammate@cammate.com *Web Site:* www.cammate.com, pg 818

The Campbell Agency, 3838 Oak Lawn Ave, Suite 900, Dallas, TX 75219 *Tel:* 214-522-8991 *Fax:* 214-522-8997 *Web Site:* www.thecampbellagency.com, pg 818

Campus Film Distributors Corp, 42 Oak Ave, Tuckahoe, NY 10707 *Tel:* 914-961-1900 *Fax:* 914-395-1091 *Web Site:* www.campusgroup.com, pg 818

CamTec Motion Picture Cameras, 4221 W Magnolia Blvd, Burbank, CA 91505 *Tel:* 818-841-8700 *Fax:* 818-841-8777 *Web Site:* www.camtec.tv, pg 818

Can-Am Merchandising Systems, 70 Shields Ct, Markham, ON L3R 9T5, Canada *Tel:* 905-475-6622 *Toll Free Tel:* 800-387-9790 *Fax:* 905-475-1154 *E-mail:* mail@can-am.ca *Web Site:* www.can-am.ca, pg 818

Canadian Academy of Recording Arts & Sciences (CARAS), 345 Adelaide St W, 2nd fl, Toronto, ON M5V 1R5, Canada *Tel:* 416-485-3135 *Toll Free Tel:* 888-440-JUNO (440-5866, CN only) *Fax:* 416-485-4978 *E-mail:* submissions@junoawards.ca *Web Site:* www.carasonline.ca; junoawards.ca, pg 1080

Canadian American Records, PO Box 808, Lititz, PA 17543-0538 *Tel:* 717-627-4800 *Fax:* 717-627-4800 *E-mail:* canadianamerican@dejazzd.com *Web Site:* www.canadianamericanrecords.net; www.joeywelz.com, pg 818

Canadian Broadcast Standards Council (CBSC), PO Box 3265, Sta D, Ottawa, ON K1P 6H8, Canada *Tel:* 613-233-4607 *Toll Free Tel:* 866-696-4718 (CN only) *Fax:* 613-233-4826 *E-mail:* info@cbsc.ca *Web Site:* www.ccnr.ca, pg 1080

Canadian Filmmakers Distribution Center (CFMDC), 401 Richmond St W, Suite 245, Toronto, ON M5V 3A8, Canada *Tel:* 416-588-0725 *Fax:* 416-588-7956 *Web Site:* www.cfmdc.org, pg 818

Canadian Learning Co Inc, 95 Vansittart Ave, Woodstock, ON N4S 6E3, Canada *Tel:* 519-537-2360 *Toll Free Tel:* 800-267-2977 (CN) *Fax:* 519-537-1035 *Web Site:* www.canlearn.com, pg 818

Canadian Screen Awards, 49 Ontario St, Suite 501, Toronto, ON M5A 2V1, Canada *Tel:* 416-366-2227 *Toll Free Tel:* 800-644-5194 *Fax:* 416-366-8454 *E-mail:* academie@acct.ca *Web Site:* www.acct.ca/prixgemeaux; www.academy.ca/awards, pg 1111

Canadian Student Film Festival, 1432 de Bleury St, Montreal, QC H3A 2J1, Canada *Tel:* 514-848-3883 *Fax:* 514-848-3886 *E-mail:* info@ffm-montreal.org *Web Site:* www.ffm-montreal.org, pg 1111

Canamedia Inc, 1540 Cornwall Rd, Suite 216, Oakville, ON L6J 7W5, Canada *Tel:* 416-363-6765 *Toll Free Tel:* 866-999-5292 *Fax:* 416-363-7834 *Web Site:* www.canamedia.com, pg 818

Canare Corporation of America, 45 Commerce Way, Unit C, Totowa, NJ 07512 *Tel:* 973-837-0070 *Fax:* 973-837-0080 *E-mail:* sales@canare.com *Web Site:* www.canare.com, pg 819

Canavan Scenic & Light LLC, 2440 Dinneen Ave, Orlando, FL 32804 *Tel:* 407-888-8002 *Fax:* 407-888-8171 *Web Site:* www.csandl.com, pg 819

C&C Studios Corp, 20 W 37 St, New York, NY 10018 *Tel:* 212-967-6427 *Web Site:* www.candcstudios.tv, pg 819

Candee Productions Inc, 301 W Deer Valley Rd, Suite 7, Phoenix, AZ 85027 *Tel:* 623-266-3070 *Fax:* 623-581-7020 *Web Site:* www.candeeproductions.com, pg 819

C&I Studios, 541 NW First Ave, Fort Lauderdale, FL 33301 *Tel:* 954-357-3934 *E-mail:* contact@c-istudios.com *Web Site:* www.c-istudios.com, pg 819

Cannon Stage Lighting Inc, 1717 Whitehead Rd, Baltimore, MD 21207 *Tel:* 410-298-0636 *Fax:* 410-298-7950 *Web Site:* www.cannonstage.com, pg 819

Canon Broadcast & Communications Division, One Canon Park, Melville, NY 11747-3336 *Toll Free Tel:* 800-321-4388 *E-mail:* bctv@cusa.canon.com *Web Site:* www.canon.com/bctv; www.usa.canon.com/cusa/professional, pg 819

Canon USA Inc, One Canon Park, Melville, NY 11747 *Tel:* 613-330-5000 *E-mail:* pr@cusa.canon.com *Web Site:* www.usa.canon.com, pg 819

Cantrax Recorders, 2119 Fidler Ave, Long Beach, CA 90815 *Tel:* 562-498-6492 *E-mail:* cantrax@verizon.net, pg 819

Canvys™, 40W267 Keslinger Rd, La Fox, IL 60147-0393 *Toll Free Tel:* 888-735-7373 *Fax:* 630-208-2830 *Web Site:* www.canvys.com, pg 819

Canyon Cinema Inc, 1777 Yosemite Ave, Suite 210, San Francisco, CA 94124 *Tel:* 415-626-2255 *E-mail:* info@canyoncinema.com *Web Site:* www.canyoncinema.com, pg 819

Cape Girardeau Convention & Visitors Bureau, 400 Broadway St, Suite 100, Cape Girardeau, MO 63701 *Tel:* 573-335-1631 *Toll Free Tel:* 800-777-0068 *Fax:* 573-334-6702 *E-mail:* info@visitcape.com *Web Site:* visitcape.com, pg 1099

Capital Communications Inc, 2357-3, S Tamiami Trail, Venice, FL 34293 *Tel:* 941-539-6741 *E-mail:* cap5678@isp.com, pg 819

Capital - Saratoga Film Commission, 28 Clinton St, Saratoga Springs, NY 12866 *Tel:* 518-584-3255 *Fax:* 518-587-0318 *E-mail:* info@capital-saratogafilm.com *Web Site:* www.saratoga.org, pg 1100

Capitol Records, 1750 N Vine St, Hollywood, CA 90028 *Tel:* 323-871-5001 *E-mail:* mark.moreno@emimusic.com *Web Site:* www.capitalstudios.com; www.capitolrecords.com, pg 819

Caprock Developments Inc, 475 Speedwell, Morris Plains, NJ 07950 *Tel:* 973-267-9292 *Toll Free Tel:* 800-222-0325 *Fax:* 973-292-0614 *E-mail:* info@caprockdev.com *Web Site:* www.caprockdev.com, pg 819

Capron Lighting & Sound Co Inc, 278 West St, Needham, MA 02494 *Tel:* 781-444-8850 *Fax:* 781-444-1408 *E-mail:* info@capron.net *Web Site:* www.capron.net, pg 819

Captain Fiddle Music & Publications, 94 Wiswall Rd, Lee, NH 03861 *Tel:* 603-659-2658 *E-mail:* cfiddle@tiac.net *Web Site:* captainfiddle.com, pg 820

Caption Colorado LLC, 5690 DTC Blvd, Suite 500W, Greenwood Village, CO 80111 *Tel:* 720-489-5662 *Toll Free Tel:* 800-775-7838 *Fax:* 720-489-5664 *Web Site:* www.captioncolorado.com, pg 820

CaptionMax, 2438 27 Ave S, Minneapolis, MN 55406 *Tel:* 612-341-3566 *Toll Free Tel:* 800-822-3566 *Fax:* 612-341-2345 *Web Site:* www.captionmax.com, pg 820

Captions & Subtitle Services Ltd, 101 Hempstead Place, Suite 1A, Joliet, IL 60433 *Tel:* 815-740-1009 *Toll Free Tel:* 866-230-1009 *E-mail:* info@capsubservices.com; quote@capsubservices.com *Web Site:* www.capsubservices.com, pg 820

Cardinal Sound & Video, 2219 Kansas Ave, Silver Spring, MD 20910 *Tel:* 301-589-3700 *Fax:* 301-589-4284 *E-mail:* info@cardinalsound.us *Web Site:* www.cardinalsound.us, pg 820

Career & Self Directed Extended Programs at Purdue University, Stewart Ctr, G-53, 128 Memorial Mall, West Lafayette, IN 47907-2034 *Tel:* 765-494-8619 *Toll Free Tel:* 800-830-0269 *Fax:* 765-496-2484 *E-mail:* distance@purdue.edu *Web Site:* www.distance.purdue.edu/training, pg 820

Chester F Carlson Award, 7003 Kilworth Lane, Springfield, VA 22151 *Tel:* 703-642-9090 *Fax:* 703-642-9094 *E-mail:* info@imaging.org *Web Site:* www.imaging.org, pg 1111

Carlton-Bates Co, 3600 W 69 St, Little Rock, AR 72209 *Tel:* 501-562-9100 *Toll Free Tel:* 866-600-6040 *E-mail:* customerservicecb@carltonbates.com; sales@carltonbates.com *Web Site:* www.carltonbates.com, pg 820

Carolina Biological Supply Co, 2700 York Rd, Burlington, NC 27215-3398 *Tel:* 336-584-0381 (outside US & CN) *Toll Free Tel:* 800-334-5551 *Toll Free Fax:* 800-222-7112 *E-mail:* customer_service@carolina.com; internationalsales@carolina.com *Web Site:* www.carolina.com, pg 820

Carolina Film & Video Festival (CFVF), 210 Brown Bldg, UNC Greensboro, Greensboro, NC 27402 *Tel:* 336-334-5360 *Fax:* 336-334-5039 *E-mail:* cfvf@uncg.edu *Web Site:* cfvf.uncg.edu; www.carolinafilmandvideofestival.org, pg 1111

Carpel Video Inc, 429 E Patrick St, Frederick, MD 21701 *Tel:* 301-694-3500 *Toll Free Tel:* 800-238-4300 *Fax:* 301-694-9510 *Web Site:* www.carpelvideoonline.com, pg 820

Carr McLean Ltd, 461 Horner Ave, Toronto, ON M8W 4X2, Canada *Tel:* 416-252-3371 *Toll Free Tel:* 800-268-2123 (CN) *Fax:* 416-252-9203 *Toll Free Fax:* 800-871-2397 *E-mail:* sales@carrmclean.ca *Web Site:* www.carrmclean.ca, pg 820

Carvin Corp, 12340 World Trade Dr, San Diego, CA 92128 *Tel:* 858-487-1600 *Toll Free Tel:* 800-854-2235 *Fax:* 858-487-8160 *Web Site:* www.carvin.com, pg 820

CAS Video Productions, 820 White Marsh Ct, Huntingtown, MD 20639 *Tel:* 301-760-7301; 301-674-2000 (cell) *Web Site:* www.casvideo.com, pg 820

Case Design Corp, 333 School Lane, Telford, PA 18969 *Tel:* 215-703-0130 *Toll Free Tel:* 800-847-4176 *Fax:* 215-703-0139 *E-mail:* sales@casedesigncorp.com *Web Site:* www.casedesigncorp.com, pg 820

Case Logic Inc, 6303 Dry Creek Pkwy, Longmont, CO 80503 *Tel:* 303-652-1000 *Toll Free Tel:* 800-925-8111 *Fax:* 303-652-1094 *E-mail:* customer.service@caselogic.com *Web Site:* www.caselogic.com, pg 820

Cashmark Media Inc, 4702 Eastern Ave, Kansas City, MO 64129 *Tel:* 816-861-4200 *Fax:* 816-861-4205 *E-mail:* info@cashmarkmedia.com *Web Site:* www.cashmarkmedia.com, pg 820

Casio America Inc, 570 Mount Pleasant Ave, Dover, NJ 07801 *Tel:* 973-361-5400 *Fax:* 973-537-8929 *E-mail:* projectors@casio.com *Web Site:* www.casioprojector.com, pg 820

Castillo Theater, 543 W 42 St, New York, NY 10036 *Tel:* 212-941-5800 *Toll Free Tel:* 800-435-7453 *E-mail:* castillo@allstars.org *Web Site:* www.castillo.org, pg 820

Castleview Productions, 1100 W 41 St, Austin, TX 78756 *Tel:* 512-442-9944 *Fax:* 512-442-8823 *E-mail:* contact@castleviewproductions.com *Web Site:* www.castleviewproductions.com, pg 821

Catalina Island Film Commission, One Green Pier, Avalon, CA 90704-0217 *Tel:* 310-510-7649 *Fax:* 310-510-7607 *Web Site:* www.catalinachamber.com/mediafilming/contact, pg 1092

Catapult Films Inc, 832 Third St, Suite 303, Santa Monica, CA 90403 *Tel:* 310-395-1470, pg 821

Catholic Books & Tapes, PO Box 350333, Fort Lauderdale, FL 33335-0333 *Tel:* 954-583-5108 *Fax:* 954-583-5108 *E-mail:* mascmen7@yahoo.com *Web Site:* www.catholicbook.com, pg 821

Catholic Library Association (CLA), 8550 United Plaza Blvd, Suite 1001, Baton Rouge, LA 70809 *Tel:* 225-408-4417 *E-mail:* cla2@cathla.org *Web Site:* www.cathla.org, pg 1080

Catman & Mary Productions, 336 W 37 St, Suite 800, New York, NY 10018 *Tel:* 212-947-4777 *Fax:* 212-947-4779 *Web Site:* www.catmanandmary.com, pg 821

Cavalcade Productions Inc, PO Box 2480, Nevada City, CA 95959-1948 *Tel:* 530-477-0701 (outside US & CN) *Toll Free Tel:* 800-345-5530 *Fax:* 530-477-0701 (outside US & CN) *Toll Free Fax:* 800-345-5530 *E-mail:* info@cavalcadeproductions.com *Web Site:* www.cavalcadeproductions.com, pg 821

Cavanaugh Tocci Associates Inc, 327F Boston Post Rd, Sudbury, MA 01776 *Tel:* 978-443-7871 *E-mail:* cta@cavtocci.com *Web Site:* www.cavtocci.com, pg 821

Cavision Enterprises Ltd, 2323 Boundary Rd, Suite 210, Vancouver, BC V5M 4V8, Canada *Tel:* 604-298-9053 *Fax:* 604-298-9051 *E-mail:* info@cavision.com *Web Site:* www.cavision.com, pg 821

Cayman Islands Department of Tourism, Empire State Bldg, 350 Fifth Ave, Suite 2720, New York, NY 10018 *Tel:* 212-889-9009 *Toll Free Tel:* 877-4-CAYMAN (422-9626) *Fax:* 212-889-9125 *Web Site:* www.caymanislands.ky; www.divecayman.ky, pg 1100

CBC/Radio-Canada, 181 Queen St, Ottawa, ON K1P 1K9, Canada *Toll Free Tel:* 866-306-4636 (CN) *Fax:* 613-288-6245 *E-mail:* liaison@cbc.ca; liaison@radio-canada.ca *Web Site:* www.cbc.radio-canada.ca, pg 821

CBM Metal, High Point Business Park, 8750 Holgate Cresent, Milton, ON L9T 0K3, Canada *Tel:* 905-878-0648 *Toll Free Tel:* 800-387-4834 *Fax:* 905-878-6748 *Toll Free Fax:* 888-554-5501 *E-mail:* sales@cbmmetal.com *Web Site:* www.cbmmetal.com, pg 821

CCH Continuing Education, 4025 W Peterson Ave, Chicago, IL 60646-6085 *Tel:* 773-866-3648 *Toll Free Tel:* 800-248-3248 *Fax:* 773-866-3084 *Web Site:* www.cch.com, pg 821

CCH Inc, A Wolters Kluwer business, 2700 Lake Cook Rd, Riverwoods, IL 60015 *Tel:* 847-267-7000 *Web Site:* www.cch.com, pg 821

CCI Communications Inc, 1440 Phoenixville Pike, West Chester, PA 19380 *Tel:* 610-296-7233 *Fax:* 610-296-7358 *E-mail:* info@ccivideo.com *Web Site:* www.ccivideo.com, pg 821

CCI Digital, 2921 W Alameda Ave, Burbank, CA 91505 *Tel:* 818-562-6300 *Fax:* 818-562-8222 *E-mail:* info@ccidigital.com *Web Site:* www.ccidigital.com, pg 821

CCI Solutions, 1342 88 Ave SE, Olympia, WA 98501 *Tel:* 360-943-5378 *Toll Free Tel:* 800-562-6006 *Fax:* 360-754-1566 *E-mail:* info@ccisolutions.com *Web Site:* www.ccisolutions.com, pg 821

CCore Media Inc, 1421 Lowe Dr, Algonquin, IL 60102 *Tel:* 847-854-1111 *Web Site:* www.creativecore.com, pg 821

CD Meyer Inc, 91 Clinton Rd, Suite 2C, Fairfield, NJ 07004 *Tel:* 973-882-9411 *Fax:* 973-808-4087 *E-mail:* info@cdmeyer.com *Web Site:* www.cdmeyer.com; www.point2explore.com; museumdigitalsignage.com, pg 822

The CD Recycling Center of America, 68 Stiles Rd, Salem, NH 03079 *Tel:* 603-894-5553 *Fax:* 603-898-4319 *E-mail:* info@cdrecyclingcenter.org *Web Site:* www.cdrecyclingcenter.org, pg 822

CD ROM™ Inc, 3131 E Riverside Dr, Fort Myers, FL 33916 *Tel:* 952-832-5424 (sales) *Toll Free Tel:* 866-662-3766 (orders) *Fax:* 239-332-2808; 715-372-6702 (orders) *E-mail:* sales@cdrominc.com *Web Site:* www.cdrominc.com, pg 822

CDAI Innovative Design Solutions, 4279 Roswell Rd NE, Suite 102, No 135, Atlanta, GA 30342 *Tel:* 404-633-8861 *Fax:* 404-636-5089 *E-mail:* info@cdai.com *Web Site:* www.cdai.com, pg 822

CDR Communications Inc, 9310-B Old Keene Mill Rd, Burke, VA 22015 *Tel:* 703-569-3400 *Toll Free Tel:* 800-729-2237 *Fax:* 703-569-3448 *E-mail:* info@cdrcommunications.com *Web Site:* www.cdrcommunications.com, pg 822

Ceavco Audio/Visual Co, 6240 W 54 Ave, Arvada, CO 80002 *Tel:* 303-539-3500 *Fax:* 303-539-3501 *E-mail:* solutions@ceavco.com *Web Site:* www.ceavco.com, pg 822

Cedar Crest Studio, 17 CR 830, Henderson, AR 72544 *Tel:* 870-488-5777 *E-mail:* cedarcrest@springfield.net *Web Site:* www.cedarcreststudio.com, pg 822

CELCO-Constantine Engineering Labs Co, 14 Industrial Ave, Suite 3, Mahwah, NJ 07430 *Tel:* 201-327-1123 *Fax:* 201-327-7047 *E-mail:* info@celco-nj.com *Web Site:* www.celco.com; www.celco-nj.com, pg 822

Celebration of Service to America Awards, 1771 "N" St NW, Washington, DC 20036-2891 *Tel:* 202-421-3191 *E-mail:* nabef@nab.org *Web Site:* www.nabef.org, pg 1111

Celebrities Productions, c/o Clayton-Davis & Associates, 230 S Bemiston Ave, Suite 1400, St Louis, MO 63105 *Tel:* 314-862-7800 *Fax:* 314-721-5171 *E-mail:* idcda@aol.com *Web Site:* www.claytondavis.com, pg 822

Celebrity Helicopters Inc, 961 W Alondra Blvd, Compton, CA 90220 *Tel:* 310-618-1155 *Toll Free Tel:* 877-999-2099 *Fax:* 424-785-8768 *Toll Free Fax:* 877-999-2099 *Web Site:* www.celebheli.com, pg 822

Celestial Harmonies/Fortuna Records/Kuckuck Schallplatten/Black Sun Music/MonteVideo, 1951 N Wilmot Rd, Bldg 2, Unit 7, Tucson, AZ 85712-8000 *Tel:* 520-326-4400 *Fax:* 520-326-3333 *E-mail:* celestial@harmonies.com *Web Site:* www.harmonies.com, pg 822

Centaur Records Inc, 136 Saint Joseph St, Baton Rouge, LA 70802 *Tel:* 225-336-4877 *Fax:* 225-336-9678 *E-mail:* info@centaurrecords.com *Web Site:* www.centaurrecords.com, pg 822

Centennial Electric Sound Co Ltd, 545 W 45 St, New York, NY 10036 *Tel:* 212-581-4150 *Fax:* 212-581-4152, pg 822

Center City Film & Video Inc, 1501-1503 Walnut St, Philadelphia, PA 19102 *Tel:* 215-568-4134 *Fax:* 215-568-6011 *E-mail:* info@ccfv.com; sales@ccfv.com *Web Site:* www.ccfv.com, pg 822

Center for Asian American Media (CAAM), 145 Ninth St, Suite 350, San Francisco, CA 94103 *Tel:* 415-863-0814 *Fax:* 415-863-7428 *E-mail:* info@caamedia.org *Web Site:* www.caamedia.org, pg 1080

Center for Southern Folklore Inc, 119 S Main St, Memphis, TN 38103 *Tel:* 901-525-3655 *Fax:* 901-544-9965 *E-mail:* info@southernfolklore.com *Web Site:* www.southernfolklore.com, pg 822

Center for Touch Drawing, PO Box 1595, Langley, WA 98260 *Tel:* 360-221-5745 *Toll Free Tel:* 800-989-6334 (orders) *E-mail:* center@touchdrawing.com *Web Site:* www.touchdrawing.com, pg 822

CenterStaging LLC, 3407 Winona Ave, Burbank, CA 91504 *Tel:* 818-559-4333 *Fax:* 818-848-4016 *E-mail:* info@centerstaging.com *Web Site:* centerstaging.com, pg 822

Central Audio-Visual Equipment Inc, 375 Roma Jean Pkwy, Streamwood, IL 60107 *Tel:* 630-372-8100 *Toll Free Tel:* 800-323-4239 *Fax:* 630-372-9281 *Web Site:* www.cavinc.com, pg 823

Central Florida Visitors & Convention Bureau, 2701 Lake Myrtle Park Rd, Auburndale, FL 33823-9360 *Tel:* 863-551-4750 *Toll Free Tel:* 800-828-7655 *Fax:* 863-551-4740 *Web Site:* www.visitcentralflorida.org, pg 1095

Central Lighting & Equipment Inc (CLE), 4103 E 16 St, Des Moines, IA 50313 *Tel:* 515-277-4190 *Toll Free Tel:* 877-977-4190 *Fax:* 515-277-2295 *E-mail:* info@cleproductions.com *Web Site:* www.cleproductions.com, pg 823

Central Texas College KNCT-TV & Radio FM, PO Box 1800, Killeen, TX 76540-1800 *Tel:* 254-526-1176 *Fax:* 254-526-1850 *E-mail:* knct@knct.org *Web Site:* www.knct.org, pg 823

Centralite Systems Inc, 1000 Cody Rd S, Mobile, AL 36695 *Tel:* 251-607-9119 *Toll Free Tel:* 877-466-5483 *Fax:* 251-607-9117 *Web Site:* www.centralite.com, pg 823

Centrax Corp, 22 W Washington, Suite 1500, Chicago, IL 60602 *Tel:* 312-946-2000 *Toll Free Tel:* 800-556-1909 *Toll Free Fax:* 888-661-7030 *E-mail:* info@centrax.com *Web Site:* www.centrax.com, pg 823

Centre Communications Inc, 75 Manhattan Dr, Suite 200, Boulder, CO 80303 *Tel:* 303-444-1166 *E-mail:* centre@ecentral.com *Web Site:* www.centrecommunicationinc.com; www.centredm.com, pg 823

Centre for Art Tapes (CFAT), 2238 Maitland St, Halifax, NS B3K 2Z9, Canada *Tel:* 902-422-6822 *Fax:* 902-422-6823 *E-mail:* info@cfat.ca *Web Site:* cfat.ca, pg 1080

Century Business Solutions, 2340 Brighton Henrietta Town Line Rd, Rochester, NY 14623 *Toll Free Tel:* 800-975-6429 *Toll Free Fax:* 800-975-6429 *E-mail:* customerservice@ncd-brands.com *Web Site:* www.centurybusinesssolutions.com, pg 823

Century Color Labs Inc, 494 School St, East Hartford, CT 06108 *Tel:* 860-289-9501 *Toll Free Tel:* 800-242-9501 *Fax:* 860-291-9098 *E-mail:* production@centurycolor.com *Web Site:* www.centurycolor.com, pg 823

Cerutti Productions Inc, 18211 Bulverde Rd, Suite 10202, San Antonio, TX 78259 *Tel:* 210-403-0800 *Fax:* 210-403-0801 *Web Site:* www.cerutti.org, pg 823

Cerwin-Vega! Inc, 309 Plus Park Blvd, Nashville, TN 37217 *Tel:* 615-871-4500 *Toll Free Tel:* 800-444-2766 *Web Site:* www.cerwinvega.com, pg 823

Thomas Cestare Inc, 188 Herricks Rd, Mineola, NY 11502 *Tel:* 516-742-5550 *Fax:* 516-742-5551 *E-mail:* cestare@aol.com *Web Site:* www.thomascestareinc.com, pg 823

CET, 1223 Central Pkwy, Cincinnati, OH 45214 *Tel:* 513-381-4033 *Fax:* 513-381-7520 *E-mail:* wcet@cetconnect.org *Web Site:* www.cetconnect.org, pg 823

CEV Multimedia Ltd, 1020 SE Loop 289, Lubbock, TX 79404 *Toll Free Tel:* 800-922-9965 *Toll Free Fax:* 800-243-6398 *E-mail:* cev@cevmultimedia.com *Web Site:* www.cevmultimedia.com, pg 823

CFP Video Productions Inc, PO Box 86, Caldwell, NJ 07006-0086 *Tel:* 973-226-2481 *Fax:* 973-226-2480 *Web Site:* cfpvideo.com, pg 823

Chace Audio by Deluxe, 201 S Victory Blvd, Burbank, CA 91502-2349 *Toll Free Tel:* 800-842-8346 *Web Site:* www.chace.com, pg 823

Chalk Dust Co, 16107 Kensington Dr, PMB 256, Sugar Land, TX 77479-4401 *Tel:* 281-265-2495 *Toll Free Tel:* 800-588-7564 *Fax:* 281-265-3197 *E-mail:* sales@chalkdust.com *Web Site:* www.chalkdust.com, pg 823

Challenge Productions, 400 E George St, Marion, OH 43302 *Tel:* 740-531-3077 *E-mail:* info@challenge-pro.com *Web Site:* challenge-pro.com, pg 823

Championship Productions Inc, Ames Community Development Park, 2730 Graham St, Ames, IA 50010 *Tel:* 515-232-3687 *Toll Free Tel:* 800-873-2730 *Fax:* 515-232-3739 *E-mail:* info@championshipproductions.com *Web Site:* www.championshipproductions.com, pg 823

Channel Productions, 1964 Filer Ave E, Twin Falls, ID 83301 *Fax:* 208-734-6550 *E-mail:* chanpro@mindspring.com, pg 823

Channell One Video, PO Box 399, Epping, NH 03042-0399 *Tel:* 603-679-6796 *Toll Free Tel:* 888-722-3843 (natl) *E-mail:* racevid@earthlink.net *Web Site:* www.racevideo.com, pg 824

Chapman/Leonard Studios & Production Center, 12950 Raymer St, North Hollywood, CA 91605 *Tel:* 818-764-6726 *Toll Free Tel:* 888-883-6559 *Fax:* 818-764-6730 *Web Site:* www.chapman-leonard.com, pg 824

Chapman Recording & Mastering, 8805 Monrovia, Lenexa, KS 66215 *Tel:* 913-894-6854 *Fax:* 913-894-6857 *Web Site:* www.chapmanrecording.com, pg 824

Charles Beseler Co, 2018 W Main St, Stroudsburg, PA 18360 *Toll Free Tel:* 800-237-3537 *Toll Free Fax:* 800-966-4515 *Web Site:* www.beselerphoto.com, pg 824

Charleston International Film Festival (CIFF), 915 Folly Rd, No 78, Charleston, SC 29412 *Tel:* 843-817-1617 *E-mail:* info@charlestoniff.org *Web Site:* charlestoniff.org, pg 1111

Charlex Inc, 2 W 45 St, 7th fl, New York, NY 10036 *Tel:* 212-719-4600 *Fax:* 212-840-2747 *Web Site:* www.charlex.com, pg 824

Charlotte Regional Film Commission, 500 S College St, Suite 300, Charlotte, NC 28202 *Tel:* 704-331-2723 *Toll Free Tel:* 800-722-1994 *Fax:* 704-342-3972 *Toll Free Fax:* 800-722-1994 *Web Site:* www.charlottefilm.com, pg 1101

Chartpak Inc, One River Rd, Leeds, MA 01053 *Tel:* 413-584-5446 *Toll Free Tel:* 800-628-1910 *Fax:* 413-584-6781 *E-mail:* info@chartpak.com *Web Site:* www.chartpak.com, pg 824

Chater Camera Inc, 1336 Ninth St, Berkeley, CA 94710 *Tel:* 510-525-5400 *Fax:* 510-295-2478 *E-mail:* rentals@chatercamera.com *Web Site:* www.chatercamera.com, pg 824

Chatterbox Productions Inc, 2311 S Bayshore Dr, Coconut Grove, FL 33133-4728 *Tel:* 305-285-1058 *Web Site:* www.ampersandcom.com/chatterbox, pg 824

Chauvet Lighting, 5200 NW 108 Ave, Sunrise, FL 33351-8040 *Tel:* 954-577-4455 *Toll Free Tel:* 800-762-1084 *Fax:* 954-929-5560 *Toll Free Fax:* 800-544-4898 *E-mail:* info@chauvetlighting.com *Web Site:* www.chauvetlighting.com, pg 824

Checkers Industrial Products LLC, 620 Compton St, Broomfield, CO 80020 *Tel:* 720-890-1187 *Toll Free Tel:* 800-438-9336 *Fax:* 720-890-1191 *E-mail:* sales@checkersindustrial.com *Web Site:* www.checkersindustrial.com, pg 824

Chelsea Decorative Metal Co, 8212 Braewick Dr, Dept AV, Houston, TX 77074 *Tel:* 713-721-9200 *Fax:* 713-776-8661 *E-mail:* tinman83@earthlink.net *Web Site:* www.tinman.com, pg 824

Chelsea Green Publishing Co, 85 N Main St, Suite 120, White River Junction, VT 05001 *Tel:* 802-295-6300 *Toll Free Tel:* 800-639-4099 *Fax:* 802-295-6444 *Web Site:* www.chelseagreen.com, pg 824

Cheng & Tsui Co, 25 West St, 2nd fl, Boston, MA 02111-1213 *Tel:* 617-988-2400 *Toll Free Tel:* 800-554-1963 (orders) *Fax:* 617-426-3669 *E-mail:* orders@cheng-tsui.com *Web Site:* www.cheng-tsui.com, pg 824

Cherry Multimedia, 2129 Colorado Blvd, Los Angeles, CA 90041 *Toll Free Tel:* 800-378-7598 *E-mail:* info@cherrymultimedia.com *Web Site:* cherrymultimedia.com, pg 824

Chesney Communications, PO Box 61945, Irvine, CA 92602-1945 *Tel:* 949-263-5500 *E-mail:* videocc@aol.com *Web Site:* www.speakersdemos.com; www.videocc.com, pg 824

Cheuvront Studios, 4607 NW Sixth St Ext, Studio I, Gainesville, FL 32609 *Tel:* 352-378-4671 *Fax:* 352-338-9215 *E-mail:* allen@cheuvront.com *Web Site:* www.cheuvront.com, pg 824

Bruce Chianese, 719 S Main St, Burbank, CA 91506 *Tel:* 818-841-6607 *E-mail:* bruce@brucechianese.com *Web Site:* www.brucechianese.com, pg 824

Chicago Film Critics Association, 155 E Algonquin Rd, Arlington Heights, IL 60006 *Tel:* 847-427-4530 *Fax:* 847-427-1301 *E-mail:* critics@chicagofilmcritics.org *Web Site:* www.chicagofilmcritics.org, pg 1080

Chicago Film Office, Chicago Cultural Center, 78 E Washington, Rm 108, Chicago, IL 60602 *Tel:* 312-744-6415 *Fax:* 312-744-1378 *E-mail:* filmoffice@cityofchicago.org *Web Site:* www.cityofchicago.org/city/en/depts/dca/provdrs/chicago_film_office.html, pg 1097

Chicago International Children's Film Festival, 1517 W Fullerton Ave, Chicago, IL 60614 *Tel:* 773-281-9075 (ext 3011) *Fax:* 773-929-0266 *E-mail:* kids@facets.org *Web Site:* www.cicff.org; www.facets.org, pg 1111

Chicago International Film Festival, 30 E Adams St, Suite 800, Chicago, IL 60603 *Tel:* 312-683-0121 *Fax:* 312-683-0122 *E-mail:* info@chicagofilmfestival.com *Web Site:* www.chicagofilmfestival.com, pg 1111

Chicago International REEL Shorts Festival, 428 N Wolcott, Chicago, IL 60622 *Web Site:* www.projectchicago.com, pg 1111

Chicago Irish Film Festival (CIFF), c/o Society for Arts, 1112 N Milwaukee Ave, Chicago, IL 60642 *Tel:* 773-486-9612 *Fax:* 773-486-9613 *Web Site:* www.chicagoirishfilmfestival.com, pg 1111

Chicago Latino Film Festival, 676 N La Salle Dr, Suite 520, Chicago, IL 60654 *Tel:* 312-431-1330 *Fax:* 312-786-0126 *E-mail:* info@latinoculturalcenter.org *Web Site:* www.chicagolatinofilmfestival.org, pg 1111

The Chicago Production Center, 5400 N Saint Louis Ave, Chicago, IL 60625-4698 *Tel:* 773-509-5571 *Fax:* 773-509-5303 *Web Site:* www.wttw.com, pg 825

Chicago Satellite & Video, 6749 N Keeler Ave, Lincolnwood, IL 60712-3513 *Tel:* 312-907-3057 *E-mail:* chicagosatellite@hotmail.com, pg 825

Chicago Scenic Studios Inc, 1315 N Branch St, Chicago, IL 60642 *Tel:* 312-274-9900 *Fax:* 312-274-9901 *E-mail:* info@chicagoscenic.com *Web Site:* www.chicagoscenic.com, pg 825

Chicago South Asian Film Festival (CSAFF), 2909 N Sheridan Rd, Unit 1902, Chicago, IL 60657 *Tel:* 773-980-9285 *E-mail:* info@csaff.org *Web Site:* www.csaff.org, pg 1111

Chicago Spotlight Inc, 1658 W Carroll St, Chicago, IL 60612 *Tel:* 312-455-1171 *Fax:* 312-455-1744 *Web Site:* www.chicagospotlight.com, pg 825

Chicago Underground Film Festival, 2044 W Chicago Ave, PMB 155, Chicago, IL 60622 *Tel:* 773-341-6727 *E-mail:* info@cuff.org *Web Site:* www.cuff.org, pg 1112

Chick Russell Communications, 490 Castano Ave, Pasadena, CA 91107 *Tel:* 407-406-2899 *E-mail:* info@chickrussell.com *Web Site:* www.chickrussell.com, pg 825

Chico Chamber of Commerce/Butte County Film Commission, 441 Main St, Suite 150, Chico, CA 95928 *Tel:* 530-891-5556 *Toll Free Tel:* 800-852-8570 *Fax:* 530-891-3613 *E-mail:* info@chicochamber.com *Web Site:* chicochamber.com, pg 1092

Chief, 6436 City West Pkwy, Eden Prairie, MN 55344 *Tel:* 952-894-6280 *Toll Free Tel:* 800-582-6480 *Fax:* 952-894-6918 *Toll Free Fax:* 877-894-6918 *E-mail:* chief@chiefmfg.com; orders@chiefmfg.com *Web Site:* www.chiefmfg.com, pg 825

Children of Mary, PO Box 350333, Fort Lauderdale, FL 33335-0333 *Tel:* 954-583-5108 *Fax:* 954-583-5108 *E-mail:* mascmen7@yahoo.com *Web Site:* www.catholicbook.com, pg 825

The Children's Book Store Distribution (CBSD), 14-3245 Harvester Rd, Burlington, ON L7N 3T7, Canada *Tel:* 905-681-8160; 905-831-1995 (intl) *Toll Free Tel:* 800-668-0242; 800-757-8372 (cust serv-CN & US) *Fax:* 905-831-1142 (intl) *E-mail:* info@childrensgroup.com *Web Site:* www.childrensgroup.com, pg 825

Chimera®, 1812 Valtec Lane, Boulder, CO 80301 *Tel:* 303-444-8000 *Toll Free Tel:* 888-444-1812 *Fax:* 303-444-8303 *E-mail:* salesinfo@chimeralighting.com *Web Site:* chimeralighting.com, pg 825

Chinmaya Publications, 560 Bridgetown Pike, Langhorne, PA 19053-7210 *Tel:* 215-396-0390 *Toll Free Tel:* 888-CMW-READ (269-7323) *Fax:* 215-396-9710 *E-mail:* publications@chinmayamission.org *Web Site:* www.chinmayamission.org; www.chinmayapublications.org, pg 825

Richard Chisolm Cinematography, 300 Oakdale Rd, Baltimore, MD 21210 *Tel:* 410-467-2997 *E-mail:* mail@richardchisolm.com *Web Site:* www.richardchisolm.com, pg 825

CHK Electronics, 6021 SW 29 St, Suite A311, Topeka, KS 66614 *Tel:* 785-862-2543 *Fax:* 707-361-0230 *E-mail:* sales@chk-electronics.com *Web Site:* www.chk-electronics.com, pg 825

The Chris Awards, 1021 E Broad St, Columbus, OH 43205-1357 *Tel:* 614-444-7460 *E-mail:* info@columbusfilmcouncil.org *Web Site:* www.columbusfilmcouncil.org, pg 1112

Christian Media Network, PO Box 728, Garberville, CA 95542-8728 *Web Site:* www.christianmedianetwork.com, pg 825

Christian TV Services of Ellicottville, NY, 6490 Pine Tree Rd, Bldg 5, Apt 315, Ellicottville, NY 14731-9603 *Tel:* 716-699-2549 (off & home); 716-257-2096 (cell); 716-397-9825 (cell) *Web Site:* www.christiantvservices.com; www.angelfire.com/ny/christiantvservices; home.sbu.edu/christ; www.christiantvservices.net; www.sauen.com/george/adm; www.christiantvservices.us; www.christiantvservices.info, pg 825

ChristianAnswers.Net™, PO Box 1167, Marysville, WA 98270-1167 *Tel:* 480-507-3621 *Toll Free Tel:* 800-332-2261 (orders only) *Fax:* 480-507-3623 *E-mail:* mail@eden.org *Web Site:* www.christiananswers.net; www.christiananswers.net/eden/home.html, pg 825

Christie Digital Systems USA Inc, 10550 Camden Dr, Cypress, CA 90630 *Tel:* 714-236-8610 *Toll Free Tel:* 866-880-4462 (cust serv) *Fax:* 714-503-3375 *E-mail:* sales-us@christiedigital.com *Web Site:* www.christiedigital.com, pg 825

Christie Lites, 6990 Lake Ellenor Dr, Orlando, FL 32809 *Tel:* 407-856-0016 *Fax:* 407-856-0765 *Web Site:* www.christielites.com, pg 825

Christopher Gray Post Production, 3918 Michael Ave, Los Angeles, CA 90066 *Tel:* 310-395-9845 *E-mail:* cgray@cgpost.com *Web Site:* www.cgpost.com, pg 826

The Christophers, 5 Hanover Sq, 22nd fl, New York, NY 10004 *Tel:* 212-759-4050 *Toll Free Tel:* 888-298-4050 (orders) *Fax:* 212-838-5073 *E-mail:* mail@christophers.org *Web Site:* www.christophers.org, pg 826

Christy's Editorial, 3625 W Pacific Ave, Burbank, CA 91505 *Tel:* 818-845-1755 *Toll Free Tel:* 800-468-6391; 800-556-5706 (CA) *Fax:* 818-845-1756 *E-mail:* info@christys.net *Web Site:* www.christys.net, pg 826

Chromavision Corp, The Radio Wave Bldg, 8th fl, 49 W 27 St, New York, NY 10001 *Tel:* 212-686-7366 *E-mail:* info@chromavision.net *Web Site:* www.chromavision.net, pg 826

ChronTrol Corp, 7525-D Mission Gorge Rd, San Diego, CA 92120 *Tel:* 619-282-8686 *Toll Free Tel:* 800-854-1999 *Fax:* 619-563-6563 *E-mail:* info@chrontrol.com *Web Site:* www.chrontrol.com, pg 826

ChyronHego Corp, 5 Hub Dr, Melville, NY 11747 *Tel:* 631-845-2000 *Fax:* 631-845-2058 *E-mail:* usa@chyronhego.com *Web Site:* www.chyronhego.com, pg 826

Cibola Systems, 180 S Cypress St, Orange, CA 92866 *Tel:* 714-480-0272 *Fax:* 714-480-0768 *E-mail:* info@cibolasystems.com *Web Site:* cibolasystems.com, pg 826

Cifex Corp, 20547 Linksview Way, Boca Raton, FL 33434 *Tel:* 561-883-5548 *Fax:* 561-883-2712 *E-mail:* 2cifex@gmail.com, pg 826

Cine Audio Visual Sales & Service Ltd, 10251 106 St, Edmonton, AB T5J 1H5, Canada *Tel:* 780-423-5081 *Toll Free Tel:* 877-423-5081 *Fax:* 780-424-0309 *E-mail:* cineav@cineav.com; sales@cineav.com; info@cineav.com *Web Site:* www.cineav.com, pg 826

CINE Golden Eagle Awards, 1003 "K" St NW, Suite 208, Washington, DC 20001 *Tel:* 507-400-CINE (400-2463) *E-mail:* info@cine.org *Web Site:* www.cine.org, pg 1112

Cine Las Americas International Film Festival (CLAIFF), 81 San Marcos St, Austin, TX 78702 *Tel:* 512-535-0765 *Fax:* 512-535-6268 *E-mail:* cine@

cinelasamericas.org *Web Site:* www.cinelasamericas.org; www.facebook.com/cinelasamericasaustin, pg 1112

Cine-Med Inc, 127 Main St N, Woodbury, CT 06798 *Tel:* 203-263-0006 *Toll Free Tel:* 800-253-7657 *Fax:* 203-263-4839 *E-mail:* support@cine-med.net *Web Site:* www.cine-med.com, pg 826

Cine Photo Tech, 1240 Oakleigh Dr, Atlanta, GA 30344 *Tel:* 404-684-7100 *Fax:* 404-684-7080 *E-mail:* info@cinephototech.com *Web Site:* www.cinephototech.com, pg 826

Cine 60 Inc, 630 Ninth Ave, New York, NY 10036 *Tel:* 347-460-3971 *E-mail:* cine60nyc@gmail.com *Web Site:* cine60.jimdo.com, pg 826

Cine-World Film Festival, 10715 Rodeo Dr, Suite 8, Lakewood Ranch, FL 34202 *Tel:* 941-364-8478 *Fax:* 941-364-8478 *E-mail:* mail@filmsociety.org *Web Site:* www.filmsociety.org, pg 1112

CineBags Inc, 825 Western Ave, Suite 17, Glendale, CA 91201 *Tel:* 818-662-0605 *Fax:* 818-662-0613 *Web Site:* www.cinebags.com, pg 826

Cinebar Productions Inc, 763 J Clyde Morris Blvd, Suite 1-C, Newport News, VA 23601 *Tel:* 757-873-3232 *Fax:* 757-873-3790 *E-mail:* cinebar@cinebarproductions.com *Web Site:* www.cinebarproductions.com, pg 826

Cinecraft Productions Inc, 2515 Franklin Blvd, Cleveland, OH 44113 *Tel:* 216-781-2300 *Toll Free Tel:* 800-959-2463 *Fax:* 216-781-1067 *E-mail:* info@cinecraft.com *Web Site:* cinecraft.com, pg 827

CineFilm Lab, 2156 Faulkner Rd NE, Atlanta, GA 30324 *Tel:* 404-633-1448 *Toll Free Tel:* 800-633-1448 *Fax:* 404-633-3867 *E-mail:* csr@cinefilmlab.com *Web Site:* www.cinefilmlab.com, pg 827

Cinema Camera Rentals, 113 Fleet St, Marina del Rey, CA 90292 *Tel:* 310-574-1524 *E-mail:* info@cinemacamerarentals.com *Web Site:* www.cinemacamerarentals.com, pg 827

Cinema Concepts, 2030 Powers Ferry Rd, Suite 214, Atlanta, GA 30339 *Tel:* 770-956-7460 *Toll Free Tel:* 800-SHOWADS (746-9237) *Fax:* 770-956-8358 *E-mail:* info@cinemaconcepts.com *Web Site:* www.cinemaconcepts.com, pg 827

Cinema East, 7111 Biscayne Blvd, Miami, FL 33138 *Tel:* 305-757-5859 *Fax:* 305-751-2329 *Web Site:* www.cinemaeast.com, pg 827

Cinema Engineering Co, 14737 Arminta St, Unit B, Panorama City, CA 91402 *Tel:* 818-780-5404 *Fax:* 818-780-5405 *E-mail:* cinemaengineering@tcsn.net; cinemagear@cinemagear.com *Web Site:* www.cinema-engineering.com; www.cinemagear.com, pg 827

Cinema Entertainment Inc, 1779 NW 79 Ave, Doral, FL 33126 *Tel:* 561-899-0721 *E-mail:* info@cinemaent.com *Web Site:* cinemaent.com, pg 827

Cinema Equipment & Supplies Inc, 12457 SW 130 St, Miami, FL 33186 *Tel:* 305-232-8182 *Toll Free Tel:* 800-759-5905 *E-mail:* sales@cinemaequip.com *Web Site:* www.cinemaequip.com, pg 827

Cinema Equipment Sales of California Inc, 24881 Alicia Pkwy, Suite E-326, Laguna Hills, CA 92653 *Tel:* 949-470-0298 *Fax:* 949-470-0835 *E-mail:* cinemadealer@cinemadealer.com *Web Site:* www.cinema-equip.com, pg 827

The Cinema Guild Inc, 115 W 30 St, Suite 800, New York, NY 10001-4061 *Tel:* 212-685-6242 *Toll Free Tel:* 800-723-5522 *Fax:* 212-685-4717 *E-mail:* info@cinemaguild.com *Web Site:* www.cinemaguild.com, pg 827

The Cinema Lab, 2735 S Raritan St, Englewood, CO 80110-1101 *Tel:* 303-783-1020 *Fax:* 303-806-0555 *Web Site:* www.cinemalab.com, pg 827

Cinema Rentals Inc, 25876 The Old Rd, Suite 174, Stevenson Ranch, CA 91381 *Tel:* 661-222-7342 *E-mail:* ocxinc@gmail.com *Web Site:* www.cinemarentals.com, pg 827

Cinema Stage Inc, 110 Saunders Rd, Unit 4, Barrie, ON L4N 9A8, Canada *Tel:* 705-733-8740 *Toll Free Tel:* 800-387-6205 *Fax:* 705-733-8742 *E-mail:* info@cinemastage.ca *Web Site:* www.cinemastage.ca, pg 827

Cinema-Vision, 424 W 33 St, Suite 370, New York, NY 10001 *Tel:* 212-620-8191 *Fax:* 212-620-8198 *E-mail:* info@motionpicturerentals.com *Web Site:* www.motionpicturerentals.com, pg 827

Cinema Xenon International Inc, 261 Valley Vista Dr, Camarillo, CA 93010-1655 *Tel:* 805-383-5548 *Toll Free Tel:* 888-669-7271 *Fax:* 805-389-9611 *E-mail:* info@cxilamps.com *Web Site:* www.cxilamps.com, pg 827

Cinemarr Entertainment, 104 Church St, Sevierville, TN 37862 *E-mail:* cinemarrstudios@aol.com *Web Site:* cinemarrstudios.com, pg 827

Cinemat Inc, 2350 NW 96 Ave, Doral, FL 33172 *Tel:* 305-887-7726 *E-mail:* info@cinematusa.com *Web Site:* cinematusa.com, pg 827

Cinematography Electronics Inc, 5321 Derry Ave, Suite G, Agoura Hills, CA 91301 *Tel:* 818-706-3334 *Fax:* 818-706-3335 *E-mail:* info@cinemaelec.com *Web Site:* www.cinematographyelectronics.com, pg 828

Cinemills Corp, 2021 N Lincoln St, Burbank, CA 91504 *Tel:* 818-843-4560 *Toll Free Tel:* 877-CMC-HMIS (262-4647) *Fax:* 818-843-7834 *E-mail:* sales@cinemills.com *Web Site:* www.cinemills.com, pg 828

Cinequest Film Festival (CQFF), PO Box 720040, San Jose, CA 95172-0040 *Tel:* 408-295-FEST (295-3378); 408-995-5033 (off) *Fax:* 408-995-5713 *E-mail:* contact@cinequest.org *Web Site:* www.cinequest.org, pg 1112

Cinequipt Inc, 2601 49 Ave N, Suite 500, Minneapolis, MN 55430 *Tel:* 612-627-9080 *Toll Free Tel:* 800-809-9080 *Fax:* 612-627-9789 *Web Site:* www.cinequipt.com, pg 828

Cinetel Films Inc, 8255 Sunset Blvd, Los Angeles, CA 90046-2432 *Tel:* 323-654-4000 *Fax:* 323-650-6400 *E-mail:* info@cinetelfilms.com *Web Site:* cinetelfilms.com, pg 828

CineVantage LLC, 8560 W Sunset Blvd, 5th fl, West Hollywood, CA 90069 *Toll Free Tel:* 888-518-7571 *Web Site:* www.cinevantage.com, pg 828

Cinevest, 21956 Carbon Mesa Rd, Malibu, CA 90265 *Tel:* 310-913-0284 *Web Site:* www.cinevest.com, pg 828

CineVideotech Inc, 7330 NE Fourth Ct, Miami, FL 33138 *Tel:* 305-754-2611 *Fax:* 305-759-2463 *Web Site:* www.cinevideotech.com, pg 828

Cinevision Corp, 3300 Northeast Expwy NE, Bldg 2-A, Atlanta, GA 30341 *Tel:* 770-455-8988 *Fax:* 770-455-4066 *E-mail:* cvcorp@bellsouth.net, pg 828

Cineworks Inc, 8125 Lankershim Blvd, North Hollywood, CA 91605 *Tel:* 818-252-0001 *Fax:* 818-252-0003 *E-mail:* cineworks@cineworksinc.com *Web Site:* www.cineworksinc.com, pg 828

Cinram Inc, 2255 Markham Rd, Scarborough, ON M1B 2W3, Canada *Tel:* 416-298-8190 *Fax:* 416-298-0612 *E-mail:* sales@cinram.com *Web Site:* www.cinramgroup.com, pg 828

Cintrex Audio Visual, 656 Axminister Dr, Fenton, MO 63026 *Tel:* 636-343-0178 *Toll Free Tel:* 800-325-9541 *Fax:* 636-343-3513 *E-mail:* websales@cintrexav.com *Web Site:* www.cintrexav.com, pg 828

CircuitWerkes Inc, 2805 NW Sixth St, Gainesville, FL 32609 *Tel:* 352-335-6555 *Fax:* 352-380-0230 *E-mail:* sales@circuitwerkes.com *Web Site:* www.broadcastboxes.com; www.circuitwerkes.com, pg 828

Circulating Film & Video Library, 11 W 53 St, New York, NY 10019-5401 *Tel:* 212-708-9530 *Fax:* 212-708-9531 *E-mail:* circfilm@moma.org *Web Site:* www.moma.org, pg 828

Tim Cissell Music, 10732 W 107 Circle, Westminster, CO 80021 *Tel:* 303-955-4436 *E-mail:* tcissell@wt.net *Web Site:* web.wt.net/~tcissell, pg 828

The Citation of Outstanding Service to the Society Award, 3 Barker Ave, 5th fl, White Plains, NY 10601 *Tel:* 914-761-1100 *Fax:* 914-761-3115 *E-mail:* smpte@smpte.org *Web Site:* www.smpte.org, pg 1112

Citizens Systems America Corp, 363 Van Ness Way, Suite 404, Torrance, CA 90501 *Tel:* 310-781-1460 *Toll Free Tel:* 800-421-6516 *Fax:* 310-781-9152 *Web Site:* www.citizen-systems.com, pg 828

City Color, 1825 W Mockingbird Lane, Dallas, TX 75235 *Tel:* 214-951-9696 *Fax:* 214-951-9697 *Web Site:* www.citycolor.com, pg 828

City Events Group, 57 Park Dr, Troy, MI 48083-2724 *Tel:* 248-589-0600 *Toll Free Tel:* 800-872-8295 *Fax:* 248-589-2020 *E-mail:* info@cityeventsgroups.com *Web Site:* www.cityeventsgroup.com, pg 828

City of Boston Office of Cable Communications, 43 Hawkins St, Boston, MA 02114 *Tel:* 617-635-3112 *Fax:* 617-635-4475 *E-mail:* cable@cityofboston.gov *Web Site:* www.cityofboston.gov/cable, pg 1080

City of Calgary Film Commission, 731 First St SE, Calgary, AB T2G 2G9, Canada *Tel:* 403-221-7831 *Toll Free Tel:* 888-222-5855 *Fax:* 403-221-7828 *Web Site:* www.calgaryeconomicdevelopment.com, pg 1104

City of Montrose Office of Business & Tourism, 107 S Cascade Ave, Montrose, CO 81401 *Tel:* 970-497-8558 *Toll Free Tel:* 855-497-8558 *Web Site:* www.visitmontrose.com, pg 1095

City of Phoenix Film Office, 200 W Washington St, 20th fl, Phoenix, AZ 85003 *Tel:* 602-262-4850 *E-mail:* filmphx@phoenix.gov *Web Site:* www.phoenix.gov/econdev/filming/, pg 1091

City of Port St Lucie Community Relations/Film Office, 121 SW Port St Lucie Blvd, Bldg A, 1st fl, Rm 145, Port St Lucie, FL 34984 *Tel:* 772-871-5219 *Fax:* 772-344-4111 *E-mail:* info@cityofpsl.com *Web Site:* www.cityofpsl.com, pg 1096

City of Prescott Film Office, 201 S Cortez St, Prescott, AZ 86303 *Tel:* 928-777-1204 *Fax:* 928-777-1255 *Web Site:* www.cityofprescott.net/business/film, pg 1091

City of Regina Film Office, Queen Elizabeth II Ct, 2476 Victoria Ave, Regina, SK S4P 3C8, Canada *Tel:* 306-777-7000; 306-777-7529 (scheduling) *Web Site:* www.regina.ca/business/filming, pg 1106

City of Savannah Film Office, One Waring Dr, Savannah, GA 31404 *Tel:* 912-651-2360 *Fax:* 912-651-0982 *E-mail:* info@savannahfilm.org *Web Site:* www.savannahfilm.org, pg 1096

City of Scottsdale, 3939 N Drinkwater Blvd, Scottsdale, AZ 85251 *Tel:* 480-312-2550; 480-312-3111; 480-312-2500 (permit servs) *Fax:* 480-312-2888 *Web Site:* www.scottsdaleaz.gov, pg 1091

City of Stamford, 888 Washington Blvd, Stamford, CT 06901 *Tel:* 203-977-5858 *Fax:* 203-977-5545 *Web Site:* www.cityofstamford.org, pg 1095

City of West Hollywood Film Office, 8300 Santa Monica Blvd, West Hollywood, CA 90069-6216 *Tel:* 323-848-6489 *Fax:* 323-848-6561 *E-mail:* wehofilm@weho.org/film *Web Site:* www.weho.org/film, pg 1094

City Stage, 435 W 19 St, New York, NY 10011 *Tel:* 212-627-3400 *Fax:* 212-633-1228 *Web Site:* www.citystage.com, pg 828

Civins Productions Inc, 5881 NW 122 Dr, Coral Springs, FL 33076 *Tel:* 954-938-8600 *E-mail:* info@civins.com *Web Site:* www.civins.com, pg 828

Clair Brothers Audio Systems Inc, One Clair Blvd, Manheim, PA 17545 *Tel:* 717-665-4000 *Fax:* 717-665-8000 *Web Site:* www.clairsystems.com, pg 829

Clairmont Camera Inc, 4343 Lankershim Blvd, North Hollywood, CA 91602 *Tel:* 818-761-4440 *Fax:* 818-761-0861 *E-mail:* hollywood@clairmont.com *Web Site:* www.clairmont.com, pg 829

Clarion Awards, 3337 Duke St, Alexandria, VA 22314 *Tel:* 703-370-7436 *Fax:* 703-342-4311 *E-mail:* clarion@womcom.org *Web Site:* www.womcom.org, pg 1112

Clarity Media Group, 166 Fifth Ave, 6th fl, New York, NY 10010 *Tel:* 212-262-7015 *E-mail:* info@claritymediagroup.com *Web Site:* www.claritymediagroup.com, pg 829

Clarity Sound & Light, 14618 Tyler Foote Rd, Nevada City, CA 95959 *Tel:* 530-478-7600 *Toll Free Tel:* 800-424-1055 *Fax:* 530-478-7610 *E-mail:* clarity@crystalclarity.com *Web Site:* www.crystalclarity.com, pg 829

Clark, 1225 Old Alpharetta Rd, Suite 295, Alpharetta, GA 85296 *Tel:* 770-888-5088 *Toll Free Tel:* 888-621-8841 *Fax:* 678-513-8206 *Web Site:* www.clark.is, pg 829

Clark Services Audio Visual & Exhibit Inc, 113 Board Rd, Lafayette, LA 70508 *Tel:* 337-234-5653 *Fax:* 337-232-0243 *E-mail:* clarkservices@bellsouth.net *Web Site:* www.clarkservices.biz, pg 829

Clark Wire & Cable, 408 Washington Blvd, Mundelein, IL 60060-3102 *Tel:* 847-949-9944 *Toll Free Tel:* 800-222-5348 *Fax:* 847-949-9595 *E-mail:* sales@clarkwire.com *Web Site:* www.clarkwire.com, pg 829

Clark's Audio Visual Services Ltd, 1615 Venables St, Vancouver, BC V5L 2H1, Canada *Tel:* 604-877-8558 *Toll Free Tel:* 800-667-1819 *Fax:* 604-879-2993 *Toll Free Fax:* 800-665-2932 *E-mail:* info@clarksav.com *Web Site:* www.clarksav.com, pg 829

Clarkson Studio, 401 N Hoback St, Helena, MT 59601 *Tel:* 406-442-2046 *Web Site:* www.clarksonstudio.com, pg 829

Classic Images, 469 S Bedford Dr, Beverly Hills, CA 90212 *Tel:* 310-277-0400 *Toll Free Tel:* 800-949-CLIP (949-2547) *Fax:* 310-277-0412 *E-mail:* sales@classicimg.com *Web Site:* www.classicimg.com, pg 829

Clayton-Davis & Associates, 230 S Bemiston Ave, St Louis, MO 63105 *Tel:* 314-862-7800 *E-mail:* info@claytondavis.com *Web Site:* www.claytondavis.com, pg 829

Clean Slate Video, 3070 Kerner Blvd, Unit O, San Rafael, CA 94901 *Tel:* 415-485-0727 *E-mail:* info@cleanslatevideo.com *Web Site:* www.cleanslatevideo.com, pg 829

Clear Blue Audio Video, 1650 Cold Creek Dr, Layafette, CO 80026 *Tel:* 303-412-9477 *Fax:* 303-412-9457, pg 829

Clear Choice Creative Corp, 4013 E Market St, Warren, OH 44484 *Tel:* 330-469-9542; 330-469-9524 *Web Site:* www.clearchoicecreative.com, pg 829

Clear-Com®, 1301 Marina Village Pkwy, Suite 105, Alameda, CA 94501 *Tel:* 510-337-6600 *Toll Free Tel:* 800-462-HELP (462-4357) *Fax:* 510-337-6699 *E-mail:* CustomerServicesUS@clearcom.com *Web Site:* www.clearcom.com, pg 829

Clear Gravy Productions, PO Box 270, Frederick, CO 80530-0270 *Tel:* 303-833-2029 *E-mail:* studio@cleargravy.com *Web Site:* www.cleargravy.com, pg 829

ClearOne Inc, Edgewater Corporate Park, South Tower, Suite 500, 5225 Wiley Post Way, Salt Lake City, UT 84116 *Tel:* 801-974-3760 *Toll Free Tel:* 800-705-2103 (tech sales) *Fax:* 801-977-0087 *E-mail:* techsales@clearone.com *Web Site:* www.clearone.com, pg 830

ClearOne MagicBox Inc, 408 SW Monroe, Suite M236, Corvallis, OR 97333 *Tel:* 541-752-5654 (sales); 541-752-5542 (tech support) *Fax:* 541-752-5614 *E-mail:* info@magicboxinc.com; sales@magicboxinc.com; support@magicboxinc.com *Web Site:* www.magicboxinc.com, pg 830

Wally Cleaver's Recording Service, 2200 Airport Ave, Fredericksburg, VA 22401-7220 *Tel:* 540-373-6511 *Fax:* 540-370-0645 *E-mail:* wallycleavers@mac.com *Web Site:* www.facebook.com/wallycleavers, pg 830

Cleveland Costume & Display Corp, 18489 Pearl Rd, Strongsville, OH 44136 *Tel:* 440-846-9292 *E-mail:* info@clevelandcostume.com *Web Site:* www.clevelandcostume.com, pg 830

Cleveland International Film Festival, 2510 Market Ave, Cleveland, OH 44113-3434 *Tel:* 216-623-3456 *Fax:* 216-623-0103 *Web Site:* www.clevelandfilm.org, pg 1112

Clever Cleaver Productions, 11397 Legacy Canyon Place, San Diego, CA 92131 *Tel:* 619-522-6760 *Fax:* 619-522-6763 *E-mail:* info@clevercleaver.com *Web Site:* www.clevercleaver.com, pg 830

Clever Devices Ltd, 300 Crossways Park Dr, Woodburg, NY 11797 *Tel:* 516-433-6100 *Toll Free Tel:* 800-872-6129 *Web Site:* www.cleverdevices.com, pg 830

The Clio Awards, 770 Broadway, 15th fl, New York, NY 10003 *Tel:* 212-683-4300 *Toll Free Tel:* 800-WIN-CLIO (946-2546) *Fax:* 212-683-4796 *Web Site:* www.clioawards.com, pg 1112

Close Up Foundation, 1330 Braddock Place, Suite 400, Alexandria, VA 22314 *Tel:* 703-706-3300 *Toll Free Tel:* 800-CLOSEUP (256-7387) *E-mail:* info@closeup.org *Web Site:* www.closeup.org, pg 830

CMEInfo, 2700 Corporate Dr, Suite 100, Birmingham, AL 35242 *Tel:* 205-991-5188 *Toll Free Tel:* 800-284-8433 *Toll Free Fax:* 800-284-5964 *Web Site:* www.cmeinfo.com, pg 830

CMI, 612 Hampton Dr, Venice, CA 90291 *Tel:* 310-392-8771 *Fax:* 310-392-5704 *E-mail:* cmi@cmifilms.com *Web Site:* www.cmifilms.com, pg 830

CMI Communications, 400 Mile Crossing Blvd, Rochester, NY 14624 *Tel:* 585-424-1900 *Toll Free Tel:* 888-736-8264 *Fax:* 585-424-1913 *E-mail:* info@cmiav.com *Web Site:* www.cmiav.com, pg 830

CMI Media Management, 100 Business Park Dr, Armonk, NY 10504-1750 *Tel:* 914-273-7500 *Toll Free Tel:* 800-431-1102 *Fax:* 914-273-7575 *Web Site:* www.cinemagnetics.com, pg 830

CNIB Library for the Blind, 1929 Bayview Ave, Toronto, ON M4G 3E8, Canada *Toll Free Tel:* 800-563-2642 *Fax:* 416-480-7700 *E-mail:* library@cnib.ca; info@cnib.ca *Web Site:* www.cnib.ca, pg 830

CNS Productions Inc, 11 Almond St, Medford, OR 97504 *Tel:* 541-779-3361 *Toll Free Tel:* 800-888-0617 *Fax:* 541-773-5905 *E-mail:* info@cnsproductions.com *Web Site:* www.cnsproductions.com, pg 830

Coast Learning Systems, 11460 Warner Ave, Fountain Valley, CA 92708 *Tel:* 714-241-6109 *Toll Free Tel:* 800-547-4748 *Fax:* 714-241-6286 *Web Site:* www.coastlearning.org, pg 830

Coastal Training Technologies Corp, 500 Studio Dr, Virginia Beach, VA 23452 *Tel:* 757-498-9014 *Toll Free Tel:* 877-262-7825 *Fax:* 757-498-3657 *E-mail:* info@training.dupont.com *Web Site:* www.training.dupont.com, pg 831

Coastline Licensing International Inc, 7345 Topanga Canyon Blvd, Canoga Park, CA 91303 *Tel:* 818-226-0488 *Fax:* 818-226-0489 *Web Site:* www.coastlinelicensing.com, pg 831

Coastline Productions, 2647 Gateway Rd, No 105-355, Carlsbad, CA 92009 *Tel:* 760-598-1860 *Toll Free Tel:* 888-781-5714 *E-mail:* productions@coastlinevideo.com *Web Site:* www.coastlinevideo.com, pg 831

Cobalt Studios Inc, 134 Royce Rd, White Lake, NY 12786 *Tel:* 845-583-7025 *Fax:* 845-583-7025 *E-mail:* mail@cobaltstudios.net; rentals@cobaltstudios.net *Web Site:* www.cobaltstudios.net, pg 831

Cobham Tactical Communications & Surveillance, 3845 Gateway Centre Blvd, Pinellas Park, FL 33782 *Tel:* 571-392-2500 *Web Site:* www.cobham.com, pg 831

Cochise County Arizona, Queen Mine Tour Bldg, 478 Dart Rd, Bisbee, AZ 85603 *Tel:* 520-432-3554 *Toll Free Tel:* 866-2BISBEE (224-7233) *E-mail:* ilona@discoverbisbee.com *Web Site:* www.explorecochise.com, pg 1091

Don Cohen - The Mathman, 809 Stratford Dr, Champaign, IL 61821-4140 *Tel:* 217-356-4555 *Web Site:* www.mathman.biz, pg 831

Steven Cohen Motion Picture Production, 1182 Coral Club Dr, Coral Springs, FL 33071 *Tel:* 954-346-7370 *Fax:* 954-346-7370, pg 831

Cohn Creative Group LLC, 244 W 54 St, 5th fl, New York, NY 10019 *Tel:* 212-333-3241 *Fax:* 212-246-5727 *E-mail:* info@cohncreative.com *Web Site:* www.cohncreativegroup.com, pg 831

CohuHD, 12367 Crosthwaite Circle, Poway, CA 92064 *Tel:* 858-391-1800 *E-mail:* info@cohuhd.com *Web Site:* www.cohuhd.com, pg 831

Cokesbury, 201 Eighth Ave, Nashville, TN 37203 *Tel:* 615-749-6000 *Toll Free Tel:* 800-672-1789 *Fax:* 615-749-6079 *E-mail:* cokes_serv@cokesbury.com *Web Site:* www.cokesbury.com, pg 831

Colby Systems Corp, 2991 Alexis Dr, Palo Alto, CA 94304 *Tel:* 650-941-9090 *Web Site:* www.colbysystems.com, pg 831

Cole Wire & Cable Co Inc, 620 Margate Dr, Lincolnshire, IL 60069-4247 *Toll Free Tel:* 800-323-1403 *Fax:* 847-634-4988 *E-mail:* sales@colewire.com *Web Site:* www.colewire.com, pg 831

College of Nursing, Washington State University, 103 E Spokane Falls Blvd, Spokane, WA 99202 *Tel:* 509-324-7360 *Fax:* 509-324-7341 *Web Site:* nursing.wsu.edu, pg 831

Colonel Buster Doss Music Group, 341 Billy Goat Hill Rd, Winchester, TN 37398 *Tel:* 931-649-2577 *E-mail:* cbd@united.net *Web Site:* www.stardustcountrymusic.com, pg 831

Colonial Williamsburg Foundation, PO Box 1776, Williamsburg, VA 23187-1776 *Tel:* 757-229-1000 *E-mail:* geninfo@cwf.org *Web Site:* www.colonialwilliamsburg.org, pg 831

The Color Lab Inc, 4442 Lawnview Ave, Dallas, TX 75227 *Tel:* 214-381-2105 *Fax:* 214-381-5168 *E-mail:* color.lab@airmail.net *Web Site:* thecolorlab.com, pg 831

Color Leasing Studios, 330 Rte 46 E, Fairfield, NJ 07004 *Tel:* 973-575-1118 *Fax:* 973-575-1170 *Web Site:* www.colorleasingstudios.com, pg 831

Colorado Display Systems, 1551 E 11 St, Loveland, CO 80537 *Tel:* 970-667-1000 *Toll Free Tel:* 800-279-0111 *Fax:* 970-667-5876 *E-mail:* info@coloradotime.com *Web Site:* www.coloradotime.com, pg 831

Colorado Office of Film, Television & Media, 1625 Broadway, Suite 2700, Denver, CO 80202 *Tel:* 303-892-3840 *Fax:* 303-892-3848 *E-mail:* info@coloradofilm.org *Web Site:* www.coloradofilm.org, pg 1094

Colorado Sound Recording Studios, 3100 W 71 Ave, Westminster, CO 80030 *Tel:* 303-430-8811 *E-mail:* colosnd@coloradosound.com *Web Site:* www.coloradosound.com, pg 831

Colorado Springs Film Commission, 515 S Cascade Ave, Colorado Springs, CO 80903 *Tel:* 719-685-7637 *Toll Free Tel:* 800-888-4748 (ext 137) *Fax:* 719-635-4968 *Web Site:* www.filmcoloradosprings.com, pg 1094

Colorado Studios, 8269 E 23 Ave, Denver, CO 80238 *Fax:* 303-388-9600 *E-mail:* info@coloradostudios.com *Web Site:* www.coloradostudios.com, pg 832

Colorado Video Inc, 6595 Odell Place, Mezzanine S, Boulder, CO 80301 *Tel:* 303-530-9580 *Fax:* 303-530-9569 *E-mail:* sales@colorado-video.com *Web Site:* www.colorado-video.com, pg 832

Coloredge, 1919 Empire Ave, Burbank, CA 91504 *Tel:* 818-842-1121 *Fax:* 818-840-0185 *Web Site:* coloredge.com, pg 832

Colortek of Boston, 727 Atlantic Ave, Boston, MA 02111 *Tel:* 617-451-0894 *Fax:* 617-451-2714 *E-mail:* info@colortekofboston.com *Web Site:* www.colortekofboston.com, pg 832

Colortone Audio Visual, 75 Virginia Rd, White Plains, NY 10603 *Tel:* 914-592-4151 *Fax:* 914-592-2833 *Web Site:* www.colortone-av.com, pg 832

Columbia Lighting, 701 Millennium Blvd, Greenville, SC 29607 *Tel:* 864-678-1000; 864-678-1664 (cust support) *Toll Free Fax:* 866-898-0131 *Web Site:* www.columbialighting.com, pg 832

Columbia Pictures Inc, 10202 W Washington Blvd, Culver City, CA 90232 *Tel:* 310-244-4000; 310-244-6926 (studio opers) *Fax:* 310-244-8090 *Web Site:* www.sonypicturesstudios.com; www.sonypictures.com, pg 832

Columbus Film Commission, 117 Third St S, Columbus, MS 39701 *Tel:* 662-329-1191 *Toll Free Tel:* 800-327-2686 *Fax:* 662-329-8969 *E-mail:* ccvb@columbus-ms.org *Web Site:* visitcolumbusms.org, pg 1099

Comex Systems Inc, 101 Pleasant Hill Rd, Chester, NJ 07930 *Tel:* 908-881-6301 (cell) *Toll Free Tel:* 800-543-6959 *Fax:* 908-879-0070 *E-mail:* mail@comexsystems.com *Web Site:* www.comexsystems.com, pg 832

Comm-Arts, 2512 E 71 St, Suite A, Tulsa, OK 74136 *Tel:* 918-493-5700 *Fax:* 918-493-3526 *E-mail:* info@comm-arts.com *Web Site:* www.comm-arts.com, pg 832

CommCreative, 345 Union Ave, Framingham, MA 01702 *Tel:* 508-620-6664 *Toll Free Tel:* 877-620-6664 *Fax:* 508-620-0592 *Web Site:* www.commcreative.com, pg 832

Commercial Electronics Ltd, 1565 W Seventh St, Vancouver, BC V6J 1S1, Canada *Tel:* 604-669-5525; 604-669-6626 *Fax:* 604-669-6347 *E-mail:* info@commercialelectronics.ca *Web Site:* commercialelectronics.ca, pg 832

Commercial Video, PO Box 360247, Cleveland, OH 44136-0005 *Tel:* 330-273-8795 *E-mail:* info@comvid.com *Web Site:* www.comvid.com, pg 832

Commonwealth Films Inc, 223 Commonwealth Ave, Boston, MA 02116 *Tel:* 617-262-5634 *E-mail:* info@commonwealthfilms.com *Web Site:* www.commonwealthfilms.com, pg 832

CommScope Inc, 1100 CommScope Place SE, Hickory, NC 28602 *Tel:* 828-324-2200 *Toll Free Tel:* 800-982-1708 *Web Site:* www.commscope.com, pg 832

Communication Arts Design & Advertising Competition, 110 Constitution Dr, Menlo Park, CA 94025-1107 *Tel:* 650-326-6040 *Fax:* 650-326-1648 *E-mail:* competition@commarts.com *Web Site:* www.commarts.com, pg 1113

Communication Arts Multimedia Inc, 1618 Williams Dr, No 5, Georgetown, TX 78628 *Tel:* 512-868-0548 *Toll Free Tel:* 888-742-0074 *Fax:* 512-868-0548 *E-mail:* mail@commartsmultimedia.com *Web Site:* commartsmultimedia.com, pg 832

Communication Corner Inc, PO Box 210, Brightwater, NY 11718 *Tel:* 631-567-2626 *Fax:* 631-665-3473 *Web Site:* www.commcorner.com, pg 832

Communication Ministries, PO Box 1986, Indianapolis, IN 46206-1986 *Tel:* 317-713-2492 *Fax:* 317-635-3700 *Toll Free Fax:* 800-458-3318 *Web Site:* disciples.org/dns, pg 833

Communications & Power Industries, Satcom Division, 811 Hansen Way, Bldg 2, Palo Alto, CA 94304-1031 *Tel:* 650-846-3803; 650-846-2801 *Fax:* 650-424-1744 *E-mail:* satcommarketing@cpii.com *Web Site:* www.cpii.com, pg 833

Communications Concepts Inc (CCI), 7980 N Atlantic Ave, Cape Canaveral, FL 32920 *Tel:* 321-783-5232 *Toll Free Tel:* 800-783-2368 *Fax:* 321-799-1016 *E-mail:* info@cciflorida.com *Web Site:* www.cciflorida.com, pg 833

Communications Corporation of America, PO Box 14262, Chicago, IL 60614-0262 *Tel:* 773-348-0001 *E-mail:* comcorp30@aol.com, pg 833

The Communications Department Inc, 3724 Amherst Ave, Dallas, TX 75225-7201 *Tel:* 214-369-1281, pg 833

Communications Design Associates, 437 Turnpike St, Canton, MA 02021 *Tel:* 339-502-6551 *Fax:* 339-502-6595 *E-mail:* information@cdaconsultants.com *Web Site:* www.cdaconsultants.com, pg 833

The Communications Group Inc, 502 S West St, Raleigh, NC 27601 *Tel:* 919-828-4086 *Toll Free Tel:* 800-595-2937 *E-mail:* info@cgfilm.com *Web Site:* www.cgfilm.com, pg 833

Communications Media Management Association (CMMA), c/o The Association Source LLC, 20423 State Rd 7, Suite F6-491, Boca Raton, FL 33498 *Tel:* 561-477-8100 *Web Site:* www.cmma.org, pg 1080

Communications Specialists Inc, 7272 Jackson Ave, Mechanicsville, VA 23111 *Tel:* 804-559-4274 *Fax:* 804-559-4479 *E-mail:* info@csisystems.net *Web Site:* www.csisystems.net, pg 833

Communications Specialties Inc, 125 Comac St, Ronkonkoma, NY 11779 *Tel:* 631-273-0404 *Fax:* 631-273-1638 *E-mail:* info@commspecial.com *Web Site:* www.commspecial.com, pg 833

Communilux Productions, 4001 East Side Ave, Dallas, TX 75226 *Tel:* 214-821-8706 *Toll Free Tel:* 877-323-5189 *E-mail:* info@communilux.com *Web Site:* www.communilux.com, pg 833

Communitronics Corp, 970 Bolger Ct, Fenton, MO 63026 *Tel:* 314-771-7160 *Fax:* 314-771-9144 *E-mail:* info@communitronics.com *Web Site:* www.communitronics.com, pg 833

Community Arts Grants Program, 200 Ridge Rd W, Suite 214, Rochester, NY 14615 *Tel:* 585-473-4000 *Fax:* 585-473-4051 *E-mail:* artsandculturalcouncil@artsrochester.org *Web Site:* www.artsrochester.org, pg 1113

Community Professional Loudspeakers, 333 E Fifth St, Chester, PA 19013-4511 *Tel:* 610-876-3400 *Toll Free Tel:* 800-523-4934 *Fax:* 610-874-0190 *E-mail:* info@communitypro.com *Web Site:* www.communitypro.com, pg 833

Compact Storage Systems Inc, 9757 Reseda Blvd, Suite 68, Northridge, CA 91324 *Tel:* 818-772-0996 *E-mail:* info@halfthespace.com *Web Site:* www.halfthespace.com, pg 833

Compass Learning Inc, 203 Colorado St, Austin, TX 78701 *Tel:* 512-478-9600 *Toll Free Tel:* 866-586-7387 (sales); 800-678-1412 (cust support) *Web Site:* www.compasslearning.com, pg 833

Compix Media, 26 Edelman, Irvine, CA 92618 *Tel:* 949-585-0055 *Fax:* 949-585-0320 *E-mail:* info@compix.tv *Web Site:* www.compix.tv, pg 833

Comprehensive Cable & Connectivity Co, 80 Little Falls Rd, Fairfield, NJ 07004 *Toll Free Tel:* 800-526-0242 *Fax:* 201-814-0510 *E-mail:* sales@comprehensivecable.com; customerservice@comprehensivecable.com *Web Site:* www.comprehensivecable.com, pg 833

Comprehensive Technical Group, 2030 Powers Ferry Rd SE, Suite 130, Atlanta, GA 30339 *Tel:* 404-352-3000 *Toll Free Tel:* 888-557-4284 *Fax:* 404-352-2962 *E-mail:* info@ctgatlanta.com *Web Site:* www.ctgatlanta.com, pg 833

COMPRO Productions Inc, 2055 Boar Tusk Rd NE, Conyers, GA 30012-3801 *Tel:* 770-918-8163 *E-mail:* compro@compro-atl.com *Web Site:* www.compro-atl.com, pg 834

Comprompter Inc, 1601 Caledonia St, Suite E, La Crosse, WI 54603 *Tel:* 608-785-7766 *E-mail:* sales@comprompter.com *Web Site:* www.comprompter.com, pg 834

Computer Dynamics, 3030 Whitehall Park Dr, Charlotte, NC 28273 *Tel:* 704-227-4600 *Toll Free Tel:* 866-599-6512 *Fax:* 704-583-9671 *Web Site:* www.cdynamics.com, pg 834

The Computer Language Co Inc, 5521 State Park Rd, Point Pleasant, PA 18950 *Tel:* 215-297-8082 *E-mail:* sales@computerlanguage.com; comments@computerlanguage.com *Web Site:* www.computerlanguage.com, pg 834

Computer Modules Inc, 11409 W Bernardo Ct, San Diego, CA 92127 *Tel:* 858-613-1818 *Fax:* 858-613-1815 *E-mail:* info@computermodules.com *Web Site:* www.dveo.com, pg 834

Computer Sciences Corp, 3170 Fairview Park Dr, Falls Church, VA 22042 *Tel:* 703-876-1000 *Web Site:* www.csc.com, pg 834

Computing & Information Technology, South Hall 119, One College Circle, Geneseo, NY 14454 *Tel:* 585-245-5577 *Fax:* 585-245-5579 *Web Site:* www.geneseo.edu/cit, pg 834

Compuvideo Sales USA Ltd, 7255 Brunswick Circle, Boynton Beach, FL 33472 *Tel:* 561-733-4780 *E-mail:* sales@compuvideo.com; customerservice@compuvideo.com *Web Site:* www.compuvideo.com, pg 834

CompuWeather Inc, 2566 Rte 52, Hopewell Junction, NY 12533 *Tel:* 845-227-8500 *Toll Free Tel:* 800-825-4445 *Fax:* 845-227-8400 *Toll Free Fax:* 800-825-4441 *Web Site:* www.compuweather.com, pg 834

Comrex Corp, 19 Pine Rd, Devens, MA 01434 *Tel:* 978-784-1776 (intl) *Toll Free Tel:* 800-237-1776 *Fax:* 978-784-1717 *E-mail:* info@comrex.com *Web Site:* www.comrex.com, pg 834

Comtech Multimedia Marketing, 6048 Broadcast Pkwy, Loves Park, IL 61111 *Tel:* 779-774-3188 *Fax:* 779-423-0090 *E-mail:* info@comtechcorporation.com *Web Site:* www.comtechcorporation.com, pg 834

Comtek Communications Technology Inc, 357 W 2700 S, Salt Lake City, UT 84115 *Tel:* 801-466-3463 *Toll Free Tel:* 800-496-3463 *Fax:* 801-484-6906 *E-mail:* sales@comtek.com *Web Site:* www.comtek.com, pg 834

Comtel Inc, 14901 NE 20 Ave, Miami, FL 33181 *Tel:* 305-948-9116 *Fax:* 305-947-9306 *E-mail:* info@comtelinc.com *Web Site:* www.comtelinc.com, pg 834

Concept Associates Inc, 5371 Punta Alta, Unit 1-E, Laguna Woods, CA 92637 *Toll Free Tel:* 800-333-8252 *E-mail:* customerservice@preschoolpower.com *Web Site:* www.preschoolpower.com, pg 834

Concept Audio-Visual, 4295 rue d'Iberville, Montreal, QC H2H 2L5, Canada *Tel:* 514-954-0000 *Toll Free Tel:* 800-567-7076 (CN only) *Fax:* 514-954-1425 *E-mail:* info@conceptav.ca *Web Site:* www.conceptav.ca, pg 834

Concept Productions Inc, 7878 Big Sky Dr, Madison, WI 53719 *Tel:* 608-833-8273 *E-mail:* info@conceptpro.biz *Web Site:* www.conceptpro.biz, pg 834

Concepts TV Production, 328 W Main St, Boonton, NJ 07005 *Tel:* 973-331-1500 *Fax:* 973-331-1550 *E-mail:* sales@conceptstv.com *Web Site:* www.conceptstv.com, pg 834

Concoction Lab, 520 Frederick St, No 8, San Francisco, CA 94117 *Tel:* 415-294-2032 *Fax:* 415-294-2178 *E-mail:* info@concoctionlab.com *Web Site:* www.concoctionlab.com, pg 835

Concord Communications, 26 Denise Place, Stamford, CT 06905 *Tel:* 203-322-9322, pg 835

Concord Jazz Inc, 100 N Crescent Dr, Garden Level, Beverly Hills, CA 90210 *Tel:* 310-385-4455 *Fax:* 310-385-4466 *Web Site:* www.concordmusicgroup.com, pg 835

Concord Records Inc, 100 N Crescent Dr, Garden Level, Beverly Hills, CA 90210 *Tel:* 310-385-4455 *Fax:* 310-385-4466 *Web Site:* www.concordmusicgroup.com, pg 835

Concrete Images, 1301 Main St, Venice, CA 90291 *Tel:* 310-452-9655 *Fax:* 310-452-9866 *E-mail:* office@concreteimages.com *Web Site:* www.concreteimages.com, pg 835

Conex Electro-Systems Inc, 789 W Smith Rd, Bellingham, WA 98226-9613 *Tel:* 360-734-4323 *Fax:* 360-676-4822 *E-mail:* sales@conex-electro.com *Web Site:* www.conex-electro.com, pg 835

Conference Technologies Inc, 11653 Adie Rd, Maryland Heights, MO 63043 *Tel:* 314-993-1400 *Toll Free Tel:* 800-743-6051 *Toll Free Fax:* 855-329-2844 *Web Site:* www.conferencetech.com, pg 835

Conly Productions, 1563 Oneida St, Denver, CO 80220 *Tel:* 303-393-6240 *Fax:* 303-393-6240, pg 835

Connecticut Audio & Theatrical Supply, 775 Bloomfield Ave, Windsor, CT 06095 *Tel:* 860-298-9141 *Fax:* 860-298-9142 *Web Site:* www.ctaudio.com, pg 835

Connecticut Office of Film, Television & Digital Media, c/o Dept of Economic & Community Development, 505 Hudson St, Hartford, CT 06106 *Tel:* 860-270-8198 *Web Site:* www.ctfilm.com, pg 1095

Connections Film & Video Inc, PO Box 110929, Anchorage, AK 99511 *Tel:* 907-561-6450 *Web Site:* www.filmalaska.com, pg 835

Conquest Sound Co Inc, 26113 S Ridgeland Ave, Monee, IL 60449 *Tel:* 708-534-0390 *Toll Free Tel:* 800-323-7671 *Fax:* 708-534-0398 *E-mail:* info@conquestsound.com; customerservice@conquestsound.com *Web Site:* www.conquestsound.com, pg 835

Consolidated Communications Consultants, 1837 SE Harold St, Portland, OR 97202-4932 *Tel:* 503-232-9787 *Toll Free Tel:* 800-929-5119 *Fax:* 503-232-9787 *Toll Free Fax:* 800-929-5119 *E-mail:* acmrl@myexcel.com *Web Site:* www.acmusicresearch.com, pg 835

Consolidated Display Co Inc, 1210 US Hwy 34, Oswego, IL 60543 *Tel:* 630-851-8666 *Toll Free Tel:* 888-851-7669 *Fax:* 630-851-8756 *E-mail:* info@letitsnow.com *Web Site:* www.letitsnow.com, pg 835

Consortium of College & University Media Centers (CCUMC), c/o Indiana University, 306 N Union St, Bloomington, IN 47405-3888 *Tel:* 812-855-6049 *Fax:* 812-855-2103 *E-mail:* ccumc@ccumc.org *Web Site:* www.ccumc.org, pg 1080

Consumer Electronics Association (CEA), 1919 S Eads St, Arlington, VA 22202 *Tel:* 703-907-7600 *Toll Free Tel:* 866-858-1555 *Fax:* 703-907-7675 *Toll Free Fax:* 866-858-2555 *E-mail:* cea@ce.org *Web Site:* www.ce.org, pg 1080

Contemporary Research, 4355 Excel Pkwy, Suite 600, Addison, TX 75001 *Tel:* 972-931-2728 *Toll Free Tel:* 888-972-2728 *Fax:* 972-931-2765 *E-mail:* contact@crwww.com *Web Site:* contemporaryresearch.com, pg 835

Continental Film, 1466 Riverside Dr, Suite E, Chattanooga, TN 37406 *Tel:* 423-622-1193 *Toll Free Tel:* 888-909-3456 *Fax:* 423-629-0853 *Web Site:* www.continentalfilm.com, pg 835

Continental Film & Video, PO Box 250627, Atlanta, GA 30325 *Tel:* 404-844-6374 *Web Site:* www.continentalfilmvideo.com, pg 835

Continental Recordings Inc, 23 Mirimichi St, Plainville, MA 02762 *Tel:* 508-699-0003 *Toll Free Tel:* 888-729-3130 *Fax:* 508-699-0004, pg 835

Convenience, 3012 N Long Ave, Chicago, IL 60641-4930 *Tel:* 773-545-3073 *Fax:* 773-545-3073, pg 835

Convergent Media Systems, 190 Bluegrass Valley Pkwy, Alpharetta, GA 30005-2204 *Tel:* 770-369-9000 *Toll Free Tel:* 800-877-7804 *Fax:* 770-369-9100 *E-mail:* convergent@convergent.com *Web Site:* www.convergent.com, pg 836

Conversation Arts Media, PO Box 715, Brooklyn, NY 11215 *Tel:* 718-768-0824 *Web Site:* www.dongabor.com, pg 836

Cooking by the Book, 13475 N Applegate Rd, Grants Pass, OR 97527 *Tel:* 541-846-0654 *Toll Free Tel:* 800-655-9071 *Fax:* 541-846-0654 *Web Site:* www.atasteofnature.org, pg 836

Cool-Lux, 1268 Humbracht Circle, Bartlett, IL 60103 *Toll Free Tel:* 800-ACDC-LUX (223-2589) *Fax:* 630-830-2525 *Web Site:* www.cool-lux.com, pg 836

Cooper Controls, 203 Cooper Circle, Peachtree City, GA 30269 *Tel:* 770-486-4782 *Toll Free Tel:* 800-553-3879 *Toll Free Fax:* 800-954-7016 *E-mail:* controlssales@cooperindustries.com *Web Site:* www.coopercontrol.com, pg 836

Copp Integrated Systems, 123 S Keowee St, Dayton, OH 45402 *Tel:* 937-228-4188 *Toll Free Tel:* 877-450-2677 *Fax:* 937-228-2901 *Web Site:* www.copp.com, pg 836

CopShopMiami.com, 160 E 35 St, Hialeah, FL 33013 *Tel:* 305-333-5791 *E-mail:* omar@copshopmiami.com *Web Site:* www.copshopmiami.com, pg 836

Corbis, 710 Second Ave, Suite 200, Seattle, WA 98104 *Tel:* 206-373-6000 *Fax:* 206-373-6100 *Web Site:* www.corbisimages.com, pg 836

Corbis Motion, 250 Hudson St, 4th fl, New York, NY 10013-1413 *Tel:* 212-375-7622 *Toll Free Tel:* 800-260-0444 *Fax:* 212-375-7700 *Toll Free Fax:* 877-297-7977 *E-mail:* sales@corbis.com *Web Site:* www.corbismotion.com, pg 836

Corinth Films Inc, 3117 Bursonville Rd, Riegelsville, PA 18077 *Tel:* 610-346-7446 *Fax:* 610-346-6345 *E-mail:* sales@corinthfilms.com *Web Site:* www.corinthreleasing.com; www.corinthfilms.com, pg 836

Cornell Laboratory of Ornithology, Cornell University, 159 Sapsucker Woods Rd, Ithaca, NY 14850 *Tel:* 607-254-BIRD (254-2473) *Toll Free Tel:* 800-843-BIRD (843-2473) *Fax:* 607-254-2415 *E-mail:* cornellbirds@cornell.edu *Web Site:* www.birds.cornell.edu, pg 836

Cornerstone Media Productions Inc, 41 Bramhall St, Georgetown, DE 19947 *Tel:* 302-855-9380 *Web Site:* www.cornerstonemedia.com, pg 836

Corplex, 915 Sherwood Dr, Lake Bluff, IL 60044 *Tel:* 847-582-8800 *Fax:* 847-582-8730 *Web Site:* www.nepinc.com/welcome/corplex, pg 836

Corporate Color Graphics Inc, 3525 Lousma Dr SE, Grand Rapids, MI 49548 *Tel:* 616-774-9583 *Toll Free Tel:* 800-776-9583 *Fax:* 616-774-8235 *E-mail:* production@corpcolor.com *Web Site:* www.corpcolor.com, pg 836

Corporation for Public Broadcasting (CPB), 401 Ninth St NW, Washington, DC 20004-2129 *Tel:* 202-879-9600 *Toll Free Tel:* 800-272-2190 (general comments) *Fax:* 202-879-9700 *E-mail:* comments@cpb.org *Web Site:* www.cpb.org, pg 1080

Corpus Christi Convention & Visitors Bureau, 101 N Shoreline Blvd, Suite 430, Corpus Christi, TX 78401 *Tel:* 361-881-1888 *Toll Free Tel:* 800-678-6232 *Fax:* 361-887-9023 *Web Site:* www.corpuschristicvb.com, pg 1103

Cosumnes River College, 8401 Center Pkwy, Sacramento, CA 95823 *Tel:* 916-691-7289 *Fax:* 916-691-7375 *Web Site:* www.crc.losrios.edu, pg 836

Council on Foundations, 2121 Crystal Dr, Suite 700, Arlington, VA 22202 *Toll Free Tel:* 800-673-9036 *Web Site:* www.cof.org, pg 836

Council on International Nontheatrical Events (CINE), 1003 "K" St NW, Suite 208, Washington, DC 20001 *Tel:* 507-400-CINE (400-2463) *E-mail:* info@cine.org *Web Site:* www.cine.org, pg 1081

Countdown Productions Inc, PO Box 180220, Dallas, TX 75218 *Tel:* 214-321-3233; 214-808-9988 (cell) *Web Site:* www.countdownproductions.com, pg 837

Countryman Associates Inc, 195 Constitution Dr, Menlo Park, CA 94025 *Tel:* 650-364-9988 *Toll Free Tel:* 800-669-1422 *Fax:* 650-364-2794 *E-mail:* sales@countryman.com *Web Site:* www.countryman.com, pg 837

County Sales, 117A W Main St, Floyd, VA 24091 *Tel:* 540-745-2001 *Fax:* 540-745-2008 *E-mail:* sales@countysales.com; info@countysales.com *Web Site:* www.countysales.com, pg 837

Courter Films LLC, 121 NW Crystal St, Crystal River, FL 34428 *Tel:* 352-795-2156 *Fax:* 352-795-6144 *E-mail:* info@courterfilms.com *Web Site:* www.courterfilms.com, pg 837

Coustic Car Audio, 4545 E Baseline Rd, Phoenix, AZ 85042 *Tel:* 602-438-2020 *Toll Free Tel:* 800-225-5689 *E-mail:* coustic@coustic.com *Web Site:* www.coustic.com, pg 837

Covenant Productions®, c/o Anderson University, 1100 E Fifth St, Anderson, IN 46012 *Tel:* 765-641-4348 *Fax:* 765-641-3825 *Web Site:* www.covenantproductions.com, pg 837

Covid Inc, 1723 W Fourth St, Tempe, AZ 85281 *Tel:* 480-966-2221 *Toll Free Tel:* 800-638-6104 *Fax:* 480-966-6728 *E-mail:* sales@covid.com *Web Site:* www.covid.com, pg 837

Cox Creative Studios, 17602 N Black Canyon Hwy, Phoenix, AZ 85053 *Tel:* 623-328-4778 *Web Site:* www.coxcreativestudios.com, pg 837

Cox Media, 350 Tenth Ave, Suite 500, San Diego, CA 92101 *Tel:* 619-686-1900 *Toll Free Tel:* 855-755-2691 *Fax:* 619-867-4996 *Web Site:* www.coxmedia.com, pg 837

Coyote Cowboy Co, PO Box 2190, Benson, AZ 85602-2190 *Tel:* 520-586-1077 *Toll Free Tel:* 800-654-2550 *Web Site:* baxterblack.com, pg 837

CP Communications, 200 Clearbrook Rd, Suite 148, Elmsford, NY 10523 *Tel:* 914-345-9292 *Toll Free Tel:* 800-762-4254 *Fax:* 914-345-9222 *E-mail:* info@cpcomms.com; sales@cpcomms.com *Web Site:* www.cpcomms.com, pg 837

CPdigital, 102 Madison Ave, New York, NY 10016 *Tel:* 212-328-5177 *Web Site:* www.cpdigital.com, pg 837

CPI Malibu, 3760-A Calle Tecate, Camarillo, CA 93012-5060 *Tel:* 805-383-1829 *Fax:* 805-383-1859 *E-mail:* malibu.sales@cpii.com *Web Site:* www.cpii.com/division.cfm/10, pg 837

CPR MultiMedia Solutions, 7812 Cessna Ave, Gaithersburg, MD 20879 *Tel:* 301-590-9400 *Fax:* 301-590-9402 *E-mail:* info@cprmms.com *Web Site:* www.cprmms.com, pg 837

CPT Rental Inc, 36-01A 48 Ave, Long Island City, NY 11101 *Tel:* 718-424-1600 *Fax:* 718-457-4778 *E-mail:* rental@cptrental.com *Web Site:* www.cptrental.com, pg 837

Craig Recording Studios, 2381 Philmont Ave, Suite 112, Huntingdon Valley, PA 19006 *Tel:* 215-947-8900 *Web Site:* www.craigrecording.com; www.craigrecordingstudios.com, pg 837

Cramer Productions, 425 University Ave, Norwood, MA 02062 *Tel:* 781-278-2300 *Fax:* 781-255-0721 *E-mail:* info@cramer.com *Web Site:* cramer.com, pg 837

Crash Video Productions, 713 N Mansfield Ave, Los Angeles, CA 90038 *Tel:* 310-489-6848 *E-mail:* crash@crashproductions.com *Web Site:* www.crashproductions.com, pg 837

Thomas Craven Film Corp, 5 W 19 St, New York, NY 10011-4216 *Tel:* 212-463-7190 *Fax:* 212-627-4761 *E-mail:* info@cravenfilms.com *Web Site:* cravenfilms.com, pg 837

Crawford Media Services, 6 W Druid Hills Dr NE, Atlanta, GA 30329 *Tel:* 404-876-0333 *Toll Free Tel:* 800-831-8029 *Fax:* 678-536-4912 *Web Site:* www.crawford.com, pg 838

Creation Technologies Inc, 102-8977 Fraserton Ct, Burnaby, BC V5J 5H8, Canada *Tel:* 604-430-4336 *Toll Free Tel:* 800-736-1271 *Fax:* 604-430-4337 *E-mail:* info@creationtech.com *Web Site:* www.creationtech.com, pg 838

Creative Arts Film Festival (CAFF), PO Box 823, Frazer, PA 19355 *Tel:* 610-889-4928 *Web Site:* www.creativeartsfilmfestival.com, pg 1113

Creative Arts Television, PO Box 739, Kent, CT 06757-0739 *Tel:* 860-868-1771 *Fax:* 860-868-9999 *E-mail:* catarchive@aol.com; info@catarchive.com *Web Site:* www.catarchive.com, pg 838

Creative Backstage, 4829 S 36 St, Suite 1, Phoenix, AZ 85040 *Tel:* 480-580-2222 *E-mail:* sales@creativebackstage.com *Web Site:* www.creativebackstage.com, pg 838

Creative BC (CrBC), 2225 W Broadway, Vancouver, BC V6K 2E4, Canada *Tel:* 604-730-2732 *Fax:* 604-736-7290 *E-mail:* info@creativebc.com *Web Site:* www.creativebc.com, pg 1104

Creative Custom Cases, 14946 Shoemaker Ave, Suite D, Santa Fe Springs, CA 90670 *Tel:* 562-404-5500 *Fax:* 562-404-5505 *E-mail:* info@creativecc.net *Web Site:* www.creativecc.net, pg 838

Creative Impulse Awards (Impies), c/o RIIFF, 36 Rhode Island Ave, Newport, RI 02840 *Tel:* 401-861-4445 *Fax:* 401-490-6735 *E-mail:* info@film-fesitval.org *Web Site:* www.film-festival.org/CreativeIM.php, pg 1113

Creative Media Development, 1631 NW Thurman St, Portland, OR 97209 *Tel:* 503-223-6794 *Fax:* 503-223-2430 *E-mail:* info@cmdpdx.com *Web Site:* www.cmdpdx.com, pg 838

Creative Media Recording, 11105 Knott Ave, Suite G, Cypress, CA 90630 *Tel:* 714-892-9469 *E-mail:* info@creativemediarecording.com *Web Site:* www.creativemediarecording.com, pg 838

Creative Realities Inc, 55 Broadway, 9th fl, New York, NY 10006 *Tel:* 212-324-6660 *Toll Free Tel:* 888-432-7328 *E-mail:* info@cri.com *Web Site:* www.cri.com, pg 838

Creative Services Inc, 806 Westchester Dr, High Point, NC 27262 *Tel:* 336-889-3010; 336-883-8800 *Toll Free Tel:* 800-989-3010 *Fax:* 336-885-1829 *E-mail:* info@nidoqubein.com *Web Site:* www.nidoqubein.com; www.getcreativeservices.com, pg 838

Creative Sound Corp, 5515 Medea Valley Dr, Agoura Hills, CA 91301 *Tel:* 818-707-8986 *E-mail:* info@csoundcorp.com *Web Site:* www.csoundcorp.com, pg 838

Creative Stage Lighting Co Inc, 149 Rte 28 N, North Creek, NY 12853 *Tel:* 518-251-3302 *Fax:* 518-251-2908 *E-mail:* info@creativestagelighting.com *Web Site:* www.creativestagelighting.com, pg 838

Creative Support Services/CSS Music, 1948 Riverside Dr, Los Angeles, CA 90039 *Tel:* 323-666-7968 *Toll Free Tel:* 800-468-6874 *Fax:* 323-660-2070 *E-mail:* info@cssmusic.com *Web Site:* www.cssmusic.com, pg 838

Creative Technology, 1455 Estes Ave, Elk Grove Village, IL 60007 *Tel:* 847-671-9670 *Toll Free Tel:* 800-826-4761 *Fax:* 847-640-6559 *E-mail:* info@ctchicago.com *Web Site:* us.ct-group.com, pg 838

Creative Technology, 137 Heritage Woods Dr, Akron, OH 44321 *Tel:* 330-668-7777 *Fax:* 330-665-3718 *Web Site:* www.creativetechnology.com, pg 838

Creative Video, 26 Colonial Ave, Woodbury, NJ 08096 *Tel:* 856-848-0046 *Toll Free Tel:* 888-988-2877 *Fax:* 856-848-8905 *E-mail:* contact@creativevideo.org *Web Site:* www.creativevideo.org, pg 838

Creative Video of Washington Inc, 1410 Spring Hill Rd, Suite 100, McLean, VA 22102 *Tel:* 703-891-2620 *Fax:* 703-891-2625 *Web Site:* www.creativevideo.com, pg 839

Creativity Unlimited Press®, 30819 Casilina Dr, Rancho Palos Verdes, CA 90275 *Tel:* 310-541-4844 *Fax:* 310-377-7946 *E-mail:* ihf@cox.net *Web Site:* drshelleynicholas.com; hypnosisfederation.com, pg 839

Cre-a-tv Studios, 1332 Londontown Blvd, Suite 102, Eldesburg, MD 21784 *Toll Free Tel:* 800-628-0112 *E-mail:* production@cre-a-tv.com *Web Site:* cre-a-tv.com, pg 839

Credo Interactive Inc, 4612 Strathcona Rd, North Vancouver, BC V7O 1G3, Canada *Tel:* 604-291-6717 *E-mail:* info@charactermotion.com *Web Site:* www.charactermotion.com, pg 839

Crescendo Designs Inc, 641 County Rd 39-A, Southampton, NY 11968 *Tel:* 631-283-2133 *Fax:* 631-204-1066 *E-mail:* sales@crescendodesigns.com *Web Site:* www.crescendodesigns.com, pg 839

Crescent/Stonco, 200 Franklin Square Dr, Somerset, NJ 08873 *Toll Free Tel:* 800-334-2212 *Web Site:* www.crescent-stonco.com/led; www.csgreenlightingsolutions.com, pg 839

Crest Audio Inc, 5022 Hwy 493, Meridian, MS 39305 *Toll Free Tel:* 866-812-7378 *Fax:* 601-486-1380 *E-mail:* webmaster@crestaudio.com *Web Site:* www.crestaudio.com, pg 839

Crest Electronics Inc, 3706 Alliance Dr, Greensboro, NC 27407 *Tel:* 336-855-6422 *Toll Free Tel:* 888-502-7378 *Fax:* 336-855-6676 *E-mail:* info@crestelectronics.com; custserv@crestelectronics.com *Web Site:* www.crestelectronics.com, pg 839

Cresta Creative, 1050 N State St, Chicago, IL 60610 *Tel:* 312-944-4700 *Fax:* 312-944-1582 *E-mail:* info@crestagroup.com *Web Site:* www.crestacreative.com, pg 839

Crestron Electronics Inc, 15 Volvo Dr, Rockleigh, NJ 07647 *Tel:* 201-767-3400 *Toll Free Tel:* 800-237-2041 *Fax:* 201-767-1903 *E-mail:* crestronhq@crestron.com *Web Site:* www.crestron.com, pg 839

Crew West Inc, 1515 W Deer Valley Rd, Suite C109, Phoenix, AZ 85027 *Tel:* 480-367-6888 *Toll Free Tel:* 888-444-2739 *Fax:* 480-367-6688 *E-mail:* tvcrews@crewwestinc.com *Web Site:* www.crewwestinc.com, pg 839

Crispin Corp, 600 Wade Ave, Raleigh, NC 27605 *Tel:* 919-845-7744 *Fax:* 919-845-7766 *E-mail:* welisten@crispincorp.com *Web Site:* www.crispincorp.com, pg 839

Criterion Collection, 215 Park Ave S, 5th fl, New York, NY 10003 *Tel:* 212-756-8822 *E-mail:* orders@criterion.com *Web Site:* www.criterion.com, pg 839

Critical Information Network, 17300 N Dallas Pkwy, Suite 3010, Dallas, TX 75248 *Tel:* 972-309-4000 *Toll Free Tel:* 800-624-2272 *Fax:* 972-309-5402; 972-309-5432 *E-mail:* info@criticalinfonet.com *Web Site:* www.criticalinfonet.com, pg 839

Cross-Cultural Communications, 239 Wynsum Ave, Merrick, NY 11566-4725 *Tel:* 516-868-5635 *Fax:* 516-379-1901 *E-mail:* info@cross-culturalcommunications.com *Web Site:* www.cross-culturalcommunications.com, pg 839

Crosscreek Television Productions Inc, 100 Airpark Ct, Alabaster, AL 35007 *Tel:* 205-663-4411 *Fax:* 205-621-1389 *E-mail:* tvmcree@gmail.com *Web Site:* www.crosscreektv.com, pg 839

Crossroads Audio Inc, 2623 Myrtle Springs Ave, Dallas, TX 75220 *Tel:* 214-358-2623 *Toll Free Tel:* 800-287-0436 *Fax:* 214-358-0185 *E-mail:* mail@crossroadsaudio.com *Web Site:* www.crossroadsaudio.com, pg 840

Crossroads Video, 65 Church Rd, Sherman, CT 06784-1334 *Tel:* 860-350-0010 *Toll Free Tel:* 866-746-7111 (orders) *Fax:* 860-350-0010 *E-mail:* info@crossroadsvideo.com; crossroadsvideo@charter.net *Web Site:* www.crossroadsvideo.com, pg 840

Crown Audio Inc, 1718 W Mishawaka Rd, Elkhart, IN 46517 *Tel:* 574-294-8000 *Toll Free Tel:* 800-342-6939 *Fax:* 574-294-8301 *Web Site:* www.crownaudio.com, pg 840

Crown Ministries International, PO Box 26479, Colorado Springs, CO 80936-6479 *Tel:* 719-591-2767 *Toll Free Tel:* 800-433-4685 *E-mail:* crownmin@intlcom.org *Web Site:* www.crownmin.org, pg 840

CRT Custom Products Inc, 7532 Hickory Hills Ct, Whites Creek, TN 37189 *Tel:* 615-876-5490 *Toll Free Tel:* 800-453-2533 *Fax:* 615-876-0096 *E-mail:* sales@crtcustomproducts.com *Web Site:* www.crtcustomproducts.com, pg 840

Crunch Bird Studios Inc, 9537 Whetstone Dr, Montgomery Village, MD 20886 *Tel:* 301-947-2927 *Web Site:* www.crunchbirdstudios.com, pg 840

Crystal Clear Media Group, 6737 E 30 St, Indianapolis, IN 46219 *Toll Free Tel:* 800-880-0073 *E-mail:* info@crystalclearcds.com *Web Site:* www.crystalclearcds.com, pg 840

Crystal Pictures Inc, 2000 Riverside Dr, Asheville, NC 28804 *Tel:* 828-285-9995 *Toll Free Tel:* 800-669-4057 *Fax:* 828-285-9997 *E-mail:* cryspic@aol.com *Web Site:* www.ivyvideo.com, pg 840

Crystal Productions, 5320 Carpinteria Ave, Suite K, Carpinteria, CA 93013-2107 *Tel:* 847-657-8144 *Toll Free Tel:* 800-255-8629 *Fax:* 847-657-8149 *Toll Free Fax:* 800-657-8149 *E-mail:* custserv@crystalproductions.com *Web Site:* www.crystalproductions.com, pg 840

Crystal Pyramid Productions™, 7323 Rondel Ct, San Diego, CA 92119-1530 *Tel:* 619-644-3000 *E-mail:* cpp@newuniquevideos.com *Web Site:* www.crystalpyramid.com, pg 840

Crystal Records Inc, 28818 NE Hancock Rd, Camas, WA 98607 *Tel:* 360-834-7022 *Fax:* 360-834-9680 *E-mail:* info@crystalrecords.com *Web Site:* www.crystalrecords.com, pg 840

Crystalite Industries Inc, 101 Palm Harbor Pkwy, Unit 117, Palm Coast, FL 32137 *Tel:* 561-330-8742; 561-330-8660 *Toll Free Tel:* 800-328-5483; 800-468-8673 *Fax:* 561-330-8659; 561-330-8665 *E-mail:* phcrystalite@aol.com *Web Site:* www.phcled.com, pg 840

CSC Awards, 3007 Kingston Rd, Suite 131, Toronto, ON M1M 1P1, Canada *Tel:* 416-266-0591 *Fax:* 416-266-3996 *E-mail:* admin@csc.ca *Web Site:* www.csc.ca, pg 1113

CSI Films, 1913 Sonora St, Fort Collins, CO 80525 *Tel:* 970-282-1622 *E-mail:* mail@airhat.com *Web Site:* www.airhat.com, pg 840

CSI/Orion, 1709 Utica Sq, Tulsa, OK 74114 *Tel:* 918-743-7881 *Toll Free Tel:* 888-579-1850 *Web Site:* www.csihealthcarecommunications.com; www.csiorion.com, pg 840

CSI Rentals, 133 W 19 St, Ground Level, New York, NY 10011 *Tel:* 212-243-7368 *Fax:* 212-243-2102 *E-mail:* info@csirentals.com; orders@csirentals.com *Web Site:* www.csirentals.com, pg 840

CSPI, 43 Manning Rd, Billerica, MA 01821 *Tel:* 978-663-7598 *Toll Free Tel:* 800-325-3110 *Fax:* 978-663-0150 *E-mail:* info@cspi.com *Web Site:* www.cspi.com, pg 840

CSPMedia.com, PO Box 3474, Capitol Heights, MD 20791-3474 *Tel:* 301-350-3181 *Web Site:* www.soundstore.com, pg 840

CTG Audio, 2100 Constitution Blvd, Sarasota, FL 34231 *Tel:* 941-922-2322 *Fax:* 941-922-5445 *E-mail:* orders@ctgaudio.com; info@ctgaudio.com *Web Site:* www.ctgaudio.com, pg 840

C2 Imaging LLC, 423 W 55 St, New York, NY 10019 *Tel:* 646-557-6300 *Fax:* 646-557-6400 *Web Site:* www.vomela.com/locations/c2_imaging, pg 841

Cucalorus Film Festival, Jengo's Playhouse, 815 Princess St, Wilmington, NC 28401 *Tel:* 910-343-5995 *Fax:* 910-343-5227 *E-mail:* development@cucalorus.org *Web Site:* www.cucalorus.org, pg 1113

Cue Tech Teleprompting, 5527 Satsuma Ave, North Hollywood, CA 91601 *Tel:* 818-487-2700 *Fax:* 818-487-2750 *E-mail:* info@cue-tech.com *Web Site:* www.cue-tech.com, pg 841

Culver Pictures Inc, 51-02 21 St, Suite 4B, Long Island City, NY 11101 *Tel:* 718-752-9393 *Fax:* 718-752-9394 *E-mail:* research@culverpictures.com *Web Site:* www.culverpictures.com, pg 841

Cupit Music Group, PO Box 121904, Nashville, TN 37212 *Tel:* 615-731-0100 *Fax:* 615-731-3005 *Web Site:* www.cupitmusic.com, pg 841

Curb Entertainment International Corp, 3907 W Alameda Ave, Burbank, CA 91505 *Tel:* 818-843-8580 *Fax:* 818-566-1719 *Web Site:* www.curbentertainment.com, pg 841

Curious Pictures, 440 Lafayette St, 5th fl, New York, NY 10003, pg 841

Curtis Company, PO Box 210-215, Montgomery, AL 36121 *Tel:* 334-279-7127 *Toll Free Tel:* 800-228-5937 *Fax:* 334-270-8787 *Toll Free Fax:* 800-325-6341 *Web Site:* www.curtisav.com, pg 841

Curtis Inc, 1105 Western Ave, Cincinnati, OH 45203 *Tel:* 513-621-8895 *Toll Free Tel:* 800-733-2878 *Fax:* 513-621-0942 *E-mail:* info@curtisinc.com; clientservices@curtisinc.com *Web Site:* www.curtisinc.com, pg 841

Custom Color Corp, 14320 W 101 Terr, Lenexa, KS 66215 *Tel:* 913-730-3100 *Toll Free Tel:* 888-605-4050 *Fax:* 913-730-3101 *E-mail:* info@customcolor.com *Web Site:* www.customcolor.com, pg 841

Custom Computer Specialists Inc, 6 Blackstone Valley Place, Suite 402, Lincoln, RI 02865 *Tel:* 401-765-3000 *Toll Free Tel:* 800-556-2828 *Fax:* 401-765-6440 *Web Site:* www.customonline.com, pg 841

Custom Media Environments, 299 Duffy Ave, Hicksville, NY 11801 *Tel:* 516-586-3600 *Toll Free Tel:* 800-80-SOUND (807-6863) *Fax:* 516-586-3487 *E-mail:* info@custommediaenvironments.com; sales@custommediaenvironments.com *Web Site:* custommediaenvironments.com, pg 841

Custom Medical Stock Photo Inc, 3660 W Irving Park Rd, Chicago, IL 60618 *Tel:* 773-267-3100 *Toll Free Tel:* 800-373-2677 *Fax:* 773-267-6071 *E-mail:* info@cmsp.com *Web Site:* www.cmsp.com, pg 841

Custom Video Productions Inc, 707 Torrance Blvd, Suite 105, Redondo Beach, CA 90277 *Tel:* 310-543-4901 *E-mail:* info@customvideo.tv *Web Site:* www.customvideo.tv, pg 841

Custom Video Productions Inc, 15 Lake Shore Dr, Red Bank, NJ 07701 *Tel:* 732-936-1001 *Fax:* 732-741-9204 *E-mail:* info@cvpnj.com *Web Site:* www.cvpnj.com, pg 841

The Cutting Corp, 4940 Hampden Lane, Suite 300, Bethesda, MD 20814 *Tel:* 301-654-CUTS (654-2887) *Fax:* 301-654-3271 *E-mail:* info@cuttingarchives.com *Web Site:* www.cuttingarchives.com, pg 841

Cutting Edge Productions, 22904 Lockness Ave, Torrance, CA 90501 *Tel:* 310-326-4500; 818-503-0400 *E-mail:* info@cuttingedgeproductions.tv *Web Site:* www.cuttingedgeproductions.tv, pg 841

Cuyahoga Community College Media Center, 2900 Community College Ave, Cleveland, OH 44115 *Tel:* 216-987-6000 *Toll Free Tel:* 800-954-8742 *Web Site:* www.tri-c.edu, pg 841

CyberIconics International, 1752 N 74 Place, Mesa, AZ 85207-2932 *Tel:* 480-396-8731, pg 841

Cybernetics, 111 Cybernetics Way, Yorktown, VA 23693 *Tel:* 757-833-9000 *Fax:* 757-833-9300 *E-mail:* customer_service@cybernetics.com; techsales@cybernetics.com *Web Site:* www.cybernetics.com, pg 841

CyberOptics, 5900 Golden Hills Dr, Minneapolis, MN 55416 *Tel:* 763-542-5000 *Fax:* 763-542-5100 *E-mail:* info@cyberoptics.com *Web Site:* cyberoptics.com, pg 841

Czar Productions Inc, 809 New Britain Ave, Hartford, CT 06106 *Tel:* 860-953-0809 *E-mail:* czar.productions@snet.net, pg 842

D A S Audio of America Inc, Sunset Palmetto Park, 6900 NW 52 St, Miami, FL 33166 *Tel:* 305-436-0521 *Fax:* 305-436-0528 *E-mail:* sales@dasaudio.com *Web Site:* www.dasaudio.com, pg 842

D A Sound, 12932 SE Kent Kangley Rd, Box 460, Kent, WA 98030 *Tel:* 206-632-7773 *Toll Free Tel:* 855-DASOUND (327-6863) *Toll Free Fax:* 866-859-8650 *E-mail:* info@dasound.biz *Web Site:* www.dasound.biz, pg 842

Da-Lite, 3100 N Detroit St, Warsaw, IN 46582 *Tel:* 574-267-8101 *Toll Free Tel:* 800-622-3737 *Fax:* 574-267-7804 *Toll Free Fax:* 877-325-4832 *E-mail:* info@da-lite.com *Web Site:* www.da-lite.com, pg 842

Daburn Electronics & Cable Corp, 44 Richboynton Rd, Dover, NJ 07801 *Tel:* 973-328-3200 *Fax:* 973-328-3130 *E-mail:* daburn@daburn.com *Web Site:* www.daburn.com, pg 842

daCapo Productions, 516 Hargrave St, Winnipeg, MB R3A 0X8, Canada *Tel:* 204-956-2867 *Fax:* 204-956-2869 *Web Site:* www.dacapo.ca, pg 842

Dadco, 11078 Fleetwood St, Sun Valley, CA 91352 *Tel:* 818-768-8886 *Fax:* 818-765-0914 *Web Site:* www.dadcopowerandlights.com, pg 842

Dage-MTI, 701 N Roeske Ave, Michigan City, IN 46360 *Tel:* 219-872-5514 *Fax:* 219-872-5559 *E-mail:* info@dagemti.com; sales@dagemti.com; service@dagemti.com *Web Site:* www.dagemti.com, pg 842

Dailey & Vincent Land Fest, 1072 Cranford Rd, Denton, NC 27239-7930 *Tel:* 336-859-2755 *Fax:* 336-859-2567 *E-mail:* manager@threshers.com *Web Site:* www.daileyvincentfest.com; www.farmpark.com, pg 1113

Daily Electronics Corp, PO Box 822437, Vancouver, WA 98682-0053 *Tel:* 360-896-8856 *Toll Free Tel:* 800-346-6667 *Fax:* 360-896-5476 *E-mail:* daily@worldaccessnet.com *Web Site:* dailyelectronics.net, pg 842

Dake Publishing Inc, 764 Martins Chapel Rd, Lawrenceville, GA 30045 *Toll Free Tel:* 800-241-1239 *Fax:* 770-963-7700 *E-mail:* info@dake.com *Web Site:* www.dake.com, pg 842

Dalet Digital Media Systems, 100 Wall St, 15th fl, New York, NY 10005 *Tel:* 212-269-6700 *Fax:* 212-269-6709 *E-mail:* ddms@dalet.com *Web Site:* www.dalet.com, pg 842

Dallas Learning Solutions, 9596 Walnut St, Dallas, TX 75243-2112 *Tel:* 972-669-6650 *Toll Free Tel:* 866-DISTLRN (347-8576) *Fax:* 972-669-6668 *E-mail:* tlearn@dcccd.edu *Web Site:* dls.dcccd.edu, pg 842

Dallas Prompter, PO Box 571233, Dallas, TX 75357 *Tel:* 214-275-9000 *Web Site:* www.dallasprompter.com, pg 842

Dallas Video Festival, 1405 Woodlawn Ave, Dallas, TX 75208 *E-mail:* info@videofest.org *Web Site:* www.videofest.org, pg 1113

Dance Horizons Video, 614 Rte 130, Hightstown, NJ 08520 *Tel:* 609-426-0602 *Toll Free Tel:* 800-220-7149 *Fax:* 609-426-1344 *E-mail:* pbc@dancehorizons.com *Web Site:* www.dancehorizons.com, pg 842

Dance on Camera Festival, 252 Java St, Suite 333, Brooklyn, NY 11222 *Tel:* 347-505-8649 *E-mail:* info@dancefilms.org *Web Site:* www.dancefilms.org, pg 1113

Dances With Films, Formosa Bldg, 2nd fl, 1041 N Formosa Ave, West Hollywood, CA 90046 *Tel:* 323-850-2929 *E-mail:* info@danceswithfilms.com *Web Site:* www.danceswithfilms.com, pg 1113

D&B Television & Video Productions Inc, 1400 Riverbend Dr, Rocky Mount, VA 24151 *Tel:* 305-542-7000 *Web Site:* www.dbvideoproductions.net, pg 842

Dark Star Lighting & Production, 102 Commerce St, Hinesburg, VT 05461 *Tel:* 802-482-4802 *Toll Free Tel:* 877-375-7827 *Fax:* 802-482-4803 *E-mail:* sales@darkstarlighting.com *Web Site:* www.darkstarlighting.com, pg 842

Data Check Video Inc, 5148-E Commerce Ave, Moorpark, CA 93021 *Tel:* 805-517-1907 *Fax:* 805-552-0744 *E-mail:* mail@datacheck.com *Web Site:* www.datacheck.com, pg 843

Data Display Audio Visual Co LP, 3720 Dacoma, Houston, TX 77092-8906 *Tel:* 713-688-7900 *Toll Free Tel:* 800-840-2500 *Fax:* 713-688-5840 *E-mail:* tech@ddav.com *Web Site:* www.ddav.com, pg 843

Data Projections Inc, 3700 W Sam Houston Pkwy S, Suite 525, Houston, TX 77042 *Tel:* 713-781-1999 *Toll Free Tel:* 866-225-5374 *Fax:* 713-781-3338 *Web Site:* www.dataprojections.com, pg 843

Data Security Inc, 300 S Seventh St, Lincoln, NE 68508 *Tel:* 402-434-5959 *Toll Free Tel:* 800-225-7554 *Fax:* 402-434-3291 *E-mail:* sales@telesis-inc.com *Web Site:* www.datasecurityinc.com, pg 843

Data Translation Inc, 100 Locke Dr, Marlboro, MA 01752-1192 *Tel:* 508-481-3700 *Toll Free Tel:* 800-525-8528 (sales) *Fax:* 508-481-8620 *E-mail:* info@datatranslation.com *Web Site:* www.datatranslation.com, pg 843

DataDirect Networks, 2929 Patrick Henry Dr, Santa Clara, CA 95054 *Tel:* 818-700-4000 *Toll Free Tel:* 800-TERABYTE (837-2298) *E-mail:* info@ddn.com; sales@ddn.com *Web Site:* www.ddn.com, pg 843

Dav Tronics Ltd, 1543 Venables St, Suite 200, Vancouver, BC V5L 2G8, Canada *Tel:* 604-255-2200 *Fax:* 604-255-4083 *Web Site:* www.broadcasttechnical.com, pg 843

Davenport Music Library, PO Box 690536, Charlotte, NC 28227-7009 *E-mail:* info@davenportmusic.com *Web Site:* www.davenportmusic.com, pg 843

David Clark Co Inc, 360 Franklin St, Worcester, MA 01604 *Tel:* 508-751-5800 *Toll Free Tel:* 800-900-3434 *Fax:* 508-753-5827 *E-mail:* sales@davidclark.com *Web Site:* www.davidclark.com, pg 843

Davidson Films Inc, PO Box 664, Santa Margarita, CA 93453 *Toll Free Tel:* 888-437-4200 *Fax:* 805-594-0532 *E-mail:* dfi@davidsonfilms.com *Web Site:* davidsonfilms.com, pg 843

Davies Publishing Inc, 32 S Raymond Ave, Suite 4, Pasadena, CA 91105-1935 *Tel:* 626-792-3046 *Toll Free Tel:* 877-792-0005 *Fax:* 626-792-5308 *E-mail:* order@daviespublishing.com *Web Site:* daviespublishing.com, pg 843

Davis Art Images, 50 Portland St, Worcester, MA 01608 *Tel:* 508-754-7201 *Toll Free Tel:* 800-533-2847 *Fax:* 508-753-3834 *E-mail:* das@davisart.com *Web Site:* www.davisartimages.com, pg 843

John J Davis & Associates Consulting Engineers, PO Box 128, Sierra Madre, CA 91025-0128 *Tel:* 626-355-6909, pg 843

DaviSound, 1504 Sunset Ave, Newberry, SC 29108 *Tel:* 803-944-7972 (messages only) *E-mail:* davisound@davisound.com; davisound@hotmail.com *Web Site:* www.davisound.com, pg 843

DAWNco, 3340 S Lapeer Rd, Orion, MI 48359 *Tel:* 248-391-9200 *Fax:* 248-391-9206 *E-mail:* sales@dawnco.com *Web Site:* www.dawnco.com, pg 843

DawnSignPress, 6130 Nancy Ridge Dr, San Diego, CA 92121-3223 *Tel:* 858-625-0600 *Toll Free Tel:* 800-549-5350 *Fax:* 858-625-2336 *E-mail:* contactus@dawnsign.com *Web Site:* www.dawnsign.com, pg 844

Day Star Productions, 1042 S 130 St, Bonner Springs, KS 66012 *Tel:* 913-422-3400 *Fax:* 913-422-3401 *E-mail:* daystar@day-star.org *Web Site:* www.day-star.org, pg 844

Daylight Productions & Rentals, 4700 Sterling Dr, Suite I, Boulder, CO 80301 *Tel:* 303-440-3334 *Fax:* 303-442-8180 *E-mail:* info@daylightav.com *Web Site:* www.daylightav.com, pg 844

Dazian Inc, 18 Central Blvd, South Hackensack, NJ 07606 *Toll Free Tel:* 877-232-9426 *Fax:* 201-641-2728; 201-549-1055 *E-mail:* info@dazian.com *Web Site:* www.dazian.com, pg 844

Dazor Manufacturing Corp, 2079 Congressional, St Louis, MO 63146 *Tel:* 314-652-2400 *Toll Free Tel:* 800-345-9103 *Fax:* 314-652-2069 *E-mail:* info@dazor.com *Web Site:* www.dazor.com, pg 844

db interactive Inc, PO Box 302064, Austin, TX 78703 *Tel:* 512-436-8586 *E-mail:* info@dbinteractive.com *Web Site:* dbinteractive.com, pg 844

dbF a Media Company, 9683 Charles St, La Plata, MD 20646 *Tel:* 301-645-6110 *Fax:* 301-392-6111 *E-mail:* service@dbfmedia.com *Web Site:* dbfmedia.com, pg 844

DBM Communications Inc, 606 Baltimore Ave, Suite 200, Towson, MD 21204 *Tel:* 410-825-7400 *Fax:* 443-269-0213 *Web Site:* www.dbmcommunications.com, pg 844

dbx Professional Products, 8760 S Sandy Pkwy, Sandy, UT 84070 *Tel:* 801-566-8800; 801-568-7660 (cust serv) *Fax:* 801-568-7662 *E-mail:* customer@dbxpro.com *Web Site:* www.dbxpro.com, pg 844

DC Asian Pacific American Film Festival, 2515 Virginia Ave NW, No 58205, Washington, DC 20037 *Tel:* 703-507-4375 *E-mail:* info@apafilm.org; admin@apafilm.org *Web Site:* www.apafilm.org, pg 1113

De Nonno Productions Inc (DPI), 7119 Shore Rd, Suite 6-F, Brooklyn, NY 11209 *Tel:* 917-304-6610 *E-mail:* info@denonnoproductions.com *Web Site:* www.denonnoproductions.com; www.denonnoscelebrityphotos.com, pg 844

De Sisti Lighting/Desmar Corp, 1011 Rte 22 E, Unit D, Mountainside, NJ 07092 *Tel:* 908-317-0020 *Fax:* 908-317-0021 *Web Site:* www.desisti.it, pg 844

De Wolfe Music USA, 37 W 17 St, 7th fl, Suite E, New York, NY 10011 *Tel:* 212-259-0524 *E-mail:* info@dewolfmusicusa.com *Web Site:* dewolfemusic.com, pg 844

Debbie Regan Locations Ltd, PO Box 353, Old Westbury, NY 11568 *Tel:* 516-626-1928 *Fax:* 516-626-2337 *E-mail:* info@debbiereganlocations.com *Web Site:* www.debbiereganlocations.com, pg 844

DebsVoice, 19 Park Trail, Midhurst, ON L0L 1X0, Canada *Tel:* 604-459-5559 (cell) *E-mail:* info@debsvoice.com *Web Site:* www.debsvoice.com, pg 844

DEC Grants, 696 Dutchess Tpke, Suite F, Poughkeepsie, NY 12603 *Tel:* 845-454-3222 *Fax:* 845-454-6902 *E-mail:* info@artsmidhudson.org *Web Site:* www.artsmidhudson.org, pg 1113

DecisionOne, 426 W Lancaster Ave, Devon, PA 19333 *Tel:* 610-296-6000 *Toll Free Tel:* 800-767-2876; 800-777-8800 (cust serv); 888-287-9202 (sales); 800-554-5179 (CN) *Fax:* 610-296-2910 *Web Site:* www.decisionone.com, pg 844

Deck Hand Inc, 1905 Victory Blvd, Suite 8, Glendale, CA 91201 *Tel:* 818-557-8403 *Fax:* 818-557-8406 *E-mail:* info@deckhand.com *Web Site:* www.deckhand.com, pg 844

Dedotec USA Inc, 48 Sheffield Business Park, Ashley Falls, MA 01222 *Tel:* 413-229-2550 *Fax:* 413-229-2556 *E-mail:* info@dedolight.com *Web Site:* www.dedolight.com, pg 844

Deerfield Laboratory Inc, 524 San Anselmo Ave, Suite 136, San Anselmo, CA 94960 *Tel:* 650-632-4090 *Fax:* 650-632-4091 *E-mail:* info@deerfieldlab.com *Web Site:* www.deerfieldlab.com, pg 844

Definitive Technology LLP, 11433 Cronridge Dr, Suite K, Owings Mills, MD 21117-2294 *Tel:* 410-363-7148 *Toll Free Tel:* 800-228-7148 *Fax:* 410-363-9998 *E-mail:* info@definitivetech.com *Web Site:* www.definitivetech.com, pg 845

Deja View Video, 417 S Eldorado St, San Mateo, CA 94402-1374 *Tel:* 650-343-8899 *Web Site:* www.dejaview.com, pg 845

deKramer Productions Inc, 515 Western Ave, Petaluma, CA 94952 *Tel:* 707-765-0888 *E-mail:* dekramer@sonic.net *Web Site:* www.dekramerproductions.com, pg 845

Delaware Tourism Office, 99 Kings Hwy, Dover, DE 19901 *Tel:* 302-739-4271 *Toll Free Tel:* 866-284-7483 *Fax:* 302-739-5749 *Web Site:* www.visitdelaware.com, pg 1095

Delicate Electronics Sales Inc, 874 Verdulera St, Camarillo, CA 93010 *Tel:* 805-484-8139 *Toll Free Tel:* 800-350-3555 *Fax:* 805-388-1037 *Web Site:* www.delicatesales.com, pg 845

deLise Studios, 83 Park Dr, Cherry Hill, NJ 08002-3002 *Tel:* 856-616-2867 *E-mail:* info@delisestudios.com *Web Site:* www.delisestudios.com, pg 845

Delmark Records, 4121 N Rockwell, Chicago, IL 60618 *Tel:* 773-539-5001 *Fax:* 773-539-5004 *E-mail:* delmark@delmark.com; jazzmart@delmark.com *Web Site:* www.delmark.com, pg 845

Delta Consolidated Industries Inc, 14600 York Rd, Suite A, Sparks, MD 21152 *Toll Free Tel:* 800-643-0084 (cust serv) *Fax:* 870-935-4994 *Toll Free Fax:* 877-356-4081 *Web Site:* www.deltastorage.com; www.apextoolgroup.com, pg 845

Delta Electronics Inc, 5730 General Washington Dr, Alexandria, VA 22312 *Tel:* 703-354-3350 *Toll Free Tel:* 800-833-5828 *Fax:* 703-354-0216 *E-mail:* sales@deltaelectronics.com *Web Site:* www.deltaelectronics.com, pg 845

Deluxe Laboratories Inc, 5433 Fernwood Ave, Hollywood, CA 90027 *Tel:* 323-960-3600 *Fax:* 323-960-7016 *Web Site:* www.bydeluxe.com, pg 845

Deluxe Media Services, 235 Pegasus Ave, Northvale, NJ 07647 *Tel:* 201-767-3800 *Fax:* 201-784-2769 *Web Site:* www.bydeluxe.com, pg 845

Demco Inc, 4810 Forest Run Rd, Madison, WI 53704 *Tel:* 608-241-1201 *Toll Free Tel:* 800-962-4463; 800-279-1586 *Toll Free Fax:* 800-245-1329 *Web Site:* www.demco.com, pg 845

Denecke Inc, 25209 Ave Tibbitts, Valencia, CA 91355 *Tel:* 661-607-0206 *Fax:* 661-257-2236 *E-mail:* info@denecke.com *Web Site:* www.denecke.com, pg 845

Denver Film Society, 1510 York St, 3rd fl, Denver, CO 80206 *Tel:* 303-595-3456 *Fax:* 303-595-0956 *E-mail:* info@denverfilm.org *Web Site:* www.denverfilm.org, pg 1081

Denver Media Center, 3853 S Broadway, Englewood, CO 80113 *Tel:* 303-872-9993 *Web Site:* denvermediacenter.com, pg 845

The Denver Office of Economic Development, Wellington E Webb Municipal Bldg, 2nd fl, 201 W Colfax Ave, Dept 1005, Denver, CO 80202 *Tel:* 720-913-1999 *Fax:* 720-913-1802 *E-mail:* oed@denvergov.org *Web Site:* www.milehigh.com, pg 1095

Department of Education Resources, 2000-B S Club Dr, Landover, MD 20785 *Tel:* 202-842-6280 *Fax:* 202-842-6935 *E-mail:* edresources@nga.gov *Web Site:* www.nga.gov; www.nga.gov/education, pg 845

Derksen (USA) Inc, 4934 Pathway Ct, Fair Oaks, CA 95628 *Tel:* 916-903-7275 *Fax:* 916-903-7022 *E-mail:* info@derksen.com *Web Site:* www.derksen.com, pg 845

Desert Hot Springs Chamber of Commerce & Visitors Center, 11999 Palm Dr, Desert Hot Springs, CA 92240 *Tel:* 760-329-6403 *E-mail:* info@deserthotsprings.com *Web Site:* www.deserthotsprings.com, pg 1092

Design & Production Inc, 7110 Rainwater Place, Lorton, VA 22079 *Tel:* 703-550-8640 *Fax:* 703-339-0296 *E-mail:* email@d-and-p.com *Web Site:* www.d-and-p.com, pg 845

Design Audio Visual Inc, 195-A Central Ave, Farmingdale, NY 11735 *Tel:* 631-694-3334 *Toll Free Tel:* 800-886-1328 *Fax:* 631-694-3549 *Web Site:* www.design-av.com, pg 845

Design FX Audio, PO Box 491087, Los Angeles, CA 90049 *Tel:* 818-843-6555 *Toll Free Tel:* 800-441-4415 *Fax:* 818-562-6978 *Web Site:* www.dfxaudio.com, pg 845

Design Media, 650 Alabama St, Suite 203, San Francisco, CA 94110-2038 *Tel:* 415-641-4848 *Fax:* 415-641-5245 *E-mail:* info@designmedia.com *Web Site:* www.designmedia.com, pg 845

Designomotion, 67 E 11 St, Suite 324, New York, NY 10003 *Tel:* 917-532-0738 *E-mail:* info@designomotion.com *Web Site:* designomotion.com, pg 846

Desktop Video Systems, 9052 Parkhill, Lenexa, KS 66215 *Tel:* 913-782-8888 *Toll Free Tel:* 800-662-6901 *Fax:* 913-492-6908 *E-mail:* sales@desktopvideosystems.com *Web Site:* www.desktopvideosystems.com, pg 846

Detroit Windsor International Film Festival (DWIFF), 15206 Mack Ave, Suite 9, Detroit, MI 48230 *Tel:* 313-881-0122 *E-mail:* info@dwiff.org *Web Site:* www.dwiff.org, pg 1114

Developmental Studies Center, 1250 53 St, Suite 3, Emeryville, CA 94608 *Tel:* 510-533-0213 *Toll Free Tel:* 800-666-7270 *Fax:* 510-464-3670 *E-mail:* info@devstu.org; customer_service@devstu.org *Web Site:* www.devstu.org, pg 846

Devlin Video International, 1501 Broadway, Suite 408, New York, NY 10036 *Tel:* 212-391-1313 *Fax:* 212-391-2744 *Web Site:* www.devlinvideo.com, pg 846

DG Mijo, 635 E Queen St, East Toronto, ON M4M 1G4, Canada *Tel:* 416-964-7539 *Toll Free Tel:* 800-463-MIJO (463-6456) *Fax:* 416-964-5920 *Web Site:* www.mijo.com, pg 846

DGA Awards, 7920 Sunset Blvd, Los Angeles, CA 90046 *Tel:* 310-289-2038 *E-mail:* dgaawards@dga.org *Web Site:* www.dga.org, pg 1114

DGI-Invisuals LLC, 101 Billerica Ave, Bldg 6, North Billerica, MA 01862 *Toll Free Tel:* 800-344-0432 *Fax:* 781-270-3663 *E-mail:* sales@dgi-invisuals.com *Web Site:* www.dgi-invisuals.com, pg 846

DH Satellite, 600 N Marquette Rd, Prairie du Chien, WI 53821 *Tel:* 608-326-8406 *Toll Free Tel:* 800-627-9443 *Fax:* 608-326-4233 *E-mail:* dhsat@mhtc.net *Web Site:* www.dhsatellite.com, pg 846

Dialect Accent Specialists Inc, PO Box 44, Lyndonville, VT 05851-0044 *Toll Free Tel:* 800-753-1016 *E-mail:* dasinc@kingcon.com; info@dialectaccentspecialists.com *Web Site:* www.dialectaccentspecialists.com; www.learnaccent.com, pg 846

Diamond Dreams Music Productions, North Ocean County, Carbon Canyon, Chino Hills, CA 91709 *Tel:* 909-393-6120 *Fax:* 909-606-5779 *E-mail:* info@diamonddreamsmusic.com *Web Site:* www.diamonddreamsmusic.com, pg 846

Diamond Studios, Woods Point 1, 1855 Data Dr, Suite 255, Hoover, AL 35244 *Tel:* 205-987-2121 *Fax:* 205-987-2128 *Web Site:* www.tvstuff.com, pg 846

Diaquest, 5808 Vallejo St, Emeryville, CA 94608 *Tel:* 510-547-4544 *Fax:* 510-654-8370 *E-mail:* sales@diaquest.com; support@diaquest.com *Web Site:* www.diaquest.com, pg 846

Dickensheets Design Associates, 12335 Hymeadow Dr, Suite 200, Austin, TX 78750 *Tel:* 512-331-8977 *Toll Free Tel:* 800-545-5734 *Web Site:* www.dickensheets.com, pg 846

DiCon Fiberoptics Inc, 1689 Regatta Blvd, Richmond, CA 94804 *Tel:* 510-620-5000; 510-620-5200 (sales) *Fax:* 510-620-4100; 510-620-4102 (sales) *E-mail:* info@diconfiber.com; sales@diconfiber.com *Web Site:* www.diconfiberoptics.com, pg 846

Dielectric Communications, 22 Tower Rd, Raymond, ME 04071 *Tel:* 207-655-4555 *Toll Free Tel:* 800-341-9678 *Fax:* 207-655-8174 *E-mail:* dcsales@dielectric.com *Web Site:* www.dielectric.com, pg 846

Diemer Amp & Keyboard Repair, 12814 Landale St, Studio City, CA 91604-1351 *Tel:* 818-762-0804 *Web Site:* bustedgear.com, pg 846

The Richard Diercks Co Inc, 3140 Harbor Lane N, Suite 223, Minneapolis, MN 55447 *Tel:* 763-231-3303 *Fax:* 763-231-3307 *E-mail:* rdiercks@diercks.com *Web Site:* www.dvdauthor.com, pg 846

Different Fur Recording Ltd, 3470 19 St, San Francisco, CA 94110 *Tel:* 415-864-1967; 415-828-4060 (bookings) *Fax:* 415-864-1965 *Web Site:* www.differentfurstudios.com, pg 846

Digi-matics, 4472 Spring Valley Rd, Dallas, TX 75244 *Tel:* 469-644-1390 *Web Site:* www.digi-matics.com, pg 847

Digi Sign Design LLC, 28533 Greenfield Rd, Suite 2, Southfield, MI 48076 *Tel:* 248-569-5422 *Web Site:* www.digisigndesign.com, pg 847

Digimation, 250 International Pkwy, Suite 320, Lake Mary, FL 32746 *Tel:* 407-833-0600 *Toll Free Tel:* 800-854-4496 *Fax:* 813-283-4906 *E-mail:* sales@digimation.com *Web Site:* www.digimation.com, pg 847

Digital Art Video Inc, 8506 60 Ave, 3rd fl, Middle Village, NY 11379-5430 *Tel:* 718-457-5388 *Web Site:* www.digital-art.com, pg 847

Digital Audio Labs, 1266 Park Rd, Chanhassen, MN 55317 *Tel:* 952-401-7700 *Fax:* 952-401-7725 *E-mail:* sales@digitalaudio.com *Web Site:* www.digitalaudio.com, pg 847

Digital Comm Link Inc, 10450 W State Rd 84, Davie, FL 33324-4206 *Tel:* 954-236-2993 *Toll Free Tel:* 877-532-5438 *Fax:* 954-236-3633 *E-mail:* booking@dclinc.net *Web Site:* www.dclinc.net, pg 847

Digital Designs, 1141 NW First St, Oklahoma City, OK 73106 *Tel:* 405-239-2800 *Fax:* 405-239-7100 *E-mail:* ddtech@ddaudio.com *Web Site:* www.ddaudio.com, pg 847

Digital Display Solutions Inc, 12081 Starcrest, San Antonio, TX 78216 *Tel:* 210-404-1233; 210-523-7368 (rentals) *Fax:* 210-979-6585 *E-mail:* lharbert@ddssa.com *Web Site:* www.ddssa.com, pg 847

Digital Film Studios, 11800 Sheldon St, Unit C/D, Sun Valley, CA 91352 *Tel:* 818-771-0019 *Fax:* 818-351-1155 *E-mail:* info@digitalfilmstudios.com *Web Site:* www.digitalfilmstudios.com, pg 847

Digital Force, 149 Madison Ave, 12th fl, New York, NY 10016 *Tel:* 212-252-9300 *Toll Free Tel:* 877-DISC-USA (347-2872) *Fax:* 212-252-7377 *E-mail:* frontdesk@digitalforce.com *Web Site:* www.digitalforce.com, pg 847

Digital FX Inc, 6010 Perkins Rd, Suite B, Baton Rouge, LA 70808 *Tel:* 225-763-6010 *Toll Free Tel:* 888-898-6010 *Fax:* 225-763-6059 *E-mail:* info@digitalfx.tv; rentals@digitalfx.tv *Web Site:* www.digitalfx.tv, pg 847

Digital Image Studios LLC, 23400 Commerce Dr, Farmington Hills, MI 48335 *Tel:* 248-477-5600 *Toll Free Tel:* 888-434-7839 *Fax:* 248-477-4322 *Web Site:* www.dimage.com, pg 847

Digital Jungle, 6363 Santa Monica Blvd, Hollywood, CA 90038 *Tel:* 323-962-0867 *Fax:* 323-962-9960 *E-mail:* info@digijungle.com *Web Site:* www.digijungle.com, pg 847

Digital Lighting Systems Inc, 12302 SW 128 Ct, Suite 105, Miami, FL 33186 *Tel:* 305-969-8442 *Fax:* 305-969-8675 *E-mail:* info@digitallighting.com; sales@digitallighting.com *Web Site:* www.digitallighting.com, pg 847

Digital Media West, 573 Jones St, Ventura, CA 93003 *Tel:* 805-559-1318 *Web Site:* www.digitalmediawest.com, pg 847

Digital Music Corp, 3165 Coffey Lane, Santa Rosa, CA 95403 *Tel:* 707-545-0600 *Fax:* 707-545-9777 *E-mail:* info@voodoolab.com *Web Site:* www.voodoolab.com, pg 847

Digital Outpost, 2772 Loker Ave W, Carlsbad, CA 92010 *Tel:* 760-431-3575 *Toll Free Tel:* 800-464-6434 *Fax:* 760-431-8717 *E-mail:* info@dop.com; sales@dop.com *Web Site:* www.dop.com, pg 847

Digital Projection, 55 Chastain Rd, Suite 115, Kennesaw, GA 30144 *Tel:* 770-420-1350 *Fax:* 770-420-1360 *E-mail:* contact@digitalprojection.com *Web Site:* www.digitalprojection.com, pg 847

Digital Rain LLC, 640 Wilson St, Danville, IN 46122 *Tel:* 317-563-1208 *E-mail:* avmarket@digitalrainllc.com *Web Site:* www.digitalrainllc.com, pg 847

Digital Services Recording Studios, 1601 S Cherry St, Tomball, TX 77375 *Tel:* 281-290-8500 *Fax:* 281-290-8510 *E-mail:* studio@dsrecordings.com *Web Site:* www.dsrecordings.com, pg 848

Digital Video Arts, 7775 Belfort Pkwy, Jacksonville, FL 32256 *Tel:* 904-281-1001 *Toll Free Tel:* 888-340-1010 *Fax:* 904-281-0051 *Web Site:* www.digitalvideoarts.com, pg 848

Digital Video Productions, 257 Federal Rd, Brookfield, CT 06804 *Tel:* 203-743-7663 *Fax:* 203-743-1658 *E-mail:* info@dvpllc.com *Web Site:* www.dvpllc.com, pg 848

Digital Video Systems Inc, 3270 Executive Way, Miramar, FL 33025 *Tel:* 954-239-4410 *Fax:* 954-239-4485 *E-mail:* info@digitalvideosystems.net *Web Site:* www.digitalvideosystems.net, pg 848

Digital Zoetrope Productions, 1902 Oak St, Melbourne, FL 32901 *Tel:* 321-821-7404 *Fax:* 321-821-2287 *Web Site:* digitalzoetrope.com, pg 848

DigiTech, 10653 S River Front Pkwy, Suite 300, South Jordan, UT 84095 *Tel:* 801-566-8800 *Toll Free Tel:* 800-999-9363 *E-mail:* support@digitech.com *Web Site:* www.digitech.com, pg 848

Digitron Electronics, 7801 E Telegraph Rd, Montebello, CA 90640 *Tel:* 323-629-4518 *Fax:* 323-887-0891 *E-mail:* repairs@digitronelectronics.com *Web Site:* digitronelectronics.com, pg 848

DimcoGray Co, 900 Dimco Way, Centerville, OH 45458-2710 *Tel:* 937-433-7600 *Fax:* 937-433-0520 *E-mail:* dgsales@dimcogray.com; dginfo@dimcogray.com *Web Site:* www.dimcogray.com, pg 848

Direct Broadcast Services Inc (DBS), 711 Executive Blvd, Suite F, Valley Cottage, NY 10989 *Tel:* 845-267-2800 *Fax:* 845-267-2123 *E-mail:* dbs@directbroadcast.com *Web Site:* www.directbroadcast.com, pg 848

Direct Cinema Ltd Inc, PO Box 10003, Santa Monica, CA 90410-1003 *Tel:* 310-636-8200 *Toll Free Tel:* 800-525-0000 *Fax:* 310-636-8228 *E-mail:* dclvideo@aol.com *Web Site:* www.directcinema.com, pg 848

Direct Current Video Productions, 1928 E Highland, Suite F-104-448, Phoenix, AZ 85016 *Tel:* 602-263-7717 *Fax:* 602-263-7719 *Web Site:* www.directcurrentproductions.com, pg 848

Direct Images Interactive Inc, 1933 Davis St, Suite 308, San Leandro, CA 94577 *Tel:* 510-613-8299 *E-mail:* info@directimages.com *Web Site:* www.directimages.com, pg 848

Direct Marketing Association Inc (DMA), 1120 Avenue of the Americas, New York, NY 10036-6700 *Tel:* 212-768-7277 *Fax:* 212-302-6714 *Web Site:* thedma.org, pg 1081

Directed Electronics, One Viper Way, Vista, CA 92081 *Tel:* 760-598-6200 *Toll Free Tel:* 800-876-0800 *Fax:* 760-598-6400 *E-mail:* customerfeedback@directed.com *Web Site:* www.directed.com, pg 848

Directors Guild of America (DGA), 7920 Sunset Blvd, Los Angeles, CA 90046 *Tel:* 310-289-2000 *Toll Free Tel:* 800-421-4173 *Web Site:* www.dga.org, pg 1081

Disc Makers, 7905 N Rte 130, Pennsauken, NJ 08110-1402 *Tel:* 856-663-9030 *Toll Free Tel:* 800-468-9353 *Fax:* 856-661-3450 *E-mail:* info@discmakers.com *Web Site:* www.discmakers.com, pg 848

Discovery Education - Chicago, 111 E Wacker Dr, Suite 3000, Chicago, IL 60601 *Web Site:* www.discoveryeducation.com, pg 848

Discovery Education - Los Angeles, 10100 Santa Monica Blvd, Suite 1500, Los Angeles, CA 90067 *Tel:* 310-551-1611 *Fax:* 310-551-1684 *Web Site:* www.discoveryeducation.com, pg 848

Discovery Education - Silver Spring, One Discovery Place, Silver Spring, MD 20910 *Toll Free Tel:* 800-323-9084 *Fax:* 847-328-6706 *Web Site:* discoveryeducation.com, pg 848

Discovery Education - South Burlington, PO Box 3400, Lancaster, PA 17604 *Toll Free Tel:* 888-892-3484 *Toll Free Fax:* 877-324-6830 *E-mail:* education_info@discovery.com *Web Site:* teacherstore.discovery.com, pg 848

Discovery Toys, 3037 Independence Dr, Suite G, Livermore, CA 94551 *Tel:* 925-606-2600 *Toll Free Tel:* 800-341-TOYS (341-8697, sales) *Fax:* 925-447-0626 *E-mail:* contact@discoverytoys.net *Web Site:* www.discoverytoys.net, pg 848

Disk Productions, 1100 Perkins Rd, Baton Rouge, LA 70802 *Tel:* 225-343-5438 *E-mail:* disk_productions@yahoo.com, pg 849

DiskFaktory Direct, 17173 Gillette Ave, Suite A, Irvine, CA 92614 *Tel:* 949-477-1700 *Toll Free Tel:* 888-464-9664 *E-mail:* customercare@diskfaktory.com *Web Site:* www.direct.diskfaktory.com, pg 849

Display Devices, 10828 Hwy 93, Golden, CO 80403 *Tel:* 303-412-0399 *Toll Free Tel:* 877-862-6865 *Fax:* 303-412-9346 *E-mail:* sales@displaydevices.com *Web Site:* www.displaydevices.com, pg 849

Display Systems International, 2214 Hanselman Ave, Saskatoon, SK S7L 6A4, Canada *Tel:* 306-934-6884 *Toll Free Tel:* 877-934-6884 *Fax:* 306-934-6447 *E-mail:* sales@displaysystemsintl.com *Web Site:* www.displaysystemsintl.com, pg 849

Les Disques Artiste, 154 Grande Cote, Rosemere, QC J7A 1H3, Canada *Tel:* 450-437-7625 *Web Site:* www.disquesartiste.com, pg 849

Distribution Video & Audio (DVA), 15232 US 19 N, Suite B, Clearwater, FL 33764 *Tel:* 727-447-4147 *Toll Free Tel:* 800-683-4147 *Fax:* 727-441-3069 *Web Site:* www.dvaspecial.com, pg 849

District of Columbia Office of Motion Picture & TV Development, 200 "I" St SE, Suite 1800, Washington, DC 20003 *Tel:* 202-727-6608 *Fax:* 202-727-3246 *E-mail:* film@dc.gov *Web Site:* www.film.dc.gov, pg 1095

Diversified Imaging Supply, 333 Alondra Blvd, Gardena, CA 90248, pg 849

Diversified Systems Inc, 363 Market St, Kenilworth, NJ 07033 *Tel:* 908-245-4833 *Fax:* 908-245-0011 *E-mail:* info@divsystems.com *Web Site:* www.divsystems.com, pg 849

Division Camera, 7022 W Sunset Blvd, Hollywood, CA 90028 *Tel:* 323-465-7700 *Fax:* 323-293-2773 *E-mail:* rent@divisioncamera.com *Web Site:* divisioncamera.com, pg 849

Dixie Theatre Service & Supply Co Inc, 311 N Washington, Albany, GA 31701 *Tel:* 229-435-4566 *E-mail:* dixietheatre@aol.com, pg 849

DL Sound & Lighting Productions Ltd, 450 Banga Place, Victoria, BC V8Z 6X5, Canada *Tel:* 250-216-7898 *Fax:* 250-590-1280 *Web Site:* www.dlsound.net, pg 849

dM works, 246 Rockaway Ave, Valley Stream, NY 11580 *Tel:* 516-255-0100 *Toll Free Tel:* 888-914-6639 *E-mail:* info@dmworks.com *Web Site:* www.dmworks.com, pg 849

DME Studios, 1025 Greenwood Blvd, Suite 191, Lake Mary, FL 32746 *Tel:* 407-585-7500 *E-mail:* creativeteam@dmestudios.com *Web Site:* www.dmestudios.com, pg 849

DNASTAR Inc, 3801 Regent St, Madison, WI 53705-5204 *Tel:* 608-258-7420 *Toll Free Tel:* 866-511-5090 *Fax:* 608-258-7439 *E-mail:* info@dnastar.com *Web Site:* www.dnastar.com, pg 849

DNP Photo Imaging America Corp, 101 Uhland Rd, Suite 210, San Marcos, TX 78666 *Tel:* 512-753-7280 *Toll Free Tel:* 800-467-4935 *Fax:* 512-753-7299 *E-mail:* info@pixelmagic.com; sales@pixelmagic.com; customercare@pixelmagic.com *Web Site:* www.dnpphoto.com; www.pixelmagic.com; www.pmimaging.com, pg 849

Do It Yourself Inc - DIY Video Corp, 200 N Greensboro St, Suite A5, Carrboro, NC 27510 *Tel:* 919-904-7343; 828-773-8878 (cell) *Web Site:* www.do-it-yourself-dvds.com, pg 849

DocMiami International Film Festival, 8770 Sunset Dr, No 274, Miami, FL 33173-3512 *Tel:* 786-493-8308 *E-mail:* info@docmiami.org *Web Site:* www.docmiami.org, pg 1114

Docter Optics Inc, 1425 W Elliot Rd, Suite A-105, Gilbert, AZ 85233 *Tel:* 480-844-7585 *Fax:* 480-844-7826 *E-mail:* doi@docteroptics.com *Web Site:* www.docteroptics.com, pg 849

Documentary Educational Resources Inc, 101 Morse St, Watertown, MA 02472 *Tel:* 617-926-0491 *Toll Free Tel:* 800-569-6621 *Fax:* 617-926-9519 *E-mail:* docued@der.org *Web Site:* www.der.org, pg 850

Dog & Pony Productions Inc, 8928 "L" St, Omaha, NE 68127 *Tel:* 402-391-7691 *Fax:* 402-341-2751 *Web Site:* dogandponyinc.com, pg 850

Dogma Studios, 10559 Jefferson Blvd, Culver City, CA 90232 *Tel:* 310-838-2973 *Fax:* 310-838-2975 *E-mail:* info@dogmastudios.com *Web Site:* www.dogmastudios.com, pg 850

Dogwood Recording Studios, 757 Government St, Mobile, AL 36602 *Tel:* 251-476-0858 *Toll Free Tel:* 800-254-9903 *Fax:* 251-479-0364 *E-mail:* info@dogwoodproductions.com *Web Site:* www.dogwoodproductions.com, pg 850

Dolby Labs Inc, 100 Potrero Ave, San Francisco, CA 94103-4813 *Tel:* 415-558-0200 *Fax:* 415-645-4000 *E-mail:* info@dolby.com *Web Site:* www.dolby.com, pg 850

Dollar Bank Three Rivers Arts Festival, 803 Liberty Ave, Pittsburgh, PA 15222 *Tel:* 412-471-3191 *Web Site:* www.3riversartsfest.org, pg 1114

Dollarhide Film Inc, 764 Lake Cavalier Rd, Madison, MS 39110 *Tel:* 601-946-8407 *Web Site:* www.dollarhide.net, pg 850

Dolphin MultiMedia Inc, 1660 Belleville Way, Sunnyvale, CA 94087 *Tel:* 650-354-0800 *Fax:* 408-737-8404 *E-mail:* dolphin@dolphinmm.com *Web Site:* www.dolphinmm.com, pg 850

Domino Film Ltd, 4004 Grey Ave, Montreal, QC H4A 3P1, Canada *Tel:* 514-484-0446 *Fax:* 514-484-0468 *E-mail:* domino@dominofilm.ca *Web Site:* www.dominofilm.ca, pg 850

Tom Donald Films, 601 Fourth St, Suite 320, San Francisco, CA 94107 *Tel:* 415-546-4966 *Fax:* 415-546-5145 *Web Site:* www.tomdonaldfilms.com, pg 850

Doomsday Studios Ltd, 212 James St, Ottawa, ON K1R 5M7, Canada *Tel:* 613-230-9769 *Fax:* 613-230-6004 *E-mail:* info@doomsdaystudios.com, pg 850

Doppler Studios, 1922 Piedmont Circle, Atlanta, GA 30324 *Tel:* 404-873-6941 *Fax:* 404-249-7148 *E-mail:* info@dopplerstudios.com *Web Site:* www.dopplerstudios.com, pg 851

Doremi Labs, 1020 Chestnut St, Burbank, CA 91506 *Tel:* 818-562-1101 *Fax:* 818-562-1109 *E-mail:* info@doremilabs.com *Web Site:* www.doremilabs.com, pg 851

Dorfman Museum Figures Inc, 6224 Holabird Ave, Baltimore, MD 21224 *Tel:* 410-284-3248 *Toll Free Tel:* 800-634-4873 *Fax:* 410-284-3249 *E-mail:* info@museumfigures.com *Web Site:* www.museumfigures.com, pg 851

Dorian Color, 24 Mill St, Arlington, MA 02476 *Tel:* 781-648-8040 *Fax:* 781-641-1231 *E-mail:* images@dorianlabcolor.com (gallery) *Web Site:* www.doriancolor.com, pg 851

Dorrough Electronics Inc, 5221 Collier Place, Woodland Hills, CA 91364 *Tel:* 818-998-2824 *Fax:* 818-998-1507 *E-mail:* dorroughel@aol.com *Web Site:* www.dorrough.com, pg 851

Dorst MediaWorks Inc, 209 N Filmore St, Arlington, VA 22201 *Tel:* 202-258-9612 *Fax:* 571-312-9212 *Web Site:* www.stevedorst.com, pg 851

Dot C Software Inc, 117 Waihili Place, Honolulu, HI 96825 *Tel:* 808-744-0836 *E-mail:* info@dotcsw.com *Web Site:* www.dotcsw.com, pg 851

Dot Hill Systems Corp, 1351 S Sunset St, Longmont, CO 80501-6533 *Tel:* 303-845-3200 *Toll Free Tel:* 800-872-2783 *Fax:* 303-845-3655 *E-mail:* support@dothill.com; websales@dothill.com *Web Site:* www.dothill.com, pg 851

Dotronix Technology Inc, 160 First St SE, New Brighton, MN 55112 *Tel:* 651-633-1742 *Fax:* 651-633-2152 *E-mail:* service@dotronix.com; sales@dotronix.com *Web Site:* www.dotronix.com, pg 851

Douglas House Inc, 275 Kings Hwy, Orangeburg, NY 10962 *Tel:* 845-359-1477 *Fax:* 845-359-2945 *E-mail:* thedouglashouse@earthlink.net *Web Site:* www.thedouglashouse.com, pg 851

Dover Publications Inc, 31 E Second St, Mineola, NY 11501 *Tel:* 516-294-7000 *Fax:* 516-742-5049 (wholesale orders); 516-742-6953 (cust care) *Web Site:* store.doverpublications.com, pg 851

Dow-Key Microwave Corp, 4822 McGrath St, Ventura, CA 93003 *Tel:* 805-650-0260 *Toll Free Tel:* 800-266-3695 *Fax:* 805-650-1734 *E-mail:* askdk@dowkey.com *Web Site:* www.dowkey.com, pg 851

Down East Books, 680 Commercial St, Rockport, ME 04856 *Tel:* 207-594-9544 *Toll Free Tel:* 800-766-1670 *Fax:* 207-594-0147 *E-mail:* editorial@downeast.com *Web Site:* www.downeast.com, pg 851

Downpour.com, 31 Mistletoe Rd, Ashland, OR 97520 *Toll Free Tel:* 855-369-6768 *Toll Free Fax:* 800-482-9294 *E-mail:* customercare@downpour.com *Web Site:* www.downpour.com, pg 851

Downtown Community Television Center (DCTV), 87 Lafayette St, New York, NY 10013 *Tel:* 212-966-4510 *Fax:* 212-226-3053 *E-mail:* info@dctvny.org *Web Site:* www.dctvny.org, pg 851

R L Drake Co, 9900 Springboro Pike, Miamisburg, OH 45342 *Tel:* 937-746-4556 *Fax:* 937-806-1510 (sales); 937-806-1511 (gen) *E-mail:* salesgroup@rldrake.net *Web Site:* www.rldrake.com, pg 852

The Dramatists Guild of America, 1501 Broadway, Suite 701, New York, NY 10036 *Tel:* 212-398-9366 *Fax:* 212-944-0420 *E-mail:* info@dramatistsguild.com *Web Site:* www.dramatistsguild.com, pg 1081

DR&A Inc, 45 Willow St, Nashville, TN 37210 *Tel:* 615-256-6200 *Fax:* 615-256-6236 *Web Site:* www.griptruck.com, pg 852

Draper Inc, 411 S Pearl St, Spiceland, IN 47385 *Tel:* 765-987-7999 *Toll Free Tel:* 800-238-7999 *Fax:* 765-987-7142 *Web Site:* www.draperinc.com; blog.draperinc.com, pg 852

Drastic Technologies Ltd, 523 The Queensway, Suite 102, Toronto, ON M8Y 1J7, Canada *Tel:* 416-255-5636 *Fax:* 416-255-8780 *Web Site:* www.drastic.tv, pg 852

Dreambox Media Inc, PO Box 8132, Philadelphia, PA 19101-8132 *E-mail:* mail@dreamboxmedia.com *Web Site:* www.dreamboxmedia.com, pg 852

Dreamhire LLC, 36-36 33 St, Suite 102, Long Island City, NY 11106 *Tel:* 212-691-5544 *Toll Free Tel:* 800-234-7536 *E-mail:* info@dreamhire.com *Web Site:* www.dreamhire.com, pg 852

The Dreaming Tree, 1112 Chestnut St, Unit B, Burbank, CA 91506 *Tel:* 818-845-3230 *Fax:* 818-333-0795 *E-mail:* info@dreamingtreeproductions.com *Web Site:* www.dreamingtreeproductions.com, pg 852

Dreamscape Lighting Mfg Inc, 5521 W Washington Blvd, Los Angeles, CA 90016 *Tel:* 323-933-5760 *Fax:* 323-933-3607 *E-mail:* info@dreamscapelighting.com *Web Site:* www.dreamscapelighting.com, pg 852

DreamWorks Animation SKG Inc, 1000 Flower St, Glendale, CA 91201 *Tel:* 818-695-5000 *Fax:* 818-695-4190 *Web Site:* www.dreamworksanimation.com, pg 852

DRG Records Inc, 22 Harbor Park Dr, Port Washington, NY 11050 *Tel:* 516-484-1000 (ext 147); 212-614-2800 *Toll Free Tel:* 866-293-2854 *Fax:* 516-484-2365 *E-mail:* info@drgrecords.com *Web Site:* drgrecords.com, pg 852

DRM: sir reel sound, 10520 Beard Ave, Austin, TX 78748 *Tel:* 214-752-5000 (studio) *E-mail:* drmuzik@mac.com *Web Site:* www.drm-sirreelsound.com, pg 852

DRT Mastering, 20 Vine St, Peterborough, NH 03458 *Tel:* 603-924-2277 *Web Site:* www.drtmastering.com, pg 852

Mark Druck Productions, 300 E 40 St, New York, NY 10016 *Tel:* 212-682-5980 *Fax:* 212-682-5981, pg 852

Drumbeat Indian Arts Inc, 4143 N 16 St, Phoenix, AZ 85016 *Tel:* 602-266-4823 *Toll Free Tel:* 800-895-4859 *Fax:* 602-265-2402 *E-mail:* info@drumbeatindianarts.com *Web Site:* www.drumbeatindianarts.com, pg 852

Drytac Corp, 5601 Eastport Blvd, Richmond, VA 23231 *Toll Free Tel:* 800-280-6013 *E-mail:* customerservice@drytac.com *Web Site:* www.drytac.com, pg 852

DSan Corp, 142 Mineola Ave, Roslyn Heights, NY 11577 *Tel:* 516-625-5608 *Fax:* 516-625-0878 *E-mail:* sales@dsan.com *Web Site:* www.dsan.com, pg 852

DSI RF Systems Inc, 26-H World's Fair Dr, Somerset, NJ 08873 *Tel:* 732-563-1144 *Toll Free Tel:* 888-374-7388 *Fax:* 732-563-1818 *E-mail:* info@dsirf.com; sales@dsirf.com *Web Site:* www.dsirf.com, pg 853

DSR Computer Technology Specialists Inc, 921-P Mercantile Dr, Hanover, MD 21076 *Tel:* 410-579-4508 *Toll Free Tel:* 800-875-0037 *Fax:* 410-579-8412 *E-mail:* dsr@dsr-inc.com *Web Site:* www.dsr-inc.com, pg 853

DTC Lighting & Grip, 1280 65 St, Emeryville, CA 94608 *Tel:* 510-595-0770 *Toll Free Tel:* 877-382-3456 *Fax:* 510-595-0772 *E-mail:* sales@dtcgrip.com; rentals@dtcgrip.com *Web Site:* www.dtcgrip.com, pg 853

DuArt, 245 W 55 St, New York, NY 10019 *Tel:* 212-757-4580 *Fax:* 212-977-5609 *E-mail:* info@duart.com *Web Site:* www.duart.com, pg 853

Dub King, 8133 Callaghan Rd, San Antonio, TX 78230 *Tel:* 210-979-8779 *Toll Free Tel:* 800-542-1187 *E-mail:* dubking@dubking.com *Web Site:* www.dubking.com, pg 853

The DubHouse, 404 SE 15 St, Fort Lauderdale, FL 33316 *Tel:* 954-524-3658 *Toll Free Tel:* 877-900-DUBS (900-3827) *Fax:* 954-522-1905 *Web Site:* www.thedubhouse.net, pg 853

Dubuque Convention & Visitors Bureau, 300 Main St, Suite 200, Dubuque, IA 52001 *Tel:* 563-557-9200 *Fax:* 563-557-1591 *E-mail:* office@dubuquechamber.com *Web Site:* www.dubuquechamber.com, pg 1097

Duck Studios, 2205 Stoner Ave, Los Angeles, CA 90064 *Tel:* 310-478-0771 *Fax:* 310-478-0773 *E-mail:* info@duckstudios.com *Web Site:* www.duckstudios.com, pg 853

Dudley Theatrical, 3401 Indiana Ave, Winston-Salem, NC 27105 *Tel:* 336-722-3255 *Fax:* 336-722-4641 *E-mail:* sales@dudleytheatrical.com *Web Site:* www.dudleytheatrical.com, pg 853

Dan Dugan Sound Design Inc, 290 Napoleon St, Suite E, San Francisco, CA 94124 *Tel:* 415-821-9776 *Fax:* 415-826-7699 *Web Site:* www.dandugan.com, pg 853

Duggal Visual Solutions, 29 W 23 St, New York, NY 10010 *Tel:* 212-924-8100 *Fax:* 212-242-6660 *E-mail:* info@duggal.com *Web Site:* duggal.com, pg 853

Dukane Corp, Audio Visual Products Division, 2900 Dukane Dr, St Charles, IL 60174 *Tel:* 630-762-4040 *Toll Free Tel:* 888-245-1966 *Fax:* 630-584-5156 *E-mail:* avsales@dukane.com *Web Site:* dukaneav.com, pg 853

Duke Media Services, 0052 Bryan Ctr, Durham, NC 27708 *Tel:* 919-660-1740 *Fax:* 919-660-1719 *Web Site:* sites.duke.edu/mediaservices, pg 853

Michael Dunn Productions, 25 Sunlit Dr W, Santa Fe, NM 87508 *Tel:* 847-940-0150, pg 853

Dunning Photo Equipment Inc, 605 W Needles St, Bixby, OK 74008 *Tel:* 918-366-4917 *Fax:* 918-366-4918 *Web Site:* www.dunningphoto.com, pg 853

Duplication Depot Inc, 7 Brookstan Rd, Nesconset, NY 11767 *Tel:* 631-752-0608 *E-mail:* copymydisc@gmail.com *Web Site:* www.duplicationdepot.com, pg 853

Duplication Media, 8126 Douglas Ave, Urbandale, IA 50322 *Tel:* 515-334-DUPS (334-3877) *E-mail:* info@duplicationmedia.com *Web Site:* www.duplicationmedia.com, pg 853

Duplication Specialists Inc, 843 Merrick Rd, Baldwin, NY 11510 *Tel:* 516-867-7300; 212-754-2044 *Toll Free Tel:* 800-227-1382 *Fax:* 516-867-7597 *E-mail:* sales@dupespec.com *Web Site:* www.dupespec.com, pg 853

DuQuaine Manufacturing, PO Box 56, Kewaunee, WI 54216-0056 *Tel:* 920-388-3790 *Web Site:* www.duquaine.com, pg 853

Duray Lighting, 500 E Touhy Ave, Suite F, Des Plaines, IL 60018 *Tel:* 773-271-2800 *Fax:* 773-271-4410 *E-mail:* info@duraylighting.com; sales@duraylighting.com *Web Site:* www.duraylighting.com, pg 854

Durrell LLC, 801 Fifth Ave S, Nashville, TN 37203 *Tel:* 615-313-8877 *Fax:* 615-313-8873 *Web Site:* www.durrellsports.com, pg 854

Durrenberger Engineering Inc, 2037 Powell Dr, El Cajon, CA 92020 *Tel:* 858-578-3363 *Web Site:* www.dfrfx.com, pg 854

Durrin Productions Inc, 4926 Sedgwick St NW, Washington, DC 20016 *Tel:* 202-237-6700 *Toll Free Tel:* 800-536-6843 *Fax:* 202-237-6738 *E-mail:* info@durrinproductions.com *Web Site:* www.durrinproductions.com, pg 854

Duxbury Systems Inc, 270 Littleton Rd, Unit 6, Westford, MA 01886-3523 *Tel:* 978-692-3000 *Fax:* 978-692-7912 *E-mail:* info@duxsys.com *Web Site:* www.duxburysystems.com, pg 854

DV Awards, 6300 N Sagewood Dr, Suite H-383, Park City, UT 84098 *E-mail:* info@dvawards.com *Web Site:* www.dvawards.com, pg 1114

DV Post, 505 N Tustin Ave, Suite 220, Santa Ana, CA 92705 *Tel:* 714-550-0925 *Web Site:* www.dvpostvideo.com, pg 854

DVDs4Less, 6519 Jamon Dr, Sparks, NV 89436-9142 *Tel:* 775-323-0965 *Toll Free Tel:* 800-852-2330 *Fax:* 775-323-1055 *E-mail:* info@dvds4less.net *Web Site:* www.dvds4less.net, pg 854

The DVI Group, 1486 Mecaslin St NW, Atlanta, GA 30309 *Tel:* 404-873-6283 *Toll Free Tel:* 888-736-7384 *E-mail:* makeitbetter@thedvigroup.com *Web Site:* www.thedvigroup.com, pg 854

DVS InteleStream, 2600 W Olive Ave, Burbank, CA 91505 *Tel:* 818-566-4151 *Fax:* 818-566-4453 *E-mail:* info@dvs.tv *Web Site:* www.dvs.tv, pg 854

DW Electrochemicals Ltd, 3-97 Newkirk Rd N, Richmond Hill, ON L4C 3G4, Canada *Tel:* 905-508-7500 *Fax:* 905-508-7502 *E-mail:* dwel@stabilant.com *Web Site:* www.stabilant.com, pg 854

DWD Theatre Design & Consulting, Suite 485, 425 Carrall St, Vancouver, BC V6B 6E3, Canada *Tel:* 604-874-0552 *E-mail:* info@d-w-d.com *Web Site:* www.d-w-d.com, pg 854

DWJ Television, One Robinson Lane, Ridgewood, NJ 07450 *Tel:* 201-445-1711 *Toll Free Tel:* 800-766-1711 *Fax:* 201-445-8352, pg 854

Dyer-Bennet Records, 792 Columbus Ave, Rm 16-0, New York, NY 10025 *Tel:* 212-866-3675, pg 854

Dykeman Associates Inc, 4115 Rawlins St, Dallas, TX 75219 *E-mail:* info@dykemanassociates.com *Web Site:* www.dykemanassociates.com, pg 854

Dyna-Lite Inc, 1050 Commerce Ave, Union, NJ 07083 *Tel:* 908-687-8800 *Toll Free Tel:* 800-722-6638 *Fax:* 908-686-6682 *E-mail:* flash@dynalite.com *Web Site:* www.dynalite.com, pg 854

Dynamic Digital Depth Inc (DDD), 6100 Center Dr W, Suite 1100, Los Angeles, CA 90045 *Tel:* 310-566-3340 *Toll Free Tel:* 877-884-4333 *Fax:* 310-566-3380 *E-mail:* info@ddd.com *Web Site:* www.ddd.com, pg 854

Dystopian Studios, 651 Clover St, Bldg 1, Los Angeles, CA 90031 *Tel:* 310-503-2365 *Web Site:* dystopianstudios.com, pg 854

e-MEDIAtely, 6778 Cibola, San Diego, CA 92120 *Tel:* 619-583-2008 *Toll Free Tel:* 866-816-6845 *Fax:* 619-501-1425 *E-mail:* sdweb@cox.net *Web Site:* www.e-mediately.com, pg 855

E Video Productions, 17 Washington St, Toms River, NJ 08753 *Tel:* 732-349-4762 *Toll Free Tel:* 877-384-3365 *Web Site:* www.evideoproductions.net, pg 855

Eagle Camera Support Systems Ltd, 1783 Draycott Rd, North Vancouver, BC V7J 1W5, Canada *Tel:* 604-649-6350 *Web Site:* eaglecss.com, pg 855

Eagle Films, 2806 Cameron Rd, Falls Church, VA 22042-2004 *Tel:* 703-237-8160 *Web Site:* www.eaglefilms.com, pg 855

Eagle Inc, PO Box 579, Clarkdale, AZ 86324 *Tel:* 928-204-2597 *Fax:* 928-204-2568 *E-mail:* hier_bosch@yahoo.com *Web Site:* www.eagle-1st.com, pg 855

Eagle Multimedia, 6024 Paseo Palmilla, Goleta, CA 93117 *Tel:* 805-964-7041 *Fax:* 805-964-1338 *E-mail:* dicepoo@aol.com *Web Site:* www.eaglemultimedia.com, pg 855

Eagle Photographics & Digital Imaging Inc, 3612 W Swann Ave, Tampa, FL 33609 *Tel:* 813-870-2495 *Fax:* 813-876-5093 *Web Site:* www.eaglefineartimaging.com, pg 855

EagleVision Inc, 1200 High Ridge Rd, 2nd fl, Stamford, CT 06905 *Tel:* 203-359-8777 *Fax:* 203-348-6000 *E-mail:* info@evtv.net *Web Site:* www.evtv.net, pg 855

EAR Professional Audio/Video, 2641 E McDowell Rd, Phoenix, AZ 85008 *Tel:* 602-267-0600 *Toll Free Tel:* 800-473-6914 *Fax:* 602-275-3277 *E-mail:* info@ear.net *Web Site:* www.ear.net, pg 855

Earl Girls Inc, 1648 White Horse Pike, Egg Harbor City, NJ 08215 *Tel:* 609-965-6900 *Toll Free Tel:* 888-777-EARL (777-3275) *Fax:* 609-965-3330 *E-mail:* sales@earlgirlsinc.com *Web Site:* earlgirlsinc.com, pg 855

Early Films, 9 Richter St, Randolph, NJ 07869-3309 *Tel:* 973-361-5817 *Fax:* 973-361-2748 *E-mail:* info@earlyfilms.net *Web Site:* www.earlyfilms.net, pg 855

Earmark LLC, 1125 Dixwell Ave, Hamden, CT 06514 *Tel:* 203-777-2130 *Toll Free Tel:* 888-327-6275 *Fax:* 203-777-2886 *E-mail:* staff@earmark.com *Web Site:* www.earmark.com, pg 855

Earth Mother Productions Inc™, PO Box 43204, Tucson, AZ 85733-3204 *Tel:* 520-790-7061 *Fax:* 801-740-6397 *E-mail:* art4wall@aol.com *Web Site:* www.earthmotherproductions.com, pg 855

EarthDesign Inc, 9 Riverfront Dr, Venice, FL 34293 *Tel:* 941-276-8689 *Toll Free Tel:* 800-327-8433 *E-mail:* gp@jamilin.com *Web Site:* www.jamilin.com, pg 855

Earthworks Inc, 37 Wilton Rd, Milford, NH 03055 *Tel:* 603-654-6427 (sales); 603-654-2433 *Fax:* 603-654-6107 *E-mail:* info@earthworksaudio.com *Web Site:* www.earthworksaudio.com, pg 855

Earwax Productions Inc, 916 Kearny St, San Francisco, CA 94133 *Tel:* 415-860-9403 *Web Site:* www.earwaxproductions.com, pg 855

Earwig Music Co Inc, 2054 W Farwell Ave, Unit G, Chicago, IL 60645-4963 *Tel:* 773-262-0278 *E-mail:* orders@earwigmusic.com *Web Site:* www.earwigmusic.com, pg 855

EASI, 2296 Country Club Dr, Mason City, IA 50401 *Tel:* 641-424-5079 *Toll Free Tel:* 888-327-4797 *Fax:* 641-424-8869 *Web Site:* www.easisat.com, pg 855

East Lansing Film Festival (ELFF), 210 Abbot Rd, Suite 48, East Lansing, MI 48823-4348 *Tel:* 517-980-5802 *Web Site:* elff.com, pg 1114

East of Hollywood NY, 140 53 St, Brooklyn, NY 11232 *Tel:* 718-492-7400 *Fax:* 718-439-3930 *E-mail:* info@eastofhollywoodny.com *Web Site:* www.eastofhollywoodny.com, pg 855

Eastco Multimedia Solutions Inc, 3646 California Rd, Orchard Park, NY 14127 *Tel:* 716-662-0536 *Toll Free Tel:* 800-365-8273 (orders) *Fax:* 716-662-3360 *E-mail:* info@eastcomultimedia.com *Web Site:* www.eastcomultimedia.com, pg 856

Eastern Acoustic Works Inc (EAW), One Main St, Whitinsville, MA 01588-2238 *Tel:* 508-234-6158 *Toll Free Tel:* 800-992-5013 *Fax:* 508-234-8251 *Toll Free Fax:* 800-322-8251 *E-mail:* info@eaw.com *Web Site:* www.eaw.com, pg 856

Eastern Effects Inc, 99 Ninth St, Brooklyn, NY 11215 *Tel:* 718-855-1197 *Fax:* 212-504-9534 *E-mail:* geteffected@easterneffects.com *Web Site:* www.easterneffects.com, pg 856

Eastern Video, 7111 Biscayne Blvd, Miami, FL 33138 *Tel:* 305-759-7111 *Fax:* 305-759-7111; 305-751-2329 *E-mail:* miami@easternvideo.com *Web Site:* www.easternvideo.com, pg 856

Eastman Corp, 7447 Via de Fortuna, Carlsbad, CA 92009 *Tel:* 760-603-8646 *Web Site:* www.kbwfoundation.com, pg 856

Eastman Kodak Professional, 343 State St, Rochester, NY 14650 *Toll Free Tel:* 800-698-3324 *Web Site:* www.kodak.com, pg 856

Easy Edit Video Inc, 8431 Baymeadows Way, Jacksonville, FL 32256 *Tel:* 904-730-9999 *Fax:* 904-730-0412 *Web Site:* www.easyeditvideo.com, pg 856

Easy Street Productions, 118 Redhaven Ct, Thurmont, MD 21788 *Tel:* 301-471-8058 *E-mail:* info@publicdomainfootage.com *Web Site:* www.publicdomainfootage.com, pg 856

Eaton Corp, 8609 Six Forks Rd, Raleigh, NC 27615 *Tel:* 919-872-3020 *Toll Free Tel:* 800-356-5794 *E-mail:* powerquality@eaton.com *Web Site:* powerquality.eaton.com, pg 856

ECG Productions, 120 Interstate N Pkwy SE, Suite 435, Atlanta, GA 30339 *Tel:* 678-855-5169 *E-mail:* info@ecgprod.com *Web Site:* www.ecgprod.com, pg 856

Eco-Greenlighting Inc, 7718 San Fernando Rd N, Sun Valley, CA 91352 *Tel:* 818-768-4300 *Fax:* 818-768-4988 *E-mail:* info@eco-greenlighting.com *Web Site:* www.eco-greenlighting.com, pg 856

ECONEWS (Environmental Television Series) & (Environmental Directions Radio Series), PO Box 351419, Los Angeles, CA 90035-9119 *Tel:* 310-559-9160 *Fax:* 310-559-9160 *E-mail:* ecnp@aol.com *Web Site:* www.ecoprojects.org, pg 856

ECS Inc, 5665 Tremont Ave, Davenport, IA 52807-2658 *Tel:* 563-322-1525 *Fax:* 563-322-5920 *Web Site:* www.ecsdav.com, pg 856

Edcom Multimedia Products, 2386 Main St, Unit 1, London, ON N6P 1A9, Canada *Tel:* 519-652-3533 *Toll Free Tel:* 800-265-1069 *Fax:* 519-652-5045 *E-mail:* sales-l@edcom.ca; info@edcom.ca *Web Site:* www.edcom.ca, pg 856

EDCOR Electronics Corp, 7130 National Parks Hwy, Carlsbad, NM 88220 *Tel:* 575-887-6790 *Toll Free Tel:* 800-854-0259 *Fax:* 575-887-6880 *E-mail:* sales@edcorusa.com *Web Site:* www.edcorusa.com, pg 856

Edgeware Associates/Travel Arts Syndicate, 377 Rector Place, Suite 10-H, New York, NY 10280 *Tel:* 212-807-7509 *Web Site:* www.travelartssyndicate.blogspot.com, pg 856

Edgewise Media Inc, 602 N Cypress St, Orange, CA 92867 *Toll Free Tel:* 800-959-5156 *Fax:* 323-466-6815 *E-mail:* sales@edgewise-media.com *Web Site:* www.edgewise-media.com, pg 856

Edgewood Studios, Howe Ctr, Unit 12-B, Suite 90, Rutland, VT 05701-4459 *Tel:* 802-773-0510 *Fax:* 802-773-3481 *Web Site:* www.edgewoodstudios.com, pg 857

Edison Price Lighting, 41-50 22 St, Long Island City, NY 11101 *Tel:* 718-685-0700 *Fax:* 718-786-8530 *E-mail:* info@epl.com *Web Site:* www.epl.com, pg 857

Edit House Chicago, 5325 W Berenice Ave, Chicago, IL 60641 *Tel:* 773-725-1525 *Web Site:* www.edithousechicago.com, pg 857

The Editing Co, 7030 Empire Central Dr, Houston, TX 77040 *Tel:* 713-783-2655 *Fax:* 713-783-8642 *Web Site:* www.editingco.com, pg 857

Les Editions CEC Inc, 9001 boul Louis-H-La Fontaine, Anjou, QC H1J 2C5, Canada *Tel:* 514-351-6010 *Toll Free Tel:* 800-363-0494 *Fax:* 514-351-3534 *Web Site:* www.editionscec.com, pg 857

Edmund Scientific, 532 Main St, Tonawanda, NY 14150 *Toll Free Tel:* 800-728-6999; 800-818-4955 *Toll Free Fax:* 800-828-3299 *E-mail:* scientifics@edsci.com *Web Site:* www.scientificsonline.com, pg 857

EDR Media LLC, 23330 Commerce Park, Beachwood, OH 44122-5811 *Tel:* 216-292-7300 *Web Site:* www.edrmedia.com; www.beachwoodstudios.com, pg 857

Education Development Center Inc (EDC), 43 Foundry Ave, Waltham, MA 02453-8313 *Tel:* 617-969-7100 *Fax:* 617-969-5979 *E-mail:* contact@edc.org *Web Site:* www.edc.org, pg 857

Education Works, 735 Iwilei Rd, Suite 330, Honolulu, HI 96817 *Tel:* 808-237-5350 *Toll Free Tel:* 800-573-3822 *Fax:* 808-545-8341 *E-mail:* info@educationworkshawaii.com *Web Site:* catalog.educationworkshawaii.com, pg 857

Educational Activities Inc, PO Box 87, Baldwin, NY 11510-0087 *Tel:* 516-223-4666 *Toll Free Tel:* 800-797-3223 *Fax:* 516-623-9282 *E-mail:* learn@edact.com *Web Site:* www.edact.com, pg 857

Educational Film Center, 3314 Newark St NW, Washington, DC 20008 *Tel:* 202-243-1048 *Fax:* 202-243-1048 *Web Site:* www.efcvideo.com, pg 857

Educational Images Ltd, 660 Fassett Rd, Elmira, NY 14901 *Tel:* 607-732-1090 *Toll Free Tel:* 800-527-4264, pg 857

Educational Impressions, 785 Franklin Ave, Franklin Lakes, NJ 07417 *Tel:* 201-644-0908 *Toll Free Tel:* 800-451-7450 *Fax:* 201-644-0907 *E-mail:* awpeller@optonline.net *Web Site:* www.edimpressions.com, pg 857

Educational Insights, 380 N Fairway Dr, Vernon Hills, IL 60061 *Toll Free Tel:* 888-591-9334 (cust serv) *Toll Free Fax:* 888-995-0506 (cust serv) *E-mail:* info@edin.com; cs@educationalinsights.com *Web Site:* www.educationalinsights.com, pg 857

Educational Media LLC, 1300 W Main St, Oklahoma City, OK 73106 *Tel:* 405-239-2955 *Toll Free Tel:* 800-654-8428 *Fax:* 405-236-4261 *E-mail:* mail@educationalmediallc.com *Web Site:* www.educationalmediallc.com, pg 857

Educational Technology Services (ETS), Medical Sciences, Rm SB-43, 513 Parnassus Ave, San Francisco, CA 94143-0702 *Tel:* 415-476-4310 *Fax:* 415-514-3735 *E-mail:* edtech@ucsf.edu *Web Site:* edtech.ucsf.edu, pg 857

Educational Video Group Inc, 291 Southwind Way, Greenwood, IN 46142-9190 *Tel:* 317-889-8253 *Fax:* 317-888-5857 *E-mail:* service@evgonline.com *Web Site:* www.evgonline.com, pg 857

Educational Video Network, 1401 19 St, Huntsville, TX 77340 *Tel:* 936-295-5767 *Toll Free Tel:* 800-762-0060 *Fax:* 936-294-0233 *Toll Free Fax:* 866-814-1714 *Web Site:* www.evndirect.com, pg 857

EduMedia of Sugar Land, Texas, PO Box 2428, Sugar Land, TX 77487-2428 *Tel:* 281-277-3970 *E-mail:* service@history2u.com *Web Site:* www.history2u.com, pg 857

EEG Enterprises Inc, 586 Main St, Farmingdale, NY 11735 *Tel:* 516-293-7472 *Fax:* 516-293-7417 *E-mail:* sales@eegent.com *Web Site:* www.eegent.com, pg 858

Effective Engineering, 2805 W Empire Ave, Burbank, CA 91504 *Tel:* 818-841-4437 *Fax:* 818-841-4389 *E-mail:* info@effeng.com *Web Site:* www.effeng.com, pg 858

Effective Learning Systems Inc, 7740 W 78 St, Bloomington, MN 55439 *Tel:* 952-943-1660 *Toll Free Tel:* 800-966-5683 (orders) *E-mail:* info@efflearn.com *Web Site:* www.efflearn.com, pg 858

eFootage LLC, 65 N Raymond Ave, Suite 220, Pasadena, CA 91103 *Tel:* 626-395-9593 *Fax:* 626-792-5394 *E-mail:* info@efootage.com *Web Site:* www.efootage.com, pg 858

EFX Media, 2300 S Ninth St, Suite 136, Arlington, VA 22204 *Tel:* 703-486-2303 *Fax:* 703-553-9813 *E-mail:* info@efxmedia.com; sales@efxmedia.com *Web Site:* www.efxmedia.com, pg 858

Egan Visual Inc/Egan TeamBoard Inc, 300 Hanlan Rd, Woodbridge, ON L4L 3P6, Canada *Tel:* 905-851-2826 *Toll Free Tel:* 800-263-2387 (US & CN) *Toll Free Fax:* 888-609-8886 *E-mail:* marketing@egan.com *Web Site:* www.egan.com; www.teamboard.com, pg 858

Egripment USA Inc, 201 Center Park Dr, Suite 1010, Knoxville, TN 37922 *Tel:* 865-357-7535 *Fax:* 865-357-7536 *Web Site:* www.egripment.com, pg 858

18 Label Studios, 18 Label St, Montclair, NJ 07042 *Tel:* 973-744-7382 *E-mail:* info@18label.com *Web Site:* 18label.com, pg 858

8K Productions, 11952 Blue Heron Dr, Draper, UT 84020 *Tel:* 801-671-8357 *E-mail:* rentals@8kproductions.com *Web Site:* www.8kproductions.com, pg 858

Eiki International, 30251 Esperanza, Rancho Santa Margarita, CA 92688-2130 *Tel:* 949-457-0200 *Toll Free Tel:* 800-242-3454 *Fax:* 949-457-7877 *Toll Free Fax:* 800-457-3454 *E-mail:* usa@eiki.com *Web Site:* www.eiki.com, pg 858

EiKO Ltd, 23220 W 84 St, Shawnee Mission, KS 66227 *Tel:* 913-441-8500 *Toll Free Tel:* 800-852-2217 *Fax:* 913-441-6679 *E-mail:* eiko@eiko.com *Web Site:* www.eiko-ltd.com, pg 858

eInstruction Corp, 14400 N 87 St, Suite 250, Scottsdale, AZ 85260 *Tel:* 480-948-6540 *Toll Free Tel:* 800-856-0732 *Fax:* 480-948-5508 *Web Site:* www.einstruction.com, pg 858

El Dorado Lake Tahoe Film & Media Office, 542 Main St, Placerville, CA 95667 *Tel:* 530-626-4400 *Toll Free Tel:* 800-457-6279 *Fax:* 530-642-1624 *E-mail:* film@eldoradocounty.org *Web Site:* filmtahoe.com, pg 1093

El Mar Plastics Inc, 967 E Sandhill Ave, Carson, CA 90746 *Tel:* 310-436-6444 *Toll Free Tel:* 800-255-5210 *Fax:* 310-436-6445 *E-mail:* sales@elmarplastics.com *Web Site:* www.elmarplastics.com, pg 858

El Paso Film Commission, One Civic Center Plaza, El Paso, TX 79901 *Toll Free Tel:* 800-351-6024 *Fax:* 915-532-2963 *Web Site:* www.visitelpaso.com/film, pg 1103

ELC Sales & Service Inc, 3100 S Congress Ave, Suite 6, Boynton Beach, FL 33426 *Tel:* 561-756-2210 *E-mail:* tvman@gate.net, pg 858

Electric Lady Studios, 52 W Eighth St, New York, NY 10011 *Tel:* 212-677-4700 *Web Site:* electricladystudios.com, pg 858

Electriduct Inc, 6250 NW 27 Way, Fort Lauderdale, FL 33309 *Tel:* 954-867-9100 *Toll Free Tel:* 866-673-9590 *Fax:* 954-206-0799 *E-mail:* sales@electriduct.com *Web Site:* www.electriduct.com, pg 858

Electro Impulse Laboratory Inc, 1805 Rte 33, Neptune, NJ 07754 *Tel:* 732-776-5800 *Fax:* 732-776-6793 *E-mail:* sales@electroimpulse.com *Web Site:* www.electroimpulse.com, pg 858

Electron Microscopy Sciences (EMS), 1560 Industry Rd, Hatfield, PA 19440 *Tel:* 215-412-8400 *Toll Free Tel:* 800-523-5874 *Fax:* 215-412-8450 *E-mail:* sgkcck@aol.com *Web Site:* www.emsdiasum.com/microscopy, pg 859

Electronic Arts, 209 Redwood Shores Pkwy, Redwood City, CA 94065 *Tel:* 650-628-1500 *Web Site:* www.ea.com, pg 859

Electronic Service Dealers Association, 4925 W Irving Park Rd, Chicago, IL 60641 *Tel:* 773-282-9400, pg 1081

Electronic Vision Inc (EV), 5 Depot St, Athens, OH 45701 *Tel:* 740-592-2433 *Fax:* 740-592-2650 *E-mail:* info@ev.net *Web Site:* www.electronicvision.com, pg 859

Electronics Representatives Association (ERA), 111 N Canal St, Suite 885, Chicago, IL 60606 *Tel:* 312-559-3050 *Fax:* 312-559-4566 *E-mail:* info@era.org *Web Site:* www.era.org, pg 1081

Electronics Technicians Association International Inc, 5 Depot St, Greencastle, IN 46135 *Tel:* 765-653-8262 *Toll Free Tel:* 800-288-3824 *Fax:* 765-653-4287 *E-mail:* eta@eta-i.org *Web Site:* www.eta-i.org, pg 1081

Electrorack Legrand Division, 1443 S Sunkist St, Anaheim, CA 92806 *Tel:* 714-776-5420 *Toll Free Tel:* 800-433-6745 *Fax:* 714-776-9683 *E-mail:* sales@electrorack.com *Web Site:* www.electrorack.com, pg 859

Electrosonic Inc, 3320 N San Fernando Blvd, Burbank, CA 91504 *Tel:* 818-333-3600 *Toll Free Tel:* 888-343-3604 (sales) *Fax:* 818-230-1017 *E-mail:* info@electrosonic.com *Web Site:* www.electrosonic.com, pg 859

Elegant Packaging Corp, 5253 W Roosevelt Rd, Cicero, IL 60804 *Tel:* 708-652-3400 *Toll Free Tel:* 800-367-5493 *Fax:* 708-652-6444 *E-mail:* info@elegantpackaging.com *Web Site:* www.elegantpackaging.com, pg 859

Elektrashock, 1320 Main St, Venice, CA 90291 *Tel:* 310-399-4985 *Fax:* 310-399-4972 *E-mail:* info@elektrashock.com *Web Site:* www.elektrashock.com, pg 859

Eli Research Group, 2222 Sedwick Rd, Suite 102, Durham, NC 27713 *Toll Free Tel:* 800-223-8720 *Toll Free Fax:* 800-508-2592 *E-mail:* customerservice@dartnellcorp.com *Web Site:* www.dartnellcorp.com, pg 859

Elite Video, 209 E Emerson Rd, Lexington, MA 02420 *Tel:* 781-862-6606 *E-mail:* sales@elitevision.com *Web Site:* www.elitevision.com, pg 859

Elite Video & Photography Services Inc, 250 Mount Sinai Coram Rd, Coram, NY 11727 *Tel:* 631-696-1635 *E-mail:* info@cantbeatelite.com *Web Site:* www.cantbeatelite.com, pg 859

Albert Ellis Institute (AEI), 145 E 32 St, 9th fl, New York, NY 10016 *Tel:* 212-535-0822 *Fax:* 212-249-3582 *E-mail:* info@albertellis.org *Web Site:* www.albertellis.org, pg 859

Ellison Educational Equipment Inc, 25862 Commercentre Dr, Lake Forest, CA 92630-8804 *Tel:* 949-598-8822 *Toll Free Tel:* 800-253-2238 *Fax:* 949-598-8840 *Toll Free Fax:* 800-253-2240 *E-mail:* customersupport@ellison.com *Web Site:* www.ellison.com, pg 859

ELMO USA Corp, 1478 Old Country Rd, Plainview, NY 11803 *Tel:* 516-501-1400 *Toll Free Tel:* 800-947-3566 *Fax:* 516-501-0429 *E-mail:* elmo@elmousa.com *Web Site:* www.elmousa.com, pg 859

Elo TouchSystems, 1033 McCarthy Blvd, Milpitas, CA 95035 *Toll Free Tel:* 800-356-8682; 800-557-1458 *Fax:* 650-361-4722 *E-mail:* eloinfo@elotouch.com; customerservice@elotouch.com *Web Site:* www.elotouch.com, pg 859

ELS Productions Inc, 3287 Sanborn Dr, Riverton, UT 84065 *Tel:* 801-676-0807 *Toll Free Tel:* 800-927-3472 *E-mail:* customerservice@elsproductions.com *Web Site:* www.elsproductions.com, pg 860

Em Gee Film Library, 13502 Erwin St, Van Nuys, CA 91401 *Tel:* 818-997-0410, pg 860

eMagin Corp, 3006 Northup Way, Suite 103, Bellevue, WA 98004 *Tel:* 425-284-5200 *Toll Free Tel:* 877-362-4461 *Fax:* 425-284-5201 *E-mail:* info@emagin.com *Web Site:* www.emagin.com, pg 860

Emanuel Audiovisual Consultants, 303 County Rd, Cresskill, NJ 07626 *Tel:* 201-569-5328 *Toll Free Fax:* 888-397-1302 *E-mail:* emanuelav@att.net *Web Site:* www.audiovisualconsultant.com, pg 860

EMC/Paradigm Publishing, 875 Montreal Way, St Paul, MN 55102 *Tel:* 651-290-2800 (corp) *Toll Free Tel:* 800-535-6865 (cust care); 800-328-1452 *Fax:* 651-290-2899 *Toll Free Fax:* 800-328-4564 (cust care) *E-mail:* educate@emcp.com *Web Site:* www.emcp.com, pg 860

Emcor Enclosures-Crenlo, 1600 Fourth Ave NW, Rochester, MN 55901 *Tel:* 507-287-3535 *Fax:* 507-287-3405 *E-mail:* emcorenclosures@crenlo.com *Web Site:* www.emcorenclosures.com, pg 860

Emerald Coast Film Commission, PO Box 609, Fort Walton Beach, FL 32549-0609 *Tel:* 850-651-7644 *Fax:* 850-651-7149 *E-mail:* emeraldfilm@co.okaloosa.fl.us *Web Site:* filmemeraldcoast.com, pg 1095

Emerald Records, PO Box 17059, Nashville, TN 37217-0059 *Tel:* 615-361-7902 *E-mail:* entertainernet@comcast.net *Web Site:* www.entertainernet.net, pg 860

Emergency Film Group, 140 Cooke St, Edgartown, MA 02539 *Tel:* 508-627-8844 *Toll Free Tel:* 800-842-0999 *Fax:* 508-627-8863 *E-mail:* info@efilmgroup.com *Web Site:* www.efilmgroup.com, pg 860

Emerson Network Power Surge Protection Inc, 100 Emerson Pkwy, Binghamton, NY 13905 *Tel:* 607-721-8840 *Toll Free Tel:* 800-288-6169 *Fax:* 607-722-8713 *E-mail:* contactsurge@emerson.com *Web Site:* www.emersonnetworkpower.com, pg 860

Emerson Radio Corp, 3 University Plaza, Suite 405, Hackensack, NJ 07601 *Tel:* 973-884-5800 *Toll Free Tel:* 800-909-1240 (cust serv) *Fax:* 973-428-2067 *E-mail:* internet@emersonradio.com *Web Site:* www.emersonradio.com, pg 860

Emery-Pratt Co, 1966 W M-21, Owosso, MI 48867-1379 *Tel:* 989-723-5291 *Toll Free Tel:* 800-248-3887 *Fax:* 989-723-4677 *Toll Free Fax:* 800-523-6379 *E-mail:* mail@emery-pratt.com *Web Site:* www.emery-pratt.com, pg 860

EMI CMG Distribution, 101 Winners Circle, Brentwood, TN 37027 *Tel:* 615-371-4300 *Toll Free Tel:* 800-877-4443 *Fax:* 615-371-6555; 615-371-6980 (sales) *E-mail:* distribution@emicmg.com *Web Site:* www.emicmg.com; www.emicmgdistribution.com, pg 860

Emlight Design, 1179 N Eastman Ave, Suite 1, Los Angeles, CA 90063 *Tel:* 323-261-5162 *Toll Free Fax:* 866-728-9164 *E-mail:* service@dimmer.com *Web Site:* www.dimmer.com; www.emlightdesign.com, pg 860

Emmy Awards (Primetime), 5220 Lankershim Blvd, North Hollywood, CA 91601-3109 *Tel:* 818-754-2800 *Fax:* 818-754-2836 *Web Site:* www.emmys.com, pg 1114

eMotion Studios, 85 Liberty Ship Way, Suite 110, Sausalito, CA 94965 *Tel:* 415-331-6975 *Fax:* 415-331-6124 *E-mail:* sales@emotionstudios.com *Web Site:* www.emotionstudios.com, pg 860

Empire Wholesale Inc, 5675 Mansfield Way, Bell, CA 90201 *Tel:* 213-748-5200 *Toll Free Tel:* 866-748-5200 *Fax:* 213-748-5505 *E-mail:* sales@empirepro.com *Web Site:* www.empirepro.com, pg 860

ENCO Systems Inc, 29444 Northwestern Hwy, Southfield, MI 48034 *Tel:* 248-827-4440 *Toll Free Tel:* 800-362-6797 (sales) *Fax:* 248-827-4441 *E-mail:* sales@enco.com *Web Site:* www.enco.com, pg 860

Encore Broadcast Solutions, 2104 W Kennedy Blvd, Tampa, FL 33606 *Tel:* 813-253-2774 *Toll Free Tel:* 800-780-8857 *Fax:* 813-254-5907 *Web Site:* www.encorebroadcast.com, pg 860

Encore Cases, 8818 Lankershim Blvd, Sun Valley, CA 91352 *Tel:* 818-768-8803 *Toll Free Tel:* 800-743-6267 *Fax:* 818-768-3993 *Web Site:* www.encorecases.com; www.giantcases.com, pg 861

Encore Home Video, PO Box 25, Frankenmuth, MI 48734-0025 *Tel:* 989-652-9699 *E-mail:* sales@encorehomevideo.com *Web Site:* www.encorehomevideo.com, pg 861

Encore Productions Inc, 5150 S Decatur Blvd, Las Vegas, NV 89119 *Tel:* 702-739-8803 *Toll Free Tel:* 800-287-7469 *Fax:* 702-739-8831 *Web Site:* www.encore-us.com, pg 861

Encore Video Productions, 811 Main St, Myrtle Beach, SC 29577 *Tel:* 843-448-9900 *E-mail:* crew@encorevideo.biz *Web Site:* www.encorevideo.biz, pg 861

Encounter Video Inc, 14825 NW Ash St, Portland, OR 97231-2620 *Tel:* 503-285-8974 *Fax:* 503-285-3726 *E-mail:* encountvid@aol.com *Web Site:* www.encountervideo.com, pg 861

Encyclomedia, 1526 Dekalb Ave, Atlanta, GA 30307 *Tel:* 404-527-3600 *Fax:* 404-584-5171 *E-mail:* info@encyclomedia.net *Web Site:* www.encyclomedia.net, pg 861

Encyclopaedia Britannica Inc, 331 N La Salle St, Chicago, IL 60654 *Tel:* 312-347-7000 (all other countries) *Toll Free Tel:* 800-323-1229 (US & CN) *Fax:* 312-294-2104 *Web Site:* www.britannica.com, pg 861

Endtime Inc, 2701 E George Bush Tpke, Suite 100, Plano, TX 75074 *Tel:* 972-422-0857 *Toll Free Tel:* 800-363-8463 (cust serv) *Fax:* 972-423-4370 *E-mail:* questions@endtime.com; customerservice@endtime.com *Web Site:* www.endtime.com, pg 861

Enhanced View Services Inc, 12360 SW 132 Ct, Suite 114, Miami, FL 33186 *Tel:* 305-971-2916 *Toll Free Tel:* 877-873-3843 *Web Site:* www.usedvideogear.com, pg 861

Enright Co, 1801-I Parkcourt Place, Suite 100, Santa Ana, CA 92701 *Toll Free Tel:* 888-334-7773 *Fax:* 714-285-1905 *E-mail:* admin@enrightcompany.com *Web Site:* www.enrightcompany.com, pg 861

Ensemble Designs Inc, 870 Gold Flat Rd, Nevada City, CA 95959 *Tel:* 530-478-1830 *Fax:* 530-478-1832 *E-mail:* info@ensembledesigns.com *Web Site:* www.ensembledesigns.com, pg 861

Entel Systems Inc, 230 W Parkway, Pompton Plains, NJ 07444 *Tel:* 201-447-2000 *Toll Free Tel:* 888-914-7100 *Fax:* 201-447-2880 *E-mail:* service@entelsystems.com *Web Site:* www.entelsystems.com, pg 861

Enterprise Media LLC, 91 Harvey St, Cambridge, MA 02140 *Tel:* 617-354-0017 *Toll Free Tel:* 800-423-6021 *Fax:* 617-354-1637 *E-mail:* orders@enterprisemedia.com *Web Site:* www.enterprisemedia.com, pg 861

The Entertainment Merchants Association (EMA), 16530 Ventura Blvd, Suite 400, Encino, CA 91436-4551 *Tel:* 818-385-1500 *Fax:* 818-933-0910 *E-mail:* emaoffice@entmerch.org *Web Site:* www.entmerch.org, pg 1081

Entertainment One Distribution, 22 Harbor Park Dr, Port Washington, NY 11050 *Tel:* 516-484-1000 *E-mail:* musicdistribution@entonegroup.com; videosales@entonegroup.com *Web Site:* entertainmentone.com; us.eonedistribution.com, pg 861

Entertainment One Distribution, 70 Driver Rd, Unit 1, Brampton, ON L6T 5V2, Canada *Tel:* 905-624-7337 *Toll Free Tel:* 800-387-0184 *Fax:* 905-624-7310; 905-463-9755 (cust serv) *E-mail:* info@entertainmentone.ca *Web Site:* entertainmentone.com; ca.eonedistribution.com, pg 861

Envirovision, PO Box 4136, Laguna Beach, CA 92652-4136 *Tel:* 949-673-2555 *Fax:* 949-673-2555 *Web Site:* www.beverlyfactor.com, pg 861

Envision Communications Inc, 2002 N 204 St, Elkhorn, NE 68022 *Tel:* 402-289-2220, pg 861

Epic Software Group Inc, 701 Sawdust Rd, The Woodlands, TX 77380 *Tel:* 281-363-3742 *Fax:* 281-419-4509 *E-mail:* epic@epicsoftware.com *Web Site:* www.epicsoftware.com, pg 862

Epitome Pictures Inc, 220 Bartley Dr, Toronto, ON M4A 1G1, Canada *Tel:* 416-752-7627 *Fax:* 416-752-7837 *E-mail:* info@epitomepictures.com *Web Site:* www.epitomepictures.com, pg 862

EPIX Inc, 381 Lexington Dr, Buffalo Grove, IL 60089 *Tel:* 847-465-1818 *Fax:* 847-465-1919 *E-mail:* epix@epixinc.com *Web Site:* epixinc.com, pg 862

Kat Epple Music Productions, PO Box 3156, North Fort Myers, FL 33918-3156 *Tel:* 239-997-0323 *E-mail:* music@katepple.com *Web Site:* www.katepple.com, pg 862

EPRAD Inc, 6979 Wales Rd, Northwood, OH 43619 *Tel:* 419-666-3266 *Fax:* 419-666-8109 *E-mail:* info@eprad.com *Web Site:* www.eprad.com, pg 862

Equi=Tech Corp, PO Box 249, Selma, OR 97538-0249 *Toll Free Tel:* 877-378-4832 *Fax:* 541-787-8740 *E-mail:* sales@equitech.com *Web Site:* www.equitech.com, pg 862

Equiservices Publishing, 4343 Garfoot Rd, Cross Plains, WI 53528 *Tel:* 608-798-4910 *E-mail:* info@equipub.com *Web Site:* www.equipub.com, pg 862

ERA Learning, PO Box 8795, Portland, OR 97207-8795 *Tel:* 503-228-6345 *Toll Free Tel:* 800-827-2499 (orders) *Fax:* 810-885-5811 *E-mail:* info@eralearning.com; customerservice@eralearning.com *Web Site:* www.eralearning.com, pg 862

Ergo Media Inc, 668 American Legion Dr, Teaneck, NJ 07666 *Tel:* 201-692-0404 *Fax:* 201-692-0663 *E-mail:* info@jewishvideo.com *Web Site:* www.jewishvideo.com; www.ergomedia.com, pg 862

ESE, 142 Sierra St, El Segundo, CA 90245 *Tel:* 310-322-2136 *Fax:* 310-322-8127 *E-mail:* ese@ese-web.com *Web Site:* www.ese-web.com, pg 862

ESECO Speedmaster, 730 E Eseco Rd, Cushing, OK 74023-5505 *Tel:* 918-225-1266 *Toll Free Tel:* 800-331-5904 (US & CN) *Fax:* 918-225-1284 *E-mail:* info@eseco-speedmaster.com *Web Site:* www.eseco-speedmaster.com, pg 862

Esoteric Sound, 1608 Hemstock Ave, Wheaton, IL 60189 *Tel:* 630-933-9801 *Fax:* 630-933-9801 *E-mail:* esotericct@aol.com *Web Site:* www.esotericsound.com, pg 862

ESPN Inc, ESPN Plaza, 545 Middle St, Bristol, CT 06010 *Tel:* 860-766-2000 *Web Site:* espn.go.com, pg 862

Essex Television Group Inc, 7 Vista Dr, Old Lyme, CT 06371 *Tel:* 860-434-7200 *Fax:* 860-434-7210 *E-mail:* contact@essextelevision.com *Web Site:* www.essextelevision.com, pg 862

Estes Park Film Commission, 1200 Graves Ave, Estes Park, CO 80517 *Tel:* 970-586-0500 *Fax:* 970-586-4036, pg 1095

Estiluz Inc, 235 Moonachie Rd, Moonachie, NJ 07074 *Tel:* 201-641-1997 *Fax:* 201-641-2092 *E-mail:* estiluzinc@estiluz.com *Web Site:* www.estiluzusa.com, pg 862

ETA Systems, 1601 Jack McKay Blvd, Ennis, TX 75119 *Tel:* 972-875-8413 *Toll Free Tel:* 800-321-6699 *Toll Free Fax:* 800-996-3821 *E-mail:* etacustomerrelations@etasys.com *Web Site:* www.mitekcorp.com; www.etasys.com, pg 862

ETC, 3031 Pleasant View Rd, Middleton, WI 53562-4809 *Tel:* 608-831-4116 *Toll Free Tel:* 800-688-4116 *Fax:* 608-836-1736 *E-mail:* mail@etcconnect.com; americas@etcconnect.com *Web Site:* www.etcconnect.com, pg 862

Eternal Word Television Network (EWTN), 5817 Old Leeds Rd, Irondale, AL 35210-2164 *Tel:* 205-271-2900 *Fax:* 205-271-2920 *E-mail:* viewer@ewtn.com *Web Site:* www.ewtn.com, pg 862

ETHOS Ltd, 4981 Hwy 7 E, Unit 12-A, Suite 235, Markham, ON L3R 1N1, Canada *Tel:* 905-471-7654 *Toll Free Tel:* 800-471-0737 *Fax:* 905-471-7976 *E-mail:* ethoseducation@rogers.com *Web Site:* www.ethoseducation.ca, pg 863

Ed Ethridge Productions Inc, 1215 E Broward Blvd, Suite 200, Fort Lauderdale, FL 33301 *Tel:* 954-533-7100 *Fax:* 954-306-3261 *Web Site:* www.ethridgeproductions.com, pg 863

EUE/Screen Gems Studios, 1223 N 23 St, Wilmington, NC 28405 *Tel:* 910-343-3500 *Fax:* 910-343-3574 *E-mail:* info@euescreengems.com *Web Site:* euescreengems.com, pg 863

Eugene, Cascades & Coast-Travel Lane County, 754 Olive St, Eugene, OR 97401 *Tel:* 541-484-5307 *Toll Free Tel:* 800-547-5445 *Fax:* 541-343-6335 *E-mail:* film@eugenecascadescoast.org *Web Site:* www.eugenecascadescoast.org, pg 1101

Eureka Springs Advertising & Promotions Commission, PO Box 522, Eureka Springs, AR 72632-0522 *Tel:* 479-253-7333 *Toll Free Tel:* 866-566-9387 *Fax:* 479-363-9380 *E-mail:* info@eurekasprings.org *Web Site:* www.eurekasprings.org, pg 1092

Euro-Pacific Film & Video Productions Inc, PO Box 7986, Shrewsbury, NJ 07702 *Tel:* 732-530-4451 *Toll Free Tel:* 800-387-6776 *E-mail:* info@euro-pacific.com *Web Site:* www.euro-pacific.com, pg 863

Eurotech Seating, c/o Marketec, 419 S Flower St, Burbank, CA 91502 *Tel:* 818-847-0200 *Toll Free Tel:* 800-557-8861 *Toll Free Fax:* 888-262-1726 *E-mail:* info@marketec.com *Web Site:* www.marketec.com, pg 863

Event Essentials, 6485 Blanchar's Crossing, Windsor, WI 53598 *Tel:* 608-846-5004 *Toll Free Tel:* 800-220-4991 *Fax:* 608-222-5063 *Web Site:* www.eventessentials.com, pg 863

Event Tech, 7601 Brandon Woods Blvd, Baltimore, MD 21226 *Tel:* 410-360-5006 *Toll Free Tel:* 866-950-8343 *Fax:* 410-360-5002 *E-mail:* info@eventtech.com *Web Site:* www.eventtech.com, pg 863

Eventide Inc, One Alsan Way, Little Ferry, NJ 07643 *Tel:* 201-641-1200 *Fax:* 201-641-1640 *E-mail:* audio@eventide.com; support@eventide.com *Web Site:* www.eventide.com, pg 863

Ever-Ready Media Packaging, 8192 Gatherly Circle, Easton, MD 21601 *Tel:* 973-566-9333 *Fax:* 201-387-1530 *E-mail:* packages@erpack.com *Web Site:* www.erpack.com, pg 863

Everett Hall Associates Inc, 76 Progress Dr, Stamford, CT 06902 *Tel:* 203-325-4328 *Fax:* 203-323-8078 *E-mail:* info@everetthall.com *Web Site:* www.everetthall.com, pg 863

Everlast Productions, 59 SW 12 Ave, Unit 109, Dania Beach, FL 33004 *Tel:* 954-456-7167 *Fax:* 954-456-1243 *E-mail:* info@everlastproductions.com *Web Site:* everlastproductions.com, pg 863

Evertz Microsystems Ltd, 5292 John Lucas Dr, Burlington, ON L7L 5Z9, Canada *Tel:* 905-335-3700 *Toll Free Tel:* 877-995-3700 *Fax:* 905-335-3573 *E-mail:* sales@evertz.com *Web Site:* www.evertz.com, pg 863

Evidence Audio Inc, PO Box 473, Lake Oswego, OR 97034 *Tel:* 949-306-7390 *E-mail:* info@evidenceaudio.com *Web Site:* www.evidenceaudio.com, pg 863

Evolution Presentation Technologies, 6910 Farrell Rd SE, Calgary, AB T2H 0T1, Canada *Tel:* 403-259-3793 *Toll Free Tel:* 800-561-9820 *Fax:* 403-259-2374 *Web Site:* www.evolutionav.ca, pg 863

Evolution Presentation Technologies, 971 Wall St, Winnipeg, MB R3G 2V4, Canada *Tel:* 204-775-6662 *Toll Free Fax:* 888-775-4693 *E-mail:* sstephens@evolutionav.com *Web Site:* www.evolutionav.ca, pg 863

Evolve Inc, 1210 E Arlington Blvd, Greenville, NC 27858 *Tel:* 252-754-2957 *Fax:* 252-754-2832 *Web Site:* www.evolveinc.com, pg 863

Jasper Ewing & Sons Inc, 1220 E Northside Dr, Suite 370, Jackson, MS 39211 *Tel:* 601-981-2178 *Fax:* 601-981-2178 *E-mail:* jasperewing@comcast.net *Web Site:* jasperewing.com, pg 864

Excel Duplication Services, 1219 N Cass St, Milwaukee, WI 53202 *Tel:* 414-225-9235 *Fax:* 414-225-9236 *E-mail:* info@excelduplication.com *Web Site:* www.excelduplication.com, pg 864

Executive Development Systems, 3818 Vinecrest Dr, Dallas, TX 75229 *Tel:* 214-351-0055 *Toll Free Tel:* 800-955-7353 *Fax:* 214-351-5024 *Web Site:* www.edforeman.com, pg 864

Exeltech Inc, 7317 Jack Newell Blvd N, Fort Worth, TX 76118 *Tel:* 817-595-4969 *Toll Free Tel:* 800-886-4683 *Fax:* 817-595-1290 *E-mail:* exlsales@exeltech.com *Web Site:* www.exeltech.com, pg 864

Exemplar Global, 600 N Plankington Ave, Milwaukee, WI 53201 *Tel:* 414-272-3937 *Toll Free Tel:* 888-722-2440 *Fax:* 414-765-8661 *Web Site:* www.exemplarglobal.org, pg 1081

Exhibit & Event Marketers Association (E2MA), 2214 NW Fifth St, Bend, OR 97701 *Tel:* 541-317-8768 *Fax:* 541-317-8749 *Web Site:* www.e2ma.org, pg 1081

Explore Media LLC, 113 1/2 E Lexington Ave, Elkhart, IN 46516 *Tel:* 574-875-5565 *Fax:* 574-830-0200 *E-mail:* info@explore-media.com *Web Site:* www.explore-media.com, pg 864

Explore Minnesota Tourism, Metro Sq, Suite 100, 121 E Seventh Place, St Paul, MN 55101-2112 *Tel:* 651-757-1870 *Toll Free Tel:* 800-657-3638 *Fax:* 651-296-7095 *E-mail:* explore@state.mn.us *Web Site:* www.exploreminnesota.com, pg 1099

ExpoDisplays, 3401 Mary Taylor Rd, Birmingham, AL 35235 *Tel:* 205-439-8200 *Toll Free Tel:* 800-367-3976 *Fax:* 205-439-8201 *E-mail:* info@expodisplays.com *Web Site:* www.expodisplays.com, pg 864

Express Media Inc, 2225 Palou Ave, San Francisco, CA 94124 *Tel:* 415-255-9883 *Fax:* 415-255-0139 *Web Site:* www.expressmedia.tv, pg 864

Express Media Inc, 2225 Palou Ave, San Francisco, CA 94124 *Tel:* 415-255-9883 *Fax:* 415-255-0139 *Web Site:* www.rentvideo.com; www.expressmedia.tv, pg 864

Express Video Supply Inc, 1819 Victory Blvd, Glendale, CA 91201 *Tel:* 818-552-4590 *Toll Free Tel:* 800-238-8480 *Fax:* 818-552-4591 *E-mail:* rentals@evsonline.com; sales@evsonline.com *Web Site:* www.evsonline.com, pg 864

Extraordinary Demos, 2131 Yellowstar Lane, Naperville, IL 60564-5330 *Tel:* 630-904-3636 *Web Site:* www.extraordinarydemos.com, pg 864

Extreme Reach Inc, 75 Second Ave, Suite 720, Needham, MA 02494 *Tel:* 781-577-2016 *E-mail:* sales@extremereach.com; press@extremereach.com *Web Site:* www.extremereach.com, pg 864

Extron Electronics, 1025 E Ball Rd, Suite 100, Anaheim, CA 92805-5957 *Tel:* 714-491-1500 *Toll Free Tel:* 800-633-9876 (sales & tech support); 800-633-9873 (order support) *Fax:* 714-491-1517 *E-mail:* sales-usa@extron.com *Web Site:* www.extron.com, pg 864

Eye & I Productions, 1250 Kay Lane, Oakley, CA 94561 *Tel:* 925-625-7888 *Toll Free Tel:* 800-720-9014 *E-mail:* contact@voicecrystal.com *Web Site:* www.voicecrystal.com, pg 864

Eye on Dance, 70 E Tenth St, Suite 19-D, New York, NY 10003 *Tel:* 212-206-6492 *E-mail:* eyeonthearts@gmail.com *Web Site:* www.eyeondance.org, pg 865

Eyecon Video Productions, 1865 Summit Ave, Suite 605, Plano, TX 75074 *Tel:* 972-881-3200 *Toll Free Tel:* 877-704-1517 *E-mail:* info@eyeconvideo.com *Web Site:* www.eyeconvideo.com, pg 865

Eyeline Teleprompting, 1313 Mound St, Alameda, CA 94501 *Tel:* 510-205-6762 *Web Site:* www.eyeline.tv, pg 865

EZ FX Inc, 324 Maguire Rd, Ocoee, FL 34761 *Tel:* 407-877-2335 *Toll Free Tel:* 800-541-5706 *Fax:* 407-877-6603 *E-mail:* sales@ezfx.com *Web Site:* www.ezfx.com, pg 865

Face Digital Post, 9753 Via Roma, Burbank, CA 91504 *Tel:* 818-842-9081 *Fax:* 818-768-6313 *E-mail:* face@facedigitalpost.com *Web Site:* www.facedigitalpost.com, pg 865

Facet Media, 5821 Rodman St, Hollywood, FL 33023 *Tel:* 954-589-0535 *Fax:* 954-593-0411 *E-mail:* info@facetmedia.com *Web Site:* www.facetmedia.com, pg 865

Facets Multi-Media Inc, 1517 W Fullerton Ave, Chicago, IL 60614 *Tel:* 773-281-9075 (ext 3011) *Toll Free Tel:* 800-331-6197 *Fax:* 773-929-5437 *E-mail:* sales@facets.org *Web Site:* www.facets.org, pg 865

Faith Fellowship Ministries World Outreach Center, 2707 Main St Ext, Sayreville, NJ 08872 *Tel:* 732-727-9500 *E-mail:* information@ffmwoc.org *Web Site:* www.ffmwoc.org, pg 865

Falcon Safety Products Inc, 25 Imclone Dr, Branchburg, NJ 08876 *Tel:* 908-707-4900 *Toll Free Tel:* 800-332-5266 (cust serv ext 1) *Fax:* 908-707-8855 *Web Site:* www.falconsafety.com, pg 865

Fambrough & Associates Inc, 13501 Leatha's Ct, Suite 100, Kansas City, MO 64089-7701 *Tel:* 816-471-1717 *Fax:* 816-256-5283 *E-mail:* we_work_for_you@fambrough.com *Web Site:* www.fambrough.com, pg 865

Family Health Media, PO Box 5832, Charlottesville, VA 22905-5832 *Tel:* 434-566-0123 *Toll Free Tel:* 800-366-3641 *Toll Free Fax:* 888-234-2579 *E-mail:* support@familyhealthmedia.com *Web Site:* www.familyhealthmedia.com, pg 865

F&F Productions, 14333 Myerlake Circle, Clearwater, FL 33760 *Tel:* 727-530-5000 *Fax:* 727-535-6547 *Web Site:* www.fandfhd.tv, pg 865

Fanlight Productions, c/o Icarus Films, 32 Court St, Brooklyn, NY 11201 *Tel:* 718-488-8900 *Toll Free Tel:* 800-876-1710 *Fax:* 781-488-8642 *E-mail:* info@fanlight.com *Web Site:* www.fanlight.com; www.icarusfilms.com, pg 865

Fanon Courier, 17171 Murphy Ave, Irvine, CA 92614-5915 *Tel:* 949-417-8085 *Toll Free Tel:* 800-345-1354 *Fax:* 949-417-8075 *E-mail:* info@fanon.com *Web Site:* www.fanon.com, pg 865

Fantasee Lighting Inc, 14857 Martinsville Rd, Belleville, MI 48111 *Tel:* 734-699-7200 *Fax:* 734-699-7400 *E-mail:* info@fantaseelighting.com *Web Site:* www.fantaseelighting.com, pg 865

Fantasy Creations FX, 2060 E McDaniel St, Springfield, MO 65802 *Tel:* 417-619-1138 *E-mail:* fcfxmike@yahoo.com *Web Site:* www.fantasycreationsfx.com, pg 865

Fantasy Studios, 2600 Tenth St, Berkeley, CA 94710 *Tel:* 510-486-2038 *Fax:* 510-486-2248 *Web Site:* www.fantasystudios.com, pg 865

Far West Media Services Inc, 4140 Norse Way, Long Beach, CA 90808 *Tel:* 562-496-3342 *Fax:* 562-496-4329 *Web Site:* www.farwestmedia.com, pg 865

Fastlane Productions LLC, 7 Riverdale Rd, Billerica, MA 01821 *Tel:* 978-667-8399 *Fax:* 978-667-8398 *E-mail:* info@fastlaneproductions.net *Web Site:* www.fastlaneproductions.net, pg 866

Fax Animation Co, 5625 Melrose Ave, Hollywood, CA 90038 *Tel:* 323-466-3561 *Fax:* 323-871-2193 *E-mail:* contactus@alangordon.com *Web Site:* www.alangordon.com, pg 866

D W Fearn, PO Box 57, Pocopson, PA 19366 *Tel:* 610-793-2526 *Fax:* 610-793-1479 *E-mail:* dwfearn@dwfearn.com *Web Site:* www.dwfearn.com, pg 866

Feature Systems Inc, 223 Veterans Blvd, Carlstadt, NJ 07072 *Tel:* 201-531-2299; 212-736-0447 *Fax:* 201-531-2290; 212-465-1987 *Web Site:* www.featuresystems.com, pg 866

Edward Feil Productions, 36980 Wallace Creek Rd, Springfield, OH 97478 *Tel:* 541-521-2411 *Toll Free Fax:* 877-582-1158 *Web Site:* www.edwardfeilproductions.com, pg 866

Feldenkrais® Movement Institute, 721 The Alameda, Berkeley, CA 94707 *Tel:* 510-527-2634 *Toll Free Tel:* 800-342-3424 *Fax:* 510-528-1332 *E-mail:* info@feldenkraisinstitute.org *Web Site:* www.feldenkraisinstitute.org, pg 866

Ronald Feldman Fine Arts Inc, 31 Mercer St, New York, NY 10013 *Tel:* 212-226-3232 *Fax:* 212-941-1536 *E-mail:* info@feldmangallery.com *Web Site:* www.feldmangallery.com, pg 866

Federico Fellini Award, 6 Beach Rd, 544, Tiburon, CA 94920 *Tel:* 415-251-8433 *Fax:* 633-444-8433 *E-mail:* info@tiburonfilmfestival.com *Web Site:* www.tiburonfilmfestival.com, pg 1114

Femme Productions Inc, PO Box 268, New York, NY 10012 *Toll Free Tel:* 800-456-LOVE (456-5683); 800-955-0888 (CN) *E-mail:* inquiries@candidaroyalle.com *Web Site:* candidaroyalle.com, pg 866

Fender Musical Instruments Corp, 17600 N Perimeter Dr, Suite 100, Scottsdale, AZ 85255 *Tel:* 480-596-9690 *Fax:* 480-596-1384 *E-mail:* consumerrelations@fender.com *Web Site:* www.fender.com, pg 866

Ferrari Color®, 1550 S Gladiola St, Salt Lake City, UT 84104 *Tel:* 801-355-4124 *Toll Free Tel:* 888-312-6567 *Fax:* 801-355-4152 *E-mail:* info.slc@ferraricolor.com *Web Site:* www.ferraricolor.com, pg 866

Ferrari Productions, 11717 Sorrento Valley Rd, San Diego, CA 92121 *Tel:* 858-792-8011 *Fax:* 858-481-6499 *E-mail:* info@ferrariproductions.com *Web Site:* www.ferrariproductions.com, pg 866

Festival Films, 6115 Chestnut Terr, Shorewood, MN 55331 *Tel:* 952-470-2172 *Fax:* 952-470-2172 *E-mail:* fesfilms@aol.com *Web Site:* www.fesfilms.com, pg 866

Fiber Optic Cable Shop, 136 S Second St, Richmond, CA 94804 *Tel:* 510-234-9090 *Toll Free Tel:* 800-777-6269 *Fax:* 510-233-8888 *E-mail:* sales@fibermailbox.com *Web Site:* www.fiberopticcableshop.com, pg 866

Fiber Optic Systems Inc (FOSI), 2 Railroad Ave, Whitehouse Station, NJ 08889 *Tel:* 908-534-5500 *Toll Free Tel:* 800-809-3674 *Fax:* 908-534-2272 *E-mail:* info@fosi.com *Web Site:* www.fosi.com, pg 866

Fibre Case Corp, 160 Broadway, Suite 1105, New York, NY 10038 *Tel:* 212-566-2720 *Toll Free Tel:* 800-394-6871 *Fax:* 212-566-2726 *E-mail:* sales@fibrecase.com *Web Site:* www.fibrecase.com, pg 866

Fiddler Films, 1111 Fifth Ave S, Naples, FL 34102 *Tel:* 239-435-1818 *E-mail:* lou@fiddlerfilms.com *Web Site:* www.fiddlerfilms.com, pg 866

Fidelity Information Services (FIS), 601 Riverside Ave, Jacksonville, FL 32204 *Tel:* 904-438-6000 *Toll Free Tel:* 888-323-0310 (US only) *Fax:* 904-357-1105 *E-mail:* moreinformation@fisglobal.com *Web Site:* www.fisglobal.com, pg 866

FIDM Productions, 919 S Grand Ave, Los Angeles, CA 90015-1421 *Tel:* 213-624-1201 *Toll Free Tel:* 800-624-1200 *Fax:* 213-624-4799 *Toll Free Fax:* 800-624-1200 *Web Site:* fidm.edu, pg 866

5th Floor Recording Co, 316 N Milwaukee St, Suite 501, Milwaukee, WI 53202 *Tel:* 414-276-1919 *Fax:* 414-271-6621 *Web Site:* www.5thfloorrecording.com, pg 867

Film & Creative Industries Nova Scotia, Historic Properties, Collins Bank Bldg, 3rd fl, 1883 Upper Water St, Suite 302, Halifax, NS B3J 1S9, Canada *Tel:* 902-424-7177 *Toll Free Tel:* 888-360-2111 *Fax:* 902-424-0617 *E-mail:* filmandcreativens@gov.ns.ca *Web Site:* www.filmandcreativens.ca, pg 1105

FILM Archives Inc, 35 W 35 St, Suite 904, New York, NY 10001-2238 *Tel:* 212-696-2616 *Fax:* 503-210-9927 *E-mail:* info@filmarchives.com *Web Site:* www.filmarchivesonline.com, pg 867

Film Commission of Greater Kansas City, 1906 Wyandotte, Kansas City, MO 64108 *Tel:* 816-471-2215 *Fax:* 816-471-6500 *E-mail:* contact@kcfilm.com; greaterkcfilmcommission@gmail.com *Web Site:* kcfilm.com, pg 1099

Film Converter Co of America Inc, 10 W Burbank Blvd, Burbank, CA 91502 *Tel:* 818-845-7651 *Fax:* 818-845-7651 *Web Site:* www.filmconverterco.com, pg 867

Film Creations Ltd, 2021 E Broadway Blvd, Tucson, AZ 85719 *Tel:* 520-624-4444 *Toll Free Tel:* 888-877-2490 *Fax:* 520-624-9659 *E-mail:* info@filmcreations.com *Web Site:* www.filmcreations.com, pg 867

Film Detroit, 211 W Fort St, Suite 1000, Detroit, MI 48226 *Tel:* 313-202-1990 *Toll Free Tel:* 877-478-7883 *Web Site:* www.filmdetroit.com, pg 1098

Film Emporium, 1890 Palmer Ave, Suite 403, Larchmont, NY 10538 *Tel:* 914-833-2433 *Toll Free Tel:* 800-371-2555 *Fax:* 914-833-2430 *E-mail:* info@filmemporium.com *Web Site:* www.filmemporium.com, pg 867

Film Florida, c/o Jennifer Parramore, St Petersburg-Clearwater Film Commission, 13805 58 St N, Suite 2-200, Clearwater, FL 33760 *E-mail:* info@filmflorida.org *Web Site:* www.filmflorida.org, pg 1081

Film House Inc, 810 Dominican Dr, Nashville, TN 37228 *Tel:* 615-255-4000 *Fax:* 615-255-4111 *E-mail:* results@filmhouse.com *Web Site:* www.filmhouse.com, pg 867

Film Ideas, 308 N Wolf Rd, Wheeling, IL 60090 *Tel:* 847-419-0255 *Toll Free Tel:* 800-475-3456 (US only) *Fax:* 847-419-8933 *E-mail:* info@filmideas.com *Web Site:* www.filmideas.com, pg 867

Film Indiana, One N Capitol, Suite 700, Indianapolis, IN 46204-2288 *Tel:* 317-234-2087 *Fax:* 317-232-4146 *E-mail:* filminfo@iedc.in.gov *Web Site:* www.filmindiana.com, pg 1097

Film Liaison of Escambia County, 1401 E Gregory St, Pensacola, FL 32501 *Tel:* 850-390-3974 *Toll Free Tel:* 800-874-1234 *Web Site:* filmnorthflorida.com, pg 1096

Film Liaisons In California Statewide (FLICS), c/o Placer-Lake Tahoe Film Off, 175 Fulweiler Ave, Auburn, CA 95603 *Tel:* 530-889-4091 *Toll Free Tel:* 877-228-3456 *Fax:* 530-889-4095 *Web Site:* www.filmcalifornia.com, pg 1082

Film-Makers Cooperative, 475 Park Ave S, 6th fl, New York, NY 10016 *Tel:* 212-267-5665 *Fax:* 212-267-5666 *E-mail:* film6000@aol.com; filmmakerscoop@gmail.com *Web Site:* film-makerscoop.com, pg 867

Film Marketing Services Inc, 4640 Admiralty Way, Suite 500, Marina del Rey, CA 90292 *E-mail:* info@filmmarketingservices.com *Web Site:* filmmarketingservices.com, pg 867

Film Police, 4310 Mozart St, Chicago, IL 60618-1528 *Tel:* 773-463-4010 *E-mail:* info@filmpolice.com *Web Site:* www.filmpolice.com, pg 867

Film Technology Co Inc, 726 N Cole Ave, Hollywood, CA 90038 *Tel:* 323-464-3456 *Fax:* 323-464-7439 *Web Site:* www.filmtech.com, pg 867

Film TV Sound, PO Box 950207, Mission Hills, CA 91395-0207 *Tel:* 818-231-1038 *Fax:* 818-892-9236 *E-mail:* editorial@filmtvsound.com; eqe-media@filmtvsound.com *Web Site:* www.filmtvsound.com, pg 867

Film/Video Fellowship Grants, 109 E Jones St, Raleigh, NC 27601 *Tel:* 919-807-6500 (main) *Fax:* 919-807-6532 *E-mail:* ncarts@ncdcr.gov *Web Site:* www.ncarts.org, pg 1114

Film Wisconsin Inc, PO Box 93, Waunakee, WI 53597 *Tel:* 414-333-2366 *E-mail:* info@filmwisconsin.net *Web Site:* www.filmwisconsin.net, pg 1104

Filmakers Library, 3212 Duke St, Alexandria, VA 22314 *Tel:* 703-212-8520 *E-mail:* sales@alexanderstreet.com; orders@alexanderstreet.com *Web Site:* www.academicvideostore.com/filmakers; www.academicvideostore.com, pg 867

Filmdex Inc, 14016 Sullyfield Circle, Chantilly, VA 20151 *Tel:* 703-631-0600 *Toll Free Tel:* 888-FILMDEX (345-6339) *Fax:* 703-818-0237 *E-mail:* webinquiry@filmdex.com *Web Site:* www.filmdex.com, pg 867

FilmL.A., Inc, 6255 W Sunset Blvd, 12th fl, Los Angeles, CA 90028 *Tel:* 213-977-8600 *Fax:* 213-977-8610; 213-977-8601 (permits) *E-mail:* info@filmla.com *Web Site:* www.filmla.com, pg 1082, 1093

Filmlites Montana, 6465 River Rd, Bozeman, MT 59718 *Tel:* 406-587-0226 *Fax:* 406-551-4555 *E-mail:* info@filmlitesmt.com *Web Site:* www.filmlitesmt.com, pg 867

Filmmakers Alliance (FA), 1317 N San Fernando Blvd, Unit 366, Burbank, CA 91504 *Tel:* 310-568-0633 *Fax:* 818-301-2257 *E-mail:* info@filmmakersalliance.org *Web Site:* filmmakersalliance.org, pg 1082

FilmNation Entertainment, 150 W 22 St, 9th fl, New York, NY 10011 *Web Site:* www.filmnation.com, pg 867

Films by Huey, 103 Montrose Ave, Portland, ME 04103 *Tel:* 207-773-1130 *E-mail:* huey@filmsbyhuey.com *Web Site:* www.filmsbyhuey.com, pg 867

Films for the Humanities & Sciences, 132 W 31 St, 17th fl, New York, NY 10001 *Toll Free Tel:* 800-257-5126 *Fax:* 609-671-0266 *E-mail:* custserv@films.com *Web Site:* ffh.films.com, pg 868

Films Media Group, 132 W 31 St, 17th fl, New York, NY 10001 *Tel:* 212-967-8800 *Toll Free Tel:* 800-322-8755 *Toll Free Fax:* 800-678-3633 *E-mail:* custserv@films.com; order@films.com *Web Site:* www.films.com, pg 868

Films of the Nations, PO Box 449, Clarksburg, NJ 08510-0449 *Tel:* 732-462-3522 *Toll Free Tel:* 800-832-0980 *Fax:* 732-294-0330 *E-mail:* info@aldenfilms.com *Web Site:* www.aldenfilms.com, pg 868

Filmtools®, 1400 W Burbank Blvd, Burbank, CA 91506 *Tel:* 818-845-8066 *Toll Free Tel:* 888-807-1900 *Fax:* 818-845-8138 *Web Site:* www.filmtools.com, pg 868

Filmworkers, 232 E Ohio, Chicago, IL 60611 *Tel:* 312-664-9333 *Web Site:* www.filmworkersastro.com, pg 868

FilmWorks Pacific, PO Box 61281, Honolulu, HI 96839-1281 *Tel:* 808-599-6403 (studio) *Fax:* 808-537-9272 *E-mail:* studio@filmworkspacific.com *Web Site:* www.filmworkspacific.com, pg 868

Final Draft Inc, 26707 W Agoura Rd, Suite 205, Calabasas, CA 91302 *Tel:* 818-995-8995; 818-906-8930 (tech support) *Toll Free Tel:* 800-231-4055 *Fax:* 818-995-4422 *E-mail:* info@finaldraft.com *Web Site:* www.finaldraft.com, pg 868

Finale Editworks, 2339 Columbia, Suite 100, Vancouver, BC V5Y 3V5, Canada *Tel:* 604-876-7678 *Fax:* 604-876-3299 *E-mail:* info@finale.tv *Web Site:* www.finale.tv, pg 868

Fingerpaint, 13 Walker Way, Albany, NY 12205 *Tel:* 518-869-1968 *Fax:* 518-869-1969 *Web Site:* fingerpaintmarketing.com, pg 868

Stuart Finley Films, 3428 Mansfield Rd, Falls Church, VA 22041 *Tel:* 703-820-7700 *Web Site:* www.stufin.com, pg 868

Fire Power Music Inc, 9913 E Main St, No 171, Tempe, AZ 85207 *Tel:* 602-463-2988, pg 868

Fire Station Studios, 224 N Guadalupe St, San Marcos, TX 78666 *Tel:* 512-396-1144 *Fax:* 512-396-1169 *E-mail:* info@firestationstudios.com *Web Site:* www.firestationstudios.com, pg 868

Firefly Book Club, 557 Broadway, New York, NY 10012 *Tel:* 212-343-6100 *Toll Free Tel:* 800-724-6527 (cust serv) *Fax:* 212-343-4535 *E-mail:* info@scholastic.com; custserv@scholastic.com *Web Site:* www.scholastic.com, pg 868

Firehouse Studios, 155 W Rosemont Ave, Chicago, IL 60660 *Tel:* 773-271-3100 *Toll Free Fax:* 866-540-1091 *E-mail:* folks@firehousestudios.com *Web Site:* firehousestudios.com, pg 868

First Camera, 2472 Third St, San Francisco, CA 94107 *Tel:* 415-647-3400 *Fax:* 415-647-3410 *E-mail:* sfvideo@firstcamera.com *Web Site:* www.firstcamera.com, pg 868

First Cut Communications LLC, 301 W Broome St, Suite 100, LaGrange, GA 30240 *Tel:* 706-882-5581 *E-mail:* info@firstcutcommunications.com *Web Site:* www.firstcutcommunications.com, pg 868

1st Financial Training Services Inc, 1515 E Woodfield Rd, Suite 3730, Schaumburg, IL 60173 *Tel:* 847-969-0900 *Toll Free Tel:* 800-442-8662 *Fax:* 847-969-0521 *E-mail:* sales@1stfinancialtraining.com *Web Site:* www.1stfinancialtraining.com, pg 868

First Group Communications Inc, 10994 Ranch Stone Dr, Houston, TX 77064 *Tel:* 281-890-9999 *Fax:* 281-890-9989 *E-mail:* info@firstgroupmedia.com *Web Site:* www.firstgroupmedia.com, pg 868

First Person™, 550 Bryant St, San Francisco, CA 94107 *Tel:* 415-495-5595 *Fax:* 415-543-8370, pg 868

First Run Features, The Film Center Bldg, Suite 1213, 630 Ninth Ave, New York, NY 10036-3708 *Tel:* 212-243-0600 *Fax:* 212-989-7649 *E-mail:* info@firstrunfeatures.com *Web Site:* www.firstrunfeatures.com, pg 869

1st Wave Productions, 2017 Pacific Ave, Venice, CA 90291 *Tel:* 310-474-2439 *Fax:* 310-474-5282 *Web Site:* www.1stwaveproductions.com, pg 869

FirstCom Music, 1325 Capital Pkwy, Suite 109, Carrollton, TX 75006 *Tel:* 972-446-8742 *Toll Free Tel:* 800-858-8880 *Fax:* 972-242-6526 *E-mail:* info@firstcom.com *Web Site:* www.firstcom.com, pg 869

FirstGeneration Audio/Visual Services, 410 Allentown Dr, Allentown, PA 18109 *Tel:* 610-437-4300 *Fax:* 610-437-3200 *E-mail:* information@firstgencom.com; contact@firstgencom.com *Web Site:* www.firstgenav.com, pg 869

Fish Films Footage World, 4548 Van Noord Ave, Studio City, CA 91604 *Tel:* 818-905-1071 *E-mail:* footageworld@aol.com *Web Site:* www.footageworld.com, pg 869

FitzCo Sound Inc, 4300 W Wall St, Bldg B, Midland, TX 79703 *Tel:* 432-684-0861 *Fax:* 432-682-9978 *Web Site:* www.fitzcosound.com, pg 869

5 Alarm Music, 35 W Dayton St, Pasadena, CA 91105 *Tel:* 626-304-1698 *Toll Free Tel:* 800-322-7879 *Fax:* 626-795-2058 *E-mail:* info@5alarmmusic.com *Web Site:* www.5alarmmusic.com, pg 869

FJ Productions Inc, 14900 Ventura Blvd, Suite 350, Sherman Oaks, CA 91403-3465 *Tel:* 818-788-0153 *Fax:* 818-788-0186 *Web Site:* www.fjproductions.com, pg 869

FJW Optical Systems Inc, 322 N Woodwork Lane, Palatine, IL 60067-4933 *Tel:* 847-358-2500 *Toll Free Tel:* 800-355-4FJW (355-4359) *Fax:* 847-358-2533 *E-mail:* irsales@findrscope.com *Web Site:* www.findrscope.com, pg 869

FlagHouse, 601 Flaghouse Dr, Hasbrouck Heights, NJ 07604-3116 *Tel:* 201-288-7600 *Toll Free Tel:* 800-793-7900 *Fax:* 201-288-7887 *Toll Free Fax:* 800-793-7922 *E-mail:* sales@flaghouse.com *Web Site:* www.flaghouse.com, pg 869

Flagstaff Convention & Visitors Bureau, One E Rte 66, Flagstaff, AZ 86001-5303 *Tel:* 928-213-2910 *Toll Free Tel:* 800-842-7293 *E-mail:* cvb@flagstaffaz.gov *Web Site:* www.flagstaffarizona.org, pg 1091

Robert Flaherty Film Seminar, 6 E 39 St, 12th fl, New York, NY 10016 *Tel:* 212-448-0457 *Fax:* 212-448-0458 *E-mail:* ifs@flahertyseminar.org *Web Site:* www.flahertyseminar.org, pg 1114

Paul Flanagan Productions, 1623 S Hearthside Dr, Richmond, TX 77406-1369 *Tel:* 281-799-4832 *Web Site:* www.productionhub.com, pg 869

Flash Clinic Inc, 164 W 25 St, New York, NY 10001 *Tel:* 212-337-0447 *Toll Free Tel:* 800-752-7536 *Fax:* 212-337-8088 *E-mail:* info@flashclinic.com *Web Site:* www.flashclinic.com, pg 869

Flash Electronics Inc, Brooklyn Army Terminal, Suite 1-A, Mail Box 3, 140 58 St, Brooklyn, NY 11220 *Tel:* 718-492-4040 *Toll Free Tel:* 800-831-3127 *Fax:* 718-492-4590 *E-mail:* flashdistr@aol.com; customercare@flashdistributors.com *Web Site:* www.flashdistributors.com, pg 869

Flashback Media Productions, 510 E Sutton Circle, Lafayette, CO 80026 *Tel:* 303-545-9955 *Fax:* 303-545-6658 *E-mail:* info@flashback.tv *Web Site:* www.flashback.tv, pg 869

Flashback Stage Lighting, 8151 Commercial St, La Mesa, CA 91924 *Tel:* 619-697-2729 *Fax:* 619-697-2782 *E-mail:* mail@flashbackstagelighting.com *Web Site:* www.flashbackstagelighting.com, pg 869

Flat Town Music Co, 238 E Main St, Ville Platte, LA 70856 *Tel:* 337-363-2177 *Fax:* 337-363-2094 *E-mail:* info@flattownmusic.com *Web Site:* www.flattownmusic.com, pg 869

Doug Fleenor Design Inc, 396 Corbett Canyon Rd, Arroyo Grande, CA 93420 *Tel:* 805-481-9599 *Toll Free Tel:* 888-436-9512 *Fax:* 805-481-9599 *E-mail:* info@dfd.com *Web Site:* www.dfd.com, pg 869

Fleetwood Group Inc, 11832 James St, Holland, MI 49424 *Tel:* 616-396-1142 *Toll Free Tel:* 800-257-6390 *Fax:* 616-820-8301 *E-mail:* sales@fleetwoodgroup.com *Web Site:* www.fleetwoodgroup.com; www.replysystems.com (electronics div), pg 870

Flex-A-Lite West, 10250 Aldebaran Dr, Reno, NV 89508 *Tel:* 775-677-7711 *Fax:* 775-677-7577, pg 870

FLICKERS: Rhode Island International Film Festival™ (RIIFF), 83 Park St, Suite 1, Providence, RI 02903 *Tel:* 401-861-4445 *Fax:* 401-490-6735 *E-mail:* info@film-festival.org *Web Site:* film-festival.org/enteraskidseye.php, pg 1114

Flight Form Cases Inc, 6543 S Laramie Ave, Bedford Park, IL 60638 *Tel:* 708-458-8989 *Toll Free Tel:* 800-334-4884 *Fax:* 708-458-9023 *E-mail:* info@flightform.com; info@caseyguys.net; sales@caseyguys.com *Web Site:* www.flightform.com, pg 870

Flip 2 Media Inc, 1067 Serpentine Lane, Pleasanton, CA 94566-4759 *Tel:* 925-417-1420 *E-mail:* info@flip2media.com *Web Site:* www.flip2media.com, pg 870

FLIR Systems Inc, 27700 SW Parkway Ave, Wilsonville, OR 97070 *Tel:* 503-498-3547 *Toll Free Tel:* 800-322-3731 *Fax:* 503-498-3904 *E-mail:* marketing@flir.com *Web Site:* www.flir.com, pg 870

Florentine Films, 136 E 56 St, Suite 4-B, New York, NY 10022 *Tel:* 212-980-5966 *Fax:* 212-980-5944 *Web Site:* www.florentinefilms.com/sherman, pg 870

Florical Systems Inc, 4500 NW 27 Ave, Bldg B-1, Gainesville, FL 32606 *Tel:* 352-372-8326 *Toll Free Tel:* 800-372-4613 *Fax:* 352-375-0859 *E-mail:* support@florical.com *Web Site:* www.florical.com, pg 870

Florida Digital Studios, 10781 75 St, Largo, FL 33777 *Tel:* 727-546-7900 *Fax:* 727-546-8640 *Web Site:* www.floridadigitalstudios.com, pg 870

Florida Film & Tape, 3417 Lake Breeze Rd, Orlando, FL 32808 *Tel:* 407-297-0091 *Fax:* 407-297-0094 *Web Site:* www.ffandt.com, pg 870

Florida Film & Video, 4461 38 Way S, St Petersburg, FL 33711 *Tel:* 727-369-0732 *E-mail:* info@flhd.tv *Web Site:* www.flhd.tv, pg 870

Florida Film Festival, c/o Enzian, 1300 S Orlando Ave, Maitland, FL 32751 *Tel:* 407-629-1088 *Fax:* 407-629-6870 *E-mail:* filmfest@enzian.org *Web Site:* www.floridafilmfestival.com; enzian.org, pg 1114

Florida Keys & Key West Film Commission, 1201 White St, Suite 102, Key West, FL 33040 *Tel:* 305-293-1800 *Toll Free Tel:* 800-FILM-KEYS (345-6539) *Fax:* 305-296-0788 *Web Site:* www.filmkeys.com, pg 1096

The Florida Office of Film & Entertainment, 107 E Madison St, MSC 80, Tallahassee, FL 32399 *Tel:* 850-717-8990; 818-508-7772 *Toll Free Tel:* 877-FLA-FILM (352-3456) *Fax:* 850-410-4770 *Web Site:* www.filminflorida.com, pg 1096

Fluke Corp, 6920 Seaway Blvd, Everett, WA 98203 *Tel:* 425-347-6100 *Toll Free Tel:* 800-443-5853 *Fax:* 425-446-5116 *E-mail:* fluke-info@fluke.com *Web Site:* www.fluke.com, pg 870

The Fluorescent Co Inc, c/o Red*D*Mix Rentals Inc, 388 Carlaw Ave, Suite 116, Toronto, ON M4M 2T4, Canada *Tel:* 416-879-3761 *Fax:* 905-681-8520 *E-mail:* reddmix@cogeco.ca *Web Site:* www.flo-co.com, pg 870

Flying Colors Broadcasts, 2000 "M" St NW, Suite 345, Washington, DC 20036 *Tel:* 202-293-5300 *E-mail:* info@fc-tv.com *Web Site:* www.fc-tv.com, pg 870

FM Systems Inc, 3877 S Main St, Santa Ana, CA 92707 *Tel:* 714-979-3355 *Toll Free Tel:* 800-235-6960 *Fax:* 714-979-0913 *E-mail:* fmsystemsinc@sbcglobal.net *Web Site:* www.fmsystems-inc.com, pg 870

FMP Media Solutions Inc, 1010 Spring Mill Ave, Suite 100, Conshohocken, PA 19428 *Tel:* 610-825-4000 *Toll Free Tel:* 800-346-5071 *Fax:* 610-825-4430 *E-mail:* info@fmpmedia.com *Web Site:* www.fmpmedia.com, pg 870

Focus Features, 1540 Second St, No 200, Santa Monica, CA 90401 *Web Site:* www.focusfeatures.com, pg 870

Focus on Animals, PO Box 340, Charles Town, WV 25414-0340 *Tel:* 304-725-0506 *Fax:* 304-725-1523 *E-mail:* information@nhes.org *Web Site:* www.nhes.org, pg 870

Folk Era Productions Inc, 705 S Washington St, Suite 3, Naperville, IL 60540-6654 *Tel:* 630-637-2303; 630-305-0770 (cust serv) *Toll Free Tel:* 800-232-7328 (orders) *Fax:* 630-305-0782 *E-mail:* info@folkera.com *Web Site:* www.rediscovermusic.com, pg 870

Folk-Legacy, 85 Sharon Mountain Rd, Sharon, CT 06069 *Tel:* 860-364-5661 *Toll Free Tel:* 800-836-0901 (orders) *Fax:* 860-364-1050 *E-mail:* sales@folk-legacy.com *Web Site:* www.folk-legacy.com, pg 871

Folkcraft Instruments, 22133 Main St, Woodburn, IN 46797 *Tel:* 317-522-1635 *Toll Free Tel:* 800-433-3655 *Fax:* 317-245-2378 *E-mail:* sales@folkcraft.com *Web Site:* www.folkcraft.com; www.richardash.com, pg 871

Follett Software Co, 1391 Corporate Dr, McHenry, IL 60050-7041 *Tel:* 815-344-8700 *Toll Free Tel:* 800-323-3397 *Fax:* 815-344-8774; 815-578-5575 *Toll Free Fax:* 800-807-3623 (cust serv) *Web Site:* www.follettsoftware.com, pg 871

The Food & Beverage Institute, 1946 Campus Dr, Hyde Park, NY 12538-1499 *Tel:* 845-905-4417 *Toll Free Tel:* 800-888-7850 *Fax:* 845-451-1078 *E-mail:* ciaprochef@culinary.edu *Web Site:* www.ciachef.edu; www.ciaprochef.com, pg 871

FootageBank HD, 13470 Washington Blvd, Suite 210, Marina Del Rey, CA 90292 *Tel:* 310-822-1400 *Toll Free Tel:* 888-653-1400 *Fax:* 310-822-4100 *E-mail:* info@footagebank.com *Web Site:* www.footagebank.com, pg 871

Foothill Digital Inc, 217 Storer Ave, New Rochelle, NY 10801 *Tel:* 914-235-5670 *E-mail:* info@foothilldigital.com *Web Site:* www.foothilldigital.com; www.tuckersound.com, pg 871

For-A Corp of America, 11155 Knott Ave, Suite G & H, Cypress, CA 90630 *Tel:* 714-894-3311 *Fax:* 714-894-5399 *E-mail:* info@for-a.com *Web Site:* www.for-a.com, pg 871

Forensic Video Deposition Service, 2823 N 48 St, Suite 8, Phoenix, AZ 85008 *Tel:* 602-840-1222 *Fax:* 602-840-1313 *Web Site:* forensicvideo.net, pg 871

Foresight Imaging, One Executive Dr, Suite 102, Chelmsford, MA 01824 *Tel:* 978-458-4624 *Fax:* 978-458-5488 *E-mail:* info@fi-llc.com *Web Site:* www.fi-llc.com, pg 871

Forge Recording LLC, 100 Mill Rd, Oreland, PA 19075 *Tel:* 215-885-7000 *Toll Free Tel:* 800-331-0405 *Fax:* 215-887-3501 *E-mail:* info@forgerecording.com *Web Site:* www.forgerecording.com, pg 871

Forte Productions, PO Box 17, San Geronimo, CA 94963-0325 *Tel:* 415-488-9446 *Fax:* 415-488-9446 *Web Site:* www.pianovideos.com, pg 871

48 Windows, 1661 N Lincoln Blvd, Suite 220, Santa Monica, CA 90404 *Tel:* 310-392-9545 *Fax:* 310-392-9445 *E-mail:* ziv@48windows.com *Web Site:* www.48windows.com, pg 871

J E Foss Co, 3328-B Industrial Blvd, Bethel Park, PA 15102 *Tel:* 412-564-5644 *Toll Free Tel:* 800-245-6240 *Fax:* 412-564-5646 *E-mail:* jefoss@earthlink.net *Web Site:* www.jefoss.com, pg 871

FotoKem Film & Video, 2801 W Alameda Ave, Burbank, CA 91505 *Tel:* 818-846-3101 *Fax:* 818-841-2130 *E-mail:* sales@fotokem.com *Web Site:* www.fotokem.com, pg 871

FOTON Hawaii, 98-021 Kamehameha Hwy, Aiea, HI 96701 *Tel:* 808-206-5244 *Web Site:* www.fotonhawaii.com, pg 871

Fotosearch Stock Photography, 21155 Watertown Rd, Waukesha, WI 53186 *Tel:* 262-717-0740 *Toll Free Tel:* 800-827-3920 *Fax:* 262-717-0745 *E-mail:* fotosearch@fotosearch.com *Web Site:* www.fotosearch.com, pg 871

Foundation for Economic Education, 30 S Broadway, Irvington-on-Hudson, NY 10533 *Tel:* 914-591-7230 *Toll Free Tel:* 800-960-4333 *E-mail:* editor@fee.org; info@fee.org *Web Site:* www.fee.org, pg 1082

Four Corners Productions, 38 W Tenth St, New York, NY 10011 *Tel:* 212-228-6492 *Fax:* 212-228-6492 *Web Site:* www.operatitles.net; www.gracepaleyvideo.com, pg 871

4-D Creative Media, 16 W 46 St, 12th fl, New York, NY 10036 *Tel:* 212-994-3300 *Fax:* 212-499-9081 *Web Site:* www.4-dcreative.com, pg 871

411 Video Information, PO Box 1223, Pebble Beach, CA 93953-1223 *Tel:* 831-656-0553 *Fax:* 831-656-0555 *Web Site:* www.411videoinfo.com, pg 872

4 Wall Entertainment, 3325 W Sunset Rd, Suite F, Las Vegas, NV 89118 *Tel:* 702-263-3858 *Toll Free Tel:* 877-789-8167 (Western US); 866-492-5540 (Eastern US) *Fax:* 702-263-3863 *E-mail:* info@4wall.com *Web Site:* www.4wall.com; www.usedlighting.com, pg 872

4th Street Recording, 1211 Fourth St, Santa Monica, CA 90401 *Tel:* 310-395-9114 *E-mail:* info@4thstreetrecording.com *Web Site:* www.4thstreetrecording.com, pg 872

Fox Connecticut, 285 Broad St, Hartford, CT 06115 *Tel:* 860-527-6161 *Fax:* 860-727-0158 *Web Site:* www.ctnow.com, pg 872

Fox 40 KTXL TV, 4655 Fruitridge Rd, Sacramento, CA 95820 *Tel:* 916-454-4422 *Fax:* 916-739-8139 *Web Site:* www.fox40.com, pg 872

Fox Television Center, 1999 S Bundy Dr, Los Angeles, CA 90025 *Tel:* 310-584-2000 *Fax:* 310-584-2023 *Web Site:* www.myfoxla.com, pg 872

Fox 10 Productions (KSAZ-TV), 511 W Adams, Phoenix, AZ 85003 *Tel:* 602-257-1234 *Fax:* 602-262-0177 *E-mail:* fox10.desk@foxtv.com *Web Site:* www.myfoxphoenix.com; www.my45.com, pg 872

Foxtrot Teleprompt, 20 Clifford Place, East Norwich, NY 11732-1306 *Tel:* 516-428-3063 (cell) *Toll Free Tel:* 888-365-0808 *E-mail:* nyprompter@hotmail.com *Web Site:* foxtrotteleprompt.com, pg 872

Frame 30 Productions Ltd, 10816A-82 Ave, No 202, Edmonton, AB T6E 2B3, Canada *Tel:* 780-439-5322 *E-mail:* frame30@frame30.com *Web Site:* www.frame30.com, pg 872

Frameline Completion Fund, 145 Ninth St, Suite 300, San Francisco, CA 94103 *Tel:* 415-703-8650 *Fax:* 415-861-1404 *E-mail:* info@frameline.org *Web Site:* www.frameline.org, pg 1114

Framepool, 150 Alhambre Circle, Suite 800, Miami, FL 33134 *Tel:* 305-401-8597 *Toll Free Tel:* 800-331-1314 *Fax:* 305-428-2800 *E-mail:* americas@framepool.com *Web Site:* usa2.framepool.com, pg 872

Franciscan Media, 28 W Liberty St, Cincinnati, OH 45202-6498 *Tel:* 513-241-5615 *Toll Free Tel:* 800-488-0488 *Fax:* 513-241-0399 *Web Site:* www.americancatholic.org, pg 872

Karen Frankel Productions, 520 E 84 St, New York, NY 10028 *Tel:* 212-744-6446 *Fax:* 212-570-2820 *E-mail:* izcrystal@aol.com, pg 872

Franklin Video Inc, 931 Marilyn Dr, Raleigh, NC 27607 *Tel:* 919-833-8888 *Web Site:* www.franklinvideo.com, pg 872

Freedoms Foundation National Awards, 1601 Valley Forge Rd, Valley Forge, PA 19482 *Tel:* 610-933-8825 *Fax:* 610-935-0522 *E-mail:* info@ffvf.org *Web Site:* www.freedomsfoundation.com, pg 1115

Freeman, 1600 Viceroy, Suite 100, Dallas, TX 75235 *Tel:* 214-445-1000 *Fax:* 214-445-0200 *Web Site:* www.freemanco.com, pg 872

Freeman Pictures Inc, 1234 Sherman Ave, Suite 201, Evanston, IL 60602 *Tel:* 847-733-0717 *Web Site:* www.freemanpictures.com, pg 872

Freestyle Photographic Supplies, 5124 Sunset Blvd, Los Angeles, CA 90027 *Tel:* 323-660-3460 *Toll Free Tel:* 800-292-6137 *Fax:* 323-660-4885 *Web Site:* www.freestylephoto.biz, pg 872

Freestyle Productions Inc, 7160 Madison Ave W, Minneapolis, MN 55427 *Tel:* 763-417-9575 *Fax:* 763-417-9576 *E-mail:* info@freestyle-productions.com *Web Site:* freestyleproductions.com, pg 872

Freewheelin' Films, 44895 Hwy 82, Aspen, CO 81611 *Tel:* 970-925-2640 *Fax:* 970-925-9369 *Web Site:* www.fwf.com, pg 872

FremantleMedia, 4000 W Alameda Ave, 3rd fl, Burbank, CA 91505 *Tel:* 818-748-1100 *Fax:* 818-563-6410 *E-mail:* contactus@fremantlemedia.com *Web Site:* www.fremantlemedia.com, pg 873

Fremont/Custer County Film Commission, 403 Royal Gorge Blvd, Canon City, CO 81212 *Tel:* 719-275-2331 *Toll Free Tel:* 800-876-7922 *Fax:* 719-275-2332 *E-mail:* chamber@canoncity.com *Web Site:* www.canoncitychamber.com, pg 1094

French American Cultural Exchange (FACE), 972 Fifth Ave, New York, NY 10021 *Tel:* 212-439-1449 *Fax:* 212-439-1455 *E-mail:* info@facecouncil.org *Web Site:* www.facecouncil.org, pg 873

French American Music Enterprises, 5 Junkins Ave, Suite 106, Portsmouth, NH 03801 *Tel:* 603-430-9524 *Web Site:* www.luciet.com, pg 873

Fresh Film Northwest (FFNW), 934 SW Salmon St, Portland, OR 97205 *Tel:* 503-221-1156 (ext 10) *Fax:* 503-294-0874 *E-mail:* info@nwfilm.org *Web Site:* www.nwfilm.org, pg 1115

Fresh Music Library, 320 South St, Agawam, MA 01001 *Toll Free Tel:* 888-211-8576 *Web Site:* www.freshmusic.com, pg 873

Fresno County Film Commission, 2220 Tulare St, 8th fl, Fresno, CA 93721 *Tel:* 559-600-4271 *Fax:* 559-600-4549 *Web Site:* www.filmfresno.com, pg 1092

Fresno Film Commission, 5241 E Townsend Ave, Fresno, CA 93727 *Tel:* 559-908-0539 *Fax:* 559-354-5980 *E-mail:* fresnofilm@gmail.com *Web Site:* www.fresnofilm.com, pg 1092

Frey Scientific, 80 Northwest Blvd, Nashua, NH 03063-4067 *Toll Free Tel:* 800-225-3739 *Toll Free Fax:* 877-256-3739 *E-mail:* customercare@freyscientific.com *Web Site:* www.freyscientific.com, pg 873

Frezzi Energy Systems, 7 Valley St, Hawthorne, NJ 07506 *Tel:* 973-427-1160 *Fax:* 973-427-0934 *E-mail:* info@frezzi.com *Web Site:* www.frezzi.com, pg 873

Fricon Entertainment Co Inc, 134 Bluegrass Circle, Hendersonville, TN 37075 *Tel:* 615-826-2288 *Fax:* 615-826-0500, pg 873

Robert Fried Photography, 610 Eldridge Ct, Novato, CA 94947 *Tel:* 415-898-6153 *Fax:* 415-897-0353 *Web Site:* www.robertfriedphotography.com, pg 873

Gene Friedman, PO Box 275, Wainscott, NY 11975-0275 *Tel:* 631-537-0178 *E-mail:* genfried@optonline.net, pg 873

Frontier Communications Corp, PO Box 939, Portland, OR 97207-0939 *Tel:* 503-246-8080 *Fax:* 541-549-1809, pg 873

Frontier Software Inc, PO Box 56505, Houston, TX 77256 *Tel:* 713-622-8167 *Toll Free Tel:* 800-634-3306 *Fax:* 713-622-0058 *E-mail:* webmaster@frontiertex.com *Web Site:* www.frontiertex.com, pg 873

Frontline Communications, 12770 44 St N, Clearwater, FL 33762 *Tel:* 727-573-0400 *Fax:* 727-571-3295 *Web Site:* www.frontlinecomm.com, pg 873

FSL Media Inc, 122 Amity St, Suite 1, Brooklyn, NY 11201 *Tel:* 347-463-9729 *E-mail:* info@fslmedia.com *Web Site:* www.fslmedia.com, pg 873

FSR Inc, 244 Bergen Blvd, West Paterson, NJ 07424 *Tel:* 973-785-4347 *Toll Free Tel:* 800-332-3771 (tech support) *Fax:* 973-785-4207 *E-mail:* sales@fsrinc.com *Web Site:* www.fsrinc.com, pg 873

Fugro EarthData, 7320 Executive Way, Frederick, MD 21704 *Tel:* 301-948-8550 *Fax:* 301-963-2064 *E-mail:* info@fugroearthdata.com *Web Site:* www.fugroearthdata.com, pg 873

FUJIFILM Canada Inc, 600 Suffolk Ct, Mississauga, ON L5R 4G4, Canada *Tel:* 905-890-6611 *Toll Free Tel:* 800-263-5018 *Fax:* 905-890-6446 *Web Site:* www.fujifilm.ca, pg 873

FUJIFILM Graphic Systems Division, 850 Central Ave, Hanover Park, IL 60133 *Tel:* 630-259-7200 *Toll Free Tel:* 800-877-0555 *Fax:* 630-259-7078 *E-mail:* contact@fujifilmgs.com *Web Site:* www.fujifilmgs.com, pg 873

FUJIFILM North America Corp, 200 Summit Lake Dr, Valhalla, NY 10595-1356 *Tel:* 914-789-8100 *Toll Free Tel:* 800-755-3854 *Fax:* 914-789-8530 *Web Site:* www.fujifilmusa.com/northamerica, pg 873

FUJIFILM Optical Devices Division, 10 High Point Dr, Wayne, NJ 07470 *Tel:* 973-633-5600 *Fax:* 973-633-5216 *Web Site:* www.fujifilmusa.com/products/optical_devices, pg 873

Full Compass Systems, 9770 Silicon Prairie Pkwy, Madison, WI 53593 *Tel:* 608-831-7330 *Toll Free Tel:* 800-356-5844 *Fax:* 608-831-8846 *E-mail:* customerservice@fullcompass.com *Web Site:* www.fullcompass.com, pg 874

Full Moon & High Tide Productions & Studios, 424 Main St, El Segundo, CA 90245-3002 *Tel:* 310-647-1958 *Fax:* 310-647-1960 *Web Site:* fmht.net, pg 874

Full Scale Effects, 6869 Tujunga Ave, North Hollywood, CA 91605 *Tel:* 818-760-0875; 818-760-0042 *Fax:* 818-760-0876 *Web Site:* fullscalefx.com, pg 874

Full Spectrum Arts & Services, PO Box 1032, Littleton, CO 80160 *Tel:* 303-798-7906 *Web Site:* www.fullspectrumarts.com, pg 874

Fuller Street Productions, 10702 Hathaway Dr, No 2, Santa Fe Springs, CA 90670 *Toll Free Tel:* 877-637-8733 *Toll Free Fax:* 877-637-8733 *E-mail:* contact@fullerstreet.com *Web Site:* www.fullerstreet.com, pg 874

Furman, 1800 S McDowell Blvd, Petaluma, CA 94954 *Tel:* 707-763-1010 *Fax:* 707-763-1310 *E-mail:* info@furmansound.com *Web Site:* www.furmansound.com, pg 874

Furnace MFG, 2719-B Dorr Ave, Fairfax, VA 22031 *Tel:* 703-205-0007 *Toll Free Tel:* 888-599-9883 *Fax:* 703-205-2951 *E-mail:* sales@furnacemfg.com *Web Site:* www.furnacemfg.com, pg 874

Fusion Brand Experiences, 421 Chestnut St, Philadelphia, PA 19123 *Tel:* 215-629-2000 *Web Site:* www.fusionexperiences.com, pg 874

Future Disc LLC, 15851 NW Willis Rd, McMinnville, OR 97128 *Tel:* 213-361-0603 *Fax:* 503-472-1951 *Web Site:* www.futurediscsystems.com, pg 874

Future Light Inc, 23420 Lorain Rd, Suite 200, North Olmsted, OH 44070 *Tel:* 440-801-1310 *Toll Free Tel:* 800-581-5536 *Fax:* 440-779-4159 *E-mail:* info@future-light.com *Web Site:* www.future-light.com, pg 874

Future US Inc, 4000 Shoreline Ct, Suite 400, South San Francisco, CA 94080 *Tel:* 650-872-1642 *Fax:* 650-872-2207 *Web Site:* www.futureus.com, pg 874

Future View Inc, 6035 Blair Rd NW, Washington, DC 20011 *Tel:* 202-882-7400 *Fax:* 202-882-7450 *E-mail:* info@futureview.com *Web Site:* www.futureview.com, pg 874

FutureVideo, 28202 Cabot Rd, Suite 300, Laguna Niguel, CA 92677 *Tel:* 949-363-1286 *Toll Free Fax:* 866-261-1686 *E-mail:* sales@futurevideo.com *Web Site:* www.futurevideo.com, pg 874

FWT LLC, 5750 E I-20, Fort Worth, TX 76119 *Tel:* 817-255-3060 *Toll Free Tel:* 800-433-1816 *Fax:* 817-255-2957 *E-mail:* info@fwtllc.com *Web Site:* fwtllc.com, pg 874

FXC Communications, 970 S Second St, San Jose, CA 95112-5825 *Tel:* 408-293-2000 *Fax:* 408-294-2000, pg 874

FXF Productions Inc, 1024 Harding Ave, Suite 201, Venice Beach, CA 90291 *Tel:* 310-577-5009 *Fax:* 310-577-1960 *E-mail:* info@fxfproductions.com *Web Site:* www.fxfproductions.com, pg 874

Gabriel Awards, 1645 Brook Lynn Dr, Suite 2, Dayton, OH 45432-1944 *Tel:* 937-458-0265 *Fax:* 937-458-0263 *E-mail:* admin@catholicacademy.org *Web Site:* www.catholicacademy.org; www.gabrielawards.com, pg 1115

Gage-Line Technology Inc, 121 LaGrange Ave, Rochester, NY 14613-1577 *Tel:* 585-458-2000 *Toll Free Tel:* 800-291-3724 *Fax:* 585-458-0524 *E-mail:* sales@gage-line.com *Web Site:* www.gage-line.com, pg 874

Gagne Inc, 41 Commercial Dr, Johnson City, NY 13790 *Tel:* 607-729-3366 *Toll Free Tel:* 800-800-5954 *Fax:* 607-729-7644 *E-mail:* sales@gagneinc.com *Web Site:* www.gagneinc.com, pg 875

Gaiam Inc, 833 W South Boulder Rd, PO Box 3095, Boulder, CO 80307-3095 *Tel:* 303-222-3600 *Toll Free Tel:* 877-989-6321 (cust serv) *Fax:* 303-222-3700 *E-mail:* customerservice@gaiam.com *Web Site:* www.gaiam.com, pg 875

Gaither Studios LLC, 1705 S Park Ave, Alexandria, IN 46001 *Toll Free Tel:* 800-333-7859 *E-mail:* info@gaitherstudios.com *Web Site:* www.gaitherstudios.com, pg 875

Galaxy Audio, 601 E Pawnee Ave, Wichita, KS 67211 *Tel:* 316-263-2852 *Toll Free Tel:* 800-369-7768 *Fax:* 316-263-0642 *E-mail:* sales@galaxyaudio.com; orders@galaxyaudio.com *Web Site:* www.galaxyaudio.com, pg 875

Gallien/Krueger, 2234 Industrial Dr, Stockton, CA 95206 *Tel:* 209-234-7300 *Fax:* 209-234-8420 *E-mail:* sales@gallien.com *Web Site:* www.gallien.com, pg 875

GAMfilm Productions, 7559 Willoughby Ave, Suite 5, Los Angeles, CA 90046 *Tel:* 213-840-6212 *E-mail:* gamfilm@gmail.com *Web Site:* director-writer-producer.com, pg 875

Gamma Imaging, 222 N DesPlaines St, Chicago, IL 60661 *Tel:* 312-441-0091 *Toll Free Tel:* 877-441-4830 *Fax:* 312-441-0092 *E-mail:* digital@gammaimaging.com *Web Site:* gammaimaging.com, pg 875

G&G Technologies Inc, 280 N Midland Ave, Bldg F, Suite 202, Saddle Brook, NJ 07663 *Tel:* 201-791-1400 *Toll Free Tel:* 800-422-2920 *Fax:* 201-791-1401 *E-mail:* staff@ggvideo.com *Web Site:* www.ggvideo.com, pg 875

GAPC (General Assembly Production Centre), 1550 Laperriere Ave, Suite 102, Ottawa, ON K1Z 7T2, Canada *Tel:* 613-723-3316 *Fax:* 613-723-8583 *Web Site:* www.gapc.com, pg 875

Garcia Marketing Inc, 400 Ninth St, Conway, PA 15027-1663 *Tel:* 724-869-0100 *Toll Free Tel:* 800-683-1925 *Fax:* 724-869-1925 *E-mail:* gmavfoto@verizon.net, pg 875

Garden Valley Productions, 240 Crystal Springs Lane, Roseburg, OR 97471 *Tel:* 541-440-1926 *Fax:* 541-440-1008, pg 875

Garman Productions LLC, 2828 NW 58 St, Oklahoma City, OK 73112 *Tel:* 405-254-2500 *Toll Free Tel:* 800-747-5699 *Fax:* 405-254-2507 *E-mail:* info@garman.com *Web Site:* www.garman.com, pg 875

Garner Products Inc, 10620 Industrial Ave, Suite 100, Roseville, CA 95678 *Tel:* 916-784-0200 *Toll Free Tel:* 800-624-1903 *Fax:* 916-784-1425 *E-mail:* info@garner-products.com *Web Site:* www.garner-products.com, pg 875

Gary Camera & Digital, 6750 Broadway Ave, Merrillville, IN 46410 *Tel:* 219-769-2451 *Fax:* 219-769-2488 *Web Site:* garycameradigital.com, pg 875

The Gary-Paul Agency, 1549 Main St, Stratford, CT 06615 *Tel:* 203-345-6167 *Web Site:* www.thegarypaulagency.com, pg 875

Joe Gastwirt Mastering, 4750 Rhapsody Dr, Oak Park, CA 91377 *Tel:* 310-444-9904 *Web Site:* www.gastwirtmastering.com, pg 875

GatesAir, 5300 Kings Island Dr, Suite 101, Mason, OH 45040 *Tel:* 513-459-3400 *Fax:* 513-459-3796 *E-mail:* information@gatesair.com; orders@gatesair.com; support@gatesair.com *Web Site:* www.gatesair.com, pg 875

Gateways, PO Box 1706, Ojai, CA 93024-1706 *Tel:* 805-649-5367 *Toll Free Tel:* 800-477-8908 *Fax:* 805-649-5302 *E-mail:* gwgateways@sbcglobal.net, pg 876

Gateways Books & Tapes, PO Box 370, Nevada City, CA 95959 *Tel:* 530-271-2239 *Toll Free Tel:* 800-869-0658 *Fax:* 530-272-0184 *E-mail:* info@gatewaysbooksandtapes.com *Web Site:* www.gatewaysbooksandtapes.com, pg 876

Gaylord Brothers, PO Box 4901, Syracuse, NY 13221-4901 *Tel:* 315-634-8243 (intl) *Toll Free Tel:* 800-962-9580 (cust serv) *Fax:* 315-453-5030 (intl) *Toll Free Fax:* 800-272-3412 *E-mail:* customerservice@gaylord.com *Web Site:* www.gaylord.com, pg 876

GBC Document Finishing, 4 Corporate Dr, Lake Zurich, IL 60047 *Toll Free Tel:* 800-723-4000 (orders) *Toll Free Fax:* 800-914-8178 *Web Site:* www.gbcconnect.com; www.gbcoffice.com, pg 876

GEAR Cameras & Lighting, 4822 E Cesar Chavez, Austin, TX 78702 *Tel:* 512-485-3131 *Fax:* 512-474-6098 *E-mail:* austin@hdgear.tv *Web Site:* www.hdgear.tv, pg 876

Gear Monkey, 630 The City Dr, Suite 175, Orange, CA 92868 *Tel:* 714-705-6088 *Toll Free Tel:* 877-411-4445 *Fax:* 714-705-6080 *Web Site:* www.gearmonkey.tv, pg 876

Gearhead Rentals, 69 O'Conner Rd, Suite 6, Fairport, NY 14450 *Tel:* 585-236-4272 *Web Site:* www.gearheadrentals.com, pg 876

Gearhouse Broadcast LLC, 9440 Chivers Ave, Sun Valley, CA 91352 *Tel:* 818-955-9449 *Fax:* 818-955-9779 *E-mail:* sales@gearhousebroadcast.us *Web Site:* www.gearhousebroadcast.com, pg 876

Geddes Productions LLC, PO Box 41761, Los Angeles, CA 90041-0761 *Tel:* 323-344-8045 *Fax:* 323-257-7209 *E-mail:* orders@geddesproduction.com *Web Site:* www.geddesproduction.com, pg 876

Gefen, 20600 Nordhoff St, Chatsworth, CA 91311 *Tel:* 818-772-9100 *Toll Free Tel:* 800-545-6900 *Fax:* 818-772-9120 *E-mail:* gsinfo@gefen.com *Web Site:* www.gefen.com, pg 876

Gemini, 2000 Penncraft Ct, Ann Arbor, MI 48103 *Tel:* 734-665-0165 *Toll Free Tel:* 800-317-9929 *Fax:* 734-786-4007 *E-mail:* info@geminichildrensmusic.com *Web Site:* www.geminichildrensmusic.com, pg 876

Gemini Sound, 107 Trumbull St, Bldg F8, 2nd fl, Elizabeth, NJ 07206-2171 *Tel:* 732-346-0061 *Fax:* 732-346-0065 *E-mail:* sales@geminisound.com *Web Site:* www.geminisound.com, pg 876

General Audio-Visual Inc (GAVI), 92 E Merrick Rd, Freeport, NY 11520 *Tel:* 516-623-8500 *Fax:* 516-623-9155 *E-mail:* miked@gavi.com *Web Site:* www.gavi.com, pg 876

General Devices Co Inc, 1410 S Post Rd, Indianapolis, IN 46239 *Tel:* 317-897-7000 *Fax:* 317-898-2917 *E-mail:* sales@generaldevices.com *Web Site:* www.generaldevices.com, pg 876

General Electric Co, 3135 Easton Tpke, Fairfield, CT 06828 *Tel:* 203-373-2211 *Fax:* 203-373-3131 *Web Site:* www.ge.com, pg 876

General Production Services, 883 S East St, Anaheim, CA 92805 *Tel:* 714-535-2271 *Fax:* 714-535-0952 *E-mail:* lensclens@yahoo.com *Web Site:* www.lensclens.com, pg 877

General Projection Systems Inc, 707 Platinum Point, Lake Mary, FL 32746-5702 *Tel:* 407-260-5511 *Toll Free Tel:* 888-GENPROJ (436-7765) *Fax:* 407-833-4990 *E-mail:* solutions@genproj.com *Web Site:* www.genproj.com, pg 877

Genesis Creative, 1006 Hafely Ct, Cayce, SC 29033 *Tel:* 803-796-9666 *E-mail:* geninfo@gencreative.com *Web Site:* genesisstudiossc.com, pg 877

Genigraphics®, PO Box 860111, Shawnee, KS 66286-0111 *Tel:* 913-441-1410 *Toll Free Tel:* 800-790-4001 (cust serv) *E-mail:* info@genigraphics.com *Web Site:* www.genigraphics.com, pg 877

Gary Gentile Productions (GGP), 3 Lehigh Gorge Dr, Jim Thorpe, PA 18229 *Tel:* 252-394-6974 *Web Site:* www.ggentile.com, pg 877

A Gentle Wind, 14 S Pine Ave, Albany, NY 12208 *Tel:* 518-FUN-SONG (482-9023) *Toll Free Tel:* 888-386-7664 (orders) *E-mail:* hello@gentlewind.com *Web Site:* www.gentlewind.com, pg 877

Geomatrix Productions, 270 Amity Rd, Woodbridge, CT 06525-2267 *Tel:* 203-389-0001 *Web Site:* www.geomatrixproductions.com, pg 877

Georgia Film, Music & Digital Entertainment Office, 75 Fifth St W, Suite 1200, Atlanta, GA 30308 *Tel:* 404-962-4052 *Toll Free Tel:* 877-SHOOTGA (746-6842) *Fax:* 404-962-4053 *E-mail:* film@georgia.org *Web Site:* www.georgia.org, pg 1096

Georgia-Pacific Television & Photography, 133 Peachtree St NE, Atlanta, GA 30303 *Tel:* 404-652-5690 *Fax:* 404-487-5352 *Web Site:* www.gp.com; g-ptv.com, pg 877

Gepco®, a General Cable brand, 500 Thorndale Ave, Suite F, Wood Dale, IL 60191-1267 *Tel:* 847-795-9555 *Toll Free Tel:* 800-966-0069 *Fax:* 847-795-8770 *Web Site:* www.gepco.com; www.generalcable.com, pg 877

Bob Gerardi Music Productions, 160 W 73 St, New York, NY 10023-3012 *Tel:* 212-874-6436, pg 877

Gerriets International, 130 Winterwood Ave, Ewing, NJ 08638 *Tel:* 609-771-8111 *Toll Free Tel:* 800-369-3695 *Fax:* 609-771-8118 *E-mail:* info@gerriets.us *Web Site:* www.gerriets.us, pg 877

GES Audio Visual, 7000 Lindell Rd, Las Vegas, NV 89118 *Tel:* 702-515-5500 *Toll Free Tel:* 800-443-9767 *Fax:* 702-515-5765 *E-mail:* lasvegas@ges.com *Web Site:* ges.com, pg 877

Gesturetek, 317 Adelaide St W, Suite 903, Toronto, ON M5V 1P9, Canada *Tel:* 416-340-9290 *Toll Free Tel:* 800-315-1189 *Fax:* 416-348-9809 *E-mail:* info@gesturetek.com *Web Site:* www.gesturetek.com, pg 877

Get Organized, 328 Canham Rd, Scotts Valley, CA 95066 *Tel:* 831-438-0259 *Fax:* 831-438-0359, pg 877

Get Smart Products, 30 S Highland Ave, Ossining, NY 10562 *Tel:* 914-762-3500 *Toll Free Tel:* 800-827-0673 *Fax:* 914-923-5818 *Toll Free Fax:* 866-827-0673 *E-mail:* getsmart@pfile.com *Web Site:* www.pfile.com, pg 877

Gettinger Feather Corp, 16 W 36 St, New York, NY 10018 *Tel:* 212-695-9470 *Fax:* 212-695-9471 *E-mail:* gettfeath@aol.com *Web Site:* www.gettingerfeather.com, pg 877

Getty-Dubay Productions, PO Box 91084, Portland, OR 97291-0084 *Tel:* 503-223-7268 (orders) *Toll Free Tel:* 800-777-2844 *Fax:* 503-223-9182 (orders) *E-mail:* info@handwritingsuccess.com; info@allport.com (orders) *Web Site:* www.handwritingsuccess.com; www.allport.com (orders), pg 877

Getty Images, 605 Fifth Ave S, Suite 400, Seattle, WA 98104 *Tel:* 206-925-5000 *Toll Free Tel:* 888-888-5889; 800-462-4379 (sales) *Fax:* 206-925-5001 *E-mail:* sales@gettyimages.com *Web Site:* www.gettyimages.com, pg 877

Gettysburg Bluegrass Festival, 3340 Fairfield Rd, Gettysburg, PA 17325 *Tel:* 717-642-8749 *E-mail:* bluegrass@granitehillcampingresort.com *Web Site:* www.gettysburgbluegrass.com, pg 1115

Ghent Manufacturing, 2999 Henkle Dr, Lebanon, OH 45036-9260 *Tel:* 513-932-3445 *Toll Free Tel:* 800-543-0550 *Fax:* 513-932-9252 *E-mail:* customer_service@ghent.com *Web Site:* www.ghent.com, pg 878

GHO Group LLC, 340 W 55 St, Suite 5E, New York, NY 10019 *Tel:* 212-319-7716 *E-mail:* info@ghogroup.com *Web Site:* www.ghogroup.com, pg 878

Giant Audio Visual Inc, 111 Canfield Ave, Unit B-6, Randolph, NJ 07869-1114 *Tel:* 973-927-1112 *Toll Free Tel:* 866-GIANTAV (442-6828) *Fax:* 973-927-9977 *E-mail:* staging@giantav.com *Web Site:* www.giantav.com, pg 878

Giant Interactive, 88 Tenth Ave, Suite 6-W, New York, NY 10011 *Tel:* 212-675-7300 *Fax:* 212-765-9336 *E-mail:* info@giant-interactive.com *Web Site:* www.giant-interactive.com, pg 878

Giant Screen Cinema Association (GSCA), 624 Holly Springs Rd, Suite 243, Holly Springs, NC 27540 *Tel:* 919-346-1123 *Fax:* 919-573-9100 *E-mail:* info@giantscreencinema.com *Web Site:* www.giantscreencinema.com, pg 1082

GigaSonic, 260 E Gish Rd, San Jose, CA 95112 *Tel:* 408-573-1400 *Toll Free Tel:* 888-246-4442 *Fax:* 408-573-0602 *Web Site:* www.gigasonic.com, pg 878

Gilderfluke & Co Inc, 205 S Flower St, Burbank, CA 91502 *Tel:* 818-840-9484 *Toll Free Tel:* 800-776-5972 *Fax:* 818-840-9485 *E-mail:* info@gilderfluke.com *Web Site:* www.gilderfluke.com, pg 878

Jim Gill Music Inc, PO Box 2263, Oak Park, IL 60303-2263 *Tel:* 708-763-9864 *Fax:* 708-763-9888 *Web Site:* www.jimgill.com, pg 878

Gingerbread Group, 1337 Kittredge Ct, Atlanta, GA 30329 *Tel:* 404-634-8678; 404-663-9050 *Fax:* 404-601-9387 *E-mail:* books2gogh@gmail.com, pg 878

Gingerbread Productions, 1323 Shepard Dr, Unit I, Sterling, VA 20164 *Tel:* 703-450-7722; 571-432-6920 *Toll Free Tel:* 877-219-3562 *Fax:* 703-450-6836 *E-mail:* bakegingerbread@aol.com *Web Site:* www.gingerbreadproductions.com, pg 878

GKM Broadcast Racks, 200 Finn Ct, Farmingdale, NY 11735 *Tel:* 631-249-7816 *Fax:* 631-249-9450 *E-mail:* info@gkmbroadcastracks.com *Web Site:* www.gkmbroadcastracks.com, pg 878

Glanz Technologies Inc, 687 NE 124 St, North Miami, FL 33161 *Tel:* 305-893-1269 *Fax:* 305-899-8526 *E-mail:* mglanz@glanztech.com *Web Site:* www.glanztechnologies.com, pg 878

Glendale Media Center, 9494 W Maryland Ave, Glendale, AZ 85305 *Tel:* 623-930-4510 *Web Site:* www.glendalemediacenter.com, pg 878

Glendale Production Centre, 1239 S Glendale Ave, Glendale, CA 91205 *Tel:* 818-550-6000 *E-mail:* info@glendalestudios.com *Web Site:* www.glendalestudios.com, pg 878

Glenn Photo Supply, 13502 Erwin St, Van Nuys, CA 91401 *Tel:* 818-997-0410 *Web Site:* www.emgee.freeyellow.com, pg 878

Glenn Video Vistas Ltd, 13502 Erwin St, Van Nuys, CA 91401 *Tel:* 818-997-0410 *Web Site:* www.emgee.freeyellow.com, pg 878

Glenray Productions Inc, 1265 E Calaveras St, Altadena, CA 91001-2535 *Tel:* 626-797-5462 *E-mail:* 2glenray@sbcglobal.net *Web Site:* www.childrensmedia.com, pg 878

GLI Sound Systems, 2691 W 15 St, Brooklyn, NY 11224 *Tel:* 718-372-7849 *Toll Free Tel:* 800-GLI-PRO-1 (454-7761) *Fax:* 718-946-4151 *E-mail:* info@glipro.com; sales@glipro.com *Web Site:* www.glipro.com, pg 878

Glidecam Industries Inc, 23 Joseph St, Kingston, MA 02364 *Tel:* 781-585-7900 *Toll Free Tel:* 800-949-2089; 800-600-2011 *Fax:* 781-585-7903 *E-mail:* sales@glidecam.com *Web Site:* www.glidecam.com, pg 878

Glix Studios, 437 N Varney St, Burbank, CA 91502 *Tel:* 818-441-4065 *E-mail:* info@glixstudios.com *Web Site:* www.glixstudios.com, pg 879

The Global Awards, 260 W 39 St, 10th fl, New York, NY 10018 *Tel:* 212-643-4800 *Fax:* 212-643-0170 *E-mail:* info@newyorkfestivals.com *Web Site:* www.theglobalawards.com, pg 1115

Global Cyber-Visions, 21 Valley Lane, Venus, FL 33960 *Tel:* 863-465-0321 *E-mail:* tvp@thevenusproject.com *Web Site:* www.thevenusproject.com, pg 879

Global ImageWorks LLC, 65 Beacon St, Haworth, NJ 07641 *Tel:* 201-384-7715 *Fax:* 201-501-8971 *E-mail:* info@globalimageworks.com *Web Site:* www.globalimageworks.com, pg 879

Global Net Productions Inc, 568 Iverson Beach Rd, Camano Island, WA 98282-8597 *Tel:* 360-387-8222 *Toll Free Tel:* 800-862-6247 *E-mail:* contact@globalnetproductions.com *Web Site:* www.globalnetproductions.com, pg 879

Global Peace Film Festival (GPFF), 1000 Universal Studios Plaza, Bldg 22-A, Orlando, FL 32819 *Tel:* 407-224-6625 *E-mail:* info@peacefilmfest.org *Web Site:* www.peacefilmfest.org, pg 1115

Global Television, 222 23 St NE, Calgary, AB T2E 7N2, Canada *Tel:* 403-235-7777 *Fax:* 403-248-0252 *E-mail:* globalnews.calg@globaltv.com *Web Site:* www.globaltv.com, pg 879

Global Television Station, 5325 Allard Way, Edmonton, AB T6H 5B8, Canada *Tel:* 780-436-1250; 780-989-4683 *Fax:* 780-989-4686 *E-mail:* globalnews.ed@globaltv.com *Web Site:* www.globaltv.com, pg 879

Global Video Distributors Inc, 8181 NW 91 Terr, Suite 7, Medley, FL 33166 *Tel:* 305-887-2000 *Fax:* 305-887-2000 *Web Site:* global.myvideostore.com, pg 879

Global Village Productions, 6914 B Sebastapol Ave, Sebastopol, CA 95472 *Tel:* 707-823-1451 *Toll Free Tel:* 800-798-FIND (798-3463) *Fax:* 707-829-5545 *E-mail:* production@videosource.com; video@videosource.com *Web Site:* www.videosource.com, pg 879

Global Village Stock Footage Library, 1717 Darby Rd, Sebastopol, CA 95472 *Tel:* 707-823-1451 *Toll Free Tel:* 800-798-FIND (798-3463) *Fax:* 707-829-5545 *E-mail:* contact@hdenvironments.com *Web Site:* www.videosource.com; hdenvironments.com, pg 879

GlobalStreams™ Corp, 20353 W 108 St, Olathe, KS 66061 *Tel:* 314-423-6700 *Toll Free Tel:* 800-788-7205; 866-558-7830 (cust support) *Fax:* 314-423-6705 *E-mail:* gsinfo@globalstreams.com; support@globalstreams.com; sales@globalstreams.com *Web Site:* www.globalstreams.com, pg 879

Globe/Miami Film Commission, 1360 N Broad St, US 60, Globe, AZ 85501 *Tel:* 928-425-4495 *Toll Free Tel:* 800-804-5623 *Fax:* 928-425-3410 *E-mail:* gmr@cableone.net *Web Site:* www.globemiamichamber.com, pg 1091

Globe Photos Inc, 24 Edmore Lane S, West Islip, NY 11795 *Tel:* 631-661-3131 *Fax:* 631-321-4063 *E-mail:* info@globephotos.com *Web Site:* www.globephotos.com, pg 879

Gluskin's Custom Audio Video, 2087 Grand Canal Blvd, Suite 11, Stockton, CA 95204 *Tel:* 209-888-4609 *Fax:* 209-888-4629 *E-mail:* audio@gluskins.com *Web Site:* www.gluskins.com, pg 879

GMF Sound Inc, 1961 N Main, Orange, CA 92865 *Tel:* 714-282-1559 *Fax:* 714-282-1942 *E-mail:* generalinfo@gmfsound.com; sales@gmfsound.com *Web Site:* www.gmfsound.com, pg 879

GMI Productions, One General Mills Blvd, Minneapolis, MN 55426 *Tel:* 763-764-7600 *Toll Free Tel:* 800-248-7310 *Fax:* 763-764-2739 *Web Site:* www.generalmills.com, pg 879

GMP Music, 1103 North St, Niles, MI 49120 *Tel:* 269-687-9100 *Toll Free Tel:* 800-955-0619 *Fax:* 269-687-9200 *E-mail:* info@gmpmusic.com *Web Site:* www.gmpmusic.com; www.reservemusic.com, pg 879

GNP Crescendo Records, 1405 N Avon St, Burbank, CA 91505-1885 *Tel:* 818-566-8900 *E-mail:* gnp@pacificnet.net *Web Site:* www.gnpcrescendo.com, pg 879

Go To Team, 359-C Wando Place Dr, Mount Pleasant, SC 29464 *Tel:* 843-884-6222 *Toll Free Tel:* 888-455-4333 *E-mail:* crew@gototeam.com *Web Site:* www.gototeam.com, pg 879

Goal Productions, 1905 Victory Blvd, Suite 6, Glendale, CA 91201 *Tel:* 818-588-3900 *Fax:* 818-588-3903 *E-mail:* info@goalproductions.com *Web Site:* www.goalproductions.com, pg 879

Goddard Design Co, 51 Nassau Ave, Brooklyn, NY 11222 *Tel:* 718-599-0170 *Fax:* 718-599-0172 *E-mail:* sales@goddarddesign.com *Web Site:* www.goddarddesign.com, pg 880

The Godfrey Group Inc, 4102 S Miami Blvd, Durham, NC 27703 *Tel:* 919-544-6504 *Toll Free Tel:* 800-789-9394 *Fax:* 919-544-6729 *E-mail:* sales@godfreygroup.com *Web Site:* www.godfreygroup.com, pg 880

Goin' Mobile, PO Box 470627, Brookline, MA 02447 *Tel:* 617-232-7969 (cell) *Web Site:* www.goin-mobile.com, pg 880

Gold Line/TEF, PO Box 500, West Redding, CT 06896-0500 *Tel:* 203-938-2588 *Fax:* 203-938-8740 *E-mail:* sales@gold-line.com *Web Site:* www.gold-line.com, pg 880

Gold Link Productions Inc, 176 Ridge Rd, Bolton, ON L7E 4V4, Canada *Tel:* 416-560-3864 *Web Site:* www.toronto-cameraman.com, pg 880

Gold Standard Productions, 12952 Miriam Place, Santa Ana, CA 92705-1334 *Tel:* 714-544-7000 *Fax:* 714-544-7010 *Web Site:* www.goldstandardproductions.com, pg 880

Goldberg Brothers Inc, 8000 E 40 Ave, Denver, CO 80207 *Tel:* 303-321-1099 *Fax:* 303-388-0749 *E-mail:* reelservice@goldbergbrothers.com *Web Site:* www.goldbergbrothers.com, pg 880

Bruce Goldberg Inc, 5354 Quakertown Ave, Woodland Hills, CA 91364 *Tel:* 818-713-8190 *Toll Free Tel:* 800-527-6248 *Fax:* 818-704-9189 *E-mail:* drbg@sbcglobal.net *Web Site:* www.drbrucegoldberg.com, pg 880

Golden Gate Awards, c/o San Francisco Film Society, The Presidio, Suite 110, 39 Mesa St, San Francisco, CA 94129-1025 *Tel:* 415-561-5000 *Fax:* 415-440-1760 *E-mail:* info@sffs.org *Web Site:* festival.sffs.org; www.sffs.org, pg 1115

Golden Gate Studios, 100 Pelican Way, Suite E, San Rafael, CA 94901 *Tel:* 415-485-5856 *Fax:* 415-256-9262 *Web Site:* www.goldengatestudios.com, pg 880

Golden Globe Awards, 646 N Robertson Blvd, West Hollywood, CA 90069 *Tel:* 310-657-1731 *Fax:* 310-657-5576 *E-mail:* info@hfpa.org *Web Site:* www.hfpa.org, pg 1115

Golden Lamb Productions, 47 Schoolhouse Rd, Nassau, NY 12123 *Tel:* 518-766-4358 *Web Site:* www.glpvideoproduction.com, pg 880

Golden Mike Award, 125 W 55 St, 3rd fl, New York, NY 10019-5366 *Tel:* 212-373-8250 *Fax:* 212-373-8254 *E-mail:* info@thebfoa.org *Web Site:* www.broadcastersfoundation.org, pg 1115

Golden Reel Award, 6 Beach Rd, 544, Tiburon, CA 94920 *Tel:* 415-251-8433 *Fax:* 633-444-8433 *E-mail:* info@tiburonfilmfestival.com *Web Site:* www.tiburonfilmfestival.com, pg 1115

Golden Reel Awards, 10061 Riverside Dr, PMB 751, Toluca Lake, CA 91602-2550 *Tel:* 818-506-7731 *Fax:* 818-506-7732 *E-mail:* mail@mpse.org; info@mpse.org *Web Site:* www.mpse.org, pg 1115

Golden Sheaf Awards, 49 Smith St E, Yorkton, SK S3N 0H4, Canada *Tel:* 306-782-7077 *Fax:* 306-782-1550 *E-mail:* info@yorktonfilm.com *Web Site:* yorktonfilm.com/golden-sheaf-awards/, pg 1115

Golden Space Needle Awards, 305 Harrison St, Seattle, WA 98109 *Tel:* 206-464-5830 *Fax:* 206-264-7919 *E-mail:* info@siff.net *Web Site:* www.siff.net, pg 1116

Golden State Dance Teachers Association (GSDTA), 10804 Woodruff Ave, Downey, CA 90241-3910 *Tel:* 562-869-8949 *Web Site:* www.swingworld.com, pg 880

Golf Digest, 20 Westport Rd, Wilton, CT 06897 *Tel:* 203-761-5100 *Toll Free Tel:* 800-727-4653 *Fax:* 203-761-5129 *Web Site:* www.golfdigest.com, pg 880

Goodman Associates Inc, 718 S 22 St, Philadelphia, PA 19146 *Tel:* 215-546-1448 *E-mail:* goodman@histories.com, pg 880

Goose Creek Music & Entertainment, 17723 Tranquility Rd, Purcellville, VA 20132 *Tel:* 540-751-1395 *E-mail:* info@goosecreekmusic.com *Web Site:* www.goosecreekmusic.com, pg 880

Alan Gordon Enterprises Inc, 5625 Melrose Ave, Hollywood, CA 90038 *Tel:* 323-466-3561 *Fax:* 323-871-2193 *E-mail:* contactus@alangordon.com *Web Site:* www.alangordon.com, pg 880

Gordon Productions Inc, 1730 Pacheco St, San Francisco, CA 94116 *Tel:* 415-776-7484 *Web Site:* www.gpvideo.com, pg 880

Gordon Visual Solutions, 504 Reiman St, Buffalo, NY 14212-2250 *Tel:* 716-894-5930 *Fax:* 630-839-5930 *E-mail:* info@gordonvisualsolutions.com; service@gordonvisualsolutions.com *Web Site:* www.gordonvisualsolutions.com, pg 880

Gospel Folio Press, 304 Killaly St W, Port Colborne, ON L3K 6A6, Canada *Tel:* 905-835-9166 *Toll Free Tel:* 800-952-2382 *Fax:* 905-834-0012 *E-mail:* info@gospelfolio.com; orders@gospelfolio.com *Web Site:* www.gospelfolio.com, pg 880

Gotham City Studios, 2219 Freedom Dr, Charlotte, NC 28208 *Tel:* 704-333-2349 *E-mail:* info@gothamcitystudios.us *Web Site:* www.gothamcitystudios.us, pg 880

Gotham Sound & Communications Inc, 330 W 38 St, No 105, New York, NY 10018 *Tel:* 212-629-9430 *Toll Free Tel:* 866-468-4268 *Fax:* 212-629-9436 *E-mail:* nyc@gothamsound.com *Web Site:* www.gothamsound.com, pg 881

Grace Church - St Louis, 2695 Creve Coeur Mill Rd, Maryland Heights, MO 63043 *Tel:* 314-292-8300 *Fax:* 314-291-0918 *E-mail:* info@gracestl.org *Web Site:* www.gracestl.org, pg 881

The Gracies®, 1250 24 St NW, Suite 300, Washington, DC 20037 *Tel:* 202-750-3664 *Fax:* 202-750-3664 *Web Site:* www.allwomeninmedia.org; www.thegracies.org, pg 1116

Grafco Inc, PO Box 431, Stroudsburg, PA 18360 *Toll Free Tel:* 800-367-6169 *Toll Free Fax:* 800-443-4329 *E-mail:* grafcofurniture@grafco.com *Web Site:* www.grafco.com, pg 881

Graftek Imaging Inc, 8900 Shoal Creek Blvd, Bldg 300, Suite B, Austin, TX 78757 *Tel:* 512-416-1099 *Toll Free Tel:* 800-441-2118 *Fax:* 512-416-1014 *E-mail:* graftek@graftek.com *Web Site:* www.graftek.com, pg 881

Graham-Patten, 119 E McKnight Way, Unit A, Grass Valley, CA 95949 *Tel:* 530-477-2984 *Fax:* 530-477-2986 *E-mail:* support@isis-group.com *Web Site:* www.gpsys.com, pg 881

Grammy Awards, 3030 Olympic Blvd, Santa Monica, CA 90404 *Tel:* 310-392-3777 *Fax:* 310-392-2306 *Web Site:* www.grammy.org; www.grammy.com, pg 1116

Grand Stage Co Inc, 630 W Lake St, Chicago, IL 60661 *Tel:* 312-332-5611 *Toll Free Tel:* 800-621-2181 *Fax:* 312-258-0056 *E-mail:* info@grandstage.com *Web Site:* www.grandstage.com, pg 881

Grande Vitesse Systems Inc (GVS), 390 Fremont St, San Francisco, CA 94105-9275 *Tel:* 415-777-0320 *Toll Free Tel:* 800-794-4622 (sales) *Fax:* 415-777-9544 *Web Site:* www.gvs9000.com, pg 881

Granger, 25 Chapel St, Suite 605, New York, NY 11201 *Tel:* 212-447-1789 *Fax:* 212-447-1492 *E-mail:* info@granger.com *Web Site:* www.granger.com, pg 881

Granny Press LLC, 101 Gedney St, Apt 5-D, Nyack, NY 10960 *Tel:* 845-875-4422; 845-875-4423 *E-mail:* webmaster@grannypress.com *Web Site:* www.grannypress.com, pg 881

Graphic Artists Guild, 32 Broadway, Suite 1114, New York, NY 10004 *Tel:* 212-791-3400 *Fax:* 212-791-0333 *E-mail:* admin@gag.org; sales@gag.org *Web Site:* www.graphicartistsguild.org, pg 1082

Graphic Laminating LLC, 6185 Cochran Rd, Solon, OH 44139 *Tel:* 440-498-3400 *Toll Free Tel:* 800-345-5300 *Fax:* 440-498-3410 *E-mail:* info@graphiclaminating.com *Web Site:* www.graphiclaminating.com, pg 881

Graphic Products Corp, 455 Maple Ave, Carpentersville, IL 60110 *Tel:* 847-836-9600 *Toll Free Tel:* 800-323-1660 (cust serv) *Fax:* 847-836-9666 *E-mail:* info@gpcpapers.com *Web Site:* www.gpcpapers.com, pg 881

Graphics Depot Inc, 11 Middlebury Blvd, Unit 4, Randolph, NJ 07869 *Tel:* 973-927-8200 *Fax:* 973-927-8253 *E-mail:* info@graphicsdepotinc.com; sales@graphicsdepotinc.com *Web Site:* www.graphicsdepotinc.com, pg 881

Graphx Inc, 400 W Cummings Park, Suite 3900, Woburn, MA 01801 *Tel:* 781-932-0430 *Fax:* 781-932-0855 *E-mail:* info@graphx.com *Web Site:* www.graphx.com, pg 881

Grass Valley, 3030 NW Aloclek Dr, Hillsboro, OR 97124 *Tel:* 503-526-8160 *Fax:* 503-526-8109, pg 881

Grass Valley/Nevada County Chamber of Commerce, 128 E Main St, Grass Valley, CA 95945 *Tel:* 530-273-4667 *Toll Free Tel:* 800-655-4667 *Fax:* 530-272-5440 *E-mail:* info@grassvalleychamber.com *Web Site:* www.grassvalleychamber.com, pg 1093

Grassland Media Inc, 5944 Seminole Centre Ct, Suite 120, Fitchburg, WI 53711-5019 *Tel:* 608-238-7575 *Toll Free Tel:* 800-236-7575 *Fax:* 608-270-9301 *Web Site:* www.grasslandmedia.com, pg 881

Great Chefs/Leisure Jazz Video, 747 Magazine St, New Orleans, LA 70130 *Tel:* 504-581-5000 *Toll Free Tel:* 800-321-1499 *Fax:* 504-581-1188 *E-mail:* info@greatchefs.com *Web Site:* www.greatchefs.com, pg 881

Great Recordings LLC, 1812 Procter St, Port Arthur, TX 77640 *Tel:* 409-982-7121 *Fax:* 409-982-0643 *E-mail:* music@great-recordings.com *Web Site:* www.great-recordings.com, pg 881

Great River Electronics, 164 Hardman Ave S, South St Paul, MN 55075 *Tel:* 651-455-1846 *Fax:* 651-455-3224 *E-mail:* info@greweb.com *Web Site:* www.greatriverelectronics.com, pg 881

The Great Southern Studios, 15221 NE 21 Ave, North Miami Beach, FL 33162 *Tel:* 305-944-2464 *Fax:* 305-944-9920 *E-mail:* info@gssmiami.com *Web Site:* www.greatsouthernstudios.com, pg 882

Greater Cincinnati & Northern Kentucky Film Commission, 602 Main St, Suite 712, Cincinnati, OH 45202 *Tel:* 513-784-1744 *Fax:* 513-768-8963 *E-mail:* info@filmcincinnati.com *Web Site:* www.filmcincinnati.com, pg 1101

Greater Columbus Film Commission, PO Box 12735, Columbus, OH 43212 *Tel:* 614-450-0264 *E-mail:* info@columbusfilmcommission.com *Web Site:* www.filmcolumbus.com, pg 1101

Greater Fort Lauderdale/Broward Office of Film & Entertainment, 110 E Broward, Suite 1990, Fort Lauderdale, FL 33301 *Tel:* 954-524-3113 *Toll Free Tel:* 800-741-1420 *Fax:* 954-524-3167 *E-mail:* info@browardalliance.org *Web Site:* www.browardalliance.org/film; www.sunny.org, pg 1095

Greater Omaha Film Commission, 1819 Farnam St, Suite 300, Omaha, NE 68183 *Tel:* 402-444-5000, pg 1100

Greater Philadelphia Film Office, One Parkway Bldg, 11th fl, 1515 Arch St, Philadelphia, PA 19102 *Tel:* 215-686-2668 *Fax:* 215-686-3659 *E-mail:* mail@film.org *Web Site:* www.film.org, pg 1102

Greater Wichita Convention & Visitors Bureau/Wichita Film Commission, 515 S Main St, Suite 115, Wichita, KS 67202 *Tel:* 316-265-2800 *Toll Free Tel:* 800-288-9424 *Fax:* 316-265-0162 *Web Site:* www.gowichita.com, pg 1098

William Greaves Productions Inc, 475 W 57 St, No 17A, New York, NY 10019 *Toll Free Tel:* 800-874-8314 *Fax:* 212-315-0027 *Web Site:* www.williamgreaves.com, pg 882

Greeley/Weld Film Commission, 902 Seventh Ave, Greeley, CO 80631 *Tel:* 970-352-3567 *Toll Free Tel:* 800-449-3866 *Fax:* 970-352-3572 *E-mail:* info@greeleycvb.com *Web Site:* www.greeleychamber.com, pg 1095

Green Dot Audio Electronics, PO Box 290609, Nashville, TN 37229-0609 *Tel:* 615-366-5964 *Fax:* 615-366-7069 *E-mail:* greendotaudio@bellsouth.net *Web Site:* www.greendotaudio.com, pg 882

Green Linnet Records, 916 19 Ave S, Nashville, TN 37212 *Tel:* 615-320-7672 *Toll Free Tel:* 800-468-6644 *Fax:* 615-320-7378 *E-mail:* info@compassrecords.com *Web Site:* greenlinnet.com; www.compassrecords.com, pg 882

Green Mountain Audio Inc, 955 E Fillmore St, Colorado Springs, CO 80907-6315 *Tel:* 719-636-2500 *E-mail:* greenmountainaudio@comcast.net *Web Site:* www.greenmountainaudio.com, pg 882

Green Mountain Post Films (GMP), PO Box 229, Turners Falls, MA 01376-0229 *Tel:* 413-863-4754 *Fax:* 413-863-8248 *E-mail:* info@gmpfilms.com *Web Site:* www.gmpfilms.com, pg 882

Greenery Studios, 7764 San Fernando Rd, Burbank, CA 91352 *Tel:* 818-253-9990 *E-mail:* info@greenerystudios.com *Web Site:* greenerystudios.com, pg 882

Greenwood Convention & Visitors Bureau & Film Commission, 111 E Market St, Greenwood, MS 38935 *Tel:* 662-453-9197 *Toll Free Tel:* 800-748-9064 *Fax:* 662-453-5526 *E-mail:* info@gcvb.com *Web Site:* www.greenwoodms.org, pg 1099

Greyfalcon House, 124 Waverly Place, New York, NY 10011 *Tel:* 212-777-9042, pg 882

Griesinger Films LLC, 7300 Old Mill Rd, Gates Mills, OH 44040 *Tel:* 440-423-1601 *Toll Free Tel:* 800-872-4456 *Fax:* 440-423-1601 *E-mail:* orders@griesingerfilms.com *Web Site:* www.griesingerfilms.com, pg 882

Griffith Productions, 1750 Donelson Dr, Eads, TN 38028 *Tel:* 901-351-1899 *Fax:* 901-465-1787 *E-mail:* info@griffithproductions.tv *Web Site:* www.griffithproductions.tv, pg 882

Griffiths Broadcast Co Inc, 2981 Le Conte St, Viera, FL 32940 *Tel:* 321-622-4619 *Fax:* 321-622-4619 *E-mail:* griffiths.broadcast@usa.net *Web Site:* www.griffithsbroadcast.com, pg 882

Griggs Productions Inc, Kappas Marina, 29 W Pier, Sausalito, CA 94965 *Tel:* 415-999-1079 *Toll Free Tel:* 800-210-4200 *Web Site:* www.griggs.com, pg 882

Grise Audio Visual Center Inc, 2402 Cherry St, Erie, PA 16502 *Tel:* 814-452-4465 *Toll Free Tel:* 888-404-2719 *Fax:* 814-452-4479 *E-mail:* grise@erie.net *Web Site:* www.griseav.com, pg 882

Grocery Manufacturers Association (GMA), 1350 "I" St NW, Suite 300, Washington, DC 20005 *Tel:* 202-639-5900 *Toll Free Tel:* 800-355-0983 *Fax:* 202-639-5932 *E-mail:* info@gmaonline.org *Web Site:* gmaonline.org, pg 882

GrooveWorx, 1418 Second St, Santa Monica, CA 90401 *Tel:* 310-260-2626 *Toll Free Tel:* 800-400-6767 *Fax:* 310-260-2662 *E-mail:* contact@grooveworx.com *Web Site:* www.grooveworx.com, pg 882

Groovy Like a Movie, 5205 Kearny Villa Way, Suite 100, San Diego, CA 92123 *Tel:* 858-715-0300 *E-mail:* info@groovylikeamovie.com *Web Site:* www.groovylikeamovie.com, pg 882

Group One Ltd, 70 Sea Lane, Farmingdale, NY 11735 *Tel:* 516-249-1399 *Fax:* 516-249-8870 *E-mail:* sales@g1limited.com *Web Site:* www.g1limited.com, pg 882

Group PVP, 296 Saint Pierre St, Matane, QC G4W 2B9, Canada *Tel:* 418-566-2040 *Toll Free Tel:* 877-320-2040 *Fax:* 418-562-4643 *E-mail:* info@pvp.ca *Web Site:* www.pvp.ca, pg 882

GTI (Graphic Technology Inc), PO Box 3138, Newburgh, NY 12550-0651 *Tel:* 845-562-7066 *Toll Free Tel:* 888-562-7066 *Fax:* 845-562-2543 *E-mail:* sales@gtilite.com *Web Site:* www.gtilite.com, pg 883

Guerrilla Film Fest, 1421 Massachusetts Ave NW, Suite 202, Washington, DC 20005 *Tel:* 202-234-2889 *E-mail:* gfilmfest@yahoo.com *Web Site:* www.gfilmfest.com, pg 1116

Guerrilla Productions LLC, 1119 E 50 St, Savannah, GA 31404 *Tel:* 919-349-7643; 912-354-4518 *Fax:* 912-354-1176 *E-mail:* info@guerrillapro.com *Web Site:* www.guerrillapro.com, pg 883

Guidance Associates Inc Center for Humanities, 31 Pine View Rd, Mount Kisco, NY 10549 *Tel:* 914-666-4100 *Toll Free Tel:* 800-431-1242 *Fax:* 914-666-5319 *Web Site:* www.guidanceassociates.com, pg 883

Guild of Italian American Actors (GIAA), Canal Street Sta, PO Box 123, New York, NY 10013-0123 *Tel:* 201-344-3411 *E-mail:* info@giaa.us *Web Site:* www.giaa.us, pg 1082

Guilford Publications, 72 Spring St, 4th fl, New York, NY 10012 *Tel:* 212-431-9800 *Toll Free Tel:* 800-365-7006 *Fax:* 212-966-6708 *E-mail:* info@guilford.com *Web Site:* www.guilford.com, pg 883

Gulf Coast Audio Visual Producers Inc, c/o National Park Bookshop, 3720 N Pace Blvd, Pensacola, FL 32506 *Tel:* 850-433-3016 *Toll Free Tel:* 800-722-2057 *Fax:* 850-438-4807 *E-mail:* gcavp@aol.com *Web Site:* www.gcavp.com, pg 883

Gurrilla Video Solutions, 233 Fillmore Ave, Suite 8, Tonawanda, NY 14150 *Tel:* 716-692-0064 *E-mail:* info@gvideosolutions.com *Web Site:* www.gvideosolutions.com, pg 883

Guymark Studios LLC, 3019 Dixwell Ave, Hamden, CT 06518 *Tel:* 203-248-9323 *Fax:* 203-248-9325 *E-mail:* guymark.studios@snet.net *Web Site:* www.guymarkstudios.com, pg 883

GVISION USA Inc, 20532 Crescent Bay Dr, Lake Forest, CA 92630 *Tel:* 949-586-3338 *Fax:* 949-586-3398 *E-mail:* info@gvision-usa.com; gsales@gvision-usa.com *Web Site:* www.gvision-usa.com, pg 883

Gypsum Association, 6525 Belcrest Rd, Suite 480, Hyattsville, MD 20782 *Tel:* 301-277-8686 *Fax:* 301-277-8747 *E-mail:* info@gypsum.org *Web Site:* www.gypsum.org, pg 883

Gyration, 3601-B Calle Tecate, Camarillo, CA 93012 *Toll Free Tel:* 888-340-0033 (tech support) *E-mail:* gsupport@smkusa.com *Web Site:* www.gyration.com, pg 883

Gyrus ACMI, 136 Turnpike Rd, Southborough, MA 01772-2104 *Tel:* 508-804-2600 *Toll Free Tel:* 800-852-9361 (cust serv) *Fax:* 508-804-2624; 763-416-3001 (cust serv) *E-mail:* customercare@gyrusacmi.com *Web Site:* www.gyrusacmi.com, pg 883

Hakuba Sunpak Velbon, 53 Green Pond Rd, Suite 5, Rockaway, NJ 07866 *Tel:* 973-627-9600 *Toll Free Tel:* 800-886-2236 *Fax:* 973-664-2438 *E-mail:* info@tocad.com *Web Site:* www.tocad.com, pg 883

Half Moon Video Productions, 79 Central Ave, Jersey City, NJ 07306-2124 *Tel:* 201-792-1066 *Fax:* 201-792-1523 *E-mail:* pavonia@home.com, pg 883

Howard Hall Productions, 2171 La Amatista Rd, Del Mar, CA 92014-3031 *Tel:* 858-259-8989 *Fax:* 858-792-1467 *E-mail:* info@howardhall.com *Web Site:* www.howardhall.com, pg 883

Hall Productions, 951 Front St, Grover Beach, CA 93433 *Tel:* 805-473-1042 *Toll Free Tel:* 800-366-6057 *Fax:* 805-473-2202 *Web Site:* hallpro.com, pg 884

HallBrook Productions, 565 Dutch Valley Rd, Atlanta, GA 30324 *Tel:* 404-892-0042 *E-mail:* hallbrook@hallbrookproductions.com *Web Site:* hallbrookproductions.com, pg 884

Hallel Communications, Hallel Institute, 175 Rte 340, Sparkill, NY 10976-1047 *Tel:* 845-365-2277 *Toll Free Tel:* 800-445-7477 *Fax:* 845-365-2279 *E-mail:* hallel@hallel.net *Web Site:* www.hallelvideos.com, pg 884

Steven Halpern's Inner Peace Music, PO Box 2644, San Anselmo, CA 94979-2644 *Tel:* 541-488-7870 *Toll Free Tel:* 888-765-9697 (shipping); 800-909-0707 (orders) *Fax:* 541-488-7870 *E-mail:* info@innerpeacemusic.com *Web Site:* www.innerpeacemusic.com, pg 884

Hamilton Buhl, 80 Little Falls Rd, Fairfield, NJ 07004 *Toll Free Tel:* 800-631-0868 *Toll Free Fax:* 800-398-1812 (cust serv & sales) *E-mail:* customerservice@hamiltonbuhl.com *Web Site:* www.hamiltonbuhl.com, pg 884

Hamilton Studio, 1427 W Dean Ave, Spokane, WA 99201 *Tel:* 509-327-9501 *Web Site:* www.hamiltonstudio.com, pg 884

Hammond Communications Group, 173 Trade St, Lexington, KY 40511-2608 *Tel:* 859-254-1878 *E-mail:* info@hammondcg.com *Web Site:* www.hammondcg.com, pg 884

Hampshire Street Studios, 540A Hampshire St, San Francisco, CA 94110 *Tel:* 415-643-5580 *E-mail:* info@hampshirestreetstudios.com *Web Site:* www.hampshirestreetstudios.com, pg 884

The Hamptons International Film Festival, 47 Newtown Lane, East Hampton, NY 11937 *Tel:* 631-324-4600; 631-747-7978 *Fax:* 631-324-1558 *E-mail:* info@hamptonsfilmfest.org *Web Site:* www.hamptonsfilmfest.org, pg 1116

Hand Held Films, 129 W 27 St, New York, NY 10001 *Tel:* 212-627-2781; 212-502-0900 (rentals) *Fax:* 212-502-0906 *E-mail:* rentals@handheldfilms.com *Web Site:* handheldfilms.com, pg 884

Howard Hanger, 31 Park Ave N, Asheville, NC 28801 *Tel:* 828-280-8419 *Fax:* 828-280-8419 *E-mail:* hangerhall@prodigy.net *Web Site:* www.howardhanger.com, pg 884

Terry Hanley Audio Systems Inc, 20 Industrial Pkwy, Woburn, MA 01801 *Tel:* 781-932-5300 *Fax:* 781-932-5354 *E-mail:* mail@terryhanleyaudio.com *Web Site:* www.terryhanleyaudio.com, pg 884

G W Hannaway & Associates, 839 Pearl St, Boulder, CO 80302 *Tel:* 303-440-9631 *Fax:* 303-440-4421 *E-mail:* sales@gwha.com; services@gwha.com; technology@gwha.com *Web Site:* www.gwha.com, pg 884

Hannay Reels Inc, 553 State Rte 143, Westerlo, NY 12193-0159 *Tel:* 518-797-3791 *Toll Free Tel:* 877-467-3357 *Fax:* 518-797-3259 *Toll Free Fax:* 800-733-5464 *E-mail:* reels@hannay.com *Web Site:* www.hannay.com, pg 884

Hannecke Display Systems Inc, 91 Fulton St, Boonton, NJ 07005 *Tel:* 973-335-0434 *Toll Free Tel:* 800-345-8631 *Fax:* 973-335-1274 *E-mail:* info.usa@hannecke.com *Web Site:* www.hannecke.com, pg 884

Hanovia Specialty Lighting LLC, 6 Evans St, Fairfield, NJ 07004 *Tel:* 973-651-5510 *Fax:* 973-651-5550 *E-mail:* sales@hanovia-uv.com *Web Site:* www.hanovia-uv.com, pg 884

Har-Ken Specialties, PO Box 37, Parkesburg, PA 19365-0037 *Tel:* 610-384-2161 *Fax:* 610-384-8258 *E-mail:* harken1@comcast.net *Web Site:* www.har-kenspecialties.com; www.har-ken.com, pg 884

Harbor House Studios, 2525 Florence Rd, Suite B, Keller, TX 76262 *Tel:* 817-379-1500 *Fax:* 817-337-5104 *E-mail:* info@harborhousestudios.com *Web Site:* www.harborhousestudios.com, pg 884

Harbro Corp, 2691 W 15 St, Brooklyn, NY 11224-2705 *Tel:* 718-946-4134 *Fax:* 718-946-4151, pg 884

Hard Hat Radio Music Service, 519 N Halifax Ave, Daytona Beach, FL 32118-4017 *Tel:* 386-252-0381 *Fax:* 386-252-0381 *E-mail:* hardhatrecords@aol.com *Web Site:* www.hardhatrecords.com, pg 884

Hardcastle Films & Video, 7319 Wise Ave, St Louis, MO 63117-1718 *Tel:* 314-647-4200 *Fax:* 314-647-4201, pg 885

Hargrove Inc, One Hargrove Dr, Lanham, MD 20706 *Tel:* 301-306-9000 *Fax:* 301-306-9318 *E-mail:* exhibitorservices@hargroveinc.com *Web Site:* www.hargroveinc.com, pg 885

Harman International Industries Inc, 400 Atlantic St, 15th fl, Stamford, CT 06901 *Tel:* 203-328-3500 *Web Site:* www.harman.com, pg 885

Harman Pro North America, 8500 Balboa Blvd, Northridge, CA 91329 *Tel:* 818-894-8850; 818-893-8411 *Fax:* 818-920-3208 *E-mail:* info@harman.com *Web Site:* www.harman.com, pg 885

Harmonia Mundi USA, 1117 Chestnut St, Burbank, CA 91506 *Tel:* 818-333-1500 *Fax:* 818-333-1502 *E-mail:* info-usa@harmoniamundi.com *Web Site:* www.harmoniamundi.com, pg 885

Harmon's Audio-Visual Services, 2533 Crystal Dr, Fort Myers, FL 33966 *Tel:* 239-939-2273 *Fax:* 239-939-5966 *E-mail:* info@harmonsav.com *Web Site:* www.harmonsav.com, pg 885

Harnel Case Co, 1600 Marshall Ave SE, Grand Rapids, MI 49507 *Tel:* 616-452-4522 *Fax:* 616-452-5514 *E-mail:* info@harnelcase.com *Web Site:* www.harnelcase.com, pg 885

HarperAudio, 10 E 53 St, New York, NY 10022 *Tel:* 212-207-7000 *Toll Free Tel:* 800-242-7737 *Fax:* 212-207-2582 *Toll Free Fax:* 800-822-4090 *Web Site:* www.harpercollins.com, pg 885

Harpers Ferry Historical Association, c/o National Park Bookshop, 723 Shenandoah St, Harpers Ferry, WV 25425 *Tel:* 304-535-6881 *Fax:* 304-535-6749 *E-mail:* hfha@earthlink.net *Web Site:* www.harpersferryhistory.org, pg 885

Harrah's Theatre Equipment Co, 25613 Dollar St, Unit 1, Hayward, CA 94544 *Tel:* 510-881-4989 *Fax:* 510-881-0448, pg 885

Harris Canada Systems, 26 Peppler St, Waterloo, ON N2J 3C4, Canada *Tel:* 519-570-9111 *Toll Free Tel:* 800-363-3400 *Fax:* 519-570-9140 *E-mail:* info@inscriber.com *Web Site:* www.broadcast.harris.com, pg 885

Harris Communications Inc, 15155 Technology Dr, Eden Prairie, MN 55344 *Tel:* 952-906-1180 *Toll Free Tel:* 800-825-6758 *Fax:* 952-906-1099 *E-mail:* info@harriscomm.com *Web Site:* www.harriscomm.com, pg 885

Harris Corp, 1025 W NASA Blvd, Melbourne, FL 32919-0001 *Tel:* 321-727-9100 *Toll Free Tel:* 800-442-7747 *E-mail:* webmaster@harris.com *Web Site:* www.harris.com, pg 885

Harrison Brothers, 47 N Chatham Pkwy, Chapel Hill, NC 27517 *Toll Free Tel:* 866-386-8335; 800-327-4414 *Toll Free Fax:* 800-327-6651 *E-mail:* info@harrisonbros.com *Web Site:* www.thetapeworks.com, pg 885

Harrison Consoles, 1024 Firestone Pkwy, La Vergne, TN 37086-3505 *Tel:* 615-641-7200 *Fax:* 615-641-7224 *E-mail:* info@harrisonconsoles.com *Web Site:* www.harrisonconsoles.com, pg 885

Hart Inc, 320 New Stock Rd, Asheville, NC 28804 *Tel:* 828-645-4734 *Toll Free Tel:* 800-654-8012 *Fax:* 828-645-4294 *Toll Free Fax:* 866-390-4278 *E-mail:* mail@hart-inc.com *Web Site:* www.hart-inc.com, pg 885

Hartley Film Foundation, 49 Richmondville Ave, Suite 204, Westport, CT 06880 *Tel:* 203-226-9500 *Toll Free Tel:* 800-937-1819 *Fax:* 203-227-6938 *E-mail:* info@hartleyfoundation.org *Web Site:* www.hartleyfoundation.org, pg 885

Harvest Studios, 2880 Vision Ct, Aurora, IL 60506 *Tel:* 630-801-3658 *Fax:* 630-801-3839 *E-mail:* info@harveststudios.org *Web Site:* harveststudios.org, pg 885

Hasselblad Bron Inc, 1080A Garden State Rd, Union, NJ 07083 *Tel:* 908-754-5800 *Toll Free Tel:* 800-456-0203; 800-367-6434 *Fax:* 908-754-5807 *E-mail:* production@hasselbladbron.com; sales@hasselbladbron.com; servicedept@hasselbladbron.com *Web Site:* www.hasselbladbron.com, pg 885

Havana Film Festival New York (HFFNY), 4 W 43 St, Suite 304, New York, NY 10036 *Tel:* 212-687-2146 *Fax:* 212-681-8037 *E-mail:* info@hffny.com; info@aflfc.org *Web Site:* www.hffny.com, pg 1116

Havas Edge, 6922 Hollywood Blvd, Hollywood, CA 90028 *Tel:* 310-734-1333 *E-mail:* info@havasedge.com *Web Site:* www.havasedge.com, pg 885

Havas Worldwide, 200 Hudson St, New York, NY 10013 *Tel:* 212-886-2000 *Fax:* 212-886-5013 *Web Site:* havasworldwide.com, pg 886

HAVE Inc, 309 Power Ave, Hudson, NY 12534 *Tel:* 518-828-2000 *Toll Free Tel:* 888-999-HAVE (999-4283) *Fax:* 518-828-2008 *E-mail:* pro_sales@haveinc.com; have@haveinc.com *Web Site:* www.haveinc.com, pg 886

Hawaii International Film Festival, 680 Iwilei Rd, Suite 100, Honolulu, HI 96817 *Tel:* 808-792-1577 *Fax:* 808-749-7783 *E-mail:* info@hiff.org *Web Site:* www.hiff.org, pg 1116

Hawaii Sound & Vision, PO Box 2267, Kailua-Kona, HI 96745 *Tel:* 808-982-8330 *Toll Free Tel:* 877-982-8330 *Fax:* 808-982-8340 *E-mail:* aloha@hawaiisav.com *Web Site:* www.hawaiisav.com, pg 886

Hay House Inc, PO Box 5100, Carlsbad, CA 92018-5100 *Tel:* 760-431-7695 (ext 2, intl) *Toll Free Tel:* 800-654-5126 (ext 2, US); 800-650-5115 *Fax:* 760-431-6948 *Web Site:* www.hayhouse.com, pg 886

Hayden 5 Media LLC, 22 W 27 St, 6th fl, New York, NY 10001 *Tel:* 212-871-9316 *E-mail:* info@hayden5.com *Web Site:* www.hayden5.com, pg 886

Hazelden Publishing & Educational Services, 15251 Pleasant Valley Rd, Center City, MN 55012-0011 *Tel:* 651-213-4200 *Toll Free Tel:* 800-328-9000 *Fax:* 651-213-4590 *E-mail:* info@hazelden.org; customersupport@hazelden.org *Web Site:* www.hazelden.org, pg 886

HB Communications Inc, 60 Dodge Ave, North Haven, CT 06473 *Tel:* 203-234-9246 *Toll Free Tel:* 800-243-4414 *Fax:* 203-234-2013 *E-mail:* info@hbcommunications.com *Web Site:* www.hbcommunications.com, pg 886

HB-Content, 105 Butler St, Suite 2B, Brooklyn, NY 11231 *Tel:* 212-213-8824 *E-mail:* hb@hb-content.com *Web Site:* www.hb-content.com, pg 886

HBO Archives, 1100 Avenue of the Americas, New York, NY 10036 *Toll Free Tel:* 877-426-1121 *Web Site:* www.hboarchives.com, pg 886

HBO Home Video Inc, 1100 Avenue of the Americas, New York, NY 10036 *Tel:* 212-512-1000 *Fax:* 212-512-7458 *Web Site:* www.hbo.com, pg 886

HBO Studio Productions, 120-A E 23 St, New York, NY 10010 *Tel:* 212-512-7800 *E-mail:* hsp@hsptv.com *Web Site:* www.hbo.com, pg 886

HBW Entertainment Inc, 62 Massey Place, SW, T2V 2G5 Calgary, AB T2H 2H1, Canada *Tel:* 403-228-1900 *Fax:* 403-259-3860, pg 886

HD Cinema, 12233 W Olympic Blvd, Suite 120, Los Angeles, CA 90064 *Tel:* 310-434-9500 *Fax:* 310-499-5237 (efax) *Web Site:* www.hd-cinema.com, pg 886

HD House, 6312 NW 77 Ct, Miami, FL 33166 *Tel:* 305-597-7359 *Fax:* 305-597-7027 *Web Site:* thehdhouse.com, pg 886

HD Source, 1333 Matheson Blvd E, Mississauga, ON L4W 1R1, Canada *Tel:* 416-449-3030; 905-890-6905 *Fax:* 416-449-5230 *Web Site:* www.hdsource.ca, pg 886

HDrental.com, 16129 Covello St, Van Nuys, CA 91406 *Tel:* 818-994-3461 *Fax:* 818-994-3471 *Web Site:* hdrental.com, pg 886

HDTV Productions Inc, 2620 S Maryland Pkwy, Suite 816, Las Vegas, NV 89109 *Tel:* 702-499-4880 *E-mail:* hdtv@hdtvproductions.com *Web Site:* www.hdtvproductions.com, pg 886

Headlight Audio Visual Inc, 74 Evergreen Dr, Portland, ME 04103-1066 *Tel:* 207-774-5998 *Toll Free Tel:* 800-247-0540 *Fax:* 207-774-4917 *Web Site:* www.headlightaudiovisual.com, pg 887

Headroom Digital Audio, 11 E 26 St, 19th fl, New York, NY 10010 *Tel:* 212-246-8400 *Fax:* 212-245-0370 *E-mail:* info@headroomdigi.com *Web Site:* www.headroomdigi.com, pg 887

Health Communications Inc, 3201 SW 15 St, Deerfield Beach, FL 33442-8124 *Tel:* 954-360-0909 *Toll Free Tel:* 800-441-5569 *Fax:* 954-360-0034 *Web Site:* www.hcibooks.com, pg 887

Health Education Services, 10200 Jefferson Blvd, Culver City, CA 90232 *Tel:* 310-839-2436 *Toll Free Tel:* 800-421-4246 *Fax:* 310-839-2249 *Toll Free Fax:* 800-944-5432 *E-mail:* access@socialstudies.com *Web Site:* www.socialstudies.com, pg 887

Hearing Loss Association of America (HLAA), 7910 Woodmont Ave, Suite 1200, Bethesda, MD 20814 *Tel:* 301-657-2248; 301-657-2249 (TTY) *Fax:* 301-913-9413 *E-mail:* info@hearingloss.org *Web Site:* www.hearingloss.org, pg 887

Hearst Entertainment & Syndication, 300 W 57 St, New York, NY 10019-5238 *Tel:* 212-969-7553 *Toll Free Tel:* 800-526-5464 *Fax:* 646-280-1553 *E-mail:* hearstentertainment@hearst.com *Web Site:* www.hearst.com, pg 887

Heart Breaker Entertainment LLC, 10094 Lacy Rd, Hagerstown, IN 47346 *Tel:* 765-489-4048; 765-489-5558 *Toll Free Tel:* 800-843-3635 *Fax:* 765-489-4899 *E-mail:* info@videodj.com *Web Site:* videodj.com, pg 887

Heart Music Inc, PO Box 160326, Austin, TX 78716-0326 *Tel:* 512-795-2375 *Fax:* 512-795-9573 *E-mail:* info@heartmusic.com *Web Site:* www.heartmusic.com, pg 887

Heartland Film Festival, 1043 Virginia Ave, Suite 2, Indianapolis, IN 46203 *Tel:* 317-464-9405 *Web Site:* www.heartlandfilmfestival.org, pg 1116

Heavy Melody, 307 Seventh Ave, Suite 1203, New York, NY 10001 *Tel:* 212-675-9585 *Fax:* 212-675-9565 *E-mail:* contact_hm@heavymelodymusic.com (studio inquiries) *Web Site:* www.heavymelodymusic.com, pg 887

HEC Reading Horizons, 60 N Cutler Dr, Suite 101, North Salt Lake, UT 84054 *Tel:* 801-295-7054 *Toll Free Tel:* 800-333-0054 *Fax:* 801-295-7088 *E-mail:* info@readinghorizons.com *Web Site:* www.readinghorizons.com, pg 887

Hedquist Productions Inc, PO Box 1475, Fairfield, IA 52556-1475 *Tel:* 641-472-6708 *Toll Free Fax:* 855-510-5726 *Web Site:* www.hedquist.com, pg 887

Heffernan Audio Visual, 616 W Rhapsody, San Antonio, TX 78216 *Tel:* 210-732-4333 *Fax:* 210-732-5906 *E-mail:* sales@heffernanav.com *Web Site:* www.heffernanav.com, pg 887

Grant Heilman Photography Inc, 506 W Lincoln Ave, Lititz, PA 17543 *Tel:* 717-626-0296 *Toll Free Tel:* 800-622-2046 *Fax:* 717-626-0971 *E-mail:* info@heilmanphoto.com *Web Site:* www.heilmanphoto.com, pg 887

Heinemann, 361 Hanover St, Portsmouth, NH 03801-3912 *Tel:* 603-431-7894 *Toll Free Tel:* 800-225-5800 *Fax:* 603-431-2214 *Toll Free Fax:* 877-231-6980 *E-mail:* custserv@heinemann.com *Web Site:* www.heinemann.com, pg 887

Heliotrope Studios, 44 Oak St, Newton Upper Falls, MA 02464 *Tel:* 617-964-8181 *Fax:* 617-964-8030 *E-mail:* heliotropestudios@earthlink.net *Web Site:* www.heliotropestudios.com, pg 887

Helix Camera & Video, 310 S Racine Ave, Chicago, IL 60607 *Tel:* 312-421-6000 *Toll Free Tel:* 800-33-HELIX (334-3549 orders) *Fax:* 312-421-1586 *E-mail:* info@helixcamera.com *Web Site:* www.helixcamera.com, pg 887

Hellman Associates Inc, 1225 W Fourth St, Waterloo, IA 50702-2903 *Tel:* 319-234-7055 *Toll Free Tel:* 800-747-7055 *Fax:* 319-234-2089 *E-mail:* info@hellman.com *Web Site:* www.hellman.com, pg 887

Hello World Communications, 118 W 22 St, 2nd fl, New York, NY 10011 *Tel:* 212-243-8800 *Fax:* 212-691-6961 *E-mail:* excitable01@gmail.com *Web Site:* www.hwc.tv, pg 888

HeloAir Inc, 5721 Gulfstream Rd, Richmond, VA 23250 *Tel:* 804-226-3400 *Toll Free Tel:* 888-FLY-HELO (359-4356) *Fax:* 804-226-3494 *E-mail:* info@heloair.com *Web Site:* www.heloair.com, pg 888

Henninger Media Services, 2601-A Wilson Blvd, Arlington, VA 22201 *Tel:* 703-243-3444 *Toll Free Tel:* 888-243-3444 *Fax:* 703-243-5697 *E-mail:* hmsinfo@henninger.com; hmsquotes@henninger.com *Web Site:* www.henninger.com, pg 888

Henry Engineering, PO Box 3796, Seal Beach, CA 90740 *Tel:* 562-493-3589 *E-mail:* info@henryeng.com *Web Site:* www.henryeng.com, pg 888

Henry's Camera, 119 Church St, Toronto, ON M5C 2G5, Canada *Tel:* 416-941-0579 *Toll Free Tel:* 800-461-7960 *Fax:* 416-868-4951 *Toll Free Fax:* 800-645-6431 *E-mail:* info@henrys.com *Web Site:* www.henrys.com, pg 888

Greg Hensley Productions, 200 S "E" Ave, Unit 113, New Castle, CO 81647 *Tel:* 970-984-3158 *E-mail:* hensley@sopris.net *Web Site:* www.greghensley.com, pg 888

Her Own Words LLC, PO Box 5264, Madison, WI 53705-0264 *Tel:* 608-271-7083 *Fax:* 608-271-0209 *Web Site:* herownwords.com; nontraditionalcareers.com, pg 888

Herbach & Rademan Co Inc, 353 Crider Ave, Moorestown, NJ 08057 *Tel:* 856-802-0422 *Toll Free Tel:* 800-848-8001 *Fax:* 856-802-0465 *E-mail:* sales@herbach.com *Web Site:* www.herbach.com, pg 888

Herff Jones | Nystrom, 4719 W 62 St, Indianapolis, IN 46268-2593 *Toll Free Tel:* 800-621-8086 *Fax:* 317-329-3305 *Web Site:* www.herffjonesnystrom.com, pg 888

Ken Herkes Productions & Entertainment (KHPE), PO Box 313, Volcano, HI 96785 *Tel:* 808-640-0730 *Web Site:* www.khpe-hawaii.com, pg 888

Herman Pro AV, 10110 USA Today Way, Miramar, FL 33025 *Tel:* 305-477-0063 *Toll Free Tel:* 888-736-6888 *Fax:* 305-392-3377 *E-mail:* sales@hermanproav.com; info@hermanproav.com *Web Site:* www.hermanproav.com, pg 888

Hewlett-Packard Co, 3000 Hanover St, Palo Alto, CA 94304-1185 *Tel:* 650-857-1501 *Toll Free Tel:* 800-752-0900 *Fax:* 650-857-5518 *Web Site:* www.hp.com, pg 888

Hi-Tech Audio Systems Inc, 3382 Enterprise Ave, Hayward, CA 94545 *Tel:* 650-742-9166 *Fax:* 650-648-0573 *E-mail:* consoles@hi-techaudio.com *Web Site:* www.hi-techaudio.com, pg 888

Hi-Tech Enterprises Inc, 4250 114 Terr, Clearwater, FL 33762 *Tel:* 727-573-9600 *Toll Free Tel:* 800-350-4862 *Fax:* 727-573-9606 *E-mail:* hitech@videoequipment.com *Web Site:* www.videoequipment.com, pg 888

Hi-Tech Import Export Corp, 1101 W McNab Rd, Pompano Beach, FL 33069 *Tel:* 954-946-0603 *Fax:* 954-946-0652, pg 888

Hi-Tech Lamps Inc, 922 San Leandro Ave, Suite B, Mountain View, CA 94043 *Tel:* 650-961-9031 *Toll Free Tel:* 800-229-6509 *Fax:* 650-961-9033 *E-mail:* info@hi-techlamps.com *Web Site:* www.hi-techlamps.com, pg 888

HiFi House, 2304 Concord Pike, Wilmington, DE 19803 *Tel:* 302-655-4780 *Toll Free Tel:* 800-990-HIFI (990-4434) *Web Site:* www.hifihousegroup.com; www.hifihouse.com, pg 888

High End Systems Inc, 2105 Gracy Farms Lane, Austin, TX 78758 *Tel:* 512-836-2242 *Toll Free Tel:* 800-890-8989 *Fax:* 512-837-5290 *E-mail:* info@highend.com *Web Site:* www.highend.com, pg 888

High Output Inc, 495 Turnpike St, Canton, MA 02021 *Tel:* 781-364-1800 *Fax:* 781-364-1900 *Web Site:* www.highoutput.com, pg 888

High Plains Films, PO Box 8796, Missoula, MT 59807 *Tel:* 406-543-6726 *E-mail:* yak@highplainsfilms.org *Web Site:* www.highplainsfilms.org, pg 889

High-Tech Special Effects Inc, PO Box 193, Eads, TN 38028-0193 *Tel:* 901-850-5522 *Fax:* 901-850-8317 *Web Site:* www.hightechspecialeffects.com, pg 889

High Water, University of Memphis, Rudi E Scheidt School of Music, Memphis, TN 38152 *Tel:* 901-678-3317 *Fax:* 901-678-3096, pg 889

High Windy Audio/Banjoman Inc, PO Box 553, Fairview, NC 28730 *Tel:* 828-628-1728 *Toll Free Tel:* 800-637-8679 *Fax:* 828-628-4435 *E-mail:* office@davidholt.com *Web Site:* www.davidholt.com, pg 889

HighBridge Audio, 201 Sixth St, Suite 220, Minneapolis, MN 55414 *Toll Free Tel:* 800-755-8532 *Fax:* 612-436-4005 *E-mail:* highbridge@highbridgeaudio.com *Web Site:* www.highbridgeaudio.com, pg 889

HighScope Press, 600 N River St, Ypsilanti, MI 48198-2898 *Tel:* 734-485-2000 *Toll Free Tel:* 800-407-7377 *Fax:* 734-485-0704 *Toll Free Fax:* 800-442-4329 *E-mail:* info@highscope.org; press@highscope.org *Web Site:* www.highscope.org, pg 889

Hilferty & Associates Inc, 14240 State Rte 550, Athens, OH 45701 *Tel:* 740-448-3821 *Fax:* 740-448-2331 *E-mail:* gha@hilferty.com *Web Site:* www.hilferty.com, pg 889

Jerry Hill Steadicam Products, 19160 Arminta St, Reseda, CA 91335-1105 *Tel:* 818-772-9256 *Fax:* 818-772-9251 *E-mail:* jerry@steadimoves.com *Web Site:* www.steadimoves.com, pg 889

Ron Hill Imagery, 2994 S Richards St, Salt Lake City, UT 84115 *Tel:* 801-486-3300 *Fax:* 801-486-3310 *Web Site:* ronhillimagery.com, pg 889

Hillman Prizes in Journalism, 12 W 31 St, 12th fl, New York, NY 10001 *Tel:* 646-448-6413 *Web Site:* www.hillmanfoundation.org, pg 1116

Hillmann & Carr Inc, 2233 Wisconsin Ave, Washington, DC 20007 *Tel:* 202-342-0001 *Fax:* 202-342-0117 *E-mail:* mail@hillmanncarr.com *Web Site:* www.hillmanncarr.com, pg 889

Himalayan Institute Audio/Video, 952 Bethany Tpke, Honesdale, PA 18431 *Tel:* 570-253-5551 *Toll Free Tel:* 800-822-4547 *Fax:* 570-253-9078 *E-mail:* info@himalayaninstitute.org *Web Site:* www.himalayaninstitute.org, pg 889

Historic Films, 211 Third St, Greenport, NY 11944 *Tel:* 631-477-9700 *Toll Free Tel:* 800-249-1940 *Fax:* 631-477-9800 *E-mail:* info@historicfilms.com *Web Site:* www.historicfilms.com, pg 889

Hitachi Kokusai Electric America Ltd, 150 Crossways Park Dr, Woodbury, NY 11797 *Tel:* 516-921-7200 *Fax:* 516-496-3718 *E-mail:* info@hitachikokusai.us *Web Site:* hitachikokusai.us, pg 889

Hite Co, 3101 Beale Ave, Altoona, PA 16601 *Tel:* 814-944-6121 *Toll Free Tel:* 800-252-3598 *Fax:* 814-944-3052 *Web Site:* www.hiteco.com, pg 889

HM Electronics Inc (HME), 14110 Stowe Dr, Poway, CA 92064 *Tel:* 858-535-6000 *Toll Free Tel:* 800-848-4468 (domestic sales) *Fax:* 858-452-7207; 858-552-0139 (domestic sales) *E-mail:* info@hme.com *Web Site:* www.hme.com, pg 889

HMC Electronics, 33 Springdale Ave, Canton, MA 02021 *Tel:* 781-821-1870 *Toll Free Tel:* 800-482-4440 *Fax:* 781-821-4133 *E-mail:* sales@hmcelectronics.com *Web Site:* www.hmcelectronics.com, pg 889

Hogpenny Studios, Ship Bottom Studio Ctr, 123 E 14 St, Ship Bottom, Long Beach Island, NJ 08008 *Tel:* 609-494-6640 *E-mail:* hogpenny@verizon.net; info@hogpenny.com *Web Site:* mysite.verizon.net/vzep5xhw, pg 890

Holbrook Film Commission, 465 N First Ave, Holbrook, AZ 86025 *Tel:* 928-524-6227 *Toll Free Tel:* 800-524-2459 *Fax:* 928-524-1719 *E-mail:* holbrook@gotouraz.com *Web Site:* www.gotouraz.com, pg 1091

The Hollaender Manufacturing Co, 10285 Wayne Ave, Cincinnati, OH 45215 *Tel:* 513-772-8800 *Toll Free Tel:* 800-772-8800 (orders) *Fax:* 513-772-8806 *Web Site:* www.hollaender.com, pg 890

Hollywood Center Studios, 1040 N Las Palmas, Los Angeles, CA 90038 *Tel:* 323-860-0000 *E-mail:* info@hollywoodcenter.com *Web Site:* www.hollywoodcenter.com, pg 890

The Hollywood Edge, 7080 Hollywood Blvd, Suite 519, Hollywood, CA 90028 *Tel:* 323-603-3252 *Toll Free Tel:* 800-292-3755 *Fax:* 323-603-3298 *E-mail:* info@hollywoodedge.com; sales@hollywoodedge.com *Web Site:* www.hollywoodedge.com, pg 890

Hollywood Lights Inc, 5251 SE McLoughlin Blvd, Portland, OR 97202-4836 *Tel:* 503-232-9001; 503-232-8855 *Toll Free Tel:* 800-826-9881 *Fax:* 503-517-8686 *E-mail:* portland@hollywoodlights.biz *Web Site:* www.hollywoodlights.biz, pg 890

Hollywood Loft, 6161 Santa Monica Blvd, Los Angeles, CA 90038 *Tel:* 323-957-9398 *Web Site:* hollywoodloft.com, pg 890

Hollywood Post Alliance, 846 S Broadway, Suite 601, Los Angeles, CA 90014 *Tel:* 213-614-0860 *Fax:* 213-614-0890 *Web Site:* www.hpaonline.com, pg 1082

Hollywood Rentals Production Services, 12800 Foothill Blvd, Sylmar, CA 91342 *Tel:* 818-407-7800 *Toll Free Tel:* 800-233-7830 *Fax:* 818-407-7868 *E-mail:* info@hollywoodrentals.com *Web Site:* www.hollywoodrentals.com, pg 890

Hollywood Sound Systems, 1541 N Wilcox Ave, Hollywood, CA 90028 *Tel:* 323-466-2416 *Fax:* 323-460-2676 *Web Site:* www.hollywoodsound.com, pg 890

Hollywood Theatre Equipment Inc, 1941 N 66 Ave, Hollywood, FL 33024 *Tel:* 954-920-2832 *Fax:* 954-986-6914 *E-mail:* hwdtheatre@aol.com, pg 890

Hollywood Vaults Inc, 742 N Seward St, Hollywood, CA 90038-3504 *Tel:* 323-461-6464 *Toll Free Tel:* 800-569-5336 *Fax:* 323-461-6479 *E-mail:* vault@hollywoodvaults.com *Web Site:* www.hollywoodvaults.com, pg 890

Holo-Spectra Inc, 7742B Gloria Ave, Van Nuys, CA 91406 *Tel:* 818-994-9577 *Fax:* 818-994-4709 *E-mail:* info@lasershs.com *Web Site:* www.lasershs.com, pg 890

Home Inc, 566 Columbus Ave, Boston, MA 02118 *Tel:* 617-427-4663 *Fax:* 617-427-4664 *Web Site:* homeinc.org, pg 890

Home Shopping Network (HSN), PO Box 9090, Clearwater, FL 33758 *Tel:* 727-872-1000 *Toll Free Tel:* 800-933-2887 (cust serv, orders online); 800-284-3900 (cust serv, orders by phone); 800-557-0714 (cust serv, auto ship orders); 800-284-5757 (orders) *Fax:* 727-872-6559 *Web Site:* www.hsn.com, pg 890

Homespun Video, 1610 Rte 212, Saugerties, NY 12477 *Tel:* 845-246-2550 *Toll Free Tel:* 800-338-2737 (orders-US & CN) *Fax:* 845-246-5282 *E-mail:* info@homespuntapes.com *Web Site:* www.homespuntapes.com, pg 890

Honolulu Film Office, 530 S King St, Rm 306, Honolulu, HI 96813 *Tel:* 808-768-6108 *Fax:* 808-768-6102 *E-mail:* info@filmhonolulu.com *Web Site:* www.filmhonolulu.com, pg 1097

Hoodman Corp, 20445 Gramercy Place, Suite 201, Torrence, CA 90501 *Tel:* 310-222-8608 *Toll Free Tel:* 800-818-3946 *Fax:* 310-222-8623 *E-mail:* sales@hoodmanusa.com *Web Site:* www.hoodmanusa.com, pg 891

Hooper Camera & Imaging, 21902 Devonshire St, Chatsworth, CA 91311-2907 *Tel:* 818-709-0014 *Fax:* 818-709-0130 *E-mail:* sales@hoopercamera.com *Web Site:* hoopercamera.com, pg 891

Hope Productions, 3116 Arrowhead Dr, Hollywood, CA 90068 *Tel:* 323-460-4995, pg 891

Hopkins Technology LLC, 421 Hazel Lane, Hopkins, MN 55343-7116 *Tel:* 952-856-0467 *E-mail:* infodesk5@hoptechno.com *Web Site:* www.hoptechno.com, pg 891

Tom Hopkins International Inc, 465 E Chilton Dr, Suite 4, Chandler, AZ 85225 *Tel:* 480-949-0786 *Toll Free Tel:* 800-528-0446 *Fax:* 480-949-1590 *E-mail:* info@tomhopkins.com *Web Site:* www.tomhopkins.com, pg 891

Hoppmann Audio Visual, 4170 Lafayette Center Dr, Suite 100, Chantilly, VA 20151-1255 *Tel:* 703-502-4080 *Toll Free Tel:* 800-220-3038 *Fax:* 703-222-0038 *E-mail:* info@hoppmann-av.com; sales@hoppmann-av.com *Web Site:* www.hoppmann-av.net, pg 891

Horita Co Inc, PO Box 3993, Mission Viejo, CA 92690-3993 *Tel:* 949-489-0240 *Fax:* 949-489-0242 *E-mail:* sales@horita.com *Web Site:* www.horita.com, pg 891

Horizon Film + Video Productions, 808 E 34 St, Austin, TX 78705 *Tel:* 512-459-3100 *Toll Free Tel:* 800-540-2785 *Fax:* 512-459-3477 *Web Site:* www.horizonvideo.com, pg 891

Horizon Films & Media LLC, PO Box 1087, Shelbyville, KY 40066 *Tel:* 502-647-9966 *Fax:* 502-647-9968 *E-mail:* horizonfilms@insightbb.com *Web Site:* www.horizon-films.com, pg 891

Horizon Video Productions Inc, 6114 Fayetteville St, Suite 106, Durham, NC 27713 *Tel:* 919-941-0901 *Toll Free Tel:* 800-768-3776 *Fax:* 919-941-1939 *E-mail:* info@horizonvp.com *Web Site:* www.horizonvp.com, pg 891

Horizon Worldwide, 1765 Stebbins Dr, Houston, TX 77043 *Tel:* 713-647-7400 *Fax:* 713-647-6664 *E-mail:* info@horizonworldwide.com *Web Site:* horizonworldwide.com, pg 891

Susan Hormuth, Visual Resource Consultant, 3356 Pennsylvania Ave SE, Washington, DC 20020 *Tel:* 202-584-3994 *E-mail:* susanhormuth@verizon.net, pg 891

Hosa Technology Inc, 6650 Caballero Blvd, Buena Park, CA 90620 *Tel:* 714-522-8878 *Fax:* 714-522-4540 *E-mail:* info@hosatech.com; sales@hosatech.com; orders@hosatech.com *Web Site:* www.hosatech.com, pg 891

Hot House Professional Audio, 275 Martin Ave, Highland, NY 12528 *Tel:* 845-691-6077 *E-mail:* info@hothousepro.com *Web Site:* www.hothousepro.com, pg 891

Hot Springs Documentary Film Festival, 659 Ouchita Ave, Hot Springs, AR 71901 *Tel:* 501-538-2290 *Web Site:* www.hsdfi.org, pg 1116

HOThead, 56 W 45 St, 17th fl, New York, NY 10036 *Tel:* 212-575-5566 *Fax:* 212-575-1070 *E-mail:* info@hothead.tv *Web Site:* www.hothead.tv, pg 891

Hotronic Inc, 1875 S Winchester Blvd, Campbell, CA 95008 *Tel:* 408-378-3883 *Fax:* 408-378-3888 *E-mail:* sales@hotronics.com *Web Site:* www.hotronics.com, pg 891

Hottrax Records, 1957 Kilburn Dr, Atlanta, GA 30324-4852 *Tel:* 770-662-6661 *E-mail:* info@hottrax.com; hotwax@hottrax.com *Web Site:* www.hottrax.com, pg 891

House of Cinemagraphics, 4802 Quail Ave N, Minneapolis, MN 55429 *Tel:* 612-339-7803; 763-458-8244 *Toll Free Tel:* 888-813-0413 *E-mail:* film@visi.com *Web Site:* www.houseofcinemagraphics.com, pg 891

House of Moves, 5419 McConnell Ave, Los Angeles, CA 90066-7027 *Tel:* 310-306-6131 *E-mail:* info@moves.com *Web Site:* www.moves.com, pg 891

The House Studios, 325 Second Ave W, Seattle, WA 98119 *Tel:* 206-218-6810 *E-mail:* book@thehousestudios.com *Web Site:* thehousestudios.com, pg 891

Houston Film Commission, 4 Houston Ctr, 1331 Lamar St, 7th fl, Houston, TX 77010 *Tel:* 713-437-5251 *Toll Free Tel:* 800-365-7575 *Fax:* 713-223-3816 *E-mail:* jmontgomery@ghcvb.org *Web Site:* www.houstonfilmcommission.com, pg 1103

Houston Photo Imaging, 5250 Gulfton, Suite 3-B, Houston, TX 77081 *Tel:* 713-666-0282 *Toll Free Tel:* 800-664-0282 *Fax:* 713-667-9625 *E-mail:* info@houstonphotoimaging.com *Web Site:* www.houstonphotoimaging.com, pg 892

Hover-Views Unlimited, PO Box 1164, Syosset, NY 11791 *Tel:* 516-496-2946 *Fax:* 516-496-8029 *Web Site:* www.hoverviews.com, pg 892

HP Marketing Corp, 16 Chapin Rd, Unit 908, Pine Brook, NJ 07058 *Tel:* 973-808-9010 *Toll Free Tel:* 800-735-4373 *Fax:* 973-808-9004 *E-mail:* info@hpmarketingcorp.com *Web Site:* www.hpmarketingcorp.com, pg 892

HSA Inc, 1717 E Sixth St, Mishawaka, IN 46544 *Tel:* 574-255-6100 *Fax:* 574-255-8131 *E-mail:* hsainfo@hsarolltops.com *Web Site:* www.hsarolltops.com, pg 892

Hubbard Supply Co, 901 W Second St, Flint, MI 48503 *Tel:* 810-234-8681 *Toll Free Tel:* 800-875-4811 *Fax:* 810-234-6142 *E-mail:* information@hubbardsupply.com *Web Site:* www.hubbardsupply.com, pg 892

Hubbell Wiring Device-Kellems, 40 Waterview Dr, Shelton, CT 06484 *Tel:* 475-882-4800 *Toll Free Tel:* 800-288-6000 (cust serv) *Fax:* 475-882-4849 *Toll Free Fax:* 800-255-1031 (cust serv) *E-mail:* techserv@hubbell.com *Web Site:* www.hubbell-wiring.com, pg 892

Hughie's Event Production Services, 1260 E 38 St, Cleveland, OH 44114 *Tel:* 216-361-4600 *Toll Free Tel:* 800-449-4115 *Fax:* 216-361-2570 *Web Site:* www.hughies.com, pg 892

Charles A Hulcher Co Inc, 909 "G" St, Hampton, VA 23661 *Tel:* 757-245-6190 *Fax:* 757-245-2882 *E-mail:* hulcher@hulchercamera.com *Web Site:* www.hulchercamera.com, pg 892

Human Circuit, 9120 Gaither Rd, Gaithersburg, MD 20877 *Tel:* 240-864-4000 *Toll Free Tel:* 800-638-8071 *Fax:* 240-864-4000 *E-mail:* info@humancircuit.com *Web Site:* www.humancircuit.com, pg 892

Human Relations Media, 41 Kensico Dr, Mount Kisco, NY 10549 *Tel:* 914-666-9151 *Toll Free Tel:* 800-431-2050 (cust serv) *Fax:* 914-666-9506 *E-mail:* service@hrmvideo.com; orders@hrmvideo.com; help@hrmvideo.com; letters@hrmvideo.com *Web Site:* www.hrmvideo.com, pg 892

Humanities Extension Publications, North Carolina State Univ, Campus Box 8101, Raleigh, NC 27695 *Tel:* 919-515-2468 *Fax:* 919-515-9419 *Web Site:* www.ncsu.edu/chass/extension, pg 892

Humboldt-Del Norte Film Commission, 1385 Eighth St, Suite 106, Arcata, CA 95521 *Tel:* 707-825-7600 *Web Site:* www.filmhumboldtdelnorte.org, pg 1092

Humboldt International Film Festival, Dept Theatre, Film & Dance, One Harpst St, Arcata, CA 95521 *Tel:* 707-826-4113 *Fax:* 707-826-4112 *E-mail:* filmfest@humboldt.edu *Web Site:* hsufilmfestival.com, pg 1116

Hunter Electronics LLC, 7553 Lake Harbor Terr, Lake Worth, FL 33467 *Tel:* 561-568-2063 *Fax:* 561-491-8030 *E-mail:* hunterelectronics@comcast.net; hunterelectronics201@gmail.com, pg 892

Hunt's Photo, Video & Digital, 100 Main St, Melrose, MA 02176-6104 *Tel:* 781-662-8822 (retail sales) *Toll Free Tel:* 800-924-8682 (retail sales); 800-221-1830 (ext 2340, corp sales) *Fax:* 781-662-6524 *E-mail:* ecommerce@wbhunt.com (retail online sales) *Web Site:* www.huntsphotoandvideo.com, pg 892

Frank D Hurst Corp dba Pechman Imaging, 106 E Second St, Kaukauna, WI 54130 *Tel:* 920-766-6160 *Toll Free Tel:* 800-777-0221 *Fax:* 920-766-6161 *E-mail:* customerservice@pechmanimaging.com *Web Site:* www.pechmanimaging.com, pg 892

Editions Hurtubise HMH Ltee, 1815 Avenue De Lorimier, Montreal, QC H2K 3W6, Canada *Tel:* 514-523-1523 *Toll Free Tel:* 800-361-1664 *Fax:* 514-523-9969 *Web Site:* www.editionshurtubise.com, pg 892

Hybrid Cases, 1121-20 Lincoln Ave, Holbrook, NY 11741 *Tel:* 631-563-1181 *Toll Free Tel:* 800-645-1707 (orders) *Fax:* 631-563-1390 *E-mail:* sales@hybridcases.com *Web Site:* www.hybridcases.com, pg 892

Hybrid Studios, 3021 S Shannon St, Santa Ana, CA 92704 *Tel:* 714-850-1499 *E-mail:* info@hybridstudiosca.com; rentals@hybridstudiosca.com *Web Site:* hybridstudiosca.com, pg 892

Hydrogen Whiskey Studios, 1640 Fifth St, Suite 226, Santa Monica, CA 90401 *Tel:* 310-394-8130 *Fax:* 310-394-8129 *Web Site:* www.hydrogenwhiskey.com, pg 893

Hyperspective Studios Inc, 2800 Woodlawn Dr, Suite 253, Honolulu, HI 96822 *Tel:* 808-353-3618 *E-mail:* info@hyperspective.com *Web Site:* www.hyperspective.com, pg 893

I M P A C T Publishing Inc, 3409 47 Ave E, Bradenton, FL 34203 *Tel:* 941-739-2611 *Toll Free Tel:* 800-221-6121; 800-426-3963 *Fax:* 941-756-0315 *E-mail:* potentialsunlimitedcs@gmail.com *Web Site:* www.potentialsunlimited.com, pg 893

I-25 Studios, 9201 Pan American Fwy NE, Albuquerque, NM 87113 *Tel:* 505-822-7115 *Fax:* 505-314-7094 *E-mail:* info@i-25studios.com *Web Site:* i-25studios.com, pg 893

IAAVC (International Association of Audio Visual Communicators), PO Box 270779, Flower Mound, TX 75027-0779 *Tel:* 469-464-4180 *Fax:* 469-464-4170 *Web Site:* www.iaavc.org, pg 1082

IAC Acoustics, 1160 Commerce Ave, Bronx, NY 10462 *Tel:* 718-931-8000 *Fax:* 718-863-1138 *E-mail:* newyork@iac-acoustics.com *Web Site:* www.iac-acoustics.com/us, pg 893

IAI Video, 33 Lancaster St, Cherry Valley, NY 13320 *Tel:* 646-696-5645 *E-mail:* iai@improvart.com *Web Site:* www.improvart.com, pg 893

IAMP Professional Audio, 218 Reindollar, Marina, CA 93933 *Tel:* 831-884-9558 *Fax:* 831-643-2131 *E-mail:* iamp-pro-audio@comcast.net *Web Site:* www.iampproaudio.com, pg 893

IATSE, 207 W 25 St, 4th fl, New York, NY 10001 *Tel:* 212-730-1770 *Fax:* 212-730-7809 *Web Site:* www.iatse-intl.org, pg 1082

IBM SPSS, 200 W Madison Ave, 23rd fl, Chicago, IL 60606 *Toll Free Tel:* 800-543-2185 *Toll Free Fax:* 800-841-0064 *E-mail:* salesbox@us.ibm.com *Web Site:* www-01.ibm.com/software/analytics/spss, pg 893

IBPA, Independent Book Publishers Association, 1020 Manhattan Beach Blvd, Suite 204, Manhattan Beach, CA 90266 *Tel:* 310-546-1818 *Fax:* 310-546-3939 *E-mail:* info@ibpa-online.org *Web Site:* www.ibpa-online.org, pg 1082

Icarus Film Inc, 32 Court St, 21st fl, Brooklyn, NY 11201 *Tel:* 718-488-8900 *Toll Free Tel:* 800-876-1710 *Fax:* 718-488-8642 *E-mail:* mail@icarusfilms.com *Web Site:* www.icarusfilms.com, pg 893

ICL Imaging Inc, 51 Mellen St, Framingham, MA 01702 *Tel:* 508-872-3280 *Toll Free Tel:* 800-660-3280 *Fax:* 508-872-7364 *E-mail:* csr@icl-imaging.com *Web Site:* www.icl-imaging.com, pg 893

Icom Multimedia, 294 E Long St, Columbus, OH 43215-1829 *Tel:* 614-224-4400 *Fax:* 614-457-8050 *Web Site:* www.icommultimedia.com, pg 893

Icontent, 149 Fifth Ave, New York, NY 10010 *Tel:* 212-462-0022 *E-mail:* info@icontent.tv; tania@icontent.tv *Web Site:* www.icontent.tv, pg 893

iCorpTv, PO Box 461172, Los Angeles, CA 90046 *Tel:* 818-492-4623 *E-mail:* contact@icorptv.com *Web Site:* www.icorptv.com, pg 893

iCrossing Inc, 300 W 57 St, New York, NY 10019 *Tel:* 212-649-3900 *Fax:* 646-280-1091 *Web Site:* www.icrossing.com, pg 893

IDA Documentary Awards, 3470 Wilshire Blvd, Suite 980, Los Angeles, CA 90010 *Tel:* 213-232-1660 *Fax:* 213-232-1669 *E-mail:* info@documentary.org *Web Site:* www.documentary.org, pg 1116

Idaho Camera Inc, 1310 N Orchard Ave, Boise, ID 83706 *Tel:* 208-377-3686 (corp) *Toll Free Tel:* 877-323-8734 *E-mail:* info@idahocamera.com; orchard@idahocamera.com; sales@idahocamera.com *Web Site:* www.idahocamera.com, pg 893

Idaho Film Office, 700 W State St, Boise, ID 83702 *Tel:* 208-334-2470 *Toll Free Tel:* 800-942-8338 *Fax:* 208-334-2631 *Web Site:* www.filmidaho.com, pg 1097

Ideal Large Format Imaging Services, 15737 Crabbs Branch Way, Rockville, MD 20855 *Tel:* 301-468-0123 *Toll Free Tel:* 800-76IDEAL (764-3325) *Fax:* 301-230-0813 *E-mail:* sales@ideal.com *Web Site:* www.ideal.com, pg 893

Ideascape Inc, PO Box 1966, Lake Oswego, OR 97035 *Tel:* 503-246-2439 *E-mail:* info@ideascapeinc.com *Web Site:* www.ideascapeinc.com, pg 894

IDenticard Systems Inc, 25 Race Ave, 1st fl, Lancaster, PA 17603 *Tel:* 717-569-5797 *Toll Free Tel:* 800-233-0298 *Fax:* 717-427-1654 *E-mail:* identicard.info@identicard.com *Web Site:* www.identicard.com, pg 894

Idle Minds Productions Inc, 3405 Pepperhill Rd, Lexington, KY 40502 *Tel:* 859-268-8500 *Fax:* 859-268-8500 *E-mail:* idleminds@twc.com, pg 894

IDX System Technology Inc, 19001 Harborgate Way, Suite 105, Torrance, CA 90501 *Tel:* 310-328-2850 *Fax:* 310-328-8202 *E-mail:* idx.usa@idx.tv *Web Site:* www.idx.tv, pg 894

IEEE Computer Society Press, 10662 Los Vaqueros Circle, Los Alamitos, CA 90720-1314 *Tel:* 714-821-8380 *Toll Free Tel:* 800-272-6657 (cust serv) *Fax:* 714-821-4010 *E-mail:* help@computer.org *Web Site:* www.computer.org, pg 894

IFM World Releasing Inc, 1328 E Palmer Ave, Glendale, CA 91205 *Tel:* 818-243-4976 *Fax:* 818-550-9728 *E-mail:* contact@ifmfilm.com *Web Site:* www.ifmfilm.com, pg 894

Ikegami Electronics (USA) Inc, 37 Brook Ave, Maywood, NJ 07607 *Tel:* 201-368-9171 *Fax:* 201-569-1626 *E-mail:* sales@ikegami.com; service@ikegami.com *Web Site:* www.ikegami.com, pg 894

ILFORD America Inc, 30 Tower Lane, Avon, CT 06001 *Tel:* 860-321-7602 *Toll Free Tel:* 888-453-6731 *Fax:* 860-321-7519 *E-mail:* usinfo@ilford.com *Web Site:* www.ilford.ch/en/contact/contactusa.asp, pg 894

Ilio Enterprises LLC, PO Box 6211, Malibu, CA 90265 *Tel:* 818-707-7222; 818-707-3655 *Toll Free Tel:* 800-747-4546 *Fax:* 818-707-8552 *E-mail:* ilioquestions@ilio.com *Web Site:* www.ilio.com, pg 894

Illinois Film Office, James R Thompson Ctr, Suite 3-400, 100 W Randolph, Chicago, IL 60601 *Tel:* 312-814-3600 *Fax:* 312-814-8874 *E-mail:* film@illinois.gov *Web Site:* www.illinoisfilm.biz, pg 1097

Illuma Studios, 16601 N 90 St, Scottsdale, AZ 85260 *Tel:* 480-222-4396 *E-mail:* info@illumastudios.com *Web Site:* www.illumastudios.com, pg 894

Illuminart Lighting, 7320 Griffin Rd, Suite 111, Davie, FL 33314 *Tel:* 954-327-0564 *Fax:* 954-327-0367 *E-mail:* lightisart@aol.com *Web Site:* www.illuminart-inc.com, pg 894

Illuminate Post/Digital Finishing, 3575 Cahuenga Blvd W, 4th fl, Hollywood, CA 90068 *Tel:* 323-969-8822 *Fax:* 323-969-8860 *Web Site:* illuminatehollywood.com, pg 894

Illuminate Studios, 10900 Ventura Blvd, Studio City, CA 90068 *Tel:* 818-769-4500 *Fax:* 818-769-7150 *Web Site:* illuminatehollywood.com, pg 894

Illuminating Engineering Society (IES), 120 Wall St, 17th fl, New York, NY 10005-4001 *Tel:* 212-248-5000 *Fax:* 212-248-5017; 212-248-5018 *E-mail:* ies@ies.org *Web Site:* www.ies.org, pg 1082

Image Associates Inc, 5311 S Miami Blvd, Suite G, Durham, NC 27703 *Tel:* 919-876-6400 *Fax:* 919-876-6400 *E-mail:* info@imageassociates.com *Web Site:* www.imageassociates.com, pg 894

Image Audiovisuals, 2130 S Dahlia St, Denver, CO 80222 *Tel:* 303-758-1818 *Toll Free Tel:* 800-818-1857 *Fax:* 303-758-5722 *E-mail:* commercialsales@imageav.com *Web Site:* www.imageav.com, pg 894

Image Craft LLC, 3401 E Broadway Rd, Phoenix, AZ 85040 *Tel:* 602-276-2082 *Toll Free Tel:* 800-274-2422 *Fax:* 602-232-0719 *E-mail:* designgroup@imcraft.com *Web Site:* www.imcraft.com, pg 894

Image Entertainment, 20525 Nordhoff St, Suite 200, Chatsworth, CA 91311 *Tel:* 818-407-9100 *Toll Free Tel:* 800-473-3475 *E-mail:* inquiries@rljentertainment.com *Web Site:* www.image-entertainment.com, pg 895

Image G, 28490 Westinghouse Place, Unit 160, Valencia, CA 91355 *Tel:* 818-761-6644 *Fax:* 661-775-8900 *E-mail:* production@imageg.com *Web Site:* sites.google.com/site/imagegwebsite, pg 895

The Image Generators, 18156 Darnell Dr, Olney, MD 20832 *Tel:* 301-924-5700 *Fax:* 240-363-0062 *E-mail:* info@imagegenerators.com *Web Site:* www.imagegenerators.com, pg 895

Image Innovations Inc, 8607 Wurzbach Rd, San Antonio, TX 78240 *Tel:* 210-696-5900 *Web Site:* www.slidescribe.com, pg 895

Image Integration, 2619 Benvenue Ave, No A, Berkeley, CA 94704 *Tel:* 510-504-2605, pg 895

Image Labs Corp, 20 Arden Dr, Garrison, NY 10524 *Tel:* 845-737-4420 *Fax:* 845-737-0426 *E-mail:* imagelabs@optonline.net, pg 895

Image Logic Corp, 6807 Brennon Lane, Chevy Chase, MD 20815-3255 *Tel:* 202-223-2888 *E-mail:* info@imagelogic.com *Web Site:* www.imagelogic.com, pg 895

Image Makers of Pittsford/Image Maker Productions, 6 Wood Gate, Pittsford, NY 14534-1826 *Tel:* 585-385-4567 *Fax:* 585-586-6568, pg 895

Image Management Systems Inc, 239 W 15 St, New York, NY 10011 *Tel:* 212-741-8765 *Fax:* 212-243-2344 *E-mail:* ims@imagemgt.com *Web Site:* www.imagemgt.com, pg 895

Image Marketing Corp, 1636 N 24 St, Mesa, AZ 85213 *Tel:* 480-969-7032 *Fax:* 480-969-0939 *E-mail:* info@image4u.com *Web Site:* www.image4u.com, pg 895

Image Media Farm, 1090 E Georgia St, Vancouver, BC V6A 2A7, Canada *Tel:* 604-874-7513 *Toll Free Tel:* 800-352-1454 (prodn rentals); 800-567-0037 (equip rentals) *Fax:* 604-874-7516 *E-mail:* info@imagemediafarm.com *Web Site:* www.imagemediafarm.com, pg 895

Image Technical Services, 720 Crown Point Cross Rd, Winter Garden, FL 34787 *Tel:* 407-905-2100 *Toll Free Tel:* 800-393-4300 *Fax:* 407-905-2150 *E-mail:* moreinfo@goimage.com *Web Site:* www.goimage.com, pg 895

Image Technologies Corp, 523 Hanley Industrial Ct, St Louis, MO 63144 *Tel:* 314-646-1800 *Toll Free Tel:* 800-962-2344 *Fax:* 314-646-1818 *Web Site:* www.imagetechnologies.com, pg 895

Image Up, 176 Main St, Metuchen, NJ 08840 *Tel:* 732-549-1845 *Web Site:* www.imageup.com, pg 895

Image Video, 1620 Midland Ave, Scarborough, ON M1P 3C2, Canada *Tel:* 416-750-8872 *Fax:* 416-750-8015 *E-mail:* sales@imagevideo.com *Web Site:* www.imagevideo.com, pg 895

Image Video Services & Productions, 1210 Southview Dr, Sudbury, ON P3E 2L6, Canada *Tel:* 705-698-1212 *Fax:* 705-805-0110 *E-mail:* info@imagevideo.ca *Web Site:* www.imagevideo.ca, pg 895

Image Video Teleproductions Inc, 6755 Freedom Ave NW, North Canton, OH 44720 *Tel:* 330-494-9303 *Fax:* 330-966-1792 *E-mail:* info@image-video.com *Web Site:* www.image-video.com, pg 895

Image Zone Inc, 11 W 69 St, Suite 10A, New York, NY 10023 *Tel:* 212-924-8804 *Web Site:* www.imagezone.com, pg 896

Imagecraft Productions, 3318 Burton Ave, Burbank, CA 91504 *Tel:* 818-954-0187 *Fax:* 818-954-0189 *Web Site:* www.imagecraftproductions.com, pg 896

imageReal Pictures LLC, 4 Lighthouse St, No 8, Marina del Rey, CA 90292 *E-mail:* info@imagereal.com *Web Site:* www.imagereal.com, pg 896

Imagers, 1575 Northside Dr, Bldg 400, Suite 490, Atlanta, GA 30318-5411 *Tel:* 404-351-5800 *Toll Free Tel:* 800-232-5411 *Fax:* 404-351-9020 *E-mail:* imagers@imagers.com *Web Site:* www.imagers.com, pg 896

Images in Motion Media Inc, 720 Ladera Dr, Sonoma, CA 95476 *Tel:* 707-996-9474 *E-mail:* images@vom.com *Web Site:* www.imagesmedia.com, pg 896

Images II Inc, 1700 "O" St, Lincoln, NE 68508 *Tel:* 402-475-4000 *Toll Free Tel:* 800-669-4001 *E-mail:* graphics@images2.com *Web Site:* www.images2.com, pg 896

Imageworks, 1039 Meade Ave, San Diego, CA 92116-1038 *Tel:* 619-239-6161 *E-mail:* info@imageworks.tv *Web Site:* www.imageworks.tv, pg 896

ImageWorks Communications, 10155 High Point Lane, Suite 100, Sandy, UT 84092 *Tel:* 801-231-7234 (cell) *Web Site:* www.imageworkscommunications.com, pg 896

Imagine Communications Corp, 3001 Dallas Pkwy, Suite 300, Frisco, TX 75034 *Tel:* 469-803-4900 *Toll Free Tel:* 866-4-IMAGINE (446-2446) *Fax:* 469-803-4899 *E-mail:* insidesales@imaginecommunications.com *Web Site:* www.imaginecommunications.com, pg 896

Imagivations, 11314 Sheldon St, Sun Valley, CA 91352 *Tel:* 818-767-6767 *Fax:* 818-767-3637 *E-mail:* info@imagivations.com *Web Site:* www.imagivations.com, pg 896

Imation Corp, One Imation Way, Oakdale, MN 55128-3421 *Tel:* 651-704-4000 *Toll Free Tel:* 888-466-3456 *Fax:* 651-704-3444 *Toll Free Fax:* 888-704-4200 *E-mail:* info@imation.com *Web Site:* www.imation.com, pg 896

IMAX Corp, 2525 Speakman Dr, Mississauga, ON L5K 1B1, Canada *Tel:* 905-403-6500 *Fax:* 905-403-6450 *E-mail:* info@imax.com *Web Site:* www.imax.com, pg 896

Imig Audio/Video Inc, 2611 Fairbanks St, Suite 100, Anchorage, AK 99503 *Tel:* 907-274-2161 *Fax:* 907-279-0219 *E-mail:* info@imigav.com *Web Site:* www.imigav.com, pg 896

Immersion Corp, 310 Rio Robles, San Jose, CA 95134 *Tel:* 408-467-1900 *Fax:* 408-467-1901 *E-mail:* info@immersion.com *Web Site:* www.immersion.com, pg 896

IMP Digital Studios, 120 Rte 17N, Paramus, NJ 07652 *Tel:* 201-261-3959 *Fax:* 201-261-3959 *E-mail:* info@impdigital.us *Web Site:* impdigitalstudios.com, pg 896

Impact Christian Books Inc, 332 Leffingwell Ave, Suite 101, Kirkwood, MO 63122 *Tel:* 314-822-3309 *E-mail:* info@impactchristianbooks.com *Web Site:* www.impactchristianbooks.com, pg 897

Impact Group, 410 Bryant Circle, Bldg F, Ojai, CA 93023 *Toll Free Tel:* 800-675-2200 *E-mail:* sales@impact-group.com *Web Site:* impact-group.com, pg 897

IMR Limited, 1104 Fernwood Ave, 4th fl, Camp Hill, PA 17011 *Tel:* 717-364-3700 *Toll Free Tel:* 800-446-2826 *Fax:* 717-364-3750 *E-mail:* information@imrdigital.com *Web Site:* www.imrdigital.com, pg 897

Imtronics Industries Inc, 11930 31 Ct N, St Petersburg, FL 33716 *Tel:* 727-572-9010 *Fax:* 727-572-9012 *E-mail:* imtronics@imtronics.com *Web Site:* imtronics.com, pg 897

In Concert Production Inc (ICP), 2750 S Cobb Industrial Blvd, Smyrna, GA 30082 *Tel:* 404-355-7943 *Fax:* 404-350-9045 *Web Site:* icpatlanta.com, pg 897

In-Plant Printing & Mailing Association, 155 S Sam Barr Dr, Suite 203, Kearney, MO 64060 *Tel:* 816-903-4762 *E-mail:* ipmainfo@ipma.org *Web Site:* www.ipma.org, pg 1082

In the Wild Productions, PO Box 1443, Provincetown, MA 02657-5443 *Tel:* 508-241-5990; 508-487-2887 *E-mail:* info@inthewildproductions.com *Web Site:* www.inthewildproductions.com, pg 897

Increase Video/Silver Mine Video, 5776 D Lindero Canyon Rd, Westlake Village, CA 91362 *Tel:* 805-480-0303 *Fax:* 805-375-1606, pg 897

Independent Audio Inc, 43 Deerfield Rd, Portland, ME 04101 *Tel:* 207-773-2424 *Fax:* 207-773-2422 *E-mail:* info@independentaudio.com *Web Site:* www.independentaudio.com, pg 897

Independent Film & Television Alliance® (IFTA), 10850 Wilshire Blvd, 9th fl, Los Angeles, CA 90024-4311 *Tel:* 310-446-1000 *Fax:* 310-446-1600 *E-mail:* info@ifta-online.org *Web Site:* www.ifta-online.org, pg 1083

Independent Film Week, 68 Jay St, Rm 425, Brooklyn, NY 11201-8361 *Tel:* 212-465-8200 *Fax:* 212-465-8525 *Web Site:* www.ifp.org/programs/independent-film-week, pg 1117

The Independent Filmmaker Project (IFP), 68 Jay St, Rm 425, Brooklyn, NY 11201-8361 *Tel:* 212-465-8200 *Fax:* 212-465-8525 *Web Site:* www.ifp.org, pg 1083

Independent Studios, 4701 Conti, New Orleans, LA 70119 *Tel:* 504-915-IJOE (915-4563), pg 897

Indian House, PO Box 472, Taos, NM 87571-0472 *Tel:* 575-776-2953 *Toll Free Tel:* 800-748-0522 *Fax:* 575-776-2804 *E-mail:* music@indianhouse.com *Web Site:* www.indianhouse.com, pg 897

Indiana University Press, Office of Scholarly Publishing, Herman B Wells Library 350, 1320 E Tenth St, Bloomington, IN 47405-3907 *Tel:* 812-855-8817 *Toll Free Tel:* 800-842-6796 *Fax:* 812-855-8507 *E-mail:* iupress@indiana.edu *Web Site:* www.iupress.indiana.edu, pg 897

Indianapolis International Film Festival, PO Box 1917, Indianapolis, IN 46206 *Tel:* 317-560-4433 *E-mail:* info@indyfilmfest.org *Web Site:* indyfilmfest.org, pg 1117

Indie Aerials, 16425 Hart St, Van Nuys, CA 91406 *Tel:* 818-988-9382 *E-mail:* info@indieaerials.com *Web Site:* indieaerials.com, pg 897

Indigo Productions, 313 Kensington Ave, Buffalo, NY 14214 *Tel:* 716-836-2930 *Fax:* 716-836-6830 *E-mail:* indigo@indigoproductions.net *Web Site:* www.indigoproductions.net, pg 897

Individual Artist Fellowship, Carvel State Off Bldg, 4th fl, 820 N French St, Wilmington, DE 19801 *Tel:* 302-577-8278 *Fax:* 302-577-6561 *E-mail:* delarts@state.de.us *Web Site:* www.artsdel.org, pg 1117

Individual Artist Fellowship Program, 193 State St, 25 State House Sta, Augusta, ME 04330-0025 *Tel:* 207-287-2724 *Fax:* 207-287-2725 *E-mail:* mainearts.info@maine.gov *Web Site:* mainearts.maine.gov/Pages/Grants/Individual-Artist-Fellowships, pg 1117

Induro, 75 Virginia Rd, North White Plains, NY 10603 *Tel:* 914-347-3300 *Fax:* 914-347-3309 *E-mail:* info@indurogear.com *Web Site:* www.indurogear.com, pg 897

Indus International Inc, 340 S Oak St, West Salem, WI 54669 *Tel:* 608-786-0300 *Toll Free Tel:* 800-843-9377 *Fax:* 608-786-0786 *E-mail:* info@indususa.com *Web Site:* www.indususa.com, pg 897

Industrial Audio/Video Inc, 2617 Bissonnet, Houston, TX 77005 *Tel:* 713-524-1956 *Toll Free Tel:* 800-392-4384 (TX only) *Fax:* 713-524-2823 *E-mail:* info@iavdigital.com *Web Site:* www.iavdigital.com, pg 897

Industrial Light & Magic (ILM), 1110 Gorgas St, San Francisco, CA 94129 *Tel:* 415-746-3000 *Fax:* 415-746-3015 *E-mail:* prdepartment@ilm.com *Web Site:* www.ilm.com, pg 897

Industrial Strength Inc, 3232 44 Ave N, St Petersburg, FL 33714 *Tel:* 727-528-2877 *Toll Free Fax:* 888-804-7680 *E-mail:* sales@industrialstrengthstaging.com *Web Site:* www.worryfreeav.com, pg 897

Industrial Timer Co, 30 Industrial Park Rd, Centerbrook, CT 06409 *Tel:* 860-767-7130 *Toll Free Tel:* 800-394-7130 *Fax:* 860-767-9137 *Toll Free Fax:* 800-767-9137 *E-mail:* sales@epg-inc.com *Web Site:* www.industrialtimercompany.com, pg 897

Inferno Film Productions LLC, PO Box 696, Littleton, CO 80160-0696 *Tel:* 303-587-9792 *E-mail:* sales@infernofilm.com *Web Site:* www.infernofilm.com, pg 897

Inferno Films, 3404 Guadalupe St, Austin, TX 78705 *Tel:* 512-302-9009 *Fax:* 512-302-9022 *Web Site:* www.infernofilms.com, pg 898

InfoComm International®, 11242 Waples Mill Rd, Suite 200, Fairfax, VA 22030 *Tel:* 703-273-7200 *Toll Free Tel:* 800-659-SHOW (659-7469) *Fax:* 703-278-8082 *E-mail:* customerservice@infocomm.org *Web Site:* www.infocomm.org, pg 1083

InFocus Corp, 13190 SW 68 Pkwy, Suite 200, Portland, OR 97223-8368 *Tel:* 503-207-4700 *Toll Free Tel:* 877-388-8385 *Fax:* 503-207-4707 *E-mail:* sales@infocus.com *Web Site:* www.infocus.com, pg 898

Infonics Inc, 2302 E Michigan Blvd, Michigan City, IN 46360 *Tel:* 219-879-3381 *Fax:* 219-879-3383 *E-mail:* infonics@sbcglobal.net, pg 898

Infosat Communications Inc, 3130 114 Ave SE, Calgary, AB T2Z 3V6, Canada *Tel:* 403-543-8188 *Toll Free Tel:* 888-524-3038 *Fax:* 403-289-8133 *Web Site:* infosat.com, pg 898

Ingram Book Group, One Ingram Blvd, La Vergne, TN 37086 *Tel:* 615-793-5000 *E-mail:* customer.service@ingramcontent.com; inquiry@ingramcontent.com *Web Site:* www.ingramcontent.com, pg 898

Ingram Entertainment Inc, 2 Ingram Blvd, La Vergne, TN 37089-7006 *Tel:* 615-287-4000 (corp) *Toll Free Tel:* 800-621-1333 (sales & cust serv) *Fax:* 615-287-4982 *Web Site:* www.ingramentertainment.com, pg 898

Ingram Micro, 1600 E Saint Andrew Place, Santa Ana, CA 92705 *Tel:* 714-566-1000 *Web Site:* www.ingrammicro.com, pg 898

InJoy Birth & Parenting Education, 7107 La Vista Place, Longmont, CO 80503 *Tel:* 303-447-2082 (ext 2) *Toll Free Tel:* 800-326-2082 (ext 2) *Fax:* 303-449-8788 *E-mail:* custserv@injoyvideos.com *Web Site:* www.injoyvideos.com, pg 898

Inland Audio Visual Co, 1414 N Fiske St, Suite E, Spokane, WA 99202 *Tel:* 509-328-0706 *Toll Free Tel:* 888-9INLAND (946-5263) *Fax:* 509-328-0730 *E-mail:* inland@inlandav.com *Web Site:* www.inlandav.com, pg 898

Inland Audio Visual Ltd, 422 Lucas Ave, Box 102, Group 200, RR 2, Winnipeg, MB R3C 2E6, Canada *Tel:* 204-786-6521 *Toll Free Tel:* 800-933-6006 *Fax:* 204-783-6281 *E-mail:* winnipeg@inlandav.ca *Web Site:* www.inlandav.ca, pg 898

Inland Empire Film Commission (IEFC), 1601 E Third St, Suite 102, San Bernardino, CA 92408 *Fax:* 909-382-6060 *E-mail:* info@filminlandempire.com *Web Site:* www.filminlandempire.com, pg 1094

Inner Explorations, PO Box 37, Midland, OR 97634-0037 *Tel:* 541-851-1534 *Web Site:* www.innerexplorations.com, pg 898

Inner Traditions International, One Park St, Rochester, VT 05767 *Tel:* 802-767-3174 *Toll Free Tel:* 800-246-8648 *Fax:* 802-767-3726 *E-mail:* customerservice@innertraditions.com *Web Site:* www.innertraditions.com, pg 898

Innocinema, 10130 Perimeter Pkwy, Suite 180, Charlotte, NC 28216 *Tel:* 704-665-1945 *Fax:* 704-665-1956 *E-mail:* info@innocinema.com; sales@innocinema.com *Web Site:* www.innocinema.com, pg 898

Innovative Electronic Designs LLC, 9701 Taylorsville Rd, Louisville, KY 40299 *Tel:* 502-267-7436 *Fax:* 502-267-9070 *E-mail:* info@iedaudio.com *Web Site:* www.iedaudio.com, pg 898

Innovision Media Group, 307 W Johnson Hwy, Norristown, PA 19401 *Tel:* 484-688-1200 *Fax:* 484-688-0148 *E-mail:* info@innovision.net; sales@innovision.net *Web Site:* www.innovision.net, pg 899

Innovision Optics, 1719 21 St, Santa Monica, CA 90404 *Tel:* 310-453-4866 *Fax:* 310-453-4677 *Web Site:* www.innovision-optics.com, pg 899

Institute for Teaching & Learning Excellence (ITLE), 100 ITLE, Oklahoma State University, Stillwater, OK 74078 *Tel:* 405-744-1000 *Fax:* 405-744-8563 *E-mail:* itle@okstate.edu *Web Site:* itle.okstate.edu, pg 899

The Institute Inc, 787 East Ave, Brockport, NY 14420 *Tel:* 585-637-6531 *Web Site:* www.the-institute-ny.com, pg 899

Institute of Industrial Engineers (IIE), 3577 Parkway Lane, Suite 200, Norcross, GA 30092 *Tel:* 770-449-0460 *Toll Free Tel:* 800-494-0460 *Fax:* 770-441-3295 *E-mail:* cs@iienet.org *Web Site:* www.iienet2.org, pg 1083

Institute of Precision Muscle Balancing, 6035 Vantage Ave, North Hollywood, CA 91616-4637 *Tel:* 818-766-8555 *Fax:* 818-766-8645 *Web Site:* www.dralexander.com, pg 899

Institute of Texan Cultures, UTSA HemisFair Park Campus, 801 E Cesar E Chavez Blvd, San Antonio, TX 78205-3296 *Tel:* 210-458-2300 *Toll Free Tel:* 800-776-7651 *Fax:* 210-458-2205 *Web Site:* www.texancultures.com, pg 899

Institute on Religious Life Inc, PO Box 7500, Libertyville, IL 60048-7500 *Tel:* 847-573-8975 *Fax:* 847-573-8960 *Web Site:* www.religiouslife.com, pg 899

Instructional Materials & Equipment Distributors (I-Med), 1520 Cotner Ave, Los Angeles, CA 90025 *Tel:* 323-879-0377; 323-272-5260; 310-473-5558 *Toll Free Tel:* 800-352-7423 (CA only) *Fax:* 310-312-1743 *Web Site:* www.i-med-inc.com, pg 899

Instructional Resources Corp, 1819 Bay Ridge Ave, Annapolis, MD 21403 *Tel:* 410-263-0025 *Toll Free Tel:* 800-922-1711 *Fax:* 410-268-8320 *Web Site:* www.historypictures.com, pg 899

Instrumentation Marketing Corp, 820 S Mariposa St, Burbank, CA 91506-3196 *Tel:* 818-842-2141 *Fax:* 818-842-2610 *E-mail:* mail@photosonics.com *Web Site:* www.photosonics.com/imc.htm, pg 899

IntegraColor, 3210 Innovative Way, Mesquite, TX 75149 *Tel:* 972-289-0705 *Toll Free Tel:* 800-933-9511 *Fax:* 972-285-4881 *E-mail:* salesinfo@integracolor.com *Web Site:* www.integracolor.com, pg 899

Integrated Event Management, 1239 Vista Leaf Dr, Decatur, GA 30033 *Tel:* 404-633-8541 *Fax:* 404-633-8691 *Web Site:* www.integratedevents.com, pg 899

Intel-A-Jib™, 409 Calle San Pablo, No 108, Camarillo, CA 93012 *Web Site:* www.intel-a-jib.com, pg 899

Intelix LLC, 8001 Terrace Ave, Suite 201, Middleton, WI 53562 *Tel:* 608-831-0880 *Toll Free Tel:* 866-4-MATMIX (462-8649) *Fax:* 608-831-1833 *E-mail:* intelix@intelix.com *Web Site:* www.intelix.com, pg 899

The Intellications Co, 1110 Northshore Dr, Roswell, GA 30076-2812 *Tel:* 678-643-8468 *Web Site:* www.johnatwood.com, pg 899

Intellidyne LLC, 5203 Leesburg Pike, Suite 400, 2 Skyline Place, Falls Church, VA 22041 *Tel:* 703-575-9715 *Fax:* 703-575-9718 *Web Site:* www.intellidyne-llc.com, pg 899

Inter-Media Electronics, 192 Willard St, Quincy, MA 02169 *Tel:* 617-773-9688 *Fax:* 617-696-6327 *E-mail:* intermedia.ex@verizon.net; info@ime-imaging.com *Web Site:* www.viapolonia.net/IME, pg 899

Inter Video, 2000 N Lincoln St, Burbank, CA 91504 *Tel:* 818-843-3624 *Fax:* 818-843-6884 *Web Site:* www.intervideo24.com, pg 899

Interactive International Inc, 290 West End Ave, New York, NY 10023-8106 *Tel:* 212-580-5015 *Fax:* 212-580-5017 *E-mail:* ivie@erols.com, pg 899

Interactive Multimedia & Collaborative Communications Alliance (IMCCA), PO Box 756, Syosset, NY 11791 *Web Site:* www.imcca.org, pg 1083

Interactive Products, 101 Commerce Dr, Montgomeryville, PA 18936 *Tel:* 215-362-2766 *Toll Free Tel:* 800-523-6716 *Fax:* 215-361-0167 *E-mail:* numonics@numonics.com *Web Site:* www.numonics.com, pg 899

InterAmerica Stage Inc, 4300 St Johns Pkwy, Sanford, FL 32771 *Tel:* 407-302-0881 *Toll Free Tel:* 877-302-4274 *Fax:* 407-302-0882 *E-mail:* info@iastage.com *Web Site:* www.iastage.com, pg 900

Intercollegiate Studies Institute Inc (ISI), 3901 Centerville Rd, Wilmington, DE 19807 *Tel:* 302-652-4600 *Toll Free Tel:* 800-526-7022 *Fax:* 302-652-1760 *E-mail:* info@isi.org *Web Site:* www.isi.org, pg 900

InterCom, 3 Grogan's Park, Suite 200, The Woodlands, TX 77380 *Tel:* 281-367-4277 *Toll Free Tel:* 800-298-7070 *Fax:* 281-364-7032 *E-mail:* intercom@intercomtraining.com *Web Site:* www.intercom-interactive.com, pg 900

INTERCOM, 30 E Adams St, Suite 800, Chicago, IL 60603 *Tel:* 312-683-0121 *Fax:* 312-683-0122 *E-mail:* info@chicagofilmfestival.com *Web Site:* www.chicagofilmfestival.com, pg 1117

InterComm, 1520 E Winona Ave, Warsaw, IN 46590 *Tel:* 574-267-5774 *Fax:* 574-267-5876 *E-mail:* info@intercommedia.org *Web Site:* www.intercommedia.org, pg 900

Intercon 1, 7746 Goedderz Rd, Suite 110, Baxter, MN 56425 *Tel:* 218-828-3157 *Toll Free Tel:* 800-237-9576 *Fax:* 218-828-1096 *E-mail:* intercon@nortechsys.com *Web Site:* www.intercon-1.com, pg 900

Interface Media Group, 1233 20 St NW, Washington, DC 20036 *Tel:* 202-861-0500 *E-mail:* info@interfacevideo.com *Web Site:* www.interfacevideo.com, pg 900

Interlink Technologies, 139 W Indiana Ave, Suite 203, Perrysburg, OH 43552 *Tel:* 419-893-9011 *Toll Free Tel:* 800-655-5465 *Fax:* 419-893-7280 *E-mail:* info@interlinktech.com; info@thinkinterlink.com *Web Site:* www.interlinktech.com; www.thinkinterlink.com, pg 900

Intermark Industries Inc, 2980 NW 74 Ave, Miami, FL 33122 *Tel:* 305-591-8930 *Fax:* 305-593-1091 *E-mail:* info@intermarkindustries.com *Web Site:* www.intermarkindustries.com, pg 900

Intermed Video Technologies Inc, 18 Commerce Rd, Newtown, CT 06470 *Tel:* 203-270-0677; 203-270-9100 *Fax:* 203-270-9619 *E-mail:* sales@intermedvideo.com *Web Site:* www.intermedvideo.com, pg 900

Intermedia Inc, 5600 Rainier Ave S, Suite 203, Seattle, WA 98118 *Tel:* 206-284-2995 *Toll Free Tel:* 800-553-8336 *Toll Free Fax:* 800-553-1655 *E-mail:* info@intermedia-inc.com *Web Site:* www.intermedia-inc.com, pg 900

Intermedia Technologies, 1720 Kaliste Saloom, Bldg 2, Suite B-2, Lafayette, LA 70508 *Tel:* 337-406-9428 *Toll Free Tel:* 877-268-9574 *Fax:* 337-406-9582 *Web Site:* www.intermedia-technologies.com, pg 900

InterNation Inc, 299 Broadway, Suite 1400, New York, NY 10007 *Tel:* 212-619-5545 *Toll Free Tel:* 800-222-8799 *Fax:* 212-619-5887 *E-mail:* info@internation.com *Web Site:* www.internation.com, pg 900

International Association of Business Communicators (IABC), 601 Montgomery St, Suite 1900, San Francisco, CA 94111 *Tel:* 415-544-4700 *Toll Free Tel:* 800-776-4222 *Fax:* 415-544-4747 *E-mail:* member_relations@iabc.com *Web Site:* www.iabc.com, pg 1083

International Audio Visual Inc, 622 Rte 10, Unit 21, Whippany, NJ 07981 *Tel:* 973-887-7744 *Toll Free Tel:* 888-887-7749 *Fax:* 973-887-7272 *E-mail:* iav@iavnj.com *Web Site:* www.iavnj.com, pg 900

International Cellulose Corp, 12315 Robin Blvd, Houston, TX 77045 *Tel:* 713-433-6701 *Toll Free Tel:* 800-444-1252 *Fax:* 713-433-2029 *E-mail:* icc@spray-on.com *Web Site:* www.spray-on.com, pg 900

International CINDY Competitions, PO Box 270779, Flower Mound, TX 75027-0779 *Tel:* 469-464-4180 *Fax:* 469-464-4170 *E-mail:* cindy@cindys.com *Web Site:* www.cindys.com, pg 1117

International Cinema Technology Association (ICTA), 770 Broadway, 5th fl, New York, NY 10003-9595 *Tel:* 212-493-4097; 212-493-4058 *Fax:* 212-257-6428 *E-mail:* info@itea.com *Web Site:* www.internationalcinematechnologyassociation.com, pg 1083

International Contact Inc, 351 15 St, Oakland, CA 94612 *Tel:* 510-836-1180 *Toll Free Tel:* 800-430-7705 *Fax:* 510-835-1314 *E-mail:* info@intlcontact.com *Web Site:* www.intlcontact.com, pg 900

International Datacasting, 50 Frank Nighbor Place, Kanata, ON K2V 1B9, Canada *Tel:* 613-596-4120 *Fax:* 613-596-4863 *E-mail:* marketing@datacast.com *Web Site:* www.datacast.com, pg 900

International Digital Centre, 216 E 45 St, 7th fl, New York, NY 10017 *Tel:* 212-581-3940 *Fax:* 212-581-3979 *E-mail:* info@idcdigital.com *Web Site:* www.idcdigital.com, pg 901

International Display & Exhibit Corp, 60 Shawmut Rd, Suite 5, Canton, MA 02021 *Tel:* 617-527-7878 *Toll Free Tel:* 800-533-7878 *Fax:* 617-964-5099 *E-mail:* sales@idec-displays.com *Web Site:* www.idecdisplays.com, pg 901

International Documentary Association, 3470 Wilshire Blvd, Suite 980, Los Angeles, CA 90010 *Tel:* 213-232-1660 *Fax:* 213-232-1669 *E-mail:* info@documentary.org *Web Site:* www.documentary.org, pg 1083

International E-Z UP Inc, 1900 Second St, Norco, CA 92860 *Tel:* 951-279-0999 *Toll Free Tel:* 800-45SHADE (457-4233) *Fax:* 951-279-0888 *Web Site:* www.ezup.com, pg 901

International Electro-Magnetics Inc, 1033A S Noel Ave, Wheeling, IL 60090 *Tel:* 847-358-4622 *Toll Free Tel:* 800-227-4323 (sales) *Fax:* 847-947-8239 *E-mail:* information@iemmag.com; service@iemmag.com; sales@iemmag.com *Web Site:* www.iemmag.com, pg 901

International Emmy® Awards, 25 W 52 St, New York, NY 10019 *Tel:* 212-489-6969 *Fax:* 212-489-6557 *E-mail:* iemmys@iemmys.tv; awardsdept@iemmys.tv *Web Site:* www.iemmys.tv, pg 1117

International Film Festival in Abitibi-Teiscamingue/ Festival du cinema international en Abitibi-Temiscamingue, 215 Ave Mercier, Rouyn-Noranda, QC J9X 5W8, Canada *Tel:* 819-762-6212 *Fax:* 819-762-6762 *E-mail:* info@festivalcinema.ca *Web Site:* www.festivalcinema.ca, pg 1117

International Fun-Shop, 2114 Seabrook Circle, Seabrook, TX 77586 *Tel:* 281-291-0707 *Fax:* 281-291-0718 *E-mail:* fssales@fun-shop.com *Web Site:* www.fun-shop.com, pg 901

International Historic Films Inc, 3533 S Archer Ave, Chicago, IL 60609 *Tel:* 773-927-2900 *Fax:* 773-927-9211 *E-mail:* info@ihffilm.com *Web Site:* www.ihffilm.com, pg 901

International Light Technologies Inc, 10 Technology Dr, Peabody, MA 01960-7976 *Tel:* 978-818-6180 *Fax:* 978-818-6181 *E-mail:* ilsales@intl-lighttech.com *Web Site:* www.intl-lighttech.com, pg 901

International Loving Touch Foundation Inc, 2122 SE Division St, Portland, OR 97202 *Tel:* 503-253-8482 *Fax:* 503-256-6753 *E-mail:* info@lovingtouch.com *Web Site:* www.lovingtouch.com, pg 901

International Marketing Group, 1900 Elm Hill Pike, Nashville, TN 37210 *Tel:* 615-889-8000 *Fax:* 615-871-4817, pg 901

International Radio & Television Society Foundation (IRTS), 1697 Broadway, 10th fl, New York, NY 10019 *Tel:* 212-867-6650 *Web Site:* irtsfoundation.org, pg 1083

International Robotics Inc, 2001 Palmer Ave, Suite LL-1, Larchmont, NY 10538 *Tel:* 914-630-1060 *Fax:* 203-630-1733 *E-mail:* info@internationalrobotics.com *Web Site:* www.internationalrobotics.com, pg 901

International Society for Performance Improvement® (ISPI), PO Box 13035, Silver Spring, MD 20910 *Tel:* 301-587-8570 *Fax:* 301-587-8573 *E-mail:* info@ispi.org *Web Site:* www.ispi.org, pg 1083

The International Society of Automation (ISA), 67 T W Alexander Dr, Research Triangle Park, NC 27709 *Tel:* 919-549-8411 *Fax:* 919-549-8288 *E-mail:* info@isa.org *Web Site:* www.isa.org, pg 901

International Storytelling Center, 116 W Main St, Jonesborough, TN 37659 *Tel:* 423-753-2171 *Toll Free Tel:* 800-952-8392 *Fax:* 423-913-8219 *E-mail:* customerservice@storytellingcenter.net *Web Site:* www.storytellingcenter.net, pg 1083

International Tae Kwon Do Association (ITA Institute), PO Box 281, Grand Blanc, MI 48480 *Tel:* 810-232-6482 *Fax:* 810-235-8594 *E-mail:* hq@itatkd.com *Web Site:* www.itatkd.com, pg 901

International Ticketing Association Inc (INTIX), 2 Meridian Plaza, 10401 N Meridian St, Suite 300, Indianapolis, IN 46290 *Tel:* 212-629-4036 *Fax:* 212-629-8532 *E-mail:* info@intix.org *Web Site:* www.intix.org, pg 1084

International Wildlife Film Festival, Roxy Theater, 718 S Higgins Ave, Missoula, MT 59801 *Tel:* 406-728-9380 *Fax:* 406-728-2881 *E-mail:* iwff@wildlifefilms.org *Web Site:* www.wildlifefilms.org, pg 1117

Interscope, Geffen, A&M Records, 2220 Colorado Ave, Santa Monica, CA 90404 *Tel:* 310-865-4500 *Web Site:* www.interscope.com, pg 901

Interscreen America Inc, 13191 56 Ct, Suite 104, Clearwater, FL 33760 *Tel:* 727-546-8515 *Toll Free Tel:* 800-520-9642 *Toll Free Fax:* 866-476-0440 *E-mail:* info@interscreen.tv *Web Site:* www.interscreen.us, pg 901

Intersect Video, 25749 SW Canyon Creek Rd, Suite 300, Wilsonville, OR 97070 *Tel:* 971-224-4808 *E-mail:* info@intersectvideo.com *Web Site:* www.intersectvideo.com, pg 901

Intersil Americas LLC, 1001 Murphy Ranch Rd, Milpitas, CA 95035 *Tel:* 408-432-8888 *Toll Free Tel:* 888-INTERSIL (468-3774) *Fax:* 408-434-5351 *Web Site:* www.intersil.com, pg 901

Interstate Connecting Components, 120 Mount Holly Bypass, Lumberton, NJ 08048-1112 *Tel:* 856-722-5535 *Toll Free Tel:* 888-881-5420 *Fax:* 856-813-5419 *E-mail:* info@connecticc.com *Web Site:* www.connecticc.com, pg 901

Intervideo Duplication Services, 3533 S Archer Ave, Chicago, IL 60609 *Tel:* 773-927-9091 *Fax:* 773-927-9211 *E-mail:* info@intervideoduplication.com *Web Site:* www.intervideoduplication.com, pg 902

InterVision Media, 44 W Broadway, Suite 426, Eugene, OR 97401 *Tel:* 541-343-7993 *Fax:* 541-345-5951 *E-mail:* info@intervisionmedia.com *Web Site:* www.intervisionmedia.com, pg 902

InVision Productions, 821 Las Colindas Rd, San Rafael, CA 94903 *Tel:* 415-492-0414 *E-mail:* invision@goinvision.com *Web Site:* www.goinvision.com, pg 902

Iowa Cable & Telecommunications Association (ICTA), 2024 NW 92 Ct, Suite 6, Clive, IA 50325 *Tel:* 515-276-0006 *E-mail:* info@iacable.com *Web Site:* www.iacable.com, pg 1084

Iowa State University-Information Technology Services, 1200 Communications Bldg, Ames, IA 50011-3243 *Tel:* 515-294-6014 (multimedia & streaming prodn) *Fax:* 515-294-8089 *Web Site:* www.it.iastate.edu, pg 902

Ipitek, 2330 Faraday Ave, Carlsbad, CA 92008 *Tel:* 760-438-1010 *Toll Free Tel:* 888-4-IPITEK (447-4835, US) *Fax:* 760-438-2412 *E-mail:* sales@ipitek.com *Web Site:* www.ipitek.com, pg 902

IPRO, 34157 W 9 Mile Rd, Farmington Hills, MI 48335 *Tel:* 248-474-0522 *Toll Free Tel:* 800-420-4268 *Web Site:* www.avreps.org, pg 1084

iProbe Multilingual Solutions Inc, 273 E Third St, New York, NY 10009 *Tel:* 212-489-6035 *Toll Free Tel:* 888-489-6035 *Fax:* 212-202-4790 *E-mail:* info@iprobesolutions.com *Web Site:* www.iprobesolutions.com, pg 902

iQstor Networks Inc, 2001 Corporate Center Dr, Newbury Park, CA 91320 *Tel:* 805-376-1000 *E-mail:* sales@iqstor.com *Web Site:* www.iqstor.com, pg 902

IRE Annual Awards for Investigative Reporting, Missouri School of Journalism, 141 Neff Annex, Columbia, MO 65211 *Tel:* 573-882-2042 *Fax:* 573-882-5431 *E-mail:* rescntr@ire.org; info@ire.org *Web Site:* www.ire.org/awards, pg 1117

Irish Music Corp, PO Box 1515, Green Island, NY 12183-1515 *Tel:* 518-266-0765 *Toll Free Tel:* 800-458-7346; 800-854-3746 (sales) *E-mail:* info@regorecords.com *Web Site:* www.regorecords.com, pg 902

Iron Ring Communications Ltd, 431 Brookmill Rd, Unit 1, Oakville, ON L6J 5K6, Canada *Tel:* 905-849-5922 *Fax:* 905-849-6188 *Web Site:* www.ironringltd.com, pg 902

Ironbound Film & Television Studios LLC, Newark Arts & Entertainment Bldg, 169 Malvern St, Newark, NJ 07105 *Tel:* 201-456-4754 *Web Site:* www.ironboundfilmstudios.com, pg 902

Ironik Design & Post, 56 E Main St, Suite 203, Avon, CT 06001 *Tel:* 860-404-2386 *Fax:* 860-404-2735 *E-mail:* info@ironikdesign.com *Web Site:* www.ironikdesign.com, pg 902

Ironstone Technologies, 534 Berry St, Winnipeg, MB R3H 0R9, Canada *Tel:* 204-697-0159 *Toll Free Tel:* 800-665-4766 *Fax:* 204-694-9355 *E-mail:* info@ironstone.ca *Web Site:* www.ironstone.ca, pg 902

ISCAN Inc, 21 Cabot Rd, Woburn, MA 01801 *Tel:* 781-932-1199 *Fax:* 781-932-1155 *E-mail:* info@iscaninc.com *Web Site:* www.iscaninc.com, pg 902

Ishtar Films, 12400 Moorpark St, Suite 2, Studio City, CA 91604 *Toll Free Tel:* 800-428-7136 *Fax:* 818-985-0567 *E-mail:* ishtarfilms2@sbcglobal.net *Web Site:* www.ishtarfilms.com, pg 902

Island Cases, 1121-20 Lincoln Ave, Holbrook, NY 11741 *Tel:* 631-563-0633 *Toll Free Tel:* 877-824-3199 *Fax:* 631-563-1390; 631-563-0608 *E-mail:* sales@roadcasesusa.com *Web Site:* www.islandcases.com; www.roadcasesusa.com, pg 902

Israel Film Festival, 324 S Beverly Dr, No 424, Beverly Hills, CA 90212 *Tel:* 323-966-4166 *E-mail:* info@israelfilmfestival.org *Web Site:* www.israelfilmfestival.com, pg 1118

ITA Audio Visual Solutions, 2162 Dana Ave & I-71, Cincinnati, OH 45207 *Tel:* 513-631-7000 *Toll Free Tel:* 800-899-8877 *Fax:* 513-631-3290; 513-631-8877 *E-mail:* csr@ita.com *Web Site:* www.ita.com, pg 902

ITC Learning LLC, 1616 Anderson Rd, Suite 109, McLean, VA 22102 *Toll Free Tel:* 800-638-3757 *E-mail:* sales@itclearning.com *Web Site:* www.itclearning.com, pg 903

ITEC Entertainment Corp, 8544 Commodity Circle, Orlando, FL 32819 *Tel:* 407-226-0200 *Fax:* 407-226-0201 *E-mail:* productionsinfo@itec.com *Web Site:* www.itec.com, pg 903

ITT Veam LLC, 100 New Wood Rd, Watertown, CT 06795 *Tel:* 860-274-9681 *Fax:* 860-274-4963 *Web Site:* www.ittcannon.com, pg 903

ITV Productions, 1649 S Robertson Blvd, Los Angeles, CA 90035 *Tel:* 310-204-1234 *E-mail:* itvproductions1@gmail.com *Web Site:* www.itvproductions.com, pg 903

IV Media Resources, 910 Redwing Dr, Geneva, IL 60134 *Tel:* 630-389-0000 *Fax:* 630-389-0208 *E-mail:* info@infinitevideo.com *Web Site:* www.infinitevideo.com, pg 903

iVideo Technologies, 14885 Sprague Rd, Cleveland, OH 44136 *Tel:* 440-891-9440 *Toll Free Tel:* 800-352-6150 *Fax:* 440-891-9450 *E-mail:* info@ivideo.com *Web Site:* www.ivideo.com, pg 903

Ivie Technologies Inc, 1195 Spring Creek Place, Suite B, Springville, UT 84663 *Tel:* 801-489-8703 *Toll Free Fax:* 877-829-6567 *E-mail:* ivie@ivie.com *Web Site:* www.ivie.com, pg 903

Ivory Productions, 529 Plymouth Rd, Gwynedd Valley, PA 19437 *Tel:* 215-591-9900 *E-mail:* divory@comcast.net *Web Site:* www.ivoryproductions.com, pg 903

IVS Imaging, 101 Wrangler Dr, Suite 201, Coppell, TX 75019 *Toll Free Tel:* 888-446-1301 *Fax:* 469-635-6800 *E-mail:* info@ivsimaging.com *Web Site:* www.ivsimaging.com, pg 903

J & D Laboratories Inc, 27 E 21 St, New York, NY 10010 *Tel:* 212-982-3330 *Toll Free Tel:* 800-535-2201 *Fax:* 212-982-3332 *E-mail:* jdvideolab@aol.com *Web Site:* jdvideolab.com, pg 903

J & R Film Co, 1135 N Mansfield Ave, Hollywood, CA 90038 *Tel:* 323-467-1116 *Toll Free Tel:* 877-668-4652 *Fax:* 323-464-1518 *Web Site:* www.moviola.com, pg 903

J K Audio Inc, 1311 E Sixth St, Sandwich, IL 60548 *Tel:* 815-786-2929 *Toll Free Tel:* 800-552-8346 *Fax:* 815-786-8502 *E-mail:* info@jkaudio.com *Web Site:* www.jkaudio.com, pg 903

Jack's Camera Shop, 300 E Main St, Muncie, IN 47305 *Tel:* 765-282-0204 *Fax:* 765-284-6405 *E-mail:* info@jackscamera.com *Web Site:* jackscamera.com, pg 903

Jackson Hole Film Commission, 112 Center St, Jackson, WY 83001 *Tel:* 307-733-3316 (ext 104) *Fax:* 307-733-5585 *Web Site:* www.jacksonholechamber.com, pg 1104

Jacksonville Office of Economic Development, Film & Television Office, 117 W Duval St, Suite 280, Jacksonville, FL 32202 *Tel:* 904-630-2522 *Fax:* 904-630-3693 *Web Site:* www.filmjax.com, pg 1096

JaffeHolden, 114-A Washington St, Norwalk, CT 06854 *Tel:* 203-838-4167 *Fax:* 203-838-4168 *Web Site:* www.jaffeholden.com, pg 903

Jaguar Distribution Corp, 12711 Ventura Blvd, Suite 300, Studio City, CA 91604 *Tel:* 818-508-3377 *Fax:* 818-508-3340 *Web Site:* www.jaguardc.com, pg 903

Jaguar Productions, PO Box 121014, Nashville, TN 37212-1014 *Tel:* 615-391-4393 (off); 615-390-4161 (cell) *Web Site:* www.jaguarvideoproductions.com, pg 903

Jalbert Productions International, 230 New York Ave, Huntington, NY 11743 *Tel:* 631-351-5878 *Fax:* 631-351-5875 *E-mail:* info@jalbertfilm.com *Web Site:* www.jalbertfilm.com, pg 903

JAM Industries Ltd, 21000 Trans-Canadienne, Baie D'Urfe, QC H9X 4B7, Canada *Tel:* 514-457-2555 *Fax:* 514-457-0055 *E-mail:* info@jamindustries.com *Web Site:* www.jamindustries.com, pg 903

Jameco Electronics, 1355 Shoreway Rd, Belmont, CA 94002-4105 *Tel:* 650-592-8097 *Toll Free Tel:* 800-831-4242 (orders); 800-536-4316 (cust serv) *Fax:* 650-592-2503 *Toll Free Fax:* 800-237-6948 *E-mail:* info@jameco.com; sales@jameco.com *Web Site:* www.jameco.com, pg 903

James Agee Film Project, PO Box 73, Riverdale, MD 20738-0073 *Tel:* 301-277-3880 *E-mail:* jagee@cstone.net *Web Site:* www.ageefilms.org, pg 904

Jamieson & Associates Inc, 4133 W 45 St, Minneapolis, MN 55424-1040 *Tel:* 952-920-3770 *E-mail:* info@jamieson.com *Web Site:* www.jamieson.com, pg 904

Jams Productions Inc, Production Trailer No 1, 2206 Holt Rd, Bowmanville, ON L1C 3K7, Canada *Tel:* 647-273-4844 *Fax:* 905-623-2895 *E-mail:* info@jamsproductions.ca *Web Site:* www.jamsproductions.ca, pg 904

JamSync, Music Row, 1232 17 Ave S, Nashville, TN 37212-2802 *Tel:* 615-320-5050 *Fax:* 615-340-9559 *E-mail:* info@jamsync.com *Web Site:* www.jamsync.com, pg 904

Jan-Al Cases, 3339 Union Pacific Ave, Los Angeles, CA 90023 *Tel:* 323-260-7212 *Toll Free Tel:* 800-735-2625 *Fax:* 323-260-4696 *Web Site:* www.janalcase.com, pg 904

J&S Audio Visual Inc, 9150 N Royal Lane, Suite 150, Irving, TX 75063 *Tel:* 972-241-5444 *Toll Free Tel:* 800-852-8771 *Fax:* 972-247-2590 *E-mail:* info@jsav.com *Web Site:* www.jsav.com, pg 904

Janson Industries, 1200 Garfield Ave SW, Canton, OH 44706 *Tel:* 330-455-7029 *Toll Free Tel:* 800-548-8982 *Fax:* 330-455-5919 *Web Site:* www.jansonindustries.com, pg 904

Janson Media, 118 Main St, Tappan, NY 10983 *Tel:* 845-359-8488 *E-mail:* info@janson.com *Web Site:* www.janson.com, pg 904

Janus Films Inc, 215 Park Ave S, 5th fl, New York, NY 10003 *Tel:* 212-756-8822 *Fax:* 212-756-8850 *Web Site:* www.criterion.com, pg 904

Javboy Records, 408 Kingston Dr, Douglassville, PA 19518 *Tel:* 215-285-7444 *E-mail:* contact@javboyrecords.com *Web Site:* www.javboyrecords.com, pg 904

Jay Jay Record & Tape Co, 102 Brookfield Lane, Geneva, IL 60134 *Tel:* 305-758-0000 *Fax:* 305-758-0000, pg 904

Jazzology, 61 French Market Place, New Orleans, LA 70116 *Tel:* 504-525-5000 *Fax:* 504-525-1776 *E-mail:* info@jazzology.com *Web Site:* www.jazzology.com, pg 904

JBK Cinequipt LLC, 17940 N Tamiami Trail, No 222, North Fort Myers, FL 33903 *Tel:* 954-607-8440 *E-mail:* jbkfilm@yahoo.com; jbkcine@gmail.com *Web Site:* www.jbkcinequipt.com, pg 904

JBL Professional, 8500 Balboa Blvd, Northridge, CA 91329 *Tel:* 818-894-8850; 818-895-3498 *Fax:* 818-894-3479; 818-830-7865 (mktg); 818-830-7801 (sales) *E-mail:* info@jblpro.com *Web Site:* www.jblpro.com; www.harman.com, pg 904

JCS Video Productions, 4617 Sequoia Park Ave, Las Vegas, NV 89139 *Tel:* 702-596-9291 (cell); 702-546-0150 *Toll Free Tel:* 800-791-8671 *Fax:* 702-546-0150 *E-mail:* jcsvideo@cox.net *Web Site:* www.jcsvideo.com, pg 904

JD Audio Visual Inc, 1713 E Walnut St, Pasadena, CA 91106 *Tel:* 626-792-6682 *Toll Free Tel:* 800-532-8346 *Fax:* 626-796-6635 *E-mail:* sales@jdav.com *Web Site:* www.jdav.com, pg 904

JDS Video & Media Productions Inc, 39870 Camden Ct, Temecula, CA 92591 *Tel:* 951-296-6715 *Toll Free Fax:* 866-737-2239 *E-mail:* info@jds-productions.com *Web Site:* www.jds-productions.com, pg 904

JDSU, 430 N McCarthy Blvd, Milpitas, CA 95035 *Tel:* 408-546-5000 *Fax:* 408-546-4300 *Web Site:* www.jdsu.com, pg 905

Jeep Jazz Media Solutions, 8 Graham Terr, Montclair, NJ 07042 *Tel:* 973-222-5737 *E-mail:* jeepjazz@hotmail.com *Web Site:* www.jeepjazz.com, pg 905

JEM Smoke Machine Co Ltd, 700 Sawgrass Corporate Pkwy, Sunrise, FL 33325 *Tel:* 954-858-1800 *Toll Free Tel:* 800-832-4180 *Fax:* 954-858-1811 *E-mail:* martinus@martinpro.com *Web Site:* www.martinpro.com, pg 905

Jensen Transformers Inc, 9304 Deering Ave, Chatsworth, CA 91311 *Tel:* 818-374-5857 *Toll Free Tel:* 866-476-6291 *Fax:* 818-374-5856 *E-mail:* sales@jensen-transformers.com *Web Site:* www.jensen-transformers.com, pg 905

Jeppesen, 55 Inverness Dr E, Englewood, CO 80112 *Tel:* 303-799-9090 *Toll Free Tel:* 800-621-5377; 800-353-2107 *Fax:* 303-328-4153 *Web Site:* www.jeppesen.com, pg 905

Jereco Studios Inc, 627 E Peach St, Suite E, Bozeman, MT 59715 *Tel:* 406-586-5262 *Fax:* 406-586-5262 *Web Site:* www.jerecostudios.com, pg 905

Jeron Electronic Systems Inc, 1743-55 W Rosehill Dr, Chicago, IL 60660 *Tel:* 773-275-1900 *Toll Free Tel:* 800-621-1903 *Fax:* 773-275-0283 *E-mail:* sales@jeron.com *Web Site:* www.jeron.com, pg 905

JFA Studio, 3062 N Lima St, Burbank, CA 91504 *Tel:* 818-861-9090 *E-mail:* info@jfastudio.com *Web Site:* www.jfastudio.com, pg 905

JFB Communications, 3 Haig Ave, Toronto, ON M1N 2W2, Canada *Tel:* 416-691-5001 *E-mail:* jfb@jfb.ca *Web Site:* jfb.ca, pg 905

JFW Industries Inc, 5134 Commerce Square Dr, Indianapolis, IN 46237 *Tel:* 317-887-1340 *Toll Free Tel:* 877-887-4539 *Fax:* 317-881-6790 *E-mail:* sales@jfwindustries.com; jfwengr@jfwindustries.com *Web Site:* www.jfwindustries.com, pg 905

JIB Shots Equipment Inc, 1828 Lorraine Ave, Ottawa, ON K1H 6Z8, Canada *Tel:* 613-293-3318 *Fax:* 613-521-9312 *Web Site:* www.jibshots.com, pg 905

Jin, 238 E Main St, Ville Platte, LA 70586 *Tel:* 337-363-2177 *Fax:* 337-363-2094 *E-mail:* info@flattownmusic.com *Web Site:* www.flattownmusic.com, pg 905

JIST Publishing, 875 Montreal Way, St Paul, MN 55102 *Toll Free Tel:* 800-328-1452 *Toll Free Fax:* 800-328-4564 *E-mail:* info@jist.com *Web Site:* www.jist.com, pg 905

JL Recording Studios, 270 Adelaide St W, Suite 202, Toronto, ON M5H 1X6, Canada *Tel:* 416-598-7979 *Web Site:* www.jlstudios.ca; www.facebook.com/jlrecordingstudios; twitter.com/JLStudios, pg 905

JLCooper Electronics, 142 Arena St, El Segundo, CA 90245-3901 *Tel:* 310-322-9990 *Fax:* 310-335-0110 *E-mail:* sales@jlcooper.com; service@jlcooper.com *Web Site:* www.jlcooper.com, pg 905

JLG Industries, One JLG Dr, McConnellsburg, PA 17233 *Tel:* 717-485-5161 *Toll Free Tel:* 877-JLG-LIFT (554-5438) *Fax:* 717-485-6417 *E-mail:* comments@jlg.com *Web Site:* www.jlg.com, pg 905

JMC Photo & Digital Services Inc, 10 Westport Ct, Bloomington, IL 61704-8233 *Tel:* 309-663-4677 *Fax:* 309-664-3973 *E-mail:* jmcpds@jmcpds.com *Web Site:* www.jmcpds.com, pg 905

JoeAudio, 10850 John Galt Blvd, Omaha, NE 68137 *Tel:* 402-341-9153 *Toll Free Tel:* 866-JOE-AUDIO (563-2834) *Web Site:* www.joeaudioproductions.com, pg 905

John McLean Media, 802 Newton, Penthouse 3, Seattle, WA 98109 *Tel:* 206-285-2603 *E-mail:* info@johnmcleanmedia.com *Web Site:* www.johnmcleanmedia.com, pg 905

Alan Johnson Recording, 5763 Park Plaza Ct, Indianapolis, IN 46220 *Tel:* 317-439-6521 *E-mail:* alan@alanjohnsonrecording.com *Web Site:* www.alanjohnsonrecording.com, pg 905

Johnson Systems Inc (JSI), 1923 Highfield Crescent SE, Calgary, AB T2G 5M1, Canada *Tel:* 403-287-8003 *Fax:* 403-287-9003 *E-mail:* info@johnsonsystems.com *Web Site:* www.johnsonsystems.com, pg 906

Pamela Johnston Voice Talent, 249 Eighth Ave, Cramerton, NC 28032 *Tel:* 703-371-7341 *Fax:* 703-997-8971 *Web Site:* www.pjvoicetalent.com, pg 906

Jointure for Community Adult Education Inc, Centre at Raritan, Suite B-11, 1124 US Hwy 202 S, Raritan, NJ 08869 *Tel:* 908-722-0233; 908-874-4852 *Fax:* 908-722-0388 *E-mail:* jcaeinc@aol.com *Web Site:* www.jointure.org, pg 906

JoLida Inc, 21310 Ridgecroft Dr, Brookeville, MD 20833 *Tel:* 301-953-2014 *Fax:* 301-498-0554 *E-mail:* jolidacorp@msn.com *Web Site:* www.jolida.com, pg 906

Jones Film Video, 916 W Sixth St, Little Rock, AR 72201 *Tel:* 501-372-1981 *Toll Free Tel:* 800-880-1981 *Fax:* 501-372-4286 *E-mail:* info@jonesfilmvideo.com *Web Site:* www.jonesfilmvideo.com, pg 906

Jordan Klein Film & Video (JKFV), 10197 SE 144 Place, Summerfield, FL 34491 *Tel:* 352-288-3999 *Fax:* 352-288-5538 *Web Site:* www.jordy.com, pg 906

Joseph Electronics, 6633 W Howard St, Niles, IL 60714 *Tel:* 847-588-3800 *Toll Free Tel:* 800-323-5925 *Fax:* 847-588-3300 *Toll Free Fax:* 800-446-8366 *E-mail:* sales@josephelectronics.com *Web Site:* www.josephelectronics.com, pg 906

Harry Joseph & Associates Inc, PO Box 20993, New York, NY 10025 *Tel:* 212-244-5900 *E-mail:* harry@hja.com *Web Site:* www.hja.com, pg 906

Josephson Engineering Inc, 329-A Ingalls St, Santa Cruz, CA 95060 *Tel:* 831-420-0888 *Fax:* 831-420-0890 *E-mail:* info@josephson.com *Web Site:* www.josephson.com, pg 906

Jossey-Bass, One Montgomery St, Suite 1200, San Francisco, CA 94104 *Tel:* 415-433-1740 *Fax:* 415-433-0499 *Web Site:* www.josseybass.com; www.wiley.com, pg 906

The Journal Award & SMPTE Journal Certificate of Merit, 3 Barker Ave, 5th fl, White Plains, NY 10601 *Tel:* 914-761-1100 *Fax:* 914-761-3115 *E-mail:* smpte@smpte.org *Web Site:* www.smpte.org, pg 1118

Joyce Media Inc, 3413 Soledad Canyon Rd, Acton, CA 93510 *Tel:* 661-269-1169 *Fax:* 661-269-2139 *E-mail:* help@joycemediainc.com *Web Site:* www.joycemediainc.com, pg 906

JPL, 471 JPL Wick Dr, Harrisburg, PA 17111-2504 *Tel:* 717-558-8048 *Toll Free Tel:* 800-421-7697 *Fax:* 717-558-8349 *E-mail:* jpl@jplcreative.com *Web Site:* www.jplcreative.com; www.facebook.com/jplcreative, pg 906

JR Media Services, 2501 W Burbank Blvd, Suite 200, Burbank, CA 91505 *Tel:* 818-557-0200 *Fax:* 818-557-0201 *E-mail:* info@jrmediaservices.com *Web Site:* www.jrmediaservices.com, pg 906

JRF Magnetic Sciences Inc, 249 Kennedy Rd, Greendell, NJ 07839 *Tel:* 973-579-5773 *Fax:* 973-579-6021 *E-mail:* jrf@jrfmagnetics.com *Web Site:* www.jrfmagnetics.com, pg 906

JSC Wire & Cable, 7861 Airport Hwy, Pennsauken, NJ 08109 *Tel:* 856-324-2929 *Toll Free Tel:* 800-572-9473 *Fax:* 973-694-8297 *E-mail:* sales@jscwire.com *Web Site:* www.jscwire.com, pg 906

JT Communications, 579 NE 44 Ave, Ocala, FL 34470-1421 *Tel:* 352-236-0744 *Fax:* 352-236-5130 *E-mail:* general_info@jtcomms.com *Web Site:* www.jtcomms.com, pg 906

Juice, 1648 Tenth St, Santa Monica, CA 90404 *Tel:* 310-460-7830 *Fax:* 310-460-7845 *Web Site:* www.juicewest.com, pg 906

Juice Goose, 7320 Ashcroft, Suite 104, Houston, TX 77081 *Tel:* 713-772-1404 *Fax:* 713-772-7360 *E-mail:* info@juicegoose.com *Web Site:* www.juicegoose.com, pg 906

JungleTV, 571 NW Mercantile Place, Port St Lucie, FL 34986 *Tel:* 772-370-0043 *E-mail:* info@jungletv.com *Web Site:* www.jungletv.com, pg 906

Juno Awards, 345 Adelaide St W, 2nd fl, Toronto, ON M5V 1R5, Canada *Tel:* 416-485-3135 *Toll Free Tel:* 888-440-JUNO (440-5866, CN only) *Fax:* 416-485-4978 *E-mail:* info@junoawards.ca; info@carasonline.ca; submissions@junoawards.ca *Web Site:* junoawards.ca; www.facebook.com/theJunoAwards, pg 1118

Jupiter Moon Productions, 53 Grand Haven Dr, Commack, NY 11725 *Tel:* 631-553-9750 *Web Site:* www.jupitermoonproductions.com, pg 907

Jupiter Systems, 31015 Huntwood Ave, Hayward, CA 94544 *Tel:* 510-675-1000 *Fax:* 510-675-1001 *E-mail:* sales@jupiter.com *Web Site:* www.jupiter.com, pg 907

Just Bulbs - The Light Bulb Store, 220 E 60 St, New York, NY 10022 *Tel:* 212-888-5707 *Fax:* 212-888-5704 *E-mail:* sales@justbulbsnyc.com *Web Site:* www.justbulbsnyc.com, pg 907

Juston Records, PO Box 362, New York, NY 10113-0362 *Tel:* 973-379-5538 *Fax:* 973-379-5538 *E-mail:* justonrecords@att.net, pg 907

JVC Professional Products Co, 1700 Valley Rd, Wayne, NJ 07470 *Tel:* 973-317-5000 *Toll Free Tel:* 800-582-5825; 800-247-3608; 800-252-5722 *Fax:* 973-317-5030 *Toll Free Fax:* 800-582-5825 (option 2) *E-mail:* proinfo@jvc.com *Web Site:* www.jvc.com, pg 907

JWP Inc, PO Box 14867, Fort Worth, TX 76117 *Tel:* 817-233-6462 *Fax:* 817-439-2353 *Web Site:* www.jwproductions.org, pg 907

K-SAR Video & DVD Productions, Center for Persons with Disabilities, Utah Univ Ctr of Excellence, 6800 Old Main Hill, Logan, UT 84322-6800 *Tel:* 435-797-1981 *Fax:* 435-797-3944 *Web Site:* www.cpdusa.org, pg 907

K2B2 Records, 1748 Roosevelt Ave, Los Angeles, CA 90006 *Web Site:* k2b2.com, pg 907

Ka Io Productions Inc, PO Box 5150, Hilo, HI 96720-1150 *Tel:* 808-959-3885 *Toll Free Tel:* 888-458-7538 *Fax:* 808-959-3885 *E-mail:* lava@volcanovideo.com *Web Site:* www.volcanovideo.com, pg 907

KABA Audio Productions, PO Box 5357, Petaluma, CA 94955 *Tel:* 707-765-9900 *E-mail:* info@kabaaudio.com *Web Site:* www.kabaaudio.com, pg 907

Kaboom Productions, 1465 Illinois St, San Francisco, CA 94107 *Tel:* 415-434-2666 *Fax:* 415-970-8548 *E-mail:* updates@kaboomproductions.com *Web Site:* kaboomproductions.com, pg 907

Kabuki, 63 rue Gaudet, Cap-Pele, NB E4N 1T8, Canada *Tel:* 506-577-6326 *Toll Free Tel:* 800-461-7625 *Fax:* 506-577-2875 *Toll Free Fax:* 800-461-4329 *E-mail:* info@kabuki.com *Web Site:* www.kabuki.com, pg 907

KAE Corp, 955 E 500 S, Salt Lake City, UT 84102 *Tel:* 801-238-2300 *Fax:* 801-238-3900 *E-mail:* kaecorp@xmission.com *Web Site:* www.kaecorp.com, pg 907

KahBang Festival, 84 Harlow St, Suite 1, Bangor, ME 04401 *E-mail:* info@kahbang.com; press@kahbang.com *Web Site:* www.kahbang.com, pg 1118

Kajo Co, 2081 E Bellerive Place, Chandler, AZ 85249-4131 *Tel:* 480-830-9798 *Fax:* 480-883-3022 *Web Site:* www.kajoco.com, pg 907

KAKE-TV, 1500 N West St, Wichita, KS 67203-1323 *Tel:* 316-943-4221; 316-946-1314 (sales) *Fax:* 316-943-5493 *Web Site:* kake.com, pg 907

Kaleidosound, 3883 Campolindo Dr, Moraga, CA 94556 *Tel:* 925-283-9901 *Web Site:* www.k-sound.com, pg 907

Kalglo Electronics Co Inc, 5911 Colony Dr, Bethlehem, PA 18017-9348 *Tel:* 610-837-0700 *Fax:* 610-837-7978 *E-mail:* kalglo@kalglo.com *Web Site:* www.kalglo.com, pg 907

Kamen Entertainment Group Inc, 200 E 94 St, New York, NY 10128 *Tel:* 212-575-4660 *Fax:* 212-575-4799 *E-mail:* kamen@kamen.com *Web Site:* www.kamen.com, pg 908

Kanab/Kane County Film Commission, Kane County Utah Off of Tourism, 78 S 100 E, Kanab, UT 84741 *Tel:* 435-644-5033 *Toll Free Tel:* 800-733-5263 *Fax:* 435-644-5923 *E-mail:* filmcomm@xpressweb.com *Web Site:* www.kaneutah.com, pg 1103

K&R All Media Productions Inc, 28533 Greenfield, Southfield, MI 48076 *Tel:* 248-557-8276 *Toll Free Tel:* 888-802-0420 *Web Site:* www.knr.net, pg 908

K&R Photo Digital, 538 Terry Lane, Fort Mitchell, KY 41017 *Tel:* 859-341-6998 *Fax:* 859-341-6987 *E-mail:* photodigitalpro@mac.com *Web Site:* www.krphotodigital.com, pg 908

K&R's Recording Studios Inc, 28533 Greenfield, Southfield, MI 48076 *Tel:* 248-557-8276 *E-mail:* recordav@knr.net *Web Site:* www.knr.net, pg 908

Kangaroo Cases, 4027 Main St, Dallas, TX 75226 *Tel:* 214-823-5264 *Toll Free Tel:* 800-890-1073 *Fax:* 214-824-1179 *E-mail:* info@kangaroocases.com *Web Site:* www.kangaroocases.com, pg 908

Kansas City FilmFest, 4741 Central, Suite 306, Kansas City, MO 64112 *Tel:* 816-286-4777 *E-mail:* contact@jubilee.org *Web Site:* kcfilmfest.org, pg 1118

Kansas Film Commission, 1000 SW Jackson St, Suite 100, Topeka, KS 66612-1354 *Tel:* 785-296-2178 *Fax:* 785-296-3490 *Web Site:* www.filmkansas.com, pg 1097

Kantola Productions LLC, 55 Sunnyside Ave, Mill Valley, CA 94941 *Tel:* 415-381-9363 *Toll Free Tel:* 800-280-1180 *Fax:* 415-381-9801 *E-mail:* kantola@kantola.com *Web Site:* www.kantola.com, pg 908

The David Kaplan Award, 40 W 45 St, New York, NY 10036 *Tel:* 212-626-9220 *Fax:* 212-626-9210 *Web Site:* www.opcofamerica.org, pg 1118

Richard Kaplan Productions, 455 N End Ave, Apt 1114, New York, NY 10282-1139 *Tel:* 212-787-0258 *Fax:* 212-787-0268 *E-mail:* richardkaplan33@gmail.com *Web Site:* www.richardkaplanproductions.com, pg 908

Kappa Map Group LLC, 112 E New York Ave, Deland, FL 32724 *Tel:* 386-873-3010 *Toll Free Tel:* 800-829-6277 (cust serv) *Fax:* 386-873-3011 *E-mail:* info@kappamapgroup.com *Web Site:* kappamapgroup.com, pg 908

Kappa optronics Inc, 825 S Primrose Ave, Suite I, Monrovia, CA 91016 *Tel:* 626-256-4343 *Fax:* 626-256-6484 *E-mail:* info@kappa-optronics.com *Web Site:* www.kappa-optronics.com, pg 908

Karol Media Inc, Hanover Industrial Estates, 375 Stewart Rd, Wilkes-Barre, PA 18703 *Tel:* 570-822-8899 *Toll Free Tel:* 800-526-4773 *Fax:* 570-822-8226 *E-mail:* sales@karolmedia.com *Web Site:* www.karolmedia.com, pg 908

Karst Productions Inc, 5779 NE County Rd 340, High Springs, FL 32643 *Tel:* 386-454-2376 *Fax:* 386-454-2369 *E-mail:* images@karstproductions.com *Web Site:* www.karstproductions.com, pg 908

Kart-A-Bag Manufacturing Inc, 510 Manhattan Rd, Joliet, IL 60433 *Tel:* 815-723-1940 *Toll Free Tel:* 800-423-9328 *Fax:* 815-723-2495 *E-mail:* bks@kart-a-bag.com *Web Site:* www.kart-a-bag.com, pg 908

KAS Music & Sound, 34-12 36 St, Astoria, NY 11106 *Tel:* 718-786-3400 *Fax:* 718-729-3007 *Web Site:* www.kasmusic.com, pg 908

Kavanagh Productions Inc, 32 Broadway, Suite 1711-12, New York, NY 10004 *Tel:* 212-480-0065 *Fax:* 212-480-0149 *E-mail:* mail@kavanaghproductions.com *Web Site:* www.kavanaghproductions.com, pg 908

Kavich Reynolds Productions Inc, 6381 Hollywood Blvd, Suite 580, Hollywood, CA 90028 *Tel:* 323-466-2490 *Fax:* 323-466-3655 *E-mail:* info@kavichreynolds.com *Web Site:* www.kavichreynolds.com, pg 908

Kay Industries Inc, 227 N Dixie Way, South Bend, IN 46637 *Tel:* 574-236-6220 *Toll Free Tel:* 800-348-5257 *Fax:* 574-289-5932 *E-mail:* phasemaster@kayind.com; techsupp@kayind.com *Web Site:* www.kayind.com, pg 908

KB Systems, 10407 62 Place W, Mukilteo, WA 98275 *Tel:* 425-355-8740 *E-mail:* kbsystem@kbsystem.com *Web Site:* www.kbsystem.com, pg 908

KCFW Television, 401 First Ave E, Kalispell, MT 59901 *Tel:* 406-755-5239 *Fax:* 406-752-8002 *E-mail:* news@kcfw.com *Web Site:* www.nbcmontana.com; www.kcfw.com, pg 908

KD Kanopy Inc, 1921 E 68 Ave, Denver, CO 80229 *Tel:* 303-650-1310 *Toll Free Tel:* 800-432-4435 *Fax:* 303-650-5211 *E-mail:* sales@kdkanopy.com *Web Site:* www.kdkanopy.com, pg 908

KDM Electronics Inc, 55 Mills Rd, Unit 3, Ajax, ON L1S 2H2, Canada *Tel:* 416-439-7158 *Toll Free Tel:* 800-567-6282 *Fax:* 416-439-7232 *E-mail:* kdm@octasound.com *Web Site:* www.octasound.com, pg 908

KEF Media, 1161 Concord Rd, Smyrna, GA 30080 *Tel:* 404-605-0009 *Toll Free Tel:* 866-219-2477 *Fax:* 404-605-0639 *Web Site:* www.kefmedia.com, pg 908

Kelmscott Communications, 1665 Mallette Rd, Aurora, IL 60505-1354 *Tel:* 630-898-0800 *Fax:* 630-898-2183 *Web Site:* kelmscottcommunications.com, pg 909

Ken-A-Vision Manufacturing Co Inc, 5615 Raytown Rd, Kansas City, MO 64133 *Tel:* 816-353-4787 *Toll Free Tel:* 800-501-7366; 800-627-1953 (cust serv) *Fax:* 816-358-5072 *E-mail:* info@ken-a-vision.com *Web Site:* www.ken-a-vision.com, pg 909

Ken-Del Productions Inc, 1500 First State Blvd, Wilmington, DE 19804-3596 *Tel:* 302-999-1111; 302-999-1110; 302-999-1164 *Toll Free Tel:* 800-249-1110 *Fax:* 302-999-1656 *E-mail:* info@ken-del.com *Web Site:* www.ken-del.com, pg 909

Ken-Del Studios, 1500 First State Blvd, Wilmington, DE 19804-3596 *Tel:* 302-999-1111 *Toll Free Tel:* 800-249-1110 *Fax:* 302-999-1656 *E-mail:* info@ken-del.com *Web Site:* www.ken-del.com, pg 909

Kendall/Hunt Publishing Co, 4050 Westmark Dr, Dubuque, IA 52002 *Tel:* 563-589-1000 *Toll Free Tel:* 800-228-0810 *Fax:* 563-589-1237 *Toll Free Fax:* 800-772-9165 *E-mail:* orders@kendallhunt.com *Web Site:* www.kendallhunt.com, pg 909

Kenexa, 650 E Swedesford Rd, 2nd fl, Wayne, PA 19087 *Tel:* 407-548-1444 *Fax:* 610-971-9181 *E-mail:* kenexa_learn_sales@kenexa.com *Web Site:* www.outstart.com, pg 909

Keng Seng Enterprises Inc, 4000 Rue St Ambroise, Suite 103, Montreal, QC H4C 2C7, Canada *Tel:* 514-939-3971 *Fax:* 514-989-1922 *E-mail:* canada@kengseng.com *Web Site:* www.kengseng.com, pg 909

Robert F Kennedy Journalism Awards, 1300 19 St NW, Suite 750, Washington, DC 20036 *Tel:* 202-463-7575 *E-mail:* info@rfkcenter.org *Web Site:* www.rfkcenter.org, pg 1118

Kensington Falls Animation, 1680 Hillsdale Ave, Ambridge, PA 15003 *Tel:* 724-266-0329 *Fax:* 724-266-4016 *E-mail:* kensingtonfalls@aol.com *Web Site:* kensingtonfalls.com, pg 909

Kensington Technology Group, 333 Twin Dolphin Dr, 6th fl, Redwood Shores, CA 94065 *Tel:* 650-572-2700 *Toll Free Tel:* 800-235-6708 (cust serv); 800-535-4242 (tech support) *Fax:* 650-267-2800 *E-mail:* sales@kensington.com *Web Site:* www.kensington.com, pg 909

Norman Kent Productions, PO Box 1749, Flagler Beach, FL 32136 *Tel:* 386-446-0505 *Web Site:* www.normankent.com, pg 909

Kentucky Film Office, 2200 Capital Plaza Tower, 500 Mero St, Frankfort, KY 40601 *Tel:* 502-564-3456 *Toll Free Tel:* 800-345-6591 *Fax:* 502-564-5695 *E-mail:* kentucky.filmoffice@ky.gov *Web Site:* filmoffice.ky.gov, pg 1098

Kentucky Grip & Lighting, 1340 Connor Station Rd, Simpsonville, KY 40067 *Tel:* 502-548-5833 *E-mail:* sstaley@iglou.com *Web Site:* www.kentuckyvideo.net; www.kentuckygrip.com, pg 909

The Kenwood Group, 75 Varney Place, San Francisco, CA 94107 *Tel:* 415-957-5333 *Fax:* 415-957-5311 *E-mail:* newbusiness@kenwoodgroup.com *Web Site:* www.kenwoodgroup.com, pg 909

Kenyon Laboratories LLC, 12 Scovil Rd, Higganum, CT 06441 *Tel:* 860-345-2097 *Toll Free Tel:* 800-253-4681 *Fax:* 860-345-8652 *E-mail:* kenyonlabs@comcast.net *Web Site:* www.ken-lab.com, pg 909

Kern County Film Commission, 2101 Oak St, Bakersfield, CA 93301 *Tel:* 661-868-KERN (868-5376) *Toll Free Tel:* 800-500-KERN (500-5376) *Fax:* 661-861-2017 *E-mail:* kerninfo@co.kern.ca.us *Web Site:* www.filmkern.com, pg 1092

Kerrigan Productions Inc, 3877 Draper Ave, Montreal, QC H4A 2N9, Canada *Tel:* 514-486-8456 *Fax:* 514-488-4550 *Web Site:* www.kerrigan.ca, pg 910

Kerrville Convention & Visitors Bureau, 2108 Sidney Baker St, Kerrville, TX 78028 *Tel:* 830-792-3535 *Toll Free Tel:* 800-221-7958 *Fax:* 830-792-3230 *E-mail:* info@kerrvilletexascvb.com; kerrcvb@ktc.com *Web Site:* www.kerrvilletexascvb.com, pg 1103

Keslow Camera Inc, 11260 Playa Ct, Culver City, CA 90230 *Tel:* 310-636-4600 *Fax:* 310-915-5335 *E-mail:* info@keslowcamera.com *Web Site:* www.keslowcamera.com, pg 910

KESSPRO Studios, 435 S Molino St, Los Angeles, CA 90013 *Tel:* 213-253-2623 *Fax:* 213-253-2629 *E-mail:* info@kessprostudios.com *Web Site:* www.kessprostudios.com, pg 910

KET The Kentucky Network, 600 Cooper Dr, Lexington, KY 40502 *Tel:* 859-258-7000 *Toll Free Tel:* 800-432-0951 *Fax:* 859-258-7396 *E-mail:* adulted@ket.org *Web Site:* www.ket.org, pg 910

Ketchum Pleon Change, 1285 Avenue of the Americas, 3rd fl, New York, NY 10019 *Tel:* 646-935-3900 *Web Site:* www.ketchum.com/change, pg 910

Key Digital Systems, 521 E Third St, Mount Vernon, NY 10553 *Tel:* 914-667-9700 *Fax:* 914-668-8666 *E-mail:* info@keydigital.com *Web Site:* www.keydigital.com, pg 910

Key of David Publications, PO Box 153, Merion, PA 19066 *Tel:* 610-896-1970 *Fax:* 610-896-1970 *Web Site:* www.keyofdavidpublications.org, pg 910

The Keyboard Workshop, PO Box 700, Medford, OR 97501 *Tel:* 541-664-7052 *Fax:* 541-664-7052 *Web Site:* www.playpiano.com, pg 910

Keystone Entertainment, 23410 Civic Ctr Way, Suite E-9, Malibu, CA 90265 *Tel:* 310-317-4883 *Fax:* 310-317-4903 *E-mail:* films@keypics.com *Web Site:* www.keypics.com, pg 910

Keystone View, 2200 Dickerson Rd, Reno, NV 89503 *Tel:* 775-324-2799; 510-931-7747 *Toll Free Tel:* 866-574-6360 *Fax:* 775-324-5375 *Toll Free Fax:* 866-574-6395 *E-mail:* sales@keystoneview.com *Web Site:* www.keystoneview.com, pg 910

Keywest Technology Inc, 14563 W 96 Terr, Lenexa, KS 66215 *Tel:* 913-492-4666 *Toll Free Tel:* 800-331-2019 *Fax:* 913-322-1864 *E-mail:* info@keywesttechnology.com; sales@keywesttechnology.com *Web Site:* www.keywesttechnology.com, pg 910

KFOR-TV, 444 E Britton Rd, Oklahoma City, OK 73114 *Tel:* 405-424-4444 *Fax:* 405-478-6337 *Web Site:* www.kfor.com, pg 910

KHNL/KGMB, 420 Waiakamilo Rd, Suite 205, Honolulu, HI 96817 *Tel:* 808-847-3246 *Fax:* 808-845-3616 *E-mail:* info8@khnl.com; news8@khnl.com *Web Site:* www.hawaiinewsnow.com, pg 910

KickedUp Media Group Inc, 2 Amherst Dr, Hastings-on-Hudson, NY 10706 *Tel:* 914-693-KICK (693-5425) *E-mail:* info@kickedupmediagroup.com *Web Site:* www.kickedupmediagroup.com, pg 910

KidFilm®, 6116 N Central Expwy, Suite 105, Dallas, TX 75206 *Tel:* 214-821-6300; 214-821-FILM (821-3456) *Fax:* 214-821-6364 *E-mail:* usafilmfestival@aol.com *Web Site:* www.usafilmfestival.com, pg 1118

Kids on the Block Inc, 9 Westminster Shopping Ctr, Suite 344, Westminster, MD 21157 *Tel:* 443-297-9564 *Toll Free Tel:* 800-368-KIDS (368-5437) *Fax:* 410-290-9358 *E-mail:* kob@kotb.com *Web Site:* www.kotb.com, pg 910

KidsEye™ International Film Festival, 83 Park St, Suite 1, Providence, RI 02903 *Tel:* 401-861-4445 *Fax:* 401-490-6735 *E-mail:* info@film-festival.org *Web Site:* film-festival.org/enteraskidseye.php, pg 1118

Killer Tracks, 2110 Colorado Ave, Suite 110, Santa Monica, CA 90404 *Tel:* 310-865-4455 *Toll Free Tel:* 800-4-KILLER (454-5537) *Fax:* 310-865-4470 *Toll Free Fax:* 800-787-2257 *E-mail:* info@killertracks.com; sales@killertracks.com *Web Site:* www.killertracks.com, pg 910

Kimbo Educational, 10 N Third Ave, Long Branch, NJ 07740 *Tel:* 732-229-4949 *Toll Free Tel:* 800-631-2187 *Fax:* 732-870-3340 *E-mail:* kimboed@aol.com *Web Site:* www.kimboed.com, pg 910

Kimono Surf Studios, 401 Logan Ave, Suite 109, Toronto, ON M4M 1S1, Canada *Tel:* 416-405-8111 *Fax:* 416-405-8751 *E-mail:* studio@kimonosurf.com *Web Site:* www.kimonosurf.com, pg 911

Kinetic Arts, 306 Gold St, No 5-I, Brooklyn, NY 11201 *Tel:* 917-439-4008 *E-mail:* info@kineticarts.tv *Web Site:* www.kineticarts.tv, pg 911

Kinetic Corp, 200 Distillery Commons, Suite 200, Louisville, KY 40206-1990 *Tel:* 502-719-9500 *Fax:* 502-719-9509 *E-mail:* info@thetechnologyagency.com *Web Site:* kinetic.thetechnologyagency.com, pg 911

Kineticvideo.com, 16 Munition St, Toronto, ON M5A 1G7, Canada *Tel:* 416-538-6613 *Toll Free Tel:* 800-263-6910 (CN only) *Fax:* 416-538-9984 *E-mail:* info@kineticvideo.com *Web Site:* www.kineticvideo.com, pg 911

Kinetronics Corp, 1459 Tallevast Rd, Sarasota, FL 34243 *Tel:* 941-951-2432 *Toll Free Tel:* 800-624-3204 (US & CN) *Fax:* 941-955-5992 *E-mail:* info@kinetronics.com; order@kinetronics.com *Web Site:* www.kinetronics.com, pg 911

Kingsway Motion Picture Ltd, 200 Evans Ave, Unit 4, Toronto, ON M8Z 1J7, Canada *Tel:* 416-463-4345 *Fax:* 416-469-2609 *E-mail:* info@kingswaycanada.com *Web Site:* kingswaycanada.com, pg 911

Kingswood Productions, 810 12 Ave S, Nashville, TN 37203 *Toll Free Tel:* 800-476-7766 *E-mail:* info@kingswoodproductions.com *Web Site:* kingswoodproductions.com, pg 911

Kino Flo Lighting Systems, 2840 N Hollywood Way, Burbank, CA 91505 *Tel:* 818-767-6528 *Fax:* 818-252-0290 (rental); 818-767-7517 (sales) *E-mail:* sales@kinoflo.com *Web Site:* www.kinoflo.com, pg 911

Kino International Corp, 333 W 39 St, Suite 503, New York, NY 10018 *Tel:* 212-629-6880 *Toll Free Tel:* 800-562-3330 *Fax:* 212-714-0871 *E-mail:* contact@kino.com *Web Site:* www.kinolorber.com, pg 911

Kino Mountain Productions LLC, 307 S Salem St, No 311, Apex, NC 27502 *Tel:* 919-210-1379 *Web Site:* www.kinomountain.com, pg 911

KION-TV, 1550 Moffett St, Salinas, CA 93905 *Tel:* 831-784-1702; 831-422-3500 *Fax:* 831-757-1766 *Web Site:* www.kionrightnow.com, pg 911

Kipp Visual Systems Inc, 3600 Clipper Mill Rd, Suite 105, Baltimore, MD 21211 *Tel:* 410-235-9900 *Toll Free Tel:* 800-278-6912 *Fax:* 410-235-7122 *Web Site:* kippvisual.com, pg 911

Kirkwood Community College, Linn Hall, Rm 102, 6301 Kirkwood Blvd SW, Cedar Rapids, IA 52406 *Tel:* 319-398-5517 *Toll Free Tel:* 800-363-2220 *Fax:* 319-398-5413 *E-mail:* info@kirkwood.edu *Web Site:* www.kirkwood.edu, pg 911

The Kitchen, 4119 W Burbank Blvd, Burbank, CA 91505 *Tel:* 818-306-5300 *Fax:* 305-415-6201 *E-mail:* info@thekitchen.tv *Web Site:* www.thekitchen.tv, pg 911

Kits & Expendables, 45-27 37 St, Long Island, NY 11101 *Tel:* 718-482-1824; 718-482-1993; 917-842-8394 (emergencies after hrs) *Fax:* 718-482-1853 *E-mail:* orders@kitsandexpendables.com *Web Site:* www.kitsandexpendables.com, pg 911

KJfilms LLC, 33 Serra Dr, Middletown, CT 06457 *Tel:* 860-894-2363; 860-995-5106 (cell) *E-mail:* info@kjfilms.com *Web Site:* www.kjfilms.com, pg 911

KK Office Solutions Inc, 3910 N Bridgeport Circle, Wichita, KS 67219 *Tel:* 316-944-5464 *Toll Free Tel:* 800-362-1317 *Fax:* 316-944-0605 *Toll Free Fax:* 888-319-9600 *E-mail:* info@kkofficesolutions.com *Web Site:* kkosinc.com, pg 911

Klipsch Audio Technologies, 3502 Woodview Trace, Suite 200, Indianapolis, IN 46268 *Tel:* 317-860-8100 *Toll Free Tel:* 877-412-7467 (orders); 800-544-1482 *Fax:* 317-860-9170 (sales & mktg) *E-mail:* support@klipsch.com *Web Site:* www.klipsch.com, pg 912

Kloss Studios Co, 1441 Jericho Rd, Abington, PA 19001 *Tel:* 215-885-1203 *Toll Free Tel:* 800-885-1203 (PA only) *E-mail:* kloss@kloss-studios.com *Web Site:* kloss-studios.com, pg 912

Klutz, 450 Lambert Ave, Palo Alto, CA 94306 *Tel:* 650-857-0888 *Toll Free Tel:* 800-737-4123 *Fax:* 650-857-9110 *E-mail:* thefolks@klutz.com *Web Site:* www.klutz.com, pg 912

Knowledge Unlimited Inc, 2320 Pleasant View, Middleton, WI 53562 *Tel:* 608-661-5666 *Toll Free Tel:* 800-356-2303 *Fax:* 608-836-6684 *Toll Free Fax:* 800-618-1570 *E-mail:* csis@newscurrents.com *Web Site:* www.knowledgeunlimited.com, pg 912

Knowles Video Inc (KVI), 5450 Buck Lake Rd, Tallahassee, FL 32317 *Tel:* 850-878-2298 *E-mail:* info@knowlesvideo.com *Web Site:* www.knowlesvideo.com, pg 912

Knox Video Technologies, 15875 Crabbs Branch Way, Suite A, Rockville, MD 20855 *Tel:* 301-840-5805 *Fax:* 301-840-2946 *E-mail:* sales@knoxvideo.com *Web Site:* www.knoxvideo.com, pg 912

KO Creative, 465 S Beverly Dr, 3rd fl, Beverly Hills, CA 90212 *Tel:* 310-288-3820 *Web Site:* www.ko-creative.com, pg 912

Kodak Canada Inc, 4225 Kincaid St, Burnaby, BC V5G 4P5, Canada *Tel:* 604-320-1777 *Toll Free Tel:* 800-465-6325 *Fax:* 604-570-3501 *Web Site:* www.kodak.ca, pg 912

Koerner Camera Systems, 2323 N Williams Ave, Portland, OR 97227 *Tel:* 503-274-6533 *Toll Free Tel:* 800-377-1132 *Fax:* 503-274-5446 *E-mail:* michael@koernercamera.com *Web Site:* www.koernercamera.com, pg 912

Kofax Image Products, 15211 Laguna Canyon Rd, Irvine, CA 92618-3603 *Tel:* 949-727-1733 *Fax:* 949-727-3144 *E-mail:* info@kofax.com *Web Site:* www.kofax.com, pg 912

KOH Design Inc, 540 Barnum Ave, Bridgeport, CT 06608 *Tel:* 203-336-1334 *Fax:* 203-335-9361 *E-mail:* info@kohdesign.com *Web Site:* www.kohdesign.com, pg 913

Konica Minolta Business Solutions, 100 Williams Dr, Ramsey, NJ 07446 *Tel:* 201-825-4000 *Fax:* 201-825-7567 *Web Site:* kmbs.konicaminolta.us, pg 913

Kontron America, 14118 Stowe Dr, Poway, CA 92064-7147 *Tel:* 858-677-0877 *Toll Free Tel:* 888-294-4558; 800-480-0044 (cust serv & tech support) *Fax:* 858-677-0898 *E-mail:* sales@us.kontron.com *Web Site:* www.kontron.com, pg 913

KOOL FM Radio, 840 N Central Ave, Phoenix, AZ 85004 *Tel:* 602-452-1000; 602-260-9494 (request line) *Fax:* 602-440-6530 *Web Site:* www.koolradio.com, pg 913

Kool Music, 9 Hector Ave, Toronto, ON M6G 3G2, Canada *Tel:* 416-533-3520 *E-mail:* host@koolmusic.com *Web Site:* www.koolmusic.com, pg 913

Kopp Glass, 2108 Palmer St, Pittsburgh, PA 15218 *Tel:* 412-271-0190 *Fax:* 412-271-4103 *E-mail:* sales@koppglass.com *Web Site:* www.koppglass.com, pg 913

Korg USA Inc, 316 S Service Rd, Melville, NY 11747 *Tel:* 631-390-6500; 631-390-8737 *Fax:* 631-390-6501 *Web Site:* www.korgusa.com, pg 913

Koss Corp, 4129 N Port Washington Ave, Milwaukee, WI 53212 *Tel:* 414-964-5000 *Toll Free Tel:* 800-USA-KOSS (872-5677) *Fax:* 414-964-8615 *E-mail:* customersupport@koss.com *Web Site:* www.koss.com, pg 913

Kostov Productions, Whispering Wind Ranch, 16320 High Bridge Rd, Monroe, WA 98272 *Tel:* 206-755-0050 *E-mail:* info@kostov.com *Web Site:* www.kostov.com, pg 913

Kozmic Lazer Show LLC, PO Box 140197, Nashville, TN 37214-0197 *Tel:* 615-391-3226 *Toll Free Tel:* 800-MRLASER (675-2737) *Fax:* 615-391-3265 *E-mail:* mrlaser800@aol.com *Web Site:* www.kozmiclazershow.com, pg 913

KPBS TV FM-San Diego, 5200 Campanille Dr, San Diego, CA 92182 *Tel:* 619-594-1515; 619-265-6438 (newsroom) *Toll Free Tel:* 888-399-5727 *Fax:* 619-594-3812 *Web Site:* www.kpbs.org, pg 913

KPDX-TV Production Center, 14975 NW Greenbrier Pkwy, Beaverton, OR 97006-5731 *Tel:* 503-906-1249 *Fax:* 503-548-6920 *E-mail:* ezone@kpdx.com; fox12news@kptv.com *Web Site:* www.kptv.com; www.kpdx.com, pg 913

KPHO-TV5, 4016 N Black Canyon Hwy, Phoenix, AZ 85017 *Tel:* 602-264-1000 *Fax:* 602-274-1596 *E-mail:* cbs5news@kpho.com *Web Site:* www.news5.tv, pg 913

KPLR-TV, 2250 Ball Dr, St Louis, MO 63146 *Tel:* 314-213-2222; 314-213-7831 (newsroom) *E-mail:* kplradmin@tribune.com *Web Site:* www.cw11tv.com; www.kplr11.com, pg 913

Kramer Communications Video Production, 12504 Quarterhorse Dr, Bowie, MD 20720 *Tel:* 301-352-3042 *Fax:* 301-352-3559 *E-mail:* kcam@his.com *Web Site:* www.kramercommunications.tv, pg 913

Kramer Electronics USA Inc, 6 Rte 173 W, Clinton, NJ 08809 *Tel:* 908-735-0018 *Toll Free Tel:* 888-275-6311 *Fax:* 908-735-0515 *E-mail:* info@kramerus.com *Web Site:* www.kramerus.com, pg 913

Joan Kramer & Associates Inc, 10490 Wilshire Blvd, Suite 1701, Los Angeles, CA 90024 *Tel:* 310-446-1866 *Fax:* 310-446-1856 *E-mail:* ekeeeek@earthlink.net, pg 913

Krishnamurti Foundation of America, 1070 McAndrew Rd, Ojai, CA 93023 *Tel:* 805-646-2726 (ext 10) *Fax:* 805-646-6674 *E-mail:* kfa@kfa.org *Web Site:* www.kfa.org, pg 913

KRK Systems, c/o Gibson Pro Audio, 309 Plus Park Blvd, Nashville, TN 37217 *Toll Free Tel:* 800-444-2799 *E-mail:* service@gibson.com *Web Site:* www.krksys.com, pg 914

Kroy LLC, 3830 Kelley Ave, Cleveland, OH 44114 *Tel:* 216-426-5600 *Toll Free Tel:* 888-888-5769 (cust serv) *Fax:* 216-426-5601 *Web Site:* www.kroy.com, pg 914

KTHV Television, a Gannett Company, 720 Izard St, Little Rock, AR 72201 *Tel:* 501-376-1111 *Fax:* 501-376-9928 (sales); 501-376-3324 (admin); 501-376-1645 (news) *Web Site:* www.todaysthv.com, pg 914

KTVB-TV, 5407 Fairview Ave, Boise, ID 83706 *Tel:* 208-375-7277 *Toll Free Tel:* 800-559-7277 *Fax:* 208-378-1762; 208-375-7770 (news fax) *E-mail:* info@ktvb.com; ktvbnews@ktvb.com *Web Site:* www.ktvb.com, pg 914

KTVU-Retail Services, 2 Jack London Sq, Oakland, CA 94607 *Tel:* 510-834-1212 *Web Site:* www.ktvu.com, pg 914

K2 Productions, 4214 Shoal Creek Dr, Greensboro, NC 27410 *Tel:* 336-664-8036 *E-mail:* info@k2production.com *Web Site:* www.k2production.com, pg 914

Kuhn Productions LLC, 321 E Walnut St, Suite 340, Des Moines, IA 50309 *Tel:* 515-244-1618, pg 914

Kultur International Films Ltd Inc, 195 Hwy 36, West Long Branch, NJ 07764 *Tel:* 732-229-2343 *Toll Free Tel:* 800-573-3782 *Toll Free Fax:* 866-205-2744 *E-mail:* support@kultur.com *Web Site:* www.kultur.com, pg 914

KUSM TV, Visual Communications Bldg 183, Montana State University, Bozeman, MT 59717 *Tel:* 406-994-3437 *Toll Free Tel:* 866-832-0829 *Fax:* 406-994-6545 *E-mail:* kusm@montanapbs.org *Web Site:* www.montanapbs.org, pg 914

KVAL, 4575 Blanton Rd, Eugene, OR 97405 *Tel:* 541-342-4961 *Fax:* 541-342-2635 *E-mail:* kvalnews@kval.com *Web Site:* www.kval.com, pg 914

KVIE-Channel 6, 2030 W El Camino Ave, Sacramento, CA 95833 *Tel:* 916-929-5843 *Toll Free Tel:* 800-347-5843 *Fax:* 916-929-7215 *E-mail:* member@kvie.org *Web Site:* www.kvie.org, pg 914

KVL Audio Visual Services Inc, 466 Saw Mill River Rd, Ardsley, NY 10502-2112 *Tel:* 914-479-3300 *Toll Free Tel:* 800-862-3210 *Fax:* 914-479-3395 *E-mail:* info@kvlav.com *Web Site:* www.kvlav.com, pg 914

L A Bruell Inc, 30 W 26 St, New York, NY 10010 *Tel:* 646-336-5977 *Fax:* 646-336-8317 *Web Site:* www.labruell.com, pg 914

L A Management Co LLC, 8131 Bay Pointe Dr, Denver, NC 28037 *Tel:* 704-560-6274 *Toll Free Tel:* 800-651-7818 *Fax:* 704-973-7968 *E-mail:* info@managementco.com *Web Site:* lamanagementco.com, pg 914

L Acoustics US, 2201 Celsius Ave, Unit E, Oxnard, CA 93030 *Tel:* 805-604-0577 *Fax:* 805-604-0858 *E-mail:* info@l-acoustics-us.com *Web Site:* www.l-acoustics.com, pg 914

L'AIR International, 117 Vacek St, Fort Worth, TX 76107 *Tel:* 817-237-9390 *Toll Free Tel:* 844-243-8574 *Fax:* 817-237-9407 *E-mail:* info@lairfloors.com *Web Site:* www.lairfloors.com, pg 914

L & S Video Inc, 45 Stornowaye, Chappaqua, NY 10514 *Tel:* 914-238-9366 *Fax:* 914-238-6324 *E-mail:* videopaint2@msn.com *Web Site:* www.landsvideo.com, pg 914

L R Light & Sound, 5317 54 St, Drayton Valley, AB T7A 1R6, Canada *Tel:* 780-542-4242; 780-542-9363 *Fax:* 780-542-4283 *E-mail:* lrlightandsound@yahoo.ca *Web Site:* www.lrlightandsound.ca, pg 915

L-3 ESSCO, 90 Nemco Way, Ayer, MA 01432 *Tel:* 978-568-5100 *Fax:* 978-772-7581 *Web Site:* www2.l-3com.com/essco/wolfcoach, pg 915

L-3 GCS, 7640 Omnitech Place, Victor, NY 14564 *Tel:* 585-742-9100 *Toll Free Tel:* 888-SAT1USA (728-1872); 877-247-1207 (tech support) *Fax:* 585-742-1914 *E-mail:* gcs.info@l-3com.com *Web Site:* www.globalcoms.com, pg 915

L-3 Integrated Optical Systems, 4040 Lakeside Dr, Richmond, CA 94806-1963 *Tel:* 510-222-8110 *Fax:* 510-223-4534 *E-mail:* sales@asphere.com *Web Site:* www.asphere.com, pg 915

LA Castle Studios, 154 S Victory Blvd, Burbank, CA 91502 *Tel:* 818-861-7317 *Web Site:* lacastlestudios.com, pg 915

LA Femme International Film Festival, 324 S Beverly Dr, Suite 436, Beverly Hills, CA 90212 *Tel:* 310-441-1645 *Fax:* 310-475-8213 *Web Site:* www.lafemme.org, pg 1118

La Paloma Films, 719 Dorr Edson Rd, Suite 1, Oneonta, NY 13820 *Tel:* 607-287-5175 *E-mail:* lapalomafilms@yahoo.com *Web Site:* www.lapalomafilms.net, pg 915

LA Sound Co, 9001 Canoga Ave, Canoga Park, CA 91304 *Tel:* 818-772-9200 *Fax:* 818-772-9977 *E-mail:* rentals@lasoundco.com; sales@lasoundco.com *Web Site:* lasoundco.com, pg 915

Labor Saving Devices Inc, 5678 Eudora St, Commerce City, CO 80022-3809 *Tel:* 303-287-2121 *Toll Free Tel:* 800-648-4714 *Fax:* 303-287-9044 *E-mail:* info@lsdinc.com *Web Site:* www.lsdinc.com, pg 915

Labrecque Creative Sound, 2825 Main St, Becket, MA 01223, pg 915

Lacquer-Mat Inc, 13035 Wayne Rd, Livonia, MI 48150 *Toll Free Tel:* 800-942-2223 (cust serv) *Fax:* 734-422-4205 (orders) *Web Site:* www.lacquer-mat.com, pg 915

Ladyslipper Inc, PO Box 14, Cedar Grove, NC 27231 *Tel:* 919-245-3737 *E-mail:* info@ladyslipper.org *Web Site:* www.ladyslipper.org, pg 915

Lagoon Video, 3323 Marble Front Rd, Caldwell, ID 83605 *Tel:* 208-455-3457 *Fax:* 208-453-1136 *E-mail:* kapsm@aol.com, pg 915

Laird Digital Cinema, One Tower Dr, Saugerties, NY 12477 *Tel:* 845-339-9555 *Toll Free Tel:* 800-898-0759 *Fax:* 845-339-0231 *E-mail:* info@lairddigitalcinema.com; sales@lairddigitalcinema.com *Web Site:* www.lairddigitalcinema.com, pg 915

Lake Tahoe Visitors Authority (LTVA), 169 Hwy 50, Stateline, NV 89449 *Tel:* 775-588-5900 *Toll Free Tel:* 800-288-2463 (reservations) *Fax:* 775-588-1941 *E-mail:* info@ltva.org *Web Site:* ltva.org, pg 1100

Lakeshore Productions, 8625 Indiana Place, Merriville, IN 46410 *Tel:* 219-756-5656 *Toll Free Tel:* 888-694-5253 *Fax:* 219-755-4312 *Web Site:* lakeshoreproduction.com, pg 915

Lamb & Lion Ministries, PO Box 919, McKinney, TX 75070 *Tel:* 972-736-3567 *Toll Free Tel:* 800-705-8316 (sales) *E-mail:* lamblion@lamblion.com *Web Site:* www.lamblion.com, pg 915

Laminex Inc, 4209 Pleasant Rd, Fort Mill, SC 29708 *Tel:* 704-679-4170 *Toll Free Tel:* 800-438-8850 *Fax:* 704-679-8453 *E-mail:* info@laminex.com *Web Site:* www.laminex.com, pg 915

Landmark Media Inc, 3450 Slade Run Dr, Falls Church, VA 22042 *Tel:* 703-241-2030 *Toll Free Tel:* 800-342-4336 *Fax:* 703-536-9540 *E-mail:* info@landmarkmedia.com; landmrkmed@aol.com *Web Site:* www.landmarkmedia.com, pg 915

L&P Media, 255 River St, Troy, NY 12180 *Tel:* 518-880-0300 *Toll Free Tel:* 800-201-5949 *Fax:* 518-880-0390 *E-mail:* information@lpmedia.net *Web Site:* www.light-power.com, pg 915

Langie Audio Visual Systems, Piano Works Mall, 349 W Commercial St, East Rochester, NY 14445 *Tel:* 585-385-4880 *Fax:* 585-385-4882 *E-mail:* info@langieav.com; sales@langieav.com; rental@langieav.com *Web Site:* www.langieav.com, pg 915

Language Plus Inc, 4110 Rio Bravo, Suite 202, El Paso, TX 79902 *Tel:* 915-544-8600 *Fax:* 915-544-8640 *E-mail:* speak@languageplus.com *Web Site:* www.languageplus.com, pg 916

LANGUAGE/30™, 1222 S Amphlett Blvd, San Mateo, CA 94403 *Tel:* 650-872-7100 *Fax:* 650-872-7133 *Web Site:* www.lang30.com, pg 916

Lank/Beach Productions Inc, 341 Wardlaw Ave, Winnipeg, MB R3L 0L5, Canada *Tel:* 204-452-9422 *E-mail:* info@lankbeach.com *Web Site:* www.lankbeach.com, pg 916

Lannan Foundation, 313 Read St, Santa Fe, NM 87501-2628 *Tel:* 505-986-8160 *Fax:* 505-986-8195 *E-mail:* info@lannan.org *Web Site:* www.lannan.org, pg 916

Larrabee Sound Studio, 4162 Lankershim Blvd, North Hollywood, CA 91602 *Tel:* 818-753-0717 *Fax:* 818-753-8046 *E-mail:* info@larrabeestudios.com *Web Site:* www.larrabeestudios.com, pg 916

Las Cruces Film Commission, 700 N Main St, Las Cruces, NM 88001 *Tel:* 575-541-2271 *E-mail:* econdev@las-cruces.org *Web Site:* www.las-cruces-film.org, pg 1100

Laser Fantasy/HECK Industries/Photon Manufacturing, 4228 159 Ave SE, Bellevue, WA 98006 *Tel:* 425-890-6026 (software & creative support); 425-214-0771 (hardware & tech support) *Fax:* 425-296-4255 *E-mail:* info@heckindustries.com; info@photonmanufacturing.com *Web Site:* www.heckindustries.com; www.photonmanufacturing.com, pg 916

Laser Magic Productions, 722 N Orlando Ave, No 207, Los Angeles, CA 90069 *Tel:* 323-951-9392 *Web Site:* www.laser-magic.com, pg 916

Laser Rentals Inc, 1953 S County Lane 282, Joplin, MO 64804 *Tel:* 417-782-8484; 417-437-9149 (after hours) *Toll Free Tel:* 800-285-2737 *Web Site:* www.laserrentalsinc.com, pg 916

Laser Spectacles Inc, PO Box 1535, San Marcos, TX 78667 *Tel:* 512-392-4600 *Fax:* 512-392-4601 *E-mail:* laserinfo@laserspectacles.com *Web Site:* www.laserspectacles.com, pg 916

Laser Video Corp, 401 Germantown Pike, Lafayette Hill, PA 19444 *Tel:* 610-825-2500 *Toll Free Tel:* 800-448-8772 *Fax:* 610-941-9989 *E-mail:* customerservice@laservideousa.com *Web Site:* www.lvconline.com, pg 916

Lasergraphics Inc, 20 Ada, Irvine, CA 92618 *Tel:* 949-753-8282 *Fax:* 949-727-9282 *E-mail:* info@lasergraphics.com *Web Site:* www.lasergraphics.com, pg 916

Laserium, 6911 Hayvenhurst Ave, Suite 102, Van Nuys, CA 91406 *Tel:* 818-429-0454 *E-mail:* info@laserium.com *Web Site:* www.laserium.com, pg 916

The LAST Factory, 2015 Research Dr, Livermore, CA 94550-3803 *Tel:* 925-449-9449 *Fax:* 925-447-0662 *E-mail:* thelastfactory@gmail.com *Web Site:* thelastfactory.com, pg 916

Latham Foundation Publications, Latham Plaza Bldg, 1826 Clement Ave, Alameda, CA 94501 *Tel:* 510-521-0920 *Fax:* 510-521-9861 *E-mail:* info@latham.org *Web Site:* www.latham.org, pg 916

Laughing Dog Studio Inc, 59 Hylan Blvd, Apt 1C, Staten Island, NY 10305 *Tel:* 917-496-7752 *E-mail:* lafndog@inch.com *Web Site:* billdonnelly.com, pg 916

Launch Media, Celtic Media Ctr, 10000 Celtic Dr, Baton Rouge, LA 70809 *Tel:* 225-612-2112 *E-mail:* contactus@launchmedia.tv *Web Site:* www.launchmedia.tv, pg 916

Laurel Canyon Stages, 9337 Laurel Canyon Blvd, Arleta, CA 91331-4315 *Tel:* 818-768-8935 *Fax:* 818-768-6852 *E-mail:* info@lcstages.com *Web Site:* www.lcstages.com, pg 916

Laurel Hill Press, PO Box 16516, Chapel Hill, NC 27516-6516 *Toll Free Tel:* 800-942-6516 *Fax:* 919-942-9533 *E-mail:* plantsforus@gmail.com *Web Site:* www.laurelhillpress.com, pg 916

Laurel Video Productions, 1999 Marlton Pike, Suite 11, Cherry Hill, NJ 08003 *Tel:* 856-424-3300 *E-mail:* inquiries@laurelvideo.net *Web Site:* www.laurelvideo.net, pg 916

Lavine Production Group, 189 Dean St, Brooklyn, NY 11217 *Tel:* 917-804-1870 *Web Site:* www.lavinegroup.com, pg 917

Lawrence Convention & Visitors Bureau, 402 N Second St, Lawrence, KS 66044 *Tel:* 785-856-3040; 785-856-5282 *Fax:* 785-856-5303 *E-mail:* visinfo@visitlawrence.com *Web Site:* www.visitlawrence.com, pg 1097

Donna Lawrence Productions, 624 Baxter Ave, Louisville, KY 40204 *Tel:* 502-589-9617 *E-mail:* dlp@dlproductions.com *Web Site:* www.dlproductions.com, pg 917

Lawrence Productions Inc, 6146 W Main St, Suite A, Kalamazoo, MI 49009 *Tel:* 269-903-2395 *E-mail:* sales@lpi.com *Web Site:* www.lpi.com, pg 917

Lex Lawson Associates, 2002 Platinum St, Garland, TX 75042 *Tel:* 972-272-8482 *Toll Free Tel:* 800-783-9395 *Fax:* 972-276-8120 *Web Site:* www.lexlawson.com, pg 917

LBA Technology Inc, 3400 Tupper Dr, Greenville, NC 27834 *Tel:* 252-757-0279 *Toll Free Tel:* 800-522-4464 *Fax:* 252-752-9155 *E-mail:* lbagrp@lbagroup.com *Web Site:* www.lbagroup.com, pg 917

LCW Productions LLC, 3019 Hayden Dr, Wilmington, NC 28411-9625 *Tel:* 910-681-0835 *Fax:* 910-524-2736 *Web Site:* www.lcwproductions.com, pg 917

LEA International, 10701 Airport Rd, Hayden, ID 83835 *Tel:* 208-762-6121 *Toll Free Tel:* 800-882-9110, pg 917

LEAD Technologies Inc, 1927 S Tryon St, Suite 200, Charlotte, NC 28203 *Tel:* 704-332-5532 *Toll Free Tel:* 800-637-4699 *Fax:* 704-372-8161 *E-mail:* sales@leadtools.com *Web Site:* www.leadtools.com, pg 917

Leader Instruments Corp, 6484 Commerce Dr, Cypress, CA 90630 *Tel:* 714-527-9300 *Toll Free Tel:* 800-645-5104 *Fax:* 714-527-7490 *E-mail:* sales@leaderusa.com *Web Site:* www.leaderusa.com, pg 917

Learn Quickly, PO Box 3114, Palm Springs, CA 92263-3114 *Toll Free Tel:* 888-LRN-FAST (576-3278) *Toll Free Fax:* 888-LRN-FAST (576-3278) *Web Site:* www.learnquickly.com, pg 917

Learning Ally, 20 Roszel Rd, Princeton, NJ 08540 *Tel:* 609-750-1830 *Toll Free Tel:* 800-221-4792 (memb support) *E-mail:* custserv@learningally.org *Web Site:* www.learningally.org, pg 917

Learning Communications LLC, 5520 Trabuco Rd, Irvine, CA 92620 *Toll Free Tel:* 800-622-3610 *Fax:* 949-727-4323 *E-mail:* sales@learncom.com *Web Site:* www.learncom.com, pg 917

The Learning House Inc, 427 S Fourth St, Suite 300, Louisville, KY 40202 *Tel:* 502-589-9878 *Fax:* 502-589-9825 *E-mail:* sales@learninghouse.com *Web Site:* www.learninghouse.com, pg 917

Learning Seed, 208 S Jefferson St, Suite 402, Chicago, IL 60661 *Toll Free Tel:* 800-634-4941 *Toll Free Fax:* 800-998-0854 *E-mail:* info@learningseed.com *Web Site:* www.learningseed.com, pg 917

Learning Strategies Corp, 2000 Plymouth Rd, Minnetonka, MN 55305-2335 *Tel:* 952-767-9800 *Toll Free Tel:* 888-800-2688 (cust serv); 866-292-1861 (24 hour order line) *Fax:* 952-475-2373 *E-mail:* info@learningstrategies.com *Web Site:* www.learningstrategies.com, pg 917

Learning Technology Services, 301 Millennium Hall, Menomonie, WI 54751 *Tel:* 715-232-1289 *Fax:* 715-232-2456 *E-mail:* helpdesk@uwec.edu *Web Site:* www.unwec.edu/lts, pg 917

Lectrosonics Inc, 581 Laser Rd NE, Rio Rancho, NM 87124 *Tel:* 505-892-4501 *Toll Free Tel:* 800-821-1121 *Fax:* 505-892-6243 *E-mail:* sales@lectrosonics.com *Web Site:* www.lectrosonics.com, pg 918

LEDtronics Inc, 23105 Kashiva Ct, Torrance, CA 90505 *Tel:* 310-534-1505 *Toll Free Tel:* 800-579-4875 *Fax:* 310-534-1424 *E-mail:* info@ledtronics.com *Web Site:* www.ledtronics.com, pg 918

Lee Co Inc, 27 S 12 St, Terre Haute, IN 47807 *Tel:* 812-235-8155 *Fax:* 812-235-3587 *E-mail:* leeco@leecompanyinc.com *Web Site:* www.leecompanyinc.com, pg 918

Lee Dan® Communications Inc, 155 Adams Ave, Hauppauge, NY 11788-3699 *Tel:* 631-231-1414 *Toll Free Tel:* 800-231-1414 *Fax:* 631-231-1498 *E-mail:* info@leedan.com *Web Site:* www.leedan.com, pg 918

Lee Filters, 2237 N Hollywood Way, Burbank, CA 91505 *Tel:* 818-238-1220 *Toll Free Tel:* 800-576-5055 *Fax:* 818-238-1228 *E-mail:* mail@leefiltersusa.com *Web Site:* www.leefilters.com, pg 918

Lee Hartman & Sons Inc, 3236 Cove Rd NW, Roanoke, VA 24017 *Tel:* 540-366-3493 *Toll Free Tel:* 800-344-1832 *Fax:* 540-362-4659 *E-mail:* info@leehartman.com *Web Site:* www.leehartman.com, pg 918

Leedal Inc, 3453 Commercial Ave, Northbrook, IL 60062 *Tel:* 847-498-0111 *Fax:* 847-498-0198 *E-mail:* sink@leedal.com *Web Site:* www.leedal.com, pg 918

Lefco Video Services Inc, 600 W Sunset Rd, Suite 103, Henderson, NV 89011 *Tel:* 702-566-1770 *Fax:* 702-566-1798 *E-mail:* info1@lefco.com *Web Site:* www.lefco.com, pg 918

Legendary Entertainment, 160 Torrance Woods, Brampton, ON L6Y 4K2, Canada *Tel:* 416-712-9994 *E-mail:* info@legendaryentertainment.com *Web Site:* legendaryentertainment.com, pg 918

Legendary Pictures LLC, 2900 W Alameda Ave, 15th fl, Burbank, CA 91505 *Tel:* 818-688-7003 *E-mail:* info@legendary.com *Web Site:* www.legendary.com, pg 918

Legion Lighting Co Inc, 221 Glenmore Ave, Brooklyn, NY 11207 *Tel:* 718-498-1770 *Fax:* 718-498-0128 *Toll Free Fax:* 800-4-LEGION (453-4466) *E-mail:* sales@legionlighting.com *Web Site:* www.legionlighting.com, pg 918

Lehigh Electric Products Co, 6265 Hamilton Blvd, Allentown, PA 18106 *Tel:* 610-395-3386 *Fax:* 610-395-7735 *E-mail:* sales@lehighdim.com *Web Site:* www.lehighdim.com, pg 918

Lehigh Phoenix™, 18249 Phoenix Dr, Hagerstown, MD 21742 *Tel:* 301-733-0018 *Toll Free Tel:* 800-632-4111 *Fax:* 301-733-1733 *Web Site:* www.phoenixcolor.com, pg 918

Leica Camera Inc, One Pearl Ct, Unit A, Allendale, NJ 07401 *Toll Free Tel:* 800-222-0118 *Fax:* 201-995-1686 *Web Site:* en.leica-camera.com, pg 918

Leightronix Inc, 2330 Jarco Dr, Holt, MI 48842 *Tel:* 517-694-8000 *Toll Free Tel:* 800-243-5589 *Fax:* 517-694-1600 *E-mail:* support@leightronix.com; sales@leightronix.com *Web Site:* www.leightronix.com, pg 918

Leisure Video, 747 Magazine St, New Orleans, LA 70130 *Tel:* 504-299-9000 *Toll Free Tel:* 800-432-3853 *Fax:* 504-299-9090 *E-mail:* info@dukesofdixieland.com *Web Site:* www.dukesofdixieland.com; www.leisurejazz.com, pg 918

LEMO USA Inc, 635 Park Ct, Rohnert Park, CA 94928 *Tel:* 707-578-8811 *Toll Free Tel:* 800-444-LEMO (444-5366) *Fax:* 707-578-0869 *E-mail:* info@lemousa.com *Web Site:* www.lemousa.com; www.lemo.com, pg 918

Lenel Systems International Inc, 1212 Pittsford-Victor Rd, Pittsford, NY 14534-3820 *Tel:* 585-248-9720 *Toll Free Tel:* 866-788-5095 *Fax:* 585-248-9185 *E-mail:* pr@lenel.com *Web Site:* www.lenel.com, pg 919

Lensless Camera Manufacturing Co, 809 Lark Dr, Fernley, NV 89408 *Tel:* 775-575-5189 *E-mail:* info@pinholecamera.com *Web Site:* www.pinholecamera.com, pg 919

Leo Films, 6548 Country Squire Lane, Omaha, NE 68152 *Tel:* 323-459-5574 *Web Site:* www.leofilms.com, pg 919

Leonardo Software, 11726 San Vicente Blvd, Suite 520, Los Angeles, CA 90049 *Tel:* 310-820-9961 *Toll Free Tel:* 800-606-4536 *Fax:* 310-820-9970 *E-mail:* info@leonardosoft.com *Web Site:* www.leonardosoft.com, pg 919

Leprecon®, 10087 Industrial Dr, Hamburg, MI 48139 *Tel:* 810-852-4300 *Toll Free Tel:* 888-422-3537 *Fax:* 810-231-1631 *E-mail:* lepsls@leprecon.com *Web Site:* www.leprecon.com, pg 919

The Lerro Corp, Valley Forge Corporate Ctr, 905 Madison Ave, Norristown, PA 19403 *Tel:* 610-650-4100 *Fax:* 610-650-4110 *E-mail:* lerrocorp@lerro.com *Web Site:* www.lerro.com, pg 919

Leucos USA Inc, 11 Mayfield Ave, Edison, NJ 08837 *Tel:* 732-225-0010 *Toll Free Tel:* 800-832-3360 *Fax:* 732-225-0250 *E-mail:* info@leucosusa.com *Web Site:* www.leucos.com, pg 919

Level 3 Communications Inc, 1025 Eldorado Blvd, Broomfield, CO 80021 *Tel:* 720-888-1000 *Toll Free Tel:* 877-2LEVEL3 (253-8357) *Web Site:* www.level3.com, pg 919

Leviton LES, 20497 SW Teton Ave, Tualatin, OR 97062 *Toll Free Tel:* 800-736-6682 *Fax:* 503-404-5594 *Web Site:* www.leviton.com, pg 919

Levy Lighting NYC Inc, 347 W 36 St, Ground fl, New York, NY 10018 *Tel:* 212-925-4640 *Fax:* 212-925-4216 *E-mail:* info@levylighting.com *Web Site:* www.levylighting.com, pg 919

Lex Products Corp, 15 Progress Dr, Shelton, CT 06484 *Tel:* 203-363-3738 *Toll Free Tel:* 800-643-4460 *Fax:* 203-363-3742 *E-mail:* info@lexproducts.com *Web Site:* www.lexproducts.com, pg 919

LHV Audio Services, 3417 Lake Breeze Rd, Orlando, FL 32808 *Tel:* 407-295-3565 *E-mail:* service@lhvaudio.com *Web Site:* www.lhvaudio.com, pg 919

Liberty Photo Products, 1041 Calle Trepadora, San Clemente, CA 92673 *Tel:* 949-361-1100 *Toll Free Tel:* 800-572-3600 *Fax:* 949-498-4441 *E-mail:* info@liberty2create.com; sales-info@libertyphoto.com *Web Site:* www.liberty2create.com, pg 919

Liberty Publishing Co Inc, PO Box 4485, Deerfield Beach, FL 33442-4248 *Tel:* 954-573-7236 *Web Site:* www.bullsorbears.com, pg 919

Liberty Uplink, 2547 Yellow Springs Rd, Malvern, PA 19355 *Tel:* 215-964-5222; 917-254-0155 *E-mail:* info@libertyuplink.com *Web Site:* www.libertyuplink.com, pg 919

LibertyPak Co Inc, 420 Bryant Circle, Bldg B, Ojai, CA 93023 *Tel:* 805-640-6700 *E-mail:* sales@libertypak.com; service@libertypak.com *Web Site:* www.libertypak.com, pg 919

Library & Information Technology Association (LITA), c/o American Library Association, 50 E Huron St, Chicago, IL 60611-2795 *Toll Free Tel:* 800-545-2433 (ext 4270) *Fax:* 312-280-3257 *E-mail:* lita@ala.org *Web Site:* www.ala.org/lita, pg 1084

Library of Congress, Motion Picture, Broadcasting & Recorded Sound Division, James Madison Bldg, LM 336, 101 Independence Ave SE, Washington, DC 20540-1000 *Tel:* 202-707-8572 *Fax:* 202-707-2371 *Web Site:* www.loc.gov/rr/mopic, pg 919

Library Video Company, 7 E Wynnewood Rd, Wynnewood, PA 19096 *Tel:* 610-645-4000 *Toll Free Tel:* 800-843-3620 *Fax:* 610-645-4040 *E-mail:* sales@libraryvideo.com; comments@libraryvideo.com *Web Site:* www.libraryvideo.com, pg 920

Library Video Network (LVN), 320 York Rd, Towson, MD 21204 *Tel:* 410-887-2090 *Toll Free Tel:* 800-441-8273 *Fax:* 410-887-2091 *E-mail:* lvn@bcpl.net *Web Site:* www.lvn.org, pg 920

Ken Lieberman Labs Inc, 69 Fairview Dr, Albertson, NY 11507-1007 *Tel:* 212-633-0500 *Web Site:* lieberman-labs.com, pg 920

Lieberman Productions, 455 Ninth St, San Francisco, CA 94103-4410 *Tel:* 415-955-0855 *Fax:* 415-955-0822 *E-mail:* lpinfo@lieberman.com *Web Site:* www.lieberman.com, pg 920

Life Cycle Books Ltd, 1085 Bellamy Rd N, Unit 20, Toronto, ON M1H 1H7, Canada *Tel:* 416-690-5860 *Toll Free Tel:* 866-880-5860 *Fax:* 416-690-8532 *Toll Free Fax:* 866-690-8532 *E-mail:* support@lifecyclebooks.com; billing@lifecyclebooks.com; orders@lifecyclebooks.com *Web Site:* www.lifecyclebooks.com, pg 920

Life House Productions LLC, PO Box 4007, Manchester, CT 06045-4007 *Tel:* 860-432-9177 *Web Site:* www.lifehouseproductions.com, pg 920

Lifetime Television®, 235 E 45 St, New York, NY 10017 *Tel:* 212-424-7000 *Web Site:* www.mylifetime.com, pg 920

Light Impressions, 2340 Brighton Henrietta Town Line Rd, Rochester, NY 14623 *Toll Free Tel:* 800-975-6429 *Toll Free Fax:* 800-975-6429 (orders) *E-mail:* info@lightimpressionsdirect.com *Web Site:* www.lightimpressionsdirect.com, pg 920

The Light Source, 3935 Westinghouse Blvd, Charlotte, NC 28273 *Tel:* 704-504-8399 *Fax:* 704-588-4693 (acctg); 704-588-4637 (orders) *E-mail:* mail@thelightsource.com; sales@thelightsource.com *Web Site:* www.thelightsource.com, pg 920

Light Tec, 1311 Chemical St, Dallas, TX 75207 *Tel:* 214-350-8990 *Toll Free Tel:* 888-548-3832 *Fax:* 214-638-2038 *E-mail:* info@lighttec.com *Web Site:* www.lighttec.com, pg 920

LightBox-NY, 841 Barretto St, Bronx, NY 10474 *Tel:* 718-759-6419 *E-mail:* lightboxny@gmail.com *Web Site:* www.lightbox-ny.com, pg 920

LightCraft Graphics Inc, 1269 Rand Rd, Des Plaines, IL 60016 *Tel:* 847-759-8500 *Fax:* 847-759-8540 *Web Site:* www.lightcraft.com, pg 920

LightHouse Films, 115 W 29 St, Suite 903, New York, NY 10001 *Tel:* 646-649-3600 *Fax:* 646-398-7122 *E-mail:* contact@lhfny.com; rent@lhfny.com *Web Site:* www.light-house-films.com, pg 920

Lighthouse Photo & Video Productions, 1100 Chicago Ave, Suite 2C, Goshen, IN 46528 *Tel:* 574-533-1400 (off); 574-202-5502 (studio) *E-mail:* lighthousevideo@gmail.com *Web Site:* www.lighthousephotoandvideo.com, pg 920

Lighting & Production Equipment Inc, 590 Travis St, Atlanta, GA 30318 *Tel:* 404-352-0464 *Toll Free Tel:* 800-275-3721 *Fax:* 404-351-4399 *Web Site:* www.lpe.com, pg 920

The Lighting Design Alliance, 2830 Temple Ave, Long Beach, CA 90806-2213 *Tel:* 562-989-3843 *Fax:* 562-989-3847 *E-mail:* info@lightingdesignalliance.com *Web Site:* www.lightingdesignalliance.com, pg 920

Lighting Design Group, 49 W 27 St, Suite 920, New York, NY 10001 *Tel:* 212-685-4940 *Fax:* 212-685-4927 *E-mail:* lighting@ldg.com *Web Site:* www.ldg.com, pg 920

Lighting Industry Resource Council, 440 N Wells St, Suite 210, Chicago, IL 60654 *Tel:* 312-527-3677 *Fax:* 312-527-3680 *E-mail:* iald@iald.org *Web Site:* www.iald.org/council, pg 920

Lighting Sales Connections, 757 SE 17 St, PMB 254, Fort Lauderdale, FL 33316 *Tel:* 954-764-6928 *Fax:* 954-791-8450 *E-mail:* info@lightingsales.com *Web Site:* www.lightingsales.com, pg 920

Lighting Services Inc, 2 Holt Dr, Stony Point, NY 10980-1996 *Tel:* 845-942-2800 *Toll Free Tel:* 800-999-9574 (US & CN) *Fax:* 845-942-2177 *E-mail:* applications@maillsi.com; sales@maillsi.com *Web Site:* www.lightingservicesinc.com, pg 921

Lightning Eliminators & Consultants Inc, 6687 Arapahoe Rd, Boulder, CO 80303 *Tel:* 303-447-2828 *Toll Free Tel:* 800-521-6101 *Fax:* 303-447-8122 *E-mail:* info@lightningprotection.com *Web Site:* www.lightningprotection.com, pg 921

Lightning Master Corp, 1770 Calumet St, Clearwater, FL 33765 *Tel:* 727-447-6800 *Toll Free Tel:* 877-334-8006 *Fax:* 727-499-0138 *E-mail:* info@lightningmaster.com *Web Site:* www.lightningmaster.com, pg 921

Lightning Media, 1415 Cahuenga Blvd, Hollywood, CA 90028 *Tel:* 323-957-9255 *E-mail:* info@lightningmedia.com *Web Site:* www.lightningmedia.com, pg 921

Lightolier, 631 Airport Rd, Fall River, MA 02720 *Tel:* 508-679-8131 *Toll Free Tel:* 800-215-1068 *Fax:* 508-674-4710 *Web Site:* www.lightolier.com, pg 921

Lightronics Inc, 509 Central Dr, Virginia Beach, VA 23454 *Tel:* 757-486-3588 *Toll Free Tel:* 800-472-8541 *Fax:* 757-486-3391 *Web Site:* www.lightronics.com, pg 921

Lights On, 61 Bedford St SE, Minneapolis, MN 55414 *Tel:* 612-331-6620 *Toll Free Tel:* 800-336-6620 *Fax:* 612-331-6601 *E-mail:* minneapolis@lightson.com *Web Site:* www.lightson.com, pg 921

Lights On Nebraska, 7520 Burlington St, Omaha, NE 68127 *Tel:* 402-331-4340 *Fax:* 402-331-4556 *E-mail:* ne@lightsonrentals.com *Web Site:* www.lightsonrentals.com, pg 921

LightSpace Studios, 1115 Flushing Ave, Brooklyn, NY 11237 *Tel:* 212-202-0372 *E-mail:* reserve@lightspace.tv *Web Site:* www.lightspace.tv, pg 921

Lightspeed Technologies Inc, 11509 SW Herman Rd, Tualatin, OR 97062 *Tel:* 503-684-5538 *Toll Free Tel:* 800-732-8999 *Fax:* 503-684-3197 *Web Site:* www.lightspeed-tek.com, pg 921

Lighttech Group Inc, 161-15 Rockaway Blvd, Jamaica, NY 11434 *Tel:* 718-525-2900 *Fax:* 718-525-2488 *E-mail:* info@lighttech.com *Web Site:* www.lighttech.com, pg 921

Lightware Inc, 1329 W Byers Place, Denver, CO 80223-1723 *Tel:* 303-744-0202 *Fax:* 303-722-4545 *E-mail:* info@lightwareinc.com *Web Site:* www.lightwareinc.com; www.lightwaredirect.com, pg 921

Lightworks Audio & Video Inc, PO Box 661593, Los Angeles, CA 90066 *Tel:* 310-398-4949 *Fax:* 310-397-4401 *E-mail:* sales1@lightworksav.com *Web Site:* www.lightworksav.com, pg 921

Lightyear Entertainment, 4011 Alcove Ave, Studio City, CA 91604 *Tel:* 818-855-1318 *Fax:* 818-855-1320 *E-mail:* mail@lightyear.com *Web Site:* www.lightyear.com, pg 921

Ligos Corporation, 6001 Chatham Ctr Dr, Suite 300, Savannah, GA 31405 *Tel:* 912-236-8993 *Fax:* 912-234-1366 *Web Site:* www.ligos.com, pg 921

Limbo Films, 2223 NE Martin Luther King Jr Blvd, Portland, OR 97212 *Tel:* 503-228-0844 *Fax:* 503-228-0857 *E-mail:* info@limbofilms.com *Web Site:* www.limbofilms.com, pg 921

Limelight Communications Inc, 2812 Roesh Way, Vienna, VA 22181 *Tel:* 703-242-4596 *Fax:* 703-991-0616 *E-mail:* moreinfo@limelightdc.com *Web Site:* www.limelightdc.com, pg 921

Limelight Productions Inc, 471 Pleasant St, Lee, MA 01238-9322 *Tel:* 413-243-4950 *Toll Free Tel:* 800-243-4950 *Fax:* 413-243-4993 *Toll Free Fax:* 800-243-4951 *E-mail:* info@limelightproductions.com *Web Site:* www.limelightproductions.com, pg 921

Linear LLC, 1950 Camino Vida Roble, Suite 150, Carlsbad, CA 92008-6517 *Tel:* 760-438-7000 *Toll Free Tel:* 800-421-1587 *Fax:* 760-931-1340 *Toll Free Fax:* 800-468-1340 *E-mail:* sales@linearcorp.com *Web Site:* www.linearcorp.com, pg 922

Lineco, 517 Main St, Holyoke, MA 01040 *Toll Free Tel:* 800-322-7775 *Fax:* 413-532-9281 *Toll Free Fax:* 800-298-7815 *E-mail:* info@lineco.com *Web Site:* www.lineco.com, pg 922

Linguistic Systems Inc, 201 Broadway, Cambridge, MA 02139 *Tel:* 617-528-7400 *Toll Free Tel:* 877-654-5006 *Fax:* 617-528-7491 *Web Site:* linguist.com, pg 922

Linguist's Software Inc, PO Box 580, Edmonds, WA 98020-0580 *Tel:* 425-775-1130 *Fax:* 425-771-5911 *E-mail:* fonts@linguistsoftware.com *Web Site:* www.linguistsoftware.com, pg 922

Linhoff Photo & Digital Imaging, 4400 France Ave S, Edina, MN 55410 *Tel:* 952-927-7333 *E-mail:* info@linhoff.com *Web Site:* linhoff.com, pg 922

Link Electronics Inc, 2137 Rust Ave, Cape Girardeau, MO 63703-7668 *Tel:* 573-334-4433 *Toll Free Tel:* 800-776-4411 *Fax:* 573-334-9255 *E-mail:* sales@linkelectronics.com *Web Site:* www.linkelectronics.com, pg 922

Linkabit, 9890 Towne Centre Dr, San Diego, CA 92121 *Toll Free Tel:* 800-331-9401 *E-mail:* linkabitproducts@l-3com.com *Web Site:* www2.l-3com.com/linkabit, pg 922

Linker Systems Inc, 13612 Onkayha Circle, Irvine, CA 92620 *Tel:* 949-552-1904 *Toll Free Tel:* 800-315-1174 *Web Site:* linkersystems.com, pg 922

Linsman Film, 329 N Windsor Blvd, Los Angeles, CA 90004 *Tel:* 310-903-3009 *Web Site:* www.linsman.com, pg 922

Lion & Fox Recording Studios, 9517 Baltimore Ave, College Park, MD 20740 *Tel:* 301-982-4431 *E-mail:* mail@lionfox.com *Web Site:* www.lionfox.com, pg 922

Lion Recording Services Inc, 7532 Fullerton Ct, Springfield, VA 22153 *Tel:* 703-569-3200 *Fax:* 703-891-3220 *E-mail:* mail@lionrecording.com *Web Site:* www.lionrecording.com, pg 922

Lions Gate Entertainment Corp, 2700 Colorado Ave, Santa Monica, CA 90404 *Tel:* 310-449-9200 *Fax:* 310-255-3870 *E-mail:* general-inquiries@lionsgate.com *Web Site:* www.lionsgate.com; corporate.lionsgate.com, pg 922

Lippincott Williams & Wilkins, Two Commerce Sq, 2001 Market St, Philadephia, PA 19103 *Tel:* 215-521-8300; 301-223-2300 (cust serv) *Toll Free Tel:* 800-638-3030 (cust serv) *Fax:* 215-521-8902 *E-mail:* orders@lww.com *Web Site:* www.lww.com, pg 922

Lipsner-Smith Co, 4700 Chase Ave, Lincolnwood, IL 60712-1689 *Tel:* 847-677-3000 *Toll Free Tel:* 800-323-7520 *Fax:* 847-677-1311 *Toll Free Fax:* 800-784-6733 *E-mail:* sales@lipsner.com; sales@rtico.com *Web Site:* www.lipsner.com, pg 922

A Liss & Co, 51-55 59 Place, Woodside, NY 11377-7408 *Tel:* 718-728-0600 *Toll Free Tel:* 800-221-0938 *Fax:* 718-728-1227 *E-mail:* sales@alissco.com *Web Site:* www.alissco.com, pg 922

Listec Video Corp, 90 Oser Ave, Hauppauge, NY 11788 *Tel:* 631-273-2500 *Toll Free Tel:* 800-645-2522 *Fax:* 631-273-2557 *E-mail:* orders@tiffen.com; techsupport@tiffen.com *Web Site:* www.tiffen.com, pg 923

Listen & Live Audio Inc, 1700 Manhattan Ave, Union City, NJ 07068 *Tel:* 201-558-9000 *Toll Free Tel:* 800-653-9400 (orders) *Fax:* 201-558-9800 *Web Site:* www.listenandlive.com, pg 923

Listen Technologies Corp, 14912 Heritage Crest Way, Bluffdale, UT 84065-4818 *Tel:* 801-233-8992 *Toll Free Tel:* 800-330-0891 *Fax:* 801-233-8995 *E-mail:* info@listentech.com *Web Site:* www.listentech.com, pg 923

Listening Library, 1745 Broadway, New York, NY 10019 *Tel:* 212-782-9000 *Toll Free Tel:* 800-733-3000 *E-mail:* audio@randomhouse.com *Web Site:* www.randomhouse.com/audio/listeninglibrary, pg 923

LITE-IT Grip Truck Rentals, 450 Saint Andrews Ct, West Chicago, IL 60185 *Tel:* 630-231-1671 *Fax:* 630-231-1672 *E-mail:* liteit1@sbcglobal.net *Web Site:* www.liteit1.com, pg 923

Little Big Bang Design Inc, 287 NE 90 St, Miami, FL 33138 *Tel:* 786-218-0713 *E-mail:* info@littlebigbangdesign.com *Web Site:* www.littlebigbangdesign.com, pg 923

The Larry Little Co, 10120 W Flamingo Rd, Suite 4-160, Las Vegas, NV 89147 *Tel:* 262-518-2014 *Toll Free Fax:* 800-452-8273 *E-mail:* larrylittlecompany@gmail.com *Web Site:* www.larrylittle.com, pg 923

Little Mammoth Media, 750 Ralph McGill Blvd, NE, Atlanta, GA 30312 *Toll Free Tel:* 800-KIDVIDEO (543-8433) *E-mail:* bv@vanderkloot.com *Web Site:* www.littlemammoth.com, pg 923

The Little Warehouse Inc, 900 Resource Dr, Suite 8, Brooklyn Heights, OH 44131 *Tel:* 216-398-0022 *Toll Free Tel:* 800-445-8273 *Fax:* 216-398-9980 *E-mail:* tlwtape@sbcglobal.net *Web Site:* www.thelittlewarehouse.com, pg 923

Littlite LLC, PO Box 430, Hamburg, MI 48139-0430 *Tel:* 810-852-4242 *Fax:* 810-231-1631 *E-mail:* sales@littlite.com *Web Site:* www.littlite.com, pg 923

Liturgy Training Publications, 3949 S Racine Ave, Chicago, IL 60609-2523 *Tel:* 773-579-4900 *Toll Free Tel:* 800-933-1800 (orders) *Fax:* 773-579-4929 *E-mail:* orders@ltp.org *Web Site:* www.ltp.org, pg 923

Live Oak Media, PO Box 652, Pine Plains, NY 12567-0652 *Toll Free Tel:* 800-788-1121 *Toll Free Fax:* 866-398-1070 *E-mail:* info@liveoakmedia.com *Web Site:* www.liveoakmedia.com, pg 923

Live Spark Inc, 700 Raymond Ave, Suite 100, St Paul, MN 55114 *Tel:* 651-289-7375 *E-mail:* info@live-spark.com *Web Site:* www.live-spark.com, pg 923

Live Wire Media, PO Box 848, Mill Valley, CA 94942 *Tel:* 415-564-9500 *Toll Free Tel:* 800-359-KIDS (359-5437) *Fax:* 415-552-4087 *E-mail:* sales@livewiremedia.com *Web Site:* www.livewiremedia.com, pg 923

Live'N'Loud, One Lindsay Way, Hot Springs Village, AR 71909 *Tel:* 501-414-2845 *Web Site:* www.livenloud.net, pg 923

The Livingston Awards for Young Journalists, Wallace House, 620 Oxford Rd, Ann Arbor, MI 48104 *Tel:* 734-998-7575 *Fax:* 734-998-7979 *E-mail:* livawards@umich.edu *Web Site:* www.livawards.org, pg 1118

LKG Industries Inc, 3660 Publishers Dr, Rockford, IL 61109 *Tel:* 815-874-2301 *Toll Free Tel:* 800-645-2262 *Fax:* 815-874-2896 *E-mail:* sales-lkgindustries@t6b.com *Web Site:* www.philmore-datak.com, pg 923

Llewellyn Publications, 2143 Wooddale Dr, Woodbury, MN 55125-2989 *Tel:* 651-291-1970 *Toll Free Tel:* 877-NEWWRLD (639-9753) *Fax:* 651-291-1908 *E-mail:* publicity@llewellyn.com; customerservice@llewellyn.com *Web Site:* www.llewellyn.com, pg 923

C V Lloyde, 102 S Neil St, Champaign, IL 61820 *Tel:* 217-352-7031 *Toll Free Tel:* 800-779-7031 *E-mail:* sales@cvlloyde.com *Web Site:* www.cvlloyde.com, pg 923

LM Cases/LM Engineering Inc, 2720 Intertech Dr, Youngstown, OH 44509 *Tel:* 330-270-2400 *Toll Free Tel:* 800-874-8326 *Fax:* 330-270-2424 *E-mail:* info@lmcases.com *Web Site:* www.lmcases.com, pg 923

Location Camera Ltd, 300 Pennsylvania Ave, Oreland, PA 19075 *Tel:* 215-576-5600 *Fax:* 215-576-6022 *E-mail:* mail@locationcamera.com *Web Site:* www.locationcamera.com, pg 923

The Location Connection Inc, 1600 Rosecrans Ave, Bldg 5, Manhattan Beach, CA 90266 *Tel:* 310-376-9797 *Fax:* 310-376-9796 *E-mail:* lconnect@aol.com *Web Site:* www.locationconnection.com, pg 924

Location Lighting Ltd, 300 Pennsylvania Ave, Oreland, PA 19075 *Tel:* 215-576-5600 *Fax:* 215-576-6022 *E-mail:* mail@locationlighting.com; rentals@locationlighting.com *Web Site:* www.locationlighting.com, pg 924

Location Sound Corp, 10639 Riverside Dr, North Hollywood, CA 91602 *Tel:* 818-980-9891 *Toll Free Tel:* 800-228-4429 *Fax:* 818-980-9911 *E-mail:* information@locationsound.com; salesdept@locationsound.com *Web Site:* www.locationsound.com, pg 924

Location 05 Studios, 509 W 34 St, 2nd fl, New York, NY 10001 *Tel:* 212-219-2144 *Fax:* 212-344-8032 *E-mail:* info@location05.com *Web Site:* location05.com, pg 924

Loft 19, 21618 N Ninth Ave, Suite A, Phoenix, AZ 85027 *Tel:* 623-434-3791 *Fax:* 623-434-5003 *E-mail:* info@loft19.com *Web Site:* loft19.com, pg 924

Loftin Productions, PO Box 78, New York, NY 10116 *Tel:* 917-825-5412 *E-mail:* loftin.productions@gmail.com *Web Site:* www.loftinpro.com, pg 924

Logan Productions Inc, 8035 N Port Washington Rd, Milwaukee, WI 53217 *Tel:* 414-352-9691 *Fax:* 414-352-4993 *E-mail:* sales@loganproductions.com *Web Site:* www.loganproductions.com, pg 924

Logitech, 7600 Gateway Blvd, Newark, CA 94560 *Tel:* 510-795-8500 *Toll Free Tel:* 800-231-7717 (sales) *Web Site:* www.logitech.com, pg 924

Logitek Electronic Systems Inc, 5622 Edgemoor Dr, Houston, TX 77081 *Tel:* 713-664-4470 *Toll Free Tel:* 800-231-5870 (sales); 877-231-5870 (tech support) *Fax:* 713-664-4479 *E-mail:* northamericansales@logitekaudio.com *Web Site:* www.logitekaudio.com, pg 924

Loma Scientific International (LSI), 3115 Kashiwa St, Torrance, CA 90505 *Tel:* 310-539-8655 *Fax:* 310-539-8634 *E-mail:* info@lomasci.com *Web Site:* www.lomasci.com, pg 924

Long Island University Media Arts Dept, One University Plaza, Brooklyn, NY 11201-8423 *Tel:* 718-488-1052 *Fax:* 718-780-4578 *E-mail:* mediart@brooklyn.liu.edu *Web Site:* www.liu.edu/brooklyn.aspx, pg 924

Long Island Video Enterprises Live Inc, 110 Pratt Oval, Glen Cove, NY 11542 *Tel:* 516-759-5483 *Fax:* 516-671-5874 *E-mail:* info@longislandvideo.com *Web Site:* www.longislandvideo.com, pg 924

Long-Term Success Publishing, 766 Ninth Ave N, Suite 1, Fort Dodge, IA 50501 *Tel:* 515-571-8880 *Web Site:* judypayne.com, pg 924

Loopmedia Inc, 401 Richmond St W, Suite 243, Toronto, ON M5V 3A8, Canada *Tel:* 416-595-6496 *Fax:* 416-595-0306 *E-mail:* info@loopmedia.com *Web Site:* www.loopmedia.com, pg 924

The Los Angeles Asian Pacific Film Festival, 120 Judge John Aiso St, Basement Level, Los Angeles, CA 90012-3805 *Tel:* 213-680-4462 *Fax:* 213-687-4848 *E-mail:* festival@vconline.org *Web Site:* asianfilmfestla.org, pg 1119

Los Angeles Center Studios, 450 S Bixel St, Los Angeles, CA 90017 *Tel:* 213-534-3000 *E-mail:* productionservices@lacenterstudios.com *Web Site:* lacenterstudios.com, pg 924

Los Angeles Film Festival, 9911 W Pico Blvd, Suite 1100, Los Angeles, CA 90035 *Toll Free Tel:* 866-345-6337 *E-mail:* lafilmfest@filmindependent.org *Web Site:* www.lafilmfest.com, pg 1119

Los Angeles Latino International Film Festival (LALIFF), 453 S Spring St, Suite 1030, Los Angeles, CA 90013 *Tel:* 323-446-2770 *Fax:* 323-446-2770 *E-mail:* info@latinofilm.org *Web Site:* latinofilm.org, pg 1119

Los Angeles Post Music Inc, 4340 E Kentucky Ave, Suite 308, Glendale, CO 80246 *Tel:* 310-896-5176 *Web Site:* www.lapostmusic.com, pg 924

Los Feliz Post, 6767 Forest Lawn Dr, Suite 211, Los Angeles, CA 90068 *Tel:* 818-859-3500, pg 924

The Lot (Skye Partners), 1041 N Formosa Ave, West Hollywood, CA 90046 *Tel:* 323-850-3180 *Fax:* 323-850-3190 *E-mail:* info@skyepartners.com *Web Site:* www.thelotstudios.com, pg 925

Lotus Development Corp, an IBM Company, One Rogers St, Cambridge, MA 02142 *Tel:* 617-693-4235; 914-499-1900 (IBM) *Web Site:* www.lotus.com, pg 925

LOUD Technologies Inc, 16220 Wood-Red Rd NE, Woodinville, WA 98072 *Tel:* 425-487-4333; 415-892-6500 *Toll Free Tel:* 866-858-LTEC (858-5832) *Fax:* 425-487-4337 *Web Site:* www.mackie.com; www.loudtechinc.com, pg 925

Louisiana Entertainment, Off of Entertainment Indus Devt, Capital Annex Bldg, 1051 N Third St, Baton Rouge, LA 70802 *Tel:* 225-342-5403 *Fax:* 225-342-5554 *E-mail:* led-entertainment@la.gov *Web Site:* louisianaentertainment.gov, pg 1098

Louisiana State University Health Sciences Center - Shreveport, Dept of Video Servs & TeleHealth, 1501 Kings Hwy, Shreveport, LA 71103-4228 *Tel:* 318-675-5268 *Fax:* 318-675-7757 *Web Site:* www.lsuhscshreveport.edu, pg 925

James Loupas Associates Inc, 134 Carrington Dr, Coppell, TX 75019 *Tel:* 972-304-0455 *Web Site:* jimloupas.com, pg 925

Love Shack Recording Studios, 909 18 Ave S, Nashville, TN 37212 *Tel:* 615-843-0019 *E-mail:* book@loveshackstudios.com *Web Site:* loveshackstudios.com, pg 925

Love Your Shorts Film Festival, 608 S Elm Ave, Sanford, FL 32771 *E-mail:* contact@loveyourshorts.com *Web Site:* www.loveyourshorts.com, pg 1119

Lowel-Light Manufacturing Inc, 90 Oser Ave, Hauppauge, NY 11788 *Tel:* 631-273-2500 *Toll Free Tel:* 800-645-2522 *Fax:* 631-273-2557 *E-mail:* info@lowel.com *Web Site:* www.lowel.com, pg 925

Lowell Manufacturing, 100 Integram Dr, Pacific, MO 63069-3476 *Toll Free Tel:* 800-325-9660 *Toll Free Fax:* 800-456-9355 *E-mail:* sales@lowellmfg.com *Web Site:* www.lowellmfg.com, pg 925

Lowing Light & Grip Inc, 1500 Whiting St SW, Wyoming, MI 49509-1056 *Tel:* 616-530-7440 *Toll Free Tel:* 888-530-7440 *Fax:* 616-249-8947 *Web Site:* www.lowinglight.com, pg 925

Lowrance Sound Co Inc, 2132 Nailling Dr, Union City, TN 38261 *Tel:* 731-885-4504 *Toll Free Tel:* 800-852-5418 *E-mail:* info@lowrancesoundcompany.com *Web Site:* www.lowrancesoundcompany.com, pg 925

Loyal Studios, 3513 W Pacific Ave, Burbank, CA 91505 *Tel:* 818-845-5123 (studio); 818-399-9499 *Web Site:* www.loyalstudios.tv, pg 925

LT Sound Inc, 7980 LT Pkwy, Lithonia, GA 30058 *Tel:* 770-482-4836 *E-mail:* info3@ltsound.com *Web Site:* www.ltsound.com, pg 925

LTM Corp of America, 7357 1/2 Atoll Ave, North Hollywood, CA 91605 *Tel:* 818-780-9828 *Toll Free Tel:* 800-762-4291 *Fax:* 818-780-9848 *E-mail:* sales@ltmlighting.com; info@ltmlighting.com, pg 925

Lubbock Audio Visual Inc, 2120 Ave "Q", Lubbock, TX 79405 *Tel:* 806-744-2559 *Toll Free Tel:* 800-850-2559 *Fax:* 806-747-6939 *E-mail:* sales@lav.com *Web Site:* www.lav.com, pg 925

Lubell Labs Inc, 21 N Stanwood Rd, Columbus, OH 43209 *Tel:* 614-235-6740 *E-mail:* lubell_labs@wowway.com *Web Site:* www.lubell.com, pg 925

David Lubman Acoustics, 14301 Middletown Lane, Westminster, CA 92683 *Tel:* 714-373-3050 *Fax:* 714-373-3050 *Web Site:* www.dlacoustics.com, pg 925

Lucasey Manufacturing Corp, 2744 E 11 St, Oakland, CA 94601 *Tel:* 510-534-1435 *Toll Free Tel:* 800-582-2739 *Fax:* 510-534-6828 *E-mail:* sales@lucasey.com *Web Site:* www.lucasey.com, pg 925

Lucerne Media, 37 Ground Pine Rd, Morris Plains, NJ 07950 *Tel:* 973-538-1401 *Fax:* 973-538-0855 *E-mail:* lucernemedia@optonline.net, pg 925

Ludlow Media Solutions, 15501 San Pablo Ave, Suite G320, San Pablo, CA 94806 *Tel:* 415-927-1300 *E-mail:* info@ludlowmedia.com *Web Site:* www.ludlowmedia.com, pg 926

Lumalaser, 84777 Charlottes Way, Eugene, OR 97405 *Tel:* 541-687-1414 *Toll Free Tel:* 800-606-2597 *Fax:* 541-687-1438 *E-mail:* info@lumalaser.com *Web Site:* www.lumalaser.com, pg 926

Lumedyne Inc, 6010 Wall St, Port Richey, FL 34668 *Tel:* 727-847-2777; 727-847-5394 *Toll Free Tel:* 800-586-3396 *Fax:* 727-841-0000 *E-mail:* info@lumedyne.com; sales@lumedyne.com; service@lumedyne.com *Web Site:* www.lumedyne.com, pg 926

Lumeni Productions Inc, 1632 Flower St, Glendale, CA 91201 *Tel:* 818-956-2200 *Fax:* 818-956-3298 *E-mail:* info@lumeni.com *Web Site:* www.lumeni.com, pg 926

Luminaud Inc, 8688 Tyler Blvd, Mentor, OH 44060 *Tel:* 440-255-9082 *Toll Free Tel:* 800-255-3408 *Fax:* 440-255-2250 *E-mail:* info@luminaud.com *Web Site:* www.luminaud.com, pg 926

Luminys Systems Corp, 11961 Sherman Rd, North Hollywood, CA 91605 *Tel:* 323-461-6361 *Toll Free Tel:* 800-321-3644 *Fax:* 323-461-3067 *E-mail:* info@luminyscorp.com *Web Site:* www.luminyscorp.com, pg 926

Lumisphere™ USA, 9429 Everett Ct, Spotsylvania, VA 22553 *Tel:* 540-582-7897 *Fax:* 540-582-5233 *E-mail:* jrbent@starpower.net *Web Site:* www.lumisphereusa.com, pg 926

G T Luscombe Co Inc, 106 Kansas St, Frankfort, IL 60423 *Tel:* 815-469-2478 *Toll Free Tel:* 800-435-7855 *Fax:* 815-469-5429 *Toll Free Fax:* 888-469-5429 *E-mail:* info@gtluscombe.com *Web Site:* www.gtluscombe.com, pg 926

Lux Mundi Production House, 1405 16 St, Racine, WI 53403 *Tel:* 262-619-1622 *E-mail:* producer@luxmundistudio.com *Web Site:* www.luxmundistudio.com, pg 926

Luxor, 2245 Delany Rd, Waukegan, IL 60087 *Tel:* 847-244-1800 *Toll Free Tel:* 800-323-4656 *Fax:* 847-244-1818 *Toll Free Fax:* 800-327-1698 *E-mail:* info@luxorfurn.com; customerservice@luxorfurn.com *Web Site:* www.luxorfurn.com, pg 926

LuXout Brand Stage Curtains, 1221 Admiral St, Richmond, VA 23220 *Tel:* 804-264-3000; 804-264-3700 *Toll Free Tel:* 800-817-1204 *Toll Free Fax:* 888-227-8064 *E-mail:* luxoutinfo@luxout.com *Web Site:* www.luxout.com, pg 926

Luzerne County Community College, 1333 S Prospect St, Nanticoke, PA 18634-3899 *Tel:* 570-740-0200 *Toll Free Tel:* 800-377-5222 *Fax:* 570-740-0250 *Web Site:* www.luzerne.edu/index.jsp, pg 926

LW Media Group, 107 W Valencia Ave, Burbank, CA 91502 *Tel:* 818-439-2989 *E-mail:* lwmgbooking@gmail.com *Web Site:* www.lwmgstudios.com, pg 926

Lylofilm Productions, 503 Beech St, New Hyde Park, NY 11040 *Tel:* 516-587-0567 *E-mail:* lylofilm@gmail.com; cdigitalv@yahoo.com *Web Site:* www.lylofilm.com, pg 926

Lyn Norstad & Associates Inc, 2470 E Oakton St, Arlington Heights, IL 60005 *Tel:* 847-640-6400 *Fax:* 847-640-1677 *E-mail:* contact@lnainc.com *Web Site:* www.lnainc.com, pg 926

Lynch Communications, 22 Canada Cove Ave, Half Moon Bay, CA 94019 *Tel:* 678-939-1212 *Web Site:* www.lynchcommunications.com, pg 926

Lynx Broadband, 12219 Wood Lake Dr, Burnsville, MN 55337 *Tel:* 952-894-9590 *Fax:* 952-894-9380 *E-mail:* info@lynxbroadband.com *Web Site:* www.lynxbroadband.com, pg 926

LYNX Signal Management Systems LLC, 4407 Vineland Rd, Suite D-18, Orlando, FL 32811 *Tel:* 407-428-1071 *Fax:* 407-428-1075 *E-mail:* sales1@intelligentmedia.us; support1@intelligentmedia.us *Web Site:* www.intelligentmedia.us, pg 926

Lynx Studio Technology Inc, 190 McCormick Ave, Costa Mesa, CA 92626-3307 *Tel:* 714-545-4700 *Fax:* 714-545-4777 *E-mail:* sales@lynxstudio.com *Web Site:* www.lynxstudio.com, pg 927

Fred Lyon Pictures, 3609 Buchanan St, San Francisco, CA 94123 *Tel:* 415-922-5100 *Fax:* 415-922-5762 *E-mail:* images@winetravelandfood.com *Web Site:* www.fredlyon.com; www.winetravelandfood.com, pg 927

Lyon Video Inc, 2091 Arlingate Lane, Columbus, OH 43228 *Tel:* 614-297-0001 *Web Site:* www.lyonvideo.com, pg 927

Lyon Workspace Products LLC, 420 N Main St, Montgomery, IL 60538 *Tel:* 630-892-8941 *Toll Free Tel:* 800-433-8488 *Fax:* 630-892-8966 *Toll Free Fax:* 800-367-6681 *E-mail:* lyon@lyonworkspace.com *Web Site:* www.lyonworkspace.com, pg 927

LYRASIS, 1438 W Peachtree NW, Suite 200, Atlanta, GA 30309 *Tel:* 404-892-0943 *Toll Free Tel:* 800-999-8558 *Fax:* 404-892-7879 *Web Site:* www.lyrasis.org, pg 927

Lyrichord Discs Inc, PO Box 1977, Old Chelsea Sta, New York, NY 10011-1726 *Tel:* 212-404-8290 *Fax:* 212-404-8291 *E-mail:* info@lyrichord.com *Web Site:* www.lyrichord.com, pg 927

M-Audio, 2000 Scenic View Dr, Cumberland, RI 02864 *Tel:* 401-658-5765 *Fax:* 401-658-3640 *Web Site:* www.m-audio.com, pg 927

M M Newman Corp, 24 Tioga Way, Marblehead, MA 01945 *Tel:* 781-631-7100 *Toll Free Tel:* 800-777-6309 *Fax:* 781-631-8887 *E-mail:* sales@mmnewman.com *Web Site:* www.mmnewman.com, pg 927

M Works Mastering Studios, 1035 Cambridge St, Suite 17-B, Cambridge, MA 02141 *Tel:* 617-577-0089 *Fax:* 617-577-0098 *E-mail:* studio@m-works.com *Web Site:* www.m-works.com, pg 927

MAC Production Group, 3172 Greenwood St, Winter Park, FL 32792 *Tel:* 407-234-8898 *Fax:* 407-671-5360 *E-mail:* info@macproav.com *Web Site:* macproav.com, pg 927

MacGillivray Freeman Films Inc, PO Box 205, Laguna Beach, CA 92652-0205 *Tel:* 949-494-1055 *Fax:* 949-494-2079 *E-mail:* info@macfreefilms.com *Web Site:* www.macfreefilms.com, pg 927

Mach 1 Productions, 1101 N Himes Ave, Tampa, FL 33607 *Tel:* 813-873-7700 *Fax:* 813-875-6633 *E-mail:* info@mach1pro.com *Web Site:* www.mach1pro.com, pg 927

Mackenzie Laboratories Inc, 1163 Nicole Ct, Glendora, CA 91740 *Tel:* 909-394-9007 *Fax:* 909-394-9411 *E-mail:* info@macklabs.com *Web Site:* www.macklabs.com, pg 927

Macmillan Audio, 175 Fifth Ave, New York, NY 10010 *Tel:* 646-600-7856; 646-307-5742 *Toll Free Tel:* 888-330-8477 (orders); 800-221-7945 *Toll Free Fax:* 800-672-7703 (orders) *E-mail:* macmillan.audio@macmillanusa.com *Web Site:* us.macmillan.com/audio.aspx, pg 927

Macrosystem US Inc, 5541 Central Ave, Suite 135, Boulder, CO 80301 *Tel:* 303-440-5311 *Toll Free Tel:* 877-554-2846 *Fax:* 303-440-5396 *E-mail:* info@macrosystem.us *Web Site:* www.macrosystem.us, pg 927

Madera County Film Commission, PO Box 3690, Oakhurst, CA 93644 *Tel:* 559-760-1143 *Fax:* 559-658-2851 *Web Site:* www.yosemite-sierra.com; www.filmcalifornia.com/yosemite.html, pg 1093

Madera Video, 501 N E St, Suite A, Madera, CA 93638-3102 *Tel:* 559-661-6000 *Toll Free Tel:* 800-828-8118 *Fax:* 559-674-3650, pg 927

Madison Square Garden, 4 Pennsylvania Plaza, New York, NY 10001 *Tel:* 212-465-6000; 212-465-6741 *Fax:* 212-465-4416 *E-mail:* msgnetpr@msgnetwork.com *Web Site:* www.thegarden.com; www.msg.com, pg 927

Madisound Speaker Components Inc, 8608 University Green, Suite 10, Middleton, WI 53562 *Tel:* 608-831-3433 *Toll Free Tel:* 866-883-1488 (orders) *Fax:* 608-831-3771 *E-mail:* info@madisound.com *Web Site:* www.madisound.com, pg 928

Magic By Bruce Chadwick, PO Box 12345, Fort Worth, TX 76110-8345 *Tel:* 817-832-6062 *E-mail:* chadwickillusionist@yahoo.com *Web Site:* www.magicbybrucechadwick.com, pg 928

Magic Gadgets™, 12986 Mapleleaf Ct NE, Aurora, OR 97002-8418 *Tel:* 503-678-6236; 818-655-5465 (rentals) *Fax:* 503-678-6237 *E-mail:* info@magicgadgets.com *Web Site:* www.magicgadgets.com, pg 928

Magic Teleprompting Inc, 1390 Waller St, San Francisco, CA 94117 *Tel:* 415-626-5283 *Toll Free Tel:* 800-646-6244 *Fax:* 415-626-2762 *E-mail:* info@magicscroll.com *Web Site:* www.magicscroll.com, pg 928

Magick Lantern, 750 Ralph McGill Blvd, Atlanta, GA 30312 *Tel:* 404-688-3348 *Fax:* 404-584-5247 *E-mail:* info@magicklantern.com *Web Site:* magicklantern.com, pg 928

Magna Systems Inc, 208 S Jefferson St, Suite 402, Chicago, IL 60661 *Toll Free Tel:* 800-634-4941 *Toll Free Fax:* 800-998-0854 *E-mail:* info@magnasystems.com *Web Site:* www.learningseed.com, pg 928

Magna-Tech Electronic Co Inc, 1998 NE 150 St, North Miami, FL 33181 *Tel:* 305-573-7339 *Fax:* 305-573-8101 *E-mail:* magnatech@iceco.com; sales@iceco.com *Web Site:* www.magna-tech.com, pg 928

Magna Visual Inc, 9400 Watson Rd, St Louis, MO 63126-1596 *Tel:* 314-843-9000 *Toll Free Tel:* 800-843-3399 *Fax:* 314-843-0000 *E-mail:* magna@magnavisual.com *Web Site:* www.magnavisual.com, pg 928

Magnanimous Media, 600 W Cermak, Chicago, IL 60616 *Tel:* 312-465-2366 *E-mail:* rentals@magnanimous.biz; production@magnanimous.biz *Web Site:* www.magnanimous.biz, pg 928

Magnaplan Corp, 1320 Rte 9, No 3314, Champlain, NY 12919 *Tel:* 518-298-8404 *Toll Free Tel:* 800-361-1192 *Fax:* 518-298-2368 *Toll Free Fax:* 888-563-8730 *E-mail:* info@visualplanning.com *Web Site:* www.visualplanning.com, pg 928

Magnepan Inc, 1645 Ninth St, White Bear Lake, MN 55110 *Tel:* 651-426-1645 *Toll Free Tel:* 800-474-1646 *Fax:* 651-426-0441 *Web Site:* www.magnepan.com, pg 928

Magnet Sales & Manufacturing Co Inc, 11248 Playa Ct, Culver City, CA 90230 *Tel:* 310-391-7213 *Toll Free Tel:* 800-421-6692 *Fax:* 310-391-7463 *E-mail:* info@magnetsales.com *Web Site:* www.magnetsales.com, pg 928

Magnetek Inc, N49 W13650 Campbell Dr, Menomonee Falls, WI 53051 *Tel:* 262-783-3500 *Toll Free Tel:* 800-288-8178 *Toll Free Fax:* 800-298-3503 *E-mail:* sales@magnetek.com *Web Site:* www.magnetek.com, pg 928

Magnetic Music Publishing Co, 20 Jane St, Suite 2-C, New York, NY 10014-1945 *Tel:* 212-255-8527 *Fax:* 212-595-2067 *E-mail:* info@magneticmusic.ws *Web Site:* magneticmusic.ws, pg 928

Magnetic Post Production, 4 Marshall Rd, Wappingers Falls, NY 12590-4105 *Tel:* 212-598-3000 *Fax:* 212-228-3664 *E-mail:* contact@magneticimage.com *Web Site:* www.magneticimage.com, pg 928

Magnetic Reference Laboratory Inc, 165 Wyandotte Dr, San Jose, CA 95123 *Tel:* 408-227-8631 *Fax:* 408-227-8631 *E-mail:* mrltapes@comcast.net *Web Site:* www.mrltapes.com, pg 928

Magnetic Shield Corp, 740 N Thomas Dr, Bensenville, IL 60106 *Tel:* 630-766-7800 *Toll Free Tel:* 888-766-7800 *Fax:* 630-766-2813 *E-mail:* shields@magnetic-shield.com *Web Site:* www.magnetic-shield.com, pg 928

Magnicon Media/Image d'Or, PO Box 1898, Dearborn, MI 48121-1898 *Tel:* 313-846-8694; 313-574-3546 (cell) *Fax:* 815-361-2869, pg 928

Magno Sound & Video, 729 Seventh Ave, New York, NY 10019 *Tel:* 212-302-2505 *Fax:* 212-819-1282 *E-mail:* staff@magnosound.com *Web Site:* www.magnosoundandvideo.com, pg 929

MAGNUM Companies Ltd, 205 Armour Dr NE, Atlanta, GA 30324 *Tel:* 404-872-0553 *Toll Free Tel:* 800-255-1774 *Fax:* 404-875-5629 *E-mail:* buy@magnumco.com; rent@magnumco.com; design@magnumco.com; production@magnumco.com *Web Site:* www.magnumco.com, pg 929

Magnum Towers Inc, 9370 Elder Creek Rd, Sacramento, CA 95829 *Tel:* 916-381-5053 *Fax:* 916-381-2144 *E-mail:* office@magnumtowers.com *Web Site:* www.magnumtowers.com, pg 929

Carl F & Viola V Mahnke Multimedia Award, 320 W Eighth St, Suite 101, Bloomington, IN 47404-3745 *Tel:* 812-335-7675 *Toll Free Tel:* 877-677-AECT (677-2328) *Fax:* 812-335-7678 *E-mail:* aect@aect.org *Web Site:* www.aect.org, pg 1119

Mailing Avenue Stageworks, 1144 Mailing Ave, Atlanta, GA 30315 *Tel:* 404-601-9500 (ext 11) *Web Site:* www.mailingavenuestageworks.com, pg 929

Main Point Productions, 295 Lobachsville Rd, Oley, PA 19547 *Tel:* 610-987-9320 *E-mail:* mainpoint@dejazzd.com, pg 929

Main Street Media Inc, 185 Pier Ave, Suite 105, Santa Monica, CA 90405 *Tel:* 310-450-1846 *E-mail:* info@mainstreetmediainc.com *Web Site:* www.mainstreetmediainc.com, pg 929

Maine Film Office, 59 State House Sta, Augusta, ME 04333 *Tel:* 207-624-9828 *Fax:* 207-287-8070 *E-mail:* film@maine.gov *Web Site:* www.filminmaine.com, pg 1098

Maine Imaging, PO Box 753, Wiscasset, ME 04578 *Tel:* 207-380-6343 *Web Site:* maineaerial.com, pg 929

Maine Student Film & Video Festival, 103 Montrose Ave, Portland, ME 04103 *Tel:* 207-415-7154 *E-mail:* info@msfvf.com *Web Site:* www.msfvf.com, pg 1119

MainSail Production Services Inc, 521 Byers Rd, Suite 109, Miamisburg, OH 45342 *Tel:* 937-866-7800 *Toll Free Tel:* 800-877-0093 *Fax:* 937-866-8088 *E-mail:* discover@mainsailproductions.com *Web Site:* www.mainsailproductions.com, pg 929

Maison de Soul Records, 238 E Main St, Ville Platte, LA 70586 *Tel:* 337-363-2177 *Fax:* 337-363-2094 *E-mail:* info@flattownmusic.com *Web Site:* www.flattownmusic.com, pg 929

Major Media Inc, PO Box 209, Deerfield, IL 60015 *Tel:* 847-433-1682 *E-mail:* webmaster@major-media.com *Web Site:* www.major-media.com, pg 929

Major Media Productions Inc, PO Box 209, Deerfield, IL 60015 *Tel:* 847-433-1682 *E-mail:* webmaster@major-media.com *Web Site:* www.major-media.com, pg 929

Major Reproductions Equipment Co, PO Box 209, Deerfield, IL 60015 *Tel:* 847-433-1682 *E-mail:* webmaster@major-media.com *Web Site:* www.major-media.com, pg 929

Majortech Inc, 8464 Ninth Line RR-1, Norval, ON L0P 1K0, Canada *Tel:* 905-873-0778 *Fax:* 905-873-1244 *Web Site:* www.majortech.com, pg 929

MakeMusic® Inc, 7615 Golden Triangle Dr, Suite M, Eden Prairie, MN 55344 *Tel:* 952-937-9611 *Toll Free Tel:* 800-843-2066 (cust serv) *Fax:* 952-937-9760 *Web Site:* www.makemusic.com, pg 929

MALCO Electronics, 5 Wolcott Ave, Lawrence, MA 01844 *Tel:* 978-685-4383 *Toll Free Tel:* 800-937-6252 *Fax:* 978-975-4038 *E-mail:* info@malcoelectronics.com *Web Site:* www.malcoelectronics.com, pg 929

MAM-A Inc, 4250 Buckingham Dr, Suite 100, Colorado Springs, CO 80907 *Toll Free Tel:* 888-626-3472 *Fax:* 719-592-0057 *Toll Free Fax:* 888-923-7203 *E-mail:* info@mam-a.com *Web Site:* www.mam-a.com, pg 929

Mamiya, 75 Virginia Rd, Suite 1, North White Plains, NY 10603 *Tel:* 914-347-3300 *Fax:* 914-347-3309 *E-mail:* info@mamiya-usa.com *Web Site:* www.mamiya-usa.com; www.mamiyaleaf.com, pg 929

Mammoth HD, PO Box 2064, Evergreen, CO 80437 *Tel:* 303-670-7973 *E-mail:* mammothhd@me.com; info@mammothhd.com *Web Site:* www.mammothhd.com, pg 929

Mammoth Location Services, One Minaret Rd, Mammoth Lakes, CA 93546 *Tel:* 760-934-0628 *Fax:* 760-924-7026, pg 1093

Manatee County Film Commission, One Haben Blvd, Palmetto, FL 34221 *Tel:* 941-729-9177 *Toll Free Tel:* 800-822-2017 *Fax:* 941-729-1820 *Web Site:* www.bradentongulfislands.com, pg 1096

Manchester Music Library Inc, 26 Ivalou St, Somerville, MA 02143 *Tel:* 413-369-4331 *Web Site:* www.manchestermusiclibrary.com, pg 929

maney-logic, 6117 Thornebury Dr, Madison, WI 53719-4834 *Tel:* 608-277-8001 *Fax:* 608-277-8001 *Web Site:* maney-logic.com, pg 929

Manfrotto Distribution Inc, 10 Mountainview Rd, Suite 320 S, Upper Saddle River, NJ 07458 *Tel:* 201-818-9500 *Fax:* 201-818-9177 *E-mail:* info@manfrottodistribution.us *Web Site:* www.manfrottodistribution.us, pg 930

Manhattan Center Studios Inc, 311 W 34 St, New York, NY 10001 *Tel:* 212-279-7740 *Fax:* 212-564-1072 *E-mail:* info@mcstudios.com *Web Site:* www.mcstudios.com, pg 930

Manhattan Film Commission, 501 Poyntz Ave, Manhattan, KS 66502 *Tel:* 785-776-8829 *Toll Free Tel:* 800-759-0134 *Fax:* 785-776-0679 *E-mail:* cvb@manhattan.org *Web Site:* www.manhattancvb.org, pg 1097

Manhattan Production Music Inc, 1650 Broadway, Suite 900, New York, NY 10019 *Tel:* 212-333-5766 *Fax:* 212-262-0814 *E-mail:* info@mpmmusic.com *Web Site:* www.mpmmusic.com, pg 930

Maniac Productions, 3888 Viewpoint Way, Lafayette, CO 80026 *Tel:* 303-661-0920 *Toll Free Tel:* 888-626-4227 *Fax:* 303-661-0995 *E-mail:* mpcl@aol.com; info@maniacproductions.com *Web Site:* www.maniacproductions.com, pg 930

Maniglia Media, 7925 Jones Branch Dr, Suite LL110, Tysons, VA 22102 *Tel:* 703-283-8532 *Web Site:* www.manigliamedia.com, pg 930

Manios Digital & Film, 10663 Burbank Blvd, North Hollywood, CA 91601 *Tel:* 818-760-8290 *Toll Free Tel:* 800-845-6619 *Fax:* 818-760-8805 *E-mail:* sales@maniosdigital.com *Web Site:* www.maniosdigital.com, pg 930

Manitoba Film & Music, 410-93 Lombard Ave, Suite 410, Winnipeg, MB R3B 3B1, Canada *Tel:* 204-947-2040 *Fax:* 204-956-5261 *E-mail:* info@mbfilmmusic.ca *Web Site:* www.mbfilmmusic.ca, pg 930, 1105

Manley Laboratories Inc, 13880 Magnolia Ave, Chino, CA 91710 *Tel:* 909-627-4256 *Fax:* 909-628-2482 *Web Site:* www.manley.com, pg 930

Manning Productions, 115 N Morgan St, Chicago, IL 60607 *Tel:* 312-756-1100 *Fax:* 312-756-1200 *E-mail:* info@manningproductions.com *Web Site:* www.manningproductions.com, pg 930

Map Resources, 50 S Union St, Lambertville, NJ 08530 *Tel:* 609-397-1611 *Toll Free Tel:* 800-334-4291 *Fax:* 609-751-9378 *E-mail:* info@mapresources.com; sales@mapresources.com *Web Site:* www.mapresources.com, pg 930

MAPS Production House, 212 Collins Ave, Miami Beach, FL 33139 *Tel:* 305-532-7880; 786-245-2491 (equipment rentals) *Fax:* 305-532-7673 *E-mail:* info@mapsproduction.com; equipment@mapsproduction.com *Web Site:* mapsproduction.com, pg 930

MarathonNorco Aerospace Inc, c/o Christie Electric Div, 8301 Imperial Dr, Waco, TX 76712-6588 *Tel:* 254-776-0650 *Fax:* 254-776-6558 *E-mail:* marathon@mptc.com *Web Site:* www.mnaerospace.com, pg 930

Marblemedia, 74 Fraser Ave, Suite 100, Toronto, ON M6K 3E1, Canada *Tel:* 416-646-2711 *E-mail:* connect@marblemedia.com *Web Site:* www.marblemedia.com, pg 930

March Manufacturing Inc, 1819 Pickwick Ave, Glenview, IL 60026 *Tel:* 847-729-5300 *Fax:* 847-729-7062 *E-mail:* sales@marchpump.com *Web Site:* www.marchpump.com, pg 930

March of Dimes Foundation, 1275 Mamaroneck Ave, White Plains, NY 10605 *Tel:* 914-997-4488 *Toll Free Tel:* 888-663-4637 *E-mail:* contactus@marchofdimes.com *Web Site:* www.marchofdimes.com, pg 930

Marco Inc, 451 Carson Rd N, Birmingham, AL 35215 *Tel:* 205-856-1110 *Toll Free Tel:* 888-465-2514 *Fax:* 205-856-1136 *E-mail:* marco@marcoconsoles.com *Web Site:* www.marcoconsoles.com, pg 930

Mardi Gras Costume Shop, 5895 N Granite Reef Rd, Scottsdale, AZ 85250 *Tel:* 480-948-4030 *Fax:* 480-948-0754 *E-mail:* info@mardigrascostumeshop.com *Web Site:* mardigrascostumeshop.com, pg 930

Marengo Films, 27206 Waterfall Hill Pkwy, Spicewood, TX 78669 *Tel:* 972-365-0406 *Fax:* 830-693-0949 *E-mail:* marengodvd@texasdata.net *Web Site:* www.marengofilms.com, pg 931

Marinco Electrical Group, N85 W12545 Westbrook Crossing, Menomonee Falls, WI 53051-3330 *Tel:* 262-293-0600 *Toll Free Tel:* 800-307-6702 *Fax:* 262-293-7022 *E-mail:* swdsales@marinco.com *Web Site:* www.marinco.com, pg 931

Marine Geographic, 3636 Division St, Knoxville, TN 37919 *Tel:* 865-237-0291; 865-524-0001 *Web Site:* www.marinegeographic.net; www.marinegeographic.com, pg 931

Maritz Performance Improvement Co, 1000 Town Ctr, Suite 1200, Southfield, MI 48075 *Tel:* 248-948-4500 *Toll Free Tel:* 877-462-7489 *Fax:* 248-948-4598 *Web Site:* www.maritz.com, pg 931

Mark Custom Recording Service Inc, 10815 Bodine Rd, Clarence, NY 14031-2252 *Tel:* 716-759-2600 *Fax:* 716-759-2329 *E-mail:* info@markcustom.com *Web Site:* www.markcustom.com, pg 931

Mark Sonder Productions Inc, 2479 Freezeland Rd, Linden, VA 22642 *Tel:* 540-636-1640 *E-mail:* inquiry@marksonderproductions.com *Web Site:* www.marksonderproductions.com, pg 931

Markertek Video Supply, One Tower Dr, Saugerties, NY 12477 *Tel:* 845-246-3036 *Toll Free Tel:* 800-522-2025 *Fax:* 845-246-1757 *E-mail:* sales@markertek.com *Web Site:* www.markertek.com, pg 931

Market Data Retrieval (MDR), 6 Armstrong Rd, Suite 301, Shelton, CT 06484 *Tel:* 203-926-4800 *Toll Free Tel:* 800-333-8802 *Toll Free Fax:* 866-532-7097 *E-mail:* mdrinfo@dnb.com *Web Site:* www.schooldata.com, pg 931

The Market Place, PO Box 4126, Rockford, IL 61110-0626 *Tel:* 815-877-1514, pg 931

Marketec, 419 S Flower St, Burbank, CA 91502 *Tel:* 818-847-0200 *Toll Free Tel:* 800-557-8861 *Toll Free Fax:* 888-262-1726 *E-mail:* info@marketec.com *Web Site:* www.marketec.com, pg 931

Marketron Broadcast Solutions, 101 Empty Saddle Trail, Hailey, ID 83333 *Tel:* 208-788-6800 *Toll Free Tel:* 888-239-8878 (support); 800-476-7226 *E-mail:* info@wicksbroadcastsolutions.com *Web Site:* www.wicksbroadcastsolutions.com; www.marketron.com, pg 931

Marlboro Film & Video Productions, 1076 Moss Hollow Rd, Marlboro, VT 05344 *Tel:* 802-257-0743 *Toll Free Tel:* 888-867-7581 (orders) *Fax:* 802-257-0743 *E-mail:* mfilmpro@sover.net *Web Site:* marlboroproductions.com, pg 931

Marsand Inc, 6100 S IH-35W, Alvarado, TX 76009 *Tel:* 817-783-5566 *Fax:* 817-783-5577 *Web Site:* www.marsand.com, pg 931

Marsh Media, 200 Avila Circle, Kansas City, MO 64114 *Tel:* 816-523-1059 *Toll Free Tel:* 800-821-3303 *Fax:* 816-333-7421 *Toll Free Fax:* 866-333-7421 *E-mail:* order@marshmedia.com; info@marshmedia.com *Web Site:* www.marshmedia.com, pg 931

Neal Marshad Productions, 99 Hudson St, 5th fl, New York, NY 10013 *Tel:* 212-925-8656 *Fax:* 212-292-8912 *E-mail:* info@marshad.com *Web Site:* www.marshad.com, pg 931

Marshad Technology Group, 99 Hudson St, 5th fl, New York, NY 10013 *Tel:* 212-925-8656 *E-mail:* info@marshad.com *Web Site:* www.marshad.com, pg 932

Marshall Electronics Inc, 1910 E Maple Ave, El Segundo, CA 90245 *Tel:* 310-333-0606 *Toll Free Tel:* 800-800-6608 *Fax:* 310-333-0688 *E-mail:* sales@mars-cam.com; sales@marshall-usa.com *Web Site:* www.mars-cam.com; www.marshall-usa.com, pg 932

Marshall Furniture Inc, 999 Anita Ave, Antioch, IL 60002 *Tel:* 847-395-9350 *Fax:* 847-395-9351 *E-mail:* info@marshallfurniture.com *Web Site:* www.marshallfurniture.com, pg 932

Martel Electronics Sales Inc, Yorba Linda Hills Business Park, 23221 E La Palma Ave, Yorba Linda, CA 92887 *Tel:* 714-692-6690 *Toll Free Tel:* 800-553-5536 *Fax:* 714-692-1799 *E-mail:* martelsales@marteldirect.com *Web Site:* www.martelelectronics.com, pg 932

The Martha's Vineyard Film Festival (MVFF), PO Box 592, 9 State Rd, Chilmark, MA 02535 *Tel:* 508-645-9599 *Fax:* 508-645-9893 *Web Site:* www.tmvff.org, pg 1119

Martha's Vineyard International Film Festival, PO Box 4423, Vineyard Haven, MA 02568 *Tel:* 508-696-9369 *E-mail:* info@mvfilmsociety.com *Web Site:* www.mvfilmfest.com, pg 1119

Marti Electronics Inc, 4100 N 24 St, Quincy, IL 62305 *Tel:* 217-224-9600 *Fax:* 217-224-9607 *E-mail:* sales@martielectronics.com *Web Site:* martielectronics.com, pg 932

The Martin Guitar Co, 510 Sycamore St, Nazareth, PA 18064 *Tel:* 610-759-2837 *Toll Free Tel:* 800-633-2060; 888-433-9177 *Fax:* 610-759-5757 *E-mail:* info@martinguitar.com *Web Site:* www.martinguitar.com, pg 932

Martin Professional Inc, 700 Sawgrass Corporate Pkwy, Sunrise, FL 33325 *Tel:* 954-858-1800 *Fax:* 954-858-1811 *E-mail:* martinus@martinpro.com *Web Site:* www.martinpro.com, pg 932

Martinsound Inc, 1151 W Valley Blvd, Alhambra, CA 91803-2493 *Tel:* 626-281-3555 *Toll Free Tel:* 800-582-3555 *Fax:* 626-284-3092 *E-mail:* info@martinsound.com *Web Site:* www.martinsound.com, pg 932

Marvel Photo Inc, 1720 N Sheridan Rd, Tulsa, OK 74115 *Tel:* 918-836-0741 *Toll Free Tel:* 800-806-3616 *Fax:* 918-836-0949 *Web Site:* www.marvelphoto.com, pg 932

Marvell Semiconductor Inc, 5488 Marvell Lane, Santa Clara, CA 95054 *Tel:* 408-222-2500 *Fax:* 408-988-8279 *Web Site:* www.marvell.com, pg 932

MarVista Entertainment Inc, 10277 W Olympic Blvd, 3rd fl, Los Angeles, CA 90067 *Tel:* 424-274-3000 *Fax:* 424-274-3050 *E-mail:* info@marvista.net *Web Site:* www.marvista.net, pg 933

Marx InDigital, 7921 Skylake Dr, Fort Worth, TX 76179 *Tel:* 414-351-5060 *Web Site:* www.marxindigital.com, pg 933

Maryknoll Productions, PO Box 308, Maryknoll, NY 10545-0308 *Tel:* 914-941-7590 *Toll Free Tel:* 888-627-9566 *Fax:* 914-944-3613 *E-mail:* mkweb@maryknoll.org *Web Site:* www.maryknoll.org, pg 933

Maryland Film Office, 401 E Pratt St, 14th fl, Baltimore, MD 21202 *Tel:* 410-767-6340 *Toll Free Tel:* 800-333-6632 *Fax:* 410-333-0044 *E-mail:* filminfo@marylandfilm.org *Web Site:* www.marylandfilm.org, pg 1098

Maryland Sound International Holding Co LLC, 4900 Wetheredsville Rd, Baltimore, MD 21207 *Tel:* 410-448-1400 *Toll Free Tel:* 800-76SOUND (767-6863) *Fax:* 410-448-1467 *E-mail:* martha@msihc.com *Web Site:* www.marylandsound.com, pg 933

Maslowski Productions, 1219 Eversole Rd, Cincinnati, OH 45230 *Tel:* 513-231-7301 *Fax:* 513-231-7301 *Web Site:* www.maslowskiwildlife.com, pg 933

Mason Video, 9632 N 34 St, Omaha, NE 68112 *Tel:* 402-455-9422 *E-mail:* mason.video@mac.com *Web Site:* www.masonvideo.com, pg 933

massAV, 755 Middlesex Tpke, Billerica, MA 01821 *Tel:* 978-670-0027 *Toll Free Tel:* 800-423-7830 *Fax:* 978-670-0037 *E-mail:* info@massav.com *Web Site:* www.massav.com, pg 933

Mastech, 1000 Commerce Dr, Suite 500, Pittsburgh, PA 15275 *Tel:* 412-787-2100 *Toll Free Tel:* 800-627-8323 *Fax:* 412-494-9272 *E-mail:* info@mastech.com *Web Site:* www.mastech.com, pg 933

Master Bond, 154 Hobart St, Hackensack, NJ 07601 *Tel:* 201-343-8983 *Fax:* 201-343-2132 *E-mail:* main@masterbond.com *Web Site:* www.masterbond.com, pg 933

Master Books, 3142 Hwy 103 N, Green Forest, AR 72638 *Tel:* 870-438-5288 *Toll Free Tel:* 800-999-3777 *Fax:* 870-438-5120 *E-mail:* nlp@newleafpress.net *Web Site:* www.nlpg.com, pg 933

Master Communications Group, 3410 Winnetka Ave, Suite 107, New Hope, MN 55427 *Tel:* 763-231-1881 *Fax:* 763-231-1885 *E-mail:* info@mastcom.com *Web Site:* www.mastcom.com, pg 933

Master Mind Publishing Co, 11200 E 11 Mile Rd, Warren, MI 48089 *Tel:* 586-353-2300 *Toll Free Tel:* 800-758-3055 *Fax:* 586-758-7249 *E-mail:* info@renaissanceunity.org *Web Site:* www.renaissanceunity.org, pg 933

Master Video Disc & Design, 7349 N Via Paseo del Sur, Suite 515-455, Scottsdale, AZ 85238 *Tel:* 480-948-0305 *Fax:* 480-948-8628 *Web Site:* www.mastervdd.com, pg 933

Masterclock Inc, 2484 W Clay St, St Charles, MO 63301-2548 *Tel:* 636-724-3666 *Toll Free Tel:* 800-940-2248 *Fax:* 636-724-3776 *E-mail:* info@masterclock.com; sales@masterclock.com *Web Site:* www.masterclock.com, pg 933

Masterdisk Corp, 545 W 45 St, 5th fl, New York, NY 10036 *Tel:* 212-541-5022 *Fax:* 212-581-4093 *E-mail:* info@masterdisk.com *Web Site:* www.masterdisk.com, pg 933

Mastervision Inc, 969 Park Ave, New York, NY 10028 *Tel:* 212-879-0448 *Toll Free Tel:* 800-876-0091 (order info) *Fax:* 212-744-3560 *Web Site:* www.mastervision.com, pg 933

Mastery Technologies Inc, 41216 Bridge St, Novi, MI 48375 *Tel:* 972-943-9214 *Toll Free Tel:* 800-258-3837 *Fax:* 248-888-8424 *E-mail:* sales@masterytech.com *Web Site:* www.masterytech.com, pg 933

Mathmadeeasy.com, 4914 13 Ave, Brooklyn, NY 11219 *Toll Free Tel:* 800-USA-MATH (872-6284) *Web Site:* www.mathmadeeasy.com, pg 934

Matrix Video Communications Corp (MVCC), 120 2331 50 Ave SE, Calgary, AB T2G 0N1, Canada *Tel:* 403-640-4490 *Toll Free Tel:* 800-320-3974 *Fax:* 403-640-9012 *Web Site:* www.matrixvideocom.com, pg 934

Matrox Video Products Group, 1055 Saint Regis Blvd, Dorval, QC H9P 2T4, Canada *Tel:* 514-822-6364; 514-685-7230 *Toll Free Tel:* 800-361-4903 *Fax:* 514-685-2853 *Web Site:* www.matrox.com/video, pg 934

Matson Multi-Media, 403 E Ramsey Rd, Suite 101, San Antonio, TX 78216 *Tel:* 210-349-3674 *Fax:* 210-340-5710 *E-mail:* sales@matsonmultimedia.com *Web Site:* www.matsonmultimedia.com, pg 934

Matthews Studio Equipment Inc, 4520 W Valerio St, Burbank, CA 91505 *Tel:* 818-843-6715 *Toll Free Tel:* 800-237-8263 *Fax:* 818-480-5808 *E-mail:* info@msegrip.com *Web Site:* www.msegrip.com, pg 934

Maui County Film Office, Off of Economic Devt, One Main Plaza, 2200 S Main St, Suite 305, Wailuku, HI 96793 *Tel:* 808-270-7710 *Fax:* 808-270-7995 *Web Site:* www.co.maui.hi.us, pg 1097

MAVCO, 77 S Main St, Newtown, CT 06470 *Tel:* 203-270-8292 *Fax:* 203-270-8292, pg 934

Maverick Awards, 13 Rock City Rd, Woodstock, NY 12498 *Tel:* 845-679-4265; 845-810-0131 *Fax:* 509-479-5414 *E-mail:* info@woodstockfilmfestival.com *Web Site:* www.woodstockfilmfestival.com, pg 1119

Maverick Video Productions, 121 Interpark, Suite 601, San Antonio, TX 78216 *Tel:* 210-495-1111 *Fax:* 210-495-8033 *Web Site:* www.maverickstudio.com, pg 934

Max Films Inc, 1751 Richardson St, Suite 5101, Montreal, QC H3K 1G6, Canada *Tel:* 514-282-8444 *Fax:* 514-282-9222 *E-mail:* info@maxfilms.ca *Web Site:* www.maxfilms.ca, pg 934

Max USA, 257 E Second St, Mineola, NY 11501 *Tel:* 516-741-3151 *Toll Free Tel:* 800-223-4293 *Fax:* 516-741-3272 *E-mail:* maxcorp@maxusacorp.com *Web Site:* www.maxusacorp.com, pg 934

Maxell Corp of America, 3 Garret Mountain Plaza, Suite 300, Woodland Park, NJ 07424-3352 *Tel:* 973-653-2400 *Toll Free Tel:* 800-533-2836; 800-377-5887 (tech support) *Fax:* 201-796-8790 *E-mail:* techsupp@maxell.com *Web Site:* www.maxell-usa.com, pg 934

Maximus Media Inc, 2727 N Grove Industrial Dr, Suite 111, Fresno, CA 93727 *Tel:* 559-255-1688 *Toll Free Tel:* 800-2THEMAX (284-3629) *Fax:* 559-255-0323 *Web Site:* www.tothemax.com, pg 934

MAXON Computer Inc, 2640 Lavery Ct, Suite A, Newbury Park, CA 91320 *Tel:* 805-376-3333 *Fax:* 805-376-3331 *E-mail:* info_us@maxon.net *Web Site:* www.maxon.net, pg 934

Mayor's Office of Economic & Community Development, Metropolitan Courthouse, Suite 102, One Public Sq, Nashville, TN 37219 *Tel:* 615-862-4700 *Fax:* 615-862-6025 *Web Site:* www.nashville.gov, pg 1102

Mayor's Office of Film & Video, 222 NW Fifth Ave, Portland, OR 97209-3859 *Tel:* 503-823-4039 *Fax:* 503-865-3791 *Web Site:* www.portlandonline.com/filmandvideo; www.pdc.us/film, pg 1101

MB Productions, 4 Edison Place, Fairfield, NJ 07004 *Tel:* 973-439-0044 *Toll Free Tel:* 800-622-2224 *Fax:* 973-439-9844 *E-mail:* mbp@mbvideo.com *Web Site:* www.mbvideo.com, pg 934

Annual MCA-I Media Festival, PO Box 5135, Madison, WI 53705-0135 *Tel:* 608-836-0722 *Toll Free Tel:* 888-899-MCAI (899-6224) *Toll Free Fax:* 888-862-8150 *E-mail:* info@mca-i.org; mcaimediafestival@gmail.com *Web Site:* www.mca-i.org, pg 1119

McAlister Electronics, 926 E Fremont Ave, Sunnyvale, CA 94087 *Tel:* 408-739-2605 *Fax:* 408-733-2895 *E-mail:* mcalelect@aol.com *Web Site:* www.werepairallbrands.com, pg 935

McBain Audio Visual Ltd, 10805 107 Ave, Edmonton, AB T5H 0W9, Canada *Tel:* 780-420-0404 *Toll Free Tel:* 800-661-6980 *Fax:* 780-421-1188 *Web Site:* www.mcbaincamera.com, pg 935

MCC Films, 7 Rabbit Lane, Brookfield, CT 06804 *Tel:* 203-775-9473 *Fax:* 734-310-6328 *E-mail:* info@mcc-films.com *Web Site:* www.mcc-films.com, pg 935

McCauley Sound Inc, 16607 Meridian Ave E, Puyallup, WA 98375 *Tel:* 253-848-0363 *Toll Free Tel:* 877-622-2853 *Fax:* 253-841-3050 *Web Site:* www.mccauleysound.com, pg 935

MCCOM Inc, 383 Rte 206, Chester, NJ 07930 *Tel:* 908-879-9590 *Fax:* 908-879-9679 *E-mail:* info@mccominc.com *Web Site:* www.mccom.tv, pg 935

Robert McConnell Productions, 4303 67 Ave NW, Gig Harbor, WA 98335 *Tel:* 253-265-3184 *Toll Free Tel:* 800-532-4017 *Fax:* 253-265-1550 *Toll Free Fax:* 800-948-8463 *E-mail:* info@parli.com; drvideo@earthlink.net *Web Site:* parli.com, pg 935

McCune Audio-Video-Lighting, 101 Utah Ave, South San Francisco, CA 94080 *Tel:* 650-873-1111 *Toll Free Tel:* 800-899-7686 *Fax:* 650-246-6702 *E-mail:* info@mccune.com *Web Site:* www.mccune.com, pg 935

McCune Design, 6836 Valjean Ave, Van Nuys, CA 91406 *Tel:* 818-779-1920 *Web Site:* www.mccune-design.com, pg 935

McCurdy Radio Ltd, 75 First St, Suite 108, Orangeville, ON L9W 5B6, Canada *Tel:* 416-248-6155 *Fax:* 416-248-6755 *E-mail:* sales8800@mcradio.com *Web Site:* www.mcradio.com; www.mccurdytel.com, pg 935

McGraw Hill Financial, 1221 Avenue of the Americas, New York, NY 10020-1095 *Tel:* 212-512-2000; 212-904-2000 *Web Site:* www.mhfi.com, pg 935

McGraw-Hill School Education Group, 8787 Orion Place, Columbus, OH 43240-4027 *Tel:* 614-430-4000 *Toll Free Tel:* 800-334-7734 *Fax:* 614-755-5682 *E-mail:* customer.service@mcgraw-hill.com *Web Site:* www.mcgraw-hill.com, pg 935

McGuane Studio Inc, 36 Horatio St, Suite 5-B, New York, NY 10014-1691 *Tel:* 212-463-7259, pg 935

McIntyre Media Inc, 203-75 First St, Orangeville, ON L9W 5B6, Canada *Tel:* 519-942-9640 *Toll Free Tel:* 800-565-3036 *Fax:* 519-942-8489 *E-mail:* info@mcintyre.ca *Web Site:* www.mcintyre.ca, pg 935

McKay Conant Hoover Inc, 5655 Lindero Canyon Rd, Suite 325, Westlake Village, CA 91362 *Tel:* 818-991-9300 *Fax:* 818-991-2324 *E-mail:* info@mchinc.com *Web Site:* www.mchinc.com, pg 935

Lloyd F McKinney Associates Inc, 25350 Cypress Ave, Hayward, CA 94544 *Tel:* 510-783-8043 *Fax:* 510-783-2130 *Web Site:* www.mckinneyassoc.com, pg 935

McNabb & Connolly, 60 Briarwood Ave, Mississauga, ON L5G 3N6, Canada *Tel:* 905-278-0566 *Toll Free Tel:* 866-722-1522 *Fax:* 905-278-2801 *Toll Free Fax:* 866-722-1822 *E-mail:* info@mcnabbconnolly.ca *Web Site:* www.mcnabbconnolly.ca, pg 935

McNee Productions Inc, 3301 W Alabama St, Houston, TX 77098 *Tel:* 713-526-5333 *Fax:* 713-526-4634 *E-mail:* mcnee@mcnee.com *Web Site:* www.mcnee.com, pg 935

MCS Recording Studios, 550 Queen St E, Suite G100, Toronto, ON M5A 1V2, Canada *Tel:* 416-361-1688 *Toll Free Tel:* 866-322-8555 *Fax:* 416-361-5088 *E-mail:* info@mcsrecording.com *Web Site:* www.mcsrecording.com, pg 936

MDS Power Inc, PO Box 532, Champlain, NY 12919-0532 *Tel:* 514-369-4919 *Toll Free Tel:* 800-931-4919 *Fax:* 514-369-4817 *Toll Free Fax:* 800-931-4817 *E-mail:* sales@mdspower.com; support@mdspower.com *Web Site:* www.mdspower.com, pg 936

Medcom Inc, 6060 Phyllis Dr, Cypress, CA 90630-5243 *Tel:* 714-891-1443 *Toll Free Tel:* 800-877-1443; 800-541-0253 *Fax:* 714-891-3140 *E-mail:* customerservice@medcominc.com *Web Site:* www.medcominc.com, pg 936

Media Alliance, 1904 Franklin St, Suite 818, Oakland, CA 94612 *Tel:* 510-832-9000 *Fax:* 510-238-8557 *E-mail:* information@media-alliance.org *Web Site:* www.media-alliance.org, pg 1084

Media Arts Grants, 400 Sibley St, Suite 125, St Paul, MN 55101 *Tel:* 651-224-9431 *Toll Free Tel:* 800-995-3766 *Fax:* 651-224-3439 *E-mail:* info@jeromefdn.org *Web Site:* www.jeromefdn.org, pg 1119

Media Bridge Gamekids, PO Box 513, Koloa, HI 96703 *Tel:* 808-280-9591 *Web Site:* www.gamekids.com, pg 936

The Media Collaboratory, 215 E High St, Lexington, KY 40507 *Tel:* 859-255-9049 *Fax:* 859-281-6537 *E-mail:* info@veslex.com *Web Site:* www.veslex.com, pg 936

Media-Comm, 9700 S Pine Blvd, Charlotte, NC 28273 *Tel:* 704-527-8853 *Web Site:* www.media-comm.com, pg 936

Media Communications Association-International (MCA-I), PO Box 5135, Madison, WI 53705-0135 *Tel:* 608-836-0722 *Toll Free Tel:* 888-899-MCAI (899-6224) *Fax:* 608-443-2474; 608-443-2478 *Toll Free Fax:* 888-862-8150 *E-mail:* info@mca-i.org *Web Site:* www.mca-i.org, pg 936, 1084

Media Computing Inc, PO Box 4169, Cave Creek, AZ 85327-4169 *Tel:* 602-614-2091 *E-mail:* info@mediacomputing.com *Web Site:* www.mediacomputing.com, pg 936

Media Concepts Inc, 559 49 St S, St Petersburg, FL 33707 *Tel:* 727-321-2122 *Toll Free Tel:* 800-330-3873 *Fax:* 727-321-2272 *E-mail:* mcifl@tampabay.rr.com *Web Site:* www.mcifl.com, pg 936

Media Consultants Inc, 3908 E Valley Ct, Raleigh, NC 27606 *Tel:* 919-821-2190 *Toll Free Tel:* 800-560-7379 *Toll Free Fax:* 866-881-9331 *Web Site:* www.mediaconsultants.com, pg 936

Media Control Systems LLC, 1050 Pioneer Way, Suite Q, El Cajon, CA 92020 *Tel:* 619-599-1050 *Fax:* 619-599-1051 *Web Site:* www.mediacontrolsystems.com, pg 936

Media Cybernetics Inc, 401 N Washington St, Suite 350, Rockville, MD 20850 *Tel:* 301-495-3305 *Toll Free Tel:* 800-263-2088 *Fax:* 240-328-6193 *E-mail:* info@mediacy.com *Web Site:* www.mediacy.com, pg 936

Media Dimensions Inc, 2212 Autumn Glow Ct, Bel Air, MD 21015 *Tel:* 410-561-4550 *Fax:* 410-561-4550 *E-mail:* info@mediadimensions.com *Web Site:* www.mediadimensions.com, pg 936

Media Distributors, 4518 W Vanowen St, Burbank, CA 91505 *Tel:* 818-980-9916 *Toll Free Tel:* 800-851-3113 *Fax:* 818-566-8989 *E-mail:* la@mediadistributors.com *Web Site:* www.mediadistributors.com, pg 936

Media Elite Productions, 800 Bellevue Way, Suite 600, Bellevue, WA 98004 *Tel:* 425-336-3707 *Toll Free Fax:* 877-391-3778 *E-mail:* mediaeliteproductions@yahoo.com *Web Site:* mediaeliteproductions.com, pg 936

Media Entertainment Inc, 13194 US Hwy 301 S, Suite 320, Riverview, FL 33569 *Tel:* 813-495-5821 *Toll Free Tel:* 888-886-7793 *Fax:* 813-741-1152 *Web Site:* www.mediaent.net, pg 936

Media Event Concepts Inc, 2036 Centimeter Circle, Austin, TX 78758 *Tel:* 512-832-1142 *Toll Free Tel:* 800-299-1142 *Fax:* 512-832-0236 *Web Site:* www.mecteam.com, pg 936

Media Fabricators Inc, 8509 Washington Blvd, Culver City, CA 90232 *Tel:* 323-937-3344 *Fax:* 323-937-1142 *E-mail:* mediafab@mediafab.com; info@mediafab.com *Web Site:* www.mediafab.com; www.mfi-law.com, pg 936

Media Financial Management Association (MFM), 550 W Frontage Rd, Suite 3600, Northfield, IL 60093 *Tel:* 847-716-7000 *Fax:* 847-716-7004 *E-mail:* info@mediafinance.org *Web Site:* www.mediafinance.org, pg 1084

Media Inc, PO Box 496, Media, PA 19063 *Tel:* 610-565-2844 *Fax:* 610-565-3614 *Web Site:* www.mediaincorporated.com, pg 936

Media Loft Inc, 615 First Ave NE, Suite 100, Minneapolis, MN 55413 *Tel:* 612-375-1086 *Fax:* 612-375-0913 *E-mail:* info@medialoft.net *Web Site:* www.medialoft.net, pg 937

Media Magic, 11 Tanzanite, Rancho Santa Margarita, CA 92688 *Tel:* 949-713-9696 *Fax:* 270-716-9696 *E-mail:* request@mediamagic.tv *Web Site:* www.mediamagic.tv, pg 937

Media Management LLC, 1801 Royal Lane, Suite 906, Dallas, TX 75229 *Tel:* 972-409-0900 *Fax:* 972-409-0903 *E-mail:* info@mmgt.com *Web Site:* www.mmgt.com, pg 937

Media Marketing Associates Inc, 12 Colgate Rd, Beverly, MA 01915, pg 937

Media Productions, 3241 S University Dr, Fargo, ND 58104 *Tel:* 701-237-6863 *Toll Free Tel:* 800-480-6863 *Fax:* 701-280-1226 *Web Site:* www.mediaproductions.com, pg 937

Media Resources, 102 Perkins Bldg, 521 Lancaster Ave, Richmond, KY 40475 *Tel:* 859-622-6671 *Fax:* 859-622-1116 *Web Site:* www.mpc.eku.edu, pg 937

Media Resources Inc, 9012 NW Holly Rd, Bremerton, WA 98312-9595 *Tel:* 360-830-0302 *Toll Free Tel:* 800-666-0106, pg 937

The Media Staff Inc, 8425 W Third St, Suite 401, Los Angeles, CA 90048 *Tel:* 323-658-8996 *Fax:* 323-658-8990 *E-mail:* info@themediastaff.com *Web Site:* www.themediastaff.com, pg 937

Media Supply Inc, 611 Jeffers Circle, Exton, PA 19341 *Tel:* 610-884-4400 *Toll Free Tel:* 800-944-4237 *Fax:* 610-884-4500 *E-mail:* info@mediasupply.com *Web Site:* www.mediasupply.com, pg 937

Media Systems Design Group, 4253 Stewart Ave, Los Angeles, CA 90066 *Tel:* 310-398-0281 *Fax:* 310-398-9451 *Web Site:* www.msd-group.com, pg 937

Media 3 Ltd, 535 Fifth Ave, 13th fl, New York, NY 10017 *Tel:* 212-983-5200 *Fax:* 212-983-5200 *E-mail:* media3@liveshots.com *Web Site:* liveshots.com, pg 937

Media Vision Productions Inc, 1049 Asylum Ave, Hartford, CT 06105 *Tel:* 860-278-5310 *Web Site:* cpbn.org, pg 937

Media Vision USA, 1078 60 St, Oakland, CA 94608 *Tel:* 415-391-9090 *Toll Free Tel:* 877-746-8375 *Fax:* 415-391-9192 *E-mail:* info@mediavision-usa.com *Web Site:* mediavision-usa.com, pg 937

Media Visions Inc, 5875 Old Leeds Rd, Birmingham, AL 35210 *Tel:* 205-324-4600 *Toll Free Tel:* 800-254-0876 *Fax:* 205-324-4688 *Web Site:* www.mediavisions.com, pg 937

Mediaforce Productions, 5960 W Parker Rd, Suite 278-183, Plano, TX 75093 *Tel:* 972-473-6888 *Web Site:* www.mediaforcepro.com, pg 937

MediaFX, 10445 SW Canyon Rd, Suite 220, Beaverton, OR 97005 *Tel:* 503-646-9884 *Fax:* 503-646-7115 *Web Site:* www.mediafxvideo.com, pg 937

Mediaimage Communications Group, 10 Sacks Ave, Grimsby, ON L3M 4Y4, Canada *Tel:* 905-309-5554 *Fax:* 905-309-0999, pg 937

MediaMation Inc, 387 Maple Ave, Torrance, CA 90503 *Tel:* 310-320-0696 *Fax:* 310-320-0699 *E-mail:* sales@mediamation.com *Web Site:* www.mediamation.com, pg 937

MediaMix Inc, 4 Pearl Ct, Allendale, NJ 07401 *Tel:* 201-262-3700 (day); 201-378-3035 (nights/weekends) *Fax:* 201-262-3798 *E-mail:* info@mmix.net *Web Site:* www.mmix.net, pg 937

MediaNow, One Maple Ave, 1-E, Netcong, NJ 07857 *Tel:* 973-347-2155 *Toll Free Tel:* 888-515-2255 *Fax:* 973-215-2121 *E-mail:* info@medianow.com; rfq@medianow.com (quote) *Web Site:* www.medianow.com, pg 938

MediaOne Services, 901 Battery St, Suite 220, San Francisco, CA 94111 *Tel:* 415-262-4222 *E-mail:* sales@mediaoneservices.com *Web Site:* mediaoneservices.com, pg 938

MediaPOINTE, 667 Rancho Conejo Blvd, Newbury Park, CA 91320 *Tel:* 805-480-3700 *Fax:* 805-480-3770 *E-mail:* info@mediapointe.com; sales@mediapointe.com *Web Site:* www.mediapointe.com, pg 938

MediaWorks, 843 W Elna Rae St, Tempe, AZ 85281-5421 *Tel:* 480-968-4392 *Fax:* 480-968-4679 *Web Site:* www.mediaworks-az.com, pg 938

Medical Media Systems, 2916 NW Bucklin Hill Rd, No 481, Silverdale, WA 98383 *Tel:* 360-516-6110 *Fax:* 360-516-6100 *Web Site:* medicalmediasystems.com, pg 938

Medical Visual Creations (MVC), 1700 California St, Suite 350, San Francisco, CA 94109 *Tel:* 415-928-1623 *Fax:* 415-928-4642 *E-mail:* info@lifestyleinmotion.com *Web Site:* www.mvcvideodvd.com, pg 938

Medifecta Healthcare Training, 8740 SE Sunnybrook Blvd, Suite 300, Clackamas, OR 97015 *Toll Free Tel:* 877-843-8374 (sales & prog info) *Fax:* 541-858-6696 *E-mail:* info@medifecta.com *Web Site:* medifecta.com, pg 938

Medina Software Inc, PO Box 952440, Lake Mary, FL 32795-2440 *Tel:* 407-227-4112 *E-mail:* info@medinasoft.com *Web Site:* www.medinasoft.com, pg 938

The Meetinghouse Companies Inc, 781 N Church Rd, Elmhurst, IL 60126-1413 *Tel:* 630-941-0600 *Fax:* 630-941-7777 *E-mail:* info@meetinghouse.com *Web Site:* www.meetinghouse.com, pg 938

Megatrax, 7629 Fulton Ave, North Hollywood, CA 91605 *Tel:* 818-255-7100 *Toll Free Tel:* 888-MEGA-555 (634-2555) *Fax:* 818-255-7199 *E-mail:* info@megatrax.com *Web Site:* www.megatrax.com, pg 938

Megavideo Productions, 22 Cedar St, No 2, Garfield, NJ 07026 *Tel:* 973-478-1921 *E-mail:* megamail@megadv.com *Web Site:* www.megadv.com, pg 938

Melbourne Independent Filmmakers Festival (MIFF), 1399 S Harbor City Blvd, Melbourne, FL 32901 *Tel:* 321-726-1711 *Fax:* 321-726-1715 *Web Site:* www.3boysproductions.com, pg 1119

Mellow Hollow Studio, 3030 River Rd, Ashland City, TN 37015 *Tel:* 615-971-0146 *Fax:* 615-792-1787 *Web Site:* www.mellowhollow.com, pg 938

Melmat Inc, 5333 Industrial Dr, Huntington Beach, CA 92649 *Tel:* 714-379-4555 *Toll Free Tel:* 800-635-6289 *Fax:* 714-379-4554 *E-mail:* info@melmat.com; sales@melmat.com *Web Site:* www.melmat.com, pg 938

Meltzer Media Productions, 70 W 36 St, Suite 1000, New York, NY 10018 *Tel:* 212-868-4600 *E-mail:* contact@meltzermedia.com *Web Site:* www.meltzermedia.com, pg 938

Memory Lane Productions, 4323 Mundymill Rd, Oakwood, GA 30566 *Tel:* 770-531-1444 *Fax:* 770-531-1444 *E-mail:* memlane1@aol.com, pg 938

Memory Lane Videos, 676 Lone Oak Ave, Eugene, OR 97404 *Tel:* 541-688-0484 *Fax:* 541-688-0484, pg 938

The Memphis & Shelby County Film & TV Commission, 496 S Main St, Suite 101, Memphis, TN 38103 *Tel:* 901-527-8300 (ext 2) *Fax:* 901-527-8326 *E-mail:* info@memphisfilmcomm.org *Web Site:* www.filmmemphis.org, pg 1102

Memphis Communications Corp, 4771 Summer Ave, Memphis, TN 38122 *Tel:* 901-725-9271 *Fax:* 901-272-3577, pg 938

Merced Visitor Services, California Welcome Ctr, 710 W 16 St, Merced, CA 95340 *Tel:* 209-724-8104 *Toll Free Tel:* 800-446-5353 *E-mail:* info@visitmerced.travel *Web Site:* www.yosemite-gateway.org, pg 1093

Merck & Hill Consultants Inc, 1995 N Park Place, Suite 450, Atlanta, GA 30339 *Tel:* 770-937-0185 *Fax:* 770-937-0919 *E-mail:* info@merckhill.com *Web Site:* www.merckhill.com, pg 938

Merestone, 7232 E First St, Scottsdale, AZ 85251 *Tel:* 480-945-4631 *Fax:* 480-945-0590 *Web Site:* www.merestone.com, pg 938

Meridia Audience Response, 5207 Militia Hill Rd, Plymouth Meeting, PA 19462 *Tel:* 610-260-6800 *Fax:* 610-260-6810 *E-mail:* rsvp@meridiaars.com *Web Site:* www.meridiaars.com, pg 939

Meridian Education Corp, c/o Films Media Group, 132 W 31 St, 17th fl, New York, NY 10001 *Tel:* 609-671-1000 *Toll Free Tel:* 800-257-5126; 800-322-8755 *Toll Free Fax:* 800-678-3633 *E-mail:* custserv@films.com *Web Site:* meridian.films.com, pg 939

Meridian Studios, 1020 Highland Park Rd, Neenah, WI 54956 *Tel:* 920-720-4200 *E-mail:* info@meridianstudiosusa.com *Web Site:* www.meridianstudiosusa.com, pg 939

Meriwether Publishing Ltd, 885 Elkton Dr, Colorado Springs, CO 80907-3522 *Tel:* 719-594-4422 *Toll Free Tel:* 800-937-5297 *Fax:* 719-594-9916 *Toll Free Fax:* 888-594-4436 *E-mail:* customerservice@meriwether.com; orders@meriwether.com *Web Site:* www.meriwether.com, pg 939

Mermaid7seas Productions, 970 Ninth St, Boulder, CO 80302-7226 *Tel:* 303-545-0202; 303-818-5771 (cell) *E-mail:* mermaid7seas@gmail.com, pg 939

Merrimack Films, 530 Concord Ave, Belmont, MA 02478 *Tel:* 617-489-4729 *E-mail:* sales@merrimack-films.com *Web Site:* www.merrimack-films.com, pg 939

MeshTel-Intelite, PO Box 747, Genoa, NV 89411 *Tel:* 775-267-5959 *Fax:* 775-267-5958 *E-mail:* info@meshtel.com *Web Site:* www.meshtel.com, pg 939

MessageMakers, 1217 Turner St, Lansing, MI 48906 *Tel:* 517-482-3333 *Toll Free Tel:* 888-482-6688 *E-mail:* info@messagemakers.com *Web Site:* www.messagemakers.com, pg 939

Metalworks Recording Studios Inc, 3611 Mavis Rd, Mississauga, ON L5C 1T7, Canada *Tel:* 905-279-4000 *Fax:* 905-279-4006 *Web Site:* www.metalworksstudios.com, pg 939

Method Studios, 730 Arizona Ave, Santa Monica, CA 90401 *Tel:* 310-434-6500 *Web Site:* www.methodstudios.com, pg 939

Metric Splicer Inc, 3930 E Miraloma Ave, Suite C, Anaheim, CA 92806 *Tel:* 714-630-2999 *Fax:* 714-630-2268 *Web Site:* www.metricsplicer.com, pg 939

Metro Orlando Film Commission, 301 E Pine St, Suite 900, Orlando, FL 32801 *Tel:* 407-422-7159 *Fax:* 407-425-6428 *E-mail:* info@filmorlando.com *Web Site:* www.filmorlando.com, pg 1096

Metro Productions, 8570 Magellan Pkwy, Suite 400, Richmond, VA 23227 *Tel:* 804-261-1172 *Toll Free Tel:* 877-669-4687 *Fax:* 804-261-1885 *E-mail:* contactmetro@metro-productions.com *Web Site:* www.metro-productions.com, pg 939

Metro Teleproductions Inc (MTI), 2500 Virginia Ave NW, 416-S, Washington, DC 20037 *Tel:* 301-608-9077 *Fax:* 301-608-9078 *Web Site:* www.mtitv.com, pg 939

Metro Video Systems Inc, 1220 E Imperial Ave, El Segundo, CA 90245 *Tel:* 310-640-9250 *Fax:* 310-640-9347 *E-mail:* sales@metrovideosystems.com *Web Site:* www.metrovideosystems.com, pg 940

Metromotion Productions LLC, 450 W 31 St, 8th & 9th fl, New York, NY 10001 *Tel:* 212-967-2000 *Fax:* 212-967-1988 *E-mail:* info@metromotion.com; pr@metromotion.com *Web Site:* www.metromotion.com, pg 940

Metropolitan Acoustics LLC, 40 W Evergreen Ave, Suite 108, Philadelphia, PA 19118 *Tel:* 215-248-4352 *Fax:* 215-248-4353 *E-mail:* info@metro-acoustics.com *Web Site:* www.metro-acoustics.com, pg 940

Metropolitan Audio Visual Co LLC, 2862 Hartland Rd, Falls Church, VA 22043 *Tel:* 703-834-0004 *Toll Free Tel:* 800-966-4333 *Fax:* 703-834-0866 *E-mail:* sales@metroav.com *Web Site:* www.metroav.com, pg 940

Metropolitan Audio-Visual Inc, 35333 N 27 Lane, Phoenix, AZ 85086 *Tel:* 480-948-9008 *Fax:* 480-948-9130 *Web Site:* www.metroav.tv, pg 940

Metropolitan Museum of Art, 1000 Fifth Ave, New York, NY 10028-0198 *Tel:* 212-535-7710 *Fax:* 212-472-2764 *E-mail:* customer.service@metmuseum.org; communications@metmuseum.org *Web Site:* www.metmuseum.org, pg 940

Metropolitan Opera Guild, Samuel B & David Rose Bldg, 70 Lincoln Center Plaza, 6th fl, New York, NY 10023-6593 *Tel:* 212-769-7000 *E-mail:* info@metguild.org *Web Site:* www.metguild.org, pg 940

MetroSonic Recording Studio, 143 Roebling St, 3rd fl, Brooklyn, NY 11211 *Tel:* 718-782-1872 *E-mail:* manager@metrosonic.net *Web Site:* www.metrosonic.net, pg 940

Meuninck's Media Methods Inc, 24097 North Shore Dr, Edwardsburg, MI 49112 *Web Site:* www.herbvideos.com, pg 940

Meyer Sound Laboratories Inc, 2832 San Pablo Ave, Berkeley, CA 94702 *Tel:* 510-486-1166 *Toll Free Tel:* 855-641-3288 (US & CN) *Fax:* 510-486-8356 *E-mail:* sales@meyersound.com; techsupport@meyersound.com; service@meyersound.com *Web Site:* www.meyersound.com, pg 940

MFJ Enterprises Inc, 300 Industrial Park Rd, Starkville, MS 39759-3992 *Tel:* 662-323-5869 *Toll Free Tel:* 800-647-1800 *Fax:* 662-323-6551 *E-mail:* mfjcustserv@mfjenterprises.com *Web Site:* www.mfjenterprises.com, pg 940

MG Electronics, 32 Ranick Rd, Hauppauge, NY 11788 *Tel:* 631-582-3400 *Fax:* 631-582-3229 *E-mail:* info@mgelectronics.com *Web Site:* www.mgelectronics.com, pg 940

MG Studio, 6625 S Valley View Blvd, Suite C-304, Las Vegas, NV 89118 *Tel:* 702-836-3686 *Toll Free Tel:* 866-478-8340 *E-mail:* office@mgstudio.com *Web Site:* mgstudio.com, pg 940

MGE UPS Systems, 1660 Scenic Ave, Costa Mesa, CA 92626 *Tel:* 714-557-1636 *Toll Free Tel:* 800-344-0570 *Web Site:* www.apc.com, pg 940

MGM & Associates Inc, 16026 S 36 St, Phoenix, AZ 85048-7322 *Tel:* 480-759-6251 *Toll Free Tel:* 800-485-0065 *Fax:* 480-759-6257 *E-mail:* mgm@mgmsuperstar.com *Web Site:* www.mgmsuperstar.com; www.thewomensmillionaireclub.com, pg 940

MGM Home Video, 245 N Beverly Dr, Beverly Hills, CA 90210 *Tel:* 310-449-3000 *Web Site:* www.mgm.com, pg 941

MGM United Artists, 245 N Beverly Dr, Beverly Hills, CA 90210 *Tel:* 310-449-3000 *Web Site:* www.mgm.com, pg 941

MHS-TV, Mamaroneck High School, 1000 W Boston Post Rd, Mamaroneck, NY 10543 *Tel:* 914-220-3100 *Fax:* 914-220-3115 *Web Site:* www.mhstv.org; www.mamkschools.org, pg 941

Mia Mind Music, 254 Sixth St, Suite 2, Hoboken, NJ 07030-6916 *Toll Free Tel:* 800-843-8575 *Fax:* 201-216-1186 *E-mail:* mimimus@aol.com *Web Site:* www.miamindmusic.com, pg 941

Miami-Dade Office of Film & Entertainment, 111 NW First St, Suite 2200, Miami, FL 33128 *Tel:* 305-375-3288 *Fax:* 305-375-3266 *E-mail:* filmoffice@miamigov.com *Web Site:* www.filmiami.org, pg 1096

Miami Daylight Studios, 1819 West Ave, Bay 5, Miami Beach, FL 33139 *Tel:* 305-763-8490 *E-mail:* info@miamidaylightstudios.com *Web Site:* miamidaylightstudios.com, pg 941

Miami International Film Festival, 300 NE Second Ave, Miami, FL 33132 *Tel:* 305-237-FILM (237-3456) *Fax:* 305-237-7344 *E-mail:* info@miamifilmfestival.com *Web Site:* miamifilmfestival.com, pg 1119

Miami short Film Festival (MsFF), 247 SW Eighth St, Suite 44, Miami, FL 33130 *E-mail:* info@miamishortfilmfestival.com *Web Site:* www.miamishortfilmfestival.com, pg 1120

Miami Stagecraft Inc, 2855 E 11 Ave, Hialeah, FL 33013 *Tel:* 305-836-9356 *Fax:* 305-696-3322 *E-mail:* info@miamistagecraft.com *Web Site:* www.miamistagecraft.com, pg 941

MIB Mediaworks, 85 Main St, Little Falls, NJ 07424 *Tel:* 973-403-1133 *E-mail:* info@mibmediaworks.com *Web Site:* www.mibmediaworks.com, pg 941

Michigan Film Office, 300 N Washington Sq, 4th fl, Lansing, MI 48913 *Tel:* 517-373-3456 *Toll Free Tel:* 800-477-FILM (477-3456) *Fax:* 517-241-0867 *E-mail:* mfo@michigan.org *Web Site:* www.michiganfilmoffice.org, pg 1098

Michigan Office Solutions, 2859 Walkent Dr NW, Grand Rapids, MI 49544 *Tel:* 616-454-1198 *Toll Free Tel:* 800-442-9070 *Fax:* 616-459-8705 *Web Site:* www.miofficesolutions.com, pg 941

Michigan Recording Arts Institute & Technologies, 28533 Greenfield, Southfield, MI 48076 *Tel:* 248-569-5422 *Toll Free Tel:* 888-802-0402 *Web Site:* mirecordingarts.com, pg 941

Micor Analytics, 7538 Saint Louis Ave, Skokie, IL 60076 *Tel:* 847-329-8590 *Fax:* 847-329-8599 *Web Site:* www.micoranalytics.com, pg 941

Micro Express, 8 Hammond, Suite 105, Irvine, CA 92618-1601 *Tel:* 949-460-9911 *Toll Free Tel:* 800-989-9900 *Fax:* 949-269-3070 *E-mail:* info@microexpress.net *Web Site:* www.microexpress.net, pg 941

Micro Innovations Inc, 910 Belle Ave, Suite 1046, Winter Springs, FL 32708 *Tel:* 407-696-9800 *Fax:* 407-696-8511 *E-mail:* avail@avail-software.com *Web Site:* www.avail-software.com, pg 941

Micro Technology Unlimited, PO Box 80124, Raleigh, NC 27623 *Tel:* 919-870-0344 *Web Site:* www.mtu.com, pg 941

Microboards Technology LLC, 8150 Mallory Ct, Chanhassen, MN 55317 *Tel:* 952-556-1600 *Toll Free Tel:* 800-646-8881; 800-290-9012 *Fax:* 952-556-1620 *E-mail:* sales@microboards.com *Web Site:* www.microboards.com, pg 941

Microdolly Hollywood, 135 N Victory Blvd, Burbank, CA 91502 *Tel:* 818-845-8383 *E-mail:* microdolly@microdolly.com *Web Site:* www.microdolly.com, pg 941

MicroImage Video Systems, PO Box 331, Boyertown, PA 19512-0331 *Tel:* 610-754-6800 *Fax:* 610-754-9766 *E-mail:* sales@mivs.com *Web Site:* www.mivs.com, pg 941

MicrophoneRentals.com, 103-1075 Marine Dr, Suite 501, North Vancouver, BC V7P 3T6, Canada *Tel:* 604-980-5703 *E-mail:* info@microphonerentals.com *Web Site:* www.microphonerentals.com, pg 941

Microsemi, 2300 Orchard Pkwy, San Jose, CA 95131-1017 *Tel:* 408-433-0910; 408-428-7907 (tech support) *Fax:* 408-428-6960 *E-mail:* info@symmetricom.com *Web Site:* www.symmetricom.com, pg 941

Microspace Communications Corp, 3100 Highwoods Blvd, Suite 120, Raleigh, NC 27604 *Tel:* 919-850-4500 *Fax:* 919-850-4518 *Web Site:* www.microspace.com, pg 942

Microtraining LLC, 3212 Duke St, Alexandria, VA 22314 *Tel:* 703-212-8520 *Toll Free Tel:* 888-505-5576 *Fax:* 703-212-8540 *Toll Free Fax:* 888-505-5576 *E-mail:* marketing@astreetpress.com *Web Site:* www.academicvideostore.com/microtraining, pg 942

Microtran Manufacturing, 1040 S Andreasen Dr, Suite 100, Escondido, CA 92029 *Tel:* 951-699-1270 *Toll Free Tel:* 800-472-6624 *Fax:* 951-676-9482 *Web Site:* www.tamuracorp.com, pg 942

Microwave Filter Co Inc, 6743 Kinne St, East Syracuse, NY 13057 *Tel:* 315-438-4700 *Toll Free Tel:* 800-448-1666 *Fax:* 315-463-1467 *Toll Free Fax:* 888-411-8860 *E-mail:* mfcsales@microwavefilter.com *Web Site:* www.microwavefilter.com, pg 942

Mid-South Color Labs Inc, 496 Emmett St, Jackson, TN 38301 *Tel:* 731-422-6691 *Toll Free Tel:* 800-221-3920 *Fax:* 731-424-1902 *E-mail:* info@midsouthcolor.com *Web Site:* www.midsouthcolor.com, pg 942

Midas Consoles North America, 5270 Procyon St, Las Vegas, NV 89118 *Tel:* 702-371-0103 *Toll Free Tel:* 866-929-9074 *Fax:* 702-554-2367 *Toll Free Fax:* 800-955-6831 *E-mail:* custsuppprofus@music-group.com *Web Site:* www.midasconsoles.com, pg 942

MidCanada Production Services Inc (MidCan), 509 Century St, Winnipeg, MB R3H 0L8, Canada *Tel:* 204-772-0368 *Toll Free Tel:* 800-772-0368 *Fax:* 204-772-0360 *E-mail:* info@midcan.com *Web Site:* www.midcan.com, pg 942

Middle Atlantic Products Inc, 300 Fairfield Rd, Fairfield, NJ 07004 *Tel:* 973-839-1011 *Fax:* 973-839-1976 *E-mail:* info@middleatlantic.com *Web Site:* www.middleatlantic.com, pg 942

Midland Video Productions Inc, 126 N Jefferson St, Milwaukee, WI 53202 *Tel:* 414-276-8300 *E-mail:* request@midlandvideo.com *Web Site:* midlandvideo.com, pg 942

Midnight Media Group Inc, 45 E Willow St, Millburn, NJ 07041-1416 *Tel:* 973-379-5959 *E-mail:* info@mmgi.tv *Web Site:* www.mmgi.tv, pg 942

Midtown Video Inc, 4824 SW 74 Ct, Miami, FL 33155 *Tel:* 305-669-1117 *Toll Free Tel:* 800-232-4564 *Fax:* 305-662-2860 *E-mail:* info@midtownvideo.com *Web Site:* www.midtownvideo.com, pg 942

Midwest Digital Corp, 10150 Virginia Ave, Suite H, Chicago Ridge, IL 60415 *Tel:* 708-790-4040 *E-mail:* midwestdig@gmail.com *Web Site:* www.midwestdigitalcorp.com, pg 942

Midwest Photo Exchange, 3313 N High St, Columbus, OH 43202 *Tel:* 614-261-1264 *Toll Free Tel:* 866-940-3686 *Fax:* 614-261-1637 *E-mail:* mpex@mpex.com; orders@mpex.com *Web Site:* mpex.com, pg 942

Midwest Uplink Inc, 911 N East St, Indianapolis, IN 46202 *Tel:* 317-423-8684 *Toll Free Tel:* 866-886-6247 *Fax:* 317-423-3061 *Web Site:* midwestuplink.com, pg 942

MIGHTYbYTES Inc, 4001 N Ravenswood Ave, Suite 404, Chicago, IL 60613 *Tel:* 773-561-7529 *E-mail:* info@mightybytes.com *Web Site:* www.mightybytes.com, pg 942

Milbrodt/Music & Sound Design, 1835 US Hwy 9, Howell, NJ 07731 *Tel:* 848-459-4965 *E-mail:* info@ideasinmedia.com *Web Site:* www.ideasinmedia.com; www.carmusicproject.com, pg 943

Milestone Film & Video Inc, PO Box 128, Harrington Park, NJ 07640-0128 *Tel:* 201-767-3117 *Toll Free Tel:* 800-603-1104 *Fax:* 201-767-3035 *E-mail:* milefilms@gmail.com *Web Site:* www.milestonefilms.com, pg 943

Milgrom Productions, 50 Kent Rd, Glen Rock, NJ 07452 *Tel:* 201-444-8838 *E-mail:* info@milgromproductions.com *Web Site:* milgrom.adcstudio.com, pg 943

Milky Way Press, 317 Ridge Run Dr, Georgetown, TX 78628 *Tel:* 512-869-6455 *Toll Free Tel:* 888-756-6455 (orders only) *Web Site:* www.milkywaypress.com, pg 943

Mill Valley Film Festival, 1001 Lootens Place, Suite 220, San Rafael, CA 94901 *Tel:* 415-383-5256 *Fax:* 415-383-8606 *E-mail:* mvff@cafilm.org; info@cafilm.org *Web Site:* www.mvff.com; www.cafilm.org, pg 1120

Millennia Media FPC, 4600 Missouri Flat Rd, Suite 11, Placerville, CA 95667 *Tel:* 530-647-0750 *Fax:* 530-647-9921 *E-mail:* sales@mil-media.com *Web Site:* www.mil-media.com, pg 943

Millennium Entertainment LLC, 5900 Wilshire Blvd, 18th fl, Los Angeles, CA 90036 *Tel:* 310-893-6289 *E-mail:* info@millenniumentertainment.me *Web Site:* www.millenniumentertainment.me, pg 943

Miller Camera Support LLC, 216 Little Falls Rd, Unit 15 & 16, Cedar Grove, NJ 07009-1276 *Tel:* 973-857-8300 *Fax:* 973-857-8188 *E-mail:* service@millertripods.us *Web Site:* www.millertripods.com, pg 943

Earl Miller Productions Inc, 1702 W Koenig Lane, Austin, TX 78756 *Tel:* 512-458-4343 *Fax:* 512-458-4485 *E-mail:* info@earlmillerproductions.com *Web Site:* www.earlmillerproductions.com, pg 943

The Miller Group, Multiplex Division, 1610 Design Way, Dupo, IL 62239-1820 *Tel:* 636-343-5700 *Toll Free Tel:* 800-325-3350 *Fax:* 618-286-6202 *E-mail:* info@miller-group.com *Web Site:* www.multiplexdisplays.com, pg 943

Robin Miller, Filmaker Inc, 606 W Broad St, Bethlehem, PA 18018 *Tel:* 610-691-0900 *Fax:* 610-691-0952 *E-mail:* enquire@filmaker.com *Web Site:* www.filmaker.com, pg 943

Barney Miller's Inc, 232 E Main St, Lexington, KY 40507-1310 *Tel:* 859-252-2216 *Toll Free Tel:* 800-755-6799 *Fax:* 859-253-1115 *Web Site:* www.barneymillers.com, pg 943

Mills James Productions, 3545 Fishinger Blvd, Columbus, OH 43026-9489 *Tel:* 614-777-9933 *Toll Free Tel:* 800-860-8436 *Fax:* 614-777-9943 *E-mail:* info@mjp.com *Web Site:* www.millsjames.com, pg 943

Milner-Fenwick Inc, 119 Lakefront Dr, Hunt Valley, MD 21030-2216 *Tel:* 410-252-1700 *Toll Free Tel:* 800-432-8433 *Fax:* 410-252-6316 *E-mail:* mail@milner-fenwick.com *Web Site:* www.milner-fenwick.com, pg 943

Mimi Productions, 329 W 18 St, Suite 405, Chicago, IL 60616 *Tel:* 312-829-0162 *E-mail:* info@mimiproductions.com *Web Site:* www.mimiproductions.com, pg 943

Mind Over Eye Inc, 2221 Rosecrans Ave, Suite 195, El Segundo, CA 90245 *Tel:* 310-396-4663 *Fax:* 310-297-9526 *E-mail:* info@mindovereye.com *Web Site:* www.mindovereye.com, pg 943

Mind Resources Inc, 130 Shoemaker St, Unit 1, Kitchener, ON N2E 3G4, Canada *Tel:* 519-895-0330 *Toll Free Tel:* 877-414-6463 *Fax:* 519-895-0331 *Toll Free Fax:* 877-585-2992 *E-mail:* sales@mindresources.com *Web Site:* www.mindresources.com, pg 943

MindPlay, 4400 E Broadway Blvd, Suite 400, Tucson, AZ 85711 *Tel:* 520-888-1800 *Toll Free Tel:* 800-221-7911 *E-mail:* mail@mindplay.com *Web Site:* www.mindplay.com, pg 943

Saul Mineroff Electronics Inc, 574 Meacham Ave, Elmont, NY 11003 *Tel:* 516-775-1370 *Fax:* 516-775-1371 *E-mail:* tapenixon@aol.com *Web Site:* www.mineroff.com, pg 943

Minneapolis Licenses & Consumer Services, 350 S Fifth St, Rm 1C, Minneapolis, MN 55415-1391 *Tel:* 612-673-2080 *Fax:* 612-673-3399 *Web Site:* www.minneapolismn.gov/business-licensing, pg 1098

Minneapolis St Paul International Film Festival (MSPIFF), 125 SE Main St, Suite 125A, Minneapolis, MN 55414 *Tel:* 612-331-7563 *Fax:* 612-378-7750 *E-mail:* info@mspfilmsociety.org; submissions@mspfilmsociety.org *Web Site:* www.mspfilmsociety.org, pg 1120

Minnesota Film & TV, 401 N Third St, Suite 245, Minneapolis, MN 55401 *Tel:* 612-767-0095 *Fax:* 612-767-2425 *Web Site:* www.mnfilmtv.org, pg 1098

Miranda Technologies, 3499 Douglas-B Floreani, Montreal, QC H4S 2C6, Canada *Tel:* 514-333-1772 *Toll Free Tel:* 800-224-7882 *Fax:* 514-333-9828 *E-mail:* salesamericas@miranda.com *Web Site:* www.miranda.com; www.belden.com, pg 944

Miranda Telecast Fiber Systems Inc, 102 Grove St, Worcester, MA 01605 *Tel:* 508-754-4858 *Fax:* 508-752-1520 *E-mail:* telecast.sales@belden.com *Web Site:* www.miranda.com; www.belden.com, pg 944

MIS Technologies, 555-B NW Blue Pkwy, Lees Summit, MO 64063 *Tel:* 816-966-4529 *Fax:* 816-966-2915 *Web Site:* www.mistechnologies.com, pg 944

MISCO, 2637 32 Ave S, Minneapolis, MN 55406-1641 *Tel:* 612-825-1010 *Toll Free Tel:* 800-276-9955 *Fax:* 612-825-7010 *E-mail:* info@miscospeakers.com *Web Site:* www.miscospeakers.com, pg 944

Mississippi Film Office, 501 N West St, Suite B-01, Jackson, MS 39201 *Tel:* 601-359-3297 *Fax:* 601-359-5048 *Web Site:* www.filmmississippi.org, pg 1099

Missouri Film Commission, 301 W High St, Suite 720, Jefferson City, MO 65101 *Tel:* 573-526-3566 *E-mail:* mofilm@ded.mo.gov *Web Site:* www.mofilm.org, pg 1099

Missouri Honor Medal for Distinguished Service in Journalism, School of Journalism, 120 Neff Hall, Columbia, MO 65211-1200 *Tel:* 573-882-4821 *Fax:* 573-884-5400 *E-mail:* journalism@missouri.edu *Web Site:* journalism.missouri.edu, pg 1120

Mist Media Inc, 10845 Acama St, Toluca Lake, CA 91602 *Tel:* 818-508-1097 *Fax:* 818-508-1097 *E-mail:* mistmedia@sbcglobal.net *Web Site:* www.mistmedia.tv, pg 944

Mr Mark's Used Musical, Stereo & Studio Equipment Store, 109 Grizzard Ave, Nashville, TN 37207-4413 *Tel:* 615-242-2907 *E-mail:* mrmarksmusic@aol.com, pg 944

Mitchell Acoustics Research, 2005B Industrial Blvd, Rockwall, TX 75087 *Tel:* 214-741-7136 *Toll Free Fax:* 866-492-2470 *E-mail:* info@frazierspeakers.com *Web Site:* www.frazierspeakers.com, pg 944

Mitsubishi Electric Visual Solutions America Inc (MEVSA), 10833 Valley View St, Suite 300, Cypress, CA 90630 *Toll Free Tel:* 800-332-2119 *E-mail:* tvsupport@mevsa.com *Web Site:* www.mitsubishi-tv.com, pg 944

MKE Production Rental, 710 N Plankinton Ave, Suite 300, Milwaukee, WI 53213 *Tel:* 414-939-3653 *E-mail:* rent1@mkeproductionrental.com *Web Site:* www.mkeproductionrental.com, pg 944

MMI Corp, 2950 Wyman Pkwy, Baltimore, MD 21211-2802 *Tel:* 410-366-1222 *Fax:* 410-366-6311 *E-mail:* mail@mmicorporation.com *Web Site:* www.mmicorporation.com, pg 944

Moab to Monument Valley Film Commission, 217 E Center St, Moab, UT 84532 *Tel:* 435-259-4341 *Fax:* 435-259-4135 *Web Site:* www.filmmoab.com; film.utah.gov, pg 1103

Mobile Film Office, 164 Saint Emanuel St, Mobile, AL 36602 *Tel:* 251-438-7102 *Fax:* 251-438-7104 *Web Site:* www.mobilefilmoffice.com, pg 1091

Mobile-Video Productions Inc, 7315 Wisconsin Ave, Suite 1300 W, Bethesda, MD 20814 *Tel:* 301-656-2525 *Fax:* 301-656-4343 *E-mail:* mobilevp@verizon.net *Web Site:* www.mobilevideoproductions.tv, pg 944

Mobilized Tech Systems, 4015 Blackthorn Dr, Vacaville, CA 95688 *Tel:* 707-602-5548 *Toll Free Tel:* 888-293-0869 *Fax:* 707-602-5549 *E-mail:* info@bigfootmobilecarts.com *Web Site:* www.bigfootmobilecarts.com, pg 944

The Mobius Advertising Awards, 713 S Pacific Coast Hwy, Suite A, Redondo Beach, CA 90277-4233 *Tel:* 310-540-0959 *Fax:* 310-316-8905 *E-mail:* mobiusinfo@mobiusawards.com *Web Site:* www.mobiusawards.com, pg 1120

Modern Communications Inc, 1231 Horan Dr, Fenton, MO 63026 *Tel:* 636-343-0800 *Toll Free Tel:* 800-428-2442 *Fax:* 636-343-0906 *Web Site:* www.modcomm.com, pg 944

Modernage Photographic Services Inc, 555 Eighth Ave, New York, NY 10018 *Tel:* 212-997-1800 *Toll Free Tel:* 800-997-2510 *Fax:* 212-869-4796 *E-mail:* info@modernage.com *Web Site:* www.modernage.com, pg 944

Modesto Convention & Visitors Bureau, 1150 Ninth St, Suite C, Modesto, CA 95354 *Tel:* 209-526-5588 *Toll Free Tel:* 888-640-8467 *Fax:* 209-526-5586 *E-mail:* films@visitmodesto.com; info@visitmodesto.com *Web Site:* www.visitmodesto.com, pg 1093

modprop.com, 1044 Madison Ave, New York, NY 10021 *Tel:* 212-628-7582 *E-mail:* info@modprop.com *Web Site:* www.modprop.com, pg 945

Modulation Sciences Inc, 14 Worlds Fair Dr, Suite K, Somerset, NJ 08873 *Tel:* 732-302-3090 *Toll Free Tel:* 800-826-2603 *Fax:* 732-302-0206 *E-mail:* info@modsci.com; sales@modsci.com *Web Site:* www.modsci.com, pg 945

Moe AV LLC, 133 Deerfield Rd, Sayreville, NJ 08872-1618 *Tel:* 732-257-3760 *Web Site:* www.moeco.net, pg 945

Mohawk, 324 Clark St, Worcester, MA 01606 *Tel:* 978-537-9961 *Toll Free Tel:* 800-422-9961 *Fax:* 978-537-4358 *E-mail:* info@mohawk-cable.com *Web Site:* www.mohawk-cable.com, pg 945

Mole-Richardson Co, 937 N Sycamore Ave, Hollywood, CA 90038-2384 *Tel:* 323-851-0111 *Fax:* 323-851-5593 *E-mail:* info@mole.com *Web Site:* www.mole.com, pg 945

Monaco Digital Films Labs, 234 Ninth St, San Francisco, CA 94103 *Tel:* 415-864-5350 *Fax:* 415-864-5682 *E-mail:* admin@monacosf.com, pg 945

Monaco LLC, 145 Grassy Plain St, Bethel, CT 06801-2806 *Tel:* 203-744-3398 *Toll Free Tel:* 800-448-4877 *Fax:* 203-744-3228 *E-mail:* monaco@hangupbags.com *Web Site:* www.hangupbags.com, pg 945

Monad Trainer's Aide Inc, 163-60 22 Ave, Whitestone, NY 11357 *Tel:* 718-352-2314 *Toll Free Tel:* 800-344-6088 *Fax:* 718-352-8276 *Web Site:* www.monadtrainersaide.com, pg 945

Monadnock Media Inc, 112 Amherst Rd, Sunderland, MA 01375 *Tel:* 413-665-1390 *Fax:* 413-665-1394 *E-mail:* info@monadnock.org *Web Site:* www.monadnock.org, pg 945

Monarch Instrument, 15 Columbia Dr, Amherst, NH 03031-2305 *Tel:* 603-883-3390 *Toll Free Tel:* 800-999-3390 *Fax:* 603-886-3300 *E-mail:* sales@monarchinstrument.com *Web Site:* www.monarchinstrument.com, pg 945

Monotype Inc, 500 Unicorn Park Dr, Woburn, MA 01801 *Tel:* 781-970-6000 *Toll Free Tel:* 800-424-8973 *Fax:* 781-970-6001; 781-970-6002 (gen questions) *Web Site:* www.monotype.com, pg 945

Monroe Electronics Inc, 100 Housel Ave, Lyndonville, NY 14098 *Tel:* 585-765-2254 *Fax:* 585-765-9330 *Web Site:* www.monroe-electronics.com, pg 945

Monroe-West Monroe Convention & Visitors Bureau, 601 Constitution Dr, West Monroe, LA 71292 *Tel:* 318-387-5691 *Toll Free Tel:* 800-843-1872 *Fax:* 318-324-1752 *E-mail:* mwmcvb@monroe-westmonroe.org *Web Site:* www.monroe-westmonroe.org, pg 1098

Monster Cable Products Inc, 455 Valley Dr, Brisbane, CA 94005-1209 *Tel:* 415-840-2000 *Fax:* 415-468-0311 *Web Site:* www.monstercable.com, pg 945

Monster Tracks, 1821 Ranstead St, Philadelphia, PA 19103 *Tel:* 215-567-0400 *Toll Free Tel:* 800-369-1280 *Fax:* 215-567-0350 *Web Site:* www.monstertracks.com, pg 945

Montana Film Office, 301 S Park Ave, Helena, MT 59620 *Tel:* 406-841-2876 *Toll Free Tel:* 800-553-4563 *Fax:* 406-841-2877 *E-mail:* montanafilm@mt.gov *Web Site:* www.montanafilm.com, pg 1099

Monterey County Film Commission, 801 Lighthouse Ave, Suite 104, Monterey, CA 93940 *Tel:* 831-646-0910 *Fax:* 831-655-9250 *E-mail:* info@filmmonterey.org *Web Site:* www.filmmonterey.org, pg 1093

monterey media inc, 566 Saint Charles Dr, Thousand Oaks, CA 91360-3953 *Tel:* 805-494-7199 *Toll Free Tel:* 800-424-2593 *Fax:* 805-496-6061 *E-mail:* customerservice@montereymedia.com; publicity@montereymedia.com *Web Site:* www.montereymedia.com, pg 945

monterey video, 566 Saint Charles Dr, Thousand Oaks, CA 91360-3953 *Tel:* 805-494-7199 *Toll Free Tel:* 800-424-2593 *Fax:* 805-496-6061 *E-mail:* customerservice@montereymedia.com; publicity@montereymedia.com *Web Site:* www.montereymedia.com, pg 946

Montreal Film & TV Commission, Duke Pavilion, 5th fl, 801 Brennan St, Montreal, QC H3C 0G4, Canada *Tel:* 514-872-2883 *Fax:* 514-872-3409 *E-mail:* film.tv@ville.montreal.qc.ca *Web Site:* www.montrealfilm.com, pg 1105

Montreal International Festival of Films on Art, 2130 Crescent St, Montreal, QC H3G 2B8, Canada *Tel:* 514-874-1637 *Fax:* 514-874-9929 *E-mail:* info@artfifa.com *Web Site:* www.artfifa.com, pg 1120

Montreal International Festival of Nouveau Cinema, 3805 Blvd Ste-Laurent, Montreal, QC H2W 1X9, Canada *Tel:* 514-282-0004 *Fax:* 514-282-6664 *E-mail:* info@nouveaucinema.ca *Web Site:* www.nouveaucinema.ca, pg 1120

Montreal World Film Festival, 1432 de Bleury St, Montreal, QC H3A 2J1, Canada *Tel:* 514-848-3883 *Fax:* 514-848-3886 *E-mail:* info@ffm-montreal.org *Web Site:* www.ffm-montreal.org, pg 1120

Mood Creations Ltd, One Depot Plaza, Ossining, NY 10562 *Tel:* 914-941-2357 *Fax:* 914-941-3142 *E-mail:* moodcreations@optonline.net *Web Site:* www.moodcreations.com, pg 946

Moog Music Inc, 160 Broadway St, Asheville, NC 28801 *Tel:* 828-251-0090 *Toll Free Tel:* 800-948-1990 *Fax:* 828-254-6233 *E-mail:* info@moogmusic.com *Web Site:* www.moogmusic.com, pg 946

Moondance International Film Festival, 970 Ninth St, Boulder, CO 80302-7226 *Tel:* 303-545-0202 *Web Site:* moondancefilmfestival.com, pg 1120

Moore Creative Talent Inc, 3130 Excelsior Blvd, Minneapolis, MN 55416 *Tel:* 612-827-3823 *Web Site:* www.mooretalent.com, pg 946

MooreCo Inc, 2885 Lorraine Ave, Temple, TX 76501 *Tel:* 254-778-4727 (CN) *Toll Free Tel:* 800-749-2258 (US) *Fax:* 254-773-0500 (CN) *Toll Free Fax:* 800-697-6258 (US) *Web Site:* moorecoinc.com, pg 946

Moose School Productions, Box 960, Topanga, CA 90290-0960 *Tel:* 310-455-2318 *Toll Free Tel:* 800-676-5480 *Fax:* 310-455-4192 *Web Site:* www.peteralsop.com, pg 946

Morefield Communications Inc, 35 N 35 St, Camp Hill, PA 17011-2707 *Tel:* 717-761-6170 *Toll Free Tel:* 800-382-1266 *E-mail:* info@morefield.com *Web Site:* www.morefield.com, pg 946

Morehouse Publishing, 4775 Linglestown Rd, Harrisburg, PA 17112 *Tel:* 212-592-1800 (intl) *Toll Free Tel:* 800-242-1918 *Fax:* 717-541-8136 *E-mail:* churchpublishing@cpg.org *Web Site:* www.morehousepublishing.com; churchpublishing.org, pg 946

Morning Music Ltd, 5200 Dixie Rd, Suite 203, Mississauga, ON L4W 1E4, Canada *Tel:* 905-625-2676 *Fax:* 905-625-2092 *E-mail:* info@morningmusic.ca *Web Site:* www.morningmusic.ca, pg 946

MorphoTrust USA, 296 Concord Rd, Billerica, MA 01821 *Tel:* 978-215-2400 *Fax:* 978-215-2500 *Web Site:* www.morphotrust.com, pg 946

Rex Morris Productions, 5521 S Firethorn Place, Boise, ID 83716 *Tel:* 208-344-9878 *Fax:* 208-344-9878 *Web Site:* rexmorrisproductions.com, pg 946

Morrisound Recording, 12111 N 56 St, Tampa, FL 33617 *Tel:* 813-989-2108 *Fax:* 813-980-6950 *E-mail:* info@morrisound.com *Web Site:* morrisound.com, pg 946

Morro Bay Chamber of Commerce & Business Center, 695 Harbor St, Morro Bay, CA 93442 *Tel:* 805-772-4467 *Toll Free Tel:* 800-231-0592 *Web Site:* www.morrobay.org, pg 1093

Jack Morton Worldwide, 909 Third Ave, New York, NY 10022 *Tel:* 212-401-7000 *E-mail:* experience@jackmorton.com *Web Site:* www.jackmorton.com, pg 946

Mosby Inc, 3251 Riverport Lane, Maryland Heights, MO 63043 *Tel:* 314-872-8370 *Toll Free Tel:* 800-325-4177 *Fax:* 314-432-1380 *Web Site:* www.us.elsevierhealth.com, pg 947

Mother Basilea Films, 9849 N 40 St, Phoenix, AZ 85028-4099 *Tel:* 602-996-4040 *Fax:* 602-953-1303 *E-mail:* cid@integrity.com *Web Site:* www.canaaninthedesert.com, pg 947

Mother West, 37 W 20 St, Suite 1006, New York, NY 10011 *Tel:* 212-807-0405 *E-mail:* info@motherwest.com *Web Site:* www.motherwest.com, pg 947

Motion & Graphic Image Corp Inc (MAGIC), 1106 Dauphin St, Mobile, AL 36604 *Tel:* 251-433-7733 *E-mail:* magicians@magichd.com *Web Site:* magichd.com, pg 947

Motion Image Group LLC, 2140 S Dixie Hwy, Suite 301, Coconut Grove, FL 33133 *Tel:* 305-859-2000 *Fax:* 305-859-2412, pg 947

Motion Picture Association of America (MPAA), 15301 Ventura Blvd, Bldg E, Sherman Oaks, CA 91403-5885 *Tel:* 818-995-6600 *Fax:* 818-285-4403 *E-mail:* contactus@mpaa.org *Web Site:* www.mpaa.org, pg 1084

Motion Picture Editors Guild Local 700, 7715 Sunset Blvd, Suite 200, Hollywood, CA 90046 *Tel:* 323-876-4770 *Toll Free Tel:* 800-705-8700 *Fax:* 323-876-0861 *E-mail:* mail@editorsguild.com *Web Site:* www.editorsguild.com, pg 1084

Motion Picture Enterprises Inc, 432 W 45 St, New York, NY 10036 *Tel:* 212-245-0969 *Toll Free Tel:* 800-673-3348 *Fax:* 212-245-0974 *E-mail:* sales@mpenyc.com *Web Site:* www.mpenyc.com, pg 947

Motion Picture Licensing Corp (MPLC), 5455 Centinela Ave, Los Angeles, CA 90066 *Tel:* 310-822-8855 (intl calls) *Toll Free Tel:* 800-462-8855 *Fax:* 310-822-4440 *Web Site:* www.mplc.org, pg 947

Motion Picture Marine, 616 Venice Blvd, Marina Del Rey, CA 90291 *Tel:* 310-822-1100 *Fax:* 310-822-2679 *E-mail:* info@motionpicturemarine.com *Web Site:* www.motionpicturemarine.com, pg 947

Motion Picture Services, 5121 Ooltewah-Ringgold Rd, Suite E, Ooltewah, TN 37363 *Tel:* 423-238-7000 *E-mail:* info@motionpictureservices.net *Web Site:* www.motionpictureservices.net, pg 947

MotionArt Studios, 27 Common St, Boston, MA 02129 *Tel:* 617-242-2228 *Web Site:* www.motionart.org; www.linestorm.com, pg 947

MotionMasters, 2288 Roxalana Rd, Dunbar, WV 25064 *Tel:* 304-345-8800 *Fax:* 304-345-8809 *E-mail:* storytellers@motionmasters.com *Web Site:* motionmasters.com, pg 947

Motown Record Co, c/o Universal Music Group, 1755 Broadway, 6th fl, New York, NY 10019 *Tel:* 212-841-8000 *Web Site:* www.motown.com, pg 947

Mountainair Films, 1623 Camino De Cruz Blanca, Santa Fe, NM 87505 *Tel:* 505-471-9293 *Fax:* 505-438-0294 *E-mail:* produce@mountainairfilms.com *Web Site:* mountainairfilms.com, pg 947

Mountainfilm in Telluride, 109 E Colorado Ave, Suite 1, Telluride, CO 81435 *Tel:* 970-728-4123 *Fax:* 970-728-6458 *E-mail:* contact@mountainfilm.org *Web Site:* www.mountainfilm.org, pg 1121

Mouser Electronics, 1000 N Main St, Mansfield, TX 76063-1514 *Tel:* 817-804-3888 *Toll Free Tel:* 800-346-6873 *Fax:* 817-804-3899 *Web Site:* www.mouser.com, pg 947

Moviecraft Inc, PO Box 438, Orland Park, IL 60462-0438 *Tel:* 708-460-9082 *Fax:* 708-460-9099 *E-mail:* stock@moviecraft.com *Web Site:* www.moviecraft.com, pg 947

Movies Unlimited, 3015 Darnell Rd, Philadelphia, PA 19154 *Tel:* 215-637-4444 *Toll Free Tel:* 800-4-MOVIES (466-8437) *Fax:* 215-637-2350 *E-mail:* movies@moviesunlimited.com *Web Site:* www.moviesunlimited.com, pg 947

Moving Art by Louie Schwartzberg, 3371 Cahuenga Blvd W, Los Angeles, CA 90068 *Tel:* 323-436-7070 *Fax:* 323-436-2230 *E-mail:* team@movingart.com *Web Site:* www.movingart.com, pg 947

Moving Picture, 748 N Victoria Park Rd, Fort Lauderdale, FL 33304 *Tel:* 954-522-1361 *Toll Free Tel:* 800-800-1361 *Fax:* 954-523-1361 *E-mail:* info@movingpicture.com *Web Site:* www.movingpicture.com, pg 947

Moving Pictures, 200 Court St, Middletown, CT 06457 *Tel:* 860-704-6900 *Fax:* 860-704-6800 *E-mail:* inquiry@gener8or.com *Web Site:* www.movingpix.com; www.gener8or.com, pg 947

Moving Pictures, 655-H Pressley Rd, Charlotte, NC 28217 *Tel:* 704-676-0868 *Fax:* 704-676-0813 *E-mail:* info@mpicts.com *Web Site:* www.mpicts.com, pg 948

Moviola, 1135 N Mansfield Ave, Hollywood, CA 90038 *Tel:* 323-467-3107 *Toll Free Tel:* 877-MOVIOLA (668-4652) *Fax:* 323-464-1518 *Web Site:* www.moviola.com, pg 948

Moviola, 545 W 45 St, New York, NY 10036 *Tel:* 212-247-0972 *Fax:* 212-265-9820 *Web Site:* www.moviola.com, pg 948

Moxie Media, 1301 Dealers Ave, New Orleans, LA 70123 *Tel:* 504-733-6907 *Toll Free Tel:* 800-346-6943 *Fax:* 504-733-9493 *E-mail:* info@moxiemedia.com *Web Site:* www.moxiemedia.com; www.moxietraining.com, pg 948

Moxie Video Productions Inc, 7046 Sugar Magnolia Circle, Naples, FL 34109 *Tel:* 239-682-2129 *Toll Free Fax:* 888-349-8197 *Web Site:* moxievideo.com, pg 948

MQ Power Corp, 1800 Waters Ridge Dr, Suite 500, Lewisville, TX 75057 *Tel:* 972-459-5650 *Toll Free Tel:* 800-883-2551 *Fax:* 972-315-1847 *E-mail:* mqpowersales@multiquip.com *Web Site:* www.multiquip.com, pg 948

MRG Productions Inc, 286 Horton Hwy, Mineola, NY 11501 *Tel:* 516-214-6644 *Toll Free Tel:* 866-300-5121 *E-mail:* info@mrgproductions.com *Web Site:* mrgproductions.com, pg 948

MRM Worldwide, 622 Third Ave, New York, NY 10017 *Tel:* 646-865-6230 *E-mail:* info@mrmworldwide.com *Web Site:* www.mrmworldwide.com, pg 948

MRN Radio, 555 MRN Dr, Concord, NC 28027 *Tel:* 704-262-6700 *Fax:* 704-262-6811 *E-mail:* sales@mrnradio.com *Web Site:* www.mrnradio.com, pg 948

MRV Communications Inc, 20415 Nordhoff St, Chatsworth, CA 91311 *Tel:* 818-773-0900 *Toll Free Tel:* 800-338-5316 *Fax:* 818-773-0906 *E-mail:* info@mrv.com *Web Site:* www.mrv-corporate.com, pg 948

MRY, 11 W 19 St, 3rd fl, New York, NY 10011 *Tel:* 212-274-0470 *Toll Free Fax:* 888-847-5321 *Web Site:* mry.com, pg 949

MSE Media Solutions, 6013 Scott Way, Los Angeles, CA 90040 *Tel:* 323-721-1656 *Toll Free Tel:* 800-626-1955 *Fax:* 323-721-1506 *E-mail:* info@msemedia.com *Web Site:* www.msemedia.com, pg 949

MSI Productions, 9220 Activity Rd, San Diego, CA 92126 *Tel:* 858-348-0100 *Fax:* 858-348-0076 *Web Site:* www.msiprod.com, pg 949

MSR Mobile Stage Rentals, 2331 N State Rd 7, Suite 221, Fort Lauderdale, FL 33313 *Toll Free Tel:* 877-882-8889 *Toll Free Fax:* 866-704-1194 *E-mail:* info@mobilestagerentals.com *Web Site:* www.mobilestagerentals.com, pg 949

MSU Technologies, 325 E Grand River, Suite 350, East Lansing, MI 48823 *Tel:* 517-355-2186 *Fax:* 517-432-3880 *E-mail:* msut@msu.edu *Web Site:* www.technologies.msu.edu, pg 949

MTI Home Video, 14216 SW 136 St, Miami, FL 33186 *Tel:* 305-255-8684 *Fax:* 305-233-6943 *Web Site:* www.mtivideo.com, pg 949

MTM Equipment Rentals Ltd, 604 46 Ave NE, Calgary, AB T2E 8M9, Canada *Tel:* 403-276-1505 *E-mail:* contact@mtmequipment.com *Web Site:* www.mtmequipment.com, pg 949

MTV Networks Co, c/o MTV Studios, 1515 Broadway, New York, NY 10036 *Tel:* 212-258-8000 *Web Site:* www.mtv.com; www.mtvpress.com, pg 949

M2 Communications, 235 Bellefontaine St, Pasadena, CA 91105 *Tel:* 626-441-2024 *Toll Free Tel:* 800-423-8273 *Fax:* 626-441-2694 *E-mail:* m2com@aol.com *Web Site:* www.m2com.com, pg 949

MTX Audio, 4545 E Baseline Rd, Phoenix, AZ 85042 *Tel:* 602-438-4545 *Toll Free Tel:* 800-225-5689 *Fax:* 602-438-8692 *E-mail:* mtx@mtx.com *Web Site:* www.mtx.com, pg 949

Muderick Media, 101 Earlington Rd, Havertown, PA 19083 *Tel:* 610-449-6970, pg 949

Michael Mueller Productions, 1654 Airport Rd, Hot Springs, AR 71913 *Tel:* 501-520-5905 *Web Site:* muellervideo.com, pg 949

Ray Mueller Productions, 5 E Waterloo Rd, Stanhope, NJ 07874 *Tel:* 973-691-2088; 973-801-6004 *Web Site:* www.muellerproductions.com, pg 949

Muller Entertainment, 540 Commerce St, Southlake, TX 76092 *Tel:* 972-869-7704 *Fax:* 972-869-7791 *E-mail:* info@mullerentertainment.com *Web Site:* www.mullerentertainment.com, pg 949

Mullikin Agency, 1391 Plaza Place, Suite A, Springdale, AR 72764-5225 *Tel:* 479-750-0871 *Toll Free Tel:* 800-750-0871 *Fax:* 479-750-2685 *Web Site:* www.mullikinad.com, pg 949

Multi-Media Mathematics, 11224 Seawind Cove, San Diego, CA 92126-1119 *Tel:* 858-578-3421 *E-mail:* phyl.hil@gmail.com *Web Site:* www.miracosta.edu/home/pmcguire, pg 949

Multicom Inc, 1076 Florida Central Pkwy, Longwood, FL 32750 *Tel:* 407-331-7779 *Toll Free Tel:* 800-423-2594 *Fax:* 407-339-0204 *E-mail:* multicom@multicominc.com *Web Site:* www.multicominc.com, pg 949

Multicultural Media, 56 Browns Mill Rd, Montpelier, VT 05602 *E-mail:* support@worldmusicstore.com *Web Site:* www.worldmusicstore.com; www.multiculturalmedia.com, pg 950

MultiDyne Video & Fiber Optics Systems, 191 Forest Ave, Locust Valley, NY 11560 *Tel:* 516-671-7278 *Toll Free Tel:* 877-MULTIDYNE (685-8439) *Fax:* 516-671-3362 *E-mail:* sales@multidyne.com *Web Site:* www.multidyne.com, pg 950

MultiMedia, 333 Washington Ave N, Suite 212, Minneapolis, MN 55401 *Tel:* 612-767-1660 *Fax:* 612-339-5121 *E-mail:* info@multimedia-inc.com *Web Site:* www.multimedia-inc.com, pg 950

Multimedia Audio Visual Inc, 2640 S Raritan Circle, Denver, CO 80110 *Tel:* 303-623-2324 *Toll Free Tel:* 800-756-6118 *Fax:* 303-623-0829 *E-mail:* info@multimedia-av.com *Web Site:* www.multimedia-av.com, pg 950

Multimedia LED, 4225 Prado Rd, Suite 108, Corona, CA 92880 *Tel:* 951-280-7500 *Toll Free Tel:* 888-98-MMLED (986-6533 sales); 800-888-3007 (cust serv) *Fax:* 951-279-1773 *E-mail:* info@multimedialed.com *Web Site:* www.multimedialed.com, pg 950

Multivision Video & Film, 4006 Aurora St, Coral Gables, FL 33146 *Tel:* 305-662-6011 *E-mail:* info@multivisionvideo.com *Web Site:* www.multivisionvideo.com, pg 950

Munday & Collins AV, 2122 Zanker Rd, San Jose, CA 95131-2108 *Tel:* 408-451-9155 *Toll Free Tel:* 800-834-5551 *Fax:* 408-451-9192 *E-mail:* info@avevents.com *Web Site:* www.avevents.com, pg 950

Edward R Murrow Award, 401 Ninth St NW, Washington, DC 20004-2129 *Tel:* 202-879-9600 *Toll Free Tel:* 800-272-2190 *Fax:* 202-879-9700 *E-mail:* comments@cpb.org *Web Site:* www.cpb.org, pg 1121

The Edward R Murrow Award, 40 W 45 St, New York, NY 10036 *Tel:* 212-626-9220 *Fax:* 212-626-9210 *Web Site:* www.opcofamerica.org, pg 1121

Musco Lighting, 100 First Ave W, Oskaloosa, IA 52577 *Tel:* 641-673-0411 *Toll Free Tel:* 800-825-6030 *Fax:* 641-673-4852 *E-mail:* lighting@musco.com *Web Site:* www.musco.com, pg 950

Muse Entertainment Enterprises, 3451 Rue Saint Jacques, Montreal, QC H4C 1H1, Canada *Tel:* 514-866-6873 *Fax:* 514-876-3911 *E-mail:* bpalik@muse.ca *Web Site:* www.muse.ca, pg 950

Muse Presentation Technologies, 3510 S Susan St, Santa Ana, CA 92704 *Tel:* 714-850-1008 *Toll Free Tel:* 800-950-4955 *Fax:* 714-850-1018 *Web Site:* www.museprestech.com, pg 950

Museum of the City of New York, 1220 Fifth Ave, New York, NY 10029 *Tel:* 212-534-1672 *Fax:* 212-423-0758 *E-mail:* info@mcny.org *Web Site:* www.mcny.org, pg 950

Music & Entertainment Industry Educators Association (MEIEA), 1900 Belmont Blvd, Nashville, TN 37212-3758 *Tel:* 615-460-6946 *E-mail:* office@meiea.org *Web Site:* www.meiea.org, pg 1084

The Music Bakery, 7522 Campbell Rd, Suite 113, Dallas, TX 75248 *Tel:* 972-578-7863 *Toll Free Tel:* 800-229-0313 *Fax:* 214-884-6068 *E-mail:* helpnow@musicbakery.com *Web Site:* www.musicbakery.com, pg 950

Music Business Association (Music Biz), One Eves Dr, Suite 138, Marlton, NJ 08053 *Tel:* 856-596-2221 *Fax:* 856-596-7299 *Web Site:* www.musicbiz.org, pg 1084

Music Hall LLC, 108 Station Rd, Great Neck, NY 11023 *Tel:* 516-487-3663 *Fax:* 516-773-3891 *E-mail:* info@musichallaudio.com *Web Site:* musichall.biz, pg 950

The Music Kitchen Inc, 12400 Connery Way, Bakersfield, CA 93312 *Tel:* 661-338-4749 *Fax:* 661-338-2514 *Web Site:* www.themusickitchen.com, pg 950

Music Lab Inc, 500 E Saint Elmo Rd, Austin, TX 78745 *Tel:* 512-707-0560 *Fax:* 512-707-2946 *E-mail:* rentals@musiclab.net *Web Site:* www.musiclab.net, pg 950

Music Manufacturing Services, 636 King St W, Toronto, ON M5V 1M7, Canada *Tel:* 416-364-1943 *Toll Free Tel:* 800-MMS-4CDS (667-4237) *Fax:* 416-364-3616 *E-mail:* info@musicmanufacturing.com *Web Site:* www.musicmanufacturing.com; www.mmsdirect.com, pg 950

The Music People Inc, 154 Woodlawn Rd, Suite C, Berlin, CT 06037-1500 *Toll Free Tel:* 800-289-8889 *Fax:* 860-828-1353 *E-mail:* sales@musicpeopleinc.com *Web Site:* www.musicpeopleinc.com, pg 951

The Music Place, 844 Rte 73, West Berlin, NJ 08091 *Tel:* 856-768-2226 *Fax:* 856-768-7135 *E-mail:* zeronemusic@aol.com, pg 951

Music Rhapsody, 1603 Aviation Blvd, Redondo Beach, CA 90278 *Tel:* 310-376-8646 *Toll Free Tel:* 888-TRY-MUSIC (879-6874) *Fax:* 310-376-8490 *E-mail:* info@musicrhapsody.com *Web Site:* musicrhapsody.com, pg 951

Music Sales Corp, 180 Madison Ave, 24th fl, New York, NY 10016 *Tel:* 212-254-2100 *Fax:* 212-254-2013 *E-mail:* info@musicsales.com *Web Site:* www.musicsales.com, pg 951

Music 2 Hues, 54 Hazard Ave, Suite 315, Enfield, CT 06082 *Tel:* 860-745-1312 *Fax:* 860-745-1312 (orders) *E-mail:* info@music2hues.com *Web Site:* www.music2hues.com, pg 951

Music World/Vocal Power School, 9826 Columbus Ave, North Hills, CA 91343 *Tel:* 818-895-7464 *Toll Free Tel:* 800-929-7464 *E-mail:* MusicMan@music-world.com *Web Site:* www.BornToSing.com, pg 951

Musicol Recording, 780 Oakland Park Ave, Columbus, OH 43224 *Tel:* 614-267-3133 *Toll Free Tel:* 800-240-5963 *Fax:* 614-267-3135 *E-mail:* info@musicolrecording.com *Web Site:* www.musicolrecording.com, pg 951

Musikvergnuegen, 1545 Wilcox Ave, Suite 202, Hollywood, CA 90028 *Tel:* 323-856-5900 *Fax:* 323-856-5917 *E-mail:* info@musikv.com *Web Site:* www.musikvergnuegen.com, pg 951

Musivision Inc, 8 Deepwood Rd, Weston, CT 06883 *Tel:* 203-227-1017 *E-mail:* info@musivision.com, pg 951

Mutoh America Inc, 2602 S 47 St, Phoenix, AZ 85034-7401 *Tel:* 480-968-7772 *Toll Free Tel:* 800-99-MUTOH (996-8864) *Fax:* 480-968-7990 *E-mail:* sales@mutoh.com *Web Site:* mutoh.com, pg 951

Mutual Hardware, 36-27 Vernon Blvd, Long Island City, NY 11106 *Toll Free Tel:* 866-361-2480 *Fax:* 718-786-9591 *E-mail:* info@mutualhardware.com *Web Site:* www.mutualhardware.com, pg 951

MVD Entertainment Group, 203 Windsor Rd, Pottstown, PA 19464 *Tel:* 610-650-8200 *Toll Free Tel:* 800-888-0486 *Fax:* 610-650-9102 *Toll Free Fax:* 888-536-7998 *Web Site:* mvdb2b.com, pg 951

MVI Multivision Inc, 120 McLevin Ave, Unit 3, Toronto, ON M1B 3E9, Canada *Tel:* 416-449-1080 *Toll Free Tel:* 800-563-5902 (ext 228) *Fax:* 416-449-5131 *E-mail:* business@mvidisplay.com *Web Site:* www.mvidisplay.com, pg 951

MVP International Inc, 9000 Southwest Fwy, Suite 320, Houston, TX 77074-1521 *Tel:* 713-771-1132 *Toll Free Tel:* 800-432-0687 *Fax:* 713-771-3806 *E-mail:* info@mvp-av.com *Web Site:* www.mvp-av.com, pg 951

Myriad Productions, 415 Barlow Ct, Johns Creek, GA 30022 *Tel:* 678-417-0043 *Fax:* 678-417-0043, pg 951

Mystery Electronics, 6438 Morton Rd, Greenbrier, TN 37073 *Tel:* 615-643-8460 *Toll Free Tel:* 800-798-2256 *Fax:* 615-643-8464 *E-mail:* sales@mysteryelectronics.com *Web Site:* www.mysteryelectronics.com, pg 951

Mystic Seaport (Film & Video Archives), 75 Greenmanville Ave, Mystic, CT 06355 *Tel:* 860-572-5367 *Toll Free Tel:* 888-973-2767 *E-mail:* collections@mysticseaport.org; info@mysticseaport.org *Web Site:* www.mysticseaport.org, pg 951

Myton Industries Inc, 1981 S Park Rd, Pembroke Park, FL 33009 *Tel:* 954-989-0113 *Toll Free Tel:* 800-544-2406 *Fax:* 954-989-1488 *E-mail:* myton@msn.com; sales@mytonindustries.com *Web Site:* www.mytonindustries.com, pg 952

NAB Distinguished Service Award, 1771 "N" St NW, Washington, DC 20036 *Tel:* 202-429-5300 *Fax:* 202-775-3516 *E-mail:* nab@nab.org *Web Site:* www.nab.org, pg 1121

Nady Systems Inc, 6701 Shellmound St, Emeryville, CA 94608 *Tel:* 510-652-2411 *Fax:* 510-652-5075 *E-mail:* ussales@nady.com *Web Site:* www.nady.com, pg 952

Nalpak Inc, 1267 Vernon Way, El Cajon, CA 92020 *Tel:* 619-258-1200 *Toll Free Tel:* 888-488-3372 (help desk) *Fax:* 619-258-0925 *E-mail:* service@nalpak.com *Web Site:* www.nalpak.com, pg 952

NAMM, the National Association of Music Merchants, 5790 Armada Dr, Carlsbad, CA 92008 *Tel:* 760-438-8001 *Toll Free Tel:* 800-767-6266 (memb hotline) *Fax:* 760-438-7327 *E-mail:* info@namm.org *Web Site:* www.namm.org, pg 1085

Nancy's Notions, 333 Beichl Ave, Beaver Dam, WI 53916 *Tel:* 920-887-0391 *Toll Free Tel:* 800-833-0690 (orders) *Fax:* 920-887-2133 *Toll Free Fax:* 800-255-8119 (orders) *E-mail:* custserv@nancysnotions.com *Web Site:* www.nancysnotions.com, pg 952

Nandar Entertainment Pictures, 650 N Bronson Ave, Suite B145, Los Angeles, CA 90004 *Toll Free Tel:* 800-969-6022 *E-mail:* mail@nandarent.com *Web Site:* nandarentertainment.com, pg 952

N&N Productions Ltd, 5540 High Rock Way, Sparks, NV 89431 *Tel:* 775-355-9080 *Fax:* 775-355-7859 *E-mail:* sales@brassgobos.com *Web Site:* www.brassgobos.com, pg 952

Nantucket Film Festival (NFF), 68 Jay St, Suite 319, Brooklyn, NY 11201 *Tel:* 646-480-1900; 508-325-6274 *Fax:* 646-365-3367 *E-mail:* info@nantucketfilmfestival.org *Web Site:* www.nantucketfilmfestival.org, pg 1121

The Napoleon Group, 48 W 25 St, New York, NY 10010 *Tel:* 212-692-9200 *Toll Free Tel:* 800-579-4019 *Fax:* 212-692-0309 *E-mail:* info@napny.com *Web Site:* www.napny.com, pg 952

NASCAR Media Group LLC, 550 S Caldwell St, Suite 2000, Charlotte, NC 28202 *Tel:* 704-348-7100 *Web Site:* www.nascarmediagroup.com, pg 952

Nashville Production Rentals (NPR), 3401 Ambrose Ave, Nashville, TN 37207 *Tel:* 615-775-7609 *Fax:* 615-515-5985 *E-mail:* mail@nashvilleproductionrentals.com *Web Site:* www.nashvilleproductionrentals.com, pg 952

Nassau County Film Office, Executive Bldg, One West St, Mineola, NY 11501 *Tel:* 516-571-3168 *Fax:* 516-571-6195 *Web Site:* www.longislandfilm.com, pg 1100

Natchez Film Commission, 640 S Canal St, Box C, Natchez, MS 39120 *Tel:* 601-446-6345 *Toll Free Tel:* 800-647-6724 *Fax:* 601-442-0814 *E-mail:* info@visitnatchez.org *Web Site:* www.visitnatchez.org, pg 1099

The National Academy of Television Arts & Sciences (NATAS), 1697 Broadway, Suite 1001, New York, NY 10019 *Tel:* 212-586-8424 *Fax:* 212-246-8129 *Web Site:* www.emmyonline.org, pg 1085

National Association for Music Education (NAfME), 1806 Robert Fulton Dr, Reston, VA 20191 *Tel:* 703-860-4000 *Toll Free Tel:* 800-336-3768 *Fax:* 703-860-1531 *E-mail:* memberservices@nafme2.org *Web Site:* www.menc.org; www.nafme.org, pg 1085

National Association of Biology Teachers (NABT), 1313 Dolley Madison Blvd, Suite 402, McLean, VA 22101 *Tel:* 703-264-9696 *Toll Free Tel:* 888-501-NABT (501-6228) *Fax:* 703-790-2672 *Toll Free Fax:* 800-883-0698 *E-mail:* office@nabt.org *Web Site:* www.nabt.org, pg 1085

National Association of Black Journalists (NABJ), 1100 Knight Hall, Suite 3100, College Park, MD 20742 *Tel:* 301-405-0248 *Fax:* 301-314-1714 *E-mail:* nabj@nabj.org *Web Site:* www.nabj.org, pg 1085

National Association of Broadcasters (NAB), 1771 "N" St NW, Washington, DC 20036 *Tel:* 202-429-5300 *Fax:* 202-429-4199 *E-mail:* nab@nab.org *Web Site:* www.nab.org, pg 1085

National Association of Elementary School Principals (NAESP), 1615 Duke St, Alexandria, VA 22314 *Tel:* 703-684-3345 *Toll Free Tel:* 800-386-2377 *Fax:* 703-549-5568 *Toll Free Fax:* 800-396-2377 *E-mail:* naesp@naesp.org *Web Site:* www.naesp.org, pg 952

National Association of Photo Equipment Technicians (NAPET), 2282 Springport Rd, Suite F, Jackson, MI 49202 *Tel:* 517-788-8100 *Toll Free Tel:* 800-762-9287 *Fax:* 517-788-8371 *Web Site:* www.pmai.org/napet, pg 1085

National Association of Record Industry Professionals (NARIP), PO Box 2446, Toluca Lake, CA 91610-2446 *Tel:* 818-769-7007; 559-271-7900 (Pollstar Live!) *Fax:* 818-769-6191 *E-mail:* info@narip.com *Web Site:* www.narip.com, pg 1085

National Association of Video Distributors (NAVD), 5584 Prestwick Dr, Newburgh, IN 47630 *Tel:* 270-860-8904 *Web Site:* www.navdonline.org, pg 1085

National Audio-Visual Supply, 80 Little Falls Rd, Fairfield, NJ 07004 *Toll Free Tel:* 800-222-0109 *Toll Free Fax:* 800-628-1329 *E-mail:* info@nationalavsupply.com *Web Site:* www.nationalaudiovisualsupply.com, pg 952

National Audiovisual Center - National Technical Information Service (NTIS), 5301 Shawnee Rd, Alexandria, VA 22312 *Tel:* 703-605-6000 *Toll Free Tel:* 800-553-6847 *Fax:* 703-605-6900 *E-mail:* info@ntis.gov *Web Site:* www.ntis.gov, pg 952

National Board of Review (of Motion Pictures), 40 W 37 St, Suite 501, New York, NY 10018 *Tel:* 212-465-9166 *Fax:* 212-465-9168 *E-mail:* nbr@nbrmp.org *Web Site:* www.nationalboardofreview.org, pg 1085

National Boston, 115 Dummer St, Brookline, MA 02446 *Tel:* 617-734-4800 *Fax:* 617-734-6323 *E-mail:* info@nationalboston.com *Web Site:* www.nationalboston.com, pg 952

National Council of Acoustical Consultants (NCAC), 9100 Purdue Rd, Suite 200, Indianapolis, IN 46268 *Tel:* 317-328-0642 *Fax:* 317-328-4629 *E-mail:* info@ncac.com *Web Site:* www.ncac.com, pg 1085

National Council of Churches, 110 Maryland Ave NE, Suite 10-B, Washington, DC 20002 *Tel:* 202-544-2350 *Fax:* 202-543-1297 *E-mail:* info@ncccusa.org *Web Site:* www.ncccusa.org, pg 952

National Council of Teachers of English (NCTE), 1111 W Kenyon Rd, Urbana, IL 61801-1096 *Tel:* 217-328-3870 *Toll Free Tel:* 877-369-6283 *Fax:* 217-328-9645 *Web Site:* www.ncte.org, pg 1086

National Education Association (NEA), 1201 16 St NW, Washington, DC 20036-3290 *Tel:* 202-833-4000 *Fax:* 202-822-7974 *Web Site:* www.nea.org, pg 952

National Film Board of Canada/Office National du Film du Canada, Norman-McLaren Bldg, 3155 Cote-de-Liesse Rd, Montreal, QC H4N 2N4, Canada *Tel:* 514-283-9000 *Toll Free Tel:* 800-267-7710 (CN only) *Fax:* 514-283-7564 *Web Site:* www.nfb.ca, pg 952

National Fire Protection Association (NFPA), One Batterymarch Park, Quincy, MA 02169-7471 *Tel:* 617-770-3000 *Toll Free Tel:* 800-344-3555 *Fax:* 617-770-0700 *E-mail:* custserv@nfpa.org *Web Site:* www.nfpa.org, pg 952

National Freedom of Information Coalition (NFOIC), Missouri School of Journalism, 101E Reynolds Journalism Institute, Columbia, MO 65211 *Tel:* 573-882-4856 *E-mail:* info@nfoic.org *Web Site:* www.nfoic.org, pg 1086

National Geographic Learning, 10650 Toebben Dr, Independence, KY 41051 *Toll Free Tel:* 888-915-3276 *E-mail:* schoolcustomerservice@cengage.com *Web Site:* ngl.cengage.com, pg 952

National Headliner Awards, PO Box 239, Northfield, NJ 08225-0239 *Tel:* 609-601-2116 *E-mail:* info@headlinerawards.org *Web Site:* www.headlinerawards.org, pg 1121

National Information Center for Educational Media (NICEM)/MediaSleuth, c/o Access Innovations Inc, 4725 Indian School Rd NE, Suite 100, Albuquerque, NM 87110-3980 *Tel:* 505-265-3591 *Toll Free Tel:* 800-926-8328 *Fax:* 505-256-1080 *E-mail:* info-request@nicem.com; orders@mediasleuth.com *Web Site:* www.nicem.com; www.mediasleuth.com, pg 952

National Institute for Trial Advocacy (NITA), 1685 38 St, Suite 200, Boulder, CO 80301-2735 *Tel:* 720-890-4860 *Toll Free Tel:* 800-225-6482 *Fax:* 720-890-7069 *E-mail:* receptionist@nita.org *Web Site:* www.nita.org, pg 953

National Instruments Corp, 11500 N Mopac Expwy, Austin, TX 78759-3504 *Toll Free Tel:* 888-280-7645 (sales); 800-531-5066 (cust serv) *Fax:* 512-683-8411 *Web Site:* www.ni.com, pg 953

National Lampoon, 8228 W Sunset Blvd, West Hollywood, CA 90046-2414 *Tel:* 310-474-5252 *Fax:* 310-474-1219 *E-mail:* feedback@nationallampoon.com *Web Site:* www.nationallampoon.com, pg 953

National Media Services Inc, 613 N Commerce Ave, Front Royal, VA 22630 *Tel:* 540-635-4181 *Fax:* 540-636-4240 *E-mail:* info@nationalmediaservices.com *Web Site:* www.nationalmediaservices.com, pg 953

National Old Time Country Bluegrass & Folk Music Festival, PO Box 492, Anita, IA 50020 *Tel:* 712-762-4363 *Web Site:* ntcma.net, pg 1121

National Press Photographers Association (NPPA), 3200 Croasdaile Dr, Suite 306, Durham, NC 27705 *Tel:* 919-383-7246 *Fax:* 919-383-7261 *E-mail:* info@nppa.org *Web Site:* www.nppa.org, pg 1086

National Products Inc, 8410 Dallas Ave S, Seattle, WA 98108 *Tel:* 206-763-8361 *Toll Free Tel:* 800-497-7479 *Fax:* 206-763-9615 *Web Site:* www.rammount.com, pg 953

National Public Radio (NPR), 1111 N Capitol St NE, Washington, DC 20002 *Tel:* 202-513-2000 *Web Site:* www.npr.org, pg 1086

National Religious Broadcasters (NRB), 9510 Technology Dr, Manassas, VA 20110 *Tel:* 703-330-7000 *Fax:* 703-330-7100 *E-mail:* info@nrb.org *Web Site:* www.nrb.org, pg 1086

National Safety Council (NSC), 1121 Spring Lake Dr, Itasca, IL 60143-3201 *Tel:* 630-285-1121 *Toll Free Tel:* 800-621-7615; 800-621-7619 (cust serv) *Fax:* 630-285-1315; 630-285-1434 (cust serv) *E-mail:* customerservice@nsc.org *Web Site:* www.nsc.org, pg 953

National School Boards Association (NSBA), 1680 Duke St, Alexandria, VA 22314 *Tel:* 703-838-6722 *Fax:* 703-683-7590 *E-mail:* info@nsba.org *Web Site:* www.nsba.org, pg 1086

National School Products, 1523 Old Niles Ferry Rd, Maryville, TN 37803 *Tel:* 865-984-3960 *Toll Free Tel:* 800-627-9393 *Fax:* 865-983-9355 *Toll Free Fax:* 800-289-3960 *Web Site:* www.nationalschoolproducts.com, pg 953

National Short Film & Video Competition, 6116 N Central Expwy, Suite 105, Dallas, TX 75206 *Tel:* 214-821-6300; 214-821-FILM (821-3456) *Fax:* 214-821-6364 *E-mail:* usafilmfestival@aol.com *Web Site:* www.usafilmfestival.com, pg 1121

National Storytelling Festival, 116 W Main St, Jonesborough, TN 37659 *Tel:* 423-753-2171 *Toll Free Tel:* 800-952-8392 *Fax:* 423-913-8219 *E-mail:* customerservice@storytellingcenter.net *Web Site:* www.storytellingfestival.net; www.storytellingcenter.net, pg 1121

National Student Production Awards, Hershey Square Ctr, 1152 Mae St, Hummelstown, PA 17036 *Toll Free Tel:* 855-ASK-4CBI (275-4224) *Web Site:* www.askcbi.org, pg 1121

National Systems Contractors Association (NSCA), 3950 River Ridge Dr NE, Cedar Rapids, IA 52402 *Tel:* 319-366-6722 *Toll Free Tel:* 800-446-6722 *Fax:* 319-366-4164 *E-mail:* nsca@nsca.org *Web Site:* www.nsca.org, pg 1086

National Teaching Aids Inc, 401 Hickory St, Fort Collins, CO 80524 *Tel:* 970-484-7445 *Toll Free Tel:* 800-289-9299 *Fax:* 970-484-1198 *E-mail:* custserv@amep.com *Web Site:* www.amep.com, pg 953

National Telemedia Council Inc, 1922 University Ave, Madison, WI 53726 *Tel:* 608-218-1182 *E-mail:* ntelemedia@aol.com *Web Site:* www.nationaltelemediacouncil.org, pg 1086

National Teleproductions Inc, PO Box 1804, West Palm Beach, FL 33402-1804 *Tel:* 561-689-9271 *Fax:* 561-640-4677 *E-mail:* ntp@ntpworldwide.com, pg 953

National Traditional Country Music Association Inc (NTCMA), PO Box 492, Anita, IA 50020-0492 *Tel:* 712-762-4363; 712-249-5989 (cell) *E-mail:* ruralcountrymusic@gmail.com *Web Site:* ntcma.net, pg 1086

National Undergraduate Student Electronic Media Competition, PO Box 4206, Chesterfield, MO 63006 *Tel:* 636-536-1943 *Fax:* 636-898-6920 *E-mail:* national-office@nbs-aerho.org *Web Site:* www.nbs-aerho.org, pg 1121

Nationwide Audio Visual Co, 4100-B Sladeview Crescent, Units 1 & 2, Mississauga, ON L5L 5Z3, Canada *Tel:* 905-608-8899 *Fax:* 905-608-8890 *E-mail:* sales@nationwideav.com *Web Site:* www.nationwideav.com, pg 953

Nautilus Entertainment Design Inc (NED), 1010 Turquoise St, Suite 215, San Diego, CA 92109 *Tel:* 858-456-6395 *E-mail:* info@n-e-d.com *Web Site:* www.n-e-d.com, pg 953

Navigator Systems US, 1312 W Main St, Suite E, Lebanon, TN 37087 *Tel:* 615-547-1895 *Fax:* 615-547-1897 *E-mail:* sales@hiretrack.com *Web Site:* www.hiretrack.com, pg 953

Navitar Inc, 200 Commerce Dr, Rochester, NY 14623 *Tel:* 585-359-4000 *Toll Free Tel:* 800-828-6778 *Fax:* 585-359-4999 *E-mail:* info@navitar.com *Web Site:* www.navitar.com, pg 953

Nazdar®, 8501 Hedge Lane Terr, Shawnee, KS 66227-3290 *Tel:* 913-422-1888 *Toll Free Tel:* 800-767-9942 (cust serv) *Fax:* 913-422-2296 *E-mail:* custserv@nazdar.com *Web Site:* www.nazdar.com, pg 953

NBA Entertainment Inc, 450 Harmon Meadow Blvd, Secaucus, NJ 07094 *Tel:* 201-865-1500 *Fax:* 201-865-2626 *Web Site:* www.nba.com, pg 953

NBC-5, 4805 Amon Carter Blvd, Fort Worth, TX 76155 *Tel:* 817-429-5555 *Fax:* 817-654-6325 *E-mail:* newstips@nbcdfw.com *Web Site:* www.nbcdfw.com, pg 953

NBC Production Facilities, 30 Rockefeller Plaza, New York, NY 10112 *Tel:* 212-664-3687 *Fax:* 212-664-5056 *Web Site:* www.nbc.com, pg 953

NBCUniversal Archives, 30 Rockefeller Plaza, New York, NY 10112 *Tel:* 212-664-5015 *Toll Free Tel:* 855-NBC-VIDEO (622-8433) *Fax:* 212-703-8558; 212-664-4472 *E-mail:* nbcu.archives@nbcuni.com *Web Site:* www.nbcuniversalarchives.com, pg 954

NDS Surgical Imaging LLC, 5750 Hellyer Ave, San Jose, CA 95138 *Tel:* 408-776-0085 *Toll Free Tel:* 866-637-5237 *Fax:* 408-776-9878 *E-mail:* info@ndssi.com *Web Site:* www.ndssi.com, pg 954

Malcolm Neal Productions, 111 Everest Dr, Thomaston, GA 30286-4603 *Tel:* 706-646-2749; 706-647-5372 *Fax:* 706-938-1138 *E-mail:* nealritz@charter.net, pg 954

Nebraska Film Office, PO Box 98907, Lincoln, NE 68509-8907 *Tel:* 402-471-3746 *Toll Free Tel:* 800-228-4307 *E-mail:* info@filmnebraska.org *Web Site:* www.filmnebraska.org; www.neded.org/nebraska-film-office-home, pg 1099

NEC Display Solutions of America, 500 Park Blvd, Suite 1100, Itasca, IL 60143 *Tel:* 630-467-3000 *Web Site:* www.necdisplay.com, pg 954

Nelson Education Ltd, 1120 Birchmount Rd, Scarborough, ON M1K 5G4, Canada *Tel:* 416-752-9100 *Toll Free Tel:* 800-268-2222 (cust support) *Fax:* 416-752-8101 *Toll Free Fax:* 800-430-4445 *E-mail:* inquire@nelson.com *Web Site:* www.nelson.com, pg 954

Nelson Enterprises Theatrical Supply Co, 1014 Rte 173 E, Bloomsbury, NJ 08804 *Tel:* 908-479-6902 *Fax:* 908-479-6903 *E-mail:* sales@nelson-enterprises.com; rentals@nelson-enterprises.com *Web Site:* www.nelson-enterprises.com, pg 954

L E Nelson Sales Corp, 6050 S Valley View Blvd, Las Vegas, NV 89118 *Tel:* 702-367-3656 *Fax:* 702-367-7058, pg 954

Scott Nelson HD Productions Inc, PO Box 1198, Bend, OR 97709-1198 *Tel:* 541-410-8680 *E-mail:* snp@bendcable.com *Web Site:* vimeo.com/scottnelson, pg 954

Nelson White Systems Inc, 8725-A Loch Raven Blvd, Baltimore, MD 21286 *Tel:* 410-668-9628 *Toll Free Tel:* 800-296-7555 *Fax:* 410-668-9629 *E-mail:* sales@nelsonwhite.com; service@nelsonwhite.com; rentals@nelsonwhite.com *Web Site:* www.nelsonwhite.com, pg 954

Nemal Electronics International Inc, 12240 NE 14 Ave, North Miami, FL 33161 *Tel:* 305-899-0900 *Toll Free Tel:* 800-522-2253 *Fax:* 305-895-8178 *E-mail:* info@nemal.com *Web Site:* www.nemal.com, pg 954

Otto Nemenz International Inc, 870 N Vine St, Los Angeles, CA 90038 *Tel:* 323-469-2774 *Fax:* 323-469-1217 *E-mail:* info@ottonemenz.com *Web Site:* www.ottonemenz.com, pg 954

Neo Studios, 628 Broadway, Suite 302, New York, NY 10012 *Tel:* 212-533-4195 *E-mail:* mail@neostudiosnyc.com *Web Site:* www.neostudiosnyc.com, pg 954

NeoSoft Corp, PO Box 5667, Bend, OR 97708-5667 *Tel:* 541-389-5489 *Toll Free Tel:* 877-389-5489 (orders only) *Fax:* 541-388-8221 *E-mail:* sales@neosoftware.com *Web Site:* www.neosoftware.com, pg 954

Neptune Photo Inc, 130 Seventh St, Garden City, NY 11530 *Tel:* 516-741-4484 *Toll Free Tel:* 800-955-1110 *Fax:* 516-741-1225 *E-mail:* sales@neptunephoto.com *Web Site:* www.neptunephoto.com, pg 954

Nesbit Systems Inc, 243 N Union St, Suite 112, Lambertville, NJ 08530 *Tel:* 609-397-7720 *E-mail:* info@nesbit.com *Web Site:* www.nesbit.com, pg 954

NetWell Noise Control, 18525 37 Ave N, Minneapolis, MN 55446-2855 *Tel:* 763-694-8908 *Toll Free Tel:* 800-638-9355 *Fax:* 763-694-8909 *E-mail:* help@controlnoise.com *Web Site:* www.controlnoise.com, pg 954

Network Entertainment Inc, 23 W Pender St, Suite 290, Vancouver, BC V6B 1R3, Canada *Tel:* 604-739-8825 *Fax:* 604-739-8835 *E-mail:* info@networkentertainment.com *Web Site:* www.networkentertainment.ca, pg 954

Network Technologies Inc, 1275 Danner Dr, Aurora, OH 44202 *Tel:* 330-562-7070 *Toll Free Tel:* 800-742-8324 *Fax:* 330-562-1999 *E-mail:* sales@ntigo.com *Web Site:* www.networktechinc.com, pg 955

Neumann USA, One Enterprise Dr, Old Lyme, CT 06371 *Tel:* 860-434-9190 *Fax:* 860-434-1759 *E-mail:* neumann-help@neumannusa.com *Web Site:* www.neumannusa.com, pg 955

Neutrik® USA Inc, 4115 Taggart Creek Rd, Charlotte, NC 28208-5479 *Tel:* 704-972-3050 *Fax:* 704-438-9202 *E-mail:* info@neutrikusa.com *Web Site:* www.neutrik.us, pg 955

Nevada Broadcasters Association, 1050 E Flamingo Rd, No 102, Las Vegas, NV 89119 *Tel:* 702-794-4994 *Web Site:* www.nevadabroadcasters.org, pg 1086

Nevada Film Office, 6655 W Sahara, Suite C106, Las Vegas, NV 89146 *Tel:* 702-486-2711 *Toll Free Tel:* 877-638-3456 *Fax:* 702-486-2712 *E-mail:* lvnfo@nevadafilm.com *Web Site:* www.nevadafilm.com, pg 1100

Nevion, 1600 Emerson Ave, Oxnard, CA 93033 *Tel:* 805-247-8560 *E-mail:* ussales@nevion.com *Web Site:* www.nevion.com, pg 955

New & Unique Videos™, 7323 Rondel Ct, San Diego, CA 92119-1530 *Tel:* 619-644-3000 *E-mail:* video@newuniquevideos.com *Web Site:* www.newuniquevideos.com, pg 955

New Art Miami, 175 SW Seventh St, Suite 2201, Miami, FL 33130 *Tel:* 305-857-0350 *Fax:* 305-857-0175 *E-mail:* info@newartmiami.com *Web Site:* www.newartmiami.com, pg 955

New Brunswick Film (NB Film), c/o New Brunswick Division of Tourism, Heritage & Culture, Place 2000, 250 King St, Fredericton, NB E3B 9M9, Canada *Tel:* 506-453-2909 *Fax:* 506-453-2416, pg 1105

New Circuit Films LLC, 403 S Central Ave, No 12, Glendale, CA 91204 *Tel:* 818-378-0033 *E-mail:* info@newcircuit.com *Web Site:* www.newcircuit.com, pg 955

New Cyberian Systems Inc, 1919 O'Toole Way, San Jose, CA 95131 *Tel:* 408-922-0682 *Toll Free Tel:* 877-423-4383 *Fax:* 408-884-2257 *E-mail:* sales@newcyberian.com *Web Site:* www.newcyberian.com, pg 955

New Day Films, 190 Rte 17 M, Suite D, Harriman, NY 10926 *Toll Free Tel:* 888-367-9154 *Fax:* 845-774-2945 *E-mail:* curator@newday.com; orders@newday.com *Web Site:* www.newday.com, pg 955

New Deal Studios, 15392 Cobalt St, Los Angeles, CA 91342 *Tel:* 310-578-9929 *Web Site:* www.newdealstudios.com, pg 955

New England Keyboard Inc, One Princeton Rd, Fitchburg, MA 01420 *Tel:* 978-345-8332 *Fax:* 978-345-4329 *E-mail:* info@newenglandkeyboard.com *Web Site:* www.newenglandkeyboard.com, pg 955

New England Technology Group Inc (NETG), One Davenport St, Cambridge, MA 02140 *Tel:* 617-864-5551 *Fax:* 520-844-5551 *E-mail:* teamnetg@netgworld.com *Web Site:* netgworld.com, pg 955

New Era Media, PO Box 410685, San Francisco, CA 94141-0685 *Tel:* 415-863-3555 *Fax:* 415-864-5437 *E-mail:* sales@arkmedia.com, pg 955

The New Film Company Inc, 7 Scott St, Cambridge, MA 02138 *Tel:* 617-520-5005 *Fax:* 617-491-9201 *E-mail:* newfilmco@aol.com *Web Site:* www.newfilmco.com, pg 955

New Hampshire Film & TV Office, 19 Pillsbury St, 1st fl, Concord, NH 03301 *Tel:* 603-271-2220 *Fax:* 603-271-3584 *E-mail:* film@nh.gov *Web Site:* www.nh.gov/film, pg 1100

New Harbinger Publications, 5674 Shattuck Ave, Oakland, CA 94609 *Tel:* 510-652-0215 *Toll Free Tel:* 800-748-6273 *Fax:* 510-652-5472 *E-mail:* customerservice@newharbinger.com *Web Site:* www.newharbinger.com, pg 955

New Horizon Studios, 202 E 42 St, New York, NY 10017 *Tel:* 212-490-0355 *Fax:* 212-490-0355, pg 955

New Horizons Computer Learning Centers Inc, One W Elm St, Suite 125, Conshohocken, PA 19428 *Tel:* 484-567-3000 *Toll Free Tel:* 888-236-3625 *Web Site:* www.newhorizons.com, pg 955

New Jersey Film Festival, Admin Off, 30 Bedford Rd, Somerset, NJ 08873 *Tel:* 848-932-8482 *Fax:* 732-932-1935 *E-mail:* njmac@aol.com *Web Site:* www.njfilmfest.com, pg 1122

New Jersey International Film Festival, Admin Off, 30 Bedford Rd, Somerset, NJ 08873 *Tel:* 848-932-8482 *Fax:* 732-932-1935 *E-mail:* njmac@aol.com *Web Site:* www.njfilmfest.com, pg 1122

New Jersey Motion Picture & Television Commission, 153 Halsey St, 5th fl, Newark, NJ 07102-2807 *Tel:* 973-648-6279 *Fax:* 973-648-7350 *E-mail:* njfilm@njfilm.org *Web Site:* www.njfilm.org, pg 1100

New Leaf Distributing Co, 401 Thornton Rd, Lithia Springs, GA 30122-1557 *Tel:* 770-948-7845 *Toll Free Tel:* 800-326-2665 (orders) *Fax:* 770-944-2313 *E-mail:* newleaf@newleaf-dist.com *Web Site:* www.newleaf-dist.com, pg 955

New Letters on the Air, c/o University of Missouri, Kansas City, 5101 Rockhill Rd, Kansas City, MO 64110 *Tel:* 816-235-1159 *Toll Free Tel:* 888-548-2477 *Fax:* 816-235-2611 *E-mail:* radio@newletters.org *Web Site:* www.newletters.org, pg 956

New Life Communications Inc, 905 Hwy 71 NE, Willmar, MN 56201-2654 *Tel:* 320-235-6404 *Toll Free Tel:* 800-233-6470 *Fax:* 320-235-6418 *E-mail:* nlc@newlifecomm.com *Web Site:* www.newlifecomm.com, pg 956

New Line Cinema, 116 N Robertson Blvd, Suite 200, Los Angeles, CA 90048 *Tel:* 310-854-5811 *Fax:* 310-854-1824 *Web Site:* www.warnerbros.com/studio/divisions/motion-pictures/new-line-cinema.html, pg 956

New London Media, 78 Washington St, New London, CT 06320 *Tel:* 860-961-6300 *Web Site:* www.andrewclydebell.com, pg 956

New Mexico Film Office, Joseph M Montoya Bldg, 1st fl, 1100 St Francis Dr, Suite 1213, Santa Fe, NM 87505 *Tel:* 505-476-5600 *Toll Free Tel:* 800-545-9871 *Fax:* 505-476-5601 *E-mail:* info@nmfilm.com *Web Site:* www.nmfilm.com, pg 1100

New Orleans Film Festival, 900 Camp St, New Orleans, LA 70130 *Tel:* 504-309-6633 *Fax:* 504-309-0923 *E-mail:* info@neworleansfilmfest.com *Web Site:* www.neworleansfilmsociety.org, pg 1122

New Wave Entertainment, 2660 W Olive Ave, Burbank, CA 91505 *Tel:* 818-295-5000 *E-mail:* pr@nwe.com *Web Site:* nwe.com, pg 956

New World Records, 20 Jay St, Suite 1001, Brooklyn, NY 11201 *Tel:* 212-290-1680 *Fax:* 646-224-9638 *E-mail:* info@newworldrecords.org *Web Site:* www.newworldrecords.org, pg 956

New York Audio Productions, 344 W 38 St, 6th fl, New York, NY 10018 *Tel:* 212-244-1114 *Fax:* 212-243-7210 *E-mail:* info@nyaudio.com *Web Site:* www.nyaudio.com, pg 956

New York Camera & Video, 1139 Street Rd, Southampton, PA 18966 *Tel:* 215-357-6222 *E-mail:* rentals@nycv.com *Web Site:* www.nycv.com, pg 956

New York City Mayor's Office of Film, Theatre & Broadcasting, 1697 Broadway, 6th fl, Suite 602, New York, NY 10019 *Tel:* 212-489-6710 *Fax:* 212-307-6237 *E-mail:* info@film.nyc.gov *Web Site:* www.nyc.gov/film, pg 1100

New York Emmy Awards, 1375 Broadway, Suite 2103, New York, NY 10018 *Tel:* 212-459-3630 *Fax:* 212-459-9772 *Web Site:* www.nyemmys.org, pg 1122

New York Festivals®-International Advertising Awards, 260 W 39 St, 10th fl, New York, NY 10018 *Tel:* 212-643-4800 *Fax:* 212-643-0170 *E-mail:* info@newyorkfestivals.com *Web Site:* www.newyorkfestivals.com, pg 1122

New York Festivals®-International Radio Program Awards, 260 W 39 St, 10th fl, New York, NY 10018 *Tel:* 212-643-4800 *Fax:* 212-643-0170 *E-mail:* info@newyorkfestivals.com *Web Site:* www.newyorkfestivals.com, pg 1122

New York Festivals®-International TV & Film Awards, 260 W 39 St, 10th fl, New York, NY 10018 *Tel:* 212-643-4800 *Fax:* 212-643-0170 *E-mail:* info@newyorkfestivals.com *Web Site:* www.newyorkfestivals.com, pg 1122

New York Film/Video Council (NYFVC), PO Box 1685, New York, NY 10185-1685 *Tel:* 212-330-0450 *E-mail:* info@nyfvc.org *Web Site:* www.nyfvc.org, pg 1086

New York Graphic Society, 130 Scott Rd, Waterburg, CT 06750 *Tel:* 203-847-2000 *Toll Free Tel:* 800-677-6947 *Fax:* 203-757-5526 *E-mail:* mail@nygs.com *Web Site:* www.nygs.com, pg 956

The New York Historical Society, 170 Central Park W, New York, NY 10024 *Tel:* 212-873-3400 *Fax:* 212-787-9474 *Web Site:* www.nyhistory.org, pg 956

New York Sound Inc, 166 Fifth Ave, No 6, New York, NY 10010 *Tel:* 917-523-0770; 212-929-5719, pg 956

New York State Governor's Office for Motion Picture & Television Development, 633 Third Ave, 33rd fl, New York, NY 10017 *Tel:* 212-803-2330 *Fax:* 212-803-2339 *E-mail:* nyfilm@esd.ny.gov *Web Site:* www.nylovesfilm.com, pg 1100

New York Times Photo Sales, c/o Redux Pictures, 11 Hanover Sq, 26th fl, New York, NY 10005 *Tel:* 212-253-0399 *Fax:* 212-253-0397 *E-mail:* submissions@reduxpictures.com *Web Site:* reduxpictures.com, pg 956

Newark Beth Israel Medical Center, c/o Creative Media Services, 201 Lyons Ave at Osborne Terr, Newark, NJ 07112 *Tel:* 973-926-7000 *Toll Free Tel:* 800-843-2384 *Web Site:* www.newarkbeth.com, pg 956

Newark Black Film Festival (NBFF), 49 Washington St, Newark, NJ 07102-3176 *Tel:* 973-596-6550 *Fax:* 973-642-0459 *E-mail:* nbff@newarkmuseum.org *Web Site:* www.newarkmuseum.org/nbff, pg 1122

Newbury Media, 80 Industrial Way, Wilmington, MA 01887 *Tel:* 617-267-4095 *E-mail:* info@newburymedia.com *Web Site:* newburymedia.com, pg 956

Newdoll Enterprises LLC, 3515-B Edison Way, Menlo Park, CA 94025 *Tel:* 650-365-2843 *Fax:* 650-365-3057 *E-mail:* info@newdollenterprises.com *Web Site:* www.newdollenterprises.com, pg 956

Newfoundland & Labrador Film Development Corp, 12 King's Bridge Rd, St John's, NL A1C 3K3, Canada *Tel:* 709-738-3456 *Toll Free Tel:* 877-738-3456 (CN) *Fax:* 709-739-1680 *E-mail:* info@nlfdc.ca *Web Site:* www.nlfdc.ca, pg 1105

The Newhouse Media Group, 6907 Silvermill Dr, Tampa, FL 33635 *Tel:* 813-625-2326 *E-mail:* newhousemediagroup@yahoo.com *Web Site:* www.newhousemediagroup.com, pg 956

NEWIST/CESA 7, 2420 Nicolet Dr, IS 1040, Green Bay, WI 54311 *Tel:* 920-465-2599 *Toll Free Tel:* 800-633-7445 *Fax:* 920-465-2723 *E-mail:* newist@cesa7.k12.wi.us *Web Site:* www.newist.org/home.html, pg 956

Julye Newlin Productions Inc, 129 E 13 St, Houston, TX 77008 *Tel:* 713-869-3609; 832-689-3609 (cell) *E-mail:* julye@julyenewlin.com *Web Site:* www.julyenewlin.com, pg 956

News Broadcast Network, 75 Broad St, 15th fl, New York, NY 10004 *Tel:* 212-684-8910 *Fax:* 212-684-9650 *Web Site:* www.newsbroadcastnetwork.com, pg 956

The News Corp, 1211 Avenue of the Americas, 8th fl, New York, NY 10036 *Tel:* 212-416-3400 *Web Site:* newscorp.com, pg 956

NewsBank Inc, 5801 Pelican Bay Blvd, Suite 600, Naples, FL 34108 *Toll Free Tel:* 800-762-8182 *Fax:* 239-263-3004 *E-mail:* sales@newsbank.com; custservice@newsbank.com *Web Site:* www.newsbank.com, pg 956

Newtec America Inc, 1055 Washington Blvd, Stamford, CT 06901 *Tel:* 203-323-0042 *Fax:* 203-323-8406 *E-mail:* sales@newtec.eu *Web Site:* www.newtec.eu, pg 957

Newton Instrument Co Inc, 111 E "A" St, Butner, NC 27509-2426 *Tel:* 919-575-6426 *Fax:* 919-575-4708 *Web Site:* www.enewton.com, pg 957

Newtown Psychological Center, 660 Newtown Yardley Rd, Suite 102, Newtown, PA 18940 *Tel:* 215-968-5378, pg 957

NewWave Technologies Inc, 4635 Wedgewood Blvd, Suite 107, Frederick, MD 21703 *Tel:* 301-624-5300 *Toll Free Tel:* 800-536-5222 *Fax:* 301-948-5883 (sales & serv); 301-668-7808 (acctg, opers & mktg) *E-mail:* sales@newwavetech.com; custsupport@newwavetech.com *Web Site:* www.newwavetech.com, pg 957

Next Arts, 1300 25 St, Unit C, San Francisco, CA 94107 *Tel:* 415-970-9005 *E-mail:* mail@nextarts.org *Web Site:* www.nextarts.org, pg 957

NFL Films Inc, One Sabol Way, Mount Laurel, NJ 08054 *Tel:* 856-222-3500 *Fax:* 856-638-0754 *E-mail:* nflfilms@nfl.com *Web Site:* www.nflfilms.com, pg 957

NFL Films Music Library, One Sabol Way, Mount Laurel, NJ 08054 *Tel:* 856-222-3500 *Fax:* 856-638-0754 *E-mail:* nflfilms@nfl.com *Web Site:* www.nflfilms.com, pg 957

NH Movies Inc, 16 Gulf Rd, Deerfield, NH 03037 *Tel:* 603-463-5900 *E-mail:* info@nhmovies.com *Web Site:* www.nhmovies.com, pg 957

Niagara Region-Economic Development, Campbell East, 3rd fl, 2201 Saint David's Rd, Thorold, ON L2V 4T7, Canada *Tel:* 905-685-4225 *Toll Free Tel:* 800-263-7215 *Fax:* 905-688-5907 *E-mail:* info@niagaracanada.com *Web Site:* www.niagaracanada.com, pg 1105

Nicholl Fellowships in Screenwriting, 8949 Wilshire Blvd, Beverly Hills, CA 90211 *Tel:* 310-247-3010 *E-mail:* nicholl@oscars.org *Web Site:* www.oscars.org, pg 1122

Nickelodeon, 1515 Broadway, 44th fl, New York, NY 10036 *Tel:* 212-258-8000 *Fax:* 212-258-1822 *Web Site:* www.nick.com, pg 957

Joseph Nicoletti Consulting-Promotion/California International Records/Global Village Records, PO Box 386, Laguna Beach, CA 92652 *Tel:* 949-446-8005 *E-mail:* music-film@att.net, pg 957

Nightingale-Conant Corp, 1400 S Wolf Rd, Bldg 300, Suite 103, Wheeling, IL 60090 *Toll Free Tel:* 800-557-1660 (sales); 800-560-6081 (cust serv) *E-mail:* customerservice@nightingale.com *Web Site:* www.nightingale.com, pg 957

Nightingale Music Productions Inc, 5460 Yonge St, Suite 1611, Toronto, ON M2N 6K7, Canada *Tel:* 416-221-2393 *Fax:* 416-221-2676 *E-mail:* admin@nightingalemusic.com *Web Site:* www.nightingalemusic.com, pg 957

Nikon Inc, 6420 Wilshire Blvd, Suite 100, Los Angeles, CA 90048-5501 *Tel:* 323-658-2100 *Toll Free Tel:* 800-NIKONUS (645-6687 - cust rel) *Web Site:* www.nikonusa.com, pg 957

Nikon Small World, 1300 Walt Whitman Rd, Melville, NY 11747 *Tel:* 631-547-8500 *Toll Free Tel:* 800-52-NIKON (526-4566 - US only) *Fax:* 631-547-0306 *E-mail:* info@nikonsmallworld.com *Web Site:* www.nikonsmallworld.com; www.nikoninstruments.com, pg 1122

Nilfisk-Advance America Inc, 740 Hemlock Rd, Suite 100, Morgantown, PA 19543 *Toll Free Tel:* 800-NILFISK (645-3475) *Fax:* 610-286-7350 *E-mail:* questions@nilfisk.com *Web Site:* www.nilfiskcfm.com, pg 957

Nilgiri Press, PO Box 256, Tomales, CA 94971-0256 *Tel:* 707-878-2369 *Toll Free Tel:* 800-475-2369 *Fax:* 707-878-2375 *E-mail:* info@easwaran.org *Web Site:* www.easwaran.org, pg 957

NIMCO Inc, 102 Hwy 81 N, Calhoun, KY 42327 *Tel:* 270-273-5000 *Toll Free Tel:* 800-962-6662 *Fax:* 270-273-5844 *Toll Free Fax:* 800-541-0007 *E-mail:* info@nimcoinc.com *Web Site:* www.nimcoinc.com, pg 957

911 Media Arts Center, 909 NE 43 St, Suite 206, Seattle, WA 98105 *Tel:* 206-682-6552 *E-mail:* info@911media.org *Web Site:* www.911media.org, pg 957

99 Productions LLC, 760 Conger St, Suite 1, Eugene, OR 97402 *Tel:* 541-343-0099 *E-mail:* email@99productions.com *Web Site:* www.99productions.com, pg 957

NKK Switches, 7850 E Gelding Dr, Scottsdale, AZ 85260 *Tel:* 480-991-0942 *Toll Free Tel:* 877-228-9655 *Fax:* 480-998-1435 *E-mail:* sales@nkkswitches.com *Web Site:* www.nkkswitches.com, pg 957

No Soap Productions, 936 Broadway, 4th fl, New York, NY 10010 *Tel:* 212-581-5572 *Fax:* 212-586-0045 *Web Site:* www.nosoap.net, pg 957

J P Nolan & Co, 4027 E 52 St, Maywood, CA 90270-2298 *Tel:* 323-581-7158 *Toll Free Tel:* 800-34-NOLAN (346-6526) *Fax:* 323-583-1824 *E-mail:* jpnolan@jpnolan.com *Web Site:* www.jpnolan.com, pg 958

Nolte Media, 12 Pierson St, Santa Rosa, CA 95401 *Tel:* 707-579-3902 *Web Site:* www.noltemedia.com, pg 958

Noontide Press, PO Box 2719, Newport Beach, CA 92759 *Tel:* 714-593-9725 *E-mail:* orders@noontidepress.com *Web Site:* www.noontidepress.com, pg 958

NOR-COM Inc, 2126 Petersburg Rd, Hebron, KY 41048 *Tel:* 859-689-7451 *Toll Free Tel:* 800-689-6889 *Fax:* 859-689-7483 *E-mail:* norcom@nor-com.com *Web Site:* www.nor-com.com, pg 958

Noramco Wire & Cable, 70 Glacier St, Coquitlam, BC V3K 5Y9, Canada *Tel:* 604-472-6980 *Toll Free Tel:* 800-663-8434 *Fax:* 604-472-6973 *E-mail:* norcorp@noramco.ca *Web Site:* www.noramco.ca, pg 958

Norcostco Inc, 825 Rhode Island Ave S, Minneapolis, MN 55426-1611 *Tel:* 763-544-0601 *Toll Free Tel:* 800-220-6920 *Fax:* 763-525-8676 *E-mail:* theatretechmn@norcostco.com; makeupmn@norcostco.com; costumesmn@norcostco.com *Web Site:* www.norcostco.com, pg 958

Noritsu America Corp, 6900 Noritsu Ave, Buena Park, CA 90620 *Tel:* 714-521-9040 *Toll Free Tel:* 800-521-3686; 888-435-7448 (tech support) *E-mail:* sales@noritsu.com *Web Site:* www.noritsu.com, pg 958

Norlake Manufacturing Co, 39301 Taylor Pkwy, Elyria, OH 44036 *Tel:* 440-353-3200 *Fax:* 440-353-3232 *E-mail:* info@norlakemfg.com *Web Site:* www.norlakemfg.com, pg 958

Norlynn Audio Visual Services, 1858 Beaulynn Place, North Vancouver, BC V7J 2T1, Canada *Tel:* 604-988-4996 *Fax:* 604-988-4996 *E-mail:* sales@norlynn.ca *Web Site:* www.norlynn.ca; www.reason-for-hope.com, pg 958

Norman Beerger Productions, 4508 Logan Lane, Tolovana Park, OR 97145 *Tel:* 503-919-3453 *E-mail:* nbeerger@yahoo.com *Web Site:* www.thegrandcanyonvideo.com, pg 958

Norsat International Inc, 110-4020 Viking Way, Richmond, BC V6V 2L4, Canada *Tel:* 604-821-2800 *Toll Free Tel:* 800-644-4562 *Fax:* 604-821-2801 *E-mail:* inquiries@norsat.com; support@norsat.com *Web Site:* www.norsat.com, pg 958

North American Broadcasters Association (NABA), Canadian Broadcasting Centre, 25 John St, Suite 6C300, Toronto, ON M5V 3G7, Canada *Tel:* 416-598-9877 *Fax:* 416-598-9774 *E-mail:* contact@nabanet.com *Web Site:* www.nabanet.com, pg 1086

North American Retail Dealers Association (NARDA), 222 S Riverside Plaza, Suite 2100, Chicago, IL 60606 *Tel:* 312-648-0649 *Toll Free Tel:* 800-621-0298 (US only) *Fax:* 312-648-1212 *E-mail:* nardasvc.@narda.com *Web Site:* www.narda.com, pg 1087

North Atlantic Books, 2526 Martin Luther King Jr Way, Berkeley, CA 94704 *Tel:* 510-549-4270 *Fax:* 510-549-4276 *Web Site:* www.northatlanticbooks.com, pg 958

North-by-Northwest Productions, 903 W Broadway Ave, Spokane, WA 99201 *Tel:* 509-324-2949 *Fax:* 509-324-2959 *E-mail:* contact@nxnw.net *Web Site:* www.nxnw.net, pg 958

North Carolina Film Office, 301 N Wilmington St, Raleigh, NC 27601 *Tel:* 919-733-9900 *Toll Free Tel:* 866-468-2273 *Fax:* 919-715-0151 *Web Site:* www.ncfilm.com, pg 1101

North Carolina's Piedmont Triad Film Commission, 416 Gallimore Dairy Rd, Suite M, Greensboro, NC 27409 *Tel:* 336-393-0001 *E-mail:* info@piedmontfilm.com *Web Site:* www.piedmontfilm.com, pg 1101

North Coast Studios Inc, 29181 Calahan Rd, Roseville, MI 48066 *Tel:* 586-359-6630 *Toll Free Tel:* 888-866-0652 *Fax:* 586-359-6638 *E-mail:* sales@northcoaststudiosinc.com, pg 959

North Country Media Group, 721 Second St S, Great Falls, MT 59405-1852 *Tel:* 406-761-7877 *Fax:* 406-761-2029 *E-mail:* info@ncmg.com *Web Site:* www.ncmg.com, pg 959

North County Media Center, 1130 N Melrose Dr, Suite 404, Vista, CA 92083 *Toll Free Tel:* 888-393-0580 *E-mail:* info@northcountymediacenter.com *Web Site:* northcountymediacenter.com, pg 959

North Dakota Tourism Division/Film Commission, Century Ctr, 1600 E Century Ave, Suite 2, Bismarck, ND 58502-2057 *Tel:* 701-328-2525 *Toll Free Tel:* 800-435-5663 *Fax:* 701-328-4878 *E-mail:* tourism@nd.gov *Web Site:* www.ndtourism.com, pg 1101

North Star Satellite Communications Inc, 2547 Yellow Springs Rd, Malvern, PA 19355 *Tel:* 610-407-9290 *Fax:* 610-407-9304 *E-mail:* north.star@comcast.net *Web Site:* www.northstarsatellite.net, pg 959

North West Digital Ltd, 400-116 W Sixth Ave, Vancouver, BC V5Y 1K6, Canada *Tel:* 604-709-3444 *Fax:* 604-687-7600 *Web Site:* www.nwdigi.com, pg 959

NorthCountry Distributors, Cadence Bldg, Redwood, NY 13679 *Tel:* 315-287-2852 *Fax:* 315-287-2860 *E-mail:* info@ncdsales.com *Web Site:* www.ncdsales.com, pg 959

Northeast Conference on the Teaching of Foreign Languages (NECTFL), c/o Dickinson College, PO Box 1773, Carlisle, PA 17013-2896 *Tel:* 717-245-1977 *Fax:* 717-245-1976 *E-mail:* nectfl@dickinson.edu *Web Site:* www.nectfl.org, pg 1087

Northeast Video Productions Inc, Box 8425, Sleepy Hollow, NY 10591 *Tel:* 914-714-0703, pg 959

Northeastern Digital Recording Inc, 2 Hidden Meadow Lane, Southboro, MA 01772 *Tel:* 508-481-9322 *Web Site:* www.northeasterndigital.com, pg 959

Northern Kentucky University, Nunn Dr, Highland Heights, KY 41099 *Tel:* 859-572-5100 *Fax:* 859-572-6172 *Web Site:* www.nku.edu, pg 959

Northern Light Productions, 300 Western Ave, 2nd fl, Boston, MA 02134 *Tel:* 617-789-4344 *Fax:* 617-789-4744 *E-mail:* info@nlprod.com *Web Site:* www.nlprod.com, pg 959

Northern Lights, 25 Burlingham Rd, Pine Bush, NY 12566 *Tel:* 845-361-4356 *Toll Free Tel:* 888-353-5134 *Fax:* 845-361-4900, pg 959

Northern Lights & Pro Audio, 5503 232 St SW, Mountlake Terrace, WA 98043 *Tel:* 425-774-1905 *E-mail:* sales@loud.net *Web Site:* www.loud.net, pg 959

NorthTown Sounds Inc, 275 Wickerberry Hollow, Roswell, GA 30075 *Tel:* 770-587-9350 *E-mail:* info@northtownsounds.com *Web Site:* www.northtownsounds.com, pg 959

Northwest Colorado Film Commission, 125 Anglers Dr, Steamboat Springs, CO 80487 *Tel:* 970-879-0880 *Fax:* 970-285-3550 *E-mail:* info@steamboatchamber.com; media@steamboatchamber.com *Web Site:* www.steamboat-chamber.com, pg 1095

Northwest Film Center, 934 SW Salmon St, Portland, OR 97205 *Tel:* 503-221-1156 (ext 10) *Fax:* 503-294-0874 *E-mail:* info@nwfilm.org *Web Site:* www.nwfilm.org, pg 959

Northwest Filmmakers' Festival, 934 SW Salmon St, Portland, OR 97205 *Tel:* 503-221-1156 (ext 10) *Fax:* 503-294-0874 *E-mail:* info@nwfilm.org *Web Site:* www.nwfilm.org, pg 1122

Northwest Territories Film Commission, PO Box 1320, Yellowknife, NT X1A 2L9, Canada *Tel:* 867-920-8793 *Fax:* 867-873-0101 *Toll Free Fax:* 877-445-2787 (ext 6) *E-mail:* nwtfilm@gov.nt.ca *Web Site:* www.nwtfilm.com, pg 1105

Nostalgia Family Video Inc, 2345 11 St, Baker City, OR 97814 *Tel:* 541-523-9034 *Toll Free Tel:* 800-784-3362 *Fax:* 541-523-7115, pg 959

Noteworthy Enterprises, 3829 NE 167 St, North Miami Beach, FL 33160 *Tel:* 305-949-9192 *E-mail:* shenote@comcast.net, pg 959

Nova Electric, 100 School St, Bergenfield, NJ 07621-2915 *Tel:* 201-385-0500 *Fax:* 201-385-0702 *E-mail:* novasales@theallpower.com *Web Site:* www.novaelectric.com, pg 959

Novalis, 10 Lower Spadina Ave, Suite 400, Toronto, ON M5V 2Z2, Canada *Tel:* 416-363-3303 *Toll Free Tel:* 877-702-7773; 800-387-7164 (US & CN only) *Fax:* 416-363-9409 *Toll Free Fax:* 877-702-7775; 800-204-4140 (cust serv) *E-mail:* books@novalis.ca; resources@novalis.ca *Web Site:* www.novalis.ca, pg 959

Novell Inc, 1800 S Novell Place, Provo, UT 84606 *Tel:* 801-861-4272 *Toll Free Tel:* 888-321-4272 (sales); 800-858-4000 (support) *E-mail:* crc@novell.com *Web Site:* www.novell.com, pg 959

Novelty Scenic Studios Inc, 3 Kosnitz Dr, Unit 111, Monroe, NY 10950-1163 *Tel:* 516-671-5245 *E-mail:* noveltyscenic@verizon.net, pg 959

Noventri, 20940 Twin Springs Dr, Smithsburg, MD 21783-1510 *Tel:* 301-790-0103 *Fax:* 301-790-0173 *E-mail:* sale@noventri.com *Web Site:* www.noventri.com, pg 960

Now Hear This, 250 W 49 St, Suite 704, New York, NY 10019 *Tel:* 212-265-1188 *Fax:* 212-265-6363 *E-mail:* info@nhtsound.com *Web Site:* www.nhtsound.com, pg 960

NPES The Association for Suppliers of Printing, Publishing & Converting Technologies, 1899 Preston White Dr, Reston, VA 20191 *Tel:* 703-264-7200 *Fax:* 703-620-0994 *E-mail:* npes@npes.org *Web Site:* www.npes.org, pg 1087

NPR Satellite Services, 1111 N Capitol St NE, Washington, DC 20002 *Tel:* 202-513-2626 *Fax:* 202-513-3035 *Web Site:* www.nprss.org, pg 960

NRD LLC, A Mark IV Industries Co, 2937 Alt Blvd, Grand Island, NY 14072-1285 *Tel:* 716-773-7634 *Toll Free Tel:* 800-525-8076 (US only) *Fax:* 716-773-7744 *E-mail:* sales@nrdinc.com *Web Site:* www.nrdstaticcontrol.com, pg 960

NSI Sound & Video Inc, 105 S Sparks St, Burbank, CA 91506 *Tel:* 818-848-1004 *Fax:* 818-848-1571 *E-mail:* info@nsisound.com *Web Site:* www.nsisound.com, pg 960

NSM Surveillance, 2709 Via Orange Way, Suite B, Spring Valley, CA 91978 *Tel:* 619-670-0616 *Fax:* 619-670-7040 *E-mail:* sales@nsmsurveillance.com *Web Site:* www.nsmsurveillance.com, pg 960

NSR Productions Inc & Capricorn Five Films, 110 Second St, Hicksville, NY 11801 *Tel:* 516-681-2171 *Fax:* 516-681-2171 *E-mail:* nsrproductions@verizon.net, pg 960

NTI Americas Inc, PO Box 231027, Tigard, OR 97281 *Tel:* 503-684-7050 *Fax:* 503-684-7051 *E-mail:* americas@nti-audio.com *Web Site:* www.nti-audio.com, pg 960

NTS ProMedia, 1201 Villa Place, Suite 106, Nashville, TN 37212 *Tel:* 615-254-8178 *Toll Free Tel:* 800-591-4804 *Web Site:* www.ntspromedia.com, pg 960

Nuance, One Wayside Rd, Burlington, MA 01803 *Tel:* 781-565-5000 *Toll Free Tel:* 888-372-1908 (cust serv) *Fax:* 781-565-5001 *Web Site:* www.nuance.com, pg 960

Numark Industries Inc, 200 Scenic View Dr, Cumberland, RI 02864 *Tel:* 401-658-3131 *Fax:* 401-658-3640 *Web Site:* www.numark.com, pg 960

NuMynd Studios, 915 Twin Elms Ct, Nashville, TN 37210 *Tel:* 615-259-1143 *Fax:* 615-259-1141 *E-mail:* hello@numyndstudios.com *Web Site:* www.numyndstudios.com, pg 960

Nutmeg Post, 45 W 45 St, New York, NY 10036 *Tel:* 212-921-8005 *Fax:* 212-921-7728 *E-mail:* info@nutmegpost.com *Web Site:* www.nutmegpost.com, pg 960

NVerzion, 296 E 3900 S, Salt Lake City, UT 84107-1531 *Tel:* 801-293-8420 *Fax:* 801-293-8616 *E-mail:* info@nverzion.com; sales@nverzion.com *Web Site:* www.nverzion.com, pg 960

NWT Arts Council, Box 1320, Govt NW Territories, Yellowknife, NT X1A 2L9, Canada *Tel:* 867-920-6370 *Fax:* 867-873-0205 *Web Site:* www.pwnhc.ca; www.pwnhc.ca/artscouncil, pg 1123

Oakland Film Office, One Frank H Ogawa Plaza, 9th fl, Oakland, CA 94612-1406 *Tel:* 510-238-4734 *Fax:* 510-238-6149 *E-mail:* filmoakland@filmoakland.com *Web Site:* www.filmoakland.com, pg 1093

OAP Audio Products, 310 Peachtree Industrial Blvd, Buford, GA 30518 *Tel:* 770-945-1033 *Toll Free Tel:* 800-788-1OAP (788-1627) *Fax:* 770-945-1843 *E-mail:* info@oapaudio.com *Web Site:* www.oapaudio.com, pg 960

Oasis Audio, 289 S Main Place, Carol Stream, IL 60188-2425 *Toll Free Tel:* 800-323-2500 *E-mail:* questions@oasisaudio.com *Web Site:* www.oasisaudio.com, pg 960

Oasis CD Manufacturing, 7905 N Crescent Blvd, Delair, NJ 08110 *Toll Free Tel:* 888-296-2747 *Fax:* 540-987-8812 *Toll Free Fax:* 866-929-8402 *E-mail:* info@oasisrecording.com *Web Site:* www.oasisrecording.com, pg 960

Ocala/Marion County Chamber of Commerce, 310 SE Third St, Ocala, FL 34471 *Tel:* 352-629-8051 *Fax:* 352-629-7651 *Web Site:* www.ocalacc.com, pg 1096

Oceanic Time Warner Cable, 200 Akamainui St, Mililani, HI 96789-3999 *Tel:* 808-625-2100 *Toll Free Tel:* 800-643-2100 (cust serv) *Fax:* 808-625-5888 *Web Site:* www.oceanic.com, pg 961

O'Connor Engineering Labs, 2701 N Ontario St, Burbank, CA 91504 *Tel:* 818-847-8666 *Fax:* 818-847-1205 *E-mail:* info@ocon.com; sales@ocon.com *Web Site:* www.ocon.com, pg 961

ODC Nimbus Inc, 490 E Princeland Ct, Suites 3 & 4, Corona, CA 92879 *Tel:* 951-372-9800 *Fax:* 951-372-9119 *E-mail:* sales@odc-nimbus.com *Web Site:* www.optical-disc.com, pg 961

ODC Publishing, PO Box 60609, Santa Barbara, CA 93160-0609 *Toll Free Tel:* 800-551-2800 *Toll Free Fax:* 800-551-2800 *Web Site:* www.frederickelias.com, pg 961

Oddball Film + Video, 275 Capp St, San Francisco, CA 94110 *Tel:* 415-558-8112 *Fax:* 415-558-8116 *E-mail:* info@oddballfilm.com *Web Site:* www.oddballfilm.com, pg 961

Odyssey Productions Inc, 2800 NW Thurman, Portland, OR 97210 *Tel:* 503-223-3480 *Fax:* 503-223-3493 *E-mail:* info@odysseypro.com *Web Site:* www.odysseypro.com, pg 961

OGM Production Music, 6464 Sunset Blvd, Suite 770, Hollywood, CA 90028 *Tel:* 323-461-2701 *Toll Free Tel:* 800-421-4163 (sales) *Fax:* 323-461-1543 *E-mail:* ogmmusic@gmail.com *Web Site:* www.ogmmusic.com, pg 961

Ohio HD Video, 3465 Noe Bixby Rd, Columbus, OH 43232 *Tel:* 614-656-1162 *Fax:* 614-656-4343 *E-mail:* info@ohiohdvideo.com *Web Site:* ohiohdvideo.com, pg 961

Ohio Independent Film Festival, 6516 Detroit Ave, Suite 3, Cleveland, OH 44102-3057 *Tel:* 216-926-6166 *E-mail:* ohiofilms@yahoo.com *Web Site:* www.ohiofilms.com, pg 1123

Ohio Independent Screenplay Awards, 6516 Detroit Ave, Suite 3, Cleveland, OH 44102-3057 *Tel:* 216-926-6166 *E-mail:* ohiofilms@yahoo.com *Web Site:* www.ohiofilms.com, pg 1123

Ohio State University Foreign Language Publications, 198 Hagerty Hall, 1775 S College Rd, Columbus, OH 43210-1309 *Tel:* 614-292-3838 *Toll Free Tel:* 800-678-6999 *Fax:* 614-688-3355 *E-mail:* flpubs@osu.edu *Web Site:* flpubs.osu.edu, pg 961

Ojai Valley Chamber of Commerce, 206 N Signal St, Suite P, Ojai, CA 93023 *Tel:* 805-646-8126 *Fax:* 805-646-9762 *E-mail:* info@ojaichamber.org *Web Site:* www.ojaichamber.org, pg 1093

Okanagan Film Commission, 1450 KLO Rd, Kelowna, BC V1W 3Z4, Canada *Tel:* 250-717-0087 *Fax:* 250-868-0512 *E-mail:* info@okanaganfilm.com *Web Site:* www.okanaganfilm.com, pg 1104

O'Keefe Communications Inc, 4301 Connecticut Ave NW, Suite 200, Washington, DC 20008-2304 *Tel:* 202-363-2101 *E-mail:* info@okeefecom.com *Web Site:* www.okeefecom.com, pg 961

Oklahoma City Convention & Visitors Bureau, 123 Park Ave, Oklahoma City, OK 73102 *Tel:* 405-297-8912 *Toll Free Tel:* 800-225-5652 *Fax:* 405-297-8888 *E-mail:* contact@visitokc.com *Web Site:* www.visitokc.org, pg 1101

Oklahoma Film Commission & Music Office, 120 N Robinson, Suite 600, Oklahoma City, OK 73102 *Tel:* 405-230-8440 *Toll Free Tel:* 800-766-3456 *Fax:* 405-230-8640 *Web Site:* www.oklahomafilm.org; thebuffalolounge.com, pg 1101

Oklahoma Sound Corp, 149 Entin Rd, Clifton, NJ 07014 *Tel:* 973-594-9000 *Toll Free Tel:* 800-261-4112 *Fax:* 201-322-2104 *E-mail:* info@oklahomasound.com *Web Site:* www.oklahomasound.com, pg 961

Old Army Press (OAP), 218 Alabaster Way, Johnstown, CO 80534 *Tel:* 970-587-9530 *Toll Free Tel:* 800-627-0079 *Fax:* 970-490-2709 *E-mail:* oldarmypress@msn.com *Web Site:* oldarmypress.com, pg 961

Old Dominion Broadcasting, 9505 Lakewater Ct, Richmond, VA 23229 *Tel:* 804-740-4717 *Fax:* 804-740-4717, pg 961

The Old Rhinebeck Aerodome®, 9 Norton Rd, Red Hook, NY 12571 *Tel:* 845-752-3200 *Fax:* 845-758-6481 *E-mail:* info@oldrhinebeck.org *Web Site:* www.oldrhinebeck.org, pg 961

Old School Cameras, 2819 N San Fernando Blvd, Burbank, CA 91504 *Tel:* 818-847-1555 *Fax:* 818-847-1556 *Web Site:* www.oldschoolcameras.com, pg 961

Olden Camera & Lens Co Inc, 1263 Broadway, 4th fl, New York, NY 10001-3593 *Tel:* 212-725-1234 *Fax:* 212-725-1325, pg 962

Olden Lighting, 2008 Alexander Ave, Austin, TX 78722 *Tel:* 512-416-8080 *Fax:* 512-416-8096 *E-mail:* rental@oldenlighting.com; sales@oldenlighting.com *Web Site:* www.oldenlighting.com, pg 962

Olsen Audio Group Inc, 7845 E Evans Rd, Scottsdale, AZ 85260-2919 *Tel:* 480-998-7140 *Fax:* 480-998-7192 *E-mail:* information@olsenaudio.com *Web Site:* www.olsenaudio.com, pg 962

Olson Visual Inc, 13000 Weber Way, Hawthorne, CA 90250 *Tel:* 310-355-1681 *Toll Free Tel:* 800-480-6643 *Fax:* 310-263-6980 *E-mail:* graphics@olsonvisual.com *Web Site:* www.olsonvisual.com, pg 962

Olympic Case Co, 9110 King Palm Dr, Suite 101, Tampa, FL 33619 *Tel:* 813-246-5525 *Toll Free Tel:* 888-246-5525 *Fax:* 813-246-4748 *E-mail:* info@olycase.com *Web Site:* www.olycase.com, pg 962

Olympus America Inc, 3500 Corporate Pkwy, Center Valley, PA 18034 *Tel:* 484-896-5000 *Web Site:* www.olympusamerica.com, pg 962

Olympusat Entertainment, 560 Village Blvd, Suite 250W, Palm Beach, FL 33409 *Tel:* 561-283-2888 *E-mail:* info@olympusatent.com *Web Site:* www.olympusatent.com, pg 962

Omega Broadcast Group, 817 W Howard Lane, Austin, TX 78753 *Tel:* 512-251-7778 *Fax:* 512-251-8633 *E-mail:* rental@omegabroadcast.com; sales@omegabroadcast.com *Web Site:* www.omegabroadcast.com, pg 962

Omega Media Group Inc, 3100 Medlock Bridge Rd, Suite 100, Norcross, GA 30071 *Tel:* 770-449-8870 *Web Site:* www.omegamediagroup.com, pg 962

Omega Productions, PO Box 606, Palacios, TX 77465 *Tel:* 214-891-9585 *Fax:* 214-722-1442 *E-mail:* getinfo@omegalive.com *Web Site:* www.omegalive.com, pg 962

Omega Recording Studios, 5609 Fishers Lane, Suite 14-A, Rockville, MD 20852 *Tel:* 301-230-9100 *Toll Free Tel:* 800-93-OMEGA (936-6342) *Fax:* 301-230-9103 *E-mail:* omega@omegastudios.com; info@omegastudios.com *Web Site:* www.omegastudios.com, pg 962

OmegaBrandess Distribution, 626 Hanover Pike, Suite 102, Hampstead, MD 21074-2036 *Tel:* 410-374-3250 *Fax:* 410-374-3184 *E-mail:* customerservice@omegabrandess.com *Web Site:* www.omegabrandess.com, pg 962

Omni Intercommunications Inc, 2825 Wilcrest Dr, Suite 400, Houston, TX 77042 *Tel:* 713-781-2188 *Toll Free Tel:* 800-777-2304 *Fax:* 713-781-2315 *E-mail:* info@omni-inter.com *Web Site:* www.omni-inter.com, pg 962

Omni International Inc, 435 12 St SW, Vernon, AL 35592 *Tel:* 205-695-9173 *Toll Free Tel:* 800-844-6664 *Fax:* 205-695-6465 *E-mail:* omni-brewster@centurytel.net *Web Site:* www.omniinternational.com, pg 962

OMNI Productions, PO Box 302, Carmel, IN 46082-0302 *Tel:* 317-846-2345 (ext 111) *Fax:* 317-846-6664 *E-mail:* omni@omniproductions.com *Web Site:* www.omniproductions.com, pg 962

Omnia Audio, 1241 Superior Ave E, Cleveland, OH 44114 *Tel:* 216-241-7225 *Fax:* 216-241-4103 *E-mail:* omnia-info@omniaaudio.com *Web Site:* www.omniaaudio.com, pg 962

Omnimedia Inc, 3085 Maple Cove Dr, Loganville, GA 30052 *Toll Free Tel:* 800-433-2091 *Fax:* 678-623-3940 *E-mail:* sales@omni-media.com *Web Site:* www.omni-media.com, pg 962

OmniMount Systems, 4409 E Baseline Rd, Suite 130, Phoenix, AZ 85042 *Tel:* 480-829-8000 *Toll Free Tel:* 800-MOUNT-IT (668-6848) *Fax:* 480-756-9000 *E-mail:* info@omnimount.com *Web Site:* www.omnimount.com, pg 962

Omnimusic, 52 Main St, Port Washington, NY 11050 *Tel:* 516-883-0121 *Toll Free Tel:* 800-828-6664 *Fax:* 516-883-0271 *E-mail:* omni@omnimusic.com *Web Site:* www.omnimusic.com, pg 962

Omnirax, PO Box 1792, Sausalito, CA 94966-1792 *Tel:* 415-332-3392 *Toll Free Tel:* 800-332-3393 *Fax:* 415-332-2607 *E-mail:* info@omnirax.com *Web Site:* www.omnirax.com, pg 963

OMNISound Recording Studio, 1806 Division St, Nashville, TN 37203 *Tel:* 615-482-1151 *Fax:* 615-321-5528 *Web Site:* www.omnisoundstudios.com, pg 963

ON Event Services, 6550 McDonough Dr, Norcross, GA 30093-1211 *Tel:* 404-875-0966 *Fax:* 404-874-7925 *E-mail:* av@techrentals.com *Web Site:* www.oneventservices.com, pg 963

On-Line Productions, 2515 Hawthorne Dr, Atlanta, GA 30345 *Tel:* 404-634-5572 *E-mail:* esptv@mindspring.com *Web Site:* on-lineproductions.com, pg 963

On Location North Carolina, 2121 Atlantic Ave, Suite 106, Raleigh, NC 27604 *Tel:* 919-755-9488 *Toll Free Tel:* 888-469-4747 *Fax:* 919-832-7797 *E-mail:* info@onlocation-nc.com *Web Site:* www.onlocation-nc.com, pg 963

On Site Video, PO Box 1865, Palatine, IL 60078-1865 *Tel:* 847-980-9808 *Fax:* 847-358-8697 *E-mail:* producersvideo@hotmail.com, pg 963

On-Site Video, 201 E Southern Ave, Suite 112, Tempe, AZ 85282 *Tel:* 480-967-5062 *Fax:* 480-967-4806 *E-mail:* on_sitevideo@yahoo.com *Web Site:* www.on-sitevideo.com, pg 963

On Stage Audio, 537 N Edgewood Ave, Wood Dale, IL 60191 *Tel:* 630-227-1008 *Toll Free Tel:* 877-672-4685 *Toll Free Fax:* 866-OSA-FAX2 (672-3292) *E-mail:* welisten@osacorp.com *Web Site:* www.osacorp.com, pg 963

On Stage Visuals, 420 Baker St, Lansing, MI 48910-1543 *Tel:* 517-393-7800 *Toll Free Tel:* 800-373-LIVE (373-5483) *Fax:* 517-481-2482 *E-mail:* support@onstagevisuals.com *Web Site:* www.onstagevisuals.com, pg 963

On-Trax Inc, 3052 Vine St, Riverside, CA 92507 *Tel:* 951-786-3921 *Fax:* 951-786-3922 *Web Site:* www.on-trax.com, pg 963

Once Around, 194 Castle Lane, Kilmarnock, VA 22482 *Tel:* 804-436-8904 *E-mail:* wardjudy56@verizon.net, pg 963

Oncourt Offcourt Ltd, 6301 Gaston Ave, Suite 650, Dallas, TX 75214 *Tel:* 214-823-3078 *Toll Free Tel:* 888-366-4711 (88-TENNIS-11) *Fax:* 214-823-3082 *E-mail:* info@oncourtoffcourt.com *Web Site:* www.oncourtoffcourt.com, pg 963

168 Film Festival, 100 E Cedar, Burbank, CA 91502 *Tel:* 818-557-8507 *Fax:* 818-942-6076 *E-mail:* info@168project.com *Web Site:* www.168project.com, pg 1123

One Stop CD Shop LLC, 3149 S State St, Salt Lake City, UT 84115 *Tel:* 801-303-6100 *Fax:* 801-303-6129 *E-mail:* info2@1stopcdshop.com *Web Site:* www.1stopcdshop.com, pg 963

One Touch Systems Inc, 2346 Bering Dr, San Jose, CA 95131 *Tel:* 408-660-8435 *Fax:* 408-436-4699 *E-mail:* info@onetouchsys.com *Web Site:* www.onetouchsys.com, pg 963

Onkyo USA Corp, 18 Park Way, Upper Saddle River, NJ 07458 *Tel:* 201-785-2600 *Toll Free Tel:* 800-229-1687 *Fax:* 201-785-2650 *Web Site:* www.onkyousa.com, pg 963

OnLine Power Inc, 5701 Smithway St, Commerce, CA 90040 *Tel:* 323-721-5017 *Toll Free Tel:* 800-227-8899 *Fax:* 323-721-3929 *E-mail:* sales@onlinepower.com *Web Site:* www.onlinepower.com, pg 963

Onstage Systems, 10930 Petal St, Dallas, TX 75238 *Tel:* 972-686-4488 *Fax:* 972-686-7732 *E-mail:* inquiry@onstagesystems.com *Web Site:* www.onstagesystems.com, pg 963

Ontario Media Development Corp, South Tower, Suite 501, 175 Bloor St E, Toronto, ON M4W 3R8, Canada *Tel:* 416-314-6858 *Fax:* 416-314-6876 *E-mail:* reception@omdc.on.ca *Web Site:* www.omdc.on.ca, pg 1105

Ontario Safety League, 2595 Skymark Ave, Suite 212, Mississauga, ON L4W 4Y4, Canada *Tel:* 905-625-0556 *Fax:* 905-625-0677 *E-mail:* info@osl.org *Web Site:* www.osl.org; ontariosafetyleague.com, pg 964

ooLite Media, 1702 Nelson Rd, Bozeman, MT 59718 *Tel:* 406-587-1456 *Toll Free Tel:* 800-798-9980 *Fax:* 406-587-1459 *Web Site:* www.oolitemedia.com/earthtalk, pg 964

Opamp Labs Inc, 1033 N Sycamore Ave, Los Angeles, CA 90038 *Tel:* 323-934-3566 *Fax:* 323-462-6490 *E-mail:* opamplabs@gmail.com *Web Site:* www.opamplabs.com, pg 964

Open Media Foundation, 700 Kalamath St, Denver, CO 80204 *Tel:* 720-222-0159 *Fax:* 303-534-5098 *E-mail:* info@openmediafoundation.org *Web Site:* openmediafoundation.org; denveropenmedia.org, pg 964

Open Text Corp, 275 Frank Tompa Dr, Waterloo, ON N2L 0A1, Canada *Tel:* 519-888-7111 *Toll Free Tel:* 800-499-6544; 800-4996-5440 (intl) *Fax:* 519-888-0677 *E-mail:* support@opentext.com *Web Site:* www.opentext.com, pg 964

Oppenheimer Camera Products, 7400 Third Ave S, Seattle, WA 98108-4143 *Tel:* 206-467-8666 *Toll Free Tel:* 877-467-8666 *Fax:* 206-467-9165 *Web Site:* oppenheimercameraproducts.com, pg 964

Opterna AM, 44901 Falcon Place, Suite 116, Sterling, VA 20166-9531 *Tel:* 703-653-1130 *Toll Free Tel:* 800-248-9004 *Fax:* 703-803-8313 *Web Site:* www.opterna-am.com, pg 964

Opti-Case Inc, 1175 CR 481 W, Henderson, TX 75654 *Tel:* 903-657-5666 *Toll Free Tel:* 800-637-6635 *Fax:* 903-657-6030 *E-mail:* sales@opti-case.net *Web Site:* www.opti-case.net, pg 964

Optibase Inc, 931 Benecia Ave, Sunnyvale, CA 94085 *Toll Free Tel:* 800-451-5101 *Fax:* 408-739-1706 *Web Site:* www.optibase.com, pg 964

Optic Bindery & Packaging, 407 Fair Hill Ct, Annapolis, MD 21403-1649 *Toll Free Tel:* 877-767-0099 *Fax:* 410-295-0079 *Web Site:* www.pointofpurchasestore.com, pg 964

Optical Disc Solutions Inc, 1767 Sheridan St, Richmond, IN 47374 *Tel:* 765-935-7574 *Toll Free Tel:* 800-704-7648 *Fax:* 765-935-0174 *Web Site:* www.odiscs.com, pg 964

Opticomm-EMCORE, 2015 Chestnut St, Alhambra, CA 91803 *Tel:* 626-293-3400; 626-293-3670 (west coast team); 540-626-3381 (east coast team) *Toll Free Tel:* 800-8OPTICOMM (867-8426) *Fax:* 626-293-3427 *E-mail:* video-sales@emcore.com *Web Site:* www.opticomm.com, pg 964

Optics 1 Inc, 2 Cooper Lane, Bedford, NH 03110 *Tel:* 603-296-0469 *Fax:* 603-296-0473 *Web Site:* www.optics1.com, pg 964

Optikinetics Ltd - The Americas, 11211 Air Park Rd, Suite 1, Ashland, VA 23005 *Tel:* 804-752-2570 *Toll Free Tel:* 800-575-6784 *Fax:* 804-752-2888 *E-mail:* optius@optikinetics.com *Web Site:* www.optikinetics.com, pg 964

The Optikon Corp, 1099 Guelph St, Kitchener, ON N2B 2E4, Canada *Tel:* 519-745-4115 *Fax:* 519-745-6922 *E-mail:* info@optikon.ca *Web Site:* www.optikon.ca, pg 964

Optimum Production Services Inc, 1490 S Sheridan Way, Mississauga, ON L5H 1Z8, Canada *Tel:* 905-278-2125 *Toll Free Tel:* 800-461-4979 *E-mail:* optimum@optimumprod.com *Web Site:* www.optimumprod.com, pg 964

Optimus, 161 E Grand Ave, Chicago, IL 60611 *Tel:* 312-321-0880 *Web Site:* www.optimus.com, pg 964

Optisonics Productions, 311 South Pkwy, Clifton, NJ 07014 *Tel:* 973-458-0951 *Fax:* 973-458-0983 *E-mail:* optisonics@aol.com *Web Site:* www.optisonics.com, pg 965

Optix Digital Pictures & Sound, 157 Princess St, Toronto, ON M5A 4M4, Canada *Tel:* 416-214-9911 *Fax:* 416-214-9912 *Web Site:* www.optix.ca, pg 965

Optronics®, 175 Cremona Dr, Goleta, CA 93117 *Tel:* 805-968-3568 *Toll Free Tel:* 800-796-8909 *Fax:* 805-968-0933 *E-mail:* oeinfo@optronics.com *Web Site:* www.optronics.com, pg 965

Opulen Studios, 1309 S Flower St, Los Angeles, CA 90015 *Tel:* 310-867-5023; 310-902-6996 *E-mail:* info@opulenstudios.com *Web Site:* opulenstudios.com, pg 965

Oral Tradition Sound & Music, PO Box 51155, Pacific Grove, CA 93950-6155 *Tel:* 831-372-0352 *Toll Free Tel:* 800-779-1116 (orders), pg 965

Orange County Film Commission, 800 N State College Blvd, MH 133, Fullerton, CA 92834-6850 *Tel:* 657-278-7569 *Fax:* 657-278-7521 *Web Site:* www.filmorangecounty.org, pg 1092

Orange County Sound Stage, 17518 Von Karman Ave, Irvine, CA 92614 *Tel:* 714-598-6557 *E-mail:* sm@ocsoundstage.com *Web Site:* orangecountysoundstage.com, pg 965

Orban, 8350 E Evans Rd, Suite C-4, Scottsdale, AZ 85260 *Tel:* 480-403-8300 *Fax:* 480-403-8302 *E-mail:* info@orban.com; sales@orban.com *Web Site:* www.orban.com, pg 965

Oregon Film & Video Office, 123 NE Third Ave, Suite 210, Portland, OR 97232 *Tel:* 503-229-5832 *Fax:* 503-229-6869 *E-mail:* shoot@oregonfilm.org *Web Site:* www.oregonfilm.org, pg 1101

Orevox USA Corp, 240 N Puente Ave, City of Industry, CA 91746-2303 *Tel:* 626-336-0516 *Toll Free Tel:* 800-237-0700 *Fax:* 626-336-3748 *Web Site:* www.dynavox.com, pg 965

Oriental Records Inc, 96 E Williston Ave, East Williston Park, NY 11596-2017 *Tel:* 516-746-0140 *Fax:* 516-747-4285 *E-mail:* info@orientalrecords.com; orientalcd@aol.com *Web Site:* www.orientalrecords.com, pg 965

Origin Instruments Corp, 854 Greenview Dr, Grand Prairie, TX 75050-2438 *Tel:* 972-606-8740 *Fax:* 972-606-8741 *E-mail:* support@orin.com; marketing@orin.com *Web Site:* www.orin.com, pg 965

Original Cast Records, PO Box 496, Georgetown, CT 06829-0496 *Tel:* 203-544-8288 *Fax:* 203-544-8288 *E-mail:* originalcast@aol.com *Web Site:* www.originalcastrecords.com; footlight.com, pg 965

Orion Software, 6000 Cote-des-Neiges, Suite 240, Montreal, QC H3S 1Z8, Canada *Tel:* 514-484-9661 *Toll Free Tel:* 877-755-2012 *Fax:* 514-484-1339 *E-mail:* info@orion-soft.com *Web Site:* www.orion-soft.com, pg 965

Orlando Special Effects, 14222 Lake Mary Jane Rd, Orlando, FL 32832 *Tel:* 407-648-1867 *Fax:* 407-273-0328 *Web Site:* www.orlandospfx.com, pg 965

Rob Orr Productions Ltd, 1336 Pine St, Glenview, IL 60025 *Tel:* 847-724-5228 *Fax:* 847-729-7319 *E-mail:* rob@roborrproductions.com *Web Site:* www.roborrproductions.com, pg 965

Orson Welles Award, 6 Beach Rd, 544, Tiburon, CA 94920 *Tel:* 415-251-8433 *Fax:* 633-444-8433 *E-mail:* info@tiburonfilmfestival.com *Web Site:* www.tiburonfilmfestival.com, pg 1123

Orvac Electronics, 1645 E Orangethorpe Ave, Fullerton, CA 92831 *Tel:* 714-871-1020 *Fax:* 714-871-1951 *E-mail:* myorvac@orvac.com *Web Site:* www.orvac.com, pg 965

Osho Viha Information Center & Book Distributors, PO Box 352, Mill Valley, CA 94942-0352 *Tel:* 415-472-5381 *Toll Free Tel:* 866-856-7019 *Fax:* 415-472-5149 *E-mail:* oshoviha@oshoviha.org *Web Site:* www.oshoviha.org, pg 965

Osram Sylvania Inc, 100 Endicott St, Danvers, MA 01923 *Tel:* 978-777-1900 *Toll Free Tel:* 800-842-7010 *Fax:* 978-750-2152 *Web Site:* www.sylvania.com, pg 965

Osram Sylvania Ltd/LTEE, 2001 Drew Rd, Mississauga, ON L5S 1S4, Canada *Tel:* 905-673-6171 *Toll Free Tel:* 800-LIGHTBULB (544-4828) *Fax:* 905-671-5584 *Web Site:* www.sylvania.com, pg 966

Ostergaard Acoustical Associates, 200 Executive Dr, Suite 350, West Orange, NJ 07052 *Tel:* 973-731-7002 *Fax:* 973-731-6680 *E-mail:* info@acousticalconsultant.com *Web Site:* www.acousticalconsultant.com, pg 966

Osum Event Rentals, 562 First Ave S, Suite 100, Seattle, WA 98104 *Tel:* 206-209-2012 *Fax:* 206-209-2013 *E-mail:* info@osumeventrentals.com *Web Site:* osumeventrentals.com, pg 966

OSV Studios, 29605 Lorain Rd N, Olmsted, OH 44070 *Tel:* 440-779-1900 *Web Site:* www.osvstudios.com, pg 966

OTR Studios, PO Box 874, Belmont, CA 94002 *Tel:* 650-595-8475 *E-mail:* info@otrstudios.com *Web Site:* www.otrstudios.com, pg 966

Ott Film Rentals, 6901 Castor Ave, Philadelphia, PA 19149 *Tel:* 215-745-8964 *Toll Free Tel:* 800-545-4558 *Fax:* 215-745-8965, pg 966

Ottawa International Animation Festival, 2 Daly Ave, Suite 120, Ottawa, ON K1N 6E2, Canada *Tel:* 613-232-8769 *Fax:* 613-232-6315 *E-mail:* info@animationfestival.ca *Web Site:* www.animationfestival.ca, pg 1123

Our Sunday Visitor Inc, 200 Noll Plaza, Huntington, IN 46750 *Tel:* 260-356-8400 *Toll Free Tel:* 800-348-2440 *Fax:* 260-356-8472 *E-mail:* osvsales@osv.com *Web Site:* www.osv.com, pg 966

Out of the BLUE Media, 1413 Brenda Lane, Allen, TX 75002 *Tel:* 469-853-9015 *Web Site:* www.outofthebluemedia.com, pg 966

Outfest, 3470 Wilshire Blvd, Suite 935, Los Angeles, CA 90010 *Tel:* 213-480-7088 *Fax:* 213-480-7099 *E-mail:* outfest@outfest.org *Web Site:* www.outfest.org, pg 1123

Outland Technology Inc, 38190 Commercial Ct, Slidell, LA 70458 *Tel:* 985-847-1104 *Fax:* 985-847-1106 *E-mail:* sales@outlandtech.com *Web Site:* www.outlandtech.com, pg 966

Outside The Box Interactive LLC, 150 Bay St, Suite 706, Jersey City, NJ 07302 *Tel:* 201-610-0625 *Fax:* 201-610-0627 *E-mail:* theoffice@outboxin.com *Web Site:* www.outboxin.com, pg 966

Outsource Engineering & Manufacturing Inc dba Texscan MSI, 11800 Wills Rd, Suite 150, Alpharetta, GA 30009 *Tel:* 678-689-0146; 770-642-7440 (support) *E-mail:* sales@texscan-msi.com *Web Site:* www.texscan-msi.com, pg 966

Outwater Plastics Industries Inc, 24 River Rd, Bogota, NJ 07603 *Tel:* 201-498-8750 *Toll Free Tel:* 800-631-8375 *Fax:* 201-498-8751 *Toll Free Fax:* 800-888-3315 *E-mail:* info@outwaterplastics.com *Web Site:* www.outwater.com, pg 966

Oval Window Audio, 33 Wildflower Ct, Nederland, CO 80466 *Tel:* 303-447-3607 *Fax:* 303-447-3607 *E-mail:* info@ovalwindowaudio.com *Web Site:* www.ovalwindowaudio.com, pg 966

OWI Inc, 17141 Kingsview Ave, Carson, CA 90746 *Tel:* 310-515-1900 *Toll Free Tel:* 800-638-1694 *Fax:* 310-515-1606 *E-mail:* info@owi-inc.com *Web Site:* www.owi-inc.com, pg 966

Oxford Film Commission, 415 S Lamar Blvd, Oxford, MS 38655 *Tel:* 662-232-2477 *Toll Free Tel:* 800-758-9177 *E-mail:* tourism@visitoxfordms.com *Web Site:* visitoxfordms.com, pg 1099

Ozam Production, 1516 Equestrian Rd, Ozark, MO 65721 *Tel:* 417-866-3232 *Web Site:* ozam.com, pg 966

Pace Systems, 824 Dakin St, New Orleans, LA 70121 *Tel:* 504-837-4224 *Toll Free Tel:* 800-722-3797 *Fax:* 504-837-4307 *E-mail:* info@pacesys.com *Web Site:* www.pacesys.com, pg 966

PACE Worldwide, 255 Air Tool Dr, Southern Pines, NC 28387 *Tel:* 910-695-7223 *Fax:* 910-695-1594 *E-mail:* support@paceworldwide.com; sales@paceworldwide.com *Web Site:* www.paceworldwide.com, pg 966

Pacific Audio-Visual Enterprises, 3807 E Green St, Pasadena, CA 91107-3904 *Tel:* 626-449-9353 *Toll Free Tel:* 888-240-8012 *Fax:* 626-395-9793 *Web Site:* www.stereosoundbook.com, pg 967

Pacific Grip & Lighting Inc, 6550 NE Portland Hwy, Portland, OR 97218 *Tel:* 503-233-4747 *Fax:* 503-233-5830 *E-mail:* info@pacific-grip.com *Web Site:* pacific-grip.com, pg 967

Pacific International Enterprises Inc (PIE), 401 Crater Lake Ave, Suite 2, Medford, OR 97504 *Tel:* 541-779-0990 *Toll Free Tel:* 800-547-2316 *Fax:* 541-779-0880 *E-mail:* info@family-films.com *Web Site:* www.family-films.com, pg 967

Pacific Light Studios, 265 Caspian Dr, Sunnyvale, CA 94089 *Tel:* 408-541-1800 *Web Site:* www.pacificlightstudios.com, pg 967

Pacific Media, 21730 Nordhoff St, Chatsworth, CA 91311 *Tel:* 818-341-3156 *Toll Free Tel:* 800-262-7367 *Fax:* 818-341-3562 *E-mail:* info@pac-media.com *Web Site:* www.pac-media.com, pg 967

Pacific Multimedia Inc, 4917 Seaview Way, Everett, WA 98203 *Tel:* 425-347-4110 *Toll Free Tel:* 888-373-8273 *Fax:* 425-710-9932 *Web Site:* www.pacmultimedia.com, pg 967

Pacific Northwest Theatre Associates Inc (PNTA), 2414 SW Andover St, Bldg C100, Seattle, WA 98106 *Tel:* 206-622-7850 *Toll Free Tel:* 800-622-7850 *Fax:* 206-267-1789 *E-mail:* sales@pnta.com *Web Site:* www.pnta.com, pg 967

Pacific Radio Electronics, 3031 Thornton Ave, Burbank, CA 91504 *Tel:* 818-556-4177 *Toll Free Tel:* 800-634-9476 *Fax:* 818-556-4185 *E-mail:* sales@pacrad.com *Web Site:* www.pacrad.com, pg 967

Pacific Video Image, 9065 E Rosecrans Ave, Bellflower, CA 90706 *Tel:* 562-634-4200 *Fax:* 562-634-4700 *E-mail:* info@pvideo.com *Web Site:* www.pvideo.com, pg 967

Pacific Video Products Inc, 14312 Franklin Ave, Suite 100, Tustin, CA 92780 *Tel:* 714-508-2750 *Toll Free Tel:* 800-576-0060 *Fax:* 714-508-2136 *Web Site:* www.pacvideo.com, pg 967

Pacifica Radio Archives, 3729 Cahuenga Blvd W, North Hollywood, CA 91604 *Tel:* 818-506-1077 *Toll Free Tel:* 800-735-0230 *Fax:* 818-506-1084 *E-mail:* pacarchive@aol.com *Web Site:* www.pacificaradioarchives.org, pg 967

PACSAT, 1629 "S" St, Sacramento, CA 95811 *Tel:* 916-446-7890; 916-335-1649 (after hours) *Toll Free Tel:* 800-672-2728 *Fax:* 916-446-7893 *E-mail:* pacsat@pacsat.com *Web Site:* www.pacsat.com, pg 967

Padgitt's, 7801 N Lamar Blvd, Suite D84, Austin, TX 78752 *Tel:* 512-832-9900 *Toll Free Tel:* 800-388-3130 *Fax:* 512-832-0003 *E-mail:* padgitts@padgitts.com *Web Site:* www.padgitts.com, pg 967

Page-Lake Powell Film Commission, PO Box 1180, Page, AZ 86040 *Tel:* 928-645-3410 *Toll Free Tel:* 888-261-PAGE (261-7243) *Fax:* 928-645-4250 *Web Site:* visitpagealakepowell.com, pg 1091

Pak-Wik Corp, 128 Tivoli St, Albany, NY 12207 *Tel:* 518-465-4556 *Toll Free Tel:* 800-372-5945 *Fax:* 518-465-4559 *E-mail:* sales@pakwik.com *Web Site:* www.pakwik.com, pg 967

Pal Productions Inc, 4056 NE 174 St, Seattle, WA 98155 *Tel:* 206-361-9366 *E-mail:* info@paladventurevideos.com *Web Site:* www.paladventurevideos.com, pg 967

Palace Costume & Prop Co, 835 N Fairfax Ave, Hollywood, CA 90046 *Tel:* 323-651-5458 *Fax:* 323-658-7133 *E-mail:* rentals@palacecostume.com *Web Site:* www.palacecostume.com, pg 967

Palace Digital Studios, 29 N Main St, South Norwalk, CT 06854 *Tel:* 203-853-1740 *Fax:* 203-855-9608 *Web Site:* www.palacedigital.com, pg 967

Palardo Productions, 1807 Taft Ave, Suite 4, Hollywood, CA 90028 *Tel:* 323-469-8991 *E-mail:* palardo2@msn.com, pg 968

Palm Beach County Film & Television Commission, 1555 Palm Beach Lakes Blvd, Suite 900, West Palm Beach, FL 33401 *Tel:* 561-233-1000 *Toll Free Tel:* 800-745-FILM (745-3456) *Fax:* 561-233-3113 *Web Site:* www.pbfilm.com, pg 1096

Palm Beach International Film Festival (PBIFF), 2101 S Congress Ave, Delray Beach, FL 33445 *Tel:* 561-362-0003 *E-mail:* info@pbifilmfest.org; submissions@pbifilmfest.org *Web Site:* www.pbifilmfest.org, pg 1123

Palm Springs International Film Festival, 1700 E Tahquitz Canyon Way, Suite 3, Palm Springs, CA 92262 *Tel:* 760-322-2930 *Toll Free Tel:* 800-898-7256 *Fax:* 760-322-4087 *E-mail:* info@psfilmfest.org *Web Site:* www.psfilmfest.org, pg 1123

Palmdale Chamber of Commerce, 817 E Avenue Q-9, Palmdale, CA 93550 *Tel:* 661-273-3232 *Fax:* 661-273-8508 *E-mail:* chamberstaff@palmdalechamber.org *Web Site:* www.palmdalechamber.org, pg 1093

Shelly Palmer Production, PO Box 1877, New York, NY 10156-1877 *Tel:* 212-532-3880 *E-mail:* info@shellypalmer.com *Web Site:* www.shellypalmer.com, pg 968

Pan African Film & Arts Festival, 6820 La Tijera Blvd, Suite 200, Los Angeles, CA 90045 *Tel:* 310-337-4737 *Fax:* 310-337-4736 *E-mail:* info@paff.org *Web Site:* www.paff.org, pg 1123

Panamax, 1800 S McDowell Blvd, 2nd fl, Petaluma, CA 94954 *Tel:* 707-283-5900 (intl) *Toll Free Tel:* 800-472-5555 (US & CN) *Fax:* 707-283-5901 *E-mail:* custrelations@panamax.com *Web Site:* www.panamax.com, pg 968

Panasonic Broadcast & Digital Systems Co, 3330 Cahuenga Blvd W, Los Angeles, CA 90068 *Tel:* 323-436-3507 *Fax:* 323-436-3615 *Web Site:* www.panasonic.com, pg 968

Panasonic Consumer Electronics Co, One Panasonic Way, Secaucus, NJ 07094 *Tel:* 201-348-7066 *Toll Free Tel:* 800-211-PANA (211-7262) *Web Site:* www.panasonic.com, pg 968

Panasonic Corp, One Panasonic Way, Secaucus, NJ 07094 *Tel:* 201-348-7000 *Toll Free Tel:* 800-211-7262; 888-275-2595 *Fax:* 201-348-7807 *Web Site:* www.panasonic.com, pg 968

Panasonic Professional Audio Systems, 3330 Cahuenga Blvd W, Los Angeles, CA 90068 *Tel:* 323-436-3616 *Fax:* 323-436-3618 *Web Site:* www.panasonic.com, pg 968

Panavideo Inc, 347 Marie de l'Incarnation, Quebec, QC G1N 3G9, Canada *Tel:* 418-687-3150 *Toll Free Tel:* 800-463-5076 *Fax:* 418-687-0366 *E-mail:* info@panavideo.net *Web Site:* www.panavideo.net, pg 968

Panavision Dallas, 8000 Jetstar Dr, Irving, TX 75063 *Tel:* 972-929-8585 *Toll Free Tel:* 800-260-1846 *Fax:* 972-929-8686 *Web Site:* www.panavision.com, pg 968

P&H Chrystalite Inc, 101 Palm Harbor Pkwy, Unit 117, Palm Coast, FL 32137 *Tel:* 561-330-8660 *Fax:* 561-330-8665 *Toll Free Fax:* 800-468-8673 *E-mail:* phcrystalite@aol.com *Web Site:* www.phcled.com, pg 968

Pandisc Music Corp, 247 SW Eighth St, Suite 349, Miami, FL 33130 *Tel:* 305-557-1914 *Toll Free Fax:* 888-493-7778 *Web Site:* www.pandisc.com, pg 968

P&P Studios Inc, 110 Lenox Ave, Suite 210, Stamford, CT 06906 *Tel:* 203-359-9292 *Toll Free Tel:* 888-WEPRODUCE (937-7638) *E-mail:* ppstudios@weproduce.com *Web Site:* www.weproduce.com, pg 968

Pangolin Laser Systems Inc, 9501 Satellite Blvd, Suite 109, Orlando, FL 32837 *Tel:* 407-299-2088 *Toll Free Tel:* 800-PAN-GOLIN (726-4654) *Fax:* 407-299-6066 *E-mail:* contact@pangolin.com *Web Site:* www.pangolin.com, pg 968

Panorama Productions, 5320 Croy Rd, Morgan Hill, CA 95037 *Tel:* 408-727-7500 *E-mail:* information@panorama-productions.com *Web Site:* www.panorama-productions.com, pg 968

Panorama Publishing Co, 18607 Ventura Blvd, Suite 310, Tarzana, CA 91356-4158 *Tel:* 818-758-2747 *Toll Free Tel:* 800-634-5620; 800-479-9464 (home study school) *Fax:* 818-344-2262 *Web Site:* www.hypnosis.edu, pg 968

Panta Rhei Media Inc, 565 Beulah Rd, Turtle Creek, PA 15145 *Tel:* 412-824-8858 *E-mail:* info@panta-rhei.com *Web Site:* www.panta-rhei.com, pg 968

Tom Pantages, 87 Short St, Marlboro, MA 01752 *Tel:* 508-305-2828 *Fax:* 508-305-2828 *E-mail:* pantages@comcast.net, pg 968

Pantomime Pictures Inc, 12144 Riverside Dr, North Hollywood, CA 91607 *Tel:* 818-980-5555, pg 968

Parabola Audio/Video, 20 W 20 St, 2nd fl, New York, NY 10011 *Tel:* 212-822-8806 (edit & publg); 201-656-7220 (ad) *Toll Free Tel:* 800-560-MYTH (560-6984); 877-593-2521 (subns) *Fax:* 212-822-8823 *E-mail:* info@parabola.org *Web Site:* www.parabola.org, pg 968

Paradigm Marketing & Creative, 8275 Tournament Dr, Suite 330, Memphis, TN 38125 *Tel:* 901-685-7703 *Fax:* 901-531-8513 *E-mail:* info@2dimes.com *Web Site:* www.2dimes.com, pg 969

The Paradise Coast Film Commission, 755 Eighth Ave S, Naples, FL 34102 *Tel:* 239-659-FILM (659-3456) *Fax:* 239-213-3053 *Web Site:* www.shootinparadise.com, pg 1096

Paradise Show & Design Inc, 4653 35 St, Orlando, FL 32811 *Tel:* 407-649-7220 *Fax:* 407-649-7225 *E-mail:* info@paradiseshow.com *Web Site:* www.paradiseshow.com, pg 969

Paradise Video & Film, 10148 NW 47 St, Sunrise, FL 33351 *Tel:* 954-747-1118 *Fax:* 954-747-3380 *E-mail:* info@paradisevideo.com *Web Site:* www.paradisevideo.com, pg 969

Paradoxal Inc, 540 Broadway, New York, NY 10012 *Tel:* 212-366-5526; 917-400-4507 (cell) *E-mail:* contact@paradoxal.net *Web Site:* www.paradoxal.net, pg 969

Paragon Studios Inc, 820 W Fulton Market, Chicago, IL 60607-1302 *Tel:* 312-942-0075 *Fax:* 312-942-2488 *E-mail:* info@paragonstudiosinc.com *Web Site:* www.paragonstudiosinc.com, pg 969

Parallax Press, 2236-B Sixth St, Berkeley, CA 94710 *Tel:* 510-525-0101 *Toll Free Tel:* 800-863-5290 (book orders) *Fax:* 510-525-7129 *E-mail:* info@parallax.org *Web Site:* www.parallax.org, pg 969

Parallax Productions Inc, 1711 Longwood Rd, Suite B, Haverhill, FL 33409 *Tel:* 561-842-7788 *Toll Free Tel:* 844-892-9289 *Fax:* 561-842-4566 *E-mail:* parllaxpro@aol.com *Web Site:* www.parallaxvideoproductions.com, pg 969

Paramount Motion Pictures Group, 1515 Broadway, 3rd fl, New York, NY 10019 *Tel:* 212-258-6000 *Fax:* 212-846-4315 *Web Site:* www.viacom.com, pg 969

Paramount Pictures Corporation, 5555 Melrose Ave, Los Angeles, CA 90038 *Tel:* 323-956-8398 *Web Site:* www.paramount.com, pg 969

Parasound Products Inc, 2250 McKinnon Ave, San Francisco, CA 94124 *Tel:* 415-397-7100 *Fax:* 415-397-0144 *E-mail:* sales@parasound.com; marketing@parasound.com; service@parasound.com *Web Site:* www.parasound.com, pg 969

Jeff Davis Parish Tourist Commission, 100 Rue de l'Acadie, Jennings, LA 70546 *Tel:* 337-821-5521 *Toll Free Tel:* 800-264-5521 *Fax:* 337-821-5536 *Web Site:* www.jeffdavis.org; www.louisianatravel.com, pg 1098

Park City Film Commission, 1910 Prospector Ave, Park City, UT 84060 *Tel:* 435-649-6100 *Toll Free Tel:* 800-453-1360 *Fax:* 435-649-4132 *Web Site:* www.visitparkcity.com/media/park-city-film-commission/, pg 1103

Parker Area Chamber of Commerce, 1217 California Ave, Parker, AZ 85344 *Tel:* 928-669-2174 *Fax:* 928-669-6304 *E-mail:* info@parkeraz.org *Web Site:* www.parkeraz.org, pg 1091

Parlato Productions, 8632 US Rte 2, North Hero, VT 05474 *Tel:* 802-264-2902 *E-mail:* info@parlatoproductions.com *Web Site:* www.parlatoproductions.com, pg 969

Parlights Inc, One Wormans Mill Ct, Suite 7, Frederick, MD 21701 *Tel:* 301-698-9242 *Fax:* 301-846-0369 *E-mail:* sales@parlights.com *Web Site:* www.parlights.com, pg 969

Partech Lighting Systems Inc, 8711 Reading Rd, Cincinnati, OH 45215 *Tel:* 513-761-5678 *Toll Free Tel:* 800-701-9551 *Fax:* 513-679-8282 *E-mail:* info@partechlighting.com *Web Site:* www.partechlighting.com, pg 969

Parts Express, 725 Pleasant Valley Dr, Springboro, OH 45066-1158 *Tel:* 937-743-3000 *Toll Free Tel:* 866-366-4909; 800-338-0531 (cust serv & tech support) *Fax:* 937-743-1677 *Toll Free Fax:* 866-755-7557 *E-mail:* sales@parts-express.com *Web Site:* www.parts-express.com, pg 969

PASCO, 224 48 St, Brooklyn, NY 11220 *Tel:* 718-833-9100 *Fax:* 718-833-9118 *E-mail:* pasco2@aol.com, pg 969

Paso Sound Products Inc, 4750-F Goer Dr, Charleston, SC 29406 *Tel:* 843-308-9005 *Toll Free Tel:* 800-231-3034 *Fax:* 843-308-0904 *E-mail:* info@pasosound.com *Web Site:* www.pasosound.com, pg 969

Jim Passin Productions, 1900 W Berwyn Ave, Chicago, IL 60640 *Tel:* 773-334-0408, pg 970

Pat Kogan Productions Inc, 615 Half Moon Bay, Croton-on-Hudson, NY 10520 *Tel:* 914-661-0049 *Web Site:* www.pkpmedia.com, pg 970

PatchAmp, 20 E Kennedy St, Hackensack, NJ 07601 *Tel:* 201-457-1504 *Fax:* 201-457-1507 *E-mail:* sales@patchamp.com *Web Site:* www.patchamp.com, pg 970

Patco Resources Inc, 9 Washington Circle, Suffern, NY 10901 *Tel:* 845-357-5300 *Fax:* 845-357-6427 *E-mail:* musicinfo@patcoresources.com *Web Site:* www.patcoresources.com, pg 970

Pathway Connectivity Inc, 1439 17 Ave SE, Unit 103, Calgary, AB T2G 1J9, Canada *Tel:* 403-243-8110 *Fax:* 403-287-1281 *E-mail:* sales@pathwayconnect.com *Web Site:* www.pathwayconnect.com, pg 970

Pauline Books & Media, 50 St Paul's Ave, Boston, MA 02130-3491 *Tel:* 617-522-8911 *Toll Free Tel:* 800-876-4463 (orders); 800-836-9723 (cust serv) *Fax:* 617-541-9805 *E-mail:* records@pauline.org *Web Site:* www.pauline.org, pg 970

Paulist Press, 997 Macarthur Blvd, Mahwah, NJ 07430-9990 *Tel:* 201-825-7300 *Toll Free Tel:* 800-218-1903 (orders) *Toll Free Fax:* 800-836-3161 *E-mail:* info@paulistpress.com *Web Site:* www.paulistpress.com, pg 970

Paulist Productions, 17575 Pacific Coast Hwy, Pacific Palisades, CA 90272-4128 *Tel:* 310-454-0688 *Toll Free Tel:* 800-624-8613 *Fax:* 310-459-6549 *E-mail:* paulistmail@paulistproductions.org *Web Site:* www.paulistproductions.org, pg 970

PBS Video, 1320 Braddock Place, Alexandria, VA 22314 *Tel:* 703-739-5021 *E-mail:* video@pbs.org *Web Site:* video.pbs.org; www.shoppbs.org, pg 970

"PBTM" Music, 1160 W 26 Ave, Eugene, OR 97405 *Tel:* 541-345-8117 *E-mail:* support@pbtmlive.com *Web Site:* www.pbtmlive.com; pbtm.com, pg 970

PC&E, 2235 DeFoor Hills Rd, Atlanta, GA 30318 *Tel:* 404-609-9001 *Toll Free Tel:* 800-537-4021 *Fax:* 404-609-9926 *Web Site:* www.pce-atlanta.com, pg 970

PCO-TECH Inc, 6930 Metroplex Dr, Romulus, MI 48174 *Tel:* 248-276-8820 *Fax:* 248-276-8825 *E-mail:* info@pco-tech.com; service@pco-tech.com *Web Site:* www.pco-tech.com, pg 970

PDC Productions, 3217 N Flood Ave, Norman, OK 73069 *Tel:* 405-360-5130 *Fax:* 405-360-0524 *E-mail:* info@pdcproductions.com *Web Site:* www.pdcproductions.com, pg 970

George Foster Peabody Awards, c/o University of Georgia, Grady College of Journalism & Mass Communication, 120 Hooper St, Athens, GA 30602-3018 *Tel:* 706-542-3787 *Fax:* 706-542-9273 *E-mail:* peabody@uga.edu *Web Site:* www.peabodyawards.com, pg 1123

Peak Performance Publishing, 14728 Shirley St, Omaha, NE 68144 *Tel:* 402-334-1676 *Toll Free Tel:* 800-293-1676 *Fax:* 402-334-4437 *Web Site:* www.peakperformanceconsult.com, pg 970

Peak Performance Sports LLC, 7380 Sand Lake Rd, PMB 5012, Orlando, FL 32819-5248 *Tel:* 407-909-1700 *Toll Free Tel:* 888-742-7225 *Fax:* 407-909-1789 *E-mail:* pgapack@aol.com *Web Site:* www.peaksports.com, pg 970

Pearson Education Canada, 26 Prince Andrew Place, North York, ON M3C 2T8, Canada *Tel:* 416-447-5101 *Toll Free Tel:* 800-361-6128 *Fax:* 416-447-2551 *Toll Free Fax:* 800-563-9196 *Web Site:* www.pearsonschoolcanada.ca, pg 970

Peavey Electronics Corp, 5022 Hartley Peavey Dr, Meridian, MS 39305 *Tel:* 601-483-5365 *Fax:* 601-486-1278 *E-mail:* domesticsales@peavey.com *Web Site:* www.peavey.com, pg 970

Peckham Productions Inc, 50 S Buckhout St, Irvington, NY 10533 *Tel:* 914-591-4140 *Fax:* 914-591-4149 *E-mail:* info@peckhampix.com *Web Site:* www.peckhampix.com, pg 970

Peerbolte Creative, PO Box 754, Warrensburg, MO 64093 *Tel:* 660-429-1383 *Fax:* 660-429-3666 *E-mail:* solutions@peerbolte.com *Web Site:* www.peerbolte.com, pg 970

Peerless Industries, 2300 White Oak Circle, Aurora, IL 60502 *Tel:* 630-375-5100 *Toll Free Tel:* 800-865-2112 *Fax:* 630-820-8537 *Toll Free Fax:* 800-359-6500 *E-mail:* info@peerlessmounts.com *Web Site:* www.peerlessmounts.com, pg 971

Peerless Lighting, 2246 Fifth St, Berkeley, CA 94710 *Tel:* 510-845-2760 *Fax:* 510-845-2776 *Web Site:* www.peerless-lighting.com, pg 971

Pelco, 3500 Pelco Way, Clovis, CA 93612-5699 *Tel:* 559-292-1981 (intl) *Toll Free Tel:* 800-289-9100 (US & CN) *Fax:* 559-348-1120 (intl) *Toll Free Fax:* 800-289-9150 (US & CN) *E-mail:* sales@pelco.com *Web Site:* www.pelco.com, pg 971

Pelican Products, 147 N Main St, South Deerfield, MA 01373 *Tel:* 413-665-2163 *Toll Free Tel:* 800-542-7344 *Fax:* 413-665-8330 *Web Site:* www.pelican.com, pg 971

Pelican Publishing Co, 1000 Burmaster St, Gretna, LA 70053-2246 *Tel:* 504-368-1175 *Toll Free Tel:* 800-843-1724; 888-PELICAN (735-4226 - cust serv); 888-5PELICAN (888-573-5422) *Fax:* 504-368-1195 *E-mail:* sales@pelicanpub.com *Web Site:* www.pelicanpub.com, pg 971

A W Peller & Associates Inc, PO Box 377, Franklin Lakes, NJ 07414-0377 *Tel:* 201-644-0908 *Toll Free Tel:* 800-451-7450 *Fax:* 201-644-0907 *E-mail:* awpeller@optonline.net *Web Site:* www.brightideascatalog.com, pg 971

Pemcor LLC, 2100 State Rd, Lancaster, PA 17601 *Tel:* 717-898-1555 *Toll Free Tel:* 800-735-1555 *Fax:* 717-898-3191 *E-mail:* support@pemcor.com *Web Site:* www.pemcor.com, pg 971

Pendle Hill Bookstore, 338 Plush Mill Rd, Wallingford, PA 19086-6099 *Tel:* 610-566-4507 (ext 2) *Toll Free Tel:* 800-742-3150 (ext 2) *Fax:* 610-566-3679 *E-mail:* bookstore@pendlehill.org *Web Site:* www.pendlehill.org, pg 971

Pendulum Entertainment, 444 Dufferin St, Studio 1, Toronto, ON M6K 2A3, Canada *Tel:* 416-721-7593 *E-mail:* info@pendulumentertainment.com *Web Site:* www.pendulumentertainment.com, pg 971

Penfield Productions Ltd, 35 Springfield St, Agawam, MA 01001 *Tel:* 413-786-4454 *Fax:* 413-789-4240 *E-mail:* info@penfieldprod.com *Web Site:* www.penfieldprod.com, pg 971

Penguin Audiobooks, 375 Hudson St, New York, NY 10014 *Tel:* 212-366-2000 *E-mail:* online@penguinputnam.com *Web Site:* www.penguinputnam.com; us.penguingroup.com, pg 971

Penn Elcom Inc, 12691 Monarch St, Garden Grove, CA 92841 *Tel:* 714-230-6200 *Toll Free Tel:* 800-228-9122 (orders) *Fax:* 714-230-6222 *Toll Free Fax:* 800-619-0808 *E-mail:* california@penn-elcom.com *Web Site:* www.penn-elcom.com, pg 971

Penn State University MediaTech, 14 Wagner Annex, State College, PA 16803-1886 *Tel:* 814-865-6314; 814-863-3202 *Toll Free Tel:* 800-826-0132 *Fax:* 814-863-2574 *E-mail:* mtssmed@psulias.psu.edu *Web Site:* www.libraries.psu.edu/mtss; www.medianet.libraries.psu.edu, pg 972

Pennebaker Hegedus Films Inc, 262 W 91 St, New York, NY 10024 *Tel:* 212-496-9195 *Fax:* 212-496-8195 *Web Site:* phfilms.com, pg 972

Pennsylvania Film Office, Commonwealth Keystone Bldg, 4th fl, 400 North St, Harrisburg, PA 17120-0225 *Tel:* 717-783-3456 *Fax:* 717-787-6825 *E-mail:* info@filminpa.com *Web Site:* www.filminpa.com, pg 1101

Penny + Giles, 665 N Baldwin Park Blvd, City of Industry, CA 91746 *Tel:* 626-480-2150 *Fax:* 626-369-6318 *E-mail:* us.sales@pennyandgiles.com *Web Site:* www.pennyandgiles.com, pg 972

Penrose Productions, 1674 N Shoreline Blvd, Suite 130, Mountain View, CA 94043 *Tel:* 650-969-TAPE (969-8273) *Fax:* 650-969-6816 *E-mail:* info@penroseproductions.com *Web Site:* www.penroseproductions.com, pg 972

PentaVision Communications Inc, 52303 Emmons Rd, Suite A-4, South Bend, IN 46637 *Tel:* 574-272-8365 *Fax:* 574-272-8366 *Web Site:* pentavision.net, pg 972

Pentrex Media Group LLC, 2652 E Walnut St, Pasadena, CA 91107-3723 *Tel:* 626-793-3400 *Toll Free Tel:* 800-950-9333 *Fax:* 626-793-3797 *E-mail:* pentrex@pentrex.com *Web Site:* www.pentrex.com, pg 972

People Productions, 1737 15 St, Suite 200, Boulder, CO 80302 *Tel:* 303-449-6086 *Fax:* 303-449-9526 *E-mail:* info@peopleproductions.com *Web Site:* www.peopleproductions.com, pg 972

People Skills International, 2910 Baily Ave, San Diego, CA 92105 *Tel:* 619-262-9951 *Fax:* 619-262-0505 *Web Site:* www.idagreene.com, pg 972

PeopleVisionFX, 311 E First Ave, Bldg A, Roselle, NJ 07203 *Tel:* 973-509-2056 *Web Site:* peoplevisionfx.com, pg 972

The Pepper Group, 220 N Smith St, Suite 406, Palatine, IL 60067 *Tel:* 847-963-0333 *Fax:* 847-963-0888 *E-mail:* pepper@peppergroup.com *Web Site:* www.peppergroup.com, pg 972

Peppers Ghost HD®, c/o Bob Thomas Productions Inc, 2 Franklin Ct, Montville, NJ 07045 *Tel:* 973-335-9100 *Web Site:* www.peppersghosthd.com, pg 973

Perception Publications, 8711 E Pinnacle Peak Rd, PMB 345, Scottsdale, AZ 85255 *Toll Free Tel:* 800-338-5831 *Fax:* 480-451-9372 *E-mail:* info@iqbooster.com, pg 973

Perceptions Inc, 1030 Hinesburg Rd, Charlotte, VT 05445 *Tel:* 802-425-2783 *Fax:* 802-425-3628 *E-mail:* perceptivt@aol.com *Web Site:* perceptionsvermont.com; perceptionsmaple.com; perceptionspics.com, pg 973

Perennial Pictures Film Corp, 2102 E 52 St, Indianapolis, IN 46205 *Tel:* 317-253-1519 *E-mail:* mail@perennialpictures.com *Web Site:* www.perennialpictures.com, pg 973

Perfection Learning Corp, 1000 N Second Ave, Logan, IA 51546 *Tel:* 712-644-2831 *Toll Free Tel:* 800-831-4190 (US & CN) *Toll Free Fax:* 800-543-2745 *E-mail:* orders@perfectionlearning.com *Web Site:* www.perfectionlearning.com, pg 973

Performance Audio, 2456 S West Temple St, Salt Lake City, UT 84115 *Tel:* 801-466-3196 *Toll Free Tel:* 800-771-8330 *Fax:* 801-484-1538 *E-mail:* sales@performanceaudio.com; rental@performanceaudio.com *Web Site:* www.performanceaudio.com, pg 973

Permlight Products Inc, 422 W Sixth St, Tustin, CA 92780 *Tel:* 714-508-0729 *Fax:* 714-508-0920 *E-mail:* sales@brillialed.com (brillia div); sales@permlightforsigns.com (sign div) *Web Site:* www.permlight.com; www.permlightforsigns.com (signs div); www.brillialed.com (brillia div), pg 973

Personal Achievement Institute, One Speaking Success Rd, Kingman, AZ 86402 *Tel:* 928-753-5315 *Web Site:* www.speakingsuccess.com, pg 973

Personal Communications Industry Association (PCIA), 500 Montgomery St, Suite 500, Alexandria, VA 22314 *Tel:* 703-739-0300 *Toll Free Tel:* 800-759-0300 *Fax:* 703-836-1608 *Web Site:* www.pcia.com, pg 1087

Perspectives Media, 410 S Michigan Ave, Chicago, IL 60605 *Tel:* 312-212-1492, pg 973

PESA, 103 Quality Circle, Suite 210, Huntsville, AL 35806 *Tel:* 256-726-9200 *Toll Free Tel:* 800-323-7372 *E-mail:* sales@pesa.com *Web Site:* www.pesa.com, pg 973

Peterson's Video Transfer Services, 10051 E Estates Dr, Cupertino, CA 95014 *Tel:* 408-255-4925 *Toll Free Tel:* 800-888-0426 *Fax:* 408-255-6404 *E-mail:* contact@petersonsvideotransfer.com *Web Site:* www.petersonsvideotransfer.com, pg 973

Petra Productions Ltd, 52 Sycamore Rd, Mahopac, NY 10541 *E-mail:* information@petraproductions.org *Web Site:* www.petraproductions.org, pg 973

Phase One Studios, 3015 Kennedy Rd, Suite 10, Toronto, ON M1V 1E7, Canada *Tel:* 416-291-9553 *Toll Free Tel:* 888-728-3333 *Fax:* 416-291-7898 *E-mail:* info@phaseonestudios.com *Web Site:* www.phaseonestudios.com, pg 973

Phase Technology, 6400 Youngerman Circle, Jacksonville, FL 32244 *Tel:* 913-663-5600 *Toll Free Tel:* 800-874-7076; 888-PHASE-TK (742-7385) *Fax:* 913-663-3200 *E-mail:* sales@phasetech.com *Web Site:* www.phasetech.com, pg 973

Phat Planet Recording Studios, 3473 Parkway Center Ct, Orlando, FL 32808 *Tel:* 407-295-7270 *Toll Free Tel:* 800-667-4893 *Fax:* 407-295-7207 *E-mail:* info@phatplanetstudios.com *Web Site:* www.phatplanetstudios.com, pg 973

Phelan Productions Inc, 9201 E Mississippi Ave, Apt C205, Denver, CO 80247-6875, pg 973

Phil Lights, 1903 Redlands, Austin, TX 78757 *Tel:* 512-452-2930; 512-627-4991 (cell) *Web Site:* www.pcurry.com, pg 973

Phil Sykes & Associates Inc, 692 Sunset Ct, Shoreview, MN 55126 *Tel:* 651-481-4940 *Fax:* 651-481-3290 *E-mail:* mail@sykesnet.com *Web Site:* www.sykesnet.com, pg 974

Philadelphia Film Festival, 1600 N Fifth St, Philadelphia, PA 19122 *Tel:* 267-239-2941 *E-mail:* info@filmadelphia.org *Web Site:* www.filmadelphia.org, pg 1123

Philadelphia International Film Festival & Market, PO Box 48134, Philadelphia, PA 19144 *Tel:* 215-849-2716 (festival) *Toll Free Tel:* 877-347-FILM (347-3456) *E-mail:* info@philafilm.org *Web Site:* www.philafilm.org, pg 1123

Philadelphia Soundstages, 1600 N Fifth St, Philadelphia, PA 19122 *Tel:* 267-773-8971 *Fax:* 267-773-8972 *E-mail:* info@philastudios.com *Web Site:* philastudios.com, pg 974

Philips Lighting Controls, 2828 Trade Center Dr, Suite 130B, Carrollton, TX 75007 *Toll Free Tel:* 800-526-2731 *Fax:* 972-389-6174 *E-mail:* controls.support@philips.com *Web Site:* philipslightingcontrols.com, pg 974

Phillips MediaSource, 750 N St Paul, Suite 1000, Dallas, TX 75201 *Tel:* 214-741-1300 *Toll Free Tel:* 800-TEXAS13 (839-2713) *Fax:* 214-741-3942 *Web Site:* phillipsmediasource.com, pg 974

Phoebus Lighting, 2800 Third St, San Francisco, CA 94107 *Tel:* 415-550-0770 *Fax:* 415-550-2655 *Web Site:* www.phoebus.com, pg 974

Phoebus Manufacturing, 2800 Third St, San Francisco, CA 94107 *Tel:* 415-550-0770 *Fax:* 415-550-2655 *Web Site:* www.phoebus.com/phoebusmanufactu.html; www.phoebus.com, pg 974

Phoenix Aerial Photography Inc, 613 Skyview Dr, Nashville, TN 37206 *Tel:* 615-255-2000; 615-975-4226 (cell) *E-mail:* info@phoenixaerialphoto.com *Web Site:* www.phoenixaerialphoto.com, pg 974

Phoenix/BFA/Coronet, 141 Milllwell Dr, Suite A, St Louis, MO 63043-2509 *Tel:* 314-569-0211 (ext 104) *Toll Free Tel:* 800-221-1274 (ext 104) *Fax:* 314-569-2834 (orders) *E-mail:* info@phoenixlearninggroup.com; customerservice@phoenixlearninggroup.com *Web Site:* www.phoenixlearninggroup.com, pg 974

The Phoenix Learning Group Inc, 141 Millwell Dr, Suite A, St Louis, MO 63043-2509 *Tel:* 314-569-0211 *Toll Free Tel:* 800-221-1274 *Fax:* 314-569-2834 (orders) *E-mail:* customerservice@phoenixlearninggroup.com; info@phoenixlearninggroup.com *Web Site:* www.phoenixlearninggroup.com, pg 974

Phoenix Society for Burn Survivors Inc, 1835 RW Berends Dr SW, Grand Rapids, MI 49519-4955 *Tel:* 616-458-2773 *Toll Free Tel:* 800-888-BURN (888-2876) *Fax:* 616-458-2831 *E-mail:* info@phoenix-society.org *Web Site:* www.phoenix-society.org, pg 974

Phoenix VideoFilms®, 2925 W Indian School Rd, Phoenix, AZ 85017 *Tel:* 602-266-4198; 801-226-8209 *Web Site:* www.phoenixvideofilms.com, pg 974

Phonic Ear Inc (FrontRow), 2080 Lakeville Hwy, Petaluma, CA 94954 *Tel:* 707-769-1110 *Toll Free Tel:* 800-227-0735 *Fax:* 707-769-9624 *E-mail:* customerservice@phonicear.com; customercare@gofrontrow.com *Web Site:* www.phonicear.com; www.gofrontrow.com, pg 974

Photo Film Stage, 820 Thompson Ave, Suite 34, Glendale, CA 91201 *Tel:* 213-304-5608 *E-mail:* photofilmstage@yahoo.com *Web Site:* photofilmstage.com, pg 974

Photo Marketing Association International (PMA), 2282 Springport Rd, Suite F, Jackson, MI 49202 *Tel:* 517-788-8100 *Toll Free Tel:* 800-762-9287 *Fax:* 517-788-8371 *Web Site:* www.pmai.org, pg 1087

Photo Tech Inc, 7200 Hudson Blvd N, Suite 170, St Paul, MN 55128 *Tel:* 651-702-6717 *Toll Free Tel:* 800-525-6486 *Fax:* 651-702-6745 *E-mail:* rolleasy@juno.com *Web Site:* www.phototechinc.com, pg 974

Photo Technicians Inc, 3664 N River Rd, Freeland, MI 48623 *Tel:* 989-751-8517 *Web Site:* www.phototechnicians.com, pg 974

Photodyne Technologies, 8531 Alcott St, Suite 201, Los Angeles, CA 90035 *Tel:* 310-497-0968 *Toll Free Tel:* 800-660-2147 *Fax:* 310-652-2820 *E-mail:* info@photodyne.com *Web Site:* www.photodyne.com, pg 974

Photoflex Inc, 97 Hangar Way, Watsonville, CA 95076 *Tel:* 831-786-1370 *Toll Free Tel:* 800-486-2674 *Fax:* 831-786-1372 *E-mail:* sales@photoflex.com; marketing@photoflex.com *Web Site:* www.photoflex.com, pg 974

Photogenic Professional Lighting, 1268 Humbracht Circle, Bartlett, IL 60103-1631 *Tel:* 630-830-2500 *Toll Free Tel:* 800-682-7668 *Fax:* 630-830-2525 *E-mail:* sales@photogenicpro.com *Web Site:* www.photogenicpro.com, pg 974

Photographers' Formulary Inc, 7079 Hwy 83 N, Condon, MT 59826 *Tel:* 406-754-2891 *Toll Free Tel:* 800-922-5255 *Fax:* 406-754-2896 *E-mail:* formulary@blackfoot.net *Web Site:* www.photoformulary.com, pg 975

Photographic Society of America® (PSA®), 3000 United Founders Blvd, Suite 103, Oklahoma City, OK 73112 *Tel:* 405-843-1437 *Toll Free Tel:* 855-PSA-INFO (772-4636) *Fax:* 405-843-1438 *E-mail:* hq@psa-photo.org *Web Site:* www.psa-photo.org, pg 1087

Photographic Solutions Inc, 430-G Ansin Blvd, Hallendale, FL 33009 *Tel:* 954-458-4744 *Toll Free Tel:* 800-637-3212 *Fax:* 954-458-4745 *E-mail:* orders@photosol.com *Web Site:* www.photosol.com, pg 975

Photogroup Studios, 321 W Ben White, Suite 106A & 107, Austin, TX 78704 *Tel:* 512-373-8547 *E-mail:* photogroup@photogroupaustin.com *Web Site:* www.photogroupaustin.com, pg 975

Photoimaging Manufacturers & Distributors Association Inc, 7600 Jericho Tpke, Suite 301, Woodbury, NY 11797 *Tel:* 516-802-0895 *Fax:* 516-364-0140 *Web Site:* www.pmda.com, pg 1087

Photomart Cine-Video Inc, 6869 Stapoint Ct, Suite 112, Winter Park, FL 32792 *Tel:* 407-381-5606 *Toll Free Tel:* 800-443-2901 *Fax:* 407-381-5610 *E-mail:* info@photomartusa.com *Web Site:* www.photomartusa.com, pg 975

Photoquip Inc, 3070 S Eighth St, Fernandina Beach, FL 32034-8680 *Tel:* 904-261-4075, pg 975

Photosound of Orlando Inc, 6438 University Blvd, Unit 14, Winter Park, FL 32792 *Tel:* 407-898-8841 *Toll Free Tel:* 800-552-8776 *Fax:* 407-898-0300 *E-mail:* photosound@cfl.rr.com *Web Site:* www.photosoundav.com, pg 975

Phylco Audio Duplication, 10431 Blackwell Rd, Central Point, OR 97502 *Tel:* 541-855-7484 *Toll Free Tel:* 800-348-6194 *E-mail:* info@phylcoaudio.com *Web Site:* www.phylcoaudio.com, pg 975

Physical Optics Corp, 1845 E 205 St, Torrance, CA 90501-1510 *Tel:* 310-320-3088 *Fax:* 310-320-5961 *Web Site:* www.poc.com, pg 975

Pico Digital, 8880 Rehco Rd, San Diego, CA 92121 *Tel:* 858-546-5050 *Toll Free Tel:* 800-421-6511 *Fax:* 858-546-5051; 858-546-5055 (intl) *E-mail:* sales@picodigital.com *Web Site:* picodigital.com, pg 975

Picture Box Distribution Inc, 141 E 23 Ave, Vancouver, BC V5V 1X1, Canada *Tel:* 604-681-3174 *Fax:* 604-608-9081 *E-mail:* info@picturebox.ca *Web Site:* www.picturebox.ca, pg 975

Picture This Production Services, 2223 NE Oregon St, Portland, OR 97232 *Tel:* 503-235-3456 *Fax:* 503-236-2302 *E-mail:* info@pixthis.com *Web Site:* pixthis.com, pg 975

PicturePhone Inc, 200 Commerce Dr, Rochester, NY 14623 *Tel:* 585-334-9040 *Toll Free Tel:* 800-521-5454 *Fax:* 585-486-1919 *E-mail:* info@picturephone.com *Web Site:* www.picturephone.com, pg 975

Pictures of Record Inc, 119 Kettle Creek Rd, Weston, CT 06883 *Tel:* 203-227-3387 *Fax:* 203-222-9673 *E-mail:* picturesofrecord@aol.com *Web Site:* www.picturesofrecord.com, pg 975

Pieces of Learning, 1990 Market Rd, Marion, IL 62959 *Tel:* 618-964-9426 *Toll Free Tel:* 800-729-5137 *Toll Free Fax:* 800-844-0455 *E-mail:* info@piecesoflearning.com *Web Site:* www.piecesoflearning.com, pg 975

Pignose-Gorilla, 570 W Cheyenne Ave, Suite 80, North Las Vegas, NV 89030 *Tel:* 702-648-2444 *Toll Free Tel:* 800-9-PIGNOSE (974-4667) *Fax:* 702-648-2440 *E-mail:* sales@pignoseamps.com *Web Site:* www.pignoseamps.com, pg 975

Pinewood Sound, 555 Brooksbank Ave, Stage S, North Vancouver, BC V7J 3S5, Canada *Tel:* 604-669-6900; 604-983-5200 *Fax:* 604-983-5204 *E-mail:* info@pinewoodsound.com; sales@pinewoodsound.com *Web Site:* www.pinewoodsound.com, pg 975

Pinnacle Systems Inc, 385 Ravendale Dr, Mountain View, CA 94043-5240 *Tel:* 650-526-1600 *Toll Free Tel:* 877-582-6735 *Fax:* 650-526-1601 *E-mail:* sales@pinnaclesys.com *Web Site:* www.pinnaclesys.com; www.corel.com, pg 975

pinta acoustic inc, 2601 49 Ave N, Suite 400, Minneapolis, MN 55430 *Tel:* 612-355-4200 *Toll Free Tel:* 800-662-0032 *Fax:* 612-355-4299 *E-mail:* sales@pinta-acoustic.com; info@pinta-acoustic.com *Web Site:* www.pinta-acoustic.com, pg 976

Pioneer Electronics (USA) Inc, 1925 E Dominguez St, Long Beach, CA 90810 *Tel:* 310-952-2000 *Toll Free Tel:* 800-421-1404 (cust serv); 800-228-7221 (parts dept) *Fax:* 310-952-2821 (parts dept) *Web Site:* www.pioneerelectronics.com, pg 976

Pioneer Research Inc, 97 Foster Rd, Suite 5, Moorestown, NJ 08057 *Tel:* 856-866-9191 *Toll Free Tel:* 800-257-7742 *Fax:* 856-866-8615 *E-mail:* info@pioneer-research.com *Web Site:* www.pioneer-research.com, pg 976

PipelineFX LLC, 1000 Bishop St, Suite 509, Honolulu, HI 96813 *Tel:* 808-685-7823 *Toll Free Tel:* 866-856-7823 *Fax:* 808-685-7800 *E-mail:* sales@pipelinefx.com *Web Site:* www.pipelinefx.com, pg 976

Piper Media Services Inc, 904 W Kenosha St, Broken Arrow, OK 74014 *Tel:* 918-251-0477 *Toll Free Tel:* 800-752-5346 *Fax:* 918-258-1476 *Web Site:* www.pipermediaservices.com, pg 976

Nicholas P Pipino Associates Inc, 9159-A Red Branch Rd, Columbia, MD 21045 *Tel:* 202-603-9319; 301-596-3397; 410-995-0041 *Toll Free Tel:* 888-596-0014 *Fax:* 410-964-1191 *Web Site:* www.pipinoinc.com, pg 976

Lee Pitts Enterprises, 8765 Azalea Ct, Suite 103, Tamarac, FL 33321 *Toll Free Tel:* 877-830-0391 *E-mail:* swimvideo@leepitts.com; speaking@leepitts.com (request speaking engagements) *Web Site:* www.leepitts.com, pg 976

Pittsburgh Film Office, The Century Bldg, Suite 202, 130 Seventh St, Pittsburgh, PA 15222 *Tel:* 412-261-2744 *Toll Free Tel:* 888-744-3456 *Fax:* 412-471-7317 *E-mail:* info@pghfilm.org *Web Site:* www.pghfilm.org, pg 1102

PIX, 1109 S La Brea Ave, Los Angeles, CA 90019 *Tel:* 323-936-8488 *Toll Free Tel:* 888-697-0081 *Fax:* 323-936-5209 *E-mail:* rental@pixcamera.com *Web Site:* www.pixcamera.com, pg 976

Pixar Animation Studios, 1200 Park Ave, Emeryville, CA 94608 *Tel:* 510-922-3000 *Toll Free Tel:* 800-888-9856 *Fax:* 510-922-3151 *E-mail:* ir@pixar.com (investor rel) *Web Site:* www.pixar.com, pg 976

PixeLINK, 1900 City Park Dr, Suite 410, Ottawa, ON K1J 1A3, Canada *Tel:* 613-247-1211 *Fax:* 613-247-2001 *E-mail:* sales@pixelink.com *Web Site:* www.pixelink.com, pg 976

PixMix Video Services, 23 Elm St, Bldg 2, Watertown, MA 02472 *Tel:* 617-923-0102 *Fax:* 617-923-0105 *E-mail:* info@pixmix.net *Web Site:* www.pixmix.net, pg 976

piXvfm, 1805 E Dyer, Suite 107, Santa Ana, CA 92705-5701 *Tel:* 949-250-1749 *Fax:* 949-419-3485 *E-mail:* infoweb@pixvfm.com *Web Site:* www.pixvfm.com, pg 976

PK Photo & Electronic Repair, 1760 S Carr St, Lakewood, CO 80232-6643 *Tel:* 303-777-1311 *Fax:* 303-777-1332, pg 976

Placer-Lake Tahoe Film Office, 145 Fulweiler Ave, Auburn, CA 95603 *Tel:* 530-889-4091 *Toll Free Tel:* 877-228-3456 *Fax:* 530-889-4095 *Web Site:* www.placer.ca.gov/films, pg 1092

Planet Blue, 1250 Sixth St, Suite 102, Santa Monica, CA 90401 *Tel:* 310-899-3877 *Fax:* 310-899-3787 *Web Site:* www.planetblue.com, pg 976

Planet Dallas Recording Studios, PO Box 110995, Carrollton, TX 75011 *Tel:* 214-521-2216; 214-893-1130 (cell) *Fax:* 214-528-1299 *E-mail:* planetd@ix.netcom.com *Web Site:* planetdallas.com, pg 976

Plank Road Publishing Inc, 11111 W Plank Ct, Wauwatosa, WI 53226 *Tel:* 262-790-5210 *Toll Free Tel:* 800-437-0832 *Fax:* 262-781-8818 *Toll Free Fax:* 888-272-0212 *E-mail:* custsvc@musick8.com *Web Site:* www.musick8.com, pg 976

plan9films, 1926B Alberta Ave, Saskatoon, SK S7K 1R9, Canada *Tel:* 306-955-6463 *Toll Free Fax:* 866-795-4503 *E-mail:* info@plan9films.com *Web Site:* www.plan9films.com, pg 976

Plantronics Inc, 345 Encinal St, Santa Cruz, CA 95060 *Tel:* 831-426-5858 *Toll Free Tel:* 800-544-4660 *Fax:* 831-426-6098 *Toll Free Fax:* 888-290-4519 *E-mail:* plantronics@custhelp.com *Web Site:* www.plantronics.com, pg 976

Platt Luggage Inc, 4051 W 51 St, Chicago, IL 60632 *Tel:* 773-838-2000 *Toll Free Tel:* 800-222-1555 *Fax:* 773-838-2010 *E-mail:* info@plattcases.com *Web Site:* www.plattcases.com, pg 977

Platypi Studios, 1245 Champa St, 4th fl, Denver, CO 80204 *Tel:* 720-935-7497 *Web Site:* platypistudios.com, pg 977

Playback Now, 3139 Campus Dr, Suite 700, Norcross, GA 30071-1402 *Tel:* 770-447-0616 *Toll Free Tel:* 800-241-7785 *Fax:* 770-447-0543 *E-mail:* sales@playbacknow.com *Web Site:* www.playbacknow.com, pg 977

Playback Recording Studio, 400 E Gutierrez, Santa Barbara, CA 93101 *Tel:* 805-730-7529 *Web Site:* www.playbackrecording.com, pg 977

Playboy Entertainment Group Inc, 9346 Civic Center Dr, Suite 200, Beverly Hills, CA 90210 *Tel:* 312-751-8000 *Web Site:* www.playboy.com; www.playboyenterprises.com, pg 977

Players Press, PO Box 1132, Studio City, CA 91614-0132 *Tel:* 818-789-4980 *Web Site:* ppeps.com, pg 977

PLS Staging, 371 Little Falls Rd, Cedar Grove, NJ 07009-1250 *Tel:* 973-857-7242 *Toll Free Tel:* 800-783-4757 *Fax:* 973-857-8867 *Web Site:* www.plsstaging.com, pg 977

Captain J Charles Plumb, 3917 Fairbreeze Circle, Westlake, CA 91361 *Tel:* 818-991-1964 *Web Site:* www.charlieplumb.com, pg 977

Plume Ltd, 888 Main St, Silver Plume, CO 80476 *Tel:* 303-569-3236 *Toll Free Tel:* 866-569-3236 *Fax:* 303-569-2932 *Web Site:* www.plumeltd.com, pg 977

PLUS Corp of America, 9610 SW Sunshine Ct, Suite 100, Beaverton, OR 97005 *Tel:* 503-748-8700 *Toll Free Tel:* 800-211-9001 *Fax:* 503-643-9756 *E-mail:* sales@plus-america.com *Web Site:* www.plus-america.com, pg 977

Plus 24, 1155 N La Brea Ave, West Hollywood, CA 90038 *Tel:* 323-845-1171; 323-845-1168 (support) *Toll Free Tel:* 800-330-7753 (orders) *Fax:* 323-845-1170 *E-mail:* info@plus24.net; sales@plus24.net *Web Site:* www.plus24.net, pg 977

PM Productions, 5882 Bowcroft St, Suite 2, Los Angeles, CA 90016-4907 *Tel:* 310-559-3127 *Fax:* 310-559-3168 *Web Site:* www.pmproductionsvideos.com, pg 977

PME Audio/Video, 2003 S El Camino Rd, Suite 108, Oceanside, CA 92054 *Tel:* 760-439-0281 *E-mail:* solutions@pmevideo.com *Web Site:* www.pmevideo.com, pg 977

PMP Marketing Inc, 13006 E Philadelphia St, Suite 402, Whittier, CA 90601 *Tel:* 562-698-0088 *Fax:* 562-320-8139 *Web Site:* www.pmpmarketing.com, pg 977

The Pocket Studios, 920 Eastern Ave, Top fl, Toronto, ON M4L 1A4, Canada *Tel:* 416-466-0029 *E-mail:* info@thepocketstudios.com *Web Site:* www.thepocketstudios.com, pg 977

Pogo Pictures, 114 E Ponce de Leon Ave, Suite B, Decatur, GA 30030 *Tel:* 404-892-9490 *Fax:* 404-892-9491 *E-mail:* info@pogopictures.com *Web Site:* www.pogopictures.com, pg 977

Point Lobos Productions, 20417 Califa St, Woodland Hills, CA 91367 *Tel:* 818-340-4201, pg 977

Point of View Productions, 2477 Folsom St, San Francisco, CA 94110 *Fax:* 415-821-0434 *Web Site:* www.karildaniels.com, pg 977

Point Source Audio, 1129 Industrial Ave, No 205, Petaluma, CA 94952 *Tel:* 415-226-1122 *Fax:* 415-520-2110 *E-mail:* info@point-sourceaudio.com; sales@point-sourceaudio.com; support@point-sourceaudio.com *Web Site:* www.point-sourceaudio.com, pg 977

Point 360, 2701 Media Center Dr, Los Angeles, CA 90065 *Tel:* 818-565-1400 *Fax:* 818-847-2503 *E-mail:* sales-point360@point360.com *Web Site:* www.point360.com, pg 978

Polarity Post Production, 69 Green St, San Francisco, CA 94111 *Tel:* 415-421-6622 *Fax:* 415-391-4995 *E-mail:* info@polaritypost.com *Web Site:* www.polaritypost.com, pg 978

Polestar Films & Associated Arts Ltd, PO Box 20104, West Village Sta, New York, NY 10014-0708 *Tel:* 212-352-1375, pg 978

Polhemus, 40 Hercules Dr, Colchester, VT 05446-5835 *Tel:* 802-655-3159 *Toll Free Tel:* 800-357-4777 (US & CN) *E-mail:* sales@polhemus.com *Web Site:* polhemus.com, pg 978

George Polk Awards in Journalism, Journalism Dept, One University Plaza, Brooklyn, NY 11201-5372 *Tel:* 718-488-1009 *Fax:* 718-780-4046 *Web Site:* www.liu.edu/polk, pg 1124

Pollstar, 4697 W Jacquelyn Ave, Fresno, CA 93722-6413 *Tel:* 559-271-7900 *Fax:* 559-271-7979 *E-mail:* info@pollstar.com *Web Site:* www.pollstar.com; www.pollstarpro.com, pg 978

Pollution Studios, 3239 Union Pacific Ave, Los Angeles, CA 90023 *Tel:* 323-380-8033 *E-mail:* info@pollutionstudios.com *Web Site:* pollutionstudios.com, pg 978

Gabriel Polonsky Studio, 33 Harvard Rd, Suite 2, Belmont, MA 02478 *Tel:* 617-489-3331 *E-mail:* gp-studio@verizon.net *Web Site:* www.gp-studio.com, pg 978

Polyline LLC, 845 N Church Ct, Elmhurst, IL 60126-1036 *Tel:* 630-993-2700 *Toll Free Tel:* 800-701-7689 *Toll Free Fax:* 800-816-3330 *E-mail:* sales@polylinecorp.com *Web Site:* www.polylinecorp.com, pg 978

PolyPhaser Corp, 10701 Airport Rd, Hayden, ID 83835 *Tel:* 208-772-8515 *Toll Free Tel:* 800-882-9110 *Fax:* 208-762-6117 *Web Site:* www.smithspower.com/brands/polyphaser, pg 978

PolyScience, 6600 W Touhy Ave, Niles, IL 60714-4516 *Tel:* 847-647-0611 *Toll Free Tel:* 800-229-7569 *Fax:* 847-647-1155 *E-mail:* sales@polyscience.com *Web Site:* www.polyscience.com, pg 978

PolyVision Corporation, 10700 Abbotts Bridge Rd, Suite 100, Duluth, GA 30097 *Tel:* 678-542-3100 *Toll Free Tel:* 888-325-6351 *Fax:* 678-542-3200 *E-mail:* info@polyvision.com *Web Site:* polyvision.com, pg 978

Pook Diemont & Ohl Inc, 701 E 132 St, Bronx, NY 10454 *Tel:* 718-402-2677 *Fax:* 718-402-2859 *E-mail:* info@pdoinc.com *Web Site:* www.pdoinc.com, pg 978

POP TV, 5069 Maureen Lane, Moorpark, CA 93021-7127 *Tel:* 805-499-8513 *Toll Free Tel:* 800-331-4626 *Fax:* 805-499-8206 *E-mail:* sales@mpo-video.com *Web Site:* www.mpo-video.com, pg 978

Popless Voice Screens, PO Box 1014, New Paltz, NY 12561-3063 *Tel:* 845-255-3367 *Toll Free Tel:* 800-252-1503 *Fax:* 845-255-3367 *E-mail:* info@popfilter.com *Web Site:* www.popfilter.com, pg 978

Porta-Jib, 1033 N Sycamore Ave, Los Angeles, CA 90038 *Tel:* 323-462-2855 *Fax:* 323-462-2682 *E-mail:* info@porta-jib.com *Web Site:* www.porta-jib.com, pg 978

PortaBrace Inc, PO Box 220, North Bennington, VT 05257-0220 *Tel:* 802-442-8171 *Fax:* 802-442-9118 *E-mail:* info@portabrace.com *Web Site:* www.portabrace.com, pg 978

Porter Case Inc, 3718 W Western Ave, South Bend, IN 46619 *Tel:* 574-289-2616 *Toll Free Tel:* 800-356-8348 *Fax:* 574-289-2747 *E-mail:* sales@portercase.com *Web Site:* www.portercase.com, pg 978

James Porter Photography, 211 E Columbine Ave, Suite A-1, Santa Ana, CA 92707 *Tel:* 714-546-4148 *E-mail:* info@jamesporterphotography.com *Web Site:* www.jamesporterphotography.com, pg 979

Porter Productions, 211 E Columbine Ave, Suite A-1, Santa Ana, CA 92707 *Tel:* 714-546-4148 *E-mail:* studio@porterproductions.info *Web Site:* www.porterproductions.info, pg 979

Portland Models & Talent LLC, PO Box 4727, Portland, ME 04112-4727 *Tel:* 207-741-2850; 207-799-9758 *E-mail:* PortlandModels@aol.com *Web Site:* www.portlandmodels.com, pg 979

Post Josh Productions, 375 Greenwich St, New York, NY 10013 *Tel:* 212-699-2642 *E-mail:* info@postjosh.com *Web Site:* www.postjosh.com, pg 979

Posthorn Recordings, 142 W 26 St, 10th fl, New York, NY 10001-6814 *Tel:* 212-242-3737 *Fax:* 212-924-1243 *Web Site:* www.posthorn.com, pg 979

PostWorks, 100 Avenue of the Americas, 10th fl, New York, NY 10013 *Tel:* 212-894-4000 *Fax:* 212-941-0439 *E-mail:* inquiry@postworks.com *Web Site:* www.postworks.com, pg 979

Potentials Unlimited, 3409 47 Ave E, Bradenton, FL 34203-3974 *Tel:* 941-739-2611 *Toll Free Tel:* 800-221-6121; 800-426-3963 *Fax:* 941-756-0315 *Web Site:* www.potentialsunlimited.com, pg 979

Potomac Instruments Inc, 7309 Grove Rd, Unit D, Frederick, MD 21704 *Tel:* 301-696-5550 *Fax:* 301-696-5553 *E-mail:* comments@pi-usa.com *Web Site:* www.pi-usa.com, pg 979

Pounds Photographic Labs Inc, 901 Regal Row, Dallas, TX 75247 *Tel:* 214-688-1425 *Toll Free Tel:* 800-350-5671 *Fax:* 214-688-1429 *Web Site:* www.poundslabs.com, pg 979

Power & Light, 1313 Mound St, Alameda, CA 94501 *Tel:* 510-205-4101 (cell) *Web Site:* www.powerlight.net, pg 979

Power & Telephone Supply Co, 44 Hull St, Suite 2, Randolph, VT 05060 *Toll Free Tel:* 800-451-4381 *Fax:* 802-234-5006 *E-mail:* cablesales@ptsupply.com *Web Site:* www.ptsupply.com, pg 979

Power Factory Productions, 14518 Hempstead Rd, No 4CC, Houston, TX 77040 *Tel:* 281-630-6900 *E-mail:* info@powerfactoryproductions.com *Web Site:* www.powerfactoryproductions.com, pg 979

Power Integrity Corporation, PO Box 9682, Greensboro, NC 27429-0682 *Tel:* 336-379-9773 *Toll Free Tel:* 800-237-6260 (tech support) *E-mail:* info@powerintegritycorp.com *Web Site:* www.powerintegritycorp.com, pg 979

Power-Sonic Corp, 7550 Panasonic Way, San Diego, CA 92154 *Tel:* 619-661-2020 *Fax:* 619-661-3650 *E-mail:* customer-service@power-sonic.com; technical-support@power-sonic.com *Web Site:* www.power-sonic.com, pg 979

PowerPhysics Inc, 877 Production Place, Newport Beach, CA 92663-2809 *Tel:* 949-371-6202 *Fax:* 815-572-8936 *E-mail:* contact@powerphysics.com *Web Site:* www.powerphysics.com, pg 979

Melvin Powers Television Marketing, 9731 Variel Ave, Chatsworth, CA 91311-4315 *Tel:* 818-700-1522 *E-mail:* mpowers@mpowers.com *Web Site:* www.mpowers.com, pg 979

Powerstation Events, 1486 Highland Ave, Bldg 2, Suite 6, Cheshire, CT 06410 *Tel:* 203-250-8500 *Toll Free Tel:* 800-423-7835 *Fax:* 203-250-8575 *E-mail:* sales@powerstationevents.com *Web Site:* www.powerstationevents.com, pg 979

PowerTechnology Southeast Inc, 634 State Rd 44, Leesburg, FL 34748 *Tel:* 352-365-2777 *Toll Free Tel:* 800-760-0027 *Fax:* 352-787-5545 *E-mail:* powertech@powertech-gen.com *Web Site:* www.powertech-gen.com, pg 979

The PPS Group, 424 Scott St, Covington, KY 41011 *Tel:* 859-291-5100 *Toll Free Tel:* 800-978-3445 *Fax:* 859-291-5150 *E-mail:* info@theppsgroup.com *Web Site:* www.pps-inc.com; www.theppsgroup.com, pg 980

Practising Law Institute, 1177 Avenue of the Americas, New York, NY 10036 *Tel:* 212-824-5700 *Toll Free Tel:* 800-260-4PLI (260-4754, cust serv) *Toll Free Fax:* 800-321-0093 *E-mail:* info@pli.edu (cust serv) *Web Site:* www.pli.edu, pg 980

Prairie Pictures Film & Video, PO Box 122020, Arlington, TX 76012-8020 *Tel:* 817-276-9500 *E-mail:* info@prairiepictures.com *Web Site:* prairiepictures.com, pg 980

The Prairie Production Group, 509 S Country Fair Dr, Suite A, Champaign, IL 61821 *Tel:* 217-359-4675 *Fax:* 217-359-4689 *E-mail:* ppg@prairie-production.com *Web Site:* www.prairie-production.com, pg 980

Prakken Publications Inc, 2851 Boardwalk Dr, Ann Arbor, MI 48104 *Tel:* 734-975-2800 *Toll Free Tel:* 800-530-9673 *Fax:* 734-975-2787 *E-mail:* matt@techdirections.com *Web Site:* www.techdirections.com, pg 980

PRC Digital Media, 250-A Park St, Jacksonville, FL 32204 *Tel:* 904-354-1500 *E-mail:* info@prcdigital.com *Web Site:* www.prcdigital.com, pg 980

Precision Camera & Video, 2438 W Anderson Lane, Suite B-4, Austin, TX 78757 *Tel:* 512-467-7676 *Toll Free Tel:* 800-677-1023 *Fax:* 512-467-0607 *Web Site:* www.precision-camera.com, pg 980

Precision Camera & Video Repair Inc, 4 Anngina Dr, Enfield, CT 06082-3222 *Tel:* 860-749-7380 *Toll Free Tel:* 800-665-6515 *Fax:* 860-763-7100 *E-mail:* info@precisioncamera.com *Web Site:* www.precisioncamera.com, pg 980

Precision Electronics Inc, 1331 Estes Ave, Gurnee, IL 60031 *Tel:* 847-599-1799 *Toll Free Tel:* 800-SINCE-46 (746-2346) *Fax:* 847-599-6178 *E-mail:* info@grommesprecision.com; sales@grommesprecision.com *Web Site:* www.grommesprecision.com, pg 980

Precision Microproducts of America, One Comac Loop, Unit 13, Ronkonkoma, NY 11779 *Tel:* 631-580-3456 *Toll Free Tel:* 800-932-9215 *Fax:* 631-580-3003 *E-mail:* sales@p-m-a.com *Web Site:* www.p-m-a.com, pg 980

Precision Projection Systems Inc, 17508 Studebaker Rd, Cerritos, CA 90703 *Tel:* 562-865-8552 *Fax:* 562-924-7133 *E-mail:* info@ppsfx.com *Web Site:* www.ppsfx.com, pg 980

Prelinger Archives, PO Box 590622, San Francisco, CA 94159-0622 *Tel:* 415-750-0445 *Fax:* 415-750-0607 *E-mail:* footage@panix.com *Web Site:* www.prelinger.com, pg 980

Premier™, 251 Wedcor Ave, Wabash, IN 46992 *Tel:* 260-563-0641 *Toll Free Tel:* 800-225-5644 *Fax:* 260-563-4575 *Toll Free Fax:* 800-654-8339 (orders) *E-mail:* info@martinyale.com *Web Site:* www.martinyale.com/premier.aspx, pg 980

Premier A/V Sales Ltd, 28 Howden Rd, Scarborough, ON M1R 3E4, Canada *Tel:* 416-755-1148 *Toll Free Tel:* 800-267-0700 *Fax:* 416-755-6996 *E-mail:* sales@premierav.ca *Web Site:* www.premierav.ca, pg 980

Premier Lighting & Production Co, 12023 Victory Blvd, North Hollywood, CA 91606 *Tel:* 818-762-0884 *Toll Free Tel:* 800-770-0884 *Fax:* 818-762-0896 *E-mail:* premier@premier-lighting.com *Web Site:* www.premier-lighting.com, pg 980

Premiere Locations, 25 Clyden Rd, Wainscott, NY 11975 *Tel:* 631-537-1669; 917-690-1075 (cell) *E-mail:* info@premierelocations.com *Web Site:* www.premierelocations.com, pg 980

Premio Mesquite, 723 S Brazos St, San Antonio, TX 78207 *Tel:* 210-271-3151 (ext 232) *Fax:* 210-271-3480 *E-mail:* cine@guadalupeculturalarts.org *Web Site:* www.guadalupeculturalarts.org, pg 1124

Pres-On Merchandising Corp, 2600 E 107 St, Bolingbrook, IL 60440 *Toll Free Tel:* 800-323-7467 *Fax:* 630-628-8025 *Web Site:* www.pres-on.com, pg 981

Presagis, 4700 de la Savane, Suite 300, Montreal, QC H4P 1T7, Canada *Tel:* 514-341-3874 *Toll Free Tel:* 800-361-6424 *E-mail:* info@presagis.com *Web Site:* www.presagis.com, pg 981

Prescolite, 701 Millennium Blvd, Greenville, SC 29607 *Tel:* 864-678-1000 *Fax:* 864-678-1415 *Web Site:* www.prescolite.com, pg 981

Presence Records, 67 Candace Lane, Chatham Township, NJ 07928-1115 *Tel:* 973-701-0707 *Web Site:* www.paulpayton.com; www.presenceproductions.com, pg 981

Presence Studios Westport, 80 Wells Hill Rd, Suite 100, Weston, CT 06883 *Tel:* 203-221-8061 *E-mail:* info@presencestudios.com *Web Site:* www.presencestudios.com, pg 981

Presentation Products Inc, 632 W 28 St, 7th fl, New York, NY 10001 *Tel:* 212-736-6350 *Toll Free Tel:* 877-774-4523 *Fax:* 212-736-6353 *E-mail:* info@presentationstore.com; sales@pproducts.com *Web Site:* www.ppidirect.com; www.presentationproducts.com, pg 981

The Presidential Proclamation Award, 3 Barker Ave, 5th fl, White Plains, NY 10601 *Tel:* 914-761-1100 *Fax:* 914-761-3115 *E-mail:* smpte@smpte.org *Web Site:* www.smpte.org, pg 1124

Preston Cinema Systems, 1659 11 St, Suite 100, Santa Monica, CA 90404 *Tel:* 310-453-1852 *Fax:* 310-453-5672 *E-mail:* sales@prestoncinema.com *Web Site:* www.prestoncinema.com, pg 981

Preston Productions Inc, 128 Bartlett St, Marlborough, MA 01752 *Toll Free Tel:* 800-822-2299 *E-mail:* ideas@prestonevents.com *Web Site:* www.prestonproductions.com; www.prestonevents.com, pg 981

Prevent Blindness America, 211 W Wacker Dr, Suite 1700, Chicago, IL 60606 *Tel:* 312-363-6001 *Toll Free Tel:* 800-331-2020 *Fax:* 312-363-6052 *E-mail:* info@preventblindness.org *Web Site:* www.preventblindness.org, pg 981

PRG, 1053 Willingham Dr, Atlanta, GA 30344 *Tel:* 404-214-4800 *Toll Free Tel:* 888-844-4225 *Fax:* 404-214-4801 *E-mail:* info@hitechrent.com *Web Site:* www.prg.com, pg 981

PRG Lighting, 6050 S Valley View Blvd, Las Vegas, NV 89118 *Tel:* 702-942-4774 *Fax:* 702-942-4668 *E-mail:* info@prg.com *Web Site:* www.prg.com, pg 981

PRI Productions, 1819 Kings Ave, Jacksonville, FL 32207 *Tel:* 904-398-8179 *Fax:* 904-398-1569 *E-mail:* generalmailbox@priproductions.com *Web Site:* www.priproductions.com, pg 981

Price Stern Sloan, 375 Hudson St, 14th fl, New York, NY 10014 *Tel:* 212-414-3607; 212-366-2000; 212-366-2372 *Fax:* 212-414-3396; 212-366-2933 *Web Site:* us.penguingroup.com, pg 981

Primacoustic, 1588 Kebet Way, Port Coquitlam, BC V3C 5M5, Canada *Tel:* 604-942-1001 *Fax:* 604-942-1010 *E-mail:* info@primacoustic.com *Web Site:* www.primacoustic.com, pg 982

PrimaLux Video Inc, 555 Eighth Ave, Suite 1002, New York, NY 10018 *Tel:* 212-206-1402 *Fax:* 212-206-1826 *E-mail:* primalux@aol.com *Web Site:* www.primalux.com, pg 982

Primary Color Laboratory Inc, 3550 Williams Blvd, Suite A, Kenner, LA 70065 *Tel:* 504-468-3750 *Toll Free Tel:* 800-535-7799 *Fax:* 504-468-3751 *E-mail:* info@primarycolorlab.com *Web Site:* www.primarycolorlab.com, pg 982

Primary Press, PO Box 83, St Peters, PA 19470-0083 *Tel:* 610-469-9029, pg 982

Prime Cut Productions, 6418 Via Baron, Rancho Palo Verdes, CA 90275 *Tel:* 310-750-6109 *Web Site:* www.primecutproductions.com, pg 982

Prime Image Inc, 200 Highpoint Dr, Suite 215, Chalfont, PA 18914 *Tel:* 215-822-1561; 215-817-2713 (tech support) *Toll Free Tel:* 877-PRIME-40 (774-6340) *E-mail:* info@primeimage.com *Web Site:* www.primeimage.com, pg 982

PrimeArray Systems Inc, 48 Maple St, Lowell, MA 01852 *Tel:* 978-649-0090 *Toll Free Tel:* 800-433-5133 *Fax:* 978-498-0190 *E-mail:* info@primearray.com; sales@primearray.com *Web Site:* www.primearray.com, pg 982

PrimeLight Productions Inc, 750 Kappock St, Suite 805, Riverdale, NY 10463 *Tel:* 718-543-3991; 917-680-5780 *E-mail:* info@primelight.net *Web Site:* www.primelight.net, pg 982

Princeton Acoustics Corp, 40 Benford Dr, Princeton Junction, NJ 08550 *Tel:* 609-936-0006 *Web Site:* www.nccnewyork.com, pg 982

Princeton Architectural Press, 37 E Seventh St, New York, NY 10003 *Tel:* 212-995-9620 *Fax:* 212-995-9454 *E-mail:* sales@papress.com *Web Site:* www.papress.com, pg 982

Princeton Book Company, Publishers, 614 Rte 130, Hightstown, NJ 08520 *Tel:* 609-426-0602 *Toll Free Tel:* 800-220-7149 *Fax:* 609-426-1344 *E-mail:* pbc@dancehorizons.com *Web Site:* www.dancehorizons.com, pg 982

Print File Inc, 1846 S Orange Blossom Trail, Apopka, FL 32703 *Tel:* 407-886-3100 *Toll Free Tel:* 800-508-8539 *Fax:* 407-886-0008 *Toll Free Fax:* 800-546-4145 *E-mail:* support@printfile.com *Web Site:* www.printfile.com, pg 982

Printing Industries of America, 200 Deer Run Rd, Sewickley, PA 15143 *Tel:* 412-741-6860 *Toll Free Tel:* 800-910-4283 *Fax:* 412-741-2311 *E-mail:* printing@printing.org *Web Site:* www.printing.org, pg 1087

Prior Scientific Inc, 80 Reservoir Park Dr, Rockland, MA 02370-1062 *Tel:* 781-878-8442 *Toll Free Tel:* 800-877-2234 *Fax:* 781-878-8736 *E-mail:* info@prior.com; techsupportus@prior.com *Web Site:* www.prior.com, pg 982

Prism Media Products Inc, 21 Pine St, Rockaway, NJ 07866 *Tel:* 973-983-9577 *Fax:* 973-983-9588 *E-mail:* sales@prismmpi.com *Web Site:* www.prismsound.com, pg 982

Pristine Systems Inc, 1891 N Gaffey St, Suite I, San Pedro, CA 90731-1268 *Tel:* 310-831-2234 *Fax:* 310-831-6287 *E-mail:* sales@pristinesys.com *Web Site:* www.pristinesys.com, pg 982

Private Island Trax, 1882 S Cochran Ave, Los Angeles, CA 90019 *Tel:* 323-856-8729 *Fax:* 323-965-8732 *E-mail:* info@privateislandtrax.com *Web Site:* www.privateislandtrax.com, pg 982

Prix Gemeaux (French language TV), 225 rue Roy E, bureau 106, Montreal, QC H2W 1M5, Canada *Tel:* 514-849-7448 *Fax:* 514-849-5069 *E-mail:* academie@acct.ca *Web Site:* www.acct.ca/prixgemeaux; www.acct.ca; www.academy.ca, pg 1124

Pro Camera Repair, 7910 Raytheon Rd, San Diego, CA 92111 *Tel:* 858-277-3700 *Fax:* 858-277-5332 *E-mail:* prophotorepair@hotmail.com *Web Site:* www.procamerarepair.com, pg 982

Pro Cuts Editing Services, 2138 Priest Bridge Ct, Suite 1, Crofton, MD 21114 *Tel:* 301-464-5067; 443-274-6115 *E-mail:* info@procutsediting.com *Web Site:* www.procutsediting.com, pg 982

Pro8mm, 2805 W Magnolia Blvd, Burbank, CA 91505-3037 *Tel:* 818-848-5522 *Fax:* 818-848-5956 *E-mail:* sales@pro8mm.com; info@pro8mm.com *Web Site:* www.pro8mm.com, pg 983

Pro HD Rentals, 2201 N Hollywood Way, Suite 1, Burbank, CA 91505 *Tel:* 818-450-1115 *E-mail:* sales@prohdrentals.com *Web Site:* www.prohdrentals.com, pg 983

Pro Image, 1716 Terrace Ave, Snohomish, WA 98290 *Tel:* 206-284-5000 *Toll Free Tel:* 888-284-6400, pg 983

Pro Media Productions, 2593 Hamline Ave N, Roseville, MN 55113 *Tel:* 651-631-3681 *E-mail:* info@promediaproductions.com *Web Site:* www.promediaproductions.com, pg 983

Pro Media/Ultra Sound, 800 Alfred Nobel Dr, Hercules, CA 94547 *Tel:* 510-741-2925 *Toll Free Tel:* 800-969-7686 (sales) *Fax:* 510-741-0790 *E-mail:* service@ultrapromedia.com *Web Site:* www.promediausa.com, pg 983

Pro Power Products Inc, 913 S Victory Blvd, Burbank, CA 91502-2430 *Tel:* 818-558-6222 *Toll Free Tel:* 800-395-8466 *Fax:* 818-558-3999 *Web Site:* propowerproducts.com, pg 983

Pro Stage Inc, 567 Ocoee Business Pkwy, Ocoee, FL 34761 *Tel:* 407-654-5822 *Fax:* 407-654-5826 *E-mail:* info@prostage.com *Web Site:* www.prostage.com, pg 983

Pro Studio Supply, 140 S Park St, Oconomowoc, WI 53066 *Tel:* 262-567-8047 *Toll Free Tel:* 800-558-0114 *Fax:* 262-567-8479 *E-mail:* mail2@prostudiousa.com; sales@prostudiousa.com *Web Site:* www.prostudiousa.com, pg 983

Pro-Tape & Specialities Inc, 621 Rte 1 S, Suite B, North Brunswick, NJ 08902 *Tel:* 732-346-0900 *Toll Free Tel:* 800-345-0234 *Fax:* 732-729-7373 *Web Site:* www.protapes.com, pg 983

Pro Video, 600 First Ave NW, Cedar Rapids, IA 52405 *Tel:* 319-368-7779 *Toll Free Tel:* 800-234-7680 *E-mail:* service@provideoweb.com *Web Site:* www.provideoweb.com, pg 983

Pro Video & Film Equipment Co Inc, 11425 Mathis Ave, Studio 404, Dallas, TX 75234 *Tel:* 972-869-9990 *Toll Free Tel:* 888-869-9998 *Fax:* 972-869-0145 *E-mail:* providfilm@aol.com *Web Site:* www.provideofilm.com; www.usedequipmentnewsletter.com, pg 983

PROCAM, 13624 Black Elk Trail, Prescott, AZ 86305 *Tel:* 928-708-9901 *Fax:* 928-708-9897 *E-mail:* camradoc@hotmail.com *Web Site:* bolex-usa.com, pg 983

Producer East Productions, 43 Mandrake Rd, Monroe Township, NJ 08831 *Tel:* 631-455-9636 *Web Site:* www.producereast.com, pg 983

Producers Group Ltd, 713 S Pacific Coast Hwy, Suite B, Redondo Beach, CA 90277-4233 *Tel:* 310-316-0481 *Fax:* 310-316-1482 *Web Site:* www.producers-group.tv, pg 983

Producers Guild of America Inc (PGA), 8530 Wilshire Blvd, Suite 400, Beverly Hills, CA 90211 *Tel:* 310-358-9020 *E-mail:* info@producersguild.org *Web Site:* www.producersguild.org, pg 1087

Producers Library, 10832 Chandler Blvd, North Hollywood, CA 91601 *Tel:* 818-752-9097 *Toll Free Tel:* 800-944-2135 *Fax:* 818-752-9196 *E-mail:* research@producerslibrary.com *Web Site:* www.producerslibrary.com, pg 983

The Producer's Loft, 2773 Folsom St, Suite 101, San Francisco, CA 94110 *Tel:* 415-334-4700 *Web Site:* theproducersloft.com, pg 983

Producers Management Television (PMTV), 681 Moore Rd, Suite 100, King of Prussia, PA 19406 *Tel:* 610-768-1770 *Fax:* 610-768-1773 *E-mail:* info@pmtv.com *Web Site:* www.pmtv.com, pg 983

Producers Playhouse, 117 NW 142 St, Edmond, OK 73013 *Tel:* 405-858-0700 *Toll Free Tel:* 888-607-6856 *Fax:* 405-302-0703 *Web Site:* www.producersplayhouse.com, pg 983

Producers Studio, PO Box 7846, Eugene, OR 97401-0032 *Tel:* 541-683-1400 *Fax:* 541-683-1401 *E-mail:* producer@cyberis.net *Web Site:* www.producers-studio.com, pg 984

Producers Video, 3700 Malden Ave, Baltimore, MD 21211 *Tel:* 410-523-7520 *Fax:* 410-669-3347; 410-523-0281 *Web Site:* producers.tv, pg 984

Product Productions, 1806 W Grand Ave, Chicago, IL 60622 *Tel:* 312-421-9030 *Fax:* 312-243-5051 *E-mail:* info@productproductions.com *Web Site:* www.productproductions.com, pg 984

Production Advantage Inc, 301 Avenue "D", Suite 10, Williston, VT 05495 *Tel:* 802-651-6915 *Toll Free Tel:* 800-424-9991 *Fax:* 802-651-6914 *Toll Free Fax:* 877-424-9991 *E-mail:* sales@proadv.com; orders@proadv.com *Web Site:* www.productionadvantageonline.com, pg 984

Production Central, 873 Broadway, Suite 205, New York, NY 10003 *Tel:* 212-631-0435 *Fax:* 212-631-0436 *E-mail:* info@prodcentral.com *Web Site:* www.prodcentral.com, pg 984

Production Consultants, 1408 Thomas Mason Place, St Louis, MO 63011-4423 *Tel:* 636-391-8611 *Fax:* 636-391-4044 *E-mail:* info@productionconsultants.com *Web Site:* www.productionconsultants.com, pg 984

Production Craft Inc, 1437 W Grand Ave, Chicago, IL 60642-6332 *Tel:* 312-829-0272 *Fax:* 312-829-8936 *E-mail:* info@productioncraft.com *Web Site:* www.productioncraft.com, pg 984

Production Garden Music, 510 E Ramsey, Suite 4, San Antonio, TX 78216 *Tel:* 210-530-5200 *Toll Free Tel:* 800-247-5317 *Fax:* 210-530-5230 *E-mail:* sales@productiongarden.com *Web Site:* www.productiongarden.com, pg 984

Production Gear Rentals (PGR), 16140 Runnymede St, Van Nuys, CA 91406 *Tel:* 818-989-8640 *Fax:* 818-989-8644 *E-mail:* oscar@pgr.tv *Web Site:* pgr.tv, pg 984

The Production Group Studios, 6767 W Sunset Blvd, No 8-496, Hollywood, CA 90028-7177 *Tel:* 323-469-8111 *Fax:* 323-962-2182 *E-mail:* info@productiongroup.tv *Web Site:* www.productiongroup.tv, pg 984

The Production House, Innovative Teaching & Technology Ctr, 108 ITTC Bldg, Cedar Falls, IA 50614 *Tel:* 319-273-7820 *Fax:* 319-273-2917 *E-mail:* pro-house@uni.edu *Web Site:* www.uni.edu/its/labs/production-house, pg 984

Production Intercom Inc, 4 Hillview Dr, Unit A, Lake Barrington, IL 60010 *Tel:* 847-381-5350 *Fax:* 847-381-4360 *E-mail:* beltpack@beltpack.com *Web Site:* www.beltpack.com, pg 984

Production Masters Inc (PMI), 202 Fifth Ave, Pittsburgh, PA 15222 *Tel:* 412-281-8500 *Fax:* 412-391-7529 *E-mail:* info@pmi.tv *Web Site:* www.pmi.tv, pg 984

Production Outfitters, 1833 San Mateo Blvd NE, Albuquerque, NM 87110 *Tel:* 505-237-0770 *Fax:* 505-232-4419 *E-mail:* info@productionoutfitters.com *Web Site:* www.productionoutfitters.com, pg 984

Production Partners Media, 520 Enterprise Dr, Suite C, Lewis Center, OH 43035 *Tel:* 614-888-4888 *Web Site:* productionpartnersmedia.com, pg 984

Production Radio Rentals Inc, 249 Ferris Ave, White Plains, NY 10603-3420 *Tel:* 914-686-3525 *Fax:* 914-686-3374 *E-mail:* info@productionradio.com *Web Site:* www.productionradio.com, pg 984

Production Resource Group LLC (PRG), 539 Temple Hill Rd, New Windsor, NY 12553-5533 *Tel:* 845-567-5700 *Fax:* 845-567-5800 *E-mail:* info@prg.com *Web Site:* www.prg.com, pg 984

Production Solutions Inc, PO Box 49431, Dayton, OH 45449-0431 *Tel:* 937-866-2028 *Fax:* 253-423-8997 *E-mail:* proso@worldnet.att.net *Web Site:* www.psiohio.com, pg 984

Production Solutions Inc, PO Box 8146, Reading, PA 19603-8146 *Tel:* 610-374-6998 *Fax:* 610-374-7284 *E-mail:* info@prod-sol.com *Web Site:* www.prod-sol.com, pg 985

Production Support Services Inc, 827 Koeln Ave, St Louis, MO 63111 *Tel:* 314-535-8548 *Toll Free Tel:* 800-394-1257 *Fax:* 314-236-0735 *E-mail:* info@productionsupportservices.com *Web Site:* www.productionsupportservices.com, pg 985

Production West, 207 NW Park Ave, Portland, OR 97209 *Tel:* 503-222-0025 *Fax:* 503-573-1941 *E-mail:* info@r2cgroup.com *Web Site:* www.r2cgroup.com, pg 985

Productions Grand Nord Quebec Inc, 5141 Notre Dame de Grace Ave, Montreal, QC H4A 1K4, Canada *Tel:* 514-521-7433 *Fax:* 514-522-3013, pg 985

Les Productions Via Le Monde (Daniel Bertolino) Inc, 1222 rue MacKay, Suite 201, Montreal, QC H3G 2H4, Canada *Tel:* 514-285-1658 *Fax:* 514-285-1970 *Web Site:* www.vialemonde.com, pg 985

Productiontrax.com, 11811 N Tatum Blvd, Suite 3031, Phoenix, AZ 85028 *Tel:* 480-331-8729 *Fax:* 480-240-9324 *E-mail:* sales@productiontrax.com *Web Site:* www.productiontrax.com, pg 985

Professional Advancement Enterprises (PAE), 2182 Saginaw SE, Grand Rapids, MI 49506 *Tel:* 616-956-9443 *Fax:* 616-956-7973 *E-mail:* paeworld@comcast.net *Web Site:* www.paeworld.com, pg 985

Professional Audio Design Inc, 90 Corporate Park Dr, Suite 1420, Pembroke, MA 02359 *Tel:* 781-982-2600 *Toll Free Tel:* 877-223-8858 *Fax:* 781-982-2610 *E-mail:* info@proaudiodesign.com *Web Site:* www.proaudiodesign.com, pg 985

Professional Education Institute (PEI), 7020 High Grove Blvd, Burr Ridge, IL 60527 *Tel:* 630-382-1000 *Fax:* 630-325-0825 *E-mail:* kpalmer@pei.com *Web Site:* www.thepei.com, pg 985

Professional Label Inc, 3415 Olandwood Ct, Olney, MD 20832 *Tel:* 301-570-0774 *Fax:* 301-570-0776 *E-mail:* prolabel@msn.com *Web Site:* www.professionallabel.com; www.prolabel.com, pg 985

Professional Management Services Inc, 100 Lewis Dr, No 2C, Greenville, SC 29605 *Tel:* 864-325-7240; 864-498-5118 *Fax:* 413-683-7431 *E-mail:* sales@pm-systems.com *Web Site:* pm-systems.com, pg 985

Professional Marketing Services Inc, 105 S Southgate Dr, Chandler, AZ 85226 *Tel:* 480-940-5400 *Fax:* 480-940-5488 *E-mail:* pmsi@promarketinc.com *Web Site:* www.promarketinc.com, pg 985

Professional Photographers of America (PPA), 229 Peachtree St NE, Suite 2200, Atlanta, GA 30303 *Tel:* 404-522-8600 *Toll Free Tel:* 800-786-6277 *Fax:* 404-614-6400 *E-mail:* csc@ppa.com *Web Site:* www.ppa.com, pg 1087

Professional Photographers of Canada –Ontario (PPOC-ON), 209 Light St, Woodstock, ON N4S 6H6, Canada *Tel:* 519-537-2555 *Toll Free Tel:* 888-643-7762 *Toll Free Fax:* 888-831-4036 *E-mail:* info@ppocontario.com *Web Site:* www.ppocontario.com, pg 1087

Professional Sound Corp, 28085 Smyth Dr, Valencia, CA 91355 *Tel:* 661-295-9395 *Fax:* 661-295-8398 *E-mail:* sales@professionalsound.com; service@professionalsound.com *Web Site:* www.professionalsound.com, pg 985

Professional Women Photographers (PWP), 119 W 72 St, Suite 223, New York, NY 10023 *E-mail:* info@pwponline.org *Web Site:* www.pwponline.org, pg 1087

Proforma GW Marketing, 3839 E 17 Ave, Spokane, WA 99223 *Tel:* 509-534-9677; 509-534-7477 *Toll Free Tel:* 800-845-6956 *Fax:* 509-534-9703 *E-mail:* lulupromotion@aol.com *Web Site:* www.proforma.com, pg 985

The Program Source International, 2494 Loch Creek Way, Bloomfield Hills, MI 48304 *Tel:* 248-333-2010 *E-mail:* info@program-source.com *Web Site:* www.program-source.com, pg 985

The Progress Medal Award, 3 Barker Ave, 5th fl, White Plains, NY 10601 *Tel:* 914-761-1100 *Fax:* 914-761-3115 *E-mail:* smpte@smpte.org *Web Site:* www.smpte.org, pg 1124

Progressive AE, 1811 Four Mile Rd NE, Grand Rapids, MI 49525 *Tel:* 616-361-2664 *Fax:* 616-361-1493 *E-mail:* info@progressiveae.com *Web Site:* www.progressiveae.com, pg 985

Progressive Media & Music, 2116 Southview Ave, Tampa, FL 33606 *Tel:* 813-251-8093 *Fax:* 813-251-6050 *E-mail:* info@progressivecds.com *Web Site:* www.progressivecds.com/index.html, pg 985

Projection Presentation Technology, 5803 Rolling Rd, Suite 207, Springfield, VA 22152 *Tel:* 703-912-1334 *Toll Free Tel:* 800-377-7650 *Fax:* 703-912-1350 *E-mail:* info@projection.com *Web Site:* www.projection.com, pg 985

Projector Protector Inc, 131 SW 35 Terr, Cape Coral, FL 33914 *Tel:* 239-945-0792 *Fax:* 239-945-0792 *E-mail:* projectorprotector@excite.com *Web Site:* www.projectorprotector.com, pg 986

Projector SuperStore LLC, 17350 N Hartford Dr, Scottsdale, AZ 85255 *Tel:* 480-922-9420 *Toll Free Tel:* 888-525-6696 *Fax:* 480-348-0273 *Web Site:* www.projectorsuperstore.com, pg 986

Projects in Knowledge Inc, 290 W Mount Pleasant Ave, Suite 2350, Livingston, NJ 07039 *Tel:* 973-890-8988 *Toll Free Tel:* 800-772-8277 *Fax:* 973-992-5810 *E-mail:* info@projectsinknowledge.com *Web Site:* www.projectsinknowledge.com, pg 986

ProLine Digital, PO Box 27682, Denver, CO 80227-0682 *Tel:* 303-761-3999 *Toll Free Tel:* 800-325-0853 *Fax:* 303-761-1818 *E-mail:* info@prolinedigital.com *Web Site:* www.prolinedigital.com, pg 986

Promax Systems, 2850 S Fairview St, Santa Ana, CA 97204 *Tel:* 949-861-2700 *Toll Free Tel:* 800-977-6629 *Fax:* 949-727-2040 *E-mail:* customer@promax.com; sales@promax.com *Web Site:* www.promax.com, pg 986

PromaxBDA, 1522e Cloverfield Blvd, Santa Monica, CA 90404 *Tel:* 310-788-7600 *Fax:* 310-788-7616 *Web Site:* www.promaxbda.org, pg 1087

PromaxBDA Design Awards, 1522e Cloverfield Blvd, Santa Monica, CA 90404 *Tel:* 310-788-7600 *Fax:* 310-788-7616 *Web Site:* www.promaxbda.org, pg 1124

Promedia Digital, 6520 Singletree Dr, Columbus, OH 43229 *Tel:* 614-274-1600 *Toll Free Tel:* 800-837-3827 *Fax:* 614-275-0100 *E-mail:* info@promediaohio.com *Web Site:* www.promediadigital.com, pg 986

Promidi Music, 1980 NE 148 St, Miami, FL 33181 *Tel:* 305-956-9116 *Fax:* 305-947-8220 *E-mail:* info@promidi.biz *Web Site:* www.promidimusic.com, pg 986

Propeller Music Group, 30 Prescott Ave, Mont Clair, NJ 07042 *Tel:* 212-768-3400 *E-mail:* info@propellermusic.com *Web Site:* www.propellermusic.com, pg 986

ProPhotonix Ltd, 32 Hampshire Rd, Salem, NH 03079 *Tel:* 603-893-8778 *Toll Free Tel:* 800-472-4633 (North & South America sales) *Fax:* 603-907-0255 *E-mail:* sales@stockeryale.com *Web Site:* www.prophotonix.com, pg 986

Prosper Media Group Inc, 348 E Main St, Lexington, KY 40507 *Tel:* 859-400-0136 *Toll Free Tel:* 888-528-1999 *E-mail:* producer@prosperproductions.com *Web Site:* www.prospermg.com, pg 986

Protech Audio Corp, 192 Cedar River Rd, Indian Lake, NY 12842 *Tel:* 518-648-6410 *Fax:* 518-648-6395 *E-mail:* proinfo@protechaudio.com; prosales@protechaudio.com *Web Site:* www.protechaudio.com, pg 986

PROTOCOL, 16844 Saticoy St, Van Nuys, CA 91406 *Tel:* 818-782-5705 *Toll Free Tel:* 800-400-5705 *Fax:* 818-782-5817 *E-mail:* orders@walkietalkie.com *Web Site:* www.walkietalkie.com, pg 986

Providence Underground Film Festival, 83 Park St, Suite 1, Providence, RI 02903 *Tel:* 401-861-4445 *Fax:* 401-490-6735 *E-mail:* info@film-festival.org *Web Site:* www.film-festival.org/Prov.Underground.php, pg 1124

Provident-Integrity Distribution, 741 Cool Springs Blvd, Franklin, TN 37067 *Tel:* 615-261-6500 *Toll Free Tel:* 800-333-9000 *Fax:* 615-261-5904 *Toll Free Fax:* 800-333-9408 *E-mail:* info@providentmusicgroup.com, pg 986

ProVideo, 2302 W Badger Rd, Madison, WI 53713-2322 *Tel:* 608-271-1226 *Toll Free Tel:* 800-569-6810 *Fax:* 608-271-2737 *E-mail:* info@provideo.com *Web Site:* www.provideo.com, pg 986

ProVision Video Sales & Rentals Inc, 143 W Third Ave, Vancouver, BC V5Y 1E6, Canada *Tel:* 604-876-0940 *Toll Free Tel:* 877-337-0940 *Fax:* 604-876-8269 *E-mail:* sales@provisionvideo.com; rentals@provisionvideo.com *Web Site:* www.provisionvideo.com, pg 986

PSAV® Presentation Services, 111 W Ocean Blvd, Suite 1110, Long Beach, CA 90802-4688 *Tel:* 562-366-0620 *Toll Free Tel:* 877-430-7728 *Fax:* 562-366-0628 *Web Site:* www.psav.com, pg 986

PSAV® Presentation Services (Hotel Services Division), 1700 E Golf Rd, Suite 400, Schaumburg, IL 60173-5820 *Tel:* 847-222-9800 *Toll Free Tel:* 800-486-9509 *E-mail:* info@psav.com *Web Site:* www.psav.com, pg 987

PSB Speakers International, 633 Granite Ct, Pickering, ON L1W 3K1, Canada *Tel:* 905-831-6555 *Toll Free Tel:* 800-263-4641 (cust serv) *Fax:* 905-837-6357 *E-mail:* info@psbspeakers.com *Web Site:* www.psbspeakers.com, pg 987

PSI Inc, 15375 Barranca Pkwy, Suite A 208, Irvine, CA 92618 *Tel:* 949-261-6119 *E-mail:* psiinfo@psivideoinc.com *Web Site:* www.psivideoinc.com, pg 987

PsiTech Inc, 18368 Bandilier Circle, Fountain Valley, CA 92708 *Tel:* 714-964-7818 *Toll Free Tel:* 800-872-7385 *Fax:* 714-968-7884 *E-mail:* info@psitech.com; sales@psitech.com *Web Site:* www.psitech.com, pg 987

PSNI (Professional Systems Network Inc), 1831 E 71 St, Tulsa, OK 74136 *Tel:* 918-388-1343 *Web Site:* www.psni.org, pg 1088

PSSI, 7030 Hayvenhurst Ave, Van Nuys, CA 91406 *Tel:* 310-575-4400 *Toll Free Tel:* 800-SAT-LINK (728-5465) *Fax:* 310-575-4451 *E-mail:* operations@pssiglobal.com *Web Site:* www.pssiglobal.com, pg 987

Psych Soft Inc, PO Box 232, North Quincy, MA 02171 *Tel:* 617-471-8733 *E-mail:* psoft@psych-soft.com *Web Site:* www.psych-soft.com, pg 987

Psychological Assessment Resources Inc (PAR), 16204 N Florida Ave, Lutz, FL 33549 *Tel:* 813-968-3003; 813-449-4065 (cust serv) *Toll Free Tel:* 800-331-8378 (tech support) *Fax:* 813-968-2598 *Toll Free Fax:* 800-727-9329 *Web Site:* www4.parinc.com, pg 987

PTL Test Equipment Inc, 612 N Orange Ave, Suite D-10, Jupiter, FL 33458 *Tel:* 561-747-3647 *Fax:* 561-575-4635 *E-mail:* ptltest@bellsouth.net *Web Site:* www.ptltest.com, pg 987

Public Eye Productions, 409 Meeker St, South Orange, NJ 07079 *Tel:* 917-446-8977 *Web Site:* www.publiceyeproductions.com, pg 987

Publishers Group West Inc, 1700 Fourth St, Berkeley, CA 94710 *Tel:* 510-809-3700 *Toll Free Tel:* 800-788-3123 (cust serv) *Fax:* 510-809-3777 *E-mail:* info@pgw.com *Web Site:* www.pgw.com, pg 987

Puerto Rico Film Commission, 355 FD Roosevelt Ave, Suite 106, Hato Rey, PR 00918 *Tel:* 787-754-6444 *Fax:* 787-756-5706 *E-mail:* info@puertoricofilm.pr.gov *Web Site:* www.puertoricofilm.com, pg 1104

Jai Pulnix, 625 River Oaks Pkwy, San Jose, CA 95134 *Tel:* 408-383-0300 *Toll Free Tel:* 800-445-5444 *Fax:* 408-383-0301 *E-mail:* camerasales.americas@jai.com *Web Site:* www.jai.com, pg 987

Pumpkin Recording Studio Inc, 8453 Rob Roy Dr, Orland Park, IL 60462 *Tel:* 708-349-1485 *E-mail:* pumpkin1@flash.net, pg 987

Purefire Communications Inc, 200 Evans Ave, Unit 3, Toronto, ON M8Z 1J7, Canada *Tel:* 416-503-2323 *E-mail:* info@purefire.ca *Web Site:* www.purefire.ca, pg 987

PXL This Video Festival, 2427 1/2 Glyndon Ave, Venice, CA 90291 *Tel:* 310-306-7330 *E-mail:* pfsuzy@aol.com *Web Site:* laughtears.com, pg 1124

Pyramid Media, 3200 Airport Ave, No 19, Santa Monica, CA 90405 *Tel:* 310-398-6149 *Toll Free Tel:* 800-421-2304 *Fax:* 310-398-7869 *E-mail:* info@pyramidmedia.com; sales@pyramidmedia.com *Web Site:* www.pyramidmedia.com, pg 987

Pyramind Studios, 880 Folsom St, San Francisco, CA 94107 *Tel:* 415-896-9800 *Toll Free Tel:* 888-378-6463 *Fax:* 415-896-5943 *E-mail:* news@pyramind.com *Web Site:* www.pyramind.com, pg 988

Pyro Spectaculars, 3196 N Locust Ave, Rialto, CA 92377 *Tel:* 909-355-8120 *Toll Free Tel:* 888-477-7976 *Fax:* 909-355-9813 *E-mail:* info@pyrospectaculars.com *Web Site:* www.pyrospectaculars.com, pg 988

Pyrotek Special Effects Inc, 7676 Woodbine Ave, Suites 7 & 8, Markham, ON L3R 2N2, Canada *Tel:* 905-479-9991 *Toll Free Tel:* 800-481-9910 *Fax:* 905-479-3515 *E-mail:* info@pyrotekfx.com *Web Site:* www.pyrotekfx.com, pg 988

Pyxis Industries Inc, 25695 Jefferson Ave, Suite 8, Murrieta, CA 92562 *Tel:* 951-526-1999 *Toll Free Tel:* 888-799-4728 *Fax:* 951-253-9290 *Web Site:* pyxisindustries.com, pg 988

Q-Prompt Inc, 5356 Vail Ct, Mississauga, ON L5M 6G9, Canada *Tel:* 905-601-3826 *Toll Free Tel:* 888-848-4134 *Fax:* 905-567-5665 *E-mail:* info@qprompt.com *Web Site:* www.qprompt.com, pg 988

QCA, 2832 Spring Grove Ave, Cincinnati, OH 45225 *Tel:* 513-681-8400 *Toll Free Tel:* 800-859-8401 *E-mail:* info@go-qca.com *Web Site:* www.go-qca.com, pg 988

QCI International, PO Box 1769, Chico, CA 95927-1769 *Tel:* 530-893-4095 *Fax:* 530-893-0395 *E-mail:* info@qci-intl.com *Web Site:* www.qualitydigest.com, pg 988

Qioptiq, 78 Shuyler Baldwin, Fairport, NY 14450 *Tel:* 585-223-2370 *Toll Free Tel:* 800-429-0257 *Fax:* 585-223-1999 *E-mail:* info@qioptiqlinos.com *Web Site:* www.qioptiqlinos.com, pg 988

QRS Software Services, 11879 Woodbury Rd, Garden Grove, CA 92843 *Tel:* 714-537-5100 *Toll Free Tel:* 800-228-9699 *Fax:* 714-539-9448 *E-mail:* qrs@qrssoftware.com; sales@qrssoftware.com *Web Site:* www.qrssoftware.com, pg 988

QSC Audio Products LLC, 1675 MacArthur Blvd, Costa Mesa, CA 92626 *Tel:* 714-754-6175 *Toll Free Tel:* 800-854-4079 *Fax:* 714-754-6174 *E-mail:* info@qscaudio.com *Web Site:* www.qsc.com, pg 988

QSound Labs Inc, 2816 11 St NE, Suite 102, Calgary, AB T2E 7S7, Canada *Tel:* 403-291-2492 *Fax:* 403-250-1521 *E-mail:* info@qsound.com; sales@qsound.com *Web Site:* www.qsound.com, pg 988

QTV, 124 W 30 St, Suite 312, New York, NY 10001 *Tel:* 212-929-7755 *Fax:* 212-929-2105 *E-mail:* info@qtv.com *Web Site:* www.autocue.com/teleprompter, pg 988

Quabbin Wire & Cable Co Inc, 10 Maple St, Ware, MA 01082-1597 *Tel:* 413-967-6281 *Toll Free Tel:* 800-368-3311 *Fax:* 413-967-7564 *E-mail:* sales@quabbin.com *Web Site:* www.quabbin.com, pg 988

Quad Cities First, 130 W Second St, Davenport, IA 52801 *Tel:* 563-326-1005 *Web Site:* www.quadcitiesfirst.com, pg 1097

Quad Recording Studios, 346 Jersey Ave, Greenwood Lake, NY 10925 *Tel:* 845-477-0338 *Web Site:* www.quadstudios.com, pg 988

Qualiton Imports Ltd, 24-02 40 Ave, Long Island City, NY 11101 *Tel:* 718-937-8515 *Fax:* 718-729-3239 *E-mail:* qualiton@qualiton.com; steve@qualiton.com *Web Site:* www.qualiton.com, pg 988

Quality Audio Visual Service Inc, 6938 Boulevard 26, Fort Worth, TX 76180-8808 *Tel:* 817-284-3192 *Toll Free Tel:* 800-371-6741 *Fax:* 817-595-2942 *E-mail:* info@qualityaudiovisual.com *Web Site:* www.qualityaudiovisual.com, pg 988

Quality Clones, 3940 Laurel Canyon Blvd, Suite 405, Studio City, CA 91604 *Tel:* 323-464-5853 *E-mail:* info@qualityclones.com *Web Site:* www.qualityclones.com, pg 988

Quality Film & Video, 3321 Main St, Suite B-1, Manchester, MD 21102 *Tel:* 410-785-1920 *E-mail:* quality3321@comcast.net *Web Site:* www.qualityfilmvideo.com, pg 988

Quantel Inc, 25 W 43 St, Suite 1118, New York, NY 10036-7406 *Tel:* 212-944-6820 *Toll Free Tel:* 800-331-8327 (cust serv) *Fax:* 212-944-6813 *Web Site:* www.quantel.com, pg 989

Quantum Data Inc, 2111 Big Timber Rd, Elgin, IL 60123-1100 *Tel:* 847-888-0450 *Toll Free Tel:* 888-252-6133 (tech support) *Fax:* 847-888-2802 *E-mail:* sales@quantumdata.com *Web Site:* www.quantumdata.com, pg 989

Quantum Instruments Inc, 1268 Humbracht Circle, Bartlett, IL 60103-1631 *Tel:* 631-656-7400 *Fax:* 631-656-7410 *E-mail:* quantumhelp@qtm.com *Web Site:* www.qtm.com, pg 989

Quartet Manufacturing Co, 4 Corporate Dr, Lake Zurich, IL 60047-8997 *Toll Free Tel:* 800-541-0094 *Toll Free Fax:* 800-247-1317 *Web Site:* www.quartet.com; www.gbc.com; www.accobrands.com, pg 989

Quatrefoil Associates Inc, 29 "C" St, Laurel, MD 20707 *Tel:* 301-470-4748 *Fax:* 301-470-4749 *E-mail:* info@quatrefoil.com *Web Site:* www.quatrefoil.com, pg 989

Questar Corp, 6204 Ingham Rd, New Hope, PA 18938 *Tel:* 215-862-5277 *Toll Free Tel:* 800-247-9607 *Fax:* 215-862-0512 *E-mail:* questar@erols.com *Web Site:* www.questarcorporation.com, pg 989

Questar Inc, 307 N Michigan Ave, 5th fl, Chicago, IL 60601-5305 *Tel:* 312-266-9400 *Toll Free Tel:* 800-544-8422 (cust serv) *Fax:* 312-266-9523 *E-mail:* info@questar1.com *Web Site:* questarentertainment.com, pg 989

Quickbeam Systems Inc (QSI), 4411 McLeod Rd NE, Suite E, Albuquerque, NM 87109 *Tel:* 505-345-9230 *Fax:* 505-345-4604 *E-mail:* sales@quickbeam.com *Web Site:* www.quickbeam.com, pg 989

Quickdraw Animation Society, 351 11 Ave SW, Suite 201, Calgary, AB T2R 0C7, Canada *Tel:* 403-261-5767 *Fax:* 403-261-5644 *E-mail:* info@quickdrawanimation.ca; production@quickdrawanimation.ca; programming@quickdrawanimation.ca *Web Site:* quickdrawanimation.ca; www.giraffest.ca, pg 1088

QuickSet International Inc, 3650 Woodhead Dr, Northbrook, IL 60062-1895 *Tel:* 847-498-0700 *Toll Free Tel:* 800-247-6563 *Fax:* 847-498-1258 *E-mail:* info@quickset.com *Web Site:* www.quickset.com, pg 989

Quiet Planet LLC, PO Box 900, Indianola, WA 98342 *Tel:* 360-477-9588 *Web Site:* www.quietplanet.com, pg 989

Quilt in a Day, 1955 Diamond St, San Marcos, CA 92078 *Tel:* 760-591-0082 *Toll Free Tel:* 800-777-4852 *Fax:* 760-591-4424 *E-mail:* customerservice@quiltinaday.com *Web Site:* www.quiltinaday.com, pg 989

Quince Imaging Inc, 2810 Towerview Rd, Herndon, VA 20171-3206 *Tel:* 703-742-7520 *Toll Free Tel:* 888-252-4960 *Fax:* 703-742-7586 *E-mail:* info@quinceimaging.com; sales@quinceimaging.com; operations@quinceimaging.com *Web Site:* www.quinceimaging.com, pg 989

Bill Quinn Productions, PO Box 213, Ocean Gate, NJ 08740 *Tel:* 732-237-0525, pg 989

Quintessence Audio Ltd, 5701 W Dempster St, Morton Grove, IL 60053 *Tel:* 847-966-4434 *Fax:* 847-966-0932 *E-mail:* info@quintessenceaudio.com *Web Site:* www.quintessenceaudio.com, pg 989

R & R Cases & Cabinets, 1217 Rand Rd, Des Plaines, IL 60016 *Tel:* 847-299-8100 *Fax:* 847-299-8110 *E-mail:* sales@rrcases.com *Web Site:* www.rrcases.com, pg 989

R/GA, 350 W 39 St, New York, NY 10018 *Tel:* 212-946-4000 *Fax:* 212-946-4010 *E-mail:* web@rga.com *Web Site:* www.rga.com, pg 990

Radial Engineering Ltd, 1588 Kebet Way, Port Coquitlam, BC V3C 5M5, Canada *Tel:* 604-942-1001 *Toll Free Tel:* 800-939-1001 (orders) *Fax:* 604-942-1010 *E-mail:* info@radialeng.com *Web Site:* www.radialeng.com, pg 990

Radian Audio Engineering Inc, 600 N Batavia St, Orange, CA 92868 *Tel:* 714-288-8900 *Fax:* 714-288-1133 *E-mail:* info@radianaudio.com *Web Site:* www.radianaudio.com, pg 990

Radiant Images, 4125 W Jefferson Blvd, Los Angeles, CA 90016 *Tel:* 323-737-1314 *Fax:* 310-861-0163 *E-mail:* info@radiantimages.com *Web Site:* www.radiantimages.com, pg 990

Radio Advertising Bureau (RAB), 125 W 55 St, 5th fl, New York, NY 10019 *Tel:* 212-681-7200 *Toll Free Tel:* 800-252-7234 *Fax:* 212-681-7223 *Web Site:* www.rab.com, pg 1088

Radio & TV Engineering Achievement Awards, 1771 "N" St NW, Washington, DC 20036 *Tel:* 202-429-5300 *Fax:* 202-429-4199 *E-mail:* nab@nab.org *Web Site:* www.nab.org, pg 1124

Radio Design Labs (RDL), 659 N Sixth St, Prescott, AZ 86301 *Tel:* 928-443-9391 (sales); 928-778-3554 (cust serv) *Toll Free Tel:* 800-281-2683 (sales); 800-933-1780 (cust serv) *Fax:* 928-443-9392 (sales); 928-778-3506 (cust serv) *Toll Free Fax:* 800-289-7338 (sales) *E-mail:* sales@rdlnet.com; service@rdlnet.com; exportsales@rdlnet.com (Latin America & Asia/Pacific sales) *Web Site:* www.rdlnet.com, pg 990

Radio Systems Inc, 601 Heron Dr, Logan Township, NJ 08085 *Tel:* 856-467-8000 *Fax:* 856-467-3044 *E-mail:* sales@radiosystems.com; tech@radiosystems.com *Web Site:* www.radiosystems.com, pg 990

Radio Television Digital News Association (RTDNA), The National Press Bldg, 529 14 St NW, Suite 425, Washington, DC 20045 *Tel:* 202-659-6510 *Fax:* 202-223-4007 *Web Site:* www.rtdna.org, pg 1088

Radio Vision Inc, 531 W Main St, Denison, TX 75020 *Tel:* 903-337-4200 *Toll Free Tel:* 800-326-3198 *Fax:* 903-337-4296 *E-mail:* info@radiovisioninc.com *Web Site:* www.radiovisioninc.com, pg 990

Radio Visions, PO Box 4732, Toms River, NJ 08754-4732 *Tel:* 732-240-3119 *E-mail:* sales@radiovisions.com *Web Site:* www.radiovisions.com, pg 990

RadioArt/Bob & Ray CDs & MP3 Files, PO Box 519, Plantarium Sta, New York, NY 10024-0519 *Tel:* 212-595-1837 *E-mail:* reply@bobandray.com *Web Site:* www.bobandray.com, pg 990

RadioShack Corp, Riverfront Campus, 300 RadioShack Circle, Fort Worth, TX 76102-1964 *Tel:* 817-415-3700; 817-415-3011 *E-mail:* media.relations@radioshack.com; radioshack.customer.care@radioshack.com *Web Site:* www.radioshackcorporation.com, pg 990

Radiotechniques Engineering LLC, 402 Tenth Ave, Haddon Heights, NJ 08035-1838 *Tel:* 856-546-8008 *Fax:* 856-546-1841 *E-mail:* sales@radiotechniques.com *Web Site:* www.radiotechniques.com, pg 990

Radius® Display Products Inc, 800 Fabric X-Press Way, Dallas, TX 75234 *Tel:* 972-406-1221 *Toll Free Tel:* 800-FABRIC-X (322-7429); 866-966-4066 (sales); 866-966-8266 (hospitality) *Fax:* 972-406-1321 *Toll Free Fax:* 888-322-7429 *Web Site:* www.radiusdp.com, pg 990

RADMAR Inc, PO Box 425, Northbrook, IL 60065-0425 *Tel:* 847-298-7980 *E-mail:* radmarinc@gmail.com *Web Site:* www.radmarinc.com, pg 990

Rafik, 812 Broadway, Suite 4, New York, NY 10003 *Tel:* 212-475-7884 *E-mail:* info@rafikvideo.com; sales@rafikvideo.com *Web Site:* www.rafikvideo.com, pg 990

Rahlic Publishing Co, 301 Keithwood Rd, Wynnewood, PA 19096 *Tel:* 610-649-0982, pg 990

Rainbow International Inc/Rainbow Productions Inc, 1103 Canyon Rd, Santa Fe, NM 87501 *Tel:* 773-505-6264 *Fax:* 773-525-6278 *Web Site:* www.rainbowplace.com, pg 990

Rainbow Media Taos, 27 Valencia Rd, Taos, NM 87571 *Tel:* 575-776-2268 *Toll Free Tel:* 800-748-1540 *Fax:* 575-776-2804, pg 991

Rainbow Rentals, 6705-A Electronic Dr, Springfield, VA 22151 *Tel:* 703-916-0800 *Fax:* 703-916-8013 *E-mail:* party@rainbow-rental.com *Web Site:* www.rainbow-rental.com, pg 991

Rainbow Video Productions Inc, 23803 S 162 St, Adams, NE 68301 *Tel:* 402-430-7343 *Web Site:* www.rainbowvideo.com, pg 991

Raincoast Books, 2440 Viking Way, Richmond, BC V6V 1N2, Canada *Tel:* 604-323-7100 *Toll Free Tel:* 800-663-5714 (cust serv & book orders) *Fax:* 604-270-7161 *Toll Free Fax:* 800-565-3770 (cust serv & book orders) *E-mail:* info@raincoast.com; customerservice@raincoast.com *Web Site:* www.raincoast.com, pg 991

RAM Systems LLC, 27992 W Rte 120, Unit 138, Lakemoor, IL 60051 *Tel:* 847-487-7575 *Fax:* 847-487-2440 *E-mail:* sales@ramsyscom.com *Web Site:* www.ramsyscom.com, pg 991

Rand McNally Education, 9855 Woods Dr, Skokie, IL 60077 *Toll Free Tel:* 800-333-0136 *Web Site:* www.randmcnally.com, pg 991

Randall House Publications, 114 Bush Rd, Nashville, TN 37217 *Tel:* 615-361-1221 *Toll Free Tel:* 800-877-7030 *Fax:* 615-367-0535 *Web Site:* www.randallhouse.com, pg 991

R&B Communications Inc, 2397 Somrack Dr, Willoughby Hills, OH 44094 *Tel:* 440-946-9511 *Web Site:* www.rbcommunications.net, pg 991

R&O Studios, 5805 N 39 St, McAllen, TX 78504 *Tel:* 956-203-0520 *E-mail:* rostudiosrgv@gmail.com *Web Site:* www.randostudios.com, pg 991

Randolf Productions Inc, 17935 Skypark Circle, Suite K, Irvine, CA 92614 *Tel:* 949-794-9109 *Toll Free Tel:* 800-266-7741 *Fax:* 949-794-9117 *E-mail:* sales@go2rpi.com *Web Site:* www.go2rpi.com, pg 991

Random House Audio Publishing Group, 1745 Broadway, New York, NY 10019 *Tel:* 212-782-9205 *Toll Free Tel:* 800-733-3000 *E-mail:* customerservice@randomhouse.com; audio@randomhouse.com *Web Site:* www.randomhouse.com/audio, pg 991

Random House Children's Books, 1745 Broadway, 10th fl, New York, NY 10019 *Tel:* 212-782-9000 *Web Site:* www.randomhousekids.com, pg 991

Random House of Canada Limited, One Toronto St, Unit 300, Toronto, ON M5C 2V6, Canada *Tel:* 416-364-4449 *Fax:* 416-364-6863 *Web Site:* www.randomhouse.ca, pg 991

Rane, 10802 47 Ave W, Mukilteo, WA 98275-5000 *Tel:* 425-355-6000 *E-mail:* info@rane.com *Web Site:* www.rane.com, pg 991

The RapcoHorizon Co, 3581 Larch Lane, Jackson, MO 63755 *Tel:* 573-243-1433 *Toll Free Tel:* 800-325-0266 *Fax:* 573-243-4913 *E-mail:* info@rapcohorizon.com *Web Site:* www.rapcohorizon.com, pg 991

David Rapkin Audio Production, 473 West End Ave, Unit 6A, New York, NY 10024 *Tel:* 212-362-7236 *E-mail:* drapco@aol.com, pg 991

Rauland-Borg Corp, 1802 W Central Rd, Mount Prospect, IL 60056 *Tel:* 847-590-7100 *Toll Free Tel:* 800-752-7725 *Web Site:* www.rauland.com, pg 991

RAVA Films, 67 West St, Suite 604, Brooklyn, NY 11222 *Web Site:* www.ravafilms.com, pg 991

Raven Rental, 2617 Peach St, Erie, PA 16508 *Tel:* 814-456-0331 *Fax:* 814-451-0557 *Web Site:* www.ravensound.com, pg 991

Raven Screen Corp, PO Box 691, Harriman, NY 10926 *Tel:* 845-782-1844 *Toll Free Tel:* 800-847-6906 *Fax:* 845-782-1840 *E-mail:* info@ravenscreen.com *Web Site:* www.ravenscreen.com, pg 992

Ray Supply Inc, 871 Rte 9, Queensbury, NY 12804 *Tel:* 518-792-5848 *Toll Free Tel:* 800-347-5851 (orders) *Fax:* 518-792-1727 *E-mail:* sales@raysupply.com *Web Site:* www.raysupply.com, pg 992

Raymond Entertainment Direct (RED), 3450 Cahuenga Blvd W, Suite 410, Los Angeles, CA 90068 *Tel:* 323-785-4700 *Fax:* 323-785-4701 *E-mail:* info@raymondentertainment.com *Web Site:* www.raymondentertainment.com, pg 992

Rayven Inc, 431 Griggs St N, St Paul, MN 55104 *Tel:* 651-642-1112 *Toll Free Tel:* 800-878-3776 *Fax:* 651-642-9497 *E-mail:* info@rayven.com *Web Site:* www.rayven.com, pg 992

RB Productions, 3-4191 Longmoor Dr, Burlington, ON L7L 5J9, Canada *Tel:* 905-633-7474 *Toll Free Tel:* 866-633-7474 *E-mail:* sales@radicalbob.com *Web Site:* www.rbproductionz.com, pg 992

RBR Productions, 117 W Rockland Rd, Libertyville, IL 60048 *Tel:* 847-362-4060 *Toll Free Tel:* 888-278-0558 *E-mail:* info@rbrproductions.com *Web Site:* www.rbrproductions.com, pg 992

RC Communications, 3900 N River Rd, Schiller Park, IL 60176-2345 *Tel:* 847-678-7000 *Fax:* 847-678-9378 *E-mail:* rccsales@rentcom.com; rent@rentcom.com *Web Site:* www.rentcom.com; www.rc-communications.com, pg 992

RCA Records, 550 Madison Ave, New York, NY 10022 *Tel:* 212-833-8000 *E-mail:* info@rcarecords.com *Web Site:* www.rcarecords.com; www.sonymusic.com, pg 992

RCI Custom Products, 801 N East St, Suite 2-A, Frederick, MD 21701 *Tel:* 301-620-9130 *Toll Free Tel:* 800-546-4724 *Fax:* 301-620-9103 *Toll Free Fax:* 800-546-6175 *E-mail:* info@rcicustom.com *Web Site:* www.rcicustom.com, pg 992

RCS Enterprises, 445 Hamilton Ave, 7th fl, White Plains, NY 10601 *Tel:* 914-428-4600 *Fax:* 914-428-5922 *E-mail:* info@rcsworks.com *Web Site:* www.rcsworks.com, pg 992

Jimmy Rea Electronics Inc, 540 W Broad St, Columbus, OH 43215 *Tel:* 614-221-5170 *Fax:* 614-221-8898 *Web Site:* www.jimmyrea.com, pg 992

Real Cool TV Productions, 800 S Main St, Suite 203, Mansfield, MA 02048 *Tel:* 508-337-8520 *E-mail:* info@realcooltv.com *Web Site:* www.realcooltv.com, pg 992

Real to Reel International Film Festival, 111 S Washington St, Shelby, NC 28150 *Tel:* 704-484-2787 *Fax:* 704-481-1822 *E-mail:* info@ccartscouncil.org *Web Site:* www.ccartscouncil.org/realtoreel, pg 1124

Real to Reel Studios Inc, 4141 Office Pkwy, Dallas, TX 75204 *Tel:* 214-528-4242 *Web Site:* www.rtrstudios.com, pg 992

Reality Check Systems, 726 S Flower St, Burbank, CA 91502 *Tel:* 323-465-3900 *Fax:* 323-465-3600 *E-mail:* info@realitychecksystems.com *Web Site:* www.realityx.com, pg 992

Really Good Stuff, 448 Pepper St, Monroe, CT 06468 *Tel:* 203-261-1920 *Toll Free Tel:* 800-366-1920 (orders); 877-867-1920 (cust serv) *Fax:* 203-268-1796 *Web Site:* www.reallygoodstuff.com, pg 992

RealNetworks Inc, 1501 First Ave S, Suite 600, Seattle, WA 98134 *Tel:* 206-674-2700 *Toll Free Tel:* 800-444-8011 *Fax:* 206-674-2696 *Web Site:* www.real.com; www.realnetworks.com; service.real.com/localized (cust serv); service.real.com (tech support), pg 992

Rebel Records, PO Box 7405, Charlottesville, VA 22906-7405 *Tel:* 434-973-5151 *E-mail:* questions@rebelrecords.com *Web Site:* rebelrecords.com, pg 993

Rebirth/Wenha Records, 81 Chandler St, Detroit, MI 48202 *Tel:* 313-875-0289, pg 993

Record Plant Remote, 1170 Greenwood Lake Tpke, Ringwood, NJ 07456 *Tel:* 973-728-8114 *Fax:* 973-728-8761 *E-mail:* info@recordplantremote.com *Web Site:* www.recordplantremote.com, pg 993

Recorded Books LLC, 270 Skipjack Rd, Prince Frederick, MD 20678 *Tel:* 410-535-5590 *Toll Free Tel:* 800-638-1304 *Fax:* 410-535-5499 *E-mail:* customerservice@recordedbooks.com *Web Site:* www.recordedbooks.com, pg 993

Recordex USA Inc, 10-50 46 Ave, Long Island City, NY 11101 *Tel:* 718-392-5380 *Fax:* 718-392-5485 *E-mail:* sales@recordexusa.com; support@recordexusa.com *Web Site:* www.recordexmfg.com, pg 993

The Recording Academy, 3030 Olympic Blvd, Santa Monica, CA 90404 *Tel:* 310-392-3777 *Fax:* 310-392-2306 *E-mail:* losangeles@grammy.com *Web Site:* www.grammy.org/recording-academy, pg 1088

Recording Industry Association of America (RIAA), 1025 "F" St NW, 10th fl, Washington, DC 20004 *Tel:* 202-775-0101 *Web Site:* www.riaa.com, pg 1088

Recording Media & Equipment Inc (RM&E), 3736 SW 30 Ave, Fort Lauderdale, FL 33312 *Tel:* 954-791-9797 *Toll Free Tel:* 800-541-9797 *Fax:* 954-791-6662 *E-mail:* info@rmeinc.com *Web Site:* www.rmeinc.com, pg 993

Recortec Inc, 3329 Kifer Rd, Santa Clara, CA 95051-0719 *Tel:* 408-928-1480 *Toll Free Tel:* 800-729-7654 *Fax:* 408-928-1489 *E-mail:* info@recortec.com; support@recortec.com; sales@recortec.com *Web Site:* www.recortec.com, pg 993

The Recruiters Library, 14728 Shirley St, Omaha, NE 68144 *Tel:* 402-334-1676 *Toll Free Tel:* 800-293-1676 *Fax:* 402-334-4437 *Web Site:* www.thebestcollegerecruiter.com, pg 993

Red Fox Enterprises, Rte 209 E, Elizabethville, PA 17023 *Tel:* 717-362-3391 *Fax:* 717-362-8577 *E-mail:* redfox1@pa.net, pg 993

Red Hill Corp, 1540 Biglerville Rd, Gettysburg, PA 17325 *Tel:* 717-337-3038 *Toll Free Tel:* 800-822-4003 *Fax:* 717-337-0732 *E-mail:* customerservice@supergrit.com *Web Site:* www.supergrit.com, pg 993

Red Onion Records, PO Box 366, Dayton, OH 45401-0366 *Tel:* 937-277-3079 *Toll Free Tel:* 800-876-4467 *Fax:* 513-672-0213 *Web Site:* www.landofjazz.com, pg 993

Red Sky Studios, 184 Everett St, Allston, MA 02134 *Tel:* 617-903-3373 *E-mail:* mail@redsky-studios.com *Web Site:* redsky-studios.com, pg 993

RED Studios Hollywood, 846 N Cahuenga Blvd, Los Angeles, CA 90038 *Tel:* 323-463-0808 *Web Site:* www.redstudio.com, pg 993

Redco Audio Inc, 1701 Stratford Ave, Stratford, CT 06615 *Tel:* 203-502-7600 *Toll Free Tel:* 800-572-7280 *Fax:* 203-502-7610 *E-mail:* orders@redco.com *Web Site:* www.redco.com, pg 993

Rediscover Music, 705 S Washington St, Suite 3, Naperville, IL 60540 *Tel:* 630-305-0770 *Toll Free Tel:* 800-232-7328 (orders) *Fax:* 630-305-0782 *E-mail:* rediscovermusic@rediscovermusic.com *Web Site:* www.rediscovermusic.com, pg 993

Redman Movies & Stories, 1075 S 700 W, Salt Lake City, UT 84104 *Tel:* 801-978-9292 *Fax:* 801-978-2299 *E-mail:* info@redmanmovies.com *Web Site:* www.redmanmovies.com, pg 993

Redwood Audiobooks, 10375 Nichols Lane, Mendocino, CA 95460 *Tel:* 707-937-1225 *E-mail:* audiobks@mcn.org *Web Site:* www.universitypressaudiobooks.com, pg 993

Reed Presentations Inc (RPI), 17 Water St, Lebanon, NJ 08833 *Tel:* 908-753-8800 *Fax:* 908-753-8823 *E-mail:* info@reedpresentations.com *Web Site:* www.reedpresentations.com, pg 993

Reef Photo & Video, 2303 N Andrews Ave, Fort Lauderdale, FL 33311 *Tel:* 954-537-0644 *Toll Free Tel:* 877-453-8927 *Fax:* 954-537-0645 *Web Site:* reefphoto.com, pg 993

Reel Men Rentals Inc, 2225 E McDowell Rd, Phoenix, AZ 85006 *Tel:* 602-286-6800 *Fax:* 602-286-0080 *E-mail:* rentals@reelmen.com *Web Site:* www.reelmen.com, pg 994

Reel Picture, 5330 Eastgate Mall, San Diego, CA 92121 *Tel:* 858-587-0301 *Toll Free Tel:* 866 502-3472 (US & CN) *Fax:* 858-587-8838 *Web Site:* www.reelpicture.com, pg 994

Reelout Queer Film + Video Festival, 82 Sydenham St, Kingston, ON K7L 3H4, Canada *Tel:* 613-549-REEL (549-7335) *Web Site:* www.reelout.com, pg 1124

Reelsound Recording Co, 701 Southern Dr, Buda, TX 78610 *Tel:* 512-312-1610; 512-422-7098 (cell) *Web Site:* www.reelsound-usa.com, pg 994

ReelWorld Film Festival, 438 Parliament St, Suite 300, Toronto, ON M5A 3A2, Canada *Tel:* 416-598-7933 *E-mail:* info@reelworld.ca; events@reelworld.ca *Web Site:* www.reelworld.ca, pg 1125

Rees Associates, Rees Plaza at East Wharf, Suite 300, 9211 Lake Hefner Pkwy, Oklahoma City, OK 73120 *Tel:* 405-942-7337 *Fax:* 405-948-1261 *E-mail:* rees@rees-associates.com *Web Site:* www.rees.com, pg 994

Reference Recordings, PO Box 77225, San Francisco, CA 94107 *Tel:* 650-355-1845 *Toll Free Tel:* 800-336-8866 *Fax:* 650-355-1949 *E-mail:* referencerecordings@gmail.com *Web Site:* www.referencerecordings.com, pg 994

Refinery, 16 W 46 St, 12th fl, New York, NY 10036 *Tel:* 212-391-8166 *Fax:* 212-391-8783 *Web Site:* refinerynyc.com, pg 994

Regal Photo Products Inc/Arkay Corp, 2769 S 34 St, Milwaukee, WI 53215-3541 *Tel:* 414-645-2050 *Toll Free Tel:* 800-695-2055 (sales) *Fax:* 414-645-9515, pg 994

Regent Press Publishers & Printers, 2747 Regent St, Berkeley, CA 94705 *Tel:* 510-845-1196 *E-mail:* regentpress@mindspring.com *Web Site:* www.regentpress.net, pg 994

Regional Artist Project Grants Program, 227 W Trade St, Suite 250, Charlotte, NC 28202 *Tel:* 704-333-2272 *Fax:* 704-333-2720 *E-mail:* asc@artsandscience.org *Web Site:* www.artsandscience.org, pg 1125

Register Data Systems, 1691 Forsyth St, Macon, GA 31201 *Tel:* 478-745-5500 *Toll Free Tel:* 800-521-5222 *Fax:* 478-745-0500 *E-mail:* sales@registerdata.com, pg 994

REI - Radio Engineering Industries, 6534 "L" St, Omaha, NE 68117 *Tel:* 402-339-2200 *Toll Free Tel:* 800-228-9275 (sales); 877-726-4617 (tech support) *Fax:* 402-339-1704 *E-mail:* info@radioeng.com; orderdesk@radioeng.com *Web Site:* www.radioeng.com, pg 994

Reider Photography & Video Productions, 2174 Morris Ave, Union, NJ 07083 *Tel:* 908-688-8808 *E-mail:* info@njphotographer.com *Web Site:* www.njphotographer.com, pg 994

Reinhardt Productions Inc, 242-17 Van Zandt Ave, Douglaston, NY 11362 *Tel:* 718-225-4163 *Fax:* 212-338-0505, pg 994

Richard Reiter Productions Inc, 36 Catherine Ct, Cedar Grove, NJ 07009 *Tel:* 973-857-2935; 973-857-2557 *Fax:* 973-857-2935 *E-mail:* reiterjazz@gmail.com; reiterjazz@yahoo.com; reiterjazz@optonline.net *Web Site:* www.richardreiter.com, pg 994

Dick Reizner Film & Video, 7179 Via Maria, San Jose, CA 95139 *Tel:* 408-226-6339 *Web Site:* www.reizner.com, pg 994

Related Visual Inc, 2941 E Miraloma Ave, Suite 3, Anaheim, CA 92806 *Tel:* 714-535-1414 *Toll Free Tel:* 800-733-1415 *Fax:* 714-630-3518 *E-mail:* relatedvis@aol.com *Web Site:* www.relatedvisual.com, pg 994

Remote Audio Products, 220 Great Circle Rd, Suite 114, Nashville, TN 37228-1737 *Tel:* 615-256-3513 *Fax:* 615-634-2277 *E-mail:* info@remoteaudio.com *Web Site:* www.remoteaudio.com, pg 994

Renaissance Media, 909 Logan St, Suite 11F, Denver, CO 80204 *Tel:* 303-892-1415 *Web Site:* www.renaissancemedia.com, pg 994

Renegade Animation, 111 E Broadway, Suite 208, Glendale, CA 91205 *Tel:* 818-551-2351 *Fax:* 818-551-2350 *Web Site:* www.renegadeanimation.com, pg 994

Renkus-Heinz Inc, 19201 Cook St, Foothill Ranch, CA 92610-3501 *Tel:* 949-588-9997 *Fax:* 949-588-9514 *E-mail:* sales@renkus-heinz.com *Web Site:* www.renkus-heinz.com, pg 994

RentACamera.com, 1805 Hayes St, Nashville, TN 37203 *Tel:* 615-320-3200 *Toll Free Tel:* 855-588-2882 *E-mail:* info@tvcnashville.com *Web Site:* www.rentacamera.com, pg 995

Replicopy Digital Media Center, 2101 Midway Rd, Suite 200, Carrollton, TX 75006 *Tel:* 972-702-8388 *Fax:* 972-387-DUBS (387-3827) *E-mail:* replicopy@replicopy.com *Web Site:* www.replicopy.com, pg 995

Reprise Records Burbank, 3300 Warner Blvd, Burbank, CA 91505 *Tel:* 818-846-9090 *E-mail:* reprise@wbr.com *Web Site:* www.warnerbrosrecords.com, pg 995

Research Press Co, 2612 N Mattis Ave, Champaign, IL 61822 *Tel:* 217-352-3273 *Toll Free Tel:* 800-519-2707 *Fax:* 217-352-1221 *E-mail:* orders@researchpress.com *Web Site:* www.researchpress.com, pg 995

Research Technology International (RTI), 4700 Chase Ave, Lincolnwood, IL 60712-1689 *Tel:* 847-677-3000 *Toll Free Tel:* 800-323-7520 *Fax:* 847-677-1311 *Toll Free Fax:* 800-784-6733 *E-mail:* sales@rtico.com *Web Site:* www.rtico.com, pg 995

Residency Fellowship, 154 San Angelo Dr, Amherst, VA 24521 *Tel:* 434-946-7236 *Fax:* 434-946-7239 *E-mail:* vcca@vcca.com *Web Site:* www.vcca.com, pg 1125

The Resource Centre, Box 190, Waterloo, ON N2J 3Z9, Canada *Tel:* 519-885-0826 *Toll Free Tel:* 800-923-0330 *Fax:* 519-747-5629 *E-mail:* sales@theresourcecentre.com, pg 995

Resource Development Co LLC, 280 Daines St, Suite 200, Birmingham, MI 48009 *Tel:* 248-646-2300 *Toll Free Tel:* 800-360-7222 *Fax:* 248-646-0789 *E-mail:* inquiries@resourcedev.com *Web Site:* www.resourcedev.com, pg 995

RetinaVision Productions, 19 Barker Ave, Fairfax, CA 94930 *Tel:* 415-459-3926 *Toll Free Tel:* 877-738-4628, pg 995

Rev Up Transmedia, 20929 Ventura Blvd, Suite 47-212, Woodland Hills, CA 91364 *Tel:* 818-995-1719 *Toll Free Tel:* 877-372-0005 *Fax:* 818-979-9599 *E-mail:* info@revuptransmedia.com *Web Site:* revuptransmedia.com, pg 995

Revelli, PO Box 150098, San Rafael, CA 94915 *Tel:* 415-460-9898 *E-mail:* colorstyledesign@aol.com, pg 995

Revels Records, 80 Mount Auburn St, Watertown, MA 02472 *Tel:* 617-972-8300 *E-mail:* info@revels.org *Web Site:* www.revels.org, pg 995

Revolt Pro Media Inc, 7625 Hayvenhurst Ave, Suite 27, Van Nuys, CA 91406 *Tel:* 818-904-0001 *Fax:* 819-904-0005 *E-mail:* info@revoltpromedia.com *Web Site:* www.revoltpromedia.com, pg 995

Revolution Cinema Rentals, 1102 Arroyo St, Unit A, San Fernando, CA 91340 *Tel:* 818-837-5981 *Fax:* 818-837-5986 *E-mail:* info@revolutioncinemarentals.com *Web Site:* revolutioncinemarentals.com, pg 995

Revolution Lighting Technologies Inc, 177 Broad St, 12th fl, Stamford, CT 06901 *Tel:* 203-504-1111 *Fax:* 203-504-1150 *Web Site:* www.rvlti.com, pg 995

Rex, 610 SW 17 Ave, Portland, OR 97205 *Tel:* 503-238-4525 *E-mail:* info@rexpost.com *Web Site:* www.rexpost.com, pg 995

RF Industries, 7610 Miramar Rd, San Diego, CA 92126 *Tel:* 858-549-6340 *Toll Free Tel:* 800-233-1728 *Fax:* 858-549-6345 *E-mail:* rfi@rfindustries.com *Web Site:* www.rfindustries.com, pg 995

RF Specialties of California Inc, PO Box 16655, San Diego, CA 92176 *Tel:* 619-501-3936 *Fax:* 619-342-8511 *Web Site:* www.rfspec.com, pg 995

RF Specialties of Texas LLC, PO Box 1010, Newark, TX 76071-1010 *Tel:* 214-697-3477 (cell); 817-489-2730 *Toll Free Tel:* 800-537-1801 (Newark) *E-mail:* rfstx@swbell.net *Web Site:* www.rfspecialties.com, pg 996

RGB Spectrum, 950 Marina Village Pkwy, Alameda, CA 94501 *Tel:* 510-814-7000 *Fax:* 510-814-7026 *E-mail:* sales@rgb.com *Web Site:* www.rgb.com, pg 996

RGB Technology Inc, 590 Herndon Pkwy, Suite 500, Herndon, VA 20170-5267 *Tel:* 703-834-1500 *Fax:* 703-834-1506 *Web Site:* www.rgbtec.com, pg 996

RGH Lighting LLC, 546 W 48 St, New York, NY 10036 *Tel:* 212-244-8300 *Fax:* 212-244-8769 *E-mail:* info@scheimpflug.net *Web Site:* www.scheimpflug.net, pg 996

Rhino Home Video, 3400 W Olive Ave, Burbank, CA 91505 *Tel:* 818-238-6100; 410-568-3713 (intl) *Toll Free Tel:* 877-RHINO-51 (744-6651 - cust serv) *E-mail:* customerservice@rhino.com *Web Site:* www.rhino.com, pg 996

Rhode Island Film & Television Office, One Capitol Hill, 3rd fl, Providence, RI 02908 *Tel:* 401-222-3456; 401-222-6666 (hotline) *Fax:* 401-222-3018 *Web Site:* www.film.ri.gov, pg 1102

Rhode Island State Council on the Arts Fellowships & Grants Program, One Capitol Hill, 3rd fl, Providence, RI 02908 *Tel:* 401-222-3880 *Fax:* 401-222-3018 *E-mail:* info@arts.ri.gov *Web Site:* www.arts.ri.gov, pg 1125

Rhythm & Hues, 2100 E Grand Ave, Suite A, El Segundo, CA 90245-5024 *Tel:* 310-448-7500 *Fax:* 310-448-7600 *E-mail:* info-la@rhythm.com *Web Site:* www.rhythm.com, pg 996

Rhythmic Medicine, 10425 W 177 Terr, Olathe, KS 66062 *Tel:* 913-851-5100 *Fax:* 913-402-8510 *E-mail:* music@rhythmicmedicine.com *Web Site:* www.rhythmicmedicine.com, pg 996

Rhythms Productions (Tom Thumb Music), PO Box 786, Malibu, CA 90265-0786 *Tel:* 310-836-4678, pg 996

RIA Corp, 1615 W 2200 S, Suite B, Salt Lake City, UT 84119 *Tel:* 801-486-8822 *Fax:* 801-486-2741 *E-mail:* sales@riacorp.com *Web Site:* www.riacorp.com, pg 996

The RIAA® Gold® & Platinum® Awards, 1025 "F" St NW, 10th fl, Washington, DC 20004 *Tel:* 202-775-0101 *Web Site:* www.riaa.com, pg 1125

Rich-Heape Films Inc, 5952 Royal Lane, Suite 254, Dallas, TX 75230 *Tel:* 214-696-6916 *Toll Free Tel:* 888-600-2922 *Fax:* 214-696-6306 *Web Site:* www.richheape.com, pg 996

The Bart Richards Award for Media Criticism, 302 James Bldg, University Park, PA 16801-3867 *Tel:* 814-865-8801 *Fax:* 814-863-6134 *Web Site:* comm.psu.edu/news-events/awards/bart-richards-award-for-media-criticism, pg 1125

Lynda Richardson Photography, 7239 Lookout Dr, Richmond, VA 23225 *Tel:* 804-347-9668 *E-mail:* lynda@lyndarichardsonphotography.com *Web Site:* www.lyndarichardsonphotography.com, pg 996

Richie Media Productions LLC, 2035 Royal Lane, Suite 203, Dallas, TX 75229 *Tel:* 214-696-9040 *Web Site:* www.richiemedia.com, pg 996

Richmond Sound Design Ltd, 5264 Ross St, Vancouver, BC V5W 3K7, Canada *Web Site:* www.richmondsounddesign.com, pg 996

Richter Productions Inc, 521 E 14 St, Suite 4F, New York, NY 10009 *Tel:* 917-608-7427 *E-mail:* rrprod@aol.com; richter330@aol.com *Web Site:* www.richtervideos.com, pg 996

Richter Studios, 1143 W Rundell Place, Chicago, IL 60607 *Tel:* 312-861-9999 *Fax:* 312-997-2387 *E-mail:* info@richterstudios.com *Web Site:* www.richterstudios.com, pg 996

The Ridenhour Documentary Film Prize, 116 E 16 St, 8th fl, New York, NY 10003 *Tel:* 212-822-0250 *Fax:* 212-253-5356 *E-mail:* ridenhour@nationinstitute.org *Web Site:* www.ridenhour.org, pg 1125

Ridgecrest Film Commission, 634 N China Lake Blvd, Suite C, Ridgecrest, CA 93555 *Tel:* 760-375-8202 *Toll Free Tel:* 800-847-4830 *Fax:* 760-375-9850 *E-mail:* racvb@filmdeserts.com *Web Site:* www.filmdeserts.com, pg 1093

Riggs Production Associates Inc, 6532 Wahl Rd, Freeland, WA 98249 *Tel:* 360-331-5155 *Fax:* 360-331-4558 *E-mail:* sales@riggspfx.com *Web Site:* www.riggspfx.com, pg 996

Right Coast Recording Inc, 349 Chestnut St, Columbia, PA 17512-1259 *Tel:* 717-681-9801 *Fax:* 717-681-9801 *E-mail:* rightcoastrecording@gmail.com *Web Site:* www.rightcoastrecording.com, pg 997

Right Stuf Inc, 512 NE Main St, Grimes, IA 50111-0680 *Tel:* 515-986-1028 *Toll Free Tel:* 800-338-6827 *Fax:* 515-986-1129 *E-mail:* info@rightstuf.com *Web Site:* www.rightstuf.com, pg 997

RingSide Creative, 13320 Northend, Suite 3000, Oak Park, MI 48237 *Tel:* 248-548-2500 *E-mail:* info@ringsidecreative.com; newbiz@ringsidecreative.com *Web Site:* www.ringsidecreative.com, pg 997

Rink Rat Productions Inc, 2 Monk Lane, St John's, NL A1E 1M8, Canada *Tel:* 709-739-9055 *Fax:* 709-739-9065 *E-mail:* info@rinkratproductions.com *Web Site:* www.rinkratproductions.com, pg 997

The Rip-Tie Co, 883 San Leandro Blvd, San Leandro, CA 94577 *Tel:* 510-577-0200 *Toll Free Tel:* 800-7-RIPTIE (774-7843) *Fax:* 510-553-0160 *E-mail:* info@riptie.com *Web Site:* www.riptie.com, pg 997

Risk International & Associates Inc, 8803 W Ontario Ave, Littleton, CO 80128 *Tel:* 720-922-0707 *Fax:* 720-922-0707 *E-mail:* info@riskit.com *Web Site:* www.riskit.com, pg 997

Ritchie's Perfect Press, 500 Aloha, Suite 105, Seattle, WA 98109 *Tel:* 206-498-9208 (cell) *Web Site:* www.emeralda.com, pg 997

Ritz Camera & Image, 6900 Virginia Manor Rd, Suite 113, Beltsville, MD 20705 *Toll Free Tel:* 866-849-3045 *E-mail:* ritzpix@ritzcamera.com *Web Site:* www.ritzcamera.com, pg 997

River Road Recorders (RRR), 122 Crislaur Ave, Harahan, LA 70123-5025 *Tel:* 504-737-9880 *Fax:* 504-324-1920 *E-mail:* info@rivrd.com, pg 997

RJ Video Productions, 15585 Tilden St, San Leandro, CA 94579-2316 *Tel:* 510-357-6535 *Fax:* 510-357-6535 *E-mail:* tuffnut56@att.net, pg 997

RJS Productions, PO Box 739, Westminster, MD 21158 *Tel:* 410-876-6300 *Fax:* 410-857-0608, pg 997

RKO Pictures Inc, 2034 Broadway, Santa Monica, CA 90404 *Tel:* 310-277-0707 *Fax:* 310-566-8940 *E-mail:* info@rko.com *Web Site:* www.rko.com, pg 997

RLJ Entertainment Inc, 8515 Georgia Ave, Suite 650, Silver Spring, MD 20910 *Tel:* 301-608-2115 *Toll Free Tel:* 800-999-0212 *Fax:* 301-608-9312 *E-mail:* inquiries@rljentertainment.com *Web Site:* www.us.rljentertainment.com, pg 997

RLX Media LLC, 720 SW 12 Ave, Pompano Beach, FL 33069 *Tel:* 954-946-7575 *Toll Free Tel:* 800-555-9704 *Fax:* 954-946-7576 *E-mail:* info@rlxmedia.com *Web Site:* www.rlxmedia.com; www.rlxvideo.net, pg 997

RM Films International, PO Box 3748, Hollywood, CA 90078-3748 *Tel:* 323-466-7791 *Fax:* 323-461-4152 *E-mail:* rmf@rmfilms.com *Web Site:* www.rmfilms.com; www.russmeyer.com, pg 997

RNJ Electronics, 202 New Hwy, Amityville, NY 11701 *Tel:* 631-226-2700 *Toll Free Tel:* 800-645-5833 *Fax:* 631-226-2770 *Toll Free Fax:* 800-765-3291 *E-mail:* sales@rnjelectronics.com *Web Site:* www.rnjelectronics.com, pg 997

Road Pictures, 5420 N College Ave, Suite 201, Indianapolis, IN 46220 *Tel:* 317-267-9590 *Toll Free Tel:* 800-267-9590 *Fax:* 317-267-9677 *Web Site:* www.roadpictures.com, pg 997

Roadworthy Image Magnification, 1501 N Magnolia Ave, Chicago, IL 60642 *Tel:* 312-649-1800 *Toll Free Tel:* 800-C-DA SHOW (232-7469) *Fax:* 312-642-7441 *E-mail:* imag@atomicimaging.com *Web Site:* www.atomicimaging.com; www.golan.tv/roadworthy/index.html, pg 998

Robbins Media Inc, 375 Greenwich St, New York, NY 10013 *Tel:* 212-661-7670 *Fax:* 212-656-1997 *E-mail:* info@robbinsmedia.com *Web Site:* www.robbinsmedia.com, pg 998

Robertson Worldwide, 13611 Thornton Rd, Blue Island, IL 60406 *Toll Free Tel:* 800-323-5633 *Toll Free Fax:* 877-388-2420 *E-mail:* info@robertsonww.com *Web Site:* www.robertsonww.com, pg 998

Robertstock.com, 4203 Locust St, Philadelphia, PA 19104 *Tel:* 215-386-6300 *Toll Free Tel:* 800-786-6300 *Toll Free Fax:* 800-786-1920 *E-mail:* info@robertstock.com *Web Site:* www.robertstock.com, pg 998

Paul Robeson Awards, 49 Washington St, Newark, NJ 07102-3176 *Tel:* 973-596-6550 *Fax:* 973-642-0459 *E-mail:* nbff@newarkmuseum.org *Web Site:* www.newarkmuseum.org/nbff, pg 1125

Rochester/Finger Lakes Film & Video Office, 45 East Ave, Suite 400, Rochester, NY 14604-2294 *Tel:* 585-279-8308 *Fax:* 585-232-4822 *Web Site:* www.filmrochester.org, pg 1100

Rochester International Film Festival, PO Box 17746, Rochester, NY 14617 *Tel:* 585-234-7411 (voice mail) *E-mail:* president@rochesterfilmfest.org (use MOAS on subject) *Web Site:* www.rochesterfilmfest.org, pg 1125

Rockeffects Canada Inc/KABUKI, 42 Calder St, Shediac, NB E4P 1K8, Canada *Tel:* 506-577-6326 *Toll Free Tel:* 800-461-7625 *Fax:* 506-577-2832 *Toll Free Fax:* 800-461-4329 *E-mail:* info@kabuki.com *Web Site:* www.kabuki.com, pg 998

Rockie Awards, 21 St Clair Ave E, Suite 700, Toronto, ON M4T 1L9, Canada *Tel:* 416-921-3171 *E-mail:* info@achillesmedia.com *Web Site:* www.banffmediafestival.com, pg 1125

Rocking Horse Studio, 1380 Upper City Rd, Pittsfield, NH 03263 *Tel:* 603-512-5347 *E-mail:* info@rockinghorsestudio.com *Web Site:* www.rockinghorsestudio.com, pg 998

Rockland Colloid LLC, PO Box 3120, Oregon City, OR 97045-0306 *Tel:* 503-655-4152 (sales); 914-413-3000 (tech) *Toll Free Fax:* 866-737-0174 *E-mail:* info@rockaloid.com; orders@rockaloid.com *Web Site:* www.rockaloid.com, pg 998

Rocktown Media, 1361 Lincolnshire Dr, Harrisonburg, VA 22802 *Tel:* 540-433-7700 *Toll Free Tel:* 888-433-8700 *E-mail:* info@rocktown.tv *Web Site:* www.rocktown.tv, pg 998

Rockwell Communications Inc, 321 Burnham St, East Hartford, CT 06108 *Tel:* 860-528-9091 *Toll Free Tel:* 800-566-6681 *Fax:* 860-289-2334 *E-mail:* rockwellservice@aol.com *Web Site:* www.rockwellcommunications.com, pg 998

Rocky Mountain Audio/Video Productions Inc, 7950 S Lincoln St, Littleton, CO 80122 *Tel:* 303-730-1100 *Toll Free Tel:* 877-856-4644 *Fax:* 303-468-9811 *E-mail:* sales@rmavp.com *Web Site:* www.rmavp.com, pg 998

Roconex Corp, 20 Marybill Dr S, Troy, OH 45373 *Tel:* 937-339-2616 *Fax:* 937-339-1470 *E-mail:* info@roconex.com *Web Site:* www.roconex.com, pg 998

Rodeo Video Inc, 412 S Main, Snowflake, AZ 85937 *Tel:* 928-536-7111 *Toll Free Tel:* 800-331-1269 *Fax:* 928-536-7120 *E-mail:* info@rodeovideo.com *Web Site:* www.rodeovideo.com, pg 998

The Fred Rogers Co, 2100 Wharton St, Suite 700, Pittsburgh, PA 15203 *Tel:* 412-687-2990 *Fax:* 412-687-1226 *Web Site:* www.fredrogers.org, pg 998

Rohde & Schwarz Inc, 6821 Benjamin Franklin Dr, Columbia, MD 21046 *Tel:* 410-910-7800 *Toll Free Tel:* 888-837-8772 *Fax:* 410-910-7801 *E-mail:* info@rsa.rohde-schwarz.com *Web Site:* www.rohde-schwarz.us, pg 998

Roland Corp US, 5100 S Eastern Ave, Los Angeles, CA 90040-2938 *Tel:* 323-890-3700 *Fax:* 323-721-4875 *Web Site:* www.rolandus.com, pg 998

Glenn Roland Films, 10711 Wellworth Ave, Los Angeles, CA 90024 *Tel:* 310-475-0937 *Fax:* 310-475-0939, pg 998

Rollin Studios, 199 Green St, Brooklyn, NY 11222 *E-mail:* more@rollin-studios.com *Web Site:* www.rollin-studios.com, pg 998

Rolls Corp, 5968 S 350 W, Murray, UT 84107 *Tel:* 801-263-9053 *Fax:* 801-263-9068 *E-mail:* info@rolls.com *Web Site:* www.rolls.com, pg 999

Romar Learning, 6700 Woodlands Pkwy, Suite 230-292, Woodlands, TX 77382 *Tel:* 281-292-5508 *Fax:* 281-363-2309 *E-mail:* info@romarlearning.com *Web Site:* www.romarlearning.com, pg 999

Rosco Laboratories Inc, 52 Harbor View, Stamford, CT 06902 *Tel:* 203-708-8900 *Toll Free Tel:* 800-ROSCO NY (767-2669) *Fax:* 203-708-8919 *E-mail:* info@rosco.com *Web Site:* www.rosco.com, pg 999

Rose Brand, 4 Emerson Lane, Secaucus, NJ 07094 *Tel:* 201-809-1730 *Toll Free Tel:* 800-223-1624 *Fax:* 201-809-1851 *E-mail:* info@rosebrand.com *Web Site:* www.rosebrand.com, pg 999

Rose City Sound, 4811 SE 16 Ave, Portland, OR 97202 *Tel:* 503-238-6330 *Toll Free Tel:* 877-503-7673 *Fax:* 503-238-9872 *E-mail:* sales@rosecitysound.com *Web Site:* www.rosecitysound.com, pg 999

Rose Packaging & Design Inc, 4000 Sopris Mountain Rd, Basalt, CO 81621-9179 *Tel:* 970-927-6515 *Toll Free Tel:* 800-308-1003 *Fax:* 970-927-6514 *E-mail:* sales@rosepkg.com *Web Site:* www.rosepkg.com, pg 999

Judson Rosebush Co Inc, 630 Ninth Ave, Suite 507, New York, NY 10036 *Tel:* 212-581-3000 *E-mail:* judson@rosebush.com *Web Site:* www.rosebush.com, pg 999

Peter Rosen Productions Inc, 9 E 78 St, Suite 5-A, New York, NY 10075 *Tel:* 212-535-8927 *Fax:* 212-517-5337 *E-mail:* rosenprod@aol.com *Web Site:* www.peterrosenproductions.com, pg 999

The Rosenthal Group, 10625 Cohasset St, Sun Valley, CA 91352 *Tel:* 818-252-1010 *Fax:* 818-252-1070 *Web Site:* www.therosenthalgroup.com, pg 999

The Madeline Dane Ross Award, 40 W 45 St, New York, NY 10036 *Tel:* 212-626-9220 *Fax:* 212-626-9210 *Web Site:* www.opcofamerica.org, pg 1125

Mary Riepma Ross Media Arts Center, University of Nebraska-Lincoln, 313 N 13 St, Lincoln, NE 68588 *Tel:* 402-472-9100; 402-472-5353 *Fax:* 402-472-2576 *Web Site:* www.theross.org, pg 999

Ross Video Ltd, 8 John St, Iroquois, ON K0E 1K0, Canada *Tel:* 613-652-4886 *Fax:* 613-652-4425 *E-mail:* solutions@rossvideo.com *Web Site:* www.rossvideo.com, pg 999

Rossman Audio LLC, 597 W Hillside Ave, Suite 100, State College, PA 16803-1509 *Tel:* 814-234-2044 *Fax:* 814-689-1036 *E-mail:* info@rossmanaudio.com *Web Site:* www.rossmanaudio.com, pg 1000

Rough House, 550 Bryant St, San Francisco, CA 94107-1217 *Tel:* 415-561-4544 *Fax:* 415-543-8390 *E-mail:* info@roughhouse.com *Web Site:* www.roughhouse.com, pg 1000

Roundabout Entertainment Inc, 217 S Lake St, Burbank, CA 91502 *Tel:* 818-842-9300 *Fax:* 818-842-9301 *E-mail:* info@roundabout.com *Web Site:* www.roundabout.com, pg 1000

Rounder Records, 1209 Pine St, Suite 100, Nashville, TN 37203 *Web Site:* www.rounder.com, pg 1000

Rovi Corp, 2830 De La Cruz Blvd, Santa Clara, CA 95050 *Tel:* 408-562-8400 *Fax:* 408-567-1800 *Web Site:* www.rovicorp.com, pg 1000

Ron Roy Productions/Moodtapes, 2219 W Olive, Suite 312, Burbank, CA 91506 *E-mail:* info@moodtapes.com *Web Site:* www.moodtapes.com, pg 1000

RPG Diffusor Systems Inc, 651-C Commerce Dr, Upper Marlboro, MD 20774 *Tel:* 301-249-0044 *Fax:* 301-390-3602 *E-mail:* info@rpginc.com *Web Site:* www.rpginc.com, pg 1000

RPM-PSI, 8750 Shirley Ave, Northridge, CA 91324 *Tel:* 818-349-8680 *Fax:* 818-772-7577 *E-mail:* info@rpm-psi.com *Web Site:* www.rpm-psi.com, pg 1000

RSS Distributors, 7930 Old Auction Rd, Manheim, PA 17545 *Toll Free Tel:* 800-233-0175 *E-mail:* orders@rssd.com *Web Site:* www.rssd.com, pg 1000

RTDNA Edward R Murrow Awards, The National Press Bldg, 529 14 St NW, Suite 425, Washington, DC 20045 *Tel:* 202-659-6510 *Fax:* 202-223-4007 *E-mail:* awards@rtdna.org *Web Site:* www.rtdna.org, pg 1125

RTS Inc, 40-11 Burt Dr, Deer Park, NY 11729 *Tel:* 631-242-6801 *Fax:* 631-242-6808 *E-mail:* rtsinc@rcn.com *Web Site:* www.rtsphoto.com, pg 1000

RTZ Audio Visual, 6725 Santa Barbara Ct, Suite 103, Elkridge, MD 21075 *Tel:* 443-757-0480 *Toll Free Tel:* 800-543-0582 *Fax:* 443-757-0487 *E-mail:* sales@rtzav.com *Web Site:* www.rtzav.com, pg 1000

Rucinski & Reetz Communications LLC, 2155 Terrebonne, Mosinee, WI 54455 *Tel:* 715-355-9159; 715-241-7316 *Web Site:* www.rucinskireetz.com, pg 1000

Ben Rudnick & Friends, PO Box 1426, Arlington, MA 02474 *Tel:* 781-643-5137 *Web Site:* www.benrudnick.com, pg 1000

RuffHouse LLC, 2823 Lariat Trail, Austin, TX 78734 *Tel:* 512-965-2957 *E-mail:* info@ruffhousin.com *Web Site:* www.ruffhousin.com, pg 1000

Rule Broadcast Systems, 1284 Soldier's Field Rd, Boston, MA 02135 *Tel:* 617-277-2200 *Toll Free Tel:* 800-785-3266 *Fax:* 617-277-6800 *E-mail:* answers@rule.com *Web Site:* www.rule.com, pg 1000

Rum Jungle Media, 5295 Eden Rd, Mound, MN 55364 *Tel:* 952-472-5525 *E-mail:* rumjungle@rumjungle.com *Web Site:* www.rumjungle.com, pg 1000

Running Pony Productions LLC, 1770 Kirby Pkwy, Suite 118, Memphis, TN 38138 *Tel:* 901-683-6693 *Toll Free Tel:* 877-891-7669 *Fax:* 901-683-3093 *E-mail:* info@runningpony.com *Web Site:* www.runningpony.com, pg 1000

Russ Bassett Corp, 8189 Byron Rd, Whittier, CA 90606-2615 *Tel:* 562-945-2445 *Toll Free Tel:* 800-350-2445 *Fax:* 562-698-8972 *E-mail:* info@russbassett.com *Web Site:* www.russbassett.com, pg 1001

Russ InVision Co/AbridgeClub.com, 3219 Conquista Ave, Long Beach, CA 90808 *Tel:* 562-421-1836 *Toll Free Tel:* 888-421-7488 *Fax:* 562-420-9101 *E-mail:* info@abridgeclub.com *Web Site:* abridgeclub.com, pg 1001

Russell Industries Inc, 40 Horton Ave, Lynbrook, NY 11563 *Tel:* 516-536-5000 *Toll Free Tel:* 800-645-2202 *Fax:* 516-764-5747 *Toll Free Fax:* 800-645-2200 *E-mail:* sales@russellind.com *Web Site:* www.russellind.com, pg 1001

Norman Russell Design, 5266 Hollister Ave, Suite 233, Santa Barbara, CA 93111 *Tel:* 805-964-9375 *Fax:* 805-964-9386 *E-mail:* normruss@normanrusselldesign.com *Web Site:* www.normanrusselldesign.com, pg 1001

Russound, 5 Forbes Rd, Newmarket, NH 03857 *Tel:* 603-659-5170 *Toll Free Tel:* 800-638-8055 (US) *Fax:* 603-659-5388 *E-mail:* sales@russound.com; tech@russound.com *Web Site:* www.russound.com, pg 1001

S I Video Sales Group, 1318 S Carlisle St, Philadelphia, PA 19146 *Tel:* 267-519-2222 *Web Site:* www.sivideo.com; www.capclassics.com; takinglasvegas.com, pg 1001

Saah Video, 12221 Parklawn Dr, Rockville, MD 20852 *Tel:* 301-770-6699 *Toll Free Tel:* 800-225-9690 *Fax:* 301-770-3250 *Web Site:* www.saahvideo.com, pg 1001

Sabine® Inc, 13301 US Hwy 441, Alachua, FL 32615-8544 *Tel:* 386-418-2000 *Toll Free Tel:* 800-626-7394 *Fax:* 386-418-2001 *E-mail:* sabine@sabine.com *Web Site:* www.sabine.com, pg 1001

Sacramento Film Commission, 1608 "I" St, Sacramento, CA 95814-2042 *Tel:* 916-808-7777 *Fax:* 916-808-7788 *Web Site:* www.filmsacramento.com, pg 1093

Sacramento Theatrical Lighting Ltd (STL), 950 Richards Blvd, Sacramento, CA 95811 *Tel:* 916-447-3258 *Toll Free Tel:* 800-283-2785 *Fax:* 916-447-5012 *E-mail:* info@stlltd.com *Web Site:* www.stlltd.com, pg 1001

SADiE Inc, 21 Pine St, Rockaway, NJ 07866 *Tel:* 973-983-9577 *Fax:* 973-983-9588 *E-mail:* sales@prismmpi.com *Web Site:* www.sadie.com, pg 1001

Safe Harbor Computers, 530 W Oklahoma Ave, Suite 500, Milwaukee, WI 53207 *Tel:* 414-615-4560 *Toll Free Tel:* 800-544-6599 *Fax:* 414-615-4567 *E-mail:* sales@sharbor.com *Web Site:* www.sharbor.com, pg 1001

Sagebrush Video Productions, 2304 County Rd 370, Otis, KS 67565 *Tel:* 785-222-3313 *Toll Free Tel:* 800-457-3453 *Web Site:* www.sagebrushvideo.com, pg 1001

Sahara Records & Filmworks Entertainment Co, 10573 W Pico Blvd, Suite 352, Los Angeles, CA 90064-2348 *Tel:* 310-948-9652 *E-mail:* info@edmsahara.com *Web Site:* www.edmsahara.com, pg 1001

St Augustine, Ponte Vedra & The Beaches Visitors and Convention Bureau, 29 Old Mission Ave, St Augustine, FL 32084 *Tel:* 904-829-1711 *Toll Free Tel:* 800-653-2489 *Web Site:* www.floridashistoriccoast.com, pg 1096

St Barth Film Festival, 410 W 24 St, New York, NY 10011 *Tel:* 212-989-8004 *Fax:* 212-727-1774 *E-mail:* staff@stbarthff.org *Web Site:* www.stbarthff.org, pg 1126

St Bede's Publications, 271 N Main St, Petersham, MA 01366-9503 *Tel:* 978-724-3213, pg 1001

Saint Elmo Soundstage, 415 E St Elmo, Austin, TX 78745 *Tel:* 512-535-5113 *E-mail:* contact@saintelmo.info *Web Site:* saintelmo.info, pg 1001

St John's International Women's Film Festival, 28 Cochrane St, Suite 101, St John's, NL A1C 3L3, Canada *Tel:* 709-754-3141 *E-mail:* info@womensfilmfestival.com *Web Site:* www.womensfilmfestival.com, pg 1126

St Petersburg/Clearwater Film Commission, 8200 Bryan Dairy Rd, Suite 200, Largo, FL 33777 *Tel:* 727-464-7241 *Toll Free Tel:* 877-352-3224 *E-mail:* info@filmspc.com *Web Site:* www.filmspc.com, pg 1096

Saint Vincent & The Grenadines Tourist Office, 801 Second Ave, 1st fl, New York, NY 10017 *Tel:* 212-687-4981 *Toll Free Tel:* 800-729-1726 *Fax:* 212-949-5946 *E-mail:* svgtony@aol.com *Web Site:* www.discoversvg.com, pg 1100

Salesmaker Carts, 403 Roberts Ave, Louisville, KY 40214 *Toll Free Tel:* 800-281-2278 *Toll Free Fax:* 800-418-2525 *Web Site:* www.salesmakercarts.com, pg 1001

Salina Film Commission, 120 W Ash St, Salina, KS 67402 *Tel:* 785-827-9301 *Fax:* 785-827-9758 *E-mail:* info@salinakansas.org *Web Site:* www.salinakansas.org, pg 1097

Sally Mountain Park Bluegrass Festival, Rte 2, Box 15, Greentop, MO 63546 *Tel:* 660-949-2345 *E-mail:* festival@marktwain.net *Web Site:* www.sallymountainshow.com, pg 1126

Charles M Salter Associates Inc, 130 Sutter St, Suite 500, San Francisco, CA 94104 *Tel:* 415-397-0442 *Fax:* 415-397-0454 *E-mail:* info@cmsalter.com *Web Site:* www.cmsalter.com, pg 1001

Steven Samler Music & Sound, 1298 Green Knolls Dr, Buffalo Grove, IL 60089 *Tel:* 847-400-5080 *Fax:* 815-366-8227 *Web Site:* www.stevensamler.com, pg 1002

Samson Technologies Corp, 45 Gilpin Ave, Hauppauge, NY 11788-4723 *Tel:* 631-784-2200 *Fax:* 631-784-2201 *E-mail:* info@samsontech.com *Web Site:* www.samsontech.com, pg 1002

Samsung Electronics America, 85 Challenger Rd, Ridgefield Park, NJ 07660 *Toll Free Tel:* 800-SAMSUNG (726-7864) *Fax:* 864-752-1632 *Web Site:* www.samsung.com, pg 1002

The Samuels Co, Box 770874, Houston, TX 77215-0874 *Tel:* 281-564-1055 *Fax:* 530-420-4631 *E-mail:* staff@thesamuelsco.com *Web Site:* www.thesamuelsco.com, pg 1002

Samy's Camera, 431 S Fairfax Ave, Los Angeles, CA 90036 *Tel:* 323-938-4400 *Toll Free Tel:* 800-321-4726 *Fax:* 323-937-2919 *E-mail:* lacamera@samys.com *Web Site:* www.samys.com, pg 1002

San Antonio Film Commission, 203 S Saint Mary's St, Suite 360, San Antonio, TX 78205 *Tel:* 210-207-6730 *Toll Free Tel:* 800-447-3372 *Fax:* 210-207-4526 *E-mail:* filmsa@filmsanantonio.com *Web Site:* www.filmsanantonio.com, pg 1103

San Antonio Film Festival, 1633 Babcock Rd, Suite 111, San Antonio, TX 78229 *Tel:* 210-885-5888 *E-mail:* safilm@gmail.com *Web Site:* www.safilm.com, pg 1126

San Diego Film Festival, 2683 Via de la Valle, Suite G210, Del Mar, CA 92014 *Tel:* 619-818-2221 *E-mail:* info@sdff.org *Web Site:* www.sdfilmfest.com, pg 1126

San Diego Stage & Lighting Supply Inc, 2203 Verus St, San Diego, CA 92154 *Tel:* 619-299-2300 *Fax:* 619-299-0058 *E-mail:* info@sdstagelighting.com *Web Site:* www.sdstagelighting.com, pg 1002

San Francisco Black Film Festival, PO Box 15490, San Francisco, CA 94115 *Tel:* 415-400-4602 *Fax:* 415-346-9046 *E-mail:* sfbff@sfbff.org *Web Site:* www.sfbff.org, pg 1126

San Francisco Film Commission, City Hall, Rm 473, One Dr Carlton B Goodlett Place, San Francisco, CA 94102-4649 *Tel:* 415-554-6241 *Fax:* 415-554-6503 *E-mail:* film@sfgov.org *Web Site:* www.filmsf.org, pg 1094

San Francisco International Film Festival, 39 Mesa St, Suite 110, The Presidio, San Francisco, CA 94129-1025 *Tel:* 415-561-5000 *Fax:* 415-440-1760 *E-mail:* info@sffs.org *Web Site:* festival.sffs.org; www.sffs.org; www.sf360.org, pg 1126

San Francisco International LGBT Film Festival, 145 Ninth St, Suite 300, San Francisco, CA 94103 *Tel:* 415-703-8650 *Fax:* 415-861-1404 *E-mail:* info@frameline.org *Web Site:* www.frameline.org, pg 1126

San Francisco Jewish Film Festival, 145 Ninth St, Suite 200, San Francisco, CA 94103 *Tel:* 415-621-0556 *Fax:* 415-621-0568 *E-mail:* jewishfilm@sfjff.org *Web Site:* www.sfjff.org, pg 1126

San Jose Film & Video Commission, c/o San Jose Convention & Visitors Bureau, 408 Almaden Blvd, San Jose, CA 95110 *Tel:* 408-295-9600 *Toll Free Tel:* 800-SAN-JOSE (726-5673) *Web Site:* www.sanjose.org/film, pg 1094

San Juan School District Heritage Language Resource Center, 28 W 200 N, Blanding, UT 84511 *Tel:* 435-678-1230; 435-678-1229 *Fax:* 435-678-1283 *Web Site:* media.sjsd.org, pg 1002

San Luis Obispo County Film Commission, 811 El Capitan, Suite 200, San Luis Obispo, CA 93401 *Tel:* 805-541-8000 *Fax:* 805-543-9498 *Web Site:* www.sanluisobispocounty.com, pg 1094

San Mateo County Film Commission, Seabreeze Plaza, Suite 410, 111 Anza Blvd, Burlingame, CA 94010 *Tel:* 650-348-7600 *Fax:* 650-348-7687 *E-mail:* info@filmsanmateocounty.com *Web Site:* www.sanmateocountycvb.com, pg 1092

Sanako Inc, 500 Linden Oaks, Rochester, NY 14625 *Toll Free Tel:* 888-611-4785 *Toll Free Fax:* 888-389-3858 *E-mail:* info@sanako.com *Web Site:* www.sanako.com, pg 1002

Sand Box Studio, 555 Minnesota St, San Francisco, CA 94107 *Tel:* 415-550-8732 *E-mail:* inquiries@sandboxstudio.com *Web Site:* www.sandboxstudio.com, pg 1002

Sandusky Lee Corp, PO Box 6, Littlestown, PA 17340 *Toll Free Tel:* 800-233-7076 *Fax:* 717-359-4414 *E-mail:* customerserv@sanduskycabinets.com *Web Site:* www.sanduskylee.com, pg 1002

Sano Videos, Columbia Plaza, 2450 Virginia Ave NW, Suite E 322, Washington, DC 20037 *Tel:* 202-293-0454, pg 1002

Santa Barbara County Film Commission, 500 E Montecito St, Santa Barbara, CA 93103 *Tel:* 805-966-9222 *Toll Free Tel:* 800-676-1266 *Fax:* 805-966-1728 *Web Site:* www.filmsantabarbara.com, pg 1094

Santa Barbara International Film Festival, 1528 Chapala St, Suite 203, Santa Barbara, CA 93101 *Tel:* 805-963-0023 *Fax:* 805-962-2524 *E-mail:* generalinfo@sbfilmfestival.org *Web Site:* sbiff.org, pg 1126

Santa Barbara Location Services, 403 Orilla del Mar, Unit 2, Santa Barbara, CA 93108 *Tel:* 805-969-5555; 805-565-1562 *Fax:* 805-969-9595 *E-mail:* production@sblsonline.com *Web Site:* www.santabarbara-locations.com, pg 1002

Santa Clarita Film Office, 23920 Valencia Blvd, Suite 100, Santa Clarita, CA 91355 *Tel:* 661-284-1425 *Fax:* 661-286-4001 *E-mail:* film@santa-clarita.com *Web Site:* www.filmsantaclarita.com, pg 1094

Santa Clarita Studios, 25135 Anza Dr, Santa Clarita, CA 91355 *Tel:* 661-294-2000 *Fax:* 661-294-2020 *E-mail:* mike@sc-studios.com *Web Site:* www.santaclaritastudios.com, pg 1002

Santa Monica Mountains NRA, 401 W Hillcrest Dr, Thousand Oaks, CA 91360 *Tel:* 805-370-2301 *Fax:* 805-370-2351 *Web Site:* www.nps.gov/samo, pg 1094

SANYO Fisher Co, 2055 Sanyo Ave, San Diego, CA 92154 *Tel:* 619-661-1134 *Fax:* 619-661-6795 *Web Site:* us.sanyo.com; www.fisherav.com, pg 1002

SAPSIS Rigging Inc, 233 N Lansdowne Ave, Lansdowne, PA 19050 *Tel:* 215-228-0888 *Toll Free Tel:* 800-SAPSIS-1 (727-7471) *Fax:* 215-228-1786 *E-mail:* sales@sapsis-rigging.com *Web Site:* www.sapsis-rigging.com, pg 1002

Sarasota County Film & Entertainment Office, 1680 Fruitville Rd, Suite 402, Sarasota, FL 34236 *Tel:* 941-309-1200 *Fax:* 941-309-1209 *E-mail:* info@filmsarasota.com *Web Site:* www.filmsarasota.com, pg 1096

Sargent-Welch, 5100 W Henrietta Rd, Rochester, NY 14692-9012 *Toll Free Tel:* 800-727-4368 *Toll Free Fax:* 800-676-2540 *E-mail:* sargentwelchcs@vwr.com *Web Site:* www.sargentwelch.com, pg 1002

SAS Institute Inc, 100 SAS Campus Dr, Cary, NC 27513-2414 *Tel:* 919-677-8000 *Toll Free Tel:* 800-727-0025 *Fax:* 919-677-4444 *Web Site:* www.sas.com, pg 1002

Sascom Marketing Group Inc, 34 Nelson St, Oakville, ON L6L 3H6, Canada *Tel:* 905-469-8080 *Fax:* 647-439-1510 *Web Site:* www.sascom.com, pg 1003

Satellite Broadcasting & Communications Association, 1100 17 St NW, Suite 1150, Washington, DC 20036 *Tel:* 202-349-3620 *Toll Free Tel:* 800-541-5981 *Fax:* 202-349-3621 *E-mail:* info@sbca.org *Web Site:* www.sbca.com, pg 1088

Satellite Center, 2535 Williams Blvd, Kenner, LA 70062 *Tel:* 504-466-3474 *Toll Free Tel:* 800-256-4010 *Web Site:* satctr.com, pg 1003

Satellite Digital Teleproductions (SDTV), 4004 La Salle St, San Diego, CA 92110-5124 *Tel:* 619-293-7777 *Toll Free Tel:* 800-SKY-PROD (759-7763 US) *Fax:* 619-223-3626 *E-mail:* info@sdtv.com *Web Site:* www.sdtv.com, pg 1003

Satellite Media Production, 8379 Inspiration Ave, Walkersville, MD 21793 *Tel:* 301-845-2737 *Toll Free Tel:* 800-747-0856 *Web Site:* www.satellitemediaproduction.com; www.oldietv.com, pg 1003

Satellite Technology Systems Inc, 4702 State Rte 176, Unit F, Crystal Lake, IL 60014 *Tel:* 815-482-0224 *Toll Free Tel:* 800-838-1472 *Fax:* 815-568-8478 *E-mail:* sts@mc.net *Web Site:* www.satellitetechsys.com, pg 1003

Saturn Awards, 334 W 54 St, Los Angeles, CA 90037 *Tel:* 323-752-5811 *Web Site:* www.saturnawards.org, pg 1126

Saturn Productions Inc, 305 E 86 St, Suite 14-JW, New York, NY 10028 *Tel:* 212-348-7300 *Fax:* 212-426-7907 *E-mail:* saturnnyc@aol.com, pg 1003

Saturn Studios, PO Box 3687, Hollywood, CA 90078-3687 *Tel:* 323-871-4134 *Web Site:* rollingplanet.com, pg 1003

Alwin Sauers Audio Productions (ASAP), PO Box 50957, Oxnard, CA 93031 *Tel:* 206-484-6144 *E-mail:* alwinaudio@yahoo.com, pg 1003

Savage Universal Corp, 550 E Elliot Rd, Chandler, AZ 85225 *Tel:* 480-632-1320 *Toll Free Tel:* 800-624-8891 *Fax:* 480-632-1322 *Web Site:* savageuniversal.com, pg 1003

Savant Systems LLC, 45 Perseverance Way, Hyannis, MA 02601 *Tel:* 508-683-2500 *Fax:* 508-683-2600 *Web Site:* www.savantsystems.com, pg 1003

Save the Children Federation Inc, 54 Wilton Rd, Westport, CT 06880 *Tel:* 203-221-4030 *Toll Free Tel:* 800-728-3843 *E-mail:* twebster@savechildren.org *Web Site:* www.savethechildren.org, pg 1003

SBS Productions, 1646 Livonia Ave, Los Angeles, CA 90035 *Tel:* 310-557-1545 *E-mail:* eindigo2@pacbell.net, pg 1003

SC Media Canada, 2100 Onesime-Gagnon, Lachine, QC H8T 3M8, Canada *Tel:* 514-780-0808 *Toll Free Tel:* 888-595-3966 *Fax:* 514-780-1604 *Toll Free Fax:* 800-790-2000 *E-mail:* information@scmediacanada.com *Web Site:* www.scmediacanada.com, pg 1003

Scala Inc, 350 Eagleview Blvd, Suite 350, Exton, PA 19341 *Tel:* 610-363-3350 *Toll Free Tel:* 888-SCALA-96 (722-5296) *Fax:* 610-363-4010 *E-mail:* marketing@scala.com *Web Site:* scala.com, pg 1003

Sceno Plus, 5423 ave de Lorimier, Montreal, QC H2H 2C3, Canada *Tel:* 514-529-4364 *Fax:* 514-529-9164 *E-mail:* project@sceno-plus.com *Web Site:* www.sceno-plus.com, pg 1004

Schafer World Communications Corp, PO Box 1047, Marion, VA 24354-1047 *Tel:* 276-783-2000, pg 1004

Scheimpflug Digital, 546 W 48 St, New York, NY 10036 *Tel:* 212-244-8300 *Fax:* 212-244-8769 *E-mail:* info@scheimpflug.net *Web Site:* www.scheimpflug.net, pg 1004

Randall Schiller Productions, 1207 Fifth Ave, San Francisco, CA 94122 *Tel:* 415-661-7553 *Fax:* 415-566-6238 *E-mail:* rsp7@pacbell.net *Web Site:* www.randallschillerproductions.com, pg 1004

Schiller's Audio-Visual, 9240 Manchester Rd, St Louis, MO 63144-2636 *Tel:* 314-968-3650 *Toll Free Tel:* 800-366-7244 *Fax:* 314-968-1184 *E-mail:* sales@schillers.com; av@schillers.com *Web Site:* www.schillersav.com, pg 1004

Peter Schleger Co, 200 Central Park S, Suite 27B, New York, NY 10019-1415 *Tel:* 212-245-4973 *E-mail:* schleger@nyc.rr.com, pg 1004

Schlessinger Media, PO Box 580, Wynnewood, PA 19096-0580 *Tel:* 610-645-4000 *Toll Free Tel:* 800-843-3620 *Fax:* 610-645-4040 *E-mail:* comments@libraryvideo.com *Web Site:* www.libraryvideo.com, pg 1004

Schneider Optics Inc, 285 Oser Ave, Hauppauge, NY 11788 *Tel:* 631-761-5000 *Toll Free Tel:* 800-645-7239 *Fax:* 631-761-5090 *E-mail:* info@schneideroptics.com *Web Site:* www.schneideroptics.com, pg 1004

Scholastic Canada Ltd, 175 Hillmount Rd, Markham, ON L6C 1Z7, Canada *Tel:* 905-887-7323 *Toll Free Tel:* 800-268-3860 *Fax:* 905-887-1131 *Toll Free Fax:* 800-387-4944 *E-mail:* custserv@scholastic.ca *Web Site:* www.scholastic.ca, pg 1004

Scholastic Library Publishing, 90 Sherman Tpke, Danbury, CT 06816 *Toll Free Tel:* 800-621-1115 (cust serv) *Toll Free Fax:* 866-783-4361 *Web Site:* www.scholastic.com/aboutscholastic/librarypublishing.htm, pg 1004

Scholastic Media, 557 Broadway, New York, NY 10012 *Fax:* 212-343-7592 *Web Site:* www.scholastic.com/aboutscholastic/librarypublishing.htm, pg 1004

School Media Associates LLC, 5815 Live Oak Pkwy, Suite 2-B, Norcross, GA 30093-1700 *Tel:* 770-441-0600 *Toll Free Tel:* 800-451-5226 (orders) *Fax:* 770-441-8529 *E-mail:* info@smavideo.net *Web Site:* www.smavideo.net, pg 1004

School Specialty Inc, W6316 Design Dr, Greenville, WI 54942 *Tel:* 419-589-1425 *Toll Free Tel:* 888-388-3224 *Fax:* 419-589-1600 *Toll Free Fax:* 888-388-6344 *E-mail:* internationalorders@schoolspecialty.com *Web Site:* www.schoolspecialty.com, pg 1004

Schoolhouse Audio Visual, 1000 20 St, Plano, TX 75074 *Tel:* 972-423-5874 *Toll Free Tel:* 800-338-8116 *Fax:* 972-424-3501 *E-mail:* sav@schoolhouseav.com *Web Site:* www.schoolhouseav.com, pg 1004

Schroder Music Co, PO Box 2067, Berkeley, CA 94702-0067 *Tel:* 510-843-0533 *Fax:* 510-834-5201 *Web Site:* www.sisterschoice.com, pg 1004

SCI Television Productions LLC, 160 E Grand Ave, Suite 5W, Chicago, IL 60611 *Tel:* 312-643-2080 *E-mail:* info@scitvproductions.com *Web Site:* www.scitvproductions.com, pg 1004

Science First/STARLAB™, 86475 Gene Lasserre Blvd, Yulee, FL 32097 *Tel:* 904-225-5558 *Toll Free Tel:* 800-875-3214 *Fax:* 904-225-2228 *E-mail:* starlab@starlab.com; info@starlab.com *Web Site:* starlab.com, pg 1005

Science for Kids, 1941 Brooke Dr, New Hope, PA 18938 *Tel:* 215-794-7718 *Fax:* 215-794-7718, pg 1005

Science Museum of Minnesota, 120 W Kellogg Blvd, St Paul, MN 55102 *Tel:* 651-221-9444 *Toll Free Tel:* 800-221-9444 *Fax:* 651-221-4533 *E-mail:* info@smm.org *Web Site:* www.smm.org, pg 1005

Science Seeking, 705 Gurley Ave, Gallup, NM 87301 *Tel:* 505-863-7647 *Web Site:* fs.gallup.unm.edu, pg 1005

Science Television Co, 460 W 24 St, Unit 3A, New York, NY 10011 *Tel:* 917-593-2537 *E-mail:* admin@scitv.com *Web Site:* www.scitv.com, pg 1005

Score Productions Inc, 219 E 49 St, New York, NY 10017 *Tel:* 212-751-2510 *Fax:* 212-754-6305 *E-mail:* score@scoreproductions.com *Web Site:* www.artgraphica.com/preview/ScoreProductions/index.html, pg 1005

Scott Resources Inc, 401 Hickory St, Fort Collins, CO 80524-1125 *Tel:* 970-484-7445 *Toll Free Tel:* 800-289-9299 *Fax:* 970-484-1198 *E-mail:* custserv@amep.com *Web Site:* amep.com, pg 1005

Ron Scott Inc, 2020 Colquitt St, Houston, TX 77098 *Web Site:* www.ronscott.com; www.qfx.com, pg 1005

Screamfest® Horror Film Festival & Screenplay Competition, 8840 Wilshire Blvd, 3rd fl, Beverly Hills, CA 90211 *Tel:* 310-358-3273 *Fax:* 310-358-3272 *E-mail:* info@screamfestla.com *Web Site:* www.screamfestla.com, pg 1126

Screen Actors Guild & American Federation of Television & Radio Artists (SAG-AFTRA), 5757 Wilshire Blvd, 7th fl, Los Angeles, CA 90036-3600 *Tel:* 323-954-1600 (former SAG); 323-634-8100 (former AFTRA) *Toll Free Tel:* 855-SAG-AFTRA (724-2387) *Fax:* 323-634-8194 *E-mail:* sagaftrainfo@sagaftra.org *Web Site:* www.sagaftra.org/ny, pg 1088

Screen Door Entertainment Inc, PO Box 1002, Agoura Hills, CA 91376 *Tel:* 818-781-5600 *E-mail:* info@sdetv.com *Web Site:* www.sdetv.com, pg 1005

The Screen Works®, 2201 W Fulton St, Chicago, IL 60612 *Tel:* 312-243-8265 *Toll Free Tel:* 800-294-8111 *Fax:* 312-243-8290 *E-mail:* screens@thescreenworks.com *Web Site:* www.thescreenworks.com, pg 1005

Scripps Networks, 9721 Sherrill Blvd, Knoxville, TN 37932 *Tel:* 865-694-2700 *Fax:* 865-693-6576 *Web Site:* www.scrippsnetworks.com, pg 1005

Scriptware, 100 Technology Dr, Suite 315C, Broomfield, CO 80021 *Tel:* 303-786-7899 *Toll Free Tel:* 800-788-7090 (orders) *Fax:* 303-786-9292 *E-mail:* info@scriptware.com *Web Site:* www.scriptware.com, pg 1005

Roger Scruggs Films, PO Box 321054, Cocoa Beach, FL 32932-1054 *Tel:* 321-783-6545 (off); 321-795-6545 (cell) *Web Site:* www.tvphotog.com, pg 1005

SDI Technologies Inc, 1299 Main St, Rahway, NJ 07065 *Tel:* 732-574-9000 *Toll Free Tel:* 800-333-3092; 800-888-4491 (cust serv) *Web Site:* www.sditechnologies.com; www.ihomeaudio.com, pg 1005

Sea Studios Foundation, PO Box 267, Carmel Valley, CA 93924 *E-mail:* info@seastudios.org; jete@seastudios.org *Web Site:* www.seastudios.org, pg 1005

SeaChange International Inc, 50 Nagog Park, Acton, MA 01720 *Tel:* 978-897-0100 *Fax:* 978-897-0132 *Web Site:* www.schange.com, pg 1005

Seaport Graphics, 12 Channel St, Suite 802, Boston, MA 02210 *Tel:* 617-330-1200 *Fax:* 617-330-1222 *E-mail:* jobs@seaportgraphics.com *Web Site:* www.seaportgraphics.com, pg 1005

Sear Sound, 353 W 48 St, 6th fl, New York, NY 10036 *Tel:* 212-582-5380 *Fax:* 212-581-2731 *E-mail:* waltersear@aol.com *Web Site:* www.searsound.com, pg 1005

Seattle International Film Festival (SIFF), 305 Harrison St, Seattle, WA 98109 *Tel:* 206-464-5830 *Fax:* 206-264-7919 *E-mail:* info@siff.net *Web Site:* www.siff.net, pg 1127

Seattle Jewish Film Festival (SJFF), 3801 E Mercer Way, Mercer Island, WA 98040 *Tel:* 206-232-7115 *Fax:* 206-232-7119 *E-mail:* sjff@sjcc.org *Web Site:* www.seattlejewishfilmfestival.org, pg 1127

Seattle Mayor's Office of Film & Music, 700 Fifth Ave, Suite 5752, Seattle, WA 98104 *Tel:* 206-684-8090 *Fax:* 206-684-0379 *E-mail:* filmandmusicoffice@seattle.gov *Web Site:* www.seattle.gov/filmandmusic, pg 1103

2nd Cine, 1035 Donna Dr, Belvidere, IL 61008 *Tel:* 773-398-1452 *E-mail:* info@2ndcine.com *Web Site:* www.2ndcine.com, pg 1006

Second Line Stages, 800 Richard St, New Orleans, LA 70130 *Tel:* 504-528-3050 *E-mail:* info@secondlinestages.com *Web Site:* secondlinestages.com, pg 1006

Sedona Film Office, 45 Sunset Dr, Sedona, AZ 86336 *Tel:* 928-204-1123 ext 130 *Fax:* 928-204-1064 *E-mail:* pr@sedonachamber.com *Web Site:* www.sedonafilmoffice.com, pg 1091

See Factor Industry Inc, 37-11 30 St, Long Island City, NY 11101 *Tel:* 718-784-4200 *Fax:* 718-784-0617 *Web Site:* www.seefactor.com, pg 1006

See Production Services, 3330 Cobb Pkwy, Suite 17-327, Acworth, GA 30101 *Tel:* 404-474-4416 *E-mail:* info@seeproductionservices.com *Web Site:* seeproductionservices.com, pg 1006

SEK'D™ America, 1155 N La Brea Ave, West Hollywood, CA 90038 *Tel:* 323-845-1171 *Toll Free Tel:* 800-330-7753 (orders) *Fax:* 323-845-1170 *E-mail:* sales@plus24.net *Web Site:* www.sekd.com, pg 1006

Sekonic, 75 Virginia Rd, North White Plains, NY 10603 *Tel:* 914-347-3300 *Fax:* 914-347-3309 *E-mail:* info@macgroupus.com *Web Site:* www.sekonic.com; www.macgroupus.com, pg 1006

Selco Products Co, 8780 Technology Way, Reno, NV 89521-5908 *Toll Free Tel:* 877-807-5426 *Fax:* 775-674-5111 *E-mail:* sales@selcoproducts.com *Web Site:* www.selcoproducts.com, pg 1006

Selden Associates, 150 S Mountain Ave, Montclair, NJ 07042 *Tel:* 973-746-0421 *Fax:* 973-509-1498, pg 1006

Select Media Inc, 333 Hudson St, 4th fl, New York, NY 10013 *Tel:* 212-925-9101 *Toll Free Tel:* 800-707-6334 *Fax:* 212-925-9102 *E-mail:* info@selectmedia.org *Web Site:* www.selectmedia.org, pg 1006

Semiconductor Services, 2269 Chestnut St, No 735, San Francisco, CA 94123 *Tel:* 650-369-7890 *Fax:* 415-346-8099 *E-mail:* moreinfo@semiconductorservices.com *Web Site:* www.semiconductorservices.com, pg 1006

Semtech, 4281 Harvester Rd, Burlington, ON L7L 5M4, Canada *Tel:* 905-632-2996 *Fax:* 905-632-2055 *E-mail:* corporate@gennum.com *Web Site:* www.semtech.com, pg 1006

Sencore Inc, 3200 Sencore Dr, Sioux Falls, SD 57107 *Tel:* 605-978-4600 *Toll Free Tel:* 800-SENCORE (736-2673) *Fax:* 605-335-6379 *E-mail:* info@sencore.com *Web Site:* www.sencore.com, pg 1006

The Mack Sennett Studios, 1215 Bates Ave, Los Angeles, CA 90029 *Tel:* 323-660-8466 *E-mail:* info@macksennettstage.com *Web Site:* www.macksennettstage.com, pg 1006

Sennheiser (Canada) Inc, 221 ave Labrosse, Pointe Claire, QC H9R 1A3, Canada *Tel:* 514-426-3013 *Toll Free Tel:* 800-463-1006 *Fax:* 514-426-3953 *Toll Free Fax:* 800-463-3013 *E-mail:* info@sennheiser.ca *Web Site:* www.sennheiser.ca, pg 1006

Sennheiser Electronic Corp, One Enterprise Dr, Old Lyme, CT 06371 *Tel:* 860-434-9190 *Toll Free Tel:* 877-SENNHEISER (736-6434) *Fax:* 860-434-1759 *E-mail:* info@sennheiserusa.com *Web Site:* en-us.sennheiser.com, pg 1006

Sensaphone, 901 Tryens Rd, Aston, PA 19014 *Tel:* 610-558-2700 *Toll Free Tel:* 877-373-2700 *Fax:* 610-558-0222 *E-mail:* sales@sensaphone.com *Web Site:* www.sensaphone.com, pg 1006

Sensormatic®, 6600 Congress Ave, Boca Raton, FL 33487 *Tel:* 561-912-6000 *Toll Free Tel:* 800-507-6268 *Web Site:* www.tyco.com; www.sensormatic.com, pg 1006

Sensory Technologies LLC, 6951 Corporate Circle, Indianapolis, IN 46278 *Tel:* 317-347-5252 *Toll Free Tel:* 800-488-4336 (help desk) *Fax:* 317-347-5262 *E-mail:* sales@sensorytechnologies.com *Web Site:* sensorytechnologies.com, pg 1006

Sentry Industries Inc, One Bridge St, Hillburn, NY 10931-0885 *Tel:* 845-753-2910 *Fax:* 845-753-2920 *E-mail:* techsupport@sentryindustries.com *Web Site:* www.sentryindustries.com, pg 1007

Serendipity Recordings, 511 Slab City Rd, Lincolnville, ME 04849 *Tel:* 207-763-3677, pg 1007

Service Quality Institute, 9201 E Bloomington Fwy, Minneapolis, MN 55420-3437 *Tel:* 952-884-3311 *Toll Free Tel:* 800-548-0538 *Fax:* 952-884-8901 *E-mail:* quality@servicequality.com *Web Site:* www.customer-service.com, pg 1007

Servoreeler Systems, 218-31 97 Ave, Queens Village, NY 11429 *Tel:* 718-464-9400 *Toll Free Tel:* 800-431-8900 *E-mail:* srsystems@servoreelers.com *Web Site:* www.servoreelers.com, pg 1007

SES World Skies, 4 Research Way, Princeton, NJ 08540 *Tel:* 609-987-4000; 609-987-4200 *Fax:* 609-987-4517 *E-mail:* info@ses.com *Web Site:* www.ses.com, pg 1007

SESAC Inc, 55 Music Sq E, Nashville, TN 37203 *Tel:* 615-320-0055 *Fax:* 615-963-3527 *Web Site:* www.sesac.com, pg 1088

Sesame Workshop, 1900 Broadway, 4th fl, New York, NY 10023 *Tel:* 212-595-3456 *Fax:* 212-875-6113 *Web Site:* www.sesameworkshop.org, pg 1088

Sescom Inc, PO Box 720, Mount Marion, NY 12456 *Tel:* 845-246-1915 *Fax:* 845-246-0626 *E-mail:* info@sescom.com *Web Site:* www.sescom.com, pg 1007

Set Decorators Society of America (SDSA), 7100 Tujunga Ave, Suite A, North Hollywood, CA 91605 *Tel:* 818-255-2425 *Fax:* 818-982-8597 *E-mail:* sdsa@setdecorators.org *Web Site:* www.setdecorators.org, pg 1088

The Set Shop, 428 Colyton St, Los Angeles, CA 90013 *Tel:* 213-680-1668 *Fax:* 213-680-4269 *Web Site:* www.thesetshop.tv, pg 1007

Set To Go Studios, 86 Lackawana Ave, Suite 235, Woodland Park, NJ 07424 *Tel:* 973-638-1646 *E-mail:* settogostudio@gmail.com *Web Site:* www.settogostudio.com, pg 1007

Setcom Corp™, 3019 Alvin De Vane Blvd, Suite 560, Austin, TX 78741 *Tel:* 650-965-8020 *Fax:* 650-965-1193 *E-mail:* info@setcomcorp.com; sales@setcomcorp.com *Web Site:* www.setcomcorp.com, pg 1007

SevenStar Communications, 13315 W Washington Blvd, Suite 200, Los Angeles, CA 90066 *Toll Free Tel:* 800-578-9526 (orders) *Fax:* 310-302-1208 *E-mail:* info@taostar.com *Web Site:* www.taostar.com, pg 1007

SF Global Sourcing, 1000 Sansome St, Suite 280, San Francisco, CA 94111 *Tel:* 415-288-9400 *Toll Free Tel:* 855-SF-GLOBAL (734-5622) *Fax:* 415-288-9410 *E-mail:* info@sfglobalsourcing.com *Web Site:* www.sfglobalsourcing.com, pg 1007

SGW Teleprompter Solutions Inc, 844 Eighth Ave, La Grange, IL 60525-2949 *Tel:* 773-402-0105 *Fax:* 708-482-9159 *E-mail:* teleprompter@sbcglobal.net *Web Site:* telepromptersolutions.com, pg 1007

Shadow Pictures Inc, 319 Sixth Ave, No 4-F, New York, NY 10014 *Tel:* 212-929-8906; 917-545-9870 *E-mail:* info@shadowpictures.com *Web Site:* www.shadowpictures.com; laurabelsey.com, pg 1007

Shadow Play Records & Video, 8127 Mesa Dr, Suite B206-277, Austin, TX 78759 *Tel:* 512-349-9962 *Toll Free Tel:* 800-274-8804 *Fax:* 512-345-9515 *Web Site:* www.hellojoe.com, pg 1007

Shadowbox Video Productions, 304 Westfield Dr, North Little Rock, AR 72118 *Tel:* 501-374-3322 *E-mail:* info@shadowboxvideo.com *Web Site:* shadowboxvideo.com, pg 1007

Shadowstone R & R™, 813 Silver Spring Ave, Silver Spring, MD 20910 *Tel:* 301-589-4997 *Fax:* 301-565-5156 *Web Site:* www.shadowstone.com, pg 1008

Shaker Microphones & Promotions Inc, PO Box 1070, Diamond City, AR 72630-1070 *Tel:* 870-422-2988 *E-mail:* shakermicrophone@shakermicrophone.net *Web Site:* www.shakermicrophone.net, pg 1008

Shakticom, 108 Yogaville Way, Buckingham, VA 23921 *Tel:* 434-969-1347 *Toll Free Tel:* 800-476-1347 (orders) *E-mail:* shop@shakticom.org *Web Site:* www.shakticom.org, pg 1008

Shambhala Publications, Horticultural Hall, 300 Massachusetts Ave, Boston, MA 02115 *Tel:* 617-424-0030; 978-829-2599 (intl orders) *Toll Free Tel:* 888-424-2329 (orders & cust serv) *Fax:* 617-236-1563 *E-mail:* editors@shambhala.com *Web Site:* www.shambhala.com, pg 1008

Shamrock Communications, 200 Tornillo Way, Suite 110, Tinton Falls, NJ 07712 *Tel:* 732-686-1140 *Fax:* 732-686-1148 *E-mail:* info@shamrockcommunications.com *Web Site:* www.shamrockcommunications.com, pg 1008

Shanachie Entertainment Corp, 37 E Clinton St, Newton, NJ 07860 *Tel:* 973-579-7763 *Web Site:* shanachie.com, pg 1008

Shanix Inc, 40 Worthington Rd, Cranston, RI 02920 *Tel:* 401-941-4222 *Toll Free Tel:* 800-783-2067 *Fax:* 401-941-4333 *E-mail:* info@shanix.com *Web Site:* www.shanix.com, pg 1008

Shapeshifter, 3405 Cahuenga Blvd W, Los Angeles, CA 90068 *Tel:* 323-876-3444 *Fax:* 323-876-1444 *E-mail:* sales@shapeshifterpost.com *Web Site:* www.shapeshifterpost.com, pg 1008

Steve Shapiro Music, 7777 Skyline Blvd, Oakland, CA 94611 *Tel:* 510-339-7930 *Web Site:* www.stevemusic.com, pg 1008

Sharp Electronics Corp, Professional Display Division, One Sharp Plaza, Mahwah, NJ 07495-1163 *Tel:* 201-529-8200 *Fax:* 201-529-8425 *E-mail:* prolcd@sharpsec.com *Web Site:* www.sharpusa.com, pg 1008

Sharp's Audio-Visual Ltd, 3636 Seventh St SE, Calgary, AB T2G 2Y8, Canada *Tel:* 403-255-4123 *Toll Free Tel:* 800-491-1121 *Fax:* 403-255-3478 *E-mail:* sales@sharpsav.com *Web Site:* www.sharpsav.com, pg 1008

Shasta County Film Commission, 2334 Washington Ave, Suite B, Redding, CA 96001 *Tel:* 530-225-4103 *Toll Free Tel:* 800-874-7562 *Fax:* 530-225-4354 *Web Site:* www.visitredding.org/film, pg 1093

Brad Shaw Productions Inc, 9950 Roan Meadows Dr, Boise, ID 83709 *Tel:* 208-362-5500 *Web Site:* bradshawproductions.com, pg 1008

Shaw Street Productions, 51 Halton St, Unit 127, Toronto, ON M6J 1R5, Canada *Tel:* 416-588-9443 *E-mail:* info@shawstreetpro.com *Web Site:* www.shawstreetpro.com, pg 1008

The Fulton J Sheen Co Inc, 73 State St, Rochester, NY 14614 *Tel:* 585-232-1150 *Toll Free Tel:* 866-357-4336 *Web Site:* www.bishopsheen.com, pg 1008

Sheffield Audio/Video Productions, 13816 Sunnybrook Rd, Phoenix, MD 21131 *Tel:* 410-628-7260 *Toll Free Tel:* 800-355-6613 *Fax:* 410-628-1977 *E-mail:* info@sheffieldav.com *Web Site:* www.sheffieldav.com/production, pg 1008

Shelburne Films, 54545 SR 681, Reedsville, OH 45772 *Tel:* 740-378-6297 *E-mail:* info@shelburnefilms.com *Web Site:* www.shelburnefilms.com, pg 1008

Shen Milsom & Wilke LLC, 417 Fifth Ave, New York, NY 10016 *Tel:* 212-725-6800 *Fax:* 212-725-0864 *E-mail:* info@smwllc.com *Web Site:* www.smwllc.com, pg 1008

Sherwood America Inc, 6120 Valley View Ave, Buena Park, CA 90620 *Tel:* 714-739-2000 *Toll Free Tel:* 800-962-3203 *Fax:* 714-739-2009 *E-mail:* sales@sherwoodamerica.com *Web Site:* www.sherwoodamerica.com, pg 1009

ShiftFocus Productions, 5126 N Ravenswood Ave, Chicago, IL 60640 *Tel:* 773-231-2000 *Web Site:* www.shiftfocusproductions.com, pg 1009

Shimad Corp, 45 Parsons Way, Los Altos, CA 94022 *Tel:* 650-962-1234 (Outside USA) *Toll Free Tel:* 888-474-4623 *Fax:* 650-948-3378 *E-mail:* sales@shimad.com *Web Site:* www.shimad.com, pg 1009

Shokus Video, PO Box 3125, Chatsworth, CA 91313-3125 *Tel:* 818-538-9985 *Toll Free Tel:* 800-SHOKUS-1 (746-5871 - orders) *Fax:* 818-701-0560 *E-mail:* info@shokus.com *Web Site:* www.shokus.com, pg 1009

Stan Sholik Photography, 1946 E Blair Ave, Santa Ana, CA 92705 *Tel:* 949-250-9275 *Fax:* 949-756-2623 *E-mail:* stan@stansholik.com *Web Site:* www.stansholik.com, pg 1009

Shook Mobile Technology LP, 7451 FM 3009, Schertz, TX 78154 *Tel:* 210-651-5700 *Toll Free Tel:* 888-651-5775 *Fax:* 210-651-5220 *E-mail:* shook@shook-usa.com *Web Site:* www.shook-usa.com, pg 1009

Shooting Star Video, 256 Shearwater Isle, Foster City, CA 94404 *Tel:* 650-345-0919 *Fax:* 650-573-6615 *E-mail:* rent@ssv.com *Web Site:* www.ssv.com, pg 1009

Shooting Stars Post Inc, 3106 W North "A" St, Tampa, FL 33609 *Tel:* 813-873-0100 *Web Site:* www.sspmedia.com, pg 1009

Shopware, c/o Films Media Group, 132 W 31 St, 17th fl, New York, NY 10001 *Toll Free Tel:* 800-322-8755 *Toll Free Fax:* 800-678-3633 *E-mail:* custserv@films.com *Web Site:* shopware.films.com, pg 1009

Shore Manufacturing Co, 222 Beade St, Plymouth, PA 18651 *Tel:* 570-779-4042 *Toll Free Tel:* 800-321-5153 (orders) *Fax:* 570-779-7607 *Toll Free Fax:* 800-272-4334 *E-mail:* shoremfg@att.net *Web Site:* shoremfg.com, pg 1009

Shotmaker Co, 10909 Vanowen St, North Hollywood, CA 91605-6408 *Tel:* 818-219-2043 *E-mail:* info@shotmaker.com; info@bigshot.tv *Web Site:* www.shotmaker.com, pg 1009

Shoulder High Productions, 50 Elsie St, San Francisco, CA 94110 *Tel:* 415-235-1984 *Fax:* 415-357-9747 *E-mail:* info@shoulderhigh.com *Web Site:* shoulderhigh.com, pg 1009

Show Canada Industries Inc, 5555 Maurice-Cullen, Laval, QC H7C 2T8, Canada *Tel:* 450-664-5155 *Toll Free Tel:* 888-329-5556 *Fax:* 450-664-0852 *E-mail:* info@show-canada.ca *Web Site:* www.show-canada.com, pg 1009

Show Department Inc, 2201 W Fulton St, Chicago, IL 60612 *Tel:* 312-243-8215 *Toll Free Tel:* 800-294-4111 *Fax:* 312-243-8236 *E-mail:* info@showdepartment.com *Web Site:* www.showdepartment.com, pg 1009

Show-Me Audio-Visual, Corporate Ridge, 4501 Blue Ridge Cutoff, Kansas City, MO 64133 *Tel:* 816-358-8700 *Toll Free Tel:* 800-2-SHOWME (274-6963) *Fax:* 816-358-8701 *E-mail:* info@showmeav.com *Web Site:* www.showmeav.com, pg 1009

ShowBiz Studios, 15521 Lanark St, Van Nuys, CA 91406 *Tel:* 818-989-7007 *Fax:* 818-989-8272 *Web Site:* www.showbizstudios.com, pg 1009

Showcase Photo & Video, 2323 Cheshire Bridge Rd, Atlanta, GA 30324 *Tel:* 404-325-7676 *Toll Free Tel:* 800-886-1976 *Fax:* 404-321-3636 *E-mail:* sales@showcaseinc.com *Web Site:* www.showcaseinc.com, pg 1009

Showman Fabricators Inc, 47-22 Pearson Place, Long Island City, NY 11101 *Tel:* 718-935-9899 *Fax:* 718-855-9823 *E-mail:* info@showfab.com *Web Site:* www.showfab.com, pg 1010

Showorks Audio Visual Inc, 100 Naamans Rd, Suite 1-C, Claymont, DE 19703 *Tel:* 302-798-7999 *Toll Free Tel:* 800-942-7469 *Fax:* 302-798-9705 *E-mail:* info@showorksav.com *Web Site:* showorksav.com, pg 1010

Showreel International Inc, 1021 N McCadden Place, Hollywood, CA 90038 *Tel:* 323-464-5111 *E-mail:* information@showreel.com *Web Site:* www.showreel.com, pg 1010

Showtime Networks Inc, 1633 Broadway, 9th fl, New York, NY 10019 *Tel:* 212-708-1600 *Fax:* 212-708-1217 *Web Site:* www.sho.com, pg 1010

SHP Electronics, 1225 Hulman St, Terre Haute, IN 47802 *Tel:* 812-232-1003 *Fax:* 812-232-3170 *Web Site:* www.shpelectronics.com, pg 1010

Shure Inc, 5800 W Touhy Ave, Niles, IL 60714-4608 *Tel:* 847-600-2000; 847-600-8440 (tech support); 847-600-8699 (cust serv) *Toll Free Tel:* 800-25-SHURE (257-4873); 800-516-2525 (cust serv) *Fax:* 847-600-1212; 847-600-8444 (tech support); 847-600-8686 (cust serv); 847-600-8688 (parts) *E-mail:* info@shure.com; support@shure.com (tech support); service@shure.com (cust serv) *Web Site:* www.shure.com, pg 1010

Shure Manufacturing Corp, 1901 W Main St, Washington, MO 63090 *Tel:* 636-390-7100 *Toll Free Tel:* 800-227-4873 *Fax:* 636-390-7171 *E-mail:* sales@shureusa.com *Web Site:* www.shureusa.com, pg 1010

Side Door Studio Inc, 69 Albe Dr, Newark, DE 19702 *Tel:* 302-738-8777 *Fax:* 302-731-7601 *E-mail:* sdseng@sidedoorstudioinc.com, pg 1010

Side 3 Studios, 725 Mariposa St, Denver, CO 80204 *Tel:* 720-515-2649 *E-mail:* info@side3.com *Web Site:* www.side3.com, pg 1010

Sierra Automated Systems, 2821 Burton Ave, Burbank, CA 91504 *Tel:* 818-840-6749 *Fax:* 818-840-6751 *E-mail:* sales@sasaudio.com; marketing@sasaudio.com *Web Site:* www.sasaudio.com, pg 1010

Sight & Sound Production Services Inc, 1143 Boland Place, St Louis, MO 63117-1411 *Tel:* 314-647-0665 *Web Site:* www.sspsinc.com, pg 1010

Sight & Sound Productions, 11193 Saint Johns Industrial Pkwy N, Jacksonville, FL 32246 *Tel:* 904-645-7880 *Toll Free Tel:* 800-339-0846 *Fax:* 904-645-7787 *E-mail:* info@ssav.net *Web Site:* www.ssav.net, pg 1010

Sight & Sound Studios, 66 Queen St, Suite 1705, Honolulu, HI 96813 *Tel:* 808-599-7600 *Fax:* 808-599-7601 *Web Site:* www.sightandsoundhawaii.com, pg 1010

Sight Creative, 400 First Ave N, Suite 100, Minneapolis, MN 55401 *Tel:* 651-646-2442 *Fax:* 651-646-1461 *E-mail:* info@sightcreative.com *Web Site:* www.sightcreative.com, pg 1010

Sigma Corp of America, 15 Fleetwood Ct, Ronkonkoma, NY 11779 *Tel:* 631-585-1144 *Toll Free Tel:* 800-896-6858 (cust serv) *Fax:* 631-585-1895 *E-mail:* info@sigmaphoto.com *Web Site:* www.sigmaphoto.com, pg 1010

Sigma Delta Chi Awards in Journalism, Eugene S Pulliam National Journalism Ctr, 3909 N Meridian St, Indianapolis, IN 46208 *Tel:* 317-927-8000 *Fax:* 317-920-4789 *E-mail:* awards@spj.org *Web Site:* www.spj.org, pg 1127

Sign Media Inc, 4020 Blackburn Lane, Burtonsville, MD 20866-1167 *Tel:* 301-421-0268 *Toll Free Tel:* 800-475-4756 *Fax:* 301-421-0270 *E-mail:* info@signmedia.com *Web Site:* www.signmedia.com, pg 1011

Signal Transport, PO Box 1028, Lake Forest, CA 92609-1028 *Tel:* 714-641-5665 *Fax:* 714-641-5664 *E-mail:* sales@sigt.com; sales@smcpanels.com *Web Site:* www.sigt.com; www.smcpanels.com, pg 1011

Signature Entertainment, 8306 Wilshire Blvd, Suite 791, Beverly Hills, CA 90211 *Tel:* 310-498-1805 *Fax:* 310-276-2521 *Web Site:* www.signature-ent.com, pg 1011

Silent Source, 58 Nonotuck St, Northampton, MA 01062 *Tel:* 413-584-7944 *Toll Free Tel:* 800-583-7174 (orders) *Fax:* 413-584-2377 *E-mail:* info@silentsource.com *Web Site:* www.silentsource.com, pg 1011

Silver Anvil Awards, 33 Maiden Lane, 11th fl, New York, NY 10038-5150 *Tel:* 212-460-1400 *Toll Free Tel:* 800-350-0111 *Fax:* 212-995-0757 *E-mail:* awards@prsa.org *Web Site:* www.prsa.org, pg 1127

Silver Gavel Awards for Media and the Arts, Div for Public Education, 321 N Clark St, Chicago, IL 60654 *Tel:* 312-988-5733 *Toll Free Tel:* 800-285-2221 *Fax:* 312-988-5494 (Attn: Gavel Awards) *E-mail:* publiceducation@americanbar.org *Web Site:* www.americanbar.org, pg 1127

Silvestri California, 8125 Beach St, Los Angeles, CA 90001 *Tel:* 323-277-4420 *Toll Free Tel:* 800-647-8874 *Fax:* 323-585-0861 *E-mail:* info@silvestricalifornia.com *Web Site:* www.silvestricalifornia.com, pg 1011

SIM Digital, One Atlantic Ave, Suite 110, Toronto, ON M6K 3E7, Canada *Tel:* 416-979-9958 *Fax:* 416-979-7770 *E-mail:* info@simdigital.com *Web Site:* www.simdigital.com, pg 1011

Sima Products Corp, 125 Commerce Dr, Hauppauge, NY 11788 *Tel:* 631-435-0200 *Toll Free Tel:* 800-345-7462; 800-274-7824 *Fax:* 631-435-4545 *Toll Free Fax:* 800-274-7828 *E-mail:* info@simacorp.com; custserv@simacorp.com; customerservice@aristagroup.com *Web Site:* www.aristagroup.com, pg 1011

Simco-Ion, 2257 N Penn Rd, Hatfield, PA 19440 *Tel:* 215-822-6401 *Toll Free Tel:* 800-203-3419 *Fax:* 215-822-3795 *E-mail:* customerservice@simco-ion.com *Web Site:* www.simco-ion.com, pg 1011

Simkar Corporation, 700 Ramona Ave, Philadelphia, PA 19120-4691 *Tel:* 215-831-7700 *Toll Free Tel:* 800-523-3602 *Fax:* 215-831-7703 *E-mail:* lighting@simkar.com *Web Site:* www.simkar.com, pg 1011

Simon & Schuster, Inc, 1230 Avenue of the Americas, New York, NY 10020 *Tel:* 212-698-7000 *Toll Free Tel:* 800-223-2348 (cust serv) *Toll Free Fax:* 800-943-9831 *E-mail:* customer.service@simonandschuster.net *Web Site:* www.simonandschuster.net; www.simonandschuster.biz, pg 1011

D S Simon Productions, 229 W 36 St, 9th fl, New York, NY 10018 *Tel:* 212-736-2727 *Toll Free Tel:* 800-377-4666 *Fax:* 212-736-7040 *E-mail:* news@dssimon.com *Web Site:* dssimon.com, pg 1011

Simon - Kaloi Engineering, 31192 La Baya Dr, Unit G, Westlake Village, CA 91362 *Tel:* 818-707-8400 *Fax:* 818-707-8401, pg 1011

Simplex Grinnell LP, 50 Technology Dr, Westminster, MA 01441 *Tel:* 978-731-2500 *Web Site:* www.simplexgrinnell.com, pg 1011

Simply Audiobooks, 935 Sheldon Ct, Burlington, ON L7L 5K6, Canada *Tel:* 905-634-3035 *Toll Free Tel:* 877-554-4332 *E-mail:* customerservice@simplyaudiobooks.com *Web Site:* www.simplyaudiobooks.com, pg 1011

Simpson Electric Co, 520 Simpson Ave, Lac du Flambeau, WI 54538 *Tel:* 715-588-3947 (cust serv); 715-588-3311 *Fax:* 715-588-1248 (cust serv); 715-588-3326 *E-mail:* cservice@simpsonelectric.com *Web Site:* www.simpsonelectric.com, pg 1011

Simtrol Inc, Northwinds 600 Bldg, Suite 250, 11675 Rainwater Dr, Alpharetta, GA 30009 *Tel:* 678-365-2315 *Fax:* 678-365-2315 *Web Site:* www.simtrol.com, pg 1011

Sinauer Associates Inc, 23 Plumtree Rd, Sunderland, MA 01375 *Tel:* 413-549-4300 *Fax:* 413-549-1118 *E-mail:* orders@sinauer.com (orders); custserv@sinauer.com (cust serv); publish@sinauer.com (general edit correspondence) *Web Site:* www.sinauer.com, pg 1011

Sinclair Institute, 402 Millstone Dr, Hillsborough, NC 27278 *Tel:* 919-732-6005 *Toll Free Tel:* 888-736-2247 *Fax:* 919-732-6146 *E-mail:* sales@sinclairwholesale.com *Web Site:* www.sinclairwholesale.com; www.bettersex.com, pg 1012

Barbara Singer Productions, 319 E 24 St, No 3-A, New York, NY 10010 *Tel:* 212-689-0395 *Fax:* 212-686-4890 *E-mail:* barbara@barbarasinger.com *Web Site:* www.barbarasinger.com, pg 1012

SintecMedia, 425 Madison Ave, Suite 1602, New York, NY 10017 *Tel:* 917-606-5310 *Fax:* 917-606-5311 *E-mail:* sales@sintecmedia.com *Web Site:* www.sintecmedia.com, pg 1012

Sioux Falls Convention & Visitors Bureau, 200 N Phillips Ave, Suite 102, Sioux Falls, SD 57104 *Tel:* 605-275-6060 *Toll Free Tel:* 800-333-2072 *Fax:* 605-338-0682 *E-mail:* sfcvb@siouxfalls.com *Web Site:* www.siouxfallscvb.com; visitsiouxfalls.com, pg 1102

Sirius Images Corp dba WaveGuide Studios, 2062 Weems Rd, Tucker, GA 30084 *Tel:* 770-939-2004 *Toll Free Tel:* 800-578-2004 *E-mail:* info@waveguidestudios.com *Web Site:* www.waveguidestudios.com, pg 1012

SirsiDynix, 3300 N Ashton Blvd, Suite 500, Lehi, UT 84043-5340 *Tel:* 801-223-5200 *Toll Free Tel:* 800-288-8020 *Fax:* 801-223-5202 *E-mail:* info@sirsidynix.com; sales@sirsidynix.com *Web Site:* www.sirsidynix.com, pg 1012

Sisters' Choice Press, PO Box 2067, Berkeley, CA 94702-0067 *Tel:* 510-843-0533 *Fax:* 510-834-5201 *Web Site:* www.sisterschoice.com, pg 1012

SISU Home Entertainment Inc, 340 W 39 St, 6th fl, New York, NY 10018 *Tel:* 212-947-7888 *Toll Free Tel:* 800-223-7478 *Fax:* 212-947-8388 *Toll Free Fax:* 888-221-7478 *E-mail:* sisu@sisuent.com *Web Site:* www.sisuent.com, pg 1012

Frank Siteman Photography, 136 Pond St, Winchester, MA 01890 *Tel:* 781-729-3747 *Fax:* 781-729-2549 *Web Site:* www.franksiteman.com, pg 1012

Sitler's Supplies Inc, 702 E Washington St, Washington, IA 52353 *Tel:* 319-653-2123 *Toll Free Tel:* 800-426-3938 *Fax:* 319-653-3198 *E-mail:* info@sitlersupplies.com *Web Site:* www.sitlersupplies.com, pg 1012

16 x 9 Inc, 28314 Constellation Rd, Valencia, CA 91355 *Tel:* 661-295-3313 *Toll Free Tel:* 866-800-1699 *Fax:* 661-295-3314 *E-mail:* info@16x9inc.com *Web Site:* www.16x9inc.com, pg 1012

SKC Communication Products Inc, 8320 Hedge Lane Terr, Shawnee Mission, KS 66227 *Tel:* 913-422-4222 *Toll Free Tel:* 800-882-7779 *Toll Free Fax:* 800-454-4752 *E-mail:* contact.us@skccom.com *Web Site:* www.skccom.com, pg 1012

Skjonberg Controls Inc, 1363 Donlon St, Suite 6, Ventura, CA 93003 *Tel:* 805-650-0877 *Toll Free Fax:* 800-650-0360 *E-mail:* sales@skjonberg.com *Web Site:* www.skjonberg.com, pg 1012

Skotel Corp, 118-6185 boul Teschereau, Suite 144, Brossard, QC J4Z 0E4, Canada *Tel:* 514-806-2340 *E-mail:* skotel@videotron.ca, pg 1012

Sky-View Co, 2800 NE Loop 410, San Antonio, TX 78218 *Tel:* 210-590-8100 *Toll Free Tel:* 800-562-8439 (US & CN) *Fax:* 210-967-8787 *E-mail:* sales@sky-view.com *Web Site:* www.sky-view.com, pg 1013

Skyfire Video, PO Box 2266, Sparks, NV 89432 *Tel:* 775-323-0965 *Toll Free Tel:* 800-852-2330 *Web Site:* www.skyfirevideo.com, pg 1013

Skyhoundz, 660 Hembree Pkwy, Suite 110, Roswell, GA 30076 *Tel:* 770-751-3882 *Fax:* 770-740-1665 *E-mail:* info@skyhoundz.com *Web Site:* www.skyhoundz.com, pg 1013

Skyline Broadcast, 30 Skyline Dr, Lake Mary, FL 32771 *Tel:* 407-484-1089 *Fax:* 518-684-2593 *E-mail:* sales@skylinebroadcast.com *Web Site:* www.skylinebroadcast.com, pg 1013

Skyriver Films, 6251 Tuttle Place, Suite 102, Anchorage, AK 99507-2099 *Tel:* 907-243-3332; 907-248-9999 *Toll Free Tel:* 888-660-2257 *Fax:* 907-243-2044 *E-mail:* info@alaskajacks.com *Web Site:* www.alaskajacks.com; www.skyriver.com, pg 1013

Skystorm Productions, 103 Commerce St, Suite 100, Lake Mary, FL 32746 *Tel:* 407-328-4747 *Toll Free Tel:* 800-783-8508 *Fax:* 407-328-4479 *E-mail:* info@skystorm.com *Web Site:* www.skystorm.com, pg 1013

Skyviews Survey Inc, 32 Highline Trail, Stamford, CT 06902 *Tel:* 203-359-3754 *Fax:* 203-359-3791 *Web Site:* www.skyviewsurvey.com, pg 1013

Slamdance Film Festival, 5634 Melrose Ave, Los Angeles, CA 90038 *Tel:* 323-466-1786 *Fax:* 323-466-1784 *E-mail:* submissions@slamdance.com *Web Site:* www.slamdance.com, pg 1127

Slate Media Group, 1111 S Victory Blvd, Burbank, CA 91502 *Tel:* 818-569-6500 *Fax:* 818-846-9399 *Web Site:* www.slatemediagroup.com, pg 1013

SLD Lighting, 36-05 Broadway, Fair Lawn, NJ 07410 *Tel:* 201-373-2700 *Toll Free Tel:* 800-245-6630 *Fax:* 201-793-7618 *E-mail:* sales@sldlighting.com *Web Site:* www.sldlighting.com, pg 1013

SLI Manufacturing Inc, 550 McNicholl Ave, Toronto, ON M2H 2E1, Canada *Tel:* 416-493-8900 *Toll Free Tel:* 888-216-2382 *Fax:* 416-493-8901 *E-mail:* salesinfo@slicanada.com *Web Site:* www.slicanada.com, pg 1013

Slim Goodbody Corp, 161 Narrows Rd, Lincolnville, ME 04850 *Tel:* 207-763-2820 *Toll Free Tel:* 800-962-7546 *Fax:* 207-763-4804 *E-mail:* info@slimgoodbody.com *Web Site:* www.slimgoodbody.com, pg 1013

Slow Motion Film & Digital Inc, 7211 Clybourn Ave, Los Angeles, CA 91352 *Tel:* 818-982-4400 *Fax:* 818-982-8500 *Web Site:* www.slowmotioninc.com, pg 1013

SLR Enterprises LLC, PO Box 1111, Orleans, MA 02653 *Tel:* 508-737-7788 *Fax:* 508-240-6878 *E-mail:* stephenroth@c4.net, pg 1013

SmackDab Media, 1033 Third Ave S, Nashville, TN 37210 *Toll Free Tel:* 888-248-8197 *Web Site:* smackdabmedia.com, pg 1013

Small Planet Communications Inc, 15 Union St, Lawrence, MA 01840 *Tel:* 978-794-2201 *E-mail:* planet@smplanet.com *Web Site:* www.smplanet.com, pg 1013

Small Press Distribution Inc, 1341 Seventh St, Berkeley, CA 94710-1409 *Tel:* 510-524-1668 *Toll Free Tel:* 800-869-7553 *Fax:* 510-524-0852 *E-mail:* spd@spdbooks.org *Web Site:* www.spdbooks.org, pg 1013

Small World Productions Inc, 140 Lakeside Ave, Suite 200, Seattle, WA 98122 *Tel:* 206-329-7167 *Toll Free Tel:* 800-866-7425 (orders) *E-mail:* info@travelsmallworld.com *Web Site:* www.smarttravels.tv, pg 1013

Smart Concepts Ltd, 4525 S Jamestown, Tulsa, OK 74135 *Tel:* 918-636-2376 *Web Site:* www.smartconceptsinc.com, pg 1013

SMART Technologies Inc, 3636 Research Rd NW, Calgary, AB T2L 1Y1, Canada *Tel:* 403-245-0333 *Toll Free Tel:* 888-42-SMART (427-6278 US & Canada) *Fax:* 403-228-2500 *E-mail:* info@smarttech.com *Web Site:* www.smarttech.com, pg 1013

SmartPros Ltd, 12 Skyline Dr, Hawthorne, NY 10532-2133 *Tel:* 914-345-2620 *Fax:* 914-345-2603 *E-mail:* admin@smartpros.com *Web Site:* www.smartpros.com, pg 1014

SmartSource Computer & AV Rentals, 265 Oser Ave, Hauppauge, NY 11788 *Tel:* 631-273-8888 *Toll Free Tel:* 800-888-8686 *Fax:* 631-273-8889 *E-mail:* info@smartsourcerentals.com; longisland@smartsourcerentals.com *Web Site:* www.smartsourcerentals.com, pg 1014

SMI Inc, PO Box 7216, Waco, TX 76714-7216 *Tel:* 254-717-8917 *Fax:* 254-776-1230 *E-mail:* dmcminn@lmi-inc.com *Web Site:* www.success-motivation.com, pg 1014

Smith Audio-Visual Inc, 310 SW Sixth Ave, Topeka, KS 66603-3109 *Tel:* 785-235-3481 *Fax:* 785-235-3485 *E-mail:* sales@smithav.com *Web Site:* www.smithav.com, pg 1014

Smith System Inc, 1714 E 14 St, Plano, TX 75074 *Toll Free Tel:* 800-328-1061 *Fax:* 972-398-4051 *E-mail:* furniture@smithsystem.com *Web Site:* www.smithsystem.com, pg 1014

Smith-Victor Corp, 1268 Humbracht Circle, Bartlett, IL 60103-1631 *Tel:* 630-830-9200 *Toll Free Tel:* 800-348-9862 *Fax:* 630-830-9201 *Toll Free Fax:* 800-352-0490 *E-mail:* sales@smithvictor.com, pg 1014

Smithall Electronics Inc, 2001 Vine St, Cincinnati, OH 45202 *Tel:* 513-381-2828 *Fax:* 513-381-5160 *Web Site:* www.smithall.com, pg 1014

Smithsonian Folkways Recordings, 600 Maryland Ave SW, Suite 2001, Washington, DC 20024 *Tel:* 202-633-6450 *Toll Free Tel:* 888-FOLKWAYS (365-5929) *Fax:* 202-633-6477 *E-mail:* smithsonianfolkways@si.edu *Web Site:* www.folkways.si.edu, pg 1014

Smithsonian National Museum of the American Indian, c/o Film & Video Ctr, Natl Museum of the American Indian, One Bowling Green, New York, NY 10004-1415 *Tel:* 212-514-3700 *Fax:* 212-514-3725 *E-mail:* fvc@si.edu *Web Site:* www.nmai.si.edu, pg 1014

Smolian Sound Studios, One Worman's Mill Ct, Frederick, MD 21701 *Tel:* 301-694-5134 *E-mail:* smolians@erols.com *Web Site:* www.soundsaver.com, pg 1014

SMP Digital Graphics, 163 W 22 St, New York, NY 10011 *Tel:* 212-691-6766 *E-mail:* info@smpdigitalgraphics.com *Web Site:* www.smpdigitalgraphics.com, pg 1014

SNAP, 18653 Ventura, Suite 295, Tarzana, CA 91356 *Tel:* 818-340-0283 *E-mail:* hdcine@gmail.com *Web Site:* www.facebook.com/barry.seybert, pg 1014

Snell, 3519 Pacific Ave, Burbank, CA 91505 *Tel:* 818-556-2616 *Fax:* 818-556-2626 *E-mail:* americas@snellgroup.com *Web Site:* www.snellgroup.com, pg 1014

SNL Kagan Media & Communications, One SNL Plaza, 212 Seventh St NE, Charlottesville, VA 22902 *Tel:* 434-977-1600 *Toll Free Tel:* 866-296-3743 *Fax:* 434-977-4466 *E-mail:* snlkagansales@snl.com *Web Site:* www.snl.com, pg 1014

So Smart Productions, 701 Sharpley Rd, Wilmington, DE 19803 *Tel:* 484-753-1520 *E-mail:* info@sosmart.com *Web Site:* store.sosmart.com, pg 1015

Social Studies School Service, 10200 Jefferson Blvd, Culver City, CA 90232 *Tel:* 310-839-2436 *Toll Free Tel:* 800-421-4246 *Fax:* 310-839-2249 *Toll Free Fax:* 800-944-5432 *E-mail:* access@socialstudies.com *Web Site:* www.socialstudies.com, pg 1015

Society for Applied Learning Technology (SALT®), 50 Culpeper St, Warrenton, VA 20186 *Tel:* 540-347-0055 *Fax:* 540-349-3169 *E-mail:* info@lti.org *Web Site:* www.salt.org, pg 1089

Society for Imaging Science and Technology (IS&T), 7003 Kilworth Lane, Springfield, VA 22151 *Tel:* 703-642-9090 *Fax:* 703-642-9094 *E-mail:* info@imaging.org *Web Site:* www.imaging.org, pg 1089

Society for Information Display (SID), 1475 S Bascom Ave, Suite 114, Campbell, CA 95008-4006 *Tel:* 408-879-3901 *Fax:* 408-879-3833 *E-mail:* office@sid.org *Web Site:* www.sid.org, pg 1089

Society of Broadcast Engineers Inc (SBE), 9102 N Meridian St, Suite 150, Indianapolis, IN 46260 *Tel:* 317-846-9000 *Web Site:* www.sbe.org, pg 1089

Society of Cable Telecommunications Engineers Inc (SCTE), 140 Philips Rd, Exton, PA 19341-1318 *Tel:* 610-363-6888 *Toll Free Tel:* 800-542-5040 (cust care) *Fax:* 610-363-5898 *E-mail:* information@scte.org *Web Site:* www.scte.org, pg 1089

Society of Camera Operators, PO Box 2006, Toluca Lake, CA 91610-0006 *Tel:* 818-382-7070 *E-mail:* info@soc.org *Web Site:* www.soc.org, pg 1089

Society of Manufacturing Engineers (SME), One SME Dr, Dearborn, MI 48128 *Tel:* 313-425-3000 *Toll Free Tel:* 800-733-4763 *E-mail:* service@sme.org (cust care) *Web Site:* www.sme.org, pg 1015

Society of Motion Picture & Television Engineers (SMPTE), 3 Barker Ave, 5th fl, White Plains, NY 10601 *Tel:* 914-761-1100 *Fax:* 914-761-3115 *E-mail:* smpte@smpte.org *Web Site:* www.smpte.org, pg 1015

Society of Motion Picture & Television Engineers (SMPTE), 3 Barker Ave, 5th fl, White Plains, NY 10601 *Tel:* 914-761-1100 *Fax:* 914-761-3115 *E-mail:* membership@smpte.org *Web Site:* www.smpte.org, pg 1089

The Society of Professional Audio Recording Services (SPARS), PO Box 606, Palacios, TX 77465 *Toll Free Tel:* 800-771-7727 *Fax:* 214-722-1442 *E-mail:* spars@spars.com *Web Site:* spars.com, pg 1089

Sodanceabit, 11372 Kelly Lane, Los Alamitos, CA 90720 *Tel:* 562-799-4340 *Toll Free Tel:* 800-64-DANCE (643-2623) *E-mail:* sodanceabit@live.com *Web Site:* www.sodanceabit.com, pg 1015

SODEC, 215 rue Saint-Jacques St, Rm 800, Montreal, QC H2Y 1M6, Canada *Tel:* 514-841-2200 *Toll Free Tel:* 800-363-0401 (CN only) *Fax:* 514-841-8606 *E-mail:* info@sodec.gouv.qc.ca *Web Site:* www.sodec.gouv.qc.ca, pg 1089

Sofradir EC, 373 Rte 46 W, Fairfield, NJ 07004-2442 *Tel:* 973-882-0211 *Toll Free Tel:* 800-759-9577 *Fax:* 973-882-0997 *E-mail:* info@sofradir-ec.com *Web Site:* www.nightvisioncameras.com, pg 1015

Software & Information Industry Association (SIIA), 1090 Vermont Ave NW, 6th fl, Washington, DC 20005-4095 *Tel:* 202-289-7442 *Fax:* 202-289-7097 *Web Site:* www.siia.net, pg 1089

SoftWright LLC, PO Box 7205, Charlotte, VA 22906 *Tel:* 303-344-5486 *Toll Free Tel:* 800-728-4033 *Fax:* 303-265-9399 *E-mail:* sales@softwright.com *Web Site:* www.softwright.com, pg 1015

Elliot Sokolov Music, 149 Mountainview Rd, Patterson, NY 12563 *Tel:* 917-690-5487 *E-mail:* elliotsoko@aol.com *Web Site:* www.elliotsokolov.com, pg 1015

Solar Studios, 1601 S Central Ave, Glendale, CA 91204 *Tel:* 818-240-1893 *Fax:* 818-240-4187 *Web Site:* www.solarstudios.com, pg 1015

Solid Sound Recording Studio, 2400 Hassell Rd, Suite 430, Hoffman Estates, IL 60169 *Tel:* 847-490-2101 *E-mail:* solidsoundrecordingstudios@gmail.com, pg 1015

Solid State Logic Inc, 320 W 46 St, 2nd fl, New York, NY 10036-8398 *Tel:* 212-315-1111 *E-mail:* sales@solidstatelogic.com *Web Site:* www.solid-state-logic.com, pg 1015

Solutek Corp, 94 Shirley St, Boston, MA 02119 *Tel:* 617-445-5335 *Toll Free Tel:* 800-403-0770 *Fax:* 617-445-9623 *E-mail:* bflanagan@solutek.com *Web Site:* www.solutekphotochemicals.com, pg 1015

Solution Tree, 555 N Morton St, Bloomington, IN 47404-3730 *Tel:* 812-336-7700 *Toll Free Tel:* 800-733-6786 *Fax:* 812-336-7790 *E-mail:* info@solution-tree.com *Web Site:* www.solution-tree.com, pg 1015

SOM Publishing Co, 163 Moon Valley Rd, Windyville, MO 65783 *Tel:* 417-345-8411 *E-mail:* som@som.org *Web Site:* www.som.org, pg 1015

Sonalysts Media, 215 Parkway N, Waterford, CT 06385 *Tel:* 860-326-3848 *Toll Free Tel:* 800-526-8091 (ext 3848) *E-mail:* tour_rehearsals@sonalysts.com *Web Site:* www.sonalystsmedia.com, pg 1015

Sonance, 212 Avenida Fabricante, San Clemente, CA 92672-7531 *Tel:* 949-492-7777 *Toll Free Tel:* 800-592-4644; 800-582-0772 (tech support); 800-582-7777 *Toll Free Fax:* 800-538-5151 *E-mail:* customerservice@sonance.com *Web Site:* www.sonance.com, pg 1015

Sonar Radio Corp, 3000 Stirling Rd, Hollywood, FL 33021-2039 *Tel:* 954-981-8800 *Fax:* 954-981-8800, pg 1015

Sonic Gravy, 2515 Laurel Path, Los Angeles, CA 90046 *Tel:* 323-650-2751 *Fax:* 323-822-1003 *Web Site:* www.johnswihart.tumblr.com, pg 1015

Sonic Science Inc, 79 Denlow Blvd, Toronto, ON M3B 1P8, Canada *Tel:* 416-383-0260 *Toll Free Tel:* 800-267-6642 *Fax:* 416-383-0261 *E-mail:* sales@sonicscience.com *Web Site:* www.sonicscience.com, pg 1016

SonicPool, 6860 Lexington Ave, Hollywood, CA 90038 *Tel:* 323-460-4649 *Toll Free Tel:* 866-203-7213 *Fax:* 323-460-6063 *E-mail:* production@sonicpool.com *Web Site:* www.sonicpool.com, pg 1016

SoNo Studios, 18 Leonard St, Norwalk, CT 06850 *Tel:* 203-354-4002 *Fax:* 203-354-7018 *E-mail:* info@sonostudios.com *Web Site:* www.sonostudios.com, pg 1016

Sonoma County Film Office, 141 Stony Circle, Suite 110, Santa Rosa, CA 95401-4154 *Tel:* 707-565-7170 *Fax:* 707-565-7231 *E-mail:* film@sonoma-county.org *Web Site:* www.sonoma-county.org/film, pg 1094

Sonoma Valley Chamber of Commerce, 651-A Broadway, Sonoma, CA 95476-7041 *Tel:* 707-996-1033 *Fax:* 707-996-9402 *E-mail:* info@sonomachamber.com *Web Site:* sonomachamber.org, pg 1016, 1094

Sonora Recorders, 3222 Los Feliz Blvd, Los Angeles, CA 90039 *Tel:* 323-663-2500 *E-mail:* ductape@aol.com *Web Site:* www.sonorarecorders.com, pg 1016

Sonoton Music Library, 6255 Sunset Blvd, Suite 820, Hollywood, CA 90028 *Tel:* 323-461-3211 *Toll Free Tel:* 800-543-4276 *Fax:* 323-461-9102 *Web Site:* www.apmmusic.com, pg 1016

Sony Electronics Inc, 16530 Via Esprillo, San Diego, CA 92127 *Tel:* 858-942-2400 *Web Site:* www.sony.com, pg 1016

Sony Music Custom Marketing, 550 Madison Ave, New York, NY 10022 *Tel:* 212-833-8000 *Web Site:* www.sonymusic.com, pg 1016

Sony Music Entertainment, 550 Madison Ave, New York, NY 10022 *Tel:* 212-833-8000 *Fax:* 212-833-8336 *Web Site:* www.sonymusic.com, pg 1016

Sony Pictures Entertainment, 10202 W Washington Blvd, Culver City, CA 90232 *Tel:* 310-244-4000 *Web Site:* www.sonypictures.com, pg 1016

Sony Pictures Home Entertainment, 10202 W Washington Blvd, Culver City, CA 90232-3119 *Tel:* 310-244-4000 *Fax:* 310-244-2485 *Web Site:* www.sonypictures.com, pg 1016

Sony Pro Audio (Broadcast & Professional Systems Division), One Sony Dr, Park Ridge, NJ 07656 *Tel:* 201-930-1000 *Web Site:* pro.sony.com/bbsc/ssr/home.do, pg 1016

SOS Film Works (Space Ordnance Systems), 34855 Petersen Rd, Agua Dulce, CA 91390 *Tel:* 661-251-2365 *Fax:* 661-268-7680 *Web Site:* www.sosfilmworks.com, pg 1016

SOS Worldwide Productions Inc, 2000 Towerside Terr, Suite 607, Miami, FL 33138 *Tel:* 305-891-9133; 305-653-5321 (cell) *Fax:* 305-603-8111 *E-mail:* info@safesongs.com; info@safesongs4kids.com *Web Site:* www.safesongs.com; www.safesongs4kids.com; www.safesongsforkids.com, pg 1016

SOTA Sales & Service Center, 10830 S Nagle Ave, Worth, IL 60482 *Tel:* 608-538-3500 *Toll Free Tel:* 800-772-7682 *Fax:* 608-538-3502 *E-mail:* sotaturntables@kwom.com *Web Site:* www.sotaturntables.com, pg 1016

Soularium Recording Studios, 702 S Alpine Hwy, Alpine, UT 84004 *Tel:* 801-492-0505 *E-mail:* solariumstudios@gmail.com *Web Site:* www.soulariumstudios.com, pg 1016

Sound Advantage, 93 Shaw Rd, Little Compton, RI 02837 *Tel:* 508-653-1644 *E-mail:* soundadvantage@mac.com, pg 1016

Sound & Images Inc, 104 Corporate Blvd, Suite 411, West Columbia, SC 29169 *Tel:* 803-791-3925 *E-mail:* marketing@s-and-i.com *Web Site:* www.s-and-i.com, pg 1016

Sound & Video Creations Inc, 2408 Felts Ave, Nashville, TN 37211 *Tel:* 615-460-7330 *Fax:* 615-460-7331 *Web Site:* www.clickeffects.com, pg 1016

Sound & Vision Communications Inc, 4601 N "A" St, Tampa, FL 33609-1909 *Tel:* 813-642-4706 *Web Site:* www.gosvc.com, pg 1016

Sound & Vision Media, 372 Squire Rd, Revere, MA 02151 *Tel:* 781-284-9707 *Web Site:* www.soundandvisionmedia.com, pg 1017

Sound Arts Recording Studio, 8377 Westview Dr, Houston, TX 77055-5737 *Tel:* 713-464-4653 *Web Site:* www.soundartsrecording.com, pg 1017

Sound Associates Inc, 424 W 45 St, New York, NY 10036 *Tel:* 212-757-5679 *Toll Free Tel:* 888-772-7686 *Fax:* 212-265-1250 *E-mail:* newyork@soundassociates.com *Web Site:* www.soundassociates.com, pg 1017

Sound by Fitch, 1134 Ridge Rd, Pottstown, PA 19465 *Tel:* 610-469-6082 *Fax:* 610-469-0559, pg 1017

Sound by Singer Ltd, 242 W 27 St, 2nd fl, New York, NY 10001 *Tel:* 212-924-8600 *Fax:* 212-366-6351 *E-mail:* info@soundbysinger.com *Web Site:* www.soundbysinger.com, pg 1017

Sound Control Technologies Inc, 28 Knight St, Norwalk, CT 06851 *Tel:* 203-854-5701 *Fax:* 203-854-5702 *E-mail:* sales@soundcontrol.net *Web Site:* www.soundcontrol.net, pg 1017

Sound-Craft Systems Inc, 1584 Petit Jean Mountain Rd, Morrilton, AR 72110 *Tel:* 501-727-5476 *Toll Free Tel:* 800-643-8747 *Fax:* 501-727-5402 *E-mail:* sales@sound-craft.com *Web Site:* www.sound-craft.com, pg 1017

Sound Feelings Records, 18375 Ventura Blvd, No 8000, Tarzana, CA 91356 *Tel:* 818-757-0600 *Web Site:* www.soundfeelings.com, pg 1017

Sound-FX-Design, PO Box 3541, Newport, RI 02840 *Tel:* 401-952-1186 *E-mail:* info@sound-fx-design.com *Web Site:* www.sound-fx-design.com, pg 1017

Sound Ideas, 105 W Beaver Creek Rd, Suite 4, Richmond Hill, ON L4B 1C6, Canada *Tel:* 905-886-5000 *Toll Free Tel:* 800-387-3030 *Fax:* 905-886-6800 *E-mail:* info@sound-ideas.com *Web Site:* www.sound-ideas.com, pg 1017

The Sound Lab Inc, 3355 Bee Cave Rd, Bldg 7, Suite 705, Austin, TX 78746 *Tel:* 512-476-2122 *Fax:* 512-476-2127 *E-mail:* info@thesoundlabinc.com *Web Site:* www.thesoundlabinc.com, pg 1017

Sound*Light, 5438 Tennessee Ave, New Port Richey, FL 34652 *Tel:* 727-842-6788 *Fax:* 727-842-6788 *Web Site:* www.awakening-healing.com; www.soundlight.org, pg 1017

Sound of Birmingham Productions, 3625 Fifth Ave S, Birmingham, AL 35222 *Tel:* 205-595-8497 *Fax:* 205-595-5220 *Web Site:* www.soundofbirmingham.com, pg 1017

Sound Physics Labs Inc, PO Box 319, Glenview, IL 60025 *Tel:* 847-380-9390 *E-mail:* sales@soundphysics.com; info@soundphysics.com *Web Site:* www.soundphysics.com, pg 1017

Sound Service Co, 6630 Morella Ave, North Hollywood, CA 91606-1651 *Tel:* 818-503-4440, pg 1017

Sound Sound/Savage Fruitarian Productions, 843 Hiawatha Place S, Unit 304, Seattle, WA 98144 *Tel:* 206-322-6866 *Web Site:* www.soundsound.com, pg 1017

Sound Strations Audio Productions Inc, 3120 South Ave, La Crosse, WI 54601 *Tel:* 608-787-8133 *Fax:* 608-787-0012 *Web Site:* soundstrations.com, pg 1017

Sound Venture International, 441 MacLaren St, Suite 401, Ottawa, ON K2P 2H3, Canada *Tel:* 613-241-5111 *Fax:* 613-241-5010 *E-mail:* info@soundventure.com *Web Site:* www.soundventure.com, pg 1017

Sound/Video Impressions Inc, 110 S River Rd, Des Plaines, IL 60016 *Tel:* 847-297-4360 *Fax:* 847-297-6870 *E-mail:* info@soundvideoimpressions.com *Web Site:* www.soundvideoimpressions.com, pg 1018

Sound Vision Inc, 1450 Davis Rd, Elgin, IL 60123 *Tel:* 847-742-6000 *Fax:* 847-742-7585 *E-mail:* info@svi-avsystems.com *Web Site:* www.svi-avsystems.com, pg 1018

Sound Works, 7110 Gary St, Houston, TX 77055 *Tel:* 713-960-8222 (ext 1) *Fax:* 713-960-0122 *E-mail:* w3@soundworks.com; sworks@soundworks.com *Web Site:* www.soundworks.com, pg 1018

SoundByte Productions Inc, 353 W 48 St, 6th fl, New York, NY 10036 *Tel:* 212-675-0600 *Fax:* 212-675-3724 *E-mail:* info@soundbyte.com *Web Site:* www.soundbyte.com, pg 1018

Soundcraft USA, 8500 Balboa Blvd, North Ridge, CA 91329 *Tel:* 818-920-3212 *Fax:* 818-920-3209 *E-mail:* soundcraft-usa@harman.com *Web Site:* usa.soundcraft.com, pg 1018

Soundfold International, 9200 N State Rte 48, Centerville, OH 45458 *Tel:* 937-885-5100 *Toll Free Tel:* 800-782-8018 *Fax:* 937-885-5115 *Web Site:* www.soundfold.com, pg 1018

Soundmaster Group, 89 Barford Rd, Toronto, ON M9W 4H8, Canada *Tel:* 416-741-7057 *Fax:* 416-410-7057 *E-mail:* mail@soundmaster.com *Web Site:* www.soundmaster.com, pg 1018

Sounds Interesting Studios, 112 Fuller St, Middleboro, MA 02346 *Tel:* 508-947-7387 *Web Site:* www.soundsinterestingstudio.com, pg 1018

Sounds Unique, 1721-A Little Orchard St, San Jose, CA 95125 *Tel:* 408-287-3002 *Web Site:* www.soundsunique.com, pg 1018

SoundSpace Inc, 845 Dayton St, Yellow Springs, OH 45387 *Tel:* 937-767-7353 *Fax:* 937-767-7348 *E-mail:* soundspace@sbcglobal.net, pg 1018

Soundsphere, 10 Research Dr, Stratford, CT 06615 *Tel:* 203-386-9200 *Fax:* 203-386-0773 *E-mail:* info@soundsphere.com *Web Site:* www.soundsphere.com, pg 1018

SoundTech, 1000 Corporate Grove Dr, Buffalo Grove, IL 60089 *Tel:* 847-949-0444 *Toll Free Tel:* 800-US-SOUND (877-6863) *Fax:* 847-949-8444; 775-898-4891 *E-mail:* soundtech@soundtech.com *Web Site:* www.usmusiccorp.com; www.soundtech.com, pg 1018

Soundtrack Recording Studios, 162 Columbus Ave, Boston, MA 02116 *Tel:* 617-303-7500 *Fax:* 617-303-7555 *Web Site:* www.soundtrackboston.com, pg 1018

Soundtracks Production Services LLC, 22 N Central Ave, Sicklerville, NJ 08081 *Tel:* 856-728-8112 *Fax:* 856-728-8075 *E-mail:* info@soundtracksnj.com *Web Site:* www.soundtracksnj.com, pg 1018

Soundtrax Optical Sound Recording, 8116 Brucar Ct, Gaithersburg, MD 20877 *Tel:* 301-948-4288 *Fax:* 301-869-9061, pg 1018

SoundTube Entertainment, 6430 N Business Park Loop, Park City, UT 84098 *Tel:* 435-647-9555 *Toll Free Tel:* 800-647-TUBE (647-8823) *Fax:* 435-647-9666 *E-mail:* sales@soundtube.com *Web Site:* www.soundtube.com, pg 1018

SoundView Services Inc, One Phillips Dr NW, Leesburg, VA 20176 *Tel:* 703-777-9570 *Toll Free Tel:* 866-680-8189 *E-mail:* info@soundviewservices.com *Web Site:* www.soundviewservices.com, pg 1018

Source Film Studio, 1111 N Beachwood Dr, Hollywood, CA 90038 *Tel:* 323-463-5555 *E-mail:* info@sourcefilmstudio.com *Web Site:* www.sourcefilmstudio.com, pg 1018

Source School of Tantra Yoga Inc, PO Box 368, Kahului, HI 96733 *Tel:* 808-572-8364 *Toll Free Tel:* 888-6-TANTRA (682-6872) *Fax:* 831-703-4221 *E-mail:* school@sourcetantra.com *Web Site:* www.sourcetantra.com, pg 1019

The Source Stock Footage Library Inc, 140 S Camino Seco, Suite 308, Tucson, AZ 85710 *Tel:* 520-298-4810 *Fax:* 520-290-4376 *E-mail:* requests@sourcefootage.com *Web Site:* www.sourcefootage.com, pg 1019

South Carolina Film Commission, 1205 Pendleton St, Rm 225, Columbia, SC 29201-3261 *Tel:* 803-737-0490 *Fax:* 803-734-0670 *E-mail:* filmsc@scprt.com *Web Site:* www.filmsc.com, pg 1102

South Coast Film & Video, 5234 Elm St, Houston, TX 77081 *Tel:* 713-661-3550 *Toll Free Tel:* 800-229-3550 *Fax:* 713-661-4357 *E-mail:* info@scfilmvideo.com *Web Site:* www.scfilmvideo.com, pg 1019

South Dakota Film Office, Dept of Tourism, 711 E Wells Ave, Pierre, SD 57501-3369 *Tel:* 605-773-3301 *Toll Free Tel:* 800-952-3625 *Fax:* 605-773-3256 *E-mail:* filmsd@state.sd.us *Web Site:* www.filmsd.com, pg 1102

South Florida Rehearsal Studios, 1885 NE 149 St, Suite 100, North Miami, FL 33181 *Tel:* 305-949-5303 *Fax:* 305-947-3030 *E-mail:* sfrsmusic@gmail.com *Web Site:* www.sfrs.net, pg 1019

South Trunk Studios, 825 S Trunk Ave, Dallas, TX 75210 *Tel:* 214-826-2513 *E-mail:* southtrunk@earthlink.net *Web Site:* www.southtrunk.com, pg 1019

South-Western Publishing Co, 5191 Natorp Blvd, Mason, OH 45040 *Tel:* 513-229-1000 *Toll Free Tel:* 800-543-0487 *Fax:* 513-229-1020 *E-mail:* esales@cengage.com *Web Site:* www.cengage.com, pg 1019

Southern Audio Visual, 11700 NW 102 Rd, Suite 15, Miami, FL 33178 *Tel:* 305-591-3888 *Fax:* 305-591-7105 *Web Site:* www.southernav.com, pg 1019

Southern California Sound Image Inc, 2415 Auto Park Way, Escondido, CA 92029-1222 *Tel:* 760-737-3900 *Fax:* 760-737-3929 *Web Site:* www.sound-image.com, pg 1019

Southern Illinois University, 605 Agriculture Dr, Mailcode 6632, Carbondale, IL 62901 *Tel:* 618-453-2258 *Fax:* 618-453-3010 *Web Site:* www.lib.siu.edu/departments/iss, pg 1019

Southwest Audio-Visual Inc, 3058 E Cairo, Springfield, MO 65802 *Tel:* 417-887-4900 *Fax:* 417-866-6500 *E-mail:* info@southwestav.com *Web Site:* www.southwestav.com, pg 1019

Southwest Binding & Laminating, 109 Millwell Ct, Maryland Heights, MO 63043-2509 *Tel:* 314-739-4400 *Toll Free Tel:* 800-325-3628 *Toll Free Fax:* 800-942-2010 *E-mail:* orders@swbindinglaminating.com *Web Site:* swbindinglaminating.com, pg 1019

SouthWest Organizing Project (SWOP), 211 Tenth St SW, Albuquerque, NM 87102-2919 *Tel:* 505-247-8832 *Fax:* 505-247-9972 *E-mail:* swop@swop.net *Web Site:* www.swop.net, pg 1019

Southwest Sound & Electronics Inc, 2323 Loop 410 NW, San Antonio, TX 78230-5348 *Tel:* 210-341-4411 *Fax:* 210-349-8300 *Web Site:* www.swsoundinc.com, pg 1019

Sovfoto/Eastfoto Inc, 263 W 20 St, Suite 3, New York, NY 10011 *Tel:* 212-727-8170 *Fax:* 212-727-8228 *E-mail:* info@sovfoto.com *Web Site:* www.sovfoto.com, pg 1019

Space Coast Film Commission, 430 Brevard Ave, Suite 150, Cocoa Village, FL 32922 *Tel:* 321-433-4470 *Toll Free Tel:* 877-57-BEACH (572-3224) *Fax:* 321-433-4476 *Web Site:* www.visitspacecoast.com/space-coast-film-commission, pg 1095

SpaceCam, 31111 Via Colinas, Suite 202, Westlake Village, CA 91362 *Tel:* 818-889-6060 *Fax:* 818-889-6062 *E-mail:* rentals@spacecam.com *Web Site:* spacecam.com, pg 1019

Sparkfactor, 1644 N Honore St, Suite 100, Chicago, IL 60622 *Tel:* 773-292-8000 *E-mail:* info@sparkfactor.com *Web Site:* www.sparkfactor.com, pg 1019

Sparkworks Media, 325 W Republican St, Seattle, WA 98119 *Tel:* 206-284-5500 *Fax:* 206-284-6611 *E-mail:* info@sparkworksmedia.com *Web Site:* sparkworksmedia.com, pg 1019

Sparrow Sound Design, 3501 N Southport, 2nd fl, Chicago, IL 60657-1435 *Tel:* 773-281-8510 *Fax:* 773-472-4330 *E-mail:* studio@chicagosound.com; southport@chicagosound.com *Web Site:* www.chicagosound.com, pg 1019

SPEAK HOUSE Audio™, 1844 E Montecito Ave, Phoenix, AZ 85016 *Tel:* 602-279-0900 *Fax:* 602-279-0980 *Web Site:* www.speakhouseaudio.com, pg 1019

Speakeasy Productions, 3616-B Falls Rd, Baltimore, MD 21211 *Tel:* 410-889-0374 *Web Site:* www.voiceover.com, pg 1020

Speakers Unlimited, 5565 Woodridge Dr, Columbus, OH 43213 *Tel:* 614-864-3703 *Fax:* 614-864-3876 *E-mail:* prospeak@aol.com *Web Site:* www.speakersunlimited.com, pg 1020

Special Archives Division, Motion Picture Branch, 8601 Adelphi Rd, College Park, MD 20740-6001 *Tel:* 301-837-2000 *Toll Free Tel:* 866-272-6272 (cust serv) *Fax:* 301-837-0483 *E-mail:* mopix@nara.gov *Web Site:* www.archives.gov, pg 1020

Special Effects Systems Inc, 6130 Edgewater Dr, Suite A, Orlando, FL 32810 *Tel:* 407-297-6520 *Toll Free Tel:* 877-297-1900 *Fax:* 407-297-4041 *E-mail:* sales@spfx.com; confetti.info@spfx.com *Web Site:* www.spfx.com, pg 1020

Special Effects Unlimited Inc, 1005 N Lillian Way, Hollywood, CA 90038 *Tel:* 323-466-3361 *Fax:* 323-466-5712 *E-mail:* seuefx@aol.com *Web Site:* www.specialefxunltd.com, pg 1020

Special Event Services, 3135 Indiana Ave, Winston-Salem, NC 27105 *Tel:* 336-725-7799 *Toll Free Tel:* 800-423-3996 *Fax:* 336-725-0019 *Web Site:* www.specialeventservices.com, pg 1020

Special Projects, 345 Glen Iris Dr NE, Atlanta, GA 30312-1445 *Tel:* 404-588-2800 *Toll Free Tel:* 888-588-2800 *Fax:* 678-904-6629 *E-mail:* info@specialprojects.tv *Web Site:* www.specialprojects.tv, pg 1020

Speciality Bulb Products Inc, 20010-100A Ave, Unit 2, Langley, BC V1M 3G4, Canada *Tel:* 604-513-8500 *Toll Free Tel:* 800-663-1120 *Fax:* 604-513-8200 *E-mail:* info@specialtybulb.com; bulbexpert@specialtybulb.com *Web Site:* www.specialtybulb.com, pg 1020

Specialized Audio-Visual Inc, 14 Solar Dr, Clifton Park, NY 12065 *Tel:* 518-383-6501 *Fax:* 518-383-6506 *E-mail:* info@saviusa.com; sales@saviusa.com *Web Site:* www.saviusa.com, pg 1020

Specialized Products Co, 1100 S Kimball Ave, Southlake, TX 76092 *Tel:* 817-329-6647 *Toll Free Tel:* 800-866-5353 *Fax:* 817-329-6195 *Toll Free Fax:* 800-234-8286 *E-mail:* info@specialized.net *Web Site:* www.specialized.net, pg 1020

Specialty Bulb Co Inc, 80 Orville Dr, Bohemia, NY 11716 *Tel:* 631-589-3393 *Toll Free Tel:* 800-331-BULB (331-2852) *Fax:* 631-563-3089 *E-mail:* info@bulbspecialists.com *Web Site:* www.bulbspecialists.com, pg 1020

Specialty Tapes LLC, 4221 Courtney Rd, Franksville, WI 53126 *Tel:* 262-835-0748 *Toll Free Tel:* 800-545-8273 *Fax:* 262-835-0749 *E-mail:* sales@specialtytapes.net *Web Site:* www.specialtytapes.net, pg 1020

Speco/Systems & Products Engineering Co, 709 N Sixth St, Kansas City, KS 66101 *Tel:* 913-321-3978 *Toll Free Tel:* 800-633-5913 *Fax:* 913-321-7439, pg 1020

Spectra Cine Inc, 3607 W Magnolia Blvd, Burbank, CA 91505 *Tel:* 818-954-9222 *Fax:* 818-954-0016 *E-mail:* info@spectracine.com *Web Site:* www.spectracine.com, pg 1020

Spectra Film & Video, 5626 Vineland Ave, North Hollywood, CA 91601 *Tel:* 818-762-4545 *Fax:* 818-762-5454 *E-mail:* sales@spectrafilmandvideo.com *Web Site:* www.spectrafilmandvideo.com, pg 1020

Spectra Sonics Applied Technology Inc, 860 W Riverdale Rd, Unit D6, Riverdale, UT 84405 *Tel:* 801-605-8849 *Fax:* 801-689-2967 *Web Site:* www.spectra-sonics.com, pg 1020

Spectra Video Productions Ltd, 309 Wardlaw Ave, Winnipeg, MB R3L 0L5, Canada *Tel:* 204-452-9832 *Web Site:* www.spectra-productions.com, pg 1020

Spectrum Audio Visual Services, 351 W 45 Ave, Denver, CO 80216 *Tel:* 303-477-4456 *Toll Free Tel:* 800-477-4752 *Fax:* 303-477-0114 *E-mail:* info@spectrumav.com *Web Site:* www.spectrumav.com, pg 1020

Spectrum Engineers, 324 S State St, Suite 400, Salt Lake City, UT 84111 *Tel:* 801-328-5151 *Toll Free Tel:* 800-678-7077 *Fax:* 801-328-5155 *E-mail:* info@spectrum-engineers.com *Web Site:* www.spectrum-engineers.com, pg 1021

Spectrum Industries Inc, 925 First Ave, Chippewa Falls, WI 54729 *Tel:* 715-723-6750 *Toll Free Tel:* 800-235-1262 *Toll Free Fax:* 800-335-0473 *E-mail:* info@spectrumfurniture.com *Web Site:* www.spectrumfurniture.com, pg 1021

Spectrum Productions, 565 Pinedale Dr, Annapolis, MD 21401 *Web Site:* www.markgoldberg.com, pg 1021

Spectrum Sound Inc, 1040 Acorn Dr, Suite C, Nashville, TN 37210 *Tel:* 615-391-3700 *Web Site:* www.spectrumsound.net, pg 1021

Spectrum Systems Design, 937 SW 14 Ave, Suite 101, Portland, OR 97205 *Tel:* 503-248-0248 *Toll Free Tel:* 800-288-3492 *Fax:* 503-274-7684 *Web Site:* www.spectrumsd.com, pg 1021

Speedotron Corp, 1268 Humbracht Circle, Bartlett, IL 60103-1631 *Tel:* 630-246-5001 *Fax:* 630-830-2525 *E-mail:* support@speedotron.com *Web Site:* www.speedotron.com, pg 1021

Spence-Thomas Audio Post, 70 Richmond St E, Suite 300, Toronto, ON M5C 1N8, Canada *Tel:* 416-361-6383 *Toll Free Tel:* 866-547-2617 *Fax:* 416-361-2970 *E-mail:* info@spence-thomas.com; bookings@spence-thomas.com *Web Site:* www.spence-thomas.com, pg 1021

Spider Support Systems, 11654 Plaza America Dr, Suite 180, Reston, VA 20190 *Tel:* 703-758-0699 *Fax:* 703-935-8899 *Web Site:* www.spidersupport.com, pg 1021

SPIE, PO Box 10, Bellingham, WA 98227-0010 *Tel:* 360-676-3290 *Toll Free Tel:* 888-504-8171 *Fax:* 360-647-1445 *E-mail:* customerservice@spie.org *Web Site:* www.spie.org, pg 1089

Spina Bifida Association, 4590 MacArthur Blvd NW, Suite 250, Washington, DC 20007 *Tel:* 202-944-3285 *Toll Free Tel:* 800-621-3141 (outside DC) *Fax:* 202-944-3295 *E-mail:* sbaa@sbaa.org *Web Site:* www.sbaa.org, pg 1021

Spire Audio Visual Co Inc, 12170 SW 128 Ct, Unit 105, Miami, FL 33186 *Tel:* 305-378-5334; 786-367-3408 (cell) *Fax:* 786-397-7462 *Web Site:* www.spireav.com, pg 1021

Spirig Advanced Technologies Inc (SAT), 144 Oakland St, Springfield, MA 01108 *Tel:* 413-788-6191 *Toll Free Tel:* 866-977-4744 *Fax:* 413-788-0490 *E-mail:* sat@spirig.com; order@spirig.com *Web Site:* www.spirig.com, pg 1021

Spirit Media, 12042 SE Sunnyside Rd, Suite 700, Happy Valley, OR 97015 *Tel:* 503-698-5540 *Fax:* 503-698-8408 *E-mail:* info@spiritmedia.com *Web Site:* www.spiritmedia.com, pg 1021

Spizzirri Press Inc, PO Box 9397, Rapid City, SD 57709-9397 *Tel:* 605-348-2749 *Toll Free Tel:* 800-325-9819 *Fax:* 605-348-6251 *Toll Free Fax:* 800-322-9819 *E-mail:* spizzpub@aol.com *Web Site:* www.spizzirri.com, pg 1021

Split Image Productions, 4134 243 St, Flushing, NY 11363-1658 *Tel:* 718-428-1438 *Fax:* 718-428-1438, pg 1021

Spoken Arts Inc, 195 S White Rock Rd, Holmes, NY 12531 *Tel:* 845-878-9600 *Toll Free Tel:* 800-326-4090 *Fax:* 845-878-9009 *E-mail:* sales@spokenartsmedia.com *Web Site:* www.spokenartsmedia.com, pg 1021

Spoken Language Services Inc, PO Box 17113, Urbana, IL 61803 *Tel:* 217-328-0173 *Fax:* 217-328-0177 *E-mail:* orders@spokenlanguage.com, pg 1021

Sports Cinematography Group, 73 Market St, Venice, CA 90291-3606 *Tel:* 310-785-9100 *Fax:* 310-564-7500 *E-mail:* sportscinema@earthlink.net *Web Site:* www.sportscinematographygroup.com, pg 1021

Sportsmen on Film Inc, 231 Earl Garrett, Suite 300, Kerrville, TX 78028 *Tel:* 830-792-4200 *Toll Free Tel:* 800-910-HUNT (910-4868) *Fax:* 830-792-4224 *Web Site:* www.sportsmenonfilm.com, pg 1021

Spot Media Production Group, 2745 Locust St, St Louis, MO 63103 *Tel:* 314-667-5915 *E-mail:* info@spotmpg.com *Web Site:* www.spotmpg.com, pg 1022

Sprayway Inc, 1005 S Westgate Ave, Addison, IL 60101 *Tel:* 630-628-3000 *Toll Free Tel:* 800-332-9000 *Fax:* 630-543-7797 *E-mail:* info@spraywayinc.com *Web Site:* www.spraywayinc.com, pg 1022

Spring Arbor Distributors, One Ingram Blvd, LaVergne, TN 37086-1986 *Tel:* 615-793-5000 (Ingram) *Toll Free Tel:* 800-395-4340 (Christian); 800-395-5599 (sales); 800-234-6737 (electronic ordering); 877-846-6989 (software support); 800-395-7234 (cust serv) *Fax:* 615-213-5192 *E-mail:* custserv@springarbor.com; orders@springarbor.com *Web Site:* www.ingramcontent.com, pg 1022

Sprocket Digital, PO Box 1420, Claremont, CA 91711 *Tel:* 909-946-2364 *Fax:* 909-946-2631 *E-mail:* sdsales@sprocketdigital.com *Web Site:* www.sprocketdigital.com, pg 1022

SSL Industries Inc, 4935 Anne Louise Lane, Suite 2, Placerville, CA 95667 *Tel:* 530-644-0233 *E-mail:* sslind@starband.net *Web Site:* www.sslinc.net, pg 1022

ST Productions, 900 Whitehall Rd, Chattanooga, TN 37405 *Tel:* 423-267-5412 *Fax:* 423-267-6840 *E-mail:* stps@wrcbtv.com *Web Site:* www.wrcbtv.com, pg 1022

Tom Stack & Associates Inc, 154 Tequesta St, Tavernier, FL 33070 *Tel:* 305-852-5520 *E-mail:* tomstack@earthlink.net *Web Site:* tomstackassociates.photoshelter.com, pg 1022

Staco Energy Products Co, 301 Gaddis Blvd, Dayton, OH 45403 *Tel:* 937-253-1191 *Toll Free Tel:* 866-261-1191 *Fax:* 937-253-1723 *E-mail:* sales@stacoenergy.com; service@stacoenergy.com *Web Site:* www.stacoenergy.com, pg 1022

Staedtler-Mars Ltd, 5725 McLaughlin Rd, Mississauga, ON L5R 3K5, Canada *Tel:* 905-501-9008 *Toll Free Tel:* 800-776-5544; 800-387-5872 *Fax:* 905-501-9117 *Toll Free Fax:* 800-675-8249 *E-mail:* info@staedtler.ca *Web Site:* www.staedtler.ca, pg 1022

Stage America LLC, 4001 S Decatur 37, Suite 532, Las Vegas, NV 89103 *Tel:* 702-879-8177 *Toll Free Fax:* 877-488-6663 *E-mail:* info@stageamerica.com *Web Site:* www.stageamerica.com, pg 1022

Stage Crew Audiovisual Inc, PO Box 6097, San Juan, PR 00914-6097 *Tel:* 787-723-6398 *Fax:* 787-721-1410 *E-mail:* scav@stagecrewav.com *Web Site:* www.stagecrewav.com, pg 1022

Stage Directions, 8311 Hempstead Rd, Houston, TX 77008 *Tel:* 713-863-7469 *Fax:* 713-863-9418 *E-mail:* sales@stagedirections.com *Web Site:* www.stagedirections.com, pg 1022

Stage Equipment & Lighting Inc, 4600 SW 36 St, Orlando, FL 32811 *Tel:* 407-425-2010 *Fax:* 407-648-2604 *E-mail:* mail@seal-fla.com *Web Site:* www.seal-fla.com, pg 1022

Stage Front Presentation Systems, 6 Southern Oaks Dr, Savannah, GA 31405 *Tel:* 912-236-1345 *Toll Free Tel:* 800-736-9242 *Fax:* 912-233-5350 *Web Site:* www.sfps.net; www.stagefrontproductions.com, pg 1022

Stage Post, 255 French Landing Dr, Nashville, TN 37228 *Tel:* 615-248-1978 *Toll Free Tel:* 877-250-1839 *Fax:* 615-242-8861 *E-mail:* mail@stagepost.com *Web Site:* www.stagepost.com, pg 1022

Stage 3 Productions, 27500 Donald Ct, Warren, MI 48092 *Tel:* 586-576-0625 *Toll Free Tel:* 888-330-5179 *Web Site:* www.stage3.com, pg 1022

Stageline Mobile Stage Inc, 700 Marsolais St, L'Assomption, QC J5W 2G9, Canada *Tel:* 450-589-1063 *Toll Free Tel:* 800-26-STAGE (267-8243) *Fax:* 450-589-1711 *E-mail:* info@stageline.com *Web Site:* www.stageline.com, pg 1023

Stageright Corp, 495 Pioneer Pkwy, Clare, MI 48617 *Toll Free Tel:* 800-438-4499; 888-577-8243 (sales) *Fax:* 989-386-7393 *E-mail:* info@stageright.com *Web Site:* www.stageright.com, pg 1023

Stages Video Productions, 514 29 Ave N, Myrtle Beach, SC 29577 *Tel:* 843-626-7466 *E-mail:* info@stagesvideo.com *Web Site:* www.stagesvideo.com, pg 1023

StageSound, 2240 Shenandoah Ave NW, Roanoke, VA 24017 *Tel:* 540-342-2040 *Toll Free Tel:* 800-778-9839 *Fax:* 540-345-5158 *Web Site:* stagesound.com, pg 1023

Stagestep Inc, 4701 Bath St, No 46, Philadelphia, PA 19137 *Tel:* 215-636-9000 *Toll Free Tel:* 800-523-0960 (US & CN) *Fax:* 267-672-2912 *E-mail:* stagestep@stagestep.com; info@stagestep.com *Web Site:* www.stagestep.com, pg 1023

Staging Concepts, 7008 Northland Dr N, Suite 150, Minneapolis, MN 55428 *Tel:* 763-533-2094 *Toll Free Tel:* 800-337-5339 *E-mail:* info@stagingconcepts.com *Web Site:* www.stagingconcepts.com, pg 1023

Staging Directions Inc, 1327 Northbrook Pkwy, Suite 440, Suwanee, GA 30024 *Tel:* 770-409-9909 *Toll Free Tel:* 800-782-4322 *Fax:* 770-409-0277 *E-mail:* info@teamsdi.net; sales@teamsdi.net *Web Site:* www.stagingdirections.com, pg 1023

Staging Resources Inc, 257 E Helen Rd, Palatine, IL 60067 *Tel:* 847-963-6600 *Toll Free Tel:* 877-963-6600 *Fax:* 847-963-6601 *E-mail:* info@stagingresources.com *Web Site:* www.stagingresources.com, pg 1023

Stampede Presentation Products Inc, 55 Woodridge Dr, Amherst, NY 14228 *Tel:* 716-635-9474 *Toll Free Tel:* 800-398-5652 *Fax:* 716-635-9484 *E-mail:* stampedenews@stampedeglobal.com *Web Site:* www.stampede-us.com, pg 1023

Stanco Sales LLC, 1529 S Terry St, Longmont, CO 80501 *Tel:* 303-776-3770 *E-mail:* stancosales@comcast.net, pg 1023

James Stanfield Co Inc, 129 S Quarantina St, Santa Barbara, CA 93103 *Tel:* 805-897-1185 *Toll Free Tel:* 800-421-6534 *Fax:* 805-897-1187 *E-mail:* maindesk@stanfield.com *Web Site:* www.stanfield.com, pg 1023

Stanford Research Systems Inc, 1290-D Reamwood Ave, Sunnyvale, CA 94089 *Tel:* 408-744-9040 *Fax:* 408-744-9049 *E-mail:* info@thinksrs.com *Web Site:* www.thinksrs.com, pg 1023

Stanislaus Audio Video Inc, 1431 Kansas Ave, Modesto, CA 95351 *Tel:* 209-529-2700 *Fax:* 209-529-7355 *E-mail:* info@stanav.com *Web Site:* www.stanav.com, pg 1023

Stanley Film Festival, 1510 York St, 3rd fl, Denver, CO 80206 *Tel:* 970-577-4111 *E-mail:* stanley@denverfilm.org *Web Site:* www.stanleyfilmfest.com, pg 1127

Jay S Stanley & Associates Inc, 5313 McClanahan Dr, Suite G-5, North Little Rock, AR 72116 *Tel:* 501-758-8029 *Toll Free Tel:* 888-758-4728 *Fax:* 501-758-8037 *E-mail:* info@jaystanley.com *Web Site:* www.jaystanley.com, pg 1023

Stanley Supply & Services Inc, 335 Willow St, North Andover, MA 01845-5995 *Tel:* 978-682-9844 *Toll Free Tel:* 800-225-5370 (sales) *Toll Free Fax:* 800-743-8141 *E-mail:* sales@stanleyworks.com *Web Site:* www.stanleysupplyservices.com, pg 1023

Stanton Magnetics, c/o Gibson Pro Audio, 309 Plus Park Blvd, Nashville, TN 37217 *Toll Free Tel:* 800-4GIBSON (444-2766) *Web Site:* stantondj.com, pg 1023

Star Case Manufacturing Co Inc, 648 Superior Ave, Munster, IN 46321 *Tel:* 219-922-4440 *Toll Free Tel:* 800-822-STAR (822-7827); 800-782-CASE (782-2273) *Fax:* 219-922-4442 *E-mail:* star@starcase.com *Web Site:* www.starcase.com, pg 1023

Star Video Duplicating, 6910 E Fifth Ave, Scottsdale, AZ 85251 *Tel:* 480-946-3699 *Toll Free Tel:* 800-238-7827 *Fax:* 480-946-4722 *Web Site:* www.starvideo.com, pg 1024

Starburns Industries, 1700 W Burbank Blvd, Burbank, CA 91506 *Tel:* 818-433-3300 *Fax:* 818-433-3383 *Web Site:* www.starburnsindustries.com, pg 1024

Starline Costume, 1286 Bandera Rd, San Antonio, TX 78228 *Tel:* 210-435-3535 *Fax:* 210-435-9425 *Web Site:* starlinecostumes.com, pg 1024

Starlite Productions, 9 Whittendale Dr, Moorestown, NJ 08057 *Tel:* 856-780-8000 *Toll Free Tel:* 800-738-7400 *Fax:* 856-780-8001 *E-mail:* info@starlite.com *Web Site:* www.starlite.com, pg 1024

StarTrak Studios Inc, 36 Vermont Ave, Unit 1, Warwick, RI 02888 *Tel:* 401-732-1880 *E-mail:* info@startrakstudios.com *Web Site:* www.startrakstudios.com, pg 1024

Starwest Productions, 8760 W 68 Place, Arvada, CO 80004 *Tel:* 303-295-2222 *E-mail:* info@starwest.com, pg 1024

Starz Denver Film Festival, 1510 York St, 3rd fl, Denver, CO 80206 *Tel:* 303-595-3456 *Fax:* 303-595-0956 *E-mail:* info@denverfilm.org *Web Site:* www.denverfilm.org/festival, pg 1127

State of Hawaii Film Office, 250 S Hotel St, Suite 510-A, Honolulu, HI 96813 *Tel:* 808-586-2570 *Fax:* 808-586-2572 *E-mail:* info@hawaiifilmoffice.com *Web Site:* www.filmoffice.hawaii.gov, pg 1097

State of the Art Acoustik Inc, 43-1010 Polytek St, Ottawa, ON K1J 9J3, Canada *Tel:* 613-745-2003 *Fax:* 613-745-9687 *E-mail:* sota@sota.ca *Web Site:* www.sota.ca, pg 1024

Staylor-Made Communications Inc, 11835 Carmel Mountain Rd, Suite 1304-365, San Diego, CA 92128-4609 *Tel:* 858-779-4266 *Toll Free Tel:* 800-711-6699 *E-mail:* info@staylor-made.com *Web Site:* staylor-made.com, pg 1024

Stedman Corp, 4167 Stedman Dr, Richland, MI 49083 *Tel:* 269-629-5930 *Toll Free Tel:* 888-629-5960 *E-mail:* info@stedmancorp.com *Web Site:* www.stedmancorp.com, pg 1024

Steeldeck® Inc, 3339 Exposition Place, Los Angeles, CA 90018-4034 *Tel:* 323-290-2100 *Toll Free Tel:* 800-50STAGE (507-8243) *Fax:* 323-290-9600 *E-mail:* sales@steeldeck.com; rentals@steeldeck.com *Web Site:* www.steeldeck.com, pg 1024

Steiner Studios, 15 Washington Ave, Brooklyn Navy Yard, Brooklyn, NY 11205 *Tel:* 718-858-1600 *Web Site:* www.steinerstudios.com, pg 1024

Stereo Sales Inc, 1530 S Monroe St, Tallahassee, FL 32301 *Tel:* 850-224-2635 *Fax:* 850-224-0950 *E-mail:* sales@stereosales.net *Web Site:* www.stereosales.org; www.stereosales.net, pg 1024

StereoScope International, 727 N Victory Blvd, Burbank, CA 91502 *Tel:* 818-919-6253 *E-mail:* stereoscope3d@gmail.com, pg 1024

Stevens Design & Animation LLC, 3405 Calle Cuervo NW, Unit 912, Albuquerque, NM 87114 *Tel:* 505-200-2042 *Web Site:* stevensanimation.com, pg 1024

Kris Stevens Enterprises, 22362 Dardenne St, Calabasas, CA 91302 *Tel:* 818-225-7585 *E-mail:* inquiry@kriserikstevens.com *Web Site:* www.kriserikstevens.com, pg 1024

Stevenson Photography, 530 E Erie Dr, Tempe, AZ 85282 *Tel:* 480-967-6312 *E-mail:* info@stevensonphotography.com *Web Site:* www.stevensonphotography.com, pg 1024

Stewart Acoustical Consultants, 7330 Chapel Hill Rd, Suite 101, Raleigh, NC 27607 *Tel:* 919-858-0899 *Fax:* 919-858-0878 *Web Site:* www.sacnc.com, pg 1025

Stewart Audio, 14397 Cuesta Ct, Suite D1, Sonora, CA 95370 *Tel:* 209-588-8111 *Fax:* 209-588-8113 *E-mail:* sales@stewartaudio.com; support@stewartaudio.com *Web Site:* www.stewartaudio.com, pg 1025

Stewart Filmscreen Corp, 1161 Sepulveda Blvd, Torrance, CA 90502-2754 *Tel:* 310-784-5300 *Toll Free Tel:* 800-762-4999 (North America only) *Fax:* 310-326-6870 *E-mail:* request@stewartfilmscreen.com *Web Site:* www.stewartfilmscreen.com, pg 1025

STIL Casing Solution, 76 Saint Paul, Suite 301, Quebec City, QC G1K 3V9, Canada *Tel:* 418-694-0449 (ext 10); 418-694-0449 (ext 11, sales & cust serv); 418-694-0449 (ext 12, admin) *Toll Free Tel:* 888-414-0449 (CN & US) *Fax:* 418-694-1621 *E-mail:* info@stilcasing.com; sales@stilcasing.com; admin@stilcasing.com *Web Site:* www.stilcasing.com, pg 1025

Still N'Motion, 1727 Little Orchard St, Suite A, San Jose, CA 95125 *Tel:* 408-292-9982 *Fax:* 408-292-9987 *E-mail:* info1@stillnmotion.com *Web Site:* www.stillnmotion.com, pg 1025

Stockfootage.com, 231 S Mountain Way Dr, Orem, UT 84058 *Tel:* 801-221-9570; 801-361-0012 (cell) *E-mail:* sales@stockfootage.com *Web Site:* www.stockfootage.com, pg 1025

StockMusic.com, 105 W Beaver Creek Rd, Suite 4, Richmond Hill, ON L4B 1C6, Canada *Tel:* 905-886-0077 *Fax:* 905-886-6800 *E-mail:* info@stockmusic.com *Web Site:* www.stockmusic.com, pg 1025

Stockton/San Joaquin Film Liaison, 125 Bridge Place, Stockton, CA 95202 *Tel:* 209-938-1555 *Toll Free Tel:* 877-778-6258 *Fax:* 209-938-1554 *Web Site:* visitstockton.org/footer/resources/stockton-film-commission, pg 1094

Stockyard Photos/Jim Olive Photography, 1520 Center St, Studio 2, Houston, TX 77007 *Tel:* 713-520-0898 *Fax:* 713-820-6965 *Web Site:* www.stockyard.com, pg 1025

Stoney-Wolf Productions Inc, 130 W Columbia Ct, Chaska, MN 55318-2304 *Tel:* 952-556-0075 *Toll Free Tel:* 800-237-7583 *Fax:* 952-361-4217 *E-mail:* sales@stoneywolf.com *Web Site:* www.stoneywolf.com, pg 1025

StoryTrack, 212 S Bemiston, St Louis, MO 63105 *Tel:* 314-725-3003 *Web Site:* www.storytrack.com, pg 1025

Stouffer Graphic Arts, 922 S Cleveland St, Mishawaka, IN 46544 *Tel:* 574-252-5772 *Fax:* 574-252-5776 *E-mail:* info@stouffer.net *Web Site:* www.stouffer.net, pg 1025

Straight Shoot'r Cranes Inc, 18434 Oxnard St, Unit H, Tarzana, CA 91356 *Tel:* 818-609-8310 *Fax:* 818-609-8311 *Web Site:* www.straightshootr.com, pg 1025

Straight Wire Inc, 2032 Scott St, Hollywood, FL 33020 *Tel:* 954-925-2470 *Toll Free Tel:* 800-683-4434 *Fax:* 954-925-7253 *E-mail:* info@straightwire.com *Web Site:* www.straightwire.com, pg 1025

Strand Lighting Inc, 10911 Petal St, Dallas, TX 75238 *Tel:* 214-647-7880 *Fax:* 214-647-8031 *E-mail:* sales@strandlighting.com *Web Site:* www.strandlighting.com, pg 1025

Strata™, 3013 Santa Clara Dr, Santa Clara, UT 84765 *Tel:* 435-628-5218 *Toll Free Tel:* 800-STRATA-3D (787-2823); 800-6-STRATA (678-7282) *Fax:* 435-628-9756 *E-mail:* sales@strata.com *Web Site:* www.strata.com, pg 1025

Strategic Connections, 2721 Spring Forest Rd, Raleigh, NC 27616 *Tel:* 919-878-0550 *Fax:* 919-875-8712 *E-mail:* info@strategicmail.net *Web Site:* www.strategicconnections.net, pg 1026

Strauss Photo Technical Service Inc, 4574 Beech Rd, Temple Hills, MD 20748 *Tel:* 202-529-3200 *Fax:* 202-526-6465 *E-mail:* info@straussphototech.com *Web Site:* www.straussphototech.com, pg 1026

Stray Angel Films, 2236 S Barrington Ave, Los Angeles, CA 90064 *Tel:* 310-277-6900 *Fax:* 801-438-5009 *E-mail:* rentals@strayangel.com *Web Site:* www.strayangel.com, pg 1026

Stretching Inc, PO Box 767, Palmer Lake, CO 80133-0767 *Tel:* 719-481-3928 *Toll Free Tel:* 800-333-1307 *Fax:* 719-481-9058 *E-mail:* office@stretching.com *Web Site:* www.stretching.com, pg 1026

Stricker Books, 8 Main St N, Unit C, Acton, ON L7J 1W1, Canada *Tel:* 519-853-2780 *Toll Free Tel:* 800-924-3966 *Fax:* 519-853-2847 *E-mail:* stricker@strickerbooks.com *Web Site:* www.strickerbooks.com, pg 1026

Strong Cinema Products, 13710 FNB Pkwy, Suite 400, Omaha, NE 68145 *Tel:* 402-453-4444 *Toll Free Tel:* 800-424-1215 *Fax:* 402-453-7238 *E-mail:* info@btn-inc.com *Web Site:* www.strong-world.com, pg 1026

Strong Entertainment Lighting, 13710 FNB Pkwy, Suite 400, Omaha, NE 68154 *Tel:* 402-453-4444 *Toll Free Tel:* 800-424-1215 *Fax:* 402-453-7238 *E-mail:* info@btn-inc.com *Web Site:* www.strong-world.com, pg 1026

Strong Screen Systems, 1440 Raoul-Charrette, Joliette, QC J6E 8S7, Canada *Tel:* 450-755-3795 *Toll Free Tel:* 877-755-3795 *Fax:* 450-755-3122 *E-mail:* sales@strong-mdicinema.com *Web Site:* www.strong-world.com; www.mdicinema.com, pg 1026

Joseph Struhl Co Inc, 195 Atlantic Ave, Garden City Park, NY 11040 *Tel:* 516-741-3660 *Toll Free Tel:* 800-552-0023 *Fax:* 516-742-3617 *E-mail:* info@magicmaster.com; orders@magicmaster.com *Web Site:* www.magicmaster.com, pg 1026

Student Academy Awards Competition, 8949 Wilshire Blvd, Beverly Hills, CA 90211 *Tel:* 310-247-3000 *Fax:* 310-859-9619 *E-mail:* SAA@oscars.org *Web Site:* www.oscars.org/saa, pg 1127

Studio A Recording Inc, 5619 N Beech Daly, Dearborn Heights, MI 48127-3927 *Tel:* 313-561-7489 *Fax:* 313-561-6736 *Web Site:* www.studioarecording.com, pg 1026

Studio B Mastering, 821 Louise Ave, Charlotte, NC 28204 *Tel:* 704-372-9661 *Web Site:* www.studiobmastering.com, pg 1026

The Studio Center, 915 Fee Dr, Sacramento, CA 95815 *Tel:* 916-564-9333 *E-mail:* info@thestudiocenter.com *Web Site:* www.thestudiocenter.com, pg 1026

Studio Center Corp, 161 Business Park Dr, Virginia Beach, VA 23462 *Tel:* 757-286-3080 (24 hour cell) *Toll Free Tel:* 866-515-2111 *Fax:* 757-622-0583 (acctg) *Web Site:* www.studiocenter.com, pg 1026

Studio Charleston, 620 Dobbin Rd, Charleston, SC 29414 *Tel:* 843-376-1190 *Fax:* 843-737-4282 *E-mail:* info@studiocharleston.com *Web Site:* www.studiocharleston.com, pg 1026

Studio Consulting & Construction Inc, 2805 Oakview Dr, Dryden, MI 48428-9740 *Tel:* 810-796-3235; 248-496-9000 *E-mail:* scc@hdakers.com *Web Site:* www.hdakers.com, pg 1026

Studio Dynamics, 7703 Alondra Blvd, Paramount, CA 90723 *Tel:* 562-531-6700 *Toll Free Tel:* 800-595-4273 *Fax:* 562-531-6769 *E-mail:* sales@studiodynamics.com *Web Site:* www.studiodynamics.com, pg 1026

Studio 1444, 1444 N Highland Ave, Hollywood, CA 90028 *Tel:* 323-482-1004 *E-mail:* info@studio1444.com *Web Site:* www.studio1444.com, pg 1026

Studio Instrument Rentals (SIR), 475 Tenth Ave, 2nd fl, New York, NY 10018 *Tel:* 212-627-4900 *Fax:* 212-627-7079 *E-mail:* nyinfo@sir-usa.com *Web Site:* www.sir-usa.com, pg 1027

The Studio of David Inocencio/Minette Siegel, 41 Fairlawn Ave, Daly City, CA 94015 *Tel:* 415-716-2791 *Fax:* 415-716-2796 *Web Site:* www.ino-sieg.com, pg 1027

Studio 1 Productions™ Inc, 1700 Destino Ct, Port Orange, FL 32128 *Tel:* 386-788-6075 *Fax:* 386-760-5474 *E-mail:* studio1@studio1productions.com *Web Site:* www.studio1productions.com, pg 1027

Studio 132, 6802 Gunn Dr, Oakland, CA 94611-1443 *Tel:* 510-338-1240 *E-mail:* info@studio132.com *Web Site:* www.studio132.com, pg 1027

Studio 6429, 6429 Independence Ave, Woodland Hills, CA 91367 *Tel:* 818-710-0016 *E-mail:* paulformanek@studio6429.tv *Web Site:* studio6429.tv, pg 1027

Studio 637, 637 Cypress Ave, Hermosa Beach, CA 90254 *Tel:* 310-372-8218 *Web Site:* studio-637.com, pg 1027

Studio South, 4912 Old Pineville Rd, Charlotte, NC 28217 *Tel:* 704-525-0296 *Fax:* 704-525-0136 *E-mail:* studiosouthvideo@earthlink.net *Web Site:* www.studiosouthmedia.com, pg 1027

Studio Space Atlanta, 3080 McCall Dr, Suite 2, Atlanta, GA 30340 *Tel:* 404-630-0508 *E-mail:* info@studiospaceatl.com *Web Site:* www.studiospaceatl.com, pg 1027

Studio Technologies Inc, 5520 W Touhy Ave, Skokie, IL 60077 *Tel:* 847-676-9177 *Fax:* 847-982-0747 *E-mail:* stisales-2014@studio-tech.com *Web Site:* www.studio-tech.com, pg 1027

Studio Worx Inc, 8252 Brentwood Industrial Dr, Brentwood, MO 63144 *Tel:* 314-968-2626 *Fax:* 314-968-9866 *E-mail:* studioworxinc@studioworxinc.com *Web Site:* www.studioworxinc.com, pg 1027

Studio14DC, 1121 14 St, 5th fl, Washington, DC 20005 *Tel:* 202-216-8944 *E-mail:* info@studio14dc.com *Web Site:* studio14dc.com, pg 1027

The Studios at Paramount, 5555 Melrose Ave, Hollywood, CA 90038 *Tel:* 323-956-5000 *Web Site:* www.paramountstudios.com, pg 1027

Stunt Wings Adventure Sports Talent & Equipment, 12623 Gridley St, Sylmar, CA 91342 *Tel:* 818-367-2430; 818-353-5580 (home); 818-266-0874 (cell) *Fax:* 818-367-5363 *E-mail:* stuntwings@me.com *Web Site:* www.stuntwings.com, pg 1027

Russ Sturgeon Productions/RSVP, 916 Third Ave S, Nashville, TN 37210 *Tel:* 615-255-7787 *Fax:* 615-254-7788 *Web Site:* www.rsvpnashville.com, pg 1027

Style-City Music Inc, 7826 Rhodes Rd, Suite 6, Hudson, FL 34667 *Tel:* 727-520-2336 *E-mail:* mail@stylecitymusic.com; stylecitymusic@yahoo.com *Web Site:* www.stylecitymusic.com, pg 1027

Substation K, 3947 State Line Rd, Kansas City, MO 64111 *Tel:* 816-531-3838 *Fax:* 816-531-3839 *Web Site:* www.substationk.com, pg 1027

Suede Interactive, 693 Main St, Hackensack, NJ 07601-4713 *Tel:* 201-646-0416 *E-mail:* suede@suede.tv *Web Site:* www.suede.tv, pg 1027

Suffolk County Film Commission, H Lee Dennison Bldg, 2nd fl, 100 Veterans Memorial Hwy, Hauppauge, NY 11788-0099 *Tel:* 631-853-4800 *Fax:* 631-853-4888 *Web Site:* www.suffolkcountyfilmcommission.com, pg 1100

Sugar Mountain PR, 5505 SW Illinois St, Portland, OR 97221-1643 *Tel:* 503-293-9498 *E-mail:* sugarmountainnews@msn.com *Web Site:* www.sugarmountainpr.com, pg 1028

Suggs Media Productions Inc, 156 W 44 St, New York, NY 10036 *Tel:* 212-398-4200 *Fax:* 212-382-0922, pg 1028

Sullivan Home Entertainment, 110 Davenport Rd, Toronto, ON M5R 3R3, Canada *Tel:* 416-921-7177 *Fax:* 416-921-7538 *E-mail:* inquire@sullivan-ent.com *Web Site:* www.sullivanmovies.com, pg 1028

Sumiko Inc, 2431 Fifth St, Berkeley, CA 94710 *Tel:* 510-843-4500 *Toll Free Tel:* 800-301-0799 *Fax:* 510-843-7120 *E-mail:* mail@sumikoaudio.net *Web Site:* www.sumikoaudio.net, pg 1028

Summit Audio Inc, 5706 Corsa Ave, Suite 102, Westlake Village, CA 91362 *Tel:* 775-782-8838 *Fax:* 775-782-8350 *E-mail:* sound@summitaudio.com *Web Site:* www.summitaudio.com, pg 1028

Summit Electronics Corp, 1060 Holland Dr, Suite M, Boca Raton, FL 33487 *Tel:* 561-226-8500 *Toll Free Tel:* 800-226-6960 *Fax:* 561-226-8523 *E-mail:* sales@summitelectronics.com *Web Site:* www.summitelectronics.com; www.partsprocurement.com; bocasemi.com, pg 1028

Sun Entertainment Corp, 3106 Belmont Blvd, Nashville, TN 37212 *Tel:* 615-385-1960 *E-mail:* info@sunrecords.com *Web Site:* www.sunrecords.com, pg 1028

Sunburst Digital, 3150 W Higgins Rd, Suite 140, Hoffman Estates, IL 60619 *Toll Free Tel:* 800-321-7511 *E-mail:* service@sunburst.com; sales@sunburst.com *Web Site:* sunburst.com, pg 1028

Sunburst Recording, 10313 Jefferson Blvd, Culver City, CA 90232 *Tel:* 310-204-2222 *E-mail:* info@sunburstrecording.com *Web Site:* sunburstrecording.com, pg 1028

Sundance Film Festival, 1825 Three Kings Dr, Park City, UT 84060 *Tel:* 435-658-3456 *Fax:* 435-658-3457 *E-mail:* customerservice@sundance.org; press@sundance.org; institute@sundance.org *Web Site:* www.sundance.org/festival/, pg 1127

Sundance Systems, Fibox Products Division, 7411 Hines Place, Suite 123, Dallas, TX 75235 *Tel:* 214-920-9190 (Dallas) *Toll Free Tel:* 800-525-3443 *Fax:* 214-920-9339 *E-mail:* info@sundancesys.com *Web Site:* www.sundancesys.com, pg 1028

Sunfire Communications Inc, 7751 Kingspointe Pkwy, Suite 105, Orlando, FL 32819 *Tel:* 407-226-8226 *Fax:* 407-226-1660 *E-mail:* info@sunfirecommunications.com *Web Site:* www.sunfirecommunications.com, pg 1028

Sunnex Inc, 9319 Forsyth Park Dr, Charlotte, NC 28273 *Toll Free Tel:* 800-445-7869 *Fax:* 508-651-0099 *E-mail:* sunnex@sunnex.com; info@sunnex.com *Web Site:* www.sunnexonline.com, pg 1028

Sunnyside Communications Inc, 348 W 38 St, Suite 12-B, New York, NY 10018 *Tel:* 212-564-4606 *Fax:* 212-967-2968 *Web Site:* www.sunnysiderecords.com, pg 1028

Sunrise Media LLC, 200 Central Park S, Suite 12F, New York, NY 10019 *Tel:* 212-221-6310 *Fax:* 212-302-1854 *E-mail:* info@ipfmedia.org *Web Site:* www.ipfmedia.org/vetc.htm, pg 1028

Sunrise Packaging Inc, 9937 Goodhue St NE, Blaine, MN 55449-4433 *Tel:* 763-785-2505 *Toll Free Tel:* 800-634-8160 *Fax:* 763-785-2210 *E-mail:* customerservice@sunpack.com *Web Site:* www.sunpack.com, pg 1028

Sunrise Studios, 1471 SW 96 Terr, Davie, FL 33324 *Tel:* 954-581-0026 *Fax:* 954-581-0204 *E-mail:* info@dvdcopypros.com *Web Site:* www.dvdcopypros.com, pg 1028

Sunset Bronson Studios, 1438 N Gower St, Box 88, Hollywood, CA 90028 *Tel:* 323-460-5858 *Fax:* 323-460-3844 *E-mail:* sbs.reception@sgsandsbs.com *Web Site:* sgsandsbs.com, pg 1028

Sunset Gower Studios, 1438 N Gower St, Box 21, Hollywood, CA 90028 *Tel:* 323-467-1001 *Fax:* 323-467-2717 *E-mail:* sgsreception@sgsandsbs.com *Web Site:* sgsandsbs.com, pg 1028

Supercircuits, 11000 N Mopac Expwy, Bldg 300, Austin, TX 78759 *Toll Free Tel:* 877-995-2288 *E-mail:* operations@supercircuits.com; customercare@supercircuits.com *Web Site:* www.supercircuits.com, pg 1029

SuperDigital Ltd, 1150 NW 17 Ave, Portland, OR 97209-2403 *Tel:* 503-228-2222 *Toll Free Tel:* 888-79AUDIO (792-8346) *Fax:* 503-228-6819 *E-mail:* audiosales@superdigital.com *Web Site:* www.superdigital.com, pg 1029

Superior Electric, One Cowles Rd, Plainville, CT 06062 *Tel:* 860-507-2025 *Toll Free Tel:* 800-787-3532 *Fax:* 860-507-2050 *Toll Free Fax:* 800-821-1369 *E-mail:* info@superiorelectric.com *Web Site:* www.superiorelectric.com, pg 1029

Superior Graphics, 10440 Brockwood Rd, Dallas, TX 75238 *Tel:* 972-437-0542 *Toll Free Tel:* 800-969-8228 *Fax:* 972-690-6029 *E-mail:* info@superiorgraphics.com *Web Site:* www.superiorgraphics.com, pg 1029

Superscope Technologies Inc, 1508 Batavia Ave, Geneva, IL 60134-3302 *Tel:* 630-232-8900 *Toll Free Tel:* 800-374-4118 *Fax:* 630-232-8905 *Web Site:* www.superscopetechnologies.com, pg 1029

SuperStock Inc, 6622 Southpoint Dr S, Suite 240, Jacksonville, FL 32216 *Tel:* 904-565-0066 *Toll Free Tel:* 800-828-4545 *Fax:* 904-565-1620 *E-mail:* yourfriends@superstock.com *Web Site:* www.superstock.com, pg 1029

SuperVision, Pacific Design Ctr, Suite B-120, 8687 Melrose Ave, Los Angeles, CA 90069 *Tel:* 310-652-9510 *Toll Free Tel:* 877-287-9783 *Fax:* 310-652-9516 *E-mail:* mail@supervisionav.com *Web Site:* www.supervisionav.com, pg 1029

Sure Shot Transmissions Inc, 10314 Main St, New Middletown, OH 44442 *Tel:* 330-542-0900 *Fax:* 330-542-1020 *Web Site:* www.sureshotsat.com, pg 1029

SurgeX, 800 Knightdale Blvd, Suite 121, Knightdale, NC 27545 *Toll Free Tel:* 800-645-9721 (tech & cust support) *Fax:* 919-269-0454 *Web Site:* www.surgex.com, pg 1029

SVAT Electronics, 4080 Montrose Rd, Niagara Falls, ON L2H 1J9, Canada *Tel:* 905-353-0732 *Toll Free Tel:* 866-946-7828 *Fax:* 905-353-1701 *Toll Free Fax:* 888-771-1701 *E-mail:* sales@svat.com *Web Site:* www.svat.com, pg 1029

SVS Inc, 2513 Jenks Ave, Panama City, FL 32405 *Tel:* 850-522-4747 *Fax:* 850-522-4739 *E-mail:* sales@svslifts.com *Web Site:* www.svslifts.com, pg 1029

Swallow, 238 E Main St, Drawer 10, Ville Platte, LA 70586 *Tel:* 337-363-2177 *Fax:* 337-363-2094 *E-mail:* info@flattownmusic.com *Web Site:* www.flattownmusic.com, pg 1029

Swank Audio Visuals, 639-E Gravois Bluffs, St Louis, MO 63026 *Tel:* 636-680-9000 *Toll Free Tel:* 877-792-6528 *Fax:* 636-680-2853 *Web Site:* www.swankav.com, pg 1029

Sweetsong Productions, 193 Meadsville Rd, Parkersburg, WV 26104 *Tel:* 304-428-7773 *E-mail:* sweetsonginfo@sweetsong.com *Web Site:* www.sweetsong.com, pg 1029

Sweetwater Sound Inc, 5501 US Hwy 30 W, Fort Wayne, IN 46818 *Tel:* 260-432-8176 *Toll Free Tel:* 800-222-4700 *Fax:* 260-432-1758 *Web Site:* www.sweetwater.com, pg 1029

Switch, 6600 Manchester Ave, St Louis, MO 63139 *Tel:* 314-206-7700 *Toll Free Tel:* 800-445-0633 *Fax:* 314-206-4570 *E-mail:* switch@theswitch.us *Web Site:* www.liberateyourbrand.com, pg 1030

Switchcraft® Inc, 5555 N Elston Ave, Chicago, IL 60630 *Tel:* 773-792-2700 *Fax:* 773-792-2129 *E-mail:* sales@switchcraft.com *Web Site:* www.switchcraft.com, pg 1030

Swivelier, 600 Bradley Hill Rd, Blauvelt, NY 10913 *Tel:* 845-353-1455 *Fax:* 845-353-1512 *E-mail:* info@swivelier.com *Web Site:* www.swivelier.com, pg 1030

Symbolic Sound Corp, PO Box 2549, Champaign, IL 61825-2549 *Tel:* 217-355-6273 *Fax:* 217-355-6562 *E-mail:* info-kyma@symbolicsound.com *Web Site:* www.symbolicsound.com, pg 1030

SYMCO Inc, 29 Poplar Dr, Stirling, NJ 07980 *Tel:* 908-647-6262 *Fax:* 908-647-4904 *E-mail:* orders@symcoinc.com *Web Site:* www.symcoinc.com, pg 1030

Symetrix Inc, 6408 216 St SW, Mountlake Terrace, WA 98043-2093 *Tel:* 425-778-7728 *E-mail:* support@symetrix.co; sales@symetrix.co *Web Site:* www.symetrix.co, pg 1030

Symmes Systems, 3977 Briarcliff Rd NE, Atlanta, GA 30345 *Tel:* 404-320-1012 *Fax:* 404-320-3465, pg 1030

Synaptic Digital, 79 Fifth Ave, 14th fl, New York, NY 10003 *Tel:* 212-682-8300 *Toll Free Tel:* 800-843-0677 *Fax:* 212-682-5260 *E-mail:* learnmore@synapticdigital.com *Web Site:* www.synapticdigital.com, pg 1030

SynAudCon, 8780 Rufing Rd, Greenville, IN 47124 *Tel:* 812-923-0174 *Toll Free Fax:* 800-547-0298 *Web Site:* www.synaudcon.com, pg 1030

Synergem, 2323 Randolph Ave, Avenel, NJ 07001 *Tel:* 732-225-0001 *Fax:* 732-225-7555 *E-mail:* info@synergem.com *Web Site:* www.synergem.com, pg 1030

Synergistic Batteries Inc, 5975 Providence Lane, Cumming, GA 30040 *Tel:* 770-886-6621 *Toll Free Tel:* 800-634-6000 *Fax:* 770-886-6522 *E-mail:* sbicas@synbat.com *Web Site:* www.synergisticbatteries.com, pg 1030

Synergy Group Inc, 23930 Craftsman Rd, Calabasas, CA 91302-1437 *Tel:* 818-223-9009 *Fax:* 818-223-8999 *Web Site:* www.jeffcooper.com, pg 1030

Synsor Corp, 1920 Merrill Creek Pkwy, Everett, WA 98203-5859 *Tel:* 425-551-1300 *Toll Free Tel:* 800-426-0193 *Fax:* 425-551-1313 *E-mail:* info@synsor.com *Web Site:* www.synsor.com, pg 1030

Synthesizer Rental Service, 2268 Ben Lomond Dr, Los Angeles, CA 90027-2905 *Tel:* 323-660-4065 *Fax:* 323-660-4597 *E-mail:* info@2srs.com *Web Site:* synthesizerrentalservice.com, pg 1030

Synthesizer Systems Technologies (SST), 10907 Magnolia Blvd, Suite 425, North Hollywood, CA 91601 *Tel:* 818-907-7780 *E-mail:* sst.shop@yahoo.com, pg 1030

Syracuse Scenery & Stage Lighting Co Inc, 101 Monarch Dr, Liverpool, NY 13088-4514 *Tel:* 315-453-8096 *Toll Free Tel:* 800-453-7775 *Fax:* 315-453-7897 *E-mail:* info@syracusescenery.com *Web Site:* www.syracusescenery.com, pg 1031

Systems Impact Inc, 3515 Woodley Rd NW, Washington, DC 20016 *Toll Free Tel:* 888-568-6284 *E-mail:* support@mathmastery.com *Web Site:* mathmastery.com, pg 1031

T & M Digital Services, 54 Flint Ridge Rd, Monroe, CT 06468 *Tel:* 203-268-5290 *Fax:* 203-268-5290, pg 1031

T-stop Inc, 957 Cole Ave, Hollywood, CA 90038 *Tel:* 323-544-1000 *Fax:* 323-544-4970 *E-mail:* info@t-stopinc.com *Web Site:* www.t-stopinc.com, pg 1031

Tacoma-Regional Film Commission, 1119 Pacific Ave, Suite 1400, Tacoma, WA 98402 *Tel:* 253-627-2836 (ext 26) *Fax:* 253-627-8783 *Web Site:* www.traveltacoma.com/press-room/film-commission, pg 1103

TAI Audio, 5828 Old Winter Garden Rd, Orlando, FL 32835 *Tel:* 407-296-9959 *Toll Free Tel:* 800-486-6444 *Fax:* 407-648-1352 *E-mail:* sales@taiaudio.com *Web Site:* www.taiaudio.com, pg 1031

Take 1 Media Services, 31335 Center Ridge Rd, Cleveland, OH 44145 *Tel:* 440-899-0101 *Web Site:* www.take1media.com, pg 1031

Take One Productions Ltd, 11010 Lake Grove Blvd, Suite 100, Morrisville, NC 27560 *Tel:* 919-481-0000 *Fax:* 919-460-8809 *E-mail:* marketing@takeonepro.com *Web Site:* www.takeonepro.com, pg 1031

Talas, 330 Morgan Ave, Brooklyn, NY 11211 *Tel:* 212-219-0770 *Fax:* 212-219-0735 *E-mail:* info@talasonline.com *Web Site:* www.talasonline.com, pg 1031

Talk-A-Phone Co, 7530 N Natchez Ave, Niles, IL 60714 *Tel:* 773-539-1100 *Fax:* 773-539-1241 *E-mail:* info@talkaphone.com *Web Site:* www.talkaphone.com, pg 1031

Tallahassee Audio Visual, 2880 Apalachee Pkwy, Tallahassee, FL 32301 *Tel:* 850-877-1152 (photo); 850-877-1154 (AV) *Toll Free Tel:* 800-356-9631 *Fax:* 850-878-4026; 850-656-1384 *E-mail:* info@talcam.com *Web Site:* www.talcam.com, pg 1031

Tally Display Corp, 19 Gardner Rd, Fairfield, NJ 07004 *Tel:* 973-777-7760 *Toll Free Tel:* 800-758-2559 *Fax:* 973-777-6220 *E-mail:* info@tallydisplay.com *Web Site:* www.tallydisplay.com, pg 1031

Tam Communications Inc, 5610 Scotts Valley Dr, Suite B552, Scotts Valley, CA 95066 *Tel:* 831-439-1500 *Toll Free Fax:* 866-390-1218 *E-mail:* info@tamcom.com *Web Site:* www.tamcom.com, pg 1031

Tampa Bay Film Commission, 401 E Jackson St, Suite 2100, Tampa, FL 33602 *Tel:* 813-223-1111 (ext 4058) *Toll Free Tel:* 800-826-8358 *Fax:* 813-218-3328 *Web Site:* www.filmtampabay.com, pg 1096

Tamrac® Inc, 9240 Jordan Ave, Chatsworth, CA 91311 *Tel:* 818-407-9500 *Toll Free Tel:* 800-662-0717 *Fax:* 818-407-9501 *Web Site:* www.tamrac.com, pg 1031

Tamron USA Inc, 10 Austin Blvd, Commack, NY 11725 *Tel:* 631-858-8400 *Toll Free Tel:* 800-827-8880 *Fax:* 631-543-5666 *E-mail:* custserv@tamron.com *Web Site:* www.tamron-usa.com, pg 1031

Tanglewood Productions, 125 Brinkby Ave, Reno, NV 89509 *Tel:* 775-688-6282 *Toll Free Tel:* 877-671-8933 *E-mail:* info@tanglewoodproductions.com *Web Site:* www.tanglewoodproductions.com, pg 1031

Tannoy North America Inc, 335 Gage Ave, Suite 1, Kitchener, ON N2M 5E1, Canada *Tel:* 519-745-1158 *Fax:* 519-745-2364 *E-mail:* info@tcgroup-americas.com *Web Site:* www.tannoy.com, pg 1031

Tantor Media Inc, 2 Business Park Rd, Unit 2, Old Saybrook, CT 06475 *Tel:* 860-395-1155 *Toll Free Tel:* 877-7-TANTOR (782-6867) *Toll Free Fax:* 888-782-7821 *E-mail:* orders@tantor.com; service@tantor.com *Web Site:* www.tantor.com, pg 1031

Tape Resources, 845 N Church St, Elmhurst, IL 60126 *Tel:* 630-993-4673 *Toll Free Tel:* 800-827-3462; 888-496-3282 (sales) *Toll Free Fax:* 888-827-3329 *Web Site:* www.taperesources.com, pg 1031

Tape World, 309 Wagner Ave, Butler, PA 16001 *Tel:* 724-283-8621 *Toll Free Tel:* 800-245-6000; 800-322-8273 *Fax:* 724-283-8298 *Toll Free Fax:* 800-322-8273 *E-mail:* info@tapeworld.com *Web Site:* www.tapeworld.com, pg 1031

Tapemaker, 48 Urban Ave, Westbury, NY 11590 *Tel:* 516-333-2700 *Fax:* 516-333-0643 *E-mail:* tapemaker@aol.com, pg 1032

Taperwire, c/o Fuller Manufacturing, 523 S Flower St, Burbank, CA 91502 *Tel:* 818-238-9911 *Fax:* 818-238-9959 *E-mail:* taperwire@taperwire.com *Web Site:* www.taperwire.com, pg 1032

TapeStockOnline.com, 602 N Cypress St, Orange, CA 92867 *Tel:* 310-352-4230 *Toll Free Tel:* 888-322-TAPE (322-8273) *Fax:* 310-352-4233 *E-mail:* sales@tapestockonline.com *Web Site:* www.tapestockonline.com, pg 1032

TapeWorks Texas Inc, 4930-B Dacoma, Houston, TX 77092 *Tel:* 713-688-0696 *Toll Free Tel:* 866-827-3489 *Fax:* 713-688-2509 *E-mail:* sales@tapeworkstexas.com *Web Site:* www.tapeworkstexas.com, pg 1032

TAPPI, 15 Technology Pkwy S, Norcross, GA 30092 *Tel:* 770-446-1400 *Toll Free Tel:* 800-332-8686 (US); 800-446-9431 (CN) *Fax:* 770-446-6947 *E-mail:* memberconnection@tappi.org *Web Site:* www.tappi.org, pg 1032

TARA Labs, 1020 Benson Way, Ashland, OR 97520 *Tel:* 541-488-6465 *Fax:* 541-488-6463 *E-mail:* sales@taralabs.com *Web Site:* www.taralabs.com, pg 1032

Tarpley Media Systems, 3737 50 St, Lubbock, TX 79413 *Tel:* 806-797-5833 *Toll Free Tel:* 800-600-5833 *Fax:* 806-797-5139 *E-mail:* tms@tarpleymedia.com *Web Site:* www.tarpleymedia.com, pg 1032

TASCAM, 7733 Telegraph Rd, Montebello, CA 90640 *Tel:* 323-726-0303; 323-727-7617 (support) *Toll Free Tel:* 800-447-8322 *Fax:* 323-727-4805 *E-mail:* tascamrepair@teac.com *Web Site:* www.tascam.com, pg 1032

Tasman Group Pacific Rim, 4850 Gregg Rd, Pico Rivera, CA 90660 *Tel:* 562-695-8877 *Toll Free Tel:* 888-355-8889 *Fax:* 562-908-3912 *Web Site:* www.tasmangrouppr.com, pg 1032

Tatum Video, 103 S Davis St, Telluride, CO 81435 *Tel:* 213-999-5970 (cell); 970-728-4892 *Fax:* 970-728-4892 *E-mail:* utemtn@aol.com, pg 1032

Tatung Co of America Inc, 2850 El Presidio St, Long Beach, CA 90810 *Tel:* 310-637-2105 *Toll Free Tel:* 800-827-2850 *E-mail:* tus@tatungusa.com *Web Site:* www.tatungusa.com, pg 1032

Carl Tatz Design, 6666 Brookmont Terr, Suite 1109, Nashville, TN 37205 *Tel:* 615-354-6242 *Fax:* 615-356-4791 *E-mail:* carl@carltatzdesign.com *Web Site:* www.carltatzdesign.com, pg 1032

The Taunton Press Inc, 63 S Main St, Newtown, CT 06470 *Tel:* 203-426-8171 *Toll Free Tel:* 800-926-8776 (ext 3893 - PR); 800-888-8286 (orders) *Fax:* 203-426-3434 *Web Site:* www.taunton.com, pg 1032

Taylor Associates, 110 W Canal St, Suite 301, Winooski, VT 05404 *Tel:* 802-735-1942 *Toll Free Tel:* 800-READ-PLUS (732-3758) *Fax:* 802-419-4786 *E-mail:* info@readingplus.com *Web Site:* www.readingplus.com, pg 1032

Chip Taylor Communications LLC, 2 East View Dr, Derry, NH 03038 *Tel:* 603-434-9262 *Toll Free Tel:* 800-876-CHIP (876-2447) *Fax:* 603-432-2723 *E-mail:* chip.taylor@chiptaylor.com *Web Site:* www.chiptaylor.com, pg 1032

TBA Global Events, 220 W 42 St, 10th fl, New York, NY 10036 *Tel:* 646-445-7000 *Fax:* 646-445-7001 *E-mail:* newyorkinfo@tbaglobal.com *Web Site:* www.tbaglobal.com, pg 1032

TBC Consoles Inc, 170 Rodeo Dr, Edgewood, NY 11717 *Tel:* 631-293-4068 *Toll Free Tel:* 888-CONSOLE (266-7653) *Fax:* 631-293-4075 *E-mail:* info@tbcconsoles.com; sales@tbcconsoles.com; support@tbcconsoles.com *Web Site:* www.tbcconsoles.com, pg 1033

TBC Studios, 10201 W Appleton Ave, Milwaukee, WI 53225 *Tel:* 414-536-7337 *E-mail:* info@tbcstudios.com *Web Site:* www.tbcstudios.com, pg 1033

TEAC America Inc, 7733 Telegraph Rd, Montebello, CA 90640 *Tel:* 323-726-0303 *Fax:* 323-727-7656 *E-mail:* custser@teac.com *Web Site:* www.teac.com, pg 1033

Teach America Corp, 121 N Love St, Quincy, FL 32351-2440 *Tel:* 850-875-0491 *Web Site:* teachamerica.com; www.accessmanagement.info, pg 1033

TeachLogic Inc, 1688 Ord Way, Oceanside, CA 92056 *Tel:* 760-631-7800 *Toll Free Tel:* 800-588-0018 *Fax:* 760-631-1283 *E-mail:* sales@teachlogic.com; info@teachlogic.com *Web Site:* www.teachlogic.com, pg 1033

Team Volusia Economic Development Corp, One Daytona Blvd, Suite 240, Daytona Beach, FL 32114 *Tel:* 386-255-6332 *E-mail:* dmott@tvedc.com *Web Site:* tvedc.com, pg 1095

Teatown Communications Group, 1560 Broadway, New York, NY 10036 *Tel:* 212-302-0722 *E-mail:* info@teatown.tv *Web Site:* www.teatown.tv, pg 1033

TEC/West USA Inc, 3050 E Victoria St, Rancho Dominguez, CA 90221 *Tel:* 310-961-3491 *Toll Free Tel:* 800-421-7215 *Fax:* 310-464-9210 *E-mail:* info@tecwest.com *Web Site:* www.tecwest.com, pg 1033

Tecfilms Inc, 6310 Lemmon Ave, Suite 210, Dallas, TX 75209-5850 *Tel:* 214-904-0414 *E-mail:* mail@tecfilms.com *Web Site:* www.tecfilms.com, pg 1033

Tech 21 USA Inc, 790 Bloomfield Ave, Clifton, NJ 07012 *Tel:* 973-777-6996 *Fax:* 973-777-9899 *E-mail:* info@tech21nyc.com *Web Site:* www.tech21nyc.com, pg 1033

Techflex Inc, 29 Brookfield Dr, Sparta, NJ 07871 *Tel:* 973-300-9242 *Toll Free Tel:* 800-323-5140 *Fax:* 973-300-9409 *E-mail:* techflex@techflex.com *Web Site:* www.techflex.com, pg 1033

Technet® Systems Group, PO Box 422, Auburn, NH 03032-0422 *Tel:* 603-483-5365 *Toll Free Tel:* 888-TECHNET (832-4638) *Fax:* 603-483-0512 *E-mail:* sales@technetsystems.com *Web Site:* www.technetsystems.com, pg 1033

Techni-Lux Inc, 10900 Palmbay Dr, Orlando, FL 32824 *Tel:* 407-857-8770 *Fax:* 407-857-8771 *E-mail:* sales@techni-lux.com *Web Site:* www.techni-lux.com, pg 1033

Techni-Tool Inc, 1547 N Trooper Rd, Worcester, PA 19490 *Tel:* 610-941-2400 *Toll Free Tel:* 800-832-4866 *Fax:* 610-828-5623 *Toll Free Fax:* 800-854-8665 *E-mail:* sales@techni-tool.com *Web Site:* www.techni-tool.com, pg 1033

Technical Audio Devices (TAD)™, 1925 E Dominguez St, Long Beach, CA 90810 *Tel:* 213-746-6337 (cust support) *Toll Free Tel:* 800-421-1404 *Fax:* 310-952-2821 *E-mail:* tadpioneer@pioneerservice.com *Web Site:* www.pioneerelectronics.com/pusa, pg 1033

Technical Exhibits Corp, 6155 S Oak Park Ave, Chicago, IL 60638 *Tel:* 773-586-3377 *Fax:* 773-586-6575 *Web Site:* www.technicalexhibits.net, pg 1033

Technical Innovation, 2975 Northwoods Pkwy, Norcross, GA 30071 *Tel:* 770-447-1001 *Toll Free Tel:* 866-447-1004 *Fax:* 770-441-5285 *Web Site:* www.technical-innovation.com, pg 1033

Technical Services, 10567 Oak Creek Dr, Lakeside, CA 92040 *Tel:* 619-561-4410 *Web Site:* www.widcoinc.com, pg 1034

Technical Services, 2480 Southwell Rd, Dallas, TX 75229 *Tel:* 972-421-4230 *Fax:* 972-421-4231, pg 1034

Technical Support Systems LLC, 2232 Central Ave, Memphis, TN 38104 *Tel:* 901-398-5908 *Fax:* 901-398-5914 *Web Site:* www.techsupportsys.com, pg 1034

Technicolor, 3233 E Mission Oaks Blvd, Camarillo, CA 93012 *Tel:* 805-445-1122 *Fax:* 805-445-4340 *E-mail:* info@technicolor.com *Web Site:* www.technicolor.com, pg 1034

Technicolor-Herbert T Kalmus Gold Medal Award, 3 Barker Ave, 5th fl, White Plains, NY 10601 *Tel:* 914-761-1100 *Fax:* 914-761-3115 *E-mail:* smpte@smpte.org *Web Site:* www.smpte.org, pg 1128

Technicolor SA, 10330 N Meridian St, Indianapolis, IN 46290 *Tel:* 317-587-3000 *Fax:* 317-587-6763 *Web Site:* www.thomsonconsumer.com, pg 1034

Technics, One Panasonic Way, Secaucus, NJ 07094 *Tel:* 201-348-7000 *Toll Free Tel:* 800-211-7262 (support); 800-405-0652 (orders) *Web Site:* www.panasonic.com, pg 1034

Technisphere Corp, 134 W 26 St, Ground fl, New York, NY 10001 *Tel:* 212-777-5100 *Toll Free Tel:* 800-343-9500 *E-mail:* info@technisphere.com *Web Site:* www.technispherecorp.com, pg 1034

Technologies at Excelitas, 200 West St, Waltham, MA 02451 *Toll Free Tel:* 800-775-OPTO (775-6786); 855-382-2677 *Fax:* 781-290-4702 *Web Site:* www.excelitas.com, pg 1034

Technology and Engineering Emmy Awards, 1697 Broadway, Suite 1001, New York, NY 10019 *Tel:* 212-586-8424 *Fax:* 212-246-8129 *E-mail:* techemmys@emmyonline.tv *Web Site:* www.emmyonline.org, pg 1128

Technology Learning Services, 36600 Schoolcraft Rd, Livonia, MI 48150-1173 *Tel:* 734-432-5800 *Toll Free Tel:* 800-852-4951 *Web Site:* ww3.madonna.edu/tls, pg 1035

Technomad™ Inc, PO Box 273, South Deerfield, MA 01373 *Tel:* 617-275-8898 *Toll Free Tel:* 800-464-7757 *Fax:* 617-535-9712 *E-mail:* sales@technomad.com; customercare@technomad.com *Web Site:* www.technomad.com, pg 1035

Technomedia Solutions, 4545 36 St, Orlando, FL 32811 *Tel:* 407-351-0909 *Fax:* 407-248-9484 *E-mail:* sales@gotechnomedia.com *Web Site:* www.gotechnomedia.com, pg 1035

Technovision® Interactive Inc, 1845 Sandstone Manor, Unit 2, Pickering, ON L1W 3X9, Canada *Tel:* 905-420-5153 *E-mail:* sales@technovision.com *Web Site:* www.technovision.com, pg 1035

TecNec Distributing, 812 Kings Hwy, Saugerties, NY 12477 *Tel:* 845-246-0428 *Toll Free Tel:* 800-543-0909 *Fax:* 845-246-0626 *E-mail:* sales@tecnec.com *Web Site:* www.tecnec.com, pg 1035

Tecplot Inc, 3535 Factoria Blvd SE, Suite 550, Bellevue, WA 98006 *Tel:* 425-653-1200; 425-653-9393 (tech support) *Toll Free Tel:* 800-763-7005 (orders) *E-mail:* info@tecplot.com; sales@tecplot.com *Web Site:* www.tecplot.com, pg 1035

Tectonics Industries Inc, 24680 Mound Rd, Warren, MI 48091 *Tel:* 586-755-6522 *Toll Free Tel:* 888-638-3671 *Fax:* 586-755-6562 *E-mail:* info@techtonicsindustries.com *Web Site:* www.techtonicsindustries.com, pg 1035

Ted The Fiddler Music, 103 S Main St, Spring City, PA 19475-1820 *Tel:* 610-948-0345 *Web Site:* www.tfiddler.com, pg 1035

Tek Data Systems Co, 1111 W Park Ave, Libertyville, IL 60048 *Tel:* 847-367-8800 *Fax:* 847-367-0235 *E-mail:* tekdata@tekdata.com; sales@tekdata.com *Web Site:* www.tekdata.com, pg 1035

Tek Gear, 938 Corydon Ave, Winnipeg, MB R3M 0Y5, Canada *Tel:* 204-988-3001 *Fax:* 204-988-3050 *E-mail:* sales@tekgear.com *Web Site:* tekgear.com, pg 1035

TEK Media Group, 711 S Victory Blvd, Burbank, CA 91502 *Tel:* 818-244-4440; 818-255-5045 *Toll Free Tel:* 800-255-5045 (support) *Fax:* 818-855-8762 *E-mail:* mshank@tekmg.com *Web Site:* www.tekmg.com, pg 1035

Tekskil Industries Inc, 102-998 Harbourside Dr, North Vancouver, BC V7P 3T2, Canada *Tel:* 604-985-2250 *Toll Free Tel:* 877-835-7545 *Toll Free Fax:* 877-576-8361 *E-mail:* tekskilprompters2012@tekskil.com *Web Site:* www.tekskil.com, pg 1035

Tel-Air Interests Inc, 2040 Sherman St, Hollywood, FL 33020 *Tel:* 954-924-4949 *Fax:* 954-924-4980 *E-mail:* telair@aol.com *Web Site:* www.telairint.com, pg 1035

TeL Systems, 7235 Jackson Rd, Ann Arbor, MI 48103 *Tel:* 734-761-4506 *Toll Free Tel:* 800-686-7235 *Fax:* 734-761-9776 *E-mail:* sales@telsystemsusa.com *Web Site:* www.telsystemsusa.com, pg 1035

Tel-Test, 605 NW 53 Ave, Suite A-17, Gainesville, FL 32609 *Tel:* 352-335-0901 *Fax:* 352-376-3260, pg 1035

Telarc International Corp, 23412 Commerce Park Rd, Cleveland, OH 44122 *Tel:* 216-464-2313 *Fax:* 216-360-9663 *Web Site:* www.concordmusicgroup.com/labels/Telarc/; www.concordmusicgroup.com, pg 1035

Tele-Measurements Inc, 145 Main Ave, Clifton, NJ 07014 *Tel:* 973-473-8822 *Toll Free Tel:* 800-223-0052 (ext 207) *Fax:* 973-473-0521 *E-mail:* contact@tele-measurements.com *Web Site:* www.tele-measurements.com, pg 1035

Tele-Time Systems, 313 Parkway Dr, Cary, IL 60013 *Tel:* 847-640-1420 *E-mail:* teletimesystems@netzero.com *Web Site:* www.teletimesystems.com, pg 1036

Tele-Video Production Services (TVPS), 3655 Grand Ave, 2nd fl, Oakland, CA 94610-2009 *Tel:* 510-893-0555 *Toll Free Tel:* 800-893-0555 *Fax:* 510-893-0552 *E-mail:* tvps893@yahoo.com *Web Site:* www.tvpsonline.com, pg 1036

Telect Inc, 23321 E Knox Ave, Liberty Lake, WA 99019 *Tel:* 509-926-6000 *Toll Free Tel:* 800-551-4567 *E-mail:* getinfo@telect.com *Web Site:* www.telect.com, pg 1036

Teledac Inc, 635, rue De La Noue IDS, Verdun, QC H3E 1W1, Canada *Tel:* 514-362-6362 *Toll Free Tel:* 888-659-6362 *E-mail:* general@teledac.com *Web Site:* www.teledac.com, pg 1036

Teledyne DALSA Inc, 605 McMurray Rd, Waterloo, ON N2V 2E9, Canada *Tel:* 519-886-6000 *Fax:* 519-886-8023 *E-mail:* sales.americas@teledynedalsa.com *Web Site:* www.teledynedalsa.com, pg 1036

Teledyne Energy Systems Inc, 10707 Gilroy Rd, Hunt Valley, MD 21031 *Tel:* 410-771-8600 *Fax:* 410-771-8620 *E-mail:* energy.systems@teledynees.com *Web Site:* www.teledynees.com, pg 1036

Telemanagement Resources International Inc (TRI), 124 Thomas Lane, Manahawkin, NJ 08050 *Tel:* 609-597-6334 *Web Site:* www.triinc.com, pg 1036

Telemetrics Inc, 6 Leighton Place, Mahwah, NJ 07430 *Tel:* 201-848-9818 *Fax:* 201-848-9819 *E-mail:* info@telemetricsinc.com *Web Site:* www.telemetricsinc.com, pg 1036

Telemotions LLC, 405 E 54 St, Suite 3-N, New York, NY 10022 *Tel:* 212-486-3010 *Web Site:* www.telemotions.net, pg 1036

Teleometrics International, 4567 Lake Shore Dr, Waco, TX 76710 *Tel:* 254-776-2060 *Toll Free Tel:* 800-876-2389 *Fax:* 254-772-9588 *E-mail:* teleocsrv@teleometrics.com *Web Site:* www.teleometrics.com, pg 1036

Telepro Video Inc, 14730 Adams Circle, Omaha, NE 68137 *Tel:* 402-593-0999; 402-690-2198 *Fax:* 402-593-6117 *E-mail:* tmtelepro@aol.com *Web Site:* www.teleprovideo.com, pg 1036

Telequest Inc, 66 Witherspoon St, Suite 383, Princeton, NJ 08542 *Tel:* 609-430-3004 *E-mail:* contact@telequestinc.com *Web Site:* www.telequestinc.com, pg 1036

Telescript International, 55 Walnut St, Norwood, NJ 07648 *Tel:* 201-767-6733 *Toll Free Tel:* 888-767-6713 *Fax:* 201-784-0323 *E-mail:* info@telescript.com *Web Site:* telescript.com, pg 1036

Telestream Inc, 848 Gold Flat Rd, Nevada City, CA 95959 *Tel:* 530-470-1300 *Toll Free Tel:* 877-257-6245 *Fax:* 530-470-1301 *E-mail:* info@telestream.net *Web Site:* www.telestream.net, pg 1036

Teletech Inc, 38235 Executive Dr, Westland, MI 48185 *Tel:* 734-641-2300, pg 1036

TeleTime Productions, 100 Atlantic Ave, Lynbrook, NY 11563 *Tel:* 516-255-8383 *E-mail:* info@teletimevideo.com *Web Site:* www.teletimevideo.com, pg 1036

Televersions, 747 N May St, Chicago, IL 60642 *Tel:* 312-642-9488 *Toll Free Tel:* 800-942-9488 *Fax:* 312-642-9491 *E-mail:* convert@televersions.com *Web Site:* www.televersions.com, pg 1036

TeleVideos, 1566 Dola St, Eugene, OR 97402 *Toll Free Tel:* 800-2-VIDEOS (284-3367) *E-mail:* televideos@msn.com *Web Site:* televideos.com, pg 1036

Television Academy, 5220 Lankershim Blvd, North Hollywood, CA 91601-3109 *Tel:* 818-754-2800 *Fax:* 818-761-2827 *Web Site:* www.emmys.com, pg 1089

Television Bureau of Advertising Inc (TVB), 120 Wall St, 15th fl, New York, NY 10005-3908 *Tel:* 212-486-1111 *Fax:* 212-935-5631 *E-mail:* info@tvb.org *Web Site:* www.tvb.org, pg 1089

Television Equipment Associates Inc (TEA), 16 Mount Ebo Rd S, Suite 6, Brewster, NY 10509 *Tel:* 845-278-0960 *Fax:* 845-278-0964 *E-mail:* info@swatheadsets.com *Web Site:* www.swatheadsets.com, pg 1036

Telex Communications Inc, 12000 Portland Ave, Burnsville, MN 55337-1522 *Tel:* 952-884-4051 *Toll Free Tel:* 877-863-4166 *Fax:* 952-884-0043 *E-mail:* info@telex.com *Web Site:* www.telex.com, pg 1037

Telex EVI, 12000 Portland Ave S, Burnsville, MN 55337-1522 *Tel:* 952-884-4051 *Toll Free Tel:* 877-863-4166 *Fax:* 952-884-0043; 952-887-5585 *E-mail:* info@telex.com *Web Site:* www.telex.com, pg 1037

Tellabs Inc, One Tellabs Ctr, 1415 W Diehl Rd, Naperville, IL 60563 *Tel:* 630-798-8800 *Fax:* 630-798-2000 *Web Site:* www.tellabs.com, pg 1037

Tellens Inc, 770 W Landoran Lane, Tucson, AZ 85737 *Tel:* 520-742-0649 *Fax:* 520-742-0652 *E-mail:* infotellens@aol.com *Web Site:* www.tellens.com, pg 1037

Telluride Film Festival, 800 Jones St, Berkeley, CA 94710 *Tel:* 510-665-9494 *Fax:* 510-665-9589 *E-mail:* mail@telluridefilmfestival.org *Web Site:* www.telluridefilmfestival.org, pg 1128

Telos Systems, 1241 Superior Ave E, Cleveland, OH 44114 *Tel:* 216-241-7225 *Fax:* 216-241-4103 *E-mail:* inquiry@telos-systems.com *Web Site:* www.telos-systems.com, pg 1037

Tempe Camera, 606 W University, Tempe, AZ 85281 *Tel:* 480-966-6954 *Toll Free Tel:* 800-836-7374 *E-mail:* rent@tempecamera.com; sales@tempecamera.com *Web Site:* www.tempecamera.biz, pg 1037

Tempe Tape & Disc, 2737 W Baseline Rd, Suite 21, Tempe, AZ 85283 *Tel:* 602-453-9663 *Web Site:* www.tempetape.com, pg 1037

1013 Integrated, 1013 Kawaiahao St, Honolulu, HI 96814 *Tel:* 808-593-8848 *Fax:* 808-593-9427 *E-mail:* info@1013integrated.com *Web Site:* www.1013i.com, pg 1037

10-20 Productions, 11120 Indian Oaks Dr, Tampa, FL 33625 *Tel:* 813-300-4221 *Web Site:* 1020tv.com, pg 1037

Tenba, 75 Virginia Rd, North White Plains, NY 10603 *Tel:* 914-347-3300 *Fax:* 914-347-3309 *E-mail:* info@tenba.com *Web Site:* www.tenba.com, pg 1037

Tennessee Film, Entertainment & Music Commission, 312 Rosa L Parks Ave, 26th fl, Nashville, TN 37243 *Tel:* 615-741-FILM (741-3456) *Toll Free Tel:* 877-818-FILM (818-3456) *Fax:* 615-741-5554 *E-mail:* tn.film@tn.gov *Web Site:* www.state.tn.us/film, pg 1102

Tennessee Prompters, 727 Wildview Dr, Nashville, TN 37211-1142 *Tel:* 615-834-9655 *Fax:* 615-834-1086 *E-mail:* info@tennesseeprompters.com *Web Site:* www.tennesseeprompters.com, pg 1037

Tennessee Visual Service Co, 912 Main St, Nashville, TN 37206 *Tel:* 615-226-0162 *Toll Free Tel:* 800-359-6132 *Fax:* 615-228-1876 *E-mail:* sales@tennvisual.com *Web Site:* www.tennvisual.com, pg 1037

Tepco Corp, 2603 Bridgeview Dr, Rapid City, SD 57701-5801 *Tel:* 605-343-7200 *Fax:* 605-343-7240 *E-mail:* tepco@rapidnet.com *Web Site:* www.rapidnet.com/~tepco, pg 1037

Terra Nova Films Inc, 9848 S Winchester Ave, Chicago, IL 60643 *Tel:* 773-881-8491 *Toll Free Tel:* 800-779-8491 *Fax:* 773-881-3368 *E-mail:* tnf@terranova.org *Web Site:* www.terranova.org, pg 1037

Terra Productions LLC, 2017 Fairview Ave E, Suite G, Seattle, WA 98102 *Tel:* 206-328-3080 *Web Site:* www.terraproductions.com, pg 1037

Tetrahedron LLC, 5348 Las Vegas Dr, Suite 353, Las Vegas, NV 89108 *Tel:* 208-265-8065 *Toll Free Tel:* 888-923-9936 *E-mail:* tetra@tetrahedron.org *Web Site:* www.tetrahedron.org, pg 1037

Texas Association of Motion Media Professionals (TAMMP), 9629 Carnegie Dr, Dallas, TX 75228 *Tel:* 214-766-1924 *E-mail:* info@taftp.com *Web Site:* taftp.com, pg 1090

Texas Film Commission, 1100 San Jacinto, Suite 3.410, Austin, TX 78701 *Tel:* 512-463-9200 *Fax:* 512-463-4114 *E-mail:* film@governor.state.tx.us *Web Site:* www.governor.state.tx.us/film, pg 1102

Texas Heart Institute Visual Communication Services, Denton A Cooley Bldg, Suite C530, 6770 Bertner Ave, Houston, TX 77030 *Tel:* 832-355-9558 *Fax:* 832-355-9511 *Web Site:* www.texasheartinstitute.org, pg 1037

Texas Rebel Radio Network, 210 Woodcrest, Fredericksburg, TX 78624 *Tel:* 830-997-2197 *Fax:* 830-997-2198 *E-mail:* txradio@ktc.net *Web Site:* www.kfanfmradio.com, pg 1037

Texas Wesleyan University, 1201 Wesleyan St, Fort Worth, TX 76105 *Tel:* 817-531-5850 *Web Site:* www.txwes.edu, pg 1038

Texcam Inc, 1323 N First St, Bellaire, TX 77401 *Tel:* 713-524-2774 *Toll Free Tel:* 800-735-2774 *Fax:* 713-524-2779 *E-mail:* info@texcam.com *Web Site:* www.texcam.com, pg 1038

TFT Inc, 105 Bonaventura Dr, San Jose, CA 95134 *Tel:* 408-943-9323 *Fax:* 408-432-9218; 408-432-9219 *E-mail:* info@tftinc.com *Web Site:* www.tftinc.com, pg 1038

TGA Recording Co, 295 Urbandale Ave, Benton Harbor, MI 49022 *Tel:* 269-926-7581 *Fax:* 269-926-7589 *E-mail:* tgarecording@sbcglobal.net *Web Site:* www.tgarecording.com, pg 1038

Thayer Birding Software, 12650 Colliers Reserve Dr, Naples, FL 34110 *Tel:* 239-596-1637 *Toll Free Tel:* 800-865-2473 *Fax:* 239-596-0232 *Web Site:* www.thayerbirding.com, pg 1038

Theatre Arts Video Library, 174 Andrew Ave, Leucadia, CA 92024 *Tel:* 760-632-6355 *Toll Free Tel:* 800-456-8285 *Fax:* 760-632-6859 *E-mail:* admin@theatreartsvideo.com *Web Site:* www.theatreartsvideo.com, pg 1038

Theatre Effects, 1810 Airport Exchange Blvd, Suite 400, Erlanger, KY 41018-3184 *Tel:* 513-772-7646 (intl) *Toll Free Tel:* 800-791-7646 *Fax:* 513-772-3579 *E-mail:* service@theatrefx.com *Web Site:* www.theatrefx.com, pg 1038

Theatre House Inc, 400 W Third St, Covington, KY 41011-1306 *Tel:* 859-431-2414 *Toll Free Tel:* 800-827-2414 *Fax:* 859-431-1837 *E-mail:* theatreh@one.net; info@theatrehouse.com *Web Site:* www.theatrehouse.com, pg 1038

Theatre Service & Supply Corp, 1792 Union Ave, Baltimore, MD 21211 *Tel:* 410-467-1225 *Fax:* 410-467-1289 *E-mail:* sales@stage-n-studio.com *Web Site:* www.stage-n-studio.com, pg 1038

Theatrical Services & Supplies Inc, 415Q Oser Ave, Hauppauge, NY 11788 *Tel:* 631-873-4790 *Fax:* 631-873-4795 *E-mail:* sales@gotheatrical.com *Web Site:* www.gotheatrical.com, pg 1038

Theatrical Services Inc, 128 S Washington St, Wichita, KS 67202 *Tel:* 316-263-4415 *Toll Free Tel:* 888-874-2649 *Fax:* 316-263-9927 *Web Site:* www.theatricalservices.com, pg 1038

Theatrical Technicians Inc (TTI), 2700 Connecticut Ave NW, Suite 109, Washington, DC 20008-5308 *Tel:* 202-332-4907 *Fax:* 202-332-4907 *E-mail:* info@perfect-pickup.com *Web Site:* www.perfect-pickup.com, pg 1038

Theosophical Publishing House, 306 W Geneva Rd, Wheaton, IL 60187 *Tel:* 630-665-0130 *Toll Free Tel:* 800-669-9425 *Fax:* 630-665-8791 *Web Site:* www.questbooks.net, pg 1038

Thermodyne Cases, 1841 Business Pkwy, Ontario, CA 91761 *Tel:* 909-923-9945 *Toll Free Tel:* 877-307-8425 *Fax:* 909-923-7505 *E-mail:* request@thermodyne-online.com *Web Site:* www.thermodyne-online.com, pg 1038

Thin-Lite Corp, 530 Constitution Ave, Camarillo, CA 93012 *Tel:* 805-987-5021 *Fax:* 805-388-0921 *E-mail:* thinlite@thinlite.com; thinlitesales@thinlite.com *Web Site:* www.thinlite.com, pg 1038

Think 3-D.com, 180 Cross Hwy, Westport, CT 06880 *Tel:* 646-732-9197 *Web Site:* www.think3-d.com, pg 1038

Thinking Allowed Productions, 5966 Zinn Dr, Oakland, CA 94611 *Tel:* 510-339-8004 *Toll Free Tel:* 800-999-4415 *E-mail:* thinking@thinkingallowed.com *Web Site:* www.thinkingallowed.com, pg 1038

Thinking Maps Inc, 401 Cascade Pointe Lane, Cary, NC 27513-5780 *Tel:* 919-678-8778 *Toll Free Tel:* 800-243-9169 *Fax:* 919-678-8782 *E-mail:* office@thinkingmaps.com *Web Site:* thinkingmaps.com, pg 1038

Third Ear Sound Co, 30965 San Benito St, Hayward, CA 94544 *Tel:* 510-429-1000 *Toll Free Tel:* 800-587-1115 *Fax:* 510-429-1001 *E-mail:* raul@thirdearsound.com *Web Site:* www.thirdearsound.com, pg 1038

Third World Newsreel/Camera News Inc, 545 Eighth Ave, Suite 550, New York, NY 10018 *Tel:* 212-947-9277 *Fax:* 212-594-6417 *E-mail:* twn@twn.org *Web Site:* www.twn.org, pg 1039

ThirdWave Learning Inc, 120 E Oakland Park Blvd, Suite 105-623, Fort Lauderdale, FL 33334 *Toll Free Tel:* 888-630-9555 *Fax:* 954-630-9050 *Web Site:* www.thirdwavelearning.com, pg 1039

31st Street Studios, 77 31 St, Pittsburgh, PA 15201 *Tel:* 412-228-0231 *E-mail:* info@31ststreetstudios.com *Web Site:* www.31ststreetstudios.com, pg 1039

30 Second Films, 3019 Pico Blvd, Santa Monica, CA 90405 *Tel:* 310-315-1750 *Fax:* 310-315-1757 *E-mail:* sales@30secondfilms.com *Web Site:* www.30secondfilms.com, pg 1039

30 Second Street Ltd, 1209 Mountain Road Place NE, Albuquerque, NM 87110 *Tel:* 505-265-0224 *E-mail:* info@thirtysecst.com *Web Site:* www.thirtysecst.com, pg 1039

THK Photo Products Inc, 7642 Woodwind Dr, Huntington Beach, CA 92647 *Tel:* 714-849-5700 *Toll Free Tel:* 800-421-1141 *Fax:* 714-849-5677 *E-mail:* support@thkphoto.com *Web Site:* www.thkphoto.com, pg 1039

Thomas & Betts Power Solutions, 5900 Eastport Blvd, Bldg V, Richmond, VA 23231-4453 *Tel:* 804-236-3300 *Toll Free Tel:* 800-238-5000; 800-CYBEREX (292-3739) *Fax:* 804-236-4040; 804-236-4841 *Web Site:* www.tnbpowersolutions.com, pg 1039

The Lowell Thomas Award, 40 W 45 St, New York, NY 10036 *Tel:* 212-626-9220 *Fax:* 212-626-9210 *Web Site:* www.opcofamerica.org, pg 1128

Thomas Reprographics, 801 Second Ave N, Minneapolis, MN 55405 *Tel:* 612-374-1120 *Toll Free Tel:* 800-328-7154 *Fax:* 612-374-1129 *E-mail:* orders501@thomasrepro.com *Web Site:* thomasrepro.com, pg 1039

Thomega Entertainment Inc, 3027 Miller Ave, Bay D, Saskatoon, SK S7K 6G5, Canada *Tel:* 306-373-3765 *Fax:* 306-242-5845 *E-mail:* thomega@sasktel.net *Web Site:* www.thomega.com, pg 1039

Thompson-Mitchell & Associates Inc, 1205 Johnson Ferry Rd, No 136, Marietta, GA 30068 *Tel:* 404-233-5435 *Toll Free Tel:* 800-554-1389 *Fax:* 404-521-4643, pg 1039

Thompson-Nicola Film Commission, 300-465 Victoria St, Kamloops, BC V2C 2A9, Canada *Tel:* 250-377-8673 *Toll Free Tel:* 877-377-8673 (BC only) *Fax:* 250-372-5048 *E-mail:* admin@tnrd.bc.ca *Web Site:* www.tnrdfilm.com, pg 1104

Thompson Rivers University Open Learning, BC Centre for Open Learning, 4th fl, 900 McGill Rd, Kamloops, BC V2C 0C8, Canada *Tel:* 250-852-7000 *Toll Free Tel:* 800-663-9711 *E-mail:* student@tru.ca; olmarketing@tru.ca *Web Site:* www.tru.ca/distance, pg 1039

Thorburn Associates, Acoustic, Technology, Lighting Design, 20880 Baker St, Castro Valley, CA 94546 *Tel:* 510-886-7826 *Fax:* 510-886-7828 *E-mail:* ta@ta-inc.com *Web Site:* www.ta-inc.com, pg 1039

Thread Marketing Group, 4635 W Alexis Rd, Toledo, OH 43623-1005 *Tel:* 419-887-6801 *Toll Free Tel:* 800-397-0126 *Fax:* 419-887-6802 *E-mail:* contact@experiencethread.com *Web Site:* www.experiencethread.com, pg 1039

Three D Graphics Inc, 11340 W Olympic Blvd, Suite 352, Los Angeles, CA 90064-1613 *Tel:* 310-231-3330 *Toll Free Tel:* 800-913-0008 *Fax:* 310-231-3303 *E-mail:* info@threedgraphics.com *Web Site:* www.threedgraphics.com, pg 1039

360 Systems, 3281 Grande Vista Dr, Newbury Park, CA 91320-1193 *Tel:* 818-991-0360 *Fax:* 818-991-1360 *E-mail:* info@360systems.com; sales@360systems.com *Web Site:* www.360systems.com, pg 1039

3M Touch Systems, 501 Griffin Book Park Dr, Methuen, MA 01844 *Tel:* 978-659-9000 *Toll Free Tel:* 888-659-1080 *Web Site:* www.3mtouch.com; www.3m.com/touch, pg 1039

Three Pillars Media, 140 N Eighth St, Suite 440, Lincoln, NE 68508 *Tel:* 402-937-0984 *E-mail:* contact@threepillarsmedia.com *Web Site:* www.threepillarsmedia.com, pg 1040

Three Rivers Publishing Co, 218 Country Wood, San Antonio, TX 78216 *Tel:* 210-490-2433 *E-mail:* cowboyhouse@aol.com *Web Site:* www.kurthouse.com, pg 1040

3008, 3008 Ross Ave, Suite 100, Dallas, TX 75204 *Tel:* 214-922-9232 *Fax:* 214-922-8861 *Web Site:* www.3008.com, pg 1040

Tiburon International Film Festival (TIFF), 6 Beach Rd, 544, Tiburon, CA 94920 *Tel:* 415-251-8433 *Fax:* 633-444-8433 *E-mail:* info@tiburonfilmfestival.com *Web Site:* www.tiburonfilmfestival.com, pg 1128

Leo Ticheli Productions, 2801 University Blvd, Suite 101, Birmingham, AL 35233 *Tel:* 205-930-0500 *Fax:* 205-930-0505 *Web Site:* www.ltpro.com, pg 1040

Tickets.com, 555 Anton Blvd, Costa Mesa, CA 92626 *Tel:* 714-327-5400 *Toll Free Tel:* 800-352-0212 (cust serv) *Fax:* 714-327-5410 *E-mail:* sales@tickets.com *Web Site:* www.tickets.com, pg 1040

Tierney Brothers Inc, 3300 University Ave SE, Minneapolis, MN 55414-3326 *Tel:* 612-331-5500 *Toll Free Tel:* 866-557-6062 *Fax:* 612-331-3424 *E-mail:* contactform@tierneybrothers.com *Web Site:* www.tierneybrothers.com, pg 1040

The Tiffen Co LLC, 90 Oser Ave, Hauppauge, NY 11788-3886 *Tel:* 631-273-2500 *Toll Free Tel:* 800-989-6013; 800-645-8500; 800-645-2522 *Fax:* 631-273-2557 *E-mail:* techsupport@tiffen.com *Web Site:* www.tiffen.com, pg 1040

Tigar Hare Studios, 4485 Matilija Ave, Sherman Oaks, CA 91423 *Tel:* 818-907-6663 *Fax:* 818-907-0693 *E-mail:* info@tigarhare.com *Web Site:* www.tigarhare.com, pg 1040

Tight Line Productions, 1902 Oak St, Melbourne, FL 32901 *Tel:* 321-725-4668 *Fax:* 321-768-6528 *E-mail:* info@tightlinetv.com *Web Site:* www.tightlinetv.com, pg 1040

Tiki Recording Studios Inc, 30-A Glen St, Suite 204, Glen Cove, NY 11542 *Tel:* 516-671-4300 (ext 101) *Fax:* 516-671-8754 *Web Site:* www.tikirecording.com, pg 1040

Time Warner Cable, 60 Columbus Circle, 17th fl, New York, NY 10023 *Tel:* 212-364-8200 *Web Site:* www.timewarnercable.com, pg 1040

Time Warner Cable Business Class, 120 E 23 St, 8th fl, New York, NY 10010 *Tel:* 212-379-5826 *Web Site:* www.twcbc.com/nyc, pg 1040

Timecode Multimedia, 12340 Santa Monica Blvd, Suite 230, West Los Angeles, CA 90025 *Tel:* 310-826-9199 *E-mail:* info@timecodemedia.com *Web Site:* www.timecodemultimedia.com, pg 1040

Timed Exposures Films, 122 Old Rd, Germantown, NY 12526-6014 *Tel:* 518-537-2012 *E-mail:* info@timedexposures.com *Web Site:* www.timedexposures.com, pg 1040

Timeless Books, Box 9, Kootenay Bay, BC V0B 1X0, Canada *Tel:* 250-227-9224 *Toll Free Tel:* 800-661-8711 *Fax:* 250-227-9494 *E-mail:* contact@timeless.org *Web Site:* www.timeless.org, pg 1040

Timeless Productions, 5050 Traverse Creek Rd, Garden Valley, CA 95633 *Tel:* 530-333-1335 *Toll Free Tel:* 800-729-1325 *E-mail:* 4info@timelessproductions.com *Web Site:* www.timelessproductions.com, pg 1040

TimeLogic Corp, 1914 Palomar Oaks Way, Suite 150, Carlsbad, CA 92008 *Tel:* 760-431-1263 *Toll Free Tel:* 877-222-9543 *Fax:* 760-431-1351 *Web Site:* www.timelogic.com, pg 1040

Times-Square Fantasy Theatre, 519 N Halifax Ave, Daytona Beach, FL 32118 *Tel:* 386-252-0381 *Fax:* 386-252-0381 *E-mail:* timessquare@bellsouth.net *Web Site:* www.timessquarefantasytheatre.com; www.broadwaymusicdownload.com, pg 1041

TimeSteps Productions Inc, 2 Glenside Dr, West Orange, NJ 07052 *Tel:* 973-669-1930 *Fax:* 973-731-8546 *E-mail:* info@timesteps.com *Web Site:* timesteps.com, pg 1041

Timestream Video, 11821 N Circle Dr, Whittier, CA 90601-2338 *Tel:* 562-699-8797 *Fax:* 562-695-0252 *Web Site:* www.timestreamvideo.com, pg 1041

Rik Tinory Productions, PO Box 311, Cohasset, MA 02025-0311 *Tel:* 781-383-9494 *E-mail:* riktinory@aol.com, pg 1041

Tisch School of the Arts, 721 Broadway, 10th & 11th fl, New York, NY 10003 *Tel:* 212-998-1700; 212-998-1780 *Fax:* 212-995-4063; 212-995-4062 *Web Site:* www.tisch.nyu.edu, pg 1041

Titus Technological Laboratories (TTL), 77 Kreiger Lane, Glastonbury, CT 06033 *Tel:* 860-633-5472 *Toll Free Tel:* 800-806-TTL1 (806-8851) *Fax:* 860-633-8244 *E-mail:* sales1@tituslabs.com *Web Site:* www.tituslabs.com, pg 1041

TKH Security Solutions USA Inc, 12920 Cloverleaf Center Dr, Germantown, MD 20874 *Tel:* 301-444-2200 *Toll Free Tel:* 800-BY-FIBER (293-4237) *Fax:* 301-444-2299 *Toll Free Fax:* 800-293-4237 *E-mail:* sales.us@tkhsecurity.com *Web Site:* www.tkhsecurity.com, pg 1041

TM Studios Inc, 2002 Academy Lane, Suite 110, Dallas, TX 75234 *Tel:* 972-406-6800 *Fax:* 972-406-6890 *E-mail:* info@tmstudios.com; tmcustomerservice@tmstudios.com *Web Site:* www.tmstudios.com, pg 1041

TMW Media Group, 2321 Abbot Kinney Blvd, Suite 101, Venice, CA 90291 *Tel:* 310-577-8581 *Toll Free Tel:* 800-262-8862 *Fax:* 310-574-0886 *E-mail:* sale@tmwmedia.com *Web Site:* www.tmwmedia.com, pg 1041

TOA Electronics Inc, 1350 Bayshore Hwy, Suite 270, Burlingame, CA 94010 *Toll Free Tel:* 800-733-7088 (cust serv); 800-733-4750 (main) *Fax:* 650-588-3349 *Toll Free Fax:* 800-733-9766 *E-mail:* info@toaelectronics.com *Web Site:* www.toaelectronics.com, pg 1041

Tobias Associates Inc, 50 Industrial Dr, Warminster, PA 18974-1433 *Tel:* 215-322-1500 *Toll Free Tel:* 800-877-3367 *Fax:* 215-322-1504 *E-mail:* sales@tobiasinc.com *Web Site:* www.densitometers.net, pg 1041

Tobin Cinema Systems Inc, 6116 N Ormond Rd, Otis Orchards, WA 99027 *Tel:* 509-621-0323 *E-mail:* filmstodvd@comcast.net *Web Site:* www.tobincinemasystems.com, pg 1041

Tobin Productions Inc, 630 Ninth Ave, Suite 215, New York, NY 10036 *Tel:* 212-727-1500 *Toll Free Tel:* 800-877-8273 *Fax:* 212-727-1766 *E-mail:* info@tobinproductions.com *Web Site:* www.tobinproductions.com, pg 1041

Tobins Lake Sales, 11035 Hi Tech Dr, Whitmore Lake, MI 48189 *Tel:* 734-449-9810 *Toll Free Tel:* 888-525-3753 *Fax:* 734-449-9812 *Web Site:* www.tobinslakesales.com, pg 1041

Dorothy Tod Films, 41 Hazel Brown Rd, Warren, VT 05674 *Tel:* 802-496-5280 *Fax:* 802-496-5280, pg 1041

Todd-AO Studios, 900 N Seward St, Hollywood, CA 90038 *Tel:* 323-962-4000 *Fax:* 323-466-4062 *Web Site:* www.toddao.com, pg 1041

Toko America Inc, 1250 Feehanville Dr, Mount Prospect, IL 60056 *Tel:* 847-297-0070 *Toll Free Tel:* 800-PIK-TOKO (745-8656) *Fax:* 847-699-7864 *E-mail:* info@tokoam.com *Web Site:* www.tokoam.com, pg 1041

TOMCAT USA Inc, 5427 N National Dr, Knoxville, TN 37914 *Tel:* 865-219-3700 *Fax:* 865-673-5818 *E-mail:* info@tomcatusa.com; sales@tomcatusa.com *Web Site:* www.tomcatglobal.com, pg 1041

Tommy Boy Entertainment LLC, 902 Broadway, No 14, New York, NY 10010 *Tel:* 212-388-8300 *Fax:* 212-388-8431 *E-mail:* info@tommyboy.com *Web Site:* shop.tommyboy.com, pg 1042

Tomorrow River Music, PO Box 245, Cambridge, WI 53523 *Tel:* 608-217-5039 *Web Site:* www.robbieclement.com, pg 1042

Tone Zone Recording, 1316 N Clybourn, Chicago, IL 60610-1710 *Tel:* 312-664-5353 *Fax:* 312-664-6560 *E-mail:* tonezonerecording@sbcglobal.net, pg 1042

Toon Makers, 17333 Ludlow St, Granada Hills, CA 91344 *Tel:* 818-832-8666 *E-mail:* info@toonmakers.com *Web Site:* toonmakers.com, pg 1042

Top Hat Productions, 6615 Boynton Beach Blvd, Suite 310, Boynton Beach, FL 33437 *Tel:* 561-963-6442 *Toll Free Tel:* 888-794-0528 *Fax:* 561-880-6988 *E-mail:* info@tophatproductions.net *Web Site:* www.tophatproductions.net, pg 1042

TopCat Records LLC, PO Box 670234, Dallas, TX 75367-0234 *Tel:* 972-484-4141 *E-mail:* info@topcatrecords.com *Web Site:* topcatrecords.com, pg 1042

Toronto Film, Television & Digital Media Office, Toronto City Hall, Main fl, Rotunda N, 100 Queen St W, Toronto, ON M5H 2N2, Canada *Tel:* 416-338-FILM (338-3456) *Fax:* 416-338-0685 *E-mail:* filmtoronto@toronto.ca *Web Site:* www.toronto.ca/tfto, pg 1105

Toronto Reel Asian International Film Festival, 401 Richmond St W, Suite 309, Toronto, ON M5V 3A8, Canada *Tel:* 416-703-9333 *Fax:* 416-703-9986 *E-mail:* info@reelasian.com; programming@reelasian.com *Web Site:* www.reelasian.com, pg 1128

Torpey Time, 580 Danforth Rd, Toronto, ON M1K 1E3, Canada *Tel:* 416-261-3773 *E-mail:* helpdesk@dixonsystems.com; technicalsupport@dixonsystems.com *Web Site:* www.dixonsystems.com, pg 1042

Toshiba America Information Systems Inc, 9740 Irvine Blvd, Irvine, CA 92618 *Tel:* 949-583-3000 *Fax:* 949-583-3437 *Web Site:* www.toshiba.com, pg 1042

Tosoh USA Inc, 3600 Gantz Rd, Grove City, OH 43123 *Tel:* 614-277-4348 *Toll Free Tel:* 866-844-6953 *Fax:* 614-875-8086 *E-mail:* info.tusa@tosoh.com *Web Site:* www.tosohusa.com, pg 1042

Total AV Systems, 923 Sligo Ave, Silver Spring, MD 20910 *Tel:* 301-589-3337 *Toll Free Tel:* 800-447-7632 *Fax:* 301-494-4770 *E-mail:* info@total-av.com *Web Site:* total-av.com, pg 1042

Total Concept Sales, 2505 Foothill Blvd, Suite G, La Crescentia, CA 91214 *Tel:* 818-236-3966 *Toll Free Tel:* 800-488-0589 *Fax:* 818-236-3969 *E-mail:* info@smartups.com *Web Site:* www.smartups.com, pg 1042

Total Impact Multimedia Group Ltd, 1475 Pea Pond Rd, North Bellmore, NY 11710 *Tel:* 516-783-8800 *E-mail:* info@totalimpactltd.com *Web Site:* www.totalimpactltd.com, pg 1042

Total Media, 2 N Corporate Dr, 2nd fl, Riverdale, NJ 07457 *Tel:* 973-248-9700 *Toll Free Tel:* 800-355-4400 *Fax:* 973-248-9707 *E-mail:* info@totalmedia.com *Web Site:* www.totalmedia.com, pg 1042

Total Media Group, 432 N Canal St, Suite 12, South San Francisco, CA 94080 *Tel:* 650-583-8236 *Fax:* 650-583-4708 *E-mail:* info@mediagroup.com *Web Site:* www.totalmediagroup.com, pg 1042

Total Video Products Inc, 414 Southgate Ct, Mickleton, NJ 08056 *Tel:* 856-423-7400 *Toll Free Tel:* 800-447-0920 *Fax:* 856-423-4747 *E-mail:* info@totalvideoproducts.com *Web Site:* www.totalvideoproducts.com, pg 1042

ToteVision, 1319 Dexter Ave N, Suite 020, Seattle, WA 98109 *Tel:* 206-623-6000 *Fax:* 206-623-6609 *E-mail:* info@totevision.com *Web Site:* www.totevision.com, pg 1042

TouchStar Productions Inc, 522 Jackson Park Dr, Meadville, PA 16335 *Tel:* 814-337-8192 *Toll Free Tel:* 800-759-1294 *Fax:* 814-337-0699 *E-mail:* doctorb@touchstarpro.com *Web Site:* www.touchstarpro.com, pg 1042

Touchstone Center Publications, 141 E 88 St, New York, NY 10128 *Tel:* 212-831-7717 *Web Site:* www.touchstonecenter.net, pg 1043

Towards 2000 Inc, 215 W Palm Ave, Suite 101, Burbank, CA 91502 *Tel:* 818-557-0903 *Toll Free Fax:* 866-836-5725 *E-mail:* info@t2k.com *Web Site:* www.t2k.com, pg 1043

Toys From The Attic, 203 Mamaroneck Ave, Suite 2, White Plains, NY 10601 *Tel:* 914-421-0069 *Fax:* 914-328-3852 *E-mail:* info@tfta.com *Web Site:* tfta.com, pg 1043

TPR Enterprises Ltd, 644 Fayette Ave, Mamaroneck, NY 10543 *Tel:* 914-698-1141 *Fax:* 914-698-9419 *E-mail:* info@tprlights.com *Web Site:* www.tprlights.com, pg 1043

TR Productions, 2 13 St, 3rd fl, Charlestown, MA 02129 *Tel:* 617-241-5500 *E-mail:* info@trprod.com *Web Site:* www.trprod.com, pg 1043

Trac Record Co & Recording Studio, 180 E Warner Ave, Fresno, CA 93710 *Tel:* 559-448-8722 *E-mail:* tracsell@sbcglobal.net, pg 1043

Trafalgar Square Books, 388 Howe Hill Rd, North Pomfret, VT 05053 *Tel:* 802-457-1911 *Toll Free Tel:* 800-423-4525 *Fax:* 802-457-1913 *E-mail:* info@horseandriderbooks.com *Web Site:* www.horseandriderbooks.com, pg 1043

Trailblazer Studios®, 1610 Midtown Place, Raleigh, NC 27609 *Tel:* 919-645-6600 *Fax:* 919-645-6601 *Web Site:* www.trailblazerstudios.com, pg 1043

Trance Formations Unlimited, 1425 Steele St, Laramie, WY 82070 *Tel:* 307-745-7897, pg 1043

Tranquil Technology Music, PO Box 20463, Oakland, CA 94620-0463 *Tel:* 510-658-2560 *Web Site:* michaelmantra.com, pg 1043

Trans-Lux Multimedia Corp, 950 Third Ave, Suite 2804, New York, NY 10022 *Tel:* 203-853-4321 *Toll Free Tel:* 800-243-5544; 800-462-2716 *Fax:* 203-229-0691 *Web Site:* www.trans-lux.com, pg 1043

The Transfer Zone®, 4301 Orchard Lake Rd, Suite 180-191, West Bloomfield, MI 48323 *Tel:* 248-225-0477, pg 1043

Transformational Education Initiatives, PO Box 344, Phoenicia, NY 12464 *Tel:* 310-795-4910 *E-mail:* lioneltv@aol.com *Web Site:* transformationaledu.org, pg 1043

Transistor Devices Inc, 36 Newburgh Rd, Hackettstown, NJ 07840 *Tel:* 908-850-5088 *Fax:* 908-850-1607 *E-mail:* info@tdipower.com *Web Site:* www.tdipower.com, pg 1043

Transparent Office Products LLC, 2550 Haddonfield Rd, Pennsauken, NJ 08110 *Tel:* 856-488-5455 *Fax:* 856-488-5411 *E-mail:* sales@transoffprod.biz *Web Site:* www.transoffprod.biz, pg 1043

Transtar Entertainment Co Inc, 10650 E Bethany Dr, Suite E, Aurora, CO 80014 *Tel:* 303-695-4207 *Web Site:* www.transtarfilm.com, pg 1043

Transtector Systems Inc, 10701 N Airport Dr, Hayden Lake, ID 83835 *Tel:* 208-772-8515 *Toll Free Tel:* 800-882-9110 *Fax:* 208-762-6133 *E-mail:* sales@transtector.com *Web Site:* www.transtector.com, pg 1043

Transvideo International, 11712 Moorpark St, Suite 112-B, North Hollywood, CA 91604 *Tel:* 818-985-4903 *Fax:* 818-985-4921 *Web Site:* www.transvideointl.com, pg 1044

Traverse City Convention & Visitors Bureau, 101 W Grandview Pkwy, Traverse City, MI 49684 *Tel:* 231-947-1120 *Toll Free Tel:* 800-940-1120 *Fax:* 231-947-2621 *Web Site:* www.visittraversecity.com, pg 1098

TRC Interactive Inc, 4200 Crums Mill Rd, Harrisburg, PA 17112 *Tel:* 717-652-3100 *Toll Free Tel:* 800-222-9909 *Fax:* 717-652-8281 *E-mail:* customerservicetrc01@trcinteractive.com; info@trcinteractive.com *Web Site:* www.trcinteractive.com, pg 1044

Trebas Institute, 550 Sherbrooke St W, Suite 600, Montreal, QC H3A 1B9, Canada *Tel:* 514-845-4141 *Toll Free Tel:* 866-5TREBAS (587-3227) *Fax:* 514-845-2581 *E-mail:* infomtl@trebas.com *Web Site:* www.trebas.com, pg 1044

Treehaus Communications Inc, 906 W Loveland Ave, Loveland, OH 45140-2150 *Tel:* 513-683-5716 *Toll Free Tel:* 800-638-4287 *Fax:* 513-683-2882 *E-mail:* treehaus@treehaus1.com *Web Site:* www.treehaus1.com, pg 1044

Tremetrics Inc Industrial Instruments Division, 7625 Golden Triangle Dr, Eden Prairie, MN 55344 *Toll Free Tel:* 800-825-0121 *Fax:* 952-903-4100 *E-mail:* info@tremetrics.com *Web Site:* www.tremetrics.com, pg 1044

Trendy Studio LLC, 196 NW 24 St, Miami, FL 33127 *Tel:* 305-438-4244 *Fax:* 305-438-4243 *E-mail:* studio@trendygroup.com *Web Site:* trendystudio.net, pg 1044

Trew Audio Inc, 220 Great Circle Rd, Suite 116, Nashville, TN 37228 *Tel:* 615-256-3542 *Toll Free Tel:* 800-241-8994 *Fax:* 615-259-2699 *E-mail:* info@trewaudio.com; sales@trewaudio.com *Web Site:* www.trewaudio.com, pg 1044

TRF Production Music Libraries, 106 Apple St, Suite 302, Tinton Falls, NJ 07724 *Tel:* 201-335-0005 *Toll Free Tel:* 800-899-MUSIC (899-6874) *Fax:* 201-335-0004 *E-mail:* info@trfmusic.com *Web Site:* www.trfmusic.com, pg 1044

Tri-Color, 4303 Normandy Ct, Royal Oak, MI 48073-2266 *Tel:* 248-549-0150 *Toll Free Tel:* 800-886-5661 *Fax:* 248-549-5270 *Web Site:* www.tricolorphoto.com, pg 1044

Tri-Digital Software Inc, 8424 154 Ave NE, Redmond, WA 98052 *Tel:* 425-284-3888 *Toll Free Tel:* 800-206-2547 *Fax:* 425-883-3887 *E-mail:* tdp@tri-digital.com *Web Site:* www.tri-digital.com, pg 1044

Tri-Ed, 3625 Cincinnati Ave, Rocklin, CA 95765 *Tel:* 916-543-4000 *Toll Free Tel:* 800-366-4472 *Fax:* 916-543-4020 *E-mail:* info@northernvideo.com *Web Site:* www.tri-ed.com, pg 1044

Tri-State Audio Visual Co, 2901 Glendora Ave, Cincinnati, OH 45219 *Tel:* 513-281-7500 *Toll Free Tel:* 800-348-8728 *Fax:* 513-281-7539 *E-mail:* sales@tristateav.com *Web Site:* www.tristateav.com, pg 1044

Tri-State Loudspeaker, 650 Franklin Ave, Aliquippa, PA 15001 *Tel:* 724-375-9203, pg 1044

Tri-State Visual Products, 885 Ohio Pike, Suite C, Cincinnati, OH 45245 *Tel:* 513-471-7111 *Toll Free Tel:* 800-473-4474 *Fax:* 513-471-7140 *E-mail:* info@trivisual.com *Web Site:* www.trivisual.com, pg 1044

Triad Communications Ltd, 2751 Oxford St, Vancouver, BC V5K 1N5, Canada *Tel:* 604-253-5351; 604-253-3990 *E-mail:* triadc@comwave.com *Web Site:* www.triadcommunications.ca, pg 1044

Triangle Regional Film Commission, PO Box 13041, Research Triangle Park, NC 27709-3041 *Tel:* 919-544-5501 *E-mail:* triangleregionalfilm@gmail.com *Web Site:* www.trianglencfilm.com, pg 1101

Tribeca Film Festival, 375 Greenwich St, New York, NY 10013 *Tel:* 212-941-2400 *Fax:* 212-941-3939 *E-mail:* festival@tribecafilmfestival.org *Web Site:* tribecafilm.com/festival/; tribecafilmfestival.org/festival, pg 1128

Tricycle Studios, 1905 E Seventh Ave, Tampa, FL 33605 *Tel:* 813-258-6867 *Fax:* 813-258-8595 *E-mail:* hi@tricyclestudios.com *Web Site:* www.tricyclestudios.com, pg 1044

Trinidad Film Commission, 136 W Main St, Trinidad, CO 81082 *Tel:* 719-846-7324 *Toll Free Tel:* 866-480-4750 *Fax:* 719-846-3545 *Web Site:* www.trinidadchamber.com, pg 1095

The Trinity Recording Studio, PO Box 1417, Corpus Christi, TX 78403 *Tel:* 361-854-7464 *E-mail:* info@trinitystudio.com *Web Site:* www.trinitystudio.com, pg 1045

Trio Video, 915 Sherwood Dr, Lake Bluff, IL 60044 *Tel:* 312-421-7060 *Fax:* 312-421-0361 *Web Site:* www.triovideo.com, pg 1045

Tripp Lite, 1111 W 35 St, Chicago, IL 60609 *Tel:* 773-869-1111; 773-869-1234 *Fax:* 773-869-1935 *E-mail:* av@tripplite.com *Web Site:* www.tripplite.com, pg 1045

Tritech Communications, 625 Locust St, Suite 300, Garden City, NY 11530 *Tel:* 631-254-4500 *Fax:* 631-254-4499 *E-mail:* sales@tritechcomm.com *Web Site:* www.tritechcomm.com, pg 1045

Triumph Learning LLC, PO Box 1270, Littleton, MA 01460-4270 *Toll Free Tel:* 800-338-6519 *Toll Free Fax:* 866-805-5723 *E-mail:* customerservice@triumphlearning.com *Web Site:* www.triumphlearning.com, pg 1045

Triune Arts, RR 5, 1804 Bedell Rd, Kemptville, ON K0G 1J0, Canada *E-mail:* triune@triune.ca *Web Site:* www.triune.ca, pg 1045

Trod Nossel Productions & Recording Studios, 10 George St, Wallingford, CT 06492 *Tel:* 203-269-4465 *Toll Free Tel:* 800-800-HITS (800-4487) *Fax:* 203-294-1745 *E-mail:* info@trodnossel.com *Web Site:* www.trodnossel.com, pg 1045

Troll Touch, 33302 Santiago Rd, Suite C, Acton, CA 93510 *Tel:* 661-257-1160 *Fax:* 661-257-1161 *Web Site:* www.trolltouch.com, pg 1045

Trompeter Electronics Inc, 299 Johnson Ave, Suite 100, Waseca, MN 56093 *Tel:* 507-833-8822 *Fax:* 507-833-6287 *E-mail:* connectivityinfo@emerson.com; connectivitysales@emerson.com *Web Site:* emersonconnectivity.com, pg 1045

Tropical Visions Video Inc, 62 Halaulani Place, Hilo, HI 96720 *Tel:* 808-935-5557 *Fax:* 808-935-0066 *E-mail:* redhotlava@hawaii.rr.com *Web Site:* www.volcanoscapes.com, pg 1045

Tropikal Productions, 137 Sequoia Rd, Rockwall, TX 75032 *Tel:* 972-771-3797 *Fax:* 972-771-0853 *E-mail:* tropikalproductions@gmail.com *Web Site:* www.tropikalproductions.com, pg 1045

The Troupe, 3 Industrial Dr, Windham, NH 03087 *Tel:* 603-893-4554 *Fax:* 603-893-9717 *E-mail:* info@thetroupe.com *Web Site:* www.thetroupe.com, pg 1045

Troxell Communications Inc, 4830 S 38 St, Phoenix, AZ 85040 *Tel:* 602-437-7240 *Toll Free Tel:* 800-578-8858 *Fax:* 602-437-7265 *Toll Free Fax:* 800-589-5939 *Web Site:* www.trox.com, pg 1045

True Audio, 387 Duncan Lane, Andersonville, TN 37705 *Tel:* 865-494-3388 *Toll Free Tel:* 800-621-4411 *Fax:* 865-494-3388 *E-mail:* sales@trueaudio.com *Web Site:* www.trueaudio.com, pg 1045

TRUMATCH Inc, PO Box 501, Water Mill, NY 11976-0501 *Tel:* 631-204-9100 *Toll Free Tel:* 800-TRU-9100 (878-9100) *Fax:* 631-204-0002 *E-mail:* info@trumatch.com *Web Site:* www.trumatch.com, pg 1045

Trusty Tuneshop Recording Studios, 8771 Rose Creek Rd, Nebo, KY 42441 *Tel:* 270-249-3194 *E-mail:* etrusty@vci.net *Web Site:* trustytuneshop.com, pg 1045

Truth Consciousness Publications, Desert Ashram, 3403 W Sweetwater Dr, Tucson, AZ 85745-9301 *Tel:* 520-743-8821 *Fax:* 520-743-3394 *E-mail:* info@truthconsciousness.org *Web Site:* truthconsciousness.org, pg 1045

TSG Publishing Foundation Inc USA, 28641 N 63 Place, Cave Creek, AZ 85331 *Tel:* 480-502-1909 *Fax:* 480-502-0713 *E-mail:* info@tsgfoundation.org *Web Site:* www.tsgfoundation.org, pg 1046

TSR/Baja Damabi Records, 18653 Ventura Blvd, Suite 513, Tarzana, CA 91356 *Tel:* 818-702-9902, pg 1046

T3Media, 1530 16 St, 6th fl, Denver, CO 80202 *Tel:* 720-382-2869 *Toll Free Tel:* 866-815-6599 *Fax:* 720-382-2719 *E-mail:* content@t3media.com *Web Site:* www.t3licensing.com, pg 1046

Tubeworks Video Productions, 1626 Wilcox Ave, Los Angeles, CA 90028 *Tel:* 323-469-6003 *Web Site:* www.tubeworksvideo.com, pg 1046

Tucson Film Office, 100 S Church Ave, Tucson, AZ 85701 *Tel:* 520-770-2151 *Fax:* 520-629-0160 *Web Site:* www.filmtucson.com, pg 1091

Tufnut Theft Protection, 2910 San Isidro Ct, Santa Fe, NM 87501 *Tel:* 505-424-1954 *Toll Free Tel:* 800-227-0949 *Fax:* 505-424-1956 *E-mail:* tufnut@tufnut.com *Web Site:* www.tufnut.com, pg 1046

Tuolumne County Film Commission, 542 W Stockton St, Sonora, CA 95370 *Tel:* 209-533-4420 *Toll Free Tel:* 800-446-1333 *Fax:* 209-532-2502 *E-mail:* info@tcfilm.org *Web Site:* www.tcfilm.org, pg 1094

Tupelo Film Commission, 399 E Main St, Tupelo, MS 38804 *Tel:* 662-841-6521 *Toll Free Tel:* 800-533-0611 *Fax:* 662-841-6558 *E-mail:* visittupelo@tupelo.net *Web Site:* www.tupelo.net, pg 1099

Turner Broadcasting System Inc, One CNN Ctr, Atlanta, GA 30303 *Tel:* 404-827-1700 *Web Site:* www.turner.com, pg 1046

Turner Engineering Inc, 14 Morris Ave, Mountain Lakes, NJ 07046-1433 *Tel:* 973-263-1000 *Fax:* 973-334-1620 *E-mail:* adair@turnereng.com *Web Site:* www.turnereng.com, pg 1046

TV Crews, 2135-B Defoor Hills Rd, Atlanta, GA 30318 *Tel:* 404-351-8898 *Toll Free Tel:* 800-TV-CREWS (882-7397) *Fax:* 404-351-8893 *E-mail:* info@tvcrews.com *Web Site:* www.tvcrews.com, pg 1046

TV Juice Productions Inc, PO Box 843, Kilauea, HI 96754-0843 *Tel:* 808-828-0101; 808-828-0434 *E-mail:* fido@tvjuice.com *Web Site:* www.tvjuice.com, pg 1046

TV One Multimedia Solutions, 2791 Circleport Dr, Erlanger, KY 41018 *Tel:* 859-282-7303 *Toll Free Tel:* 800-721-4044 *Fax:* 859-282-8225 *E-mail:* sales@tvone.com; info@tvone.com *Web Site:* www.tvone.com, pg 1046

TV Pro Gear, 1630 Flower St, Glendale, CA 91201 *Tel:* 818-246-7100 *Fax:* 818-246-1945 *Web Site:* www.tvprogear.com, pg 1046

TV Specialists Inc, 180 E 2100 S, Salt Lake City, UT 84115 *Tel:* 801-486-5757 *Toll Free Tel:* 888-486-5757 *Fax:* 801-486-7566 *E-mail:* info@tvspecialists.com *Web Site:* www.tvspecialists.com, pg 1046

TVA Productions, 3950 Vantage Ave, Studio City, CA 91604 *Tel:* 818-505-8300 *Toll Free Tel:* 888-322-4296 *E-mail:* info@tvaproductions.com *Web Site:* www.tvaproductions.com, pg 1046

TVN-The Video Network, 31 Cutler Dr, Ashland, MA 01721-1210 *Tel:* 508-881-1800 *E-mail:* info@tvnvideo.com *Web Site:* www.tvnvideo.com, pg 1046

TVO/Ontario Educational Communications Authority (OECA), 2180 Yonge St, Toronto, ON M4S 2B9, Canada *Tel:* 416-484-2600; 416-484-2665 (cust rel) *Toll Free Tel:* 800-613-0513; 800-INFO-TVO (463-6886) *E-mail:* asktvo@tvo.org *Web Site:* tvo.org, pg 1046

Twentieth Century Fox Film Corp, 10201 W Pico Blvd, Bldg 88, Rm 311, Los Angeles, CA 90035 *Tel:* 310-369-1000 *Fax:* 310-369-8825 *Web Site:* www.foxmovies.com, pg 1046

21st Century Video Productions, 890 S Higley Rd, Pahrump, NV 89048 *Tel:* 775-727-9400 *Fax:* 775-727-8750 *Web Site:* www.kpvm.tv, pg 1047

24 Frames Film & Video, 15 Fourth Ave E, Vancouver, BC V5T 1E9, Canada *Tel:* 604-877-2299 *Fax:* 604-877-2298 *E-mail:* info@24frames.ca *Web Site:* www.24frames.ca, pg 1047

Twenty-Third Publications/Bayard, One Montauk Ave, Suite 200, New London, CT 06320 *Tel:* 860-437-3012 *Toll Free Tel:* 800-321-0411; 877-944-5844 (subns) *Toll Free Fax:* 800-572-0788 *E-mail:* resources@pastoralplanning.com *Web Site:* www.23rdpublications.com, pg 1047

20/20 Communications Inc, 10112 Voss Rd, Marengo, IL 60152 *Tel:* 847-364-7666 *Fax:* 847-364-7672 *Web Site:* www.2020communications.com, pg 1047

20k, 3535 Blvd Ste-Anne, Suite 300, Quebec, QC G1E 3L6, Canada *Tel:* 418-694-2220 *Toll Free Tel:* 855-933-2220 *E-mail:* info@20k.ca *Web Site:* www.20k.ca, pg 1047

Twin Peaks Creative, 445 W Seventh St, San Pedro, CA 90731 *Tel:* 310-832-3303 *E-mail:* postmaster@bestmedia.com *Web Site:* www.twinpeakscreative.com, pg 1047

Twin Sisters Productions LLC, 4710 Hudson Dr, Stow, OH 44224 *Toll Free Tel:* 800-248-TWIN (248-8946) *Toll Free Fax:* 800-480-TWIN (480-8946) *E-mail:* twinsisters@twinsisters.com *Web Site:* www.twinsisters.com, pg 1047

Twisted Media Inc, 1341 W Granville, Suite 1, Chicago, IL 60660 *Tel:* 773-856-6586 *E-mail:* info@twistedtracks.com *Web Site:* www.twistedtracks.com, pg 1047

Two Animators LLP, PO Box 3174, Mercerville, NJ 08619 *Tel:* 609-532-6138 *E-mail:* cartoons@twoanimators.com *Web Site:* www.twoanimators.com, pg 1047

2BruceStudio, 2 Wall St, Suite 119, Asheville, NC 28801 *Tel:* 828-255-2700 *E-mail:* info@2brucestudio.com *Web Site:* 2brucestudio.com, pg 1047

Two Door Productions, 416 N Harper Ave, Los Angeles, CA 90048 *E-mail:* shoot@usphotograph.com *Web Site:* www.twodoorfx.com, pg 1047

2BK9 Acting Animals, 1470 Catherine Ave, Winnipeg, MB R3E 1V8, Canada *Tel:* 204-338-1474; 204-997-9247 (cell), pg 1047

Tyler Camera Systems, 14218 Aetna St, Van Nuys, CA 91401 *Tel:* 818-989-4420 *Toll Free Tel:* 800-390-6070 *Fax:* 818-989-0423 *E-mail:* info@tylermount.com *Web Site:* www.tylermount.com, pg 1047

U-Direct Productions, 10 White St, 1st fl, New York, NY 10013 *Tel:* 212-647-9200 *Fax:* 212-625-9400 *E-mail:* udirect@udirectnyc.com *Web Site:* www.udirectnyc.com, pg 1047

U-Edit Video, 1002 N Central Expwy, Suite 555, Richardson, TX 75080 *Tel:* 972-690-EDIT (690-3348) *Fax:* 214-884-3687 *Web Site:* www.ueditvideo.com, pg 1047

Ultimate Presentation Systems Inc, 901 S Hohokam Dr, Tempe, AZ 85281 *Tel:* 480-966-2000 *Toll Free Tel:* 800-866-4066 *Fax:* 480-968-3009 *E-mail:* sales@ult.com *Web Site:* www.ult.com, pg 1047

Ultimate Support Systems Inc, 5836 Wright Dr, Loveland, CO 80538 *Toll Free Tel:* 800-525-5628 *Fax:* 970-776-1941 *E-mail:* info@ultimatesupport.com *Web Site:* www.ultimatesupport.com, pg 1047

Ultimatte Corp, 20945 Plummer St, Chatsworth, CA 91311 *Tel:* 818-993-8007 *Fax:* 818-993-3762 *E-mail:* sales@ultimatte.com *Web Site:* www.ultimatte.com, pg 1047

Ultralife Corporation, 2000 Technology Pkwy, Newark, NY 14513 *Tel:* 315-332-7100 *Toll Free Tel:* 800-332-5000 (US & CN) *Fax:* 315-331-7800 *E-mail:* orders@ulbi.com *Web Site:* ultralifecorporation.com, pg 1047

Ulysses Travel Guides Inc, 4176 Rue St-Denis, Montreal, QC H2W 2M5, Canada *Tel:* 514-843-9882 *Fax:* 514-843-9448 *E-mail:* info@ulysse.ca; st-denis@ulysse.ca *Web Site:* www.ulysse.ca (French); www.ulyssesguides.com (English), pg 1048

Umbra of Newburgh LLC, 9 Scobie Dr, Newburgh, NY 12550 *Toll Free Tel:* 855-536-6973 *Fax:* 845-569-9063 *E-mail:* info@umbranewburgh.com *Web Site:* www.umbranewburgh.com, pg 1048

UMCom Productions, 810 12 Ave S, Nashville, TN 37203 *Tel:* 615-742-5400 *Fax:* 615-742-5469 *E-mail:* umcom@umcom.org *Web Site:* www.umcom.org, pg 1048

Uncharted Country Publishing, PO Box 756, Taos, NM 87571 *Tel:* 575-776-3470 *Toll Free Tel:* 800-488-4940 *E-mail:* ucp@taichihealth.com *Web Site:* www.taichihealth.com, pg 1048

UND Television Center, 4300 James Ray Dr, Stop 7307, Grand Forks, ND 58202 *Tel:* 701-777-4346 *Toll Free Tel:* 800-CALL-UND (225-5863) *Fax:* 701-777-4342 *E-mail:* tv@und.edu *Web Site:* www.und.nodak.edu/dept/tvcenter, pg 1048

Ungar Video & Film, 1001 Guilford, Medina, OH 44256 *Tel:* 216-661-5090 *E-mail:* donungarvideo@yahoo.com, pg 1048

Uniconn Productions, 8485 Valley Circle Blvd, Suite 203, West Hills, CA 91304 *Tel:* 818-887-9108 *Fax:* 818-348-6544 *E-mail:* measeburl@aol.com *Web Site:* www.uniconnproductions.com, pg 1048

Unifour Productions Inc, 25 First Ave NE, Suite 105, Hickory, NC 28601 *Tel:* 828-324-1314 *Toll Free Tel:* 888-843-8644 *Fax:* 828-324-1318 *Web Site:* www.uni4.com, pg 1048

Unilux Inc, 59 N Fifth St, Saddle Brook, NJ 07663 *Tel:* 201-712-1266 *Toll Free Tel:* 800-522-0801 (US only) *Fax:* 201-712-1366 *Web Site:* www.unilux.com, pg 1048

Union Connector Co Inc, 8182 Baymeadow Way W, Jacksonville, FL 32256 *Tel:* 631-753-9550 *Fax:* 631-753-9560 *E-mail:* sales@unionconnector.com *Web Site:* www.unionconnector.com, pg 1048

Unique Business Systems, 1100 Colorado Ave, Santa Monica, CA 90401 *Tel:* 310-396-3929 *Toll Free Tel:* 800-669-4827 *Fax:* 310-396-6114 *E-mail:* sales@unibiz.com *Web Site:* www.unibiz.com, pg 1048

Unique Communications Ltd, 2232 Pegasus Way NE, Calgary, AB T2E 8M5, Canada *Tel:* 403-250-3763 *Toll Free Tel:* 800-661-8575 *Fax:* 403-250-2604 *Web Site:* www.uniquecommunications.ca, pg 1048

Uniset Co LLC, 449 Avenue "A", Rochester, NY 14621 *Tel:* 585-544-3820 *Fax:* 585-544-1110 *E-mail:* info@unisetcorp.com *Web Site:* www.unisetcorp.com, pg 1048

United Audio Video Group Inc, 6855 Vineland Ave, North Hollywood, CA 91605 *Tel:* 818-980-6700 *Toll Free Tel:* 800-247-8606 *Fax:* 818-508-8273 *Web Site:* www.unitedavg.com, pg 1048

United Nations Department of Public Information-News & Media Division, 405 E 42 St, Rm IN-913B, New York, NY 10017 *Tel:* 917-367-5007 *E-mail:* mediapartnerships@un.org *Web Site:* www.un.org, pg 1048

United Nations Multimedia Resources Unit, c/o Audio Library, UN Dept of Public Information, Rm S-1046 & S-1083, New York, NY 10017 *Tel:* 212-963-9268; 212-963-4501 *Fax:* 212-963-4501 *E-mail:* avlibrary@un.org *Web Site:* www.unmultimedia.org, pg 1048

United Scenic Artists Local 829, 29 W 38 St, 15th fl, New York, NY 10018 *Tel:* 212-581-0300 *Fax:* 212-977-2011 *E-mail:* businessoffice@usa829.org *Web Site:* www.usa829.org; vfx.usa829.org, pg 1090

United Sound & Electronics, 525 E Main St, Bridgeport, WV 26330 *Tel:* 304-842-6030 *E-mail:* questions@unitedsound.net *Web Site:* www.unitedsound.net, pg 1048

United States Super 8mm Film & Digital Video Festival, Admin Off, 30 Bedford Rd, Somerset, NJ 08873 *Tel:* 848-932-8482 *Fax:* 732-932-1935 *E-mail:* njmac@aol.com *Web Site:* www.njfilmfest.com, pg 1128

United Way Worldwide, 701 N Fairfax St, Alexandria, VA 22314-2045 *Tel:* 703-836-7112 *Fax:* 703-519-0097 *Web Site:* www.unitedway.org, pg 1048

Unitron Ltd, 73 Mall Dr, Commack, NY 11725 *Tel:* 631-543-2000 *Fax:* 631-589-6975 *E-mail:* info@unitronusa.com *Web Site:* www.unitronusa.com, pg 1048

Univenture Inc, 13311 Industrial Pkwy, Marysville, OH 43040 *Tel:* 937-645-4600 *Toll Free Tel:* 877-831-9428 *Fax:* 937-645-4700 *E-mail:* sales@univenture.com; orders@univenture.com *Web Site:* www.univenture.com, pg 1049

Universal Audio Inc, 4585 Scotts Valley Dr, Scotts Valley, CA 95066 *Tel:* 831-466-3737 *Toll Free Tel:* 866-823-1176; 877-698-2834 (tech support) *Fax:* 831-461-1550 *E-mail:* info@uaudio.com *Web Site:* www.uaudio.com, pg 1049

Universal Images, 20750 Civic Center Dr, Suite 100, Southfield, MI 48076 *Tel:* 248-357-4160, pg 1049

Universal Music Group, 2220 Colorado Ave, Santa Monica, CA 90404 *Tel:* 310-865-5000 *Web Site:* www.universalmusic.com, pg 1049

Universal Radio Inc, 6830 Americana Pkwy, Reynoldsburg, OH 43068 *Tel:* 614-866-4267 *Toll Free Tel:* 800-431-3939 (orders) *Fax:* 614-866-2339 *E-mail:* dx@universal-radio.com *Web Site:* www.universal-radio.com, pg 1049

Universal Rehearsal, 17 W 20 St, Suite 4-W, New York, NY 10011 *Tel:* 212-929-3277 *E-mail:* univ318277@aol.com *Web Site:* www.universalrehearsalnyc.com, pg 1049

Universal Satellite Communications Inc, 1530 Nandina Ave, Perris, CA 92571 *Tel:* 562-483-4800; 951-943-4420 (corp off) *Toll Free Tel:* 888-867-6620 *Fax:* 954-943-0263 *Web Site:* www.unisatmobile.com, pg 1049

Universal Studios, 100 Universal City Plaza, Universal City, CA 91608-1002 *Toll Free Tel:* 800-892-1979 *Fax:* 818-866-3600 *E-mail:* studio.operations2@nbcuni.com *Web Site:* www.filmmakersdestination.com; www.nbcuni.com, pg 1049

Universal Studios Canada Inc, 2450 Victoria Park Ave, Willowdale, ON M2J 4A2, Canada *Tel:* 416-491-3000 *Web Site:* www.universalpictures.ca, pg 1049

Universal Studios Florida® Production Group, 1000 Universal Studios Plaza, Bldg 22-A, Orlando, FL 32819 *Tel:* 407-363-8400 *Toll Free Tel:* 877-612-3737 (outside FL) *Fax:* 407-363-8869

E-mail: productiongroup@universalorlando.com *Web Site:* www.universalstudios.com/studio/florida, pg 1049

Universal Studios Home Entertainment, 10 Universal City Plaza, 4th fl, Universal City, CA 91608 *Tel:* 818-777-5159 *Fax:* 818-866-3330 *Web Site:* www.universalstudiosentertainment.com, pg 1049

Universal Training, 736 N Western Ave, Suite 323, Lake Forest, IL 60045 *Tel:* 847-235-2170 *Web Site:* www.universaltraining.com, pg 1049

Universe Kogaku America Inc, 116 Audrey Ave, Oyster Bay, NY 11771 *Tel:* 516-624-2444 *Fax:* 516-624-3109 *E-mail:* info@universeoptics.com *Web Site:* universeoptics.com, pg 1049

University Film & Video Association (UFVA), c/o University of Illinois Press, 1325 S Oak St, Champaign, IL 61820 *Tel:* 217-244-0626 (journals); 217-333-0950 (main) *Toll Free Tel:* 866-244-0626 (journals); 866-647-8382 (main) *Fax:* 217-244-9910 *E-mail:* ufvahome@gmail.com *Web Site:* www.ufva.org, pg 1090

University Media Services, University of Delaware, 85 E Delaware Ave, Newark, DE 19716 *Tel:* 302-831-3546; 302-831-3557 *Fax:* 302-831-3642 *Web Site:* www.ums.udel.edu; www.udel.edu/ums, pg 1049

University of Florida, Warrington College of Business Administration, 100 BRY, Gainesville, FL 32611 *Tel:* 352-392-2397 *Fax:* 352-392-2086 *E-mail:* ufwcba@warrington.ufl.edu *Web Site:* www.cba.ufl.edu, pg 1049

University of Idaho Engineering Outreach, 875 Perimeter Dr MS 1014, Moscow, ID 83844-1014 *Tel:* 208-885-6373 *Toll Free Tel:* 800-824-2889 *Fax:* 208-885-9249 *E-mail:* outreach@uidaho.edu *Web Site:* eo.uidaho.edu, pg 1049

University of Maine Audio Visual Services, 28 Shibles Hall, Orono, ME 04469 *Tel:* 207-581-2500; 207-581-2516 *Web Site:* www.umaine.edu/it/divisions/av, pg 1049

University of Memphis, Music Industry Division, Music Bldg, Rm 123, 3775 Central Ave, Memphis, TN 38152-3160 *Tel:* 901-678-2559; 901-678-2541 *E-mail:* music@memphis.edu *Web Site:* www.memphis.edu/music/index.php, pg 1050

University of Michigan, Center for Middle Eastern & North African Studies, 1080 S University, Suite 3603, Ann Arbor, MI 48109-1106 *Tel:* 734-647-4143 *Fax:* 734-936-0996 *E-mail:* cmenas@umich.edu *Web Site:* www.ii.umich.edu/cmenas, pg 1050

University of Missouri-Columbia, Film & Video Library, 505 E Stewart Rd, Columbia, MO 65211-2040 *Tel:* 573-882-3608 *Fax:* 573-882-6110 *E-mail:* asc@missouri.edu *Web Site:* asc.missouri.edu, pg 1050

University of Missouri-Kansas City School of Dentistry, 650 E 25 St, Kansas City, MO 64108 *Tel:* 816-235-2100 *Fax:* 816-235-5001 *Web Site:* dentistry.umkc.edu, pg 1050

University of Oklahoma Academic Media & Digital Services, 1000 Stanton L Young Blvd, Rm 251, Oklahoma City, OK 73117 *Tel:* 405-271-2318 *E-mail:* amds@ouohsc.edu *Web Site:* www.ouhsc.edu/amds, pg 1050

University of South Carolina Press, 1600 Hampton St, Colimbia, SC 29208 *Tel:* 803-777-5243 *Toll Free Tel:* 800-768-2500 *Toll Free Fax:* 800-868-0740 *Web Site:* www.sc.edu/uscpress, pg 1050

University of Southern California, Davidson Continuing Educ Conference Ctr, Rm 103, 3415 S Figueroa St, Los Angeles, CA 90089-0871 *Tel:* 213-740-5956; 213-740-5679 *Fax:* 213-740-9366 *Web Site:* hospitality.usc.edu/catering, pg 1050

University of Texas at Austin - Petroleum Extension Service, J J Pickle Research Campus, Petroleum Extension Service, Bldg 2, 10100 Burnet Rd, Austin, TX 78758-4445 *Tel:* 512-471-5940 *Toll Free Tel:* 800-687-4132 *Fax:* 512-471-9410 *Toll Free Fax:* 800-687-7839 *E-mail:* petex@www.utexas.edu *Web Site:* www.utexas.edu/ce/petex, pg 1050

University of Toronto Academic & Campus Events, St George Campus, McMurrich Bldg, 4th fl, 12 Queen's Park Crescent W, Toronto, ON M5S 1S8, Canada *Tel:* 416-978-2187; 416-978-8613 (film & photo shoot permits) *Fax:* 416-978-4802 *E-mail:* ace.team@utoronto.ca *Web Site:* www.ace.utoronto.ca, pg 1105

University of Toronto, Classroom Technology Support, Saint George Campus, McMurrich Bldg, 4th fl, 12 Queen's Park Crescent W, Toronto, ON M5S 1S8, Canada *Tel:* 416-978-6544 *Fax:* 416-978-4802 *E-mail:* avrequests@utoronto.ca *Web Site:* www.osm.utoronto.ca, pg 1050

University of Vermont, Instructional Television Dept, 234 Rowell Bldg, Burlington, VT 05405 *Tel:* 802-656-2927 *Fax:* 802-656-8816 *E-mail:* video@zoo.uvm.edu *Web Site:* www.uvm.edu; www.uvm.edu/~video, pg 1050

University of Wisconsin-Oshkosh Radio-TV-Film Dept, Arts & Communications Bldg, W-112, 800 Algoma Blvd, Oshkosh, WI 54901 *Tel:* 920-424-3131 *Fax:* 920-424-7041 *E-mail:* rtf@uwosh.edu *Web Site:* www.uwosh.edu/rtf, pg 1050

University Products Inc, 517 Main St, Holyoke, MA 01040-0073 *Tel:* 413-532-3372 *Toll Free Tel:* 800-628-1912 *Fax:* 413-532-9281 *Toll Free Fax:* 800-532-9281 *E-mail:* custserv@universityproducts.com; info@universityproducts.com *Web Site:* www.universityproducts.com, pg 1050

UPN 20 WDCA-TV, 5151 Wisconsin Ave NW, 2nd fl, Washington, DC 20016 *Tel:* 202-244-5151 *Web Site:* www.my20dc.com, pg 1050

Upstage Video, 212 Shoemaker Rd, Pottstown, PA 19464 *Tel:* 610-323-7200 *Toll Free Tel:* 877-484-3887 *Fax:* 484-727-9056 *E-mail:* info@upstagevideo.com *Web Site:* www.upstagevideo.com, pg 1050

Urbanski Film, PO Box 438, Orland Park, IL 60462-0438 *Tel:* 708-460-9082 *Fax:* 708-460-9099 *E-mail:* info@urbanskifilm.com *Web Site:* www.urbanskifilm.com, pg 1050

US Case Corp, 6301 J Richard Dr, Raleigh, NC 27617 *Tel:* 919-783-6166 *Toll Free Tel:* 800-648-8474 *Fax:* 919-783-0740 *E-mail:* customersupport@uscase.com *Web Site:* www.uscase.com, pg 1050

US Holocaust Memorial Museum, 100 Raoul Wallenberg Place SW, Washington, DC 20024-2126 *Tel:* 202-488-0400 *Fax:* 202-488-2695 *E-mail:* membership@ushmm.org *Web Site:* www.ushmm.org, pg 1050

US International Film & Video Festival Awards, 713 S Pacific Coast Hwy, Suite A, Redondo Beach, CA 90277-4233 *Tel:* 310-540-0959 *Fax:* 310-316-8905 *E-mail:* filmfestinfo@filmfestawards.com *Web Site:* www.filmfestawards.com, pg 1128

US Virgin Islands Film Promotion Office, PO Box 6400, St Thomas, VI 00804-6400 *Tel:* 340-775-1444 (ext 2243) *Fax:* 340-774-4390 *E-mail:* info@filmusvi.com *Web Site:* www.filmusvi.com, pg 1104

USA Film Festival, 6116 N Central Expwy, Suite 105, Dallas, TX 75206 *Tel:* 214-821-6300 *Fax:* 214-821-6364 *E-mail:* usafilmfestival@aol.com *Web Site:* www.usafilmfestival.com, pg 1128

USA Studios, 253 W 35 St, 2nd fl, New York, NY 10001 *Tel:* 212-398-6400 *Fax:* 212-398-4145 *E-mail:* sales@usastudios.tv; info@usastudios.tv *Web Site:* www.usastudios.tv, pg 1050

USAV Group Inc, 5485 S Westridge Dr, New Berlin, WI 53151-7948 *Tel:* 262-814-2000 *Toll Free Tel:* 800-596-USAV (596-8728) *Fax:* 262-814-2006 *Web Site:* www.usavgroup.com, pg 1050

USCCB Publishing, 3211 Fourth St NE, Washington, DC 20017 *Tel:* 202-541-3090 *Toll Free Tel:* 800-235-8722 (cust serv) *Fax:* 202-722-8709 (cust serv) *E-mail:* publications@usccb.org *Web Site:* www.usccbpublishing.org, pg 1051

USDA/FSA Aerial Photography Field Office, 2222 W 2300 S, Salt Lake City, UT 84119-2020 *Tel:* 801-844-2922 *Toll Free Fax:* 855-415-2014 *E-mail:* apfo.sales@slc.usda.gov *Web Site:* www.apfo.usda.gov, pg 1051

Ushio America Inc, 5440 Cerritos Ave, Cypress, CA 90630-4567 *Tel:* 714-236-8600 *Toll Free Tel:* 800-838-7446 (cust serv) *Fax:* 714-229-3180 *Toll Free Fax:* 800-776-3641 (cust serv) *E-mail:* customerservice@ushio.com *Web Site:* www.ushio.com, pg 1051

USI Inc, 98 Fort Path Rd, Suite A, Madison, CT 06443 *Tel:* 203-245-8586 *Toll Free Tel:* 800-282-9290 *Fax:* 203-245-8619 *E-mail:* customers@usi-corp.com *Web Site:* www.usi-laminate.com, pg 1051

USITT: United States Institute for Theatre Technology Inc, 315 S Crouse Ave, Suite 200, Syracuse, NY 13210-1844 *Tel:* 315-463-6463 *Toll Free Tel:* 800-938-7488 *Fax:* 315-463-6525 *Toll Free Fax:* 866-398-7488 *E-mail:* info@office.usitt.org *Web Site:* www.usitt.org, pg 1090

USMotivation, 7840 Roswell Rd, USM Bldg 100, 3rd fl, Atlanta, GA 30350 *Tel:* 770-290-4700 *Toll Free Tel:* 800-476-0496 *Fax:* 770-290-4701 *E-mail:* information@usmotivation.com *Web Site:* www.usmotivation.com, pg 1051

Utah Film Commission, Council Hall/Capitol Hill, 300 N State St, Salt Lake City, UT 84114 *Tel:* 801-538-8740 *Toll Free Tel:* 800-453-8824 *Fax:* 801-538-1397 *Web Site:* www.film.utah.gov, pg 1103

Utah Scientific Inc, 4750 Wiley Post Way, Suite 150, Salt Lake City, UT 84116 *Tel:* 801-575-8801 *Toll Free Tel:* 800-453-8782 *Fax:* 801-537-3099 *E-mail:* info@utahscientific.com *Web Site:* www.utahscientific.com, pg 1051

Utah Valley Film Commission, 220 W Center St, Suite 100, Provo, UT 84601 *Tel:* 801-851-2100 *Toll Free Tel:* 800-222-8824 *Fax:* 801-851-2109 *E-mail:* visitors@utahvalley.com *Web Site:* www.utahvalley.com/film, pg 1103

Utopia Films, 1976 S La Cienega Blvd, No 130, Los Angeles, CA 90034 *Tel:* 310-338-0580 *Fax:* 313-557-0580 *E-mail:* reception@utopiafilms.com; utopiafilms2@gmail.com (large e-mails); production@utopiafilms.com (reels) *Web Site:* utopiafilms.com, pg 1051

Vaddio, 131 Cheshire Lane, Suite 500, Minnetonka, MN 55305 *Tel:* 763-971-4400 *Toll Free Tel:* 800-572-2011 *Fax:* 763-971-4464 *E-mail:* info@vaddio.com *Web Site:* www.vaddio.com, pg 1051

Valencia Studios, 26030 Avenue Hall, Studio 5, Valencia, CA 91355 *Tel:* 661-702-9102 *E-mail:* info@valenciastudios.com *Web Site:* www.valenciastudios.com, pg 1051

Vallejo/Solano County Film Office, 289 Mare Island Way, Vallejo, CA 94590 *Tel:* 707-642-3653 *Toll Free Tel:* 800-4-VALLEJO (482-5535) *Fax:* 707-644-2206 *Web Site:* www.visitvallejo.com/film-office, pg 1094

Valley Media, 421 Roanoke Dr, Martinez, CA 94553-6240 *Tel:* 925-937-5207; 510-612-5215 (cell) *Web Site:* www.valleymedia.com, pg 1051

Valley of the Sun Publishing Co, PO Box 2053, Sedona, AZ 86339 *Tel:* 928-554-1333 *E-mail:* info@dicksutphen.com *Web Site:* www.dicksutphen.com, pg 1051

Jack Van Impe Ministries International, 1718 Northfield Dr, Rochester Hills, MI 48309 *Tel:* 248-852-2244; 248-852-5225 (orders) *Fax:* 248-852-2692 *E-mail:* jvimi@jvim.com *Web Site:* www.jvim.com, pg 1051

Vancouver Film & Special Events Office, 126 Keefer St, Vancouver, BC V6A 1X4, Canada *Tel:* 604-257-8840 *Fax:* 604-257-8859 *E-mail:* film.office@vancouver.ca *Web Site:* www.vancouver.ca/engsvcs/filmandevents, pg 1105

Vancouver Film Studios Ltd, 3500 Cornett Rd, Vancouver, BC V5M 2H5, Canada *Tel:* 604-453-5000 *Fax:* 604-453-5045 *Web Site:* www.vancouverfilmstudios.com, pg 1051

Vancouver International Film Festival, Vancouver International Film Centre, 1181 Seymour St, Vancouver, BC V6B 3M7, Canada *Tel:* 604-685-0260 *Fax:* 604-688-8221 *E-mail:* viff@viff.org *Web Site:* www.viff.org, pg 1129

Vancouver Island South Film & Media Commission, 100-852 Fort St, Victoria, BC V8W 1H8, Canada *Tel:* 250-386-3976 *Toll Free Tel:* 888-537-3456 *Fax:* 250-386-3967 *E-mail:* admin@filmvictoria.com *Web Site:* www.filmvictoria.com, pg 1105

Vanguard Documentaries, PO Box 26635, Brooklyn, NY 11202 *Tel:* 347-725-1677 *Web Site:* www.vanguarddocumentaries.com, pg 1051

Vanner Inc, 4282 Reynolds Dr, Hilliard, OH 43026 *Tel:* 614-771-2718 *Toll Free Tel:* 800-ACPOWER (227-6937) *Fax:* 614-771-4904 *E-mail:* info@vanner.com; pwrsales@vanner.com *Web Site:* www.vanner.com, pg 1051

Vantage/Legrand, 1061 S 800 E, Orem, UT 84097 *Tel:* 801-229-2800 *Toll Free Tel:* 800-555-9891 *Fax:* 801-224-0355 *E-mail:* vantage.info@vantagecontrols.com *Web Site:* www.vantagecontrols.com, pg 1051

Vantage Point Products Corp, PO Box 2485, Santa Fe Springs, CA 90670 *Tel:* 562-946-1718 *Toll Free Tel:* 888-886-6868 *Fax:* 562-946-3898 *Web Site:* www.thinkvp.com, pg 1051

Varese Sarabande Records Inc, 9100 Wilshire Blvd, Suite 455E, Beverly Hills, CA 90212 *Tel:* 310-853-5400 *Toll Free Tel:* 800-827-3734 *E-mail:* info@varesesarabande.com; orders@varesesarabande.com *Web Site:* www.varesesarabande.com, pg 1052

Vari-Lite, 10911 Petal St, Dallas, TX 75238 *Tel:* 214-647-7880 *Toll Free Tel:* 877-VARILITE (877-827-4548) *Fax:* 214-647-8038 *E-mail:* entertainment.service@philips.com *Web Site:* www.vari-lite.com, pg 1052

Varitronics LLC, 2355 Polaris Lane N, Suite 100, Plymouth, MN 55447 *Tel:* 763-536-6400 *Toll Free Tel:* 800-328-0585 *Toll Free Fax:* 800-543-8966 *Web Site:* www.variquest.com, pg 1052

Varta Microbattery Inc, 555 Theodore Fremd Ave, Suite C304, Rye, NY 10580 *Tel:* 914-592-2500 *Toll Free Tel:* 800-468-2782 *Fax:* 914-345-0488 *Web Site:* www.varta-microbattery.com; www.varta-microbattery.us, pg 1052

Varto Technologies, 195 Hackensack St, East Rutherford, NJ 07073 *Toll Free Tel:* 888-656-6233 *Fax:* 201-604-2661 *E-mail:* sales@vartotechnologies.com *Web Site:* www.vartotechnologies.com, pg 1052

Mike Vasilinda Productions Inc, 310 N Monroe St, Tallahassee, FL 32301 *Tel:* 850-224-5420 *Web Site:* mvptv.tv, pg 1052

VCI Entertainment, 11333 E 60 Place, Tulsa, OK 74146-6828 *Tel:* 918-254-6337 *Toll Free Tel:* 800-331-4077 *Fax:* 918-254-6117 *E-mail:* vci@vcientertainment.com *Web Site:* www.vcientertainment.com, pg 1052

VCom International Multimedia Corp, 80 Little Falls Rd, Fairfield, NJ 07004 *Toll Free Tel:* 800-572-6373 *E-mail:* info@vcomimc.com *Web Site:* www.vcomimc.com, pg 1052

VCSvideo, 2807 Hunterdon Dr, Cinnaminson, NJ 08077 *Tel:* 856-273-8800 *Toll Free Tel:* 877-VCS-VIDEO (827-8433) *Web Site:* www.vcsvideo.com, pg 1052

VDO Lab Inc, 400 Tarrytown Rd, White Plains, NY 10607-1314 *Tel:* 914-681-0849; 914-949-1741 *Fax:* 914-949-5743 *E-mail:* sales@vdolab.net *Web Site:* vdolab.net, pg 1052

Vedanta Press & Catalog, 1946 Vedanta Place, Hollywood, CA 90068 *Tel:* 323-960-1727 (bookstores); 323-960-1736 (outside US) *Toll Free Tel:* 800-816-2242 *E-mail:* info@vedanta.com *Web Site:* www.vedanta.com, pg 1052

Vedanta Society of St Louis, 205 S Skinker Blvd, St Louis, MO 63105 *Tel:* 314-721-5118 *Web Site:* vedantastl.org, pg 1052

Veetronix Inc, 1311 W Pacific St, Lexington, NE 68850 *Tel:* 308-324-6661 *Toll Free Tel:* 800-445-0007 *Fax:* 308-324-4985 *E-mail:* sales@veetronix.com *Web Site:* www.veetronix.com, pg 1052

Vela Research, 5540 Rio Vista Dr, Clearwater, FL 33760-3107 *Tel:* 727-507-5300 *Fax:* 727-507-5312 *E-mail:* vela_info@vela.com *Web Site:* www.vela.com, pg 1052

Velodyne Acoustics Inc, 345 Digital Dr, Morgan Hill, CA 95037 *Tel:* 408-465-2800 *Toll Free Tel:* 866-243-0789 *Fax:* 408-779-9227; 408-779-9208 (cust serv); 408-779-9377 (orders) *E-mail:* service@velodyne.com; orders@velodyne.com *Web Site:* www.velodyne.com, pg 1052

Venice Media Group, 101 W Venice Ave, Unit 10, Venice, FL 34285 *Tel:* 941-485-0699 *E-mail:* info@venicemediagroup.com *Web Site:* www.venicemediagroup.com, pg 1052

Venture Media, 902 Harvest Pointe Dr, Fort Mill, SC 29708 *Tel:* 803-547-3878 *E-mail:* info@venturemedia.tv *Web Site:* www.venturemedia.tv, pg 1052

Ver Sales Inc, 2509 N Naomi St, Burbank, CA 91504 *Tel:* 818-567-3000 *Toll Free Tel:* 800-229-0518; 800-300-WIRE (300-9479, CA only) *Fax:* 818-567-3018 *E-mail:* sales@versales.com *Web Site:* www.versales.com, pg 1052

VER-Video Equipment Rentals, 912 Ruberta Ave, Glendale, CA 91201 *Tel:* 818-956-1444 *Toll Free Tel:* 800-794-1407 (cust serv); 888-584-TECH (584-8324) *Fax:* 818-241-4519 *E-mail:* rentals@verrents.com; info@verrents.com *Web Site:* www.verrents.com, pg 1053

Verilux® - The Healthy Lighting Co, 340 Mad River Park, Suite 1, Waitsfield, VT 05673 *Tel:* 802-496-3101 *Toll Free Tel:* 888-544-4865 (cust support); 800-454-4408 (orders) *Fax:* 802-496-3105 (orders) *E-mail:* info@verilux.com *Web Site:* www.verilux.com, pg 1053

Veritech Corp, 80 Denslow Rd, East Longmeadow, MA 01028 *Tel:* 413-525-3368 *Toll Free Tel:* 800-525-5912 *Fax:* 413-525-7449 *E-mail:* info@veritechmedia.com *Web Site:* www.veritechmedia.com, pg 1053

Vermont International Film Festival, 230 College St, Burlington, VT 05401 *Tel:* 802-660-2600 *Fax:* 802-860-9555 *E-mail:* info@vtiff.org *Web Site:* www.vtiff.org, pg 1129

Versatech Industries Inc, 14750 S Grant St, Bixby, OK 74008 *Tel:* 918-366-7400, pg 1053

Versatruss, 5028 Hwy 43, Perth, ON K7H 3C7, Canada *Tel:* 613-264-0074 *Toll Free Tel:* 888-430-7613 *Fax:* 613-264-0889 *E-mail:* info@versatruss.com *Web Site:* www.versatruss.com, pg 1053

The Verve Music Group, 134 W 25 St, 5th fl, New York, NY 10001 *Tel:* 212-494-0078 *E-mail:* contact@vervemusicgroup.com *Web Site:* www.vervemusicgroup.com; www.umusic.com, pg 1053

Vexcel Corp, 5775 Flatiron Pkwy, Suite 220, Boulder, CO 80301 *Tel:* 303-415-6000 *Fax:* 303-442-2956 *E-mail:* vexcel@microsoft.com *Web Site:* www.vexcel.com, pg 1053

La Vezzi Precision Inc, 999 Regency Dr, Glendale Heights, IL 60139-2281 *Tel:* 630-582-1230 *Toll Free Tel:* 800-323-1772 (outside IL) *Fax:* 630-582-1238 (orders) *E-mail:* lpi@lavezzi.com *Web Site:* www.lavezzi.com, pg 1053

VFGadgets Inc, 22 Elmer Ave, Toronto, ON M4L 3R7, Canada *Tel:* 416-686-1452 *E-mail:* sales@vfgadgets.com; customerservice@vfgadgets.com *Web Site:* www.vfgadgets.com, pg 1053

VGI Productions, 3655 Tolland Rd, Shaker Heights, OH 44122 *Tel:* 216-464-3635 *Fax:* 216-464-5630 *Web Site:* www.vgipro.com, pg 1053

Via Verde Productions, 22631 Pacific Coast Hwy, Suite 480, Malibu, CA 90265-5036 *Tel:* 310-458-3778 *Fax:* 310-496-2992 *E-mail:* info@viaverdedigital.com *Web Site:* www.viaverdedigital.com, pg 1053

Via-Vision Film & Video Productions, 18 College St, Lewiston, ME 04240 *Tel:* 207-783-2550 *Web Site:* www.viavisionproductions.com, pg 1053

Vicon Industries Inc, 131 Heartland Blvd, Edgewood, NY 11717 *Tel:* 631-952-2288 *Toll Free Tel:* 800-645-9116 *Fax:* 631-951-2288 *Web Site:* www.vicon-security.com, pg 1053

Victoria Supply Inc/Topbulb.com, 5204 Indianapolis Blvd, East Chicago, IN 46312-3838 *Tel:* 219-398-2362 *Toll Free Tel:* 800-TOP-BULB (867-2852) *Toll Free Fax:* 877-329-2852 *E-mail:* sales@topbulb.com *Web Site:* www.topbulb.com, pg 1054

Victory Cinevideo Battery Corp, 10509 Burbank Blvd, N Hollywood, CA 91601 *Tel:* 818-754-0647 *Toll Free Tel:* 800-292-6565 *Fax:* 818-754-0640 *Web Site:* www.victorycinevideobattery.com, pg 1054

Victory Studios, 2247 15 Ave W, Seattle, WA 98119 *Tel:* 206-282-1776 *Toll Free Tel:* 888-282-1776 *Fax:* 206-282-3535 *Toll Free Fax:* 888-765-9563 *E-mail:* info@victorystudios.com *Web Site:* www.victorystudios.com, pg 1054

VidCAD by Commsys Design LLC, 2010 E Lohman Ave, Suite 2, Las Cruces, NM 88001 *Tel:* 575-522-0003 *Toll Free Tel:* 800-VIDCAD-6 (843-2236 sales); 888-4-VIDTEC (484-3832 tech support) *Fax:* 575-635-4518 *E-mail:* sales@vidcad.com *Web Site:* www.vidcad.com, pg 1054

VidCan Media Solutions, 24133 Del Monte Dr, Unit 204, Valencia, CA 91355 *Tel:* 818-239-4729; 818-312-5128 *Web Site:* www.vidcan.com, pg 1054

Vidcraft Productions Ltd, 425 Curling St, Corner Brook, NL A2H 3K4, Canada *Tel:* 709-785-1157 *E-mail:* info@vidcraft.com *Web Site:* www.vidcraft.com, pg 1054

Vide-O-Go/That's Infotainment!, 206 Winding Ridge Dr, Cary, NC 27518-8934 *Tel:* 919-363-7920 *E-mail:* videogo@aol.com *Web Site:* www.videogo.com, pg 1054

Video Accessory Corp, 1243 Sherman Dr, Suite 8, Longmont, CO 80501 *Tel:* 303-443-1319 *Toll Free Tel:* 800-821-0426 *Fax:* 303-440-8878 *E-mail:* sales@vac-brick.net *Web Site:* www.vac-brick.com, pg 1054

Video Advantage, 90 Houseman Crescent, Richmond Hill, ON L4C 7S6, Canada *Tel:* 905-883-5332 *E-mail:* info@videoadvantage.ca *Web Site:* www.videoadvantage.ca, pg 1054

Video Aided Instruction Inc, 485-34 S Broadway, Hicksville, NY 11801-5071 *Tel:* 516-939-0707 *Toll Free Tel:* 800-238-1512 *Toll Free Fax:* 800-588-1419 *E-mail:* custsvc@videoaidedinstruction.com *Web Site:* www.videoaidedinstruction.com, pg 1054

Video Artists International & VAI Audio, 109 Wheeler Ave, Pleasantville, NY 10570 *Tel:* 914-769-3691 *Toll Free Tel:* 800-477-7146 *Fax:* 914-769-5407 *E-mail:* orders@vaimusic.com *Web Site:* www.vaimusic.com, pg 1054

Video Associates Labs Inc, 2201 Denton Dr, Suite 109 B, Austin, TX 78758 *Tel:* 512-491-7091 *Toll Free Tel:* 800-331-0547 *Fax:* 512-491-7619 *E-mail:* sales@val.com *Web Site:* www.val.com, pg 1054

Video Automation Systems Inc, 13 Arrow Meadow Rd, New Fairfield, CT 06812 *Tel:* 203-312-0152 *Fax:* 203-312-0157 *Web Site:* www.videoautomation.com/videoautomation.html, pg 1054

Video Caption Corp, 88 Hunns Lake Rd, Stanfordville, NY 12581 *Tel:* 845-868-1200 *Toll Free Tel:* 800-705-1203 *Fax:* 845-868-1188 *Toll Free Fax:* 800-705-1207 *E-mail:* mail@vicaps.com *Web Site:* www.vicaps.com, pg 1054

Video Catalogue Co Inc, 105 E 34 St, Suite 105, New York, NY 10016 *Toll Free Tel:* 866-843-2282 *E-mail:* info@vidcat.com *Web Site:* www.vidcat.com, pg 1054

Video Communication Productions Inc, 446 Salem Dr, Pittsburgh, PA 15243 *Tel:* 412-915-6776 *Web Site:* www.pittsburghvideoguy.com, pg 1054

Video Concepts Unlimited, PO Box 577, North Chili, NY 14514 *Tel:* 585-293-2222 *Toll Free Tel:* 800-930-5411 *E-mail:* videocu@aol.com *Web Site:* www.dvdtransferservices.com, pg 1055

Video Copy Services Inc, 3980 Dekalb Technology Pkwy, Suite 670, Atlanta, GA 30340 *Toll Free Tel:* 800-553-3616 *E-mail:* info@video-copy.com *Web Site:* www.video-copy.com, pg 1055

Video Corporation of America (VCA), 7 Veronica Ave, Somerset, NJ 08873 *Tel:* 732-545-8000 *Fax:* 732-545-5101 *E-mail:* njsales@vcaglobal.com *Web Site:* www.vcaglobal.com, pg 1055

Video Design Group, 51 Hattertown Rd, Monroe, CT 06468 *Tel:* 203-261-7995 *Web Site:* www.videodesigngroup.com, pg 1055

Video Excellence Productions, 94 Breckonwood Crescent, Thornhill, ON L3T 5E8, Canada *Tel:* 905-731-4355 *Web Site:* www.videoexcellence.com, pg 1055

Video Express, 181 Newbury St, 5th fl, Boston, MA 02116 *Tel:* 617-267-7900 *Fax:* 617-267-6306 *E-mail:* information@evideoexpress.com *Web Site:* www.evideoexpress.com, pg 1055

Video/Film Associates, 3310 W Queen Lane, Philadelphia, PA 19129 *Tel:* 215-922-3333, pg 1055

Video Gear Rentals Inc, 8969 Kenamar Dr, Suite 104, San Diego, CA 92121 *Tel:* 858-356-0200 *Fax:* 858-356-0204 *Web Site:* www.video-gear.com, pg 1055

Video I-D Teleproductions Inc, 105 Muller Rd, Washington, IL 61571 *Tel:* 309-444-4323 *Toll Free Tel:* 800-333-9123 *Fax:* 309-444-4333 *Web Site:* www.videoid.com, pg 1055

Video Ideas Productions, 1501 64 St, North Bergen, NJ 07047 *Tel:* 201-951-3798 *Fax:* 201-662-4846 *Web Site:* osoriomedia.com, pg 1055

Video Impressions, 2505 Diehl Rd, Aurora, IL 60502 *Tel:* 630-851-1663 *Fax:* 630-851-2688 *E-mail:* office@video-impressions.com *Web Site:* www.video-impressions.com, pg 1055

Video In Studios/Video Out Distribution, 2625 Kaslo St, Vancouver, BC V5M 3G9, Canada *Tel:* 604-872-8337; 604-872-8449 *Fax:* 604-876-1185 *E-mail:* info@vivomediaarts.com; info@videoout.ca *Web Site:* www.videoinstudios.com; www.videoout.ca, pg 1055

Video International Development Inc, PO Box 349, Locust Valley, NY 11560 *Tel:* 516-671-6765 *Fax:* 516-730-5084 *E-mail:* info@videointernational.org *Web Site:* www.videointernational.org, pg 1055

Video Labs, 15237 Display Ct, Rockville, MD 20850 *Tel:* 301-217-0000 *Toll Free Tel:* 800-800-8240 *Fax:* 301-217-0044 *E-mail:* sales@videolabs.net *Web Site:* www.videolabs.net, pg 1055

Video Learning Library, 15838 N 62 St, Scottsdale, AZ 85254-1988 *Tel:* 480-596-9970 *Toll Free Tel:* 800-383-8811 (orders) *E-mail:* videos@videolearning.com *Web Site:* www.videolearning.com, pg 1055

Video Media Productions (VMP), 175 S Hamilton Place, Gilbert, AZ 85233 *Tel:* 480-745-2776 *E-mail:* question@videomediaproductions.com; video@videomediaproductions.com *Web Site:* www.videomediaproductions.com, pg 1055

The Video Messenger Co, 862 Judson Place, Stratford, CT 06615 *Tel:* 203-358-8842 *Toll Free Tel:* 800-800-7128 *Fax:* 203-547-6216 *E-mail:* vmc@videomessenger.com *Web Site:* www.videomessenger.com, pg 1055

Video Mount Products (VMP), 345 Log Canoe Circle, Stevensville, MD 21666 *Tel:* 410-643-6390 *Toll Free Tel:* 877-281-2169 *Fax:* 410-643-6615 *E-mail:* sales@videomount.com *Web Site:* www.videomount.com, pg 1055

Video Movie Magic, 26941 Cabot Rd, Suite 127, Laguna Hills, CA 92653 *Tel:* 949-582-8596 *Fax:* 949-582-8223 *E-mail:* sales@videomoviemagic.com *Web Site:* www.videomoviemagic.com, pg 1056

Video Perspective, PO Box 591843, Houston, TX 77259-1843 *Tel:* 281-996-7974 *Toll Free Tel:* 888-996-7974 *E-mail:* vp@vidper.com *Web Site:* www.videoperspective.com, pg 1056

Video Production Associates Inc, 525 Bridgeport Ave, Shelton, CT 06484-1397 *Tel:* 203-929-8869 *Toll Free Tel:* 800-394-8869 *Fax:* 203-925-0344 *Web Site:* www.vpa-inc.com, pg 1056

The Video Project, 145 Ninth St, Suite 102, San Francisco, CA 94103 *Tel:* 415-981-9710 *Toll Free Tel:* 800-475-2638 *Toll Free Fax:* 888-562-9012 *E-mail:* orders@videoproject.com; support@videoproject.com *Web Site:* www.videoproject.com, pg 1056

Video Resources Inc, 1809 E Dyer Rd, Suite 307, Santa Ana, CA 92705 *Tel:* 949-261-7266 *Toll Free Tel:* 800-261-7266 *Fax:* 949-261-5908 *E-mail:* info@videoresources.com *Web Site:* www.videoresources.com, pg 1056

Video Service of America Inc (VSA), 6929 Seward Ave, Lincoln, NE 68507 *Tel:* 402-467-3668 *Toll Free Tel:* 800-888-2140 (orders) *Fax:* 402-325-8033 *E-mail:* sales@vsa1.com *Web Site:* www.vsa1.com, pg 1056

Video Solutions, 2121 Eisenhower Ave, Suite 103, Alexandria, VA 22314 *Tel:* 703-683-5305; 703-628-0702 (cell) *E-mail:* inquiries@thevideosolution.com *Web Site:* www.thevideosolution.com, pg 1056

The Video Store Shopper, 3987 Heritage Oak Ct, Simi Valley, CA 93063 *Tel:* 805-583-8500 *Toll Free Tel:* 800-462-9040; 800-325-6867 (cust serv) *Fax:* 805-583-8546 *Toll Free Fax:* 800-947-2060 *E-mail:* sales@shopperinc.com; customerservice@shopperinc.com *Web Site:* www.thevideostoreshopper.com, pg 1056

Video Symphony TV & Film School, 266 E Magnolia Blvd, Burbank, CA 91502 *Tel:* 818-557-7200 *Toll Free Tel:* 800-871-2843 *Fax:* 818-845-1951 *E-mail:* info@videosymphony.com *Web Site:* www.videosymphony.com, pg 1056

Video Techniques Inc, 3306 26 St W, Bradenton, FL 34205-3608 *Tel:* 941-758-3077 *Fax:* 941-301-4696 *E-mail:* vti1@videotechniques.com, pg 1056

Video Technology Services Inc, 5 Ariel Way, Suite 300, Syosset, NY 11791 *Tel:* 516-937-9700 *Fax:* 516-937-9704 *E-mail:* vts1@optonline.net *Web Site:* www.videotechnologyservices.com, pg 1056

Video Visions Inc, 3600 Boundbrook Ave, Trevose, PA 19053 *Tel:* 215-942-6642 *Fax:* 267-684-6819 *E-mail:* sales@video-visions.com *Web Site:* www.video-visions.com, pg 1056

Video West Inc, 570 W Southern Ave, Tempe, AZ 85282 *Tel:* 480-222-3180 *Fax:* 480-222-3191 *E-mail:* info@videowestinc.com *Web Site:* www.videowestinc.com, pg 1056

Video Wisconsin Inc, 18110 W Bluemound Rd, Brookfield, WI 53045 *Tel:* 262-785-1110 *Fax:* 262-785-9827 *Web Site:* www.videowisconsin.tv, pg 1056

Videobotics, 220 N Palisade Dr, Santa Maria, CA 93454 *Tel:* 805-349-1104 *E-mail:* videobotics@megagem.com; megagem@megagem.com *Web Site:* www.videobotics.com; camrobot.com, pg 1056

Videofashion Network, 611 Broadway, Suite 307, New York, NY 10012 *Tel:* 212-274-1600 *Fax:* 212-219-1969 *E-mail:* licensing@videofashion.com *Web Site:* www.videofashion.com, pg 1056

Videofax, 1750 Cesar Chavez St, Unit G, San Francisco, CA 94124 *Tel:* 415-641-0100 *E-mail:* rentals@videofax.com *Web Site:* www.videofax.com, pg 1056

Videofilm Systems Inc, 7 Islandbrook Ave, Unit D-1, Bridgeport, CT 06606 *Tel:* 203-870-6013 *Web Site:* www.videofilmsystems.com, pg 1057

Videograf, 144 W 27 St, 12th fl, New York, NY 10001 *Tel:* 212-242-7871 *E-mail:* videograf@verizon.net, pg 1057

Videografix LLC, 2530 Berryessa Rd, Suite 314, San Jose, CA 95132-2903 *Tel:* 408-499-1280 *Fax:* 408-583-4018 *E-mail:* info@videografix.com *Web Site:* www.videografix.com, pg 1057

Videography Productions, PO Box 653, Amagansett, NY 11930-0653 *Tel:* 520-907-1900 *Web Site:* www.dickfisher.net, pg 1057

Videoguys, 10-12 Charles St, Glen Cove, NY 11542 *Tel:* 516-759-1611 *Toll Free Tel:* 800-323-2325 *Fax:* 516-671-3092 *E-mail:* sales@videoguys.com *Web Site:* www.videoguys.com, pg 1057

The Videohouse Inc, 975 Greentree Rd, Pittsburgh, PA 15220 *Tel:* 412-921-7577 *Fax:* 412-921-5535 *E-mail:* tvirjb@aol.com *Web Site:* www.thevideohouse.com, pg 1057

Videolady, PO Box 2276, San Bernardino, CA 92406-2276 *Tel:* 909-882-4057 *Fax:* 909-882-4057 *E-mail:* vldy@aol.com *Web Site:* videoladystudios.com, pg 1057

VideoLink Inc, 1230 Washington St, Newton, MA 02465 *Tel:* 617-340-4100 *Fax:* 617-340-4101 *Web Site:* www.videolinktv.com, pg 1057

Videomagnetics, 3970 Clearview Frontage Rd, Colorado Springs, CO 80911 *Tel:* 719-390-1313 *Toll Free Tel:* 800-432-3887 *Fax:* 719-390-1316 *E-mail:* vmi@csprings.com *Web Site:* www.videomagnetics.com, pg 1057

Videorama Industries LLC, 1119 N Hudson Ave, Hollywood, CA 90038 *Tel:* 323-466-7232 *Fax:* 323-466-7228 *Web Site:* www.videorama.com, pg 1057

Videoscope, 7711 NW 46 St, Miami, FL 33166 *Tel:* 305-436-1684 *Fax:* 305-438-3743 *E-mail:* info@videoscopeusa.com *Web Site:* www.videoscopeusa.com, pg 1057

Videosmith Inc, 200 Spring Garden St, Suite C, Philadelphia, PA 19123 *Tel:* 215-238-5070 *Fax:* 215-238-5075 *E-mail:* info@videosmith.com *Web Site:* videosmith.com, pg 1057

Videotex Systems Inc, 10255 Miller Rd, Dallas, TX 75238 *Tel:* 972-231-9200 *Toll Free Tel:* 800-88-VIDEO (888-4336) *Fax:* 972-231-2420 *E-mail:* info@videotexsystems.com *Web Site:* www.videotexsystems.com, pg 1057

Videowerks, 3435 Ocean Park Blvd, Suite 107, Santa Monica, CA 90405 *Tel:* 310-393-8754; 310-780-4156 (cell) *Fax:* 310-399-1829 *E-mail:* videowerks@earthlink.net *Web Site:* www.videowerks.com, pg 1057

Videssence, 10768 Lower Azusa Rd, El Monte, CA 91731 *Tel:* 626-579-0943 *Fax:* 626-579-6803 *E-mail:* contact@videssence.tv *Web Site:* www.videssence.tv, pg 1057

Vidicom Inc, 520 Eighth Ave, Suite 2206, New York, NY 10018 *Tel:* 212-895-8300 *E-mail:* info@vidicom.com *Web Site:* vidicom.com, pg 1057

Vidox Motion Imagery, 204 Winchester Dr, Lafayette, LA 70506 *Tel:* 337-237-1700 *Fax:* 337-237-1712 *Web Site:* www.vidox.com, pg 1057

VIEW Inc (Video International Entertainment World Inc), 11 Reservoir Rd, Saugerties, NY 12477 *Tel:* 845-246-9955 *Toll Free Tel:* 800-843-9843 *Fax:* 845-246-9966 *E-mail:* viewvid@aol.com *Web Site:* www.view.com, pg 1058

Viewpoint Production Services Inc, 419 Mount Nebo Rd, Pittsburgh, PA 15237 *Tel:* 412-369-7171 *Toll Free Tel:* 800-820-0402 *Web Site:* viewpoint.tv, pg 1058

ViewSonic, 381 Brea Canyon Rd, Walnut, CA 91789-0708 *Tel:* 909-444-8888 *Toll Free Tel:* 800-688-6688; 800-888-8583 *Fax:* 909-468-1240 *Web Site:* www.viewsonic.com, pg 1058

Viking Cases, 10480 Oak St NE, St Petersburg, FL 33716 *Tel:* 727-577-1216 *Toll Free Tel:* 800-237-8560 *Fax:* 727-577-2082 *E-mail:* sales@vikingcases.com *Web Site:* www.vikingcases.com, pg 1058

Vincent Associates, 803 Linden Ave, Rochester, NY 14625 *Tel:* 585-385-5930 *Toll Free Tel:* 800-828-6972 *Fax:* 585-385-6004 *E-mail:* info@uniblitz.com *Web Site:* www.uniblitz.com, pg 1058

Vincent Lighting Systems, 6161 Cochran Rd, Suite D, Solon, OH 44139 *Tel:* 216-475-7600 *Toll Free Tel:* 800-922-5356 *Fax:* 216-475-6376 *E-mail:* info@vls.com *Web Site:* www.vincentlighting.com, pg 1058

Vineyard Productions, 3640 Lovall Valley Rd, Sonoma, CA 95476 *Tel:* 707-939-3566 *Web Site:* www.vineyardproductions.com, pg 1058

Vineyard Video & Photography, 4193 Concord Ave, Santa Rosa, CA 95407 *Tel:* 707-591-9999; 707-591-1927 (cell) *Web Site:* www.vineyardvideo.com, pg 1058

VIP Presentation Products, 69 S Dixie Hwy, Suite A, St Augustine, FL 32084 *Tel:* 904-824-0824 *Toll Free Tel:* 800-874-0855 *Fax:* 904-829-6903 *E-mail:* info@vippresentationproducts.com *Web Site:* vippresentationproducts.com, pg 1058

The Virginia Film Festival, 617 W Main St, 2nd fl, Charlottesville, VA 22903 *Tel:* 434-982-5277 *Fax:* 434-924-3374 *E-mail:* info@virginiafilmfestival.org *Web Site:* www.virginiafilmfestival.org, pg 1129

Virginia Film Office, 901 E Byrd St, Richmond, VA 23219-4048 *Tel:* 804-545-5530 *Toll Free Tel:* 800-854-6233 *Fax:* 804-545-5501 *E-mail:* vafilm@virginia.org *Web Site:* www.film.virginia.org, pg 1103

Virtual Research Systems Inc, 3824 Vienna Dr, Aptos, CA 95003 *Tel:* 408-748-8712 *Fax:* 408-748-8714 *Web Site:* www.virtualresearch.com, pg 1058

VirtualMix, 311 W Third St, Suite 2914, Carson City, NV 89703 *Tel:* 818-209-6176 *E-mail:* virtualmixpost@gmail.com *Web Site:* www.virtualmix.com, pg 1058

Vision Identics Systems Inc, 110 Villa Ave, Mamaroneck, NY 10543 *Tel:* 914-381-2625 *Toll Free Tel:* 800-750-8840 *Fax:* 914-381-2752 *E-mail:* inquiry@visionid.com *Web Site:* www.visionid.com, pg 1058

Vision Maker Media, 1800 N 33 St, Lincoln, NE 68503 *Tel:* 402-472-3522 *Fax:* 402-472-8675 *E-mail:* visionmaker@unl.edu *Web Site:* www.visionmakermedia.org, pg 1058

Vision Quest Productions Inc, PO Box 1896, Wayne, NJ 07470-1896 *Tel:* 973-686-9400 *Fax:* 973-694-8314 *Web Site:* vqpi.yolasite.com, pg 1058

Vision Video, 2030 Wentz Church Rd, Lansdale, PA 19446 *Tel:* 610-584-3500 *Toll Free Tel:* 800-523-0226 *Fax:* 610-584-6643 *E-mail:* support@visionvideo.com *Web Site:* www.visionvideo.com, pg 1058

Visionary Solutions Inc, 2060 Alameda Padre Serra, Suite 100, Santa Barbara, CA 93103 *Tel:* 805-845-8900 *Fax:* 805-845-8889 *E-mail:* info@vsicam.com; sales@vsicam.com *Web Site:* www.vsicam.com, pg 1058

Visioneering International Inc, 659 Auburn Ave NE, Suite 267, Atlanta, GA 30312 *Tel:* 404-681-9028 *Fax:* 404-681-5947 *E-mail:* design@visioneering.com *Web Site:* www.visioneering.com, pg 1058

Visions Plus, 200 Valley Dr, Suite 5, Brisbane, CA 94005 *Tel:* 415-467-3300 *E-mail:* web_inquiry@visionsplus.com *Web Site:* visionsplus.com, pg 1058

Visionworks Design Services Inc, 204 Peach Way, Suite H, Columbia, MO 65203 *Tel:* 573-449-8567 *Fax:* 573-449-6714 *E-mail:* info@visionworksgroup.com *Web Site:* visionworksgroup.com, pg 1059

VISIT Milwaukee, 648 N Plankinton Ave, Suite 425, Milwaukee, WI 53203-2917 *Tel:* 414-273-3950 *Toll Free Tel:* 800-554-1448 *Fax:* 414-273-5596 *E-mail:* info@milwaukee.org *Web Site:* www.visitmilwaukee.org, pg 1104

Visit Topeka Inc, 618 S Kansas Ave, Topeka, KS 66603 *Tel:* 785-234-1030 *Toll Free Tel:* 800-235-1030 *Fax:* 785-234-8282 *E-mail:* info@visittopeka.com *Web Site:* www.visittopeka.com, pg 1097

Visix™ Inc, 230 Scientific Dr, Suite 80, Norcross, GA 30092 *Tel:* 770-446-1416 *Toll Free Tel:* 800-572-4935 *Fax:* 770-448-5724 *E-mail:* info@visix.com *Web Site:* www.visix.com, pg 1059

Vista Color Imaging Inc, 2048 Fulton Rd, Cleveland, OH 44113 *Tel:* 216-651-2830 *Toll Free Tel:* 800-890-0062 *Fax:* 216-651-5004 *E-mail:* info@vistacolorimaging.com *Web Site:* www.vistacolorimaging.com, pg 1059

Vista Group International Inc, 25 Van Zant St, Unit 8-D, Norwalk, CT 06855 *Tel:* 203-852-5557 *Toll Free Tel:* 800-866-2113 *Fax:* 203-852-5559 *E-mail:* info@vistagroupinternational.com *Web Site:* www.vistagroupinternational.com, pg 1059

Vistacom Inc, 1902 Vultee St, Allentown, PA 18103-2998 *Tel:* 610-791-9081 *Toll Free Tel:* 800-747-0459 *Fax:* 610-791-9510 *Web Site:* www.vistacominc.com, pg 1059

Vistamax Productions, 9705 Little Pond Way, Tampa, FL 33647 *Tel:* 813-907-1010 *Fax:* 813-907-1991 *E-mail:* info@vistamax.com; sales@vistamax.com *Web Site:* www.vistamax.com, pg 1059

Visual Aids Electronics Corp, 12900 Cloverleaf Center Dr, Suite C, Germantown, MD 20874 *Tel:* 301-330-6900 *Fax:* 301-330-6901 *Web Site:* www.vaecorp.com, pg 1059

Visual Aids Electronics of North Carolina Inc, 245 Executive Park Blvd, Winston-Salem, NC 27103 *Tel:* 336-768-5454 *Toll Free Tel:* 855-934-2828 *Fax:* 336-768-5054 *E-mail:* avrentals@avconnectionsusa.com *Web Site:* avconnectionsusa.com, pg 1059

Visual Communications Group Inc, 5721 Arapahoe Ave, Suite A-2, Boulder, CO 80303 *Tel:* 303-413-0878 *Fax:* 303-413-0683 *E-mail:* vcg@visualcomgroup.com *Web Site:* www.visualcomgroup.com, pg 1059

Visual Communications - Southern California Asian American Studies Central Inc, 120 Judge John Aiso St, Basement Level, Los Angeles, CA 90012 *Tel:* 213-680-4462 *Fax:* 213-687-4848 *E-mail:* info@vconline.org *Web Site:* www.vconline.org, pg 1059

Visual Departures Ltd, 48 Sheffield Business Park, Ashley Falls, MA 01222 *Tel:* 413-229-2272 *Toll Free Tel:* 800-628-2003 *Fax:* 413-229-2274 *E-mail:* sales@visualdepartures.com *Web Site:* www.visualdepartures.com, pg 1059

Visual Education, PO Box 1666, Springfield, OH 45501-1666 *Toll Free Tel:* 800-243-7070 *Fax:* 937-324-5697 *E-mail:* sales@vis-ed.com *Web Site:* www.vis-ed.com, pg 1059

Visual Instrumentation Corp, 1110 West Ave L-12, Unit 2, Lancaster, CA 93534-7039 *Tel:* 661-945-7999 *Fax:* 661-723-5667 *E-mail:* visinst@earthlink.net *Web Site:* www.visinst.com, pg 1059

Visual Products Inc, 790 Shiloh Ave, Wellington, OH 44090 *Tel:* 440-647-4999 *Fax:* 440-647-4998 *E-mail:* sales@visualproducts.com *Web Site:* www.visualproducts.com, pg 1059

Visual Sound Inc, 485 Park Way, Broomall, PA 19008 *Tel:* 610-544-8700 *Toll Free Tel:* 800-523-7525 *Fax:* 610-544-3385 *Web Site:* www.visualsound.com, pg 1059

The Visual Studies Workshop (VSW), 31 Prince St, Rochester, NY 14607 *Tel:* 585-442-8676 *Fax:* 585-442-1992 *E-mail:* info@vsw.org *Web Site:* www.vsw.org, pg 1059

Visual Systems, 845 Encino Place, Santa Paula, CA 93060 *Tel:* 805-933-8044 *Fax:* 805-933-9744 *E-mail:* info@visualsystemsonline.com *Web Site:* www.visualsystemsonline.com, pg 1060

Visual Technologies Corp, 1620 Burnet Ave, Syracuse, NY 13206 *Tel:* 315-423-2000 *Toll Free Tel:* 888-423-0004 *Fax:* 315-423-0004 *E-mail:* contact@visualtec.com *Web Site:* www.visualtec.com; www.vtcspecialties.com, pg 1060

Visual Word Systems Inc, 35 W 36 St, 8th fl, New York, NY 10018 *Tel:* 212-629-8383 *Fax:* 212-629-8333 *Web Site:* www.visualword.com, pg 1060

Vital Learning LLC, 1675 Larimer St, No 410, Denver, CO 80202 *Tel:* 402-592-1602 *Toll Free Tel:* 800-243-5858 *Fax:* 402-592-7142 *E-mail:* sales@vital-learning.com; info@vital-learning.com *Web Site:* www.vital-learning.com, pg 1060

VITEC Multimedia, 931 Benecia, Sunnyvale, CA 94085 *Tel:* 650-230-2400 *Toll Free Tel:* 800-451-5101 *Fax:* 404-320-3132 *E-mail:* info@vitec.com *Web Site:* www.vitec.com, pg 1060

Vitec Videocom Inc, 709 Executive Blvd, Valley Cottage, NY 10989 *Tel:* 845-268-0100 *Fax:* 845-268-0113 *E-mail:* info-cd-usa@vitecgroup.com *Web Site:* www.vitecgroup.com, pg 1060

Vitruvian Entertainment, 727 N Victory Blvd, Burbank, CA 91502 *Tel:* 818-244-3575; 818-720-3250 *Web Site:* vitruvianent.com, pg 1060

ViVi Co, PO Box 750, Glendale, CA 91209 *Tel:* 818-500-8889 *Fax:* 818-507-6600 *E-mail:* zibreathe@aol.com *Web Site:* www.theartofbreathing.com, pg 1060

VMI Inc, 211 E Weddell Dr, Sunnyvale, CA 94089 *Tel:* 408-745-1700 *Fax:* 408-745-6721 *E-mail:* sales@vmivideo.com *Web Site:* www.vmivideo.com, pg 1060

VMI (Video Masters Inc), PO Box 681100, Kansas City, MO 64168-1100 *E-mail:* sales@vmi.com *Web Site:* www.vmi.com, pg 1060

VMS Inc, 805 Airway Dr, Allegan, MI 49101-8516 *Tel:* 269-673-2200 *Toll Free Tel:* 800-343-6430 *Fax:* 269-673-9509 *E-mail:* sales@vms-online.com *Web Site:* www.vms-online.com, pg 1060

The Vocal Point/Profile Communications Ltd, 1196 Habgood St, White Rock, BC V4B 4W9, Canada *Tel:* 604-531-6908 *Web Site:* www.profilecomm.com, pg 1060

Voice & Video Rentals, 4909 Ruffner St, San Diego, CA 92111 *Tel:* 858-560-5000 *Toll Free Tel:* 800-638-8878 *Fax:* 858-560-9900 *Web Site:* www.voiceandvideo.com, pg 1060

Voice of Democracy Scholarship Program, 406 W 34 St, Kansas City, MO 64111 *Tel:* 816-968-1117 *Fax:* 816-968-1149 *Web Site:* www.vfw.org, pg 1129

VO2 Mix Studios, 116 Spadina Ave, Suite 208, Toronto, ON M5V 2K6, Canada *Tel:* 416-603-3954 *Fax:* 416-603-3957 *E-mail:* info@vo2mix.ca *Web Site:* www.vo2mix.ca, pg 1060

Voyager Recordings & Publications, 424 35 Ave, Seattle, WA 98122 *Tel:* 206-323-1112 *E-mail:* info@voyagerrecords.com *Web Site:* www.voyagerrecords.com, pg 1060

Voyetra Turtle Beach, 100 Summit Lake Dr, Suite 100, Valhalla, NY 10595 *Tel:* 914-345-2255 *Fax:* 914-345-2266 *E-mail:* sales@turtlebeach.com *Web Site:* www.turtlebeach.com, pg 1061

VRSim Inc, 222 Pitkin St, Suite 119, East Hartford, CT 06108-3220 *Tel:* 860-893-0080 *E-mail:* info@vrsim.net *Web Site:* www.vrsim.net, pg 1061

VSA, 2700 "F" St NW, Washington, DC 20566 *Tel:* 202-416-8898 *Fax:* 202-416-4840 *E-mail:* vsainfo@kennedy-center.org *Web Site:* www.vsarts.org, pg 1061

VSG Digital Media Solutions, 11126 Lindbergh Business Ct, St Louis, MO 63123 *Tel:* 314-487-8045 *Toll Free Tel:* 800-737-8045 *Fax:* 314-487-9387 *Web Site:* www.vsginc.net, pg 1061

VTP Inc, 2721 W Magnolia Blvd, Burbank, CA 91505 *Tel:* 818-566-9898 *Toll Free Tel:* 800-422-2444 *E-mail:* sales@vtpcorp.com *Web Site:* www.myvtp.com, pg 1061

VTS Video & Media, 3121D Fire Rd, Suite 105, Egg Harbor Township, NJ 08234 *Toll Free Tel:* 877-891-1002 *E-mail:* info@videotapingservice.com *Web Site:* www.videotapingservice.com, pg 1061

Vutec Corp, Video Products Division, 11711 W Sample Rd, Coral Springs, FL 33065-3155 *Tel:* 954-545-9000 *Toll Free Tel:* 800-770-4700 *Fax:* 954-545-9011 *Toll Free Fax:* 800-548-5885 *E-mail:* info@vutec.com; sales@vutec.com *Web Site:* www.vutec.com, pg 1061

VWR International LLC, Radnor Corporate Ctr, Bldg 1, 100 Matsonford Rd, Suite 200, Radnor, PA 19087-8660 *Tel:* 610-431-1700 (corp off) *Toll Free Tel:* 800-932-5000 (cust serv) *E-mail:* solutions@vwr.com; vwrcustomerservice@vwr.com *Web Site:* www.vwr.com; us.vwr.com, pg 1061

WAC Lighting Co, 44 Harbor Park Dr, Port Washington, NY 11050 *Tel:* 516-515-5000 *Toll Free Tel:* 800-526-2588 *Fax:* 516-515-5050 *Toll Free Fax:* 800-526-2585 *E-mail:* sales@waclighting.com *Web Site:* www.waclighting.com, pg 1061

Wacom Technology Corp, 1311 SE Cardinal Ct, Vancouver, WA 98683 *Tel:* 360-896-9833 *Toll Free Tel:* 800-922-6613 *Fax:* 360-896-9734 *Web Site:* www.wacom.com, pg 1061

Waldom Electronics Corp, 1801 Morgan St, Rockford, IL 61102-2690 *Tel:* 815-968-9661 *Toll Free Tel:* 800-435-2931 (cust serv) *Fax:* 815-968-9029 *E-mail:* sales@waldom.com; corp@waldom.com *Web Site:* www.waldom.com, pg 1061

WalkerVision Interarts, PO Box 22533, San Diego, CA 92192-2533 *Tel:* 858-458-9038 *Fax:* 858-458-9104 *Web Site:* www.walkervisioninterarts.com, pg 1061

Wallace Creative Inc, 1705 NW 25 Ave, Portland, OR 97210 *Tel:* 503-224-9660 *E-mail:* info@wallyhood.com *Web Site:* www.wallyhood.com, pg 1061

Wallace Film Studios, 258 Wallace Ave, Toronto, ON M6P 3N9, Canada *Tel:* 416-538-3535 *E-mail:* info@wallacefilmstudios.ca *Web Site:* wallacefilmstudios.ca, pg 1061

Wallach Entertainment, 1400 Braeridge Dr, Beverly Hills, CA 90210 *Tel:* 310-278-4574 *Fax:* 310-273-0548 *E-mail:* gwallach@roadrunner.com, pg 1061

Walltalkers, 3875 Embassy Pkwy, Fairlawn, OH 44333 *Tel:* 330-668-7600 *Toll Free Tel:* 800-820-9255 *Fax:* 330-668-7703 *E-mail:* customerservice@koroseal.com *Web Site:* www.walltalkers.com, pg 1061

The Walt Disney Co, 500 S Buena Vista St, Burbank, CA 91521 *Tel:* 818-560-1000 *Web Site:* disney.com, pg 1061

Walt Disney Records Consumer Products Division, 1201 Flower St, Glendale, AZ 91201 *Tel:* 818-560-1000 *Web Site:* disney.com; www.disneyconsumerproducts.com, pg 1061

Walt Disney Studio, 500 S Buena Vista St, Burbank, CA 91521 *Tel:* 818-560-1000 *Web Site:* studioservices.go.com, pg 1061

Walters-Storyk Design Group Inc (WSDG), 262 Martin Ave, Highland, NY 12528 *Tel:* 845-691-9300 *Fax:* 845-691-9361 *E-mail:* info@wsdg.com *Web Site:* www.wsdg.com, pg 1061

Walterscheid Productions, PO Box 995, Wichita, KS 67201 *Tel:* 316-258-1152 *E-mail:* bobwalter1@aol.com *Web Site:* www.wponline.com, pg 1062

Wanted! Sound + Picture, 409 King St W, Suite 300, Toronto, ON M5V 1K1, Canada *Tel:* 416-596-1101 *Fax:* 416-596-0690 *E-mail:* info@wantedsp.com *Web Site:* www.wantedsp.com, pg 1062

Ward-Beck Systems Ltd, 945 Middlefield Rd, Unit 9, Toronto, ON M1V 5E1, Canada *Tel:* 416-335-5999 *Toll Free Tel:* 800-771-2556 *Fax:* 416-335-5202 *E-mail:* sales@ward-beck.com *Web Site:* www.ward-beck.com, pg 1062

Warner Bros Animation, 4000 Warner Blvd, Burbank, CA 91522 *Tel:* 818-954-6000 *Web Site:* www.warnerbros.com, pg 1062

Warner Bros Entertainment Inc, 4000 Warner Blvd, Burbank, CA 91522 *Tel:* 818-954-3000 *Fax:* 818-954-4918 *E-mail:* wbsf@warnerbros.com *Web Site:* www.warnerbros.com; studiofacilities.warnerbros.com, pg 1062

Warner Bros Production Sound & Video Services, 4000 Warner Blvd, Burbank, CA 91522 *Tel:* 818-954-2511 *Fax:* 818-954-1037 *E-mail:* wbsf@warnerbros.com; wbsfproductionsound@warnerbros.com *Web Site:* www.wbsf.com; www.wbsoundandvideo.com, pg 1062

Warner/Chappell Production Music, 1030 16 Ave S, Nashville, TN 37212 *Toll Free Tel:* 888-615-8729 *Fax:* 615-242-2455 *E-mail:* info@warnerchappellpm.com *Web Site:* www.warnerchappellpm.com/615-music, pg 1062

Warner Home Video Inc, 4000 Warner Blvd, Bldg 160, Burbank, CA 91522 *Tel:* 818-954-6000 *Fax:* 818-954-6480 *Web Site:* www.warnerbros.com, pg 1062

The Samuel L Warner Memorial Award, 3 Barker Ave, 5th fl, White Plains, NY 10601 *Tel:* 914-761-1100 *Fax:* 914-761-3115 *E-mail:* smpte@smpte.org *Web Site:* www.smpte.org, pg 1129

WARPed Pictures, 2447 Benedict Canyon Dr, Beverly Hills, CA 90210 *Tel:* 310-777-8828; 310-999-1219 (cell) *Fax:* 310-777-8805 *Web Site:* www.warpedpictures.com, pg 1062

Washington DC International Film Festival, PO Box 21396, Washington, DC 20009-0896 *Tel:* 202-274-5782 *Fax:* 202-274-6690 *E-mail:* filmfestdc@filmfestdc.org *Web Site:* www.filmfestdc.org, pg 1129

Washington Filmworks, 1411 Fourth Ave, Suite 420, Seattle, WA 98101 *Tel:* 206-264-0667 *Fax:* 206-382-4343 *E-mail:* info@washingtonfilmworks.org *Web Site:* washingtonfilmworks.org, pg 1103

Water Bearer Films Inc, 3239 Gateway Circle, Charlottesville, VA 22911 *Tel:* 434-923-8686 *Toll Free Tel:* 800-551-8304 *E-mail:* sales@waterbearerfilms.com *Web Site:* store.waterbearerfilms.com, pg 1062

Waterfront Film Festival (WFF), PO Box 387, Saugatuck, MI 49453-0387 *Tel:* 269-857-8351 *Fax:* 269-857-1072 *E-mail:* info@waterfrontfilm.org *Web Site:* www.waterfrontfilm.org, pg 1129

Waterworks Acoustics, 1038 44 Ave, Oakland, CA 94601 *Tel:* 510-653-4300 *Fax:* 510-437-9231 *E-mail:* waterworksacoustics@earthlink.net *Web Site:* www.soundpipes.com, pg 1062

WATL-TV Inc, One Monroe Place NE, Atlanta, GA 30324 *Tel:* 404-892-1611 *Fax:* 404-881-3635 *Web Site:* www.myatltv.com, pg 1062

Watson Desking, 26246 Twelve Trees Lane NW, Poulsbo, WA 98370 *Tel:* 360-394-1300 *Toll Free Tel:* 800-426-1202 *Fax:* 360-394-1322 *E-mail:* service@watsondesking.com; info@watsondesking.com *Web Site:* www.watsonfurniture.com, pg 1062

Watts Communications Inc, 149 N 120 St, Wauwatosa, WI 53226 *Tel:* 414-727-9505 *Fax:* 414-727-9506 *E-mail:* sales@wattscom.com *Web Site:* www.wattscom.com, pg 1062

Waveland Software Inc, 1900 W Berwyn Ave, Suite 2, Chicago, IL 60640 *Tel:* 773-334-0408 *Fax:* 773-334-0408, pg 1062

Wavemaker Media Design, PO Box 226, Duncans Mills, CA 95430 *Tel:* 707-788-6040 *Fax:* 707-788-6040 *E-mail:* sales@wavemakermediadesign.com *Web Site:* www.wavemakermediadesign.com, pg 1062

WaxWorks VideoWorks, 325 E Third St, Owensboro, KY 42303 *Tel:* 270-926-0008 *Toll Free Tel:* 800-825-8558 *Fax:* 270-663-0737 *Web Site:* www.waxworksonline.com, pg 1063

Don Wayne Magic Inc, 10907 Magnolia Blvd, Suite 467, North Hollywood, CA 91601 *Tel:* 818-763-3192 *E-mail:* info@donwaynemagic.com *Web Site:* www.donwaynemagic.com, pg 1063

Wayne State University Media Services, Purdy/Kresge Library, 5244 Gullen Mall, Detroit, MI 48202 *Tel:* 313-577-1980 *Fax:* 313-577-6777 *E-mail:* mediaservices@wayne.edu *Web Site:* library.wayne.edu, pg 1063

WCJB TV20, 6220 NW 43 St, Gainesville, FL 32653 *Tel:* 352-416-0623 *Fax:* 352-373-6516 *E-mail:* comments@divcom.com *Web Site:* divcom.com, pg 1063

Weapons of Choice™, 4075 Browns Valley Rd, Napa, CA 94558-4144 *Tel:* 707-226-2845 *E-mail:* info@weaponsofchoice.com *Web Site:* weaponsofchoicetheatrical.com, pg 1063

Webb Audio Visual Communication, 3020 S West Temple, Salt Lake City, UT 84115 *Tel:* 801-484-8567 (installation) *Toll Free Tel:* 877-909-8567 *Fax:* 801-484-8589 *Web Site:* www.webbav.com, pg 1063

Webster Communications, 607 N Avenue 64, Los Angeles, CA 90042 *Tel:* 323-258-6741 *E-mail:* info@vanwebster.com *Web Site:* www.vanwebster.com, pg 1063

WEEK TV, 2907 Springfield Rd, East Peoria, IL 61611 *Tel:* 309-698-2525 *Fax:* 309-698-9335 *Web Site:* www.week.com, pg 1063

Wegener Communications, Technology Park, 11350 Technology Circle, Johns Creek, GA 30097 *Tel:* 770-814-4000; 770-814-4021 (sales); 770-814-4057 (cust serv) *Toll Free Tel:* 800-848-9467 (cust serv) *Fax:* 770-623-0698; 770-232-0621 (cust serv) *E-mail:* info@wegener.com; globalsales@wegener.com; service@wegener.com *Web Site:* www.wegener.com, pg 1063

Weigl Publishers Inc, 350 Fifth Ave, 59th fl, New York, NY 10118 *Toll Free Tel:* 866-649-3445 *Toll Free Fax:* 866-449-3445 *Web Site:* www.weigl.com, pg 1063

Alan Weiss Productions, 270 White Plains Rd, Suite 2N, East Chester, NY 10709 *Tel:* 212-974-0606 *E-mail:* awpinfo@awptv.com *Web Site:* www.awptv.com, pg 1063

Welk Music Group, 11400 W Olympic Blvd, Suite 1450, Los Angeles, CA 90064 *Tel:* 310-829-9355 *Fax:* 310-315-9996 *E-mail:* info@vanguardrecords.com; order@vanguardrecords.com *Web Site:* www.vanguardrecords.com, pg 1063

The Well-Tempered Music Library, PO Box 465, Middleboro, MA 02346-0465 *Tel:* 508-947-7387 *Fax:* 508-947-7387 *E-mail:* info@arfarfrecords.com; page@arfarfrecords.com *Web Site:* www.arfarfrecords.com, pg 1063

Wells-Gardner Electronics Corp, 9500 W 55 St, Suite A, McCook, IL 60525-3605 *Tel:* 708-290-2100 *Toll Free Tel:* 800-336-6630 *Fax:* 708-290-2200 *Web Site:* www.wellsgardner.com, pg 1063

Welocalize, 241 E Fourth St, Suite 207, Frederick, MD 21701 *Tel:* 301-668-0330 *Toll Free Tel:* 800-370-9515 *Fax:* 301-668-0335 *E-mail:* info@welocalize.com *Web Site:* www.welocalize.com, pg 1063

WESCAM Inc, 649 N Service Rd W, Burlington, ON L7P 5B9, Canada *Tel:* 905-633-4000 *Toll Free Tel:* 800-668-4355 *Fax:* 905-633-4100 *E-mail:* sales.wescam@l-3com.com *Web Site:* www.wescam.com, pg 1063

Wespen Audio Visual Co, 101 Riverside Dr, Hawthorn, PA 16230, pg 1063

West Coast Projections Inc, 12463 Rancho Bernardo Rd, No 149, San Diego, CA 92128-2143 *Tel:* 858-674-7334 *E-mail:* wcpinfo@westcoastprojections.com *Web Site:* westcoastprojections.com, pg 1063

West Eagle Films Inc, 800 Lower Ganges Rd, Salt Spring Island, BC V8K 2N5, Canada *Tel:* 250-538-1780 *E-mail:* mailbox@westeaglefilms.com *Web Site:* www.westeaglefilms.com, pg 1064

West Penn Wire, 2833 W Chestnut St, Washington, PA 15301 *Tel:* 724-222-7060 *Toll Free Tel:* 800-245-4964 *Fax:* 724-222-6420 *E-mail:* info@westpenn-wpw.com *Web Site:* www.westpenn-wpw.com, pg 1064

West Virginia Film Office, 90 MacCorkle Ave SW, South Charleston, WV 25303 *Toll Free Tel:* 866-6WV-FILM (698-3456) *Fax:* 304-558-1662 *Web Site:* wvfilm.wvcommerce.org, pg 1103

Westar Music, 105 W Beaver Creek Rd, Suite 4, Richmond Hill, ON L4B 1C6, Canada *Tel:* 905-886-3100 *Toll Free Tel:* 800-665-3000 *Fax:* 905-886-6800 *E-mail:* info@westarmusic.com *Web Site:* www.westarmusic.com, pg 1064

Westbrook Technologies Inc, 35 Thorpe Ave, Suite 201, Wallingford, CT 06492 *Tel:* 203-871-4984 *Fax:* 203-269-0322 *E-mail:* info@westbrooktech.com *Web Site:* www.westbrooktech.com, pg 1064

Westbury National Show Systems Ltd, 772 Warden Ave, Toronto, ON M1L 4T7, Canada *Tel:* 416-752-1371 *Fax:* 416-752-1382 *E-mail:* mail@westbury.com *Web Site:* www.westbury.com, pg 1064

Westcoast Video Productions Inc, 14141 Covello St, Suite 9-A, Van Nuys, CA 91405 *Tel:* 818-785-8033 *Toll Free Tel:* 800-477-8417 *Fax:* 818-785-8035 *E-mail:* mail@wvpinc.com *Web Site:* www.wvpinc.com, pg 1064

Western Connecticut Convention & Visitors Bureau, PO Box 968, Litchfield, CT 06759-0968 *Tel:* 860-567-4506 *Toll Free Tel:* 800-663-1273 *Fax:* 860-567-5214 *E-mail:* info@litchfieldhills.com *Web Site:* www.visitwesternct.com; www.litchfieldhills.com; www.visitfairfieldcountyct.com, pg 1095

Western Digital Corp, 3355 Michelson Dr, Suite 100, Irvine, CA 92612 *Tel:* 949-672-7000 *Toll Free Tel:* 888-935-8893 *Fax:* 408-717-9282 *Web Site:* www.wdc.com, pg 1064

Western Heritage Awards, 1700 NE 63 St, Oklahoma City, OK 73111 *Tel:* 405-478-2250 *Fax:* 405-478-4714 *Web Site:* nationalcowboymuseum.org, pg 1129

Western Instructional Television Inc, 1438 Gower St, No 18, Los Angeles, CA 90028 *Tel:* 323-466-8601, pg 1064

Western North Carolina Film Commission, 134 Wright Brothers Way, Fletcher, NC 28732 *Tel:* 828-687-7234 *Toll Free Tel:* 888-595-7234 *Fax:* 828-687-7552 *E-mail:* film@awnc.org *Web Site:* www.wncfilm.com; www.advantagewest.com, pg 1101

Westlake Recording Studios, 7265 Santa Monica Blvd, Los Angeles, CA 90046 *Tel:* 323-851-9800 *E-mail:* bookings@thelakestudios.com; info@thelakestudios.com *Web Site:* www.thelakestudios.com, pg 1064

Stuart Westmorland Photography, 14128 11 Dr SE, Mill Creek, WA 98012 *Tel:* 425-225-5733 *Fax:* 425-225-5733 *E-mail:* info@stuartwestmorland.com *Web Site:* stuartwestmorland.com, pg 1064

Weston Woods Canada, 60 Briarwood Ave, Mississauga, ON L5G 3N6, Canada *Tel:* 905-278-0566 *Toll Free Tel:* 866-722-1522 *Fax:* 905-278-2801 *Toll Free Fax:* 866-722-1822 *E-mail:* info@mcnabbconnolly.ca *Web Site:* www.mcnabbconnolly.ca, pg 1064

Weston Woods Studios Inc, 90 Old Sherman Tpke, Danbury, CT 06816 *Tel:* 203-797-3520 *Toll Free Tel:* 800-243-5020 *Fax:* 203-797-3531 *E-mail:* westonwoodsquestions@scholastic.com *Web Site:* www.scholastic.com/westonwoods, pg 1064

Westworks Studios, 4100 E Dry Creek Rd, Littleton, CO 80122 *Toll Free Tel:* 800-491-1947 *E-mail:* info@westworksstudios.com *Web Site:* westworksstudios.com, pg 1064

WETA Production Center, 3620 S 27 St, Arlington, VA 22206 *Tel:* 703-998-2054 *Fax:* 703-998-2706 *Web Site:* www.weta.org/tv/productioncenter, pg 1064

David Wexler & Co, 7807 E Greenway Rd, Suite 8, Scottsdale, AZ 85260-1717 *Tel:* 480-675-8888 *Fax:* 480-675-8900 *E-mail:* wexlermusic@aol.com *Web Site:* www.wexlermusic.com, pg 1064

WFRV-TV 5 CBS, 1181 E Mason St, Green Bay, WI 54301 *Tel:* 920-437-5411 *Fax:* 920-437-4576 *E-mail:* mailbox@wfrv.com *Web Site:* www.wfrv.com, pg 1064

WGBH Production Group, One Guest St, Boston, MA 02135 *Tel:* 617-300-2200 *Fax:* 617-300-3460 *Web Site:* www.wgbh.org/productionservices, pg 1065

WGBH Stock Sales, One Guest St, Boston, MA 02135 *Tel:* 617-300-3939 *Fax:* 617-300-1056 *E-mail:* stock_sales@wgbh.org *Web Site:* www.wgbhstocksales.org, pg 1065

WGME-TV, 81 Northport Dr, Portland, ME 04103 *Tel:* 207-797-1313 *Fax:* 207-878-7842 *E-mail:* tvmail@wgme.com *Web Site:* www.wgme.com, pg 1065

WGVU TV, 301 Fulton St W, Grand Rapids, MI 49504-6492 *Tel:* 616-331-6666 *Toll Free Tel:* 800-442-2771 *E-mail:* wgvu@gvsu.edu *Web Site:* www.wgvu.org, pg 1065

The Whale Video Co, 225 Indian Creek Dr, Mechanicsburg, PA 17050 *Tel:* 717-763-9507 *Web Site:* www.whalevideo.com, pg 1065

Whalley-Abbey Media Holdings Inc, 1303 Greene Ave, Suite 300, Westmount, QC H3Z 2A7, Canada *Tel:* 514-846-1940 *Fax:* 514-846-1550 *Web Site:* whalleyabbey.com, pg 1065

Wheatstone Corp, 600 Industrial Dr, New Bern, NC 28562 *Tel:* 252-638-7000 *Fax:* 252-635-1285 *E-mail:* sales@wheatstone.com *Web Site:* www.wheatstone.com, pg 1065

Whirlwind Music Distributors Inc, 99 Ling Rd, Rochester, NY 14612 *Tel:* 585-663-8820 *Toll Free Tel:* 800-733-9473 (US only) *Fax:* 585-865-8930 *E-mail:* sales@whirlwindusa.com; techsupport@whirlwindusa.com; darylg@whirlwindusa.com (Canadian inquiries) *Web Site:* whirlwindusa.com, pg 1065

WhisperRoom™ Inc, 116 S Sugar Hollow Rd, Morristown, TN 37813 *Tel:* 423-585-5827 *Toll Free Tel:* 800-200-8168 *Fax:* 423-585-5831 *E-mail:* info@whisperroom.com *Web Site:* www.whisperroom.com, pg 1065

White Buffalo Multimedia, 13 Charles Bach Rd, Saugerties, NY 12477 *Tel:* 845-246-9995, pg 1065

White Diamond Productions, 2267 Hwy 43 S, Harrison, AR 72601 *Tel:* 870-365-7374, pg 1065

White Dog Studios, 587 Virginia Ave NE, Suite 1, Atlanta, GA 30306 *Tel:* 404-355-2200 *E-mail:* info@whitedogstudios.net *Web Site:* www.whitedogstudios.net, pg 1065

White Lotus Foundation, 2500 San Marcos Pass, Santa Barbara, CA 93105 *Tel:* 805-964-1944 *Fax:* 805-964-9617 *E-mail:* info@whitelotus.org *Web Site:* www.whitelotus.org, pg 1065

White Rain Films Ltd, 2009 Dexter Ave N, Seattle, WA 98109 *Tel:* 206-682-5417 *Toll Free Tel:* 800-816-5244 *Fax:* 206-682-3038 *E-mail:* info@whiterainfilms.com *Web Site:* www.whiterainfilms.com, pg 1065

White Swan Music Inc, 6395 Gunpark Dr, Suite A, Boulder, CO 80301 *Tel:* 303-527-0770 *Toll Free Tel:* 800-825-8656 *Fax:* 303-527-0771 *E-mail:* info@whiteswanmusic.com *Web Site:* whiteswanmusic.com, pg 1065

William F White International Inc, 800 Islington Ave, Toronto, ON M8Z 6A1, Canada *Tel:* 416-239-5050 *Toll Free Tel:* 800-465-0160 (CN only); 800-268-2200 *Fax:* 416-207-2777 *E-mail:* info@cinequipwhite.com *Web Site:* www.whites.com, pg 1065

The Whitlock Group, 12820 West Creek Pkwy, Richmond, VA 23238 *Tel:* 804-273-9100 *Toll Free Tel:* 800-726-9843 *Fax:* 804-273-9380 *E-mail:* information@whitlock.com *Web Site:* www.whitlock.com, pg 1065

Whole Person Associates Inc, 101 W Second St, Suite 203, Duluth, MN 55802-5004 *Tel:* 218-727-0500 *Toll Free Tel:* 800-247-6789 *Fax:* 218-727-0505 *E-mail:* books@wholeperson.com *Web Site:* www.wholeperson.com, pg 1066

WHYY Inc, Independence Mall West, 150 N Sixth St, Philadelphia, PA 19106 *Tel:* 215-351-1200 *Fax:* 215-351-0398 *E-mail:* talkback@whyy.org *Web Site:* www.whyy.org, pg 1066

Wickenburg Film Commission, 216 N Frontier St, Wickenburg, AZ 85390 *Tel:* 928-684-5479; 928-684-0977 *Toll Free Tel:* 800-942-5242 *Fax:* 928-684-5470 *E-mail:* info@wickenburgchamber.com *Web Site:* www.wickenburgchamber.com/film-commission, pg 1091

Wide Eye Productions, 1018 W Hays St, Boise, ID 83702 *Tel:* 208-336-0391 *Fax:* 208-336-6644 *E-mail:* info@wideeye.tv *Web Site:* wideeye.tv, pg 1066

WIFR-TV, 2523 N Meridian Rd, Rockford, IL 61101 *Tel:* 815-987-5300 *Fax:* 815-965-0981 *E-mail:* talkto23@wifr.com *Web Site:* www.wifr.com, pg 1066

Wild Plum, 2128 Narcissus Ct, Venice, CA 90291 *Tel:* 310-823-7445 *Fax:* 310-578-1445 *Web Site:* www.wildplum.tv, pg 1066

Wild Visions Inc, PO Box 42194, Phoenix, AZ 85080 *Tel:* 623-512-9810 *Web Site:* www.wildvisions.net, pg 1066

Wilderness Video, 888 Beswick Way, Ashland, OR 97520 *Tel:* 541-488-9363 *Web Site:* www.wildernessvideo.com, pg 1066

Wildfire Lighting & Visual Effects, 2908 Oregon Ct, Suite G1, Torrance, CA 90503 *Tel:* 310-755-6780 *Toll Free Tel:* 800-937-8065 *Fax:* 310-755-6781 *E-mail:* mail@wildfirefx.com; sales@wildfirefx.com *Web Site:* www.wildfirefx.com, pg 1066

Wildfire Post Production Studios, 640 S San Vicente Blvd, Los Angeles, CA 90048 *Tel:* 323-951-1700 *Fax:* 323-951-1710 *Web Site:* www.wildfirepost.com, pg 1066

John Wiley & Sons Inc, 111 River St, Hoboken, NJ 07030 *Tel:* 201-748-6000 *Toll Free Tel:* 800-225-5945 *Fax:* 201-748-6088 *E-mail:* info@wiley.com *Web Site:* www.wiley.com, pg 1066

The Will-Burt Co, 169 S Main St, Orrville, OH 44667 *Tel:* 330-682-7015; 330-684-4000 (cust serv) *Fax:* 330-684-1190 *E-mail:* contact_us@willburt.com *Web Site:* www.willburt.com, pg 1066

Williams Sound Corp, 10300 Valley View Rd, Eden Prairie, MN 55344-3446 *Tel:* 952-943-2252 *Toll Free Tel:* 800-328-6190 *Fax:* 952-943-2174 *E-mail:* info@williamssound.com *Web Site:* www.williamssound.com, pg 1067

Willoughby's Imaging Center, 298 Fifth Ave, New York, NY 10001 *Tel:* 212-564-1600 *Toll Free Tel:* 800-378-1898 *Fax:* 212-564-1608 *E-mail:* sales@willoughbys.com; customersupport@willoughbys.com *Web Site:* www.willoughbys.com, pg 1067

Willow Creek Press Inc, PO Box 147, Minocqua, WI 54548-0147 *Tel:* 715-358-7010 *Toll Free Tel:* 800-850-9453 *Fax:* 715-358-2807 *E-mail:* info@willowcreekpress.com *Web Site:* www.willowcreekpress.com, pg 1067

Willow Mixed Media Inc, 25 Lennox Ave, Glenford, NY 12433 *Tel:* 845-657-2914 *E-mail:* video@hvc.rr.com *Web Site:* www.willowmixedmedia.org; www.documentaryworld.com, pg 1067

Wilmington Camera Services, 905 N 23 St, Wilmington, NC 28405 *Tel:* 910-343-1089 *Fax:* 910-343-0247 *E-mail:* info@wilmingtoncameraservices.com, pg 1067

Wilmington Regional Film Commission Inc, 1223 N 23 St, Wilmington, NC 28405 *Tel:* 910-343-3456 *Fax:* 910-343-3457 *E-mail:* commish@wilmingtonfilm.com *Web Site:* www.wilmingtonfilm.com, pg 1101

Wilray Audio Visual Corp, 615 Jackson Valley Rd, Port Murray, NJ 07865 *Tel:* 908-689-1300 *Toll Free Tel:* 800-452-9184 *Fax:* 908-689-8839 *E-mail:* wilray@mindspring.com, pg 1067

Wilson Case Inc, 113 Road 3168, Hastings, NE 68901-9418 *Tel:* 402-463-5040 *Toll Free Tel:* 800-322-5493 *Fax:* 402-463-5276 *E-mail:* sales@wilsoncase.com *Web Site:* www.wilsoncase.com, pg 1067

H Wilson Co, 2245 Delany Rd, Waukegan, IL 60087 *Tel:* 847-244-1800 *Toll Free Tel:* 800-245-7224; 800-323-4656 (sales) *Fax:* 708-210-2069; 847-244-1818 (sales) *Toll Free Fax:* 800-245-8224; 800-327-1698 (sales) *E-mail:* sales@hwilson.com; info@wilson.com; customerservice@wilson.com *Web Site:* www.hwilson.com, pg 1067

Wilson McLeran Inc, 41 Corey Hill Rd, Saxtons River, VT 05154 *Tel:* 802-869-3111 *Toll Free Tel:* 800-562-9646 *Fax:* 802-869-3111 *Web Site:* www.job-bridge.com, pg 1067

Wiltronix, 16850 Oakmont Ave, Washington Grove, MD 20880 *Tel:* 301-258-7676 *Toll Free Tel:* 800-848-7870 *Fax:* 301-854-3434 *E-mail:* equipsales@wiltronix.com *Web Site:* www.wiltronix.com, pg 1067

Win Media Inc, 317 N Dodge St, Burlington, WI 53105 *Tel:* 262-763-6397 *E-mail:* info@winmediainc.com *Web Site:* www.winmediainc.com, pg 1067

Winchester Electronics Corp, 68 Water St, Norwalk, CT 06854 *Tel:* 203-741-5400 *E-mail:* info@winchesterelectronics.com *Web Site:* www.winchesterelectronics.com, pg 1067

Wind River Broadcast Center, 117 E 11 St, Loveland, CO 80537 *Tel:* 970-669-3442 *Toll Free Tel:* 800-669-3993 *Fax:* 970-663-6081 *Web Site:* www.windriverbroadcast.com, pg 1067

Windel International/Weyel, 3714 Illinois Ave, St Charles, IL 60174-2421 *Toll Free Tel:* 800-395-7093 *Fax:* 630-587-2833 *Web Site:* www.windel.com, pg 1067

WindTech™ Microphone Windscreens & Accessories, 7845 E Evans Rd, Scottsdale, AZ 85260-2919 *Tel:* 480-998-7140 *Fax:* 480-998-7192 *E-mail:* information@olsenaudio.com; web-info3@olsenaudio.com *Web Site:* www.olsenaudio.com; www.windtech.tv, pg 1067

The Wine Appreciation Guild Ltd, 360 Swift Ave, Unit 30-40, South San Francisco, CA 94080 *Tel:* 650-866-3020 *Toll Free Tel:* 800-231-9463 *Fax:* 650-866-3513 *E-mail:* info@wineappreciation.com *Web Site:* www.wineappreciation.com, pg 1067

Winegard Co, 2736 Mt Pleasant St, Suite 140, Burlington, IA 52601 *Tel:* 319-754-0600 *Toll Free Tel:* 800-288-8094 *Fax:* 319-754-0787 *Toll Free Fax:* 800-247-8221 *Web Site:* www.winegard.com, pg 1067

Babe Winkelman Productions Inc, 7119 Forthun Rd S, Baxter, MN 56425 *Tel:* 218-822-4424 *Toll Free Tel:* 800-333-0471 *Fax:* 218-822-7436 *Web Site:* www.winkelman.com, pg 1068

Winsted Corp, 10901 Hampshire Ave S, Minneapolis, MN 55438 *Tel:* 952-944-9050 *Toll Free Tel:* 800-447-2257 *Fax:* 952-944-1546 *Toll Free Fax:* 800-421-3839 *E-mail:* info@winsted.com *Web Site:* www.winsted.com, pg 1068

Winter Film Awards, 419 Lafayette St, New York, NY 10003 *Tel:* 646-355-4371 *E-mail:* info@winterfilmawards.com *Web Site:* www.winterfilmawards.com, pg 1129

Winter Film Awards Independent Film Festival, 419 Lafayette St, New York, NY 10003 *Tel:* 646-355-4371 *E-mail:* info@winterfilmawards.com; submissions@winterfilmawards.com *Web Site:* www.winterfilmawards.com, pg 1129

Winter Productions, 10625 S Hoyne, Chicago, IL 60643 *E-mail:* winterpr@aol.com *Web Site:* www.winterproductions.com, pg 1068

Wintergreen Learning Materials, 3075 Line 8, RR2, Bradford, ON L3Z 2A5, Canada *Toll Free Tel:* 800-268-1268 *Toll Free Fax:* 800-567-8054 *E-mail:* info@wintergreen.ca *Web Site:* www.wintergreen.ca, pg 1068

Winterland Studios, 5417 Boone Ave N, New Hope, MN 55428 *Tel:* 763-971-8943 *Fax:* 763-971-8952 *E-mail:* studio@winterlandstudios.com *Web Site:* www.winterlandstudios.com, pg 1068

Wired 4 Sound Inc, PO Box 683, Clifton, NJ 07012-0683 *Tel:* 973-773-2565 *Toll Free Fax:* 888-453-8819 *E-mail:* info@wired4sound.com *Web Site:* www.wired4sound.com, pg 1068

Wireless Xcessories Group Inc, 1840 County Line Rd, Suite 301, Huntingdon Valley, PA 19006 *Tel:* 215-322-4600 *Toll Free Tel:* 800-233-0013 *Toll Free Fax:* 866-570-7686 *E-mail:* sales@wirexgroup.com *Web Site:* store.wirexgroup.com, pg 1068

Wirestrippers.com, 34925 Cherry St, Wildomar, CA 92595 *Tel:* 951-245-6212 *Toll Free Tel:* 800-490-8520 *Fax:* 951-245-6213 *E-mail:* wirestrippers@verizon.net *Web Site:* www.wirestrippers.com, pg 1068

Wireworks Corp, 380 Hillside Ave, Hillside, NJ 07205 *Tel:* 908-686-7400 *Toll Free Tel:* 800-642-9473 *Fax:* 908-686-0483 *E-mail:* sales@wireworks.com; info@wireworks.com *Web Site:* www.wireworks.com, pg 1068

Wisconsin Public Television, 821 University Ave, Madison, WI 53706 *Tel:* 608-263-2121 *Toll Free Tel:* 800-422-9707 *Fax:* 608-263-9763 *E-mail:* comments@wpt.org *Web Site:* www.wpt.org, pg 1068

Wisconsin Technical College System Foundation Inc, One Foundation Circle, Waunakee, WI 53597-8914 *Tel:* 608-849-2424; 608-849-2400 *Toll Free Tel:* 800-821-6313 *Fax:* 608-849-2468 *E-mail:* foundation@wtcsf.tec.wi.us *Web Site:* www.wtcsf.tec.wi.us, pg 1068

Wise Audio Video, PO Box 105523, Jefferson City, MO 65110 *Tel:* 573-761-7888 *Toll Free Tel:* 877-775-7888 *Web Site:* www.wiseaudiovideo.com, pg 1068

WKMG-TV Channel 6, 4466 N John Young Pkwy, Orlando, FL 32804 *Tel:* 407-521-1200 *Fax:* 407-521-1204 *Web Site:* www.clickorlando.com, pg 1068

WKPT-TV, 222 Commerce St, Kingsport, TN 37660 *Tel:* 423-246-9578 *Fax:* 423-246-1863 *Web Site:* www.abc19.tv, pg 1068

WKYT Productions, 2851 Winchester Rd, Lexington, KY 40509 *Tel:* 859-299-0411; 859-299-2727 (newsroom) *Fax:* 859-299-2494 *Web Site:* www.wkyt.com, pg 1068

WMAR-TV, 6400 York Rd, Baltimore, MD 21212 *Tel:* 410-377-2222 *E-mail:* newsroom@wmar.com *Web Site:* www.abc2news.com, pg 1068

WMS Media Inc, 555 Bryant St, Suite 361, Palo Alto, CA 94301 *Toll Free Tel:* 800-487-1073 *Fax:* 510-796-0924 *E-mail:* info@wmsmedia.com *Web Site:* www.wmsmedia.com, pg 1069

WNET/NET TELECON, 825 Eighth Ave, New York, NY 10019 *Tel:* 212-560-1313 *Fax:* 212-560-1314 *E-mail:* programming@thirteen.org *Web Site:* www.thirteen.org; www.wnet.org, pg 1069

Wohler Technologies Inc, 31055 Huntwood Ave, Hayward, CA 94544 *Tel:* 510-870-0810 *Toll Free Tel:* 888-5-WOHLER (596-4537) *Fax:* 510-870-0811 *E-mail:* sales@wohler.com; info@wohler.com *Web Site:* www.wohler.com, pg 1069

WolfVision Inc, 1601 Bayshore Hwy, Suite 168, Burlingame, CA 94010 *Tel:* 650-648-0002 *Toll Free Tel:* 800-356-9653 *Fax:* 650-648-0009 *E-mail:* sales@wolfvision.us; support@wolfvision.us *Web Site:* www.wolfvision.com, pg 1069

Women In Animation, PO Box 17706, Encino, CA 91416-7706 *Tel:* 818-759-9596 *E-mail:* wia@womeninanimation.org; info@womeninanimation.org *Web Site:* www.womeninanimation.org, pg 1090

Women In Film, 6100 Wilshire Blvd, Suite 710, Los Angeles, CA 90048-5117 *Tel:* 323-935-2211 *Fax:* 323-935-2212 *E-mail:* info@wif.org *Web Site:* www.wif.org, pg 1090

Women in Film & Television-Florida (WIFT-FL), PO Box 533541, Orlando, FL 32853-3541 *E-mail:* info@womeninfilmfl.org *Web Site:* womeninfilmfl.org, pg 1090

Women in Film Foundation Film Finishing Fund, 6100 Wilshire Blvd, Suite 710, Los Angeles, CA 90048 *Tel:* 323-935-2211 *Fax:* 323-935-2212 *E-mail:* info@wif.org *Web Site:* www.wif.org, pg 1129

Women Make Movies Inc, 115 W 29 St, Suite 1200, New York, NY 10001 *Tel:* 212-925-0606 *Fax:* 212-925-2052 *E-mail:* info@wmm.com *Web Site:* www.wmm.com, pg 1069

Wonderwomen™ Enterprises, 485 Rugby Rd, Brooklyn, NY 11226 *Tel:* 646-456-3266; 718-693-4322 *E-mail:* info@wonderwomen.com, pg 1069

WoodenBoat Publications, 41 WoodenBoat Lane, Brooklin, ME 04616 *Tel:* 207-359-4651 *Toll Free Tel:* 800-877-5284 (subns); 800-487-2084 (subns) *Fax:* 207-359-8920; 818-487-4550 (subns) *E-mail:* woodenboat@woodenboat.com *Web Site:* www.woodenboat.com, pg 1069

Woodside Avenue Music Productions Inc, 2906 Central St, No 117, Evanston, IL 60201 *Tel:* 847-864-6655 *E-mail:* music@woodsideavenue.com *Web Site:* www.woodsideavenue.com, pg 1069

Mark Woollen & Associates, 207 Ashland Ave, Santa Monica, CA 90405 *Tel:* 310-399-2690 *E-mail:* info@markwoollen.com *Web Site:* www.markwoollen.com, pg 1069

Word Label Group, 25 Music Sq W, Nashville, TN 37203 *Tel:* 615-251-0600 *Fax:* 615-726-7886 (publicity) *E-mail:* wbrc.publicity@wbr.com *Web Site:* www.wordlabelgroup.com, pg 1069

World Beat Studio, 137 Sequoia Rd, Rockwall, TX 75032 *Tel:* 972-771-3797 *Fax:* 972-771-0853 *E-mail:* tropikalproductions@gmail.com *Web Site:* www.tropikalproductions.com, pg 1069

World Class Learning Materials Inc, PO Box 639, Candler, NC 28715 *Toll Free Tel:* 800-638-6470 *Toll Free Fax:* 800-638-6499 *E-mail:* dealers@wclm.com *Web Site:* www.wclm.com; learningwelled.com, pg 1069

World Events Productions Ltd, 50 Maryland Plaza, Suite 300, St Louis, MO 63108 *Tel:* 314-345-1060 *Fax:* 314-345-1093 *E-mail:* wep@wep.com *Web Site:* www.wep.com, pg 1069

World Media Group Inc, 6737 E 30 St, Indianapolis, IN 46219 *Tel:* 317-549-8484 *Toll Free Tel:* 800-400-4964 *Fax:* 317-549-8480 *E-mail:* getstarted@worldmediagroup.com *Web Site:* www.worldmediagroup.com, pg 1069

World Video Sales Co Inc, PO Box 117, Boyertown, PA 19512-0117 *Tel:* 610-754-6800 *Fax:* 610-754-9766 *E-mail:* sales@mivs.com *Web Site:* www.mivs.com, pg 1070

World Wide Pictures Inc, One Billy Graham Pkwy, Charlotte, NC 28266-8029 *Tel:* 704-401-2432 *Toll Free Tel:* 800-745-4318 *Fax:* 704-401-3045 *Web Site:* www.wwp.org, pg 1070

WorldFest-Houston, 9898 Bissonnet St, Suite 650, Houston, TX 77036 *Tel:* 713-965-9955 *Toll Free Tel:* 866-965-9955 *Fax:* 713-965-9960 *E-mail:* mail@worldfest.org; entry@worldfest.org *Web Site:* www.worldfest.org, pg 1129

WorldStage, 259 W 30 St, 12th fl, New York, NY 10001-2863 *Tel:* 212-582-2345 *Fax:* 718-610-1750 *E-mail:* info@worldstage.com *Web Site:* www.worldstage.com, pg 1070

Worldview Entertainment Holdings Inc, 1384 Broadway, 25th fl, New York, NY 10018 *Tel:* 212-431-3090 *Fax:* 212-431-0390 *E-mail:* info@worldviewent.com *Web Site:* www.worldviewent.com, pg 1070

WorldView Software, 76 N Broadway, Suite 2002, Hicksville, NY 11801 *Tel:* 516-681-1773 *Toll Free Tel:* 800-347-8839 *Fax:* 516-681-1775 *E-mail:* history@worldviewsoftware.com *Web Site:* www.worldviewsoftware.com, pg 1070

Worldwide Entertainment Corp, 135 S McCarty Dr, Suite 101, Beverly Hills, CA 90212 *Tel:* 310-858-1272 *Fax:* 310-858-3774, pg 1070

Worthwhile Films, 317 Winona St, Northfield, MN 55057 *Toll Free Tel:* 877-507-5077 *Web Site:* worthwhilefilms.org, pg 1070

WOUB Public Media, 35 S College St, Athens, OH 45701 *Tel:* 740-593-1771 *Fax:* 740-593-0240 *E-mail:* woub@woub.org *Web Site:* woub.org, pg 1070

The WPA Film Library, 16101 S 108 Ave, Orland Park, IL 60467 *Tel:* 708-460-0555 *Toll Free Tel:* 800-323-0442 *Fax:* 708-460-0187 *E-mail:* sales@wpafilmlibrary.com *Web Site:* www.wpafilmlibrary.com, pg 1070

WPGH-TV, 750 Ivory Ave, Pittsburgh, PA 15214 *Tel:* 412-931-5300 *Fax:* 412-931-4284 *Web Site:* www.sbgi.net; www.wpgh53.com, pg 1070

WPHL-TV, 5001 Wynnefield Ave, Philadelphia, PA 19131 *Tel:* 215-878-1700 *Fax:* 215-879-7683; 215-877-4912 *E-mail:* feedback@phl17.com *Web Site:* www.phl17.com, pg 1070

WQED-Multimedia, 4802 Fifth Ave, Pittsburgh, PA 15213 *Tel:* 412-622-1300; 412-622-1370 *Fax:* 412-622-1488 *E-mail:* wqed@wqed.org *Web Site:* www.wqed.org, pg 1070

The Wright Group, 860 Taylor Station Rd, Blacklick, OH 43004 *Toll Free Tel:* 800-334-7344 *E-mail:* customer.service@mheducation.com *Web Site:* www.mheonline.com, pg 1070

Writers Anonymous, 34225 Acton Canyon Rd, Acton, CA 93510-1309 *Tel:* 661-269-0260, pg 1090

Writer's AudioShop/Davenport Productions, 1316 Overland Stage Rd, Dripping Springs, TX 78620 *Tel:* 512-476-1616 *Fax:* 512-264-7067 *E-mail:* wrtaudshop@aol.com *Web Site:* www.writersaudio.com, pg 1070

Writers Guild of America, West (WGAW), 7000 W Third St, Los Angeles, CA 90048 *Tel:* 323-951-4000 *Toll Free Tel:* 800-548-4532 *Fax:* 323-782-4800 *Web Site:* www.wga.org, pg 1090

The Writing Co, 10200 Jefferson Blvd, Culver City, CA 90232 *Tel:* 310-839-2436 *Toll Free Tel:* 800-421-4246 *Fax:* 310-839-2249 *Toll Free Fax:* 800-944-5432 *E-mail:* access@writingco.com; access@socialstudies.com *Web Site:* www.socialstudies.com; www.writingco.com, pg 1070

WSAZ-TV 3/WSAZ Productions, 645 Fifth Ave, Huntington, WV 25701 *Tel:* 304-697-4780 *Fax:* 304-690-3061 (sales); 304-690-3065 (news) *E-mail:* newschannel3@wsaz.com *Web Site:* www.wsaz.com, pg 1070

WSI, 400 Minuteman Rd, Andover, MA 01810 *Tel:* 978-983-6300 *Fax:* 978-983-6400 *Web Site:* www.wsi.com, pg 1070

WTL Productions, 345 E 52 St, Suite 1, New York, NY 10022 *Tel:* 212-355-1893 *E-mail:* wtlvideo@aol.com, pg 1071

WTMJ-TV, 720 E Capitol Dr, Milwaukee, WI 53212 *Tel:* 414-332-9611; 414-967-5444 *Fax:* 414-967-5255 *E-mail:* tmj4feedback@todaystmj4.com *Web Site:* www.jrn.com/tmj4, pg 1071

WTVS-Station Enterprises, Riley Broadcast Ctr, One Clover Ct, Wixom, MI 48393-2247 *Tel:* 248-305-DPTV (305-3788) *Fax:* 248-305-3990 *E-mail:* email@dptv.org *Web Site:* www.dptv.org, pg 1071

WVLA-TV, 10000 Perkins Rd, Baton Rouge, LA 70810 *Tel:* 225-766-3233 *Fax:* 225-768-9293 *Web Site:* www.nbc33tv.com, pg 1071

WVP Boston, 50 Hunt St, Watertown, MA 02472 *Tel:* 617-926-2089 *Fax:* 617-926-7965 *E-mail:* info@wvp.com *Web Site:* www.weismanvideo.com, pg 1071

The Wyland Group, 101 W Cochran St, Simi Valley, CA 93065 *Tel:* 805-955-7680 *Fax:* 805-522-1082 *Web Site:* www.adventistmediacenter.com, pg 1071

Wyoming Film Office, 5611 High Plains Rd, Cheyenne, WY 82007 *Tel:* 307-777-3400 *Toll Free Tel:* 800-458-6657 *Fax:* 307-777-2877 *E-mail:* info@filmwyoming.com *Web Site:* www.filmwyoming.com, pg 1104

Xantech LLC, 1800 S McDowell Blvd, Petaluma, CA 94954 *Tel:* 707-283-5900 *Toll Free Tel:* 800-472-5555 *Fax:* 707-283-5901 *E-mail:* info@xantech.com; customerservice@xantech.com *Web Site:* www.xantech.com, pg 1071

Xenon Pictures Inc, 3521 Jack Northrop Ave, Hawthorne, CA 90250 *Tel:* 310-451-5510 *Fax:* 310-395-4058 *E-mail:* info@xenonpictures.com; sales@xenonpictures.com *Web Site:* xenonpictures.com, pg 1071

Xetron, 460 W Crescentville Rd, Cincinnati, OH 45246-1221 *Tel:* 513-881-3100, pg 1071

Xintekvideo Inc, 56 W Broad St, Stamford, CT 06902 *Tel:* 203-348-9229 *Web Site:* www.xintekvideo.com, pg 1071

Xplor® International, 24156 State Rd 54, Suite 4, Lutz, FL 33559 *Tel:* 813-949-6170 *Toll Free Tel:* 800-669-7567 *Fax:* 813-949-9977 *E-mail:* info@xplor.org *Web Site:* www.xplor.org, pg 1090

X-Rite, 4300 44 St SE, Grand Rapids, MI 49512 *Tel:* 616-803-2100 *Toll Free Tel:* 800-248-9748 *E-mail:* info@xrite.com *Web Site:* www.xrite.com, pg 1071

XTA Electronics Ltd, 70 Sea Lane, Farmingdale, NY 11735 *Tel:* 516-249-1399 *Fax:* 516-249-8870 *E-mail:* sales@g1limited.com *Web Site:* www.g1limited.com, pg 1071

Xtech Inc, 241 Rock Creek Lane, Suite B, Scarsdale, NY 10583 *Tel:* 718-543-1222 *Toll Free Fax:* 888-528-6511 *E-mail:* info@xtechsystems.com *Web Site:* www.xtechsystems.com, pg 1071

Xytech Systems Corp, 15451 San Fernando Mission Blvd, Suite 400, Mission Hills, CA 91345 *Tel:* 818-698-4900 *Fax:* 818-698-4901 *E-mail:* sales@xytechsystems.com *Web Site:* www.xytechsystems.com, pg 1071

Yada/Levine Video Productions, 1253 Vine St, Suite 21-A, Hollywood, CA 90038 *Tel:* 323-461-1616 *Fax:* 323-461-2288 *E-mail:* video@yadalevine.com *Web Site:* www.yadalevine.com, pg 1071

Yale Film & Video, 25601 Avenue Stanford, Valencia, CA 91355 *Tel:* 661-295-7170; 661-295-7160 *E-mail:* info@yalefilmandvideo.com *Web Site:* www.yalefilmandvideo.com, pg 1071

Yamaha Electronics Corp, 6660 Orangethorpe Ave, Buena Park, CA 90620 *Tel:* 714-522-9105 *Toll Free Tel:* 800-292-2982 (cust support) *Toll Free Fax:* 800-782-8484 *Web Site:* www.yamaha.com, pg 1071

Yanchar Design & Consulting Group, 26741 Portola Pkwy, Suite 1-E, Foothill Ranch, CA 92610-1763 *Tel:* 949-770-6601 *Fax:* 949-770-6575 *E-mail:* info@yanchardesign.com *Web Site:* www.yanchardesign.com, pg 1072

YAP Films, 96 Spadina Ave, Suite 205, Toronto, ON M5V 2J6, Canada *Tel:* 416-504-3662 *Fax:* 416-504-3667 *E-mail:* thedog@yapfilms.com *Web Site:* www.yapfilms.com, pg 1072

Yarn Barn of Kansas, 930 Massachusetts St, Lawrence, KS 66044 *Tel:* 785-842-4333 *Toll Free Tel:* 800-468-0035 *Fax:* 785-842-0794 *E-mail:* info@yarnbarn-ks.com *Web Site:* www.yarnbarn-ks.com, pg 1072

Yellow Cat Productions Inc, 505 11 St SE, Washington, DC 20003 *Tel:* 202-543-2221 *E-mail:* yellowcat@yellowcat.com *Web Site:* www.yellowcat.com, pg 1072

Yellow Moon Press, PO Box 381316, Cambridge, MA 02238-1316 *Tel:* 617-776-2230 *Toll Free Tel:* 800-497-4385 *Fax:* 617-776-8246 *E-mail:* story@yellowmoon.com *Web Site:* www.yellowmoon.com, pg 1072

Yellowknife Films Inc, 5021 53 St, Yellowknife, NT X1A 1V5, Canada *Tel:* 867-873-8610 *E-mail:* ykf@theedge.ca *Web Site:* www.ykfilms.ca, pg 1072

YES Productions, 916 Navarre Ave, New Orleans, LA 70124 *Tel:* 504-840-4891 *Toll Free Tel:* 800-736-8812 *Fax:* 504-840-4895 *Web Site:* www.yesproductions.com, pg 1072

Yessian, 137 Fifth Ave, 3rd fl, New York, NY 10010 *Tel:* 212-533-3443 *E-mail:* info-ny@yessian.com *Web Site:* www.yessian.com, pg 1072

The Yesterday USA Radio Networks, 2001 Plymouth Rock Dr, Richardson, TX 75081-3946 *Tel:* 972-889-9872 *Fax:* 972-889-2329 *Web Site:* www.yesterdayusa.com, pg 1072

YMAA Publication Center Inc, 16 Lehner St, Wolfeboro, NH 03894 *Tel:* 603-569-7988 *Toll Free Tel:* 800-669-8892 *Fax:* 603-569-1889 *E-mail:* info@ymaa.com *Web Site:* www.ymaa.com, pg 1072

Yoga 1 Inc, 3128 Carlisle St, Columbia, SC 29205 *Tel:* 803-254-6121 *Toll Free Tel:* 888-364-1310 (orders) *Web Site:* www.yogaone.com, pg 1072

York Telecom, 81 Corbett Way, Eatontown, NJ 07724 *Tel:* 732-413-6000 *Toll Free Tel:* 866-836-8463 *Fax:* 732-413-6060 *E-mail:* knowmore@yorktel.com *Web Site:* yorktel.com, pg 1072

Yorkton Film Festival (YFF), 49 Smith St E, Yorkton, SK S3N 0H4, Canada *Tel:* 306-782-7077 *Fax:* 306-782-1550 *E-mail:* info@yorktonfilm.com *Web Site:* yorktonfilm.com, pg 1130

Yorkville Sound Inc, 4625 Witmer Industrial Estate, Niagara Falls, NY 14305 *Tel:* 716-297-2920 *Fax:* 716-297-3689 *E-mail:* usa@yorkville.com *Web Site:* www.yorkville.com, pg 1072

Young Chang America, 6000 Phyllis Dr, Cypress, CA 90630 *Toll Free Tel:* 866-798-6979 *Fax:* 657-200-3477 *E-mail:* marketing@ycapiano.com *Web Site:* www.youngchang.com, pg 1072

Young Minds Inc, 1014 E Cooley Dr, Suite H, Colton, CA 92324 *Tel:* 909-426-4860 *Fax:* 909-426-4866 *E-mail:* info@ymi.com; sales@ymi.com *Web Site:* www.ymi.com, pg 1072

Yukon Film & Sound Commission (YFSC), Box 2703, Whitehorse, YT Y1A 2C6, Canada *Tel:* 867-667-5400; 867-661-0408 (ext 5400, no charge for calls from within Yukon) *Fax:* 867-393-7040 *E-mail:* info@reelyukon.com *Web Site:* www.reelyukon.com, pg 1106

Yuma Film Commission, 180 W First St, Suite D, Yuma, AZ 85364 *Tel:* 928-314-9247 *Fax:* 928-373-0133 *Web Site:* www.filmyuma.com, pg 1092

Z-Axis Corp, 4600 S Ulster St, Suite 270, Denver, CO 80237 *Tel:* 303-713-0200 *Toll Free Tel:* 800-827-2947 *E-mail:* info@zaxis.com *Web Site:* www.zaxis.com, pg 1073

Z-Systems Audio Engineering, 1325 NW 53 Ave, Suite B, Gainesville, FL 32609 *Tel:* 352-371-0990 *E-mail:* z-sys@z-sys.com *Web Site:* www.z-sys.com, pg 1073

Z-Ville Productions, 34710 Lancaster Rd, Gorman, CA 93536 *Tel:* 310-422-9590 *Fax:* 310-422-9590 *E-mail:* info@zvpro.com *Web Site:* www.z-ville.com, pg 1073

Zachry Associates Inc, 500 Chestnut St, Suite 2000, Abilene, TX 79602 *Tel:* 325-677-1342 *Fax:* 325-672-2001 *E-mail:* info@zachryinc.com *Web Site:* zachryinc.com, pg 1073

Zack Electronics Inc, 1075 Hamilton Rd, Duarte, CA 91010 *Tel:* 626-303-0655 *Toll Free Tel:* 800-466-0449 *Fax:* 626-303-8694 *E-mail:* info@zackelectronics.com *Web Site:* www.zackelectronics.com, pg 1073

Zacuto, 401 W Ontario Ave, Chicago, IL 60654 *Tel:* 312-863-3456; 312-863-3453 (rentals) *Toll Free Tel:* 888-294-3456 *Fax:* 312-863-3455; 312-377-3016 (rentals) *E-mail:* rentals@zacuto.com *Web Site:* www.zacuto.com, pg 1073

Zamacona Productions, 2600 Tenth St, Suite 302, Berkeley, CA 94710 *Tel:* 510-704-4011 *Fax:* 510-704-4013 *E-mail:* admin@zamacona-productions.com *Web Site:* www.zamacona-productions.com, pg 1073

ZBS Foundation, 174 N River Rd, Fort Edward, NY 12828-9713 *Tel:* 518-695-6406 *Toll Free Tel:* 800-662-3345 *Fax:* 518-695-4041 *E-mail:* custserv@zbs.org *Web Site:* www.zbs.org, pg 1073

Zebedee Productions, 231 SW Fifth Ct, Pompano Beach, FL 33060 *Tel:* 954-942-0044 *E-mail:* info@zbd.us *Web Site:* zebedeeproductions.com, pg 1073

Zeitgeist Films Ltd, 247 Centre St, 2nd fl, New York, NY 10013 *Tel:* 212-274-1989 *Fax:* 212-274-1644 *E-mail:* mail@zeitgeistfilms.com *Web Site:* www.zeitgeistfilms.com, pg 1073

Zelco Industries Inc, 110 Hartford Ave, Mount Vernon, NY 10553 *Tel:* 914-699-6230 *Toll Free Tel:* 800-431-2486 *E-mail:* office@zelco.com *Web Site:* www.zelco.com, pg 1073

Zelman Studios Ltd, 623 Cortelyou Rd, Brooklyn, NY 11218 *Tel:* 718-941-5500 *E-mail:* kaforce@yahoo.com, pg 1073

Zelo Productions Inc, 3 S Newton St, Denver, CO 80219 *Tel:* 303-936-8995; 303-898-0911 (cell) *Fax:* 303-936-0799 *E-mail:* zelo@earthlink.net *Web Site:* www.zeloproductions.com, pg 1073

Zenith Electronics LLC, 2000 Millbrook Dr, Lincolnshire, IL 60069 *Tel:* 847-941-8000 *Toll Free Tel:* 877-9-ZENITH (993-6484) *Fax:* 847-941-8177 *E-mail:* customer.service@zenith.com *Web Site:* www.zenith.com, pg 1073

ZERO Manufacturing Inc, 500 W 200 N, North Salt Lake, UT 84054 *Tel:* 801-298-5900 *Toll Free Tel:* 800-500-ZERO (500-9376) *Fax:* 801-299-7389 *E-mail:* sales@zerocases.com *Web Site:* www.zerocases.com, pg 1073

ZGC Inc, 264 Morris Ave, Mountain Lakes, NJ 07046 *Tel:* 973-335-4460 *Fax:* 973-335-4560 *E-mail:* sales@zgc.com *Web Site:* www.zgc.com, pg 1073

Zhone Technologies Inc, 7195 Oakport St, Oakland, CA 94621 *Tel:* 510-777-7000 *Toll Free Tel:* 877-ZHONE-20 (946-6320, US & CN) *Fax:* 510-777-7001 *E-mail:* info@zhone.com; sales@zhone.com *Web Site:* www.zhone.com, pg 1073

Zim Records, 18 Ivy Dr, Jericho, NY 11753 *Tel:* 516-681-7102 *E-mail:* zimrecords@msn.com, pg 1074

Zion Music Group, 357 Riverside Dr, Suite 200, Franklin, TN 37064 *Tel:* 615-262-2600 *Toll Free Tel:* 800-883-1772 *Fax:* 615-226-4070 *Web Site:* www.zionmusic.com, pg 1074

Zippertubing® Co, 7150 W Erie St, Chandler, AZ 85226 *Tel:* 480-285-3900 *Toll Free Tel:* 800-321-8178 *Fax:* 480-285-3997 *E-mail:* info@zippertubing.com; orders@zippertubing.com *Web Site:* www.zippertubing.com, pg 1074

Zondervan, A HarperCollins Company, 3900 Sparks Dr, Grand Rapids, MI 49546 *Tel:* 616-698-6900 *Toll Free Tel:* 800-226-1122; 800-727-3480 (retail orders) *Fax:* 616-698-3255 (retail orders) *E-mail:* zinfo@zondervan.com *Web Site:* www.zondervan.com, pg 1074

ZTV Broadcast Services Inc, 1333 Matheson Blvd E, Mississauga, ON L4W 1R1, Canada *Tel:* 905-290-4430 *Fax:* 905-290-3370 *Web Site:* ztvbroadcast.com, pg 1074

Zygote Media Group Inc, 1045 S 500 E, Suite 200, American Fork, UT 84003 *Tel:* 801-765-4141 *Fax:* 801-705-2234 *E-mail:* customerservices@zygote.com *Web Site:* www.zygote.com, pg 1074

Personnel Index

Included in this index are the personnel included in the entries of *AVMP*, along with the page number(s) on which they appear. Not included in this index are those individuals associated with listings in the **Calendar of Events; Periodicals for the Trade** and **Reference Books for the Trade** sections. Also, personnel associated with secondary addresses within listings (such as branch offices, sales offices, etc.) are not included.

Abbey, Susan M, Humboldt International Film Festival, Dept Theatre, Film & Dance, One Harpst St, Arcata, CA 95521 *Tel:* 707-826-4113 *Fax:* 707-826-4112 *E-mail:* filmfest@humboldt.edu *Web Site:* hsufilmfestival.com, pg 1116

Abbott, Travis, JLG Industries, One JLG Dr, McConnellsburg, PA 17233 *Tel:* 717-485-5161 *Toll Free Tel:* 877-JLG-LIFT (554-5438) *Fax:* 717-485-6417 *E-mail:* comments@jlg.com *Web Site:* www.jlg.com, pg 905

Abed, Ramzi, Birns & Sawyer Inc, 5275 Craner Ave, North Hollywood, CA 91601 *Tel:* 323-466-8211 *Fax:* 323-466-1868; 818-358-4395 (rental) *E-mail:* info@birnsandsawyer.com *Web Site:* www.birnsandsawyer.com, pg 808

Abernathy, Susan, MGM & Associates Inc, 16026 S 36 St, Phoenix, AZ 85048-7322 *Tel:* 480-759-6251 *Toll Free Tel:* 800-485-0065 *Fax:* 480-759-6257 *E-mail:* mgm@mgmsuperstar.com *Web Site:* www.mgmsuperstar.com; www.thewomensmillionaireclub.com, pg 940

Abitbol, Larry, Bay Photo Lab, 920 Disc Dr, Scotts Valley, CA 95066 *Tel:* 831-475-6686 *Toll Free Tel:* 800-435-6686 *Fax:* 831-475-5275 *E-mail:* support@bayphoto.com (cust serv) *Web Site:* www.bayphoto.com, pg 803

Abney, Bradley, Audio Visual Techniques Inc, 1489 Leestown Rd, Lexington, KY 40511 *Tel:* 859-254-8954 *Fax:* 859-233-4754 *E-mail:* info@avtav.com *Web Site:* avtav.com, pg 796

Abramson, Karen, CCH Inc, A Wolters Kluwer business, 2700 Lake Cook Rd, Riverwoods, IL 60015 *Tel:* 847-267-7000 *Web Site:* www.cch.com, pg 821

Abramson, Steve, TRUMATCH Inc, PO Box 501, Water Mill, NY 11976-0501 *Tel:* 631-204-9100 *Toll Free Tel:* 800-TRU-9100 (878-9100) *Fax:* 631-204-0002 *E-mail:* info@trumatch.com *Web Site:* www.trumatch.com, pg 1045

Achlimbari, Robert, All Access Staging & Productions, 1320 Storm Pkwy, Torrance, CA 90501 *Tel:* 310-784-2464 *Toll Free Tel:* 877-784-2464 *Fax:* 310-517-0899 *E-mail:* usinfo@allaccessinc.com *Web Site:* www.allaccessinc.com, pg 780

Ackerman, Gary S, Thermodyne Cases, 1841 Business Pkwy, Ontario, CA 91761 *Tel:* 909-923-9945 *Toll Free Tel:* 877-307-8425 *Fax:* 909-923-7505 *E-mail:* request@thermodyne-online.com *Web Site:* www.thermodyne-online.com, pg 1038

Ackie, Eleen, Saint Vincent & The Grenadines Tourist Office, 801 Second Ave, 1st fl, New York, NY 10017 *Tel:* 212-687-4981 *Toll Free Tel:* 800-729-1726 *Fax:* 212-949-5946 *E-mail:* svgtony@aol.com *Web Site:* www.discoversvg.com, pg 1100

Acklin, Deborah L, WQED-Multimedia, 4802 Fifth Ave, Pittsburgh, PA 15213 *Tel:* 412-622-1300; 412-622-1370 *Fax:* 412-622-1488 *E-mail:* wqed@wqed.org *Web Site:* www.wqed.org, pg 1070

Acosta, Alex, Tampa Bay Film Commission, 401 E Jackson St, Suite 2100, Tampa, FL 33602 *Tel:* 813-223-1111 (ext 4058) *Toll Free Tel:* 800-826-8358 *Fax:* 813-218-3328 *Web Site:* www.filmtampabay.com, pg 1096

Acosta, Bill, Data Check Video Inc, 5148-E Commerce Ave, Moorpark, CA 93021 *Tel:* 805-517-1907 *Fax:* 805-552-0744 *E-mail:* mail@datacheck.com *Web Site:* www.datacheck.com, pg 843

Acton, Amy, Phoenix Society for Burn Survivors Inc, 1835 RW Berends Dr SW, Grand Rapids, MI 49519-4955 *Tel:* 616-458-2773 *Toll Free Tel:* 800-888-BURN (888-2876) *Fax:* 616-458-2831 *E-mail:* info@phoenix-society.org *Web Site:* www.phoenix-society.org, pg 974

Adachi, Joe, Canon USA Inc, One Canon Park, Melville, NY 11747 *Tel:* 613-330-5000 *E-mail:* pr@cusa.canon.com *Web Site:* www.usa.canon.com, pg 819

Adalid, Joanne, SpaceCam, 31111 Via Colinas, Suite 202, Westlake Village, CA 91362 *Tel:* 818-889-6060 *Fax:* 818-889-6062 *E-mail:* rentals@spacecam.com *Web Site:* spacecam.com, pg 1019

Adam, Susanne, Commercial Electronics Ltd, 1565 W Seventh St, Vancouver, BC V6J 1S1, Canada *Tel:* 604-669-5525; 604-669-6626 *Fax:* 604-669-6347 *E-mail:* info@commercialelectronics.ca *Web Site:* commercialelectronics.ca, pg 832

Adami, Anne V, Videofashion Network, 611 Broadway, Suite 307, New York, NY 10012 *Tel:* 212-274-1600 *Fax:* 212-219-1969 *E-mail:* licensing@videofashion.com *Web Site:* www.videofashion.com, pg 1056

Adamo, Louis, Hi-Tech Audio Systems Inc, 3382 Enterprise Ave, Hayward, CA 94545 *Tel:* 650-742-9166 *Fax:* 650-648-0573 *E-mail:* consoles@hi-techaudio.com *Web Site:* www.hi-techaudio.com, pg 888

Adams, Andrea, American Chemical Society (ACS), Dept of Professional Education, 1155 16 St NW, Washington, DC 20036 *Tel:* 202-872-4508 *Toll Free Tel:* 800-ACS-5558 (227-5558 ext 4508) *Fax:* 202-872-6336 *E-mail:* proed@acs.org *Web Site:* proed.acs.org, pg 784

Adams, Bruce, Cadex Electronics Inc, 22000 Fraserwood Way, Richmond, BC V6W 1J6, Canada *Tel:* 604-231-7777 *Toll Free Tel:* 800-565-5228 *Fax:* 604-231-7755 *E-mail:* info@cadex.com *Web Site:* www.cadex.com, pg 816

Adams, Dan, Adams Creative & Production Services, PO Box 98636, Des Moines, WA 98198-0636 *Tel:* 206-824-6970 *Fax:* 206-824-7036 *E-mail:* adamscreative@isomedia.com *Web Site:* www.adamscreative.net, pg 775

Adams, David L, DL Adams Associates Ltd, 970 N Kalaheo Ave, Suite A-311, Kailua, HI 96734 *Tel:* 808-254-3318 *Fax:* 808-254-5295 *E-mail:* infohawaii@dlaa.com *Web Site:* www.dlaa.com, pg 775

Adams, Denise, Pyramid Media, 3200 Airport Ave, No 19, Santa Monica, CA 90405 *Tel:* 310-398-6149 *Toll Free Tel:* 800-421-2304 *Fax:* 310-398-7869 *E-mail:* info@pyramidmedia.com; sales@pyramidmedia.com *Web Site:* www.pyramidmedia.com, pg 987

Adams, Doug, Pyrotek Special Effects Inc, 7676 Woodbine Ave, Suites 7 & 8, Markham, ON L3R 2N2, Canada *Tel:* 905-479-9991 *Toll Free Tel:* 800-481-9910 *Fax:* 905-479-3515 *E-mail:* info@pyrotekfx.com *Web Site:* www.pyrotekfx.com, pg 988

Adams, J D, 5 Alarm Music, 35 W Dayton St, Pasadena, CA 91105 *Tel:* 626-304-1698 *Toll Free Tel:* 800-322-7879 *Fax:* 626-795-2058 *E-mail:* info@5alarmmusic.com *Web Site:* www.5alarmmusic.com, pg 869

Adams, Jack, Writers Anonymous, 34225 Acton Canyon Rd, Acton, CA 93510-1309 *Tel:* 661-269-0260, pg 1090

Adams, Mike, Moog Music Inc, 160 Broadway St, Asheville, NC 28801 *Tel:* 828-251-0090 *Toll Free Tel:* 800-948-1990 *Fax:* 828-254-6233 *E-mail:* info@moogmusic.com *Web Site:* www.moogmusic.com, pg 946

Adams, Robin C, Brooklyn Films, PO Box 20412, New York, NY 10021-0066 *Tel:* 212-744-2845 *E-mail:* inquiries@brooklynfilms.com *Web Site:* www.brooklynfilms.com, pg 814

Adamson, Lee, Utah Valley Film Commission, 220 W Center St, Suite 100, Provo, UT 84601 *Tel:* 801-851-2100 *Toll Free Tel:* 800-222-8824 *Fax:* 801-851-2109 *E-mail:* visitors@utahvalley.com *Web Site:* www.utahvalley.com/film, pg 1103

Adelman, Jon, Nutmeg Post, 45 W 45 St, New York, NY 10036 *Tel:* 212-921-8005 *Fax:* 212-921-7728 *E-mail:* info@nutmegpost.com *Web Site:* www.nutmegpost.com, pg 960

Adelstein, Jonathan S, Personal Communications Industry Association (PCIA), 500 Montgomery St, Suite 500, Alexandria, VA 22314 *Tel:* 703-739-0300 *Toll Free Tel:* 800-759-0300 *Fax:* 703-836-1608 *Web Site:* www.pcia.com, pg 1087

Adema, Polly, DEC Grants, 696 Dutchess Tpke, Suite F, Poughkeepsie, NY 12603 *Tel:* 845-454-3222 *Fax:* 845-454-6902 *E-mail:* info@artsmidhudson.org *Web Site:* www.artsmidhudson.org, pg 1114

Ader, Ben, MG Studio, 6625 S Valley View Blvd, Suite C-304, Las Vegas, NV 89118 *Tel:* 702-836-3686 *Toll Free Tel:* 866-478-8340 *E-mail:* office@mgstudio.com *Web Site:* mgstudio.com, pg 940

Adjemian, Robert, Vedanta Press & Catalog, 1946 Vedanta Place, Hollywood, CA 90068 *Tel:* 323-960-1727 (bookstores); 323-960-1736 (outside US) *Toll Free Tel:* 800-816-2242 *E-mail:* info@vedanta.com *Web Site:* www.vedanta.com, pg 1052

Adler, Allan R, Association of American Publishers (AAP), 71 Fifth Ave, 2nd fl, New York, NY 10003-3004 *Tel:* 212-255-0200 *Fax:* 212-255-7007 *E-mail:* info@publishers.org *Web Site:* www.publishers.org, pg 1078

Adler, Eli, Clean Slate Video, 3070 Kerner Blvd, Unit O, San Rafael, CA 94901 *Tel:* 415-485-0727 *E-mail:* info@cleanslatevideo.com *Web Site:* www.cleanslatevideo.com, pg 829

Adler, Maura, Conly Productions, 1563 Oneida St, Denver, CO 80220 *Tel:* 303-393-6240 *Fax:* 303-393-6240, pg 835

Adriao, Antonio, American Artists Representatives Inc, 4700 Mamaroneck Ave, White Plains, NY 10605 *Tel:* 212-682-2462; 646-286-5633 (cell) *E-mail:* info@aareps.com *Web Site:* www.aareps.com, pg 783

Adwar, Michael, Adwar Video, 125 Gazza Blvd, Farmingdale, NY 11735 *Tel:* 631-777-7070 *Toll Free Tel:* 877-GOADWAR (462-3927) *Fax:* 631-777-7011 *E-mail:* sales@adwarvideo.com *Web Site:* adwarvideo.com, pg 778

Agard, Stacey, ReelWorld Film Festival, 438 Parliament St, Suite 300, Toronto, ON M5A 3A2, Canada *Tel:* 416-598-7933 *E-mail:* info@reelworld.ca; events@reelworld.ca *Web Site:* www.reelworld.ca, pg 1125

Agbenya, Allohn, Pan African Film & Arts Festival, 6820 La Tijera Blvd, Suite 200, Los Angeles, CA 90045 *Tel:* 310-337-4737 *Fax:* 310-337-4736 *E-mail:* info@paff.org *Web Site:* www.paff.org, pg 1123

Agrama, Frank, Agrama Film Enterprises Inc, 7655 Sunset Blvd, Los Angeles, CA 90046 *Tel:* 323-851-4900 *Fax:* 323-851-5599 *E-mail:* sales@harmonygold.com *Web Site:* harmonygold.com, pg 778

Agulian, Dan, Videografix LLC, 2530 Berryessa Rd, Suite 314, San Jose, CA 95132-2903 *Tel:* 408-499-1280 *Fax:* 408-583-4018 *E-mail:* info@videografix.com *Web Site:* www.videografix.com, pg 1057

Agustin, Rafael, Los Angeles Latino International Film Festival (LALIFF), 453 S Spring St, Suite 1030, Los Angeles, CA 90013 *Tel:* 323-446-2770 *Fax:* 323-446-2770 *E-mail:* info@latinofilm.org *Web Site:* latinofilm.org, pg 1119

Ahern, Donald, The Ahern Group, 3701 Malden Ave, Unit A, Baltimore, MD 21211 *Tel:* 410-367-9660 *Fax:* 410-367-9661 *E-mail:* videoahern@aol.com *Web Site:* www.theaherngroup.com, pg 779

Ahern, Lynne, The Ahern Group, 3701 Malden Ave, Unit A, Baltimore, MD 21211 *Tel:* 410-367-9660 *Fax:* 410-367-9661 *E-mail:* videoahern@aol.com *Web Site:* www.theaherngroup.com, pg 779

Ahern, Robert, The Ahern Group, 3701 Malden Ave, Unit A, Baltimore, MD 21211 *Tel:* 410-367-9660 *Fax:* 410-367-9661 *E-mail:* videoahern@aol.com *Web Site:* www.theaherngroup.com, pg 779

Ahlborg, Michelle S, A&M Productions, 86 Weybosset St, 5th fl, Providence, RI 02903 *Tel:* 401-453-6161 *Fax:* 401-421-6443 *E-mail:* info@a-mproductions.com *Web Site:* www.a-mproductions.com, pg 771

Ahmadi, Ali, O'Connor Engineering Labs, 2701 N Ontario St, Burbank, CA 91504 *Tel:* 818-847-8666 *Fax:* 818-847-1205 *E-mail:* info@ocon.com; sales@ocon.com *Web Site:* www.ocon.com, pg 961

Ahmadi, Mohammad, Be Media, 9729 Lurline Ave, Chatsworth, CA 91311 *Tel:* 310-725-8500 *Toll Free Tel:* 877-210-7664 *Fax:* 310-725-9500 *Web Site:* www.bemedia.com, pg 804

Ahmed, Mobasher, Winter Film Awards, 419 Lafayette St, New York, NY 10003 *Tel:* 646-355-4371 *E-mail:* info@winterfilmawards.com *Web Site:* www.winterfilmawards.com, pg 1129

Ahmed, Mobasher, Winter Film Awards Independent Film Festival, 419 Lafayette St, New York, NY 10003 *Tel:* 646-355-4371 *E-mail:* info@winterfilmawards.com; submissions@winterfilmawards.com *Web Site:* www.winterfilmawards.com, pg 1129

Ahuile, Yamil, ABSA Productions Inc, 125 N Halsted St, Chicago, IL 60661 *Tel:* 312-382-1029 *Web Site:* www.absaproductions.com, pg 772

Aicher, Scott, Mastech, 1000 Commerce Dr, Suite 500, Pittsburgh, PA 15275 *Tel:* 412-787-2100 *Toll Free Tel:* 800-627-8323 *Fax:* 412-494-9272 *E-mail:* info@mastech.com *Web Site:* www.mastech.com, pg 933

Aidikoff, Josh, The Charles Aidikoff Screening Room, 150 S Rodeo Dr, Suite 140, Beverly Hills, CA 90212 *Tel:* 310-274-0866 *Fax:* 310-550-1794 *E-mail:* info@aidikoff.com *Web Site:* www.aidikoff.tv, pg 779

Aihara, Douglas, Visual Communications - Southern California Asian American Studies Central Inc, 120 Judge John Aiso St, Basement Level, Los Angeles, CA 90012 *Tel:* 213-680-4462 *Fax:* 213-687-4848 *E-mail:* info@vconline.org *Web Site:* www.vconline.org, pg 1059

Aitchison, Janet, Cambridge University Press, 32 Avenue of the Americas, New York, NY 10013-2473 *Tel:* 212-337-5000 *Toll Free Tel:* 800-221-4512 *Fax:* 212-691-3239 *E-mail:* information@cambridge.org; newyork@cambridge.org *Web Site:* www.cambridge.org, pg 818

Akers, Harry D, Studio Consulting & Construction Inc, 2805 Oakview Dr, Dryden, MI 48428-9740 *Tel:* 810-796-3235; 248-496-9000 *E-mail:* scc@hdakers.com *Web Site:* www.hdakers.com, pg 1026

Akhamlich, Patrick, Hybrid Studios, 3021 S Shannon St, Santa Ana, CA 92704 *Tel:* 714-850-1499 *E-mail:* info@hybridstudiosca.com; rentals@hybridstudiosca.com *Web Site:* hybridstudiosca.com, pg 893

Akoury, Tom, Delicate Electronics Sales Inc, 874 Verdulera St, Camarillo, CA 93010 *Tel:* 805-484-8139 *Toll Free Tel:* 800-350-3555 *Fax:* 805-388-1037 *Web Site:* www.delicatesales.com, pg 845

Albert, Alan, Clairmont Camera Inc, 4343 Lankershim Blvd, North Hollywood, CA 91602 *Tel:* 818-761-4440 *Fax:* 818-761-0861 *E-mail:* hollywood@clairmont.com *Web Site:* www.clairmont.com, pg 829

Alberti, Cliff, Tritech Communications, 625 Locust St, Suite 300, Garden City, NY 11530 *Tel:* 631-254-4500 *Fax:* 631-254-4499 *E-mail:* sales@tritechcomm.com *Web Site:* www.tritechcomm.com, pg 1045

Albiniak, Paige, PromaxBDA, 1522e Cloverfield Blvd, Santa Monica, CA 90404 *Tel:* 310-788-7600 *Fax:* 310-788-7616 *Web Site:* www.promaxbda.org, pg 1087

Albonico, Don, Third Ear Sound Co, 30965 San Benito St, Hayward, CA 94544 *Tel:* 510-429-1000 *Toll Free Tel:* 800-587-1115 *Fax:* 510-429-1001 *E-mail:* raul@thirdearsound.com *Web Site:* www.thirdearsound.com, pg 1039

Alejandro, Jan M, Jan-Al Cases, 3339 Union Pacific Ave, Los Angeles, CA 90023 *Tel:* 323-260-7212 *Toll Free Tel:* 800-735-2625 *Fax:* 323-260-4696 *Web Site:* www.janalcase.com, pg 904

Alejandro, Miriam (Muffie), Jan-Al Cases, 3339 Union Pacific Ave, Los Angeles, CA 90023 *Tel:* 323-260-7212 *Toll Free Tel:* 800-735-2625 *Fax:* 323-260-4696 *Web Site:* www.janalcase.com, pg 904

Alemany, Joshua, Rosco Laboratories Inc, 52 Harbor View, Stamford, CT 06902 *Tel:* 203-708-8900 *Toll Free Tel:* 800-ROSCO NY (767-2669) *Fax:* 203-708-8919 *E-mail:* info@rosco.com *Web Site:* www.rosco.com, pg 999

Alexander, Ann, KidFilm®, 6116 N Central Expwy, Suite 105, Dallas, TX 75206 *Tel:* 214-821-6300; 214-821-FILM (821-3456) *Fax:* 214-821-6364 *E-mail:* usafilmfestival@aol.com *Web Site:* www.usafilmfestival.com, pg 1118

Alexander, Ann, National Short Film & Video Competition, 6116 N Central Expwy, Suite 105, Dallas, TX 75206 *Tel:* 214-821-6300; 214-821-FILM (821-3456) *Fax:* 214-821-6364 *E-mail:* usafilmfestival@aol.com *Web Site:* www.usafilmfestival.com, pg 1121

Alexander, Ann, USA Film Festival, 6116 N Central Expwy, Suite 105, Dallas, TX 75206 *Tel:* 214-821-6300 *Fax:* 214-821-6364 *E-mail:* usafilmfestival@aol.com *Web Site:* www.usafilmfestival.com, pg 1128

Alexander, Geoff, Santa Barbara County Film Commission, 500 E Montecito St, Santa Barbara, CA 93103 *Tel:* 805-966-9222 *Toll Free Tel:* 800-676-1266 *Fax:* 805-966-1728 *Web Site:* www.filmsantabarbara.com, pg 1094

Alexander, Heather, Alexander Media Productions, 1901 Diamond Ridge Dr, Carrollton, TX 75010 *Tel:* 214-274-3456 *Web Site:* www.heatheralexander.net, pg 780

Alexander, Kimberlee, Vancouver Film Studios Ltd, 3500 Cornett Rd, Vancouver, BC V5M 2H5, Canada *Tel:* 604-453-5000 *Fax:* 604-453-5045 *Web Site:* www.vancouverfilmstudios.com, pg 1051

Alexander, Marcie, Classic Images, 469 S Bedford Dr, Beverly Hills, CA 90212 *Tel:* 310-277-0400 *Toll Free Tel:* 800-949-CLIP (949-2547) *Fax:* 310-277-0412 *E-mail:* sales@classicimg.com *Web Site:* www.classicimg.com, pg 829

Alexander, Mary Lou, Spring Arbor Distributors, One Ingram Blvd, LaVergne, TN 37086-1986 *Tel:* 615-793-5000 (Ingram) *Toll Free Tel:* 800-395-4340 (Christian); 800-395-5599 (sales); 800-234-6737 (electronic ordering); 877-846-6989 (software support); 800-395-7234 (cust serv) *Fax:* 615-213-5192 *E-mail:* custserv@springarbor.com; orders@springarbor.com *Web Site:* www.ingramcontent.com, pg 1022

Alexander, Neil, Cokesbury, 201 Eighth Ave, Nashville, TN 37203 *Tel:* 615-749-6000 *Toll Free Tel:* 800-672-1789 *Fax:* 615-749-6079 *E-mail:* cokes_serv@cokesbury.com *Web Site:* www.cokesbury.com, pg 831

Alexander, Peter, Westar Music, 105 W Beaver Creek Rd, Suite 4, Richmond Hill, ON L4B 1C6, Canada *Tel:* 905-886-3100 *Toll Free Tel:* 800-665-3000 *Fax:* 905-886-6800 *E-mail:* info@westarmusic.com *Web Site:* www.westarmusic.com, pg 1064

Alexander, Dr Ric D, Institute of Precision Muscle Balancing, 6035 Vantage Ave, North Hollywood, CA 91616-4637 *Tel:* 818-766-8555 *Fax:* 818-766-8645 *Web Site:* www.dralexander.com, pg 899

Alexander, Victoria, The Learning House Inc, 427 S Fourth St, Suite 300, Louisville, KY 40202 *Tel:* 502-589-9878 *Fax:* 502-589-9825 *E-mail:* sales@learninghouse.com *Web Site:* www.learninghouse.com, pg 917

Alfano, Richard, IAC Acoustics, 1160 Commerce Ave, Bronx, NY 10462 *Tel:* 718-931-8000 *Fax:* 718-863-1138 *E-mail:* newyork@iac-acoustics.com *Web Site:* www.iac-acoustics.com/us, pg 893

Alfonzo, Amy, International Digital Centre, 216 E 45 St, 7th fl, New York, NY 10017 *Tel:* 212-581-3940 *Fax:* 212-581-3979 *E-mail:* info@idcdigital.com *Web Site:* www.idcdigital.com, pg 901

Alford, Chris, A&V Company, 4238 Piedmont Pkwy, Greensboro, NC 27410-8111 *Tel:* 336-292-9700 *Toll Free Tel:* 800-292-9700 *Fax:* 336-854-5282 *E-mail:* info@avcompany.com *Web Site:* www.avcompany.com, pg 772

Alford, Steve, Alford Media Services, 296 Freeport Pkwy, Coppell, TX 75019 *Tel:* 972-538-9400 *Toll Free Tel:* 800-554-9144 *Fax:* 972-538-0800 *E-mail:* info@alfordmedia.com; sales@alfordmedia.com *Web Site:* www.alfordmedia.com, pg 780

Alford, Tom, Alford Media Services, 296 Freeport Pkwy, Coppell, TX 75019 *Tel:* 972-538-9400 *Toll Free Tel:* 800-554-9144 *Fax:* 972-538-0800 *E-mail:* info@alfordmedia.com; sales@alfordmedia.com *Web Site:* www.alfordmedia.com, pg 780

Ali, Ed, Langie Audio Visual Systems, Piano Works Mall, 349 W Commercial St, East Rochester, NY 14445 *Tel:* 585-385-4880 *Fax:* 585-385-4882 *E-mail:* info@langieav.com; sales@langieav.com; rental@langieav.com *Web Site:* www.langieav.com, pg 916

Alires, Kristi, Xenon Pictures Inc, 3521 Jack Northrop Ave, Hawthorne, CA 90250 *Tel:* 310-451-5510 *Fax:* 310-395-4058 *E-mail:* info@xenonpictures.com; sales@xenonpictures.com *Web Site:* xenonpictures.com, pg 1071

Allain, Chris, Vidox Motion Imagery, 204 Winchester Dr, Lafayette, LA 70506 *Tel:* 337-237-1700 *Fax:* 337-237-1712 *Web Site:* www.vidox.com, pg 1057

Allain, Jean-Marc L, Trans-Lux Multimedia Corp, 950 Third Ave, Suite 2804, New York, NY 10022 *Tel:* 203-853-4321 *Toll Free Tel:* 800-243-5544; 800-462-2716 *Fax:* 203-229-0691 *Web Site:* www.trans-lux.com, pg 1043

Allain, Stephanie, Los Angeles Film Festival, 9911 W Pico Blvd, Suite 1100, Los Angeles, CA 90035 *Toll Free Tel:* 866-345-6337 *E-mail:* lafilmfest@filmindependent.org *Web Site:* www.lafilmfest.com, pg 1119

Allard, Pierre-Paul, Avaya Inc, 211 Mount Airy Rd, Basking Ridge, NJ 07920 *Tel:* 908-953-6000 *Toll Free Tel:* 866-GO-AVAYA (462-8292 US & CN) *Web Site:* www.avaya.com, pg 798

Allen, Alisa, Wild Plum, 2128 Narcissus Ct, Venice, CA 90291 *Tel:* 310-823-7445 *Fax:* 310-578-1445 *Web Site:* www.wildplum.tv, pg 1066

Allen, Brian, AMPLUS Productions, 1484 Liveoak Dr, Mississauga, ON L5E 2X1, Canada *Tel:* 416-889-7664 *Fax:* 905-274-7687 *Web Site:* www.amplusproductions.com, pg 786

Allen, Charles, Cinema East, 7111 Biscayne Blvd, Miami, FL 33138 *Tel:* 305-757-5859 *Fax:* 305-751-2329 *Web Site:* www.cinemaeast.com, pg 827

Allen, Chris, Sear Sound, 353 W 48 St, 6th fl, New York, NY 10036 *Tel:* 212-582-5380 *Fax:* 212-581-2731 *E-mail:* waltersear@aol.com *Web Site:* www.searsound.com, pg 1005

Allen, John E, John E Allen Inc, PO Box 452, Newfoundland, PA 18445 *Tel:* 570-676-4152 *Fax:* 570-676-9194 *E-mail:* jeainc@gmail.com *Web Site:* www.allenarchive.com/wordpress, pg 781

Allen, Layman G (Buzz), Accelerated Learning Foundation, 118 N Court St, Fairfield, IA 52556 *Tel:* 641-954-5443 *Toll Free Tel:* 800-289-2377 *Fax:* 641-954-5851 *E-mail:* info@gamesforthinkers.org *Web Site:* gamesforthinkers.org, pg 773

Allen, Mike, JoLida Inc, 21310 Ridgecroft Dr, Brookeville, MD 20833 *Tel:* 301-953-2014 *Fax:* 301-498-0554 *E-mail:* jolidacorp@msn.com *Web Site:* www.jolida.com, pg 906

Allen, Paul, Adaptive Video Walls & Displays, 1635 E Burnett St, Signal Hill, CA 90755 *Tel:* 562-424-1100 *Fax:* 562-424-3520 *E-mail:* info@adapttechgroup.com *Web Site:* www.adapttechgroup.com, pg 776

Allen, Paul, Allen Products Co Inc, 1635 E Burnett St, Signal Hill, CA 90755 *Tel:* 562-424-1100 *Fax:* 562-424-3520 *E-mail:* info@adapttechgroup.com *Web Site:* www.adapttechgroup.com, pg 781

Allen, Paul, ATM Fly-Ware, 1635 E Burnett St, Signal Hill, CA 90755 *Tel:* 562-424-1100 *Fax:* 562-424-3520 *E-mail:* info@adapttechgroup.com; marketing@adapttechgroup.com *Web Site:* www.adapttechgroup.com/atmflyware.html, pg 793

Allen, Robert, Macmillan Audio, 175 Fifth Ave, New York, NY 10010 *Tel:* 646-600-7856; 646-307-5742 *Toll Free Tel:* 888-330-8477 (orders); 800-221-7945 *Toll Free Fax:* 800-672-7703 (orders) *E-mail:* macmillan.audio@macmillanusa.com *Web Site:* us.macmillan.com/audio.aspx, pg 927

Allen, Susan, Eastern Video, 7111 Biscayne Blvd, Miami, FL 33138 *Tel:* 305-759-7111 *Fax:* 305-759-7111; 305-751-2329 *E-mail:* miami@easternvideo.com *Web Site:* www.easternvideo.com, pg 856

Allen, Tom, Association of American Publishers (AAP), 71 Fifth Ave, 2nd fl, New York, NY 10003-3004 *Tel:* 212-255-0200 *Fax:* 212-255-7007 *E-mail:* info@publishers.org *Web Site:* www.publishers.org, pg 1078

Allen, Van, Radio Advertising Bureau (RAB), 125 W 55 St, 5th fl, New York, NY 10019 *Tel:* 212-681-7200 *Toll Free Tel:* 800-252-7234 *Fax:* 212-681-7223 *Web Site:* www.rab.com, pg 1088

Allen, Walter, Elite Video, 209 E Emerson Rd, Lexington, MA 02420 *Tel:* 781-862-6606 *E-mail:* sales@elitevision.com *Web Site:* www.elitevision.com, pg 859

Allessi, Ana Marie, HarperAudio, 10 E 53 St, New York, NY 10022 *Tel:* 212-207-7000 *Toll Free Tel:* 800-242-7737 *Fax:* 212-207-2582 *Toll Free Fax:* 800-822-4090 *Web Site:* www.harpercollins.com, pg 885

Allhands, Ellen, Rane, 10802 47 Ave W, Mukilteo, WA 98275-5000 *Tel:* 425-355-6000 *E-mail:* info@rane.com *Web Site:* www.rane.com, pg 991

Alli, Brian, Roland Corp US, 5100 S Eastern Ave, Los Angeles, CA 90040-2938 *Tel:* 323-890-3700 *Fax:* 323-721-4875 *Web Site:* www.rolandus.com, pg 998

Allin, Mark, John Wiley & Sons Inc, 111 River St, Hoboken, NJ 07030 *Tel:* 201-748-6000 *Toll Free Tel:* 800-225-5945 *Fax:* 201-748-6088 *E-mail:* info@wiley.com *Web Site:* www.wiley.com, pg 1066

Allison, Mark, Dake Publishing Inc, 764 Martins Chapel Rd, Lawrenceville, GA 30045 *Toll Free Tel:* 800-241-1239 *Fax:* 770-963-7700 *E-mail:* info@dake.com *Web Site:* www.dake.com, pg 842

Allsop, James, Allsop Inc, PO Box 23, Bellingham, WA 98227-0023 *Tel:* 360-734-9090 *Toll Free Tel:* 800-426-4303 *Fax:* 360-734-9858 (sales); 360-733-4302 (corp) *E-mail:* info@allsop.com *Web Site:* www.allsop.com, pg 781

Allyn, Jon, American Society of Photographers (ASP), 3120 N Argonne Dr, Milwaukee, WI 53222 *Tel:* 414-871-6600 *Web Site:* s17670789.onlinehome-server.com/, pg 1077

Almanza-Lumpkin, Carlota, WTVS-Station Enterprises, Riley Broadcast Ctr, One Clover Ct, Wixom, MI 48393-2247 *Tel:* 248-305-DPTV (305-3788) *Fax:* 248-305-3990 *E-mail:* email@dptv.org *Web Site:* www.dptv.org, pg 1071

Alonso, John, Kenexa, 650 E Swedesford Rd, 2nd fl, Wayne, PA 19087 *Tel:* 407-548-1444 *Fax:* 610-971-9181 *E-mail:* kenexa_learn_sales@kenexa.com *Web Site:* www.outstart.com, pg 909

Alpert, Daniel, WTVS-Station Enterprises, Riley Broadcast Ctr, One Clover Ct, Wixom, MI 48393-2247 *Tel:* 248-305-DPTV (305-3788) *Fax:* 248-305-3990 *E-mail:* email@dptv.org *Web Site:* www.dptv.org, pg 1071

Alpert, Jon, Downtown Community Television Center (DCTV), 87 Lafayette St, New York, NY 10013 *Tel:* 212-966-4510 *Fax:* 212-226-3053 *E-mail:* info@dctvny.org *Web Site:* www.dctvny.org, pg 851

Alsop, Peter, Moose School Productions, Box 960, Topanga, CA 90290-0960 *Tel:* 310-455-2318 *Toll Free Tel:* 800-676-5480 *Fax:* 310-455-4192 *Web Site:* www.peteralsop.com, pg 946

Alsup, Sharon, True Audio, 387 Duncan Lane, Andersonville, TN 37705 *Tel:* 865-494-3388 *Toll Free Tel:* 800-621-4411 *Fax:* 865-494-3388 *E-mail:* sales@trueaudio.com *Web Site:* www.trueaudio.com, pg 1045

Alti, Thomas, TGA Recording Co, 295 Urbandale Ave, Benton Harbor, MI 49022 *Tel:* 269-926-7581 *Fax:* 269-926-7589 *E-mail:* tgarecording@sbcglobal.net *Web Site:* www.tgarecording.com, pg 1038

Altman, Allan, Video Artists International & VAI Audio, 109 Wheeler Ave, Pleasantville, NY 10570 *Tel:* 914-769-3691 *Toll Free Tel:* 800-477-7146 *Fax:* 914-769-5407 *E-mail:* orders@vaimusic.com *Web Site:* www.vaimusic.com, pg 1054

Altman, Mark, Morning Music Ltd, 5200 Dixie Rd, Suite 203, Mississauga, ON L4W 1E4, Canada *Tel:* 905-625-2676 *Fax:* 905-625-2092 *E-mail:* info@morningmusic.ca *Web Site:* www.morningmusic.ca, pg 946

Altomare, Brent, Groovy Like a Movie, 5205 Kearny Villa Way, Suite 100, San Diego, CA 92123 *Tel:* 858-715-0300 *E-mail:* info@groovylikeamovie.com *Web Site:* www.groovylikeamovie.com, pg 882

Alvarado, Maritza, The Kitchen, 4119 W Burbank Blvd, Burbank, CA 91505 *Tel:* 818-306-5300 *Fax:* 305-415-6201 *E-mail:* info@thekitchen.tv *Web Site:* www.thekitchen.tv, pg 911

Alvarado, Tony, Audio Visual Concepts Inc, PO Box 3915, Guaynabo, PR 00970-3915 *Tel:* 787-753-7700 *Fax:* 787-766-7712 *Web Site:* www.mig-avc.com, pg 795

Alvarez, Beth, Seaport Graphics, 12 Channel St, Suite 802, Boston, MA 02210 *Tel:* 617-330-1200 *Fax:* 617-330-1222 *E-mail:* jobs@seaportgraphics.com *Web Site:* www.seaportgraphics.com, pg 1005

Alvarez, Brian, Dogma Studios, 10559 Jefferson Blvd, Culver City, CA 90232 *Tel:* 310-838-2973 *Fax:* 310-838-2975 *E-mail:* info@dogmastudios.com *Web Site:* www.dogmastudios.com, pg 850

Alvarez, Milt, Planet Blue, 1250 Sixth St, Suite 102, Santa Monica, CA 90401 *Tel:* 310-899-3877 *Fax:* 310-899-3787 *Web Site:* www.planetblue.com, pg 976

Alway, Curt, SoftWright LLC, PO Box 7205, Charlotte, VA 22906 *Tel:* 303-344-5486 *Toll Free Tel:* 800-728-4033 *Fax:* 303-265-9399 *E-mail:* sales@softwright.com *Web Site:* www.softwright.com, pg 1015

Amadril, Richard, Luminys Systems Corp, 11961 Sherman Rd, North Hollywood, CA 91605 *Tel:* 323-461-6361 *Toll Free Tel:* 800-321-3644 *Fax:* 323-461-3067 *E-mail:* info@luminyscorp.com *Web Site:* www.luminyscorp.com, pg 926

Amat, Mark, Print File Inc, 1846 S Orange Blossom Trail, Apopka, FL 32703 *Tel:* 407-886-3100 *Toll Free Tel:* 800-508-8539 *Fax:* 407-886-0008 *Toll Free Fax:* 800-546-4145 *E-mail:* support@printfile.com *Web Site:* www.printfile.com, pg 982

Ambrose, William V, Ambrose Video Publishing Inc, 145 W 45 St, Suite 1115, New York, NY 10036 *Tel:* 212-768-7373 *Toll Free Tel:* 800-526-4663 *Fax:* 212-768-9282 *E-mail:* customerservice@ambrosevideo.com *Web Site:* www.ambrosevideo.com, pg 783

Ambrosh, Karen, National Telemedia Council Inc, 1922 University Ave, Madison, WI 53726 *Tel:* 608-218-1182 *E-mail:* ntelemedia@aol.com *Web Site:* www.nationaltelemediacouncil.org, pg 1086

Ames, David, Stanford Research Systems Inc, 1290-D Reamwood Ave, Sunnyvale, CA 94089 *Tel:* 408-744-9040 *Fax:* 408-744-9049 *E-mail:* info@thinksrs.com *Web Site:* www.thinksrs.com, pg 1023

Ames, Howard, Osram Sylvania Inc, 100 Endicott St, Danvers, MA 01923 *Tel:* 978-777-1900 *Toll Free Tel:* 800-842-7010 *Fax:* 978-750-2152 *Web Site:* www.sylvania.com, pg 965

Ames, Justin, Ames Recording Studios, 840 Danit St, Prescott, AZ 86301 *Tel:* 928-830-2313 *Web Site:* www.amesrecordingstudios.com, pg 785

Amici, Tom, Tobin Productions Inc, 630 Ninth Ave, Suite 215, New York, NY 10036 *Tel:* 212-727-1500 *Toll Free Tel:* 800-877-8273 *Fax:* 212-727-1766 *E-mail:* info@tobinproductions.com *Web Site:* www.tobinproductions.com, pg 1041

Amick, Gray, Carolina Biological Supply Co, 2700 York Rd, Burlington, NC 27215-3398 *Tel:* 336-584-0381 (outside US & CN) *Toll Free Tel:* 800-334-5551 *Toll Free Fax:* 800-222-7112 *E-mail:* customer_service@carolina.com; internationalsales@carolina.com *Web Site:* www.carolina.com, pg 820

Amico, Lou, L A Management Co LLC, 8131 Bay Pointe Dr, Denver, NC 28037 *Tel:* 704-560-6274 *Toll Free Tel:* 800-651-7818 *Fax:* 704-973-7968 *E-mail:* info@managementco.com *Web Site:* lamanagementco.com, pg 914

Amir-Fazli, Andrew, Phoenix/BFA/Coronet, 141 Milllwell Dr, Suite A, St Louis, MO 63043-2509 *Tel:* 314-569-0211 (ext 104) *Toll Free Tel:* 800-221-1274 (ext 104) *Fax:* 314-569-2834 (orders) *E-mail:* info@phoenixlearninggroup.com; customerservice@phoenixlearninggroup.com *Web Site:* www.phoenixlearninggroup.com, pg 974

Amir-Fazli, Andrew, The Phoenix Learning Group Inc, 141 Millwell Dr, Suite A, St Louis, MO 63043-2509 *Tel:* 314-569-0211 *Toll Free Tel:* 800-221-1274 *Fax:* 314-569-2834 (orders) *E-mail:* customerservice@phoenixlearninggroup.com; info@phoenixlearninggroup.com *Web Site:* www.phoenixlearninggroup.com, pg 974

Amir-Hamzeh, Mark, Sigma Corp of America, 15 Fleetwood Ct, Ronkonkoma, NY 11779 *Tel:* 631-585-1144 *Toll Free Tel:* 800-896-6858 (cust serv) *Fax:* 631-585-1895 *E-mail:* info@sigmaphoto.com *Web Site:* www.sigmaphoto.com, pg 1010

Ammeen, Charlie, SKC Communication Products Inc, 8320 Hedge Lane Terr, Shawnee Mission, KS 66227 *Tel:* 913-422-4222 *Toll Free Tel:* 800-882-7779 *Toll Free Fax:* 800-454-4752 *E-mail:* contact.us@skccom.com *Web Site:* www.skccom.com, pg 1012

Amor, Joseph L III, Microspace Communications Corp, 3100 Highwoods Blvd, Suite 120, Raleigh, NC 27604 *Tel:* 919-850-4500 *Fax:* 919-850-4518 *Web Site:* www.microspace.com, pg 942

Anastasi, Joseph, PASCO, 224 48 St, Brooklyn, NY 11220 *Tel:* 718-833-9100 *Fax:* 718-833-9118 *E-mail:* pasco2@aol.com, pg 969

Anastasio, Russo, Shapeshifter, 3405 Cahuenga Blvd W, Los Angeles, CA 90068 *Tel:* 323-876-3444 *Fax:* 323-876-1444 *E-mail:* sales@shapeshifterpost.com *Web Site:* www.shapeshifterpost.com, pg 1008

Anderson, Bob, HB Communications Inc, 60 Dodge Ave, North Haven, CT 06473 *Tel:* 203-234-9246 *Toll Free Tel:* 800-243-4414 *Fax:* 203-234-2013 *E-mail:* info@hbcommunications.com *Web Site:* www.hbcommunications.com, pg 886

Anderson, Bob, Stretching Inc, PO Box 767, Palmer Lake, CO 80133-0767 *Tel:* 719-481-3928 *Toll Free Tel:* 800-333-1307 *Fax:* 719-481-9058 *E-mail:* office@stretching.com *Web Site:* www.stretching.com, pg 1026

Anderson, Bruce, McCauley Sound Inc, 16607 Meridian Ave E, Puyallup, WA 98375 *Tel:* 253-848-0363 *Toll Free Tel:* 877-622-2853 *Fax:* 253-841-3050 *Web Site:* www.mccauleysound.com, pg 935

Anderson, Caryn, Automatic Devices Co, 2121 S 12 St, Allentown, PA 18103 *Tel:* 610-797-6000 *Toll Free Tel:* 800-360-2321 *Fax:* 610-797-4088 *E-mail:* info@automaticdevices.com *Web Site:* www.automaticdevices.com, pg 797

Anderson, Chad, Osum Event Rentals, 562 First Ave S, Suite 100, Seattle, WA 98104 *Tel:* 206-209-2012 *Fax:* 206-209-2013 *E-mail:* info@osumeventrentals.com *Web Site:* osumeventrentals.com, pg 966

Anderson, Daniel, ATTCO Inc, 825 Ilaniwai St, Honolulu, HI 96813 *Tel:* 808-836-1191 *Fax:* 808-834-1046 *E-mail:* information@attcoinc.com *Web Site:* www.attcoinc.com, pg 793

Anderson, Derek, D&B Television & Video Productions Inc, 1400 Riverbend Dr, Rocky Mount, VA 24151 *Tel:* 305-542-7000 *Web Site:* www.dbvideoproductions.net, pg 842

Anderson, Erin, Chater Camera Inc, 1336 Ninth St, Berkeley, CA 94710 *Tel:* 510-525-5400 *Fax:* 510-295-2478 *E-mail:* rentals@chatercamera.com *Web Site:* www.chatercamera.com, pg 824

Anderson, Gary, NH Movies Inc, 16 Gulf Rd, Deerfield, NH 03037 *Tel:* 603-463-5900 *E-mail:* info@nhmovies.com *Web Site:* www.nhmovies.com, pg 957

Anderson, Gary, Score Productions Inc, 219 E 49 St, New York, NY 10017 *Tel:* 212-751-2510 *Fax:* 212-754-6305 *E-mail:* score@scoreproductions.com *Web Site:* www.artgraphica.com/preview/ScoreProductions/index.html, pg 1005

Anderson, Jackie, Colortek of Boston, 727 Atlantic Ave, Boston, MA 02111 *Tel:* 617-451-0894 *Fax:* 617-451-2714 *E-mail:* info@colortekofboston.com *Web Site:* www.colortekofboston.com, pg 832

Anderson, Jane, PDC Productions, 3217 N Flood Ave, Norman, OK 73069 *Tel:* 405-360-5130 *Fax:* 405-360-0524 *E-mail:* info@pdcproductions.com *Web Site:* www.pdcproductions.com, pg 970

Anderson, Jason, Phillips MediaSource, 750 N St Paul, Suite 1000, Dallas, TX 75201 *Tel:* 214-741-1300 *Toll Free Tel:* 800-TEXAS13 (839-2713) *Fax:* 214-741-3942 *Web Site:* phillipsmediasource.com, pg 974

Anderson, Jean E, Stretching Inc, PO Box 767, Palmer Lake, CO 80133-0767 *Tel:* 719-481-3928 *Toll Free Tel:* 800-333-1307 *Fax:* 719-481-9058 *E-mail:* office@stretching.com *Web Site:* www.stretching.com, pg 1026

Anderson, Jeff, Superscope Technologies Inc, 1508 Batavia Ave, Geneva, IL 60134-3302 *Tel:* 630-232-8900 *Toll Free Tel:* 800-374-4118 *Fax:* 630-232-8905 *Web Site:* www.superscopetechnologies.com, pg 1029

Anderson, Joseph, Mutoh America Inc, 2602 S 47 St, Phoenix, AZ 85034-7401 *Tel:* 480-968-7772 *Toll Free Tel:* 800-99-MUTOH (996-8864) *Fax:* 480-968-7990 *E-mail:* sales@mutoh.com *Web Site:* mutoh.com, pg 951

Anderson, Keith C, Yale Film & Video, 25601 Avenue Stanford, Valencia, CA 91355 *Tel:* 661-295-7170; 661-295-7160 *E-mail:* info@yalefilmandvideo.com *Web Site:* www.yalefilmandvideo.com, pg 1071

Anderson, Kim, COMPRO Productions Inc, 2055 Boar Tusk Rd NE, Conyers, GA 30012-3801 *Tel:* 770-918-8163 *E-mail:* compro@compro-atl.com *Web Site:* www.compro-atl.com, pg 834

Anderson, Mr Lane, InterComm, 1520 E Winona Ave, Warsaw, IN 46590 *Tel:* 574-267-5774 *Fax:* 574-267-5876 *E-mail:* info@intercommedia.org *Web Site:* www.intercommedia.org, pg 900

Anderson, Leslie, Explore Minnesota Tourism, Metro Sq, Suite 100, 121 E Seventh Place, St Paul, MN 55101-2112 *Tel:* 651-757-1870 *Toll Free Tel:* 800-657-3638 *Fax:* 651-296-7095 *E-mail:* explore@state.mn.us *Web Site:* www.exploreminnesota.com, pg 1099

Anderson, Mark C, ACCO Brands Corp, 4 Corporate Dr, Lake Zurick, IL 60047-8997 *Toll Free Tel:* 800-541-0094 *Toll Free Fax:* 800-941-4463 *E-mail:* contactus@gbc.com *Web Site:* www.accobrands.com, pg 773

Anderson, Mary, Countryman Associates Inc, 195 Constitution Dr, Menlo Park, CA 94025 *Tel:* 650-364-9988 *Toll Free Tel:* 800-669-1422 *Fax:* 650-364-2794 *E-mail:* sales@countryman.com *Web Site:* www.countryman.com, pg 837

Anderson, Max, The Market Place, PO Box 4126, Rockford, IL 61110-0626 *Tel:* 815-877-1514, pg 931

Anderson, Nancy, BingoLewis, 203 NE Weidler St, Portland, OR 97232 *Tel:* 503-223-2224 *E-mail:* info@bingolewis.com *Web Site:* www.bingolewis.com, pg 807

Anderson, Nels, COMPRO Productions Inc, 2055 Boar Tusk Rd NE, Conyers, GA 30012-3801 *Tel:* 770-918-8163 *E-mail:* compro@compro-atl.com *Web Site:* www.compro-atl.com, pg 834

Anderson, Paul, Paul L Anderson Productions Inc, 2107 Constitution Ave, Fort Collins, CO 80526 *Web Site:* www.paulanderson.com, pg 786

Anderson, Rob, BingoLewis, 203 NE Weidler St, Portland, OR 97232 *Tel:* 503-223-2224 *E-mail:* info@bingolewis.com *Web Site:* www.bingolewis.com, pg 807

Anderson, Robyn, Musco Lighting, 100 First Ave W, Oskaloosa, IA 52577 *Tel:* 641-673-0411 *Toll Free Tel:* 800-825-6030 *Fax:* 641-673-4852 *E-mail:* lighting@musco.com *Web Site:* www.musco.com, pg 950

Anderson, Rose, The Global Awards, 260 W 39 St, 10th fl, New York, NY 10018 *Tel:* 212-643-4800 *Fax:* 212-643-0170 *E-mail:* info@newyorkfestivals.com *Web Site:* www.theglobalawards.com, pg 1115

Anderson, Rose, New York Festivals®-International Radio Program Awards, 260 W 39 St, 10th fl, New York, NY 10018 *Tel:* 212-643-4800 *Fax:* 212-643-0170 *E-mail:* info@newyorkfestivals.com *Web Site:* www.newyorkfestivals.com, pg 1122

Anderson, Rose, New York Festivals®-International TV & Film Awards, 260 W 39 St, 10th fl, New York, NY 10018 *Tel:* 212-643-4800 *Fax:* 212-643-0170 *E-mail:* info@newyorkfestivals.com *Web Site:* www.newyorkfestivals.com, pg 1122

Anderson, Sarah, G W Hannaway & Associates, 839 Pearl St, Boulder, CO 80302 *Tel:* 303-440-9631 *Fax:* 303-440-4421 *E-mail:* sales@gwha.com; services@gwha.com; technology@gwha.com *Web Site:* www.gwha.com, pg 884

Anderson, Stan, Trac Record Co & Recording Studio, 180 E Warner Ave, Fresno, CA 93710 *Tel:* 559-448-8722 *E-mail:* tracsell@sbcglobal.net, pg 1043

Anderson, Steve, Freeman, 1600 Viceroy, Suite 100, Dallas, TX 75235 *Tel:* 214-445-1000 *Fax:* 214-445-0200 *Web Site:* www.freemanco.com, pg 872

Andonov, Vlatko, Bethesda Softworks LLC, 1370 Piccard Dr, Suite 120, Rockville, MD 20850 *Tel:* 301-926-8300 *E-mail:* info@bethsoft.com *Web Site:* www.bethsoft.com, pg 806

Andrews, Craig, Beholder Productions Inc, 1515 Market St, Suite 1200, Philadelphia, PA 19102 *Toll Free Tel:* 844-BEHOLD-R (234-6537) *E-mail:* info@beholderproductions.com *Web Site:* www.beholderproductions.com, pg 804

Andrews, Emilia, Beholder Productions Inc, 1515 Market St, Suite 1200, Philadelphia, PA 19102 *Toll Free Tel:* 844-BEHOLD-R (234-6537) *E-mail:* info@beholderproductions.com *Web Site:* www.beholderproductions.com, pg 804

Andrews, Rev Eric, Paulist Productions, 17575 Pacific Coast Hwy, Pacific Palisades, CA 90272-4128 *Tel:* 310-454-0688 *Toll Free Tel:* 800-624-8613 *Fax:* 310-459-6549 *E-mail:* paulistmail@paulistproductions.org *Web Site:* www.paulistproductions.org, pg 970

Andrews, Fred G, Kansas City FilmFest, 4741 Central, Suite 306, Kansas City, MO 64112 *Tel:* 816-286-4777 *E-mail:* contact@jubilee.org *Web Site:* kcfilmfest.org, pg 1118

Andrle, Chuck, Out of the BLUE Media, 1413 Brenda Lane, Allen, TX 75002 *Tel:* 469-853-9015 *Web Site:* www.outofthebluemedia.com, pg 966

Angel, Fel, Creative Arts Film Festival (CAFF), PO Box 823, Frazer, PA 19355 *Tel:* 610-889-4928 *Web Site:* www.creativeartsfilmfestival.com, pg 1113

Angelich, Chris, AM Stock-Cameo Film Library, 1663 Sawtelle Blvd, Suite 305, Los Angeles, CA 90025 *Tel:* 310-479-4800 *Fax:* 310-933-6979 *E-mail:* researcher@amstockcameo.com *Web Site:* www.amstockcameo.com, pg 783

Anglim, Mike, American Playback Images, 27748 Caraway Lane, Santa Clarita, CA 91350 *Tel:* 818-427-8292 *Fax:* 661-263-2387 *E-mail:* americanplayback@aol.com, pg 785

Anglin, Tami, Sure Shot Transmissions Inc, 10314 Main St, New Middletown, OH 44442 *Tel:* 330-542-0900 *Fax:* 330-542-1020 *Web Site:* www.sureshotsat.com, pg 1029

Anguiano, Sonia, Castleview Productions, 1100 W 41 St, Austin, TX 78756 *Tel:* 512-442-9944 *Fax:* 512-442-8823 *E-mail:* contact@castleviewproductions.com *Web Site:* www.castleviewproductions.com, pg 821

Ankeny, James, Blue Earth Pictures, 5532 Code Ave, Minneapolis, MN 55436 *Tel:* 612-619-5909 *E-mail:* missioncontrol@blueearthpictures.com *Web Site:* www.blueearthpictures.com, pg 809

Annella, Chris, Joseph Electronics, 6633 W Howard St, Niles, IL 60714 *Tel:* 847-588-3800 *Toll Free Tel:* 800-323-5925 *Fax:* 847-588-3300 *Toll Free Fax:* 800-446-8366 *E-mail:* sales@josephelectronics.com *Web Site:* www.josephelectronics.com, pg 906

Anselmo, Rick, Tekskil Industries Inc, 102-998 Harbourside Dr, North Vancouver, BC V7P 3T2, Canada *Tel:* 604-985-2250 *Toll Free Tel:* 877-835-7545 *Toll Free Fax:* 877-576-8361 *E-mail:* tekskilprompters2012@tekskil.com *Web Site:* www.tekskil.com, pg 1035

Ansen, David, Los Angeles Film Festival, 9911 W Pico Blvd, Suite 1100, Los Angeles, CA 90035 *Toll Free Tel:* 866-345-6337 *E-mail:* lafilmfest@filmindependent.org *Web Site:* www.lafilmfest.com, pg 1119

Anthony, David, Giant Interactive, 88 Tenth Ave, Suite 6-W, New York, NY 10011 *Tel:* 212-675-7300 *Fax:* 212-765-9336 *E-mail:* info@giant-interactive.com *Web Site:* www.giant-interactive.com, pg 878

Anthony, Geoffrey, 24 Frames Film & Video, 15 Fourth Ave E, Vancouver, BC V5T 1E9, Canada *Tel:* 604-877-2299 *Fax:* 604-877-2298 *E-mail:* info@24frames.ca *Web Site:* www.24frames.ca, pg 1047

Anthony, Graham, August House Audio, 3500 Piedmont Rd NE, Suite 310, Atlanta, GA 30305 *Tel:* 404-442-4420 *Toll Free Tel:* 800-284-8784 *Fax:* 404-442-4435 *E-mail:* ahinfo@augusthouse.com *Web Site:* www.augusthouse.com, pg 796

Anthony, Josie A, Leucos USA Inc, 11 Mayfield Ave, Edison, NJ 08837 *Tel:* 732-225-0010 *Toll Free Tel:* 800-832-3360 *Fax:* 732-225-0250 *E-mail:* info@leucosusa.com *Web Site:* www.leucos.com, pg 919

Antl, Tom, Groovy Like a Movie, 5205 Kearny Villa Way, Suite 100, San Diego, CA 92123 *Tel:* 858-715-0300 *E-mail:* info@groovylikeamovie.com *Web Site:* www.groovylikeamovie.com, pg 882

Antonio, Sheril, Tisch School of the Arts, 721 Broadway, 10th & 11th fl, New York, NY 10003 *Tel:* 212-998-1700; 212-998-1780 *Fax:* 212-995-4063; 212-995-4062 *Web Site:* www.tisch.nyu.edu, pg 1041

Antrim, David, Antex Electronics Corp, 19160 Van Ness Ave, Torrance, CA 90501 *Tel:* 310-532-3092 *Toll Free Tel:* 800-338-4231 *Fax:* 310-532-8509 *E-mail:* ainfo@antex.com; asales@antex.com *Web Site:* www.antex.com, pg 787

Anweiler, Shaun, DR&A Inc, 45 Willow St, Nashville, TN 37210 *Tel:* 615-256-6200 *Fax:* 615-256-6236 *Web Site:* www.griptruck.com, pg 852

Anzalone, Robert, Location Sound Corp, 10639 Riverside Dr, North Hollywood, CA 91602 *Tel:* 818-980-9891 *Toll Free Tel:* 800-228-4429 *Fax:* 818-980-9911 *E-mail:* information@locationsound.com; salesdept@locationsound.com *Web Site:* www.locationsound.com, pg 924

Apel, Johan, ChyronHego Corp, 5 Hub Dr, Melville, NY 11747 *Tel:* 631-845-2000 *Fax:* 631-845-2058 *E-mail:* usa@chyronhego.com *Web Site:* www.chyronhego.com, pg 826

Apfelbaum, Marc Lawrence, Time Warner Cable, 60 Columbus Circle, 17th fl, New York, NY 10023 *Tel:* 212-364-8200 *Web Site:* www.timewarnercable.com, pg 1040

Apley, Alice, Documentary Educational Resources Inc, 101 Morse St, Watertown, MA 02472 *Tel:* 617-926-0491 *Toll Free Tel:* 800-569-6621 *Fax:* 617-926-9519 *E-mail:* docued@der.org *Web Site:* www.der.org, pg 850

Appelbaum, Moshie, Midwest Photo Exchange, 3313 N High St, Columbus, OH 43202 *Tel:* 614-261-1264 *Toll Free Tel:* 866-940-3686 *Fax:* 614-261-1637 *E-mail:* mpex@mpex.com; orders@mpex.com *Web Site:* mpex.com, pg 942

Appell, Richard, DVS InteleStream, 2600 W Olive Ave, Burbank, CA 91505 *Tel:* 818-566-4151 *Fax:* 818-566-4453 *E-mail:* info@dvs.tv *Web Site:* www.dvs.tv, pg 854

Appleman, Linda C, Dixie Theatre Service & Supply Co Inc, 311 N Washington, Albany, GA 31701 *Tel:* 229-435-4566 *E-mail:* dixietheatre@aol.com, pg 849

Appleson, Patrick G, Pat Appleson Studios Inc, 2359 Hwy 70 SE, Suite 102, Hickory, NC 28602 *Tel:* 828-994-4361; 828-461-3003 (cell) *Web Site:* www.appleson.com, pg 788

Apter, Monique, Zhone Technologies Inc, 7195 Oakport St, Oakland, CA 94621 *Tel:* 510-777-7000 *Toll Free Tel:* 877-ZHONE-20 (946-6320, US & CN) *Fax:* 510-777-7001 *E-mail:* info@zhone.com; sales@zhone.com *Web Site:* www.zhone.com, pg 1073

Arana, Benjamin, Arkon Resources Inc, 20 La Porte St, Arcadia, CA 91006 *Tel:* 626-254-9005 *Toll Free Tel:* 800-841-0884 *Fax:* 626-254-9266 *E-mail:* arkon5@arkon.com *Web Site:* www.arkon.com, pg 790

Araujo, Hilary, The Tiffen Co LLC, 90 Oser Ave, Hauppauge, NY 11788-3886 *Tel:* 631-273-2500 *Toll Free Tel:* 800-989-6013; 800-645-8500; 800-645-2522 *Fax:* 631-273-2557 *E-mail:* techsupport@tiffen.com *Web Site:* www.tiffen.com, pg 1040

Archambault, Karen, Montreal International Festival of Films on Art, 2130 Crescent St, Montreal, QC H3G 2B8, Canada *Tel:* 514-874-1637 *Fax:* 514-874-9929 *E-mail:* info@artfifa.com *Web Site:* www.artfifa.com, pg 1120

Archambault, Steven, International Datacasting, 50 Frank Nighbor Place, Kanata, ON K2V 1B9, Canada *Tel:* 613-596-4120 *Fax:* 613-596-4863 *E-mail:* marketing@datacast.com *Web Site:* www.datacast.com, pg 900

Archibald, Rachel, Meyer Sound Laboratories Inc, 2832 San Pablo Ave, Berkeley, CA 94702 *Tel:* 510-486-1166 *Toll Free Tel:* 855-641-3288 (US & CN) *Fax:* 510-486-8356 *E-mail:* sales@meyersound.com; techsupport@meyersound.com; service@meyersound.com *Web Site:* www.meyersound.com, pg 940

Arco, Joseph, Comtech Multimedia Marketing, 6048 Broadcast Pkwy, Loves Park, IL 61111 *Tel:* 779-774-3188 *Fax:* 779-423-0090 *E-mail:* info@comtechcorporation.com *Web Site:* www.comtechcorporation.com, pg 834

Arco, Susan, Comtech Multimedia Marketing, 6048 Broadcast Pkwy, Loves Park, IL 61111 *Tel:* 779-774-3188 *Fax:* 779-423-0090 *E-mail:* info@comtechcorporation.com *Web Site:* www.comtechcorporation.com, pg 834

Ardolino, Paul, Palardo Productions, 1807 Taft Ave, Suite 4, Hollywood, CA 90028 *Tel:* 323-469-8991 *E-mail:* palardo2@msn.com, pg 968

Ardolino, Tommy, Palardo Productions, 1807 Taft Ave, Suite 4, Hollywood, CA 90028 *Tel:* 323-469-8991 *E-mail:* palardo2@msn.com, pg 968

Arena, Joseph M, York Telecom, 81 Corbett Way, Eatontown, NJ 07724 *Tel:* 732-413-6000 *Toll Free Tel:* 866-836-8463 *Fax:* 732-413-6060 *E-mail:* knowmore@yorktel.com *Web Site:* yorktel.com, pg 1072

Argentine, Peter, Argentine Productions Inc, 603 Washington Rd, Suite 501, Pittsburgh, PA 15228 *Tel:* 412-341-6448 *E-mail:* info@argentineproductions.com *Web Site:* www.argentineproductions.com, pg 789

Argento, Anthony, Rollin Studios, 199 Green St, Brooklyn, NY 11222 *E-mail:* more@rollin-studios.com *Web Site:* www.rollin-studios.com, pg 998

Argomaniz, Fidel, Silvestri California, 8125 Beach St, Los Angeles, CA 90001 *Tel:* 323-277-4420 *Toll Free Tel:* 800-647-8874 *Fax:* 323-585-0861 *E-mail:* info@silvestricalifornia.com *Web Site:* www.silvestricalifornia.com, pg 1011

Argyris, Phil, GatesAir, 5300 Kings Island Dr, Suite 101, Mason, OH 45040 *Tel:* 513-459-3400 *Fax:* 513-459-3796 *E-mail:* information@gatesair.com; orders@gatesair.com; support@gatesair.com *Web Site:* www.gatesair.com, pg 875

Arias, Washington, Everlast Productions, 59 SW 12 Ave, Unit 109, Dania Beach, FL 33004 *Tel:* 954-456-7167 *Fax:* 954-456-1243 *E-mail:* info@everlastproductions.com *Web Site:* everlastproductions.com, pg 863

Ariosa, John, Sheffield Audio/Video Productions, 13816 Sunnybrook Rd, Phoenix, MD 21131 *Tel:* 410-628-7260 *Toll Free Tel:* 800-355-6613 *Fax:* 410-628-1977 *E-mail:* info@sheffieldav.com *Web Site:* www.sheffieldav.com/production, pg 1008

Arkin, Robert, Holo-Spectra Inc, 7742B Gloria Ave, Van Nuys, CA 91406 *Tel:* 818-994-9577 *Fax:* 818-994-4709 *E-mail:* info@lasershs.com *Web Site:* www.lasershs.com, pg 890

Arkin, William, Holo-Spectra Inc, 7742B Gloria Ave, Van Nuys, CA 91406 *Tel:* 818-994-9577 *Fax:* 818-994-4709 *E-mail:* info@lasershs.com *Web Site:* www.lasershs.com, pg 890

Arking, Paul, GLI Sound Systems, 2691 W 15 St, Brooklyn, NY 11224 *Tel:* 718-372-7849 *Toll Free Tel:* 800-GLI-PRO-1 (454-7761) *Fax:* 718-946-4151 *E-mail:* info@glipro.com; sales@glipro.com *Web Site:* www.glipro.com, pg 878

Arlyck, Ralph, Timed Exposures Films, 122 Old Rd, Germantown, NY 12526-6014 *Tel:* 518-537-2012 *E-mail:* info@timedexposures.com *Web Site:* www.timedexposures.com, pg 1040

Armer, Tony, St Petersburg/Clearwater Film Commission, 8200 Bryan Dairy Rd, Suite 200, Largo, FL 33777 *Tel:* 727-464-7241 *Toll Free Tel:* 877-352-3224 *E-mail:* info@filmspc.com *Web Site:* www.filmspc.com, pg 1096

Armistead, John, DME Studios, 1025 Greenwood Blvd, Suite 191, Lake Mary, FL 32746 *Tel:* 407-585-7500 *E-mail:* creativeteam@dmestudios.com *Web Site:* www.dmestudios.com, pg 849

Armon, Norma, International Contact Inc, 351 15 St, Oakland, CA 94612 *Tel:* 510-836-1180 *Toll Free Tel:* 800-430-7705 *Fax:* 510-835-1314 *E-mail:* info@intlcontact.com *Web Site:* www.intlcontact.com, pg 900

Armour, Ronda, Capital Communications Inc, 2357-3, S Tamiami Trail, Venice, FL 34293 *Tel:* 941-539-6741 *E-mail:* cap5678@isp.com, pg 819

Arms, Diane, Arms Communications, 1517 Maurice Dr, Woodbridge, VA 22191 *Tel:* 703-690-3338 *Fax:* 703-490-3810 (call first) *E-mail:* info@armscomm.com *Web Site:* www.armscomm.com, pg 790

Armstrong, David, Covenant Productions®, c/o Anderson University, 1100 E Fifth St, Anderson, IN 46012 *Tel:* 765-641-4348 *Fax:* 765-641-3825 *Web Site:* www.covenantproductions.com, pg 837

Armstrong, Doug, KTVB-TV, 5407 Fairview Ave, Boise, ID 83706 *Tel:* 208-375-7277 *Toll Free Tel:* 800-559-7277 *Fax:* 208-378-1762; 208-375-7770 (news fax) *E-mail:* info@ktvb.com; ktvbnews@ktvb.com *Web Site:* www.ktvb.com, pg 914

Armstrong, Lee, Images in Motion Media Inc, 720 Ladera Dr, Sonoma, CA 95476 *Tel:* 707-996-9474 *E-mail:* images@vom.com *Web Site:* www.imagesmedia.com, pg 896

Armstrong, Tina, Medcom Inc, 6060 Phyllis Dr, Cypress, CA 90630-5243 *Tel:* 714-891-1443 *Toll Free Tel:* 800-877-1443; 800-541-0253 *Fax:* 714-891-3140 *E-mail:* customerservice@medcominc.com *Web Site:* www.medcominc.com, pg 936

Arnero, Carlos, NSM Surveillance, 2709 Via Orange Way, Suite B, Spring Valley, CA 91978 *Tel:* 619-670-0616 *Fax:* 619-670-7040 *E-mail:* sales@nsmsurveillance.com *Web Site:* www.nsmsurveillance.com, pg 960

Arnold, Andrea, Zebedee Productions, 231 SW Fifth Ct, Pompano Beach, FL 33060 *Tel:* 954-942-0044 *E-mail:* info@zbd.us *Web Site:* zebedeeproductions.com, pg 1073

Arnold, Clara, TVO/Ontario Educational Communications Authority (OECA), 2180 Yonge St, Toronto, ON M4S 2B9, Canada *Tel:* 416-484-2600; 416-484-2665 (cust rel) *Toll Free Tel:* 800-613-0513; 800-INFO-TVO (463-6886) *E-mail:* asktvo@tvo.org *Web Site:* tvo.org, pg 1046

Arnold, Dawn, Production Craft Inc, 1437 W Grand Ave, Chicago, IL 60642-6332 *Tel:* 312-829-0272 *Fax:* 312-829-8936 *E-mail:* info@productioncraft.com *Web Site:* www.productioncraft.com, pg 984

Arnold, Lori, J Arnold Productions Inc, 147 Cove Creek Rd, Mooresville, NC 28117-8910 *Tel:* 704-663-4444 *Web Site:* www.jarnoldproductions.com, pg 790

Arnold, Nick, Denver Media Center, 3853 S Broadway, Englewood, CO 80113 *Tel:* 303-872-9993 *Web Site:* denvermediacenter.com, pg 845

Arnold, Sandy, Zebedee Productions, 231 SW Fifth Ct, Pompano Beach, FL 33060 *Tel:* 954-942-0044 *E-mail:* info@zbd.us *Web Site:* zebedeeproductions.com, pg 1073

Arocho, Hector, Astoria Communications Inc, 12054 Miramar Pkwy, Miami, FL 33025 *Tel:* 305-728-4280 *Toll Free Tel:* 877-GETMEAV (438-6328) *Fax:* 305-728-4285 *Web Site:* www.getmeav.com, pg 792

Aron, Dan, No Soap Productions, 936 Broadway, 4th fl, New York, NY 10010 *Tel:* 212-581-5572 *Fax:* 212-586-0045 *Web Site:* www.nosoap.net, pg 958

Arp, Fredrik, Qioptiq, 78 Shuyler Baldwin, Fairport, NY 14450 *Tel:* 585-223-2370 *Toll Free Tel:* 800-429-0257 *Fax:* 585-223-1999 *E-mail:* info@qioptiqlinos.com *Web Site:* www.qioptiqlinos.com, pg 988

Arraj, Tyra, Inner Explorations, PO Box 37, Midland, OR 97634-0037 *Tel:* 541-851-1534 *Web Site:* www.innerexplorations.com, pg 898

Arrington, Janice, Orange County Film Commission, 800 N State College Blvd, MH 133, Fullerton, CA 92834-6850 *Tel:* 657-278-7569 *Fax:* 657-278-7521 *Web Site:* www.filmorangecounty.org, pg 1092

Arsenault, Chill, Concept Audio-Visual, 4295 rue d'Iberville, Montreal, QC H2H 2L5, Canada *Tel:* 514-954-0000 *Toll Free Tel:* 800-567-7076 (CN only) *Fax:* 514-954-1425 *E-mail:* info@conceptav.ca *Web Site:* www.conceptav.ca, pg 834

Arsenault, Jessica, Inner Traditions International, One Park St, Rochester, VT 05767 *Tel:* 802-767-3174 *Toll Free Tel:* 800-246-8648 *Fax:* 802-767-3726 *E-mail:* customerservice@innertraditions.com *Web Site:* www.innertraditions.com, pg 898

Arsenault, Vanessa, Concept Audio-Visual, 4295 rue d'Iberville, Montreal, QC H2H 2L5, Canada *Tel:* 514-954-0000 *Toll Free Tel:* 800-567-7076 (CN only) *Fax:* 514-954-1425 *E-mail:* info@conceptav.ca *Web Site:* www.conceptav.ca, pg 834

Arth, Violet, Real to Reel International Film Festival, 111 S Washington St, Shelby, NC 28150 *Tel:* 704-484-2787 *Fax:* 704-481-1822 *E-mail:* info@ccartscouncil.org *Web Site:* www.ccartscouncil.org/realtoreel, pg 1124

Arthur, Michael, Beekman Books Inc, 300 Old All Angels Hill Rd, Wappingers Falls, NY 12590 *Tel:* 845-297-2690 *Fax:* 845-297-1002 *E-mail:* manager@beekmanbooks.com *Web Site:* www.beekmanbooks.com, pg 804

Arthur, Ray, Fresno Film Commission, 5241 E Townsend Ave, Fresno, CA 93727 *Tel:* 559-908-0539 *Fax:* 559-354-5980 *E-mail:* fresnofilm@gmail.com *Web Site:* www.fresnofilm.com, pg 1092

Aruta, Rose, DC Asian Pacific American Film Festival, 2515 Virginia Ave NW, No 58205, Washington, DC 20037 *Tel:* 703-507-4375 *E-mail:* info@apafilm.org; admin@apafilm.org *Web Site:* www.apafilm.org, pg 1113

Arvidson, Wayne P, ATTO Technology Inc, 155 CrossPoint Pkwy, Amherst, NY 14068 *Tel:* 716-691-1999 *Fax:* 716-691-9353 *Web Site:* www.attotech.com, pg 793

Asadorian, Alan, Dorian Color, 24 Mill St, Arlington, MA 02476 *Tel:* 781-648-8040 *Fax:* 781-641-1231 *E-mail:* images@dorianlabcolor.com (gallery) *Web Site:* www.doriancolor.com, pg 851

Asbury, Kenneth, CACI Productions Group, 14370 Newbrook Dr, Chantilly, VA 20151 *Tel:* 703-679-3100 *Web Site:* www.caci.com, pg 816

Ascanio, Lucille, East of Hollywood NY, 140 53 St, Brooklyn, NY 11232 *Tel:* 718-492-7400 *Fax:* 718-439-3930 *E-mail:* info@eastofhollywoodny.com *Web Site:* www.eastofhollywoodny.com, pg 855

Ash, Jeff, Welocalize, 241 E Fourth St, Suite 207, Frederick, MD 21701 *Tel:* 301-668-0330 *Toll Free Tel:* 800-370-9515 *Fax:* 301-668-0335 *E-mail:* info@welocalize.com *Web Site:* www.welocalize.com, pg 1063

Ash, Richard, Folkcraft Instruments, 22133 Main St, Woodburn, IN 46797 *Tel:* 317-522-1635 *Toll Free Tel:* 800-433-3655 *Fax:* 317-245-2378 *E-mail:* sales@folkcraft.com *Web Site:* www.folkcraft.com; www.richardash.com, pg 871

Ashbaugh, Scott, OmniMount Systems, 4409 E Baseline Rd, Suite 130, Phoenix, AZ 85042 *Tel:* 480-829-8000 *Toll Free Tel:* 800-MOUNT-IT (668-6848) *Fax:* 480-756-9000 *E-mail:* info@omnimount.com *Web Site:* www.omnimount.com, pg 962

Asher, Howard, Stray Angel Films, 2236 S Barrington Ave, Los Angeles, CA 90064 *Tel:* 310-277-6900 *Fax:* 801-438-5009 *E-mail:* rentals@strayangel.com *Web Site:* www.strayangel.com, pg 1026

Asher, Timothy, Idle Minds Productions Inc, 3405 Pepperhill Rd, Lexington, KY 40502 *Tel:* 859-268-8500 *Fax:* 859-268-8500 *E-mail:* idleminds@twc.com, pg 894

Ashram, Satchidananda, Shakticom, 108 Yogaville Way, Buckingham, VA 23921 *Tel:* 434-969-1347 *Toll Free Tel:* 800-476-1347 (orders) *E-mail:* shop@shakticom.org *Web Site:* www.shakticom.org, pg 1008

Ashton, David, Cinram Inc, 2255 Markham Rd, Scarborough, ON M1B 2W3, Canada *Tel:* 416-298-8190 *Fax:* 416-298-0612 *E-mail:* sales@cinram.com *Web Site:* www.cinramgroup.com, pg 828

Ashton, Jonathan, Agfa Graphics, 611 River Dr, Ctr 3, Elmwood Park, NJ 07407 *Tel:* 201-440-2500 *Toll Free Tel:* 800-540-2432 *Web Site:* www.agfagraphics.com; www.agfa.com, pg 778

Aslan, Ines, Havana Film Festival New York (HFFNY), 4 W 43 St, Suite 304, New York, NY 10036 *Tel:* 212-687-2146 *Fax:* 212-681-8037 *E-mail:* info@hffny.com; info@aflfc.org *Web Site:* www.hffny.com, pg 1116

Astor, Eric, Furnace MFG, 2719-B Dorr Ave, Fairfax, VA 22031 *Tel:* 703-205-0007 *Toll Free Tel:* 888-599-9883 *Fax:* 703-205-2951 *E-mail:* sales@furnacemfg.com *Web Site:* www.furnacemfg.com, pg 874

Atamanenko, Boris, NWT Arts Council, Box 1320, Govt NW Territories, Yellowknife, NT X1A 2L9, Canada *Tel:* 867-920-6370 *Fax:* 867-873-0205 *Web Site:* www.pwnhc.ca; www.pwnhc.ca/artscouncil, pg 1123

Atherton, Jay, Freeman, 1600 Viceroy, Suite 100, Dallas, TX 75235 *Tel:* 214-445-1000 *Fax:* 214-445-0200 *Web Site:* www.freemanco.com, pg 872

Atkin, Michael, Broadview Software Inc, 110 Adelaide St E, Toronto, ON M5C 1K9, Canada *Tel:* 416-778-0623 *Fax:* 416-778-0648 *E-mail:* sales@broadviewsoftware.com *Web Site:* www.broadviewsoftware.com, pg 813

Atkins, Michele, Kaboom Productions, 1465 Illinois St, San Francisco, CA 94107 *Tel:* 415-434-2666 *Fax:* 415-970-8548 *E-mail:* updates@kaboomproductions.com *Web Site:* kaboomproductions.com, pg 907

Atkins, Ricky, Communications Media Management Association (CMMA), c/o The Association Source LLC, 20423 State Rd 7, Suite F6-491, Boca Raton, FL 33498 *Tel:* 561-477-8100 *Web Site:* www.cmma.org, pg 1080

Atkinson, Dennis, Encore Home Video, PO Box 25, Frankenmuth, MI 48734-0025 *Tel:* 989-652-9699 *E-mail:* sales@encorehomevideo.com *Web Site:* www.encorehomevideo.com, pg 861

Atkinson, Jason, University Media Services, University of Delaware, 85 E Delaware Ave, Newark, DE 19716 *Tel:* 302-831-3546; 302-831-3557 *Fax:* 302-831-3642 *Web Site:* www.ums.udel.edu; www.udel.edu/ums, pg 1049

Atkinson, Kelly, Transistor Devices Inc, 36 Newburgh Rd, Hackettstown, NJ 07840 *Tel:* 908-850-5088 *Fax:* 908-850-1607 *E-mail:* info@tdipower.com *Web Site:* www.tdipower.com, pg 1043

Atwood, John, The Intellications Co, 1110 Northshore Dr, Roswell, GA 30076-2812 *Tel:* 678-643-8468 *Web Site:* www.johnatwood.com, pg 899

Auclair, James, WGBH Stock Sales, One Guest St, Boston, MA 02135 *Tel:* 617-300-3939 *Fax:* 617-300-1056 *E-mail:* stock_sales@wgbh.org *Web Site:* www.wgbhstocksales.org, pg 1065

Auerbach, Abby, Television Bureau of Advertising Inc (TVB), 120 Wall St, 15th fl, New York, NY 10005-3908 *Tel:* 212-486-1111 *Fax:* 212-935-5631 *E-mail:* info@tvb.org *Web Site:* www.tvb.org, pg 1090

Auerbach, Richard, Z-Systems Audio Engineering, 1325 NW 53 Ave, Suite B, Gainesville, FL 32609 *Tel:* 352-371-0990 *E-mail:* z-sys@z-sys.com *Web Site:* www.z-sys.com, pg 1073

Auernheimer, C Curly, ALC (Auernheimer Labs & Co), 4561 E Florence Ave, Fresno, CA 93725 *Tel:* 559-442-1048, pg 780

Auffret, Laurent, French American Cultural Exchange (FACE), 972 Fifth Ave, New York, NY 10021 *Tel:* 212-439-1449 *Fax:* 212-439-1455 *E-mail:* info@facecouncil.org *Web Site:* www.facecouncil.org, pg 873

Aug, Mike, Event Tech, 7601 Brandon Woods Blvd, Baltimore, MD 21226 *Tel:* 410-360-5006 *Toll Free Tel:* 866-950-8343 *Fax:* 410-360-5002 *E-mail:* info@eventtech.com *Web Site:* www.eventtech.com, pg 863

Auger, Chris, White Rain Films Ltd, 2009 Dexter Ave N, Seattle, WA 98109 *Tel:* 206-682-5417 *Toll Free Tel:* 800-816-5244 *Fax:* 206-682-3038 *E-mail:* info@whiterainfilms.com *Web Site:* www.whiterainfilms.com, pg 1065

Augustine, Jackie, Photoimaging Manufacturers & Distributors Association Inc, 7600 Jericho Tpke, Suite 301, Woodbury, NY 11797 *Tel:* 516-802-0895 *Fax:* 516-364-0140 *Web Site:* www.pmda.com, pg 1087

Augustine-Pierce, Gregory F, ACTA Publications, 4848 N Clark St, Chicago, IL 60640 *Tel:* 773-271-1030 *Toll Free Tel:* 800-397-2282 *Fax:* 773-271-7399 *Toll Free Fax:* 800-397-0079 *Web Site:* www.actapublications.com, pg 775

Augusto, Carl R, American Foundation for the Blind (AFB), 2 Penn Plaza, Suite 1102, New York, NY 10121 *Tel:* 212-502-7600; 212-502-7662 (TDD) *Toll Free Tel:* 800-232-5463 *Fax:* 212-502-7777 *Toll Free Fax:* 888-545-8331 *E-mail:* afbinfo@afb.net *Web Site:* www.afb.org, pg 1076

Aukerman, Gregg, Visioneering International Inc, 659 Auburn Ave NE, Suite 267, Atlanta, GA 30312 *Tel:* 404-681-9028 *Fax:* 404-681-5947 *E-mail:* design@visioneering.com *Web Site:* www.visioneering.com, pg 1058

Aurichio, Jeffrey, Agfa Graphics, 611 River Dr, Ctr 3, Elmwood Park, NJ 07407 *Tel:* 201-440-2500 *Toll Free Tel:* 800-540-2432 *Web Site:* www.agfagraphics.com; www.agfa.com, pg 778

Auslender, Leland, Auslender Productions/Celestial Images, 6036 Comey Ave, Los Angeles, CA 90034-2204 *Tel:* 323-931-3277 *Fax:* 323-937-1720 *Web Site:* celestial-images.net; auslender.com, pg 797

Austin, Howard, Music World/Vocal Power School, 9826 Columbus Ave, North Hills, CA 91343 *Tel:* 818-895-7464 *Toll Free Tel:* 800-929-7464 *E-mail:* MusicMan@music-world.com *Web Site:* www.BornToSing.com, pg 951

Austin, James W, Parallax Productions Inc, 1711 Longwood Rd, Suite B, Haverhill, FL 33409 *Tel:* 561-842-7788 *Toll Free Tel:* 844-892-9289 *Fax:* 561-842-4566 *E-mail:* parllaxpro@aol.com *Web Site:* www.parallaxvideoproductions.com, pg 969

Austman, Eric, Tek Gear, 938 Corydon Ave, Winnipeg, MB R3M 0Y5, Canada *Tel:* 204-988-3001 *Fax:* 204-988-3050 *E-mail:* sales@tekgear.com *Web Site:* tekgear.com, pg 1035

AuYeung, PoChu, Vancouver International Film Festival, Vancouver International Film Centre, 1181 Seymour St, Vancouver, BC V6B 3M7, Canada *Tel:* 604-685-0260 *Fax:* 604-688-8221 *E-mail:* viff@viff.org *Web Site:* www.viff.org, pg 1129

Avanzino, Angela, Jameco Electronics, 1355 Shoreway Rd, Belmont, CA 94002-4105 *Tel:* 650-592-8097 *Toll Free Tel:* 800-831-4242 (orders); 800-536-4316 (cust serv) *Fax:* 650-592-2503 *Toll Free Fax:* 800-237-6948 *E-mail:* info@jameco.com; sales@jameco.com *Web Site:* www.jameco.com, pg 904

Avgerakis, George, Avekta Productions Inc, One Rock Place, Yonkers, NY 10705 *Tel:* 914-378-8000 *Web Site:* avekta.com, pg 798

Avgerakis, Maria, Avekta Productions Inc, One Rock Place, Yonkers, NY 10705 *Tel:* 914-378-8000 *Web Site:* avekta.com, pg 798

Avigkos, David, Digimation, 250 International Pkwy, Suite 320, Lake Mary, FL 32746 *Tel:* 407-833-0600 *Toll Free Tel:* 800-854-4496 *Fax:* 813-283-4906 *E-mail:* sales@digimation.com *Web Site:* www.digimation.com, pg 847

Awad, Dennis, Zack Electronics Inc, 1075 Hamilton Rd, Duarte, CA 91010 *Tel:* 626-303-0655 *Toll Free Tel:* 800-466-0449 *Fax:* 626-303-8694 *E-mail:* info@zackelectronics.com *Web Site:* www.zackelectronics.com, pg 1073

Axelrod, Dr Norman N, Norman N Axelrod Associates, 445 E 86 St, New York, NY 10028 *Tel:* 212-741-6302 *E-mail:* naxelrod@axelrodassociates.com *Web Site:* www.axelrodassociates.com, pg 800

Ayers, Cliff, Cliff Ayers Enterprises, American Big Band Hall of Fame, 608 SW 75 Terr, North Lauderdale, FL 33068 *Tel:* 615-361-7902 *Fax:* 615-336-2480 *E-mail:* info@entertainernet.net *Web Site:* www.entertainernet.net, pg 801

Ayers, Cliff, Emerald Records, PO Box 17059, Nashville, TN 37217-0059 *Tel:* 615-361-7902 *E-mail:* entertainernet@comcast.net *Web Site:* www.entertainernet.net, pg 860

Ayoob, Ameen, Indus International Inc, 340 S Oak St, West Salem, WI 54669 *Tel:* 608-786-0300 *Toll Free Tel:* 800-843-9377 *Fax:* 608-786-0786 *E-mail:* info@indususa.com *Web Site:* www.indususa.com, pg 897

Ayoub, Paul, Digital Video Productions, 257 Federal Rd, Brookfield, CT 06804 *Tel:* 203-743-7663 *Fax:* 203-743-1658 *E-mail:* info@dvpllc.com *Web Site:* www.dvpllc.com, pg 848

Ayscough, Suzan, Canadian Screen Awards, 49 Ontario St, Suite 501, Toronto, ON M5A 2V1, Canada *Tel:* 416-366-2227 *Toll Free Tel:* 800-644-5194 *Fax:* 416-366-8454 *E-mail:* academie@acct.ca *Web Site:* www.acct.ca/prixgemeaux; www.academy.ca/awards, pg 1111

Azevedo, Luke, City of Calgary Film Commission, 731 First St SE, Calgary, AB T2G 2G9, Canada *Tel:* 403-221-7831 *Toll Free Tel:* 888-222-5855 *Fax:* 403-221-7828 *Web Site:* www.calgaryeconomicdevelopment.com, pg 1104

Azize, Hamid, Stage Crew Audiovisual Inc, PO Box 6097, San Juan, PR 00914-6097 *Tel:* 787-723-6398 *Fax:* 787-721-1410 *E-mail:* scav@stagecrewav.com *Web Site:* www.stagecrewav.com, pg 1022

Azorsky, Greg, Audio-VideoGraphics Inc, 17501 E 40 Hwy, Suite 219, Independence, MO 64055 *Tel:* 816-350-0800 *Toll Free Tel:* 800-322-2832 *Fax:* 816-350-0804 *E-mail:* mail@avginc.com *Web Site:* www.avginc.com, pg 795

Azua, Dawn, The Videohouse Inc, 975 Greentree Rd, Pittsburgh, PA 15220 *Tel:* 412-921-7577 *Fax:* 412-921-5535 *E-mail:* tvirjb@aol.com *Web Site:* www.thevideohouse.com, pg 1057

Azure, Andrew, Alpha Technologies, 3767 Alpha Way, Bellingham, WA 98226 *Tel:* 360-647-2360 *Fax:* 360-671-4936 *E-mail:* alpha@alpha.com *Web Site:* www.alpha.com, pg 782

B, Stevie, Mia Mind Music, 254 Sixth St, Suite 2, Hoboken, NJ 07030-6916 *Toll Free Tel:* 800-843-8575 *Fax:* 201-216-1186 *E-mail:* mimimus@aol.com *Web Site:* www.miamindmusic.com, pg 941

Baade, Andy, Tempe Tape & Disc, 2737 W Baseline Rd, Suite 21, Tempe, AZ 85283 *Tel:* 602-453-9663 *Web Site:* www.tempetape.com, pg 1037

Babb, Paul, MAXON Computer Inc, 2640 Lavery Ct, Suite A, Newbury Park, CA 91320 *Tel:* 805-376-3333 *Fax:* 805-376-3331 *E-mail:* info_us@maxon.net *Web Site:* www.maxon.net, pg 934

Babin, Denise, PSB Speakers International, 633 Granite Ct, Pickering, ON L1W 3K1, Canada *Tel:* 905-831-6555 *Toll Free Tel:* 800-263-4641 (cust serv) *Fax:* 905-837-6357 *E-mail:* info@psbspeakers.com *Web Site:* www.psbspeakers.com, pg 987

Babu, Ayuko, Pan African Film & Arts Festival, 6820 La Tijera Blvd, Suite 200, Los Angeles, CA 90045 *Tel:* 310-337-4737 *Fax:* 310-337-4736 *E-mail:* info@paff.org *Web Site:* www.paff.org, pg 1123

Baca, Kathy, Lectrosonics Inc, 581 Laser Rd NE, Rio Rancho, NM 87124 *Tel:* 505-892-4501 *Toll Free Tel:* 800-821-1121 *Fax:* 505-892-6243 *E-mail:* sales@lectrosonics.com *Web Site:* www.lectrosonics.com, pg 918

Bacarella, Mary, Golden Space Needle Awards, 305 Harrison St, Seattle, WA 98109 *Tel:* 206-464-5830 *Fax:* 206-264-7919 *E-mail:* info@siff.net *Web Site:* www.siff.net, pg 1116

Bacarella, Mary, Seattle International Film Festival (SIFF), 305 Harrison St, Seattle, WA 98109 *Tel:* 206-464-5830 *Fax:* 206-264-7919 *E-mail:* info@siff.net *Web Site:* www.siff.net, pg 1127

Bachmann, Bill, Bill Bachmann Studios, PO Box 950833, Lake Mary, FL 32795 *Tel:* 407-333-9988 *Web Site:* www.billbachmann.com, pg 807

Back, Tara, Jack Morton Worldwide, 909 Third Ave, New York, NY 10022 *Tel:* 212-401-7000 *E-mail:* experience@jackmorton.com *Web Site:* www.jackmorton.com, pg 946

Backus, Don, ENCO Systems Inc, 29444 Northwestern Hwy, Southfield, MI 48034 *Tel:* 248-827-4440 *Toll Free Tel:* 800-362-6797 (sales) *Fax:* 248-827-4441 *E-mail:* sales@enco.com *Web Site:* www.enco.com, pg 860

Bacon, Paul, KABA Audio Productions, PO Box 5357, Petaluma, CA 94955 *Tel:* 707-765-9900 *E-mail:* info@kabaaudio.com *Web Site:* www.kabaaudio.com, pg 907

Baczkowski, Antoinette, Gordon Visual Solutions, 504 Reiman St, Buffalo, NY 14212-2250 *Tel:* 716-894-5930 *Fax:* 630-839-5930 *E-mail:* info@gordonvisualsolutions.com; service@gordonvisualsolutions.com *Web Site:* www.gordonvisualsolutions.com, pg 880

Badagliacca, Mark, Paramount Pictures Corporation, 5555 Melrose Ave, Los Angeles, CA 90038 *Tel:* 323-956-8398 *Web Site:* www.paramount.com, pg 969

Badeaux, Floyd J, Great Recordings LLC, 1812 Procter St, Port Arthur, TX 77640 *Tel:* 409-982-7121 *Fax:* 409-982-0643 *E-mail:* music@great-recordings.com *Web Site:* www.great-recordings.com, pg 881

Bader, Carl, Aviom Inc, 1157 Phoenixville Pike, Suite 201, West Chester, PA 19380-4254 *Tel:* 610-738-9005 *Fax:* 610-738-9950 *E-mail:* info@aviom.com *Web Site:* www.aviom.com, pg 799

Bader, Jamie, NDS Surgical Imaging LLC, 5750 Hellyer Ave, San Jose, CA 95138 *Tel:* 408-776-0085 *Toll Free Tel:* 866-637-5237 *Fax:* 408-776-9878 *E-mail:* info@ndssi.com *Web Site:* www.ndssi.com, pg 954

Badiyan, Fred, Badiyan Inc, 720 W 94 St, Bloomington, MN 55420 *Tel:* 952-888-5507 *Fax:* 952-888-0360 *E-mail:* info@badiyan.com *Web Site:* www.badiyan.com, pg 801

Badke, John, Vicon Industries Inc, 131 Heartland Blvd, Edgewood, NY 11717 *Tel:* 631-952-2288 *Toll Free Tel:* 800-645-9116 *Fax:* 631-951-2288 *Web Site:* www.vicon-security.com, pg 1053

Bagerdjian, Haig, Point 360, 2701 Media Center Dr, Los Angeles, CA 90065 *Tel:* 818-565-1400 *Fax:* 818-847-2503 *E-mail:* sales-point360@point360.com *Web Site:* www.point360.com, pg 978

Bagley, Dave, Penn State University MediaTech, 14 Wagner Annex, State College, PA 16803-1886 *Tel:* 814-865-6314; 814-863-3202 *Toll Free Tel:* 800-826-0132 *Fax:* 814-863-2574 *E-mail:* mtssmed@psulias.psu.edu *Web Site:* www.libraries.psu.edu/mtss; www.medianet.libraries.psu.edu, pg 972

Bagley, Pierre, District of Columbia Office of Motion Picture & TV Development, 200 "I" St SE, Suite 1800, Washington, DC 20003 *Tel:* 202-727-6608 *Fax:* 202-727-3246 *E-mail:* film@dc.gov *Web Site:* www.film.dc.gov, pg 1095

Bailey, Brena, San Mateo County Film Commission, Seabreeze Plaza, Suite 410, 111 Anza Blvd, Burlingame, CA 94010 *Tel:* 650-348-7600 *Fax:* 650-348-7687 *E-mail:* info@filmsanmateocounty.com *Web Site:* www.sanmateocountycvb.com, pg 1092

Bailey, Carole, WQED-Multimedia, 4802 Fifth Ave, Pittsburgh, PA 15213 *Tel:* 412-622-1300; 412-622-1370 *Fax:* 412-622-1488 *E-mail:* wqed@wqed.org *Web Site:* www.wqed.org, pg 1070

Bailey, Debbie, The Food & Beverage Institute, 1946 Campus Dr, Hyde Park, NY 12538-1499 *Tel:* 845-905-4417 *Toll Free Tel:* 800-888-7850 *Fax:* 845-451-1078 *E-mail:* ciaprochef@culinary.edu *Web Site:* www.ciachef.edu; www.ciaprochef.com, pg 871

Bailey, Eric, Dorian Color, 24 Mill St, Arlington, MA 02476 *Tel:* 781-648-8040 *Fax:* 781-641-1231 *E-mail:* images@dorianlabcolor.com (gallery) *Web Site:* www.doriancolor.com, pg 851

Bailey, Glenda, Camcor Inc, 2273 S Church St, Burlington, NC 27215 *Tel:* 336-228-0251 *Toll Free Tel:* 800-868-2462 *Fax:* 336-222-8011 *Toll Free Fax:* 800-298-1181 *E-mail:* info@camcor.com *Web Site:* www.camcor.com, pg 818

Bailey, Ray E Sr, Camcor Inc, 2273 S Church St, Burlington, NC 27215 *Tel:* 336-228-0251 *Toll Free Tel:* 800-868-2462 *Fax:* 336-222-8011 *Toll Free Fax:* 800-298-1181 *E-mail:* info@camcor.com *Web Site:* www.camcor.com, pg 818

Bailey, Steven, University of Toronto Academic & Campus Events, St George Campus, McMurrich Bldg, 4th fl, 12 Queen's Park Crescent W, Toronto, ON M5S 1S8, Canada *Tel:* 416-978-2187; 416-978-8613 (film & photo shoot permits) *Fax:* 416-978-4802 *E-mail:* ace.team@utoronto.ca *Web Site:* www.ace.utoronto.ca, pg 1105

Bailey, Steven A Sr, Lloyd F McKinney Associates Inc, 25350 Cypress Ave, Hayward, CA 94544 *Tel:* 510-783-8043 *Fax:* 510-783-2130 *Web Site:* www.mckinneyassoc.com, pg 935

Bailin, Robert, Feature Systems Inc, 223 Veterans Blvd, Carlstadt, NJ 07072 *Tel:* 201-531-2299; 212-736-0447 *Fax:* 201-531-2290; 212-465-1987 *Web Site:* www.featuresystems.com, pg 866

Bakala, Joe, Warner Home Video Inc, 4000 Warner Blvd, Bldg 160, Burbank, CA 91522 *Tel:* 818-954-6000 *Fax:* 818-954-6480 *Web Site:* www.warnerbros.com, pg 1062

Baker, Aaron J, AGF Media Services, 14932 Delano St, Van Nuys, CA 91411-2122 *Tel:* 818-780-7400; 818-780-8085 (24 hours) *Fax:* 818-904-9905 *E-mail:* info@agfmedia.com *Web Site:* www.agfmedia.com, pg 778

Baker, Brandon, C&I Studios, 541 NW First Ave, Fort Lauderdale, FL 33301 *Tel:* 954-357-3934 *E-mail:* contact@c-istudios.com *Web Site:* www.c-istudios.com, pg 819

Baker, Brian, Sound Arts Recording Studio, 8377 Westview Dr, Houston, TX 77055-5737 *Tel:* 713-464-4653 *Web Site:* www.soundartsrecording.com, pg 1017

Baker, Carolyn C, American Counseling Association, 6101 Stevenson Ave, Alexandria, VA 22304 *Tel:* 703-823-9800 (ext 222) *Toll Free Tel:* 800-422-2648 (ext 222) *Fax:* 703-370-4833 *Toll Free Fax:* 800-473-2329 *E-mail:* membership@counseling.org *Web Site:* www.counseling.org, pg 784

Baker, Dave, Go To Team, 359-C Wando Place Dr, Mount Pleasant, SC 29464 *Tel:* 843-884-6222 *Toll Free Tel:* 888-455-4333 *E-mail:* crew@gototeam.com *Web Site:* www.gototeam.com, pg 879

Baker, Jeffrey, AGF Media Services, 14932 Delano St, Van Nuys, CA 91411-2122 *Tel:* 818-780-7400; 818-780-8085 (24 hours) *Fax:* 818-904-9905 *E-mail:* info@agfmedia.com *Web Site:* www.agfmedia.com, pg 778

Baker, Jim, Blue Barn Pictures Inc, 68 Jay St, Suite 311, Brooklyn, NY 11201 *Tel:* 718-852-1403 *Web Site:* www.bluebarnpictures.com, pg 809

Baker, Karen, Merced Visitor Services, California Welcome Ctr, 710 W 16 St, Merced, CA 95340 *Tel:* 209-724-8104 *Toll Free Tel:* 800-446-5353 *E-mail:* info@visitmerced.travel *Web Site:* www.yosemite-gateway.org, pg 1093

Baker, Laurie, Shasta County Film Commission, 2334 Washington Ave, Suite B, Redding, CA 96001 *Tel:* 530-225-4103 *Toll Free Tel:* 800-874-7562 *Fax:* 530-225-4354 *Web Site:* www.visitredding.org/film, pg 1093

Baker, Mark, The Whitlock Group, 12820 West Creek Pkwy, Richmond, VA 23238 *Tel:* 804-273-9100 *Toll Free Tel:* 800-726-9843 *Fax:* 804-273-9380 *E-mail:* information@whitlock.com *Web Site:* www.whitlock.com, pg 1065

Baker, Megan, Hot Springs Documentary Film Festival, 659 Ouchita Ave, Hot Springs, AR 71901 *Tel:* 501-538-2290 *Web Site:* www.hsdfi.org, pg 1116

Baker, Nick, Show-Me Audio-Visual, Corporate Ridge, 4501 Blue Ridge Cutoff, Kansas City, MO 64133 *Tel:* 816-358-8700 *Toll Free Tel:* 800-2-SHOWME (274-6963) *Fax:* 816-358-8701 *E-mail:* info@showmeav.com *Web Site:* www.showmeav.com, pg 1009

Baker, Richard, FilmNation Entertainment, 150 W 22 St, 9th fl, New York, NY 10011 *Web Site:* www.filmnation.com, pg 867

Baker, Rick, Meridia Audience Response, 5207 Militia Hill Rd, Plymouth Meeting, PA 19462 *Tel:* 610-260-6800 *Fax:* 610-260-6810 *E-mail:* rsvp@meridiaars.com *Web Site:* www.meridiaars.com, pg 939

Baker, Robert, Westworks Studios, 4100 E Dry Creek Rd, Littleton, CO 80122 *Toll Free Tel:* 800-491-1947 *E-mail:* info@westworksstudios.com *Web Site:* westworksstudios.com, pg 1064

Bakerville, Joanne, Technologies at Excelitas, 200 West St, Waltham, MA 02451 *Toll Free Tel:* 800-775-OPTO (775-6786); 855-382-2677 *Fax:* 781-290-4702 *Web Site:* www.excelitas.com, pg 1034

Balcharan, Christine, Strauss Photo Technical Service Inc, 4574 Beech Rd, Temple Hills, MD 20748 *Tel:* 202-529-3200 *Fax:* 202-526-6465 *E-mail:* info@straussphototech.com *Web Site:* www.straussphototech.com, pg 1026

Balcharan, Jeremy, Strauss Photo Technical Service Inc, 4574 Beech Rd, Temple Hills, MD 20748 *Tel:* 202-529-3200 *Fax:* 202-526-6465 *E-mail:* info@straussphototech.com *Web Site:* www.straussphototech.com, pg 1026

Baldovino, Ester, Jameco Electronics, 1355 Shoreway Rd, Belmont, CA 94002-4105 *Tel:* 650-592-8097 *Toll Free Tel:* 800-831-4242 (orders); 800-536-4316 (cust serv) *Fax:* 650-592-2503 *Toll Free Fax:* 800-237-6948 *E-mail:* info@jameco.com; sales@jameco.com *Web Site:* www.jameco.com, pg 904

Baldwin, Jim, Baldwin Productions, 160 Tioga Lane, Greenbrae, CA 94904 *Tel:* 415-925-9262 *Fax:* 415-925-1040 *Web Site:* www.baldwinproductions.com, pg 802

Baldwin, Margo, Chelsea Green Publishing Co, 85 N Main St, Suite 120, White River Junction, VT 05001 *Tel:* 802-295-6300 *Toll Free Tel:* 800-639-4099 *Fax:* 802-295-6444 *Web Site:* www.chelseagreen.com, pg 824

Baldwin, Maureen, Russound, 5 Forbes Rd, Newmarket, NH 03857 *Tel:* 603-659-5170 *Toll Free Tel:* 800-638-8055 (US) *Fax:* 603-659-5388 *E-mail:* sales@russound.com; tech@russound.com *Web Site:* www.russound.com, pg 1001

Baldwin, Whit, HeloAir Inc, 5721 Gulfstream Rd, Richmond, VA 23250 *Tel:* 804-226-3400 *Toll Free Tel:* 888-FLY-HELO (359-4356) *Fax:* 804-226-3494 *E-mail:* info@heloair.com *Web Site:* www.heloair.com, pg 888

Balino, Alexandra, FilmNation Entertainment, 150 W 22 St, 9th fl, New York, NY 10011 *Web Site:* www.filmnation.com, pg 867

Balistrieri, Pete, USAV Group Inc, 5485 S Westridge Dr, New Berlin, WI 53151-7948 *Tel:* 262-814-2000 *Toll Free Tel:* 800-596-USAV (596-8728) *Fax:* 262-814-2006 *Web Site:* www.usavgroup.com, pg 1051

Ball, Darrin, Blueyed Pictures Inc, 8950 W Olympic Blvd, Suite 324, Beverly Hills, CA 90211 *Tel:* 310-295-0848 *Fax:* 310-295-0260 *E-mail:* la@blueyedpictures.com *Web Site:* www.blueyedpictures.com, pg 810

Ballard, Kristen, Bexel Corp, 2701 N Ontario St, Burbank, CA 91504 *Tel:* 818-565-4322 *Toll Free Tel:* 800-225-6185 (tech support) *E-mail:* rentals@bexel.com *Web Site:* www.bexel.com, pg 806

Ballard, Stevie, American Visions, One Deerfield Lane, Cedar Rapids, IA 52403 *Tel:* 319-360-3211 *E-mail:* info@americanvisions.org *Web Site:* www.americanvisions.org, pg 785

Ballingham, Pamala, Earth Mother Productions Inc™, PO Box 43204, Tucson, AZ 85733-3204 *Tel:* 520-790-7061 *Fax:* 801-740-6397 *E-mail:* art4wall@aol.com *Web Site:* www.earthmotherproductions.com, pg 855

Ballingham, Tim, Earth Mother Productions Inc™, PO Box 43204, Tucson, AZ 85733-3204 *Tel:* 520-790-7061 *Fax:* 801-740-6397 *E-mail:* art4wall@aol.com *Web Site:* www.earthmotherproductions.com, pg 855

Ballo, Robert, Goal Productions, 1905 Victory Blvd, Suite 6, Glendale, CA 91201 *Tel:* 818-588-3900 *Fax:* 818-588-3903 *E-mail:* info@goalproductions.com *Web Site:* www.goalproductions.com, pg 880

Balsamo, Kathy, Pieces of Learning, 1990 Market Rd, Marion, IL 62959 *Tel:* 618-964-9426 *Toll Free Tel:* 800-729-5137 *Toll Free Fax:* 800-844-0455 *E-mail:* info@piecesoflearning.com *Web Site:* www.piecesoflearning.com, pg 975

Balsmeyer, Randall, Big Film Design, 375 S End Ave, No 9S, New York, NY 10280 *Tel:* 212-627-3430 *E-mail:* info@bigfilmdesign.com *Web Site:* www.bigfilmdesign.com, pg 807

Baltazar, Mark, Broad Street Inc, 242 W 30 St, 2nd fl, New York, NY 10001 *Tel:* 212-780-5700 *E-mail:* newyork@broadstreet.com *Web Site:* www.broadstreet.com, pg 812

Baltes, Casey, Tribeca Film Festival, 375 Greenwich St, New York, NY 10013 *Tel:* 212-941-2400 *Fax:* 212-941-3939 *E-mail:* festival@tribecafilmfestival.org *Web Site:* tribecafilm.com/festival/; tribecafilmfestival.org/festival, pg 1128

Band, Amnon H, Band Pro Film & Digital Inc, 3403 W Pacific Ave, Burbank, CA 91505 *Tel:* 818-841-9655 *Toll Free Tel:* 888-BANDPRO (226-3776) *Fax:* 818-841-7649 *Web Site:* www.bandpro.com, pg 802

Bandolik, Keith A, Switchcraft® Inc, 5555 N Elston Ave, Chicago, IL 60630 *Tel:* 773-792-2700 *Fax:* 773-792-2129 *E-mail:* sales@switchcraft.com *Web Site:* www.switchcraft.com, pg 1030

Banfill, Stephanie, I M P A C T Publishing Inc, 3409 47 Ave E, Bradenton, FL 34203 *Tel:* 941-739-2611 *Toll Free Tel:* 800-221-6121; 800-426-3963 *Fax:* 941-756-0315 *E-mail:* potentialsunlimitedcs@gmail.com *Web Site:* www.potentialsunlimited.com, pg 893

Banfill, Stephanie, Potentials Unlimited, 3409 47 Ave E, Bradenton, FL 34203-3974 *Tel:* 941-739-2611 *Toll Free Tel:* 800-221-6121; 800-426-3963 *Fax:* 941-756-0315 *Web Site:* www.potentialsunlimited.com, pg 979

Banks, Jonathan A, Lipsner-Smith Co, 4700 Chase Ave, Lincolnwood, IL 60712-1689 *Tel:* 847-677-3000 *Toll Free Tel:* 800-323-7520 *Fax:* 847-677-1311 *Toll Free Fax:* 800-784-6733 *E-mail:* sales@lipsner.com; sales@rtico.com *Web Site:* www.lipsner.com, pg 922

Banks, Larry, Long Island University Media Arts Dept, One University Plaza, Brooklyn, NY 11201-8423 *Tel:* 718-488-1052 *Fax:* 718-780-4578 *E-mail:* mediart@brooklyn.liu.edu *Web Site:* www.liu.edu/brooklyn.aspx, pg 924

Banks, Martin, Video Gear Rentals Inc, 8969 Kenamar Dr, Suite 104, San Diego, CA 92121 *Tel:* 858-356-0200 *Fax:* 858-356-0204 *Web Site:* www.video-gear.com, pg 1055

Banks, William D, Impact Christian Books Inc, 332 Leffingwell Ave, Suite 101, Kirkwood, MO 63122 *Tel:* 314-822-3309 *E-mail:* info@impactchristianbooks.com *Web Site:* www.impactchristianbooks.com, pg 897

Bannister, Brian, Loft 19, 21618 N Ninth Ave, Suite A, Phoenix, AZ 85027 *Tel:* 623-434-3791 *Fax:* 623-434-5003 *E-mail:* info@loft19.com *Web Site:* loft19.com, pg 924

Bannister, Floyd, Loft 19, 21618 N Ninth Ave, Suite A, Phoenix, AZ 85027 *Tel:* 623-434-3791 *Fax:* 623-434-5003 *E-mail:* info@loft19.com *Web Site:* loft19.com, pg 924

Bannister, Nancy, Paramount Motion Pictures Group, 1515 Broadway, 3rd fl, New York, NY 10019 *Tel:* 212-258-6000 *Fax:* 212-846-4315 *Web Site:* www.viacom.com, pg 969

Bannister, Paul, Electric Lady Studios, 52 W Eighth St, New York, NY 10011 *Tel:* 212-677-4700 *Web Site:* electricladystudios.com, pg 858

Baran, Ericka C, Jeron Electronic Systems Inc, 1743-55 W Rosehill Dr, Chicago, IL 60660 *Tel:* 773-275-1900 *Toll Free Tel:* 800-621-1903 *Fax:* 773-275-0283 *E-mail:* sales@jeron.com *Web Site:* www.jeron.com, pg 905

Baranski, Amanda, Western North Carolina Film Commission, 134 Wright Brothers Way, Fletcher, NC 28732 *Tel:* 828-687-7234 *Toll Free Tel:* 888-595-7234 *Fax:* 828-687-7552 *E-mail:* film@awnc.org *Web Site:* www.wncfilm.com; www.advantagewest.com, pg 1101

Barbarino, Rick, White Rain Films Ltd, 2009 Dexter Ave N, Seattle, WA 98109 *Tel:* 206-682-5417 *Toll Free Tel:* 800-816-5244 *Fax:* 206-682-3038 *E-mail:* info@whiterainfilms.com *Web Site:* www.whiterainfilms.com, pg 1065

Barbarossa, Nadia, Puerto Rico Film Commission, 355 FD Roosevelt Ave, Suite 106, Hato Rey, PR 00918 *Tel:* 787-754-6444 *Fax:* 787-756-5706 *E-mail:* info@puertoricofilm.pr.gov *Web Site:* www.puertoricofilm.com, pg 1104

Barber, Cindy, BMI Supply, 571 Queensbury Ave, Queensbury, NY 12804 *Tel:* 518-793-6706 *Toll Free Tel:* 800-836-0524 *Fax:* 518-793-6181 *E-mail:* bminy@bmisupply.com *Web Site:* www.bmisupply.com, pg 810

Barber, Eddie, Barber Tech Video Products, 205 E Anaheim St, Long Beach, CA 90813 *Tel:* 818-982-7775 *Toll Free Tel:* 877-887-6388 *E-mail:* info@barbertvp.com *Web Site:* www.barbertvp.com, pg 802

Barber, Raymond, Hollywood Vaults Inc, 742 N Seward St, Hollywood, CA 90038-3504 *Tel:* 323-461-6464 *Toll Free Tel:* 800-569-5336 *Fax:* 323-461-6479 *E-mail:* vault@hollywoodvaults.com *Web Site:* www.hollywoodvaults.com, pg 890

Barbero, James, Transistor Devices Inc, 36 Newburgh Rd, Hackettstown, NJ 07840 *Tel:* 908-850-5088 *Fax:* 908-850-1607 *E-mail:* info@tdipower.com *Web Site:* www.tdipower.com, pg 1043

Barbieri, Ernest, Thomas Craven Film Corp, 5 W 19 St, New York, NY 10011-4216 *Tel:* 212-463-7190 *Fax:* 212-627-4761 *E-mail:* info@cravenfilms.com *Web Site:* cravenfilms.com, pg 837

Barbosa, Gordon, Barbosa Video Services, 11 Plaza, Suite E, Patterson, CA 95363 *Tel:* 209-324-5327 *Web Site:* barbosavideo.com, pg 802

Barbour, Lee, Charleston International Film Festival (CIFF), 915 Folly Rd, No 78, Charleston, SC 29412 *Tel:* 843-817-1617 *E-mail:* info@charlestoniff.org *Web Site:* charlestoniff.org, pg 1111

Barchick, Jacqueline, Thread Marketing Group, 4635 W Alexis Rd, Toledo, OH 43623-1005 *Tel:* 419-887-6801 *Toll Free Tel:* 800-397-0126 *Fax:* 419-887-6802 *E-mail:* contact@experiencethread.com *Web Site:* www.experiencethread.com, pg 1039

Barclay, Paris, Directors Guild of America (DGA), 7920 Sunset Blvd, Los Angeles, CA 90046 *Tel:* 310-289-2000 *Toll Free Tel:* 800-421-4173 *Web Site:* www.dga.org, pg 1081

Barclay, Paul, Carr McLean Ltd, 461 Horner Ave, Toronto, ON M8W 4X2, Canada *Tel:* 416-252-3371 *Toll Free Tel:* 800-268-2123 (CN) *Fax:* 416-252-9203 *Toll Free Fax:* 800-871-2397 *E-mail:* sales@carrmclean.ca *Web Site:* www.carrmclean.ca, pg 820

Barey, Pat, Tellens Inc, 770 W Landoran Lane, Tucson, AZ 85737 *Tel:* 520-742-0649 *Fax:* 520-742-0652 *E-mail:* infotellens@aol.com *Web Site:* www.tellens.com, pg 1037

Barger, Ed, Barger-Lite, PO Box 90294, Venice, CA 90294 *Tel:* 310-401-0633 *Fax:* 310-392-6791 *Web Site:* www.bargerlite.com, pg 803

Barger, Steven, Express Media Inc, 2225 Palou Ave, San Francisco, CA 94124 *Tel:* 415-255-9883 *Fax:* 415-255-0139 *Web Site:* www.expressmedia.tv, pg 864

Barger, Steven, Express Media Inc, 2225 Palou Ave, San Francisco, CA 94124 *Tel:* 415-255-9883 *Fax:* 415-255-0139 *Web Site:* www.rentvideo.com; www.expressmedia.tv, pg 864

Barkan, Bebe, Cross-Cultural Communications, 239 Wynsum Ave, Merrick, NY 11566-4725 *Tel:* 516-868-5635 *Fax:* 516-379-1901 *E-mail:* info@cross-culturalcommunications.com *Web Site:* www.cross-culturalcommunications.com, pg 839

Barkan, Stanley H, Cross-Cultural Communications, 239 Wynsum Ave, Merrick, NY 11566-4725 *Tel:* 516-868-5635 *Fax:* 516-379-1901 *E-mail:* info@cross-culturalcommunications.com *Web Site:* www.cross-culturalcommunications.com, pg 839

Barker, Bruce, Kris Stevens Enterprises, 22362 Dardenne St, Calabasas, CA 91302 *Tel:* 818-225-7585 *E-mail:* inquiry@kriserikstevens.com *Web Site:* www.kriserikstevens.com, pg 1024

Barker, James, Caption Colorado LLC, 5690 DTC Blvd, Suite 500W, Greenwood Village, CO 80111 *Tel:* 720-489-5662 *Toll Free Tel:* 800-775-7838 *Fax:* 720-489-5664 *Web Site:* www.captioncolorado.com, pg 820

Barker, Nicholas, Montreal Film & TV Commission, Duke Pavilion, 5th fl, 801 Brennan St, Montreal, QC H3C 0G4, Canada *Tel:* 514-872-2883 *Fax:* 514-872-3409 *E-mail:* film.tv@ville.montreal.qc.ca *Web Site:* www.montrealfilm.com, pg 1105

Barnes, Charlotte, Bill Barnes Video Productions LLC, 14238 Honeysuckle Ridge, Matthews, NC 28105-6403 *Tel:* 704-847-8685 *Toll Free Tel:* 888-893-7331 *Fax:* 704-847-7279 *E-mail:* bill@bbvp.tv *Web Site:* bbvp.tv, pg 803

Barnes, William R, Bill Barnes Video Productions LLC, 14238 Honeysuckle Ridge, Matthews, NC 28105-6403 *Tel:* 704-847-8685 *Toll Free Tel:* 888-893-7331 *Fax:* 704-847-7279 *E-mail:* bill@bbvp.tv *Web Site:* bbvp.tv, pg 803

Barnett, Eddie, Petra Productions Ltd, 52 Sycamore Rd, Mahopac, NY 10541 *E-mail:* information@petraproductions.org *Web Site:* www.petraproductions.org, pg 973

Barnett, Kasie, Baker Audio Inc, 2195 N Norcross Tucker Rd, Norcross, GA 30071 *Tel:* 770-441-2000 *Toll Free Tel:* 800-847-3523 *Fax:* 770-449-7719 *E-mail:* sales@bakeraudiovisual.com *Web Site:* www.bakeraudiovisual.com, pg 802

Barnett, Melody, Palace Costume & Prop Co, 835 N Fairfax Ave, Hollywood, CA 90046 *Tel:* 323-651-5458 *Fax:* 323-658-7133 *E-mail:* rentals@palacecostume.com *Web Site:* www.palacecostume.com, pg 967

Barnhill, Ted, Castleview Productions, 1100 W 41 St, Austin, TX 78756 *Tel:* 512-442-9944 *Fax:* 512-442-8823 *E-mail:* contact@castleviewproductions.com *Web Site:* www.castleviewproductions.com, pg 821

Barnwell, Allan, Omega Broadcast Group, 817 W Howard Lane, Austin, TX 78753 *Tel:* 512-251-7778 *Fax:* 512-251-8633 *E-mail:* rental@omegabroadcast.com; sales@omegabroadcast.com *Web Site:* www.omegabroadcast.com, pg 962

Baroco, Molly, Beast Atlanta, 3399 Peachtree Rd NE, Suite 200, Atlanta, GA 30326-1149 *Tel:* 404-237-9977 *Fax:* 404-237-3923 *E-mail:* info@riotatlanta.com *Web Site:* www.beast.tv, pg 804

Baron, Sara R, Catholic Library Association (CLA), 8550 United Plaza Blvd, Suite 1001, Baton Rouge, LA 70809 *Tel:* 225-408-4417 *E-mail:* cla2@cathla.org *Web Site:* www.cathla.org, pg 1080

Baronet, Jim, WVLA-TV, 10000 Perkins Rd, Baton Rouge, LA 70810 *Tel:* 225-766-3233 *Fax:* 225-768-9293 *Web Site:* www.nbc33tv.com, pg 1071

Barr, Wayne, Barron's Educational Series Inc, 250 Wireless Blvd, Hauppauge, NY 11788 *Tel:* 631-434-3311 *Toll Free Tel:* 800-645-3476 *Fax:* 631-434-3723 *E-mail:* barrons@barronseduc.com *Web Site:* www.barronseduc.com, pg 803

Barrett, Beth, Golden Space Needle Awards, 305 Harrison St, Seattle, WA 98109 *Tel:* 206-464-5830 *Fax:* 206-264-7919 *E-mail:* info@siff.net *Web Site:* www.siff.net, pg 1116

Barrett, Beth, Seattle International Film Festival (SIFF), 305 Harrison St, Seattle, WA 98109 *Tel:* 206-464-5830 *Fax:* 206-264-7919 *E-mail:* info@siff.net *Web Site:* www.siff.net, pg 1127

Barrett, Joe, Sand Box Studio, 555 Minnesota St, San Francisco, CA 94107 *Tel:* 415-550-8732 *E-mail:* inquiries@sandboxstudio.com *Web Site:* www.sandboxstudio.com, pg 1002

Barrett, Lauren, Ohio State University Foreign Language Publications, 198 Hagerty Hall, 1775 S College Rd, Columbus, OH 43210-1309 *Tel:* 614-292-3838 *Toll Free Tel:* 800-678-6999 *Fax:* 614-688-3355 *E-mail:* flpubs@osu.edu *Web Site:* flpubs.osu.edu, pg 961

Barrett, Linda, Executive Development Systems, 3818 Vinecrest Dr, Dallas, TX 75229 *Tel:* 214-351-0055 *Toll Free Tel:* 800-955-7353 *Fax:* 214-351-5024 *Web Site:* www.edforeman.com, pg 864

Barrett, Rick, MAXON Computer Inc, 2640 Lavery Ct, Suite A, Newbury Park, CA 91320 *Tel:* 805-376-3333 *Fax:* 805-376-3331 *E-mail:* info_us@maxon.net *Web Site:* www.maxon.net, pg 934

Barrette, Francois, Strong Screen Systems, 1440 Raoul-Charrette, Joliette, QC J6E 8S7, Canada *Tel:* 450-755-3795 *Toll Free Tel:* 877-755-3795 *Fax:* 450-755-3122 *E-mail:* sales@strong-mdicinema.com *Web Site:* www.strong-world.com; www.mdicinema.com, pg 1026

Barron, Dana, HB Communications Inc, 60 Dodge Ave, North Haven, CT 06473 *Tel:* 203-234-9246 *Toll Free Tel:* 800-243-4414 *Fax:* 203-234-2013 *E-mail:* info@hbcommunications.com *Web Site:* www.hbcommunications.com, pg 886

Barron, Mackey, HB Communications Inc, 60 Dodge Ave, North Haven, CT 06473 *Tel:* 203-234-9246 *Toll Free Tel:* 800-243-4414 *Fax:* 203-234-2013 *E-mail:* info@hbcommunications.com *Web Site:* www.hbcommunications.com, pg 886

Barron, Manuel H, Barron's Educational Series Inc, 250 Wireless Blvd, Hauppauge, NY 11788 *Tel:* 631-434-3311 *Toll Free Tel:* 800-645-3476 *Fax:* 631-434-3723 *E-mail:* barrons@barronseduc.com *Web Site:* www.barronseduc.com, pg 803

Barron, Matt, Beast Atlanta, 3399 Peachtree Rd NE, Suite 200, Atlanta, GA 30326-1149 *Tel:* 404-237-9977 *Fax:* 404-237-3923 *E-mail:* info@riotatlanta.com *Web Site:* www.beast.tv, pg 804

Barron, Richard, Sonora Recorders, 3222 Los Feliz Blvd, Los Angeles, CA 90039 *Tel:* 323-663-2500 *E-mail:* ductape@aol.com *Web Site:* www.sonorarecorders.com, pg 1016

Barron, Tom, Image G, 28490 Westinghouse Place, Unit 160, Valencia, CA 91355 *Tel:* 818-761-6644 *Fax:* 661-775-8900 *E-mail:* production@imageg.com *Web Site:* sites.google.com/site/imagegwebsite, pg 895

Barros, Glen, Concord Jazz Inc, 100 N Crescent Dr, Garden Level, Beverly Hills, CA 90210 *Tel:* 310-385-4455 *Fax:* 310-385-4466 *Web Site:* www.concordmusicgroup.com, pg 835

Barros, Glen, Concord Records Inc, 100 N Crescent Dr, Garden Level, Beverly Hills, CA 90210 *Tel:* 310-385-4455 *Fax:* 310-385-4466 *Web Site:* www.concordmusicgroup.com, pg 835

Barros, Glen, Telarc International Corp, 23412 Commerce Park Rd, Cleveland, OH 44122 *Tel:* 216-464-2313 *Fax:* 216-360-9663 *Web Site:* www.concordmusicgroup.com/labels/Telarc/; www.concordmusicgroup.com, pg 1035

Barry, Ben, Ben Barry & Associates Inc, 10246 Briarwood Dr, Los Angeles, CA 90077 *Tel:* 310-274-1523 *Fax:* 310-274-1523 *E-mail:* benbarryfilms@sbcglobal.net, pg 803

Barry, Luann, 1st Wave Productions, 2017 Pacific Ave, Venice, CA 90291 *Tel:* 310-474-2439 *Fax:* 310-474-5282 *Web Site:* www.1stwaveproductions.com, pg 869

Barry, Mimi, Ben Barry & Associates Inc, 10246 Briarwood Dr, Los Angeles, CA 90077 *Tel:* 310-274-1523 *Fax:* 310-274-1523 *E-mail:* benbarryfilms@sbcglobal.net, pg 803

Barry, Steven, Style-City Music Inc, 7826 Rhodes Rd, Suite 6, Hudson, FL 34667 *Tel:* 727-520-2336 *E-mail:* mail@stylecitymusic.com; stylecitymusic@yahoo.com *Web Site:* www.stylecitymusic.com, pg 1027

Barta, B Andrew, Tech 21 USA Inc, 790 Bloomfield Ave, Clifton, NJ 07012 *Tel:* 973-777-6996 *Fax:* 973-777-9899 *E-mail:* info@tech21nyc.com *Web Site:* www.tech21nyc.com, pg 1033

Barth, Andy, TecNec Distributing, 812 Kings Hwy, Saugerties, NY 12477 *Tel:* 845-246-0428 *Toll Free Tel:* 800-543-0909 *Fax:* 845-246-0626 *E-mail:* sales@tecnec.com *Web Site:* www.tecnec.com, pg 1035

Barth, Carl, Carl Barth Images, PO Box 5325, Santa Barbara, CA 93150-5325 *Tel:* 805-637-0881 *E-mail:* carlbarthimages@cox.net, pg 803

Bartlett, Alan, Wayne State University Media Services, Purdy/Kresge Library, 5244 Gullen Mall, Detroit, MI 48202 *Tel:* 313-577-1980 *Fax:* 313-577-6777 *E-mail:* mediaservices@wayne.edu *Web Site:* library.wayne.edu, pg 1063

Bartlett, Kevin, Aural Gratification Inc, 32 Nissen Lane, West Hurley, NY 12491-5903 *Tel:* 845-679-5674 *E-mail:* auralg@gmail.com, pg 796

Bartlett, Tim, Adrenaline Films, 5224 S Orange Ave, Orlando, FL 32809 *Tel:* 407-850-0711 *Fax:* 407-859-6527 *E-mail:* contact@adrenalinefilms.com *Web Site:* www.adrenalinefilms.com, pg 777

Bartling, Tab, Heart Music Inc, PO Box 160326, Austin, TX 78716-0326 *Tel:* 512-795-2375 *Fax:* 512-795-9573 *E-mail:* info@heartmusic.com *Web Site:* www.heartmusic.com, pg 887

Bartok, Peter, Bartok Records & Publications, PO Box 399, Homosassa, FL 34487 *Tel:* 352-382-2015 *Fax:* 352-382-0341 *E-mail:* bartok@atlantic.net *Web Site:* www.bartokrecords.com, pg 803

Barton, Larry, Cinematography Electronics Inc, 5321 Derry Ave, Suite G, Agoura Hills, CA 91301 *Tel:* 818-706-3334 *Fax:* 818-706-3335 *E-mail:* info@cinemaelec.com *Web Site:* www.cinematographyelectronics.com, pg 828

Barton, Paul, PSB Speakers International, 633 Granite Ct, Pickering, ON L1W 3K1, Canada *Tel:* 905-831-6555 *Toll Free Tel:* 800-263-4641 (cust serv) *Fax:* 905-837-6357 *E-mail:* info@psbspeakers.com *Web Site:* www.psbspeakers.com, pg 987

Barton, Ridgie, piXvfm, 1805 E Dyer, Suite 107, Santa Ana, CA 92705-5701 *Tel:* 949-250-1749 *Fax:* 949-419-3485 *E-mail:* infoweb@pixvfm.com *Web Site:* www.pixvfm.com, pg 976

Barton, Sue, Lake Tahoe Visitors Authority (LTVA), 169 Hwy 50, Stateline, NV 89449 *Tel:* 775-588-5900 *Toll Free Tel:* 800-288-2463 (reservations) *Fax:* 775-588-1941 *E-mail:* info@ltva.org *Web Site:* ltva.org, pg 1100

Bartos, Marlene, Yessian, 137 Fifth Ave, 3rd fl, New York, NY 10010 *Tel:* 212-533-3443 *E-mail:* info-ny@yessian.com *Web Site:* www.yessian.com, pg 1072

Bartzke, Roger, HP Marketing Corp, 16 Chapin Rd, Unit 908, Pine Brook, NJ 07058 *Tel:* 973-808-9010 *Toll Free Tel:* 800-735-4373 *Fax:* 973-808-9004 *E-mail:* info@hpmarketingcorp.com *Web Site:* www.hpmarketingcorp.com, pg 892

Basgen, Fritz, Blue 60 Pictures, 555 First Ave NE, Suite 200, Minneapolis, MN 55413 *Tel:* 612-871-6800 *E-mail:* info@blue-60.com *Web Site:* www.blue-60.com, pg 810

Bashir, Irene, Central Audio-Visual Equipment Inc, 375 Roma Jean Pkwy, Streamwood, IL 60107 *Tel:* 630-372-8100 *Toll Free Tel:* 800-323-4239 *Fax:* 630-372-9281 *Web Site:* www.cavinc.com, pg 823

Bashir, Jonathan, Central Audio-Visual Equipment Inc, 375 Roma Jean Pkwy, Streamwood, IL 60107 *Tel:* 630-372-8100 *Toll Free Tel:* 800-323-4239 *Fax:* 630-372-9281 *Web Site:* www.cavinc.com, pg 823

Bashir, Michael, Central Audio-Visual Equipment Inc, 375 Roma Jean Pkwy, Streamwood, IL 60107 *Tel:* 630-372-8100 *Toll Free Tel:* 800-323-4239 *Fax:* 630-372-9281 *Web Site:* www.cavinc.com, pg 823

Bashore, Dan, Bartha, 600 N Cassady Ave, Columbus, OH 43219 *Tel:* 614-252-7455 *Toll Free Tel:* 800-363-2698 *Fax:* 614-252-7641 *E-mail:* info@bartha.com *Web Site:* www.bartha.com, pg 803

Basileo, Patricia, American Harlequin Corp, 1531 Glen Ave, Moorestown, NJ 08057 *Tel:* 856-234-5505 *Toll Free Tel:* 800-642-6440 *Fax:* 856-231-4403 *E-mail:* dance@harlequinfloors.com *Web Site:* www.harlequinfloors.com, pg 784

Basner, Glen, FilmNation Entertainment, 150 W 22 St, 9th fl, New York, NY 10011 *Web Site:* www.filmnation.com, pg 867

Bass, Carl, Autodesk Inc, 111 McInnis Pkwy, San Rafael, CA 94903 *Tel:* 415-507-5000 *Fax:* 415-507-5100 *Web Site:* www.autodesk.com, pg 797

Bast, Randy, High-Tech Special Effects Inc, PO Box 193, Eads, TN 38028-0193 *Tel:* 901-850-5522 *Fax:* 901-850-8317 *Web Site:* www.hightechspecialeffects.com, pg 889

Basta, Chris, Beast Atlanta, 3399 Peachtree Rd NE, Suite 200, Atlanta, GA 30326-1149 *Tel:* 404-237-9977 *Fax:* 404-237-3923 *E-mail:* info@riotatlanta.com *Web Site:* www.beast.tv, pg 804

Basta, Eric, Preston Productions Inc, 128 Bartlett St, Marlborough, MA 01752 *Toll Free Tel:* 800-822-2299 *E-mail:* ideas@prestonevents.com *Web Site:* www.prestonproductions.com; www.prestonevents.com, pg 981

Basteri, Patricia, massAV, 755 Middlesex Tpke, Billerica, MA 01821 *Tel:* 978-670-0027 *Toll Free Tel:* 800-423-7830 *Fax:* 978-670-0037 *E-mail:* info@massav.com *Web Site:* www.massav.com, pg 933

Bastian, Don, Attainment Co Inc, 504 Commerce Pkwy, Verona, WI 53593 *Tel:* 608-845-7880 *Toll Free Tel:* 800-327-4269 *Fax:* 608-845-8040 *Toll Free Fax:* 800-942-3865 *E-mail:* customerservice@attainmentcompany.com; international@attainmentcompany.com *Web Site:* www.attainmentcompany.com, pg 793

Batavick, Catherine, Maryland Film Office, 401 E Pratt St, 14th fl, Baltimore, MD 21202 *Tel:* 410-767-6340 *Toll Free Tel:* 800-333-6632 *Fax:* 410-333-0044 *E-mail:* filminfo@marylandfilm.org *Web Site:* www.marylandfilm.org, pg 1098

Bateman, Susan, Yarn Barn of Kansas, 930 Massachusetts St, Lawrence, KS 66044 *Tel:* 785-842-4333 *Toll Free Tel:* 800-468-0035 *Fax:* 785-842-0794 *E-mail:* info@yarnbarn-ks.com *Web Site:* www.yarnbarn-ks.com, pg 1072

Bates, Carolyn, Buttercup Pictures, 2415 Michigan Ave, Bldg H, Santa Monica, CA 90404 *Tel:* 323-692-0909 *E-mail:* info@buttercuppictures.com *Web Site:* buttercuppictures.com, pg 816

Bates, Phil, Artbeats, 1405 N Myrtle Rd, Myrtle Creek, OR 97457 *Tel:* 541-863-4429 *Toll Free Tel:* 800-444-9392 *Fax:* 541-863-4547 *E-mail:* info@artbeats.com *Web Site:* www.artbeats.com, pg 791

Bates, Rick, Big Bear Chamber of Commerce, 630 Bartlett Rd, 1st fl, Big Bear Lake, CA 92315 *Tel:* 909-866-4607 *Fax:* 909-866-5412 *E-mail:* contact@bigbearchamber.com *Web Site:* www.bigbearchamber.com, pg 1092

Bates, Ron, WCJB TV20, 6220 NW 43 St, Gainesville, FL 32653 *Tel:* 352-416-0623 *Fax:* 352-373-6516 *E-mail:* comments@divcom.com *Web Site:* divcom.com, pg 1063

Bates, Vicki, University of South Carolina Press, 1600 Hampton St, Colimbia, SC 29208 *Tel:* 803-777-5243 *Toll Free Tel:* 800-768-2500 *Toll Free Fax:* 800-868-0740 *Web Site:* www.sc.edu/uscpress, pg 1050

Battaglia, Frank, Cine Photo Tech, 1240 Oakleigh Dr, Atlanta, GA 30344 *Tel:* 404-684-7100 *Fax:* 404-684-7080 *E-mail:* info@cinephototech.com *Web Site:* www.cinephototech.com, pg 826

Bauer, Gary H, Alpha Video Productions, 441 Biscay Dr, Garland, TX 75043 *Tel:* 972-497-9959 *E-mail:* alphaghb@sbcglobal.net *Web Site:* www.alphavideo.net, pg 782

Bauer, Susan, Alpha Video Productions, 441 Biscay Dr, Garland, TX 75043 *Tel:* 972-497-9959 *E-mail:* alphaghb@sbcglobal.net *Web Site:* www.alphavideo.net, pg 782

Bauersfeld, Kris, All Communications Rentals Inc (ALLCOMM), 1402 SW 13 Ct, Pompano Beach, FL 33069 *Tel:* 954-788-9555 *Web Site:* www.allcommrentals.com, pg 780

Baum, Bruce, Pyrotek Special Effects Inc, 7676 Woodbine Ave, Suites 7 & 8, Markham, ON L3R 2N2, Canada *Tel:* 905-479-9991 *Toll Free Tel:* 800-481-9910 *Fax:* 905-479-3515 *E-mail:* info@pyrotekfx.com *Web Site:* www.pyrotekfx.com, pg 988

Baum, Gene, Laser Magic Productions, 722 N Orlando Ave, No 207, Los Angeles, CA 90069 *Tel:* 323-951-9392 *Web Site:* www.laser-magic.com, pg 916

Bauman, Dan, PSAV® Presentation Services, 111 W Ocean Blvd, Suite 1110, Long Beach, CA 90802-4688 *Tel:* 562-366-0620 *Toll Free Tel:* 877-430-7728 *Fax:* 562-366-0628 *Web Site:* www.psav.com, pg 986

Bauman, Dan, Swank Audio Visuals, 639-E Gravois Bluffs, St Louis, MO 63026 *Tel:* 636-680-9000 *Toll Free Tel:* 877-792-6528 *Fax:* 636-680-2853 *Web Site:* www.swankav.com, pg 1029

Bauman, Margy, Redwood Audiobooks, 10375 Nichols Lane, Mendocino, CA 95460 *Tel:* 707-937-1225 *E-mail:* audiobks@mcn.org *Web Site:* www.universitypressaudiobooks.com, pg 993

Baumberger, Randall, The Studios at Paramount, 5555 Melrose Ave, Hollywood, CA 90038 *Tel:* 323-956-5000 *Web Site:* www.paramountstudios.com, pg 1027

Bausch, Romain, SES World Skies, 4 Research Way, Princeton, NJ 08540 *Tel:* 609-987-4000; 609-987-4200 *Fax:* 609-987-4517 *E-mail:* info@ses.com *Web Site:* www.ses.com, pg 1007

Bauske, Mark, Producers Playhouse, 117 NW 142 St, Edmond, OK 73013 *Tel:* 405-858-0700 *Toll Free Tel:* 888-607-6856 *Fax:* 405-302-0703 *Web Site:* www.producersplayhouse.com, pg 984

Bauske, Matt, Producers Playhouse, 117 NW 142 St, Edmond, OK 73013 *Tel:* 405-858-0700 *Toll Free Tel:* 888-607-6856 *Fax:* 405-302-0703 *Web Site:* www.producersplayhouse.com, pg 984

Bavin, Clark, Video Solutions, 2121 Eisenhower Ave, Suite 103, Alexandria, VA 22314 *Tel:* 703-683-5305; 703-628-0702 (cell) *E-mail:* inquiries@thevideosolution.com *Web Site:* www.thevideosolution.com, pg 1056

Baxter, Irvin Jr, Endtime Inc, 2701 E George Bush Tpke, Suite 100, Plano, TX 75074 *Tel:* 972-422-0857 *Toll Free Tel:* 800-363-8463 (cust serv) *Fax:* 972-423-4370 *E-mail:* questions@endtime.com; customerservice@endtime.com *Web Site:* www.endtime.com, pg 861

Baxter, Peter, Slamdance Film Festival, 5634 Melrose Ave, Los Angeles, CA 90038 *Tel:* 323-466-1786 *Fax:* 323-466-1784 *E-mail:* submissions@slamdance.com *Web Site:* www.slamdance.com, pg 1127

Bayer, Robert F, Theatrical Services & Supplies Inc, 415Q Oser Ave, Hauppauge, NY 11788 *Tel:* 631-873-4790 *Fax:* 631-873-4795 *E-mail:* sales@gotheatrical.com *Web Site:* www.gotheatrical.com, pg 1038

Bayley, Roger, National Boston, 115 Dummer St, Brookline, MA 02446 *Tel:* 617-734-4800 *Fax:* 617-734-6323 *E-mail:* info@nationalboston.com *Web Site:* www.nationalboston.com, pg 952

Bays, Greg, EMI CMG Distribution, 101 Winners Circle, Brentwood, TN 37027 *Tel:* 615-371-4300 *Toll Free Tel:* 800-877-4443 *Fax:* 615-371-6555; 615-371-6980 (sales) *E-mail:* distribution@emicmg.com *Web Site:* www.emicmg.com; www.emicmgdistribution.com, pg 860

Bazley, Christopher, Antenna International, 383 Main Ave, Norwalk, CT 06851 *Tel:* 203-523-0320 *Fax:* 203-354-5519 *E-mail:* inquiry@antennainternational.com *Web Site:* www.antennainternational.com, pg 787

Beadle, Beth, Winchester Electronics Corp, 68 Water St, Norwalk, CT 06854 *Tel:* 203-741-5400 *E-mail:* info@winchesterelectronics.com *Web Site:* www.winchesterelectronics.com, pg 1067

Beadle, Sarah, Emerson Network Power Surge Protection Inc, 100 Emerson Pkwy, Binghamton, NY 13905 *Tel:* 607-721-8840 *Toll Free Tel:* 800-288-6169 *Fax:* 607-722-8713 *E-mail:* contactsurge@emerson.com *Web Site:* www.emersonnetworkpower.com, pg 860

Beal, Greg, Nicholl Fellowships in Screenwriting, 8949 Wilshire Blvd, Beverly Hills, CA 90211 *Tel:* 310-247-3010 *E-mail:* nicholl@oscars.org *Web Site:* www.oscars.org, pg 1122

Bealor, Tim, Marti Electronics Inc, 4100 N 24 St, Quincy, IL 62305 *Tel:* 217-224-9600 *Fax:* 217-224-9607 *E-mail:* sales@martielectronics.com *Web Site:* martielectronics.com, pg 932

Beard, Charles, Frontier Software Inc, PO Box 56505, Houston, TX 77256 *Tel:* 713-622-8167 *Toll Free Tel:* 800-634-3306 *Fax:* 713-622-0058 *E-mail:* webmaster@frontiertex.com *Web Site:* www.frontiertex.com, pg 873

Beasley, Coty, MIS Technologies, 555-B NW Blue Pkwy, Lees Summit, MO 64063 *Tel:* 816-966-4529 *Fax:* 816-966-2915 *Web Site:* www.mistechnologies.com, pg 944

Beattie, Michael, Brookline Books, 8 Trumbull Rd, Suite B-001, Northampton, MA 01060 *Tel:* 413-584-0184; 603-669-7032 (orders) *Toll Free Tel:* 800-666-BOOK (666-2665 cust serv) *Fax:* 413-584-6184 *E-mail:* brbooks@yahoo.com *Web Site:* www.brooklinebooks.com, pg 814

Beatty, David E, Beatty TeleVisual Productions, 1287 Wabash Ave, Springfield, IL 62704 *Tel:* 217-787-4747 *Toll Free Tel:* 800-777-2043 *Fax:* 217-787-4857 *E-mail:* bargins@beattytelevisual.com *Web Site:* www.beattytelevisual.com, pg 804

Beatty, Wilma, Beatty TeleVisual Productions, 1287 Wabash Ave, Springfield, IL 62704 *Tel:* 217-787-4747 *Toll Free Tel:* 800-777-2043 *Fax:* 217-787-4857 *E-mail:* bargins@beattytelevisual.com *Web Site:* www.beattytelevisual.com, pg 804

Beaulieu, Julie, Trafalgar Square Books, 388 Howe Hill Rd, North Pomfret, VT 05053 *Tel:* 802-457-1911 *Toll Free Tel:* 800-423-4525 *Fax:* 802-457-1913 *E-mail:* info@horseandriderbooks.com *Web Site:* www.horseandriderbooks.com, pg 1043

Beautyman, William, Limelight Productions Inc, 471 Pleasant St, Lee, MA 01238-9322 *Tel:* 413-243-4950 *Toll Free Tel:* 800-243-4950 *Fax:* 413-243-4993 *Toll Free Fax:* 800-243-4951 *E-mail:* info@limelightproductions.com *Web Site:* www.limelightproductions.com, pg 921

Beaver, Nick, Media Cybernetics Inc, 401 N Washington St, Suite 350, Rockville, MD 20850 *Tel:* 301-495-3305 *Toll Free Tel:* 800-263-2088 *Fax:* 240-328-6193 *E-mail:* info@mediacy.com *Web Site:* www.mediacy.com, pg 936

Beazley, Sara, American Hospital Association, 155 N Wacker Dr, Suite 400, Chicago, IL 60606-1725 *Tel:* 312-422-3000 *Fax:* 312-422-4700 *Web Site:* www.aha.org, pg 784

Bebb, Bruce, Lightspeed Technologies Inc, 11509 SW Herman Rd, Tualatin, OR 97062 *Tel:* 503-684-5538 *Toll Free Tel:* 800-732-8999 *Fax:* 503-684-3197 *Web Site:* www.lightspeed-tek.com, pg 921

Becher, James, FXC Communications, 970 S Second St, San Jose, CA 95112-5825 *Tel:* 408-293-2000 *Fax:* 408-294-2000, pg 874

Beck, Chris, Cosumnes River College, 8401 Center Pkwy, Sacramento, CA 95823 *Tel:* 916-691-7289 *Fax:* 916-691-7375 *Web Site:* www.crc.losrios.edu, pg 836

Beck, Doug, Bil-Jax Inc, 125 Taylor Pkwy, Archbold, OH 43502 *Tel:* 419-445-8915 *Toll Free Tel:* 800-537-0540 *Fax:* 419-445-0367 *E-mail:* sales@biljax.com *Web Site:* www.biljax.com, pg 807

Beck, James, Eagle Inc, PO Box 579, Clarkdale, AZ 86324 *Tel:* 928-204-2597 *Fax:* 928-204-2568 *E-mail:* hier_bosch@yahoo.com *Web Site:* www.eagle-1st.com, pg 855

Becker, Glenn, Grand Stage Co Inc, 630 W Lake St, Chicago, IL 60661 *Tel:* 312-332-5611 *Toll Free Tel:* 800-621-2181 *Fax:* 312-258-0056 *E-mail:* info@grandstage.com *Web Site:* www.grandstage.com, pg 881

Beckert, Sabine, Telemotions LLC, 405 E 54 St, Suite 3-N, New York, NY 10022 *Tel:* 212-486-3010 *Web Site:* www.telemotions.net, pg 1036

Beckman, Janet, Williams Sound Corp, 10300 Valley View Rd, Eden Prairie, MN 55344-3446 *Tel:* 952-943-2252 *Toll Free Tel:* 800-328-6190 *Fax:* 952-943-2174 *E-mail:* info@williamssound.com *Web Site:* www.williamssound.com, pg 1067

Beckman, Kathleen, Chicago International Children's Film Festival, 1517 W Fullerton Ave, Chicago, IL 60614 *Tel:* 773-281-9075 (ext 3011) *Fax:* 773-929-0266 *E-mail:* kids@facets.org *Web Site:* www.cicff.org; www.facets.org, pg 1111

Beckner, Jenni, Russ Beckner Pictures, 2100 Heatherwood Ct, Middletown, OH 45042 *Tel:* 513-422-9552 *Web Site:* www.russbecknerpictures.com, pg 804

Beckner, Russ, Russ Beckner Pictures, 2100 Heatherwood Ct, Middletown, OH 45042 *Tel:* 513-422-9552 *Web Site:* www.russbecknerpictures.com, pg 804

Bedall, Patrick, Metro Productions, 8570 Magellan Pkwy, Suite 400, Richmond, VA 23227 *Tel:* 804-261-1172 *Toll Free Tel:* 877-669-4687 *Fax:* 804-261-1885 *E-mail:* contactmetro@metro-productions.com *Web Site:* www.metro-productions.com, pg 939

Bedell, Lonnie, Goin' Mobile, PO Box 470627, Brookline, MA 02447 *Tel:* 617-232-7969 (cell) *Web Site:* www.goin-mobile.com, pg 880

Bedichek, Louise, Sano Videos, Columbia Plaza, 2450 Virginia Ave NW, Suite E 322, Washington, DC 20037 *Tel:* 202-293-0454, pg 1002

Beebe, Greg, Sennheiser Electronic Corp, One Enterprise Dr, Old Lyme, CT 06371 *Tel:* 860-434-9190 *Toll Free Tel:* 877-SENNHEISER (736-6434) *Fax:* 860-434-1759 *E-mail:* info@sennheiserusa.com *Web Site:* en-us.sennheiser.com, pg 1006

Beegle, Bruce, Vanner Inc, 4282 Reynolds Dr, Hilliard, OH 43026 *Tel:* 614-771-2718 *Toll Free Tel:* 800-ACPOWER (227-6937) *Fax:* 614-771-4904 *E-mail:* info@vanner.com; pwrsales@vanner.com *Web Site:* www.vanner.com, pg 1051

Been, Jason, Imagecraft Productions, 3318 Burton Ave, Burbank, CA 91504 *Tel:* 818-954-0187 *Fax:* 818-954-0189 *Web Site:* www.imagecraftproductions.com, pg 896

Beerger, Norman, Norman Beerger Productions, 4508 Logan Lane, Tolovana Park, OR 97145 *Tel:* 503-919-3453 *E-mail:* nbeerger@yahoo.com *Web Site:* www.thegrandcanyonvideo.com, pg 958

Behr, Lawrence, LBA Technology Inc, 3400 Tupper Dr, Greenville, NC 27834 *Tel:* 252-757-0279 *Toll Free Tel:* 800-522-4464 *Fax:* 252-752-9155 *E-mail:* lbagrp@lbagroup.com *Web Site:* www.lbagroup.com, pg 917

Beimfohr, Rik W, Image Marketing Corp, 1636 N 24 St, Mesa, AZ 85213 *Tel:* 480-969-7032 *Fax:* 480-969-0939 *E-mail:* info@image4u.com *Web Site:* www.image4u.com, pg 895

Beiriger, Lindsay, CaptionMax, 2438 27 Ave S, Minneapolis, MN 55406 *Tel:* 612-341-3566 *Toll Free Tel:* 800-822-3566 *Fax:* 612-341-2345 *Web Site:* www.captionmax.com, pg 820

Bekian, Bob, Loyal Studios, 3513 W Pacific Ave, Burbank, CA 91505 *Tel:* 818-845-5123 (studio); 818-399-9499 *Web Site:* www.loyalstudios.tv, pg 925

Bekian, Bob, Pro HD Rentals, 2201 N Hollywood Way, Suite 1, Burbank, CA 91505 *Tel:* 818-450-1115 *E-mail:* sales@prohdrentals.com *Web Site:* www.prohdrentals.com, pg 983

Belcher, Charles, Onstage Systems, 10930 Petal St, Dallas, TX 75238 *Tel:* 972-686-4488 *Fax:* 972-686-7732 *E-mail:* inquiry@onstagesystems.com *Web Site:* www.onstagesystems.com, pg 963

Belcher, Vickie, Onstage Systems, 10930 Petal St, Dallas, TX 75238 *Tel:* 972-686-4488 *Fax:* 972-686-7732 *E-mail:* inquiry@onstagesystems.com *Web Site:* www.onstagesystems.com, pg 963

Belden, Steve, IVS Imaging, 101 Wrangler Dr, Suite 201, Coppell, TX 75019 *Toll Free Tel:* 888-446-1301 *Fax:* 469-635-6800 *E-mail:* info@ivsimaging.com *Web Site:* www.ivsimaging.com, pg 903

Belding, Carol, Cambridge Documentary Films Inc, 3099 Hidden Valley Lane, Santa Barbara, CA 93108 *Tel:* 617-484-3993 *E-mail:* info@cambridgedocumentaryfilms.org *Web Site:* www.cambridgedocumentaryfilms.org, pg 818

Belew, Sam B, Belew Enterprises, 524 Vance Dr, Bristol, TN 37620 *Tel:* 423-764-4116 *E-mail:* bsv@tricon.net, pg 804

Belgique, Jon, Comtek Communications Technology Inc, 357 W 2700 S, Salt Lake City, UT 84115 *Tel:* 801-466-3463 *Toll Free Tel:* 800-496-3463 *Fax:* 801-484-6906 *E-mail:* sales@comtek.com *Web Site:* www.comtek.com, pg 834

Belgique, Ralph, Comtek Communications Technology Inc, 357 W 2700 S, Salt Lake City, UT 84115 *Tel:* 801-466-3463 *Toll Free Tel:* 800-496-3463 *Fax:* 801-484-6906 *E-mail:* sales@comtek.com *Web Site:* www.comtek.com, pg 834

Belgrad, Doug, Columbia Pictures Inc, 10202 W Washington Blvd, Culver City, CA 90232 *Tel:* 310-244-4000; 310-244-6926 (studio opers) *Fax:* 310-244-8090 *Web Site:* www.sonypicturesstudios.com; www.sonypictures.com, pg 832

Belicove, Jamie, Axxis Inc, 845 S Ninth St, Louisville, KY 40203 *Tel:* 502-568-6030 *Fax:* 502-568-6204 *E-mail:* info@axxisinc.com *Web Site:* www.axxisinc.com, pg 800

Belinky, Charles R PhD, Educational Images Ltd, 660 Fassett Rd, Elmira, NY 14901 *Tel:* 607-732-1090 *Toll Free Tel:* 800-527-4264, pg 857

Belisle, Samuel, Prix Gemeaux (French language TV), 225 rue Roy E, bureau 106, Montreal, QC H2W 1M5, Canada *Tel:* 514-849-7448 *Fax:* 514-849-5069 *E-mail:* academie@acct.ca *Web Site:* www.acct.ca/prixgemeaux; www.acct.ca; www.academy.ca, pg 1124

Belknap, Lori, Cahokia Mounds Museum Society, 30 Ramey Dr, Collinsville, IL 62234 *Tel:* 618-344-7316 *Fax:* 618-346-5162 *E-mail:* museumsociety@cahokiamounds.org *Web Site:* www.cahokiamounds.org, pg 816

Bell, Andrew, New London Media, 78 Washington St, New London, CT 06320 *Tel:* 860-961-6300 *Web Site:* www.andrewclydebell.com, pg 956

Bell, Dr C Ritchie, Laurel Hill Press, PO Box 16516, Chapel Hill, NC 27516-6516 *Toll Free Tel:* 800-942-6516 *Fax:* 919-942-9533 *E-mail:* plantsforus@gmail.com *Web Site:* www.laurelhillpress.com, pg 916

Bell, Dave, Crossroads Audio Inc, 2623 Myrtle Springs Ave, Dallas, TX 75220 *Tel:* 214-358-2623 *Toll Free Tel:* 800-287-0436 *Fax:* 214-358-0185 *E-mail:* mail@crossroadsaudio.com *Web Site:* www.crossroadsaudio.com, pg 840

Bell, Douglas, Cavanaugh Tocci Associates Inc, 327F Boston Post Rd, Sudbury, MA 01776 *Tel:* 978-443-7871 *E-mail:* cta@cavtocci.com *Web Site:* www.cavtocci.com, pg 821

Bell, Emily, CaptionMax, 2438 27 Ave S, Minneapolis, MN 55406 *Tel:* 612-341-3566 *Toll Free Tel:* 800-822-3566 *Fax:* 612-341-2345 *Web Site:* www.captionmax.com, pg 820

Bell, Keith, A & J Cases, 11121 Hindry Ave, Los Angeles, CA 90045 *Tel:* 310-216-2170 *Toll Free Tel:* 800-537-4000 *Fax:* 310-216-2694 *Web Site:* www.ajcases.com, pg 771

Bell, Michael D, Technical Services, 10567 Oak Creek Dr, Lakeside, CA 92040 *Tel:* 619-561-4410 *Web Site:* www.widcoinc.com, pg 1034

Bell, Tona, Tricycle Studios, 1905 E Seventh Ave, Tampa, FL 33605 *Tel:* 813-258-6867 *Fax:* 813-258-8595 *E-mail:* hi@tricyclestudios.com *Web Site:* www.tricyclestudios.com, pg 1045

Bellantoni, Annamaria, Capital - Saratoga Film Commission, 28 Clinton St, Saratoga Springs, NY 12866 *Tel:* 518-584-3255 *Fax:* 518-587-0318 *E-mail:* info@capital-saratogafilm.com *Web Site:* www.saratoga.org, pg 1101

Bellavia, Michael, Animax, 6627 Valjean Ave, Van Nuys, CA 91406 *Tel:* 818-787-4444 *E-mail:* hello@animaxent.com *Web Site:* www.animaxent.com, pg 787

Belliveau, Richard, High End Systems Inc, 2105 Gracy Farms Lane, Austin, TX 78758 *Tel:* 512-836-2242 *Toll Free Tel:* 800-890-8989 *Fax:* 512-837-5290 *E-mail:* info@highend.com *Web Site:* www.highend.com, pg 888

Bellovin, Sheldon, Legion Lighting Co Inc, 221 Glenmore Ave, Brooklyn, NY 11207 *Tel:* 718-498-1770 *Fax:* 718-498-0128 *Toll Free Fax:* 800-4-LEGION (453-4466) *E-mail:* sales@legionlighting.com *Web Site:* www.legionlighting.com, pg 918

Belmont, Al, Final Draft Inc, 26707 W Agoura Rd, Suite 205, Calabasas, CA 91302 *Tel:* 818-995-8995; 818-906-8930 (tech support) *Toll Free Tel:* 800-231-4055 *Fax:* 818-995-4422 *E-mail:* info@finaldraft.com *Web Site:* www.finaldraft.com, pg 868

Belofsky, Rachel, Screamfest® Horror Film Festival & Screenplay Competition, 8840 Wilshire Blvd, 3rd fl, Beverly Hills, CA 90211 *Tel:* 310-358-3273 *Fax:* 310-358-3272 *E-mail:* info@screamfestla.com *Web Site:* www.screamfestla.com, pg 1126

Belsey, Laura, Shadow Pictures Inc, 319 Sixth Ave, No 4-F, New York, NY 10014 *Tel:* 212-929-8906; 917-545-9870 *E-mail:* info@shadowpictures.com *Web Site:* www.shadowpictures.com; laurabelsey.com, pg 1007

Belz, Dee, Miami-Dade Office of Film & Entertainment, 111 NW First St, Suite 2200, Miami, FL 33128 *Tel:* 305-375-3288 *Fax:* 305-375-3266 *E-mail:* filmoffice@miamigov.com *Web Site:* www.filmiami.org, pg 1096

Bena, Thomas, The Martha's Vineyard Film Festival (MVFF), PO Box 592, 9 State Rd, Chilmark, MA 02535 *Tel:* 508-645-9599 *Fax:* 508-645-9893 *Web Site:* www.tmvff.org, pg 1119

Benatar, Owen, U-Edit Video, 1002 N Central Expwy, Suite 555, Richardson, TX 75080 *Tel:* 972-690-EDIT (690-3348) *Fax:* 214-884-3687 *Web Site:* www.ueditvideo.com, pg 1047

Bendell, Curtis A, Tele-Time Systems, 313 Parkway Dr, Cary, IL 60013 *Tel:* 847-640-1420 *E-mail:* teletimesystems@netzero.com *Web Site:* www.teletimesystems.com, pg 1036

Bender, William, Tobias Associates Inc, 50 Industrial Dr, Warminster, PA 18974-1433 *Tel:* 215-322-1500 *Toll Free Tel:* 800-877-3367 *Fax:* 215-322-1504 *E-mail:* sales@tobiasinc.com *Web Site:* www.densitometers.net, pg 1041

Bendesky, Eitan, Pico Digital, 8880 Rehco Rd, San Diego, CA 92121 *Tel:* 858-546-5050 *Toll Free Tel:* 800-421-6511 *Fax:* 858-546-5051; 858-546-5055 (intl) *E-mail:* sales@picodigital.com *Web Site:* picodigital.com, pg 975

Benedetto, Cindy, Robert Benedetto, 10 Mall Terr, Suite A, Savannah, GA 31406 *Tel:* 912-692-1400 *Fax:* 912-692-1403 *Web Site:* www.benedettoguitars.com, pg 805

Benedetto, Robert, Robert Benedetto, 10 Mall Terr, Suite A, Savannah, GA 31406 *Tel:* 912-692-1400 *Fax:* 912-692-1403 *Web Site:* www.benedettoguitars.com, pg 805

Benghiat, Michael, The Music Kitchen Inc, 12400 Connery Way, Bakersfield, CA 93312 *Tel:* 661-338-4749 *Fax:* 661-338-2514 *Web Site:* www.themusickitchen.com, pg 950

Benioff, Louis, Leonardo Software, 11726 San Vicente Blvd, Suite 520, Los Angeles, CA 90049 *Tel:* 310-820-9961 *Toll Free Tel:* 800-606-4536 *Fax:* 310-820-9970 *E-mail:* info@leonardosoft.com *Web Site:* www.leonardosoft.com, pg 919

Benjamin, Cary M, TR Productions, 2 13 St, 3rd fl, Charlestown, MA 02129 *Tel:* 617-241-5500 *E-mail:* info@trprod.com *Web Site:* www.trprod.com, pg 1043

Benjamin, Chris, Benjamin Creative Productions, 577 Lakeside Dr, Waterford, MI 48328 *Tel:* 248-682-6566 *Fax:* 248-682-0508 *Web Site:* www.benjaminvideo.com, pg 805

Benko, James S, International Tae Kwon Do Association (ITA Institute), PO Box 281, Grand Blanc, MI 48480 *Tel:* 810-232-6482 *Fax:* 810-235-8594 *E-mail:* hq@itatkd.com *Web Site:* www.itatkd.com, pg 901

Benner, William R, Pangolin Laser Systems Inc, 9501 Satellite Blvd, Suite 109, Orlando, FL 32837 *Tel:* 407-299-2088 *Toll Free Tel:* 800-PAN-GOLIN (726-4654) *Fax:* 407-299-6066 *E-mail:* contact@pangolin.com *Web Site:* www.pangolin.com, pg 968

Bennett, Betty, Apogee Electronics Corp, 1715 Berkeley St, Santa Monica, CA 90404 *Tel:* 310-584-9394 *Fax:* 310-584-9385 *Web Site:* www.apogeedigital.com, pg 788

Bennett, David, Westbury National Show Systems Ltd, 772 Warden Ave, Toronto, ON M1L 4T7, Canada *Tel:* 416-752-1371 *Fax:* 416-752-1382 *E-mail:* mail@westbury.com *Web Site:* www.westbury.com, pg 1064

Bennett, Julie, New Harbinger Publications, 5674 Shattuck Ave, Oakland, CA 94609 *Tel:* 510-652-0215 *Toll Free Tel:* 800-748-6273 *Fax:* 510-652-5472 *E-mail:* customerservice@newharbinger.com *Web Site:* www.newharbinger.com, pg 955

Bennett, Lisa, The CD Recycling Center of America, 68 Stiles Rd, Salem, NH 03079 *Tel:* 603-894-5553 *Fax:* 603-898-4319 *E-mail:* info@cdrecyclingcenter.org *Web Site:* www.cdrecyclingcenter.org, pg 822

Bennett, Lynn, Stage Post, 255 French Landing Dr, Nashville, TN 37228 *Tel:* 615-248-1978 *Toll Free Tel:* 877-250-1839 *Fax:* 615-242-8861 *E-mail:* mail@stagepost.com *Web Site:* www.stagepost.com, pg 1022

Bennett, Michael, TMW Media Group, 2321 Abbot Kinney Blvd, Suite 101, Venice, CA 90291 *Tel:* 310-577-8581 *Toll Free Tel:* 800-262-8862 *Fax:* 310-574-0886 *E-mail:* sale@tmwmedia.com *Web Site:* www.tmwmedia.com, pg 1041

Bennett, Patrick, Xytech Systems Corp, 15451 San Fernando Mission Blvd, Suite 400, Mission Hills, CA 91345 *Tel:* 818-698-4900 *Fax:* 818-698-4901 *E-mail:* sales@xytechsystems.com *Web Site:* www.xytechsystems.com, pg 1071

Bennett, Richard, Cinema Engineering Co, 14737 Arminta St, Unit B, Panorama City, CA 91402 *Tel:* 818-780-5404 *Fax:* 818-780-5405 *E-mail:* cinemaengineering@tcsn.net; cinemagear@cinemagear.com *Web Site:* www.cinema-engineering.com; www.cinemagear.com, pg 827

Bennett, Stewart, Crossroads Audio Inc, 2623 Myrtle Springs Ave, Dallas, TX 75220 *Tel:* 214-358-2623 *Toll Free Tel:* 800-287-0436 *Fax:* 214-358-0185 *E-mail:* mail@crossroadsaudio.com *Web Site:* www.crossroadsaudio.com, pg 840

Bennett, Tracy, Maui County Film Office, Off of Economic Devt, One Main Plaza, 2200 S Main St, Suite 305, Wailuku, HI 96793 *Tel:* 808-270-7710 *Fax:* 808-270-7995 *Web Site:* www.co.maui.hi.us, pg 1097

Beno, Max, JR Media Services, 2501 W Burbank Blvd, Suite 200, Burbank, CA 91505 *Tel:* 818-557-0200 *Fax:* 818-557-0201 *E-mail:* info@jrmediaservices.com *Web Site:* www.jrmediaservices.com, pg 906

Benoit, Byrnes, Spectra Video Productions Ltd, 309 Wardlaw Ave, Winnipeg, MB R3L 0L5, Canada *Tel:* 204-452-9832 *Web Site:* www.spectra-productions.com, pg 1020

Benson, Chip, Technical Support Systems LLC, 2232 Central Ave, Memphis, TN 38104 *Tel:* 901-398-5908 *Fax:* 901-398-5914 *Web Site:* www.techsupportsys.com, pg 1034

Benson, James, Vision Quest Productions Inc, PO Box 1896, Wayne, NJ 07470-1896 *Tel:* 973-686-9400 *Fax:* 973-694-8314 *Web Site:* vqpi.yolasite.com, pg 1058

Benson, Mike, Stage America LLC, 4001 S Decatur 37, Suite 532, Las Vegas, NV 89103 *Tel:* 702-879-8177 *Toll Free Fax:* 877-488-6663 *E-mail:* info@stageamerica.com *Web Site:* www.stageamerica.com, pg 1022

Bentley, Anne, PBS Video, 1320 Braddock Place, Alexandria, VA 22314 *Tel:* 703-739-5021 *E-mail:* video@pbs.org *Web Site:* video.pbs.org; www.shoppbs.org, pg 970

Bentley, Craig, Imageworks, 1039 Meade Ave, San Diego, CA 92116-1038 *Tel:* 619-239-6161 *E-mail:* info@imageworks.tv *Web Site:* www.imageworks.tv, pg 896

Bentley, Ginny, Limelight Productions Inc, 471 Pleasant St, Lee, MA 01238-9322 *Tel:* 413-243-4950 *Toll Free Tel:* 800-243-4950 *Fax:* 413-243-4993 *Toll Free Fax:* 800-243-4951 *E-mail:* info@limelightproductions.com *Web Site:* www.limelightproductions.com, pg 921

Benton, Darrell, Diversified Imaging Supply, 333 Alondra Blvd, Gardena, CA 90248, pg 849

Benton, Paul, TPR Enterprises Ltd, 644 Fayette Ave, Mamaroneck, NY 10543 *Tel:* 914-698-1141 *Fax:* 914-698-9419 *E-mail:* info@tprlights.com *Web Site:* www.tprlights.com, pg 1043

Benton, Thomas J, Direct Marketing Association Inc (DMA), 1120 Avenue of the Americas, New York, NY 10036-6700 *Tel:* 212-768-7277 *Fax:* 212-302-6714 *Web Site:* thedma.org, pg 1081

Beran, Angela, Sonoma Valley Chamber of Commerce, 651-A Broadway, Sonoma, CA 95476-7041 *Tel:* 707-996-1033 *Fax:* 707-996-9402 *E-mail:* info@sonomachamber.com *Web Site:* sonomachamber.org, pg 1016, 1094

Berardi, John, Wildfire Lighting & Visual Effects, 2908 Oregon Ct, Suite G1, Torrance, CA 90503 *Tel:* 310-755-6780 *Toll Free Tel:* 800-937-8065 *Fax:* 310-755-6781 *E-mail:* mail@wildfirefx.com; sales@wildfirefx.com *Web Site:* www.wildfirefx.com, pg 1066

Berberian, Jack, Color Leasing Studios, 330 Rte 46 E, Fairfield, NJ 07004 *Tel:* 973-575-1118 *Fax:* 973-575-1170 *Web Site:* www.colorleasingstudios.com, pg 831

Berdelle, Robert, United Way Worldwide, 701 N Fairfax St, Alexandria, VA 22314-2045 *Tel:* 703-836-7112 *Fax:* 703-519-0097 *Web Site:* www.unitedway.org, pg 1048

Berg, James, Matson Multi-Media, 403 E Ramsey Rd, Suite 101, San Antonio, TX 78216 *Tel:* 210-349-3674 *Fax:* 210-340-5710 *E-mail:* sales@matsonmultimedia.com *Web Site:* www.matsonmultimedia.com, pg 934

Bergan, William, Championship Productions Inc, Ames Community Development Park, 2730 Graham St, Ames, IA 50010 *Tel:* 515-232-3687 *Toll Free Tel:* 800-873-2730 *Fax:* 515-232-3739 *E-mail:* info@championshipproductions.com *Web Site:* www.championshipproductions.com, pg 823

Berge, Patrick, Sceno Plus, 5423 ave de Lorimier, Montreal, QC H2H 2C3, Canada *Tel:* 514-529-4364 *Fax:* 514-529-9164 *E-mail:* project@sceno-plus.com *Web Site:* www.sceno-plus.com, pg 1004

Bergens, Arthur, Bell & Howell LLC, 760 S Wolf Rd, Wheeling, IL 60090 *Tel:* 847-675-7600 *Toll Free Tel:* 800-220-3030 (cust serv) *E-mail:* marketing@bhemail.com *Web Site:* www.bellhowell.net, pg 804

Berger, Lee, Rhythm & Hues, 2100 E Grand Ave, Suite A, El Segundo, CA 90245-5024 *Tel:* 310-448-7500 *Fax:* 310-448-7600 *E-mail:* info-la@rhythm.com *Web Site:* www.rhythm.com, pg 996

Berger, Sherwin, Lipsner-Smith Co, 4700 Chase Ave, Lincolnwood, IL 60712-1689 *Tel:* 847-677-3000 *Toll Free Tel:* 800-323-7520 *Fax:* 847-677-1311 *Toll Free Fax:* 800-784-6733 *E-mail:* sales@lipsner.com; sales@rtico.com *Web Site:* www.lipsner.com, pg 922

Berger, Sherwin, Research Technology International (RTI), 4700 Chase Ave, Lincolnwood, IL 60712-1689 *Tel:* 847-677-3000 *Toll Free Tel:* 800-323-7520 *Fax:* 847-677-1311 *Toll Free Fax:* 800-784-6733 *E-mail:* sales@rtico.com *Web Site:* www.rtico.com, pg 995

Bergeron, Mike, Dolby Labs Inc, 100 Potrero Ave, San Francisco, CA 94103-4813 *Tel:* 415-558-0200 *Fax:* 415-645-4000 *E-mail:* info@dolby.com *Web Site:* www.dolby.com, pg 850

Bergin, Fran, Vancouver International Film Festival, Vancouver International Film Centre, 1181 Seymour St, Vancouver, BC V6B 3M7, Canada *Tel:* 604-685-0260 *Fax:* 604-688-8221 *E-mail:* viff@viff.org *Web Site:* www.viff.org, pg 1129

Bergman, Richard I, The Bergman Collection of Medical/Technical/Scientific Stock Images, 134 Leabrook Lane, Princeton, NJ 08540-3622 *Tel:* 609-921-0749 *E-mail:* information@pmiprinceton.com *Web Site:* pmiprinceton.com, pg 805

Bergman, Victoria B, The Bergman Collection of Medical/Technical/Scientific Stock Images, 134 Leabrook Lane, Princeton, NJ 08540-3622 *Tel:* 609-921-0749 *E-mail:* information@pmiprinceton.com *Web Site:* pmiprinceton.com, pg 805

Bergs, M J, TARA Labs, 1020 Benson Way, Ashland, OR 97520 *Tel:* 541-488-6465 *Fax:* 541-488-6463 *E-mail:* sales@taralabs.com *Web Site:* www.taralabs.com, pg 1032

Berk, Robert C, Creative Technology, 137 Heritage Woods Dr, Akron, OH 44321 *Tel:* 330-668-7777 *Fax:* 330-665-3718 *Web Site:* www.creativetechnology.com, pg 838

Berk, Roger, Creative Technology, 137 Heritage Woods Dr, Akron, OH 44321 *Tel:* 330-668-7777 *Fax:* 330-665-3718 *Web Site:* www.creativetechnology.com, pg 838

Berke, Nancy, Berke Creative Inc, 50 Mendell St, Suite 11, San Francisco, CA 94124 *Tel:* 415-285-8800 *Fax:* 415-285-8847 *Web Site:* www.berkesound.com, pg 805

Berkeley, Brian, Society for Information Display (SID), 1475 S Bascom Ave, Suite 114, Campbell, CA 95008-4006 *Tel:* 408-879-3901 *Fax:* 408-879-3833 *E-mail:* office@sid.org *Web Site:* www.sid.org, pg 1089

Berkowitz, Robert, Multivision Video & Film, 4006 Aurora St, Coral Gables, FL 33146 *Tel:* 305-662-6011 *E-mail:* info@multivisionvideo.com *Web Site:* www.multivisionvideo.com, pg 950

Berlin, David M, Video Corporation of America (VCA), 7 Veronica Ave, Somerset, NJ 08873 *Tel:* 732-545-8000 *Fax:* 732-545-5101 *E-mail:* njsales@vcaglobal.com *Web Site:* www.vcaglobal.com, pg 1055

Berlin, Jack, Accusoft, 4001 N Riverside Dr, Tampa, FL 33603 *Tel:* 813-875-7575 *Toll Free Tel:* 800-875-7009 *Fax:* 813-875-7705 *E-mail:* sales@accusoft.com *Web Site:* www.accusoft.com, pg 774

Berman, Jan, Developmental Studies Center, 1250 53 St, Suite 3, Emeryville, CA 94608 *Tel:* 510-533-0213 *Toll Free Tel:* 800-666-7270 *Fax:* 510-464-3670 *E-mail:* info@devstu.org; customer_service@devstu.org *Web Site:* www.devstu.org, pg 846

Berman, Scott E, Advanced Imaging Concepts Inc, 301 N Harrison St, Bldg B, Suite 266, Princeton, NJ 08540 *Tel:* 609-921-3629; 609-529-9200 *Fax:* 609-924-3010 *E-mail:* info@aic-imagecentral.com; sales@aic-imagecentral.com *Web Site:* www.aic-imagecentral.com, pg 777

Berman-Bogdan, Jessica, Global ImageWorks LLC, 65 Beacon St, Haworth, NJ 07641 *Tel:* 201-384-7715 *Fax:* 201-501-8971 *E-mail:* info@globalimageworks.com *Web Site:* www.globalimageworks.com, pg 879

Bernard, John, Lumisphere™ USA, 9429 Everett Ct, Spotsylvania, VA 22553 *Tel:* 540-582-7897 *Fax:* 540-582-5233 *E-mail:* jrbent@starpower.net *Web Site:* www.lumisphereusa.com, pg 926

Bernatsky, Peter, Advance Pro, 1300 Portage Ave, Winnipeg, MB R3G 0V1, Canada *Tel:* 204-772-0386 *Toll Free Tel:* 800-392-1295 *Fax:* 204-783-2177 *E-mail:* ap@advance.mb.ca *Web Site:* www.advance-pro.com, pg 777

Berne, Ellen, Ideal Large Format Imaging Services, 15737 Crabbs Branch Way, Rockville, MD 20855 *Tel:* 301-468-0123 *Toll Free Tel:* 800-76IDEAL (764-3325) *Fax:* 301-230-0813 *E-mail:* sales@ideal.com *Web Site:* www.ideal.com, pg 894

Berney, Ellen, Satellite Media Production, 8379 Inspiration Ave, Walkersville, MD 21793 *Tel:* 301-845-2737 *Toll Free Tel:* 800-747-0856 *Web Site:* www.satellitemediaproduction.com; www.oldietv.com, pg 1003

Berney, Fred, Satellite Media Production, 8379 Inspiration Ave, Walkersville, MD 21793 *Tel:* 301-845-2737 *Toll Free Tel:* 800-747-0856 *Web Site:* www.satellitemediaproduction.com; www.oldietv.com, pg 1003

Bernotas, Peter, International Historic Films Inc, 3533 S Archer Ave, Chicago, IL 60609 *Tel:* 773-927-2900 *Fax:* 773-927-9211 *E-mail:* info@ihffilm.com *Web Site:* www.ihffilm.com, pg 901

Bernotas, Peter, Intervideo Duplication Services, 3533 S Archer Ave, Chicago, IL 60609 *Tel:* 773-927-9091 *Fax:* 773-927-9211 *E-mail:* info@intervideoduplication.com *Web Site:* www.intervideoduplication.com, pg 902

Bernstein, David, Graphics Depot Inc, 11 Middlebury Blvd, Unit 4, Randolph, NJ 07869 *Tel:* 973-927-8200 *Fax:* 973-927-8253 *E-mail:* info@graphicsdepotinc.com; sales@graphicsdepotinc.com *Web Site:* www.graphicsdepotinc.com, pg 881

Berry, Denise, A&S Case Co Inc, 5260 Vineland Ave, North Hollywood, CA 91601 *Tel:* 818-509-5920 *Toll Free Tel:* 800-394-6181 *Fax:* 818-509-1397 *E-mail:* info@ascase.com *Web Site:* www.ascase.com, pg 772

Berry, Jack, Image Management Systems Inc, 239 W 15 St, New York, NY 10011 *Tel:* 212-741-8765 *Fax:* 212-243-2344 *E-mail:* ims@imagemgt.com *Web Site:* www.imagemgt.com, pg 895

Berry, Kirk, Mastery Technologies Inc, 41216 Bridge St, Novi, MI 48375 *Tel:* 972-943-9214 *Toll Free Tel:* 800-258-3837 *Fax:* 248-888-8424 *E-mail:* sales@masterytech.com *Web Site:* www.masterytech.com, pg 934

Berry, Scot, Memphis Communications Corp, 4771 Summer Ave, Memphis, TN 38122 *Tel:* 901-725-9271 *Fax:* 901-272-3577, pg 938

Berry, Shane, Memphis Communications Corp, 4771 Summer Ave, Memphis, TN 38122 *Tel:* 901-725-9271 *Fax:* 901-272-3577, pg 938

Bersell, Sean, The Entertainment Merchants Association (EMA), 16530 Ventura Blvd, Suite 400, Encino, CA 91436-4551 *Tel:* 818-385-1500 *Fax:* 818-933-0910 *E-mail:* emaoffice@entmerch.org *Web Site:* www.entmerch.org, pg 1081

Bertelsen, Jeffrey, CyberOptics, 5900 Golden Hills Dr, Minneapolis, MN 55416 *Tel:* 763-542-5000 *Fax:* 763-542-5100 *E-mail:* info@cyberoptics.com *Web Site:* cyberoptics.com, pg 841

Berthiaume, Lorraine, Sceno Plus, 5423 ave de Lorimier, Montreal, QC H2H 2C3, Canada *Tel:* 514-529-4364 *Fax:* 514-529-9164 *E-mail:* project@sceno-plus.com *Web Site:* www.sceno-plus.com, pg 1004

Bertolino, Daniel, Les Productions Via Le Monde (Daniel Bertolino) Inc, 1222 rue MacKay, Suite 201, Montreal, QC H3G 2H4, Canada *Tel:* 514-285-1658 *Fax:* 514-285-1970 *Web Site:* www.vialemonde.com, pg 985

Bertoni, Elliot, Showman Fabricators Inc, 47-22 Pearson Place, Long Island City, NY 11101 *Tel:* 718-935-9899 *Fax:* 718-855-9823 *E-mail:* info@showfab.com *Web Site:* www.showfab.com, pg 1010

Bertrand, Bruce, Early Films, 9 Richter St, Randolph, NJ 07869-3309 *Tel:* 973-361-5817 *Fax:* 973-361-2748 *E-mail:* info@earlyfilms.net *Web Site:* www.earlyfilms.net, pg 855

Bertrand, Marc, Tannoy North America Inc, 335 Gage Ave, Suite 1, Kitchener, ON N2M 5E1, Canada *Tel:* 519-745-1158 *Fax:* 519-745-2364 *E-mail:* info@tcgroup-americas.com *Web Site:* www.tannoy.com, pg 1031

Berzan, Jane, Direct Marketing Association Inc (DMA), 1120 Avenue of the Americas, New York, NY 10036-6700 *Tel:* 212-768-7277 *Fax:* 212-302-6714 *Web Site:* thedma.org, pg 1081

Bettan, Gary, Videoguys, 10-12 Charles St, Glen Cove, NY 11542 *Tel:* 516-759-1611 *Toll Free Tel:* 800-323-2325 *Fax:* 516-671-3092 *E-mail:* sales@videoguys.com *Web Site:* www.videoguys.com, pg 1057

Betts, D R, Schoolhouse Audio Visual, 1000 20 St, Plano, TX 75074 *Tel:* 972-423-5874 *Toll Free Tel:* 800-338-8116 *Fax:* 972-424-3501 *E-mail:* sav@schoolhouseav.com *Web Site:* www.schoolhouseav.com, pg 1004

Betts, Susan, Actors Attic, 540 Otis Dr, Dover, DE 19901 *Tel:* 302-734-8214 *Fax:* 302-734-8207 *E-mail:* sales@actorsattic.com *Web Site:* www.actorsattic.com, pg 775

Beugen, Joan, Cresta Creative, 1050 N State St, Chicago, IL 60610 *Tel:* 312-944-4700 *Fax:* 312-944-1582 *E-mail:* info@crestagroup.com *Web Site:* www.crestacreative.com, pg 839

Beuka, Robert, Suffolk County Film Commission, H Lee Dennison Bldg, 2nd fl, 100 Veterans Memorial Hwy, Hauppauge, NY 11788-0099 *Tel:* 631-853-4800 *Fax:* 631-853-4888 *Web Site:* www.suffolkcountyfilmcommission.com, pg 1100

Bevan, Darrel, Data Check Video Inc, 5148-E Commerce Ave, Moorpark, CA 93021 *Tel:* 805-517-1907 *Fax:* 805-552-0744 *E-mail:* mail@datacheck.com *Web Site:* www.datacheck.com, pg 843

Beverly, Morris, A/V Presentations Inc, 104 Otis St, Suite 30, Northborough, MA 01532 *Tel:* 508-393-9767 *Toll Free Tel:* 800-648-7176 *Fax:* 508-393-6698 *Web Site:* www.avpresentations.com, pg 797

Beverly, Nelson D, Love Your Shorts Film Festival, 608 S Elm Ave, Sanford, FL 32771 *E-mail:* contact@loveyourshorts.com *Web Site:* www.loveyourshorts.com, pg 1119

Bevilacqua, Joe, Bevilacqua Studios, 202 E 42 St, New York, NY 10017 *Tel:* 212-490-0355 *Fax:* 212-490-0355, pg 806

Bevilacqua, Joe, New Horizon Studios, 202 E 42 St, New York, NY 10017 *Tel:* 212-490-0355 *Fax:* 212-490-0355, pg 955

Beyers, Scott, Beyers Sound & Essay Audio, PO Box 120442, St Paul, MN 55112-0018 *Tel:* 651-633-3933 *E-mail:* info@essayaudio.com *Web Site:* www.essayaudio.com, pg 806

Bhure, Roofi, Creative Custom Cases, 14946 Shoemaker Ave, Suite D, Santa Fe Springs, CA 90670 *Tel:* 562-404-5500 *Fax:* 562-404-5505 *E-mail:* info@creativecc.net *Web Site:* www.creativecc.net, pg 838

Bhuyan, Preeti, Asia Society, 725 Park Ave, New York, NY 10021 *Tel:* 212-288-6400 *Fax:* 212-517-8315 *E-mail:* pr@asiasociety.org *Web Site:* www.asiasociety.org; www.asiasociety.org/video, pg 792

Bianco, Bob, Deluxe Laboratories Inc, 5433 Fernwood Ave, Hollywood, CA 90027 *Tel:* 323-960-3600 *Fax:* 323-960-7016 *Web Site:* www.bydeluxe.com, pg 845

Biase, Mark, The Production Group Studios, 6767 W Sunset Blvd, No 8-496, Hollywood, CA 90028-7177 *Tel:* 323-469-8111 *Fax:* 323-962-2182 *E-mail:* info@productiongroup.tv *Web Site:* www.productiongroup.tv, pg 984

Bidermann-Roizen, Camille, International Emmy® Awards, 25 W 52 St, New York, NY 10019 *Tel:* 212-489-6969 *Fax:* 212-489-6557 *E-mail:* iemmys@iemmys.tv; awardsdept@iemmys.tv *Web Site:* www.iemmys.tv, pg 1117

Bieda, Bill, The Video Store Shopper, 3987 Heritage Oak Ct, Simi Valley, CA 93063 *Tel:* 805-583-8500 *Toll Free Tel:* 800-462-9040; 800-325-6867 (cust serv) *Fax:* 805-583-8546 *Toll Free Fax:* 800-947-2060 *E-mail:* sales@shopperinc.com; customerservice@shopperinc.com *Web Site:* www.thevideostoreshopper.com, pg 1056

Bigelow, Jeff, Hubbard Supply Co, 901 W Second St, Flint, MI 48503 *Tel:* 810-234-8681 *Toll Free Tel:* 800-875-4811 *Fax:* 810-234-6142 *E-mail:* information@hubbardsupply.com *Web Site:* www.hubbardsupply.com, pg 892

Bignell, Allan, WESCAM Inc, 649 N Service Rd W, Burlington, ON L7P 5B9, Canada *Tel:* 905-633-4000 *Toll Free Tel:* 800-668-4355 *Fax:* 905-633-4100 *E-mail:* sales.wescam@l-3com.com *Web Site:* www.wescam.com, pg 1063

Bilbrey, David, Saturn Awards, 334 W 54 St, Los Angeles, CA 90037 *Tel:* 323-752-5811 *Web Site:* www.saturnawards.org, pg 1126

Bill, Jeff, IDenticard Systems Inc, 25 Race Ave, 1st fl, Lancaster, PA 17603 *Tel:* 717-569-5797 *Toll Free Tel:* 800-233-0298 *Fax:* 717-427-1654 *E-mail:* identicard.info@identicard.com *Web Site:* www.identicard.com, pg 894

Billin, Todd, Ascom Communications Contractors, 11952 James St, Holland, MI 49424 *Tel:* 616-820-1289 *Toll Free Tel:* 800-968-2444 *Fax:* 616-538-4311 *E-mail:* info@ascominc.com *Web Site:* www.ascomllc.com, pg 792

Billings, Mr, FM Systems Inc, 3877 S Main St, Santa Ana, CA 92707 *Tel:* 714-979-3355 *Toll Free Tel:* 800-235-6960 *Fax:* 714-979-0913 *E-mail:* fmsystemsinc@sbcglobal.net *Web Site:* www.fmsystems-inc.com, pg 870

Billingsley, Joseph, Pelican Publishing Co, 1000 Burmaster St, Gretna, LA 70053-2246 *Tel:* 504-368-1175 *Toll Free Tel:* 800-843-1724; 888-PELICAN (735-4226 - cust serv); 888-5PELICAN (888-573-5422) *Fax:* 504-368-1195 *E-mail:* sales@pelicanpub.com *Web Site:* www.pelicanpub.com, pg 971

Bingham, Tony, Association for Talent Development (ATD), 1640 King St, Alexandria, VA 22314-2743 *Tel:* 703-683-8100 *Toll Free Tel:* 800-628-2783 *Fax:* 703-299-8723; 703-683-1523 (cust care) *E-mail:* customercare@td.org *Web Site:* www.td.org; www.astd.org, pg 1078

Binns, Michael, Acoustical Solutions Inc, 2420 Grenoble Rd, Richmond, VA 23294 *Tel:* 804-346-8350 *Toll Free Tel:* 800-782-5742 *Fax:* 804-346-8808 *E-mail:* info@acousticalsolutions.com *Web Site:* www.acousticalsolutions.com, pg 774

Bione, John, First Run Features, The Film Center Bldg, Suite 1213, 630 Ninth Ave, New York, NY 10036-3708 *Tel:* 212-243-0600 *Fax:* 212-989-7649 *E-mail:* info@firstrunfeatures.com *Web Site:* www.firstrunfeatures.com, pg 869

Bird, Jim, The PPS Group, 424 Scott St, Covington, KY 41011 *Tel:* 859-291-5100 *Toll Free Tel:* 800-978-3445 *Fax:* 859-291-5150 *E-mail:* info@theppsgroup.com *Web Site:* www.pps-inc.com; www.theppsgroup.com, pg 980

Bird, Jolie, Quickdraw Animation Society, 351 11 Ave SW, Suite 201, Calgary, AB T2R 0C7, Canada *Tel:* 403-261-5767 *Fax:* 403-261-5644 *E-mail:* info@quickdrawanimation.ca; production@quickdrawanimation.ca; programming@quickdrawanimation.ca *Web Site:* quickdrawanimation.ca; www.giraffest.ca, pg 1088

Bird, Justin, Utopia Films, 1976 S La Cienega Blvd, No 130, Los Angeles, CA 90034 *Tel:* 310-338-0580 *Fax:* 313-557-0580 *E-mail:* reception@utopiafilms.com; utopiafilms2@gmail.com (large e-mails); production@utopiafilms.com (reels) *Web Site:* utopiafilms.com, pg 1051

Bird, Patrick, SonicPool, 6860 Lexington Ave, Hollywood, CA 90038 *Tel:* 323-460-4649 *Toll Free Tel:* 866-203-7213 *Fax:* 323-460-6063 *E-mail:* production@sonicpool.com *Web Site:* www.sonicpool.com, pg 1016

Birkmeyer, Carl, Library Video Network (LVN), 320 York Rd, Towson, MD 21204 *Tel:* 410-887-2090 *Toll Free Tel:* 800-441-8273 *Fax:* 410-887-2091 *E-mail:* lvn@bcpl.net *Web Site:* www.lvn.org, pg 920

Birks, Heather, BEA National Scholarships in Broadcasting, 1771 "N" St NW, Washington, DC 20036-2891 *Tel:* 202-602-0587 *Fax:* 202-609-9940 *E-mail:* help@beaweb.org *Web Site:* www.beaweb.org, pg 1109

Birks, Heather, Broadcast Education Association (BEA), 1771 "N" St NW, Washington, DC 20036-2891 *Fax:* 202-609-9940 *E-mail:* help@beaweb.org *Web Site:* www.beaweb.org, pg 1079

Birnbaum, Harvey M, Producer East Productions, 43 Mandrake Rd, Monroe Township, NJ 08831 *Tel:* 631-455-9636 *Web Site:* www.producereast.com, pg 983

Birnbaum, Roslyn, Producer East Productions, 43 Mandrake Rd, Monroe Township, NJ 08831 *Tel:* 631-455-9636 *Web Site:* www.producereast.com, pg 983

Bishop, David, Sony Pictures Home Entertainment, 10202 W Washington Blvd, Culver City, CA 90232-3119 *Tel:* 310-244-4000 *Fax:* 310-244-2485 *Web Site:* www.sonypictures.com, pg 1016

Bishop, Mark, Marblemedia, 74 Fraser Ave, Suite 100, Toronto, ON M6K 3E1, Canada *Tel:* 416-646-2711 *E-mail:* connect@marblemedia.com *Web Site:* www.marblemedia.com, pg 930

Bishop, William, Penn State University MediaTech, 14 Wagner Annex, State College, PA 16803-1886 *Tel:* 814-865-6314; 814-863-3202 *Toll Free Tel:* 800-826-0132 *Fax:* 814-863-2574 *E-mail:* mtssmed@psulias.psu.edu *Web Site:* www.libraries.psu.edu/mtss; www.medianet.libraries.psu.edu, pg 972

Bisk, Michael D, Bisk Education, 9417 Princess Palm Ave, Tampa, FL 33619 *Toll Free Tel:* 800-280-9718 *E-mail:* customerservice@bisk.com *Web Site:* www.bisk.com, pg 808

Bisk, Nathan, Bisk Education, 9417 Princess Palm Ave, Tampa, FL 33619 *Toll Free Tel:* 800-280-9718 *E-mail:* customerservice@bisk.com *Web Site:* www.bisk.com, pg 808

Bissen, Kathy, Wisconsin Public Television, 821 University Ave, Madison, WI 53706 *Tel:* 608-263-2121 *Toll Free Tel:* 800-422-9707 *Fax:* 608-263-9763 *E-mail:* comments@wpt.org *Web Site:* www.wpt.org, pg 1068

Bissinger, Thomas, Primary Press, PO Box 83, St Peters, PA 19470-0083 *Tel:* 610-469-9029, pg 982

Bisson, Linda, Sennheiser (Canada) Inc, 221 ave Labrosse, Pointe Claire, QC H9R 1A3, Canada *Tel:* 514-426-3013 *Toll Free Tel:* 800-463-1006 *Fax:* 514-426-3953 *Toll Free Fax:* 800-463-3013 *E-mail:* info@sennheiser.ca *Web Site:* www.sennheiser.ca, pg 1006

Bissonette, Peter, Learning Strategies Corp, 2000 Plymouth Rd, Minnetonka, MN 55305-2335 *Tel:* 952-767-9800 *Toll Free Tel:* 888-800-2688 (cust serv); 866-292-1861 (24 hour order line) *Fax:* 952-475-2373 *E-mail:* info@learningstrategies.com *Web Site:* www.learningstrategies.com, pg 917

Bissonnette, Daniel, Montreal Film & TV Commission, Duke Pavilion, 5th fl, 801 Brennan St, Montreal, QC H3C 0G4, Canada *Tel:* 514-872-2883 *Fax:* 514-872-3409 *E-mail:* film.tv@ville.montreal.qc.ca *Web Site:* www.montrealfilm.com, pg 1105

Bittman, Karen, TouchStar Productions Inc, 522 Jackson Park Dr, Meadville, PA 16335 *Tel:* 814-337-8192 *Toll Free Tel:* 800-759-1294 *Fax:* 814-337-0699 *E-mail:* doctorb@touchstarpro.com *Web Site:* www.touchstarpro.com, pg 1042

Black, Andy, Audio Media Productions, 6739 Kirby Trace Cove, Memphis, TN 38119 *Tel:* 901-751-2363 *E-mail:* ampman@aol.com *Web Site:* www.audiomediaprod.com, pg 794

Black, Betty, Mississippi Film Office, 501 N West St, Suite B-01, Jackson, MS 39201 *Tel:* 601-359-3297 *Fax:* 601-359-5048 *Web Site:* www.filmmississippi.org, pg 1099

Black, Christine, NFL Films Music Library, One Sabol Way, Mount Laurel, NJ 08054 *Tel:* 856-222-3500 *Fax:* 856-638-0754 *E-mail:* nflfilms@nfl.com *Web Site:* www.nflfilms.com, pg 957

Black, Cindy, Coyote Cowboy Co, PO Box 2190, Benson, AZ 85602-2190 *Tel:* 520-586-1077 *Toll Free Tel:* 800-654-2550 *Web Site:* baxterblack.com, pg 837

Black, Craig, Blackstone Audio Inc, 31 Mistletoe Rd, Ashland, OR 97520 *Toll Free Tel:* 800-621-0182 *Toll Free Fax:* 877-492-0793 *E-mail:* libraryservices@blackstoneaudio.com *Web Site:* www.blackstoneaudio.com; www.blackstonelibrary.com, pg 808

Black, Darold, Black Media Works, 534 21 Ave SW, Calgary, AB T2S 0H1, Canada *Tel:* 403-802-0010 *E-mail:* info@blackmediaworks.com *Web Site:* www.blackmediaworks.com, pg 808

Black, Larry, Heart Breaker Entertainment LLC, 10094 Lacy Rd, Hagerstown, IN 47346 *Tel:* 765-489-4048; 765-489-5558 *Toll Free Tel:* 800-843-3635 *Fax:* 765-489-4899 *E-mail:* info@videodj.com *Web Site:* videodj.com, pg 887

Black, Nathan, Audio Media Productions, 6739 Kirby Trace Cove, Memphis, TN 38119 *Tel:* 901-751-2363 *E-mail:* ampman@aol.com *Web Site:* www.audiomediaprod.com, pg 794

Blackburn, Jude, Chicago Irish Film Festival (CIFF), c/o Society for Arts, 1112 N Milwaukee Ave, Chicago, IL 60642 *Tel:* 773-486-9612 *Fax:* 773-486-9613 *Web Site:* www.chicagoirishfilmfestival.com, pg 1111

Blackhurst, Suzy, Estes Park Film Commission, 1200 Graves Ave, Estes Park, CO 80517 *Tel:* 970-586-0500 *Fax:* 970-586-4036, pg 1095

Blackington, Jay, Avid Technology Inc, 65-75 Network Dr, Burlington, MA 01830 *Tel:* 978-640-6789 *Fax:* 978-640-3366 *Web Site:* www.avid.com, pg 799

Blackstone, Gay, Blackstone Magik Enterprises Inc, 12800 Puesta Del Sol, Redlands, CA 92373 *Tel:* 909-792-1227 *Fax:* 909-794-2737 *E-mail:* magik@blackstonemagic.com *Web Site:* www.blackstonemagic.com, pg 808

Blackwell, George, Texas Wesleyan University, 1201 Wesleyan St, Fort Worth, TX 76105 *Tel:* 817-531-5850 *Web Site:* www.txwes.edu, pg 1038

Blackwood, Michael, Michael Blackwood Productions Inc, 6 W 18 St, Suite 2B, New York, NY 10011 *Tel:* 212-242-1805 *Fax:* 212-242-1671 *E-mail:* blackwoodfilm@aol.com *Web Site:* www.michaelblackwoodproductions.com, pg 809

Blair, Bill, Eiki International, 30251 Esperanza, Rancho Santa Margarita, CA 92688-2130 *Tel:* 949-457-0200 *Toll Free Tel:* 800-242-3454 *Fax:* 949-457-7877 *Toll Free Fax:* 800-457-3454 *E-mail:* usa@eiki.com *Web Site:* www.eiki.com, pg 858

Blair, Don, VCI Entertainment, 11333 E 60 Place, Tulsa, OK 74146-6828 *Tel:* 918-254-6337 *Toll Free Tel:* 800-331-4077 *Fax:* 918-254-6117 *E-mail:* vci@vcientertainment.com *Web Site:* www.vcientertainment.com, pg 1052

Blair, Robert A, VCI Entertainment, 11333 E 60 Place, Tulsa, OK 74146-6828 *Tel:* 918-254-6337 *Toll Free Tel:* 800-331-4077 *Fax:* 918-254-6117 *E-mail:* vci@vcientertainment.com *Web Site:* www.vcientertainment.com, pg 1052

Blair, Skippy, Golden State Dance Teachers Association (GSDTA), 10804 Woodruff Ave, Downey, CA 90241-3910 *Tel:* 562-869-8949 *Web Site:* www.swingworld.com, pg 880

Blaise, Elizabeth, Blaise Media, 3400 "J" St, Sacramento, CA 95816 *Tel:* 916-446-3126 *Fax:* 916-446-8089 *Web Site:* blaisemedia.com, pg 809

Blaise, Paul, Blaise Media, 3400 "J" St, Sacramento, CA 95816 *Tel:* 916-446-3126 *Fax:* 916-446-8089 *Web Site:* blaisemedia.com, pg 809

Blake, Jeff, Sony Pictures Entertainment, 10202 W Washington Blvd, Culver City, CA 90232 *Tel:* 310-244-4000 *Web Site:* www.sonypictures.com, pg 1016

Blakely, Christopher, Main Street Media Inc, 185 Pier Ave, Suite 105, Santa Monica, CA 90405 *Tel:* 310-450-1846 *E-mail:* info@mainstreetmediainc.com *Web Site:* www.mainstreetmediainc.com, pg 929

Blakeslee, Mike, National Association for Music Education (NAfME), 1806 Robert Fulton Dr, Reston, VA 20191 *Tel:* 703-860-4000 *Toll Free Tel:* 800-336-3768 *Fax:* 703-860-1531 *E-mail:* memberservices@nafme2.org *Web Site:* www.menc.org; www.nafme.org, pg 1085

Blakesley, Ben, Javboy Records, 408 Kingston Dr, Douglassville, PA 19518 *Tel:* 215-285-7444 *E-mail:* contact@javboyrecords.com *Web Site:* www.javboyrecords.com, pg 904

Blalock, Bill, VIP Presentation Products, 69 S Dixie Hwy, Suite A, St Augustine, FL 32084 *Tel:* 904-824-0824 *Toll Free Tel:* 800-874-0855 *Fax:* 904-829-6903 *E-mail:* info@vippresentationproducts.com *Web Site:* vippresentationproducts.com, pg 1058

Blanco, Richard J, Lighting Sales Connections, 757 SE 17 St, PMB 254, Fort Lauderdale, FL 33316 *Tel:* 954-764-6928 *Fax:* 954-791-8450 *E-mail:* info@lightingsales.com *Web Site:* www.lightingsales.com, pg 921

Blane, Barry, Gary Camera & Digital, 6750 Broadway Ave, Merrillville, IN 46410 *Tel:* 219-769-2451 *Fax:* 219-769-2488 *Web Site:* garycameradigital.com, pg 875

Blane, Mark, Gary Camera & Digital, 6750 Broadway Ave, Merrillville, IN 46410 *Tel:* 219-769-2451 *Fax:* 219-769-2488 *Web Site:* garycameradigital.com, pg 875

Blangiardi, Rick, KHNL/KGMB, 420 Waiakamilo Rd, Suite 205, Honolulu, HI 96817 *Tel:* 808-847-3246 *Fax:* 808-845-3616 *E-mail:* info8@khnl.com; news8@khnl.com *Web Site:* www.hawaiinewsnow.com, pg 910

Blank, Harrod, Les Blank Films Inc, 10341 San Pablo Ave, El Cerrito, CA 94530-3123 *Tel:* 510-525-0942 *Toll Free Tel:* 800-572-7618 *Fax:* 510-525-1204 *E-mail:* lesblankfilmsinc@gmail.com, pg 809

Blank, Matthew C, Showtime Networks Inc, 1633 Broadway, 9th fl, New York, NY 10019 *Tel:* 212-708-1600 *Fax:* 212-708-1217 *Web Site:* www.sho.com, pg 1010

Blankenship, Amy, Soundtrack Recording Studios, 162 Columbus Ave, Boston, MA 02116 *Tel:* 617-303-7500 *Fax:* 617-303-7555 *Web Site:* www.soundtrackboston.com, pg 1018

Blasko, Carolyn, Sure Shot Transmissions Inc, 10314 Main St, New Middletown, OH 44442 *Tel:* 330-542-0900 *Fax:* 330-542-1020 *Web Site:* www.sureshotsat.com, pg 1029

Blatnik, Victor, RGB Technology Films Inc, 590 Herndon Pkwy, Suite 500, Herndon, VA 20170-5267 *Tel:* 703-834-1500 *Fax:* 703-834-1506 *Web Site:* www.rgbtec.com, pg 996

Blattner, Frederick, DNASTAR Inc, 3801 Regent St, Madison, WI 53705-5204 *Tel:* 608-258-7420 *Toll Free Tel:* 866-511-5090 *Fax:* 608-258-7439 *E-mail:* info@dnastar.com *Web Site:* www.dnastar.com, pg 849

Blaustein, Meira, Maverick Awards, 13 Rock City Rd, Woodstock, NY 12498 *Tel:* 845-679-4265; 845-810-0131 *Fax:* 509-479-5414 *E-mail:* info@woodstockfilmfestival.com *Web Site:* www.woodstockfilmfestival.com, pg 1119

Blauvelt, Jeff, HD Cinema, 12233 W Olympic Blvd, Suite 120, Los Angeles, CA 90064 *Tel:* 310-434-9500 *Fax:* 310-499-5237 (efax) *Web Site:* www.hd-cinema.com, pg 886

Blaylock, Layton, Inferno Films, 3404 Guadalupe St, Austin, TX 78705 *Tel:* 512-302-9009 *Fax:* 512-302-9022 *Web Site:* www.infernofilms.com, pg 898

Bleach, Kelly, American Foundation for the Blind (AFB), 2 Penn Plaza, Suite 1102, New York, NY 10121 *Tel:* 212-502-7600; 212-502-7662 (TDD)

Toll Free Tel: 800-232-5463 *Fax:* 212-502-7777 *Toll Free Fax:* 888-545-8331 *E-mail:* afbinfo@afb.net *Web Site:* www.afb.org, pg 1076

Blenz-Clucas, Beth, Sugar Mountain PR, 5505 SW Illinois St, Portland, OR 97221-1643 *Tel:* 503-293-9498 *E-mail:* sugarmountainnews@msn.com *Web Site:* www.sugarmountainpr.com, pg 1028

Blicher, Leigh, Videofax, 1750 Cesar Chavez St, Unit G, San Francisco, CA 94124 *Tel:* 415-641-0100 *E-mail:* rentals@videofax.com *Web Site:* www.videofax.com, pg 1057

Bliss, Judith, MindPlay, 4400 E Broadway Blvd, Suite 400, Tucson, AZ 85711 *Tel:* 520-888-1800 *Toll Free Tel:* 800-221-7911 *E-mail:* mail@mindplay.com *Web Site:* www.mindplay.com, pg 943

Bloch, Arthur, Thinking Allowed Productions, 5966 Zinn Dr, Oakland, CA 94611 *Tel:* 510-339-8004 *Toll Free Tel:* 800-999-4415 *E-mail:* thinking@thinkingallowed.com *Web Site:* www.thinkingallowed.com, pg 1038

Bloch, Paul, DataDirect Networks, 2929 Patrick Henry Dr, Santa Clara, CA 95054 *Tel:* 818-700-4000 *Toll Free Tel:* 800-TERABYTE (837-2298) *E-mail:* info@ddn.com; sales@ddn.com *Web Site:* www.ddn.com, pg 843

Block, Mitchell W, Direct Cinema Ltd Inc, PO Box 10003, Santa Monica, CA 90410-1003 *Tel:* 310-636-8200 *Toll Free Tel:* 800-525-0000 *Fax:* 310-636-8228 *E-mail:* dclvideo@aol.com *Web Site:* www.directcinema.com, pg 848

Block, Roz, Premiere Locations, 25 Clyden Rd, Wainscott, NY 11975 *Tel:* 631-537-1669; 917-690-1075 (cell) *E-mail:* info@premierelocations.com *Web Site:* www.premierelocations.com, pg 980

Bloeme, Peter, Skyhoundz, 660 Hembree Pkwy, Suite 110, Roswell, GA 30076 *Tel:* 770-751-3882 *Fax:* 770-740-1665 *E-mail:* info@skyhoundz.com *Web Site:* www.skyhoundz.com, pg 1013

Blofson, Richard S, Telequest Inc, 66 Witherspoon St, Suite 383, Princeton, NJ 08542 *Tel:* 609-430-3004 *E-mail:* contact@telequestinc.com *Web Site:* www.telequestinc.com, pg 1036

Blonski, David, Timeless Productions, 5050 Traverse Creek Rd, Garden Valley, CA 95633 *Tel:* 530-333-1335 *Toll Free Tel:* 800-729-1325 *E-mail:* 4info@timelessproductions.com *Web Site:* www.timelessproductions.com, pg 1040

Bloom, Brian, Ahead Stereo Inc, 7428 Beverly Blvd, Los Angeles, CA 90036 *Tel:* 323-931-8873 *Fax:* 323-937-7285 *E-mail:* mrstereo@pacbell.net *Web Site:* www.aheadstereo.com, pg 778

Bloom, Tom, Blue 60 Pictures, 555 First Ave NE, Suite 200, Minneapolis, MN 55413 *Tel:* 612-871-6800 *E-mail:* info@blue-60.com *Web Site:* www.blue-60.com, pg 810

Bloomfield, Louise A, Posthorn Recordings, 142 W 26 St, 10th fl, New York, NY 10001-6814 *Tel:* 212-242-3737 *Fax:* 212-924-1243 *Web Site:* www.posthorn.com, pg 979

Blore, Chuck, CMI, 612 Hampton Dr, Venice, CA 90291 *Tel:* 310-392-8771 *Fax:* 310-392-5704 *E-mail:* cmi@cmifilms.com *Web Site:* www.cmifilms.com, pg 830

Bluhm, Mike, PLUS Corp of America, 9610 SW Sunshine Ct, Suite 100, Beaverton, OR 97005 *Tel:* 503-748-8700 *Toll Free Tel:* 800-211-9001 *Fax:* 503-643-9756 *E-mail:* sales@plus-america.com *Web Site:* www.plus-america.com, pg 977

Blumenthal, Raymond, Listec Video Corp, 90 Oser Ave, Hauppauge, NY 11788 *Tel:* 631-273-2500 *Toll Free Tel:* 800-645-2522 *Fax:* 631-273-2557 *E-mail:* orders@tiffen.com; techsupport@tiffen.com *Web Site:* www.tiffen.com, pg 923

Blumeyer, Brad, US Case Corp, 6301 J Richard Dr, Raleigh, NC 27617 *Tel:* 919-783-6166 *Toll Free Tel:* 800-648-8474 *Fax:* 919-783-0740 *E-mail:* customersupport@uscase.com *Web Site:* www.uscase.com, pg 1050

Bobby, Colin, American AV, 2862 Hartland Rd, Falls Church, VA 22043 *Tel:* 703-573-6910 *Fax:* 703-573-3539 *E-mail:* sales@aavevents.com *Web Site:* www.aavevents.com, pg 783

Bobo, Mrs Kris, Comrex Corp, 19 Pine Rd, Devens, MA 01434 *Tel:* 978-784-1776 (intl) *Toll Free Tel:* 800-237-1776 *Fax:* 978-784-1717 *E-mail:* info@comrex.com *Web Site:* www.comrex.com, pg 834

Bobrow, Andy, BioMedia Inc, PO Box 918, Franklin, NY 13775 *Tel:* 917-754-3274 (cell) *E-mail:* andy@bio-media.com *Web Site:* bio-media.com, pg 807

Bock, Bruce A, Tri-State Audio Visual Co, 2901 Glendora Ave, Cincinnati, OH 45219 *Tel:* 513-281-7500 *Toll Free Tel:* 800-348-8728 *Fax:* 513-281-7539 *E-mail:* sales@tristateav.com *Web Site:* www.tristateav.com, pg 1044

Bock, Karen, Applied Integration Corp, 3930 W New York Dr, Tucson, AZ 85745 *Tel:* 520-743-3095 *E-mail:* info@appliedi.com *Web Site:* www.appliedi.com, pg 789

Bodak-Smith, Tricia, The Lot (Skye Partners), 1041 N Formosa Ave, West Hollywood, CA 90046 *Tel:* 323-850-3180 *Fax:* 323-850-3190 *E-mail:* info@skyepartners.com *Web Site:* www.thelotstudios.com, pg 925

Boddicker, Michael, Synthesizer Rental Service, 2268 Ben Lomond Dr, Los Angeles, CA 90027-2905 *Tel:* 323-660-4065 *Fax:* 323-660-4597 *E-mail:* info@2srs.com *Web Site:* synthesizerrentalservice.com, pg 1030

Boddicker, Michael, Synthesizer Systems Technologies (SST), 10907 Magnolia Blvd, Suite 425, North Hollywood, CA 91601 *Tel:* 818-907-7780 *E-mail:* sst.shop@yahoo.com, pg 1030

Bodine, Shelly, eInstruction Corp, 14400 N 87 St, Suite 250, Scottsdale, AZ 85260 *Tel:* 480-948-6540 *Toll Free Tel:* 800-856-0732 *Fax:* 480-948-5508 *Web Site:* www.einstruction.com, pg 858

Bodine, Tucker, Playback Recording Studio, 400 E Gutierrez, Santa Barbara, CA 93101 *Tel:* 805-730-7529 *Web Site:* www.playbackrecording.com, pg 977

Bodinet, Donna, SOTA Sales & Service Center, 10830 S Nagle Ave, Worth, IL 60482 *Tel:* 608-538-3500 *Toll Free Tel:* 800-772-7682 *Fax:* 608-538-3502 *E-mail:* sotaturntables@kwom.com *Web Site:* www.sotaturntables.com, pg 1016

Bodinet, Kirk, SOTA Sales & Service Center, 10830 S Nagle Ave, Worth, IL 60482 *Tel:* 608-538-3500 *Toll Free Tel:* 800-772-7682 *Fax:* 608-538-3502 *E-mail:* sotaturntables@kwom.com *Web Site:* www.sotaturntables.com, pg 1016

Boegner, Ray F, Strong Cinema Products, 13710 FNB Pkwy, Suite 400, Omaha, NE 68145 *Tel:* 402-453-4444 *Toll Free Tel:* 800-424-1215 *Fax:* 402-453-7238 *E-mail:* info@btn-inc.com *Web Site:* www.strong-world.com, pg 1026

Boettcher, Michael, Advanced AV, 208 Carter Dr, Suite 7, West Chester, PA 19382 *Toll Free Tel:* 877-696-7700 *Fax:* 610-692-8421 *E-mail:* sales@advancedav.com *Web Site:* www.advancedav.com, pg 777

Boettger, Kevin, Trod Nossel Productions & Recording Studios, 10 George St, Wallingford, CT 06492 *Tel:* 203-269-4465 *Toll Free Tel:* 800-800-HITS (800-4487) *Fax:* 203-294-1745 *E-mail:* info@trodnossel.com *Web Site:* www.trodnossel.com, pg 1045

Boggs, Donald, Covenant Productions®, c/o Anderson University, 1100 E Fifth St, Anderson, IN 46012 *Tel:* 765-641-4348 *Fax:* 765-641-3825 *Web Site:* www.covenantproductions.com, pg 837

Bogosian, Karen, Visual Sound Inc, 485 Park Way, Broomall, PA 19008 *Tel:* 610-544-8700 *Toll Free Tel:* 800-523-7525 *Fax:* 610-544-3385 *Web Site:* www.visualsound.com, pg 1059

Bohnson, Jeff, AnswersMedia, 30 N Racine Ave, Suite 300, Chicago, IL 60607 *Tel:* 312-421-0113 *Fax:* 312-421-1457 *E-mail:* contactus@answersmediainc.com *Web Site:* www.answersmediainc.com, pg 787

Boire, Roseline, Sennheiser (Canada) Inc, 221 ave Labrosse, Pointe Claire, QC H9R 1A3, Canada *Tel:* 514-426-3013 *Toll Free Tel:* 800-463-1006 *Fax:* 514-426-3953 *Toll Free Fax:* 800-463-3013 *E-mail:* info@sennheiser.ca *Web Site:* www.sennheiser.ca, pg 1006

Boisvert, Charles, Sennheiser (Canada) Inc, 221 ave Labrosse, Pointe Claire, QC H9R 1A3, Canada *Tel:* 514-426-3013 *Toll Free Tel:* 800-463-1006 *Fax:* 514-426-3953 *Toll Free Fax:* 800-463-3013 *E-mail:* info@sennheiser.ca *Web Site:* www.sennheiser.ca, pg 1006

Boitnott, Keith, Boitnott Visual Communications Corp (BVC), 14201 Justice Rd, Midlothian, VA 23113 *Tel:* 804-379-9400 *Fax:* 804-379-9413 *Web Site:* www.boitnottvisual.com, pg 810

Boitnott, L Harrell, Boitnott Visual Communications Corp (BVC), 14201 Justice Rd, Midlothian, VA 23113 *Tel:* 804-379-9400 *Fax:* 804-379-9413 *Web Site:* www.boitnottvisual.com, pg 810

Boivin, Patrice, Orion Software, 6000 Cote-des-Neiges, Suite 240, Montreal, QC H3S 1Z8, Canada *Tel:* 514-484-9661 *Toll Free Tel:* 877-755-2012 *Fax:* 514-484-1339 *E-mail:* info@orion-soft.com *Web Site:* www.orion-soft.com, pg 965

Boje, Conrad F, Omnimedia Inc, 3085 Maple Cove Dr, Loganville, GA 30052 *Toll Free Tel:* 800-433-2091 *Fax:* 678-623-3940 *E-mail:* sales@omni-media.com *Web Site:* www.omni-media.com, pg 962

Boland, Michael J, Boland Communications, 16 Rancho Circle, Lake Forest, CA 92630 *Tel:* 949-465-9911 *Toll Free Tel:* 800-918-9090 *Fax:* 949-465-9944 *E-mail:* sales@bolandcom.com *Web Site:* www.bolandcom.com, pg 810

Bolchazy, Allan, Bolchazy - Carducci Publishers Inc, 1570 Baskin Rd, Mundelein, IL 60060 *Tel:* 847-526-4344 *Toll Free Tel:* 800-392-6453 *Fax:* 847-526-2867 *E-mail:* info@bolchazy.com *Web Site:* www.bolchazy.com, pg 810

Bolchazy, Marie C EdD, Bolchazy - Carducci Publishers Inc, 1570 Baskin Rd, Mundelein, IL 60060 *Tel:* 847-526-4344 *Toll Free Tel:* 800-392-6453 *Fax:* 847-526-2867 *E-mail:* info@bolchazy.com *Web Site:* www.bolchazy.com, pg 810

Bole, Angela, IBPA, Independent Book Publishers Association, 1020 Manhattan Beach Blvd, Suite 204, Manhattan Beach, CA 90266 *Tel:* 310-546-1818 *Fax:* 310-546-3939 *E-mail:* info@ibpa-online.org *Web Site:* www.ibpa-online.org, pg 1082

Bole, Curtis, Dogma Studios, 10559 Jefferson Blvd, Culver City, CA 90232 *Tel:* 310-838-2973 *Fax:* 310-838-2975 *E-mail:* info@dogmastudios.com *Web Site:* www.dogmastudios.com, pg 850

Boles, Brian K, Data Security Inc, 300 S Seventh St, Lincoln, NE 68508 *Tel:* 402-434-5959 *Toll Free Tel:* 800-225-7554 *Fax:* 402-434-3291 *E-mail:* sales@telesis-inc.com *Web Site:* www.datasecurityinc.com, pg 843

Bolin, Estle Dwayne, Media Resources, 102 Perkins Bldg, 521 Lancaster Ave, Richmond, KY 40475 *Tel:* 859-622-6671 *Fax:* 859-622-1116 *Web Site:* www.mpc.eku.edu, pg 937

Bolin, Susan, SPEAK HOUSE Audio™, 1844 E Montecito Ave, Phoenix, AZ 85016 *Tel:* 602-279-0900 *Fax:* 602-279-0980 *Web Site:* www.speakhouseaudio.com, pg 1020

Boll, Arlan, AB Audio Visual Entertainment Inc, PO Box 8020, Long Beach, CA 90808 *Tel:* 562-429-1042 *Toll Free Tel:* 877-222-8346 *Fax:* 562-429-2401 *E-mail:* media@abaudio.com *Web Site:* www.abaudio.com, pg 772

Bollard, Tom, MSI Productions, 9220 Activity Rd, San Diego, CA 92126 *Tel:* 858-348-0100 *Fax:* 858-348-0076 *Web Site:* www.msiprod.com, pg 949

Boller, Chuck, Hawaii International Film Festival, 680 Iwilei Rd, Suite 100, Honolulu, HI 96817 *Tel:* 808-792-1577 *Fax:* 808-749-7783 *E-mail:* info@hiff.org *Web Site:* www.hiff.org, pg 1116

Bolling, Brad, White Rain Films Ltd, 2009 Dexter Ave N, Seattle, WA 98109 *Tel:* 206-682-5417 *Toll Free Tel:* 800-816-5244 *Fax:* 206-682-3038 *E-mail:* info@whiterainfilms.com *Web Site:* www.whiterainfilms.com, pg 1065

Bollinger, Ted, TV Specialists Inc, 180 E 2100 S, Salt Lake City, UT 84115 *Tel:* 801-486-5757 *Toll Free Tel:* 888-486-5757 *Fax:* 801-486-7566 *E-mail:* info@tvspecialists.com *Web Site:* www.tvspecialists.com, pg 1046

Bolten, Patty, Coloredge, 1919 Empire Ave, Burbank, CA 91504 *Tel:* 818-842-1121 *Fax:* 818-840-0185 *Web Site:* coloredge.com, pg 832

Bonacum, Leslie, CCH Inc, A Wolters Kluwer business, 2700 Lake Cook Rd, Riverwoods, IL 60015 *Tel:* 847-267-7000 *Web Site:* www.cch.com, pg 821

Bond, Gary, Austin Film Commission, 301 Congress Ave, Suite 200, Austin, TX 78701 *Tel:* 512-583-7229 *Toll Free Tel:* 800-926-2282 (ext 7229) *Fax:* 512-583-7281 *Web Site:* www.austintexas.org/film; www.austinfilmcommission.com, pg 1102

Boniek, Mani, Maniac Productions, 3888 Viewpoint Way, Lafayette, CO 80026 *Tel:* 303-661-0920 *Toll Free Tel:* 888-626-4227 *Fax:* 303-661-0995 *E-mail:* mpcl@aol.com; info@maniacproductions.com *Web Site:* www.maniacproductions.com, pg 930

Boniek, Patrisha, Maniac Productions, 3888 Viewpoint Way, Lafayette, CO 80026 *Tel:* 303-661-0920 *Toll Free Tel:* 888-626-4227 *Fax:* 303-661-0995 *E-mail:* mpcl@aol.com; info@maniacproductions.com *Web Site:* www.maniacproductions.com, pg 930

Bonin, Steve G, EZ FX Inc, 324 Maguire Rd, Ocoee, FL 34761 *Tel:* 407-877-2335 *Toll Free Tel:* 800-541-5706 *Fax:* 407-877-6603 *E-mail:* sales@ezfx.com *Web Site:* www.ezfx.com, pg 865

Bonnell, Chris, Newfoundland & Labrador Film Development Corp, 12 King's Bridge Rd, St John's, NL A1C 3K3, Canada *Tel:* 709-738-3456 *Toll Free Tel:* 877-738-3456 (CN) *Fax:* 709-739-1680 *E-mail:* info@nlfdc.ca *Web Site:* www.nlfdc.ca, pg 1105

Bonner, Richard, Atlantic Illumination Entertainment Lighting, 80 Fairbanks St, Dartmouth, NS B3A 1C4, Canada *Tel:* 902-463-7418 *E-mail:* aiel@chebucto.biz *Web Site:* aiel.chebucto.biz/, pg 793

Bonnin, Carlos, Bonnin Electronics Inc, 617 Hipodromo St, San Juan, PR 00909 *Tel:* 787-725-4765 *Fax:* 787-725-0840 *Web Site:* www.bonninelectronics.com, pg 810

Bonnin, Sebastian, Bonnin Electronics Inc, 617 Hipodromo St, San Juan, PR 00909 *Tel:* 787-725-4765 *Fax:* 787-725-0840 *Web Site:* www.bonninelectronics.com, pg 810

Book, Kenneth, Total Impact Multimedia Group Ltd, 1475 Pea Pond Rd, North Bellmore, NY 11710 *Tel:* 516-783-8800 *E-mail:* info@totalimpactltd.com *Web Site:* www.totalimpactltd.com, pg 1042

Booker, Beatrice, Residency Fellowship, 154 San Angelo Dr, Amherst, VA 24521 *Tel:* 434-946-7236 *Fax:* 434-946-7239 *E-mail:* vcca@vcca.com *Web Site:* www.vcca.com, pg 1125

Booker, Robert C, Artist Research and Development Grants, 417 W Roosevelt St, Phoenix, AZ 85003-1326 *Tel:* 602-771-6501 *Fax:* 602-256-0282 *E-mail:* info@azarts.gov *Web Site:* www.azarts.gov, pg 1108

Bookout, Tim, Radius® Display Products Inc, 800 Fabric X-Press Way, Dallas, TX 75234 *Tel:* 972-406-1221 *Toll Free Tel:* 800-FABRIC-X (322-7429); 866-966-4066 (sales); 866-966-8266 (hospitality) *Fax:* 972-406-1321 *Toll Free Fax:* 888-322-7429 *Web Site:* www.radiusdp.com, pg 990

Boone, Dan, SVS Inc, 2513 Jenks Ave, Panama City, FL 32405 *Tel:* 850-522-4747 *Fax:* 850-522-4739 *E-mail:* sales@svslifts.com *Web Site:* www.svslifts.com, pg 1029

Booth, Alan, Yellowknife Films Inc, 5021 53 St, Yellowknife, NT X1A 1V5, Canada *Tel:* 867-873-8610 *E-mail:* ykf@theedge.ca *Web Site:* www.ykfilms.ca, pg 1072

Bopf, Ken, Simkar Corporation, 700 Ramona Ave, Philadelphia, PA 19120-4691 *Tel:* 215-831-7700 *Toll Free Tel:* 800-523-3602 *Fax:* 215-831-7703 *E-mail:* lighting@simkar.com *Web Site:* www.simkar.com, pg 1011

Bordeaux, John, Calbor Enterprises Two Inc, 10646 Chiquita St, Toluca Lake, CA 91602 *Tel:* 818-760-3222 *E-mail:* pyro-fx@sbcglobal.net *Web Site:* www.pyro-fx.net, pg 816

Borenstein, Richard D, Cinebar Productions Inc, 763 J Clyde Morris Blvd, Suite 1-C, Newport News, VA 23601 *Tel:* 757-873-3232 *Fax:* 757-873-3790 *E-mail:* cinebar@cinebarproductions.com *Web Site:* www.cinebarproductions.com, pg 827

Bork, Jeff, API, 8301 Patuxent Range Rd, Jessup, MD 20794 *Tel:* 301-776-7879 *Fax:* 301-776-8117 *E-mail:* service@apiaudio.com *Web Site:* www.apiaudio.com, pg 788

Borland, Susan, Logitek Electronic Systems Inc, 5622 Edgemoor Dr, Houston, TX 77081 *Tel:* 713-664-4470 *Toll Free Tel:* 800-231-5870 (sales); 877-231-5870 (tech support) *Fax:* 713-664-4479 *E-mail:* northamericansales@logitekaudio.com *Web Site:* www.logitekaudio.com, pg 924

Borland, Tag, Logitek Electronic Systems Inc, 5622 Edgemoor Dr, Houston, TX 77081 *Tel:* 713-664-4470 *Toll Free Tel:* 800-231-5870 (sales); 877-231-5870 (tech support) *Fax:* 713-664-4479 *E-mail:* northamericansales@logitekaudio.com *Web Site:* www.logitekaudio.com, pg 924

Borne, Mike, Allstar Audio Systems Inc, PO Box 541964, Merritt Island, FL 32954-1964 *Tel:* 321-455-2202 *Fax:* 321-455-2224 *E-mail:* info@allstaraudio.com *Web Site:* www.allstaraudio.com; allstarsystems.net, pg 782

Borromeo, Edward, Hollywood Lights Inc, 5251 SE McLoughlin Blvd, Portland, OR 97202-4836 *Tel:* 503-232-9001; 503-232-8855 *Toll Free Tel:* 800-826-9881 *Fax:* 503-517-8686 *E-mail:* portland@hollywoodlights.biz *Web Site:* www.hollywoodlights.biz, pg 890

Borsum, Deborah, The Meetinghouse Companies Inc, 781 N Church Rd, Elmhurst, IL 60126-1413 *Tel:* 630-941-0600 *Fax:* 630-941-7777 *E-mail:* info@meetinghouse.com *Web Site:* www.meetinghouse.com, pg 938

Borth, Randi, AVI Systems, 9675 W 76 St, Suite 200, Eden Prairie, MN 55344 *Tel:* 952-949-3700 *Toll Free Tel:* 800-488-4954 *Fax:* 952-949-6000 *E-mail:* info@avisystems.com *Web Site:* www.avisystems.com, pg 799

Bortolin, Greg, Phoebus Lighting, 2800 Third St, San Francisco, CA 94107 *Tel:* 415-550-0770 *Fax:* 415-550-2655 *Web Site:* www.phoebus.com, pg 974

Borvan, Michelle, Conquest Sound Co Inc, 26113 S Ridgeland Ave, Monee, IL 60449 *Tel:* 708-534-0390 *Toll Free Tel:* 800-323-7671 *Fax:* 708-534-0398 *E-mail:* info@conquestsound.com; customerservice@conquestsound.com *Web Site:* www.conquestsound.com, pg 835

Bosaw, Jon, Rane, 10802 47 Ave W, Mukilteo, WA 98275-5000 *Tel:* 425-355-6000 *E-mail:* info@rane.com *Web Site:* www.rane.com, pg 991

Bosch, James Vanden, Terra Nova Films Inc, 9848 S Winchester Ave, Chicago, IL 60643 *Tel:* 773-881-8491 *Toll Free Tel:* 800-779-8491 *Fax:* 773-881-3368 *E-mail:* tnf@terranova.org *Web Site:* www.terranova.org, pg 1037

Bosen, Scott, Utah Scientific Inc, 4750 Wiley Post Way, Suite 150, Salt Lake City, UT 84116 *Tel:* 801-575-8801 *Toll Free Tel:* 800-453-8782 *Fax:* 801-537-3099 *E-mail:* info@utahscientific.com *Web Site:* www.utahscientific.com, pg 1051

Boser, Timothy J, ATTO Technology Inc, 155 CrossPoint Pkwy, Amherst, NY 14068 *Tel:* 716-691-1999 *Fax:* 716-691-9353 *Web Site:* www.attotech.com, pg 793

Boseski, Cynthia Wagner, DWJ Television, One Robinson Lane, Ridgewood, NJ 07450 *Tel:* 201-445-1711 *Toll Free Tel:* 800-766-1711 *Fax:* 201-445-8352, pg 854

Bosken, Jim, QCA, 2832 Spring Grove Ave, Cincinnati, OH 45225 *Tel:* 513-681-8400 *Toll Free Tel:* 800-859-8401 *E-mail:* info@go-qca.com *Web Site:* www.go-qca.com, pg 988

Boss, Doug, Pacific Grip & Lighting Inc, 6550 NE Portland Hwy, Portland, OR 97218 *Tel:* 503-233-4747 *Fax:* 503-233-5830 *E-mail:* info@pacific-grip.com *Web Site:* pacific-grip.com, pg 967

Boster, Bob, Clear-Com®, 1301 Marina Village Pkwy, Suite 105, Alameda, CA 94501 *Tel:* 510-337-6600 *Toll Free Tel:* 800-462-HELP (462-4357) *Fax:* 510-337-6699 *E-mail:* CustomerServicesUS@clearcom.com *Web Site:* www.clearcom.com, pg 829

Bostrom, Lynn, Magnetek Inc, N49 W13650 Campbell Dr, Menomonee Falls, WI 53051 *Tel:* 262-783-3500 *Toll Free Tel:* 800-288-8178 *Toll Free Fax:* 800-298-3503 *E-mail:* sales@magnetek.com *Web Site:* www.magnetek.com, pg 928

Boswell, John, SAS Institute Inc, 100 SAS Campus Dr, Cary, NC 27513-2414 *Tel:* 919-677-8000 *Toll Free Tel:* 800-727-0025 *Fax:* 919-677-4444 *Web Site:* www.sas.com, pg 1003

Botelho, Tom, Denver Film Society, 1510 York St, 3rd fl, Denver, CO 80206 *Tel:* 303-595-3456 *Fax:* 303-595-0956 *E-mail:* info@denverfilm.org *Web Site:* www.denverfilm.org, pg 1081

Botelho, Tom, Starz Denver Film Festival, 1510 York St, 3rd fl, Denver, CO 80206 *Tel:* 303-595-3456 *Fax:* 303-595-0956 *E-mail:* info@denverfilm.org *Web Site:* www.denverfilm.org/festival, pg 1127

Bothof, Tom, Big Event Productions LLC, 77 13 Ave NE, Studio 101, Minneapolis, MN 55413 *Tel:* 612-623-7800 *Fax:* 612-455-0450 *Web Site:* www.bigeventpros.com, pg 807

Bottrell, Donna, The Wine Appreciation Guild Ltd, 360 Swift Ave, Unit 30-40, South San Francisco, CA 94080 *Tel:* 650-866-3020 *Toll Free Tel:* 800-231-9463 *Fax:* 650-866-3513 *E-mail:* info@wineappreciation.com *Web Site:* www.wineappreciation.com, pg 1067

Bourland, Annette, Zondervan, A HarperCollins Company, 3900 Sparks Dr, Grand Rapids, MI 49546 *Tel:* 616-698-6900 *Toll Free Tel:* 800-226-1122; 800-727-3480 (retail orders) *Fax:* 616-698-3255 (retail orders) *E-mail:* zinfo@zondervan.com *Web Site:* www.zondervan.com, pg 1074

Bourque, Carol, Intermedia Technologies, 1720 Kaliste Saloom, Bldg 2, Suite B-2, Lafayette, LA 70508 *Tel:* 337-406-9428 *Toll Free Tel:* 877-268-9574 *Fax:* 337-406-9582 *Web Site:* www.intermedia-technologies.com, pg 900

Bousquet, Carol, Alma-The International Loudspeaker Association, 55 Littleton Rd, Unit 13-B, Ayer, MA 01432 *Tel:* 978-772-6977 *Fax:* 617-848-9935 *E-mail:* management@almainternational.org *Web Site:* www.almainternational.org, pg 1075

Boutin, Laurin, Cox Media, 350 Tenth Ave, Suite 500, San Diego, CA 92101 *Tel:* 619-686-1900 *Toll Free Tel:* 855-755-2691 *Fax:* 619-867-4996 *Web Site:* www.coxmedia.com, pg 837

Bouzari, Alex, DataDirect Networks, 2929 Patrick Henry Dr, Santa Clara, CA 95054 *Tel:* 818-700-4000 *Toll Free Tel:* 800-TERABYTE (837-2298) *E-mail:* info@ddn.com; sales@ddn.com *Web Site:* www.ddn.com, pg 843

Bowden, Edwin, Day Star Productions, 1042 S 130 St, Bonner Springs, KS 66012 *Tel:* 913-422-3400 *Fax:* 913-422-3401 *E-mail:* daystar@day-star.org *Web Site:* www.day-star.org, pg 844

Bowden, Jay B, TRC Interactive Inc, 4200 Crums Mill Rd, Harrisburg, PA 17112 *Tel:* 717-652-3100 *Toll Free Tel:* 800-222-9909 *Fax:* 717-652-8281 *E-mail:* customerservicetrc01@trcinteractive.com; info@trcinteractive.com *Web Site:* www.trcinteractive.com, pg 1044

Bowers, Bruce, Bowers Media Group Inc, 6035 Florence Ave, Suite 100, Charlotte, NC 28212 *Tel:* 704-542-8754 *Fax:* 704-532-1058 *Web Site:* www.bowersmediagroup.com, pg 811

Bowers, Scott, Ghent Manufacturing, 2999 Henkle Dr, Lebanon, OH 45036-9260 *Tel:* 513-932-3445 *Toll Free Tel:* 800-543-0550 *Fax:* 513-932-9252 *E-mail:* customer_service@ghent.com *Web Site:* www.ghent.com, pg 878

Bowie, Clint, New Orleans Film Festival, 900 Camp St, New Orleans, LA 70130 *Tel:* 504-309-6633 *Fax:* 504-309-0923 *E-mail:* info@neworleansfilmfest.com *Web Site:* www.neworleansfilmsociety.org, pg 1122

Bowie, Jim, Electrosonic Inc, 3320 N San Fernando Blvd, Burbank, CA 91504 *Tel:* 818-333-3600 *Toll Free Tel:* 888-343-3604 (sales) *Fax:* 818-230-1017 *E-mail:* info@electrosonic.com *Web Site:* www.electrosonic.com, pg 859

Bowles, Keith, Scholastic Media, 557 Broadway, New York, NY 10012 *Fax:* 212-343-7592 *Web Site:* www.scholastic.com/aboutscholastic/librarypublishing.htm, pg 1004

Boyadjian, Mark, Neutrik® USA Inc, 4115 Taggart Creek Rd, Charlotte, NC 28208-5479 *Tel:* 704-972-3050 *Fax:* 704-438-9202 *E-mail:* info@neutrikusa.com *Web Site:* www.neutrik.us, pg 955

Boyce, Rodger, Allstar Show Industries Inc, 10331 176 St, Edmonton, AB T5S 2E4, Canada *Tel:* 780-486-4000 *Toll Free Tel:* 800-663-4063 (CN & US) *Fax:* 780-414-5724 *E-mail:* allsales@allstar-show.com *Web Site:* www.allstar-show.com, pg 782

Boyd, Alicia M, Rahlic Publishing Co, 301 Keithwood Rd, Wynnewood, PA 19096 *Tel:* 610-649-0982, pg 990

Boyd, Bill, Intellidyne LLC, 5203 Leesburg Pike, Suite 400, 2 Skyline Place, Falls Church, VA 22041 *Tel:* 703-575-9715 *Fax:* 703-575-9718 *Web Site:* www.intellidyne-llc.com, pg 899

Boyd, Dan, Technology Learning Services, 36600 Schoolcraft Rd, Livonia, MI 48150-1173 *Tel:* 734-432-5800 *Toll Free Tel:* 800-852-4951 *Web Site:* ww3.madonna.edu/tls, pg 1035

Boyd, David T, Lasergraphics Inc, 20 Ada, Irvine, CA 92618 *Tel:* 949-753-8282 *Fax:* 949-727-9282 *E-mail:* info@lasergraphics.com *Web Site:* www.lasergraphics.com, pg 916

Boyd, Greg, Avitecture Inc, One Export Dr, Sterling, VA 20164-4421 *Tel:* 703-404-8900 *Fax:* 703-404-8940 *E-mail:* info@avitecture.com *Web Site:* www.avitecture.com, pg 800

Boyd, Sue, Technology Learning Services, 36600 Schoolcraft Rd, Livonia, MI 48150-1173 *Tel:* 734-432-5800 *Toll Free Tel:* 800-852-4951 *Web Site:* ww3.madonna.edu/tls, pg 1035

Boyd, Vicky, Heinemann, 361 Hanover St, Portsmouth, NH 03801-3912 *Tel:* 603-431-7894 *Toll Free Tel:* 800-225-5800 *Fax:* 603-431-2214 *Toll Free Fax:* 877-231-6980 *E-mail:* custserv@heinemann.com *Web Site:* www.heinemann.com, pg 887

Boyd-Bradley, Leslie, Discovery Toys, 3037 Independence Dr, Suite G, Livermore, CA 94551 *Tel:* 925-606-2600 *Toll Free Tel:* 800-341-TOYS (341-8697, sales) *Fax:* 925-447-0626 *E-mail:* contact@discoverytoys.net *Web Site:* www.discoverytoys.net, pg 849

Boyer, Ray, PixMix Video Services, 23 Elm St, Bldg 2, Watertown, MA 02472 *Tel:* 617-923-0102 *Fax:* 617-923-0105 *E-mail:* info@pixmix.net *Web Site:* www.pixmix.net, pg 976

Boylan, Patrick M, PDC Productions, 3217 N Flood Ave, Norman, OK 73069 *Tel:* 405-360-5130 *Fax:* 405-360-0524 *E-mail:* info@pdcproductions.com *Web Site:* www.pdcproductions.com, pg 970

Boyle, Kenneth J, Convergent Media Systems, 190 Bluegrass Valley Pkwy, Alpharetta, GA 30005-2204 *Tel:* 770-369-9000 *Toll Free Tel:* 800-877-7804 *Fax:* 770-369-9100 *E-mail:* convergent@convergent.com *Web Site:* www.convergent.com, pg 836

Boyle, Tom, Research Technology International (RTI), 4700 Chase Ave, Lincolnwood, IL 60712-1689 *Tel:* 847-677-3000 *Toll Free Tel:* 800-323-7520 *Fax:* 847-677-1311 *Toll Free Fax:* 800-784-6733 *E-mail:* sales@rtico.com *Web Site:* www.rtico.com, pg 995

Bozeman, Rick, American Foundation for the Blind (AFB), 2 Penn Plaza, Suite 1102, New York, NY 10121 *Tel:* 212-502-7600; 212-502-7662 (TDD) *Toll Free Tel:* 800-232-5463 *Fax:* 212-502-7777 *Toll Free Fax:* 888-545-8331 *E-mail:* afbinfo@afb.net *Web Site:* www.afb.org, pg 1076

Braaten, Steve, Horizon Video Productions Inc, 6114 Fayetteville St, Suite 106, Durham, NC 27713 *Tel:* 919-941-0901 *Toll Free Tel:* 800-768-3776 *Fax:* 919-941-1939 *E-mail:* info@horizonvp.com *Web Site:* www.horizonvp.com, pg 891

Brabbee, Mystelle, Nantucket Film Festival (NFF), 68 Jay St, Suite 319, Brooklyn, NY 11201 *Tel:* 646-480-1900; 508-325-6274 *Fax:* 646-365-3367 *E-mail:* info@nantucketfilmfestival.org *Web Site:* www.nantucketfilmfestival.org, pg 1121

Brace, Collin L, Sun Entertainment Corp, 3106 Belmont Blvd, Nashville, TN 37212 *Tel:* 615-385-1960 *E-mail:* info@sunrecords.com *Web Site:* www.sunrecords.com, pg 1028

Bracey, Michael, Olson Anderson Co, 3124 Kochville Rd, Suite 121, Saginaw, MI 48604-9305 *Tel:* 989-399-3024 *E-mail:* oac100@aol.com *Web Site:* www.olsonanderson.com, pg 786

Brackett, Dan, Extreme Reach Inc, 75 Second Ave, Suite 720, Needham, MA 02494 *Tel:* 781-577-2016 *E-mail:* sales@extremereach.com; press@extremereach.com *Web Site:* www.extremereach.com, pg 864

Brackey, Kathy, Imation Corp, One Imation Way, Oakdale, MN 55128-3421 *Tel:* 651-704-4000 *Toll Free Tel:* 888-466-3456 *Fax:* 651-704-3444 *Toll Free Fax:* 888-704-4200 *E-mail:* info@imation.com *Web Site:* www.imation.com, pg 896

Bradford, Traci, Audio Rents, 1541 N Wilcox Ave, Hollywood, CA 90028 *Tel:* 323-874-1000 *Fax:* 323-460-2676 *E-mail:* info@audiorents.com *Web Site:* www.audiorents.com, pg 794

Bradley, Denise, San Francisco Film Commission, City Hall, Rm 473, One Dr Carlton B Goodlett Place, San Francisco, CA 94102-4649 *Tel:* 415-554-6241 *Fax:* 415-554-6503 *E-mail:* film@sfgov.org *Web Site:* www.filmsf.org, pg 1094

Bradley, Mark, CCI Solutions, 1342 88 Ave SE, Olympia, WA 98501 *Tel:* 360-943-5378 *Toll Free Tel:* 800-562-6006 *Fax:* 360-754-1566 *E-mail:* info@ccisolutions.com *Web Site:* www.ccisolutions.com, pg 821

Bradley, Rick, AC Lighting Inc, 88 Horner Ave, Toronto, ON M8Z 5Y3, Canada *Tel:* 416-255-9494 *Fax:* 416-255-3514 *E-mail:* northamerica@aclighting.com *Web Site:* www.aclighting.com, pg 772

Bradstock, Philip, City of Phoenix Film Office, 200 W Washington St, 20th fl, Phoenix, AZ 85003 *Tel:* 602-262-4850 *E-mail:* filmphx@phoenix.gov *Web Site:* www.phoenix.gov/econdev/filming/, pg 1091

Bradway, Amy, Draper Inc, 411 S Pearl St, Spiceland, IN 47385 *Tel:* 765-987-7999 *Toll Free Tel:* 800-238-7999 *Fax:* 765-987-7142 *Web Site:* www.draperinc.com; blog.draperinc.com, pg 852

Brady, Tim, American Audio Visual Center, 7434 E Monte Cristo Ave, Scottsdale, AZ 85260 *Tel:* 480-596-9880 *Fax:* 480-596-0942 *Web Site:* www.americanavc.com, pg 783

Bragdon, Doug, Society for Information Display (SID), 1475 S Bascom Ave, Suite 114, Campbell, CA 95008-4006 *Tel:* 408-879-3901 *Fax:* 408-879-3833 *E-mail:* office@sid.org *Web Site:* www.sid.org, pg 1089

Bragg, Bill, The Yesterday USA Radio Networks, 2001 Plymouth Rock Dr, Richardson, TX 75081-3946 *Tel:* 972-889-9872 *Fax:* 972-889-2329 *Web Site:* www.yesterdayusa.com, pg 1072

Bragg, Billy, Available Lighting & Motion Picture Services Inc, 826 Jefferson Hwy, New Orleans, LA 70120 *Tel:* 504-831-5214 *Fax:* 504-831-5361 *E-mail:* avlight@bellsouth.net *Web Site:* www.availablelighting.com, pg 798

Bragg, Greg, Bexel Corp, 2701 N Ontario St, Burbank, CA 91504 *Tel:* 818-565-4322 *Toll Free Tel:* 800-225-6185 (tech support) *E-mail:* rentals@bexel.com *Web Site:* www.bexel.com, pg 806

Brahms, Claudia, MTI Home Video, 14216 SW 136 St, Miami, FL 33186 *Tel:* 305-255-8684 *Fax:* 305-233-6943 *Web Site:* www.mtivideo.com, pg 949

Brahms, Larry, MTI Home Video, 14216 SW 136 St, Miami, FL 33186 *Tel:* 305-255-8684 *Fax:* 305-233-6943 *Web Site:* www.mtivideo.com, pg 949

Braisted, Gary, ELC Sales & Service Inc, 3100 S Congress Ave, Suite 6, Boynton Beach, FL 33426 *Tel:* 561-756-2210 *E-mail:* tvman@gate.net, pg 858

Braker, Steve, Worthwhile Films, 317 Winona St, Northfield, MN 55057 *Toll Free Tel:* 877-507-5077 *Web Site:* worthwhilefilms.org, pg 1070

Bramlet, Eileen, Software & Information Industry Association (SIIA), 1090 Vermont Ave NW, 6th fl, Washington, DC 20005-4095 *Tel:* 202-289-7442 *Fax:* 202-289-7097 *Web Site:* www.siia.net, pg 1089

Brammer, Jim, Special Event Services, 3135 Indiana Ave, Winston-Salem, NC 27105 *Tel:* 336-725-7799 *Toll Free Tel:* 800-423-3996 *Fax:* 336-725-0019 *Web Site:* www.specialeventservices.com, pg 1020

Brandon, Barry, PCO-TECH Inc, 6930 Metroplex Dr, Romulus, MI 48174 *Tel:* 248-276-8820 *Fax:* 248-276-8825 *E-mail:* info@pco-tech.com; service@pco-tech.com *Web Site:* www.pco-tech.com, pg 970

Brandon, Michael, SF Global Sourcing, 1000 Sansome St, Suite 280, San Francisco, CA 94111 *Tel:* 415-288-9400 *Toll Free Tel:* 855-SF-GLOBAL (734-5622) *Fax:* 415-288-9410 *E-mail:* info@sfglobalsourcing.com *Web Site:* www.sfglobalsourcing.com, pg 1007

Brandt, Hans-Juergen, Docter Optics Inc, 1425 W Elliot Rd, Suite A-105, Gilbert, AZ 85233 *Tel:* 480-844-7585 *Fax:* 480-844-7826 *E-mail:* doi@docteroptics.com *Web Site:* www.docteroptics.com, pg 849

Brandt, Matthew, KK Office Solutions Inc, 3910 N Bridgeport Circle, Wichita, KS 67219 *Tel:* 316-944-5464 *Toll Free Tel:* 800-362-1317 *Fax:* 316-944-0605 *Toll Free Fax:* 888-319-9600 *E-mail:* info@kkofficesolutions.com *Web Site:* kkosinc.com, pg 911

Brandwein, Mordy, Tapemaker, 48 Urban Ave, Westbury, NY 11590 *Tel:* 516-333-2700 *Fax:* 516-333-0643 *E-mail:* tapemaker@aol.com, pg 1032

Branen, Shad, Win Media Inc, 317 N Dodge St, Burlington, WI 53105 *Tel:* 262-763-6397 *E-mail:* info@winmediainc.com *Web Site:* www.winmediainc.com, pg 1067

Brantley, Bobby, Brantley Sound Associates Inc, 115 Duluth Ave, Nashville, TN 37209-1207 *Tel:* 615-256-6260 *E-mail:* ccussick@brantleysound.com *Web Site:* www.brantleysound.com, pg 812

Brar, Yash, ReelWorld Film Festival, 438 Parliament St, Suite 300, Toronto, ON M5A 3A2, Canada *Tel:* 416-598-7933 *E-mail:* info@reelworld.ca; events@reelworld.ca *Web Site:* www.reelworld.ca, pg 1125

Brasil, Diane S, Staedtler-Mars Ltd, 5725 McLaughlin Rd, Mississauga, ON L5R 3K5, Canada *Tel:* 905-501-9008 *Toll Free Tel:* 800-776-5544; 800-387-5872 *Fax:* 905-501-9117 *Toll Free Fax:* 800-675-8249 *E-mail:* info@staedtler.ca *Web Site:* www.staedtler.ca, pg 1022

Brastow, Scott, Pacific Media, 21730 Nordhoff St, Chatsworth, CA 91311 *Tel:* 818-341-3156 *Toll Free Tel:* 800-262-7367 *Fax:* 818-341-3562 *E-mail:* info@pac-media.com *Web Site:* www.pac-media.com, pg 967

Braun, Anthony, Williams Sound Corp, 10300 Valley View Rd, Eden Prairie, MN 55344-3446 *Tel:* 952-943-2252 *Toll Free Tel:* 800-328-6190 *Fax:* 952-943-2174 *E-mail:* info@williamssound.com *Web Site:* www.williamssound.com, pg 1067

Braverman, Dan, Radio Systems Inc, 601 Heron Dr, Logan Township, NJ 08085 *Tel:* 856-467-8000 *Fax:* 856-467-3044 *E-mail:* sales@radiosystems.com; tech@radiosystems.com *Web Site:* www.radiosystems.com, pg 990

Brawley, Dan, Cucalorus Film Festival, Jengo's Playhouse, 815 Princess St, Wilmington, NC 28401 *Tel:* 910-343-5995 *Fax:* 910-343-5227 *E-mail:* development@cucalorus.org *Web Site:* www.cucalorus.org, pg 1113

Bray, Dennis S, Society of Manufacturing Engineers (SME), One SME Dr, Dearborn, MI 48128 *Tel:* 313-425-3000 *Toll Free Tel:* 800-733-4763 *E-mail:* service@sme.org (cust care) *Web Site:* www.sme.org, pg 1015

Bray, Tom, Ann Arbor Film Festival, 217 N First St, Ann Arbor, MI 48104 *Tel:* 734-995-5356 *Fax:* 734-995-5396 *E-mail:* info@aafilmfest.org *Web Site:* www.aafilmfest.org, pg 1107

Breakwell, Chris, 31st Street Studios, 77 31 St, Pittsburgh, PA 15201 *Tel:* 412-228-0231 *E-mail:* info@31ststreetstudios.com *Web Site:* www.31ststreetstudios.com, pg 1039

Bredon, Tracey H, BUF Technology, 12335 World Trade Dr, Suite 11, San Diego, CA 92128 *Tel:* 858-451-1350 *Fax:* 858-451-6589 *E-mail:* info@buftek.com *Web Site:* www.buftek.com, pg 815

Breedon, Angela, Music & Entertainment Industry Educators Association (MEIEA), 1900 Belmont Blvd, Nashville, TN 37212-3758 *Tel:* 615-460-6946 *E-mail:* office@meiea.org *Web Site:* www.meiea.org, pg 1084

Bregman, Neil, Sound Venture International, 441 MacLaren St, Suite 401, Ottawa, ON K2P 2H3, Canada *Tel:* 613-241-5111 *Fax:* 613-241-5010 *E-mail:* info@soundventure.com *Web Site:* www.soundventure.com, pg 1017

Bremner, James, Varta Microbattery Inc, 555 Theodore Fremd Ave, Suite C304, Rye, NY 10580 *Tel:* 914-592-2500 *Toll Free Tel:* 800-468-2782 *Fax:* 914-345-0488 *Web Site:* www.varta-microbattery.com; www.varta-microbattery.us, pg 1052

Brennan, John, Adobe Systems Inc, 345 Park Ave, San Jose, CA 95110-2704 *Tel:* 408-536-6000 *Fax:* 408-537-6000 *Web Site:* www.adobe.com, pg 776

Brennan, Lynwen, Industrial Light & Magic (ILM), 1110 Gorgas St, San Francisco, CA 94129 *Tel:* 415-746-3000 *Fax:* 415-746-3015 *E-mail:* prdepartment@ilm.com *Web Site:* www.ilm.com, pg 897

Brennan, Stephen J PhD, Peak Performance Publishing, 14728 Shirley St, Omaha, NE 68144 *Tel:* 402-334-1676 *Toll Free Tel:* 800-293-1676 *Fax:* 402-334-4437 *Web Site:* www.peakperformanceconsult.com, pg 970

Brennan, Stephen J PhD, The Recruiters Library, 14728 Shirley St, Omaha, NE 68144 *Tel:* 402-334-1676 *Toll Free Tel:* 800-293-1676 *Fax:* 402-334-4437 *Web Site:* www.thebestcollegerecruiter.com, pg 993

Brenner, Mara-Lynne, Vitec Videocom Inc, 709 Executive Blvd, Valley Cottage, NY 10989 *Tel:* 845-268-0100 *Fax:* 845-268-0113 *E-mail:* info-cd-usa@vitecgroup.com *Web Site:* www.vitecgroup.com, pg 1060

Breslow, Jennifer, Lifetime Television®, 235 E 45 St, New York, NY 10017 *Tel:* 212-424-7000 *Web Site:* www.mylifetime.com, pg 920

Bressel, Bernd, Video International Development Inc, PO Box 349, Locust Valley, NY 11560 *Tel:* 516-671-6765 *Fax:* 516-730-5084 *E-mail:* info@videointernational.org *Web Site:* www.videointernational.org, pg 1055

Bressler, Joan, Greater Philadelphia Film Office, One Parkway Bldg, 11th fl, 1515 Arch St, Philadelphia, PA 19102 *Tel:* 215-686-2668 *Fax:* 215-686-3659 *E-mail:* mail@film.org *Web Site:* www.film.org, pg 1102

Bressler, Dr Steven H, Monadnock Media Inc, 112 Amherst Rd, Sunderland, MA 01375 *Tel:* 413-665-1390 *Fax:* 413-665-1394 *E-mail:* info@monadnock.org *Web Site:* www.monadnock.org, pg 945

Brewer, Barbara Doss, Colonel Buster Doss Music Group, 341 Billy Goat Hill Rd, Winchester, TN 37398 *Tel:* 931-649-2577 *E-mail:* cbd@united.net *Web Site:* www.stardustcountrymusic.com, pg 831

Brewer, Michael, "PBTM" Music, 1160 W 26 Ave, Eugene, OR 97405 *Tel:* 541-345-8117 *E-mail:* support@pbtmlive.com *Web Site:* www.pbtmlive.com; pbtm.com, pg 970

Brey, Pat, Boeckeler Instruments Inc, 4650 S Butterfield Dr, Tucson, AZ 85714 *Tel:* 520-745-0001 *Toll Free Tel:* 800-552-2262 *Fax:* 520-745-0004 *E-mail:* support@pointmaker.com *Web Site:* www.boeckeler.com, pg 810

Briar, John, FUJIFILM Graphic Systems Division, 850 Central Ave, Hanover Park, IL 60133 *Tel:* 630-259-7200 *Toll Free Tel:* 800-877-0555 *Fax:* 630-259-7078 *E-mail:* contact@fujifilmgs.com *Web Site:* www.fujifilmgs.com, pg 873

Brickhouse, Brian, Eaton Corp, 8609 Six Forks Rd, Raleigh, NC 27615 *Tel:* 919-872-3020 *Toll Free Tel:* 800-356-5794 *E-mail:* powerquality@eaton.com *Web Site:* powerquality.eaton.com, pg 856

Bridges, Matt, PSSI, 7030 Hayvenhurst Ave, Van Nuys, CA 91406 *Tel:* 310-575-4400 *Toll Free Tel:* 800-SAT-LINK (728-5465) *Fax:* 310-575-4451 *E-mail:* operations@pssiglobal.com *Web Site:* www.pssiglobal.com, pg 987

Bridges, Wendy, City of Prescott Film Office, 201 S Cortez St, Prescott, AZ 86303 *Tel:* 928-777-1204 *Fax:* 928-777-1255 *Web Site:* www.cityofprescott.net/business/film, pg 1091

Bridwell, Michael, Digital Projection, 55 Chastain Rd, Suite 115, Kennesaw, GA 30144 *Tel:* 770-420-1350 *Fax:* 770-420-1360 *E-mail:* contact@digitalprojection.com *Web Site:* www.digitalprojection.com, pg 847

Brienza, Gail, Spectrum Audio Visual Services, 351 W 45 Ave, Denver, CO 80216 *Tel:* 303-477-4456 *Toll Free Tel:* 800-477-4752 *Fax:* 303-477-0114 *E-mail:* info@spectrumav.com *Web Site:* www.spectrumav.com, pg 1020

Brietz, Scott, Multicom Inc, 1076 Florida Central Pkwy, Longwood, FL 32750 *Tel:* 407-331-7779 *Toll Free Tel:* 800-423-2594 *Fax:* 407-339-0204 *E-mail:* multicom@multicominc.com *Web Site:* www.multicominc.com, pg 949

Briggs, Bob, Valley Media, 421 Roanoke Dr, Martinez, CA 94553-6240 *Tel:* 925-937-5207; 510-612-5215 (cell) *Web Site:* www.valleymedia.com, pg 1051

Briggs, Christopher, International Robotics Inc, 2001 Palmer Ave, Suite LL-1, Larchmont, NY 10538 *Tel:* 914-630-1060 *Fax:* 203-630-1733 *E-mail:* info@internationalrobotics.com *Web Site:* www.internationalrobotics.com, pg 901

Briggs, Mike, MooreCo Inc, 2885 Lorraine Ave, Temple, TX 76501 *Tel:* 254-778-4727 (CN) *Toll Free Tel:* 800-749-2258 (US) *Fax:* 254-773-0500 (CN) *Toll Free Fax:* 800-697-6258 (US) *Web Site:* moorecoinc.com, pg 946

Bright, James, Sprayway Inc, 1005 S Westgate Ave, Addison, IL 60101 *Tel:* 630-628-3000 *Toll Free Tel:* 800-332-9000 *Fax:* 630-543-7797 *E-mail:* info@spraywayinc.com *Web Site:* www.spraywayinc.com, pg 1022

Brinkman, John, MSI Productions, 9220 Activity Rd, San Diego, CA 92126 *Tel:* 858-348-0100 *Fax:* 858-348-0076 *Web Site:* www.msiprod.com, pg 949

Brinson, Steve, COMPRO Productions Inc, 2055 Boar Tusk Rd NE, Conyers, GA 30012-3801 *Tel:* 770-918-8163 *E-mail:* compro@compro-atl.com *Web Site:* www.compro-atl.com, pg 834

Brinton, Jeff, Alberta Film Commission, 140 Whitemud Crossing, 4211-106 St, Edmonton, AB T6J 6L7, Canada *Tel:* 780-422-8584 *Toll Free Tel:* 888-813-1738 *Fax:* 780-422-8582 *E-mail:* info@albertafilm.ca *Web Site:* www.albertafilm.ca, pg 1104

Brinton, Lawrence, Display Devices, 10828 Hwy 93, Golden, CO 80403 *Tel:* 303-412-0399 *Toll Free Tel:* 877-862-6865 *Fax:* 303-412-9346 *E-mail:* sales@displaydevices.com *Web Site:* www.displaydevices.com, pg 849

Bristow, Myles, CommCreative, 345 Union Ave, Framingham, MA 01702 *Tel:* 508-620-6664 *Toll Free Tel:* 877-620-6664 *Fax:* 508-620-0592 *Web Site:* www.commcreative.com, pg 832

Britner, Mike, Lawrence Behr Associates Inc, 3400 Tupper Dr, Greenville, NC 27834 *Tel:* 252-757-0279 *Toll Free Tel:* 800-522-4464 *Fax:* 252-752-9155 *E-mail:* lbassc@lbagroup.com *Web Site:* www.lbagroup.com/associates, pg 804

Britt, Deb, Charleston International Film Festival (CIFF), 915 Folly Rd, No 78, Charleston, SC 29412 *Tel:* 843-817-1617 *E-mail:* info@charlestoniff.org *Web Site:* charlestoniff.org, pg 1111

Britt, Rob, Charleston International Film Festival (CIFF), 915 Folly Rd, No 78, Charleston, SC 29412 *Tel:* 843-817-1617 *E-mail:* info@charlestoniff.org *Web Site:* charlestoniff.org, pg 1111

Britton, Matt, MRY, 11 W 19 St, 3rd fl, New York, NY 10011 *Tel:* 212-274-0470 *Toll Free Fax:* 888-847-5321 *Web Site:* mry.com, pg 949

Broad, Nicola, Theatre Arts Video Library, 174 Andrew Ave, Leucadia, CA 92024 *Tel:* 760-632-6355 *Toll Free Tel:* 800-456-8285 *Fax:* 760-632-6859 *E-mail:* admin@theatreartsvideo.com *Web Site:* www.theatreartsvideo.com, pg 1038

Broadhurst, Eric L, Charles M Salter Associates Inc, 130 Sutter St, Suite 500, San Francisco, CA 94104 *Tel:* 415-397-0442 *Fax:* 415-397-0454 *E-mail:* info@cmsalter.com *Web Site:* www.cmsalter.com, pg 1001

Brode, Barry S, UND Television Center, 4300 James Ray Dr, Stop 7307, Grand Forks, ND 58202 *Tel:* 701-777-4346 *Toll Free Tel:* 800-CALL-UND (225-5863) *Fax:* 701-777-4342 *E-mail:* tv@und.edu *Web Site:* www.und.nodak.edu/dept/tvcenter, pg 1048

Brodersen, William F, FotoKem Film & Video, 2801 W Alameda Ave, Burbank, CA 91505 *Tel:* 818-846-3101 *Fax:* 818-841-2130 *E-mail:* sales@fotokem.com *Web Site:* www.fotokem.com, pg 871

Brodie, David, Southern Audio Visual, 11700 NW 102 Rd, Suite 15, Miami, FL 33178 *Tel:* 305-591-3888 *Fax:* 305-591-7105 *Web Site:* www.southernav.com, pg 1019

Brodie, Mark, MIB Mediaworks, 85 Main St, Little Falls, NJ 07424 *Tel:* 973-403-1133 *E-mail:* info@mibmediaworks.com *Web Site:* www.mibmediaworks.com, pg 941

Brody, Chris, Crescendo Designs Inc, 641 County Rd 39-A, Southampton, NY 11968 *Tel:* 631-283-2133 *Fax:* 631-204-1066 *E-mail:* sales@crescendodesigns.com *Web Site:* www.crescendodesigns.com, pg 839

Brody, Mike, Crescendo Designs Inc, 641 County Rd 39-A, Southampton, NY 11968 *Tel:* 631-283-2133 *Fax:* 631-204-1066 *E-mail:* sales@crescendodesigns.com *Web Site:* www.crescendodesigns.com, pg 839

Broen, Frank, Teach America Corp, 121 N Love St, Quincy, FL 32351-2440 *Tel:* 850-875-0491 *Web Site:* teachamerica.com; www.accessmanagement.info, pg 1033

Broening, Chris, Audio Visual Dynamics®, 8 Budd St, Morristown, NJ 07960 *Tel:* 973-993-8500 *Fax:* 973-984-0644 *Web Site:* www.avdusa.com, pg 795

Bromwell, Theodore R, Bromwell Marketing, 3 Allegheny Ctr, Suite 111, Pittsburgh, PA 15212 *Tel:* 412-321-4118 *E-mail:* bromwell@earthlink.net *Web Site:* www.bromwellmarketing.com, pg 814

Bronfman, Paul, William F White International Inc, 800 Islington Ave, Toronto, ON M8Z 6A1, Canada *Tel:* 416-239-5050 *Toll Free Tel:* 800-465-0160

(CN only); 800-268-2200 *Fax:* 416-207-2777 *E-mail:* info@cinequipwhite.com *Web Site:* www.whites.com, pg 1065

Brook, Augusta, Wanted! Sound + Picture, 409 King St W, Suite 300, Toronto, ON M5V 1K1, Canada *Tel:* 416-596-1101 *Fax:* 416-596-0690 *E-mail:* info@wantedsp.com *Web Site:* www.wantedsp.com, pg 1062

Brooker, David, Precision Camera & Video Repair Inc, 4 Anngina Dr, Enfield, CT 06082-3222 *Tel:* 860-749-7380 *Toll Free Tel:* 800-665-6515 *Fax:* 860-763-7100 *E-mail:* info@precisioncamera.com *Web Site:* www.precisioncamera.com, pg 980

Brooks, Brian, MB Productions, 4 Edison Place, Fairfield, NJ 07004 *Tel:* 973-439-0044 *Toll Free Tel:* 800-622-2224 *Fax:* 973-439-9844 *E-mail:* mbp@mbvideo.com *Web Site:* www.mbvideo.com, pg 935

Brooks, David, Just Bulbs - The Light Bulb Store, 220 E 60 St, New York, NY 10022 *Tel:* 212-888-5707 *Fax:* 212-888-5704 *E-mail:* sales@justbulbsnyc.com *Web Site:* www.justbulbsnyc.com, pg 907

Brooks, Julie, Wickenburg Film Commission, 216 N Frontier St, Wickenburg, AZ 85390 *Tel:* 928-684-5479; 928-684-0977 *Toll Free Tel:* 800-942-5242 *Fax:* 928-684-5470 *E-mail:* info@wickenburgchamber.com *Web Site:* www.wickenburgchamber.com/film-commission, pg 1091

Brooks, Robert, Drastic Technologies Ltd, 523 The Queensway, Suite 102, Toronto, ON M8Y 1J7, Canada *Tel:* 416-255-5636 *Fax:* 416-255-8780 *Web Site:* www.drastic.tv, pg 852

Brooks, Tim, Hubbard Supply Co, 901 W Second St, Flint, MI 48503 *Tel:* 810-234-8681 *Toll Free Tel:* 800-875-4811 *Fax:* 810-234-6142 *E-mail:* information@hubbardsupply.com *Web Site:* www.hubbardsupply.com, pg 892

Broome, Frances, Kineticvideo.com, 16 Munition St, Toronto, ON M5A 1G7, Canada *Tel:* 416-538-6613 *Toll Free Tel:* 800-263-6910 (CN only) *Fax:* 416-538-9984 *E-mail:* info@kineticvideo.com *Web Site:* www.kineticvideo.com, pg 911

Broughton, Brian, Broughton's Church Supplies, Religious Books & Gifts, 322 Consumers Rd, North York, ON M2J 1P8, Canada *Tel:* 416-690-4777 *Toll Free Tel:* 800-268-4449 *Fax:* 416-690-5357 *E-mail:* sales@bbroughton.com *Web Site:* www.bbroughton.com, pg 814

Broughton, Paul, Life Cycle Books Ltd, 1085 Bellamy Rd N, Unit 20, Toronto, ON M1H 1H7, Canada *Tel:* 416-690-5860 *Toll Free Tel:* 866-880-5860 *Fax:* 416-690-8532 *Toll Free Fax:* 866-690-8532 *E-mail:* support@lifecyclebooks.com; billing@lifecyclebooks.com; orders@lifecyclebooks.com *Web Site:* www.lifecyclebooks.com, pg 920

Brouillet, Joe, Russound, 5 Forbes Rd, Newmarket, NH 03857 *Tel:* 603-659-5170 *Toll Free Tel:* 800-638-8055 (US) *Fax:* 603-659-5388 *E-mail:* sales@russound.com; tech@russound.com *Web Site:* www.russound.com, pg 1001

Brouse, Katherine Hite, Hite Co, 3101 Beale Ave, Altoona, PA 16601 *Tel:* 814-944-6121 *Toll Free Tel:* 800-252-3598 *Fax:* 814-944-3052 *Web Site:* www.hiteco.com, pg 889

Broussard, Gerald, Intermedia Technologies, 1720 Kaliste Saloom, Bldg 2, Suite B-2, Lafayette, LA 70508 *Tel:* 337-406-9428 *Toll Free Tel:* 877-268-9574 *Fax:* 337-406-9582 *Web Site:* www.intermedia-technologies.com, pg 900

Brower, Ron, CRT Custom Products Inc, 7532 Hickory Hills Ct, Whites Creek, TN 37189 *Tel:* 615-876-5490 *Toll Free Tel:* 800-453-2533 *Fax:* 615-876-0096 *E-mail:* sales@crtcustomproducts.com *Web Site:* www.crtcustomproducts.com, pg 840

Brower, Travis, WPHL-TV, 5001 Wynnefield Ave, Philadelphia, PA 19131 *Tel:* 215-878-1700 *Fax:* 215-879-7683; 215-877-4912 *E-mail:* feedback@phl17.com *Web Site:* www.phl17.com, pg 1070

Brown, Alison, Green Linnet Records, 916 19 Ave S, Nashville, TN 37212 *Tel:* 615-320-7672 *Toll Free Tel:* 800-468-6644 *Fax:* 615-320-7378 *E-mail:* info@compassrecords.com *Web Site:* greenlinnet.com; www.compassrecords.com, pg 882

Brown, Anthony, Associated Sound, 1417 Del Paso Blvd, Sacramento, CA 95815 *Tel:* 916-649-8040 *Toll Free Tel:* 800-492-6800 *Fax:* 916-649-0243 *E-mail:* sales@associatedsound.com *Web Site:* www.associatedsound.com, pg 792

Brown, Art, A Go Go Films, 4324 Via Marina, Marina Del Rey, CA 90292 *Tel:* 310-576-4992 *E-mail:* art@agogofilms.com *Web Site:* www.agogofilms.com, pg 771

Brown, Ashley, Audio Visual Technologies Group, 12502 Exchange Dr, Stafford, TX 77477 *Tel:* 281-240-2100 *Toll Free Tel:* 800-522-3687 *E-mail:* avtginfo@avtg.com *Web Site:* www.avtg.com, pg 796

Brown, Avi, Extreme Reach Inc, 75 Second Ave, Suite 720, Needham, MA 02494 *Tel:* 781-577-2016 *E-mail:* sales@extremereach.com; press@extremereach.com *Web Site:* www.extremereach.com, pg 864

Brown, B, Brim Electronics, 120 Home Place, Lodi, NJ 07644 *Tel:* 201-796-2886 *Fax:* 973-778-2792 *E-mail:* info@brimelectronics.com *Web Site:* www.brimelectronics.com, pg 812

Brown, Brenda, SynAudCon, 8780 Rufing Rd, Greenville, IN 47124 *Tel:* 812-923-0174 *Toll Free Fax:* 800-547-0298 *Web Site:* www.synaudcon.com, pg 1030

Brown, Bruce, World Class Learning Materials Inc, PO Box 639, Candler, NC 28715 *Toll Free Tel:* 800-638-6470 *Toll Free Fax:* 800-638-6499 *E-mail:* dealers@wclm.com *Web Site:* www.wclm.com; learningwelled.com, pg 1069

Brown, Clark, NEC Display Solutions of America, 500 Park Blvd, Suite 1100, Itasca, IL 60143 *Tel:* 630-467-3000 *Web Site:* www.necdisplay.com, pg 954

Brown, Dan, db interactive Inc, PO Box 302064, Austin, TX 78703 *Tel:* 512-436-8586 *E-mail:* info@dbinteractive.com *Web Site:* dbinteractive.com, pg 844

Brown, George, KAKE-TV, 1500 N West St, Wichita, KS 67203-1323 *Tel:* 316-943-4221; 316-946-1314 (sales) *Fax:* 316-943-5493 *Web Site:* kake.com, pg 907

Brown, Harold W, Micro Innovations Inc, 910 Belle Ave, Suite 1046, Winter Springs, FL 32708 *Tel:* 407-696-9800 *Fax:* 407-696-8511 *E-mail:* avail@avail-software.com *Web Site:* www.avail-software.com, pg 941

Brown, Ivan, Alpha Source Inc, 6619 W Calumet Rd, Milwaukee, WI 53223-4186 *Tel:* 414-760-2222 *Toll Free Tel:* 800-654-9845 *Fax:* 414-760-2070 *Toll Free Fax:* 888-654-9840 *E-mail:* customer.service@alphasource.com; info@alphasource.com *Web Site:* www.alphasource.com, pg 782

Brown, Jerry, LBA Technology Inc, 3400 Tupper Dr, Greenville, NC 27834 *Tel:* 252-757-0279 *Toll Free Tel:* 800-522-4464 *Fax:* 252-752-9155 *E-mail:* lbagrp@lbagroup.com *Web Site:* www.lbagroup.com, pg 917

Brown, Jim, Optisonics Productions, 311 South Pkwy, Clifton, NJ 07014 *Tel:* 973-458-0951 *Fax:* 973-458-0983 *E-mail:* optisonics@aol.com *Web Site:* www.optisonics.com, pg 965

Brown, Jody A, CACI Productions Group, 14370 Newbrook Dr, Chantilly, VA 20151 *Tel:* 703-679-3100 *Web Site:* www.caci.com, pg 816

Brown, John, Brown United, PO Box 362, Monrovia, CA 91017-0362 *Tel:* 626-357-1161 *Toll Free Tel:* 800-44-BROWN (442-7696) *Fax:* 626-358-3064 *Toll Free Fax:* 800-26-BROWN (262-7696) *E-mail:* info@brownunited.com *Web Site:* www.brownunited.com, pg 814

Brown, Megan, Raymond Entertainment Direct (RED), 3450 Cahuenga Blvd W, Suite 410, Los Angeles, CA 90068 *Tel:* 323-785-4700 *Fax:* 323-785-4701 *E-mail:* info@raymondentertainment.com *Web Site:* www.raymondentertainment.com, pg 992

Brown, Monifa, Shanachie Entertainment Corp, 37 E Clinton St, Newton, NJ 07860 *Tel:* 973-579-7763 *Web Site:* shanachie.com, pg 1008

Brown, Nora, Rochester/Finger Lakes Film & Video Office, 45 East Ave, Suite 400, Rochester, NY 14604-2294 *Tel:* 585-279-8308 *Fax:* 585-232-4822 *Web Site:* www.filmrochester.org, pg 1100

Brown, Patrick, Different Fur Recording Ltd, 3470 19 St, San Francisco, CA 94110 *Tel:* 415-864-1967; 415-828-4060 (bookings) *Fax:* 415-864-1965 *Web Site:* www.differentfurstudios.com, pg 846

Brown, Paul, Star Video Duplicating, 6910 E Fifth Ave, Scottsdale, AZ 85251 *Tel:* 480-946-3699 *Toll Free Tel:* 800-238-7827 *Fax:* 480-946-4722 *Web Site:* www.starvideo.com, pg 1024

Brown, Rick, Transparent Office Products LLC, 2550 Haddonfield Rd, Pennsauken, NJ 08110 *Tel:* 856-488-5455 *Fax:* 856-488-5411 *E-mail:* sales@transoffprod.biz *Web Site:* www.transoffprod.biz, pg 1043

Brown, Rita, Florida Keys & Key West Film Commission, 1201 White St, Suite 102, Key West, FL 33040 *Tel:* 305-293-1800 *Toll Free Tel:* 800-FILM-KEYS (345-6539) *Fax:* 305-296-0788 *Web Site:* www.filmkeys.com, pg 1096

Brown, Russ, Goldberg Brothers Inc, 8000 E 40 Ave, Denver, CO 80207 *Tel:* 303-321-1099 *Fax:* 303-388-0749 *E-mail:* reelservice@goldbergbrothers.com *Web Site:* www.goldbergbrothers.com, pg 880

Brown, Ruth, Pogo Pictures, 114 E Ponce de Leon Ave, Suite B, Decatur, GA 30030 *Tel:* 404-892-9490 *Fax:* 404-892-9491 *E-mail:* info@pogopictures.com *Web Site:* www.pogopictures.com, pg 977

Brown, Sandy, monterey media inc, 566 Saint Charles Dr, Thousand Oaks, CA 91360-3953 *Tel:* 805-494-7199 *Toll Free Tel:* 800-424-2593 *Fax:* 805-496-6061 *E-mail:* customerservice@montereymedia.com; publicity@montereymedia.com *Web Site:* www.montereymedia.com, pg 946

Brown, Sandy, monterey video, 566 Saint Charles Dr, Thousand Oaks, CA 91360-3953 *Tel:* 805-494-7199 *Toll Free Tel:* 800-424-2593 *Fax:* 805-496-6061 *E-mail:* customerservice@montereymedia.com; publicity@montereymedia.com *Web Site:* www.montereymedia.com, pg 946

Brown, Steven, Cinram Inc, 2255 Markham Rd, Scarborough, ON M1B 2W3, Canada *Tel:* 416-298-8190 *Fax:* 416-298-0612 *E-mail:* sales@cinram.com *Web Site:* www.cinramgroup.com, pg 828

Brown, William, Harris Corp, 1025 W NASA Blvd, Melbourne, FL 32919-0001 *Tel:* 321-727-9100 *Toll Free Tel:* 800-442-7747 *E-mail:* webmaster@harris.com *Web Site:* www.harris.com, pg 885

Brown, William E, Communication Corner Inc, PO Box 210, Brightwater, NY 11718 *Tel:* 631-567-2626 *Fax:* 631-665-3473 *Web Site:* www.commcorner.com, pg 833

Browne, Andrew, SES World Skies, 4 Research Way, Princeton, NJ 08540 *Tel:* 609-987-4000; 609-987-4200 *Fax:* 609-987-4517 *E-mail:* info@ses.com *Web Site:* www.ses.com, pg 1007

Browning, Ben, FilmNation Entertainment, 150 W 22 St, 9th fl, New York, NY 10011 *Web Site:* www.filmnation.com, pg 867

Brownsey, Richard, Creative BC (CrBC), 2225 W Broadway, Vancouver, BC V6K 2E4, Canada *Tel:* 604-730-2732 *Fax:* 604-736-7290 *E-mail:* info@creativebc.com *Web Site:* www.creativebc.com, pg 1104

Browse, Nicholas, Cavanaugh Tocci Associates Inc, 327F Boston Post Rd, Sudbury, MA 01776 *Tel:* 978-443-7871 *E-mail:* cta@cavtocci.com *Web Site:* www.cavtocci.com, pg 821

Brozyna, J P, AGF Media Services, 14932 Delano St, Van Nuys, CA 91411-2122 *Tel:* 818-780-7400; 818-780-8085 (24 hours) *Fax:* 818-904-9905 *E-mail:* info@agfmedia.com *Web Site:* www.agfmedia.com, pg 778

Bruce, Brady O, Jupiter Systems, 31015 Huntwood Ave, Hayward, CA 94544 *Tel:* 510-675-1000 *Fax:* 510-675-1001 *E-mail:* sales@jupiter.com *Web Site:* www.jupiter.com, pg 907

Bruce, Michelle, Kenexa, 650 E Swedesford Rd, 2nd fl, Wayne, PA 19087 *Tel:* 407-548-1444 *Fax:* 610-971-9181 *E-mail:* kenexa_learn_sales@kenexa.com *Web Site:* www.outstart.com, pg 909

Bruce, Robert, Intersect Video, 25749 SW Canyon Creek Rd, Suite 300, Wilsonville, OR 97070 *Tel:* 971-224-4808 *E-mail:* info@intersectvideo.com *Web Site:* www.intersectvideo.com, pg 901

Bruck, Jerry, Posthorn Recordings, 142 W 26 St, 10th fl, New York, NY 10001-6814 *Tel:* 212-242-3737 *Fax:* 212-924-1243 *Web Site:* www.posthorn.com, pg 979

Bruckner, Lori, Convergent Media Systems, 190 Bluegrass Valley Pkwy, Alpharetta, GA 30005-2204 *Tel:* 770-369-9000 *Toll Free Tel:* 800-877-7804 *Fax:* 770-369-9100 *E-mail:* convergent@convergent.com *Web Site:* www.convergent.com, pg 836

Bruell, Lucy, L A Bruell Inc, 30 W 26 St, New York, NY 10010 *Tel:* 646-336-5977 *Fax:* 646-336-8317 *Web Site:* www.labruell.com, pg 914

Bruner, Jeremy, Nostalgia Family Video Inc, 2345 11 St, Baker City, OR 97814 *Tel:* 541-523-9034 *Toll Free Tel:* 800-784-3362 *Fax:* 541-523-7115, pg 959

Brunker, Philip, Optikinetics Ltd - The Americas, 11211 Air Park Rd, Suite 1, Ashland, VA 23005 *Tel:* 804-752-2570 *Toll Free Tel:* 800-575-6784 *Fax:* 804-752-2888 *E-mail:* optius@optikinetics.com *Web Site:* www.optikinetics.com, pg 964

Bruno, Ron, The Videohouse Inc, 975 Greentree Rd, Pittsburgh, PA 15220 *Tel:* 412-921-7577 *Fax:* 412-921-5535 *E-mail:* tvirjb@aol.com *Web Site:* www.thevideohouse.com, pg 1057

Bruno, Ross, Hellman Associates Inc, 1225 W Fourth St, Waterloo, IA 50702-2903 *Tel:* 319-234-7055 *Toll Free Tel:* 800-747-7055 *Fax:* 319-234-2089 *E-mail:* info@hellman.com *Web Site:* www.hellman.com, pg 888

Bruns, Andrew, Headlight Audio Visual Inc, 74 Evergreen Dr, Portland, ME 04103-1066 *Tel:* 207-774-5998 *Toll Free Tel:* 800-247-0540 *Fax:* 207-774-4917 *Web Site:* www.headlightaudiovisual.com, pg 887

Bruns, Chas, KahBang Festival, 84 Harlow St, Suite 1, Bangor, ME 04401 *E-mail:* info@kahbang.com; press@kahbang.com *Web Site:* www.kahbang.com, pg 1118

Bruns, Robert G, Headlight Audio Visual Inc, 74 Evergreen Dr, Portland, ME 04103-1066 *Tel:* 207-774-5998 *Toll Free Tel:* 800-247-0540 *Fax:* 207-774-4917 *Web Site:* www.headlightaudiovisual.com, pg 887

Brunzell, Jim, AGLIFF-Austin Gay & Lesbian International Film Festival, 2905 San Gabriel St, Suite 300, Austin, TX 78705 *Tel:* 512-302-9889 *Fax:* 512-302-1088 *E-mail:* info@agliff.org *Web Site:* www.agliff.org, pg 1107

Bruzzo, Chris, Electronic Arts, 209 Redwood Shores Pkwy, Redwood City, CA 94065 *Tel:* 650-628-1500 *Web Site:* www.ea.com, pg 859

Bryan, Kate, ooLite Media, 1702 Nelson Rd, Bozeman, MT 59718 *Tel:* 406-587-1456 *Toll Free Tel:* 800-798-9980 *Fax:* 406-587-1459 *Web Site:* www.oolitemedia.com/earthtalk, pg 964

Bryan, Laura, Juno Awards, 345 Adelaide St W, 2nd fl, Toronto, ON M5V 1R5, Canada *Tel:* 416-485-3135 *Toll Free Tel:* 888-440-JUNO (440-5866, CN only) *Fax:* 416-485-4978 *E-mail:* info@junoawards.ca; info@carasonline.ca; submissions@junoawards.ca *Web Site:* junoawards.ca; www.facebook.com/theJunoAwards, pg 1118

Bryan, Robert, Cuyahoga Community College Media Center, 2900 Community College Ave, Cleveland, OH 44115 *Tel:* 216-987-6000 *Toll Free Tel:* 800-954-8742 *Web Site:* www.tri-c.edu, pg 841

Bryant, Bill, Ingram Entertainment Inc, 2 Ingram Blvd, La Vergne, TN 37089-7006 *Tel:* 615-287-4000 (corp) *Toll Free Tel:* 800-621-1333 (sales & cust serv) *Fax:* 615-287-4982 *Web Site:* www.ingramentertainment.com, pg 898

Bryant, Kelsey, First Person™, 550 Bryant St, San Francisco, CA 94107 *Tel:* 415-495-5595 *Fax:* 415-543-8370, pg 869

Bryant, Patrick, Go To Team, 359-C Wando Place Dr, Mount Pleasant, SC 29464 *Tel:* 843-884-6222 *Toll Free Tel:* 888-455-4333 *E-mail:* crew@gototeam.com *Web Site:* www.gototeam.com, pg 879

Bryant, Sandy, Robertson Worldwide, 13611 Thornton Rd, Blue Island, IL 60406 *Toll Free Tel:* 800-323-5633 *Toll Free Fax:* 877-388-2420 *E-mail:* info@robertsonww.com *Web Site:* www.robertsonww.com, pg 998

Bryce, Tom, Bryce Corp, 4505 Old Lamar Ave, Memphis, TN 38118 *Tel:* 901-369-4400 *Toll Free Tel:* 800-238-7277 *Web Site:* www.brycecorp.com, pg 814

Buchanan, Bob, AVForSale, 1222 Logan Cir, Atlanta, GA 30318 *Tel:* 404-355-6147 *Toll Free Tel:* 866-634-5296 *Fax:* 404-355-7462 *E-mail:* customerservice@avforsale.com *Web Site:* www.avforsale.com, pg 798

Buchanan, Martha, Wilson McLeran Inc, 41 Corey Hill Rd, Saxtons River, VT 05154 *Tel:* 802-869-3111 *Toll Free Tel:* 800-562-9646 *Fax:* 802-869-3111 *Web Site:* www.job-bridge.com, pg 1067

Buchanan, Randy, Special Effects Systems Inc, 6130 Edgewater Dr, Suite A, Orlando, FL 32810 *Tel:* 407-297-6520 *Toll Free Tel:* 877-297-1900 *Fax:* 407-297-4041 *E-mail:* sales@spfx.com; confetti.info@spfx.com *Web Site:* www.spfx.com, pg 1020

Buchenroth, Patrick, ACCO Brands Corp, 4 Corporate Dr, Lake Zurick, IL 60047-8997 *Toll Free Tel:* 800-541-0094 *Toll Free Fax:* 800-941-4463 *E-mail:* contactus@gbc.com *Web Site:* www.accobrands.com, pg 773

Buchman, Chris, Blue Mouse Studio, 26829 37 St, Gobles, MI 49055 *Tel:* 269-628-5160 *E-mail:* frogville@earthlink.net; mwivi@earthlink.net, pg 809

Buck, George H Jr, Jazzology, 61 French Market Place, New Orleans, LA 70116 *Tel:* 504-525-5000 *Fax:* 504-525-1776 *E-mail:* info@jazzology.com *Web Site:* www.jazzology.com, pg 904

Buckel, Krista, Shasta County Film Commission, 2334 Washington Ave, Suite B, Redding, CA 96001 *Tel:* 530-225-4103 *Toll Free Tel:* 800-874-7562 *Fax:* 530-225-4354 *Web Site:* www.visitredding.org/film, pg 1093

Buckley, Linda, KEF Media, 1161 Concord Rd, Smyrna, GA 30080 *Tel:* 404-605-0009 *Toll Free Tel:* 866-219-2477 *Fax:* 404-605-0639 *Web Site:* www.kefmedia.com, pg 909

Budrow, Darren, Ross Video Ltd, 8 John St, Iroquois, ON K0E 1K0, Canada *Tel:* 613-652-4886 *Fax:* 613-652-4425 *E-mail:* solutions@rossvideo.com *Web Site:* www.rossvideo.com, pg 999

Budzilek, Jim, Visual Products Inc, 790 Shiloh Ave, Wellington, OH 44090 *Tel:* 440-647-4999 *Fax:* 440-647-4998 *E-mail:* sales@visualproducts.com *Web Site:* www.visualproducts.com, pg 1059

Budzinski, Jeff, Shanix Inc, 40 Worthington Rd, Cranston, RI 02920 *Tel:* 401-941-4222 *Toll Free Tel:* 800-783-2067 *Fax:* 401-941-4333 *E-mail:* info@shanix.com *Web Site:* www.shanix.com, pg 1008

Bugden, Lisa, Film & Creative Industries Nova Scotia, Historic Properties, Collins Bank Bldg, 3rd fl, 1883 Upper Water St, Suite 302, Halifax, NS B3J 1S9, Canada *Tel:* 902-424-7177 *Toll Free Tel:* 888-360-2111 *Fax:* 902-424-0617 *E-mail:* filmandcreativens@gov.ns.ca *Web Site:* www.filmandcreativens.ca, pg 1105

Buhrman, Rob, Lion & Fox Recording Studios, 9517 Baltimore Ave, College Park, MD 20740 *Tel:* 301-982-4431 *E-mail:* mail@lionfox.com *Web Site:* www.lionfox.com, pg 922

Buksbaum, Larry, Now Hear This, 250 W 49 St, Suite 704, New York, NY 10019 *Tel:* 212-265-1188 *Fax:* 212-265-6363 *E-mail:* info@nhtsound.com *Web Site:* www.nhtsound.com, pg 960

Bulgaretti, Silvio, Gold Link Productions Inc, 176 Ridge Rd, Bolton, ON L7E 4V4, Canada *Tel:* 416-560-3864 *Web Site:* www.toronto-cameraman.com, pg 880

Bull, Kevin, KDM Electronics Inc, 55 Mills Rd, Unit 3, Ajax, ON L1S 2H2, Canada *Tel:* 416-439-7158 *Toll Free Tel:* 800-567-6282 *Fax:* 416-439-7232 *E-mail:* kdm@octasound.com *Web Site:* www.octasound.com, pg 908

Bull, Martin, KDM Electronics Inc, 55 Mills Rd, Unit 3, Ajax, ON L1S 2H2, Canada *Tel:* 416-439-7158 *Toll Free Tel:* 800-567-6282 *Fax:* 416-439-7232 *E-mail:* kdm@octasound.com *Web Site:* www.octasound.com, pg 908

Bull, Ron, KDM Electronics Inc, 55 Mills Rd, Unit 3, Ajax, ON L1S 2H2, Canada *Tel:* 416-439-7158 *Toll Free Tel:* 800-567-6282 *Fax:* 416-439-7232 *E-mail:* kdm@octasound.com *Web Site:* www.octasound.com, pg 908

Bullock, Gary, Synsor Corp, 1920 Merrill Creek Pkwy, Everett, WA 98203-5859 *Tel:* 425-551-1300 *Toll Free Tel:* 800-426-0193 *Fax:* 425-551-1313 *E-mail:* info@synsor.com *Web Site:* www.synsor.com, pg 1030

Bullock, Joe, Blair Packaging, 1515 Independence St, Cape Girardeau, MO 63703 *Tel:* 573-264-2146 *Toll Free Tel:* 800-624-3150 *Fax:* 573-264-3730 *E-mail:* info@blairpkg.com *Web Site:* www.blairpkg.com, pg 809

Bulow, George M, Interactive International Inc, 290 West End Ave, New York, NY 10023-8106 *Tel:* 212-580-5015 *Fax:* 212-580-5017 *E-mail:* ivie@erols.com, pg 899

Bundschuh, Andy, Mike Vasilinda Productions Inc, 310 N Monroe St, Tallahassee, FL 32301 *Tel:* 850-224-5420 *Web Site:* mvptv.tv, pg 1052

Bunke, Jerome, Digital Force, 149 Madison Ave, 12th fl, New York, NY 10016 *Tel:* 212-252-9300 *Toll Free Tel:* 877-DISC-USA (347-2872) *Fax:* 212-252-7377 *E-mail:* frontdesk@digitalforce.com *Web Site:* www.digitalforce.com, pg 847

Bunney, Graham, Broadcast Microwave Services (BMS), 12367 Crosthwaite Circle, Poway, CA 92064 *Tel:* 858-391-3050 *Toll Free Tel:* 800-669-9667 *Fax:* 858-391-3049 *E-mail:* sales@bms-inc.com *Web Site:* www.bms-inc.com, pg 813

Bunyard, Sharon, Tecfilms Inc, 6310 Lemmon Ave, Suite 210, Dallas, TX 75209-5850 *Tel:* 214-904-0414 *E-mail:* mail@tecfilms.com *Web Site:* www.tecfilms.com, pg 1033

Burd, Adam, Avast! Recording Co, 601 NW 80 St, Seattle, WA 98117 *Tel:* 206-633-3926 *Fax:* 206-789-7569 *E-mail:* avast@comcast.net *Web Site:* www.avastrecording.com, pg 798

Burden, Danny, Canadian American Records, PO Box 808, Lititz, PA 17543-0538 *Tel:* 717-627-4800 *Fax:* 717-627-4800 *E-mail:* canadianamerican@dejazzd.com *Web Site:* www.canadianamericanrecords.net; www.joeywelz.com, pg 818

Burden, Richard W, Richard W Burden Associates, 20944 Sherman Way, Canoga Park, CA 91303 *Tel:* 818-340-4590, pg 815

Burdick, Steve, Westlake Recording Studios, 7265 Santa Monica Blvd, Los Angeles, CA 90046 *Tel:* 323-851-9800 *E-mail:* bookings@thelakestudios.com; info@thelakestudios.com *Web Site:* www.thelakestudios.com, pg 1064

Burford, Robert, Foxtrot Teleprompt, 20 Clifford Place, East Norwich, NY 11732-1306 *Tel:* 516-428-3063 (cell) *Toll Free Tel:* 888-365-0808 *E-mail:* nyprompter@hotmail.com *Web Site:* foxtrotteleprompt.com, pg 872

Burger, Gregg, Precision Camera & Video, 2438 W Anderson Lane, Suite B-4, Austin, TX 78757 *Tel:* 512-467-7676 *Toll Free Tel:* 800-677-1023 *Fax:* 512-467-0607 *Web Site:* www.precision-camera.com, pg 980

Burgess, Glenn, Matrix Video Communications Corp (MVCC), 120 2331 50 Ave SE, Calgary, AB T2G 0N1, Canada *Tel:* 403-640-4490 *Toll Free Tel:* 800-320-3974 *Fax:* 403-640-9012 *Web Site:* www.matrixvideocom.com, pg 934

Burgess, Richard, Smithsonian Folkways Recordings, 600 Maryland Ave SW, Suite 2001, Washington, DC 20024 *Tel:* 202-633-6450 *Toll Free Tel:* 888-FOLKWAYS (365-5929) *Fax:* 202-633-6477 *E-mail:* smithsonianfolkways@si.edu *Web Site:* www.folkways.si.edu, pg 1014

Burgess, William III, Ken-Del Productions Inc, 1500 First State Blvd, Wilmington, DE 19804-3596 *Tel:* 302-999-1111; 302-999-1110; 302-999-1164 *Toll Free Tel:* 800-249-1110 *Fax:* 302-999-1656 *E-mail:* info@ken-del.com *Web Site:* www.ken-del.com, pg 909

Burgess, William III, Ken-Del Studios, 1500 First State Blvd, Wilmington, DE 19804-3596 *Tel:* 302-999-1111 *Toll Free Tel:* 800-249-1110 *Fax:* 302-999-1656 *E-mail:* info@ken-del.com *Web Site:* www.ken-del.com, pg 909

Burke, Bryant, GatesAir, 5300 Kings Island Dr, Suite 101, Mason, OH 45040 *Tel:* 513-459-3400 *Fax:* 513-459-3796 *E-mail:* information@gatesair.com; orders@gatesair.com; support@gatesair.com *Web Site:* www.gatesair.com, pg 875

Burke, David, Commonwealth Films Inc, 223 Commonwealth Ave, Boston, MA 02116 *Tel:* 617-262-5634 *E-mail:* info@commonwealthfilms.com *Web Site:* www.commonwealthfilms.com, pg 832

Burke, James, HB Communications Inc, 60 Dodge Ave, North Haven, CT 06473 *Tel:* 203-234-9246 *Toll Free Tel:* 800-243-4414 *Fax:* 203-234-2013 *E-mail:* info@hbcommunications.com *Web Site:* www.hbcommunications.com, pg 886

Burke, Rose, Ken-Del Productions Inc, 1500 First State Blvd, Wilmington, DE 19804-3596 *Tel:* 302-999-1111; 302-999-1110; 302-999-1164 *Toll Free Tel:* 800-249-1110 *Fax:* 302-999-1656 *E-mail:* info@ken-del.com *Web Site:* www.ken-del.com, pg 909

Burke, Rose, Ken-Del Studios, 1500 First State Blvd, Wilmington, DE 19804-3596 *Tel:* 302-999-1111 *Toll Free Tel:* 800-249-1110 *Fax:* 302-999-1656 *E-mail:* info@ken-del.com *Web Site:* www.ken-del.com, pg 909

Burke, Sean, Gefen, 20600 Nordhoff St, Chatsworth, CA 91311 *Tel:* 818-772-9100 *Toll Free Tel:* 800-545-6900 *Fax:* 818-772-9120 *E-mail:* gsinfo@gefen.com *Web Site:* www.gefen.com, pg 876

Burkette, Jay, ExpoDisplays, 3401 Mary Taylor Rd, Birmingham, AL 35235 *Tel:* 205-439-8200 *Toll Free Tel:* 800-367-3976 *Fax:* 205-439-8201 *E-mail:* info@expodisplays.com *Web Site:* www.expodisplays.com, pg 864

Burkhart, Dennis, Encounter Video Inc, 14825 NW Ash St, Portland, OR 97231-2620 *Tel:* 503-285-8974 *Fax:* 503-285-3726 *E-mail:* encountvid@aol.com *Web Site:* www.encountervideo.com, pg 861

Burkholder, Jason O PhD, SoftWright LLC, PO Box 7205, Charlotte, VA 22906 *Tel:* 303-344-5486 *Toll Free Tel:* 800-728-4033 *Fax:* 303-265-9399 *E-mail:* sales@softwright.com *Web Site:* www.softwright.com, pg 1015

Burleigh, Jon, MRM Worldwide, 622 Third Ave, New York, NY 10017 *Tel:* 646-865-6230 *E-mail:* info@mrmworldwide.com *Web Site:* www.mrmworldwide.com, pg 948

Burnett, Jennie, Method Studios, 730 Arizona Ave, Santa Monica, CA 90401 *Tel:* 310-434-6500 *Web Site:* www.methodstudios.com, pg 939

Burns, Amy, Sound & Vision Communications Inc, 4601 N "A" St, Tampa, FL 33609-1909 *Tel:* 813-642-4706 *Web Site:* www.gosvc.com, pg 1017

Burns, Barbara, Littlite LLC, PO Box 430, Hamburg, MI 48139-0430 *Tel:* 810-852-4242 *Fax:* 810-231-1631 *E-mail:* sales@littlite.com *Web Site:* www.littlite.com, pg 923

Burns, Colleen, 30 Second Street Ltd, 1209 Mountain Road Place NE, Albuquerque, NM 87110 *Tel:* 505-265-0224 *E-mail:* info@thirtysecst.com *Web Site:* www.thirtysecst.com, pg 1039

Burns, Deb, School Specialty Inc, W6316 Design Dr, Greenville, WI 54942 *Tel:* 419-589-1425 *Toll Free Tel:* 888-388-3224 *Fax:* 419-589-1600 *Toll Free Fax:* 888-388-6344 *E-mail:* internationalorders@schoolspecialty.com *Web Site:* www.schoolspecialty.com, pg 1004

Burns, Eleanor, Quilt in a Day, 1955 Diamond St, San Marcos, CA 92078 *Tel:* 760-591-0082 *Toll Free Tel:* 800-777-4852 *Fax:* 760-591-4424 *E-mail:* customerservice@quiltinaday.com *Web Site:* www.quiltinaday.com, pg 989

Burns, Kristyn, American Harlequin Corp, 1531 Glen Ave, Moorestown, NJ 08057 *Tel:* 856-234-5505 *Toll Free Tel:* 800-642-6440 *Fax:* 856-231-4403 *E-mail:* dance@harlequinfloors.com *Web Site:* www.harlequinfloors.com, pg 784

Burns, Michael, Quatrefoil Associates Inc, 29 "C" St, Laurel, MD 20707 *Tel:* 301-470-4748 *Fax:* 301-470-4749 *E-mail:* info@quatrefoil.com *Web Site:* www.quatrefoil.com, pg 989

Burns, Pat, Interactive Products, 101 Commerce Dr, Montgomeryville, PA 18936 *Tel:* 215-362-2766 *Toll Free Tel:* 800-523-6716 *Fax:* 215-361-0167 *E-mail:* numonics@numonics.com *Web Site:* www.numonics.com, pg 900

Burns, Steven J, North Coast Studios Inc, 29181 Calahan Rd, Roseville, MI 48066 *Tel:* 586-359-6630 *Toll Free Tel:* 888-866-0652 *Fax:* 586-359-6638 *E-mail:* sales@northcoaststudiosinc.com, pg 959

Burns, Tim, Edmund Scientific, 532 Main St, Tonawanda, NY 14150 *Toll Free Tel:* 800-728-6999; 800-818-4955 *Toll Free Fax:* 800-828-3299 *E-mail:* scientifics@edsci.com *Web Site:* www.scientificsonline.com, pg 857

Burr, Suzanne, Valencia Studios, 26030 Avenue Hall, Studio 5, Valencia, CA 91355 *Tel:* 661-702-9102 *E-mail:* info@valenciastudios.com *Web Site:* www.valenciastudios.com, pg 1051

Burro, Erik L, Audio Visual Systems Rental Centres, Pennjerdel House, 449 High St, Burlington, NJ 08016-4514 *Tel:* 609-387-3636 *Toll Free Tel:* 800-416-3636 *Fax:* 609-871-3636 *Web Site:* www.avsgroup.com, pg 796

Burroughs, J R, Commercial Video, PO Box 360247, Cleveland, OH 44136-0005 *Tel:* 330-273-8795 *E-mail:* info@comvid.com *Web Site:* www.comvid.com, pg 832

Burrows, Josh, Stray Angel Films, 2236 S Barrington Ave, Los Angeles, CA 90064 *Tel:* 310-277-6900 *Fax:* 801-438-5009 *E-mail:* rentals@strayangel.com *Web Site:* www.strayangel.com, pg 1026

Burrud, John, Burrud Productions Inc, 468 N Camden Dr, 2nd fl, Beverly Hills, CA 90210 *Tel:* 310-860-5158 *Fax:* 562-595-5986 *E-mail:* info@burrud.com *Web Site:* www.burrud.com, pg 815

Burson, Ben III, Padgitt's, 7801 N Lamar Blvd, Suite D84, Austin, TX 78752 *Tel:* 512-832-9900 *Toll Free Tel:* 800-388-3130 *Fax:* 512-832-0003 *E-mail:* padgitts@padgitts.com *Web Site:* www.padgitts.com, pg 967

Burst, Fran, Burst Video/Film Inc, PO Box 5354, Atlanta, GA 31107-0354, pg 815

Burstein, John, Slim Goodbody Corp, 161 Narrows Rd, Lincolnville, ME 04850 *Tel:* 207-763-2820 *Toll Free Tel:* 800-962-7546 *Fax:* 207-763-4804 *E-mail:* info@slimgoodbody.com *Web Site:* www.slimgoodbody.com, pg 1013

Burton, Bill, National Association of Video Distributors (NAVD), 5584 Prestwick Dr, Newburgh, IN 47630 *Tel:* 270-860-8904 *Web Site:* www.navdonline.org, pg 1085

Burton, Erika, Rhythm & Hues, 2100 E Grand Ave, Suite A, El Segundo, CA 90245-5024 *Tel:* 310-448-7500 *Fax:* 310-448-7600 *E-mail:* info-la@rhythm.com *Web Site:* www.rhythm.com, pg 996

Burton, Joe, Plantronics Inc, 345 Encinal St, Santa Cruz, CA 95060 *Tel:* 831-426-5858 *Toll Free Tel:* 800-544-4660 *Fax:* 831-426-6098 *Toll Free Fax:* 888-290-4519 *E-mail:* plantronics@custhelp.com *Web Site:* www.plantronics.com, pg 976

Buscher, Rob, Greater Philadelphia Film Office, One Parkway Bldg, 11th fl, 1515 Arch St, Philadelphia, PA 19102 *Tel:* 215-686-2668 *Fax:* 215-686-3659 *E-mail:* mail@film.org *Web Site:* www.film.org, pg 1102

Bush, Curt, White Dog Studios, 587 Virginia Ave NE, Suite 1, Atlanta, GA 30306 *Tel:* 404-355-2200 *E-mail:* info@whitedogstudios.net *Web Site:* www.whitedogstudios.net, pg 1065

Bush, Eric, Havas Edge, 6922 Hollywood Blvd, Hollywood, CA 90028 *Tel:* 310-734-1333 *E-mail:* info@havasedge.com *Web Site:* www.havasedge.com, pg 885

Bush, Jeff, Eye on Dance, 70 E Tenth St, Suite 19-D, New York, NY 10003 *Tel:* 212-206-6492 *E-mail:* eyeonthearts@gmail.com *Web Site:* www.eyeondance.org, pg 865

Bush, Jim, Charleston International Film Festival (CIFF), 915 Folly Rd, No 78, Charleston, SC 29412 *Tel:* 843-817-1617 *E-mail:* info@charlestoniff.org *Web Site:* charlestoniff.org, pg 1111

Bush, Ken, Bestek Lighting & Staging, 98 Mahan St, West Babylon, NY 11704 *Tel:* 631-643-0707 *Fax:* 631-643-0764 *E-mail:* production@bestek.com *Web Site:* www.bestek.com, pg 806

Busse, Glen R, Directed Electronics, One Viper Way, Vista, CA 92081 *Tel:* 760-598-6200 *Toll Free Tel:* 800-876-0800 *Fax:* 760-598-6400 *E-mail:* customerfeedback@directed.com *Web Site:* www.directed.com, pg 848

Butcher, Dane, Symetrix Inc, 6408 216 St SW, Mountlake Terrace, WA 98043-2093 *Tel:* 425-778-7728 *E-mail:* support@symetrix.co; sales@symetrix.co *Web Site:* www.symetrix.co, pg 1030

Butera, Michael A, National Association for Music Education (NAfME), 1806 Robert Fulton Dr, Reston, VA 20191 *Tel:* 703-860-4000 *Toll Free Tel:* 800-336-3768 *Fax:* 703-860-1531 *E-mail:* memberservices@nafme2.org *Web Site:* www.menc.org; www.nafme.org, pg 1085

Butler, Alton, Angstrom Lighting, 837 N Cahuenga Blvd, Hollywood, CA 90038 *Tel:* 323-462-4246 *Fax:* 323-462-8190 *Web Site:* www.angstromlighting.com, pg 786

Butler, Chuck, Monster Tracks, 1821 Ranstead St, Philadelphia, PA 19103 *Tel:* 215-567-0400 *Toll Free Tel:* 800-369-1280 *Fax:* 215-567-0350 *Web Site:* www.monstertracks.com, pg 945

Butler, David, Butler Films Inc, 108 Old Solomons Island Rd, Suite L-10, Annapolis, MD 21401 *Tel:* 410-280-1160 *Fax:* 443-458-5315 *E-mail:* info@butlerfilm.com *Web Site:* www.butlerfilm.com, pg 815

Butler, David, Manios Digital & Film, 10663 Burbank Blvd, North Hollywood, CA 91601 *Tel:* 818-760-8290 *Toll Free Tel:* 800-845-6619 *Fax:* 818-760-8805 *E-mail:* sales@maniosdigital.com *Web Site:* www.maniosdigital.com, pg 930

Butler, Patrick, Association of Public Television Stations (APTS), 2100 Crystal Dr, Suite 700, Arlington, VA 22202 *Tel:* 202-654-4200 *Fax:* 202-654-4236 *Web Site:* www.apts.org, pg 1079

Butler, Robert, Audio Book Contractors LLC, PO Box 96, Riverdale, MD 20738-0096 *Tel:* 301-439-5830 *Fax:* 301-439-5830 *E-mail:* info@audiobookcontractors.com *Web Site:* www.audiobookcontractors.com, pg 794

Butnaru, Avner, BitFlow Inc, 400 W Cummings Park, Suite 5050, Woburn, MA 01801 *Tel:* 781-932-2900 *Fax:* 781-933-9965 *E-mail:* sales@bitflow.com *Web Site:* www.bitflow.com, pg 808

Butrum, Carl, Broadcasters Foundation Awards, 125 W 55 St, 3rd fl, New York, NY 10019-5366 *Tel:* 212-373-8250 *Fax:* 212-373-8254 *E-mail:* info@thebfoa.org *Web Site:* www.broadcastersfoundation.org, pg 1110

Butt, Amy, Larrabee Sound Studio, 4162 Lankershim Blvd, North Hollywood, CA 91602 *Tel:* 818-753-0717 *Fax:* 818-753-8046 *E-mail:* info@larrabeestudios.com *Web Site:* www.larrabeestudios.com, pg 916

Butz, Holly, Logan Productions Inc, 8035 N Port Washington Rd, Milwaukee, WI 53217 *Tel:* 414-352-9691 *Fax:* 414-352-4993 *E-mail:* sales@loganproductions.com *Web Site:* www.loganproductions.com, pg 924

Buzzell, Joanne, Lineco, 517 Main St, Holyoke, MA 01040 *Toll Free Tel:* 800-322-7775 *Fax:* 413-532-9281 *Toll Free Fax:* 800-298-7815 *E-mail:* info@lineco.com *Web Site:* www.lineco.com, pg 922

Byramji, Vira, Electric Lady Studios, 52 W Eighth St, New York, NY 10011 *Tel:* 212-677-4700 *Web Site:* electricladystudios.com, pg 858

Byrd, Jeff, PrimaLux Video Inc, 555 Eighth Ave, Suite 1002, New York, NY 10018 *Tel:* 212-206-1402 *Fax:* 212-206-1826 *E-mail:* primalux@aol.com *Web Site:* www.primalux.com, pg 982

Byrd, Robert, Media Arts Grants, 400 Sibley St, Suite 125, St Paul, MN 55101 *Tel:* 651-224-9431 *Toll Free Tel:* 800-995-3766 *Fax:* 651-224-3439 *E-mail:* info@jeromefdn.org *Web Site:* www.jeromefdn.org, pg 1119

Byrne, Patrick, Balboa Capital Corp, 2010 Main St, Suite 1100, Irvine, CA 92614 *Tel:* 949-756-0800 *Toll Free Tel:* 888-BALBOA1 (225-2621) *Fax:* 949-756-2565 *E-mail:* customerservice@balboacapital.com *Web Site:* www.balboacapital.com, pg 802

Byrns, Bob, Paulist Press, 997 Macarthur Blvd, Mahwah, NJ 07430-9990 *Tel:* 201-825-7300 *Toll Free Tel:* 800-218-1903 (orders) *Toll Free Fax:* 800-836-3161 *E-mail:* info@paulistpress.com *Web Site:* www.paulistpress.com, pg 970

Caballer, Jose, Blind, 1702 Olympic Blvd, Santa Monica, CA 90404 *Tel:* 310-314-1618 *Fax:* 310-314-1718 *Web Site:* www.blind.com, pg 809

Cabasso, Artie, Gemini Sound, 107 Trumbull St, Bldg F8, 2nd fl, Elizabeth, NJ 07206-2171 *Tel:* 732-346-0061 *Fax:* 732-346-0065 *E-mail:* sales@geminisound.com *Web Site:* www.geminisound.com, pg 876

Cabeceiras, Brian, Imagine Communications Corp, 3001 Dallas Pkwy, Suite 300, Frisco, TX 75034 *Tel:* 469-803-4900 *Toll Free Tel:* 866-4-IMAGINE (446-2446) *Fax:* 469-803-4899 *E-mail:* insidesales@imaginecommunications.com *Web Site:* www.imaginecommunications.com, pg 896

Cabela, Daniel, Music Lab Inc, 500 E Saint Elmo Rd, Austin, TX 78745 *Tel:* 512-707-0560 *Fax:* 512-707-2946 *E-mail:* rentals@musiclab.net *Web Site:* www.musiclab.net, pg 950

Cabela, Joe, Music Lab Inc, 500 E Saint Elmo Rd, Austin, TX 78745 *Tel:* 512-707-0560 *Fax:* 512-707-2946 *E-mail:* rentals@musiclab.net *Web Site:* www.musiclab.net, pg 950

Cabrales, Carlos, First Person™, 550 Bryant St, San Francisco, CA 94107 *Tel:* 415-495-5595 *Fax:* 415-543-8370, pg 869

Cadigan, Katie, imageReal Pictures LLC, 4 Lighthouse St, No 8, Marina del Rey, CA 90292 *E-mail:* info@imagereal.com *Web Site:* www.imagereal.com, pg 896

Cafferillo, Nick, SNL Kagan Media & Communications, One SNL Plaza, 212 Seventh St NE, Charlottesville, VA 22902 *Tel:* 434-977-1600 *Toll Free Tel:* 866-296-3743 *Fax:* 434-977-4466 *E-mail:* snlkagansales@snl.com *Web Site:* www.snl.com, pg 1014

Cahalan, Tracy, Inland Audio Visual Co, 1414 N Fiske St, Suite E, Spokane, WA 99202 *Tel:* 509-328-0706 *Toll Free Tel:* 888-9INLAND (946-5263) *Fax:* 509-328-0730 *E-mail:* inland@inlandav.com *Web Site:* www.inlandav.com, pg 898

Cahill, Pat, American Color Imaging (ACI), 715 E 18 St, Cedar Falls, IA 50613 *Tel:* 319-277-3655 *Toll Free Tel:* 800-728-2722 *Fax:* 319-277-6522 *E-mail:* sales@acilab.com *Web Site:* www.acilab.com, pg 784

Cain, Mike, Trusty Tuneshop Recording Studios, 8771 Rose Creek Rd, Nebo, KY 42441 *Tel:* 270-249-3194 *E-mail:* etrusty@vci.net *Web Site:* trustytuneshop.com, pg 1045

Cairns, Sam, Gospel Folio Press, 304 Killaly St W, Port Colborne, ON L3K 6A6, Canada *Tel:* 905-835-9166 *Toll Free Tel:* 800-952-2382 *Fax:* 905-834-0012 *E-mail:* info@gospelfolio.com; orders@gospelfolio.com *Web Site:* www.gospelfolio.com, pg 880

Cajka, Philip, Audio-Technica US Inc, 1221 Commerce Dr, Stow, OH 44224 *Tel:* 330-686-2600 *Fax:* 330-686-0719 *E-mail:* pro@atus.com *Web Site:* www.audio-technica.com, pg 794

Calabro, Louis, Canadian Screen Awards, 49 Ontario St, Suite 501, Toronto, ON M5A 2V1, Canada *Tel:* 416-366-2227 *Toll Free Tel:* 800-644-5194 *Fax:* 416-366-8454 *E-mail:* academie@acct.ca *Web Site:* www.acct.ca/prixgemeaux; www.academy.ca/awards, pg 1111

Calabro, Thom, FUJIFILM Optical Devices Division, 10 High Point Dr, Wayne, NJ 07470 *Tel:* 973-633-5600 *Fax:* 973-633-5216 *Web Site:* www.fujifilmusa.com/products/optical_devices, pg 873

Caldero, Steve, Yamaha Electronics Corp, 6660 Orangethorpe Ave, Buena Park, CA 90620 *Tel:* 714-522-9105 *Toll Free Tel:* 800-292-2982 (cust support) *Toll Free Fax:* 800-782-8484 *Web Site:* www.yamaha.com, pg 1071

Calderon, Lauren, WorldFest-Houston, 9898 Bissonnet St, Suite 650, Houston, TX 77036 *Tel:* 713-965-9955 *Toll Free Tel:* 866-965-9955 *Fax:* 713-965-9960 *E-mail:* mail@worldfest.org; entry@worldfest.org *Web Site:* www.worldfest.org, pg 1130

Calderwood, David, Euro-Pacific Film & Video Productions Inc, PO Box 7986, Shrewsbury, NJ 07702 *Tel:* 732-530-4451 *Toll Free Tel:* 800-387-6776 *E-mail:* info@euro-pacific.com *Web Site:* www.euro-pacific.com, pg 863

Calderwood, Lisa Moss, Euro-Pacific Film & Video Productions Inc, PO Box 7986, Shrewsbury, NJ 07702 *Tel:* 732-530-4451 *Toll Free Tel:* 800-387-6776 *E-mail:* info@euro-pacific.com *Web Site:* www.euro-pacific.com, pg 863

Caler, Jennifer, Optikinetics Ltd - The Americas, 11211 Air Park Rd, Suite 1, Ashland, VA 23005 *Tel:* 804-752-2570 *Toll Free Tel:* 800-575-6784 *Fax:* 804-752-2888 *E-mail:* optius@optikinetics.com *Web Site:* www.optikinetics.com, pg 964

Califano, Carmela, Calger Lighting Inc, 200 Lexington Ave, Suite 434, New York, NY 10016 *Tel:* 212-689-9511 *Fax:* 212-779-0721 *E-mail:* sales@calgerlighting.com *Web Site:* www.calgerlighting.com, pg 816

Callagy, Dennis, Custom Computer Specialists Inc, 6 Blackstone Valley Place, Suite 402, Lincoln, RI 02865 *Tel:* 401-765-3000 *Toll Free Tel:* 800-556-2828 *Fax:* 401-765-6440 *Web Site:* www.customonline.com, pg 841

Callahan, David, New York Film/Video Council (NYFVC), PO Box 1685, New York, NY 10185-1685 *Tel:* 212-330-0450 *E-mail:* info@nyfvc.org *Web Site:* www.nyfvc.org, pg 1086

Callahan, Rod, A/V Presentations Inc, 104 Otis St, Suite 30, Northborough, MA 01532 *Tel:* 508-393-9767 *Toll Free Tel:* 800-648-7176 *Fax:* 508-393-6698 *Web Site:* www.avpresentations.com, pg 797

Callaway, Andy, Frontline Communications, 12770 44 St N, Clearwater, FL 33762 *Tel:* 727-573-0400 *Fax:* 727-571-3295 *Web Site:* www.frontlinecomm.com, pg 873

Callen, Dennis, Callen Photo Mount, 185 Sixth Ave, Paterson, NJ 07524 *Tel:* 973-925-2390 *Toll Free Tel:* 800-225-5360 *Fax:* 973-925-9615 *Web Site:* www.callencorp.com, pg 817

Callison, Kay, American Audio Prose Library Inc (AAPL), 600 Crestland Ave, Columbia, MO 65203 *Tel:* 573-443-0361 *Fax:* 573-499-0579 *E-mail:* aaplinc@centurytel.net *Web Site:* www.americanaudioprose.org, pg 783

Callner, Ben, Pogo Pictures, 114 E Ponce de Leon Ave, Suite B, Decatur, GA 30030 *Tel:* 404-892-9490 *Fax:* 404-892-9491 *E-mail:* info@pogopictures.com *Web Site:* www.pogopictures.com, pg 977

Calvert, Tom, Credo Interactive Inc, 4612 Strathcona Rd, North Vancouver, BC V7O 1G3, Canada *Tel:* 604-291-6717 *E-mail:* info@charactermotion.com *Web Site:* www.charactermotion.com, pg 839

Calvin, Marcia, PACSAT, 1629 "S" St, Sacramento, CA 95811 *Tel:* 916-446-7890; 916-335-1649 (after hours) *Toll Free Tel:* 800-672-2728 *Fax:* 916-446-7893 *E-mail:* pacsat@pacsat.com *Web Site:* www.pacsat.com, pg 967

Calzone, Joe, Calzone Anvil Case Co, 225 Black Rock Ave, Bridgeport, CT 06605 *Tel:* 203-367-5766 *Toll Free Tel:* 800-243-5152 *Fax:* 203-336-4406 *E-mail:* info@calzonecase.com *Web Site:* www.calzonecase.com, pg 817

Calzone, Joseph, Anvil Cases, 15730 Salt Lake Ave, City of Industry, CA 91745 *Tel:* 626-968-4100 *Toll Free Tel:* 800-359-2684 *Fax:* 626-968-1703 *E-mail:* web.sales@anvilcase.com *Web Site:* www.anvilcase.com, pg 787

Calzone, Vincent, Calzone Anvil Case Co, 225 Black Rock Ave, Bridgeport, CT 06605 *Tel:* 203-367-5766 *Toll Free Tel:* 800-243-5152 *Fax:* 203-336-4406 *E-mail:* info@calzonecase.com *Web Site:* www.calzonecase.com, pg 817

Camara, Alex, AudioControl®, 22410 70 Ave W, Mountlake Terrace, WA 98043 *Tel:* 425-775-8461 *Fax:* 425-778-3166 *E-mail:* sound.better@audiocontrol.com; superio.sound@audiocontrol.com *Web Site:* www.audiocontrol.com, pg 796

Cambria, Dave, Red Sky Studios, 184 Everett St, Allston, MA 02134 *Tel:* 617-903-3373 *E-mail:* mail@redsky-studios.com *Web Site:* redsky-studios.com, pg 993

Camden, Ron, BIAMP Systems, 9300 SW Gemini Dr, Beaverton, OR 97008 *Tel:* 503-641-7287 *Toll Free Tel:* 800-826-1457 (US & CN) *Fax:* 503-626-0281 *E-mail:* biampinfo@biamp.com; salesteam@biamp.com *Web Site:* www.biamp.com, pg 806

Camitta, Robert, Midnight Media Group Inc, 45 E Willow St, Millburn, NJ 07041-1416 *Tel:* 973-379-5959 *E-mail:* info@mmgi.tv *Web Site:* www.mmgi.tv, pg 942

Camp, Alysia, Goal Productions, 1905 Victory Blvd, Suite 6, Glendale, CA 91201 *Tel:* 818-588-3900 *Fax:* 818-588-3903 *E-mail:* info@goalproductions.com *Web Site:* www.goalproductions.com, pg 880

Campa, Mario A, Toys From The Attic, 203 Mamaroneck Ave, Suite 2, White Plains, NY 10601 *Tel:* 914-421-0069 *Fax:* 914-328-3852 *E-mail:* info@tfta.com *Web Site:* tfta.com, pg 1043

Campagna, George, Alliance Entertainment Corp (AEC) LLC, 4250 Coral Ridge Dr, Coral Springs, FL 33065 *Tel:* 954-346-4024 *Toll Free Tel:* 800-356-2049 (ext 4600) *Web Site:* www.aent.com, pg 781

Campagna, Mike, Peerless Industries, 2300 White Oak Circle, Aurora, IL 60502 *Tel:* 630-375-5100 *Toll Free Tel:* 800-865-2112 *Fax:* 630-820-8537 *Toll Free Fax:* 800-359-6500 *E-mail:* info@peerlessmounts.com *Web Site:* www.peerlessmounts.com, pg 971

Campbell, Colin G, Colonial Williamsburg Foundation, PO Box 1776, Williamsburg, VA 23187-1776 *Tel:* 757-229-1000 *E-mail:* geninfo@cwf.org *Web Site:* www.colonialwilliamsburg.org, pg 831

Campbell, David, Projection Presentation Technology, 5803 Rolling Rd, Suite 207, Springfield, VA 22152 *Tel:* 703-912-1334 *Toll Free Tel:* 800-377-7650 *Fax:* 703-912-1350 *E-mail:* info@projection.com *Web Site:* www.projection.com, pg 985

Campbell, Emily, Physical Optics Corp, 1845 E 205 St, Torrance, CA 90501-1510 *Tel:* 310-320-3088 *Fax:* 310-320-5961 *Web Site:* www.poc.com, pg 975

Campbell, Greg, Global Television, 222 23 St NE, Calgary, AB T2E 7N2, Canada *Tel:* 403-235-7777 *Fax:* 403-248-0252 *E-mail:* globalnews.calg@globaltv.com *Web Site:* www.globaltv.com, pg 879

Campbell, Jim, Pacific Multimedia Inc, 4917 Seaview Way, Everett, WA 98203 *Tel:* 425-347-4110 *Toll Free Tel:* 888-373-8273 *Fax:* 425-710-9932 *Web Site:* www.pacmultimedia.com, pg 967

Campbell, Matthew, Stanley Film Festival, 1510 York St, 3rd fl, Denver, CO 80206 *Tel:* 970-577-4111 *E-mail:* stanley@denverfilm.org *Web Site:* www.stanleyfilmfest.com, pg 1127

Campbell, Nancy, The Campbell Agency, 3838 Oak Lawn Ave, Suite 900, Dallas, TX 75219 *Tel:* 214-522-8991 *Fax:* 214-522-8997 *Web Site:* www.thecampbellagency.com, pg 818

Campbell, Patricia L, Portland Models & Talent LLC, PO Box 4727, Portland, ME 04112-4727 *Tel:* 207-741-2850; 207-799-9758 *E-mail:* PortlandModels@aol.com *Web Site:* www.portlandmodels.com, pg 979

Campbell, Paul C, eMagin Corp, 3006 Northup Way, Suite 103, Bellevue, WA 98004 *Tel:* 425-284-5200 *Toll Free Tel:* 877-362-4461 *Fax:* 425-284-5201 *E-mail:* info@emagin.com *Web Site:* www.emagin.com, pg 860

Campbell, Rebecca, Austin Film Society (AFS), 1901 E 51 St, Austin, TX 78723 *Tel:* 512-322-0145 *Fax:* 512-322-5192 *E-mail:* afs@austinfilm.org *Web Site:* www.austinfilm.org, pg 1079

Campbell, Wayne, Film House Inc, 810 Dominican Dr, Nashville, TN 37228 *Tel:* 615-255-4000 *Fax:* 615-255-4111 *E-mail:* results@filmhouse.com *Web Site:* www.filmhouse.com, pg 867

Campion, Patrick, ENCO Systems Inc, 29444 Northwestern Hwy, Southfield, MI 48034 *Tel:* 248-827-4440 *Toll Free Tel:* 800-362-6797 (sales) *Fax:* 248-827-4441 *E-mail:* sales@enco.com *Web Site:* www.enco.com, pg 860

Campus, Jordan, Campus Film Distributors Corp, 42 Oak Ave, Tuckahoe, NY 10707 *Tel:* 914-961-1900 *Fax:* 914-395-1091 *Web Site:* www.campusgroup.com, pg 818

Campus, Steve, Audience Response Systems Inc, 5611-C E Morgan Ave, Evansville, IN 47715 *Tel:* 812-479-7507 *Toll Free Tel:* 800-INVOLVE (468-6583) *Fax:* 812-479-1057 *Web Site:* www.audienceresponse.com, pg 794

Campus, Steven, Campus Film Distributors Corp, 42 Oak Ave, Tuckahoe, NY 10707 *Tel:* 914-961-1900 *Fax:* 914-395-1091 *Web Site:* www.campusgroup.com, pg 818

Canavan, Michael, Canavan Scenic & Light LLC, 2440 Dinneen Ave, Orlando, FL 32804 *Tel:* 407-888-8002 *Fax:* 407-888-8171 *Web Site:* www.csandl.com, pg 819

Candee, Rees W, Candee Productions Inc, 301 W Deer Valley Rd, Suite 7, Phoenix, AZ 85027 *Tel:* 623-266-3070 *Fax:* 623-581-7020 *Web Site:* www.candeeproductions.com, pg 819

Cando, Jim, Take One Productions Ltd, 11010 Lake Grove Blvd, Suite 100, Morrisville, NC 27560 *Tel:* 919-481-0000 *Fax:* 919-460-8809 *E-mail:* marketing@takeonepro.com *Web Site:* www.takeonepro.com, pg 1031

Cane, Gene, Set Decorators Society of America (SDSA), 7100 Tujunga Ave, Suite A, North Hollywood, CA 91605 *Tel:* 818-255-2425 *Fax:* 818-982-8597 *E-mail:* sdsa@setdecorators.org *Web Site:* www.setdecorators.org, pg 1088

Cannata, Richard, Cantrax Recorders, 2119 Fidler Ave, Long Beach, CA 90815 *Tel:* 562-498-6492 *E-mail:* cantrax@verizon.net, pg 819

Cannizzaro, Gerald North, Saturn Studios, PO Box 3687, Hollywood, CA 90078-3687 *Tel:* 323-871-4134 *Web Site:* rollingplanet.com, pg 1003

Cannon, Elise, Publishers Group West Inc, 1700 Fourth St, Berkeley, CA 94710 *Tel:* 510-809-3700 *Toll Free Tel:* 800-788-3123 (cust serv) *Fax:* 510-809-3777 *E-mail:* info@pgw.com *Web Site:* www.pgw.com, pg 987

Cannon, George Jr, Cannon Stage Lighting Inc, 1717 Whitehead Rd, Baltimore, MD 21207 *Tel:* 410-298-0636 *Fax:* 410-298-7950 *Web Site:* www.cannonstage.com, pg 819

Cannon, Michael, 4 Wall Entertainment, 3325 W Sunset Rd, Suite F, Las Vegas, NV 89118 *Tel:* 702-263-3858 *Toll Free Tel:* 877-789-8167 (Western US); 866-492-5540 (Eastern US) *Fax:* 702-263-3863 *E-mail:* info@4wall.com *Web Site:* www.4wall.com; www.usedlighting.com, pg 872

Cantos, Holly, CMI, 612 Hampton Dr, Venice, CA 90291 *Tel:* 310-392-8771 *Fax:* 310-392-5704 *E-mail:* cmi@cmifilms.com *Web Site:* www.cmifilms.com, pg 830

Cantu, Ana, Creation Technologies Inc, 102-8977 Fraserton Ct, Burnaby, BC V5J 5H8, Canada *Tel:* 604-430-4336 *Toll Free Tel:* 800-736-1271 *Fax:* 604-430-4337 *E-mail:* info@creationtech.com *Web Site:* www.creationtech.com, pg 838

Canuel, J F, AC Lighting Inc, 88 Horner Ave, Toronto, ON M8Z 5Y3, Canada *Tel:* 416-255-9494 *Fax:* 416-255-3514 *E-mail:* northamerica@aclighting.com *Web Site:* www.aclighting.com, pg 773

Capik, Gloria, Paulist Press, 997 Macarthur Blvd, Mahwah, NJ 07430-9990 *Tel:* 201-825-7300 *Toll Free Tel:* 800-218-1903 (orders) *Toll Free Fax:* 800-836-3161 *E-mail:* info@paulistpress.com *Web Site:* www.paulistpress.com, pg 970

Caplan, Michael, KTHV Television, a Gannett Company, 720 Izard St, Little Rock, AR 72201 *Tel:* 501-376-1111 *Fax:* 501-376-9928 (sales); 501-376-3324 (admin); 501-376-1645 (news) *Web Site:* www.todaysthv.com, pg 914

Caplan, Mike, Lion & Fox Recording Studios, 9517 Baltimore Ave, College Park, MD 20740 *Tel:* 301-982-4431 *E-mail:* mail@lionfox.com *Web Site:* www.lionfox.com, pg 922

Capodilupo, Larry III, ICL Imaging Inc, 51 Mellen St, Framingham, MA 01702 *Tel:* 508-872-3280 *Toll Free Tel:* 800-660-3280 *Fax:* 508-872-7364 *E-mail:* csr@icl-imaging.com *Web Site:* www.icl-imaging.com, pg 893

Capria, Ralph, A-V Services Inc, 99 Fairfield Rd, Fairfield, NJ 07004 *Tel:* 973-575-5222 *Fax:* 973-575-0857 *E-mail:* sales@avservices.net *Web Site:* www.avservices.net, pg 771

Capwell, Lellie, Rhino Home Video, 3400 W Olive Ave, Burbank, CA 91505 *Tel:* 818-238-6100; 410-568-3713 (intl) *Toll Free Tel:* 877-RHINO-51 (744-6651 - cust serv) *E-mail:* customerservice@rhino.com *Web Site:* www.rhino.com, pg 996

Caras, Barbara, Cine-World Film Festival, 10715 Rodeo Dr, Suite 8, Lakewood Ranch, FL 34202 *Tel:* 941-364-8478 *Fax:* 941-364-8478 *E-mail:* mail@filmsociety.org *Web Site:* www.filmsociety.org, pg 1112

Caras, Nick, Cine-World Film Festival, 10715 Rodeo Dr, Suite 8, Lakewood Ranch, FL 34202 *Tel:* 941-364-8478 *Fax:* 941-364-8478 *E-mail:* mail@filmsociety.org *Web Site:* www.filmsociety.org, pg 1112

Carballa, Nicole Justo, Bay Stage Lighting Co Inc, 4008 W Alva St, Tampa, FL 33614 *Tel:* 813-877-1089 *Fax:* 813-875-8837 *Web Site:* www.baystagelighting.com, pg 803

Carbone, Rob, 4-D Creative Media, 16 W 46 St, 12th fl, New York, NY 10036 *Tel:* 212-994-3300 *Fax:* 212-499-9081 *Web Site:* www.4-dcreative.com, pg 872

Carcamo-Birchenall, Melany, Miami short Film Festival (MsFF), 247 SW Eighth St, Suite 44, Miami, FL 33130 *E-mail:* info@miamishortfilmfestival.com *Web Site:* www.miamishortfilmfestival.com, pg 1120

Cardel, Paul Jr, Phoenix Aerial Photography Inc, 613 Skyview Dr, Nashville, TN 37206 *Tel:* 615-255-2000; 615-975-4226 (cell) *E-mail:* info@phoenixaerialphoto.com *Web Site:* www.phoenixaerialphoto.com, pg 974

Carder, Ken, Twin Sisters Productions LLC, 4710 Hudson Dr, Stow, OH 44224 *Toll Free Tel:* 800-248-TWIN (248-8946) *Toll Free Fax:* 800-480-TWIN (480-8946) *E-mail:* twinsisters@twinsisters.com *Web Site:* www.twinsisters.com, pg 1047

Cardillo, Arnold M, Live Oak Media, PO Box 652, Pine Plains, NY 12567-0652 *Toll Free Tel:* 800-788-1121 *Toll Free Fax:* 866-398-1070 *E-mail:* info@liveoakmedia.com *Web Site:* www.liveoakmedia.com, pg 923

Cardillo, Debra, Live Oak Media, PO Box 652, Pine Plains, NY 12567-0652 *Toll Free Tel:* 800-788-1121 *Toll Free Fax:* 866-398-1070 *E-mail:* info@liveoakmedia.com *Web Site:* www.liveoakmedia.com, pg 923

Cardinal, Anna, Clark, 1225 Old Alpharetta Rd, Suite 295, Alpharetta, GA 85296 *Tel:* 770-888-5088 *Toll Free Tel:* 888-621-8841 *Fax:* 678-513-8206 *Web Site:* www.clark.is, pg 829

Cardona, Edward, Video Artists International & VAI Audio, 109 Wheeler Ave, Pleasantville, NY 10570 *Tel:* 914-769-3691 *Toll Free Tel:* 800-477-7146 *Fax:* 914-769-5407 *E-mail:* orders@vaimusic.com *Web Site:* www.vaimusic.com, pg 1054

Carey, Daniel, Essex Television Group Inc, 7 Vista Dr, Old Lyme, CT 06371 *Tel:* 860-434-7200 *Fax:* 860-434-7210 *E-mail:* contact@essextelevision.com *Web Site:* www.essextelevision.com, pg 862

Carey, Tobe, Willow Mixed Media Inc, 25 Lennox Ave, Glenford, NY 12433 *Tel:* 845-657-2914 *E-mail:* video@hvc.rr.com *Web Site:* www.willowmixedmedia.org; www.documentaryworld.com, pg 1067

Carignan, Bernard, AVW-TELAV Audio Visual Solutions, a Freeman Company, 2056 32 Ave, Montreal, QC H8T 3H7, Canada *Tel:* 514-631-1821 *Toll Free Tel:* 800-868-6886 *Web Site:* freemanav-ca.com, pg 800

Carinci, David, University of Toronto, Classroom Technology Support, Saint George Campus, McMurrich Bldg, 4th fl, 12 Queen's Park Crescent W, Toronto, ON M5S 1S8, Canada *Tel:* 416-978-6544 *Fax:* 416-978-4802 *E-mail:* avrequests@utoronto.ca *Web Site:* www.osm.utoronto.ca, pg 1050

Carlisle, Dan, Soularium Recording Studios, 702 S Alpine Hwy, Alpine, UT 84004 *Tel:* 801-492-0505 *E-mail:* solariumstudios@gmail.com *Web Site:* www.soulariumstudios.com, pg 1016

Carlson, Bonnie J, Brand Activation Association, 650 First Ave, Suite 2-SW, New York, NY 10016 *Tel:* 212-420-1100 *Fax:* 212-533-7622 *Web Site:* www.baalink.org, pg 1079

Carlson, C Ray, Glenray Productions Inc, 1265 E Calaveras St, Altadena, CA 91001-2535 *Tel:* 626-797-5462 *E-mail:* 2glenray@sbcglobal.net *Web Site:* www.childrensmedia.com, pg 878

Carlson, Constance, Video Caption Corp, 88 Hunns Lake Rd, Stanfordville, NY 12581 *Tel:* 845-868-1200 *Toll Free Tel:* 800-705-1203 *Fax:* 845-868-1188 *Toll Free Fax:* 800-705-1207 *E-mail:* mail@vicaps.com *Web Site:* www.vicaps.com, pg 1054

Carlson, Jim, American Audio Visual Center, 7434 E Monte Cristo Ave, Scottsdale, AZ 85260 *Tel:* 480-596-9880 *Fax:* 480-596-0942 *Web Site:* www.americanavc.com, pg 783

Carlson, Julie, LEMO USA Inc, 635 Park Ct, Rohnert Park, CA 94928 *Tel:* 707-578-8811 *Toll Free Tel:* 800-444-LEMO (444-5366) *Fax:* 707-578-0869 *E-mail:* info@lemousa.com *Web Site:* www.lemousa.com; www.lemo.com, pg 918

Carlson, Richard, Pacific Northwest Theatre Associates Inc (PNTA), 2414 SW Andover St, Bldg C100, Seattle, WA 98106 *Tel:* 206-622-7850 *Toll Free Tel:* 800-622-7850 *Fax:* 206-267-1789 *E-mail:* sales@pnta.com *Web Site:* www.pnta.com, pg 967

Carlson, Richard D, Rockwell Communications Inc, 321 Burnham St, East Hartford, CT 06108 *Tel:* 860-528-9091 *Toll Free Tel:* 800-566-6681 *Fax:* 860-289-2334 *E-mail:* rockwellservice@aol.com *Web Site:* www.rockwellcommunications.com, pg 998

Carlson-Weber, Norine, Alpha Source Inc, 6619 W Calumet Rd, Milwaukee, WI 53223-4186 *Tel:* 414-760-2222 *Toll Free Tel:* 800-654-9845 *Fax:* 414-760-2070 *Toll Free Fax:* 888-654-9840 *E-mail:* customer.service@alphasource.com; info@alphasource.com *Web Site:* www.alphasource.com, pg 782

Carman, Jeff, JAM Industries Ltd, 21000 Trans-Canadienne, Baie D'Urfe, QC H9X 4B7, Canada *Tel:* 514-457-2555 *Fax:* 514-457-0055 *E-mail:* info@jamindustries.com *Web Site:* www.jamindustries.com, pg 903

Carman, Martin, Cantrax Recorders, 2119 Fidler Ave, Long Beach, CA 90815 *Tel:* 562-498-6492 *E-mail:* cantrax@verizon.net, pg 819

Carmel, Douglas, FlagHouse, 601 Flaghouse Dr, Hasbrouck Heights, NJ 07604-3116 *Tel:* 201-288-7600 *Toll Free Tel:* 800-793-7900 *Fax:* 201-288-7887 *Toll Free Fax:* 800-793-7922 *E-mail:* sales@flaghouse.com *Web Site:* www.flaghouse.com, pg 869

Carmel, George, FlagHouse, 601 Flaghouse Dr, Hasbrouck Heights, NJ 07604-3116 *Tel:* 201-288-7600 *Toll Free Tel:* 800-793-7900 *Fax:* 201-288-7887 *Toll Free Fax:* 800-793-7922 *E-mail:* sales@flaghouse.com *Web Site:* www.flaghouse.com, pg 869

Carmen, Fran, Baltimore Film Office, 10 E Baltimore St, 10th fl, Baltimore, MD 21202 *Tel:* 410-752-8632; 443-263-4313 *Fax:* 410-385-0361 *Web Site:* www.baltimorefilm.com, pg 1098

Carmi, Tomer, Optibase Inc, 931 Benecia Ave, Sunnyvale, CA 94085 *Toll Free Tel:* 800-451-5101 *Fax:* 408-739-1706 *Web Site:* www.optibase.com, pg 964

Carnahan, Shawn, Telestream Inc, 848 Gold Flat Rd, Nevada City, CA 95959 *Tel:* 530-470-1300 *Toll Free Tel:* 877-257-6245 *Fax:* 530-470-1301 *E-mail:* info@telestream.net *Web Site:* www.telestream.net, pg 1036

Carnevali, Jeff, National Products Inc, 8410 Dallas Ave S, Seattle, WA 98108 *Tel:* 206-763-8361 *Toll Free Tel:* 800-497-7479 *Fax:* 206-763-9615 *Web Site:* www.rammount.com, pg 953

Carney, Robert, FilmNation Entertainment, 150 W 22 St, 9th fl, New York, NY 10011 *Web Site:* www.filmnation.com, pg 867

Carpel, Andy, Carpel Video Inc, 429 E Patrick St, Frederick, MD 21701 *Tel:* 301-694-3500 *Toll Free Tel:* 800-238-4300 *Fax:* 301-694-9510 *Web Site:* www.carpelvideoonline.com, pg 820

Carpenter, Dorri, Troxell Communications Inc, 4830 S 38 St, Phoenix, AZ 85040 *Tel:* 602-437-7240 *Toll Free Tel:* 800-578-8858 *Fax:* 602-437-7265 *Toll Free Fax:* 800-589-5939 *Web Site:* www.trox.com, pg 1045

Carpenter, Manzanita, Inner Traditions International, One Park St, Rochester, VT 05767 *Tel:* 802-767-3174 *Toll Free Tel:* 800-246-8648 *Fax:* 802-767-3726 *E-mail:* customerservice@innertraditions.com *Web Site:* www.innertraditions.com, pg 898

Carpenter, Nancy, Columbus Film Commission, 117 Third St S, Columbus, MS 39701 *Tel:* 662-329-1191 *Toll Free Tel:* 800-327-2686 *Fax:* 662-329-8969 *E-mail:* ccvb@columbus-ms.org *Web Site:* visitcolumbusms.org, pg 1099

Carpenter, Peter A, Lightning Eliminators & Consultants Inc, 6687 Arapahoe Rd, Boulder, CO 80303 *Tel:* 303-447-2828 *Toll Free Tel:* 800-521-6101 *Fax:* 303-447-8122 *E-mail:* info@lightningprotection.com *Web Site:* www.lightningprotection.com, pg 921

Carpenter, Russell, Palardo Productions, 1807 Taft Ave, Suite 4, Hollywood, CA 90028 *Tel:* 323-469-8991 *E-mail:* palardo2@msn.com, pg 968

Carpenter, Valyce, Creative BC (CrBC), 2225 W Broadway, Vancouver, BC V6K 2E4, Canada *Tel:* 604-730-2732 *Fax:* 604-736-7290 *E-mail:* info@creativebc.com *Web Site:* www.creativebc.com, pg 1104

Carpowich, Tammy, KPBS TV FM-San Diego, 5200 Campanille Dr, San Diego, CA 92182 *Tel:* 619-594-1515; 619-265-6438 (newsroom) *Toll Free Tel:* 888-399-5727 *Fax:* 619-594-3812 *Web Site:* www.kpbs.org, pg 913

Carr, Bob, O'Connor Engineering Labs, 2701 N Ontario St, Burbank, CA 91504 *Tel:* 818-847-8666 *Fax:* 818-847-1205 *E-mail:* info@ocon.com; sales@ocon.com *Web Site:* www.ocon.com, pg 961

Carr, Drury Gunn, High Plains Films, PO Box 8796, Missoula, MT 59807 *Tel:* 406-543-6726 *E-mail:* yak@highplainsfilms.org *Web Site:* www.highplainsfilms.org, pg 889

Carr, James R Jr, California Stainless Manufacturing Inc, 32 N Wood Rd, Camarillo, CA 93010 *Tel:* 805-484-1038 *Toll Free Tel:* 888-712-7035 *Fax:* 805-484-1030 *E-mail:* contact@calstainless.com *Web Site:* www.calstainless.com, pg 817

Carr, Kiah, Bel-Air Film Festival (BAFF), 5900 Wilshire Blvd, 10th fl, Los Angeles, CA 90036 *Tel:* 323-801-0100 *E-mail:* info@belairfilmfestival.com *Web Site:* www.belairfilmfestival.com, pg 1109

Carr, Michal Brand, Hillmann & Carr Inc, 2233 Wisconsin Ave, Washington, DC 20007 *Tel:* 202-342-0001 *Fax:* 202-342-0117 *E-mail:* mail@hillmanncarr.com *Web Site:* www.hillmanncarr.com, pg 889

Carrasco, Emma, National Public Radio (NPR), 1111 N Capitol St NE, Washington, DC 20002 *Tel:* 202-513-2000 *Web Site:* www.npr.org, pg 1086

Carrigan, Carol B, USITT: United States Institute for Theatre Technology Inc, 315 S Crouse Ave, Suite 200, Syracuse, NY 13210-1844 *Tel:* 315-463-6463 *Toll Free Tel:* 800-938-7488 *Fax:* 315-463-6525 *Toll Free Fax:* 866-398-7488 *E-mail:* info@office.usitt.org *Web Site:* www.usitt.org, pg 1090

Carriglio, John, Camart, 6 W 20 St, New York, NY 10011 *Tel:* 212-691-8840 *E-mail:* rentals@camart.com *Web Site:* www.camart.com, pg 817

Carringer, Tom, ACS Technologies, 180 N Dunbarton Dr, Florence, SC 29501 *Tel:* 843-662-1681 *Toll Free Tel:* 800-736-7425 *Fax:* 843-669-3198 *E-mail:* info@acstechnologies.com *Web Site:* www.acstechnologies.com, pg 775

Carroll, James, GMF Sound Inc, 1961 N Main, Orange, CA 92865 *Tel:* 714-282-1559 *Fax:* 714-282-1942 *E-mail:* generalinfo@gmfsound.com; sales@gmfsound.com *Web Site:* www.gmfsound.com, pg 879

Carroll, Matt, Baker & Taylor Inc, 2550 W Tyvola Rd, Suite 300, Charlotte, NC 28217 *Tel:* 704-998-3100 *Toll Free Tel:* 800-775-1800 *E-mail:* btinfo@baker-taylor.com *Web Site:* www.btol.com, pg 801

Carroll, Mike, Foresight Imaging, One Executive Dr, Suite 102, Chelmsford, MA 01824 *Tel:* 978-458-4624 *Fax:* 978-458-5488 *E-mail:* info@fi-llc.com *Web Site:* www.fi-llc.com, pg 871

Carroll, Scott, International Digital Centre, 216 E 45 St, 7th fl, New York, NY 10017 *Tel:* 212-581-3940 *Fax:* 212-581-3979 *E-mail:* info@idcdigital.com *Web Site:* www.idcdigital.com, pg 901

Carson, Keith, Top Hat Productions, 6615 Boynton Beach Blvd, Suite 310, Boynton Beach, FL 33437 *Tel:* 561-963-6442 *Toll Free Tel:* 888-794-0528 *Fax:* 561-880-6988 *E-mail:* info@tophatproductions.net *Web Site:* www.tophatproductions.net, pg 1042

Carson, Norm, Covid Inc, 1723 W Fourth St, Tempe, AZ 85281 *Tel:* 480-966-2221 *Toll Free Tel:* 800-638-6104 *Fax:* 480-966-6728 *E-mail:* sales@covid.com *Web Site:* www.covid.com, pg 837

Carson, Tom, Rovi Corp, 2830 De La Cruz Blvd, Santa Clara, CA 95050 *Tel:* 408-562-8400 *Fax:* 408-567-1800 *Web Site:* www.rovicorp.com, pg 1000

Carstens, Peter, Framepool, 150 Alhambre Circle, Suite 800, Miami, FL 33134 *Tel:* 305-401-8597 *Toll Free Tel:* 800-331-1314 *Fax:* 305-428-2800 *E-mail:* americas@framepool.com *Web Site:* usa2.framepool.com, pg 872

Carswell, Ross, Visual Departures Ltd, 48 Sheffield Business Park, Ashley Falls, MA 01222 *Tel:* 413-229-2272 *Toll Free Tel:* 800-628-2003 *Fax:* 413-229-2274 *E-mail:* sales@visualdepartures.com *Web Site:* www.visualdepartures.com, pg 1059

Carte, Denis, RGB Spectrum, 950 Marina Village Pkwy, Alameda, CA 94501 *Tel:* 510-814-7000 *Fax:* 510-814-7026 *E-mail:* sales@rgb.com *Web Site:* www.rgb.com, pg 996

Carter, Gary, International Datacasting, 50 Frank Nighbor Place, Kanata, ON K2V 1B9, Canada *Tel:* 613-596-4120 *Fax:* 613-596-4863 *E-mail:* marketing@datacast.com *Web Site:* www.datacast.com, pg 900

Carter, Harriet, Film Detroit, 211 W Fort St, Suite 1000, Detroit, MI 48226 *Tel:* 313-202-1990 *Toll Free Tel:* 877-478-7883 *Web Site:* www.filmdetroit.com, pg 1098

Carter, Howard, Southern Illinois University, 605 Agriculture Dr, Mailcode 6632, Carbondale, IL 62901 *Tel:* 618-453-2258 *Fax:* 618-453-3010 *Web Site:* www.lib.siu.edu/departments/iss, pg 1019

Carter, James, Big Fish Productions Inc, PO Box 782, Bronx, NY 10462-0782 *Tel:* 212-860-3639 *Web Site:* www.bigfishproductioninc.com, pg 807

Carter, Jan, Sound*Light, 5438 Tennessee Ave, New Port Richey, FL 34652 *Tel:* 727-842-6788 *Fax:* 727-842-6788 *Web Site:* www.awakening-healing.com; www.soundlight.org, pg 1017

Carter, Jane, The Napoleon Group, 48 W 25 St, New York, NY 10010 *Tel:* 212-692-9200 *Toll Free Tel:* 800-579-4019 *Fax:* 212-692-0309 *E-mail:* info@napny.com *Web Site:* www.napny.com, pg 952

Cartwright, Julie, Anchor Bay Entertainment LLC, 9242 Beverly Blvd, Suite 201, Beverly Hills, CA 90210 *Tel:* 424-204-4166 *E-mail:* questions@anchorbayent.com *Web Site:* www.anchorbayentertainment.com, pg 786

Caruso, Mike, Universe Kogaku America Inc, 116 Audrey Ave, Oyster Bay, NY 11771 *Tel:* 516-624-2444 *Fax:* 516-624-3109 *E-mail:* info@universeoptics.com *Web Site:* universeoptics.com, pg 1049

Casalaina, Vincent, Image Integration, 2619 Benvenue Ave, No A, Berkeley, CA 94704 *Tel:* 510-504-2605, pg 895

Casanova, Frank, The Studio Center, 915 Fee Dr, Sacramento, CA 95815 *Tel:* 916-564-9333 *E-mail:* info@thestudiocenter.com *Web Site:* www.thestudiocenter.com, pg 1026

Cascone, Peter, 4-D Creative Media, 16 W 46 St, 12th fl, New York, NY 10036 *Tel:* 212-994-3300 *Fax:* 212-499-9081 *Web Site:* www.4-dcreative.com, pg 872

Case, David, Production Masters Inc (PMI), 202 Fifth Ave, Pittsburgh, PA 15222 *Tel:* 412-281-8500 *Fax:* 412-391-7529 *E-mail:* info@pmi.tv *Web Site:* www.pmi.tv, pg 984

Casey, Margaret, VISIT Milwaukee, 648 N Plankinton Ave, Suite 425, Milwaukee, WI 53203-2917 *Tel:* 414-273-3950 *Toll Free Tel:* 800-554-1448 *Fax:* 414-273-5596 *E-mail:* info@milwaukee.org *Web Site:* www.visitmilwaukee.org, pg 1104

Cashdollar, Madeline, Aon Hewitt, 1100 Reynolds Blvd, Winston-Salem, NC 27105-3400 *Tel:* 336-748-1120 *Fax:* 847-953-4854 *Web Site:* www.aon.com, pg 787

Cashman, Judy, PrimaLux Video Inc, 555 Eighth Ave, Suite 1002, New York, NY 10018 *Tel:* 212-206-1402 *Fax:* 212-206-1826 *E-mail:* primalux@aol.com *Web Site:* www.primalux.com, pg 982

Cashmark, Daryn, Cashmark Media Inc, 4702 Eastern Ave, Kansas City, MO 64129 *Tel:* 816-861-4200 *Fax:* 816-861-4205 *E-mail:* info@cashmarkmedia.com *Web Site:* www.cashmarkmedia.com, pg 820

Casinghino, Bob, Fresh Music Library, 320 South St, Agawam, MA 01001 *Toll Free Tel:* 888-211-8576 *Web Site:* www.freshmusic.com, pg 873

Caskey, Brian, Zhone Technologies Inc, 7195 Oakport St, Oakland, CA 94621 *Tel:* 510-777-7000 *Toll Free Tel:* 877-ZHONE-20 (946-6320, US & CN) *Fax:* 510-777-7001 *E-mail:* info@zhone.com; sales@zhone.com *Web Site:* www.zhone.com, pg 1073

Caspari, Kristina, Advanced Systems Group LLC, 1226 Powell St, Emeryville, CA 94608-2618 *Tel:* 510-654-8300 *Fax:* 510-654-8370 *Web Site:* www.asgllc.com, pg 778

Caspari, W B, Synergistic Batteries Inc, 5975 Providence Lane, Cumming, GA 30040 *Tel:* 770-886-6621 *Toll Free Tel:* 800-634-6000 *Fax:* 770-886-6522 *E-mail:* sbicas@synbat.com *Web Site:* www.synergisticbatteries.com, pg 1030

Cass, Brian, Sounds Interesting Studios, 112 Fuller St, Middleboro, MA 02346 *Tel:* 508-947-7387 *Web Site:* www.soundsinterestingstudio.com, pg 1018

Cassarino, Stephen, Clever Cleaver Productions, 11397 Legacy Canyon Place, San Diego, CA 92131 *Tel:* 619-522-6760 *Fax:* 619-522-6763 *E-mail:* info@clevercleaver.com *Web Site:* www.clevercleaver.com, pg 830

Cassels, Sean, Vidicom Inc, 520 Eighth Ave, Suite 2206, New York, NY 10018 *Tel:* 212-895-8300 *E-mail:* info@vidicom.com *Web Site:* vidicom.com, pg 1057

Cassidy, Katie, Now Hear This, 250 W 49 St, Suite 704, New York, NY 10019 *Tel:* 212-265-1188 *Fax:* 212-265-6363 *E-mail:* info@nhtsound.com *Web Site:* www.nhtsound.com, pg 960

Cassidy, M Todd, Kentucky Film Office, 2200 Capital Plaza Tower, 500 Mero St, Frankfort, KY 40601 *Tel:* 502-564-3456 *Toll Free Tel:* 800-345-6591 *Fax:* 502-564-5695 *E-mail:* kentucky.filmoffice@ky.gov *Web Site:* filmoffice.ky.gov, pg 1098

Cassidy, Tim, Marshad Technology Group, 99 Hudson St, 5th fl, New York, NY 10013 *Tel:* 212-925-8656 *E-mail:* info@marshad.com *Web Site:* www.marshad.com, pg 932

Cassin, Dan, Centaur Records Inc, 136 Saint Joseph St, Baton Rouge, LA 70802 *Tel:* 225-336-4877 *Fax:* 225-336-9678 *E-mail:* info@centaurrecords.com *Web Site:* www.centaurrecords.com, pg 822

Casso, Alan, Revels Records, 80 Mount Auburn St, Watertown, MA 02472 *Tel:* 617-972-8300 *E-mail:* info@revels.org *Web Site:* www.revels.org, pg 995

Castaneda, Jeff, MTV Networks Co, c/o MTV Studios, 1515 Broadway, New York, NY 10036 *Tel:* 212-258-8000 *Web Site:* www.mtv.com; www.mtvpress.com, pg 949

Castellon, Joe, KAS Music & Sound, 34-12 36 St, Astoria, NY 11106 *Tel:* 718-786-3400 *Fax:* 718-729-3007 *Web Site:* www.kasmusic.com, pg 908

Castillo, David, Blue Barn Pictures Inc, 68 Jay St, Suite 311, Brooklyn, NY 11201 *Tel:* 718-852-1403 *Web Site:* www.bluebarnpictures.com, pg 809

Castillo, Mauro, J&S Audio Visual Inc, 9150 N Royal Lane, Suite 150, Irving, TX 75063 *Tel:* 972-241-5444 *Toll Free Tel:* 800-852-8771 *Fax:* 972-247-2590 *E-mail:* info@jsav.com *Web Site:* www.jsav.com, pg 904

Castle, Clifford J, Audix Corp, 9400 SW Barber St, Wilsonville, OR 97070 *Tel:* 503-682-6933 *Toll Free Tel:* 800-966-8261 *Fax:* 503-682-7114 *E-mail:* info@audixusa.com *Web Site:* www.audixusa.com, pg 796

Castle, Randy, The Miller Group, Multiplex Division, 1610 Design Way, Dupo, IL 62239-1820 *Tel:* 636-343-5700 *Toll Free Tel:* 800-325-3350 *Fax:* 618-286-6202 *E-mail:* info@miller-group.com *Web Site:* www.multiplexdisplays.com, pg 943

Castles, Dan, Telestream Inc, 848 Gold Flat Rd, Nevada City, CA 95959 *Tel:* 530-470-1300 *Toll Free Tel:* 877-257-6245 *Fax:* 530-470-1301 *E-mail:* info@telestream.net *Web Site:* www.telestream.net, pg 1036

Castronovo, Joseph, Korg USA Inc, 316 S Service Rd, Melville, NY 11747 *Tel:* 631-390-6500; 631-390-8737 *Fax:* 631-390-6501 *Web Site:* www.korgusa.com, pg 913

Catalanotte, Peter, Tucson Film Office, 100 S Church Ave, Tucson, AZ 85701 *Tel:* 520-770-2151 *Fax:* 520-629-0160 *Web Site:* www.filmtucson.com, pg 1091

Catalanotto, Joseph J, Independent Studios, 4701 Conti, New Orleans, LA 70119 *Tel:* 504-915-IJOE (915-4563), pg 897

Catmull, Dr Edwin E, Pixar Animation Studios, 1200 Park Ave, Emeryville, CA 94608 *Tel:* 510-922-3000 *Toll Free Tel:* 800-888-9856 *Fax:* 510-922-3151 *E-mail:* ir@pixar.com (investor rel) *Web Site:* www.pixar.com, pg 976

Catron, Kathryn, St Augustine, Ponte Vedra & The Beaches Visitors and Convention Bureau, 29 Old Mission Ave, St Augustine, FL 32084 *Tel:* 904-829-1711 *Toll Free Tel:* 800-653-2489 *Web Site:* www.floridashistoriccoast.com, pg 1096

Catterson, Paul, Westworks Studios, 4100 E Dry Creek Rd, Littleton, CO 80122 *Toll Free Tel:* 800-491-1947 *E-mail:* info@westworksstudios.com *Web Site:* westworksstudios.com, pg 1064

Cauchard, Daniele, Canadian Student Film Festival, 1432 de Bleury St, Montreal, QC H3A 2J1, Canada *Tel:* 514-848-3883 *Fax:* 514-848-3886 *E-mail:* info@ffm-montreal.org *Web Site:* www.ffm-montreal.org, pg 1111

Cavalier, Rob, Trod Nossel Productions & Recording Studios, 10 George St, Wallingford, CT 06492 *Tel:* 203-269-4465 *Toll Free Tel:* 800-800-HITS (800-4487) *Fax:* 203-294-1745 *E-mail:* info@trodnossel.com *Web Site:* www.trodnossel.com, pg 1045

Cavalier, Tom, Trod Nossel Productions & Recording Studios, 10 George St, Wallingford, CT 06492 *Tel:* 203-269-4465 *Toll Free Tel:* 800-800-HITS (800-4487) *Fax:* 203-294-1745 *E-mail:* info@trodnossel.com *Web Site:* www.trodnossel.com, pg 1045

Cavanaugh, Dean, Moog Music Inc, 160 Broadway St, Asheville, NC 28801 *Tel:* 828-251-0090 *Toll Free Tel:* 800-948-1990 *Fax:* 828-254-6233 *E-mail:* info@moogmusic.com *Web Site:* www.moogmusic.com, pg 946

Cavender, Mike, Radio Television Digital News Association (RTDNA), The National Press Bldg, 529 14 St NW, Suite 425, Washington, DC 20045 *Tel:* 202-659-6510 *Fax:* 202-223-4007 *Web Site:* www.rtdna.org, pg 1088

Cavender, Mike, RTDNA Edward R Murrow Awards, The National Press Bldg, 529 14 St NW, Suite 425, Washington, DC 20045 *Tel:* 202-659-6510 *Fax:* 202-223-4007 *E-mail:* awards@rtdna.org *Web Site:* www.rtdna.org, pg 1126

Caves, Lucky, Fidelity Information Services (FIS), 601 Riverside Ave, Jacksonville, FL 32204 *Tel:* 904-438-6000 *Toll Free Tel:* 888-323-0310 (US only) *Fax:* 904-357-1105 *E-mail:* moreinformation@fisglobal.com *Web Site:* www.fisglobal.com, pg 866

Cavey, Gary L, Ballantyne Strong Inc, 13710 FNB Pkwy, Suite 400, Omaha, NE 68154 *Tel:* 402-453-4444 *Toll Free Tel:* 800-424-1215 *Fax:* 402-453-7238 *E-mail:* info@btn-inc.com *Web Site:* ballantynestrong.com, pg 802

Cavey, Gary L, Convergent Media Systems, 190 Bluegrass Valley Pkwy, Alpharetta, GA 30005-2204 *Tel:* 770-369-9000 *Toll Free Tel:* 800-877-7804 *Fax:* 770-369-9100 *E-mail:* convergent@convergent.com *Web Site:* www.convergent.com, pg 836

Cawthorne, Kent, Kramer Electronics USA Inc, 6 Rte 173 W, Clinton, NJ 08809 *Tel:* 908-735-0018 *Toll Free Tel:* 888-275-6311 *Fax:* 908-735-0515 *E-mail:* info@kramerus.com *Web Site:* www.kramerus.com, pg 913

Celpa, Paola, Miami short Film Festival (MsFF), 247 SW Eighth St, Suite 44, Miami, FL 33130 *E-mail:* info@miamishortfilmfestival.com *Web Site:* www.miamishortfilmfestival.com, pg 1120

Censullo, Robert, Boonton Electronics, 25 Eastmans Rd, Parsippany, NJ 07054 *Tel:* 973-386-9696 *Fax:* 973-386-9191 *E-mail:* info@boonton.com *Web Site:* www.boonton.com, pg 811

Centkowski, Mark, Innovision Optics, 1719 21 St, Santa Monica, CA 90404 *Tel:* 310-453-4866 *Fax:* 310-453-4677 *Web Site:* www.innovision-optics.com, pg 899

Cerasoli, Chris, Videosmith Inc, 200 Spring Garden St, Suite C, Philadelphia, PA 19123 *Tel:* 215-238-5070 *Fax:* 215-238-5075 *E-mail:* info@videosmith.com *Web Site:* videosmith.com, pg 1057

Cerilli, Steve, Sound-FX-Design, PO Box 3541, Newport, RI 02840 *Tel:* 401-952-1186 *E-mail:* info@sound-fx-design.com *Web Site:* www.sound-fx-design.com, pg 1017

Cerullo, Al, Hover-Views Unlimited, PO Box 1164, Syosset, NY 11791 *Tel:* 516-496-2946 *Fax:* 516-496-8029 *Web Site:* www.hoverviews.com, pg 892

Cerutti, Marc, Cerutti Productions Inc, 18211 Bulverde Rd, Suite 10202, San Antonio, TX 78259 *Tel:* 210-403-0800 *Fax:* 210-403-0801 *Web Site:* www.cerutti.org, pg 823

Cessna, Abbie, C&I Studios, 541 NW First Ave, Fort Lauderdale, FL 33301 *Tel:* 954-357-3934 *E-mail:* contact@c-istudios.com *Web Site:* www.c-istudios.com, pg 819

Cestare, Thomas, Thomas Cestare Inc, 188 Herricks Rd, Mineola, NY 11502 *Tel:* 516-742-5550 *Fax:* 516-742-5551 *E-mail:* cestare@aol.com *Web Site:* www.thomascestareinc.com, pg 823

Cetrulo, Marc E, The Hollaender Manufacturing Co, 10285 Wayne Ave, Cincinnati, OH 45215 *Tel:* 513-772-8800 *Toll Free Tel:* 800-772-8800 (orders) *Fax:* 513-772-8806 *Web Site:* www.hollaender.com, pg 890

Ceyrolles, Ronald, Best Shot, 4301 W Cayuga St, Tampa, FL 33614 *Tel:* 813-454-5768 *E-mail:* request@bestshotfootage.com *Web Site:* www.bestshotfootage.com, pg 806

Chadwick, Bruce, Magic By Bruce Chadwick, PO Box 12345, Fort Worth, TX 76110-8345 *Tel:* 817-832-6062 *E-mail:* chadwickillusionist@yahoo.com *Web Site:* www.magicbybrucechadwick.com, pg 928

Chaffee, Hal, Technical Exhibits Corp, 6155 S Oak Park Ave, Chicago, IL 60638 *Tel:* 773-586-3377 *Fax:* 773-586-6575 *Web Site:* www.technicalexhibits.net, pg 1033

Chaffee, Linda, South-Western Publishing Co, 5191 Natorp Blvd, Mason, OH 45040 *Tel:* 513-229-1000 *Toll Free Tel:* 800-543-0487 *Fax:* 513-229-1020 *E-mail:* esales@cengage.com *Web Site:* www.cengage.com, pg 1019

Chain, Herve F, Omni Intercommunications Inc, 2825 Wilcrest Dr, Suite 400, Houston, TX 77042 *Tel:* 713-781-2188 *Toll Free Tel:* 800-777-2304 *Fax:* 713-781-2315 *E-mail:* info@omni-inter.com *Web Site:* www.omni-inter.com, pg 962

Chaisson, Anne, The Hamptons International Film Festival, 47 Newtown Lane, East Hampton, NY 11937 *Tel:* 631-324-4600; 631-747-7978 *Fax:* 631-324-1558 *E-mail:* info@hamptonsfilmfest.org *Web Site:* www.hamptonsfilmfest.org, pg 1116

Chalk, Richard, TopCat Records LLC, PO Box 670234, Dallas, TX 75367-0234 *Tel:* 972-484-4141 *E-mail:* info@topcatrecords.com *Web Site:* topcatrecords.com, pg 1042

Challender, Gary, Books In Motion, 9922 E Montgomery Dr, Suite 31, Spokane Valley, WA 99206 *Tel:* 509-922-1646 *Toll Free Tel:* 800-752-3199 *Fax:* 509-922-1445 *E-mail:* sales@booksinmotion.com *Web Site:* www.booksinmotion.com, pg 811

Chamberlan, Claude, Montreal International Festival of Nouveau Cinema, 3805 Blvd Ste-Laurent, Montreal, QC H2W 1X9, Canada *Tel:* 514-282-0004 *Fax:* 514-282-6664 *E-mail:* info@nouveaucinema.ca *Web Site:* www.nouveaucinema.ca, pg 1120

Chamberlin, Amy Beth, Warner Home Video Inc, 4000 Warner Blvd, Bldg 160, Burbank, CA 91522 *Tel:* 818-954-6000 *Fax:* 818-954-6480 *Web Site:* www.warnerbros.com, pg 1062

Chambers, Dave, Apogee Sound International LLC, 50 Spring St, Ramsey, NJ 07446 *Toll Free Tel:* 800-443-3979 *Toll Free Fax:* 800-999-9016 *E-mail:* info@apogee-sound.com *Web Site:* www.apogee-sound.com, pg 788

Chambers, Steve, Nuance, One Wayside Rd, Burlington, MA 01803 *Tel:* 781-565-5000 *Toll Free Tel:* 888-372-1908 (cust serv) *Fax:* 781-565-5001 *Web Site:* www.nuance.com, pg 960

Chambers, Trey, Compass Learning Inc, 203 Colorado St, Austin, TX 78701 *Tel:* 512-478-9600 *Toll Free Tel:* 866-586-7387 (sales); 800-678-1412 (cust support) *Web Site:* www.compasslearning.com, pg 833

Champagne, Robin, Communications Concepts Inc (CCI), 7980 N Atlantic Ave, Cape Canaveral, FL 32920 *Tel:* 321-783-5232 *Toll Free Tel:* 800-783-2368 *Fax:* 321-799-1016 *E-mail:* info@cciflorida.com *Web Site:* www.cciflorida.com, pg 833

Champion, Paul, Troxell Communications Inc, 4830 S 38 St, Phoenix, AZ 85040 *Tel:* 602-437-7240 *Toll Free Tel:* 800-578-8858 *Fax:* 602-437-7265 *Toll Free Fax:* 800-589-5939 *Web Site:* www.trox.com, pg 1045

Chan, Dr Amiee, Norsat International Inc, 110-4020 Viking Way, Richmond, BC V6V 2L4, Canada *Tel:* 604-821-2800 *Toll Free Tel:* 800-644-4562 *Fax:* 604-821-2801 *E-mail:* inquiries@norsat.com; support@norsat.com *Web Site:* www.norsat.com, pg 958

Chan, Tom, Tecplot Inc, 3535 Factoria Blvd SE, Suite 550, Bellevue, WA 98006 *Tel:* 425-653-1200; 425-653-9393 (tech support) *Toll Free Tel:* 800-763-7005 (orders) *E-mail:* info@tecplot.com; sales@tecplot.com *Web Site:* www.tecplot.com, pg 1035

Chandler, David, Kangaroo Cases, 4027 Main St, Dallas, TX 75226 *Tel:* 214-823-5264 *Toll Free Tel:* 800-890-1073 *Fax:* 214-824-1179 *E-mail:* info@kangaroocases.com *Web Site:* www.kangaroocases.com, pg 908

Chandler, Steve, Videolady, PO Box 2276, San Bernardino, CA 92406-2276 *Tel:* 909-882-4057 *Fax:* 909-882-4057 *E-mail:* vldy@aol.com *Web Site:* videoladystudios.com, pg 1057

Chandy, Abraham, Opterna AM, 44901 Falcon Place, Suite 116, Sterling, VA 20166-9531 *Tel:* 703-653-1130 *Toll Free Tel:* 800-248-9004 *Fax:* 703-803-8313 *Web Site:* www.opterna-am.com, pg 964

Chang, Andrew, DreamWorks Animation SKG Inc, 1000 Flower St, Glendale, CA 91201 *Tel:* 818-695-5000 *Fax:* 818-695-4190 *Web Site:* www.dreamworksanimation.com, pg 852

Chang, C, Norman N Axelrod Associates, 445 E 86 St, New York, NY 10028 *Tel:* 212-741-6302 *E-mail:* naxelrod@axelrodassociates.com *Web Site:* www.axelrodassociates.com, pg 800

Chang, Deny, Cinema East, 7111 Biscayne Blvd, Miami, FL 33138 *Tel:* 305-757-5859 *Fax:* 305-751-2329 *Web Site:* www.cinemaeast.com, pg 827

Chang, Pearl, ASC-Tube Trap, 4275 W Fifth Ave, Eugene, OR 97402 *Tel:* 541-343-9727 *Toll Free Tel:* 800-272-8823 *Fax:* 541-343-9245 *E-mail:* info@acousticsciences.com *Web Site:* www.acousticsciences.com, pg 791

Channell, Bill, Channell One Video, PO Box 399, Epping, NH 03042-0399 *Tel:* 603-679-6796 *Toll Free Tel:* 888-722-3843 (natl) *E-mail:* racevid@earthlink.net *Web Site:* www.racevideo.com, pg 824

Channell, Kathleen, Channell One Video, PO Box 399, Epping, NH 03042-0399 *Tel:* 603-679-6796 *Toll Free Tel:* 888-722-3843 (natl) *E-mail:* racevid@earthlink.net *Web Site:* www.racevideo.com, pg 824

Channell, Leslie, Oklahoma Film Commission & Music Office, 120 N Robinson, Suite 600, Oklahoma City, OK 73102 *Tel:* 405-230-8440 *Toll Free Tel:* 800-766-3456 *Fax:* 405-230-8640 *Web Site:* www.oklahomafilm.org; thebuffalolounge.com, pg 1101

Chanti, Marc, Metromotion Productions LLC, 450 W 31 St, 8th & 9th fl, New York, NY 10001 *Tel:* 212-967-2000 *Fax:* 212-967-1988 *E-mail:* info@metromotion.com; pr@metromotion.com *Web Site:* www.metromotion.com, pg 940

Chapa, Raquel, Dallas Video Festival, 1405 Woodlawn Ave, Dallas, TX 75208 *E-mail:* info@videofest.org *Web Site:* www.videofest.org, pg 1113

Chapek, Bob, Walt Disney Records Consumer Products Division, 1201 Flower St, Glendale, AZ 91201 *Tel:* 818-560-1000 *Web Site:* disney.com; www.disneyconsumerproducts.com, pg 1061

Chapek, Bob, Walt Disney Studio, 500 S Buena Vista St, Burbank, CA 91521 *Tel:* 818-560-1000 *Web Site:* studioservices.go.com, pg 1061

Chapelle, Nancy, TVO/Ontario Educational Communications Authority (OECA), 2180 Yonge St, Toronto, ON M4S 2B9, Canada *Tel:* 416-484-2600; 416-484-2665 (cust rel) *Toll Free Tel:* 800-613-0513; 800-INFO-TVO (463-6886) *E-mail:* asktvo@tvo.org *Web Site:* tvo.org, pg 1046

Chaplin, Carol, Lake Tahoe Visitors Authority (LTVA), 169 Hwy 50, Stateline, NV 89449 *Tel:* 775-588-5900 *Toll Free Tel:* 800-288-2463 (reservations) *Fax:* 775-588-1941 *E-mail:* info@ltva.org *Web Site:* ltva.org, pg 1100

Chapman, Chuck, Chapman Recording & Mastering, 8805 Monrovia, Lenexa, KS 66215 *Tel:* 913-894-6854 *Fax:* 913-894-6857 *Web Site:* www.chapmanrecording.com, pg 824

Chapman, David E, BFS Entertainment & Multimedia Limited, 360 Newkirk Rd, Richmond Hill, ON L4C 3G7, Canada *Tel:* 905-884-2323 *Fax:* 905-884-8292 *E-mail:* info@bfsent.com; contact@bfsent.com *Web Site:* www.bfsent.com, pg 806

Chapman, Michael, Chapman/Leonard Studios & Production Center, 12950 Raymer St, North Hollywood, CA 91605 *Tel:* 818-764-6726 *Toll Free Tel:* 888-883-6559 *Fax:* 818-764-6730 *Web Site:* www.chapman-leonard.com, pg 824

Chapman, Robert, The Audio Department Inc, 119 W 57 St, Suite 400, New York, NY 10019 *Tel:* 212-586-3503 *Fax:* 212-245-1675 *E-mail:* scheduling@theaudiodepartment.com *Web Site:* www.theaudiodepartment.com, pg 794

Chapman-Huenergardt, Christine, Chapman/Leonard Studios & Production Center, 12950 Raymer St, North Hollywood, CA 91605 *Tel:* 818-764-6726 *Toll Free Tel:* 888-883-6559 *Fax:* 818-764-6730 *Web Site:* www.chapman-leonard.com, pg 824

Chapnick, Benjamin J, Black Star Publishing Co Inc, 333 Mamaroneck Ave, PMB 175, White Plains, NY 10605 *Tel:* 212-679-3288 *Fax:* 212-889-2052 *Web Site:* www.blackstar.com, pg 808

Chapnick, John P, Black Star Publishing Co Inc, 333 Mamaroneck Ave, PMB 175, White Plains, NY 10605 *Tel:* 212-679-3288 *Fax:* 212-889-2052 *Web Site:* www.blackstar.com, pg 808

Chappell, Gary, Nightingale-Conant Corp, 1400 S Wolf Rd, Bldg 300, Suite 103, Wheeling, IL 60090 *Toll Free Tel:* 800-557-1660 (sales); 800-560-6081 (cust serv) *E-mail:* customerservice@nightingale.com *Web Site:* www.nightingale.com, pg 957

Charback, Ann, JMC Photo & Digital Services Inc, 10 Westport Ct, Bloomington, IL 61704-8233 *Tel:* 309-663-4677 *Fax:* 309-664-3973 *E-mail:* jmcpds@jmcpds.com *Web Site:* www.jmcpds.com, pg 905

Charles, Doug, DuQuaine Manufacturing, PO Box 56, Kewaunee, WI 54216-0056 *Tel:* 920-388-3790 *Web Site:* www.duquaine.com, pg 853

Charney, Nick, Videofashion Network, 611 Broadway, Suite 307, New York, NY 10012 *Tel:* 212-274-1600 *Fax:* 212-219-1969 *E-mail:* licensing@videofashion.com *Web Site:* www.videofashion.com, pg 1056

Chase, Howard, HMC Electronics, 33 Springdale Ave, Canton, MA 02021 *Tel:* 781-821-1870 *Toll Free Tel:* 800-482-4440 *Fax:* 781-821-4133 *E-mail:* sales@hmcelectronics.com *Web Site:* www.hmcelectronics.com, pg 889

Chater, John, Chater Camera Inc, 1336 Ninth St, Berkeley, CA 94710 *Tel:* 510-525-5400 *Fax:* 510-295-2478 *E-mail:* rentals@chatercamera.com *Web Site:* www.chatercamera.com, pg 824

Chatfield-Taylor, Constance, Flying Colors Broadcasts, 2000 "M" St NW, Suite 345, Washington, DC 20036 *Tel:* 202-293-5300 *E-mail:* info@fc-tv.com *Web Site:* www.fc-tv.com, pg 870

Chatt, Howard, Pignose-Gorilla, 570 W Cheyenne Ave, Suite 80, North Las Vegas, NV 89030 *Tel:* 702-648-2444 *Toll Free Tel:* 800-9-PIGNOSE (974-4667) *Fax:* 702-648-2440 *E-mail:* sales@pignoseamps.com *Web Site:* www.pignoseamps.com, pg 975

Chavarria, Susan, Flying Colors Broadcasts, 2000 "M" St NW, Suite 345, Washington, DC 20036 *Tel:* 202-293-5300 *E-mail:* info@fc-tv.com *Web Site:* www.fc-tv.com, pg 870

Chavez, Oscar, Big Door, 114 Sheldon St, El Segundo, CA 90245 *Tel:* 310-546-6100 *Fax:* 310-906-4585 *E-mail:* sales@bigdoor.tv *Web Site:* www.bigdoor.tv; www.bigdoorstudio.tv, pg 807

Cheek, Doug, RingSide Creative, 13320 Northend, Suite 3000, Oak Park, MI 48237 *Tel:* 248-548-2500 *E-mail:* info@ringsidecreative.com; newbiz@ringsidecreative.com *Web Site:* www.ringsidecreative.com, pg 997

Chelew, Richard, Oral Tradition Sound & Music, PO Box 51155, Pacific Grove, CA 93950-6155 *Tel:* 831-372-0352 *Toll Free Tel:* 800-779-1116 (orders), pg 965

Chen, David, Keng Seng Enterprises Inc, 4000 Rue St Ambroise, Suite 103, Montreal, QC H4C 2C7, Canada *Tel:* 514-939-3971 *Fax:* 514-989-1922 *E-mail:* canada@kengseng.com *Web Site:* www.kengseng.com, pg 909

Chen, David W, RGB Technology Inc, 590 Herndon Pkwy, Suite 500, Herndon, VA 20170-5267 *Tel:* 703-834-1500 *Fax:* 703-834-1506 *Web Site:* www.rgbtec.com, pg 996

Chen, Edward, Tatung Co of America Inc, 2850 El Presidio St, Long Beach, CA 90810 *Tel:* 310-637-2105 *Toll Free Tel:* 800-827-2850 *E-mail:* tus@tatungusa.com *Web Site:* www.tatungusa.com, pg 1032

Chen, Ms Fang, United Nations Department of Public Information-News & Media Division, 405 E 42 St, Rm IN-913B, New York, NY 10017 *Tel:* 917-367-5007 *E-mail:* mediapartnerships@un.org *Web Site:* www.un.org, pg 1048

Chen, James C, Audio Images Corp, 701 Bryant St, 2nd fl, San Francisco, CA 94107 *Tel:* 415-957-9131 *Fax:* 415-957-1531 *Web Site:* www.audioimages.com, pg 794

Chen, Janet, Visual Communications - Southern California Asian American Studies Central Inc, 120 Judge John Aiso St, Basement Level, Los Angeles, CA 90012 *Tel:* 213-680-4462 *Fax:* 213-687-4848 *E-mail:* info@vconline.org *Web Site:* www.vconline.org, pg 1059

Chen, Jennifer, AITech International, 1288 Kifer Rd, Suite 203, Sunnyvale, CA 94086 *Tel:* 408-991-9699 *Fax:* 408-991-9691 *E-mail:* info@aitech.com; aitechproducts@aitech.com *Web Site:* www.aitech.com, pg 779

Chen, Michael, AITech International, 1288 Kifer Rd, Suite 203, Sunnyvale, CA 94086 *Tel:* 408-991-9699 *Fax:* 408-991-9691 *E-mail:* info@aitech.com; aitechproducts@aitech.com *Web Site:* www.aitech.com, pg 779

Cheney, Bill, Spectra Sonics Applied Technology Inc, 860 W Riverdale Rd, Unit D6, Riverdale, UT 84405 *Tel:* 801-605-8849 *Fax:* 801-689-2967 *Web Site:* www.spectra-sonics.com, pg 1020

Cheng, Charles, Keng Seng Enterprises Inc, 4000 Rue St Ambroise, Suite 103, Montreal, QC H4C 2C7, Canada *Tel:* 514-939-3971 *Fax:* 514-989-1922 *E-mail:* canada@kengseng.com *Web Site:* www.kengseng.com, pg 909

Cheng, Edie, People Productions, 1737 15 St, Suite 200, Boulder, CO 80302 *Tel:* 303-449-6086 *Fax:* 303-449-9526 *E-mail:* info@peopleproductions.com *Web Site:* www.peopleproductions.com, pg 972

Cheng, Jill, Cheng & Tsui Co, 25 West St, 2nd fl, Boston, MA 02111-1213 *Tel:* 617-988-2400 *Toll Free Tel:* 800-554-1963 (orders) *Fax:* 617-426-3669 *E-mail:* orders@cheng-tsui.com *Web Site:* www.cheng-tsui.com, pg 824

Cheng, Judy, Clear-Com®, 1301 Marina Village Pkwy, Suite 105, Alameda, CA 94501 *Tel:* 510-337-6600 *Toll Free Tel:* 800-462-HELP (462-4357) *Fax:* 510-337-6699 *E-mail:* CustomerServicesUS@clearcom.com *Web Site:* www.clearcom.com, pg 829

Cheremsak, Nick, Hakuba Sunpak Velbon, 53 Green Pond Rd, Suite 5, Rockaway, NJ 07866 *Tel:* 973-627-9600 *Toll Free Tel:* 800-886-2236 *Fax:* 973-664-2438 *E-mail:* info@tocad.com *Web Site:* www.tocad.com, pg 883

Cherin, L, Rhythms Productions (Tom Thumb Music), PO Box 786, Malibu, CA 90265-0786 *Tel:* 310-836-4678, pg 996

Chernick, Rick, Camera Corner Connecting Point, PO Box 248, Green Bay, WI 54305-0248 *Tel:* 920-435-5353 *Toll Free Tel:* 800-236-4950 (orders) *Fax:* 920-435-6984 *E-mail:* contactus@cccp.com; salessupport@cccp.com *Web Site:* www.cccp.com, pg 818

Cherrington, Nathan, Oregon Film & Video Office, 123 NE Third Ave, Suite 210, Portland, OR 97232 *Tel:* 503-229-5832 *Fax:* 503-229-6869 *E-mail:* shoot@oregonfilm.org *Web Site:* www.oregonfilm.org, pg 1101

Cherry, Lee, Cherry Multimedia, 2129 Colorado Blvd, Los Angeles, CA 90041 *Toll Free Tel:* 800-378-7598 *E-mail:* info@cherrymultimedia.com *Web Site:* cherrymultimedia.com, pg 824

Cherubini, Vic, Epic Software Group Inc, 701 Sawdust Rd, The Woodlands, TX 77380 *Tel:* 281-363-3742 *Fax:* 281-419-4509 *E-mail:* epic@epicsoftware.com *Web Site:* www.epicsoftware.com, pg 862

Chesky, Norman, Manhattan Production Music Inc, 1650 Broadway, Suite 900, New York, NY 10019 *Tel:* 212-333-5766 *Fax:* 212-262-0814 *E-mail:* info@mpmmusic.com *Web Site:* www.mpmmusic.com, pg 930

Chesley, Erika, University of Southern California, Davidson Continuing Educ Conference Ctr, Rm 103, 3415 S Figueroa St, Los Angeles, CA 90089-0871 *Tel:* 213-740-5956; 213-740-5679 *Fax:* 213-740-9366 *Web Site:* hospitality.usc.edu/catering, pg 1050

Chesney, Robert, Chesney Communications, PO Box 61945, Irvine, CA 92602-1945 *Tel:* 949-263-5500 *E-mail:* videocc@aol.com *Web Site:* www.speakersdemos.com; www.videocc.com, pg 824

Chessler, Abbie, Quatrefoil Associates Inc, 29 "C" St, Laurel, MD 20707 *Tel:* 301-470-4748 *Fax:* 301-470-4749 *E-mail:* info@quatrefoil.com *Web Site:* www.quatrefoil.com, pg 989

Cheung, Adolf, Dow-Key Microwave Corp, 4822 McGrath St, Ventura, CA 93003 *Tel:* 805-650-0260 *Toll Free Tel:* 800-266-3695 *Fax:* 805-650-1734 *E-mail:* askdk@dowkey.com *Web Site:* www.dowkey.com, pg 851

Cheung, Isaac, New Cyberian Systems Inc, 1919 O'Toole Way, San Jose, CA 95131 *Tel:* 408-922-0682 *Toll Free Tel:* 877-423-4383 *Fax:* 408-884-2257 *E-mail:* sales@newcyberian.com *Web Site:* www.newcyberian.com, pg 955

Chew, Albert, Freeman, 1600 Viceroy, Suite 100, Dallas, TX 75235 *Tel:* 214-445-1000 *Fax:* 214-445-0200 *Web Site:* www.freemanco.com, pg 872

Chew, Lewis, Dolby Labs Inc, 100 Potrero Ave, San Francisco, CA 94103-4813 *Tel:* 415-558-0200 *Fax:* 415-645-4000 *E-mail:* info@dolby.com *Web Site:* www.dolby.com, pg 850

Chi, Sang, Zenith Electronics LLC, 2000 Millbrook Dr, Lincolnshire, IL 60069 *Tel:* 847-941-8000 *Toll Free Tel:* 877-9-ZENITH (993-6484) *Fax:* 847-941-8177 *E-mail:* customer.service@zenith.com *Web Site:* www.zenith.com, pg 1073

Chiahemen, Fanen, CSC Awards, 3007 Kingston Rd, Suite 131, Toronto, ON M1M 1P1, Canada *Tel:* 416-266-0591 *Fax:* 416-266-3996 *E-mail:* admin@csc.ca *Web Site:* www.csc.ca, pg 1113

Chiarella, Lawrence, Ampex Data Systems Corp, 500 Broadway, Redwood City, CA 94063 *Tel:* 650-367-2011 *Fax:* 650-367-2444 *E-mail:* info@ampex.com *Web Site:* www.ampex.com, pg 785

Chicas, Ivett, Associated Press Television News, 450 W 33 St, New York, NY 10001 *Tel:* 212-621-1500 *Fax:* 212-621-7419 *Web Site:* www.aptn.com, pg 792

Chichester, Sue, Computing & Information Technology, South Hall 119, One College Circle, Geneseo, NY 14454 *Tel:* 585-245-5577 *Fax:* 585-245-5579 *Web Site:* www.geneseo.edu/cit, pg 834

Childers, Elsie, Trusty Tuneshop Recording Studios, 8771 Rose Creek Rd, Nebo, KY 42441 *Tel:* 270-249-3194 *E-mail:* etrusty@vci.net *Web Site:* trustytuneshop.com, pg 1045

Childress, Marjorie, SouthWest Organizing Project (SWOP), 211 Tenth St SW, Albuquerque, NM 87102-2919 *Tel:* 505-247-8832 *Fax:* 505-247-9972 *E-mail:* swop@swop.net *Web Site:* www.swop.net, pg 1019

Chilvers, Richard, Wireworks Corp, 380 Hillside Ave, Hillside, NJ 07205 *Tel:* 908-686-7400 *Toll Free Tel:* 800-642-9473 *Fax:* 908-686-0483 *E-mail:* sales@wireworks.com; info@wireworks.com *Web Site:* www.wireworks.com, pg 1068

Chin, Arthur, Norsat International Inc, 110-4020 Viking Way, Richmond, BC V6V 2L4, Canada *Tel:* 604-821-2800 *Toll Free Tel:* 800-644-4562 *Fax:* 604-821-2801 *E-mail:* inquiries@norsat.com; support@norsat.com *Web Site:* www.norsat.com, pg 958

Chin, Chris, Toronto Reel Asian International Film Festival, 401 Richmond St W, Suite 309, Toronto, ON M5V 3A8, Canada *Tel:* 416-703-9333 *Fax:* 416-703-9986 *E-mail:* info@reelasian.com; programming@reelasian.com *Web Site:* www.reelasian.com, pg 1128

Chin, Edward, Wisconsin Technical College System Foundation Inc, One Foundation Circle, Waunakee, WI 53597-8914 *Tel:* 608-849-2424; 608-849-2400 *Toll Free Tel:* 800-821-6313 *Fax:* 608-849-2468 *E-mail:* foundation@wtcsf.tec.wi.us *Web Site:* www.wtcsf.tec.wi.us, pg 1068

Chinn, Mike, SNL Kagan Media & Communications, One SNL Plaza, 212 Seventh St NE, Charlottesville, VA 22902 *Tel:* 434-977-1600 *Toll Free Tel:* 866-296-3743 *Fax:* 434-977-4466 *E-mail:* snlkagansales@snl.com *Web Site:* www.snl.com, pg 1014

Chirico, Jim, Avaya Inc, 211 Mount Airy Rd, Basking Ridge, NJ 07920 *Tel:* 908-953-6000 *Toll Free Tel:* 866-GO-AVAYA (462-8292 US & CN) *Web Site:* www.avaya.com, pg 798

Chirum, Bob, Video Copy Services Inc, 3980 Dekalb Technology Pkwy, Suite 670, Atlanta, GA 30340 *Toll Free Tel:* 800-553-3616 *E-mail:* info@video-copy.com *Web Site:* www.video-copy.com, pg 1055

Chisolm, Richard, Richard Chisolm Cinematography, 300 Oakdale Rd, Baltimore, MD 21210 *Tel:* 410-467-2997 *E-mail:* mail@richardchisolm.com *Web Site:* www.richardchisolm.com, pg 825

Chiu, Jason M, AITech International, 1288 Kifer Rd, Suite 203, Sunnyvale, CA 94086 *Tel:* 408-991-9699 *Fax:* 408-991-9691 *E-mail:* info@aitech.com; aitechproducts@aitech.com *Web Site:* www.aitech.com, pg 779

Chiurazzi, David, Balboa Capital Corp, 2010 Main St, Suite 1100, Irvine, CA 92614 *Tel:* 949-756-0800 *Toll Free Tel:* 888-BALBOA1 (225-2621) *Fax:* 949-756-2565 *E-mail:* customerservice@balboacapital.com *Web Site:* www.balboacapital.com, pg 802

Chmelewski, Edward, Blind Pig Records, PO Box 2344, San Francisco, CA 94126 *Tel:* 415-550-6484 *Toll Free Tel:* 888-474-4736 *Fax:* 415-550-6485 *E-mail:* info@blindpigrecords.com *Web Site:* www.blindpigrecords.com, pg 809

Cho, Peter, Masterdisk Corp, 545 W 45 St, 5th fl, New York, NY 10036 *Tel:* 212-541-5022 *Fax:* 212-581-4093 *E-mail:* info@masterdisk.com *Web Site:* www.masterdisk.com, pg 933

Chodorov, Stephan, Creative Arts Television, PO Box 739, Kent, CT 06757-0739 *Tel:* 860-868-1771 *Fax:* 860-868-9999 *E-mail:* catarchive@aol.com; info@catarchive.com *Web Site:* www.catarchive.com, pg 838

Chong, Kelly, Pro Camera Repair, 7910 Raytheon Rd, San Diego, CA 92111 *Tel:* 858-277-3700 *Fax:* 858-277-5332 *E-mail:* prophotorepair@hotmail.com *Web Site:* www.procamerarepair.com, pg 982

Chong, Larry, Westcoast Video Productions Inc, 14141 Covello St, Suite 9-A, Van Nuys, CA 91405 *Tel:* 818-785-8033 *Toll Free Tel:* 800-477-8417 *Fax:* 818-785-8035 *E-mail:* mail@wvpinc.com *Web Site:* www.wvpinc.com, pg 1064

Chorazak, James, Gordon Visual Solutions, 504 Reiman St, Buffalo, NY 14212-2250 *Tel:* 716-894-5930 *Fax:* 630-839-5930 *E-mail:* info@gordonvisualsolutions.com; service@gordonvisualsolutions.com *Web Site:* www.gordonvisualsolutions.com, pg 880

Chorazyczewski, Jennifer, Media Distributors, 4518 W Vanowen St, Burbank, CA 91505 *Tel:* 818-980-9916 *Toll Free Tel:* 800-851-3113 *Fax:* 818-566-8989 *E-mail:* la@mediadistributors.com *Web Site:* www.mediadistributors.com, pg 936

Chou, Tiffany, PMP Marketing Inc, 13006 E Philadelphia St, Suite 402, Whittier, CA 90601 *Tel:* 562-698-0088 *Fax:* 562-320-8139 *Web Site:* www.pmpmarketing.com, pg 977

Chouinard, Bob, Big Event Productions LLC, 77 13 Ave NE, Studio 101, Minneapolis, MN 55413 *Tel:* 612-623-7800 *Fax:* 612-455-0450 *Web Site:* www.bigeventpros.com, pg 807

Chouinard, Martin, Teledac Inc, 635, rue De La Noue IDS, Verdun, QC H3E 1W1, Canada *Tel:* 514-362-6362 *Toll Free Tel:* 888-659-6362 *E-mail:* general@teledac.com *Web Site:* www.teledac.com, pg 1036

Christ, Peter, Crystal Records Inc, 28818 NE Hancock Rd, Camas, WA 98607 *Tel:* 360-834-7022 *Fax:* 360-834-9680 *E-mail:* info@crystalrecords.com *Web Site:* www.crystalrecords.com, pg 840

Christensen, John, Our Sunday Visitor Inc, 200 Noll Plaza, Huntington, IN 46750 *Tel:* 260-356-8400 *Toll Free Tel:* 800-348-2440 *Fax:* 260-356-8472 *E-mail:* osvsales@osv.com *Web Site:* www.osv.com, pg 966

Christensen, Paul, The Society of Professional Audio Recording Services (SPARS), PO Box 606, Palacios, TX 77465 *Toll Free Tel:* 800-771-7727 *Fax:* 214-722-1442 *E-mail:* spars@spars.com *Web Site:* spars.com, pg 1089

Christensen, Paul A, Omega Productions, PO Box 606, Palacios, TX 77465 *Tel:* 214-891-9585 *Fax:* 214-722-1442 *E-mail:* getinfo@omegalive.com *Web Site:* www.omegalive.com, pg 962

Christiansen, Dan, Photo Tech Inc, 7200 Hudson Blvd N, Suite 170, St Paul, MN 55128 *Tel:* 651-702-6717 *Toll Free Tel:* 800-525-6486 *Fax:* 651-702-6745 *E-mail:* rolleasy@juno.com *Web Site:* www.phototechinc.com, pg 974

Christiansen, Lori, Substation K, 3947 State Line Rd, Kansas City, MO 64111 *Tel:* 816-531-3838 *Fax:* 816-531-3839 *Web Site:* www.substationk.com, pg 1027

Christiansen, Steve, InterVision Media, 44 W Broadway, Suite 426, Eugene, OR 97401 *Tel:* 541-343-7993 *Fax:* 541-345-5951 *E-mail:* info@intervisionmedia.com *Web Site:* www.intervisionmedia.com, pg 902

Christie, Aimee, The Audio Department Inc, 119 W 57 St, Suite 400, New York, NY 10019 *Tel:* 212-586-3503 *Fax:* 212-245-1675 *E-mail:* scheduling@theaudiodepartment.com *Web Site:* www.theaudiodepartment.com, pg 794

Christie, Huntly, Christie Lites, 6990 Lake Ellenor Dr, Orlando, FL 32809 *Tel:* 407-856-0016 *Fax:* 407-856-0765 *Web Site:* www.christielites.com, pg 825

Christoff, Jordan, Visionary Solutions Inc, 2060 Alameda Padre Serra, Suite 100, Santa Barbara, CA 93103 *Tel:* 805-845-8900 *Fax:* 805-845-8889 *E-mail:* info@vsicam.com; sales@vsicam.com *Web Site:* www.vsicam.com, pg 1058

Christopher, David, RuffHouse LLC, 2823 Lariat Trail, Austin, TX 78734 *Tel:* 512-965-2957 *E-mail:* info@ruffhousin.com *Web Site:* www.ruffhousin.com, pg 1000

Christy, Craig, Christy's Editorial, 3625 W Pacific Ave, Burbank, CA 91505 *Tel:* 818-845-1755 *Toll Free Tel:* 800-468-6391; 800-556-5706 (CA) *Fax:* 818-845-1756 *E-mail:* info@christys.net *Web Site:* www.christys.net, pg 826

Chu, Patrick, FilmNation Entertainment, 150 W 22 St, 9th fl, New York, NY 10011 *Web Site:* www.filmnation.com, pg 867

Chu, William, McKay Conant Hoover Inc, 5655 Lindero Canyon Rd, Suite 325, Westlake Village, CA 91362 *Tel:* 818-991-9300 *Fax:* 818-991-2324 *E-mail:* info@mchinc.com *Web Site:* www.mchinc.com, pg 935

Church, Debbie, SmartSource Computer & AV Rentals, 265 Oser Ave, Hauppauge, NY 11788 *Tel:* 631-273-8888 *Toll Free Tel:* 800-888-8686 *Fax:* 631-273-8889 *E-mail:* info@smartsourcerentals.com; longisland@smartsourcerentals.com *Web Site:* www.smartsourcerentals.com, pg 1014

Church, Mike, MIS Technologies, 555-B NW Blue Pkwy, Lees Summit, MO 64063 *Tel:* 816-966-4529 *Fax:* 816-966-2915 *Web Site:* www.mistechnologies.com, pg 944

Church, Nolan C, CSPMedia.com, PO Box 3474, Capitol Heights, MD 20791-3474 *Tel:* 301-350-3181 *Web Site:* www.soundstore.com, pg 840

Chynoweth, Kirk S, Lightning Eliminators & Consultants Inc, 6687 Arapahoe Rd, Boulder, CO 80303 *Tel:* 303-447-2828 *Toll Free Tel:* 800-521-6101 *Fax:* 303-447-8122 *E-mail:* info@lightningprotection.com *Web Site:* www.lightningprotection.com, pg 921

Ciciura, Thomas S, 2nd Cine, 1035 Donna Dr, Belvidere, IL 61008 *Tel:* 773-398-1452 *E-mail:* info@2ndcine.com *Web Site:* www.2ndcine.com, pg 1006

Cieri, Albert, Matrox Video Products Group, 1055 Saint Regis Blvd, Dorval, QC H9P 2T4, Canada *Tel:* 514-822-6364; 514-685-7230 *Toll Free Tel:* 800-361-4903 *Fax:* 514-685-2853 *Web Site:* www.matrox.com/video, pg 934

Cihi, Justin, Videofilm Systems Inc, 7 Islandbrook Ave, Unit D-1, Bridgeport, CT 06606 *Tel:* 203-870-6013 *Web Site:* www.videofilmsystems.com, pg 1057

Cilurso, Linda, Shanachie Entertainment Corp, 37 E Clinton St, Newton, NJ 07860 *Tel:* 973-579-7763 *Web Site:* shanachie.com, pg 1008

Cimino, Steve, Blonder Tongue Laboratories Inc, One Jake Brown Rd, Old Bridge, NJ 08857 *Tel:* 732-679-4000 *Toll Free Tel:* 800-523-6049 *Fax:* 732-679-4353 *E-mail:* custsvc@blondertongue.com; btglobalsales@blondertongue.com (other than US & CN) *Web Site:* www.blondertongue.com, pg 809

Cintron, Joanna, Stanley Film Festival, 1510 York St, 3rd fl, Denver, CO 80206 *Tel:* 970-577-4111 *E-mail:* stanley@denverfilm.org *Web Site:* www.stanleyfilmfest.com, pg 1127

Cissell, Tim, Tim Cissell Music, 10732 W 107 Circle, Westminster, CO 80021 *Tel:* 303-955-4436 *E-mail:* tcissell@wt.net *Web Site:* web.wt.net/~tcissell, pg 828

Civins, Gary, Civins Productions Inc, 5881 NW 122 Dr, Coral Springs, FL 33076 *Tel:* 954-938-8600 *E-mail:* info@civins.com *Web Site:* www.civins.com, pg 828

Civitella, Billy, Stray Angel Films, 2236 S Barrington Ave, Los Angeles, CA 90064 *Tel:* 310-277-6900 *Fax:* 801-438-5009 *E-mail:* rentals@strayangel.com *Web Site:* www.strayangel.com, pg 1026

Clairmont, Denny, Clairmont Camera Inc, 4343 Lankershim Blvd, North Hollywood, CA 91602 *Tel:* 818-761-4440 *Fax:* 818-761-0861 *E-mail:* hollywood@clairmont.com *Web Site:* www.clairmont.com, pg 829

Claman, Roger, Rose Brand, 4 Emerson Lane, Secaucus, NJ 07094 *Tel:* 201-809-1730 *Toll Free Tel:* 800-223-1624 *Fax:* 201-809-1851 *E-mail:* info@rosebrand.com *Web Site:* www.rosebrand.com, pg 999

Clancy, Dan, Wisconsin Technical College System Foundation Inc, One Foundation Circle, Waunakee, WI 53597-8914 *Tel:* 608-849-2424; 608-849-2400 *Toll Free Tel:* 800-821-6313 *Fax:* 608-849-2468 *E-mail:* foundation@wtcsf.tec.wi.us *Web Site:* www.wtcsf.tec.wi.us, pg 1068

Clancy, Greg, TM Studios Inc, 2002 Academy Lane, Suite 110, Dallas, TX 75234 *Tel:* 972-406-6800 *Fax:* 972-406-6890 *E-mail:* info@tmstudios.com; tmcustomerservice@tmstudios.com *Web Site:* www.tmstudios.com, pg 1041

Clappe, Megan, Society of Broadcast Engineers Inc (SBE), 9102 N Meridian St, Suite 150, Indianapolis, IN 46260 *Tel:* 317-846-9000 *Web Site:* www.sbe.org, pg 1089

Clark, Andrew, Midwest Photo Exchange, 3313 N High St, Columbus, OH 43202 *Tel:* 614-261-1264 *Toll Free Tel:* 866-940-3686 *Fax:* 614-261-1637 *E-mail:* mpex@mpex.com; orders@mpex.com *Web Site:* mpex.com, pg 942

Clark, Bill, Anchor Bay Entertainment LLC, 9242 Beverly Blvd, Suite 201, Beverly Hills, CA 90210 *Tel:* 424-204-4166 *E-mail:* questions@anchorbayent.com *Web Site:* www.anchorbayentertainment.com, pg 786

Clark, Bryce, David Clark Co Inc, 360 Franklin St, Worcester, MA 01604 *Tel:* 508-751-5800 *Toll Free Tel:* 800-900-3434 *Fax:* 508-753-5827 *E-mail:* sales@davidclark.com *Web Site:* www.davidclark.com, pg 843

Clark, Dan, The Cinema Lab, 2735 S Raritan St, Englewood, CO 80110-1101 *Tel:* 303-783-1020 *Fax:* 303-806-0555 *Web Site:* www.cinemalab.com, pg 827

Clark, Edward M, Ostergaard Acoustical Associates, 200 Executive Dr, Suite 350, West Orange, NJ 07052 *Tel:* 973-731-7002 *Fax:* 973-731-6680 *E-mail:* info@acousticalconsultant.com *Web Site:* www.acousticalconsultant.com, pg 966

Clark, Gregor, Catman & Mary Productions, 336 W 37 St, Suite 800, New York, NY 10018 *Tel:* 212-947-4777 *Fax:* 212-947-4779 *Web Site:* www.catmanandmary.com, pg 821

Clark, James M, Clark Services Audio Visual & Exhibit Inc, 113 Board Rd, Lafayette, LA 70508 *Tel:* 337-234-5653 *Fax:* 337-232-0243 *E-mail:* clarkservices@bellsouth.net *Web Site:* www.clarkservices.biz, pg 829

Clark, Jeff, WIFR-TV, 2523 N Meridian Rd, Rockford, IL 61101 *Tel:* 815-987-5300 *Fax:* 815-965-0981 *E-mail:* talkto23@wifr.com *Web Site:* www.wifr.com, pg 1066

Clark, Laurel, SOM Publishing Co, 163 Moon Valley Rd, Windyville, MO 65783 *Tel:* 417-345-8411 *E-mail:* som@som.org *Web Site:* www.som.org, pg 1015

Clark, Les, Clark's Audio Visual Services Ltd, 1615 Venables St, Vancouver, BC V5L 2H1, Canada *Tel:* 604-877-8558 *Toll Free Tel:* 800-667-1819 *Fax:* 604-879-2993 *Toll Free Fax:* 800-665-2932 *E-mail:* info@clarksav.com *Web Site:* www.clarksav.com, pg 829

Clark, Mitch, CenterStaging LLC, 3407 Winona Ave, Burbank, CA 91504 *Tel:* 818-559-4333 *Fax:* 818-848-4016 *E-mail:* info@centerstaging.com *Web Site:* centerstaging.com, pg 823

Clark, Rebecca, North Carolina's Piedmont Triad Film Commission, 416 Gallimore Dairy Rd, Suite M, Greensboro, NC 27409 *Tel:* 336-393-0001 *E-mail:* info@piedmontfilm.com *Web Site:* www.piedmontfilm.com, pg 1101

Clark, Sara, Westlake Recording Studios, 7265 Santa Monica Blvd, Los Angeles, CA 90046 *Tel:* 323-851-9800 *E-mail:* bookings@thelakestudios.com; info@thelakestudios.com *Web Site:* www.thelakestudios.com, pg 1064

Clark, Tom, South Carolina Film Commission, 1205 Pendleton St, Rm 225, Columbia, SC 29201-3261 *Tel:* 803-737-0490 *Fax:* 803-734-0670 *E-mail:* filmsc@scprt.com *Web Site:* www.filmsc.com, pg 1102

Clark, William J, Masterclock Inc, 2484 W Clay St, St Charles, MO 63301-2548 *Tel:* 636-724-3666 *Toll Free Tel:* 800-940-2248 *Fax:* 636-724-3776 *E-mail:* info@masterclock.com; sales@masterclock.com *Web Site:* www.masterclock.com, pg 933

Clarke, Dorothy, Cifex Corp, 20547 Linksview Way, Boca Raton, FL 33434 *Tel:* 561-883-5548 *Fax:* 561-883-2712 *E-mail:* 2cifex@gmail.com, pg 826

Clarke, Jeff, Eastman Kodak Professional, 343 State St, Rochester, NY 14650 *Toll Free Tel:* 800-698-3324 *Web Site:* www.kodak.com, pg 856

Clarke, Mia Barkan, Cross-Cultural Communications, 239 Wynsum Ave, Merrick, NY 11566-4725 *Tel:* 516-868-5635 *Fax:* 516-379-1901 *E-mail:* info@cross-culturalcommunications.com *Web Site:* www.cross-culturalcommunications.com, pg 839

Clarke, Roger, Zygote Media Group Inc, 1045 S 500 E, Suite 200, American Fork, UT 84003 *Tel:* 801-765-4141 *Fax:* 801-705-2234 *E-mail:* customerservices@zygote.com *Web Site:* www.zygote.com, pg 1074

Clarkson, Robert N, Clarkson Studio, 401 N Hoback St, Helena, MT 59601 *Tel:* 406-442-2046 *Web Site:* www.clarksonstudio.com, pg 829

Classe, A V, A M Graphics Products, dba Affton Graphics Inc, 2500 Third Ave, Bronx, NY 10454 *Tel:* 718-401-4040 *Toll Free Tel:* 800-777-0539 *Fax:* 718-401-3322 *E-mail:* amproducts@aol.com *Web Site:* www.amdba.com, pg 771

Claude, Lou, BroadcastStore.com, 9420 Lurline Ave, Unit C, Chatsworth, CA 91311 *Tel:* 818-998-9100 *Fax:* 818-998-9106 *E-mail:* sales@broadcaststore.com *Web Site:* www.broadcaststore.com, pg 813

Claudon, Chet, Cobham Tactical Communications & Surveillance, 3845 Gateway Centre Blvd, Pinellas Park, FL 33782 *Tel:* 571-392-2500 *Web Site:* www.cobham.com, pg 831

Claypool, Kathryn, Two Door Productions, 416 N Harper Ave, Los Angeles, CA 90048 *E-mail:* shoot@usphotograph.com *Web Site:* www.twodoorfx.com, pg 1047

Clayton, Brooks, Mid-South Color Labs Inc, 496 Emmett St, Jackson, TN 38301 *Tel:* 731-422-6691 *Toll Free Tel:* 800-221-3920 *Fax:* 731-424-1902 *E-mail:* info@midsouthcolor.com *Web Site:* www.midsouthcolor.com, pg 942

Clayton, Michael, Pentrex Media Group LLC, 2652 E Walnut St, Pasadena, CA 91107-3723 *Tel:* 626-793-3400 *Toll Free Tel:* 800-950-9333 *Fax:* 626-793-3797 *E-mail:* pentrex@pentrex.com *Web Site:* www.pentrex.com, pg 972

Cleary, Kitty, Circulating Film & Video Library, 11 W 53 St, New York, NY 10019-5401 *Tel:* 212-708-9530 *Fax:* 212-708-9531 *E-mail:* circfilm@moma.org *Web Site:* www.moma.org, pg 828

Cleaveland, Dave, Maine Imaging, PO Box 753, Wiscasset, ME 04578 *Tel:* 207-380-6343 *Web Site:* maineaerial.com, pg 929

Clemens, Paul M, Blue Dolphin Multimedia, 13340-D Grass Valley Ave, Grass Valley, CA 95945 *Tel:* 530-477-1503 *Toll Free Tel:* 800-643-0765 (orders) *Fax:* 530-477-8342 *E-mail:* bdolphin@bluedolphinpublishing.com *Web Site:* www.bluedolphinpublishing.com, pg 809

Clement, Robbie, Tomorrow River Music, PO Box 245, Cambridge, WI 53523 *Tel:* 608-217-5039 *Web Site:* www.robbieclement.com, pg 1042

Clemente, Rick, I-25 Studios, 9201 Pan American Fwy NE, Albuquerque, NM 87113 *Tel:* 505-822-7115 *Fax:* 505-314-7094 *E-mail:* info@i-25studios.com *Web Site:* i-25studios.com, pg 893

Clements, Chip, Palardo Productions, 1807 Taft Ave, Suite 4, Hollywood, CA 90028 *Tel:* 323-469-8991 *E-mail:* palardo2@msn.com, pg 968

Clements, Paul, MultiMedia, 333 Washington Ave N, Suite 212, Minneapolis, MN 55401 *Tel:* 612-767-1660 *Fax:* 612-339-5121 *E-mail:* info@multimedia-inc.com *Web Site:* www.multimedia-inc.com, pg 950

Cleveland, Rob, August House Audio, 3500 Piedmont Rd NE, Suite 310, Atlanta, GA 30305 *Tel:* 404-442-4420 *Toll Free Tel:* 800-284-8784 *Fax:* 404-442-4435 *E-mail:* ahinfo@augusthouse.com *Web Site:* www.augusthouse.com, pg 796

Clifford, Mike, WATL-TV Inc, One Monroe Place NE, Atlanta, GA 30324 *Tel:* 404-892-1611 *Fax:* 404-881-3635 *Web Site:* www.myatltv.com, pg 1062

Clifford, Stewart B, Enterprise Media LLC, 91 Harvey St, Cambridge, MA 02140 *Tel:* 617-354-0017 *Toll Free Tel:* 800-423-6021 *Fax:* 617-354-1637 *E-mail:* orders@enterprisemedia.com *Web Site:* www.enterprisemedia.com, pg 861

Clifton, Bryan, Redman Movies & Stories, 1075 S 700 W, Salt Lake City, UT 84104 *Tel:* 801-978-9292 *Fax:* 801-978-2299 *E-mail:* info@redmanmovies.com *Web Site:* www.redmanmovies.com, pg 993

Cline, Jeff, University of Memphis, Music Industry Division, Music Bldg, Rm 123, 3775 Central Ave, Memphis, TN 38152-3160 *Tel:* 901-678-2559; 901-678-2541 *E-mail:* music@memphis.edu *Web Site:* www.memphis.edu/music/index.php, pg 1050

Cline, Kim, Road Pictures, 5420 N College Ave, Suite 201, Indianapolis, IN 46220 *Tel:* 317-267-9590 *Toll Free Tel:* 800-267-9590 *Fax:* 317-267-9677 *Web Site:* www.roadpictures.com, pg 997

Cline, Terry, Challenge Productions, 400 E George St, Marion, OH 43302 *Tel:* 740-531-3077 *E-mail:* info@challenge-pro.com *Web Site:* challenge-pro.com, pg 823

Clinton, Nancy, The Editing Co, 7030 Empire Central Dr, Houston, TX 77040 *Tel:* 713-783-2655 *Fax:* 713-783-8642 *Web Site:* www.editingco.com, pg 857

Clock, Kevin, Colorado Sound Recording Studios, 3100 W 71 Ave, Westminster, CO 80030 *Tel:* 303-430-8811 *E-mail:* colosnd@coloradosound.com *Web Site:* www.coloradosound.com, pg 831

Clum, Guy C, Power-Sonic Corp, 7550 Panasonic Way, San Diego, CA 92154 *Tel:* 619-661-2020 *Fax:* 619-661-3650 *E-mail:* customer-service@power-sonic.com; technical-support@power-sonic.com *Web Site:* www.power-sonic.com, pg 979

Clyne, Arthur A Jr, PSAV® Presentation Services, 111 W Ocean Blvd, Suite 1110, Long Beach, CA 90802-4688 *Tel:* 562-366-0620 *Toll Free Tel:* 877-430-7728 *Fax:* 562-366-0628 *Web Site:* www.psav.com, pg 986

Clyne, Arthur A Jr, Swank Audio Visuals, 639-E Gravois Bluffs, St Louis, MO 63026 *Tel:* 636-680-9000 *Toll Free Tel:* 877-792-6528 *Fax:* 636-680-2853 *Web Site:* www.swankav.com, pg 1029

Coakley, Sue, SF Global Sourcing, 1000 Sansome St, Suite 280, San Francisco, CA 94111 *Tel:* 415-288-9400 *Toll Free Tel:* 855-SF-GLOBAL (734-5622) *Fax:* 415-288-9410 *E-mail:* info@sfglobalsourcing.com *Web Site:* www.sfglobalsourcing.com, pg 1007

Coan, Bill, ITEC Entertainment Corp, 8544 Commodity Circle, Orlando, FL 32819 *Tel:* 407-226-0200 *Fax:* 407-226-0201 *E-mail:* productionsinfo@itec.com *Web Site:* www.itec.com, pg 903

Cobb, Bobby, Intermedia Technologies, 1720 Kaliste Saloom, Bldg 2, Suite B-2, Lafayette, LA 70508 *Tel:* 337-406-9428 *Toll Free Tel:* 877-268-9574 *Fax:* 337-406-9582 *Web Site:* www.intermedia-technologies.com, pg 900

Coburg, Thaddeus, Flip 2 Media Inc, 1067 Serpentine Lane, Pleasanton, CA 94566-4759 *Tel:* 925-417-1420 *E-mail:* info@flip2media.com *Web Site:* www.flip2media.com, pg 870

Cochran, Heather, Television Academy, 5220 Lankershim Blvd, North Hollywood, CA 91601-3109 *Tel:* 818-754-2800 *Fax:* 818-761-2827 *Web Site:* www.emmys.com, pg 1089

Cocke, Jim, Crystal Clear Media Group, 6737 E 30 St, Indianapolis, IN 46219 *Toll Free Tel:* 800-880-0073 *E-mail:* info@crystalclearcds.com *Web Site:* www.crystalclearcds.com, pg 840

Cody, Dwight, The Boston Connection Inc, PO Box 1835, Cotuit, MA 02635 *Tel:* 617-908-6258 *Fax:* 508-428-2036 *E-mail:* bconnect@cutfilm.com *Web Site:* www.cutfilm.com, pg 811

Coe, George F, Baker & Taylor Inc, 2550 W Tyvola Rd, Suite 300, Charlotte, NC 28217 *Tel:* 704-998-3100 *Toll Free Tel:* 800-775-1800 *E-mail:* btinfo@baker-taylor.com *Web Site:* www.btol.com, pg 801

Coffey, Carolyn, Intellidyne LLC, 5203 Leesburg Pike, Suite 400, 2 Skyline Place, Falls Church, VA 22041 *Tel:* 703-575-9715 *Fax:* 703-575-9718 *Web Site:* www.intellidyne-llc.com, pg 899

Coffey, Cristy, FirstCom Music, 1325 Capital Pkwy, Suite 109, Carrollton, TX 75006 *Tel:* 972-446-8742 *Toll Free Tel:* 800-858-8880 *Fax:* 972-242-6526 *E-mail:* info@firstcom.com *Web Site:* www.firstcom.com, pg 869

Coffey, Derek, Welocalize, 241 E Fourth St, Suite 207, Frederick, MD 21701 *Tel:* 301-668-0330 *Toll Free Tel:* 800-370-9515 *Fax:* 301-668-0335 *E-mail:* info@welocalize.com *Web Site:* www.welocalize.com, pg 1063

Coffey, Shane, Sharp Electronics Corp, Professional Display Division, One Sharp Plaza, Mahwah, NJ 07495-1163 *Tel:* 201-529-8200 *Fax:* 201-529-8425 *E-mail:* prolcd@sharpsec.com *Web Site:* www.sharpusa.com, pg 1008

Coffin, Dini, Enterprise Media LLC, 91 Harvey St, Cambridge, MA 02140 *Tel:* 617-354-0017 *Toll Free Tel:* 800-423-6021 *Fax:* 617-354-1637 *E-mail:* orders@enterprisemedia.com *Web Site:* www.enterprisemedia.com, pg 861

Coffman, Candace, Scott Resources Inc, 401 Hickory St, Fort Collins, CO 80524-1125 *Tel:* 970-484-7445 *Toll Free Tel:* 800-289-9299 *Fax:* 970-484-1198 *E-mail:* custserv@amep.com *Web Site:* amep.com, pg 1005

Cogan, Michael, Bay Records, 3365 S Lucille Lane, Lafayette, LA 94549 *Tel:* 925-284-7797 *Web Site:* www.bayrec.com, pg 803

Cohen, Andy, Film House Inc, 810 Dominican Dr, Nashville, TN 37228 *Tel:* 615-255-4000 *Fax:* 615-255-4111 *E-mail:* results@filmhouse.com *Web Site:* www.filmhouse.com, pg 867

Cohen, David, Edgewise Media Inc, 602 N Cypress St, Orange, CA 92867 *Toll Free Tel:* 800-959-5156 *Fax:* 323-466-6815 *E-mail:* sales@edgewise-media.com *Web Site:* www.edgewise-media.com, pg 856

Cohen, Donald, Don Cohen - The Mathman, 809 Stratford Dr, Champaign, IL 61821-4140 *Tel:* 217-356-4555 *Web Site:* www.mathman.biz, pg 831

Cohen, Donald, Mood Creations Ltd, One Depot Plaza, Ossining, NY 10562 *Tel:* 914-941-2357 *Fax:* 914-941-3142 *E-mail:* moodcreations@optonline.net *Web Site:* www.moodcreations.com, pg 946

Cohen, Ferne, Banff World Media Festival, 102 Boulder Crescent, Suite 202, Canmore, AB T1W 1L2, Canada *Tel:* 403-678-1216 *Toll Free Tel:* 888-287-2279 *Fax:* 403-678-3357 *E-mail:* info@achillesmedia.com *Web Site:* banffmediafestival.com, pg 1109

Cohen, Henry, Production Radio Rentals Inc, 249 Ferris Ave, White Plains, NY 10603-3420 *Tel:* 914-686-3525 *Fax:* 914-686-3374 *E-mail:* info@productionradio.com *Web Site:* www.productionradio.com, pg 984

Cohen, Howard, Utopia Films, 1976 S La Cienega Blvd, No 130, Los Angeles, CA 90034 *Tel:* 310-338-0580 *Fax:* 313-557-0580 *E-mail:* reception@utopiafilms.com; utopiafilms2@gmail.com (large e-mails); production@utopiafilms.com (reels) *Web Site:* utopiafilms.com, pg 1051

Cohen, Neal, Multimedia Audio Visual Inc, 2640 S Raritan Circle, Denver, CO 80110 *Tel:* 303-623-2324 *Toll Free Tel:* 800-756-6118 *Fax:* 303-623-0829 *E-mail:* info@multimedia-av.com *Web Site:* www.multimedia-av.com, pg 950

Cohen, Oliver, Imtronics Industries Inc, 11930 31 Ct N, St Petersburg, FL 33716 *Tel:* 727-572-9010 *Fax:* 727-572-9012 *E-mail:* imtronics@imtronics.com *Web Site:* imtronics.com, pg 897

Cohen, Rob, Big Foot Productions Inc, 37-09 36 Ave, Long Island City, NY 11101 *Tel:* 718-729-1900 *Fax:* 718-729-8638 *E-mail:* info@bigfootnyc.com *Web Site:* www.bigfootnyc.com, pg 807

Cohen, Scott, Mood Creations Ltd, One Depot Plaza, Ossining, NY 10562 *Tel:* 914-941-2357 *Fax:* 914-941-3142 *E-mail:* moodcreations@optonline.net *Web Site:* www.moodcreations.com, pg 946

Cohen, Steven B, Imtronics Industries Inc, 11930 31 Ct N, St Petersburg, FL 33716 *Tel:* 727-572-9010 *Fax:* 727-572-9012 *E-mail:* imtronics@imtronics.com *Web Site:* imtronics.com, pg 897

Cohen, William, CNS Productions Inc, 11 Almond St, Medford, OR 97504 *Tel:* 541-779-3361 *Toll Free Tel:* 800-888-0617 *Fax:* 541-773-5905 *E-mail:* info@cnsproductions.com *Web Site:* www.cnsproductions.com, pg 830

Cohn, Margie, DreamWorks Animation SKG Inc, 1000 Flower St, Glendale, CA 91201 *Tel:* 818-695-5000 *Fax:* 818-695-4190 *Web Site:* www.dreamworksanimation.com, pg 852

Cohn, Dr Patrick, Peak Performance Sports LLC, 7380 Sand Lake Rd, PMB 5012, Orlando, FL 32819-5248 *Tel:* 407-909-1700 *Toll Free Tel:* 888-742-7225 *Fax:* 407-909-1789 *E-mail:* pgapack@aol.com *Web Site:* www.peaksports.com, pg 970

Cohn, Peter, Solar Studios, 1601 S Central Ave, Glendale, CA 91204 *Tel:* 818-240-1893 *Fax:* 818-240-4187 *Web Site:* www.solarstudios.com, pg 1015

Cohn, Phil, Boston Acoustics, 7 Constitution Way, Woburn, MA 01801 *Tel:* 201-762-6429 *Fax:* 978-538-6237 *E-mail:* weborders@bostonacoustics.com *Web Site:* www.bostonacoustics.com, pg 811

Cohn, Roy B, Cohn Creative Group LLC, 244 W 54 St, 5th fl, New York, NY 10019 *Tel:* 212-333-3241 *Fax:* 212-246-5727 *E-mail:* info@cohncreative.com *Web Site:* www.cohncreativegroup.com, pg 831

Coifman, Vanessa, RKO Pictures Inc, 2034 Broadway, Santa Monica, CA 90404 *Tel:* 310-277-0707 *Fax:* 310-566-8940 *E-mail:* info@rko.com *Web Site:* www.rko.com, pg 997

Cojescu, Lucian, PromaxBDA, 1522e Cloverfield Blvd, Santa Monica, CA 90404 *Tel:* 310-788-7600 *Fax:* 310-788-7616 *Web Site:* www.promaxbda.org, pg 1087

Coker, Brad, Pacific Video Image, 9065 E Rosecrans Ave, Bellflower, CA 90706 *Tel:* 562-634-4200 *Fax:* 562-634-4700 *E-mail:* info@pvideo.com *Web Site:* www.pvideo.com, pg 967

Coladonato, Heather, Desert Hot Springs Chamber of Commerce & Visitors Center, 11999 Palm Dr, Desert Hot Springs, CA 92240 *Tel:* 760-329-6403 *E-mail:* info@deserthotsprings.com *Web Site:* www.deserthotsprings.com, pg 1092

Colapinto, Maria, Big Shoulders Digital Video Productions, 875 N Michigan Ave, Suite 3750, Chicago, IL 60611 *Tel:* 312-540-5400 *E-mail:* info@bigshoulders.com; sales@bigshoulders.com *Web Site:* www.bigshoulders.com, pg 807

Colby, Charles, Colby Systems Corp, 2991 Alexis Dr, Palo Alto, CA 94304 *Tel:* 650-941-9090 *Web Site:* www.colbysystems.com, pg 831

Colby, Steve, Pogo Pictures, 114 E Ponce de Leon Ave, Suite B, Decatur, GA 30030 *Tel:* 404-892-9490 *Fax:* 404-892-9491 *E-mail:* info@pogopictures.com *Web Site:* www.pogopictures.com, pg 977

Cole, Angela, Chico Chamber of Commerce/Butte County Film Commission, 441 Main St, Suite 150, Chico, CA 95928 *Tel:* 530-891-5556 *Toll Free Tel:* 800-852-8570 *Fax:* 530-891-3613 *E-mail:* info@chicochamber.com *Web Site:* chicochamber.com, pg 1092

Cole, Dr Arnie, Back to the Bible, 6400 Cornhusker Hwy, Lincoln, NE 68507 *Tel:* 402-464-7200 *Toll Free Tel:* 800-759-6655 (inquires); 800-759-2425 (orders) *Fax:* 402-464-7474 *E-mail:* info@backtothebible.org *Web Site:* www.backtothebible.org, pg 801

Cole, David, Players Press, PO Box 1132, Studio City, CA 91614-0132 *Tel:* 818-789-4980 *Web Site:* ppeps.com, pg 977

Cole, Jeremy, Veritech Corp, 80 Denslow Rd, East Longmeadow, MA 01028 *Tel:* 413-525-3368 *Toll Free Tel:* 800-525-5912 *Fax:* 413-525-7449 *E-mail:* info@veritechmedia.com *Web Site:* www.veritechmedia.com, pg 1053

Cole, Juan, University of Michigan, Center for Middle Eastern & North African Studies, 1080 S University, Suite 3603, Ann Arbor, MI 48109-1106 *Tel:* 734-647-4143 *Fax:* 734-936-0996 *E-mail:* cmenas@umich.edu *Web Site:* www.ii.umich.edu/cmenas, pg 1050

Cole, Karl, Davis Art Images, 50 Portland St, Worcester, MA 01608 *Tel:* 508-754-7201 *Toll Free Tel:* 800-533-2847 *Fax:* 508-753-3834 *E-mail:* das@davisart.com *Web Site:* www.davisartimages.com, pg 843

Cole, Leo, Cole Wire & Cable Co Inc, 620 Margate Dr, Lincolnshire, IL 60069-4247 *Toll Free Tel:* 800-323-1403 *Fax:* 847-634-4988 *E-mail:* sales@colewire.com *Web Site:* www.colewire.com, pg 831

Cole, Michele, Univenture Inc, 13311 Industrial Pkwy, Marysville, OH 43040 *Tel:* 937-645-4600 *Toll Free Tel:* 877-831-9428 *Fax:* 937-645-4700 *E-mail:* sales@univenture.com; orders@univenture.com *Web Site:* www.univenture.com, pg 1049

Cole, Ryan, Three Pillars Media, 140 N Eighth St, Suite 440, Lincoln, NE 68508 *Tel:* 402-937-0984 *E-mail:* contact@threepillarsmedia.com *Web Site:* www.threepillarsmedia.com, pg 1040

Colebank, Kevin, Tantor Media Inc, 2 Business Park Rd, Unit 2, Old Saybrook, CT 06475 *Tel:* 860-395-1155 *Toll Free Tel:* 877-7-TANTOR (782-6867) *Toll Free Fax:* 888-782-7821 *E-mail:* orders@tantor.com; service@tantor.com *Web Site:* www.tantor.com, pg 1031

Coleman, Buddy, Clever Devices Ltd, 300 Crossways Park Dr, Woodburg, NY 11797 *Tel:* 516-433-6100 *Toll Free Tel:* 800-872-6129 *Web Site:* www.cleverdevices.com, pg 830

Coleman, Carl, Global Peace Film Festival (GPFF), 1000 Universal Studios Plaza, Bldg 22-A, Orlando, FL 32819 *Tel:* 407-224-6625 *E-mail:* info@peacefilmfest.org *Web Site:* www.peacefilmfest.org, pg 1115

Coleman, Dr Eli, Sinclair Institute, 402 Millstone Dr, Hillsborough, NC 27278 *Tel:* 919-732-6005 *Toll Free Tel:* 888-736-2247 *Fax:* 919-732-6146 *E-mail:* sales@sinclairwholesale.com *Web Site:* www.sinclairwholesale.com; www.bettersex.com, pg 1012

Coleman, James "Huey", Films by Huey, 103 Montrose Ave, Portland, ME 04103 *Tel:* 207-773-1130 *E-mail:* huey@filmsbyhuey.com *Web Site:* www.filmsbyhuey.com, pg 868

Coleman, Lew, DreamWorks Animation SKG Inc, 1000 Flower St, Glendale, CA 91201 *Tel:* 818-695-5000 *Fax:* 818-695-4190 *Web Site:* www.dreamworksanimation.com, pg 852

Coleman, Sara Otte, North Dakota Tourism Division/Film Commission, Century Ctr, 1600 E Century Ave, Suite 2, Bismarck, ND 58502-2057 *Tel:* 701-328-2525 *Toll Free Tel:* 800-435-5663 *Fax:* 701-328-4878 *E-mail:* tourism@nd.gov *Web Site:* www.ndtourism.com, pg 1101

Coles, Brian, City Stage, 435 W 19 St, New York, NY 10011 *Tel:* 212-627-3400 *Fax:* 212-633-1228 *Web Site:* www.citystage.com, pg 828

Coles, Terrence, Dogma Studios, 10559 Jefferson Blvd, Culver City, CA 90232 *Tel:* 310-838-2973 *Fax:* 310-838-2975 *E-mail:* info@dogmastudios.com *Web Site:* www.dogmastudios.com, pg 850

College, Dr Craig E, CALIBRE, Metro Park, 6354 Walker Lane, Alexandria, VA 22310-3252 *Tel:* 703-797-8500 *Toll Free Tel:* 888-CALIBRE (225-4273) *Fax:* 703-797-8501 *E-mail:* info@calibresys.com *Web Site:* www.calibresys.com, pg 817

Colleran, Rebecca, Acoustics First Corp, 2247 Tomlyn St, Richmond, VA 23230-3334 *Tel:* 804-342-2900 *Toll Free Tel:* 888-765-2900 *Fax:* 804-342-1107 *E-mail:* info@acousticsfirst.com *Web Site:* www.acousticsfirst.com, pg 775

Collier, Janice, Pennsylvania Film Office, Commonwealth Keystone Bldg, 4th fl, 400 North St, Harrisburg, PA 17120-0225 *Tel:* 717-783-3456 *Fax:* 717-787-6825 *E-mail:* info@filminpa.com *Web Site:* www.filminpa.com, pg 1101

Colligan, Megan, Paramount Pictures Corporation, 5555 Melrose Ave, Los Angeles, CA 90038 *Tel:* 323-956-8398 *Web Site:* www.paramount.com, pg 969

Collik, Bob, Elite Video & Photography Services Inc, 250 Mount Sinai Coram Rd, Coram, NY 11727 *Tel:* 631-696-1635 *E-mail:* info@cantbeatelite.com *Web Site:* www.cantbeatelite.com, pg 859

Collik, Cheryl, Elite Video & Photography Services Inc, 250 Mount Sinai Coram Rd, Coram, NY 11727 *Tel:* 631-696-1635 *E-mail:* info@cantbeatelite.com *Web Site:* www.cantbeatelite.com, pg 859

Collins, George, Memory Lane Productions, 4323 Mundymill Rd, Oakwood, GA 30566 *Tel:* 770-531-1444 *Fax:* 770-531-1444 *E-mail:* memlane1@aol.com, pg 938

Collins, Ginny, Manitoba Film & Music, 410-93 Lombard Ave, Suite 410, Winnipeg, MB R3B 3B1, Canada *Tel:* 204-947-2040 *Fax:* 204-956-5261 *E-mail:* info@mbfilmmusic.ca *Web Site:* www.mbfilmmusic.ca, pg 930

Collins, Keith, SAS Institute Inc, 100 SAS Campus Dr, Cary, NC 27513-2414 *Tel:* 919-677-8000 *Toll Free Tel:* 800-727-0025 *Fax:* 919-677-4444 *Web Site:* www.sas.com, pg 1002

Collins, Kevin, Diversified Systems Inc, 363 Market St, Kenilworth, NJ 07033 *Tel:* 908-245-4833 *Fax:* 908-245-0011 *E-mail:* info@divsystems.com *Web Site:* www.divsystems.com, pg 849

Collins, Leslie, TMW Media Group, 2321 Abbot Kinney Blvd, Suite 101, Venice, CA 90291 *Tel:* 310-577-8581 *Toll Free Tel:* 800-262-8862 *Fax:* 310-574-0886 *E-mail:* sale@tmwmedia.com *Web Site:* www.tmwmedia.com, pg 1041

Collins, Mary M, Avatar Award, 550 W Frontage Rd, Suite 3600, Northfield, IL 60093 *Tel:* 847-716-7000 *Fax:* 847-716-7004 *E-mail:* info@mediafinance.org *Web Site:* www.mediafinance.org, pg 1108

Collins, Mary M, Media Financial Management Association (MFM), 550 W Frontage Rd, Suite 3600, Northfield, IL 60093 *Tel:* 847-716-7000 *Fax:* 847-716-7004 *E-mail:* info@mediafinance.org *Web Site:* www.mediafinance.org, pg 1084

Collins, Mike, Film Ideas, 308 N Wolf Rd, Wheeling, IL 60090 *Tel:* 847-419-0255 *Toll Free Tel:* 800-475-3456 (US only) *Fax:* 847-419-8933 *E-mail:* info@filmideas.com *Web Site:* www.filmideas.com, pg 867

Collins, Stephanie, Motion Picture Licensing Corp (MPLC), 5455 Centinela Ave, Los Angeles, CA 90066 *Tel:* 310-822-8855 (intl calls) *Toll Free Tel:* 800-462-8855 *Fax:* 310-822-4440 *Web Site:* www.mplc.org, pg 947

Collins, Wendy, Films for the Humanities & Sciences, 132 W 31 St, 17th fl, New York, NY 10001 *Toll Free Tel:* 800-257-5126 *Fax:* 609-671-0266 *E-mail:* custserv@films.com *Web Site:* ffh.films.com, pg 868

Collison, Chandler, Aviom Inc, 1157 Phoenixville Pike, Suite 201, West Chester, PA 19380-4254 *Tel:* 610-738-9005 *Fax:* 610-738-9950 *E-mail:* info@aviom.com *Web Site:* www.aviom.com, pg 799

Comarov, Yaron, Optibase Inc, 931 Benecia Ave, Sunnyvale, CA 94085 *Toll Free Tel:* 800-451-5101 *Fax:* 408-739-1706 *Web Site:* www.optibase.com, pg 964

Comeau, Connie, The ADS Group, 2155 Niagara Lane N, Suite 120, Plymouth, MN 55447 *Tel:* 763-449-5500 *Toll Free Tel:* 800-759-0992 *Fax:* 763-449-5555 *E-mail:* sales@theadsgroup.com *Web Site:* www.theadsgroup.com, pg 777

Comfort, Esme, Banff World Media Festival, 102 Boulder Crescent, Suite 202, Canmore, AB T1W 1L2, Canada *Tel:* 403-678-1216 *Toll Free Tel:* 888-287-2279 *Fax:* 403-678-3357 *E-mail:* info@achillesmedia.com *Web Site:* banffmediafestival.com, pg 1109

Como, Maureen, Liturgy Training Publications, 3949 S Racine Ave, Chicago, IL 60609-2523 *Tel:* 773-579-4900 *Toll Free Tel:* 800-933-1800 (orders) *Fax:* 773-579-4929 *E-mail:* orders@ltp.org *Web Site:* www.ltp.org, pg 923

Compton, Mike, Supercircuits, 11000 N Mopac Expwy, Bldg 300, Austin, TX 78759 *Toll Free Tel:* 877-995-2288 *E-mail:* operations@supercircuits.com; customercare@supercircuits.com *Web Site:* www.supercircuits.com, pg 1029

Comstock, Beth, General Electric Co, 3135 Easton Tpke, Fairfield, CT 06828 *Tel:* 203-373-2211 *Fax:* 203-373-3131 *Web Site:* www.ge.com, pg 877

Comunale, Pat, Tri-Ed, 3625 Cincinnati Ave, Rocklin, CA 95765 *Tel:* 916-543-4000 *Toll Free Tel:* 800-366-4472 *Fax:* 916-543-4020 *E-mail:* info@northernvideo.com *Web Site:* www.tri-ed.com, pg 1044

Conahan, Jolie, Brodart Co, 500 Arch St, Williamsport, PA 17701 *Tel:* 570-769-3265 *Toll Free Tel:* 888-820-4377 *Toll Free Fax:* 800-283-6087 *E-mail:* supplies.customerservice@brodart.com *Web Site:* www.shopbrodart.com, pg 813

Conant, Vic, Nightingale-Conant Corp, 1400 S Wolf Rd, Bldg 300, Suite 103, Wheeling, IL 60090 *Toll Free Tel:* 800-557-1660 (sales); 800-560-6081 (cust serv) *E-mail:* customerservice@nightingale.com *Web Site:* www.nightingale.com, pg 957

Condiotti, Steve, DTC Lighting & Grip, 1280 65 St, Emeryville, CA 94608 *Tel:* 510-595-0770 *Toll Free Tel:* 877-382-3456 *Fax:* 510-595-0772 *E-mail:* sales@dtcgrip.com; rentals@dtcgrip.com *Web Site:* www.dtcgrip.com, pg 853

Condon, Erica, Jointure for Community Adult Education Inc, Centre at Raritan, Suite B-11, 1124 US Hwy 202 S, Raritan, NJ 08869 *Tel:* 908-722-0233; 908-874-4852 *Fax:* 908-722-0388 *E-mail:* jcaeinc@aol.com *Web Site:* www.jointure.org, pg 906

Condon, Lindsay, Caption Colorado LLC, 5690 DTC Blvd, Suite 500W, Greenwood Village, CO 80111 *Tel:* 720-489-5662 *Toll Free Tel:* 800-775-7838 *Fax:* 720-489-5664 *Web Site:* www.captioncolorado.com, pg 820

Cone, Robert, Rockland Colloid LLC, PO Box 3120, Oregon City, OR 97045-0306 *Tel:* 503-655-4152 (sales); 914-413-3000 (tech) *Toll Free Fax:* 866-737-0174 *E-mail:* info@rockaloid.com; orders@rockaloid.com *Web Site:* www.rockaloid.com, pg 998

Coneys, Ray, Crestron Electronics Inc, 15 Volvo Dr, Rockleigh, NJ 07647 *Tel:* 201-767-3400 *Toll Free Tel:* 800-237-2041 *Fax:* 201-767-1903 *E-mail:* crestronhq@crestron.com *Web Site:* www.crestron.com, pg 839

Coningsby, A Robert III, Apex Machine Co, 3000 NE 12 Terr, Fort Lauderdale, FL 33334 *Tel:* 954-566-1572 *Fax:* 954-563-2844 *E-mail:* email@apexmachine.com *Web Site:* www.apexmachine.com, pg 788

Coningsby, Todd, Apex Machine Co, 3000 NE 12 Terr, Fort Lauderdale, FL 33334 *Tel:* 954-566-1572 *Fax:* 954-563-2844 *E-mail:* email@apexmachine.com *Web Site:* www.apexmachine.com, pg 788

Conley, Tim, Extreme Reach Inc, 75 Second Ave, Suite 720, Needham, MA 02494 *Tel:* 781-577-2016 *E-mail:* sales@extremereach.com; press@extremereach.com *Web Site:* www.extremereach.com, pg 864

Conly, Paul, Conly Productions, 1563 Oneida St, Denver, CO 80220 *Tel:* 303-393-6240 *Fax:* 303-393-6240, pg 835

Connaughton, Thomas, Resource Development Co LLC, 280 Daines St, Suite 200, Birmingham, MI 48009 *Tel:* 248-646-2300 *Toll Free Tel:* 800-360-7222 *Fax:* 248-646-0789 *E-mail:* inquiries@resourcedev.com *Web Site:* www.resourcedev.com, pg 995

Connell, Nick, Transtar Entertainment Co Inc, 10650 E Bethany Dr, Suite E, Aurora, CO 80014 *Tel:* 303-695-4207 *Web Site:* www.transtarfilm.com, pg 1043

Connell, William J, Concept Associates Inc, 5371 Punta Alta, Unit 1-E, Laguna Woods, CA 92637 *Toll Free Tel:* 800-333-8252 *E-mail:* customerservice@preschoolpower.com *Web Site:* www.preschoolpower.com, pg 834

Connelly, Margaret, Tecplot Inc, 3535 Factoria Blvd SE, Suite 550, Bellevue, WA 98006 *Tel:* 425-653-1200; 425-653-9393 (tech support) *Toll Free Tel:* 800-763-7005 (orders) *E-mail:* info@tecplot.com; sales@tecplot.com *Web Site:* www.tecplot.com, pg 1035

Connelly, Maureen, Palace Digital Studios, 29 N Main St, South Norwalk, CT 06854 *Tel:* 203-853-1740 *Fax:* 203-855-9608 *Web Site:* www.palacedigital.com, pg 968

Connelly, Michael P, Uniconn Productions, 8485 Valley Circle Blvd, Suite 203, West Hills, CA 91304 *Tel:* 818-887-9108 *Fax:* 818-348-6544 *E-mail:* measeburl@aol.com *Web Site:* www.uniconnproductions.com, pg 1048

Connelly, Shawn, WFRV-TV 5 CBS, 1181 E Mason St, Green Bay, WI 54301 *Tel:* 920-437-5411 *Fax:* 920-437-4576 *E-mail:* mailbox@wfrv.com *Web Site:* www.wfrv.com, pg 1064

Conner, Saundra, Cinevision Corp, 3300 Northeast Expwy NE, Bldg 2-A, Atlanta, GA 30341 *Tel:* 770-455-8988 *Fax:* 770-455-4066 *E-mail:* cvcorp@bellsouth.net, pg 828

Conners, Molly, Worldview Entertainment Holdings Inc, 1384 Broadway, 25th fl, New York, NY 10018 *Tel:* 212-431-3090 *Fax:* 212-431-0390 *E-mail:* info@worldviewent.com *Web Site:* www.worldviewent.com, pg 1070

Connolly, Doug, Canamedia Inc, 1540 Cornwall Rd, Suite 216, Oakville, ON L6J 7W5, Canada *Tel:* 416-363-6765 *Toll Free Tel:* 866-999-5292 *Fax:* 416-363-7834 *Web Site:* www.canamedia.com, pg 818

Connolly, Patt, Saturn Studios, PO Box 3687, Hollywood, CA 90078-3687 *Tel:* 323-871-4134 *Web Site:* rollingplanet.com, pg 1003

Connolly, Steve, McNabb & Connolly, 60 Briarwood Ave, Mississauga, ON L5G 3N6, Canada *Tel:* 905-278-0566 *Toll Free Tel:* 866-722-1522 *Fax:* 905-278-2801 *Toll Free Fax:* 866-722-1822 *E-mail:* info@mcnabbconnolly.ca *Web Site:* www.mcnabbconnolly.ca, pg 935

Connolly, Steve, Weston Woods Canada, 60 Briarwood Ave, Mississauga, ON L5G 3N6, Canada *Tel:* 905-278-0566 *Toll Free Tel:* 866-722-1522 *Fax:* 905-278-2801 *Toll Free Fax:* 866-722-1822 *E-mail:* info@mcnabbconnolly.ca *Web Site:* www.mcnabbconnolly.ca, pg 1064

Connor, Donald, The American Classical League, Miami University, 422 Wells Mill Dr, Oxford, OH 45056 *Tel:* 513-529-7741 *Fax:* 513-529-7742 *E-mail:* info@aclclassics.org *Web Site:* www.aclclassics.org, pg 784

Connors, Fred Jr, The Troupe, 3 Industrial Dr, Windham, NH 03087 *Tel:* 603-893-4554 *Fax:* 603-893-9717 *E-mail:* info@thetroupe.com *Web Site:* www.thetroupe.com, pg 1045

Connors, John, The Troupe, 3 Industrial Dr, Windham, NH 03087 *Tel:* 603-893-4554 *Fax:* 603-893-9717 *E-mail:* info@thetroupe.com *Web Site:* www.thetroupe.com, pg 1045

Conover, Christopher, Arizona Public Media, 1423 E University, MLB67, Rm 223, Tucson, AZ 85719 *Tel:* 520-621-5828; 520-621-5836 (sales) *Fax:* 520-621-3360 *Web Site:* www.azpm.org, pg 790

Conover, Paul, IAC Acoustics, 1160 Commerce Ave, Bronx, NY 10462 *Tel:* 718-931-8000 *Fax:* 718-863-1138 *E-mail:* newyork@iac-acoustics.com *Web Site:* www.iac-acoustics.com/us, pg 893

Conrad, Matt, Multicom Inc, 1076 Florida Central Pkwy, Longwood, FL 32750 *Tel:* 407-331-7779 *Toll Free Tel:* 800-423-2594 *Fax:* 407-339-0204 *E-mail:* multicom@multicominc.com *Web Site:* www.multicominc.com, pg 949

Conroy, Ann, Small World Productions Inc, 140 Lakeside Ave, Suite 200, Seattle, WA 98122 *Tel:* 206-329-7167 *Toll Free Tel:* 800-866-7425 (orders) *E-mail:* info@travelsmallworld.com *Web Site:* www.smarttravels.tv, pg 1013

Conroy, Ted, Dadco, 11078 Fleetwood St, Sun Valley, CA 91352 *Tel:* 818-7768-8886 *Fax:* 818-765-0914 *Web Site:* www.dadcopowerandlights.com, pg 842

Considine, Rachelle, Future US Inc, 4000 Shoreline Ct, Suite 400, South San Francisco, CA 94080 *Tel:* 650-872-1642 *Fax:* 650-872-2207 *Web Site:* www.futureus.com, pg 874

Consiglio, Peter, HBO Studio Productions, 120-A E 23 St, New York, NY 10010 *Tel:* 212-512-7800 *E-mail:* hsp@hsptv.com *Web Site:* www.hbo.com, pg 886

Consolo, Steve, Hubbell Wiring Device-Kellems, 40 Waterview Dr, Shelton, CT 06484 *Tel:* 475-882-4800 *Toll Free Tel:* 800-288-6000 (cust serv) *Fax:* 475-882-4849 *Toll Free Fax:* 800-255-1031 (cust serv) *E-mail:* techserv@hubbell.com *Web Site:* www.hubbell-wiring.com, pg 892

Constance, Lisa, StoryTrack, 212 S Bemiston, St Louis, MO 63105 *Tel:* 314-725-3003 *Web Site:* www.storytrack.com, pg 1025

Constantinau, Walea L, Honolulu Film Office, 530 S King St, Rm 306, Honolulu, HI 96813 *Tel:* 808-768-6108 *Fax:* 808-768-6102 *E-mail:* info@filmhonolulu.com *Web Site:* www.filmhonolulu.com, pg 1097

Constantine, John Jr, CELCO-Constantine Engineering Labs Co, 14 Industrial Ave, Suite 3, Mahwah, NJ 07430 *Tel:* 201-327-1123 *Fax:* 201-327-7047 *E-mail:* info@celco-nj.com *Web Site:* www.celco.com; www.celco-nj.com, pg 822

Contrata, Curt, Stage Equipment & Lighting Inc, 4600 SW 36 St, Orlando, FL 32811 *Tel:* 407-425-2010 *Fax:* 407-648-2604 *E-mail:* mail@seal-fla.com *Web Site:* www.seal-fla.com, pg 1022

Contreras, Carlos, The Kitchen, 4119 W Burbank Blvd, Burbank, CA 91505 *Tel:* 818-306-5300 *Fax:* 305-415-6201 *E-mail:* info@thekitchen.tv *Web Site:* www.thekitchen.tv, pg 911

Contreras, Renee, Band Pro Film & Digital Inc, 3403 W Pacific Ave, Burbank, CA 91505 *Tel:* 818-841-9655 *Toll Free Tel:* 888-BANDPRO (226-3776) *Fax:* 818-841-7649 *Web Site:* www.bandpro.com, pg 802

Conway, Alan, Waldom Electronics Corp, 1801 Morgan St, Rockford, IL 61102-2690 *Tel:* 815-968-9661 *Toll Free Tel:* 800-435-2931 (cust serv) *Fax:* 815-968-9029 *E-mail:* sales@waldom.com; corp@waldom.com *Web Site:* www.waldom.com, pg 1061

Conway, Jack, Duray Lighting, 500 E Touhy Ave, Suite F, Des Plaines, IL 60018 *Tel:* 773-271-2800 *Fax:* 773-271-4410 *E-mail:* info@duraylighting.com; sales@duraylighting.com *Web Site:* www.duraylighting.com, pg 854

Conwell, Dean, Beaumont Convention & Visitors Bureau, 505 Willow St, Beaumont, TX 77701 *Tel:* 409-880-3749 *Toll Free Tel:* 800-392-4401 *Fax:* 409-880-3750 *Web Site:* www.beaumontcvb.com, pg 1102

Cook, Brad, Fuller Street Productions, 10702 Hathaway Dr, No 2, Santa Fe Springs, CA 90670 *Toll Free Tel:* 877-637-8733 *Toll Free Fax:* 877-637-8733 *E-mail:* contact@fullerstreet.com *Web Site:* www.fullerstreet.com, pg 874

Cook, Doug, SYMCO Inc, 29 Poplar Dr, Stirling, NJ 07980 *Tel:* 908-647-6262 *Fax:* 908-647-4904 *E-mail:* orders@symcoinc.com *Web Site:* www.symcoinc.com, pg 1030

Cook, Dwight, Sound Works, 7110 Gary St, Houston, TX 77055 *Tel:* 713-960-8222 (ext 1) *Fax:* 713-960-0122 *E-mail:* w3@soundworks.com; sworks@soundworks.com *Web Site:* www.soundworks.com, pg 1018

Cook, Howard, Sound & Vision Media, 372 Squire Rd, Revere, MA 02151 *Tel:* 781-284-9707 *Web Site:* www.soundandvisionmedia.com, pg 1017

Cook, Kim, Trafalgar Square Books, 388 Howe Hill Rd, North Pomfret, VT 05053 *Tel:* 802-457-1911 *Toll Free Tel:* 800-423-4525 *Fax:* 802-457-1913 *E-mail:* info@horseandriderbooks.com *Web Site:* www.horseandriderbooks.com, pg 1043

Cook, Martha, Trafalgar Square Books, 388 Howe Hill Rd, North Pomfret, VT 05053 *Tel:* 802-457-1911 *Toll Free Tel:* 800-423-4525 *Fax:* 802-457-1913 *E-mail:* info@horseandriderbooks.com *Web Site:* www.horseandriderbooks.com, pg 1043

Cook, Peter M, Juice Goose, 7320 Ashcroft, Suite 104, Houston, TX 77081 *Tel:* 713-772-1404 *Fax:* 713-772-7360 *E-mail:* info@juicegoose.com *Web Site:* www.juicegoose.com, pg 906

Cook, Phillip, Eagle Films, 2806 Cameron Rd, Falls Church, VA 22042-2004 *Tel:* 703-237-8160 *Web Site:* www.eaglefilms.com, pg 855

Cook, Roger, Educational Video Group Inc, 291 Southwind Way, Greenwood, IN 46142-9190 *Tel:* 317-889-8253 *Fax:* 317-888-5857 *E-mail:* service@evgonline.com *Web Site:* www.evgonline.com, pg 857

Cook, Terry, Visit Topeka Inc, 618 S Kansas Ave, Topeka, KS 66603 *Tel:* 785-234-1030 *Toll Free Tel:* 800-235-1030 *Fax:* 785-234-8282 *E-mail:* info@visittopeka.com *Web Site:* www.visittopeka.com, pg 1098

Cook, Thorsten, Video Automation Systems Inc, 13 Arrow Meadow Rd, New Fairfield, CT 06812 *Tel:* 203-312-0152 *Fax:* 203-312-0157 *Web Site:* www.videoautomation.com/videoautomation.html, pg 1054

Cook, Timothy D, Apple Inc, One Infinite Loop, Cupertino, CA 95014 *Tel:* 408-996-1010 *Web Site:* www.apple.com, pg 788

Cook, Wayne, Winsted Corp, 10901 Hampshire Ave S, Minneapolis, MN 55438 *Tel:* 952-944-9050 *Toll Free Tel:* 800-447-2257 *Fax:* 952-944-1546 *Toll Free Fax:* 800-421-3839 *E-mail:* info@winsted.com *Web Site:* www.winsted.com, pg 1068

Coombes, Brian, Rocking Horse Studio, 1380 Upper City Rd, Pittsfield, NH 03263 *Tel:* 603-512-5347 *E-mail:* info@rockinghorsestudio.com *Web Site:* www.rockinghorsestudio.com, pg 998

Coon, Greg, Eyecon Video Productions, 1865 Summit Ave, Suite 605, Plano, TX 75074 *Tel:* 972-881-3200 *Toll Free Tel:* 877-704-1517 *E-mail:* info@eyeconvideo.com *Web Site:* www.eyeconvideo.com, pg 865

Cooney, Chris, EUE/Screen Gems Studios, 1223 N 23 St, Wilmington, NC 28405 *Tel:* 910-343-3500 *Fax:* 910-343-3574 *E-mail:* info@euescreengems.com *Web Site:* euescreengems.com, pg 863

Cooper, Alana, Monroe-West Monroe Convention & Visitors Bureau, 601 Constitution Dr, West Monroe, LA 71292 *Tel:* 318-387-5691 *Toll Free Tel:* 800-843-1872 *Fax:* 318-324-1752 *E-mail:* mwmcvb@monroe-westmonroe.org *Web Site:* www.monroe-westmonroe.org, pg 1098

Cooper, Janita, Master Video Disc & Design, 7349 N Via Paseo del Sur, Suite 515-455, Scottsdale, AZ 85238 *Tel:* 480-948-0305 *Fax:* 480-948-8628 *Web Site:* www.mastervdd.com, pg 933

Cooper, Jason, Horizon Video Productions Inc, 6114 Fayetteville St, Suite 106, Durham, NC 27713 *Tel:* 919-941-0901 *Toll Free Tel:* 800-768-3776 *Fax:* 919-941-1939 *E-mail:* info@horizonvp.com *Web Site:* www.horizonvp.com, pg 891

Cooper, Jeff, Synergy Group Inc, 23930 Craftsman Rd, Calabasas, CA 91302-1437 *Tel:* 818-223-9009 *Fax:* 818-223-8999 *Web Site:* www.jeffcooper.com, pg 1030

Cooper, John, Sundance Film Festival, 1825 Three Kings Dr, Park City, UT 84060 *Tel:* 435-658-3456 *Fax:* 435-658-3457 *E-mail:* customerservice@sundance.org; press@sundance.org; institute@sundance.org *Web Site:* www.sundance.org/festival/, pg 1128

Cooper, Mark, Precision Camera & Video, 2438 W Anderson Lane, Suite B-4, Austin, TX 78757 *Tel:* 512-467-7676 *Toll Free Tel:* 800-677-1023 *Fax:* 512-467-0607 *Web Site:* www.precision-camera.com, pg 980

Cooper, Mike, Kentucky Film Office, 2200 Capital Plaza Tower, 500 Mero St, Frankfort, KY 40601 *Tel:* 502-564-3456 *Toll Free Tel:* 800-345-6591 *Fax:* 502-564-5695 *E-mail:* kentucky.filmoffice@ky.gov *Web Site:* filmoffice.ky.gov, pg 1098

Cooper, Phillip, Encore Productions Inc, 5150 S Decatur Blvd, Las Vegas, NV 89119 *Tel:* 702-739-8803 *Toll Free Tel:* 800-287-7469 *Fax:* 702-739-8831 *Web Site:* www.encore-us.com, pg 861

Cooper, Russell, JaffeHolden, 114-A Washington St, Norwalk, CT 06854 *Tel:* 203-838-4167 *Fax:* 203-838-4168 *Web Site:* www.jaffeholden.com, pg 903

Copeland, Alex, Auratron Systems, 3716 N Broadway, Knoxville, TN 37917-3120 *Tel:* 865-687-6060; 865-687-6006 *Fax:* 865-687-6020 *Web Site:* www.auratronsystems.com, pg 797

Copes, Brad, Audience Response Systems Inc, 5611-C E Morgan Ave, Evansville, IN 47715 *Tel:* 812-479-7507 *Toll Free Tel:* 800-INVOLVE (468-6583) *Fax:* 812-479-1057 *Web Site:* www.audienceresponse.com, pg 794

Coradeschi, Andy, Straight Shoot'r Cranes Inc, 18434 Oxnard St, Unit H, Tarzana, CA 91356 *Tel:* 818-609-8310 *Fax:* 818-609-8311 *Web Site:* www.straightshootr.com, pg 1025

Corbert, Jeanine, Brooklyn College Television Center, Whitehead Hall, 2900 Bedford Ave, Rm 018-A, Brooklyn, NY 11210-2889 *Tel:* 718-951-5585 *Fax:* 718-951-5558 *Web Site:* www.bctvr.org/tvcenter_base.php, pg 814

Corbett, Thomas, Charles M Salter Associates Inc, 130 Sutter St, Suite 500, San Francisco, CA 94104 *Tel:* 415-397-0442 *Fax:* 415-397-0454 *E-mail:* info@cmsalter.com *Web Site:* www.cmsalter.com, pg 1002

Corbitt, Tom, SNL Kagan Media & Communications, One SNL Plaza, 212 Seventh St NE, Charlottesville, VA 22902 *Tel:* 434-977-1600 *Toll Free Tel:* 866-296-3743 *Fax:* 434-977-4466 *E-mail:* snlkagansales@snl.com *Web Site:* www.snl.com, pg 1014

Corcoran, Jeanne, Sarasota County Film & Entertainment Office, 1680 Fruitville Rd, Suite 402, Sarasota, FL 34236 *Tel:* 941-309-1200 *Fax:* 941-309-1209 *E-mail:* info@filmsarasota.com *Web Site:* www.filmsarasota.com, pg 1096

Cordell, Bill, NewWave Technologies Inc, 4635 Wedgewood Blvd, Suite 107, Frederick, MD 21703 *Tel:* 301-624-5300 *Toll Free Tel:* 800-536-5222 *Fax:* 301-948-5883 (sales & serv); 301-668-7808 (acctg, opers & mktg) *E-mail:* sales@newwavetech.com; custsupport@newwavetech.com *Web Site:* www.newwavetech.com, pg 957

Cordova, Jeanne, Universal Studios, 100 Universal City Plaza, Universal City, CA 91608-1002 *Toll Free Tel:* 800-892-1979 *Fax:* 818-866-3600 *E-mail:* studio.operations2@nbcuni.com *Web Site:* www.filmmakersdestination.com; www.nbcuni.com, pg 1049

Cordova, Monica, SouthWest Organizing Project (SWOP), 211 Tenth St SW, Albuquerque, NM 87102-2919 *Tel:* 505-247-8832 *Fax:* 505-247-9972 *E-mail:* swop@swop.net *Web Site:* www.swop.net, pg 1019

Core, Jerry Del, Fox 40 KTXL TV, 4655 Fruitridge Rd, Sacramento, CA 95820 *Tel:* 916-454-4422 *Fax:* 916-739-8139 *Web Site:* www.fox40.com, pg 872

Corech, Henry, Photodyne Technologies, 8531 Alcott St, Suite 201, Los Angeles, CA 90035 *Tel:* 310-497-0968 *Toll Free Tel:* 800-660-2147 *Fax:* 310-652-2820 *E-mail:* info@photodyne.com *Web Site:* www.photodyne.com, pg 974

Coren, Chuck, Arcor Electronics Co, 5689 W Howard St, Niles, IL 60714 *Tel:* 847-588-0088 *Fax:* 847-588-0080 *E-mail:* sales@arcorelectronics.com *Web Site:* www.arcorelectronics.com, pg 789

Cornelius, Scott, Image Audiovisuals, 2130 S Dahlia St, Denver, CO 80222 *Tel:* 303-758-1818 *Toll Free Tel:* 800-818-1857 *Fax:* 303-758-5722 *E-mail:* commercialsales@imageav.com *Web Site:* www.imageav.com, pg 894

Cornell, Carl, Whirlwind Music Distributors Inc, 99 Ling Rd, Rochester, NY 14612 *Tel:* 585-663-8820 *Toll Free Tel:* 800-733-9473 (US only) *Fax:* 585-865-8930 *E-mail:* sales@whirlwindusa.com; techsupport@whirlwindusa.com; darylg@whirlwindusa.com (Canadian inquiries) *Web Site:* whirlwindusa.com, pg 1065

Cornelsen, Doug, Thomas Reprographics, 801 Second Ave N, Minneapolis, MN 55405 *Tel:* 612-374-1120 *Toll Free Tel:* 800-328-7154 *Fax:* 612-374-1129 *E-mail:* orders501@thomasrepro.com *Web Site:* thomasrepro.com, pg 1039

Cornette, Angie, The Cutting Corp, 4940 Hampden Lane, Suite 300, Bethesda, MD 20814 *Tel:* 301-654-CUTS (654-2887) *Fax:* 301-654-3271 *E-mail:* info@cuttingarchives.com *Web Site:* www.cuttingarchives.com, pg 841

Corsello, Charles P, The Video Messenger Co, 862 Judson Place, Stratford, CT 06615 *Tel:* 203-358-8842 *Toll Free Tel:* 800-800-7128 *Fax:* 203-547-6216 *E-mail:* vmc@videomessenger.com *Web Site:* www.videomessenger.com, pg 1055

Corsette, Kelly, City of Scottsdale, 3939 N Drinkwater Blvd, Scottsdale, AZ 85251 *Tel:* 480-312-2550; 480-312-3111; 480-312-2500 (permit servs) *Fax:* 480-312-2888 *Web Site:* www.scottsdaleaz.gov, pg 1091

Cort, Harvey, Dyer-Bennet Records, 792 Columbus Ave, Rm 16-0, New York, NY 10025 *Tel:* 212-866-3675, pg 854

Cort, Susan, JPL, 471 JPL Wick Dr, Harrisburg, PA 17111-2504 *Tel:* 717-558-8048 *Toll Free Tel:* 800-421-7697 *Fax:* 717-558-8349 *E-mail:* jpl@jplcreative.com *Web Site:* www.jplcreative.com; www.facebook.com/jplcreative, pg 906

Corvan, Jimmy, House of Moves, 5419 McConnell Ave, Los Angeles, CA 90066-7027 *Tel:* 310-306-6131 *E-mail:* info@moves.com *Web Site:* www.moves.com, pg 891

Cosgray, Craig, Marengo Films, 27206 Waterfall Hill Pkwy, Spicewood, TX 78669 *Tel:* 972-365-0406 *Fax:* 830-693-0949 *E-mail:* marengodvd@texasdata.net *Web Site:* www.marengofilms.com, pg 931

Cosgrove, Tracey, Rosco Laboratories Inc, 52 Harbor View, Stamford, CT 06902 *Tel:* 203-708-8900 *Toll Free Tel:* 800-ROSCO NY (767-2669) *Fax:* 203-708-8919 *E-mail:* info@rosco.com *Web Site:* www.rosco.com, pg 999

Costa, Maria, Cleveland Costume & Display Corp, 18489 Pearl Rd, Strongsville, OH 44136 *Tel:* 440-846-9292 *E-mail:* info@clevelandcostume.com *Web Site:* www.clevelandcostume.com, pg 830

Costantini, Joe, Two Animators LLP, PO Box 3174, Mercerville, NJ 08619 *Tel:* 609-532-6138 *E-mail:* cartoons@twoanimators.com *Web Site:* www.twoanimators.com, pg 1047

Costantini, Tom, Two Animators LLP, PO Box 3174, Mercerville, NJ 08619 *Tel:* 609-532-6138 *E-mail:* cartoons@twoanimators.com *Web Site:* www.twoanimators.com, pg 1047

Costantino, Gary, Air Sea Land Productions Inc (ASL), 19-69 Steinway St, Astoria, NY 11105-1108 *Tel:* 718-626-2646 *Toll Free Tel:* 888-ASL-LENS (275-5367) *Fax:* 718-626-1493 *E-mail:* sales@airsealand.com *Web Site:* www.airsealand.com, pg 779

Costanzo, Chad, Pyxis Industries Inc, 25695 Jefferson Ave, Suite 8, Murrieta, CA 92562 *Tel:* 951-526-1999 *Toll Free Tel:* 888-799-4728 *Fax:* 951-253-9290 *Web Site:* pyxisindustries.com, pg 988

Costanzo, Kelly, Pyxis Industries Inc, 25695 Jefferson Ave, Suite 8, Murrieta, CA 92562 *Tel:* 951-526-1999 *Toll Free Tel:* 888-799-4728 *Fax:* 951-253-9290 *Web Site:* pyxisindustries.com, pg 988

Cote, Bill, BC Video Inc, 152 W 25 St, 2nd fl, New York, NY 10001 *Tel:* 212-242-4065 *Toll Free Tel:* 800-846-9682 *Fax:* 212-242-4190 *Web Site:* www.bcvideo.com, pg 803

Cote, David H, Young Minds Inc, 1014 E Cooley Dr, Suite H, Colton, CA 92324 *Tel:* 909-426-4860 *Fax:* 909-426-4866 *E-mail:* info@ymi.com; sales@ymi.com *Web Site:* www.ymi.com, pg 1072

Cott, George, Eagle Photographics & Digital Imaging Inc, 3612 W Swann Ave, Tampa, FL 33609 *Tel:* 813-870-2495 *Fax:* 813-876-5093 *Web Site:* www.eaglefineartimaging.com, pg 855

Cottengim, Van, Aztec Video Productions, 2967 Montana Ave, Cincinnati, OH 45211 *Tel:* 513-481-5004 *E-mail:* aztec@fuse.net *Web Site:* www.aztecvideo.com, pg 801

Cotterell, Bob, Creative Sound Corp, 5515 Medea Valley Dr, Agoura Hills, CA 91301 *Tel:* 818-707-8986 *E-mail:* info@csoundcorp.com *Web Site:* www.csoundcorp.com, pg 838

Cottle, Karen, Adobe Systems Inc, 345 Park Ave, San Jose, CA 95110-2704 *Tel:* 408-536-6000 *Fax:* 408-537-6000 *Web Site:* www.adobe.com, pg 776

Cottrell, Ada, AM Stock-Cameo Film Library, 1663 Sawtelle Blvd, Suite 305, Los Angeles, CA 90025 *Tel:* 310-479-4800 *Fax:* 310-933-6979 *E-mail:* researcher@amstockcameo.com *Web Site:* www.amstockcameo.com, pg 783

Couris, George, The Pepper Group, 220 N Smith St, Suite 406, Palatine, IL 60067 *Tel:* 847-963-0333 *Fax:* 847-963-0888 *E-mail:* pepper@peppergroup.com *Web Site:* www.peppergroup.com, pg 973

Courter, Gay, Courter Films LLC, 121 NW Crystal St, Crystal River, FL 34428 *Tel:* 352-795-2156 *Fax:* 352-795-6144 *E-mail:* info@courterfilms.com *Web Site:* www.courterfilms.com, pg 837

Courter, Philip R, Courter Films LLC, 121 NW Crystal St, Crystal River, FL 34428 *Tel:* 352-795-2156 *Fax:* 352-795-6144 *E-mail:* info@courterfilms.com *Web Site:* www.courterfilms.com, pg 837

Cousineau, Corey D, Drastic Technologies Ltd, 523 The Queensway, Suite 102, Toronto, ON M8Y 1J7, Canada *Tel:* 416-255-5636 *Fax:* 416-255-8780 *Web Site:* www.drastic.tv, pg 852

Couyoumjian, Karl, TeL Systems, 7235 Jackson Rd, Ann Arbor, MI 48103 *Tel:* 734-761-4506 *Toll Free Tel:* 800-686-7235 *Fax:* 734-761-9776 *E-mail:* sales@telsystemsusa.com *Web Site:* www.telsystemsusa.com, pg 1035

Covert, Jeff, Wally Cleaver's Recording Service, 2200 Airport Ave, Fredericksburg, VA 22401-7220 *Tel:* 540-373-6511 *Fax:* 540-370-0645 *E-mail:* wallycleavers@mac.com *Web Site:* www.facebook.com/wallycleavers, pg 830

Cowan, Deborah A, National Public Radio (NPR), 1111 N Capitol St NE, Washington, DC 20002 *Tel:* 202-513-2000 *Web Site:* www.npr.org, pg 1086

Cowan, Mark, Spoken Language Services Inc, PO Box 17113, Urbana, IL 61803 *Tel:* 217-328-0173 *Fax:* 217-328-0177 *E-mail:* orders@spokenlanguage.com, pg 1021

Cowart, Cooper, Dot Hill Systems Corp, 1351 S Sunset St, Longmont, CO 80501-6533 *Tel:* 303-845-3200 *Toll Free Tel:* 800-872-2783 *Fax:* 303-845-3655 *E-mail:* support@dothill.com; websales@dothill.com *Web Site:* www.dothill.com, pg 851

Cowart, Janice, RM Films International, PO Box 3748, Hollywood, CA 90078-3748 *Tel:* 323-466-7791 *Fax:* 323-461-4152 *E-mail:* rmf@rmfilms.com *Web Site:* www.rmfilms.com; www.russmeyer.com, pg 997

Cowell, Bill, Buffalo Niagara Film Festival (BNFF), 3840 E Robinson Rd, Suite 166, Amherst, NY 14228 *Tel:* 716-432-1065 *E-mail:* info@buffaloniagarafilmfestival.com *Web Site:* thebnff.com, pg 1110

Cox, Brian, Audio & Light, 2209 Randleman Rd, Greensboro, NC 27406 *Tel:* 336-274-1234 *Fax:* 336-274-4022 *E-mail:* info@audio-light.com *Web Site:* www.audio-light.com, pg 794

Cox, Cheryl, The Whitlock Group, 12820 West Creek Pkwy, Richmond, VA 23238 *Tel:* 804-273-9100 *Toll Free Tel:* 800-726-9843 *Fax:* 804-273-9380 *E-mail:* information@whitlock.com *Web Site:* www.whitlock.com, pg 1065

Cox, David B, Micro Technology Unlimited, PO Box 80124, Raleigh, NC 27623 *Tel:* 919-870-0344 *Web Site:* www.mtu.com, pg 941

Cox, Don, FMP Media Solutions Inc, 1010 Spring Mill Ave, Suite 100, Conshohocken, PA 19428 *Tel:* 610-825-4000 *Toll Free Tel:* 800-346-5071 *Fax:* 610-825-4430 *E-mail:* info@fmpmedia.com *Web Site:* www.fmpmedia.com, pg 870

Cox, John, Sacramento Theatrical Lighting Ltd (STL), 950 Richards Blvd, Sacramento, CA 95811 *Tel:* 916-447-3258 *Toll Free Tel:* 800-283-2785 *Fax:* 916-447-5012 *E-mail:* info@stlltd.com *Web Site:* www.stlltd.com, pg 1001

Cox, Nancy, RCI Custom Products, 801 N East St, Suite 2-A, Frederick, MD 21701 *Tel:* 301-620-9130 *Toll Free Tel:* 800-546-4724 *Fax:* 301-620-9103 *Toll Free Fax:* 800-546-6175 *E-mail:* info@rcicustom.com *Web Site:* www.rcicustom.com, pg 992

Cox, Wendy, Da-Lite, 3100 N Detroit St, Warsaw, IN 46582 *Tel:* 574-267-8101 *Toll Free Tel:* 800-622-3737 *Fax:* 574-267-7804 *Toll Free Fax:* 877-325-4832 *E-mail:* info@da-lite.com *Web Site:* www.da-lite.com, pg 842

Coxson, Laura, New York Film/Video Council (NYFVC), PO Box 1685, New York, NY 10185-1685 *Tel:* 212-330-0450 *E-mail:* info@nyfvc.org *Web Site:* www.nyfvc.org, pg 1086

Coyle, Larry, TGA Recording Co, 295 Urbandale Ave, Benton Harbor, MI 49022 *Tel:* 269-926-7581 *Fax:* 269-926-7589 *E-mail:* tgarecording@sbcglobal.net *Web Site:* www.tgarecording.com, pg 1038

Coyne, Lauren, Communication Arts Design & Advertising Competition, 110 Constitution Dr, Menlo Park, CA 94025-1107 *Tel:* 650-326-6040 *Fax:* 650-326-1648 *E-mail:* competition@commarts.com *Web Site:* www.commarts.com, pg 1113

Crabtree, Tamara, Abingdon Press, 201 Eighth Ave S, Nashville, TN 37203 *Tel:* 615-749-6000 *Toll Free Tel:* 800-251-3320 *Fax:* 615-749-6061 *E-mail:* orders@abingdonpress.com *Web Site:* www.abingdonpress.com, pg 772

Crabtree-Ireland, Duncan, Screen Actors Guild & American Federation of Television & Radio Artists (SAG-AFTRA), 5757 Wilshire Blvd, 7th fl, Los Angeles, CA 90036-3600 *Tel:* 323-954-1600 (former SAG); 323-634-8100 (former AFTRA) *Toll Free Tel:* 855-SAG-AFTRA (724-2387) *Fax:* 323-634-8194 *E-mail:* sagaftrainfo@sagaftra.org *Web Site:* www.sagaftra.org/ny, pg 1088

Craig, Lissa, City of Calgary Film Commission, 731 First St SE, Calgary, AB T2G 2G9, Canada *Tel:* 403-221-7831 *Toll Free Tel:* 888-222-5855 *Fax:* 403-221-7828 *Web Site:* www.calgaryeconomicdevelopment.com, pg 1104

Craigie, Kim, Vincent Lighting Systems, 6161 Cochran Rd, Suite D, Solon, OH 44139 *Tel:* 216-475-7600 *Toll Free Tel:* 800-922-5356 *Fax:* 216-475-6376 *E-mail:* info@vls.com *Web Site:* www.vincentlighting.com, pg 1058

Cram, Bestor, Northern Light Productions, 300 Western Ave, 2nd fl, Boston, MA 02134 *Tel:* 617-789-4344 *Fax:* 617-789-4744 *E-mail:* info@nlprod.com *Web Site:* www.nlprod.com, pg 959

Cramer, Carl, WoodenBoat Publications, 41 WoodenBoat Lane, Brooklin, ME 04616 *Tel:* 207-359-4651 *Toll Free Tel:* 800-877-5284 (subns); 800-487-2084 (subns) *Fax:* 207-359-8920; 818-487-4550 (subns) *E-mail:* woodenboat@woodenboat.com *Web Site:* www.woodenboat.com, pg 1069

Crandall, Richard, Optronics®, 175 Cremona Dr, Goleta, CA 93117 *Tel:* 805-968-3568 *Toll Free Tel:* 800-796-8909 *Fax:* 805-968-0933 *E-mail:* oeinfo@optronics.com *Web Site:* www.optronics.com, pg 965

Crane, Bo, Pandisc Music Corp, 247 SW Eighth St, Suite 349, Miami, FL 33130 *Tel:* 305-557-1914 *Toll Free Fax:* 888-493-7778 *Web Site:* www.pandisc.com, pg 968

Crane, Christopher, Arkansas Film Commission, 900 W Capitol Ave, Suite 400, Little Rock, AR 72201 *Tel:* 501-682-7676 *Fax:* 501-682-7394 *Web Site:* www.arkansasproduction.com, pg 1092

Craton, Robert, Advanced Sound, 4611 Central Ave Pike, Suite F, Knoxville, TN 37912 *Tel:* 865-661-5961 *Fax:* 865-637-6694 *Web Site:* www.advancedsound.com, pg 778

Craven, Michael, Thomas Craven Film Corp, 5 W 19 St, New York, NY 10011-4216 *Tel:* 212-463-7190 *Fax:* 212-627-4761 *E-mail:* info@cravenfilms.com *Web Site:* cravenfilms.com, pg 837

Craven, Mike, Full Scale Effects, 6869 Tujunga Ave, North Hollywood, CA 91605 *Tel:* 818-760-0875; 818-760-0042 *Fax:* 818-760-0876 *Web Site:* fullscalefx.com, pg 874

Craven, Pamela, Avaya Inc, 211 Mount Airy Rd, Basking Ridge, NJ 07920 *Tel:* 908-953-6000 *Toll Free Tel:* 866-GO-AVAYA (462-8292 US & CN) *Web Site:* www.avaya.com, pg 798

Craven, Penny, Thomas Craven Film Corp, 5 W 19 St, New York, NY 10011-4216 *Tel:* 212-463-7190 *Fax:* 212-627-4761 *E-mail:* info@cravenfilms.com *Web Site:* cravenfilms.com, pg 837

Craven, Sally, KTVB-TV, 5407 Fairview Ave, Boise, ID 83706 *Tel:* 208-375-7277 *Toll Free Tel:* 800-559-7277 *Fax:* 208-378-1762; 208-375-7770 (news fax) *E-mail:* info@ktvb.com; ktvbnews@ktvb.com *Web Site:* www.ktvb.com, pg 914

Crawford, James, Frezzi Energy Systems, 7 Valley St, Hawthorne, NJ 07506 *Tel:* 973-427-1160 *Fax:* 973-427-0934 *E-mail:* info@frezzi.com *Web Site:* www.frezzi.com, pg 873

Crawford, Jesse, Crawford Media Services, 6 W Druid Hills Dr NE, Atlanta, GA 30329 *Tel:* 404-876-0333 *Toll Free Tel:* 800-831-8029 *Fax:* 678-536-4912 *Web Site:* www.crawford.com, pg 838

Crawford, Kevin, Frezzi Energy Systems, 7 Valley St, Hawthorne, NJ 07506 *Tel:* 973-427-1160 *Fax:* 973-427-0934 *E-mail:* info@frezzi.com *Web Site:* www.frezzi.com, pg 873

Crawford, Sandra, SpaceCam, 31111 Via Colinas, Suite 202, Westlake Village, CA 91362 *Tel:* 818-889-6060 *Fax:* 818-889-6062 *E-mail:* rentals@spacecam.com *Web Site:* spacecam.com, pg 1019

Crawford, Sandy, Illuminate Studios, 10900 Ventura Blvd, Studio City, CA 90068 *Tel:* 818-769-4500 *Fax:* 818-769-7150 *Web Site:* illuminatehollywood.com, pg 894

Crebo, Ron, The Hollaender Manufacturing Co, 10285 Wayne Ave, Cincinnati, OH 45215 *Tel:* 513-772-8800 *Toll Free Tel:* 800-772-8800 (orders) *Fax:* 513-772-8806 *Web Site:* www.hollaender.com, pg 890

Creighton, Gerry, Bang Pictures, 78 Graterford Rd, Schwenksville, PA 19473 *Tel:* 610-357-1015 *Web Site:* www.bangpictures.com, pg 802

Crenshaw, Randall W, CommScope Inc, 1100 CommScope Place SE, Hickory, NC 28602 *Tel:* 828-324-2200 *Toll Free Tel:* 800-982-1708 *Web Site:* www.commscope.com, pg 832

Crerar, Chris, Metalworks Recording Studios Inc, 3611 Mavis Rd, Mississauga, ON L5C 1T7, Canada *Tel:* 905-279-4000 *Fax:* 905-279-4006 *Web Site:* www.metalworksstudios.com, pg 939

Crescenzo, Tony, Intellidyne LLC, 5203 Leesburg Pike, Suite 400, 2 Skyline Place, Falls Church, VA 22041 *Tel:* 703-575-9715 *Fax:* 703-575-9718 *Web Site:* www.intellidyne-llc.com, pg 899

Crilly, Donna, Paulist Press, 997 Macarthur Blvd, Mahwah, NJ 07430-9990 *Tel:* 201-825-7300 *Toll Free Tel:* 800-218-1903 (orders) *Toll Free Fax:* 800-836-3161 *E-mail:* info@paulistpress.com *Web Site:* www.paulistpress.com, pg 970

Crippen, Fred, Pantomime Pictures Inc, 12144 Riverside Dr, North Hollywood, CA 91607 *Tel:* 818-980-5555, pg 968

Crippen, Julie, Pantomime Pictures Inc, 12144 Riverside Dr, North Hollywood, CA 91607 *Tel:* 818-980-5555, pg 968

Crippen, Matt, Pantomime Pictures Inc, 12144 Riverside Dr, North Hollywood, CA 91607 *Tel:* 818-980-5555, pg 968

Cristie, Art, Radiant Images, 4125 W Jefferson Blvd, Los Angeles, CA 90016 *Tel:* 323-737-1314 *Fax:* 310-861-0163 *E-mail:* info@radiantimages.com *Web Site:* www.radiantimages.com, pg 990

Critelli, Linda Lorence, SESAC Inc, 55 Music Sq E, Nashville, TN 37203 *Tel:* 615-320-0055 *Fax:* 615-963-3527 *Web Site:* www.sesac.com, pg 1088

Crochet, Charlotte, Troxell Communications Inc, 4830 S 38 St, Phoenix, AZ 85040 *Tel:* 602-437-7240 *Toll Free Tel:* 800-578-8858 *Fax:* 602-437-7265 *Toll Free Fax:* 800-589-5939 *Web Site:* www.trox.com, pg 1045

Crocker, Thomas C, Countdown Productions Inc, PO Box 180220, Dallas, TX 75218 *Tel:* 214-321-3233; 214-808-9988 (cell) *Web Site:* www.countdownproductions.com, pg 837

Cronin, Dan, National Boston, 115 Dummer St, Brookline, MA 02446 *Tel:* 617-734-4800 *Fax:* 617-734-6323 *E-mail:* info@nationalboston.com *Web Site:* www.nationalboston.com, pg 952

Cronin, Terry, Melbourne Independent Filmmakers Festival (MIFF), 1399 S Harbor City Blvd, Melbourne, FL 32901 *Tel:* 321-726-1711 *Fax:* 321-726-1715 *Web Site:* www.3boysproductions.com, pg 1119

Cross, Diane, Fanon Courier, 17171 Murphy Ave, Irvine, CA 92614-5915 *Tel:* 949-417-8085 *Toll Free Tel:* 800-345-1354 *Fax:* 949-417-8075 *E-mail:* info@fanon.com *Web Site:* www.fanon.com, pg 865

Crossley, Katera, San Francisco Black Film Festival, PO Box 15490, San Francisco, CA 94115 *Tel:* 415-400-4602 *Fax:* 415-346-9046 *E-mail:* sfbff@sfbff.org *Web Site:* www.sfbff.org, pg 1126

Crotta, Gail, Accelerated Learning Foundation, 118 N Court St, Fairfield, IA 52556 *Tel:* 641-954-5443 *Toll Free Tel:* 800-289-2377 *Fax:* 641-954-5851 *E-mail:* info@gamesforthinkers.org *Web Site:* gamesforthinkers.org, pg 773

Crowell, Lynn, Plank Road Publishing Inc, 11111 W Plank Ct, Wauwatosa, WI 53226 *Tel:* 262-790-5210 *Toll Free Tel:* 800-437-0832 *Fax:* 262-781-8818 *Toll Free Fax:* 888-272-0212 *E-mail:* custsvc@musick8.com *Web Site:* www.musick8.com, pg 976

Crowley, Rick, Intersil Americas LLC, 1001 Murphy Ranch Rd, Milpitas, CA 95035 *Tel:* 408-432-8888 *Toll Free Tel:* 888-INTERSIL (468-3774) *Fax:* 408-434-5351 *Web Site:* www.intersil.com, pg 901

Cruce, Michael, Media Visions Inc, 5875 Old Leeds Rd, Birmingham, AL 35210 *Tel:* 205-324-4600 *Toll Free Tel:* 800-254-0876 *Fax:* 205-324-4688 *Web Site:* www.mediavisions.com, pg 937

Crudo, Richard, American Society of Cinematographers, 1782 N Orange Dr, Hollywood, CA 90028 *Tel:* 323-969-4333 *Toll Free Tel:* 800-448-0145 (US only) *Fax:* 323-882-6391 *E-mail:* office@theasc.com *Web Site:* www.theasc.com, pg 1077

Crump, Mr Chris, Comrex Corp, 19 Pine Rd, Devens, MA 01434 *Tel:* 978-784-1776 (intl) *Toll Free Tel:* 800-237-1776 *Fax:* 978-784-1717 *E-mail:* info@comrex.com *Web Site:* www.comrex.com, pg 834

Cruz, Carlos, Yale Film & Video, 25601 Avenue Stanford, Valencia, CA 91355 *Tel:* 661-295-7170; 661-295-7160 *E-mail:* info@yalefilmandvideo.com *Web Site:* www.yalefilmandvideo.com, pg 1071

Cude, Bobby Lee, Hard Hat Radio Music Service, 519 N Halifax Ave, Daytona Beach, FL 32118-4017 *Tel:* 386-252-0381 *Fax:* 386-252-0381 *E-mail:* hardhatrecords@aol.com *Web Site:* www.hardhatrecords.com, pg 884

Cude, Bobby Lee, Times-Square Fantasy Theatre, 519 N Halifax Ave, Daytona Beach, FL 32118 *Tel:* 386-252-0381 *Fax:* 386-252-0381 *E-mail:* timessquare@bellsouth.net *Web Site:* www.timessquarefantasytheatre.com; www.broadwaymusicdownload.com, pg 1041

Cue, Eddy, Apple Inc, One Infinite Loop, Cupertino, CA 95014 *Tel:* 408-996-1010 *Web Site:* www.apple.com, pg 788

Cullen, Julie, Carolina Film & Video Festival (CFVF), 210 Brown Bldg, UNC Greensboro, Greensboro, NC 27402 *Tel:* 336-334-5360 *Fax:* 336-334-5039 *E-mail:* cfvf@uncg.edu *Web Site:* cfvf.uncg.edu; www.carolinafilmandvideofestival.org, pg 1111

Cullen, Mike, Polyline LLC, 845 N Church Ct, Elmhurst, IL 60126-1036 *Tel:* 630-993-2700 *Toll Free Tel:* 800-701-7689 *Toll Free Fax:* 800-816-3330 *E-mail:* sales@polylinecorp.com *Web Site:* www.polylinecorp.com, pg 978

Cully, David, Baker & Taylor Inc, 2550 W Tyvola Rd, Suite 300, Charlotte, NC 28217 *Tel:* 704-998-3100 *Toll Free Tel:* 800-775-1800 *E-mail:* btinfo@baker-taylor.com *Web Site:* www.btol.com, pg 801

Culotta, Frank Michael, SYMCO Inc, 29 Poplar Dr, Stirling, NJ 07980 *Tel:* 908-647-6262 *Fax:* 908-647-4904 *E-mail:* orders@symcoinc.com *Web Site:* www.symcoinc.com, pg 1030

Culver, Harriet, Culver Pictures Inc, 51-02 21 St, Suite 4B, Long Island City, NY 11101 *Tel:* 718-752-9393 *Fax:* 718-752-9394 *E-mail:* research@culverpictures.com *Web Site:* www.culverpictures.com, pg 841

Cummins, Tracy, Media Control Systems LLC, 1050 Pioneer Way, Suite Q, El Cajon, CA 92020 *Tel:* 619-599-1050 *Fax:* 619-599-1051 *Web Site:* www.mediacontrolsystems.com, pg 936

Cundiff, Lindsey, Different Fur Recording Ltd, 3470 19 St, San Francisco, CA 94110 *Tel:* 415-864-1967; 415-828-4060 (bookings) *Fax:* 415-864-1965 *Web Site:* www.differentfurstudios.com, pg 846

Cunningham, Brent, Small Press Distribution Inc, 1341 Seventh St, Berkeley, CA 94710-1409 *Tel:* 510-524-1668 *Toll Free Tel:* 800-869-7553 *Fax:* 510-524-0852 *E-mail:* spd@spdbooks.org *Web Site:* www.spdbooks.org, pg 1013

Cunningham, Curtis, Lawrence Productions Inc, 6146 W Main St, Suite A, Kalamazoo, MI 49009 *Tel:* 269-903-2395 *E-mail:* sales@lpi.com *Web Site:* www.lpi.com, pg 917

Cunningham, Edward, City of Port St Lucie Community Relations/Film Office, 121 SW Port St Lucie Blvd, Bldg A, 1st fl, Rm 145, Port St Lucie, FL 34984 *Tel:* 772-871-5219 *Fax:* 772-344-4111 *E-mail:* info@cityofpsl.com *Web Site:* www.cityofpsl.com, pg 1096

Cunningham, Joe, New York Sound Inc, 166 Fifth Ave, No 6, New York, NY 10010 *Tel:* 917-523-0770; 212-929-5719, pg 956

Cunningham, Kay, Psychological Assessment Resources Inc (PAR), 16204 N Florida Ave, Lutz, FL 33549 *Tel:* 813-968-3003; 813-449-4065 (cust serv) *Toll Free Tel:* 800-331-8378 (tech support) *Fax:* 813-968-2598 *Toll Free Fax:* 800-727-9329 *Web Site:* www4.parinc.com, pg 987

Cunningham, Sky, PSAV® Presentation Services, 111 W Ocean Blvd, Suite 1110, Long Beach, CA 90802-4688 *Tel:* 562-366-0620 *Toll Free Tel:* 877-430-7728 *Fax:* 562-366-0628 *Web Site:* www.psav.com, pg 986

Cunningham, Sky, PSAV® Presentation Services (Hotel Services Division), 1700 E Golf Rd, Suite 400, Schaumburg, IL 60173-5820 *Tel:* 847-222-9800 *Toll Free Tel:* 800-486-9509 *E-mail:* info@psav.com *Web Site:* www.psav.com, pg 987

Cunningham, Warren, Communilux Productions, 4001 East Side Ave, Dallas, TX 75226 *Tel:* 214-821-8706 *Toll Free Tel:* 877-323-5189 *E-mail:* info@communilux.com *Web Site:* www.communilux.com, pg 833

Cunnings, Bob, Lectrosonics Inc, 581 Laser Rd NE, Rio Rancho, NM 87124 *Tel:* 505-892-4501 *Toll Free Tel:* 800-821-1121 *Fax:* 505-892-6243 *E-mail:* sales@lectrosonics.com *Web Site:* www.lectrosonics.com, pg 918

Cuny, Mark, Telestream Inc, 848 Gold Flat Rd, Nevada City, CA 95959 *Tel:* 530-470-1300 *Toll Free Tel:* 877-257-6245 *Fax:* 530-470-1301 *E-mail:* info@telestream.net *Web Site:* www.telestream.net, pg 1036

Cuomo, Anthony E, Telemetrics Inc, 6 Leighton Place, Mahwah, NJ 07430 *Tel:* 201-848-9818 *Fax:* 201-848-9819 *E-mail:* info@telemetricsinc.com *Web Site:* www.telemetricsinc.com, pg 1036

Curb, Mike, Curb Entertainment International Corp, 3907 W Alameda Ave, Burbank, CA 91505 *Tel:* 818-843-8580 *Fax:* 818-566-1719 *Web Site:* www.curbentertainment.com, pg 841

Curran, Bill, Nantucket Film Festival (NFF), 68 Jay St, Suite 319, Brooklyn, NY 11201 *Tel:* 646-480-1900; 508-325-6274 *Fax:* 646-365-3367 *E-mail:* info@nantucketfilmfestival.org *Web Site:* www.nantucketfilmfestival.org, pg 1121

Curren, Terence, AlphaDogs Inc, 1612 W Olive Ave, Suite 200, Burbank, CA 91506-2462 *Tel:* 818-729-9262 *Fax:* 818-729-8537 *Web Site:* www.alphadogs.tv, pg 782

Currier, Ron, Quince Imaging Inc, 2810 Towerview Rd, Herndon, VA 20171-3206 *Tel:* 703-742-7520 *Toll Free Tel:* 888-252-4960 *Fax:* 703-742-7586 *E-mail:* info@quinceimaging.com; sales@quinceimaging.com; operations@quinceimaging.com *Web Site:* www.quinceimaging.com, pg 989

Curry, Adrian, Zeitgeist Films Ltd, 247 Centre St, 2nd fl, New York, NY 10013 *Tel:* 212-274-1989 *Fax:* 212-274-1644 *E-mail:* mail@zeitgeistfilms.com *Web Site:* www.zeitgeistfilms.com, pg 1073

Curry, Phil, Phil Lights, 1903 Redlands, Austin, TX 78757 *Tel:* 512-452-2930; 512-627-4991 (cell) *Web Site:* www.pcurry.com, pg 974

Curtis, Bill, Vision Video, 2030 Wentz Church Rd, Lansdale, PA 19446 *Tel:* 610-584-3500 *Toll Free Tel:* 800-523-0226 *Fax:* 610-584-6643 *E-mail:* support@visionvideo.com *Web Site:* www.visionvideo.com, pg 1058

Cushing, Gary, Camarillo Chamber of Commerce, 2400 E Ventura Blvd, Camarillo, CA 93010 *Tel:* 805-484-4383 *Fax:* 805-484-1395 *E-mail:* info@camarillochamber.org *Web Site:* www.camarillochamber.org, pg 1092

Cusick, Michael, Specialized Audio-Visual Inc, 14 Solar Dr, Clifton Park, NY 12065 *Tel:* 518-383-6501 *Fax:* 518-383-6506 *E-mail:* info@saviusa.com; sales@saviusa.com *Web Site:* www.saviusa.com, pg 1020

Cusick, Rick, Taylor Associates, 110 W Canal St, Suite 301, Winooski, VT 05404 *Tel:* 802-735-1942 *Toll Free Tel:* 800-READ-PLUS (732-3758) *Fax:* 802-419-4786 *E-mail:* info@readingplus.com *Web Site:* www.readingplus.com, pg 1032

Cusolito, Rich, Technicolor, 3233 E Mission Oaks Blvd, Camarillo, CA 93012 *Tel:* 805-445-1122 *Fax:* 805-445-4340 *E-mail:* info@technicolor.com *Web Site:* www.technicolor.com, pg 1034

Custodio, Andre, First Person™, 550 Bryant St, San Francisco, CA 94107 *Tel:* 415-495-5595 *Fax:* 415-543-8370, pg 869

Cuthbertson, Ian, Sound & Vision Communications Inc, 4601 N "A" St, Tampa, FL 33609-1909 *Tel:* 813-642-4706 *Web Site:* www.gosvc.com, pg 1017

Cypser, Darlene, Inferno Film Productions LLC, PO Box 696, Littleton, CO 80160-0696 *Tel:* 303-587-9792 *E-mail:* sales@infernofilm.com *Web Site:* www.infernofilm.com, pg 897

Czajkowski, Randy, Antelope Valley Locations & Production Services, 42848 150 St E, Lancaster, CA 93535 *Tel:* 661-946-1515 *Fax:* 661-946-0454 *E-mail:* clubed@avlocations.com *Web Site:* www.avlocations.com, pg 787

Czarnecki, Gene, Czar Productions Inc, 809 New Britain Ave, Hartford, CT 06106 *Tel:* 860-953-0809 *E-mail:* czar.productions@snet.net, pg 842

Czyzak, Timothy, iVideo Technologies, 14885 Sprague Rd, Cleveland, OH 44136 *Tel:* 440-891-9440 *Toll Free Tel:* 800-352-6150 *Fax:* 440-891-9450 *E-mail:* info@ivideo.com *Web Site:* www.ivideo.com, pg 903

Czyzewski, Matt, BIAMP Systems, 9300 SW Gemini Dr, Beaverton, OR 97008 *Tel:* 503-641-7287 *Toll Free Tel:* 800-826-1457 (US & CN) *Fax:* 503-626-0281 *E-mail:* biampinfo@biamp.com; salesteam@biamp.com *Web Site:* www.biamp.com, pg 806

D'Alessandro, Fred, Diversified Systems Inc, 363 Market St, Kenilworth, NJ 07033 *Tel:* 908-245-4833 *Fax:* 908-245-0011 *E-mail:* info@divsystems.com *Web Site:* www.divsystems.com, pg 849

D'Alessandro, Maria, Kenexa, 650 E Swedesford Rd, 2nd fl, Wayne, PA 19087 *Tel:* 407-548-1444 *Fax:* 610-971-9181 *E-mail:* kenexa_learn_sales@kenexa.com *Web Site:* www.outstart.com, pg 909

D'Alessio, Alfred W, Princeton Acoustics Corp, 40 Benford Dr, Princeton Junction, NJ 08550 *Tel:* 609-936-0006 *Web Site:* www.nccnewyork.com, pg 982

D'Allen, Nick, Staging Directions Inc, 1327 Northbrook Pkwy, Suite 440, Suwanee, GA 30024 *Tel:* 770-409-9909 *Toll Free Tel:* 800-782-4322 *Fax:* 770-409-0277 *E-mail:* info@teamsdi.net; sales@teamsdi.net *Web Site:* www.stagingdirections.com, pg 1023

D'Amato, Sally-Ann, The Citation of Outstanding Service to the Society Award, 3 Barker Ave, 5th fl, White Plains, NY 10601 *Tel:* 914-761-1100 *Fax:* 914-761-3115 *E-mail:* smpte@smpte.org *Web Site:* www.smpte.org, pg 1112

D'Amato, Sally-Ann, The Journal Award & SMPTE Journal Certificate of Merit, 3 Barker Ave, 5th fl, White Plains, NY 10601 *Tel:* 914-761-1100 *Fax:* 914-761-3115 *E-mail:* smpte@smpte.org *Web Site:* www.smpte.org, pg 1118

D'Amato, Sally-Ann, The Presidential Proclamation Award, 3 Barker Ave, 5th fl, White Plains, NY 10601 *Tel:* 914-761-1100 *Fax:* 914-761-3115 *E-mail:* smpte@smpte.org *Web Site:* www.smpte.org, pg 1124

D'Amato, Sally-Ann, The Progress Medal Award, 3 Barker Ave, 5th fl, White Plains, NY 10601 *Tel:* 914-761-1100 *Fax:* 914-761-3115 *E-mail:* smpte@smpte.org *Web Site:* www.smpte.org, pg 1124

D'Amato, Sally-Ann, Society of Motion Picture & Television Engineers (SMPTE), 3 Barker Ave, 5th fl, White Plains, NY 10601 *Tel:* 914-761-1100 *Fax:* 914-761-3115 *E-mail:* smpte@smpte.org *Web Site:* www.smpte.org, pg 1015

D'Amato, Sally-Ann, Society of Motion Picture & Television Engineers (SMPTE), 3 Barker Ave, 5th fl, White Plains, NY 10601 *Tel:* 914-761-1100 *Fax:* 914-761-3115 *E-mail:* membership@smpte.org *Web Site:* www.smpte.org, pg 1089

D'Amato, Sally-Ann, Technicolor-Herbert T Kalmus Gold Medal Award, 3 Barker Ave, 5th fl, White Plains, NY 10601 *Tel:* 914-761-1100 *Fax:* 914-761-3115 *E-mail:* smpte@smpte.org *Web Site:* www.smpte.org, pg 1128

D'Amato, Sally-Ann, The Samuel L Warner Memorial Award, 3 Barker Ave, 5th fl, White Plains, NY 10601 *Tel:* 914-761-1100 *Fax:* 914-761-3115 *E-mail:* smpte@smpte.org *Web Site:* www.smpte.org, pg 1129

D'Antonio, Dr Peter, RPG Diffusor Systems Inc, 651-C Commerce Dr, Upper Marlboro, MD 20774 *Tel:* 301-249-0044 *Fax:* 301-390-3602 *E-mail:* info@rpginc.com *Web Site:* www.rpginc.com, pg 1000

D'or, Daniel, Canamedia Inc, 1540 Cornwall Rd, Suite 216, Oakville, ON L6J 7W5, Canada *Tel:* 416-363-6765 *Toll Free Tel:* 866-999-5292 *Fax:* 416-363-7834 *Web Site:* www.canamedia.com, pg 818

Dacian, Daniel, Big Apple Films, 636 W 28 St, New York, NY 10001 *Tel:* 212-368-1111 *Fax:* 347-689-1604 *Web Site:* www.bigapplefilms.com, pg 806

Dadmun, James, DGI-Invisuals LLC, 101 Billerica Ave, Bldg 6, North Billerica, MA 01862 *Toll Free Tel:* 800-344-0432 *Fax:* 781-270-3663 *E-mail:* sales@dgi-invisuals.com *Web Site:* www.dgi-invisuals.com, pg 846

Dahlen, Peter, American Choral Catalog Ltd, 205 S Water St, Northfield, MN 55057 *Tel:* 507-645-4695 *Toll Free Tel:* 800-246-7257 *Fax:* 507-645-2474 *E-mail:* info@americanchoral.com *Web Site:* www.americanchoral.com, pg 784

Dahlquist, Nels, Chicago International REEL Shorts Festival, 428 N Wolcott, Chicago, IL 60622 *Web Site:* www.projectchicago.com, pg 1111

Dahnke, Lynn M, Coast Learning Systems, 11460 Warner Ave, Fountain Valley, CA 92708 *Tel:* 714-241-6109 *Toll Free Tel:* 800-547-4748 *Fax:* 714-241-6286 *Web Site:* www.coastlearning.org, pg 831

Daicos, Steve, PCO-TECH Inc, 6930 Metroplex Dr, Romulus, MI 48174 *Tel:* 248-276-8820 *Fax:* 248-276-8825 *E-mail:* info@pco-tech.com; service@pco-tech.com *Web Site:* www.pco-tech.com, pg 970

Dake, Ron, Show-Me Audio-Visual, Corporate Ridge, 4501 Blue Ridge Cutoff, Kansas City, MO 64133 *Tel:* 816-358-8700 *Toll Free Tel:* 800-2-SHOWME (274-6963) *Fax:* 816-358-8701 *E-mail:* info@showmeav.com *Web Site:* www.showmeav.com, pg 1009

Dalakian, Martin, International Audio Visual Inc, 622 Rte 10, Unit 21, Whippany, NJ 07981 *Tel:* 973-887-7744 *Toll Free Tel:* 888-887-7749 *Fax:* 973-887-7272 *E-mail:* iav@iavnj.com *Web Site:* www.iavnj.com, pg 900

Dallas, Julie, WPGH-TV, 750 Ivory Ave, Pittsburgh, PA 15214 *Tel:* 412-931-5300 *Fax:* 412-931-4284 *Web Site:* www.sbgi.net; www.wpgh53.com, pg 1070

Dalton, Mike, Applied Electronics Ltd, 1260 Kamato Rd, Mississauga, ON L4W 1Y1, Canada *Tel:* 905-625-4321 *Fax:* 905-625-4333 *E-mail:* ael.toronto@appliedelectronics.com *Web Site:* www.appliedelectronics.com, pg 789

Daly, Ann, DreamWorks Animation SKG Inc, 1000 Flower St, Glendale, CA 91201 *Tel:* 818-695-5000 *Fax:* 818-695-4190 *Web Site:* www.dreamworksanimation.com, pg 852

Daman, Julie, Washington Filmworks, 1411 Fourth Ave, Suite 420, Seattle, WA 98101 *Tel:* 206-264-0667 *Fax:* 206-382-4343 *E-mail:* info@washingtonfilmworks.org *Web Site:* washingtonfilmworks.org, pg 1103

Damaschke, Bill, DreamWorks Animation SKG Inc, 1000 Flower St, Glendale, CA 91201 *Tel:* 818-695-5000 *Fax:* 818-695-4190 *Web Site:* www.dreamworksanimation.com, pg 852

Dana, A William, WHYY Inc, Independence Mall West, 150 N Sixth St, Philadelphia, PA 19106 *Tel:* 215-351-1200 *Fax:* 215-351-0398 *E-mail:* talkback@whyy.org *Web Site:* www.whyy.org, pg 1066

Dancy, Paul, TVO/Ontario Educational Communications Authority (OECA), 2180 Yonge St, Toronto, ON M4S 2B9, Canada *Tel:* 416-484-2600; 416-484-2665 (cust rel) *Toll Free Tel:* 800-613-0513; 800-INFO-TVO (463-6886) *E-mail:* asktvo@tvo.org *Web Site:* tvo.org, pg 1046

Dani, Raj, AVI-SPL, 6301 Benjamin Rd, Suite 101, Tampa, FL 33634 *Tel:* 813-884-7168 *Toll Free Tel:* 866-708-5034; 800-282-6733; 866-925-8298 (cust serv); 866-559-8197 (sales) *Fax:* 813-882-9508 *E-mail:* questions@avispl.com; sales@avispl.com; customerservice@avispl.com *Web Site:* www.avispl.com, pg 798

Daniel, Donnie, Ingram Entertainment Inc, 2 Ingram Blvd, La Vergne, TN 37089-7006 *Tel:* 615-287-4000 (corp) *Toll Free Tel:* 800-621-1333 (sales & cust serv) *Fax:* 615-287-4982 *Web Site:* www.ingramentertainment.com, pg 898

Daniel, Marcus, Sacramento Theatrical Lighting Ltd (STL), 950 Richards Blvd, Sacramento, CA 95811 *Tel:* 916-447-3258 *Toll Free Tel:* 800-283-2785 *Fax:* 916-447-5012 *E-mail:* info@stlltd.com *Web Site:* www.stlltd.com, pg 1001

Daniels, John, L&P Media, 255 River St, Troy, NY 12180 *Tel:* 518-880-0300 *Toll Free Tel:* 800-201-5949 *Fax:* 518-880-0390 *E-mail:* information@lpmedia.net *Web Site:* www.light-power.com, pg 915

Daniels, Karil, Point of View Productions, 2477 Folsom St, San Francisco, CA 94110 *Fax:* 415-821-0434 *Web Site:* www.karildaniels.com, pg 977

Danowitz, Dean, Starlite Productions, 9 Whittendale Dr, Moorestown, NJ 08057 *Tel:* 856-780-8000 *Toll Free Tel:* 800-738-7400 *Fax:* 856-780-8001 *E-mail:* info@starlite.com *Web Site:* www.starlite.com, pg 1024

Danowitz, Jason, Starlite Productions, 9 Whittendale Dr, Moorestown, NJ 08057 *Tel:* 856-780-8000 *Toll Free Tel:* 800-738-7400 *Fax:* 856-780-8001 *E-mail:* info@starlite.com *Web Site:* www.starlite.com, pg 1024

Darby, Charles, DuArt, 245 W 55 St, New York, NY 10019 *Tel:* 212-757-4580 *Fax:* 212-977-5609 *E-mail:* info@duart.com *Web Site:* www.duart.com, pg 853

Daressa, Lawrence, California Newsreel, 44 Gough St, Suite 303, San Francisco, CA 94103 *Tel:* 415-284-7800 *Fax:* 415-284-7801 *E-mail:* contact@newsreel.org *Web Site:* www.newsreel.org, pg 817

Darg, Abel, Broadcast Management Group, 1625 Eye St NW, Suite 620, Washington, DC 20006 *Tel:* 202-609-7757 *E-mail:* info@broadcastmgmt.com *Web Site:* www.broadcastmgmt.com, pg 813

Darnton, John, George Polk Awards in Journalism, Journalism Dept, One University Plaza, Brooklyn, NY 11201-5372 *Tel:* 718-488-1009 *Fax:* 718-780-4046 *Web Site:* www.liu.edu/polk, pg 1124

Darroe, Aric-James, Kids on the Block Inc, 9 Westminster Shopping Ctr, Suite 344, Westminster, MD 21157 *Tel:* 443-297-9564 *Toll Free Tel:* 800-368-KIDS (368-5437) *Fax:* 410-290-9358 *E-mail:* kob@kotb.com *Web Site:* www.kotb.com, pg 910

Darrow, Richard, Hakuba Sunpak Velbon, 53 Green Pond Rd, Suite 5, Rockaway, NJ 07866 *Tel:* 973-627-9600 *Toll Free Tel:* 800-886-2236 *Fax:* 973-664-2438 *E-mail:* info@tocad.com *Web Site:* www.tocad.com, pg 883

Dashner, Mel, Origin Instruments Corp, 854 Greenview Dr, Grand Prairie, TX 75050-2438 *Tel:* 972-606-8740 *Fax:* 972-606-8741 *E-mail:* support@orin.com; marketing@orin.com *Web Site:* www.orin.com, pg 965

Dasso, Robert, Magnetic Shield Corp, 740 N Thomas Dr, Bensenville, IL 60106 *Tel:* 630-766-7800 *Toll Free Tel:* 888-766-7800 *Fax:* 630-766-2813 *E-mail:* shields@magnetic-shield.com *Web Site:* www.magnetic-shield.com, pg 928

Dasu, Dhiren, Blue Lotus Temple Studio, PO Box 888, Boulder Creek, CA 95006 *Tel:* 831-338-2544 *E-mail:* info@bluelotustemple.com *Web Site:* www.bluelotustemple.com, pg 809

Dater, Alan, Marlboro Film & Video Productions, 1076 Moss Hollow Rd, Marlboro, VT 05344 *Tel:* 802-257-0743 *Toll Free Tel:* 888-867-7581 (orders) *Fax:* 802-257-0743 *E-mail:* mfilmpro@sover.net *Web Site:* marlboroproductions.com, pg 931

Daugherty, Will, Evolve Inc, 1210 E Arlington Blvd, Greenville, NC 27858 *Tel:* 252-754-2957 *Fax:* 252-754-2832 *Web Site:* www.evolveinc.com, pg 863

Daussin, Charles, Outland Technology Inc, 38190 Commercial Ct, Slidell, LA 70458 *Tel:* 985-847-1104 *Fax:* 985-847-1106 *E-mail:* sales@outlandtech.com *Web Site:* www.outlandtech.com, pg 966

Davenport, Carla, Image Associates Inc, 5311 S Miami Blvd, Suite G, Durham, NC 27703 *Tel:* 919-876-6400 *Fax:* 919-876-6400 *E-mail:* info@imageassociates.com *Web Site:* www.imageassociates.com, pg 894

Davenport, Elaine, Writer's AudioShop/Davenport Productions, 1316 Overland Stage Rd, Dripping Springs, TX 78620 *Tel:* 512-476-1616 *Fax:* 512-264-7067 *E-mail:* wrtaudshop@aol.com *Web Site:* www.writersaudio.com, pg 1070

Davenport, Neal, Davenport Music Library, PO Box 690536, Charlotte, NC 28227-7009 *E-mail:* info@davenportmusic.com *Web Site:* www.davenportmusic.com, pg 843

Davenport, Patrick, Method Studios, 730 Arizona Ave, Santa Monica, CA 90401 *Tel:* 310-434-6500 *Web Site:* www.methodstudios.com, pg 939

David, Brian, HiFi House, 2304 Concord Pike, Wilmington, DE 19803 *Tel:* 302-655-4780 *Toll Free Tel:* 800-990-HIFI (990-4434) *Web Site:* www.hifihousegroup.com; www.hifihouse.com, pg 888

David, Joseph, J & D Laboratories Inc, 27 E 21 St, New York, NY 10010 *Tel:* 212-982-3330 *Toll Free Tel:* 800-535-2201 *Fax:* 212-982-3332 *E-mail:* jdvideolab@aol.com *Web Site:* jdvideolab.com, pg 903

David, Patricia, J & D Laboratories Inc, 27 E 21 St, New York, NY 10010 *Tel:* 212-982-3330 *Toll Free Tel:* 800-535-2201 *Fax:* 212-982-3332 *E-mail:* jdvideolab@aol.com *Web Site:* jdvideolab.com, pg 903

David, Robert, The Cinema Lab, 2735 S Raritan St, Englewood, CO 80110-1101 *Tel:* 303-783-1020 *Fax:* 303-806-0555 *Web Site:* www.cinemalab.com, pg 827

Davids, Markus, CineBags Inc, 825 Western Ave, Suite 17, Glendale, CA 91201 *Tel:* 818-662-0605 *Fax:* 818-662-0613 *Web Site:* www.cinebags.com, pg 826

Davidson, Brian, Association of National Advertisers Inc (ANA), 708 Third Ave, 33rd fl, New York, NY 10017-4270 *Tel:* 212-697-5950 *Fax:* 212-687-7310 *E-mail:* info@ana.net *Web Site:* www.ana.net, pg 1079

Davidson, Frances W, Davidson Films Inc, PO Box 664, Santa Margarita, CA 93453 *Toll Free Tel:* 888-437-4200 *Fax:* 805-594-0532 *E-mail:* dfi@davidsonfilms.com *Web Site:* davidsonfilms.com, pg 843

Davidson, Randall, University of Wisconsin-Oshkosh Radio-TV-Film Dept, Arts & Communications Bldg, W-112, 800 Algoma Blvd, Oshkosh, WI 54901 *Tel:* 920-424-3131 *Fax:* 920-424-7041 *E-mail:* rtf@uwosh.edu *Web Site:* www.uwosh.edu/rtf, pg 1050

Davidson, Dr Randall WA, Risk International & Associates Inc, 8803 W Ontario Ave, Littleton, CO 80128 *Tel:* 720-922-0707 *Fax:* 720-922-0707 *E-mail:* info@riskit.com *Web Site:* www.riskit.com, pg 997

Davidson, Richard M, RADMAR Inc, PO Box 425, Northbrook, IL 60065-0425 *Tel:* 847-298-7980 *E-mail:* radmarinc@gmail.com *Web Site:* www.radmarinc.com, pg 990

Davidson, Veronica, GAPC (General Assembly Production Centre), 1550 Laperriere Ave, Suite 102, Ottawa, ON K1Z 7T2, Canada *Tel:* 613-723-3316 *Fax:* 613-723-8583 *Web Site:* www.gapc.com, pg 875

Davies, Bill, Jack Morton Worldwide, 909 Third Ave, New York, NY 10022 *Tel:* 212-401-7000 *E-mail:* experience@jackmorton.com *Web Site:* www.jackmorton.com, pg 946

Davies, Keith, Grass Valley/Nevada County Chamber of Commerce, 128 E Main St, Grass Valley, CA 95945 *Tel:* 530-273-4667 *Toll Free Tel:* 800-655-4667 *Fax:* 530-272-5440 *E-mail:* info@grassvalleychamber.com *Web Site:* www.grassvalleychamber.com, pg 1093

Davies, Marcus, ITA Audio Visual Solutions, 2162 Dana Ave & I-71, Cincinnati, OH 45207 *Tel:* 513-631-7000 *Toll Free Tel:* 800-899-8877 *Fax:* 513-631-3290; 513-631-8877 *E-mail:* csr@ita.com *Web Site:* www.ita.com, pg 902

Davies, Michael, Davies Publishing Inc, 32 S Raymond Ave, Suite 4, Pasadena, CA 91105-1935 *Tel:* 626-792-3046 *Toll Free Tel:* 877-792-0005 *Fax:* 626-792-5308 *E-mail:* order@daviespublishing.com *Web Site:* daviespublishing.com, pg 843

Davies, Trevor, Convergent Media Systems, 190 Bluegrass Valley Pkwy, Alpharetta, GA 30005-2204 *Tel:* 770-369-9000 *Toll Free Tel:* 800-877-7804 *Fax:* 770-369-9100 *E-mail:* convergent@convergent.com *Web Site:* www.convergent.com, pg 836

Davies, Walter, The LAST Factory, 2015 Research Dr, Livermore, CA 94550-3803 *Tel:* 925-449-9449 *Fax:* 925-447-0662 *E-mail:* thelastfactory@gmail.com *Web Site:* thelastfactory.com, pg 916

Davis, Abby, Crestron Electronics Inc, 15 Volvo Dr, Rockleigh, NJ 07647 *Tel:* 201-767-3400 *Toll Free Tel:* 800-237-2041 *Fax:* 201-767-1903 *E-mail:* crestronhq@crestron.com *Web Site:* www.crestron.com, pg 839

Davis, Andrew L, Emerson Radio Corp, 3 University Plaza, Suite 405, Hackensack, NJ 07601 *Tel:* 973-884-5800 *Toll Free Tel:* 800-909-1240 (cust serv) *Fax:* 973-428-2067 *E-mail:* internet@emersonradio.com *Web Site:* www.emersonradio.com, pg 860

Davis, April, International Society for Performance Improvement® (ISPI), PO Box 13035, Silver Spring, MD 20910 *Tel:* 301-587-8570 *Fax:* 301-587-8573 *E-mail:* info@ispi.org *Web Site:* www.ispi.org, pg 1083

Davis, B Dave, Baker Audio Inc, 2195 N Norcross Tucker Rd, Norcross, GA 30071 *Tel:* 770-441-2000 *Toll Free Tel:* 800-847-3523 *Fax:* 770-449-7719 *E-mail:* sales@bakeraudiovisual.com *Web Site:* www.bakeraudiovisual.com, pg 802

Davis, Bob Jr, Tennessee Visual Service Co, 912 Main St, Nashville, TN 37206 *Tel:* 615-226-0162 *Toll Free Tel:* 800-359-6132 *Fax:* 615-228-1876 *E-mail:* sales@tennvisual.com *Web Site:* www.tennvisual.com, pg 1037

Davis, Cari, Devlin Video International, 1501 Broadway, Suite 408, New York, NY 10036 *Tel:* 212-391-1313 *Fax:* 212-391-2744 *Web Site:* www.devlinvideo.com, pg 846

Davis, Chip, American Gramaphone LLC, 9130 Mormon Bridge Rd, Omaha, NE 68152 *Tel:* 402-457-4341 *Fax:* 402-457-4332 *E-mail:* mailbox@mannheimsteamroller.com *Web Site:* www.mannheimsteamroller.com, pg 784

Davis, David A, Romar Learning, 6700 Woodlands Pkwy, Suite 230-292, Woodlands, TX 77382 *Tel:* 281-292-5508 *Fax:* 281-363-2309 *E-mail:* info@romarlearning.com *Web Site:* www.romarlearning.com, pg 999

Davis, Edward, American Fibertek Inc, 120 Belmont Dr, Somerset, NJ 08873-4243 *Tel:* 732-302-0660 *Toll Free Tel:* 877-234-7200 *Fax:* 732-302-0667 *E-mail:* sales@americanfibertek.com; techinfo@americanfibertek.com *Web Site:* www.americanfibertek.com, pg 784

Davis, Hayne, DaviSound, 1504 Sunset Ave, Newberry, SC 29108 *Tel:* 803-944-7972 (messages only) *E-mail:* davisound@davisound.com; davisound@hotmail.com *Web Site:* www.davisound.com, pg 843

Davis, Irvin, Celebrities Productions, c/o Clayton-Davis & Associates, 230 S Bemiston Ave, Suite 1400, St Louis, MO 63105 *Tel:* 314-862-7800 *Fax:* 314-721-5171 *E-mail:* idcda@aol.com *Web Site:* www.claytondavis.com, pg 822

Davis, Irvin, Clayton-Davis & Associates, 230 S Bemiston Ave, St Louis, MO 63105 *Tel:* 314-862-7800 *E-mail:* info@claytondavis.com *Web Site:* www.claytondavis.com, pg 829

Davis, James C, Communications Design Associates, 437 Turnpike St, Canton, MA 02021 *Tel:* 339-502-6551 *Fax:* 339-502-6595 *E-mail:* information@cdaconsultants.com *Web Site:* www.cdaconsultants.com, pg 833

Davis, Jennifer, Celebrities Productions, c/o Clayton-Davis & Associates, 230 S Bemiston Ave, Suite 1400, St Louis, MO 63105 *Tel:* 314-862-7800 *Fax:* 314-721-5171 *E-mail:* idcda@aol.com *Web Site:* www.claytondavis.com, pg 822

Davis, Jennifer, Clayton-Davis & Associates, 230 S Bemiston Ave, St Louis, MO 63105 *Tel:* 314-862-7800 *E-mail:* info@claytondavis.com *Web Site:* www.claytondavis.com, pg 829

Davis, Jim, SAS Institute Inc, 100 SAS Campus Dr, Cary, NC 27513-2414 *Tel:* 919-677-8000 *Toll Free Tel:* 800-727-0025 *Fax:* 919-677-4444 *Web Site:* www.sas.com, pg 1002

Davis, John J, John J Davis & Associates Consulting Engineers, PO Box 128, Sierra Madre, CA 91025-0128 *Tel:* 626-355-6909, pg 843

Davis, Jon, Sight & Sound Productions, 11193 Saint Johns Industrial Pkwy N, Jacksonville, FL 32246 *Tel:* 904-645-7880 *Toll Free Tel:* 800-339-0846 *Fax:* 904-645-7787 *E-mail:* info@ssav.net *Web Site:* www.ssav.net, pg 1010

Davis, Keith, Fender Musical Instruments Corp, 17600 N Perimeter Dr, Suite 100, Scottsdale, AZ 85255 *Tel:* 480-596-9690 *Fax:* 480-596-1384 *E-mail:* consumerrelations@fender.com *Web Site:* www.fender.com, pg 866

Davis, Kelly, St John's International Women's Film Festival, 28 Cochrane St, Suite 101, St John's, NL A1C 3L3, Canada *Tel:* 709-754-3141 *E-mail:* info@womensfilmfestival.com *Web Site:* www.womensfilmfestival.com, pg 1126

Davis, Kenneth G, Pro Cuts Editing Services, 2138 Priest Bridge Ct, Suite 1, Crofton, MD 21114 *Tel:* 301-464-5067; 443-274-6115 *E-mail:* info@procutsediting.com *Web Site:* www.procutsediting.com, pg 982

Davis, R Christopher, Tennessee Visual Service Co, 912 Main St, Nashville, TN 37206 *Tel:* 615-226-0162 *Toll Free Tel:* 800-359-6132 *Fax:* 615-228-1876 *E-mail:* sales@tennvisual.com *Web Site:* www.tennvisual.com, pg 1037

Davis, Rick, Video Advantage, 90 Houseman Crescent, Richmond Hill, ON L4C 7S6, Canada *Tel:* 905-883-5332 *E-mail:* info@videoadvantage.ca *Web Site:* www.videoadvantage.ca, pg 1054

Davis, Sheri, Inland Empire Film Commission (IEFC), 1601 E Third St, Suite 102, San Bernardino, CA 92408 *Fax:* 909-382-6060 *E-mail:* info@filminlandempire.com *Web Site:* www.filminlandempire.com, pg 1094

Davis, Stewart, Axxis Inc, 845 S Ninth St, Louisville, KY 40203 *Tel:* 502-568-6030 *Fax:* 502-568-6204 *E-mail:* info@axxisinc.com *Web Site:* www.axxisinc.com, pg 800

Davis, Timothy S Esq, Close Up Foundation, 1330 Braddock Place, Suite 400, Alexandria, VA 22314 *Tel:* 703-706-3300 *Toll Free Tel:* 800-CLOSEUP (256-7387) *E-mail:* info@closeup.org *Web Site:* www.closeup.org, pg 830

Davis-Petit, Julie, San Jose Film & Video Commission, c/o San Jose Convention & Visitors Bureau, 408 Almaden Blvd, San Jose, CA 95110 *Tel:* 408-295-9600 *Toll Free Tel:* 800-SAN-JOSE (726-5673) *Web Site:* www.sanjose.org/film, pg 1094

Davison, Bill, SirsiDynix, 3300 N Ashton Blvd, Suite 500, Lehi, UT 84043-5340 *Tel:* 801-223-5200 *Toll Free Tel:* 800-288-8020 *Fax:* 801-223-5202 *E-mail:* info@sirsidynix.com; sales@sirsidynix.com *Web Site:* www.sirsidynix.com, pg 1012

Dawson, Bob, Bias Studios, 5400 Carolina Place, Springfield, VA 22151 *Tel:* 703-941-3333 *E-mail:* info@biasstudios.com *Web Site:* www.biasstudios.com, pg 806

Dawson, Donne, State of Hawaii Film Office, 250 S Hotel St, Suite 510-A, Honolulu, HI 96813 *Tel:* 808-586-2570 *Fax:* 808-586-2572 *E-mail:* info@hawaiifilmoffice.com *Web Site:* www.filmoffice.hawaii.gov, pg 1097

Dawson, Gloria, Bias Studios, 5400 Carolina Place, Springfield, VA 22151 *Tel:* 703-941-3333 *E-mail:* info@biasstudios.com *Web Site:* www.biasstudios.com, pg 806

Dawson, Ian G, SMI Inc, PO Box 7216, Waco, TX 76714-7216 *Tel:* 254-717-8917 *Fax:* 254-776-1230 *E-mail:* dmcminn@lmi-inc.com *Web Site:* www.success-motivation.com, pg 1014

Day, Brian, Daylight Productions & Rentals, 4700 Sterling Dr, Suite I, Boulder, CO 80301 *Tel:* 303-440-3334 *Fax:* 303-442-8180 *E-mail:* info@daylightav.com *Web Site:* www.daylightav.com, pg 844

Day, Dorothy, Pendle Hill Bookstore, 338 Plush Mill Rd, Wallingford, PA 19086-6099 *Tel:* 610-566-4507 (ext 2) *Toll Free Tel:* 800-742-3150 (ext 2) *Fax:* 610-566-3679 *E-mail:* bookstore@pendlehill.org *Web Site:* www.pendlehill.org, pg 971

Day, Kenneth F, Dot Hill Systems Corp, 1351 S Sunset St, Longmont, CO 80501-6533 *Tel:* 303-845-3200 *Toll Free Tel:* 800-872-2783 *Fax:* 303-845-3655 *E-mail:* support@dothill.com; websales@dothill.com *Web Site:* www.dothill.com, pg 851

Day, Paul, Sure Shot Transmissions Inc, 10314 Main St, New Middletown, OH 44442 *Tel:* 330-542-0900 *Fax:* 330-542-1020 *Web Site:* www.sureshotsat.com, pg 1029

Dayton, Gary, Baker & Taylor Inc, 2550 W Tyvola Rd, Suite 300, Charlotte, NC 28217 *Tel:* 704-998-3100 *Toll Free Tel:* 800-775-1800 *E-mail:* btinfo@baker-taylor.com *Web Site:* www.btol.com, pg 801

De Camp, Paul, Quatrefoil Associates Inc, 29 "C" St, Laurel, MD 20707 *Tel:* 301-470-4748 *Fax:* 301-470-4749 *E-mail:* info@quatrefoil.com *Web Site:* www.quatrefoil.com, pg 989

De Cham, Paul, AlphaDogs Inc, 1612 W Olive Ave, Suite 200, Burbank, CA 91506-2462 *Tel:* 818-729-9262 *Fax:* 818-729-8537 *Web Site:* www.alphadogs.tv, pg 782

De Croix, Rick, The Source Stock Footage Library Inc, 140 S Camino Seco, Suite 308, Tucson, AZ 85710 *Tel:* 520-298-4810 *Fax:* 520-290-4376 *E-mail:* requests@sourcefootage.com *Web Site:* www.sourcefootage.com, pg 1019

De Francesco, Jim, Hogpenny Studios, Ship Bottom Studio Ctr, 123 E 14 St, Ship Bottom, Long Beach Island, NJ 08008 *Tel:* 609-494-6640 *E-mail:* hogpenny@verizon.net; info@hogpenny.com *Web Site:* mysite.verizon.net/vzep5xhw, pg 890

de Freitas, Bob, Petra Productions Ltd, 52 Sycamore Rd, Mahopac, NY 10541 *E-mail:* information@petraproductions.org *Web Site:* www.petraproductions.org, pg 973

De Galbert, Camille, LightHouse Films, 115 W 29 St, Suite 903, New York, NY 10001 *Tel:* 646-649-3600 *Fax:* 646-398-7122 *E-mail:* contact@lhfny.com; rent@lhfny.com *Web Site:* www.light-house-films.com, pg 920

De Jong, Dirk, University of Southern California, Davidson Continuing Educ Conference Ctr, Rm 103, 3415 S Figueroa St, Los Angeles, CA 90089-0871 *Tel:* 213-740-5956; 213-740-5679 *Fax:* 213-740-9366 *Web Site:* hospitality.usc.edu/catering, pg 1050

De Lia, Tony, Photomart Cine-Video Inc, 6869 Stapoint Ct, Suite 112, Winter Park, FL 32792 *Tel:* 407-381-5606 *Toll Free Tel:* 800-443-2901 *Fax:* 407-381-5610 *E-mail:* info@photomartusa.com *Web Site:* www.photomartusa.com, pg 975

De Long, Michelle, Mimi Productions, 329 W 18 St, Suite 405, Chicago, IL 60616 *Tel:* 312-829-0162 *E-mail:* info@mimiproductions.com *Web Site:* www.mimiproductions.com, pg 943

De Maeyer, Thomas, Synergem, 2323 Randolph Ave, Avenel, NJ 07001 *Tel:* 732-225-0001 *Fax:* 732-225-7555 *E-mail:* info@synergem.com *Web Site:* www.synergem.com, pg 1030

De Mattos, Matthew M, Cinemills Corp, 2021 N Lincoln St, Burbank, CA 91504 *Tel:* 818-843-4560 *Toll Free Tel:* 877-CMC-HMIS (262-4647) *Fax:* 818-843-7834 *E-mail:* sales@cinemills.com *Web Site:* www.cinemills.com, pg 828

De Miles, Edward, Sahara Records & Filmworks Entertainment Co, 10573 W Pico Blvd, Suite 352, Los Angeles, CA 90064-2348 *Tel:* 310-948-9652 *E-mail:* info@edmsahara.com *Web Site:* www.edmsahara.com, pg 1001

De Mita, Michael, HB-Content, 105 Butler St, Suite 2B, Brooklyn, NY 11231 *Tel:* 212-213-8824 *E-mail:* hb@hb-content.com *Web Site:* www.hb-content.com, pg 886

De Nonno, Tony, De Nonno Productions Inc (DPI), 7119 Shore Rd, Suite 6-F, Brooklyn, NY 11209 *Tel:* 917-304-6610 *E-mail:* info@denonnoproductions.com *Web Site:* www.denonnoproductions.com; www.denonnoscelebrityphotos.com, pg 844

de Silva, Antonio Carlos, United Nations Department of Public Information-News & Media Division, 405 E 42 St, Rm IN-913B, New York, NY 10017 *Tel:* 917-367-5007 *E-mail:* mediapartnerships@un.org *Web Site:* www.un.org, pg 1048

De Vaughn-Stokes, Diane, Stages Video Productions, 514 29 Ave N, Myrtle Beach, SC 29577 *Tel:* 843-626-7466 *E-mail:* info@stagesvideo.com *Web Site:* www.stagesvideo.com, pg 1023

De Vincentis, Sally, APTE Inc, 1424 Wesley Ave, Suite A, Evanston, IL 60201 *Tel:* 847-866-1872 *Fax:* 847-866-1873 *E-mail:* mail@apte.com *Web Site:* www.apte.com, pg 789

de Vlieg, Justin, Infosat Communications Inc, 3130 114 Ave SE, Calgary, AB T2Z 3V6, Canada *Tel:* 403-543-8188 *Toll Free Tel:* 888-524-3038 *Fax:* 403-289-8133 *Web Site:* infosat.com, pg 898

de Wilde, Lisa, TVO/Ontario Educational Communications Authority (OECA), 2180 Yonge St, Toronto, ON M4S 2B9, Canada *Tel:* 416-484-2600; 416-484-2665 (cust rel) *Toll Free Tel:* 800-613-0513; 800-INFO-TVO (463-6886) *E-mail:* asktvo@tvo.org *Web Site:* tvo.org, pg 1046

Deal, Joe, Wacom Technology Corp, 1311 SE Cardinal Ct, Vancouver, WA 98683 *Tel:* 360-896-9833 *Toll Free Tel:* 800-922-6613 *Fax:* 360-896-9734 *Web Site:* www.wacom.com, pg 1061

Deal, Ryan, Regional Artist Project Grants Program, 227 W Trade St, Suite 250, Charlotte, NC 28202 *Tel:* 704-333-2272 *Fax:* 704-333-2720 *E-mail:* asc@artsandscience.org *Web Site:* www.artsandscience.org, pg 1125

Deal, Tammy, Compass Learning Inc, 203 Colorado St, Austin, TX 78701 *Tel:* 512-478-9600 *Toll Free Tel:* 866-586-7387 (sales); 800-678-1412 (cust support) *Web Site:* www.compasslearning.com, pg 833

Dealey, Gary, Big Deal Custom Casings, 100 Durand Rd, Winnipeg, MB R2J 3T2, Canada *Tel:* 204-663-4870 *Toll Free Tel:* 800-337-3325 *Fax:* 204-668-7404 *E-mail:* info@bigdealcases.com *Web Site:* bigdealcases.ca, pg 807

Deame, Jed, RGB Spectrum, 950 Marina Village Pkwy, Alameda, CA 94501 *Tel:* 510-814-7000 *Fax:* 510-814-7026 *E-mail:* sales@rgb.com *Web Site:* www.rgb.com, pg 996

DeAngelis, Laura, KickedUp Media Group Inc, 2 Amherst Dr, Hastings-on-Hudson, NY 10706 *Tel:* 914-693-KICK (693-5425) *E-mail:* info@kickedupmediagroup.com *Web Site:* www.kickedupmediagroup.com, pg 910

DeAngelo, John, Educational Technology Services (ETS), Medical Sciences, Rm SB-43, 513 Parnassus Ave, San Francisco, CA 94143-0702 *Tel:* 415-476-4310 *Fax:* 415-514-3735 *E-mail:* edtech@ucsf.edu *Web Site:* edtech.ucsf.edu, pg 857

DeAngelo, Lisa, SmackDab Media, 1033 Third Ave S, Nashville, TN 37210 *Toll Free Tel:* 888-248-8197 *Web Site:* smackdabmedia.com, pg 1013

Dearth, Jan, Altruist Media LLC, 1023 Williamsport Pike, Martinsburg, WV 25404 *Tel:* 703-812-8813 *Fax:* 703-812-9710 *E-mail:* frank@altruistmedia.com *Web Site:* www.altruistmedia.com, pg 783

Debeer, Beth, Rafik, 812 Broadway, Suite 4, New York, NY 10003 *Tel:* 212-475-7884 *E-mail:* info@rafikvideo.com; sales@rafikvideo.com *Web Site:* www.rafikvideo.com, pg 990

DeBelius, Ken, Spectrum Sound Inc, 1040 Acorn Dr, Suite C, Nashville, TN 37210 *Tel:* 615-391-3700 *Web Site:* www.spectrumsound.net, pg 1021

DeBlasio, Jim, York Telecom, 81 Corbett Way, Eatontown, NJ 07724 *Tel:* 732-413-6000 *Toll Free Tel:* 866-836-8463 *Fax:* 732-413-6060 *E-mail:* knowmore@yorktel.com *Web Site:* yorktel.com, pg 1072

Debold, Joe, Boonton Electronics, 25 Eastmans Rd, Parsippany, NJ 07054 *Tel:* 973-386-9696 *Fax:* 973-386-9191 *E-mail:* info@boonton.com *Web Site:* www.boonton.com, pg 811

Deckelman, William L Jr, Computer Sciences Corp, 3170 Fairview Park Dr, Falls Church, VA 22042 *Tel:* 703-876-1000 *Web Site:* www.csc.com, pg 834

Decker, Joe, Disk Productions, 1100 Perkins Rd, Baton Rouge, LA 70802 *Tel:* 225-343-5438 *E-mail:* disk_productions@yahoo.com, pg 849

DeFrancesco, Steve, Miranda Telecast Fiber Systems Inc, 102 Grove St, Worcester, MA 01605 *Tel:* 508-754-4858 *Fax:* 508-752-1520 *E-mail:* telecast.sales@belden.com *Web Site:* www.miranda.com; www.belden.com, pg 944

DeFries, William, Copp Integrated Systems, 123 S Keowee St, Dayton, OH 45402 *Tel:* 937-228-4188 *Toll Free Tel:* 877-450-2677 *Fax:* 937-228-2901 *Web Site:* www.copp.com, pg 836

Degen, Dennis, Lightronics Inc, 509 Central Dr, Virginia Beach, VA 23454 *Tel:* 757-486-3588 *Toll Free Tel:* 800-472-8541 *Fax:* 757-486-3391 *Web Site:* www.lightronics.com, pg 921

DeGiorgio, Raphael, Diamond Dreams Music Productions, North Ocean County, Carbon Canyon, Chino Hills, CA 91709 *Tel:* 909-393-6120 *Fax:* 909-606-5779 *E-mail:* info@diamonddreamsmusic.com *Web Site:* www.diamonddreamsmusic.com, pg 846

DeHart, Barbara, Telestream Inc, 848 Gold Flat Rd, Nevada City, CA 95959 *Tel:* 530-470-1300 *Toll Free Tel:* 877-257-6245 *Fax:* 530-470-1301 *E-mail:* info@telestream.net *Web Site:* www.telestream.net, pg 1036

DeHaven, Carol, Central Florida Visitors & Convention Bureau, 2701 Lake Myrtle Park Rd, Auburndale, FL 33823-9360 *Tel:* 863-551-4750 *Toll Free Tel:* 800-828-7655 *Fax:* 863-551-4740 *Web Site:* www.visitcentralflorida.org, pg 1095

Dehmer, Mary, Rayven Inc, 431 Griggs St N, St Paul, MN 55104 *Tel:* 651-642-1112 *Toll Free Tel:* 800-878-3776 *Fax:* 651-642-9497 *E-mail:* info@rayven.com *Web Site:* www.rayven.com, pg 992

Dehn, Jelena, JIST Publishing, 875 Montreal Way, St Paul, MN 55102 *Toll Free Tel:* 800-328-1452 *Toll Free Fax:* 800-328-4564 *E-mail:* info@jist.com *Web Site:* www.jist.com, pg 905

Dehne, John, WESCAM Inc, 649 N Service Rd W, Burlington, ON L7P 5B9, Canada *Tel:* 905-633-4000 *Toll Free Tel:* 800-668-4355 *Fax:* 905-633-4100 *E-mail:* sales.wescam@l-3com.com *Web Site:* www.wescam.com, pg 1063

Dejewski, Brenda, Horizon Video Productions Inc, 6114 Fayetteville St, Suite 106, Durham, NC 27713 *Tel:* 919-941-0901 *Toll Free Tel:* 800-768-3776 *Fax:* 919-941-1939 *E-mail:* info@horizonvp.com *Web Site:* www.horizonvp.com, pg 891

DeJong, Duke, CCI Solutions, 1342 88 Ave SE, Olympia, WA 98501 *Tel:* 360-943-5378 *Toll Free Tel:* 800-562-6006 *Fax:* 360-754-1566 *E-mail:* info@ccisolutions.com *Web Site:* www.ccisolutions.com, pg 821

deKramer, Peter, deKramer Productions Inc, 515 Western Ave, Petaluma, CA 94952 *Tel:* 707-765-0888 *E-mail:* dekramer@sonic.net *Web Site:* www.dekramerproductions.com, pg 845

Delaney, Lynn, Robert F Kennedy Journalism Awards, 1300 19 St NW, Suite 750, Washington, DC 20036 *Tel:* 202-463-7575 *E-mail:* info@rfkcenter.org *Web Site:* www.rfkcenter.org, pg 1118

Delapp, Dan, Tecplot Inc, 3535 Factoria Blvd SE, Suite 550, Bellevue, WA 98006 *Tel:* 425-653-1200; 425-653-9393 (tech support) *Toll Free Tel:* 800-763-7005 (orders) *E-mail:* info@tecplot.com; sales@tecplot.com *Web Site:* www.tecplot.com, pg 1035

DeLigter, Harry, Lightworks Audio & Video Inc, PO Box 661593, Los Angeles, CA 90066 *Tel:* 310-398-4949 *Fax:* 310-397-4401 *E-mail:* sales1@lightworksav.com *Web Site:* www.lightworksav.com, pg 921

Delinski, Rachel, Love Your Shorts Film Festival, 608 S Elm Ave, Sanford, FL 32771 *E-mail:* contact@loveyourshorts.com *Web Site:* www.loveyourshorts.com, pg 1119

deLise, Louis, deLise Studios, 83 Park Dr, Cherry Hill, NJ 08002-3002 *Tel:* 856-616-2867 *E-mail:* info@delisestudios.com *Web Site:* www.delisestudios.com, pg 845

Dellenbach, Andy, Mind Over Eye Inc, 2221 Rosecrans Ave, Suite 195, El Segundo, CA 90245 *Tel:* 310-396-4663 *Fax:* 310-297-9526 *E-mail:* info@mindovereye.com *Web Site:* www.mindovereye.com, pg 943

Dellovo, Victor, CSPI, 43 Manning Rd, Billerica, MA 01821 *Tel:* 978-663-7598 *Toll Free Tel:* 800-325-3110 *Fax:* 978-663-0150 *E-mail:* info@cspi.com *Web Site:* www.cspi.com, pg 840

Deltruc, Nicolas Girard, Montreal International Festival of Nouveau Cinema, 3805 Blvd Ste-Laurent, Montreal, QC H2W 1X9, Canada *Tel:* 514-282-0004 *Fax:* 514-282-6664 *E-mail:* info@nouveaucinema.ca *Web Site:* www.nouveaucinema.ca, pg 1120

DeLuca, Joseph, Transistor Devices Inc, 36 Newburgh Rd, Hackettstown, NJ 07840 *Tel:* 908-850-5088 *Fax:* 908-850-1607 *E-mail:* info@tdipower.com *Web Site:* www.tdipower.com, pg 1043

DeMarco, Frank, Outside The Box Interactive LLC, 150 Bay St, Suite 706, Jersey City, NJ 07302 *Tel:* 201-610-0625 *Fax:* 201-610-0627 *E-mail:* theoffice@outboxin.com *Web Site:* www.outboxin.com, pg 966

Dement, Kimble, Dub King, 8133 Callaghan Rd, San Antonio, TX 78230 *Tel:* 210-979-8779 *Toll Free Tel:* 800-542-1187 *E-mail:* dubking@dubking.com *Web Site:* www.dubking.com, pg 853

Demetrescu, Dr Stefan, Lasergraphics Inc, 20 Ada, Irvine, CA 92618 *Tel:* 949-753-8282 *Fax:* 949-727-9282 *E-mail:* info@lasergraphics.com *Web Site:* www.lasergraphics.com, pg 916

Demetriades, Michael, New York Festivals®-International Advertising Awards, 260 W 39 St, 10th fl, New York, NY 10018 *Tel:* 212-643-4800 *Fax:* 212-643-0170 *E-mail:* info@newyorkfestivals.com *Web Site:* www.newyorkfestivals.com, pg 1122

Dempsey, Jamie, Artist Research and Development Grants, 417 W Roosevelt St, Phoenix, AZ 85003-1326 *Tel:* 602-771-6501 *Fax:* 602-256-0282 *E-mail:* info@azarts.gov *Web Site:* www.azarts.gov, pg 1108

Dempsey, Michael, Thread Marketing Group, 4635 W Alexis Rd, Toledo, OH 43623-1005 *Tel:* 419-887-6801 *Toll Free Tel:* 800-397-0126 *Fax:* 419-887-6802 *E-mail:* contact@experiencethread.com *Web Site:* www.experiencethread.com, pg 1039

Denado, Mario, Elegant Packaging Corp, 5253 W Roosevelt Rd, Cicero, IL 60804 *Tel:* 708-652-3400 *Toll Free Tel:* 800-367-5493 *Fax:* 708-652-6444 *E-mail:* info@elegantpackaging.com *Web Site:* www.elegantpackaging.com, pg 859

Denenberg, Peter, Acme Recording Studios Inc, 112 W Boston Post Rd, Mamaroneck, NY 10543 *Tel:* 914-381-4141 *Web Site:* www.acmerec.com, pg 774

Deniston, Donn, Littlite LLC, PO Box 430, Hamburg, MI 48139-0430 *Tel:* 810-852-4242 *Fax:* 810-231-1631 *E-mail:* sales@littlite.com *Web Site:* www.littlite.com, pg 923

Denk, Joe, WFRV-TV 5 CBS, 1181 E Mason St, Green Bay, WI 54301 *Tel:* 920-437-5411 *Fax:* 920-437-4576 *E-mail:* mailbox@wfrv.com *Web Site:* www.wfrv.com, pg 1064

Denke, Conrad W, Victory Studios, 2247 15 Ave W, Seattle, WA 98119 *Tel:* 206-282-1776 *Toll Free Tel:* 888-282-1776 *Fax:* 206-282-3535 *Toll Free Fax:* 888-765-9563 *E-mail:* info@victorystudios.com *Web Site:* www.victorystudios.com, pg 1054

Denkhaus, Don, The Kitchen, 4119 W Burbank Blvd, Burbank, CA 91505 *Tel:* 818-306-5300 *Fax:* 305-415-6201 *E-mail:* info@thekitchen.tv *Web Site:* www.thekitchen.tv, pg 911

Denman, Ron, Kenyon Laboratories LLC, 12 Scovil Rd, Higganum, CT 06441 *Tel:* 860-345-2097 *Toll Free Tel:* 800-253-4681 *Fax:* 860-345-8652 *E-mail:* kenyonlabs@comcast.net *Web Site:* www.ken-lab.com, pg 910

Dennis, Mike, Master Mind Publishing Co, 11200 E 11 Mile Rd, Warren, MI 48089 *Tel:* 586-353-2300 *Toll Free Tel:* 800-758-3055 *Fax:* 586-758-7249 *E-mail:* info@renaissanceunity.org *Web Site:* www.renaissanceunity.org, pg 933

Dennison, Richard, Eagle Multimedia, 6024 Paseo Palmilla, Goleta, CA 93117 *Tel:* 805-964-7041 *Fax:* 805-964-1338 *E-mail:* dicepoo@aol.com *Web Site:* www.eaglemultimedia.com, pg 855

Denniston, Brackett B III, General Electric Co, 3135 Easton Tpke, Fairfield, CT 06828 *Tel:* 203-373-2211 *Fax:* 203-373-3131 *Web Site:* www.ge.com, pg 877

Denny, Gary, Wisconsin Public Television, 821 University Ave, Madison, WI 53706 *Tel:* 608-263-2121 *Toll Free Tel:* 800-422-9707 *Fax:* 608-263-9763 *E-mail:* comments@wpt.org *Web Site:* www.wpt.org, pg 1068

Depper, Kristy, Centre for Art Tapes (CFAT), 2238 Maitland St, Halifax, NS B3K 2Z9, Canada *Tel:* 902-422-6822 *Fax:* 902-422-6823 *E-mail:* info@cfat.ca *Web Site:* cfat.ca, pg 1080

DePree, Dori, Waterfront Film Festival (WFF), PO Box 387, Saugatuck, MI 49453-0387 *Tel:* 269-857-8351 *Fax:* 269-857-1072 *E-mail:* info@waterfrontfilm.org *Web Site:* www.waterfrontfilm.org, pg 1129

DePree, Hopwood, Waterfront Film Festival (WFF), PO Box 387, Saugatuck, MI 49453-0387 *Tel:* 269-857-8351 *Fax:* 269-857-1072 *E-mail:* info@waterfrontfilm.org *Web Site:* www.waterfrontfilm.org, pg 1129

DePree-Minter, Dana, Waterfront Film Festival (WFF), PO Box 387, Saugatuck, MI 49453-0387 *Tel:* 269-857-8351 *Fax:* 269-857-1072 *E-mail:* info@waterfrontfilm.org *Web Site:* www.waterfrontfilm.org, pg 1129

Deputy, Dave, Techni-Tool Inc, 1547 N Trooper Rd, Worcester, PA 19490 *Tel:* 610-941-2400 *Toll Free Tel:* 800-832-4866 *Fax:* 610-828-5623 *Toll Free Fax:* 800-854-8665 *E-mail:* sales@techni-tool.com *Web Site:* www.techni-tool.com, pg 1033

Der Boghosian, Greg, Century Color Labs Inc, 494 School St, East Hartford, CT 06108 *Tel:* 860-289-9501 *Toll Free Tel:* 800-242-9501 *Fax:* 860-291-9098 *E-mail:* production@centurycolor.com *Web Site:* www.centurycolor.com, pg 823

Der, Tom, Soundcraft USA, 8500 Balboa Blvd, North Ridge, CA 91329 *Tel:* 818-920-3212 *Fax:* 818-920-3209 *E-mail:* soundcraft-usa@harman.com *Web Site:* usa.soundcraft.com, pg 1018

Derkatsch, Erick, InterNation Inc, 299 Broadway, Suite 1400, New York, NY 10007 *Tel:* 212-619-5545 *Toll Free Tel:* 800-222-8799 *Fax:* 212-619-5887 *E-mail:* info@internation.com *Web Site:* www.internation.com, pg 900

Dermer, Marlene, Los Angeles Latino International Film Festival (LALIFF), 453 S Spring St, Suite 1030, Los Angeles, CA 90013 *Tel:* 323-446-2770 *Fax:* 323-446-2770 *E-mail:* info@latinofilm.org *Web Site:* latinofilm.org, pg 1119

Dermody, William III, Techflex Inc, 29 Brookfield Dr, Sparta, NJ 07871 *Tel:* 973-300-9242 *Toll Free Tel:* 800-323-5140 *Fax:* 973-300-9409 *E-mail:* techflex@techflex.com *Web Site:* www.techflex.com, pg 1033

DeRock, Anne, Spirit Media, 12042 SE Sunnyside Rd, Suite 700, Happy Valley, OR 97015 *Tel:* 503-698-5540 *Fax:* 503-698-8408 *E-mail:* info@spiritmedia.com *Web Site:* www.spiritmedia.com, pg 1021

Derohanessian, Alfred, Total Concept Sales, 2505 Foothill Blvd, Suite G, La Crescentia, CA 91214 *Tel:* 818-236-3966 *Toll Free Tel:* 800-488-0589 *Fax:* 818-236-3969 *E-mail:* info@smartups.com *Web Site:* www.smartups.com, pg 1042

Derosier, David, Merestone, 7232 E First St, Scottsdale, AZ 85251 *Tel:* 480-945-4631 *Fax:* 480-945-0590 *Web Site:* www.merestone.com, pg 938

Derry, Patricia A, Technology Learning Services, 36600 Schoolcraft Rd, Livonia, MI 48150-1173 *Tel:* 734-432-5800 *Toll Free Tel:* 800-852-4951 *Web Site:* ww3.madonna.edu/tls, pg 1035

Des Combes, Jeff, Sprocket Digital, PO Box 1420, Claremont, CA 91711 *Tel:* 909-946-2364 *Fax:* 909-946-2631 *E-mail:* sdsales@sprocketdigital.com *Web Site:* www.sprocketdigital.com, pg 1022

DeSantis, Mark, WEEK TV, 2907 Springfield Rd, East Peoria, IL 61611 *Tel:* 309-698-2525 *Fax:* 309-698-9335 *Web Site:* www.week.com, pg 1063

Desha, Kirby, Audio Editions Books-On-Cassette & CD, 131 E Placer St, Auburn, CA 95603 *Tel:* 530-888-7801 *Toll Free Tel:* 800-231-4261 *Toll Free Fax:* 800-882-1840 *E-mail:* info@audioeditions.com *Web Site:* audioeditions.com; audioeditionslibrary.com, pg 794

DeShazor, Brian, Pacifica Radio Archives, 3729 Cahuenga Blvd W, North Hollywood, CA 91604 *Tel:* 818-506-1077 *Toll Free Tel:* 800-735-0230 *Fax:* 818-506-1084 *E-mail:* pacarchive@aol.com *Web Site:* www.pacificaradioarchives.org, pg 967

Desjardine, Elise, Thompson Rivers University Open Learning, BC Centre for Open Learning, 4th fl, 900 McGill Rd, Kamloops, BC V2C 0C8, Canada *Tel:* 250-852-7000 *Toll Free Tel:* 800-663-9711 *E-mail:* student@tru.ca; olmarketing@tru.ca *Web Site:* www.tru.ca/distance, pg 1039

Desmond, Dan, L-3 Integrated Optical Systems, 4040 Lakeside Dr, Richmond, CA 94806-1963 *Tel:* 510-222-8110 *Fax:* 510-223-4534 *E-mail:* sales@asphere.com *Web Site:* www.asphere.com, pg 915

Desplas, John, New Orleans Film Festival, 900 Camp St, New Orleans, LA 70130 *Tel:* 504-309-6633 *Fax:* 504-309-0923 *E-mail:* info@neworleansfilmfest.com *Web Site:* www.neworleansfilmsociety.org, pg 1122

DeToni, Dale, Ozam Production, 1516 Equestrian Rd, Ozark, MO 65721 *Tel:* 417-866-3232 *Web Site:* ozam.com, pg 966

Deushane, John, WATL-TV Inc, One Monroe Place NE, Atlanta, GA 30324 *Tel:* 404-892-1611 *Fax:* 404-881-3635 *Web Site:* www.myatltv.com, pg 1062

Deutsch, John, OmniMount Systems, 4409 E Baseline Rd, Suite 130, Phoenix, AZ 85042 *Tel:* 480-829-8000 *Toll Free Tel:* 800-MOUNT-IT (668-6848) *Fax:* 480-756-9000 *E-mail:* info@omnimount.com *Web Site:* www.omnimount.com, pg 962

DeVaney, Alan, Crispin Corp, 600 Wade Ave, Raleigh, NC 27605 *Tel:* 919-845-7744 *Fax:* 919-845-7766 *E-mail:* welisten@crispincorp.com *Web Site:* www.crispincorp.com, pg 839

DeVault, George Jr, WKPT-TV, 222 Commerce St, Kingsport, TN 37660 *Tel:* 423-246-9578 *Fax:* 423-246-1863 *Web Site:* www.abc19.tv, pg 1068

deVeer, James A, Advanced Lighting & Production Services Inc (ALPS), 65 Teed Dr, Randolph, MA 02368 *Tel:* 781-961-3066 *Toll Free Tel:* 866-961-3066 *Fax:* 781-961-3256 *E-mail:* info@alpsweb.com *Web Site:* www.alpsweb.com, pg 777

DeVerna, Darren, Production Resource Group LLC (PRG), 539 Temple Hill Rd, New Windsor, NY 12553-5533 *Tel:* 845-567-5700 *Fax:* 845-567-5800 *E-mail:* info@prg.com *Web Site:* www.prg.com, pg 984

DeVita, Janet, A & J Cases, 11121 Hindry Ave, Los Angeles, CA 90045 *Tel:* 310-216-2170 *Toll Free Tel:* 800-537-4000 *Fax:* 310-216-2694 *Web Site:* www.ajcases.com, pg 771

Dew, Mari, The Pocket Studios, 920 Eastern Ave, Top fl, Toronto, ON M4L 1A4, Canada *Tel:* 416-466-0029 *E-mail:* info@thepocketstudios.com *Web Site:* www.thepocketstudios.com, pg 977

Dewar, Jeff, QCI International, PO Box 1769, Chico, CA 95927-1769 *Tel:* 530-893-4095 *Fax:* 530-893-0395 *E-mail:* info@qci-intl.com *Web Site:* www.qualitydigest.com, pg 988

DeWitt, Debbie, Visix™ Inc, 230 Scientific Dr, Suite 80, Norcross, GA 30092 *Tel:* 770-446-1416 *Toll Free Tel:* 800-572-4935 *Fax:* 770-448-5724 *E-mail:* info@visix.com *Web Site:* www.visix.com, pg 1059

Dexter, Letty, Everlast Productions, 59 SW 12 Ave, Unit 109, Dania Beach, FL 33004 *Tel:* 954-456-7167 *Fax:* 954-456-1243 *E-mail:* info@everlastproductions.com *Web Site:* everlastproductions.com, pg 863

Dhanyam, Swami Prabodh, Osho Viha Information Center & Book Distributors, PO Box 352, Mill Valley, CA 94942-0352 *Tel:* 415-472-5381 *Toll Free Tel:* 866-856-7019 *Fax:* 415-472-5149 *E-mail:* oshoviha@oshoviha.org *Web Site:* www.oshoviha.org, pg 965

Di Chiera, Cristina M, Rhode Island State Council on the Arts Fellowships & Grants Program, One Capitol Hill, 3rd fl, Providence, RI 02908 *Tel:* 401-222-3880 *Fax:* 401-222-3018 *E-mail:* info@arts.ri.gov *Web Site:* www.arts.ri.gov, pg 1125

Di Giacomo, Lori, Long Island Video Enterprises Live Inc, 110 Pratt Oval, Glen Cove, NY 11542 *Tel:* 516-759-5483 *Fax:* 516-671-5874 *E-mail:* info@longislandvideo.com *Web Site:* www.longislandvideo.com, pg 924

Di Lorenzo, Gene, Media Loft Inc, 615 First Ave NE, Suite 100, Minneapolis, MN 55413 *Tel:* 612-375-1086 *Fax:* 612-375-0913 *E-mail:* info@medialoft.net *Web Site:* www.medialoft.net, pg 937

Di Yeso, Michael, Freedoms Foundation National Awards, 1601 Valley Forge Rd, Valley Forge, PA 19482 *Tel:* 610-933-8825 *Fax:* 610-935-0522 *E-mail:* info@ffvf.org *Web Site:* www.freedomsfoundation.com, pg 1115

Diamond, Ron, Acme Filmworks, 3347 Motor Ave, Suite 100, Los Angeles, CA 90034 *Tel:* 323-464-7805 *Fax:* 323-464-6614 *Web Site:* www.acmefilmworks.com, pg 774

Diaz, Chris, Dazian Inc, 18 Central Blvd, South Hackensack, NJ 07606 *Toll Free Tel:* 877-232-9426 *Fax:* 201-641-2728; 201-549-1055 *E-mail:* info@dazian.com *Web Site:* www.dazian.com, pg 844

Diaz, Jonathan, HEC Reading Horizons, 60 N Cutler Dr, Suite 101, North Salt Lake, UT 84054 *Tel:* 801-295-7054 *Toll Free Tel:* 800-333-0054 *Fax:* 801-295-7088 *E-mail:* info@readinghorizons.com *Web Site:* www.readinghorizons.com, pg 887

DiCanto, Marie, SYMCO Inc, 29 Poplar Dr, Stirling, NJ 07980 *Tel:* 908-647-6262 *Fax:* 908-647-4904 *E-mail:* orders@symcoinc.com *Web Site:* www.symcoinc.com, pg 1030

Dickensheets, Ken, Dickensheets Design Associates, 12335 Hymeadow Dr, Suite 200, Austin, TX 78750 *Tel:* 512-331-8977 *Toll Free Tel:* 800-545-5734 *Web Site:* www.dickensheets.com, pg 846

Dickerson, Brandon, Kaboom Productions, 1465 Illinois St, San Francisco, CA 94107 *Tel:* 415-434-2666 *Fax:* 415-970-8548 *E-mail:* updates@kaboomproductions.com *Web Site:* kaboomproductions.com, pg 907

Dickerson, Rich, Jai Pulnix, 625 River Oaks Pkwy, San Jose, CA 95134 *Tel:* 408-383-0300 *Toll Free Tel:* 800-445-5444 *Fax:* 408-383-0301 *E-mail:* camerasales.americas@jai.com *Web Site:* www.jai.com, pg 987

Dickey, Joey, International Cellulose Corp, 12315 Robin Blvd, Houston, TX 77045 *Tel:* 713-433-6701 *Toll Free Tel:* 800-444-1252 *Fax:* 713-433-2029 *E-mail:* icc@spray-on.com *Web Site:* www.spray-on.com, pg 900

Dickey, Teresa, Cinema Concepts, 2030 Powers Ferry Rd, Suite 214, Atlanta, GA 30339 *Tel:* 770-956-7460 *Toll Free Tel:* 800-SHOWADS (746-9237) *Fax:* 770-956-8358 *E-mail:* info@cinemaconcepts.com *Web Site:* www.cinemaconcepts.com, pg 827

Dickinson, Rik, Encore Video Productions, 811 Main St, Myrtle Beach, SC 29577 *Tel:* 843-448-9900 *E-mail:* crew@encorevideo.biz *Web Site:* www.encorevideo.biz, pg 861

Dickinson, Tom, Bexel Corp, 2701 N Ontario St, Burbank, CA 91504 *Tel:* 818-565-4322 *Toll Free Tel:* 800-225-6185 (tech support) *E-mail:* rentals@bexel.com *Web Site:* www.bexel.com, pg 806

Dickson, Natasha, Vancouver Film Studios Ltd, 3500 Cornett Rd, Vancouver, BC V5M 2H5, Canada *Tel:* 604-453-5000 *Fax:* 604-453-5045 *Web Site:* www.vancouverfilmstudios.com, pg 1051

Dickson, Steve, Primacoustic, 1588 Kebet Way, Port Coquitlam, BC V3C 5M5, Canada *Tel:* 604-942-1001 *Fax:* 604-942-1010 *E-mail:* info@primacoustic.com *Web Site:* www.primacoustic.com, pg 982

Diddell, Wendy, Canvys™, 40W267 Keslinger Rd, La Fox, IL 60147-0393 *Toll Free Tel:* 888-735-7373 *Fax:* 630-208-2830 *Web Site:* www.canvys.com, pg 819

Didier, Rebecca, Trafalgar Square Books, 388 Howe Hill Rd, North Pomfret, VT 05053 *Tel:* 802-457-1911 *Toll Free Tel:* 800-423-4525 *Fax:* 802-457-1913 *E-mail:* info@horseandriderbooks.com *Web Site:* www.horseandriderbooks.com, pg 1043

Diekemper, Gregory R, Swank Audio Visuals, 639-E Gravois Bluffs, St Louis, MO 63026 *Tel:* 636-680-9000 *Toll Free Tel:* 877-792-6528 *Fax:* 636-680-2853 *Web Site:* www.swankav.com, pg 1029

Diemer, Richard, Diemer Amp & Keyboard Repair, 12814 Landale St, Studio City, CA 91604-1351 *Tel:* 818-762-0804 *Web Site:* bustedgear.com, pg 846

Diercks, Richard, The Richard Diercks Co Inc, 3140 Harbor Lane N, Suite 223, Minneapolis, MN 55447 *Tel:* 763-231-3303 *Fax:* 763-231-3307 *E-mail:* rdiercks@diercks.com *Web Site:* www.dvdauthor.com, pg 846

Dieterich, Carrie, The Entertainment Merchants Association (EMA), 16530 Ventura Blvd, Suite 400, Encino, CA 91436-4551 *Tel:* 818-385-1500 *Fax:* 818-933-0910 *E-mail:* emaoffice@entmerch.org *Web Site:* www.entmerch.org, pg 1081

Dietrich, Kathy, The Optikon Corp, 1099 Guelph St, Kitchener, ON N2B 2E4, Canada *Tel:* 519-745-4115 *Fax:* 519-745-6922 *E-mail:* info@optikon.ca *Web Site:* www.optikon.ca, pg 964

DiGiacomio, Michael, The Old Rhinebeck Aerodome®, 9 Norton Rd, Red Hook, NY 12571 *Tel:* 845-752-3200 *Fax:* 845-758-6481 *E-mail:* info@oldrhinebeck.org *Web Site:* www.oldrhinebeck.org, pg 961

DiGiacomo, Gabe, Nilfisk-Advance America Inc, 740 Hemlock Rd, Suite 100, Morgantown, PA 19543 *Toll Free Tel:* 800-NILFISK (645-3475) *Fax:* 610-286-7350 *E-mail:* questions@nilfisk.com *Web Site:* www.nilfiskcfm.com, pg 957

Digre, Dan, MISCO, 2637 32 Ave S, Minneapolis, MN 55406-1641 *Tel:* 612-825-1010 *Toll Free Tel:* 800-276-9955 *Fax:* 612-825-7010 *E-mail:* info@miscospeakers.com *Web Site:* www.miscospeakers.com, pg 944

Dijak, Charlie, EPIX Inc, 381 Lexington Dr, Buffalo Grove, IL 60089 *Tel:* 847-465-1818 *Fax:* 847-465-1919 *E-mail:* epix@epixinc.com *Web Site:* epixinc.com, pg 862

Dillard, Felicia, Association for Information and Image Management (AIIM), 1100 Wayne Ave, Suite 1100, Silver Spring, MD 20910 *Tel:* 301-587-8202 *Toll Free Tel:* 800-477-2446 *Fax:* 301-587-2711 *E-mail:* aiim@aiim.org *Web Site:* www.aiim.org, pg 1078

Diller, Wendell, Magnepan Inc, 1645 Ninth St, White Bear Lake, MN 55110 *Tel:* 651-426-1645 *Toll Free Tel:* 800-474-1646 *Fax:* 651-426-0441 *Web Site:* www.magnepan.com, pg 928

Dilley, Michael S, Producers Studio, PO Box 7846, Eugene, OR 97401-0032 *Tel:* 541-683-1400 *Fax:* 541-683-1401 *E-mail:* producer@cyberis.net *Web Site:* www.producers-studio.com, pg 984

Diltz, Robert, RB Productions, 3-4191 Longmoor Dr, Burlington, ON L7L 5J9, Canada *Tel:* 905-633-7474 *Toll Free Tel:* 866-633-7474 *E-mail:* sales@radicalbob.com *Web Site:* www.rbproductionz.com, pg 992

Dinnell, David, Ann Arbor Film Festival, 217 N First St, Ann Arbor, MI 48104 *Tel:* 734-995-5356 *Fax:* 734-995-5396 *E-mail:* info@aafilmfest.org *Web Site:* www.aafilmfest.org, pg 1107

Dinoffer, Joe, Oncourt Offcourt Ltd, 6301 Gaston Ave, Suite 650, Dallas, TX 75214 *Tel:* 214-823-3078 *Toll Free Tel:* 888-366-4711 (88-TENNIS-11) *Fax:* 214-823-3082 *E-mail:* info@oncourtoffcourt.com *Web Site:* www.oncourtoffcourt.com, pg 963

DiPietro, Patrick, Tellabs Inc, One Tellabs Ctr, 1415 W Diehl Rd, Naperville, IL 60563 *Tel:* 630-798-8800 *Fax:* 630-798-2000 *Web Site:* www.tellabs.com, pg 1037

DiPrinzio, Kathy, Key of David Publications, PO Box 153, Merion, PA 19066 *Tel:* 610-896-1970 *Fax:* 610-896-1970 *Web Site:* www.keyofdavidpublications.org, pg 910

Dirks, Jason, Sinauer Associates Inc, 23 Plumtree Rd, Sunderland, MA 01375 *Tel:* 413-549-4300 *Fax:* 413-549-1118 *E-mail:* orders@sinauer.com (orders); custserv@sinauer.com (cust serv); publish@sinauer.com (general edit correspondence) *Web Site:* www.sinauer.com, pg 1012

DiScalfani, Robert, Bond Street Studio, 235 Bond St, Brooklyn, NY 11217 *Tel:* 718-858-2238 *Fax:* 718-858-2239 *E-mail:* info@bondstreetstudio.com *Web Site:* www.bondstreetstudio.com, pg 810

Dishong, Jay, Convergent Media Systems, 190 Bluegrass Valley Pkwy, Alpharetta, GA 30005-2204 *Tel:* 770-369-9000 *Toll Free Tel:* 800-877-7804 *Fax:* 770-369-9100 *E-mail:* convergent@convergent.com *Web Site:* www.convergent.com, pg 836

Dishong, Jay, Vitec Videocom Inc, 709 Executive Blvd, Valley Cottage, NY 10989 *Tel:* 845-268-0100 *Fax:* 845-268-0113 *E-mail:* info-cd-usa@vitecgroup.com *Web Site:* www.vitecgroup.com, pg 1060

Dissley, Susan, Enterprise Media LLC, 91 Harvey St, Cambridge, MA 02140 *Tel:* 617-354-0017 *Toll Free Tel:* 800-423-6021 *Fax:* 617-354-1637 *E-mail:* orders@enterprisemedia.com *Web Site:* www.enterprisemedia.com, pg 861

Ditchfield, Brian, The Martha's Vineyard Film Festival (MVFF), PO Box 592, 9 State Rd, Chilmark, MA 02535 *Tel:* 508-645-9599 *Fax:* 508-645-9893 *Web Site:* www.tmvff.org, pg 1119

Dittgen, Dave, The PPS Group, 424 Scott St, Covington, KY 41011 *Tel:* 859-291-5100 *Toll Free Tel:* 800-978-3445 *Fax:* 859-291-5150 *E-mail:* info@theppsgroup.com *Web Site:* www.pps-inc.com; www.theppsgroup.com, pg 980

Dittrich, Scott, Action Sports/All Stock, PO Box 301, Malibu, CA 90265-0301 *Tel:* 310-459-2526 *Fax:* 310-456-1743 *E-mail:* info@sdfilms.com *Web Site:* www.actionsportsstockfootage.com, pg 775

Dituri, Angelo, General Audio-Visual Inc (GAVI), 92 E Merrick Rd, Freeport, NY 11520 *Tel:* 516-623-8500 *Fax:* 516-623-9155 *E-mail:* miked@gavi.com *Web Site:* www.gavi.com, pg 876

Dituri, Michael, General Audio-Visual Inc (GAVI), 92 E Merrick Rd, Freeport, NY 11520 *Tel:* 516-623-8500 *Fax:* 516-623-9155 *E-mail:* miked@gavi.com *Web Site:* www.gavi.com, pg 876

Divincenzo, Diane, Manfrotto Distribution Inc, 10 Mountainview Rd, Suite 320 S, Upper Saddle River, NJ 07458 *Tel:* 201-818-9500 *Fax:* 201-818-9177 *E-mail:* info@manfrottodistribution.us *Web Site:* www.manfrottodistribution.us, pg 930

Divine, Brian, AKG Acoustics US, 8500 Balboa Blvd, Northridge, CA 91329 *Tel:* 818-920-3212 *Fax:* 818-920-3208 *E-mail:* akgusa@harman.com *Web Site:* www.akg.com/us, pg 779

Dix, Bob, Schafer World Communications Corp, PO Box 1047, Marion, VA 24354-1047 *Tel:* 276-783-2000, pg 1004

Dixon, Brian, Torpey Time, 580 Danforth Rd, Toronto, ON M1K 1E3, Canada *Tel:* 416-261-3773 *E-mail:* helpdesk@dixonsystems.com; technicalsupport@dixonsystems.com *Web Site:* www.dixonsystems.com, pg 1042

Dixon, Fred, Visual Aids Electronics Corp, 12900 Cloverleaf Center Dr, Suite C, Germantown, MD 20874 *Tel:* 301-330-6900 *Fax:* 301-330-6901 *Web Site:* www.vaecorp.com, pg 1059

Dixon, Mark, Connecticut Office of Film, Television & Digital Media, c/o Dept of Economic & Community Development, 505 Hudson St, Hartford, CT 06106 *Tel:* 860-270-8198 *Web Site:* www.ctfilm.com, pg 1095

Dixon, Wes, Keywest Technology Inc, 14563 W 96 Terr, Lenexa, KS 66215 *Tel:* 913-492-4666 *Toll Free Tel:* 800-331-2019 *Fax:* 913-322-1864 *E-mail:* info@keywesttechnology.com; sales@keywesttechnology.com *Web Site:* www.keywesttechnology.com, pg 910

Dixson, Rogers, CDAI Innovative Design Solutions, 4279 Roswell Rd NE, Suite 102, No 135, Atlanta, GA 30342 *Tel:* 404-633-8861 *Fax:* 404-636-5089 *E-mail:* info@cdai.com *Web Site:* www.cdai.com, pg 822

Djou, Benjamin, Cibola Systems, 180 S Cypress St, Orange, CA 92866 *Tel:* 714-480-0272 *Fax:* 714-480-0768 *E-mail:* info@cibolasystems.com *Web Site:* cibolasystems.com, pg 826

Do, Chris, Blind, 1702 Olympic Blvd, Santa Monica, CA 90404 *Tel:* 310-314-1618 *Fax:* 310-314-1718 *Web Site:* www.blind.com, pg 809

Dobbin, Margaret E, Open Text Corp, 275 Frank Tompa Dr, Waterloo, ON N2L 0A1, Canada *Tel:* 519-888-7111 *Toll Free Tel:* 800-499-6544; 800-4996-5440 (intl) *Fax:* 519-888-0677 *E-mail:* support@opentext.com *Web Site:* www.opentext.com, pg 964

Dobronski, Mark, Teletech Inc, 38235 Executive Dr, Westland, MI 48185 *Tel:* 734-641-2300, pg 1036

Dochard, Elaine, Bennett Media Corp, 2321 Abbot Kinney Blvd, Venice, CA 90291 *Tel:* 310-827-8064 *Toll Free Tel:* 800-733-8862 *Fax:* 310-827-8074 *E-mail:* sale@bennettmarine.com *Web Site:* www.bennettmarine.com, pg 805

Dochard, Elaine, TMW Media Group, 2321 Abbot Kinney Blvd, Suite 101, Venice, CA 90291 *Tel:* 310-577-8581 *Toll Free Tel:* 800-262-8862 *Fax:* 310-574-0886 *E-mail:* sale@tmwmedia.com *Web Site:* www.tmwmedia.com, pg 1041

Dodd, Christopher J, Motion Picture Association of America (MPAA), 15301 Ventura Blvd, Bldg E, Sherman Oaks, CA 91403-5885 *Tel:* 818-995-6600 *Fax:* 818-285-4403 *E-mail:* contactus@mpaa.org *Web Site:* www.mpaa.org, pg 1084

Dodds, Derek, Krishnamurti Foundation of America, 1070 McAndrew Rd, Ojai, CA 93023 *Tel:* 805-646-2726 (ext 10) *Fax:* 805-646-6674 *E-mail:* kfa@kfa.org *Web Site:* www.kfa.org, pg 913

Dodenhoff, Lisa, Mark Druck Productions, 300 E 40 St, New York, NY 10016 *Tel:* 212-682-5980 *Fax:* 212-682-5981, pg 852

Dodge, Kathleen, El Dorado Lake Tahoe Film & Media Office, 542 Main St, Placerville, CA 95667 *Tel:* 530-626-4400 *Toll Free Tel:* 800-457-6279 *Fax:* 530-642-1624 *E-mail:* film@eldoradocounty.org *Web Site:* filmtahoe.com, pg 1093

Dodson, Reynold, BitFlow Inc, 400 W Cummings Park, Suite 5050, Woburn, MA 01801 *Tel:* 781-932-2900 *Fax:* 781-933-9965 *E-mail:* sales@bitflow.com *Web Site:* www.bitflow.com, pg 808

Doepel, Bob, Chicago Scenic Studios Inc, 1315 N Branch St, Chicago, IL 60642 *Tel:* 312-274-9900 *Fax:* 312-274-9901 *E-mail:* info@chicagoscenic.com *Web Site:* www.chicagoscenic.com, pg 825

Doerschuk, John, Terry Hanley Audio Systems Inc, 20 Industrial Pkwy, Woburn, MA 01801 *Tel:* 781-932-5300 *Fax:* 781-932-5354 *E-mail:* mail@terryhanleyaudio.com *Web Site:* www.terryhanleyaudio.com, pg 884

Doggett, Felicia, Metropolitan Acoustics LLC, 40 W Evergreen Ave, Suite 108, Philadelphia, PA 19118 *Tel:* 215-248-4352 *Fax:* 215-248-4353 *E-mail:* info@metro-acoustics.com *Web Site:* www.metro-acoustics.com, pg 940

Doherty, Jennifer, New England Technology Group Inc (NETG), One Davenport St, Cambridge, MA 02140 *Tel:* 617-864-5551 *Fax:* 520-844-5551 *E-mail:* teamnetg@netgworld.com *Web Site:* netgworld.com, pg 955

Doiron, Paul, Down East Books, 680 Commercial St, Rockport, ME 04856 *Tel:* 207-594-9544 *Toll Free Tel:* 800-766-1670 *Fax:* 207-594-0147 *E-mail:* editorial@downeast.com *Web Site:* www.downeast.com, pg 851

Doiuchi, Frances, TEC/West USA Inc, 3050 E Victoria St, Rancho Dominguez, CA 90221 *Tel:* 310-961-3491 *Toll Free Tel:* 800-421-7215 *Fax:* 310-464-9210 *E-mail:* info@tecwest.com *Web Site:* www.tecwest.com, pg 1033

Dolak, John, Sony Electronics Inc, 16530 Via Esprillo, San Diego, CA 92127 *Tel:* 858-942-2400 *Web Site:* www.sony.com, pg 1016

Dolan, Bill, Spirit Media, 12042 SE Sunnyside Rd, Suite 700, Happy Valley, OR 97015 *Tel:* 503-698-5540 *Fax:* 503-698-8408 *E-mail:* info@spiritmedia.com *Web Site:* www.spiritmedia.com, pg 1021

Dolan, Drew, I-25 Studios, 9201 Pan American Fwy NE, Albuquerque, NM 87113 *Tel:* 505-822-7115 *Fax:* 505-314-7094 *E-mail:* info@i-25studios.com *Web Site:* i-25studios.com, pg 893

Dolan, Greg, Xytech Systems Corp, 15451 San Fernando Mission Blvd, Suite 400, Mission Hills, CA 91345 *Tel:* 818-698-4900 *Fax:* 818-698-4901 *E-mail:* sales@xytechsystems.com *Web Site:* www.xytechsystems.com, pg 1071

Dolan, James L, Madison Square Garden, 4 Pennsylvania Plaza, New York, NY 10001 *Tel:* 212-465-6000; 212-465-6741 *Fax:* 212-465-4416 *E-mail:* msgnetpr@msgnetwork.com *Web Site:* www.thegarden.com; www.msg.com, pg 928

Doll, Michael, DH Satellite, 600 N Marquette Rd, Prairie du Chien, WI 53821 *Tel:* 608-326-8406 *Toll Free Tel:* 800-627-9443 *Fax:* 608-326-4233 *E-mail:* dhsat@mhtc.net *Web Site:* www.dhsatellite.com, pg 846

Dollarhide, Jim, Dollarhide Film Inc, 764 Lake Cavalier Rd, Madison, MS 39110 *Tel:* 601-946-8407 *Web Site:* www.dollarhide.net, pg 850

Dombrovskis, Aigar, Roadworthy Image Magnification, 1501 N Magnolia Ave, Chicago, IL 60642 *Tel:* 312-649-1800 *Toll Free Tel:* 800-C-DA SHOW (232-7469) *Fax:* 312-642-7441 *E-mail:* imag@atomicimaging.com *Web Site:* www.atomicimaging.com; www.golan.tv/roadworthy/index.html, pg 998

Dombrowski, Frank, Gage-Line Technology Inc, 121 LaGrange Ave, Rochester, NY 14613-1577 *Tel:* 585-458-2000 *Toll Free Tel:* 800-291-3724 *Fax:* 585-458-0524 *E-mail:* sales@gage-line.com *Web Site:* www.gage-line.com, pg 874

Domenech, Daniel A, American Association of School Administrators (AASA), 1615 Duke St, Alexandria, VA 22314 *Tel:* 703-528-0700 *Fax:* 703-841-1543 *E-mail:* info@aasa.org *Web Site:* www.aasa.org, pg 1076

Donahue, Bob, pinta acoustic inc, 2601 49 Ave N, Suite 400, Minneapolis, MN 55430 *Tel:* 612-355-4200 *Toll Free Tel:* 800-662-0032 *Fax:* 612-355-4299 *E-mail:* sales@pinta-acoustic.com; info@pinta-acoustic.com *Web Site:* www.pinta-acoustic.com, pg 976

Donald, Kevin, Vela Research, 5540 Rio Vista Dr, Clearwater, FL 33760-3107 *Tel:* 727-507-5300 *Fax:* 727-507-5312 *E-mail:* vela_info@vela.com *Web Site:* www.vela.com, pg 1052

Donald, Tom, Tom Donald Films, 601 Fourth St, Suite 320, San Francisco, CA 94107 *Tel:* 415-546-4966 *Fax:* 415-546-5145 *Web Site:* www.tomdonaldfilms.com, pg 850

Donaldson, Eric Alan, FXF Productions Inc, 1024 Harding Ave, Suite 201, Venice Beach, CA 90291 *Tel:* 310-577-5009 *Fax:* 310-577-1960 *E-mail:* info@fxfproductions.com *Web Site:* www.fxfproductions.com, pg 874

Donhue, Ed, Rosco Laboratories Inc, 52 Harbor View, Stamford, CT 06902 *Tel:* 203-708-8900 *Toll Free Tel:* 800-ROSCO NY (767-2669) *Fax:* 203-708-8919 *E-mail:* info@rosco.com *Web Site:* www.rosco.com, pg 999

Donio, James, Music Business Association (Music Biz), One Eves Dr, Suite 138, Marlton, NJ 08053 *Tel:* 856-596-2221 *Fax:* 856-596-7299 *Web Site:* www.musicbiz.org, pg 1084

Donnelly, Bill, Laughing Dog Studio Inc, 59 Hylan Blvd, Apt 1C, Staten Island, NY 10305 *Tel:* 917-496-7752 *E-mail:* lafndog@inch.com *Web Site:* billdonnelly.com, pg 916

Donnelly, Denis BE, BFS Entertainment & Multimedia Limited, 360 Newkirk Rd, Richmond Hill, ON L4C 3G7, Canada *Tel:* 905-884-2323 *Fax:* 905-884-8292 *E-mail:* info@bfsent.com; contact@bfsent.com *Web Site:* www.bfsent.com, pg 806

Donohue, Mike, Alliance Entertainment Corp (AEC) LLC, 4250 Coral Ridge Dr, Coral Springs, FL 33065 *Tel:* 954-346-4024 *Toll Free Tel:* 800-356-2049 (ext 4600) *Web Site:* www.aent.com, pg 781

Doo, Danna, Producers Management Television (PMTV), 681 Moore Rd, Suite 100, King of Prussia, PA 19406 *Tel:* 610-768-1770 *Fax:* 610-768-1773 *E-mail:* info@pmtv.com *Web Site:* www.pmtv.com, pg 983

Doody, Brian, Teledyne DALSA Inc, 605 McMurray Rd, Waterloo, ON N2V 2E9, Canada *Tel:* 519-886-6000 *Fax:* 519-886-8023 *E-mail:* sales.americas@teledynedalsa.com *Web Site:* www.teledynedalsa.com, pg 1036

Dooley, Greg, Gluskin's Custom Audio Video, 2087 Grand Canal Blvd, Suite 11, Stockton, CA 95204 *Tel:* 209-888-4609 *Fax:* 209-888-4629 *E-mail:* audio@gluskins.com *Web Site:* www.gluskins.com, pg 879

Doornbos, Scott, Dukane Corp, Audio Visual Products Division, 2900 Dukane Dr, St Charles, IL 60174 *Tel:* 630-762-4040 *Toll Free Tel:* 888-245-1966 *Fax:* 630-584-5156 *E-mail:* avsales@dukane.com *Web Site:* dukaneav.com, pg 853

Doornick, Robert, International Robotics Inc, 2001 Palmer Ave, Suite LL-1, Larchmont, NY 10538 *Tel:* 914-630-1060 *Fax:* 203-630-1733 *E-mail:* info@internationalrobotics.com *Web Site:* www.internationalrobotics.com, pg 901

Dorfman, Robert, Dorfman Museum Figures Inc, 6224 Holabird Ave, Baltimore, MD 21224 *Tel:* 410-284-3248 *Toll Free Tel:* 800-634-4873 *Fax:* 410-284-3249 *E-mail:* info@museumfigures.com *Web Site:* www.museumfigures.com, pg 851

Dorgan, Janet Malik, Shamrock Communications, 200 Tornillo Way, Suite 110, Tinton Falls, NJ 07712 *Tel:* 732-686-1140 *Fax:* 732-686-1148 *E-mail:* info@shamrockcommunications.com *Web Site:* www.shamrockcommunications.com, pg 1008

Dorman, Cecil, AVFX Inc, 96 Holton St, Boston, MA 02135 *Tel:* 617-254-0770 *Toll Free Tel:* 888-254-0770 *E-mail:* info@avfx.com *Web Site:* www.avfx.com, pg 798

Dorn, Scott, Spectrum Industries Inc, 925 First Ave, Chippewa Falls, WI 54729 *Tel:* 715-723-6750 *Toll Free Tel:* 800-235-1262 *Toll Free Fax:* 800-335-0473 *E-mail:* info@spectrumfurniture.com *Web Site:* www.spectrumfurniture.com, pg 1021

Doros, Dennis, Milestone Film & Video Inc, PO Box 128, Harrington Park, NJ 07640-0128 *Tel:* 201-767-3117 *Toll Free Tel:* 800-603-1104 *Fax:* 201-767-3035 *E-mail:* milefilms@gmail.com *Web Site:* www.milestonefilms.com, pg 943

Dorr, Sharron, Theosophical Publishing House, 306 W Geneva Rd, Wheaton, IL 60187 *Tel:* 630-665-0130 *Toll Free Tel:* 800-669-9425 *Fax:* 630-665-8791 *Web Site:* www.questbooks.net, pg 1038

Dorrough, Kay, Dorrough Electronics Inc, 5221 Collier Place, Woodland Hills, CA 91364 *Tel:* 818-998-2824 *Fax:* 818-998-1507 *E-mail:* dorroughel@aol.com *Web Site:* www.dorrough.com, pg 851

Dorrough, Michael, Dorrough Electronics Inc, 5221 Collier Place, Woodland Hills, CA 91364 *Tel:* 818-998-2824 *Fax:* 818-998-1507 *E-mail:* dorroughel@aol.com *Web Site:* www.dorrough.com, pg 851

Dorsa, Jennifer, VMI Inc, 211 E Weddell Dr, Sunnyvale, CA 94089 *Tel:* 408-745-1700 *Fax:* 408-745-6721 *E-mail:* sales@vmivideo.com *Web Site:* www.vmivideo.com, pg 1060

Dorsey, Debbie Donaldson, Baltimore Film Office, 10 E Baltimore St, 10th fl, Baltimore, MD 21202 *Tel:* 410-752-8632; 443-263-4313 *Fax:* 410-385-0361 *Web Site:* www.baltimorefilm.com, pg 1098

Dorst, Steve, Dorst MediaWorks Inc, 209 N Filmore St, Arlington, VA 22201 *Tel:* 202-258-9612 *Fax:* 571-312-9212 *Web Site:* www.stevedorst.com, pg 851

Dortch, Chris, Stockfootage.com, 231 S Mountain Way Dr, Orem, UT 84058 *Tel:* 801-221-9570; 801-361-0012 (cell) *E-mail:* sales@stockfootage.com *Web Site:* www.stockfootage.com, pg 1025

Dottavio, Julio, RM Films International, PO Box 3748, Hollywood, CA 90078-3748 *Tel:* 323-466-7791 *Fax:* 323-461-4152 *E-mail:* rmf@rmfilms.com *Web Site:* www.rmfilms.com; www.russmeyer.com, pg 997

Doucette, Patrick, A & J Cases, 11121 Hindry Ave, Los Angeles, CA 90045 *Tel:* 310-216-2170 *Toll Free Tel:* 800-537-4000 *Fax:* 310-216-2694 *Web Site:* www.ajcases.com, pg 771

Douek, Joseph, Willoughby's Imaging Center, 298 Fifth Ave, New York, NY 10001 *Tel:* 212-564-1600 *Toll Free Tel:* 800-378-1898 *Fax:* 212-564-1608 *E-mail:* sales@willoughbys.com; customersupport@willoughbys.com *Web Site:* www.willoughbys.com, pg 1067

Dougherty, Edward, Tritech Communications, 625 Locust St, Suite 300, Garden City, NY 11530 *Tel:* 631-254-4500 *Fax:* 631-254-4499 *E-mail:* sales@tritechcomm.com *Web Site:* www.tritechcomm.com, pg 1045

Dougherty, Stephen, Close Up Foundation, 1330 Braddock Place, Suite 400, Alexandria, VA 22314 *Tel:* 703-706-3300 *Toll Free Tel:* 800-CLOSEUP (256-7387) *E-mail:* info@closeup.org *Web Site:* www.closeup.org, pg 830

Douglas, Brian, Digital Outpost, 2772 Loker Ave W, Carlsbad, CA 92010 *Tel:* 760-431-3575 *Toll Free Tel:* 800-464-6434 *Fax:* 760-431-8717 *E-mail:* info@dop.com; sales@dop.com *Web Site:* www.dop.com, pg 847

Douglas, David, West Eagle Films Inc, 800 Lower Ganges Rd, Salt Spring Island, BC V8K 2N5, Canada *Tel:* 250-538-1780 *E-mail:* mailbox@westeaglefilms.com *Web Site:* www.westeaglefilms.com, pg 1064

Douglas, Gary, International Fun-Shop, 2114 Seabrook Circle, Seabrook, TX 77586 *Tel:* 281-291-0707 *Fax:* 281-291-0718 *E-mail:* fssales@fun-shop.com *Web Site:* www.fun-shop.com, pg 901

Douglas, Greg, York Telecom, 81 Corbett Way, Eatontown, NJ 07724 *Tel:* 732-413-6000 *Toll Free Tel:* 866-836-8463 *Fax:* 732-413-6060 *E-mail:* knowmore@yorktel.com *Web Site:* yorktel.com, pg 1072

Douglas, Harry, Magnetic Post Production, 4 Marshall Rd, Wappingers Falls, NY 12590-4105 *Tel:* 212-598-3000 *Fax:* 212-228-3664 *E-mail:* contact@magneticimage.com *Web Site:* www.magneticimage.com, pg 928

Douglas, Heather, Douglas House Inc, 275 Kings Hwy, Orangeburg, NY 10962 *Tel:* 845-359-1477 *Fax:* 845-359-2945 *E-mail:* thedouglashouse@earthlink.net *Web Site:* www.thedouglashouse.com, pg 851

Douglas, Jen, Scala Inc, 350 Eagleview Blvd, Suite 350, Exton, PA 19341 *Tel:* 610-363-3350 *Toll Free Tel:* 888-SCALA-96 (722-5296) *Fax:* 610-363-4010 *E-mail:* marketing@scala.com *Web Site:* scala.com, pg 1004

Douglas, Marjorie, Douglas House Inc, 275 Kings Hwy, Orangeburg, NY 10962 *Tel:* 845-359-1477 *Fax:* 845-359-2945 *E-mail:* thedouglashouse@earthlink.net *Web Site:* www.thedouglashouse.com, pg 851

Douglas, Randy, Luxor, 2245 Delany Rd, Waukegan, IL 60087 *Tel:* 847-244-1800 *Toll Free Tel:* 800-323-4656 *Fax:* 847-244-1818 *Toll Free Fax:* 800-327-1698 *E-mail:* info@luxorfurn.com; customerservice@luxorfurn.com *Web Site:* www.luxorfurn.com, pg 926

Douglas, Vince, Twin Sisters Productions LLC, 4710 Hudson Dr, Stow, OH 44224 *Toll Free Tel:* 800-248-TWIN (248-8946) *Toll Free Fax:* 800-480-TWIN (480-8946) *E-mail:* twinsisters@twinsisters.com *Web Site:* www.twinsisters.com, pg 1047

Dow, Donald, Artograph Inc, 525 Ninth St S, Delano, MN 55328-8624 *Tel:* 763-553-1112 *Toll Free Tel:* 888-975-9555 *Fax:* 763-553-1262 *E-mail:* sales@artograph.com; info@artograph.com *Web Site:* www.artograph.com, pg 791

Dowd, Lori, StoryTrack, 212 S Bemiston, St Louis, MO 63105 *Tel:* 314-725-3003 *Web Site:* www.storytrack.com, pg 1025

Dowell, Darlene, Vanner Inc, 4282 Reynolds Dr, Hilliard, OH 43026 *Tel:* 614-771-2718 *Toll Free Tel:* 800-ACPOWER (227-6937) *Fax:* 614-771-4904 *E-mail:* info@vanner.com; pwrsales@vanner.com *Web Site:* www.vanner.com, pg 1051

Downie, Donna, Bernie's Photo Center, 525 E Ohio St, Pittsburgh, PA 15212 *Tel:* 412-231-1717 *Toll Free Tel:* 800-346-8884 *Fax:* 412-231-1217 *E-mail:* info@berniesphoto.com *Web Site:* www.berniesphoto.com, pg 805

Doyle, Denise, San Diego Stage & Lighting Supply Inc, 2203 Verus St, San Diego, CA 92154 *Tel:* 619-299-2300 *Fax:* 619-299-0058 *E-mail:* info@sdstagelighting.com *Web Site:* www.sdstagelighting.com, pg 1002

Doyle, John C, Universal Training, 736 N Western Ave, Suite 323, Lake Forest, IL 60045 *Tel:* 847-235-2170 *Web Site:* www.universaltraining.com, pg 1049

Doyle, Kristene, Albert Ellis Institute (AEI), 145 E 32 St, 9th fl, New York, NY 10016 *Tel:* 212-535-0822 *Fax:* 212-249-3582 *E-mail:* info@albertellis.org *Web Site:* www.albertellis.org, pg 859

Drabinsky, Cyril, Deluxe Laboratories Inc, 5433 Fernwood Ave, Hollywood, CA 90027 *Tel:* 323-960-3600 *Fax:* 323-960-7016 *Web Site:* www.bydeluxe.com, pg 845

Drago, Mike, Gearhead Rentals, 69 O'Conner Rd, Suite 6, Fairport, NY 14450 *Tel:* 585-236-4272 *Web Site:* www.gearheadrentals.com, pg 876

Dragoni, Nick, M Works Mastering Studios, 1035 Cambridge St, Suite 17-B, Cambridge, MA 02141 *Tel:* 617-577-0089 *Fax:* 617-577-0098 *E-mail:* studio@m-works.com *Web Site:* www.m-works.com, pg 927

Draznin, Rebecca, Advance Concepts Inc, 8453 Tyco Rd, Suite N, Vienna, VA 22182-2623 *Tel:* 703-448-0445 *Fax:* 703-893-8049 *Web Site:* www.advanceconcepts.com, pg 777

Drebin-Murphy, Layne J, Budget Films Stock Footage Inc, 706 N Vendome St, Suite 6, Los Angeles, CA 90026 *Tel:* 323-660-0187 *Fax:* 323-660-5571 *E-mail:* filmclip@aol.com; info@budgetfilms.com *Web Site:* www.budgetfilms.com, pg 814

Drendel, Frank M, CommScope Inc, 1100 CommScope Place SE, Hickory, NC 28602 *Tel:* 828-324-2200 *Toll Free Tel:* 800-982-1708 *Web Site:* www.commscope.com, pg 832

Dressendorfer, Mike, Russ Bassett Corp, 8189 Byron Rd, Whittier, CA 90606-2615 *Tel:* 562-945-2445 *Toll Free Tel:* 800-350-2445 *Fax:* 562-698-8972 *E-mail:* info@russbassett.com *Web Site:* www.russbassett.com, pg 1001

Drexler, Jefferson, North County Media Center, 1130 N Melrose Dr, Suite 404, Vista, CA 92083 *Toll Free Tel:* 888-393-0580 *E-mail:* info@northcountymediacenter.com *Web Site:* northcountymediacenter.com, pg 959

Driggs, Paul, On Stage Audio, 537 N Edgewood Ave, Wood Dale, IL 60191 *Tel:* 630-227-1008 *Toll Free Tel:* 877-672-4685 *Toll Free Fax:* 866-OSA-FAX2 (672-3292) *E-mail:* welisten@osacorp.com *Web Site:* www.osacorp.com, pg 963

Droppa, Larry, API, 8301 Patuxent Range Rd, Jessup, MD 20794 *Tel:* 301-776-7879 *Fax:* 301-776-8117 *E-mail:* service@apiaudio.com *Web Site:* www.apiaudio.com, pg 788

Druck, David, California Tape Products Inc, PO Box 177, Forest Falls, CA 92339-0177 *Tel:* 909-794-6524 *E-mail:* info@caltape.com *Web Site:* www.caltape.com, pg 817

Druck, Mark, Mark Druck Productions, 300 E 40 St, New York, NY 10016 *Tel:* 212-682-5980 *Fax:* 212-682-5981, pg 852

Drury, Marilyn, The Production House, Innovative Teaching & Technology Ctr, 108 ITTC Bldg, Cedar Falls, IA 50614 *Tel:* 319-273-7820 *Fax:* 319-273-2917 *E-mail:* pro-house@uni.edu *Web Site:* www.uni.edu/its/labs/production-house, pg 984

Dryer, Ivan, Laserium, 6911 Hayvenhurst Ave, Suite 102, Van Nuys, CA 91406 *Tel:* 818-429-0454 *E-mail:* info@laserium.com *Web Site:* www.laserium.com, pg 916

Du, Liming, Hanovia Specialty Lighting LLC, 6 Evans St, Fairfield, NJ 07004 *Tel:* 973-651-5510 *Fax:* 973-651-5550 *E-mail:* sales@hanovia-uv.com *Web Site:* www.hanovia-uv.com, pg 884

Dubay, Inga, Getty-Dubay Productions, PO Box 91084, Portland, OR 97291-0084 *Tel:* 503-223-7268 (orders) *Toll Free Tel:* 800-777-2844 *Fax:* 503-223-9182 (orders) *E-mail:* info@handwritingsuccess.com; info@allport.com (orders) *Web Site:* www.handwritingsuccess.com; www.allport.com (orders), pg 877

Dube, Steve, Russound, 5 Forbes Rd, Newmarket, NH 03857 *Tel:* 603-659-5170 *Toll Free Tel:* 800-638-8055 (US) *Fax:* 603-659-5388 *E-mail:* sales@russound.com; tech@russound.com *Web Site:* www.russound.com, pg 1001

Dubin, Burt, Personal Achievement Institute, One Speaking Success Rd, Kingman, AZ 86402 *Tel:* 928-753-5315 *Web Site:* www.speakingsuccess.com, pg 973

Dubin, Doug, CenterStaging LLC, 3407 Winona Ave, Burbank, CA 91504 *Tel:* 818-559-4333 *Fax:* 818-848-4016 *E-mail:* info@centerstaging.com *Web Site:* centerstaging.com, pg 823

DuBose, Marco, South Coast Film & Video, 5234 Elm St, Houston, TX 77081 *Tel:* 713-661-3550 *Toll Free Tel:* 800-229-3550 *Fax:* 713-661-4357 *E-mail:* info@scfilmvideo.com *Web Site:* www.scfilmvideo.com, pg 1019

Dubs, Arthur R, Pacific International Enterprises Inc (PIE), 401 Crater Lake Ave, Suite 2, Medford, OR 97504 *Tel:* 541-779-0990 *Toll Free Tel:* 800-547-2316 *Fax:* 541-779-0880 *E-mail:* info@family-films.com *Web Site:* www.family-films.com, pg 967

Dubuc, Nancy, A&E Television Networks LLC, 235 E 45 St, New York, NY 10017 *Tel:* 212-210-1400 *Web Site:* www.aetv.com, pg 771

Duchaine, Glenn, Maverick Video Productions, 121 Interpark, Suite 601, San Antonio, TX 78216 *Tel:* 210-495-1111 *Fax:* 210-495-8033 *Web Site:* www.maverickstudio.com, pg 934

Duckler, Max, CaptionMax, 2438 27 Ave S, Minneapolis, MN 55406 *Tel:* 612-341-3566 *Toll Free Tel:* 800-822-3566 *Fax:* 612-341-2345 *Web Site:* www.captionmax.com, pg 820

Ducoff, Duke, SoundTube Entertainment, 6430 N Business Park Loop, Park City, UT 84098 *Tel:* 435-647-9555 *Toll Free Tel:* 800-647-TUBE (647-8823) *Fax:* 435-647-9666 *E-mail:* sales@soundtube.com *Web Site:* www.soundtube.com, pg 1018

Duden, Kelly, Vital Learning LLC, 1675 Larimer St, No 410, Denver, CO 80202 *Tel:* 402-592-1602 *Toll Free Tel:* 800-243-5858 *Fax:* 402-592-7142 *E-mail:* sales@vital-learning.com; info@vital-learning.com *Web Site:* www.vital-learning.com, pg 1060

Dudley, Tim, Master Books, 3142 Hwy 103 N, Green Forest, AR 72638 *Tel:* 870-438-5288 *Toll Free Tel:* 800-999-3777 *Fax:* 870-438-5120 *E-mail:* nlp@newleafpress.net *Web Site:* www.nlpg.com, pg 933

Dudzinski, Tom, Renaissance Media, 909 Logan St, Suite 11F, Denver, CO 80204 *Tel:* 303-892-1415 *Web Site:* www.renaissancemedia.com, pg 994

Duff, John, FSL Media Inc, 122 Amity St, Suite 1, Brooklyn, NY 11201 *Tel:* 347-463-9729 *E-mail:* info@fslmedia.com *Web Site:* www.fslmedia.com, pg 873

Duff, Steven, Osram Sylvania Ltd/LTEE, 2001 Drew Rd, Mississauga, ON L5S 1S4, Canada *Tel:* 905-673-6171 *Toll Free Tel:* 800-LIGHTBULB (544-4828) *Fax:* 905-671-5584 *Web Site:* www.sylvania.com, pg 966

Duff, Tom, Optimus, 161 E Grand Ave, Chicago, IL 60611 *Tel:* 312-321-0880 *Web Site:* www.optimus.com, pg 964

Duffy, Jim, Venture Media, 902 Harvest Pointe Dr, Fort Mill, SC 29708 *Tel:* 803-547-3878 *E-mail:* info@venturemedia.tv *Web Site:* www.venturemedia.tv, pg 1052

Duffy, Kris, Venture Media, 902 Harvest Pointe Dr, Fort Mill, SC 29708 *Tel:* 803-547-3878 *E-mail:* info@venturemedia.tv *Web Site:* www.venturemedia.tv, pg 1052

Dufresne, Denis, Cinema Entertainment Inc, 1779 NW 79 Ave, Doral, FL 33126 *Tel:* 561-899-0721 *E-mail:* info@cinemaent.com *Web Site:* cinemaent.com, pg 827

Duga, Don, Polestar Films & Associated Arts Ltd, PO Box 20104, West Village Sta, New York, NY 10014-0708 *Tel:* 212-352-1375, pg 978

Dugan, Dan, Dan Dugan Sound Design Inc, 290 Napoleon St, Suite E, San Francisco, CA 94124 *Tel:* 415-821-9776 *Fax:* 415-826-7699 *Web Site:* www.dandugan.com, pg 853

Dugan, Katie, Scott Resources Inc, 401 Hickory St, Fort Collins, CO 80524-1125 *Tel:* 970-484-7445 *Toll Free Tel:* 800-289-9299 *Fax:* 970-484-1198 *E-mail:* custserv@amep.com *Web Site:* amep.com, pg 1005

Duggal, Michael, Duggal Visual Solutions, 29 W 23 St, New York, NY 10010 *Tel:* 212-924-8100 *Fax:* 212-242-6660 *E-mail:* info@duggal.com *Web Site:* duggal.com, pg 853

Duggan, Gene, Imagecraft Productions, 3318 Burton Ave, Burbank, CA 91504 *Tel:* 818-954-0187 *Fax:* 818-954-0189 *Web Site:* www.imagecraftproductions.com, pg 896

Duke, Channing, Wilmington Camera Services, 905 N 23 St, Wilmington, NC 28405 *Tel:* 910-343-1089 *Fax:* 910-343-0247 *E-mail:* info@wilmingtoncameraservices.com, pg 1067

Duke, Eric, All Mobile Video Inc, 221 W 26 St, New York, NY 10001 *Tel:* 212-727-1234 *Fax:* 212-255-6644 *E-mail:* contact@amvchelsea.com *Web Site:* allmobilevideo.com, pg 780

Dulmage, Debbie, Panorama Productions, 5320 Croy Rd, Morgan Hill, CA 95037 *Tel:* 408-727-7500 *E-mail:* information@panorama-productions.com *Web Site:* www.panorama-productions.com, pg 968

Dulmage, Don, Panorama Productions, 5320 Croy Rd, Morgan Hill, CA 95037 *Tel:* 408-727-7500 *E-mail:* information@panorama-productions.com *Web Site:* www.panorama-productions.com, pg 968

Dunaj, Kathy, Sound/Video Impressions Inc, 110 S River Rd, Des Plaines, IL 60016 *Tel:* 847-297-4360 *Fax:* 847-297-6870 *E-mail:* info@soundvideoimpressions.com *Web Site:* www.soundvideoimpressions.com, pg 1018

Dunbar, Clark, Mammoth HD, PO Box 2064, Evergreen, CO 80437 *Tel:* 303-670-7973 *E-mail:* mammothhd@me.com; info@mammothhd.com *Web Site:* www.mammothhd.com, pg 929

Dunbar, Rodney, Antex Electronics Corp, 19160 Van Ness Ave, Torrance, CA 90501 *Tel:* 310-532-3092 *Toll Free Tel:* 800-338-4231 *Fax:* 310-532-8509 *E-mail:* ainfo@antex.com; asales@antex.com *Web Site:* www.antex.com, pg 787

Duncan, David, Randolf Productions Inc, 17935 Skypark Circle, Suite K, Irvine, CA 92614 *Tel:* 949-794-9109 *Toll Free Tel:* 800-266-7741 *Fax:* 949-794-9117 *E-mail:* sales@go2rpi.com *Web Site:* www.go2rpi.com, pg 991

Duncan, Eason, See Production Services, 3330 Cobb Pkwy, Suite 17-327, Acworth, GA 30101 *Tel:* 404-474-4416 *E-mail:* info@seeproductionservices.com *Web Site:* seeproductionservices.com, pg 1006

Dunford, Ned, LuXout Brand Stage Curtains, 1221 Admiral St, Richmond, VA 23220 *Tel:* 804-264-3000; 804-264-3700 *Toll Free Tel:* 800-817-1204 *Toll Free Fax:* 888-227-8064 *E-mail:* luxoutinfo@luxout.com *Web Site:* www.luxout.com, pg 926

Dung, Steven, Visions Plus, 200 Valley Dr, Suite 5, Brisbane, CA 94005 *Tel:* 415-467-3300 *E-mail:* web_inquiry@visionsplus.com *Web Site:* visionsplus.com, pg 1058

Dungan, Bob, Media Management LLC, 1801 Royal Lane, Suite 906, Dallas, TX 75229 *Tel:* 972-409-0900 *Fax:* 972-409-0903 *E-mail:* info@mmgt.com *Web Site:* www.mmgt.com, pg 937

Dunham, Scott Paul, Detroit Windsor International Film Festival (DWIFF), 15206 Mack Ave, Suite 9, Detroit, MI 48230 *Tel:* 313-881-0122 *E-mail:* info@dwiff.org *Web Site:* www.dwiff.org, pg 1114

Dunmead, Dave, Switchcraft® Inc, 5555 N Elston Ave, Chicago, IL 60630 *Tel:* 773-792-2700 *Fax:* 773-792-2129 *E-mail:* sales@switchcraft.com *Web Site:* www.switchcraft.com, pg 1030

Dunmore, Herbert, National Student Production Awards, Hershey Square Ctr, 1152 Mae St, Hummelstown, PA 17036 *Toll Free Tel:* 855-ASK-4CBI (275-4224) *Web Site:* www.askcbi.org, pg 1121

Dunn, Carol, Hopkins Technology LLC, 421 Hazel Lane, Hopkins, MN 55343-7116 *Tel:* 952-856-0467 *E-mail:* infodesk5@hoptechno.com *Web Site:* www.hoptechno.com, pg 891

Dunn, Chris, Dreamhire LLC, 36-36 33 St, Suite 102, Long Island City, NY 11106 *Tel:* 212-691-5544 *Toll Free Tel:* 800-234-7536 *E-mail:* info@dreamhire.com *Web Site:* www.dreamhire.com, pg 852

Dunn, Jo Ann, Radio Systems Inc, 601 Heron Dr, Logan Township, NJ 08085 *Tel:* 856-467-8000 *Fax:* 856-467-3044 *E-mail:* sales@radiosystems.com; tech@radiosystems.com *Web Site:* www.radiosystems.com, pg 990

Dunn, Kathy, Lippincott Williams & Wilkins, Two Commerce Sq, 2001 Market St, Philadelphia, PA 19103 *Tel:* 215-521-8300; 301-223-2300 (cust serv) *Toll Free Tel:* 800-638-3030 (cust serv) *Fax:* 215-521-8902 *E-mail:* orders@lww.com *Web Site:* www.lww.com, pg 922

Dunn, Mathis, Screen Actors Guild & American Federation of Television & Radio Artists (SAG-AFTRA), 5757 Wilshire Blvd, 7th fl, Los Angeles, CA 90036-3600 *Tel:* 323-954-1600 (former SAG); 323-634-8100 (former AFTRA) *Toll Free Tel:* 855-SAG-AFTRA (724-2387) *Fax:* 323-634-8194 *E-mail:* sagaftrainfo@sagaftra.org *Web Site:* www.sagaftra.org/ny, pg 1088

Dunn, Michael, Michael Dunn Productions, 25 Sunlit Dr W, Santa Fe, NM 87508 *Tel:* 847-940-0150, pg 853

Dunn, Steven M, Ken-A-Vision Manufacturing Co Inc, 5615 Raytown Rd, Kansas City, MO 64133 *Tel:* 816-353-4787 *Toll Free Tel:* 800-501-7366; 800-627-1953 (cust serv) *Fax:* 816-358-5072 *E-mail:* info@ken-a-vision.com *Web Site:* www.ken-a-vision.com, pg 909

Dunnell, Graham, JIB Shots Equipment Inc, 1828 Lorraine Ave, Ottawa, ON K1H 6Z8, Canada *Tel:* 613-293-3318 *Fax:* 613-521-9312 *Web Site:* www.jibshots.com, pg 905

Dunning, Ernie, Dunning Photo Equipment Inc, 605 W Needles St, Bixby, OK 74008 *Tel:* 918-366-4917 *Fax:* 918-366-4918 *Web Site:* www.dunningphoto.com, pg 853

Dunphy, John A, University Products Inc, 517 Main St, Holyoke, MA 01040-0073 *Tel:* 413-532-3372 *Toll Free Tel:* 800-628-1912 *Fax:* 413-532-9281 *Toll Free Fax:* 800-532-9281 *E-mail:* custserv@universityproducts.com; info@universityproducts.com *Web Site:* www.universityproducts.com, pg 1050

Dunston, Dave, Zygote Media Group Inc, 1045 S 500 E, Suite 200, American Fork, UT 84003 *Tel:* 801-765-4141 *Fax:* 801-705-2234 *E-mail:* customerservices@zygote.com *Web Site:* www.zygote.com, pg 1074

Dunton, Joe, Wilmington Camera Services, 905 N 23 St, Wilmington, NC 28405 *Tel:* 910-343-1089 *Fax:* 910-343-0247 *E-mail:* info@wilmingtoncameraservices.com, pg 1067

Dupree, Todd, Trans-Lux Multimedia Corp, 950 Third Ave, Suite 2804, New York, NY 10022 *Tel:* 203-853-4321 *Toll Free Tel:* 800-243-5544; 800-462-2716 *Fax:* 203-229-0691 *Web Site:* www.trans-lux.com, pg 1043

Dupuis, Jacqueline, Vancouver International Film Festival, Vancouver International Film Centre, 1181 Seymour St, Vancouver, BC V6B 3M7, Canada *Tel:* 604-685-0260 *Fax:* 604-688-8221 *E-mail:* viff@viff.org *Web Site:* www.viff.org, pg 1129

Duran, Christy, Agrama Film Enterprises Inc, 7655 Sunset Blvd, Los Angeles, CA 90046 *Tel:* 323-851-4900 *Fax:* 323-851-5599 *E-mail:* sales@harmonygold.com *Web Site:* harmonygold.com, pg 778

Duran, Ramon, Cibola Systems, 180 S Cypress St, Orange, CA 92866 *Tel:* 714-480-0272 *Fax:* 714-480-0768 *E-mail:* info@cibolasystems.com *Web Site:* cibolasystems.com, pg 826

Durham, James G, ChronTrol Corp, 7525-D Mission Gorge Rd, San Diego, CA 92120 *Tel:* 619-282-8686 *Toll Free Tel:* 800-854-1999 *Fax:* 619-563-6563 *E-mail:* info@chrontrol.com *Web Site:* www.chrontrol.com, pg 826

Durkin, John, Market Data Retrieval (MDR), 6 Armstrong Rd, Suite 301, Shelton, CT 06484 *Tel:* 203-926-4800 *Toll Free Tel:* 800-333-8802 *Toll Free Fax:* 866-532-7097 *E-mail:* mdrinfo@dnb.com *Web Site:* www.schooldata.com, pg 931

Durkin, Sally, Natchez Film Commission, 640 S Canal St, Box C, Natchez, MS 39120 *Tel:* 601-446-6345 *Toll Free Tel:* 800-647-6724 *Fax:* 601-442-0814 *E-mail:* info@visitnatchez.org *Web Site:* www.visitnatchez.org, pg 1099

Durling, Roger, Santa Barbara International Film Festival, 1528 Chapala St, Suite 203, Santa Barbara, CA 93101 *Tel:* 805-963-0023 *Fax:* 805-962-2524 *E-mail:* generalinfo@sbfilmfestival.org *Web Site:* sbiff.org, pg 1126

Durrenberger, Robert S, Durrenberger Engineering Inc, 2037 Powell Dr, El Cajon, CA 92020 *Tel:* 858-578-3363 *Web Site:* www.dfrfx.com, pg 854

Durrin, Ginny, Durrin Productions Inc, 4926 Sedgwick St NW, Washington, DC 20016 *Tel:* 202-237-6700 *Toll Free Tel:* 800-536-6843 *Fax:* 202-237-6738 *E-mail:* info@durrinproductions.com *Web Site:* www.durrinproductions.com, pg 854

Durso, Vincent, Troll Touch, 33302 Santiago Rd, Suite C, Acton, CA 93510 *Tel:* 661-257-1160 *Fax:* 661-257-1161 *Web Site:* www.trolltouch.com, pg 1045

Dusinberre, Denise, Video Concepts Unlimited, PO Box 577, North Chili, NY 14514 *Tel:* 585-293-2222 *Toll Free Tel:* 800-930-5411 *E-mail:* videocu@aol.com *Web Site:* www.dvdtransferservices.com, pg 1055

Duva, Jason, Avid Technology Inc, 65-75 Network Dr, Burlington, MA 01830 *Tel:* 978-640-6789 *Fax:* 978-640-3366 *Web Site:* www.avid.com, pg 799

Dwyer, J C, Megatrax, 7629 Fulton Ave, North Hollywood, CA 91605 *Tel:* 818-255-7100 *Toll Free Tel:* 888-MEGA-555 (634-2555) *Fax:* 818-255-7199 *E-mail:* info@megatrax.com *Web Site:* www.megatrax.com, pg 938

Dyberg, Patrik, John Wiley & Sons Inc, 111 River St, Hoboken, NJ 07030 *Tel:* 201-748-6000 *Toll Free Tel:* 800-225-5945 *Fax:* 201-748-6088 *E-mail:* info@wiley.com *Web Site:* www.wiley.com, pg 1066

Dye, Tim, Intermed Video Technologies Inc, 18 Commerce Rd, Newtown, CT 06470 *Tel:* 203-270-0677; 203-270-9100 *Fax:* 203-270-9619 *E-mail:* sales@intermedvideo.com *Web Site:* www.intermedvideo.com, pg 900

Dylan, Jacob, Baker Audio Inc, 2195 N Norcross Tucker Rd, Norcross, GA 30071 *Tel:* 770-441-2000 *Toll Free Tel:* 800-847-3523 *Fax:* 770-449-7719 *E-mail:* sales@bakeraudiovisual.com *Web Site:* www.bakeraudiovisual.com, pg 802

Dymmel, Kenneth L, JD Audio Visual Inc, 1713 E Walnut St, Pasadena, CA 91106 *Tel:* 626-792-6682 *Toll Free Tel:* 800-532-8346 *Fax:* 626-796-6635 *E-mail:* sales@jdav.com *Web Site:* www.jdav.com, pg 904

Dyon, Ben, DME Studios, 1025 Greenwood Blvd, Suite 191, Lake Mary, FL 32746 *Tel:* 407-585-7500 *E-mail:* creativeteam@dmestudios.com *Web Site:* www.dmestudios.com, pg 849

Dzuban, Mark, Society of Cable Telecommunications Engineers Inc (SCTE), 140 Philips Rd, Exton, PA 19341-1318 *Tel:* 610-363-6888 *Toll Free Tel:* 800-542-5040 (cust care) *Fax:* 610-363-5898 *E-mail:* information@scte.org *Web Site:* www.scte.org, pg 1089

Eaddy, Blake, Bell & Howell LLC, 760 S Wolf Rd, Wheeling, IL 60090 *Tel:* 847-675-7600 *Toll Free Tel:* 800-220-3030 (cust serv) *E-mail:* marketing@bhemail.com *Web Site:* www.bellhowell.net, pg 804

Eaddy, Rebecca, Roland Corp US, 5100 S Eastern Ave, Los Angeles, CA 90040-2938 *Tel:* 323-890-3700 *Fax:* 323-721-4875 *Web Site:* www.rolandus.com, pg 998

Eades, David, World Wide Pictures Inc, One Billy Graham Pkwy, Charlotte, NC 28266-8029 *Tel:* 704-401-2432 *Toll Free Tel:* 800-745-4318 *Fax:* 704-401-3045 *Web Site:* www.wwp.org, pg 1070

Eaker, Brett, Hart Inc, 320 New Stock Rd, Asheville, NC 28804 *Tel:* 828-645-4734 *Toll Free Tel:* 800-654-8012 *Fax:* 828-645-4294 *Toll Free Fax:* 866-390-4278 *E-mail:* mail@hart-inc.com *Web Site:* www.hart-inc.com, pg 885

Eardley, Michael, Tanglewood Productions, 125 Brinkby Ave, Reno, NV 89509 *Tel:* 775-688-6282 *Toll Free Tel:* 877-671-8933 *E-mail:* info@tanglewoodproductions.com *Web Site:* www.tanglewoodproductions.com, pg 1031

Earl, Don, Earl Girls Inc, 1648 White Horse Pike, Egg Harbor City, NJ 08215 *Tel:* 609-965-6900 *Toll Free Tel:* 888-777-EARL (777-3275) *Fax:* 609-965-3330 *E-mail:* sales@earlgirlsinc.com *Web Site:* earlgirlsinc.com, pg 855

Earon, Dr S Ann, Telemanagement Resources International Inc (TRI), 124 Thomas Lane, Manahawkin, NJ 08050 *Tel:* 609-597-6334 *Web Site:* www.triinc.com, pg 1036

Eason, Darren, Star Case Manufacturing Co Inc, 648 Superior Ave, Munster, IN 46321 *Tel:* 219-922-4440 *Toll Free Tel:* 800-822-STAR (822-7827); 800-782-CASE (782-2273) *Fax:* 219-922-4442 *E-mail:* star@starcase.com *Web Site:* www.starcase.com, pg 1023

East, Ellen M, Time Warner Cable, 60 Columbus Circle, 17th fl, New York, NY 10023 *Tel:* 212-364-8200 *Web Site:* www.timewarnercable.com, pg 1040

East, Pauline, Antelope Valley Film Office-Lancaster, 42035 12 St W, Suite 103, Lancaster, CA 93534 *Tel:* 661-723-6090; 661-510-4231 (cell) *Web Site:* antelope-valley-film-office.hollywoodserve.com, pg 1093

Eastland, Erik, All Access Staging & Productions, 1320 Storm Pkwy, Torrance, CA 90501 *Tel:* 310-784-2464 *Toll Free Tel:* 877-784-2464 *Fax:* 310-517-0899 *E-mail:* usinfo@allaccessinc.com *Web Site:* www.allaccessinc.com, pg 780

Easton, Elmer, Three D Graphics Inc, 11340 W Olympic Blvd, Suite 352, Los Angeles, CA 90064-1613 *Tel:* 310-231-3330 *Toll Free Tel:* 800-913-0008 *Fax:* 310-231-3303 *E-mail:* info@threedgraphics.com *Web Site:* www.threedgraphics.com, pg 1039

Easton, Robert, 360 Systems, 3281 Grande Vista Dr, Newbury Park, CA 91320-1193 *Tel:* 818-991-0360 *Fax:* 818-991-1360 *E-mail:* info@360systems.com; sales@360systems.com *Web Site:* www.360systems.com, pg 1039

Eaton, Mark, Bang Pictures, 78 Graterford Rd, Schwenksville, PA 19473 *Tel:* 610-357-1015 *Web Site:* www.bangpictures.com, pg 802

Eaton, Sandi, Chelsea Green Publishing Co, 85 N Main St, Suite 120, White River Junction, VT 05001 *Tel:* 802-295-6300 *Toll Free Tel:* 800-639-4099 *Fax:* 802-295-6444 *Web Site:* www.chelseagreen.com, pg 824

Ebeling, William, Tobins Lake Sales, 11035 Hi Tech Dr, Whitmore Lake, MI 48189 *Tel:* 734-449-9810 *Toll Free Tel:* 888-525-3753 *Fax:* 734-449-9812 *Web Site:* www.tobinslakesales.com, pg 1041

Eberhart, Ronald, Hite Co, 3101 Beale Ave, Altoona, PA 16601 *Tel:* 814-944-6121 *Toll Free Tel:* 800-252-3598 *Fax:* 814-944-3052 *Web Site:* www.hiteco.com, pg 889

Eby, Debbie, The International Society of Automation (ISA), 67 T W Alexander Dr, Research Triangle Park, NC 27709 *Tel:* 919-549-8411 *Fax:* 919-549-8288 *E-mail:* info@isa.org *Web Site:* www.isa.org, pg 901

Ecarius, Christine, Kappa Map Group LLC, 112 E New York Ave, Deland, FL 32724 *Tel:* 386-873-3010 *Toll Free Tel:* 800-829-6277 (cust serv) *Fax:* 386-873-3011 *E-mail:* info@kappamapgroup.com *Web Site:* kappamapgroup.com, pg 908

Eccles, James R C, Chace Audio by Deluxe, 201 S Victory Blvd, Burbank, CA 91502-2349 *Toll Free Tel:* 800-842-8346 *Web Site:* www.chace.com, pg 823

Eck, Bob, Anixter Inc, 2301 Patriot Blvd, Glenview, IL 60026 *Tel:* 224-521-8000 *Toll Free Tel:* 800-323-8167 *Fax:* 224-521-8100 *Web Site:* www.anixter.com, pg 787

Eckel, Robert, MorphoTrust USA, 296 Concord Rd, Billerica, MA 01821 *Tel:* 978-215-2400 *Fax:* 978-215-2500 *Web Site:* www.morphotrust.com, pg 946

Ecker, Sarah, ASET - The Neurodiagnostic Society, 402 E Bannister Rd, Suite A, Kansas City, MO 64131-3019 *Tel:* 816-931-1120 *Fax:* 816-931-1145 *E-mail:* info@aset.org *Web Site:* www.aset.org, pg 792

Eckstat, Tony, Celestial Harmonies/Fortuna Records/Kuckuck Schallplatten/Black Sun Music/MonteVideo, 1951 N Wilmot Rd, Bldg 2, Unit 7, Tucson, AZ 85712-8000 *Tel:* 520-326-4400 *Fax:* 520-326-3333 *E-mail:* celestial@harmonies.com *Web Site:* www.harmonies.com, pg 822

Eckstein, Ike, Visual Word Systems Inc, 35 W 36 St, 8th fl, New York, NY 10018 *Tel:* 212-629-8383 *Fax:* 212-629-8333 *Web Site:* www.visualword.com, pg 1060

Eddy, Mary, National Teleproductions Inc, PO Box 1804, West Palm Beach, FL 33402-1804 *Tel:* 561-689-9271 *Fax:* 561-640-4677 *E-mail:* ntp@ntpworldwide.com, pg 953

Eddy, Michael, Career & Self Directed Extended Programs at Purdue University, Stewart Ctr, G-53, 128 Memorial Mall, West Lafayette, IN 47907-2034 *Tel:* 765-494-8619 *Toll Free Tel:* 800-830-0269 *Fax:* 765-496-2484 *E-mail:* distance@purdue.edu *Web Site:* www.distance.purdue.edu/training, pg 820

Edgarton, Tyler, Mailing Avenue Stageworks, 1144 Mailing Ave, Atlanta, GA 30315 *Tel:* 404-601-9500 (ext 11) *Web Site:* www.mailingavenuestageworks.com, pg 929

Edge, Denzil, The Learning House Inc, 427 S Fourth St, Suite 300, Louisville, KY 40202 *Tel:* 502-589-9878 *Fax:* 502-589-9825 *E-mail:* sales@learninghouse.com *Web Site:* www.learninghouse.com, pg 917

Edgil, Bobby, Business & Legal Reports Inc, 141 Mill Rock Rd E, Old Saybrook, CT 06475 *Tel:* 860-510-0100 *Toll Free Tel:* 800-727-5257 *Fax:* 860-510-7224 *E-mail:* service@blr.com *Web Site:* www.blr.com, pg 815

Edmonds-Merritt, Valerie A, Library & Information Technology Association (LITA), c/o American Library Association, 50 E Huron St, Chicago, IL 60611-2795 *Toll Free Tel:* 800-545-2433 (ext 4270) *Fax:* 312-280-3257 *E-mail:* lita@ala.org *Web Site:* www.ala.org/lita, pg 1084

Edmunds, Andy, Virginia Film Office, 901 E Byrd St, Richmond, VA 23219-4048 *Tel:* 804-545-5530 *Toll Free Tel:* 800-854-6233 *Fax:* 804-545-5501 *E-mail:* vafilm@virginia.org *Web Site:* www.film.virginia.org, pg 1103

Edwards, Chuck, Gulf Coast Audio Visual Producers Inc, c/o National Park Bookshop, 3720 N Pace Blvd, Pensacola, FL 32506 *Tel:* 850-433-3016 *Toll Free Tel:* 800-722-2057 *Fax:* 850-438-4807 *E-mail:* gcavp@aol.com *Web Site:* www.gcavp.com, pg 883

Edwards, Elizabeth, Chicago International Children's Film Festival, 1517 W Fullerton Ave, Chicago, IL 60614 *Tel:* 773-281-9075 (ext 3011) *Fax:* 773-929-0266 *E-mail:* kids@facets.org *Web Site:* www.cicff.org; www.facets.org, pg 1111

Edwards, Joe, Imagers, 1575 Northside Dr, Bldg 400, Suite 490, Atlanta, GA 30318-5411 *Tel:* 404-351-5800 *Toll Free Tel:* 800-232-5411 *Fax:* 404-351-9020 *E-mail:* imagers@imagers.com *Web Site:* www.imagers.com, pg 896

Edwards, Marilyn, Mayor's Office of Economic & Community Development, Metropolitan Courthouse, Suite 102, One Public Sq, Nashville, TN 37219 *Tel:* 615-862-4700 *Fax:* 615-862-6025 *Web Site:* www.nashville.gov, pg 1102

Edwards, Marvin S Jr, CommScope Inc, 1100 CommScope Place SE, Hickory, NC 28602 *Tel:* 828-324-2200 *Toll Free Tel:* 800-982-1708 *Web Site:* www.commscope.com, pg 832

Edwards, Mr Vanya, Sovfoto/Eastfoto Inc, 263 W 20 St, Suite 3, New York, NY 10011 *Tel:* 212-727-8170 *Fax:* 212-727-8228 *E-mail:* info@sovfoto.com *Web Site:* www.sovfoto.com, pg 1019

Edwardz, George L, Universal Satellite Communications Inc, 1530 Nandina Ave, Perris, CA 92571 *Tel:* 562-483-4800; 951-943-4420 (corp off) *Toll Free Tel:* 888-867-6620 *Fax:* 954-943-0263 *Web Site:* www.unisatmobile.com, pg 1049

Efrusy, Brian, RingSide Creative, 13320 Northend, Suite 3000, Oak Park, MI 48237 *Tel:* 248-548-2500 *E-mail:* info@ringsidecreative.com; newbiz@ringsidecreative.com *Web Site:* www.ringsidecreative.com, pg 997

Eftekar, Y Julian, Motion Picture Licensing Corp (MPLC), 5455 Centinela Ave, Los Angeles, CA 90066 *Tel:* 310-822-8855 (intl calls) *Toll Free Tel:* 800-462-8855 *Fax:* 310-822-4440 *Web Site:* www.mplc.org, pg 947

Eggen, Greg, Hollywood Lights Inc, 5251 SE McLoughlin Blvd, Portland, OR 97202-4836 *Tel:* 503-232-9001; 503-232-8855 *Toll Free Tel:* 800-826-9881 *Fax:* 503-517-8686 *E-mail:* portland@hollywoodlights.biz *Web Site:* www.hollywoodlights.biz, pg 890

Ehlinger, Betty Gorsegner, Association for Information Media & Equipment, PO Box 9844, Cedar Rapids, IA 52409-9844 *Tel:* 319-654-0608 *Fax:* 319-654-0609 *Web Site:* www.aime.org, pg 1078

Ehrenberger, John, Superior Graphics, 10440 Brockwood Rd, Dallas, TX 75238 *Tel:* 972-437-0542 *Toll Free Tel:* 800-969-8228 *Fax:* 972-690-6029 *E-mail:* info@superiorgraphics.com *Web Site:* www.superiorgraphics.com, pg 1029

Ehrlich, Douglas, Image Zone Inc, 11 W 69 St, Suite 10A, New York, NY 10023 *Tel:* 212-924-8804 *Web Site:* www.imagezone.com, pg 896

Eicher, David A, The Program Source International, 2494 Loch Creek Way, Bloomfield Hills, MI 48304 *Tel:* 248-333-2010 *E-mail:* info@program-source.com *Web Site:* www.program-source.com, pg 985

Eicher, Scott, Ojai Valley Chamber of Commerce, 206 N Signal St, Suite P, Ojai, CA 93023 *Tel:* 805-646-8126 *Fax:* 805-646-9762 *E-mail:* info@ojaichamber.org *Web Site:* www.ojaichamber.org, pg 1093

Eickeneier, Michael, Strategic Connections, 2721 Spring Forest Rd, Raleigh, NC 27616 *Tel:* 919-878-0550 *Fax:* 919-875-8712 *E-mail:* info@strategicmail.net *Web Site:* www.strategicconnections.net, pg 1026

Eidsin, Bonnie, 1st Financial Training Services Inc, 1515 E Woodfield Rd, Suite 3730, Schaumburg, IL 60173 *Tel:* 847-969-0900 *Toll Free Tel:* 800-442-8662 *Fax:* 847-969-0521 *E-mail:* sales@1stfinancialtraining.com *Web Site:* www.1stfinancialtraining.com, pg 868

Eiger, Neil, Russell Industries Inc, 40 Horton Ave, Lynbrook, NY 11563 *Tel:* 516-536-5000 *Toll Free Tel:* 800-645-2202 *Fax:* 516-764-5747 *Toll Free Fax:* 800-645-2200 *E-mail:* sales@russellind.com *Web Site:* www.russellind.com, pg 1001

Eisenberg, Alan, Refinery, 16 W 46 St, 12th fl, New York, NY 10036 *Tel:* 212-391-8166 *Fax:* 212-391-8783 *Web Site:* refinerynyc.com, pg 994

Eisendrath, Charles R, The Livingston Awards for Young Journalists, Wallace House, 620 Oxford Rd, Ann Arbor, MI 48104 *Tel:* 734-998-7575 *Fax:* 734-998-7979 *E-mail:* livawards@umich.edu *Web Site:* www.livawards.org, pg 1118

Eisler, Jeff, Global Television, 222 23 St NE, Calgary, AB T2E 7N2, Canada *Tel:* 403-235-7777 *Fax:* 403-248-0252 *E-mail:* globalnews.calg@globaltv.com *Web Site:* www.globaltv.com, pg 879

Eiswerth, Paul, TeL Systems, 7235 Jackson Rd, Ann Arbor, MI 48103 *Tel:* 734-761-4506 *Toll Free Tel:* 800-686-7235 *Fax:* 734-761-9776 *E-mail:* sales@telsystemsusa.com *Web Site:* www.telsystemsusa.com, pg 1035

Ejabat, Mory, Zhone Technologies Inc, 7195 Oakport St, Oakland, CA 94621 *Tel:* 510-777-7000 *Toll Free Tel:* 877-ZHONE-20 (946-6320, US & CN) *Fax:* 510-777-7001 *E-mail:* info@zhone.com; sales@zhone.com *Web Site:* www.zhone.com, pg 1073

Elam, Angela, New Letters on the Air, c/o University of Missouri, Kansas City, 5101 Rockhill Rd, Kansas City, MO 64110 *Tel:* 816-235-1159 *Toll Free Tel:* 888-548-2477 *Fax:* 816-235-2611 *E-mail:* radio@newletters.org *Web Site:* www.newletters.org, pg 956

Elatawi, Hoda, GAPC (General Assembly Production Centre), 1550 Laperriere Ave, Suite 102, Ottawa, ON K1Z 7T2, Canada *Tel:* 613-723-3316 *Fax:* 613-723-8583 *Web Site:* www.gapc.com, pg 875

Eldean, Kori, Waterfront Film Festival (WFF), PO Box 387, Saugatuck, MI 49453-0387 *Tel:* 269-857-8351 *Fax:* 269-857-1072 *E-mail:* info@waterfrontfilm.org *Web Site:* www.waterfrontfilm.org, pg 1129

Elderd, Chuck, Palm Beach County Film & Television Commission, 1555 Palm Beach Lakes Blvd, Suite 900, West Palm Beach, FL 33401 *Tel:* 561-233-1000 *Toll Free Tel:* 800-745-FILM (745-3456) *Fax:* 561-233-3113 *Web Site:* www.pbfilm.com, pg 1096

Eldridge, Glenn, Chelsea Decorative Metal Co, 8212 Braewick Dr, Dept AV, Houston, TX 77074 *Tel:* 713-721-9200 *Fax:* 713-776-8661 *E-mail:* tinman83@earthlink.net *Web Site:* www.tinman.com, pg 824

Eldridge, John, Technical Services, 2480 Southwell Rd, Dallas, TX 75229 *Tel:* 972-421-4230 *Fax:* 972-421-4231, pg 1034

Elfenbein, Reed, John Wiley & Sons Inc, 111 River St, Hoboken, NJ 07030 *Tel:* 201-748-6000 *Toll Free Tel:* 800-225-5945 *Fax:* 201-748-6088 *E-mail:* info@wiley.com *Web Site:* www.wiley.com, pg 1066

Elias, Dr Frederick G, ODC Publishing, PO Box 60609, Santa Barbara, CA 93160-0609 *Toll Free Tel:* 800-551-2800 *Toll Free Fax:* 800-551-2800 *Web Site:* www.frederickelias.com, pg 961

Eliason, Craig, Minneapolis Licenses & Consumer Services, 350 S Fifth St, Rm 1C, Minneapolis, MN 55415-1391 *Tel:* 612-673-2080 *Fax:* 612-673-3399 *Web Site:* www.minneapolismn.gov/business-licensing, pg 1098

Elifrits, Kathy, The American Classical League, Miami University, 422 Wells Mill Dr, Oxford, OH 45056 *Tel:* 513-529-7741 *Fax:* 513-529-7742 *E-mail:* info@aclclassics.org *Web Site:* www.aclclassics.org, pg 784

Elisman, Boris, ACCO Brands Corp, 4 Corporate Dr, Lake Zurick, IL 60047-8997 *Toll Free Tel:* 800-541-0094 *Toll Free Fax:* 800-941-4463 *E-mail:* contactus@gbc.com *Web Site:* www.accobrands.com, pg 773

Elkind, David, Live Wire Media, PO Box 848, Mill Valley, CA 94942 *Tel:* 415-564-9500 *Toll Free Tel:* 800-359-KIDS (359-5437) *Fax:* 415-552-4087 *E-mail:* sales@livewiremedia.com *Web Site:* www.livewiremedia.com, pg 923

Ellard, Melissa Reilly, Weston Woods Studios Inc, 90 Old Sherman Tpke, Danbury, CT 06816 *Tel:* 203-797-3520 *Toll Free Tel:* 800-243-5020 *Fax:* 203-797-3531 *E-mail:* westonwoodsquestions@scholastic.com *Web Site:* www.scholastic.com/westonwoods, pg 1064

Eller, April, K2 Productions, 4214 Shoal Creek Dr, Greensboro, NC 27410 *Tel:* 336-664-8036 *E-mail:* info@k2production.com *Web Site:* www.k2production.com, pg 914

Eller, Kevin, K2 Productions, 4214 Shoal Creek Dr, Greensboro, NC 27410 *Tel:* 336-664-8036 *E-mail:* info@k2production.com *Web Site:* www.k2production.com, pg 914

Ellett, Ed, Vaddio, 131 Cheshire Lane, Suite 500, Minnetonka, MN 55305 *Tel:* 763-971-4400 *Toll Free Tel:* 800-572-2011 *Fax:* 763-971-4464 *E-mail:* info@vaddio.com *Web Site:* www.vaddio.com, pg 1051

Elliot, Ramey, Abacus Group of Saint Louis LLC, No 11 Tower, Glen Carbon, IL 62034 *Tel:* 314-583-3747 *E-mail:* abacusgroup@agstl.com *Web Site:* www.agstl.com, pg 772

Elliott, James, Wisconsin Technical College System Foundation Inc, One Foundation Circle, Waunakee, WI 53597-8914 *Tel:* 608-849-2424; 608-849-2400 *Toll Free Tel:* 800-821-6313 *Fax:* 608-849-2468 *E-mail:* foundation@wtcsf.tec.wi.us *Web Site:* www.wtcsf.tec.wi.us, pg 1068

Elliott, Janet, Radio & TV Engineering Achievement Awards, 1771 "N" St NW, Washington, DC 20036 *Tel:* 202-429-5300 *Fax:* 202-429-4199 *E-mail:* nab@nab.org *Web Site:* www.nab.org, pg 1124

Elliott, Monica, Institute of Industrial Engineers (IIE), 3577 Parkway Lane, Suite 200, Norcross, GA 30092 *Tel:* 770-449-0460 *Toll Free Tel:* 800-494-0460 *Fax:* 770-441-3295 *E-mail:* cs@iienet.org *Web Site:* www.iienet2.org, pg 1083

Elliott, Thomas, Centre for Art Tapes (CFAT), 2238 Maitland St, Halifax, NS B3K 2Z9, Canada *Tel:* 902-422-6822 *Fax:* 902-422-6823 *E-mail:* info@cfat.ca *Web Site:* cfat.ca, pg 1080

Ellis, Chris, Blueyed Pictures Inc, 8950 W Olympic Blvd, Suite 324, Beverly Hills, CA 90211 *Tel:* 310-295-0848 *Fax:* 310-295-0260 *E-mail:* la@blueyedpictures.com *Web Site:* www.blueyedpictures.com, pg 810

Ellis, Shannon, Havas Edge, 6922 Hollywood Blvd, Hollywood, CA 90028 *Tel:* 310-734-1333 *E-mail:* info@havasedge.com *Web Site:* www.havasedge.com, pg 885

Ellis, Sister Bridget Charles, Pauline Books & Media, 50 St Paul's Ave, Boston, MA 02130-3491 *Tel:* 617-522-8911 *Toll Free Tel:* 800-876-4463 (orders); 800-836-9723 (cust serv) *Fax:* 617-541-9805 *E-mail:* records@pauline.org *Web Site:* www.pauline.org, pg 970

Elshimi, Adel, Shimad Corp, 45 Parsons Way, Los Altos, CA 94022 *Tel:* 650-962-1234 (Outside USA) *Toll Free Tel:* 888-474-4623 *Fax:* 650-948-3378 *E-mail:* sales@shimad.com *Web Site:* www.shimad.com, pg 1009

Elstrodt, John, Metropolitan Audio Visual Co LLC, 2862 Hartland Rd, Falls Church, VA 22043 *Tel:* 703-834-0004 *Toll Free Tel:* 800-966-4333 *Fax:* 703-834-0866 *E-mail:* sales@metroav.com *Web Site:* www.metroav.com, pg 940

Elton, Serona, Music & Entertainment Industry Educators Association (MEIEA), 1900 Belmont Blvd, Nashville, TN 37212-3758 *Tel:* 615-460-6946 *E-mail:* office@meiea.org *Web Site:* www.meiea.org, pg 1084

Elton, Zoe, Mill Valley Film Festival, 1001 Lootens Place, Suite 220, San Rafael, CA 94901 *Tel:* 415-383-5256 *Fax:* 415-383-8606 *E-mail:* mvff@cafilm.org; info@cafilm.org *Web Site:* www.mvff.com; www.cafilm.org, pg 1120

Eltzroth, John, American AV, 2862 Hartland Rd, Falls Church, VA 22043 *Tel:* 703-573-6910 *Fax:* 703-573-3539 *E-mail:* sales@aavevents.com *Web Site:* www.aavevents.com, pg 783

Elwood, Sim, Creative Technology, 1455 Estes Ave, Elk Grove Village, IL 60007 *Tel:* 847-671-9670 *Toll Free Tel:* 800-826-4761 *Fax:* 847-640-6559 *E-mail:* info@ctchicago.com *Web Site:* us.ct-group.com, pg 838

Elzinga, Anna, Zondervan, A HarperCollins Company, 3900 Sparks Dr, Grand Rapids, MI 49546 *Tel:* 616-698-6900 *Toll Free Tel:* 800-226-1122; 800-727-3480 (retail orders) *Fax:* 616-698-3255 (retail orders) *E-mail:* zinfo@zondervan.com *Web Site:* www.zondervan.com, pg 1074

Emanuel, Frank, Emanuel Audiovisual Consultants, 303 County Rd, Cresskill, NJ 07626 *Tel:* 201-569-5328 *Toll Free Fax:* 888-397-1302 *E-mail:* emanuelav@att.net *Web Site:* www.audiovisualconsultant.com, pg 860

Emerman, Randi, Palm Beach International Film Festival (PBIFF), 2101 S Congress Ave, Delray Beach, FL 33445 *Tel:* 561-362-0003 *E-mail:* info@pbifilmfest.org; submissions@pbifilmfest.org *Web Site:* www.pbifilmfest.org, pg 1123

Emerson, Matt, Ceavco Audio/Visual Co, 6240 W 54 Ave, Arvada, CO 80002 *Tel:* 303-539-3500 *Fax:* 303-539-3501 *E-mail:* solutions@ceavco.com *Web Site:* www.ceavco.com, pg 822

Emerson, Mike, T3Media, 1530 16 St, 6th fl, Denver, CO 80202 *Tel:* 720-382-2869 *Toll Free Tel:* 866-815-6599 *Fax:* 720-382-2719 *E-mail:* content@t3media.com *Web Site:* www.t3licensing.com, pg 1046

Emery, Bob, Media Entertainment Inc, 13194 US Hwy 301 S, Suite 320, Riverview, FL 33569 *Tel:* 813-495-5821 *Toll Free Tel:* 888-886-7793 *Fax:* 813-741-1152 *Web Site:* www.mediaent.net, pg 936

Emery, Susanne K, Media Entertainment Inc, 13194 US Hwy 301 S, Suite 320, Riverview, FL 33569 *Tel:* 813-495-5821 *Toll Free Tel:* 888-886-7793 *Fax:* 813-741-1152 *Web Site:* www.mediaent.net, pg 936

Emling, Ward, Mississippi Film Office, 501 N West St, Suite B-01, Jackson, MS 39201 *Tel:* 601-359-3297 *Fax:* 601-359-5048 *Web Site:* www.filmmississippi.org, pg 1099

Emmer, Michael, Bridger Productions Inc, 4150 Glory View Lane, Jackson, WY 83001 *Tel:* 307-733-7871 *Fax:* 307-734-1947 *E-mail:* info@bridgerproductions.com *Web Site:* www.bridgerproductions.com, pg 812

Emmerich, Toby, New Line Cinema, 116 N Robertson Blvd, Suite 200, Los Angeles, CA 90048 *Tel:* 310-854-5811 *Fax:* 310-854-1824 *Web Site:* www.warnerbros.com/studio/divisions/motion-pictures/new-line-cinema.html, pg 956

Emmerling, Dave, Midnight Media Group Inc, 45 E Willow St, Millburn, NJ 07041-1416 *Tel:* 973-379-5959 *E-mail:* info@mmgi.tv *Web Site:* www.mmgi.tv, pg 942

Emspak, Steve, Shen Milsom & Wilke LLC, 417 Fifth Ave, New York, NY 10016 *Tel:* 212-725-6800 *Fax:* 212-725-0864 *E-mail:* info@smwllc.com *Web Site:* www.smwllc.com, pg 1008

Enberg, Dick, American Sportscasters Association Inc (ASA), 225 Broadway, Suite 2030, New York, NY 10007 *Tel:* 212-227-8080 *Fax:* 212-571-0556 *Web Site:* www.americansportscasters.com; www.americansportscastersonline.com, pg 1077

Encina, Matthew, Blind, 1702 Olympic Blvd, Santa Monica, CA 90404 *Tel:* 310-314-1618 *Fax:* 310-314-1718 *Web Site:* www.blind.com, pg 809

Ender, Bruno A, Power-Sonic Corp, 7550 Panasonic Way, San Diego, CA 92154 *Tel:* 619-661-2020 *Fax:* 619-661-3650 *E-mail:* customer-service@power-sonic.com; technical-support@power-sonic.com *Web Site:* www.power-sonic.com, pg 979

Endres, W Chris, Tele-Measurements Inc, 145 Main Ave, Clifton, NJ 07014 *Tel:* 973-473-8822 *Toll Free Tel:* 800-223-0052 (ext 207) *Fax:* 973-473-0521 *E-mail:* contact@tele-measurements.com *Web Site:* www.tele-measurements.com, pg 1036

Endres, William E, Tele-Measurements Inc, 145 Main Ave, Clifton, NJ 07014 *Tel:* 973-473-8822 *Toll Free Tel:* 800-223-0052 (ext 207) *Fax:* 973-473-0521 *E-mail:* contact@tele-measurements.com *Web Site:* www.tele-measurements.com, pg 1035

Eng, Ray, Babe Winkelman Productions Inc, 7119 Forthun Rd S, Baxter, MN 56425 *Tel:* 218-822-4424 *Toll Free Tel:* 800-333-0471 *Fax:* 218-822-7436 *Web Site:* www.winkelman.com, pg 1068

Engel, Debi, Quabbin Wire & Cable Co Inc, 10 Maple St, Ware, MA 01082-1597 *Tel:* 413-967-6281 *Toll Free Tel:* 800-368-3311 *Fax:* 413-967-7564 *E-mail:* sales@quabbin.com *Web Site:* www.quabbin.com, pg 988

Engel, Mark, Rosco Laboratories Inc, 52 Harbor View, Stamford, CT 06902 *Tel:* 203-708-8900 *Toll Free Tel:* 800-ROSCO NY (767-2669) *Fax:* 203-708-8919 *E-mail:* info@rosco.com *Web Site:* www.rosco.com, pg 999

Engel, Paul, Quabbin Wire & Cable Co Inc, 10 Maple St, Ware, MA 01082-1597 *Tel:* 413-967-6281 *Toll Free Tel:* 800-368-3311 *Fax:* 413-967-7564 *E-mail:* sales@quabbin.com *Web Site:* www.quabbin.com, pg 988

Engelman, Ralph, George Polk Awards in Journalism, Journalism Dept, One University Plaza, Brooklyn, NY 11201-5372 *Tel:* 718-488-1009 *Fax:* 718-780-4046 *Web Site:* www.liu.edu/polk, pg 1124

Englehart, Ned, Paragon Studios Inc, 820 W Fulton Market, Chicago, IL 60607-1302 *Tel:* 312-942-0075 *Fax:* 312-942-2488 *E-mail:* info@paragonstudiosinc.com *Web Site:* www.paragonstudiosinc.com, pg 969

Englen, Bjorn, Palardo Productions, 1807 Taft Ave, Suite 4, Hollywood, CA 90028 *Tel:* 323-469-8991 *E-mail:* palardo2@msn.com, pg 968

English, Elizabeth, Mermaid7seas Productions, 970 Ninth St, Boulder, CO 80302-7226 *Tel:* 303-545-0202; 303-818-5771 (cell) *E-mail:* mermaid7seas@gmail.com, pg 939

English, Elizabeth, Moondance International Film Festival, 970 Ninth St, Boulder, CO 80302-7226 *Tel:* 303-545-0202 *Web Site:* moondancefilmfestival.com, pg 1120

Engstrom, John, RGH Lighting LLC, 546 W 48 St, New York, NY 10036 *Tel:* 212-244-8300 *Fax:* 212-244-8769 *E-mail:* info@scheimpflug.net *Web Site:* www.scheimpflug.net, pg 996

Ennis, Bill, Media Magic, 11 Tanzanite, Rancho Santa Margarita, CA 92688 *Tel:* 949-713-9696 *Fax:* 270-716-9696 *E-mail:* request@mediamagic.tv *Web Site:* www.mediamagic.tv, pg 937

Enright, Logan, Enright Co, 1801-I Parkcourt Place, Suite 100, Santa Ana, CA 92701 *Toll Free Tel:* 888-334-7773 *Fax:* 714-285-1905 *E-mail:* admin@enrightcompany.com *Web Site:* www.enrightcompany.com, pg 861

Enright, Pat, PSAV® Presentation Services, 111 W Ocean Blvd, Suite 1110, Long Beach, CA 90802-4688 *Tel:* 562-366-0620 *Toll Free Tel:* 877-430-7728 *Fax:* 562-366-0628 *Web Site:* www.psav.com, pg 986

Enright, Patti, Enright Co, 1801-I Parkcourt Place, Suite 100, Santa Ana, CA 92701 *Toll Free Tel:* 888-334-7773 *Fax:* 714-285-1905 *E-mail:* admin@enrightcompany.com *Web Site:* www.enrightcompany.com, pg 861

Ens, Herb, Speciality Bulb Products Inc, 20010-100A Ave, Unit 2, Langley, BC V1M 3G4, Canada *Tel:* 604-513-8500 *Toll Free Tel:* 800-663-1120 *Fax:* 604-513-8200 *E-mail:* info@specialtybulb.com; bulbexpert@specialtybulb.com *Web Site:* www.specialtybulb.com, pg 1020

Epple, Kat, Kat Epple Music Productions, PO Box 3156, North Fort Myers, FL 33918-3156 *Tel:* 239-997-0323 *E-mail:* music@katepple.com *Web Site:* www.katepple.com, pg 862

Epstein, Larry, Paradise Show & Design Inc, 4653 35 St, Orlando, FL 32811 *Tel:* 407-649-7220 *Fax:* 407-649-7225 *E-mail:* info@paradiseshow.com *Web Site:* www.paradiseshow.com, pg 969

Erbe, Walter, Samy's Camera, 431 S Fairfax Ave, Los Angeles, CA 90036 *Tel:* 323-938-4400 *Toll Free Tel:* 800-321-4726 *Fax:* 323-937-2919 *E-mail:* lacamera@samys.com *Web Site:* www.samys.com, pg 1002

Erer, Tara, FilmNation Entertainment, 150 W 22 St, 9th fl, New York, NY 10011 *Web Site:* www.filmnation.com, pg 867

Erhardt, Christian, Leica Camera Inc, One Pearl Ct, Unit A, Allendale, NJ 07401 *Toll Free Tel:* 800-222-0118 *Fax:* 201-995-1686 *Web Site:* en.leica-camera.com, pg 918

Erickson, Britta, Denver Film Society, 1510 York St, 3rd fl, Denver, CO 80206 *Tel:* 303-595-3456 *Fax:* 303-595-0956 *E-mail:* info@denverfilm.org *Web Site:* www.denverfilm.org, pg 1081

Erickson, Britta, Starz Denver Film Festival, 1510 York St, 3rd fl, Denver, CO 80206 *Tel:* 303-595-3456 *Fax:* 303-595-0956 *E-mail:* info@denverfilm.org *Web Site:* www.denverfilm.org/festival, pg 1127

Erickson, Mark C, Fire Station Studios, 224 N Guadalupe St, San Marcos, TX 78666 *Tel:* 512-396-1144 *Fax:* 512-396-1169 *E-mail:* info@firestationstudios.com *Web Site:* www.firestationstudios.com, pg 868

Ernst, Roger, Case Design Corp, 333 School Lane, Telford, PA 18969 *Tel:* 215-703-0130 *Toll Free Tel:* 800-847-4176 *Fax:* 215-703-0139 *E-mail:* sales@casedesigncorp.com *Web Site:* www.casedesigncorp.com, pg 820

Errera, Stacie, Tamron USA Inc, 10 Austin Blvd, Commack, NY 11725 *Tel:* 631-858-8400 *Toll Free Tel:* 800-827-8880 *Fax:* 631-543-5666 *E-mail:* custserv@tamron.com *Web Site:* www.tamron-usa.com, pg 1031

Errigo, Anthony, Ashly Audio Inc, 847 Holt Rd, Webster, NY 14580-9103 *Tel:* 585-872-0010 *Toll Free Tel:* 800-828-6308 *Fax:* 585-872-0739 *E-mail:* info@ashly.com; sales@ashly.com *Web Site:* www.ashly.com, pg 792

Escobar, Christopher, Atlanta Film Festival (ATLFF), 25 Park Place NE, Suite 900, Atlanta, GA 30303 *Tel:* 678-929-8103 *E-mail:* info@atlantafilmfestival.com *Web Site:* atlantafilmfestival.com, pg 1108

Esp, Jim, Association of Imaging Executives™ (AIE™), A PMA Member Association, 2282 Springport Rd, Suite F, Jackson, MI 49202 *Tel:* 517-788-8100 *Toll Free Tel:* 800-762-9287 *Fax:* 517-788-8371 *E-mail:* aie@pmai.org *Web Site:* www.pmai.org/aie, pg 1079

Esp, Jim, Photo Marketing Association International (PMA), 2282 Springport Rd, Suite F, Jackson, MI 49202 *Tel:* 517-788-8100 *Toll Free Tel:* 800-762-9287 *Fax:* 517-788-8371 *Web Site:* www.pmai.org, pg 1087

Espe, Andrew, Washington Filmworks, 1411 Fourth Ave, Suite 420, Seattle, WA 98101 *Tel:* 206-264-0667 *Fax:* 206-382-4343 *E-mail:* info@washingtonfilmworks.org *Web Site:* washingtonfilmworks.org, pg 1103

Espinoza, Richard, LTM Corp of America, 7357 1/2 Atoll Ave, North Hollywood, CA 91605 *Tel:* 818-780-9828 *Toll Free Tel:* 800-762-4291 *Fax:* 818-780-9848 *E-mail:* sales@ltmlighting.com; info@ltmlighting.com, pg 925

Esqueda, David, Coloredge, 1919 Empire Ave, Burbank, CA 91504 *Tel:* 818-842-1121 *Fax:* 818-840-0185 *Web Site:* coloredge.com, pg 832

Essma, Joe, Accu-Tech, 11350 Old Roswell Rd, Suite 100, Roswell, GA 30009 *Tel:* 770-740-2240 *Toll Free Tel:* 800-221-4767; 888-222-8832 *Fax:* 770-740-2260 *Web Site:* www.accu-tech.com, pg 773

Estellon, Thibaut, LightHouse Films, 115 W 29 St, Suite 903, New York, NY 10001 *Tel:* 646-649-3600 *Fax:* 646-398-7122 *E-mail:* contact@lhfny.com; rent@lhfny.com *Web Site:* www.light-house-films.com, pg 920

Estrada, Jr, CenterStaging LLC, 3407 Winona Ave, Burbank, CA 91504 *Tel:* 818-559-4333 *Fax:* 818-848-4016 *E-mail:* info@centerstaging.com *Web Site:* centerstaging.com, pg 823

Estremera, Estefeni, Guilford Publications, 72 Spring St, 4th fl, New York, NY 10012 *Tel:* 212-431-9800 *Toll Free Tel:* 800-365-7006 *Fax:* 212-966-6708 *E-mail:* info@guilford.com *Web Site:* www.guilford.com, pg 883

Estus, Boyd, Heliotrope Studios, 44 Oak St, Newton Upper Falls, MA 02464 *Tel:* 617-964-8181 *Fax:* 617-964-8030 *E-mail:* heliotropestudios@earthlink.net *Web Site:* www.heliotropestudios.com, pg 887

Ethier, Yan, Montreal Film & TV Commission, Duke Pavilion, 5th fl, 801 Brennan St, Montreal, QC H3C 0G4, Canada *Tel:* 514-872-2883 *Fax:* 514-872-3409 *E-mail:* film.tv@ville.montreal.qc.ca *Web Site:* www.montrealfilm.com, pg 1105

Ethridge, Ed, Ed Ethridge Productions Inc, 1215 E Broward Blvd, Suite 200, Fort Lauderdale, FL 33301 *Tel:* 954-533-7100 *Fax:* 954-306-3261 *Web Site:* www.ethridgeproductions.com, pg 863

Evangelista, Richard, Corinth Films Inc, 3117 Bursonville Rd, Riegelsville, PA 18077 *Tel:* 610-346-7446 *Fax:* 610-346-6345 *E-mail:* sales@corinthfilms.com *Web Site:* www.corinthreleasing.com; www.corinthfilms.com, pg 836

Evans, Chuck, Quantum Data Inc, 2111 Big Timber Rd, Elgin, IL 60123-1100 *Tel:* 847-888-0450 *Toll Free Tel:* 888-252-6133 (tech support) *Fax:* 847-888-2802 *E-mail:* sales@quantumdata.com *Web Site:* www.quantumdata.com, pg 989

Evans, David, High Water, University of Memphis, Rudi E Scheidt School of Music, Memphis, TN 38152 *Tel:* 901-678-3317 *Fax:* 901-678-3096, pg 889

Evans, Jeff, The Will-Burt Co, 169 S Main St, Orrville, OH 44667 *Tel:* 330-682-7015; 330-684-4000 (cust serv) *Fax:* 330-684-1190 *E-mail:* contact_us@willburt.com *Web Site:* www.willburt.com, pg 1066

Evenson, Stacey, Rainbow International Inc/Rainbow Productions Inc, 1103 Canyon Rd, Santa Fe, NM 87501 *Tel:* 773-505-6264 *Fax:* 773-525-6278 *Web Site:* www.rainbowplace.com, pg 991

Everhart, Bob, National Old Time Country Bluegrass & Folk Music Festival, PO Box 492, Anita, IA 50020 *Tel:* 712-762-4363 *Web Site:* ntcma.net, pg 1121

Everhart, Bob, National Traditional Country Music Association Inc (NTCMA), PO Box 492, Anita, IA 50020-0492 *Tel:* 712-762-4363; 712-249-5989 (cell) *E-mail:* ruralcountrymusic@gmail.com *Web Site:* ntcma.net, pg 1086

Everhart, Nick, LightHouse Films, 115 W 29 St, Suite 903, New York, NY 10001 *Tel:* 646-649-3600 *Fax:* 646-398-7122 *E-mail:* contact@lhfny.com; rent@lhfny.com *Web Site:* www.light-house-films.com, pg 920

Ewart, Heidi, Renegade Animation, 111 E Broadway, Suite 208, Glendale, CA 91205 *Tel:* 818-551-2351 *Fax:* 818-551-2350 *Web Site:* www.renegadeanimation.com, pg 994

Ewing, Malcolm P Jr, Jasper Ewing & Sons Inc, 1220 E Northside Dr, Suite 370, Jackson, MS 39211 *Tel:* 601-981-2178 *Fax:* 601-981-2178 *E-mail:* jasperewing@comcast.net *Web Site:* jasperewing.com, pg 864

Exbrayat, Marianne, Transvideo International, 11712 Moorpark St, Suite 112-B, North Hollywood, CA 91604 *Tel:* 818-985-4903 *Fax:* 818-985-4921 *Web Site:* www.transvideointl.com, pg 1044

Faber, Jeff, Sharp's Audio-Visual Ltd, 3636 Seventh St SE, Calgary, AB T2G 2Y8, Canada *Tel:* 403-255-4123 *Toll Free Tel:* 800-491-1121 *Fax:* 403-255-3478 *E-mail:* sales@sharpsav.com *Web Site:* www.sharpsav.com, pg 1008

Faber, Shane, Jeep Jazz Media Solutions, 8 Graham Terr, Montclair, NJ 07042 *Tel:* 973-222-5737 *E-mail:* jeepjazz@hotmail.com *Web Site:* www.jeepjazz.com, pg 905

Fabiano, Joe, Outsource Engineering & Manufacturing Inc dba Texscan MSI, 11800 Wills Rd, Suite 150, Alpharetta, GA 30009 *Tel:* 678-689-0146; 770-642-7440 (support) *E-mail:* sales@texscan-msi.com *Web Site:* www.texscan-msi.com, pg 966

Fabiano, Leonard J, Outsource Engineering & Manufacturing Inc dba Texscan MSI, 11800 Wills Rd, Suite 150, Alpharetta, GA 30009 *Tel:* 678-689-0146; 770-642-7440 (support) *E-mail:* sales@texscan-msi.com *Web Site:* www.texscan-msi.com, pg 966

Fackert, James, Leprecon®, 10087 Industrial Dr, Hamburg, MI 48139 *Tel:* 810-852-4300 *Toll Free Tel:* 888-422-3537 *Fax:* 810-231-1631 *E-mail:* lepsls@leprecon.com *Web Site:* www.leprecon.com, pg 919

Fackert, James H, Littlite LLC, PO Box 430, Hamburg, MI 48139-0430 *Tel:* 810-852-4242 *Fax:* 810-231-1631 *E-mail:* sales@littlite.com *Web Site:* www.littlite.com, pg 923

Facklis, Jeff, Show Department Inc, 2201 W Fulton St, Chicago, IL 60612 *Tel:* 312-243-8215 *Toll Free Tel:* 800-294-4111 *Fax:* 312-243-8236 *E-mail:* info@showdepartment.com *Web Site:* www.showdepartment.com, pg 1009

Facklis, Lee, Show Department Inc, 2201 W Fulton St, Chicago, IL 60612 *Tel:* 312-243-8215 *Toll Free Tel:* 800-294-4111 *Fax:* 312-243-8236 *E-mail:* info@showdepartment.com *Web Site:* www.showdepartment.com, pg 1009

Fackrell, Matt, Kaboom Productions, 1465 Illinois St, San Francisco, CA 94107 *Tel:* 415-434-2666 *Fax:* 415-970-8548 *E-mail:* updates@kaboomproductions.com *Web Site:* kaboomproductions.com, pg 907

Factor, Beverly, Envirovision, PO Box 4136, Laguna Beach, CA 92652-4136 *Tel:* 949-673-2555 *Fax:* 949-673-2555 *Web Site:* www.beverlyfactor.com, pg 861

Fadness, Allen, Jake Barner Studio, 120 S Barner Dr, Centralia, WA 98531 *Tel:* 360-736-1764, pg 803

Fahrbach, David, Enright Co, 1801-I Parkcourt Place, Suite 100, Santa Ana, CA 92701 *Toll Free Tel:* 888-334-7773 *Fax:* 714-285-1905 *E-mail:* admin@enrightcompany.com *Web Site:* www.enrightcompany.com, pg 861

Fahrenkrug, Carl F, Microwave Filter Co Inc, 6743 Kinne St, East Syracuse, NY 13057 *Tel:* 315-438-4700 *Toll Free Tel:* 800-448-1666 *Fax:* 315-463-1467 *Toll Free Fax:* 888-411-8860 *E-mail:* mfcsales@microwavefilter.com *Web Site:* www.microwavefilter.com, pg 942

Fairbanks, Glen, DGI-Invisuals LLC, 101 Billerica Ave, Bldg 6, North Billerica, MA 01862 *Toll Free Tel:* 800-344-0432 *Fax:* 781-270-3663 *E-mail:* sales@dgi-invisuals.com *Web Site:* www.dgi-invisuals.com, pg 846

Faison, Pat, Newark Black Film Festival (NBFF), 49 Washington St, Newark, NJ 07102-3176 *Tel:* 973-596-6550 *Fax:* 973-642-0459 *E-mail:* nbff@newarkmuseum.org *Web Site:* www.newarkmuseum.org/nbff, pg 1122

Faison, Pat, Paul Robeson Awards, 49 Washington St, Newark, NJ 07102-3176 *Tel:* 973-596-6550 *Fax:* 973-642-0459 *E-mail:* nbff@newarkmuseum.org *Web Site:* www.newarkmuseum.org/nbff, pg 1125

Falatovich, Brian J, Midwest Digital Corp, 10150 Virginia Ave, Suite H, Chicago Ridge, IL 60415 *Tel:* 708-790-4040 *E-mail:* midwestdig@gmail.com *Web Site:* www.midwestdigitalcorp.com, pg 942

Falcon, Paul, Bella Faccia Inc, 6521 Chillum Place NW, Washington, DC 20012 *Tel:* 202-291-1932 *Fax:* 202-301-7716 *E-mail:* contact@bellafaccia.net *Web Site:* www.bellafaccia.net, pg 804

Falcone, Ernie, Quatrefoil Associates Inc, 29 "C" St, Laurel, MD 20707 *Tel:* 301-470-4748 *Fax:* 301-470-4749 *E-mail:* info@quatrefoil.com *Web Site:* www.quatrefoil.com, pg 989

Fall, Martin, General Devices Co Inc, 1410 S Post Rd, Indianapolis, IN 46239 *Tel:* 317-897-7000 *Fax:* 317-898-2917 *E-mail:* sales@generaldevices.com *Web Site:* www.generaldevices.com, pg 876

Fall, Maxwell, General Devices Co Inc, 1410 S Post Rd, Indianapolis, IN 46239 *Tel:* 317-897-7000 *Fax:* 317-898-2917 *E-mail:* sales@generaldevices.com *Web Site:* www.generaldevices.com, pg 876

Fallat, Tom, Sound Sound/Savage Fruitarian Productions, 843 Hiawatha Place S, Unit 304, Seattle, WA 98144 *Tel:* 206-322-6866 *Web Site:* www.soundsound.com, pg 1017

Falotico, Russel J, PLUS Corp of America, 9610 SW Sunshine Ct, Suite 100, Beaverton, OR 97005 *Tel:* 503-748-8700 *Toll Free Tel:* 800-211-9001 *Fax:* 503-643-9756 *E-mail:* sales@plus-america.com *Web Site:* www.plus-america.com, pg 977

Falter, David A, Antenna International, 383 Main Ave, Norwalk, CT 06851 *Tel:* 203-523-0320 *Fax:* 203-354-5519 *E-mail:* inquiry@antennainternational.com *Web Site:* www.antennainternational.com, pg 787

Falzarano, Jack, Megavideo Productions, 22 Cedar St, No 2, Garfield, NJ 07026 *Tel:* 973-478-1921 *E-mail:* megamail@megadv.com *Web Site:* www.megadv.com, pg 938

Falzon, Charles, Cambium Catalyst International (CCI), 18 Dupont St, Toronto, ON M5R 1V2, Canada *Tel:* 416-964-8750 *Fax:* 416-964-1980 *E-mail:* info@ccientertainment.com *Web Site:* www.ccientertainment.com, pg 817

Fambrough, William, Fambrough & Associates Inc, 13501 Leatha's Ct, Suite 100, Kansas City, MO 64089-7701 *Tel:* 816-471-1717 *Fax:* 816-256-5283 *E-mail:* we_work_for_you@fambrough.com *Web Site:* www.fambrough.com, pg 865

Fanella, Kelly, American Society of Safety Engineers (ASSE), 1800 E Oakton St, Des Plaines, IL 60018 *Tel:* 847-699-2929 *E-mail:* customerservice@asse.org *Web Site:* www.asse.org, pg 1077

Fanelli, Duke, Association of National Advertisers Inc (ANA), 708 Third Ave, 33rd fl, New York, NY 10017-4270 *Tel:* 212-697-5950 *Fax:* 212-687-7310 *E-mail:* info@ana.net *Web Site:* www.ana.net, pg 1079

Farber, Erica, Radio Advertising Bureau (RAB), 125 W 55 St, 5th fl, New York, NY 10019 *Tel:* 212-681-7200 *Toll Free Tel:* 800-252-7234 *Fax:* 212-681-7223 *Web Site:* www.rab.com, pg 1088

Farber, Scott, Hunt's Photo, Video & Digital, 100 Main St, Melrose, MA 02176-6104 *Tel:* 781-662-8822 (retail sales) *Toll Free Tel:* 800-924-8682 (retail sales); 800-221-1830 (ext 2340, corp sales) *Fax:* 781-662-6524 *E-mail:* ecommerce@wbhunt.com (retail online sales) *Web Site:* www.huntsphotoandvideo.com, pg 892

Faria, Thom, Cramer Productions, 425 University Ave, Norwood, MA 02062 *Tel:* 781-278-2300 *Fax:* 781-255-0721 *E-mail:* info@cramer.com *Web Site:* cramer.com, pg 837

Farin, Kim, Boulder County Film Commission, 2440 Pearl St, Boulder, CO 80302 *Tel:* 303-442-2911; 303-938-2066 *Toll Free Tel:* 800-444-0447 *Fax:* 303-938-2098 *Web Site:* www.bouldercoloradousa.com/film, pg 1094

Farinella, Tony, Evidence Audio Inc, PO Box 473, Lake Oswego, OR 97034 *Tel:* 949-306-7390 *E-mail:* info@evidenceaudio.com *Web Site:* www.evidenceaudio.com, pg 863

Faris, Bill, Avatar Studios, 2675 Scott Ave, Suite G, St Louis, MO 63103 *Tel:* 314-533-2242 *Fax:* 314-533-3349 *Web Site:* www.avatar-studios.com, pg 798

Farkas, Steve, Vistamax Productions, 9705 Little Pond Way, Tampa, FL 33647 *Tel:* 813-907-1010 *Fax:* 813-907-1991 *E-mail:* info@vistamax.com; sales@vistamax.com *Web Site:* www.vistamax.com, pg 1059

Farley, George, Supercircuits, 11000 N Mopac Expwy, Bldg 300, Austin, TX 78759 *Toll Free Tel:* 877-995-2288 *E-mail:* operations@supercircuits.com; customercare@supercircuits.com *Web Site:* www.supercircuits.com, pg 1029

Farmer, Gary, American Association for Vocational Instructional Materials (AAVIM), 220 Smithonia Rd, Winterville, GA 30683 *Tel:* 706-742-5355 *Fax:* 706-742-7005 *E-mail:* sales@aavim.com *Web Site:* www.aavim.com, pg 783

Farmer, Gary, American Association for Vocational Instructional Materials (AAVIM), 220 Smithonia Rd, Winterville, GA 30683 *Tel:* 706-742-5355 *Toll Free Tel:* 800-228-4689 *Fax:* 706-742-7005 *E-mail:* sales@aavim.com *Web Site:* www.aavim.com, pg 1076

Farmer, Tiffany, Encyclomedia, 1526 Dekalb Ave, Atlanta, GA 30307 *Tel:* 404-527-3600 *Fax:* 404-584-5171 *E-mail:* info@encyclomedia.net *Web Site:* www.encyclomedia.net, pg 861

Farnsworth, Cara, Method Studios, 730 Arizona Ave, Santa Monica, CA 90401 *Tel:* 310-434-6500 *Web Site:* www.methodstudios.com, pg 939

Farr, John, Stockfootage.com, 231 S Mountain Way Dr, Orem, UT 84058 *Tel:* 801-221-9570; 801-361-0012 (cell) *E-mail:* sales@stockfootage.com *Web Site:* www.stockfootage.com, pg 1025

Farrar, Fred, Klipsch Audio Technologies, 3502 Woodview Trace, Suite 200, Indianapolis, IN 46268 *Tel:* 317-860-8100 *Toll Free Tel:* 877-412-7467 (orders); 800-544-1482 *Fax:* 317-860-9170 (sales & mktg) *E-mail:* support@klipsch.com *Web Site:* www.klipsch.com, pg 912

Farrell, Carl, SAS Institute Inc, 100 SAS Campus Dr, Cary, NC 27513-2414 *Tel:* 919-677-8000 *Toll Free Tel:* 800-727-0025 *Fax:* 919-677-4444 *Web Site:* www.sas.com, pg 1002

Farrell, Dustin, Crew West Inc, 1515 W Deer Valley Rd, Suite C109, Phoenix, AZ 85027 *Tel:* 480-367-6888 *Toll Free Tel:* 888-444-2739 *Fax:* 480-367-6688 *E-mail:* tvcrews@crewwestinc.com *Web Site:* www.crewwestinc.com, pg 839

Farrell, Frank, Custom Video Productions Inc, 15 Lake Shore Dr, Red Bank, NJ 07701 *Tel:* 732-936-1001 *Fax:* 732-741-9204 *E-mail:* info@cvpnj.com *Web Site:* www.cvpnj.com, pg 841

Farrell, Jeffrey S, 8K Productions, 11952 Blue Heron Dr, Draper, UT 84020 *Tel:* 801-671-8357 *E-mail:* rentals@8kproductions.com *Web Site:* www.8kproductions.com, pg 858

Farrell, Jim, Crew West Inc, 1515 W Deer Valley Rd, Suite C109, Phoenix, AZ 85027 *Tel:* 480-367-6888 *Toll Free Tel:* 888-444-2739 *Fax:* 480-367-6688 *E-mail:* tvcrews@crewwestinc.com *Web Site:* www.crewwestinc.com, pg 839

Farrell, Kevin, Vincent Associates, 803 Linden Ave, Rochester, NY 14625 *Tel:* 585-385-5930 *Toll Free Tel:* 800-828-6972 *Fax:* 585-385-6004 *E-mail:* info@uniblitz.com *Web Site:* www.uniblitz.com, pg 1058

Farrell, Kristy Branam, Branam Enterprises Inc, 9152 Independence Ave, Chatsworth, CA 91311 *Tel:* 818-885-6474 *Toll Free Tel:* 877-295-3390 *Fax:* 818-885-6475 *E-mail:* info@branament.com *Web Site:* www.branament.com, pg 812

Farrell, Laura, Crew West Inc, 1515 W Deer Valley Rd, Suite C109, Phoenix, AZ 85027 *Tel:* 480-367-6888 *Toll Free Tel:* 888-444-2739 *Fax:* 480-367-6688 *E-mail:* tvcrews@crewwestinc.com *Web Site:* www.crewwestinc.com, pg 839

Farrell, Lisa, Magick Lantern, 750 Ralph McGill Blvd, Atlanta, GA 30312 *Tel:* 404-688-3348 *Fax:* 404-584-5247 *E-mail:* info@magicklantern.com *Web Site:* magicklantern.com, pg 928

Farrey, James, Jameco Electronics, 1355 Shoreway Rd, Belmont, CA 94002-4105 *Tel:* 650-592-8097 *Toll Free Tel:* 800-831-4242 (orders); 800-536-4316 (cust serv) *Fax:* 650-592-2503 *Toll Free Fax:* 800-237-6948 *E-mail:* info@jameco.com; sales@jameco.com *Web Site:* www.jameco.com, pg 903

Farrington, Jay, Chater Camera Inc, 1336 Ninth St, Berkeley, CA 94710 *Tel:* 510-525-5400 *Fax:* 510-295-2478 *E-mail:* rentals@chatercamera.com *Web Site:* www.chatercamera.com, pg 824

Fasiska, Christine, Marti Electronics Inc, 4100 N 24 St, Quincy, IL 62305 *Tel:* 217-224-9600 *Fax:* 217-224-9607 *E-mail:* sales@martielectronics.com *Web Site:* martielectronics.com, pg 932

Faulk, Kathy, Alabama Film Office, Alabama Center for Commerce, 401 Adams Ave, Suite 170, Montgomery, AL 36104-1430 *Tel:* 334-242-4195 *Fax:* 334-242-2077 *Web Site:* www.alabamafilm.org, pg 1091

Faunce, Andrew, Academic & Campus Technology Services, 37 Dewey Field Rd, Hanover, NH 03755 *Tel:* 603-646-2999 *Fax:* 603-646-1343 *Web Site:* dartmouth.edu, pg 773

Favrin, Silvio, Teledyne DALSA Inc, 605 McMurray Rd, Waterloo, ON N2V 2E9, Canada *Tel:* 519-886-6000 *Fax:* 519-886-8023 *E-mail:* sales.americas@teledynedalsa.com *Web Site:* www.teledynedalsa.com, pg 1036

Fay, Douglas, Connecticut Audio & Theatrical Supply, 775 Bloomfield Ave, Windsor, CT 06095 *Tel:* 860-298-9141 *Fax:* 860-298-9142 *Web Site:* www.ctaudio.com, pg 835

Fay, Thomas, TPR Enterprises Ltd, 644 Fayette Ave, Mamaroneck, NY 10543 *Tel:* 914-698-1141 *Fax:* 914-698-9419 *E-mail:* info@tprlights.com *Web Site:* www.tprlights.com, pg 1043

Fazio, Gaston, HD House, 6312 NW 77 Ct, Miami, FL 33166 *Tel:* 305-597-7359 *Fax:* 305-597-7027 *Web Site:* thehdhouse.com, pg 886

Fazzi, Michael, Communications Specialties Inc, 125 Comac St, Ronkonkoma, NY 11779 *Tel:* 631-273-0404 *Fax:* 631-273-1638 *E-mail:* info@commspecial.com *Web Site:* www.commspecial.com, pg 833

Fazzone, Craig, Hollywood Lights Inc, 5251 SE McLoughlin Blvd, Portland, OR 97202-4836 *Tel:* 503-232-9001; 503-232-8855 *Toll Free Tel:* 800-826-9881 *Fax:* 503-517-8686 *E-mail:* portland@hollywoodlights.biz *Web Site:* www.hollywoodlights.biz, pg 890

Fearn, Douglas W, D W Fearn, PO Box 57, Pocopson, PA 19366 *Tel:* 610-793-2526 *Fax:* 610-793-1479 *E-mail:* dwfearn@dwfearn.com *Web Site:* www.dwfearn.com, pg 866

Fearnow, Vicki, Carpel Video Inc, 429 E Patrick St, Frederick, MD 21701 *Tel:* 301-694-3500 *Toll Free Tel:* 800-238-4300 *Fax:* 301-694-9510 *Web Site:* www.carpelvideoonline.com, pg 820

Feckanin, Alan, beyerdynamic Inc, 56 Central Ave, Farmingdale, NY 11735 *Tel:* 631-293-3200 *Toll Free Tel:* 800-293-4463 *Fax:* 631-293-3288 *E-mail:* info@beyerdynamic-usa.com *Web Site:* north-america.beyerdynamic.com, pg 806

Fedeli, Frank, City of Stamford, 888 Washington Blvd, Stamford, CT 06901 *Tel:* 203-977-5858 *Fax:* 203-977-5545 *Web Site:* www.cityofstamford.org, pg 1095

Federighi, Craig, Apple Inc, One Infinite Loop, Cupertino, CA 95014 *Tel:* 408-996-1010 *Web Site:* www.apple.com, pg 788

Fedotchev, Konstantin, Majortech Inc, 8464 Ninth Line RR-1, Norval, ON L0P 1K0, Canada *Tel:* 905-873-0778 *Fax:* 905-873-1244 *Web Site:* www.majortech.com, pg 929

Feely, Jim, Transistor Devices Inc, 36 Newburgh Rd, Hackettstown, NJ 07840 *Tel:* 908-850-5088 *Fax:* 908-850-1607 *E-mail:* info@tdipower.com *Web Site:* www.tdipower.com, pg 1043

Feil, Edward G, Edward Feil Productions, 36980 Wallace Creek Rd, Springfield, OH 97478 *Tel:* 541-521-2411 *Toll Free Fax:* 877-582-1158 *Web Site:* www.edwardfeilproductions.com, pg 866

Feil, Edward R, Edward Feil Productions, 36980 Wallace Creek Rd, Springfield, OH 97478 *Tel:* 541-521-2411 *Toll Free Fax:* 877-582-1158 *Web Site:* www.edwardfeilproductions.com, pg 866

Feil, Naomi, Edward Feil Productions, 36980 Wallace Creek Rd, Springfield, OH 97478 *Tel:* 541-521-2411 *Toll Free Fax:* 877-582-1158 *Web Site:* www.edwardfeilproductions.com, pg 866

Feinberg, Stan, SF Global Sourcing, 1000 Sansome St, Suite 280, San Francisco, CA 94111 *Tel:* 415-288-9400 *Toll Free Tel:* 855-SF-GLOBAL (734-5622) *Fax:* 415-288-9410 *E-mail:* info@sfglobalsourcing.com *Web Site:* www.sfglobalsourcing.com, pg 1007

Feinberg, Steven, Rhode Island Film & Television Office, One Capitol Hill, 3rd fl, Providence, RI 02908 *Tel:* 401-222-3456; 401-222-6666 (hotline) *Fax:* 401-222-3018 *Web Site:* www.film.ri.gov, pg 1102

Feinberg, Steven, SF Global Sourcing, 1000 Sansome St, Suite 280, San Francisco, CA 94111 *Tel:* 415-288-9400 *Toll Free Tel:* 855-SF-GLOBAL (734-5622) *Fax:* 415-288-9410 *E-mail:* info@sfglobalsourcing.com *Web Site:* www.sfglobalsourcing.com, pg 1007

Feingersh, Randy, Video Associates Labs Inc, 2201 Denton Dr, Suite 109 B, Austin, TX 78758 *Tel:* 512-491-7091 *Toll Free Tel:* 800-331-0547 *Fax:* 512-491-7619 *E-mail:* sales@val.com *Web Site:* www.val.com, pg 1054

Feist, Elinor, Michael Blackwood Productions Inc, 6 W 18 St, Suite 2B, New York, NY 10011 *Tel:* 212-242-1805 *Fax:* 212-242-1671 *E-mail:* blackwoodfilm@aol.com *Web Site:* www.michaelblackwoodproductions.com, pg 809

Felber, Corey, CyberOptics, 5900 Golden Hills Dr, Minneapolis, MN 55416 *Tel:* 763-542-5000 *Fax:* 763-542-5100 *E-mail:* info@cyberoptics.com *Web Site:* cyberoptics.com, pg 841

Felber, David, USCCB Publishing, 3211 Fourth St NE, Washington, DC 20017 *Tel:* 202-541-3090 *Toll Free Tel:* 800-235-8722 (cust serv) *Fax:* 202-722-8709 (cust serv) *E-mail:* publications@usccb.org *Web Site:* www.usccbpublishing.org, pg 1051

Felder, Julie, Hughie's Event Production Services, 1260 E 38 St, Cleveland, OH 44114 *Tel:* 216-361-4600 *Toll Free Tel:* 800-449-4115 *Fax:* 216-361-2570 *Web Site:* www.hughies.com, pg 892

Feldman, Frayda, Ronald Feldman Fine Arts Inc, 31 Mercer St, New York, NY 10013 *Tel:* 212-226-3232 *Fax:* 212-941-1536 *E-mail:* info@feldmangallery.com *Web Site:* www.feldmangallery.com, pg 866

Feldman, Martin P, Camera Co Inc/Broadcast Divison, 858 Boston-Providence Tpke, Norwood, MA 02062 *Tel:* 781-769-7810 *Toll Free Tel:* 866-769-0210 *Fax:* 781-769-5750 *Web Site:* www.cameraco.com, pg 818

Feldman, Ron, Ronald Feldman Fine Arts Inc, 31 Mercer St, New York, NY 10013 *Tel:* 212-226-3232 *Fax:* 212-941-1536 *E-mail:* info@feldmangallery.com *Web Site:* www.feldmangallery.com, pg 866

Felker, Bill, House of Cinemagraphics, 4802 Quail Ave N, Minneapolis, MN 55429 *Tel:* 612-339-7803; 763-458-8244 *Toll Free Tel:* 888-813-0413 *E-mail:* film@visi.com *Web Site:* www.houseofcinemagraphics.com, pg 891

Feller, Karen, Taylor Associates, 110 W Canal St, Suite 301, Winooski, VT 05404 *Tel:* 802-735-1942 *Toll Free Tel:* 800-READ-PLUS (732-3758) *Fax:* 802-419-4786 *E-mail:* info@readingplus.com *Web Site:* www.readingplus.com, pg 1032

Fellows, James, American Center for Children & Media, 5400 N Saint Louis Ave, Chicago, IL 60625 *Tel:* 773-509-5510 *Fax:* 773-509-5303 *E-mail:* info@centerforchildrenandmedia.org *Web Site:* www.centerforchildrenandmedia.org, pg 1076

Felmer, Thomas J, Brady Corp, 6555 W Good Hope Rd, Milwaukee, WI 53201-0571 *Tel:* 414-358-6600 *Toll Free Tel:* 800-541-1686 *Toll Free Fax:* 800-292-2289 *Web Site:* www.bradycorp.com, pg 811

Fels, Mark, Actors Attic, 540 Otis Dr, Dover, DE 19901 *Tel:* 302-734-8214 *Fax:* 302-734-8207 *E-mail:* sales@actorsattic.com *Web Site:* www.actorsattic.com, pg 775

Feltner, Taylor, CET, 1223 Central Pkwy, Cincinnati, OH 45214 *Tel:* 513-381-4033 *Fax:* 513-381-7520 *E-mail:* wcet@cetconnect.org *Web Site:* www.cetconnect.org, pg 823

Fenigstein, Meir, Israel Film Festival, 324 S Beverly Dr, No 424, Beverly Hills, CA 90212 *Tel:* 323-966-4166 *E-mail:* info@israelfilmfestival.org *Web Site:* www.israelfilmfestival.com, pg 1118

Fennell, Michael Paul, The Rip-Tie Co, 883 San Leandro Blvd, San Leandro, CA 94577 *Tel:* 510-577-0200 *Toll Free Tel:* 800-7-RIPTIE (774-7843) *Fax:* 510-553-0160 *E-mail:* info@riptie.com *Web Site:* www.riptie.com, pg 997

Fennessy, Rich, eInstruction Corp, 14400 N 87 St, Suite 250, Scottsdale, AZ 85260 *Tel:* 480-948-6540 *Toll Free Tel:* 800-856-0732 *Fax:* 480-948-5508 *Web Site:* www.einstruction.com, pg 858

Fennig, Jim, Photogenic Professional Lighting, 1268 Humbracht Circle, Bartlett, IL 60103-1631 *Tel:* 630-830-2500 *Toll Free Tel:* 800-682-7668 *Fax:* 630-830-2525 *E-mail:* sales@photogenicpro.com *Web Site:* www.photogenicpro.com, pg 975

Fenster, Heidi, Universal Rehearsal, 17 W 20 St, Suite 4-W, New York, NY 10011 *Tel:* 212-929-3277 *E-mail:* univ318277@aol.com *Web Site:* www.universalrehearsalnyc.com, pg 1049

Fenton, Kevin, Convergent Media Systems, 190 Bluegrass Valley Pkwy, Alpharetta, GA 30005-2204 *Tel:* 770-369-9000 *Toll Free Tel:* 800-877-7804 *Fax:* 770-369-9100 *E-mail:* convergent@convergent.com *Web Site:* www.convergent.com, pg 836

Fenton, Roger, Academy of Science Fiction, Fantasy & Horror Films, 334 W 54 St, Los Angeles, CA 90037 *Tel:* 323-752-5811 *E-mail:* scifiacademy@ca.rr.com *Web Site:* www.saturnawards.org, pg 1075

Fenwick, Neal V, ACCO Brands Corp, 4 Corporate Dr, Lake Zurick, IL 60047-8997 *Toll Free Tel:* 800-541-0094 *Toll Free Fax:* 800-941-4463 *E-mail:* contactus@gbc.com *Web Site:* www.accobrands.com, pg 773

Fercano, Cathy, IDX System Technology Inc, 19001 Harborgate Way, Suite 105, Torrance, CA 90501 *Tel:* 310-328-2850 *Fax:* 310-328-8202 *E-mail:* idx.usa@idx.tv *Web Site:* www.idx.tv, pg 894

Ferguson, Beverly, Draper Inc, 411 S Pearl St, Spiceland, IN 47385 *Tel:* 765-987-7999 *Toll Free Tel:* 800-238-7999 *Fax:* 765-987-7142 *Web Site:* www.draperinc.com; blog.draperinc.com, pg 852

Ferguson, Rick, Houston Film Commission, 4 Houston Ctr, 1331 Lamar St, 7th fl, Houston, TX 77010 *Tel:* 713-437-5251 *Toll Free Tel:* 800-365-7575 *Fax:* 713-223-3816 *E-mail:* jmontgomery@ghcvb.org *Web Site:* www.houstonfilmcommission.com, pg 1103

Ferlino, James, Vistacom Inc, 1902 Vultee St, Allentown, PA 18103-2998 *Tel:* 610-791-9081 *Toll Free Tel:* 800-747-0459 *Fax:* 610-791-9510 *Web Site:* www.vistacominc.com, pg 1059

Fermin, Stephanie, San Mateo County Film Commission, Seabreeze Plaza, Suite 410, 111 Anza Blvd, Burlingame, CA 94010 *Tel:* 650-348-7600 *Fax:* 650-348-7687 *E-mail:* info@filmsanmateocounty.com *Web Site:* www.sanmateocountycvb.com, pg 1092

Fernald, Bob, Down East Books, 680 Commercial St, Rockport, ME 04856 *Tel:* 207-594-9544 *Toll Free Tel:* 800-766-1670 *Fax:* 207-594-0147 *E-mail:* editorial@downeast.com *Web Site:* www.downeast.com, pg 851

Fernandes, Carlos, Precision Microproducts of America, One Comac Loop, Unit 13, Ronkonkoma, NY 11779 *Tel:* 631-580-3456 *Toll Free Tel:* 800-932-9215 *Fax:* 631-580-3003 *E-mail:* sales@p-m-a.com *Web Site:* www.p-m-a.com, pg 980

Fernandes, Jack, American Fibertek Inc, 120 Belmont Dr, Somerset, NJ 08873-4243 *Tel:* 732-302-0660 *Toll Free Tel:* 877-234-7200 *Fax:* 732-302-0667 *E-mail:* sales@americanfibertek.com; techinfo@americanfibertek.com *Web Site:* www.americanfibertek.com, pg 784

Fernandez-Manzano, Demetrio, Puerto Rico Film Commission, 355 FD Roosevelt Ave, Suite 106, Hato Rey, PR 00918 *Tel:* 787-754-6444 *Fax:* 787-756-5706 *E-mail:* info@puertoricofilm.pr.gov *Web Site:* www.puertoricofilm.com, pg 1104

Ferrari, Phillip, Ferrari Productions, 11717 Sorrento Valley Rd, San Diego, CA 92121 *Tel:* 858-792-8011 *Fax:* 858-481-6499 *E-mail:* info@ferrariproductions.com *Web Site:* www.ferrariproductions.com, pg 866

Ferraro, Peter, Easy Street Productions, 118 Redhaven Ct, Thurmont, MD 21788 *Tel:* 301-471-8058 *E-mail:* info@publicdomainfootage.com *Web Site:* www.publicdomainfootage.com, pg 856

Ferreira, Juan, The Clio Awards, 770 Broadway, 15th fl, New York, NY 10003 *Tel:* 212-683-4300 *Toll Free Tel:* 800-WIN-CLIO (946-2546) *Fax:* 212-683-4796 *Web Site:* www.clioawards.com, pg 1113

Ferrell, Eileen Hannan, Humanities Extension Publications, North Carolina State Univ, Campus Box 8101, Raleigh, NC 27695 *Tel:* 919-515-2468 *Fax:* 919-515-9419 *Web Site:* www.ncsu.edu/chass/extension, pg 892

Ferrer, Abraham, The Los Angeles Asian Pacific Film Festival, 120 Judge John Aiso St, Basement Level, Los Angeles, CA 90012-3805 *Tel:* 213-680-4462 *Fax:* 213-687-4848 *E-mail:* festival@vconline.org *Web Site:* asianfilmfestla.org, pg 1119

Ferrer, Vic, The Producer's Loft, 2773 Folsom St, Suite 101, San Francisco, CA 94110 *Tel:* 415-334-4700 *Web Site:* theproducersloft.com, pg 983

Ferreyra, Stuart, Timecode Multimedia, 12340 Santa Monica Blvd, Suite 230, West Los Angeles, CA 90025 *Tel:* 310-826-9199 *E-mail:* info@timecodemedia.com *Web Site:* www.timecodemultimedia.com, pg 1040

Ferri, Brian, AVP Mfg & Supply Inc, 2288-B7 Dumfries Rd RR2, Cambridge, ON N1R 5S3, Canada *Tel:* 519-740-7966 *Toll Free Tel:* 800-481-2493 *Fax:* 519-740-0131 *E-mail:* sales@jackfields.com *Web Site:* www.jackfields.com, pg 800

Ferri-Grant, Carson, Guild of Italian American Actors (GIAA), Canal Street Sta, PO Box 123, New York, NY 10013-0123 *Tel:* 201-344-3411 *E-mail:* info@giaa.us *Web Site:* www.giaa.us, pg 1082

Ferriman, Gary, Association of Progressive Rental Organizations (APRO), 1504 Robin Hood Trail, Austin, TX 78703 *Tel:* 512-794-0095 *Toll Free Tel:* 800-204-2776 *Fax:* 512-794-0097 *Web Site:* www.rtohq.org, pg 1079

Ferris, Kinney, Oxford Film Commission, 415 S Lamar Blvd, Oxford, MS 38655 *Tel:* 662-232-2477 *Toll Free Tel:* 800-758-9177 *E-mail:* tourism@visitoxfordms.com *Web Site:* visitoxfordms.com, pg 1099

Fesmire, James T, Power Integrity Corporation, PO Box 9682, Greensboro, NC 27429-0682 *Tel:* 336-379-9773 *Toll Free Tel:* 800-237-6260 (tech support) *E-mail:* info@powerintegritycorp.com *Web Site:* www.powerintegritycorp.com, pg 979

Fialka, Gerry, PXL This Video Festival, 2427 1/2 Glyndon Ave, Venice, CA 90291 *Tel:* 310-306-7330 *E-mail:* pfsuzy@aol.com *Web Site:* laughtears.com, pg 1124

Fibben, Alison, Georgia Film, Music & Digital Entertainment Office, 75 Fifth St W, Suite 1200, Atlanta, GA 30308 *Tel:* 404-962-4052 *Toll Free Tel:* 877-SHOOTGA (746-6842) *Fax:* 404-962-4053 *E-mail:* film@georgia.org *Web Site:* www.georgia.org, pg 1096

Fichera, Chris, Group One Ltd, 70 Sea Lane, Farmingdale, NY 11735 *Tel:* 516-249-1399 *Fax:* 516-249-8870 *E-mail:* sales@g1limited.com *Web Site:* www.g1limited.com, pg 882

Fidan, Aaron, CPT Rental Inc, 36-01A 48 Ave, Long Island City, NY 11101 *Tel:* 718-424-1600 *Fax:* 718-457-4778 *E-mail:* rental@cptrental.com *Web Site:* www.cptrental.com, pg 837

Fiden, Josh, Digital Music Corp, 3165 Coffey Lane, Santa Rosa, CA 95403 *Tel:* 707-545-0600 *Fax:* 707-545-9777 *E-mail:* info@voodoolab.com *Web Site:* www.voodoolab.com, pg 847

Fiegel, Douglas, NRD LLC, A Mark IV Industries Co, 2937 Alt Blvd, Grand Island, NY 14072-1285 *Tel:* 716-773-7634 *Toll Free Tel:* 800-525-8076 (US only) *Fax:* 716-773-7744 *E-mail:* sales@nrdinc.com *Web Site:* www.nrdstaticcontrol.com, pg 960

Fields, Andy, USAV Group Inc, 5485 S Westridge Dr, New Berlin, WI 53151-7948 *Tel:* 262-814-2000 *Toll Free Tel:* 800-596-USAV (596-8728) *Fax:* 262-814-2006 *Web Site:* www.usavgroup.com, pg 1051

Fields, Bob, CommCreative, 345 Union Ave, Framingham, MA 01702 *Tel:* 508-620-6664 *Toll Free Tel:* 877-620-6664 *Fax:* 508-620-0592 *Web Site:* www.commcreative.com, pg 832

Fiels, Keith Michael, American Library Association (ALA), 50 E Huron St, Chicago, IL 60611-2795 *Tel:* 312-944-6780 *Toll Free Tel:* 800-545-2433 (ext 3223, conference servs) *Fax:* 312-440-9374 *E-mail:* ala@ala.org *Web Site:* www.ala.org, pg 1076

Fieri, Joel, North County Media Center, 1130 N Melrose Dr, Suite 404, Vista, CA 92083 *Toll Free Tel:* 888-393-0580 *E-mail:* info@northcountymediacenter.com *Web Site:* northcountymediacenter.com, pg 959

Fiero, Drew, First Person™, 550 Bryant St, San Francisco, CA 94107 *Tel:* 415-495-5595 *Fax:* 415-543-8370, pg 869

Figler, Al, Rochester International Film Festival, PO Box 17746, Rochester, NY 14617 *Tel:* 585-234-7411 (voice mail) *E-mail:* president@rochesterfilmfest.org (use MOAS on subject) *Web Site:* www.rochesterfilmfest.org, pg 1125

Filarowicz, Bobby, Big House Sound Inc, 4001 Drossett Dr, Austin, TX 78744 *Tel:* 512-443-0019 *Fax:* 512-443-0916 *Web Site:* www.bighousesound.com, pg 807

Filgas, Catherine, Anthro Corp, 10450 SW Manhasset Dr, Tualatin, OR 97062 *Tel:* 503-691-2556 *Toll Free Tel:* 800-325-3841 (cust serv) *Fax:* 503-691-2409 *Toll Free Fax:* 800-325-0045 *E-mail:* sales@anthro.com *Web Site:* www.anthro.com, pg 787

Fillmore, Chris, Performance Audio, 2456 S West Temple St, Salt Lake City, UT 84115 *Tel:* 801-466-3196 *Toll Free Tel:* 800-771-8330 *Fax:* 801-484-1538 *E-mail:* sales@performanceaudio.com; rental@performanceaudio.com *Web Site:* www.performanceaudio.com, pg 973

Fimbrez, Louie, Madera Video, 501 N E St, Suite A, Madera, CA 93638-3102 *Tel:* 559-661-6000 *Toll Free Tel:* 800-828-8118 *Fax:* 559-674-3650, pg 927

Finch, Todd, MAGNUM Companies Ltd, 205 Armour Dr NE, Atlanta, GA 30324 *Tel:* 404-872-0553 *Toll Free Tel:* 800-255-1774 *Fax:* 404-875-5629 *E-mail:* buy@magnumco.com; rent@magnumco.com; design@magnumco.com; production@magnumco.com *Web Site:* www.magnumco.com, pg 929

Findlay, Roberta, Sear Sound, 353 W 48 St, 6th fl, New York, NY 10036 *Tel:* 212-582-5380 *Fax:* 212-581-2731 *E-mail:* waltersear@aol.com *Web Site:* www.searsound.com, pg 1005

Finer, Dustin, Rovi Corp, 2830 De La Cruz Blvd, Santa Clara, CA 95050 *Tel:* 408-562-8400 *Fax:* 408-567-1800 *Web Site:* www.rovicorp.com, pg 1000

Fines, Jordan, 2BK9 Acting Animals, 1470 Catherine Ave, Winnipeg, MB R3E 1V8, Canada *Tel:* 204-338-1474; 204-997-9247 (cell), pg 1047

Fingerhut, Jack, SmartPros Ltd, 12 Skyline Dr, Hawthorne, NY 10532-2133 *Tel:* 914-345-2620 *Fax:* 914-345-2603 *E-mail:* admin@smartpros.com *Web Site:* www.smartpros.com, pg 1014

Fink, Zac, Film Technology Co Inc, 726 N Cole Ave, Hollywood, CA 90038 *Tel:* 323-464-3456 *Fax:* 323-464-7439 *Web Site:* www.filmtech.com, pg 867

Finley, Robert, Stuart Finley Films, 3428 Mansfield Rd, Falls Church, VA 22041 *Tel:* 703-820-7700 *Web Site:* www.stufin.com, pg 868

Finn, Steffanie L, Winter Film Awards, 419 Lafayette St, New York, NY 10003 *Tel:* 646-355-4371 *E-mail:* info@winterfilmawards.com *Web Site:* www.winterfilmawards.com, pg 1129

Finn, Steffanie L, Winter Film Awards Independent Film Festival, 419 Lafayette St, New York, NY 10003 *Tel:* 646-355-4371 *E-mail:* info@winterfilmawards.com; submissions@winterfilmawards.com *Web Site:* www.winterfilmawards.com, pg 1129

Finnegan, Vincent, Group One Ltd, 70 Sea Lane, Farmingdale, NY 11735 *Tel:* 516-249-1399 *Fax:* 516-249-8870 *E-mail:* sales@g1limited.com *Web Site:* www.g1limited.com, pg 882

Fino, James A, Starburns Industries, 1700 W Burbank Blvd, Burbank, CA 91506 *Tel:* 818-433-3300 *Fax:* 818-433-3383 *Web Site:* www.starburnsindustries.com, pg 1024

Fiore, Franco, CPdigital, 102 Madison Ave, New York, NY 10016 *Tel:* 212-328-5177 *Web Site:* www.cpdigital.com, pg 837

Fiorese, Lisa, DEC Grants, 696 Dutchess Tpke, Suite F, Poughkeepsie, NY 12603 *Tel:* 845-454-3222 *Fax:* 845-454-6902 *E-mail:* info@artsmidhudson.org *Web Site:* www.artsmidhudson.org, pg 1114

Fiorletta, Carlo, Guild of Italian American Actors (GIAA), Canal Street Sta, PO Box 123, New York, NY 10013-0123 *Tel:* 201-344-3411 *E-mail:* info@giaa.us *Web Site:* www.giaa.us, pg 1082

Fischer, Michael, Zhone Technologies Inc, 7195 Oakport St, Oakland, CA 94621 *Tel:* 510-777-7000 *Toll Free Tel:* 877-ZHONE-20 (946-6320, US & CN) *Fax:* 510-777-7001 *E-mail:* info@zhone.com; sales@zhone.com *Web Site:* www.zhone.com, pg 1073

Fiset, Norman, Panavideo Inc, 347 Marie de l'Incarnation, Quebec, QC G1N 3G9, Canada *Tel:* 418-687-3150 *Toll Free Tel:* 800-463-5076 *Fax:* 418-687-0366 *E-mail:* info@panavideo.net *Web Site:* www.panavideo.net, pg 968

Fishback, John R, P&P Studios Inc, 110 Lenox Ave, Suite 210, Stamford, CT 06906 *Tel:* 203-359-9292 *Toll Free Tel:* 888-WEPRODUCE (937-7638) *E-mail:* ppstudios@weproduce.com *Web Site:* www.weproduce.com, pg 968

Fishback, Kathy, Florida Digital Studios, 10781 75 St, Largo, FL 33777 *Tel:* 727-546-7900 *Fax:* 727-546-8640 *Web Site:* www.floridadigitalstudios.com, pg 870

Fishbein, D, Fish Films Footage World, 4548 Van Noord Ave, Studio City, CA 91604 *Tel:* 818-905-1071 *E-mail:* footageworld@aol.com *Web Site:* www.footageworld.com, pg 869

Fisher, Bob, Nevada Broadcasters Association, 1050 E Flamingo Rd, No 102, Las Vegas, NV 89119 *Tel:* 702-794-4994 *Web Site:* www.nevadabroadcasters.org, pg 1086

Fisher, Dick, Videography Productions, PO Box 653, Amagansett, NY 11930-0653 *Tel:* 520-907-1900 *Web Site:* www.dickfisher.net, pg 1057

Fisher, Larry, Lectrosonics Inc, 581 Laser Rd NE, Rio Rancho, NM 87124 *Tel:* 505-892-4501 *Toll Free Tel:* 800-821-1121 *Fax:* 505-892-6243 *E-mail:* sales@lectrosonics.com *Web Site:* www.lectrosonics.com, pg 918

Fisher, Mark, The Entertainment Merchants Association (EMA), 16530 Ventura Blvd, Suite 400, Encino, CA 91436-4551 *Tel:* 818-385-1500 *Fax:* 818-933-0910 *E-mail:* emaoffice@entmerch.org *Web Site:* www.entmerch.org, pg 1081

Fisher, Mike, Custom Medical Stock Photo Inc, 3660 W Irving Park Rd, Chicago, IL 60618 *Tel:* 773-267-3100 *Toll Free Tel:* 800-373-2677 *Fax:* 773-267-6071 *E-mail:* info@cmsp.com *Web Site:* www.cmsp.com, pg 841

Fisher, Tim, CP Communications, 200 Clearbrook Rd, Suite 148, Elmsford, NY 10523 *Tel:* 914-345-9292 *Toll Free Tel:* 800-762-4254 *Fax:* 914-345-9222 *E-mail:* info@cpcomms.com; sales@cpcomms.com *Web Site:* www.cpcomms.com, pg 837

Fisher-Staples, Sherri, Cinebar Productions Inc, 763 J Clyde Morris Blvd, Suite 1-C, Newport News, VA 23601 *Tel:* 757-873-3232 *Fax:* 757-873-3790 *E-mail:* cinebar@cinebarproductions.com *Web Site:* www.cinebarproductions.com, pg 827

Fishkin, Mark, Mill Valley Film Festival, 1001 Lootens Place, Suite 220, San Rafael, CA 94901 *Tel:* 415-383-5256 *Fax:* 415-383-8606 *E-mail:* mvff@cafilm.org; info@cafilm.org *Web Site:* www.mvff.com; www.cafilm.org, pg 1120

Fister, Ray, 5th Floor Recording Co, 316 N Milwaukee St, Suite 501, Milwaukee, WI 53202 *Tel:* 414-276-1919 *Fax:* 414-271-6621 *Web Site:* www.5thfloorrecording.com, pg 867

Fitch, Kathleen, Crawford Media Services, 6 W Druid Hills Dr NE, Atlanta, GA 30329 *Tel:* 404-876-0333 *Toll Free Tel:* 800-831-8029 *Fax:* 678-536-4912 *Web Site:* www.crawford.com, pg 838

Fitch, Ted, Intermedia Inc, 5600 Rainier Ave S, Suite 203, Seattle, WA 98118 *Tel:* 206-284-2995 *Toll Free Tel:* 800-553-8336 *Toll Free Fax:* 800-553-1655 *E-mail:* info@intermedia-inc.com *Web Site:* www.intermedia-inc.com, pg 900

Fitch, William, Sound by Fitch, 1134 Ridge Rd, Pottstown, PA 19465 *Tel:* 610-469-6082 *Fax:* 610-469-0559, pg 1017

Fitts, David A, Time Warner Cable Business Class, 120 E 23 St, 8th fl, New York, NY 10010 *Tel:* 212-379-5826 *Web Site:* www.twcbc.com/nyc, pg 1040

Fitzer, Jon, Sescom Inc, PO Box 720, Mount Marion, NY 12456 *Tel:* 845-246-1915 *Fax:* 845-246-0626 *E-mail:* info@sescom.com *Web Site:* www.sescom.com, pg 1007

Fitzgerald, Greg, Sound Advantage, 93 Shaw Rd, Little Compton, RI 02837 *Tel:* 508-653-1644 *E-mail:* soundadvantage@mac.com, pg 1016

Fitzgerald, Jon, Slamdance Film Festival, 5634 Melrose Ave, Los Angeles, CA 90038 *Tel:* 323-466-1786 *Fax:* 323-466-1784 *E-mail:* submissions@slamdance.com *Web Site:* www.slamdance.com, pg 1127

Fitzgerald, Richard, Sound Associates Inc, 424 W 45 St, New York, NY 10036 *Tel:* 212-757-5679 *Toll Free Tel:* 888-772-7686 *Fax:* 212-265-1250 *E-mail:* newyork@soundassociates.com *Web Site:* www.soundassociates.com, pg 1017

Fitzgerald, Todd, Winterland Studios, 5417 Boone Ave N, New Hope, MN 55428 *Tel:* 763-971-8943 *Fax:* 763-971-8952 *E-mail:* studio@winterlandstudios.com *Web Site:* www.winterlandstudios.com, pg 1068

Fitzgerald, Tom, Satellite Center, 2535 Williams Blvd, Kenner, LA 70062 *Tel:* 504-466-3474 *Toll Free Tel:* 800-256-4010 *Web Site:* satctr.com, pg 1003

Fitzpatrick, John, Cornell Laboratory of Ornithology, Cornell University, 159 Sapsucker Woods Rd, Ithaca, NY 14850 *Tel:* 607-254-BIRD (254-2473) *Toll Free Tel:* 800-843-BIRD (843-2473) *Fax:* 607-254-2415 *E-mail:* cornellbirds@cornell.edu *Web Site:* www.birds.cornell.edu, pg 836

Fitzpatrick, John B, Robertstock.com, 4203 Locust St, Philadelphia, PA 19104 *Tel:* 215-386-6300 *Toll Free Tel:* 800-786-6300 *Toll Free Fax:* 800-786-1920 *E-mail:* info@robertstock.com *Web Site:* www.robertstock.com, pg 998

Fitzpatrick, Robert, Allied Artists International Inc, Production Services Ctr, 15810 E Gale Ave, Suite 133, Hacienda Heights, CA 91745 *Tel:* 626-330-0600 *Fax:* 626-961-0411 *E-mail:* info@alliedartists.net *Web Site:* us.alliedartists.com, pg 781

Fiveash, Chuck, TAPPI, 15 Technology Pkwy S, Norcross, GA 30092 *Tel:* 770-446-1400 *Toll Free Tel:* 800-332-8686 (US); 800-446-9431 (CN) *Fax:* 770-446-6947 *E-mail:* memberconnection@tappi.org *Web Site:* www.tappi.org, pg 1032

Fivek, Clark, Digital Video Arts, 7775 Belfort Pkwy, Jacksonville, FL 32256 *Tel:* 904-281-1001 *Toll Free Tel:* 888-340-1010 *Fax:* 904-281-0051 *Web Site:* www.digitalvideoarts.com, pg 848

Fix, Brenda, Hite Co, 3101 Beale Ave, Altoona, PA 16601 *Tel:* 814-944-6121 *Toll Free Tel:* 800-252-3598 *Fax:* 814-944-3052 *Web Site:* www.hiteco.com, pg 889

Fix, William, SOS Film Works (Space Ordnance Systems), 34855 Petersen Rd, Agua Dulce, CA 91390 *Tel:* 661-251-2365 *Fax:* 661-268-7680 *Web Site:* www.sosfilmworks.com, pg 1016

Flack, Dr Julien, Dynamic Digital Depth Inc (DDD), 6100 Center Dr W, Suite 1100, Los Angeles, CA 90045 *Tel:* 310-566-3340 *Toll Free Tel:* 877-884-4333 *Fax:* 310-566-3380 *E-mail:* info@ddd.com *Web Site:* www.ddd.com, pg 854

Flaherty, Lauren, CA Technologies, 520 Madison Ave, 22nd fl, New York, NY 10022 *Toll Free Tel:* 800-225-5224 *Web Site:* www.ca.com, pg 816

Flaherty, Rob, Ketchum Pleon Change, 1285 Avenue of the Americas, 3rd fl, New York, NY 10019 *Tel:* 646-935-3900 *Web Site:* www.ketchum.com/change, pg 910

Flake, Keith, Rodeo Video Inc, 412 S Main, Snowflake, AZ 85937 *Tel:* 928-536-7111 *Toll Free Tel:* 800-331-1269 *Fax:* 928-536-7120 *E-mail:* info@rodeovideo.com *Web Site:* www.rodeovideo.com, pg 998

Flanagan, Dorothy, Jay Jay Record & Tape Co, 102 Brookfield Lane, Geneva, IL 60134 *Tel:* 305-758-0000 *Fax:* 305-758-0000, pg 904

Flanagan, Mike, Video Symphony TV & Film School, 266 E Magnolia Blvd, Burbank, CA 91502 *Tel:* 818-557-7200 *Toll Free Tel:* 800-871-2843 *Fax:* 818-845-1951 *E-mail:* info@videosymphony.com *Web Site:* www.videosymphony.com, pg 1056

Flanagan, Paul, Paul Flanagan Productions, 1623 S Hearthside Dr, Richmond, TX 77406-1369 *Tel:* 281-799-4832 *Web Site:* www.productionhub.com, pg 869

Flanagan, William, Varta Microbattery Inc, 555 Theodore Fremd Ave, Suite C304, Rye, NY 10580 *Tel:* 914-592-2500 *Toll Free Tel:* 800-468-2782 *Fax:* 914-345-0488 *Web Site:* www.varta-microbattery.com; www.varta-microbattery.us, pg 1052

Flansburg, Luke, Jereco Studios Inc, 627 E Peach St, Suite E, Bozeman, MT 59715 *Tel:* 406-586-5262 *Fax:* 406-586-5262 *Web Site:* www.jerecostudios.com, pg 905

Flaska, Ashley, NEC Display Solutions of America, 500 Park Blvd, Suite 1100, Itasca, IL 60143 *Tel:* 630-467-3000 *Web Site:* www.necdisplay.com, pg 954

Fleck, Volker, WARPed Pictures, 2447 Benedict Canyon Dr, Beverly Hills, CA 90210 *Tel:* 310-777-8828; 310-999-1219 (cell) *Fax:* 310-777-8805 *Web Site:* www.warpedpictures.com, pg 1062

Fleenor, Cindy, Doug Fleenor Design Inc, 396 Corbett Canyon Rd, Arroyo Grande, CA 93420 *Tel:* 805-481-9599 *Toll Free Tel:* 888-436-9512 *Fax:* 805-481-9599 *E-mail:* info@dfd.com *Web Site:* www.dfd.com, pg 869

Fleenor, Doug, Doug Fleenor Design Inc, 396 Corbett Canyon Rd, Arroyo Grande, CA 93420 *Tel:* 805-481-9599 *Toll Free Tel:* 888-436-9512 *Fax:* 805-481-9599 *E-mail:* info@dfd.com *Web Site:* www.dfd.com, pg 869

Fleischer, Daniel, Westbrook Technologies Inc, 35 Thorpe Ave, Suite 201, Wallingford, CT 06492 *Tel:* 203-871-4984 *Fax:* 203-269-0322 *E-mail:* info@westbrooktech.com *Web Site:* www.westbrooktech.com, pg 1064

Fleischer, Ken, dM works, 246 Rockaway Ave, Valley Stream, NY 11580 *Tel:* 516-255-0100 *Toll Free Tel:* 888-914-6639 *E-mail:* info@dmworks.com *Web Site:* www.dmworks.com, pg 849

Fleischmann, Josh, New York Graphic Society, 130 Scott Rd, Waterburg, CT 06750 *Tel:* 203-847-2000 *Toll Free Tel:* 800-677-6947 *Fax:* 203-757-5526 *E-mail:* mail@nygs.com *Web Site:* www.nygs.com, pg 956

Flem, Eric, Nikon Small World, 1300 Walt Whitman Rd, Melville, NY 11747 *Tel:* 631-547-8500 *Toll Free Tel:* 800-52-NIKON (526-4566 - US only) *Fax:* 631-547-0306 *E-mail:* info@nikonsmallworld.com *Web Site:* www.nikonsmallworld.com; www.nikoninstruments.com, pg 1122

Fleming, Al, Keystone View, 2200 Dickerson Rd, Reno, NV 89503 *Tel:* 775-324-2799; 510-931-7747 *Toll Free Tel:* 866-574-6360 *Fax:* 775-324-5375 *Toll Free Fax:* 866-574-6395 *E-mail:* sales@keystoneview.com *Web Site:* www.keystoneview.com, pg 910

Fleming, Pat, Tectonics Industries Inc, 24680 Mound Rd, Warren, MI 48091 *Tel:* 586-755-6522 *Toll Free Tel:* 888-638-3671 *Fax:* 586-755-6562 *E-mail:* info@techtonicsindustries.com *Web Site:* www.techtonicsindustries.com, pg 1035

Fletcher, Cliff, University of Maine Audio Visual Services, 28 Shibles Hall, Orono, ME 04469 *Tel:* 207-581-2500; 207-581-2516 *Web Site:* www.umaine.edu/it/divisions/av, pg 1049

Fletcher, Dick, Gagne Inc, 41 Commercial Dr, Johnson City, NY 13790 *Tel:* 607-729-3366 *Toll Free Tel:* 800-800-5954 *Fax:* 607-729-7644 *E-mail:* sales@gagneinc.com *Web Site:* www.gagneinc.com, pg 875

Fletcher, J Carter, Photoquip Inc, 3070 S Eighth St, Fernandina Beach, FL 32034-8680 *Tel:* 904-261-4075, pg 975

Fletcher, Mark, 4 Wall Entertainment, 3325 W Sunset Rd, Suite F, Las Vegas, NV 89118 *Tel:* 702-263-3858 *Toll Free Tel:* 877-789-8167 (Western US); 866-492-5540 (Eastern US) *Fax:* 702-263-3863 *E-mail:* info@4wall.com *Web Site:* www.4wall.com; www.usedlighting.com, pg 872

Fletty, Eric, TAPPI, 15 Technology Pkwy S, Norcross, GA 30092 *Tel:* 770-446-1400 *Toll Free Tel:* 800-332-8686 (US); 800-446-9431 (CN) *Fax:* 770-446-6947 *E-mail:* memberconnection@tappi.org *Web Site:* www.tappi.org, pg 1032

Flinchbaugh, Dawson E, IMR Limited, 1104 Fernwood Ave, 4th fl, Camp Hill, PA 17011 *Tel:* 717-364-3700 *Toll Free Tel:* 800-446-2826 *Fax:* 717-364-3750 *E-mail:* information@imrdigital.com *Web Site:* www.imrdigital.com, pg 897

Flint, Kevin, Dystopian Studios, 651 Clover St, Bldg 1, Los Angeles, CA 90031 *Tel:* 310-503-2365 *Web Site:* dystopianstudios.com, pg 855

Flock, Carey, Intersect Video, 25749 SW Canyon Creek Rd, Suite 300, Wilsonville, OR 97070 *Tel:* 971-224-4808 *E-mail:* info@intersectvideo.com *Web Site:* www.intersectvideo.com, pg 901

Flock, Sterling, Intersect Video, 25749 SW Canyon Creek Rd, Suite 300, Wilsonville, OR 97070 *Tel:* 971-224-4808 *E-mail:* info@intersectvideo.com *Web Site:* www.intersectvideo.com, pg 901

Flood, Mike, Dot Hill Systems Corp, 1351 S Sunset St, Longmont, CO 80501-6533 *Tel:* 303-845-3200 *Toll Free Tel:* 800-872-2783 *Fax:* 303-845-3655 *E-mail:* support@dothill.com; websales@dothill.com *Web Site:* www.dothill.com, pg 851

Florence, Luiza, FJ Productions Inc, 14900 Ventura Blvd, Suite 350, Sherman Oaks, CA 91403-3465 *Tel:* 818-788-0153 *Fax:* 818-788-0186 *Web Site:* www.fjproductions.com, pg 869

Flores, Tanya, SurgeX, 800 Knightdale Blvd, Suite 121, Knightdale, NC 27545 *Toll Free Tel:* 800-645-9721 (tech & cust support) *Fax:* 919-269-0454 *Web Site:* www.surgex.com, pg 1029

Floyd, Steve, August House Audio, 3500 Piedmont Rd NE, Suite 310, Atlanta, GA 30305 *Tel:* 404-442-4420 *Toll Free Tel:* 800-284-8784 *Fax:* 404-442-4435 *E-mail:* ahinfo@augusthouse.com *Web Site:* www.augusthouse.com, pg 796

Fluster, Barry, Media Fabricators Inc, 8509 Washington Blvd, Culver City, CA 90232 *Tel:* 323-937-3344 *Fax:* 323-937-1142 *E-mail:* mediafab@mediafab.com; info@mediafab.com *Web Site:* www.mediafab.com; www.mfi-law.com, pg 936

Flynn, Bob, Novell Inc, 1800 S Novell Place, Provo, UT 84606 *Tel:* 801-861-4272 *Toll Free Tel:* 888-321-4272 (sales); 800-858-4000 (support) *E-mail:* crc@novell.com *Web Site:* www.novell.com, pg 959

Flynn, L Daniel, Continental Recordings Inc, 23 Mirimichi St, Plainville, MA 02762 *Tel:* 508-699-0003 *Toll Free Tel:* 888-729-3130 *Fax:* 508-699-0004, pg 835

Flyntz, Elizabeth, Artist Fellowships, 20 Jay St, 7th fl, Suite 740, Brooklyn, NY 11201 *Tel:* 212-366-6900 *Fax:* 212-366-1778 *E-mail:* fellowships@nyfa.org *Web Site:* nyfa.org, pg 1108

Foah, Honora, Visioneering International Inc, 659 Auburn Ave NE, Suite 267, Atlanta, GA 30312 *Tel:* 404-681-9028 *Fax:* 404-681-5947 *E-mail:* design@visioneering.com *Web Site:* www.visioneering.com, pg 1058

Foah, Robert, Visioneering International Inc, 659 Auburn Ave NE, Suite 267, Atlanta, GA 30312 *Tel:* 404-681-9028 *Fax:* 404-681-5947 *E-mail:* design@visioneering.com *Web Site:* www.visioneering.com, pg 1058

Fogg, Chris, Magick Lantern, 750 Ralph McGill Blvd, Atlanta, GA 30312 *Tel:* 404-688-3348 *Fax:* 404-584-5247 *E-mail:* info@magicklantern.com *Web Site:* magicklantern.com, pg 928

Foley, Kevin, KEF Media, 1161 Concord Rd, Smyrna, GA 30080 *Tel:* 404-605-0009 *Toll Free Tel:* 866-219-2477 *Fax:* 404-605-0639 *Web Site:* www.kefmedia.com, pg 909

Foley, Marcia Hahn, Big Foot Productions Inc, 37-09 36 Ave, Long Island City, NY 11101 *Tel:* 718-729-1900 *Fax:* 718-729-8638 *E-mail:* info@bigfootnyc.com *Web Site:* www.bigfootnyc.com, pg 807

Foley, Paul, HM Electronics Inc (HME), 14110 Stowe Dr, Poway, CA 92064 *Tel:* 858-535-6000 *Toll Free Tel:* 800-848-4468 (domestic sales) *Fax:* 858-452-7207; 858-552-0139 (domestic sales) *E-mail:* info@hme.com *Web Site:* www.hme.com, pg 889

Folkeringa, Ron, Intercon 1, 7746 Goedderz Rd, Suite 110, Baxter, MN 56425 *Tel:* 218-828-3157 *Toll Free Tel:* 800-237-9576 *Fax:* 218-828-1096 *E-mail:* intercon@nortechsys.com *Web Site:* www.intercon-1.com, pg 900

Folts, Chad, Westbrook Technologies Inc, 35 Thorpe Ave, Suite 201, Wallingford, CT 06492 *Tel:* 203-871-4984 *Fax:* 203-269-0322 *E-mail:* info@westbrooktech.com *Web Site:* www.westbrooktech.com, pg 1064

Fon-Sing, Clara, NBCUniversal Archives, 30 Rockefeller Plaza, New York, NY 10112 *Tel:* 212-664-5015 *Toll Free Tel:* 855-NBC-VIDEO (622-8433) *Fax:* 212-703-8558; 212-664-4472 *E-mail:* nbcu.archives@nbcuni.com *Web Site:* www.nbcuniversalarchives.com, pg 954

Fontaine, Michelle, Visual Technologies Corp, 1620 Burnet Ave, Syracuse, NY 13206 *Tel:* 315-423-2000 *Toll Free Tel:* 888-423-0004 *Fax:* 315-423-0004 *E-mail:* contact@visualtec.com *Web Site:* www.visualtec.com; www.vtcspecialties.com, pg 1060

Foor, David J, Visual Technologies Corp, 1620 Burnet Ave, Syracuse, NY 13206 *Tel:* 315-423-2000 *Toll Free Tel:* 888-423-0004 *Fax:* 315-423-0004 *E-mail:* contact@visualtec.com *Web Site:* www.visualtec.com; www.vtcspecialties.com, pg 1060

Forbes, Brad, AdventSource, 5120 Prescott Ave, Lincoln, NE 68506 *Tel:* 402-486-8800 *Toll Free Tel:* 800-328-0525 *Fax:* 402-486-8819 *E-mail:* service@adventsource.org *Web Site:* www.adventsource.org, pg 778

Ford, Brooke, Millennium Entertainment LLC, 5900 Wilshire Blvd, 18th fl, Los Angeles, CA 90036 *Tel:* 310-893-6289 *E-mail:* info@millenniumentertainment.me *Web Site:* www.millenniumentertainment.me, pg 943

Ford, Jason, Technomedia Solutions, 4545 36 St, Orlando, FL 32811 *Tel:* 407-351-0909 *Fax:* 407-248-9484 *E-mail:* sales@gotechnomedia.com *Web Site:* www.gotechnomedia.com, pg 1035

Ford, Michael, Yellow Cat Productions Inc, 505 11 St SE, Washington, DC 20003 *Tel:* 202-543-2221 *E-mail:* yellowcat@yellowcat.com *Web Site:* www.yellowcat.com, pg 1072

Fordin, Hugh, DRG Records Inc, 22 Harbor Park Dr, Port Washington, NY 11050 *Tel:* 516-484-1000 (ext 147); 212-614-2800 *Toll Free Tel:* 866-293-2854 *Fax:* 516-484-2365 *E-mail:* info@drgrecords.com *Web Site:* drgrecords.com, pg 852

Fordyce, Barbara, Map Resources, 50 S Union St, Lambertville, NJ 08530 *Tel:* 609-397-1611 *Toll Free Tel:* 800-334-4291 *Fax:* 609-751-9378 *E-mail:* info@mapresources.com; sales@mapresources.com *Web Site:* www.mapresources.com, pg 930

Foreman, Ed, Executive Development Systems, 3818 Vinecrest Dr, Dallas, TX 75229 *Tel:* 214-351-0055 *Toll Free Tel:* 800-955-7353 *Fax:* 214-351-5024 *Web Site:* www.edforeman.com, pg 864

Foreman, Jack, Tremetrics Inc Industrial Instruments Division, 7625 Golden Triangle Dr, Eden Prairie, MN 55344 *Toll Free Tel:* 800-825-0121 *Fax:* 952-903-4100 *E-mail:* info@tremetrics.com *Web Site:* www.tremetrics.com, pg 1044

Foreman, Steve, Imagine Communications Corp, 3001 Dallas Pkwy, Suite 300, Frisco, TX 75034 *Tel:* 469-803-4900 *Toll Free Tel:* 866-4-IMAGINE (446-2446) *Fax:* 469-803-4899 *E-mail:* insidesales@imaginecommunications.com *Web Site:* www.imaginecommunications.com, pg 896

Forish, Jim, Kopp Glass, 2108 Palmer St, Pittsburgh, PA 15218 *Tel:* 412-271-0190 *Fax:* 412-271-4103 *E-mail:* sales@koppglass.com *Web Site:* www.koppglass.com, pg 913

Forman, Glenn A, Allegro Productions Inc, 1000 Clint Moore Rd, Suite 108, Boca Raton, FL 33487 *Tel:* 561-994-9111 *Toll Free Tel:* 800-232-2133 (ext 201) *Fax:* 561-241-0707 *Web Site:* www.allegrovideo.com, pg 781

Forman, Scott J, Allegro Productions Inc, 1000 Clint Moore Rd, Suite 108, Boca Raton, FL 33487 *Tel:* 561-994-9111 *Toll Free Tel:* 800-232-2133 (ext 201) *Fax:* 561-241-0707 *Web Site:* www.allegrovideo.com, pg 781

Forrester, Clive, All Access Staging & Productions, 1320 Storm Pkwy, Torrance, CA 90501 *Tel:* 310-784-2464 *Toll Free Tel:* 877-784-2464 *Fax:* 310-517-0899 *E-mail:* usinfo@allaccessinc.com *Web Site:* www.allaccessinc.com, pg 780

Forschmidt, Don, PrimeLight Productions Inc, 750 Kappock St, Suite 805, Riverdale, NY 10463 *Tel:* 718-543-3991; 917-680-5780 *E-mail:* info@primelight.net *Web Site:* www.primelight.net, pg 982

Forster, Jeff, WTVS-Station Enterprises, Riley Broadcast Ctr, One Clover Ct, Wixom, MI 48393-2247 *Tel:* 248-305-DPTV (305-3788) *Fax:* 248-305-3990 *E-mail:* email@dptv.org *Web Site:* www.dptv.org, pg 1071

Forsythe, Kenton, Eastern Acoustic Works Inc (EAW), One Main St, Whitinsville, MA 01588-2238 *Tel:* 508-234-6158 *Toll Free Tel:* 800-992-5013 *Fax:* 508-234-8251 *Toll Free Fax:* 800-322-8251 *E-mail:* info@eaw.com *Web Site:* www.eaw.com, pg 856

Forte, Deborah A, Scholastic Media, 557 Broadway, New York, NY 10012 *Fax:* 212-343-7592 *Web Site:* www.scholastic.com/aboutscholastic/librarypublishing.htm, pg 1004

Fortier, Dr Claude, State of the Art Acoustik Inc, 43-1010 Polytek St, Ottawa, ON K1J 9J3, Canada *Tel:* 613-745-2003 *Fax:* 613-745-9687 *E-mail:* sota@sota.ca *Web Site:* www.sota.ca, pg 1024

Fortman, Fred, American Society of Safety Engineers (ASSE), 1800 E Oakton St, Des Plaines, IL 60018 *Tel:* 847-699-2929 *E-mail:* customerservice@asse.org *Web Site:* www.asse.org, pg 1077

Foss, Lori, Harris Communications Inc, 15155 Technology Dr, Eden Prairie, MN 55344 *Tel:* 952-906-1180 *Toll Free Tel:* 800-825-6758 *Fax:* 952-906-1099 *E-mail:* info@harriscomm.com *Web Site:* www.harriscomm.com, pg 885

Foster, Bill, Fresh Film Northwest (FFNW), 934 SW Salmon St, Portland, OR 97205 *Tel:* 503-221-1156 (ext 10) *Fax:* 503-294-0874 *E-mail:* info@nwfilm.org *Web Site:* www.nwfilm.org, pg 1115

Foster, Bill, Northwest Film Center, 934 SW Salmon St, Portland, OR 97205 *Tel:* 503-221-1156 (ext 10) *Fax:* 503-294-0874 *E-mail:* info@nwfilm.org *Web Site:* www.nwfilm.org, pg 959

Foster, Fred, ETC, 3031 Pleasant View Rd, Middleton, WI 53562-4809 *Tel:* 608-831-4116 *Toll Free Tel:* 800-688-4116 *Fax:* 608-836-1736 *E-mail:* mail@etcconnect.com; americas@etcconnect.com *Web Site:* www.etcconnect.com, pg 862

Foster, Kate, Jackson Hole Film Commission, 112 Center St, Jackson, WY 83001 *Tel:* 307-733-3316 (ext 104) *Fax:* 307-733-5585 *Web Site:* www.jacksonholechamber.com, pg 1104

Foster, Lee, Electric Lady Studios, 52 W Eighth St, New York, NY 10011 *Tel:* 212-677-4700 *Web Site:* electricladystudios.com, pg 858

Foster, Maurice, National Association of Black Journalists (NABJ), 1100 Knight Hall, Suite 3100, College Park, MD 20742 *Tel:* 301-405-0248 *Fax:* 301-314-1714 *E-mail:* nabj@nabj.org *Web Site:* www.nabj.org, pg 1085

Foti, Frank, Omnia Audio, 1241 Superior Ave E, Cleveland, OH 44114 *Tel:* 216-241-7225 *Fax:* 216-241-4103 *E-mail:* omnia-info@omniaaudio.com *Web Site:* www.omniaaudio.com, pg 962

Foulon, Arnaud, Editions Hurtubise HMH Ltee, 1815 Avenue De Lorimier, Montreal, QC H2K 3W6, Canada *Tel:* 514-523-1523 *Toll Free Tel:* 800-361-1664 *Fax:* 514-523-9969 *Web Site:* www.editionshurtubise.com, pg 892

Foulon, Herve, Editions Hurtubise HMH Ltee, 1815 Avenue De Lorimier, Montreal, QC H2K 3W6, Canada *Tel:* 514-523-1523 *Toll Free Tel:* 800-361-1664 *Fax:* 514-523-9969 *Web Site:* www.editionshurtubise.com, pg 892

Fourcher, Fred, Bitcentral Inc, 4340 Von Karman Ave, Suite 400, Newport Beach, CA 92660 *Tel:* 949-253-9000 *E-mail:* sales@bitcentral.com; support@bitcentral.com *Web Site:* www.bitcentral.com, pg 808

Fowler, Barbara, Diamond Studios, Woods Point 1, 1855 Data Dr, Suite 255, Hoover, AL 35244 *Tel:* 205-987-2121 *Fax:* 205-987-2128 *Web Site:* www.tvstuff.com, pg 846

Fowler, Christine, Extron Electronics, 1025 E Ball Rd, Suite 100, Anaheim, CA 92805-5957 *Tel:* 714-491-1500 *Toll Free Tel:* 800-633-9876 (sales & tech support); 800-633-9873 (order support) *Fax:* 714-491-1517 *E-mail:* sales-usa@extron.com *Web Site:* www.extron.com, pg 864

Fowler, Jennifer, RCA Records, 550 Madison Ave, New York, NY 10022 *Tel:* 212-833-8000 *E-mail:* info@rcarecords.com *Web Site:* www.rcarecords.com; www.sonymusic.com, pg 992

Fowler, Jill, International Light Technologies Inc, 10 Technology Dr, Peabody, MA 01960-7976 *Tel:* 978-818-6180 *Fax:* 978-818-6181 *E-mail:* ilsales@intl-lighttech.com *Web Site:* www.intl-lighttech.com, pg 901

Fowler, Kirk, Colorado Video Inc, 6595 Odell Place, Mezzanine S, Boulder, CO 80301 *Tel:* 303-530-9580 *Fax:* 303-530-9569 *E-mail:* sales@colorado-video.com *Web Site:* www.colorado-video.com, pg 832

Fowler, Lowell, High End Systems Inc, 2105 Gracy Farms Lane, Austin, TX 78758 *Tel:* 512-836-2242 *Toll Free Tel:* 800-890-8989 *Fax:* 512-837-5290 *E-mail:* info@highend.com *Web Site:* www.highend.com, pg 888

Fowler, Peter, Zelco Industries Inc, 110 Hartford Ave, Mount Vernon, NY 10553 *Tel:* 914-699-6230 *Toll Free Tel:* 800-431-2486 *E-mail:* office@zelco.com *Web Site:* www.zelco.com, pg 1073

Fowler, Sheena, Metro Orlando Film Commission, 301 E Pine St, Suite 900, Orlando, FL 32801 *Tel:* 407-422-7159 *Fax:* 407-425-6428 *E-mail:* info@filmorlando.com *Web Site:* www.filmorlando.com, pg 1096

Fox, Brad, Big Shoulders Digital Video Productions, 875 N Michigan Ave, Suite 3750, Chicago, IL 60611 *Tel:* 312-540-5400 *E-mail:* info@bigshoulders.com; sales@bigshoulders.com *Web Site:* www.bigshoulders.com, pg 807

Fox, Brad S, Chicago Satellite & Video, 6749 N Keeler Ave, Lincolnwood, IL 60712-3513 *Tel:* 312-907-3057 *E-mail:* chicagosatellite@hotmail.com, pg 825

Fox, David, VCSvideo, 2807 Hunterdon Dr, Cinnaminson, NJ 08077 *Tel:* 856-273-8800 *Toll Free Tel:* 877-VCS-VIDEO (827-8433) *Web Site:* www.vcsvideo.com, pg 1052

Fox, Jim, Lion & Fox Recording Studios, 9517 Baltimore Ave, College Park, MD 20740 *Tel:* 301-982-4431 *E-mail:* mail@lionfox.com *Web Site:* www.lionfox.com, pg 922

Fox, John G II, Society for Applied Learning Technology (SALT®), 50 Culpeper St, Warrenton, VA 20186 *Tel:* 540-347-0055 *Fax:* 540-349-3169 *E-mail:* info@lti.org *Web Site:* www.salt.org, pg 1089

Fox, Marion, Jeff Davis Parish Tourist Commission, 100 Rue de l'Acadie, Jennings, LA 70546 *Tel:* 337-821-5521 *Toll Free Tel:* 800-264-5521 *Fax:* 337-821-5536 *Web Site:* www.jeffdavis.org; www.louisianatravel.com, pg 1098

Fox, Richard J, Warner Bros Entertainment Inc, 4000 Warner Blvd, Burbank, CA 91522 *Tel:* 818-954-3000 *Fax:* 818-954-4918 *E-mail:* wbsf@warnerbros.com *Web Site:* www.warnerbros.com; studiofacilities.warnerbros.com, pg 1062

Fox, Stephanie, Pro Video & Film Equipment Co Inc, 11425 Mathis Ave, Studio 404, Dallas, TX 75234 *Tel:* 972-869-9990 *Toll Free Tel:* 888-869-9998 *Fax:* 972-869-0145 *E-mail:* providfilm@aol.com *Web Site:* www.provideofilm.com; www.usedequipmentnewsletter.com, pg 983

Fox, Susan E, Acoustical Society of America (ASA), 1305 Walt Whitman Rd, Suite 300, Melville, NY 11747-4300 *Tel:* 516-576-2360 *Fax:* 516-576-2377 *E-mail:* asa@aip.org *Web Site:* www.acousticalsociety.org, pg 1075

Fox, Tim, The Kitchen, 4119 W Burbank Blvd, Burbank, CA 91505 *Tel:* 818-306-5300 *Fax:* 305-415-6201 *E-mail:* info@thekitchen.tv *Web Site:* www.thekitchen.tv, pg 911

Foy, Joanne, California Independent Film Festival (CAIFF), 350 Park St, Moraga, CA 94566 *Tel:* 925-388-0752; 310-879-9188 (Los Angeles off) *E-mail:* info@caiff.org *Web Site:* caiff.org, pg 1110

Francis, Michael R, DreamWorks Animation SKG Inc, 1000 Flower St, Glendale, CA 91201 *Tel:* 818-695-5000 *Fax:* 818-695-4190 *Web Site:* www.dreamworksanimation.com, pg 852

Francis, Ramm, DVDs4Less, 6519 Jamon Dr, Sparks, NV 89436-9142 *Tel:* 775-323-0965 *Toll Free Tel:* 800-852-2330 *Fax:* 775-323-1055 *E-mail:* info@dvds4less.net *Web Site:* www.dvds4less.net, pg 854

Francis, Tom, Cibola Systems, 180 S Cypress St, Orange, CA 92866 *Tel:* 714-480-0272 *Fax:* 714-480-0768 *E-mail:* info@cibolasystems.com *Web Site:* cibolasystems.com, pg 826

Franco, James, EFX Media, 2300 S Ninth St, Suite 136, Arlington, VA 22204 *Tel:* 703-486-2303 *Fax:* 703-553-9813 *E-mail:* info@efxmedia.com; sales@efxmedia.com *Web Site:* www.efxmedia.com, pg 858

Franco, Ron, Hydrogen Whiskey Studios, 1640 Fifth St, Suite 226, Santa Monica, CA 90401 *Tel:* 310-394-8130 *Fax:* 310-394-8129 *Web Site:* www.hydrogenwhiskey.com, pg 893

Franey, Alan, Vancouver International Film Festival, Vancouver International Film Centre, 1181 Seymour St, Vancouver, BC V6B 3M7, Canada *Tel:* 604-685-0260 *Fax:* 604-688-8221 *E-mail:* viff@viff.org *Web Site:* www.viff.org, pg 1129

Franey, Christopher, ACCO Brands Corp, 4 Corporate Dr, Lake Zurick, IL 60047-8997 *Toll Free Tel:* 800-541-0094 *Toll Free Fax:* 800-941-4463 *E-mail:* contactus@gbc.com *Web Site:* www.accobrands.com, pg 773

Franey, David, Stoney-Wolf Productions Inc, 130 W Columbia Ct, Chaska, MN 55318-2304 *Tel:* 952-556-0075 *Toll Free Tel:* 800-237-7583 *Fax:* 952-361-4217 *E-mail:* sales@stoneywolf.com *Web Site:* www.stoneywolf.com, pg 1025

Frank, Alan, WPGH-TV, 750 Ivory Ave, Pittsburgh, PA 15214 *Tel:* 412-931-5300 *Fax:* 412-931-4284 *Web Site:* www.sbgi.net; www.wpgh53.com, pg 1070

Frank, Michael, Earwig Music Co Inc, 2054 W Farwell Ave, Unit G, Chicago, IL 60645-4963 *Tel:* 773-262-0278 *E-mail:* orders@earwigmusic.com *Web Site:* www.earwigmusic.com, pg 855

Frank, Mike, Speakers Unlimited, 5565 Woodridge Dr, Columbus, OH 43213 *Tel:* 614-864-3703 *Fax:* 614-864-3876 *E-mail:* prospeak@aol.com *Web Site:* www.speakersunlimited.com, pg 1020

Frank, Robby, Get Organized, 328 Canham Rd, Scotts Valley, CA 95066 *Tel:* 831-438-0259 *Fax:* 831-438-0359, pg 877

Franklin, Jerry, Media Vision Productions Inc, 1049 Asylum Ave, Hartford, CT 06105 *Tel:* 860-278-5310 *Web Site:* cpbn.org, pg 937

Franklin, Raymond W, Stage America LLC, 4001 S Decatur 37, Suite 532, Las Vegas, NV 89103 *Tel:* 702-879-8177 *Toll Free Fax:* 877-488-6663 *E-mail:* info@stageamerica.com *Web Site:* www.stageamerica.com, pg 1022

Frantz, Kittie, Geddes Productions LLC, PO Box 41761, Los Angeles, CA 90041-0761 *Tel:* 323-344-8045 *Fax:* 323-257-7209 *E-mail:* orders@geddesproduction.com *Web Site:* www.geddesproduction.com, pg 876

Franzen, J W, Precision Electronics Inc, 1331 Estes Ave, Gurnee, IL 60031 *Tel:* 847-599-1799 *Toll Free Tel:* 800-SINCE-46 (746-2346) *Fax:* 847-599-6178 *E-mail:* info@grommesprecision.com; sales@grommesprecision.com *Web Site:* www.grommesprecision.com, pg 980

Frappier, Kevin, Burk Technology Inc, 7 Beaver Brook Rd, Littleton, MA 01460 *Tel:* 978-486-0086 *Toll Free Tel:* 800-255-8090 *Fax:* 978-486-0081 *E-mail:* sales@burk.com; orders@burk.com *Web Site:* www.burk.com, pg 815

Frappier, Roger, Max Films Inc, 1751 Richardson St, Suite 5101, Montreal, QC H3K 1G6, Canada *Tel:* 514-282-8444 *Fax:* 514-282-9222 *E-mail:* info@maxfilms.ca *Web Site:* www.maxfilms.ca, pg 934

Fraser, Brendan, Tallahassee Audio Visual, 2880 Apalachee Pkwy, Tallahassee, FL 32301 *Tel:* 850-877-1152 (photo); 850-877-1154 (AV) *Toll Free Tel:* 800-356-9631 *Fax:* 850-878-4026; 850-656-1384 *E-mail:* info@talcam.com *Web Site:* www.talcam.com, pg 1031

Fraser, Dave, Heavy Melody, 307 Seventh Ave, Suite 1203, New York, NY 10001 *Tel:* 212-675-9585 *Fax:* 212-675-9565 *E-mail:* contact_hm@heavymelodymusic.com (studio inquiries) *Web Site:* www.heavymelodymusic.com, pg 887

Fraser, Michael, Tallahassee Audio Visual, 2880 Apalachee Pkwy, Tallahassee, FL 32301 *Tel:* 850-877-1152 (photo); 850-877-1154 (AV) *Toll Free Tel:* 800-356-9631 *Fax:* 850-878-4026; 850-656-1384 *E-mail:* info@talcam.com *Web Site:* www.talcam.com, pg 1031

Fraser, Susan O'Connor, Tam Communications Inc, 5610 Scotts Valley Dr, Suite B552, Scotts Valley, CA 95066 *Tel:* 831-439-1500 *Toll Free Fax:* 866-390-1218 *E-mail:* info@tamcom.com *Web Site:* www.tamcom.com, pg 1031

Fraser, Tam O'Connor, Tam Communications Inc, 5610 Scotts Valley Dr, Suite B552, Scotts Valley, CA 95066 *Tel:* 831-439-1500 *Toll Free Fax:* 866-390-1218 *E-mail:* info@tamcom.com *Web Site:* www.tamcom.com, pg 1031

Fraval, H R, Visioneering International Inc, 659 Auburn Ave NE, Suite 267, Atlanta, GA 30312 *Tel:* 404-681-9028 *Fax:* 404-681-5947 *E-mail:* design@visioneering.com *Web Site:* www.visioneering.com, pg 1058

Frazier, Michelle, J & R Film Co, 1135 N Mansfield Ave, Hollywood, CA 90038 *Tel:* 323-467-1116 *Toll Free Tel:* 877-668-4652 *Fax:* 323-464-1518 *Web Site:* www.moviola.com, pg 903

Frazier, Michelle, Moviola, 1135 N Mansfield Ave, Hollywood, CA 90038 *Tel:* 323-467-3107 *Toll Free Tel:* 877-MOVIOLA (668-4652) *Fax:* 323-464-1518 *Web Site:* www.moviola.com, pg 948

Frebowitz, Jerry, Movies Unlimited, 3015 Darnell Rd, Philadelphia, PA 19154 *Tel:* 215-637-4444 *Toll Free Tel:* 800-4-MOVIES (466-8437) *Fax:* 215-637-2350 *E-mail:* movies@moviesunlimited.com *Web Site:* www.moviesunlimited.com, pg 947

Freda, Gerald, CaptionMax, 2438 27 Ave S, Minneapolis, MN 55406 *Tel:* 612-341-3566 *Toll Free Tel:* 800-822-3566 *Fax:* 612-341-2345 *Web Site:* www.captionmax.com, pg 820

Freda, Thomas, Prior Scientific Inc, 80 Reservoir Park Dr, Rockland, MA 02370-1062 *Tel:* 781-878-8442 *Toll Free Tel:* 800-877-2234 *Fax:* 781-878-8736 *E-mail:* info@prior.com; techsupportus@prior.com *Web Site:* www.prior.com, pg 982

Fredell, Eric, Software & Information Industry Association (SIIA), 1090 Vermont Ave NW, 6th fl, Washington, DC 20005-4095 *Tel:* 202-289-7442 *Fax:* 202-289-7097 *Web Site:* www.siia.net, pg 1089

Frederick, John, Avid Technology Inc, 65-75 Network Dr, Burlington, MA 01830 *Tel:* 978-640-6789 *Fax:* 978-640-3366 *Web Site:* www.avid.com, pg 799

Frederickson, Derek, Twisted Media Inc, 1341 W Granville, Suite 1, Chicago, IL 60660 *Tel:* 773-856-6586 *E-mail:* info@twistedtracks.com *Web Site:* www.twistedtracks.com, pg 1047

Fredonchick, Michael, Sima Products Corp, 125 Commerce Dr, Hauppauge, NY 11788 *Tel:* 631-435-0200 *Toll Free Tel:* 800-345-7462; 800-274-7824 *Fax:* 631-435-4545 *Toll Free Fax:* 800-274-7828 *E-mail:* info@simacorp.com; custserv@simacorp.com; customerservice@aristagroup.com *Web Site:* www.aristagroup.com, pg 1011

Freed, Gary, Z-Axis Corp, 4600 S Ulster St, Suite 270, Denver, CO 80237 *Tel:* 303-713-0200 *Toll Free Tel:* 800-827-2947 *E-mail:* info@zaxis.com *Web Site:* www.zaxis.com, pg 1073

Freedman, Alan, The Computer Language Co Inc, 5521 State Park Rd, Point Pleasant, PA 18950 *Tel:* 215-297-8082 *E-mail:* sales@computerlanguage.com; comments@computerlanguage.com *Web Site:* www.computerlanguage.com, pg 834

Freedman, Harlan, FJ Productions Inc, 14900 Ventura Blvd, Suite 350, Sherman Oaks, CA 91403-3465 *Tel:* 818-788-0153 *Fax:* 818-788-0186 *Web Site:* www.fjproductions.com, pg 869

Freedman, Harrison, YAP Films, 96 Spadina Ave, Suite 205, Toronto, ON M5V 2J6, Canada *Tel:* 416-504-3662 *Fax:* 416-504-3667 *E-mail:* thedog@yapfilms.com *Web Site:* www.yapfilms.com, pg 1072

Freeman, Barbara, Freeman Pictures Inc, 1234 Sherman Ave, Suite 201, Evanston, IL 60602 *Tel:* 847-733-0717 *Web Site:* www.freemanpictures.com, pg 872

Freeman, David, County Sales, 117A W Main St, Floyd, VA 24091 *Tel:* 540-745-2001 *Fax:* 540-745-2008 *E-mail:* sales@countysales.com; info@countysales.com *Web Site:* www.countysales.com, pg 837

Freeman, David, Rebel Records, PO Box 7405, Charlottesville, VA 22906-7405 *Tel:* 434-973-5151 *E-mail:* questions@rebelrecords.com *Web Site:* rebelrecords.com, pg 993

Freeman, Donald S, Freeman, 1600 Viceroy, Suite 100, Dallas, TX 75235 *Tel:* 214-445-1000 *Fax:* 214-445-0200 *Web Site:* www.freemanco.com, pg 872

Freeman, Douglas, Ideascape Inc, PO Box 1966, Lake Oswego, OR 97035 *Tel:* 503-246-2439 *E-mail:* info@ideascapeinc.com *Web Site:* www.ideascapeinc.com, pg 894

Freeman, Linda, L & S Video Inc, 45 Stornowaye, Chappaqua, NY 10514 *Tel:* 914-238-9366 *Fax:* 914-238-6324 *E-mail:* videopaint2@msn.com *Web Site:* www.landsvideo.com, pg 915

Freeman, MacKenzie, Ideascape Inc, PO Box 1966, Lake Oswego, OR 97035 *Tel:* 503-246-2439 *E-mail:* info@ideascapeinc.com *Web Site:* www.ideascapeinc.com, pg 894

Freeman, Mark, Rebel Records, PO Box 7405, Charlottesville, VA 22906-7405 *Tel:* 434-973-5151 *E-mail:* questions@rebelrecords.com *Web Site:* rebelrecords.com, pg 993

Freese, Richard, Recorded Books LLC, 270 Skipjack Rd, Prince Frederick, MD 20678 *Tel:* 410-535-5590 *Toll Free Tel:* 800-638-1304 *Fax:* 410-535-5499 *E-mail:* customerservice@recordedbooks.com *Web Site:* www.recordedbooks.com, pg 993

French, Cookie, JRF Magnetic Sciences Inc, 249 Kennedy Rd, Greendell, NJ 07839 *Tel:* 973-579-5773 *Fax:* 973-579-6021 *E-mail:* jrf@jrfmagnetics.com *Web Site:* www.jrfmagnetics.com, pg 906

French, Don E, The Source Stock Footage Library Inc, 140 S Camino Seco, Suite 308, Tucson, AZ 85710 *Tel:* 520-298-4810 *Fax:* 520-290-4376 *E-mail:* requests@sourcefootage.com *Web Site:* www.sourcefootage.com, pg 1019

French, John, JRF Magnetic Sciences Inc, 249 Kennedy Rd, Greendell, NJ 07839 *Tel:* 973-579-5773 *Fax:* 973-579-6021 *E-mail:* jrf@jrfmagnetics.com *Web Site:* www.jrfmagnetics.com, pg 906

French, Matt, First Cut Communications LLC, 301 W Broome St, Suite 100, LaGrange, GA 30240 *Tel:* 706-882-5581 *E-mail:* info@firstcutcommunications.com *Web Site:* www.firstcutcommunications.com, pg 868

French, Timothy, Monarch Instrument, 15 Columbia Dr, Amherst, NH 03031-2305 *Tel:* 603-883-3390 *Toll Free Tel:* 800-999-3390 *Fax:* 603-886-3300 *E-mail:* sales@monarchinstrument.com *Web Site:* www.monarchinstrument.com, pg 945

Frenchman, Michael, Videograf, 144 W 27 St, 12th fl, New York, NY 10001 *Tel:* 212-242-7871 *E-mail:* videograf@verizon.net, pg 1057

Frericks, Thomas Jr, Copp Integrated Systems, 123 S Keowee St, Dayton, OH 45402 *Tel:* 937-228-4188 *Toll Free Tel:* 877-450-2677 *Fax:* 937-228-2901 *Web Site:* www.copp.com, pg 836

Freund, Spencer, Telemanagement Resources International Inc (TRI), 124 Thomas Lane, Manahawkin, NJ 08050 *Tel:* 609-597-6334 *Web Site:* www.triinc.com, pg 1036

Frey, Richard, Video Accessory Corp, 1243 Sherman Dr, Suite 8, Longmont, CO 80501 *Tel:* 303-443-1319 *Toll Free Tel:* 800-821-0426 *Fax:* 303-440-8878 *E-mail:* sales@vac-brick.net *Web Site:* www.vac-brick.com, pg 1054

Friberg, Leah, Fluke Corp, 6920 Seaway Blvd, Everett, WA 98203 *Tel:* 425-347-6100 *Toll Free Tel:* 800-443-5853 *Fax:* 425-446-5116 *E-mail:* fluke-info@fluke.com *Web Site:* www.fluke.com, pg 870

Friborg, Brian, JEM Smoke Machine Co Ltd, 700 Sawgrass Corporate Pkwy, Sunrise, FL 33325 *Tel:* 954-858-1800 *Toll Free Tel:* 800-832-4180 *Fax:* 954-858-1811 *E-mail:* martinus@martinpro.com *Web Site:* www.martinpro.com, pg 905

Friborg, Brian, Martin Professional Inc, 700 Sawgrass Corporate Pkwy, Sunrise, FL 33325 *Tel:* 954-858-1800 *Fax:* 954-858-1811 *E-mail:* martinus@martinpro.com *Web Site:* www.martinpro.com, pg 932

Frick, Tim, MIGHTYbYTES Inc, 4001 N Ravenswood Ave, Suite 404, Chicago, IL 60613 *Tel:* 773-561-7529 *E-mail:* info@mightybytes.com *Web Site:* www.mightybytes.com, pg 942

Fricon, Terri, Fricon Entertainment Co Inc, 134 Bluegrass Circle, Hendersonville, TN 37075 *Tel:* 615-826-2288 *Fax:* 615-826-0500, pg 873

Fried, Dan, Innovision Media Group, 307 W Johnson Hwy, Norristown, PA 19401 *Tel:* 484-688-1200 *Fax:* 484-688-0148 *E-mail:* info@innovision.net; sales@innovision.net *Web Site:* www.innovision.net, pg 899

Fried, Robert, Robert Fried Photography, 610 Eldridge Ct, Novato, CA 94947 *Tel:* 415-898-6153 *Fax:* 415-897-0353 *Web Site:* www.robertfriedphotography.com, pg 873

Friederichs, Cecilia, United Scenic Artists Local 829, 29 W 38 St, 15th fl, New York, NY 10018 *Tel:* 212-581-0300 *Fax:* 212-977-2011 *E-mail:* businessoffice@usa829.org *Web Site:* www.usa829.org; vfx.usa829.org, pg 1090

Friederichsen, Steve, Big Event Productions LLC, 77 13 Ave NE, Studio 101, Minneapolis, MN 55413 *Tel:* 612-623-7800 *Fax:* 612-455-0450 *Web Site:* www.bigeventpros.com, pg 807

Friedler, Dr Alan, Palardo Productions, 1807 Taft Ave, Suite 4, Hollywood, CA 90028 *Tel:* 323-469-8991 *E-mail:* palardo2@msn.com, pg 968

Friedman, Dan, Castillo Theater, 543 W 42 St, New York, NY 10036 *Tel:* 212-941-5800 *Toll Free Tel:* 800-435-7453 *E-mail:* castillo@allstars.org *Web Site:* www.castillo.org, pg 821

Friedman, David, Magno Sound & Video, 729 Seventh Ave, New York, NY 10019 *Tel:* 212-302-2505 *Fax:* 212-819-1282 *E-mail:* staff@magnosound.com *Web Site:* www.magnosoundandvideo.com, pg 929

Friedman, Fritz, Sony Pictures Home Entertainment, 10202 W Washington Blvd, Culver City, CA 90232-3119 *Tel:* 310-244-4000 *Fax:* 310-244-2485 *Web Site:* www.sonypictures.com, pg 1016

Friedman, Laurence, Wildfire Lighting & Visual Effects, 2908 Oregon Ct, Suite G1, Torrance, CA 90503 *Tel:* 310-755-6780 *Toll Free Tel:* 800-937-8065 *Fax:* 310-755-6781 *E-mail:* mail@wildfirefx.com; sales@wildfirefx.com *Web Site:* www.wildfirefx.com, pg 1066

Friedman, Mark, See Factor Industry Inc, 37-11 30 St, Long Island City, NY 11101 *Tel:* 718-784-4200 *Fax:* 718-784-0617 *Web Site:* www.seefactor.com, pg 1006

Friedman, Michael L, DWJ Television, One Robinson Lane, Ridgewood, NJ 07450 *Tel:* 201-445-1711 *Toll Free Tel:* 800-766-1711 *Fax:* 201-445-8352, pg 854

Friedman, Sonya, Four Corners Productions, 38 W Tenth St, New York, NY 10011 *Tel:* 212-228-6492 *Fax:* 212-228-6492 *Web Site:* www.operatitles.net; www.gracepaleyvideo.com, pg 871

Friedman, Stephen, MTV Networks Co, c/o MTV Studios, 1515 Broadway, New York, NY 10036 *Tel:* 212-258-8000 *Web Site:* www.mtv.com; www.mtvpress.com, pg 949

Friend, Dave, The ADS Group, 2155 Niagara Lane N, Suite 120, Plymouth, MN 55447 *Tel:* 763-449-5500 *Toll Free Tel:* 800-759-0992 *Fax:* 763-449-5555 *E-mail:* sales@theadsgroup.com *Web Site:* www.theadsgroup.com, pg 777

Friend, Jessie, Lee Filters, 2237 N Hollywood Way, Burbank, CA 91505 *Tel:* 818-238-1220 *Toll Free Tel:* 800-576-5055 *Fax:* 818-238-1228 *E-mail:* mail@leefiltersusa.com *Web Site:* www.leefilters.com, pg 918

Friestedt, Brad, Magnetic Shield Corp, 740 N Thomas Dr, Bensenville, IL 60106 *Tel:* 630-766-7800 *Toll Free Tel:* 888-766-7800 *Fax:* 630-766-2813 *E-mail:* shields@magnetic-shield.com *Web Site:* www.magnetic-shield.com, pg 928

Fritsch, Nick, Lyrichord Discs Inc, PO Box 1977, Old Chelsea Sta, New York, NY 10011-1726 *Tel:* 212-404-8290 *Fax:* 212-404-8291 *E-mail:* info@lyrichord.com *Web Site:* www.lyrichord.com, pg 927

Fritz, Ed, Sierra Automated Systems, 2821 Burton Ave, Burbank, CA 91504 *Tel:* 818-840-6749 *Fax:* 818-840-6751 *E-mail:* sales@sasaudio.com; marketing@sasaudio.com *Web Site:* www.sasaudio.com, pg 1010

Fritz, Jayson, Texas Rebel Radio Network, 210 Woodcrest, Fredericksburg, TX 78624 *Tel:* 830-997-2197 *Fax:* 830-997-2198 *E-mail:* txradio@ktc.net *Web Site:* www.kfanfmradio.com, pg 1037

Froechtenigt, Sylke, Kavanagh Productions Inc, 32 Broadway, Suite 1711-12, New York, NY 10004 *Tel:* 212-480-0065 *Fax:* 212-480-0149 *E-mail:* mail@kavanaghproductions.com *Web Site:* www.kavanaghproductions.com, pg 908

Frost, John, SonicPool, 6860 Lexington Ave, Hollywood, CA 90038 *Tel:* 323-460-4649 *Toll Free Tel:* 866-203-7213 *Fax:* 323-460-6063 *E-mail:* production@sonicpool.com *Web Site:* www.sonicpool.com, pg 1016

Fry, David, Omega Broadcast Group, 817 W Howard Lane, Austin, TX 78753 *Tel:* 512-251-7778 *Fax:* 512-251-8633 *E-mail:* rental@omegabroadcast.com; sales@omegabroadcast.com *Web Site:* www.omegabroadcast.com, pg 962

Fry, John, Ardent Music LLC, 2000 Madison Ave, Memphis, TN 38104 *Tel:* 901-725-0855 *Fax:* 901-725-7011 *E-mail:* info@ardentmusic.com *Web Site:* www.ardentmusic.com, pg 789

Fry, John, Ardent Studios Inc, 2000 Madison Ave, Memphis, TN 38104 *Tel:* 901-725-0855 *Fax:* 901-725-7011 *E-mail:* info@ardentstudios.com *Web Site:* www.ardentstudios.com, pg 789

Fry, Pam, Omega Broadcast Group, 817 W Howard Lane, Austin, TX 78753 *Tel:* 512-251-7778 *Fax:* 512-251-8633 *E-mail:* rental@omegabroadcast.com; sales@omegabroadcast.com *Web Site:* www.omegabroadcast.com, pg 962

Fry, Rick, Professional Label Inc, 3415 Olandwood Ct, Olney, MD 20832 *Tel:* 301-570-0774 *Fax:* 301-570-0776 *E-mail:* prolabel@msn.com *Web Site:* www.professionallabel.com; www.prolabel.com, pg 985

Frye, Greg, Mid-South Color Labs Inc, 496 Emmett St, Jackson, TN 38301 *Tel:* 731-422-6691 *Toll Free Tel:* 800-221-3920 *Fax:* 731-424-1902 *E-mail:* info@midsouthcolor.com *Web Site:* www.midsouthcolor.com, pg 942

Fryer, Caitlin, Stage Post, 255 French Landing Dr, Nashville, TN 37228 *Tel:* 615-248-1978 *Toll Free Tel:* 877-250-1839 *Fax:* 615-242-8861 *E-mail:* mail@stagepost.com *Web Site:* www.stagepost.com, pg 1022

Fuchs, Laurie, Ladyslipper Inc, PO Box 14, Cedar Grove, NC 27231 *Tel:* 919-245-3737 *E-mail:* info@ladyslipper.org *Web Site:* www.ladyslipper.org, pg 915

Fucile, John, SmackDab Media, 1033 Third Ave S, Nashville, TN 37210 *Toll Free Tel:* 888-248-8197 *Web Site:* smackdabmedia.com, pg 1013

Fuentes, Shirley, Effective Engineering, 2805 W Empire Ave, Burbank, CA 91504 *Tel:* 818-841-4437 *Fax:* 818-841-4389 *E-mail:* info@effeng.com *Web Site:* www.effeng.com, pg 858

Fulford-Brown, John, JFB Communications, 3 Haig Ave, Toronto, ON M1N 2W2, Canada *Tel:* 416-691-5001 *E-mail:* jfb@jfb.ca *Web Site:* jfb.ca, pg 905

Fulham, Paul, Zachry Associates Inc, 500 Chestnut St, Suite 2000, Abilene, TX 79602 *Tel:* 325-677-1342 *Fax:* 325-672-2001 *E-mail:* info@zachryinc.com *Web Site:* zachryinc.com, pg 1073

Fullam, Hannah, Preston Productions Inc, 128 Bartlett St, Marlborough, MA 01752 *Toll Free Tel:* 800-822-2299 *E-mail:* ideas@prestonevents.com *Web Site:* www.prestonproductions.com; www.prestonevents.com, pg 981

Fuller, Barry J, MediaWorks, 843 W Elna Rae St, Tempe, AZ 85281-5421 *Tel:* 480-968-4392 *Fax:* 480-968-4679 *Web Site:* www.mediaworks-az.com, pg 938

Fuller, Ben, Imagecraft Productions, 3318 Burton Ave, Burbank, CA 91504 *Tel:* 818-954-0187 *Fax:* 818-954-0189 *Web Site:* www.imagecraftproductions.com, pg 896

Fuller, Brad, Florida Film & Tape, 3417 Lake Breeze Rd, Orlando, FL 32808 *Tel:* 407-297-0091 *Fax:* 407-297-0094 *Web Site:* www.ffandt.com, pg 870

Fuller, Dale, Parabola Audio/Video, 20 W 20 St, 2nd fl, New York, NY 10011 *Tel:* 212-822-8806 (edit & publg); 201-656-7220 (ad) *Toll Free Tel:* 800-560-MYTH (560-6984); 877-593-2521 (subns) *Fax:* 212-822-8823 *E-mail:* info@parabola.org *Web Site:* www.parabola.org, pg 969

Fuller, Erin M, Alliance for Women in Media/Alliance for Women in Media Foundation, 1250 24 St NW, Suite 300, Washington, DC 20037 *Tel:* 703-506-3290 *Fax:* 202-750-3664 *Web Site:* www.allwomeninmedia.org, pg 1075

Fuller, Erin M, The Gracies®, 1250 24 St NW, Suite 300, Washington, DC 20037 *Tel:* 202-750-3664 *Fax:* 202-750-3664 *Web Site:* www.allwomeninmedia.org; www.thegracies.org, pg 1116

Fuller, Michael, Imagivations, 11314 Sheldon St, Sun Valley, CA 91352 *Tel:* 818-767-6767 *Fax:* 818-767-3637 *E-mail:* info@imagivations.com *Web Site:* www.imagivations.com, pg 896

Fuller, Michael M, Creative Support Services/CSS Music, 1948 Riverside Dr, Los Angeles, CA 90039 *Tel:* 323-666-7968 *Toll Free Tel:* 800-468-6874 *Fax:* 323-660-2070 *E-mail:* info@cssmusic.com *Web Site:* www.cssmusic.com, pg 838

Fuller, Mike, Florida Film & Tape, 3417 Lake Breeze Rd, Orlando, FL 32808 *Tel:* 407-297-0091 *Fax:* 407-297-0094 *Web Site:* www.ffandt.com, pg 870

Fuller, Ronald, Taperwire, c/o Fuller Manufacturing, 523 S Flower St, Burbank, CA 91502 *Tel:* 818-238-9911 *Fax:* 818-238-9959 *E-mail:* taperwire@taperwire.com *Web Site:* www.taperwire.com, pg 1032

Fuller, Susan, Monadnock Media Inc, 112 Amherst Rd, Sunderland, MA 01375 *Tel:* 413-665-1390 *Fax:* 413-665-1394 *E-mail:* info@monadnock.org *Web Site:* www.monadnock.org, pg 945

Fullerton, Eric, Vicon Industries Inc, 131 Heartland Blvd, Edgewood, NY 11717 *Tel:* 631-952-2288 *Toll Free Tel:* 800-645-9116 *Fax:* 631-951-2288 *Web Site:* www.vicon-security.com, pg 1053

Fulmer, Keith, Video Mount Products (VMP), 345 Log Canoe Circle, Stevensville, MD 21666 *Tel:* 410-643-6390 *Toll Free Tel:* 877-281-2169 *Fax:* 410-643-6615 *E-mail:* sales@videomount.com *Web Site:* www.videomount.com, pg 1056

Fulmes, Michael, Global Television Station, 5325 Allard Way, Edmonton, AB T6H 5B8, Canada *Tel:* 780-436-1250; 780-989-4683 *Fax:* 780-989-4686 *E-mail:* globalnews.ed@globaltv.com *Web Site:* www.globaltv.com, pg 879

Fulop, Dan, Universal Audio Inc, 4585 Scotts Valley Dr, Scotts Valley, CA 95066 *Tel:* 831-466-3737 *Toll Free Tel:* 866-823-1176; 877-698-2834 (tech support) *Fax:* 831-461-1550 *E-mail:* info@uaudio.com *Web Site:* www.uaudio.com, pg 1049

Fumagalli, Andrea, Blue Barn Pictures Inc, 68 Jay St, Suite 311, Brooklyn, NY 11201 *Tel:* 718-852-1403 *Web Site:* www.bluebarnpictures.com, pg 809

Funk, Kathy, SYMCO Inc, 29 Poplar Dr, Stirling, NJ 07980 *Tel:* 908-647-6262 *Fax:* 908-647-4904 *E-mail:* orders@symcoinc.com *Web Site:* www.symcoinc.com, pg 1030

Funnell, Adrian, Steeldeck® Inc, 3339 Exposition Place, Los Angeles, CA 90018-4034 *Tel:* 323-290-2100 *Toll Free Tel:* 800-50STAGE (507-8243) *Fax:* 323-290-9600 *E-mail:* sales@steeldeck.com; rentals@steeldeck.com *Web Site:* www.steeldeck.com, pg 1024

Furness, Roger K, Audio Engineering Society Inc (AES), 60 E 42 St, Rm 2520, New York, NY 10165-2520 *Tel:* 212-661-8528 *Fax:* 212-682-0477 *Web Site:* www.aes.org, pg 1079

Fuzessery, Steven, ProVision Video Sales & Rentals Inc, 143 W Third Ave, Vancouver, BC V5Y 1E6, Canada *Tel:* 604-876-0940 *Toll Free Tel:* 877-337-0940 *Fax:* 604-876-8269 *E-mail:* sales@provisionvideo.com; rentals@provisionvideo.com *Web Site:* www.provisionvideo.com, pg 986

Gabbert, Tom, Bartha, 600 N Cassady Ave, Columbus, OH 43219 *Tel:* 614-252-7455 *Toll Free Tel:* 800-363-2698 *Fax:* 614-252-7641 *E-mail:* info@bartha.com *Web Site:* www.bartha.com, pg 803

Gabor, Don, Conversation Arts Media, PO Box 715, Brooklyn, NY 11215 *Tel:* 718-768-0824 *Web Site:* www.dongabor.com, pg 836

Gaboury, Ron, York Telecom, 81 Corbett Way, Eatontown, NJ 07724 *Tel:* 732-413-6000 *Toll Free Tel:* 866-836-8463 *Fax:* 732-413-6060 *E-mail:* knowmore@yorktel.com *Web Site:* yorktel.com, pg 1072

Gabriel, J P, Filmlites Montana, 6465 River Rd, Bozeman, MT 59718 *Tel:* 406-587-0226 *Fax:* 406-551-4555 *E-mail:* info@filmlitesmt.com *Web Site:* www.filmlitesmt.com, pg 867

Gabriel, Kevin, Manitoba Film & Music, 410-93 Lombard Ave, Suite 410, Winnipeg, MB R3B 3B1, Canada *Tel:* 204-947-2040 *Fax:* 204-956-5261 *E-mail:* info@mbfilmmusic.ca *Web Site:* www.mbfilmmusic.ca, pg 930

Gadsby, Elle, Picture Box Distribution Inc, 141 E 23 Ave, Vancouver, BC V5V 1X1, Canada *Tel:* 604-681-3174 *Fax:* 604-608-9081 *E-mail:* info@picturebox.ca *Web Site:* www.picturebox.ca, pg 975

Gaetke, Brian, Shotmaker Co, 10909 Vanowen St, North Hollywood, CA 91605-6408 *Tel:* 818-219-2043 *E-mail:* info@shotmaker.com; info@bigshot.tv *Web Site:* www.shotmaker.com, pg 1009

Gage, Carrie, Studio Technologies Inc, 5520 W Touhy Ave, Skokie, IL 60077 *Tel:* 847-676-9177 *Fax:* 847-982-0747 *E-mail:* stisales-2014@studio-tech.com *Web Site:* www.studio-tech.com, pg 1027

Gagliano, Tony, Art Gallery of Ontario, 317 Dundas St W, Toronto, ON M5T 1G4, Canada *Tel:* 416-979-6660 *Toll Free Tel:* 877-225-4246 *Fax:* 416-979-6674 *E-mail:* danny_winchester@ago.net *Web Site:* www.ago.net, pg 791

Gagliardo, Coleen, Gaylord Brothers, PO Box 4901, Syracuse, NY 13221-4901 *Tel:* 315-634-8243 (intl) *Toll Free Tel:* 800-962-9580 (cust serv) *Fax:* 315-453-5030 (intl) *Toll Free Fax:* 800-272-3412 *E-mail:* customerservice@gaylord.com *Web Site:* www.gaylord.com, pg 876

Gagne, Remi, Three D Graphics Inc, 11340 W Olympic Blvd, Suite 352, Los Angeles, CA 90064-1613 *Tel:* 310-231-3330 *Toll Free Tel:* 800-913-0008 *Fax:* 310-231-3303 *E-mail:* info@threedgraphics.com *Web Site:* www.threedgraphics.com, pg 1039

Gagnon, Francis, Via-Vision Film & Video Productions, 18 College St, Lewiston, ME 04240 *Tel:* 207-783-2550 *Web Site:* www.viavisionproductions.com, pg 1053

Gagnon, Nicole, Show Canada Industries Inc, 5555 Maurice-Cullen, Laval, QC H7C 2T8, Canada *Tel:* 450-664-5155 *Toll Free Tel:* 888-329-5556 *Fax:* 450-664-0852 *E-mail:* info@show-canada.ca *Web Site:* www.show-canada.com, pg 1009

Gagon, Paul, BBE Sound Inc, 2548 Fender Ave, Fullerton, CA 92831 *Tel:* 714-897-6766 *Toll Free Tel:* 800-233-8346 *Fax:* 714-895-6728 *Web Site:* www.bbesound.com, pg 803

Gahagan, Chris, Avid Technology Inc, 65-75 Network Dr, Burlington, MA 01830 *Tel:* 978-640-6789 *Fax:* 978-640-3366 *Web Site:* www.avid.com, pg 799

Gahrahmat, Laura, Eastern Effects Inc, 99 Ninth St, Brooklyn, NY 11215 *Tel:* 718-855-1197 *Fax:* 212-504-9534 *E-mail:* geteffected@easterneffects.com *Web Site:* www.easterneffects.com, pg 856

Gaidry, Diane, Filmmakers Alliance (FA), 1317 N San Fernando Blvd, Unit 366, Burbank, CA 91504 *Tel:* 310-568-0633 *Fax:* 818-301-2257 *E-mail:* info@filmmakersalliance.org *Web Site:* filmmakersalliance.org, pg 1082

Gaines, Susie, El Paso Film Commission, One Civic Center Plaza, El Paso, TX 79901 *Toll Free Tel:* 800-351-6024 *Fax:* 915-532-2963 *Web Site:* www.visitelpaso.com/film, pg 1103

Gaither, Bill, Gaither Studios LLC, 1705 S Park Ave, Alexandria, IN 46001 *Toll Free Tel:* 800-333-7859 *E-mail:* info@gaitherstudios.com *Web Site:* www.gaitherstudios.com, pg 875

Gaither, Gloria, Gaither Studios LLC, 1705 S Park Ave, Alexandria, IN 46001 *Toll Free Tel:* 800-333-7859 *E-mail:* info@gaitherstudios.com *Web Site:* www.gaitherstudios.com, pg 875

Galdi, Gregory G, Custom Computer Specialists Inc, 6 Blackstone Valley Place, Suite 402, Lincoln, RI 02865 *Tel:* 401-765-3000 *Toll Free Tel:* 800-556-2828 *Fax:* 401-765-6440 *Web Site:* www.customonline.com, pg 841

Gale, Trevor, SESAC Inc, 55 Music Sq E, Nashville, TN 37203 *Tel:* 615-320-0055 *Fax:* 615-963-3527 *Web Site:* www.sesac.com, pg 1088

Galea, Ron, Premier A/V Sales Ltd, 28 Howden Rd, Scarborough, ON M1R 3E4, Canada *Tel:* 416-755-1148 *Toll Free Tel:* 800-267-0700 *Fax:* 416-755-6996 *E-mail:* sales@premierav.ca *Web Site:* www.premierav.ca, pg 980

Gallagher, Brian A, United Way Worldwide, 701 N Fairfax St, Alexandria, VA 22314-2045 *Tel:* 703-836-7112 *Fax:* 703-519-0097 *Web Site:* www.unitedway.org, pg 1048

Gallagher, Daniel C, North Star Satellite Communications Inc, 2547 Yellow Springs Rd, Malvern, PA 19355 *Tel:* 610-407-9290 *Fax:* 610-407-9304 *E-mail:* north.star@comcast.net *Web Site:* www.northstarsatellite.net, pg 959

Gallagher, David, QSound Labs Inc, 2816 11 St NE, Suite 102, Calgary, AB T2E 7S7, Canada *Tel:* 403-291-2492 *Fax:* 403-250-1521 *E-mail:* info@qsound.com; sales@qsound.com *Web Site:* www.qsound.com, pg 988

Gallagher, Don, Hollywood Theatre Equipment Inc, 1941 N 66 Ave, Hollywood, FL 33024 *Tel:* 954-920-2832 *Fax:* 954-986-6914 *E-mail:* hwdtheatre@aol.com, pg 890

Gallagher, Michael, Craig Recording Studios, 2381 Philmont Ave, Suite 112, Huntingdon Valley, PA 19006 *Tel:* 215-947-8900 *Web Site:* www.craigrecording.com; www.craigrecordingstudios.com, pg 837

Gallagher, Michelle, Xytech Systems Corp, 15451 San Fernando Mission Blvd, Suite 400, Mission Hills, CA 91345 *Tel:* 818-698-4900 *Fax:* 818-698-4901 *E-mail:* sales@xytechsystems.com *Web Site:* www.xytechsystems.com, pg 1071

Gallagher, Mike, VSG Digital Media Solutions, 11126 Lindbergh Business Ct, St Louis, MO 63123 *Tel:* 314-487-8045 *Toll Free Tel:* 800-737-8045 *Fax:* 314-487-9387 *Web Site:* www.vsginc.net, pg 1061

Gallagher, Mitch, Sweetwater Sound Inc, 5501 US Hwy 30 W, Fort Wayne, IN 46818 *Tel:* 260-432-8176 *Toll Free Tel:* 800-222-4700 *Fax:* 260-432-1758 *Web Site:* www.sweetwater.com, pg 1029

Gallagher, Richard, Xytech Systems Corp, 15451 San Fernando Mission Blvd, Suite 400, Mission Hills, CA 91345 *Tel:* 818-698-4900 *Fax:* 818-698-4901 *E-mail:* sales@xytechsystems.com *Web Site:* www.xytechsystems.com, pg 1071

Gallagher, Shay, National Safety Council (NSC), 1121 Spring Lake Dr, Itasca, IL 60143-3201 *Tel:* 630-285-1121 *Toll Free Tel:* 800-621-7615; 800-621-7619 (cust serv) *Fax:* 630-285-1315; 630-285-1434 (cust serv) *E-mail:* customerservice@nsc.org *Web Site:* www.nsc.org, pg 953

Gallardo, Felix, Techni-Lux Inc, 10900 Palmbay Dr, Orlando, FL 32824 *Tel:* 407-857-8770 *Fax:* 407-857-8771 *E-mail:* sales@techni-lux.com *Web Site:* www.techni-lux.com, pg 1033

Galli, Jaime, Golden Gate Awards, c/o San Francisco Film Society, The Presidio, Suite 110, 39 Mesa St, San Francisco, CA 94129-1025 *Tel:* 415-561-5000 *Fax:* 415-440-1760 *E-mail:* info@sffs.org *Web Site:* festival.sffs.org; www.sffs.org, pg 1115

Galli, Jaime, San Francisco International Film Festival, 39 Mesa St, Suite 110, The Presidio, San Francisco, CA 94129-1025 *Tel:* 415-561-5000 *Fax:* 415-440-1760 *E-mail:* info@sffs.org *Web Site:* festival.sffs.org; www.sffs.org; www.sf360.org, pg 1126

Gallien, Robert, Gallien/Krueger, 2234 Industrial Dr, Stockton, CA 95206 *Tel:* 209-234-7300 *Fax:* 209-234-8420 *E-mail:* sales@gallien.com *Web Site:* www.gallien.com, pg 875

Gallner, Larry, Total Video Products Inc, 414 Southgate Ct, Mickleton, NJ 08056 *Tel:* 856-423-7400 *Toll Free Tel:* 800-447-0920 *Fax:* 856-423-4747 *E-mail:* info@totalvideoproducts.com *Web Site:* www.totalvideoproducts.com, pg 1042

Gallo, Paul E, Vista Color Imaging Inc, 2048 Fulton Rd, Cleveland, OH 44113 *Tel:* 216-651-2830 *Toll Free Tel:* 800-890-0062 *Fax:* 216-651-5004 *E-mail:* info@vistacolorimaging.com *Web Site:* www.vistacolorimaging.com, pg 1059

Galloway, Stephen F, SurgeX, 800 Knightdale Blvd, Suite 121, Knightdale, NC 27545 *Toll Free Tel:* 800-645-9721 (tech & cust support) *Fax:* 919-269-0454 *Web Site:* www.surgex.com, pg 1029

Gallup, Kim, Moxie Media, 1301 Dealers Ave, New Orleans, LA 70123 *Tel:* 504-733-6907 *Toll Free Tel:* 800-346-6943 *Fax:* 504-733-9493 *E-mail:* info@moxiemedia.com *Web Site:* www.moxiemedia.com; www.moxietraining.com, pg 948

Galucki, Jonathan, Playback Now, 3139 Campus Dr, Suite 700, Norcross, GA 30071-1402 *Tel:* 770-447-0616 *Toll Free Tel:* 800-241-7785 *Fax:* 770-447-0543 *E-mail:* sales@playbacknow.com *Web Site:* www.playbacknow.com, pg 977

Galusha, Les, Jones Film Video, 916 W Sixth St, Little Rock, AR 72201 *Tel:* 501-372-1981 *Toll Free Tel:* 800-880-1981 *Fax:* 501-372-4286 *E-mail:* info@jonesfilmvideo.com *Web Site:* www.jonesfilmvideo.com, pg 906

Galvan-Davies, Robin, Grass Valley/Nevada County Chamber of Commerce, 128 E Main St, Grass Valley, CA 95945 *Tel:* 530-273-4667 *Toll Free Tel:* 800-655-4667 *Fax:* 530-272-5440 *E-mail:* info@grassvalleychamber.com *Web Site:* www.grassvalleychamber.com, pg 1093

Games, Greg, Tri-State Visual Products, 885 Ohio Pike, Suite C, Cincinnati, OH 45245 *Tel:* 513-471-7111 *Toll Free Tel:* 800-473-4474 *Fax:* 513-471-7140 *E-mail:* info@trivisual.com *Web Site:* www.trivisual.com, pg 1044

Gann, Jon, Council on International Nontheatrical Events (CINE), 1003 "K" St NW, Suite 208, Washington, DC 20001 *Tel:* 507-400-CINE (400-2463) *E-mail:* info@cine.org *Web Site:* www.cine.org, pg 1081

Gans, Shannon Blake, New Deal Studios, 15392 Cobalt St, Los Angeles, CA 91342 *Tel:* 310-578-9929 *Web Site:* www.newdealstudios.com, pg 955

Gansecki, Cheryl, Ka Io Productions Inc, PO Box 5150, Hilo, HI 96720-1150 *Tel:* 808-959-3885 *Toll Free Tel:* 888-458-7538 *Fax:* 808-959-3885 *E-mail:* lava@volcanovideo.com *Web Site:* www.volcanovideo.com, pg 907

Gant, Aaron, Warner/Chappell Production Music, 1030 16 Ave S, Nashville, TN 37212 *Toll Free Tel:* 888-615-8729 *Fax:* 615-242-2455 *E-mail:* info@warnerchappellpm.com *Web Site:* www.warnerchappellpm.com/615-music, pg 1062

Gantt, Ray, Kino Mountain Productions LLC, 307 S Salem St, No 311, Apex, NC 27502 *Tel:* 919-210-1379 *Web Site:* www.kinomountain.com, pg 911

Gantt, Ray, Unifour Productions Inc, 25 First Ave NE, Suite 105, Hickory, NC 28601 *Tel:* 828-324-1314 *Toll Free Tel:* 888-843-8644 *Fax:* 828-324-1318 *Web Site:* www.uni4.com, pg 1048

Garberson, John, Creative Backstage, 4829 S 36 St, Suite 1, Phoenix, AZ 85040 *Tel:* 480-580-2222 *E-mail:* sales@creativebackstage.com *Web Site:* www.creativebackstage.com, pg 838

Garcia, Alfredo, Sight & Sound Productions, 11193 Saint Johns Industrial Pkwy N, Jacksonville, FL 32246 *Tel:* 904-645-7880 *Toll Free Tel:* 800-339-0846 *Fax:* 904-645-7787 *E-mail:* info@ssav.net *Web Site:* www.ssav.net, pg 1010

Garcia, Art, Extron Electronics, 1025 E Ball Rd, Suite 100, Anaheim, CA 92805-5957 *Tel:* 714-491-1500 *Toll Free Tel:* 800-633-9876 (sales & tech support); 800-633-9873 (order support) *Fax:* 714-491-1517 *E-mail:* sales-usa@extron.com *Web Site:* www.extron.com, pg 864

Garcia, Enrique, Omega Broadcast Group, 817 W Howard Lane, Austin, TX 78753 *Tel:* 512-251-7778 *Fax:* 512-251-8633 *E-mail:* rental@omegabroadcast.com; sales@omegabroadcast.com *Web Site:* www.omegabroadcast.com, pg 962

Garcia, Eric, 48 Windows, 1661 N Lincoln Blvd, Suite 220, Santa Monica, CA 90404 *Tel:* 310-392-9545 *Fax:* 310-392-9445 *E-mail:* ziv@48windows.com *Web Site:* www.48windows.com, pg 871

Garcia, Eric, POP TV, 5069 Maureen Lane, Moorpark, CA 93021-7127 *Tel:* 805-499-8513 *Toll Free Tel:* 800-331-4626 *Fax:* 805-499-8206 *E-mail:* sales@mpo-video.com *Web Site:* www.mpo-video.com, pg 978

Garcia, Jean, Garcia Marketing Inc, 400 Ninth St, Conway, PA 15027-1663 *Tel:* 724-869-0100 *Toll Free Tel:* 800-683-1925 *Fax:* 724-869-1925 *E-mail:* gmavfoto@verizon.net, pg 875

Garcia, Jennifer, Labor Saving Devices Inc, 5678 Eudora St, Commerce City, CO 80022-3809 *Tel:* 303-287-2121 *Toll Free Tel:* 800-648-4714 *Fax:* 303-287-9044 *E-mail:* info@lsdinc.com *Web Site:* www.lsdinc.com, pg 915

Garcia, Jorge W PhD, Professional Advancement Enterprises (PAE), 2182 Saginaw SE, Grand Rapids, MI 49506 *Tel:* 616-956-9443 *Fax:* 616-956-7973 *E-mail:* paeworld@comcast.net *Web Site:* www.paeworld.com, pg 985

Garcia, Manuel, Illuminate Studios, 10900 Ventura Blvd, Studio City, CA 90068 *Tel:* 818-769-4500 *Fax:* 818-769-7150 *Web Site:* illuminatehollywood.com, pg 894

Garcia, Maurice, Emlight Design, 1179 N Eastman Ave, Suite 1, Los Angeles, CA 90063 *Tel:* 323-261-5162 *Toll Free Fax:* 866-728-9164 *E-mail:* service@dimmer.com *Web Site:* www.dimmer.com; www.emlightdesign.com, pg 860

Garcia, Stephen, MRV Communications Inc, 20415 Nordhoff St, Chatsworth, CA 91311 *Tel:* 818-773-0900 *Toll Free Tel:* 800-338-5316 *Fax:* 818-773-0906 *E-mail:* info@mrv.com *Web Site:* www.mrv-corporate.com, pg 948

Garcia, Thomas C, Garcia Marketing Inc, 400 Ninth St, Conway, PA 15027-1663 *Tel:* 724-869-0100 *Toll Free Tel:* 800-683-1925 *Fax:* 724-869-1925 *E-mail:* gmavfoto@verizon.net, pg 875

Gardner, Michael, Gypsum Association, 6525 Belcrest Rd, Suite 480, Hyattsville, MD 20782 *Tel:* 301-277-8686 *Fax:* 301-277-8747 *E-mail:* info@gypsum.org *Web Site:* www.gypsum.org, pg 883

Gardyne, Bob, Jupiter Systems, 31015 Huntwood Ave, Hayward, CA 94544 *Tel:* 510-675-1000 *Fax:* 510-675-1001 *E-mail:* sales@jupiter.com *Web Site:* www.jupiter.com, pg 907

Garey, Guy G, Quality Film & Video, 3321 Main St, Suite B-1, Manchester, MD 21102 *Tel:* 410-785-1920 *E-mail:* quality3321@comcast.net *Web Site:* www.qualityfilmvideo.com, pg 989

Garey, Peter A, Quality Film & Video, 3321 Main St, Suite B-1, Manchester, MD 21102 *Tel:* 410-785-1920 *E-mail:* quality3321@comcast.net *Web Site:* www.qualityfilmvideo.com, pg 988

Garfein, Carolyn, American Association of University Women (AAUW), 1111 16 St NW, Washington, DC 20036 *Tel:* 202-785-7700 *Toll Free Tel:* 800-326-AAUW (326-2289) *Fax:* 202-872-1425 *E-mail:* helpline@aauw.org; connect@aauw.org *Web Site:* www.aauw.org, pg 1076

Garfunkel, Sandy, Ansonia Prompting Inc, 251 W 30 St, Suite 11-FE, New York, NY 10001 *Tel:* 212-594-0500 *Fax:* 212-202-4925 *E-mail:* info@ansoniaprompting.com *Web Site:* www.ansoniaprompting.com, pg 787

Gargiulo, Marty, MRG Productions Inc, 286 Horton Hwy, Mineola, NY 11501 *Tel:* 516-214-6644 *Toll Free Tel:* 866-300-5121 *E-mail:* info@mrgproductions.com *Web Site:* mrgproductions.com, pg 948

Gargiulo, Pablo, Imagine Communications Corp, 3001 Dallas Pkwy, Suite 300, Frisco, TX 75034 *Tel:* 469-803-4900 *Toll Free Tel:* 866-4-IMAGINE (446-2446) *Fax:* 469-803-4899 *E-mail:* insidesales@imaginecommunications.com *Web Site:* www.imaginecommunications.com, pg 896

Garing, Caitlin, HarperAudio, 10 E 53 St, New York, NY 10022 *Tel:* 212-207-7000 *Toll Free Tel:* 800-242-7737 *Fax:* 212-207-2582 *Toll Free Fax:* 800-822-4090 *Web Site:* www.harpercollins.com, pg 885

Garlock, Chris, Egan Visual Inc/Egan TeamBoard Inc, 300 Hanlan Rd, Woodbridge, ON L4L 3P6, Canada *Tel:* 905-851-2826 *Toll Free Tel:* 800-263-2387 (US & CN) *Toll Free Fax:* 888-609-8886 *E-mail:* marketing@egan.com *Web Site:* www.egan.com; www.teamboard.com, pg 858

Garman, Steve, Garman Productions LLC, 2828 NW 58 St, Oklahoma City, OK 73112 *Tel:* 405-254-2500 *Toll Free Tel:* 800-747-5699 *Fax:* 405-254-2507 *E-mail:* info@garman.com *Web Site:* www.garman.com, pg 875

Garnick, Darren, Award Productions, 164 Great Rd, Acton, MA 01720 *Tel:* 978-667-3335 *E-mail:* web@awardproductions.com *Web Site:* www.awardproductions.com, pg 800

Garstick, Jeff, Lowell Manufacturing, 100 Integram Dr, Pacific, MO 63069-3476 *Toll Free Tel:* 800-325-9660 *Toll Free Fax:* 800-456-9355 *E-mail:* sales@lowellmfg.com *Web Site:* www.lowellmfg.com, pg 925

Garten, Eli, Optibase Inc, 931 Benecia Ave, Sunnyvale, CA 94085 *Toll Free Tel:* 800-451-5101 *Fax:* 408-739-1706 *Web Site:* www.optibase.com, pg 964

Garten, Eli, VITEC Multimedia, 931 Benecia, Sunnyvale, CA 94085 *Tel:* 650-230-2400 *Toll Free Tel:* 800-451-5101 *Fax:* 404-320-3132 *E-mail:* info@vitec.com *Web Site:* www.vitec.com, pg 1060

Garvin, Phillip, Colorado Studios, 8269 E 23 Ave, Denver, CO 80238 *Fax:* 303-388-9600 *E-mail:* info@coloradostudios.com *Web Site:* www.coloradostudios.com, pg 832

Garza, Abigail, Alpine Texas Chamber of Commerce, 106 N Third St, Alpine, TX 79830 *Tel:* 432-837-2326 *Toll Free Tel:* 800-561-3712 *Fax:* 432-837-1259 *E-mail:* info@alpinetexas.com *Web Site:* www.alpinetexas.com, pg 1102

Garza, Rick, University of Texas at Austin - Petroleum Extension Service, J J Pickle Research Campus, Petroleum Extension Service, Bldg 2, 10100 Burnet Rd, Austin, TX 78758-4445 *Tel:* 512-471-5940 *Toll Free Tel:* 800-687-4132 *Fax:* 512-471-9410 *Toll Free Fax:* 800-687-7839 *E-mail:* petex@www.utexas.edu *Web Site:* www.utexas.edu/ce/petex, pg 1050

Gasikowski, Hank, Beseler Photo, 2018 W Main St, Stroudsburg, PA 18360 *Toll Free Tel:* 800-237-3537 *Toll Free Fax:* 800-966-4515 *Web Site:* www.beselerphoto.com, pg 805

Gasikowski, Hank, Charles Beseler Co, 2018 W Main St, Stroudsburg, PA 18360 *Toll Free Tel:* 800-237-3537 *Toll Free Fax:* 800-966-4515 *Web Site:* www.beselerphoto.com, pg 824

Gaskell, Michael, MG Studio, 6625 S Valley View Blvd, Suite C-304, Las Vegas, NV 89118 *Tel:* 702-836-3686 *Toll Free Tel:* 866-478-8340 *E-mail:* office@mgstudio.com *Web Site:* mgstudio.com, pg 940

Gasser, John, Adolph Gasser Inc, 181 Second St, San Francisco, CA 94105 *Tel:* 415-495-3852 *Toll Free Tel:* 800-994-2773 *Fax:* 415-543-8510 *E-mail:* agivideo@yahoo.com *Web Site:* www.gasserphoto.com, pg 776

Gaster, Guy, North Carolina Film Office, 301 N Wilmington St, Raleigh, NC 27601 *Tel:* 919-733-9900 *Toll Free Tel:* 866-468-2273 *Fax:* 919-715-0151 *Web Site:* www.ncfilm.com, pg 1101

Gastwirt, Joe, Joe Gastwirt Mastering, 4750 Rhapsody Dr, Oak Park, CA 91377 *Tel:* 310-444-9904 *Web Site:* www.gastwirtmastering.com, pg 875

Gaterman, Ryan, Stanley Film Festival, 1510 York St, 3rd fl, Denver, CO 80206 *Tel:* 970-577-4111 *E-mail:* stanley@denverfilm.org *Web Site:* www.stanleyfilmfest.com, pg 1127

Gates, Katie, Yellow Cat Productions Inc, 505 11 St SE, Washington, DC 20003 *Tel:* 202-543-2221 *E-mail:* yellowcat@yellowcat.com *Web Site:* www.yellowcat.com, pg 1072

Gaughan, Tony, Marketron Broadcast Solutions, 101 Empty Saddle Trail, Hailey, ID 83333 *Tel:* 208-788-6800 *Toll Free Tel:* 888-239-8878 (support); 800-476-7226 *E-mail:* info@wicksbroadcastsolutions.com *Web Site:* www.wicksbroadcastsolutions.com; www.marketron.com, pg 931

Gaukel, Rick, Theatre House Inc, 400 W Third St, Covington, KY 41011-1306 *Tel:* 859-431-2414 *Toll Free Tel:* 800-827-2414 *Fax:* 859-431-1837 *E-mail:* theatreh@one.net; info@theatrehouse.com *Web Site:* www.theatrehouse.com, pg 1038

Gaushell, Charles T, Paradigm Marketing & Creative, 8275 Tournament Dr, Suite 330, Memphis, TN 38125 *Tel:* 901-685-7703 *Fax:* 901-531-8513 *E-mail:* info@2dimes.com *Web Site:* www.2dimes.com, pg 969

Gavin, Rick, Hite Co, 3101 Beale Ave, Altoona, PA 16601 *Tel:* 814-944-6121 *Toll Free Tel:* 800-252-3598 *Fax:* 814-944-3052 *Web Site:* www.hiteco.com, pg 889

Gaydon, Neil, SMART Technologies Inc, 3636 Research Rd NW, Calgary, AB T2L 1Y1, Canada *Tel:* 403-245-0333 *Toll Free Tel:* 888-42-SMART (427-6278 US & Canada) *Fax:* 403-228-2500 *E-mail:* info@smarttech.com *Web Site:* www.smarttech.com, pg 1013

Gazzale, Bob, American Film Institute (AFI), Attn: Facilities Off, 2021 N Western Ave, Los Angeles, CA 90027-1657 *Tel:* 323-856-7600 *Toll Free Tel:* 800-774-4AFI (774-4234 membership) *Fax:* 323-467-4578 *E-mail:* information@afi.com *Web Site:* www.afi.com, pg 1076

Gear, Christy, Visix™ Inc, 230 Scientific Dr, Suite 80, Norcross, GA 30092 *Tel:* 770-446-1416 *Toll Free Tel:* 800-572-4935 *Fax:* 770-448-5724 *E-mail:* info@visix.com *Web Site:* www.visix.com, pg 1059

Gearhart, Chris, Impact Group, 410 Bryant Circle, Bldg F, Ojai, CA 93023 *Toll Free Tel:* 800-675-2200 *E-mail:* sales@impact-group.com *Web Site:* impact-group.com, pg 897

Geary, Bill, Accu-Tech, 11350 Old Roswell Rd, Suite 100, Roswell, GA 30009 *Tel:* 770-740-2240 *Toll Free Tel:* 800-221-4767; 888-222-8832 *Fax:* 770-740-2260 *Web Site:* www.accu-tech.com, pg 773

Gebhart, Kathleen, Association of Biomedical Communications Directors (ABCD), State University of New York at Stony Brook, L3 044 Health Science Ctr, Stony Brook, NY 11794-8030 *Tel:* 631-444-3228 *Fax:* 631-444-3500 *Web Site:* www.abcdirectors.org, pg 1078

Gedden, Jeff, Digital Audio Labs, 1266 Park Rd, Chanhassen, MN 55317 *Tel:* 952-401-7700 *Fax:* 952-401-7725 *E-mail:* sales@digitalaudio.com *Web Site:* www.digitalaudio.com, pg 847

Gedzyk, Mike, Follett Software Co, 1391 Corporate Dr, McHenry, IL 60050-7041 *Tel:* 815-344-8700 *Toll Free Tel:* 800-323-3397 *Fax:* 815-344-8774; 815-578-5575 *Toll Free Fax:* 800-807-3623 (cust serv) *Web Site:* www.follettsoftware.com, pg 871

Geerling, Megan, Phoenix Society for Burn Survivors Inc, 1835 RW Berends Dr SW, Grand Rapids, MI 49519-4955 *Tel:* 616-458-2773 *Toll Free Tel:* 800-888-BURN (888-2876) *Fax:* 616-458-2831 *E-mail:* info@phoenix-society.org *Web Site:* www.phoenix-society.org, pg 974

Gefond, Richard L, IMAX Corp, 2525 Speakman Dr, Mississauga, ON L5K 1B1, Canada *Tel:* 905-403-6500 *Fax:* 905-403-6450 *E-mail:* info@imax.com *Web Site:* www.imax.com, pg 896

Gehring, Ron, Sunfire Communications Inc, 7751 Kingspointe Pkwy, Suite 105, Orlando, FL 32819 *Tel:* 407-226-8226 *Fax:* 407-226-1660 *E-mail:* info@sunfirecommunications.com *Web Site:* www.sunfirecommunications.com, pg 1028

Geist, Ryan, PentaVision Communications Inc, 52303 Emmons Rd, Suite A-4, South Bend, IN 46637 *Tel:* 574-272-8365 *Fax:* 574-272-8366 *Web Site:* pentavision.net, pg 972

Geller, Eric, Elite Video, 209 E Emerson Rd, Lexington, MA 02420 *Tel:* 781-862-6606 *E-mail:* sales@elitevision.com *Web Site:* www.elitevision.com, pg 859

Gellis, Andrew, Cinevest, 21956 Carbon Mesa Rd, Malibu, CA 90265 *Tel:* 310-913-0284 *Web Site:* www.cinevest.com, pg 828

Gelski, Marianne, Oasis Audio, 289 S Main Place, Carol Stream, IL 60188-2425 *Toll Free Tel:* 800-323-2500 *E-mail:* questions@oasisaudio.com *Web Site:* www.oasisaudio.com, pg 960

Genin, Guy, ZGC Inc, 264 Morris Ave, Mountain Lakes, NJ 07046 *Tel:* 973-335-4460 *Fax:* 973-335-4560 *E-mail:* sales@zgc.com *Web Site:* www.zgc.com, pg 1073

Genova, Paul, Boonton Electronics, 25 Eastmans Rd, Parsippany, NJ 07054 *Tel:* 973-386-9696 *Fax:* 973-386-9191 *E-mail:* info@boonton.com *Web Site:* www.boonton.com, pg 811

Gensollen, Gregoire, FilmNation Entertainment, 150 W 22 St, 9th fl, New York, NY 10011 *Web Site:* www.filmnation.com, pg 867

Gentile, Gary, Gary Gentile Productions (GGP), 3 Lehigh Gorge Dr, Jim Thorpe, PA 18229 *Tel:* 252-394-6974 *Web Site:* www.ggentile.com, pg 877

Gentilo, Bob, Right Coast Recording Inc, 349 Chestnut St, Columbia, PA 17512-1259 *Tel:* 717-681-9801 *Fax:* 717-681-9801 *E-mail:* rightcoastrecording@gmail.com *Web Site:* www.rightcoastrecording.com, pg 997

Gentner, Russell, Listen Technologies Corp, 14912 Heritage Crest Way, Bluffdale, UT 84065-4818 *Tel:* 801-233-8992 *Toll Free Tel:* 800-330-0891 *Fax:* 801-233-8995 *E-mail:* info@listentech.com *Web Site:* www.listentech.com, pg 923

Gentzel, Thomas, National School Boards Association (NSBA), 1680 Duke St, Alexandria, VA 22314 *Tel:* 703-838-6722 *Fax:* 703-683-7590 *E-mail:* info@nsba.org *Web Site:* www.nsba.org, pg 1086

Genzel, Michael, JSC Wire & Cable, 7861 Airport Hwy, Pennsauken, NJ 08109 *Tel:* 856-324-2929 *Toll Free Tel:* 800-572-9473 *Fax:* 973-694-8297 *E-mail:* sales@jscwire.com *Web Site:* www.jscwire.com, pg 906

Georg, Ole, OGM Production Music, 6464 Sunset Blvd, Suite 770, Hollywood, CA 90028 *Tel:* 323-461-2701 *Toll Free Tel:* 800-421-4163 (sales) *Fax:* 323-461-1543 *E-mail:* ogmmusic@gmail.com *Web Site:* www.ogmmusic.com, pg 961

George, J Richard, Wespen Audio Visual Co, 101 Riverside Dr, Hawthorn, PA 16230, pg 1063

George, John D, Wespen Audio Visual Co, 101 Riverside Dr, Hawthorn, PA 16230, pg 1063

George, Keith, Gaylord Brothers, PO Box 4901, Syracuse, NY 13221-4901 *Tel:* 315-634-8243 (intl) *Toll Free Tel:* 800-962-9580 (cust serv) *Fax:* 315-453-5030 (intl) *Toll Free Fax:* 800-272-3412 *E-mail:* customerservice@gaylord.com *Web Site:* www.gaylord.com, pg 876

George, Larry, Univenture Inc, 13311 Industrial Pkwy, Marysville, OH 43040 *Tel:* 937-645-4600 *Toll Free Tel:* 877-831-9428 *Fax:* 937-645-4700 *E-mail:* sales@univenture.com; orders@univenture.com *Web Site:* www.univenture.com, pg 1049

George, Peter, Jaguar Distribution Corp, 12711 Ventura Blvd, Suite 300, Studio City, CA 91604 *Tel:* 818-508-3377 *Fax:* 818-508-3340 *Web Site:* www.jaguardc.com, pg 903

George, Tom, Waterworks Acoustics, 1038 44 Ave, Oakland, CA 94601 *Tel:* 510-653-4300 *Fax:* 510-437-9231 *E-mail:* waterworksacoustics@earthlink.net *Web Site:* www.soundpipes.com, pg 1062

Georgitis, Nathan, ARSC Awards for Excellence, c/o Knight Library, 1299 University of Oregon, Eugene, OR 97403-1299 *Tel:* 541-346-1852 *Web Site:* www.arsc-audio.org, pg 1107

Georgitis, Nathan, Association for Recorded Sound Collections Inc (ARSC), c/o Knight Library, 1299 University of Oregon, Eugene, OR 97403-1299 *Web Site:* www.arsc-audio.org, pg 1078

Gerace, Christopher, Bosch Security Systems North America, 130 Perinton Pkwy, Fairport, NY 14450 *Tel:* 585-223-4060 *Toll Free Tel:* 800-289-0096 *Fax:* 585-223-9180 *Web Site:* us.boschsecurity.com, pg 811

Geramian, Sue, MRM Worldwide, 622 Third Ave, New York, NY 10017 *Tel:* 646-865-6230 *E-mail:* info@mrmworldwide.com *Web Site:* www.mrmworldwide.com, pg 948

Gerardi, Bob, Bob Gerardi Music Productions, 160 W 73 St, New York, NY 10023-3012 *Tel:* 212-874-6436, pg 877

Gerbes, Jack, Maryland Film Office, 401 E Pratt St, 14th fl, Baltimore, MD 21202 *Tel:* 410-767-6340 *Toll Free Tel:* 800-333-6632 *Fax:* 410-333-0044 *E-mail:* filminfo@marylandfilm.org *Web Site:* www.marylandfilm.org, pg 1098

Gerding, Bob, The PPS Group, 424 Scott St, Covington, KY 41011 *Tel:* 859-291-5100 *Toll Free Tel:* 800-978-3445 *Fax:* 859-291-5150 *E-mail:* info@theppsgroup.com *Web Site:* www.pps-inc.com; www.theppsgroup.com, pg 980

Germain, Kelly, Giant Screen Cinema Association (GSCA), 624 Holly Springs Rd, Suite 243, Holly Springs, NC 27540 *Tel:* 919-346-1123 *Fax:* 919-573-9100 *E-mail:* info@giantscreencinema.com *Web Site:* www.giantscreencinema.com, pg 1082

Germaine, Derrick, Dake Publishing Inc, 764 Martins Chapel Rd, Lawrenceville, GA 30045 *Toll Free Tel:* 800-241-1239 *Fax:* 770-963-7700 *E-mail:* info@dake.com *Web Site:* www.dake.com, pg 842

German, Greg, Premier™, 251 Wedcor Ave, Wabash, IN 46992 *Tel:* 260-563-0641 *Toll Free Tel:* 800-225-5644 *Fax:* 260-563-4575 *Toll Free Fax:* 800-654-8339 (orders) *E-mail:* info@martinyale.com *Web Site:* www.martinyale.com/premier.aspx, pg 980

Gerovitz, Lee, Clever Cleaver Productions, 11397 Legacy Canyon Place, San Diego, CA 92131 *Tel:* 619-522-6760 *Fax:* 619-522-6763 *E-mail:* info@clevercleaver.com *Web Site:* www.clevercleaver.com, pg 830

Gerrans, Jenny, American Color Imaging (ACI), 715 E 18 St, Cedar Falls, IA 50613 *Tel:* 319-277-3655 *Toll Free Tel:* 800-728-2722 *Fax:* 319-277-6522 *E-mail:* sales@acilab.com *Web Site:* www.acilab.com, pg 784

Gershfield, Jack, ALTINEX Inc, 592 Apollo St, Brea, CA 92821 *Tel:* 714-990-2300 *Toll Free Tel:* 800-ALTINEX (258-4639) *Fax:* 714-990-3303 *E-mail:* sales@altinex.com *Web Site:* www.altinex.com, pg 783

Gerstein, Frank, Westbury National Show Systems Ltd, 772 Warden Ave, Toronto, ON M1L 4T7, Canada *Tel:* 416-752-1371 *Fax:* 416-752-1382 *E-mail:* mail@westbury.com *Web Site:* www.westbury.com, pg 1064

Gerstman, Nancy, Zeitgeist Films Ltd, 247 Centre St, 2nd fl, New York, NY 10013 *Tel:* 212-274-1989 *Fax:* 212-274-1644 *E-mail:* mail@zeitgeistfilms.com *Web Site:* www.zeitgeistfilms.com, pg 1073

Gertz, Paul, Network Entertainment Inc, 23 W Pender St, Suite 290, Vancouver, BC V6B 1R3, Canada *Tel:* 604-739-8825 *Fax:* 604-739-8835 *E-mail:* info@networkentertainment.com *Web Site:* www.networkentertainment.ca, pg 955

Geschke, Dr Charles M, Adobe Systems Inc, 345 Park Ave, San Jose, CA 95110-2704 *Tel:* 408-536-6000 *Fax:* 408-537-6000 *Web Site:* www.adobe.com, pg 776

Gettinger, Daniel, Gettinger Feather Corp, 16 W 36 St, New York, NY 10018 *Tel:* 212-695-9470 *Fax:* 212-695-9471 *E-mail:* gettfeath@aol.com *Web Site:* www.gettingerfeather.com, pg 877

Getty, Barbara, Getty-Dubay Productions, PO Box 91084, Portland, OR 97291-0084 *Tel:* 503-223-7268 (orders) *Toll Free Tel:* 800-777-2844 *Fax:* 503-223-9182 (orders) *E-mail:* info@handwritingsuccess.com; info@allport.com (orders) *Web Site:* www.handwritingsuccess.com; www.allport.com (orders), pg 877

Getty, Mark, Getty Images, 605 Fifth Ave S, Suite 400, Seattle, WA 98104 *Tel:* 206-925-5000 *Toll Free Tel:* 888-888-5889; 800-462-4379 (sales) *Fax:* 206-925-5001 *E-mail:* sales@gettyimages.com *Web Site:* www.gettyimages.com, pg 877

Gewecke, Thomas, Warner Bros Entertainment Inc, 4000 Warner Blvd, Burbank, CA 91522 *Tel:* 818-954-3000 *Fax:* 818-954-4918 *E-mail:* wbsf@warnerbros.com *Web Site:* www.warnerbros.com; studiofacilities.warnerbros.com, pg 1062

Gharaee, Mustapha, Shanix Inc, 40 Worthington Rd, Cranston, RI 02920 *Tel:* 401-941-4222 *Toll Free Tel:* 800-783-2067 *Fax:* 401-941-4333 *E-mail:* info@shanix.com *Web Site:* www.shanix.com, pg 1008

Gianacoplos, Peter, USI Inc, 98 Fort Path Rd, Suite A, Madison, CT 06443 *Tel:* 203-245-8586 *Toll Free Tel:* 800-282-9290 *Fax:* 203-245-8619 *E-mail:* customers@usi-corp.com *Web Site:* www.usi-laminate.com, pg 1051

Giancola, David, Edgewood Studios, Howe Ctr, Unit 12-B, Suite 90, Rutland, VT 05701-4459 *Tel:* 802-773-0510 *Fax:* 802-773-3481 *Web Site:* www.edgewoodstudios.com, pg 857

Giangiuli, Jeffrey E, CALIBRE, Metro Park, 6354 Walker Lane, Alexandria, VA 22310-3252 *Tel:* 703-797-8500 *Toll Free Tel:* 888-CALIBRE (225-4273) *Fax:* 703-797-8501 *E-mail:* info@calibresys.com *Web Site:* www.calibresys.com, pg 817

Giannini, Vincent, WPHL-TV, 5001 Wynnefield Ave, Philadelphia, PA 19131 *Tel:* 215-878-1700 *Fax:* 215-879-7683; 215-877-4912 *E-mail:* feedback@phl17.com *Web Site:* www.phl17.com, pg 1070

Giannone, Ronald, FMP Media Solutions Inc, 1010 Spring Mill Ave, Suite 100, Conshohocken, PA 19428 *Tel:* 610-825-4000 *Toll Free Tel:* 800-346-5071 *Fax:* 610-825-4430 *E-mail:* info@fmpmedia.com *Web Site:* www.fmpmedia.com, pg 870

Gibbons, Ed, Broad Street Inc, 242 W 30 St, 2nd fl, New York, NY 10001 *Tel:* 212-780-5700 *E-mail:* newyork@broadstreet.com *Web Site:* www.broadstreet.com, pg 812

Gibbons, John, Mutual Hardware, 36-27 Vernon Blvd, Long Island City, NY 11106 *Toll Free Tel:* 866-361-2480 *Fax:* 718-786-9591 *E-mail:* info@mutualhardware.com *Web Site:* www.mutualhardware.com, pg 951

Gibbons, Sue, PolyScience, 6600 W Touhy Ave, Niles, IL 60714-4516 *Tel:* 847-647-0611 *Toll Free Tel:* 800-229-7569 *Fax:* 847-647-1155 *E-mail:* sales@polyscience.com *Web Site:* www.polyscience.com, pg 978

Gibbs, David, West Coast Projections Inc, 12463 Rancho Bernardo Rd, No 149, San Diego, CA 92128-2143 *Tel:* 858-674-7334 *E-mail:* wcpinfo@westcoastprojections.com *Web Site:* westcoastprojections.com, pg 1064

Gibbs, Gigi, Fresno County Film Commission, 2220 Tulare St, 8th fl, Fresno, CA 93721 *Tel:* 559-600-4271 *Fax:* 559-600-4549 *Web Site:* www.filmfresno.com, pg 1092

Gibbs, Jerry, Jaguar Productions, PO Box 121014, Nashville, TN 37212-1014 *Tel:* 615-391-4393 (off); 615-390-4161 (cell) *Web Site:* www.jaguarvideoproductions.com, pg 903

Gibbs, Mike, Videorama Industries LLC, 1119 N Hudson Ave, Hollywood, CA 90038 *Tel:* 323-466-7232 *Fax:* 323-466-7228 *Web Site:* www.videorama.com, pg 1057

Gibeau, Frank, Electronic Arts, 209 Redwood Shores Pkwy, Redwood City, CA 94065 *Tel:* 650-628-1500 *Web Site:* www.ea.com, pg 859

Gibioterra, Jim, TapeStockOnline.com, 602 N Cypress St, Orange, CA 92867 *Tel:* 310-352-4230 *Toll Free Tel:* 888-322-TAPE (322-8273) *Fax:* 310-352-4233 *E-mail:* sales@tapestockonline.com *Web Site:* www.tapestockonline.com, pg 1032

Gibson, Chip, Random House Children's Books, 1745 Broadway, 10th fl, New York, NY 10019 *Tel:* 212-782-9000 *Web Site:* www.randomhousekids.com, pg 991

Gibson, Daniel D, TV One Multimedia Solutions, 2791 Circleport Dr, Erlanger, KY 41018 *Tel:* 859-282-7303 *Toll Free Tel:* 800-721-4044 *Fax:* 859-282-8225 *E-mail:* sales@tvone.com; info@tvone.com *Web Site:* www.tvone.com, pg 1046

Gibson, Jack, Arizona Public Media, 1423 E University, MLB67, Rm 223, Tucson, AZ 85719 *Tel:* 520-621-5828; 520-621-5836 (sales) *Fax:* 520-621-3360 *Web Site:* www.azpm.org, pg 790

Gibson, Oscar, Mardi Gras Costume Shop, 5895 N Granite Reef Rd, Scottsdale, AZ 85250 *Tel:* 480-948-4030 *Fax:* 480-948-0754 *E-mail:* info@mardigrascostumeshop.com *Web Site:* mardigrascostumeshop.com, pg 931

Giella, Linda, Blue Sky Stock Footage, PO Box 177, Santa Fe, NM 87504-0177 *Tel:* 310-859-4709 *Toll Free Tel:* 877-992-5477 *Fax:* 310-823-0924 *E-mail:* sales@blueskyfootage.com *Web Site:* www.blueskyfootage.com, pg 810

Gifford, Carlyle, Avekta Productions Inc, One Rock Place, Yonkers, NY 10705 *Tel:* 914-378-8000 *Web Site:* avekta.com, pg 798

Gilbert, Brad, People Productions, 1737 15 St, Suite 200, Boulder, CO 80302 *Tel:* 303-449-6086 *Fax:* 303-449-9526 *E-mail:* info@peopleproductions.com *Web Site:* www.peopleproductions.com, pg 972

Gilbert, Chuck, Imagine Communications Corp, 3001 Dallas Pkwy, Suite 300, Frisco, TX 75034 *Tel:* 469-803-4900 *Toll Free Tel:* 866-4-IMAGINE (446-2446) *Fax:* 469-803-4899 *E-mail:* insidesales@imaginecommunications.com *Web Site:* www.imaginecommunications.com, pg 896

Gilbert, Gay, Illuma Studios, 16601 N 90 St, Scottsdale, AZ 85260 *Tel:* 480-222-4396 *E-mail:* info@illumastudios.com *Web Site:* www.illumastudios.com, pg 894

Gilbert, Kathleen, Vancouver Island South Film & Media Commission, 100-852 Fort St, Victoria, BC V8W 1H8, Canada *Tel:* 250-386-3976 *Toll Free Tel:* 888-537-3456 *Fax:* 250-386-3967 *E-mail:* admin@filmvictoria.com *Web Site:* www.filmvictoria.com, pg 1105

Gilbert, Marcy, International Digital Centre, 216 E 45 St, 7th fl, New York, NY 10017 *Tel:* 212-581-3940 *Fax:* 212-581-3979 *E-mail:* info@idcdigital.com *Web Site:* www.idcdigital.com, pg 901

Gildersleeve, Mark, WSI, 400 Minuteman Rd, Andover, MA 01810 *Tel:* 978-983-6300 *Fax:* 978-983-6400 *Web Site:* www.wsi.com, pg 1070

Giles, Betty H, Charles A Hulcher Co Inc, 909 "G" St, Hampton, VA 23661 *Tel:* 757-245-6190 *Fax:* 757-245-2882 *E-mail:* hulcher@hulchercamera.com *Web Site:* www.hulchercamera.com, pg 892

Giles, Nicole, Greater Philadelphia Film Office, One Parkway Bldg, 11th fl, 1515 Arch St, Philadelphia, PA 19102 *Tel:* 215-686-2668 *Fax:* 215-686-3659 *E-mail:* mail@film.org *Web Site:* www.film.org, pg 1102

Gilfillan, Carl, Media Consultants Inc, 3908 E Valley Ct, Raleigh, NC 27606 *Tel:* 919-821-2190 *Toll Free Tel:* 800-560-7379 *Toll Free Fax:* 866-881-9331 *Web Site:* www.mediaconsultants.com, pg 936

Gilgar, Stephanie, Method Studios, 730 Arizona Ave, Santa Monica, CA 90401 *Tel:* 310-434-6500 *Web Site:* www.methodstudios.com, pg 939

Gill, Jim, Jim Gill Music Inc, PO Box 2263, Oak Park, IL 60303-2263 *Tel:* 708-763-9864 *Fax:* 708-763-9888 *Web Site:* www.jimgill.com, pg 878

Gillen, Arlene, The Great Southern Studios, 15221 NE 21 Ave, North Miami Beach, FL 33162 *Tel:* 305-944-2464 *Fax:* 305-944-9920 *E-mail:* info@gssmiami.com *Web Site:* www.greatsouthernstudios.com, pg 882

Gillenwater, Chad, AVI-SPL, 6301 Benjamin Rd, Suite 101, Tampa, FL 33634 *Tel:* 813-884-7168 *Toll Free Tel:* 866-708-5034; 800-282-6733; 866-925-8298 (cust serv); 866-559-8197 (sales) *Fax:* 813-882-9508 *E-mail:* questions@avispl.com; sales@avispl.com; customerservice@avispl.com *Web Site:* www.avispl.com, pg 798

Gillespie, Brett, Band Pro Film & Digital Inc, 3403 W Pacific Ave, Burbank, CA 91505 *Tel:* 818-841-9655 *Toll Free Tel:* 888-BANDPRO (226-3776) *Fax:* 818-841-7649 *Web Site:* www.bandpro.com, pg 802

Gilliland, Tom, BeachWare Inc, 4980 N Campbell Ave, Tucson, AZ 85718 *Tel:* 520-577-8945 *Fax:* 520-577-8945 *Web Site:* www.beachware.com, pg 804

Gillio, Joseph, Casio America Inc, 570 Mount Pleasant Ave, Dover, NJ 07801 *Tel:* 973-361-5400 *Fax:* 973-537-8929 *E-mail:* projectors@casio.com *Web Site:* www.casioprojector.com, pg 820

Gillman, Bob, Videotex Systems Inc, 10255 Miller Rd, Dallas, TX 75238 *Tel:* 972-231-9200 *Toll Free Tel:* 800-88-VIDEO (888-4336) *Fax:* 972-231-2420 *E-mail:* info@videotexsystems.com *Web Site:* www.videotexsystems.com, pg 1057

Gillman, Elliott, Audio Visual Dynamics®, 8 Budd St, Morristown, NJ 07960 *Tel:* 973-993-8500 *Fax:* 973-984-0644 *Web Site:* www.avdusa.com, pg 795

Gillman, Joan Hogan, Time Warner Cable, 60 Columbus Circle, 17th fl, New York, NY 10023 *Tel:* 212-364-8200 *Web Site:* www.timewarnercable.com, pg 1040

Gillota, Bernadette, Ohio Independent Film Festival, 6516 Detroit Ave, Suite 3, Cleveland, OH 44102-3057 *Tel:* 216-926-6166 *E-mail:* ohiofilms@yahoo.com *Web Site:* www.ohiofilms.com, pg 1123

Gillota, Bernadette, Ohio Independent Screenplay Awards, 6516 Detroit Ave, Suite 3, Cleveland, OH 44102-3057 *Tel:* 216-926-6166 *E-mail:* ohiofilms@yahoo.com *Web Site:* www.ohiofilms.com, pg 1123

Gilstrap, Mike, Dog & Pony Productions Inc, 8928 "L" St, Omaha, NE 68127 *Tel:* 402-391-7691 *Fax:* 402-341-2751 *Web Site:* dogandponyinc.com, pg 850

Gilstrap, Susan, Dog & Pony Productions Inc, 8928 "L" St, Omaha, NE 68127 *Tel:* 402-391-7691 *Fax:* 402-341-2751 *Web Site:* dogandponyinc.com, pg 850

Gimbel, Kenneth, Voice & Video Rentals, 4909 Ruffner St, San Diego, CA 92111 *Tel:* 858-560-5000 *Toll Free Tel:* 800-638-8878 *Fax:* 858-560-9900 *Web Site:* www.voiceandvideo.com, pg 1060

Gimm, Kirsten, EPIX Inc, 381 Lexington Dr, Buffalo Grove, IL 60089 *Tel:* 847-465-1818 *Fax:* 847-465-1919 *E-mail:* epix@epixinc.com *Web Site:* epixinc.com, pg 862

Ginnane, Antony I, IFM World Releasing Inc, 1328 E Palmer Ave, Glendale, CA 91205 *Tel:* 818-243-4976 *Fax:* 818-550-9728 *E-mail:* contact@ifmfilm.com *Web Site:* www.ifmfilm.com, pg 894

Ginsberg, Ian, Audio Network US Inc, 48 W 25 St, 10th fl, New York, NY 10010 *Tel:* 646-688-4320 *E-mail:* nyoffice@audionetwork.com *Web Site:* us.audionetwork.com, pg 794

Ginsburg, Fred, Film TV Sound, PO Box 950207, Mission Hills, CA 91395-0207 *Tel:* 818-231-1038 *Fax:* 818-892-9236 *E-mail:* editorial@filmtvsound.com; eqe-media@filmtvsound.com *Web Site:* www.filmtvsound.com, pg 867

Ginther, Jane, Equiservices Publishing, 4343 Garfoot Rd, Cross Plains, WI 53528 *Tel:* 608-798-4910 *E-mail:* info@equipub.com *Web Site:* www.equipub.com, pg 862

Gionson, T. Ilihia, Big Island Film Office, 25 Aupuni St, Hilo, HI 96720 *Tel:* 808-961-8369 *Fax:* 808-935-1205 *E-mail:* film@filmbigisland.com *Web Site:* www.filmbigisland.com, pg 1097

Giordano, Don, Entel Systems Inc, 230 W Parkway, Pompton Plains, NJ 07444 *Tel:* 201-447-2000 *Toll Free Tel:* 888-914-7100 *Fax:* 201-447-2880 *E-mail:* service@entelsystems.com *Web Site:* www.entelsystems.com, pg 861

Giordano, Julie, Stanley Supply & Services Inc, 335 Willow St, North Andover, MA 01845-5995 *Tel:* 978-682-9844 *Toll Free Tel:* 800-225-5370 (sales) *Toll Free Fax:* 800-743-8141 *E-mail:* sales@stanleyworks.com *Web Site:* www.stanleysupplyservices.com, pg 1023

Giordano, Vincenzo, Custom Media Environments, 299 Duffy Ave, Hicksville, NY 11801 *Tel:* 516-586-3600 *Toll Free Tel:* 800-80-SOUND (807-6863) *Fax:* 516-586-3487 *E-mail:* info@custommediaenvironments.com; sales@custommediaenvironments.com *Web Site:* custommediaenvironments.com, pg 841

Girard, Frederick, Sennheiser (Canada) Inc, 221 ave Labrosse, Pointe Claire, QC H9R 1A3, Canada *Tel:* 514-426-3013 *Toll Free Tel:* 800-463-1006 *Fax:* 514-426-3953 *Toll Free Fax:* 800-463-3013 *E-mail:* info@sennheiser.ca *Web Site:* www.sennheiser.ca, pg 1006

Girard, Nadine, Sennheiser (Canada) Inc, 221 ave Labrosse, Pointe Claire, QC H9R 1A3, Canada *Tel:* 514-426-3013 *Toll Free Tel:* 800-463-1006 *Fax:* 514-426-3953 *Toll Free Fax:* 800-463-3013 *E-mail:* info@sennheiser.ca *Web Site:* www.sennheiser.ca, pg 1006

Giraudi, Patrick, VirtualMix, 311 W Third St, Suite 2914, Carson City, NV 89703 *Tel:* 818-209-6176 *E-mail:* virtualmixpost@gmail.com *Web Site:* www.virtualmix.com, pg 1058

Gire, Dann, Chicago Film Critics Association, 155 E Algonquin Rd, Arlington Heights, IL 60006 *Tel:* 847-427-4530 *Fax:* 847-427-1301 *E-mail:* critics@chicagofilmcritics.org *Web Site:* www.chicagofilmcritics.org, pg 1080

Giroir, Ryan, Setcom Corp™, 3019 Alvin De Vane Blvd, Suite 560, Austin, TX 78741 *Tel:* 650-965-8020 *Fax:* 650-965-1193 *E-mail:* info@setcomcorp.com; sales@setcomcorp.com *Web Site:* www.setcomcorp.com, pg 1007

Girot, Kaly Minh-Nguyen, Sand Box Studio, 555 Minnesota St, San Francisco, CA 94107 *Tel:* 415-550-8732 *E-mail:* inquiries@sandboxstudio.com *Web Site:* www.sandboxstudio.com, pg 1002

Gish, Ross, Big Event Productions LLC, 77 13 Ave NE, Studio 101, Minneapolis, MN 55413 *Tel:* 612-623-7800 *Fax:* 612-455-0450 *Web Site:* www.bigeventpros.com, pg 807

Gitow, Andi, United Nations Multimedia Resources Unit, c/o Audio Library, UN Dept of Public Information, Rm S-1046 & S-1083, New York, NY 10017

Tel: 212-963-9268; 212-963-4501 *Fax:* 212-963-4501 *E-mail:* avlibrary@un.org *Web Site:* www.unmultimedia.org, pg 1048

Gittens, Anthony, Washington DC International Film Festival, PO Box 21396, Washington, DC 20009-0896 *Tel:* 202-274-5782 *Fax:* 202-274-6690 *E-mail:* filmfestdc@filmfestdc.org *Web Site:* www.filmfestdc.org, pg 1129

Givens, John, Small World Productions Inc, 140 Lakeside Ave, Suite 200, Seattle, WA 98122 *Tel:* 206-329-7167 *Toll Free Tel:* 800-866-7425 (orders) *E-mail:* info@travelsmallworld.com *Web Site:* www.smarttravels.tv, pg 1013

Givner-Klein, Nan, TeleTime Productions, 100 Atlantic Ave, Lynbrook, NY 11563 *Tel:* 516-255-8383 *E-mail:* info@teletimevideo.com *Web Site:* www.teletimevideo.com, pg 1036

Glanz, Mark, Glanz Technologies Inc, 687 NE 124 St, North Miami, FL 33161 *Tel:* 305-893-1269 *Fax:* 305-899-8526 *E-mail:* mglanz@glanztech.com *Web Site:* www.glanztechnologies.com, pg 878

Glasband, Martin, Equi=Tech Corp, PO Box 249, Selma, OR 97538-0249 *Toll Free Tel:* 877-378-4832 *Fax:* 541-787-8740 *E-mail:* sales@equitech.com *Web Site:* www.equitech.com, pg 862

Glasofer, David, Image Up, 176 Main St, Metuchen, NJ 08840 *Tel:* 732-549-1845 *Web Site:* www.imageup.com, pg 895

Glass, Elliot, Crossroads Video, 65 Church Rd, Sherman, CT 06784-1334 *Tel:* 860-350-0010 *Toll Free Tel:* 866-746-7111 (orders) *Fax:* 860-350-0010 *E-mail:* info@crossroadsvideo.com; crossroadsvideo@charter.net *Web Site:* www.crossroadsvideo.com, pg 840

Glass, Jamie, Welocalize, 241 E Fourth St, Suite 207, Frederick, MD 21701 *Tel:* 301-668-0330 *Toll Free Tel:* 800-370-9515 *Fax:* 301-668-0335 *E-mail:* info@welocalize.com *Web Site:* www.welocalize.com, pg 1063

Glass, Murray, Em Gee Film Library, 13502 Erwin St, Van Nuys, CA 91401 *Tel:* 818-997-0410, pg 860

Glass, Murray, Glenn Photo Supply, 13502 Erwin St, Van Nuys, CA 91401 *Tel:* 818-997-0410 *Web Site:* www.emgee.freeyellow.com, pg 878

Glass, Murray, Glenn Video Vistas Ltd, 13502 Erwin St, Van Nuys, CA 91401 *Tel:* 818-997-0410 *Web Site:* www.emgee.freeyellow.com, pg 878

Glasser, David, Airshow Mastering, 3063 Sterling Circle, Suite 3, Boulder, CO 80301 *Tel:* 303-247-9035 *Toll Free Tel:* 888-545-9035 *Toll Free Fax:* 888-545-9035 *E-mail:* studio@airshowmastering.com *Web Site:* www.airshowmastering.com, pg 779

Glaysher, Monica, Moving Picture, 748 N Victoria Park Rd, Fort Lauderdale, FL 33304 *Tel:* 954-522-1361 *Toll Free Tel:* 800-800-1361 *Fax:* 954-523-1361 *E-mail:* info@movingpicture.com *Web Site:* www.movingpicture.com, pg 947

Glaza, Ken, Digi Sign Design LLC, 28533 Greenfield Rd, Suite 2, Southfield, MI 48076 *Tel:* 248-569-5422 *Web Site:* www.digisigndesign.com, pg 847

Glaza, Ken, K&R All Media Productions Inc, 28533 Greenfield, Southfield, MI 48076 *Tel:* 248-557-8276 *Toll Free Tel:* 888-802-0420 *Web Site:* www.knr.net, pg 908

Glaza, Kenneth, K&R's Recording Studios Inc, 28533 Greenfield, Southfield, MI 48076 *Tel:* 248-557-8276 *E-mail:* recordav@knr.net *Web Site:* www.knr.net, pg 908

Glaza, Kenneth, Michigan Recording Arts Institute & Technologies, 28533 Greenfield, Southfield, MI 48076 *Tel:* 248-569-5422 *Toll Free Tel:* 888-802-0402 *Web Site:* mirecordingarts.com, pg 941

Glazier, Mitch, Recording Industry Association of America (RIAA), 1025 "F" St NW, 10th fl, Washington, DC 20004 *Tel:* 202-775-0101 *Web Site:* www.riaa.com, pg 1088

Glazier, Mitch, The RIAA® Gold® & Platinum® Awards, 1025 "F" St NW, 10th fl, Washington, DC 20004 *Tel:* 202-775-0101 *Web Site:* www.riaa.com, pg 1125

Gleadall, Robin, YAP Films, 96 Spadina Ave, Suite 205, Toronto, ON M5V 2J6, Canada *Tel:* 416-504-3662 *Fax:* 416-504-3667 *E-mail:* thedog@yapfilms.com *Web Site:* www.yapfilms.com, pg 1072

Glenday, Lucy, Moxie Media, 1301 Dealers Ave, New Orleans, LA 70123 *Tel:* 504-733-6907 *Toll Free Tel:* 800-346-6943 *Fax:* 504-733-9493 *E-mail:* info@moxiemedia.com *Web Site:* www.moxiemedia.com; www.moxietraining.com, pg 948

Glenday, Martin, Moxie Media, 1301 Dealers Ave, New Orleans, LA 70123 *Tel:* 504-733-6907 *Toll Free Tel:* 800-346-6943 *Fax:* 504-733-9493 *E-mail:* info@moxiemedia.com *Web Site:* www.moxiemedia.com; www.moxietraining.com, pg 948

Gloor, Storm, Music & Entertainment Industry Educators Association (MEIEA), 1900 Belmont Blvd, Nashville, TN 37212-3758 *Tel:* 615-460-6946 *E-mail:* office@meiea.org *Web Site:* www.meiea.org, pg 1084

Gluck, Brian, National Audio-Visual Supply, 80 Little Falls Rd, Fairfield, NJ 07004 *Toll Free Tel:* 800-222-0109 *Toll Free Fax:* 800-628-1329 *E-mail:* info@nationalavsupply.com *Web Site:* www.nationalaudiovisualsupply.com, pg 952

Gluckman, Kristen, The Mobius Advertising Awards, 713 S Pacific Coast Hwy, Suite A, Redondo Beach, CA 90277-4233 *Tel:* 310-540-0959 *Fax:* 310-316-8905 *E-mail:* mobiusinfo@mobiusawards.com *Web Site:* www.mobiusawards.com, pg 1120

Gluckman, Kristen, US International Film & Video Festival Awards, 713 S Pacific Coast Hwy, Suite A, Redondo Beach, CA 90277-4233 *Tel:* 310-540-0959 *Fax:* 310-316-8905 *E-mail:* filmfestinfo@filmfestawards.com *Web Site:* www.filmfestawards.com, pg 1128

Gluckman, Lee W Jr, The Mobius Advertising Awards, 713 S Pacific Coast Hwy, Suite A, Redondo Beach, CA 90277-4233 *Tel:* 310-540-0959 *Fax:* 310-316-8905 *E-mail:* mobiusinfo@mobiusawards.com *Web Site:* www.mobiusawards.com, pg 1120

Gluckman, Lee W Jr, Producers Group Ltd, 713 S Pacific Coast Hwy, Suite B, Redondo Beach, CA 90277-4233 *Tel:* 310-316-0481 *Fax:* 310-316-1482 *Web Site:* www.producers-group.tv, pg 983

Gluckman, Lee W Jr, US International Film & Video Festival Awards, 713 S Pacific Coast Hwy, Suite A, Redondo Beach, CA 90277-4233 *Tel:* 310-540-0959 *Fax:* 310-316-8905 *E-mail:* filmfestinfo@filmfestawards.com *Web Site:* www.filmfestawards.com, pg 1128

Glusic, Robert, Wilderness Video, 888 Beswick Way, Ashland, OR 97520 *Tel:* 541-488-9363 *Web Site:* www.wildernessvideo.com, pg 1066

Gobey, Jennifer, Essex Television Group Inc, 7 Vista Dr, Old Lyme, CT 06371 *Tel:* 860-434-7200 *Fax:* 860-434-7210 *E-mail:* contact@essextelevision.com *Web Site:* www.essextelevision.com, pg 862

Goddard, Bob, Goddard Design Co, 51 Nassau Ave, Brooklyn, NY 11222 *Tel:* 718-599-0170 *Fax:* 718-599-0172 *E-mail:* sales@goddarddesign.com *Web Site:* www.goddarddesign.com, pg 880

Goddard, Doug, Gamma Imaging, 222 N DesPlaines St, Chicago, IL 60661 *Tel:* 312-441-0091 *Toll Free Tel:* 877-441-4830 *Fax:* 312-441-0092 *E-mail:* digital@gammaimaging.com *Web Site:* gammaimaging.com, pg 875

Goddard, Jeffery, TVA Productions, 3950 Vantage Ave, Studio City, CA 91604 *Tel:* 818-505-8300 *Toll Free Tel:* 888-322-4296 *E-mail:* info@tvaproductions.com *Web Site:* www.tvaproductions.com, pg 1046

Godfrey, Linda C, Comm-Arts, 2512 E 71 St, Suite A, Tulsa, OK 74136 *Tel:* 918-493-5700 *Fax:* 918-493-3526 *E-mail:* info@comm-arts.com *Web Site:* www.comm-arts.com, pg 832

Godfrey, Stephen, FutureVideo, 28202 Cabot Rd, Suite 300, Laguna Niguel, CA 92677 *Tel:* 949-363-1286 *Toll Free Fax:* 866-261-1686 *E-mail:* sales@futurevideo.com *Web Site:* www.futurevideo.com, pg 874

Godfrey, Will Daniel, The Godfrey Group Inc, 4102 S Miami Blvd, Durham, NC 27703 *Tel:* 919-544-6504 *Toll Free Tel:* 800-789-9394 *Fax:* 919-544-6729 *E-mail:* sales@godfreygroup.com *Web Site:* www.godfreygroup.com, pg 880

Goedde, Jennifer, Calculated Industries Inc, 4840 Hytech Dr, Carson City, NV 89706 *Tel:* 775-885-4900 *Toll Free Tel:* 800-854-8075 *Fax:* 775-885-4949 *E-mail:* info@calculated.com *Web Site:* www.calculated.com, pg 816

Goelzhauser, Nicola, The WPA Film Library, 16101 S 108 Ave, Orland Park, IL 60467 *Tel:* 708-460-0555 *Toll Free Tel:* 800-323-0442 *Fax:* 708-460-0187 *E-mail:* sales@wpafilmlibrary.com *Web Site:* www.wpafilmlibrary.com, pg 1070

Goertz, Elena, American Society of Media Photographers Inc (ASMP), 150 N Second St, Philadelphia, PA 19016 *Tel:* 215-451-2767 *Fax:* 215-451-0880 *E-mail:* info@asmp.org *Web Site:* www.asmp.org, pg 1077

Goff, Brian, Innocinema, 10130 Perimeter Pkwy, Suite 180, Charlotte, NC 28216 *Tel:* 704-665-1945 *Fax:* 704-665-1956 *E-mail:* info@innocinema.com; sales@innocinema.com *Web Site:* www.innocinema.com, pg 898

Goff, Daryl, Innocinema, 10130 Perimeter Pkwy, Suite 180, Charlotte, NC 28216 *Tel:* 704-665-1945 *Fax:* 704-665-1956 *E-mail:* info@innocinema.com; sales@innocinema.com *Web Site:* www.innocinema.com, pg 898

Goff, Justin, Innocinema, 10130 Perimeter Pkwy, Suite 180, Charlotte, NC 28216 *Tel:* 704-665-1945 *Fax:* 704-665-1956 *E-mail:* info@innocinema.com; sales@innocinema.com *Web Site:* www.innocinema.com, pg 898

Goforth-Hanak, Yvonne, KEF Media, 1161 Concord Rd, Smyrna, GA 30080 *Tel:* 404-605-0009 *Toll Free Tel:* 866-219-2477 *Fax:* 404-605-0639 *Web Site:* www.kefmedia.com, pg 909

Goicoechea, Barbara, ACT Productions, 407 Lincoln Rd, Suite 302, Miami Beach, FL 33139 *Tel:* 305-538-3809 *Fax:* 305-538-3814 *E-mail:* info@actproductions.com *Web Site:* www.actproductions.com, pg 775

Goiffon, Rene, Harmonia Mundi USA, 1117 Chestnut St, Burbank, CA 91506 *Tel:* 818-333-1500 *Fax:* 818-333-1502 *E-mail:* info-usa@harmoniamundi.com *Web Site:* www.harmoniamundi.com, pg 885

Goin, Carma, In-Plant Printing & Mailing Association, 155 S Sam Barr Dr, Suite 203, Kearney, MO 64060 *Tel:* 816-903-4762 *E-mail:* ipmainfo@ipma.org *Web Site:* www.ipma.org, pg 1082

Goins, Faith, Michigan Film Office, 300 N Washington Sq, 4th fl, Lansing, MI 48913 *Tel:* 517-373-3456 *Toll Free Tel:* 800-477-FILM (477-3456) *Fax:* 517-241-0867 *E-mail:* mfo@michigan.org *Web Site:* www.michiganfilmoffice.org, pg 1098

Goitiandia, Ray, Kino Flo Lighting Systems, 2840 N Hollywood Way, Burbank, CA 91505 *Tel:* 818-767-6528 *Fax:* 818-252-0290 (rental); 818-767-7517 (sales) *E-mail:* sales@kinoflo.com *Web Site:* www.kinoflo.com, pg 911

Goldberg, Bruce, Bruce Goldberg Inc, 5354 Quakertown Ave, Woodland Hills, CA 91364 *Tel:* 818-713-8190 *Toll Free Tel:* 800-527-6248 *Fax:* 818-704-9189 *E-mail:* drbg@sbcglobal.net *Web Site:* www.drbrucegoldberg.com, pg 880

Goldberg, David H, Lee Dan® Communications Inc, 155 Adams Ave, Hauppauge, NY 11788-3699 *Tel:* 631-231-1414 *Toll Free Tel:* 800-231-1414 *Fax:* 631-231-1498 *E-mail:* info@leedan.com *Web Site:* www.leedan.com, pg 918

Goldberg, Jon, Blueyed Pictures Inc, 8950 W Olympic Blvd, Suite 324, Beverly Hills, CA 90211 *Tel:* 310-295-0848 *Fax:* 310-295-0260 *E-mail:* la@blueyedpictures.com *Web Site:* www.blueyedpictures.com, pg 810

Goldberg, Mark, Spectrum Productions, 565 Pinedale Dr, Annapolis, MD 21401 *Web Site:* www.markgoldberg.com, pg 1021

Goldberg, Mike, IMP Digital Studios, 120 Rte 17N, Paramus, NJ 07652 *Tel:* 201-261-3959 *Fax:* 201-261-3959 *E-mail:* info@impdigital.us *Web Site:* impdigitalstudios.com, pg 896

Goldberg, Neil, Heavy Melody, 307 Seventh Ave, Suite 1203, New York, NY 10001 *Tel:* 212-675-9585 *Fax:* 212-675-9565 *E-mail:* contact_hm@heavymelodymusic.com (studio inquiries) *Web Site:* www.heavymelodymusic.com, pg 887

Goldberg, Ron, Manhattan Production Music Inc, 1650 Broadway, Suite 900, New York, NY 10019 *Tel:* 212-333-5766 *Fax:* 212-262-0814 *E-mail:* info@mpmmusic.com *Web Site:* www.mpmmusic.com, pg 930

Golden, Barbara, St Augustine, Ponte Vedra & The Beaches Visitors and Convention Bureau, 29 Old Mission Ave, St Augustine, FL 32084 *Tel:* 904-829-1711 *Toll Free Tel:* 800-653-2489 *Web Site:* www.floridashistoriccoast.com, pg 1096

Golden, Eric, Luminys Systems Corp, 11961 Sherman Rd, North Hollywood, CA 91605 *Tel:* 323-461-6361 *Toll Free Tel:* 800-321-3644 *Fax:* 323-461-3067 *E-mail:* info@luminyscorp.com *Web Site:* www.luminyscorp.com, pg 926

Goldenberg, Nancy, Chicago International Children's Film Festival, 1517 W Fullerton Ave, Chicago, IL 60614 *Tel:* 773-281-9075 (ext 3011) *Fax:* 773-929-0266 *E-mail:* kids@facets.org *Web Site:* www.cicff.org; www.facets.org, pg 1111

Goldin, Laurence, Aurora Films, 324 E Dowling Rd, Suite 4, Anchorage, AK 99518 *Tel:* 907-258-4686 *Fax:* 907-561-6622 *E-mail:* aurorafilms@acsalaska.net, pg 797

Golding, Emily, Anchor Audio Inc, 5931 Darwin Ct, Carlsbad, CA 92008 *Tel:* 760-827-7100 *Toll Free Tel:* 800-262-4671 *Fax:* 760-827-7105 *E-mail:* sales@anchoraudio.com *Web Site:* www.anchoraudio.com, pg 786

Goldman, Eric, Ergo Media Inc, 668 American Legion Dr, Teaneck, NJ 07666 *Tel:* 201-692-0404 *Fax:* 201-692-0663 *E-mail:* info@jewishvideo.com *Web Site:* www.jewishvideo.com; www.ergomedia.com, pg 862

Goldman, Jack, Technisphere Corp, 134 W 26 St, Ground fl, New York, NY 10001 *Tel:* 212-777-5100 *Toll Free Tel:* 800-343-9500 *E-mail:* info@technisphere.com *Web Site:* www.technispherecorp.com, pg 1034

Goldsmith, Karl, Rochester/Finger Lakes Film & Video Office, 45 East Ave, Suite 400, Rochester, NY 14604-2294 *Tel:* 585-279-8308 *Fax:* 585-232-4822 *Web Site:* www.filmrochester.org, pg 1100

Goldstein, Holly, Thread Marketing Group, 4635 W Alexis Rd, Toledo, OH 43623-1005 *Tel:* 419-887-6801 *Toll Free Tel:* 800-397-0126 *Fax:* 419-887-6802 *E-mail:* contact@experiencethread.com *Web Site:* www.experiencethread.com, pg 1039

Goldstein, Jeremy, Navitar Inc, 200 Commerce Dr, Rochester, NY 14623 *Tel:* 585-359-4000 *Toll Free Tel:* 800-828-6778 *Fax:* 585-359-4999 *E-mail:* info@navitar.com *Web Site:* www.navitar.com, pg 953

Goldstein, Jonathan, Snell, 3519 Pacific Ave, Burbank, CA 91505 *Tel:* 818-556-2616 *Fax:* 818-556-2626 *E-mail:* americas@snellgroup.com *Web Site:* www.snellgroup.com, pg 1014

Goldstein, Julian, Navitar Inc, 200 Commerce Dr, Rochester, NY 14623 *Tel:* 585-359-4000 *Toll Free Tel:* 800-828-6778 *Fax:* 585-359-4999 *E-mail:* info@navitar.com *Web Site:* www.navitar.com, pg 953

Goldstein, Robert, Maryland Sound International Holding Co LLC, 4900 Wetheredsville Rd, Baltimore, MD 21207 *Tel:* 410-448-1400 *Toll Free Tel:* 800-76SOUND (767-6863) *Fax:* 410-448-1467 *E-mail:* martha@msihc.com *Web Site:* www.marylandsound.com, pg 933

Goldstein, Samuel, B&H Photo & Video Pro Audio, 420 Ninth Ave, New York, NY 10001 *Tel:* 212-444-5000; 212-444-6615 *Toll Free Tel:* 800-606-6969 *Fax:* 212-239-7770 *Toll Free Fax:* 800-947-7008 *Web Site:* www.bhphotovideo.com, pg 802

Goldstein, Sheldon, National Audio-Visual Supply, 80 Little Falls Rd, Fairfield, NJ 07004 *Toll Free Tel:* 800-222-0109 *Toll Free Fax:* 800-628-1329 *E-mail:* info@nationalavsupply.com *Web Site:* www.nationalaudiovisualsupply.com, pg 952

Goldstein, Shelly, Alltec Stores, a Vcom IMC Company, 80 Little Falls Rd, Fairfield, NJ 07004 *Toll Free Tel:* 800-637-3181 *Toll Free Fax:* 800-965-7836 *E-mail:* sales@alltecstores.com *Web Site:* www.alltecstores.com, pg 782

Goldstein, Shelly, VCom International Multimedia Corp, 80 Little Falls Rd, Fairfield, NJ 07004 *Toll Free Tel:* 800-572-6373 *E-mail:* info@vcomimc.com *Web Site:* www.vcomimc.com, pg 1052

Goldstein, Stu, The DubHouse, 404 SE 15 St, Fort Lauderdale, FL 33316 *Tel:* 954-524-3658 *Toll Free Tel:* 877-900-DUBS (900-3827) *Fax:* 954-522-1905 *Web Site:* www.thedubhouse.net, pg 853

Goldworth, Philip, Pacific Light Studios, 265 Caspian Dr, Sunnyvale, CA 94089 *Tel:* 408-541-1800 *Web Site:* www.pacificlightstudios.com, pg 967

Golesh, John, Goldberg Brothers Inc, 8000 E 40 Ave, Denver, CO 80207 *Tel:* 303-321-1099 *Fax:* 303-388-0749 *E-mail:* reelservice@goldbergbrothers.com *Web Site:* www.goldbergbrothers.com, pg 880

Goli, Kristine, Tasman Group Pacific Rim, 4850 Gregg Rd, Pico Rivera, CA 90660 *Tel:* 562-695-8877 *Toll Free Tel:* 888-355-8889 *Fax:* 562-908-3912 *Web Site:* www.tasmangrouppr.com, pg 1032

Golombek, Fabio, FJ Productions Inc, 14900 Ventura Blvd, Suite 350, Sherman Oaks, CA 91403-3465 *Tel:* 818-788-0153 *Fax:* 818-788-0186 *Web Site:* www.fjproductions.com, pg 869

Golson, Eva H, Mobile Film Office, 164 Saint Emanuel St, Mobile, AL 36602 *Tel:* 251-438-7102 *Fax:* 251-438-7104 *Web Site:* www.mobilefilmoffice.com, pg 1091

Gomer, Allison, Fantasy Studios, 2600 Tenth St, Berkeley, CA 94710 *Tel:* 510-486-2038 *Fax:* 510-486-2248 *Web Site:* www.fantasystudios.com, pg 865

Gomez, Donna, Starlite Productions, 9 Whittendale Dr, Moorestown, NJ 08057 *Tel:* 856-780-8000 *Toll Free Tel:* 800-738-7400 *Fax:* 856-780-8001 *E-mail:* info@starlite.com *Web Site:* www.starlite.com, pg 1024

Gomez, Emilio, Sierra Automated Systems, 2821 Burton Ave, Burbank, CA 91504 *Tel:* 818-840-6749 *Fax:* 818-840-6751 *E-mail:* sales@sasaudio.com; marketing@sasaudio.com *Web Site:* www.sasaudio.com, pg 1010

Gomez, Gus, Starlite Productions, 9 Whittendale Dr, Moorestown, NJ 08057 *Tel:* 856-780-8000 *Toll Free Tel:* 800-738-7400 *Fax:* 856-780-8001 *E-mail:* info@starlite.com *Web Site:* www.starlite.com, pg 1024

Gong, Tony, Olden Camera & Lens Co Inc, 1263 Broadway, 4th fl, New York, NY 10001-3593 *Tel:* 212-725-1234 *Fax:* 212-725-1325, pg 962

Gonos, George, Leader Instruments Corp, 6484 Commerce Dr, Cypress, CA 90630 *Tel:* 714-527-9300 *Toll Free Tel:* 800-645-5104 *Fax:* 714-527-7490 *E-mail:* sales@leaderusa.com *Web Site:* www.leaderusa.com, pg 917

Gonzalez, Alex, Techni-Lux Inc, 10900 Palmbay Dr, Orlando, FL 32824 *Tel:* 407-857-8770 *Fax:* 407-857-8771 *E-mail:* sales@techni-lux.com *Web Site:* www.techni-lux.com, pg 1033

Gonzalez, Diana, Society for Imaging Science and Technology (IS&T), 7003 Kilworth Lane, Springfield, VA 22151 *Tel:* 703-642-9090 *Fax:* 703-642-9094 *E-mail:* info@imaging.org *Web Site:* www.imaging.org, pg 1089

Gonzalez, Jacqueline, New York Emmy Awards, 1375 Broadway, Suite 2103, New York, NY 10018 *Tel:* 212-459-3630 *Fax:* 212-459-9772 *Web Site:* www.nyemmys.org, pg 1122

Gonzalez, Lou, Quad Recording Studios, 346 Jersey Ave, Greenwood Lake, NY 10925 *Tel:* 845-477-0338 *Web Site:* www.quadstudios.com, pg 988

Gooden, Jim, Charleston International Film Festival (CIFF), 915 Folly Rd, No 78, Charleston, SC 29412 *Tel:* 843-817-1617 *E-mail:* info@charlestoniff.org *Web Site:* charlestoniff.org, pg 1111

Gooding, Kristina, Live Spark Inc, 700 Raymond Ave, Suite 100, St Paul, MN 55114 *Tel:* 651-289-7375 *E-mail:* info@live-spark.com *Web Site:* www.live-spark.com, pg 923

Goodman, Daniel, Goodman Associates Inc, 718 S 22 St, Philadelphia, PA 19146 *Tel:* 215-546-1448 *E-mail:* goodman@histories.com, pg 880

Goodman, Jeff, Producers Library, 10832 Chandler Blvd, North Hollywood, CA 91601 *Tel:* 818-752-9097 *Toll Free Tel:* 800-944-2135 *Fax:* 818-752-9196 *E-mail:* research@producerslibrary.com *Web Site:* www.producerslibrary.com, pg 983

Goodman, Marcie, Cleveland International Film Festival, 2510 Market Ave, Cleveland, OH 44113-3434 *Tel:* 216-623-3456 *Fax:* 216-623-0103 *Web Site:* www.clevelandfilm.org, pg 1112

Goodman, Robert, Goodman Associates Inc, 718 S 22 St, Philadelphia, PA 19146 *Tel:* 215-546-1448 *E-mail:* goodman@histories.com, pg 880

Goodman, Ron, SpaceCam, 31111 Via Colinas, Suite 202, Westlake Village, CA 91362 *Tel:* 818-889-6060 *Fax:* 818-889-6062 *E-mail:* rentals@spacecam.com *Web Site:* spacecam.com, pg 1019

Goodman, Scott, Samson Technologies Corp, 45 Gilpin Ave, Hauppauge, NY 11788-4723 *Tel:* 631-784-2200 *Fax:* 631-784-2201 *E-mail:* info@samsontech.com *Web Site:* www.samsontech.com, pg 1002

Goodman, Will, Guidance Associates Inc Center for Humanities, 31 Pine View Rd, Mount Kisco, NY 10549 *Tel:* 914-666-4100 *Toll Free Tel:* 800-431-1242 *Fax:* 914-666-5319 *Web Site:* www.guidanceassociates.com, pg 883

Goodnight, Emily, The House Studios, 325 Second Ave W, Seattle, WA 98119 *Tel:* 206-218-6810 *E-mail:* book@thehousestudios.com *Web Site:* thehousestudios.com, pg 891

Goodnight, Jim, SAS Institute Inc, 100 SAS Campus Dr, Cary, NC 27513-2414 *Tel:* 919-677-8000 *Toll Free Tel:* 800-727-0025 *Fax:* 919-677-4444 *Web Site:* www.sas.com, pg 1002

Goodson, Kara, Photographic Society of America® (PSA®), 3000 United Founders Blvd, Suite 103, Oklahoma City, OK 73112 *Tel:* 405-843-1437 *Toll Free Tel:* 855-PSA-INFO (772-4636) *Fax:* 405-843-1438 *E-mail:* hq@psa-photo.org *Web Site:* www.psa-photo.org, pg 1087

Goodwin, Crystal, Corinth Films Inc, 3117 Bursonville Rd, Riegelsville, PA 18077 *Tel:* 610-346-7446 *Fax:* 610-346-6345 *E-mail:* sales@corinthfilms.com *Web Site:* www.corinthreleasing.com; www.corinthfilms.com, pg 836

Goodwin, Randy, PRI Productions, 1819 Kings Ave, Jacksonville, FL 32207 *Tel:* 904-398-8179 *Fax:* 904-398-1569 *E-mail:* generalmailbox@priproductions.com *Web Site:* www.priproductions.com, pg 981

Goodwyn, Bill, Discovery Education - Silver Spring, One Discovery Place, Silver Spring, MD 20910 *Toll Free Tel:* 800-323-9084 *Fax:* 847-328-6706 *Web Site:* discoveryeducation.com, pg 848

Goral, Mike, Pan African Film & Arts Festival, 6820 La Tijera Blvd, Suite 200, Los Angeles, CA 90045 *Tel:* 310-337-4737 *Fax:* 310-337-4736 *E-mail:* info@paff.org *Web Site:* www.paff.org, pg 1123

Gordon, Betty, DW Electrochemicals Ltd, 3-97 Newkirk Rd N, Richmond Hill, ON L4C 3G4, Canada *Tel:* 905-508-7500 *Fax:* 905-508-7502 *E-mail:* dwel@stabilant.com *Web Site:* www.stabilant.com, pg 854

Gordon, Clayton, Illuminating Engineering Society (IES), 120 Wall St, 17th fl, New York, NY 10005-4001 *Tel:* 212-248-5000 *Fax:* 212-248-5017; 212-248-5018 *E-mail:* ies@ies.org *Web Site:* www.ies.org, pg 1082

Gordon, Gregory, Pyramind Studios, 880 Folsom St, San Francisco, CA 94107 *Tel:* 415-896-9800 *Toll Free Tel:* 888-378-6463 *Fax:* 415-896-5943 *E-mail:* news@pyramind.com *Web Site:* www.pyramind.com, pg 988

Gordon, John T, Gordon Productions Inc, 1730 Pacheco St, San Francisco, CA 94116 *Tel:* 415-776-7484 *Web Site:* www.gpvideo.com, pg 880

Gordon, Lynne Thomas, American Health Information Management Association (AHIMA), 233 N Michigan Ave, 21st fl, Chicago, IL 60601-5809 *Tel:* 312-233-1100 *Toll Free Tel:* 800-335-5535 *Fax:* 312-233-1090; 312-233-1500 (orders) *E-mail:* info@ahima.org *Web Site:* www.ahima.org, pg 1076

Gordon, Marc, Otto Nemenz International Inc, 870 N Vine St, Los Angeles, CA 90038 *Tel:* 323-469-2774 *Fax:* 323-469-1217 *E-mail:* info@ottonemenz.com *Web Site:* www.ottonemenz.com, pg 954

Gordon, Nancy, HAVE Inc, 309 Power Ave, Hudson, NY 12534 *Tel:* 518-828-2000 *Toll Free Tel:* 888-999-HAVE (999-4283) *Fax:* 518-828-2008 *E-mail:* pro_sales@haveinc.com; have@haveinc.com *Web Site:* www.haveinc.com, pg 886

Gorel, Everett, South Coast Film & Video, 5234 Elm St, Houston, TX 77081 *Tel:* 713-661-3550 *Toll Free Tel:* 800-229-3550 *Fax:* 713-661-4357 *E-mail:* info@scfilmvideo.com *Web Site:* www.scfilmvideo.com, pg 1019

Gorelick, Steven, New Jersey Motion Picture & Television Commission, 153 Halsey St, 5th fl, Newark, NJ 07102-2807 *Tel:* 973-648-6279 *Fax:* 973-648-7350 *E-mail:* njfilm@njfilm.org *Web Site:* www.njfilm.org, pg 1100

Gorman, Barret, Crescent/Stonco, 200 Franklin Square Dr, Somerset, NJ 08873 *Toll Free Tel:* 800-334-2212 *Web Site:* www.crescent-stonco.com/led; www.csgreenlightingsolutions.com, pg 839

Gorman, Laurie, Wisconsin Public Television, 821 University Ave, Madison, WI 53706 *Tel:* 608-263-2121 *Toll Free Tel:* 800-422-9707 *Fax:* 608-263-9763 *E-mail:* comments@wpt.org *Web Site:* www.wpt.org, pg 1068

Gorman, Roberta, Society of Motion Picture & Television Engineers (SMPTE), 3 Barker Ave, 5th fl, White Plains, NY 10601 *Tel:* 914-761-1100 *Fax:* 914-761-3115 *E-mail:* membership@smpte.org *Web Site:* www.smpte.org, pg 1089

Gorski, Gary, Tele-Measurements Inc, 145 Main Ave, Clifton, NJ 07014 *Tel:* 973-473-8822 *Toll Free Tel:* 800-223-0052 (ext 207) *Fax:* 973-473-0521 *E-mail:* contact@tele-measurements.com *Web Site:* www.tele-measurements.com, pg 1036

Gorsline, Russell, Rex, 610 SW 17 Ave, Portland, OR 97205 *Tel:* 503-238-4525 *E-mail:* info@rexpost.com *Web Site:* www.rexpost.com, pg 995

Gorum, Larry, Medcom Inc, 6060 Phyllis Dr, Cypress, CA 90630-5243 *Tel:* 714-891-1443 *Toll Free Tel:* 800-877-1443; 800-541-0253 *Fax:* 714-891-3140 *E-mail:* customerservice@medcominc.com *Web Site:* www.medcominc.com, pg 936

Gosnell, Linda, Scholastic Canada Ltd, 175 Hillmount Rd, Markham, ON L6C 1Z7, Canada *Tel:* 905-887-7323 *Toll Free Tel:* 800-268-3860 *Fax:* 905-887-1131 *Toll Free Fax:* 800-387-4944 *E-mail:* custserv@scholastic.ca *Web Site:* www.scholastic.ca, pg 1004

Goss, Carol, IAI Video, 33 Lancaster St, Cherry Valley, NY 13320 *Tel:* 646-696-5645 *E-mail:* iai@improvart.com *Web Site:* www.improvart.com, pg 893

Goss-Bley, A I, IAI Video, 33 Lancaster St, Cherry Valley, NY 13320 *Tel:* 646-696-5645 *E-mail:* iai@improvart.com *Web Site:* www.improvart.com, pg 893

Gottlieb, Carl, Writers Guild of America, West (WGAW), 7000 W Third St, Los Angeles, CA 90048 *Tel:* 323-951-4000 *Toll Free Tel:* 800-548-4532 *Fax:* 323-782-4800 *Web Site:* www.wga.org, pg 1090

Gotzen-Berg, Ken, Kanab/Kane County Film Commission, Kane County Utah Off of Tourism, 78 S 100 E, Kanab, UT 84741 *Tel:* 435-644-5033 *Toll Free Tel:* 800-733-5263 *Fax:* 435-644-5923 *E-mail:* filmcomm@xpressweb.com *Web Site:* www.kaneutah.com, pg 1103

Gougeon, Olivier, Ulysses Travel Guides Inc, 4176 Rue St-Denis, Montreal, QC H2W 2M5, Canada *Tel:* 514-843-9882 *Fax:* 514-843-9448 *E-mail:* info@ulysse.ca; st-denis@ulysse.ca *Web Site:* www.ulysse.ca (French); www.ulyssesguides.com (English), pg 1048

Gougerchian, Abbie, OnLine Power Inc, 5701 Smithway St, Commerce, CA 90040 *Tel:* 323-721-5017 *Toll Free Tel:* 800-227-8899 *Fax:* 323-721-3929 *E-mail:* sales@onlinepower.com *Web Site:* www.onlinepower.com, pg 963

Gouhin, Patrick, The International Society of Automation (ISA), 67 T W Alexander Dr, Research Triangle Park, NC 27709 *Tel:* 919-549-8411 *Fax:* 919-549-8288 *E-mail:* info@isa.org *Web Site:* www.isa.org, pg 901

Gould, Matthew, Illuma Studios, 16601 N 90 St, Scottsdale, AZ 85260 *Tel:* 480-222-4396 *E-mail:* info@illumastudios.com *Web Site:* www.illumastudios.com, pg 894

Goulden, Randy, Golden Sheaf Awards, 49 Smith St E, Yorkton, SK S3N 0H4, Canada *Tel:* 306-782-7077 *Fax:* 306-782-1550 *E-mail:* info@yorktonfilm.com *Web Site:* yorktonfilm.com/golden-sheaf-awards/, pg 1116

Goulden, Randy, Yorkton Film Festival (YFF), 49 Smith St E, Yorkton, SK S3N 0H4, Canada *Tel:* 306-782-7077 *Fax:* 306-782-1550 *E-mail:* info@yorktonfilm.com *Web Site:* yorktonfilm.com, pg 1130

Gourrier, Gabby, Method Studios, 730 Arizona Ave, Santa Monica, CA 90401 *Tel:* 310-434-6500 *Web Site:* www.methodstudios.com, pg 939

Gowanlock, Wayne, Edcom Multimedia Products, 2386 Main St, Unit 1, London, ON N6P 1A9, Canada *Tel:* 519-652-3533 *Toll Free Tel:* 800-265-1069 *Fax:* 519-652-5045 *E-mail:* sales-l@edcom.ca; info@edcom.ca *Web Site:* www.edcom.ca, pg 856

Goyette, Steve, South Coast Film & Video, 5234 Elm St, Houston, TX 77081 *Tel:* 713-661-3550 *Toll Free Tel:* 800-229-3550 *Fax:* 713-661-4357 *E-mail:* info@scfilmvideo.com *Web Site:* www.scfilmvideo.com, pg 1019

Grabeau, Kenneth, Monarch Instrument, 15 Columbia Dr, Amherst, NH 03031-2305 *Tel:* 603-883-3390 *Toll Free Tel:* 800-999-3390 *Fax:* 603-886-3300 *E-mail:* sales@monarchinstrument.com *Web Site:* www.monarchinstrument.com, pg 945

Grabulosa, Albert, Estiluz Inc, 235 Moonachie Rd, Moonachie, NJ 07074 *Tel:* 201-641-1997 *Fax:* 201-641-2092 *E-mail:* estiluzinc@estiluz.com *Web Site:* www.estiluzusa.com, pg 862

Gradzki, Walt, Radio Visions, PO Box 4732, Toms River, NJ 08754-4732 *Tel:* 732-240-3119 *E-mail:* sales@radiovisions.com *Web Site:* www.radiovisions.com, pg 990

Graff, Wes, University of Vermont, Instructional Television Dept, 234 Rowell Bldg, Burlington, VT 05405 *Tel:* 802-656-2927 *Fax:* 802-656-8816 *E-mail:* video@zoo.uvm.edu *Web Site:* www.uvm.edu; www.uvm.edu/~video, pg 1050

Grafinger, Paul, Advanced AV, 208 Carter Dr, Suite 7, West Chester, PA 19382 *Toll Free Tel:* 877-696-7700 *Fax:* 610-692-8421 *E-mail:* sales@advancedav.com *Web Site:* www.advancedav.com, pg 777

Graham, Andrew S, New Jersey Motion Picture & Television Commission, 153 Halsey St, 5th fl, Newark, NJ 07102-2807 *Tel:* 973-648-6279 *Fax:* 973-648-7350 *E-mail:* njfilm@njfilm.org *Web Site:* www.njfilm.org, pg 1100

Graham, Jim, Hollywood Lights Inc, 5251 SE McLoughlin Blvd, Portland, OR 97202-4836 *Tel:* 503-232-9001; 503-232-8855 *Toll Free Tel:* 800-826-9881 *Fax:* 503-517-8686 *E-mail:* portland@hollywoodlights.biz *Web Site:* www.hollywoodlights.biz, pg 890

Graham, Mark, LOUD Technologies Inc, 16220 Wood-Red Rd NE, Woodinville, WA 98072 *Tel:* 425-487-4333; 415-892-6500 *Toll Free Tel:* 866-858-LTEC (858-5832) *Fax:* 425-487-4337 *Web Site:* www.mackie.com; www.loudtechinc.com, pg 925

Graham, Ron, Freeman, 1600 Viceroy, Suite 100, Dallas, TX 75235 *Tel:* 214-445-1000 *Fax:* 214-445-0200 *Web Site:* www.freemanco.com, pg 872

Graham-White, Sean, SGW Teleprompter Solutions Inc, 844 Eighth Ave, La Grange, IL 60525-2949 *Tel:* 773-402-0105 *Fax:* 708-482-9159 *E-mail:* teleprompter@sbcglobal.net *Web Site:* telepromptersolutions.com, pg 1007

Grande, Mario, WESCAM Inc, 649 N Service Rd W, Burlington, ON L7P 5B9, Canada *Tel:* 905-633-4000 *Toll Free Tel:* 800-668-4355 *Fax:* 905-633-4100 *E-mail:* sales.wescam@l-3com.com *Web Site:* www.wescam.com, pg 1063

Grandestaff, Lauren, IRE Annual Awards for Investigative Reporting, Missouri School of Journalism, 141 Neff Annex, Columbia, MO 65211 *Tel:* 573-882-2042 *Fax:* 573-882-5431 *E-mail:* rescntr@ire.org; info@ire.org *Web Site:* www.ire.org/awards, pg 1117

Grandinetti, Andre, Wired 4 Sound Inc, PO Box 683, Clifton, NJ 07012-0683 *Tel:* 973-773-2565 *Toll Free Fax:* 888-453-8819 *E-mail:* info@wired4sound.com *Web Site:* www.wired4sound.com, pg 1068

Graney, Brian, Black Film Center Archive, Indiana University, Wells Library, Rm 044, 1320 E Tenth St, Bloomington, IN 47405 *Tel:* 812-855-6041 *Fax:* 812-856-5832 *E-mail:* bfca@indiana.edu *Web Site:* www.indiana.edu/~bfca, pg 808

Grant, Dave, KAKE-TV, 1500 N West St, Wichita, KS 67203-1323 *Tel:* 316-943-4221; 316-946-1314 (sales) *Fax:* 316-943-5493 *Web Site:* kake.com, pg 907

Grant, Sheila, Christie Lites, 6990 Lake Ellenor Dr, Orlando, FL 32809 *Tel:* 407-856-0016 *Fax:* 407-856-0765 *Web Site:* www.christielites.com, pg 825

Grant, Trudy, Sullivan Home Entertainment, 110 Davenport Rd, Toronto, ON M5R 3R3, Canada *Tel:* 416-921-7177 *Fax:* 416-921-7538 *E-mail:* inquire@sullivan-ent.com *Web Site:* www.sullivanmovies.com, pg 1028

Grant, V A, Norman N Axelrod Associates, 445 E 86 St, New York, NY 10028 *Tel:* 212-741-6302 *E-mail:* naxelrod@axelrodassociates.com *Web Site:* www.axelrodassociates.com, pg 800

Grass, Randall, Shanachie Entertainment Corp, 37 E Clinton St, Newton, NJ 07860 *Tel:* 973-579-7763 *Web Site:* shanachie.com, pg 1008

Grasser, Kerri, Marblemedia, 74 Fraser Ave, Suite 100, Toronto, ON M6K 3E1, Canada *Tel:* 416-646-2711 *E-mail:* connect@marblemedia.com *Web Site:* www.marblemedia.com, pg 930

Graves, Cindy, The BD Co, PO Box 2048, Chandler, AZ 85225-2048 *Tel:* 480-632-1160 *Toll Free Tel:* 800-704-3072 *Fax:* 480-632-1163 *E-mail:* info@bdcompany.com *Web Site:* www.bdcompany.com, pg 804

Graves, Sandra, Band Pro Film & Digital Inc, 3403 W Pacific Ave, Burbank, CA 91505 *Tel:* 818-841-9655 *Toll Free Tel:* 888-BANDPRO (226-3776) *Fax:* 818-841-7649 *Web Site:* www.bandpro.com, pg 802

Graves, Thomas P, Iowa Cable & Telecommunications Association (ICTA), 2024 NW 92 Ct, Suite 6, Clive, IA 50325 *Tel:* 515-276-0006 *E-mail:* info@iacable.com *Web Site:* www.iacable.com, pg 1084

Gravitt, Grant H Jr, Tel-Air Interests Inc, 2040 Sherman St, Hollywood, FL 33020 *Tel:* 954-924-4949 *Fax:* 954-924-4980 *E-mail:* telair@aol.com *Web Site:* www.telairint.com, pg 1035

Gravitt, Mary Lou, Tel-Air Interests Inc, 2040 Sherman St, Hollywood, FL 33020 *Tel:* 954-924-4949 *Fax:* 954-924-4980 *E-mail:* telair@aol.com *Web Site:* www.telairint.com, pg 1035

Gray, Chris, PowerTechnology Southeast Inc, 634 State Rd 44, Leesburg, FL 34748 *Tel:* 352-365-2777 *Toll Free Tel:* 800-760-0027 *Fax:* 352-787-5545 *E-mail:* powertech@powertech-gen.com *Web Site:* www.powertech-gen.com, pg 979

Graydon, Bob, MQ Power Corp, 1800 Waters Ridge Dr, Suite 500, Lewisville, TX 75057 *Tel:* 972-459-5650 *Toll Free Tel:* 800-883-2551 *Fax:* 972-315-1847 *E-mail:* mqpowersales@multiquip.com *Web Site:* www.multiquip.com, pg 948

Graziano, Steven, Veritech Corp, 80 Denslow Rd, East Longmeadow, MA 01028 *Tel:* 413-525-3368 *Toll Free Tel:* 800-525-5912 *Fax:* 413-525-7449 *E-mail:* info@veritechmedia.com *Web Site:* www.veritechmedia.com, pg 1053

Greaves, Louise, William Greaves Productions Inc, 475 W 57 St, No 17A, New York, NY 10019 *Toll Free Tel:* 800-874-8314 *Fax:* 212-315-0027 *Web Site:* www.williamgreaves.com, pg 882

Greblo, Joe, Stunt Wings Adventure Sports Talent & Equipment, 12623 Gridley St, Sylmar, CA 91342 *Tel:* 818-367-2430; 818-353-5580 (home); 818-266-0874 (cell) *Fax:* 818-367-5363 *E-mail:* stuntwings@me.com *Web Site:* www.stuntwings.com, pg 1027

Greco, Tom, Location Camera Ltd, 300 Pennsylvania Ave, Oreland, PA 19075 *Tel:* 215-576-5600 *Fax:* 215-576-6022 *E-mail:* mail@locationcamera.com *Web Site:* www.locationcamera.com, pg 924

Green, Allen, Visual Departures Ltd, 48 Sheffield Business Park, Ashley Falls, MA 01222 *Tel:* 413-229-2272 *Toll Free Tel:* 800-628-2003 *Fax:* 413-229-2274 *E-mail:* sales@visualdepartures.com *Web Site:* www.visualdepartures.com, pg 1059

Green, Deborah, Xplor® International, 24156 State Rd 54, Suite 4, Lutz, FL 33559 *Tel:* 813-949-6170 *Toll Free Tel:* 800-669-7567 *Fax:* 813-949-9977 *E-mail:* info@xplor.org *Web Site:* www.xplor.org, pg 1090

Green, John P, Advanced AV, 208 Carter Dr, Suite 7, West Chester, PA 19382 *Toll Free Tel:* 877-696-7700 *Fax:* 610-692-8421 *E-mail:* sales@advancedav.com *Web Site:* www.advancedav.com, pg 777

Green, Kirk, Ferrari Color®, 1550 S Gladiola St, Salt Lake City, UT 84104 *Tel:* 801-355-4124 *Toll Free Tel:* 888-312-6567 *Fax:* 801-355-4152 *E-mail:* info.slc@ferraricolor.com *Web Site:* www.ferraricolor.com, pg 866

Green, Morgan, Women in Film Foundation Film Finishing Fund, 6100 Wilshire Blvd, Suite 710, Los Angeles, CA 90048 *Tel:* 323-935-2211 *Fax:* 323-935-2212 *E-mail:* info@wif.org *Web Site:* www.wif.org, pg 1129

Greenberg, Bob, R/GA, 350 W 39 St, New York, NY 10018 *Tel:* 212-946-4000 *Fax:* 212-946-4010 *E-mail:* web@rga.com *Web Site:* www.rga.com, pg 990

Greenberg, Rick, Cornerstone Media Productions Inc, 41 Bramhall St, Georgetown, DE 19947 *Tel:* 302-855-9380 *Web Site:* www.cornerstonemedia.com, pg 836

Greenberg, Robert, G&G Technologies Inc, 280 N Midland Ave, Bldg F, Suite 202, Saddle Brook, NJ 07663 *Tel:* 201-791-1400 *Toll Free Tel:* 800-422-2920 *Fax:* 201-791-1401 *E-mail:* staff@ggvideo.com *Web Site:* www.ggvideo.com, pg 875

Greenblatt, Andrew, Philadelphia Film Festival, 1600 N Fifth St, Philadelphia, PA 19122 *Tel:* 267-239-2941 *E-mail:* info@filmadelphia.org *Web Site:* www.filmadelphia.org, pg 1123

Greene, Barb, Video Service of America Inc (VSA), 6929 Seward Ave, Lincoln, NE 68507 *Tel:* 402-467-3668 *Toll Free Tel:* 800-888-2140 (orders) *Fax:* 402-325-8033 *E-mail:* sales@vsa1.com *Web Site:* www.vsa1.com, pg 1056

Greene, Brighid, Dance on Camera Festival, 252 Java St, Suite 333, Brooklyn, NY 11222 *Tel:* 347-505-8649 *E-mail:* info@dancefilms.org *Web Site:* www.dancefilms.org, pg 1113

Greene, Dolly, Los Angeles Center Studios, 450 S Bixel St, Los Angeles, CA 90017 *Tel:* 213-534-3000 *E-mail:* productionservices@lacenterstudios.com *Web Site:* lacenterstudios.com, pg 924

Greene, Don, Institute of Industrial Engineers (IIE), 3577 Parkway Lane, Suite 200, Norcross, GA 30092 *Tel:* 770-449-0460 *Toll Free Tel:* 800-494-0460 *Fax:* 770-441-3295 *E-mail:* cs@iienet.org *Web Site:* www.iienet2.org, pg 1083

Greene, Ida PhD, People Skills International, 2910 Baily Ave, San Diego, CA 92105 *Tel:* 619-262-9951 *Fax:* 619-262-0505 *Web Site:* www.idagreene.com, pg 972

Greene, Mark, ITA Audio Visual Solutions, 2162 Dana Ave & I-71, Cincinnati, OH 45207 *Tel:* 513-631-7000 *Toll Free Tel:* 800-899-8877 *Fax:* 513-631-3290; 513-631-8877 *E-mail:* csr@ita.com *Web Site:* www.ita.com, pg 902

Greene, Patti, ZGC Inc, 264 Morris Ave, Mountain Lakes, NJ 07046 *Tel:* 973-335-4460 *Fax:* 973-335-4560 *E-mail:* sales@zgc.com *Web Site:* www.zgc.com, pg 1073

Greenlee, Lisa, Tecplot Inc, 3535 Factoria Blvd SE, Suite 550, Bellevue, WA 98006 *Tel:* 425-653-1200; 425-653-9393 (tech support) *Toll Free Tel:* 800-763-7005 (orders) *E-mail:* info@tecplot.com; sales@tecplot.com *Web Site:* www.tecplot.com, pg 1035

Greenstein, Josh, Paramount Pictures Corporation, 5555 Melrose Ave, Los Angeles, CA 90038 *Tel:* 323-956-8398 *Web Site:* www.paramount.com, pg 969

Greenway, Iain, The Brand Gallery, 701 W Putnam Ave, Greenwich, CT 06830 *Tel:* 203-422-3900 *Fax:* 203-531-1394 *Web Site:* www.thebrandgallery.com, pg 812

Greese, Henry, Schneider Optics Inc, 285 Oser Ave, Hauppauge, NY 11788 *Tel:* 631-761-5000 *Toll Free Tel:* 800-645-7239 *Fax:* 631-761-5090 *E-mail:* info@schneideroptics.com *Web Site:* www.schneideroptics.com, pg 1004

Grefe, Richard, AIGA, the professional association for design, 164 Fifth Ave, New York, NY 10010 *Tel:* 212-807-1990 *Toll Free Tel:* 800-548-1634 *Fax:* 212-807-1799 *E-mail:* general@aiga.org *Web Site:* www.aiga.org, pg 1075

Gregoire, Michael P, CA Technologies, 520 Madison Ave, 22nd fl, New York, NY 10022 *Toll Free Tel:* 800-225-5224 *Web Site:* www.ca.com, pg 816

Gregory, Bob, Allstar Show Industries Inc, 10331 176 St, Edmonton, AB T5S 2E4, Canada *Tel:* 780-486-4000 *Toll Free Tel:* 800-663-4063 (CN & US) *Fax:* 780-414-5724 *E-mail:* allsales@allstar-show.com *Web Site:* www.allstar-show.com, pg 782

Gregory, Jay D, SmartPros Ltd, 12 Skyline Dr, Hawthorne, NY 10532-2133 *Tel:* 914-345-2620 *Fax:* 914-345-2603 *E-mail:* admin@smartpros.com *Web Site:* www.smartpros.com, pg 1014

Gregory, John, University of Maine Audio Visual Services, 28 Shibles Hall, Orono, ME 04469 *Tel:* 207-581-2500; 207-581-2516 *Web Site:* www.umaine.edu/it/divisions/av, pg 1049

Gregory, Steven, New England Technology Group Inc (NETG), One Davenport St, Cambridge, MA 02140 *Tel:* 617-864-5551 *Fax:* 520-844-5551 *E-mail:* teamnetg@netgworld.com *Web Site:* netgworld.com, pg 955

Gregory, Trey, ECG Productions, 120 Interstate N Pkwy SE, Suite 435, Atlanta, GA 30339 *Tel:* 678-855-5169 *E-mail:* info@ecgprod.com *Web Site:* www.ecgprod.com, pg 856

Grenci, David, Tape World, 309 Wagner Ave, Butler, PA 16001 *Tel:* 724-283-8621 *Toll Free Tel:* 800-245-6000; 800-322-8273 *Fax:* 724-283-8298 *Toll Free Fax:* 800-322-8273 *E-mail:* info@tapeworld.com *Web Site:* www.tapeworld.com, pg 1032

Gresham, Brian, International Society for Performance Improvement® (ISPI), PO Box 13035, Silver Spring, MD 20910 *Tel:* 301-587-8570 *Fax:* 301-587-8573 *E-mail:* info@ispi.org *Web Site:* www.ispi.org, pg 1083

Grey, Brad, Paramount Pictures Corporation, 5555 Melrose Ave, Los Angeles, CA 90038 *Tel:* 323-956-8398 *Web Site:* www.paramount.com, pg 969

Grey, David, Varitronics LLC, 2355 Polaris Lane N, Suite 100, Plymouth, MN 55447 *Tel:* 763-536-6400 *Toll Free Tel:* 800-328-0585 *Toll Free Fax:* 800-543-8966 *Web Site:* www.variquest.com, pg 1052

Grey, Ernest, Audio & Light, 2209 Randleman Rd, Greensboro, NC 27406 *Tel:* 336-274-1234 *Fax:* 336-274-4022 *E-mail:* info@audio-light.com *Web Site:* www.audio-light.com, pg 794

Grey, Robert L, Intellidyne LLC, 5203 Leesburg Pike, Suite 400, 2 Skyline Place, Falls Church, VA 22041 *Tel:* 703-575-9715 *Fax:* 703-575-9718 *Web Site:* www.intellidyne-llc.com, pg 899

Grezechowiak, Tom, ZERO Manufacturing Inc, 500 W 200 N, North Salt Lake, UT 84054 *Tel:* 801-298-5900 *Toll Free Tel:* 800-500-ZERO (500-9376) *Fax:* 801-299-7389 *E-mail:* sales@zerocases.com *Web Site:* www.zerocases.com, pg 1073

Gridgeman, Neal, The Resource Centre, Box 190, Waterloo, ON N2J 3Z9, Canada *Tel:* 519-885-0826 *Toll Free Tel:* 800-923-0330 *Fax:* 519-747-5629 *E-mail:* sales@theresourcecentre.com, pg 995

Griebeler, Pat, Theosophical Publishing House, 306 W Geneva Rd, Wheaton, IL 60187 *Tel:* 630-665-0130 *Toll Free Tel:* 800-669-9425 *Fax:* 630-665-8791 *Web Site:* www.questbooks.net, pg 1038

Griesinger, Peter Root, Griesinger Films LLC, 7300 Old Mill Rd, Gates Mills, OH 44040 *Tel:* 440-423-1601 *Toll Free Tel:* 800-872-4456 *Fax:* 440-423-1601 *E-mail:* orders@griesingerfilms.com *Web Site:* www.griesingerfilms.com, pg 882

Grifalconi, Ann, Greyfalcon House, 124 Waverly Place, New York, NY 10011 *Tel:* 212-777-9042, pg 882

Griffin, Aaron, Saturn Awards, 334 W 54 St, Los Angeles, CA 90037 *Tel:* 323-752-5811 *Web Site:* www.saturnawards.org, pg 1126

Griffin, Johnny, Wilmington Regional Film Commission Inc, 1223 N 23 St, Wilmington, NC 28405 *Tel:* 910-343-3456 *Fax:* 910-343-3457 *E-mail:* commish@wilmingtonfilm.com *Web Site:* www.wilmingtonfilm.com, pg 1101

Griffin, Michael, 4-D Creative Media, 16 W 46 St, 12th fl, New York, NY 10036 *Tel:* 212-994-3300 *Fax:* 212-499-9081 *Web Site:* www.4-dcreative.com, pg 872

Griffin, Peter, Industrial Timer Co, 30 Industrial Park Rd, Centerbrook, CT 06409 *Tel:* 860-767-7130 *Toll Free Tel:* 800-394-7130 *Fax:* 860-767-9137 *Toll Free Fax:* 800-767-9137 *E-mail:* sales@epg-inc.com *Web Site:* www.industrialtimercompany.com, pg 897

Griffin, Ron, KET The Kentucky Network, 600 Cooper Dr, Lexington, KY 40502 *Tel:* 859-258-7000 *Toll Free Tel:* 800-432-0951 *Fax:* 859-258-7396 *E-mail:* adulted@ket.org *Web Site:* www.ket.org, pg 910

Griffith, Cary, Backstage Equipment Inc, 8052 Lankershim Blvd, North Hollywood, CA 91605 *Tel:* 818-504-6026 *Toll Free Tel:* 800-692-2787 *Fax:* 818-504-6180 *E-mail:* info@backstageweb.com *Web Site:* www.backstageweb.com, pg 801

Griffith, Ed, Griffith Productions, 1750 Donelson Dr, Eads, TN 38028 *Tel:* 901-351-1899 *Fax:* 901-465-1787 *E-mail:* info@griffithproductions.tv *Web Site:* www.griffithproductions.tv, pg 882

Griffiths, Bob, Griffiths Broadcast Co Inc, 2981 Le Conte St, Viera, FL 32940 *Tel:* 321-622-4619 *Fax:* 321-622-4619 *E-mail:* griffiths.broadcast@usa.net *Web Site:* www.griffithsbroadcast.com, pg 882

Griffiths, Naomi, Griffiths Broadcast Co Inc, 2981 Le Conte St, Viera, FL 32940 *Tel:* 321-622-4619 *Fax:* 321-622-4619 *E-mail:* griffiths.broadcast@usa.net *Web Site:* www.griffithsbroadcast.com, pg 882

Griggs, Lewis Brown, Griggs Productions Inc, Kappas Marina, 29 W Pier, Sausalito, CA 94965 *Tel:* 415-999-1079 *Toll Free Tel:* 800-210-4200 *Web Site:* www.griggs.com, pg 882

Grimes, Jim, Daily Electronics Corp, PO Box 822437, Vancouver, WA 98682-0053 *Tel:* 360-896-8856 *Toll Free Tel:* 800-346-6667 *Fax:* 360-896-5476 *E-mail:* daily@worldaccessnet.com *Web Site:* dailyelectronics.net, pg 842

Grimm, Foster, Video Artists International & VAI Audio, 109 Wheeler Ave, Pleasantville, NY 10570 *Tel:* 914-769-3691 *Toll Free Tel:* 800-477-7146 *Fax:* 914-769-5407 *E-mail:* orders@vaimusic.com *Web Site:* www.vaimusic.com, pg 1054

Grinnan, Suzanne E, Chester F Carlson Award, 7003 Kilworth Lane, Springfield, VA 22151 *Tel:* 703-642-9090 *Fax:* 703-642-9094 *E-mail:* info@imaging.org *Web Site:* www.imaging.org, pg 1111

Grinnan, Suzanne E, Society for Imaging Science and Technology (IS&T), 7003 Kilworth Lane, Springfield, VA 22151 *Tel:* 703-642-9090 *Fax:* 703-642-9094 *E-mail:* info@imaging.org *Web Site:* www.imaging.org, pg 1089

Grinole, David, USITT: United States Institute for Theatre Technology Inc, 315 S Crouse Ave, Suite 200, Syracuse, NY 13210-1844 *Tel:* 315-463-6463 *Toll Free Tel:* 800-938-7488 *Fax:* 315-463-6525 *Toll Free Fax:* 866-398-7488 *E-mail:* info@office.usitt.org *Web Site:* www.usitt.org, pg 1090

Gripp, Tom, Excel Duplication Services, 1219 N Cass St, Milwaukee, WI 53202 *Tel:* 414-225-9235 *Fax:* 414-225-9236 *E-mail:* info@excelduplication.com *Web Site:* www.excelduplication.com, pg 864

Grippi, Carolyn, The National Academy of Television Arts & Sciences (NATAS), 1697 Broadway, Suite 1001, New York, NY 10019 *Tel:* 212-586-8424 *Fax:* 212-246-8129 *Web Site:* www.emmyonline.org, pg 1085

Grise, Donald J, Grise Audio Visual Center Inc, 2402 Cherry St, Erie, PA 16502 *Tel:* 814-452-4465 *Toll Free Tel:* 888-404-2719 *Fax:* 814-452-4479 *E-mail:* grise@erie.net *Web Site:* www.griseav.com, pg 882

Grise, Jim, Grise Audio Visual Center Inc, 2402 Cherry St, Erie, PA 16502 *Tel:* 814-452-4465 *Toll Free Tel:* 888-404-2719 *Fax:* 814-452-4479 *E-mail:* grise@erie.net *Web Site:* www.griseav.com, pg 882

Griswold, Bob, Effective Learning Systems Inc, 7740 W 78 St, Bloomington, MN 55439 *Tel:* 952-943-1660 *Toll Free Tel:* 800-966-5683 (orders) *E-mail:* info@efflearn.com *Web Site:* www.efflearn.com, pg 858

Griswold, Jeff, Effective Learning Systems Inc, 7740 W 78 St, Bloomington, MN 55439 *Tel:* 952-943-1660 *Toll Free Tel:* 800-966-5683 (orders) *E-mail:* info@efflearn.com *Web Site:* www.efflearn.com, pg 858

Grober, David, Motion Picture Marine, 616 Venice Blvd, Marina Del Rey, CA 90291 *Tel:* 310-822-1100 *Fax:* 310-822-2679 *E-mail:* info@motionpicturemarine.com *Web Site:* www.motionpicturemarine.com, pg 947

Groce, Bill, FMP Media Solutions Inc, 1010 Spring Mill Ave, Suite 100, Conshohocken, PA 19428 *Tel:* 610-825-4000 *Toll Free Tel:* 800-346-5071 *Fax:* 610-825-4430 *E-mail:* info@fmpmedia.com *Web Site:* www.fmpmedia.com, pg 870

Groft, Kelly, WMAR-TV, 6400 York Rd, Baltimore, MD 21212 *Tel:* 410-377-2222 *E-mail:* newsroom@wmar.com *Web Site:* www.abc2news.com, pg 1068

Grogan, Chris, KCFW Television, 401 First Ave E, Kalispell, MT 59901 *Tel:* 406-755-5239 *Fax:* 406-752-8002 *E-mail:* news@kcfw.com *Web Site:* www.nbcmontana.com; www.kcfw.com, pg 908

Groh, David, Partech Lighting Systems Inc, 8711 Reading Rd, Cincinnati, OH 45215 *Tel:* 513-761-5678 *Toll Free Tel:* 800-701-9551 *Fax:* 513-679-8282 *E-mail:* info@partechlighting.com *Web Site:* www.partechlighting.com, pg 969

Groleau, Colette, Sennheiser (Canada) Inc, 221 ave Labrosse, Pointe Claire, QC H9R 1A3, Canada *Tel:* 514-426-3013 *Toll Free Tel:* 800-463-1006 *Fax:* 514-426-3953 *Toll Free Fax:* 800-463-3013 *E-mail:* info@sennheiser.ca *Web Site:* www.sennheiser.ca, pg 1006

Gronsbell, Scott, Soundsphere, 10 Research Dr, Stratford, CT 06615 *Tel:* 203-386-9200 *Fax:* 203-386-0773 *E-mail:* info@soundsphere.com *Web Site:* www.soundsphere.com, pg 1018

Gross, Adam, TOMCAT USA Inc, 5427 N National Dr, Knoxville, TN 37914 *Tel:* 865-219-3700 *Fax:* 865-673-5818 *E-mail:* info@tomcatusa.com; sales@tomcatusa.com *Web Site:* www.tomcatglobal.com, pg 1042

Gross, Jay, Florida Digital Studios, 10781 75 St, Largo, FL 33777 *Tel:* 727-546-7900 *Fax:* 727-546-8640 *Web Site:* www.floridadigitalstudios.com, pg 870

Grossberg, Richard, Brooklyn College Television Center, Whitehead Hall, 2900 Bedford Ave, Rm 018-A, Brooklyn, NY 11210-2889 *Tel:* 718-951-5585 *Fax:* 718-951-5558 *Web Site:* www.bctvr.org/tvcenter_base.php, pg 814

Grossinger, Richard, North Atlantic Books, 2526 Martin Luther King Jr Way, Berkeley, CA 94704 *Tel:* 510-549-4270 *Fax:* 510-549-4276 *Web Site:* www.northatlanticbooks.com, pg 958

Grossman, Jay, MTI Home Video, 14216 SW 136 St, Miami, FL 33186 *Tel:* 305-255-8684 *Fax:* 305-233-6943 *Web Site:* www.mtivideo.com, pg 949

Grossman, Jerry, Photoimaging Manufacturers & Distributors Association Inc, 7600 Jericho Tpke, Suite 301, Woodbury, NY 11797 *Tel:* 516-802-0895 *Fax:* 516-364-0140 *Web Site:* www.pmda.com, pg 1087

Grossman, Mindy, Home Shopping Network (HSN), PO Box 9090, Clearwater, FL 33758 *Tel:* 727-872-1000 *Toll Free Tel:* 800-933-2887 (cust serv, orders online); 800-284-3900 (cust serv, orders by phone); 800-557-0714 (cust serv, auto ship orders); 800-284-5757 (orders) *Fax:* 727-872-6559 *Web Site:* www.hsn.com, pg 890

Groth, Trevor, Sundance Film Festival, 1825 Three Kings Dr, Park City, UT 84060 *Tel:* 435-658-3456 *Fax:* 435-658-3457 *E-mail:* customerservice@sundance.org; press@sundance.org; institute@sundance.org *Web Site:* www.sundance.org/festival/, pg 1128

Grove, Brad, Production West, 207 NW Park Ave, Portland, OR 97209 *Tel:* 503-222-0025 *Fax:* 503-573-1941 *E-mail:* info@r2cgroup.com *Web Site:* www.r2cgroup.com, pg 985

Grove, Mark Steven, Inferno Film Productions LLC, PO Box 696, Littleton, CO 80160-0696 *Tel:* 303-587-9792 *E-mail:* sales@infernofilm.com *Web Site:* www.infernofilm.com, pg 897

Groves, Kevin, Alpha Video & Audio Inc, 7711 Computer Ave, Edina, MN 55435 *Tel:* 952-896-9898 *Toll Free Tel:* 800-388-0008 *Fax:* 952-896-9899 *E-mail:* info@alphavideo.com *Web Site:* www.alphavideo.com, pg 782

Gruber, John, On-Site Video, 201 E Southern Ave, Suite 112, Tempe, AZ 85282 *Tel:* 480-967-5062 *Fax:* 480-967-4806 *E-mail:* on_sitevideo@yahoo.com *Web Site:* www.on-sitevideo.com, pg 963

Grundstein, Frank, Logitek Electronic Systems Inc, 5622 Edgemoor Dr, Houston, TX 77081 *Tel:* 713-664-4470 *Toll Free Tel:* 800-231-5870 (sales); 877-231-5870 (tech support) *Fax:* 713-664-4479 *E-mail:* northamericansales@logitekaudio.com *Web Site:* www.logitekaudio.com, pg 924

Grzybowski, John, BFS Entertainment & Multimedia Limited, 360 Newkirk Rd, Richmond Hill, ON L4C 3G7, Canada *Tel:* 905-884-2323 *Fax:* 905-884-8292 *E-mail:* info@bfsent.com; contact@bfsent.com *Web Site:* www.bfsent.com, pg 806

Guan, Bin, York Telecom, 81 Corbett Way, Eatontown, NJ 07724 *Tel:* 732-413-6000 *Toll Free Tel:* 866-836-8463 *Fax:* 732-413-6060 *E-mail:* knowmore@yorktel.com *Web Site:* yorktel.com, pg 1072

Guarino, Anthony Guy, Guymark Studios LLC, 3019 Dixwell Ave, Hamden, CT 06518 *Tel:* 203-248-9323 *Fax:* 203-248-9325 *E-mail:* guymark.studios@snet.net *Web Site:* www.guymarkstudios.com, pg 883

Guarino, Fred, Tiki Recording Studios Inc, 30-A Glen St, Suite 204, Glen Cove, NY 11542 *Tel:* 516-671-4300 (ext 101) *Fax:* 516-671-8754 *Web Site:* www.tikirecording.com, pg 1040

Guarino, Mark L, Guymark Studios LLC, 3019 Dixwell Ave, Hamden, CT 06518 *Tel:* 203-248-9323 *Fax:* 203-248-9325 *E-mail:* guymark.studios@snet.net *Web Site:* www.guymarkstudios.com, pg 883

Guarino, Susan, Guymark Studios LLC, 3019 Dixwell Ave, Hamden, CT 06518 *Tel:* 203-248-9323 *Fax:* 203-248-9325 *E-mail:* guymark.studios@snet.net *Web Site:* www.guymarkstudios.com, pg 883

Gubler, Leron, FilmL.A., Inc, 6255 W Sunset Blvd, 12th fl, Los Angeles, CA 90028 *Tel:* 213-977-8600 *Fax:* 213-977-8610; 213-977-8601 (permits) *E-mail:* info@filmla.com *Web Site:* www.filmla.com, pg 1082, 1093

Gudnason, David, Carr McLean Ltd, 461 Horner Ave, Toronto, ON M8W 4X2, Canada *Tel:* 416-252-3371 *Toll Free Tel:* 800-268-2123 (CN) *Fax:* 416-252-9203 *Toll Free Fax:* 800-871-2397 *E-mail:* sales@carrmclean.ca *Web Site:* www.carrmclean.ca, pg 820

Guenot, Gary, Digital Media West, 573 Jones St, Ventura, CA 93003 *Tel:* 805-559-1318 *Web Site:* www.digitalmediawest.com, pg 847

Guerrette, Marie, Frame 30 Productions Ltd, 10816A-82 Ave, No 202, Edmonton, AB T6E 2B3, Canada *Tel:* 780-439-5322 *E-mail:* frame30@frame30.com *Web Site:* www.frame30.com, pg 872

Guhl, Jennifer, Florida Film Festival, c/o Enzian, 1300 S Orlando Ave, Maitland, FL 32751 *Tel:* 407-629-1088 *Fax:* 407-629-6870 *E-mail:* filmfest@enzian.org *Web Site:* www.floridafilmfestival.com; enzian.org, pg 1114

Guillaume, Stan, Elegant Packaging Corp, 5253 W Roosevelt Rd, Cicero, IL 60804 *Tel:* 708-652-3400 *Toll Free Tel:* 800-367-5493 *Fax:* 708-652-6444 *E-mail:* info@elegantpackaging.com *Web Site:* www.elegantpackaging.com, pg 859

Gumkowski, Greg, NRD LLC, A Mark IV Industries Co, 2937 Alt Blvd, Grand Island, NY 14072-1285 *Tel:* 716-773-7634 *Toll Free Tel:* 800-525-8076 (US only) *Fax:* 716-773-7744 *E-mail:* sales@nrdinc.com *Web Site:* www.nrdstaticcontrol.com, pg 960

Gumpert, Rich, Powerstation Events, 1486 Highland Ave, Bldg 2, Suite 6, Cheshire, CT 06410 *Tel:* 203-250-8500 *Toll Free Tel:* 800-423-7835 *Fax:* 203-250-8575 *E-mail:* sales@powerstationevents.com *Web Site:* www.powerstationevents.com, pg 979

Gundlach, Ralph, Olympic Case Co, 9110 King Palm Dr, Suite 101, Tampa, FL 33619 *Tel:* 813-246-5525 *Toll Free Tel:* 888-246-5525 *Fax:* 813-246-4748 *E-mail:* info@olycase.com *Web Site:* www.olycase.com, pg 962

Gunn, Brian S, Popless Voice Screens, PO Box 1014, New Paltz, NY 12561-3063 *Tel:* 845-255-3367 *Toll Free Tel:* 800-252-1503 *Fax:* 845-255-3367 *E-mail:* info@popfilter.com *Web Site:* www.popfilter.com, pg 978

Gunn, Greg, Blind, 1702 Olympic Blvd, Santa Monica, CA 90404 *Tel:* 310-314-1618 *Fax:* 310-314-1718 *Web Site:* www.blind.com, pg 809

Gupta, Jay, Backdrop Outlet, 3540 Seagate Way, Oceanside, CA 92056 *Tel:* 760-547-2900 *Toll Free Tel:* 800-466-1755 *Fax:* 760-547-2899 *E-mail:* cs@backdropoutlet.com *Web Site:* www.backdropoutlet.com, pg 801

Gupta, Naresh, Adobe Systems Inc, 345 Park Ave, San Jose, CA 95110-2704 *Tel:* 408-536-6000 *Fax:* 408-537-6000 *Web Site:* www.adobe.com, pg 776

Guthrie, Shawn, Student Academy Awards Competition, 8949 Wilshire Blvd, Beverly Hills, CA 90211 *Tel:* 310-247-3000 *Fax:* 310-859-9619 *E-mail:* SAA@oscars.org *Web Site:* www.oscars.org/saa, pg 1127

Gutierrez, Rafael, Cinema Entertainment Inc, 1779 NW 79 Ave, Doral, FL 33126 *Tel:* 561-899-0721 *E-mail:* info@cinemaent.com *Web Site:* cinemaent.com, pg 827

Gutsche, Manny, RF Industries, 7610 Miramar Rd, San Diego, CA 92126 *Tel:* 858-549-6340 *Toll Free Tel:* 800-233-1728 *Fax:* 858-549-6345 *E-mail:* rfi@rfindustries.com *Web Site:* www.rfindustries.com, pg 995

Gutz, Kris, J&S Audio Visual Inc, 9150 N Royal Lane, Suite 150, Irving, TX 75063 *Tel:* 972-241-5444 *Toll Free Tel:* 800-852-8771 *Fax:* 972-247-2590 *E-mail:* info@jsav.com *Web Site:* www.jsav.com, pg 904

Guzman, Sig, Backstage Equipment Inc, 8052 Lankershim Blvd, North Hollywood, CA 91605 *Tel:* 818-504-6026 *Toll Free Tel:* 800-692-2787 *Fax:* 818-504-6180 *E-mail:* info@backstageweb.com *Web Site:* www.backstageweb.com, pg 801

Guzzi, Jim, Gotham Sound & Communications Inc, 330 W 38 St, No 105, New York, NY 10018 *Tel:* 212-629-9430 *Toll Free Tel:* 866-468-4268 *Fax:* 212-629-9436 *E-mail:* nyc@gothamsound.com *Web Site:* www.gothamsound.com, pg 881

Guzzi, Joseph, TAI Audio, 5828 Old Winter Garden Rd, Orlando, FL 32835 *Tel:* 407-296-9959 *Toll Free Tel:* 800-486-6444 *Fax:* 407-648-1352 *E-mail:* sales@taiaudio.com *Web Site:* www.taiaudio.com, pg 1031

Gyenis, Connie, Language Plus Inc, 4110 Rio Bravo, Suite 202, El Paso, TX 79902 *Tel:* 915-544-8600 *Fax:* 915-544-8640 *E-mail:* speak@languageplus.com *Web Site:* www.languageplus.com, pg 916

Haaga, Paul G Jr, National Public Radio (NPR), 1111 N Capitol St NE, Washington, DC 20002 *Tel:* 202-513-2000 *Web Site:* www.npr.org, pg 1086

Haarstad, Jerrod, Abel Cine Tech Los Angeles, 801 S Main St, Suite 104, Burbank, CA 91506 *Tel:* 818-972-9078 *Toll Free Tel:* 888-700-4416 *Fax:* 818-972-2673 *E-mail:* orders@abelcine.com *Web Site:* www.abelcine.com, pg 772

Haas, B K, Bud Industries, 4605 E 355 St, Willoughby, OH 44094 *Tel:* 440-946-3200 *Fax:* 440-951-4015 *E-mail:* saleseast@budind.com *Web Site:* www.budind.com, pg 814

Haas, Daren, HM Electronics Inc (HME), 14110 Stowe Dr, Poway, CA 92064 *Tel:* 858-535-6000 *Toll Free Tel:* 800-848-4468 (domestic sales) *Fax:* 858-452-7207; 858-552-0139 (domestic sales) *E-mail:* info@hme.com *Web Site:* www.hme.com, pg 889

Haas, Donna, Louisiana State University Health Sciences Center - Shreveport, Dept of Video Servs & TeleHealth, 1501 Kings Hwy, Shreveport, LA 71103-4228 *Tel:* 318-675-5268 *Fax:* 318-675-7757 *Web Site:* www.lsuhscshreveport.edu, pg 925

Haas, Rick, Associated Press Television News, 450 W 33 St, New York, NY 10001 *Tel:* 212-621-1500 *Fax:* 212-621-7419 *Web Site:* www.aptn.com, pg 792

Haba, Leona, 20/20 Communications Inc, 10112 Voss Rd, Marengo, IL 60152 *Tel:* 847-364-7666 *Fax:* 847-364-7672 *Web Site:* www.2020communications.com, pg 1047

Hacker, Matt, Big Shoulders Digital Video Productions, 875 N Michigan Ave, Suite 3750, Chicago, IL 60611 *Tel:* 312-540-5400 *E-mail:* info@bigshoulders.com; sales@bigshoulders.com *Web Site:* www.bigshoulders.com, pg 807

Hadfield, Brant, StoryTrack, 212 S Bemiston, St Louis, MO 63105 *Tel:* 314-725-3003 *Web Site:* www.storytrack.com, pg 1025

Hadlock, Joe, Bear Creek Studio & Music Production Inc, 6313 Maltby Rd, Woodinville, WA 98072 *Tel:* 425-481-4100 *Fax:* 425-486-2718 *E-mail:* bearcreek@seanet.com *Web Site:* bearcreekstudio.com, pg 804

Hadlock, Manny, Bear Creek Studio & Music Production Inc, 6313 Maltby Rd, Woodinville, WA 98072 *Tel:* 425-481-4100 *Fax:* 425-486-2718 *E-mail:* bearcreek@seanet.com *Web Site:* bearcreekstudio.com, pg 804

Hadlock, Ryan, Bear Creek Studio & Music Production Inc, 6313 Maltby Rd, Woodinville, WA 98072 *Tel:* 425-481-4100 *Fax:* 425-486-2718 *E-mail:* bearcreek@seanet.com *Web Site:* bearcreekstudio.com, pg 804

Hadzor, Tom, Wide Eye Productions, 1018 W Hays St, Boise, ID 83702 *Tel:* 208-336-0391 *Fax:* 208-336-6644 *E-mail:* info@wideeye.tv *Web Site:* wideeye.tv, pg 1066

Haenelt, Joanie, Kern County Film Commission, 2101 Oak St, Bakersfield, CA 93301 *Tel:* 661-868-KERN (868-5376) *Toll Free Tel:* 800-500-KERN (500-5376) *Fax:* 661-861-2017 *E-mail:* kerninfo@co.kern.ca.us *Web Site:* www.filmkern.com, pg 1092

Hagar, Dan, Cupit Music Group, PO Box 121904, Nashville, TN 37212 *Tel:* 615-731-0100 *Fax:* 615-731-3005 *Web Site:* www.cupitmusic.com, pg 841

Hagen, Danielle, Communications Specialists Inc, 7272 Jackson Ave, Mechanicsville, VA 23111 *Tel:* 804-559-4274 *Fax:* 804-559-4479 *E-mail:* info@csisystems.net *Web Site:* www.csisystems.net, pg 833

Hagen, Doug, B-K Lighting, 40429 Brickyard Dr, Madera, CA 93636 *Tel:* 559-438-5800 *Fax:* 559-438-5900 *E-mail:* info@bklighting.com *Web Site:* www.bklighting.com, pg 801

Hager, Peter, Sight Creative, 400 First Ave N, Suite 100, Minneapolis, MN 55401 *Tel:* 651-646-2442 *Fax:* 651-646-1461 *E-mail:* info@sightcreative.com *Web Site:* www.sightcreative.com, pg 1010

Haghighat, Amin, A&V Company, 4238 Piedmont Pkwy, Greensboro, NC 27410-8111 *Tel:* 336-292-9700 *Toll Free Tel:* 800-292-9700 *Fax:* 336-854-5282 *E-mail:* info@avcompany.com *Web Site:* www.avcompany.com, pg 772

Haglund, Janiece, Badiyan Inc, 720 W 94 St, Bloomington, MN 55420 *Tel:* 952-888-5507 *Fax:* 952-888-0360 *E-mail:* info@badiyan.com *Web Site:* www.badiyan.com, pg 801

Hagstrom, Mikael, SAS Institute Inc, 100 SAS Campus Dr, Cary, NC 27513-2414 *Tel:* 919-677-8000 *Toll Free Tel:* 800-727-0025 *Fax:* 919-677-4444 *Web Site:* www.sas.com, pg 1002

Hahamy, Yohay, Joseph Electronics, 6633 W Howard St, Niles, IL 60714 *Tel:* 847-588-3800 *Toll Free Tel:* 800-323-5925 *Fax:* 847-588-3300 *Toll Free Fax:* 800-446-8366 *E-mail:* sales@josephelectronics.com *Web Site:* www.josephelectronics.com, pg 906

Hahn, Curt, Film House Inc, 810 Dominican Dr, Nashville, TN 37228 *Tel:* 615-255-4000 *Fax:* 615-255-4111 *E-mail:* results@filmhouse.com *Web Site:* www.filmhouse.com, pg 867

Hahn, Jansen, TBC Consoles Inc, 170 Rodeo Dr, Edgewood, NY 11717 *Tel:* 631-293-4068 *Toll Free Tel:* 888-CONSOLE (266-7653) *Fax:* 631-293-4075 *E-mail:* info@tbcconsoles.com; sales@tbcconsoles.com; support@tbcconsoles.com *Web Site:* www.tbcconsoles.com, pg 1033

Hahn, Jerry, TBC Consoles Inc, 170 Rodeo Dr, Edgewood, NY 11717 *Tel:* 631-293-4068 *Toll Free Tel:* 888-CONSOLE (266-7653) *Fax:* 631-293-4075 *E-mail:* info@tbcconsoles.com; sales@tbcconsoles.com; support@tbcconsoles.com *Web Site:* www.tbcconsoles.com, pg 1033

Haile-Marian, Atikem, Opterna AM, 44901 Falcon Place, Suite 116, Sterling, VA 20166-9531 *Tel:* 703-653-1130 *Toll Free Tel:* 800-248-9004 *Fax:* 703-803-8313 *Web Site:* www.opterna-am.com, pg 964

Hailigenberg, Paul, Staco Energy Products Co, 301 Gaddis Blvd, Dayton, OH 45403 *Tel:* 937-253-1191 *Toll Free Tel:* 866-261-1191 *Fax:* 937-253-1723 *E-mail:* sales@stacoenergy.com; service@stacoenergy.com *Web Site:* www.stacoenergy.com, pg 1022

Hair, Ray, American Federation of Musicians of the United States & Canada (AFM), 1501 Broadway, Suite 600, New York, NY 10036 *Tel:* 212-869-1330 *Fax:* 212-764-6134 *Web Site:* www.afm.org, pg 1076

Hakimoglu, Ms Zee, ClearOne Inc, Edgewater Corporate Park, South Tower, Suite 500, 5225 Wiley Post Way, Salt Lake City, UT 84116 *Tel:* 801-974-3760 *Toll Free Tel:* 800-705-2103 (tech sales) *Fax:* 801-977-0087 *E-mail:* techsales@clearone.com *Web Site:* www.clearone.com, pg 830

Haldenwanger, Kari, MSU Technologies, 325 E Grand River, Suite 350, East Lansing, MI 48823 *Tel:* 517-355-2186 *Fax:* 517-432-3880 *E-mail:* msut@msu.edu *Web Site:* www.technologies.msu.edu, pg 949

Hale, Kevin, Fox Television Center, 1999 S Bundy Dr, Los Angeles, CA 90025 *Tel:* 310-584-2000 *Fax:* 310-584-2023 *Web Site:* www.myfoxla.com, pg 872

Hale, Tim, Extreme Reach Inc, 75 Second Ave, Suite 720, Needham, MA 02494 *Tel:* 781-577-2016 *E-mail:* sales@extremereach.com; press@extremereach.com *Web Site:* www.extremereach.com, pg 864

Haley, Jeff, Marketron Broadcast Solutions, 101 Empty Saddle Trail, Hailey, ID 83333 *Tel:* 208-788-6800 *Toll Free Tel:* 888-239-8878 (support); 800-476-7226 *E-mail:* info@wicksbroadcastsolutions.com *Web Site:* www.wicksbroadcastsolutions.com; www.marketron.com, pg 931

Haley, Tiffany, Grass Valley, 3030 NW Aloclek Dr, Hillsboro, OR 97124 *Tel:* 503-526-8160 *Fax:* 503-526-8109, pg 881

Hall, Adam, SNL Kagan Media & Communications, One SNL Plaza, 212 Seventh St NE, Charlottesville, VA 22902 *Tel:* 434-977-1600 *Toll Free Tel:* 866-296-3743 *Fax:* 434-977-4466 *E-mail:* snlkagansales@snl.com *Web Site:* www.snl.com, pg 1014

Hall, Allen, Special Effects Unlimited Inc, 1005 N Lillian Way, Hollywood, CA 90038 *Tel:* 323-466-3361 *Fax:* 323-466-5712 *E-mail:* seuefx@aol.com *Web Site:* www.specialefxunltd.com, pg 1020

Hall, Anna Gilmore, Hearing Loss Association of America (HLAA), 7910 Woodmont Ave, Suite 1200, Bethesda, MD 20814 *Tel:* 301-657-2248; 301-657-2249 (TTY) *Fax:* 301-913-9413 *E-mail:* info@hearingloss.org *Web Site:* www.hearingloss.org, pg 887

Hall, Anna Maria, Killer Tracks, 2110 Colorado Ave, Suite 110, Santa Monica, CA 90404 *Tel:* 310-865-4455 *Toll Free Tel:* 800-4-KILLER (454-5537) *Fax:* 310-865-4470 *Toll Free Fax:* 800-787-2257 *E-mail:* info@killertracks.com; sales@killertracks.com *Web Site:* www.killertracks.com, pg 910

Hall, Casey, Extron Electronics, 1025 E Ball Rd, Suite 100, Anaheim, CA 92805-5957 *Tel:* 714-491-1500 *Toll Free Tel:* 800-633-9876 (sales & tech support); 800-633-9873 (order support) *Fax:* 714-491-1517 *E-mail:* sales-usa@extron.com *Web Site:* www.extron.com, pg 864

Hall, Curt, TapeWorks Texas Inc, 4930-B Dacoma, Houston, TX 77092 *Tel:* 713-688-0696 *Toll Free Tel:* 866-827-3489 *Fax:* 713-688-2509 *E-mail:* sales@tapeworkstexas.com *Web Site:* www.tapeworkstexas.com, pg 1032

Hall, Dan, Hall Productions, 951 Front St, Grover Beach, CA 93433 *Tel:* 805-473-1042 *Toll Free Tel:* 800-366-6057 *Fax:* 805-473-2202 *Web Site:* hallpro.com, pg 884

Hall, David, Velodyne Acoustics Inc, 345 Digital Dr, Morgan Hill, CA 95037 *Tel:* 408-465-2800 *Toll Free Tel:* 866-243-0789 *Fax:* 408-779-9227; 408-779-9208 (cust serv); 408-779-9377 (orders) *E-mail:* service@velodyne.com; orders@velodyne.com *Web Site:* www.velodyne.com, pg 1052

Hall, Diane, Mobile Film Office, 164 Saint Emanuel St, Mobile, AL 36602 *Tel:* 251-438-7102 *Fax:* 251-438-7104 *Web Site:* www.mobilefilmoffice.com, pg 1091

Hall, Doug, Propeller Music Group, 30 Prescott Ave, Mont Clair, NJ 07042 *Tel:* 212-768-3400 *E-mail:* info@propellermusic.com *Web Site:* www.propellermusic.com, pg 986

Hall, Doug, The Whitlock Group, 12820 West Creek Pkwy, Richmond, VA 23238 *Tel:* 804-273-9100 *Toll Free Tel:* 800-726-9843 *Fax:* 804-273-9380 *E-mail:* information@whitlock.com *Web Site:* www.whitlock.com, pg 1065

Hall, Heidi, Ferrari Color®, 1550 S Gladiola St, Salt Lake City, UT 84104 *Tel:* 801-355-4124 *Toll Free Tel:* 888-312-6567 *Fax:* 801-355-4152 *E-mail:* info.slc@ferraricolor.com *Web Site:* www.ferraricolor.com, pg 866

Hall, Howard, Howard Hall Productions, 2171 La Amatista Rd, Del Mar, CA 92014-3031 *Tel:* 858-259-8989 *Fax:* 858-792-1467 *E-mail:* info@howardhall.com *Web Site:* www.howardhall.com, pg 883

Hall, Jeff, Maximus Media Inc, 2727 N Grove Industrial Dr, Suite 111, Fresno, CA 93727 *Tel:* 559-255-1688 *Toll Free Tel:* 800-2THEMAX (284-3629) *Fax:* 559-255-0323 *Web Site:* www.tothemax.com, pg 934

Hall, Kegn, Sedona Film Office, 45 Sunset Dr, Sedona, AZ 86336 *Tel:* 928-204-1123 ext 130 *Fax:* 928-204-1064 *E-mail:* pr@sedonachamber.com *Web Site:* www.sedonafilmoffice.com, pg 1091

Hall, Laura, Future Disc LLC, 15851 NW Willis Rd, McMinnville, OR 97128 *Tel:* 213-361-0603 *Fax:* 503-472-1951 *Web Site:* www.futurediscsystems.com, pg 874

Hall, M B, Audio Accessories Inc, 25 Mill St, Marlow, NH 03456 *Tel:* 603-446-3335 *Fax:* 603-446-7543 *E-mail:* audioacc@patchbays.com *Web Site:* www.patchbays.com, pg 794

Hall, Marta Thoma, Velodyne Acoustics Inc, 345 Digital Dr, Morgan Hill, CA 95037 *Tel:* 408-465-2800 *Toll Free Tel:* 866-243-0789 *Fax:* 408-779-9227; 408-779-9208 (cust serv); 408-779-9377 (orders) *E-mail:* service@velodyne.com; orders@velodyne.com *Web Site:* www.velodyne.com, pg 1052

Hall, Michele, Howard Hall Productions, 2171 La Amatista Rd, Del Mar, CA 92014-3031 *Tel:* 858-259-8989 *Fax:* 858-792-1467 *E-mail:* info@howardhall.com *Web Site:* www.howardhall.com, pg 883

Hall, Ron, Festival Films, 6115 Chestnut Terr, Shorewood, MN 55331 *Tel:* 952-470-2172 *Fax:* 952-470-2172 *E-mail:* fesfilms@aol.com *Web Site:* www.fesfilms.com, pg 866

Hall, Roy, Music Hall LLC, 108 Station Rd, Great Neck, NY 11023 *Tel:* 516-487-3663 *Fax:* 516-773-3891 *E-mail:* info@musichallaudio.com *Web Site:* musichall.biz, pg 950

Hall, Scott, Blue Water Film Award, PO Box 611109, Port Huron, MI 48061 *E-mail:* bwff@bluewaterfilmfestival.com *Web Site:* bluewaterfilmfestival.com, pg 1110

Hall, Shelli, Tucson Film Office, 100 S Church Ave, Tucson, AZ 85701 *Tel:* 520-770-2151 *Fax:* 520-629-0160 *Web Site:* www.filmtucson.com, pg 1091

Hall, Steve, Future Disc LLC, 15851 NW Willis Rd, McMinnville, OR 97128 *Tel:* 213-361-0603 *Fax:* 503-472-1951 *Web Site:* www.futurediscsystems.com, pg 874

Hall, Sylvie, Sanako Inc, 500 Linden Oaks, Rochester, NY 14625 *Toll Free Tel:* 888-611-4785 *Toll Free Fax:* 888-389-3858 *E-mail:* info@sanako.com *Web Site:* www.sanako.com, pg 1002

Hallberg, Scott, Bardes Products Inc, 5245 W Clinton Ave, Milwaukee, WI 53223 *Tel:* 414-354-9000 *Toll Free Tel:* 800-223-1357 *Fax:* 414-354-1921 *E-mail:* sales@bardes.com *Web Site:* www.bardes.com, pg 803

Hallerman, Stuart, Avast! Recording Co, 601 NW 80 St, Seattle, WA 98117 *Tel:* 206-633-3926 *Fax:* 206-789-7569 *E-mail:* avast@comcast.net *Web Site:* www.avastrecording.com, pg 798

Halling, Steve, AVFX Inc, 96 Holton St, Boston, MA 02135 *Tel:* 617-254-0770 *Toll Free Tel:* 888-254-0770 *E-mail:* info@avfx.com *Web Site:* www.avfx.com, pg 798

Hallman, Anita, HallBrook Productions, 565 Dutch Valley Rd, Atlanta, GA 30324 *Tel:* 404-892-0042 *E-mail:* hallbrook@hallbrookproductions.com *Web Site:* hallbrookproductions.com, pg 884

Hallman, Wallace, ESECO Speedmaster, 730 E Eseco Rd, Cushing, OK 74023-5505 *Tel:* 918-225-1266 *Toll Free Tel:* 800-331-5904 (US & CN) *Fax:* 918-225-1284 *E-mail:* info@eseco-speedmaster.com *Web Site:* www.eseco-speedmaster.com, pg 862

Halouma, Stephanie, Scripps Networks, 9721 Sherrill Blvd, Knoxville, TN 37932 *Tel:* 865-694-2700 *Fax:* 865-693-6576 *Web Site:* www.scrippsnetworks.com, pg 1005

Halpern, Elliot, YAP Films, 96 Spadina Ave, Suite 205, Toronto, ON M5V 2J6, Canada *Tel:* 416-504-3662 *Fax:* 416-504-3667 *E-mail:* thedog@yapfilms.com *Web Site:* www.yapfilms.com, pg 1072

Halpern, Ric, Radiant Images, 4125 W Jefferson Blvd, Los Angeles, CA 90016 *Tel:* 323-737-1314 *Fax:* 310-861-0163 *E-mail:* info@radiantimages.com *Web Site:* www.radiantimages.com, pg 990

Halpern, Susan B, The Chris Awards, 1021 E Broad St, Columbus, OH 43205-1357 *Tel:* 614-444-7460 *E-mail:* info@columbusfilmcouncil.org *Web Site:* www.columbusfilmcouncil.org, pg 1112

Halt, Peter, Rovi Corp, 2830 De La Cruz Blvd, Santa Clara, CA 95050 *Tel:* 408-562-8400 *Fax:* 408-567-1800 *Web Site:* www.rovicorp.com, pg 1000

Hames, Steven, National Student Production Awards, Hershey Square Ctr, 1152 Mae St, Hummelstown, PA 17036 *Toll Free Tel:* 855-ASK-4CBI (275-4224) *Web Site:* www.askcbi.org, pg 1121

Hamilton, Christopher P, In the Wild Productions, PO Box 1443, Provincetown, MA 02657-5443 *Tel:* 508-241-5990; 508-487-2887 *E-mail:* info@inthewildproductions.com *Web Site:* www.inthewildproductions.com, pg 897

Hamilton, Dennis, Action Photo Service Inc, 1741 Clayton Rd, Concord, CA 94520 *Tel:* 925-676-7777 *Fax:* 925-676-9275 *E-mail:* actionps@sbcglobal.net *Web Site:* www.actionphotoservice.com, pg 775

Hamilton, Don, Hamilton Studio, 1427 W Dean Ave, Spokane, WA 99201 *Tel:* 509-327-9501 *Web Site:* www.hamiltonstudio.com, pg 884

Hamilton, Mary, Parker Area Chamber of Commerce, 1217 California Ave, Parker, AZ 85344 *Tel:* 928-669-2174 *Fax:* 928-669-6304 *E-mail:* info@parkeraz.org *Web Site:* www.parkeraz.org, pg 1091

Hamilton, Peter, Soundsphere, 10 Research Dr, Stratford, CT 06615 *Tel:* 203-386-9200 *Fax:* 203-386-0773 *E-mail:* info@soundsphere.com *Web Site:* www.soundsphere.com, pg 1018

Hamilton, Philip, Audio Visual Dynamics Ltd, 2360 23 Ave, Lachine, QC H8T 0A3, Canada *Tel:* 514-332-6440 *Fax:* 514-332-2009 *E-mail:* service@avd.ca *Web Site:* www.avd.ca, pg 795

Hamilton, Robert, DWD Theatre Design & Consulting, Suite 485, 425 Carrall St, Vancouver, BC V6B 6E3, Canada *Tel:* 604-874-0552 *E-mail:* info@d-w-d.com *Web Site:* www.d-w-d.com, pg 854

Hamilton, Scott, Western North Carolina Film Commission, 134 Wright Brothers Way, Fletcher, NC 28732 *Tel:* 828-687-7234 *Toll Free Tel:* 888-595-7234 *Fax:* 828-687-7552 *E-mail:* film@awnc.org *Web Site:* www.wncfilm.com; www.advantagewest.com, pg 1101

Hamkens, Jan, Docter Optics Inc, 1425 W Elliot Rd, Suite A-105, Gilbert, AZ 85233 *Tel:* 480-844-7585 *Fax:* 480-844-7826 *E-mail:* doi@docteroptics.com *Web Site:* www.docteroptics.com, pg 849

Hamlin, Brad, Burst Electronics Inc, PO Box 65947, Albuquerque, NM 87193 *Tel:* 505-898-1455 *E-mail:* sales@burstelectronics.com *Web Site:* www.burstelectronics.com, pg 815

Hamm, Michael, Frame 30 Productions Ltd, 10816A-82 Ave, No 202, Edmonton, AB T6E 2B3, Canada *Tel:* 780-439-5322 *E-mail:* frame30@frame30.com *Web Site:* www.frame30.com, pg 872

Hammagren, William P, City of Savannah Film Office, One Waring Dr, Savannah, GA 31404 *Tel:* 912-651-2360 *Fax:* 912-651-0982 *E-mail:* info@savannahfilm.org *Web Site:* www.savannahfilm.org, pg 1097

Hammerslough, Nancy, Pictures of Record Inc, 119 Kettle Creek Rd, Weston, CT 06883 *Tel:* 203-227-3387 *Fax:* 203-222-9673 *E-mail:* picturesofrecord@aol.com *Web Site:* www.picturesofrecord.com, pg 975

Hammond, Greg, Allied Artists International Inc, Production Services Ctr, 15810 E Gale Ave, Suite 133, Hacienda Heights, CA 91745 *Tel:* 626-330-0600 *Fax:* 626-961-0411 *E-mail:* info@alliedartists.net *Web Site:* us.alliedartists.com, pg 781

Hammonds, Lisa, Medcom Inc, 6060 Phyllis Dr, Cypress, CA 90630-5243 *Tel:* 714-891-1443 *Toll Free Tel:* 800-877-1443; 800-541-0253 *Fax:* 714-891-3140 *E-mail:* customerservice@medcominc.com *Web Site:* www.medcominc.com, pg 936

Hanavan, Patrick, Extreme Reach Inc, 75 Second Ave, Suite 720, Needham, MA 02494 *Tel:* 781-577-2016 *E-mail:* sales@extremereach.com; press@extremereach.com *Web Site:* www.extremereach.com, pg 864

Hancock, Dave, Spectrum Industries Inc, 925 First Ave, Chippewa Falls, WI 54729 *Tel:* 715-723-6750 *Toll Free Tel:* 800-235-1262 *Toll Free Fax:* 800-335-0473 *E-mail:* info@spectrumfurniture.com *Web Site:* www.spectrumfurniture.com, pg 1021

Hancock, Quinn, American Photographic Artisans Guild (APAG), 2269 N 400 Rd, Eudora, KS 66025 *Tel:* 785-883-4166 *Web Site:* www.apag.net, pg 1077

Hancock, Sara, North Carolina's Piedmont Triad Film Commission, 416 Gallimore Dairy Rd, Suite M, Greensboro, NC 27409 *Tel:* 336-393-0001 *E-mail:* info@piedmontfilm.com *Web Site:* www.piedmontfilm.com, pg 1101

Handel, Scott, Ohio HD Video, 3465 Noe Bixby Rd, Columbus, OH 43232 *Tel:* 614-656-1162 *Fax:* 614-656-4343 *E-mail:* info@ohiohdvideo.com *Web Site:* ohiohdvideo.com, pg 961

Hanes, Doug, Transtar Entertainment Co Inc, 10650 E Bethany Dr, Suite E, Aurora, CO 80014 *Tel:* 303-695-4207 *Web Site:* www.transtarfilm.com, pg 1043

Hanes, Frank, Big Shoulders Digital Video Productions, 875 N Michigan Ave, Suite 3750, Chicago, IL 60611 *Tel:* 312-540-5400 *E-mail:* info@bigshoulders.com; sales@bigshoulders.com *Web Site:* www.bigshoulders.com, pg 807

Haney, Kathleen, WorldFest-Houston, 9898 Bissonnet St, Suite 650, Houston, TX 77036 *Tel:* 713-965-9955 *Toll Free Tel:* 866-965-9955 *Fax:* 713-965-9960 *E-mail:* mail@worldfest.org; entry@worldfest.org *Web Site:* www.worldfest.org, pg 1130

Hanford, Lynn, Flying Colors Broadcasts, 2000 "M" St NW, Suite 345, Washington, DC 20036 *Tel:* 202-293-5300 *E-mail:* info@fc-tv.com *Web Site:* www.fc-tv.com, pg 870

Hank, Sylvester, Savage Universal Corp, 550 E Elliot Rd, Chandler, AZ 85225 *Tel:* 480-632-1320 *Toll Free Tel:* 800-624-8891 *Fax:* 480-632-1322 *Web Site:* savageuniversal.com, pg 1003

Hanley, Chris, APC by Schneider Electric, 132 Fairgrounds Rd, West Kingston, RI 02892 *Tel:* 401-789-5735 *Toll Free Tel:* 800-788-2208 *Fax:* 401-789-3710 *Web Site:* www.apc.com, pg 788

Hanley, Dan, K&R All Media Productions Inc, 28533 Greenfield, Southfield, MI 48076 *Tel:* 248-557-8276 *Toll Free Tel:* 888-802-0420 *Web Site:* www.knr.net, pg 908

Hanley, Terrence, Terry Hanley Audio Systems Inc, 20 Industrial Pkwy, Woburn, MA 01801 *Tel:* 781-932-5300 *Fax:* 781-932-5354 *E-mail:* mail@terryhanleyaudio.com *Web Site:* www.terryhanleyaudio.com, pg 884

Hannah, Maridelle, CaptionMax, 2438 27 Ave S, Minneapolis, MN 55406 *Tel:* 612-341-3566 *Toll Free Tel:* 800-822-3566 *Fax:* 612-341-2345 *Web Site:* www.captionmax.com, pg 820

Hannah, Michael, Cabbage Cases Inc, 1166-C Steelwood Rd, Columbus, OH 43212-1356 *Tel:* 614-486-2495 *Toll Free Tel:* 800-888-2495 *Fax:* 614-486-2788 *E-mail:* sales@cabbagecases.com *Web Site:* www.cabbagecases.com, pg 816

Hannam, Kevin, Yukon Film & Sound Commission (YFSC), Box 2703, Whitehorse, YT Y1A 2C6, Canada *Tel:* 867-667-5400; 867-661-0408 (ext 5400, no charge for calls from within Yukon) *Fax:* 867-393-7040 *E-mail:* info@reelyukon.com *Web Site:* www.reelyukon.com, pg 1106

Hannapel, William "Bill", Stedman Corp, 4167 Stedman Dr, Richland, MI 49083 *Tel:* 269-629-5930 *Toll Free Tel:* 888-629-5960 *E-mail:* info@stedmancorp.com *Web Site:* www.stedmancorp.com, pg 1024

Hannay, Eric, Hannay Reels Inc, 553 State Rte 143, Westerlo, NY 12193-0159 *Tel:* 518-797-3791 *Toll Free Tel:* 877-467-3357 *Fax:* 518-797-3259 *Toll Free Fax:* 800-733-5464 *E-mail:* reels@hannay.com *Web Site:* www.hannay.com, pg 884

Hannigan, Carl, Precision Projection Systems Inc, 17508 Studebaker Rd, Cerritos, CA 90703 *Tel:* 562-865-8552 *Fax:* 562-924-7133 *E-mail:* info@ppsfx.com *Web Site:* www.ppsfx.com, pg 980

Hannon, Ginger, Graphic Laminating LLC, 6185 Cochran Rd, Solon, OH 44139 *Tel:* 440-498-3400 *Toll Free Tel:* 800-345-5300 *Fax:* 440-498-3410 *E-mail:* info@graphiclaminating.com *Web Site:* www.graphiclaminating.com, pg 881

Hannon, Michael, Graphic Laminating LLC, 6185 Cochran Rd, Solon, OH 44139 *Tel:* 440-498-3400 *Toll Free Tel:* 800-345-5300 *Fax:* 440-498-3410 *E-mail:* info@graphiclaminating.com *Web Site:* www.graphiclaminating.com, pg 881

Hanrahan, Dave, Future View Inc, 6035 Blair Rd NW, Washington, DC 20011 *Tel:* 202-882-7400 *Fax:* 202-882-7450 *E-mail:* info@futureview.com *Web Site:* www.futureview.com, pg 874

Hansen, David, High End Systems Inc, 2105 Gracy Farms Lane, Austin, TX 78758 *Tel:* 512-836-2242 *Toll Free Tel:* 800-890-8989 *Fax:* 512-837-5290 *E-mail:* info@highend.com *Web Site:* www.highend.com, pg 888

Hansen, Heidi, Flagstaff Convention & Visitors Bureau, One E Rte 66, Flagstaff, AZ 86001-5303 *Tel:* 928-213-2910 *Toll Free Tel:* 800-842-7293 *E-mail:* cvb@flagstaffaz.gov *Web Site:* www.flagstaffarizona.org, pg 1091

Hansen, Lisa M, Cinetel Films Inc, 8255 Sunset Blvd, Los Angeles, CA 90046-2432 *Tel:* 323-654-4000 *Fax:* 323-650-6400 *E-mail:* info@cinetelfilms.com *Web Site:* cinetelfilms.com, pg 828

Hansen, Scott, Production Resource Group LLC (PRG), 539 Temple Hill Rd, New Windsor, NY 12553-5533 *Tel:* 845-567-5700 *Fax:* 845-567-5800 *E-mail:* info@prg.com *Web Site:* www.prg.com, pg 984

Hanshaw, John, Guerrilla Film Fest, 1421 Massachusetts Ave NW, Suite 202, Washington, DC 20005 *Tel:* 202-234-2889 *E-mail:* gfilmfest@yahoo.com *Web Site:* www.gfilmfest.com, pg 1116

Hansmire, Michel, Sparkworks Media, 325 W Republican St, Seattle, WA 98119 *Tel:* 206-284-5500 *Fax:* 206-284-6611 *E-mail:* info@sparkworksmedia.com *Web Site:* sparkworksmedia.com, pg 1019

Hanson, Kerri, Phoenix Society for Burn Survivors Inc, 1835 RW Berends Dr SW, Grand Rapids, MI 49519-4955 *Tel:* 616-458-2773 *Toll Free Tel:* 800-888-BURN (888-2876) *Fax:* 616-458-2831 *E-mail:* info@phoenix-society.org *Web Site:* www.phoenix-society.org, pg 974

Hanson, Mike, Watson Desking, 26246 Twelve Trees Lane NW, Poulsbo, WA 98370 *Tel:* 360-394-1300 *Toll Free Tel:* 800-426-1202 *Fax:* 360-394-1322 *E-mail:* service@watsondesking.com; info@watsondesking.com *Web Site:* www.watsonfurniture.com, pg 1062

Happeney, Mark, Clark's Audio Visual Services Ltd, 1615 Venables St, Vancouver, BC V5L 2H1, Canada *Tel:* 604-877-8558 *Toll Free Tel:* 800-667-1819 *Fax:* 604-879-2993 *Toll Free Fax:* 800-665-2932 *E-mail:* info@clarksav.com *Web Site:* www.clarksav.com, pg 829

Harada, Akira, Ikegami Electronics (USA) Inc, 37 Brook Ave, Maywood, NJ 07607 *Tel:* 201-368-9171 *Fax:* 201-569-1626 *E-mail:* sales@ikegami.com; service@ikegami.com *Web Site:* www.ikegami.com, pg 894

Harari, David, GLI Sound Systems, 2691 W 15 St, Brooklyn, NY 11224 *Tel:* 718-372-7849 *Toll Free Tel:* 800-GLI-PRO-1 (454-7761) *Fax:* 718-946-4151 *E-mail:* info@glipro.com; sales@glipro.com *Web Site:* www.glipro.com, pg 878

Harbert, Roger, Digital Display Solutions Inc, 12081 Starcrest, San Antonio, TX 78216 *Tel:* 210-404-1233; 210-523-7368 (rentals) *Fax:* 210-979-6585 *E-mail:* lharbert@ddssa.com *Web Site:* www.ddssa.com, pg 847

Hardcastle, Jeff, Hardcastle Films & Video, 7319 Wise Ave, St Louis, MO 63117-1718 *Tel:* 314-647-4200 *Fax:* 314-647-4201, pg 885

Harden, Scott, West Penn Wire, 2833 W Chestnut St, Washington, PA 15301 *Tel:* 724-222-7060 *Toll Free Tel:* 800-245-4964 *Fax:* 724-222-6420 *E-mail:* info@westpenn-wpw.com *Web Site:* www.westpenn-wpw.com, pg 1064

Hardesty, Bryan, EduMedia of Sugar Land, Texas, PO Box 2428, Sugar Land, TX 77487-2428 *Tel:* 281-277-3970 *E-mail:* service@history2u.com *Web Site:* www.history2u.com, pg 857

Hardesty, Todd, Alaska Video Postcards Inc, PO Box 112808, Anchorage, AK 99511-2808 *Tel:* 907-349-8002 *Toll Free Tel:* 800-248-2624 *E-mail:* mail@akvideo.com *Web Site:* www.akvideo.com, pg 780

Harding, Michael, Canadian Learning Co Inc, 95 Vansittart Ave, Woodstock, ON N4S 6E3, Canada *Tel:* 519-537-2360 *Toll Free Tel:* 800-267-2977 (CN) *Fax:* 519-537-1035 *Web Site:* www.canlearn.com, pg 818

Hardy, David, William F White International Inc, 800 Islington Ave, Toronto, ON M8Z 6A1, Canada *Tel:* 416-239-5050 *Toll Free Tel:* 800-465-0160 (CN only); 800-268-2200 *Fax:* 416-207-2777 *E-mail:* info@cinequipwhite.com *Web Site:* www.whites.com, pg 1065

Hardy, Jim, Illuminate Post/Digital Finishing, 3575 Cahuenga Blvd W, 4th fl, Hollywood, CA 90068 *Tel:* 323-969-8822 *Fax:* 323-969-8860 *Web Site:* illuminatehollywood.com, pg 894

Hardy, Jim, Illuminate Studios, 10900 Ventura Blvd, Studio City, CA 90068 *Tel:* 818-769-4500 *Fax:* 818-769-7150 *Web Site:* illuminatehollywood.com, pg 894

Hare, Dave, Tigar Hare Studios, 4485 Matilija Ave, Sherman Oaks, CA 91423 *Tel:* 818-907-6663 *Fax:* 818-907-0693 *E-mail:* info@tigarhare.com *Web Site:* www.tigarhare.com, pg 1040

Harilaou, Gus, Miller Camera Support LLC, 216 Little Falls Rd, Unit 15 & 16, Cedar Grove, NJ 07009-1276 *Tel:* 973-857-8300 *Fax:* 973-857-8188 *E-mail:* service@millertripods.us *Web Site:* www.millertripods.com, pg 943

Harlan, Shirley, Videolady, PO Box 2276, San Bernardino, CA 92406-2276 *Tel:* 909-882-4057 *Fax:* 909-882-4057 *E-mail:* vldy@aol.com *Web Site:* videoladystudios.com, pg 1057

Harlan, W Bruce, Lighting & Production Equipment Inc, 590 Travis St, Atlanta, GA 30318 *Tel:* 404-352-0464 *Toll Free Tel:* 800-275-3721 *Fax:* 404-351-4399 *Web Site:* www.lpe.com, pg 920

Harless, Joe, Shaker Microphones & Promotions Inc, PO Box 1070, Diamond City, AR 72630-1070 *Tel:* 870-422-2988 *E-mail:* shakermicrophone@shakermicrophone.net *Web Site:* www.shakermicrophone.net, pg 1008

Harlow, Rocky, Production Advantage Inc, 301 Avenue "D", Suite 10, Williston, VT 05495 *Tel:* 802-651-6915 *Toll Free Tel:* 800-424-9991 *Fax:* 802-651-6914 *Toll Free Fax:* 877-424-9991 *E-mail:* sales@proadv.com; orders@proadv.com *Web Site:* www.productionadvantageonline.com, pg 984

Harmer, Kris, Voice of Democracy Scholarship Program, 406 W 34 St, Kansas City, MO 64111 *Tel:* 816-968-1117 *Fax:* 816-968-1149 *Web Site:* www.vfw.org, pg 1129

Harmon, Bobby, Harmon's Audio-Visual Services, 2533 Crystal Dr, Fort Myers, FL 33966 *Tel:* 239-939-2273 *Fax:* 239-939-5966 *E-mail:* info@harmonsav.com *Web Site:* www.harmonsav.com, pg 885

Harmon, Dan, Starburns Industries, 1700 W Burbank Blvd, Burbank, CA 91506 *Tel:* 818-433-3300 *Fax:* 818-433-3383 *Web Site:* www.starburnsindustries.com, pg 1024

Harmon, James R, Harmon's Audio-Visual Services, 2533 Crystal Dr, Fort Myers, FL 33966 *Tel:* 239-939-2273 *Fax:* 239-939-5966 *E-mail:* info@harmonsav.com *Web Site:* www.harmonsav.com, pg 885

Harmon, Nicholas, Verilux® - The Healthy Lighting Co, 340 Mad River Park, Suite 1, Waitsfield, VT 05673 *Tel:* 802-496-3101 *Toll Free Tel:* 888-544-4865 (cust support); 800-454-4408 (orders) *Fax:* 802-496-3105 (orders) *E-mail:* info@verilux.com *Web Site:* www.verilux.com, pg 1053

Harmon, Rachel, Sagebrush Video Productions, 2304 County Rd 370, Otis, KS 67565 *Tel:* 785-222-3313 *Toll Free Tel:* 800-457-3453 *Web Site:* www.sagebrushvideo.com, pg 1001

Harmoney, Betty L, Lloyd F McKinney Associates Inc, 25350 Cypress Ave, Hayward, CA 94544 *Tel:* 510-783-8043 *Fax:* 510-783-2130 *Web Site:* www.mckinneyassoc.com, pg 935

Harms, Bjorn, Pioneer Research Inc, 97 Foster Rd, Suite 5, Moorestown, NJ 08057 *Tel:* 856-866-9191 *Toll Free Tel:* 800-257-7742 *Fax:* 856-866-8615 *E-mail:* info@pioneer-research.com *Web Site:* www.pioneer-research.com, pg 976

Harms, Fred, Extraordinary Demos, 2131 Yellowstar Lane, Naperville, IL 60564-5330 *Tel:* 630-904-3636 *Web Site:* www.extraordinarydemos.com, pg 864

Harms, Jocelyn, SESAC Inc, 55 Music Sq E, Nashville, TN 37203 *Tel:* 615-320-0055 *Fax:* 615-963-3527 *Web Site:* www.sesac.com, pg 1088

Harms, Sven E, Pioneer Research Inc, 97 Foster Rd, Suite 5, Moorestown, NJ 08057 *Tel:* 856-866-9191 *Toll Free Tel:* 800-257-7742 *Fax:* 856-866-8615 *E-mail:* info@pioneer-research.com *Web Site:* www.pioneer-research.com, pg 976

Harn, Dee Ann, Bulbman Inc, 630 Sunshine Lane, Reno, NV 89502 *Tel:* 775-788-5661 *Toll Free Tel:* 800-648-1163 *Fax:* 775-329-6599 *Toll Free Fax:* 800-548-6216 *E-mail:* service@bulbman.com *Web Site:* www.bulbman.com, pg 815

Harnell, Stewart D, Cinema Concepts, 2030 Powers Ferry Rd, Suite 214, Atlanta, GA 30339 *Tel:* 770-956-7460 *Toll Free Tel:* 800-SHOWADS (746-9237) *Fax:* 770-956-8358 *E-mail:* info@cinemaconcepts.com *Web Site:* www.cinemaconcepts.com, pg 827

Harner, Bud, The Verve Music Group, 134 W 25 St, 5th fl, New York, NY 10001 *Tel:* 212-494-0078 *E-mail:* contact@vervemusicgroup.com *Web Site:* www.vervemusicgroup.com; www.umusic.com, pg 1053

Harold, Jeremy, United Sound & Electronics, 525 E Main St, Bridgeport, WV 26330 *Tel:* 304-842-6030 *E-mail:* questions@unitedsound.net *Web Site:* www.unitedsound.net, pg 1048

Harold, Rob, United Sound & Electronics, 525 E Main St, Bridgeport, WV 26330 *Tel:* 304-842-6030 *E-mail:* questions@unitedsound.net *Web Site:* www.unitedsound.net, pg 1048

Harper, Kathryn, Astronomical Society of the Pacific, 390 Ashton Ave, San Francisco, CA 94112 *Tel:* 415-337-1100 *Toll Free Tel:* 800-335-2624 *Fax:* 415-337-5205 *E-mail:* service@astrosociety.org *Web Site:* astrosociety.org, pg 792

Harper, Malcolm H Jr, Reelsound Recording Co, 701 Southern Dr, Buda, TX 78610 *Tel:* 512-312-1610; 512-422-7098 (cell) *Web Site:* www.reelsound-usa.com, pg 994

Harrah, Jerry, Harrah's Theatre Equipment Co, 25613 Dollar St, Unit 1, Hayward, CA 94544 *Tel:* 510-881-4989 *Fax:* 510-881-0448, pg 885

Harrell, Suzanne, Sound & Vision Communications Inc, 4601 N "A" St, Tampa, FL 33609-1909 *Tel:* 813-642-4706 *Web Site:* www.gosvc.com, pg 1016

Harris, Alan I, AiH Group Inc, 709 S Aiken Ave, Pittsburgh, PA 15232 *Tel:* 412-687-5700 *E-mail:* aih@aihgroup.com *Web Site:* www.aihgroup.com, pg 779

Harris, Aleta, Spot Media Production Group, 2745 Locust St, St Louis, MO 63103 *Tel:* 314-667-5915 *E-mail:* info@spotmpg.com *Web Site:* www.spotmpg.com, pg 1022

Harris, Bill, Channell One Video, PO Box 399, Epping, NH 03042-0399 *Tel:* 603-679-6796 *Toll Free Tel:* 888-722-3843 (natl) *E-mail:* racevid@earthlink.net *Web Site:* www.racevideo.com, pg 824

Harris, Dave, Studio B Mastering, 821 Louise Ave, Charlotte, NC 28204 *Tel:* 704-372-9661 *Web Site:* www.studiobmastering.com, pg 1026

Harris, Don, Paramount Pictures Corporation, 5555 Melrose Ave, Los Angeles, CA 90038 *Tel:* 323-956-8398 *Web Site:* www.paramount.com, pg 969

Harris, Donna, Catalina Island Film Commission, One Green Pier, Avalon, CA 90704-0217 *Tel:* 310-510-7649 *Fax:* 310-510-7607 *Web Site:* www.catalinachamber.com/mediafilming/contact, pg 1092

Harris, Ed, Myriad Productions, 415 Barlow Ct, Johns Creek, GA 30022 *Tel:* 678-417-0043 *Fax:* 678-417-0043, pg 951

Harris, Greg, Jameco Electronics, 1355 Shoreway Rd, Belmont, CA 94002-4105 *Tel:* 650-592-8097 *Toll Free Tel:* 800-831-4242 (orders); 800-536-4316 (cust serv) *Fax:* 650-592-2503 *Toll Free Fax:* 800-237-6948 *E-mail:* info@jameco.com; sales@jameco.com *Web Site:* www.jameco.com, pg 903

Harris, Jack H, Worldwide Entertainment Corp, 135 S McCarty Dr, Suite 101, Beverly Hills, CA 90212 *Tel:* 310-858-1272 *Fax:* 310-858-3774, pg 1070

Harris, Joel, Avidex Inc, 13555 Bel-Red Rd, Suite 226, Bellevue, MA 98005 *Tel:* 425-643-0330 *Fax:* 425-274-7091 *E-mail:* info@avidexav.com *Web Site:* www.avidexav.com, pg 799

Harris, John, Blue Room Post, MBS Raleigh Studios, Bldg 5-A, Suite 100, 1600 Rosecrans Ave, Manhattan Beach, CA 90266 *Tel:* 310-727-2600 *Web Site:* www.blueroompost.com, pg 810

Harris, Less, Canamedia Inc, 1540 Cornwall Rd, Suite 216, Oakville, ON L6J 7W5, Canada *Tel:* 416-363-6765 *Toll Free Tel:* 866-999-5292 *Fax:* 416-363-7834 *Web Site:* www.canamedia.com, pg 818

Harris, Nancy, American Film Institute (AFI), Attn: Facilities Off, 2021 N Western Ave, Los Angeles, CA 90027-1657 *Tel:* 323-856-7600 *Toll Free Tel:* 800-774-4AFI (774-4234 membership) *Fax:* 323-467-4578 *E-mail:* information@afi.com *Web Site:* www.afi.com, pg 1076

Harris, Phillip, Association for Educational Communications & Technology (AECT), 320 W Eighth St, Suite 101, Bloomington, IN 47404-3745 *Tel:* 812-335-7675 *Toll Free Tel:* 877-677-AECT (677-2328) *Fax:* 812-335-7678 *E-mail:* aect@aect.org *Web Site:* www.aect.org, pg 1078

Harris, Phillip, James W Brown Publication Award, 320 W Eighth St, Suite 101, Bloomington, IN 47404-3745 *Tel:* 812-335-7675 *Toll Free Tel:* 877-677-AECT (677-2328) *Fax:* 812-335-7678 *E-mail:* aect@aect.org *Web Site:* www.aect.org, pg 1110

Harris, Phillip, Carl F & Viola V Mahnke Multimedia Award, 320 W Eighth St, Suite 101, Bloomington, IN 47404-3745 *Tel:* 812-335-7675 *Toll Free Tel:* 877-677-AECT (677-2328) *Fax:* 812-335-7678 *E-mail:* aect@aect.org *Web Site:* www.aect.org, pg 1119

Harris, Robert, Harris Communications Inc, 15155 Technology Dr, Eden Prairie, MN 55344 *Tel:* 952-906-1180 *Toll Free Tel:* 800-825-6758 *Fax:* 952-906-1099 *E-mail:* info@harriscomm.com *Web Site:* www.harriscomm.com, pg 885

Harris, Ron, DuArt, 245 W 55 St, New York, NY 10019 *Tel:* 212-757-4580 *Fax:* 212-977-5609 *E-mail:* info@duart.com *Web Site:* www.duart.com, pg 853

Harris, Russell, Perennial Pictures Film Corp, 2102 E 52 St, Indianapolis, IN 46205 *Tel:* 317-253-1519 *E-mail:* mail@perennialpictures.com *Web Site:* www.perennialpictures.com, pg 973

Harrison, Brad, Audioarts Engineering, 600 Industrial Dr, New Bern, NC 28562 *Tel:* 252-638-7000 *Fax:* 252-637-1285; 252-635-4857 (sales) *E-mail:* sales@wheatstone.com *Web Site:* www.wheatstone.com, pg 796

Harrison, Denise, PSNI (Professional Systems Network Inc), 1831 E 71 St, Tulsa, OK 74136 *Tel:* 918-388-1343 *Web Site:* www.psni.org, pg 1088

Harrison, Graeme, BIAMP Systems, 9300 SW Gemini Dr, Beaverton, OR 97008 *Tel:* 503-641-7287 *Toll Free Tel:* 800-826-1457 (US & CN) *Fax:* 503-626-0281 *E-mail:* biampinfo@biamp.com; salesteam@biamp.com *Web Site:* www.biamp.com, pg 806

Harrison, Jeff, Harrison Brothers, 47 N Chatham Pkwy, Chapel Hill, NC 27517 *Toll Free Tel:* 866-386-8335; 800-327-4414 *Toll Free Fax:* 800-327-6651 *E-mail:* info@harrisonbros.com *Web Site:* www.thetapeworks.com, pg 885

Harrison, Joshua, St Barth Film Festival, 410 W 24 St, New York, NY 10011 *Tel:* 212-989-8004 *Fax:* 212-727-1774 *E-mail:* staff@stbarthff.org *Web Site:* www.stbarthff.org, pg 1126

Harrison, Les, Hollywood Sound Systems, 1541 N Wilcox Ave, Hollywood, CA 90028 *Tel:* 323-466-2416 *Fax:* 323-460-2676 *Web Site:* www.hollywoodsound.com, pg 890

Harrison, Patricia de Stacy, Corporation for Public Broadcasting (CPB), 401 Ninth St NW, Washington, DC 20004-2129 *Tel:* 202-879-9600 *Toll Free Tel:* 800-272-2190 (general comments) *Fax:* 202-879-9700 *E-mail:* comments@cpb.org *Web Site:* www.cpb.org, pg 1081

Harrison, Reuben, Alliant Event Services, 196 University Pkwy, Pomona, CA 91768 *Tel:* 909-622-3306 *Toll Free Tel:* 800-851-5415 *Fax:* 909-622-3917 *E-mail:* marketing@alliantevents.com *Web Site:* www.alliantevents.com, pg 781

Harrison, Wendell, Rebirth/Wenha Records, 81 Chandler St, Detroit, MI 48202 *Tel:* 313-875-0289, pg 993

Harry, Guy, Potomac Instruments Inc, 7309 Grove Rd, Unit D, Frederick, MD 21704 *Tel:* 301-696-5550 *Fax:* 301-696-5553 *E-mail:* comments@pi-usa.com *Web Site:* www.pi-usa.com, pg 979

Hart, Barry, Pro-Tape & Specialities Inc, 621 Rte 1 S, Suite B, North Brunswick, NJ 08902 *Tel:* 732-346-0900 *Toll Free Tel:* 800-345-0234 *Fax:* 732-729-7373 *Web Site:* www.protapes.com, pg 983

Hart, Timothy S, Media Systems Design Group, 4253 Stewart Ave, Los Angeles, CA 90066 *Tel:* 310-398-0281 *Fax:* 310-398-9451 *Web Site:* www.msd-group.com, pg 937

Harter, Jim, Ghent Manufacturing, 2999 Henkle Dr, Lebanon, OH 45036-9260 *Tel:* 513-932-3445 *Toll Free Tel:* 800-543-0550 *Fax:* 513-932-9252 *E-mail:* customer_service@ghent.com *Web Site:* www.ghent.com, pg 878

Harter, Samantha, HD House, 6312 NW 77 Ct, Miami, FL 33166 *Tel:* 305-597-7359 *Fax:* 305-597-7027 *Web Site:* thehdhouse.com, pg 886

Hartley, Colleen S, Video Wisconsin Inc, 18110 W Bluemound Rd, Brookfield, WI 53045 *Tel:* 262-785-1110 *Fax:* 262-785-9827 *Web Site:* www.videowisconsin.tv, pg 1056

Hartley, Ted, RKO Pictures Inc, 2034 Broadway, Santa Monica, CA 90404 *Tel:* 310-277-0707 *Fax:* 310-566-8940 *E-mail:* info@rko.com *Web Site:* www.rko.com, pg 997

Hartman, Janelle, Heywood Broun Award, 501 Third St NW, Washington, DC 20001-2706 *Tel:* 202-434-7177 *Fax:* 202-434-1472 *Web Site:* www.newsguild.org, pg 1110

Hartman, Rob, Lee Hartman & Sons Inc, 3236 Cove Rd NW, Roanoke, VA 24017 *Tel:* 540-366-3493 *Toll Free Tel:* 800-344-1832 *Fax:* 540-362-4659 *E-mail:* info@leehartman.com *Web Site:* www.leehartman.com, pg 918

Hartman, Steve M, Lee Hartman & Sons Inc, 3236 Cove Rd NW, Roanoke, VA 24017 *Tel:* 540-366-3493 *Toll Free Tel:* 800-344-1832 *Fax:* 540-362-4659 *E-mail:* info@leehartman.com *Web Site:* www.leehartman.com, pg 918

Hartmann, Jess, Promax Systems, 2850 S Fairview St, Santa Ana, CA 97204 *Tel:* 949-861-2700 *Toll Free Tel:* 800-977-6629 *Fax:* 949-727-2040 *E-mail:* customer@promax.com; sales@promax.com *Web Site:* www.promax.com, pg 986

Hartogs, Joan, Landmark Media Inc, 3450 Slade Run Dr, Falls Church, VA 22042 *Tel:* 703-241-2030 *Toll Free Tel:* 800-342-4336 *Fax:* 703-536-9540 *E-mail:* info@landmarkmedia.com; landmrkmed@aol.com *Web Site:* www.landmarkmedia.com, pg 915

Hartogs, Michael, Landmark Media Inc, 3450 Slade Run Dr, Falls Church, VA 22042 *Tel:* 703-241-2030 *Toll Free Tel:* 800-342-4336 *Fax:* 703-536-9540 *E-mail:* info@landmarkmedia.com; landmrkmed@aol.com *Web Site:* www.landmarkmedia.com, pg 915

Hartogs, Peter, Landmark Media Inc, 3450 Slade Run Dr, Falls Church, VA 22042 *Tel:* 703-241-2030 *Toll Free Tel:* 800-342-4336 *Fax:* 703-536-9540 *E-mail:* info@landmarkmedia.com; landmrkmed@aol.com *Web Site:* www.landmarkmedia.com, pg 915

Hartogs, Richard, Landmark Media Inc, 3450 Slade Run Dr, Falls Church, VA 22042 *Tel:* 703-241-2030 *Toll Free Tel:* 800-342-4336 *Fax:* 703-536-9540 *E-mail:* info@landmarkmedia.com; landmrkmed@aol.com *Web Site:* www.landmarkmedia.com, pg 915

Harvey, Kent, Kaboom Productions, 1465 Illinois St, San Francisco, CA 94107 *Tel:* 415-434-2666 *Fax:* 415-970-8548 *E-mail:* updates@kaboomproductions.com *Web Site:* kaboomproductions.com, pg 907

Harwood, Rob, Convergent Media Systems, 190 Bluegrass Valley Pkwy, Alpharetta, GA 30005-2204 *Tel:* 770-369-9000 *Toll Free Tel:* 800-877-7804 *Fax:* 770-369-9100 *E-mail:* convergent@convergent.com *Web Site:* www.convergent.com, pg 836

Haskins, Nate, SNL Kagan Media & Communications, One SNL Plaza, 212 Seventh St NE, Charlottesville, VA 22902 *Tel:* 434-977-1600 *Toll Free Tel:* 866-296-3743 *Fax:* 434-977-4466 *E-mail:* snlkagansales@snl.com *Web Site:* www.snl.com, pg 1014

Haskins, William, Dot Hill Systems Corp, 1351 S Sunset St, Longmont, CO 80501-6533 *Tel:* 303-845-3200 *Toll Free Tel:* 800-872-2783 *Fax:* 303-845-3655 *E-mail:* support@dothill.com; websales@dothill.com *Web Site:* www.dothill.com, pg 851

Haskitt, Robert, Extreme Reach Inc, 75 Second Ave, Suite 720, Needham, MA 02494 *Tel:* 781-577-2016 *E-mail:* sales@extremereach.com; press@extremereach.com *Web Site:* www.extremereach.com, pg 864

Haspel, Gary, Thomas Cestare Inc, 188 Herricks Rd, Mineola, NY 11502 *Tel:* 516-742-5550 *Fax:* 516-742-5551 *E-mail:* cestare@aol.com *Web Site:* www.thomascestareinc.com, pg 823

Hass, Jeff, VDO Lab Inc, 400 Tarrytown Rd, White Plains, NY 10607-1314 *Tel:* 914-681-0849; 914-949-1741 *Fax:* 914-949-5743 *E-mail:* sales@vdolab.net *Web Site:* vdolab.net, pg 1052

Hassairi, Nadia, Software & Information Industry Association (SIIA), 1090 Vermont Ave NW, 6th fl, Washington, DC 20005-4095 *Tel:* 202-289-7442 *Fax:* 202-289-7097 *Web Site:* www.siia.net, pg 1089

Hasselrot, Karl, KOH Design Inc, 540 Barnum Ave, Bridgeport, CT 06608 *Tel:* 203-336-1334 *Fax:* 203-335-9361 *E-mail:* info@kohdesign.com *Web Site:* www.kohdesign.com, pg 913

Hastings, Doug, Avatar Studios, 2675 Scott Ave, Suite G, St Louis, MO 63103 *Tel:* 314-533-2242 *Fax:* 314-533-3349 *Web Site:* www.avatar-studios.com, pg 798

Hastings, Jeff, Inferno Films, 3404 Guadalupe St, Austin, TX 78705 *Tel:* 512-302-9009 *Fax:* 512-302-9022 *Web Site:* www.infernofilms.com, pg 898

Hatch, Gary S, ATCi (Antenna Technology Communication Solutions Inc), 450 N McKemy Ave, Chandler, AZ 85226 *Tel:* 480-844-8501 *Fax:* 480-898-7667 *Web Site:* www.atci.com, pg 793

Hatch, Ryan, F&F Productions, 14333 Myerlake Circle, Clearwater, FL 33760 *Tel:* 727-530-5000 *Fax:* 727-535-6547 *Web Site:* www.fandfhd.tv, pg 865

Hathaway, Milt, FitzCo Sound Inc, 4300 W Wall St, Bldg B, Midland, TX 79703 *Tel:* 432-684-0861 *Fax:* 432-682-9978 *Web Site:* www.fitzcosound.com, pg 869

Hatic, Halid, Bexel Corp, 2701 N Ontario St, Burbank, CA 91504 *Tel:* 818-565-4322 *Toll Free Tel:* 800-225-6185 (tech support) *E-mail:* rentals@bexel.com *Web Site:* www.bexel.com, pg 806

Hauck, Michael, ASPRS: The Imaging and Geospatial Information Society, 5410 Grosvenor Lane, Suite 210, Bethesda, MD 20814-2160 *Tel:* 301-493-0290 *Fax:* 301-493-0208 *E-mail:* asprs@asprs.org *Web Site:* www.asprs.org, pg 1078

Haupt, Jonathan, University of South Carolina Press, 1600 Hampton St, Colimbia, SC 29208 *Tel:* 803-777-5243 *Toll Free Tel:* 800-768-2500 *Toll Free Fax:* 800-868-0740 *Web Site:* www.sc.edu/uscpress, pg 1050

Hauschel, Raymond, Z-Axis Corp, 4600 S Ulster St, Suite 270, Denver, CO 80237 *Tel:* 303-713-0200 *Toll Free Tel:* 800-827-2947 *E-mail:* info@zaxis.com *Web Site:* www.zaxis.com, pg 1073

Hause, Julie, Open Text Corp, 275 Frank Tompa Dr, Waterloo, ON N2L 0A1, Canada *Tel:* 519-888-7111 *Toll Free Tel:* 800-499-6544; 800-4996-5440 (intl) *Fax:* 519-888-0677 *E-mail:* support@opentext.com *Web Site:* www.opentext.com, pg 964

Havelka, Tony, Tek Gear, 938 Corydon Ave, Winnipeg, MB R3M 0Y5, Canada *Tel:* 204-988-3001 *Fax:* 204-988-3050 *E-mail:* sales@tekgear.com *Web Site:* tekgear.com, pg 1035

Havers, Chuck, Crescent/Stonco, 200 Franklin Square Dr, Somerset, NJ 08873 *Toll Free Tel:* 800-334-2212 *Web Site:* www.crescent-stonco.com/led; www.csgreenlightingsolutions.com, pg 839

Hawes-Davis, Doug, High Plains Films, PO Box 8796, Missoula, MT 59807 *Tel:* 406-543-6726 *E-mail:* yak@highplainsfilms.org *Web Site:* www.highplainsfilms.org, pg 889

Hawkins, Philip, R L Drake Co, 9900 Springboro Pike, Miamisburg, OH 45342 *Tel:* 937-746-4556 *Fax:* 937-806-1510 (sales); 937-806-1511 (gen) *E-mail:* salesgroup@rldrake.net *Web Site:* www.rldrake.com, pg 852

Hay, Evan, Samson Technologies Corp, 45 Gilpin Ave, Hauppauge, NY 11788-4723 *Tel:* 631-784-2200 *Fax:* 631-784-2201 *E-mail:* info@samsontech.com *Web Site:* www.samsontech.com, pg 1002

Hayash, Ted, Digital Film Studios, 11800 Sheldon St, Unit C/D, Sun Valley, CA 91352 *Tel:* 818-771-0019 *Fax:* 818-351-1155 *E-mail:* info@digitalfilmstudios.com *Web Site:* www.digitalfilmstudios.com, pg 847

Hayashi, Michael T, Time Warner Cable, 60 Columbus Circle, 17th fl, New York, NY 10023 *Tel:* 212-364-8200 *Web Site:* www.timewarnercable.com, pg 1040

Hayden, Tom, TSR/Baja Damabi Records, 18653 Ventura Blvd, Suite 513, Tarzana, CA 91356 *Tel:* 818-702-9902, pg 1046

Hayes, Barbara, Axxis Inc, 845 S Ninth St, Louisville, KY 40203 *Tel:* 502-568-6030 *Fax:* 502-568-6204 *E-mail:* info@axxisinc.com *Web Site:* www.axxisinc.com, pg 800

Hayes, Chris, Showman Fabricators Inc, 47-22 Pearson Place, Long Island City, NY 11101 *Tel:* 718-935-9899 *Fax:* 718-855-9823 *E-mail:* info@showfab.com *Web Site:* www.showfab.com, pg 1010

Hayes, Elizabeth, French American Cultural Exchange (FACE), 972 Fifth Ave, New York, NY 10021 *Tel:* 212-439-1449 *Fax:* 212-439-1455 *E-mail:* info@facecouncil.org *Web Site:* www.facecouncil.org, pg 873

Hayes, Steve, Watson Desking, 26246 Twelve Trees Lane NW, Poulsbo, WA 98370 *Tel:* 360-394-1300 *Toll Free Tel:* 800-426-1202 *Fax:* 360-394-1322 *E-mail:* service@watsondesking.com; info@watsondesking.com *Web Site:* www.watsonfurniture.com, pg 1062

Hayes, Tom, Telemotions LLC, 405 E 54 St, Suite 3-N, New York, NY 10022 *Tel:* 212-486-3010 *Web Site:* www.telemotions.net, pg 1036

Hayman, Gerald, PowerTechnology Southeast Inc, 634 State Rd 44, Leesburg, FL 34748 *Tel:* 352-365-2777 *Toll Free Tel:* 800-760-0027 *Fax:* 352-787-5545 *E-mail:* powertech@powertech-gen.com *Web Site:* www.powertech-gen.com, pg 979

Haymes, Jeff H, Aardvark Productions LLC, 6738 S La Rosa Dr, Tempe, AZ 85283-3737 *Tel:* 480-775-8237 *Fax:* 480-775-8237 *E-mail:* aardvarkproductions@cox.net *Web Site:* www.aardvarkproductionsllc.com, pg 772

Haynes, Pam, West Virginia Film Office, 90 MacCorkle Ave SW, South Charleston, WV 25303 *Toll Free Tel:* 866-6WV-FILM (698-3456) *Fax:* 304-558-1662 *Web Site:* wvfilm.wvcommerce.org, pg 1103

Haynor, Dow, Golden Lamb Productions, 47 Schoolhouse Rd, Nassau, NY 12123 *Tel:* 518-766-4358 *Web Site:* www.glpvideoproduction.com, pg 880

Hays, John, Inner Traditions International, One Park St, Rochester, VT 05767 *Tel:* 802-767-3174 *Toll Free Tel:* 800-246-8648 *Fax:* 802-767-3726 *E-mail:* customerservice@innertraditions.com *Web Site:* www.innertraditions.com, pg 898

Hays, Ray, PRC Digital Media, 250-A Park St, Jacksonville, FL 32204 *Tel:* 904-354-1500 *E-mail:* info@prcdigital.com *Web Site:* www.prcdigital.com, pg 980

Hays, Scott, REI - Radio Engineering Industries, 6534 "L" St, Omaha, NE 68117 *Tel:* 402-339-2200 *Toll Free Tel:* 800-228-9275 (sales); 877-726-4617 (tech support) *Fax:* 402-339-1704 *E-mail:* info@radioeng.com; orderdesk@radioeng.com *Web Site:* www.radioeng.com, pg 994

Haythorn, Gregg, PortaBrace Inc, PO Box 220, North Bennington, VT 05257-0220 *Tel:* 802-442-8171 *Fax:* 802-442-9118 *E-mail:* info@portabrace.com *Web Site:* www.portabrace.com, pg 978

Hayward, Joe, Wintergreen Learning Materials, 3075 Line 8, RR2, Bradford, ON L3Z 2A5, Canada *Toll Free Tel:* 800-268-1268 *Toll Free Fax:* 800-567-8054 *E-mail:* info@wintergreen.ca *Web Site:* www.wintergreen.ca, pg 1068

Hayward, Michael, Wintergreen Learning Materials, 3075 Line 8, RR2, Bradford, ON L3Z 2A5, Canada *Toll Free Tel:* 800-268-1268 *Toll Free Fax:* 800-567-8054 *E-mail:* info@wintergreen.ca *Web Site:* www.wintergreen.ca, pg 1068

Head, Tom, EASI, 2296 Country Club Dr, Mason City, IA 50401 *Tel:* 641-424-5079 *Toll Free Tel:* 888-327-4797 *Fax:* 641-424-8869 *Web Site:* www.easisat.com, pg 855

Healey, Mike, Bitcentral Inc, 4340 Von Karman Ave, Suite 400, Newport Beach, CA 92660 *Tel:* 949-253-9000 *E-mail:* sales@bitcentral.com; support@bitcentral.com *Web Site:* www.bitcentral.com, pg 808

Healy, Eileen, Chimera®, 1812 Valtec Lane, Boulder, CO 80301 *Tel:* 303-444-8000 *Toll Free Tel:* 888-444-1812 *Fax:* 303-444-8303 *E-mail:* salesinfo@chimeralighting.com *Web Site:* chimeralighting.com, pg 825

Healy, Laura, Hartley Film Foundation, 49 Richmondville Ave, Suite 204, Westport, CT 06880 *Tel:* 203-226-9500 *Toll Free Tel:* 800-937-1819 *Fax:* 203-227-6938 *E-mail:* info@hartleyfoundation.org *Web Site:* www.hartleyfoundation.org, pg 885

Heaney, John P, Shook Mobile Technology LP, 7451 FM 3009, Schertz, TX 78154 *Tel:* 210-651-5700 *Toll Free Tel:* 888-651-5775 *Fax:* 210-651-5220 *E-mail:* shook@shook-usa.com *Web Site:* www.shook-usa.com, pg 1009

Heape, Steven R, Rich-Heape Films Inc, 5952 Royal Lane, Suite 254, Dallas, TX 75230 *Tel:* 214-696-6916 *Toll Free Tel:* 888-600-2922 *Fax:* 214-696-6306 *Web Site:* www.richheape.com, pg 996

Heard, Janet, Davies Publishing Inc, 32 S Raymond Ave, Suite 4, Pasadena, CA 91105-1935 *Tel:* 626-792-3046 *Toll Free Tel:* 877-792-0005 *Fax:* 626-792-5308 *E-mail:* order@daviespublishing.com *Web Site:* daviespublishing.com, pg 843

Hearn, Cindy, PRG, 1053 Willingham Dr, Atlanta, GA 30344 *Tel:* 404-214-4800 *Toll Free Tel:* 888-844-4225 *Fax:* 404-214-4801 *E-mail:* info@hitechrent.com *Web Site:* www.prg.com, pg 981

Hearon, Craig, ACS Technologies, 180 N Dunbarton Dr, Florence, SC 29501 *Tel:* 843-662-1681 *Toll Free Tel:* 800-736-7425 *Fax:* 843-669-3198 *E-mail:* info@acstechnologies.com *Web Site:* www.acstechnologies.com, pg 775

Heath, Rosemary F, Goddard Design Co, 51 Nassau Ave, Brooklyn, NY 11222 *Tel:* 718-599-0170 *Fax:* 718-599-0172 *E-mail:* sales@goddarddesign.com *Web Site:* www.goddarddesign.com, pg 880

Hebel, Kurt, Symbolic Sound Corp, PO Box 2549, Champaign, IL 61825-2549 *Tel:* 217-355-6273 *Fax:* 217-355-6562 *E-mail:* info-kyma@symbolicsound.com *Web Site:* www.symbolicsound.com, pg 1030

Hebert, Ray, Kabuki, 63 rue Gaudet, Cap-Pele, NB E4N 1T8, Canada *Tel:* 506-577-6326 *Toll Free Tel:* 800-461-7625 *Fax:* 506-577-2875 *Toll Free Fax:* 800-461-4329 *E-mail:* info@kabuki.com *Web Site:* www.kabuki.com, pg 907

Hecht, Ken, Phase Technology, 6400 Youngerman Circle, Jacksonville, FL 32244 *Tel:* 913-663-5600 *Toll Free Tel:* 800-874-7076; 888-PHASE-TK (742-7385) *Fax:* 913-663-3200 *E-mail:* sales@phasetech.com *Web Site:* www.phasetech.com, pg 973

Hecht, Marlen, Teatown Communications Group, 1560 Broadway, New York, NY 10036 *Tel:* 212-302-0722 *E-mail:* info@teatown.tv *Web Site:* www.teatown.tv, pg 1033

Heck, Jay, Laser Fantasy/HECK Industries/Photon Manufacturing, 4228 159 Ave SE, Bellevue, WA 98006 *Tel:* 425-890-6026 (software & creative support); 425-214-0771 (hardware & tech support) *Fax:* 425-296-4255 *E-mail:* info@heckindustries.com; info@photonmanufacturing.com *Web Site:* www.heckindustries.com; www.photonmanufacturing.com, pg 916

Hecker, Sarah, Prevent Blindness America, 211 W Wacker Dr, Suite 1700, Chicago, IL 60606 *Tel:* 312-363-6001 *Toll Free Tel:* 800-331-2020 *Fax:* 312-363-6052 *E-mail:* info@preventblindness.org *Web Site:* www.preventblindness.org, pg 981

Hedges, Mary Allyn, Oxford Film Commission, 415 S Lamar Blvd, Oxford, MS 38655 *Tel:* 662-232-2477 *Toll Free Tel:* 800-758-9177 *E-mail:* tourism@visitoxfordms.com *Web Site:* visitoxfordms.com, pg 1099

Hedges, Thomas D, American Visions, One Deerfield Lane, Cedar Rapids, IA 52403 *Tel:* 319-360-3211 *E-mail:* info@americanvisions.org *Web Site:* www.americanvisions.org, pg 785

Hedlund, Dennis M, Kultur International Films Ltd Inc, 195 Hwy 36, West Long Branch, NJ 07764 *Tel:* 732-229-2343 *Toll Free Tel:* 800-573-3782 *Toll Free Fax:* 866-205-2744 *E-mail:* support@kultur.com *Web Site:* www.kultur.com, pg 914

Hedquist, Jeffrey P, Hedquist Productions Inc, PO Box 1475, Fairfield, IA 52556-1475 *Tel:* 641-472-6708 *Toll Free Fax:* 855-510-5726 *Web Site:* www.hedquist.com, pg 887

Hedrick, Tim, EASI, 2296 Country Club Dr, Mason City, IA 50401 *Tel:* 641-424-5079 *Toll Free Tel:* 888-327-4797 *Fax:* 641-424-8869 *Web Site:* www.easisat.com, pg 855

Heffernan, Paul, Heffernan Audio Visual, 616 W Rhapsody, San Antonio, TX 78216 *Tel:* 210-732-4333 *Fax:* 210-732-5906 *E-mail:* sales@heffernanav.com *Web Site:* www.heffernanav.com, pg 887

Hefty, Gwen, CCH Continuing Education, 4025 W Peterson Ave, Chicago, IL 60646-6085 *Tel:* 773-866-3648 *Toll Free Tel:* 800-248-3248 *Fax:* 773-866-3084 *Web Site:* www.cch.com, pg 821

Hegedus, Chris, Pennebaker Hegedus Films Inc, 262 W 91 St, New York, NY 10024 *Tel:* 212-496-9195 *Fax:* 212-496-8195 *Web Site:* phfilms.com, pg 972

Hegge, Steve, Blonder Tongue Laboratories Inc, One Jake Brown Rd, Old Bridge, NJ 08857 *Tel:* 732-679-4000 *Toll Free Tel:* 800-523-6049 *Fax:* 732-679-4353 *E-mail:* custsvc@blondertongue.com; btglobalsales@blondertongue.com (other than US & CN) *Web Site:* www.blondertongue.com, pg 809

Heiber, Robert J, Chace Audio by Deluxe, 201 S Victory Blvd, Burbank, CA 91502-2349 *Toll Free Tel:* 800-842-8346 *Web Site:* www.chace.com, pg 823

Heidemann, Mark, Historic Films, 211 Third St, Greenport, NY 11944 *Tel:* 631-477-9700 *Toll Free Tel:* 800-249-1940 *Fax:* 631-477-9800 *E-mail:* info@historicfilms.com *Web Site:* www.historicfilms.com, pg 889

Heidenreich, Josh, Staging Resources Inc, 257 E Helen Rd, Palatine, IL 60067 *Tel:* 847-963-6600 *Toll Free Tel:* 877-963-6600 *Fax:* 847-963-6601 *E-mail:* info@stagingresources.com *Web Site:* www.stagingresources.com, pg 1023

Heider, Joseph S, John Wiley & Sons Inc, 111 River St, Hoboken, NJ 07030 *Tel:* 201-748-6000 *Toll Free Tel:* 800-225-5945 *Fax:* 201-748-6088 *E-mail:* info@wiley.com *Web Site:* www.wiley.com, pg 1066

Heidman, Gord, AVP Mfg & Supply Inc, 2288-B7 Dumfries Rd RR2, Cambridge, ON N1R 5S3, Canada *Tel:* 519-740-7966 *Toll Free Tel:* 800-481-2493 *Fax:* 519-740-0131 *E-mail:* sales@jackfields.com *Web Site:* www.jackfields.com, pg 800

Heilman, Grant, Grant Heilman Photography Inc, 506 W Lincoln Ave, Lititz, PA 17543 *Tel:* 717-626-0296 *Toll Free Tel:* 800-622-2046 *Fax:* 717-626-0971 *E-mail:* info@heilmanphoto.com *Web Site:* www.heilmanphoto.com, pg 887

Heilman, Larry, Smith Audio-Visual Inc, 310 SW Sixth Ave, Topeka, KS 66603-3109 *Tel:* 785-235-3481 *Fax:* 785-235-3485 *E-mail:* sales@smithav.com *Web Site:* www.smithav.com, pg 1014

Heilman, Valerie Walker, Smith Audio-Visual Inc, 310 SW Sixth Ave, Topeka, KS 66603-3109 *Tel:* 785-235-3481 *Fax:* 785-235-3485 *E-mail:* sales@smithav.com *Web Site:* www.smithav.com, pg 1014

Heim, Alan, American Cinema Editors Inc (ACE), Verna Fields Bldg 2282, Rm 190, 100 Universal City Plaza, Universal City, CA 91608 *Tel:* 818-777-2900 *Fax:* 818-733-5023 *E-mail:* americancinema@editors.com *Web Site:* www.ace-filmeditors.org, pg 1076

Heimbold, Andrew, Reality Check Systems, 726 S Flower St, Burbank, CA 91502 *Tel:* 323-465-3900 *Fax:* 323-465-3600 *E-mail:* info@realitychecksystems.com *Web Site:* www.realityx.com, pg 992

Heimbold, Steven, Reality Check Systems, 726 S Flower St, Burbank, CA 91502 *Tel:* 323-465-3900 *Fax:* 323-465-3600 *E-mail:* info@realitychecksystems.com *Web Site:* www.realityx.com, pg 992

Hein, Gordie, Hite Co, 3101 Beale Ave, Altoona, PA 16601 *Tel:* 814-944-6121 *Toll Free Tel:* 800-252-3598 *Fax:* 814-944-3052 *Web Site:* www.hiteco.com, pg 889

Heinbokel, Raymond J Jr, National Association of Photo Equipment Technicians (NAPET), 2282 Springport Rd, Suite F, Jackson, MI 49202 *Tel:* 517-788-8100 *Toll Free Tel:* 800-762-9287 *Fax:* 517-788-8371 *Web Site:* www.pmai.org/napet, pg 1085

Heine, Jeff, Kenexa, 650 E Swedesford Rd, 2nd fl, Wayne, PA 19087 *Tel:* 407-548-1444 *Fax:* 610-971-9181 *E-mail:* kenexa_learn_sales@kenexa.com *Web Site:* www.outstart.com, pg 909

Heinemann, Jayna, Rayven Inc, 431 Griggs St N, St Paul, MN 55104 *Tel:* 651-642-1112 *Toll Free Tel:* 800-878-3776 *Fax:* 651-642-9497 *E-mail:* info@rayven.com *Web Site:* www.rayven.com, pg 992

Heinemann, Joe, Rayven Inc, 431 Griggs St N, St Paul, MN 55104 *Tel:* 651-642-1112 *Toll Free Tel:* 800-878-3776 *Fax:* 651-642-9497 *E-mail:* info@rayven.com *Web Site:* www.rayven.com, pg 992

Heinrich, Aaron, International Association of Business Communicators (IABC), 601 Montgomery St, Suite 1900, San Francisco, CA 94111 *Tel:* 415-544-4700 *Toll Free Tel:* 800-776-4222 *Fax:* 415-544-4747 *E-mail:* member_relations@iabc.com *Web Site:* www.iabc.com, pg 1083

Heinz, Harro K, Renkus-Heinz Inc, 19201 Cook St, Foothill Ranch, CA 92610-3501 *Tel:* 949-588-9997 *Fax:* 949-588-9514 *E-mail:* sales@renkus-heinz.com *Web Site:* www.renkus-heinz.com, pg 994

Heinz, Ralph, Renkus-Heinz Inc, 19201 Cook St, Foothill Ranch, CA 92610-3501 *Tel:* 949-588-9997 *Fax:* 949-588-9514 *E-mail:* sales@renkus-heinz.com *Web Site:* www.renkus-heinz.com, pg 994

Heinzmann, Keith, Alpine Media, 1644 Conestoga St, Suite 3, Boulder, CO 80301 *Tel:* 303-444-1257 *Toll Free Tel:* 800-475-0872 *E-mail:* info@alpinemedia.com; production@alpinemedia.com; av@alpinemedia.com *Web Site:* www.alpinemedia.com, pg 782

Heiser, Adam, Odyssey Productions Inc, 2800 NW Thurman, Portland, OR 97210 *Tel:* 503-223-3480 *Fax:* 503-223-3493 *E-mail:* info@odysseypro.com *Web Site:* www.odysseypro.com, pg 961

Heiser, Steve, Odyssey Productions Inc, 2800 NW Thurman, Portland, OR 97210 *Tel:* 503-223-3480 *Fax:* 503-223-3493 *E-mail:* info@odysseypro.com *Web Site:* www.odysseypro.com, pg 961

Heiss, Roger, Tone Zone Recording, 1316 N Clybourn, Chicago, IL 60610-1710 *Tel:* 312-664-5353 *Fax:* 312-664-6560 *E-mail:* tonezonerecording@sbcglobal.net, pg 1042

Heitmann, Kurt, CP Communications, 200 Clearbrook Rd, Suite 148, Elmsford, NY 10523 *Tel:* 914-345-9292 *Toll Free Tel:* 800-762-4254 *Fax:* 914-345-9222 *E-mail:* info@cpcomms.com; sales@cpcomms.com *Web Site:* www.cpcomms.com, pg 837

Hejtmanek, Michael, Hasselblad Bron Inc, 1080A Garden State Rd, Union, NJ 07083 *Tel:* 908-754-5800 *Toll Free Tel:* 800-456-0203; 800-367-6434 *Fax:* 908-754-5807 *E-mail:* production@hasselbladbron.com; sales@hasselbladbron.com; servicedept@hasselbladbron.com *Web Site:* www.hasselbladbron.com, pg 885

Helland, Chris M, MAVCO, 77 S Main St, Newtown, CT 06470 *Tel:* 203-270-8292 *Fax:* 203-270-8292, pg 934

Heller, Amy, Milestone Film & Video Inc, PO Box 128, Harrington Park, NJ 07640-0128 *Tel:* 201-767-3117 *Toll Free Tel:* 800-603-1104 *Fax:* 201-767-3035 *E-mail:* milefilms@gmail.com *Web Site:* www.milestonefilms.com, pg 943

Hellman, Robert B, Hellman Associates Inc, 1225 W Fourth St, Waterloo, IA 50702-2903 *Tel:* 319-234-7055 *Toll Free Tel:* 800-747-7055 *Fax:* 319-234-2089 *E-mail:* info@hellman.com *Web Site:* www.hellman.com, pg 888

Hellmuth, Stephen M, NBA Entertainment Inc, 450 Harmon Meadow Blvd, Secaucus, NJ 07094 *Tel:* 201-865-1500 *Fax:* 201-865-2626 *Web Site:* www.nba.com, pg 953

Hellyer, Jeff, Edit House Chicago, 5325 W Berenice Ave, Chicago, IL 60641 *Tel:* 773-725-1525 *Web Site:* www.edithousechicago.com, pg 857

Helman, Michael, Brooklyn Films, PO Box 20412, New York, NY 10021-0066 *Tel:* 212-744-2845 *E-mail:* inquiries@brooklynfilms.com *Web Site:* www.brooklynfilms.com, pg 814

Helms, George, Video Copy Services Inc, 3980 Dekalb Technology Pkwy, Suite 670, Atlanta, GA 30340 *Toll Free Tel:* 800-553-3616 *E-mail:* info@video-copy.com *Web Site:* www.video-copy.com, pg 1055

Helms, Mark, Sound & Vision Media, 372 Squire Rd, Revere, MA 02151 *Tel:* 781-284-9707 *Web Site:* www.soundandvisionmedia.com, pg 1017

Heminway, Jim, Monroe Electronics Inc, 100 Housel Ave, Lyndonville, NY 14098 *Tel:* 585-765-2254 *Fax:* 585-765-9330 *Web Site:* www.monroe-electronics.com, pg 945

Hemminger, Peter, Quickdraw Animation Society, 351 11 Ave SW, Suite 201, Calgary, AB T2R 0C7, Canada *Tel:* 403-261-5767 *Fax:* 403-261-5644 *E-mail:* info@quickdrawanimation.ca; production@quickdrawanimation.ca; programming@quickdrawanimation.ca *Web Site:* quickdrawanimation.ca; www.giraffest.ca, pg 1088

Hempton, Gordon W, Quiet Planet LLC, PO Box 900, Indianola, WA 98342 *Tel:* 360-477-9588 *Web Site:* www.quietplanet.com, pg 989

Hendee, Steve, Yorkville Sound Inc, 4625 Witmer Industrial Estate, Niagara Falls, NY 14305 *Tel:* 716-297-2920 *Fax:* 716-297-3689 *E-mail:* usa@yorkville.com *Web Site:* www.yorkville.com, pg 1072

Henderson, Jane, Learning Technology Services, 301 Millennium Hall, Menomonie, WI 54751 *Tel:* 715-232-1289 *Fax:* 715-232-2456 *E-mail:* helpdesk@uwec.edu *Web Site:* www.unwec.edu/lts, pg 917

Henderson, Lyn, Women in Film & Television-Florida (WIFT-FL), PO Box 533541, Orlando, FL 32853-3541 *E-mail:* info@womeninfilmfl.org *Web Site:* womeninfilmfl.org, pg 1090

Henderson, Mark, Atlanta Filmworks, 4280 Northeast Expwy, Atlanta, GA 30340 *E-mail:* info@atlantafilmworks.com *Web Site:* atlantafilmworks.com, pg 793

Henderson, Ridge, Blue 60 Pictures, 555 First Ave NE, Suite 200, Minneapolis, MN 55413 *Tel:* 612-871-6800 *E-mail:* info@blue-60.com *Web Site:* www.blue-60.com, pg 810

Hendricks, Mark, Transtector Systems Inc, 10701 N Airport Dr, Hayden Lake, ID 83835 *Tel:* 208-772-8515 *Toll Free Tel:* 800-882-9110 *Fax:* 208-762-6133 *E-mail:* sales@transtector.com *Web Site:* www.transtector.com, pg 1043

Hendricks, Paula, Oval Window Audio, 33 Wildflower Ct, Nederland, CO 80466 *Tel:* 303-447-3607 *Fax:* 303-447-3607 *E-mail:* info@ovalwindowaudio.com *Web Site:* www.ovalwindowaudio.com, pg 966

Hendrix, Emma, Video In Studios/Video Out Distribution, 2625 Kaslo St, Vancouver, BC V5M 3G9, Canada *Tel:* 604-872-8337; 604-872-8449 *Fax:* 604-876-1185 *E-mail:* info@vivomediaarts.com; info@videoout.ca *Web Site:* www.videoinstudios.com; www.videoout.ca, pg 1055

Hengstenberg, Bill, Biomedical Media Communications Dept, 263 Farmington Ave, Farmington, CT 06030-2910 *Tel:* 860-679-2119; 860-679-2433 *Fax:* 860-679-4034 *Web Site:* video.uchc.edu, pg 807

Henk, Chad, Xplor® International, 24156 State Rd 54, Suite 4, Lutz, FL 33559 *Tel:* 813-949-6170 *Toll Free Tel:* 800-669-7567 *Fax:* 813-949-9977 *E-mail:* info@xplor.org *Web Site:* www.xplor.org, pg 1090

Henk, Skip, Xplor® International, 24156 State Rd 54, Suite 4, Lutz, FL 33559 *Tel:* 813-949-6170 *Toll Free Tel:* 800-669-7567 *Fax:* 813-949-9977 *E-mail:* info@xplor.org *Web Site:* www.xplor.org, pg 1090

Hennessey, James R, The Music People Inc, 154 Woodlawn Rd, Suite C, Berlin, CT 06037-1500 *Toll Free Tel:* 800-289-8889 *Fax:* 860-828-1353 *E-mail:* sales@musicpeopleinc.com *Web Site:* www.musicpeopleinc.com, pg 951

Hennessey, John, The Music People Inc, 154 Woodlawn Rd, Suite C, Berlin, CT 06037-1500 *Toll Free Tel:* 800-289-8889 *Fax:* 860-828-1353 *E-mail:* sales@musicpeopleinc.com *Web Site:* www.musicpeopleinc.com, pg 951

Hennessey, Larry, MicrophoneRentals.com, 103-1075 Marine Dr, Suite 501, North Vancouver, BC V7P 3T6, Canada *Tel:* 604-980-5703 *E-mail:* info@microphonerentals.com *Web Site:* www.microphonerentals.com, pg 941

Hennessey, Sharon, The Music People Inc, 154 Woodlawn Rd, Suite C, Berlin, CT 06037-1500 *Toll Free Tel:* 800-289-8889 *Fax:* 860-828-1353 *E-mail:* sales@musicpeopleinc.com *Web Site:* www.musicpeopleinc.com, pg 951

Hennige, Bob, AB Systems Amplifiers, 6120 Brace Rd, Loomis, CA 95650 *Tel:* 916-223-1133 *E-mail:* absales@abamps.com *Web Site:* www.abamps.net, pg 772

Henninger, Robert L, Henninger Media Services, 2601-A Wilson Blvd, Arlington, VA 22201 *Tel:* 703-243-3444 *Toll Free Tel:* 888-243-3444 *Fax:* 703-243-5697 *E-mail:* hmsinfo@henninger.com; hmsquotes@henninger.com *Web Site:* www.henninger.com, pg 888

Henry, Stephen, Video Perspective, PO Box 591843, Houston, TX 77259-1843 *Tel:* 281-996-7974 *Toll Free Tel:* 888-996-7974 *E-mail:* vp@vidper.com *Web Site:* www.videoperspective.com, pg 1056

Henry, Tim, Vaddio, 131 Cheshire Lane, Suite 500, Minnetonka, MN 55305 *Tel:* 763-971-4400 *Toll Free Tel:* 800-572-2011 *Fax:* 763-971-4464 *E-mail:* info@vaddio.com *Web Site:* www.vaddio.com, pg 1051

Hensel, Lynn, Spot Media Production Group, 2745 Locust St, St Louis, MO 63103 *Tel:* 314-667-5915 *E-mail:* info@spotmpg.com *Web Site:* www.spotmpg.com, pg 1022

Hensel, Rick, Spot Media Production Group, 2745 Locust St, St Louis, MO 63103 *Tel:* 314-667-5915 *E-mail:* info@spotmpg.com *Web Site:* www.spotmpg.com, pg 1022

Hensley, Bill, Furman, 1800 S McDowell Blvd, Petaluma, CA 94954 *Tel:* 707-763-1010 *Fax:* 707-763-1310 *E-mail:* info@furmansound.com *Web Site:* www.furmansound.com, pg 874

Hensley, Greg, Greg Hensley Productions, 200 S "E" Ave, Unit 113, New Castle, CO 81647 *Tel:* 970-984-3158 *E-mail:* hensley@sopris.net *Web Site:* www.greghensley.com, pg 888

Henson, Bob, Link Electronics Inc, 2137 Rust Ave, Cape Girardeau, MO 63703-7668 *Tel:* 573-334-4433 *Toll Free Tel:* 800-776-4411 *Fax:* 573-334-9255 *E-mail:* sales@linkelectronics.com *Web Site:* www.linkelectronics.com, pg 922

Henson, Kristi, Wickenburg Film Commission, 216 N Frontier St, Wickenburg, AZ 85390 *Tel:* 928-684-5479; 928-684-0977 *Toll Free Tel:* 800-942-5242 *Fax:* 928-684-5470 *E-mail:* info@wickenburgchamber.com *Web Site:* www.wickenburgchamber.com/film-commission, pg 1092

Herb, Peter, Magnicon Media/Image d'Or, PO Box 1898, Dearborn, MI 48121-1898 *Tel:* 313-846-8694; 313-574-3546 (cell) *Fax:* 815-361-2869, pg 928

Herbert, John, Northeast Video Productions Inc, Box 8425, Sleepy Hollow, NY 10591 *Tel:* 914-714-0703, pg 959

Herbst, Steve, NASCAR Media Group LLC, 550 S Caldwell St, Suite 2000, Charlotte, NC 28202 *Tel:* 704-348-7100 *Web Site:* www.nascarmediagroup.com, pg 952

Hergert, Karl, Cinema Stage Inc, 110 Saunders Rd, Unit 4, Barrie, ON L4N 9A8, Canada *Tel:* 705-733-8740 *Toll Free Tel:* 800-387-6205 *Fax:* 705-733-8742 *E-mail:* info@cinemastage.ca *Web Site:* www.cinemastage.ca, pg 827

Herkes, Ken, Ken Herkes Productions & Entertainment (KHPE), PO Box 313, Volcano, HI 96785 *Tel:* 808-640-0730 *Web Site:* www.khpe-hawaii.com, pg 888

Herman, Cheryl, Books on Tape®, c/o Library & School Servs, 400 Hahn Rd, Westminster, MD 21157 *Toll Free Tel:* 800-733-3000 *Toll Free Fax:* 800-940-7046 *E-mail:* csbot@randomhouse.com *Web Site:* www.booksontape.com, pg 811

Herman, Susan, Encore Cases, 8818 Lankershim Blvd, Sun Valley, CA 91352 *Tel:* 818-768-8803 *Toll Free Tel:* 800-743-6267 *Fax:* 818-768-3993 *Web Site:* www.encorecases.com; www.giantcases.com, pg 861

Hermann, Kevin, REI - Radio Engineering Industries, 6534 "L" St, Omaha, NE 68117 *Tel:* 402-339-2200 *Toll Free Tel:* 800-228-9275 (sales); 877-726-4617 (tech support) *Fax:* 402-339-1704 *E-mail:* info@radioeng.com; orderdesk@radioeng.com *Web Site:* www.radioeng.com, pg 994

Hermes, Randy, Aerial Video Systems, 712 S Main St, Burbank, CA 91506 *Tel:* 818-954-8842 *Fax:* 818-954-8842 *Web Site:* aerialvideo.com, pg 778

Hernandez, Carrie, HighScope Press, 600 N River St, Ypsilanti, MI 48198-2898 *Tel:* 734-485-2000 *Toll Free Tel:* 800-407-7377 *Fax:* 734-485-0704 *Toll Free Fax:* 800-442-4329 *E-mail:* info@highscope.org; press@highscope.org *Web Site:* www.highscope.org, pg 889

Hernandez, Juan, Source Film Studio, 1111 N Beachwood Dr, Hollywood, CA 90038 *Tel:* 323-463-5555 *E-mail:* info@sourcefilmstudio.com *Web Site:* www.sourcefilmstudio.com, pg 1018

Hernandez, Louis Jr, Avid Technology Inc, 65-75 Network Dr, Burlington, MA 01830 *Tel:* 978-640-6789 *Fax:* 978-640-3366 *Web Site:* www.avid.com, pg 799

Herr, Michelle, Alliance for Community Media (ACM), 4248 Park Glen Rd, Minneapolis, MN 55416 *Tel:* 952-928-4643 *E-mail:* info@allcommunitymedia.org *Web Site:* www.allcommunitymedia.org, pg 1075

Herringer, Steve, The Vocal Point/Profile Communications Ltd, 1196 Habgood St, White Rock, BC V4B 4W9, Canada *Tel:* 604-531-6908 *Web Site:* www.profilecomm.com, pg 1060

Herrington, Brent, 3008, 3008 Ross Ave, Suite 100, Dallas, TX 75204 *Tel:* 214-922-9232 *Fax:* 214-922-8861 *Web Site:* www.3008.com, pg 1040

Herrington, Mary-Kathryn, Oxford Film Commission, 415 S Lamar Blvd, Oxford, MS 38655 *Tel:* 662-232-2477 *Toll Free Tel:* 800-758-9177 *E-mail:* tourism@visitoxfordms.com *Web Site:* visitoxfordms.com, pg 1099

Herrmann, Elisa, Big Muddy Film Festival, 1100 Lincoln Dr, Rm 1101, Carbondale, IL 62901-6610 *Tel:* 618-453-8301 *Fax:* 618-453-2264 *E-mail:* info@bigmuddyfilm.com *Web Site:* www.bigmuddyfilm.com, pg 1109

Herron, Wes, Lectrosonics Inc, 581 Laser Rd NE, Rio Rancho, NM 87124 *Tel:* 505-892-4501 *Toll Free Tel:* 800-821-1121 *Fax:* 505-892-6243 *E-mail:* sales@lectrosonics.com *Web Site:* www.lectrosonics.com, pg 918

Hersey, Aaron, National Products Inc, 8410 Dallas Ave S, Seattle, WA 98108 *Tel:* 206-763-8361 *Toll Free Tel:* 800-497-7479 *Fax:* 206-763-9615 *Web Site:* www.rammount.com, pg 953

Hersh, Stuart, Split Image Productions, 4134 243 St, Flushing, NY 11363-1658 *Tel:* 718-428-1438 *Fax:* 718-428-1438, pg 1021

Hersman, Deborah, National Safety Council (NSC), 1121 Spring Lake Dr, Itasca, IL 60143-3201 *Tel:* 630-285-1121 *Toll Free Tel:* 800-621-7615; 800-621-7619 (cust serv) *Fax:* 630-285-1315; 630-285-1434 (cust serv) *E-mail:* customerservice@nsc.org *Web Site:* www.nsc.org, pg 953

Hertzberg, Paul, Cinetel Films Inc, 8255 Sunset Blvd, Los Angeles, CA 90046-2432 *Tel:* 323-654-4000 *Fax:* 323-650-6400 *E-mail:* info@cinetelfilms.com *Web Site:* cinetelfilms.com, pg 828

Hertzler, Chris, SoundSpace Inc, 845 Dayton St, Yellow Springs, OH 45387 *Tel:* 937-767-7353 *Fax:* 937-767-7348 *E-mail:* soundspace@sbcglobal.net, pg 1018

Herve, Guillaume, Presagis, 4700 de la Savane, Suite 300, Montreal, QC H4P 1T7, Canada *Tel:* 514-341-3874 *Toll Free Tel:* 800-361-6424 *E-mail:* info@presagis.com *Web Site:* www.presagis.com, pg 981

Hess, Jan, Teledyne Energy Systems Inc, 10707 Gilroy Rd, Hunt Valley, MD 21031 *Tel:* 410-771-8600 *Fax:* 410-771-8620 *E-mail:* energy.systems@teledynees.com *Web Site:* www.teledynees.com, pg 1036

Hess, Ron, Kinetic Corp, 200 Distillery Commons, Suite 200, Louisville, KY 40206-1990 *Tel:* 502-719-9500 *Fax:* 502-719-9509 *E-mail:* info@thetechnologyagency.com *Web Site:* kinetic.thetechnologyagency.com, pg 911

Hesse, Michael P, Posthorn Recordings, 142 W 26 St, 10th fl, New York, NY 10001-6814 *Tel:* 212-242-3737 *Fax:* 212-924-1243 *Web Site:* www.posthorn.com, pg 979

Hesseltine, Cassandra, Humboldt-Del Norte Film Commission, 1385 Eighth St, Suite 106, Arcata, CA 95521 *Tel:* 707-825-7600 *Web Site:* www.filmhumboldtdelnorte.org, pg 1092

Hester, Gerald, Horita Co Inc, PO Box 3993, Mission Viejo, CA 92690-3993 *Tel:* 949-489-0240 *Fax:* 949-489-0242 *E-mail:* sales@horita.com *Web Site:* www.horita.com, pg 891

Hetlinger, Bryan, Infosat Communications Inc, 3130 114 Ave SE, Calgary, AB T2Z 3V6, Canada *Tel:* 403-543-8188 *Toll Free Tel:* 888-524-3038 *Fax:* 403-289-8133 *Web Site:* infosat.com, pg 898

Hetzler, Scott, Contemporary Research, 4355 Excel Pkwy, Suite 600, Addison, TX 75001 *Tel:* 972-931-2728 *Toll Free Tel:* 888-972-2728 *Fax:* 972-931-2765 *E-mail:* contact@crwww.com *Web Site:* contemporaryresearch.com, pg 835

Heumann, Michael, Global Village Productions, 6914 B Sebastapol Ave, Sebastopol, CA 95472 *Tel:* 707-823-1451 *Toll Free Tel:* 800-798-FIND (798-3463) *Fax:* 707-829-5545 *E-mail:* production@videosource.com; video@videosource.com *Web Site:* www.videosource.com, pg 879

Heumann, Michael, Global Village Stock Footage Library, 1717 Darby Rd, Sebastopol, CA 95472 *Tel:* 707-823-1451 *Toll Free Tel:* 800-798-FIND (798-3463) *Fax:* 707-829-5545 *E-mail:* contact@hdenvironments.com *Web Site:* www.videosource.com; hdenvironments.com, pg 879

Hevia, Sylvia, Chicago Latino Film Festival, 676 N La Salle Dr, Suite 520, Chicago, IL 60654 *Tel:* 312-431-1330 *Fax:* 312-786-0126 *E-mail:* info@latinoculturalcenter.org *Web Site:* www.chicagolatinofilmfestival.org, pg 1111

Hewitt, John, Alpha Technologies, 3767 Alpha Way, Bellingham, WA 98226 *Tel:* 360-647-2360 *Fax:* 360-671-4936 *E-mail:* alpha@alpha.com *Web Site:* www.alpha.com, pg 782

Hibbard, Karen, Manhattan Film Commission, 501 Poyntz Ave, Manhattan, KS 66502 *Tel:* 785-776-8829 *Toll Free Tel:* 800-759-0134 *Fax:* 785-776-0679 *E-mail:* cvb@manhattan.org *Web Site:* www.manhattancvb.org, pg 1097

Hickey, John, Wise Audio Video, PO Box 105523, Jefferson City, MO 65110 *Tel:* 573-761-7888 *Toll Free Tel:* 877-775-7888 *Web Site:* www.wiseaudiovideo.com, pg 1068

Hickey, Paul, Phonic Ear Inc (FrontRow), 2080 Lakeville Hwy, Petaluma, CA 94954 *Tel:* 707-769-1110 *Toll Free Tel:* 800-227-0735 *Fax:* 707-769-9624 *E-mail:* customerservice@phonicear.com; customercare@gofrontrow.com *Web Site:* www.phonicear.com; www.gofrontrow.com, pg 974

Hickey, Theodore W, OAP Audio Products, 310 Peachtree Industrial Blvd, Buford, GA 30518 *Tel:* 770-945-1033 *Toll Free Tel:* 800-788-1OAP (788-1627) *Fax:* 770-945-1843 *E-mail:* info@oapaudio.com *Web Site:* www.oapaudio.com, pg 960

Hickinbotham, Gary, Fire Station Studios, 224 N Guadalupe St, San Marcos, TX 78666 *Tel:* 512-396-1144 *Fax:* 512-396-1169 *E-mail:* info@firestationstudios.com *Web Site:* www.firestationstudios.com, pg 868

Hicks, Trey, Visix™ Inc, 230 Scientific Dr, Suite 80, Norcross, GA 30092 *Tel:* 770-446-1416 *Toll Free Tel:* 800-572-4935 *Fax:* 770-448-5724 *E-mail:* info@visix.com *Web Site:* www.visix.com, pg 1059

Hicock, David, Animotion Inc, 501 W Fayette St, Syracuse, NY 13204 *Tel:* 315-471-3533 *Fax:* 315-471-2730 *E-mail:* info@animotioninc.com *Web Site:* animotioninc.com, pg 787

Hiestand, Jesse, Alliance of Motion Picture & Television Producers (AMPTP), 15301 Ventura Blvd, Bldg E, Sherman Oaks, CA 91403 *Tel:* 818-995-3600 *Fax:* 818-285-4450 *E-mail:* info@tw.amptp.org *Web Site:* www.amptp.org, pg 1075

Hiett, Richard, Rocktown Media, 1361 Lincolnshire Dr, Harrisonburg, VA 22802 *Tel:* 540-433-7700 *Toll Free Tel:* 888-433-8700 *E-mail:* info@rocktown.tv *Web Site:* www.rocktown.tv, pg 998

Higa, Wade, The Audio Visual Co (AVCO), 98-810 Moanalua Rd, Aiea, HI 96701 *Tel:* 808-485-3200 *Fax:* 808-487-0733 *Web Site:* www.theavco.com, pg 795

Higgenbotham, George W, Speco/Systems & Products Engineering Co, 709 N Sixth St, Kansas City, KS 66101 *Tel:* 913-321-3978 *Toll Free Tel:* 800-633-5913 *Fax:* 913-321-7439, pg 1020

Higgins, Clark, RetinaVision Productions, 19 Barker Ave, Fairfax, CA 94930 *Tel:* 415-459-3926 *Toll Free Tel:* 877-738-4628, pg 995

Higgins, David, Pathway Connectivity Inc, 1439 17 Ave SE, Unit 103, Calgary, AB T2G 1J9, Canada *Tel:* 403-243-8110 *Fax:* 403-287-1281 *E-mail:* sales@pathwayconnect.com *Web Site:* www.pathwayconnect.com, pg 970

Higgins, Mary Lou, Pathway Connectivity Inc, 1439 17 Ave SE, Unit 103, Calgary, AB T2G 1J9, Canada *Tel:* 403-243-8110 *Fax:* 403-287-1281 *E-mail:* sales@pathwayconnect.com *Web Site:* www.pathwayconnect.com, pg 970

Higgins, Tim, AheadTeK, 6410 Via Del Oro, San Jose, CA 95119 *Tel:* 408-226-9800; 408-226-9991 *Toll Free Tel:* 800-971-9191 *Fax:* 408-226-9195 *Web Site:* www.aheadtek.com, pg 779

Highberg, Kristin, Ellison Educational Equipment Inc, 25862 Commercentre Dr, Lake Forest, CA 92630-8804 *Tel:* 949-598-8822 *Toll Free Tel:* 800-253-2238 *Fax:* 949-598-8840 *Toll Free Fax:* 800-253-2240 *E-mail:* customersupport@ellison.com *Web Site:* www.ellison.com, pg 859

Hilbert, Stan, Telect Inc, 23321 E Knox Ave, Liberty Lake, WA 99019 *Tel:* 509-926-6000 *Toll Free Tel:* 800-551-4567 *E-mail:* getinfo@telect.com *Web Site:* www.telect.com, pg 1036

Hildebrandt, Wayne, LBA Technology Inc, 3400 Tupper Dr, Greenville, NC 27834 *Tel:* 252-757-0279 *Toll Free Tel:* 800-522-4464 *Fax:* 252-752-9155 *E-mail:* lbagrp@lbagroup.com *Web Site:* www.lbagroup.com, pg 917

Hilderbrand, Karen Mitzo, Twin Sisters Productions LLC, 4710 Hudson Dr, Stow, OH 44224 *Toll Free Tel:* 800-248-TWIN (248-8946) *Toll Free Fax:* 800-480-TWIN (480-8946) *E-mail:* twinsisters@twinsisters.com *Web Site:* www.twinsisters.com, pg 1047

Hilferty, Gerard, Hilferty & Associates Inc, 14240 State Rte 550, Athens, OH 45701 *Tel:* 740-448-3821 *Fax:* 740-448-2331 *E-mail:* gha@hilferty.com *Web Site:* www.hilferty.com, pg 889

Hill, Camille, Merestone, 7232 E First St, Scottsdale, AZ 85251 *Tel:* 480-945-4631 *Fax:* 480-945-0590 *Web Site:* www.merestone.com, pg 938

Hill, Dave, Jensen Transformers Inc, 9304 Deering Ave, Chatsworth, CA 91311 *Tel:* 818-374-5857 *Toll Free Tel:* 866-476-6291 *Fax:* 818-374-5856 *E-mail:* sales@jensen-transformers.com *Web Site:* www.jensen-transformers.com, pg 905

Hill, Howard, RF Industries, 7610 Miramar Rd, San Diego, CA 92126 *Tel:* 858-549-6340 *Toll Free Tel:* 800-233-1728 *Fax:* 858-549-6345 *E-mail:* rfi@rfindustries.com *Web Site:* www.rfindustries.com, pg 995

Hill, Jerry, Drytac Corp, 5601 Eastport Blvd, Richmond, VA 23231 *Toll Free Tel:* 800-280-6013 *E-mail:* customerservice@drytac.com *Web Site:* www.drytac.com, pg 852

Hill, Jerry, Jerry Hill Steadicam Products, 19160 Arminta St, Reseda, CA 91335-1105 *Tel:* 818-772-9256 *Fax:* 818-772-9251 *E-mail:* jerry@steadimoves.com *Web Site:* www.steadimoves.com, pg 889

Hill, Julie, Artbeats, 1405 N Myrtle Rd, Myrtle Creek, OR 97457 *Tel:* 541-863-4429 *Toll Free Tel:* 800-444-9392 *Fax:* 541-863-4547 *E-mail:* info@artbeats.com *Web Site:* www.artbeats.com, pg 791

Hill, Kassandra, Mary Riepma Ross Media Arts Center, University of Nebraska-Lincoln, 313 N 13 St, Lincoln, NE 68588 *Tel:* 402-472-9100; 402-472-5353 *Fax:* 402-472-2576 *Web Site:* www.theross.org, pg 999

Hill, McCoy, Dudley Theatrical, 3401 Indiana Ave, Winston-Salem, NC 27105 *Tel:* 336-722-3255 *Fax:* 336-722-4641 *E-mail:* sales@dudleytheatrical.com *Web Site:* www.dudleytheatrical.com, pg 853

Hill, Michael, Midas Consoles North America, 5270 Procyon St, Las Vegas, NV 89118 *Tel:* 702-371-0103 *Toll Free Tel:* 866-929-9074 *Fax:* 702-554-2367 *Toll Free Fax:* 800-955-6831 *E-mail:* custsuppprofus@music-group.com *Web Site:* www.midasconsoles.com, pg 942

Hill, Michael, News Broadcast Network, 75 Broad St, 15th fl, New York, NY 10004 *Tel:* 212-684-8910 *Fax:* 212-684-9650 *Web Site:* www.newsbroadcastnetwork.com, pg 956

Hill, Richard, Charles A Hulcher Co Inc, 909 "G" St, Hampton, VA 23661 *Tel:* 757-245-6190 *Fax:* 757-245-2882 *E-mail:* hulcher@hulchercamera.com *Web Site:* www.hulchercamera.com, pg 892

Hill, Rob, Merestone, 7232 E First St, Scottsdale, AZ 85251 *Tel:* 480-945-4631 *Fax:* 480-945-0590 *Web Site:* www.merestone.com, pg 938

Hill, Sebastian, Vidicom Inc, 520 Eighth Ave, Suite 2206, New York, NY 10018 *Tel:* 212-895-8300 *E-mail:* info@vidicom.com *Web Site:* vidicom.com, pg 1057

Hill, Steve, Luxor, 2245 Delany Rd, Waukegan, IL 60087 *Tel:* 847-244-1800 *Toll Free Tel:* 800-323-4656 *Fax:* 847-244-1818 *Toll Free Fax:* 800-327-1698 *E-mail:* info@luxorfurn.com; customerservice@luxorfurn.com *Web Site:* www.luxorfurn.com, pg 926

Hill, Steven, Straight Wire Inc, 2032 Scott St, Hollywood, FL 33020 *Tel:* 954-925-2470 *Toll Free Tel:* 800-683-4434 *Fax:* 954-925-7253 *E-mail:* info@straightwire.com *Web Site:* www.straightwire.com, pg 1025

Hill, Tracey, AC Lighting Inc, 88 Horner Ave, Toronto, ON M8Z 5Y3, Canada *Tel:* 416-255-9494 *Fax:* 416-255-3514 *E-mail:* northamerica@aclighting.com *Web Site:* www.aclighting.com, pg 773

Hiller, Ezra, Alltec Stores, a Vcom IMC Company, 80 Little Falls Rd, Fairfield, NJ 07004 *Toll Free Tel:* 800-637-3181 *Toll Free Fax:* 800-965-7836 *E-mail:* sales@alltecstores.com *Web Site:* www.alltecstores.com, pg 782

Hillery, Michelle, Palm Beach County Film & Television Commission, 1555 Palm Beach Lakes Blvd, Suite 900, West Palm Beach, FL 33401 *Tel:* 561-233-1000 *Toll Free Tel:* 800-745-FILM (745-3456) *Fax:* 561-233-3113 *Web Site:* www.pbfilm.com, pg 1096

Hillery, Parker, Moxie Media, 1301 Dealers Ave, New Orleans, LA 70123 *Tel:* 504-733-6907 *Toll Free Tel:* 800-346-6943 *Fax:* 504-733-9493 *E-mail:* info@moxiemedia.com *Web Site:* www.moxiemedia.com; www.moxietraining.com, pg 948

Hillinger, Jeffrey W, Automated Entertainment, PO Box 1079, Little Rock, CA 95343-1079 *Tel:* 661-944-2299 *Toll Free Tel:* 800-880-6567 (orders) *Fax:* 661-944-2348 *E-mail:* questions@automatedhd.com *Web Site:* www.automatedhd.com, pg 797

Hillman, Barbara, Berkeley Film Office, 2030 Addison St, Suite 102, Berkeley, CA 94704 *Tel:* 510-549-7040 *Toll Free Tel:* 800-847-4823 *Fax:* 510-644-2052 *E-mail:* film@visitberkeley.com *Web Site:* www.filmberkeley.com, pg 1092

Hillmann, Alfred J, Hillmann & Carr Inc, 2233 Wisconsin Ave, Washington, DC 20007 *Tel:* 202-342-0001 *Fax:* 202-342-0117 *E-mail:* mail@hillmanncarr.com *Web Site:* www.hillmanncarr.com, pg 889

Hilzen, Bob, SLD Lighting, 36-05 Broadway, Fair Lawn, NJ 07410 *Tel:* 201-373-2700 *Toll Free Tel:* 800-245-6630 *Fax:* 201-793-7618 *E-mail:* sales@sldlighting.com *Web Site:* www.sldlighting.com, pg 1013

Hilzen, Glenn D, SLD Lighting, 36-05 Broadway, Fair Lawn, NJ 07410 *Tel:* 201-373-2700 *Toll Free Tel:* 800-245-6630 *Fax:* 201-793-7618 *E-mail:* sales@sldlighting.com *Web Site:* www.sldlighting.com, pg 1013

Hinds, Derrick, Radio Television Digital News Association (RTDNA), The National Press Bldg, 529 14 St NW, Suite 425, Washington, DC 20045 *Tel:* 202-659-6510 *Fax:* 202-223-4007 *Web Site:* www.rtdna.org, pg 1088

Hiner, Bryce, Lyon Workspace Products LLC, 420 N Main St, Montgomery, IL 60538 *Tel:* 630-892-8941 *Toll Free Tel:* 800-433-8488 *Fax:* 630-892-8966 *Toll Free Fax:* 800-367-6681 *E-mail:* lyon@lyonworkspace.com *Web Site:* www.lyonworkspace.com, pg 927

Hines, Jeff, US Case Corp, 6301 J Richard Dr, Raleigh, NC 27617 *Tel:* 919-783-6166 *Toll Free Tel:* 800-648-8474 *Fax:* 919-783-0740 *E-mail:* customersupport@uscase.com *Web Site:* www.uscase.com, pg 1050

Hinterleiter, Scott, The Will-Burt Co, 169 S Main St, Orrville, OH 44667 *Tel:* 330-682-7015; 330-684-4000 (cust serv) *Fax:* 330-684-1190 *E-mail:* contact_us@willburt.com *Web Site:* www.willburt.com, pg 1066

Hinton, Bradford, Georgia-Pacific Television & Photography, 133 Peachtree St NE, Atlanta, GA 30303 *Tel:* 404-652-5690 *Fax:* 404-487-5352 *Web Site:* www.gp.com; g-ptv.com, pg 877

Hipps, Jeff, Amplifier Technologies Inc (ATI), 1749 Chapin Rd, Montebello, CA 90640 *Tel:* 323-278-0001 *Fax:* 323-278-0083 *E-mail:* sales@ati-amp.com *Web Site:* www.ati-amp.com, pg 785

Hipps, Jeff, B&K Components Ltd, 1749 Chapin Rd, Montebello, CA 90640 *Tel:* 323-278-0001 *Fax:* 323-278-0083 *Web Site:* www.bkcomp.com, pg 802

Hirsch, Davida, Granny Press LLC, 101 Gedney St, Apt 5-D, Nyack, NY 10960 *Tel:* 845-875-4422; 845-875-4423 *E-mail:* webmaster@grannypress.com *Web Site:* www.grannypress.com, pg 881

Hirsch, Jeffrey A, Time Warner Cable, 60 Columbus Circle, 17th fl, New York, NY 10023 *Tel:* 212-364-8200 *Web Site:* www.timewarnercable.com, pg 1040

Hirsch, Robin, Imagecraft Productions, 3318 Burton Ave, Burbank, CA 91504 *Tel:* 818-954-0187 *Fax:* 818-954-0189 *Web Site:* www.imagecraftproductions.com, pg 896

Hirt, Todd, West Penn Wire, 2833 W Chestnut St, Washington, PA 15301 *Tel:* 724-222-7060 *Toll Free Tel:* 800-245-4964 *Fax:* 724-222-6420 *E-mail:* info@westpenn-wpw.com *Web Site:* www.westpenn-wpw.com, pg 1064

Hislop, Mark W, Video Impressions, 2505 Diehl Rd, Aurora, IL 60502 *Tel:* 630-851-1663 *Fax:* 630-851-2688 *E-mail:* office@video-impressions.com *Web Site:* www.video-impressions.com, pg 1055

Hitch, Lawrence, Madisound Speaker Components Inc, 8608 University Green, Suite 10, Middleton, WI 53562 *Tel:* 608-831-3433 *Toll Free Tel:* 866-883-1488 (orders) *Fax:* 608-831-3771 *E-mail:* info@madisound.com *Web Site:* www.madisound.com, pg 928

Hite, R Lee, Hite Co, 3101 Beale Ave, Altoona, PA 16601 *Tel:* 814-944-6121 *Toll Free Tel:* 800-252-3598 *Fax:* 814-944-3052 *Web Site:* www.hiteco.com, pg 889

Hjelm, Andrea M, Moore Creative Talent Inc, 3130 Excelsior Blvd, Minneapolis, MN 55416 *Tel:* 612-827-3823 *Web Site:* www.mooretalent.com, pg 946

Hlava, Marjorie M K, National Information Center for Educational Media (NICEM)/MediaSleuth, c/o Access Innovations Inc, 4725 Indian School Rd NE, Suite 100, Albuquerque, NM 87110-3980 *Tel:* 505-265-3591 *Toll Free Tel:* 800-926-8328 *Fax:* 505-256-1080 *E-mail:* info-request@nicem.com; orders@mediasleuth.com *Web Site:* www.nicem.com; www.mediasleuth.com, pg 953

Hoban-Halvorsen, Isaiah, 911 Media Arts Center, 909 NE 43 St, Suite 206, Seattle, WA 98105 *Tel:* 206-682-6552 *E-mail:* info@911media.org *Web Site:* www.911media.org, pg 957

Hobbs, Stuart, McCurdy Radio Ltd, 75 First St, Suite 108, Orangeville, ON L9W 5B6, Canada *Tel:* 416-248-6155 *Fax:* 416-248-6755 *E-mail:* sales8800@mcradio.com *Web Site:* www.mcradio.com; www.mccurdytel.com, pg 935

Hobel, Mary-Ann, The Cinema Guild Inc, 115 W 30 St, Suite 800, New York, NY 10001-4061 *Tel:* 212-685-6242 *Toll Free Tel:* 800-723-5522 *Fax:* 212-685-4717 *E-mail:* info@cinemaguild.com *Web Site:* www.cinemaguild.com, pg 827

Hobel, Philip, The Cinema Guild Inc, 115 W 30 St, Suite 800, New York, NY 10001-4061 *Tel:* 212-685-6242 *Toll Free Tel:* 800-723-5522 *Fax:* 212-685-4717 *E-mail:* info@cinemaguild.com *Web Site:* www.cinemaguild.com, pg 827

Hobson, Charles, Vanguard Documentaries, PO Box 26635, Brooklyn, NY 11202 *Tel:* 347-725-1677 *Web Site:* www.vanguarddocumentaries.com, pg 1051

Hochheim, Frieder, Kino Flo Lighting Systems, 2840 N Hollywood Way, Burbank, CA 91505 *Tel:* 818-767-6528 *Fax:* 818-252-0290 (rental); 818-767-7517 (sales) *E-mail:* sales@kinoflo.com *Web Site:* www.kinoflo.com, pg 911

Hocker, Brian, NBC-5, 4805 Amon Carter Blvd, Fort Worth, TX 76155 *Tel:* 817-429-5555 *Fax:* 817-654-6325 *E-mail:* newstips@nbcdfw.com *Web Site:* www.nbcdfw.com, pg 953

Hockersmith, J B, Continental Film & Video, PO Box 250627, Atlanta, GA 30325 *Tel:* 404-844-6374 *Web Site:* www.continentalfilmvideo.com, pg 835

Hodges, Mike, RIA Corp, 1615 W 2200 S, Suite B, Salt Lake City, UT 84119 *Tel:* 801-486-8822 *Fax:* 801-486-2741 *E-mail:* sales@riacorp.com *Web Site:* www.riacorp.com, pg 996

Hodgson, Alan, Society for Imaging Science and Technology (IS&T), 7003 Kilworth Lane, Springfield, VA 22151 *Tel:* 703-642-9090 *Fax:* 703-642-9094 *E-mail:* info@imaging.org *Web Site:* www.imaging.org, pg 1089

Hodson, Thomas, WOUB Public Media, 35 S College St, Athens, OH 45701 *Tel:* 740-593-1771 *Fax:* 740-593-0240 *E-mail:* woub@woub.org *Web Site:* woub.org, pg 1070

Hoeye, Dan, Ultimate Support Systems Inc, 5836 Wright Dr, Loveland, CO 80538 *Toll Free Tel:* 800-525-5628 *Fax:* 970-776-1941 *E-mail:* info@ultimatesupport.com *Web Site:* www.ultimatesupport.com, pg 1047

Hofbauer, Roni, Educational Activities Inc, PO Box 87, Baldwin, NY 11510-0087 *Tel:* 516-223-4666 *Toll Free Tel:* 800-797-3223 *Fax:* 516-623-9282 *E-mail:* learn@edact.com *Web Site:* www.edact.com, pg 857

Hofer, Bruce E, Audio Precision, 5750 SW Arctic Dr, Beaverton, OR 97005 *Tel:* 503-627-0832 *Toll Free Tel:* 800-231-7350 *Fax:* 503-469-0336 *E-mail:* sales@ap.com *Web Site:* www.ap.com, pg 794

Hoff, Doan, Yamaha Electronics Corp, 6660 Orangethorpe Ave, Buena Park, CA 90620 *Tel:* 714-522-9105 *Toll Free Tel:* 800-292-2982 (cust support) *Toll Free Fax:* 800-782-8484 *Web Site:* www.yamaha.com, pg 1071

Hoffend, Daniel Jr, Freeman, 1600 Viceroy, Suite 100, Dallas, TX 75235 *Tel:* 214-445-1000 *Fax:* 214-445-0200 *Web Site:* www.freemanco.com, pg 872

Hoffend, Jack, InterAmerica Stage Inc, 4300 St Johns Pkwy, Sanford, FL 32771 *Tel:* 407-302-0881 *Toll Free Tel:* 877-302-4274 *Fax:* 407-302-0882 *E-mail:* info@iastage.com *Web Site:* www.iastage.com, pg 900

Hoffman, Ace, Animated Software Co, PO Box 1936, Carlsbad, CA 92018-1936 *Tel:* 760-720-7261 *Toll Free Tel:* 800-551-2726 *Web Site:* www.animatedsoftware.com, pg 786

Hoffman, Andrew, Noventri, 20940 Twin Springs Dr, Smithsburg, MD 21783-1510 *Tel:* 301-790-0103 *Fax:* 301-790-0173 *E-mail:* sale@noventri.com *Web Site:* www.noventri.com, pg 960

Hoffman, Clint, Kramer Electronics USA Inc, 6 Rte 173 W, Clinton, NJ 08809 *Tel:* 908-735-0018 *Toll Free Tel:* 888-275-6311 *Fax:* 908-735-0515 *E-mail:* info@kramerus.com *Web Site:* www.kramerus.com, pg 913

Hoffman, Donald, The Audio Department Inc, 119 W 57 St, Suite 400, New York, NY 10019 *Tel:* 212-586-3503 *Fax:* 212-245-1675 *E-mail:* scheduling@theaudiodepartment.com *Web Site:* www.theaudiodepartment.com, pg 794

Hoffman, Janalea, Rhythmic Medicine, 10425 W 177 Terr, Olathe, KS 66062 *Tel:* 913-851-5100 *Fax:* 913-402-8510 *E-mail:* music@rhythmicmedicine.com *Web Site:* www.rhythmicmedicine.com, pg 996

Hoffman, Jena L, International Ticketing Association Inc (INTIX), 2 Meridian Plaza, 10401 N Meridian St, Suite 300, Indianapolis, IN 46290 *Tel:* 212-629-4036 *Fax:* 212-629-8532 *E-mail:* info@intix.org *Web Site:* www.intix.org, pg 1084

Hoffman, Judy, Noventri, 20940 Twin Springs Dr, Smithsburg, MD 21783-1510 *Tel:* 301-790-0103 *Fax:* 301-790-0173 *E-mail:* sale@noventri.com *Web Site:* www.noventri.com, pg 960

Hoffman, Kevin, Event Essentials, 6485 Blanchar's Crossing, Windsor, WI 53598 *Tel:* 608-846-5004 *Toll Free Tel:* 800-220-4991 *Fax:* 608-222-5063 *Web Site:* www.eventessentials.com, pg 863

Hoffman, Norm, BroadcastStore.com, 9420 Lurline Ave, Unit C, Chatsworth, CA 91311 *Tel:* 818-998-9100 *Fax:* 818-998-9106 *E-mail:* sales@broadcaststore.com *Web Site:* www.broadcaststore.com, pg 813

Hoffman, Susan, Intermedia Inc, 5600 Rainier Ave S, Suite 203, Seattle, WA 98118 *Tel:* 206-284-2995 *Toll Free Tel:* 800-553-8336 *Toll Free Fax:* 800-553-1655 *E-mail:* info@intermedia-inc.com *Web Site:* www.intermedia-inc.com, pg 900

Hoffman-Cook, Kayla B, Freewheelin' Films, 44895 Hwy 82, Aspen, CO 81611 *Tel:* 970-925-2640 *Fax:* 970-925-9369 *Web Site:* www.fwf.com, pg 873

Hofler, Richard, Moxie Media, 1301 Dealers Ave, New Orleans, LA 70123 *Tel:* 504-733-6907 *Toll Free Tel:* 800-346-6943 *Fax:* 504-733-9493 *E-mail:* info@moxiemedia.com *Web Site:* www.moxiemedia.com; www.moxietraining.com, pg 948

Hofmann, Rick, Image Logic Corp, 6807 Brennon Lane, Chevy Chase, MD 20815-3255 *Tel:* 202-223-2888 *E-mail:* info@imagelogic.com *Web Site:* www.imagelogic.com, pg 895

Hofrenning, Maureen, Greater Wichita Convention & Visitors Bureau/Wichita Film Commission, 515 S Main St, Suite 115, Wichita, KS 67202 *Tel:* 316-265-2800 *Toll Free Tel:* 800-288-9424 *Fax:* 316-265-0162 *Web Site:* www.gowichita.com, pg 1098

Hogan, Dan, DSR Computer Technology Specialists Inc, 921-P Mercantile Dr, Hanover, MD 21076 *Tel:* 410-579-4508 *Toll Free Tel:* 800-875-0037 *Fax:* 410-579-8412 *E-mail:* dsr@dsr-inc.com *Web Site:* www.dsr-inc.com, pg 853

Hogan, Jill, POP TV, 5069 Maureen Lane, Moorpark, CA 93021-7127 *Tel:* 805-499-8513 *Toll Free Tel:* 800-331-4626 *Fax:* 805-499-8206 *E-mail:* sales@mpo-video.com *Web Site:* www.mpo-video.com, pg 978

Hogan, Kim, Luzerne County Community College, 1333 S Prospect St, Nanticoke, PA 18634-3899 *Tel:* 570-740-0200 *Toll Free Tel:* 800-377-5222 *Fax:* 570-740-0250 *Web Site:* www.luzerne.edu/index.jsp, pg 926

Hogan, Simone, Coastline Productions, 2647 Gateway Rd, No 105-355, Carlsbad, CA 92009 *Tel:* 760-598-1860 *Toll Free Tel:* 888-781-5714 *E-mail:* productions@coastlinevideo.com *Web Site:* www.coastlinevideo.com, pg 831

Hogan, Steve, Houston Photo Imaging, 5250 Gulfton, Suite 3-B, Houston, TX 77081 *Tel:* 713-666-0282 *Toll Free Tel:* 800-664-0282 *Fax:* 713-667-9625 *E-mail:* info@houstonphotoimaging.com *Web Site:* www.houstonphotoimaging.com, pg 892

Hoge, Ken, Texas Heart Institute Visual Communication Services, Denton A Cooley Bldg, Suite C530, 6770 Bertner Ave, Houston, TX 77030 *Tel:* 832-355-9558 *Fax:* 832-355-9511 *Web Site:* www.texasheartinstitute.org, pg 1037

Hogerson, Jerry, TeachLogic Inc, 1688 Ord Way, Oceanside, CA 92056 *Tel:* 760-631-7800 *Toll Free Tel:* 800-588-0018 *Fax:* 760-631-1283 *E-mail:* sales@teachlogic.com; info@teachlogic.com *Web Site:* www.teachlogic.com, pg 1033

Hoggatt, Richard Jr, Stage Directions, 8311 Hempstead Rd, Houston, TX 77008 *Tel:* 713-863-7469 *Fax:* 713-863-9418 *E-mail:* sales@stagedirections.com *Web Site:* www.stagedirections.com, pg 1022

Hohener, John, Microsemi, 2300 Orchard Pkwy, San Jose, CA 95131-1017 *Tel:* 408-433-0910; 408-428-7907 (tech support) *Fax:* 408-428-6960 *E-mail:* info@symmetricom.com *Web Site:* www.symmetricom.com, pg 941

Hohman, Robert F Jr, Media Marketing Associates Inc, 12 Colgate Rd, Beverly, MA 01915, pg 937

Hokunson, Todd, Linear LLC, 1950 Camino Vida Roble, Suite 150, Carlsbad, CA 92008-6517 *Tel:* 760-438-7000 *Toll Free Tel:* 800-421-1587 *Fax:* 760-931-1340 *Toll Free Fax:* 800-468-1340 *E-mail:* sales@linearcorp.com *Web Site:* www.linearcorp.com, pg 922

Holbrook, Dan, Maritz Performance Improvement Co, 1000 Town Ctr, Suite 1200, Southfield, MI 48075 *Tel:* 248-948-4500 *Toll Free Tel:* 877-462-7489 *Fax:* 248-948-4598 *Web Site:* www.maritz.com, pg 931

Holbrooke, David, Mountainfilm in Telluride, 109 E Colorado Ave, Suite 1, Telluride, CO 81435 *Tel:* 970-728-4123 *Fax:* 970-728-6458 *E-mail:* contact@mountainfilm.org *Web Site:* www.mountainfilm.org, pg 1121

Holden, Mark, JaffeHolden, 114-A Washington St, Norwalk, CT 06854 *Tel:* 203-838-4167 *Fax:* 203-838-4168 *Web Site:* www.jaffeholden.com, pg 903

Holguin, Robert, Academy of Science Fiction, Fantasy & Horror Films, 334 W 54 St, Los Angeles, CA 90037 *Tel:* 323-752-5811 *E-mail:* scifiacademy@ca.rr.com *Web Site:* www.saturnawards.org, pg 1075

Holguin, Robert, Saturn Awards, 334 W 54 St, Los Angeles, CA 90037 *Tel:* 323-752-5811 *Web Site:* www.saturnawards.org, pg 1126

Holiday, David, ExpoDisplays, 3401 Mary Taylor Rd, Birmingham, AL 35235 *Tel:* 205-439-8200 *Toll Free Tel:* 800-367-3976 *Fax:* 205-439-8201 *E-mail:* info@expodisplays.com *Web Site:* www.expodisplays.com, pg 864

Hollaender, Robert P II, The Hollaender Manufacturing Co, 10285 Wayne Ave, Cincinnati, OH 45215 *Tel:* 513-772-8800 *Toll Free Tel:* 800-772-8800 (orders) *Fax:* 513-772-8806 *Web Site:* www.hollaender.com, pg 890

Holland, Arnie, Lightyear Entertainment, 4011 Alcove Ave, Studio City, CA 91604 *Tel:* 818-855-1318 *Fax:* 818-855-1320 *E-mail:* mail@lightyear.com *Web Site:* www.lightyear.com, pg 921

Holland, Burt, Encyclomedia, 1526 Dekalb Ave, Atlanta, GA 30307 *Tel:* 404-527-3600 *Fax:* 404-584-5171 *E-mail:* info@encyclomedia.net *Web Site:* www.encyclomedia.net, pg 861

Holland, Lance, Encyclomedia, 1526 Dekalb Ave, Atlanta, GA 30307 *Tel:* 404-527-3600 *Fax:* 404-584-5171 *E-mail:* info@encyclomedia.net *Web Site:* www.encyclomedia.net, pg 861

Holland, Mary Ann, Gagne Inc, 41 Commercial Dr, Johnson City, NY 13790 *Tel:* 607-729-3366 *Toll Free Tel:* 800-800-5954 *Fax:* 607-729-7644 *E-mail:* sales@gagneinc.com *Web Site:* www.gagneinc.com, pg 875

Holland, Rebecca, The Video Project, 145 Ninth St, Suite 102, San Francisco, CA 94103 *Tel:* 415-981-9710 *Toll Free Tel:* 800-475-2638 *Toll Free Fax:* 888-562-9012 *E-mail:* orders@videoproject.com; support@videoproject.com *Web Site:* www.videoproject.com, pg 1056

Holley, Meagan, Replicopy Digital Media Center, 2101 Midway Rd, Suite 200, Carrollton, TX 75006 *Tel:* 972-702-8388 *Fax:* 972-387-DUBS (387-3827) *E-mail:* replicopy@replicopy.com *Web Site:* www.replicopy.com, pg 995

Hollifield, Laura, Artbeats, 1405 N Myrtle Rd, Myrtle Creek, OR 97457 *Tel:* 541-863-4429 *Toll Free Tel:* 800-444-9392 *Fax:* 541-863-4547 *E-mail:* info@artbeats.com *Web Site:* www.artbeats.com, pg 791

Hollingsworth, Schuyler, Warner Home Video Inc, 4000 Warner Blvd, Bldg 160, Burbank, CA 91522 *Tel:* 818-954-6000 *Fax:* 818-954-6480 *Web Site:* www.warnerbros.com, pg 1062

Hollingsworth, Sue, University of Missouri-Columbia, Film & Video Library, 505 E Stewart Rd, Columbia, MO 65211-2040 *Tel:* 573-882-3608 *Fax:* 573-882-6110 *E-mail:* asc@missouri.edu *Web Site:* asc.missouri.edu, pg 1050

Holloway, Chris, OMNISound Recording Studio, 1806 Division St, Nashville, TN 37203 *Tel:* 615-482-1151 *Fax:* 615-321-5528 *Web Site:* www.omnisoundstudios.com, pg 963

Holmes, Darlene, NPR Satellite Services, 1111 N Capitol St NE, Washington, DC 20002 *Tel:* 202-513-2626 *Fax:* 202-513-3035 *Web Site:* www.nprss.org, pg 960

Holmquist, Brooke, KION-TV, 1550 Moffett St, Salinas, CA 93905 *Tel:* 831-784-1702; 831-422-3500 *Fax:* 831-757-1766 *Web Site:* www.kionrightnow.com, pg 911

Holst, Robert N, Studio Instrument Rentals (SIR), 475 Tenth Ave, 2nd fl, New York, NY 10018 *Tel:* 212-627-4900 *Fax:* 212-627-7079 *E-mail:* nyinfo@sir-usa.com *Web Site:* www.sir-usa.com, pg 1027

Holt, David, High Windy Audio/Banjoman Inc, PO Box 553, Fairview, NC 28730 *Tel:* 828-628-1728 *Toll Free Tel:* 800-637-8679 *Fax:* 828-628-4435 *E-mail:* office@davidholt.com *Web Site:* www.davidholt.com, pg 889

Holt, Reba, Grace Church - St Louis, 2695 Creve Coeur Mill Rd, Maryland Heights, MO 63043 *Tel:* 314-292-8300 *Fax:* 314-291-0918 *E-mail:* info@gracestl.org *Web Site:* www.gracestl.org, pg 881

Holtane, Bill, Sound/Video Impressions Inc, 110 S River Rd, Des Plaines, IL 60016 *Tel:* 847-297-4360 *Fax:* 847-297-6870 *E-mail:* info@soundvideoimpressions.com *Web Site:* www.soundvideoimpressions.com, pg 1018

Holtmann, Peter, Exemplar Global, 600 N Plankington Ave, Milwaukee, WI 53201 *Tel:* 414-272-3937 *Toll Free Tel:* 888-722-2440 *Fax:* 414-765-8661 *Web Site:* www.exemplarglobal.org, pg 1081

Holtz, Alex, Barron's Educational Series Inc, 250 Wireless Blvd, Hauppauge, NY 11788 *Tel:* 631-434-3311 *Toll Free Tel:* 800-645-3476 *Fax:* 631-434-3723 *E-mail:* barrons@barronseduc.com *Web Site:* www.barronseduc.com, pg 803

Holyfield, Randy, Caption Colorado LLC, 5690 DTC Blvd, Suite 500W, Greenwood Village, CO 80111 *Tel:* 720-489-5662 *Toll Free Tel:* 800-775-7838 *Fax:* 720-489-5664 *Web Site:* www.captioncolorado.com, pg 820

Homan, Jason, Promedia Digital, 6520 Singletree Dr, Columbus, OH 43229 *Tel:* 614-274-1600 *Toll Free Tel:* 800-837-3827 *Fax:* 614-275-0100 *E-mail:* info@promediaohio.com *Web Site:* www.promediadigital.com, pg 986

Homberg, Rich, WTVS-Station Enterprises, Riley Broadcast Ctr, One Clover Ct, Wixom, MI 48393-2247 *Tel:* 248-305-DPTV (305-3788) *Fax:* 248-305-3990 *E-mail:* email@dptv.org *Web Site:* www.dptv.org, pg 1071

Homer, Jennifer, Association for Talent Development (ATD), 1640 King St, Alexandria, VA 22314-2743 *Tel:* 703-683-8100 *Toll Free Tel:* 800-628-2783 *Fax:* 703-299-8723; 703-683-1523 (cust care) *E-mail:* customercare@td.org *Web Site:* www.td.org; www.astd.org, pg 1078

Hon, Duncan, Emerson Radio Corp, 3 University Plaza, Suite 405, Hackensack, NJ 07601 *Tel:* 973-884-5800 *Toll Free Tel:* 800-909-1240 (cust serv) *Fax:* 973-428-2067 *E-mail:* internet@emersonradio.com *Web Site:* www.emersonradio.com, pg 860

Honda, Atsuo, TOA Electronics Inc, 1350 Bayshore Hwy, Suite 270, Burlingame, CA 94010 *Toll Free Tel:* 800-733-7088 (cust serv); 800-733-4750 (main) *Fax:* 650-588-3349 *Toll Free Fax:* 800-733-9766 *E-mail:* info@toaelectronics.com *Web Site:* www.toaelectronics.com, pg 1041

Honken, David, New Life Communications Inc, 905 Hwy 71 NE, Willmar, MN 56201-2654 *Tel:* 320-235-6404 *Toll Free Tel:* 800-233-6470 *Fax:* 320-235-6418 *E-mail:* nlc@newlifecomm.com *Web Site:* www.newlifecomm.com, pg 956

Honthaner, Eve, California Film Commission (CFC), 7080 Hollywood Blvd, Suite 900, Hollywood, CA 90028-6936 *Tel:* 323-860-2960 (24-hr serv) *Toll Free Tel:* 800-858-4749 *Fax:* 323-860-2972 *E-mail:* filmca@film.ca.gov *Web Site:* www.film.ca.gov, pg 1093

Hood, Barry, TeleVideos, 1566 Dola St, Eugene, OR 97402 *Toll Free Tel:* 800-2-VIDEOS (284-3367) *E-mail:* televideos@msn.com *Web Site:* televideos.com, pg 1036

Hooper, Bill, WMAR-TV, 6400 York Rd, Baltimore, MD 21212 *Tel:* 410-377-2222 *E-mail:* newsroom@wmar.com *Web Site:* www.abc2news.com, pg 1068

Hoopes, Ralph, Star Case Manufacturing Co Inc, 648 Superior Ave, Munster, IN 46321 *Tel:* 219-922-4440 *Toll Free Tel:* 800-822-STAR (822-7827); 800-782-CASE (782-2273) *Fax:* 219-922-4442 *E-mail:* star@starcase.com *Web Site:* www.starcase.com, pg 1023

Hoose, Tom, VIEW Inc (Video International Entertainment World Inc), 11 Reservoir Rd, Saugerties, NY 12477 *Tel:* 845-246-9955 *Toll Free Tel:* 800-843-9843 *Fax:* 845-246-9966 *E-mail:* viewvid@aol.com *Web Site:* www.view.com, pg 1058

Hoover, Roger, Sweetsong Productions, 193 Meadsville Rd, Parkersburg, WV 26104 *Tel:* 304-428-7773 *E-mail:* sweetsonginfo@sweetsong.com *Web Site:* www.sweetsong.com, pg 1029

Hope, Mark, Hope Productions, 3116 Arrowhead Dr, Hollywood, CA 90068 *Tel:* 323-460-4995, pg 891

Hopkins, Chris, ProVision Video Sales & Rentals Inc, 143 W Third Ave, Vancouver, BC V5Y 1E6, Canada *Tel:* 604-876-0940 *Toll Free Tel:* 877-337-0940 *Fax:* 604-876-8269 *E-mail:* sales@provisionvideo.com; rentals@provisionvideo.com *Web Site:* www.provisionvideo.com, pg 986

Hopkins, Keith, Accu-Tech, 11350 Old Roswell Rd, Suite 100, Roswell, GA 30009 *Tel:* 770-740-2240 *Toll Free Tel:* 800-221-4767; 888-222-8832 *Fax:* 770-740-2260 *Web Site:* www.accu-tech.com, pg 773

Hopkins, Mary Jane, Association of Catholic TV & Radio Syndicators, 518 S Alandele Ave, Los Angeles, CA 90036 *Tel:* 323-938-4861, pg 1079

Hopkins, Shae, KET The Kentucky Network, 600 Cooper Dr, Lexington, KY 40502 *Tel:* 859-258-7000 *Toll Free Tel:* 800-432-0951 *Fax:* 859-258-7396 *E-mail:* adulted@ket.org *Web Site:* www.ket.org, pg 910

Hopkins, Tom O, Tom Hopkins International Inc, 465 E Chilton Dr, Suite 4, Chandler, AZ 85225 *Tel:* 480-949-0786 *Toll Free Tel:* 800-528-0446 *Fax:* 480-949-1590 *E-mail:* info@tomhopkins.com *Web Site:* www.tomhopkins.com, pg 891

Hopwood, Cael, Vancouver Film & Special Events Office, 126 Keefer St, Vancouver, BC V6A 1X4, Canada *Tel:* 604-257-8840 *Fax:* 604-257-8859 *E-mail:* film.office@vancouver.ca *Web Site:* www.vancouver.ca/engsvcs/filmandevents, pg 1105

Horan, Shaun, Marinco Electrical Group, N85 W12545 Westbrook Crossing, Menomonee Falls, WI 53051-3330 *Tel:* 262-293-0600 *Toll Free Tel:* 800-307-6702 *Fax:* 262-293-7022 *E-mail:* swdsales@marinco.com *Web Site:* www.marinco.com, pg 931

Horan, Tom, Half Moon Video Productions, 79 Central Ave, Jersey City, NJ 07306-2124 *Tel:* 201-792-1066 *Fax:* 201-792-1523 *E-mail:* pavonia@home.com, pg 883

Horn, Donna, CaptionMax, 2438 27 Ave S, Minneapolis, MN 55406 *Tel:* 612-341-3566 *Toll Free Tel:* 800-822-3566 *Fax:* 612-341-2345 *Web Site:* www.captionmax.com, pg 820

Horn, Harry, Scala Inc, 350 Eagleview Blvd, Suite 350, Exton, PA 19341 *Tel:* 610-363-3350 *Toll Free Tel:* 888-SCALA-96 (722-5296) *Fax:* 610-363-4010 *E-mail:* marketing@scala.com *Web Site:* scala.com, pg 1004

Horn, Peter, Vicon Industries Inc, 131 Heartland Blvd, Edgewood, NY 11717 *Tel:* 631-952-2288 *Toll Free Tel:* 800-645-9116 *Fax:* 631-951-2288 *Web Site:* www.vicon-security.com, pg 1053

Hornbeck, Matthew, Young Minds Inc, 1014 E Cooley Dr, Suite H, Colton, CA 92324 *Tel:* 909-426-4860 *Fax:* 909-426-4866 *E-mail:* info@ymi.com; sales@ymi.com *Web Site:* www.ymi.com, pg 1072

Hornburg, Matt, Marblemedia, 74 Fraser Ave, Suite 100, Toronto, ON M6K 3E1, Canada *Tel:* 416-646-2711 *E-mail:* connect@marblemedia.com *Web Site:* www.marblemedia.com, pg 930

Horne, Chris, Lawrence Behr Associates Inc, 3400 Tupper Dr, Greenville, NC 27834 *Tel:* 252-757-0279 *Toll Free Tel:* 800-522-4464 *Fax:* 252-752-9155 *E-mail:* lbassc@lbagroup.com *Web Site:* www.lbagroup.com/associates, pg 804

Horner, D Kevin, Mastech, 1000 Commerce Dr, Suite 500, Pittsburgh, PA 15275 *Tel:* 412-787-2100 *Toll Free Tel:* 800-627-8323 *Fax:* 412-494-9272 *E-mail:* info@mastech.com *Web Site:* www.mastech.com, pg 933

Horner, Digby, Adobe Systems Inc, 345 Park Ave, San Jose, CA 95110-2704 *Tel:* 408-536-6000 *Fax:* 408-537-6000 *Web Site:* www.adobe.com, pg 776

Horner, Joe, AudioImage Recording, 110 N Jefferson St, Richmond, VA 23220-5022 *Tel:* 804-644-7700 *Fax:* 804-644-8801 *E-mail:* info@audioimagerecording.com *Web Site:* www.audioimagerecording.com, pg 796

Horowitz, Dr Leonard G, Tetrahedron LLC, 5348 Las Vegas Dr, Suite 353, Las Vegas, NV 89108 *Tel:* 208-265-8065 *Toll Free Tel:* 888-923-9936 *E-mail:* tetra@tetrahedron.org *Web Site:* www.tetrahedron.org, pg 1037

Horrell, Chris, Durrell LLC, 801 Fifth Ave S, Nashville, TN 37203 *Tel:* 615-313-8877 *Fax:* 615-313-8873 *Web Site:* www.durrellsports.com, pg 854

Horrell, John, Durrell LLC, 801 Fifth Ave S, Nashville, TN 37203 *Tel:* 615-313-8877 *Fax:* 615-313-8873 *Web Site:* www.durrellsports.com, pg 854

Horsley, Mike, RLX Media LLC, 720 SW 12 Ave, Pompano Beach, FL 33069 *Tel:* 954-946-7575 *Toll Free Tel:* 800-555-9704 *Fax:* 954-946-7576 *E-mail:* info@rlxmedia.com *Web Site:* www.rlxmedia.com; www.rlxvideo.net, pg 997

Horton, Starr, Skyriver Films, 6251 Tuttle Place, Suite 102, Anchorage, AK 99507-2099 *Tel:* 907-243-3332; 907-248-9999 *Toll Free Tel:* 888-660-2257 *Fax:* 907-243-2044 *E-mail:* info@alaskajacks.com *Web Site:* www.alaskajacks.com; www.skyriver.com, pg 1013

Hosier, Chad, Sigma Delta Chi Awards in Journalism, Eugene S Pulliam National Journalism Ctr, 3909 N Meridian St, Indianapolis, IN 46208 *Tel:* 317-927-8000 *Fax:* 317-920-4789 *E-mail:* awards@spj.org *Web Site:* www.spj.org, pg 1127

Hoska, Steve, Winsted Corp, 10901 Hampshire Ave S, Minneapolis, MN 55438 *Tel:* 952-944-9050 *Toll Free Tel:* 800-447-2257 *Fax:* 952-944-1546 *Toll Free Fax:* 800-421-3839 *E-mail:* info@winsted.com *Web Site:* www.winsted.com, pg 1068

Hosker, Bruce, CBM Metal, High Point Business Park, 8750 Holgate Cresent, Milton, ON L9T 0K3, Canada *Tel:* 905-878-0648 *Toll Free Tel:* 800-387-4834 *Fax:* 905-878-6748 *Toll Free Fax:* 888-554-5501 *E-mail:* sales@cbmmetal.com *Web Site:* www.cbmmetal.com, pg 821

Hoskyns-Abrahall, John, Bullfrog Films Inc, PO Box 149, Oley, PA 19547-0149 *Tel:* 610-779-8226 *Toll Free Tel:* 800-543-3764 *Fax:* 610-370-1978 *E-mail:* video@bullfrogfilms.com *Web Site:* www.bullfrogfilms.com, pg 815

Hossman, Evan, Photosound of Orlando Inc, 6438 University Blvd, Unit 14, Winter Park, FL 32792 *Tel:* 407-898-8841 *Toll Free Tel:* 800-552-8776 *Fax:* 407-898-0300 *E-mail:* photosound@cfl.rr.com *Web Site:* www.photosoundav.com, pg 975

Hott, Mondae, Ensemble Designs Inc, 870 Gold Flat Rd, Nevada City, CA 95959 *Tel:* 530-478-1830 *Fax:* 530-478-1832 *E-mail:* info@ensembledesigns.com *Web Site:* www.ensembledesigns.com, pg 861

Houghton, Deborah, SESAC Inc, 55 Music Sq E, Nashville, TN 37203 *Tel:* 615-320-0055 *Fax:* 615-963-3527 *Web Site:* www.sesac.com, pg 1088

Houlle, David, Sight & Sound Production Services Inc, 1143 Boland Place, St Louis, MO 63117-1411 *Tel:* 314-647-0665 *Web Site:* www.sspsinc.com, pg 1010

Housden, Steve, Xenon Pictures Inc, 3521 Jack Northrop Ave, Hawthorne, CA 90250 *Tel:* 310-451-5510 *Fax:* 310-395-4058 *E-mail:* info@xenonpictures.com; sales@xenonpictures.com *Web Site:* xenonpictures.com, pg 1071

House, Kurt D, Three Rivers Publishing Co, 218 Country Wood, San Antonio, TX 78216 *Tel:* 210-490-2433 *E-mail:* cowboyhouse@aol.com *Web Site:* www.kurthouse.com, pg 1040

House, Tim, Personal Communications Industry Association (PCIA), 500 Montgomery St, Suite 500, Alexandria, VA 22314 *Tel:* 703-739-0300 *Toll Free Tel:* 800-759-0300 *Fax:* 703-836-1608 *Web Site:* www.pcia.com, pg 1087

Houser, Catherine, Paramount Pictures Corporation, 5555 Melrose Ave, Los Angeles, CA 90038 *Tel:* 323-956-8398 *Web Site:* www.paramount.com, pg 969

Hovda, Heidi, Corpus Christi Convention & Visitors Bureau, 101 N Shoreline Blvd, Suite 430, Corpus Christi, TX 78401 *Tel:* 361-881-1888 *Toll Free Tel:* 800-678-6232 *Fax:* 361-887-9023 *Web Site:* www.corpuschristicvb.com, pg 1103

Howard, Christine Metz, Lawrence Convention & Visitors Bureau, 402 N Second St, Lawrence, KS 66044 *Tel:* 785-856-3040; 785-856-5282 *Fax:* 785-856-5303 *E-mail:* visinfo@visitlawrence.com *Web Site:* www.visitlawrence.com, pg 1097

Howard, Darren, Mach 1 Productions, 1101 N Himes Ave, Tampa, FL 33607 *Tel:* 813-873-7700 *Fax:* 813-875-6633 *E-mail:* info@mach1pro.com *Web Site:* www.mach1pro.com, pg 927

Howard, Diane, BCD Associates Inc, 2800 NW 36 St, Suite 220, Oklahoma City, OK 73112 *Tel:* 405-702-6888 *Toll Free Tel:* 800-223-6734 *E-mail:* salesweb@bcdusa.com; sales@bcdusa.com *Web Site:* www.bcdusa.com, pg 803

Howard, Larry, Alcorn McBride Inc, 3300 S Hiawassee Rd, Bldg 105, Orlando, FL 32835 *Tel:* 407-296-5800 *Fax:* 407-296-5801 *E-mail:* info@alcorn.com; sales@alcorn.com *Web Site:* www.alcorn.com, pg 780

Howard, Lester, Action Video, 2373 Walnut Blvd, Walnut Creek, CA 94597 *Tel:* 925-934-4366 *E-mail:* actvid@aol.com *Web Site:* actionvideo.biz, pg 775

Howard, Robert, BCD Associates Inc, 2800 NW 36 St, Suite 220, Oklahoma City, OK 73112 *Tel:* 405-702-6888 *Toll Free Tel:* 800-223-6734 *E-mail:* salesweb@bcdusa.com; sales@bcdusa.com *Web Site:* www.bcdusa.com, pg 803

Howard-Hughes, Terri, Mediaforce Productions, 5960 W Parker Rd, Suite 278-183, Plano, TX 75093 *Tel:* 972-473-6888 *Web Site:* www.mediaforcepro.com, pg 937

Howell, Adam, Heartland Film Festival, 1043 Virginia Ave, Suite 2, Indianapolis, IN 46203 *Tel:* 317-464-9405 *Web Site:* www.heartlandfilmfestival.org, pg 1116

Howell, John, GatesAir, 5300 Kings Island Dr, Suite 101, Mason, OH 45040 *Tel:* 513-459-3400 *Fax:* 513-459-3796 *E-mail:* information@gatesair.com; orders@gatesair.com; support@gatesair.com *Web Site:* www.gatesair.com, pg 875

Howell, Sharon, The Campbell Agency, 3838 Oak Lawn Ave, Suite 900, Dallas, TX 75219 *Tel:* 214-522-8991 *Fax:* 214-522-8997 *Web Site:* www.thecampbellagency.com, pg 818

Howerton, Blaine, Denver Media Center, 3853 S Broadway, Englewood, CO 80113 *Tel:* 303-872-9993 *Web Site:* denvermediacenter.com, pg 845

Howes, Lauren, Canadian Filmmakers Distribution Center (CFMDC), 401 Richmond St W, Suite 245, Toronto, ON M5V 3A8, Canada *Tel:* 416-588-0725 *Fax:* 416-588-7956 *Web Site:* www.cfmdc.org, pg 818

Howett, Tim, Alpha Wire Co, 711 Lidgerwood Ave, Elizabeth, NJ 07207-0711 *Tel:* 908-925-8000 *Toll Free Tel:* 800-52-ALPHA (522-5742) *Fax:* 908-925-6923 *E-mail:* info@alphawire.com *Web Site:* www.alphawire.com, pg 782

Howie, Thomas, Glidecam Industries Inc, 23 Joseph St, Kingston, MA 02364 *Tel:* 781-585-7900 *Toll Free Tel:* 800-949-2089; 800-600-2011 *Fax:* 781-585-7903 *E-mail:* sales@glidecam.com *Web Site:* www.glidecam.com, pg 878

Howse, Jennifer, March of Dimes Foundation, 1275 Mamaroneck Ave, White Plains, NY 10605 *Tel:* 914-997-4488 *Toll Free Tel:* 888-663-4637 *E-mail:* contactus@marchofdimes.com *Web Site:* www.marchofdimes.com, pg 930

Hoyle, Jim, Audio & Light, 2209 Randleman Rd, Greensboro, NC 27406 *Tel:* 336-274-1234 *Fax:* 336-274-4022 *E-mail:* info@audio-light.com *Web Site:* www.audio-light.com, pg 794

Hoyt, Jeff, KJfilms LLC, 33 Serra Dr, Middletown, CT 06457 *Tel:* 860-894-2363; 860-995-5106 (cell) *E-mail:* info@kjfilms.com *Web Site:* www.kjfilms.com, pg 911

Hrastar, Brian, Optimus, 161 E Grand Ave, Chicago, IL 60611 *Tel:* 312-321-0880 *Web Site:* www.optimus.com, pg 965

Hu, Dr Joe-E, York Telecom, 81 Corbett Way, Eatontown, NJ 07724 *Tel:* 732-413-6000 *Toll Free Tel:* 866-836-8463 *Fax:* 732-413-6060 *E-mail:* knowmore@yorktel.com *Web Site:* yorktel.com, pg 1072

Huang, Terry, Albumx Corp, 21 Grace Church St, Port Chester, NY 10573 *Tel:* 914-939-6878 *Toll Free Tel:* 800-961-6710 *Fax:* 914-939-8047 *E-mail:* info@renaissancealbums.com *Web Site:* www.renaissancealbums.com, pg 780

Huber, Laura, Creative Media Development, 1631 NW Thurman St, Portland, OR 97209 *Tel:* 503-223-6794 *Fax:* 503-223-2430 *E-mail:* info@cmdpdx.com *Web Site:* www.cmdpdx.com, pg 838

Hudlin, Warrington, Black Filmmaker Foundation (BFF), 131 Varick St, Suite 937, New York, NY 10013 *Tel:* 212-253-1690 *Fax:* 212-255-7575 *E-mail:* community@dvrepublic.org *Web Site:* www.dvrepublic.org, pg 1079

Hudson, Dawn, Academy Awards®, 8949 Wilshire Blvd, Beverly Hills, CA 90211 *Tel:* 310-247-3000 *Fax:* 310-859-9619 *E-mail:* awardsoffice@oscars.org; publicity@oscars.org *Web Site:* www.oscars.org, pg 1107

Hudson, Dawn, The Academy of Motion Picture Arts and Sciences (AMPAS), 8949 Wilshire Blvd, Beverly Hills, CA 90211 *Tel:* 310-247-3000 *Fax:* 310-859-9619 *E-mail:* awardsoffice@oscars.org *Web Site:* www.oscars.org, pg 1075

Hudson, Dawn, Student Academy Awards Competition, 8949 Wilshire Blvd, Beverly Hills, CA 90211 *Tel:* 310-247-3000 *Fax:* 310-859-9619 *E-mail:* SAA@oscars.org *Web Site:* www.oscars.org/saa, pg 1127

Hudson, Gary, Acoustical Solutions Inc, 2420 Grenoble Rd, Richmond, VA 23294 *Tel:* 804-346-8350 *Toll Free Tel:* 800-782-5742 *Fax:* 804-346-8808 *E-mail:* info@acousticalsolutions.com *Web Site:* www.acousticalsolutions.com, pg 774

Hudson, Paul, McCurdy Radio Ltd, 75 First St, Suite 108, Orangeville, ON L9W 5B6, Canada *Tel:* 416-248-6155 *Fax:* 416-248-6755 *E-mail:* sales8800@mcradio.com *Web Site:* www.mcradio.com; www.mccurdytel.com, pg 935

Hudson, Ruth, Chicago Spotlight Inc, 1658 W Carroll St, Chicago, IL 60612 *Tel:* 312-455-1171 *Fax:* 312-455-1744 *Web Site:* www.chicagospotlight.com, pg 825

Huelsmann, Axel, Staedtler-Mars Ltd, 5725 McLaughlin Rd, Mississauga, ON L5R 3K5, Canada *Tel:* 905-501-9008 *Toll Free Tel:* 800-776-5544; 800-387-5872 *Fax:* 905-501-9117 *Toll Free Fax:* 800-675-8249 *E-mail:* info@staedtler.ca *Web Site:* www.staedtler.ca, pg 1022

Huenergardt, Charles, Chapman/Leonard Studios & Production Center, 12950 Raymer St, North Hollywood, CA 91605 *Tel:* 818-764-6726 *Toll Free Tel:* 888-883-6559 *Fax:* 818-764-6730 *Web Site:* www.chapman-leonard.com, pg 824

Huff, Larry, Bright Star Productions Inc, 2420 Center St, Houston, TX 77007 *Tel:* 713-529-2757 *Fax:* 713-529-2329 *Web Site:* www.brightstarproductions.com, pg 812

Huff, Sherri L, Alpha Source Inc, 6619 W Calumet Rd, Milwaukee, WI 53223-4186 *Tel:* 414-760-2222 *Toll Free Tel:* 800-654-9845 *Fax:* 414-760-2070 *Toll Free Fax:* 888-654-9840 *E-mail:* customer.service@alphasource.com; info@alphasource.com *Web Site:* www.alphasource.com, pg 782

Huff, Steven, L A Management Co LLC, 8131 Bay Pointe Dr, Denver, NC 28037 *Tel:* 704-560-6274 *Toll Free Tel:* 800-651-7818 *Fax:* 704-973-7968 *E-mail:* info@managementco.com *Web Site:* lamanagementco.com, pg 914

Huffman, Tammy, SVS Inc, 2513 Jenks Ave, Panama City, FL 32405 *Tel:* 850-522-4747 *Fax:* 850-522-4739 *E-mail:* sales@svslifts.com *Web Site:* www.svslifts.com, pg 1029

Huffstetter, Larry, Curtis Company, PO Box 210-215, Montgomery, AL 36121 *Tel:* 334-279-7127 *Toll Free Tel:* 800-228-5937 *Fax:* 334-270-8787 *Toll Free Fax:* 800-325-6341 *Web Site:* www.curtisav.com, pg 841

Hugar, Tony, Audio Resource Honolulu, 1750 Kalakaua Ave, Suite 201, Honolulu, HI 96826 *Tel:* 808-944-9400 *Toll Free Fax:* 866-774-4184 *E-mail:* information@audioresourcehonolulu.com *Web Site:* www.audioresourcehonolulu.com, pg 794

Hughes, Erin, MRM Worldwide, 622 Third Ave, New York, NY 10017 *Tel:* 646-865-6230 *E-mail:* info@mrmworldwide.com *Web Site:* www.mrmworldwide.com, pg 948

Hughes, Mark, Analog Man Recording Studio, PO Box 70245, Nashville, TN 37207 *Tel:* 615-242-2908, pg 786

Hughes, Mark Stephan, Mr Mark's Used Musical, Stereo & Studio Equipment Store, 109 Grizzard Ave, Nashville, TN 37207-4413 *Tel:* 615-242-2907 *E-mail:* mrmarksmusic@aol.com, pg 944

Hughson, Susan, Thomas & Betts Power Solutions, 5900 Eastport Blvd, Bldg V, Richmond, VA 23231-4453 *Tel:* 804-236-3300 *Toll Free Tel:* 800-238-5000; 800-CYBEREX (292-3739) *Fax:* 804-236-4040; 804-236-4841 *Web Site:* www.tnbpowersolutions.com, pg 1039

Huisinga, Ron, New Life Communications Inc, 905 Hwy 71 NE, Willmar, MN 56201-2654 *Tel:* 320-235-6404 *Toll Free Tel:* 800-233-6470 *Fax:* 320-235-6418 *E-mail:* nlc@newlifecomm.com *Web Site:* www.newlifecomm.com, pg 956

Hull, Charlene, Musicol Recording, 780 Oakland Park Ave, Columbus, OH 43224 *Tel:* 614-267-3133 *Toll Free Tel:* 800-240-5963 *Fax:* 614-267-3135 *E-mail:* info@musicolrecording.com *Web Site:* www.musicolrecording.com, pg 951

Hull, David, The Screen Works®, 2201 W Fulton St, Chicago, IL 60612 *Tel:* 312-243-8265 *Toll Free Tel:* 800-294-8111 *Fax:* 312-243-8290 *E-mail:* screens@thescreenworks.com *Web Site:* www.thescreenworks.com, pg 1005

Hull, Fred, Visual Communications Group Inc, 5721 Arapahoe Ave, Suite A-2, Boulder, CO 80303 *Tel:* 303-413-0878 *Fax:* 303-413-0683 *E-mail:* vcg@visualcomgroup.com *Web Site:* www.visualcomgroup.com, pg 1059

Hull, John W, Musicol Recording, 780 Oakland Park Ave, Columbus, OH 43224 *Tel:* 614-267-3133 *Toll Free Tel:* 800-240-5963 *Fax:* 614-267-3135 *E-mail:* info@musicolrecording.com *Web Site:* www.musicolrecording.com, pg 951

Hull, Scott, Masterdisk Corp, 545 W 45 St, 5th fl, New York, NY 10036 *Tel:* 212-541-5022 *Fax:* 212-581-4093 *E-mail:* info@masterdisk.com *Web Site:* www.masterdisk.com, pg 933

Hull, Warren J, Musicol Recording, 780 Oakland Park Ave, Columbus, OH 43224 *Tel:* 614-267-3133 *Toll Free Tel:* 800-240-5963 *Fax:* 614-267-3135 *E-mail:* info@musicolrecording.com *Web Site:* www.musicolrecording.com, pg 951

Hummel, Karl, Taylor Associates, 110 W Canal St, Suite 301, Winooski, VT 05404 *Tel:* 802-735-1942 *Toll Free Tel:* 800-READ-PLUS (732-3758) *Fax:* 802-419-4786 *E-mail:* info@readingplus.com *Web Site:* www.readingplus.com, pg 1032

Humpage, Tom, WGME-TV, 81 Northport Dr, Portland, ME 04103 *Tel:* 207-797-1313 *Fax:* 207-878-7842 *E-mail:* tvmail@wgme.com *Web Site:* www.wgme.com, pg 1065

Humphrey, Doug, Films for the Humanities & Sciences, 132 W 31 St, 17th fl, New York, NY 10001 *Toll Free Tel:* 800-257-5126 *Fax:* 609-671-0266 *E-mail:* custserv@films.com *Web Site:* ffh.films.com, pg 868

Humphrey, Lori, Proforma GW Marketing, 3839 E 17 Ave, Spokane, WA 99223 *Tel:* 509-534-9677; 509-534-7477 *Toll Free Tel:* 800-845-6956 *Fax:* 509-534-9703 *E-mail:* lulupromotion@aol.com *Web Site:* www.proforma.com, pg 985

Humphrey, Rob, Kensington Technology Group, 333 Twin Dolphin Dr, 6th fl, Redwood Shores, CA 94065 *Tel:* 650-572-2700 *Toll Free Tel:* 800-235-6708 (cust serv); 800-535-4242 (tech support) *Fax:* 650-267-2800 *E-mail:* sales@kensington.com *Web Site:* www.kensington.com, pg 909

Humphries, Dave, IPRO, 34157 W 9 Mile Rd, Farmington Hills, MI 48335 *Tel:* 248-474-0522 *Toll Free Tel:* 800-420-4268 *Web Site:* www.avreps.org, pg 1084

Hung, Manuela, Filmworkers, 232 E Ohio, Chicago, IL 60611 *Tel:* 312-664-9333 *Web Site:* www.filmworkersastro.com, pg 868

Hunkele, Michael, Audio Media Productions, 6739 Kirby Trace Cove, Memphis, TN 38119 *Tel:* 901-751-2363 *E-mail:* ampman@aol.com *Web Site:* www.audiomediaprod.com, pg 794

Hunt, Bobby, Los Angeles Center Studios, 450 S Bixel St, Los Angeles, CA 90017 *Tel:* 213-534-3000 *E-mail:* productionservices@lacenterstudios.com *Web Site:* lacenterstudios.com, pg 924

Hunt, Paige, Greenwood Convention & Visitors Bureau & Film Commission, 111 E Market St, Greenwood, MS 38935 *Tel:* 662-453-9197 *Toll Free Tel:* 800-748-9064 *Fax:* 662-453-5526 *E-mail:* info@gcvb.com *Web Site:* www.greenwoodms.org, pg 1099

Hunter, Cid, ITV Productions, 1649 S Robertson Blvd, Los Angeles, CA 90035 *Tel:* 310-204-1234 *E-mail:* itvproductions1@gmail.com *Web Site:* www.itvproductions.com, pg 903

Hunter, David, D A Sound, 12932 SE Kent Kangley Rd, Box 460, Kent, WA 98030 *Tel:* 206-632-7773 *Toll Free Tel:* 855-DASOUND (327-6863) *Toll Free Fax:* 866-859-8650 *E-mail:* info@dasound.biz *Web Site:* www.dasound.biz, pg 842

Hunter, Euan, VO2 Mix Studios, 116 Spadina Ave, Suite 208, Toronto, ON M5V 2K6, Canada *Tel:* 416-603-3954 *Fax:* 416-603-3957 *E-mail:* info@vo2mix.ca *Web Site:* www.vo2mix.ca, pg 1060

Hunter, Laura, The Children's Book Store Distribution (CBSD), 14-3245 Harvester Rd, Burlington, ON L7N 3T7, Canada *Tel:* 905-681-8160; 905-831-1995 (intl) *Toll Free Tel:* 800-668-0242; 800-757-8372 (cust serv-CN & US) *Fax:* 905-831-1142 (intl) *E-mail:* info@childrensgroup.com *Web Site:* www.childrensgroup.com, pg 825

Hunter, Ron, Randall House Publications, 114 Bush Rd, Nashville, TN 37217 *Tel:* 615-361-1221 *Toll Free Tel:* 800-877-7030 *Fax:* 615-367-0535 *Web Site:* www.randallhouse.com, pg 991

Hunter, Scott, Eco-Greenlighting Inc, 7718 San Fernando Rd N, Sun Valley, CA 91352 *Tel:* 818-768-4300 *Fax:* 818-768-4988 *E-mail:* info@eco-greenlighting.com *Web Site:* www.eco-greenlighting.com, pg 856

Huntsberry, Frederick, Paramount Pictures Corporation, 5555 Melrose Ave, Los Angeles, CA 90038 *Tel:* 323-956-8398 *Web Site:* www.paramount.com, pg 969

Huntsinger, Julie, Telluride Film Festival, 800 Jones St, Berkeley, CA 94710 *Tel:* 510-665-9494 *Fax:* 510-665-9589 *E-mail:* mail@telluridefilmfestival.org *Web Site:* www.telluridefilmfestival.org, pg 1128

Hurst, Adam, Interface Media Group, 1233 20 St NW, Washington, DC 20036 *Tel:* 202-861-0500 *E-mail:* info@interfacevideo.com *Web Site:* www.interfacevideo.com, pg 900

Hurst, Andrea, Frank D Hurst Corp dba Pechman Imaging, 106 E Second St, Kaukauna, WI 54130 *Tel:* 920-766-6160 *Toll Free Tel:* 800-777-0221 *Fax:* 920-766-6161 *E-mail:* customerservice@pechmanimaging.com *Web Site:* www.pechmanimaging.com, pg 892

Hurst, Frank, Frank D Hurst Corp dba Pechman Imaging, 106 E Second St, Kaukauna, WI 54130 *Tel:* 920-766-6160 *Toll Free Tel:* 800-777-0221 *Fax:* 920-766-6161 *E-mail:* customerservice@pechmanimaging.com *Web Site:* www.pechmanimaging.com, pg 892

Hurst, Josh, Digi-matics, 4472 Spring Valley Rd, Dallas, TX 75244 *Tel:* 469-644-1390 *Web Site:* www.digi-matics.com, pg 847

Hurst, Robert, Audio Network US Inc, 48 W 25 St, 10th fl, New York, NY 10010 *Tel:* 646-688-4320 *E-mail:* nyoffice@audionetwork.com *Web Site:* us.audionetwork.com, pg 794

Hurtubise, Louis, Optimum Production Services Inc, 1490 S Sheridan Way, Mississauga, ON L5H 1Z8, Canada *Tel:* 905-278-2125 *Toll Free Tel:* 800-461-4979 *E-mail:* optimum@optimumprod.com *Web Site:* www.optimumprod.com, pg 964

Hurwitz, Jess, CompuWeather Inc, 2566 Rte 52, Hopewell Junction, NY 12533 *Tel:* 845-227-8500 *Toll Free Tel:* 800-825-4445 *Fax:* 845-227-8400 *Toll Free Fax:* 800-825-4441 *Web Site:* www.compuweather.com, pg 834

Husa, Gail M, Phylco Audio Duplication, 10431 Blackwell Rd, Central Point, OR 97502 *Tel:* 541-855-7484 *Toll Free Tel:* 800-348-6194 *E-mail:* info@phylcoaudio.com *Web Site:* www.phylcoaudio.com, pg 975

Husa, Kenneth R, Phylco Audio Duplication, 10431 Blackwell Rd, Central Point, OR 97502 *Tel:* 541-855-7484 *Toll Free Tel:* 800-348-6194 *E-mail:* info@phylcoaudio.com *Web Site:* www.phylcoaudio.com, pg 975

Hushon, Dan, Computer Sciences Corp, 3170 Fairview Park Dr, Falls Church, VA 22042 *Tel:* 703-876-1000 *Web Site:* www.csc.com, pg 834

Hussey, Halfdan, Cinequest Film Festival (CQFF), PO Box 720040, San Jose, CA 95172-0040 *Tel:* 408-295-FEST (295-3378); 408-995-5033 (off) *Fax:* 408-995-5713 *E-mail:* contact@cinequest.org *Web Site:* www.cinequest.org, pg 1112

Hussey, Michael E, Professional Education Institute (PEI), 7020 High Grove Blvd, Burr Ridge, IL 60527 *Tel:* 630-382-1000 *Fax:* 630-325-0825 *E-mail:* kpalmer@pei.com *Web Site:* www.thepei.com, pg 985

Hutcherson, Carl S, Peerbolte Creative, PO Box 754, Warrensburg, MO 64093 *Tel:* 660-429-1383 *Fax:* 660-429-3666 *E-mail:* solutions@peerbolte.com *Web Site:* www.peerbolte.com, pg 971

Hutchinson, Cheryl J, CRT Custom Products Inc, 7532 Hickory Hills Ct, Whites Creek, TN 37189 *Tel:* 615-876-5490 *Toll Free Tel:* 800-453-2533 *Fax:* 615-876-0096 *E-mail:* sales@crtcustomproducts.com *Web Site:* www.crtcustomproducts.com, pg 840

Hutchison, Roger S PhD, CD ROM™ Inc, 3131 E Riverside Dr, Fort Myers, FL 33916 *Tel:* 952-832-5424 (sales) *Toll Free Tel:* 866-662-3766 (orders) *Fax:* 239-332-2808; 715-372-6702 (orders) *E-mail:* sales@cdrominc.com *Web Site:* www.cdrominc.com, pg 822

Hutton, Irene, California Stage & Lighting, 3601 W Garry Ave, Santa Ana, CA 92704 *Tel:* 714-966-1852 *Fax:* 714-966-0104 *E-mail:* sales@calstage.com *Web Site:* www.calstage.com, pg 817

Huurman, Sean, Imagine Communications Corp, 3001 Dallas Pkwy, Suite 300, Frisco, TX 75034 *Tel:* 469-803-4900 *Toll Free Tel:* 866-4-IMAGINE (446-2446) *Fax:* 469-803-4899 *E-mail:* insidesales@imaginecommunications.com *Web Site:* www.imaginecommunications.com, pg 896

Huus, Brett, Sound Strations Audio Productions Inc, 3120 South Ave, La Crosse, WI 54601 *Tel:* 608-787-8133 *Fax:* 608-787-0012 *Web Site:* soundstrations.com, pg 1017

Hyatt, David, MRN Radio, 555 MRN Dr, Concord, NC 28027 *Tel:* 704-262-6700 *Fax:* 704-262-6811 *E-mail:* sales@mrnradio.com *Web Site:* www.mrnradio.com, pg 948

Ibanez, Michael, 16 x 9 Inc, 28314 Constellation Rd, Valencia, CA 91355 *Tel:* 661-295-3313 *Toll Free Tel:* 866-800-1699 *Fax:* 661-295-3314 *E-mail:* info@16x9inc.com *Web Site:* www.16x9inc.com, pg 1012

Iger, Robert W, The Walt Disney Co, 500 S Buena Vista St, Burbank, CA 91521 *Tel:* 818-560-1000 *Web Site:* disney.com, pg 1061

Iglauer, Bruce, Alligator Records & Artist Management Inc, 1441 W Devon Ave, Chicago, IL 60660 *Tel:* 773-973-7736 *Fax:* 773-973-2088 *E-mail:* info@allig.com *Web Site:* www.alligator.com, pg 781

Iglesias, Fernando, Midtown Video Inc, 4824 SW 74 Ct, Miami, FL 33155 *Tel:* 305-669-1117 *Toll Free Tel:* 800-232-4564 *Fax:* 305-662-2860 *E-mail:* info@midtownvideo.com *Web Site:* www.midtownvideo.com, pg 942

Igloria, Regin, Artist Residency Program, 1260 N Green Bay Rd, Lake Forest, IL 60045 *Tel:* 847-234-1063 *Fax:* 847-234-1063 *E-mail:* info@ragdale.org *Web Site:* www.ragdale.org, pg 1108

Ilarde, Tiffany, World Events Productions Ltd, 50 Maryland Plaza, Suite 300, St Louis, MO 63108 *Tel:* 314-345-1060 *Fax:* 314-345-1093 *E-mail:* wep@wep.com *Web Site:* www.wep.com, pg 1069

Ilaw, Noel, Transvideo International, 11712 Moorpark St, Suite 112-B, North Hollywood, CA 91604 *Tel:* 818-985-4903 *Fax:* 818-985-4921 *Web Site:* www.transvideointl.com, pg 1044

Imbs, Rob, Buffalo Niagara Film Festival (BNFF), 3840 E Robinson Rd, Suite 166, Amherst, NY 14228 *Tel:* 716-432-1065 *E-mail:* info@buffaloniagarafilmfestival.com *Web Site:* thebnff.com, pg 1110

Imig, Charles, Imig Audio/Video Inc, 2611 Fairbanks St, Suite 100, Anchorage, AK 99503 *Tel:* 907-274-2161 *Fax:* 907-279-0219 *E-mail:* info@imigav.com *Web Site:* www.imigav.com, pg 896

Imig, Eric, Imig Audio/Video Inc, 2611 Fairbanks St, Suite 100, Anchorage, AK 99503 *Tel:* 907-274-2161 *Fax:* 907-279-0219 *E-mail:* info@imigav.com *Web Site:* www.imigav.com, pg 896

Imlay, Dr Scott, Tecplot Inc, 3535 Factoria Blvd SE, Suite 550, Bellevue, WA 98006 *Tel:* 425-653-1200; 425-653-9393 (tech support) *Toll Free Tel:* 800-763-7005 (orders) *E-mail:* info@tecplot.com; sales@tecplot.com *Web Site:* www.tecplot.com, pg 1035

Immelt, Jeffrey, General Electric Co, 3135 Easton Tpke, Fairfield, CT 06828 *Tel:* 203-373-2211 *Fax:* 203-373-3131 *Web Site:* www.ge.com, pg 877

Indrigo, Peter, Unitron Ltd, 73 Mall Dr, Commack, NY 11725 *Tel:* 631-543-2000 *Fax:* 631-589-6975 *E-mail:* info@unitronusa.com *Web Site:* www.unitronusa.com, pg 1049

Inge, Stephen J, A-V Services Inc, 99 Fairfield Rd, Fairfield, NJ 07004 *Tel:* 973-575-5222 *Fax:* 973-575-0857 *E-mail:* sales@avservices.net *Web Site:* www.avservices.net, pg 771

Ingebrigtsen, Paul, Williams Sound Corp, 10300 Valley View Rd, Eden Prairie, MN 55344-3446 *Tel:* 952-943-2252 *Toll Free Tel:* 800-328-6190 *Fax:* 952-943-2174 *E-mail:* info@williamssound.com *Web Site:* www.williamssound.com, pg 1067

Inghram, Rick, High-Tech Special Effects Inc, PO Box 193, Eads, TN 38028-0193 *Tel:* 901-850-5522 *Fax:* 901-850-8317 *Web Site:* www.hightechspecialeffects.com, pg 889

Ingram, David, Ingram Entertainment Inc, 2 Ingram Blvd, La Vergne, TN 37089-7006 *Tel:* 615-287-4000 (corp) *Toll Free Tel:* 800-621-1333 (sales & cust serv) *Fax:* 615-287-4982 *Web Site:* www.ingramentertainment.com, pg 898

Ingram, John R, Ingram Book Group, One Ingram Blvd, La Vergne, TN 37086 *Tel:* 615-793-5000 *E-mail:* customer.service@ingramcontent.com; inquiry@ingramcontent.com *Web Site:* www.ingramcontent.com, pg 898

Ingrassia, Frank, Clever Devices Ltd, 300 Crossways Park Dr, Woodburg, NY 11797 *Tel:* 516-433-6100 *Toll Free Tel:* 800-872-6129 *Web Site:* www.cleverdevices.com, pg 830

Inman, Monique, Exemplar Global, 600 N Plankington Ave, Milwaukee, WI 53201 *Tel:* 414-272-3937 *Toll Free Tel:* 888-722-2440 *Fax:* 414-765-8661 *Web Site:* www.exemplarglobal.org, pg 1081

Innes, Fred, Technical Innovation, 2975 Northwoods Pkwy, Norcross, GA 30071 *Tel:* 770-447-1001 *Toll Free Tel:* 866-447-1004 *Fax:* 770-441-5285 *Web Site:* www.technical-innovation.com, pg 1034

Inocencio, David, The Studio of David Inocencio/Minette Siegel, 41 Fairlawn Ave, Daly City, CA 94015 *Tel:* 415-716-2791 *Fax:* 415-716-2796 *Web Site:* www.ino-sieg.com, pg 1027

Inoue, Tak, Tamron USA Inc, 10 Austin Blvd, Commack, NY 11725 *Tel:* 631-858-8400 *Toll Free Tel:* 800-827-8880 *Fax:* 631-543-5666 *E-mail:* custserv@tamron.com *Web Site:* www.tamron-usa.com, pg 1031

Inouye, Natalie, Eugene, Cascades & Coast-Travel Lane County, 754 Olive St, Eugene, OR 97401 *Tel:* 541-484-5307 *Toll Free Tel:* 800-547-5445 *Fax:* 541-343-6335 *E-mail:* film@eugenecascadescoast.org *Web Site:* www.eugenecascadescoast.org, pg 1101

Inwood, Gina, Calumet Carton Co, 16920 State St, South Holland, IL 60473 *Tel:* 708-333-6521 *Fax:* 708-333-8540 *E-mail:* info@calumetcarton.com *Web Site:* www.calumetcarton.com, pg 817

Inwood, John, Calumet Carton Co, 16920 State St, South Holland, IL 60473 *Tel:* 708-333-6521 *Fax:* 708-333-8540 *E-mail:* info@calumetcarton.com *Web Site:* www.calumetcarton.com, pg 817

Ipiotis, Celia, Eye on Dance, 70 E Tenth St, Suite 19-D, New York, NY 10003 *Tel:* 212-206-6492 *E-mail:* eyeonthearts@gmail.com *Web Site:* www.eyeondance.org, pg 865

Irwin, John, Caption Colorado LLC, 5690 DTC Blvd, Suite 500W, Greenwood Village, CO 80111 *Tel:* 720-489-5662 *Toll Free Tel:* 800-775-7838 *Fax:* 720-489-5664 *Web Site:* www.captioncolorado.com, pg 820

Irwin, Ken, Rounder Records, 1209 Pine St, Suite 100, Nashville, TN 37203 *Web Site:* www.rounder.com, pg 1000

Irwin, Tim, Heartland Film Festival, 1043 Virginia Ave, Suite 2, Indianapolis, IN 46203 *Tel:* 317-464-9405 *Web Site:* www.heartlandfilmfestival.org, pg 1116

Isaacs, Tony, Indian House, PO Box 472, Taos, NM 87571-0472 *Tel:* 575-776-2953 *Toll Free Tel:* 800-748-0522 *Fax:* 575-776-2804 *E-mail:* music@indianhouse.com *Web Site:* www.indianhouse.com, pg 897

Isaacs, Tony, Rainbow Media Taos, 27 Valencia Rd, Taos, NM 87571 *Tel:* 575-776-2268 *Toll Free Tel:* 800-748-1540 *Fax:* 575-776-2804, pg 991

Isabelle-Stark, Michelle, Suffolk County Film Commission, H Lee Dennison Bldg, 2nd fl, 100 Veterans Memorial Hwy, Hauppauge, NY 11788-0099 *Tel:* 631-853-4800 *Fax:* 631-853-4888 *Web Site:* www.suffolkcountyfilmcommission.com, pg 1100

Isenhart, Jennifer, Wide Eye Productions, 1018 W Hays St, Boise, ID 83702 *Tel:* 208-336-0391 *Fax:* 208-336-6644 *E-mail:* info@wideeye.tv *Web Site:* wideeye.tv, pg 1066

Ishii, Tom, Onkyo USA Corp, 18 Park Way, Upper Saddle River, NJ 07458 *Tel:* 201-785-2600 *Toll Free Tel:* 800-229-1687 *Fax:* 201-785-2650 *Web Site:* www.onkyousa.com, pg 963

Ishizuka, Yuichi, Canon USA Inc, One Canon Park, Melville, NY 11747 *Tel:* 613-330-5000 *E-mail:* pr@cusa.canon.com *Web Site:* www.usa.canon.com, pg 819

Israel, Chip, The Lighting Design Alliance, 2830 Temple Ave, Long Beach, CA 90806-2213 *Tel:* 562-989-3843 *Fax:* 562-989-3847 *E-mail:* info@lightingdesignalliance.com *Web Site:* www.lightingdesignalliance.com, pg 920

Israel, Robert, Score Productions Inc, 219 E 49 St, New York, NY 10017 *Tel:* 212-751-2510 *Fax:* 212-754-6305 *E-mail:* score@scoreproductions.com *Web Site:* www.artgraphica.com/preview/ScoreProductions/index.html, pg 1005

Ito, Mitsuru, Convergent Media Systems, 190 Bluegrass Valley Pkwy, Alpharetta, GA 30005-2204 *Tel:* 770-369-9000 *Toll Free Tel:* 800-877-7804 *Fax:* 770-369-9100 *E-mail:* convergent@convergent.com *Web Site:* www.convergent.com, pg 836

Itzkowich, C, International Contact Inc, 351 15 St, Oakland, CA 94612 *Tel:* 510-836-1180 *Toll Free Tel:* 800-430-7705 *Fax:* 510-835-1314 *E-mail:* info@intlcontact.com *Web Site:* www.intlcontact.com, pg 900

Iuliano, Gerry, Artaflex Inc, 96 Steelcase Rd W, Markham, ON L3R 1B5, Canada *Tel:* 905-470-0109 *Toll Free Tel:* 866-502-3378 *Fax:* 905-470-0621 *Web Site:* www.artaflex.com, pg 791

Iverson, Eric, Rose City Sound, 4811 SE 16 Ave, Portland, OR 97202 *Tel:* 503-238-6330 *Toll Free Tel:* 877-503-7673 *Fax:* 503-238-9872 *E-mail:* sales@rosecitysound.com *Web Site:* www.rosecitysound.com, pg 999

Iverson, Patricia, Maverick Video Productions, 121 Interpark, Suite 601, San Antonio, TX 78216 *Tel:* 210-495-1111 *Fax:* 210-495-8033 *Web Site:* www.maverickstudio.com, pg 934

Ives, Beth, HarperAudio, 10 E 53 St, New York, NY 10022 *Tel:* 212-207-7000 *Toll Free Tel:* 800-242-7737 *Fax:* 212-207-2582 *Toll Free Fax:* 800-822-4090 *Web Site:* www.harpercollins.com, pg 885

Ivey, Loyd, Coustic Car Audio, 4545 E Baseline Rd, Phoenix, AZ 85042 *Tel:* 602-438-2020 *Toll Free Tel:* 800-225-5689 *E-mail:* coustic@coustic.com *Web Site:* www.coustic.com, pg 837

Ivimey-Cook, Richard, Qioptiq, 78 Shuyler Baldwin, Fairport, NY 14450 *Tel:* 585-223-2370 *Toll Free Tel:* 800-429-0257 *Fax:* 585-223-1999 *E-mail:* info@qioptiqlinos.com *Web Site:* www.qioptiqlinos.com, pg 988

Ivory, David, Ivory Productions, 529 Plymouth Rd, Gwynedd Valley, PA 19437 *Tel:* 215-591-9900 *E-mail:* divory@comcast.net *Web Site:* www.ivoryproductions.com, pg 903

Iwacha, Judy, Sharp's Audio-Visual Ltd, 3636 Seventh St SE, Calgary, AB T2G 2Y8, Canada *Tel:* 403-255-4123 *Toll Free Tel:* 800-491-1121 *Fax:* 403-255-3478 *E-mail:* sales@sharpsav.com *Web Site:* www.sharpsav.com, pg 1008

Izquierdo, Joe, Sunfire Communications Inc, 7751 Kingspointe Pkwy, Suite 105, Orlando, FL 32819 *Tel:* 407-226-8226 *Fax:* 407-226-1660 *E-mail:* info@sunfirecommunications.com *Web Site:* www.sunfirecommunications.com, pg 1028

Jabara, Brock M, Galaxy Audio, 601 E Pawnee Ave, Wichita, KS 67211 *Tel:* 316-263-2852 *Toll Free Tel:* 800-369-7768 *Fax:* 316-263-0642 *E-mail:* sales@galaxyaudio.com; orders@galaxyaudio.com *Web Site:* www.galaxyaudio.com, pg 875

Jablon, Andy, WVP Boston, 50 Hunt St, Watertown, MA 02472 *Tel:* 617-926-2089 *Fax:* 617-926-7965 *E-mail:* info@wvp.com *Web Site:* www.weismanvideo.com, pg 1071

Jackman, Mike, FilmNation Entertainment, 150 W 22 St, 9th fl, New York, NY 10011 *Web Site:* www.filmnation.com, pg 867

Jackson, Barb, Agency for Instructional Technology (AIT), 8111 N Lee Paul Rd, Bloomington, IN 47404-7916 *Tel:* 812-339-2203 *Toll Free Tel:* 800-457-4509 *Fax:* 812-333-4218 *E-mail:* info@ait.net *Web Site:* www.ait.net, pg 778

Jackson, Eric, Showreel International Inc, 1021 N McCadden Place, Hollywood, CA 90038 *Tel:* 323-464-5111 *E-mail:* information@showreel.com *Web Site:* www.showreel.com, pg 1010

Jackson, Jeremy, Edgewood Studios, Howe Ctr, Unit 12-B, Suite 90, Rutland, VT 05701-4459 *Tel:* 802-773-0510 *Fax:* 802-773-3481 *Web Site:* www.edgewoodstudios.com, pg 857

Jackson, John E, Launch Media, Celtic Media Ctr, 10000 Celtic Dr, Baton Rouge, LA 70809 *Tel:* 225-612-2112 *E-mail:* contactus@launchmedia.tv *Web Site:* www.launchmedia.tv, pg 916

Jackson, Lynne B, Showreel International Inc, 1021 N McCadden Place, Hollywood, CA 90038 *Tel:* 323-464-5111 *E-mail:* information@showreel.com *Web Site:* www.showreel.com, pg 1010

Jackson, R Scott, Blair Inc, 7001 Loisdale Rd, Springfield, VA 22150 *Tel:* 703-922-0200 *Fax:* 703-924-0765 *E-mail:* info@blairinc.com *Web Site:* www.blairinc.com, pg 809

Jackson, Wayne, Preston Productions Inc, 128 Bartlett St, Marlborough, MA 01752 *Toll Free Tel:* 800-822-2299 *E-mail:* ideas@prestonevents.com *Web Site:* www.prestonproductions.com; www.prestonevents.com, pg 981

Jacob, Stacie, San Luis Obispo County Film Commission, 811 El Capitan, Suite 200, San Luis Obispo, CA 93401 *Tel:* 805-541-8000 *Fax:* 805-543-9498 *Web Site:* www.sanluisobispocounty.com, pg 1094

Jacobovici, Simcha, Associated Producers Ltd, 18 Dupont St, Toronto, ON M5R 1V2, Canada *Tel:* 416-504-6662 *Fax:* 416-504-6667 *E-mail:* general@apltd.ca *Web Site:* www.apltd.ca, pg 792

Jacobs, Alex, Anchor Audio Inc, 5931 Darwin Ct, Carlsbad, CA 92008 *Tel:* 760-827-7100 *Toll Free Tel:* 800-262-4671 *Fax:* 760-827-7105 *E-mail:* sales@anchoraudio.com *Web Site:* www.anchoraudio.com, pg 786

Jacobs, Janet, Anchor Audio Inc, 5931 Darwin Ct, Carlsbad, CA 92008 *Tel:* 760-827-7100 *Toll Free Tel:* 800-262-4671 *Fax:* 760-827-7105 *E-mail:* sales@anchoraudio.com *Web Site:* www.anchoraudio.com, pg 786

Jacobs, Jeremy, Sunset Bronson Studios, 1438 N Gower St, Box 88, Hollywood, CA 90028 *Tel:* 323-460-5858 *Fax:* 323-460-3844 *E-mail:* sbs.reception@sgsandsbs.com *Web Site:* sgsandsbs.com, pg 1028

Jacobs, Jerry, Sound/Video Impressions Inc, 110 S River Rd, Des Plaines, IL 60016 *Tel:* 847-297-4360 *Fax:* 847-297-6870 *E-mail:* info@soundvideoimpressions.com *Web Site:* www.soundvideoimpressions.com, pg 1018

Jacobs, Paul, Klipsch Audio Technologies, 3502 Woodview Trace, Suite 200, Indianapolis, IN 46268 *Tel:* 317-860-8100 *Toll Free Tel:* 877-412-7467 (orders); 800-544-1482 *Fax:* 317-860-9170 (sales & mktg) *E-mail:* support@klipsch.com *Web Site:* www.klipsch.com, pg 912

Jacobs, Robert K, Neptune Photo Inc, 130 Seventh St, Garden City, NY 11530 *Tel:* 516-741-4484 *Toll Free Tel:* 800-955-1110 *Fax:* 516-741-1225 *E-mail:* sales@neptunephoto.com *Web Site:* www.neptunephoto.com, pg 954

Jacobs, Rodney H, Freewheelin' Films, 44895 Hwy 82, Aspen, CO 81611 *Tel:* 970-925-2640 *Fax:* 970-925-9369 *Web Site:* www.fwf.com, pg 872

Jacobs, Scott, Interstate Connecting Components, 120 Mount Holly Bypass, Lumberton, NJ 08048-1112 *Tel:* 856-722-5535 *Toll Free Tel:* 888-881-5420 *Fax:* 856-813-5419 *E-mail:* info@connecticc.com *Web Site:* www.connecticc.com, pg 901

Jacobs, Stan, WorldStage, 259 W 30 St, 12th fl, New York, NY 10001-2863 *Tel:* 212-582-2345 *Fax:* 718-610-1750 *E-mail:* info@worldstage.com *Web Site:* www.worldstage.com, pg 1070

Jacovino, Frank, Vicon Industries Inc, 131 Heartland Blvd, Edgewood, NY 11717 *Tel:* 631-952-2288 *Toll Free Tel:* 800-645-9116 *Fax:* 631-951-2288 *Web Site:* www.vicon-security.com, pg 1054

Jaeckel, Kurt, Quickbeam Systems Inc (QSI), 4411 McLeod Rd NE, Suite E, Albuquerque, NM 87109 *Tel:* 505-345-9230 *Fax:* 505-345-4604 *E-mail:* sales@quickbeam.com *Web Site:* www.quickbeam.com, pg 989

Jaehnert, Neil, Midland Video Productions Inc, 126 N Jefferson St, Milwaukee, WI 53202 *Tel:* 414-276-8300 *E-mail:* request@midlandvideo.com *Web Site:* midlandvideo.com, pg 942

Jaime, Matt, North-by-Northwest Productions, 903 W Broadway Ave, Spokane, WA 99201 *Tel:* 509-324-2949 *Fax:* 509-324-2959 *E-mail:* contact@nxnw.net *Web Site:* www.nxnw.net, pg 959

Jain, Deepak, SVAT Electronics, 4080 Montrose Rd, Niagara Falls, ON L2H 1J9, Canada *Tel:* 905-353-0732 *Toll Free Tel:* 866-946-7828 *Fax:* 905-353-1701 *Toll Free Fax:* 888-771-1701 *E-mail:* sales@svat.com *Web Site:* www.svat.com, pg 1029

Jain, Dinesh C, Time Warner Cable, 60 Columbus Circle, 17th fl, New York, NY 10023 *Tel:* 212-364-8200 *Web Site:* www.timewarnercable.com, pg 1040

Jain, Raj, SVAT Electronics, 4080 Montrose Rd, Niagara Falls, ON L2H 1J9, Canada *Tel:* 905-353-0732 *Toll Free Tel:* 866-946-7828 *Fax:* 905-353-1701 *Toll Free Fax:* 888-771-1701 *E-mail:* sales@svat.com *Web Site:* www.svat.com, pg 1029

Jain, Suresh, Planet Blue, 1250 Sixth St, Suite 102, Santa Monica, CA 90401 *Tel:* 310-899-3877 *Fax:* 310-899-3787 *Web Site:* www.planetblue.com, pg 976

Jakubowski, Jill, RIA Corp, 1615 W 2200 S, Suite B, Salt Lake City, UT 84119 *Tel:* 801-486-8822 *Fax:* 801-486-2741 *E-mail:* sales@riacorp.com *Web Site:* www.riacorp.com, pg 996

Jamal, Hanif I, Dot Hill Systems Corp, 1351 S Sunset St, Longmont, CO 80501-6533 *Tel:* 303-845-3200 *Toll Free Tel:* 800-872-2783 *Fax:* 303-845-3655 *E-mail:* support@dothill.com; websales@dothill.com *Web Site:* www.dothill.com, pg 851

Jamele, Alison, MediaMation Inc, 387 Maple Ave, Torrance, CA 90503 *Tel:* 310-320-0696 *Fax:* 310-320-0699 *E-mail:* sales@mediamation.com *Web Site:* www.mediamation.com, pg 937

Jamele, Dan, MediaMation Inc, 387 Maple Ave, Torrance, CA 90503 *Tel:* 310-320-0696 *Fax:* 310-320-0699 *E-mail:* sales@mediamation.com *Web Site:* www.mediamation.com, pg 937

James, Cameron, Mills James Productions, 3545 Fishinger Blvd, Columbus, OH 43026-9489 *Tel:* 614-777-9933 *Toll Free Tel:* 800-860-8436 *Fax:* 614-777-9943 *E-mail:* info@mjp.com *Web Site:* www.millsjames.com, pg 943

James, Troy, Strong Cinema Products, 13710 FNB Pkwy, Suite 400, Omaha, NE 68145 *Tel:* 402-453-4444 *Toll Free Tel:* 800-424-1215 *Fax:* 402-453-7238 *E-mail:* info@btn-inc.com *Web Site:* www.strong-world.com, pg 1026

Jamieson, Jacqui, Quabbin Wire & Cable Co Inc, 10 Maple St, Ware, MA 01082-1597 *Tel:* 413-967-6281 *Toll Free Tel:* 800-368-3311 *Fax:* 413-967-7564 *E-mail:* sales@quabbin.com *Web Site:* www.quabbin.com, pg 988

Jamieson, Marjorie, Jamieson & Associates Inc, 4133 W 45 St, Minneapolis, MN 55424-1040 *Tel:* 952-920-3770 *E-mail:* info@jamieson.com *Web Site:* www.jamieson.com, pg 904

Jamieson, Richard N, Jamieson & Associates Inc, 4133 W 45 St, Minneapolis, MN 55424-1040 *Tel:* 952-920-3770 *E-mail:* info@jamieson.com *Web Site:* www.jamieson.com, pg 904

Jamieson, Richard S, Jamieson & Associates Inc, 4133 W 45 St, Minneapolis, MN 55424-1040 *Tel:* 952-920-3770 *E-mail:* info@jamieson.com *Web Site:* www.jamieson.com, pg 904

Jan, Han S, Total AV Systems, 923 Sligo Ave, Silver Spring, MD 20910 *Tel:* 301-589-3337 *Toll Free Tel:* 800-447-7632 *Fax:* 301-494-4770 *E-mail:* info@total-av.com *Web Site:* total-av.com, pg 1042

Jan, Josephine, Total AV Systems, 923 Sligo Ave, Silver Spring, MD 20910 *Tel:* 301-589-3337 *Toll Free Tel:* 800-447-7632 *Fax:* 301-494-4770 *E-mail:* info@total-av.com *Web Site:* total-av.com, pg 1042

Jan, Kenneth, Total AV Systems, 923 Sligo Ave, Silver Spring, MD 20910 *Tel:* 301-589-3337 *Toll Free Tel:* 800-447-7632 *Fax:* 301-494-4770 *E-mail:* info@total-av.com *Web Site:* total-av.com, pg 1042

Janis, Peter, Radial Engineering Ltd, 1588 Kebet Way, Port Coquitlam, BC V3C 5M5, Canada *Tel:* 604-942-1001 *Toll Free Tel:* 800-939-1001 (orders) *Fax:* 604-942-1010 *E-mail:* info@radialeng.com *Web Site:* www.radialeng.com, pg 990

Jankelovics, Amanda, Custom Media Environments, 299 Duffy Ave, Hicksville, NY 11801 *Tel:* 516-586-3600 *Toll Free Tel:* 800-80-SOUND (807-6863) *Fax:* 516-586-3487 *E-mail:* info@custommediaenvironments.com; sales@custommediaenvironments.com *Web Site:* custommediaenvironments.com, pg 841

Jannson, Joanna PhD, Physical Optics Corp, 1845 E 205 St, Torrance, CA 90501-1510 *Tel:* 310-320-3088 *Fax:* 310-320-5961 *Web Site:* www.poc.com, pg 975

Janocha, Paul, Ken-Del Studios, 1500 First State Blvd, Wilmington, DE 19804-3596 *Tel:* 302-999-1111 *Toll Free Tel:* 800-249-1110 *Fax:* 302-999-1656 *E-mail:* info@ken-del.com *Web Site:* www.ken-del.com, pg 909

Janoulis, Aleck, Hottrax Records, 1957 Kilburn Dr, Atlanta, GA 30324-4852 *Tel:* 770-662-6661 *E-mail:* info@hottrax.com; hotwax@hottrax.com *Web Site:* www.hottrax.com, pg 891

Jansen, Skip, The Kenwood Group, 75 Varney Place, San Francisco, CA 94107 *Tel:* 415-957-5333 *Fax:* 415-957-5311 *E-mail:* newbusiness@kenwoodgroup.com *Web Site:* www.kenwoodgroup.com, pg 909

Janson, R K, Janson Industries, 1200 Garfield Ave SW, Canton, OH 44706 *Tel:* 330-455-7029 *Toll Free Tel:* 800-548-8982 *Fax:* 330-455-5919 *Web Site:* www.jansonindustries.com, pg 904

Janson, Stephen, Janson Media, 118 Main St, Tappan, NY 10983 *Tel:* 845-359-8488 *E-mail:* info@janson.com *Web Site:* www.janson.com, pg 904

Janson, Zara, Janson Media, 118 Main St, Tappan, NY 10983 *Tel:* 845-359-8488 *E-mail:* info@janson.com *Web Site:* www.janson.com, pg 904

Janssens, Glen, eMotion Studios, 85 Liberty Ship Way, Suite 110, Sausalito, CA 94965 *Tel:* 415-331-6975 *Fax:* 415-331-6124 *E-mail:* sales@emotionstudios.com *Web Site:* www.emotionstudios.com, pg 860

Janzen, Peter, Speciality Bulb Products Inc, 20010-100A Ave, Unit 2, Langley, BC V1M 3G4, Canada *Tel:* 604-513-8500 *Toll Free Tel:* 800-663-1120 *Fax:* 604-513-8200 *E-mail:* info@specialtybulb.com; bulbexpert@specialtybulb.com *Web Site:* www.specialtybulb.com, pg 1020

Jaquint, Matt, WSAZ-TV 3/WSAZ Productions, 645 Fifth Ave, Huntington, WV 25701 *Tel:* 304-697-4780 *Fax:* 304-690-3061 (sales); 304-690-3065 (news) *E-mail:* newschannel3@wsaz.com *Web Site:* www.wsaz.com, pg 1070

Jashni, Jon, Legendary Pictures LLC, 2900 W Alameda Ave, 15th fl, Burbank, CA 91505 *Tel:* 818-688-7003 *E-mail:* info@legendary.com *Web Site:* www.legendary.com, pg 918

Jasso, Peter, Kansas Film Commission, 1000 SW Jackson St, Suite 100, Topeka, KS 66612-1354 *Tel:* 785-296-2178 *Fax:* 785-296-3490 *Web Site:* www.filmkansas.com, pg 1097

Jay, Jeff, Beast Atlanta, 3399 Peachtree Rd NE, Suite 200, Atlanta, GA 30326-1149 *Tel:* 404-237-9977 *Fax:* 404-237-3923 *E-mail:* info@riotatlanta.com *Web Site:* www.beast.tv, pg 804

Jeans, Katherine, Sound Venture International, 441 MacLaren St, Suite 401, Ottawa, ON K2P 2H3, Canada *Tel:* 613-241-5111 *Fax:* 613-241-5010 *E-mail:* info@soundventure.com *Web Site:* www.soundventure.com, pg 1018

Jedynak, Andy, North County Media Center, 1130 N Melrose Dr, Suite 404, Vista, CA 92083 *Toll Free Tel:* 888-393-0580 *E-mail:* info@northcountymediacenter.com *Web Site:* northcountymediacenter.com, pg 959

Jelenko, Amy, IDA Documentary Awards, 3470 Wilshire Blvd, Suite 980, Los Angeles, CA 90010 *Tel:* 213-232-1660 *Fax:* 213-232-1669 *E-mail:* info@documentary.org *Web Site:* www.documentary.org, pg 1116

Jelenko, Amy, International Documentary Association, 3470 Wilshire Blvd, Suite 980, Los Angeles, CA 90010 *Tel:* 213-232-1660 *Fax:* 213-232-1669 *E-mail:* info@documentary.org *Web Site:* www.documentary.org, pg 1083

Jemielita, Paul, Compact Storage Systems Inc, 9757 Reseda Blvd, Suite 68, Northridge, CA 91324 *Tel:* 818-772-0996 *E-mail:* info@halfthespace.com *Web Site:* www.halfthespace.com, pg 833

Jenkins, Kalynn, Vitruvian Entertainment, 727 N Victory Blvd, Burbank, CA 91502 *Tel:* 818-244-3575; 818-720-3250 *Web Site:* vitruvianent.com, pg 1060

Jenkins, Marc, NASCAR Media Group LLC, 550 S Caldwell St, Suite 2000, Charlotte, NC 28202 *Tel:* 704-348-7100 *Web Site:* www.nascarmediagroup.com, pg 952

Jenkins, Shirl, Intellidyne LLC, 5203 Leesburg Pike, Suite 400, 2 Skyline Place, Falls Church, VA 22041 *Tel:* 703-575-9715 *Fax:* 703-575-9718 *Web Site:* www.intellidyne-llc.com, pg 899

Jenni, Arthur, WolfVision Inc, 1601 Bayshore Hwy, Suite 168, Burlingame, CA 94010 *Tel:* 650-648-0002 *Toll Free Tel:* 800-356-9653 *Fax:* 650-648-0009 *E-mail:* sales@wolfvision.us; support@wolfvision.us *Web Site:* www.wolfvision.com, pg 1069

Jennings, Heather, Rhythm & Hues, 2100 E Grand Ave, Suite A, El Segundo, CA 90245-5024 *Tel:* 310-448-7500 *Fax:* 310-448-7600 *E-mail:* info-la@rhythm.com *Web Site:* www.rhythm.com, pg 996

Jennison, Paul, WESCAM Inc, 649 N Service Rd W, Burlington, ON L7P 5B9, Canada *Tel:* 905-633-4000 *Toll Free Tel:* 800-668-4355 *Fax:* 905-633-4100 *E-mail:* sales.wescam@l-3com.com *Web Site:* www.wescam.com, pg 1063

Jensen, Casandra Scholte, Arts Create & Arts Respond Grant, E O Thompson Off Bldg, 920 Colorado St, Suite 501, Austin, TX 78701 *Tel:* 512-463-5535 *Fax:* 512-475-2699 *E-mail:* front.desk@arts.state.tx.us *Web Site:* www.arts.state.tx.us, pg 1108

Jensen, Chris, IEEE Computer Society Press, 10662 Los Vaqueros Circle, Los Alamitos, CA 90720-1314 *Tel:* 714-821-8380 *Toll Free Tel:* 800-272-6657 (cust serv) *Fax:* 714-821-4010 *E-mail:* help@computer.org *Web Site:* www.computer.org, pg 894

Jensen, Kerry, CenterStaging LLC, 3407 Winona Ave, Burbank, CA 91504 *Tel:* 818-559-4333 *Fax:* 818-848-4016 *E-mail:* info@centerstaging.com *Web Site:* centerstaging.com, pg 823

Jensen, Mike, North Dakota Tourism Division/Film Commission, Century Ctr, 1600 E Century Ave, Suite 2, Bismarck, ND 58502-2057 *Tel:* 701-328-2525 *Toll Free Tel:* 800-435-5663 *Fax:* 701-328-4878 *E-mail:* tourism@nd.gov *Web Site:* www.ndtourism.com, pg 1101

Jensen, Ron, Chief, 6436 City West Pkwy, Eden Prairie, MN 55344 *Tel:* 952-894-6280 *Toll Free Tel:* 800-582-6480 *Fax:* 952-894-6918 *Toll Free Fax:* 877-894-6918 *E-mail:* chief@chiefmfg.com; orders@chiefmfg.com *Web Site:* www.chiefmfg.com, pg 825

Jensen, Ryan, Art Resource, 536 Broadway, 5th fl, New York, NY 10012 *Tel:* 212-505-8700 *Fax:* 212-505-2053 *E-mail:* requests@artres.com *Web Site:* www.artres.com, pg 791

Jernigan, James, TV Crews, 2135-B Defoor Hills Rd, Atlanta, GA 30318 *Tel:* 404-351-8898 *Toll Free Tel:* 800-TV-CREWS (882-7397) *Fax:* 404-351-8893 *E-mail:* info@tvcrews.com *Web Site:* www.tvcrews.com, pg 1046

Jette, Christian, Les Editions CEC Inc, 9001 boul Louis-H-La Fontaine, Anjou, QC H1J 2C5, Canada *Tel:* 514-351-6010 *Toll Free Tel:* 800-363-0494 *Fax:* 514-351-3534 *Web Site:* www.editionscec.com, pg 857

Jewell, Ray, Media Resources Inc, 9012 NW Holly Rd, Bremerton, WA 98312-9595 *Tel:* 360-830-0302 *Toll Free Tel:* 800-666-0106, pg 937

Joachim, Steve, Location Sound Corp, 10639 Riverside Dr, North Hollywood, CA 91602 *Tel:* 818-980-9891 *Toll Free Tel:* 800-228-4429 *Fax:* 818-980-9911 *E-mail:* information@locationsound.com; salesdept@locationsound.com *Web Site:* www.locationsound.com, pg 924

Jobin, Zach, Radius® Display Products Inc, 800 Fabric X-Press Way, Dallas, TX 75234 *Tel:* 972-406-1221 *Toll Free Tel:* 800-FABRIC-X (322-7429); 866-966-4066 (sales); 866-966-8266 (hospitality) *Fax:* 972-406-1321 *Toll Free Fax:* 888-322-7429 *Web Site:* www.radiusdp.com, pg 990

Joglekar, Samir, eInstruction Corp, 14400 N 87 St, Suite 250, Scottsdale, AZ 85260 *Tel:* 480-948-6540 *Toll Free Tel:* 800-856-0732 *Fax:* 480-948-5508 *Web Site:* www.einstruction.com, pg 858

Johannesen, Jeremy, Beatrice E Griggs Elementary Administrator's Award, 6021 State Farm Rd, Guilderland, NY 12084 *Tel:* 518-432-6952 *Toll Free Tel:* 800-252-6952 *Fax:* 518-427-1697 *E-mail:* info@nyla.org *Web Site:* www.nyla.org, pg 1110

Johns, Gary, Convergent Media Systems, 190 Bluegrass Valley Pkwy, Alpharetta, GA 30005-2204 *Tel:* 770-369-9000 *Toll Free Tel:* 800-877-7804 *Fax:* 770-369-9100 *E-mail:* convergent@convergent.com *Web Site:* www.convergent.com, pg 836

Johns, Jessica, MDS Power Inc, PO Box 532, Champlain, NY 12919-0532 *Tel:* 514-369-4919 *Toll Free Tel:* 800-931-4919 *Fax:* 514-369-4817 *Toll Free Fax:* 800-931-4817 *E-mail:* sales@mdspower.com; support@mdspower.com *Web Site:* www.mdspower.com, pg 936

Johns, Linda, KPDX-TV Production Center, 14975 NW Greenbrier Pkwy, Beaverton, OR 97006-5731 *Tel:* 503-906-1249 *Fax:* 503-548-6920 *E-mail:* ezone@kpdx.com; fox12news@kptv.com *Web Site:* www.kptv.com; www.kpdx.com, pg 913

Johnson, Alan, Alan Johnson Recording, 5763 Park Plaza Ct, Indianapolis, IN 46220 *Tel:* 317-439-6521 *E-mail:* alan@alanjohnsonrecording.com *Web Site:* www.alanjohnsonrecording.com, pg 905

Johnson, Bill, Modern Communications Inc, 1231 Horan Dr, Fenton, MO 63026 *Tel:* 636-343-0800 *Toll Free Tel:* 800-428-2442 *Fax:* 636-343-0906 *Web Site:* www.modcomm.com, pg 944

Johnson, Byron, Lawrence Behr Associates Inc, 3400 Tupper Dr, Greenville, NC 27834 *Tel:* 252-757-0279 *Toll Free Tel:* 800-522-4464 *Fax:* 252-752-9155 *E-mail:* lbassc@lbagroup.com *Web Site:* www.lbagroup.com/associates, pg 804

Johnson, Chris, Philadelphia International Film Festival & Market, PO Box 48134, Philadelphia, PA 19144 *Tel:* 215-849-2716 (festival) *Toll Free Tel:* 877-347-FILM (347-3456) *E-mail:* info@philafilm.org *Web Site:* www.philafilm.org, pg 1124

Johnson, Daniel R, Motion Picture Services, 5121 Ooltewah-Ringgold Rd, Suite E, Ooltewah, TN 37363 *Tel:* 423-238-7000 *E-mail:* info@motionpictureservices.net *Web Site:* www.motionpictureservices.net, pg 947

Johnson, Doug, Addlogix, 47 Peters Canyon Rd, Irvine, CA 92606 *Tel:* 949-341-0888 *Toll Free Tel:* 800-344-6921 *Fax:* 949-341-0669 *E-mail:* sales@addlogix.com *Web Site:* www.addlogix.com, pg 776

Johnson, Eric, pinta acoustic inc, 2601 49 Ave N, Suite 400, Minneapolis, MN 55430 *Tel:* 612-355-4200 *Toll Free Tel:* 800-662-0032 *Fax:* 612-355-4299 *E-mail:* sales@pinta-acoustic.com; info@pinta-acoustic.com *Web Site:* www.pinta-acoustic.com, pg 976

Johnson, Eric, Trailblazer Studios®, 1610 Midtown Place, Raleigh, NC 27609 *Tel:* 919-645-6600 *Fax:* 919-645-6601 *Web Site:* www.trailblazerstudios.com, pg 1043

Johnson, Eugene L, Ward-Beck Systems Ltd, 945 Middlefield Rd, Unit 9, Toronto, ON M1V 5E1, Canada *Tel:* 416-335-5999 *Toll Free Tel:* 800-771-2556 *Fax:* 416-335-5202 *E-mail:* sales@ward-beck.com *Web Site:* www.ward-beck.com, pg 1062

Johnson, Gloria Wolford, DWJ Television, One Robinson Lane, Ridgewood, NJ 07450 *Tel:* 201-445-1711 *Toll Free Tel:* 800-766-1711 *Fax:* 201-445-8352, pg 854

Johnson, Greg, Havas Edge, 6922 Hollywood Blvd, Hollywood, CA 90028 *Tel:* 310-734-1333 *E-mail:* info@havasedge.com *Web Site:* www.havasedge.com, pg 885

Johnson, Hamilton, Sundance Systems, Fibox Products Division, 7411 Hines Place, Suite 123, Dallas, TX 75235 *Tel:* 214-920-9190 (Dallas) *Toll Free Tel:* 800-525-3443 *Fax:* 214-920-9339 *E-mail:* info@sundancesys.com *Web Site:* www.sundancesys.com, pg 1028

Johnson, Jenda, Ka Io Productions Inc, PO Box 5150, Hilo, HI 96720-1150 *Tel:* 808-959-3885 *Toll Free Tel:* 888-458-7538 *Fax:* 808-959-3885 *E-mail:* lava@volcanovideo.com *Web Site:* www.volcanovideo.com, pg 907

Johnson, Jerry, Microdolly Hollywood, 135 N Victory Blvd, Burbank, CA 91502 *Tel:* 818-845-8383 *E-mail:* microdolly@microdolly.com *Web Site:* www.microdolly.com, pg 941

Johnson, Dr Jerry A, National Religious Broadcasters (NRB), 9510 Technology Dr, Manassas, VA 20110 *Tel:* 703-330-7000 *Fax:* 703-330-7100 *E-mail:* info@nrb.org *Web Site:* www.nrb.org, pg 1086

Johnson, Justin, ProVideo, 2302 W Badger Rd, Madison, WI 53713-2322 *Tel:* 608-271-1226 *Toll Free Tel:* 800-569-6810 *Fax:* 608-271-2737 *E-mail:* info@provideo.com *Web Site:* www.provideo.com, pg 986

Johnson, Karla, American Harlequin Corp, 1531 Glen Ave, Moorestown, NJ 08057 *Tel:* 856-234-5505 *Toll Free Tel:* 800-642-6440 *Fax:* 856-231-4403 *E-mail:* dance@harlequinfloors.com *Web Site:* www.harlequinfloors.com, pg 784

Johnson, Keith O, Reference Recordings, PO Box 77225, San Francisco, CA 94107 *Tel:* 650-355-1845 *Toll Free Tel:* 800-336-8866 *Fax:* 650-355-1949 *E-mail:* referencerecordings@gmail.com *Web Site:* www.referencerecordings.com, pg 994

Johnson, Kerry, The ADS Group, 2155 Niagara Lane N, Suite 120, Plymouth, MN 55447 *Tel:* 763-449-5500 *Toll Free Tel:* 800-759-0992 *Fax:* 763-449-5555 *E-mail:* sales@theadsgroup.com *Web Site:* www.theadsgroup.com, pg 777

Johnson, Kirk, New Harbinger Publications, 5674 Shattuck Ave, Oakland, CA 94609 *Tel:* 510-652-0215 *Toll Free Tel:* 800-748-6273 *Fax:* 510-652-5472 *E-mail:* customerservice@newharbinger.com *Web Site:* www.newharbinger.com, pg 955

Johnson, Kristi, Fresno County Film Commission, 2220 Tulare St, 8th fl, Fresno, CA 93721 *Tel:* 559-600-4271 *Fax:* 559-600-4549 *Web Site:* www.filmfresno.com, pg 1092

Johnson, Mike, Learning Communications LLC, 5520 Trabuco Rd, Irvine, CA 92620 *Toll Free Tel:* 800-622-3610 *Fax:* 949-727-4323 *E-mail:* sales@learncom.com *Web Site:* www.learncom.com, pg 917

Johnson, Paul, The Napoleon Group, 48 W 25 St, New York, NY 10010 *Tel:* 212-692-9200 *Toll Free Tel:* 800-579-4019 *Fax:* 212-692-0309 *E-mail:* info@napny.com *Web Site:* www.napny.com, pg 952

Johnson, Redge, Images II Inc, 1700 "O" St, Lincoln, NE 68508 *Tel:* 402-475-4000 *Toll Free Tel:* 800-669-4001 *E-mail:* graphics@images2.com *Web Site:* www.images2.com, pg 896

Johnson, Richard, HSA Inc, 1717 E Sixth St, Mishawaka, IN 46544 *Tel:* 574-255-6100 *Fax:* 574-255-8131 *E-mail:* hsainfo@hsarolltops.com *Web Site:* www.hsarolltops.com, pg 892

Johnson, Rick, RBR Productions, 117 W Rockland Rd, Libertyville, IL 60048 *Tel:* 847-362-4060 *Toll Free Tel:* 888-278-0558 *E-mail:* info@rbrproductions.com *Web Site:* www.rbrproductions.com, pg 992

Johnson, Roy, Green Mountain Audio Inc, 955 E Fillmore St, Colorado Springs, CO 80907-6315 *Tel:* 719-636-2500 *E-mail:* greenmountainaudio@comcast.net *Web Site:* www.greenmountainaudio.com, pg 882

Johnson, Scott, TOMCAT USA Inc, 5427 N National Dr, Knoxville, TN 37914 *Tel:* 865-219-3700 *Fax:* 865-673-5818 *E-mail:* info@tomcatusa.com; sales@tomcatusa.com *Web Site:* www.tomcatglobal.com, pg 1042

Johnson, Shaun, Johnson Systems Inc (JSI), 1923 Highfield Crescent SE, Calgary, AB T2G 5M1, Canada *Tel:* 403-287-8003 *Fax:* 403-287-9003 *E-mail:* info@johnsonsystems.com *Web Site:* www.johnsonsystems.com, pg 906

Johnson, Tom, Theatrical Services Inc, 128 S Washington St, Wichita, KS 67202 *Tel:* 316-263-4415 *Toll Free Tel:* 888-874-2649 *Fax:* 316-263-9927 *Web Site:* www.theatricalservices.com, pg 1038

Johnston, Bob, Wanted! Sound + Picture, 409 King St W, Suite 300, Toronto, ON M5V 1K1, Canada *Tel:* 416-596-1101 *Fax:* 416-596-0690 *E-mail:* info@wantedsp.com *Web Site:* www.wantedsp.com, pg 1062

Johnston, Denah, Canyon Cinema Inc, 1777 Yosemite Ave, Suite 210, San Francisco, CA 94124 *Tel:* 415-626-2255 *E-mail:* info@canyoncinema.com *Web Site:* www.canyoncinema.com, pg 819

Johnston, James, MIGHTYbYTES Inc, 4001 N Ravenswood Ave, Suite 404, Chicago, IL 60613 *Tel:* 773-561-7529 *E-mail:* info@mightybytes.com *Web Site:* www.mightybytes.com, pg 942

Johnston, Pamela, Pamela Johnston Voice Talent, 249 Eighth Ave, Cramerton, NC 28032 *Tel:* 703-371-7341 *Fax:* 703-997-8971 *Web Site:* www.pjvoicetalent.com, pg 906

Johnston, Patrick, AheadTeK, 6410 Via Del Oro, San Jose, CA 95119 *Tel:* 408-226-9800; 408-226-9991 *Toll Free Tel:* 800-971-9191 *Fax:* 408-226-9195 *Web Site:* www.aheadtek.com, pg 779

Jolly, Eric J PhD, Science Museum of Minnesota, 120 W Kellogg Blvd, St Paul, MN 55102 *Tel:* 651-221-9444 *Toll Free Tel:* 800-221-9444 *Fax:* 651-221-4533 *E-mail:* info@smm.org *Web Site:* www.smm.org, pg 1005

Joly, Julien, Directed Electronics, One Viper Way, Vista, CA 92081 *Tel:* 760-598-6200 *Toll Free Tel:* 800-876-0800 *Fax:* 760-598-6400 *E-mail:* customerfeedback@directed.com *Web Site:* www.directed.com, pg 848

Jones, Bob, Vitec Videocom Inc, 709 Executive Blvd, Valley Cottage, NY 10989 *Tel:* 845-268-0100 *Fax:* 845-268-0113 *E-mail:* info-cd-usa@vitecgroup.com *Web Site:* www.vitecgroup.com, pg 1060

Jones, Bruce, Lectrosonics Inc, 581 Laser Rd NE, Rio Rancho, NM 87124 *Tel:* 505-892-4501 *Toll Free Tel:* 800-821-1121 *Fax:* 505-892-6243 *E-mail:* sales@lectrosonics.com *Web Site:* www.lectrosonics.com, pg 918

Jones, Clint, Leo Ticheli Productions, 2801 University Blvd, Suite 101, Birmingham, AL 35233 *Tel:* 205-930-0500 *Fax:* 205-930-0505 *Web Site:* www.ltpro.com, pg 1040

Jones, Dave, Everlast Productions, 59 SW 12 Ave, Unit 109, Dania Beach, FL 33004 *Tel:* 954-456-7167 *Fax:* 954-456-1243 *E-mail:* info@everlastproductions.com *Web Site:* everlastproductions.com, pg 863

Jones, David, Crispin Corp, 600 Wade Ave, Raleigh, NC 27605 *Tel:* 919-845-7744 *Fax:* 919-845-7766 *E-mail:* welisten@crispincorp.com *Web Site:* www.crispincorp.com, pg 839

Jones, Douglas, Northern Lights & Pro Audio, 5503 232 St SW, Mountlake Terrace, WA 98043 *Tel:* 425-774-1905 *E-mail:* sales@loud.net *Web Site:* www.loud.net, pg 959

Jones, Elisabeth, DGA Awards, 7920 Sunset Blvd, Los Angeles, CA 90046 *Tel:* 310-289-2038 *E-mail:* dgaawards@dga.org *Web Site:* www.dga.org, pg 1114

Jones, Fraser, Independent Audio Inc, 43 Deerfield Rd, Portland, ME 04101 *Tel:* 207-773-2424 *Fax:* 207-773-2422 *E-mail:* info@independentaudio.com *Web Site:* www.independentaudio.com, pg 897

Jones, Gary, ATV Video Center Inc, 2424 Glendale Lane, Sacramento, CA 95825 *Tel:* 916-973-9100 *Toll Free Tel:* 800-635-1266 *Fax:* 916-973-8100 *E-mail:* info@atv.net *Web Site:* www.atv.net, pg 793

Jones, Gary W, Jones Film Video, 916 W Sixth St, Little Rock, AR 72201 *Tel:* 501-372-1981 *Toll Free Tel:* 800-880-1981 *Fax:* 501-372-4286 *E-mail:* info@jonesfilmvideo.com *Web Site:* www.jonesfilmvideo.com, pg 906

Jones, Graham, VidCan Media Solutions, 24133 Del Monte Dr, Unit 204, Valencia, CA 91355 *Tel:* 818-239-4729; 818-312-5128 *Web Site:* www.vidcan.com, pg 1054

Jones, Ian, Merestone, 7232 E First St, Scottsdale, AZ 85251 *Tel:* 480-945-4631 *Fax:* 480-945-0590 *Web Site:* www.merestone.com, pg 938

Jones, Dr Jeff, George Foster Peabody Awards, c/o University of Georgia, Grady College of Journalism & Mass Communication, 120 Hooper St, Athens, GA 30602-3018 *Tel:* 706-542-3787 *Fax:* 706-542-9273 *E-mail:* peabody@uga.edu *Web Site:* www.peabodyawards.com, pg 1123

Jones, Jeff, Solution Tree, 555 N Morton St, Bloomington, IN 47404-3730 *Tel:* 812-336-7700 *Toll Free Tel:* 800-733-6786 *Fax:* 812-336-7790 *E-mail:* info@solution-tree.com *Web Site:* www.solution-tree.com, pg 1015

Jones, Jonita, TM Studios Inc, 2002 Academy Lane, Suite 110, Dallas, TX 75234 *Tel:* 972-406-6800 *Fax:* 972-406-6890 *E-mail:* info@tmstudios.com; tmcustomerservice@tmstudios.com *Web Site:* www.tmstudios.com, pg 1041

Jones, Josh, Theatrical Services Inc, 128 S Washington St, Wichita, KS 67202 *Tel:* 316-263-4415 *Toll Free Tel:* 888-874-2649 *Fax:* 316-263-9927 *Web Site:* www.theatricalservices.com, pg 1038

Jones, Lloyd H, Lehigh Electric Products Co, 6265 Hamilton Blvd, Allentown, PA 18106 *Tel:* 610-395-3386 *Fax:* 610-395-7735 *E-mail:* sales@lehighdim.com *Web Site:* www.lehighdim.com, pg 918

Jones, Malcolm, Power-Sonic Corp, 7550 Panasonic Way, San Diego, CA 92154 *Tel:* 619-661-2020 *Fax:* 619-661-3650 *E-mail:* customer-service@power-sonic.com; technical-support@power-sonic.com *Web Site:* www.power-sonic.com, pg 979

Jones, R Mike, Video Movie Magic, 26941 Cabot Rd, Suite 127, Laguna Hills, CA 92653 *Tel:* 949-582-8596 *Fax:* 949-582-8223 *E-mail:* sales@videomoviemagic.com *Web Site:* www.videomoviemagic.com, pg 1056

Jones, Rick, Video Movie Magic, 26941 Cabot Rd, Suite 127, Laguna Hills, CA 92653 *Tel:* 949-582-8596 *Fax:* 949-582-8223 *E-mail:* sales@videomoviemagic.com *Web Site:* www.videomoviemagic.com, pg 1056

Jones, Shanin, The Banquet Sound Studios, 5870 McFarland Rd, Sebastopol, CA 95472 *Tel:* 707-823-3500 *E-mail:* info@banquetstudios.com *Web Site:* www.banquetstudios.com, pg 802

Jones, Susan Henshaw, Museum of the City of New York, 1220 Fifth Ave, New York, NY 10029 *Tel:* 212-534-1672 *Fax:* 212-423-0758 *E-mail:* info@mcny.org *Web Site:* www.mcny.org, pg 950

Jontz, Jim, Applebox Studio, 48 Kingswood Dr, Bethel, CT 06801 *Tel:* 203-762-7333 *Toll Free Fax:* 888-624-2829 *E-mail:* info@appleboxstudio.com; info@appleboxvideo.com *Web Site:* www.appleboxstudio.com, pg 788

Jordan, Peter S, Tecfilms Inc, 6310 Lemmon Ave, Suite 210, Dallas, TX 75209-5850 *Tel:* 214-904-0414 *E-mail:* mail@tecfilms.com *Web Site:* www.tecfilms.com, pg 1033

Jordan, Tina, Association of American Publishers (AAP), 71 Fifth Ave, 2nd fl, New York, NY 10003-3004 *Tel:* 212-255-0200 *Fax:* 212-255-7007 *E-mail:* info@publishers.org *Web Site:* www.publishers.org, pg 1078

Jorgensen, Allen, Quantum Data Inc, 2111 Big Timber Rd, Elgin, IL 60123-1100 *Tel:* 847-888-0450 *Toll Free Tel:* 888-252-6133 (tech support) *Fax:* 847-888-2802 *E-mail:* sales@quantumdata.com *Web Site:* www.quantumdata.com, pg 989

Josefsberg, Lisa, Catapult Films Inc, 832 Third St, Suite 303, Santa Monica, CA 90403 *Tel:* 310-395-1470, pg 821

Joseph, Harry, Harry Joseph & Associates Inc, PO Box 20993, New York, NY 10025 *Tel:* 212-244-5900 *E-mail:* harry@hja.com *Web Site:* www.hja.com, pg 906

Joseph, Kelly, QRS Software Services, 11879 Woodbury Rd, Garden Grove, CA 92843 *Tel:* 714-537-5100 *Toll Free Tel:* 800-228-9699 *Fax:* 714-539-9448 *E-mail:* qrs@qrssoftware.com; sales@qrssoftware.com *Web Site:* www.qrssoftware.com, pg 988

Joseph, Philip, Advance Concepts Inc, 8453 Tyco Rd, Suite N, Vienna, VA 22182-2623 *Tel:* 703-448-0445 *Fax:* 703-893-8049 *Web Site:* www.advanceconcepts.com, pg 777

Josephson, David, Josephson Engineering Inc, 329-A Ingalls St, Santa Cruz, CA 95060 *Tel:* 831-420-0888 *Fax:* 831-420-0890 *E-mail:* info@josephson.com *Web Site:* www.josephson.com, pg 906

Josephson, J P, Magnaplan Corp, 1320 Rte 9, No 3314, Champlain, NY 12919 *Tel:* 518-298-8404 *Toll Free Tel:* 800-361-1192 *Fax:* 518-298-2368 *Toll Free Fax:* 888-563-8730 *E-mail:* info@visualplanning.com *Web Site:* www.visualplanning.com, pg 928

Josephson, Larry, RadioArt/Bob & Ray CDs & MP3 Files, PO Box 519, Plantarium Sta, New York, NY 10024-0519 *Tel:* 212-595-1837 *E-mail:* reply@bobandray.com *Web Site:* www.bobandray.com, pg 990

Joslin, John A, DAWNco, 3340 S Lapeer Rd, Orion, MI 48359 *Tel:* 248-391-9200 *Fax:* 248-391-9206 *E-mail:* sales@dawnco.com *Web Site:* www.dawnco.com, pg 844

Jost, Kevin, J&S Audio Visual Inc, 9150 N Royal Lane, Suite 150, Irving, TX 75063 *Tel:* 972-241-5444 *Toll Free Tel:* 800-852-8771 *Fax:* 972-247-2590 *E-mail:* info@jsav.com *Web Site:* www.jsav.com, pg 904

Jost, Monroe, J&S Audio Visual Inc, 9150 N Royal Lane, Suite 150, Irving, TX 75063 *Tel:* 972-241-5444 *Toll Free Tel:* 800-852-8771 *Fax:* 972-247-2590 *E-mail:* info@jsav.com *Web Site:* www.jsav.com, pg 904

Jost, Todd, J&S Audio Visual Inc, 9150 N Royal Lane, Suite 150, Irving, TX 75063 *Tel:* 972-241-5444 *Toll Free Tel:* 800-852-8771 *Fax:* 972-247-2590 *E-mail:* info@jsav.com *Web Site:* www.jsav.com, pg 904

Joyce, Gayle, Joyce Media Inc, 3413 Soledad Canyon Rd, Acton, CA 93510 *Tel:* 661-269-1169 *Fax:* 661-269-2139 *E-mail:* help@joycemediainc.com *Web Site:* www.joycemediainc.com, pg 906

Joyce, John, Joyce Media Inc, 3413 Soledad Canyon Rd, Acton, CA 93510 *Tel:* 661-269-1169 *Fax:* 661-269-2139 *E-mail:* help@joycemediainc.com *Web Site:* www.joycemediainc.com, pg 906

Joyce, Tim, Sound Venture International, 441 MacLaren St, Suite 401, Ottawa, ON K2P 2H3, Canada *Tel:* 613-241-5111 *Fax:* 613-241-5010 *E-mail:* info@soundventure.com *Web Site:* www.soundventure.com, pg 1017

Jud, Brian, Book Marketing Works LLC, 50 Lovely St, Avon, CT 06001 *Tel:* 860-675-1344 *Web Site:* www.bookmarketingworks.com, pg 810

Judson, Charles, Atlanta Film Festival (ATLFF), 25 Park Place NE, Suite 900, Atlanta, GA 30303 *Tel:* 678-929-8103 *E-mail:* info@atlantafilmfestival.com *Web Site:* atlantafilmfestival.com, pg 1108

Jue, Martin F, MFJ Enterprises Inc, 300 Industrial Park Rd, Starkville, MS 39759-3992 *Tel:* 662-323-5869 *Toll Free Tel:* 800-647-1800 *Fax:* 662-323-6551 *E-mail:* mfjcustserv@mfjenterprises.com *Web Site:* www.mfjenterprises.com, pg 940

Jukes, Terri, REI - Radio Engineering Industries, 6534 "L" St, Omaha, NE 68117 *Tel:* 402-339-2200 *Toll Free Tel:* 800-228-9275 (sales); 877-726-4617 (tech support) *Fax:* 402-339-1704 *E-mail:* info@radioeng.com; orderdesk@radioeng.com *Web Site:* www.radioeng.com, pg 994

Julich, Alan, Sinclair Institute, 402 Millstone Dr, Hillsborough, NC 27278 *Tel:* 919-732-6005 *Toll Free Tel:* 888-736-2247 *Fax:* 919-732-6146 *E-mail:* sales@sinclairwholesale.com *Web Site:* www.sinclairwholesale.com; www.bettersex.com, pg 1012

Jung, Gabriela, Alpine Optics Inc, 150 View Rd, Brevard, NC 28712 *Tel:* 828-884-5822 *Fax:* 828-884-5884 *E-mail:* toalpine_optics@citcom.net, pg 783

Justo, Brian, Bay Stage Lighting Co Inc, 4008 W Alva St, Tampa, FL 33614 *Tel:* 813-877-1089 *Fax:* 813-875-8837 *Web Site:* www.baystagelighting.com, pg 803

Justo, Yvonne Felicione, Bay Stage Lighting Co Inc, 4008 W Alva St, Tampa, FL 33614 *Tel:* 813-877-1089 *Fax:* 813-875-8837 *Web Site:* www.baystagelighting.com, pg 803

Jzyk, Jennifer, Santa Clarita Film Office, 23920 Valencia Blvd, Suite 100, Santa Clarita, CA 91355 *Tel:* 661-284-1425 *Fax:* 661-286-4001 *E-mail:* film@santa-clarita.com *Web Site:* www.filmsantaclarita.com, pg 1094

Kahan, Douglas, America By Air Stock Footage Library, 154 Euclid Blvd, Lantana, FL 33462 *Toll Free Tel:* 800-488-6359 *Fax:* 413-235-1462 *E-mail:* footage@americabyair.com *Web Site:* www.americabyair.com; www.hdfootage.com, pg 783

Kahl, Barry, Mind Resources Inc, 130 Shoemaker St, Unit 1, Kitchener, ON N2E 3G4, Canada *Tel:* 519-895-0330 *Toll Free Tel:* 877-414-6463 *Fax:* 519-895-0331 *Toll Free Fax:* 877-585-2992 *E-mail:* sales@mindresources.com *Web Site:* www.mindresources.com, pg 943

Kahlden, Lisa, New World Records, 20 Jay St, Suite 1001, Brooklyn, NY 11201 *Tel:* 212-290-1680 *Fax:* 646-224-9638 *E-mail:* info@newworldrecords.org *Web Site:* www.newworldrecords.org, pg 956

Kahn, Warren Dennis, The Banquet Sound Studios, 5870 McFarland Rd, Sebastopol, CA 95472 *Tel:* 707-823-3500 *E-mail:* info@banquetstudios.com *Web Site:* www.banquetstudios.com, pg 802

Kain, Hannah, ALOM Technologies Corp, 48105 Warm Springs Blvd, Fremont, CA 94539-7498 *Tel:* 510-360-3600 *Toll Free Tel:* 800-500-9991 *Fax:* 510-226-7617 *E-mail:* customerservice@alom.com *Web Site:* www.alom.com, pg 782

Kairys, Mike, Ac-cetera Inc, 5049 Center Dr, Bldg D-1, Latrobe, PA 15650 *Tel:* 724-532-3363 *Fax:* 724-532-3364 *E-mail:* contact@ez-clamp.net *Web Site:* www.ac-cetera.com, pg 772

Kaiser, Bruce, Lightning Master Corp, 1770 Calumet St, Clearwater, FL 33765 *Tel:* 727-447-6800 *Toll Free Tel:* 877-334-8006 *Fax:* 727-499-0138 *E-mail:* info@lightningmaster.com *Web Site:* www.lightningmaster.com, pg 921

Kaiser, Chuck, Digital Image Studios LLC, 23400 Commerce Dr, Farmington Hills, MI 48335 *Tel:* 248-477-5600 *Toll Free Tel:* 888-434-7839 *Fax:* 248-477-4322 *Web Site:* www.dimage.com, pg 847

Kaiser, Fred, Alpha Technologies, 3767 Alpha Way, Bellingham, WA 98226 *Tel:* 360-647-2360 *Fax:* 360-671-4936 *E-mail:* alpha@alpha.com *Web Site:* www.alpha.com, pg 782

Kaiser, James, Sound Vision Inc, 1450 Davis Rd, Elgin, IL 60123 *Tel:* 847-742-6000 *Fax:* 847-742-7585 *E-mail:* info@svi-avsystems.com *Web Site:* www.svi-avsystems.com, pg 1018

Kaiser, Larry, POP TV, 5069 Maureen Lane, Moorpark, CA 93021-7127 *Tel:* 805-499-8513 *Toll Free Tel:* 800-331-4626 *Fax:* 805-499-8206 *E-mail:* sales@mpo-video.com *Web Site:* www.mpo-video.com, pg 978

Kaiser, William, ESE, 142 Sierra St, El Segundo, CA 90245 *Tel:* 310-322-2136 *Fax:* 310-322-8127 *E-mail:* ese@ese-web.com *Web Site:* www.ese-web.com, pg 862

Kalbach, Paul, Artichoke Productions, 4114 Linden St, Oakland, CA 94608 *Tel:* 510-655-1283 *Web Site:* www.artichokepro.com, pg 791

Kalber, Ann, Tropical Visions Video Inc, 62 Halaulani Place, Hilo, HI 96720 *Tel:* 808-935-5557 *Fax:* 808-935-0066 *E-mail:* redhotlava@hawaii.rr.com *Web Site:* www.volcanoscapes.com, pg 1045

Kalber, Mick, Tropical Visions Video Inc, 62 Halaulani Place, Hilo, HI 96720 *Tel:* 808-935-5557 *Fax:* 808-935-0066 *E-mail:* redhotlava@hawaii.rr.com *Web Site:* www.volcanoscapes.com, pg 1045

Kaloi, Dennis, Simon - Kaloi Engineering, 31192 La Baya Dr, Unit G, Westlake Village, CA 91362 *Tel:* 818-707-8400 *Fax:* 818-707-8401, pg 1011

Kamayatsu, Eric, PMP Marketing Inc, 13006 E Philadelphia St, Suite 402, Whittier, CA 90601 *Tel:* 562-698-0088 *Fax:* 562-320-8139 *Web Site:* www.pmpmarketing.com, pg 977

Kamcheff, Brad, Aiphone Corp, 1700 130 Ave NE, Bellevue, WA 98005 *Tel:* 425-455-0510 *Toll Free Tel:* 800-692-0200 *Fax:* 425-455-0516 (sales); 425-455-0071 *Toll Free Fax:* 800-525-3372 (cust serv) *E-mail:* info@aiphone.com; cs@aiphone.com *Web Site:* www.aiphone.com, pg 779

Kameda, Shingi, Ushio America Inc, 5440 Cerritos Ave, Cypress, CA 90630-4567 *Tel:* 714-236-8600 *Toll Free Tel:* 800-838-7446 (cust serv) *Fax:* 714-229-3180 *Toll Free Fax:* 800-776-3641 (cust serv) *E-mail:* customerservice@ushio.com *Web Site:* www.ushio.com, pg 1051

Kamen, Marina, Kamen Entertainment Group Inc, 200 E 94 St, New York, NY 10128 *Tel:* 212-575-4660 *Fax:* 212-575-4799 *E-mail:* kamen@kamen.com *Web Site:* www.kamen.com, pg 908

Kamen, Roy, Kamen Entertainment Group Inc, 200 E 94 St, New York, NY 10128 *Tel:* 212-575-4660 *Fax:* 212-575-4799 *E-mail:* kamen@kamen.com *Web Site:* www.kamen.com, pg 908

Kamienowicz, Hedy, Samy's Camera, 431 S Fairfax Ave, Los Angeles, CA 90036 *Tel:* 323-938-4400 *Toll Free Tel:* 800-321-4726 *Fax:* 323-937-2919 *E-mail:* lacamera@samys.com *Web Site:* www.samys.com, pg 1002

Kamienowicz, Samy, Samy's Camera, 431 S Fairfax Ave, Los Angeles, CA 90036 *Tel:* 323-938-4400 *Toll Free Tel:* 800-321-4726 *Fax:* 323-937-2919 *E-mail:* lacamera@samys.com *Web Site:* www.samys.com, pg 1002

Kaminshine, Jerry, ESECO Speedmaster, 730 E Eseco Rd, Cushing, OK 74023-5505 *Tel:* 918-225-1266 *Toll Free Tel:* 800-331-5904 (US & CN) *Fax:* 918-225-1284 *E-mail:* info@eseco-speedmaster.com *Web Site:* www.eseco-speedmaster.com, pg 862

Kammersgard, Dana W, Dot Hill Systems Corp, 1351 S Sunset St, Longmont, CO 80501-6533 *Tel:* 303-845-3200 *Toll Free Tel:* 800-872-2783 *Fax:* 303-845-3655 *E-mail:* support@dothill.com; websales@dothill.com *Web Site:* www.dothill.com, pg 851

Kamon, Leah, Radio Advertising Bureau (RAB), 125 W 55 St, 5th fl, New York, NY 10019 *Tel:* 212-681-7200 *Toll Free Tel:* 800-252-7234 *Fax:* 212-681-7223 *Web Site:* www.rab.com, pg 1088

Kampfe, John E, Turner Broadcasting System Inc, One CNN Ctr, Atlanta, GA 30303 *Tel:* 404-827-1700 *Web Site:* www.turner.com, pg 1046

Kampfer, Thomas D, CohuHD, 12367 Crosthwaite Circle, Poway, CA 92064 *Tel:* 858-391-1800 *E-mail:* info@cohuhd.com *Web Site:* www.cohuhd.com, pg 831

Kanarek, Mike, WKYT Productions, 2851 Winchester Rd, Lexington, KY 40509 *Tel:* 859-299-0411; 859-299-2727 (newsroom) *Fax:* 859-299-2494 *Web Site:* www.wkyt.com, pg 1068

Kanavos, Ken, Newbury Media, 80 Industrial Way, Wilmington, MA 01887 *Tel:* 617-267-4095 *E-mail:* info@newburymedia.com *Web Site:* newburymedia.com, pg 956

Kancher, Ellen, Monster Tracks, 1821 Ranstead St, Philadelphia, PA 19103 *Tel:* 215-567-0400 *Toll Free Tel:* 800-369-1280 *Fax:* 215-567-0350 *Web Site:* www.monstertracks.com, pg 945

Kane, Chris, AudioControl®, 22410 70 Ave W, Mountlake Terrace, WA 98043 *Tel:* 425-775-8461 *Fax:* 425-778-3166 *E-mail:* sound.better@audiocontrol.com; superio.sound@audiocontrol.com *Web Site:* www.audiocontrol.com, pg 796

Kane, Ursula, Award Productions, 164 Great Rd, Acton, MA 01720 *Tel:* 978-667-3335 *E-mail:* web@awardproductions.com *Web Site:* www.awardproductions.com, pg 800

Kann, Thomas, Integrated Event Management, 1239 Vista Leaf Dr, Decatur, GA 30033 *Tel:* 404-633-8541 *Fax:* 404-633-8691 *Web Site:* www.integratedevents.com, pg 899

Kannappan, Ken, Plantronics Inc, 345 Encinal St, Santa Cruz, CA 95060 *Tel:* 831-426-5858 *Toll Free Tel:* 800-544-4660 *Fax:* 831-426-6098 *Toll Free Fax:* 888-290-4519 *E-mail:* plantronics@custhelp.com *Web Site:* www.plantronics.com, pg 976

Kanter, Ron, Video/Film Associates, 3310 W Queen Lane, Philadelphia, PA 19129 *Tel:* 215-922-3333, pg 1055

Kantola, Steve, Kantola Productions LLC, 55 Sunnyside Ave, Mill Valley, CA 94941 *Tel:* 415-381-9363 *Toll Free Tel:* 800-280-1180 *Fax:* 415-381-9801 *E-mail:* kantola@kantola.com *Web Site:* www.kantola.com, pg 908

Kapes, Gordon, Studio Technologies Inc, 5520 W Touhy Ave, Skokie, IL 60077 *Tel:* 847-676-9177 *Fax:* 847-982-0747 *E-mail:* stisales-2014@studio-tech.com *Web Site:* www.studio-tech.com, pg 1027

Kapin, Kerry, JBL Professional, 8500 Balboa Blvd, Northridge, CA 91329 *Tel:* 818-894-8850; 818-895-3498 *Fax:* 818-894-3479; 818-830-7865 (mktg); 818-830-7801 (sales) *E-mail:* info@jblpro.com *Web Site:* www.jblpro.com; www.harman.com, pg 904

Kapis, Sue, Park City Film Commission, 1910 Prospector Ave, Park City, UT 84060 *Tel:* 435-649-6100 *Toll Free Tel:* 800-453-1360 *Fax:* 435-649-4132 *Web Site:* www.visitparkcity.com/media/park-city-film-commission/, pg 1103

Kaplan, Barbara, Bulbtronics Inc, 45 Banfi Plaza N, Farmingdale, NY 11735 *Tel:* 631-249-2272 *Toll Free Tel:* 800-654-8542 (sales); 800-588-2852 *Fax:* 631-249-6066 *E-mail:* marketing@bulbtronics.com *Web Site:* www.bulbtronics.com, pg 815

Kaplan, Bob, Nalpak Inc, 1267 Vernon Way, El Cajon, CA 92020 *Tel:* 619-258-1200 *Toll Free Tel:* 888-488-3372 (help desk) *Fax:* 619-258-0925 *E-mail:* service@nalpak.com *Web Site:* www.nalpak.com, pg 952

Kaplan, David, Audio Producers Group, 200 N Dearborn St, Suite 2705, Chicago, IL 60601 *Tel:* 312-977-9400 *Fax:* 312-977-9494 *E-mail:* info@apgaudio.com *Web Site:* www.audioproducersgroup.com, pg 794

Kaplan, Deeny, The Kitchen, 4119 W Burbank Blvd, Burbank, CA 91505 *Tel:* 818-306-5300 *Fax:* 305-415-6201 *E-mail:* info@thekitchen.tv *Web Site:* www.thekitchen.tv, pg 911

Kaplan, Howard, Silver Gavel Awards for Media and the Arts, Div for Public Education, 321 N Clark St, Chicago, IL 60654 *Tel:* 312-988-5733 *Toll Free Tel:* 800-285-2221 *Fax:* 312-988-5494 (Attn: Gavel Awards) *E-mail:* publiceducation@americanbar.org *Web Site:* www.americanbar.org, pg 1127

Kaplan, Lynda B, American History Workshop (NY) Inc, 588 Seventh St, Brooklyn, NY 11215-3707 *Tel:* 718-499-6500 *E-mail:* info@americanhistoryworkshop.com *Web Site:* www.americanhistoryworkshop.com, pg 784

Kaplan, Mike, Lagoon Video, 3323 Marble Front Rd, Caldwell, ID 83605 *Tel:* 208-455-3457 *Fax:* 208-453-1136 *E-mail:* kapsm@aol.com, pg 915

Kaplan, Richard, Richard Kaplan Productions, 455 N End Ave, Apt 1114, New York, NY 10282-1139 *Tel:* 212-787-0258 *Fax:* 212-787-0268 *E-mail:* richardkaplan33@gmail.com *Web Site:* www.richardkaplanproductions.com, pg 908

Kappas, George J, Panorama Publishing Co, 18607 Ventura Blvd, Suite 310, Tarzana, CA 91356-4158 *Tel:* 818-758-2747 *Toll Free Tel:* 800-634-5620; 800-479-9464 (home study school) *Fax:* 818-344-2262 *Web Site:* www.hypnosis.edu, pg 968

Kappel, Gary, Orion Software, 6000 Cote-des-Neiges, Suite 240, Montreal, QC H3S 1Z8, Canada *Tel:* 514-484-9661 *Toll Free Tel:* 877-755-2012 *Fax:* 514-484-1339 *E-mail:* info@orion-soft.com *Web Site:* www.orion-soft.com, pg 965

Karanian, Sabra, Paradise Video & Film, 10148 NW 47 St, Sunrise, FL 33351 *Tel:* 954-747-1118 *Fax:* 954-747-3380 *E-mail:* info@paradisevideo.com *Web Site:* www.paradisevideo.com, pg 969

Karasick, Jay, Feature Systems Inc, 223 Veterans Blvd, Carlstadt, NJ 07072 *Tel:* 201-531-2299; 212-736-0447 *Fax:* 201-531-2290; 212-465-1987 *Web Site:* www.featuresystems.com, pg 866

Karcy, Bob, VIEW Inc (Video International Entertainment World Inc), 11 Reservoir Rd, Saugerties, NY 12477 *Tel:* 845-246-9955 *Toll Free Tel:* 800-843-9843 *Fax:* 845-246-9966 *E-mail:* viewvid@aol.com *Web Site:* www.view.com, pg 1058

Karczmer, Claude M, Servoreeler Systems, 218-31 97 Ave, Queens Village, NY 11429 *Tel:* 718-464-9400 *Toll Free Tel:* 800-431-8900 *E-mail:* srsystems@servoreelers.com *Web Site:* www.servoreelers.com, pg 1007

Karczmer, Eileen, Servoreeler Systems, 218-31 97 Ave, Queens Village, NY 11429 *Tel:* 718-464-9400 *Toll Free Tel:* 800-431-8900 *E-mail:* srsystems@servoreelers.com *Web Site:* www.servoreelers.com, pg 1007

Kardokus, Ronald, Magnum Towers Inc, 9370 Elder Creek Rd, Sacramento, CA 95829 *Tel:* 916-381-5053 *Fax:* 916-381-2144 *E-mail:* office@magnumtowers.com *Web Site:* www.magnumtowers.com, pg 929

Karimbakas, Chris, Antronics Inc, 25 Summer Ave, Waltham, MA 02452-5634 *Tel:* 781-891-7525 *Fax:* 781-647-3667 *E-mail:* info@antronics.net *Web Site:* www.antronics.net, pg 787

Karimbakas, Jim, Antronics Inc, 25 Summer Ave, Waltham, MA 02452-5634 *Tel:* 781-891-7525 *Fax:* 781-647-3667 *E-mail:* info@antronics.net *Web Site:* www.antronics.net, pg 787

Karlowitch, Debra, The Martin Guitar Co, 510 Sycamore St, Nazareth, PA 18064 *Tel:* 610-759-2837 *Toll Free Tel:* 800-633-2060; 888-433-9177 *Fax:* 610-759-5757 *E-mail:* info@martinguitar.com *Web Site:* www.martinguitar.com, pg 932

Karns, Krys, Washington Filmworks, 1411 Fourth Ave, Suite 420, Seattle, WA 98101 *Tel:* 206-264-0667 *Fax:* 206-382-4343 *E-mail:* info@washingtonfilmworks.org *Web Site:* washingtonfilmworks.org, pg 1103

Karol, John, Apertura, 535 Main St, Orford, NH 03777 *Tel:* 603-353-9067 *Fax:* 603-353-4646 *Web Site:* www.apertura.org, pg 788

Karp, David, Access Video in Berkeley, 1442 A Walnut St, Berkeley, CA 94709 *Tel:* 510-528-6044 *E-mail:* accessvideo@hotmail.com *Web Site:* www.accessvideoproductions.com, pg 773

Karr, Cheryl, Phoenix VideoFilms®, 2925 W Indian School Rd, Phoenix, AZ 85017 *Tel:* 602-266-4198; 801-226-8209 *Web Site:* www.phoenixvideofilms.com, pg 974

Karr, Christy, Phoenix VideoFilms®, 2925 W Indian School Rd, Phoenix, AZ 85017 *Tel:* 602-266-4198; 801-226-8209 *Web Site:* www.phoenixvideofilms.com, pg 974

Karr, Kelly, Phoenix VideoFilms®, 2925 W Indian School Rd, Phoenix, AZ 85017 *Tel:* 602-266-4198; 801-226-8209 *Web Site:* www.phoenixvideofilms.com, pg 974

Karr, Marcus, Manhattan Center Studios Inc, 311 W 34 St, New York, NY 10001 *Tel:* 212-279-7740 *Fax:* 212-564-1072 *E-mail:* info@mcstudios.com *Web Site:* www.mcstudios.com, pg 930

Karr, Michael, Phoenix VideoFilms®, 2925 W Indian School Rd, Phoenix, AZ 85017 *Tel:* 602-266-4198; 801-226-8209 *Web Site:* www.phoenixvideofilms.com, pg 974

Karsten, Ralph, Atma-Sphere Music Systems Inc, 1742 Selby Ave, St Paul, MN 55104 *Tel:* 651-690-2246 *Web Site:* www.atma-sphere.com, pg 793

Karten, Mike, Calrad Electronics, 819 N Highland Ave, Los Angeles, CA 90038 *Tel:* 323-465-2131 *Toll Free Tel:* 800-821-8536 *Fax:* 323-465-3504 *E-mail:* calradelectronics@calrad.com *Web Site:* www.calrad.com, pg 817

Kasha, Kevin, Anchor Bay Entertainment LLC, 9242 Beverly Blvd, Suite 201, Beverly Hills, CA 90210 *Tel:* 424-204-4166 *E-mail:* questions@anchorbayent.com *Web Site:* www.anchorbayentertainment.com, pg 786

Kass, Hope, Chicago Spotlight Inc, 1658 W Carroll St, Chicago, IL 60612 *Tel:* 312-455-1171 *Fax:* 312-455-1744 *Web Site:* www.chicagospotlight.com, pg 825

Kassouf, Jeff, Take 1 Media Services, 31335 Center Ridge Rd, Cleveland, OH 44145 *Tel:* 440-899-0101 *Web Site:* www.take1media.com, pg 1031

Kasun, Leo, Department of Education Resources, 2000-B S Club Dr, Landover, MD 20785 *Tel:* 202-842-6280 *Fax:* 202-842-6935 *E-mail:* edresources@nga.gov *Web Site:* www.nga.gov; www.nga.gov/education, pg 845

Katt, Craig, Trans-Lux Multimedia Corp, 950 Third Ave, Suite 2804, New York, NY 10022 *Tel:* 203-853-4321 *Toll Free Tel:* 800-243-5544; 800-462-2716 *Fax:* 203-229-0691 *Web Site:* www.trans-lux.com, pg 1043

Katz, David, Camera Co Inc/Broadcast Divison, 858 Boston-Providence Tpke, Norwood, MA 02062 *Tel:* 781-769-7810 *Toll Free Tel:* 866-769-0210 *Fax:* 781-769-5750 *Web Site:* www.cameraco.com, pg 818

Katz, David M, A/V Davey, 71 Clifton Place, Bridgeport, CT 06606 *Tel:* 203-372-3286 *Toll Free Tel:* 877-AVDAVEY (283-2839) *Fax:* 203-372-3307 *Web Site:* avdavey.com, pg 797

Katz, Steve, Act One Video, PO Box 342076, Kailua, HI 96734-8997 *Tel:* 808-220-3625 *E-mail:* info@actonevideo.tv *Web Site:* www.actonevideo.tv, pg 775

Katzberger, Brian, Robertson Worldwide, 13611 Thornton Rd, Blue Island, IL 60406 *Toll Free Tel:* 800-323-5633 *Toll Free Fax:* 877-388-2420 *E-mail:* info@robertsonww.com *Web Site:* www.robertsonww.com, pg 998

Katzenberg, Jeffrey, DreamWorks Animation SKG Inc, 1000 Flower St, Glendale, CA 91201 *Tel:* 818-695-5000 *Fax:* 818-695-4190 *Web Site:* www.dreamworksanimation.com, pg 852

Katzman, Ken, Dover Publications Inc, 31 E Second St, Mineola, NY 11501 *Tel:* 516-294-7000 *Fax:* 516-742-5049 (wholesale orders); 516-742-6953 (cust care) *Web Site:* store.doverpublications.com, pg 851

Kaufman, Barney L, Magna-Tech Electronic Co Inc, 1998 NE 150 St, North Miami, FL 33181 *Tel:* 305-573-7339 *Fax:* 305-573-8101 *E-mail:* magnatech@iceco.com; sales@iceco.com *Web Site:* www.magna-tech.com, pg 928

Kaufmann, Bruce, Human Circuit, 9120 Gaither Rd, Gaithersburg, MD 20877 *Tel:* 240-864-4000 *Toll Free Tel:* 800-638-8071 *Fax:* 240-864-4000 *E-mail:* info@humancircuit.com *Web Site:* www.humancircuit.com, pg 892

Kaufmann, Harry, BeachTek Inc, 480 Osprey Ave, Kelowna, BC V1Y 5A5, Canada *Tel:* 416-690-9457 *E-mail:* info@beachtek.com *Web Site:* www.beachtek.com, pg 804

Kautz, Andrew, Love Shack Recording Studios, 909 18 Ave S, Nashville, TN 37212 *Tel:* 615-843-0019 *E-mail:* book@loveshackstudios.com *Web Site:* loveshackstudios.com, pg 925

Kavanagh, Bill, Kavanagh Productions Inc, 32 Broadway, Suite 1711-12, New York, NY 10004 *Tel:* 212-480-0065 *Fax:* 212-480-0149 *E-mail:* mail@kavanaghproductions.com *Web Site:* www.kavanaghproductions.com, pg 908

Kavich, Steve, Kavich Reynolds Productions Inc, 6381 Hollywood Blvd, Suite 580, Hollywood, CA 90028 *Tel:* 323-466-2490 *Fax:* 323-466-3655 *E-mail:* info@kavichreynolds.com *Web Site:* www.kavichreynolds.com, pg 908

Kawabata, Kazuhiro, DNP Photo Imaging America Corp, 101 Uhland Rd, Suite 210, San Marcos, TX 78666 *Tel:* 512-753-7280 *Toll Free Tel:* 800-467-4935 *Fax:* 512-753-7299 *E-mail:* info@pixelmagic.com; sales@pixelmagic.com; customercare@pixelmagic.com *Web Site:* www.dnpphoto.com; www.pixelmagic.com; www.pmimaging.com, pg 849

Kay, Judith, JDSU, 430 N McCarthy Blvd, Milpitas, CA 95035 *Tel:* 408-546-5000 *Fax:* 408-546-4300 *Web Site:* www.jdsu.com, pg 905

Kayatta, Michael, Cine-World Film Festival, 10715 Rodeo Dr, Suite 8, Lakewood Ranch, FL 34202 *Tel:* 941-364-8478 *Fax:* 941-364-8478 *E-mail:* mail@filmsociety.org *Web Site:* www.filmsociety.org, pg 1112

Kayser, Ferdinand, SES World Skies, 4 Research Way, Princeton, NJ 08540 *Tel:* 609-987-4000; 609-987-4200 *Fax:* 609-987-4517 *E-mail:* info@ses.com *Web Site:* www.ses.com, pg 1007

Kayser, Matt, KD Kanopy Inc, 1921 E 68 Ave, Denver, CO 80229 *Tel:* 303-650-1310 *Toll Free Tel:* 800-432-4435 *Fax:* 303-650-5211 *E-mail:* sales@kdkanopy.com *Web Site:* www.kdkanopy.com, pg 908

Kazaroff, John, Los Feliz Post, 6767 Forest Lawn Dr, Suite 211, Los Angeles, CA 90068 *Tel:* 818-859-3500, pg 924

Kazary, Wil, Guerrilla Productions LLC, 1119 E 50 St, Savannah, GA 31404 *Tel:* 919-349-7643; 912-354-4518 *Fax:* 912-354-1176 *E-mail:* info@guerrillapro.com *Web Site:* www.guerrillapro.com, pg 883

Kazmark, Eugene Jr, Kart-A-Bag Manufacturing Inc, 510 Manhattan Rd, Joliet, IL 60433 *Tel:* 815-723-1940 *Toll Free Tel:* 800-423-9328 *Fax:* 815-723-2495 *E-mail:* bks@kart-a-bag.com *Web Site:* www.kart-a-bag.com, pg 908

Keane, Eugene, Nevion, 1600 Emerson Ave, Oxnard, CA 93033 *Tel:* 805-247-8560 *E-mail:* ussales@nevion.com *Web Site:* www.nevion.com, pg 955

Kearns, Bob, AV Conferencing, PO Box 21606, Concord, CA 94521 *Tel:* 925-216-6319 *Fax:* 801-382-5573 *E-mail:* sales@avconferencing.com *Web Site:* www.avconferencing.com, pg 797

Kearns, Corey, Outsource Engineering & Manufacturing Inc dba Texscan MSI, 11800 Wills Rd, Suite 150, Alpharetta, GA 30009 *Tel:* 678-689-0146; 770-642-7440 (support) *E-mail:* sales@texscan-msi.com *Web Site:* www.texscan-msi.com, pg 966

Kearns, Gregg R, AV Conferencing, PO Box 21606, Concord, CA 94521 *Tel:* 925-216-6319 *Fax:* 801-382-5573 *E-mail:* sales@avconferencing.com *Web Site:* www.avconferencing.com, pg 797

Keblas, James, Seattle Mayor's Office of Film & Music, 700 Fifth Ave, Suite 5752, Seattle, WA 98104 *Tel:* 206-684-8090 *Fax:* 206-684-0379 *E-mail:* filmandmusicoffice@seattle.gov *Web Site:* www.seattle.gov/filmandmusic, pg 1103

Keck, Doug, Eternal Word Television Network (EWTN), 5817 Old Leeds Rd, Irondale, AL 35210-2164 *Tel:* 205-271-2900 *Fax:* 205-271-2920 *E-mail:* viewer@ewtn.com *Web Site:* www.ewtn.com, pg 862

Keckeisen, Donna, Associated Bag Co, 400 W Boden St, Milwaukee, WI 53207 *Tel:* 414-769-1000 *Toll Free Tel:* 800-926-6100 *Fax:* 414-769-6530 *Toll Free Fax:* 800-926-4610 *E-mail:* customerservice@associatedbag.com *Web Site:* www.associatedbag.com, pg 792

Kedas, Jeannie, MTV Networks Co, c/o MTV Studios, 1515 Broadway, New York, NY 10036 *Tel:* 212-258-8000 *Web Site:* www.mtv.com; www.mtvpress.com, pg 949

Keebler, Rachel, Cobalt Studios Inc, 134 Royce Rd, White Lake, NY 12786 *Tel:* 845-583-7025 *Fax:* 845-583-7025 *E-mail:* mail@cobaltstudios.net; rentals@cobaltstudios.net *Web Site:* www.cobaltstudios.net, pg 831

Keefe, Joe, Ostergaard Acoustical Associates, 200 Executive Dr, Suite 350, West Orange, NJ 07052 *Tel:* 973-731-7002 *Fax:* 973-731-6680 *E-mail:* info@acousticalconsultant.com *Web Site:* www.acousticalconsultant.com, pg 966

Keefe, Rich, AVFX Inc, 96 Holton St, Boston, MA 02135 *Tel:* 617-254-0770 *Toll Free Tel:* 888-254-0770 *E-mail:* info@avfx.com *Web Site:* www.avfx.com, pg 798

Keegstra, Mika, Select Media Inc, 333 Hudson St, 4th fl, New York, NY 10013 *Tel:* 212-925-9101 *Toll Free Tel:* 800-707-6334 *Fax:* 212-925-9102 *E-mail:* info@selectmedia.org *Web Site:* www.selectmedia.org, pg 1006

Keels, Nancy, Maryknoll Productions, PO Box 308, Maryknoll, NY 10545-0308 *Tel:* 914-941-7590 *Toll Free Tel:* 888-627-9566 *Fax:* 914-944-3613 *E-mail:* mkweb@maryknoll.org *Web Site:* www.maryknoll.org, pg 933

Keenan, Linda, Creative Media Recording, 11105 Knott Ave, Suite G, Cypress, CA 90630 *Tel:* 714-892-9469 *E-mail:* info@creativemediarecording.com *Web Site:* www.creativemediarecording.com, pg 838

Keenan, Tim, Creative Media Recording, 11105 Knott Ave, Suite G, Cypress, CA 90630 *Tel:* 714-892-9469 *E-mail:* info@creativemediarecording.com *Web Site:* www.creativemediarecording.com, pg 838

Keene-Kendrick, Lydia, Davis Art Images, 50 Portland St, Worcester, MA 01608 *Tel:* 508-754-7201 *Toll Free Tel:* 800-533-2847 *Fax:* 508-753-3834 *E-mail:* das@davisart.com *Web Site:* www.davisartimages.com, pg 843

Keese, William, Association of Progressive Rental Organizations (APRO), 1504 Robin Hood Trail, Austin, TX 78703 *Tel:* 512-794-0095 *Toll Free Tel:* 800-204-2776 *Fax:* 512-794-0097 *Web Site:* www.rtohq.org, pg 1079

Keezer, Dawn M, Pittsburgh Film Office, The Century Bldg, Suite 202, 130 Seventh St, Pittsburgh, PA 15222 *Tel:* 412-261-2744 *Toll Free Tel:* 888-744-3456 *Fax:* 412-471-7317 *E-mail:* info@pghfilm.org *Web Site:* www.pghfilm.org, pg 1102

Keib, John H, Time Warner Cable, 60 Columbus Circle, 17th fl, New York, NY 10023 *Tel:* 212-364-8200 *Web Site:* www.timewarnercable.com, pg 1040

Keil, Alan, Ikegami Electronics (USA) Inc, 37 Brook Ave, Maywood, NJ 07607 *Tel:* 201-368-9171 *Fax:* 201-569-1626 *E-mail:* sales@ikegami.com; service@ikegami.com *Web Site:* www.ikegami.com, pg 894

Keith, Matt, Custom Color Corp, 14320 W 101 Terr, Lenexa, KS 66215 *Tel:* 913-730-3100 *Toll Free Tel:* 888-605-4050 *Fax:* 913-730-3101 *E-mail:* info@customcolor.com *Web Site:* www.customcolor.com, pg 841

Keleman, Jackie, Theatre Service & Supply Corp, 1792 Union Ave, Baltimore, MD 21211 *Tel:* 410-467-1225 *Fax:* 410-467-1289 *E-mail:* sales@stage-n-studio.com *Web Site:* www.stage-n-studio.com, pg 1038

Kelleher, Jack, Amusement & Music Operators Association (AMOA), 600 Spring Hill Ring Rd, Suite 111, West Dundee, IL 60118 *Tel:* 847-428-7699 *Toll Free Tel:* 800-YES-AMOA (937-2662) *Fax:* 847-428-7719 *E-mail:* amoa@amoa.com *Web Site:* www.amoa.com, pg 1077

Kelleher, Kevin, Sony Music Entertainment, 550 Madison Ave, New York, NY 10022 *Tel:* 212-833-8000 *Fax:* 212-833-8336 *Web Site:* www.sonymusic.com, pg 1016

Kelleher, Roger, American Management Association®, 1601 Broadway, New York, NY 10019 *Tel:* 212-586-8100 *Toll Free Tel:* 877-566-9441 (cust serv) *Fax:* 212-903-8168; 518-891-0368 (cust serv) *E-mail:* customerservice@amanet.org *Web Site:* www.amanet.org, pg 784, 1077

Keller, Daniel, Green Mountain Post Films (GMP), PO Box 229, Turners Falls, MA 01376-0229 *Tel:* 413-863-4754 *Fax:* 413-863-8248 *E-mail:* info@gmpfilms.com *Web Site:* www.gmpfilms.com, pg 882

Keller, Dave, Furman, 1800 S McDowell Blvd, Petaluma, CA 94954 *Tel:* 707-763-1010 *Fax:* 707-763-1310 *E-mail:* info@furmansound.com *Web Site:* www.furmansound.com, pg 874

Keller, Robert J, ACCO Brands Corp, 4 Corporate Dr, Lake Zurick, IL 60047-8997 *Toll Free Tel:* 800-541-0094 *Toll Free Fax:* 800-941-4463 *E-mail:* contactus@gbc.com *Web Site:* www.accobrands.com, pg 773

Keller, Robin, The Hollaender Manufacturing Co, 10285 Wayne Ave, Cincinnati, OH 45215 *Tel:* 513-772-8800 *Toll Free Tel:* 800-772-8800 (orders) *Fax:* 513-772-8806 *Web Site:* www.hollaender.com, pg 890

Kelley, Barbara, Hearing Loss Association of America (HLAA), 7910 Woodmont Ave, Suite 1200, Bethesda, MD 20814 *Tel:* 301-657-2248; 301-657-2249 (TTY) *Fax:* 301-913-9413 *E-mail:* info@hearingloss.org *Web Site:* www.hearingloss.org, pg 887

Kelley, Chuck, Jupiter Systems, 31015 Huntwood Ave, Hayward, CA 94544 *Tel:* 510-675-1000 *Fax:* 510-675-1001 *E-mail:* sales@jupiter.com *Web Site:* www.jupiter.com, pg 907

Kelley, David, Klipsch Audio Technologies, 3502 Woodview Trace, Suite 200, Indianapolis, IN 46268 *Tel:* 317-860-8100 *Toll Free Tel:* 877-412-7467 (orders); 800-544-1482 *Fax:* 317-860-9170 (sales & mktg) *E-mail:* support@klipsch.com *Web Site:* www.klipsch.com, pg 912

Kelley, Gregg, Lynx Broadband, 12219 Wood Lake Dr, Burnsville, MN 55337 *Tel:* 952-894-9590 *Fax:* 952-894-9380 *E-mail:* info@lynxbroadband.com *Web Site:* www.lynxbroadband.com, pg 926

Kelley, Richard, Drytac Corp, 5601 Eastport Blvd, Richmond, VA 23231 *Toll Free Tel:* 800-280-6013 *E-mail:* customerservice@drytac.com *Web Site:* www.drytac.com, pg 852

Kellman, Brian, Brian Film Productions LLC, 254 W 25 St, Suite 6-A, New York, NY 10001-7325 *Tel:* 212-645-8795, pg 812

Kellner, Richard, Synaptic Digital, 79 Fifth Ave, 14th fl, New York, NY 10003 *Tel:* 212-682-8300 *Toll Free Tel:* 800-843-0677 *Fax:* 212-682-5260 *E-mail:* learnmore@synapticdigital.com *Web Site:* www.synapticdigital.com, pg 1030

Kelly, Jack, Group One Ltd, 70 Sea Lane, Farmingdale, NY 11735 *Tel:* 516-249-1399 *Fax:* 516-249-8870 *E-mail:* sales@g1limited.com *Web Site:* www.g1limited.com, pg 882

Kelly, Jack, XTA Electronics Ltd, 70 Sea Lane, Farmingdale, NY 11735 *Tel:* 516-249-1399 *Fax:* 516-249-8870 *E-mail:* sales@g1limited.com *Web Site:* www.g1limited.com, pg 1071

Kelly, John F, Detroit Windsor International Film Festival (DWIFF), 15206 Mack Ave, Suite 9, Detroit, MI 48230 *Tel:* 313-881-0122 *E-mail:* info@dwiff.org *Web Site:* www.dwiff.org, pg 1114

Kelly, Katie, Texas Film Commission, 1100 San Jacinto, Suite 3.410, Austin, TX 78701 *Tel:* 512-463-9200 *Fax:* 512-463-4114 *E-mail:* film@governor.state.tx.us *Web Site:* www.governor.state.tx.us/film, pg 1102

Kelly, Kevin, Stampede Presentation Products Inc, 55 Woodridge Dr, Amherst, NY 14228 *Tel:* 716-635-9474 *Toll Free Tel:* 800-398-5652 *Fax:* 716-635-9484 *E-mail:* stampedenews@stampedeglobal.com *Web Site:* www.stampede-us.com, pg 1023

Kelly, Sandra B, US International Film & Video Festival Awards, 713 S Pacific Coast Hwy, Suite A, Redondo Beach, CA 90277-4233 *Tel:* 310-540-0959 *Fax:* 310-316-8905 *E-mail:* filmfestinfo@filmfestawards.com *Web Site:* www.filmfestawards.com, pg 1128

Kelly, Wesley W, Morefield Communications Inc, 35 N 35 St, Camp Hill, PA 17011-2707 *Tel:* 717-761-6170 *Toll Free Tel:* 800-382-1266 *E-mail:* info@morefield.com *Web Site:* www.morefield.com, pg 946

Kelmelis, Victor, Dreamscape Lighting Mfg Inc, 5521 W Washington Blvd, Los Angeles, CA 90016 *Tel:* 323-933-5760 *Fax:* 323-933-3607 *E-mail:* info@dreamscapelighting.com *Web Site:* www.dreamscapelighting.com, pg 852

Kelsey, Audrey, KEF Media, 1161 Concord Rd, Smyrna, GA 30080 *Tel:* 404-605-0009 *Toll Free Tel:* 866-219-2477 *Fax:* 404-605-0639 *Web Site:* www.kefmedia.com, pg 909

Kelsey, David, Media Loft Inc, 615 First Ave NE, Suite 100, Minneapolis, MN 55413 *Tel:* 612-375-1086 *Fax:* 612-375-0913 *E-mail:* info@medialoft.net *Web Site:* www.medialoft.net, pg 937

Kelsey, Jesse, Hammond Communications Group, 173 Trade St, Lexington, KY 40511-2608 *Tel:* 859-254-1878 *E-mail:* info@hammondcg.com *Web Site:* www.hammondcg.com, pg 884

Kelso, Stephanie, Z-Axis Corp, 4600 S Ulster St, Suite 270, Denver, CO 80237 *Tel:* 303-713-0200 *Toll Free Tel:* 800-827-2947 *E-mail:* info@zaxis.com *Web Site:* www.zaxis.com, pg 1073

Keltz, Al, Whirlwind Music Distributors Inc, 99 Ling Rd, Rochester, NY 14612 *Tel:* 585-663-8820 *Toll Free Tel:* 800-733-9473 (US only) *Fax:* 585-865-8930 *E-mail:* sales@whirlwindusa.com; techsupport@whirlwindusa.com; darylg@whirlwindusa.com (Canadian inquiries) *Web Site:* whirlwindusa.com, pg 1065

Kendall, Charlie, Spider Support Systems, 11654 Plaza America Dr, Suite 180, Reston, VA 20190 *Tel:* 703-758-0699 *Fax:* 703-935-8899 *Web Site:* www.spidersupport.com, pg 1021

Kendrick, Kenny, AVL Systems Design LLC, 14901 Bristol Park Blvd, Edmond, OK 73013 *Tel:* 405-749-1866 *Fax:* 405-749-1851 *E-mail:* dnix@avl1.com *Web Site:* www.avl1.com, pg 800

Kennedy, Dan, Great River Electronics, 164 Hardman Ave S, South St Paul, MN 55075 *Tel:* 651-455-1846 *Fax:* 651-455-3224 *E-mail:* info@greweb.com *Web Site:* www.greatriverelectronics.com, pg 881

Kennedy, H Edwin, Ken-Del Productions Inc, 1500 First State Blvd, Wilmington, DE 19804-3596 *Tel:* 302-999-1111; 302-999-1110; 302-999-1164 *Toll Free Tel:* 800-249-1110 *Fax:* 302-999-1656 *E-mail:* info@ken-del.com *Web Site:* www.ken-del.com, pg 909

Kennedy, H Edwin, Ken-Del Studios, 1500 First State Blvd, Wilmington, DE 19804-3596 *Tel:* 302-999-1111 *Toll Free Tel:* 800-249-1110 *Fax:* 302-999-1656 *E-mail:* info@ken-del.com *Web Site:* www.ken-del.com, pg 909

Kennedy, Howard, Limbo Films, 2223 NE Martin Luther King Jr Blvd, Portland, OR 97212 *Tel:* 503-228-0844 *Fax:* 503-228-0857 *E-mail:* info@limbofilms.com *Web Site:* www.limbofilms.com, pg 921

Kennedy, Jason, SIM Digital, One Atlantic Ave, Suite 110, Toronto, ON M6K 3E7, Canada *Tel:* 416-979-9958 *Fax:* 416-979-7770 *E-mail:* info@simdigital.com *Web Site:* www.simdigital.com, pg 1011

Kennedy, Keith, The Production House, Innovative Teaching & Technology Ctr, 108 ITTC Bldg, Cedar Falls, IA 50614 *Tel:* 319-273-7820 *Fax:* 319-273-2917 *E-mail:* pro-house@uni.edu *Web Site:* www.uni.edu/its/labs/production-house, pg 984

Kennedy, Kelly, Blue Water Film Award, PO Box 611109, Port Huron, MI 48061 *E-mail:* bwff@bluewaterfilmfestival.com *Web Site:* bluewaterfilmfestival.com, pg 1110

Kennedy, Kerry, Robert F Kennedy Journalism Awards, 1300 19 St NW, Suite 750, Washington, DC 20036 *Tel:* 202-463-7575 *E-mail:* info@rfkcenter.org *Web Site:* www.rfkcenter.org, pg 1118

Kennedy, Kevin, Avaya Inc, 211 Mount Airy Rd, Basking Ridge, NJ 07920 *Tel:* 908-953-6000 *Toll Free Tel:* 866-GO-AVAYA (462-8292 US & CN) *Web Site:* www.avaya.com, pg 798

Kennedy, Valerie, SCI Television Productions LLC, 160 E Grand Ave, Suite 5W, Chicago, IL 60611 *Tel:* 312-643-2080 *E-mail:* info@scitvproductions.com *Web Site:* www.scitvproductions.com, pg 1005

Kennel, Glenn, ARRI Inc, 600 N Victory Blvd, Burbank, CA 91502-1639 *Tel:* 818-841-7070 *Fax:* 818-848-4028 *E-mail:* info@arri.com *Web Site:* www.arri.com, pg 790

Kennet, Clinton, C&C Studios Corp, 20 W 37 St, New York, NY 10018 *Tel:* 212-967-6427 *Web Site:* www.candcstudios.tv, pg 819

Kenniff, Thomas, The Best of Photojournalism (BOP), 3200 Croasdaile Dr, Suite 306, Durham, NC 27705 *Tel:* 919-383-7246 *Fax:* 919-383-7261 *E-mail:* info@nppa.org *Web Site:* www.nppa.org, pg 1109

Kenniff, Thomas, National Press Photographers Association (NPPA), 3200 Croasdaile Dr, Suite 306, Durham, NC 27705 *Tel:* 919-383-7246 *Fax:* 919-383-7261 *E-mail:* info@nppa.org *Web Site:* www.nppa.org, pg 1086

Kennison, Wes, Launch Media, Celtic Media Ctr, 10000 Celtic Dr, Baton Rouge, LA 70809 *Tel:* 225-612-2112 *E-mail:* contactus@launchmedia.tv *Web Site:* www.launchmedia.tv, pg 916

Kensinger, Nathan, Brooklyn Film Festival (BiFF), 180 S Fourth St, Suite 2-S, Brooklyn, NY 11211 *Tel:* 718-388-4306 *Fax:* 718-599-5039 *E-mail:* festival@wbff.org *Web Site:* www.brooklynfilmfestival.org, pg 1110

Kensinger, Robert, Spectrum Industries Inc, 925 First Ave, Chippewa Falls, WI 54729 *Tel:* 715-723-6750 *Toll Free Tel:* 800-235-1262 *Toll Free Fax:* 800-335-0473 *E-mail:* info@spectrumfurniture.com *Web Site:* www.spectrumfurniture.com, pg 1021

Kent, Norman, Norman Kent Productions, PO Box 1749, Flagler Beach, FL 32136 *Tel:* 386-446-0505 *Web Site:* www.normankent.com, pg 909

Kent, Phil, Turner Broadcasting System Inc, One CNN Ctr, Atlanta, GA 30303 *Tel:* 404-827-1700 *Web Site:* www.turner.com, pg 1046

Kenton, Rachel, Zacuto, 401 W Ontario Ave, Chicago, IL 60654 *Tel:* 312-863-3456; 312-863-3453 (rentals) *Toll Free Tel:* 888-294-3456 *Fax:* 312-863-3455; 312-377-3016 (rentals) *E-mail:* rentals@zacuto.com *Web Site:* www.zacuto.com, pg 1073

Kenworthy, Duncan, Quickdraw Animation Society, 351 11 Ave SW, Suite 201, Calgary, AB T2R 0C7, Canada *Tel:* 403-261-5767 *Fax:* 403-261-5644 *E-mail:* info@quickdrawanimation.ca; production@quickdrawanimation.ca; programming@quickdrawanimation.ca *Web Site:* quickdrawanimation.ca; www.giraffest.ca, pg 1088

Kenworthy, Peter, Mountainfilm in Telluride, 109 E Colorado Ave, Suite 1, Telluride, CO 81435 *Tel:* 970-728-4123 *Fax:* 970-728-6458 *E-mail:* contact@mountainfilm.org *Web Site:* www.mountainfilm.org, pg 1121

Kenworthy, Randy, School Media Associates LLC, 5815 Live Oak Pkwy, Suite 2-B, Norcross, GA 30093-1700 *Tel:* 770-441-0600 *Toll Free Tel:* 800-451-5226 (orders) *Fax:* 770-441-8529 *E-mail:* info@smavideo.net *Web Site:* www.smavideo.net, pg 1004

Kerlick, Will, CenterStaging LLC, 3407 Winona Ave, Burbank, CA 91504 *Tel:* 818-559-4333 *Fax:* 818-848-4016 *E-mail:* info@centerstaging.com *Web Site:* centerstaging.com, pg 823

Kerr, John, PsiTech Inc, 18368 Bandilier Circle, Fountain Valley, CA 92708 *Tel:* 714-964-7818 *Toll Free Tel:* 800-872-7385 *Fax:* 714-968-7884 *E-mail:* info@psitech.com; sales@psitech.com *Web Site:* www.psitech.com, pg 987

Kerrigan, Bill, Kerrigan Productions Inc, 3877 Draper Ave, Montreal, QC H4A 2N9, Canada *Tel:* 514-486-8456 *Fax:* 514-488-4550 *Web Site:* www.kerrigan.ca, pg 910

Kerris, Robert F, ADAM Inc, 5 Concourse Pkwy, Suite 3200, Atlanta, GA 30328 *Tel:* 404-604-2757 *Toll Free Tel:* 800-755-ADAM (755-2326) *E-mail:* editorialdirector@adamcorp.com *Web Site:* www.adam.com, pg 775

Kershner, Vince, Upstage Video, 212 Shoemaker Rd, Pottstown, PA 19464 *Tel:* 610-323-7200 *Toll Free Tel:* 877-484-3887 *Fax:* 484-727-9056 *E-mail:* info@upstagevideo.com *Web Site:* www.upstagevideo.com, pg 1050

Kerstin, Dave, Broadcasters General Store Inc, 2480 SE 52 St, Ocala, FL 34480 *Tel:* 352-622-7700 *Fax:* 352-629-7000 *E-mail:* sales@bgs.cc (orders) *Web Site:* www.bgs.cc, pg 813

Kesler, Eddie, Beast Atlanta, 3399 Peachtree Rd NE, Suite 200, Atlanta, GA 30326-1149 *Tel:* 404-237-9977 *Fax:* 404-237-3923 *E-mail:* info@riotatlanta.com *Web Site:* www.beast.tv, pg 804

Keslow, Robert, Keslow Camera Inc, 11260 Playa Ct, Culver City, CA 90230 *Tel:* 310-636-4600 *Fax:* 310-915-5335 *E-mail:* info@keslowcamera.com *Web Site:* www.keslowcamera.com, pg 910

Kessinger, David, KESSPRO Studios, 435 S Molino St, Los Angeles, CA 90013 *Tel:* 213-253-2623 *Fax:* 213-253-2629 *E-mail:* info@kessprostudios.com *Web Site:* www.kessprostudios.com, pg 910

Kessinger, Matt, KESSPRO Studios, 435 S Molino St, Los Angeles, CA 90013 *Tel:* 213-253-2623 *Fax:* 213-253-2629 *E-mail:* info@kessprostudios.com *Web Site:* www.kessprostudios.com, pg 910

Kesslar, Darryl, plan9films, 1926B Alberta Ave, Saskatoon, SK S7K 1R9, Canada *Tel:* 306-955-6463 *Toll Free Fax:* 866-795-4503 *E-mail:* info@plan9films.com *Web Site:* www.plan9films.com, pg 976

Kessler, Allan, Ark Media Group Ltd, PO Box 410685, San Francisco, CA 94141-0685 *Tel:* 415-863-7200 *Fax:* 415-864-5437 *E-mail:* sales@arkmedia.com *Web Site:* www.arkmedia.com, pg 790

Kessler, Allan, New Era Media, PO Box 410685, San Francisco, CA 94141-0685 *Tel:* 415-863-3555 *Fax:* 415-864-5437 *E-mail:* sales@arkmedia.com, pg 955

Kessler, Fred, Musivision Inc, 8 Deepwood Rd, Weston, CT 06883 *Tel:* 203-227-1017 *E-mail:* info@musivision.com, pg 951

Kessler, Howard, Novelty Scenic Studios Inc, 3 Kosnitz Dr, Unit 111, Monroe, NY 10950-1163 *Tel:* 516-671-5245 *E-mail:* noveltyscenic@verizon.net, pg 960

Kessler, Leslie I, Novelty Scenic Studios Inc, 3 Kosnitz Dr, Unit 111, Monroe, NY 10950-1163 *Tel:* 516-671-5245 *E-mail:* noveltyscenic@verizon.net, pg 960

Kessler, Morris, Amplifier Technologies Inc (ATI), 1749 Chapin Rd, Montebello, CA 90640 *Tel:* 323-278-0001 *Fax:* 323-278-0083 *E-mail:* sales@ati-amp.com *Web Site:* www.ati-amp.com, pg 785

Kessler, Morris, BGW Systems, an Amplifier Technologies Inc Company, 1749 Chapin Rd, Montebello, CA 90640 *Tel:* 323-278-0001 *Fax:* 323-278-0083 *E-mail:* sales@bgw.com; info@bgw.com *Web Site:* www.bgw.com, pg 806

Ketchum, Bob, Cedar Crest Studio, 17 CR 830, Henderson, AR 72544 *Tel:* 870-488-5777 *E-mail:* cedarcrest@springfield.net *Web Site:* www.cedarcreststudio.com, pg 822

Ketchum, Jane, Cedar Crest Studio, 17 CR 830, Henderson, AR 72544 *Tel:* 870-488-5777 *E-mail:* cedarcrest@springfield.net *Web Site:* www.cedarcreststudio.com, pg 822

Kettler, Judy, Limbo Films, 2223 NE Martin Luther King Jr Blvd, Portland, OR 97212 *Tel:* 503-228-0844 *Fax:* 503-228-0857 *E-mail:* info@limbofilms.com *Web Site:* www.limbofilms.com, pg 921

Keuneke, Thomas, The Alliance for Christian Media, 2715 Peachtree Rd NE, Atlanta, GA 30305 *Tel:* 404-815-0640 *Toll Free Tel:* 800-229-3788 *E-mail:* contact@allianceforchristianmedia.org *Web Site:* www.allianceforchristianmedia.org, pg 781

Key, Dave, Sky-View Co, 2800 NE Loop 410, San Antonio, TX 78218 *Tel:* 210-590-8100 *Toll Free Tel:* 800-562-8439 (US & CN) *Fax:* 210-967-8787 *E-mail:* sales@sky-view.com *Web Site:* www.sky-view.com, pg 1013

Keys, Paul, PK Photo & Electronic Repair, 1760 S Carr St, Lakewood, CO 80232-6643 *Tel:* 303-777-1311 *Fax:* 303-777-1332, pg 976

Keyser, Chris, Writers Guild of America, West (WGAW), 7000 W Third St, Los Angeles, CA 90048 *Tel:* 323-951-4000 *Toll Free Tel:* 800-548-4532 *Fax:* 323-782-4800 *Web Site:* www.wga.org, pg 1090

Khairallah, Faday, Market Data Retrieval (MDR), 6 Armstrong Rd, Suite 301, Shelton, CT 06484 *Tel:* 203-926-4800 *Toll Free Tel:* 800-333-8802 *Toll Free Fax:* 866-532-7097 *E-mail:* mdrinfo@dnb.com *Web Site:* www.schooldata.com, pg 931

Khalsa, Japji, Magic Teleprompting Inc, 1390 Waller St, San Francisco, CA 94117 *Tel:* 415-626-5283 *Toll Free Tel:* 800-646-6244 *Fax:* 415-626-2762 *E-mail:* info@magicscroll.com *Web Site:* www.magicscroll.com, pg 928

Khan, Kenny, USA Studios, 253 W 35 St, 2nd fl, New York, NY 10001 *Tel:* 212-398-6400 *Fax:* 212-398-4145 *E-mail:* sales@usastudios.tv; info@usastudios.tv *Web Site:* www.usastudios.tv, pg 1050

Khan, Said, Digital Comm Link Inc, 10450 W State Rd 84, Davie, FL 33324-4206 *Tel:* 954-236-2993 *Toll Free Tel:* 877-532-5438 *Fax:* 954-236-3633 *E-mail:* booking@dclinc.net *Web Site:* www.dclinc.net, pg 847

Khanian, Edmond, Empire Wholesale Inc, 5675 Mansfield Way, Bell, CA 90201 *Tel:* 213-748-5200 *Toll Free Tel:* 866-748-5200 *Fax:* 213-748-5505 *E-mail:* sales@empirepro.com *Web Site:* www.empirepro.com, pg 860

Khattar, Nagy, Mackenzie Laboratories Inc, 1163 Nicole Ct, Glendora, CA 91740 *Tel:* 909-394-9007 *Fax:* 909-394-9411 *E-mail:* info@macklabs.com *Web Site:* www.macklabs.com, pg 927

Khawand, Elie, Digital Lighting Systems Inc, 12302 SW 128 Ct, Suite 105, Miami, FL 33186 *Tel:* 305-969-8442 *Fax:* 305-969-8675 *E-mail:* info@digitallighting.com; sales@digitallighting.com *Web Site:* www.digitallighting.com, pg 847

Khemlani, Neerja, Hearst Entertainment & Syndication, 300 W 57 St, New York, NY 10019-5238 *Tel:* 212-969-7553 *Toll Free Tel:* 800-526-5464 *Fax:* 646-280-1553 *E-mail:* hearstentertainment@hearst.com *Web Site:* www.hearst.com, pg 887

Khosla, Victrim, Unique Business Systems, 1100 Colorado Ave, Santa Monica, CA 90401 *Tel:* 310-396-3929 *Toll Free Tel:* 800-669-4827 *Fax:* 310-396-6114 *E-mail:* sales@unibiz.com *Web Site:* www.unibiz.com, pg 1048

Kick, Randy, Tek Data Systems Co, 1111 W Park Ave, Libertyville, IL 60048 *Tel:* 847-367-8800 *Fax:* 847-367-0235 *E-mail:* tekdata@tekdata.com; sales@tekdata.com *Web Site:* www.tekdata.com, pg 1035

Kidder, Norman, Rauland-Borg Corp, 1802 W Central Rd, Mount Prospect, IL 60056 *Tel:* 847-590-7100 *Toll Free Tel:* 800-752-7725 *Web Site:* www.rauland.com, pg 991

Kidwell, Daniel, Terry Hanley Audio Systems Inc, 20 Industrial Pkwy, Woburn, MA 01801 *Tel:* 781-932-5300 *Fax:* 781-932-5354 *E-mail:* mail@terryhanleyaudio.com *Web Site:* www.terryhanleyaudio.com, pg 884

Kiehl, Stuart, Vineyard Video & Photography, 4193 Concord Ave, Santa Rosa, CA 95407 *Tel:* 707-591-9999; 707-591-1927 (cell) *Web Site:* www.vineyardvideo.com, pg 1058

Kiel, Philip, Instrumentation Marketing Corp, 820 S Mariposa St, Burbank, CA 91506-3196 *Tel:* 818-842-2141 *Fax:* 818-842-2610 *E-mail:* mail@photosonics.com *Web Site:* www.photosonics.com/imc.htm, pg 899

Kielbasa, Jody, The Virginia Film Festival, 617 W Main St, 2nd fl, Charlottesville, VA 22903 *Tel:* 434-982-5277 *Fax:* 434-924-3374 *E-mail:* info@virginiafilmfestival.org *Web Site:* www.virginiafilmfestival.org, pg 1129

Kienholz, Lyn, California/International Arts Foundation, 2737 Outpost Dr, Los Angeles, CA 90068 *Tel:* 323-874-4107 *Fax:* 323-874-8195, pg 817

Kiesel, Carson, Carvin Corp, 12340 World Trade Dr, San Diego, CA 92128 *Tel:* 858-487-1600 *Toll Free Tel:* 800-854-2235 *Fax:* 858-487-8160 *Web Site:* www.carvin.com, pg 820

Kilday, Kristi, KO Creative, 465 S Beverly Dr, 3rd fl, Beverly Hills, CA 90212 *Tel:* 310-288-3820 *Web Site:* www.ko-creative.com, pg 912

Kilgore, Jayne, Pat Appleson Studios Inc, 2359 Hwy 70 SE, Suite 102, Hickory, NC 28602 *Tel:* 828-994-4361; 828-461-3003 (cell) *Web Site:* www.appleson.com, pg 788

Kilgore, Vaughn, First Camera, 2472 Third St, San Francisco, CA 94107 *Tel:* 415-647-3400 *Fax:* 415-647-3410 *E-mail:* sfvideo@firstcamera.com *Web Site:* www.firstcamera.com, pg 868

Killacky, John, Bartha, 600 N Cassady Ave, Columbus, OH 43219 *Tel:* 614-252-7455 *Toll Free Tel:* 800-363-2698 *Fax:* 614-252-7641 *E-mail:* info@bartha.com *Web Site:* www.bartha.com, pg 803

Kilmurry, Matthew, USCCB Publishing, 3211 Fourth St NE, Washington, DC 20017 *Tel:* 202-541-3090 *Toll Free Tel:* 800-235-8722 (cust serv) *Fax:* 202-722-8709 (cust serv) *E-mail:* publications@usccb.org *Web Site:* www.usccbpublishing.org, pg 1051

Kilpatrick, Colin, Missouri Honor Medal for Distinguished Service in Journalism, School of Journalism, 120 Neff Hall, Columbia, MO 65211-1200 *Tel:* 573-882-4821 *Fax:* 573-884-5400 *E-mail:* journalism@missouri.edu *Web Site:* journalism.missouri.edu, pg 1120

Kim, Joseph, Paulist Productions, 17575 Pacific Coast Hwy, Pacific Palisades, CA 90272-4128 *Tel:* 310-454-0688 *Toll Free Tel:* 800-624-8613 *Fax:* 310-459-6549 *E-mail:* paulistmail@paulistproductions.org *Web Site:* www.paulistproductions.org, pg 970

Kim, Yong-Seog, Society for Information Display (SID), 1475 S Bascom Ave, Suite 114, Campbell, CA 95008-4006 *Tel:* 408-879-3901 *Fax:* 408-879-3833 *E-mail:* office@sid.org *Web Site:* www.sid.org, pg 1089

Kimble, Gertrude S, Kimbo Educational, 10 N Third Ave, Long Branch, NJ 07740 *Tel:* 732-229-4949 *Toll Free Tel:* 800-631-2187 *Fax:* 732-870-3340 *E-mail:* kimboed@aol.com *Web Site:* www.kimboed.com, pg 910

Kimble, James A, Kimbo Educational, 10 N Third Ave, Long Branch, NJ 07740 *Tel:* 732-229-4949 *Toll Free Tel:* 800-631-2187 *Fax:* 732-870-3340 *E-mail:* kimboed@aol.com *Web Site:* www.kimboed.com, pg 910

Kincheloe, Michael, Karol Media Inc, Hanover Industrial Estates, 375 Stewart Rd, Wilkes-Barre, PA 18703 *Tel:* 570-822-8899 *Toll Free Tel:* 800-526-4773 *Fax:* 570-822-8226 *E-mail:* sales@karolmedia.com *Web Site:* www.karolmedia.com, pg 908

Kinder, Tiffany, Red Sky Studios, 184 Everett St, Allston, MA 02134 *Tel:* 617-903-3373 *E-mail:* mail@redsky-studios.com *Web Site:* redsky-studios.com, pg 993

King, Bonnie, Space Coast Film Commission, 430 Brevard Ave, Suite 150, Cocoa Village, FL 32922 *Tel:* 321-433-4470 *Toll Free Tel:* 877-57-BEACH (572-3224) *Fax:* 321-433-4476 *Web Site:* www.visitspacecoast.com/space-coast-film-commission, pg 1095

King, Curtis L, The Black Academy of Arts & Letters Inc, Dallas Convention Ctr Theater Complex, 1309 Canton St, Dallas, TX 75201 *Tel:* 214-743-2440 *Fax:* 214-743-2451 *E-mail:* info@tbaal.org *Web Site:* www.tbaal.org, pg 808

King, Darcie, E Video Productions, 17 Washington St, Toms River, NJ 08753 *Tel:* 732-349-4762 *Toll Free Tel:* 877-384-3365 *Web Site:* www.evideoproductions.net, pg 855

King, Jan, Loopmedia Inc, 401 Richmond St W, Suite 243, Toronto, ON M5V 3A8, Canada *Tel:* 416-595-6496 *Fax:* 416-595-0306 *E-mail:* info@loopmedia.com *Web Site:* www.loopmedia.com, pg 924

King, John, Bitcentral Inc, 4340 Von Karman Ave, Suite 400, Newport Beach, CA 92660 *Tel:* 949-253-9000 *E-mail:* sales@bitcentral.com; support@bitcentral.com *Web Site:* www.bitcentral.com, pg 808

King, Kristopher, E Video Productions, 17 Washington St, Toms River, NJ 08753 *Tel:* 732-349-4762 *Toll Free Tel:* 877-384-3365 *Web Site:* www.evideoproductions.net, pg 855

King, Kristy, Stanley Film Festival, 1510 York St, 3rd fl, Denver, CO 80206 *Tel:* 970-577-4111 *E-mail:* stanley@denverfilm.org *Web Site:* www.stanleyfilmfest.com, pg 1127

King, Larry C, IntegraColor, 3210 Innovative Way, Mesquite, TX 75149 *Tel:* 972-289-0705 *Toll Free Tel:* 800-933-9511 *Fax:* 972-285-4881 *E-mail:* salesinfo@integracolor.com *Web Site:* www.integracolor.com, pg 899

King, Ralph, Comprompter Inc, 1601 Caledonia St, Suite E, La Crosse, WI 54603 *Tel:* 608-785-7766 *E-mail:* sales@comprompter.com *Web Site:* www.comprompter.com, pg 834

King, Stephen, Mobile-Video Productions Inc, 7315 Wisconsin Ave, Suite 1300 W, Bethesda, MD 20814 *Tel:* 301-656-2525 *Fax:* 301-656-4343 *E-mail:* mobilevp@verizon.net *Web Site:* www.mobilevideoproductions.tv, pg 944

King, Steve, AVS Media Group, 11193 Old Hwy 31, Suite 1, Spanish Fort, AL 36527 *Tel:* 251-621-1200 *E-mail:* info@avsmediagroup.com *Web Site:* www.avsmediagroup.com, pg 800

Kingma, Theo, Golden Globe Awards, 646 N Robertson Blvd, West Hollywood, CA 90069 *Tel:* 310-657-1731 *Fax:* 310-657-5576 *E-mail:* info@hfpa.org *Web Site:* www.hfpa.org, pg 1115

Kinlein, David, Optic Bindery & Packaging, 407 Fair Hill Ct, Annapolis, MD 21403-1649 *Toll Free Tel:* 877-767-0099 *Fax:* 410-295-0079 *Web Site:* www.pointofpurchasestore.com, pg 964

Kinney, Andre, Media Resources, 102 Perkins Bldg, 521 Lancaster Ave, Richmond, KY 40475 *Tel:* 859-622-6671 *Fax:* 859-622-1116 *Web Site:* www.mpc.eku.edu, pg 937

Kinney, Scott, Discovery Education - Silver Spring, One Discovery Place, Silver Spring, MD 20910 *Toll Free Tel:* 800-323-9084 *Fax:* 847-328-6706 *Web Site:* discoveryeducation.com, pg 848

Kinney, Tom, Attainment Co Inc, 504 Commerce Pkwy, Verona, WI 53593 *Tel:* 608-845-7880 *Toll Free Tel:* 800-327-4269 *Fax:* 608-845-8040 *Toll Free Fax:* 800-942-3865 *E-mail:* customerservice@attainmentcompany.com; international@attainmentcompany.com *Web Site:* www.attainmentcompany.com, pg 793

Kintzel, Michael, Parallax Productions Inc, 1711 Longwood Rd, Suite B, Haverhill, FL 33409 *Tel:* 561-842-7788 *Toll Free Tel:* 844-892-9289 *Fax:* 561-842-4566 *E-mail:* parllaxpro@aol.com *Web Site:* www.parallaxvideoproductions.com, pg 969

Kinzinger, Brenda, Library Video Network (LVN), 320 York Rd, Towson, MD 21204 *Tel:* 410-887-2090 *Toll Free Tel:* 800-441-8273 *Fax:* 410-887-2091 *E-mail:* lvn@bcpl.net *Web Site:* www.lvn.org, pg 920

Kirby, Alan, All Pro Media Inc, 422 S Spring St, Burlington, NC 27216 *Tel:* 336-229-7700 *Toll Free Tel:* 800-270-2207 *Fax:* 336-229-7778 *Web Site:* www.allpromedia.com, pg 780

Kirby, Rik, Renkus-Heinz Inc, 19201 Cook St, Foothill Ranch, CA 92610-3501 *Tel:* 949-588-9997 *Fax:* 949-588-9514 *E-mail:* sales@renkus-heinz.com *Web Site:* www.renkus-heinz.com, pg 994

Kircher, Roy, Big House Sound Inc, 4001 Drossett Dr, Austin, TX 78744 *Tel:* 512-443-0019 *Fax:* 512-443-0916 *Web Site:* www.bighousesound.com, pg 807

Kiriazides, George, Vision Identics Systems Inc, 110 Villa Ave, Mamaroneck, NY 10543 *Tel:* 914-381-2625 *Toll Free Tel:* 800-750-8840 *Fax:* 914-381-2752 *E-mail:* inquiry@visionid.com *Web Site:* www.visionid.com, pg 1058

Kirk, S Tobin, Blind, 1702 Olympic Blvd, Santa Monica, CA 90404 *Tel:* 310-314-1618 *Fax:* 310-314-1718 *Web Site:* www.blind.com, pg 809

Kirkland, Don, Tri-Color, 4303 Normandy Ct, Royal Oak, MI 48073-2266 *Tel:* 248-549-0150 *Toll Free Tel:* 800-886-5661 *Fax:* 248-549-5270 *Web Site:* www.tricolorphoto.com, pg 1044

Kirsch, Patrick, Stoney-Wolf Productions Inc, 130 W Columbia Ct, Chaska, MN 55318-2304 *Tel:* 952-556-0075 *Toll Free Tel:* 800-237-7583 *Fax:* 952-361-4217 *E-mail:* sales@stoneywolf.com *Web Site:* www.stoneywolf.com, pg 1025

Kirsch, Stacie, Electron Microscopy Sciences (EMS), 1560 Industry Rd, Hatfield, PA 19440 *Tel:* 215-412-8400 *Toll Free Tel:* 800-523-5874 *Fax:* 215-412-8450 *E-mail:* sgkcck@aol.com *Web Site:* www.emsdiasum.com/microscopy, pg 859

Kirsch, Tony, Stoney-Wolf Productions Inc, 130 W Columbia Ct, Chaska, MN 55318-2304 *Tel:* 952-556-0075 *Toll Free Tel:* 800-237-7583 *Fax:* 952-361-4217 *E-mail:* sales@stoneywolf.com *Web Site:* www.stoneywolf.com, pg 1025

Kirschner, Liz, Levy Lighting NYC Inc, 347 W 36 St, Ground fl, New York, NY 10018 *Tel:* 212-925-4640 *Fax:* 212-925-4216 *E-mail:* info@levylighting.com *Web Site:* www.levylighting.com, pg 919

Kislan, Andrea, Association of National Advertisers Inc (ANA), 708 Third Ave, 33rd fl, New York, NY 10017-4270 *Tel:* 212-697-5950 *Fax:* 212-687-7310 *E-mail:* info@ana.net *Web Site:* www.ana.net, pg 1079

Kite, Tom, Audio Precision, 5750 SW Arctic Dr, Beaverton, OR 97005 *Tel:* 503-627-0832 *Toll Free Tel:* 800-231-7350 *Fax:* 503-469-0336 *E-mail:* sales@ap.com *Web Site:* www.ap.com, pg 794

Kitman, Taya, The Ridenhour Documentary Film Prize, 116 E 16 St, 8th fl, New York, NY 10003 *Tel:* 212-822-0250 *Fax:* 212-253-5356 *E-mail:* ridenhour@nationinstitute.org *Web Site:* www.ridenhour.org, pg 1125

Klaar, Debbie, Guild of Italian American Actors (GIAA), Canal Street Sta, PO Box 123, New York, NY 10013-0123 *Tel:* 201-344-3411 *E-mail:* info@giaa.us *Web Site:* www.giaa.us, pg 1082

Klaine, Brian, Optical Disc Solutions Inc, 1767 Sheridan St, Richmond, IN 47374 *Tel:* 765-935-7574 *Toll Free Tel:* 800-704-7648 *Fax:* 765-935-0174 *Web Site:* www.odiscs.com, pg 964

Klarsfeld, Ted, Audio-Video Corp, 213 Broadway, Albany, NY 12204 *Tel:* 518-449-7213 *Fax:* 518-449-1205 *E-mail:* info@audiovideocorp.com; sales@audiovideocorp.com *Web Site:* www.audiovideocorp.com, pg 795

Kleckner, Shawne, Right Stuf Inc, 512 NE Main St, Grimes, IA 50111-0680 *Tel:* 515-986-1028 *Toll Free Tel:* 800-338-6827 *Fax:* 515-986-1129 *E-mail:* info@rightstuf.com *Web Site:* www.rightstuf.com, pg 997

Kleeman, David W, American Center for Children & Media, 5400 N Saint Louis Ave, Chicago, IL 60625 *Tel:* 773-509-5510 *Fax:* 773-509-5303 *E-mail:* info@centerforchildrenandmedia.org *Web Site:* www.centerforchildrenandmedia.org, pg 1076

Klein, Bernard E, Sonar Radio Corp, 3000 Stirling Rd, Hollywood, FL 33021-2039 *Tel:* 954-981-8800 *Fax:* 954-981-8800, pg 1015

Klein, Bill, Hybrid Studios, 3021 S Shannon St, Santa Ana, CA 92704 *Tel:* 714-850-1499 *E-mail:* info@hybridstudiosca.com; rentals@hybridstudiosca.com *Web Site:* hybridstudiosca.com, pg 893

Klein, Bob, Artistic Video, 87 Tyler Ave, Dept V, Sound Beach, NY 11789 *Tel:* 631-744-5999 *Toll Free Tel:* 888-982-4244 *Fax:* 631-744-5993 *E-mail:* info@movementsofmagic.com *Web Site:* www.movementsofmagic.com, pg 791

Klein, Bruce M, Bernie's Photo Center, 525 E Ohio St, Pittsburgh, PA 15212 *Tel:* 412-231-1717 *Toll Free Tel:* 800-346-8884 *Fax:* 412-231-1217 *E-mail:* info@berniesphoto.com *Web Site:* www.berniesphoto.com, pg 805

Klein, Hailey, Vaddio, 131 Cheshire Lane, Suite 500, Minnetonka, MN 55305 *Tel:* 763-971-4400 *Toll Free Tel:* 800-572-2011 *Fax:* 763-971-4464 *E-mail:* info@vaddio.com *Web Site:* www.vaddio.com, pg 1051

Klein, Harold, TeleTime Productions, 100 Atlantic Ave, Lynbrook, NY 11563 *Tel:* 516-255-8383 *E-mail:* info@teletimevideo.com *Web Site:* www.teletimevideo.com, pg 1036

Klein, Jeff, Jaguar Distribution Corp, 12711 Ventura Blvd, Suite 300, Studio City, CA 91604 *Tel:* 818-508-3377 *Fax:* 818-508-3340 *Web Site:* www.jaguardc.com, pg 903

Klein, Jonathan, Getty Images, 605 Fifth Ave S, Suite 400, Seattle, WA 98104 *Tel:* 206-925-5000 *Toll Free Tel:* 888-888-5889; 800-462-4379 (sales) *Fax:* 206-925-5001 *E-mail:* sales@gettyimages.com *Web Site:* www.gettyimages.com, pg 877

Klein, Jordan Jr, Jordan Klein Film & Video (JKFV), 10197 SE 144 Place, Summerfield, FL 34491 *Tel:* 352-288-3999 *Fax:* 352-288-5538 *Web Site:* www.jordy.com, pg 906

Klein, Randy, Crestron Electronics Inc, 15 Volvo Dr, Rockleigh, NJ 07647 *Tel:* 201-767-3400 *Toll Free Tel:* 800-237-2041 *Fax:* 201-767-1903 *E-mail:* crestronhq@crestron.com *Web Site:* www.crestron.com, pg 839

Klein, Ted, Digital Audio Labs, 1266 Park Rd, Chanhassen, MN 55317 *Tel:* 952-401-7700 *Fax:* 952-401-7725 *E-mail:* sales@digitalaudio.com *Web Site:* www.digitalaudio.com, pg 847

Klein, Timothy J, ATTO Technology Inc, 155 CrossPoint Pkwy, Amherst, NY 14068 *Tel:* 716-691-1999 *Fax:* 716-691-9353 *Web Site:* www.attotech.com, pg 793

Kleiner, Lynn, Music Rhapsody, 1603 Aviation Blvd, Redondo Beach, CA 90278 *Tel:* 310-376-8646 *Toll Free Tel:* 888-TRY-MUSIC (879-6874) *Fax:* 310-376-8490 *E-mail:* info@musicrhapsody.com *Web Site:* musicrhapsody.com, pg 951

Kleinstein, Arnold, WorldView Software, 76 N Broadway, Suite 2002, Hicksville, NY 11801 *Tel:* 516-681-1773 *Toll Free Tel:* 800-347-8839 *Fax:* 516-681-1775 *E-mail:* history@worldviewsoftware.com *Web Site:* www.worldviewsoftware.com, pg 1070

Kleinstein, Jerry, WorldView Software, 76 N Broadway, Suite 2002, Hicksville, NY 11801 *Tel:* 516-681-1773 *Toll Free Tel:* 800-347-8839 *Fax:* 516-681-1775 *E-mail:* history@worldviewsoftware.com *Web Site:* www.worldviewsoftware.com, pg 1070

Klewitz, Jean, Spirit Media, 12042 SE Sunnyside Rd, Suite 700, Happy Valley, OR 97015 *Tel:* 503-698-5540 *Fax:* 503-698-8408 *E-mail:* info@spiritmedia.com *Web Site:* www.spiritmedia.com, pg 1021

Kliavkoff, George, Hearst Entertainment & Syndication, 300 W 57 St, New York, NY 10019-5238 *Tel:* 212-969-7553 *Toll Free Tel:* 800-526-5464 *Fax:* 646-280-1553 *E-mail:* hearstentertainment@hearst.com *Web Site:* www.hearst.com, pg 887

Kline, Jack, Christie Digital Systems USA Inc, 10550 Camden Dr, Cypress, CA 90630 *Tel:* 714-236-8610 *Toll Free Tel:* 866-880-4462 (cust serv) *Fax:* 714-503-3375 *E-mail:* sales-us@christiedigital.com *Web Site:* www.christiedigital.com, pg 825

Kline, Jon, MKE Production Rental, 710 N Plankinton Ave, Suite 300, Milwaukee, WI 53213 *Tel:* 414-939-3653 *E-mail:* rent1@mkeproductionrental.com *Web Site:* www.mkeproductionrental.com, pg 944

Kline, Josh C, Final Draft Inc, 26707 W Agoura Rd, Suite 205, Calabasas, CA 91302 *Tel:* 818-995-8995; 818-906-8930 (tech support) *Toll Free Tel:* 800-231-4055 *Fax:* 818-995-4422 *E-mail:* info@finaldraft.com *Web Site:* www.finaldraft.com, pg 868

Kline, Rebecca R, Northeast Conference on the Teaching of Foreign Languages (NECTFL), c/o Dickinson College, PO Box 1773, Carlisle, PA 17013-2896 *Tel:* 717-245-1977 *Fax:* 717-245-1976 *E-mail:* nectfl@dickinson.edu *Web Site:* www.nectfl.org, pg 1087

Kline, Ron, Production Advantage Inc, 301 Avenue "D", Suite 10, Williston, VT 05495 *Tel:* 802-651-6915 *Toll Free Tel:* 800-424-9991 *Fax:* 802-651-6914 *Toll Free Fax:* 877-424-9991 *E-mail:* sales@proadv.com; orders@proadv.com *Web Site:* www.productionadvantageonline.com, pg 984

Klingelhoefer, Andy, Mammoth HD, PO Box 2064, Evergreen, CO 80437 *Tel:* 303-670-7973 *E-mail:* mammothhd@me.com; info@mammothhd.com *Web Site:* www.mammothhd.com, pg 929

Klingelhofer, Jack, Jupiter Systems, 31015 Huntwood Ave, Hayward, CA 94544 *Tel:* 510-675-1000 *Fax:* 510-675-1001 *E-mail:* sales@jupiter.com *Web Site:* www.jupiter.com, pg 907

Klinger, Joseph, J K Audio Inc, 1311 E Sixth St, Sandwich, IL 60548 *Tel:* 815-786-2929 *Toll Free Tel:* 800-552-8346 *Fax:* 815-786-8502 *E-mail:* info@jkaudio.com *Web Site:* www.jkaudio.com, pg 903

Klipsch, Fred, Klipsch Audio Technologies, 3502 Woodview Trace, Suite 200, Indianapolis, IN 46268 *Tel:* 317-860-8100 *Toll Free Tel:* 877-412-7467 (orders); 800-544-1482 *Fax:* 317-860-9170 (sales & mktg) *E-mail:* support@klipsch.com *Web Site:* www.klipsch.com, pg 912

Klipsch, Mike, Klipsch Audio Technologies, 3502 Woodview Trace, Suite 200, Indianapolis, IN 46268 *Tel:* 317-860-8100 *Toll Free Tel:* 877-412-7467 (orders); 800-544-1482 *Fax:* 317-860-9170 (sales & mktg) *E-mail:* support@klipsch.com *Web Site:* www.klipsch.com, pg 912

Kloor, Erik, Macrosystem US Inc, 5541 Central Ave, Suite 135, Boulder, CO 80301 *Tel:* 303-440-5311 *Toll Free Tel:* 877-554-2846 *Fax:* 303-440-5396 *E-mail:* info@macrosystem.us *Web Site:* www.macrosystem.us, pg 927

Klos, John, Big Time Picture Company Inc, 12210 1/2 Nebraska Ave, Los Angeles, CA 90025 *Tel:* 310-207-0921 *Fax:* 310-826-0071 *E-mail:* info@bigtimepic.com *Web Site:* www.bigtimepic.com, pg 807

Klos, Susan, Big Time Picture Company Inc, 12210 1/2 Nebraska Ave, Los Angeles, CA 90025 *Tel:* 310-207-0921 *Fax:* 310-826-0071 *E-mail:* info@bigtimepic.com *Web Site:* www.bigtimepic.com, pg 807

Kloss, John P, Kloss Studios Co, 1441 Jericho Rd, Abington, PA 19001 *Tel:* 215-885-1203 *Toll Free Tel:* 800-885-1203 (PA only) *E-mail:* kloss@kloss-studios.com *Web Site:* kloss-studios.com, pg 912

Klotz, Kelly, Manatee County Film Commission, One Haben Blvd, Palmetto, FL 34221 *Tel:* 941-729-9177 *Toll Free Tel:* 800-822-2017 *Fax:* 941-729-1820 *Web Site:* www.bradentongulfislands.com, pg 1096

Klugerman, Ira H, Educational Film Center, 3314 Newark St NW, Washington, DC 20008 *Tel:* 202-243-1048 *Fax:* 202-243-1048 *Web Site:* www.efcvideo.com, pg 857

Kmito, Brian, Advanced Battery Systems Inc, 516 Bedford St, East Bridgewater, MA 02333 *Tel:* 508-378-2284 *Toll Free Tel:* 800-634-8132 *E-mail:* abs@batteryprice.com *Web Site:* www.batteryprice.com, pg 777

Knapp, Douglas, Society of Camera Operators, PO Box 2006, Toluca Lake, CA 91610-0006 *Tel:* 818-382-7070 *E-mail:* info@soc.org *Web Site:* www.soc.org, pg 1089

Knapp, Jane, Hubbard Supply Co, 901 W Second St, Flint, MI 48503 *Tel:* 810-234-8681 *Toll Free Tel:* 800-875-4811 *Fax:* 810-234-6142 *E-mail:* information@hubbardsupply.com *Web Site:* www.hubbardsupply.com, pg 892

Knapp, Joe, A-Ware Software Inc, 330 S Executive Dr, Suite 205, Brookfield, WI 53005-4215 *Tel:* 262-717-2220 *Toll Free Tel:* 800-326-2609 *Fax:* 262-717-2230 *E-mail:* info@musicmaster.com; sales@musicmaster.com *Web Site:* www.a-ware.com, pg 771

Knapp, Steve, Audience Response Systems Inc, 5611-C E Morgan Ave, Evansville, IN 47715 *Tel:* 812-479-7507 *Toll Free Tel:* 800-INVOLVE (468-6583) *Fax:* 812-479-1057 *Web Site:* www.audienceresponse.com, pg 794

Knappenberger, Erik, Axxis Inc, 845 S Ninth St, Louisville, KY 40203 *Tel:* 502-568-6030 *Fax:* 502-568-6204 *E-mail:* info@axxisinc.com *Web Site:* www.axxisinc.com, pg 800

Knarr, David, Studio 1 Productions™ Inc, 1700 Destino Ct, Port Orange, FL 32128 *Tel:* 386-788-6075 *Fax:* 386-760-5474 *E-mail:* studio1@studio1productions.com *Web Site:* www.studio1productions.com, pg 1027

Knaub, A Daniel, The Whale Video Co, 225 Indian Creek Dr, Mechanicsburg, PA 17050 *Tel:* 717-763-9507 *Web Site:* www.whalevideo.com, pg 1065

Knell, Gary, Sesame Workshop, 1900 Broadway, 4th fl, New York, NY 10023 *Tel:* 212-595-3456 *Fax:* 212-875-6113 *Web Site:* www.sesameworkshop.org, pg 1088

Knerl, Amy, Blind, 1702 Olympic Blvd, Santa Monica, CA 90404 *Tel:* 310-314-1618 *Fax:* 310-314-1718 *Web Site:* www.blind.com, pg 809

Knight, Christopher, The New Film Company Inc, 7 Scott St, Cambridge, MA 02138 *Tel:* 617-520-5005 *Fax:* 617-491-9201 *E-mail:* newfilmco@aol.com *Web Site:* www.newfilmco.com, pg 955

Knight, Dalton, First Group Communications Inc, 10994 Ranch Stone Dr, Houston, TX 77064 *Tel:* 281-890-9999 *Fax:* 281-890-9989 *E-mail:* info@firstgroupmedia.com *Web Site:* www.firstgroupmedia.com, pg 868

Knight, Elliot PhD, Alabama State Council on the Arts Fellowships & Grants, RSA Tower, Suite 110, 201 Monroe St, Montgomery, AL 36130-1800 *Tel:* 334-242-4076 *Fax:* 334-240-3269 *E-mail:* staff@arts.alabama.gov *Web Site:* www.arts.alabama.gov, pg 1107

Knight, Tom, Zondervan, A HarperCollins Company, 3900 Sparks Dr, Grand Rapids, MI 49546 *Tel:* 616-698-6900 *Toll Free Tel:* 800-226-1122; 800-727-3480 (retail orders) *Fax:* 616-698-3255 (retail orders) *E-mail:* zinfo@zondervan.com *Web Site:* www.zondervan.com, pg 1074

Knopp, Louis Todd, Production Solutions Inc, PO Box 49431, Dayton, OH 45449-0431 *Tel:* 937-866-2028 *Fax:* 253-423-8997 *E-mail:* proso@worldnet.att.net *Web Site:* www.psiohio.com, pg 984

Knopp, Orin, Presentation Products Inc, 632 W 28 St, 7th fl, New York, NY 10001 *Tel:* 212-736-6350 *Toll Free Tel:* 877-774-4523 *Fax:* 212-736-6353 *E-mail:* info@presentationstore.com; sales@pproducts.com *Web Site:* www.ppidirect.com; www.presentationproducts.com, pg 981

Knorr, Ronald, Red Fox Enterprises, Rte 209 E, Elizabethville, PA 17023 *Tel:* 717-362-3391 *Fax:* 717-362-8577 *E-mail:* redfox1@pa.net, pg 993

Knorr, Ruth, Red Fox Enterprises, Rte 209 E, Elizabethville, PA 17023 *Tel:* 717-362-3391 *Fax:* 717-362-8577 *E-mail:* redfox1@pa.net, pg 993

Knowland, Bill, Direct Images Interactive Inc, 1933 Davis St, Suite 308, San Leandro, CA 94577 *Tel:* 510-613-8299 *E-mail:* info@directimages.com *Web Site:* www.directimages.com, pg 848

Knowles, Karl, Knowles Video Inc (KVI), 5450 Buck Lake Rd, Tallahassee, FL 32317 *Tel:* 850-878-2298 *E-mail:* info@knowlesvideo.com *Web Site:* www.knowlesvideo.com, pg 912

Knox, Gordon, Arizona State University Art Museum Annual Short Film & Video Festival, PO Box 872911, Tempe, AZ 85287-2911 *Tel:* 480-965-2787 *Toll Free Tel:* 855-278-6060 *Fax:* 480-965-5254 *E-mail:* asuartmuseum@asu.edu *Web Site:* asuartmuseum.asu.edu/filmfest, pg 1107

Kobelan, Deb, Media Event Concepts Inc, 2036 Centimeter Circle, Austin, TX 78758 *Tel:* 512-832-1142 *Toll Free Tel:* 800-299-1142 *Fax:* 512-832-0236 *Web Site:* www.mecteam.com, pg 936

Koch, Phillip, Film Police, 4310 Mozart St, Chicago, IL 60618-1528 *Tel:* 773-463-4010 *E-mail:* info@filmpolice.com *Web Site:* www.filmpolice.com, pg 867

Koch, Spencer, KPLR-TV, 2250 Ball Dr, St Louis, MO 63146 *Tel:* 314-213-2222; 314-213-7831 (newsroom) *E-mail:* kplradmin@tribune.com *Web Site:* www.cw11tv.com; www.kplr11.com, pg 913

Koczanski, Kathi, The Newhouse Media Group, 6907 Silvermill Dr, Tampa, FL 33635 *Tel:* 813-625-2326 *E-mail:* newhousemediagroup@yahoo.com *Web Site:* www.newhousemediagroup.com, pg 956

Koczanski, Zack, The Newhouse Media Group, 6907 Silvermill Dr, Tampa, FL 33635 *Tel:* 813-625-2326 *E-mail:* newhousemediagroup@yahoo.com *Web Site:* www.newhousemediagroup.com, pg 956

Koehler, Mary Ann, Vision Maker Media, 1800 N 33 St, Lincoln, NE 68503 *Tel:* 402-472-3522 *Fax:* 402-472-8675 *E-mail:* visionmaker@unl.edu *Web Site:* www.visionmakermedia.org, pg 1058

Koehnle, Jim, BMI Supply, 571 Queensbury Ave, Queensbury, NY 12804 *Tel:* 518-793-6706 *Toll Free Tel:* 800-836-0524 *Fax:* 518-793-6181 *E-mail:* bminy@bmisupply.com *Web Site:* www.bmisupply.com, pg 810

Koenig, William S, NBA Entertainment Inc, 450 Harmon Meadow Blvd, Secaucus, NJ 07094 *Tel:* 201-865-1500 *Fax:* 201-865-2626 *Web Site:* www.nba.com, pg 953

Koeppl, Todd, Chicago Spotlight Inc, 1658 W Carroll St, Chicago, IL 60612 *Tel:* 312-455-1171 *Fax:* 312-455-1744 *Web Site:* www.chicagospotlight.com, pg 825

Koester, Bob, Delmark Records, 4121 N Rockwell, Chicago, IL 60618 *Tel:* 773-539-5001 *Fax:* 773-539-5004 *E-mail:* delmark@delmark.com; jazzmart@delmark.com *Web Site:* www.delmark.com, pg 845

Koff-Chapin, Deborah, Center for Touch Drawing, PO Box 1595, Langley, WA 98260 *Tel:* 360-221-5745 *Toll Free Tel:* 800-989-6334 (orders) *E-mail:* center@touchdrawing.com *Web Site:* www.touchdrawing.com, pg 822

Kofford, Quin, HEC Reading Horizons, 60 N Cutler Dr, Suite 101, North Salt Lake, UT 84054 *Tel:* 801-295-7054 *Toll Free Tel:* 800-333-0054 *Fax:* 801-295-7088 *E-mail:* info@readinghorizons.com *Web Site:* www.readinghorizons.com, pg 887

Kogan, Patricia, Pat Kogan Productions Inc, 615 Half Moon Bay, Croton-on-Hudson, NY 10520 *Tel:* 914-661-0049 *Web Site:* www.pkpmedia.com, pg 970

Kohler, Michael, Digital Comm Link Inc, 10450 W State Rd 84, Davie, FL 33324-4206 *Tel:* 954-236-2993 *Toll Free Tel:* 877-532-5438 *Fax:* 954-236-3633 *E-mail:* booking@dclinc.net *Web Site:* www.dclinc.net, pg 847

Kohn, Moses, Baker Audio Inc, 2195 N Norcross Tucker Rd, Norcross, GA 30071 *Tel:* 770-441-2000 *Toll Free Tel:* 800-847-3523 *Fax:* 770-449-7719 *E-mail:* sales@bakeraudiovisual.com *Web Site:* www.bakeraudiovisual.com, pg 802

Kokette, Steve, Aylmer Press, PO Box 2302, Madison, WI 53701-2302 *Tel:* 608-441-5277 *Fax:* 608-251-0890 *Web Site:* www.signit2.com, pg 801

Kolarek, Dale, Set To Go Studios, 86 Lackawana Ave, Suite 235, Woodland Park, NJ 07424 *Tel:* 973-638-1646 *E-mail:* settogostudio@gmail.com *Web Site:* www.settogostudio.com, pg 1007

Kolb, Bill, MRM Worldwide, 622 Third Ave, New York, NY 10017 *Tel:* 646-865-6230 *E-mail:* info@mrmworldwide.com *Web Site:* www.mrmworldwide.com, pg 948

Kolb, Kurt, Speakeasy Productions, 3616-B Falls Rd, Baltimore, MD 21211 *Tel:* 410-889-0374 *Web Site:* www.voiceover.com, pg 1020

Kolberg, Richard, Custom Computer Specialists Inc, 6 Blackstone Valley Place, Suite 402, Lincoln, RI 02865 *Tel:* 401-765-3000 *Toll Free Tel:* 800-556-2828 *Fax:* 401-765-6440 *Web Site:* www.customonline.com, pg 841

Koller, Scott, Creative Realities Inc, 55 Broadway, 9th fl, New York, NY 10006 *Tel:* 212-324-6660 *Toll Free Tel:* 888-432-7328 *E-mail:* info@cri.com *Web Site:* www.cri.com, pg 838

Kondrat, Tim, Tobin Productions Inc, 630 Ninth Ave, Suite 215, New York, NY 10036 *Tel:* 212-727-1500 *Toll Free Tel:* 800-877-8273 *Fax:* 212-727-1766 *E-mail:* info@tobinproductions.com *Web Site:* www.tobinproductions.com, pg 1041

Kondratieff, Cynthia, Dolphin MultiMedia Inc, 1660 Belleville Way, Sunnyvale, CA 94087 *Tel:* 650-354-0800 *Fax:* 408-737-8404 *E-mail:* dolphin@dolphinmm.com *Web Site:* www.dolphinmm.com, pg 850

Kontrimas, Dr Richard, Radian Audio Engineering Inc, 600 N Batavia St, Orange, CA 92868 *Tel:* 714-288-8900 *Fax:* 714-288-1133 *E-mail:* info@radianaudio.com *Web Site:* www.radianaudio.com, pg 990

Koontz, Rob, Norcostco Inc, 825 Rhode Island Ave S, Minneapolis, MN 55426-1611 *Tel:* 763-544-0601 *Toll Free Tel:* 800-220-6920 *Fax:* 763-525-8676 *E-mail:* theatretechmn@norcostco.com; makeupmn@norcostco.com; costumesmn@norcostco.com *Web Site:* www.norcostco.com, pg 958

Kopecky, Alex, INTERCOM, 30 E Adams St, Suite 800, Chicago, IL 60603 *Tel:* 312-683-0121 *Fax:* 312-683-0122 *E-mail:* info@chicagofilmfestival.com *Web Site:* www.chicagofilmfestival.com, pg 1117

Koplar, Edward J, World Events Productions Ltd, 50 Maryland Plaza, Suite 300, St Louis, MO 63108 *Tel:* 314-345-1060 *Fax:* 314-345-1093 *E-mail:* wep@wep.com *Web Site:* www.wep.com, pg 1069

Koran, Lori, Resource Development Co LLC, 280 Daines St, Suite 200, Birmingham, MI 48009 *Tel:* 248-646-2300 *Toll Free Tel:* 800-360-7222 *Fax:* 248-646-0789 *E-mail:* inquiries@resourcedev.com *Web Site:* www.resourcedev.com, pg 995

Korngold, Honnie, CineVantage LLC, 8560 W Sunset Blvd, 5th fl, West Hollywood, CA 90069 *Toll Free Tel:* 888-518-7571 *Web Site:* www.cinevantage.com, pg 828

Korson, Brian, Video Excellence Productions, 94 Breckonwood Crescent, Thornhill, ON L3T 5E8, Canada *Tel:* 905-731-4355 *Web Site:* www.videoexcellence.com, pg 1055

Korte, Tony, Videomagnetics, 3970 Clearview Frontage Rd, Colorado Springs, CO 80911 *Tel:* 719-390-1313 *Toll Free Tel:* 800-432-3887 *Fax:* 719-390-1316 *E-mail:* vmi@csprings.com *Web Site:* www.videomagnetics.com, pg 1057

Kosak, Suzanne, The DVI Group, 1486 Mecaslin St NW, Atlanta, GA 30309 *Tel:* 404-873-6283 *Toll Free Tel:* 888-736-7384 *E-mail:* makeitbetter@thedvigroup.com *Web Site:* www.thedvigroup.com, pg 854

Koshimizu, Nobuhiko, FUJIFILM Canada Inc, 600 Suffolk Ct, Mississauga, ON L5R 4G4, Canada *Tel:* 905-890-6611 *Toll Free Tel:* 800-263-5018 *Fax:* 905-890-6446 *Web Site:* www.fujifilm.ca, pg 873

Koskella, Kelly, Hollywood Rentals Production Services, 12800 Foothill Blvd, Sylmar, CA 91342 *Tel:* 818-407-7800 *Toll Free Tel:* 800-233-7830 *Fax:* 818-407-7868 *E-mail:* info@hollywoodrentals.com *Web Site:* www.hollywoodrentals.com, pg 890

Koss, John Jr, Koss Corp, 4129 N Port Washington Ave, Milwaukee, WI 53212 *Tel:* 414-964-5000 *Toll Free Tel:* 800-USA-KOSS (872-5677) *Fax:* 414-964-8615 *E-mail:* customersupport@koss.com *Web Site:* www.koss.com, pg 913

Koss, Michael, Koss Corp, 4129 N Port Washington Ave, Milwaukee, WI 53212 *Tel:* 414-964-5000 *Toll Free Tel:* 800-USA-KOSS (872-5677) *Fax:* 414-964-8615 *E-mail:* customersupport@koss.com *Web Site:* www.koss.com, pg 913

Kostov, Michael, Kostov Productions, Whispering Wind Ranch, 16320 High Bridge Rd, Monroe, WA 98272 *Tel:* 206-755-0050 *E-mail:* info@kostov.com *Web Site:* www.kostov.com, pg 913

Kosuda, Frank, De Sisti Lighting/Desmar Corp, 1011 Rte 22 E, Unit D, Mountainside, NJ 07092 *Tel:* 908-317-0020 *Fax:* 908-317-0021 *Web Site:* www.desisti.it, pg 844

Kotcher, Ray, Ketchum Pleon Change, 1285 Avenue of the Americas, 3rd fl, New York, NY 10019 *Tel:* 646-935-3900 *Web Site:* www.ketchum.com/change, pg 910

Kotkin, Doug, Cibola Systems, 180 S Cypress St, Orange, CA 92866 *Tel:* 714-480-0272 *Fax:* 714-480-0768 *E-mail:* info@cibolasystems.com *Web Site:* cibolasystems.com, pg 826

Kotsmire, Dave, The Will-Burt Co, 169 S Main St, Orrville, OH 44667 *Tel:* 330-682-7015; 330-684-4000 (cust serv) *Fax:* 330-684-1190 *E-mail:* contact_us@willburt.com *Web Site:* www.willburt.com, pg 1066

Koury, Dee, Old Army Press (OAP), 218 Alabaster Way, Johnstown, CO 80534 *Tel:* 970-587-9530 *Toll Free Tel:* 800-627-0079 *Fax:* 970-490-2709 *E-mail:* oldarmypress@msn.com *Web Site:* oldarmypress.com, pg 961

Koury, Mike, Old Army Press (OAP), 218 Alabaster Way, Johnstown, CO 80534 *Tel:* 970-587-9530 *Toll Free Tel:* 800-627-0079 *Fax:* 970-490-2709 *E-mail:* oldarmypress@msn.com *Web Site:* oldarmypress.com, pg 961

Kovic, Adam, ITC Learning LLC, 1616 Anderson Rd, Suite 109, McLean, VA 22102 *Toll Free Tel:* 800-638-3757 *E-mail:* sales@itclearning.com *Web Site:* www.itclearning.com, pg 903

Kowalik, Joseph, Graphx Inc, 400 W Cummings Park, Suite 3900, Woburn, MA 01801 *Tel:* 781-932-0430 *Fax:* 781-932-0855 *E-mail:* info@graphx.com *Web Site:* www.graphx.com, pg 881

Kowalski, Fran, Sound & Video Creations Inc, 2408 Felts Ave, Nashville, TN 37211 *Tel:* 615-460-7330 *Fax:* 615-460-7331 *Web Site:* www.clickeffects.com, pg 1016

Kozer, Elliot, Fibre Case Corp, 160 Broadway, Suite 1105, New York, NY 10038 *Tel:* 212-566-2720 *Toll Free Tel:* 800-394-6871 *Fax:* 212-566-2726 *E-mail:* sales@fibrecase.com *Web Site:* www.fibrecase.com, pg 866

Koziell, Peter, Award Productions, 164 Great Rd, Acton, MA 01720 *Tel:* 978-667-3335 *E-mail:* web@awardproductions.com *Web Site:* www.awardproductions.com, pg 800

Koziol, Christian, Kappa optronics Inc, 825 S Primrose Ave, Suite I, Monrovia, CA 91016 *Tel:* 626-256-4343 *Fax:* 626-256-6484 *E-mail:* info@kappa-optronics.com *Web Site:* www.kappa-optronics.com, pg 908

Koziol, Jim, PLS Staging, 371 Little Falls Rd, Cedar Grove, NJ 07009-1250 *Tel:* 973-857-7242 *Toll Free Tel:* 800-783-4757 *Fax:* 973-857-8867 *Web Site:* www.plsstaging.com, pg 977

Kozlovsky, Patti, Vineyard Productions, 3640 Lovall Valley Rd, Sonoma, CA 95476 *Tel:* 707-939-3566 *Web Site:* www.vineyardproductions.com, pg 1058

Kraichley, Brian, SOM Publishing Co, 163 Moon Valley Rd, Windyville, MO 65783 *Tel:* 417-345-8411 *E-mail:* som@som.org *Web Site:* www.som.org, pg 1015

Krakauer, Daniel, Deerfield Laboratory Inc, 524 San Anselmo Ave, Suite 136, San Anselmo, CA 94960 *Tel:* 650-632-4090 *Fax:* 650-632-4091 *E-mail:* info@deerfieldlab.com *Web Site:* www.deerfieldlab.com, pg 844

Kramer, Edward, Synsor Corp, 1920 Merrill Creek Pkwy, Everett, WA 98203-5859 *Tel:* 425-551-1300 *Toll Free Tel:* 800-426-0193 *Fax:* 425-551-1313 *E-mail:* info@synsor.com *Web Site:* www.synsor.com, pg 1030

Kramer, Eileen, Hollywood Post Alliance, 846 S Broadway, Suite 601, Los Angeles, CA 90014 *Tel:* 213-614-0860 *Fax:* 213-614-0890 *Web Site:* www.hpaonline.com, pg 1082

Kramer, Jeffrey T, Kramer Communications Video Production, 12504 Quarterhorse Dr, Bowie, MD 20720 *Tel:* 301-352-3042 *Fax:* 301-352-3559 *E-mail:* kcam@his.com *Web Site:* www.kramercommunications.tv, pg 913

Kramer, Joan, Joan Kramer & Associates Inc, 10490 Wilshire Blvd, Suite 1701, Los Angeles, CA 90024 *Tel:* 310-446-1866 *Fax:* 310-446-1856 *E-mail:* ekeeeek@earthlink.net, pg 913

Kramer, Mark A, Media-Comm, 9700 S Pine Blvd, Charlotte, NC 28273 *Tel:* 704-527-8853 *Web Site:* www.media-comm.com, pg 936

Krams, Steven H, Magna-Tech Electronic Co Inc, 1998 NE 150 St, North Miami, FL 33181 *Tel:* 305-573-7339 *Fax:* 305-573-8101 *E-mail:* magnatech@iceco.com; sales@iceco.com *Web Site:* www.magna-tech.com, pg 928

Krank, Bert, Tamron USA Inc, 10 Austin Blvd, Commack, NY 11725 *Tel:* 631-858-8400 *Toll Free Tel:* 800-827-8880 *Fax:* 631-543-5666 *E-mail:* custserv@tamron.com *Web Site:* www.tamron-usa.com, pg 1031

Kranz, Patricia, The Whitman Bassow Award, 40 W 45 St, New York, NY 10036 *Tel:* 212-626-9220 *Fax:* 212-626-9210 *Web Site:* www.opcofamerica.org, pg 1109

Kranz, Patricia, The Robert Spiers Benjamin Award, 40 W 45 St, New York, NY 10036 *Tel:* 212-626-9220 *Fax:* 212-626-9210 *Web Site:* www.opcofamerica.org, pg 1109

Kranz, Patricia, The David Kaplan Award, 40 W 45 St, New York, NY 10036 *Tel:* 212-626-9220 *Fax:* 212-626-9210 *Web Site:* www.opcofamerica.org, pg 1118

Kranz, Patricia, The Edward R Murrow Award, 40 W 45 St, New York, NY 10036 *Tel:* 212-626-9220 *Fax:* 212-626-9210 *Web Site:* www.opcofamerica.org, pg 1121

Kranz, Patricia, The Madeline Dane Ross Award, 40 W 45 St, New York, NY 10036 *Tel:* 212-626-9220 *Fax:* 212-626-9210 *Web Site:* www.opcofamerica.org, pg 1125

Kranz, Patricia, The Lowell Thomas Award, 40 W 45 St, New York, NY 10036 *Tel:* 212-626-9220 *Fax:* 212-626-9210 *Web Site:* www.opcofamerica.org, pg 1128

Krasilinec, Michelle, Northwest Colorado Film Commission, 125 Anglers Dr, Steamboat Springs, CO 80487 *Tel:* 970-879-0880 *Fax:* 970-285-3550 *E-mail:* info@steamboatchamber.com; media@steamboatchamber.com *Web Site:* www.steamboat-chamber.com, pg 1095

Krasuski, Marc, DecisionOne, 426 W Lancaster Ave, Devon, PA 19333 *Tel:* 610-296-6000 *Toll Free Tel:* 800-767-2876; 800-777-8800 (cust serv); 888-287-9202 (sales); 800-554-5179 (CN) *Fax:* 610-296-2910 *Web Site:* www.decisionone.com, pg 844

Kraus, Richard, T & M Digital Services, 54 Flint Ridge Rd, Monroe, CT 06468 *Tel:* 203-268-5290 *Fax:* 203-268-5290, pg 1031

Krause, Ron, Grace Church - St Louis, 2695 Creve Coeur Mill Rd, Maryland Heights, MO 63043 *Tel:* 314-292-8300 *Fax:* 314-291-0918 *E-mail:* info@gracestl.org *Web Site:* www.gracestl.org, pg 881

Kravis, David B, Coastline Licensing International Inc, 7345 Topanga Canyon Blvd, Canoga Park, CA 91303 *Tel:* 818-226-0488 *Fax:* 818-226-0489 *Web Site:* www.coastlinelicensing.com, pg 831

Krebs, Lisa, IBPA, Independent Book Publishers Association, 1020 Manhattan Beach Blvd, Suite 204, Manhattan Beach, CA 90266 *Tel:* 310-546-1818 *Fax:* 310-546-3939 *E-mail:* info@ibpa-online.org *Web Site:* www.ibpa-online.org, pg 1082

Kreikemeier, Brian, B & B Video Productions Inc, 233 N Main St, West Point, NE 68788 *Tel:* 402-372-2628 *E-mail:* info@bandbvideo.com *Web Site:* www.bandbvideo.com, pg 801

Kremen, Dan, Intermark Industries Inc, 2980 NW 74 Ave, Miami, FL 33122 *Tel:* 305-591-8930 *Fax:* 305-593-1091 *E-mail:* info@intermarkindustries.com *Web Site:* www.intermarkindustries.com, pg 900

Kretsch, Ellen, Globe/Miami Film Commission, 1360 N Broad St, US 60, Globe, AZ 85501 *Tel:* 928-425-4495 *Toll Free Tel:* 800-804-5623 *Fax:* 928-425-3410 *E-mail:* gmr@cableone.net *Web Site:* www.globemiamichamber.com, pg 1091

Kretschmann, Richard, Amerinex Applied Imaging Inc, PO Box 6473, Monroe Township, NJ 08831-6473 *Tel:* 609-944-8855 *Toll Free Tel:* 877-664-8772 *Fax:* 609-944-8855 *E-mail:* info@amerineximaging.com *Web Site:* www.amerineximaging.com, pg 785

Kreutz, David, Image Audiovisuals, 2130 S Dahlia St, Denver, CO 80222 *Tel:* 303-758-1818 *Toll Free Tel:* 800-818-1857 *Fax:* 303-758-5722 *E-mail:* commercialsales@imageav.com *Web Site:* www.imageav.com, pg 894

Kreuzer, Terese Loeb, Edgeware Associates/Travel Arts Syndicate, 377 Rector Place, Suite 10-H, New York, NY 10280 *Tel:* 212-807-7509 *Web Site:* www.travelartssyndicate.blogspot.com, pg 856

Krevens, Dale, Tech 21 USA Inc, 790 Bloomfield Ave, Clifton, NJ 07012 *Tel:* 973-777-6996 *Fax:* 973-777-9899 *E-mail:* info@tech21nyc.com *Web Site:* www.tech21nyc.com, pg 1033

Krinsky, Santosh, New Leaf Distributing Co, 401 Thornton Rd, Lithia Springs, GA 30122-1557 *Tel:* 770-948-7845 *Toll Free Tel:* 800-326-2665 (orders) *Fax:* 770-944-2313 *E-mail:* newleaf@newleaf-dist.com *Web Site:* www.newleaf-dist.com, pg 956

Kritzell, Tom, Transtector Systems Inc, 10701 N Airport Dr, Hayden Lake, ID 83835 *Tel:* 208-772-8515 *Toll Free Tel:* 800-882-9110 *Fax:* 208-762-6133 *E-mail:* sales@transtector.com *Web Site:* www.transtector.com, pg 1043

Kritzmacher, John, John Wiley & Sons Inc, 111 River St, Hoboken, NJ 07030 *Tel:* 201-748-6000 *Toll Free Tel:* 800-225-5945 *Fax:* 201-748-6088 *E-mail:* info@wiley.com *Web Site:* www.wiley.com, pg 1066

Krivicich, Dan, Electronic Vision Inc (EV), 5 Depot St, Athens, OH 45701 *Tel:* 740-592-2433 *Fax:* 740-592-2650 *E-mail:* info@ev.net *Web Site:* www.electronicvision.com, pg 859

Kroger, Fr Dan, Franciscan Media, 28 W Liberty St, Cincinnati, OH 45202-6498 *Tel:* 513-241-5615 *Toll Free Tel:* 800-488-0488 *Fax:* 513-241-0399 *Web Site:* www.americancatholic.org, pg 872

Kron, Randy, North-by-Northwest Productions, 903 W Broadway Ave, Spokane, WA 99201 *Tel:* 509-324-2949 *Fax:* 509-324-2959 *E-mail:* contact@nxnw.net *Web Site:* www.nxnw.net, pg 959

Krone, Jerry, Zelman Studios Ltd, 623 Cortelyou Rd, Brooklyn, NY 11218 *Tel:* 718-941-5500 *E-mail:* kaforce@yahoo.com, pg 1073

Krone, William, Deja View Video, 417 S Eldorado St, San Mateo, CA 94402-1374 *Tel:* 650-343-8899 *Web Site:* www.dejaview.com, pg 845

Kronovet, Bob, 30 Second Films, 3019 Pico Blvd, Santa Monica, CA 90405 *Tel:* 310-315-1750 *Fax:* 310-315-1757 *E-mail:* sales@30secondfilms.com *Web Site:* www.30secondfilms.com, pg 1039

Krop, Dave, AutoDesSys Inc, 3518 Riverside Dr, Suite 102, Columbus, OH 43221 *Tel:* 614-488-8838 *Fax:* 614-488-0848 *E-mail:* formz@formz.com; sales@formz.com; sales@autodessys.com *Web Site:* www.formz.com, pg 797

Krout, Ed, Phat Planet Recording Studios, 3473 Parkway Center Ct, Orlando, FL 32808 *Tel:* 407-295-7270 *Toll Free Tel:* 800-667-4893 *Fax:* 407-295-7207 *E-mail:* info@phatplanetstudios.com *Web Site:* www.phatplanetstudios.com, pg 973

Kruckemyer, Gene, Love Your Shorts Film Festival, 608 S Elm Ave, Sanford, FL 32771 *E-mail:* contact@loveyourshorts.com *Web Site:* www.loveyourshorts.com, pg 1119

Krug, Margherita Petti, Fingerpaint, 13 Walker Way, Albany, NY 12205 *Tel:* 518-869-1968 *Fax:* 518-869-1969 *Web Site:* fingerpaintmarketing.com, pg 868

Krulewicz, Gerald J, Wireworks Corp, 380 Hillside Ave, Hillside, NJ 07205 *Tel:* 908-686-7400 *Toll Free Tel:* 800-642-9473 *Fax:* 908-686-0483 *E-mail:* sales@wireworks.com; info@wireworks.com *Web Site:* www.wireworks.com, pg 1068

Krutsch, Mike, R & R Cases & Cabinets, 1217 Rand Rd, Des Plaines, IL 60016 *Tel:* 847-299-8100 *Fax:* 847-299-8110 *E-mail:* sales@rrcases.com *Web Site:* www.rrcases.com, pg 990

Krystall, Marty, K2B2 Records, 1748 Roosevelt Ave, Los Angeles, CA 90006 *Web Site:* k2b2.com, pg 907

Krzyczkowski, Stan, Creation Technologies Inc, 102-8977 Fraserton Ct, Burnaby, BC V5J 5H8, Canada *Tel:* 604-430-4336 *Toll Free Tel:* 800-736-1271 *Fax:* 604-430-4337 *E-mail:* info@creationtech.com *Web Site:* www.creationtech.com, pg 838

Krzysik, Dave, The Brainwash Movie Festival, 1675 Seventh St, No 23302, Oakland, CA 94623-6009 *Tel:* 510-836-3210 *Web Site:* www.brainwashm.com, pg 1110

Kuegel, John, All Terrain Power Co Inc, PO Box 18, Bellport, NY 11713 *Tel:* 718-852-4922 *Fax:* 718-267-0002 *Web Site:* www.allterrainpower.com, pg 781

Kuehn, Case, LOUD Technologies Inc, 16220 Wood-Red Rd NE, Woodinville, WA 98072 *Tel:* 425-487-4333; 415-892-6500 *Toll Free Tel:* 866-858-LTEC (858-5832) *Fax:* 425-487-4337 *Web Site:* www.mackie.com; www.loudtechinc.com, pg 925

Kuehn, Chris, Teledyne Energy Systems Inc, 10707 Gilroy Rd, Hunt Valley, MD 21031 *Tel:* 410-771-8600 *Fax:* 410-771-8620 *E-mail:* energy.systems@teledynees.com *Web Site:* www.teledynees.com, pg 1036

Kugel, Candy, Buzzco Associates Inc, 33 Bleecker St, New York, NY 10012 *Tel:* 212-473-8800 *Fax:* 212-473-8891 *E-mail:* info@buzzzco.com *Web Site:* www.buzzzco.com, pg 816

Kugler, Brad, Distribution Video & Audio (DVA), 15232 US 19 N, Suite B, Clearwater, FL 33764 *Tel:* 727-447-4147 *Toll Free Tel:* 800-683-4147 *Fax:* 727-441-3069 *Web Site:* www.dvaspecial.com, pg 849

Kugler, Gina, Distribution Video & Audio (DVA), 15232 US 19 N, Suite B, Clearwater, FL 33764 *Tel:* 727-447-4147 *Toll Free Tel:* 800-683-4147 *Fax:* 727-441-3069 *Web Site:* www.dvaspecial.com, pg 849

Kuhn, Bill, Kuhn Productions LLC, 321 E Walnut St, Suite 340, Des Moines, IA 50309 *Tel:* 515-244-1618, pg 914

Kuhn, Edward, Frezzi Energy Systems, 7 Valley St, Hawthorne, NJ 07506 *Tel:* 973-427-1160 *Fax:* 973-427-0934 *E-mail:* info@frezzi.com *Web Site:* www.frezzi.com, pg 873

Kuhn, Shane, Slamdance Film Festival, 5634 Melrose Ave, Los Angeles, CA 90038 *Tel:* 323-466-1786 *Fax:* 323-466-1784 *E-mail:* submissions@slamdance.com *Web Site:* www.slamdance.com, pg 1127

Kuhn, Tammy, Network Technologies Inc, 1275 Danner Dr, Aurora, OH 44202 *Tel:* 330-562-7070 *Toll Free Tel:* 800-742-8324 *Fax:* 330-562-1999 *E-mail:* sales@ntigo.com *Web Site:* www.networktechinc.com, pg 955

Kulawick, Geoff, The Children's Book Store Distribution (CBSD), 14-3245 Harvester Rd, Burlington, ON L7N 3T7, Canada *Tel:* 905-681-8160; 905-831-1995 (intl) *Toll Free Tel:* 800-668-0242; 800-757-8372 (cust serv-CN & US) *Fax:* 905-831-1142 (intl) *E-mail:* info@childrensgroup.com *Web Site:* www.childrensgroup.com, pg 825

Kulesh, Robert E, Matthews Studio Equipment Inc, 4520 W Valerio St, Burbank, CA 91505 *Tel:* 818-843-6715 *Toll Free Tel:* 800-237-8263 *Fax:* 818-480-5808 *E-mail:* info@msegrip.com *Web Site:* www.msegrip.com, pg 934

Kulkami, Dr Subodh, CyberOptics, 5900 Golden Hills Dr, Minneapolis, MN 55416 *Tel:* 763-542-5000 *Fax:* 763-542-5100 *E-mail:* info@cyberoptics.com *Web Site:* cyberoptics.com, pg 841

Kull, Dennis, Lumeni Productions Inc, 1632 Flower St, Glendale, CA 91201 *Tel:* 818-956-2200 *Fax:* 818-956-3298 *E-mail:* info@lumeni.com *Web Site:* www.lumeni.com, pg 926

Kumler, Rob, K&R Photo Digital, 538 Terry Lane, Fort Mitchell, KY 41017 *Tel:* 859-341-6998 *Fax:* 859-341-6987 *E-mail:* photodigitalpro@mac.com *Web Site:* www.krphotodigital.com, pg 908

Kumst csc, Alwyn, CSC Awards, 3007 Kingston Rd, Suite 131, Toronto, ON M1M 1P1, Canada *Tel:* 416-266-0591 *Fax:* 416-266-3996 *E-mail:* admin@csc.ca *Web Site:* www.csc.ca, pg 1113

Kunce, Dennis, Sure Shot Transmissions Inc, 10314 Main St, New Middletown, OH 44442 *Tel:* 330-542-0900 *Fax:* 330-542-1020 *Web Site:* www.sureshotsat.com, pg 1029

Kung, Serena, Motion Picture Editors Guild Local 700, 7715 Sunset Blvd, Suite 200, Hollywood, CA 90046 *Tel:* 323-876-4770 *Toll Free Tel:* 800-705-8700 *Fax:* 323-876-0861 *E-mail:* mail@editorsguild.com *Web Site:* www.editorsguild.com, pg 1084

Kuniansky, Neal, Duxbury Systems Inc, 270 Littleton Rd, Unit 6, Westford, MA 01886-3523 *Tel:* 978-692-3000 *Fax:* 978-692-7912 *E-mail:* info@duxsys.com *Web Site:* www.duxburysystems.com, pg 854

Kunjufu, Jawanza, African American Images, PO Box 1799, Chicago Heights, IL 60412 *Tel:* 708-672-4909 *Toll Free Tel:* 800-552-1991 *Fax:* 708-672-0466 *E-mail:* customersvc@africanamericanimages.com *Web Site:* www.africanamericanimages.com, pg 778

Kuntz, Jay D, Video Communication Productions Inc, 446 Salem Dr, Pittsburgh, PA 15243 *Tel:* 412-915-6776 *Web Site:* www.pittsburghvideoguy.com, pg 1054

Kuntz, Tom, Image Technologies Corp, 523 Hanley Industrial Ct, St Louis, MO 63144 *Tel:* 314-646-1800 *Toll Free Tel:* 800-962-2344 *Fax:* 314-646-1818 *Web Site:* www.imagetechnologies.com, pg 895

Kunz, Jason, DigiTech, 10653 S River Front Pkwy, Suite 300, South Jordan, UT 84095 *Tel:* 801-566-8800 *Toll Free Tel:* 800-999-9363 *E-mail:* support@digitech.com *Web Site:* www.digitech.com, pg 848

Kuo, Michael, AVerMedia Technologies Inc, 47358 Fremont Blvd, Fremont, CA 94538 *Tel:* 510-403-0006 (sales) *Fax:* 510-403-0022 *E-mail:* avtsales.usa@avermedia.com; avt.pmk@avermedia.com *Web Site:* www.avermedia-usa.com, pg 798

Kurt, Ed, New Circuit Films LLC, 403 S Central Ave, No 12, Glendale, CA 91204 *Tel:* 818-378-0033 *E-mail:* info@newcircuit.com *Web Site:* www.newcircuit.com, pg 955

Kurtz, John, Ghent Manufacturing, 2999 Henkle Dr, Lebanon, OH 45036-9260 *Tel:* 513-932-3445 *Toll Free Tel:* 800-543-0550 *Fax:* 513-932-9252 *E-mail:* customer_service@ghent.com *Web Site:* www.ghent.com, pg 878

Kurtz, Justin, Showman Fabricators Inc, 47-22 Pearson Place, Long Island City, NY 11101 *Tel:* 718-935-9899 *Fax:* 718-855-9823 *E-mail:* info@showfab.com *Web Site:* www.showfab.com, pg 1010

Kushner, William, Techni-Tool Inc, 1547 N Trooper Rd, Worcester, PA 19490 *Tel:* 610-941-2400 *Toll Free Tel:* 800-832-4866 *Fax:* 610-828-5623 *Toll Free Fax:* 800-854-8665 *E-mail:* sales@techni-tool.com *Web Site:* www.techni-tool.com, pg 1033

Kussin, Al, Kool Music, 9 Hector Ave, Toronto, ON M6G 3G2, Canada *Tel:* 416-533-3520 *E-mail:* host@koolmusic.com *Web Site:* www.koolmusic.com, pg 913

Kustiak, Trevor, The Pocket Studios, 920 Eastern Ave, Top fl, Toronto, ON M4L 1A4, Canada *Tel:* 416-466-0029 *E-mail:* info@thepocketstudios.com *Web Site:* www.thepocketstudios.com, pg 977

Kutak, Ronald, Motion Picture Editors Guild Local 700, 7715 Sunset Blvd, Suite 200, Hollywood, CA 90046 *Tel:* 323-876-4770 *Toll Free Tel:* 800-705-8700 *Fax:* 323-876-0861 *E-mail:* mail@editorsguild.com *Web Site:* www.editorsguild.com, pg 1084

Kutsunai, Pamela, Cue Tech Teleprompting, 5527 Satsuma Ave, North Hollywood, CA 91601 *Tel:* 818-487-2700 *Fax:* 818-487-2750 *E-mail:* info@cue-tech.com *Web Site:* www.cue-tech.com, pg 841

Kutza, Michael J, Chicago International Film Festival, 30 E Adams St, Suite 800, Chicago, IL 60603 *Tel:* 312-683-0121 *Fax:* 312-683-0122 *E-mail:* info@chicagofilmfestival.com *Web Site:* www.chicagofilmfestival.com, pg 1111

Kutza, Michael J, INTERCOM, 30 E Adams St, Suite 800, Chicago, IL 60603 *Tel:* 312-683-0121 *Fax:* 312-683-0122 *E-mail:* info@chicagofilmfestival.com *Web Site:* www.chicagofilmfestival.com, pg 1117

Kuypers, Jeff, Creation Technologies Inc, 102-8977 Fraserton Ct, Burnaby, BC V5J 5H8, Canada *Tel:* 604-430-4336 *Toll Free Tel:* 800-736-1271 *Fax:* 604-430-4337 *E-mail:* info@creationtech.com *Web Site:* www.creationtech.com, pg 838

Kwan, Matt, Sand Box Studio, 555 Minnesota St, San Francisco, CA 94107 *Tel:* 415-550-8732 *E-mail:* inquiries@sandboxstudio.com *Web Site:* www.sandboxstudio.com, pg 1002

Kwan, Mona, Jaguar Distribution Corp, 12711 Ventura Blvd, Suite 300, Studio City, CA 91604 *Tel:* 818-508-3377 *Fax:* 818-508-3340 *Web Site:* www.jaguardc.com, pg 903

Kwon, Christine, Center for Asian American Media (CAAM), 145 Ninth St, Suite 350, San Francisco, CA 94103 *Tel:* 415-863-0814 *Fax:* 415-863-7428 *E-mail:* info@caamedia.org *Web Site:* www.caamedia.org, pg 1080

Kynaston, Marilyn, Picture Box Distribution Inc, 141 E 23 Ave, Vancouver, BC V5V 1X1, Canada *Tel:* 604-681-3174 *Fax:* 604-608-9081 *E-mail:* info@picturebox.ca *Web Site:* www.picturebox.ca, pg 975

La Cotera, Stacy, PromaxBDA, 1522e Cloverfield Blvd, Santa Monica, CA 90404 *Tel:* 310-788-7600 *Fax:* 310-788-7616 *Web Site:* www.promaxbda.org, pg 1087

La Dez, D J, Lumedyne Inc, 6010 Wall St, Port Richey, FL 34668 *Tel:* 727-847-2777; 727-847-5394 *Toll Free Tel:* 800-586-3396 *Fax:* 727-841-0000 *E-mail:* info@lumedyne.com; sales@lumedyne.com; service@lumedyne.com *Web Site:* www.lumedyne.com, pg 926

La Guardia, Jo Ann, LM Cases/LM Engineering Inc, 2720 Intertech Dr, Youngstown, OH 44509 *Tel:* 330-270-2400 *Toll Free Tel:* 800-874-8326 *Fax:* 330-270-2424 *E-mail:* info@lmcases.com *Web Site:* www.lmcases.com, pg 923

La Guardia, William, LM Cases/LM Engineering Inc, 2720 Intertech Dr, Youngstown, OH 44509 *Tel:* 330-270-2400 *Toll Free Tel:* 800-874-8326 *Fax:* 330-270-2424 *E-mail:* info@lmcases.com *Web Site:* www.lmcases.com, pg 923

La Mantia, Santo "Sandy", Shure Inc, 5800 W Touhy Ave, Niles, IL 60714-4608 *Tel:* 847-600-2000; 847-600-8440 (tech support); 847-600-8699 (cust serv) *Toll Free Tel:* 800-25-SHURE (257-4873); 800-516-2525 (cust serv) *Fax:* 847-600-1212; 847-600-8444 (tech support); 847-600-8686 (cust serv); 847-600-8688 (parts) *E-mail:* info@shure.com; support@shure.com (tech support); service@shure.com (cust serv) *Web Site:* www.shure.com, pg 1010

La Page, Leslie, LA Femme International Film Festival, 324 S Beverly Dr, Suite 436, Beverly Hills, CA 90212 *Tel:* 310-441-1645 *Fax:* 310-475-8213 *Web Site:* www.lafemme.org, pg 1118

La Velle, Mechelle, K2 Productions, 4214 Shoal Creek Dr, Greensboro, NC 27410 *Tel:* 336-664-8036 *E-mail:* info@k2production.com *Web Site:* www.k2production.com, pg 914

La Vezzi, Stephanie, La Vezzi Precision Inc, 999 Regency Dr, Glendale Heights, IL 60139-2281 *Tel:* 630-582-1230 *Toll Free Tel:* 800-323-1772 (outside IL) *Fax:* 630-582-1238 (orders) *E-mail:* lpi@lavezzi.com *Web Site:* www.lavezzi.com, pg 1053

Laatz, Robin, San Diego Film Festival, 2683 Via de la Valle, Suite G210, Del Mar, CA 92014 *Tel:* 619-818-2221 *E-mail:* info@sdff.org *Web Site:* www.sdfilmfest.com, pg 1126

Labadie, Jean, Show Canada Industries Inc, 5555 Maurice-Cullen, Laval, QC H7C 2T8, Canada *Tel:* 450-664-5155 *Toll Free Tel:* 888-329-5556 *Fax:* 450-664-0852 *E-mail:* info@show-canada.ca *Web Site:* www.show-canada.com, pg 1009

Labadie, Michael, Seaport Graphics, 12 Channel St, Suite 802, Boston, MA 02210 *Tel:* 617-330-1200 *Fax:* 617-330-1222 *E-mail:* jobs@seaportgraphics.com *Web Site:* www.seaportgraphics.com, pg 1005

Labbe, Ghislain, New Brunswick Film (NB Film), c/o New Brunswick Division of Tourism, Heritage & Culture, Place 2000, 250 King St, Fredericton, NB E3B 9M9, Canada *Tel:* 506-453-2909 *Fax:* 506-453-2416, pg 1105

Labrecque, David, Labrecque Creative Sound, 2825 Main St, Becket, MA 01223, pg 915

Labuskes, David, InfoComm International®, 11242 Waples Mill Rd, Suite 200, Fairfax, VA 22030 *Tel:* 703-273-7200 *Toll Free Tel:* 800-659-SHOW (659-7469) *Fax:* 703-278-8082 *E-mail:* customerservice@infocomm.org *Web Site:* www.infocomm.org, pg 1083

Lacelle, Sylvie, Montreal Film & TV Commission, Duke Pavilion, 5th fl, 801 Brennan St, Montreal, QC H3C 0G4, Canada *Tel:* 514-872-2883 *Fax:* 514-872-3409 *E-mail:* film.tv@ville.montreal.qc.ca *Web Site:* www.montrealfilm.com, pg 1105

Lachance, Patrice, Prix Gemeaux (French language TV), 225 rue Roy E, bureau 106, Montreal, QC H2W 1M5, Canada *Tel:* 514-849-7448 *Fax:* 514-849-5069 *E-mail:* academie@acct.ca *Web Site:* www.acct.ca/prixgemeaux; www.acct.ca; www.academy.ca, pg 1124

Lacher, Alan, Custom Computer Specialists Inc, 6 Blackstone Valley Place, Suite 402, Lincoln, RI 02865 *Tel:* 401-765-3000 *Toll Free Tel:* 800-556-2828 *Fax:* 401-765-6440 *Web Site:* www.customonline.com, pg 841

LaCombe, Kacie, San Antonio Film Festival, 1633 Babcock Rd, Suite 111, San Antonio, TX 78229 *Tel:* 210-885-5888 *E-mail:* safilm@gmail.com *Web Site:* www.safilm.com, pg 1126

Lacroix, Hubert T, CBC/Radio-Canada, 181 Queen St, Ottawa, ON K1P 1K9, Canada *Toll Free Tel:* 866-306-4636 (CN) *Fax:* 613-288-6245 *E-mail:* liaison@cbc.ca; liaison@radio-canada.ca *Web Site:* www.cbc.radio-canada.ca, pg 821

Lacroix, Rob, Immersion Corp, 310 Rio Robles, San Jose, CA 95134 *Tel:* 408-467-1900 *Fax:* 408-467-1901 *E-mail:* info@immersion.com *Web Site:* www.immersion.com, pg 896

Ladd, Steve, The Video Project, 145 Ninth St, Suite 102, San Francisco, CA 94103 *Tel:* 415-981-9710 *Toll Free Tel:* 800-475-2638 *Toll Free Fax:* 888-562-9012 *E-mail:* orders@videoproject.com; support@videoproject.com *Web Site:* www.videoproject.com, pg 1056

Ladely, Danny Lee, Mary Riepma Ross Media Arts Center, University of Nebraska-Lincoln, 313 N 13 St, Lincoln, NE 68588 *Tel:* 402-472-9100; 402-472-5353 *Fax:* 402-472-2576 *Web Site:* www.theross.org, pg 999

Laden, Susan, Biblical Archaeology Society (BAS), 4710 41 St NW, Washington, DC 20016 *Tel:* 202-364-3300 *Toll Free Tel:* 800-221-4644 *Fax:* 202-364-2636 *E-mail:* bas@bib-arch.org; merchandise@bib-arch.org *Web Site:* www.biblicalarchaeology.org, pg 806

Ladinsky, Gary, Design FX Audio, PO Box 491087, Los Angeles, CA 90049 *Tel:* 818-843-6555 *Toll Free Tel:* 800-441-4415 *Fax:* 818-562-6978 *Web Site:* www.dfxaudio.com, pg 845

LaFever, Ed, MSI Productions, 9220 Activity Rd, San Diego, CA 92126 *Tel:* 858-348-0100 *Fax:* 858-348-0076 *Web Site:* www.msiprod.com, pg 949

Lafferty, Linda, Moog Music Inc, 160 Broadway St, Asheville, NC 28801 *Tel:* 828-251-0090 *Toll Free Tel:* 800-948-1990 *Fax:* 828-254-6233 *E-mail:* info@moogmusic.com *Web Site:* www.moogmusic.com, pg 946

Lage, Alyssa, Cape Girardeau Convention & Visitors Bureau, 400 Broadway St, Suite 100, Cape Girardeau, MO 63701 *Tel:* 573-335-1631 *Toll Free Tel:* 800-777-0068 *Fax:* 573-334-6702 *E-mail:* info@visitcape.com *Web Site:* visitcape.com, pg 1099

Lagreca, Ada, FremantleMedia, 4000 W Alameda Ave, 3rd fl, Burbank, CA 91505 *Tel:* 818-748-1100 *Fax:* 818-563-6410 *E-mail:* contactus@fremantlemedia.com *Web Site:* www.fremantlemedia.com, pg 873

Lahmann, Jake, Supercircuits, 11000 N Mopac Expwy, Bldg 300, Austin, TX 78759 *Toll Free Tel:* 877-995-2288 *E-mail:* operations@supercircuits.com; customercare@supercircuits.com *Web Site:* www.supercircuits.com, pg 1029

Lai, Robin D, Academy Savant, 524 W Commonwealth Ave, Suite E, Fullerton, CA 92832 *Tel:* 714-870-7880 *Toll Free Tel:* 800-472-8268 *Fax:* 714-526-7400 *E-mail:* info@academysavant.com *Web Site:* www.academysavant.com, pg 773

Laiacona, Michael, Whirlwind Music Distributors Inc, 99 Ling Rd, Rochester, NY 14612 *Tel:* 585-663-8820 *Toll Free Tel:* 800-733-9473 (US only) *Fax:* 585-865-8930 *E-mail:* sales@whirlwindusa.com; techsupport@whirlwindusa.com; darylg@whirlwindusa.com (Canadian inquiries) *Web Site:* whirlwindusa.com, pg 1065

Laidley, Paddy, Raincoast Books, 2440 Viking Way, Richmond, BC V6V 1N2, Canada *Tel:* 604-323-7100 *Toll Free Tel:* 800-663-5714 (cust serv & book orders) *Fax:* 604-270-7161 *Toll Free Fax:* 800-565-3770 (cust serv & book orders) *E-mail:* info@raincoast.com; customerservice@raincoast.com *Web Site:* www.raincoast.com, pg 991

Laird, Heather, Film Commission of Greater Kansas City, 1906 Wyandotte, Kansas City, MO 64108 *Tel:* 816-471-2215 *Fax:* 816-471-6500 *E-mail:* contact@kcfilm.com; greaterkcfilmcommission@gmail.com *Web Site:* kcfilm.com, pg 1099

Laird, Rick, EiKO Ltd, 23220 W 84 St, Shawnee Mission, KS 66227 *Tel:* 913-441-8500 *Toll Free Tel:* 800-852-2217 *Fax:* 913-441-6679 *E-mail:* eiko@eiko.com *Web Site:* www.eiko-ltd.com, pg 858

Laitinen, Richard, CamMate Systems, 425 E Comstock, Chandler, AZ 85225 *Tel:* 480-813-9500 *Fax:* 480-813-9292 *E-mail:* cammate@cammate.com *Web Site:* www.cammate.com, pg 818

Laitman, Judith, Knowledge Unlimited Inc, 2320 Pleasant View, Middleton, WI 53562 *Tel:* 608-661-5666 *Toll Free Tel:* 800-356-2303 *Fax:* 608-836-6684 *Toll Free Fax:* 800-618-1570 *E-mail:* csis@newscurrents.com *Web Site:* www.knowledgeunlimited.com, pg 912

Laity, Jeff, TASCAM, 7733 Telegraph Rd, Montebello, CA 90640 *Tel:* 323-726-0303; 323-727-7617 (support) *Toll Free Tel:* 800-447-8322 *Fax:* 323-727-4805 *E-mail:* tascamrepair@teac.com *Web Site:* www.tascam.com, pg 1032

LaJoie, Michael L, Time Warner Cable, 60 Columbus Circle, 17th fl, New York, NY 10023 *Tel:* 212-364-8200 *Web Site:* www.timewarnercable.com, pg 1040

Lajoie, Steve, Fusion Brand Experiences, 421 Chestnut St, Philadelphia, PA 19123 *Tel:* 215-629-2000 *Web Site:* www.fusionexperiences.com, pg 874

Lake, Kyle M, Prosper Media Group Inc, 348 E Main St, Lexington, KY 40507 *Tel:* 859-400-0136 *Toll Free Tel:* 888-528-1999 *E-mail:* producer@prosperproductions.com *Web Site:* www.prospermg.com, pg 986

Lakefish, Mark, ToteVision, 1319 Dexter Ave N, Suite 020, Seattle, WA 98109 *Tel:* 206-623-6000 *Fax:* 206-623-6609 *E-mail:* info@totevision.com *Web Site:* www.totevision.com, pg 1042

Lakhter, Masha, Key Digital Systems, 521 E Third St, Mount Vernon, NY 10553 *Tel:* 914-667-9700 *Fax:* 914-668-8666 *E-mail:* info@keydigital.com *Web Site:* www.keydigital.com, pg 910

Lakhter, Michael, Key Digital Systems, 521 E Third St, Mount Vernon, NY 10553 *Tel:* 914-667-9700 *Fax:* 914-668-8666 *E-mail:* info@keydigital.com *Web Site:* www.keydigital.com, pg 910

Lamarra, Tom, Blood-Horse Publications, 3101 Beaumont Centre Circle, Lexington, KY 40513 *Toll Free Tel:* 800-866-2361; 800-582-5604 *E-mail:* customerservice@bloodhorse.com; advertise@bloodhorse.com *Web Site:* www.bloodhorse.com, pg 809

Lamb, James, Point Source Audio, 1129 Industrial Ave, No 205, Petaluma, CA 94952 *Tel:* 415-226-1122 *Fax:* 415-520-2110 *E-mail:* info@point-sourceaudio.com; sales@point-sourceaudio.com; support@point-sourceaudio.com *Web Site:* www.point-sourceaudio.com, pg 977

Lamb, Jerry, CCI Solutions, 1342 88 Ave SE, Olympia, WA 98501 *Tel:* 360-943-5378 *Toll Free Tel:* 800-562-6006 *Fax:* 360-754-1566 *E-mail:* info@ccisolutions.com *Web Site:* www.ccisolutions.com, pg 821

Lamb, Robert, PSSI, 7030 Hayvenhurst Ave, Van Nuys, CA 91406 *Tel:* 310-575-4400 *Toll Free Tel:* 800-SAT-LINK (728-5465) *Fax:* 310-575-4451 *E-mail:* operations@pssiglobal.com *Web Site:* www.pssiglobal.com, pg 987

Lambert, Rip, Producers Video, 3700 Malden Ave, Baltimore, MD 21211 *Tel:* 410-523-7520 *Fax:* 410-669-3347; 410-523-0281 *Web Site:* producers.tv, pg 984

Lambert, Ryan, TM Studios Inc, 2002 Academy Lane, Suite 110, Dallas, TX 75234 *Tel:* 972-406-6800 *Fax:* 972-406-6890 *E-mail:* info@tmstudios.com; tmcustomerservice@tmstudios.com *Web Site:* www.tmstudios.com, pg 1041

Lambert, Wendy, Palace Digital Studios, 29 N Main St, South Norwalk, CT 06854 *Tel:* 203-853-1740 *Fax:* 203-855-9608 *Web Site:* www.palacedigital.com, pg 967

Lamberti, Allan, TOA Electronics Inc, 1350 Bayshore Hwy, Suite 270, Burlingame, CA 94010 *Toll Free Tel:* 800-733-7088 (cust serv); 800-733-4750 (main) *Fax:* 650-588-3349 *Toll Free Fax:* 800-733-9766 *E-mail:* info@toaelectronics.com *Web Site:* www.toaelectronics.com, pg 1041

Lamicella, Laraine, Concepts TV Production, 328 W Main St, Boonton, NJ 07005 *Tel:* 973-331-1500 *Fax:* 973-331-1550 *E-mail:* sales@conceptstv.com *Web Site:* www.conceptstv.com, pg 835

Lammersseld, Don, Magnetic Shield Corp, 740 N Thomas Dr, Bensenville, IL 60106 *Tel:* 630-766-7800 *Toll Free Tel:* 888-766-7800 *Fax:* 630-766-2813 *E-mail:* shields@magnetic-shield.com *Web Site:* www.magnetic-shield.com, pg 928

Lamond, Joe, NAMM, the National Association of Music Merchants, 5790 Armada Dr, Carlsbad, CA 92008 *Tel:* 760-438-8001 *Toll Free Tel:* 800-767-6266 (memb hotline) *Fax:* 760-438-7327 *E-mail:* info@namm.org *Web Site:* www.namm.org, pg 1085

LaMont, Cheryl M, Dot C Software Inc, 117 Waihili Place, Honolulu, HI 96825 *Tel:* 808-744-0836 *E-mail:* info@dotcsw.com *Web Site:* www.dotcsw.com, pg 851

LaMont, Rick, Dot C Software Inc, 117 Waihili Place, Honolulu, HI 96825 *Tel:* 808-744-0836 *E-mail:* info@dotcsw.com *Web Site:* www.dotcsw.com, pg 851

LaMountain, Moira, Monterey County Film Commission, 801 Lighthouse Ave, Suite 104, Monterey, CA 93940 *Tel:* 831-646-0910 *Fax:* 831-655-9250 *E-mail:* info@filmmonterey.org *Web Site:* www.filmmonterey.org, pg 1093

Lampe, Jeanne A, Visual Education, PO Box 1666, Springfield, OH 45501-1666 *Toll Free Tel:* 800-243-7070 *Fax:* 937-324-5697 *E-mail:* sales@vis-ed.com *Web Site:* www.vis-ed.com, pg 1059

Lampert, Lori, Heinemann, 361 Hanover St, Portsmouth, NH 03801-3912 *Tel:* 603-431-7894 *Toll Free Tel:* 800-225-5800 *Fax:* 603-431-2214 *Toll Free Fax:* 877-231-6980 *E-mail:* custserv@heinemann.com *Web Site:* www.heinemann.com, pg 887

Lampert-Greaux, Ellen, St Barth Film Festival, 410 W 24 St, New York, NY 10011 *Tel:* 212-989-8004 *Fax:* 212-727-1774 *E-mail:* staff@stbarthff.org *Web Site:* www.stbarthff.org, pg 1126

Lamy, Dr Francis, X-Rite, 4300 44 St SE, Grand Rapids, MI 49512 *Tel:* 616-803-2100 *Toll Free Tel:* 800-248-9748 *E-mail:* info@xrite.com *Web Site:* www.xrite.com, pg 1071

Landers, Scott E, Monotype Inc, 500 Unicorn Park Dr, Woburn, MA 01801 *Tel:* 781-970-6000 *Toll Free Tel:* 800-424-8973 *Fax:* 781-970-6001; 781-970-6002 (gen questions) *Web Site:* www.monotype.com, pg 945

Landini, Melissa, Via Verde Productions, 22631 Pacific Coast Hwy, Suite 480, Malibu, CA 90265-5036 *Tel:* 310-458-3778 *Fax:* 310-496-2992 *E-mail:* info@viaverdedigital.com *Web Site:* www.viaverdedigital.com, pg 1053

Landow, William, Lighthouse Photo & Video Productions, 1100 Chicago Ave, Suite 2C, Goshen, IN 46528 *Tel:* 574-533-1400 (off); 574-202-5502 (studio) *E-mail:* lighthousevideo@gmail.com *Web Site:* www.lighthousephotoandvideo.com, pg 920

Landrum, Michael, Technical Innovation, 2975 Northwoods Pkwy, Norcross, GA 30071 *Tel:* 770-447-1001 *Toll Free Tel:* 866-447-1004 *Fax:* 770-441-5285 *Web Site:* www.technical-innovation.com, pg 1034

Landsberg, Hank, Henry Engineering, PO Box 3796, Seal Beach, CA 90740 *Tel:* 562-493-3589 *E-mail:* info@henryeng.com *Web Site:* www.henryeng.com, pg 888

Lane, Earl, AAAS Kavli Science Journalism Awards, 1200 New York Ave NW, Washington, DC 20005 *Tel:* 202-326-6431; 202-326-6440 *Fax:* 202-789-0455 *E-mail:* media@aaas.org *Web Site:* www.aaas.org, pg 1107

Lane, Lisa, American Color Imaging (ACI), 715 E 18 St, Cedar Falls, IA 50613 *Tel:* 319-277-3655 *Toll Free Tel:* 800-728-2722 *Fax:* 319-277-6522 *E-mail:* sales@acilab.com *Web Site:* www.acilab.com, pg 784

Lane, Mark, American Color Imaging (ACI), 715 E 18 St, Cedar Falls, IA 50613 *Tel:* 319-277-3655 *Toll Free Tel:* 800-728-2722 *Fax:* 319-277-6522 *E-mail:* sales@acilab.com *Web Site:* www.acilab.com, pg 784

Lane, Stacy Dohogne, Cape Girardeau Convention & Visitors Bureau, 400 Broadway St, Suite 100, Cape Girardeau, MO 63701 *Tel:* 573-335-1631 *Toll Free Tel:* 800-777-0068 *Fax:* 573-334-6702 *E-mail:* info@visitcape.com *Web Site:* visitcape.com, pg 1099

Lane, Woody, Garden Valley Productions, 240 Crystal Springs Lane, Roseburg, OR 97471 *Tel:* 541-440-1926 *Fax:* 541-440-1008, pg 875

Lang, David, Artech Electronics Ltd, PO Box 1547, Williston, VT 05495-1547 *Toll Free Tel:* 800-631-6448 *Toll Free Fax:* 800-934-7166 *E-mail:* info@artech-electronics.com *Web Site:* www.artech-electronics.com, pg 791

Langdon, Jonathan, Westbrook Technologies Inc, 35 Thorpe Ave, Suite 201, Wallingford, CT 06492 *Tel:* 203-871-4984 *Fax:* 203-269-0322 *E-mail:* info@westbrooktech.com *Web Site:* www.westbrooktech.com, pg 1064

Lange, Barbara, The Citation of Outstanding Service to the Society Award, 3 Barker Ave, 5th fl, White Plains, NY 10601 *Tel:* 914-761-1100 *Fax:* 914-761-3115 *E-mail:* smpte@smpte.org *Web Site:* www.smpte.org, pg 1112

Lange, Barbara, The Journal Award & SMPTE Journal Certificate of Merit, 3 Barker Ave, 5th fl, White Plains, NY 10601 *Tel:* 914-761-1100 *Fax:* 914-761-3115 *E-mail:* smpte@smpte.org *Web Site:* www.smpte.org, pg 1118

Lange, Barbara, The Presidential Proclamation Award, 3 Barker Ave, 5th fl, White Plains, NY 10601 *Tel:* 914-761-1100 *Fax:* 914-761-3115 *E-mail:* smpte@smpte.org *Web Site:* www.smpte.org, pg 1124

Lange, Barbara, The Progress Medal Award, 3 Barker Ave, 5th fl, White Plains, NY 10601 *Tel:* 914-761-1100 *Fax:* 914-761-3115 *E-mail:* smpte@smpte.org *Web Site:* www.smpte.org, pg 1124

Lange, Barbara, Society of Motion Picture & Television Engineers (SMPTE), 3 Barker Ave, 5th fl, White Plains, NY 10601 *Tel:* 914-761-1100 *Fax:* 914-761-3115 *E-mail:* smpte@smpte.org *Web Site:* www.smpte.org, pg 1015

Lange, Barbara, Society of Motion Picture & Television Engineers (SMPTE), 3 Barker Ave, 5th fl, White Plains, NY 10601 *Tel:* 914-761-1100 *Fax:* 914-761-3115 *E-mail:* membership@smpte.org *Web Site:* www.smpte.org, pg 1089

Lange, Barbara, Technicolor-Herbert T Kalmus Gold Medal Award, 3 Barker Ave, 5th fl, White Plains, NY 10601 *Tel:* 914-761-1100 *Fax:* 914-761-3115 *E-mail:* smpte@smpte.org *Web Site:* www.smpte.org, pg 1128

Lange, Barbara, The Samuel L Warner Memorial Award, 3 Barker Ave, 5th fl, White Plains, NY 10601 *Tel:* 914-761-1100 *Fax:* 914-761-3115 *E-mail:* smpte@smpte.org *Web Site:* www.smpte.org, pg 1129

Langford, Jassa, Digital Designs, 1141 NW First St, Oklahoma City, OK 73106 *Tel:* 405-239-2800 *Fax:* 405-239-7100 *E-mail:* ddtech@ddaudio.com *Web Site:* www.ddaudio.com, pg 847

Langhorst, Diane, Chicago Scenic Studios Inc, 1315 N Branch St, Chicago, IL 60642 *Tel:* 312-274-9900 *Fax:* 312-274-9901 *E-mail:* info@chicagoscenic.com *Web Site:* www.chicagoscenic.com, pg 825

Langlais, Jean, Sennheiser (Canada) Inc, 221 ave Labrosse, Pointe Claire, QC H9R 1A3, Canada *Tel:* 514-426-3013 *Toll Free Tel:* 800-463-1006 *Fax:* 514-426-3953 *Toll Free Fax:* 800-463-3013 *E-mail:* info@sennheiser.ca *Web Site:* www.sennheiser.ca, pg 1006

Langone, Christie, National Audiovisual Center - National Technical Information Service (NTIS), 5301 Shawnee Rd, Alexandria, VA 22312 *Tel:* 703-605-6000 *Toll Free Tel:* 800-553-6847 *Fax:* 703-605-6900 *E-mail:* info@ntis.gov *Web Site:* www.ntis.gov, pg 952

Lanier, James, Absolute Hollywood, 10232 Harvest Fields Dr, Woodstock, MD 21163 *Tel:* 443-341-6424 *E-mail:* events@absolutehollywood.com *Web Site:* www.absolutehollywood.com, pg 772

Lank, Barry, Lank/Beach Productions Inc, 341 Wardlaw Ave, Winnipeg, MB R3L 0L5, Canada *Tel:* 204-452-9422 *E-mail:* info@lankbeach.com *Web Site:* www.lankbeach.com, pg 916

Lank, Luanne, Lank/Beach Productions Inc, 341 Wardlaw Ave, Winnipeg, MB R3L 0L5, Canada *Tel:* 204-452-9422 *E-mail:* info@lankbeach.com *Web Site:* www.lankbeach.com, pg 916

Lannan, J Patrick Jr, Lannan Foundation, 313 Read St, Santa Fe, NM 87501-2628 *Tel:* 505-986-8160 *Fax:* 505-986-8195 *E-mail:* info@lannan.org *Web Site:* www.lannan.org, pg 916

Lansdell, Jeff, CEV Multimedia Ltd, 1020 SE Loop 289, Lubbock, TX 79404 *Toll Free Tel:* 800-922-9965 *Toll Free Fax:* 800-243-6398 *E-mail:* cev@cevmultimedia.com *Web Site:* www.cevmultimedia.com, pg 823

Lansing, John, Cable & Telecommunications Association for Marketing (CTAM), 120 Waterfront St, Suite 200, National Harbor, MD 20745 *Tel:* 301-485-8900 *Fax:* 301-560-4964 *E-mail:* info@ctam.com *Web Site:* www.ctam.com, pg 1080

Lant, Carol, Infonics Inc, 2302 E Michigan Blvd, Michigan City, IN 46360 *Tel:* 219-879-3381 *Fax:* 219-879-3383 *E-mail:* infonics@sbcglobal.net, pg 898

Lanter, Jeff, Trailblazer Studios®, 1610 Midtown Place, Raleigh, NC 27609 *Tel:* 919-645-6600 *Fax:* 919-645-6601 *Web Site:* www.trailblazerstudios.com, pg 1043

Lanza, Mark, Golden Reel Awards, 10061 Riverside Dr, PMB 751, Toluca Lake, CA 91602-2550 *Tel:* 818-506-7731 *Fax:* 818-506-7732 *E-mail:* mail@mpse.org; info@mpse.org *Web Site:* www.mpse.org, pg 1115

Lanzano, Steven, Television Bureau of Advertising Inc (TVB), 120 Wall St, 15th fl, New York, NY 10005-3908 *Tel:* 212-486-1111 *Fax:* 212-935-5631 *E-mail:* info@tvb.org *Web Site:* www.tvb.org, pg 1090

Lanzer, Mona E, Video Aided Instruction Inc, 485-34 S Broadway, Hicksville, NY 11801-5071 *Tel:* 516-939-0707 *Toll Free Tel:* 800-238-1512 *Toll Free Fax:* 800-588-1419 *E-mail:* custsvc@videoaidedinstruction.com *Web Site:* www.videoaidedinstruction.com, pg 1054

Lanzer, Peter, Video Aided Instruction Inc, 485-34 S Broadway, Hicksville, NY 11801-5071 *Tel:* 516-939-0707 *Toll Free Tel:* 800-238-1512 *Toll Free Fax:* 800-588-1419 *E-mail:* custsvc@videoaidedinstruction.com *Web Site:* www.videoaidedinstruction.com, pg 1054

Lanzet, Gary, A-V Services Inc, 99 Fairfield Rd, Fairfield, NJ 07004 *Tel:* 973-575-5222 *Fax:* 973-575-0857 *E-mail:* sales@avservices.net *Web Site:* www.avservices.net, pg 771

Lanzoni, Joe, Lightning Eliminators & Consultants Inc, 6687 Arapahoe Rd, Boulder, CO 80303 *Tel:* 303-447-2828 *Toll Free Tel:* 800-521-6101 *Fax:* 303-447-8122 *E-mail:* info@lightningprotection.com *Web Site:* www.lightningprotection.com, pg 921

Lapides, Murray, AVFX Inc, 96 Holton St, Boston, MA 02135 *Tel:* 617-254-0770 *Toll Free Tel:* 888-254-0770 *E-mail:* info@avfx.com *Web Site:* www.avfx.com, pg 798

Lapin, Philip, Falcon Safety Products Inc, 25 Imclone Dr, Branchburg, NJ 08876 *Tel:* 908-707-4900 *Toll Free Tel:* 800-332-5266 (cust serv ext 1) *Fax:* 908-707-8855 *Web Site:* www.falconsafety.com, pg 865

Laplante, Jaie, Miami International Film Festival, 300 NE Second Ave, Miami, FL 33132 *Tel:* 305-237-FILM (237-3456) *Fax:* 305-237-7344 *E-mail:* info@miamifilmfestival.com *Web Site:* miamifilmfestival.com, pg 1120

Lapointe, Frederic, STIL Casing Solution, 76 Saint Paul, Suite 301, Quebec City, QC G1K 3V9, Canada *Tel:* 418-694-0449 (ext 10); 418-694-0449 (ext 11, sales & cust serv); 418-694-0449 (ext 12, admin) *Toll Free Tel:* 888-414-0449 (CN & US) *Fax:* 418-694-1621 *E-mail:* info@stilcasing.com; sales@stilcasing.com; admin@stilcasing.com *Web Site:* www.stilcasing.com, pg 1025

Largen, Joseph, Brodart Co, 500 Arch St, Williamsport, PA 17701 *Tel:* 570-769-3265 *Toll Free Tel:* 888-820-4377 *Toll Free Fax:* 800-283-6087 *E-mail:* supplies.customerservice@brodart.com *Web Site:* www.shopbrodart.com, pg 813

Larimer, Celine, Boston Light & Sound Inc, 290 N Beacon St, Boston, MA 02135-1990 *Tel:* 617-787-3131 *Fax:* 617-787-4257 *E-mail:* info@blsi.com *Web Site:* www.blsi.com, pg 811

Larkin, Dennis, Adrenaline Films, 5224 S Orange Ave, Orlando, FL 32809 *Tel:* 407-850-0711 *Fax:* 407-859-6527 *E-mail:* contact@adrenalinefilms.com *Web Site:* www.adrenalinefilms.com, pg 777

LaRoche, Andre, Stage 3 Productions, 27500 Donald Ct, Warren, MI 48092 *Tel:* 586-576-0625 *Toll Free Tel:* 888-330-5179 *Web Site:* www.stage3.com, pg 1023

Larond, Richard, Capron Lighting & Sound Co Inc, 278 West St, Needham, MA 02494 *Tel:* 781-444-8850 *Fax:* 781-444-1408 *E-mail:* info@capron.net *Web Site:* www.capron.net, pg 820

Larrick, Robert W Jr, CALIBRE, Metro Park, 6354 Walker Lane, Alexandria, VA 22310-3252 *Tel:* 703-797-8500 *Toll Free Tel:* 888-CALIBRE (225-4273) *Fax:* 703-797-8501 *E-mail:* info@calibresys.com *Web Site:* www.calibresys.com, pg 817

Larsen, Patricia, Small World Productions Inc, 140 Lakeside Ave, Suite 200, Seattle, WA 98122 *Tel:* 206-329-7167 *Toll Free Tel:* 800-866-7425 (orders) *E-mail:* info@travelsmallworld.com *Web Site:* www.smarttravels.tv, pg 1013

Larson, Betsy, NEC Display Solutions of America, 500 Park Blvd, Suite 1100, Itasca, IL 60143 *Tel:* 630-467-3000 *Web Site:* www.necdisplay.com, pg 954

Larson, Brian, GES Audio Visual, 7000 Lindell Rd, Las Vegas, NV 89118 *Tel:* 702-515-5500 *Toll Free Tel:* 800-443-9767 *Fax:* 702-515-5765 *E-mail:* lasvegas@ges.com *Web Site:* ges.com, pg 877

Larson, Dave, Music Manufacturing Services, 636 King St W, Toronto, ON M5V 1M7, Canada *Tel:* 416-364-1943 *Toll Free Tel:* 800-MMS-4CDS (667-4237) *Fax:* 416-364-3616 *E-mail:* info@musicmanufacturing.com *Web Site:* www.musicmanufacturing.com; www.mmsdirect.com, pg 950

Larson, Elaine, Agency for Instructional Technology (AIT), 8111 N Lee Paul Rd, Bloomington, IN 47404-7916 *Tel:* 812-339-2203 *Toll Free Tel:* 800-457-4509 *Fax:* 812-333-4218 *E-mail:* info@ait.net *Web Site:* www.ait.net, pg 778

Larson, Jack, Avatar Studios, 2675 Scott Ave, Suite G, St Louis, MO 63103 *Tel:* 314-533-2242 *Fax:* 314-533-3349 *Web Site:* www.avatar-studios.com, pg 798

Larson, Jay, Genigraphics®, PO Box 860111, Shawnee, KS 66286-0111 *Tel:* 913-441-1410 *Toll Free Tel:* 800-790-4001 (cust serv) *E-mail:* info@genigraphics.com *Web Site:* www.genigraphics.com, pg 877

Larson, Keith, Winegard Co, 2736 Mt Pleasant St, Suite 140, Burlington, IA 52601 *Tel:* 319-754-0600 *Toll Free Tel:* 800-288-8094 *Fax:* 319-754-0787 *Toll Free Fax:* 800-247-8221 *Web Site:* www.winegard.com, pg 1068

Larson, Mike, StoryTrack, 212 S Bemiston, St Louis, MO 63105 *Tel:* 314-725-3003 *Web Site:* www.storytrack.com, pg 1025

Lashman, Terry O, Sun Entertainment Corp, 3106 Belmont Blvd, Nashville, TN 37212 *Tel:* 615-385-1960 *E-mail:* info@sunrecords.com *Web Site:* www.sunrecords.com, pg 1028

Laskowski, Chris, C Vision Productions, 5533 144 Ave NW, Ramsey, MN 55303-5646 *Tel:* 763-577-1358 *Toll Free Tel:* 888-827-3287 *Fax:* 763-577-1359 *Web Site:* www.cvisionproductions.com, pg 816

Lasseter, John, Pixar Animation Studios, 1200 Park Ave, Emeryville, CA 94608 *Tel:* 510-922-3000 *Toll Free Tel:* 800-888-9856 *Fax:* 510-922-3151 *E-mail:* ir@pixar.com (investor rel) *Web Site:* www.pixar.com, pg 976

Laster, Michael, Academy of Science Fiction, Fantasy & Horror Films, 334 W 54 St, Los Angeles, CA 90037 *Tel:* 323-752-5811 *E-mail:* scifiacademy@ca.rr.com *Web Site:* www.saturnawards.org, pg 1075

Laster, Michael, Saturn Awards, 334 W 54 St, Los Angeles, CA 90037 *Tel:* 323-752-5811 *Web Site:* www.saturnawards.org, pg 1126

Latenser, Elizabeth, Sundance Film Festival, 1825 Three Kings Dr, Park City, UT 84060 *Tel:* 435-658-3456 *Fax:* 435-658-3457 *E-mail:* customerservice@sundance.org; press@sundance.org; institute@sundance.org *Web Site:* www.sundance.org/festival/, pg 1128

Latimer, Bruce, WESCAM Inc, 649 N Service Rd W, Burlington, ON L7P 5B9, Canada *Tel:* 905-633-4000 *Toll Free Tel:* 800-668-4355 *Fax:* 905-633-4100 *E-mail:* sales.wescam@l-3com.com *Web Site:* www.wescam.com, pg 1063

Lau, David, The Brookwood Studio Inc, 6870 N Territorial Rd, Plymouth, MI 48170 *Tel:* 734-358-6071 *E-mail:* info@brookwoodstudio.com *Web Site:* www.brookwoodstudio.com, pg 814

Laudicina, Sal, Motion Picture Licensing Corp (MPLC), 5455 Centinela Ave, Los Angeles, CA 90066 *Tel:* 310-822-8855 (intl calls) *Toll Free Tel:* 800-462-8855 *Fax:* 310-822-4440 *Web Site:* www.mplc.org, pg 947

Lauer, Jean Anne, Cine Las Americas International Film Festival (CLAIFF), 81 San Marcos St, Austin, TX 78702 *Tel:* 512-535-0765 *Fax:* 512-535-6268 *E-mail:* cine@cinelasamericas.org *Web Site:* www.cinelasamericas.org; www.facebook.com/cinelasamericasaustin, pg 1112

Laufer, Amy, Kimbo Educational, 10 N Third Ave, Long Branch, NJ 07740 *Tel:* 732-229-4949 *Toll Free Tel:* 800-631-2187 *Fax:* 732-870-3340 *E-mail:* kimboed@aol.com *Web Site:* www.kimboed.com, pg 910

Laukys, Amanda, Picture Box Distribution Inc, 141 E 23 Ave, Vancouver, BC V5V 1X1, Canada *Tel:* 604-681-3174 *Fax:* 604-608-9081 *E-mail:* info@picturebox.ca *Web Site:* www.picturebox.ca, pg 975

Lauman, Ellis, Interactive Products, 101 Commerce Dr, Montgomeryville, PA 18936 *Tel:* 215-362-2766 *Toll Free Tel:* 800-523-6716 *Fax:* 215-361-0167 *E-mail:* numonics@numonics.com *Web Site:* www.numonics.com, pg 900

Laurance, James, Audiomoxie®, PO Box 304, Georgetown, TX 78627 *E-mail:* info@audiomoxie.com *Web Site:* www.audiomoxie.com, pg 796

Lauro, Joseph, Historic Films, 211 Third St, Greenport, NY 11944 *Tel:* 631-477-9700 *Toll Free Tel:* 800-249-1940 *Fax:* 631-477-9800 *E-mail:* info@historicfilms.com *Web Site:* www.historicfilms.com, pg 889

Lauten, Bill, Action Sports/All Stock, PO Box 301, Malibu, CA 90265-0301 *Tel:* 310-459-2526 *Fax:* 310-456-1743 *E-mail:* info@sdfilms.com *Web Site:* www.actionsportsstockfootage.com, pg 775

Lauzon-Rosato, Nadine, Agfa Graphics, 611 River Dr, Ctr 3, Elmwood Park, NJ 07407 *Tel:* 201-440-2500 *Toll Free Tel:* 800-540-2432 *Web Site:* www.agfagraphics.com; www.agfa.com, pg 778

Lavi, Amir, SintecMedia, 425 Madison Ave, Suite 1602, New York, NY 10017 *Tel:* 917-606-5310 *Fax:* 917-606-5311 *E-mail:* sales@sintecmedia.com *Web Site:* www.sintecmedia.com, pg 1012

LaVine, Jerry, Connections Film & Video Inc, PO Box 110929, Anchorage, AK 99511 *Tel:* 907-561-6450 *Web Site:* www.filmalaska.com, pg 835

Lavitt, Pamela, Seattle Jewish Film Festival (SJFF), 3801 E Mercer Way, Mercer Island, WA 98040 *Tel:* 206-232-7115 *Fax:* 206-232-7119 *E-mail:* sjff@sjcc.org *Web Site:* www.seattlejewishfilmfestival.org, pg 1127

Lawhead, Scott, Hite Co, 3101 Beale Ave, Altoona, PA 16601 *Tel:* 814-944-6121 *Toll Free Tel:* 800-252-3598 *Fax:* 814-944-3052 *Web Site:* www.hiteco.com, pg 889

Lawler, Frank C, Lannan Foundation, 313 Read St, Santa Fe, NM 87501-2628 *Tel:* 505-986-8160 *Fax:* 505-986-8195 *E-mail:* info@lannan.org *Web Site:* www.lannan.org, pg 916

Lawrence, Dean, Hooper Camera & Imaging, 21902 Devonshire St, Chatsworth, CA 91311-2907 *Tel:* 818-709-0014 *Fax:* 818-709-0130 *E-mail:* sales@hoopercamera.com *Web Site:* hoopercamera.com, pg 891

Lawrence, Donna, Donna Lawrence Productions, 624 Baxter Ave, Louisville, KY 40204 *Tel:* 502-589-9617 *E-mail:* dlp@dlproductions.com *Web Site:* www.dlproductions.com, pg 917

Lawrence, Nate, ECS Inc, 5665 Tremont Ave, Davenport, IA 52807-2658 *Tel:* 563-322-1525 *Fax:* 563-322-5920 *Web Site:* www.ecsdav.com, pg 856

Lawrence, R Scott, Videorama Industries LLC, 1119 N Hudson Ave, Hollywood, CA 90038 *Tel:* 323-466-7232 *Fax:* 323-466-7228 *Web Site:* www.videorama.com, pg 1057

Lawrence, Rex, ECS Inc, 5665 Tremont Ave, Davenport, IA 52807-2658 *Tel:* 563-322-1525 *Fax:* 563-322-5920 *Web Site:* www.ecsdav.com, pg 856

Lawrie, Mike, Computer Sciences Corp, 3170 Fairview Park Dr, Falls Church, VA 22042 *Tel:* 703-876-1000 *Web Site:* www.csc.com, pg 834

Lawson, Bill, Linguistic Systems Inc, 201 Broadway, Cambridge, MA 02139 *Tel:* 617-528-7400 *Toll Free Tel:* 877-654-5006 *Fax:* 617-528-7491 *Web Site:* linguist.com, pg 922

Lawson, David, Lex Lawson Associates, 2002 Platinum St, Garland, TX 75042 *Tel:* 972-272-8482 *Toll Free Tel:* 800-783-9395 *Fax:* 972-276-8120 *Web Site:* www.lexlawson.com, pg 917

Lawson, Stephen, Biomorph Desks, 11 Broadway, Rm 905, New York, NY 10004 *Tel:* 212-809-4323 *Toll Free Tel:* 888-302-DESK (302-3375) *Toll Free Fax:* 888-652-7137 *E-mail:* info@biomorphdesk.com *Web Site:* www.biomorphdesk.com, pg 807

Lawson, Stephen E, Rees Associates, Rees Plaza at East Wharf, Suite 300, 9211 Lake Hefner Pkwy, Oklahoma City, OK 73120 *Tel:* 405-942-7337 *Fax:* 405-948-1261 *E-mail:* rees@rees-associates.com *Web Site:* www.rees.com, pg 994

Lay, Bruno, Amerinex Applied Imaging Inc, PO Box 6473, Monroe Township, NJ 08831-6473 *Tel:* 609-944-8855 *Toll Free Tel:* 877-664-8772 *Fax:* 609-944-8855 *E-mail:* info@amerineximaging.com *Web Site:* www.amerineximaging.com, pg 785

Lazaris, Spyros, Audio Precision, 5750 SW Arctic Dr, Beaverton, OR 97005 *Tel:* 503-627-0832 *Toll Free Tel:* 800-231-7350 *Fax:* 503-469-0336 *E-mail:* sales@ap.com *Web Site:* www.ap.com, pg 794

Lazaros, Nancy, Extreme Reach Inc, 75 Second Ave, Suite 720, Needham, MA 02494 *Tel:* 781-577-2016 *E-mail:* sales@extremereach.com; press@extremereach.com *Web Site:* www.extremereach.com, pg 864

Lazarus, Alison, Macmillan Audio, 175 Fifth Ave, New York, NY 10010 *Tel:* 646-600-7856; 646-307-5742 *Toll Free Tel:* 888-330-8477 (orders); 800-221-7945 *Toll Free Fax:* 800-672-7703 (orders) *E-mail:* macmillan.audio@macmillanusa.com *Web Site:* us.macmillan.com/audio.aspx, pg 927

Lazarus, Ann, International Association of Business Communicators (IABC), 601 Montgomery St, Suite 1900, San Francisco, CA 94111 *Tel:* 415-544-4700 *Toll Free Tel:* 800-776-4222 *Fax:* 415-544-4747 *E-mail:* member_relations@iabc.com *Web Site:* www.iabc.com, pg 1083

Lazarus, Margaret, Cambridge Documentary Films Inc, 3099 Hidden Valley Lane, Santa Barbara, CA 93108 *Tel:* 617-484-3993 *E-mail:* info@cambridgedocumentaryfilms.org *Web Site:* www.cambridgedocumentaryfilms.org, pg 818

Lazarus, Marty, Chicago Spotlight Inc, 1658 W Carroll St, Chicago, IL 60612 *Tel:* 312-455-1171 *Fax:* 312-455-1744 *Web Site:* www.chicagospotlight.com, pg 825

Le, Anderson, Hawaii International Film Festival, 680 Iwilei Rd, Suite 100, Honolulu, HI 96817 *Tel:* 808-792-1577 *Fax:* 808-749-7783 *E-mail:* info@hiff.org *Web Site:* www.hiff.org, pg 1116

Le Duc, Greg, Aaron & Le Duc, 2210 Third St, No 316, Santa Monica, CA 90405 *Tel:* 310-452-2034, pg 772

Le Fever, Don, Tepco Corp, 2603 Bridgeview Dr, Rapid City, SD 57701-5801 *Tel:* 605-343-7200 *Fax:* 605-343-7240 *E-mail:* tepco@rapidnet.com *Web Site:* www.rapidnet.com/~tepco, pg 1037

Le Hardy, Ward, Once Around, 194 Castle Lane, Kilmarnock, VA 22482 *Tel:* 804-436-8904 *E-mail:* wardjudy56@verizon.net, pg 963

Le Porte, Steven, Syracuse Scenery & Stage Lighting Co Inc, 101 Monarch Dr, Liverpool, NY 13088-4514 *Tel:* 315-453-8096 *Toll Free Tel:* 800-453-7775 *Fax:* 315-453-7897 *E-mail:* info@syracusescenery.com *Web Site:* www.syracusescenery.com, pg 1031

Lea, Michael, River Road Recorders (RRR), 122 Crislaur Ave, Harahan, LA 70123-5025 *Tel:* 504-737-9880 *Fax:* 504-324-1920 *E-mail:* info@rivrd.com, pg 997

Leach, Jim, JFW Industries Inc, 5134 Commerce Square Dr, Indianapolis, IN 46237 *Tel:* 317-887-1340 *Toll Free Tel:* 877-887-4539 *Fax:* 317-881-6790 *E-mail:* sales@jfwindustries.com; jfwengr@jfwindustries.com *Web Site:* www.jfwindustries.com, pg 905

Leadore, D, ASC Systems, Mack Place, 566, St Clair Shores, MI 48080-0566 *Tel:* 313-882-1133 *E-mail:* ascsystems@live.com *Web Site:* www.airi.com, pg 791

Leake, Harry, UMCom Productions, 810 12 Ave S, Nashville, TN 37203 *Tel:* 615-742-5400 *Fax:* 615-742-5469 *E-mail:* umcom@umcom.org *Web Site:* www.umcom.org, pg 1048

Leamon, Scott, American Visions, One Deerfield Lane, Cedar Rapids, IA 52403 *Tel:* 319-360-3211 *E-mail:* info@americanvisions.org *Web Site:* www.americanvisions.org, pg 785

Leamy, Ted, Pro Media/Ultra Sound, 800 Alfred Nobel Dr, Hercules, CA 94547 *Tel:* 510-741-2925 *Toll Free Tel:* 800-969-7686 (sales) *Fax:* 510-741-0790 *E-mail:* service@ultrapromedia.com *Web Site:* www.promediausa.com, pg 983

Leard, Leland, Music Hall LLC, 108 Station Rd, Great Neck, NY 11023 *Tel:* 516-487-3663 *Fax:* 516-773-3891 *E-mail:* info@musichallaudio.com *Web Site:* musichall.biz, pg 950

Leasure, Mary, CADint, 10517 W Bellarose Dr, Sun City, AZ 85351-2241 *Tel:* 303-520-0907 *Toll Free Tel:* 800-553-1177 (ext 12) *Fax:* 707-924-0907 *E-mail:* info@cadint.com; sales@cadint.com *Web Site:* www.cadint.com, pg 816

Leathers, Craig, Convergent Media Systems, 190 Bluegrass Valley Pkwy, Alpharetta, GA 30005-2204 *Tel:* 770-369-9000 *Toll Free Tel:* 800-877-7804 *Fax:* 770-369-9100 *E-mail:* convergent@convergent.com *Web Site:* www.convergent.com, pg 836

Leavelle, Kaye, Romar Learning, 6700 Woodlands Pkwy, Suite 230-292, Woodlands, TX 77382 *Tel:* 281-292-5508 *Fax:* 281-363-2309 *E-mail:* info@romarlearning.com *Web Site:* www.romarlearning.com, pg 999

Leban, Lexi, San Francisco Jewish Film Festival, 145 Ninth St, Suite 200, San Francisco, CA 94103 *Tel:* 415-621-0556 *Fax:* 415-621-0568 *E-mail:* jewishfilm@sfjff.org *Web Site:* www.sfjff.org, pg 1126

LeBlanc, Brenda, Mohawk, 324 Clark St, Worcester, MA 01606 *Tel:* 978-537-9961 *Toll Free Tel:* 800-422-9961 *Fax:* 978-537-4358 *E-mail:* info@mohawk-cable.com *Web Site:* www.mohawk-cable.com, pg 945

LeBrecht, James, Berkeley Sound Artists Inc, 2600 Tenth St, Suite 312, Berkeley, CA 94710 *Tel:* 510-486-2290 *Fax:* 510-549-0287 *E-mail:* info@berkeleysoundartists.com *Web Site:* www.berkeleysoundartists.com, pg 805

LeClair, Jeffrey, JL Recording Studios, 270 Adelaide St W, Suite 202, Toronto, ON M5H 1X6, Canada *Tel:* 416-598-7979 *Web Site:* www.jlstudios.ca; www.facebook.com/jlrecordingstudios; twitter.com/JLStudios, pg 905

Leddy, Kevin J, Time Warner Cable, 60 Columbus Circle, 17th fl, New York, NY 10023 *Tel:* 212-364-8200 *Web Site:* www.timewarnercable.com, pg 1040

Lederman, Jan, Benro, 75 Virginia Rd, Suite 1, North White Plains, NY 10603 *Tel:* 914-347-3300 *Fax:* 914-347-3309 *E-mail:* info@benrousa.com *Web Site:* www.benrousa.com, pg 805

Lederman, Jan, Bowens USA, 75 Virginia Rd, North White Plains, NY 10603 *Tel:* 914-347-3300 *Fax:* 914-347-3309 *Web Site:* www.bowensusa.com, pg 811

Lederman, Jan, Induro, 75 Virginia Rd, North White Plains, NY 10603 *Tel:* 914-347-3300 *Fax:* 914-347-3309 *E-mail:* info@indurogear.com *Web Site:* www.indurogear.com, pg 897

Lederman, Jan, Mamiya, 75 Virginia Rd, Suite 1, North White Plains, NY 10603 *Tel:* 914-347-3300 *Fax:* 914-347-3309 *E-mail:* info@mamiya-usa.com *Web Site:* www.mamiya-usa.com; www.mamiyaleaf.com, pg 929

Lederman, Mr Jan, Sekonic, 75 Virginia Rd, North White Plains, NY 10603 *Tel:* 914-347-3300 *Fax:* 914-347-3309 *E-mail:* info@macgroupus.com *Web Site:* www.sekonic.com; www.macgroupus.com, pg 1006

Lederman, Mr Jan, Tenba, 75 Virginia Rd, North White Plains, NY 10603 *Tel:* 914-347-3300 *Fax:* 914-347-3309 *E-mail:* info@tenba.com *Web Site:* www.tenba.com, pg 1037

Lederman, Janet, Flash Clinic Inc, 164 W 25 St, New York, NY 10001 *Tel:* 212-337-0447 *Toll Free Tel:* 800-752-7536 *Fax:* 212-337-8088 *E-mail:* info@flashclinic.com *Web Site:* www.flashclinic.com, pg 869

Lederman, Marvin, Colortone Audio Visual, 75 Virginia Rd, White Plains, NY 10603 *Tel:* 914-592-4151 *Fax:* 914-592-2833 *Web Site:* www.colortone-av.com, pg 832

Lederman, Norman, Oval Window Audio, 33 Wildflower Ct, Nederland, CO 80466 *Tel:* 303-447-3607 *Fax:* 303-447-3607 *E-mail:* info@ovalwindowaudio.com *Web Site:* www.ovalwindowaudio.com, pg 966

Lee, Edgy, FilmWorks Pacific, PO Box 61281, Honolulu, HI 96839-1281 *Tel:* 808-599-6403 (studio) *Fax:* 808-537-9272 *E-mail:* studio@filmworkspacific.com *Web Site:* www.filmworkspacific.com, pg 868

Lee, Finley, Alien Skin Software LLC, 1111 Haynes St, Suite 113, Raleigh, NC 27604 *Tel:* 919-832-4124 *Toll Free Tel:* 888-921-7546 *Fax:* 919-832-4065 *E-mail:* sales@alienskin.com *Web Site:* www.alienskin.com, pg 780

Lee, Ho-Shang, DiCon Fiberoptics Inc, 1689 Regatta Blvd, Richmond, CA 94804 *Tel:* 510-620-5000; 510-620-5200 (sales) *Fax:* 510-620-4100; 510-620-4102 (sales) *E-mail:* info@diconfiber.com; sales@diconfiber.com *Web Site:* www.diconfiberoptics.com, pg 846

Lee, James, 16 x 9 Inc, 28314 Constellation Rd, Valencia, CA 91355 *Tel:* 661-295-3313 *Toll Free Tel:* 866-800-1699 *Fax:* 661-295-3314 *E-mail:* info@16x9inc.com *Web Site:* www.16x9inc.com, pg 1012

Lee, Julia, Community Professional Loudspeakers, 333 E Fifth St, Chester, PA 19013-4511 *Tel:* 610-876-3400 *Toll Free Tel:* 800-523-4934 *Fax:* 610-874-0190 *E-mail:* info@communitypro.com *Web Site:* www.communitypro.com, pg 833

Lee, Julie, Arizona Production Association, 6615 N Scottsdale Rd, Suite 101, Scottsdale, AZ 85250 *Tel:* 480-345-6464 *Toll Free Tel:* 866-345-6469 *Fax:* 480-941-2557 *E-mail:* info@azproduction.com *Web Site:* www.azproduction.com, pg 1077

Lee, Dr Lester, Recortec Inc, 3329 Kifer Rd, Santa Clara, CA 95051-0719 *Tel:* 408-928-1480 *Toll Free Tel:* 800-729-7654 *Fax:* 408-928-1489 *E-mail:* info@recortec.com; support@recortec.com; sales@recortec.com *Web Site:* www.recortec.com, pg 993

Lee, Linda, Weston Woods Studios Inc, 90 Old Sherman Tpke, Danbury, CT 06816 *Tel:* 203-797-3520 *Toll Free Tel:* 800-243-5020 *Fax:* 203-797-3531 *E-mail:* westonwoodsquestions@scholastic.com *Web Site:* www.scholastic.com/westonwoods, pg 1064

Lee, Lori, American Optometric Association (AOA), 243 N Lindbergh Blvd, 1st fl, St Louis, MO 63141-7881 *Tel:* 314-991-4100 *Toll Free Tel:* 800-365-2219 *Fax:* 314-991-4101 *Web Site:* www.aoa.org, pg 1077

Lee, Noel, Monster Cable Products Inc, 455 Valley Dr, Brisbane, CA 94005-1209 *Tel:* 415-840-2000 *Fax:* 415-468-0311 *Web Site:* www.monstercable.com, pg 945

Lee, Thomas, The Audio Visual Co (AVCO), 98-810 Moanalua Rd, Aiea, HI 96701 *Tel:* 808-485-3200 *Fax:* 808-487-0733 *Web Site:* www.theavco.com, pg 795

Lefebvre, Alan J, Best Film & Video, 3913 Fall Wheat Dr, Plano, TX 75075 *Tel:* 214-395-4070 *Web Site:* www.bestfilmandvideo.com, pg 805

Lefebvre, Gilles, Les Editions CEC Inc, 9001 boul Louis-H-La Fontaine, Anjou, QC H1J 2C5, Canada *Tel:* 514-351-6010 *Toll Free Tel:* 800-363-0494 *Fax:* 514-351-3534 *Web Site:* www.editionscec.com, pg 857

Leffingwell, Ken, Wegener Communications, Technology Park, 11350 Technology Circle, Johns Creek, GA 30097 *Tel:* 770-814-4000; 770-814-4021 (sales); 770-814-4057 (cust serv) *Toll Free Tel:* 800-848-9467 (cust serv) *Fax:* 770-623-0698; 770-232-0621 (cust serv) *E-mail:* info@wegener.com; globalsales@wegener.com; service@wegener.com *Web Site:* www.wegener.com, pg 1063

Legband, Nate, Convergent Media Systems, 190 Bluegrass Valley Pkwy, Alpharetta, GA 30005-2204 *Tel:* 770-369-9000 *Toll Free Tel:* 800-877-7804 *Fax:* 770-369-9100 *E-mail:* convergent@convergent.com *Web Site:* www.convergent.com, pg 836

Legg, Pat, MotionMasters, 2288 Roxalana Rd, Dunbar, WV 25064 *Tel:* 304-345-8800 *Fax:* 304-345-8809 *E-mail:* storytellers@motionmasters.com *Web Site:* motionmasters.com, pg 947

Leggett, Robert, Tellabs Inc, One Tellabs Ctr, 1415 W Diehl Rd, Naperville, IL 60563 *Tel:* 630-798-8800 *Fax:* 630-798-2000 *Web Site:* www.tellabs.com, pg 1037

Legnini, Ray, Aviom Inc, 1157 Phoenixville Pike, Suite 201, West Chester, PA 19380-4254 *Tel:* 610-738-9005 *Fax:* 610-738-9950 *E-mail:* info@aviom.com *Web Site:* www.aviom.com, pg 799

Legniowski, William, PixeLINK, 1900 City Park Dr, Suite 410, Ottawa, ON K1J 1A3, Canada *Tel:* 613-247-1211 *Fax:* 613-247-2001 *E-mail:* sales@pixelink.com *Web Site:* www.pixelink.com, pg 976

Legris, Paul T, PTL Test Equipment Inc, 612 N Orange Ave, Suite D-10, Jupiter, FL 33458 *Tel:* 561-747-3647 *Fax:* 561-575-4635 *E-mail:* ptltest@bellsouth.net *Web Site:* www.ptltest.com, pg 987

Lehman, Allison, KickedUp Media Group Inc, 2 Amherst Dr, Hastings-on-Hudson, NY 10706 *Tel:* 914-693-KICK (693-5425) *E-mail:* info@kickedupmediagroup.com *Web Site:* www.kickedupmediagroup.com, pg 910

LeHoven, Susan, TV Juice Productions Inc, PO Box 843, Kilauea, HI 96754-0843 *Tel:* 808-828-0101; 808-828-0434 *E-mail:* fido@tvjuice.com *Web Site:* www.tvjuice.com, pg 1046

LeHoven, Tony, TV Juice Productions Inc, PO Box 843, Kilauea, HI 96754-0843 *Tel:* 808-828-0101; 808-828-0434 *E-mail:* fido@tvjuice.com *Web Site:* www.tvjuice.com, pg 1046

Leibrecht, Gina, Les Blank Films Inc, 10341 San Pablo Ave, El Cerrito, CA 94530-3123 *Tel:* 510-525-0942 *Toll Free Tel:* 800-572-7618 *Fax:* 510-525-1204 *E-mail:* lesblankfilmsinc@gmail.com, pg 809

Leif, Laura, Quickdraw Animation Society, 351 11 Ave SW, Suite 201, Calgary, AB T2R 0C7, Canada *Tel:* 403-261-5767 *Fax:* 403-261-5644 *E-mail:* info@quickdrawanimation.ca; production@quickdrawanimation.ca; programming@quickdrawanimation.ca *Web Site:* quickdrawanimation.ca; www.giraffest.ca, pg 1088

Leifert, Robert, Sima Products Corp, 125 Commerce Dr, Hauppauge, NY 11788 *Tel:* 631-435-0200 *Toll Free Tel:* 800-345-7462; 800-274-7824 *Fax:* 631-435-4545 *Toll Free Fax:* 800-274-7828 *E-mail:* info@simacorp.com; custserv@simacorp.com; customerservice@aristagroup.com *Web Site:* www.aristagroup.com, pg 1011

Leighton-Levy, Marian, Rounder Records, 1209 Pine St, Suite 100, Nashville, TN 37203 *Web Site:* www.rounder.com, pg 1000

Leitensdorfer, Rita, Communitronics Corp, 970 Bolger Ct, Fenton, MO 63026 *Tel:* 314-771-7160 *Fax:* 314-771-9144 *E-mail:* info@communitronics.com *Web Site:* www.communitronics.com, pg 833

Leitner, Marc, Safe Harbor Computers, 530 W Oklahoma Ave, Suite 500, Milwaukee, WI 53207 *Tel:* 414-615-4560 *Toll Free Tel:* 800-544-6599 *Fax:* 414-615-4567 *E-mail:* sales@sharbor.com *Web Site:* www.sharbor.com, pg 1001

Leland, Matt, Burk Technology Inc, 7 Beaver Brook Rd, Littleton, MA 01460 *Tel:* 978-486-0086 *Toll Free Tel:* 800-255-8090 *Fax:* 978-486-0081 *E-mail:* sales@burk.com; orders@burk.com *Web Site:* www.burk.com, pg 815

Lemisch, Amy, California Film Commission (CFC), 7080 Hollywood Blvd, Suite 900, Hollywood, CA 90028-6936 *Tel:* 323-860-2960 (24-hr serv) *Toll Free Tel:* 800-858-4749 *Fax:* 323-860-2972 *E-mail:* filmca@film.ca.gov *Web Site:* www.film.ca.gov, pg 1093

Lemke, Dale, Display Systems International, 2214 Hanselman Ave, Saskatoon, SK S7L 6A4, Canada *Tel:* 306-934-6884 *Toll Free Tel:* 877-934-6884 *Fax:* 306-934-6447 *E-mail:* sales@displaysystemsintl.com *Web Site:* www.displaysystemsintl.com, pg 849

Lemmons, Mark, T3Media, 1530 16 St, 6th fl, Denver, CO 80202 *Tel:* 720-382-2869 *Toll Free Tel:* 866-815-6599 *Fax:* 720-382-2719 *E-mail:* content@t3media.com *Web Site:* www.t3licensing.com, pg 1046

LeMoine, Heather, North Dakota Tourism Division/Film Commission, Century Ctr, 1600 E Century Ave, Suite 2, Bismarck, ND 58502-2057 *Tel:* 701-328-2525 *Toll Free Tel:* 800-435-5663 *Fax:* 701-328-4878 *E-mail:* tourism@nd.gov *Web Site:* www.ndtourism.com, pg 1101

Lennox, Stuart, LibertyPak Co Inc, 420 Bryant Circle, Bldg B, Ojai, CA 93023 *Tel:* 805-640-6700 *E-mail:* sales@libertypak.com; service@libertypak.com *Web Site:* www.libertypak.com, pg 919

Lennox, Thomas, Luminaud Inc, 8688 Tyler Blvd, Mentor, OH 44060 *Tel:* 440-255-9082 *Toll Free Tel:* 800-255-3408 *Fax:* 440-255-2250 *E-mail:* info@luminaud.com *Web Site:* www.luminaud.com, pg 926

Lentner, Sean, Antenna International, 383 Main Ave, Norwalk, CT 06851 *Tel:* 203-523-0320 *Fax:* 203-354-5519 *E-mail:* inquiry@antennainternational.com *Web Site:* www.antennainternational.com, pg 787

Lenzo, Anthony S, Air Sea Land Productions Inc (ASL), 19-69 Steinway St, Astoria, NY 11105-1108 *Tel:* 718-626-2646 *Toll Free Tel:* 888-ASL-LENS (275-5367) *Fax:* 718-626-1493 *E-mail:* sales@airsealand.com *Web Site:* www.airsealand.com, pg 779

Lenzo, Edward, Air Sea Land Productions Inc (ASL), 19-69 Steinway St, Astoria, NY 11105-1108 *Tel:* 718-626-2646 *Toll Free Tel:* 888-ASL-LENS (275-5367) *Fax:* 718-626-1493 *E-mail:* sales@airsealand.com *Web Site:* www.airsealand.com, pg 779

Leonard, Betty M, Compact Storage Systems Inc, 9757 Reseda Blvd, Suite 68, Northridge, CA 91324 *Tel:* 818-772-0996 *E-mail:* info@halfthespace.com *Web Site:* www.halfthespace.com, pg 833

Leonard, David P, Trebas Institute, 550 Sherbrooke St W, Suite 600, Montreal, QC H3A 1B9, Canada *Tel:* 514-845-4141 *Toll Free Tel:* 866-5TREBAS (587-3227) *Fax:* 514-845-2581 *E-mail:* infomtl@trebas.com *Web Site:* www.trebas.com, pg 1044

Leonard, Jeff, Baker & Taylor Inc, 2550 W Tyvola Rd, Suite 300, Charlotte, NC 28217 *Tel:* 704-998-3100 *Toll Free Tel:* 800-775-1800 *E-mail:* btinfo@baker-taylor.com *Web Site:* www.btol.com, pg 801

Leone, Raymond, Myton Industries Inc, 1981 S Park Rd, Pembroke Park, FL 33009 *Tel:* 954-989-0113 *Toll Free Tel:* 800-544-2406 *Fax:* 954-989-1488 *E-mail:* myton@msn.com; sales@mytonindustries.com *Web Site:* www.mytonindustries.com, pg 952

Leone, Ron, West Penn Wire, 2833 W Chestnut St, Washington, PA 15301 *Tel:* 724-222-7060 *Toll Free Tel:* 800-245-4964 *Fax:* 724-222-6420 *E-mail:* info@westpenn-wpw.com *Web Site:* www.westpenn-wpw.com, pg 1064

Leopard, Colby, FilmNation Entertainment, 150 W 22 St, 9th fl, New York, NY 10011 *Web Site:* www.filmnation.com, pg 867

Lepejian, Baret, A&I, 257 S Lake St, Burbank, CA 91502 *Tel:* 323-856-5280; 818-848-9001 *Fax:* 323-856-5110 *E-mail:* mail@aandi.com *Web Site:* www.aandi.com, pg 771

Leporati, Ray, EDR Media LLC, 23330 Commerce Park, Beachwood, OH 44122-5811 *Tel:* 216-292-7300 *Web Site:* www.edrmedia.com; www.beachwoodstudios.com, pg 857

Leposky, Marjory E, Chatterbox Productions Inc, 2311 S Bayshore Dr, Coconut Grove, FL 33133-4728 *Tel:* 305-285-1058 *Web Site:* www.ampersandcom.com/chatterbox, pg 824

Lepp, L Sue, Design & Production Inc, 7110 Rainwater Place, Lorton, VA 22079 *Tel:* 703-550-8640 *Fax:* 703-339-0296 *E-mail:* email@d-and-p.com *Web Site:* www.d-and-p.com, pg 845

Lerner, Ann, Albuquerque Film Office, Economic Development Dept, One Civic Plaza NW, Albuquerque, NM 87102 *Tel:* 505-768-3283 *Fax:* 505-768-3280 *Web Site:* www.cabq.gov/film, pg 1100

Leroux, Vincent, Group PVP, 296 Saint Pierre St, Matane, QC G4W 2B9, Canada *Tel:* 418-566-2040 *Toll Free Tel:* 877-320-2040 *Fax:* 418-562-4643 *E-mail:* info@pvp.ca *Web Site:* www.pvp.ca, pg 883

Lescaze, Alexandra, Hillman Prizes in Journalism, 12 W 31 St, 12th fl, New York, NY 10001 *Tel:* 646-448-6413 *Web Site:* www.hillmanfoundation.org, pg 1116

Lesch, Donna, Computer Sciences Corp, 3170 Fairview Park Dr, Falls Church, VA 22042 *Tel:* 703-876-1000 *Web Site:* www.csc.com, pg 834

Lesemann, Mara, Guild of Italian American Actors (GIAA), Canal Street Sta, PO Box 123, New York, NY 10013-0123 *Tel:* 201-344-3411 *E-mail:* info@giaa.us *Web Site:* www.giaa.us, pg 1082

Lesnick, Jim, The Little Warehouse Inc, 900 Resource Dr, Suite 8, Brooklyn Heights, OH 44131 *Tel:* 216-398-0022 *Toll Free Tel:* 800-445-8273 *Fax:* 216-398-9980 *E-mail:* tlwtape@sbcglobal.net *Web Site:* www.thelittlewarehouse.com, pg 923

Lessans, Ryan, Kipp Visual Systems Inc, 3600 Clipper Mill Rd, Suite 105, Baltimore, MD 21211 *Tel:* 410-235-9900 *Toll Free Tel:* 800-278-6912 *Fax:* 410-235-7122 *Web Site:* kippvisual.com, pg 911

Levai, George, Optix Digital Pictures & Sound, 157 Princess St, Toronto, ON M5A 4M4, Canada *Tel:* 416-214-9911 *Fax:* 416-214-9912 *Web Site:* www.optix.ca, pg 965

Leverence, Dr John, Emmy Awards (Primetime), 5220 Lankershim Blvd, North Hollywood, CA 91601-3109 *Tel:* 818-754-2800 *Fax:* 818-754-2836 *Web Site:* www.emmys.com, pg 1114

Leverence, Dr John, Television Academy, 5220 Lankershim Blvd, North Hollywood, CA 91601-3109 *Tel:* 818-754-2800 *Fax:* 818-761-2827 *Web Site:* www.emmys.com, pg 1089

Levesque, Paul, Les Disques Artiste, 154 Grande Cote, Rosemere, QC J7A 1H3, Canada *Tel:* 450-437-7625 *Web Site:* www.disquesartiste.com, pg 849

Levey, Jodie, Golden Space Needle Awards, 305 Harrison St, Seattle, WA 98109 *Tel:* 206-464-5830 *Fax:* 206-264-7919 *E-mail:* info@siff.net *Web Site:* www.siff.net, pg 1116

Levin, A J, Leedal Inc, 3453 Commercial Ave, Northbrook, IL 60062 *Tel:* 847-498-0111 *Fax:* 847-498-0198 *E-mail:* sink@leedal.com *Web Site:* www.leedal.com, pg 918

Levin, Claudia, Monadnock Media Inc, 112 Amherst Rd, Sunderland, MA 01375 *Tel:* 413-665-1390 *Fax:* 413-665-1394 *E-mail:* info@monadnock.org *Web Site:* www.monadnock.org, pg 945

Levin, Irwin, The Writing Co, 10200 Jefferson Blvd, Culver City, CA 90232 *Tel:* 310-839-2436 *Toll Free Tel:* 800-421-4246 *Fax:* 310-839-2249 *Toll Free Fax:* 800-944-5432 *E-mail:* access@writingco.com; access@socialstudies.com *Web Site:* www.socialstudies.com; www.writingco.com, pg 1070

Levin, Joel, Final Draft Inc, 26707 W Agoura Rd, Suite 205, Calabasas, CA 91302 *Tel:* 818-995-8995; 818-906-8930 (tech support) *Toll Free Tel:* 800-231-4055 *Fax:* 818-995-4422 *E-mail:* info@finaldraft.com *Web Site:* www.finaldraft.com, pg 868

Levin, Sheldon, Leedal Inc, 3453 Commercial Ave, Northbrook, IL 60062 *Tel:* 847-498-0111 *Fax:* 847-498-0198 *E-mail:* sink@leedal.com *Web Site:* www.leedal.com, pg 918

Levin, Steve, International Display & Exhibit Corp, 60 Shawmut Rd, Suite 5, Canton, MA 02021 *Tel:* 617-527-7878 *Toll Free Tel:* 800-533-7878 *Fax:* 617-964-5099 *E-mail:* sales@idec-displays.com *Web Site:* www.idecdisplays.com, pg 901

Levine, Felice J, American Educational Research Association (AERA), 1430 "K" St NW, Suite 1200, Washington, DC 20005 *Tel:* 202-238-3200 *Fax:* 202-238-3250 *Web Site:* www.aera.net, pg 1076

Levine, Michael, Crash Video Productions, 713 N Mansfield Ave, Los Angeles, CA 90038 *Tel:* 310-489-6848 *E-mail:* crash@crashproductions.com *Web Site:* www.crashproductions.com, pg 837

Levitt, Cary, Parlights Inc, One Wormans Mill Ct, Suite 7, Frederick, MD 21701 *Tel:* 301-698-9242 *Fax:* 301-846-0369 *E-mail:* sales@parlights.com *Web Site:* www.parlights.com, pg 969

Levy, Arthur J, Apogee Communications Group, 159 Alpine Way, Boulder, CO 80304 *Tel:* 303-443-8473 *Toll Free Tel:* 800-210-5700 *Fax:* 303-443-0500 *E-mail:* sales@apogeevideo.com; orders@apogeevideo.com *Web Site:* www.apogeevideo.com, pg 788

Levy, Charles, Lensless Camera Manufacturing Co, 809 Lark Dr, Fernley, NV 89408 *Tel:* 775-575-5189 *E-mail:* info@pinholecamera.com *Web Site:* www.pinholecamera.com, pg 919

Levy, Ira, Levy Lighting NYC Inc, 347 W 36 St, Ground fl, New York, NY 10018 *Tel:* 212-925-4640 *Fax:* 212-925-4216 *E-mail:* info@levylighting.com *Web Site:* www.levylighting.com, pg 919

Levy, L J, MMI Corp, 2950 Wyman Pkwy, Baltimore, MD 21211-2802 *Tel:* 410-366-1222 *Fax:* 410-366-6311 *E-mail:* mail@mmicorporation.com *Web Site:* www.mmicorporation.com, pg 944

Levy, Lawrence, Catapult Films Inc, 832 Third St, Suite 303, Santa Monica, CA 90403 *Tel:* 310-395-1470, pg 821

Levy, Mel, Breeze Productions Inc, 1660 Edgewood Rd, Highland Park, IL 60035 *Tel:* 312-860-1710 *Web Site:* www.breezeprod.com, pg 812

Levy, Ralph C, MMI Corp, 2950 Wyman Pkwy, Baltimore, MD 21211-2802 *Tel:* 410-366-1222 *Fax:* 410-366-6311 *E-mail:* mail@mmicorporation.com *Web Site:* www.mmicorporation.com, pg 944

Levy, Scott, Eastern Effects Inc, 99 Ninth St, Brooklyn, NY 11215 *Tel:* 718-855-1197 *Fax:* 212-504-9534 *E-mail:* geteffected@easterneffects.com *Web Site:* www.easterneffects.com, pg 856

Lewin, Miriam, Lavine Production Group, 189 Dean St, Brooklyn, NY 11217 *Tel:* 917-804-1870 *Web Site:* www.lavinegroup.com, pg 917

Lewis, B Z, Studio 132, 6802 Gunn Dr, Oakland, CA 94611-1443 *Tel:* 510-338-1240 *E-mail:* info@studio132.com *Web Site:* www.studio132.com, pg 1027

Lewis, Beth A, Augsburg Fortress Publishers, 100 S Fifth St, Suite 600, Minneapolis, MN 55402 *Tel:* 612-330-3300 *Toll Free Tel:* 800-328-4648 *Fax:* 612-330-3455 *Toll Free Fax:* 800-722-7766 *E-mail:* info@augsburgfortress.org *Web Site:* www.augsburgfortress.org, pg 796

Lewis, Beverly, Film Liaisons In California Statewide (FLICS), c/o Placer-Lake Tahoe Film Off, 175 Fulweiler Ave, Auburn, CA 95603 *Tel:* 530-889-4091 *Toll Free Tel:* 877-228-3456 *Fax:* 530-889-4095 *Web Site:* www.filmcalifornia.com, pg 1082

Lewis, Beverly, Placer-Lake Tahoe Film Office, 145 Fulweiler Ave, Auburn, CA 95603 *Tel:* 530-889-4091 *Toll Free Tel:* 877-228-3456 *Fax:* 530-889-4095 *Web Site:* www.placer.ca.gov/films, pg 1092

Lewis, Daniel, NuMynd Studios, 915 Twin Elms Ct, Nashville, TN 37210 *Tel:* 615-259-1143 *Fax:* 615-259-1141 *E-mail:* hello@numyndstudios.com *Web Site:* www.numyndstudios.com, pg 960

Lewis, Dianne, Jointure for Community Adult Education Inc, Centre at Raritan, Suite B-11, 1124 US Hwy 202 S, Raritan, NJ 08869 *Tel:* 908-722-0233; 908-874-4852 *Fax:* 908-722-0388 *E-mail:* jcaeinc@aol.com *Web Site:* www.jointure.org, pg 906

Lewis, Harold G, ATA Trading Corp/Favorite TV Inc, 877 Oceanfront, Long Beach, NY 11561-1542 *Tel:* 516-431-2302 *Fax:* 516-431-2302 *E-mail:* atat@verizon.net, pg 792

Lewis, Jim, Communications Concepts Inc (CCI), 7980 N Atlantic Ave, Cape Canaveral, FL 32920 *Tel:* 321-783-5232 *Toll Free Tel:* 800-783-2368 *Fax:* 321-799-1016 *E-mail:* info@cciflorida.com *Web Site:* www.cciflorida.com, pg 833

Lewis, John, Staging Concepts, 7008 Northland Dr N, Suite 150, Minneapolis, MN 55428 *Tel:* 763-533-2094 *Toll Free Tel:* 800-337-5339 *E-mail:* info@stagingconcepts.com *Web Site:* www.stagingconcepts.com, pg 1023

Lewis, Ken, Midwest Photo Exchange, 3313 N High St, Columbus, OH 43202 *Tel:* 614-261-1264 *Toll Free Tel:* 866-940-3686 *Fax:* 614-261-1637 *E-mail:* mpex@mpex.com; orders@mpex.com *Web Site:* mpex.com, pg 942

Lewis, Mark, Tight Line Productions, 1902 Oak St, Melbourne, FL 32901 *Tel:* 321-725-4668 *Fax:* 321-768-6528 *E-mail:* info@tightlinetv.com *Web Site:* www.tightlinetv.com, pg 1040

Lewis, Noland L, ACO Pacific Inc, 2604 Read Ave, Belmont, CA 94002 *Tel:* 650-595-8588 *Fax:* 650-591-2891 *E-mail:* sales@acopacific.com; info@acopacific.com; support@acopacific.com *Web Site:* www.acopacific.com, pg 774

Lewis, Richard, PipelineFX LLC, 1000 Bishop St, Suite 509, Honolulu, HI 96813 *Tel:* 808-685-7823 *Toll Free Tel:* 866-856-7823 *Fax:* 808-685-7800 *E-mail:* sales@pipelinefx.com *Web Site:* www.pipelinefx.com, pg 976

Lewis, Richard, Touchstone Center Publications, 141 E 88 St, New York, NY 10128 *Tel:* 212-831-7717 *Web Site:* www.touchstonecenter.net, pg 1043

Lewis, Robert, Visual Instrumentation Corp, 1110 West Ave L-12, Unit 2, Lancaster, CA 93534-7039 *Tel:* 661-945-7999 *Fax:* 661-723-5667 *E-mail:* visinst@earthlink.net *Web Site:* www.visinst.com, pg 1059

Lewis, Tim, Master Communications Group, 3410 Winnetka Ave, Suite 107, New Hope, MN 55427 *Tel:* 763-231-1881 *Fax:* 763-231-1885 *E-mail:* info@mastcom.com *Web Site:* www.mastcom.com, pg 933

Lewis, Vel, Los Angeles Post Music Inc, 4340 E Kentucky Ave, Suite 308, Glendale, CO 80246 *Tel:* 310-896-5176 *Web Site:* www.lapostmusic.com, pg 924

Lewnes, Ann, Adobe Systems Inc, 345 Park Ave, San Jose, CA 95110-2704 *Tel:* 408-536-6000 *Fax:* 408-537-6000 *Web Site:* www.adobe.com, pg 776

Lhyne, Robinie, Semiconductor Services, 2269 Chestnut St, No 735, San Francisco, CA 94123 *Tel:* 650-369-7890 *Fax:* 415-346-8099 *E-mail:* moreinfo@semiconductorservices.com *Web Site:* www.semiconductorservices.com, pg 1006

Li, Nancy Zi, ViVi Co, PO Box 750, Glendale, CA 91209 *Tel:* 818-500-8889 *Fax:* 818-507-6600 *E-mail:* zibreathe@aol.com *Web Site:* www.theartofbreathing.com, pg 1060

Liantonio, Collette, Concepts TV Production, 328 W Main St, Boonton, NJ 07005 *Tel:* 973-331-1500 *Fax:* 973-331-1550 *E-mail:* sales@conceptstv.com *Web Site:* www.conceptstv.com, pg 834

Libby, Jim, Petra Productions Ltd, 52 Sycamore Rd, Mahopac, NY 10541 *E-mail:* information@petraproductions.org *Web Site:* www.petraproductions.org, pg 973

Liberatore, George, Midland Video Productions Inc, 126 N Jefferson St, Milwaukee, WI 53202 *Tel:* 414-276-8300 *E-mail:* request@midlandvideo.com *Web Site:* midlandvideo.com, pg 942

Librach, Larry, JVC Professional Products Co, 1700 Valley Rd, Wayne, NJ 07470 *Tel:* 973-317-5000 *Toll Free Tel:* 800-582-5825; 800-247-3608; 800-252-5722 *Fax:* 973-317-5030 *Toll Free Fax:* 800-582-5825 (option 2) *E-mail:* proinfo@jvc.com *Web Site:* www.jvc.com, pg 907

Lidderdale, William, The Set Shop, 428 Colyton St, Los Angeles, CA 90013 *Tel:* 213-680-1668 *Fax:* 213-680-4269 *Web Site:* www.thesetshop.tv, pg 1007

Lieberman, Jason, AV Workshop, 500 W 37 St, 3rd fl, New York, NY 10018 *Tel:* 212-643-0040 *Fax:* 212-564-5277 *E-mail:* sales@avworkshop.com *Web Site:* avworkshop.com, pg 797

Lieberman, Ken, Ken Lieberman Labs Inc, 69 Fairview Dr, Albertson, NY 11507-1007 *Tel:* 212-633-0500 *Web Site:* lieberman-labs.com, pg 920

Lieberman, Lenny, Lieberman Productions, 455 Ninth St, San Francisco, CA 94103-4410 *Tel:* 415-955-0855 *Fax:* 415-955-0822 *E-mail:* lpinfo@lieberman.com *Web Site:* www.lieberman.com, pg 920

Lieberman, Les, KVL Audio Visual Services Inc, 466 Saw Mill River Rd, Ardsley, NY 10502-2112 *Tel:* 914-479-3300 *Toll Free Tel:* 800-862-3210 *Fax:* 914-479-3395 *E-mail:* info@kvlav.com *Web Site:* www.kvlav.com, pg 914

Lieberman, Michael, Barbizon Electric Co Inc, 456 W 55 St, New York, NY 10019-4403 *Tel:* 212-586-1620 *Toll Free Tel:* 800-582-9941 *Fax:* 212-247-8818 *E-mail:* benysales@barbizon.com *Web Site:* www.barbizon.com, pg 802

Liebman, Seymour, Canon USA Inc, One Canon Park, Melville, NY 11747 *Tel:* 613-330-5000 *E-mail:* pr@cusa.canon.com *Web Site:* www.usa.canon.com, pg 819

Lien, Chris, Bell & Howell LLC, 760 S Wolf Rd, Wheeling, IL 60090 *Tel:* 847-675-7600 *Toll Free Tel:* 800-220-3030 (cust serv) *E-mail:* marketing@bhemail.com *Web Site:* www.bellhowell.net, pg 804

Lienau, Michael, Global Net Productions Inc, 568 Iverson Beach Rd, Camano Island, WA 98282-8597 *Tel:* 360-387-8222 *Toll Free Tel:* 800-862-6247 *E-mail:* contact@globalnetproductions.com *Web Site:* www.globalnetproductions.com, pg 879

Lietz, Tom, MessageMakers, 1217 Turner St, Lansing, MI 48906 *Tel:* 517-482-3333 *Toll Free Tel:* 888-482-6688 *E-mail:* info@messagemakers.com *Web Site:* www.messagemakers.com, pg 939

Lifvendahl, Amanda, Broadway Costumes Inc, 1100 W Cermak Rd, 2nd fl, Chicago, IL 60608 *Tel:* 312-829-6400 *Toll Free Tel:* 800-397-3316 *Fax:* 312-829-8621 *E-mail:* rentals@broadwaycostumes.com *Web Site:* www.broadwaycostumes.com, pg 813

Light, Charles, Green Mountain Post Films (GMP), PO Box 229, Turners Falls, MA 01376-0229 *Tel:* 413-863-4754 *Fax:* 413-863-8248 *E-mail:* info@gmpfilms.com *Web Site:* www.gmpfilms.com, pg 882

Lighterman, Sandy, Miami-Dade Office of Film & Entertainment, 111 NW First St, Suite 2200, Miami, FL 33128 *Tel:* 305-375-3288 *Fax:* 305-375-3266 *E-mail:* filmoffice@miamigov.com *Web Site:* www.filmiami.org, pg 1096

Lightfoot, Tim, Radius® Display Products Inc, 800 Fabric X-Press Way, Dallas, TX 75234 *Tel:* 972-406-1221 *Toll Free Tel:* 800-FABRIC-X (322-7429); 866-966-4066 (sales); 866-966-8266 (hospitality) *Fax:* 972-406-1321 *Toll Free Fax:* 888-322-7429 *Web Site:* www.radiusdp.com, pg 990

Lillard, Amy, Washington Filmworks, 1411 Fourth Ave, Suite 420, Seattle, WA 98101 *Tel:* 206-264-0667 *Fax:* 206-382-4343 *E-mail:* info@washingtonfilmworks.org *Web Site:* washingtonfilmworks.org, pg 1103

Lilling, Dave, Metro Teleproductions Inc (MTI), 2500 Virginia Ave NW, 416-S, Washington, DC 20037 *Tel:* 301-608-9077 *Fax:* 301-608-9078 *Web Site:* www.mtitv.com, pg 939

Lin, Alen, Studio 1444, 1444 N Highland Ave, Hollywood, CA 90028 *Tel:* 323-482-1004 *E-mail:* info@studio1444.com *Web Site:* www.studio1444.com, pg 1027

Lin, Jami, EarthDesign Inc, 9 Riverfront Dr, Venice, FL 34293 *Tel:* 941-276-8689 *Toll Free Tel:* 800-327-8433 *E-mail:* gp@jamilin.com *Web Site:* www.jamilin.com, pg 855

Lindberg, Greg E, Eli Research Group, 2222 Sedwick Rd, Suite 102, Durham, NC 27713 *Toll Free Tel:* 800-223-8720 *Toll Free Fax:* 800-508-2592 *E-mail:* customerservice@dartnellcorp.com *Web Site:* www.dartnellcorp.com, pg 859

Linder, Jason, Telarc International Corp, 23412 Commerce Park Rd, Cleveland, OH 44122 *Tel:* 216-464-2313 *Fax:* 216-360-9663 *Web Site:* www.concordmusicgroup.com/labels/Telarc/; www.concordmusicgroup.com, pg 1035

Lindgren, Erik, ARF!ARF!, PO Box 465, Middleboro, MA 02346-0465 *Tel:* 508-947-7387 *Fax:* 508-947-7387 *E-mail:* page@arfarfrecords.com *Web Site:* www.arfarfrecords.com, pg 789

Lindgren, Erik, Sounds Interesting Studios, 112 Fuller St, Middleboro, MA 02346 *Tel:* 508-947-7387 *Web Site:* www.soundsinterestingstudio.com, pg 1018

Lindgren, Erik, The Well-Tempered Music Library, PO Box 465, Middleboro, MA 02346-0465 *Tel:* 508-947-7387 *Fax:* 508-947-7387 *E-mail:* info@arfarfrecords.com; page@arfarfrecords.com *Web Site:* www.arfarfrecords.com, pg 1063

Lindo, Todd, Rough House, 550 Bryant St, San Francisco, CA 94107-1217 *Tel:* 415-561-4544 *Fax:* 415-543-8390 *E-mail:* info@roughhouse.com *Web Site:* www.roughhouse.com, pg 1000

Lindsey, Charisse, Hyperspective Studios Inc, 2800 Woodlawn Dr, Suite 253, Honolulu, HI 96822 *Tel:* 808-353-3618 *E-mail:* info@hyperspective.com *Web Site:* www.hyperspective.com, pg 893

Lindsey, Dwight, Schneider Optics Inc, 285 Oser Ave, Hauppauge, NY 11788 *Tel:* 631-761-5000 *Toll Free Tel:* 800-645-7239 *Fax:* 631-761-5090 *E-mail:* info@schneideroptics.com *Web Site:* www.schneideroptics.com, pg 1004

Lindstrom, Mel, Pacific Light Studios, 265 Caspian Dr, Sunnyvale, CA 94089 *Tel:* 408-541-1800 *Web Site:* www.pacificlightstudios.com, pg 967

Lines, Kevin, Southwest Audio-Visual Inc, 3058 E Cairo, Springfield, MO 65802 *Tel:* 417-887-4900 *Fax:* 417-866-6500 *E-mail:* info@southwestav.com *Web Site:* www.southwestav.com, pg 1019

Lines, Thomas S, Imagers, 1575 Northside Dr, Bldg 400, Suite 490, Atlanta, GA 30318-5411 *Tel:* 404-351-5800 *Toll Free Tel:* 800-232-5411 *Fax:* 404-351-9020 *E-mail:* imagers@imagers.com *Web Site:* www.imagers.com, pg 896

Linetsky, David, Noventri, 20940 Twin Springs Dr, Smithsburg, MD 21783-1510 *Tel:* 301-790-0103 *Fax:* 301-790-0173 *E-mail:* sale@noventri.com *Web Site:* www.noventri.com, pg 960

Linhoff, John, Linhoff Photo & Digital Imaging, 4400 France Ave S, Edina, MN 55410 *Tel:* 952-927-7333 *E-mail:* info@linhoff.com *Web Site:* linhoff.com, pg 922

Linker, Sheldon, Linker Systems Inc, 13612 Onkayha Circle, Irvine, CA 92620 *Tel:* 949-552-1904 *Toll Free Tel:* 800-315-1174 *Web Site:* linkersystems.com, pg 922

Linker, Tara, Thread Marketing Group, 4635 W Alexis Rd, Toledo, OH 43623-1005 *Tel:* 419-887-6801 *Toll Free Tel:* 800-397-0126 *Fax:* 419-887-6802 *E-mail:* contact@experiencethread.com *Web Site:* www.experiencethread.com, pg 1039

Lins, Vicki, United Way Worldwide, 701 N Fairfax St, Alexandria, VA 22314-2045 *Tel:* 703-836-7112 *Fax:* 703-519-0097 *Web Site:* www.unitedway.org, pg 1048

Linsley, James L, Shadowbox Video Productions, 304 Westfield Dr, North Little Rock, AR 72118 *Tel:* 501-374-3322 *E-mail:* info@shadowboxvideo.com *Web Site:* shadowboxvideo.com, pg 1007

Linsman, William, Linsman Film, 329 N Windsor Blvd, Los Angeles, CA 90004 *Tel:* 310-903-3009 *Web Site:* www.linsman.com, pg 922

Lintner, Jim, The Learning House Inc, 427 S Fourth St, Suite 300, Louisville, KY 40202 *Tel:* 502-589-9878 *Fax:* 502-589-9825 *E-mail:* sales@learninghouse.com *Web Site:* www.learninghouse.com, pg 917

Liodice, Bob, Association of National Advertisers Inc (ANA), 708 Third Ave, 33rd fl, New York, NY 10017-4270 *Tel:* 212-697-5950 *Fax:* 212-687-7310 *E-mail:* info@ana.net *Web Site:* www.ana.net, pg 1079

Lion, Richard, Lion Recording Services Inc, 7532 Fullerton Ct, Springfield, VA 22153 *Tel:* 703-569-3200 *Fax:* 703-891-3220 *E-mail:* mail@lionrecording.com *Web Site:* www.lionrecording.com, pg 922

Lionel, David, Transformational Education Initiatives, PO Box 344, Phoenicia, NY 12464 *Tel:* 310-795-4910 *E-mail:* lioneltv@aol.com *Web Site:* transformationaledu.org, pg 1043

Liotta, Charles J, Moxie Video Productions Inc, 7046 Sugar Magnolia Circle, Naples, FL 34109 *Tel:* 239-682-2129 *Toll Free Fax:* 888-349-8197 *Web Site:* moxievideo.com, pg 948

Liou, Ming, Beta Electronics Inc, 130 S Barranca St, Apt 314, West Covina, CA 91791-2279 *Tel:* 614-538-8207 *Toll Free Tel:* 800-546-2382 *Fax:* 614-538-8209 *Toll Free Fax:* 888-329-2382 *E-mail:* sales@betalaser.com *Web Site:* www.betalaser.com, pg 806

Lipkin, Marc, Alligator Records & Artist Management Inc, 1441 W Devon Ave, Chicago, IL 60660 *Tel:* 773-973-7736 *Fax:* 773-973-2088 *E-mail:* info@allig.com *Web Site:* www.alligator.com, pg 781

Lipp, Jonathan, Full Compass Systems, 9770 Silicon Prairie Pkwy, Madison, WI 53593 *Tel:* 608-831-7330 *Toll Free Tel:* 800-356-5844 *Fax:* 608-831-8846 *E-mail:* customerservice@fullcompass.com *Web Site:* www.fullcompass.com, pg 874

Lipp, Susan W, Full Compass Systems, 9770 Silicon Prairie Pkwy, Madison, WI 53593 *Tel:* 608-831-7330 *Toll Free Tel:* 800-356-5844 *Fax:* 608-831-8846 *E-mail:* customerservice@fullcompass.com *Web Site:* www.fullcompass.com, pg 874

Lippincott, Evan, Aztek Inc, 13765-F Alton Pkwy, Irvine, CA 92618 *Tel:* 949-770-8787 *Toll Free Tel:* 800-GRAPH-55 (472-7455) *Fax:* 949-770-4986 *E-mail:* mail@aztek.com *Web Site:* www.aztek.com, pg 801

Lippincott, Phil, Aztek Inc, 13765-F Alton Pkwy, Irvine, CA 92618 *Tel:* 949-770-8787 *Toll Free Tel:* 800-GRAPH-55 (472-7455) *Fax:* 949-770-4986 *E-mail:* mail@aztek.com *Web Site:* www.aztek.com, pg 801

Lipton, Martin, Argraph Corp, 111 Asia Place, Carlstadt, NJ 07072 *Tel:* 201-939-7722 *Toll Free Tel:* 800-526-6290 *Fax:* 201-939-7782 *E-mail:* info@argraph.com; sales@argraph.com *Web Site:* www.argraph.com, pg 789

Lipton, Shelli, White Buffalo Multimedia, 13 Charles Bach Rd, Saugerties, NY 12477 *Tel:* 845-246-9995, pg 1065

Lisch, Denise, Hamilton Buhl, 80 Little Falls Rd, Fairfield, NJ 07004 *Toll Free Tel:* 800-631-0868 *Toll Free Fax:* 800-398-1812 (cust serv & sales) *E-mail:* customerservice@hamiltonbuhl.com *Web Site:* www.hamiltonbuhl.com, pg 884

Lisius, Martin, Prairie Pictures Film & Video, PO Box 122020, Arlington, TX 76012-8020 *Tel:* 817-276-9500 *E-mail:* info@prairiepictures.com *Web Site:* prairiepictures.com, pg 980

Lisk, Travis A, Advanced AV, 208 Carter Dr, Suite 7, West Chester, PA 19382 *Toll Free Tel:* 877-696-7700 *Fax:* 610-692-8421 *E-mail:* sales@advancedav.com *Web Site:* www.advancedav.com, pg 777

Liss, Jeffery, A Liss & Co, 51-55 59 Place, Woodside, NY 11377-7408 *Tel:* 718-728-0600 *Toll Free Tel:* 800-221-0938 *Fax:* 718-728-1227 *E-mail:* sales@alissco.com *Web Site:* www.alissco.com, pg 922

Lissner, Sidney L, Avitecture Inc, One Export Dr, Sterling, VA 20164-4421 *Tel:* 703-404-8900 *Fax:* 703-404-8940 *E-mail:* info@avitecture.com *Web Site:* www.avitecture.com, pg 800

Listorti, Joe, LM Cases/LM Engineering Inc, 2720 Intertech Dr, Youngstown, OH 44509 *Tel:* 330-270-2400 *Toll Free Tel:* 800-874-8326 *Fax:* 330-270-2424 *E-mail:* info@lmcases.com *Web Site:* www.lmcases.com, pg 923

Litchfield, Steven, Microsemi, 2300 Orchard Pkwy, San Jose, CA 95131-1017 *Tel:* 408-433-0910; 408-428-7907 (tech support) *Fax:* 408-428-6960 *E-mail:* info@symmetricom.com *Web Site:* www.symmetricom.com, pg 941

Litinsky, Irene, Muse Entertainment Enterprises, 3451 Rue Saint Jacques, Montreal, QC H4C 1H1, Canada *Tel:* 514-866-6873 *Fax:* 514-876-3911 *E-mail:* bpalik@muse.ca *Web Site:* www.muse.ca, pg 950

Little, Benjamin, Clean Slate Video, 3070 Kerner Blvd, Unit O, San Rafael, CA 94901 *Tel:* 415-485-0727 *E-mail:* info@cleanslatevideo.com *Web Site:* www.cleanslatevideo.com, pg 829

Little, David, Keywest Technology Inc, 14563 W 96 Terr, Lenexa, KS 66215 *Tel:* 913-492-4666 *Toll Free Tel:* 800-331-2019 *Fax:* 913-322-1864 *E-mail:* info@keywesttechnology.com; sales@keywesttechnology.com *Web Site:* www.keywesttechnology.com, pg 910

Little, Jeffrey B, Liberty Publishing Co Inc, PO Box 4485, Deerfield Beach, FL 33442-4248 *Tel:* 954-573-7236 *Web Site:* www.bullsorbears.com, pg 919

Little, Judith A, Liberty Publishing Co Inc, PO Box 4485, Deerfield Beach, FL 33442-4248 *Tel:* 954-573-7236 *Web Site:* www.bullsorbears.com, pg 919

Little, Kent, Xenon Pictures Inc, 3521 Jack Northrop Ave, Hawthorne, CA 90250 *Tel:* 310-451-5510 *Fax:* 310-395-4058 *E-mail:* info@xenonpictures.com; sales@xenonpictures.com *Web Site:* xenonpictures.com, pg 1071

Little, Larry, The Larry Little Co, 10120 W Flamingo Rd, Suite 4-160, Las Vegas, NV 89147 *Tel:* 262-518-2014 *Toll Free Fax:* 800-452-8273 *E-mail:* larrylittlecompany@gmail.com *Web Site:* www.larrylittle.com, pg 923

Little, Pamela A, CALIBRE, Metro Park, 6354 Walker Lane, Alexandria, VA 22310-3252 *Tel:* 703-797-8500 *Toll Free Tel:* 888-CALIBRE (225-4273) *Fax:* 703-797-8501 *E-mail:* info@calibresys.com *Web Site:* www.calibresys.com, pg 817

Little, Pat, PRG Lighting, 6050 S Valley View Blvd, Las Vegas, NV 89118 *Tel:* 702-942-4774 *Fax:* 702-942-4668 *E-mail:* info@prg.com *Web Site:* www.prg.com, pg 981

Little, Richard, LEAD Technologies Inc, 1927 S Tryon St, Suite 200, Charlotte, NC 28203 *Tel:* 704-332-5532 *Toll Free Tel:* 800-637-4699 *Fax:* 704-372-8161 *E-mail:* sales@leadtools.com *Web Site:* www.leadtools.com, pg 917

Little, Robert, Allied Photo Color Co, 4221 Forest Park Ave, St Louis, MO 63108 *Tel:* 314-652-4000 *Fax:* 314-652-8203 *Web Site:* alliedphotocolor.com, pg 781

Little, Sherwin, The American Classical League, Miami University, 422 Wells Mill Dr, Oxford, OH 45056 *Tel:* 513-529-7741 *Fax:* 513-529-7742 *E-mail:* info@aclclassics.org *Web Site:* www.aclclassics.org, pg 784

Little, Suzanne, Liberty Publishing Co Inc, PO Box 4485, Deerfield Beach, FL 33442-4248 *Tel:* 954-573-7236 *Web Site:* www.bullsorbears.com, pg 919

Littlejohn, Tara, RF Specialties of Texas LLC, PO Box 1010, Newark, TX 76071-1010 *Tel:* 214-697-3477 (cell); 817-489-2730 *Toll Free Tel:* 800-537-1801 (Newark) *E-mail:* rfstx@swbell.net *Web Site:* www.rfspecialties.com, pg 996

Littman, Ryan, Tribeca Film Festival, 375 Greenwich St, New York, NY 10013 *Tel:* 212-941-2400 *Fax:* 212-941-3939 *E-mail:* festival@tribecafilmfestival.org *Web Site:* tribecafilm.com/festival/; tribecafilmfestival.org/festival, pg 1128

Litwin, Gary, Boland Communications, 16 Rancho Circle, Lake Forest, CA 92630 *Tel:* 949-465-9911 *Toll Free Tel:* 800-918-9090 *Fax:* 949-465-9944 *E-mail:* sales@bolandcom.com *Web Site:* www.bolandcom.com, pg 810

Litwin, Tracy, Monadnock Media Inc, 112 Amherst Rd, Sunderland, MA 01375 *Tel:* 413-665-1390 *Fax:* 413-665-1394 *E-mail:* info@monadnock.org *Web Site:* www.monadnock.org, pg 945

Liu, Gary G, Sun Entertainment Corp, 3106 Belmont Blvd, Nashville, TN 37212 *Tel:* 615-385-1960 *E-mail:* info@sunrecords.com *Web Site:* www.sunrecords.com, pg 1028

Livernoche, Johanne, Editions Hurtubise HMH Ltee, 1815 Avenue De Lorimier, Montreal, QC H2K 3W6, Canada *Tel:* 514-523-1523 *Toll Free Tel:* 800-361-1664 *Fax:* 514-523-9969 *Web Site:* www.editionshurtubise.com, pg 892

Livolsi, Joe, Big Foot Productions Inc, 37-09 36 Ave, Long Island City, NY 11101 *Tel:* 718-729-1900 *Fax:* 718-729-8638 *E-mail:* info@bigfootnyc.com *Web Site:* www.bigfootnyc.com, pg 807

Llamas, Jeff, Brown United, PO Box 362, Monrovia, CA 91017-0362 *Tel:* 626-357-1161 *Toll Free Tel:* 800-44-BROWN (442-7696) *Fax:* 626-358-3064 *Toll Free Fax:* 800-26-BROWN (262-7696) *E-mail:* info@brownunited.com *Web Site:* www.brownunited.com, pg 814

Lloyd, James, Christian Media Network, PO Box 728, Garberville, CA 95542-8728 *Web Site:* www.christianmedianetwork.com, pg 825

Lo, Jason, iQstor Networks Inc, 2001 Corporate Center Dr, Newbury Park, CA 91320 *Tel:* 805-376-1000 *E-mail:* sales@iqstor.com *Web Site:* www.iqstor.com, pg 902

Lo, Paul, DiCon Fiberoptics Inc, 1689 Regatta Blvd, Richmond, CA 94804 *Tel:* 510-620-5000; 510-620-5200 (sales) *Fax:* 510-620-4100; 510-620-4102 (sales) *E-mail:* info@diconfiber.com; sales@diconfiber.com *Web Site:* www.diconfiberoptics.com, pg 846

Lo, Timothy, KahBang Festival, 84 Harlow St, Suite 1, Bangor, ME 04401 *E-mail:* info@kahbang.com; press@kahbang.com *Web Site:* www.kahbang.com, pg 1118

Lobasco, Frank, Herbach & Rademan Co Inc, 353 Crider Ave, Moorestown, NJ 08057 *Tel:* 856-802-0422 *Toll Free Tel:* 800-848-8001 *Fax:* 856-802-0465 *E-mail:* sales@herbach.com *Web Site:* www.herbach.com, pg 888

Locascio, James, Dukane Corp, Audio Visual Products Division, 2900 Dukane Dr, St Charles, IL 60174 *Tel:* 630-762-4040 *Toll Free Tel:* 888-245-1966 *Fax:* 630-584-5156 *E-mail:* avsales@dukane.com *Web Site:* dukaneav.com, pg 853

Lockard, Sue, Attainment Co Inc, 504 Commerce Pkwy, Verona, WI 53593 *Tel:* 608-845-7880 *Toll Free Tel:* 800-327-4269 *Fax:* 608-845-8040 *Toll Free Fax:* 800-942-3865 *E-mail:* customerservice@attainmentcompany.com; international@attainmentcompany.com *Web Site:* www.attainmentcompany.com, pg 793

Locke, Frank, Hollywood Lights Inc, 5251 SE McLoughlin Blvd, Portland, OR 97202-4836 *Tel:* 503-232-9001; 503-232-8855 *Toll Free Tel:* 800-826-9881 *Fax:* 503-517-8686 *E-mail:* portland@hollywoodlights.biz *Web Site:* www.hollywoodlights.biz, pg 890

Lockhart, Betty Ann, Perceptions Inc, 1030 Hinesburg Rd, Charlotte, VT 05445 *Tel:* 802-425-2783 *Fax:* 802-425-3628 *E-mail:* perceptivt@aol.com *Web Site:* perceptionsvermont.com; perceptionsmaple.com; perceptionspics.com, pg 973

Lockwood, Ben, SPIE, PO Box 10, Bellingham, WA 98227-0010 *Tel:* 360-676-3290 *Toll Free Tel:* 888-504-8171 *Fax:* 360-647-1445 *E-mail:* customerservice@spie.org *Web Site:* www.spie.org, pg 1089

Lockwood, Karen, National Institute for Trial Advocacy (NITA), 1685 38 St, Suite 200, Boulder, CO 80301-2735 *Tel:* 720-890-4860 *Toll Free Tel:* 800-225-6482 *Fax:* 720-890-7069 *E-mail:* receptionist@nita.org *Web Site:* www.nita.org, pg 953

Lode, Trygve, Inferno Film Productions LLC, PO Box 696, Littleton, CO 80160-0696 *Tel:* 303-587-9792 *E-mail:* sales@infernofilm.com *Web Site:* www.infernofilm.com, pg 897

Loeb, Matthew D, IATSE, 207 W 25 St, 4th fl, New York, NY 10001 *Tel:* 212-730-1770 *Fax:* 212-730-7809 *Web Site:* www.iatse-intl.org, pg 1082

Loeffel, Eric, Compass Learning Inc, 203 Colorado St, Austin, TX 78701 *Tel:* 512-478-9600 *Toll Free Tel:* 866-586-7387 (sales); 800-678-1412 (cust support) *Web Site:* www.compasslearning.com, pg 833

Loehr, Gregory, Video Design Group, 51 Hattertown Rd, Monroe, CT 06468 *Tel:* 203-261-7995 *Web Site:* www.videodesigngroup.com, pg 1055

Loewen, Collin G, Data Display Audio Visual Co LP, 3720 Dacoma, Houston, TX 77092-8906 *Tel:* 713-688-7900 *Toll Free Tel:* 800-840-2500 *Fax:* 713-688-5840 *E-mail:* tech@ddav.com *Web Site:* www.ddav.com, pg 843

Loewenstein, Peter, National Public Radio (NPR), 1111 N Capitol St NE, Washington, DC 20002 *Tel:* 202-513-2000 *Web Site:* www.npr.org, pg 1086

Lofgren, Gunnar, Sunnex Inc, 9319 Forsyth Park Dr, Charlotte, NC 28273 *Toll Free Tel:* 800-445-7869 *Fax:* 508-651-0099 *E-mail:* sunnex@sunnex.com; info@sunnex.com *Web Site:* www.sunnexonline.com, pg 1028

Loftus, Karen, Dazian Inc, 18 Central Blvd, South Hackensack, NJ 07606 *Toll Free Tel:* 877-232-9426 *Fax:* 201-641-2728; 201-549-1055 *E-mail:* info@dazian.com *Web Site:* www.dazian.com, pg 844

Loftus, Timothy, PSI Inc, 15375 Barranca Pkwy, Suite A 208, Irvine, CA 92618 *Tel:* 949-261-6119 *E-mail:* psiinfo@psivideoinc.com *Web Site:* www.psivideoinc.com, pg 987

Logan, Beth, Logan Productions Inc, 8035 N Port Washington Rd, Milwaukee, WI 53217 *Tel:* 414-352-9691 *Fax:* 414-352-4993 *E-mail:* sales@loganproductions.com *Web Site:* www.loganproductions.com, pg 924

Logan, David, Animax, 6627 Valjean Ave, Van Nuys, CA 91406 *Tel:* 818-787-4444 *E-mail:* hello@animaxent.com *Web Site:* www.animaxent.com, pg 787

Logan, Jesse, Showorks Audio Visual Inc, 100 Naamans Rd, Suite 1-C, Claymont, DE 19703 *Tel:* 302-798-7999 *Toll Free Tel:* 800-942-7469 *Fax:* 302-798-9705 *E-mail:* info@showorksav.com *Web Site:* showorksav.com, pg 1010

Logan, Jim, Logan Productions Inc, 8035 N Port Washington Rd, Milwaukee, WI 53217 *Tel:* 414-352-9691 *Fax:* 414-352-4993 *E-mail:* sales@loganproductions.com *Web Site:* www.loganproductions.com, pg 924

Logsdon, Ed, D L Adams Associates Inc, 1536 Augden St, Denver, CO 80218 *Tel:* 303-455-1900 *Fax:* 303-455-9187 *E-mail:* denver@dlaa.com *Web Site:* www.dlaa.com, pg 775

Logsdon, Lucy, The Video Project, 145 Ninth St, Suite 102, San Francisco, CA 94103 *Tel:* 415-981-9710 *Toll Free Tel:* 800-475-2638 *Toll Free Fax:* 888-562-9012 *E-mail:* orders@videoproject.com; support@videoproject.com *Web Site:* www.videoproject.com, pg 1056

Logue, Trish, QuickSet International Inc, 3650 Woodhead Dr, Northbrook, IL 60062-1895 *Tel:* 847-498-0700 *Toll Free Tel:* 800-247-6563 *Fax:* 847-498-1258 *E-mail:* info@quickset.com *Web Site:* www.quickset.com, pg 989

Loh-Berri, Vikki, Prime Cut Productions, 6418 Via Baron, Rancho Palo Verdes, CA 90275 *Tel:* 310-750-6109 *Web Site:* www.primecutproductions.com, pg 982

Lohr, Michael, Hollywood Loft, 6161 Santa Monica Blvd, Los Angeles, CA 90038 *Tel:* 323-957-9398 *Web Site:* hollywoodloft.com, pg 890

Lohre, Kathryn Mary, National Council of Churches, 110 Maryland Ave NE, Suite 10-B, Washington, DC 20002 *Tel:* 202-544-2350 *Fax:* 202-543-1297 *E-mail:* info@ncccusa.org *Web Site:* www.ncccusa.org, pg 952

Loizzo, Gary, Pumpkin Recording Studio Inc, 8453 Rob Roy Dr, Orland Park, IL 60462 *Tel:* 708-349-1485 *E-mail:* pumpkin1@flash.net, pg 987

Lombardi, Adelio, Side 3 Studios, 725 Mariposa St, Denver, CO 80204 *Tel:* 720-515-2649 *E-mail:* info@side3.com *Web Site:* www.side3.com, pg 1010

Lombardo, Joseph, Magna Systems Inc, 208 S Jefferson St, Suite 402, Chicago, IL 60661 *Toll Free Tel:* 800-634-4941 *Toll Free Fax:* 800-998-0854 *E-mail:* info@magnasystems.com *Web Site:* www.learningseed.com, pg 928

Loncar, Veronica Elliott, Kansas City FilmFest, 4741 Central, Suite 306, Kansas City, MO 64112 *Tel:* 816-286-4777 *E-mail:* contact@jubilee.org *Web Site:* kcfilmfest.org, pg 1118

London, Dr Jack P, CACI Productions Group, 14370 Newbrook Dr, Chantilly, VA 20151 *Tel:* 703-679-3100 *Web Site:* www.caci.com, pg 816

Long, Chris, Intercollegiate Studies Institute Inc (ISI), 3901 Centerville Rd, Wilmington, DE 19807 *Tel:* 302-652-4600 *Toll Free Tel:* 800-526-7022 *Fax:* 302-652-1760 *E-mail:* info@isi.org *Web Site:* www.isi.org, pg 900

Long, Jan, Apache Junction Chamber of Commerce, 567 W Apache Trail, Apache Junction, AZ 85120 *Tel:* 480-982-3141 *Toll Free Tel:* 800-252-3141 *Fax:* 480-982-3234 *Web Site:* www.ajchamber.com, pg 1091

Long, Kent, Thomas Reprographics, 801 Second Ave N, Minneapolis, MN 55405 *Tel:* 612-374-1120 *Toll Free Tel:* 800-328-7154 *Fax:* 612-374-1129 *E-mail:* orders501@thomasrepro.com *Web Site:* thomasrepro.com, pg 1039

Long, Kerrie, Frame 30 Productions Ltd, 10816A-82 Ave, No 202, Edmonton, AB T6E 2B3, Canada *Tel:* 780-439-5322 *E-mail:* frame30@frame30.com *Web Site:* www.frame30.com, pg 872

Long, S M, OMNI Productions, PO Box 302, Carmel, IN 46082-0302 *Tel:* 317-846-2345 (ext 111) *Fax:* 317-846-6664 *E-mail:* omni@omniproductions.com *Web Site:* www.omniproductions.com, pg 962

Long, Tim, Laminex Inc, 4209 Pleasant Rd, Fort Mill, SC 29708 *Tel:* 704-679-4170 *Toll Free Tel:* 800-438-8850 *Fax:* 704-679-8453 *E-mail:* info@laminex.com *Web Site:* www.laminex.com, pg 915

Long, W H, OMNI Productions, PO Box 302, Carmel, IN 46082-0302 *Tel:* 317-846-2345 (ext 111) *Fax:* 317-846-6664 *E-mail:* omni@omniproductions.com *Web Site:* www.omniproductions.com, pg 962

Lonsdale, Martha, StockMusic.com, 105 W Beaver Creek Rd, Suite 4, Richmond Hill, ON L4B 1C6, Canada *Tel:* 905-886-0077 *Fax:* 905-886-6800 *E-mail:* info@stockmusic.com *Web Site:* www.stockmusic.com, pg 1025

Loper, Kevin, Pristine Systems Inc, 1891 N Gaffey St, Suite I, San Pedro, CA 90731-1268 *Tel:* 310-831-2234 *Fax:* 310-831-6287 *E-mail:* sales@pristinesys.com *Web Site:* www.pristinesys.com, pg 982

Lopes, Matthew, The DVI Group, 1486 Mecaslin St NW, Atlanta, GA 30309 *Tel:* 404-873-6283 *Toll Free Tel:* 888-736-7384 *E-mail:* makeitbetter@thedvigroup.com *Web Site:* www.thedvigroup.com, pg 854

Lopez, David, Industrial Audio/Video Inc, 2617 Bissonnet, Houston, TX 77005 *Tel:* 713-524-1956 *Toll Free Tel:* 800-392-4384 (TX only) *Fax:* 713-524-2823 *E-mail:* info@iavdigital.com *Web Site:* www.iavdigital.com, pg 897

Lopez, David, Pacific Video Image, 9065 E Rosecrans Ave, Bellflower, CA 90706 *Tel:* 562-634-4200 *Fax:* 562-634-4700 *E-mail:* info@pvideo.com *Web Site:* www.pvideo.com, pg 967

Lopez, Dennis, Automatic Devices Co, 2121 S 12 St, Allentown, PA 18103 *Tel:* 610-797-6000 *Toll Free Tel:* 800-360-2321 *Fax:* 610-797-4088 *E-mail:* info@automaticdevices.com *Web Site:* www.automaticdevices.com, pg 797

Lopez, Gloria, Fish Films Footage World, 4548 Van Noord Ave, Studio City, CA 91604 *Tel:* 818-905-1071 *E-mail:* footageworld@aol.com *Web Site:* www.footageworld.com, pg 869

Lopez, Mike, DME Studios, 1025 Greenwood Blvd, Suite 191, Lake Mary, FL 32746 *Tel:* 407-585-7500 *E-mail:* creativeteam@dmestudios.com *Web Site:* www.dmestudios.com, pg 849

Lopez, Rosie, Tommy Boy Entertainment LLC, 902 Broadway, No 14, New York, NY 10010 *Tel:* 212-388-8300 *Fax:* 212-388-8431 *E-mail:* info@tommyboy.com *Web Site:* shop.tommyboy.com, pg 1042

Lopez, Thomas, ZBS Foundation, 174 N River Rd, Fort Edward, NY 12828-9713 *Tel:* 518-695-6406 *Toll Free Tel:* 800-662-3345 *Fax:* 518-695-4041 *E-mail:* custserv@zbs.org *Web Site:* www.zbs.org, pg 1073

Lopinto, John, Communications Specialties Inc, 125 Comac St, Ronkonkoma, NY 11779 *Tel:* 631-273-0404 *Fax:* 631-273-1638 *E-mail:* info@commspecial.com *Web Site:* www.commspecial.com, pg 833

Lorber, Ken, The Kitchen, 4119 W Burbank Blvd, Burbank, CA 91505 *Tel:* 818-306-5300 *Fax:* 305-415-6201 *E-mail:* info@thekitchen.tv *Web Site:* www.thekitchen.tv, pg 911

Lorber, Richard, Kino International Corp, 333 W 39 St, Suite 503, New York, NY 10018 *Tel:* 212-629-6880 *Toll Free Tel:* 800-562-3330 *Fax:* 212-714-0871 *E-mail:* contact@kino.com *Web Site:* www.kinolorber.com, pg 911

Lord, Cassie, 5 Alarm Music, 35 W Dayton St, Pasadena, CA 91105 *Tel:* 626-304-1698 *Toll Free Tel:* 800-322-7879 *Fax:* 626-795-2058 *E-mail:* info@5alarmmusic.com *Web Site:* www.5alarmmusic.com, pg 869

Lord, Dennis, SESAC Inc, 55 Music Sq E, Nashville, TN 37203 *Tel:* 615-320-0055 *Fax:* 615-963-3527 *Web Site:* www.sesac.com, pg 1088

Lorentzen, Bob, Video Techniques Inc, 3306 26 St W, Bradenton, FL 34205-3608 *Tel:* 941-758-3077 *Fax:* 941-301-4696 *E-mail:* vti1@videotechniques.com, pg 1056

Losik, Tim, ProPhotonix Ltd, 32 Hampshire Rd, Salem, NH 03079 *Tel:* 603-893-8778 *Toll Free Tel:* 800-472-4633 (North & South America sales) *Fax:* 603-907-0255 *E-mail:* sales@stockeryale.com *Web Site:* www.prophotonix.com, pg 986

Losique, Serge, Montreal World Film Festival, 1432 de Bleury St, Montreal, QC H3A 2J1, Canada *Tel:* 514-848-3883 *Fax:* 514-848-3886 *E-mail:* info@ffm-montreal.org *Web Site:* www.ffm-montreal.org, pg 1120

Losmandy, Bel, Opamp Labs Inc, 1033 N Sycamore Ave, Los Angeles, CA 90038 *Tel:* 323-934-3566 *Fax:* 323-462-6490 *E-mail:* opamplabs@gmail.com *Web Site:* www.opamplabs.com, pg 964

Losmandy, I, Opamp Labs Inc, 1033 N Sycamore Ave, Los Angeles, CA 90038 *Tel:* 323-934-3566 *Fax:* 323-462-6490 *E-mail:* opamplabs@gmail.com *Web Site:* www.opamplabs.com, pg 964

Losmandy, Scott, Porta-Jib, 1033 N Sycamore Ave, Los Angeles, CA 90038 *Tel:* 323-462-2855 *Fax:* 323-462-2682 *E-mail:* info@porta-jib.com *Web Site:* www.porta-jib.com, pg 978

Lott, Laura, American Alliance of Museums (AAM), 1575 Eye St NW, Suite 400, Washington, DC 20005 *Tel:* 202-289-1818 *Fax:* 202-289-6578 *Web Site:* www.aam-us.org, pg 1075

Loucks, Grant, Fax Animation Co, 5625 Melrose Ave, Hollywood, CA 90038 *Tel:* 323-466-3561 *Fax:* 323-871-2193 *E-mail:* contactus@alangordon.com *Web Site:* www.alangordon.com, pg 866

Loucks, Grant, Alan Gordon Enterprises Inc, 5625 Melrose Ave, Hollywood, CA 90038 *Tel:* 323-466-3561 *Fax:* 323-871-2193 *E-mail:* contactus@alangordon.com *Web Site:* www.alangordon.com, pg 880

Lough, Richard, Williams Sound Corp, 10300 Valley View Rd, Eden Prairie, MN 55344-3446 *Tel:* 952-943-2252 *Toll Free Tel:* 800-328-6190 *Fax:* 952-943-2174 *E-mail:* info@williamssound.com *Web Site:* www.williamssound.com, pg 1067

Loughboro, Jeff, Loma Scientific International (LSI), 3115 Kashiwa St, Torrance, CA 90505 *Tel:* 310-539-8655 *Fax:* 310-539-8634 *E-mail:* info@lomasci.com *Web Site:* www.lomasci.com, pg 924

Loughboro, Patrick, Loma Scientific International (LSI), 3115 Kashiwa St, Torrance, CA 90505 *Tel:* 310-539-8655 *Fax:* 310-539-8634 *E-mail:* info@lomasci.com *Web Site:* www.lomasci.com, pg 924

Loughhead, Roland, Triad Communications Ltd, 2751 Oxford St, Vancouver, BC V5K 1N5, Canada *Tel:* 604-253-5351; 604-253-3990 *E-mail:* triadc@comwave.com *Web Site:* www.triadcommunications.ca, pg 1044

Loughran, William Jr, Shore Manufacturing Co, 222 Beade St, Plymouth, PA 18651 *Tel:* 570-779-4042 *Toll Free Tel:* 800-321-5153 (orders) *Fax:* 570-779-7607 *Toll Free Fax:* 800-272-4334 *E-mail:* shoremfg@att.net *Web Site:* shoremfg.com, pg 1009

Loupas, James, James Loupas Associates Inc, 134 Carrington Dr, Coppell, TX 75019 *Tel:* 972-304-0455 *Web Site:* jimloupas.com, pg 925

Lourie, Iven, Gateways Books & Tapes, PO Box 370, Nevada City, CA 95959 *Tel:* 530-271-2239 *Toll Free Tel:* 800-869-0658 *Fax:* 530-272-0184 *E-mail:* info@gatewaysbooksandtapes.com *Web Site:* www.gatewaysbooksandtapes.com, pg 876

Lovallo, Christopher L, Horita Co Inc, PO Box 3993, Mission Viejo, CA 92690-3993 *Tel:* 949-489-0240 *Fax:* 949-489-0242 *E-mail:* sales@horita.com *Web Site:* www.horita.com, pg 891

Love, Brian, Westbrook Technologies Inc, 35 Thorpe Ave, Suite 201, Wallingford, CT 06492 *Tel:* 203-871-4984 *Fax:* 203-269-0322 *E-mail:* info@westbrooktech.com *Web Site:* www.westbrooktech.com, pg 1064

Love, Candace, New & Unique Videos™, 7323 Rondel Ct, San Diego, CA 92119-1530 *Tel:* 619-644-3000 *E-mail:* video@newuniquevideos.com *Web Site:* www.newuniquevideos.com, pg 955

Love, Kristen, ATCi (Antenna Technology Communication Solutions Inc), 450 N McKemy Ave, Chandler, AZ 85226 *Tel:* 480-844-8501 *Fax:* 480-898-7667 *Web Site:* www.atci.com, pg 793

Love, Lisa, Georgia Film, Music & Digital Entertainment Office, 75 Fifth St W, Suite 1200, Atlanta, GA 30308 *Tel:* 404-962-4052 *Toll Free Tel:* 877-SHOOTGA (746-6842) *Fax:* 404-962-4053 *E-mail:* film@georgia.org *Web Site:* www.georgia.org, pg 1096

Lovejoy, Meredith, Shen Milsom & Wilke LLC, 417 Fifth Ave, New York, NY 10016 *Tel:* 212-725-6800 *Fax:* 212-725-0864 *E-mail:* info@smwllc.com *Web Site:* www.smwllc.com, pg 1008

Lovelace, Steve, Moving Pictures, 200 Court St, Middletown, CT 06457 *Tel:* 860-704-6900 *Fax:* 860-704-6800 *E-mail:* inquiry@gener8or.com *Web Site:* www.movingpix.com; www.gener8or.com, pg 948

Loveridge, Doug, ST Productions, 900 Whitehall Rd, Chattanooga, TN 37405 *Tel:* 423-267-5412 *Fax:* 423-267-6840 *E-mail:* stps@wrcbtv.com *Web Site:* www.wrcbtv.com, pg 1022

Lovette, Tony, LuXout Brand Stage Curtains, 1221 Admiral St, Richmond, VA 23220 *Tel:* 804-264-3000; 804-264-3700 *Toll Free Tel:* 800-817-1204 *Toll Free Fax:* 888-227-8064 *E-mail:* luxoutinfo@luxout.com *Web Site:* www.luxout.com, pg 926

Low, Bob, O'Connor Engineering Labs, 2701 N Ontario St, Burbank, CA 91504 *Tel:* 818-847-8666 *Fax:* 818-847-1205 *E-mail:* info@ocon.com; sales@ocon.com *Web Site:* www.ocon.com, pg 961

Lowe, David, KVIE-Channel 6, 2030 W El Camino Ave, Sacramento, CA 95833 *Tel:* 916-929-5843 *Toll Free Tel:* 800-347-5843 *Fax:* 916-929-7215 *E-mail:* member@kvie.org *Web Site:* www.kvie.org, pg 914

Lowe, George F, Sparkfactor, 1644 N Honore St, Suite 100, Chicago, IL 60622 *Tel:* 773-292-8000 *E-mail:* info@sparkfactor.com *Web Site:* www.sparkfactor.com, pg 1019

Lowe, Walter, Blackburst Entertainment, 1830 Longwood Lake Mary Rd, No 1024, Longwood, FL 32750 *Tel:* 407-599-5353 *E-mail:* info@blackburst.net *Web Site:* www.blackburstentertainment.com, pg 808

Lowell, John, Lowell Manufacturing, 100 Integram Dr, Pacific, MO 63069-3476 *Toll Free Tel:* 800-325-9660 *Toll Free Fax:* 800-456-9355 *E-mail:* sales@lowellmfg.com *Web Site:* www.lowellmfg.com, pg 925

Lowen, Cynthia, HB-Content, 105 Butler St, Suite 2B, Brooklyn, NY 11231 *Tel:* 212-213-8824 *E-mail:* hb@hb-content.com *Web Site:* www.hb-content.com, pg 886

Lowenstein, Rick, Avid Technology Inc, 65-75 Network Dr, Burlington, MA 01830 *Tel:* 978-640-6789 *Fax:* 978-640-3366 *Web Site:* www.avid.com, pg 799

Lowenthal, Paul, Southern Audio Visual, 11700 NW 102 Rd, Suite 15, Miami, FL 33178 *Tel:* 305-591-3888 *Fax:* 305-591-7105 *Web Site:* www.southernav.com, pg 1019

Lowery, Dr Dan, Calumet College of Saint Joseph, 2400 New York Ave, Whiting, IN 46394 *Tel:* 219-473-7770 *Fax:* 219-473-4259 *Web Site:* www.ccsj.edu, pg 817

Lowery, Shawn, NAMM, the National Association of Music Merchants, 5790 Armada Dr, Carlsbad, CA 92008 *Tel:* 760-438-8001 *Toll Free Tel:* 800-767-6266 (memb hotline) *Fax:* 760-438-7327 *E-mail:* info@namm.org *Web Site:* www.namm.org, pg 1085

Lowing, David R, Lowing Light & Grip Inc, 1500 Whiting St SW, Wyoming, MI 49509-1056 *Tel:* 616-530-7440 *Toll Free Tel:* 888-530-7440 *Fax:* 616-249-8947 *Web Site:* www.lowinglight.com, pg 925

Lowman, Paul, Case Design Corp, 333 School Lane, Telford, PA 18969 *Tel:* 215-703-0130 *Toll Free Tel:* 800-847-4176 *Fax:* 215-703-0139 *E-mail:* sales@casedesigncorp.com *Web Site:* www.casedesigncorp.com, pg 820

Lowman, Quincy, Inferno Films, 3404 Guadalupe St, Austin, TX 78705 *Tel:* 512-302-9009 *Fax:* 512-302-9022 *Web Site:* www.infernofilms.com, pg 898

Lowrance, Mark, Lowrance Sound Co Inc, 2132 Nailling Dr, Union City, TN 38261 *Tel:* 731-885-4504 *Toll Free Tel:* 800-852-5418 *E-mail:* info@lowrancesoundcompany.com *Web Site:* www.lowrancesoundcompany.com, pg 925

Lowther, Doug, International Datacasting, 50 Frank Nighbor Place, Kanata, ON K2V 1B9, Canada *Tel:* 613-596-4120 *Fax:* 613-596-4863 *E-mail:* marketing@datacast.com *Web Site:* www.datacast.com, pg 900

Lozowski, Stanley, Lylofilm Productions, 503 Beech St, New Hyde Park, NY 11040 *Tel:* 516-587-0567 *E-mail:* lylofilm@gmail.com; cdigitalv@yahoo.com *Web Site:* www.lylofilm.com, pg 926

Lubash, Rob, Kenexa, 650 E Swedesford Rd, 2nd fl, Wayne, PA 19087 *Tel:* 407-548-1444 *Fax:* 610-971-9181 *E-mail:* kenexa_learn_sales@kenexa.com *Web Site:* www.outstart.com, pg 909

Lubeck, Chris, Accusoft, 4001 N Riverside Dr, Tampa, FL 33603 *Tel:* 813-875-7575 *Toll Free Tel:* 800-875-7009 *Fax:* 813-875-7705 *E-mail:* sales@accusoft.com *Web Site:* www.accusoft.com, pg 774

Lubell, Alan H, Lubell Labs Inc, 21 N Stanwood Rd, Columbus, OH 43209 *Tel:* 614-235-6740 *E-mail:* lubell_labs@wowway.com *Web Site:* www.lubell.com, pg 925

Lubliner, Larry, Acoustone Corp, 140 58 St, Unit 9 W, Bldg A, Brooklyn, NY 11220 *Tel:* 718-782-5560 *Fax:* 718-782-7367 *E-mail:* acoustone@newcastlefabrics.com *Web Site:* www.acoustonegrillecloth.com, pg 775

Lubman, David, David Lubman Acoustics, 14301 Middletown Lane, Westminster, CA 92683 *Tel:* 714-373-3050 *Fax:* 714-373-3050 *Web Site:* www.dlacoustics.com, pg 925

Lubotta, Barry, Phase One Studios, 3015 Kennedy Rd, Suite 10, Toronto, ON M1V 1E7, Canada *Tel:* 416-291-9553 *Toll Free Tel:* 888-728-3333 *Fax:* 416-291-7898 *E-mail:* info@phaseonestudios.com *Web Site:* www.phaseonestudios.com, pg 973

Luca, Gerry, Spectra Film & Video, 5626 Vineland Ave, North Hollywood, CA 91601 *Tel:* 818-762-4545 *Fax:* 818-762-5454 *E-mail:* sales@spectrafilmandvideo.com *Web Site:* www.spectrafilmandvideo.com, pg 1020

Lucas, Barbara E R, USITT: United States Institute for Theatre Technology Inc, 315 S Crouse Ave, Suite 200, Syracuse, NY 13210-1844 *Tel:* 315-463-6463 *Toll Free Tel:* 800-938-7488 *Fax:* 315-463-6525 *Toll Free Fax:* 866-398-7488 *E-mail:* info@office.usitt.org *Web Site:* www.usitt.org, pg 1090

Lucas, Bill, Fox 10 Productions (KSAZ-TV), 511 W Adams, Phoenix, AZ 85003 *Tel:* 602-257-1234 *Fax:* 602-262-0177 *E-mail:* fox10.desk@foxtv.com *Web Site:* www.myfoxphoenix.com; www.my45.com, pg 872

Lucas, Katherine, Gurrilla Video Solutions, 233 Fillmore Ave, Suite 8, Tonawanda, NY 14150 *Tel:* 716-692-0064 *E-mail:* info@gvideosolutions.com *Web Site:* www.gvideosolutions.com, pg 883

Lucas, Mark, Imation Corp, One Imation Way, Oakdale, MN 55128-3421 *Tel:* 651-704-4000 *Toll Free Tel:* 888-466-3456 *Fax:* 651-704-3444 *Toll Free Fax:* 888-704-4200 *E-mail:* info@imation.com *Web Site:* www.imation.com, pg 896

Lucasey, Charles, Lucasey Manufacturing Corp, 2744 E 11 St, Oakland, CA 94601 *Tel:* 510-534-1435 *Toll Free Tel:* 800-582-2739 *Fax:* 510-534-6828 *E-mail:* sales@lucasey.com *Web Site:* www.lucasey.com, pg 925

Lucci, Ralph, Automobile Film Club of America Inc, 10 Cross St, Staten Island, NY 10304 *Tel:* 718-447-2255 *Fax:* 718-447-2289 *E-mail:* autofilm@aol.com *Web Site:* www.autofilmclub.com, pg 797

Luce, Rich, Rosco Laboratories Inc, 52 Harbor View, Stamford, CT 06902 *Tel:* 203-708-8900 *Toll Free Tel:* 800-ROSCO NY (767-2669) *Fax:* 203-708-8919 *E-mail:* info@rosco.com *Web Site:* www.rosco.com, pg 999

Lucero, John, The Denver Office of Economic Development, Wellington E Webb Municipal Bldg, 2nd fl, 201 W Colfax Ave, Dept 1005, Denver, CO 80202 *Tel:* 720-913-1999 *Fax:* 720-913-1802 *E-mail:* oed@denvergov.org *Web Site:* www.milehigh.com, pg 1095

Lucich, Marko, Butte-Silver Bow Chamber of Commerce, 1000 George St, Butte, MT 59701 *Tel:* 406-723-3177 *Toll Free Tel:* 800-735-6814 *Fax:* 406-723-1215 *E-mail:* chamber@buttechamber.org; marketing@buttechamber.org *Web Site:* www.buttechamber.org, pg 1099

Luckhardt, Wolfgang, beyerdynamic Inc, 56 Central Ave, Farmingdale, NY 11735 *Tel:* 631-293-3200 *Toll Free Tel:* 800-293-4463 *Fax:* 631-293-3288 *E-mail:* info@beyerdynamic-usa.com *Web Site:* north-america.beyerdynamic.com, pg 806

Luckhart, Brad, Visual Aids Electronics of North Carolina Inc, 245 Executive Park Blvd, Winston-Salem, NC 27103 *Tel:* 336-768-5454 *Toll Free Tel:* 855-934-2828 *Fax:* 336-768-5054 *E-mail:* avrentals@avconnectionsusa.com *Web Site:* avconnectionsusa.com, pg 1059

Lucy, Ray, MSI Productions, 9220 Activity Rd, San Diego, CA 92126 *Tel:* 858-348-0100 *Fax:* 858-348-0076 *Web Site:* www.msiprod.com, pg 949

Luddy, Tom, Telluride Film Festival, 800 Jones St, Berkeley, CA 94710 *Tel:* 510-665-9494 *Fax:* 510-665-9589 *E-mail:* mail@telluridefilmfestival.org *Web Site:* www.telluridefilmfestival.org, pg 1128

Ludlow, Gay, Triad Communications Ltd, 2751 Oxford St, Vancouver, BC V5K 1N5, Canada *Tel:* 604-253-5351; 604-253-3990 *E-mail:* triadc@comwave.com *Web Site:* www.triadcommunications.ca, pg 1044

Ludlow, Rhys, Ludlow Media Solutions, 15501 San Pablo Ave, Suite G320, San Pablo, CA 94806 *Tel:* 415-927-1300 *E-mail:* info@ludlowmedia.com *Web Site:* www.ludlowmedia.com, pg 926

Lueck, Doug, Ridgecrest Film Commission, 634 N China Lake Blvd, Suite C, Ridgecrest, CA 93555 *Tel:* 760-375-8202 *Toll Free Tel:* 800-847-4830 *Fax:* 760-375-9850 *E-mail:* racvb@filmdeserts.com *Web Site:* www.filmdeserts.com, pg 1093

Luedtke, Luther, Education Development Center Inc (EDC), 43 Foundry Ave, Waltham, MA 02453-8313 *Tel:* 617-969-7100 *Fax:* 617-969-5979 *E-mail:* contact@edc.org *Web Site:* www.edc.org, pg 857

Luff, Monica, Manatee County Film Commission, One Haben Blvd, Palmetto, FL 34221 *Tel:* 941-729-9177 *Toll Free Tel:* 800-822-2017 *Fax:* 941-729-1820 *Web Site:* www.bradentongulfislands.com, pg 1096

Lugo, Fernando, Cinema Entertainment Inc, 1779 NW 79 Ave, Doral, FL 33126 *Tel:* 561-899-0721 *E-mail:* info@cinemaent.com *Web Site:* cinemaent.com, pg 827

Lujan, Kelly, 30 Second Street Ltd, 1209 Mountain Road Place NE, Albuquerque, NM 87110 *Tel:* 505-265-0224 *E-mail:* info@thirtysecst.com *Web Site:* www.thirtysecst.com, pg 1039

Lukacs, Ann, Blue River Productions, PO Box 1535, Breckenridge, CO 80424-1535 *Tel:* 970-390-8568 *E-mail:* filmbreckenridge@gmail.com *Web Site:* www.filmcolorado.com, pg 810

Lukasik, Diana, TBC Consoles Inc, 170 Rodeo Dr, Edgewood, NY 11717 *Tel:* 631-293-4068 *Toll Free Tel:* 888-CONSOLE (266-7653) *Fax:* 631-293-4075 *E-mail:* info@tbcconsoles.com; sales@tbcconsoles.com; support@tbcconsoles.com *Web Site:* www.tbcconsoles.com, pg 1033

Luke, Keth, Sound*Light, 5438 Tennessee Ave, New Port Richey, FL 34652 *Tel:* 727-842-6788 *Fax:* 727-842-6788 *Web Site:* www.awakening-healing.com; www.soundlight.org, pg 1017

Luksch, James A, Blonder Tongue Laboratories Inc, One Jake Brown Rd, Old Bridge, NJ 08857 *Tel:* 732-679-4000 *Toll Free Tel:* 800-523-6049 *Fax:* 732-679-4353 *E-mail:* custsvc@blondertongue.com; btglobalsales@blondertongue.com (other than US & CN) *Web Site:* www.blondertongue.com, pg 809

Lumbard, Paula, FootageBank HD, 13470 Washington Blvd, Suite 210, Marina Del Rey, CA 90292 *Tel:* 310-822-1400 *Toll Free Tel:* 888-653-1400 *Fax:* 310-822-4100 *E-mail:* info@footagebank.com *Web Site:* www.footagebank.com, pg 871

Lumpkin, Michael, IDA Documentary Awards, 3470 Wilshire Blvd, Suite 980, Los Angeles, CA 90010 *Tel:* 213-232-1660 *Fax:* 213-232-1669 *E-mail:* info@documentary.org *Web Site:* www.documentary.org, pg 1116

Lumpkin, Michael, International Documentary Association, 3470 Wilshire Blvd, Suite 980, Los Angeles, CA 90010 *Tel:* 213-232-1660 *Fax:* 213-232-1669 *E-mail:* info@documentary.org *Web Site:* www.documentary.org, pg 1083

Lumsden, Rick, Britannica Film & Video, 331 N LaSalle St, Chicago, IL 60654 *Toll Free Tel:* 800-621-3900 *Toll Free Fax:* 800-344-9624 *E-mail:* contact@eb.com *Web Site:* info.eb.com, pg 812

Lund, Michael Paul, Serendipity Recordings, 511 Slab City Rd, Lincolnville, ME 04849 *Tel:* 207-763-3677, pg 1007

Lundahl, Paul, eMotion Studios, 85 Liberty Ship Way, Suite 110, Sausalito, CA 94965 *Tel:* 415-331-6975 *Fax:* 415-331-6124 *E-mail:* sales@emotionstudios.com *Web Site:* www.emotionstudios.com, pg 860

Lunder, Karen, FilmNation Entertainment, 150 W 22 St, 9th fl, New York, NY 10011 *Web Site:* www.filmnation.com, pg 867

Lunsford, Gary, RTZ Audio Visual, 6725 Santa Barbara Ct, Suite 103, Elkridge, MD 21075 *Tel:* 443-757-0480 *Toll Free Tel:* 800-543-0582 *Fax:* 443-757-0487 *E-mail:* sales@rtzav.com *Web Site:* www.rtzav.com, pg 1000

Lupien, Leo, Audio Visual Sales & Service Inc, 2601 Curry Rd, Schenectady, NY 12303 *Tel:* 518-688-0640 *Fax:* 518-688-0634 *E-mail:* info@avssi.com, pg 796

Luscombe, George, G T Luscombe Co Inc, 106 Kansas St, Frankfort, IL 60423 *Tel:* 815-469-2478 *Toll Free Tel:* 800-435-7855 *Fax:* 815-469-5429 *Toll Free Fax:* 888-469-5429 *E-mail:* info@gtluscombe.com *Web Site:* www.gtluscombe.com, pg 926

Luscombe, John, G T Luscombe Co Inc, 106 Kansas St, Frankfort, IL 60423 *Tel:* 815-469-2478 *Toll Free Tel:* 800-435-7855 *Fax:* 815-469-5429 *Toll Free Fax:* 888-469-5429 *E-mail:* info@gtluscombe.com *Web Site:* www.gtluscombe.com, pg 926

Lustgarten, Steve, Leo Films, 6548 Country Squire Lane, Omaha, NE 68152 *Tel:* 323-459-5574 *Web Site:* www.leofilms.com, pg 919

Luther, Bob, Lex Products Corp, 15 Progress Dr, Shelton, CT 06484 *Tel:* 203-363-3738 *Toll Free Tel:* 800-643-4460 *Fax:* 203-363-3742 *E-mail:* info@lexproducts.com *Web Site:* www.lexproducts.com, pg 919

Luther, Jessica, Digital Music Corp, 3165 Coffey Lane, Santa Rosa, CA 95403 *Tel:* 707-545-0600 *Fax:* 707-545-9777 *E-mail:* info@voodoolab.com *Web Site:* www.voodoolab.com, pg 847

Lyanga, Jacqueline, AFI FEST, 2021 N Western Ave, Los Angeles, CA 90027-1657 *Tel:* 323-856-7600 *Toll Free Tel:* 866-AFI-FEST (234-3378) *Fax:* 323-467-4578 *E-mail:* afifest@afi.com; festpublicity@afi.com *Web Site:* www.afi.com, pg 1107

Lynch, Fernando, Permlight Products Inc, 422 W Sixth St, Tustin, CA 92780 *Tel:* 714-508-0729 *Fax:* 714-508-0920 *E-mail:* sales@brillialed.com (brillia div); sales@permlightforsigns.com (sign div) *Web Site:* www.permlight.com; www.permlightforsigns.com (signs div); www.brillialed.com (brillia div), pg 973

Lynch, John, Forensic Video Deposition Service, 2823 N 48 St, Suite 8, Phoenix, AZ 85008 *Tel:* 602-840-1222 *Fax:* 602-840-1313 *Web Site:* forensicvideo.net, pg 871

Lynch, Kevin, Adobe Systems Inc, 345 Park Ave, San Jose, CA 95110-2704 *Tel:* 408-536-6000 *Fax:* 408-537-6000 *Web Site:* www.adobe.com, pg 776

Lynch, Marcella O, Cooking by the Book, 13475 N Applegate Rd, Grants Pass, OR 97527 *Tel:* 541-846-0654 *Toll Free Tel:* 800-655-9071 *Fax:* 541-846-0654 *Web Site:* www.atasteofnature.org, pg 836

Lynch, Michael, City of Boston Office of Cable Communications, 43 Hawkins St, Boston, MA 02114 *Tel:* 617-635-3112 *Fax:* 617-635-4475 *E-mail:* cable@cityofboston.gov *Web Site:* www.cityofboston.gov/cable, pg 1080

Lynch, Nicky, Banff Mountain Film & Book Festival, 107 Tunnel Mountain Dr, Banff, AB T1L 1H5, Canada *Tel:* 403-762-6347 *Fax:* 403-762-6277 *E-mail:* banffmountainfestival@banffcentre.ca *Web Site:* www.banffcentre.ca/mountainfestival, pg 1109

Lynch, Paul, Lynch Communications, 22 Canada Cove Ave, Half Moon Bay, CA 94019 *Tel:* 678-939-1212 *Web Site:* www.lynchcommunications.com, pg 926

Lyngard, Doug, DL Sound & Lighting Productions Ltd, 450 Banga Place, Victoria, BC V8Z 6X5, Canada *Tel:* 250-216-7898 *Fax:* 250-590-1280 *Web Site:* www.dlsound.net, pg 849

Lyngdal, Reynir, Kaboom Productions, 1465 Illinois St, San Francisco, CA 94107 *Tel:* 415-434-2666 *Fax:* 415-970-8548 *E-mail:* updates@kaboomproductions.com *Web Site:* kaboomproductions.com, pg 907

Lynton, Michael, Columbia Pictures Inc, 10202 W Washington Blvd, Culver City, CA 90232 *Tel:* 310-244-4000; 310-244-6926 (studio opers) *Fax:* 310-244-8090 *Web Site:* www.sonypicturesstudios.com; www.sonypictures.com, pg 832

Lynton, Michael, Sony Pictures Entertainment, 10202 W Washington Blvd, Culver City, CA 90232 *Tel:* 310-244-4000 *Web Site:* www.sonypictures.com, pg 1016

Lyon, Fred, Fred Lyon Pictures, 3609 Buchanan St, San Francisco, CA 94123 *Tel:* 415-922-5100 *Fax:* 415-922-5762 *E-mail:* images@winetravelandfood.com *Web Site:* www.fredlyon.com; www.winetravelandfood.com, pg 927

Lyon, Jim, ICL Imaging Inc, 51 Mellen St, Framingham, MA 01702 *Tel:* 508-872-3280 *Toll Free Tel:* 800-660-3280 *Fax:* 508-872-7364 *E-mail:* csr@icl-imaging.com *Web Site:* www.icl-imaging.com, pg 893

Lyon, Robert, Lyon Video Inc, 2091 Arlingate Lane, Columbus, OH 43228 *Tel:* 614-297-0001 *Web Site:* www.lyonvideo.com, pg 927

Lyons, Anthony J, IFM World Releasing Inc, 1328 E Palmer Ave, Glendale, CA 91205 *Tel:* 818-243-4976 *Fax:* 818-550-9728 *E-mail:* contact@ifmfilm.com *Web Site:* www.ifmfilm.com, pg 894

Lyons, Jim, Allen Avionics Inc, 255 E Second St, Mineola, NY 11501 *Tel:* 516-248-8080 *Fax:* 516-747-6724 *E-mail:* info@allenavionics.com *Web Site:* www.allenavionics.com, pg 781

Lyriti, Simona, Lylofilm Productions, 503 Beech St, New Hyde Park, NY 11040 *Tel:* 516-587-0567 *E-mail:* lylofilm@gmail.com; cdigitalv@yahoo.com *Web Site:* www.lylofilm.com, pg 926

Lytle, Moe, International Marketing Group, 1900 Elm Hill Pike, Nashville, TN 37210 *Tel:* 615-889-8000 *Fax:* 615-871-4817, pg 901

Lyver, Kevin, Ward-Beck Systems Ltd, 945 Middlefield Rd, Unit 9, Toronto, ON M1V 5E1, Canada *Tel:* 416-335-5999 *Toll Free Tel:* 800-771-2556 *Fax:* 416-335-5202 *E-mail:* sales@ward-beck.com *Web Site:* www.ward-beck.com, pg 1062

Macaluso, Andre, Deluxe Media Services, 235 Pegasus Ave, Northvale, NJ 07647 *Tel:* 201-767-3800 *Fax:* 201-784-2769 *Web Site:* www.bydeluxe.com, pg 845

Macan, John, Keywest Technology Inc, 14563 W 96 Terr, Lenexa, KS 66215 *Tel:* 913-492-4666 *Toll Free Tel:* 800-331-2019 *Fax:* 913-322-1864 *E-mail:* info@keywesttechnology.com; sales@keywesttechnology.com *Web Site:* www.keywesttechnology.com, pg 910

Macaraeg, Angela, PME Audio/Video, 2003 S El Camino Rd, Suite 108, Oceanside, CA 92054 *Tel:* 760-439-0281 *E-mail:* solutions@pmevideo.com *Web Site:* www.pmevideo.com, pg 977

Macari, Anthony, CPI Malibu, 3760-A Calle Tecate, Camarillo, CA 93012-5060 *Tel:* 805-383-1829 *Fax:* 805-383-1859 *E-mail:* malibu.sales@cpii.com *Web Site:* www.cpii.com/division.cfm/10, pg 837

Macari, Michael Jr, EagleVision Inc, 1200 High Ridge Rd, 2nd fl, Stamford, CT 06905 *Tel:* 203-359-8777 *Fax:* 203-348-6000 *E-mail:* info@evtv.net *Web Site:* www.evtv.net, pg 855

Macaulay, Doug, Kingsway Motion Picture Ltd, 200 Evans Ave, Unit 4, Toronto, ON M8Z 1J7, Canada *Tel:* 416-463-4345 *Fax:* 416-469-2609 *E-mail:* info@kingswaycanada.com *Web Site:* kingswaycanada.com, pg 911

MacDonald, Bill, Spectrum Audio Visual Services, 351 W 45 Ave, Denver, CO 80216 *Tel:* 303-477-4456 *Toll Free Tel:* 800-477-4752 *Fax:* 303-477-0114 *E-mail:* info@spectrumav.com *Web Site:* www.spectrumav.com, pg 1020

Macdonald, Darryl, Palm Springs International Film Festival, 1700 E Tahquitz Canyon Way, Suite 3, Palm Springs, CA 92262 *Tel:* 760-322-2930 *Toll Free Tel:* 800-898-7256 *Fax:* 760-322-4087 *E-mail:* info@psfilmfest.org *Web Site:* www.psfilmfest.org, pg 1123

MacDonald, Jesse, Old School Cameras, 2819 N San Fernando Blvd, Burbank, CA 91504 *Tel:* 818-847-1555 *Fax:* 818-847-1556 *Web Site:* www.oldschoolcameras.com, pg 961

Macdonald, Ramona, Doomsday Studios Ltd, 212 James St, Ottawa, ON K1R 5M7, Canada *Tel:* 613-230-9769 *Fax:* 613-230-6004 *E-mail:* info@doomsdaystudios.com, pg 850

MacDougall, R Bruce, Kalglo Electronics Co Inc, 5911 Colony Dr, Bethlehem, PA 18017-9348 *Tel:* 610-837-0700 *Fax:* 610-837-7978 *E-mail:* kalglo@kalglo.com *Web Site:* www.kalglo.com, pg 907

MacEachern, Camilla, Northwest Territories Film Commission, PO Box 1320, Yellowknife, NT X1A 2L9, Canada *Tel:* 867-920-8793 *Fax:* 867-873-0101 *Toll Free Fax:* 877-445-2787 (ext 6) *E-mail:* nwtfilm@gov.nt.ca *Web Site:* www.nwtfilm.com, pg 1105

Macey, Todd, Vital Learning LLC, 1675 Larimer St, No 410, Denver, CO 80202 *Tel:* 402-592-1602 *Toll Free Tel:* 800-243-5858 *Fax:* 402-592-7142 *E-mail:* sales@vital-learning.com; info@vital-learning.com *Web Site:* www.vital-learning.com, pg 1060

MacFadden, Lisa, TPR Enterprises Ltd, 644 Fayette Ave, Mamaroneck, NY 10543 *Tel:* 914-698-1141 *Fax:* 914-698-9419 *E-mail:* info@tprlights.com *Web Site:* www.tprlights.com, pg 1043

MacIlvaine, Jim, Oakland Film Office, One Frank H Ogawa Plaza, 9th fl, Oakland, CA 94612-1406 *Tel:* 510-238-4734 *Fax:* 510-238-6149 *E-mail:* filmoakland@filmoakland.com *Web Site:* www.filmoakland.com, pg 1093

Maciocia, Gabriel, Canadian American Records, PO Box 808, Lititz, PA 17543-0538 *Tel:* 717-627-4800 *Fax:* 717-627-4800 *E-mail:* canadianamerican@dejazzd.com *Web Site:* www.canadianamericanrecords.net; www.joeywelz.com, pg 818

Mack, Joseph, GatesAir, 5300 Kings Island Dr, Suite 101, Mason, OH 45040 *Tel:* 513-459-3400 *Fax:* 513-459-3796 *E-mail:* information@gatesair.com; orders@gatesair.com; support@gatesair.com *Web Site:* www.gatesair.com, pg 875

Mack, Odell, PM Productions, 5882 Bowcroft St, Suite 2, Los Angeles, CA 90016-4907 *Tel:* 310-559-3127 *Fax:* 310-559-3168 *Web Site:* www.pmproductionsvideos.com, pg 977

Mackell, Susan E, Brooklyn Film Festival (BiFF), 180 S Fourth St, Suite 2-S, Brooklyn, NY 11211 *Tel:* 718-388-4306 *Fax:* 718-599-5039 *E-mail:* festival@wbff.org *Web Site:* www.brooklynfilmfestival.org, pg 1110

MacKinnon, Gail G, Time Warner Cable, 60 Columbus Circle, 17th fl, New York, NY 10023 *Tel:* 212-364-8200 *Web Site:* www.timewarnercable.com, pg 1040

Macklin, Nancy, Hearing Loss Association of America (HLAA), 7910 Woodmont Ave, Suite 1200, Bethesda, MD 20814 *Tel:* 301-657-2248; 301-657-2249 (TTY) *Fax:* 301-913-9413 *E-mail:* info@hearingloss.org *Web Site:* www.hearingloss.org, pg 887

MacNab, John, Canadian Broadcast Standards Council (CBSC), PO Box 3265, Sta D, Ottawa, ON K1P 6H8, Canada *Tel:* 613-233-4607 *Toll Free Tel:* 866-696-4718 (CN only) *Fax:* 613-233-4826 *E-mail:* info@cbsc.ca *Web Site:* www.ccnr.ca, pg 1080

Macuch, Doug, RCI Custom Products, 801 N East St, Suite 2-A, Frederick, MD 21701 *Tel:* 301-620-9130 *Toll Free Tel:* 800-546-4724 *Fax:* 301-620-9103 *Toll Free Fax:* 800-546-6175 *E-mail:* info@rcicustom.com *Web Site:* www.rcicustom.com, pg 992

Madalengoitia, Eve, DEC Grants, 696 Dutchess Tpke, Suite F, Poughkeepsie, NY 12603 *Tel:* 845-454-3222 *Fax:* 845-454-6902 *E-mail:* info@artsmidhudson.org *Web Site:* www.artsmidhudson.org, pg 1114

Madar, Paul, SOM Publishing Co, 163 Moon Valley Rd, Windyville, MO 65783 *Tel:* 417-345-8411 *E-mail:* som@som.org *Web Site:* www.som.org, pg 1015

Maddox, Angela, Cooper Controls, 203 Cooper Circle, Peachtree City, GA 30269 *Tel:* 770-486-4782 *Toll Free Tel:* 800-553-3879 *Toll Free Fax:* 800-954-7016 *E-mail:* controlssales@cooperindustries.com *Web Site:* www.coopercontrol.com, pg 836

Maddox, Douglas B, DBM Communications Inc, 606 Baltimore Ave, Suite 200, Towson, MD 21204 *Tel:* 410-825-7400 *Fax:* 443-269-0213 *Web Site:* www.dbmcommunications.com, pg 844

Madison, Cheryl, Sensormatic®, 6600 Congress Ave, Boca Raton, FL 33487 *Tel:* 561-912-6000 *Toll Free Tel:* 800-507-6268 *Web Site:* www.tyco.com; www.sensormatic.com, pg 1006

Madison, Jeff, RPG Diffusor Systems Inc, 651-C Commerce Dr, Upper Marlboro, MD 20774 *Tel:* 301-249-0044 *Fax:* 301-390-3602 *E-mail:* info@rpginc.com *Web Site:* www.rpginc.com, pg 1000

Madnick, Marc, Final Draft Inc, 26707 W Agoura Rd, Suite 205, Calabasas, CA 91302 *Tel:* 818-995-8995; 818-906-8930 (tech support) *Toll Free Tel:* 800-231-4055 *Fax:* 818-995-4422 *E-mail:* info@finaldraft.com *Web Site:* www.finaldraft.com, pg 868

Maestri, Luca, Apple Inc, One Infinite Loop, Cupertino, CA 95014 *Tel:* 408-996-1010 *Web Site:* www.apple.com, pg 788

Magabni, Fabian, MediaOne Services, 901 Battery St, Suite 220, San Francisco, CA 94111 *Tel:* 415-262-4222 *E-mail:* sales@mediaoneservices.com *Web Site:* mediaoneservices.com, pg 938

Magdael, David, The Los Angeles Asian Pacific Film Festival, 120 Judge John Aiso St, Basement Level, Los Angeles, CA 90012-3805 *Tel:* 213-680-4462 *Fax:* 213-687-4848 *E-mail:* festival@vconline.org *Web Site:* asianfilmfestla.org, pg 1119

Magenheim, Jay, Ideal Large Format Imaging Services, 15737 Crabbs Branch Way, Rockville, MD 20855 *Tel:* 301-468-0123 *Toll Free Tel:* 800-76IDEAL (764-3325) *Fax:* 301-230-0813 *E-mail:* sales@ideal.com *Web Site:* www.ideal.com, pg 894

Magidson, Phyllis, Museum of the City of New York, 1220 Fifth Ave, New York, NY 10029 *Tel:* 212-534-1672 *Fax:* 212-423-0758 *E-mail:* info@mcny.org *Web Site:* www.mcny.org, pg 950

Magnuson, Ingrid, MAGNUM Companies Ltd, 205 Armour Dr NE, Atlanta, GA 30324 *Tel:* 404-872-0553 *Toll Free Tel:* 800-255-1774 *Fax:* 404-875-5629 *E-mail:* buy@magnumco.com; rent@magnumco.com; design@magnumco.com; production@magnumco.com *Web Site:* www.magnumco.com, pg 929

Magnuson, Julie, Mullikin Agency, 1391 Plaza Place, Suite A, Springdale, AR 72764-5225 *Tel:* 479-750-0871 *Toll Free Tel:* 800-750-0871 *Fax:* 479-750-2685 *Web Site:* www.mullikinad.com, pg 949

Magnuson, Mark, Anode Inc, 926 Main St, Nashville, TN 37206 *Tel:* 615-742-1490 *Toll Free Tel:* 866-802-2436 *Fax:* 615-742-1487 *E-mail:* inquiry@anode.com *Web Site:* www.anode.com, pg 787

Magoon, Scott, Lineco, 517 Main St, Holyoke, MA 01040 *Toll Free Tel:* 800-322-7775 *Fax:* 413-532-9281 *Toll Free Fax:* 800-298-7815 *E-mail:* info@lineco.com *Web Site:* www.lineco.com, pg 922

Magoon, Scott E, University Products Inc, 517 Main St, Holyoke, MA 01040-0073 *Tel:* 413-532-3372 *Toll Free Tel:* 800-628-1912 *Fax:* 413-532-9281 *Toll Free Fax:* 800-532-9281 *E-mail:* custserv@universityproducts.com; info@universityproducts.com *Web Site:* www.universityproducts.com, pg 1050

Magoun, David, Full Spectrum Arts & Services, PO Box 1032, Littleton, CO 80160 *Tel:* 303-798-7906 *Web Site:* www.fullspectrumarts.com, pg 874

Magrill, Kyle, CircuitWerkes Inc, 2805 NW Sixth St, Gainesville, FL 32609 *Tel:* 352-335-6555 *Fax:* 352-380-0230 *E-mail:* sales@circuitwerkes.com *Web Site:* www.broadcastboxes.com; www.circuitwerkes.com, pg 828

Magruder, Robin, Crossroads Audio Inc, 2623 Myrtle Springs Ave, Dallas, TX 75220 *Tel:* 214-358-2623 *Toll Free Tel:* 800-287-0436 *Fax:* 214-358-0185 *E-mail:* mail@crossroadsaudio.com *Web Site:* www.crossroadsaudio.com, pg 840

Maguire, Dennis, Paramount Pictures Corporation, 5555 Melrose Ave, Los Angeles, CA 90038 *Tel:* 323-956-8398 *Web Site:* www.paramount.com, pg 969

Maguire, William, Intellidyne LLC, 5203 Leesburg Pike, Suite 400, 2 Skyline Place, Falls Church, VA 22041 *Tel:* 703-575-9715 *Fax:* 703-575-9718 *Web Site:* www.intellidyne-llc.com, pg 899

Maher, Teresa, Electronics Technicians Association International Inc, 5 Depot St, Greencastle, IN 46135 *Tel:* 765-653-8262 *Toll Free Tel:* 800-288-3824 *Fax:* 765-653-4287 *E-mail:* eta@eta-i.org *Web Site:* www.eta-i.org, pg 1081

Maheras, William, Sight & Sound Studios, 66 Queen St, Suite 1705, Honolulu, HI 96813 *Tel:* 808-599-7600 *Fax:* 808-599-7601 *Web Site:* www.sightandsoundhawaii.com, pg 1010

Mahle, Robin, Rum Jungle Media, 5295 Eden Rd, Mound, MN 55364 *Tel:* 952-472-5525 *E-mail:* rumjungle@rumjungle.com *Web Site:* www.rumjungle.com, pg 1000

Mahoney, Pat, Hollywood Center Studios, 1040 N Las Palmas, Los Angeles, CA 90038 *Tel:* 323-860-0000 *E-mail:* info@hollywoodcenter.com *Web Site:* www.hollywoodcenter.com, pg 890

Mahoney, Tim, Hollywood Center Studios, 1040 N Las Palmas, Los Angeles, CA 90038 *Tel:* 323-860-0000 *E-mail:* info@hollywoodcenter.com *Web Site:* www.hollywoodcenter.com, pg 890

Maier, Charlie, Sand Box Studio, 555 Minnesota St, San Francisco, CA 94107 *Tel:* 415-550-8732 *E-mail:* inquiries@sandboxstudio.com *Web Site:* www.sandboxstudio.com, pg 1002

Main, Steve, The Prairie Production Group, 509 S Country Fair Dr, Suite A, Champaign, IL 61821 *Tel:* 217-359-4675 *Fax:* 217-359-4689 *E-mail:* ppg@prairie-production.com *Web Site:* www.prairie-production.com, pg 980

Main, Valerie, Stage Post, 255 French Landing Dr, Nashville, TN 37228 *Tel:* 615-248-1978 *Toll Free Tel:* 877-250-1839 *Fax:* 615-242-8861 *E-mail:* mail@stagepost.com *Web Site:* www.stagepost.com, pg 1022

Mainardi, Don, IDX System Technology Inc, 19001 Harborgate Way, Suite 105, Torrance, CA 90501 *Tel:* 310-328-2850 *Fax:* 310-328-8202 *E-mail:* idx.usa@idx.tv *Web Site:* www.idx.tv, pg 894

Maines, Lauri, Videssence, 10768 Lower Azusa Rd, El Monte, CA 91731 *Tel:* 626-579-0943 *Fax:* 626-579-6803 *E-mail:* contact@videssence.tv *Web Site:* www.videssence.tv, pg 1057

Maisner, Andrew, TV Pro Gear, 1630 Flower St, Glendale, CA 91201 *Tel:* 818-246-7100 *Fax:* 818-246-1945 *Web Site:* www.tvprogear.com, pg 1046

Makhlout, David, IFM World Releasing Inc, 1328 E Palmer Ave, Glendale, CA 91205 *Tel:* 818-243-4976 *Fax:* 818-550-9728 *E-mail:* contact@ifmfilm.com *Web Site:* www.ifmfilm.com, pg 894

Makofske, Thomas, LYNX Signal Management Systems LLC, 4407 Vineland Rd, Suite D-18, Orlando, FL 32811 *Tel:* 407-428-1071 *Fax:* 407-428-1075 *E-mail:* sales1@intelligentmedia.us; support1@intelligentmedia.us *Web Site:* www.intelligentmedia.us, pg 927

Malcolm, Brian, Rule Broadcast Systems, 1284 Soldier's Field Rd, Boston, MA 02135 *Tel:* 617-277-2200 *Toll Free Tel:* 800-785-3266 *Fax:* 617-277-6800 *E-mail:* answers@rule.com *Web Site:* www.rule.com, pg 1000

Malejko, Ray, Wilray Audio Visual Corp, 615 Jackson Valley Rd, Port Murray, NJ 07865 *Tel:* 908-689-1300 *Toll Free Tel:* 800-452-9184 *Fax:* 908-689-8839 *E-mail:* wilray@mindspring.com, pg 1067

Malekpour, Dave, Professional Audio Design Inc, 90 Corporate Park Dr, Suite 1420, Pembroke, MA 02359 *Tel:* 781-982-2600 *Toll Free Tel:* 877-223-8858 *Fax:* 781-982-2610 *E-mail:* info@proaudiodesign.com *Web Site:* www.proaudiodesign.com, pg 985

Malijan, Edith, International Cinema Technology Association (ICTA), 770 Broadway, 5th fl, New York, NY 10003-9595 *Tel:* 212-493-4097; 212-493-4058 *Fax:* 212-257-6428 *E-mail:* info@itea.com *Web Site:* www.internationalcinematechnologyassociation.com, pg 1083

Malina, Craig, The Video Project, 145 Ninth St, Suite 102, San Francisco, CA 94103 *Tel:* 415-981-9710 *Toll Free Tel:* 800-475-2638 *Toll Free Fax:* 888-562-9012 *E-mail:* orders@videoproject.com; support@videoproject.com *Web Site:* www.videoproject.com, pg 1056

Malinosky, John, Precision Camera & Video Repair Inc, 4 Anngina Dr, Enfield, CT 06082-3222 *Tel:* 860-749-7380 *Toll Free Tel:* 800-665-6515 *Fax:* 860-763-7100 *E-mail:* info@precisioncamera.com *Web Site:* www.precisioncamera.com, pg 980

Mallett, Mark, Kroy LLC, 3830 Kelley Ave, Cleveland, OH 44114 *Tel:* 216-426-5600 *Toll Free Tel:* 888-888-5769 (cust serv) *Fax:* 216-426-5601 *Web Site:* www.kroy.com, pg 914

Mallory, Steve, PACSAT, 1629 "S" St, Sacramento, CA 95811 *Tel:* 916-446-7890; 916-335-1649 (after hours) *Toll Free Tel:* 800-672-2728 *Fax:* 916-446-7893 *E-mail:* pacsat@pacsat.com *Web Site:* www.pacsat.com, pg 967

Malloy, Gary, Kineticvideo.com, 16 Munition St, Toronto, ON M5A 1G7, Canada *Tel:* 416-538-6613 *Toll Free Tel:* 800-263-6910 (CN only) *Fax:* 416-538-9984 *E-mail:* info@kineticvideo.com *Web Site:* www.kineticvideo.com, pg 911

Malloy, Tom, Adobe Systems Inc, 345 Park Ave, San Jose, CA 95110-2704 *Tel:* 408-536-6000 *Fax:* 408-537-6000 *Web Site:* www.adobe.com, pg 776

Malone, Greg, Road Pictures, 5420 N College Ave, Suite 201, Indianapolis, IN 46220 *Tel:* 317-267-9590 *Toll Free Tel:* 800-267-9590 *Fax:* 317-267-9677 *Web Site:* www.roadpictures.com, pg 997

Malone, Kristy, Kendall/Hunt Publishing Co, 4050 Westmark Dr, Dubuque, IA 52002 *Tel:* 563-589-1000 *Toll Free Tel:* 800-228-0810 *Fax:* 563-589-1237 *Toll Free Fax:* 800-772-9165 *E-mail:* orders@kendallhunt.com *Web Site:* www.kendallhunt.com, pg 909

Malone, Matthew, Research Technology International (RTI), 4700 Chase Ave, Lincolnwood, IL 60712-1689 *Tel:* 847-677-3000 *Toll Free Tel:* 800-323-7520 *Fax:* 847-677-1311 *Toll Free Fax:* 800-784-6733 *E-mail:* sales@rtico.com *Web Site:* www.rtico.com, pg 995

Maloney, Mike, Eureka Springs Advertising & Promotions Commission, PO Box 522, Eureka Springs, AR 72632-0522 *Tel:* 479-253-7333 *Toll Free Tel:* 866-566-9387 *Fax:* 479-363-9380 *E-mail:* info@eurekasprings.org *Web Site:* www.eurekasprings.org, pg 1092

Malouche, Paige, Prescolite, 701 Millennium Blvd, Greenville, SC 29607 *Tel:* 864-678-1000 *Fax:* 864-678-1415 *Web Site:* www.prescolite.com, pg 981

Maltz, Elliott, MG Electronics, 32 Ranick Rd, Hauppauge, NY 11788 *Tel:* 631-582-3400 *Fax:* 631-582-3229 *E-mail:* info@mgelectronics.com *Web Site:* www.mgelectronics.com, pg 940

Malvin, Justin, Face Digital Post, 9753 Via Roma, Burbank, CA 91504 *Tel:* 818-842-9081 *Fax:* 818-768-6313 *E-mail:* face@facedigitalpost.com *Web Site:* www.facedigitalpost.com, pg 865

Malvin, Ron, Face Digital Post, 9753 Via Roma, Burbank, CA 91504 *Tel:* 818-842-9081 *Fax:* 818-768-6313 *E-mail:* face@facedigitalpost.com *Web Site:* www.facedigitalpost.com, pg 865

Manchester, John, Manchester Music Library Inc, 26 Ivalou St, Somerville, MA 02143 *Tel:* 413-369-4331 *Web Site:* www.manchestermusiclibrary.com, pg 929

Mancini, John F, Association for Information and Image Management (AIIM), 1100 Wayne Ave, Suite 1100, Silver Spring, MD 20910 *Tel:* 301-587-8202 *Toll Free Tel:* 800-477-2446 *Fax:* 301-587-2711 *E-mail:* aiim@aiim.org *Web Site:* www.aiim.org, pg 1078

Mancini, Lew, American Federation of Musicians of the United States & Canada (AFM), 1501 Broadway, Suite 600, New York, NY 10036 *Tel:* 212-869-1330 *Fax:* 212-764-6134 *Web Site:* www.afm.org, pg 1076

Mancuso, Janice, Reference Recordings, PO Box 77225, San Francisco, CA 94107 *Tel:* 650-355-1845 *Toll Free Tel:* 800-336-8866 *Fax:* 650-355-1949 *E-mail:* referencerecordings@gmail.com *Web Site:* www.referencerecordings.com, pg 994

Mancuso, Mike, 4 Wall Entertainment, 3325 W Sunset Rd, Suite F, Las Vegas, NV 89118 *Tel:* 702-263-3858 *Toll Free Tel:* 877-789-8167 (Western US); 866-492-5540 (Eastern US) *Fax:* 702-263-3863 *E-mail:* info@4wall.com *Web Site:* www.4wall.com; www.usedlighting.com, pg 872

Mandel, Gayle, The Global Awards, 260 W 39 St, 10th fl, New York, NY 10018 *Tel:* 212-643-4800 *Fax:* 212-643-0170 *E-mail:* info@newyorkfestivals.com *Web Site:* www.theglobalawards.com, pg 1115

Mandilaras, Nick, Sennheiser (Canada) Inc, 221 ave Labrosse, Pointe Claire, QC H9R 1A3, Canada *Tel:* 514-426-3013 *Toll Free Tel:* 800-463-1006 *Fax:* 514-426-3953 *Toll Free Fax:* 800-463-3013 *E-mail:* info@sennheiser.ca *Web Site:* www.sennheiser.ca, pg 1006

Maney, Dan, maney-logic, 6117 Thornebury Dr, Madison, WI 53719-4834 *Tel:* 608-277-8001 *Fax:* 608-277-8001 *Web Site:* maney-logic.com, pg 930

Mangione, Richard, Marshall Furniture Inc, 999 Anita Ave, Antioch, IL 60002 *Tel:* 847-395-9350 *Fax:* 847-395-9351 *E-mail:* info@marshallfurniture.com *Web Site:* www.marshallfurniture.com, pg 932

Mangoba, Mark, Visual Communications - Southern California Asian American Studies Central Inc, 120 Judge John Aiso St, Basement Level, Los Angeles, CA 90012 *Tel:* 213-680-4462 *Fax:* 213-687-4848 *E-mail:* info@vconline.org *Web Site:* www.vconline.org, pg 1059

Maniatis, Nick, New Mexico Film Office, Joseph M Montoya Bldg, 1st fl, 1100 St Francis Dr, Suite 1213, Santa Fe, NM 87505 *Tel:* 505-476-5600 *Toll Free Tel:* 800-545-9871 *Fax:* 505-476-5601 *E-mail:* info@nmfilm.com *Web Site:* www.nmfilm.com, pg 1100

Manies, Keith, Lawrence Convention & Visitors Bureau, 402 N Second St, Lawrence, KS 66044 *Tel:* 785-856-3040; 785-856-5282 *Fax:* 785-856-5303 *E-mail:* visinfo@visitlawrence.com *Web Site:* www.visitlawrence.com, pg 1097

Maniglia, Frank Jr, Maniglia Media, 7925 Jones Branch Dr, Suite LL110, Tysons, VA 22102 *Tel:* 703-283-8532 *Web Site:* www.manigliamedia.com, pg 930

Manios, Steven Jr, Manios Digital & Film, 10663 Burbank Blvd, North Hollywood, CA 91601 *Tel:* 818-760-8290 *Toll Free Tel:* 800-845-6619 *Fax:* 818-760-8805 *E-mail:* sales@maniosdigital.com *Web Site:* www.maniosdigital.com, pg 930

Mankins, Christopher, Antex Electronics Corp, 19160 Van Ness Ave, Torrance, CA 90501 *Tel:* 310-532-3092 *Toll Free Tel:* 800-338-4231 *Fax:* 310-532-8509 *E-mail:* ainfo@antex.com; asales@antex.com *Web Site:* www.antex.com, pg 787

Manley, EveAnna, Manley Laboratories Inc, 13880 Magnolia Ave, Chino, CA 91710 *Tel:* 909-627-4256 *Fax:* 909-628-2482 *Web Site:* www.manley.com, pg 930

Manlulu, Pamela, Electrosonic Inc, 3320 N San Fernando Blvd, Burbank, CA 91504 *Tel:* 818-333-3600 *Toll Free Tel:* 888-343-3604 (sales) *Fax:* 818-230-1017 *E-mail:* info@electrosonic.com *Web Site:* www.electrosonic.com, pg 859

Mann, Doug, Flip 2 Media Inc, 1067 Serpentine Lane, Pleasanton, CA 94566-4759 *Tel:* 925-417-1420 *E-mail:* info@flip2media.com *Web Site:* www.flip2media.com, pg 870

Mann, Jennifer, SAS Institute Inc, 100 SAS Campus Dr, Cary, NC 27513-2414 *Tel:* 919-677-8000 *Toll Free Tel:* 800-727-0025 *Fax:* 919-677-4444 *Web Site:* www.sas.com, pg 1003

Mann, Mary Ellen, Ipitek, 2330 Faraday Ave, Carlsbad, CA 92008 *Tel:* 760-438-1010 *Toll Free Tel:* 888-4-IPITEK (447-4835, US) *Fax:* 760-438-2412 *E-mail:* sales@ipitek.com *Web Site:* www.ipitek.com, pg 902

Manna, Christine, Association of National Advertisers Inc (ANA), 708 Third Ave, 33rd fl, New York, NY 10017-4270 *Tel:* 212-697-5950 *Fax:* 212-687-7310 *E-mail:* info@ana.net *Web Site:* www.ana.net, pg 1079

Manning, Char, Manning Productions, 115 N Morgan St, Chicago, IL 60607 *Tel:* 312-756-1100 *Fax:* 312-756-1200 *E-mail:* info@manningproductions.com *Web Site:* www.manningproductions.com, pg 930

Manning, Douglas, Manning Productions, 115 N Morgan St, Chicago, IL 60607 *Tel:* 312-756-1100 *Fax:* 312-756-1200 *E-mail:* info@manningproductions.com *Web Site:* www.manningproductions.com, pg 930

Manning, James, Astronomical Society of the Pacific, 390 Ashton Ave, San Francisco, CA 94112 *Tel:* 415-337-1100 *Toll Free Tel:* 800-335-2624 *Fax:* 415-337-5205 *E-mail:* service@astrosociety.org *Web Site:* astrosociety.org, pg 792

Mannschreck, Mark, TVA Productions, 3950 Vantage Ave, Studio City, CA 91604 *Tel:* 818-505-8300 *Toll Free Tel:* 888-322-4296 *E-mail:* info@tvaproductions.com *Web Site:* www.tvaproductions.com, pg 1046

Manocchio, Jennifer, monterey media inc, 566 Saint Charles Dr, Thousand Oaks, CA 91360-3953 *Tel:* 805-494-7199 *Toll Free Tel:* 800-424-2593 *Fax:* 805-496-6061 *E-mail:* customerservice@montereymedia.com; publicity@montereymedia.com *Web Site:* www.montereymedia.com, pg 946

Manocchio, Jennifer, monterey video, 566 Saint Charles Dr, Thousand Oaks, CA 91360-3953 *Tel:* 805-494-7199 *Toll Free Tel:* 800-424-2593 *Fax:* 805-496-6061 *E-mail:* customerservice@montereymedia.com; publicity@montereymedia.com *Web Site:* www.montereymedia.com, pg 946

Mans, Dawn, Cinequipt Inc, 2601 49 Ave N, Suite 500, Minneapolis, MN 55430 *Tel:* 612-627-9080 *Toll Free Tel:* 800-809-9080 *Fax:* 612-627-9789 *Web Site:* www.cinequipt.com, pg 828

Mansfield, Scott, monterey media inc, 566 Saint Charles Dr, Thousand Oaks, CA 91360-3953 *Tel:* 805-494-7199 *Toll Free Tel:* 800-424-2593 *Fax:* 805-496-6061 *E-mail:* customerservice@montereymedia.com; publicity@montereymedia.com *Web Site:* www.montereymedia.com, pg 946

Mansfield, Scott, monterey video, 566 Saint Charles Dr, Thousand Oaks, CA 91360-3953 *Tel:* 805-494-7199 *Toll Free Tel:* 800-424-2593 *Fax:* 805-496-6061 *E-mail:* customerservice@montereymedia.com; publicity@montereymedia.com *Web Site:* www.montereymedia.com, pg 946

Mansour, Robert, ETHOS Ltd, 4981 Hwy 7 E, Unit 12-A, Suite 235, Markham, ON L3R 1N1, Canada *Tel:* 905-471-7654 *Toll Free Tel:* 800-471-0737 *Fax:* 905-471-7976 *E-mail:* ethoseducation@rogers.com *Web Site:* www.ethoseducation.ca, pg 863

Mansouri, Michael, Radiant Images, 4125 W Jefferson Blvd, Los Angeles, CA 90016 *Tel:* 323-737-1314 *Fax:* 310-861-0163 *E-mail:* info@radiantimages.com *Web Site:* www.radiantimages.com, pg 990

Manzo, Robert, Hunter Electronics LLC, 7553 Lake Harbor Terr, Lake Worth, FL 33467 *Tel:* 561-568-2063 *Fax:* 561-491-8030 *E-mail:* hunterelectronics@comcast.net; hunterelectronics201@gmail.com, pg 892

Maquet, Alain, Ingram Micro, 1600 E Saint Andrew Place, Santa Ana, CA 92705 *Tel:* 714-566-1000 *Web Site:* www.ingrammicro.com, pg 898

Marado, Linda, Alegra House Publishers, PO Box 1443, Warren, OH 44482-1443 *Tel:* 330-372-2951 *Fax:* 330-399-1619, pg 780

Maranville, Richard, Freeman, 1600 Viceroy, Suite 100, Dallas, TX 75235 *Tel:* 214-445-1000 *Fax:* 214-445-0200 *Web Site:* www.freemanco.com, pg 872

Marcel, Jo Ellen, Library of Congress, Motion Picture, Broadcasting & Recorded Sound Division, James Madison Bldg, LM 336, 101 Independence Ave SE, Washington, DC 20540-1000 *Tel:* 202-707-8572 *Fax:* 202-707-2371 *Web Site:* www.loc.gov/rr/mopic, pg 920

Marcellus, Simona, TAPPI, 15 Technology Pkwy S, Norcross, GA 30092 *Tel:* 770-446-1400 *Toll Free Tel:* 800-332-8686 (US); 800-446-9431 (CN) *Fax:* 770-446-6947 *E-mail:* memberconnection@tappi.org *Web Site:* www.tappi.org, pg 1032

March, Jon, Powerstation Events, 1486 Highland Ave, Bldg 2, Suite 6, Cheshire, CT 06410 *Tel:* 203-250-8500 *Toll Free Tel:* 800-423-7835 *Fax:* 203-250-8575 *E-mail:* sales@powerstationevents.com *Web Site:* www.powerstationevents.com, pg 979

March, Joseph H, American Legion Fourth Estate Award, Public Relations Div, 700 N Pennsylvania St, Indianapolis, IN 46204 *Tel:* 317-630-1253 *Fax:* 317-630-1368 *E-mail:* pr@legion.org *Web Site:* www.legion.org, pg 1107

Marcheterre, Claude, Les Disques Artiste, 154 Grande Cote, Rosemere, QC J7A 1H3, Canada *Tel:* 450-437-7625 *Web Site:* www.disquesartiste.com, pg 849

Marchetti, Tom, Burlington A/V Recording Media, 106 Mott St, Oceanside, NY 11572 *Tel:* 516-678-4414 *Toll Free Tel:* 800-331-3191 *Fax:* 516-678-8959 *E-mail:* burlington@optonline.net *Web Site:* www.recordingstore.com, pg 815

Marciano, Eric A, American Montage Inc, PO Box 1042, New York, NY 10003 *Tel:* 212-334-8283 *Web Site:* americanmontage.com, pg 784

Marcon, Tony, ProLine Digital, PO Box 27682, Denver, CO 80227-0682 *Tel:* 303-761-3999 *Toll Free Tel:* 800-325-0853 *Fax:* 303-761-1818 *E-mail:* info@prolinedigital.com *Web Site:* www.prolinedigital.com, pg 986

Marcus, Aaron, Aaron Marcus & Associates Inc, 1196 Euclid Ave, Suite 1-F, Berkeley, CA 94708-1640 *Tel:* 510-601-0994 *Fax:* 510-527-1994 *Web Site:* www.amanda.com, pg 772

Marcus, Barbara, Random House Children's Books, 1745 Broadway, 10th fl, New York, NY 10019 *Tel:* 212-782-9000 *Web Site:* www.randomhousekids.com, pg 991

Marcus, Carol, RGB Spectrum, 950 Marina Village Pkwy, Alameda, CA 94501 *Tel:* 510-814-7000 *Fax:* 510-814-7026 *E-mail:* sales@rgb.com *Web Site:* www.rgb.com, pg 996

Marcus, Robert, RGB Spectrum, 950 Marina Village Pkwy, Alameda, CA 94501 *Tel:* 510-814-7000 *Fax:* 510-814-7026 *E-mail:* sales@rgb.com *Web Site:* www.rgb.com, pg 996

Marcus, Robert D, Time Warner Cable, 60 Columbus Circle, 17th fl, New York, NY 10023 *Tel:* 212-364-8200 *Web Site:* www.timewarnercable.com, pg 1040

Marcusson, Reese P, The Chicago Production Center, 5400 N Saint Louis Ave, Chicago, IL 60625-4698 *Tel:* 773-509-5571 *Fax:* 773-509-5303 *Web Site:* www.wttw.com, pg 825

Marenco, Cookie, OTR Studios, PO Box 874, Belmont, CA 94002 *Tel:* 650-595-8475 *E-mail:* info@otrstudios.com *Web Site:* www.otrstudios.com, pg 966

Margerum, Barry, Plantronics Inc, 345 Encinal St, Santa Cruz, CA 95060 *Tel:* 831-426-5858 *Toll Free Tel:* 800-544-4660 *Fax:* 831-426-6098 *Toll Free Fax:* 888-290-4519 *E-mail:* plantronics@custhelp.com *Web Site:* www.plantronics.com, pg 976

Margolis, David, Skyviews Survey Inc, 32 Highline Trail, Stamford, CT 06902 *Tel:* 203-359-3754 *Fax:* 203-359-3791 *Web Site:* www.skyviewsurvey.com, pg 1013

Marhewka, Guy, Gaylord Brothers, PO Box 4901, Syracuse, NY 13221-4901 *Tel:* 315-634-8243 (intl) *Toll Free Tel:* 800-962-9580 (cust serv) *Fax:* 315-453-5030 (intl) *Toll Free Fax:* 800-272-3412 *E-mail:* customerservice@gaylord.com *Web Site:* www.gaylord.com, pg 876

Marini, Dean, Image Video Teleproductions Inc, 6755 Freedom Ave NW, North Canton, OH 44720 *Tel:* 330-494-9303 *Fax:* 330-966-1792 *E-mail:* info@image-video.com *Web Site:* www.image-video.com, pg 895

Mariotti, Mark, Foresight Imaging, One Executive Dr, Suite 102, Chelmsford, MA 01824 *Tel:* 978-458-4624 *Fax:* 978-458-5488 *E-mail:* info@fi-llc.com *Web Site:* www.fi-llc.com, pg 871

Maritz, Steve, Maritz Performance Improvement Co, 1000 Town Ctr, Suite 1200, Southfield, MI 48075 *Tel:* 248-948-4500 *Toll Free Tel:* 877-462-7489 *Fax:* 248-948-4598 *Web Site:* www.maritz.com, pg 931

Markert, John R, Accel Video Productions, 14056 Golden Eagle Dr, Jacksonville, FL 32226 *Tel:* 904-677-9063; 848-467-6299 *E-mail:* accelv@yahoo.com *Web Site:* www.accelvideo.com, pg 773

Markey, Kevin, Sensory Technologies LLC, 6951 Corporate Circle, Indianapolis, IN 46278 *Tel:* 317-347-5252 *Toll Free Tel:* 800-488-4336 (help desk) *Fax:* 317-347-5262 *E-mail:* sales@sensorytechnologies.com *Web Site:* sensorytechnologies.com, pg 1007

Markham, Peter, Shadow Play Records & Video, 8127 Mesa Dr, Suite B206-277, Austin, TX 78759 *Tel:* 512-349-9962 *Toll Free Tel:* 800-274-8804 *Fax:* 512-345-9515 *Web Site:* www.hellojoe.com, pg 1007

Markowitz, Debra, Nassau County Film Office, Executive Bldg, One West St, Mineola, NY 11501 *Tel:* 516-571-3168 *Fax:* 516-571-6195 *Web Site:* www.longislandfilm.com, pg 1100

Marks, David, Qioptiq, 78 Shuyler Baldwin, Fairport, NY 14450 *Tel:* 585-223-2370 *Toll Free Tel:* 800-429-0257 *Fax:* 585-223-1999 *E-mail:* info@qioptiqlinos.com *Web Site:* www.qioptiqlinos.com, pg 988

Marks, Mona, Videofax, 1750 Cesar Chavez St, Unit G, San Francisco, CA 94124 *Tel:* 415-641-0100 *E-mail:* rentals@videofax.com *Web Site:* www.videofax.com, pg 1057

Markus, James, Norlake Manufacturing Co, 39301 Taylor Pkwy, Elyria, OH 44036 *Tel:* 440-353-3200 *Fax:* 440-353-3232 *E-mail:* info@norlakemfg.com *Web Site:* www.norlakemfg.com, pg 958

Marotti, Carol, The Taunton Press Inc, 63 S Main St, Newtown, CT 06470 *Tel:* 203-426-8171 *Toll Free Tel:* 800-926-8776 (ext 3893 - PR); 800-888-8286 (orders) *Fax:* 203-426-3434 *Web Site:* www.taunton.com, pg 1032

Marr, Doris, Cinemarr Entertainment, 104 Church St, Sevierville, TN 37862 *E-mail:* cinemarrstudios@aol.com *Web Site:* cinemarrstudios.com, pg 827

Marr, Shane, Cinemarr Entertainment, 104 Church St, Sevierville, TN 37862 *E-mail:* cinemarrstudios@aol.com *Web Site:* cinemarrstudios.com, pg 827

Marraccini, Jason, ECG Productions, 120 Interstate N Pkwy SE, Suite 435, Atlanta, GA 30339 *Tel:* 678-855-5169 *E-mail:* info@ecgprod.com *Web Site:* www.ecgprod.com, pg 856

Marrazzo, William J, WHYY Inc, Independence Mall West, 150 N Sixth St, Philadelphia, PA 19106 *Tel:* 215-351-1200 *Fax:* 215-351-0398 *E-mail:* talkback@whyy.org *Web Site:* www.whyy.org, pg 1066

Marriott, Brent, MIS Technologies, 555-B NW Blue Pkwy, Lees Summit, MO 64063 *Tel:* 816-966-4529 *Fax:* 816-966-2915 *Web Site:* www.mistechnologies.com, pg 944

Marrow, Rosemary, New York Times Photo Sales, c/o Redux Pictures, 11 Hanover Sq, 26th fl, New York, NY 10005 *Tel:* 212-253-0399 *Fax:* 212-253-0397 *E-mail:* submissions@reduxpictures.com *Web Site:* reduxpictures.com, pg 956

Marrullier, Adrian, Bisk Education, 9417 Princess Palm Ave, Tampa, FL 33619 *Toll Free Tel:* 800-280-9718 *E-mail:* customerservice@bisk.com *Web Site:* www.bisk.com, pg 808

Marschall, Sally, Film Police, 4310 Mozart St, Chicago, IL 60618-1528 *Tel:* 773-463-4010 *E-mail:* info@filmpolice.com *Web Site:* www.filmpolice.com, pg 867

Marsh, Gary, Production Outfitters, 1833 San Mateo Blvd NE, Albuquerque, NM 87110 *Tel:* 505-237-0770 *Fax:* 505-232-4419 *E-mail:* info@productionoutfitters.com *Web Site:* www.productionoutfitters.com, pg 984

Marshad, Neal, Neal Marshad Productions, 99 Hudson St, 5th fl, New York, NY 10013 *Tel:* 212-925-8656 *Fax:* 212-292-8912 *E-mail:* info@marshad.com *Web Site:* www.marshad.com, pg 931

Marshad, Neal, Marshad Technology Group, 99 Hudson St, 5th fl, New York, NY 10013 *Tel:* 212-925-8656 *E-mail:* info@marshad.com *Web Site:* www.marshad.com, pg 932

Marshall, Debbie, Cleveland International Film Festival, 2510 Market Ave, Cleveland, OH 44113-3434 *Tel:* 216-623-3456 *Fax:* 216-623-0103 *Web Site:* www.clevelandfilm.org, pg 1112

Marshall, George T, Creative Impulse Awards (Impies), c/o RIIFF, 36 Rhode Island Ave, Newport, RI 02840 *Tel:* 401-861-4445 *Fax:* 401-490-6735 *E-mail:* info@film-fesitval.org *Web Site:* www.film-festival.org/CreativeIM.php, pg 1113

Marshall, George T, FLICKERS: Rhode Island International Film Festival™ (RIIFF), 83 Park St, Suite 1, Providence, RI 02903 *Tel:* 401-861-4445 *Fax:* 401-490-6735 *E-mail:* info@film-festival.org *Web Site:* film-festival.org/enteraskidseye.php, pg 1114

Marshall, George T, KidsEye™ International Film Festival, 83 Park St, Suite 1, Providence, RI 02903 *Tel:* 401-861-4445 *Fax:* 401-490-6735 *E-mail:* info@film-festival.org *Web Site:* film-festival.org/enteraskidseye.php, pg 1118

Marshall, George T, Providence Underground Film Festival, 83 Park St, Suite 1, Providence, RI 02903 *Tel:* 401-861-4445 *Fax:* 401-490-6735 *E-mail:* info@film-festival.org *Web Site:* www.film-festival.org/Prov.Underground.php, pg 1124

Marshall, Lisa, National Student Production Awards, Hershey Square Ctr, 1152 Mae St, Hummelstown, PA 17036 *Toll Free Tel:* 855-ASK-4CBI (275-4224) *Web Site:* www.askcbi.org, pg 1121

Marsico, Frank, Shadowstone R & R™, 813 Silver Spring Ave, Silver Spring, MD 20910 *Tel:* 301-589-4997 *Fax:* 301-565-5156 *Web Site:* www.shadowstone.com, pg 1008

Marsico, Maryann P, Pennsylvania Film Office, Commonwealth Keystone Bldg, 4th fl, 400 North St, Harrisburg, PA 17120-0225 *Tel:* 717-783-3456 *Fax:* 717-787-6825 *E-mail:* info@filminpa.com *Web Site:* www.filminpa.com, pg 1101

Marston-Reid, Linda, DEC Grants, 696 Dutchess Tpke, Suite F, Poughkeepsie, NY 12603 *Tel:* 845-454-3222 *Fax:* 845-454-6902 *E-mail:* info@artsmidhudson.org *Web Site:* www.artsmidhudson.org, pg 1114

Martel, Valerie, Montreal Film & TV Commission, Duke Pavilion, 5th fl, 801 Brennan St, Montreal, QC H3C 0G4, Canada *Tel:* 514-872-2883 *Fax:* 514-872-3409 *E-mail:* film.tv@ville.montreal.qc.ca *Web Site:* www.montrealfilm.com, pg 1105

Martello, Carolyn, Max USA, 257 E Second St, Mineola, NY 11501 *Tel:* 516-741-3151 *Toll Free Tel:* 800-223-4293 *Fax:* 516-741-3272 *E-mail:* maxcorp@maxusacorp.com *Web Site:* www.maxusacorp.com, pg 934

Martin, Andrew, Miami Stagecraft Inc, 2855 E 11 Ave, Hialeah, FL 33013 *Tel:* 305-836-9356 *Fax:* 305-696-3322 *E-mail:* info@miamistagecraft.com *Web Site:* www.miamistagecraft.com, pg 941

Martin, Bill, Quad Cities First, 130 W Second St, Davenport, IA 52801 *Tel:* 563-326-1005 *Web Site:* www.quadcitiesfirst.com, pg 1097

Martin, Brad, Random House of Canada Limited, One Toronto St, Unit 300, Toronto, ON M5C 2V6, Canada *Tel:* 416-364-4449 *Fax:* 416-364-6863 *Web Site:* www.randomhouse.ca, pg 991

Martin, Carol, FootageBank HD, 13470 Washington Blvd, Suite 210, Marina Del Rey, CA 90292 *Tel:* 310-822-1400 *Toll Free Tel:* 888-653-1400 *Fax:* 310-822-4100 *E-mail:* info@footagebank.com *Web Site:* www.footagebank.com, pg 871

Martin, Christian Frederick IV, The Martin Guitar Co, 510 Sycamore St, Nazareth, PA 18064 *Tel:* 610-759-2837 *Toll Free Tel:* 800-633-2060; 888-433-9177 *Fax:* 610-759-5757 *E-mail:* info@martinguitar.com *Web Site:* www.martinguitar.com, pg 932

Martin, Chuck, Cape Girardeau Convention & Visitors Bureau, 400 Broadway St, Suite 100, Cape Girardeau, MO 63701 *Tel:* 573-335-1631 *Toll Free Tel:* 800-777-0068 *Fax:* 573-334-6702 *E-mail:* info@visitcape.com *Web Site:* visitcape.com, pg 1099

Martin, David, Visual Aids Electronics Corp, 12900 Cloverleaf Center Dr, Suite C, Germantown, MD 20874 *Tel:* 301-330-6900 *Fax:* 301-330-6901 *Web Site:* www.vaecorp.com, pg 1059

Martin, Debra, Love Your Shorts Film Festival, 608 S Elm Ave, Sanford, FL 32771 *E-mail:* contact@loveyourshorts.com *Web Site:* www.loveyourshorts.com, pg 1119

Martin, Debra, NKK Switches, 7850 E Gelding Dr, Scottsdale, AZ 85260 *Tel:* 480-991-0942 *Toll Free Tel:* 877-228-9655 *Fax:* 480-998-1435 *E-mail:* sales@nkkswitches.com *Web Site:* www.nkkswitches.com, pg 957

Martin, George, HallBrook Productions, 565 Dutch Valley Rd, Atlanta, GA 30324 *Tel:* 404-892-0042 *E-mail:* hallbrook@hallbrookproductions.com *Web Site:* hallbrookproductions.com, pg 884

Martin, John, Turner Broadcasting System Inc, One CNN Ctr, Atlanta, GA 30303 *Tel:* 404-827-1700 *Web Site:* www.turner.com, pg 1046

Martin, Lenny, NewWave Technologies Inc, 4635 Wedgewood Blvd, Suite 107, Frederick, MD 21703 *Tel:* 301-624-5300 *Toll Free Tel:* 800-536-5222 *Fax:* 301-948-5883 (sales & serv); 301-668-7808 (acctg, opers & mktg) *E-mail:* sales@newwavetech.com; custsupport@newwavetech.com *Web Site:* www.newwavetech.com, pg 957

Martin, Lynn, American Music & Sound (AM&S), 925 Broadbeck Dr, No 220, Newbury Park, CA 91320 *Toll Free Tel:* 800-431-2609 *Toll Free Fax:* 866-707-0717 *E-mail:* info@americanmusicandsound.com *Web Site:* www.americanmusicandsound.com, pg 785

Martin, Marcia, Reference Recordings, PO Box 77225, San Francisco, CA 94107 *Tel:* 650-355-1845 *Toll Free Tel:* 800-336-8866 *Fax:* 650-355-1949 *E-mail:* referencerecordings@gmail.com *Web Site:* www.referencerecordings.com, pg 994

Martin, Marianne, Truth Consciousness Publications, Desert Ashram, 3403 W Sweetwater Dr, Tucson, AZ 85745-9301 *Tel:* 520-743-8821 *Fax:* 520-743-3394 *E-mail:* info@truthconsciousness.org *Web Site:* truthconsciousness.org, pg 1046

Martin, Michael T PhD, Black Film Center Archive, Indiana University, Wells Library, Rm 044, 1320 E Tenth St, Bloomington, IN 47405 *Tel:* 812-855-6041 *Fax:* 812-856-5832 *E-mail:* bfca@indiana.edu *Web Site:* www.indiana.edu/~bfca, pg 808

Martin, Paul, Snell, 3519 Pacific Ave, Burbank, CA 91505 *Tel:* 818-556-2616 *Fax:* 818-556-2626 *E-mail:* americas@snellgroup.com *Web Site:* www.snellgroup.com, pg 1014

Martin, Paul, Vineyard Productions, 3640 Lovall Valley Rd, Sonoma, CA 95476 *Tel:* 707-939-3566 *Web Site:* www.vineyardproductions.com, pg 1058

Martin, Paul A, Sun Entertainment Corp, 3106 Belmont Blvd, Nashville, TN 37212 *Tel:* 615-385-1960 *E-mail:* info@sunrecords.com *Web Site:* www.sunrecords.com, pg 1028

Martin, Phil, Sodanceabit, 11372 Kelly Lane, Los Alamitos, CA 90720 *Tel:* 562-799-4340 *Toll Free Tel:* 800-64-DANCE (643-2623) *E-mail:* sodanceabit@live.com *Web Site:* www.sodanceabit.com, pg 1015

Martin, R, ASC Systems, Mack Place, 566, St Clair Shores, MI 48080-0566 *Tel:* 313-882-1133 *E-mail:* ascsystems@live.com *Web Site:* www.airi.com, pg 791

Martin, Rick, Audio-Video Resources Inc, 1043 Adams Ave, Montgomery, AL 36104 *Tel:* 334-262-4806 *Fax:* 334-240-0000 *E-mail:* avrinc@bellsouth.net, pg 795

Martin, Sean, Uniset Co LLC, 449 Avenue "A", Rochester, NY 14621 *Tel:* 585-544-3820 *Fax:* 585-544-1110 *E-mail:* info@unisetcorp.com *Web Site:* www.unisetcorp.com, pg 1048

Martin, Thomas, Cramer Productions, 425 University Ave, Norwood, MA 02062 *Tel:* 781-278-2300 *Fax:* 781-255-0721 *E-mail:* info@cramer.com *Web Site:* cramer.com, pg 837

Martin, Tony, Visix™ Inc, 230 Scientific Dr, Suite 80, Norcross, GA 30092 *Tel:* 770-446-1416 *Toll Free Tel:* 800-572-4935 *Fax:* 770-448-5724 *E-mail:* info@visix.com *Web Site:* www.visix.com, pg 1059

Martinez, Carlos, HD House, 6312 NW 77 Ct, Miami, FL 33166 *Tel:* 305-597-7359 *Fax:* 305-597-7027 *Web Site:* thehdhouse.com, pg 886

Martinez, Catherine, Downtown Community Television Center (DCTV), 87 Lafayette St, New York, NY 10013 *Tel:* 212-966-4510 *Fax:* 212-226-3053 *E-mail:* info@dctvny.org *Web Site:* www.dctvny.org, pg 851

Martinez, Frank, Antex Electronics Corp, 19160 Van Ness Ave, Torrance, CA 90501 *Tel:* 310-532-3092 *Toll Free Tel:* 800-338-4231 *Fax:* 310-532-8509 *E-mail:* ainfo@antex.com; asales@antex.com *Web Site:* www.antex.com, pg 787

Martini, Paul, BMI Supply, 571 Queensbury Ave, Queensbury, NY 12804 *Tel:* 518-793-6706 *Toll Free Tel:* 800-836-0524 *Fax:* 518-793-6181 *E-mail:* bminy@bmisupply.com *Web Site:* www.bmisupply.com, pg 810

Martino, Alfred C, Listen & Live Audio Inc, 1700 Manhattan Ave, Union City, NJ 07068 *Tel:* 201-558-9000 *Toll Free Tel:* 800-653-9400 (orders) *Fax:* 201-558-9800 *Web Site:* www.listenandlive.com, pg 923

Martinsen, Dan, Nickelodeon, 1515 Broadway, 44th fl, New York, NY 10036 *Tel:* 212-258-8000 *Fax:* 212-258-1822 *Web Site:* www.nick.com, pg 957

Martinson, Joe, Martinsound Inc, 1151 W Valley Blvd, Alhambra, CA 91803-2493 *Tel:* 626-281-3555 *Toll Free Tel:* 800-582-3555 *Fax:* 626-284-3092 *E-mail:* info@martinsound.com *Web Site:* www.martinsound.com, pg 932

Martore, Joseph A, CALIBRE, Metro Park, 6354 Walker Lane, Alexandria, VA 22310-3252 *Tel:* 703-797-8500 *Toll Free Tel:* 888-CALIBRE (225-4273) *Fax:* 703-797-8501 *E-mail:* info@calibresys.com *Web Site:* www.calibresys.com, pg 817

Martyn, John, Audacity Creative, 2734 Polk St, Suite B, Hollywood, FL 33020 *Tel:* 954-920-4418 *Toll Free Fax:* 877-229-6298 *E-mail:* info@audacitycreative.com; audacityrecording@mac.com *Web Site:* audacitycreative.com; audacityrecording.com, pg 793

Maruca, Dante, Tri-State Loudspeaker, 650 Franklin Ave, Aliquippa, PA 15001 *Tel:* 724-375-9203, pg 1044

Maruca, John, Image Associates Inc, 5311 S Miami Blvd, Suite G, Durham, NC 27703 *Tel:* 919-876-6400 *Fax:* 919-876-6400 *E-mail:* info@imageassociates.com *Web Site:* www.imageassociates.com, pg 894

Marugg, Brandon, ALOM Technologies Corp, 48105 Warm Springs Blvd, Fremont, CA 94539-7498 *Tel:* 510-360-3600 *Toll Free Tel:* 800-500-9991 *Fax:* 510-226-7617 *E-mail:* customerservice@alom.com *Web Site:* www.alom.com, pg 782

Marulli, Mike, Faith Fellowship Ministries World Outreach Center, 2707 Main St Ext, Sayreville, NJ 08872 *Tel:* 732-727-9500 *E-mail:* information@ffmwoc.org *Web Site:* www.ffmwoc.org, pg 865

Marullo, Gary, Memory Lane Videos, 676 Lone Oak Ave, Eugene, OR 97404 *Tel:* 541-688-0484 *Fax:* 541-688-0484, pg 938

Marx, David, Marx InDigital, 7921 Skylake Dr, Fort Worth, TX 76179 *Tel:* 414-351-5060 *Web Site:* www.marxindigital.com, pg 933

Marx, Troy, Omega Broadcast Group, 817 W Howard Lane, Austin, TX 78753 *Tel:* 512-251-7778 *Fax:* 512-251-8633 *E-mail:* rental@omegabroadcast.com; sales@omegabroadcast.com *Web Site:* www.omegabroadcast.com, pg 962

Marzano, Vincent, John Wiley & Sons Inc, 111 River St, Hoboken, NJ 07030 *Tel:* 201-748-6000 *Toll Free Tel:* 800-225-5945 *Fax:* 201-748-6088 *E-mail:* info@wiley.com *Web Site:* www.wiley.com, pg 1066

Marzec, Randy, VTP Inc, 2721 W Magnolia Blvd, Burbank, CA 91505 *Tel:* 818-566-9898 *Toll Free Tel:* 800-422-2444 *E-mail:* sales@vtpcorp.com *Web Site:* www.myvtp.com, pg 1061

Mascarenas, Nate, Lightning Eliminators & Consultants Inc, 6687 Arapahoe Rd, Boulder, CO 80303 *Tel:* 303-447-2828 *Toll Free Tel:* 800-521-6101 *Fax:* 303-447-8122 *E-mail:* info@lightningprotection.com *Web Site:* www.lightningprotection.com, pg 921

Masch, Travis, Parallax Press, 2236-B Sixth St, Berkeley, CA 94710 *Tel:* 510-525-0101 *Toll Free Tel:* 800-863-5290 (book orders) *Fax:* 510-525-7129 *E-mail:* info@parallax.org *Web Site:* www.parallax.org, pg 969

Masciangelo, Joe, Starlite Productions, 9 Whittendale Dr, Moorestown, NJ 08057 *Tel:* 856-780-8000 *Toll Free Tel:* 800-738-7400 *Fax:* 856-780-8001 *E-mail:* info@starlite.com *Web Site:* www.starlite.com, pg 1024

Masiello, James F, ATTO Technology Inc, 155 CrossPoint Pkwy, Amherst, NY 14068 *Tel:* 716-691-1999 *Fax:* 716-691-9353 *Web Site:* www.attotech.com, pg 793

Maslowski, Steve, Maslowski Productions, 1219 Eversole Rd, Cincinnati, OH 45230 *Tel:* 513-231-7301 *Fax:* 513-231-7301 *Web Site:* www.maslowskiwildlife.com, pg 933

Mason, Mele, Mason Video, 9632 N 34 St, Omaha, NE 68112 *Tel:* 402-455-9422 *E-mail:* mason.video@mac.com *Web Site:* www.masonvideo.com, pg 933

Mason, Michael, CP Communications, 200 Clearbrook Rd, Suite 148, Elmsford, NY 10523 *Tel:* 914-345-9292 *Toll Free Tel:* 800-762-4254 *Fax:* 914-345-9222 *E-mail:* info@cpcomms.com; sales@cpcomms.com *Web Site:* www.cpcomms.com, pg 837

Mason, Todd, Broadcast Management Group, 1625 Eye St NW, Suite 620, Washington, DC 20006 *Tel:* 202-609-7757 *E-mail:* info@broadcastmgmt.com *Web Site:* www.broadcastmgmt.com, pg 813

Massey, Lee, Media Productions, 3241 S University Dr, Fargo, ND 58104 *Tel:* 701-237-6863 *Toll Free Tel:* 800-480-6863 *Fax:* 701-280-1226 *Web Site:* www.mediaproductions.com, pg 937

Massingham, Gordon, Emergency Film Group, 140 Cooke St, Edgartown, MA 02539 *Tel:* 508-627-8844 *Toll Free Tel:* 800-842-0999 *Fax:* 508-627-8863 *E-mail:* info@efilmgroup.com *Web Site:* www.efilmgroup.com, pg 860

Masters, Mary Jo, Twin Peaks Creative, 445 W Seventh St, San Pedro, CA 90731 *Tel:* 310-832-3303 *E-mail:* postmaster@bestmedia.com *Web Site:* www.twinpeakscreative.com, pg 1047

Masters, Robert, Twin Peaks Creative, 445 W Seventh St, San Pedro, CA 90731 *Tel:* 310-832-3303 *E-mail:* postmaster@bestmedia.com *Web Site:* www.twinpeakscreative.com, pg 1047

Masters, Sarah, Hartley Film Foundation, 49 Richmondville Ave, Suite 204, Westport, CT 06880 *Tel:* 203-226-9500 *Toll Free Tel:* 800-937-1819 *Fax:* 203-227-6938 *E-mail:* info@hartleyfoundation.org *Web Site:* www.hartleyfoundation.org, pg 885

Mastrangelo, Paul, Paso Sound Products Inc, 4750-F Goer Dr, Charleston, SC 29406 *Tel:* 843-308-9005 *Toll Free Tel:* 800-231-3034 *Fax:* 843-308-0904 *E-mail:* info@pasosound.com *Web Site:* www.pasosound.com, pg 969

Mata, Julie, Meridian Studios, 1020 Highland Park Rd, Neenah, WI 54956 *Tel:* 920-720-4200 *E-mail:* info@meridianstudiosusa.com *Web Site:* www.meridianstudiosusa.com, pg 939

Mata, Tony, Meridian Studios, 1020 Highland Park Rd, Neenah, WI 54956 *Tel:* 920-720-4200 *E-mail:* info@meridianstudiosusa.com *Web Site:* www.meridianstudiosusa.com, pg 939

Matasker, Charles, Practising Law Institute, 1177 Avenue of the Americas, New York, NY 10036 *Tel:* 212-824-5700 *Toll Free Tel:* 800-260-4PLI (260-4754, cust serv) *Toll Free Fax:* 800-321-0093 *E-mail:* info@pli.edu (cust serv) *Web Site:* www.pli.edu, pg 980

Matey, Janet, Matrox Video Products Group, 1055 Saint Regis Blvd, Dorval, QC H9P 2T4, Canada *Tel:* 514-822-6364; 514-685-7230 *Toll Free Tel:* 800-361-4903 *Fax:* 514-685-2853 *Web Site:* www.matrox.com/video, pg 934

Mathe, Barbara, American Museum of Natural History (AMNH), c/o Moving Image Collection, Library Services Dept, Central Park W & 79 St, New York, NY 10024-5192 *Tel:* 212-769-5420 *Fax:* 212-769-5009 *E-mail:* speccol@amnh.org *Web Site:* www.amnh.org, pg 785

Mathews, Gary, Quickbeam Systems Inc (QSI), 4411 McLeod Rd NE, Suite E, Albuquerque, NM 87109 *Tel:* 505-345-9230 *Fax:* 505-345-4604 *E-mail:* sales@quickbeam.com *Web Site:* www.quickbeam.com, pg 989

Mathews, Mark, RPM-PSI, 8750 Shirley Ave, Northridge, CA 91324 *Tel:* 818-349-8680 *Fax:* 818-772-7577 *E-mail:* info@rpm-psi.com *Web Site:* www.rpm-psi.com, pg 1000

Mathias, Darian, The Location Connection Inc, 1600 Rosecrans Ave, Bldg 5, Manhattan Beach, CA 90266 *Tel:* 310-376-9797 *Fax:* 310-376-9796 *E-mail:* lconnect@aol.com *Web Site:* www.locationconnection.com, pg 924

Mathuny, Rob, PsiTech Inc, 18368 Bandilier Circle, Fountain Valley, CA 92708 *Tel:* 714-964-7818 *Toll Free Tel:* 800-872-7385 *Fax:* 714-968-7884 *E-mail:* info@psitech.com; sales@psitech.com *Web Site:* www.psitech.com, pg 987

Mathy, Kevin, Related Visual Inc, 2941 E Miraloma Ave, Suite 3, Anaheim, CA 92806 *Tel:* 714-535-1414 *Toll Free Tel:* 800-733-1415 *Fax:* 714-630-3518 *E-mail:* relatedvis@aol.com *Web Site:* www.relatedvisual.com, pg 994

Mathy, William W, Related Visual Inc, 2941 E Miraloma Ave, Suite 3, Anaheim, CA 92806 *Tel:* 714-535-1414 *Toll Free Tel:* 800-733-1415 *Fax:* 714-630-3518 *E-mail:* relatedvis@aol.com *Web Site:* www.relatedvisual.com, pg 994

Matlin, Julie, National Film Board of Canada/Office National du Film du Canada, Norman-McLaren Bldg, 3155 Cote-de-Liesse Rd, Montreal, QC H4N 2N4, Canada *Tel:* 514-283-9000 *Toll Free Tel:* 800-267-7710 (CN only) *Fax:* 514-283-7564 *Web Site:* www.nfb.ca, pg 952

Matson, Donna, Western Instructional Television Inc, 1438 Gower St, No 18, Los Angeles, CA 90028 *Tel:* 323-466-8601, pg 1064

Matsubara, Masaki, Ikegami Electronics (USA) Inc, 37 Brook Ave, Maywood, NJ 07607 *Tel:* 201-368-9171 *Fax:* 201-569-1626 *E-mail:* sales@ikegami.com; service@ikegami.com *Web Site:* www.ikegami.com, pg 894

Mattes, Kim, The Chicago Production Center, 5400 N Saint Louis Ave, Chicago, IL 60625-4698 *Tel:* 773-509-5571 *Fax:* 773-509-5303 *Web Site:* www.wttw.com, pg 825

Matthews, Andrew, RKO Pictures Inc, 2034 Broadway, Santa Monica, CA 90404 *Tel:* 310-277-0707 *Fax:* 310-566-8940 *E-mail:* info@rko.com *Web Site:* www.rko.com, pg 997

Matthews, Dan, Sullivan Home Entertainment, 110 Davenport Rd, Toronto, ON M5R 3R3, Canada *Tel:* 416-921-7177 *Fax:* 416-921-7538 *E-mail:* inquire@sullivan-ent.com *Web Site:* www.sullivanmovies.com, pg 1028

Matthews, Dena, Life House Productions LLC, PO Box 4007, Manchester, CT 06045-4007 *Tel:* 860-432-9177 *Web Site:* www.lifehouseproductions.com, pg 920

Matthews, Edward D II, Visix™ Inc, 230 Scientific Dr, Suite 80, Norcross, GA 30092 *Tel:* 770-446-1416 *Toll Free Tel:* 800-572-4935 *Fax:* 770-448-5724 *E-mail:* info@visix.com *Web Site:* www.visix.com, pg 1059

Matthews, John, Marco Inc, 451 Carson Rd N, Birmingham, AL 35215 *Tel:* 205-856-1110 *Toll Free Tel:* 888-465-2514 *Fax:* 205-856-1136 *E-mail:* marco@marcoconsoles.com *Web Site:* www.marcoconsoles.com, pg 930

Matthews, Lisa, Technical Innovation, 2975 Northwoods Pkwy, Norcross, GA 30071 *Tel:* 770-447-1001 *Toll Free Tel:* 866-447-1004 *Fax:* 770-441-5285 *Web Site:* www.technical-innovation.com, pg 1034

Matthews, Sean, Visix™ Inc, 230 Scientific Dr, Suite 80, Norcross, GA 30092 *Tel:* 770-446-1416 *Toll Free Tel:* 800-572-4935 *Fax:* 770-448-5724 *E-mail:* info@visix.com *Web Site:* www.visix.com, pg 1059

Matthews, William, Life House Productions LLC, PO Box 4007, Manchester, CT 06045-4007 *Tel:* 860-432-9177 *Web Site:* www.lifehouseproductions.com, pg 920

Mattice, Kevin, Aztech Productions LLC, 400 Bethlehem Pike, Erdenheim, PA 19038 *Tel:* 215-836-5490 *Fax:* 215-836-0577 *Web Site:* aztechproductions.com, pg 801

Mattice, Linda, Aztech Productions LLC, 400 Bethlehem Pike, Erdenheim, PA 19038 *Tel:* 215-836-5490 *Fax:* 215-836-0577 *Web Site:* aztechproductions.com, pg 801

Matys, Frank, Audio Visual Communications Inc, 1336 Cherry St, Boothwyn, PA 19061 *Tel:* 610-272-8500 *E-mail:* audiovc@verizon.net *Web Site:* www.audiovc.com, pg 795

Matz, Bret A, Opterna AM, 44901 Falcon Place, Suite 116, Sterling, VA 20166-9531 *Tel:* 703-653-1130 *Toll Free Tel:* 800-248-9004 *Fax:* 703-803-8313 *Web Site:* www.opterna-am.com, pg 964

Matzen, Robert, R&B Communications Inc, 2397 Somrack Dr, Willoughby Hills, OH 44094 *Tel:* 440-946-9511 *Web Site:* www.rbcommunications.net, pg 991

Mau, Rennie, Media Bridge Gamekids, PO Box 513, Koloa, HI 96703 *Tel:* 808-280-9591 *Web Site:* www.gamekids.com, pg 936

Mauel, Anne, Adams Evidence Grade Technology Inc, 4123 N Little Creek Rd, Utopia, TX 78884 *Tel:* 830-966-4210 *Toll Free Tel:* 877-643-4900 *Fax:* 830-966-4214 *E-mail:* info1@evidencegrade.com; customerservice@evidencegrade.com *Web Site:* www.evidencegrade.com, pg 775

Mauro, Cheryl, North Carolina Film Office, 301 N Wilmington St, Raleigh, NC 27601 *Tel:* 919-733-9900 *Toll Free Tel:* 866-468-2273 *Fax:* 919-715-0151 *Web Site:* www.ncfilm.com, pg 1101

Mavin, Steve, Grafco Inc, PO Box 431, Stroudsburg, PA 18360 *Toll Free Tel:* 800-367-6169 *Toll Free Fax:* 800-443-4329 *E-mail:* grafcofurniture@grafco.com *Web Site:* www.grafco.com, pg 881

Maxey, Kent, Encyclomedia, 1526 Dekalb Ave, Atlanta, GA 30307 *Tel:* 404-527-3600 *Fax:* 404-584-5171 *E-mail:* info@encyclomedia.net *Web Site:* www.encyclomedia.net, pg 861

Maxey, Mark, York Telecom, 81 Corbett Way, Eatontown, NJ 07724 *Tel:* 732-413-6000 *Toll Free Tel:* 866-836-8463 *Fax:* 732-413-6060 *E-mail:* knowmore@yorktel.com *Web Site:* yorktel.com, pg 1072

Maxwell, Deborah, Cineworks Inc, 8125 Lankershim Blvd, North Hollywood, CA 91605 *Tel:* 818-252-0001 *Fax:* 818-252-0003 *E-mail:* cineworks@cineworksinc.com *Web Site:* www.cineworksinc.com, pg 828

Maxwell, Ray, Eventide Inc, One Alsan Way, Little Ferry, NJ 07643 *Tel:* 201-641-1200 *Fax:* 201-641-1640 *E-mail:* audio@eventide.com; support@eventide.com *Web Site:* www.eventide.com, pg 863

Maxwell, Willie, DG Mijo, 635 E Queen St, East Toronto, ON M4M 1G4, Canada *Tel:* 416-964-7539 *Toll Free Tel:* 800-463-MIJO (463-6456) *Fax:* 416-964-5920 *Web Site:* www.mijo.com, pg 846

May, Edward J, John Wiley & Sons Inc, 111 River St, Hoboken, NJ 07030 *Tel:* 201-748-6000 *Toll Free Tel:* 800-225-5945 *Fax:* 201-748-6088 *E-mail:* info@wiley.com *Web Site:* www.wiley.com, pg 1066

May, Mike, Rane, 10802 47 Ave W, Mukilteo, WA 98275-5000 *Tel:* 425-355-6000 *E-mail:* info@rane.com *Web Site:* www.rane.com, pg 991

May, Pamela, Design Media, 650 Alabama St, Suite 203, San Francisco, CA 94110-2038 *Tel:* 415-641-4848 *Fax:* 415-641-5245 *E-mail:* info@designmedia.com *Web Site:* www.designmedia.com, pg 846

Maybrook, Jerry, The Media Staff Inc, 8425 W Third St, Suite 401, Los Angeles, CA 90048 *Tel:* 323-658-8996 *Fax:* 323-658-8990 *E-mail:* info@themediastaff.com *Web Site:* www.themediastaff.com, pg 937

Maye, Karen, Airshow Mastering, 3063 Sterling Circle, Suite 3, Boulder, CO 80301 *Tel:* 303-247-9035 *Toll Free Tel:* 888-545-9035 *Toll Free Fax:* 888-545-9035 *E-mail:* studio@airshowmastering.com *Web Site:* www.airshowmastering.com, pg 779

Mayer, Andrea, WolfVision Inc, 1601 Bayshore Hwy, Suite 168, Burlingame, CA 94010 *Tel:* 650-648-0002 *Toll Free Tel:* 800-356-9653 *Fax:* 650-648-0009 *E-mail:* sales@wolfvision.us; support@wolfvision.us *Web Site:* www.wolfvision.com, pg 1069

Mayer-Oakes, Drew, San Antonio Film Commission, 203 S Saint Mary's St, Suite 360, San Antonio, TX 78205 *Tel:* 210-207-6730 *Toll Free Tel:* 800-447-3372 *Fax:* 210-207-4526 *E-mail:* filmsa@filmsanantonio.com *Web Site:* www.filmsanantonio.com, pg 1103

Mayfield, Buddy, Outland Technology Inc, 38190 Commercial Ct, Slidell, LA 70458 *Tel:* 985-847-1104 *Fax:* 985-847-1106 *E-mail:* sales@outlandtech.com *Web Site:* www.outlandtech.com, pg 966

Mayl, Gene, Red Onion Records, PO Box 366, Dayton, OH 45401-0366 *Tel:* 937-277-3079 *Toll Free Tel:* 800-876-4467 *Fax:* 513-672-0213 *Web Site:* www.landofjazz.com, pg 993

Maynard, Eric, Event Tech, 7601 Brandon Woods Blvd, Baltimore, MD 21226 *Tel:* 410-360-5006 *Toll Free Tel:* 866-950-8343 *Fax:* 410-360-5002 *E-mail:* info@eventtech.com *Web Site:* www.eventtech.com, pg 863

Maynard, Gary, The Gary-Paul Agency, 1549 Main St, Stratford, CT 06615 *Tel:* 203-345-6167 *Web Site:* www.thegarypaulagency.com, pg 875

Maynard, Shawn, Florical Systems Inc, 4500 NW 27 Ave, Bldg B-1, Gainesville, FL 32606 *Tel:* 352-372-8326 *Toll Free Tel:* 800-372-4613 *Fax:* 352-375-0859 *E-mail:* support@florical.com *Web Site:* www.florical.com, pg 870

Mayne, Erik, MediaFX, 10445 SW Canyon Rd, Suite 220, Beaverton, OR 97005 *Tel:* 503-646-9884 *Fax:* 503-646-7115 *Web Site:* www.mediafxvideo.com, pg 937

Mayo, Lisa, Tuolumne County Film Commission, 542 W Stockton St, Sonora, CA 95370 *Tel:* 209-533-4420 *Toll Free Tel:* 800-446-1333 *Fax:* 209-532-2502 *E-mail:* info@tcfilm.org *Web Site:* www.tcfilm.org, pg 1094

Mays, Jenny, The Virginia Film Festival, 617 W Main St, 2nd fl, Charlottesville, VA 22903 *Tel:* 434-982-5277 *Fax:* 434-924-3374 *E-mail:* info@virginiafilmfestival.org *Web Site:* www.virginiafilmfestival.org, pg 1129

Mazovick, John A, Convenience, 3012 N Long Ave, Chicago, IL 60641-4930 *Tel:* 773-545-3073 *Fax:* 773-545-3073, pg 836

Mazzei, Kelly, Alaska Film Office, 550 W Seventh Ave, Suite 500, Anchorage, AK 99501 *Tel:* 907-269-1018 *Fax:* 907-269-6644 *E-mail:* alaskafilmoffice@alaska.gov *Web Site:* tax.alaska.gov/AlaskaFilmOffice/, pg 1091

McAleer, V J, The Chicago Production Center, 5400 N Saint Louis Ave, Chicago, IL 60625-4698 *Tel:* 773-509-5571 *Fax:* 773-509-5303 *Web Site:* www.wttw.com, pg 825

McAlister, William, McAlister Electronics, 926 E Fremont Ave, Sunnyvale, CA 94087 *Tel:* 408-739-2605 *Fax:* 408-733-2895 *E-mail:* mcalelect@aol.com *Web Site:* www.werepairallbrands.com, pg 935

McAllister, Gregg C, TVN-The Video Network, 31 Cutler Dr, Ashland, MA 01721-1210 *Tel:* 508-881-1800 *E-mail:* info@tvnvideo.com *Web Site:* www.tvnvideo.com, pg 1046

McAllister, Robert "Kooster", Record Plant Remote, 1170 Greenwood Lake Tpke, Ringwood, NJ 07456 *Tel:* 973-728-8114 *Fax:* 973-728-8761 *E-mail:* info@recordplantremote.com *Web Site:* www.recordplantremote.com, pg 993

McArthur, Gary L, Harris Corp, 1025 W NASA Blvd, Melbourne, FL 32919-0001 *Tel:* 321-727-9100 *Toll Free Tel:* 800-442-7747 *E-mail:* webmaster@harris.com *Web Site:* www.harris.com, pg 885

McArthur, Sean, Apogee Electronics Corp, 1715 Berkeley St, Santa Monica, CA 90404 *Tel:* 310-584-9394 *Fax:* 310-584-9385 *Web Site:* www.apogeedigital.com, pg 788

McArthur, Stephen, Multicultural Media, 56 Browns Mill Rd, Montpelier, VT 05602 *E-mail:* support@worldmusicstore.com *Web Site:* www.worldmusicstore.com; www.multiculturalmedia.com, pg 950

McAtee, Todd S, Mouser Electronics, 1000 N Main St, Mansfield, TX 76063-1514 *Tel:* 817-804-3888 *Toll Free Tel:* 800-346-6873 *Fax:* 817-804-3899 *Web Site:* www.mouser.com, pg 947

McBrayer, Steve, All Communications Rentals Inc (ALLCOMM), 1402 SW 13 Ct, Pompano Beach, FL 33069 *Tel:* 954-788-9555 *Web Site:* www.allcommrentals.com, pg 780

McBride, Sean, Grocery Manufacturers Association (GMA), 1350 "I" St NW, Suite 300, Washington, DC 20005 *Tel:* 202-639-5900 *Toll Free Tel:* 800-355-0983 *Fax:* 202-639-5932 *E-mail:* info@gmaonline.org *Web Site:* gmaonline.org, pg 882

McCabe, Glenn, MCC Films, 7 Rabbit Lane, Brookfield, CT 06804 *Tel:* 203-775-9473 *Fax:* 734-310-6328 *E-mail:* info@mcc-films.com *Web Site:* www.mcc-films.com, pg 935

McCabe, Meghan, Canadian Academy of Recording Arts & Sciences (CARAS), 345 Adelaide St W, 2nd fl, Toronto, ON M5V 1R5, Canada *Tel:* 416-485-3135 *Toll Free Tel:* 888-440-JUNO (440-5866, CN only) *Fax:* 416-485-4978 *E-mail:* submissions@junoawards.ca *Web Site:* www.carasonline.ca; junoawards.ca, pg 1080

McCabe, Meghan, Juno Awards, 345 Adelaide St W, 2nd fl, Toronto, ON M5V 1R5, Canada *Tel:* 416-485-3135 *Toll Free Tel:* 888-440-JUNO (440-5866, CN only) *Fax:* 416-485-4978 *E-mail:* info@junoawards.ca; info@carasonline.ca; submissions@junoawards.ca *Web Site:* junoawards.ca; www.facebook.com/theJunoAwards, pg 1118

McCabe, Scott, IMR Limited, 1104 Fernwood Ave, 4th fl, Camp Hill, PA 17011 *Tel:* 717-364-3700 *Toll Free Tel:* 800-446-2826 *Fax:* 717-364-3750 *E-mail:* information@imrdigital.com *Web Site:* www.imrdigital.com, pg 897

McCall, Andy, Media Supply Inc, 611 Jeffers Circle, Exton, PA 19341 *Tel:* 610-884-4400 *Toll Free Tel:* 800-944-4237 *Fax:* 610-884-4500 *E-mail:* info@mediasupply.com *Web Site:* www.mediasupply.com, pg 937

McCall, Josh, Jack Morton Worldwide, 909 Third Ave, New York, NY 10022 *Tel:* 212-401-7000 *E-mail:* experience@jackmorton.com *Web Site:* www.jackmorton.com, pg 946

McCann, Heather, House of Moves, 5419 McConnell Ave, Los Angeles, CA 90066-7027 *Tel:* 310-306-6131 *E-mail:* info@moves.com *Web Site:* www.moves.com, pg 891

McCann, Tammy, Sunset Gower Studios, 1438 N Gower St, Box 21, Hollywood, CA 90028 *Tel:* 323-467-1001 *Fax:* 323-467-2717 *E-mail:* sgsreception@sgsandsbs.com *Web Site:* sgsandsbs.com, pg 1028

McCann, Thomas, Commonwealth Films Inc, 223 Commonwealth Ave, Boston, MA 02116 *Tel:* 617-262-5634 *E-mail:* info@commonwealthfilms.com *Web Site:* www.commonwealthfilms.com, pg 832

McCarthy, Debbie, Lawrence Convention & Visitors Bureau, 402 N Second St, Lawrence, KS 66044 *Tel:* 785-856-3040; 785-856-5282 *Fax:* 785-856-5303 *E-mail:* visinfo@visitlawrence.com *Web Site:* www.visitlawrence.com, pg 1097

McCarthy, Kari, Magna Systems Inc, 208 S Jefferson St, Suite 402, Chicago, IL 60661 *Toll Free Tel:* 800-634-4941 *Toll Free Fax:* 800-998-0854 *E-mail:* info@magnasystems.com *Web Site:* www.learningseed.com, pg 928

McCarthy, Malachy R, Catholic Library Association (CLA), 8550 United Plaza Blvd, Suite 1001, Baton Rouge, LA 70809 *Tel:* 225-408-4417 *E-mail:* cla2@cathla.org *Web Site:* www.cathla.org, pg 1080

McCarthy, Padraig, SES World Skies, 4 Research Way, Princeton, NJ 08540 *Tel:* 609-987-4000; 609-987-4200 *Fax:* 609-987-4517 *E-mail:* info@ses.com *Web Site:* www.ses.com, pg 1007

McCarty, Maggie, The Paradise Coast Film Commission, 755 Eighth Ave S, Naples, FL 34102 *Tel:* 239-659-FILM (659-3456) *Fax:* 239-213-3053 *Web Site:* www.shootinparadise.com, pg 1096

McCauley, Dan, General Devices Co Inc, 1410 S Post Rd, Indianapolis, IN 46239 *Tel:* 317-897-7000 *Fax:* 317-898-2917 *E-mail:* sales@generaldevices.com *Web Site:* www.generaldevices.com, pg 876

McCauley, James, MCC Films, 7 Rabbit Lane, Brookfield, CT 06804 *Tel:* 203-775-9473 *Fax:* 734-310-6328 *E-mail:* info@mcc-films.com *Web Site:* www.mcc-films.com, pg 935

McCauley, Thomas, McCauley Sound Inc, 16607 Meridian Ave E, Puyallup, WA 98375 *Tel:* 253-848-0363 *Toll Free Tel:* 877-622-2853 *Fax:* 253-841-3050 *Web Site:* www.mccauleysound.com, pg 935

McClain, Kim, Filmtools®, 1400 W Burbank Blvd, Burbank, CA 91506 *Tel:* 818-845-8066 *Toll Free Tel:* 888-807-1900 *Fax:* 818-845-8138 *Web Site:* www.filmtools.com, pg 868

McClain, Stan, Filmtools®, 1400 W Burbank Blvd, Burbank, CA 91506 *Tel:* 818-845-8066 *Toll Free Tel:* 888-807-1900 *Fax:* 818-845-8138 *Web Site:* www.filmtools.com, pg 868

McClanathan, Bob, Frontier Communications Corp, PO Box 939, Portland, OR 97207-0939 *Tel:* 503-246-8080 *Fax:* 541-549-1809, pg 873

McClatchie, Donald, FM Systems Inc, 3877 S Main St, Santa Ana, CA 92707 *Tel:* 714-979-3355 *Toll Free Tel:* 800-235-6960 *Fax:* 714-979-0913 *E-mail:* fmsystemsinc@sbcglobal.net *Web Site:* www.fmsystems-inc.com, pg 870

McClatchie, Frank, FM Systems Inc, 3877 S Main St, Santa Ana, CA 92707 *Tel:* 714-979-3355 *Toll Free Tel:* 800-235-6960 *Fax:* 714-979-0913 *E-mail:* fmsystemsinc@sbcglobal.net *Web Site:* www.fmsystems-inc.com, pg 870

McClea, Robin, Arkansas Arts Council Fellowships & Grants Program, 323 Center St, Suite 1500, Little Rock, AR 72201-2606 *Tel:* 501-324-9766 *Fax:* 501-324-9207 *E-mail:* info@arkansasarts.com *Web Site:* www.arkansasarts.org, pg 1107

McCleary, Sandy, Lex Lawson Associates, 2002 Platinum St, Garland, TX 75042 *Tel:* 972-272-8482 *Toll Free Tel:* 800-783-9395 *Fax:* 972-276-8120 *Web Site:* www.lexlawson.com, pg 917

McClellan, Jon Paul, Audio Art, 124 Forsythe Dr, Chapel Hill, NC 27517 *Tel:* 919-260-1507, pg 794

McClure, Colleen, The Florida Office of Film & Entertainment, 107 E Madison St, MSC 80, Tallahassee, FL 32399 *Tel:* 850-717-8990; 818-508-7772 *Toll Free Tel:* 877-FLA-FILM (352-3456) *Fax:* 850-410-4770 *Web Site:* www.filminflorida.com, pg 1096

McClure, Leslie, 411 Video Information, PO Box 1223, Pebble Beach, CA 93953-1223 *Tel:* 831-656-0553 *Fax:* 831-656-0555 *Web Site:* www.411videoinfo.com, pg 872

McClure, Thomas, Greater Columbus Film Commission, PO Box 12735, Columbus, OH 43212 *Tel:* 614-450-0264 *E-mail:* info@columbusfilmcommission.com *Web Site:* www.filmcolumbus.com, pg 1101

McCone, Mark, Substation K, 3947 State Line Rd, Kansas City, MO 64111 *Tel:* 816-531-3838 *Fax:* 816-531-3839 *Web Site:* www.substationk.com, pg 1027

McConnell, Robert, Robert McConnell Productions, 4303 67 Ave NW, Gig Harbor, WA 98335 *Tel:* 253-265-3184 *Toll Free Tel:* 800-532-4017 *Fax:* 253-265-1550 *Toll Free Fax:* 800-948-8463 *E-mail:* info@parli.com; drvideo@earthlink.net *Web Site:* parli.com, pg 935

McCool, Michael D, National Media Services Inc, 613 N Commerce Ave, Front Royal, VA 22630 *Tel:* 540-635-4181 *Fax:* 540-636-4240 *E-mail:* info@nationalmediaservices.com *Web Site:* www.nationalmediaservices.com, pg 953

McCord, Kenneth G, Permlight Products Inc, 422 W Sixth St, Tustin, CA 92780 *Tel:* 714-508-0729 *Fax:* 714-508-0920 *E-mail:* sales@brillialed.com (brillia div); sales@permlightforsigns.com (sign div) *Web Site:* www.permlight.com; www.permlightforsigns.com (signs div); www.brillialed.com (brillia div), pg 973

McCord-Morelli, Kerry, WSI, 400 Minuteman Rd, Andover, MA 01810 *Tel:* 978-983-6300 *Fax:* 978-983-6400 *Web Site:* www.wsi.com, pg 1070

McCormick, Brian, Stewart Audio, 14397 Cuesta Ct, Suite D1, Sonora, CA 95370 *Tel:* 209-588-8111 *Fax:* 209-588-8113 *E-mail:* sales@stewartaudio.com; support@stewartaudio.com *Web Site:* www.stewartaudio.com, pg 1025

McCormick, Neil G, Cinecraft Productions Inc, 2515 Franklin Blvd, Cleveland, OH 44113 *Tel:* 216-781-2300 *Toll Free Tel:* 800-959-2463 *Fax:* 216-781-1067 *E-mail:* info@cinecraft.com *Web Site:* cinecraft.com, pg 827

McCormick, Peter M, Magnetek Inc, N49 W13650 Campbell Dr, Menomonee Falls, WI 53051 *Tel:* 262-783-3500 *Toll Free Tel:* 800-288-8178 *Toll Free Fax:* 800-298-3503 *E-mail:* sales@magnetek.com *Web Site:* www.magnetek.com, pg 928

McCoy, Charles E, Audio-Video Resources Inc, 1043 Adams Ave, Montgomery, AL 36104 *Tel:* 334-262-4806 *Fax:* 334-240-0000 *E-mail:* avrinc@bellsouth.net, pg 795

McCrainie, David, Everlast Productions, 59 SW 12 Ave, Unit 109, Dania Beach, FL 33004 *Tel:* 954-456-7167 *Fax:* 954-456-1243 *E-mail:* info@everlastproductions.com *Web Site:* everlastproductions.com, pg 863

McCreery, Patrick, KPDX-TV Production Center, 14975 NW Greenbrier Pkwy, Beaverton, OR 97006-5731 *Tel:* 503-906-1249 *Fax:* 503-548-6920 *E-mail:* ezone@kpdx.com; fox12news@kptv.com *Web Site:* www.kptv.com; www.kpdx.com, pg 913

McCue, Monette, Film & Creative Industries Nova Scotia, Historic Properties, Collins Bank Bldg, 3rd fl, 1883 Upper Water St, Suite 302, Halifax, NS B3J 1S9, Canada *Tel:* 902-424-7177 *Toll Free Tel:* 888-360-2111 *Fax:* 902-424-0617 *E-mail:* filmandcreativens@gov.ns.ca *Web Site:* www.filmandcreativens.ca, pg 1105

McCulley, Bruce, Cavalcade Productions Inc, PO Box 2480, Nevada City, CA 95959-1948 *Tel:* 530-477-0701 (outside US & CN) *Toll Free Tel:* 800-345-5530 *Fax:* 530-477-0701 (outside US & CN) *Toll Free Fax:* 800-345-5530 *E-mail:* info@cavalcadeproductions.com *Web Site:* www.cavalcadeproductions.com, pg 821

McCune, Allan, McCune Audio-Video-Lighting, 101 Utah Ave, South San Francisco, CA 94080 *Tel:* 650-873-1111 *Toll Free Tel:* 800-899-7686 *Fax:* 650-246-6702 *E-mail:* info@mccune.com *Web Site:* www.mccune.com, pg 935

McCune, Grant, McCune Design, 6836 Valjean Ave, Van Nuys, CA 91406 *Tel:* 818-779-1920 *Web Site:* www.mccune-design.com, pg 935

McCune, Thomas, Navitar Inc, 200 Commerce Dr, Rochester, NY 14623 *Tel:* 585-359-4000 *Toll Free Tel:* 800-828-6778 *Fax:* 585-359-4999 *E-mail:* info@navitar.com *Web Site:* www.navitar.com, pg 953

McCurdy, Robert, GTI (Graphic Technology Inc), PO Box 3138, Newburgh, NY 12550-0651 *Tel:* 845-562-7066 *Toll Free Tel:* 888-562-7066 *Fax:* 845-562-2543 *E-mail:* sales@gtilite.com *Web Site:* www.gtilite.com, pg 883

McDonald, Dennis, Keslow Camera Inc, 11260 Playa Ct, Culver City, CA 90230 *Tel:* 310-636-4600 *Fax:* 310-915-5335 *E-mail:* info@keslowcamera.com *Web Site:* www.keslowcamera.com, pg 910

McDonald, Gregory, iCorpTv, PO Box 461172, Los Angeles, CA 90046 *Tel:* 818-492-4623 *E-mail:* contact@icorptv.com *Web Site:* www.icorptv.com, pg 893

McDonald, Jim, Wind River Broadcast Center, 117 E 11 St, Loveland, CO 80537 *Tel:* 970-669-3442 *Toll Free Tel:* 800-669-3993 *Fax:* 970-663-6081 *Web Site:* www.windriverbroadcast.com, pg 1067

McDonald, Michael, Private Island Trax, 1882 S Cochran Ave, Los Angeles, CA 90019 *Tel:* 323-856-8729 *Fax:* 323-965-8732 *E-mail:* info@privateislandtrax.com *Web Site:* www.privateislandtrax.com, pg 982

McDonnell, Mark, Films for the Humanities & Sciences, 132 W 31 St, 17th fl, New York, NY 10001 *Toll Free Tel:* 800-257-5126 *Fax:* 609-671-0266 *E-mail:* custserv@films.com *Web Site:* ffh.films.com, pg 868

McDonnell, Mark, Shopware, c/o Films Media Group, 132 W 31 St, 17th fl, New York, NY 10001 *Toll Free Tel:* 800-322-8755 *Toll Free Fax:* 800-678-3633 *E-mail:* custserv@films.com *Web Site:* shopware.films.com, pg 1009

McDonnough, Paul A, Direct Marketing Association Inc (DMA), 1120 Avenue of the Americas, New York, NY 10036-6700 *Tel:* 212-768-7277 *Fax:* 212-302-6714 *Web Site:* thedma.org, pg 1081

McDonough, Pete, Harvest Studios, 2880 Vision Ct, Aurora, IL 60506 *Tel:* 630-801-3658 *Fax:* 630-801-3839 *E-mail:* info@harveststudios.org *Web Site:* harveststudios.org, pg 885

McDowell, John, NewsBank Inc, 5801 Pelican Bay Blvd, Suite 600, Naples, FL 34108 *Toll Free Tel:* 800-762-8182 *Fax:* 239-263-3004 *E-mail:* sales@newsbank.com; custservice@newsbank.com *Web Site:* www.newsbank.com, pg 957

McDuff, Chris, ChronTrol Corp, 7525-D Mission Gorge Rd, San Diego, CA 92120 *Tel:* 619-282-8686 *Toll Free Tel:* 800-854-1999 *Fax:* 619-563-6563 *E-mail:* info@chrontrol.com *Web Site:* www.chrontrol.com, pg 826

McElfresh, Jeff, Palmdale Chamber of Commerce, 817 E Avenue Q-9, Palmdale, CA 93550 *Tel:* 661-273-3232 *Fax:* 661-273-8508 *E-mail:* chamberstaff@palmdalechamber.org *Web Site:* www.palmdalechamber.org, pg 1093

McElwee, Joni, Technomedia Solutions, 4545 36 St, Orlando, FL 32811 *Tel:* 407-351-0909 *Fax:* 407-248-9484 *E-mail:* sales@gotechnomedia.com *Web Site:* www.gotechnomedia.com, pg 1035

McErlain, Eric, EEG Enterprises Inc, 586 Main St, Farmingdale, NY 11735 *Tel:* 516-293-7472 *Fax:* 516-293-7417 *E-mail:* sales@eegent.com *Web Site:* www.eegent.com, pg 858

McEwen, Michael, North American Broadcasters Association (NABA), Canadian Broadcasting Centre, 25 John St, Suite 6C300, Toronto, ON M5V 3G7, Canada *Tel:* 416-598-9877 *Fax:* 416-598-9774 *E-mail:* contact@nabanet.com *Web Site:* www.nabanet.com, pg 1086

McFarland, Judy, Thread Marketing Group, 4635 W Alexis Rd, Toledo, OH 43623-1005 *Tel:* 419-887-6801 *Toll Free Tel:* 800-397-0126 *Fax:* 419-887-6802 *E-mail:* contact@experiencethread.com *Web Site:* www.experiencethread.com, pg 1039

McGarty, Kevin, Staging Directions Inc, 1327 Northbrook Pkwy, Suite 440, Suwanee, GA 30024 *Tel:* 770-409-9909 *Toll Free Tel:* 800-782-4322 *Fax:* 770-409-0277 *E-mail:* info@teamsdi.net; sales@teamsdi.net *Web Site:* www.stagingdirections.com, pg 1023

McGill, Carla Hargrove, Hargrove Inc, One Hargrove Dr, Lanham, MD 20706 *Tel:* 301-306-9000 *Fax:* 301-306-9318 *E-mail:* exhibitorservices@hargroveinc.com *Web Site:* www.hargroveinc.com, pg 885

McGill, Jackie, Spectrum Engineers, 324 S State St, Suite 400, Salt Lake City, UT 84111 *Tel:* 801-328-5151 *Toll Free Tel:* 800-678-7077 *Fax:* 801-328-5155 *E-mail:* info@spectrum-engineers.com *Web Site:* www.spectrum-engineers.com, pg 1021

McGill, Lindsey L, Spectrum Systems Design, 937 SW 14 Ave, Suite 101, Portland, OR 97205 *Tel:* 503-248-0248 *Toll Free Tel:* 800-288-3492 *Fax:* 503-274-7684 *Web Site:* www.spectrumsd.com, pg 1021

McGill, Tim, Hargrove Inc, One Hargrove Dr, Lanham, MD 20706 *Tel:* 301-306-9000 *Fax:* 301-306-9318 *E-mail:* exhibitorservices@hargroveinc.com *Web Site:* www.hargroveinc.com, pg 885

McGinnis, Amanda, Videssence, 10768 Lower Azusa Rd, El Monte, CA 91731 *Tel:* 626-579-0943 *Fax:* 626-579-6803 *E-mail:* contact@videssence.tv *Web Site:* www.vid務sence.tv, pg 1057

McGinty, Eugene, Welocalize, 241 E Fourth St, Suite 207, Frederick, MD 21701 *Tel:* 301-668-0330 *Toll Free Tel:* 800-370-9515 *Fax:* 301-668-0335 *E-mail:* info@welocalize.com *Web Site:* www.welocalize.com, pg 1063

McGlothlin, Ron, iVideo Technologies, 14885 Sprague Rd, Cleveland, OH 44136 *Tel:* 440-891-9440 *Toll Free Tel:* 800-352-6150 *Fax:* 440-891-9450 *E-mail:* info@ivideo.com *Web Site:* www.ivideo.com, pg 903

McGovern, Kevin, Cine-Med Inc, 127 Main St N, Woodbury, CT 06798 *Tel:* 203-263-0006 *Toll Free Tel:* 800-253-7657 *Fax:* 203-263-4839 *E-mail:* support@cine-med.net *Web Site:* www.cine-med.com, pg 826

McGovern, Mark, AMS Pictures, 16986 N Dallas Pkwy, Dallas, TX 75248 *Tel:* 972-818-7400 *Toll Free Tel:* 866-691-3660 *Fax:* 972-818-1257 *Web Site:* www.amspictures.com, pg 786

McGowan, Bill, Clarity Media Group, 166 Fifth Ave, 6th fl, New York, NY 10010 *Tel:* 212-262-7015 *E-mail:* info@claritymediagroup.com *Web Site:* www.claritymediagroup.com, pg 829

McGowan, Bret, Vicon Industries Inc, 131 Heartland Blvd, Edgewood, NY 11717 *Tel:* 631-952-2288 *Toll Free Tel:* 800-645-9116 *Fax:* 631-951-2288 *Web Site:* www.vicon-security.com, pg 1053

McGrath, Dick, Albany Theatre Supply Co Inc, 445 N Pearl St, Albany, NY 12204 *Tel:* 518-465-8895 *Fax:* 518-465-8908 *E-mail:* sales@albanytheatresupply.com *Web Site:* www.albanytheatresupply.com, pg 780

McGrath, Kyra G, WHYY Inc, Independence Mall West, 150 N Sixth St, Philadelphia, PA 19106 *Tel:* 215-351-1200 *Fax:* 215-351-0398 *E-mail:* talkback@whyy.org *Web Site:* www.whyy.org, pg 1066

McGrath, Matt, Advanced Designs Corp, 1169 W Second St, Bloomington, IN 47403 *Tel:* 812-333-1922 *Fax:* 812-333-2030 *Web Site:* www.doprad.com, pg 777

McGrath, Thomas, Albany Theatre Supply Co Inc, 445 N Pearl St, Albany, NY 12204 *Tel:* 518-465-8895 *Fax:* 518-465-8908 *E-mail:* sales@albanytheatresupply.com *Web Site:* www.albanytheatresupply.com, pg 780

McGraw, Brian, Cine Photo Tech, 1240 Oakleigh Dr, Atlanta, GA 30344 *Tel:* 404-684-7100 *Fax:* 404-684-7080 *E-mail:* info@cinephototech.com *Web Site:* www.cinephototech.com, pg 826

McGrew, Casey, Tarpley Media Systems, 3737 50 St, Lubbock, TX 79413 *Tel:* 806-797-5833 *Toll Free Tel:* 800-600-5833 *Fax:* 806-797-5139 *E-mail:* tms@tarpleymedia.com *Web Site:* www.tarpleymedia.com, pg 1032

McGuane, James P, McGuane Studio Inc, 36 Horatio St, Suite 5-B, New York, NY 10014-1691 *Tel:* 212-463-7259, pg 935

McGugan, Phil, Nazdar®, 8501 Hedge Lane Terr, Shawnee, KS 66227-3290 *Tel:* 913-422-1888 *Toll Free Tel:* 800-767-9942 (cust serv) *Fax:* 913-422-2296 *E-mail:* custserv@nazdar.com *Web Site:* www.nazdar.com, pg 953

McGuire, Hilary Paul, Multi-Media Mathematics, 11224 Seawind Cove, San Diego, CA 92126-1119 *Tel:* 858-578-3421 *E-mail:* phyl.hil@gmail.com *Web Site:* www.miracosta.edu/home/pmcguire, pg 949

McGuire, John, Kajo Co, 2081 E Bellerive Place, Chandler, AZ 85249-4131 *Tel:* 480-830-9798 *Fax:* 480-883-3022 *Web Site:* www.kajoco.com, pg 907

McHugh, Daniel, National Institute for Trial Advocacy (NITA), 1685 38 St, Suite 200, Boulder, CO 80301-2735 *Tel:* 720-890-4860 *Toll Free Tel:* 800-225-6482 *Fax:* 720-890-7069 *E-mail:* receptionist@nita.org *Web Site:* www.nita.org, pg 953

McHugh, Eric, Dogma Studios, 10559 Jefferson Blvd, Culver City, CA 90232 *Tel:* 310-838-2973 *Fax:* 310-838-2975 *E-mail:* info@dogmastudios.com *Web Site:* www.dogmastudios.com, pg 850

McIlvain, Carlie, Kerrville Convention & Visitors Bureau, 2108 Sidney Baker St, Kerrville, TX 78028 *Tel:* 830-792-3535 *Toll Free Tel:* 800-221-7958 *Fax:* 830-792-3230 *E-mail:* info@kerrvilletexascvb.com; kerrcvb@ktc.com *Web Site:* www.kerrvilletexascvb.com, pg 1103

McIlwain, J Michael, PSAV® Presentation Services, 111 W Ocean Blvd, Suite 1110, Long Beach, CA 90802-4688 *Tel:* 562-366-0620 *Toll Free Tel:* 877-430-7728 *Fax:* 562-366-0628 *Web Site:* www.psav.com, pg 986

McIlwain, J Michael, PSAV® Presentation Services (Hotel Services Division), 1700 E Golf Rd, Suite 400, Schaumburg, IL 60173-5820 *Tel:* 847-222-9800 *Toll Free Tel:* 800-486-9509 *E-mail:* info@psav.com *Web Site:* www.psav.com, pg 987

McIntire, Bill, Magic Gadgets™, 12986 Mapleleaf Ct NE, Aurora, OR 97002-8418 *Tel:* 503-678-6236; 818-655-5465 (rentals) *Fax:* 503-678-6237 *E-mail:* info@magicgadgets.com *Web Site:* www.magicgadgets.com, pg 928

McIntire, Kathryn, Magic Gadgets™, 12986 Mapleleaf Ct NE, Aurora, OR 97002-8418 *Tel:* 503-678-6236; 818-655-5465 (rentals) *Fax:* 503-678-6237 *E-mail:* info@magicgadgets.com *Web Site:* www.magicgadgets.com, pg 928

McIntire, Steve, Broadcast Management Group, 1625 Eye St NW, Suite 620, Washington, DC 20006 *Tel:* 202-609-7757 *E-mail:* info@broadcastmgmt.com *Web Site:* www.broadcastmgmt.com, pg 813

McIntosh, Alex, YAP Films, 96 Spadina Ave, Suite 205, Toronto, ON M5V 2J6, Canada *Tel:* 416-504-3662 *Fax:* 416-504-3667 *E-mail:* thedog@yapfilms.com *Web Site:* www.yapfilms.com, pg 1072

McIntyre, Jaime, Aspen Systems Inc, 3900 Youngfield St, Wheat Ridge, CO 80033-3865 *Tel:* 303-431-4606 *Toll Free Tel:* 800-992-9242 *Fax:* 303-431-7196 *E-mail:* sales@aspsys.com *Web Site:* www.aspsys.com, pg 792

McIntyre, Maury, Television Academy, 5220 Lankershim Blvd, North Hollywood, CA 91601-3109 *Tel:* 818-754-2800 *Fax:* 818-761-2827 *Web Site:* www.emmys.com, pg 1089

McIntyre, Phil, The Brand Gallery, 701 W Putnam Ave, Greenwich, CT 06830 *Tel:* 203-422-3900 *Fax:* 203-531-1394 *Web Site:* www.thebrandgallery.com, pg 812

McIntyre, Ron L, CyberIconics International, 1752 N 74 Place, Mesa, AZ 85207-2932 *Tel:* 480-396-8731, pg 841

McKay, Matthew PhD, New Harbinger Publications, 5674 Shattuck Ave, Oakland, CA 94609 *Tel:* 510-652-0215 *Toll Free Tel:* 800-748-6273 *Fax:* 510-652-5472 *E-mail:* customerservice@newharbinger.com *Web Site:* www.newharbinger.com, pg 955

McKay, Nathan, Salesmaker Carts, 403 Roberts Ave, Louisville, KY 40214 *Toll Free Tel:* 800-281-2278 *Toll Free Fax:* 800-418-2525 *Web Site:* www.salesmakercarts.com, pg 1001

McKechney, Bill, F&F Productions, 14333 Myerlake Circle, Clearwater, FL 33760 *Tel:* 727-530-5000 *Fax:* 727-535-6547 *Web Site:* www.fandfhd.tv, pg 865

McKee, Jeffrey, X-Rite, 4300 44 St SE, Grand Rapids, MI 49512 *Tel:* 616-803-2100 *Toll Free Tel:* 800-248-9748 *E-mail:* info@xrite.com *Web Site:* www.xrite.com, pg 1071

McKee, Jim, Earwax Productions Inc, 916 Kearny St, San Francisco, CA 94133 *Tel:* 415-860-9403 *Web Site:* www.earwaxproductions.com, pg 855

McKeever, Pat, PSB Speakers International, 633 Granite Ct, Pickering, ON L1W 3K1, Canada *Tel:* 905-831-6555 *Toll Free Tel:* 800-263-4641 (cust serv) *Fax:* 905-837-6357 *E-mail:* info@psbspeakers.com *Web Site:* www.psbspeakers.com, pg 987

McKenna, Megan, Total Media Group, 432 N Canal St, Suite 12, South San Francisco, CA 94080 *Tel:* 650-583-8236 *Fax:* 650-583-4708 *E-mail:* info@mediagroup.com *Web Site:* www.totalmediagroup.com, pg 1042

McKenzie, Clif, Watson Desking, 26246 Twelve Trees Lane NW, Poulsbo, WA 98370 *Tel:* 360-394-1300 *Toll Free Tel:* 800-426-1202 *Fax:* 360-394-1322 *E-mail:* service@watsondesking.com; info@watsondesking.com *Web Site:* www.watsonfurniture.com, pg 1062

McKiernan, Patricia, Graphic Artists Guild, 32 Broadway, Suite 1114, New York, NY 10004 *Tel:* 212-791-3400 *Fax:* 212-791-0333 *E-mail:* admin@gag.org; sales@gag.org *Web Site:* www.graphicartistsguild.org, pg 1082

McKinney, Michael, M2 Communications, 235 Bellefontaine St, Pasadena, CA 91105 *Tel:* 626-441-2024 *Toll Free Tel:* 800-423-8273 *Fax:* 626-441-2694 *E-mail:* m2com@aol.com *Web Site:* www.m2com.com, pg 949

McKinney-Browning, Mabel, Silver Gavel Awards for Media and the Arts, Div for Public Education, 321 N Clark St, Chicago, IL 60654 *Tel:* 312-988-5733 *Toll Free Tel:* 800-285-2221 *Fax:* 312-988-5494 (Attn: Gavel Awards) *E-mail:* publiceducation@americanbar.org *Web Site:* www.americanbar.org, pg 1127

McKinnon, Brian, Uniset Co LLC, 449 Avenue "A", Rochester, NY 14621 *Tel:* 585-544-3820 *Fax:* 585-544-1110 *E-mail:* info@unisetcorp.com *Web Site:* www.unisetcorp.com, pg 1048

McKnight, Jay, Magnetic Reference Laboratory Inc, 165 Wyandotte Dr, San Jose, CA 95123 *Tel:* 408-227-8631 *Fax:* 408-227-8631 *E-mail:* mrltapes@comcast.net *Web Site:* www.mrltapes.com, pg 928

McLachlan, Neil, ACCO Brands Corp, 4 Corporate Dr, Lake Zurick, IL 60047-8997 *Toll Free Tel:* 800-541-0094 *Toll Free Fax:* 800-941-4463 *E-mail:* contactus@gbc.com *Web Site:* www.accobrands.com, pg 773

McLaren, David C, BBE Sound Inc, 2548 Fender Ave, Fullerton, CA 92831 *Tel:* 714-897-6766 *Toll Free Tel:* 800-233-8346 *Fax:* 714-895-6728 *Web Site:* www.bbesound.com, pg 803

McLaren, Ian, Productions Grand Nord Quebec Inc, 5141 Notre Dame de Grace Ave, Montreal, QC H4A 1K4, Canada *Tel:* 514-521-7433 *Fax:* 514-522-3013, pg 985

McLaren, John C, BBE Sound Inc, 2548 Fender Ave, Fullerton, CA 92831 *Tel:* 714-897-6766 *Toll Free Tel:* 800-233-8346 *Fax:* 714-895-6728 *Web Site:* www.bbesound.com, pg 803

McLaughlin, John, Sure Shot Transmissions Inc, 10314 Main St, New Middletown, OH 44442 *Tel:* 330-542-0900 *Fax:* 330-542-1020 *Web Site:* www.sureshotsat.com, pg 1029

McLaughlin, Scott, Strategic Connections, 2721 Spring Forest Rd, Raleigh, NC 27616 *Tel:* 919-878-0550 *Fax:* 919-875-8712 *E-mail:* info@strategicmail.net *Web Site:* www.strategicconnections.net, pg 1026

McLean, John, John McLean Media, 802 Newton, Penthouse 3, Seattle, WA 98109 *Tel:* 206-285-2603 *E-mail:* info@johnmcleanmedia.com *Web Site:* www.johnmcleanmedia.com, pg 905

McLean, Randy, Kenexa, 650 E Swedesford Rd, 2nd fl, Wayne, PA 19087 *Tel:* 407-548-1444 *Fax:* 610-971-9181 *E-mail:* kenexa_learn_sales@kenexa.com *Web Site:* www.outstart.com, pg 909

McLean, Randy, Toronto Film, Television & Digital Media Office, Toronto City Hall, Main fl, Rotunda N, 100 Queen St W, Toronto, ON M5H 2N2, Canada *Tel:* 416-338-FILM (338-3456) *Fax:* 416-338-0685 *E-mail:* filmtoronto@toronto.ca *Web Site:* www.toronto.ca/tfto, pg 1105

McLelland, Dawn, ELS Productions Inc, 3287 Sanborn Dr, Riverton, UT 84065 *Tel:* 801-676-0807 *Toll Free Tel:* 800-927-3472 *E-mail:* customerservice@elsproductions.com *Web Site:* www.elsproductions.com, pg 860

McLelland, Mark, ELS Productions Inc, 3287 Sanborn Dr, Riverton, UT 84065 *Tel:* 801-676-0807 *Toll Free Tel:* 800-927-3472 *E-mail:* customerservice@elsproductions.com *Web Site:* www.elsproductions.com, pg 860

McLeod, Michele, Annenberg Learner, PO Box 26983, St Louis, MO 63118 *Tel:* 202-783-0500 (outside US) *Toll Free Tel:* 800-LEARNER (532-7637) *Fax:* 202-783-0333 *E-mail:* order@learner.org *Web Site:* www.learner.org, pg 787

McManus, Beverly Cohron, Zion Music Group, 357 Riverside Dr, Suite 200, Franklin, TN 37064 *Tel:* 615-262-2600 *Toll Free Tel:* 800-883-1772 *Fax:* 615-226-4070 *Web Site:* www.zionmusic.com, pg 1074

McManus, Kevin T, Zion Music Group, 357 Riverside Dr, Suite 200, Franklin, TN 37064 *Tel:* 615-262-2600 *Toll Free Tel:* 800-883-1772 *Fax:* 615-226-4070 *Web Site:* www.zionmusic.com, pg 1074

McManus, Sean, HarperAudio, 10 E 53 St, New York, NY 10022 *Tel:* 212-207-7000 *Toll Free Tel:* 800-242-7737 *Fax:* 212-207-2582 *Toll Free Fax:* 800-822-4090 *Web Site:* www.harpercollins.com, pg 885

McMaster, Margot, HDTV Productions Inc, 2620 S Maryland Pkwy, Suite 816, Las Vegas, NV 89109 *Tel:* 702-499-4880 *E-mail:* hdtv@hdtvproductions.com *Web Site:* www.hdtvproductions.com, pg 886

McMenamin, Scott, Final Draft Inc, 26707 W Agoura Rd, Suite 205, Calabasas, CA 91302 *Tel:* 818-995-8995; 818-906-8930 (tech support) *Toll Free Tel:* 800-231-4055 *Fax:* 818-995-4422 *E-mail:* info@finaldraft.com *Web Site:* www.finaldraft.com, pg 868

McMichael, Lee, Page-Lake Powell Film Commission, PO Box 1180, Page, AZ 86040 *Tel:* 928-645-3410 *Toll Free Tel:* 888-261-PAGE (261-7243) *Fax:* 928-645-4250 *Web Site:* visitpagealakepowell.com, pg 1091

McMillen, Rick, SuperDigital Ltd, 1150 NW 17 Ave, Portland, OR 97209-2403 *Tel:* 503-228-2222 *Toll Free Tel:* 888-79AUDIO (792-8346) *Fax:* 503-228-6819 *E-mail:* audiosales@superdigital.com *Web Site:* www.superdigital.com, pg 1029

McMillian, Ray, The Fluorescent Co Inc, c/o Red*D*Mix Rentals Inc, 388 Carlaw Ave, Suite 116, Toronto, ON M4M 2T4, Canada *Tel:* 416-879-3761 *Fax:* 905-681-8520 *E-mail:* reddmix@cogeco.ca *Web Site:* www.flo-co.com, pg 870

McMullen, Daniel, Blackwater Video Productions, PO Box 909, Morgantown, WV 26507 *Tel:* 304-296-4048 *E-mail:* blackwatervideo@hotmail.com *Web Site:* www.blackwatervideo.com, pg 808

McMullian, Matt, Audio Network US Inc, 48 W 25 St, 10th fl, New York, NY 10010 *Tel:* 646-688-4320 *E-mail:* nyoffice@audionetwork.com *Web Site:* us.audionetwork.com, pg 794

McNabb, Dennis, Staylor-Made Communications Inc, 11835 Carmel Mountain Rd, Suite 1304-365, San Diego, CA 92128-4609 *Tel:* 858-779-4266 *Toll Free Tel:* 800-711-6699 *E-mail:* info@staylor-made.com *Web Site:* staylor-made.com, pg 1024

McNay, Bonnie Southard, Microspace Communications Corp, 3100 Highwoods Blvd, Suite 120, Raleigh, NC 27604 *Tel:* 919-850-4500 *Fax:* 919-850-4518 *Web Site:* www.microspace.com, pg 942

McNee, Doug, McNee Productions Inc, 3301 W Alabama St, Houston, TX 77098 *Tel:* 713-526-5333 *Fax:* 713-526-4634 *E-mail:* mcnee@mcnee.com *Web Site:* www.mcnee.com, pg 936

McNee, Jim, McNee Productions Inc, 3301 W Alabama St, Houston, TX 77098 *Tel:* 713-526-5333 *Fax:* 713-526-4634 *E-mail:* mcnee@mcnee.com *Web Site:* www.mcnee.com, pg 936

McNee, Sheryl, McNee Productions Inc, 3301 W Alabama St, Houston, TX 77098 *Tel:* 713-526-5333 *Fax:* 713-526-4634 *E-mail:* mcnee@mcnee.com *Web Site:* www.mcnee.com, pg 936

McNeil, Gary, Noramco Wire & Cable, 70 Glacier St, Coquitlam, BC V3K 5Y9, Canada *Tel:* 604-472-6980 *Toll Free Tel:* 800-663-8434 *Fax:* 604-472-6973 *E-mail:* norcorp@noramco.ca *Web Site:* www.noramco.ca, pg 958

McNeil, Steve, Enright Co, 1801-I Parkcourt Place, Suite 100, Santa Ana, CA 92701 *Toll Free Tel:* 888-334-7773 *Fax:* 714-285-1905 *E-mail:* admin@enrightcompany.com *Web Site:* www.enrightcompany.com, pg 861

McNutt, Don, Leo Ticheli Productions, 2801 University Blvd, Suite 101, Birmingham, AL 35233 *Tel:* 205-930-0500 *Fax:* 205-930-0505 *Web Site:* www.ltpro.com, pg 1040

McNutt, Jim, Marine Geographic, 3636 Division St, Knoxville, TN 37919 *Tel:* 865-237-0291; 865-524-0001 *Web Site:* www.marinegeographic.net; www.marinegeographic.com, pg 931

McQuay, John, Angstrom Lighting, 837 N Cahuenga Blvd, Hollywood, CA 90038 *Tel:* 323-462-4246 *Fax:* 323-462-8190 *Web Site:* www.angstromlighting.com, pg 786

McQuillan, Maia, California Teleprompter, PO Box 13024, La Jolla, CA 92039-3024 *Tel:* 858-945-2076 *E-mail:* caprompter@aol.com *Web Site:* www.sandiegoteleprompter.com, pg 817

McQuillen, Charles, Heinemann, 361 Hanover St, Portsmouth, NH 03801-3912 *Tel:* 603-431-7894 *Toll Free Tel:* 800-225-5800 *Fax:* 603-431-2214 *Toll Free Fax:* 877-231-6980 *E-mail:* custserv@heinemann.com *Web Site:* www.heinemann.com, pg 887

McRae, Cefus, Omega Media Group Inc, 3100 Medlock Bridge Rd, Suite 100, Norcross, GA 30071 *Tel:* 770-449-8870 *Web Site:* www.omegamediagroup.com, pg 962

McRoberts, Anna, Keystone Entertainment, 23410 Civic Ctr Way, Suite E-9, Malibu, CA 90265 *Tel:* 310-317-4883 *Fax:* 310-317-4903 *E-mail:* films@keypics.com *Web Site:* www.keypics.com, pg 910

McShea, Dennis, Moviola, 545 W 45 St, New York, NY 10036 *Tel:* 212-247-0972 *Fax:* 212-265-9820 *Web Site:* www.moviola.com, pg 948

McTammany, Britt, Digital Video Arts, 7775 Belfort Pkwy, Jacksonville, FL 32256 *Tel:* 904-281-1001 *Toll Free Tel:* 888-340-1010 *Fax:* 904-281-0051 *Web Site:* www.digitalvideoarts.com, pg 848

McTigue, Kelly, Sound Physics Labs Inc, PO Box 319, Glenview, IL 60025 *Tel:* 847-380-9390 *E-mail:* sales@soundphysics.com; info@soundphysics.com *Web Site:* www.soundphysics.com, pg 1017

Meacham, JoAnne, Communications & Power Industries, Satcom Division, 811 Hansen Way, Bldg 2, Palo Alto, CA 94304-1031 *Tel:* 650-846-3803; 650-846-2801 *Fax:* 650-424-1744 *E-mail:* satcommarketing@cpii.com *Web Site:* www.cpii.com, pg 833

Meade, Joe, Kaboom Productions, 1465 Illinois St, San Francisco, CA 94107 *Tel:* 415-434-2666 *Fax:* 415-970-8548 *E-mail:* updates@kaboomproductions.com *Web Site:* kaboomproductions.com, pg 907

Meador, Walter, Laser Rentals Inc, 1953 S County Lane 282, Joplin, MO 64804 *Tel:* 417-782-8484; 417-437-9149 (after hours) *Toll Free Tel:* 800-285-2737 *Web Site:* www.laserrentalsinc.com, pg 916

Meadows, Roxanne, Global Cyber-Visions, 21 Valley Lane, Venus, FL 33960 *Tel:* 863-465-0321 *E-mail:* tvp@thevenusproject.com *Web Site:* www.thevenusproject.com, pg 879

Mealey, Joseph, Deck Hand Inc, 1905 Victory Blvd, Suite 8, Glendale, CA 91201 *Tel:* 818-557-8403 *Fax:* 818-557-8406 *E-mail:* info@deckhand.com *Web Site:* www.deckhand.com, pg 844

Mearns, Geoffrey, Northern Kentucky University, Nunn Dr, Highland Heights, KY 41099 *Tel:* 859-572-5100 *Fax:* 859-572-6172 *Web Site:* www.nku.edu, pg 959

Medellin, Alan, Muller Entertainment, 540 Commerce St, Southlake, TX 76092 *Tel:* 972-869-7704 *Fax:* 972-869-7791 *E-mail:* info@mullerentertainment.com *Web Site:* www.mullerentertainment.com, pg 949

Medernach, Mark, Duck Studios, 2205 Stoner Ave, Los Angeles, CA 90064 *Tel:* 310-478-0771 *Fax:* 310-478-0773 *E-mail:* info@duckstudios.com *Web Site:* www.duckstudios.com, pg 853

Medina, Carmen, Medina Software Inc, PO Box 952440, Lake Mary, FL 32795-2440 *Tel:* 407-227-4112 *E-mail:* info@medinasoft.com *Web Site:* www.medinasoft.com, pg 938

Medina, Jorge, Medina Software Inc, PO Box 952440, Lake Mary, FL 32795-2440 *Tel:* 407-227-4112 *E-mail:* info@medinasoft.com *Web Site:* www.medinasoft.com, pg 938

Meding, Mark, Aviom Inc, 1157 Phoenixville Pike, Suite 201, West Chester, PA 19380-4254 *Tel:* 610-738-9005 *Fax:* 610-738-9950 *E-mail:* info@aviom.com *Web Site:* www.aviom.com, pg 799

Medori, Ernie, Majortech Inc, 8464 Ninth Line RR-1, Norval, ON L0P 1K0, Canada *Tel:* 905-873-0778 *Fax:* 905-873-1244 *Web Site:* www.majortech.com, pg 929

Medvitz, Ryan, Premier Lighting & Production Co, 12023 Victory Blvd, North Hollywood, CA 91606 *Tel:* 818-762-0884 *Toll Free Tel:* 800-770-0884 *Fax:* 818-762-0896 *E-mail:* premier@premier-lighting.com *Web Site:* www.premier-lighting.com, pg 980

Meeks, Philip G, Time Warner Cable, 60 Columbus Circle, 17th fl, New York, NY 10023 *Tel:* 212-364-8200 *Web Site:* www.timewarnercable.com, pg 1040

Meeuwsen, Jeffrey, Artist Residency Program, 1260 N Green Bay Rd, Lake Forest, IL 60045 *Tel:* 847-234-1063 *Fax:* 847-234-1063 *E-mail:* info@ragdale.org *Web Site:* www.ragdale.org, pg 1108

Megerian, Haig, Convergent Media Systems, 190 Bluegrass Valley Pkwy, Alpharetta, GA 30005-2204 *Tel:* 770-369-9000 *Toll Free Tel:* 800-877-7804 *Fax:* 770-369-9100 *E-mail:* convergent@convergent.com *Web Site:* www.convergent.com, pg 836

Mehalko, Michael, MCCOM Inc, 383 Rte 206, Chester, NJ 07930 *Tel:* 908-879-9590 *Fax:* 908-879-9679 *E-mail:* info@mccominc.com *Web Site:* www.mccom.tv, pg 935

Mehrabian, Dr Robert, Teledyne Energy Systems Inc, 10707 Gilroy Rd, Hunt Valley, MD 21031 *Tel:* 410-771-8600 *Fax:* 410-771-8620 *E-mail:* energy.systems@teledynees.com *Web Site:* www.teledynees.com, pg 1036

Meier, Lynda, Butler Films Inc, 108 Old Solomons Island Rd, Suite L-10, Annapolis, MD 21401 *Tel:* 410-280-1160 *Fax:* 443-458-5315 *E-mail:* info@butlerfilm.com *Web Site:* www.butlerfilm.com, pg 815

Meihls, Debbie, Manatee County Film Commission, One Haben Blvd, Palmetto, FL 34221 *Tel:* 941-729-9177 *Toll Free Tel:* 800-822-2017 *Fax:* 941-729-1820 *Web Site:* www.bradentongulfislands.com, pg 1096

Meister, Peter, Ironbound Film & Television Studios LLC, Newark Arts & Entertainment Bldg, 169 Malvern St, Newark, NJ 07105 *Tel:* 201-456-4754 *Web Site:* www.ironboundfilmstudios.com, pg 902

Meister, Scott, Attainment Co Inc, 504 Commerce Pkwy, Verona, WI 53593 *Tel:* 608-845-7880 *Toll Free Tel:* 800-327-4269 *Fax:* 608-845-8040 *Toll Free Fax:* 800-942-3865 *E-mail:* customerservice@attainmentcompany.com; international@attainmentcompany.com *Web Site:* www.attainmentcompany.com, pg 793

Mejudhon, Kittikarn, LKG Industries Inc, 3660 Publishers Dr, Rockford, IL 61109 *Tel:* 815-874-2301 *Toll Free Tel:* 800-645-2262 *Fax:* 815-874-2896 *E-mail:* sales-lkgindustries@t6b.com *Web Site:* www.philmore-datak.com, pg 923

Melando, Edward J, John Wiley & Sons Inc, 111 River St, Hoboken, NJ 07030 *Tel:* 201-748-6000 *Toll Free Tel:* 800-225-5945 *Fax:* 201-748-6088 *E-mail:* info@wiley.com *Web Site:* www.wiley.com, pg 1066

Melendy, Christopher, Intelix LLC, 8001 Terrace Ave, Suite 201, Middleton, WI 53562 *Tel:* 608-831-0880 *Toll Free Tel:* 866-4-MATMIX (462-8649) *Fax:* 608-831-1833 *E-mail:* intelix@intelix.com *Web Site:* www.intelix.com, pg 899

Melfa, Joseph, Tritech Communications, 625 Locust St, Suite 300, Garden City, NY 11530 *Tel:* 631-254-4500 *Fax:* 631-254-4499 *E-mail:* sales@tritechcomm.com *Web Site:* www.tritechcomm.com, pg 1045

Melhorn, Erika, National Headliner Awards, PO Box 239, Northfield, NJ 08225-0239 *Tel:* 609-601-2116 *E-mail:* info@headlinerawards.org *Web Site:* www.headlinerawards.org, pg 1121

Melkom, A G, GAMfilm Productions, 7559 Willoughby Ave, Suite 5, Los Angeles, CA 90046 *Tel:* 213-840-6212 *E-mail:* gamfilm@gmail.com *Web Site:* director-writer-producer.com, pg 875

Mellen, Ronnie Haran, Santa Barbara Location Services, 403 Orilla del Mar, Unit 2, Santa Barbara, CA 93108 *Tel:* 805-969-5555; 805-565-1562 *Fax:* 805-969-9595 *E-mail:* production@sblsonline.com *Web Site:* www.santabarbara-locations.com, pg 1002

Mellentine, Jeff, World Media Group Inc, 6737 E 30 St, Indianapolis, IN 46219 *Tel:* 317-549-8484 *Toll Free Tel:* 800-400-4964 *Fax:* 317-549-8480 *E-mail:* getstarted@worldmediagroup.com *Web Site:* www.worldmediagroup.com, pg 1069

Mellentine, Josh, World Media Group Inc, 6737 E 30 St, Indianapolis, IN 46219 *Tel:* 317-549-8484 *Toll Free Tel:* 800-400-4964 *Fax:* 317-549-8480 *E-mail:* getstarted@worldmediagroup.com *Web Site:* www.worldmediagroup.com, pg 1069

Mellott, John, Melmat Inc, 5333 Industrial Dr, Huntington Beach, CA 92649 *Tel:* 714-379-4555 *Toll Free Tel:* 800-635-6289 *Fax:* 714-379-4554 *E-mail:* info@melmat.com; sales@melmat.com *Web Site:* www.melmat.com, pg 938

Mellott, Shelly, Final Draft Inc, 26707 W Agoura Rd, Suite 205, Calabasas, CA 91302 *Tel:* 818-995-8995; 818-906-8930 (tech support) *Toll Free Tel:* 800-231-4055 *Fax:* 818-995-4422 *E-mail:* info@finaldraft.com *Web Site:* www.finaldraft.com, pg 868

Melton, Eric, University of Vermont, Instructional Television Dept, 234 Rowell Bldg, Burlington, VT 05405 *Tel:* 802-656-2927 *Fax:* 802-656-8816 *E-mail:* video@zoo.uvm.edu *Web Site:* www.uvm.edu; www.uvm.edu/~video, pg 1050

Meltzer, Jeff, Meltzer Media Productions, 70 W 36 St, Suite 1000, New York, NY 10018 *Tel:* 212-868-4600 *E-mail:* contact@meltzermedia.com *Web Site:* www.meltzermedia.com, pg 938

Melville, Jack, Foresight Imaging, One Executive Dr, Suite 102, Chelmsford, MA 01824 *Tel:* 978-458-4624 *Fax:* 978-458-5488 *E-mail:* info@fi-llc.com *Web Site:* www.fi-llc.com, pg 871

Memoli, Rich, Savage Universal Corp, 550 E Elliot Rd, Chandler, AZ 85225 *Tel:* 480-632-1320 *Toll Free Tel:* 800-624-8891 *Fax:* 480-632-1322 *Web Site:* savageuniversal.com, pg 1003

Menard, Karen, Artel Video Systems, 5B Lyberty Way, Westford, MA 01886 *Tel:* 978-263-5775 *Toll Free Tel:* 800-225-0228 *Fax:* 978-263-9755 *E-mail:* sales@artel.com *Web Site:* www.artel.com, pg 791

Menasco, Richard W, Stereo Sales Inc, 1530 S Monroe St, Tallahassee, FL 32301 *Tel:* 850-224-2635 *Fax:* 850-224-0950 *E-mail:* sales@stereosales.net *Web Site:* www.stereosales.org; www.stereosales.net, pg 1024

Mendelsohn, Michael R, American Artists Representatives Inc, 4700 Mamaroneck Ave, White Plains, NY 10605 *Tel:* 212-682-2462; 646-286-5633 (cell) *E-mail:* info@aareps.com *Web Site:* www.aareps.com, pg 783

Mendelsohn, Ron, Megatrax, 7629 Fulton Ave, North Hollywood, CA 91605 *Tel:* 818-255-7100 *Toll Free Tel:* 888-MEGA-555 (634-2555) *Fax:* 818-255-7199 *E-mail:* info@megatrax.com *Web Site:* www.megatrax.com, pg 938

Menendez, Francisco, University Film & Video Association (UFVA), c/o University of Illinois Press, 1325 S Oak St, Champaign, IL 61820 *Tel:* 217-244-0626 (journals); 217-333-0950 (main) *Toll Free Tel:* 866-244-0626 (journals); 866-647-8382 (main) *Fax:* 217-244-9910 *E-mail:* ufvahome@gmail.com *Web Site:* www.ufva.org, pg 1090

Mengel, Arthur V, Aydin Displays Inc, One Riga Lane, Birdsboro, PA 19508 *Tel:* 610-404-7400; 610-404-5353 (sales) *Toll Free Tel:* 866-367-2934 *Fax:* 610-404-8190 *E-mail:* sales1@aydindisplays.com; orders@aydindisplays.com *Web Site:* www.aydindisplays.com, pg 800

Menghi, Mark, Samson Technologies Corp, 45 Gilpin Ave, Hauppauge, NY 11788-4723 *Tel:* 631-784-2200 *Fax:* 631-784-2201 *E-mail:* info@samsontech.com *Web Site:* www.samsontech.com, pg 1002

Menon, Krish, Synaptic Digital, 79 Fifth Ave, 14th fl, New York, NY 10003 *Tel:* 212-682-8300 *Toll Free Tel:* 800-843-0677 *Fax:* 212-682-5260 *E-mail:* learnmore@synapticdigital.com *Web Site:* www.synapticdigital.com, pg 1030

Menschik, Andrew, Imagivations, 11314 Sheldon St, Sun Valley, CA 91352 *Tel:* 818-767-6767 *Fax:* 818-767-3637 *E-mail:* info@imagivations.com *Web Site:* www.imagivations.com, pg 896

Mensink, Andrea, Tacoma-Regional Film Commission, 1119 Pacific Ave, Suite 1400, Tacoma, WA 98402 *Tel:* 253-627-2836 (ext 26) *Fax:* 253-627-8783 *Web Site:* www.traveltacoma.com/press-room/film-commission, pg 1103

Mercado, David, SoundView Services Inc, One Phillips Dr NW, Leesburg, VA 20176 *Tel:* 703-777-9570 *Toll Free Tel:* 866-680-8189 *E-mail:* info@soundviewservices.com *Web Site:* www.soundviewservices.com, pg 1018

Mercado, Rick, Rayven Inc, 431 Griggs St N, St Paul, MN 55104 *Tel:* 651-642-1112 *Toll Free Tel:* 800-878-3776 *Fax:* 651-642-9497 *E-mail:* info@rayven.com *Web Site:* www.rayven.com, pg 992

Mercer, Mark, Southwest Binding & Laminating, 109 Millwell Ct, Maryland Heights, MO 63043-2509 *Tel:* 314-739-4400 *Toll Free Tel:* 800-325-3628 *Toll Free Fax:* 800-942-2010 *E-mail:* orders@swbindinglaminating.com *Web Site:* swbindinglaminating.com, pg 1019

Mercer, Theo, Telepro Video Inc, 14730 Adams Circle, Omaha, NE 68137 *Tel:* 402-593-0999; 402-690-2198 *Fax:* 402-593-6117 *E-mail:* tmtelepro@aol.com *Web Site:* www.teleprovideo.com, pg 1036

Merchant, Fazal, DreamWorks Animation SKG Inc, 1000 Flower St, Glendale, CA 91201 *Tel:* 818-695-5000 *Fax:* 818-695-4190 *Web Site:* www.dreamworksanimation.com, pg 852

Merchant, Irfan, Vitruvian Entertainment, 727 N Victory Blvd, Burbank, CA 91502 *Tel:* 818-244-3575; 818-720-3250 *Web Site:* vitruvianent.com, pg 1060

Merchant, Steve, Stereo Sales Inc, 1530 S Monroe St, Tallahassee, FL 32301 *Tel:* 850-224-2635 *Fax:* 850-224-0950 *E-mail:* sales@stereosales.net *Web Site:* www.stereosales.org; www.stereosales.net, pg 1024

Merck, Harold, Merck & Hill Consultants Inc, 1995 N Park Place, Suite 450, Atlanta, GA 30339 *Tel:* 770-937-0185 *Fax:* 770-937-0919 *E-mail:* info@merckhill.com *Web Site:* www.merckhill.com, pg 938

Mergaman, Steve, The Clio Awards, 770 Broadway, 15th fl, New York, NY 10003 *Tel:* 212-683-4300 *Toll Free Tel:* 800-WIN-CLIO (946-2546) *Fax:* 212-683-4796 *Web Site:* www.clioawards.com, pg 1113

Merrell, Don, Ivie Technologies Inc, 1195 Spring Creek Place, Suite B, Springville, UT 84663 *Tel:* 801-489-8703 *Toll Free Fax:* 877-829-6567 *E-mail:* ivie@ivie.com *Web Site:* www.ivie.com, pg 903

Merrell, Scott, Ivie Technologies Inc, 1195 Spring Creek Place, Suite B, Springville, UT 84663 *Tel:* 801-489-8703 *Toll Free Fax:* 877-829-6567 *E-mail:* ivie@ivie.com *Web Site:* www.ivie.com, pg 903

Merrill, Dina, RKO Pictures Inc, 2034 Broadway, Santa Monica, CA 90404 *Tel:* 310-277-0707 *Fax:* 310-566-8940 *E-mail:* info@rko.com *Web Site:* www.rko.com, pg 997

Merrill, Lan, Compix Media, 26 Edelman, Irvine, CA 92618 *Tel:* 949-585-0055 *Fax:* 949-585-0320 *E-mail:* info@compix.tv *Web Site:* www.compix.tv, pg 833

Merritt, Iris, Yukon Film & Sound Commission (YFSC), Box 2703, Whitehorse, YT Y1A 2C6, Canada *Tel:* 867-667-5400; 867-661-0408 (ext 5400, no charge for calls from within Yukon) *Fax:* 867-393-7040 *E-mail:* info@reelyukon.com *Web Site:* www.reelyukon.com, pg 1106

Merritt, Monica L, USITT: United States Institute for Theatre Technology Inc, 315 S Crouse Ave, Suite 200, Syracuse, NY 13210-1844 *Tel:* 315-463-6463 *Toll Free Tel:* 800-938-7488 *Fax:* 315-463-6525 *Toll Free Fax:* 866-398-7488 *E-mail:* info@office.usitt.org *Web Site:* www.usitt.org, pg 1090

Merritts, Tim, Hite Co, 3101 Beale Ave, Altoona, PA 16601 *Tel:* 814-944-6121 *Toll Free Tel:* 800-252-3598 *Fax:* 814-944-3052 *Web Site:* www.hiteco.com, pg 889

Merz, Herbert, Tellabs Inc, One Tellabs Ctr, 1415 W Diehl Rd, Naperville, IL 60563 *Tel:* 630-798-8800 *Fax:* 630-798-2000 *Web Site:* www.tellabs.com, pg 1037

Messina, Robert L, The Color Lab Inc, 4442 Lawnview Ave, Dallas, TX 75227 *Tel:* 214-381-2105 *Fax:* 214-381-5168 *E-mail:* color.lab@airmail.net *Web Site:* thecolorlab.com, pg 831

Metcalfe, Tony, Acorn Productions, 620 Homewood Dr, Plano, TX 75025 *Tel:* 972-385-9977 *Fax:* 972-385-9944 *E-mail:* acornprod@aol.com, pg 774

Metz, Steve, The Sound Lab Inc, 3355 Bee Cave Rd, Bldg 7, Suite 705, Austin, TX 78746 *Tel:* 512-476-2122 *Fax:* 512-476-2127 *E-mail:* info@thesoundlabinc.com *Web Site:* www.thesoundlabinc.com, pg 1017

Metzger, Heather, Biblical Archaeology Society (BAS), 4710 41 St NW, Washington, DC 20016 *Tel:* 202-364-3300 *Toll Free Tel:* 800-221-4644 *Fax:* 202-364-2636 *E-mail:* bas@bib-arch.org; merchandise@bib-arch.org *Web Site:* www.biblicalarchaeology.org, pg 806

Metzger, Steve, BIAMP Systems, 9300 SW Gemini Dr, Beaverton, OR 97008 *Tel:* 503-641-7287 *Toll Free Tel:* 800-826-1457 (US & CN) *Fax:* 503-626-0281 *E-mail:* biampinfo@biamp.com; salesteam@biamp.com *Web Site:* www.biamp.com, pg 806

Meuninck, Jim, Meuninck's Media Methods Inc, 24097 North Shore Dr, Edwardsburg, MI 49112 *Web Site:* www.herbvideos.com, pg 940

Meurer, Bill, Birns & Sawyer Inc, 5275 Craner Ave, North Hollywood, CA 91601 *Tel:* 323-466-8211 *Fax:* 323-466-1868; 818-358-4395 (rental) *E-mail:* info@birnsandsawyer.com *Web Site:* www.birnsandsawyer.com, pg 808

Meyer, Arno, Belar Electronics Laboratory Inc, 1140 McDermott Dr, Suite 105, West Chester, PA 19380-4043 *Tel:* 610-687-5550 *Fax:* 610-687-2686 *E-mail:* sales@belar.com *Web Site:* www.belar.com, pg 804

Meyer, Carolyn, Skjonberg Controls Inc, 1363 Donlon St, Suite 6, Ventura, CA 93003 *Tel:* 805-650-0877 *Toll Free Fax:* 800-650-0360 *E-mail:* sales@skjonberg.com *Web Site:* www.skjonberg.com, pg 1012

Meyer, Chris, CD Meyer Inc, 91 Clinton Rd, Suite 2C, Fairfield, NJ 07004 *Tel:* 973-882-9411 *Fax:* 973-808-4087 *E-mail:* info@cdmeyer.com *Web Site:* www.cdmeyer.com; www.point2explore.com; museumdigitalsignage.com, pg 822

Meyer, Dean, Pelco, 3500 Pelco Way, Clovis, CA 93612-5699 *Tel:* 559-292-1981 (intl) *Toll Free Tel:* 800-289-9100 (US & CN) *Fax:* 559-348-1120 (intl) *Toll Free Fax:* 800-289-9150 (US & CN) *E-mail:* sales@pelco.com *Web Site:* www.pelco.com, pg 971

Meyer, Gary, Telluride Film Festival, 800 Jones St, Berkeley, CA 94710 *Tel:* 510-665-9494 *Fax:* 510-665-9589 *E-mail:* mail@telluridefilmfestival.org *Web Site:* www.telluridefilmfestival.org, pg 1128

Meyer, John, Meyer Sound Laboratories Inc, 2832 San Pablo Ave, Berkeley, CA 94702 *Tel:* 510-486-1166 *Toll Free Tel:* 855-641-3288 (US & CN) *Fax:* 510-486-8356 *E-mail:* sales@meyersound.com; techsupport@meyersound.com; service@meyersound.com *Web Site:* www.meyersound.com, pg 940

Meyer, Lutz, Recording Media & Equipment Inc (RM&E), 3736 SW 30 Ave, Fort Lauderdale, FL 33312 *Tel:* 954-791-9797 *Toll Free Tel:* 800-541-9797 *Fax:* 954-791-6662 *E-mail:* info@rmeinc.com *Web Site:* www.rmeinc.com, pg 993

Meyer, Mary, Recording Media & Equipment Inc (RM&E), 3736 SW 30 Ave, Fort Lauderdale, FL 33312 *Tel:* 954-791-9797 *Toll Free Tel:* 800-541-9797 *Fax:* 954-791-6662 *E-mail:* info@rmeinc.com *Web Site:* www.rmeinc.com, pg 993

Meyer, Ron, Centre Communications Inc, 75 Manhattan Dr, Suite 200, Boulder, CO 80303 *Tel:* 303-444-1166 *E-mail:* centre@ecentral.com *Web Site:* www.centrecommunicationinc.com; www.centredm.com, pg 823

Meyer, Ron, Professional Sound Corp, 28085 Smyth Dr, Valencia, CA 91355 *Tel:* 661-295-9395 *Fax:* 661-295-8398 *E-mail:* sales@professionalsound.com; service@professionalsound.com *Web Site:* www.professionalsound.com, pg 985

Meyers, Denise, National Freedom of Information Coalition (NFOIC), Missouri School of Journalism, 101E Reynolds Journalism Institute, Columbia, MO 65211 *Tel:* 573-882-4856 *E-mail:* info@nfoic.org *Web Site:* www.nfoic.org, pg 1086

Meztista, Chris, Motion & Graphic Image Corp Inc (MAGIC), 1106 Dauphin St, Mobile, AL 36604 *Tel:* 251-433-7733 *E-mail:* magicians@magichd.com *Web Site:* magichd.com, pg 947

Mezzetti, Phil, The Sound Lab Inc, 3355 Bee Cave Rd, Bldg 7, Suite 705, Austin, TX 78746 *Tel:* 512-476-2122 *Fax:* 512-476-2127 *E-mail:* info@thesoundlabinc.com *Web Site:* www.thesoundlabinc.com, pg 1017

Micallef, Joseph, Allegro Corp/Allegro Entertainment Canada Ltd, 20048 NE San Rafael St, Portland, OR 97230-7459 *Tel:* 503-491-8480 *Toll Free Tel:* 800-288-2007 (ext 2500, cust serv) *Fax:* 503-491-8488 *E-mail:* mailcs@allegro-music.com (cust serv) *Web Site:* www.allegromediagroup.com, pg 781

Miceli, John, Technomedia Solutions, 4545 36 St, Orlando, FL 32811 *Tel:* 407-351-0909 *Fax:* 407-248-9484 *E-mail:* sales@gotechnomedia.com *Web Site:* www.gotechnomedia.com, pg 1035

Michaelis, Norm, Global Television, 222 23 St NE, Calgary, AB T2E 7N2, Canada *Tel:* 403-235-7777 *Fax:* 403-248-0252 *E-mail:* globalnews.calg@globaltv.com *Web Site:* www.globaltv.com, pg 879

Michaeloff, Scott, Vidicom Inc, 520 Eighth Ave, Suite 2206, New York, NY 10018 *Tel:* 212-895-8300 *E-mail:* info@vidicom.com *Web Site:* vidicom.com, pg 1057

Michaud, Arthur C, AM Productions, 1141 S Pasadena Ave, Pasadena, CA 91105 *Tel:* 626-403-0258 *Fax:* 626-403-0138, pg 783

Michel, Alan, Home Inc, 566 Columbus Ave, Boston, MA 02118 *Tel:* 617-427-4663 *Fax:* 617-427-4664 *Web Site:* homeinc.org, pg 890

Michelsen, Geri, ThirdWave Learning Inc, 120 E Oakland Park Blvd, Suite 105-623, Fort Lauderdale, FL 33334 *Toll Free Tel:* 888-630-9555 *Fax:* 954-630-9050 *Web Site:* www.thirdwavelearning.com, pg 1039

Michelson, Steve, The Video Project, 145 Ninth St, Suite 102, San Francisco, CA 94103 *Tel:* 415-981-9710 *Toll Free Tel:* 800-475-2638 *Toll Free Fax:* 888-562-9012 *E-mail:* orders@videoproject.com; support@videoproject.com *Web Site:* www.videoproject.com, pg 1056

Michielsen, Ken, Nesbit Systems Inc, 243 N Union St, Suite 112, Lambertville, NJ 08530 *Tel:* 609-397-7720 *E-mail:* info@nesbit.com *Web Site:* www.nesbit.com, pg 954

Midani, Sami, SC Media Canada, 2100 Onesime-Gagnon, Lachine, QC H8T 3M8, Canada *Tel:* 514-780-0808 *Toll Free Tel:* 888-595-3966 *Fax:* 514-780-1604 *Toll Free Fax:* 800-790-2000 *E-mail:* information@scmediacanada.com *Web Site:* www.scmediacanada.com, pg 1003

Midthun, Shelley, Mayor's Office of Film & Video, 222 NW Fifth Ave, Portland, OR 97209-3859 *Tel:* 503-823-4039 *Fax:* 503-865-3791 *Web Site:* www.portlandonline.com/filmandvideo; www.pdc.us/film, pg 1101

Miele, Joe, Diamond Studios, Woods Point 1, 1855 Data Dr, Suite 255, Hoover, AL 35244 *Tel:* 205-987-2121 *Fax:* 205-987-2128 *Web Site:* www.tvstuff.com, pg 846

Miesner, Charles, Broadway Digital, 1014 E Broadway, Louisville, KY 40204 *Tel:* 502-540-5301 *Fax:* 502-540-5565 *E-mail:* msworkscm@mindspring.com *Web Site:* www.broadwaydigital.us, pg 813

Miga, Mike, Superior Electric, One Cowles Rd, Plainville, CT 06062 *Tel:* 860-507-2025 *Toll Free Tel:* 800-787-3532 *Fax:* 860-507-2050 *Toll Free Fax:* 800-821-1369 *E-mail:* info@superiorelectric.com *Web Site:* www.superiorelectric.com, pg 1029

Mignola, Pete, MetroSonic Recording Studio, 143 Roebling St, 3rd fl, Brooklyn, NY 11211 *Tel:* 718-782-1872 *E-mail:* manager@metrosonic.net *Web Site:* www.metrosonic.net, pg 940

Mikeska, Fred, AC Lighting Inc, 88 Horner Ave, Toronto, ON M8Z 5Y3, Canada *Tel:* 416-255-9494 *Fax:* 416-255-3514 *E-mail:* northamerica@aclighting.com *Web Site:* www.aclighting.com, pg 773

Mikhitarian, A J, ACM Productions Ltd, 38 Bob Hill Rd, Ridgefield, CT 06877 *Tel:* 203-431-9575 *E-mail:* info@acmproductions.tv *Web Site:* www.acmproductions.tv, pg 774

Mikhitarian, Craig, ACM Productions Ltd, 38 Bob Hill Rd, Ridgefield, CT 06877 *Tel:* 203-431-9575 *E-mail:* info@acmproductions.tv *Web Site:* www.acmproductions.tv, pg 774

Mikuriya, Sean, Blue Dolphin Multimedia, 13340-D Grass Valley Ave, Grass Valley, CA 95945 *Tel:* 530-477-1503 *Toll Free Tel:* 800-643-0765 (orders) *Fax:* 530-477-8342 *E-mail:* bdolphin@bluedolphinpublishing.com *Web Site:* www.bluedolphinpublishing.com, pg 809

Milanese-Distasio, Mary Ellen, Video Visions Inc, 3600 Boundbrook Ave, Trevose, PA 19053 *Tel:* 215-942-6642 *Fax:* 267-684-6819 *E-mail:* sales@video-visions.com *Web Site:* www.video-visions.com, pg 1056

Milbery, Pete, Neutrik® USA Inc, 4115 Taggart Creek Rd, Charlotte, NC 28208-5479 *Tel:* 704-972-3050 *Fax:* 704-438-9202 *E-mail:* info@neutrikusa.com *Web Site:* www.neutrik.us, pg 955

Milbourn, Wes, KFOR-TV, 444 E Britton Rd, Oklahoma City, OK 73114 *Tel:* 405-424-4444 *Fax:* 405-478-6337 *Web Site:* www.kfor.com, pg 910

Milbrodt, Bill, Milbrodt/Music & Sound Design, 1835 US Hwy 9, Howell, NJ 07731 *Tel:* 848-459-4965 *E-mail:* info@ideasinmedia.com *Web Site:* www.ideasinmedia.com; www.carmusicproject.com, pg 943

Miles, Arik, Tropikal Productions, 137 Sequoia Rd, Rockwall, TX 75032 *Tel:* 972-771-3797 *Fax:* 972-771-0853 *E-mail:* tropikalproductions@gmail.com *Web Site:* www.tropikalproductions.com, pg 1045

Miles, Arik, World Beat Studio, 137 Sequoia Rd, Rockwall, TX 75032 *Tel:* 972-771-3797 *Fax:* 972-771-0853 *E-mail:* tropikalproductions@gmail.com *Web Site:* www.tropikalproductions.com, pg 1069

Milgrom, Al, Minneapolis St Paul International Film Festival (MSPIFF), 125 SE Main St, Suite 125A, Minneapolis, MN 55414 *Tel:* 612-331-7563 *Fax:* 612-378-7750 *E-mail:* info@mspfilmsociety.org; submissions@mspfilmsociety.org *Web Site:* www.mspfilmsociety.org, pg 1120

Miller, Ali, Furnace MFG, 2719-B Dorr Ave, Fairfax, VA 22031 *Tel:* 703-205-0007 *Toll Free Tel:* 888-599-9883 *Fax:* 703-205-2951 *E-mail:* sales@furnacemfg.com *Web Site:* www.furnacemfg.com, pg 874

Miller, Anne, Semiconductor Services, 2269 Chestnut St, No 735, San Francisco, CA 94123 *Tel:* 650-369-7890 *Fax:* 415-346-8099 *E-mail:* moreinfo@semiconductorservices.com *Web Site:* www.semiconductorservices.com, pg 1006

Miller, Barney, Barney Miller's Inc, 232 E Main St, Lexington, KY 40507-1310 *Tel:* 859-252-2216 *Toll Free Tel:* 800-755-6799 *Fax:* 859-253-1115 *Web Site:* www.barneymillers.com, pg 943

Miller, Beverly, United Scenic Artists Local 829, 29 W 38 St, 15th fl, New York, NY 10018 *Tel:* 212-581-0300 *Fax:* 212-977-2011 *E-mail:* businessoffice@usa829.org *Web Site:* www.usa829.org; vfx.usa829.org, pg 1090

Miller, Blake, CSI Films, 1913 Sonora St, Fort Collins, CO 80525 *Tel:* 970-282-1622 *E-mail:* mail@airhat.com *Web Site:* www.airhat.com, pg 840

Miller, Brainard, Point Lobos Productions, 20417 Califa St, Woodland Hills, CA 91367 *Tel:* 818-340-4201, pg 977

Miller, Chris, PSNI (Professional Systems Network Inc), 1831 E 71 St, Tulsa, OK 74136 *Tel:* 918-388-1343 *Web Site:* www.psni.org, pg 1088

Miller, Craig, Hammond Communications Group, 173 Trade St, Lexington, KY 40511-2608 *Tel:* 859-254-1878 *E-mail:* info@hammondcg.com *Web Site:* www.hammondcg.com, pg 884

Miller, Daniel, U-Direct Productions, 10 White St, 1st fl, New York, NY 10013 *Tel:* 212-647-9200 *Fax:* 212-625-9400 *E-mail:* udirect@udirectnyc.com *Web Site:* www.udirectnyc.com, pg 1047

Miller, Debra, Midtown Video Inc, 4824 SW 74 Ct, Miami, FL 33155 *Tel:* 305-669-1117 *Toll Free Tel:* 800-232-4564 *Fax:* 305-662-2860 *E-mail:* info@midtownvideo.com *Web Site:* www.midtownvideo.com, pg 942

Miller, Doug, The Napoleon Group, 48 W 25 St, New York, NY 10010 *Tel:* 212-692-9200 *Toll Free Tel:* 800-579-4019 *Fax:* 212-692-0309 *E-mail:* info@napny.com *Web Site:* www.napny.com, pg 952

Miller, Eric, Amarillo Film Commission, 1000 S Polk St, Amarillo, TX 79101 *Tel:* 806-342-2016 *Toll Free Tel:* 800-692-1338 *Fax:* 806-373-3909 *Web Site:* www.amarillofilm.org; www.visitamarillotx.com, pg 1102

Miller, Eric, Landmark Media Inc, 3450 Slade Run Dr, Falls Church, VA 22042 *Tel:* 703-241-2030 *Toll Free Tel:* 800-342-4336 *Fax:* 703-536-9540 *E-mail:* info@landmarkmedia.com; landmrkmed@aol.com *Web Site:* www.landmarkmedia.com, pg 915

Miller, Geoff, OmniMount Systems, 4409 E Baseline Rd, Suite 130, Phoenix, AZ 85042 *Tel:* 480-829-8000 *Toll Free Tel:* 800-MOUNT-IT (668-6848) *Fax:* 480-756-9000 *E-mail:* info@omnimount.com *Web Site:* www.omnimount.com, pg 962

Miller, Glenn, Side Door Studio Inc, 69 Albe Dr, Newark, DE 19702 *Tel:* 302-738-8777 *Fax:* 302-731-7601 *E-mail:* sdseng@sidedoorstudioinc.com, pg 1010

Miller, Herb, Cable Films & Video, PO Box 7171, Country Club Sta, Kansas City, MO 64113-0171 *Tel:* 913-362-2804 *Toll Free Tel:* 800-514-2804 *Fax:* 913-362-2804 *E-mail:* cablefilms@kc.rr.com, pg 816

Miller, Jacob Troy, Pendulum Entertainment, 444 Dufferin St, Studio 1, Toronto, ON M6K 2A3, Canada *Tel:* 416-721-7593 *E-mail:* info@pendulumentertainment.com *Web Site:* www.pendulumentertainment.com, pg 971

Miller, James, Dreambox Media Inc, PO Box 8132, Philadelphia, PA 19101-8132 *E-mail:* mail@dreamboxmedia.com *Web Site:* www.dreamboxmedia.com, pg 852

Miller, James E, WoodenBoat Publications, 41 WoodenBoat Lane, Brooklin, ME 04616 *Tel:* 207-359-4651 *Toll Free Tel:* 800-877-5284 (subns); 800-487-2084 (subns) *Fax:* 207-359-8920; 818-487-4550 (subns) *E-mail:* woodenboat@woodenboat.com *Web Site:* www.woodenboat.com, pg 1069

Miller, Jeane P, Unitron Ltd, 73 Mall Dr, Commack, NY 11725 *Tel:* 631-543-2000 *Fax:* 631-589-6975 *E-mail:* info@unitronusa.com *Web Site:* www.unitronusa.com, pg 1049

Miller, Jesse, Midtown Video Inc, 4824 SW 74 Ct, Miami, FL 33155 *Tel:* 305-669-1117 *Toll Free Tel:* 800-232-4564 *Fax:* 305-662-2860 *E-mail:* info@midtownvideo.com *Web Site:* www.midtownvideo.com, pg 942

Miller, Jessie, Interlink Technologies, 139 W Indiana Ave, Suite 203, Perrysburg, OH 43552 *Tel:* 419-893-9011 *Toll Free Tel:* 800-655-5465 *Fax:* 419-893-7280 *E-mail:* info@interlinktech.com; info@thinkinterlink.com *Web Site:* www.interlinktech.com; www.thinkinterlink.com, pg 900

Miller, Jim, Metro Productions, 8570 Magellan Pkwy, Suite 400, Richmond, VA 23227 *Tel:* 804-261-1172 *Toll Free Tel:* 877-669-4687 *Fax:* 804-261-1885 *E-mail:* contactmetro@metro-productions.com *Web Site:* www.metro-productions.com, pg 939

Miller, Jim, RSS Distributors, 7930 Old Auction Rd, Manheim, PA 17545 *Toll Free Tel:* 800-233-0175 *E-mail:* orders@rssd.com *Web Site:* www.rssd.com, pg 1000

Miller, Jonathan, Icarus Film Inc, 32 Court St, 21st fl, Brooklyn, NY 11201 *Tel:* 718-488-8900 *Toll Free Tel:* 800-876-1710 *Fax:* 718-488-8642 *E-mail:* mail@icarusfilms.com *Web Site:* www.icarusfilms.com, pg 893

Miller, Joshua, C&I Studios, 541 NW First Ave, Fort Lauderdale, FL 33301 *Tel:* 954-357-3934 *E-mail:* contact@c-istudios.com *Web Site:* www.c-istudios.com, pg 819

Miller, Kenneth J, Midtown Video Inc, 4824 SW 74 Ct, Miami, FL 33155 *Tel:* 305-669-1117 *Toll Free Tel:* 800-232-4564 *Fax:* 305-662-2860 *E-mail:* info@midtownvideo.com *Web Site:* www.midtownvideo.com, pg 942

Miller, Kevin, Staging Directions Inc, 1327 Northbrook Pkwy, Suite 440, Suwanee, GA 30024 *Tel:* 770-409-9909 *Toll Free Tel:* 800-782-4322 *Fax:* 770-409-0277 *E-mail:* info@teamsdi.net; sales@teamsdi.net *Web Site:* www.stagingdirections.com, pg 1023

Miller, Leonard, Vari-Lite, 10911 Petal St, Dallas, TX 75238 *Tel:* 214-647-7880 *Toll Free Tel:* 877-VARILITE (877-827-4548) *Fax:* 214-647-8038 *E-mail:* entertainment.service@philips.com *Web Site:* www.vari-lite.com, pg 1052

Miller, Marilyn, Rhythmic Medicine, 10425 W 177 Terr, Olathe, KS 66062 *Tel:* 913-851-5100 *Fax:* 913-402-8510 *E-mail:* music@rhythmicmedicine.com *Web Site:* www.rhythmicmedicine.com, pg 996

Miller, Marjorie, Gold Line/TEF, PO Box 500, West Redding, CT 06896-0500 *Tel:* 203-938-2588 *Fax:* 203-938-8740 *E-mail:* sales@gold-line.com *Web Site:* www.gold-line.com, pg 880

Miller, Matt, Association of Independent Commercial Producers (AICP), 3 W 18 St, 5th fl, New York, NY 10011 *Tel:* 212-929-3000 *Fax:* 212-929-3359 *E-mail:* info@aicp.com *Web Site:* www.aicp.com, pg 1079

Miller, Mike, Hybrid Studios, 3021 S Shannon St, Santa Ana, CA 92704 *Tel:* 714-850-1499 *E-mail:* info@hybridstudiosca.com; rentals@hybridstudiosca.com *Web Site:* hybridstudiosca.com, pg 893

Miller, Mike, Earl Miller Productions Inc, 1702 W Koenig Lane, Austin, TX 78756 *Tel:* 512-458-4343 *Fax:* 512-458-4485 *E-mail:* info@earlmillerproductions.com *Web Site:* www.earlmillerproductions.com, pg 943

Miller, Noreen, Custom Video Productions Inc, 15 Lake Shore Dr, Red Bank, NJ 07701 *Tel:* 732-936-1001 *Fax:* 732-741-9204 *E-mail:* info@cvpnj.com *Web Site:* www.cvpnj.com, pg 841

Miller, Noreen, Shamrock Communications, 200 Tornillo Way, Suite 110, Tinton Falls, NJ 07712 *Tel:* 732-686-1140 *Fax:* 732-686-1148 *E-mail:* info@shamrockcommunications.com *Web Site:* www.shamrockcommunications.com, pg 1008

Miller, Robin, Robin Miller, Filmaker Inc, 606 W Broad St, Bethlehem, PA 18018 *Tel:* 610-691-0900 *Fax:* 610-691-0952 *E-mail:* enquire@filmaker.com *Web Site:* www.filmaker.com, pg 943

Miller, Scott, DWD Theatre Design & Consulting, Suite 485, 425 Carrall St, Vancouver, BC V6B 6E3, Canada *Tel:* 604-874-0552 *E-mail:* info@d-w-d.com *Web Site:* www.d-w-d.com, pg 854

Miller, Sherman G, Multicom Inc, 1076 Florida Central Pkwy, Longwood, FL 32750 *Tel:* 407-331-7779 *Toll Free Tel:* 800-423-2594 *Fax:* 407-339-0204 *E-mail:* multicom@multicominc.com *Web Site:* www.multicominc.com, pg 949

Miller, Stan, Rosco Laboratories Inc, 52 Harbor View, Stamford, CT 06902 *Tel:* 203-708-8900 *Toll Free Tel:* 800-ROSCO NY (767-2669) *Fax:* 203-708-8919 *E-mail:* info@rosco.com *Web Site:* www.rosco.com, pg 999

Milligan, Steve, Western Digital Corp, 3355 Michelson Dr, Suite 100, Irvine, CA 92612 *Tel:* 949-672-7000 *Toll Free Tel:* 888-935-8893 *Fax:* 408-717-9282 *Web Site:* www.wdc.com, pg 1064

Mills, Bill, Florida Film & Video, 4461 38 Way S, St Petersburg, FL 33711 *Tel:* 727-369-0732 *E-mail:* info@flhd.tv *Web Site:* www.flhd.tv, pg 870

Mills, Jan, Ross Video Ltd, 8 John St, Iroquois, ON K0E 1K0, Canada *Tel:* 613-652-4886 *Fax:* 613-652-4425 *E-mail:* solutions@rossvideo.com *Web Site:* www.rossvideo.com, pg 999

Mills, Kevin, Larrabee Sound Studio, 4162 Lankershim Blvd, North Hollywood, CA 91602 *Tel:* 818-753-0717 *Fax:* 818-753-8046 *E-mail:* info@larrabeestudios.com *Web Site:* www.larrabeestudios.com, pg 916

Milne, Craig, SIM Digital, One Atlantic Ave, Suite 110, Toronto, ON M6K 3E7, Canada *Tel:* 416-979-9958 *Fax:* 416-979-7770 *E-mail:* info@simdigital.com *Web Site:* www.simdigital.com, pg 1011

Milne, Matt, Rovi Corp, 2830 De La Cruz Blvd, Santa Clara, CA 95050 *Tel:* 408-562-8400 *Fax:* 408-567-1800 *Web Site:* www.rovicorp.com, pg 1000

Milneck, Greg, Digital FX Inc, 6010 Perkins Rd, Suite B, Baton Rouge, LA 70808 *Tel:* 225-763-6010 *Toll Free Tel:* 888-898-6010 *Fax:* 225-763-6059 *E-mail:* info@digitalfx.tv; rentals@digitalfx.tv *Web Site:* www.digitalfx.tv, pg 847

Milner, David, Milner-Fenwick Inc, 119 Lakefront Dr, Hunt Valley, MD 21030-2216 *Tel:* 410-252-1700 *Toll Free Tel:* 800-432-8433 *Fax:* 410-252-6316 *E-mail:* mail@milner-fenwick.com *Web Site:* www.milner-fenwick.com, pg 943

Milner, Richard, Milner-Fenwick Inc, 119 Lakefront Dr, Hunt Valley, MD 21030-2216 *Tel:* 410-252-1700 *Toll Free Tel:* 800-432-8433 *Fax:* 410-252-6316 *E-mail:* mail@milner-fenwick.com *Web Site:* www.milner-fenwick.com, pg 943

Milner, Stan, ON Event Services, 6550 McDonough Dr, Norcross, GA 30093-1211 *Tel:* 404-875-0966 *Fax:* 404-874-7925 *E-mail:* av@techrentals.com *Web Site:* www.oneventservices.com, pg 963

Minardi, Dan, Clear Blue Audio Video, 1650 Cold Creek Dr, Layafette, CO 80026 *Tel:* 303-412-9477 *Fax:* 303-412-9457, pg 829

Mince, Craig, Indianapolis International Film Festival, PO Box 1917, Indianapolis, IN 46206 *Tel:* 317-560-4433 *E-mail:* info@indyfilmfest.org *Web Site:* indyfilmfest.org, pg 1117

Minchella, James, Micor Analytics, 7538 Saint Louis Ave, Skokie, IL 60076 *Tel:* 847-329-8590 *Fax:* 847-329-8599 *Web Site:* www.micoranalytics.com, pg 941

Minchew, Daniel, Atlanta Filmworks, 4280 Northeast Expwy, Atlanta, GA 30340 *E-mail:* info@atlantafilmworks.com *Web Site:* atlantafilmworks.com, pg 793

Minchew, Daniel, Studio Space Atlanta, 3080 McCall Dr, Suite 2, Atlanta, GA 30340 *Tel:* 404-630-0508 *E-mail:* info@studiospaceatl.com *Web Site:* www.studiospaceatl.com, pg 1027

Mineroff, Saul, Saul Mineroff Electronics Inc, 574 Meacham Ave, Elmont, NY 11003 *Tel:* 516-775-1370 *Fax:* 516-775-1371 *E-mail:* tapenixon@aol.com *Web Site:* www.mineroff.com, pg 944

Ming, Melvin, Sesame Workshop, 1900 Broadway, 4th fl, New York, NY 10023 *Tel:* 212-595-3456 *Fax:* 212-875-6113 *Web Site:* www.sesameworkshop.org, pg 1088

Minguez, Karen, Applause Learning Resources, 85 Fernwood Lane, Roslyn, NY 11576 *Tel:* 516-625-1145 *Toll Free Tel:* 800-277-5287 *Toll Free Fax:* 877-365-7484 *E-mail:* info@applauselearning.com *Web Site:* www.applauselearning.com, pg 788

Minkoff, Michael, Lefco Video Services Inc, 600 W Sunset Rd, Suite 103, Henderson, NV 89011 *Tel:* 702-566-1770 *Fax:* 702-566-1798 *E-mail:* info1@lefco.com *Web Site:* www.lefco.com, pg 918

Minor, Debbie, Audience Response Systems Inc, 5611-C E Morgan Ave, Evansville, IN 47715 *Tel:* 812-479-7507 *Toll Free Tel:* 800-INVOLVE (468-6583) *Fax:* 812-479-1057 *Web Site:* www.audienceresponse.com, pg 794

Minson, Arthur T Jr, Time Warner Cable, 60 Columbus Circle, 17th fl, New York, NY 10023 *Tel:* 212-364-8200 *Web Site:* www.timewarnercable.com, pg 1040

Mintner, Thomas E, NTI Americas Inc, PO Box 231027, Tigard, OR 97281 *Tel:* 503-684-7050 *Fax:* 503-684-7051 *E-mail:* americas@nti-audio.com *Web Site:* www.nti-audio.com, pg 960

Mirabella, Dennis, Pro-Tape & Specialities Inc, 621 Rte 1 S, Suite B, North Brunswick, NJ 08902 *Tel:* 732-346-0900 *Toll Free Tel:* 800-345-0234 *Fax:* 732-729-7373 *Web Site:* www.protapes.com, pg 983

Mire, Scott, Peavey Electronics Corp, 5022 Hartley Peavey Dr, Meridian, MS 39305 *Tel:* 601-483-5365 *Fax:* 601-486-1278 *E-mail:* domesticsales@peavey.com *Web Site:* www.peavey.com, pg 970

Miron, Maryanne, Stageline Mobile Stage Inc, 700 Marsolais St, L'Assomption, QC J5W 2G9, Canada *Tel:* 450-589-1063 *Toll Free Tel:* 800-26-STAGE (267-8243) *Fax:* 450-589-1711 *E-mail:* info@stageline.com *Web Site:* www.stageline.com, pg 1023

Miron, Steven, John Wiley & Sons Inc, 111 River St, Hoboken, NJ 07030 *Tel:* 201-748-6000 *Toll Free Tel:* 800-225-5945 *Fax:* 201-748-6088 *E-mail:* info@wiley.com *Web Site:* www.wiley.com, pg 1066

Mirrer, Louise, The New York Historical Society, 170 Central Park W, New York, NY 10024 *Tel:* 212-873-3400 *Fax:* 212-787-9474 *Web Site:* www.nyhistory.org, pg 956

Mirvish, Dan, Slamdance Film Festival, 5634 Melrose Ave, Los Angeles, CA 90038 *Tel:* 323-466-1786 *Fax:* 323-466-1784 *E-mail:* submissions@slamdance.com *Web Site:* www.slamdance.com, pg 1127

Misaka, Kirk, Zhone Technologies Inc, 7195 Oakport St, Oakland, CA 94621 *Tel:* 510-777-7000 *Toll Free Tel:* 877-ZHONE-20 (946-6320, US & CN) *Fax:* 510-777-7001 *E-mail:* info@zhone.com; sales@zhone.com *Web Site:* www.zhone.com, pg 1073

Misconi, Michael, Digital Zoetrope Productions, 1902 Oak St, Melbourne, FL 32901 *Tel:* 321-821-7404 *Fax:* 321-821-2287 *Web Site:* digitalzoetrope.com, pg 848

Mislawchuk, Fred, MidCanada Production Services Inc (MidCan), 509 Century St, Winnipeg, MB R3H 0L8, Canada *Tel:* 204-772-0368 *Toll Free Tel:* 800-772-0368 *Fax:* 204-772-0360 *E-mail:* info@midcan.com *Web Site:* www.midcan.com, pg 942

Mistretta, Mary Lee, Mist Media Inc, 10845 Acama St, Toluca Lake, CA 91602 *Tel:* 818-508-1097 *Fax:* 818-508-1097 *E-mail:* mistmedia@sbcglobal.net *Web Site:* www.mistmedia.tv, pg 944

Mistretta, William, Mist Media Inc, 10845 Acama St, Toluca Lake, CA 91602 *Tel:* 818-508-1097 *Fax:* 818-508-1097 *E-mail:* mistmedia@sbcglobal.net *Web Site:* www.mistmedia.tv, pg 944

Misunas, David, Zhone Technologies Inc, 7195 Oakport St, Oakland, CA 94621 *Tel:* 510-777-7000 *Toll Free Tel:* 877-ZHONE-20 (946-6320, US & CN) *Fax:* 510-777-7001 *E-mail:* info@zhone.com; sales@zhone.com *Web Site:* www.zhone.com, pg 1073

Mitchell, Bill, Blue Sky Stock Footage, PO Box 177, Santa Fe, NM 87504-0177 *Tel:* 310-859-4709 *Toll Free Tel:* 877-992-5477 *Fax:* 310-823-0924 *E-mail:* sales@blueskyfootage.com *Web Site:* www.blueskyfootage.com, pg 810

Mitchell, Brian L, Parts Express, 725 Pleasant Valley Dr, Springboro, OH 45066-1158 *Tel:* 937-743-3000 *Toll Free Tel:* 866-366-4909; 800-338-0531 (cust serv & tech support) *Fax:* 937-743-1677 *Toll Free Fax:* 866-755-7557 *E-mail:* sales@parts-express.com *Web Site:* www.parts-express.com, pg 969

Mitchell, Eric, Blood-Horse Publications, 3101 Beaumont Centre Circle, Lexington, KY 40513 *Toll Free Tel:* 800-866-2361; 800-582-5604 *E-mail:* customerservice@bloodhorse.com; advertise@bloodhorse.com *Web Site:* www.bloodhorse.com, pg 809

Mitchell, J E, Mitchell Acoustics Research, 2005B Industrial Blvd, Rockwall, TX 75087 *Tel:* 214-741-7136 *Toll Free Fax:* 866-492-2470 *E-mail:* info@frazierspeakers.com *Web Site:* www.frazierspeakers.com, pg 944

Mitchell, James, ACCO Brands Corp, 4 Corporate Dr, Lake Zurick, IL 60047-8997 *Toll Free Tel:* 800-541-0094 *Toll Free Fax:* 800-941-4463 *E-mail:* contactus@gbc.com *Web Site:* www.accobrands.com, pg 773

Mitchell, James F, DVDs4Less, 6519 Jamon Dr, Sparks, NV 89436-9142 *Tel:* 775-323-0965 *Toll Free Tel:* 800-852-2330 *Fax:* 775-323-1055 *E-mail:* info@dvds4less.net *Web Site:* www.dvds4less.net, pg 854

Mitchell, Jim, Skyfire Video, PO Box 2266, Sparks, NV 89432 *Tel:* 775-323-0965 *Toll Free Tel:* 800-852-2330 *Web Site:* www.skyfirevideo.com, pg 1013

Mitchell, Linda, CamMate Systems, 425 E Comstock, Chandler, AZ 85225 *Tel:* 480-813-9500 *Fax:* 480-813-9292 *E-mail:* cammate@cammate.com *Web Site:* www.cammate.com, pg 818

Mitchell, Pete, Vancouver Film Studios Ltd, 3500 Cornett Rd, Vancouver, BC V5M 2H5, Canada *Tel:* 604-453-5000 *Fax:* 604-453-5045 *Web Site:* www.vancouverfilmstudios.com, pg 1051

Mitchell, Ron, Blood-Horse Publications, 3101 Beaumont Centre Circle, Lexington, KY 40513 *Toll Free Tel:* 800-866-2361; 800-582-5604 *E-mail:* customerservice@bloodhorse.com; advertise@bloodhorse.com *Web Site:* www.bloodhorse.com, pg 809

Mitchell, Ron, RAM Systems LLC, 27992 W Rte 120, Unit 138, Lakemoor, IL 60051 *Tel:* 847-487-7575 *Fax:* 847-487-2440 *E-mail:* sales@ramsyscom.com *Web Site:* www.ramsyscom.com, pg 991

Mitchell, Steve, ACDC Audio CD & Cassette, 606 Alamo Pintado Rd, Suite 3-281, Solvang, CA 93463 *Tel:* 818-762-ACDC (762-2232) *Web Site:* www.acdc-cdr.com, pg 774

Mitrano, Patricia, Newark Beth Israel Medical Center, c/o Creative Media Services, 201 Lyons Ave at Osborne Terr, Newark, NJ 07112 *Tel:* 973-926-7000 *Toll Free Tel:* 800-843-2384 *Web Site:* www.newarkbeth.com, pg 956

Mitsui, Scott, Mark Woollen & Associates, 207 Ashland Ave, Santa Monica, CA 90405 *Tel:* 310-399-2690 *E-mail:* info@markwoollen.com *Web Site:* www.markwoollen.com, pg 1069

Mittenberg, Paul, Palardo Productions, 1807 Taft Ave, Suite 4, Hollywood, CA 90028 *Tel:* 323-469-8991 *E-mail:* palardo2@msn.com, pg 968

Miyahira, Chuck, HM Electronics Inc (HME), 14110 Stowe Dr, Poway, CA 92064 *Tel:* 858-535-6000 *Toll Free Tel:* 800-848-4468 (domestic sales) *Fax:* 858-452-7207; 858-552-0139 (domestic sales) *E-mail:* info@hme.com *Web Site:* www.hme.com, pg 889

Miyazaki, Go, FUJIFILM North America Corp, 200 Summit Lake Dr, Valhalla, NY 10595-1356 *Tel:* 914-789-8100 *Toll Free Tel:* 800-755-3854 *Fax:* 914-789-8530 *Web Site:* www.fujifilmusa.com/northamerica, pg 873

Mizzi, Lee, The Children's Book Store Distribution (CBSD), 14-3245 Harvester Rd, Burlington, ON L7N 3T7, Canada *Tel:* 905-681-8160; 905-831-1995 (intl) *Toll Free Tel:* 800-668-0242; 800-757-8372 (cust serv-CN & US) *Fax:* 905-831-1142 (intl) *E-mail:* info@childrensgroup.com *Web Site:* www.childrensgroup.com, pg 825

Mizzo, Rick, ALOM Technologies Corp, 48105 Warm Springs Blvd, Fremont, CA 94539-7498 *Tel:* 510-360-3600 *Toll Free Tel:* 800-500-9991 *Fax:* 510-226-7617 *E-mail:* customerservice@alom.com *Web Site:* www.alom.com, pg 782

Mobley, Douglas C, Gilderfluke & Co Inc, 205 S Flower St, Burbank, CA 91502 *Tel:* 818-840-9484 *Toll Free Tel:* 800-776-5972 *Fax:* 818-840-9485 *E-mail:* info@gilderfluke.com *Web Site:* www.gilderfluke.com, pg 878

Mobley, Marge, Calaveras County Film Commission, 183 Three "M" Lane, Mountain Ranch, CA 95246 *Tel:* 209-754-3053, pg 1093

Mocarski, Derek, Trod Nossel Productions & Recording Studios, 10 George St, Wallingford, CT 06492 *Tel:* 203-269-4465 *Toll Free Tel:* 800-800-HITS (800-4487) *Fax:* 203-294-1745 *E-mail:* info@trodnossel.com *Web Site:* www.trodnossel.com, pg 1045

Mockensturm, Dan, Mach 1 Productions, 1101 N Himes Ave, Tampa, FL 33607 *Tel:* 813-873-7700 *Fax:* 813-875-6633 *E-mail:* info@mach1pro.com *Web Site:* www.mach1pro.com, pg 927

Moe, Erik, Kaboom Productions, 1465 Illinois St, San Francisco, CA 94107 *Tel:* 415-434-2666 *Fax:* 415-970-8548 *E-mail:* updates@kaboomproductions.com *Web Site:* kaboomproductions.com, pg 907

Moffatt, Shawn, Go To Team, 359-C Wando Place Dr, Mount Pleasant, SC 29464 *Tel:* 843-884-6222 *Toll Free Tel:* 888-455-4333 *E-mail:* crew@gototeam.com *Web Site:* www.gototeam.com, pg 879

Moffit, John, Art Directors Guild (ADG), 11969 Ventura Blvd, 2nd fl, Studio City, CA 91604 *Tel:* 818-762-9995 *Fax:* 818-762-9997 *Web Site:* www.adg.org, pg 1078

Moggre, Martin, Freeman, 1600 Viceroy, Suite 100, Dallas, TX 75235 *Tel:* 214-445-1000 *Fax:* 214-445-0200 *Web Site:* www.freemanco.com, pg 872

Mohamed, Joe, Chicago Spotlight Inc, 1658 W Carroll St, Chicago, IL 60612 *Tel:* 312-455-1171 *Fax:* 312-455-1744 *Web Site:* www.chicagospotlight.com, pg 825

Mohiuddin, Sameer, Bitcentral Inc, 4340 Von Karman Ave, Suite 400, Newport Beach, CA 92660 *Tel:* 949-253-9000 *E-mail:* sales@bitcentral.com; support@bitcentral.com *Web Site:* www.bitcentral.com, pg 808

Molina, Stephanie, Beaumont Convention & Visitors Bureau, 505 Willow St, Beaumont, TX 77701 *Tel:* 409-880-3749 *Toll Free Tel:* 800-392-4401 *Fax:* 409-880-3750 *Web Site:* www.beaumontcvb.com, pg 1102

Molinari, Fred, Data Translation Inc, 100 Locke Dr, Marlboro, MA 01752-1192 *Tel:* 508-481-3700 *Toll Free Tel:* 800-525-8528 (sales) *Fax:* 508-481-8620 *E-mail:* info@datatranslation.com *Web Site:* www.datatranslation.com, pg 843

Molinari, Tony, Foresight Imaging, One Executive Dr, Suite 102, Chelmsford, MA 01824 *Tel:* 978-458-4624 *Fax:* 978-458-5488 *E-mail:* info@fi-llc.com *Web Site:* www.fi-llc.com, pg 871

Molnar, David, McCune Audio-Video-Lighting, 101 Utah Ave, South San Francisco, CA 94080 *Tel:* 650-873-1111 *Toll Free Tel:* 800-899-7686 *Fax:* 650-246-6702 *E-mail:* info@mccune.com *Web Site:* www.mccune.com, pg 935

Molnar, Michael F, Society of Manufacturing Engineers (SME), One SME Dr, Dearborn, MI 48128 *Tel:* 313-425-3000 *Toll Free Tel:* 800-733-4763 *E-mail:* service@sme.org (cust care) *Web Site:* www.sme.org, pg 1015

Moloney, Steven, Precision Camera & Video Repair Inc, 4 Anngina Dr, Enfield, CT 06082-3222 *Tel:* 860-749-7380 *Toll Free Tel:* 800-665-6515 *Fax:* 860-763-7100 *E-mail:* info@precisioncamera.com *Web Site:* www.precisioncamera.com, pg 980

Moloney, Wes, Hi-Tech Lamps Inc, 922 San Leandro Ave, Suite B, Mountain View, CA 94043 *Tel:* 650-961-9031 *Toll Free Tel:* 800-229-6509 *Fax:* 650-961-9033 *E-mail:* info@hi-techlamps.com *Web Site:* www.hi-techlamps.com, pg 888

Monaco, Rob, Monaco Digital Films Labs, 234 Ninth St, San Francisco, CA 94103 *Tel:* 415-864-5350 *Fax:* 415-864-5682 *E-mail:* admin@monacosf.com, pg 945

Monahan, Terry, Chimera®, 1812 Valtec Lane, Boulder, CO 80301 *Tel:* 303-444-8000 *Toll Free Tel:* 888-444-1812 *Fax:* 303-444-8303 *E-mail:* salesinfo@chimeralighting.com *Web Site:* chimeralighting.com, pg 825

Monge, Joe, DuArt, 245 W 55 St, New York, NY 10019 *Tel:* 212-757-4580 *Fax:* 212-977-5609 *E-mail:* info@duart.com *Web Site:* www.duart.com, pg 853

Monie, Alain, Ingram Micro, 1600 E Saint Andrew Place, Santa Ana, CA 92705 *Tel:* 714-566-1000 *Web Site:* www.ingrammicro.com, pg 898

Monrean, Mark, Tri-Digital Software Inc, 8424 154 Ave NE, Redmond, WA 98052 *Tel:* 425-284-3888 *Toll Free Tel:* 800-206-2547 *Fax:* 425-883-3887 *E-mail:* tdp@tri-digital.com *Web Site:* www.tri-digital.com, pg 1044

Montague, Larry N, TAPPI, 15 Technology Pkwy S, Norcross, GA 30092 *Tel:* 770-446-1400 *Toll Free Tel:* 800-332-8686 (US); 800-446-9431 (CN) *Fax:* 770-446-6947 *E-mail:* memberconnection@tappi.org *Web Site:* www.tappi.org, pg 1032

Montague, Timothy L, Analog Free Media, 111 E Ninth St, Lockport, IL 60441 *Tel:* 815-588-5000 *Toll Free Tel:* 877-4MYVIDEO (469-8433) *E-mail:* analogfreemedia@yahoo.com *Web Site:* www.analogfreemedia.com, pg 786

Montague-Devaud, Adrianna, American Foundation for the Blind (AFB), 2 Penn Plaza, Suite 1102, New York, NY 10121 *Tel:* 212-502-7600; 212-502-7662 (TDD) *Toll Free Tel:* 800-232-5463 *Fax:* 212-502-7777 *Toll Free Fax:* 888-545-8331 *E-mail:* afbinfo@afb.net *Web Site:* www.afb.org, pg 1076

Montfort, Matthew, Ancient Future, PO Box 264, Kentfield, CA 94914-0264 *Tel:* 415-459-1892 *E-mail:* info@ancient-future.com *Web Site:* www.ancient-future.com, pg 786

Moody, Bruce A, American Production Services LLC, 150 Nims Spring Dr, Fort Mill, SC 29715 *Tel:* 803-548-2290 *Toll Free Tel:* 888-506-2400 *Fax:* 803-548-3406 *Web Site:* www.apsvideo.com, pg 785

Mooney, Carol, Donna Lawrence Productions, 624 Baxter Ave, Louisville, KY 40204 *Tel:* 502-589-9617 *E-mail:* dlp@dlproductions.com *Web Site:* www.dlproductions.com, pg 917

Mooney, Patty, Crystal Pyramid Productions™, 7323 Rondel Ct, San Diego, CA 92119-1530 *Tel:* 619-644-3000 *E-mail:* cpp@newuniquevideos.com *Web Site:* www.crystalpyramid.com, pg 840

Mooney, Patty, New & Unique Videos™, 7323 Rondel Ct, San Diego, CA 92119-1530 *Tel:* 619-644-3000 *E-mail:* video@newuniquevideos.com *Web Site:* www.newuniquevideos.com, pg 955

Moore, Diana, International Loving Touch Foundation Inc, 2122 SE Division St, Portland, OR 97202 *Tel:* 503-253-8482 *Fax:* 503-256-6753 *E-mail:* info@lovingtouch.com *Web Site:* www.lovingtouch.com, pg 901

Moore, Fred, FWT LLC, 5750 E I-20, Fort Worth, TX 76119 *Tel:* 817-255-3060 *Toll Free Tel:* 800-433-1816 *Fax:* 817-255-2957 *E-mail:* info@fwtllc.com *Web Site:* fwtllc.com, pg 874

Moore, Gordon, Lectrosonics Inc, 581 Laser Rd NE, Rio Rancho, NM 87124 *Tel:* 505-892-4501 *Toll Free Tel:* 800-821-1121 *Fax:* 505-892-6243 *E-mail:* sales@lectrosonics.com *Web Site:* www.lectrosonics.com, pg 918

Moore, Greg, MooreCo Inc, 2885 Lorraine Ave, Temple, TX 76501 *Tel:* 254-778-4727 (CN) *Toll Free Tel:* 800-749-2258 (US) *Fax:* 254-773-0500 (CN) *Toll Free Fax:* 800-697-6258 (US) *Web Site:* moorecoinc.com, pg 946

Moore, Jeff, Ross Video Ltd, 8 John St, Iroquois, ON K0E 1K0, Canada *Tel:* 613-652-4886 *Fax:* 613-652-4425 *E-mail:* solutions@rossvideo.com *Web Site:* www.rossvideo.com, pg 999

Moore, Jeff, StageSound, 2240 Shenandoah Ave NW, Roanoke, VA 24017 *Tel:* 540-342-2040 *Toll Free Tel:* 800-778-9839 *Fax:* 540-345-5158 *Web Site:* stagesound.com, pg 1023

Moore, John, Dage-MTI, 701 N Roeske Ave, Michigan City, IN 46360 *Tel:* 219-872-5514 *Fax:* 219-872-5559 *E-mail:* info@dagemti.com; sales@dagemti.com; service@dagemti.com *Web Site:* www.dagemti.com, pg 842

Moore, Jonathan, NuMynd Studios, 915 Twin Elms Ct, Nashville, TN 37210 *Tel:* 615-259-1143 *Fax:* 615-259-1141 *E-mail:* hello@numyndstudios.com *Web Site:* www.numyndstudios.com, pg 960

Moore Kech, Julie, Starline Costume, 1286 Bandera Rd, San Antonio, TX 78228 *Tel:* 210-435-3535 *Fax:* 210-435-9425 *Web Site:* starlinecostumes.com, pg 1024

Moore, Megan, Focus on Animals, PO Box 340, Charles Town, WV 25414-0340 *Tel:* 304-725-0506 *Fax:* 304-725-1523 *E-mail:* information@nhes.org *Web Site:* www.nhes.org, pg 870

Moore, Michael, Universal Studios, 100 Universal City Plaza, Universal City, CA 91608-1002 *Toll Free Tel:* 800-892-1979 *Fax:* 818-866-3600 *E-mail:* studio.operations2@nbcuni.com *Web Site:* www.filmmakersdestination.com; www.nbcuni.com, pg 1049

Moore, Peggy, Dage-MTI, 701 N Roeske Ave, Michigan City, IN 46360 *Tel:* 219-872-5514 *Fax:* 219-872-5559 *E-mail:* info@dagemti.com; sales@dagemti.com; service@dagemti.com *Web Site:* www.dagemti.com, pg 842

Moore, R T Jr, Audio/Video Supply Inc, 4575 Ruffner St, San Diego, CA 92111 *Tel:* 858-565-1101 *Toll Free Tel:* 800-284-2288 *Fax:* 858-565-7845 *E-mail:* sales@avsupply.com *Web Site:* www.avsupply.com, pg 795

Moore, Rob, Paramount Pictures Corporation, 5555 Melrose Ave, Los Angeles, CA 90038 *Tel:* 323-956-8398 *Web Site:* www.paramount.com, pg 969

Moore, Tim, Baha'i Distribution Service (BDS), 401 Greenleaf Ave, Wilmette, IL 60091 *Tel:* 847-425-7950 *Toll Free Tel:* 800-999-9019 *Fax:* 847-425-7951 *E-mail:* bds@usbnc.org *Web Site:* www.bahaibookstore.com, pg 801

Moore, Trish, Random House of Canada Limited, One Toronto St, Unit 300, Toronto, ON M5C 2V6, Canada *Tel:* 416-364-4449 *Fax:* 416-364-6863 *Web Site:* www.randomhouse.ca, pg 991

Moossmann, Christine, Sigma Corp of America, 15 Fleetwood Ct, Ronkonkoma, NY 11779 *Tel:* 631-585-1144 *Toll Free Tel:* 800-896-6858 (cust serv) *Fax:* 631-585-1895 *E-mail:* info@sigmaphoto.com *Web Site:* www.sigmaphoto.com, pg 1010

Mopsik, Eugene, American Society of Media Photographers Inc (ASMP), 150 N Second St, Philadelphia, PA 19016 *Tel:* 215-451-2767 *Fax:* 215-451-0880 *E-mail:* info@asmp.org *Web Site:* www.asmp.org, pg 1077

Moquist, Burton, Stanco Sales LLC, 1529 S Terry St, Longmont, CO 80501 *Tel:* 303-776-3770 *E-mail:* stancosales@comcast.net, pg 1023

Morales, Jan, Fricon Entertainment Co Inc, 134 Bluegrass Circle, Hendersonville, TN 37075 *Tel:* 615-826-2288 *Fax:* 615-826-0500, pg 873

Morales, Oscar, Juice, 1648 Tenth St, Santa Monica, CA 90404 *Tel:* 310-460-7830 *Fax:* 310-460-7845 *Web Site:* www.juicewest.com, pg 906

Moran, Bob, Antenna International, 383 Main Ave, Norwalk, CT 06851 *Tel:* 203-523-0320 *Fax:* 203-354-5519 *E-mail:* inquiry@antennainternational.com *Web Site:* www.antennainternational.com, pg 787

Moran, Debbie, Zachry Associates Inc, 500 Chestnut St, Suite 2000, Abilene, TX 79602 *Tel:* 325-677-1342 *Fax:* 325-672-2001 *E-mail:* info@zachryinc.com *Web Site:* zachryinc.com, pg 1073

Moran, John C, The Hollywood Edge, 7080 Hollywood Blvd, Suite 519, Hollywood, CA 90028 *Tel:* 323-603-3252 *Toll Free Tel:* 800-292-3755 *Fax:* 323-603-3298 *E-mail:* info@hollywoodedge.com; sales@hollywoodedge.com *Web Site:* www.hollywoodedge.com, pg 890

Moran, Sean, Hitachi Kokusai Electric America Ltd, 150 Crossways Park Dr, Woodbury, NY 11797 *Tel:* 516-921-7200 *Fax:* 516-496-3718 *E-mail:* info@hitachikokusai.us *Web Site:* hitachikokusai.us, pg 889

Moreen, Steve, RF Specialties of California Inc, PO Box 16655, San Diego, CA 92176 *Tel:* 619-501-3936 *Fax:* 619-342-8511 *Web Site:* www.rfspec.com, pg 995

Morefield, John D, Morefield Communications Inc, 35 N 35 St, Camp Hill, PA 17011-2707 *Tel:* 717-761-6170 *Toll Free Tel:* 800-382-1266 *E-mail:* info@morefield.com *Web Site:* www.morefield.com, pg 946

Moreira, Adrian, RCA Records, 550 Madison Ave, New York, NY 10022 *Tel:* 212-833-8000 *E-mail:* info@rcarecords.com *Web Site:* www.rcarecords.com; www.sonymusic.com, pg 992

Morette, Cecilia M, Mark Custom Recording Service Inc, 10815 Bodine Rd, Clarence, NY 14031-2252 *Tel:* 716-759-2600 *Fax:* 716-759-2329 *E-mail:* info@markcustom.com *Web Site:* www.markcustom.com, pg 931

Morette, Mark J, Mark Custom Recording Service Inc, 10815 Bodine Rd, Clarence, NY 14031-2252 *Tel:* 716-759-2600 *Fax:* 716-759-2329 *E-mail:* info@markcustom.com *Web Site:* www.markcustom.com, pg 931

Moretti, Tom, Markertek Video Supply, One Tower Dr, Saugerties, NY 12477 *Tel:* 845-246-3036 *Toll Free Tel:* 800-522-2025 *Fax:* 845-246-1757 *E-mail:* sales@markertek.com *Web Site:* www.markertek.com, pg 931

Morgan, Barbara, Austin Film Festival, 1801 Salina St, Austin, TX 78702 *Tel:* 512-478-4795 *Toll Free Tel:* 800-310-FEST (310-3378) *Fax:* 512-478-6205 *E-mail:* info@austinfilmfestival.com *Web Site:* www.austinfilmfestival.com, pg 1108

Morgan, Beth, Real to Reel Studios Inc, 4141 Office Pkwy, Dallas, TX 75204 *Tel:* 214-528-4242 *Web Site:* www.rtrstudios.com, pg 992

Morgan, Beverly, Milky Way Press, 317 Ridge Run Dr, Georgetown, TX 78628 *Tel:* 512-869-6455 *Toll Free Tel:* 888-756-6455 (orders only) *Web Site:* www.milkywaypress.com, pg 943

Morgan, Linda, Gefen, 20600 Nordhoff St, Chatsworth, CA 91311 *Tel:* 818-772-9100 *Toll Free Tel:* 800-545-6900 *Fax:* 818-772-9120 *E-mail:* gsinfo@gefen.com *Web Site:* www.gefen.com, pg 876

Morgan, Linda, Yuma Film Commission, 180 W First St, Suite D, Yuma, AZ 85364 *Tel:* 928-314-9247 *Fax:* 928-373-0133 *Web Site:* www.filmyuma.com, pg 1092

Morgan, Mark D, MainSail Production Services Inc, 521 Byers Rd, Suite 109, Miamisburg, OH 45342 *Tel:* 937-866-7800 *Toll Free Tel:* 800-877-0093 *Fax:* 937-866-8088 *E-mail:* discover@mainsailproductions.com *Web Site:* www.mainsailproductions.com, pg 929

Morgan, Randy, All Service Musical Electronics Repair, 617 SE Morrison St, Portland, OR 97214 *Tel:* 503-231-6552 *Fax:* 503-239-7157 *E-mail:* service@asmusic.org *Web Site:* www.all-service-musical.com, pg 780

Morgan, Ron, Real to Reel Studios Inc, 4141 Office Pkwy, Dallas, TX 75204 *Tel:* 214-528-4242 *Web Site:* www.rtrstudios.com, pg 992

Morgenstern, Fred, Neutrik® USA Inc, 4115 Taggart Creek Rd, Charlotte, NC 28208-5479 *Tel:* 704-972-3050 *Fax:* 704-438-9202 *E-mail:* info@neutrikusa.com *Web Site:* www.neutrik.us, pg 955

Morgenstern, Ira, Antenna International, 383 Main Ave, Norwalk, CT 06851 *Tel:* 203-523-0320 *Fax:* 203-354-5519 *E-mail:* inquiry@antennainternational.com *Web Site:* www.antennainternational.com, pg 787

Morgenthaler, Lynelle, Compass Learning Inc, 203 Colorado St, Austin, TX 78701 *Tel:* 512-478-9600 *Toll Free Tel:* 866-586-7387 (sales); 800-678-1412 (cust support) *Web Site:* www.compasslearning.com, pg 833

Morgeson, Eric, Studio A Recording Inc, 5619 N Beech Daly, Dearborn Heights, MI 48127-3927 *Tel:* 313-561-7489 *Fax:* 313-561-6736 *Web Site:* www.studioarecording.com, pg 1026

Morgeson, Marilyn, Studio A Recording Inc, 5619 N Beech Daly, Dearborn Heights, MI 48127-3927 *Tel:* 313-561-7489 *Fax:* 313-561-6736 *Web Site:* www.studioarecording.com, pg 1026

Moriano, Rob, PostWorks, 100 Avenue of the Americas, 10th fl, New York, NY 10013 *Tel:* 212-894-4000 *Fax:* 212-941-0439 *E-mail:* inquiry@postworks.com *Web Site:* www.postworks.com, pg 979

Moriarty, Jim, YES Productions, 916 Navarre Ave, New Orleans, LA 70124 *Tel:* 504-840-4891 *Toll Free Tel:* 800-736-8812 *Fax:* 504-840-4895 *Web Site:* www.yesproductions.com, pg 1072

Moridani, Sahar, DGA Awards, 7920 Sunset Blvd, Los Angeles, CA 90046 *Tel:* 310-289-2038 *E-mail:* dgaawards@dga.org *Web Site:* www.dga.org, pg 1114

Morningstar, Nancy, Crew West Inc, 1515 W Deer Valley Rd, Suite C109, Phoenix, AZ 85027 *Tel:* 480-367-6888 *Toll Free Tel:* 888-444-2739 *Fax:* 480-367-6688 *E-mail:* tvcrews@crewwestinc.com *Web Site:* www.crewwestinc.com, pg 839

Moro, Justyn, LW Media Group, 107 W Valencia Ave, Burbank, CA 91502 *Tel:* 818-439-2989 *E-mail:* lwmgbooking@gmail.com *Web Site:* www.lwmgstudios.com, pg 926

Morris, Bert, Theatrical Technicians Inc (TTI), 2700 Connecticut Ave NW, Suite 109, Washington, DC 20008-5308 *Tel:* 202-332-4907 *Fax:* 202-332-4907 *E-mail:* info@perfect-pickup.com *Web Site:* www.perfect-pickup.com, pg 1038

Morris, Bill, High End Systems Inc, 2105 Gracy Farms Lane, Austin, TX 78758 *Tel:* 512-836-2242 *Toll Free Tel:* 800-890-8989 *Fax:* 512-837-5290 *E-mail:* info@highend.com *Web Site:* www.highend.com, pg 888

Morris, Clark, 30 Second Street Ltd, 1209 Mountain Road Place NE, Albuquerque, NM 87110 *Tel:* 505-265-0224 *E-mail:* info@thirtysecst.com *Web Site:* www.thirtysecst.com, pg 1039

Morris, Donna, Adobe Systems Inc, 345 Park Ave, San Jose, CA 95110-2704 *Tel:* 408-536-6000 *Fax:* 408-537-6000 *Web Site:* www.adobe.com, pg 776

Morris, Lori, Magnum Towers Inc, 9370 Elder Creek Rd, Sacramento, CA 95829 *Tel:* 916-381-5053 *Fax:* 916-381-2144 *E-mail:* office@magnumtowers.com *Web Site:* www.magnumtowers.com, pg 929

Morris, Rex, Rex Morris Productions, 5521 S Firethorn Place, Boise, ID 83716 *Tel:* 208-344-9878 *Fax:* 208-344-9878 *Web Site:* rexmorrisproductions.com, pg 946

Morris, Stephen, C V Lloyde, 102 S Neil St, Champaign, IL 61820 *Tel:* 217-352-7031 *Toll Free Tel:* 800-779-7031 *E-mail:* sales@cvlloyde.com *Web Site:* www.cvlloyde.com, pg 923

Morris, Tom, Morrisound Recording, 12111 N 56 St, Tampa, FL 33617 *Tel:* 813-989-2108 *Fax:* 813-980-6950 *E-mail:* info@morrisound.com *Web Site:* morrisound.com, pg 946

Morrison, Irma, The Computer Language Co Inc, 5521 State Park Rd, Point Pleasant, PA 18950 *Tel:* 215-297-8082 *E-mail:* sales@computerlanguage.com; comments@computerlanguage.com *Web Site:* www.computerlanguage.com, pg 834

Morrison, Steve, Mammoth Location Services, One Minaret Rd, Mammoth Lakes, CA 93546 *Tel:* 760-934-0628 *Fax:* 760-924-7026, pg 1093

Morrone, Frank, Golden Reel Awards, 10061 Riverside Dr, PMB 751, Toluca Lake, CA 91602-2550 *Tel:* 818-506-7731 *Fax:* 818-506-7732 *E-mail:* mail@mpse.org; info@mpse.org *Web Site:* www.mpse.org, pg 1115

Morrow, Kirby, Metric Splicer Inc, 3930 E Miraloma Ave, Suite C, Anaheim, CA 92806 *Tel:* 714-630-2999 *Fax:* 714-630-2268 *Web Site:* www.metricsplicer.com, pg 939

Morrow, Trey, Metric Splicer Inc, 3930 E Miraloma Ave, Suite C, Anaheim, CA 92806 *Tel:* 714-630-2999 *Fax:* 714-630-2268 *Web Site:* www.metricsplicer.com, pg 939

Morse, Eric, Audio Network US Inc, 48 W 25 St, 10th fl, New York, NY 10010 *Tel:* 646-688-4320 *E-mail:* nyoffice@audionetwork.com *Web Site:* us.audionetwork.com, pg 794

Morse, Tracy, CamTec Motion Picture Cameras, 4221 W Magnolia Blvd, Burbank, CA 91505 *Tel:* 818-841-8700 *Fax:* 818-841-8777 *Web Site:* www.camtec.tv, pg 818

Morten, Pat, Norlynn Audio Visual Services, 1858 Beaulynn Place, North Vancouver, BC V7J 2T1, Canada *Tel:* 604-988-4996 *Fax:* 604-988-4996 *E-mail:* sales@norlynn.ca *Web Site:* www.norlynn.ca; www.reason-for-hope.com, pg 958

Mortensen, Tom, Tobin Productions Inc, 630 Ninth Ave, Suite 215, New York, NY 10036 *Tel:* 212-727-1500 *Toll Free Tel:* 800-877-8273 *Fax:* 212-727-1766 *E-mail:* info@tobinproductions.com *Web Site:* www.tobinproductions.com, pg 1041

Mortimer, Sandy, Horizon Films & Media LLC, PO Box 1087, Shelbyville, KY 40066 *Tel:* 502-647-9966 *Fax:* 502-647-9968 *E-mail:* horizonfilms@insightbb.com *Web Site:* www.horizon-films.com, pg 891

Mortweet, Brian, Intellidyne LLC, 5203 Leesburg Pike, Suite 400, 2 Skyline Place, Falls Church, VA 22041 *Tel:* 703-575-9715 *Fax:* 703-575-9718 *Web Site:* www.intellidyne-llc.com, pg 899

Mosakowski, Michael "Moe", Moe AV LLC, 133 Deerfield Rd, Sayreville, NJ 08872-1618 *Tel:* 732-257-3760 *Web Site:* www.moeco.net, pg 945

Mosallam, Mike, Sunset Gower Studios, 1438 N Gower St, Box 21, Hollywood, CA 90028 *Tel:* 323-467-1001 *Fax:* 323-467-2717 *E-mail:* sgsreception@sgsandsbs.com *Web Site:* sgsandsbs.com, pg 1028

Mosby, Karen, SOM Publishing Co, 163 Moon Valley Rd, Windyville, MO 65783 *Tel:* 417-345-8411 *E-mail:* som@som.org *Web Site:* www.som.org, pg 1015

Moseley, Ellis, Freeman, 1600 Viceroy, Suite 100, Dallas, TX 75235 *Tel:* 214-445-1000 *Fax:* 214-445-0200 *Web Site:* www.freemanco.com, pg 872

Mosely, Dana, Chalk Dust Co, 16107 Kensington Dr, PMB 256, Sugar Land, TX 77479-4401 *Tel:* 281-265-2495 *Toll Free Tel:* 800-588-7564 *Fax:* 281-265-3197 *E-mail:* sales@chalkdust.com *Web Site:* www.chalkdust.com, pg 823

Mosely, Richard, Chalk Dust Co, 16107 Kensington Dr, PMB 256, Sugar Land, TX 77479-4401 *Tel:* 281-265-2495 *Toll Free Tel:* 800-588-7564 *Fax:* 281-265-3197 *E-mail:* sales@chalkdust.com *Web Site:* www.chalkdust.com, pg 823

Moser, Star, Hollywood Lights Inc, 5251 SE McLoughlin Blvd, Portland, OR 97202-4836 *Tel:* 503-232-9001; 503-232-8855 *Toll Free Tel:* 800-826-9881 *Fax:* 503-517-8686 *E-mail:* portland@hollywoodlights.biz *Web Site:* www.hollywoodlights.biz, pg 890

Moses, Bob, Audio Engineering Society Inc (AES), 60 E 42 St, Rm 2520, New York, NY 10165-2520 *Tel:* 212-661-8528 *Fax:* 212-682-0477 *Web Site:* www.aes.org, pg 1079

Moskal, Richard, Chicago Film Office, Chicago Cultural Center, 78 E Washington, Rm 108, Chicago, IL 60602 *Tel:* 312-744-6415 *Fax:* 312-744-1378 *E-mail:* filmoffice@cityofchicago.org *Web Site:* www.cityofchicago.org/city/en/depts/dca/provdrs/chicago_film_office.html, pg 1097

Mosley, Don, Sound of Birmingham Productions, 3625 Fifth Ave S, Birmingham, AL 35222 *Tel:* 205-595-8497 *Fax:* 205-595-5220 *Web Site:* www.soundofbirmingham.com, pg 1017

Mosovic, Steven, Big Foot Productions Inc, 37-09 36 Ave, Long Island City, NY 11101 *Tel:* 718-729-1900 *Fax:* 718-729-8638 *E-mail:* info@bigfootnyc.com *Web Site:* www.bigfootnyc.com, pg 807

Moss, E B, Euro-Pacific Film & Video Productions Inc, PO Box 7986, Shrewsbury, NJ 07702 *Tel:* 732-530-4451 *Toll Free Tel:* 800-387-6776 *E-mail:* info@euro-pacific.com *Web Site:* www.euro-pacific.com, pg 863

Mossman, Chris, WKYT Productions, 2851 Winchester Rd, Lexington, KY 40509 *Tel:* 859-299-0411; 859-299-2727 (newsroom) *Fax:* 859-299-2494 *Web Site:* www.wkyt.com, pg 1068

Mossotti, Ron, Hammond Communications Group, 173 Trade St, Lexington, KY 40511-2608 *Tel:* 859-254-1878 *E-mail:* info@hammondcg.com *Web Site:* www.hammondcg.com, pg 884

Mostin, Michael, J & R Film Co, 1135 N Mansfield Ave, Hollywood, CA 90038 *Tel:* 323-467-1116 *Toll Free Tel:* 877-668-4652 *Fax:* 323-464-1518 *Web Site:* www.moviola.com, pg 903

Mostin, Michael, Moviola, 1135 N Mansfield Ave, Hollywood, CA 90038 *Tel:* 323-467-3107 *Toll Free Tel:* 877-MOVIOLA (668-4652) *Fax:* 323-464-1518 *Web Site:* www.moviola.com, pg 948

Motta, Chuck, SYMCO Inc, 29 Poplar Dr, Stirling, NJ 07980 *Tel:* 908-647-6262 *Fax:* 908-647-4904 *E-mail:* orders@symcoinc.com *Web Site:* www.symcoinc.com, pg 1030

Motter, Gussie, Cochise County Arizona, Queen Mine Tour Bldg, 478 Dart Rd, Bisbee, AZ 85603 *Tel:* 520-432-3554 *Toll Free Tel:* 866-2BISBEE (224-7233) *E-mail:* ilona@discoverbisbee.com *Web Site:* www.explorecochise.com, pg 1091

Motu, Nick, Hazelden Publishing & Educational Services, 15251 Pleasant Valley Rd, Center City, MN 55012-0011 *Tel:* 651-213-4200 *Toll Free Tel:* 800-328-9000 *Fax:* 651-213-4590 *E-mail:* info@hazelden.org; customersupport@hazelden.org *Web Site:* www.hazelden.org, pg 886

Mountain, Toby, Northeastern Digital Recording Inc, 2 Hidden Meadow Lane, Southboro, MA 01772 *Tel:* 508-481-9322 *Web Site:* www.northeasterndigital.com, pg 959

Mower, Lorne, JL Recording Studios, 270 Adelaide St W, Suite 202, Toronto, ON M5H 1X6, Canada *Tel:* 416-598-7979 *Web Site:* www.jlstudios.ca; www.facebook.com/jlrecordingstudios; twitter.com/JLStudios, pg 905

Moyer, Charles, Science for Kids, 1941 Brooke Dr, New Hope, PA 18938 *Tel:* 215-794-7718 *Fax:* 215-794-7718, pg 1005

Moynihan, Frank, Billy Budd Films Inc, 235 E 57 St, New York, NY 10022 *Tel:* 212-755-3968 *E-mail:* info@billybuddfilms.com *Web Site:* www.billybuddfilms.com, pg 814

Mpistolarides, Paul, Midwest Uplink Inc, 911 N East St, Indianapolis, IN 46202 *Tel:* 317-423-8684 *Toll Free Tel:* 866-886-6247 *Fax:* 317-423-3061 *Web Site:* midwestuplink.com, pg 942

Mroz, John, RingSide Creative, 13320 Northend, Suite 3000, Oak Park, MI 48237 *Tel:* 248-548-2500 *E-mail:* info@ringsidecreative.com; newbiz@ringsidecreative.com *Web Site:* www.ringsidecreative.com, pg 997

Muderick, Michael, Muderick Media, 101 Earlington Rd, Havertown, PA 19083 *Tel:* 610-449-6970, pg 949

Muehlhoff, Ken, Jack Van Impe Ministries International, 1718 Northfield Dr, Rochester Hills, MI 48309 *Tel:* 248-852-2244; 248-852-5225 (orders) *Fax:* 248-852-2692 *E-mail:* jvimi@jvim.com *Web Site:* www.jvim.com, pg 1051

Mueller, Dave, Stage Front Presentation Systems, 6 Southern Oaks Dr, Savannah, GA 31405 *Tel:* 912-236-1345 *Toll Free Tel:* 800-736-9242 *Fax:* 912-233-5350 *Web Site:* www.sfps.net; www.stagefrontproductions.com, pg 1022

Mueller, David, Image Audiovisuals, 2130 S Dahlia St, Denver, CO 80222 *Tel:* 303-758-1818 *Toll Free Tel:* 800-818-1857 *Fax:* 303-758-5722 *E-mail:* commercialsales@imageav.com *Web Site:* www.imageav.com, pg 894

Mueller, Diana, Image Audiovisuals, 2130 S Dahlia St, Denver, CO 80222 *Tel:* 303-758-1818 *Toll Free Tel:* 800-818-1857 *Fax:* 303-758-5722 *E-mail:* commercialsales@imageav.com *Web Site:* www.imageav.com, pg 894

Mueller, Judy, DSI RF Systems Inc, 26-H World's Fair Dr, Somerset, NJ 08873 *Tel:* 732-563-1144 *Toll Free Tel:* 888-374-7388 *Fax:* 732-563-1818 *E-mail:* info@dsirf.com; sales@dsirf.com *Web Site:* www.dsirf.com, pg 853

Mueller, Michael, Michael Mueller Productions, 1654 Airport Rd, Hot Springs, AR 71913 *Tel:* 501-520-5905 *Web Site:* muellervideo.com, pg 949

Mueller, Ray, Ray Mueller Productions, 5 E Waterloo Rd, Stanhope, NJ 07874 *Tel:* 973-691-2088; 973-801-6004 *Web Site:* www.muellerproductions.com, pg 949

Muertens, Gunther, Agfa Graphics, 611 River Dr, Ctr 3, Elmwood Park, NJ 07407 *Tel:* 201-440-2500 *Toll Free Tel:* 800-540-2432 *Web Site:* www.agfagraphics.com; www.agfa.com, pg 778

Muir, Charles, Source School of Tantra Yoga Inc, PO Box 368, Kahului, HI 96733 *Tel:* 808-572-8364 *Toll Free Tel:* 888-6-TANTRA (682-6872) *Fax:* 831-703-4221 *E-mail:* school@sourcetantra.com *Web Site:* www.sourcetantra.com, pg 1019

Muldowney, Oisin, French American Cultural Exchange (FACE), 972 Fifth Ave, New York, NY 10021 *Tel:* 212-439-1449 *Fax:* 212-439-1455 *E-mail:* info@facecouncil.org *Web Site:* www.facecouncil.org, pg 873

Mulica, Joe, Gotham Sound & Communications Inc, 330 W 38 St, No 105, New York, NY 10018 *Tel:* 212-629-9430 *Toll Free Tel:* 866-468-4268 *Fax:* 212-629-9436 *E-mail:* nyc@gothamsound.com *Web Site:* www.gothamsound.com, pg 881

Mulieri, Andrew, Carpel Video Inc, 429 E Patrick St, Frederick, MD 21701 *Tel:* 301-694-3500 *Toll Free Tel:* 800-238-4300 *Fax:* 301-694-9510 *Web Site:* www.carpelvideoonline.com, pg 820

Mullen, Jennifer, Modesto Convention & Visitors Bureau, 1150 Ninth St, Suite C, Modesto, CA 95354 *Tel:* 209-526-5588 *Toll Free Tel:* 888-640-8467 *Fax:* 209-526-5586 *E-mail:* films@visitmodesto.com; info@visitmodesto.com *Web Site:* www.visitmodesto.com, pg 1093

Mullen, Robb, Noventri, 20940 Twin Springs Dr, Smithsburg, MD 21783-1510 *Tel:* 301-790-0103 *Fax:* 301-790-0173 *E-mail:* sale@noventri.com *Web Site:* www.noventri.com, pg 960

Muller, Alan, Pat Appleson Studios Inc, 2359 Hwy 70 SE, Suite 102, Hickory, NC 28602 *Tel:* 828-994-4361; 828-461-3003 (cell) *Web Site:* www.appleson.com, pg 788

Muller, Arlene, Moxie Media, 1301 Dealers Ave, New Orleans, LA 70123 *Tel:* 504-733-6907 *Toll Free Tel:* 800-346-6943 *Fax:* 504-733-9493 *E-mail:* info@moxiemedia.com *Web Site:* www.moxiemedia.com; www.moxietraining.com, pg 948

Muller, Justin K, Muller Entertainment, 540 Commerce St, Southlake, TX 76092 *Tel:* 972-869-7704 *Fax:* 972-869-7791 *E-mail:* info@mullerentertainment.com *Web Site:* www.mullerentertainment.com, pg 949

Mullet, J A, OMNI Productions, PO Box 302, Carmel, IN 46082-0302 *Tel:* 317-846-2345 (ext 111) *Fax:* 317-846-6664 *E-mail:* omni@omniproductions.com *Web Site:* www.omniproductions.com, pg 962

Mullikin, Randy, Mullikin Agency, 1391 Plaza Place, Suite A, Springdale, AR 72764-5225 *Tel:* 479-750-0871 *Toll Free Tel:* 800-750-0871 *Fax:* 479-750-2685 *Web Site:* www.mullikinad.com, pg 949

Mullis, Glenn, Production Intercom Inc, 4 Hillview Dr, Unit A, Lake Barrington, IL 60010 *Tel:* 847-381-5350 *Fax:* 847-381-4360 *E-mail:* beltpack@beltpack.com *Web Site:* www.beltpack.com, pg 984

Mullis, Sibbelina, Production Intercom Inc, 4 Hillview Dr, Unit A, Lake Barrington, IL 60010 *Tel:* 847-381-5350 *Fax:* 847-381-4360 *E-mail:* beltpack@beltpack.com *Web Site:* www.beltpack.com, pg 984

Mulvaney, Jon, Janus Films Inc, 215 Park Ave S, 5th fl, New York, NY 10003 *Tel:* 212-756-8822 *Fax:* 212-756-8850 *Web Site:* www.criterion.com, pg 904

Mulvaney, Maureen G, MGM & Associates Inc, 16026 S 36 St, Phoenix, AZ 85048-7322 *Tel:* 480-759-6251 *Toll Free Tel:* 800-485-0065 *Fax:* 480-759-6257 *E-mail:* mgm@mgmsuperstar.com *Web Site:* www.mgmsuperstar.com; www.thewomensmillionaireclub.com, pg 940

Munday, Robert, Munday & Collins AV, 2122 Zanker Rd, San Jose, CA 95131-2108 *Tel:* 408-451-9155 *Toll Free Tel:* 800-834-5551 *Fax:* 408-451-9192 *E-mail:* info@avevents.com *Web Site:* www.avevents.com, pg 950

Munn, Jim, Dorian Color, 24 Mill St, Arlington, MA 02476 *Tel:* 781-648-8040 *Fax:* 781-641-1231 *E-mail:* images@dorianlabcolor.com (gallery) *Web Site:* www.doriancolor.com, pg 851

Munoz, Alma, Calrad Electronics, 819 N Highland Ave, Los Angeles, CA 90038 *Tel:* 323-465-2131 *Toll Free Tel:* 800-821-8536 *Fax:* 323-465-3504 *E-mail:* calradelectronics@calrad.com *Web Site:* www.calrad.com, pg 817

Munro, Debbie, DebsVoice, 19 Park Trail, Midhurst, ON L0L 1X0, Canada *Tel:* 604-459-5559 (cell) *E-mail:* info@debsvoice.com *Web Site:* www.debsvoice.com, pg 844

Munro, Douglas, HDTV Productions Inc, 2620 S Maryland Pkwy, Suite 816, Las Vegas, NV 89109 *Tel:* 702-499-4880 *E-mail:* hdtv@hdtvproductions.com *Web Site:* www.hdtvproductions.com, pg 886

Murphy, Courtney, Alabama Film Office, Alabama Center for Commerce, 401 Adams Ave, Suite 170, Montgomery, AL 36104-1430 *Tel:* 334-242-4195 *Fax:* 334-242-2077 *Web Site:* www.alabamafilm.org, pg 1091

Murphy, Don, Big Shoulders Digital Video Productions, 875 N Michigan Ave, Suite 3750, Chicago, IL 60611 *Tel:* 312-540-5400 *E-mail:* info@bigshoulders.com; sales@bigshoulders.com *Web Site:* www.bigshoulders.com, pg 807

Murphy, Elaine, Kimbo Educational, 10 N Third Ave, Long Branch, NJ 07740 *Tel:* 732-229-4949 *Toll Free Tel:* 800-631-2187 *Fax:* 732-870-3340 *E-mail:* kimboed@aol.com *Web Site:* www.kimboed.com, pg 910

Murphy, Erin, Flying Colors Broadcasts, 2000 "M" St NW, Suite 345, Washington, DC 20036 *Tel:* 202-293-5300 *E-mail:* info@fc-tv.com *Web Site:* www.fc-tv.com, pg 870

Murphy, Karen, Wanted! Sound + Picture, 409 King St W, Suite 300, Toronto, ON M5V 1K1, Canada *Tel:* 416-596-1101 *Fax:* 416-596-0690 *E-mail:* info@wantedsp.com *Web Site:* www.wantedsp.com, pg 1062

Murphy, Marion E, The Lerro Corp, Valley Forge Corporate Ctr, 905 Madison Ave, Norristown, PA 19403 *Tel:* 610-650-4100 *Fax:* 610-650-4110 *E-mail:* lerrocorp@lerro.com *Web Site:* www.lerro.com, pg 919

Murphy, Matt, WoodenBoat Publications, 41 WoodenBoat Lane, Brooklin, ME 04616 *Tel:* 207-359-4651 *Toll Free Tel:* 800-877-5284 (subns); 800-487-2084 (subns) *Fax:* 207-359-8920; 818-487-4550 (subns) *E-mail:* woodenboat@woodenboat.com *Web Site:* www.woodenboat.com, pg 1069

Murphy, Matthew E, The Lerro Corp, Valley Forge Corporate Ctr, 905 Madison Ave, Norristown, PA 19403 *Tel:* 610-650-4100 *Fax:* 610-650-4110 *E-mail:* lerrocorp@lerro.com *Web Site:* www.lerro.com, pg 919

Murphy, Peter, The Video Messenger Co, 862 Judson Place, Stratford, CT 06615 *Tel:* 203-358-8842 *Toll Free Tel:* 800-800-7128 *Fax:* 203-547-6216 *E-mail:* vmc@videomessenger.com *Web Site:* www.videomessenger.com, pg 1055

Murphy, Randy, South Trunk Studios, 825 S Trunk Ave, Dallas, TX 75210 *Tel:* 214-826-2513 *E-mail:* southtrunk@earthlink.net *Web Site:* www.southtrunk.com, pg 1019

Murphy, Scott, NVerzion, 296 E 3900 S, Salt Lake City, UT 84107-1531 *Tel:* 801-293-8420 *Fax:* 801-293-8616 *E-mail:* info@nverzion.com; sales@nverzion.com *Web Site:* www.nverzion.com, pg 960

Murphy, Sean, Miranda Technologies, 3499 Douglas-B Floreani, Montreal, QC H4S 2C6, Canada *Tel:* 514-333-1772 *Toll Free Tel:* 800-224-7882 *Fax:* 514-333-9828 *E-mail:* salesamericas@miranda.com *Web Site:* www.miranda.com; www.belden.com, pg 944

Murphy, Shalyn, Visit Topeka Inc, 618 S Kansas Ave, Topeka, KS 66603 *Tel:* 785-234-1030 *Toll Free Tel:* 800-235-1030 *Fax:* 785-234-8282 *E-mail:* info@visittopeka.com *Web Site:* www.visittopeka.com, pg 1098

Murphy, Siobhan, Education Development Center Inc (EDC), 43 Foundry Ave, Waltham, MA 02453-8313 *Tel:* 617-969-7100 *Fax:* 617-969-5979 *E-mail:* contact@edc.org *Web Site:* www.edc.org, pg 857

Murphy, William, Protech Audio Corp, 192 Cedar River Rd, Indian Lake, NY 12842 *Tel:* 518-648-6410 *Fax:* 518-648-6395 *E-mail:* proinfo@protechaudio.com; prosales@protechaudio.com *Web Site:* www.protechaudio.com, pg 986

Murray, Derik, Network Entertainment Inc, 23 W Pender St, Suite 290, Vancouver, BC V6B 1R3, Canada *Tel:* 604-739-8825 *Fax:* 604-739-8835 *E-mail:* info@networkentertainment.com *Web Site:* www.networkentertainment.ca, pg 955

Murray, Doug, Upstage Video, 212 Shoemaker Rd, Pottstown, PA 19464 *Tel:* 610-323-7200 *Toll Free Tel:* 877-484-3887 *Fax:* 484-727-9056 *E-mail:* info@upstagevideo.com *Web Site:* www.upstagevideo.com, pg 1050

Murray, Karla, Film Detroit, 211 W Fort St, Suite 1000, Detroit, MI 48226 *Tel:* 313-202-1990 *Toll Free Tel:* 877-478-7883 *Web Site:* www.filmdetroit.com, pg 1098

Murray, Michael, Adrenaline Films, 5224 S Orange Ave, Orlando, FL 32809 *Tel:* 407-850-0711 *Fax:* 407-859-6527 *E-mail:* contact@adrenalinefilms.com *Web Site:* www.adrenalinefilms.com, pg 777

Murray, Sean, AnswersMedia, 30 N Racine Ave, Suite 300, Chicago, IL 60607 *Tel:* 312-421-0113 *Fax:* 312-421-1457 *E-mail:* contactus@answersmediainc.com *Web Site:* www.answersmediainc.com, pg 787

Murray, Steve, KVAL, 4575 Blanton Rd, Eugene, OR 97405 *Tel:* 541-342-4961 *Fax:* 541-342-2635 *E-mail:* kvalnews@kval.com *Web Site:* www.kval.com, pg 914

Murray, Tim, Symetrix Inc, 6408 216 St SW, Mountlake Terrace, WA 98043-2093 *Tel:* 425-778-7728 *E-mail:* support@symetrix.co; sales@symetrix.co *Web Site:* www.symetrix.co, pg 1030

Murrell, Debra, American Legion Fourth Estate Award, Public Relations Div, 700 N Pennsylvania St, Indianapolis, IN 46204 *Tel:* 317-630-1253 *Fax:* 317-630-1368 *E-mail:* pr@legion.org *Web Site:* www.legion.org, pg 1107

Murski, Paul, Horizon Film + Video Productions, 808 E 34 St, Austin, TX 78705 *Tel:* 512-459-3100 *Toll Free Tel:* 800-540-2785 *Fax:* 512-459-3477 *Web Site:* www.horizonvideo.com, pg 891

Muscari, Julia, Eternal Word Television Network (EWTN), 5817 Old Leeds Rd, Irondale, AL 35210-2164 *Tel:* 205-271-2900 *Fax:* 205-271-2920 *E-mail:* viewer@ewtn.com *Web Site:* www.ewtn.com, pg 862

Musci, Andrew M, ALTEL Systems Inc, 601 N Main St, Brewster, NY 10509 *Tel:* 845-278-4400 *Toll Free Tel:* 800-88ALTEL (882-5835) *Fax:* 845-278-2824 *E-mail:* info@altel-av.com *Web Site:* www.altel-av.com, pg 783

Muse, Jim, Muse Presentation Technologies, 3510 S Susan St, Santa Ana, CA 92704 *Tel:* 714-850-1008 *Toll Free Tel:* 800-950-4955 *Fax:* 714-850-1018 *Web Site:* www.museprestech.com, pg 950

Musumarra, Joseph, MALCO Electronics, 5 Wolcott Ave, Lawrence, MA 01844 *Tel:* 978-685-4383 *Toll Free Tel:* 800-937-6252 *Fax:* 978-975-4038 *E-mail:* info@malcoelectronics.com *Web Site:* www.malcoelectronics.com, pg 929

Mutarelli, John C, CALIBRE, Metro Park, 6354 Walker Lane, Alexandria, VA 22310-3252 *Tel:* 703-797-8500 *Toll Free Tel:* 888-CALIBRE (225-4273) *Fax:* 703-797-8501 *E-mail:* info@calibresys.com *Web Site:* www.calibresys.com, pg 817

Mutterperl, Jeff, RNJ Electronics, 202 New Hwy, Amityville, NY 11701 *Tel:* 631-226-2700 *Toll Free Tel:* 800-645-5833 *Fax:* 631-226-2770 *Toll Free Fax:* 800-765-3291 *E-mail:* sales@rnjelectronics.com *Web Site:* www.rnjelectronics.com, pg 997

Myers, Barry, AccuWeather Inc, 385 Science Park Rd, State College, PA 16803 *Tel:* 814-235-8600 *Toll Free Tel:* 800-566-6606 *Fax:* 814-235-8609 *E-mail:* sales@accuweather.com *Web Site:* www.accuweather.com, pg 774

Myers, Dee Dee, Warner Bros Entertainment Inc, 4000 Warner Blvd, Burbank, CA 91522 *Tel:* 818-954-3000 *Fax:* 818-954-4918 *E-mail:* wbsf@warnerbros.com *Web Site:* www.warnerbros.com; studiofacilities.warnerbros.com, pg 1062

Myers, Evan A, AccuWeather Inc, 385 Science Park Rd, State College, PA 16803 *Tel:* 814-235-8600 *Toll Free Tel:* 800-566-6606 *Fax:* 814-235-8609 *E-mail:* sales@accuweather.com *Web Site:* www.accuweather.com, pg 774

Myers, Irv, New Leaf Distributing Co, 401 Thornton Rd, Lithia Springs, GA 30122-1557 *Tel:* 770-948-7845 *Toll Free Tel:* 800-326-2665 (orders) *Fax:* 770-944-2313 *E-mail:* newleaf@newleaf-dist.com *Web Site:* www.newleaf-dist.com, pg 956

Myers, Jeff, Brush Industries Inc, 301 Reagan St, Sunbury, PA 17801 *Tel:* 570-286-5611 *Fax:* 570-286-2649 *E-mail:* info@brushindustries.com *Web Site:* www.brushindustries.com, pg 814

Myers, Dr Joel N, AccuWeather Inc, 385 Science Park Rd, State College, PA 16803 *Tel:* 814-235-8600 *Toll Free Tel:* 800-566-6606 *Fax:* 814-235-8609 *E-mail:* sales@accuweather.com *Web Site:* www.accuweather.com, pg 774

Myers, Katharine, Princeton Architectural Press, 37 E Seventh St, New York, NY 10003 *Tel:* 212-995-9620 *Fax:* 212-995-9454 *E-mail:* sales@papress.com *Web Site:* www.papress.com, pg 982

Myers, Patrick G, KAKE-TV, 1500 N West St, Wichita, KS 67203-1323 *Tel:* 316-943-4221; 316-946-1314 (sales) *Fax:* 316-943-5493 *Web Site:* kake.com, pg 907

Myers, Rodney A, Digital Rain LLC, 640 Wilson St, Danville, IN 46122 *Tel:* 317-563-1208 *E-mail:* avmarket@digitalrainllc.com *Web Site:* www.digitalrainllc.com, pg 847

Myers, Tim, WIFR-TV, 2523 N Meridian Rd, Rockford, IL 61101 *Tel:* 815-987-5300 *Fax:* 815-965-0981 *E-mail:* talkto23@wifr.com *Web Site:* www.wifr.com, pg 1066

Myles, Patrick, Teledyne DALSA Inc, 605 McMurray Rd, Waterloo, ON N2V 2E9, Canada *Tel:* 519-886-6000 *Fax:* 519-886-8023 *E-mail:* sales.americas@teledynedalsa.com *Web Site:* www.teledynedalsa.com, pg 1036

Myres, Donald R, Omni International Inc, 435 12 St SW, Vernon, AL 35592 *Tel:* 205-695-9173 *Toll Free Tel:* 800-844-6664 *Fax:* 205-695-6465 *E-mail:* omni-brewster@centurytel.net *Web Site:* www.omniinternational.com, pg 962

Nabatian, Syrous, Radiant Images, 4125 W Jefferson Blvd, Los Angeles, CA 90016 *Tel:* 323-737-1314 *Fax:* 310-861-0163 *E-mail:* info@radiantimages.com *Web Site:* www.radiantimages.com, pg 990

Nachlis, Gayle, Women In Film, 6100 Wilshire Blvd, Suite 710, Los Angeles, CA 90048-5117 *Tel:* 323-935-2211 *Fax:* 323-935-2212 *E-mail:* info@wif.org *Web Site:* www.wif.org, pg 1090

Nachlis, Gayle, Women in Film Foundation Film Finishing Fund, 6100 Wilshire Blvd, Suite 710, Los Angeles, CA 90048 *Tel:* 323-935-2211 *Fax:* 323-935-2212 *E-mail:* info@wif.org *Web Site:* www.wif.org, pg 1129

Nadeau, Guy, Giant Audio Visual Inc, 111 Canfield Ave, Unit B-6, Randolph, NJ 07869-1114 *Tel:* 973-927-1112 *Toll Free Tel:* 866-GIANTAV (442-6828) *Fax:* 973-927-9977 *E-mail:* staging@giantav.com *Web Site:* www.giantav.com, pg 878

Nadlin, Mark, Green Dot Audio Electronics, PO Box 290609, Nashville, TN 37229-0609 *Tel:* 615-366-5964 *Fax:* 615-366-7069 *E-mail:* greendotaudio@bellsouth.net *Web Site:* www.greendotaudio.com, pg 882

Nady, Toby Garten, Nady Systems Inc, 6701 Shellmound St, Emeryville, CA 94608 *Tel:* 510-652-2411 *Fax:* 510-652-5075 *E-mail:* ussales@nady.com *Web Site:* www.nady.com, pg 952

Nagel, Dennis, Idaho Camera Inc, 1310 N Orchard Ave, Boise, ID 83706 *Tel:* 208-377-3686 (corp) *Toll Free Tel:* 877-323-8734 *E-mail:* info@idahocamera.com; orchard@idahocamera.com; sales@idahocamera.com *Web Site:* www.idahocamera.com, pg 893

Nagel, Jan, Women In Animation, PO Box 17706, Encino, CA 91416-7706 *Tel:* 818-759-9596 *E-mail:* wia@womeninanimation.org; info@womeninanimation.org *Web Site:* www.womeninanimation.org, pg 1090

Nagel, Patrick F, Idaho Camera Inc, 1310 N Orchard Ave, Boise, ID 83706 *Tel:* 208-377-3686 (corp) *Toll Free Tel:* 877-323-8734 *E-mail:* info@idahocamera.com; orchard@idahocamera.com; sales@idahocamera.com *Web Site:* www.idahocamera.com, pg 893

Nagle, Don, Asia Society, 725 Park Ave, New York, NY 10021 *Tel:* 212-288-6400 *Fax:* 212-517-8315 *E-mail:* pr@asiasociety.org *Web Site:* www.asiasociety.org; www.asiasociety.org/video, pg 792

Nagorski, Tom, Asia Society, 725 Park Ave, New York, NY 10021 *Tel:* 212-288-6400 *Fax:* 212-517-8315 *E-mail:* pr@asiasociety.org *Web Site:* www.asiasociety.org; www.asiasociety.org/video, pg 792

Nahte, Ethan, Live'N'Loud, One Lindsay Way, Hot Springs Village, AR 71909 *Tel:* 501-414-2845 *Web Site:* www.livenloud.net, pg 923

Naidu, Bobby, Source Film Studio, 1111 N Beachwood Dr, Hollywood, CA 90038 *Tel:* 323-463-5555 *E-mail:* info@sourcefilmstudio.com *Web Site:* www.sourcefilmstudio.com, pg 1018

Nall, Terry, Autogram/Crl, 920 Edison Ave, Suite 4, Benton, AR 72015 *Tel:* 480-893-7080 *Fax:* 501-776-0357 *Web Site:* www.orban.com, pg 797

Nance, Hank, Boxlight Inc, NE 151 Hwy 300, Suite A, Belfair, WA 98528 *Tel:* 360-464-2119 *Fax:* 360-282-6141 *E-mail:* sales@boxlight.com *Web Site:* www.boxlight.com, pg 811

Nanji, Anil, Magnet Sales & Manufacturing Co Inc, 11248 Playa Ct, Culver City, CA 90230 *Tel:* 310-391-7213 *Toll Free Tel:* 800-421-6692 *Fax:* 310-391-7463 *E-mail:* info@magnetsales.com *Web Site:* www.magnetsales.com, pg 928

Napoleon, Marty, The Napoleon Group, 48 W 25 St, New York, NY 10010 *Tel:* 212-692-9200 *Toll Free Tel:* 800-579-4019 *Fax:* 212-692-0309 *E-mail:* info@napny.com *Web Site:* www.napny.com, pg 952

Nappi, Ralph J, NPES The Association for Suppliers of Printing, Publishing & Converting Technologies, 1899 Preston White Dr, Reston, VA 20191 *Tel:* 703-264-7200 *Fax:* 703-620-0994 *E-mail:* npes@npes.org *Web Site:* www.npes.org, pg 1087

Narayen, Shantanu, Adobe Systems Inc, 345 Park Ave, San Jose, CA 95110-2704 *Tel:* 408-536-6000 *Fax:* 408-537-6000 *Web Site:* www.adobe.com, pg 776

Nardelli, Scott, Bexel Corp, 2701 N Ontario St, Burbank, CA 91504 *Tel:* 818-565-4322 *Toll Free Tel:* 800-225-6185 (tech support) *E-mail:* rentals@bexel.com *Web Site:* www.bexel.com, pg 806

Naruwa, Hiroki, Noritsu America Corp, 6900 Noritsu Ave, Buena Park, CA 90620 *Tel:* 714-521-9040 *Toll Free Tel:* 800-521-3686; 888-435-7448 (tech support) *E-mail:* sales@noritsu.com *Web Site:* www.noritsu.com, pg 958

Nash, Anthony, Charles M Salter Associates Inc, 130 Sutter St, Suite 500, San Francisco, CA 94104 *Tel:* 415-397-0442 *Fax:* 415-397-0454 *E-mail:* info@cmsalter.com *Web Site:* www.cmsalter.com, pg 1001

Natale, Dave, Right Coast Recording Inc, 349 Chestnut St, Columbia, PA 17512-1259 *Tel:* 717-681-9801 *Fax:* 717-681-9801 *E-mail:* rightcoastrecording@gmail.com *Web Site:* www.rightcoastrecording.com, pg 997

Natella, Jamee, Blueyed Pictures Inc, 8950 W Olympic Blvd, Suite 324, Beverly Hills, CA 90211 *Tel:* 310-295-0848 *Fax:* 310-295-0260 *E-mail:* la@blueyedpictures.com *Web Site:* www.blueyedpictures.com, pg 810

Nathan, Terry, IBPA, Independent Book Publishers Association, 1020 Manhattan Beach Blvd, Suite 204, Manhattan Beach, CA 90266 *Tel:* 310-546-1818 *Fax:* 310-546-3939 *E-mail:* info@ibpa-online.org *Web Site:* www.ibpa-online.org, pg 1082

Nathani, Andy, 24 Frames Film & Video, 15 Fourth Ave E, Vancouver, BC V5T 1E9, Canada *Tel:* 604-877-2299 *Fax:* 604-877-2298 *E-mail:* info@24frames.ca *Web Site:* www.24frames.ca, pg 1047

Naughton, Brandon, Platypi Studios, 1245 Champa St, 4th fl, Denver, CO 80204 *Tel:* 720-935-7497 *Web Site:* platypistudios.com, pg 977

Nauman, J Michael, Brady Corp, 6555 W Good Hope Rd, Milwaukee, WI 53201-0571 *Tel:* 414-358-6600 *Toll Free Tel:* 800-541-1686 *Toll Free Fax:* 800-292-2289 *Web Site:* www.bradycorp.com, pg 811

Nawrocki, Nancy, Video Associates Labs Inc, 2201 Denton Dr, Suite 109 B, Austin, TX 78758 *Tel:* 512-491-7091 *Toll Free Tel:* 800-331-0547 *Fax:* 512-491-7619 *E-mail:* sales@val.com *Web Site:* www.val.com, pg 1054

Neaderland, Adolph, Sound Control Technologies Inc, 28 Knight St, Norwalk, CT 06851 *Tel:* 203-854-5701 *Fax:* 203-854-5702 *E-mail:* sales@soundcontrol.net *Web Site:* www.soundcontrol.net, pg 1017

Neaderland, David, Sound Control Technologies Inc, 28 Knight St, Norwalk, CT 06851 *Tel:* 203-854-5701 *Fax:* 203-854-5702 *E-mail:* sales@soundcontrol.net *Web Site:* www.soundcontrol.net, pg 1017

Neal, Malcolm, Malcolm Neal Productions, 111 Everest Dr, Thomaston, GA 30286-4603 *Tel:* 706-646-2749; 706-647-5372 *Fax:* 706-938-1138 *E-mail:* nealritz@charter.net, pg 954

Neal, Pete, Annenberg Learner, PO Box 26983, St Louis, MO 63118 *Tel:* 202-783-0500 (outside US) *Toll Free Tel:* 800-LEARNER (532-7637) *Fax:* 202-783-0333 *E-mail:* order@learner.org *Web Site:* www.learner.org, pg 787

Neall, Kelly, Ottawa International Animation Festival, 2 Daly Ave, Suite 120, Ottawa, ON K1N 6E2, Canada *Tel:* 613-232-8769 *Fax:* 613-232-6315 *E-mail:* info@animationfestival.ca *Web Site:* www.animationfestival.ca, pg 1123

Neall, Sallie, HighBridge Audio, 201 Sixth St, Suite 220, Minneapolis, MN 55414 *Toll Free Tel:* 800-755-8532 *Fax:* 612-436-4005 *E-mail:* highbridge@highbridgeaudio.com *Web Site:* www.highbridgeaudio.com, pg 889

Necuze, Jorge J, Digital Video Systems Inc, 3270 Executive Way, Miramar, FL 33025 *Tel:* 954-239-4410 *Fax:* 954-239-4485 *E-mail:* info@digitalvideosystems.net *Web Site:* www.digitalvideosystems.net, pg 848

Neddermeyer, Andrew, InVision Productions, 821 Las Colindas Rd, San Rafael, CA 94903 *Tel:* 415-492-0414 *E-mail:* invision@goinvision.com *Web Site:* www.goinvision.com, pg 902

Neel, David, Production Solutions Inc, PO Box 8146, Reading, PA 19603-8146 *Tel:* 610-374-6998 *Fax:* 610-374-7284 *E-mail:* info@prod-sol.com *Web Site:* www.prod-sol.com, pg 985

Neger, Kim, WGBH Production Group, One Guest St, Boston, MA 02135 *Tel:* 617-300-2200 *Fax:* 617-300-3460 *Web Site:* www.wgbh.org/productionservices, pg 1065

Negron, David, Productiontrax.com, 11811 N Tatum Blvd, Suite 3031, Phoenix, AZ 85028 *Tel:* 480-331-8729 *Fax:* 480-240-9324 *E-mail:* sales@productiontrax.com *Web Site:* www.productiontrax.com, pg 985

Neilson, Stefan, AEON Communications Inc, PO Box 96, Mountlake Terrace, WA 98043 *Tel:* 425-672-8222 *E-mail:* winningcolors@mindspring.com *Web Site:* winningcolors.com, pg 778

Neimann, Aaron, Ilio Enterprises LLC, PO Box 6211, Malibu, CA 90265 *Tel:* 818-707-7222; 818-707-3655 *Toll Free Tel:* 800-747-4546 *Fax:* 818-707-8552 *E-mail:* ilioquestions@ilio.com *Web Site:* www.ilio.com, pg 894

Nelligan, Helena, Brady Corp, 6555 W Good Hope Rd, Milwaukee, WI 53201-0571 *Tel:* 414-358-6600 *Toll Free Tel:* 800-541-1686 *Toll Free Fax:* 800-292-2289 *Web Site:* www.bradycorp.com, pg 811

Nelson, Carrie, Flagstaff Convention & Visitors Bureau, One E Rte 66, Flagstaff, AZ 86001-5303 *Tel:* 928-213-2910 *Toll Free Tel:* 800-842-7293 *E-mail:* cvb@flagstaffaz.gov *Web Site:* www.flagstaffarizona.org, pg 1091

Nelson, Esther, Granny Press LLC, 101 Gedney St, Apt 5-D, Nyack, NY 10960 *Tel:* 845-875-4422; 845-875-4423 *E-mail:* webmaster@grannypress.com *Web Site:* www.grannypress.com, pg 881

Nelson, Ken, FirstCom Music, 1325 Capital Pkwy, Suite 109, Carrollton, TX 75006 *Tel:* 972-446-8742 *Toll Free Tel:* 800-858-8880 *Fax:* 972-242-6526 *E-mail:* info@firstcom.com *Web Site:* www.firstcom.com, pg 869

Nelson, Mary, Virginia Film Office, 901 E Byrd St, Richmond, VA 23219-4048 *Tel:* 804-545-5530 *Toll Free Tel:* 800-854-6233 *Fax:* 804-545-5501 *E-mail:* vafilm@virginia.org *Web Site:* www.film.virginia.org, pg 1103

Nelson, Richard, ACCO Brands Corp, 4 Corporate Dr, Lake Zurick, IL 60047-8997 *Toll Free Tel:* 800-541-0094 *Toll Free Fax:* 800-941-4463 *E-mail:* contactus@gbc.com *Web Site:* www.accobrands.com, pg 773

Nelson, Richard, GBC Document Finishing, 4 Corporate Dr, Lake Zurich, IL 60047 *Toll Free Tel:* 800-723-4000 (orders) *Toll Free Fax:* 800-914-8178 *Web Site:* www.gbcconnect.com; www.gbcoffice.com, pg 876

Nelson, Rob, Sound & Images Inc, 104 Corporate Blvd, Suite 411, West Columbia, SC 29169 *Tel:* 803-791-3925 *E-mail:* marketing@s-and-i.com *Web Site:* www.s-and-i.com, pg 1016

Nelson, Scott, Scott Nelson HD Productions Inc, PO Box 1198, Bend, OR 97709-1198 *Tel:* 541-410-8680 *E-mail:* snp@bendcable.com *Web Site:* vimeo.com/scottnelson, pg 954

Nelson, Tony, Spectrum Industries Inc, 925 First Ave, Chippewa Falls, WI 54729 *Tel:* 715-723-6750 *Toll Free Tel:* 800-235-1262 *Toll Free Fax:* 800-335-0473 *E-mail:* info@spectrumfurniture.com *Web Site:* www.spectrumfurniture.com, pg 1021

Nelson, William A III, Nelson Enterprises Theatrical Supply Co, 1014 Rte 173 E, Bloomsbury, NJ 08804 *Tel:* 908-479-6902 *Fax:* 908-479-6903 *E-mail:* sales@nelson-enterprises.com; rentals@nelson-enterprises.com *Web Site:* www.nelson-enterprises.com, pg 954

Nelson-Dowd, Heidi, L E Nelson Sales Corp, 6050 S Valley View Blvd, Las Vegas, NV 89118 *Tel:* 702-367-3656 *Fax:* 702-367-7058, pg 954

Nemenz, Otto, Otto Nemenz International Inc, 870 N Vine St, Los Angeles, CA 90038 *Tel:* 323-469-2774 *Fax:* 323-469-1217 *E-mail:* info@ottonemenz.com *Web Site:* www.ottonemenz.com, pg 954

Nemoy, Carole Curb, Curb Entertainment International Corp, 3907 W Alameda Ave, Burbank, CA 91505 *Tel:* 818-843-8580 *Fax:* 818-566-1719 *Web Site:* www.curbentertainment.com, pg 841

Nemser, Benjamin L, Nemal Electronics International Inc, 12240 NE 14 Ave, North Miami, FL 33161 *Tel:* 305-899-0900 *Toll Free Tel:* 800-522-2253 *Fax:* 305-895-8178 *E-mail:* info@nemal.com *Web Site:* www.nemal.com, pg 954

Nesbit, Irene S, Nesbit Systems Inc, 243 N Union St, Suite 112, Lambertville, NJ 08530 *Tel:* 609-397-7720 *E-mail:* info@nesbit.com *Web Site:* www.nesbit.com, pg 954

Ness, Verden A, Sign Media Inc, 4020 Blackburn Lane, Burtonsville, MD 20866-1167 *Tel:* 301-421-0268 *Toll Free Tel:* 800-475-4756 *Fax:* 301-421-0270 *E-mail:* info@signmedia.com *Web Site:* www.signmedia.com, pg 1011

Nettles, Amy, Metro Orlando Film Commission, 301 E Pine St, Suite 900, Orlando, FL 32801 *Tel:* 407-422-7159 *Fax:* 407-425-6428 *E-mail:* info@filmorlando.com *Web Site:* www.filmorlando.com, pg 1096

Nettleton, John, Majortech Inc, 8464 Ninth Line RR-1, Norval, ON L0P 1K0, Canada *Tel:* 905-873-0778 *Fax:* 905-873-1244 *Web Site:* www.majortech.com, pg 929

Netzley, Steve, Havas Edge, 6922 Hollywood Blvd, Hollywood, CA 90028 *Tel:* 310-734-1333 *E-mail:* info@havasedge.com *Web Site:* www.havasedge.com, pg 885

Neuman, Mark D, Association of Federal Communications Consulting Engineers (AFCCE), PO Box 19333, Washington, DC 20036-0333 *E-mail:* secretary@afcce.org *Web Site:* www.afcce.org, pg 1079

Neumann, Rachel, Parallax Press, 2236-B Sixth St, Berkeley, CA 94710 *Tel:* 510-525-0101 *Toll Free Tel:* 800-863-5290 (book orders) *Fax:* 510-525-7129 *E-mail:* info@parallax.org *Web Site:* www.parallax.org, pg 969

Nevins, David, Showtime Networks Inc, 1633 Broadway, 9th fl, New York, NY 10019 *Tel:* 212-708-1600 *Fax:* 212-708-1217 *Web Site:* www.sho.com, pg 1010

Nevins, Kate, LYRASIS, 1438 W Peachtree NW, Suite 200, Atlanta, GA 30309 *Tel:* 404-892-0943 *Toll Free Tel:* 800-999-8558 *Fax:* 404-892-7879 *Web Site:* www.lyrasis.org, pg 927

Nevins, Richard, Shanachie Entertainment Corp, 37 E Clinton St, Newton, NJ 07860 *Tel:* 973-579-7763 *Web Site:* shanachie.com, pg 1008

Newdoll, Ronald, Newdoll Enterprises LLC, 3515-B Edison Way, Menlo Park, CA 94025 *Tel:* 650-365-2843 *Fax:* 650-365-3057 *E-mail:* info@newdollenterprises.com *Web Site:* www.newdollenterprises.com, pg 956

Newell, David, The Fred Rogers Co, 2100 Wharton St, Suite 700, Pittsburgh, PA 15203 *Tel:* 412-687-2990 *Fax:* 412-687-1226 *Web Site:* www.fredrogers.org, pg 998

Newell, Robert, Main Street Media Inc, 185 Pier Ave, Suite 105, Santa Monica, CA 90405 *Tel:* 310-450-1846 *E-mail:* info@mainstreetmediainc.com *Web Site:* www.mainstreetmediainc.com, pg 929

Newhouse, Roxane B, The Transfer Zone®, 4301 Orchard Lake Rd, Suite 180-191, West Bloomfield, MI 48323 *Tel:* 248-225-0477, pg 1043

Newlin, Julye, Julye Newlin Productions Inc, 129 E 13 St, Houston, TX 77008 *Tel:* 713-869-3609; 832-689-3609 (cell) *E-mail:* julye@julyenewlin.com *Web Site:* www.julyenewlin.com, pg 956

Newman, Charles, Mother West, 37 W 20 St, Suite 1006, New York, NY 10011 *Tel:* 212-807-0405 *E-mail:* info@motherwest.com *Web Site:* www.motherwest.com, pg 947

Newman, Dave J, CTG Audio, 2100 Constitution Blvd, Sarasota, FL 34231 *Tel:* 941-922-2322 *Fax:* 941-922-5445 *E-mail:* orders@ctgaudio.com; info@ctgaudio.com *Web Site:* www.ctgaudio.com, pg 840

Newman, Judith A, Firefly Book Club, 557 Broadway, New York, NY 10012 *Tel:* 212-343-6100 *Toll Free Tel:* 800-724-6527 (cust serv) *Fax:* 212-343-4535 *E-mail:* info@scholastic.com; custserv@scholastic.com *Web Site:* www.scholastic.com, pg 868

Newman, Todd, K-SAR Video & DVD Productions, Center for Persons with Disabilities, Utah Univ Ctr of Excellence, 6800 Old Main Hill, Logan, UT 84322-6800 *Tel:* 435-797-1981 *Fax:* 435-797-3944 *Web Site:* www.cpdusa.org, pg 907

Newmann, Kassandra, Muse Presentation Technologies, 3510 S Susan St, Santa Ana, CA 92704 *Tel:* 714-850-1008 *Toll Free Tel:* 800-950-4955 *Fax:* 714-850-1018 *Web Site:* www.museprestech.com, pg 950

Newsome, Tina, Angstrom Lighting, 837 N Cahuenga Blvd, Hollywood, CA 90038 *Tel:* 323-462-4246 *Fax:* 323-462-8190 *Web Site:* www.angstromlighting.com, pg 786

Newton, Matthew W, New Hampshire Film & TV Office, 19 Pillsbury St, 1st fl, Concord, NH 03301 *Tel:* 603-271-2220 *Fax:* 603-271-3584 *E-mail:* film@nh.gov *Web Site:* www.nh.gov/film, pg 1100

Newton, Stephen A, Cinevision Corp, 3300 Northeast Expwy NE, Bldg 2-A, Atlanta, GA 30341 *Tel:* 770-455-8988 *Fax:* 770-455-4066 *E-mail:* cvcorp@bellsouth.net, pg 828

Newton, Walter, Newton Instrument Co Inc, 111 E "A" St, Butner, NC 27509-2426 *Tel:* 919-575-6426 *Fax:* 919-575-4708 *Web Site:* www.enewton.com, pg 957

Ng, Ricky, PESA, 103 Quality Circle, Suite 210, Huntsville, AL 35806 *Tel:* 256-726-9200 *Toll Free Tel:* 800-323-7372 *E-mail:* sales@pesa.com *Web Site:* www.pesa.com, pg 973

Ngo, Anh, North American Broadcasters Association (NABA), Canadian Broadcasting Centre, 25 John St, Suite 6C300, Toronto, ON M5V 3G7, Canada *Tel:* 416-598-9877 *Fax:* 416-598-9774 *E-mail:* contact@nabanet.com *Web Site:* www.nabanet.com, pg 1086

Ni, Dr Mao Shing, SevenStar Communications, 13315 W Washington Blvd, Suite 200, Los Angeles, CA 90066 *Toll Free Tel:* 800-578-9526 (orders) *Fax:* 310-302-1208 *E-mail:* info@taostar.com *Web Site:* www.taostar.com, pg 1007

Nicassio, Sam, Los Angeles Center Studios, 450 S Bixel St, Los Angeles, CA 90017 *Tel:* 213-534-3000 *E-mail:* productionservices@lacenterstudios.com *Web Site:* lacenterstudios.com, pg 924

Nicholls, Andrew, Orlando Special Effects, 14222 Lake Mary Jane Rd, Orlando, FL 32832 *Tel:* 407-648-1867 *Fax:* 407-273-0328 *Web Site:* www.orlandospfx.com, pg 965

Nicholls, Ronald, USDA/FSA Aerial Photography Field Office, 2222 W 2300 S, Salt Lake City, UT 84119-2020 *Tel:* 801-844-2922 *Toll Free Fax:* 855-415-2014 *E-mail:* apfo.sales@slc.usda.gov *Web Site:* www.apfo.usda.gov, pg 1051

Nichols, Betty, High Windy Audio/Banjoman Inc, PO Box 553, Fairview, NC 28730 *Tel:* 828-628-1728 *Toll Free Tel:* 800-637-8679 *Fax:* 828-628-4435 *E-mail:* office@davidholt.com *Web Site:* www.davidholt.com, pg 889

Nichols, Clayton, WaxWorks VideoWorks, 325 E Third St, Owensboro, KY 42303 *Tel:* 270-926-0008 *Toll Free Tel:* 800-825-8558 *Fax:* 270-663-0737 *Web Site:* www.waxworksonline.com, pg 1063

Nichols, Dan, Indiana University Press, Office of Scholarly Publishing, Herman B Wells Library 350, 1320 E Tenth St, Bloomington, IN 47405-3907 *Tel:* 812-855-8817 *Toll Free Tel:* 800-842-6796 *Fax:* 812-855-8507 *E-mail:* iupress@indiana.edu *Web Site:* www.iupress.indiana.edu, pg 897

Nichols, Heather, Chicago Underground Film Festival, 2044 W Chicago Ave, PMB 155, Chicago, IL 60622 *Tel:* 773-341-6727 *E-mail:* info@cuff.org *Web Site:* www.cuff.org, pg 1112

Nichols, Jason, Avitecture Inc, One Export Dr, Sterling, VA 20164-4421 *Tel:* 703-404-8900 *Fax:* 703-404-8940 *E-mail:* info@avitecture.com *Web Site:* www.avitecture.com, pg 800

Nichols, Koytt O, Keywest Technology Inc, 14563 W 96 Terr, Lenexa, KS 66215 *Tel:* 913-492-4666 *Toll Free Tel:* 800-331-2019 *Fax:* 913-322-1864 *E-mail:* info@keywesttechnology.com; sales@keywesttechnology.com *Web Site:* www.keywesttechnology.com, pg 910

Nichols, Michael, Missouri Film Commission, 301 W High St, Suite 720, Jefferson City, MO 65101 *Tel:* 573-526-3566 *E-mail:* mofilm@ded.mo.gov *Web Site:* www.mofilm.org, pg 1099

Nichols, Peggy, Artbeats, 1405 N Myrtle Rd, Myrtle Creek, OR 97457 *Tel:* 541-863-4429 *Toll Free Tel:* 800-444-9392 *Fax:* 541-863-4547 *E-mail:* info@artbeats.com *Web Site:* www.artbeats.com, pg 791

Nichols, Shannon, Broadcast Supply World Wide, 2237 S 19 St, Tacoma, WA 98405 *Tel:* 253-565-2301 (intl) *Toll Free Tel:* 800-426-8434 *Fax:* 253-565-8114 (intl)

Toll Free Fax: 800-231-7055 *E-mail:* sales@bswusa.com; info@bswusa.com; customersupport@bswusa.com *Web Site:* www.bswusa.com, pg 813

Nickel, John, Switch, 6600 Manchester Ave, St Louis, MO 63139 *Tel:* 314-206-7700 *Toll Free Tel:* 800-445-0633 *Fax:* 314-206-4570 *E-mail:* switch@theswitch.us *Web Site:* www.liberateyourbrand.com, pg 1030

Nickolauson, Karen, Brush Industries Inc, 301 Reagan St, Sunbury, PA 17801 *Tel:* 570-286-5611 *Fax:* 570-286-2649 *E-mail:* info@brushindustries.com *Web Site:* www.brushindustries.com, pg 814

Nicol, Donna, Rosco Laboratories Inc, 52 Harbor View, Stamford, CT 06902 *Tel:* 203-708-8900 *Toll Free Tel:* 800-ROSCO NY (767-2669) *Fax:* 203-708-8919 *E-mail:* info@rosco.com *Web Site:* www.rosco.com, pg 999

Nicoletti, Joseph Jr, Joseph Nicoletti Consulting-Promotion/California International Records/Global Village Records, PO Box 386, Laguna Beach, CA 92652 *Tel:* 949-446-8005 *E-mail:* music-film@att.net, pg 957

Nicotera, Stan, S I Video Sales Group, 1318 S Carlisle St, Philadelphia, PA 19146 *Tel:* 267-519-2222 *Web Site:* www.sivideo.com; www.capclassics.com; takinglasvegas.com, pg 1001

Niebauer, Carl "Skip", American Artist Studio, 1114 W 26 St, Erie, PA 16508-1518 *Tel:* 814-455-4796 *Toll Free Tel:* 888-462-7813 *Web Site:* americanartiststudio.com, pg 783

Nielsen, Bruce, Docter Optics Inc, 1425 W Elliot Rd, Suite A-105, Gilbert, AZ 85233 *Tel:* 480-844-7585 *Fax:* 480-844-7826 *E-mail:* doi@docteroptics.com *Web Site:* www.docteroptics.com, pg 850

Nielsen, Rod, Big House Sound Inc, 4001 Drossett Dr, Austin, TX 78744 *Tel:* 512-443-0019 *Fax:* 512-443-0916 *Web Site:* www.bighousesound.com, pg 807

Nielsen, Scott, Telequest Inc, 66 Witherspoon St, Suite 383, Princeton, NJ 08542 *Tel:* 609-430-3004 *E-mail:* contact@telequestinc.com *Web Site:* www.telequestinc.com, pg 1036

Nieves, Ivan, Stage Crew Audiovisual Inc, PO Box 6097, San Juan, PR 00914-6097 *Tel:* 787-723-6398 *Fax:* 787-721-1410 *E-mail:* scav@stagecrewav.com *Web Site:* www.stagecrewav.com, pg 1022

Nightingale, Caron, Nightingale Music Productions Inc, 5460 Yonge St, Suite 1611, Toronto, ON M2N 6K7, Canada *Tel:* 416-221-2393 *Fax:* 416-221-2676 *E-mail:* admin@nightingalemusic.com *Web Site:* www.nightingalemusic.com, pg 957

Nigrin, Albert Gabriel, New Jersey Film Festival, Admin Off, 30 Bedford Rd, Somerset, NJ 08873 *Tel:* 848-932-8482 *Fax:* 732-932-1935 *E-mail:* njmac@aol.com *Web Site:* www.njfilmfest.com, pg 1122

Nigrin, Albert Gabriel, New Jersey International Film Festival, Admin Off, 30 Bedford Rd, Somerset, NJ 08873 *Tel:* 848-932-8482 *Fax:* 732-932-1935 *E-mail:* njmac@aol.com *Web Site:* www.njfilmfest.com, pg 1122

Nigrin, Albert Gabriel, United States Super 8mm Film & Digital Video Festival, Admin Off, 30 Bedford Rd, Somerset, NJ 08873 *Tel:* 848-932-8482 *Fax:* 732-932-1935 *E-mail:* njmac@aol.com *Web Site:* www.njfilmfest.com, pg 1128

Nikoo, Emily M, Blonder Tongue Laboratories Inc, One Jake Brown Rd, Old Bridge, NJ 08857 *Tel:* 732-679-4000 *Toll Free Tel:* 800-523-6049 *Fax:* 732-679-4353 *E-mail:* custsvc@blondertongue.com; btglobalsales@blondertongue.com (other than US & CN) *Web Site:* www.blondertongue.com, pg 809

Nilo, Robert, 360 Systems, 3281 Grande Vista Dr, Newbury Park, CA 91320-1193 *Tel:* 818-991-0360 *Fax:* 818-991-1360 *E-mail:* info@360systems.com; sales@360systems.com *Web Site:* www.360systems.com, pg 1039

Nimens, Brian, Sound Ideas, 105 W Beaver Creek Rd, Suite 4, Richmond Hill, ON L4B 1C6, Canada *Tel:* 905-886-5000 *Toll Free Tel:* 800-387-3030 *Fax:* 905-886-6800 *E-mail:* info@sound-ideas.com *Web Site:* www.sound-ideas.com, pg 1017

Nimens, Brian, StockMusic.com, 105 W Beaver Creek Rd, Suite 4, Richmond Hill, ON L4B 1C6, Canada *Tel:* 905-886-0077 *Fax:* 905-886-6800 *E-mail:* info@stockmusic.com *Web Site:* www.stockmusic.com, pg 1025

Nimens, Brian, Westar Music, 105 W Beaver Creek Rd, Suite 4, Richmond Hill, ON L4B 1C6, Canada *Tel:* 905-886-3100 *Toll Free Tel:* 800-665-3000 *Fax:* 905-886-6800 *E-mail:* info@westarmusic.com *Web Site:* www.westarmusic.com, pg 1064

Nirakarananda, Swami, Vedanta Society of St Louis, 205 S Skinker Blvd, St Louis, MO 63105 *Tel:* 314-721-5118 *Web Site:* vedantastl.org, pg 1052

Nisbet, Sandra, Small World Productions Inc, 140 Lakeside Ave, Suite 200, Seattle, WA 98122 *Tel:* 206-329-7167 *Toll Free Tel:* 800-866-7425 (orders) *E-mail:* info@travelsmallworld.com *Web Site:* www.smarttravels.tv, pg 1013

Niwano, Masashi, Center for Asian American Media (CAAM), 145 Ninth St, Suite 350, San Francisco, CA 94103 *Tel:* 415-863-0814 *Fax:* 415-863-7428 *E-mail:* info@caamedia.org *Web Site:* www.caamedia.org, pg 1080

Nix, Danny, AVL Systems Design LLC, 14901 Bristol Park Blvd, Edmond, OK 73013 *Tel:* 405-749-1866 *Fax:* 405-749-1851 *E-mail:* dnix@avl1.com *Web Site:* www.avl1.com, pg 800

Nix, Tom, Scala Inc, 350 Eagleview Blvd, Suite 350, Exton, PA 19341 *Tel:* 610-363-3350 *Toll Free Tel:* 888-SCALA-96 (722-5296) *Fax:* 610-363-4010 *E-mail:* marketing@scala.com *Web Site:* scala.com, pg 1004

Nobiletti, Mechelle, Timed Exposures Films, 122 Old Rd, Germantown, NY 12526-6014 *Tel:* 518-537-2012 *E-mail:* info@timedexposures.com *Web Site:* www.timedexposures.com, pg 1040

Noble, Debbie, Whirlwind Music Distributors Inc, 99 Ling Rd, Rochester, NY 14612 *Tel:* 585-663-8820 *Toll Free Tel:* 800-733-9473 (US only) *Fax:* 585-865-8930 *E-mail:* sales@whirlwindusa.com; techsupport@whirlwindusa.com; darylg@whirlwindusa.com (Canadian inquiries) *Web Site:* whirlwindusa.com, pg 1065

Noble, Denise, Colorado Springs Film Commission, 515 S Cascade Ave, Colorado Springs, CO 80903 *Tel:* 719-685-7637 *Toll Free Tel:* 800-888-4748 (ext 137) *Fax:* 719-635-4968 *Web Site:* www.filmcoloradosprings.com, pg 1094

Noble, Paul, Activu Corp, 301 Roundhill Dr, Rockaway, NJ 07866 *Tel:* 973-366-5550 *Toll Free Tel:* 888-ACTIVU1 (228-4881) *Fax:* 973-625-7775 *E-mail:* info@activu.com *Web Site:* www.activu.com, pg 775

Noble, Randy, Image Technical Services, 720 Crown Point Cross Rd, Winter Garden, FL 34787 *Tel:* 407-905-2100 *Toll Free Tel:* 800-393-4300 *Fax:* 407-905-2150 *E-mail:* moreinfo@goimage.com *Web Site:* www.goimage.com, pg 895

Nocita, Anthony, IAMP Professional Audio, 218 Reindollar, Marina, CA 93933 *Tel:* 831-884-9558 *Fax:* 831-643-2131 *E-mail:* iamp-pro-audio@comcast.net *Web Site:* www.iampproaudio.com, pg 893

Noel, Andree I, Canadian Broadcast Standards Council (CBSC), PO Box 3265, Sta D, Ottawa, ON K1P 6H8, Canada *Tel:* 613-233-4607 *Toll Free Tel:* 866-696-4718 (CN only) *Fax:* 613-233-4826 *E-mail:* info@cbsc.ca *Web Site:* www.ccnr.ca, pg 1080

Nolan, Angela, Vistacom Inc, 1902 Vultee St, Allentown, PA 18103-2998 *Tel:* 610-791-9081 *Toll Free Tel:* 800-747-0459 *Fax:* 610-791-9510 *Web Site:* www.vistacominc.com, pg 1059

Nolan, James, J P Nolan & Co, 4027 E 52 St, Maywood, CA 90270-2298 *Tel:* 323-581-7158 *Toll Free Tel:* 800-34-NOLAN (346-6526) *Fax:* 323-583-1824 *E-mail:* jpnolan@jpnolan.com *Web Site:* www.jpnolan.com, pg 958

Noll, Robert, Boston Productions Inc, 290 Vanderbilt Ave, Suite 1, Norwood, MA 02062 *Tel:* 781-255-1555 *E-mail:* imagine@bostonproductions.com *Web Site:* www.bostonproductions.com, pg 811

Nolte, Carolyn, SuperStock Inc, 6622 Southpoint Dr S, Suite 240, Jacksonville, FL 32216 *Tel:* 904-565-0066 *Toll Free Tel:* 800-828-4545 *Fax:* 904-565-1620 *E-mail:* yourfriends@superstock.com *Web Site:* www.superstock.com, pg 1029

Nolton, Gary, Limbo Films, 2223 NE Martin Luther King Jr Blvd, Portland, OR 97212 *Tel:* 503-228-0844 *Fax:* 503-228-0857 *E-mail:* info@limbofilms.com *Web Site:* www.limbofilms.com, pg 921

Nom's, Drew, MediaOne Services, 901 Battery St, Suite 220, San Francisco, CA 94111 *Tel:* 415-262-4222 *E-mail:* sales@mediaoneservices.com *Web Site:* mediaoneservices.com, pg 938

Noorbhai, Munir, William F White International Inc, 800 Islington Ave, Toronto, ON M8Z 6A1, Canada *Tel:* 416-239-5050 *Toll Free Tel:* 800-465-0160 (CN only); 800-268-2200 *Fax:* 416-207-2777 *E-mail:* info@cinequipwhite.com *Web Site:* www.whites.com, pg 1065

Noorigian, Carol, The Production Group Studios, 6767 W Sunset Blvd, No 8-496, Hollywood, CA 90028-7177 *Tel:* 323-469-8111 *Fax:* 323-962-2182 *E-mail:* info@productiongroup.tv *Web Site:* www.productiongroup.tv, pg 984

Norberg, Eric, Consolidated Communications Consultants, 1837 SE Harold St, Portland, OR 97202-4932 *Tel:* 503-232-9787 *Toll Free Tel:* 800-929-5119 *Fax:* 503-232-9787 *Toll Free Fax:* 800-929-5119 *E-mail:* acmrl@myexcel.com *Web Site:* www.acmusicresearch.com, pg 835

Nordal, Greg, Nelson Education Ltd, 1120 Birchmount Rd, Scarborough, ON M1K 5G4, Canada *Tel:* 416-752-9100 *Toll Free Tel:* 800-268-2222 (cust support) *Fax:* 416-752-8101 *Toll Free Fax:* 800-430-4445 *E-mail:* inquire@nelson.com *Web Site:* www.nelson.com, pg 954

Nordstrand, Karen, Monterey County Film Commission, 801 Lighthouse Ave, Suite 104, Monterey, CA 93940 *Tel:* 831-646-0910 *Fax:* 831-655-9250 *E-mail:* info@filmmonterey.org *Web Site:* www.filmmonterey.org, pg 1093

Nordyke, David, Music Lab Inc, 500 E Saint Elmo Rd, Austin, TX 78745 *Tel:* 512-707-0560 *Fax:* 512-707-2946 *E-mail:* rentals@musiclab.net *Web Site:* www.musiclab.net, pg 950

Norfleet, George, Connecticut Office of Film, Television & Digital Media, c/o Dept of Economic & Community Development, 505 Hudson St, Hartford, CT 06106 *Tel:* 860-270-8198 *Web Site:* www.ctfilm.com, pg 1095

Norinsky, Mitch, Backstar Creative Media Inc, 676 N La Salle Dr, Suite 424, Chicago, IL 60654 *Tel:* 312-467-0425 *Toll Free Tel:* 800-955-8900 *E-mail:* solutions@backstar.com *Web Site:* www.backstar.com, pg 801

Norman, Neil, GNP Crescendo Records, 1405 N Avon St, Burbank, CA 91505-1885 *Tel:* 818-566-8900 *E-mail:* gnp@pacificnet.net *Web Site:* www.gnpcrescendo.com, pg 879

Norman, Ray, Dogwood Recording Studios, 757 Government St, Mobile, AL 36602 *Tel:* 251-476-0858 *Toll Free Tel:* 800-254-9903 *Fax:* 251-479-0364 *E-mail:* info@dogwoodproductions.com *Web Site:* www.dogwoodproductions.com, pg 850

Norrie, Mark, Transtector Systems Inc, 10701 N Airport Dr, Hayden Lake, ID 83835 *Tel:* 208-772-8515 *Toll Free Tel:* 800-882-9110 *Fax:* 208-762-6133 *E-mail:* sales@transtector.com *Web Site:* www.transtector.com, pg 1043

Norris, Jade, 30 Second Street Ltd, 1209 Mountain Road Place NE, Albuquerque, NM 87110 *Tel:* 505-265-0224 *E-mail:* info@thirtysecst.com *Web Site:* www.thirtysecst.com, pg 1039

Norris, Mark, Antenna International, 383 Main Ave, Norwalk, CT 06851 *Tel:* 203-523-0320 *Fax:* 203-354-5519 *E-mail:* inquiry@antennainternational.com *Web Site:* www.antennainternational.com, pg 787

Norris, Paul, Immersion Corp, 310 Rio Robles, San Jose, CA 95134 *Tel:* 408-467-1900 *Fax:* 408-467-1901 *E-mail:* info@immersion.com *Web Site:* www.immersion.com, pg 896

Norris, Rich, N&N Productions Ltd, 5540 High Rock Way, Sparks, NV 89431 *Tel:* 775-355-9080 *Fax:* 775-355-7859 *E-mail:* sales@brassgobos.com *Web Site:* www.brassgobos.com, pg 952

Norrod, Jim, Zhone Technologies Inc, 7195 Oakport St, Oakland, CA 94621 *Tel:* 510-777-7000 *Toll Free Tel:* 877-ZHONE-20 (946-6320, US & CN) *Fax:* 510-777-7001 *E-mail:* info@zhone.com; sales@zhone.com *Web Site:* www.zhone.com, pg 1073

Norstad, Mr Lyn, Lyn Norstad & Associates Inc, 2470 E Oakton St, Arlington Heights, IL 60005 *Tel:* 847-640-6400 *Fax:* 847-640-1677 *E-mail:* contact@lnainc.com *Web Site:* www.lnainc.com, pg 926

Northrop, Tom, NorthTown Sounds Inc, 275 Wickerberry Hollow, Roswell, GA 30075 *Tel:* 770-587-9350 *E-mail:* info@northtownsounds.com *Web Site:* www.northtownsounds.com, pg 959

Norton, Bill, Earthworks Inc, 37 Wilton Rd, Milford, NH 03055 *Tel:* 603-654-6427 (sales); 603-654-2433 *Fax:* 603-654-6107 *E-mail:* info@earthworksaudio.com *Web Site:* www.earthworksaudio.com, pg 855

Norton, Diane, Idaho Film Office, 700 W State St, Boise, ID 83702 *Tel:* 208-334-2470 *Toll Free Tel:* 800-942-8338 *Fax:* 208-334-2631 *Web Site:* www.filmidaho.com, pg 1097

Norton, Janice, Prism Media Products Inc, 21 Pine St, Rockaway, NJ 07866 *Tel:* 973-983-9577 *Fax:* 973-983-9588 *E-mail:* sales@prismmpi.com *Web Site:* www.prismsound.com, pg 982

Norton, Janice, SADiE Inc, 21 Pine St, Rockaway, NJ 07866 *Tel:* 973-983-9577 *Fax:* 973-983-9588 *E-mail:* sales@prismmpi.com *Web Site:* www.sadie.com, pg 1001

Nottingham, Ken, Knox Video Technologies, 15875 Crabbs Branch Way, Suite A, Rockville, MD 20855 *Tel:* 301-840-5805 *Fax:* 301-840-2946 *E-mail:* sales@knoxvideo.com *Web Site:* www.knoxvideo.com, pg 912

Novacek, Eugene, ENCO Systems Inc, 29444 Northwestern Hwy, Southfield, MI 48034 *Tel:* 248-827-4440 *Toll Free Tel:* 800-362-6797 (sales) *Fax:* 248-827-4441 *E-mail:* sales@enco.com *Web Site:* www.enco.com, pg 860

Novak, Joseph, Delta Electronics Inc, 5730 General Washington Dr, Alexandria, VA 22312 *Tel:* 703-354-3350 *Toll Free Tel:* 800-833-5828 *Fax:* 703-354-0216 *E-mail:* sales@deltaelectronics.com *Web Site:* www.deltaelectronics.com, pg 845

Novey, Dr Donald W, Medical Media Systems, 2916 NW Bucklin Hill Rd, No 481, Silverdale, WA 98383 *Tel:* 360-516-6110 *Fax:* 360-516-6100 *Web Site:* medicalmediasystems.com, pg 938

Nowell, John, National School Products, 1523 Old Niles Ferry Rd, Maryville, TN 37803 *Tel:* 865-984-3960 *Toll Free Tel:* 800-627-9393 *Fax:* 865-983-9355 *Toll Free Fax:* 800-289-3960 *Web Site:* www.nationalschoolproducts.com, pg 953

Nowell, Robert, Professional Photographers of Canada –Ontario (PPOC-ON), 209 Light St, Woodstock, ON N4S 6H6, Canada *Tel:* 519-537-2555 *Toll Free Tel:* 888-643-7762 *Toll Free Fax:* 888-831-4036 *E-mail:* info@ppocontario.com *Web Site:* www.ppocontario.com, pg 1087

Nowicki, Brenda, Caption Colorado LLC, 5690 DTC Blvd, Suite 500W, Greenwood Village, CO 80111 *Tel:* 720-489-5662 *Toll Free Tel:* 800-775-7838 *Fax:* 720-489-5664 *Web Site:* www.captioncolorado.com, pg 820

Nowlin, Bill, Rounder Records, 1209 Pine St, Suite 100, Nashville, TN 37203 *Web Site:* www.rounder.com, pg 1000

Nowlin, Carol, Xytech Systems Corp, 15451 San Fernando Mission Blvd, Suite 400, Mission Hills, CA 91345 *Tel:* 818-698-4900 *Fax:* 818-698-4901 *E-mail:* sales@xytechsystems.com *Web Site:* www.xytechsystems.com, pg 1071

Noxon, Arthur, ASC-Tube Trap, 4275 W Fifth Ave, Eugene, OR 97402 *Tel:* 541-343-9727 *Toll Free Tel:* 800-272-8823 *Fax:* 541-343-9245 *E-mail:* info@acousticsciences.com *Web Site:* www.acousticsciences.com, pg 791

Nunez, Ray, Rockwell Communications Inc, 321 Burnham St, East Hartford, CT 06108 *Tel:* 860-528-9091 *Toll Free Tel:* 800-566-6681 *Fax:* 860-289-2334 *E-mail:* rockwellservice@aol.com *Web Site:* www.rockwellcommunications.com, pg 998

Nunez, Rudy, Instrumentation Marketing Corp, 820 S Mariposa St, Burbank, CA 91506-3196 *Tel:* 818-842-2141 *Fax:* 818-842-2610 *E-mail:* mail@photosonics.com *Web Site:* www.photosonics.com/imc.htm, pg 899

Nunn, Robin, Production Support Services Inc, 827 Koeln Ave, St Louis, MO 63111 *Tel:* 314-535-8548 *Toll Free Tel:* 800-394-1257 *Fax:* 314-236-0735 *E-mail:* info@productionsupportservices.com *Web Site:* www.productionsupportservices.com, pg 985

Nurko, Eric, TRF Production Music Libraries, 106 Apple St, Suite 302, Tinton Falls, NJ 07724 *Tel:* 201-335-0005 *Toll Free Tel:* 800-899-MUSIC (899-6874) *Fax:* 201-335-0004 *E-mail:* info@trfmusic.com *Web Site:* www.trfmusic.com, pg 1044

Nurko, Michael, TRF Production Music Libraries, 106 Apple St, Suite 302, Tinton Falls, NJ 07724 *Tel:* 201-335-0005 *Toll Free Tel:* 800-899-MUSIC (899-6874) *Fax:* 201-335-0004 *E-mail:* info@trfmusic.com *Web Site:* www.trfmusic.com, pg 1044

Nursall, John, Black Media Works, 534 21 Ave SW, Calgary, AB T2S 0H1, Canada *Tel:* 403-802-0010 *E-mail:* info@blackmediaworks.com *Web Site:* www.blackmediaworks.com, pg 808

Nuss, Robert, Drumbeat Indian Arts Inc, 4143 N 16 St, Phoenix, AZ 85016 *Tel:* 602-266-4823 *Toll Free Tel:* 800-895-4859 *Fax:* 602-265-2402 *E-mail:* info@drumbeatindianarts.com *Web Site:* www.drumbeatindianarts.com, pg 852

Nutini, Mark, KPHO-TV5, 4016 N Black Canyon Hwy, Phoenix, AZ 85017 *Tel:* 602-264-1000 *Fax:* 602-274-1596 *E-mail:* cbs5news@kpho.com *Web Site:* www.news5.tv, pg 913

Nutt, Bob, Zachry Associates Inc, 500 Chestnut St, Suite 2000, Abilene, TX 79602 *Tel:* 325-677-1342 *Fax:* 325-672-2001 *E-mail:* info@zachryinc.com *Web Site:* zachryinc.com, pg 1073

Nuzum, Eric, National Public Radio (NPR), 1111 N Capitol St NE, Washington, DC 20002 *Tel:* 202-513-2000 *Web Site:* www.npr.org, pg 1086

Nye, Foster, University of Vermont, Instructional Television Dept, 234 Rowell Bldg, Burlington, VT 05405 *Tel:* 802-656-2927 *Fax:* 802-656-8816 *E-mail:* video@zoo.uvm.edu *Web Site:* www.uvm.edu; www.uvm.edu/~video, pg 1050

Nye, Joshua, Hawaii International Film Festival, 680 Iwilei Rd, Suite 100, Honolulu, HI 96817 *Tel:* 808-792-1577 *Fax:* 808-749-7783 *E-mail:* info@hiff.org *Web Site:* www.hiff.org, pg 1116

Nyquist, Eric, NASCAR Media Group LLC, 550 S Caldwell St, Suite 2000, Charlotte, NC 28202 *Tel:* 704-348-7100 *Web Site:* www.nascarmediagroup.com, pg 952

O'Brien, Chris, Telescript International, 55 Walnut St, Norwood, NJ 07648 *Tel:* 201-767-6733 *Toll Free Tel:* 888-767-6713 *Fax:* 201-784-0323 *E-mail:* info@telescript.com *Web Site:* telescript.com, pg 1036

O'Brien, M Kathleen, Institute on Religious Life Inc, PO Box 7500, Libertyville, IL 60048-7500 *Tel:* 847-573-8975 *Fax:* 847-573-8960 *Web Site:* www.religiouslife.com, pg 899

O'Brien, Michael, Video Advantage, 90 Houseman Crescent, Richmond Hill, ON L4C 7S6, Canada *Tel:* 905-883-5332 *E-mail:* info@videoadvantage.ca *Web Site:* www.videoadvantage.ca, pg 1054

O'Brien, Obie, Manhattan Center Studios Inc, 311 W 34 St, New York, NY 10001 *Tel:* 212-279-7740 *Fax:* 212-564-1072 *E-mail:* info@mcstudios.com *Web Site:* www.mcstudios.com, pg 930

O'Brien, Regina, Set Decorators Society of America (SDSA), 7100 Tujunga Ave, Suite A, North Hollywood, CA 91605 *Tel:* 818-255-2425 *Fax:* 818-982-8597 *E-mail:* sdsa@setdecorators.org *Web Site:* www.setdecorators.org, pg 1088

O'Brien, Tim, Univenture Inc, 13311 Industrial Pkwy, Marysville, OH 43040 *Tel:* 937-645-4600 *Toll Free Tel:* 877-831-9428 *Fax:* 937-645-4700 *E-mail:* sales@univenture.com; orders@univenture.com *Web Site:* www.univenture.com, pg 1049

O'Brien-Moran, Louise, Manitoba Film & Music, 410-93 Lombard Ave, Suite 410, Winnipeg, MB R3B 3B1, Canada *Tel:* 204-947-2040 *Fax:* 204-956-5261 *E-mail:* info@mbfilmmusic.ca *Web Site:* www.mbfilmmusic.ca, pg 1105

O'Connell, Paula, Vidcraft Productions Ltd, 425 Curling St, Corner Brook, NL A2H 3K4, Canada *Tel:* 709-785-1157 *E-mail:* info@vidcraft.com *Web Site:* www.vidcraft.com, pg 1054

O'Connell, Ron, Vidcraft Productions Ltd, 425 Curling St, Corner Brook, NL A2H 3K4, Canada *Tel:* 709-785-1157 *E-mail:* info@vidcraft.com *Web Site:* www.vidcraft.com, pg 1054

O'Connor, Gordon, Versatruss, 5028 Hwy 43, Perth, ON K7H 3C7, Canada *Tel:* 613-264-0074 *Toll Free Tel:* 888-430-7613 *Fax:* 613-264-0889 *E-mail:* info@versatruss.com *Web Site:* www.versatruss.com, pg 1053

O'Connor, Mary Beth, Ironbound Film & Television Studios LLC, Newark Arts & Entertainment Bldg, 169 Malvern St, Newark, NJ 07105 *Tel:* 201-456-4754 *Web Site:* www.ironboundfilmstudios.com, pg 902

O'Connor, Michael, Adolph Gasser Inc, 181 Second St, San Francisco, CA 94105 *Tel:* 415-495-3852 *Toll Free Tel:* 800-994-2773 *Fax:* 415-543-8510 *E-mail:* agivideo@yahoo.com *Web Site:* www.gasserphoto.com, pg 776

O'Connor, Patrick, OTR Studios, PO Box 874, Belmont, CA 94002 *Tel:* 650-595-8475 *E-mail:* info@otrstudios.com *Web Site:* www.otrstudios.com, pg 966

O'Connor, Susan, International Storytelling Center, 116 W Main St, Jonesborough, TN 37659 *Tel:* 423-753-2171 *Toll Free Tel:* 800-952-8392 *Fax:* 423-913-8219 *E-mail:* customerservice@storytellingcenter.net *Web Site:* www.storytellingcenter.net, pg 1084

O'Connor, Susan, National Storytelling Festival, 116 W Main St, Jonesborough, TN 37659 *Tel:* 423-753-2171 *Toll Free Tel:* 800-952-8392 *Fax:* 423-913-8219 *E-mail:* customerservice@storytellingcenter.net *Web Site:* www.storytellingfestival.net; www.storytellingcenter.net, pg 1121

O'Connor, Tom, Desktop Video Systems, 9052 Parkhill, Lenexa, KS 66215 *Tel:* 913-782-8888 *Toll Free Tel:* 800-662-6901 *Fax:* 913-492-6908 *E-mail:* sales@desktopvideosystems.com *Web Site:* www.desktopvideosystems.com, pg 846

O'Daniel, Paul, PC&E, 2235 DeFoor Hills Rd, Atlanta, GA 30318 *Tel:* 404-609-9001 *Toll Free Tel:* 800-537-4021 *Fax:* 404-609-9926 *Web Site:* www.pce-atlanta.com, pg 970

O'Donnell, Kerry, Emergency Film Group, 140 Cooke St, Edgartown, MA 02539 *Tel:* 508-627-8844 *Toll Free Tel:* 800-842-0999 *Fax:* 508-627-8863 *E-mail:* info@efilmgroup.com *Web Site:* www.efilmgroup.com, pg 860

O'Gorman, Jerry, B&B Electronics Manufacturing Co, 707 Dayton Rd, Ottawa, IL 61350 *Tel:* 815-433-5100 *Toll Free Tel:* 800-346-3119 *Fax:* 815-433-5109 *E-mail:* info@bb-elec.com; orders@bb-elec.com *Web Site:* www.bb-elec.com, pg 802

O'Grady, Martha, Panta Rhei Media Inc, 565 Beulah Rd, Turtle Creek, PA 15145 *Tel:* 412-824-8858 *E-mail:* info@panta-rhei.com *Web Site:* www.panta-rhei.com, pg 968

O'Guin, Sharon Fox, The Memphis & Shelby County Film & TV Commission, 496 S Main St, Suite 101, Memphis, TN 38103 *Tel:* 901-527-8300 (ext 2) *Fax:* 901-527-8326 *E-mail:* info@memphisfilmcomm.org *Web Site:* www.filmmemphis.org, pg 1102

O'Guinn Condron, Barbara, SOM Publishing Co, 163 Moon Valley Rd, Windyville, MO 65783 *Tel:* 417-345-8411 *E-mail:* som@som.org *Web Site:* www.som.org, pg 1015

O'Hare, Thomas, Studio Dynamics, 7703 Alondra Blvd, Paramount, CA 90723 *Tel:* 562-531-6700 *Toll Free Tel:* 800-595-4273 *Fax:* 562-531-6769 *E-mail:* sales@studiodynamics.com *Web Site:* www.studiodynamics.com, pg 1026

O'Hearen, Tracey, Telemanagement Resources International Inc (TRI), 124 Thomas Lane, Manahawkin, NJ 08050 *Tel:* 609-597-6334 *Web Site:* www.triinc.com, pg 1036

O'Keefe, Carrie, Freestyle Productions Inc, 7160 Madison Ave W, Minneapolis, MN 55427 *Tel:* 763-417-9575 *Fax:* 763-417-9576 *E-mail:* info@freestyle-productions.com *Web Site:* freestyleproductions.com, pg 872

O'Keefe, Catie, O'Keefe Communications Inc, 4301 Connecticut Ave NW, Suite 200, Washington, DC 20008-2304 *Tel:* 202-363-2101 *E-mail:* info@okeefecom.com *Web Site:* www.okeefecom.com, pg 961

O'Keefe, David, VFGadgets Inc, 22 Elmer Ave, Toronto, ON M4L 3R7, Canada *Tel:* 416-686-1452 *E-mail:* sales@vfgadgets.com; customerservice@vfgadgets.com *Web Site:* www.vfgadgets.com, pg 1053

O'Keefe, James J, All Jersey Studios, 222 Cavour St, Colonia, NJ 07067 *Tel:* 732-382-2333 *E-mail:* info@alljerseystudios.com *Web Site:* www.alljerseystudios.com, pg 780

O'Keefe, Kevin, O'Keefe Communications Inc, 4301 Connecticut Ave NW, Suite 200, Washington, DC 20008-2304 *Tel:* 202-363-2101 *E-mail:* info@okeefecom.com *Web Site:* www.okeefecom.com, pg 961

O'Keefe, Tony, CAD Audio, 6573 Cochran Rd, Bldg I, Solon, OH 44139 *Tel:* 440-349-4900 *Toll Free Tel:* 800-762-9266 (ext 211) *Fax:* 440-248-4902 *E-mail:* sales@cadaudio.com *Web Site:* www.cadaudio.com, pg 816

O'Leary, MJ, John Wiley & Sons Inc, 111 River St, Hoboken, NJ 07030 *Tel:* 201-748-6000 *Toll Free Tel:* 800-225-5945 *Fax:* 201-748-6088 *E-mail:* info@wiley.com *Web Site:* www.wiley.com, pg 1066

O'Neil, Mike, Freeman, 1600 Viceroy, Suite 100, Dallas, TX 75235 *Tel:* 214-445-1000 *Fax:* 214-445-0200 *Web Site:* www.freemanco.com, pg 872

O'Neill, Denise, The Pepper Group, 220 N Smith St, Suite 406, Palatine, IL 60067 *Tel:* 847-963-0333 *Fax:* 847-963-0888 *E-mail:* pepper@peppergroup.com *Web Site:* www.peppergroup.com, pg 973

O'Neill, Ken, Laser Video Corp, 401 Germantown Pike, Lafayette Hill, PA 19444 *Tel:* 610-825-2500 *Toll Free Tel:* 800-448-8772 *Fax:* 610-941-9989 *E-mail:* customerservice@laservideousa.com *Web Site:* www.lvconline.com, pg 916

O'Neill, Kerrigan, Hollywood Lights Inc, 5251 SE McLoughlin Blvd, Portland, OR 97202-4836 *Tel:* 503-232-9001; 503-232-8855 *Toll Free Tel:* 800-826-9881 *Fax:* 503-517-8686 *E-mail:* portland@hollywoodlights.biz *Web Site:* www.hollywoodlights.biz, pg 890

O'Neill, Michael, Switch, 6600 Manchester Ave, St Louis, MO 63139 *Tel:* 314-206-7700 *Toll Free Tel:* 800-445-0633 *Fax:* 314-206-4570 *E-mail:* switch@theswitch.us *Web Site:* www.liberateyourbrand.com, pg 1030

O'Neill, Thomas P Jr, ACCO Brands Corp, 4 Corporate Dr, Lake Zurick, IL 60047-8997 *Toll Free Tel:* 800-541-0094 *Toll Free Fax:* 800-941-4463 *E-mail:* contactus@gbc.com *Web Site:* www.accobrands.com, pg 773

O'Neill, Trudie, Laser Video Corp, 401 Germantown Pike, Lafayette Hill, PA 19444 *Tel:* 610-825-2500 *Toll Free Tel:* 800-448-8772 *Fax:* 610-941-9989 *E-mail:* customerservice@laservideousa.com *Web Site:* www.lvconline.com, pg 916

O'Pecko, Paul, Mystic Seaport (Film & Video Archives), 75 Greenmanville Ave, Mystic, CT 06355 *Tel:* 860-572-5367 *Toll Free Tel:* 888-973-2767 *E-mail:* collections@mysticseaport.org; info@mysticseaport.org *Web Site:* www.mysticseaport.org, pg 951

O'Reilly, Matthew P, Tritech Communications, 625 Locust St, Suite 300, Garden City, NY 11530 *Tel:* 631-254-4500 *Fax:* 631-254-4499 *E-mail:* sales@tritechcomm.com *Web Site:* www.tritechcomm.com, pg 1045

O'Riley, Margaret, Michigan Film Office, 300 N Washington Sq, 4th fl, Lansing, MI 48913 *Tel:* 517-373-3456 *Toll Free Tel:* 800-477-FILM (477-3456) *Fax:* 517-241-0867 *E-mail:* mfo@michigan.org *Web Site:* www.michiganfilmoffice.org, pg 1098

Oakley, Jeff, Crossroads Audio Inc, 2623 Myrtle Springs Ave, Dallas, TX 75220 *Tel:* 214-358-2623 *Toll Free Tel:* 800-287-0436 *Fax:* 214-358-0185 *E-mail:* mail@crossroadsaudio.com *Web Site:* www.crossroadsaudio.com, pg 840

Oatley, Steve, Axis Films, 3138 Cumberland Rd, Berkley, MI 48072 *Tel:* 248-722-1734 *Web Site:* www.axisfilms.tv, pg 800

Oatman, Steve, Pounds Photographic Labs Inc, 901 Regal Row, Dallas, TX 75247 *Tel:* 214-688-1425 *Toll Free Tel:* 800-350-5671 *Fax:* 214-688-1429 *Web Site:* www.poundslabs.com, pg 979

Ocean, Evgueni Sam, McCauley Sound Inc, 16607 Meridian Ave E, Puyallup, WA 98375 *Tel:* 253-848-0363 *Toll Free Tel:* 877-622-2853 *Fax:* 253-841-3050 *Web Site:* www.mccauleysound.com, pg 935

Odehnal, Steve, Sacramento Theatrical Lighting Ltd (STL), 950 Richards Blvd, Sacramento, CA 95811 *Tel:* 916-447-3258 *Toll Free Tel:* 800-283-2785 *Fax:* 916-447-5012 *E-mail:* info@stlltd.com *Web Site:* www.stlltd.com, pg 1001

Oden, Ecar, Video Resources Inc, 1809 E Dyer Rd, Suite 307, Santa Ana, CA 92705 *Tel:* 949-261-7266 *Toll Free Tel:* 800-261-7266 *Fax:* 949-261-5908 *E-mail:* info@videoresources.com *Web Site:* www.videoresources.com, pg 1056

Odunsi, Yolanda, Annenberg Learner, PO Box 26983, St Louis, MO 63118 *Tel:* 202-783-0500 (outside US) *Toll Free Tel:* 800-LEARNER (532-7637) *Fax:* 202-783-0333 *E-mail:* order@learner.org *Web Site:* www.learner.org, pg 787

Oehlers, Paul, The American University, Dept of Performing Arts, 4400 Massachusetts Ave NW, Washington, DC 20016-8053 *Tel:* 202-885-2746 *Fax:* 202-885-1092 *E-mail:* audiotech@american.edu *Web Site:* www.american.edu, pg 785

Oei, Elisabeth, Sonoton Music Library, 6255 Sunset Blvd, Suite 820, Hollywood, CA 90028 *Tel:* 323-461-3211 *Toll Free Tel:* 800-543-4276 *Fax:* 323-461-9102 *Web Site:* www.apmmusic.com, pg 1016

Ogburn, Jim, CineFilm Lab, 2156 Faulkner Rd NE, Atlanta, GA 30324 *Tel:* 404-633-1448 *Toll Free Tel:* 800-633-1448 *Fax:* 404-633-3867 *E-mail:* csr@cinefilmlab.com *Web Site:* www.cinefilmlab.com, pg 827

Oglesby, Alan, HSA Inc, 1717 E Sixth St, Mishawaka, IN 46544 *Tel:* 574-255-6100 *Fax:* 574-255-8131 *E-mail:* hsainfo@hsarolltops.com *Web Site:* www.hsarolltops.com, pg 892

Oh, Christian, DC Asian Pacific American Film Festival, 2515 Virginia Ave NW, No 58205, Washington, DC 20037 *Tel:* 703-507-4375 *E-mail:* info@apafilm.org; admin@apafilm.org *Web Site:* www.apafilm.org, pg 1113

Ohl, Ted, Pook Diemont & Ohl Inc, 701 E 132 St, Bronx, NY 10454 *Tel:* 718-402-2677 *Fax:* 718-402-2859 *E-mail:* info@pdoinc.com *Web Site:* www.pdoinc.com, pg 978

Ohlhaber, Ron, Dukane Corp, Audio Visual Products Division, 2900 Dukane Dr, St Charles, IL 60174 *Tel:* 630-762-4040 *Toll Free Tel:* 888-245-1966 *Fax:* 630-584-5156 *E-mail:* avsales@dukane.com *Web Site:* dukaneav.com, pg 853

Ohtsuki, Mike, Universe Kogaku America Inc, 116 Audrey Ave, Oyster Bay, NY 11771 *Tel:* 516-624-2444 *Fax:* 516-624-3109 *E-mail:* info@universeoptics.com *Web Site:* universeoptics.com, pg 1049

Oien, Laura, Tom Hopkins International Inc, 465 E Chilton Dr, Suite 4, Chandler, AZ 85225 *Tel:* 480-949-0786 *Toll Free Tel:* 800-528-0446 *Fax:* 480-949-1590 *E-mail:* info@tomhopkins.com *Web Site:* www.tomhopkins.com, pg 891

Oishi, Tsutomu (Tom), PLUS Corp of America, 9610 SW Sunshine Ct, Suite 100, Beaverton, OR 97005 *Tel:* 503-748-8700 *Toll Free Tel:* 800-211-9001 *Fax:* 503-643-9756 *E-mail:* sales@plus-america.com *Web Site:* www.plus-america.com, pg 977

Okamoto, Keith, Konica Minolta Business Solutions, 100 Williams Dr, Ramsey, NJ 07446 *Tel:* 201-825-4000 *Fax:* 201-825-7567 *Web Site:* kmbs.konicaminolta.us, pg 913

Olden, Robert, Olden Camera & Lens Co Inc, 1263 Broadway, 4th fl, New York, NY 10001-3593 *Tel:* 212-725-1234 *Fax:* 212-725-1325, pg 962

Olden, Walter L, Olden Lighting, 2008 Alexander Ave, Austin, TX 78722 *Tel:* 512-416-8080 *Fax:* 512-416-8096 *E-mail:* rental@oldenlighting.com; sales@oldenlighting.com *Web Site:* www.oldenlighting.com, pg 962

Olechny, Steven, NDS Surgical Imaging LLC, 5750 Hellyer Ave, San Jose, CA 95138 *Tel:* 408-776-0085 *Toll Free Tel:* 866-637-5237 *Fax:* 408-776-9878 *E-mail:* info@ndssi.com *Web Site:* www.ndssi.com, pg 954

Oleno, Andee, Swank Audio Visuals, 639-E Gravois Bluffs, St Louis, MO 63026 *Tel:* 636-680-9000 *Toll Free Tel:* 877-792-6528 *Fax:* 636-680-2853 *Web Site:* www.swankav.com, pg 1029

Olinsky, David, Disc Makers, 7905 N Rte 130, Pennsauken, NJ 08110-1402 *Tel:* 856-663-9030 *Toll Free Tel:* 800-468-9353 *Fax:* 856-661-3450 *E-mail:* info@discmakers.com *Web Site:* www.discmakers.com, pg 848

Oliva, Krystal, DocMiami International Film Festival, 8770 Sunset Dr, No 274, Miami, FL 33173-3512 *Tel:* 786-493-8308 *E-mail:* info@docmiami.org *Web Site:* www.docmiami.org, pg 1114

Olive, James "Jim" Lee, Stockyard Photos/Jim Olive Photography, 1520 Center St, Studio 2, Houston, TX 77007 *Tel:* 713-520-0898 *Fax:* 713-820-6965 *Web Site:* www.stockyard.com, pg 1025

Oliver, Katherine, New York City Mayor's Office of Film, Theatre & Broadcasting, 1697 Broadway, 6th fl, Suite 602, New York, NY 10019 *Tel:* 212-489-6710 *Fax:* 212-307-6237 *E-mail:* info@film.nyc.gov *Web Site:* www.nyc.gov/film, pg 1100

Oliver, Lee, Arizona Cine Equipment, 2125 E 20 St, Tucson, AZ 85719 *Tel:* 520-623-8268 *Fax:* 520-623-1092 *Web Site:* www.azcine.com, pg 789

Oliver, Linda, Arizona Cine Equipment, 2125 E 20 St, Tucson, AZ 85719 *Tel:* 520-623-8268 *Fax:* 520-623-1092 *Web Site:* www.azcine.com, pg 789

Olsen, Craig N, WindTech™ Microphone Windscreens & Accessories, 7845 E Evans Rd, Scottsdale, AZ 85260-2919 *Tel:* 480-998-7140 *Fax:* 480-998-7192 *E-mail:* information@olsenaudio.com; web-info3@olsenaudio.com *Web Site:* www.olsenaudio.com; www.windtech.tv, pg 1067

Olsen, David, Right Stuf Inc, 512 NE Main St, Grimes, IA 50111-0680 *Tel:* 515-986-1028 *Toll Free Tel:* 800-338-6827 *Fax:* 515-986-1129 *E-mail:* info@rightstuf.com *Web Site:* www.rightstuf.com, pg 997

Olsen, Keith, Interscreen America Inc, 13191 56 Ct, Suite 104, Clearwater, FL 33760 *Tel:* 727-546-8515 *Toll Free Tel:* 800-520-9642 *Toll Free Fax:* 866-476-0440 *E-mail:* info@interscreen.tv *Web Site:* www.interscreen.us, pg 901

Olson, Dan, Olson Visual Inc, 13000 Weber Way, Hawthorne, CA 90250 *Tel:* 310-355-1681 *Toll Free Tel:* 800-480-6643 *Fax:* 310-263-6980 *E-mail:* graphics@olsonvisual.com *Web Site:* www.olsonvisual.com, pg 962

Olson, Doug, Image Craft LLC, 3401 E Broadway Rd, Phoenix, AZ 85040 *Tel:* 602-276-2082 *Toll Free Tel:* 800-274-2422 *Fax:* 602-232-0719 *E-mail:* designgroup@imcraft.com *Web Site:* www.imcraft.com, pg 895

Olson, Gary H, GHO Group LLC, 340 W 55 St, Suite 5E, New York, NY 10019 *Tel:* 212-319-7716 *E-mail:* info@ghogroup.com *Web Site:* www.ghogroup.com, pg 878

Olson, Jason, Duplication Media, 8126 Douglas Ave, Urbandale, IA 50322 *Tel:* 515-334-DUPS (334-3877) *E-mail:* info@duplicationmedia.com *Web Site:* www.duplicationmedia.com, pg 853

Olson, Mark A, CommScope Inc, 1100 CommScope Place SE, Hickory, NC 28602 *Tel:* 828-324-2200 *Toll Free Tel:* 800-982-1708 *Web Site:* www.commscope.com, pg 832

Olson, Tom, Olson Visual Inc, 13000 Weber Way, Hawthorne, CA 90250 *Tel:* 310-355-1681 *Toll Free Tel:* 800-480-6643 *Fax:* 310-263-6980 *E-mail:* graphics@olsonvisual.com *Web Site:* www.olsonvisual.com, pg 962

Olson-Scovill, Sarah, Science Museum of Minnesota, 120 W Kellogg Blvd, St Paul, MN 55102 *Tel:* 651-221-9444 *Toll Free Tel:* 800-221-9444 *Fax:* 651-221-4533 *E-mail:* info@smm.org *Web Site:* www.smm.org, pg 1005

Olsson, Martin, Stage Post, 255 French Landing Dr, Nashville, TN 37228 *Tel:* 615-248-1978 *Toll Free Tel:* 877-250-1839 *Fax:* 615-242-8861 *E-mail:* mail@stagepost.com *Web Site:* www.stagepost.com, pg 1022

Ombao, Satti, Rollin Studios, 199 Green St, Brooklyn, NY 11222 *E-mail:* more@rollin-studios.com *Web Site:* www.rollin-studios.com, pg 998

Omps, Jon, PC&E, 2235 DeFoor Hills Rd, Atlanta, GA 30318 *Tel:* 404-609-9001 *Toll Free Tel:* 800-537-4021 *Fax:* 404-609-9926 *Web Site:* www.pce-atlanta.com, pg 970

Ontiveros, Arianna, R&O Studios, 5805 N 39 St, McAllen, TX 78504 *Tel:* 956-203-0520 *E-mail:* rostudiosrgv@gmail.com *Web Site:* www.randostudios.com, pg 991

Oono, Junichiro, Canare Corporation of America, 45 Commerce Way, Unit C, Totowa, NJ 07512 *Tel:* 973-837-0070 *Fax:* 973-837-0080 *E-mail:* sales@canare.com *Web Site:* www.canare.com, pg 819

Oosterhuis, Marc, Drytac Corp, 5601 Eastport Blvd, Richmond, VA 23231 *Toll Free Tel:* 800-280-6013 *E-mail:* customerservice@drytac.com *Web Site:* www.drytac.com, pg 852

Oppenheimer, Marty, Oppenheimer Camera Products, 7400 Third Ave S, Seattle, WA 98108-4143 *Tel:* 206-467-8666 *Toll Free Tel:* 877-467-8666 *Fax:* 206-467-9165 *Web Site:* oppenheimercameraproducts.com, pg 964

Orbegoso, Louise, Lenel Systems International Inc, 1212 Pittsford-Victor Rd, Pittsford, NY 14534-3820 *Tel:* 585-248-9720 *Toll Free Tel:* 866-788-5095 *Fax:* 585-248-9185 *E-mail:* pr@lenel.com *Web Site:* www.lenel.com, pg 919

Ordelheide, Whitney K, CPI Malibu, 3760-A Calle Tecate, Camarillo, CA 93012-5060 *Tel:* 805-383-1829 *Fax:* 805-383-1859 *E-mail:* malibu.sales@cpii.com *Web Site:* www.cpii.com/division.cfm/10, pg 837

Orgera, George, F&F Productions, 14333 Myerlake Circle, Clearwater, FL 33760 *Tel:* 727-530-5000 *Fax:* 727-535-6547 *Web Site:* www.fandfhd.tv, pg 865

Orlando, Ken, Cool-Lux, 1268 Humbracht Circle, Bartlett, IL 60103 *Toll Free Tel:* 800-ACDC-LUX (223-2589) *Fax:* 630-830-2525 *Web Site:* www.cool-lux.com, pg 836

Orlando, Ken, Quantum Instruments Inc, 1268 Humbracht Circle, Bartlett, IL 60103-1631 *Tel:* 631-656-7400 *Fax:* 631-656-7410 *E-mail:* quantumhelp@qtm.com *Web Site:* www.qtm.com, pg 989

Orlando, Ken, Speedotron Corp, 1268 Humbracht Circle, Bartlett, IL 60103-1631 *Tel:* 630-246-5001 *Fax:* 630-830-2525 *E-mail:* support@speedotron.com *Web Site:* www.speedotron.com, pg 1021

Orlando, Kenneth, Smith-Victor Corp, 1268 Humbracht Circle, Bartlett, IL 60103-1631 *Tel:* 630-830-9200 *Toll Free Tel:* 800-348-9862 *Fax:* 630-830-9201 *Toll Free Fax:* 800-352-0490 *E-mail:* sales@smithvictor.com, pg 1014

Orlando, Ron, ATS Cases Inc, 172 Otis St, Northborough, MA 01532 *Tel:* 508-393-9110 *Toll Free Tel:* 800-451-4242; 800-519-2771 *Fax:* 508-393-9508 *E-mail:* casemakers@mac.com *Web Site:* atscases.com, pg 793

Orosz, Bruce, ACT Productions, 407 Lincoln Rd, Suite 302, Miami Beach, FL 33139 *Tel:* 305-538-3809 *Fax:* 305-538-3814 *E-mail:* info@actproductions.com *Web Site:* www.actproductions.com, pg 775

Orr, Bill, Michigan Office Solutions, 2859 Walkent Dr NW, Grand Rapids, MI 49544 *Tel:* 616-454-1198 *Toll Free Tel:* 800-442-9070 *Fax:* 616-459-8705 *Web Site:* www.miofficesolutions.com, pg 941

Orr, Henry, Gaylord Brothers, PO Box 4901, Syracuse, NY 13221-4901 *Tel:* 315-634-8243 (intl) *Toll Free Tel:* 800-962-9580 (cust serv) *Fax:* 315-453-5030 (intl) *Toll Free Fax:* 800-272-3412 *E-mail:* customerservice@gaylord.com *Web Site:* www.gaylord.com, pg 876

Orr, Rob, Rob Orr Productions Ltd, 1336 Pine St, Glenview, IL 60025 *Tel:* 847-724-5228 *Fax:* 847-729-7319 *E-mail:* rob@roborrproductions.com *Web Site:* www.roborrproductions.com, pg 965

Ort, Gene, GMP Music, 1103 North St, Niles, MI 49120 *Tel:* 269-687-9100 *Toll Free Tel:* 800-955-0619 *Fax:* 269-687-9200 *E-mail:* info@gmpmusic.com *Web Site:* www.gmpmusic.com; www.reservemusic.com, pg 879

Ortabasi, Leslie, The Dreaming Tree, 1112 Chestnut St, Unit B, Burbank, CA 91506 *Tel:* 818-845-3230 *Fax:* 818-333-0795 *E-mail:* info@dreamingtreeproductions.com *Web Site:* www.dreamingtreeproductions.com, pg 852

Ortabasi, Oktay, The Dreaming Tree, 1112 Chestnut St, Unit B, Burbank, CA 91506 *Tel:* 818-845-3230 *Fax:* 818-333-0795 *E-mail:* info@dreamingtreeproductions.com *Web Site:* www.dreamingtreeproductions.com, pg 852

Ortiz, Mark, Paulist Productions, 17575 Pacific Coast Hwy, Pacific Palisades, CA 90272-4128 *Tel:* 310-454-0688 *Toll Free Tel:* 800-624-8613 *Fax:* 310-459-6549 *E-mail:* paulistmail@paulistproductions.org *Web Site:* www.paulistproductions.org, pg 970

Ortiz, Patty, Premio Mesquite, 723 S Brazos St, San Antonio, TX 78207 *Tel:* 210-271-3151 (ext 232) *Fax:* 210-271-3480 *E-mail:* cine@guadalupeculturalarts.org *Web Site:* www.guadalupeculturalarts.org, pg 1124

Ortiz, Vidal, Cine 60 Inc, 630 Ninth Ave, New York, NY 10036 *Tel:* 347-460-3971 *E-mail:* cine60nyc@gmail.com *Web Site:* cine60.jimdo.com, pg 826

Osawa, Hogan, Yamaha Electronics Corp, 6660 Orangethorpe Ave, Buena Park, CA 90620 *Tel:* 714-522-9105 *Toll Free Tel:* 800-292-2982 (cust support) *Toll Free Fax:* 800-782-8484 *Web Site:* www.yamaha.com, pg 1071

Osborn, Jeff, Audience Response Systems Inc, 5611-C E Morgan Ave, Evansville, IN 47715 *Tel:* 812-479-7507 *Toll Free Tel:* 800-INVOLVE (468-6583) *Fax:* 812-479-1057 *Web Site:* www.audienceresponse.com, pg 794

Osborn, Pell, MotionArt Studios, 27 Common St, Boston, MA 02129 *Tel:* 617-242-2228 *Web Site:* www.motionart.org; www.linestorm.com, pg 947

Osborne, Bud, AVA Productions, 4760 E 65 St, Indianapolis, IN 46220 *Tel:* 317-255-6457 *E-mail:* avaprods@comcast.net *Web Site:* www.avavideoproductions.com, pg 798

Oslund, Deborah, Broadcast Rentals, 2343 W University Dr, Suite 101, Tempe, AZ 85281 *Tel:* 480-894-1456 *Toll Free Tel:* 888-686-7368 *Fax:* 480-894-1023 *E-mail:* rent@broadcastrentals.com *Web Site:* www.broadcastrentals.com, pg 813

Oslund, Steve, Broadcast Rentals, 2343 W University Dr, Suite 101, Tempe, AZ 85281 *Tel:* 480-894-1456 *Toll Free Tel:* 888-686-7368 *Fax:* 480-894-1023 *E-mail:* rent@broadcastrentals.com *Web Site:* www.broadcastrentals.com, pg 813

Osorio, William, Video Ideas Productions, 1501 64 St, North Bergen, NJ 07047 *Tel:* 201-951-3798 *Fax:* 201-662-4846 *Web Site:* osoriomedia.com, pg 1055

Oster, Doran, Sabine® Inc, 13301 US Hwy 441, Alachua, FL 32615-8544 *Tel:* 386-418-2000 *Toll Free Tel:* 800-626-7394 *Fax:* 386-418-2001 *E-mail:* sabine@sabine.com *Web Site:* www.sabine.com, pg 1001

Osterman, Fred, Universal Radio Inc, 6830 Americana Pkwy, Reynoldsburg, OH 43068 *Tel:* 614-866-4267 *Toll Free Tel:* 800-431-3939 (orders) *Fax:* 614-866-2339 *E-mail:* dx@universal-radio.com *Web Site:* www.universal-radio.com, pg 1049

Ostrover, Lewis, Warner Home Video Inc, 4000 Warner Blvd, Bldg 160, Burbank, CA 91522 *Tel:* 818-954-6000 *Fax:* 818-954-6480 *Web Site:* www.warnerbros.com, pg 1062

Oswald, Andy, West Penn Wire, 2833 W Chestnut St, Washington, PA 15301 *Tel:* 724-222-7060 *Toll Free Tel:* 800-245-4964 *Fax:* 724-222-6420 *E-mail:* info@westpenn-wpw.com *Web Site:* www.westpenn-wpw.com, pg 1064

Oswald, Dan, Business & Legal Reports Inc, 141 Mill Rock Rd E, Old Saybrook, CT 06475 *Tel:* 860-510-0100 *Toll Free Tel:* 800-727-5257 *Fax:* 860-510-7224 *E-mail:* service@blr.com *Web Site:* www.blr.com, pg 815

Otrusina, Edward, Flight Form Cases Inc, 6543 S Laramie Ave, Bedford Park, IL 60638 *Tel:* 708-458-8989 *Toll Free Tel:* 800-334-4884 *Fax:* 708-458-9023 *E-mail:* info@flightform.com; info@caseyguys.net; sales@caseguys.com *Web Site:* www.flightform.com, pg 870

Otsuka, Yuichi, Hitachi Kokusai Electric America Ltd, 150 Crossways Park Dr, Woodbury, NY 11797 *Tel:* 516-921-7200 *Fax:* 516-496-3718 *E-mail:* info@hitachikokusai.us *Web Site:* hitachikokusai.us, pg 889

Ott, Robert M, Ott Film Rentals, 6901 Castor Ave, Philadelphia, PA 19149 *Tel:* 215-745-8964 *Toll Free Tel:* 800-545-4558 *Fax:* 215-745-8965, pg 966

Ottolenghi, Arturo M, Red Hill Corp, 1540 Biglerville Rd, Gettysburg, PA 17325 *Tel:* 717-337-3038 *Toll Free Tel:* 800-822-4003 *Fax:* 717-337-0732 *E-mail:* customerservice@supergrit.com *Web Site:* www.supergrit.com, pg 993

Ouimet, Francois, Auriga Productions Ltd, 2856 rue du Comtois, Ste-Lazare, QC J7T 0E7, Canada *Tel:* 514-984-4202 *E-mail:* aurigapix@gmail.com *Web Site:* www.aurigapix.com, pg 797

Owen, Lisa, Applause Productions & Publications, PO Box 820024, Dallas, TX 75382-0024 *Tel:* 214-652-4300 *Fax:* 214-652-4075 *E-mail:* info@applauseproductions.com *Web Site:* applauseproductions.com, pg 788

Owen, Marvin, ACS Technologies, 180 N Dunbarton Dr, Florence, SC 29501 *Tel:* 843-662-1681 *Toll Free Tel:* 800-736-7425 *Fax:* 843-669-3198 *E-mail:* info@acstechnologies.com *Web Site:* www.acstechnologies.com, pg 775

Owens, Earl E, BSW Records, PO Box 2297, Universal City, TX 78148-1297 *Tel:* 210-653-3989 *Fax:* 210-653-3989 *E-mail:* bswr18@att.net *Web Site:* www.bsw-records.com, pg 814

Owens, Peg, Idaho Film Office, 700 W State St, Boise, ID 83702 *Tel:* 208-334-2470 *Toll Free Tel:* 800-942-8338 *Fax:* 208-334-2631 *Web Site:* www.filmidaho.com, pg 1097

Owens, Robert, Method Studios, 730 Arizona Ave, Santa Monica, CA 90401 *Tel:* 310-434-6500 *Web Site:* www.methodstudios.com, pg 939

Oyung, Alec, Ludlow Media Solutions, 15501 San Pablo Ave, Suite G320, San Pablo, CA 94806 *Tel:* 415-927-1300 *E-mail:* info@ludlowmedia.com *Web Site:* www.ludlowmedia.com, pg 926

Ozzanto, Arianna, Screen Actors Guild & American Federation of Television & Radio Artists (SAG-AFTRA), 5757 Wilshire Blvd, 7th fl, Los Angeles, CA 90036-3600 *Tel:* 323-954-1600 (former SAG); 323-634-8100 (former AFTRA) *Toll Free Tel:* 855-SAG-AFTRA (724-2387) *Fax:* 323-634-8194 *E-mail:* sagaftrainfo@sagaftra.org *Web Site:* www.sagaftra.org/ny, pg 1088

Pace, Jenna, Vidicom Inc, 520 Eighth Ave, Suite 2206, New York, NY 10018 *Tel:* 212-895-8300 *E-mail:* info@vidicom.com *Web Site:* vidicom.com, pg 1057

Pace, Jim, Plus 24, 1155 N La Brea Ave, West Hollywood, CA 90038 *Tel:* 323-845-1171; 323-845-1168 (support) *Toll Free Tel:* 800-330-7753 (orders) *Fax:* 323-845-1170 *E-mail:* info@plus24.net; sales@plus24.net *Web Site:* www.plus24.net, pg 977

Pace-Stall, Angela, Ironik Design & Post, 56 E Main St, Suite 203, Avon, CT 06001 *Tel:* 860-404-2386 *Fax:* 860-404-2735 *E-mail:* info@ironikdesign.com *Web Site:* www.ironikdesign.com, pg 902

Packard, Ellen, Wiltronix, 16850 Oakmont Ave, Washington Grove, MD 20880 *Tel:* 301-258-7676 *Toll Free Tel:* 800-848-7870 *Fax:* 301-854-3434 *E-mail:* equipsales@wiltronix.com *Web Site:* www.wiltronix.com, pg 1067

Padgett, Tim, The Pepper Group, 220 N Smith St, Suite 406, Palatine, IL 60067 *Tel:* 847-963-0333 *Fax:* 847-963-0888 *E-mail:* pepper@peppergroup.com *Web Site:* www.peppergroup.com, pg 973

Padgitt, Jason, Fender Musical Instruments Corp, 17600 N Perimeter Dr, Suite 100, Scottsdale, AZ 85255 *Tel:* 480-596-9690 *Fax:* 480-596-1384 *E-mail:* consumerrelations@fender.com *Web Site:* www.fender.com, pg 866

Page, Catherine, Western Heritage Awards, 1700 NE 63 St, Oklahoma City, OK 73111 *Tel:* 405-478-2250 *Fax:* 405-478-4714 *Web Site:* nationalcowboymuseum.org, pg 1129

Page, Greg, NuMynd Studios, 915 Twin Elms Ct, Nashville, TN 37210 *Tel:* 615-259-1143 *Fax:* 615-259-1141 *E-mail:* hello@numyndstudios.com *Web Site:* www.numyndstudios.com, pg 960

Paglia, Karen, York Telecom, 81 Corbett Way, Eatontown, NJ 07724 *Tel:* 732-413-6000 *Toll Free Tel:* 866-836-8463 *Fax:* 732-413-6060 *E-mail:* knowmore@yorktel.com *Web Site:* yorktel.com, pg 1072

Pagliante, Nick, Gerriets International, 130 Winterwood Ave, Ewing, NJ 08638 *Tel:* 609-771-8111 *Toll Free Tel:* 800-369-3695 *Fax:* 609-771-8118 *E-mail:* info@gerriets.us *Web Site:* www.gerriets.us, pg 877

Paine McBrien, Judith, Perspectives Media, 410 S Michigan Ave, Chicago, IL 60605 *Tel:* 312-212-1492, pg 973

Painter, Brad, Dot Hill Systems Corp, 1351 S Sunset St, Longmont, CO 80501-6533 *Tel:* 303-845-3200 *Toll Free Tel:* 800-872-2783 *Fax:* 303-845-3655 *E-mail:* support@dothill.com; websales@dothill.com *Web Site:* www.dothill.com, pg 851

Pair, Laura, Synaptic Digital, 79 Fifth Ave, 14th fl, New York, NY 10003 *Tel:* 212-682-8300 *Toll Free Tel:* 800-843-0677 *Fax:* 212-682-5260 *E-mail:* learnmore@synapticdigital.com *Web Site:* www.synapticdigital.com, pg 1030

Pajerski, Maureen, Rauland-Borg Corp, 1802 W Central Rd, Mount Prospect, IL 60056 *Tel:* 847-590-7100 *Toll Free Tel:* 800-752-7725 *Web Site:* www.rauland.com, pg 991

Pal, Laszlo, Pal Productions Inc, 4056 NE 174 St, Seattle, WA 98155 *Tel:* 206-361-9366 *E-mail:* info@paladventurevideos.com *Web Site:* www.paladventurevideos.com, pg 967

Palakovich, Ben, Gluskin's Custom Audio Video, 2087 Grand Canal Blvd, Suite 11, Stockton, CA 95204 *Tel:* 209-888-4609 *Fax:* 209-888-4629 *E-mail:* audio@gluskins.com *Web Site:* www.gluskins.com, pg 879

Palazzola, John L, VTP Inc, 2721 W Magnolia Blvd, Burbank, CA 91505 *Tel:* 818-566-9898 *Toll Free Tel:* 800-422-2444 *E-mail:* sales@vtpcorp.com *Web Site:* www.myvtp.com, pg 1061

Palfrey, Deanna, Palardo Productions, 1807 Taft Ave, Suite 4, Hollywood, CA 90028 *Tel:* 323-469-8991 *E-mail:* palardo2@msn.com, pg 968

Paliwal, Dinesh C, Harman International Industries Inc, 400 Atlantic St, 15th fl, Stamford, CT 06901 *Tel:* 203-328-3500 *Web Site:* www.harman.com, pg 885

Pallatto, Joanie, Sparrow Sound Design, 3501 N Southport, 2nd fl, Chicago, IL 60657-1435 *Tel:* 773-281-8510 *Fax:* 773-472-4330 *E-mail:* studio@chicagosound.com; southport@chicagosound.com *Web Site:* www.chicagosound.com, pg 1019

Palle, Robert J, Blonder Tongue Laboratories Inc, One Jake Brown Rd, Old Bridge, NJ 08857 *Tel:* 732-679-4000 *Toll Free Tel:* 800-523-6049 *Fax:* 732-679-4353 *E-mail:* custsvc@blondertongue.com; btglobalsales@blondertongue.com (other than US & CN) *Web Site:* www.blondertongue.com, pg 809

Paller, Craig, dbx Professional Products, 8760 S Sandy Pkwy, Sandy, UT 84070 *Tel:* 801-566-8800; 801-568-7660 (cust serv) *Fax:* 801-568-7662 *E-mail:* customer@dbxpro.com *Web Site:* www.dbxpro.com, pg 844

Palm, Richard, Staging Directions Inc, 1327 Northbrook Pkwy, Suite 440, Suwanee, GA 30024 *Tel:* 770-409-9909 *Toll Free Tel:* 800-782-4322 *Fax:* 770-409-0277 *E-mail:* info@teamsdi.net; sales@teamsdi.net *Web Site:* www.stagingdirections.com, pg 1023

Palmer, Ben, Arrakis Systems, 6604 Powell St, Loveland, CO 80538 *Tel:* 970-461-0730 *Fax:* 970-663-1010 *E-mail:* support@arrakis-systems.com *Web Site:* www.arrakis-systems.com, pg 790

Palmer, Cora, Westworks Studios, 4100 E Dry Creek Rd, Littleton, CO 80122 *Toll Free Tel:* 800-491-1947 *E-mail:* info@westworksstudios.com *Web Site:* westworksstudios.com, pg 1064

Palmer, Michael, American Music & Sound (AM&S), 925 Broadbeck Dr, No 220, Newbury Park, CA 91320 *Toll Free Tel:* 800-431-2609 *Toll Free Fax:* 866-707-0717 *E-mail:* info@americanmusicandsound.com *Web Site:* www.americanmusicandsound.com, pg 785

Palmer, Patricia, SVS Inc, 2513 Jenks Ave, Panama City, FL 32405 *Tel:* 850-522-4747 *Fax:* 850-522-4739 *E-mail:* sales@svslifts.com *Web Site:* www.svslifts.com, pg 1029

Palmer, Shelly, Shelly Palmer Production, PO Box 1877, New York, NY 10156-1877 *Tel:* 212-532-3880 *E-mail:* info@shellypalmer.com *Web Site:* www.shellypalmer.com, pg 968

Palmucci, Gary, Kino International Corp, 333 W 39 St, Suite 503, New York, NY 10018 *Tel:* 212-629-6880 *Toll Free Tel:* 800-562-3330 *Fax:* 212-714-0871 *E-mail:* contact@kino.com *Web Site:* www.kinolorber.com, pg 911

Pan, Steven, MFJ Enterprises Inc, 300 Industrial Park Rd, Starkville, MS 39759-3992 *Tel:* 662-323-5869 *Toll Free Tel:* 800-647-1800 *Fax:* 662-323-6551 *E-mail:* mfjcustserv@mfjenterprises.com *Web Site:* www.mfjenterprises.com, pg 940

Panayioto, Steven, On-Line Productions, 2515 Hawthorne Dr, Atlanta, GA 30345 *Tel:* 404-634-5572 *E-mail:* esptv@mindspring.com *Web Site:* on-lineproductions.com, pg 963

Panek, Ted, Wells-Gardner Electronics Corp, 9500 W 55 St, Suite A, McCook, IL 60525-3605 *Tel:* 708-290-2100 *Toll Free Tel:* 800-336-6630 *Fax:* 708-290-2200 *Web Site:* www.wellsgardner.com, pg 1063

Paolini, Patrick, UPN 20 WDCA-TV, 5151 Wisconsin Ave NW, 2nd fl, Washington, DC 20016 *Tel:* 202-244-5151 *Web Site:* www.my20dc.com, pg 1050

Papa, Bruce, Hybrid Cases, 1121-20 Lincoln Ave, Holbrook, NY 11741 *Tel:* 631-563-1181 *Toll Free Tel:* 800-645-1707 (orders) *Fax:* 631-563-1390 *E-mail:* sales@hybridcases.com *Web Site:* www.hybridcases.com, pg 892

Papa, Bruce, Island Cases, 1121-20 Lincoln Ave, Holbrook, NY 11741 *Tel:* 631-563-0633 *Toll Free Tel:* 877-824-3199 *Fax:* 631-563-1390; 631-563-0608 *E-mail:* sales@roadcasesusa.com *Web Site:* www.islandcases.com; www.roadcasesusa.com, pg 902

Papa, Patricia, Boston Film Bureau, One City Hall Sq, Rm 802, Boston, MA 02201-2029 *Tel:* 617-635-3911 *Fax:* 617-635-4428 *E-mail:* filmbureau@cityofboston.gov *Web Site:* www.cityofboston.gov/arts/film, pg 1098

Papasadero, Otto, North American Retail Dealers Association (NARDA), 222 S Riverside Plaza, Suite 2100, Chicago, IL 60606 *Tel:* 312-648-0649 *Toll Free Tel:* 800-621-0298 (US only) *Fax:* 312-648-1212 *E-mail:* nardasvc.@narda.com *Web Site:* www.narda.com, pg 1087

Papotnik, Phil, Raven Rental, 2617 Peach St, Erie, PA 16508 *Tel:* 814-456-0331 *Fax:* 814-451-0557 *Web Site:* www.ravensound.com, pg 992

Pappas, Will, SNL Kagan Media & Communications, One SNL Plaza, 212 Seventh St NE, Charlottesville, VA 22902 *Tel:* 434-977-1600 *Toll Free Tel:* 866-296-3743 *Fax:* 434-977-4466 *E-mail:* snlkagansales@snl.com *Web Site:* www.snl.com, pg 1015

Paquin, Derek, Sensory Technologies LLC, 6951 Corporate Circle, Indianapolis, IN 46278 *Tel:* 317-347-5252 *Toll Free Tel:* 800-488-4336 (help desk) *Fax:* 317-347-5262 *E-mail:* sales@sensorytechnologies.com *Web Site:* sensorytechnologies.com, pg 1007

Paradis, Charles, Alliance Quebecoise des Techniciens de l'Image et du Son (AQTIS), 533 Ontario St E, Suite 300, Montreal, QC H2L 1N8, Canada *Tel:* 514-844-2113 *Toll Free Tel:* 888-647-0681 *Fax:* 514-844-3540 *E-mail:* info@aqtis.qc.ca *Web Site:* www.aqtis.qc.ca, pg 1075

Paradise, Richard, Martha's Vineyard International Film Festival, PO Box 4423, Vineyard Haven, MA 02568 *Tel:* 508-696-9369 *E-mail:* info@mvfilmsociety.com *Web Site:* www.mvfilmfest.com, pg 1119

Pardo, Michael, The DubHouse, 404 SE 15 St, Fort Lauderdale, FL 33316 *Tel:* 954-524-3658 *Toll Free Tel:* 877-900-DUBS (900-3827) *Fax:* 954-522-1905 *Web Site:* www.thedubhouse.net, pg 853

Pardovany, Jacques F, Lighttech Group Inc, 161-15 Rockaway Blvd, Jamaica, NY 11434 *Tel:* 718-525-2900 *Fax:* 718-525-2488 *E-mail:* info@lighttech.com *Web Site:* www.lighttech.com, pg 921

Parikh, Nina, Mississippi Film Office, 501 N West St, Suite B-01, Jackson, MS 39201 *Tel:* 601-359-3297 *Fax:* 601-359-5048 *Web Site:* www.filmmississippi.org, pg 1099

Paris, Jason, North American Broadcasters Association (NABA), Canadian Broadcasting Centre, 25 John St, Suite 6C300, Toronto, ON M5V 3G7, Canada *Tel:* 416-598-9877 *Fax:* 416-598-9774 *E-mail:* contact@nabanet.com *Web Site:* www.nabanet.com, pg 1086

Paris, Stan, Video International Development Inc, PO Box 349, Locust Valley, NY 11560 *Tel:* 516-671-6765 *Fax:* 516-730-5084 *E-mail:* info@videointernational.org *Web Site:* www.videointernational.org, pg 1055

Parker, Darryl E, TFT Inc, 105 Bonaventura Dr, San Jose, CA 95134 *Tel:* 408-943-9323 *Fax:* 408-432-9218; 408-432-9219 *E-mail:* info@tftinc.com *Web Site:* www.tftinc.com, pg 1038

Parker, Don, SAS Institute Inc, 100 SAS Campus Dr, Cary, NC 27513-2414 *Tel:* 919-677-8000 *Toll Free Tel:* 800-727-0025 *Fax:* 919-677-4444 *Web Site:* www.sas.com, pg 1002

Parker, Herbert K, Harman International Industries Inc, 400 Atlantic St, 15th fl, Stamford, CT 06901 *Tel:* 203-328-3500 *Web Site:* www.harman.com, pg 885

Parker, Michael, Mole-Richardson Co, 937 N Sycamore Ave, Hollywood, CA 90038-2384 *Tel:* 323-851-0111 *Fax:* 323-851-5593 *E-mail:* info@mole.com *Web Site:* www.mole.com, pg 945

Parker-Sparrow, Bradley, Sparrow Sound Design, 3501 N Southport, 2nd fl, Chicago, IL 60657-1435 *Tel:* 773-281-8510 *Fax:* 773-472-4330 *E-mail:* studio@chicagosound.com; southport@chicagosound.com *Web Site:* www.chicagosound.com, pg 1019

Parkinson, Judy, Research Press Co, 2612 N Mattis Ave, Champaign, IL 61822 *Tel:* 217-352-3273 *Toll Free Tel:* 800-519-2707 *Fax:* 217-352-1221 *E-mail:* orders@researchpress.com *Web Site:* www.researchpress.com, pg 995

Parkowski, Linda, Delaware Tourism Office, 99 Kings Hwy, Dover, DE 19901 *Tel:* 302-739-4271 *Toll Free Tel:* 866-284-7483 *Fax:* 302-739-5749 *Web Site:* www.visitdelaware.com, pg 1095

Parks, Aaron, Institute of Texan Cultures, UTSA HemisFair Park Campus, 801 E Cesar E Chavez Blvd, San Antonio, TX 78205-3296 *Tel:* 210-458-2300 *Toll Free Tel:* 800-776-7651 *Fax:* 210-458-2205 *Web Site:* www.texancultures.com, pg 899

Parlato, Richard, Parlato Productions, 8632 US Rte 2, North Hero, VT 05474 *Tel:* 802-264-2902 *E-mail:* info@parlatoproductions.com *Web Site:* www.parlatoproductions.com, pg 969

Parmenter, Debbie, Roland Corp US, 5100 S Eastern Ave, Los Angeles, CA 90040-2938 *Tel:* 323-890-3700 *Fax:* 323-721-4875 *Web Site:* www.rolandus.com, pg 998

Parr, Allen R, Rees Associates, Rees Plaza at East Wharf, Suite 300, 9211 Lake Hefner Pkwy, Oklahoma City, OK 73120 *Tel:* 405-942-7337 *Fax:* 405-948-1261 *E-mail:* rees@rees-associates.com *Web Site:* www.rees.com, pg 994

Parr, Ann, NSI Sound & Video Inc, 105 S Sparks St, Burbank, CA 91506 *Tel:* 818-848-1004 *Fax:* 818-848-1571 *E-mail:* info@nsisound.com *Web Site:* www.nsisound.com, pg 960

Parr, Stephen, Oddball Film + Video, 275 Capp St, San Francisco, CA 94110 *Tel:* 415-558-8112 *Fax:* 415-558-8116 *E-mail:* info@oddballfilm.com *Web Site:* www.oddballfilm.com, pg 961

Parr, Steve, NSI Sound & Video Inc, 105 S Sparks St, Burbank, CA 91506 *Tel:* 818-848-1004 *Fax:* 818-848-1571 *E-mail:* info@nsisound.com *Web Site:* www.nsisound.com, pg 960

Parra, Kimberly, Denecke Inc, 25209 Ave Tibbitts, Valencia, CA 91355 *Tel:* 661-607-0206 *Fax:* 661-257-2236 *E-mail:* info@denecke.com *Web Site:* www.denecke.com, pg 845

Parrent, Lauren, Kris Stevens Enterprises, 22362 Dardenne St, Calabasas, CA 91302 *Tel:* 818-225-7585 *E-mail:* inquiry@kriserikstevens.com *Web Site:* www.kriserikstevens.com, pg 1024

Parry, Christopher, MVI Multivision Inc, 120 McLevin Ave, Unit 3, Toronto, ON M1B 3E9, Canada *Tel:* 416-449-1080 *Toll Free Tel:* 800-563-5902 (ext 228) *Fax:* 416-449-5131 *E-mail:* business@mvidisplay.com *Web Site:* www.mvidisplay.com, pg 951

Parry, Hugh R, Prevent Blindness America, 211 W Wacker Dr, Suite 1700, Chicago, IL 60606 *Tel:* 312-363-6001 *Toll Free Tel:* 800-331-2020 *Fax:* 312-363-6052 *E-mail:* info@preventblindness.org *Web Site:* www.preventblindness.org, pg 981

Parshall, Craig, National Religious Broadcasters (NRB), 9510 Technology Dr, Manassas, VA 20110 *Tel:* 703-330-7000 *Fax:* 703-330-7100 *E-mail:* info@nrb.org *Web Site:* www.nrb.org, pg 1086

Parson, Donald H Jr, Instructional Materials & Equipment Distributors (I-Med), 1520 Cotner Ave, Los Angeles, CA 90025 *Tel:* 323-879-0377; 323-272-5260; 310-473-5558 *Toll Free Tel:* 800-352-7423 (CA only) *Fax:* 310-312-1743 *Web Site:* www.i-med-inc.com, pg 899

Parsons, Ben, Fiber Optic Cable Shop, 136 S Second St, Richmond, CA 94804 *Tel:* 510-234-9090 *Toll Free Tel:* 800-777-6269 *Fax:* 510-233-8888 *E-mail:* sales@fibermailbox.com *Web Site:* www.fiberopticcableshop.com, pg 866

Parsons, Carrie Freeman, Freeman, 1600 Viceroy, Suite 100, Dallas, TX 75235 *Tel:* 214-445-1000 *Fax:* 214-445-0200 *Web Site:* www.freemanco.com, pg 872

Parthasarthy, Mr Rangasami, Oriental Records Inc, 96 E Williston Ave, East Williston Park, NY 11596-2017 *Tel:* 516-746-0140 *Fax:* 516-747-4285 *E-mail:* info@orientalrecords.com; orientalcd@aol.com *Web Site:* www.orientalrecords.com, pg 965

Partington, Griff, Goal Productions, 1905 Victory Blvd, Suite 6, Glendale, CA 91201 *Tel:* 818-588-3900 *Fax:* 818-588-3903 *E-mail:* info@goalproductions.com *Web Site:* www.goalproductions.com, pg 880

Partridge, Jim, Tele-Video Production Services (TVPS), 3655 Grand Ave, 2nd fl, Oakland, CA 94610-2009 *Tel:* 510-893-0555 *Toll Free Tel:* 800-893-0555 *Fax:* 510-893-0552 *E-mail:* tvps893@yahoo.com *Web Site:* www.tvpsonline.com, pg 1036

Paryzka, Eva, Angenieux, 40-G Commerce Way, Totowa, NJ 07512 *Tel:* 973-812-3858 *Fax:* 973-812-9049 *E-mail:* angenieux@tccus.com *Web Site:* www.angenieux.com, pg 786

Pascal, Amy, Columbia Pictures Inc, 10202 W Washington Blvd, Culver City, CA 90232 *Tel:* 310-244-4000; 310-244-6926 (studio opers) *Fax:* 310-244-8090 *Web Site:* www.sonypicturesstudios.com; www.sonypictures.com, pg 832

Pascal, Amy, Sony Pictures Entertainment, 10202 W Washington Blvd, Culver City, CA 90232 *Tel:* 310-244-4000 *Web Site:* www.sonypictures.com, pg 1016

Pascale, Jan, Set Decorators Society of America (SDSA), 7100 Tujunga Ave, Suite A, North Hollywood, CA 91605 *Tel:* 818-255-2425 *Fax:* 818-982-8597 *E-mail:* sdsa@setdecorators.org *Web Site:* www.setdecorators.org, pg 1088

Paskal, Joe, J & R Film Co, 1135 N Mansfield Ave, Hollywood, CA 90038 *Tel:* 323-467-1116 *Toll Free Tel:* 877-668-4652 *Fax:* 323-464-1518 *Web Site:* www.moviola.com, pg 903

Paskal, Randy, J & R Film Co, 1135 N Mansfield Ave, Hollywood, CA 90038 *Tel:* 323-467-1116 *Toll Free Tel:* 877-668-4652 *Fax:* 323-464-1518 *Web Site:* www.moviola.com, pg 903

Paskal, Randy, Moviola, 1135 N Mansfield Ave, Hollywood, CA 90038 *Tel:* 323-467-3107 *Toll Free Tel:* 877-MOVIOLA (668-4652) *Fax:* 323-464-1518 *Web Site:* www.moviola.com, pg 948

Paskos, Cynthia, Art Directors Guild (ADG), 11969 Ventura Blvd, 2nd fl, Studio City, CA 91604 *Tel:* 818-762-9995 *Fax:* 818-762-9997 *Web Site:* www.adg.org, pg 1078

Pass, Greg, SuperVision, Pacific Design Ctr, Suite B-120, 8687 Melrose Ave, Los Angeles, CA 90069 *Tel:* 310-652-9510 *Toll Free Tel:* 877-287-9783 *Fax:* 310-652-9516 *E-mail:* mail@supervisionav.com *Web Site:* www.supervisionav.com, pg 1029

Passarello, Janice, Immersion Corp, 310 Rio Robles, San Jose, CA 95134 *Tel:* 408-467-1900 *Fax:* 408-467-1901 *E-mail:* info@immersion.com *Web Site:* www.immersion.com, pg 896

Passin, Jim, Waveland Software Inc, 1900 W Berwyn Ave, Suite 2, Chicago, IL 60640 *Tel:* 773-334-0408 *Fax:* 773-334-0408, pg 1062

Passman, Hap, Adelphi Records Inc, PO Box 7688, Silver Spring, MD 20907-7688 *Tel:* 301-434-6958 *Fax:* 301-434-3056 *E-mail:* adelphi@adelphirecords.com *Web Site:* www.adelphirecords.com, pg 776

Pastorelli, Patricia, Avekta Productions Inc, One Rock Place, Yonkers, NY 10705 *Tel:* 914-378-8000 *Web Site:* avekta.com, pg 798

Patafio, Tony, Purefire Communications Inc, 200 Evans Ave, Unit 3, Toronto, ON M8Z 1J7, Canada *Tel:* 416-503-2323 *E-mail:* info@purefire.ca *Web Site:* www.purefire.ca, pg 987

Patel, Parinda, Philadelphia Film Festival, 1600 N Fifth St, Philadelphia, PA 19122 *Tel:* 267-239-2941 *E-mail:* info@filmadelphia.org *Web Site:* www.filmadelphia.org, pg 1123

Patel, Sanjay, Alliant Event Services, 196 University Pkwy, Pomona, CA 91768 *Tel:* 909-622-3306 *Toll Free Tel:* 800-851-5415 *Fax:* 909-622-3917 *E-mail:* marketing@alliantevents.com *Web Site:* www.alliantevents.com, pg 781

Patel, Sunit, Level 3 Communications Inc, 1025 Eldorado Blvd, Broomfield, CO 80021 *Tel:* 720-888-1000 *Toll Free Tel:* 877-2LEVEL3 (253-8357) *Web Site:* www.level3.com, pg 919

Paterson, Kelly, Limbo Films, 2223 NE Martin Luther King Jr Blvd, Portland, OR 97212 *Tel:* 503-228-0844 *Fax:* 503-228-0857 *E-mail:* info@limbofilms.com *Web Site:* www.limbofilms.com, pg 921

Paton, Caroline, Folk-Legacy, 85 Sharon Mountain Rd, Sharon, CT 06069 *Tel:* 860-364-5661 *Toll Free Tel:* 800-836-0901 (orders) *Fax:* 860-364-1050 *E-mail:* sales@folk-legacy.com *Web Site:* www.folk-legacy.com, pg 871

Patota, Anne, Guilford Publications, 72 Spring St, 4th fl, New York, NY 10012 *Tel:* 212-431-9800 *Toll Free Tel:* 800-365-7006 *Fax:* 212-966-6708 *E-mail:* info@guilford.com *Web Site:* www.guilford.com, pg 883

Patrick, Priscilla, Yoga 1 Inc, 3128 Carlisle St, Columbia, SC 29205 *Tel:* 803-254-6121 *Toll Free Tel:* 888-364-1310 (orders) *Web Site:* www.yogaone.com, pg 1072

Patrick, Roger, The Whitlock Group, 12820 West Creek Pkwy, Richmond, VA 23238 *Tel:* 804-273-9100 *Toll Free Tel:* 800-726-9843 *Fax:* 804-273-9380 *E-mail:* information@whitlock.com *Web Site:* www.whitlock.com, pg 1065

Patten, Forrest G, Kaleidosound, 3883 Campolindo Dr, Moraga, CA 94556 *Tel:* 925-283-9901 *Web Site:* www.k-sound.com, pg 907

Patterson, Alice, Chico Chamber of Commerce/Butte County Film Commission, 441 Main St, Suite 150, Chico, CA 95928 *Tel:* 530-891-5556 *Toll Free Tel:* 800-852-8570 *Fax:* 530-891-3613 *E-mail:* info@chicochamber.com *Web Site:* chicochamber.com, pg 1092

Patterson, Brian J, Ontario Safety League, 2595 Skymark Ave, Suite 212, Mississauga, ON L4W 4Y4, Canada *Tel:* 905-625-0556 *Fax:* 905-625-0677 *E-mail:* info@osl.org *Web Site:* www.osl.org; ontariosafetyleague.com, pg 964

Patton, Patrick, Newton Instrument Co Inc, 111 E "A" St, Butner, NC 27509-2426 *Tel:* 919-575-6426 *Fax:* 919-575-4708 *Web Site:* www.enewton.com, pg 957

Pavett, Jim, Allusion Studios & Pure Wave Audio, 248 W Elm St, Tucson, AZ 85705 *Tel:* 520-622-3895 *Fax:* 520-622-3895 *E-mail:* contact@allusionstudios.com *Web Site:* www.allusionstudios.com; www.purewaveaudio.com, pg 782

Payaslyan, Anush, PromaxBDA, 1522e Cloverfield Blvd, Santa Monica, CA 90404 *Tel:* 310-788-7600 *Fax:* 310-788-7616 *Web Site:* www.promaxbda.org, pg 1088

Payberg-Torroija, Holly, Two Door Productions, 416 N Harper Ave, Los Angeles, CA 90048 *E-mail:* shoot@usphotograph.com *Web Site:* www.twodoorfx.com, pg 1047

Payne, Chris, Eastman Kodak Professional, 343 State St, Rochester, NY 14650 *Toll Free Tel:* 800-698-3324 *Web Site:* www.kodak.com, pg 856

Payne, Frank, Encore Video Productions, 811 Main St, Myrtle Beach, SC 29577 *Tel:* 843-448-9900 *E-mail:* crew@encorevideo.biz *Web Site:* www.encorevideo.biz, pg 861

Payne, Judy, Long-Term Success Publishing, 766 Ninth Ave N, Suite 1, Fort Dodge, IA 50501 *Tel:* 515-571-8880 *Web Site:* judypayne.com, pg 924

Payne, Philip B, Linguist's Software Inc, PO Box 580, Edmonds, WA 98020-0580 *Tel:* 425-775-1130 *Fax:* 425-771-5911 *E-mail:* fonts@linguistsoftware.com *Web Site:* www.linguistsoftware.com, pg 922

Payton, Paul, Presence Records, 67 Candace Lane, Chatham Township, NJ 07928-1115 *Tel:* 973-701-0707 *Web Site:* www.paulpayton.com; www.presenceproductions.com, pg 981

Peace, Kerry, Alligator Records & Artist Management Inc, 1441 W Devon Ave, Chicago, IL 60660 *Tel:* 773-973-7736 *Fax:* 773-973-2088 *E-mail:* info@allig.com *Web Site:* www.alligator.com, pg 781

Peacher, Brian, Charleston International Film Festival (CIFF), 915 Folly Rd, No 78, Charleston, SC 29412 *Tel:* 843-817-1617 *E-mail:* info@charlestoniff.org *Web Site:* charlestoniff.org, pg 1111

Peacher, Summer, Charleston International Film Festival (CIFF), 915 Folly Rd, No 78, Charleston, SC 29412 *Tel:* 843-817-1617 *E-mail:* info@charlestoniff.org *Web Site:* charlestoniff.org, pg 1111

Peal, Lorna-Kay, Vermont International Film Festival, 230 College St, Burlington, VT 05401 *Tel:* 802-660-2600 *Fax:* 802-860-9555 *E-mail:* info@vtiff.org *Web Site:* www.vtiff.org, pg 1129

Pearce, Sara, Sundance Film Festival, 1825 Three Kings Dr, Park City, UT 84060 *Tel:* 435-658-3456 *Fax:* 435-658-3457 *E-mail:* customerservice@sundance.org; press@sundance.org; institute@sundance.org *Web Site:* www.sundance.org/festival/, pg 1128

Pearce, Stewart, Metropolitan Opera Guild, Samuel B & David Rose Bldg, 70 Lincoln Center Plaza, 6th fl, New York, NY 10023-6593 *Tel:* 212-769-7000 *E-mail:* info@metguild.org *Web Site:* www.metguild.org, pg 940

Pearce, Virginia, Utah Film Commission, Council Hall/Capitol Hill, 300 N State St, Salt Lake City, UT 84114 *Tel:* 801-538-8740 *Toll Free Tel:* 800-453-8824 *Fax:* 801-538-1397 *Web Site:* www.film.utah.gov, pg 1103

Pearlman, Nancy, ECONEWS (Environmental Television Series) & (Environmental Directions Radio Series), PO Box 351419, Los Angeles, CA 90035-9119 *Tel:* 310-559-9160 *Fax:* 310-559-9160 *E-mail:* ecnp@aol.com *Web Site:* www.ecoprojects.org, pg 856

Pearlman, Sandy, Alpha & Omega Recording, 150 Bellam Blvd, Suite 255, San Rafael, CA 94901, pg 782

Pearson, Jim, Cinema Rentals Inc, 25876 The Old Rd, Suite 174, Stevenson Ranch, CA 91381 *Tel:* 661-222-7342 *E-mail:* ocxinc@gmail.com *Web Site:* www.cinemarentals.com, pg 827

Pearson, Margo, InterCom, 3 Grogan's Park, Suite 200, The Woodlands, TX 77380 *Tel:* 281-367-4277 *Toll Free Tel:* 800-298-7070 *Fax:* 281-364-7032 *E-mail:* intercom@intercomtraining.com *Web Site:* www.intercom-interactive.com, pg 900

Pearson, Wade A, Institute for Teaching & Learning Excellence (ITLE), 100 ITLE, Oklahoma State University, Stillwater, OK 74078 *Tel:* 405-744-1000 *Fax:* 405-744-8563 *E-mail:* itle@okstate.edu *Web Site:* itle.okstate.edu, pg 899

Pease, Chris, Lightronics Inc, 509 Central Dr, Virginia Beach, VA 23454 *Tel:* 757-486-3588 *Toll Free Tel:* 800-472-8541 *Fax:* 757-486-3391 *Web Site:* www.lightronics.com, pg 921

Peck, Eliott, Canon USA Inc, One Canon Park, Melville, NY 11747 *Tel:* 613-330-5000 *E-mail:* pr@cusa.canon.com *Web Site:* www.usa.canon.com, pg 819

Peckham, Peter H, Peckham Productions Inc, 50 S Buckhout St, Irvington, NY 10533 *Tel:* 914-591-4140 *Fax:* 914-591-4149 *E-mail:* info@peckhampix.com *Web Site:* www.peckhampix.com, pg 970

Peckham, Russell C, Peckham Productions Inc, 50 S Buckhout St, Irvington, NY 10533 *Tel:* 914-591-4140 *Fax:* 914-591-4149 *E-mail:* info@peckhampix.com *Web Site:* www.peckhampix.com, pg 970

Peckham, Susanne, Prakken Publications Inc, 2851 Boardwalk Dr, Ann Arbor, MI 48104 *Tel:* 734-975-2800 *Toll Free Tel:* 800-530-9673 *Fax:* 734-975-2787 *E-mail:* matt@techdirections.com *Web Site:* www.techdirections.com, pg 980

Peckham, Tom, AVFX Inc, 96 Holton St, Boston, MA 02135 *Tel:* 617-254-0770 *Toll Free Tel:* 888-254-0770 *E-mail:* info@avfx.com *Web Site:* www.avfx.com, pg 798

Peckham, Waldine E, Peckham Productions Inc, 50 S Buckhout St, Irvington, NY 10533 *Tel:* 914-591-4140 *Fax:* 914-591-4149 *E-mail:* info@peckhampix.com *Web Site:* www.peckhampix.com, pg 970

Pecot, Alain, GatesAir, 5300 Kings Island Dr, Suite 101, Mason, OH 45040 *Tel:* 513-459-3400 *Fax:* 513-459-3796 *E-mail:* information@gatesair.com; orders@gatesair.com; support@gatesair.com *Web Site:* www.gatesair.com, pg 875

Pedisich, Peter, TBC Consoles Inc, 170 Rodeo Dr, Edgewood, NY 11717 *Tel:* 631-293-4068 *Toll Free Tel:* 888-CONSOLE (266-7653) *Fax:* 631-293-4075 *E-mail:* info@tbcconsoles.com; sales@tbcconsoles.com; support@tbcconsoles.com *Web Site:* www.tbcconsoles.com, pg 1033

Peel, Carl, Killer Tracks, 2110 Colorado Ave, Suite 110, Santa Monica, CA 90404 *Tel:* 310-865-4455 *Toll Free Tel:* 800-4-KILLER (454-5537) *Fax:* 310-865-4470 *Toll Free Fax:* 800-787-2257 *E-mail:* info@killertracks.com; sales@killertracks.com *Web Site:* www.killertracks.com, pg 910

Peerbolte, David R, Peerbolte Creative, PO Box 754, Warrensburg, MO 64093 *Tel:* 660-429-1383 *Fax:* 660-429-3666 *E-mail:* solutions@peerbolte.com *Web Site:* www.peerbolte.com, pg 971

Peery, Mike, Tecplot Inc, 3535 Factoria Blvd SE, Suite 550, Bellevue, WA 98006 *Tel:* 425-653-1200; 425-653-9393 (tech support) *Toll Free Tel:* 800-763-7005 (orders) *E-mail:* info@tecplot.com; sales@tecplot.com *Web Site:* www.tecplot.com, pg 1035

Peiser, Judy, Center for Southern Folklore Inc, 119 S Main St, Memphis, TN 38103 *Tel:* 901-525-3655 *Fax:* 901-544-9965 *E-mail:* info@southernfolklore.com *Web Site:* www.southernfolklore.com, pg 822

Pelino, Robert, Robertson Worldwide, 13611 Thornton Rd, Blue Island, IL 60406 *Toll Free Tel:* 800-323-5633 *Toll Free Fax:* 877-388-2420 *E-mail:* info@robertsonww.com *Web Site:* www.robertsonww.com, pg 998

Pelkowski, Chet, Definitive Technology LLP, 11433 Cronridge Dr, Suite K, Owings Mills, MD 21117-2294 *Tel:* 410-363-7148 *Toll Free Tel:* 800-228-7148 *Fax:* 410-363-9998 *E-mail:* info@definitivetech.com *Web Site:* www.definitivetech.com, pg 845

Pell, David T, Rainbow Rentals, 6705-A Electronic Dr, Springfield, VA 22151 *Tel:* 703-916-0800 *Fax:* 703-916-8013 *E-mail:* party@rainbow-rental.com *Web Site:* www.rainbow-rental.com, pg 991

Pelland, Gene, Clair Brothers Audio Systems Inc, One Clair Blvd, Manheim, PA 17545 *Tel:* 717-665-4000 *Fax:* 717-665-8000 *Web Site:* www.clairsystems.com, pg 829

Pellat, Philip, Shaw Street Productions, 51 Halton St, Unit 127, Toronto, ON M6J 1R5, Canada *Tel:* 416-588-9443 *E-mail:* info@shawstreetpro.com *Web Site:* www.shawstreetpro.com, pg 1008

Pellegatti, Mike, Wild Visions Inc, PO Box 42194, Phoenix, AZ 85080 *Tel:* 623-512-9810 *Web Site:* www.wildvisions.net, pg 1066

Peller, Allan W, Educational Impressions, 785 Franklin Ave, Franklin Lakes, NJ 07417 *Tel:* 201-644-0908 *Toll Free Tel:* 800-451-7450 *Fax:* 201-644-0907 *E-mail:* awpeller@optonline.net *Web Site:* www.edimpressions.com, pg 857

Peller, Allan W, A W Peller & Associates Inc, PO Box 377, Franklin Lakes, NJ 07414-0377 *Tel:* 201-644-0908 *Toll Free Tel:* 800-451-7450 *Fax:* 201-644-0907 *E-mail:* awpeller@optonline.net *Web Site:* www.brightideascatalog.com, pg 971

Peller, Barbara, Educational Impressions, 785 Franklin Ave, Franklin Lakes, NJ 07417 *Tel:* 201-644-0908 *Toll Free Tel:* 800-451-7450 *Fax:* 201-644-0907 *E-mail:* awpeller@optonline.net *Web Site:* www.edimpressions.com, pg 857

Peller, Neil, Educational Impressions, 785 Franklin Ave, Franklin Lakes, NJ 07417 *Tel:* 201-644-0908 *Toll Free Tel:* 800-451-7450 *Fax:* 201-644-0907 *E-mail:* awpeller@optonline.net *Web Site:* www.edimpressions.com, pg 857

Peller, Neil, A W Peller & Associates Inc, PO Box 377, Franklin Lakes, NJ 07414-0377 *Tel:* 201-644-0908 *Toll Free Tel:* 800-451-7450 *Fax:* 201-644-0907 *E-mail:* awpeller@optonline.net *Web Site:* www.brightideascatalog.com, pg 971

Pelletier, Vic, Group PVP, 296 Saint Pierre St, Matane, QC G4W 2B9, Canada *Tel:* 418-566-2040 *Toll Free Tel:* 877-320-2040 *Fax:* 418-562-4643 *E-mail:* info@pvp.ca *Web Site:* www.pvp.ca, pg 883

Peluse, Michael, Cambridge University Press, 32 Avenue of the Americas, New York, NY 10013-2473 *Tel:* 212-337-5000 *Toll Free Tel:* 800-221-4512 *Fax:* 212-691-3239 *E-mail:* information@cambridge.org; newyork@cambridge.org *Web Site:* www.cambridge.org, pg 818

Pelzl, Jeff, High End Systems Inc, 2105 Gracy Farms Lane, Austin, TX 78758 *Tel:* 512-836-2242 *Toll Free Tel:* 800-890-8989 *Fax:* 512-837-5290 *E-mail:* info@highend.com *Web Site:* www.highend.com, pg 888

Penella, Miguel, RLJ Entertainment Inc, 8515 Georgia Ave, Suite 650, Silver Spring, MD 20910 *Tel:* 301-608-2115 *Toll Free Tel:* 800-999-0212 *Fax:* 301-608-9312 *E-mail:* inquiries@rljentertainment.com *Web Site:* www.us.rljentertainment.com, pg 997

Penkala, Peter, MVI Multivision Inc, 120 McLevin Ave, Unit 3, Toronto, ON M1B 3E9, Canada *Tel:* 416-449-1080 *Toll Free Tel:* 800-563-5902 (ext 228) *Fax:* 416-449-5131 *E-mail:* business@mvidisplay.com *Web Site:* www.mvidisplay.com, pg 951

Pennebaker, Frazer, Pennebaker Hegedus Films Inc, 262 W 91 St, New York, NY 10024 *Tel:* 212-496-9195 *Fax:* 212-496-8195 *Web Site:* phfilms.com, pg 972

Penner, Tara S, Moab to Monument Valley Film Commission, 217 E Center St, Moab, UT 84532 *Tel:* 435-259-4341 *Fax:* 435-259-4135 *Web Site:* www.filmmoab.com; film.utah.gov, pg 1103

Pennie, Jane, Videomagnetics, 3970 Clearview Frontage Rd, Colorado Springs, CO 80911 *Tel:* 719-390-1313 *Toll Free Tel:* 800-432-3887 *Fax:* 719-390-1316 *E-mail:* vmi@csprings.com *Web Site:* www.videomagnetics.com, pg 1057

Penny, Stuart, SMP Digital Graphics, 163 W 22 St, New York, NY 10011 *Tel:* 212-691-6766 *E-mail:* info@smpdigitalgraphics.com *Web Site:* www.smpdigitalgraphics.com, pg 1014

Pennycook, Glenn, Belden, 401 Pennsylvania Pkwy, Suite 200, Indianapolis, IN 46280 *Tel:* 317-818-6300 (ext 6334) *Toll Free Tel:* 800-235-3362; 800-BELDEN-1 (235-3361) *Fax:* 317-818-6365 *E-mail:* info@belden.com *Web Site:* www.belden.com, pg 804

Penrod, Linda, Visual Sound Inc, 485 Park Way, Broomall, PA 19008 *Tel:* 610-544-8700 *Toll Free Tel:* 800-523-7525 *Fax:* 610-544-3385 *Web Site:* www.visualsound.com, pg 1059

Penrose, Jim, Penrose Productions, 1674 N Shoreline Blvd, Suite 130, Mountain View, CA 94043 *Tel:* 650-969-TAPE (969-8273) *Fax:* 650-969-6816 *E-mail:* info@penroseproductions.com *Web Site:* www.penroseproductions.com, pg 972

Pentland, Jake, Full Moon & High Tide Productions & Studios, 424 Main St, El Segundo, CA 90245-3002 *Tel:* 310-647-1958 *Fax:* 310-647-1960 *Web Site:* fmht.net, pg 874

Peoples, Kym, WKMG-TV Channel 6, 4466 N John Young Pkwy, Orlando, FL 32804 *Tel:* 407-521-1200 *Fax:* 407-521-1204 *Web Site:* www.clickorlando.com, pg 1068

Perales, Conchita, Eyeline Teleprompting, 1313 Mound St, Alameda, CA 94501 *Tel:* 510-205-6762 *Web Site:* www.eyeline.tv, pg 865

Peralta, L Lonnie, FXF Productions Inc, 1024 Harding Ave, Suite 201, Venice Beach, CA 90291 *Tel:* 310-577-5009 *Fax:* 310-577-1960 *E-mail:* info@fxfproductions.com *Web Site:* www.fxfproductions.com, pg 874

Perchuk, Neal, RCS Enterprises, 445 Hamilton Ave, 7th fl, White Plains, NY 10601 *Tel:* 914-428-4600 *Fax:* 914-428-5922 *E-mail:* info@rcsworks.com *Web Site:* www.rcsworks.com, pg 992

Perciasepe, Julia, Documentary Educational Resources Inc, 101 Morse St, Watertown, MA 02472 *Tel:* 617-926-0491 *Toll Free Tel:* 800-569-6621 *Fax:* 617-926-9519 *E-mail:* docued@der.org *Web Site:* www.der.org, pg 850

Percy, Rev Maryanne, Faith Fellowship Ministries World Outreach Center, 2707 Main St Ext, Sayreville, NJ 08872 *Tel:* 732-727-9500 *E-mail:* information@ffmwoc.org *Web Site:* www.ffmwoc.org, pg 865

Peregrine, Paul, Lightware Inc, 1329 W Byers Place, Denver, CO 80223-1723 *Tel:* 303-744-0202 *Fax:* 303-722-4545 *E-mail:* info@lightwareinc.com *Web Site:* www.lightwareinc.com; www.lightwaredirect.com, pg 921

Pereira, Mark, Brilliance Audio, 1704 Eaton Dr, Grand Haven, MI 49417 *Tel:* 616-846-5256 *Toll Free Tel:* 800-648-2312 (orders) *Fax:* 616-846-0630 *E-mail:* customerservice@brillianceaudio.com *Web Site:* www.brillianceaudio.com, pg 812

Perez, Bernadette, Spectra Cine Inc, 3607 W Magnolia Blvd, Burbank, CA 91505 *Tel:* 818-954-9222 *Fax:* 818-954-0016 *E-mail:* info@spectracine.com *Web Site:* www.spectracine.com, pg 1020

Perez, Brenda, DigiTech, 10653 S River Front Pkwy, Suite 300, South Jordan, UT 84095 *Tel:* 801-566-8800 *Toll Free Tel:* 800-999-9363 *E-mail:* support@digitech.com *Web Site:* www.digitech.com, pg 848

Perez, Jerry, Follett Software Co, 1391 Corporate Dr, McHenry, IL 60050-7041 *Tel:* 815-344-8700 *Toll Free Tel:* 800-323-3397 *Fax:* 815-344-8774; 815-578-5575 *Toll Free Fax:* 800-807-3623 (cust serv) *Web Site:* www.follettsoftware.com, pg 871

Perez, Tony, HD House, 6312 NW 77 Ct, Miami, FL 33166 *Tel:* 305-597-7359 *Fax:* 305-597-7027 *Web Site:* thehdhouse.com, pg 886

Perhamus, Kevin, Winchester Electronics Corp, 68 Water St, Norwalk, CT 06854 *Tel:* 203-741-5400 *E-mail:* info@winchesterelectronics.com *Web Site:* www.winchesterelectronics.com, pg 1067

Perkins, David, Morehouse Publishing, 4775 Linglestown Rd, Harrisburg, PA 17112 *Tel:* 212-592-1800 (intl) *Toll Free Tel:* 800-242-1918 *Fax:* 717-541-8136 *E-mail:* churchpublishing@cpg.org *Web Site:* www.morehousepublishing.com; churchpublishing.org, pg 946

Perkins, Eric, Display Devices, 10828 Hwy 93, Golden, CO 80403 *Tel:* 303-412-0399 *Toll Free Tel:* 877-862-6865 *Fax:* 303-412-9346 *E-mail:* sales@displaydevices.com *Web Site:* www.displaydevices.com, pg 849

Perkins, James A, Questar Corp, 6204 Ingham Rd, New Hope, PA 18938 *Tel:* 215-862-5277 *Toll Free Tel:* 800-247-9607 *Fax:* 215-862-0512 *E-mail:* questar@erols.com *Web Site:* www.questarcorporation.com, pg 989

Perkins, Mervin, Display Devices, 10828 Hwy 93, Golden, CO 80403 *Tel:* 303-412-0399 *Toll Free Tel:* 877-862-6865 *Fax:* 303-412-9346 *E-mail:* sales@displaydevices.com *Web Site:* www.displaydevices.com, pg 849

Perkins, Nancy L, National Fire Protection Association (NFPA), One Batterymarch Park, Quincy, MA 02169-7471 *Tel:* 617-770-3000 *Toll Free Tel:* 800-344-3555 *Fax:* 617-770-0700 *E-mail:* custserv@nfpa.org *Web Site:* www.nfpa.org, pg 952

Perlmutter, Alvin H, Sunrise Media LLC, 200 Central Park S, Suite 12F, New York, NY 10019 *Tel:* 212-221-6310 *Fax:* 212-302-1854 *E-mail:* info@ipfmedia.org *Web Site:* www.ipfmedia.org/vetc.htm, pg 1028

Perlmutter, Tom, National Film Board of Canada/Office National du Film du Canada, Norman-McLaren Bldg, 3155 Cote-de-Liesse Rd, Montreal, QC H4N 2N4, Canada *Tel:* 514-283-9000 *Toll Free Tel:* 800-267-7710 (CN only) *Fax:* 514-283-7564 *Web Site:* www.nfb.ca, pg 952

Perotto, Rick, William F White International Inc, 800 Islington Ave, Toronto, ON M8Z 6A1, Canada *Tel:* 416-239-5050 *Toll Free Tel:* 800-465-0160 (CN only); 800-268-2200 *Fax:* 416-207-2777 *E-mail:* info@cinequipwhite.com *Web Site:* www.whites.com, pg 1065

Perovic, Sonja, Loopmedia Inc, 401 Richmond St W, Suite 243, Toronto, ON M5V 3A8, Canada *Tel:* 416-595-6496 *Fax:* 416-595-0306 *E-mail:* info@loopmedia.com *Web Site:* www.loopmedia.com, pg 924

Perrault, Anthony, Marvel Photo Inc, 1720 N Sheridan Rd, Tulsa, OK 74115 *Tel:* 918-836-0741 *Toll Free Tel:* 800-806-3616 *Fax:* 918-836-0949 *Web Site:* www.marvelphoto.com, pg 932

Perrine, Lisa, Cibola Systems, 180 S Cypress St, Orange, CA 92866 *Tel:* 714-480-0272 *Fax:* 714-480-0768 *E-mail:* info@cibolasystems.com *Web Site:* cibolasystems.com, pg 826

Perrotta, David, SurgeX, 800 Knightdale Blvd, Suite 121, Knightdale, NC 27545 *Toll Free Tel:* 800-645-9721 (tech & cust support) *Fax:* 919-269-0454 *Web Site:* www.surgex.com, pg 1029

Perry, Alex, A to Z Theatrical Supply & Service, 307 W 80 St, Kansas City, MO 64114-2376 *Tel:* 816-523-1655 *Toll Free Tel:* 800-732-8252 *Fax:* 816-523-1690 *E-mail:* atoz@atoztheatrical.com *Web Site:* www.atoztheatrical.com, pg 771

Perry, Jay, Simco-Ion, 2257 N Penn Rd, Hatfield, PA 19440 *Tel:* 215-822-6401 *Toll Free Tel:* 800-203-3419 *Fax:* 215-822-3795 *E-mail:* customerservice@simco-ion.com *Web Site:* www.simco-ion.com, pg 1011

Person, Jill, A Gentle Wind, 14 S Pine Ave, Albany, NY 12208 *Tel:* 518-FUN-SONG (482-9023) *Toll Free Tel:* 888-386-7664 (orders) *E-mail:* hello@gentlewind.com *Web Site:* www.gentlewind.com, pg 877

Peters, Robert C, Alegra House Publishers, PO Box 1443, Warren, OH 44482-1443 *Tel:* 330-372-2951 *Fax:* 330-399-1619, pg 780

Peters, Sandy, North Country Media Group, 721 Second St S, Great Falls, MT 59405-1852 *Tel:* 406-761-7877 *Fax:* 406-761-2029 *E-mail:* info@ncmg.com *Web Site:* www.ncmg.com, pg 959

Petersen, Barbara, Rockwell Communications Inc, 321 Burnham St, East Hartford, CT 06108 *Tel:* 860-528-9091 *Toll Free Tel:* 800-566-6681 *Fax:* 860-289-2334 *E-mail:* rockwellservice@aol.com *Web Site:* www.rockwellcommunications.com, pg 998

Peterson, Brian, MotionMasters, 2288 Roxalana Rd, Dunbar, WV 25064 *Tel:* 304-345-8800 *Fax:* 304-345-8809 *E-mail:* storytellers@motionmasters.com *Web Site:* motionmasters.com, pg 947

Peterson, Dave, Full Scale Effects, 6869 Tujunga Ave, North Hollywood, CA 91605 *Tel:* 818-760-0875; 818-760-0042 *Fax:* 818-760-0876 *Web Site:* fullscalefx.com, pg 874

Peterson, Edward, Omega Recording Studios, 5609 Fishers Lane, Suite 14-A, Rockville, MD 20852 *Tel:* 301-230-9100 *Toll Free Tel:* 800-93-OMEGA (936-6342) *Fax:* 301-230-9103 *E-mail:* omega@omegastudios.com; info@omegastudios.com *Web Site:* www.omegastudios.com, pg 962

Peterson, Gary, Encore Cases, 8818 Lankershim Blvd, Sun Valley, CA 91352 *Tel:* 818-768-8803 *Toll Free Tel:* 800-743-6267 *Fax:* 818-768-3993 *Web Site:* www.encorecases.com; www.giantcases.com, pg 861

Peterson, James J, Microsemi, 2300 Orchard Pkwy, San Jose, CA 95131-1017 *Tel:* 408-433-0910; 408-428-7907 (tech support) *Fax:* 408-428-6960 *E-mail:* info@symmetricom.com *Web Site:* www.symmetricom.com, pg 941

Peterson, Jeff, Peterson's Video Transfer Services, 10051 E Estates Dr, Cupertino, CA 95014 *Tel:* 408-255-4925 *Toll Free Tel:* 800-888-0426 *Fax:* 408-255-6404 *E-mail:* contact@petersonsvideotransfer.com *Web Site:* www.petersonsvideotransfer.com, pg 973

Peterson, Lara, Golden Gate Studios, 100 Pelican Way, Suite E, San Rafael, CA 94901 *Tel:* 415-485-5856 *Fax:* 415-256-9262 *Web Site:* www.goldengatestudios.com, pg 880

Peterson, Pam, Phoenix Society for Burn Survivors Inc, 1835 RW Berends Dr SW, Grand Rapids, MI 49519-4955 *Tel:* 616-458-2773 *Toll Free Tel:* 800-888-BURN (888-2876) *Fax:* 616-458-2831 *E-mail:* info@phoenix-society.org *Web Site:* www.phoenix-society.org, pg 974

Peterson, Patricia, Projects in Knowledge Inc, 290 W Mount Pleasant Ave, Suite 2350, Livingston, NJ 07039 *Tel:* 973-890-8988 *Toll Free Tel:* 800-772-8277 *Fax:* 973-992-5810 *E-mail:* info@projectsinknowledge.com *Web Site:* www.projectsinknowledge.com, pg 986

Peterson, Robert M, National Teleproductions Inc, PO Box 1804, West Palm Beach, FL 33402-1804 *Tel:* 561-689-9271 *Fax:* 561-640-4677 *E-mail:* ntp@ntpworldwide.com, pg 953

Peterson, Terry, Peterson's Video Transfer Services, 10051 E Estates Dr, Cupertino, CA 95014 *Tel:* 408-255-4925 *Toll Free Tel:* 800-888-0426 *Fax:* 408-255-6404 *E-mail:* contact@petersonsvideotransfer.com *Web Site:* www.petersonsvideotransfer.com, pg 973

Peterson, Verle G, Envision Communications Inc, 2002 N 204 St, Elkhorn, NE 68022 *Tel:* 402-289-2220, pg 861

Petgrave, Robin, Celebrity Helicopters Inc, 961 W Alondra Blvd, Compton, CA 90220 *Tel:* 310-618-1155 *Toll Free Tel:* 877-999-2099 *Fax:* 424-785-8768 *Toll Free Fax:* 877-999-2099 *Web Site:* www.celebheli.com, pg 822

Petit, George S, SHP Electronics, 1225 Hulman St, Terre Haute, IN 47802 *Tel:* 812-232-1003 *Fax:* 812-232-3170 *Web Site:* www.shpelectronics.com, pg 1010

Petit, Jim, WVP Boston, 50 Hunt St, Watertown, MA 02472 *Tel:* 617-926-2089 *Fax:* 617-926-7965 *E-mail:* info@wvp.com *Web Site:* www.weismanvideo.com, pg 1071

Petok, Fred, Crunch Bird Studios Inc, 9537 Whetstone Dr, Montgomery Village, MD 20886 *Tel:* 301-947-2927 *Web Site:* www.crunchbirdstudios.com, pg 840

Petrick, Chris, Bretford Manufacturing Inc, 11000 Seymour Ave, Franklin Park, IL 60131 *Tel:* 847-678-2545 *Toll Free Tel:* 800-521-9614 *Fax:* 847-678-0852 *Toll Free Fax:* 800-343-1779 *E-mail:* customerservice@bretford.com *Web Site:* bretford.com, pg 812

Petrie, Jeremy, Willow Creek Press Inc, PO Box 147, Minocqua, WI 54548-0147 *Tel:* 715-358-7010 *Toll Free Tel:* 800-850-9453 *Fax:* 715-358-2807 *E-mail:* info@willowcreekpress.com *Web Site:* www.willowcreekpress.com, pg 1067

Petrikin, Chris, Twentieth Century Fox Film Corp, 10201 W Pico Blvd, Bldg 88, Rm 311, Los Angeles, CA 90035 *Tel:* 310-369-1000 *Fax:* 310-369-8825 *Web Site:* www.foxmovies.com, pg 1046

Petrokubi, Marilyn, TimeSteps Productions Inc, 2 Glenside Dr, West Orange, NJ 07052 *Tel:* 973-669-1930 *Fax:* 973-731-8546 *E-mail:* info@timesteps.com *Web Site:* timesteps.com, pg 1041

Petrosino, Ralph, Studio Instrument Rentals (SIR), 475 Tenth Ave, 2nd fl, New York, NY 10018 *Tel:* 212-627-4900 *Fax:* 212-627-7079 *E-mail:* nyinfo@sir-usa.com *Web Site:* www.sir-usa.com, pg 1027

Pettit, Steven, Starwest Productions, 8760 W 68 Place, Arvada, CO 80004 *Tel:* 303-295-2222 *E-mail:* info@starwest.com, pg 1024

Pettus, Jeff, Film/Video Fellowship Grants, 109 E Jones St, Raleigh, NC 27601 *Tel:* 919-807-6500 (main) *Fax:* 919-807-6532 *E-mail:* ncarts@ncdcr.gov *Web Site:* www.ncarts.org, pg 1114

Petty, Beth, Charlotte Regional Film Commission, 500 S College St, Suite 300, Charlotte, NC 28202 *Tel:* 704-331-2723 *Toll Free Tel:* 800-722-1994 *Fax:* 704-342-3972 *Toll Free Fax:* 800-722-1994 *Web Site:* www.charlottefilm.com, pg 1101

Pezald, Steve, Celebrities Productions, c/o Clayton-Davis & Associates, 230 S Bemiston Ave, Suite 1400, St Louis, MO 63105 *Tel:* 314-862-7800 *Fax:* 314-721-5171 *E-mail:* idcda@aol.com *Web Site:* www.claytondavis.com, pg 822

Pfister, Ann, Visual Sound Inc, 485 Park Way, Broomall, PA 19008 *Tel:* 610-544-8700 *Toll Free Tel:* 800-523-7525 *Fax:* 610-544-3385 *Web Site:* www.visualsound.com, pg 1059

Phail, Kevin, Fantasee Lighting Inc, 14857 Martinsville Rd, Belleville, MI 48111 *Tel:* 734-699-7200 *Fax:* 734-699-7400 *E-mail:* info@fantaseelighting.com *Web Site:* www.fantaseelighting.com, pg 865

Pham, Joe, QSC Audio Products LLC, 1675 MacArthur Blvd, Costa Mesa, CA 92626 *Tel:* 714-754-6175 *Toll Free Tel:* 800-854-4079 *Fax:* 714-754-6174 *E-mail:* info@qscaudio.com *Web Site:* www.qsc.com, pg 988

Phelan, James M, Phelan Productions Inc, 9201 E Mississippi Ave, Apt C205, Denver, CO 80247-6875, pg 973

Phelan, Patrick, National Safety Council (NSC), 1121 Spring Lake Dr, Itasca, IL 60143-3201 *Tel:* 630-285-1121 *Toll Free Tel:* 800-621-7615; 800-621-7619 (cust serv) *Fax:* 630-285-1315; 630-285-1434 (cust serv) *E-mail:* customerservice@nsc.org *Web Site:* www.nsc.org, pg 953

Phelps, David, FilmL.A., Inc, 6255 W Sunset Blvd, 12th fl, Los Angeles, CA 90028 *Tel:* 213-977-8600 *Fax:* 213-977-8610; 213-977-8601 (permits) *E-mail:* info@filmla.com *Web Site:* www.filmla.com, pg 1082, 1093

Phelps, Steve, NASCAR Media Group LLC, 550 S Caldwell St, Suite 2000, Charlotte, NC 28202 *Tel:* 704-348-7100 *Web Site:* www.nascarmediagroup.com, pg 952

Phelps, Thomas, Sabine® Inc, 13301 US Hwy 441, Alachua, FL 32615-8544 *Tel:* 386-418-2000 *Toll Free Tel:* 800-626-7394 *Fax:* 386-418-2001 *E-mail:* sabine@sabine.com *Web Site:* www.sabine.com, pg 1001

Phelus, Dean, American Alliance of Museums (AAM), 1575 Eye St NW, Suite 400, Washington, DC 20005 *Tel:* 202-289-1818 *Fax:* 202-289-6578 *Web Site:* www.aam-us.org, pg 1075

Phillips, Bill, White Rain Films Ltd, 2009 Dexter Ave N, Seattle, WA 98109 *Tel:* 206-682-5417 *Toll Free Tel:* 800-816-5244 *Fax:* 206-682-3038 *E-mail:* info@whiterainfilms.com *Web Site:* www.whiterainfilms.com, pg 1065

Phillips, Bob, Phillips MediaSource, 750 N St Paul, Suite 1000, Dallas, TX 75201 *Tel:* 214-741-1300 *Toll Free Tel:* 800-TEXAS13 (839-2713) *Fax:* 214-741-3942 *Web Site:* phillipsmediasource.com, pg 974

Phillips, Jeff, Projector SuperStore LLC, 17350 N Hartford Dr, Scottsdale, AZ 85255 *Tel:* 480-922-9420 *Toll Free Tel:* 888-525-6696 *Fax:* 480-348-0273 *Web Site:* www.projectorsuperstore.com, pg 986

Phillips, Jill, SKC Communication Products Inc, 8320 Hedge Lane Terr, Shawnee Mission, KS 66227 *Tel:* 913-422-4222 *Toll Free Tel:* 800-882-7779 *Toll Free Fax:* 800-454-4752 *E-mail:* contact.us@skccom.com *Web Site:* www.skccom.com, pg 1012

Phillips, Kirsten, Consortium of College & University Media Centers (CCUMC), c/o Indiana University, 306 N Union St, Bloomington, IN 47405-3888 *Tel:* 812-855-6049 *Fax:* 812-855-2103 *E-mail:* ccumc@ccumc.org *Web Site:* www.ccumc.org, pg 1080

Phillips, Marc, Airwave Recording Studio, 5176 Hollow Log Lane, Birmingham, AL 35244 *Tel:* 205-427-4675, pg 779

Phillips, Michael, Kineticvideo.com, 16 Munition St, Toronto, ON M5A 1G7, Canada *Tel:* 416-538-6613 *Toll Free Tel:* 800-263-6910 (CN only) *Fax:* 416-538-9984 *E-mail:* info@kineticvideo.com *Web Site:* www.kineticvideo.com, pg 911

Phillips, Mike, City of Scottsdale, 3939 N Drinkwater Blvd, Scottsdale, AZ 85251 *Tel:* 480-312-2550; 480-312-3111; 480-312-2500 (permit servs) *Fax:* 480-312-2888 *Web Site:* www.scottsdaleaz.gov, pg 1091

Phillips, Rick, A KTVA Production LLC, 9818 SE 17 Ave, Suite B, Milwaukie, OR 97222 *Tel:* 503-659-4417 *Toll Free Tel:* 800-282-KTVA (282-5882, OR & WA only) *E-mail:* mail@ktvavideo.com *Web Site:* www.ktvavideo.com, pg 771

Phillips, Stephanie, Sirius Images Corp dba WaveGuide Studios, 2062 Weems Rd, Tucker, GA 30084 *Tel:* 770-939-2004 *Toll Free Tel:* 800-578-2004 *E-mail:* info@waveguidestudios.com *Web Site:* www.waveguidestudios.com, pg 1012

Phillipson, Thomas, Northwest Filmmakers' Festival, 934 SW Salmon St, Portland, OR 97205 *Tel:* 503-221-1156 (ext 10) *Fax:* 503-294-0874 *E-mail:* info@nwfilm.org *Web Site:* www.nwfilm.org, pg 1122

Phippard, Mike, Lehigh Phoenix™, 18249 Phoenix Dr, Hagerstown, MD 21742 *Tel:* 301-733-0018 *Toll Free Tel:* 800-632-4111 *Fax:* 301-733-1733 *Web Site:* www.phoenixcolor.com, pg 918

Phipps, Brian, Mutoh America Inc, 2602 S 47 St, Phoenix, AZ 85034-7401 *Tel:* 480-968-7772 *Toll Free Tel:* 800-99-MUTOH (996-8864) *Fax:* 480-968-7990 *E-mail:* sales@mutoh.com *Web Site:* mutoh.com, pg 951

Phipps, Jeanne K, Alpine Media, 1644 Conestoga St, Suite 3, Boulder, CO 80301 *Tel:* 303-444-1257 *Toll Free Tel:* 800-475-0872 *E-mail:* info@alpinemedia.com; production@alpinemedia.com; av@alpinemedia.com *Web Site:* www.alpinemedia.com, pg 782

Pianka, Robert, Sunrise Studios, 1471 SW 96 Terr, Davie, FL 33324 *Tel:* 954-581-0026 *Fax:* 954-581-0204 *E-mail:* info@dvdcopypros.com *Web Site:* www.dvdcopypros.com, pg 1028

Picard, Karine, The Bessies Awards, 160 Bloor St E, Suite 1005, Toronto, ON M4W 1B9, Canada *Tel:* 416-923-8813 *Toll Free Tel:* 800-231-0051 (CN only) *Fax:* 416-413-3879 *E-mail:* tvb@tvb.ca *Web Site:* www.tvb.ca/pages/thebessies.htm; thebessies.ca, pg 1109

Piche, Danielle, AVW-TELAV Audio Visual Solutions, a Freeman Company, 2056 32 Ave, Montreal, QC H8T 3H7, Canada *Tel:* 514-631-1821 *Toll Free Tel:* 800-868-6886 *Web Site:* freemanav-ca.com, pg 800

Piche, Lorna, Gyrus ACMI, 136 Turnpike Rd, Southborough, MA 01772-2104 *Tel:* 508-804-2600 *Toll Free Tel:* 800-852-9361 (cust serv) *Fax:* 508-804-2624; 763-416-3001 (cust serv) *E-mail:* customercare@gyrusacmi.com *Web Site:* www.gyrusacmi.com, pg 883

Pidgeon, John D, Draper Inc, 411 S Pearl St, Spiceland, IN 47385 *Tel:* 765-987-7999 *Toll Free Tel:* 800-238-7999 *Fax:* 765-987-7142 *Web Site:* www.draperinc.com; blog.draperinc.com, pg 852

Piechota, Pauline, FilmNation Entertainment, 150 W 22 St, 9th fl, New York, NY 10011 *Web Site:* www.filmnation.com, pg 867

Pierce, Clifton, Manhattan Center Studios Inc, 311 W 34 St, New York, NY 10001 *Tel:* 212-279-7740 *Fax:* 212-564-1072 *E-mail:* info@mcstudios.com *Web Site:* www.mcstudios.com, pg 930

Pierce, John W, Quality Audio Visual Service Inc, 6938 Boulevard 26, Fort Worth, TX 76180-8808 *Tel:* 817-284-3192 *Toll Free Tel:* 800-371-6741 *Fax:* 817-595-2942 *E-mail:* info@qualityaudiovisual.com *Web Site:* www.qualityaudiovisual.com, pg 988

Pierce, Larry, Advanced Audio-Visual Inc, 11978 Riverwood Dr, Burnsville, MN 55337 *Tel:* 952-881-4500 *Web Site:* www.aavmn.com, pg 777

Pierce, Marc, AVL Systems Design LLC, 14901 Bristol Park Blvd, Edmond, OK 73013 *Tel:* 405-749-1866 *Fax:* 405-749-1851 *E-mail:* dnix@avl1.com *Web Site:* www.avl1.com, pg 800

Pierce, Stacy, AVL Systems Design LLC, 14901 Bristol Park Blvd, Edmond, OK 73013 *Tel:* 405-749-1866 *Fax:* 405-749-1851 *E-mail:* dnix@avl1.com *Web Site:* www.avl1.com, pg 800

Pieri, Dennis, Bext Inc, 1045 Tenth Ave, San Diego, CA 92101 *Tel:* 619-BEXTINC (239-8462) *Toll Free Tel:* 888-BEXTINC (239-8462) *Fax:* 619-239-8474 *E-mail:* bext@bext.com *Web Site:* www.bext.com, pg 806

Pierucci, Jerry, Moviola, 1135 N Mansfield Ave, Hollywood, CA 90038 *Tel:* 323-467-3107 *Toll Free Tel:* 877-MOVIOLA (668-4652) *Fax:* 323-464-1518 *Web Site:* www.moviola.com, pg 948

Piggott, Andrew, Big Bear Lake International Film Festival, PO Box 1981, Big Bear Lake, CA 92315 *Tel:* 909-547-4019 *E-mail:* info@bigbearfilmfestival.com *Web Site:* www.bigbearfilmfestival.com, pg 1109

Pike, Robert, C & M Publishing Co, 1076 Torrey Pines Rd, Chula Vista, CA 91915 *Tel:* 619-656-6462, pg 816

Pila, Jerry, Can-Am Merchandising Systems, 70 Shields Ct, Markham, ON L3R 9T5, Canada *Tel:* 905-475-6622 *Toll Free Tel:* 800-387-9790 *Fax:* 905-475-1154 *E-mail:* mail@can-am.ca *Web Site:* www.can-am.ca, pg 818

Pilar, Daniel, SYMCO Inc, 29 Poplar Dr, Stirling, NJ 07980 *Tel:* 908-647-6262 *Fax:* 908-647-4904 *E-mail:* orders@symcoinc.com *Web Site:* www.symcoinc.com, pg 1030

Pillitteri, Paul, The National Academy of Television Arts & Sciences (NATAS), 1697 Broadway, Suite 1001, New York, NY 10019 *Tel:* 212-586-8424 *Fax:* 212-246-8129 *Web Site:* www.emmyonline.org, pg 1085

Pillitteri, Paul, Technology and Engineering Emmy Awards, 1697 Broadway, Suite 1001, New York, NY 10019 *Tel:* 212-586-8424 *Fax:* 212-246-8129 *E-mail:* techemmys@emmyonline.tv *Web Site:* www.emmyonline.org, pg 1128

Pimlott, Duncan, Evolution Presentation Technologies, 971 Wall St, Winnipeg, MB R3G 2V4, Canada *Tel:* 204-775-6662 *Toll Free Fax:* 888-775-4693 *E-mail:* sstephens@evolutionav.com *Web Site:* www.evolutionav.ca, pg 863

Pinand-Dumpert, Kristy, Concepts TV Production, 328 W Main St, Boonton, NJ 07005 *Tel:* 973-331-1500 *Fax:* 973-331-1550 *E-mail:* sales@conceptstv.com *Web Site:* www.conceptstv.com, pg 835

Pinckert, Jeremy, Explore Media LLC, 113 1/2 E Lexington Ave, Elkhart, IN 46516 *Tel:* 574-875-5565 *Fax:* 574-830-0200 *E-mail:* info@explore-media.com *Web Site:* www.explore-media.com, pg 864

Pinder, Jolene, New Orleans Film Festival, 900 Camp St, New Orleans, LA 70130 *Tel:* 504-309-6633 *Fax:* 504-309-0923 *E-mail:* info@neworleansfilmfest.com *Web Site:* www.neworleansfilmsociety.org, pg 1122

Pingal, Frederick, Applied Integration Corp, 3930 W New York Dr, Tucson, AZ 85745 *Tel:* 520-743-3095 *E-mail:* info@appliedi.com *Web Site:* www.appliedi.com, pg 789

Pink, Gary, Camera Co Inc/Broadcast Divison, 858 Boston-Providence Tpke, Norwood, MA 02062 *Tel:* 781-769-7810 *Toll Free Tel:* 866-769-0210 *Fax:* 781-769-5750 *Web Site:* www.cameraco.com, pg 818

Pinkenson, Sharon, Greater Philadelphia Film Office, One Parkway Bldg, 11th fl, 1515 Arch St, Philadelphia, PA 19102 *Tel:* 215-686-2668 *Fax:* 215-686-3659 *E-mail:* mail@film.org *Web Site:* www.film.org, pg 1102

Pinkerton, Bob, T3Media, 1530 16 St, 6th fl, Denver, CO 80202 *Tel:* 720-382-2869 *Toll Free Tel:* 866-815-6599 *Fax:* 720-382-2719 *E-mail:* content@t3media.com *Web Site:* www.t3licensing.com, pg 1046

Pinney, Jessica, Stray Angel Films, 2236 S Barrington Ave, Los Angeles, CA 90064 *Tel:* 310-277-6900 *Fax:* 801-438-5009 *E-mail:* rentals@strayangel.com *Web Site:* www.strayangel.com, pg 1026

Pinnick, Tony, Design FX Audio, PO Box 491087, Los Angeles, CA 90049 *Tel:* 818-843-6555 *Toll Free Tel:* 800-441-4415 *Fax:* 818-562-6978 *Web Site:* www.dfxaudio.com, pg 845

Pinnock, Henry, ZTV Broadcast Services Inc, 1333 Matheson Blvd E, Mississauga, ON L4W 1R1, Canada *Tel:* 905-290-4430 *Fax:* 905-290-3370 *Web Site:* ztvbroadcast.com, pg 1074

Pinsker, Jeff, Klutz, 450 Lambert Ave, Palo Alto, CA 94306 *Tel:* 650-857-0888 *Toll Free Tel:* 800-737-4123 *Fax:* 650-857-9110 *E-mail:* thefolks@klutz.com *Web Site:* www.klutz.com, pg 912

Piotrowski, Mary, Mutual Hardware, 36-27 Vernon Blvd, Long Island City, NY 11106 *Toll Free Tel:* 866-361-2480 *Fax:* 718-786-9591 *E-mail:* info@mutualhardware.com *Web Site:* www.mutualhardware.com, pg 951

Piper, Daniel B, Piper Media Services Inc, 904 W Kenosha St, Broken Arrow, OK 74014 *Tel:* 918-251-0477 *Toll Free Tel:* 800-752-5346 *Fax:* 918-258-1476 *Web Site:* www.pipermediaservices.com, pg 976

Piper, Timothy, Pro Stage Inc, 567 Ocoee Business Pkwy, Ocoee, FL 34761 *Tel:* 407-654-5822 *Fax:* 407-654-5826 *E-mail:* info@prostage.com *Web Site:* www.prostage.com, pg 983

Pipher, Tim, LA Castle Studios, 154 S Victory Blvd, Burbank, CA 91502 *Tel:* 818-861-7317 *Web Site:* lacastlestudios.com, pg 915

Pipino, Stephen J, Nicholas P Pipino Associates Inc, 9159-A Red Branch Rd, Columbia, MD 21045 *Tel:* 202-603-9319; 301-596-3397; 410-995-0041 *Toll Free Tel:* 888-596-0014 *Fax:* 410-964-1191 *Web Site:* www.pipinoinc.com, pg 976

Pirkle, Leonard, California Independent Film Festival (CAIFF), 350 Park St, Moraga, CA 94566 *Tel:* 925-388-0752; 310-879-9188 (Los Angeles off) *E-mail:* info@caiff.org *Web Site:* caiff.org, pg 1110

Pirooz, Patti, Penguin Audiobooks, 375 Hudson St, New York, NY 10014 *Tel:* 212-366-2000 *E-mail:* online@penguinputnam.com *Web Site:* www.penguinputnam.com; us.penguingroup.com, pg 971

Pisano, Marty, MediaNow, One Maple Ave, 1-E, Netcong, NJ 07857 *Tel:* 973-347-2155 *Toll Free Tel:* 888-515-2255 *Fax:* 973-215-2121 *E-mail:* info@medianow.com; rfq@medianow.com (quote) *Web Site:* www.medianow.com, pg 938

Pitterle, Ryan, Dukane Corp, Audio Visual Products Division, 2900 Dukane Dr, St Charles, IL 60174 *Tel:* 630-762-4040 *Toll Free Tel:* 888-245-1966 *Fax:* 630-584-5156 *E-mail:* avsales@dukane.com *Web Site:* dukaneav.com, pg 853

Pittman, Bruce, Avitecture Inc, One Export Dr, Sterling, VA 20164-4421 *Tel:* 703-404-8900 *Fax:* 703-404-8940 *E-mail:* info@avitecture.com *Web Site:* www.avitecture.com, pg 800

Pitts, Lee, Lee Pitts Enterprises, 8765 Azalea Ct, Suite 103, Tamarac, FL 33321 *Toll Free Tel:* 877-830-0391 *E-mail:* swimvideo@leepitts.com; speaking@leepitts.com (request speaking engagements) *Web Site:* www.leepitts.com, pg 976

Pitts, Tim, Kinetic Corp, 200 Distillery Commons, Suite 200, Louisville, KY 40206-1990 *Tel:* 502-719-9500 *Fax:* 502-719-9509 *E-mail:* info@thetechnologyagency.com *Web Site:* kinetic.thetechnologyagency.com, pg 911

Placek, Robert, Wegener Communications, Technology Park, 11350 Technology Circle, Johns Creek, GA 30097 *Tel:* 770-814-4000; 770-814-4021 (sales); 770-814-4057 (cust serv) *Toll Free Tel:* 800-848-9467 (cust serv) *Fax:* 770-623-0698; 770-232-0621 (cust serv) *E-mail:* info@wegener.com; globalsales@wegener.com; service@wegener.com *Web Site:* www.wegener.com, pg 1063

Plaideau, Ralph Jr, Primary Color Laboratory Inc, 3550 Williams Blvd, Suite A, Kenner, LA 70065 *Tel:* 504-468-3750 *Toll Free Tel:* 800-535-7799 *Fax:* 504-468-3751 *E-mail:* info@primarycolorlab.com *Web Site:* www.primarycolorlab.com, pg 982

Plambeck, Lynne, Film Converter Co of America Inc, 10 W Burbank Blvd, Burbank, CA 91502 *Tel:* 818-845-7651 *Fax:* 818-845-7651 *Web Site:* www.filmconverterco.com, pg 867

Plantell, Laura, Chimera®, 1812 Valtec Lane, Boulder, CO 80301 *Tel:* 303-444-8000 *Toll Free Tel:* 888-444-1812 *Fax:* 303-444-8303 *E-mail:* salesinfo@chimeralighting.com *Web Site:* chimeralighting.com, pg 825

Plasenia, Sergio, Dorrough Electronics Inc, 5221 Collier Place, Woodland Hills, CA 91364 *Tel:* 818-998-2824 *Fax:* 818-998-1507 *E-mail:* dorroughel@aol.com *Web Site:* www.dorrough.com, pg 851

Plattner, John, Conex Electro-Systems Inc, 789 W Smith Rd, Bellingham, WA 98226-9613 *Tel:* 360-734-4323 *Fax:* 360-676-4822 *E-mail:* sales@conex-electro.com *Web Site:* www.conex-electro.com, pg 835

Pleasanton, Kristin, Individual Artist Fellowship, Carvel State Off Bldg, 4th fl, 820 N French St, Wilmington, DE 19801 *Tel:* 302-577-8278 *Fax:* 302-577-6561 *E-mail:* delarts@state.de.us *Web Site:* www.artsdel.org, pg 1117

Pleasants, Sheila Gulley, Residency Fellowship, 154 San Angelo Dr, Amherst, VA 24521 *Tel:* 434-946-7236 *Fax:* 434-946-7239 *E-mail:* vcca@vcca.com *Web Site:* www.vcca.com, pg 1125

Pledger, Courtney, Hot Springs Documentary Film Festival, 659 Ouchita Ave, Hot Springs, AR 71901 *Tel:* 501-538-2290 *Web Site:* www.hsdfi.org, pg 1116

Plotkin, Jerry, Headroom Digital Audio, 11 E 26 St, 19th fl, New York, NY 10010 *Tel:* 212-246-8400 *Fax:* 212-245-0370 *E-mail:* info@headroomdigi.com *Web Site:* www.headroomdigi.com, pg 887

Plouin, Carla, Professional Photographers of America (PPA), 229 Peachtree St NE, Suite 2200, Atlanta, GA 30303 *Tel:* 404-522-8600 *Toll Free Tel:* 800-786-6277 *Fax:* 404-614-6400 *E-mail:* csc@ppa.com *Web Site:* www.ppa.com, pg 1087

Podevin, J F, Timestream Video, 11821 N Circle Dr, Whittier, CA 90601-2338 *Tel:* 562-699-8797 *Fax:* 562-695-0252 *Web Site:* www.timestreamvideo.com, pg 1041

Poehler, Rance, Panasonic Broadcast & Digital Systems Co, 3330 Cahuenga Blvd W, Los Angeles, CA 90068 *Tel:* 323-436-3507 *Fax:* 323-436-3615 *Web Site:* www.panasonic.com, pg 968

Poggioli, Richard H, aurora productions, 315 Walt Whitman Rd, Suite 210, Huntington Station, NY 11746-4112 *Tel:* 631-549-8933 *E-mail:* info@auroraproductions.tv *Web Site:* www.auroraproductions.tv, pg 797

Pohl, Martin, Big Foot Productions Inc, 37-09 36 Ave, Long Island City, NY 11101 *Tel:* 718-729-1900 *Fax:* 718-729-8638 *E-mail:* info@bigfootnyc.com *Web Site:* www.bigfootnyc.com, pg 807

Pohlman, Ruth, Schroder Music Co, PO Box 2067, Berkeley, CA 94702-0067 *Tel:* 510-843-0533 *Fax:* 510-834-5201 *Web Site:* www.sisterschoice.com, pg 1004

Pohlman, Ruth, Sisters' Choice Press, PO Box 2067, Berkeley, CA 94702-0067 *Tel:* 510-843-0533 *Fax:* 510-834-5201 *Web Site:* www.sisterschoice.com, pg 1012

Poimbeauf, Bob, Texcam Inc, 1323 N First St, Bellaire, TX 77401 *Tel:* 713-524-2774 *Toll Free Tel:* 800-735-2774 *Fax:* 713-524-2779 *E-mail:* info@texcam.com *Web Site:* www.texcam.com, pg 1038

Poirier, Milene, International Film Festival in Abitibi-Teiscamingue/Festival du cinema international en Abitibi-Temiscamingue, 215 Ave Mercier, Rouyn-Noranda, QC J9X 5W8, Canada *Tel:* 819-762-6212 *Fax:* 819-762-6762 *E-mail:* info@festivalcinema.ca *Web Site:* www.festivalcinema.ca, pg 1117

Poisson, Nicole, Lumalaser, 84777 Charlottes Way, Eugene, OR 97405 *Tel:* 541-687-1414 *Toll Free Tel:* 800-606-2597 *Fax:* 541-687-1438 *E-mail:* info@lumalaser.com *Web Site:* www.lumalaser.com, pg 926

Polanski, Boris, Magnaplan Corp, 1320 Rte 9, No 3314, Champlain, NY 12919 *Tel:* 518-298-8404 *Toll Free Tel:* 800-361-1192 *Fax:* 518-298-2368 *Toll Free Fax:* 888-563-8730 *E-mail:* info@visualplanning.com *Web Site:* www.visualplanning.com, pg 928

Polder, Mike, Alcorn McBride Inc, 3300 S Hiawassee Rd, Bldg 105, Orlando, FL 32835 *Tel:* 407-296-5800 *Fax:* 407-296-5801 *E-mail:* info@alcorn.com; sales@alcorn.com *Web Site:* www.alcorn.com, pg 780

Polito, John, Audio Mechanics, 1200 W Magnolia Blvd, Burbank, CA 91506 *Tel:* 818-846-5525 *Fax:* 818-846-5501 *E-mail:* info@audiomechanics.com *Web Site:* audiomechanics.com, pg 794

Pollack, Evelyn, Applause Learning Resources, 85 Fernwood Lane, Roslyn, NY 11576 *Tel:* 516-625-1145 *Toll Free Tel:* 800-277-5287 *Toll Free Fax:* 877-365-7484 *E-mail:* info@applauselearning.com *Web Site:* www.applauselearning.com, pg 788

Pollack, Michael, Applause Learning Resources, 85 Fernwood Lane, Roslyn, NY 11576 *Tel:* 516-625-1145 *Toll Free Tel:* 800-277-5287 *Toll Free Fax:* 877-365-7484 *E-mail:* info@applauselearning.com *Web Site:* www.applauselearning.com, pg 788

Pollak, Ruth, Educational Film Center, 3314 Newark St NW, Washington, DC 20008 *Tel:* 202-243-1048 *Fax:* 202-243-1048 *Web Site:* www.efcvideo.com, pg 857

Pollara, John, Milner-Fenwick Inc, 119 Lakefront Dr, Hunt Valley, MD 21030-2216 *Tel:* 410-252-1700 *Toll Free Tel:* 800-432-8433 *Fax:* 410-252-6316 *E-mail:* mail@milner-fenwick.com *Web Site:* www.milner-fenwick.com, pg 943

Pollock, Bill, Furman, 1800 S McDowell Blvd, Petaluma, CA 94954 *Tel:* 707-763-1010 *Fax:* 707-763-1310 *E-mail:* info@furmansound.com *Web Site:* www.furmansound.com, pg 874

Polonsky, Gabriel, Gabriel Polonsky Studio, 33 Harvard Rd, Suite 2, Belmont, MA 02478 *Tel:* 617-489-3331 *E-mail:* gp-studio@verizon.net *Web Site:* www.gp-studio.com, pg 978

Polster, W Michael, CALIBRE, Metro Park, 6354 Walker Lane, Alexandria, VA 22310-3252 *Tel:* 703-797-8500 *Toll Free Tel:* 888-CALIBRE (225-4273) *Fax:* 703-797-8501 *E-mail:* info@calibresys.com *Web Site:* www.calibresys.com, pg 817

Polumbus, Tad, Caption Colorado LLC, 5690 DTC Blvd, Suite 500W, Greenwood Village, CO 80111 *Tel:* 720-489-5662 *Toll Free Tel:* 800-775-7838 *Fax:* 720-489-5664 *Web Site:* www.captioncolorado.com, pg 820

Pomialowski, Peter, Evolution Presentation Technologies, 971 Wall St, Winnipeg, MB R3G 2V4, Canada *Tel:* 204-775-6662 *Toll Free Fax:* 888-775-4693 *E-mail:* sstephens@evolutionav.com *Web Site:* www.evolutionav.ca, pg 863

Ponczek, Mike, Crossroads Audio Inc, 2623 Myrtle Springs Ave, Dallas, TX 75220 *Tel:* 214-358-2623 *Toll Free Tel:* 800-287-0436 *Fax:* 214-358-0185 *E-mail:* mail@crossroadsaudio.com *Web Site:* www.crossroadsaudio.com, pg 840

Pond, Gary E, Porter Case Inc, 3718 W Western Ave, South Bend, IN 46619 *Tel:* 574-289-2616 *Toll Free Tel:* 800-356-8348 *Fax:* 574-289-2747 *E-mail:* sales@portercase.com *Web Site:* www.portercase.com, pg 979

Poole, Angie, Hammond Communications Group, 173 Trade St, Lexington, KY 40511-2608 *Tel:* 859-254-1878 *E-mail:* info@hammondcg.com *Web Site:* www.hammondcg.com, pg 884

Poole, John M Jr, Corinth Films Inc, 3117 Bursonville Rd, Riegelsville, PA 18077 *Tel:* 610-346-7446 *Fax:* 610-346-6345 *E-mail:* sales@corinthfilms.com *Web Site:* www.corinthreleasing.com; www.corinthfilms.com, pg 836

Poole, John M, Corinth Films Inc, 3117 Bursonville Rd, Riegelsville, PA 18077 *Tel:* 610-346-7446 *Fax:* 610-346-6345 *E-mail:* sales@corinthfilms.com *Web Site:* www.corinthreleasing.com; www.corinthfilms.com, pg 836

Poole, Wesley, MotionMasters, 2288 Roxalana Rd, Dunbar, WV 25064 *Tel:* 304-345-8800 *Fax:* 304-345-8809 *E-mail:* storytellers@motionmasters.com *Web Site:* motionmasters.com, pg 947

Poon, Virginia, Keng Seng Enterprises Inc, 4000 Rue St Ambroise, Suite 103, Montreal, QC H4C 2C7, Canada *Tel:* 514-939-3971 *Fax:* 514-989-1922 *E-mail:* canada@kengseng.com *Web Site:* www.kengseng.com, pg 909

Poorman, Andy, EiKO Ltd, 23220 W 84 St, Shawnee Mission, KS 66227 *Tel:* 913-441-8500 *Toll Free Tel:* 800-852-2217 *Fax:* 913-441-6679 *E-mail:* eiko@eiko.com *Web Site:* www.eiko-ltd.com, pg 858

Pope, Nic, Different Fur Recording Ltd, 3470 19 St, San Francisco, CA 94110 *Tel:* 415-864-1967; 415-828-4060 (bookings) *Fax:* 415-864-1965 *Web Site:* www.differentfurstudios.com, pg 846

Popelka, Milan, FilmNation Entertainment, 150 W 22 St, 9th fl, New York, NY 10011 *Web Site:* www.filmnation.com, pg 867

Poper, Toni, Linker Systems Inc, 13612 Onkayha Circle, Irvine, CA 92620 *Tel:* 949-552-1904 *Toll Free Tel:* 800-315-1174 *Web Site:* linkersystems.com, pg 922

Popolo, Joseph V Jr, Freeman, 1600 Viceroy, Suite 100, Dallas, TX 75235 *Tel:* 214-445-1000 *Fax:* 214-445-0200 *Web Site:* www.freemanco.com, pg 872

Popper, Frank, StoryTrack, 212 S Bemiston, St Louis, MO 63105 *Tel:* 314-725-3003 *Web Site:* www.storytrack.com, pg 1025

Poray, John, Society of Broadcast Engineers Inc (SBE), 9102 N Meridian St, Suite 150, Indianapolis, IN 46260 *Tel:* 317-846-9000 *Web Site:* www.sbe.org, pg 1089

Porcelli, Dan, PostWorks, 100 Avenue of the Americas, 10th fl, New York, NY 10013 *Tel:* 212-894-4000 *Fax:* 212-941-0439 *E-mail:* inquiry@postworks.com *Web Site:* www.postworks.com, pg 979

Poremba, Peter, Dyna-Lite Inc, 1050 Commerce Ave, Union, NJ 07083 *Tel:* 908-687-8800 *Toll Free Tel:* 800-722-6638 *Fax:* 908-686-6682 *E-mail:* flash@dynalite.com *Web Site:* www.dynalite.com, pg 854

Porritt, Charlie, Russound, 5 Forbes Rd, Newmarket, NH 03857 *Tel:* 603-659-5170 *Toll Free Tel:* 800-638-8055 (US) *Fax:* 603-659-5388 *E-mail:* sales@russound.com; tech@russound.com *Web Site:* www.russound.com, pg 1001

Port, George, MarVista Entertainment Inc, 10277 W Olympic Blvd, 3rd fl, Los Angeles, CA 90067 *Tel:* 424-274-3000 *Fax:* 424-274-3050 *E-mail:* info@marvista.net *Web Site:* www.marvista.net, pg 933

Porter, David, Critical Information Network, 17300 N Dallas Pkwy, Suite 3010, Dallas, TX 75248 *Tel:* 972-309-4000 *Toll Free Tel:* 800-624-2272 *Fax:* 972-309-5402; 972-309-5432 *E-mail:* info@criticalinfonet.com *Web Site:* www.criticalinfonet.com, pg 839

Porter, James, James Porter Photography, 211 E Columbine Ave, Suite A-1, Santa Ana, CA 92707 *Tel:* 714-546-4148 *E-mail:* info@jamesporterphotography.com *Web Site:* www.jamesporterphotography.com, pg 979

Porter, James, Porter Productions, 211 E Columbine Ave, Suite A-1, Santa Ana, CA 92707 *Tel:* 714-546-4148 *E-mail:* studio@porterproductions.info *Web Site:* www.porterproductions.info, pg 979

Porter, Ken, Spectrum Sound Inc, 1040 Acorn Dr, Suite C, Nashville, TN 37210 *Tel:* 615-391-3700 *Web Site:* www.spectrumsound.net, pg 1021

Porter, Steve, Techni-Tool Inc, 1547 N Trooper Rd, Worcester, PA 19490 *Tel:* 610-941-2400 *Toll Free Tel:* 800-832-4866 *Fax:* 610-828-5623 *Toll Free Fax:* 800-854-8665 *E-mail:* sales@techni-tool.com *Web Site:* www.techni-tool.com, pg 1033

Porter, Vince, Oregon Film & Video Office, 123 NE Third Ave, Suite 210, Portland, OR 97232 *Tel:* 503-229-5832 *Fax:* 503-229-6869 *E-mail:* shoot@oregonfilm.org *Web Site:* www.oregonfilm.org, pg 1101

Portnow, Neil, Grammy Awards, 3030 Olympic Blvd, Santa Monica, CA 90404 *Tel:* 310-392-3777 *Fax:* 310-392-2306 *Web Site:* www.grammy.org; www.grammy.com, pg 1116

Portnow, Neil, The Recording Academy, 3030 Olympic Blvd, Santa Monica, CA 90404 *Tel:* 310-392-3777 *Fax:* 310-392-2306 *E-mail:* losangeles@grammy.com *Web Site:* www.grammy.org/recording-academy, pg 1088

Portuges, Kamela, Images in Motion Media Inc, 720 Ladera Dr, Sonoma, CA 95476 *Tel:* 707-996-9474 *E-mail:* images@vom.com *Web Site:* www.imagesmedia.com, pg 896

Poss, Joe, WTMJ-TV, 720 E Capitol Dr, Milwaukee, WI 53212 *Tel:* 414-332-9611; 414-967-5444 *Fax:* 414-967-5255 *E-mail:* tmj4feedback@todaystmj4.com *Web Site:* www.jrn.com/tmj4, pg 1071

Postlewaite, Ashley, Renegade Animation, 111 E Broadway, Suite 208, Glendale, CA 91205 *Tel:* 818-551-2351 *Fax:* 818-551-2350 *Web Site:* www.renegadeanimation.com, pg 994

Poston, Bob III, Kinetic Corp, 200 Distillery Commons, Suite 200, Louisville, KY 40206-1990 *Tel:* 502-719-9500 *Fax:* 502-719-9509 *E-mail:* info@thetechnologyagency.com *Web Site:* kinetic.thetechnologyagency.com, pg 911

Potier, Robert, Studio Dynamics, 7703 Alondra Blvd, Paramount, CA 90723 *Tel:* 562-531-6700 *Toll Free Tel:* 800-595-4273 *Fax:* 562-531-6769 *E-mail:* sales@studiodynamics.com *Web Site:* www.studiodynamics.com, pg 1026

Pottebaum, Gerard A, Treehaus Communications Inc, 906 W Loveland Ave, Loveland, OH 45140-2150 *Tel:* 513-683-5716 *Toll Free Tel:* 800-638-4287 *Fax:* 513-683-2882 *E-mail:* treehaus@treehaus1.com *Web Site:* www.treehaus1.com, pg 1044

Potter, Meredith, Sundance Film Festival, 1825 Three Kings Dr, Park City, UT 84060 *Tel:* 435-658-3456 *Fax:* 435-658-3457 *E-mail:* customerservice@sundance.org; press@sundance.org; institute@sundance.org *Web Site:* www.sundance.org/festival/, pg 1128

Potter, Rob, Charleston International Film Festival (CIFF), 915 Folly Rd, No 78, Charleston, SC 29412 *Tel:* 843-817-1617 *E-mail:* info@charlestoniff.org *Web Site:* charlestoniff.org, pg 1111

Pounds, Danny, Pounds Photographic Labs Inc, 901 Regal Row, Dallas, TX 75247 *Tel:* 214-688-1425 *Toll Free Tel:* 800-350-5671 *Fax:* 214-688-1429 *Web Site:* www.poundslabs.com, pg 979

Powell, Katherine, Cinequest Film Festival (CQFF), PO Box 720040, San Jose, CA 95172-0040 *Tel:* 408-295-FEST (295-3378); 408-995-5033 (off) *Fax:* 408-995-5713 *E-mail:* contact@cinequest.org *Web Site:* www.cinequest.org, pg 1112

Powell, Rick, Vela Research, 5540 Rio Vista Dr, Clearwater, FL 33760-3107 *Tel:* 727-507-5300 *Fax:* 727-507-5312 *E-mail:* vela_info@vela.com *Web Site:* www.vela.com, pg 1052

Power, Kathleen, ChyronHego Corp, 5 Hub Dr, Melville, NY 11747 *Tel:* 631-845-2000 *Fax:* 631-845-2058 *E-mail:* usa@chyronhego.com *Web Site:* www.chyronhego.com, pg 826

Powers, Brian, Producers Management Television (PMTV), 681 Moore Rd, Suite 100, King of Prussia, PA 19406 *Tel:* 610-768-1770 *Fax:* 610-768-1773 *E-mail:* info@pmtv.com *Web Site:* www.pmtv.com, pg 983

Powers, Glen, MultiDyne Video & Fiber Optics Systems, 191 Forest Ave, Locust Valley, NY 11560 *Tel:* 516-671-7278 *Toll Free Tel:* 877-MULTIDYNE (685-8439) *Fax:* 516-671-3362 *E-mail:* sales@multidyne.com *Web Site:* www.multidyne.com, pg 950

Powers, Kevin, Technical Innovation, 2975 Northwoods Pkwy, Norcross, GA 30071 *Tel:* 770-447-1001 *Toll Free Tel:* 866-447-1004 *Fax:* 770-441-5285 *Web Site:* www.technical-innovation.com, pg 1034

Powers, Lynn, Gaiam Inc, 833 W South Boulder Rd, PO Box 3095, Boulder, CO 80307-3095 *Tel:* 303-222-3600 *Toll Free Tel:* 877-989-6321 (cust serv) *Fax:* 303-222-3700 *E-mail:* customerservice@gaiam.com *Web Site:* www.gaiam.com, pg 875

Powers, Sherri, Leightronix Inc, 2330 Jarco Dr, Holt, MI 48842 *Tel:* 517-694-8000 *Toll Free Tel:* 800-243-5589 *Fax:* 517-694-1600 *E-mail:* support@leightronix.com; sales@leightronix.com *Web Site:* www.leightronix.com, pg 918

Powley, Bryan, iCrossing Inc, 300 W 57 St, New York, NY 10019 *Tel:* 212-649-3900 *Fax:* 646-280-1091 *Web Site:* www.icrossing.com, pg 893

Praeger, Gretchen, Optimus, 161 E Grand Ave, Chicago, IL 60611 *Tel:* 312-321-0880 *Web Site:* www.optimus.com, pg 964

Prafullchandra, Sunil, Alpec®, 1231 Midas Way, Sunnyvale, CA 94085 *Tel:* 408-735-6180 *Toll Free Tel:* 800-854-6686 *Fax:* 408-735-6190 *Web Site:* www.alpec.com, pg 782

Pratt, Earle, New Horizons Computer Learning Centers Inc, One W Elm St, Suite 125, Conshohocken, PA 19428 *Tel:* 484-567-3000 *Toll Free Tel:* 888-236-3625 *Web Site:* www.newhorizons.com, pg 955

Pratt, Sean, Santa Barbara International Film Festival, 1528 Chapala St, Suite 203, Santa Barbara, CA 93101 *Tel:* 805-963-0023 *Fax:* 805-962-2524 *E-mail:* generalinfo@sbfilmfestival.org *Web Site:* sbiff.org, pg 1126

Predovich, Robert, Soundmaster Group, 89 Barford Rd, Toronto, ON M9W 4H8, Canada *Tel:* 416-741-7057 *Fax:* 416-410-7057 *E-mail:* mail@soundmaster.com *Web Site:* www.soundmaster.com, pg 1018

Preiss, Eric, Nevada Film Office, 6655 W Sahara, Suite C106, Las Vegas, NV 89146 *Tel:* 702-486-2711 *Toll Free Tel:* 877-638-3456 *Fax:* 702-486-2712 *E-mail:* lvnfo@nevadafilm.com *Web Site:* www.nevadafilm.com, pg 1100

Prelinger, Richard, Prelinger Archives, PO Box 590622, San Francisco, CA 94159-0622 *Tel:* 415-750-0445 *Fax:* 415-750-0607 *E-mail:* footage@panix.com *Web Site:* www.prelinger.com, pg 980

Prentice, Kim, Gagne Inc, 41 Commercial Dr, Johnson City, NY 13790 *Tel:* 607-729-3366 *Toll Free Tel:* 800-800-5954 *Fax:* 607-729-7644 *E-mail:* sales@gagneinc.com *Web Site:* www.gagneinc.com, pg 875

Prentice, Melissa, Library & Information Technology Association (LITA), c/o American Library Association, 50 E Huron St, Chicago, IL 60611-2795 *Toll Free Tel:* 800-545-2433 (ext 4270) *Fax:* 312-280-3257 *E-mail:* lita@ala.org *Web Site:* www.ala.org/lita, pg 1084

Pressimone, Dawn, Beatrice E Griggs Elementary Administrator's Award, 6021 State Farm Rd, Guilderland, NY 12084 *Tel:* 518-432-6952 *Toll Free Tel:* 800-252-6952 *Fax:* 518-427-1697 *E-mail:* info@nyla.org *Web Site:* www.nyla.org, pg 1110

Presti, Tony, Electronic Vision Inc (EV), 5 Depot St, Athens, OH 45701 *Tel:* 740-592-2433 *Fax:* 740-592-2650 *E-mail:* info@ev.net *Web Site:* www.electronicvision.com, pg 859

Preston, Coral, AudioImage Recording, 110 N Jefferson St, Richmond, VA 23220-5022 *Tel:* 804-644-7700 *Fax:* 804-644-8801 *E-mail:* info@audioimagerecording.com *Web Site:* www.audioimagerecording.com, pg 796

Preston, Dan, Telequest Inc, 66 Witherspoon St, Suite 383, Princeton, NJ 08542 *Tel:* 609-430-3004 *E-mail:* contact@telequestinc.com *Web Site:* www.telequestinc.com, pg 1036

Preston, George, Permlight Products Inc, 422 W Sixth St, Tustin, CA 92780 *Tel:* 714-508-0729 *Fax:* 714-508-0920 *E-mail:* sales@brillialed.com (brillia div); sales@permlightforsigns.com (sign div) *Web Site:* www.permlight.com; www.permlightforsigns.com (signs div); www.brillialed.com (brillia div), pg 973

Preston, Howard, Preston Cinema Systems, 1659 11 St, Suite 100, Santa Monica, CA 90404 *Tel:* 310-453-1852 *Fax:* 310-453-5672 *E-mail:* sales@prestoncinema.com *Web Site:* www.prestoncinema.com, pg 981

Preston, Philip, PolyScience, 6600 W Touhy Ave, Niles, IL 60714-4516 *Tel:* 847-647-0611 *Toll Free Tel:* 800-229-7569 *Fax:* 847-647-1155 *E-mail:* sales@polyscience.com *Web Site:* www.polyscience.com, pg 978

Preston, Rick, Preston Productions Inc, 128 Bartlett St, Marlborough, MA 01752 *Toll Free Tel:* 800-822-2299 *E-mail:* ideas@prestonevents.com *Web Site:* www.prestonproductions.com; www.prestonevents.com, pg 981

Preston, Susan, Preston Productions Inc, 128 Bartlett St, Marlborough, MA 01752 *Toll Free Tel:* 800-822-2299 *E-mail:* ideas@prestonevents.com *Web Site:* www.prestonproductions.com; www.prestonevents.com, pg 981

Presworsky, Eric, Zhone Technologies Inc, 7195 Oakport St, Oakland, CA 94621 *Tel:* 510-777-7000 *Toll Free Tel:* 877-ZHONE-20 (946-6320, US & CN) *Fax:* 510-777-7001 *E-mail:* info@zhone.com; sales@zhone.com *Web Site:* www.zhone.com, pg 1073

Pretto, Anthony, International Electro-Magnetics Inc, 1033A S Noel Ave, Wheeling, IL 60090 *Tel:* 847-358-4622 *Toll Free Tel:* 800-227-4323 (sales) *Fax:* 847-947-8239 *E-mail:* information@iemmag.com; service@iemmag.com; sales@iemmag.com *Web Site:* www.iemmag.com, pg 901

Prettyman, William "Woody", Studio Center Corp, 161 Business Park Dr, Virginia Beach, VA 23462 *Tel:* 757-286-3080 (24 hour cell) *Toll Free Tel:* 866-515-2111 *Fax:* 757-622-0583 (acctg) *Web Site:* www.studiocenter.com, pg 1026

Prewitt, Jean M, Independent Film & Television Alliance® (IFTA), 10850 Wilshire Blvd, 9th fl, Los Angeles, CA 90024-4311 *Tel:* 310-446-1000 *Fax:* 310-446-1600 *E-mail:* info@ifta-online.org *Web Site:* www.ifta-online.org, pg 1083

Price, Emma, Edison Price Lighting, 41-50 22 St, Long Island City, NY 11101 *Tel:* 718-685-0700 *Fax:* 718-786-8530 *E-mail:* info@epl.com *Web Site:* www.epl.com, pg 857

Price, Jim, R & R Cases & Cabinets, 1217 Rand Rd, Des Plaines, IL 60016 *Tel:* 847-299-8100 *Fax:* 847-299-8110 *E-mail:* sales@rrcases.com *Web Site:* www.rrcases.com, pg 990

Price, John, Cinema Concepts, 2030 Powers Ferry Rd, Suite 214, Atlanta, GA 30339 *Tel:* 770-956-7460 *Toll Free Tel:* 800-SHOWADS (746-9237) *Fax:* 770-956-8358 *E-mail:* info@cinemaconcepts.com *Web Site:* www.cinemaconcepts.com, pg 827

Price, K C, San Francisco International LGBT Film Festival, 145 Ninth St, Suite 300, San Francisco, CA 94103 *Tel:* 415-703-8650 *Fax:* 415-861-1404 *E-mail:* info@frameline.org *Web Site:* www.frameline.org, pg 1126

Price, Paul, Creative Realities Inc, 55 Broadway, 9th fl, New York, NY 10006 *Tel:* 212-324-6660 *Toll Free Tel:* 888-432-7328 *E-mail:* info@cri.com *Web Site:* www.cri.com, pg 838

Priest-Heck, Bob, Freeman, 1600 Viceroy, Suite 100, Dallas, TX 75235 *Tel:* 214-445-1000 *Fax:* 214-445-0200 *Web Site:* www.freemanco.com, pg 872

Priestman, Ginny, Terra Nova Films Inc, 9848 S Winchester Ave, Chicago, IL 60643 *Tel:* 773-881-8491 *Toll Free Tel:* 800-779-8491 *Fax:* 773-881-3368 *E-mail:* tnf@terranova.org *Web Site:* www.terranova.org, pg 1037

Primm, John, DV Post, 505 N Tustin Ave, Suite 220, Santa Ana, CA 92705 *Tel:* 714-550-0925 *Web Site:* www.dvpostvideo.com, pg 854

Pringle, David, Luminys Systems Corp, 11961 Sherman Rd, North Hollywood, CA 91605 *Tel:* 323-461-6361 *Toll Free Tel:* 800-321-3644 *Fax:* 323-461-3067 *E-mail:* info@luminyscorp.com *Web Site:* www.luminyscorp.com, pg 926

Pringle, Rebecca S "Becky", National Education Association (NEA), 1201 16 St NW, Washington, DC 20036-3290 *Tel:* 202-833-4000 *Fax:* 202-822-7974 *Web Site:* www.nea.org, pg 952

Pritz, Arthur, Tubeworks Video Productions, 1626 Wilcox Ave, Los Angeles, CA 90028 *Tel:* 323-469-6003 *Web Site:* www.tubeworksvideo.com, pg 1046

Proal, Pia, Real Cool TV Productions, 800 S Main St, Suite 203, Mansfield, MA 02048 *Tel:* 508-337-8520 *E-mail:* info@realcooltv.com *Web Site:* www.realcooltv.com, pg 992

Prochaska, Jason, Sitler's Supplies Inc, 702 E Washington St, Washington, IA 52353 *Tel:* 319-653-2123 *Toll Free Tel:* 800-426-3938 *Fax:* 319-653-3198 *E-mail:* info@sitlersupplies.com *Web Site:* www.sitlersupplies.com, pg 1012

Proctor, Bill, Golden Gate Awards, c/o San Francisco Film Society, The Presidio, Suite 110, 39 Mesa St, San Francisco, CA 94129-1025 *Tel:* 415-561-5000 *Fax:* 415-440-1760 *E-mail:* info@sffs.org *Web Site:* festival.sffs.org; www.sffs.org, pg 1115

Proctor, Bill, San Francisco International Film Festival, 39 Mesa St, Suite 110, The Presidio, San Francisco, CA 94129-1025 *Tel:* 415-561-5000 *Fax:* 415-440-1760 *E-mail:* info@sffs.org *Web Site:* festival.sffs.org; www.sffs.org; www.sf360.org, pg 1126

Proctor, Robert, LYNX Signal Management Systems LLC, 4407 Vineland Rd, Suite D-18, Orlando, FL 32811 *Tel:* 407-428-1071 *Fax:* 407-428-1075 *E-mail:* sales1@intelligentmedia.us; support1@intelligentmedia.us *Web Site:* www.intelligentmedia.us, pg 927

Proffitt, K K, JamSync, Music Row, 1232 17 Ave S, Nashville, TN 37212-2802 *Tel:* 615-320-5050 *Fax:* 615-340-9559 *E-mail:* info@jamsync.com *Web Site:* www.jamsync.com, pg 904

Prokop, Robert, Alegra House Publishers, PO Box 1443, Warren, OH 44482-1443 *Tel:* 330-372-2951 *Fax:* 330-399-1619, pg 780

Proto, Joseph, Electriduct Inc, 6250 NW 27 Way, Fort Lauderdale, FL 33309 *Tel:* 954-867-9100 *Toll Free Tel:* 866-673-9590 *Fax:* 954-206-0799 *E-mail:* sales@electriduct.com *Web Site:* www.electriduct.com, pg 858

Prudencio, Archi, Blind, 1702 Olympic Blvd, Santa Monica, CA 90404 *Tel:* 310-314-1618 *Fax:* 310-314-1718 *Web Site:* www.blind.com, pg 809

Prupas, Jesse, Muse Entertainment Enterprises, 3451 Rue Saint Jacques, Montreal, QC H4C 1H1, Canada *Tel:* 514-866-6873 *Fax:* 514-876-3911 *E-mail:* bpalik@muse.ca *Web Site:* www.muse.ca, pg 950

Prupas, Michael, Muse Entertainment Enterprises, 3451 Rue Saint Jacques, Montreal, QC H4C 1H1, Canada *Tel:* 514-866-6873 *Fax:* 514-876-3911 *E-mail:* bpalik@muse.ca *Web Site:* www.muse.ca, pg 950

Prybylowski, Doug, Comex Systems Inc, 101 Pleasant Hill Rd, Chester, NJ 07930 *Tel:* 908-881-6301 (cell) *Toll Free Tel:* 800-543-6959 *Fax:* 908-879-0070 *E-mail:* mail@comexsystems.com *Web Site:* www.comexsystems.com, pg 832

Przyborski, Lisa, WQED-Multimedia, 4802 Fifth Ave, Pittsburgh, PA 15213 *Tel:* 412-622-1300; 412-622-1370 *Fax:* 412-622-1488 *E-mail:* wqed@wqed.org *Web Site:* www.wqed.org, pg 1070

Pschetter, Gerry, QSC Audio Products LLC, 1675 MacArthur Blvd, Costa Mesa, CA 92626 *Tel:* 714-754-6175 *Toll Free Tel:* 800-854-4079 *Fax:* 714-754-6174 *E-mail:* info@qscaudio.com *Web Site:* www.qsc.com, pg 988

Puccio, Sebastian J, Consolidated Display Co Inc, 1210 US Hwy 34, Oswego, IL 60543 *Tel:* 630-851-8666 *Toll Free Tel:* 888-851-7669 *Fax:* 630-851-8756 *E-mail:* info@letitsnow.com *Web Site:* www.letitsnow.com, pg 835

Puffenberger, David, Advent Media Inc, 5629 Fraley Ct, Columbus, OH 43235 *Tel:* 614-538-1622 *Toll Free Tel:* 877-538-1622 *Fax:* 614-538-1621 *Web Site:* www.adventmediainc.com, pg 778

Puffenberger, Stephen F, Advent Media Inc, 5629 Fraley Ct, Columbus, OH 43235 *Tel:* 614-538-1622 *Toll Free Tel:* 877-538-1622 *Fax:* 614-538-1621 *Web Site:* www.adventmediainc.com, pg 778

Pugh, Daniel, Bitcentral Inc, 4340 Von Karman Ave, Suite 400, Newport Beach, CA 92660 *Tel:* 949-253-9000 *E-mail:* sales@bitcentral.com; support@bitcentral.com *Web Site:* www.bitcentral.com, pg 808

Pugh, Mike, Goose Creek Music & Entertainment, 17723 Tranquility Rd, Purcellville, VA 20132 *Tel:* 540-751-1395 *E-mail:* info@goosecreekmusic.com *Web Site:* www.goosecreekmusic.com, pg 880

Pulig, Judi, York Telecom, 81 Corbett Way, Eatontown, NJ 07724 *Tel:* 732-413-6000 *Toll Free Tel:* 866-836-8463 *Fax:* 732-413-6060 *E-mail:* knowmore@yorktel.com *Web Site:* yorktel.com, pg 1072

Purcell, Nicole, The Clio Awards, 770 Broadway, 15th fl, New York, NY 10003 *Tel:* 212-683-4300 *Toll Free Tel:* 800-WIN-CLIO (946-2546) *Fax:* 212-683-4796 *Web Site:* www.clioawards.com, pg 1113

Purdy, Brian E, Mediaimage Communications Group, 10 Sacks Ave, Grimsby, ON L3M 4Y4, Canada *Tel:* 905-309-5554 *Fax:* 905-309-0999, pg 937

Purtee, Chris, Sky-View Co, 2800 NE Loop 410, San Antonio, TX 78218 *Tel:* 210-590-8100 *Toll Free Tel:* 800-562-8439 (US & CN) *Fax:* 210-967-8787 *E-mail:* sales@sky-view.com *Web Site:* www.sky-view.com, pg 1013

Pusey, Ron, Communications Specialists Inc, 7272 Jackson Ave, Mechanicsville, VA 23111 *Tel:* 804-559-4274 *Fax:* 804-559-4479 *E-mail:* info@csisystems.net *Web Site:* www.csisystems.net, pg 833

Pushman, Parmita, White Swan Music Inc, 6395 Gunpark Dr, Suite A, Boulder, CO 80301 *Tel:* 303-527-0770 *Toll Free Tel:* 800-825-8656 *Fax:* 303-527-0771 *E-mail:* info@whiteswanmusic.com *Web Site:* whiteswanmusic.com, pg 1065

Puskaric, Russ, Accusoft, 4001 N Riverside Dr, Tampa, FL 33603 *Tel:* 813-875-7575 *Toll Free Tel:* 800-875-7009 *Fax:* 813-875-7705 *E-mail:* sales@accusoft.com *Web Site:* www.accusoft.com, pg 774

Putnam, Ned, L A Bruell Inc, 30 W 26 St, New York, NY 10010 *Tel:* 646-336-5977 *Fax:* 646-336-8317 *Web Site:* www.labruell.com, pg 914

Pyette, Craig, Random House of Canada Limited, One Toronto St, Unit 300, Toronto, ON M5C 2V6, Canada *Tel:* 416-364-4449 *Fax:* 416-364-6863 *Web Site:* www.randomhouse.ca, pg 991

Pytowski, Janet, Video Catalogue Co Inc, 105 E 34 St, Suite 105, New York, NY 10016 *Toll Free Tel:* 866-843-2282 *E-mail:* info@vidcat.com *Web Site:* www.vidcat.com, pg 1054

Qin, Lesley Yiping, Asian American International Film Festival (AAIFF), 115 W 30 St, Suite 708, New York, NY 10001-4068 *Tel:* 212-989-1422 *Fax:* 212-727-3584 *E-mail:* festival@asiancinevision.org; info@asiancinevision.org *Web Site:* aaiff.org; www.asiancinevision.org, pg 1108

Qubein, Dr Deena, Creative Services Inc, 806 Westchester Dr, High Point, NC 27262 *Tel:* 336-889-3010; 336-883-8800 *Toll Free Tel:* 800-989-3010 *Fax:* 336-885-1829 *E-mail:* info@nidoqubein.com *Web Site:* www.nidoqubein.com; www.getcreativeservices.com, pg 838

Queri, Chuck, TKH Security Solutions USA Inc, 12920 Cloverleaf Center Dr, Germantown, MD 20874 *Tel:* 301-444-2200 *Toll Free Tel:* 800-BY-FIBER (293-4237) *Fax:* 301-444-2299 *Toll Free Fax:* 800-293-4237 *E-mail:* sales.us@tkhsecurity.com *Web Site:* www.tkhsecurity.com, pg 1041

Quigley, Ken, AVFX Inc, 96 Holton St, Boston, MA 02135 *Tel:* 617-254-0770 *Toll Free Tel:* 888-254-0770 *E-mail:* info@avfx.com *Web Site:* www.avfx.com, pg 798

Quigley, Kevin, Switch, 6600 Manchester Ave, St Louis, MO 63139 *Tel:* 314-206-7700 *Toll Free Tel:* 800-445-0633 *Fax:* 314-206-4570 *E-mail:* switch@theswitch.us *Web Site:* www.liberateyourbrand.com, pg 1030

Quiles, Danny, Barbizon Electric Co Inc, 456 W 55 St, New York, NY 10019-4403 *Tel:* 212-586-1620 *Toll Free Tel:* 800-582-9941 *Fax:* 212-247-8818 *E-mail:* benysales@barbizon.com *Web Site:* www.barbizon.com, pg 802

Quilliam, Christian, Q-Prompt Inc, 5356 Vail Ct, Mississauga, ON L5M 6G9, Canada *Tel:* 905-601-3826 *Toll Free Tel:* 888-848-4134 *Fax:* 905-567-5665 *E-mail:* info@qprompt.com *Web Site:* www.qprompt.com, pg 988

Quinlan, David, Marshall Electronics Inc, 1910 E Maple Ave, El Segundo, CA 90245 *Tel:* 310-333-0606 *Toll Free Tel:* 800-800-6608 *Fax:* 310-333-0688 *E-mail:* sales@mars-cam.com; sales@marshall-usa.com *Web Site:* www.mars-cam.com; www.marshall-usa.com, pg 932

Quinlan, Shawn, Nationwide Audio Visual Co, 4100-B Sladeview Crescent, Units 1 & 2, Mississauga, ON L5L 5Z3, Canada *Tel:* 905-608-8899 *Fax:* 905-608-8890 *E-mail:* sales@nationwideav.com *Web Site:* www.nationwideav.com, pg 953

Quinn, Bill, Doppler Studios, 1922 Piedmont Circle, Atlanta, GA 30324 *Tel:* 404-873-6941 *Fax:* 404-249-7148 *E-mail:* info@dopplerstudios.com *Web Site:* www.dopplerstudios.com, pg 851

Quinn, Bill, Bill Quinn Productions, PO Box 213, Ocean Gate, NJ 08740 *Tel:* 732-237-0525, pg 989

Quinn, Chris, Bill Quinn Productions, PO Box 213, Ocean Gate, NJ 08740 *Tel:* 732-237-0525, pg 989

Quinn, Pamela K, Dallas Learning Solutions, 9596 Walnut St, Dallas, TX 75243-2112 *Tel:* 972-669-6650 *Toll Free Tel:* 866-DISTLRN (347-8576) *Fax:* 972-669-6668 *E-mail:* tlearn@dcccd.edu *Web Site:* dls.dcccd.edu, pg 842

Quinn, Terry, WGBH Production Group, One Guest St, Boston, MA 02135 *Tel:* 617-300-2200 *Fax:* 617-300-3460 *Web Site:* www.wgbh.org/productionservices, pg 1065

Quinniey, Charles, Buffalo Niagara Film Festival (BNFF), 3840 E Robinson Rd, Suite 166, Amherst, NY 14228 *Tel:* 716-432-1065 *E-mail:* info@buffaloniagarafilmfestival.com *Web Site:* thebnff.com, pg 1110

Quist, Len, Chauvet Lighting, 5200 NW 108 Ave, Sunrise, FL 33351-8040 *Tel:* 954-577-4455 *Toll Free Tel:* 800-762-1084 *Fax:* 954-929-5560 *Toll Free Fax:* 800-544-4898 *E-mail:* info@chauvetlighting.com *Web Site:* www.chauvetlighting.com, pg 824

Quitt, Michael, Milner-Fenwick Inc, 119 Lakefront Dr, Hunt Valley, MD 21030-2216 *Tel:* 410-252-1700 *Toll Free Tel:* 800-432-8433 *Fax:* 410-252-6316 *E-mail:* mail@milner-fenwick.com *Web Site:* www.milner-fenwick.com, pg 943

Rabbach, Glenn, Duggal Visual Solutions, 29 W 23 St, New York, NY 10010 *Tel:* 212-924-8100 *Fax:* 212-242-6660 *E-mail:* info@duggal.com *Web Site:* duggal.com, pg 853

Rabbitt, Jay, In Concert Production Inc (ICP), 2750 S Cobb Industrial Blvd, Smyrna, GA 30082 *Tel:* 404-355-7943 *Fax:* 404-350-9045 *Web Site:* icpatlanta.com, pg 897

Rabehl, Mike, Cinequest Film Festival (CQFF), PO Box 720040, San Jose, CA 95172-0040 *Tel:* 408-295-FEST (295-3378); 408-995-5033 (off) *Fax:* 408-995-5713 *E-mail:* contact@cinequest.org *Web Site:* www.cinequest.org, pg 1112

Rabern, Sebastian, Artbeats, 1405 N Myrtle Rd, Myrtle Creek, OR 97457 *Tel:* 541-863-4429 *Toll Free Tel:* 800-444-9392 *Fax:* 541-863-4547 *E-mail:* info@artbeats.com *Web Site:* www.artbeats.com, pg 791

Rabin, Ed, Monaco LLC, 145 Grassy Plain St, Bethel, CT 06801-2806 *Tel:* 203-744-3398 *Toll Free Tel:* 800-448-4877 *Fax:* 203-744-3228 *E-mail:* monaco@hangupbags.com *Web Site:* www.hangupbags.com, pg 945

Rabinovitz, Frank, AVES Audio Visual Systems Inc, PO Box 500, Sugar Land, TX 77487-0500 *Tel:* 281-295-1300 *Toll Free Tel:* 800-365-AVES (365-2837) *Fax:* 281-295-1310 *E-mail:* sales@avesav.com *Web Site:* www.avesav.com, pg 798

Rabinowitz, Richard, American History Workshop (NY) Inc, 588 Seventh St, Brooklyn, NY 11215-3707 *Tel:* 718-499-6500 *E-mail:* info@americanhistoryworkshop.com *Web Site:* www.americanhistoryworkshop.com, pg 784

Rachal, Scott, Vidox Motion Imagery, 204 Winchester Dr, Lafayette, LA 70506 *Tel:* 337-237-1700 *Fax:* 337-237-1712 *Web Site:* www.vidox.com, pg 1057

Racher, Cora, Nady Systems Inc, 6701 Shellmound St, Emeryville, CA 94608 *Tel:* 510-652-2411 *Fax:* 510-652-5075 *E-mail:* ussales@nady.com *Web Site:* www.nady.com, pg 952

Racine, Remi, CBC/Radio-Canada, 181 Queen St, Ottawa, ON K1P 1K9, Canada *Toll Free Tel:* 866-306-4636 (CN) *Fax:* 613-288-6245 *E-mail:* liaison@cbc.ca; liaison@radio-canada.ca *Web Site:* www.cbc.radio-canada.ca, pg 821

Radbill, Catherine, Music & Entertainment Industry Educators Association (MEIEA), 1900 Belmont Blvd, Nashville, TN 37212-3758 *Tel:* 615-460-6946 *E-mail:* office@meiea.org *Web Site:* www.meiea.org, pg 1084

Rade, Susan, Wireless Xcessories Group Inc, 1840 County Line Rd, Suite 301, Huntingdon Valley, PA 19006 *Tel:* 215-322-4600 *Toll Free Tel:* 800-233-0013 *Toll Free Fax:* 866-570-7686 *E-mail:* sales@wirexgroup.com *Web Site:* store.wirexgroup.com, pg 1068

Rader, Mike, Univenture Inc, 13311 Industrial Pkwy, Marysville, OH 43040 *Tel:* 937-645-4600 *Toll Free Tel:* 877-831-9428 *Fax:* 937-645-4700 *E-mail:* sales@univenture.com; orders@univenture.com *Web Site:* www.univenture.com, pg 1049

Radner, Karen, HarperAudio, 10 E 53 St, New York, NY 10022 *Tel:* 212-207-7000 *Toll Free Tel:* 800-242-7737 *Fax:* 212-207-2582 *Toll Free Fax:* 800-822-4090 *Web Site:* www.harpercollins.com, pg 885

Radonovich, John, American Audio Visual Center, 7434 E Monte Cristo Ave, Scottsdale, AZ 85260 *Tel:* 480-596-9880 *Fax:* 480-596-0942 *Web Site:* www.americanavc.com, pg 783

Radzak, Joe, Sencore Inc, 3200 Sencore Dr, Sioux Falls, SD 57107 *Tel:* 605-978-4600 *Toll Free Tel:* 800-SENCORE (736-2673) *Fax:* 605-335-6379 *E-mail:* info@sencore.com *Web Site:* www.sencore.com, pg 1006

Rae, Darrell, monterey media inc, 566 Saint Charles Dr, Thousand Oaks, CA 91360-3953 *Tel:* 805-494-7199 *Toll Free Tel:* 800-424-2593 *Fax:* 805-496-6061 *E-mail:* customerservice@montereymedia.com; publicity@montereymedia.com *Web Site:* www.montereymedia.com, pg 946

Rae, Darrell, monterey video, 566 Saint Charles Dr, Thousand Oaks, CA 91360-3953 *Tel:* 805-494-7199 *Toll Free Tel:* 800-424-2593 *Fax:* 805-496-6061 *E-mail:* customerservice@montereymedia.com; publicity@montereymedia.com *Web Site:* www.montereymedia.com, pg 946

Rae, Susan, Burnaby Film Office, 6450 Deerlake Ave, Burnaby, BC V5G 2J3, Canada *Tel:* 604-294-7314 *Fax:* 604-205-3001 *Web Site:* www.burnaby.ca, pg 1104

Rae-Mansfield, Jere, monterey media inc, 566 Saint Charles Dr, Thousand Oaks, CA 91360-3953 *Tel:* 805-494-7199 *Toll Free Tel:* 800-424-2593 *Fax:* 805-496-6061 *E-mail:* customerservice@montereymedia.com; publicity@montereymedia.com *Web Site:* www.montereymedia.com, pg 946

Rae-Mansfield, Jere, monterey video, 566 Saint Charles Dr, Thousand Oaks, CA 91360-3953 *Tel:* 805-494-7199 *Toll Free Tel:* 800-424-2593 *Fax:* 805-496-6061 *E-mail:* customerservice@montereymedia.com; publicity@montereymedia.com *Web Site:* www.montereymedia.com, pg 946

Rael, Teena, ESE, 142 Sierra St, El Segundo, CA 90245 *Tel:* 310-322-2136 *Fax:* 310-322-8127 *E-mail:* ese@ese-web.com *Web Site:* www.ese-web.com, pg 862

Rafferty, Emily K, Metropolitan Museum of Art, 1000 Fifth Ave, New York, NY 10028-0198 *Tel:* 212-535-7710 *Fax:* 212-472-2764 *E-mail:* customer.service@metmuseum.org; communications@metmuseum.org *Web Site:* www.metmuseum.org, pg 940

Rafferty, John, CNIB Library for the Blind, 1929 Bayview Ave, Toronto, ON M4G 3E8, Canada *Toll Free Tel:* 800-563-2642 *Fax:* 416-480-7700 *E-mail:* library@cnib.ca; info@cnib.ca *Web Site:* www.cnib.ca, pg 830

Ragozzino, Julie C, Universal Satellite Communications Inc, 1530 Nandina Ave, Perris, CA 92571 *Tel:* 562-483-4800; 951-943-4420 (corp off) *Toll Free Tel:* 888-867-6620 *Fax:* 954-943-0263 *Web Site:* www.unisatmobile.com, pg 1049

Ragsdale, David, HB-Content, 105 Butler St, Suite 2B, Brooklyn, NY 11231 *Tel:* 212-213-8824 *E-mail:* hb@hb-content.com *Web Site:* www.hb-content.com, pg 886

Rahe, Keith, Dubuque Convention & Visitors Bureau, 300 Main St, Suite 200, Dubuque, IA 52001 *Tel:* 563-557-9200 *Fax:* 563-557-1591 *E-mail:* office@dubuquechamber.com *Web Site:* www.dubuquechamber.com, pg 1097

Rahn, Eckart, Celestial Harmonies/Fortuna Records/Kuckuck Schallplatten/Black Sun Music/MonteVideo, 1951 N Wilmot Rd, Bldg 2, Unit 7, Tucson, AZ 85712-8000 *Tel:* 520-326-4400 *Fax:* 520-326-3333 *E-mail:* celestial@harmonies.com *Web Site:* www.harmonies.com, pg 822

Rahr, Tim, The Taunton Press Inc, 63 S Main St, Newtown, CT 06470 *Tel:* 203-426-8171 *Toll Free Tel:* 800-926-8776 (ext 3893 - PR); 800-888-8286 (orders) *Fax:* 203-426-3434 *Web Site:* www.taunton.com, pg 1032

Raina, Robin, ADAM Inc, 5 Concourse Pkwy, Suite 3200, Atlanta, GA 30328 *Tel:* 404-604-2757 *Toll Free Tel:* 800-755-ADAM (755-2326) *E-mail:* editorialdirector@adamcorp.com *Web Site:* www.adam.com, pg 775

Rainer, Tammy, Specialty Tapes LLC, 4221 Courtney Rd, Franksville, WI 53126 *Tel:* 262-835-0748 *Toll Free Tel:* 800-545-8273 *Fax:* 262-835-0749 *E-mail:* sales@specialtytapes.net *Web Site:* www.specialtytapes.net, pg 1020

Raines, Bob, Tennessee Film, Entertainment & Music Commission, 312 Rosa L Parks Ave, 26th fl, Nashville, TN 37243 *Tel:* 615-741-FILM (741-3456) *Toll Free Tel:* 877-818-FILM (818-3456) *Fax:* 615-741-5554 *E-mail:* tn.film@tn.gov *Web Site:* www.state.tn.us/film, pg 1102

Rainey, Dave, Glendale Media Center, 9494 W Maryland Ave, Glendale, AZ 85305 *Tel:* 623-930-4510 *Web Site:* www.glendalemediacenter.com, pg 878

Ralke, Richard, LA Sound Co, 9001 Canoga Ave, Canoga Park, CA 91304 *Tel:* 818-772-9200 *Fax:* 818-772-9977 *E-mail:* rentals@lasoundco.com; sales@lasoundco.com *Web Site:* lasoundco.com, pg 915

Rall, Rory, Benchmark Media Systems Inc, 203 E Hampton Place, Suite 2, Syracuse, NY 13206 *Tel:* 315-437-6300 *Toll Free Tel:* 800-262-4675 *Fax:* 315-437-5119 *E-mail:* info@benchmarkmedia.com *Web Site:* www.benchmarkmedia.com, pg 805

Ramadan, Alan S, Adobe Systems Inc, 345 Park Ave, San Jose, CA 95110-2704 *Tel:* 408-536-6000 *Fax:* 408-537-6000 *Web Site:* www.adobe.com, pg 776

Rametta, Jack, StarTrak Studios Inc, 36 Vermont Ave, Unit 1, Warwick, RI 02888 *Tel:* 401-732-1880 *E-mail:* info@startrakstudios.com *Web Site:* www.startrakstudios.com, pg 1024

Ramey, Ken, Northern Kentucky University, Nunn Dr, Highland Heights, KY 41099 *Tel:* 859-572-5100 *Fax:* 859-572-6172 *Web Site:* www.nku.edu, pg 959

Ramirez, Joseph, Covid Inc, 1723 W Fourth St, Tempe, AZ 85281 *Tel:* 480-966-2221 *Toll Free Tel:* 800-638-6104 *Fax:* 480-966-6728 *E-mail:* sales@covid.com *Web Site:* www.covid.com, pg 837

Ramirez, Julio, Freeman, 1600 Viceroy, Suite 100, Dallas, TX 75235 *Tel:* 214-445-1000 *Fax:* 214-445-0200 *Web Site:* www.freemanco.com, pg 872

Ramirez, Stephen, R&O Studios, 5805 N 39 St, McAllen, TX 78504 *Tel:* 956-203-0520 *E-mail:* rostudiosrgv@gmail.com *Web Site:* www.randostudios.com, pg 991

Raml, Gregory, American Museum of Natural History (AMNH), c/o Moving Image Collection, Library Services Dept, Central Park W & 79 St, New York, NY 10024-5192 *Tel:* 212-769-5420 *Fax:* 212-769-5009 *E-mail:* speccol@amnh.org *Web Site:* www.amnh.org, pg 785

Ramos, Sandra, AVES Audio Visual Systems Inc, PO Box 500, Sugar Land, TX 77487-0500 *Tel:* 281-295-1300 *Toll Free Tel:* 800-365-AVES (365-2837) *Fax:* 281-295-1310 *E-mail:* sales@avesav.com *Web Site:* www.avesav.com, pg 798

Rampino, Frank, Flash Electronics Inc, Brooklyn Army Terminal, Suite 1-A, Mail Box 3, 140 58 St, Brooklyn, NY 11220 *Tel:* 718-492-4040 *Toll Free Tel:* 800-831-3127 *Fax:* 718-492-4590 *E-mail:* flashdistr@aol.com; customercare@flashdistributors.com *Web Site:* www.flashdistributors.com, pg 869

Rampmeyer, Mike, Applied Electronics, 722 Blue Crab Rd, Newport News, VA 23606 *Tel:* 757-591-9371 *Toll Free Tel:* 800-883-0008 *Fax:* 757-591-9514 *E-mail:* sales@appliednn.com *Web Site:* www.appliednn.com, pg 788

Ramsay, Ashley, Okanagan Film Commission, 1450 KLO Rd, Kelowna, BC V1W 3Z4, Canada *Tel:* 250-717-0087 *Fax:* 250-868-0512 *E-mail:* info@okanaganfilm.com *Web Site:* www.okanaganfilm.com, pg 1104

Ramsey, Chris, VSG Digital Media Solutions, 11126 Lindbergh Business Ct, St Louis, MO 63123 *Tel:* 314-487-8045 *Toll Free Tel:* 800-737-8045 *Fax:* 314-487-9387 *Web Site:* www.vsginc.net, pg 1061

Rana, Amit, Chicago South Asian Film Festival (CSAFF), 2909 N Sheridan Rd, Unit 1902, Chicago, IL 60657 *Tel:* 773-980-9285 *E-mail:* info@csaff.org *Web Site:* www.csaff.org, pg 1112

Ranaldi, Robert, Far West Media Services Inc, 4140 Norse Way, Long Beach, CA 90808 *Tel:* 562-496-3342 *Fax:* 562-496-4329 *Web Site:* www.farwestmedia.com, pg 865

Randall, Charlie, Boston Acoustics, 7 Constitution Way, Woburn, MA 01801 *Tel:* 201-762-6429 *Fax:* 978-538-6237 *E-mail:* weborders@bostonacoustics.com *Web Site:* www.bostonacoustics.com, pg 811

Randall, Gene B Jr, Versatech Industries Inc, 14750 S Grant St, Bixby, OK 74008 *Tel:* 918-366-7400, pg 1053

Randall, Greg, KTVU-Retail Services, 2 Jack London Sq, Oakland, CA 94607 *Tel:* 510-834-1212 *Web Site:* www.ktvu.com, pg 914

Randall, Scott, Cross-Cultural Communications, 239 Wynsum Ave, Merrick, NY 11566-4725 *Tel:* 516-868-5635 *Fax:* 516-379-1901 *E-mail:* info@cross-culturalcommunications.com *Web Site:* www.cross-culturalcommunications.com, pg 839

Randall, Stewart B, Communications Design Associates, 437 Turnpike St, Canton, MA 02021 *Tel:* 339-502-6551 *Fax:* 339-502-6595 *E-mail:* information@cdaconsultants.com *Web Site:* www.cdaconsultants.com, pg 833

Randall, Todd, Cable Films & Video, PO Box 7171, Country Club Sta, Kansas City, MO 64113-0171 *Tel:* 913-362-2804 *Toll Free Tel:* 800-514-2804 *Fax:* 913-362-2804 *E-mail:* cablefilms@kc.rr.com, pg 816

Randel, Carol, Jalbert Productions International, 230 New York Ave, Huntington, NY 11743 *Tel:* 631-351-5878 *Fax:* 631-351-5875 *E-mail:* info@jalbertfilm.com *Web Site:* www.jalbertfilm.com, pg 903

Ranieri, Ron, AMV/Unitel, 515 W 57 St, New York, NY 10019 *Tel:* 212-265-3600 (studios); 212-586-8616 (sales) *Fax:* 212-246-5059 *E-mail:* hdsales@allmobilevideo.com *Web Site:* www.allmobilevideo.com, pg 786

Ranjel, Susan, San Antonio Film Festival, 1633 Babcock Rd, Suite 111, San Antonio, TX 78229 *Tel:* 210-885-5888 *E-mail:* safilm@gmail.com *Web Site:* www.safilm.com, pg 1126

Rankin, Scott, Mills James Productions, 3545 Fishinger Blvd, Columbus, OH 43026-9489 *Tel:* 614-777-9933 *Toll Free Tel:* 800-860-8436 *Fax:* 614-777-9943 *E-mail:* info@mjp.com *Web Site:* www.millsjames.com, pg 943

Rankin, Scott, Voyetra Turtle Beach, 100 Summit Lake Dr, Suite 100, Valhalla, NY 10595 *Tel:* 914-345-2255 *Fax:* 914-345-2266 *E-mail:* sales@turtlebeach.com *Web Site:* www.turtlebeach.com, pg 1061

Ranney, Chuck, Liberty Uplink, 2547 Yellow Springs Rd, Malvern, PA 19355 *Tel:* 215-964-5222; 917-254-0155 *E-mail:* info@libertyuplink.com *Web Site:* www.libertyuplink.com, pg 919

Ranson, Ron, Theatre Arts Video Library, 174 Andrew Ave, Leucadia, CA 92024 *Tel:* 760-632-6355 *Toll Free Tel:* 800-456-8285 *Fax:* 760-632-6859 *E-mail:* admin@theatreartsvideo.com *Web Site:* www.theatreartsvideo.com, pg 1038

Ranta, Richard, High Water, University of Memphis, Rudi E Scheidt School of Music, Memphis, TN 38152 *Tel:* 901-678-3317 *Fax:* 901-678-3096, pg 889

Rapkin, David, David Rapkin Audio Production, 473 West End Ave, Unit 6A, New York, NY 10024 *Tel:* 212-362-7236 *E-mail:* drapco@aol.com, pg 991

Rappolt, Tom, AMP Services Inc, 3111 Fortune Way, Suite B-18, West Palm Beach, FL 33414 *Tel:* 561-333-0335 *Fax:* 561-333-0370 *Web Site:* www.audiomagnetics.com, pg 785

Rappoport, Beulah, Cifex Corp, 20547 Linksview Way, Boca Raton, FL 33434 *Tel:* 561-883-5548 *Fax:* 561-883-2712 *E-mail:* 2cifex@gmail.com, pg 826

Rappoport, Jerry, Cifex Corp, 20547 Linksview Way, Boca Raton, FL 33434 *Tel:* 561-883-5548 *Fax:* 561-883-2712 *E-mail:* 2cifex@gmail.com, pg 826

Rasberry, Pat, Tupelo Film Commission, 399 E Main St, Tupelo, MS 38804 *Tel:* 662-841-6521 *Toll Free Tel:* 800-533-0611 *Fax:* 662-841-6558 *E-mail:* visittupelo@tupelo.net *Web Site:* www.tupelo.net, pg 1099

Raschio, Greg, KVAL, 4575 Blanton Rd, Eugene, OR 97405 *Tel:* 541-342-4961 *Fax:* 541-342-2635 *E-mail:* kvalnews@kval.com *Web Site:* www.kval.com, pg 914

Rash, Edward, Hannay Reels Inc, 553 State Rte 143, Westerlo, NY 12193-0159 *Tel:* 518-797-3791 *Toll Free Tel:* 877-467-3357 *Fax:* 518-797-3259 *Toll Free Fax:* 800-733-5464 *E-mail:* reels@hannay.com *Web Site:* www.hannay.com, pg 884

Rashid, Bea, Woodside Avenue Music Productions Inc, 2906 Central St, No 117, Evanston, IL 60201 *Tel:* 847-864-6655 *E-mail:* music@woodsideavenue.com *Web Site:* www.woodsideavenue.com, pg 1069

Rashid, Steve, Woodside Avenue Music Productions Inc, 2906 Central St, No 117, Evanston, IL 60201 *Tel:* 847-864-6655 *E-mail:* music@woodsideavenue.com *Web Site:* www.woodsideavenue.com, pg 1069

Rasmussen, Dawn, Down East Books, 680 Commercial St, Rockport, ME 04856 *Tel:* 207-594-9544 *Toll Free Tel:* 800-766-1670 *Fax:* 207-594-0147 *E-mail:* editorial@downeast.com *Web Site:* www.downeast.com, pg 851

Rasmussen, Ken, One Stop CD Shop LLC, 3149 S State St, Salt Lake City, UT 84115 *Tel:* 801-303-6100 *Fax:* 801-303-6129 *E-mail:* info2@1stopcdshop.com *Web Site:* www.1stopcdshop.com, pg 963

Rasmussen, Robert, Balboa Capital Corp, 2010 Main St, Suite 1100, Irvine, CA 92614 *Tel:* 949-756-0800 *Toll Free Tel:* 888-BALBOA1 (225-2621) *Fax:* 949-756-2565 *E-mail:* customerservice@balboacapital.com *Web Site:* www.balboacapital.com, pg 802

Rasnake, Eileen, PromaxBDA, 1522e Cloverfield Blvd, Santa Monica, CA 90404 *Tel:* 310-788-7600 *Fax:* 310-788-7616 *Web Site:* www.promaxbda.org, pg 1088

Rasnake, Eileen, PromaxBDA Design Awards, 1522e Cloverfield Blvd, Santa Monica, CA 90404 *Tel:* 310-788-7600 *Fax:* 310-788-7616 *Web Site:* www.promaxbda.org, pg 1124

Ratan, Ramesh, Bell & Howell LLC, 760 S Wolf Rd, Wheeling, IL 60090 *Tel:* 847-675-7600 *Toll Free Tel:* 800-220-3030 (cust serv) *E-mail:* marketing@bhemail.com *Web Site:* www.bellhowell.net, pg 804

Ratcliffe, Kim, GatesAir, 5300 Kings Island Dr, Suite 101, Mason, OH 45040 *Tel:* 513-459-3400 *Fax:* 513-459-3796 *E-mail:* information@gatesair.com; orders@gatesair.com; support@gatesair.com *Web Site:* www.gatesair.com, pg 875

Rau, Raghu, SeaChange International Inc, 50 Nagog Park, Acton, MA 01720 *Tel:* 978-897-0100 *Fax:* 978-897-0132 *Web Site:* www.schange.com, pg 1005

Raughter, John, American Legion Fourth Estate Award, Public Relations Div, 700 N Pennsylvania St, Indianapolis, IN 46204 *Tel:* 317-630-1253 *Fax:* 317-630-1368 *E-mail:* pr@legion.org *Web Site:* www.legion.org, pg 1107

Raulet, John, Mailing Avenue Stageworks, 1144 Mailing Ave, Atlanta, GA 30315 *Tel:* 404-601-9500 (ext 11) *Web Site:* www.mailingavenuestageworks.com, pg 929

Raulet, Paul, Mailing Avenue Stageworks, 1144 Mailing Ave, Atlanta, GA 30315 *Tel:* 404-601-9500 (ext 11) *Web Site:* www.mailingavenuestageworks.com, pg 929

Rausch, Brian, House of Moves, 5419 McConnell Ave, Los Angeles, CA 90066-7027 *Tel:* 310-306-6131 *E-mail:* info@moves.com *Web Site:* www.moves.com, pg 891

Raven, Abbe, A&E Television Networks LLC, 235 E 45 St, New York, NY 10017 *Tel:* 212-210-1400 *Web Site:* www.aetv.com, pg 771

Raventos, Bill, Ivie Technologies Inc, 1195 Spring Creek Place, Suite B, Springville, UT 84663 *Tel:* 801-489-8703 *Toll Free Fax:* 877-829-6567 *E-mail:* ivie@ivie.com *Web Site:* www.ivie.com, pg 903

Ravn, Jorgen, Signal Transport, PO Box 1028, Lake Forest, CA 92609-1028 *Tel:* 714-641-5665 *Fax:* 714-641-5664 *E-mail:* sales@sigt.com; sales@smcpanels.com *Web Site:* www.sigt.com; www.smcpanels.com, pg 1011

Ray, Charlie, Digital Services Recording Studios, 1601 S Cherry St, Tomball, TX 77375 *Tel:* 281-290-8500 *Fax:* 281-290-8510 *E-mail:* studio@dsrecordings.com *Web Site:* www.dsrecordings.com, pg 848

Ray, Randy, Randolf Productions Inc, 17935 Skypark Circle, Suite K, Irvine, CA 92614 *Tel:* 949-794-9109 *Toll Free Tel:* 800-266-7741 *Fax:* 949-794-9117 *E-mail:* sales@go2rpi.com *Web Site:* www.go2rpi.com, pg 991

Raymond, Greg, e-MEDIAtely, 6778 Cibola, San Diego, CA 92120 *Tel:* 619-583-2008 *Toll Free Tel:* 866-816-6845 *Fax:* 619-501-1425 *E-mail:* sdweb@cox.net *Web Site:* www.e-mediately.com, pg 855

Raymond, Leslie, Ann Arbor Film Festival, 217 N First St, Ann Arbor, MI 48104 *Tel:* 734-995-5356 *Fax:* 734-995-5396 *E-mail:* info@aafilmfest.org *Web Site:* www.aafilmfest.org, pg 1107

Raymond, Patrick, Raymond Entertainment Direct (RED), 3450 Cahuenga Blvd W, Suite 410, Los Angeles, CA 90068 *Tel:* 323-785-4700 *Fax:* 323-785-4701 *E-mail:* info@raymondentertainment.com *Web Site:* www.raymondentertainment.com, pg 992

Raz, Karen, AJA Video Systems Inc, 180 Litton Dr, Grass Valley, CA 95945 *Tel:* 530-274-2048 *Fax:* 530-274-9442 *E-mail:* sales@aja.com *Web Site:* www.aja.com, pg 779

Razdan, Rikki, ISCAN Inc, 21 Cabot Rd, Woburn, MA 01801 *Tel:* 781-932-1199 *Fax:* 781-932-1155 *E-mail:* info@iscaninc.com *Web Site:* www.iscaninc.com, pg 902

Rea, Jimmy, Jimmy Rea Electronics Inc, 540 W Broad St, Columbus, OH 43215 *Tel:* 614-221-5170 *Fax:* 614-221-8898 *Web Site:* www.jimmyrea.com, pg 992

Read, Jennifer, Thompson Rivers University Open Learning, BC Centre for Open Learning, 4th fl, 900 McGill Rd, Kamloops, BC V2C 0C8, Canada *Tel:* 250-852-7000 *Toll Free Tel:* 800-663-9711 *E-mail:* student@tru.ca; olmarketing@tru.ca *Web Site:* www.tru.ca/distance, pg 1039

Read, Steve, Evolution Presentation Technologies, 6910 Farrell Rd SE, Calgary, AB T2H 0T1, Canada *Tel:* 403-259-3793 *Toll Free Tel:* 800-561-9820 *Fax:* 403-259-2374 *Web Site:* www.evolutionav.ca, pg 863

Reagan, Dr David R, Lamb & Lion Ministries, PO Box 919, McKinney, TX 75070 *Tel:* 972-736-3567 *Toll Free Tel:* 800-705-8316 (sales) *E-mail:* lamblion@lamblion.com *Web Site:* www.lamblion.com, pg 915

Reagan, Patrick, VSG Digital Media Solutions, 11126 Lindbergh Business Ct, St Louis, MO 63123 *Tel:* 314-487-8045 *Toll Free Tel:* 800-737-8045 *Fax:* 314-487-9387 *Web Site:* www.vsginc.net, pg 1061

Rebala, Gopinath, One Touch Systems Inc, 2346 Bering Dr, San Jose, CA 95131 *Tel:* 408-660-8435 *Fax:* 408-436-4699 *E-mail:* info@onetouchsys.com *Web Site:* www.onetouchsys.com, pg 963

Reber, Mark, JaffeHolden, 114-A Washington St, Norwalk, CT 06854 *Tel:* 203-838-4167 *Fax:* 203-838-4168 *Web Site:* www.jaffeholden.com, pg 903

Reches, Nir, Band Pro Film & Digital Inc, 3403 W Pacific Ave, Burbank, CA 91505 *Tel:* 818-841-9655 *Toll Free Tel:* 888-BANDPRO (226-3776) *Fax:* 818-841-7649 *Web Site:* www.bandpro.com, pg 802

Rechner, Coni, Discovery Education - Chicago, 111 E Wacker Dr, Suite 3000, Chicago, IL 60601 *Web Site:* www.discoveryeducation.com, pg 848

Record, James, SNL Kagan Media & Communications, One SNL Plaza, 212 Seventh St NE, Charlottesville, VA 22902 *Tel:* 434-977-1600 *Toll Free Tel:* 866-296-3743 *Fax:* 434-977-4466 *E-mail:* snlkagansales@snl.com *Web Site:* www.snl.com, pg 1015

Rector, Adam, RentACamera.com, 1805 Hayes St, Nashville, TN 37203 *Tel:* 615-320-3200 *Toll Free Tel:* 855-588-2882 *E-mail:* info@tvcnashville.com *Web Site:* www.rentacamera.com, pg 995

Redd, Daniel L, Replicopy Digital Media Center, 2101 Midway Rd, Suite 200, Carrollton, TX 75006 *Tel:* 972-702-8388 *Fax:* 972-387-DUBS (387-3827) *E-mail:* replicopy@replicopy.com *Web Site:* www.replicopy.com, pg 995

Redd, Robert, Replicopy Digital Media Center, 2101 Midway Rd, Suite 200, Carrollton, TX 75006 *Tel:* 972-702-8388 *Fax:* 972-387-DUBS (387-3827) *E-mail:* replicopy@replicopy.com *Web Site:* www.replicopy.com, pg 995

Redhead, Paul, Sanako Inc, 500 Linden Oaks, Rochester, NY 14625 *Toll Free Tel:* 888-611-4785 *Toll Free Fax:* 888-389-3858 *E-mail:* info@sanako.com *Web Site:* www.sanako.com, pg 1002

Redman, Patrick, American Management Association International, 600 AMA Way, Saranac Lake, NY 12983 *Tel:* 518-891-1500 (ext 300) *Toll Free Tel:* 877-566-9441 (cust serv) *Fax:* 518-891-0368 *E-mail:* customerservice@amanet.org *Web Site:* www.amanet.org, pg 784

Redmond, Rich, GatesAir, 5300 Kings Island Dr, Suite 101, Mason, OH 45040 *Tel:* 513-459-3400 *Fax:* 513-459-3796 *E-mail:* information@gatesair.com; orders@gatesair.com; support@gatesair.com *Web Site:* www.gatesair.com, pg 875

Reed, Alene, Reed Presentations Inc (RPI), 17 Water St, Lebanon, NJ 08833 *Tel:* 908-753-8800 *Fax:* 908-753-8823 *E-mail:* info@reedpresentations.com *Web Site:* www.reedpresentations.com, pg 993

Reed, Art, Bradley Broadcast & Pro Audio, PO Box 756, New Market, MD 21774 *Tel:* 301-682-8700 *Toll Free Tel:* 800-732-7665 *Fax:* 301-263-7042 *E-mail:* beburg@bradleybroadcast.com *Web Site:* www.bradleybroadcast.com, pg 811

Reed, Barry A, Reed Presentations Inc (RPI), 17 Water St, Lebanon, NJ 08833 *Tel:* 908-753-8800 *Fax:* 908-753-8823 *E-mail:* info@reedpresentations.com *Web Site:* www.reedpresentations.com, pg 993

Reed, Doug, Brown Bag Imaging, 111 Presidential Blvd, Suite 100, Bala Cynwyd, PA 19004 *Toll Free Tel:* 800-533-8686 *E-mail:* sales@brownbagimaging.com *Web Site:* brownbag.sourceaudio.com, pg 814

Reed, James, Selco Products Co, 8780 Technology Way, Reno, NV 89521-5908 *Toll Free Tel:* 877-807-5426 *Fax:* 775-674-5111 *E-mail:* sales@selcoproducts.com *Web Site:* www.selcoproducts.com, pg 1006

Reed, Lawrence, Foundation for Economic Education, 30 S Broadway, Irvington-on-Hudson, NY 10533 *Tel:* 914-591-7230 *Toll Free Tel:* 800-960-4333 *E-mail:* editor@fee.org; info@fee.org *Web Site:* www.fee.org, pg 1082

Reeder, Bill, Hughie's Event Production Services, 1260 E 38 St, Cleveland, OH 44114 *Tel:* 216-361-4600 *Toll Free Tel:* 800-449-4115 *Fax:* 216-361-2570 *Web Site:* www.hughies.com, pg 892

Reese, Cathie, Geomatrix Productions, 270 Amity Rd, Woodbridge, CT 06525-2267 *Tel:* 203-389-0001 *Web Site:* www.geomatrixproductions.com, pg 877

Reese, Diane, Ultimate Presentation Systems Inc, 901 S Hohokam Dr, Tempe, AZ 85281 *Tel:* 480-966-2000 *Toll Free Tel:* 800-866-4066 *Fax:* 480-968-3009 *E-mail:* sales@ult.com *Web Site:* www.ult.com, pg 1047

Reese, Michael, Ultimate Presentation Systems Inc, 901 S Hohokam Dr, Tempe, AZ 85281 *Tel:* 480-966-2000 *Toll Free Tel:* 800-866-4066 *Fax:* 480-968-3009 *E-mail:* sales@ult.com *Web Site:* www.ult.com, pg 1047

Reetz, Susan, Rucinski & Reetz Communications LLC, 2155 Terrebonne, Mosinee, WI 54455 *Tel:* 715-355-9159; 715-241-7316 *Web Site:* www.rucinskireetz.com, pg 1000

Reeves, Sharon, Photoflex Inc, 97 Hangar Way, Watsonville, CA 95076 *Tel:* 831-786-1370 *Toll Free Tel:* 800-486-2674 *Fax:* 831-786-1372 *E-mail:* sales@photoflex.com; marketing@photoflex.com *Web Site:* www.photoflex.com, pg 974

Reeves-Pepin, Jaclyn, National Association of Biology Teachers (NABT), 1313 Dolley Madison Blvd, Suite 402, McLean, VA 22101 *Tel:* 703-264-9696 *Toll Free Tel:* 888-501-NABT (501-6228) *Fax:* 703-790-2672 *Toll Free Fax:* 800-883-0698 *E-mail:* office@nabt.org *Web Site:* www.nabt.org, pg 1085

Reff, Kenny, Limelight Communications Inc, 2812 Roesh Way, Vienna, VA 22181 *Tel:* 703-242-4596 *Fax:* 703-991-0616 *E-mail:* moreinfo@limelightdc.com *Web Site:* www.limelightdc.com, pg 921

Regal, Kelly, Turner Broadcasting System Inc, One CNN Ctr, Atlanta, GA 30303 *Tel:* 404-827-1700 *Web Site:* www.turner.com, pg 1046

Regan, Debbie, Debbie Regan Locations Ltd, PO Box 353, Old Westbury, NY 11568 *Tel:* 516-626-1928 *Fax:* 516-626-2337 *E-mail:* info@debbiereganlocations.com *Web Site:* www.debbiereganlocations.com, pg 844

Regan, Jeff, Shooting Star Video, 256 Shearwater Isle, Foster City, CA 94404 *Tel:* 650-345-0919 *Fax:* 650-573-6615 *E-mail:* rent@ssv.com *Web Site:* www.ssv.com, pg 1009

Regan, Marie, New York Film/Video Council (NYFVC), PO Box 1685, New York, NY 10185-1685 *Tel:* 212-330-0450 *E-mail:* info@nyfvc.org *Web Site:* www.nyfvc.org, pg 1086

Regester, Gary, Plume Ltd, 888 Main St, Silver Plume, CO 80476 *Tel:* 303-569-3236 *Toll Free Tel:* 866-569-3236 *Fax:* 303-569-2932 *Web Site:* www.plumeltd.com, pg 977

Register, Lowell, Register Data Systems, 1691 Forsyth St, Macon, GA 31201 *Tel:* 478-745-5500 *Toll Free Tel:* 800-521-5222 *Fax:* 478-745-0500 *E-mail:* sales@registerdata.com, pg 994

Register, Sam, Warner Bros Animation, 4000 Warner Blvd, Burbank, CA 91522 *Tel:* 818-954-6000 *Web Site:* www.warnerbros.com, pg 1062

Reher, Anita, Robert Flaherty Film Seminar, 6 E 39 St, 12th fl, New York, NY 10016 *Tel:* 212-448-0457 *Fax:* 212-448-0458 *E-mail:* ifs@flahertyseminar.org *Web Site:* www.flahertyseminar.org, pg 1114

Reichman, Barry, Mathmadeeasy.com, 4914 13 Ave, Brooklyn, NY 11219 *Toll Free Tel:* 800-USA-MATH (872-6284) *Web Site:* www.mathmadeeasy.com, pg 934

Reid, Allan, Canadian Academy of Recording Arts & Sciences (CARAS), 345 Adelaide St W, 2nd fl, Toronto, ON M5V 1R5, Canada *Tel:* 416-485-3135 *Toll Free Tel:* 888-440-JUNO (440-5866, CN only) *Fax:* 416-485-4978 *E-mail:* submissions@junoawards.ca *Web Site:* www.carasonline.ca; junoawards.ca, pg 1080

Reid, Allan, Juno Awards, 345 Adelaide St W, 2nd fl, Toronto, ON M5V 1R5, Canada *Tel:* 416-485-3135 *Toll Free Tel:* 888-440-JUNO (440-5866, CN only) *Fax:* 416-485-4978 *E-mail:* info@junoawards.ca; info@carasonline.ca; submissions@junoawards.ca *Web Site:* junoawards.ca; www.facebook.com/theJunoAwards, pg 1118

Reid, Bill, KB Systems, 10407 62 Place W, Mukilteo, WA 98275 *Tel:* 425-355-8740 *E-mail:* kbsystem@kbsystem.com *Web Site:* www.kbsystem.com, pg 908

Reid, Kay, KB Systems, 10407 62 Place W, Mukilteo, WA 98275 *Tel:* 425-355-8740 *E-mail:* kbsystem@kbsystem.com *Web Site:* www.kbsystem.com, pg 908

Reider, Allan, Reider Photography & Video Productions, 2174 Morris Ave, Union, NJ 07083 *Tel:* 908-688-8808 *E-mail:* info@njphotographer.com *Web Site:* www.njphotographer.com, pg 994

Reidinger, Scott, Cardinal Sound & Video, 2219 Kansas Ave, Silver Spring, MD 20910 *Tel:* 301-589-3700 *Fax:* 301-589-4284 *E-mail:* info@cardinalsound.us *Web Site:* www.cardinalsound.us, pg 820

Reidy, Carolyn, Simon & Schuster, Inc, 1230 Avenue of the Americas, New York, NY 10020 *Tel:* 212-698-7000 *Toll Free Tel:* 800-223-2348 (cust serv) *Toll Free Fax:* 800-943-9831 *E-mail:* customer.service@simonandschuster.net *Web Site:* www.simonandschuster.net; www.simonandschuster.biz, pg 1011

Reighard, Aaron, West Penn Wire, 2833 W Chestnut St, Washington, PA 15301 *Tel:* 724-222-7060 *Toll Free Tel:* 800-245-4964 *Fax:* 724-222-6420 *E-mail:* info@westpenn-wpw.com *Web Site:* www.westpenn-wpw.com, pg 1064

Reighard, Jessica, Paul H Brookes Publishing Co, PO Box 10624, Baltimore, MD 21285-0624 *Tel:* 410-337-9580 *Toll Free Tel:* 800-638-3775 (cust serv) *Fax:* 410-337-8539 *E-mail:* custserv@brookespublishing.com *Web Site:* www.brookespublishing.com, pg 814

Reikowsky, Jim, Vallejo/Solano County Film Office, 289 Mare Island Way, Vallejo, CA 94590 *Tel:* 707-642-3653 *Toll Free Tel:* 800-4-VALLEJO (482-5535) *Fax:* 707-644-2206 *Web Site:* www.visitvallejo.com/film-office, pg 1094

Reil, Doug, North Atlantic Books, 2526 Martin Luther King Jr Way, Berkeley, CA 94704 *Tel:* 510-549-4270 *Fax:* 510-549-4276 *Web Site:* www.northatlanticbooks.com, pg 958

Reilly, Edward T, American Management Association®, 1601 Broadway, New York, NY 10019 *Tel:* 212-586-8100 *Toll Free Tel:* 877-566-9441 (cust serv) *Fax:* 212-903-8168; 518-891-0368 (cust serv) *E-mail:* customerservice@amanet.org *Web Site:* www.amanet.org, pg 784, 1077

Reilly, John J, SoftWright LLC, PO Box 7205, Charlotte, VA 22906 *Tel:* 303-344-5486 *Toll Free Tel:* 800-728-4033 *Fax:* 303-265-9399 *E-mail:* sales@softwright.com *Web Site:* www.softwright.com, pg 1015

Reilly, Kevin, AVFX Inc, 96 Holton St, Boston, MA 02135 *Tel:* 617-254-0770 *Toll Free Tel:* 888-254-0770 *E-mail:* info@avfx.com *Web Site:* www.avfx.com, pg 798

Reimnitz, Arlen, ASET - The Neurodiagnostic Society, 402 E Bannister Rd, Suite A, Kansas City, MO 64131-3019 *Tel:* 816-931-1120 *Fax:* 816-931-1145 *E-mail:* info@aset.org *Web Site:* www.aset.org, pg 792

Reinartz, Joe, Pollstar, 4697 W Jacquelyn Ave, Fresno, CA 93722-6413 *Tel:* 559-271-7900 *Fax:* 559-271-7979 *E-mail:* info@pollstar.com *Web Site:* www.pollstar.com; www.pollstarpro.com, pg 978

Reiner, Keith, Meridia Audience Response, 5207 Militia Hill Rd, Plymouth Meeting, PA 19462 *Tel:* 610-260-6800 *Fax:* 610-260-6810 *E-mail:* rsvp@meridiaars.com *Web Site:* www.meridiaars.com, pg 939

Reinhardt, Bob, Reinhardt Productions Inc, 242-17 Van Zandt Ave, Douglaston, NY 11362 *Tel:* 718-225-4163 *Fax:* 212-338-0505, pg 994

Reischmann, Angela, Hi-Tech Enterprises Inc, 4250 114 Terr, Clearwater, FL 33762 *Tel:* 727-573-9600 *Toll Free Tel:* 800-350-4862 *Fax:* 727-573-9606 *E-mail:* hitech@videoequipment.com *Web Site:* www.videoequipment.com, pg 888

Reiser, Rich, Savage Universal Corp, 550 E Elliot Rd, Chandler, AZ 85225 *Tel:* 480-632-1320 *Toll Free Tel:* 800-624-8891 *Fax:* 480-632-1322 *Web Site:* savageuniversal.com, pg 1003

Reiter, Bill, Pro Video & Film Equipment Co Inc, 11425 Mathis Ave, Studio 404, Dallas, TX 75234 *Tel:* 972-869-9990 *Toll Free Tel:* 888-869-9998 *Fax:* 972-869-0145 *E-mail:* providfilm@aol.com *Web Site:* www.provideofilm.com; www.usedequipmentnewsletter.com, pg 983

Reiter, Richard, Richard Reiter Productions Inc, 36 Catherine Ct, Cedar Grove, NJ 07009 *Tel:* 973-857-2935; 973-857-2557 *Fax:* 973-857-2935 *E-mail:* reiterjazz@gmail.com; reiterjazz@yahoo.com; reiterjazz@optonline.net *Web Site:* www.richardreiter.com, pg 994

Reizner, Dick, Dick Reizner Film & Video, 7179 Via Maria, San Jose, CA 95139 *Tel:* 408-226-6339 *Web Site:* www.reizner.com, pg 994

Rejto, Laurent, Maverick Awards, 13 Rock City Rd, Woodstock, NY 12498 *Tel:* 845-679-4265; 845-810-0131 *Fax:* 509-479-5414 *E-mail:* info@woodstockfilmfestival.com *Web Site:* www.woodstockfilmfestival.com, pg 1119

Remes, Mark, BES Studios, 6829 Atmore Dr, Suite E, Richmond, VA 23225 *Tel:* 804-276-0806 *Toll Free Tel:* 800-995-2371 *E-mail:* info@besstudios.com *Web Site:* www.besstudios.com, pg 805

Remington, Paul, Westbrook Technologies Inc, 35 Thorpe Ave, Suite 201, Wallingford, CT 06492 *Tel:* 203-871-4984 *Fax:* 203-269-0322 *E-mail:* info@westbrooktech.com *Web Site:* www.westbrooktech.com, pg 1064

Remis, Joel, Ironstone Technologies, 534 Berry St, Winnipeg, MB R3H 0R9, Canada *Tel:* 204-697-0159 *Toll Free Tel:* 800-665-4766 *Fax:* 204-694-9355 *E-mail:* info@ironstone.ca *Web Site:* www.ironstone.ca, pg 902

Remmers, Chad, National Products Inc, 8410 Dallas Ave S, Seattle, WA 98108 *Tel:* 206-763-8361 *Toll Free Tel:* 800-497-7479 *Fax:* 206-763-9615 *Web Site:* www.rammount.com, pg 953

Remoaldo, Michelle, ALOM Technologies Corp, 48105 Warm Springs Blvd, Fremont, CA 94539-7498 *Tel:* 510-360-3600 *Toll Free Tel:* 800-500-9991 *Fax:* 510-226-7617 *E-mail:* customerservice@alom.com *Web Site:* www.alom.com, pg 782

Remote, Steven, Aura Sonic Ltd, PO Box 520791, Flushing, NY 11352-0791 *Tel:* 718-886-6500 *E-mail:* somebody@aurasonic.com *Web Site:* www.aurasonicltd.com, pg 796

Rene, Michele, Bill Bachmann Studios, PO Box 950833, Lake Mary, FL 32795 *Tel:* 407-333-9988 *Web Site:* www.billbachmann.com, pg 807

Renell, Ellen, Action Sports/All Stock, PO Box 301, Malibu, CA 90265-0301 *Tel:* 310-459-2526 *Fax:* 310-456-1743 *E-mail:* info@sdfilms.com *Web Site:* www.actionsportsstockfootage.com, pg 775

Renteria, Juan, Universal Satellite Communications Inc, 1530 Nandina Ave, Perris, CA 92571 *Tel:* 562-483-4800; 951-943-4420 (corp off) *Toll Free Tel:* 888-867-6620 *Fax:* 954-943-0263 *Web Site:* www.unisatmobile.com, pg 1049

Repola, Cathy, Motion Picture Editors Guild Local 700, 7715 Sunset Blvd, Suite 200, Hollywood, CA 90046 *Tel:* 323-876-4770 *Toll Free Tel:* 800-705-8700 *Fax:* 323-876-0861 *E-mail:* mail@editorsguild.com *Web Site:* www.editorsguild.com, pg 1084

Reppert, Tim, AirCraft Production Libraries, 162 Columbus Ave, Boston, MA 02116-5222 *Tel:* 617-303-7600 *Toll Free Tel:* 800-343-2514 *Fax:* 617-303-7666 *E-mail:* info@aircraftmusiclibrary.com; acsales@aircraftmusiclibrary.com *Web Site:* www.aircraftmusiclibrary.com, pg 779

Restivo-Alessi, Chantal, HarperAudio, 10 E 53 St, New York, NY 10022 *Tel:* 212-207-7000 *Toll Free Tel:* 800-242-7737 *Fax:* 212-207-2582 *Toll Free Fax:* 800-822-4090 *Web Site:* www.harpercollins.com, pg 885

Rettig, Ray, Fingerpaint, 13 Walker Way, Albany, NY 12205 *Tel:* 518-869-1968 *Fax:* 518-869-1969 *Web Site:* fingerpaintmarketing.com, pg 868

Revelli, Clare, Revelli, PO Box 150098, San Rafael, CA 94915 *Tel:* 415-460-9898 *E-mail:* colorstyledesign@aol.com, pg 995

Reynolds, G Brian, Perennial Pictures Film Corp, 2102 E 52 St, Indianapolis, IN 46205 *Tel:* 317-253-1519 *E-mail:* mail@perennialpictures.com *Web Site:* www.perennialpictures.com, pg 973

Reynolds, Jerry, College of Nursing, Washington State University, 103 E Spokane Falls Blvd, Spokane, WA 99202 *Tel:* 509-324-7360 *Fax:* 509-324-7341 *Web Site:* nursing.wsu.edu, pg 831

Reynolds, John, Kavich Reynolds Productions Inc, 6381 Hollywood Blvd, Suite 580, Hollywood, CA 90028 *Tel:* 323-466-2490 *Fax:* 323-466-3655 *E-mail:* info@kavichreynolds.com *Web Site:* www.kavichreynolds.com, pg 908

Reynolds, Steve, Imagine Communications Corp, 3001 Dallas Pkwy, Suite 300, Frisco, TX 75034 *Tel:* 469-803-4900 *Toll Free Tel:* 866-4-IMAGINE (446-2446) *Fax:* 469-803-4899 *E-mail:* insidesales@imaginecommunications.com *Web Site:* www.imaginecommunications.com, pg 896

Reynolds, Will, Tennessee Prompters, 727 Wildview Dr, Nashville, TN 37211-1142 *Tel:* 615-834-9655 *Fax:* 615-834-1086 *E-mail:* info@tennesseeprompters.com *Web Site:* www.tennesseeprompters.com, pg 1037

Reznick, Evi, Gingerbread Group, 1337 Kittredge Ct, Atlanta, GA 30329 *Tel:* 404-634-8678; 404-663-9050 *Fax:* 404-601-9387 *E-mail:* books2gogh@gmail.com, pg 878

Rhea, Wes, Stockton/San Joaquin Film Liaison, 125 Bridge Place, Stockton, CA 95202 *Tel:* 209-938-1555 *Toll Free Tel:* 877-778-6258 *Fax:* 209-938-1554 *Web Site:* visitstockton.org/footer/resources/stockton-film-commission, pg 1094

Rheinstein, Fred, The Production Group Studios, 6767 W Sunset Blvd, No 8-496, Hollywood, CA 90028-7177 *Tel:* 323-469-8111 *Fax:* 323-962-2182 *E-mail:* info@productiongroup.tv *Web Site:* www.productiongroup.tv, pg 984

Rhoads, Kevin, Kontron America, 14118 Stowe Dr, Poway, CA 92064-7147 *Tel:* 858-677-0877 *Toll Free Tel:* 888-294-4558; 800-480-0044 (cust serv & tech support) *Fax:* 858-677-0898 *E-mail:* sales@us.kontron.com *Web Site:* www.kontron.com, pg 913

Rhodes, Diane, Films for the Humanities & Sciences, 132 W 31 St, 17th fl, New York, NY 10001 *Toll Free Tel:* 800-257-5126 *Fax:* 609-671-0266 *E-mail:* custserv@films.com *Web Site:* ffh.films.com, pg 868

Rhodes, Ken, Instrumentation Marketing Corp, 820 S Mariposa St, Burbank, CA 91506-3196 *Tel:* 818-842-2141 *Fax:* 818-842-2610 *E-mail:* mail@photosonics.com *Web Site:* www.photosonics.com/imc.htm, pg 899

Rhodes, Martin, DV Awards, 6300 N Sagewood Dr, Suite H-383, Park City, UT 84098 *E-mail:* info@dvawards.com *Web Site:* www.dvawards.com, pg 1114

Rhodes, William, Heinemann, 361 Hanover St, Portsmouth, NH 03801-3912 *Tel:* 603-431-7894 *Toll Free Tel:* 800-225-5800 *Fax:* 603-431-2214 *Toll Free Fax:* 877-231-6980 *E-mail:* custserv@heinemann.com *Web Site:* www.heinemann.com, pg 887

Ribeiro, Tom, Real Cool TV Productions, 800 S Main St, Suite 203, Mansfield, MA 02048 *Tel:* 508-337-8520 *E-mail:* info@realcooltv.com *Web Site:* www.realcooltv.com, pg 992

Ricca, Aimee, The Citation of Outstanding Service to the Society Award, 3 Barker Ave, 5th fl, White Plains, NY 10601 *Tel:* 914-761-1100 *Fax:* 914-761-3115 *E-mail:* smpte@smpte.org *Web Site:* www.smpte.org, pg 1112

Ricca, Aimee, The Journal Award & SMPTE Journal Certificate of Merit, 3 Barker Ave, 5th fl, White Plains, NY 10601 *Tel:* 914-761-1100 *Fax:* 914-761-3115 *E-mail:* smpte@smpte.org *Web Site:* www.smpte.org, pg 1118

Ricca, Aimee, The Presidential Proclamation Award, 3 Barker Ave, 5th fl, White Plains, NY 10601 *Tel:* 914-761-1100 *Fax:* 914-761-3115 *E-mail:* smpte@smpte.org *Web Site:* www.smpte.org, pg 1124

Ricca, Aimee, The Progress Medal Award, 3 Barker Ave, 5th fl, White Plains, NY 10601 *Tel:* 914-761-1100 *Fax:* 914-761-3115 *E-mail:* smpte@smpte.org *Web Site:* www.smpte.org, pg 1124

Ricca, Aimee, Society of Motion Picture & Television Engineers (SMPTE), 3 Barker Ave, 5th fl, White Plains, NY 10601 *Tel:* 914-761-1100 *Fax:* 914-761-3115 *E-mail:* smpte@smpte.org *Web Site:* www.smpte.org, pg 1015

Ricca, Aimee, Technicolor-Herbert T Kalmus Gold Medal Award, 3 Barker Ave, 5th fl, White Plains, NY 10601 *Tel:* 914-761-1100 *Fax:* 914-761-3115 *E-mail:* smpte@smpte.org *Web Site:* www.smpte.org, pg 1128

Ricca, Aimee, The Samuel L Warner Memorial Award, 3 Barker Ave, 5th fl, White Plains, NY 10601 *Tel:* 914-761-1100 *Fax:* 914-761-3115 *E-mail:* smpte@smpte.org *Web Site:* www.smpte.org, pg 1129

Ricciardi, Charles, New Jersey Motion Picture & Television Commission, 153 Halsey St, 5th fl, Newark, NJ 07102-2807 *Tel:* 973-648-6279 *Fax:* 973-648-7350 *E-mail:* njfilm@njfilm.org *Web Site:* www.njfilm.org, pg 1100

Rice, Bill, Videografix LLC, 2530 Berryessa Rd, Suite 314, San Jose, CA 95132-2903 *Tel:* 408-499-1280 *Fax:* 408-583-4018 *E-mail:* info@videografix.com *Web Site:* www.videografix.com, pg 1057

Rice, Doug, DR&A Inc, 45 Willow St, Nashville, TN 37210 *Tel:* 615-256-6200 *Fax:* 615-256-6236 *Web Site:* www.griptruck.com, pg 852

Rice, Jennifer, ACCO Brands Corp, 4 Corporate Dr, Lake Zurick, IL 60047-8997 *Toll Free Tel:* 800-541-0094 *Toll Free Fax:* 800-941-4463 *E-mail:* contactus@gbc.com *Web Site:* www.accobrands.com, pg 773

Rice, Sylvia, Salina Film Commission, 120 W Ash St, Salina, KS 67402 *Tel:* 785-827-9301 *Fax:* 785-827-9758 *E-mail:* info@salinakansas.org *Web Site:* www.salinakansas.org, pg 1097

Rice, Van Allen, Bestek Lighting & Staging, 98 Mahan St, West Babylon, NY 11704 *Tel:* 631-643-0707 *Fax:* 631-643-0764 *E-mail:* production@bestek.com *Web Site:* www.bestek.com, pg 806

Rice, Willard, PrimeArray Systems Inc, 48 Maple St, Lowell, MA 01852 *Tel:* 978-649-0090 *Toll Free Tel:* 800-433-5133 *Fax:* 978-498-0190 *E-mail:* info@primearray.com; sales@primearray.com *Web Site:* www.primearray.com, pg 982

Rich, Gerald, Concord Communications, 26 Denise Place, Stamford, CT 06905 *Tel:* 203-322-9322, pg 835

Rich, Michael, Media Computing Inc, PO Box 4169, Cave Creek, AZ 85327-4169 *Tel:* 602-614-2091 *E-mail:* info@mediacomputing.com *Web Site:* www.mediacomputing.com, pg 936

Rich, Todd, KFOR-TV, 444 E Britton Rd, Oklahoma City, OK 73114 *Tel:* 405-424-4444 *Fax:* 405-478-6337 *Web Site:* www.kfor.com, pg 910

Rich, Tracey, White Lotus Foundation, 2500 San Marcos Pass, Santa Barbara, CA 93105 *Tel:* 805-964-1944 *Fax:* 805-964-9617 *E-mail:* info@whitelotus.org *Web Site:* www.whitelotus.org, pg 1065

Richard, Dr James T, Newtown Psychological Center, 660 Newtown Yardley Rd, Suite 102, Newtown, PA 18940 *Tel:* 215-968-5378, pg 957

Richard, Julie, Individual Artist Fellowship Program, 193 State St, 25 State House Sta, Augusta, ME 04330-0025 *Tel:* 207-287-2724 *Fax:* 207-287-2725 *E-mail:* mainearts.info@maine.gov *Web Site:* mainearts.maine.gov/Pages/Grants/Individual-Artist-Fellowships, pg 1117

Richard, T J, 99 Productions LLC, 760 Conger St, Suite 1, Eugene, OR 97402 *Tel:* 541-343-0099 *E-mail:* email@99productions.com *Web Site:* www.99productions.com, pg 957

Richards, Kim, Allied Artists International Inc, Production Services Ctr, 15810 E Gale Ave, Suite 133, Hacienda Heights, CA 91745 *Tel:* 626-330-0600 *Fax:* 626-961-0411 *E-mail:* info@alliedartists.net *Web Site:* us.alliedartists.com, pg 781

Richards, Laurie, Nebraska Film Office, PO Box 98907, Lincoln, NE 68509-8907 *Tel:* 402-471-3746 *Toll Free Tel:* 800-228-4307 *E-mail:* info@filmnebraska.org *Web Site:* www.filmnebraska.org; www.neded.org/nebraska-film-office-home, pg 1100

Richardson, Andrew T, Shure Manufacturing Corp, 1901 W Main St, Washington, MO 63090 *Tel:* 636-390-7100 *Toll Free Tel:* 800-227-4873 *Fax:* 636-390-7171 *E-mail:* sales@shureusa.com *Web Site:* www.shureusa.com, pg 1010

Richardson, David T, The Learning House Inc, 427 S Fourth St, Suite 300, Louisville, KY 40202 *Tel:* 502-589-9878 *Fax:* 502-589-9825 *E-mail:* sales@learninghouse.com *Web Site:* www.learninghouse.com, pg 917

Richardson, David W, Perception Publications, 8711 E Pinnacle Peak Rd, PMB 345, Scottsdale, AZ 85255 *Toll Free Tel:* 800-338-5831 *Fax:* 480-451-9372 *E-mail:* info@iqbooster.com, pg 973

Richardson, Hal, Paramount Pictures Corporation, 5555 Melrose Ave, Los Angeles, CA 90038 *Tel:* 323-956-8398 *Web Site:* www.paramount.com, pg 969

Richardson, Lynda, Lynda Richardson Photography, 7239 Lookout Dr, Richmond, VA 23225 *Tel:* 804-347-9668 *E-mail:* lynda@lyndarichardsonphotography.com *Web Site:* www.lyndarichardsonphotography.com, pg 996

Richardson, Scott, Media Concepts Inc, 559 49 St S, St Petersburg, FL 33707 *Tel:* 727-321-2122 *Toll Free Tel:* 800-330-3873 *Fax:* 727-321-2272 *E-mail:* mcifl@tampabay.rr.com *Web Site:* www.mcifl.com, pg 936

Richeson, Parke, The Chicago Production Center, 5400 N Saint Louis Ave, Chicago, IL 60625-4698 *Tel:* 773-509-5571 *Fax:* 773-509-5303 *Web Site:* www.wttw.com, pg 825

Richie, Chip, Rich-Heape Films Inc, 5952 Royal Lane, Suite 254, Dallas, TX 75230 *Tel:* 214-696-6916 *Toll Free Tel:* 888-600-2922 *Fax:* 214-696-6306 *Web Site:* www.richheape.com, pg 996

Richie, Chip, Richie Media Productions LLC, 2035 Royal Lane, Suite 203, Dallas, TX 75229 *Tel:* 214-696-9040 *Web Site:* www.richiemedia.com, pg 996

Richier, Pierre, NEC Display Solutions of America, 500 Park Blvd, Suite 1100, Itasca, IL 60143 *Tel:* 630-467-3000 *Web Site:* www.necdisplay.com, pg 954

Richman, Carol, Monad Trainer's Aide Inc, 163-60 22 Ave, Whitestone, NY 11357 *Tel:* 718-352-2314 *Toll Free Tel:* 800-344-6088 *Fax:* 718-352-8276 *Web Site:* www.monadtrainersaide.com, pg 945

Richman, Eugene, Monad Trainer's Aide Inc, 163-60 22 Ave, Whitestone, NY 11357 *Tel:* 718-352-2314 *Toll Free Tel:* 800-344-6088 *Fax:* 718-352-8276 *Web Site:* www.monadtrainersaide.com, pg 945

Richman, Howard, Sound Feelings Records, 18375 Ventura Blvd, No 8000, Tarzana, CA 91356 *Tel:* 818-757-0600 *Web Site:* www.soundfeelings.com, pg 1017

Richmond, Charlie, Richmond Sound Design Ltd, 5264 Ross St, Vancouver, BC V5W 3K7, Canada *Web Site:* www.richmondsounddesign.com, pg 996

Richter, David, Richter Studios, 1143 W Rundell Place, Chicago, IL 60607 *Tel:* 312-861-9999 *Fax:* 312-997-2387 *E-mail:* info@richterstudios.com *Web Site:* www.richterstudios.com, pg 996

Richter, Jeremy, Richter Studios, 1143 W Rundell Place, Chicago, IL 60607 *Tel:* 312-861-9999 *Fax:* 312-997-2387 *E-mail:* info@richterstudios.com *Web Site:* www.richterstudios.com, pg 996

Richter, Katlyn, South Dakota Film Office, Dept of Tourism, 711 E Wells Ave, Pierre, SD 57501-3369 *Tel:* 605-773-3301 *Toll Free Tel:* 800-952-3625 *Fax:* 605-773-3256 *E-mail:* filmsd@state.sd.us *Web Site:* www.filmsd.com, pg 1102

Richter, Robert, Richter Productions Inc, 521 E 14 St, Suite 4F, New York, NY 10009 *Tel:* 917-608-7427 *E-mail:* rrprod@aol.com; richter330@aol.com *Web Site:* www.richtervideos.com, pg 996

Ricker-Rosato, Debra A, Boston Acoustics, 7 Constitution Way, Woburn, MA 01801 *Tel:* 201-762-6429 *Fax:* 978-538-6237 *E-mail:* weborders@bostonacoustics.com *Web Site:* www.bostonacoustics.com, pg 811

Ridabock, W, Silent Source, 58 Nonotuck St, Northampton, MA 01062 *Tel:* 413-584-7944 *Toll Free Tel:* 800-583-7174 (orders) *Fax:* 413-584-2377 *E-mail:* info@silentsource.com *Web Site:* www.silentsource.com, pg 1011

Ridgell, Jeff, Lightolier, 631 Airport Rd, Fall River, MA 02720 *Tel:* 508-679-8131 *Toll Free Tel:* 800-215-1068 *Fax:* 508-674-4710 *Web Site:* www.lightolier.com, pg 921

Ridgway, Tim, Califone International Inc, 1145 Arroyo Ave, No A, San Fernando, CA 91340 *Tel:* 818-407-2400 *Toll Free Tel:* 800-722-0500 *Fax:* 818-407-2405 *Toll Free Fax:* 877-402-2248 *Web Site:* www.califone.com, pg 817

Ridley, Jane, Oregon Film & Video Office, 123 NE Third Ave, Suite 210, Portland, OR 97232 *Tel:* 503-229-5832 *Fax:* 503-229-6869 *E-mail:* shoot@oregonfilm.org *Web Site:* www.oregonfilm.org, pg 1101

Riffert, Carol, FirstCom Music, 1325 Capital Pkwy, Suite 109, Carrollton, TX 75006 *Tel:* 972-446-8742 *Toll Free Tel:* 800-858-8880 *Fax:* 972-242-6526 *E-mail:* info@firstcom.com *Web Site:* www.firstcom.com, pg 869

Riley, David, NeoSoft Corp, PO Box 5667, Bend, OR 97708-5667 *Tel:* 541-389-5489 *Toll Free Tel:* 877-389-5489 (orders only) *Fax:* 541-388-8221 *E-mail:* sales@neosoftware.com *Web Site:* www.neosoftware.com, pg 954

Riley, James L, Omni International Inc, 435 12 St SW, Vernon, AL 35592 *Tel:* 205-695-9173 *Toll Free Tel:* 800-844-6664 *Fax:* 205-695-6465 *E-mail:* omni-brewster@centurytel.net *Web Site:* www.omniinternational.com, pg 962

Riley, Jocelyn, Her Own Words LLC, PO Box 5264, Madison, WI 53705-0264 *Tel:* 608-271-7083 *Fax:* 608-271-0209 *Web Site:* herownwords.com; nontraditionalcareers.com, pg 888

Riley, Melissa, The Livingston Awards for Young Journalists, Wallace House, 620 Oxford Rd, Ann Arbor, MI 48104 *Tel:* 734-998-7575 *Fax:* 734-998-7979 *E-mail:* livawards@umich.edu *Web Site:* www.livawards.org, pg 1118

Riley, Rod, Word Label Group, 25 Music Sq W, Nashville, TN 37203 *Tel:* 615-251-0600 *Fax:* 615-726-7886 (publicity) *E-mail:* wbrc.publicity@wbr.com *Web Site:* www.wordlabelgroup.com, pg 1069

Rimm, Christopher, Image Labs Corp, 20 Arden Dr, Garrison, NY 10524 *Tel:* 845-737-4420 *Fax:* 845-737-0426 *E-mail:* imagelabs@optonline.net, pg 895

Rimm, Robert, Image Labs Corp, 20 Arden Dr, Garrison, NY 10524 *Tel:* 845-737-4420 *Fax:* 845-737-0426 *E-mail:* imagelabs@optonline.net, pg 895

Rinck, Gary M, John Wiley & Sons Inc, 111 River St, Hoboken, NJ 07030 *Tel:* 201-748-6000 *Toll Free Tel:* 800-225-5945 *Fax:* 201-748-6088 *E-mail:* info@wiley.com *Web Site:* www.wiley.com, pg 1066

Ringrose, James, Real Cool TV Productions, 800 S Main St, Suite 203, Mansfield, MA 02048 *Tel:* 508-337-8520 *E-mail:* info@realcooltv.com *Web Site:* www.realcooltv.com, pg 992

Ripianzi, David, YMAA Publication Center Inc, 16 Lehner St, Wolfeboro, NH 03894 *Tel:* 603-569-7988 *Toll Free Tel:* 800-669-8892 *Fax:* 603-569-1889 *E-mail:* info@ymaa.com *Web Site:* www.ymaa.com, pg 1072

Risdall, Charlie, Smith System Inc, 1714 E 14 St, Plano, TX 75074 *Toll Free Tel:* 800-328-1061 *Fax:* 972-398-4051 *E-mail:* furniture@smithsystem.com *Web Site:* www.smithsystem.com, pg 1014

Risey, Paul, eFootage LLC, 65 N Raymond Ave, Suite 220, Pasadena, CA 91103 *Tel:* 626-395-9593 *Fax:* 626-792-5394 *E-mail:* info@efootage.com *Web Site:* www.efootage.com, pg 858

Riske, Lois, Leprecon®, 10087 Industrial Dr, Hamburg, MI 48139 *Tel:* 810-852-4300 *Toll Free Tel:* 888-422-3537 *Fax:* 810-231-1631 *E-mail:* lepsls@leprecon.com *Web Site:* www.leprecon.com, pg 919

Ritchhart, Jim, BAI Distributors Inc, 2312 NE 29 Ave, Ocala, FL 34470-3999 *Tel:* 352-732-7009 *Toll Free Tel:* 888-224-3446 *Fax:* 352-732-1616 *E-mail:* sales@baionline.com *Web Site:* www.baionline.com, pg 801

Ritchie, Bill H Jr, Ritchie's Perfect Press, 500 Aloha, Suite 105, Seattle, WA 98109 *Tel:* 206-498-9208 (cell) *Web Site:* www.emeralda.com, pg 997

Rittenberg, Durrell, Tecplot Inc, 3535 Factoria Blvd SE, Suite 550, Bellevue, WA 98006 *Tel:* 425-653-1200; 425-653-9393 (tech support) *Toll Free Tel:* 800-763-7005 (orders) *E-mail:* info@tecplot.com; sales@tecplot.com *Web Site:* www.tecplot.com, pg 1035

Ritter, Jeanne, Domino Film Ltd, 4004 Grey Ave, Montreal, QC H4A 3P1, Canada *Tel:* 514-484-0446 *Fax:* 514-484-0468 *E-mail:* domino@dominofilm.ca *Web Site:* www.dominofilm.ca, pg 850

Rizko, Emil, Doremi Labs, 1020 Chestnut St, Burbank, CA 91506 *Tel:* 818-562-1101 *Fax:* 818-562-1109 *E-mail:* info@doremilabs.com *Web Site:* www.doremilabs.com, pg 851

Rizor, Joel, Screen Door Entertainment Inc, PO Box 1002, Agoura Hills, CA 91376 *Tel:* 818-781-5600 *E-mail:* info@sdetv.com *Web Site:* www.sdetv.com, pg 1005

Roach, Dan, Dav Tronics Ltd, 1543 Venables St, Suite 200, Vancouver, BC V5L 2G8, Canada *Tel:* 604-255-2200 *Fax:* 604-255-4083 *Web Site:* www.broadcasttechnical.com, pg 843

Roark, Joseph, Broadcast Electronics, 4100 N 24 St, Quincy, IL 62305 *Tel:* 217-224-9600 *Fax:* 217-224-9607 *E-mail:* bdcast@bdcast.com *Web Site:* www.bdcast.com, pg 813

Robbins, Ashley, Lighting Industry Resource Council, 440 N Wells St, Suite 210, Chicago, IL 60654 *Tel:* 312-527-3677 *Fax:* 312-527-3680 *E-mail:* iald@iald.org *Web Site:* www.iald.org/council, pg 920

Robbins, Blair, Terra Productions LLC, 2017 Fairview Ave E, Suite G, Seattle, WA 98102 *Tel:* 206-328-3080 *Web Site:* www.terraproductions.com, pg 1037

Robbins, Caroline, Trafalgar Square Books, 388 Howe Hill Rd, North Pomfret, VT 05053 *Tel:* 802-457-1911 *Toll Free Tel:* 800-423-4525 *Fax:* 802-457-1913 *E-mail:* info@horseandriderbooks.com *Web Site:* www.horseandriderbooks.com, pg 1043

Robbins, Dave, Endtime Inc, 2701 E George Bush Tpke, Suite 100, Plano, TX 75074 *Tel:* 972-422-0857 *Toll Free Tel:* 800-363-8463 (cust serv) *Fax:* 972-423-4370 *E-mail:* questions@endtime.com; customerservice@endtime.com *Web Site:* www.endtime.com, pg 861

Robbins, Kim, BTX Technologies, 5 Skyline Dr, Hawthorne, NY 10532 *Tel:* 914-592-1800 *Toll Free Tel:* 800-666-0996 *Toll Free Fax:* 800-569-4244 *E-mail:* info@btx.com *Web Site:* www.btx.com, pg 814

Robbins, Nick, University of Maine Audio Visual Services, 28 Shibles Hall, Orono, ME 04469 *Tel:* 207-581-2500; 207-581-2516 *Web Site:* www.umaine.edu/it/divisions/av, pg 1049

Robbins, Sally, Kinetronics Corp, 1459 Tallevast Rd, Sarasota, FL 34243 *Tel:* 941-951-2432 *Toll Free Tel:* 800-624-3204 (US & CN) *Fax:* 941-955-5992 *E-mail:* info@kinetronics.com; order@kinetronics.com *Web Site:* www.kinetronics.com, pg 911

Robbins, Shawn, Robbins Media Inc, 375 Greenwich St, New York, NY 10013 *Tel:* 212-661-7670 *Fax:* 212-656-1997 *E-mail:* info@robbinsmedia.com *Web Site:* www.robbinsmedia.com, pg 998

Robbins, Susannah Greason, San Francisco Film Commission, City Hall, Rm 473, One Dr Carlton B Goodlett Place, San Francisco, CA 94102-4649 *Tel:* 415-554-6241 *Fax:* 415-554-6503 *E-mail:* film@sfgov.org *Web Site:* www.filmsf.org, pg 1094

Robbins-Pianka, Orson, National Board of Review (of Motion Pictures), 40 W 37 St, Suite 501, New York, NY 10018 *Tel:* 212-465-9166 *Fax:* 212-465-9168 *E-mail:* nbr@nbrmp.org *Web Site:* www.nationalboardofreview.org, pg 1085

Roberson, Angi, Telos Systems, 1241 Superior Ave E, Cleveland, OH 44114 *Tel:* 216-241-7225 *Fax:* 216-241-4103 *E-mail:* inquiry@telos-systems.com *Web Site:* www.telos-systems.com, pg 1037

Roberson, Robert, Merestone, 7232 E First St, Scottsdale, AZ 85251 *Tel:* 480-945-4631 *Fax:* 480-945-0590 *Web Site:* www.merestone.com, pg 938

Roberson, Sean, Theatrical Services Inc, 128 S Washington St, Wichita, KS 67202 *Tel:* 316-263-4415 *Toll Free Tel:* 888-874-2649 *Fax:* 316-263-9927 *Web Site:* www.theatricalservices.com, pg 1038

Roberts, Diane, West Eagle Films Inc, 800 Lower Ganges Rd, Salt Spring Island, BC V8K 2N5, Canada *Tel:* 250-538-1780 *E-mail:* mailbox@westeaglefilms.com *Web Site:* www.westeaglefilms.com, pg 1064

Roberts, Don, Tecplot Inc, 3535 Factoria Blvd SE, Suite 550, Bellevue, WA 98006 *Tel:* 425-653-1200; 425-653-9393 (tech support) *Toll Free Tel:* 800-763-7005 (orders) *E-mail:* info@tecplot.com; sales@tecplot.com *Web Site:* www.tecplot.com, pg 1035

Roberts, H Armstrong III, Robertstock.com, 4203 Locust St, Philadelphia, PA 19104 *Tel:* 215-386-6300 *Toll Free Tel:* 800-786-6300 *Toll Free Fax:* 800-786-1920 *E-mail:* info@robertstock.com *Web Site:* www.robertstock.com, pg 998

Roberts, Jennifer, Anchor Bay Entertainment LLC, 9242 Beverly Blvd, Suite 201, Beverly Hills, CA 90210 *Tel:* 424-204-4166 *E-mail:* questions@anchorbayent.com *Web Site:* www.anchorbayentertainment.com, pg 786

Roberts, Jim, Broadcast Electronics, 4100 N 24 St, Quincy, IL 62305 *Tel:* 217-224-9600 *Fax:* 217-224-9607 *E-mail:* bdcast@bdcast.com *Web Site:* www.bdcast.com, pg 813

Roberts, Martin, Linguistic Systems Inc, 201 Broadway, Cambridge, MA 02139 *Tel:* 617-528-7400 *Toll Free Tel:* 877-654-5006 *Fax:* 617-528-7491 *Web Site:* linguist.com, pg 922

Roberts, Marty, White Diamond Productions, 2267 Hwy 43 S, Harrison, AR 72601 *Tel:* 870-365-7374, pg 1065

Roberts, Randy, American Cinema Editors Inc (ACE), Verna Fields Bldg 2282, Rm 190, 100 Universal City Plaza, Universal City, CA 91608 *Tel:* 818-777-2900 *Fax:* 818-733-5023 *E-mail:* americancinema@editors.com *Web Site:* www.ace-filmeditors.org, pg 1076

Roberts, Richard H, Image Makers of Pittsford/Image Maker Productions, 6 Wood Gate, Pittsford, NY 14534-1826 *Tel:* 585-385-4567 *Fax:* 585-586-6568, pg 895

Roberts-Negron, Emily, VIEW Inc (Video International Entertainment World Inc), 11 Reservoir Rd, Saugerties, NY 12477 *Tel:* 845-246-9955 *Toll Free Tel:* 800-843-9843 *Fax:* 845-246-9966 *E-mail:* viewvid@aol.com *Web Site:* www.view.com, pg 1058

Robertson, Bill, Shadowstone R & R™, 813 Silver Spring Ave, Silver Spring, MD 20910 *Tel:* 301-589-4997 *Fax:* 301-565-5156 *Web Site:* www.shadowstone.com, pg 1008

Robertson, Douglas, Fire Power Music Inc, 9913 E Main St, No 171, Tempe, AZ 85207 *Tel:* 602-463-2988, pg 868

Robertson, Laurel, Comtek Communications Technology Inc, 357 W 2700 S, Salt Lake City, UT 84115 *Tel:* 801-466-3463 *Toll Free Tel:* 800-496-3463 *Fax:* 801-484-6906 *E-mail:* sales@comtek.com *Web Site:* www.comtek.com, pg 834

Robertson, Patti, CompuWeather Inc, 2566 Rte 52, Hopewell Junction, NY 12533 *Tel:* 845-227-8500 *Toll Free Tel:* 800-825-4445 *Fax:* 845-227-8400 *Toll Free Fax:* 800-825-4441 *Web Site:* www.compuweather.com, pg 834

Robertson, Todd J, Hyperspective Studios Inc, 2800 Woodlawn Dr, Suite 253, Honolulu, HI 96822 *Tel:* 808-353-3618 *E-mail:* info@hyperspective.com *Web Site:* www.hyperspective.com, pg 893

Robeson, Jim, Bias Studios, 5400 Carolina Place, Springfield, VA 22151 *Tel:* 703-941-3333 *E-mail:* info@biasstudios.com *Web Site:* www.biasstudios.com, pg 806

Robey, Elizabeth, Microtraining LLC, 3212 Duke St, Alexandria, VA 22314 *Tel:* 703-212-8520 *Toll Free Tel:* 888-505-5576 *Fax:* 703-212-8540 *Toll Free Fax:* 888-505-5576 *E-mail:* marketing@astreetpress.com *Web Site:* www.academicvideostore.com/microtraining, pg 942

Robichaud, Heidi B, Earthworks Inc, 37 Wilton Rd, Milford, NH 03055 *Tel:* 603-654-6427 (sales); 603-654-2433 *Fax:* 603-654-6107 *E-mail:* info@earthworksaudio.com *Web Site:* www.earthworksaudio.com, pg 855

Robin, Anna, Crystalite Industries Inc, 101 Palm Harbor Pkwy, Unit 117, Palm Coast, FL 32137 *Tel:* 561-330-8742; 561-330-8660 *Toll Free Tel:* 800-328-5483; 800-468-8673 *Fax:* 561-330-8659; 561-330-8665 *E-mail:* phcrystalite@aol.com *Web Site:* www.phcled.com, pg 840

Robins, Lynn B, Xplor® International, 24156 State Rd 54, Suite 4, Lutz, FL 33559 *Tel:* 813-949-6170 *Toll Free Tel:* 800-669-7567 *Fax:* 813-949-9977 *E-mail:* info@xplor.org *Web Site:* www.xplor.org, pg 1090

Robinson, Chris, Ottawa International Animation Festival, 2 Daly Ave, Suite 120, Ottawa, ON K1N 6E2, Canada *Tel:* 613-232-8769 *Fax:* 613-232-6315 *E-mail:* info@animationfestival.ca *Web Site:* www.animationfestival.ca, pg 1123

Robinson, Eddie, City of West Hollywood Film Office, 8300 Santa Monica Blvd, West Hollywood, CA 90069-6216 *Tel:* 323-848-6489 *Fax:* 323-848-6561 *E-mail:* wehofilm@weho.org/film *Web Site:* www.weho.org/film, pg 1094

Robinson, Jeffrey, massAV, 755 Middlesex Tpke, Billerica, MA 01821 *Tel:* 978-670-0027 *Toll Free Tel:* 800-423-7830 *Fax:* 978-670-0037 *E-mail:* info@massav.com *Web Site:* www.massav.com, pg 933

Robinson, Joe, Hasselblad Bron Inc, 1080A Garden State Rd, Union, NJ 07083 *Tel:* 908-754-5800 *Toll Free Tel:* 800-456-0203; 800-367-6434 *Fax:* 908-754-5807 *E-mail:* production@hasselbladbron.com; sales@hasselbladbron.com; servicedept@hasselbladbron.com *Web Site:* www.hasselbladbron.com, pg 885

Robinson, Marian, Guilford Publications, 72 Spring St, 4th fl, New York, NY 10012 *Tel:* 212-431-9800 *Toll Free Tel:* 800-365-7006 *Fax:* 212-966-6708 *E-mail:* info@guilford.com *Web Site:* www.guilford.com, pg 883

Robinson, Peter, 168 Film Festival, 100 E Cedar, Burbank, CA 91502 *Tel:* 818-557-8507 *Fax:* 818-942-6076 *E-mail:* info@168project.com *Web Site:* www.168project.com, pg 1123

Rocha, Adam, San Antonio Film Festival, 1633 Babcock Rd, Suite 111, San Antonio, TX 78229 *Tel:* 210-885-5888 *E-mail:* safilm@gmail.com *Web Site:* www.safilm.com, pg 1126

Roche, Mary Beth, Macmillan Audio, 175 Fifth Ave, New York, NY 10010 *Tel:* 646-600-7856; 646-307-5742 *Toll Free Tel:* 888-330-8477 (orders); 800-221-7945 *Toll Free Fax:* 800-672-7703 (orders) *E-mail:* macmillan.audio@macmillanusa.com *Web Site:* us.macmillan.com/audio.aspx, pg 927

Rochefort, Josee, Montreal Film & TV Commission, Duke Pavilion, 5th fl, 801 Brennan St, Montreal, QC H3C 0G4, Canada *Tel:* 514-872-2883 *Fax:* 514-872-3409 *E-mail:* film.tv@ville.montreal.qc.ca *Web Site:* www.montrealfilm.com, pg 1105

Rocheleau, Jean-Claude, Alliance Quebecoise des Techniciens de l'Image et du Son (AQTIS), 533 Ontario St E, Suite 300, Montreal, QC H2L 1N8, Canada *Tel:* 514-844-2113 *Toll Free Tel:* 888-647-0681 *Fax:* 514-844-3540 *E-mail:* info@aqtis.qc.ca *Web Site:* www.aqtis.qc.ca, pg 1075

Rochon, Josee, Montreal Film & TV Commission, Duke Pavilion, 5th fl, 801 Brennan St, Montreal, QC H3C 0G4, Canada *Tel:* 514-872-2883 *Fax:* 514-872-3409 *E-mail:* film.tv@ville.montreal.qc.ca *Web Site:* www.montrealfilm.com, pg 1105

Rockefeller, Shawn, Data Display Audio Visual Co LP, 3720 Dacoma, Houston, TX 77092-8906 *Tel:* 713-688-7900 *Toll Free Tel:* 800-840-2500 *Fax:* 713-688-5840 *E-mail:* tech@ddav.com *Web Site:* www.ddav.com, pg 843

Rockwell, Don, Spot Media Production Group, 2745 Locust St, St Louis, MO 63103 *Tel:* 314-667-5915 *E-mail:* info@spotmpg.com *Web Site:* www.spotmpg.com, pg 1022

Rocky, Colleen, Brilliance Audio, 1704 Eaton Dr, Grand Haven, MI 49417 *Tel:* 616-846-5256 *Toll Free Tel:* 800-648-2312 (orders) *Fax:* 616-846-0630 *E-mail:* customerservice@brillianceaudio.com *Web Site:* www.brillianceaudio.com, pg 812

Rodak, Bob, Chartpak Inc, One River Rd, Leeds, MA 01053 *Tel:* 413-584-5446 *Toll Free Tel:* 800-628-1910 *Fax:* 413-584-6781 *E-mail:* info@chartpak.com *Web Site:* www.chartpak.com, pg 824

Rode, Scott, Hollywood Lights Inc, 5251 SE McLoughlin Blvd, Portland, OR 97202-4836 *Tel:* 503-232-9001; 503-232-8855 *Toll Free Tel:* 800-826-9881 *Fax:* 503-517-8686 *E-mail:* portland@hollywoodlights.biz *Web Site:* www.hollywoodlights.biz, pg 890

Rodgers, Al, Polhemus, 40 Hercules Dr, Colchester, VT 05446-5835 *Tel:* 802-655-3159 *Toll Free Tel:* 800-357-4777 (US & CN) *E-mail:* sales@polhemus.com *Web Site:* polhemus.com, pg 978

Rodgers, Skip, Polhemus, 40 Hercules Dr, Colchester, VT 05446-5835 *Tel:* 802-655-3159 *Toll Free Tel:* 800-357-4777 (US & CN) *E-mail:* sales@polhemus.com *Web Site:* polhemus.com, pg 978

Rodman, Howard A, Writers Guild of America, West (WGAW), 7000 W Third St, Los Angeles, CA 90048 *Tel:* 323-951-4000 *Toll Free Tel:* 800-548-4532 *Fax:* 323-782-4800 *Web Site:* www.wga.org, pg 1090

Rodney, Layne, P&P Studios Inc, 110 Lenox Ave, Suite 210, Stamford, CT 06906 *Tel:* 203-359-9292 *Toll Free Tel:* 888-WEPRODUCE (937-7638) *E-mail:* ppstudios@weproduce.com *Web Site:* www.weproduce.com, pg 968

Rodriguez Abad, Maria, Seattle International Film Festival (SIFF), 305 Harrison St, Seattle, WA 98109 *Tel:* 206-464-5830 *Fax:* 206-264-7919 *E-mail:* info@siff.net *Web Site:* www.siff.net, pg 1127

Rodriguez, Charles, A-V Services Inc, 99 Fairfield Rd, Fairfield, NJ 07004 *Tel:* 973-575-5222 *Fax:* 973-575-0857 *E-mail:* sales@avservices.net *Web Site:* www.avservices.net, pg 771

Rodriguez, Sergio, MarathonNorco Aerospace Inc, c/o Christie Electric Div, 8301 Imperial Dr, Waco, TX 76712-6588 *Tel:* 254-776-0650 *Fax:* 254-776-6558 *E-mail:* marathon@mptc.com *Web Site:* www.mnaerospace.com, pg 930

Rodriguez Tressler, Claudia, Broad Street Inc, 242 W 30 St, 2nd fl, New York, NY 10001 *Tel:* 212-780-5700 *E-mail:* newyork@broadstreet.com *Web Site:* www.broadstreet.com, pg 812

Roe, Bruce, Zhone Technologies Inc, 7195 Oakport St, Oakland, CA 94621 *Tel:* 510-777-7000 *Toll Free Tel:* 877-ZHONE-20 (946-6320, US & CN) *Fax:* 510-777-7001 *E-mail:* info@zhone.com; sales@zhone.com *Web Site:* www.zhone.com, pg 1073

Roemer, Jason, Indianapolis International Film Festival, PO Box 1917, Indianapolis, IN 46206 *Tel:* 317-560-4433 *E-mail:* info@indyfilmfest.org *Web Site:* indyfilmfest.org, pg 1117

Rogers, Brack, Media-Comm, 9700 S Pine Blvd, Charlotte, NC 28273 *Tel:* 704-527-8853 *Web Site:* www.media-comm.com, pg 936

Rogers, Christopher D, CDR Communications Inc, 9310-B Old Keene Mill Rd, Burke, VA 22015 *Tel:* 703-569-3400 *Toll Free Tel:* 800-729-2237 *Fax:* 703-569-3448 *E-mail:* info@cdrcommunications.com *Web Site:* www.cdrcommunications.com, pg 822

Rogers, Chuck, Axxis Inc, 845 S Ninth St, Louisville, KY 40203 *Tel:* 502-568-6030 *Fax:* 502-568-6204 *E-mail:* info@axxisinc.com *Web Site:* www.axxisinc.com, pg 800

Rogers, Mandy, Zacuto, 401 W Ontario Ave, Chicago, IL 60654 *Tel:* 312-863-3456; 312-863-3453 (rentals) *Toll Free Tel:* 888-294-3456 *Fax:* 312-863-3455; 312-377-3016 (rentals) *E-mail:* rentals@zacuto.com *Web Site:* www.zacuto.com, pg 1073

Rogers, Nancy, CDR Communications Inc, 9310-B Old Keene Mill Rd, Burke, VA 22015 *Tel:* 703-569-3400 *Toll Free Tel:* 800-729-2237 *Fax:* 703-569-3448 *E-mail:* info@cdrcommunications.com *Web Site:* www.cdrcommunications.com, pg 822

Rogers, O David, Stageright Corp, 495 Pioneer Pkwy, Clare, MI 48617 *Toll Free Tel:* 800-438-4499; 888-577-8243 (sales) *Fax:* 989-386-7393 *E-mail:* info@stageright.com *Web Site:* www.stageright.com, pg 1023

Rogers, Tim, Follett Software Co, 1391 Corporate Dr, McHenry, IL 60050-7041 *Tel:* 815-344-8700 *Toll Free Tel:* 800-323-3397 *Fax:* 815-344-8774; 815-578-5575 *Toll Free Fax:* 800-807-3623 (cust serv) *Web Site:* www.follettsoftware.com, pg 871

Rogers, Tyme, Tech 21 USA Inc, 790 Bloomfield Ave, Clifton, NJ 07012 *Tel:* 973-777-6996 *Fax:* 973-777-9899 *E-mail:* info@tech21nyc.com *Web Site:* www.tech21nyc.com, pg 1033

Rogg, Jesse, The Mack Sennett Studios, 1215 Bates Ave, Los Angeles, CA 90029 *Tel:* 323-660-8466 *E-mail:* info@macksennettstage.com *Web Site:* www.macksennettstage.com, pg 1006

Rogovin, John, Warner Bros Entertainment Inc, 4000 Warner Blvd, Burbank, CA 91522 *Tel:* 818-954-3000 *Fax:* 818-954-4918 *E-mail:* wbsf@warnerbros.com *Web Site:* www.warnerbros.com; studiofacilities.warnerbros.com, pg 1062

Rohan, Lucie, Northeast Video Productions Inc, Box 8425, Sleepy Hollow, NY 10591 *Tel:* 914-714-0703, pg 959

Rohrback, Chad, Filmworkers, 232 E Ohio, Chicago, IL 60611 *Tel:* 312-664-9333 *Web Site:* www.filmworkersastro.com, pg 868

Rohy, Eric, eInstruction Corp, 14400 N 87 St, Suite 250, Scottsdale, AZ 85260 *Tel:* 480-948-6540 *Toll Free Tel:* 800-856-0732 *Fax:* 480-948-5508 *Web Site:* www.einstruction.com, pg 858

Roi, Michele, Big Kids Productions Inc, 2620 Barton Hills Dr, Austin, TX 78704 *Tel:* 512-441-0737 *Toll Free Tel:* 800-477-7811 *Fax:* 512-441-0339 *E-mail:* customerservice@bigkids.com *Web Site:* bigkids.com, pg 807

Roibal, Robert, SouthWest Organizing Project (SWOP), 211 Tenth St SW, Albuquerque, NM 87102-2919 *Tel:* 505-247-8832 *Fax:* 505-247-9972 *E-mail:* swop@swop.net *Web Site:* www.swop.net, pg 1019

Roland, Glenn, Glenn Roland Films, 10711 Wellworth Ave, Los Angeles, CA 90024 *Tel:* 310-475-0937 *Fax:* 310-475-0939, pg 998

Roland, John, Extreme Reach Inc, 75 Second Ave, Suite 720, Needham, MA 02494 *Tel:* 781-577-2016 *E-mail:* sales@extremereach.com; press@extremereach.com *Web Site:* www.extremereach.com, pg 864

Rolin, Jim, Videofax, 1750 Cesar Chavez St, Unit G, San Francisco, CA 94124 *Tel:* 415-641-0100 *E-mail:* rentals@videofax.com *Web Site:* www.videofax.com, pg 1057

Rollins, Joel R, Everett Hall Associates Inc, 76 Progress Dr, Stamford, CT 06902 *Tel:* 203-325-4328 *Fax:* 203-323-8078 *E-mail:* info@everetthall.com *Web Site:* www.everetthall.com, pg 863

Rollinson, Simona, Follett Software Co, 1391 Corporate Dr, McHenry, IL 60050-7041 *Tel:* 815-344-8700 *Toll Free Tel:* 800-323-3397 *Fax:* 815-344-8774; 815-578-5575 *Toll Free Fax:* 800-807-3623 (cust serv) *Web Site:* www.follettsoftware.com, pg 871

Rollwagen, Jack, The Institute Inc, 787 East Ave, Brockport, NY 14420 *Tel:* 585-637-6531 *Web Site:* www.the-institute-ny.com, pg 899

Roloff, Phil, ALOM Technologies Corp, 48105 Warm Springs Blvd, Fremont, CA 94539-7498 *Tel:* 510-360-3600 *Toll Free Tel:* 800-500-9991 *Fax:* 510-226-7617 *E-mail:* customerservice@alom.com *Web Site:* www.alom.com, pg 782

Romaguera, Ralph, Professional Photographers of America (PPA), 229 Peachtree St NE, Suite 2200, Atlanta, GA 30303 *Tel:* 404-522-8600 *Toll Free Tel:* 800-786-6277 *Fax:* 404-614-6400 *E-mail:* csc@ppa.com *Web Site:* www.ppa.com, pg 1087

Romano, Edward A, Warner Bros Entertainment Inc, 4000 Warner Blvd, Burbank, CA 91522 *Tel:* 818-954-3000 *Fax:* 818-954-4918 *E-mail:* wbsf@warnerbros.com *Web Site:* www.warnerbros.com; studiofacilities.warnerbros.com, pg 1062

Romine, Barry, VSG Digital Media Solutions, 11126 Lindbergh Business Ct, St Louis, MO 63123 *Tel:* 314-487-8045 *Toll Free Tel:* 800-737-8045 *Fax:* 314-487-9387 *Web Site:* www.vsginc.net, pg 1061

Romo, Terezita (Tere), Artadia James D Phelan Award in the Visual Arts, One Embarcadero Ctr, Suite 1400, San Francisco, CA 94111 *Tel:* 415-733-8500 *Fax:* 415-477-2783 *E-mail:* artsinfo@sff.org; info@sff.org *Web Site:* www.sff.org, pg 1108

Rone, Katye, Trailblazer Studios®, 1610 Midtown Place, Raleigh, NC 27609 *Tel:* 919-645-6600 *Fax:* 919-645-6601 *Web Site:* www.trailblazerstudios.com, pg 1043

Rone, Melissa, Da-Lite, 3100 N Detroit St, Warsaw, IN 46582 *Tel:* 574-267-8101 *Toll Free Tel:* 800-622-3737 *Fax:* 574-267-7804 *Toll Free Fax:* 877-325-4832 *E-mail:* info@da-lite.com *Web Site:* www.da-lite.com, pg 842

Roobin, Todd, Jacksonville Office of Economic Development, Film & Television Office, 117 W Duval St, Suite 280, Jacksonville, FL 32202 *Tel:* 904-630-2522 *Fax:* 904-630-3693 *Web Site:* www.filmjax.com, pg 1096

Rooke, Bernie, Pathway Connectivity Inc, 1439 17 Ave SE, Unit 103, Calgary, AB T2G 1J9, Canada *Tel:* 403-243-8110 *Fax:* 403-287-1281 *E-mail:* sales@pathwayconnect.com *Web Site:* www.pathwayconnect.com, pg 970

Rooney, Daniel, Special Archives Division, Motion Picture Branch, 8601 Adelphi Rd, College Park, MD 20740-6001 *Tel:* 301-837-2000 *Toll Free Tel:* 866-272-6272 (cust serv) *Fax:* 301-837-0483 *E-mail:* mopix@nara.gov *Web Site:* www.archives.gov, pg 1020

Rooney, Rick, Planet Dallas Recording Studios, PO Box 110995, Carrollton, TX 75011 *Tel:* 214-521-2216; 214-893-1130 (cell) *Fax:* 214-528-1299 *E-mail:* planetd@ix.netcom.com *Web Site:* planetdallas.com, pg 976

Rosa, Mary, Adrenaline Films, 5224 S Orange Ave, Orlando, FL 32809 *Tel:* 407-850-0711 *Fax:* 407-859-6527 *E-mail:* contact@adrenalinefilms.com *Web Site:* www.adrenalinefilms.com, pg 777

Rosa, TerriLynn, 5 Alarm Music, 35 W Dayton St, Pasadena, CA 91105 *Tel:* 626-304-1698 *Toll Free Tel:* 800-322-7879 *Fax:* 626-795-2058 *E-mail:* info@5alarmmusic.com *Web Site:* www.5alarmmusic.com, pg 869

Rosales, Monica, DocMiami International Film Festival, 8770 Sunset Dr, No 274, Miami, FL 33173-3512 *Tel:* 786-493-8308 *E-mail:* info@docmiami.org *Web Site:* www.docmiami.org, pg 1114

Rose, Frederic, Technicolor, 3233 E Mission Oaks Blvd, Camarillo, CA 93012 *Tel:* 805-445-1122 *Fax:* 805-445-4340 *E-mail:* info@technicolor.com *Web Site:* www.technicolor.com, pg 1034

Rose, John, Canon Broadcast & Communications Division, One Canon Park, Melville, NY 11747-3336 *Toll Free Tel:* 800-321-4388 *E-mail:* bctv@cusa.canon.com *Web Site:* www.canon.com/bctv; www.usa.canon.com/cusa/professional, pg 819

Rose, Marco, Illuminart Lighting, 7320 Griffin Rd, Suite 111, Davie, FL 33314 *Tel:* 954-327-0564 *Fax:* 954-327-0367 *E-mail:* lightisart@aol.com *Web Site:* www.illuminart-inc.com, pg 894

Rose, Max, LW Media Group, 107 W Valencia Ave, Burbank, CA 91502 *Tel:* 818-439-2989 *E-mail:* lwmgbooking@gmail.com *Web Site:* www.lwmgstudios.com, pg 926

Rose, Mike, A T Products Inc, 1600 S Division St, Harvard, IL 60033 *Tel:* 815-943-3590 *Toll Free Tel:* 800-848-2205 *Fax:* 815-943-3604 *E-mail:* atprod@mc.net *Web Site:* atproducts.com, pg 771

Rose, Paul, Film Creations Ltd, 2021 E Broadway Blvd, Tucson, AZ 85719 *Tel:* 520-624-4444 *Toll Free Tel:* 888-877-2490 *Fax:* 520-624-9659 *E-mail:* info@filmcreations.com *Web Site:* www.filmcreations.com, pg 867

Rose, Richard, Hot House Professional Audio, 275 Martin Ave, Highland, NY 12528 *Tel:* 845-691-6077 *E-mail:* info@hothousepro.com *Web Site:* www.hothousepro.com, pg 891

Rose, Richard A, Film Creations Ltd, 2021 E Broadway Blvd, Tucson, AZ 85719 *Tel:* 520-624-4444 *Toll Free Tel:* 888-877-2490 *Fax:* 520-624-9659 *E-mail:* info@filmcreations.com *Web Site:* www.filmcreations.com, pg 867

Rose, Robert, Rose Packaging & Design Inc, 4000 Sopris Mountain Rd, Basalt, CO 81621-9179 *Tel:* 970-927-6515 *Toll Free Tel:* 800-308-1003 *Fax:* 970-927-6514 *E-mail:* sales@rosepkg.com *Web Site:* www.rosepkg.com, pg 999

Rose, Steven, Tally Display Corp, 19 Gardner Rd, Fairfield, NJ 07004 *Tel:* 973-777-7760 *Toll Free Tel:* 800-758-2559 *Fax:* 973-777-6220 *E-mail:* info@tallydisplay.com *Web Site:* www.tallydisplay.com, pg 1031

Rosebush, Judson, Judson Rosebush Co Inc, 630 Ninth Ave, Suite 507, New York, NY 10036 *Tel:* 212-581-3000 *E-mail:* judson@rosebush.com *Web Site:* www.rosebush.com, pg 999

Rosen, Daniel, Sentry Industries Inc, One Bridge St, Hillburn, NY 10931-0885 *Tel:* 845-753-2910 *Fax:* 845-753-2920 *E-mail:* techsupport@sentryindustries.com *Web Site:* www.sentryindustries.com, pg 1007

Rosen, Dave, Absolute Rentals, 2633 N San Fernando Blvd, Burbank, CA 91504 *Tel:* 818-842-2828 *Web Site:* www.absoluterentals.com, pg 772

Rosen, Dave, Argyle Post, 2633 N San Fernando Blvd, Burbank, CA 91504 *Tel:* 818-845-5555; 310-560-2373 *Fax:* 818-842-8115 *E-mail:* info@argylepost.com *Web Site:* www.argylepost.com, pg 789

Rosen, David, Slate Media Group, 1111 S Victory Blvd, Burbank, CA 91502 *Tel:* 818-569-6500 *Fax:* 818-846-9399 *Web Site:* www.slatemediagroup.com, pg 1013

Rosen, Peter, Peter Rosen Productions Inc, 9 E 78 St, Suite 5-A, New York, NY 10075 *Tel:* 212-535-8927 *Fax:* 212-517-5337 *E-mail:* rosenprod@aol.com *Web Site:* www.peterrosenproductions.com, pg 999

Rosen, Rachel, Golden Gate Awards, c/o San Francisco Film Society, The Presidio, Suite 110, 39 Mesa St, San Francisco, CA 94129-1025 *Tel:* 415-561-5000 *Fax:* 415-440-1760 *E-mail:* info@sffs.org *Web Site:* festival.sffs.org; www.sffs.org, pg 1115

Rosen, Rachel, San Francisco International Film Festival, 39 Mesa St, Suite 110, The Presidio, San Francisco, CA 94129-1025 *Tel:* 415-561-5000 *Fax:* 415-440-1760 *E-mail:* info@sffs.org *Web Site:* festival.sffs.org; www.sffs.org; www.sf360.org, pg 1126

Rosen, Tammie, Tribeca Film Festival, 375 Greenwich St, New York, NY 10013 *Tel:* 212-941-2400 *Fax:* 212-941-3939 *E-mail:* festival@tribecafilmfestival.org *Web Site:* tribecafilm.com/festival/; tribecafilmfestival.org/festival, pg 1128

Rosenberg, Carole, Havana Film Festival New York (HFFNY), 4 W 43 St, Suite 304, New York, NY 10036 *Tel:* 212-687-2146 *Fax:* 212-681-8037 *E-mail:* info@hffny.com; info@aflfc.org *Web Site:* www.hffny.com, pg 1116

Rosenberg, Jason, MMI Corp, 2950 Wyman Pkwy, Baltimore, MD 21211-2802 *Tel:* 410-366-1222 *Fax:* 410-366-6311 *E-mail:* mail@mmicorporation.com *Web Site:* www.mmicorporation.com, pg 944

Rosenberg, Leo, Direct Broadcast Services Inc (DBS), 711 Executive Blvd, Suite F, Valley Cottage, NY 10989 *Tel:* 845-267-2800 *Fax:* 845-267-2123 *E-mail:* dbs@directbroadcast.com *Web Site:* www.directbroadcast.com, pg 848

Rosenberg, Murray, Bestwell Optical Instrument Corp, 46 Henry St, Merrick, NY 11566 *Tel:* 516-379-2280 *Fax:* 516-706-1744 *Web Site:* www.bestwelloptical.com, pg 806

Rosenberg, Tracy, Media Alliance, 1904 Franklin St, Suite 818, Oakland, CA 94612 *Tel:* 510-832-9000 *Fax:* 510-238-8557 *E-mail:* information@media-alliance.org *Web Site:* www.media-alliance.org, pg 1084

Rosenblad, David, DRM: sir reel sound, 10520 Beard Ave, Austin, TX 78748 *Tel:* 214-752-5000 (studio) *E-mail:* drmuzik@mac.com *Web Site:* www.drm-sirreelsound.com, pg 852

Rosenblatt, Jay, San Francisco Jewish Film Festival, 145 Ninth St, Suite 200, San Francisco, CA 94103 *Tel:* 415-621-0556 *Fax:* 415-621-0568 *E-mail:* jewishfilm@sfjff.org *Web Site:* www.sfjff.org, pg 1126

Rosenbloom, Jerry, SBS Productions, 1646 Livonia Ave, Los Angeles, CA 90035 *Tel:* 310-557-1545 *E-mail:* eindigo2@pacbell.net, pg 1003

Rosenblum, Victor, Sight & Sound Productions, 11193 Saint Johns Industrial Pkwy N, Jacksonville, FL 32246 *Tel:* 904-645-7880 *Toll Free Tel:* 800-339-0846 *Fax:* 904-645-7787 *E-mail:* info@ssav.net *Web Site:* www.ssav.net, pg 1010

Rosenfeld, Irene, Bestwell Optical Instrument Corp, 46 Henry St, Merrick, NY 11566 *Tel:* 516-379-2280 *Fax:* 516-706-1744 *Web Site:* www.bestwelloptical.com, pg 806

Rosenfeld, Maury, Planet Blue, 1250 Sixth St, Suite 102, Santa Monica, CA 90401 *Tel:* 310-899-3877 *Fax:* 310-899-3787 *Web Site:* www.planetblue.com, pg 976

Rosenstein, Hans, Whalley-Abbey Media Holdings Inc, 1303 Greene Ave, Suite 300, Westmount, QC H3Z 2A7, Canada *Tel:* 514-846-1940 *Fax:* 514-846-1550 *Web Site:* whalleyabbey.com, pg 1065

Rosenstein, Richard, Summit Electronics Corp, 1060 Holland Dr, Suite M, Boca Raton, FL 33487 *Tel:* 561-226-8500 *Toll Free Tel:* 800-226-6960 *Fax:* 561-226-8523 *E-mail:* sales@summitelectronics.com *Web Site:* www.summitelectronics.com; www.partsprocurement.com; bocasemi.com, pg 1028

Rosenstein, Sam, Summit Electronics Corp, 1060 Holland Dr, Suite M, Boca Raton, FL 33487 *Tel:* 561-226-8500 *Toll Free Tel:* 800-226-6960 *Fax:* 561-226-8523 *E-mail:* sales@summitelectronics.com *Web Site:* www.summitelectronics.com; www.partsprocurement.com; bocasemi.com, pg 1028

Rosenstein, Scott, Summit Electronics Corp, 1060 Holland Dr, Suite M, Boca Raton, FL 33487 *Tel:* 561-226-8500 *Toll Free Tel:* 800-226-6960 *Fax:* 561-226-8523 *E-mail:* sales@summitelectronics.com *Web Site:* www.summitelectronics.com; www.partsprocurement.com; bocasemi.com, pg 1028

Rosenthal, Fred, Ametron Audio/Video, 1546 N Argyle Ave, Hollywood, CA 90028-6410 *Tel:* 323-466-4321 *Fax:* 323-871-0127 *E-mail:* info@ametron.com *Web Site:* www.ametron.com, pg 785

Rosenthal, Gene, Adelphi Records Inc, PO Box 7688, Silver Spring, MD 20907-7688 *Tel:* 301-434-6958 *Fax:* 301-434-3056 *E-mail:* adelphi@adelphirecords.com *Web Site:* www.adelphirecords.com, pg 776

Rosenthal, Jim, The Rosenthal Group, 10625 Cohasset St, Sun Valley, CA 91352 *Tel:* 818-252-1010 *Fax:* 818-252-1070 *Web Site:* www.therosenthalgroup.com, pg 999

Rosenthal, Phil, American Melody, PO Box 270, Guilford, CT 06437-0270 *Tel:* 203-457-0881 *Web Site:* www.americanmelody.com, pg 784

Rosenthal, Randy, Tricycle Studios, 1905 E Seventh Ave, Tampa, FL 33605 *Tel:* 813-258-6867 *Fax:* 813-258-8595 *E-mail:* hi@tricyclestudios.com *Web Site:* www.tricyclestudios.com, pg 1045

Rosica, Jeff, Avid Technology Inc, 65-75 Network Dr, Burlington, MA 01830 *Tel:* 978-640-6789 *Fax:* 978-640-3366 *Web Site:* www.avid.com, pg 799

Rosing, Richard, Trew Audio Inc, 220 Great Circle Rd, Suite 116, Nashville, TN 37228 *Tel:* 615-256-3542 *Toll Free Tel:* 800-241-8994 *Fax:* 615-259-2699 *E-mail:* info@trewaudio.com; sales@trewaudio.com *Web Site:* www.trewaudio.com, pg 1044

Roskind, Robert, Do It Yourself Inc - DIY Video Corp, 200 N Greensboro St, Suite A5, Carrboro, NC 27510 *Tel:* 919-904-7343; 828-773-8878 (cell) *Web Site:* www.do-it-yourself-dvds.com, pg 849

Ross, Ben, Wild Plum, 2128 Narcissus Ct, Venice, CA 90291 *Tel:* 310-823-7445 *Fax:* 310-578-1445 *Web Site:* www.wildplum.tv, pg 1066

Ross, David, Ross Video Ltd, 8 John St, Iroquois, ON K0E 1K0, Canada *Tel:* 613-652-4886 *Fax:* 613-652-4425 *E-mail:* solutions@rossvideo.com *Web Site:* www.rossvideo.com, pg 999

Ross, George, Velodyne Acoustics Inc, 345 Digital Dr, Morgan Hill, CA 95037 *Tel:* 408-465-2800 *Toll Free Tel:* 866-243-0789 *Fax:* 408-779-9227; 408-779-9208 (cust serv); 408-779-9377 (orders) *E-mail:* service@velodyne.com; orders@velodyne.com *Web Site:* www.velodyne.com, pg 1052

Ross, Jason, Replicopy Digital Media Center, 2101 Midway Rd, Suite 200, Carrollton, TX 75006 *Tel:* 972-702-8388 *Fax:* 972-387-DUBS (387-3827) *E-mail:* replicopy@replicopy.com *Web Site:* www.replicopy.com, pg 995

Ross, Karen, PACSAT, 1629 "S" St, Sacramento, CA 95811 *Tel:* 916-446-7890; 916-335-1649 (after hours) *Toll Free Tel:* 800-672-2728 *Fax:* 916-446-7893 *E-mail:* pacsat@pacsat.com *Web Site:* www.pacsat.com, pg 967

Ross, Lonnie, L R Light & Sound, 5317 54 St, Drayton Valley, AB T7A 1R6, Canada *Tel:* 780-542-4242; 780-542-9363 *Fax:* 780-542-4283 *E-mail:* lrlightandsound@yahoo.ca *Web Site:* www.lrlightandsound.ca, pg 915

Ross, Mark, BMI Supply, 571 Queensbury Ave, Queensbury, NY 12804 *Tel:* 518-793-6706 *Toll Free Tel:* 800-836-0524 *Fax:* 518-793-6181 *E-mail:* bminy@bmisupply.com *Web Site:* www.bmisupply.com, pg 810

Ross, Mike, Flex-A-Lite West, 10250 Aldebaran Dr, Reno, NV 89508 *Tel:* 775-677-7711 *Fax:* 775-677-7577, pg 870

Ross, Peter D, Manhattan Center Studios Inc, 311 W 34 St, New York, NY 10001 *Tel:* 212-279-7740 *Fax:* 212-564-1072 *E-mail:* info@mcstudios.com *Web Site:* www.mcstudios.com, pg 930

Ross, Peter John, Production Partners Media, 520 Enterprise Dr, Suite C, Lewis Center, OH 43035 *Tel:* 614-888-4888 *Web Site:* productionpartnersmedia.com, pg 984

Rossi, John, Xintekvideo Inc, 56 W Broad St, Stamford, CT 06902 *Tel:* 203-348-9229 *Web Site:* www.xintekvideo.com, pg 1071

Rossi, Tony, The Christophers, 5 Hanover Sq, 22nd fl, New York, NY 10004 *Tel:* 212-759-4050 *Toll Free Tel:* 888-298-4050 (orders) *Fax:* 212-838-5073 *E-mail:* mail@christophers.org *Web Site:* www.christophers.org, pg 826

Rossini, Giovanni, OWI Inc, 17141 Kingsview Ave, Carson, CA 90746 *Tel:* 310-515-1900 *Toll Free Tel:* 800-638-1694 *Fax:* 310-515-1606 *E-mail:* info@owi-inc.com *Web Site:* www.owi-inc.com, pg 966

Rossman, Russ Jr, Rossman Audio LLC, 597 W Hillside Ave, Suite 100, State College, PA 16803-1509 *Tel:* 814-234-2044 *Fax:* 814-689-1036 *E-mail:* info@rossmanaudio.com *Web Site:* www.rossmanaudio.com, pg 1000

Roth, Aaron, Arkon Resources Inc, 20 La Porte St, Arcadia, CA 91006 *Tel:* 626-254-9005 *Toll Free Tel:* 800-841-0884 *Fax:* 626-254-9266 *E-mail:* arkon5@arkon.com *Web Site:* www.arkon.com, pg 790

Roth, Betty, Cape Girardeau Convention & Visitors Bureau, 400 Broadway St, Suite 100, Cape Girardeau, MO 63701 *Tel:* 573-335-1631 *Toll Free Tel:* 800-777-0068 *Fax:* 573-334-6702 *E-mail:* info@visitcape.com *Web Site:* visitcape.com, pg 1099

Roth, Don, AmpliVox Portable Sound Systems, 650 Anthony Trail, Suite D, Northbrook, IL 60062-2512 *Tel:* 847-498-9000 *Toll Free Tel:* 800-267-5486 *Toll Free Fax:* 800-267-5489 *E-mail:* info@ampli.com *Web Site:* www.ampli.com, pg 785

Roth, Mark, Argraph Corp, 111 Asia Place, Carlstadt, NJ 07072 *Tel:* 201-939-7722 *Toll Free Tel:* 800-526-6290 *Fax:* 201-939-7782 *E-mail:* info@argraph.com; sales@argraph.com *Web Site:* www.argraph.com, pg 789

Roth, Rob, HBO Home Video Inc, 1100 Avenue of the Americas, New York, NY 10036 *Tel:* 212-512-1000 *Fax:* 212-512-7458 *Web Site:* www.hbo.com, pg 886

Roth, Scott, Art Directors Guild (ADG), 11969 Ventura Blvd, 2nd fl, Studio City, CA 91604 *Tel:* 818-762-9995 *Fax:* 818-762-9997 *Web Site:* www.adg.org, pg 1078

Roth, Stephen, SLR Enterprises LLC, PO Box 1111, Orleans, MA 02653 *Tel:* 508-737-7788 *Fax:* 508-240-6878 *E-mail:* stephenroth@c4.net, pg 1013

Roth, Steve, Tri-Ed, 3625 Cincinnati Ave, Rocklin, CA 95765 *Tel:* 916-543-4000 *Toll Free Tel:* 800-366-4472 *Fax:* 916-543-4020 *E-mail:* info@northernvideo.com *Web Site:* www.tri-ed.com, pg 1044

Roth, Steven, Chartpak Inc, One River Rd, Leeds, MA 01053 *Tel:* 413-584-5446 *Toll Free Tel:* 800-628-1910 *Fax:* 413-584-6781 *E-mail:* info@chartpak.com *Web Site:* www.chartpak.com, pg 824

Rothe, Robert, Association of National Advertisers Inc (ANA), 708 Third Ave, 33rd fl, New York, NY 10017-4270 *Tel:* 212-697-5950 *Fax:* 212-687-7310 *E-mail:* info@ana.net *Web Site:* www.ana.net, pg 1079

Rothschild, Brad, Big Foot Productions Inc, 37-09 36 Ave, Long Island City, NY 11101 *Tel:* 718-729-1900 *Fax:* 718-729-8638 *E-mail:* info@bigfootnyc.com *Web Site:* www.bigfootnyc.com, pg 807

Rothstein, James, Tri-Ed, 3625 Cincinnati Ave, Rocklin, CA 95765 *Tel:* 916-543-4000 *Toll Free Tel:* 800-366-4472 *Fax:* 916-543-4020 *E-mail:* info@northernvideo.com *Web Site:* www.tri-ed.com, pg 1044

Rothstein, Scott, Blind, 1702 Olympic Blvd, Santa Monica, CA 90404 *Tel:* 310-314-1618 *Fax:* 310-314-1718 *Web Site:* www.blind.com, pg 809

Rotondelli, Gary, Vitec Videocom Inc, 709 Executive Blvd, Valley Cottage, NY 10989 *Tel:* 845-268-0100 *Fax:* 845-268-0113 *E-mail:* info-cd-usa@vitecgroup.com *Web Site:* www.vitecgroup.com, pg 1060

Roudebush, Steve, BMI Supply, 571 Queensbury Ave, Queensbury, NY 12804 *Tel:* 518-793-6706 *Toll Free Tel:* 800-836-0524 *Fax:* 518-793-6181 *E-mail:* bminy@bmisupply.com *Web Site:* www.bmisupply.com, pg 810

Roundtree, Carol, Provident-Integrity Distribution, 741 Cool Springs Blvd, Franklin, TN 37067 *Tel:* 615-261-6500 *Toll Free Tel:* 800-333-9000 *Fax:* 615-261-5904 *Toll Free Fax:* 800-333-9408 *E-mail:* info@providentmusicgroup.com, pg 986

Rouse, Arthur, The Media Collaboratory, 215 E High St, Lexington, KY 40507 *Tel:* 859-255-9049 *Fax:* 859-281-6537 *E-mail:* info@veslex.com *Web Site:* www.veslex.com, pg 936

Rouse, Tim, Audio Visual of Milwaukee Inc, 285 N Janacek Rd, Brookfield, WI 53045 *Tel:* 262-432-1077 *Toll Free Tel:* 800-236-6909 *Fax:* 262-432-1078 *E-mail:* avm@avmonline.com *Web Site:* www.avmonline.com, pg 795

Roush, Kimberly, Academy Awards®, 8949 Wilshire Blvd, Beverly Hills, CA 90211 *Tel:* 310-247-3000 *Fax:* 310-859-9619 *E-mail:* awardsoffice@oscars.org; publicity@oscars.org *Web Site:* www.oscars.org, pg 1107

Roush, Kimberly, The Academy of Motion Picture Arts and Sciences (AMPAS), 8949 Wilshire Blvd, Beverly Hills, CA 90211 *Tel:* 310-247-3000 *Fax:* 310-859-9619 *E-mail:* awardsoffice@oscars.org *Web Site:* www.oscars.org, pg 1075

Roush, Tom, Film Liaison of Escambia County, 1401 E Gregory St, Pensacola, FL 32501 *Tel:* 850-390-3974 *Toll Free Tel:* 800-874-1234 *Web Site:* filmnorthflorida.com, pg 1096

Rousseau, Gaetan, Paradoxal Inc, 540 Broadway, New York, NY 10012 *Tel:* 212-366-5526; 917-400-4507 (cell) *E-mail:* contact@paradoxal.net *Web Site:* www.paradoxal.net, pg 969

Routson, Ron, Film House Inc, 810 Dominican Dr, Nashville, TN 37228 *Tel:* 615-255-4000 *Fax:* 615-255-4111 *E-mail:* results@filmhouse.com *Web Site:* www.filmhouse.com, pg 867

Rowe, Chris, Love Shack Recording Studios, 909 18 Ave S, Nashville, TN 37212 *Tel:* 615-843-0019 *E-mail:* book@loveshackstudios.com *Web Site:* loveshackstudios.com, pg 925

Rowe, Marieli, National Telemedia Council Inc, 1922 University Ave, Madison, WI 53726 *Tel:* 608-218-1182 *E-mail:* ntelemedia@aol.com *Web Site:* www.nationaltelemediacouncil.org, pg 1086

Rowlands, David, Antenna International, 383 Main Ave, Norwalk, CT 06851 *Tel:* 203-523-0320 *Fax:* 203-354-5519 *E-mail:* inquiry@antennainternational.com *Web Site:* www.antennainternational.com, pg 787

Rowlands, Mark, Towards 2000 Inc, 215 W Palm Ave, Suite 101, Burbank, CA 91502 *Tel:* 818-557-0903 *Toll Free Fax:* 866-836-5725 *E-mail:* info@t2k.com *Web Site:* www.t2k.com, pg 1043

Rowley, Carolyn, Gilderfluke & Co Inc, 205 S Flower St, Burbank, CA 91502 *Tel:* 818-840-9484 *Toll Free Tel:* 800-776-5972 *Fax:* 818-840-9485 *E-mail:* info@gilderfluke.com *Web Site:* www.gilderfluke.com, pg 878

Roy, Rahul, ARC Document Solutions, 1981 N Broadway, Suite 385, Walnut Creek, CA 94596 *Tel:* 925-949-5100 *Fax:* 925-949-5101 *E-mail:* info@e-arc.com *Web Site:* www.e-arc.com, pg 789

Roy, Ron, Ron Roy Productions/Moodtapes, 2219 W Olive, Suite 312, Burbank, CA 91506 *E-mail:* info@moodtapes.com *Web Site:* www.moodtapes.com, pg 1000

Royalle, Candida, Femme Productions Inc, PO Box 268, New York, NY 10012 *Toll Free Tel:* 800-456-LOVE (456-5683); 800-955-0888 (CN) *E-mail:* inquiries@candidaroyalle.com *Web Site:* candidaroyalle.com, pg 866

Royce, Michael L, Artist Fellowships, 20 Jay St, 7th fl, Suite 740, Brooklyn, NY 11201 *Tel:* 212-366-6900 *Fax:* 212-366-1778 *E-mail:* fellowships@nyfa.org *Web Site:* nyfa.org, pg 1108

Royer, Larry, Animotion Inc, 501 W Fayette St, Syracuse, NY 13204 *Tel:* 315-471-3533 *Fax:* 315-471-2730 *E-mail:* info@animotioninc.com *Web Site:* animotioninc.com, pg 787

Rozon, Rene, Montreal International Festival of Films on Art, 2130 Crescent St, Montreal, QC H3G 2B8, Canada *Tel:* 514-874-1637 *Fax:* 514-874-9929 *E-mail:* info@artfifa.com *Web Site:* www.artfifa.com, pg 1120

Ruballos, Fernando, MSE Media Solutions, 6013 Scott Way, Los Angeles, CA 90040 *Tel:* 323-721-1656 *Toll Free Tel:* 800-626-1955 *Fax:* 323-721-1506 *E-mail:* info@msemedia.com *Web Site:* www.msemedia.com, pg 949

Rubenstein, Herb, Associated Bag Co, 400 W Boden St, Milwaukee, WI 53207 *Tel:* 414-769-1000 *Toll Free Tel:* 800-926-6100 *Fax:* 414-769-6530 *Toll Free Fax:* 800-926-4610 *E-mail:* customerservice@associatedbag.com *Web Site:* www.associatedbag.com, pg 792

Rubin, Barry, Schneider Optics Inc, 285 Oser Ave, Hauppauge, NY 11788 *Tel:* 631-761-5000 *Toll Free Tel:* 800-645-7239 *Fax:* 631-761-5090 *E-mail:* info@schneideroptics.com *Web Site:* www.schneideroptics.com, pg 1004

Rubin, Kelly Andrea, Signature Entertainment, 8306 Wilshire Blvd, Suite 791, Beverly Hills, CA 90211 *Tel:* 310-498-1805 *Fax:* 310-276-2521 *Web Site:* www.signature-ent.com, pg 1011

Rubin, Mark, Electro Impulse Laboratory Inc, 1805 Rte 33, Neptune, NJ 07754 *Tel:* 732-776-5800 *Fax:* 732-776-6793 *E-mail:* sales@electroimpulse.com *Web Site:* www.electroimpulse.com, pg 859

Rubin, Richard, Fibre Case Corp, 160 Broadway, Suite 1105, New York, NY 10038 *Tel:* 212-566-2720 *Toll Free Tel:* 800-394-6871 *Fax:* 212-566-2726 *E-mail:* sales@fibrecase.com *Web Site:* www.fibrecase.com, pg 866

Rubin, Richard, P&H Chrystalite Inc, 101 Palm Harbor Pkwy, Unit 117, Palm Coast, FL 32137 *Tel:* 561-330-8660 *Fax:* 561-330-8665 *Toll Free Fax:* 800-468-8673 *E-mail:* phcrystalite@aol.com *Web Site:* www.phcled.com, pg 968

Rubin, Scot, Big Door, 114 Sheldon St, El Segundo, CA 90245 *Tel:* 310-546-6100 *Fax:* 310-906-4585 *E-mail:* sales@bigdoor.tv *Web Site:* www.bigdoor.tv; www.bigdoorstudio.tv, pg 807

Rubino, Victor J, Practising Law Institute, 1177 Avenue of the Americas, New York, NY 10036 *Tel:* 212-824-5700 *Toll Free Tel:* 800-260-4PLI (260-4754, cust serv) *Toll Free Fax:* 800-321-0093 *E-mail:* info@pli.edu (cust serv) *Web Site:* www.pli.edu, pg 980

Rubinstein, Neal, NSR Productions Inc & Capricorn Five Films, 110 Second St, Hicksville, NY 11801 *Tel:* 516-681-2171 *Fax:* 516-681-2171 *E-mail:* nsrproductions@verizon.net, pg 960

Rucinski, Pamela, Rucinski & Reetz Communications LLC, 2155 Terrebonne, Mosinee, WI 54455 *Tel:* 715-355-9159; 715-241-7316 *Web Site:* www.rucinskireetz.com, pg 1000

Rucska, Susie, Kimono Surf Studios, 401 Logan Ave, Suite 109, Toronto, ON M4M 1S1, Canada *Tel:* 416-405-8111 *Fax:* 416-405-8751 *E-mail:* studio@kimonosurf.com *Web Site:* www.kimonosurf.com, pg 911

Rude, Nick, Sunrise Packaging Inc, 9937 Goodhue St NE, Blaine, MN 55449-4433 *Tel:* 763-785-2505 *Toll Free Tel:* 800-634-8160 *Fax:* 763-785-2210 *E-mail:* customerservice@sunpack.com *Web Site:* www.sunpack.com, pg 1028

Rudnick, Ben, Ben Rudnick & Friends, PO Box 1426, Arlington, MA 02474 *Tel:* 781-643-5137 *Web Site:* www.benrudnick.com, pg 1000

Rudolph, Fred, Cinram Inc, 2255 Markham Rd, Scarborough, ON M1B 2W3, Canada *Tel:* 416-298-8190 *Fax:* 416-298-0612 *E-mail:* sales@cinram.com *Web Site:* www.cinramgroup.com, pg 828

Rudolph, Max, Central Texas College KNCT-TV & Radio FM, PO Box 1800, Killeen, TX 76540-1800 *Tel:* 254-526-1176 *Fax:* 254-526-1850 *E-mail:* knct@knct.org *Web Site:* www.knct.org, pg 823

Rudolph, Scott, Chicago International REEL Shorts Festival, 428 N Wolcott, Chicago, IL 60622 *Web Site:* www.projectchicago.com, pg 1111

Ruehrdanz, Carter, Corplex, 915 Sherwood Dr, Lake Bluff, IL 60044 *Tel:* 847-582-8800 *Fax:* 847-582-8730 *Web Site:* www.nepinc.com/welcome/corplex, pg 836

Ruesch, Tracey, Adrienne Electronics Corp (AEC), 901 American Pacific Dr, Suite 170, Henderson, NV 89014 *Tel:* 702-896-1858 *Toll Free Tel:* 800-782-2321 *Fax:* 702-896-3034 *E-mail:* info@adrielec.com; orders@adrielec.com; support@adrielec.com *Web Site:* www.adrielec.com, pg 777

Ruff, Allison, Location Lighting Ltd, 300 Pennsylvania Ave, Oreland, PA 19075 *Tel:* 215-576-5600 *Fax:* 215-576-6022 *E-mail:* mail@locationlighting.com; rentals@locationlighting.com *Web Site:* www.locationlighting.com, pg 924

Ruff, Dave, Unique Communications Ltd, 2232 Pegasus Way NE, Calgary, AB T2E 8M5, Canada *Tel:* 403-250-3763 *Toll Free Tel:* 800-661-8575 *Fax:* 403-250-2604 *Web Site:* www.uniquecommunications.ca, pg 1048

Ruffin, Andy, R L Drake Co, 9900 Springboro Pike, Miamisburg, OH 45342 *Tel:* 937-746-4556 *Fax:* 937-806-1510 (sales); 937-806-1511 (gen) *E-mail:* salesgroup@rldrake.net *Web Site:* www.rldrake.com, pg 852

Ruggiero, Ed, Connecticut Office of Film, Television & Digital Media, c/o Dept of Economic & Community Development, 505 Hudson St, Hartford, CT 06106 *Tel:* 860-270-8198 *Web Site:* www.ctfilm.com, pg 1095

Ruggiero, Michael, Perennial Pictures Film Corp, 2102 E 52 St, Indianapolis, IN 46205 *Tel:* 317-253-1519 *E-mail:* mail@perennialpictures.com *Web Site:* www.perennialpictures.com, pg 973

Ruggles, Sam, Keywest Technology Inc, 14563 W 96 Terr, Lenexa, KS 66215 *Tel:* 913-492-4666 *Toll Free Tel:* 800-331-2019 *Fax:* 913-322-1864 *E-mail:* info@keywesttechnology.com; sales@keywesttechnology.com *Web Site:* www.keywesttechnology.com, pg 910

Rule, John, Rule Broadcast Systems, 1284 Soldier's Field Rd, Boston, MA 02135 *Tel:* 617-277-2200 *Toll Free Tel:* 800-785-3266 *Fax:* 617-277-6800 *E-mail:* answers@rule.com *Web Site:* www.rule.com, pg 1000

Rummell, Grant, Linear LLC, 1950 Camino Vida Roble, Suite 150, Carlsbad, CA 92008-6517 *Tel:* 760-438-7000 *Toll Free Tel:* 800-421-1587 *Fax:* 760-931-1340 *Toll Free Fax:* 800-468-1340 *E-mail:* sales@linearcorp.com *Web Site:* www.linearcorp.com, pg 922

Runnels, Susan, Captain J Charles Plumb, 3917 Fairbreeze Circle, Westlake, CA 91361 *Tel:* 818-991-1964 *Web Site:* www.charlieplumb.com, pg 977

Runyon, Randy, dbF a Media Company, 9683 Charles St, La Plata, MD 20646 *Tel:* 301-645-6110 *Fax:* 301-392-6111 *E-mail:* service@dbfmedia.com *Web Site:* dbfmedia.com, pg 844

Rupert, Grant, Wirestrippers.com, 34925 Cherry St, Wildomar, CA 92595 *Tel:* 951-245-6212 *Toll Free Tel:* 800-490-8520 *Fax:* 951-245-6213 *E-mail:* wirestrippers@verizon.net *Web Site:* www.wirestrippers.com, pg 1068

Rupkalvis, John A, StereoScope International, 727 N Victory Blvd, Burbank, CA 91502 *Tel:* 818-919-6253 *E-mail:* stereoscope3d@gmail.com, pg 1024

Ruppert, Jim, Associated Video, 2542 MacLaren Circle, Atlanta, GA 30360 *Tel:* 404-873-6411, pg 792

Rusch, David, Orban, 8350 E Evans Rd, Suite C-4, Scottsdale, AZ 85260 *Tel:* 480-403-8300 *Fax:* 480-403-8302 *E-mail:* info@orban.com; sales@orban.com *Web Site:* www.orban.com, pg 965

Russ, John C, SSL Industries Inc, 4935 Anne Louise Lane, Suite 2, Placerville, CA 95667 *Tel:* 530-644-0233 *E-mail:* sslind@starband.net *Web Site:* www.sslinc.net, pg 1022

Russ, Robin, Studio Center Corp, 161 Business Park Dr, Virginia Beach, VA 23462 *Tel:* 757-286-3080 (24 hour cell) *Toll Free Tel:* 866-515-2111 *Fax:* 757-622-0583 (acctg) *Web Site:* www.studiocenter.com, pg 1026

Russ-Ayon, Angela, Russ InVision Co/AbridgeClub.com, 3219 Conquista Ave, Long Beach, CA 90808 *Tel:* 562-421-1836 *Toll Free Tel:* 888-421-7488 *Fax:* 562-420-9101 *E-mail:* info@abridgeclub.com *Web Site:* abridgeclub.com, pg 1001

Russell, Adam, Russell Industries Inc, 40 Horton Ave, Lynbrook, NY 11563 *Tel:* 516-536-5000 *Toll Free Tel:* 800-645-2202 *Fax:* 516-764-5747 *Toll Free Fax:* 800-645-2200 *E-mail:* sales@russellind.com *Web Site:* www.russellind.com, pg 1001

Russell, Angie, Captions & Subtitle Services Ltd, 101 Hempstead Place, Suite 1A, Joliet, IL 60433 *Tel:* 815-740-1009 *Toll Free Tel:* 866-230-1009 *E-mail:* info@capsubservices.com; quote@capsubservices.com *Web Site:* www.capsubservices.com, pg 820

Russell, Bill, ARRI Inc, 600 N Victory Blvd, Burbank, CA 91502-1639 *Tel:* 818-841-7070 *Fax:* 818-848-4028 *E-mail:* info@arri.com *Web Site:* www.arri.com, pg 790

Russell, Brian W, Bryston Ltd, 677 Neal Dr, Peterborough, ON K9J 6X7, Canada *Tel:* 705-742-5325 *Fax:* 705-742-0882 *Web Site:* bryston.com, pg 814

Russell, Chick, Chick Russell Communications, 490 Castano Ave, Pasadena, CA 91107 *Tel:* 407-406-2899 *E-mail:* info@chickrussell.com *Web Site:* www.chickrussell.com, pg 825

Russell, Christopher, Bryston Ltd, 677 Neal Dr, Peterborough, ON K9J 6X7, Canada *Tel:* 705-742-5325 *Fax:* 705-742-0882 *Web Site:* bryston.com, pg 814

Russell, David, Image Video, 1620 Midland Ave, Scarborough, ON M1P 3C2, Canada *Tel:* 416-750-8872 *Fax:* 416-750-8015 *E-mail:* sales@imagevideo.com *Web Site:* www.imagevideo.com, pg 895

Russell, George H, Educational Video Network, 1401 19 St, Huntsville, TX 77340 *Tel:* 936-295-5767 *Toll Free Tel:* 800-762-0060 *Fax:* 936-294-0233 *Toll Free Fax:* 866-814-1714 *Web Site:* www.evndirect.com, pg 857

Russell, Jon, Presence Studios Westport, 80 Wells Hill Rd, Suite 100, Weston, CT 06883 *Tel:* 203-221-8061 *E-mail:* info@presencestudios.com *Web Site:* www.presencestudios.com, pg 981

Russell, Norman, Norman Russell Design, 5266 Hollister Ave, Suite 233, Santa Barbara, CA 93111 *Tel:* 805-964-9375 *Fax:* 805-964-9386 *E-mail:* normruss@normanrusselldesign.com *Web Site:* www.normanrusselldesign.com, pg 1001

Russell, Penny, Eurotech Seating, c/o Marketec, 419 S Flower St, Burbank, CA 91502 *Tel:* 818-847-0200 *Toll Free Tel:* 800-557-8861 *Toll Free Fax:* 888-262-1726 *E-mail:* info@marketec.com *Web Site:* www.marketec.com, pg 863

Russell, Penny, Marketec, 419 S Flower St, Burbank, CA 91502 *Tel:* 818-847-0200 *Toll Free Tel:* 800-557-8861 *Toll Free Fax:* 888-262-1726 *E-mail:* info@marketec.com *Web Site:* www.marketec.com, pg 931

Russo, Anne Marie, TRF Production Music Libraries, 106 Apple St, Suite 302, Tinton Falls, NJ 07724 *Tel:* 201-335-0005 *Toll Free Tel:* 800-899-MUSIC (899-6874) *Fax:* 201-335-0004 *E-mail:* info@trfmusic.com *Web Site:* www.trfmusic.com, pg 1044

Russo, Dan, Ardent Studios Inc, 2000 Madison Ave, Memphis, TN 38104 *Tel:* 901-725-0855 *Fax:* 901-725-7011 *E-mail:* info@ardentstudios.com *Web Site:* www.ardentstudios.com, pg 789

Russo, Emily, Zeitgeist Films Ltd, 247 Centre St, 2nd fl, New York, NY 10013 *Tel:* 212-274-1989 *Fax:* 212-274-1644 *E-mail:* mail@zeitgeistfilms.com *Web Site:* www.zeitgeistfilms.com, pg 1073

Russo, Joe II, Starburns Industries, 1700 W Burbank Blvd, Burbank, CA 91506 *Tel:* 818-433-3300 *Fax:* 818-433-3383 *Web Site:* www.starburnsindustries.com, pg 1024

Russo, Lynne, Blonder Tongue Laboratories Inc, One Jake Brown Rd, Old Bridge, NJ 08857 *Tel:* 732-679-4000 *Toll Free Tel:* 800-523-6049 *Fax:* 732-679-4353 *E-mail:* custsvc@blondertongue.com; btglobalsales@blondertongue.com (other than US & CN) *Web Site:* www.blondertongue.com, pg 809

Russo, Mary, Dorian Color, 24 Mill St, Arlington, MA 02476 *Tel:* 781-648-8040 *Fax:* 781-641-1231 *E-mail:* images@dorianlabcolor.com (gallery) *Web Site:* www.doriancolor.com, pg 851

Rustad, Mark, NetWell Noise Control, 18525 37 Ave N, Minneapolis, MN 55446-2855 *Tel:* 763-694-8908 *Toll Free Tel:* 800-638-9355 *Fax:* 763-694-8909 *E-mail:* help@controlnoise.com *Web Site:* www.controlnoise.com, pg 954

Ruth, Eric, Delaware Tourism Office, 99 Kings Hwy, Dover, DE 19901 *Tel:* 302-739-4271 *Toll Free Tel:* 866-284-7483 *Fax:* 302-739-5749 *Web Site:* www.visitdelaware.com, pg 1095

Rutherford, Dennis, CyberOptics, 5900 Golden Hills Dr, Minneapolis, MN 55416 *Tel:* 763-542-5000 *Fax:* 763-542-5100 *E-mail:* info@cyberoptics.com *Web Site:* cyberoptics.com, pg 841

Rutherford, Gerry, Vancouver Film Studios Ltd, 3500 Cornett Rd, Vancouver, BC V5M 2H5, Canada *Tel:* 604-453-5000 *Fax:* 604-453-5045 *Web Site:* www.vancouverfilmstudios.com, pg 1051

Rutledge, Corey Scott, Big Apple Films, 636 W 28 St, New York, NY 10001 *Tel:* 212-368-1111 *Fax:* 347-689-1604 *Web Site:* www.bigapplefilms.com, pg 806

Ryan, Andy, Mystery Electronics, 6438 Morton Rd, Greenbrier, TN 37073 *Tel:* 615-643-8460 *Toll Free Tel:* 800-798-2256 *Fax:* 615-643-8464 *E-mail:* sales@mysteryelectronics.com *Web Site:* www.mysteryelectronics.com, pg 951

Ryan, Becky, DawnSignPress, 6130 Nancy Ridge Dr, San Diego, CA 92121-3223 *Tel:* 858-625-0600 *Toll Free Tel:* 800-549-5350 *Fax:* 858-625-2336 *E-mail:* contactus@dawnsign.com *Web Site:* www.dawnsign.com, pg 844

Ryan, Craig, Ver Sales Inc, 2509 N Naomi St, Burbank, CA 91504 *Tel:* 818-567-3000 *Toll Free Tel:* 800-229-0518; 800-300-WIRE (300-9479, CA only) *Fax:* 818-567-3018 *E-mail:* sales@versales.com *Web Site:* www.versales.com, pg 1052

Ryan, Cyr A, Fiber Optic Systems Inc (FOSI), 2 Railroad Ave, Whitehouse Station, NJ 08889 *Tel:* 908-534-5500 *Toll Free Tel:* 800-809-3674 *Fax:* 908-534-2272 *E-mail:* info@fosi.com *Web Site:* www.fosi.com, pg 866

Ryan, Michael, Techni-Tool Inc, 1547 N Trooper Rd, Worcester, PA 19490 *Tel:* 610-941-2400 *Toll Free Tel:* 800-832-4866 *Fax:* 610-828-5623 *Toll Free Fax:* 800-854-8665 *E-mail:* sales@techni-tool.com *Web Site:* www.techni-tool.com, pg 1033

Ryan, Paul, Ver Sales Inc, 2509 N Naomi St, Burbank, CA 91504 *Tel:* 818-567-3000 *Toll Free Tel:* 800-229-0518; 800-300-WIRE (300-9479, CA only) *Fax:* 818-567-3018 *E-mail:* sales@versales.com *Web Site:* www.versales.com, pg 1052

Ryback, Andrew, Broadcast Management Group, 1625 Eye St NW, Suite 620, Washington, DC 20006 *Tel:* 202-609-7757 *E-mail:* info@broadcastmgmt.com *Web Site:* www.broadcastmgmt.com, pg 813

Ryder, Aaron, FilmNation Entertainment, 150 W 22 St, 9th fl, New York, NY 10011 *Web Site:* www.filmnation.com, pg 867

Rysavy, Jirka, Gaiam Inc, 833 W South Boulder Rd, PO Box 3095, Boulder, CO 80307-3095 *Tel:* 303-222-3600 *Toll Free Tel:* 877-989-6321 (cust serv) *Fax:* 303-222-3700 *E-mail:* customerservice@gaiam.com *Web Site:* www.gaiam.com, pg 875

Rytman, Peggy, Logan Productions Inc, 8035 N Port Washington Rd, Milwaukee, WI 53217 *Tel:* 414-352-9691 *Fax:* 414-352-4993 *E-mail:* sales@loganproductions.com *Web Site:* www.loganproductions.com, pg 924

Rzepka, Jason, MTV Networks Co, c/o MTV Studios, 1515 Broadway, New York, NY 10036 *Tel:* 212-258-8000 *Web Site:* www.mtv.com; www.mtvpress.com, pg 949

Saah, Richard, Saah Video, 12221 Parklawn Dr, Rockville, MD 20852 *Tel:* 301-770-6699 *Toll Free Tel:* 800-225-9690 *Fax:* 301-770-3250 *Web Site:* www.saahvideo.com, pg 1001

Sabatino, Diana, Juston Records, PO Box 362, New York, NY 10113-0362 *Tel:* 973-379-5538 *Fax:* 973-379-5538 *E-mail:* justonrecords@att.net, pg 907

Sabella, John A, Lehigh Phoenix™, 18249 Phoenix Dr, Hagerstown, MD 21742 *Tel:* 301-733-0018 *Toll Free Tel:* 800-632-4111 *Fax:* 301-733-1733 *Web Site:* www.phoenixcolor.com, pg 918

Sabini, Lucy, Welk Music Group, 11400 W Olympic Blvd, Suite 1450, Los Angeles, CA 90064 *Tel:* 310-829-9355 *Fax:* 310-315-9996 *E-mail:* info@vanguardrecords.com; order@vanguardrecords.com *Web Site:* www.vanguardrecords.com, pg 1063

Saboya, Adriana, FJ Productions Inc, 14900 Ventura Blvd, Suite 350, Sherman Oaks, CA 91403-3465 *Tel:* 818-788-0153 *Fax:* 818-788-0186 *Web Site:* www.fjproductions.com, pg 869

Sachse, Victor E, Centaur Records Inc, 136 Saint Joseph St, Baton Rouge, LA 70802 *Tel:* 225-336-4877 *Fax:* 225-336-9678 *E-mail:* info@centaurrecords.com *Web Site:* www.centaurrecords.com, pg 822

Sacks, Marty, Omnia Audio, 1241 Superior Ave E, Cleveland, OH 44114 *Tel:* 216-241-7225 *Fax:* 216-241-4103 *E-mail:* omnia-info@omniaaudio.com *Web Site:* www.omniaaudio.com, pg 962

Sad, Wally, Wells-Gardner Electronics Corp, 9500 W 55 St, Suite A, McCook, IL 60525-3605 *Tel:* 708-290-2100 *Toll Free Tel:* 800-336-6630 *Fax:* 708-290-2200 *Web Site:* www.wellsgardner.com, pg 1063

Saddler, Leon R, Lighttech Group Inc, 161-15 Rockaway Blvd, Jamaica, NY 11434 *Tel:* 718-525-2900 *Fax:* 718-525-2488 *E-mail:* info@lighttech.com *Web Site:* www.lighttech.com, pg 921

Sadler, Kurt, Dotronix Technology Inc, 160 First St SE, New Brighton, MN 55112 *Tel:* 651-633-1742 *Fax:* 651-633-2152 *E-mail:* service@dotronix.com; sales@dotronix.com *Web Site:* www.dotronix.com, pg 851

Sadorf, Nedra, Demco Inc, 4810 Forest Run Rd, Madison, WI 53704 *Tel:* 608-241-1201 *Toll Free Tel:* 800-962-4463; 800-279-1586 *Toll Free Fax:* 800-245-1329 *Web Site:* www.demco.com, pg 845

Saechow, Nai, Hollywood Lights Inc, 5251 SE McLoughlin Blvd, Portland, OR 97202-4836 *Tel:* 503-232-9001; 503-232-8855 *Toll Free Tel:* 800-826-9881 *Fax:* 503-517-8686 *E-mail:* portland@hollywoodlights.biz *Web Site:* www.hollywoodlights.biz, pg 890

Saenz, Daniel, Crown Audio Inc, 1718 W Mishawaka Rd, Elkhart, IN 46517 *Tel:* 574-294-8000 *Toll Free Tel:* 800-342-6939 *Fax:* 574-294-8301 *Web Site:* www.crownaudio.com, pg 840

Safran, Jeff, Varese Sarabande Records Inc, 9100 Wilshire Blvd, Suite 455E, Beverly Hills, CA 90212 *Tel:* 310-853-5400 *Toll Free Tel:* 800-827-3734 *E-mail:* info@varesesarabande.com; orders@varesesarabande.com *Web Site:* www.varesesarabande.com, pg 1052

Sagar, Lou, Rafik, 812 Broadway, Suite 4, New York, NY 10003 *Tel:* 212-475-7884 *E-mail:* info@rafikvideo.com; sales@rafikvideo.com *Web Site:* www.rafikvideo.com, pg 990

Sage, Bill, Delicate Electronics Sales Inc, 874 Verdulera St, Camarillo, CA 93010 *Tel:* 805-484-8139 *Toll Free Tel:* 800-350-3555 *Fax:* 805-388-1037 *Web Site:* www.delicatesales.com, pg 845

Sager, Stephanie, Harpers Ferry Historical Association, c/o National Park Bookshop, 723 Shenandoah St, Harpers Ferry, WV 25425 *Tel:* 304-535-6881 *Fax:* 304-535-6749 *E-mail:* hfha@earthlink.net *Web Site:* www.harpersferryhistory.org, pg 885

Sahlein, Don, Fax Animation Co, 5625 Melrose Ave, Hollywood, CA 90038 *Tel:* 323-466-3561 *Fax:* 323-871-2193 *E-mail:* contactus@alangordon.com *Web Site:* www.alangordon.com, pg 866

Sahlein, Don, Alan Gordon Enterprises Inc, 5625 Melrose Ave, Hollywood, CA 90038 *Tel:* 323-466-3561 *Fax:* 323-871-2193 *E-mail:* contactus@alangordon.com *Web Site:* www.alangordon.com, pg 880

Sainvil, Max, Facet Media, 5821 Rodman St, Hollywood, FL 33023 *Tel:* 954-589-0535 *Fax:* 954-593-0411 *E-mail:* info@facetmedia.com *Web Site:* www.facetmedia.com, pg 865

Sakamoto-Jog, Sonia, Toronto Reel Asian International Film Festival, 401 Richmond St W, Suite 309, Toronto, ON M5V 3A8, Canada *Tel:* 416-703-9333 *Fax:* 416-703-9986 *E-mail:* info@reelasian.com; programming@reelasian.com *Web Site:* www.reelasian.com, pg 1128

Sakatia, Toshio, TOA Electronics Inc, 1350 Bayshore Hwy, Suite 270, Burlingame, CA 94010 *Toll Free Tel:* 800-733-7088 (cust serv); 800-733-4750 (main) *Fax:* 650-588-3349 *Toll Free Fax:* 800-733-9766 *E-mail:* info@toaelectronics.com *Web Site:* www.toaelectronics.com, pg 1041

Salazar, Carlos, Intellidyne LLC, 5203 Leesburg Pike, Suite 400, 2 Skyline Place, Falls Church, VA 22041 *Tel:* 703-575-9715 *Fax:* 703-575-9718 *Web Site:* www.intellidyne-llc.com, pg 899

Salazar, Rafael, RAVA Films, 67 West St, Suite 604, Brooklyn, NY 11222 *Web Site:* www.ravafilms.com, pg 991

Salci, Al, Sierra Automated Systems, 2821 Burton Ave, Burbank, CA 91504 *Tel:* 818-840-6749 *Fax:* 818-840-6751 *E-mail:* sales@sasaudio.com; marketing@sasaudio.com *Web Site:* www.sasaudio.com, pg 1010

Saldana, Selena, FilmNation Entertainment, 150 W 22 St, 9th fl, New York, NY 10011 *Web Site:* www.filmnation.com, pg 867

Saleh, Paul N, Computer Sciences Corp, 3170 Fairview Park Dr, Falls Church, VA 22042 *Tel:* 703-876-1000 *Web Site:* www.csc.com, pg 834

Sales, Bill, FWT LLC, 5750 E I-20, Fort Worth, TX 76119 *Tel:* 817-255-3060 *Toll Free Tel:* 800-433-1816 *Fax:* 817-255-2957 *E-mail:* info@fwtllc.com *Web Site:* fwtllc.com, pg 874

Sales, Bruce, 2BruceStudio, 2 Wall St, Suite 119, Asheville, NC 28801 *Tel:* 828-255-2700 *E-mail:* info@2brucestudio.com *Web Site:* 2brucestudio.com, pg 1047

Saliba, Liz, Stricker Books, 8 Main St N, Unit C, Acton, ON L7J 1W1, Canada *Tel:* 519-853-2780 *Toll Free Tel:* 800-924-3966 *Fax:* 519-853-2847 *E-mail:* stricker@strickerbooks.com *Web Site:* www.strickerbooks.com, pg 1026

Salik, Jake, Talas, 330 Morgan Ave, Brooklyn, NY 11211 *Tel:* 212-219-0770 *Fax:* 212-219-0735 *E-mail:* info@talasonline.com *Web Site:* www.talasonline.com, pg 1031

Salik, Marjorie, Talas, 330 Morgan Ave, Brooklyn, NY 11211 *Tel:* 212-219-0770 *Fax:* 212-219-0735 *E-mail:* info@talasonline.com *Web Site:* www.talasonline.com, pg 1031

Sall, John, SAS Institute Inc, 100 SAS Campus Dr, Cary, NC 27513-2414 *Tel:* 919-677-8000 *Toll Free Tel:* 800-727-0025 *Fax:* 919-677-4444 *Web Site:* www.sas.com, pg 1002

Salmon, Annabel, The Napoleon Group, 48 W 25 St, New York, NY 10010 *Tel:* 212-692-9200 *Toll Free Tel:* 800-579-4019 *Fax:* 212-692-0309 *E-mail:* info@napny.com *Web Site:* www.napny.com, pg 952

Salms, Rebecca, Bella Faccia Inc, 6521 Chillum Place NW, Washington, DC 20012 *Tel:* 202-291-1932 *Fax:* 202-301-7716 *E-mail:* contact@bellafaccia.net *Web Site:* www.bellafaccia.net, pg 804

Salomon, Robert, HP Marketing Corp, 16 Chapin Rd, Unit 908, Pine Brook, NJ 07058 *Tel:* 973-808-9010 *Toll Free Tel:* 800-735-4373 *Fax:* 973-808-9004 *E-mail:* info@hpmarketingcorp.com *Web Site:* www.hpmarketingcorp.com, pg 892

Salour, Michael, Ipitek, 2330 Faraday Ave, Carlsbad, CA 92008 *Tel:* 760-438-1010 *Toll Free Tel:* 888-4-IPITEK (447-4835, US) *Fax:* 760-438-2412 *E-mail:* sales@ipitek.com *Web Site:* www.ipitek.com, pg 902

Salser, Mark, ERA Learning, PO Box 8795, Portland, OR 97207-8795 *Tel:* 503-228-6345 *Toll Free Tel:* 800-827-2499 (orders) *Fax:* 810-885-5811 *E-mail:* info@eralearning.com; customerservice@eralearning.com *Web Site:* www.eralearning.com, pg 862

Salter, Ann C, Community Arts Grants Program, 200 Ridge Rd W, Suite 214, Rochester, NY 14615 *Tel:* 585-473-4000 *Fax:* 585-473-4051 *E-mail:* artsandculturalcouncil@artsrochester.org *Web Site:* www.artsrochester.org, pg 1113

Salter, Charles M, Charles M Salter Associates Inc, 130 Sutter St, Suite 500, San Francisco, CA 94104 *Tel:* 415-397-0442 *Fax:* 415-397-0454 *E-mail:* info@cmsalter.com *Web Site:* www.cmsalter.com, pg 1001

Salton, Matt, Reelout Queer Film + Video Festival, 82 Sydenham St, Kingston, ON K7L 3H4, Canada *Tel:* 613-549-REEL (549-7335) *Web Site:* www.reelout.com, pg 1124

Samaha, John, Shooting Stars Post Inc, 3106 W North "A" St, Tampa, FL 33609 *Tel:* 813-873-0100 *Web Site:* www.sspmedia.com, pg 1009

Samler, Steven, Steven Samler Music & Sound, 1298 Green Knolls Dr, Buffalo Grove, IL 60089 *Tel:* 847-400-5080 *Fax:* 815-366-8227 *Web Site:* www.stevensamler.com, pg 1002

Sample, Melissa, The Visual Studies Workshop (VSW), 31 Prince St, Rochester, NY 14607 *Tel:* 585-442-8676 *Fax:* 585-442-1992 *E-mail:* info@vsw.org *Web Site:* www.vsw.org, pg 1059

Sampsell, Steve, The Bart Richards Award for Media Criticism, 302 James Bldg, University Park, PA 16801-3867 *Tel:* 814-865-8801 *Fax:* 814-863-6134 *Web Site:* comm.psu.edu/news-events/awards/bart-richards-award-for-media-criticism, pg 1125

Sams, Louise, Turner Broadcasting System Inc, One CNN Ctr, Atlanta, GA 30303 *Tel:* 404-827-1700 *Web Site:* www.turner.com, pg 1046

Sams, Mark, West Penn Wire, 2833 W Chestnut St, Washington, PA 15301 *Tel:* 724-222-7060 *Toll Free Tel:* 800-245-4964 *Fax:* 724-222-6420 *E-mail:* info@westpenn-wpw.com *Web Site:* www.westpenn-wpw.com, pg 1064

Samuel, Fred M, Avtech Systems Inc, 7-01 Bellair Ave, Fairlawn, NJ 07410 *Tel:* 201-833-8777 *Fax:* 201-833-4995 *E-mail:* sales@avtechsystems.com *Web Site:* www.avtechsystems.com, pg 800

Samuels, Ron, The Samuels Co, Box 770874, Houston, TX 77215-0874 *Tel:* 281-564-1055 *Fax:* 530-420-4631 *E-mail:* staff@thesamuelsco.com *Web Site:* www.thesamuelsco.com, pg 1002

Sanagan, Kate, Picture Box Distribution Inc, 141 E 23 Ave, Vancouver, BC V5V 1X1, Canada *Tel:* 604-681-3174 *Fax:* 604-608-9081 *E-mail:* info@picturebox.ca *Web Site:* www.picturebox.ca, pg 975

Sanchez, Jose, Available Lighting & Motion Picture Services Inc, 826 Jefferson Hwy, New Orleans, LA 70120 *Tel:* 504-831-5214 *Fax:* 504-831-5361 *E-mail:* avlight@bellsouth.net *Web Site:* www.availablelighting.com, pg 798

Sand, Chris, International Wildlife Film Festival, Roxy Theater, 718 S Higgins Ave, Missoula, MT 59801 *Tel:* 406-728-9380 *Fax:* 406-728-2881 *E-mail:* iwff@wildlifefilms.org *Web Site:* www.wildlifefilms.org, pg 1117

Sanderford, David, Marsand Inc, 6100 S IH-35W, Alvarado, TX 76009 *Tel:* 817-783-5566 *Fax:* 817-783-5577 *Web Site:* www.marsand.com, pg 931

Sanderford, Matthew A Jr, Marsand Inc, 6100 S IH-35W, Alvarado, TX 76009 *Tel:* 817-783-5566 *Fax:* 817-783-5577 *Web Site:* www.marsand.com, pg 931

Sanders, Barry, Spectrum Sound Inc, 1040 Acorn Dr, Suite C, Nashville, TN 37210 *Tel:* 615-391-3700 *Web Site:* www.spectrumsound.net, pg 1021

Sanders, Denny, Telos Systems, 1241 Superior Ave E, Cleveland, OH 44114 *Tel:* 216-241-7225 *Fax:* 216-241-4103 *E-mail:* inquiry@telos-systems.com *Web Site:* www.telos-systems.com, pg 1037

Sanders, Julie, Leprecon®, 10087 Industrial Dr, Hamburg, MI 48139 *Tel:* 810-852-4300 *Toll Free Tel:* 888-422-3537 *Fax:* 810-231-1631 *E-mail:* lepsls@leprecon.com *Web Site:* www.leprecon.com, pg 919

Sanders, Ken, Freeman, 1600 Viceroy, Suite 100, Dallas, TX 75235 *Tel:* 214-445-1000 *Fax:* 214-445-0200 *Web Site:* www.freemanco.com, pg 872

Sanders, Philip N, Charles M Salter Associates Inc, 130 Sutter St, Suite 500, San Francisco, CA 94104 *Tel:* 415-397-0442 *Fax:* 415-397-0454 *E-mail:* info@cmsalter.com *Web Site:* www.cmsalter.com, pg 1001

Sanders, William B "Beau", Professional Management Services Inc, 100 Lewis Dr, No 2C, Greenville, SC 29605 *Tel:* 864-325-7240; 864-498-5118 *Fax:* 413-683-7431 *E-mail:* sales@pm-systems.com *Web Site:* pm-systems.com, pg 985

Sanderson, Kim, Kingswood Productions, 810 12 Ave S, Nashville, TN 37203 *Toll Free Tel:* 800-476-7766 *E-mail:* info@kingswoodproductions.com *Web Site:* kingswoodproductions.com, pg 911

Sandidge, Robert L, CCore Media Inc, 1421 Lowe Dr, Algonquin, IL 60102 *Tel:* 847-854-1111 *Web Site:* www.creativecore.com, pg 821

Sandler, Adam, Nevada Broadcasters Association, 1050 E Flamingo Rd, No 102, Las Vegas, NV 89119 *Tel:* 702-794-4994 *Web Site:* www.nevadabroadcasters.org, pg 1086

Sandolowich, Rob, Westbury National Show Systems Ltd, 772 Warden Ave, Toronto, ON M1L 4T7, Canada *Tel:* 416-752-1371 *Fax:* 416-752-1382 *E-mail:* mail@westbury.com *Web Site:* www.westbury.com, pg 1064

Sandri, Janice, FSR Inc, 244 Bergen Blvd, West Paterson, NJ 07424 *Tel:* 973-785-4347 *Toll Free Tel:* 800-332-3771 (tech support) *Fax:* 973-785-4207 *E-mail:* sales@fsrinc.com *Web Site:* www.fsrinc.com, pg 873

Sanduski, James, Panasonic Consumer Electronics Co, One Panasonic Way, Secaucus, NJ 07094 *Tel:* 201-348-7066 *Toll Free Tel:* 800-211-PANA (211-7262) *Web Site:* www.panasonic.com, pg 968

Sandwell, Mike, Majortech Inc, 8464 Ninth Line RR-1, Norval, ON L0P 1K0, Canada *Tel:* 905-873-0778 *Fax:* 905-873-1244 *Web Site:* www.majortech.com, pg 929

Sanett, Martin, ARS Electronics, 7110 DeCelis Place, Van Nuys, CA 91406 *Tel:* 818-997-6279 *Fax:* 818-997-6158 *E-mail:* info@arselectronics.com *Web Site:* www.arselectronics.com, pg 791

Sangary, Pascal, All Video Productions, 726 Santa Monica Blvd, Suite 212, Santa Monica, CA 90401 *Tel:* 310-666-5606 *Fax:* 310-656-1155 *E-mail:* info@allvideoproductions.com *Web Site:* www.allvideoproductions.com, pg 781

Sanny, Tom, University Film & Video Association (UFVA), c/o University of Illinois Press, 1325 S Oak St, Champaign, IL 61820 *Tel:* 217-244-0626 (journals); 217-333-0950 (main) *Toll Free Tel:* 866-244-0626 (journals); 866-647-8382 (main) *Fax:* 217-244-9910 *E-mail:* ufvahome@gmail.com *Web Site:* www.ufva.org, pg 1090

Santangelo, Carolyn E, Freedoms Foundation National Awards, 1601 Valley Forge Rd, Valley Forge, PA 19482 *Tel:* 610-933-8825 *Fax:* 610-935-0522 *E-mail:* info@ffvf.org *Web Site:* www.freedomsfoundation.com, pg 1115

Santos, Norman, Oceanic Time Warner Cable, 200 Akamainui St, Mililani, HI 96789-3999 *Tel:* 808-625-2100 *Toll Free Tel:* 800-643-2100 (cust serv) *Fax:* 808-625-5888 *Web Site:* www.oceanic.com, pg 961

Saout, Mostapha, Allied Media Corp, 5252 Cherokee Ave, Suite 200, Alexandria, VA 22312 *Tel:* 703-333-2008 *Fax:* 703-997-7539 *Toll Free Fax:* 888-747-0957 *E-mail:* info@allied-media.com; contact@allied-media.com *Web Site:* www.allied-media.com, pg 781

Saperstein, Larry, KickedUp Media Group Inc, 2 Amherst Dr, Hastings-on-Hudson, NY 10706 *Tel:* 914-693-KICK (693-5425) *E-mail:* info@kickedupmediagroup.com *Web Site:* www.kickedupmediagroup.com, pg 910

Sapp, Laurie Berg, Glendale Media Center, 9494 W Maryland Ave, Glendale, AZ 85305 *Tel:* 623-930-4510 *Web Site:* www.glendalemediacenter.com, pg 878

Sapsis, Bill, SAPSIS Rigging Inc, 233 N Lansdowne Ave, Lansdowne, PA 19050 *Tel:* 215-228-0888 *Toll Free Tel:* 800-SAPSIS-1 (727-7471) *Fax:* 215-228-1786 *E-mail:* sales@sapsis-rigging.com *Web Site:* www.sapsis-rigging.com, pg 1002

Saranchuk, Susan, CSC Awards, 3007 Kingston Rd, Suite 131, Toronto, ON M1M 1P1, Canada *Tel:* 416-266-0591 *Fax:* 416-266-3996 *E-mail:* admin@csc.ca *Web Site:* www.csc.ca, pg 1113

Saraydarian, Gita, TSG Publishing Foundation Inc USA, 28641 N 63 Place, Cave Creek, AZ 85331 *Tel:* 480-502-1909 *Fax:* 480-502-0713 *E-mail:* info@tsgfoundation.org *Web Site:* www.tsgfoundation.org, pg 1046

Sardinsky, Elizabeth, 18 Label Studios, 18 Label St, Montclair, NJ 07042 *Tel:* 973-744-7382 *E-mail:* info@18label.com *Web Site:* 18label.com, pg 858

Sargent, Ralph, Film Technology Co Inc, 726 N Cole Ave, Hollywood, CA 90038 *Tel:* 323-464-3456 *Fax:* 323-464-7439 *Web Site:* www.filmtech.com, pg 867

Saritzky, Marlene Sharon, San Francisco Film Commission, City Hall, Rm 473, One Dr Carlton B Goodlett Place, San Francisco, CA 94102-4649 *Tel:* 415-554-6241 *Fax:* 415-554-6503 *E-mail:* film@sfgov.org *Web Site:* www.filmsf.org, pg 1094

Sashen, Steven, Scriptware, 100 Technology Dr, Suite 315C, Broomfield, CO 80021 *Tel:* 303-786-7899 *Toll Free Tel:* 800-788-7090 (orders) *Fax:* 303-786-9292 *E-mail:* info@scriptware.com *Web Site:* www.scriptware.com, pg 1005

Satterfield, Rob, Video Media Productions (VMP), 175 S Hamilton Place, Gilbert, AZ 85233 *Tel:* 480-745-2776 *E-mail:* question@videomediaproductions.com; video@videomediaproductions.com *Web Site:* www.videomediaproductions.com, pg 1055

Satterthwaite, Dan, DreamWorks Animation SKG Inc, 1000 Flower St, Glendale, CA 91201 *Tel:* 818-695-5000 *Fax:* 818-695-4190 *Web Site:* www.dreamworksanimation.com, pg 852

Sauers, Alwin, Alwin Sauers Audio Productions (ASAP), PO Box 50957, Oxnard, CA 93031 *Tel:* 206-484-6144 *E-mail:* alwinaudio@yahoo.com, pg 1003

Saul, Terri, Parallax Press, 2236-B Sixth St, Berkeley, CA 94710 *Tel:* 510-525-0101 *Toll Free Tel:* 800-863-5290 (book orders) *Fax:* 510-525-7129 *E-mail:* info@parallax.org *Web Site:* www.parallax.org, pg 969

Saunders, Avram, Lightning Eliminators & Consultants Inc, 6687 Arapahoe Rd, Boulder, CO 80303 *Tel:* 303-447-2828 *Toll Free Tel:* 800-521-6101 *Fax:* 303-447-8122 *E-mail:* info@lightningprotection.com *Web Site:* www.lightningprotection.com, pg 921

Saunders, Heather, Method Studios, 730 Arizona Ave, Santa Monica, CA 90401 *Tel:* 310-434-6500 *Web Site:* www.methodstudios.com, pg 939

Sauve, Lynne, Ultimatte Corp, 20945 Plummer St, Chatsworth, CA 91311 *Tel:* 818-993-8007 *Fax:* 818-993-3762 *E-mail:* sales@ultimatte.com *Web Site:* www.ultimatte.com, pg 1047

Savage, John, Gordon Visual Solutions, 504 Reiman St, Buffalo, NY 14212-2250 *Tel:* 716-894-5930 *Fax:* 630-839-5930 *E-mail:* info@gordonvisualsolutions.com; service@gordonvisualsolutions.com *Web Site:* www.gordonvisualsolutions.com, pg 880

Savage, Kathryn, State of the Art Acoustik Inc, 43-1010 Polytek St, Ottawa, ON K1J 9J3, Canada *Tel:* 613-745-2003 *Fax:* 613-745-9687 *E-mail:* sota@sota.ca *Web Site:* www.sota.ca, pg 1024

Savage, Kim, Dielectric Communications, 22 Tower Rd, Raymond, ME 04071 *Tel:* 207-655-4555 *Toll Free Tel:* 800-341-9678 *Fax:* 207-655-8174 *E-mail:* dcsales@dielectric.com *Web Site:* www.dielectric.com, pg 846

Savidge, Leigh, Xenon Pictures Inc, 3521 Jack Northrop Ave, Hawthorne, CA 90250 *Tel:* 310-451-5510 *Fax:* 310-395-4058 *E-mail:* info@xenonpictures.com; sales@xenonpictures.com *Web Site:* xenonpictures.com, pg 1071

Sawyer, Joan, Cambridge Documentary Films Inc, 3099 Hidden Valley Lane, Santa Barbara, CA 93108 *Tel:* 617-484-3993 *E-mail:* info@cambridgedocumentaryfilms.org *Web Site:* www.cambridgedocumentaryfilms.org, pg 818

Sawyer, John, Raincoast Books, 2440 Viking Way, Richmond, BC V6V 1N2, Canada *Tel:* 604-323-7100 *Toll Free Tel:* 800-663-5714 (cust serv & book orders) *Fax:* 604-270-7161 *Toll Free Fax:* 800-565-3770 (cust serv & book orders) *E-mail:* info@raincoast.com; customerservice@raincoast.com *Web Site:* www.raincoast.com, pg 991

Sawyer, Rachel White, Seattle Mayor's Office of Film & Music, 700 Fifth Ave, Suite 5752, Seattle, WA 98104 *Tel:* 206-684-8090 *Fax:* 206-684-0379 *E-mail:* filmandmusicoffice@seattle.gov *Web Site:* www.seattle.gov/filmandmusic, pg 1103

Sayah, David, Be Media, 9729 Lurline Ave, Chatsworth, CA 91311 *Tel:* 310-725-8500 *Toll Free Tel:* 877-210-7664 *Fax:* 310-725-9500 *Web Site:* www.bemedia.com, pg 804

Sayed, Anita, Colorado Display Systems, 1551 E 11 St, Loveland, CO 80537 *Tel:* 970-667-1000 *Toll Free Tel:* 800-279-0111 *Fax:* 970-667-5876 *E-mail:* info@coloradotime.com *Web Site:* www.coloradotime.com, pg 831

Sayiner, Necip, Intersil Americas LLC, 1001 Murphy Ranch Rd, Milpitas, CA 95035 *Tel:* 408-432-8888 *Toll Free Tel:* 888-INTERSIL (468-3774) *Fax:* 408-434-5351 *Web Site:* www.intersil.com, pg 901

Scales, Aileen, Consortium of College & University Media Centers (CCUMC), c/o Indiana University, 306 N Union St, Bloomington, IN 47405-3888 *Tel:* 812-855-6049 *Fax:* 812-855-2103 *E-mail:* ccumc@ccumc.org *Web Site:* www.ccumc.org, pg 1080

Scaletti, Carla, Symbolic Sound Corp, PO Box 2549, Champaign, IL 61825-2549 *Tel:* 217-355-6273 *Fax:* 217-355-6562 *E-mail:* info-kyma@symbolicsound.com *Web Site:* www.symbolicsound.com, pg 1030

Scallon, Leslee, Dances With Films, Formosa Bldg, 2nd fl, 1041 N Formosa Ave, West Hollywood, CA 90046 *Tel:* 323-850-2929 *E-mail:* info@danceswithfilms.com *Web Site:* www.danceswithfilms.com, pg 1113

Scanell, Kelly, Taylor Associates, 110 W Canal St, Suite 301, Winooski, VT 05404 *Tel:* 802-735-1942 *Toll Free Tel:* 800-READ-PLUS (732-3758) *Fax:* 802-419-4786 *E-mail:* info@readingplus.com *Web Site:* www.readingplus.com, pg 1032

Scanlon, Jamye, Shamrock Communications, 200 Tornillo Way, Suite 110, Tinton Falls, NJ 07712 *Tel:* 732-686-1140 *Fax:* 732-686-1148 *E-mail:* info@shamrockcommunications.com *Web Site:* www.shamrockcommunications.com, pg 1008

Scanlon, Mr Pat, Shamrock Communications, 200 Tornillo Way, Suite 110, Tinton Falls, NJ 07712 *Tel:* 732-686-1140 *Fax:* 732-686-1148 *E-mail:* info@shamrockcommunications.com *Web Site:* www.shamrockcommunications.com, pg 1008

Scannell, Pam, Big Bear Chamber of Commerce, 630 Bartlett Rd, 1st fl, Big Bear Lake, CA 92315 *Tel:* 909-866-4607 *Fax:* 909-866-5412 *E-mail:* contact@bigbearchamber.com *Web Site:* www.bigbearchamber.com, pg 1092

Scarpone, Janet, Learn Quickly, PO Box 3114, Palm Springs, CA 92263-3114 *Toll Free Tel:* 888-LRN-FAST (576-3278) *Toll Free Fax:* 888-LRN-FAST (576-3278) *Web Site:* www.learnquickly.com, pg 917

Scauzzo, Buddy, Express Media Inc, 2225 Palou Ave, San Francisco, CA 94124 *Tel:* 415-255-9883 *Fax:* 415-255-0139 *Web Site:* www.expressmedia.tv, pg 864

Scauzzo, Buddy, Express Media Inc, 2225 Palou Ave, San Francisco, CA 94124 *Tel:* 415-255-9883 *Fax:* 415-255-0139 *Web Site:* www.rentvideo.com; www.expressmedia.tv, pg 864

Scavelli, Steven V, Flash Electronics Inc, Brooklyn Army Terminal, Suite 1-A, Mail Box 3, 140 58 St, Brooklyn, NY 11220 *Tel:* 718-492-4040 *Toll Free Tel:* 800-831-3127 *Fax:* 718-492-4590 *E-mail:* flashdistr@aol.com; customercare@flashdistributors.com *Web Site:* www.flashdistributors.com, pg 869

Scavotto, Marie A, Sinauer Associates Inc, 23 Plumtree Rd, Sunderland, MA 01375 *Tel:* 413-549-4300 *Fax:* 413-549-1118 *E-mail:* orders@sinauer.com (orders); custserv@sinauer.com (cust serv); publish@sinauer.com (general edit correspondence) *Web Site:* www.sinauer.com, pg 1012

Scavulli, Stephen, Groovy Like a Movie, 5205 Kearny Villa Way, Suite 100, San Diego, CA 92123 *Tel:* 858-715-0300 *E-mail:* info@groovylikeamovie.com *Web Site:* www.groovylikeamovie.com, pg 882

Schachinger, Christian, Tritech Communications, 625 Locust St, Suite 300, Garden City, NY 11530 *Tel:* 631-254-4500 *Fax:* 631-254-4499 *E-mail:* sales@tritechcomm.com *Web Site:* www.tritechcomm.com, pg 1045

Schaefer, Dieter, PROCAM, 13624 Black Elk Trail, Prescott, AZ 86305 *Tel:* 928-708-9901 *Fax:* 928-708-9897 *E-mail:* camradoc@hotmail.com *Web Site:* bolex-usa.com, pg 983

Schaefer, Scott, Comprehensive Cable & Connectivity Co, 80 Little Falls Rd, Fairfield, NJ 07004 *Toll Free Tel:* 800-526-0242 *Fax:* 201-814-0510 *E-mail:* sales@comprehensivecable.com; customerservice@comprehensivecable.com *Web Site:* www.comprehensivecable.com, pg 833

Schaeffer, Cory, Listen Technologies Corp, 14912 Heritage Crest Way, Bluffdale, UT 84065-4818 *Tel:* 801-233-8992 *Toll Free Tel:* 800-330-0891 *Fax:* 801-233-8995 *E-mail:* info@listentech.com *Web Site:* www.listentech.com, pg 923

Schafer, Charles, Revolution Lighting Technologies Inc, 177 Broad St, 12th fl, Stamford, CT 06901 *Tel:* 203-504-1111 *Fax:* 203-504-1150 *Web Site:* www.rvlti.com, pg 995

Schafer, Renee, Data Security Inc, 300 S Seventh St, Lincoln, NE 68508 *Tel:* 402-434-5959 *Toll Free Tel:* 800-225-7554 *Fax:* 402-434-3291 *E-mail:* sales@telesis-inc.com *Web Site:* www.datasecurityinc.com, pg 843

Schaffel, Martin, AVI-SPL, 6301 Benjamin Rd, Suite 101, Tampa, FL 33634 *Tel:* 813-884-7168 *Toll Free Tel:* 866-708-5034; 800-282-6733; 866-925-8298 (cust serv); 866-559-8197 (sales) *Fax:* 813-882-9508 *E-mail:* questions@avispl.com; sales@avispl.com; customerservice@avispl.com *Web Site:* www.avispl.com, pg 798

Schaffer, Julie, Printing Industries of America, 200 Deer Run Rd, Sewickley, PA 15143 *Tel:* 412-741-6860 *Toll Free Tel:* 800-910-4283 *Fax:* 412-741-2311 *E-mail:* printing@printing.org *Web Site:* www.printing.org, pg 1087

Schaffer, Kirsten, Outfest, 3470 Wilshire Blvd, Suite 935, Los Angeles, CA 90010 *Tel:* 213-480-7088 *Fax:* 213-480-7099 *E-mail:* outfest@outfest.org *Web Site:* www.outfest.org, pg 1123

Schau, Allan, Kirkwood Community College, Linn Hall, Rm 102, 6301 Kirkwood Blvd SW, Cedar Rapids, IA 52406 *Tel:* 319-398-5517 *Toll Free Tel:* 800-363-2220 *Fax:* 319-398-5413 *E-mail:* info@kirkwood.edu *Web Site:* www.kirkwood.edu, pg 911

Schauer, Tim, Pemcor LLC, 2100 State Rd, Lancaster, PA 17601 *Tel:* 717-898-1555 *Toll Free Tel:* 800-735-1555 *Fax:* 717-898-3191 *E-mail:* support@pemcor.com *Web Site:* www.pemcor.com, pg 971

Schecker, Gabrielle, Charleston International Film Festival (CIFF), 915 Folly Rd, No 78, Charleston, SC 29412 *Tel:* 843-817-1617 *E-mail:* info@charlestoniff.org *Web Site:* charlestoniff.org, pg 1111

Scheinberg, Jeremy, Alcorn McBride Inc, 3300 S Hiawassee Rd, Bldg 105, Orlando, FL 32835 *Tel:* 407-296-5800 *Fax:* 407-296-5801 *E-mail:* info@alcorn.com; sales@alcorn.com *Web Site:* www.alcorn.com, pg 780

Scheininger, Haim, SISU Home Entertainment Inc, 340 W 39 St, 6th fl, New York, NY 10018 *Tel:* 212-947-7888 *Toll Free Tel:* 800-223-7478 *Fax:* 212-947-8388 *Toll Free Fax:* 888-221-7478 *E-mail:* sisu@sisuent.com *Web Site:* www.sisuent.com, pg 1012

Schellenger, Jon, JungleTV, 571 NW Mercantile Place, Port St Lucie, FL 34986 *Tel:* 772-370-0043 *E-mail:* info@jungletv.com *Web Site:* www.jungletv.com, pg 907

Schenk, Michael, One Touch Systems Inc, 2346 Bering Dr, San Jose, CA 95131 *Tel:* 408-660-8435 *Fax:* 408-436-4699 *E-mail:* info@onetouchsys.com *Web Site:* www.onetouchsys.com, pg 963

Scher, Larry, Timestream Video, 11821 N Circle Dr, Whittier, CA 90601-2338 *Tel:* 562-699-8797 *Fax:* 562-695-0252 *Web Site:* www.timestreamvideo.com, pg 1041

Scherrer, Winifred, Bullfrog Films Inc, PO Box 149, Oley, PA 19547-0149 *Tel:* 610-779-8226 *Toll Free Tel:* 800-543-3764 *Fax:* 610-370-1978 *E-mail:* video@bullfrogfilms.com *Web Site:* www.bullfrogfilms.com, pg 815

Scheuer, Greg, AVForSale, 1222 Logan Cir, Atlanta, GA 30318 *Tel:* 404-355-6147 *Toll Free Tel:* 866-634-5296 *Fax:* 404-355-7462 *E-mail:* customerservice@avforsale.com *Web Site:* www.avforsale.com, pg 798

Scheuren, Eduardo, Cinemat Inc, 2350 NW 96 Ave, Doral, FL 33172 *Tel:* 305-887-7726 *E-mail:* info@cinematusa.com *Web Site:* cinematusa.com, pg 827

Scheuren, Jose Vicente, Cinemat Inc, 2350 NW 96 Ave, Doral, FL 33172 *Tel:* 305-887-7726 *E-mail:* info@cinematusa.com *Web Site:* cinematusa.com, pg 827

Schiavo, Jen, AVA Electronics Corp, 4000 Bridge St, Drexel Hill, PA 19026 *Tel:* 610-284-2500 *Fax:* 610-259-8379, pg 798

Schildt, Deborah, Alaska Film Services Inc, 11050 Cange St, Anchorage, AK 99516 *Tel:* 907-230-6870 *Fax:* 907-272-6778 *E-mail:* filmservices@alaska.net *Web Site:* www.alaskafilmservices.com, pg 779

Schiller, Brad, Vari-Lite, 10911 Petal St, Dallas, TX 75238 *Tel:* 214-647-7880 *Toll Free Tel:* 877-VARILITE (877-827-4548) *Fax:* 214-647-8038 *E-mail:* entertainment.service@philips.com *Web Site:* www.vari-lite.com, pg 1052

Schiller, Craig, Bexel Corp, 2701 N Ontario St, Burbank, CA 91504 *Tel:* 818-565-4322 *Toll Free Tel:* 800-225-6185 (tech support) *E-mail:* rentals@bexel.com *Web Site:* www.bexel.com, pg 806

Schiller, Philip W, Apple Inc, One Infinite Loop, Cupertino, CA 95014 *Tel:* 408-996-1010 *Web Site:* www.apple.com, pg 788

Schiller, Randy, Randall Schiller Productions, 1207 Fifth Ave, San Francisco, CA 94122 *Tel:* 415-661-7553 *Fax:* 415-566-6238 *E-mail:* rsp7@pacbell.net *Web Site:* www.randallschillerproductions.com, pg 1004

Schilling, Ron, Nolte Media, 12 Pierson St, Santa Rosa, CA 95401 *Tel:* 707-579-3902 *Web Site:* www.noltemedia.com, pg 958

Schimek, Chris, Freeman, 1600 Viceroy, Suite 100, Dallas, TX 75235 *Tel:* 214-445-1000 *Fax:* 214-445-0200 *Web Site:* www.freemanco.com, pg 872

Schimmel, Nancy, Schroder Music Co, PO Box 2067, Berkeley, CA 94702-0067 *Tel:* 510-843-0533 *Fax:* 510-834-5201 *Web Site:* www.sisterschoice.com, pg 1004

Schimmel, Nancy, Sisters' Choice Press, PO Box 2067, Berkeley, CA 94702-0067 *Tel:* 510-843-0533 *Fax:* 510-834-5201 *Web Site:* www.sisterschoice.com, pg 1012

Schindler, Max J, Broadcast Management Group, 1625 Eye St NW, Suite 620, Washington, DC 20006 *Tel:* 202-609-7757 *E-mail:* info@broadcastmgmt.com *Web Site:* www.broadcastmgmt.com, pg 813

Schindler, Thomas, Charles M Salter Associates Inc, 130 Sutter St, Suite 500, San Francisco, CA 94104 *Tel:* 415-397-0442 *Fax:* 415-397-0454 *E-mail:* info@cmsalter.com *Web Site:* www.cmsalter.com, pg 1001

Schinman, William J, Studio South, 4912 Old Pineville Rd, Charlotte, NC 28217 *Tel:* 704-525-0296 *Fax:* 704-525-0136 *E-mail:* studiosouthvideo@earthlink.net *Web Site:* www.studiosouthmedia.com, pg 1027

Schlessinger, Andrew, Library Video Company, 7 E Wynnewood Rd, Wynnewood, PA 19096 *Tel:* 610-645-4000 *Toll Free Tel:* 800-843-3620 *Fax:* 610-645-4040 *E-mail:* sales@libraryvideo.com; comments@libraryvideo.com *Web Site:* www.libraryvideo.com, pg 920

Schlessinger, Andrew, Schlessinger Media, PO Box 580, Wynnewood, PA 19096-0580 *Tel:* 610-645-4000 *Toll Free Tel:* 800-843-3620 *Fax:* 610-645-4040 *E-mail:* comments@libraryvideo.com *Web Site:* www.libraryvideo.com, pg 1004

Schlichter, Scott, Dogma Studios, 10559 Jefferson Blvd, Culver City, CA 90232 *Tel:* 310-838-2973 *Fax:* 310-838-2975 *E-mail:* info@dogmastudios.com *Web Site:* www.dogmastudios.com, pg 850

Schloat, Anson W, Human Relations Media, 41 Kensico Dr, Mount Kisco, NY 10549 *Tel:* 914-666-9151 *Toll Free Tel:* 800-431-2050 (cust serv) *Fax:* 914-666-9506 *E-mail:* service@hrmvideo.com; orders@hrmvideo.com; help@hrmvideo.com; letters@hrmvideo.com *Web Site:* www.hrmvideo.com, pg 892

Schlobohm, Michael, Polyline LLC, 845 N Church Ct, Elmhurst, IL 60126-1036 *Tel:* 630-993-2700 *Toll Free Tel:* 800-701-7689 *Toll Free Fax:* 800-816-3330 *E-mail:* sales@polylinecorp.com *Web Site:* www.polylinecorp.com, pg 978

Schlosser, Kathy M, Aero-Tech Light Bulb Co Inc, 534 Pratt Ave N, Schaumburg, IL 60193 *Tel:* 847-352-4900 *Toll Free Tel:* 800-955-2376 *Fax:* 847-352-4999 *E-mail:* info@aerolights.com *Web Site:* www.aerolights.com, pg 778

Schlosser, Ray M, Aero-Tech Light Bulb Co Inc, 534 Pratt Ave N, Schaumburg, IL 60193 *Tel:* 847-352-4900 *Toll Free Tel:* 800-955-2376 *Fax:* 847-352-4999 *E-mail:* info@aerolights.com *Web Site:* www.aerolights.com, pg 778

Schluntz, Bryan, All Access Staging & Productions, 1320 Storm Pkwy, Torrance, CA 90501 *Tel:* 310-784-2464 *Toll Free Tel:* 877-784-2464 *Fax:* 310-517-0899 *E-mail:* usinfo@allaccessinc.com *Web Site:* www.allaccessinc.com, pg 780

Schlussler, Bob, Bill Bachmann Studios, PO Box 950833, Lake Mary, FL 32795 *Tel:* 407-333-9988 *Web Site:* www.billbachmann.com, pg 807

Schluter, Bob, Middle Atlantic Products Inc, 300 Fairfield Rd, Fairfield, NJ 07004 *Tel:* 973-839-1011 *Fax:* 973-839-1976 *E-mail:* info@middleatlantic.com *Web Site:* www.middleatlantic.com, pg 942

Schmaling, Bob, Oregon Film & Video Office, 123 NE Third Ave, Suite 210, Portland, OR 97232 *Tel:* 503-229-5832 *Fax:* 503-229-6869 *E-mail:* shoot@oregonfilm.org *Web Site:* www.oregonfilm.org, pg 1101

Schmidlapp, Jason, Southern California Sound Image Inc, 2415 Auto Park Way, Escondido, CA 92029-1222 *Tel:* 760-737-3900 *Fax:* 760-737-3929 *Web Site:* www.sound-image.com, pg 1019

Schmidt, Bob, CCI Solutions, 1342 88 Ave SE, Olympia, WA 98501 *Tel:* 360-943-5378 *Toll Free Tel:* 800-562-6006 *Fax:* 360-754-1566 *E-mail:* info@ccisolutions.com *Web Site:* www.ccisolutions.com, pg 821

Schmidt, Craig, Morro Bay Chamber of Commerce & Business Center, 695 Harbor St, Morro Bay, CA 93442 *Tel:* 805-772-4467 *Toll Free Tel:* 800-231-0592 *Web Site:* www.morrobay.org, pg 1093

Schmidt, Daniel J, The Chicago Production Center, 5400 N Saint Louis Ave, Chicago, IL 60625-4698 *Tel:* 773-509-5571 *Fax:* 773-509-5303 *Web Site:* www.wttw.com, pg 825

Schmidt, Eric, Richter Studios, 1143 W Rundell Place, Chicago, IL 60607 *Tel:* 312-861-9999 *Fax:* 312-997-2387 *E-mail:* info@richterstudios.com *Web Site:* www.richterstudios.com, pg 996

Schmidt, Lou, Hoodman Corp, 20445 Gramercy Place, Suite 201, Torrence, CA 90501 *Tel:* 310-222-8608 *Toll Free Tel:* 800-818-3946 *Fax:* 310-222-8623 *E-mail:* sales@hoodmanusa.com *Web Site:* www.hoodmanusa.com, pg 891

Schmidt, Mike, Grace Church - St Louis, 2695 Creve Coeur Mill Rd, Maryland Heights, MO 63043 *Tel:* 314-292-8300 *Fax:* 314-291-0918 *E-mail:* info@gracestl.org *Web Site:* www.gracestl.org, pg 881

Schmidt, Teri, Sioux Falls Convention & Visitors Bureau, 200 N Phillips Ave, Suite 102, Sioux Falls, SD 57104 *Tel:* 605-275-6060 *Toll Free Tel:* 800-333-2072 *Fax:* 605-338-0682 *E-mail:* sfcvb@siouxfalls.com *Web Site:* www.siouxfallscvb.com; visitsiouxfalls.com, pg 1102

Schmitz, Brad, A to Z Theatrical Supply & Service, 307 W 80 St, Kansas City, MO 64114-2376 *Tel:* 816-523-1655 *Toll Free Tel:* 800-732-8252 *Fax:* 816-523-1690 *E-mail:* atoz@atoztheatrical.com *Web Site:* www.atoztheatrical.com, pg 771

Schmitz, Leonard, Soundtrax Optical Sound Recording, 8116 Brucar Ct, Gaithersburg, MD 20877 *Tel:* 301-948-4288 *Fax:* 301-869-9061, pg 1018

Schmoldt, David, Audio Precision, 5750 SW Arctic Dr, Beaverton, OR 97005 *Tel:* 503-627-0832 *Toll Free Tel:* 800-231-7350 *Fax:* 503-469-0336 *E-mail:* sales@ap.com *Web Site:* www.ap.com, pg 794

Schmoll, Rob, Producers Management Television (PMTV), 681 Moore Rd, Suite 100, King of Prussia, PA 19406 *Tel:* 610-768-1770 *Fax:* 610-768-1773 *E-mail:* info@pmtv.com *Web Site:* www.pmtv.com, pg 983

Schmuckler, Hannah, Clarion Awards, 3337 Duke St, Alexandria, VA 22314 *Tel:* 703-370-7436 *Fax:* 703-342-4311 *E-mail:* clarion@womcom.org *Web Site:* www.womcom.org, pg 1112

Schneck, Thomas, Westbrook Technologies Inc, 35 Thorpe Ave, Suite 201, Wallingford, CT 06492 *Tel:* 203-871-4984 *Fax:* 203-269-0322 *E-mail:* info@westbrooktech.com *Web Site:* www.westbrooktech.com, pg 1064

Schneider, Erin Newell, Film Indiana, One N Capitol, Suite 700, Indianapolis, IN 46204-2288 *Tel:* 317-234-2087 *Fax:* 317-232-4146 *E-mail:* filminfo@iedc.in.gov *Web Site:* www.filmindiana.com, pg 1097

Schneider, John, HDrental.com, 16129 Covello St, Van Nuys, CA 91406 *Tel:* 818-994-3461 *Fax:* 818-994-3471 *Web Site:* hdrental.com, pg 886

Schneider, Leslie, Parallax Press, 2236-B Sixth St, Berkeley, CA 94710 *Tel:* 510-525-0101 *Toll Free Tel:* 800-863-5290 (book orders) *Fax:* 510-525-7129 *E-mail:* info@parallax.org *Web Site:* www.parallax.org, pg 969

Schneider, Lori, Amusement & Music Operators Association (AMOA), 600 Spring Hill Ring Rd, Suite 111, West Dundee, IL 60118 *Tel:* 847-428-7699 *Toll Free Tel:* 800-YES-AMOA (937-2662) *Fax:* 847-428-7719 *E-mail:* amoa@amoa.com *Web Site:* www.amoa.com, pg 1077

Schneider, Michele, OSV Studios, 29605 Lorain Rd N, Olmsted, OH 44070 *Tel:* 440-779-1900 *Web Site:* www.osvstudios.com, pg 966

Schneider, Pamela R, ACCO Brands Corp, 4 Corporate Dr, Lake Zurick, IL 60047-8997 *Toll Free Tel:* 800-541-0094 *Toll Free Fax:* 800-941-4463 *E-mail:* contactus@gbc.com *Web Site:* www.accobrands.com, pg 773

Schneider, Peter, Gotham Sound & Communications Inc, 330 W 38 St, No 105, New York, NY 10018 *Tel:* 212-629-9430 *Toll Free Tel:* 866-468-4268 *Fax:* 212-629-9436 *E-mail:* nyc@gothamsound.com *Web Site:* www.gothamsound.com, pg 881

Schneider, Rex, Blue Mouse Studio, 26829 37 St, Gobles, MI 49055 *Tel:* 269-628-5160 *E-mail:* frogville@earthlink.net; mwivi@earthlink.net, pg 809

Schnitzer, Diane, American Law Institute Continuing Legal Education (ALICLE), 4025 Chestnut St, Philadelphia, PA 19104-3099 *Toll Free Tel:* 800-253-6397 *Fax:* 215-243-1664 *Web Site:* www.ali-cle.org, pg 784

Schober, Edward A, Radiotechniques Engineering LLC, 402 Tenth Ave, Haddon Heights, NJ 08035-1838 *Tel:* 856-546-8008 *Fax:* 856-546-1841 *E-mail:* sales@radiotechniques.com *Web Site:* www.radiotechniques.com, pg 990

Schock, Kathleen, Automatic Devices Co, 2121 S 12 St, Allentown, PA 18103 *Tel:* 610-797-6000 *Toll Free Tel:* 800-360-2321 *Fax:* 610-797-4088 *E-mail:* info@automaticdevices.com *Web Site:* www.automaticdevices.com, pg 797

Schoebel, Doug, Concept Productions Inc, 7878 Big Sky Dr, Madison, WI 53719 *Tel:* 608-833-8273 *E-mail:* info@conceptpro.biz *Web Site:* www.conceptpro.biz, pg 834

Schoeknecht, Walter, Midnight Media Group Inc, 45 E Willow St, Millburn, NJ 07041-1416 *Tel:* 973-379-5959 *E-mail:* info@mmgi.tv *Web Site:* www.mmgi.tv, pg 942

Schoenwald, Mark, Zondervan, A HarperCollins Company, 3900 Sparks Dr, Grand Rapids, MI 49546 *Tel:* 616-698-6900 *Toll Free Tel:* 800-226-1122; 800-727-3480 (retail orders) *Fax:* 616-698-3255 (retail orders) *E-mail:* zinfo@zondervan.com *Web Site:* www.zondervan.com, pg 1074

Schoner, David W Jr, New Jersey Motion Picture & Television Commission, 153 Halsey St, 5th fl, Newark, NJ 07102-2807 *Tel:* 973-648-6279 *Fax:* 973-648-7350 *E-mail:* njfilm@njfilm.org *Web Site:* www.njfilm.org, pg 1100

Schor, Allen, El Mar Plastics Inc, 967 E Sandhill Ave, Carson, CA 90746 *Tel:* 310-436-6444 *Toll Free Tel:* 800-255-5210 *Fax:* 310-436-6445 *E-mail:* sales@elmarplastics.com *Web Site:* www.elmarplastics.com, pg 858

Schrader, Laurie, Blue Sky Stock Footage, PO Box 177, Santa Fe, NM 87504-0177 *Tel:* 310-859-4709 *Toll Free Tel:* 877-992-5477 *Fax:* 310-823-0924 *E-mail:* sales@blueskyfootage.com *Web Site:* www.blueskyfootage.com, pg 810

Schraffenberger, David W, Production Advantage Inc, 301 Avenue "D", Suite 10, Williston, VT 05495 *Tel:* 802-651-6915 *Toll Free Tel:* 800-424-9991 *Fax:* 802-651-6914 *Toll Free Fax:* 877-424-9991 *E-mail:* sales@proadv.com; orders@proadv.com *Web Site:* www.productionadvantageonline.com, pg 984

Schram, Richard, Parasound Products Inc, 2250 McKinnon Ave, San Francisco, CA 94124 *Tel:* 415-397-7100 *Fax:* 415-397-0144 *E-mail:* sales@parasound.com; marketing@parasound.com; service@parasound.com *Web Site:* www.parasound.com, pg 969

Schramm, Craig, Troxell Communications Inc, 4830 S 38 St, Phoenix, AZ 85040 *Tel:* 602-437-7240 *Toll Free Tel:* 800-578-8858 *Fax:* 602-437-7265 *Toll Free Fax:* 800-589-5939 *Web Site:* www.trox.com, pg 1045

Schramm, R C, Broadway Costumes Inc, 1100 W Cermak Rd, 2nd fl, Chicago, IL 60608 *Tel:* 312-829-6400 *Toll Free Tel:* 800-397-3316 *Fax:* 312-829-8621 *E-mail:* rentals@broadwaycostumes.com *Web Site:* www.broadwaycostumes.com, pg 813

Schrank, Christine, Learning Seed, 208 S Jefferson St, Suite 402, Chicago, IL 60661 *Toll Free Tel:* 800-634-4941 *Toll Free Fax:* 800-998-0854 *E-mail:* info@learningseed.com *Web Site:* www.learningseed.com, pg 917

Schreiber, Trilby, New York Film/Video Council (NYFVC), PO Box 1685, New York, NY 10185-1685 *Tel:* 212-330-0450 *E-mail:* info@nyfvc.org *Web Site:* www.nyfvc.org, pg 1086

Schrieber, David, Music & Entertainment Industry Educators Association (MEIEA), 1900 Belmont Blvd, Nashville, TN 37212-3758 *Tel:* 615-460-6946 *E-mail:* office@meiea.org *Web Site:* www.meiea.org, pg 1084

Schrieber, John, Bexel Corp, 2701 N Ontario St, Burbank, CA 91504 *Tel:* 818-565-4322 *Toll Free Tel:* 800-225-6185 (tech support) *E-mail:* rentals@bexel.com *Web Site:* www.bexel.com, pg 806

Schrier, Howard, Nova Electric, 100 School St, Bergenfield, NJ 07621-2915 *Tel:* 201-385-0500 *Fax:* 201-385-0702 *E-mail:* novasales@theallpower.com *Web Site:* www.novaelectric.com, pg 959

Schrimpf, John, Panavision Dallas, 8000 Jetstar Dr, Irving, TX 75063 *Tel:* 972-929-8585 *Toll Free Tel:* 800-260-1846 *Fax:* 972-929-8686 *Web Site:* www.panavision.com, pg 968

Schroeder, Brad, Canamedia Inc, 1540 Cornwall Rd, Suite 216, Oakville, ON L6J 7W5, Canada *Tel:* 416-363-6765 *Toll Free Tel:* 866-999-5292 *Fax:* 416-363-7834 *Web Site:* www.canamedia.com, pg 818

Schroeder, Chris, Padgitt's, 7801 N Lamar Blvd, Suite D84, Austin, TX 78752 *Tel:* 512-832-9900 *Toll Free Tel:* 800-388-3130 *Fax:* 512-832-0003 *E-mail:* padgitts@padgitts.com *Web Site:* www.padgitts.com, pg 967

Schroeder, Joseph, Sunrise Media LLC, 200 Central Park S, Suite 12F, New York, NY 10019 *Tel:* 212-221-6310 *Fax:* 212-302-1854 *E-mail:* info@ipfmedia.org *Web Site:* www.ipfmedia.org/vetc.htm, pg 1028

Schroeder, Karen, Padgitt's, 7801 N Lamar Blvd, Suite D84, Austin, TX 78752 *Tel:* 512-832-9900 *Toll Free Tel:* 800-388-3130 *Fax:* 512-832-0003 *E-mail:* padgitts@padgitts.com *Web Site:* www.padgitts.com, pg 967

Schroeder, Paul, American Foundation for the Blind (AFB), 2 Penn Plaza, Suite 1102, New York, NY 10121 *Tel:* 212-502-7600; 212-502-7662 (TDD) *Toll Free Tel:* 800-232-5463 *Fax:* 212-502-7777 *Toll Free Fax:* 888-545-8331 *E-mail:* afbinfo@afb.net *Web Site:* www.afb.org, pg 1076

Schroeder, Steve, Calgary International Film Festival, 214 11 Ave SE, Unit 207, Calgary, AB T2G 0X8, Canada *Tel:* 403-283-1490 *E-mail:* info@calgaryfilm.com *Web Site:* www.calgaryfilm.com, pg 1110

Schuch, Joe, Baker Audio Inc, 2195 N Norcross Tucker Rd, Norcross, GA 30071 *Tel:* 770-441-2000 *Toll Free Tel:* 800-847-3523 *Fax:* 770-449-7719 *E-mail:* sales@bakeraudiovisual.com *Web Site:* www.bakeraudiovisual.com, pg 802

Schuhmann, G Raymond, Kinetic Corp, 200 Distillery Commons, Suite 200, Louisville, KY 40206-1990 *Tel:* 502-719-9500 *Fax:* 502-719-9509 *E-mail:* info@thetechnologyagency.com *Web Site:* kinetic.thetechnologyagency.com, pg 911

Schulenburg, Bill, Production Consultants, 1408 Thomas Mason Place, St Louis, MO 63011-4423 *Tel:* 636-391-8611 *Fax:* 636-391-4044 *E-mail:* info@productionconsultants.com *Web Site:* www.productionconsultants.com, pg 984

Schulenburg, David, Production Consultants, 1408 Thomas Mason Place, St Louis, MO 63011-4423 *Tel:* 636-391-8611 *Fax:* 636-391-4044 *E-mail:* info@productionconsultants.com *Web Site:* www.productionconsultants.com, pg 984

Schulman, Larry, Communications Specialties Inc, 125 Comac St, Ronkonkoma, NY 11779 *Tel:* 631-273-0404 *Fax:* 631-273-1638 *E-mail:* info@commspecial.com *Web Site:* www.commspecial.com, pg 833

Schulman, Patricia, Pace Systems, 824 Dakin St, New Orleans, LA 70121 *Tel:* 504-837-4224 *Toll Free Tel:* 800-722-3797 *Fax:* 504-837-4307 *E-mail:* info@pacesys.com *Web Site:* www.pacesys.com, pg 966

Schulman, Peter, Pace Systems, 824 Dakin St, New Orleans, LA 70121 *Tel:* 504-837-4224 *Toll Free Tel:* 800-722-3797 *Fax:* 504-837-4307 *E-mail:* info@pacesys.com *Web Site:* www.pacesys.com, pg 966

Schultz, Eric D, City Events Group, 57 Park Dr, Troy, MI 48083-2724 *Tel:* 248-589-0600 *Toll Free Tel:* 800-872-8295 *Fax:* 248-589-2020 *E-mail:* info@cityeventsgroups.com *Web Site:* www.cityeventsgroup.com, pg 828

Schultz, Greg, Astronomical Society of the Pacific, 390 Ashton Ave, San Francisco, CA 94112 *Tel:* 415-337-1100 *Toll Free Tel:* 800-335-2624 *Fax:* 415-337-5205 *E-mail:* service@astrosociety.org *Web Site:* astrosociety.org, pg 792

Schultz, Kim, Trinidad Film Commission, 136 W Main St, Trinidad, CO 81082 *Tel:* 719-846-7324 *Toll Free Tel:* 866-480-4750 *Fax:* 719-846-3545 *Web Site:* www.trinidadchamber.com, pg 1095

Schulze, Mark, Crystal Pyramid Productions™, 7323 Rondel Ct, San Diego, CA 92119-1530 *Tel:* 619-644-3000 *E-mail:* cpp@newuniquevideos.com *Web Site:* www.crystalpyramid.com, pg 840

Schulze, Mark, New & Unique Videos™, 7323 Rondel Ct, San Diego, CA 92119-1530 *Tel:* 619-644-3000 *E-mail:* video@newuniquevideos.com *Web Site:* www.newuniquevideos.com, pg 955

Schulze, Tom, VMI (Video Masters Inc), PO Box 681100, Kansas City, MO 64168-1100 *E-mail:* sales@vmi.com *Web Site:* www.vmi.com, pg 1060

Schuman, Paula, Quatrefoil Associates Inc, 29 "C" St, Laurel, MD 20707 *Tel:* 301-470-4748 *Fax:* 301-470-4749 *E-mail:* info@quatrefoil.com *Web Site:* www.quatrefoil.com, pg 989

Schumann, Karen, Gateways, PO Box 1706, Ojai, CA 93024-1706 *Tel:* 805-649-5367 *Toll Free Tel:* 800-477-8908 *Fax:* 805-649-5302 *E-mail:* gwgateways@sbcglobal.net, pg 876

Schutt, Paul, Helix Camera & Video, 310 S Racine Ave, Chicago, IL 60607 *Tel:* 312-421-6000 *Toll Free Tel:* 800-33-HELIX (334-3549 orders) *Fax:* 312-421-1586 *E-mail:* info@helixcamera.com *Web Site:* www.helixcamera.com, pg 887

Schuyler, Linda, Epitome Pictures Inc, 220 Bartley Dr, Toronto, ON M4A 1G1, Canada *Tel:* 416-752-7627 *Fax:* 416-752-7837 *E-mail:* info@epitomepictures.com *Web Site:* www.epitomepictures.com, pg 862

Schwab, Michael C, Kensington Falls Animation, 1680 Hillsdale Ave, Ambridge, PA 15003 *Tel:* 724-266-0329 *Fax:* 724-266-4016 *E-mail:* kensingtonfalls@aol.com *Web Site:* kensingtonfalls.com, pg 909

Schwab, Toby, Kensington Falls Animation, 1680 Hillsdale Ave, Ambridge, PA 15003 *Tel:* 724-266-0329 *Fax:* 724-266-4016 *E-mail:* kensingtonfalls@aol.com *Web Site:* kensingtonfalls.com, pg 909

Schwartz, Alan, Caprock Developments Inc, 475 Speedwell, Morris Plains, NJ 07950 *Tel:* 973-267-9292 *Toll Free Tel:* 800-222-0325 *Fax:* 973-292-0614 *E-mail:* info@caprockdev.com *Web Site:* www.caprockdev.com, pg 819

Schwartz, David, Duplication Specialists Inc, 843 Merrick Rd, Baldwin, NY 11510 *Tel:* 516-867-7300; 212-754-2044 *Toll Free Tel:* 800-227-1382 *Fax:* 516-867-7597 *E-mail:* sales@dupespec.com *Web Site:* www.dupespec.com, pg 853

Schwartz, Howard J, VGI Productions, 3655 Tolland Rd, Shaker Heights, OH 44122 *Tel:* 216-464-3635 *Fax:* 216-464-5630 *Web Site:* www.vgipro.com, pg 1053

Schwartz, Jan, Burlington A/V Recording Media, 106 Mott St, Oceanside, NY 11572 *Tel:* 516-678-4414 *Toll Free Tel:* 800-331-3191 *Fax:* 516-678-8959 *E-mail:* burlington@optonline.net *Web Site:* www.recordingstore.com, pg 815

Schwartz, Jeff, PrimaLux Video Inc, 555 Eighth Ave, Suite 1002, New York, NY 10018 *Tel:* 212-206-1402 *Fax:* 212-206-1826 *E-mail:* primalux@aol.com *Web Site:* www.primalux.com, pg 982

Schwartz, Jordan M, Center City Film & Video Inc, 1501-1503 Walnut St, Philadelphia, PA 19102 *Tel:* 215-568-4134 *Fax:* 215-568-6011 *E-mail:* info@ccfv.com; sales@ccfv.com *Web Site:* www.ccfv.com, pg 822

Schwartz, Lauren, Kaboom Productions, 1465 Illinois St, San Francisco, CA 94107 *Tel:* 415-434-2666 *Fax:* 415-970-8548 *E-mail:* updates@kaboomproductions.com *Web Site:* kaboomproductions.com, pg 907

Schwartz, Lauren, Outside The Box Interactive LLC, 150 Bay St, Suite 706, Jersey City, NJ 07302 *Tel:* 201-610-0625 *Fax:* 201-610-0627 *E-mail:* theoffice@outboxin.com *Web Site:* www.outboxin.com, pg 966

Schwartz, Louis O, American Sportscasters Association Inc (ASA), 225 Broadway, Suite 2030, New York, NY 10007 *Tel:* 212-227-8080 *Fax:* 212-571-0556 *Web Site:* www.americansportscasters.com; www.americansportscastersonline.com, pg 1077

Schwartz, Michael, Swivelier, 600 Bradley Hill Rd, Blauvelt, NY 10913 *Tel:* 845-353-1455 *Fax:* 845-353-1512 *E-mail:* info@swivelier.com *Web Site:* www.swivelier.com, pg 1030

Schwartz, Phil, Canadian American Records, PO Box 808, Lititz, PA 17543-0538 *Tel:* 717-627-4800 *Fax:* 717-627-4800 *E-mail:* canadianamerican@dejazzd.com *Web Site:* www.canadianamericanrecords.net; www.joeywelz.com, pg 818

Schwartz, Stan, Rosco Laboratories Inc, 52 Harbor View, Stamford, CT 06902 *Tel:* 203-708-8900 *Toll Free Tel:* 800-ROSCO NY (767-2669) *Fax:* 203-708-8919 *E-mail:* info@rosco.com *Web Site:* www.rosco.com, pg 999

Schwartzberg, Louis, Moving Art by Louie Schwartzberg, 3371 Cahuenga Blvd W, Los Angeles, CA 90068 *Tel:* 323-436-7070 *Fax:* 323-436-2230 *E-mail:* team@movingart.com *Web Site:* www.movingart.com, pg 947

Schwarz, Alan J, Jams Productions Inc, Production Trailer No 1, 2206 Holt Rd, Bowmanville, ON L1C 3K7, Canada *Tel:* 647-273-4844 *Fax:* 905-623-2895 *E-mail:* info@jamsproductions.ca *Web Site:* www.jamsproductions.ca, pg 904

Schwarz, Joshua, Post Josh Productions, 375 Greenwich St, New York, NY 10013 *Tel:* 212-699-2642 *E-mail:* info@postjosh.com *Web Site:* www.postjosh.com, pg 979

Schwarz, Susan, Jams Productions Inc, Production Trailer No 1, 2206 Holt Rd, Bowmanville, ON L1C 3K7, Canada *Tel:* 647-273-4844 *Fax:* 905-623-2895 *E-mail:* info@jamsproductions.ca *Web Site:* www.jamsproductions.ca, pg 904

Schweickart, Mark, Porta-Jib, 1033 N Sycamore Ave, Los Angeles, CA 90038 *Tel:* 323-462-2855 *Fax:* 323-462-2682 *E-mail:* info@porta-jib.com *Web Site:* www.porta-jib.com, pg 978

Schweinhart, Larry, HighScope Press, 600 N River St, Ypsilanti, MI 48198-2898 *Tel:* 734-485-2000 *Toll Free Tel:* 800-407-7377 *Fax:* 734-485-0704 *Toll Free Fax:* 800-442-4329 *E-mail:* info@highscope.org; press@highscope.org *Web Site:* www.highscope.org, pg 889

Schwenner, Marty J, Magnetek Inc, N49 W13650 Campbell Dr, Menomonee Falls, WI 53051 *Tel:* 262-783-3500 *Toll Free Tel:* 800-288-8178 *Toll Free Fax:* 800-298-3503 *E-mail:* sales@magnetek.com *Web Site:* www.magnetek.com, pg 928

Schwieger, Tim, Broadcast Supply World Wide, 2237 S 19 St, Tacoma, WA 98405 *Tel:* 253-565-2301 (intl) *Toll Free Tel:* 800-426-8434 *Fax:* 253-565-8114 (intl) *Toll Free Fax:* 800-231-7055 *E-mail:* sales@bswusa.com; info@bswusa.com; customersupport@bswusa.com *Web Site:* www.bswusa.com, pg 813

Schwind, David R, Charles M Salter Associates Inc, 130 Sutter St, Suite 500, San Francisco, CA 94104 *Tel:* 415-397-0442 *Fax:* 415-397-0454 *E-mail:* info@cmsalter.com *Web Site:* www.cmsalter.com, pg 1001

Sciannella, Chris, CAS Video Productions, 820 White Marsh Ct, Huntingtown, MD 20639 *Tel:* 301-760-7301; 301-674-2000 (cell) *Web Site:* www.casvideo.com, pg 820

Scicchitano, Stephen, Gaylord Brothers, PO Box 4901, Syracuse, NY 13221-4901 *Tel:* 315-634-8243 (intl) *Toll Free Tel:* 800-962-9580 (cust serv) *Fax:* 315-453-5030 (intl) *Toll Free Fax:* 800-272-3412 *E-mail:* customerservice@gaylord.com *Web Site:* www.gaylord.com, pg 876

Scofield, Kara, Thayer Birding Software, 12650 Colliers Reserve Dr, Naples, FL 34110 *Tel:* 239-596-1637 *Toll Free Tel:* 800-865-2473 *Fax:* 239-596-0232 *Web Site:* www.thayerbirding.com, pg 1038

Scott, Ed, KAE Corp, 955 E 500 S, Salt Lake City, UT 84102 *Tel:* 801-238-2300 *Fax:* 801-238-3900 *E-mail:* kaecorp@xmission.com *Web Site:* www.kaecorp.com, pg 907

Scott, Larry, Broadcast Center Studios, 700 Millbridge Gardens, Clementon, NJ 08021 *Tel:* 856-751-3500 *Web Site:* www.broadcastcenterstudios.com, pg 813

Scott, Lesa, Heinemann, 361 Hanover St, Portsmouth, NH 03801-3912 *Tel:* 603-431-7894 *Toll Free Tel:* 800-225-5800 *Fax:* 603-431-2214 *Toll Free Fax:* 877-231-6980 *E-mail:* custserv@heinemann.com *Web Site:* www.heinemann.com, pg 887

Scott, Michael, R B Annis Instruments Inc, 117 W Franklin St, Greencastle, IN 46135-1223 *Tel:* 765-848-1621 *Fax:* 765-848-1625 *E-mail:* info@rbannis.com *Web Site:* www.rbannis.com, pg 787

Scott, Ron, Ron Scott Inc, 2020 Colquitt St, Houston, TX 77098 *Web Site:* www.ronscott.com; www.qfx.com, pg 1005

Scott, Rusty, Encore Cases, 8818 Lankershim Blvd, Sun Valley, CA 91352 *Tel:* 818-768-8803 *Toll Free Tel:* 800-743-6267 *Fax:* 818-768-3993 *Web Site:* www.encorecases.com; www.giantcases.com, pg 861

Scott, Stephen, Skotel Corp, 118-6185 boul Teschereau, Suite 144, Brossard, QC J4Z 0E4, Canada *Tel:* 514-806-2340 *E-mail:* skotel@videotron.ca, pg 1013

Scott, Tom, LITE-IT Grip Truck Rentals, 450 Saint Andrews Ct, West Chicago, IL 60185 *Tel:* 630-231-1671 *Fax:* 630-231-1672 *E-mail:* liteit1@sbcglobal.net *Web Site:* www.liteit1.com, pg 923

Scovill, Scott, CenterStaging LLC, 3407 Winona Ave, Burbank, CA 91504 *Tel:* 818-559-4333 *Fax:* 818-848-4016 *E-mail:* info@centerstaging.com *Web Site:* centerstaging.com, pg 823

Scruggs, Roger, Roger Scruggs Films, PO Box 321054, Cocoa Beach, FL 32932-1054 *Tel:* 321-783-6545 (off); 321-795-6545 (cell) *Web Site:* www.tvphotog.com, pg 1005

Scudder, Dean H, Sinauer Associates Inc, 23 Plumtree Rd, Sunderland, MA 01375 *Tel:* 413-549-4300 *Fax:* 413-549-1118 *E-mail:* orders@sinauer.com (orders); custserv@sinauer.com (cust serv); publish@sinauer.com (general edit correspondence) *Web Site:* www.sinauer.com, pg 1012

Sculley, Andrew G, eMagin Corp, 3006 Northup Way, Suite 103, Bellevue, WA 98004 *Tel:* 425-284-5200 *Toll Free Tel:* 877-362-4461 *Fax:* 425-284-5201 *E-mail:* info@emagin.com *Web Site:* www.emagin.com, pg 860

Seabaugh, Darius, The RapcoHorizon Co, 3581 Larch Lane, Jackson, MO 63755 *Tel:* 573-243-1433 *Toll Free Tel:* 800-325-0266 *Fax:* 573-243-4913 *E-mail:* info@rapcohorizon.com *Web Site:* www.rapcohorizon.com, pg 991

Seaman, John, Future Light Inc, 23420 Lorain Rd, Suite 200, North Olmsted, OH 44070 *Tel:* 440-801-1310 *Toll Free Tel:* 800-581-5536 *Fax:* 440-779-4159 *E-mail:* info@future-light.com *Web Site:* www.future-light.com, pg 874

Seaman, Tom, MVD Entertainment Group, 203 Windsor Rd, Pottstown, PA 19464 *Tel:* 610-650-8200 *Toll Free Tel:* 800-888-0486 *Fax:* 610-650-9102 *Toll Free Fax:* 888-536-7998 *Web Site:* mvdb2b.com, pg 951

Searcy, Tom, ClearOne MagicBox Inc, 408 SW Monroe, Suite M236, Corvallis, OR 97333 *Tel:* 541-752-5654 (sales); 541-752-5542 (tech support) *Fax:* 541-752-5614 *E-mail:* info@magicboxinc.com; sales@magicboxinc.com; support@magicboxinc.com *Web Site:* www.magicboxinc.com, pg 830

Searfoss, Len, American Color Imaging (ACI), 715 E 18 St, Cedar Falls, IA 50613 *Tel:* 319-277-3655 *Toll Free Tel:* 800-728-2722 *Fax:* 319-277-6522 *E-mail:* sales@acilab.com *Web Site:* www.acilab.com, pg 784

Sears, Ric, Intellidyne LLC, 5203 Leesburg Pike, Suite 400, 2 Skyline Place, Falls Church, VA 22041 *Tel:* 703-575-9715 *Fax:* 703-575-9718 *Web Site:* www.intellidyne-llc.com, pg 899

Sedita, Francesco, Price Stern Sloan, 375 Hudson St, 14th fl, New York, NY 10014 *Tel:* 212-414-3607; 212-366-2000; 212-366-2372 *Fax:* 212-414-3396; 212-366-2933 *Web Site:* us.penguingroup.com, pg 982

See, Robert, See Factor Industry Inc, 37-11 30 St, Long Island City, NY 11101 *Tel:* 718-784-4200 *Fax:* 718-784-0617 *Web Site:* www.seefactor.com, pg 1006

Seetzen, Helge, Society for Information Display (SID), 1475 S Bascom Ave, Suite 114, Campbell, CA 95008-4006 *Tel:* 408-879-3901 *Fax:* 408-879-3833 *E-mail:* office@sid.org *Web Site:* www.sid.org, pg 1089

Segal, Sylvia Ozner, SOS Worldwide Productions Inc, 2000 Towerside Terr, Suite 607, Miami, FL 33138 *Tel:* 305-891-9133; 305-653-5321 (cell) *Fax:* 305-603-8111 *E-mail:* info@safesongs.com; info@

safesongs4kids.com *Web Site:* www.safesongs.com; www.safesongs4kids.com; www.safesongsforkids.com, pg 1016

Segarra, Aaron, CP Communications, 200 Clearbrook Rd, Suite 148, Elmsford, NY 10523 *Tel:* 914-345-9292 *Toll Free Tel:* 800-762-4254 *Fax:* 914-345-9222 *E-mail:* info@cpcomms.com; sales@cpcomms.com *Web Site:* www.cpcomms.com, pg 837

Segrist, Dennis, ITA Audio Visual Solutions, 2162 Dana Ave & I-71, Cincinnati, OH 45207 *Tel:* 513-631-7000 *Toll Free Tel:* 800-899-8877 *Fax:* 513-631-3290; 513-631-8877 *E-mail:* csr@ita.com *Web Site:* www.ita.com, pg 902

Seguin, John L, Monotype Inc, 500 Unicorn Park Dr, Woburn, MA 01801 *Tel:* 781-970-6000 *Toll Free Tel:* 800-424-8973 *Fax:* 781-970-6001; 781-970-6002 (gen questions) *Web Site:* www.monotype.com, pg 945

Seiberling, Kelly, Creative Technology, 137 Heritage Woods Dr, Akron, OH 44321 *Tel:* 330-668-7777 *Fax:* 330-665-3718 *Web Site:* www.creativetechnology.com, pg 838

Seidel, Jeff, OmegaBrandess Distribution, 626 Hanover Pike, Suite 102, Hampstead, MD 21074-2036 *Tel:* 410-374-3250 *Fax:* 410-374-3184 *E-mail:* customerservice@omegabrandess.com *Web Site:* www.omegabrandess.com, pg 962

Seiden, Paul, Communications Specialties Inc, 125 Comac St, Ronkonkoma, NY 11779 *Tel:* 631-273-0404 *Fax:* 631-273-1638 *E-mail:* info@commspecial.com *Web Site:* www.commspecial.com, pg 833

Seifert, Sam, Bismeaux Studio, PO Box 463, Austin, TX 78767-0463 *Tel:* 512-444-9885 *Fax:* 512-444-4699 *Web Site:* www.bismeauxstudio.com, pg 808

Selden, Charles J, Selden Associates, 150 S Mountain Ave, Montclair, NJ 07042 *Tel:* 973-746-0421 *Fax:* 973-509-1498, pg 1006

Seldon, Tammy, Giant Screen Cinema Association (GSCA), 624 Holly Springs Rd, Suite 243, Holly Springs, NC 27540 *Tel:* 919-346-1123 *Fax:* 919-573-9100 *E-mail:* info@giantscreencinema.com *Web Site:* www.giantscreencinema.com, pg 1082

Selesnich, Lou, All Communications Rentals Inc (ALLCOMM), 1402 SW 13 Ct, Pompano Beach, FL 33069 *Tel:* 954-788-9555 *Web Site:* www.allcommrentals.com, pg 780

Seligman, Stephen, MediaOne Services, 901 Battery St, Suite 220, San Francisco, CA 94111 *Tel:* 415-262-4222 *E-mail:* sales@mediaoneservices.com *Web Site:* mediaoneservices.com, pg 938

Selim, Hani, Concrete Images, 1301 Main St, Venice, CA 90291 *Tel:* 310-452-9655 *Fax:* 310-452-9866 *E-mail:* office@concreteimages.com *Web Site:* www.concreteimages.com, pg 835

Seline, Gary M, Horizon Worldwide, 1765 Stebbins Dr, Houston, TX 77043 *Tel:* 713-647-7400 *Fax:* 713-647-6664 *E-mail:* info@horizonworldwide.com *Web Site:* horizonworldwide.com, pg 891

Selinger, Kenneth R, CCI Communications Inc, 1440 Phoenixville Pike, West Chester, PA 19380 *Tel:* 610-296-7233 *Fax:* 610-296-7358 *E-mail:* info@ccivideo.com *Web Site:* www.ccivideo.com, pg 821

Sell, Dan, Welk Music Group, 11400 W Olympic Blvd, Suite 1450, Los Angeles, CA 90064 *Tel:* 310-829-9355 *Fax:* 310-315-9996 *E-mail:* info@vanguardrecords.com; order@vanguardrecords.com *Web Site:* www.vanguardrecords.com, pg 1063

Sellers, Andrew, Sensory Technologies LLC, 6951 Corporate Circle, Indianapolis, IN 46278 *Tel:* 317-347-5252 *Toll Free Tel:* 800-488-4336 (help desk) *Fax:* 317-347-5262 *E-mail:* sales@sensorytechnologies.com *Web Site:* sensorytechnologies.com, pg 1007

Sellers, Anne, Sensory Technologies LLC, 6951 Corporate Circle, Indianapolis, IN 46278 *Tel:* 317-347-5252 *Toll Free Tel:* 800-488-4336 (help desk) *Fax:* 317-347-5262 *E-mail:* sales@sensorytechnologies.com *Web Site:* sensorytechnologies.com, pg 1007

Sellers, Karen, Curtis Inc, 1105 Western Ave, Cincinnati, OH 45203 *Tel:* 513-621-8895 *Toll Free Tel:* 800-733-2878 *Fax:* 513-621-0942 *E-mail:* info@curtisinc.com; clientservices@curtisinc.com *Web Site:* www.curtisinc.com, pg 841

Sellers, Peter, Freewheelin' Films, 44895 Hwy 82, Aspen, CO 81611 *Tel:* 970-925-2640 *Fax:* 970-925-9369 *Web Site:* www.fwf.com, pg 873

Seltz, Judy, ASCD, 1703 N Beauregard St, Alexandria, VA 22311-1714 *Tel:* 703-578-9600 *Toll Free Tel:* 800-933-2723 *Fax:* 703-575-5400 *E-mail:* exhibits@ascd.org *Web Site:* www.ascd.org, pg 1078

Seman, Mark, API, 8301 Patuxent Range Rd, Jessup, MD 20794 *Tel:* 301-776-7879 *Fax:* 301-776-8117 *E-mail:* service@apiaudio.com *Web Site:* www.apiaudio.com, pg 788

Sembritzky, Stephen D, Smart Concepts Ltd, 4525 S Jamestown, Tulsa, OK 74135 *Tel:* 918-636-2376 *Web Site:* www.smartconceptsinc.com, pg 1013

Semegram, Harriet Rita, Wonderwomen™ Enterprises, 485 Rugby Rd, Brooklyn, NY 11226 *Tel:* 646-456-3266; 718-693-4322 *E-mail:* info@wonderwomen.com, pg 1069

Semel, John, John Wiley & Sons Inc, 111 River St, Hoboken, NJ 07030 *Tel:* 201-748-6000 *Toll Free Tel:* 800-225-5945 *Fax:* 201-748-6088 *E-mail:* info@wiley.com *Web Site:* www.wiley.com, pg 1066

Semmer, Bob, FotoKem Film & Video, 2801 W Alameda Ave, Burbank, CA 91505 *Tel:* 818-846-3101 *Fax:* 818-841-2130 *E-mail:* sales@fotokem.com *Web Site:* www.fotokem.com, pg 871

Semone, Gigi, New York State Governor's Office for Motion Picture & Television Development, 633 Third Ave, 33rd fl, New York, NY 10017 *Tel:* 212-803-2330 *Fax:* 212-803-2339 *E-mail:* nyfilm@esd.ny.gov *Web Site:* www.nylovesfilm.com, pg 1100

Sengupta, Sohini, Mark Woollen & Associates, 207 Ashland Ave, Santa Monica, CA 90405 *Tel:* 310-399-2690 *E-mail:* info@markwoollen.com *Web Site:* www.markwoollen.com, pg 1069

Senseman, Ken, Lee Co Inc, 27 S 12 St, Terre Haute, IN 47807 *Tel:* 812-235-8155 *Fax:* 812-235-3587 *E-mail:* leeco@leecompanyinc.com *Web Site:* www.leecompanyinc.com, pg 918

Serafin, Robert, Graphic Products Corp, 455 Maple Ave, Carpentersville, IL 60110 *Tel:* 847-836-9600 *Toll Free Tel:* 800-323-1660 (cust serv) *Fax:* 847-836-9666 *E-mail:* info@gpcpapers.com *Web Site:* www.gpcpapers.com, pg 881

Serb, Andrew C, Pro Media/Ultra Sound, 800 Alfred Nobel Dr, Hercules, CA 94547 *Tel:* 510-741-2925 *Toll Free Tel:* 800-969-7686 (sales) *Fax:* 510-741-0790 *E-mail:* service@ultrapromedia.com *Web Site:* www.promediausa.com, pg 983

Seron, Suren M, Stray Angel Films, 2236 S Barrington Ave, Los Angeles, CA 90064 *Tel:* 310-277-6900 *Fax:* 801-438-5009 *E-mail:* rentals@strayangel.com *Web Site:* www.strayangel.com, pg 1026

Serpico, Laura, Jupiter Moon Productions, 53 Grand Haven Dr, Commack, NY 11725 *Tel:* 631-553-9750 *Web Site:* www.jupitermoonproductions.com, pg 907

Serr, Marilyn A, Spence-Thomas Audio Post, 70 Richmond St E, Suite 300, Toronto, ON M5C 1N8, Canada *Tel:* 416-361-6383 *Toll Free Tel:* 866-547-2617 *Fax:* 416-361-2970 *E-mail:* info@spence-thomas.com; bookings@spence-thomas.com *Web Site:* www.spence-thomas.com, pg 1021

Serra, Janet, Western Connecticut Convention & Visitors Bureau, PO Box 968, Litchfield, CT 06759-0968 *Tel:* 860-567-4506 *Toll Free Tel:* 800-663-1273 *Fax:* 860-567-5214 *E-mail:* info@litchfieldhills.com *Web Site:* www.visitwesternct.com; www.litchfieldhills.com; www.visitfairfieldcountyct.com, pg 1095

Serra, M M, Film-Makers Cooperative, 475 Park Ave S, 6th fl, New York, NY 10016 *Tel:* 212-267-5665 *Fax:* 212-267-5666 *E-mail:* film6000@aol.com; filmmakerscoop@gmail.com *Web Site:* film-makerscoop.com, pg 867

Sessler, Dan, RF Specialties of Texas LLC, PO Box 1010, Newark, TX 76071-1010 *Tel:* 214-697-3477 (cell); 817-489-2730 *Toll Free Tel:* 800-537-1801 (Newark) *E-mail:* rfstx@swbell.net *Web Site:* www.rfspecialties.com, pg 996

Setterstrom, Andrea, Mole-Richardson Co, 937 N Sycamore Ave, Hollywood, CA 90038-2384 *Tel:* 323-851-0111 *Fax:* 323-851-5593 *E-mail:* info@mole.com *Web Site:* www.mole.com, pg 945

Settle, Raymond, Maximus Media Inc, 2727 N Grove Industrial Dr, Suite 111, Fresno, CA 93727 *Tel:* 559-255-1688 *Toll Free Tel:* 800-2THEMAX (284-3629) *Fax:* 559-255-0323 *Web Site:* www.tothemax.com, pg 934

Seubert, Emelia, Smithsonian National Museum of the American Indian, c/o Film & Video Ctr, Natl Museum of the American Indian, One Bowling Green, New York, NY 10004-1415 *Tel:* 212-514-3700 *Fax:* 212-514-3725 *E-mail:* fvc@si.edu *Web Site:* www.nmai.si.edu, pg 1014

Sevush, Ralph, The Dramatists Guild of America, 1501 Broadway, Suite 701, New York, NY 10036 *Tel:* 212-398-9366 *Fax:* 212-944-0420 *E-mail:* info@dramatistsguild.com *Web Site:* www.dramatistsguild.com, pg 1081

Sexton, Mary, Rink Rat Productions Inc, 2 Monk Lane, St John's, NL A1E 1M8, Canada *Tel:* 709-739-9055 *Fax:* 709-739-9065 *E-mail:* info@rinkratproductions.com *Web Site:* www.rinkratproductions.com, pg 997

Sexton, Shelby, Wild Plum, 2128 Narcissus Ct, Venice, CA 90291 *Tel:* 310-823-7445 *Fax:* 310-578-1445 *Web Site:* www.wildplum.tv, pg 1066

Seybert, Barry, SNAP, 18653 Ventura, Suite 295, Tarzana, CA 91356 *Tel:* 818-340-0283 *E-mail:* hdcine@gmail.com *Web Site:* www.facebook.com/barry.seybert, pg 1014

Shadbolt, Melvin, ATV Research Inc, 1301 Broadway, Dakota City, NE 68731 *Tel:* 402-987-3771 *Toll Free Tel:* 800-392-3922 *Fax:* 402-987-3709 *E-mail:* sales@atvresearch.com *Web Site:* www.atvresearch.com, pg 793

Shadbolt, Scott, ATV Research Inc, 1301 Broadway, Dakota City, NE 68731 *Tel:* 402-987-3771 *Toll Free Tel:* 800-392-3922 *Fax:* 402-987-3709 *E-mail:* sales@atvresearch.com *Web Site:* www.atvresearch.com, pg 793

Shadoan, Dave, Southern California Sound Image Inc, 2415 Auto Park Way, Escondido, CA 92029-1222 *Tel:* 760-737-3900 *Fax:* 760-737-3929 *Web Site:* www.sound-image.com, pg 1019

Shafer, Viktor, Cibola Systems, 180 S Cypress St, Orange, CA 92866 *Tel:* 714-480-0272 *Fax:* 714-480-0768 *E-mail:* info@cibolasystems.com *Web Site:* cibolasystems.com, pg 826

Shaffer, Gary, Kaboom Productions, 1465 Illinois St, San Francisco, CA 94107 *Tel:* 415-434-2666 *Fax:* 415-970-8548 *E-mail:* updates@kaboomproductions.com *Web Site:* kaboomproductions.com, pg 907

Shaffer, Susan M, Northeast Conference on the Teaching of Foreign Languages (NECTFL), c/o Dickinson College, PO Box 1773, Carlisle, PA 17013-2896 *Tel:* 717-245-1977 *Fax:* 717-245-1976 *E-mail:* nectfl@dickinson.edu *Web Site:* www.nectfl.org, pg 1087

Shah, Jatan, QSC Audio Products LLC, 1675 MacArthur Blvd, Costa Mesa, CA 92626 *Tel:* 714-754-6175 *Toll Free Tel:* 800-854-4079 *Fax:* 714-754-6174 *E-mail:* info@qscaudio.com *Web Site:* www.qsc.com, pg 988

Shah, Jay, Hi-Tech Import Export Corp, 1101 W McNab Rd, Pompano Beach, FL 33069 *Tel:* 954-946-0603 *Fax:* 954-946-0652, pg 888

Shakes, Dave, KOOL FM Radio, 840 N Central Ave, Phoenix, AZ 85004 *Tel:* 602-452-1000; 602-260-9494 (request line) *Fax:* 602-440-6530 *Web Site:* www.koolradio.com, pg 913

Shakra, Ramzi, Electrosonic Inc, 3320 N San Fernando Blvd, Burbank, CA 91504 *Tel:* 818-333-3600 *Toll Free Tel:* 888-343-3604 (sales) *Fax:* 818-230-1017 *E-mail:* info@electrosonic.com *Web Site:* www.electrosonic.com, pg 859

Shalom, Morris, GLI Sound Systems, 2691 W 15 St, Brooklyn, NY 11224 *Tel:* 718-372-7849 *Toll Free Tel:* 800-GLI-PRO-1 (454-7761) *Fax:* 718-946-4151 *E-mail:* info@glipro.com; sales@glipro.com *Web Site:* www.glipro.com, pg 878

Shalom, Morris, Harbro Corp, 2691 W 15 St, Brooklyn, NY 11224-2705 *Tel:* 718-946-4134 *Fax:* 718-946-4151, pg 884

Shanahan, John, Penfield Productions Ltd, 35 Springfield St, Agawam, MA 01001 *Tel:* 413-786-4454 *Fax:* 413-789-4240 *E-mail:* info@penfieldprod.com *Web Site:* www.penfieldprod.com, pg 971

Shanahan, Julie, Lenel Systems International Inc, 1212 Pittsford-Victor Rd, Pittsford, NY 14534-3820 *Tel:* 585-248-9720 *Toll Free Tel:* 866-788-5095 *Fax:* 585-248-9185 *E-mail:* pr@lenel.com *Web Site:* www.lenel.com, pg 919

Shanahan, Thomas J, Electronics Representatives Association (ERA), 111 N Canal St, Suite 885, Chicago, IL 60606 *Tel:* 312-559-3050 *Fax:* 312-559-4566 *E-mail:* info@era.org *Web Site:* www.era.org, pg 1081

Shanes, Bob, Talk-A-Phone Co, 7530 N Natchez Ave, Niles, IL 60714 *Tel:* 773-539-1100 *Fax:* 773-539-1241 *E-mail:* info@talkaphone.com *Web Site:* www.talkaphone.com, pg 1031

Shanks, Hershel, Biblical Archaeology Society (BAS), 4710 41 St NW, Washington, DC 20016 *Tel:* 202-364-3300 *Toll Free Tel:* 800-221-4644 *Fax:* 202-364-2636 *E-mail:* bas@bib-arch.org; merchandise@bib-arch.org *Web Site:* www.biblicalarchaeology.org, pg 806

Shanks, Leigh, Christie Digital Systems USA Inc, 10550 Camden Dr, Cypress, CA 90630 *Tel:* 714-236-8610 *Toll Free Tel:* 866-880-4462 (cust serv) *Fax:* 714-503-3375 *E-mail:* sales-us@christiedigital.com *Web Site:* www.christiedigital.com, pg 825

Shannon, James M, National Fire Protection Association (NFPA), One Batterymarch Park, Quincy, MA 02169-7471 *Tel:* 617-770-3000 *Toll Free Tel:* 800-344-3555 *Fax:* 617-770-0700 *E-mail:* custserv@nfpa.org *Web Site:* www.nfpa.org, pg 952

Shaper, Richard, Quantum Instruments Inc, 1268 Humbracht Circle, Bartlett, IL 60103-1631 *Tel:* 631-656-7400 *Fax:* 631-656-7410 *E-mail:* quantumhelp@qtm.com *Web Site:* www.qtm.com, pg 989

Shapiro, Brad, Location Camera Ltd, 300 Pennsylvania Ave, Oreland, PA 19075 *Tel:* 215-576-5600 *Fax:* 215-576-6022 *E-mail:* mail@locationcamera.com *Web Site:* www.locationcamera.com, pg 924

Shapiro, Brad, Location Lighting Ltd, 300 Pennsylvania Ave, Oreland, PA 19075 *Tel:* 215-576-5600 *Fax:* 215-576-6022 *E-mail:* mail@locationlighting.com; rentals@locationlighting.com *Web Site:* www.locationlighting.com, pg 924

Shapiro, Gary, Consumer Electronics Association (CEA), 1919 S Eads St, Arlington, VA 22202 *Tel:* 703-907-7600 *Toll Free Tel:* 866-858-1555 *Fax:* 703-907-7675 *Toll Free Fax:* 866-858-2555 *E-mail:* cea@ce.org *Web Site:* www.ce.org, pg 1080

Shapiro, Neal, WNET/NET TELECON, 825 Eighth Ave, New York, NY 10019 *Tel:* 212-560-1313 *Fax:* 212-560-1314 *E-mail:* programming@thirteen.org *Web Site:* www.thirteen.org; www.wnet.org, pg 1069

Shapiro, Stephanie, VTS Video & Media, 3121D Fire Rd, Suite 105, Egg Harbor Township, NJ 08234 *Toll Free Tel:* 877-891-1002 *E-mail:* info@videotapingservice.com *Web Site:* www.videotapingservice.com, pg 1061

Shapiro, Steve, Steve Shapiro Music, 7777 Skyline Blvd, Oakland, CA 94611 *Tel:* 510-339-7930 *Web Site:* www.stevemusic.com, pg 1008

Sharenow, Rob, Lifetime Television®, 235 E 45 St, New York, NY 10017 *Tel:* 212-424-7000 *Web Site:* www.mylifetime.com, pg 920

Sharma, Nick, DecisionOne, 426 W Lancaster Ave, Devon, PA 19333 *Tel:* 610-296-6000 *Toll Free Tel:* 800-767-2876; 800-777-8800 (cust serv); 888-287-9202 (sales); 800-554-5179 (CN) *Fax:* 610-296-2910 *Web Site:* www.decisionone.com, pg 844

Sharoni, Erez, Talk-A-Phone Co, 7530 N Natchez Ave, Niles, IL 60714 *Tel:* 773-539-1100 *Fax:* 773-539-1241 *E-mail:* info@talkaphone.com *Web Site:* www.talkaphone.com, pg 1031

Sharp, David, Technical Innovation, 2975 Northwoods Pkwy, Norcross, GA 30071 *Tel:* 770-447-1001 *Toll Free Tel:* 866-447-1004 *Fax:* 770-441-5285 *Web Site:* www.technical-innovation.com, pg 1034

Sharp, Joe, Thread Marketing Group, 4635 W Alexis Rd, Toledo, OH 43623-1005 *Tel:* 419-887-6801 *Toll Free Tel:* 800-397-0126 *Fax:* 419-887-6802 *E-mail:* contact@experiencethread.com *Web Site:* www.experiencethread.com, pg 1039

Sharpe, Michele, VRSim Inc, 222 Pitkin St, Suite 119, East Hartford, CT 06108-3220 *Tel:* 860-893-0080 *E-mail:* info@vrsim.net *Web Site:* www.vrsim.net, pg 1061

Shatsoff, Steve, SmartSource Computer & AV Rentals, 265 Oser Ave, Hauppauge, NY 11788 *Tel:* 631-273-8888 *Toll Free Tel:* 800-888-8686 *Fax:* 631-273-8889 *E-mail:* info@smartsourcerentals.com; longisland@smartsourcerentals.com *Web Site:* www.smartsourcerentals.com, pg 1014

Shattuck, Byron E, Emery-Pratt Co, 1966 W M-21, Owosso, MI 48867-1379 *Tel:* 989-723-5291 *Toll Free Tel:* 800-248-3887 *Fax:* 989-723-4677 *Toll Free Fax:* 800-523-6379 *E-mail:* mail@emery-pratt.com *Web Site:* www.emery-pratt.com, pg 860

Shaw, Allan, Folk Era Productions Inc, 705 S Washington St, Suite 3, Naperville, IL 60540-6654 *Tel:* 630-637-2303; 630-305-0770 (cust serv) *Toll Free Tel:* 800-232-7328 (orders) *Fax:* 630-305-0782 *E-mail:* info@folkera.com *Web Site:* www.rediscovermusic.com, pg 871

Shaw, Allan, Rediscover Music, 705 S Washington St, Suite 3, Naperville, IL 60540 *Tel:* 630-305-0770 *Toll Free Tel:* 800-232-7328 (orders) *Fax:* 630-305-0782 *E-mail:* rediscovermusic@rediscovermusic.com *Web Site:* www.rediscovermusic.com, pg 993

Shaw, Beth Portnoi, Professional Women Photographers (PWP), 119 W 72 St, Suite 223, New York, NY 10023 *E-mail:* info@pwponline.org *Web Site:* www.pwponline.org, pg 1087

Shaw, Brad W, Brad Shaw Productions Inc, 9950 Roan Meadows Dr, Boise, ID 83709 *Tel:* 208-362-5500 *Web Site:* bradshawproductions.com, pg 1008

Shaw, Douglas J, Monotype Inc, 500 Unicorn Park Dr, Woburn, MA 01801 *Tel:* 781-970-6000 *Toll Free Tel:* 800-424-8973 *Fax:* 781-970-6001; 781-970-6002 (gen questions) *Web Site:* www.monotype.com, pg 945

Shaw, Morris, AMA Nystrom Printing/Finishing, 920 N Valley Mills Dr, Waco, TX 76710 *Tel:* 254-776-8860 *Toll Free Tel:* 800-369-9226 *Fax:* 254-751-2127 *E-mail:* info@amanystrom.com *Web Site:* www.amanystrom.com, pg 783

Shaw, Tate, The Visual Studies Workshop (VSW), 31 Prince St, Rochester, NY 14607 *Tel:* 585-442-8676 *Fax:* 585-442-1992 *E-mail:* info@vsw.org *Web Site:* www.vsw.org, pg 1059

Shawcross, Tony, Open Media Foundation, 700 Kalamath St, Denver, CO 80204 *Tel:* 720-222-0159 *Fax:* 303-534-5098 *E-mail:* info@openmediafoundation.org *Web Site:* openmediafoundation.org; denveropenmedia.org, pg 964

Shedden, Ray, Multicom Inc, 1076 Florida Central Pkwy, Longwood, FL 32750 *Tel:* 407-331-7779 *Toll Free Tel:* 800-423-2594 *Fax:* 407-339-0204 *E-mail:* multicom@multicominc.com *Web Site:* www.multicominc.com, pg 949

Sheehan, Dennis, Immersion Corp, 310 Rio Robles, San Jose, CA 95134 *Tel:* 408-467-1900 *Fax:* 408-467-1901 *E-mail:* info@immersion.com *Web Site:* www.immersion.com, pg 896

Sheehan, Jim, SeaChange International Inc, 50 Nagog Park, Acton, MA 01720 *Tel:* 978-897-0100 *Fax:* 978-897-0132 *Web Site:* www.schange.com, pg 1005

Sheeley, Rob, Vaddio, 131 Cheshire Lane, Suite 500, Minnetonka, MN 55305 *Tel:* 763-971-4400 *Toll Free Tel:* 800-572-2011 *Fax:* 763-971-4464 *E-mail:* info@vaddio.com *Web Site:* www.vaddio.com, pg 1051

Sheeran, Josette, Asia Society, 725 Park Ave, New York, NY 10021 *Tel:* 212-288-6400 *Fax:* 212-517-8315 *E-mail:* pr@asiasociety.org *Web Site:* www.asiasociety.org; www.asiasociety.org/video, pg 792

Sheilley, Kevin, Ocala/Marion County Chamber of Commerce, 310 SE Third St, Ocala, FL 34471 *Tel:* 352-629-8051 *Fax:* 352-629-7651 *Web Site:* www.ocalacc.com, pg 1096

Shelburne, David, Shelburne Films, 54545 SR 681, Reedsville, OH 45772 *Tel:* 740-378-6297 *E-mail:* info@shelburnefilms.com *Web Site:* www.shelburnefilms.com, pg 1008

Shelburne, Ellen, Shelburne Films, 54545 SR 681, Reedsville, OH 45772 *Tel:* 740-378-6297 *E-mail:* info@shelburnefilms.com *Web Site:* www.shelburnefilms.com, pg 1008

Sheldon, Wayne, MidCanada Production Services Inc (MidCan), 509 Century St, Winnipeg, MB R3H 0L8, Canada *Tel:* 204-772-0368 *Toll Free Tel:* 800-772-0368 *Fax:* 204-772-0360 *E-mail:* info@midcan.com *Web Site:* www.midcan.com, pg 942

Shelley, Mark, Sea Studios Foundation, PO Box 267, Carmel Valley, CA 93924 *E-mail:* info@seastudios.org; jete@seastudios.org *Web Site:* www.seastudios.org, pg 1005

Shelley, Suzanne, Spirit Media, 12042 SE Sunnyside Rd, Suite 700, Happy Valley, OR 97015 *Tel:* 503-698-5540 *Fax:* 503-698-8408 *E-mail:* info@spiritmedia.com *Web Site:* www.spiritmedia.com, pg 1021

Shelnutt, Genna, Charleston International Film Festival (CIFF), 915 Folly Rd, No 78, Charleston, SC 29412 *Tel:* 843-817-1617 *E-mail:* info@charlestoniff.org *Web Site:* charlestoniff.org, pg 1111

Shelton, Brad, Avatar Studios, 2675 Scott Ave, Suite G, St Louis, MO 63103 *Tel:* 314-533-2242 *Fax:* 314-533-3349 *Web Site:* www.avatar-studios.com, pg 798

Shen, Fred, Shen Milsom & Wilke LLC, 417 Fifth Ave, New York, NY 10016 *Tel:* 212-725-6800 *Fax:* 212-725-0864 *E-mail:* info@smwllc.com *Web Site:* www.smwllc.com, pg 1008

Shenk, Gary, Corbis, 710 Second Ave, Suite 200, Seattle, WA 98104 *Tel:* 206-373-6000 *Fax:* 206-373-6100 *Web Site:* www.corbisimages.com, pg 836

Shenk, Gary, Corbis Motion, 250 Hudson St, 4th fl, New York, NY 10013-1413 *Tel:* 212-375-7622 *Toll Free Tel:* 800-260-0444 *Fax:* 212-375-7700 *Toll Free Fax:* 877-297-7977 *E-mail:* sales@corbis.com *Web Site:* www.corbismotion.com, pg 836

Shenk, Joe, PRG Lighting, 6050 S Valley View Blvd, Las Vegas, NV 89118 *Tel:* 702-942-4774 *Fax:* 702-942-4668 *E-mail:* info@prg.com *Web Site:* www.prg.com, pg 981

Shepherd, Kyle, Spectrum Sound Inc, 1040 Acorn Dr, Suite C, Nashville, TN 37210 *Tel:* 615-391-3700 *Web Site:* www.spectrumsound.net, pg 1021

Sherman, Cary, Recording Industry Association of America (RIAA), 1025 "F" St NW, 10th fl, Washington, DC 20004 *Tel:* 202-775-0101 *Web Site:* www.riaa.com, pg 1088

Sherman, Cary, The RIAA® Gold® & Platinum® Awards, 1025 "F" St NW, 10th fl, Washington, DC 20004 *Tel:* 202-775-0101 *Web Site:* www.riaa.com, pg 1125

Sherman, Greg, American Video Inc, 780 Third Ave, 5th fl, New York, NY 10017-2024 *Tel:* 212-527-9000 *Toll Free Tel:* 800-582-4184 *E-mail:* sales@accnewyork.com *Web Site:* www.americanvideo.com, pg 785

Sherman, Lesley, Wallace Film Studios, 258 Wallace Ave, Toronto, ON M6P 3N9, Canada *Tel:* 416-538-3535 *E-mail:* info@wallacefilmstudios.ca *Web Site:* wallacefilmstudios.ca, pg 1061

Sherman, Lisa, MediaFX, 10445 SW Canyon Rd, Suite 220, Beaverton, OR 97005 *Tel:* 503-646-9884 *Fax:* 503-646-7115 *Web Site:* www.mediafxvideo.com, pg 937

Sherman, Matt, Three Pillars Media, 140 N Eighth St, Suite 440, Lincoln, NE 68508 *Tel:* 402-937-0984 *E-mail:* contact@threepillarsmedia.com *Web Site:* www.threepillarsmedia.com, pg 1040

Sherman, Roger, Florentine Films, 136 E 56 St, Suite 4-B, New York, NY 10022 *Tel:* 212-980-5966 *Fax:* 212-980-5944 *Web Site:* www.florentinefilms.com/sherman, pg 870

Sherry, Jim, SPEAK HOUSE Audio™, 1844 E Montecito Ave, Phoenix, AZ 85016 *Tel:* 602-279-0900 *Fax:* 602-279-0980 *Web Site:* www.speakhouseaudio.com, pg 1020

Sherwood, Duane, Lowel-Light Manufacturing Inc, 90 Oser Ave, Hauppauge, NY 11788 *Tel:* 631-273-2500 *Toll Free Tel:* 800-645-2522 *Fax:* 631-273-2557 *E-mail:* info@lowel.com *Web Site:* www.lowel.com, pg 925

Shew, Jeff, Electrorack Legrand Division, 1443 S Sunkist St, Anaheim, CA 92806 *Tel:* 714-776-5420 *Toll Free Tel:* 800-433-6745 *Fax:* 714-776-9683 *E-mail:* sales@electrorack.com *Web Site:* www.electrorack.com, pg 859

Shewchuk, Joseph, A-V Services Inc, 99 Fairfield Rd, Fairfield, NJ 07004 *Tel:* 973-575-5222 *Fax:* 973-575-0857 *E-mail:* sales@avservices.net *Web Site:* www.avservices.net, pg 771

Shie, Rick, Physical Optics Corp, 1845 E 205 St, Torrance, CA 90501-1510 *Tel:* 310-320-3088 *Fax:* 310-320-5961 *Web Site:* www.poc.com, pg 975

Shields, Anaite, FilmNation Entertainment, 150 W 22 St, 9th fl, New York, NY 10011 *Web Site:* www.filmnation.com, pg 867

Shihadeh, Eileen, Compass Learning Inc, 203 Colorado St, Austin, TX 78701 *Tel:* 512-478-9600 *Toll Free Tel:* 866-586-7387 (sales); 800-678-1412 (cust support) *Web Site:* www.compasslearning.com, pg 833

Shimm, Joey, Outwater Plastics Industries Inc, 24 River Rd, Bogota, NJ 07603 *Tel:* 201-498-8750 *Toll Free Tel:* 800-631-8375 *Fax:* 201-498-8751 *Toll Free Fax:* 800-888-3315 *E-mail:* info@outwaterplastics.com *Web Site:* www.outwater.com, pg 966

Shiner, Nicole, Greater Philadelphia Film Office, One Parkway Bldg, 11th fl, 1515 Arch St, Philadelphia, PA 19102 *Tel:* 215-686-2668 *Fax:* 215-686-3659 *E-mail:* mail@film.org *Web Site:* www.film.org, pg 1102

Shinn, Duane, The Keyboard Workshop, PO Box 700, Medford, OR 97501 *Tel:* 541-664-7052 *Fax:* 541-664-7052 *Web Site:* www.playpiano.com, pg 910

Shipe, Coty, Delicate Electronics Sales Inc, 874 Verdulera St, Camarillo, CA 93010 *Tel:* 805-484-8139 *Toll Free Tel:* 800-350-3555 *Fax:* 805-388-1037 *Web Site:* www.delicatesales.com, pg 845

Shipley, Eric, Showcase Photo & Video, 2323 Cheshire Bridge Rd, Atlanta, GA 30324 *Tel:* 404-325-7676 *Toll Free Tel:* 800-886-1976 *Fax:* 404-321-3636 *E-mail:* sales@showcaseinc.com *Web Site:* www.showcaseinc.com, pg 1010

Shoaf, Rob, Triangle Regional Film Commission, PO Box 13041, Research Triangle Park, NC 27709-3041 *Tel:* 919-544-5501 *E-mail:* triangleregionalfilm@gmail.com *Web Site:* www.trianglencfilm.com, pg 1101

Shockley, Glen, Flip 2 Media Inc, 1067 Serpentine Lane, Pleasanton, CA 94566-4759 *Tel:* 925-417-1420 *E-mail:* info@flip2media.com *Web Site:* www.flip2media.com, pg 870

Shoel, Michael Jack, Ariztical Entertainment Inc, 12400 Ventura Blvd, Suite 686, Studio City, CA 91604-2406 *Tel:* 818-760-3739 *Fax:* 818-760-3581 *E-mail:* info@ariztical.com *Web Site:* www.ariztical.com, pg 790

Shook, Ken, Xytech Systems Corp, 15451 San Fernando Mission Blvd, Suite 400, Mission Hills, CA 91345 *Tel:* 818-698-4900 *Fax:* 818-698-4901 *E-mail:* sales@xytechsystems.com *Web Site:* www.xytechsystems.com, pg 1071

Shore, Greg, PixeLINK, 1900 City Park Dr, Suite 410, Ottawa, ON K1J 1A3, Canada *Tel:* 613-247-1211 *Fax:* 613-247-2001 *E-mail:* sales@pixelink.com *Web Site:* www.pixelink.com, pg 976

Shore, Julie, Emmy Awards (Primetime), 5220 Lankershim Blvd, North Hollywood, CA 91601-3109 *Tel:* 818-754-2800 *Fax:* 818-754-2836 *Web Site:* www.emmys.com, pg 1114

Shore, Julie, Television Academy, 5220 Lankershim Blvd, North Hollywood, CA 91601-3109 *Tel:* 818-754-2800 *Fax:* 818-761-2827 *Web Site:* www.emmys.com, pg 1089

Shore, Mark, High Output Inc, 495 Turnpike St, Canton, MA 02021 *Tel:* 781-364-1800 *Fax:* 781-364-1900 *Web Site:* www.highoutput.com, pg 888

Shorrock, Rick, Big Byte Video Productions, 223 Washington Blvd, Lake Placid, FL 33852 *Tel:* 863-699-6229 *Fax:* 863-699-0145 *E-mail:* bigbytevideo@yahoo.com *Web Site:* www.bigbytevideo.us, pg 806

Short, Matthew, Flashback Stage Lighting, 8151 Commercial St, La Mesa, CA 91924 *Tel:* 619-697-2729 *Fax:* 619-697-2782 *E-mail:* mail@flashbackstagelighting.com *Web Site:* www.flashbackstagelighting.com, pg 869

Short, Ray, Research Technology International (RTI), 4700 Chase Ave, Lincolnwood, IL 60712-1689 *Tel:* 847-677-3000 *Toll Free Tel:* 800-323-7520 *Fax:* 847-677-1311 *Toll Free Fax:* 800-784-6733 *E-mail:* sales@rtico.com *Web Site:* www.rtico.com, pg 995

Shostak, Stuart, Shokus Video, PO Box 3125, Chatsworth, CA 91313-3125 *Tel:* 818-538-9985 *Toll Free Tel:* 800-SHOKUS-1 (746-5871 - orders) *Fax:* 818-701-0560 *E-mail:* info@shokus.com *Web Site:* www.shokus.com, pg 1009

Shoup, John, Great Chefs/Leisure Jazz Video, 747 Magazine St, New Orleans, LA 70130 *Tel:* 504-581-5000 *Toll Free Tel:* 800-321-1499 *Fax:* 504-581-1188 *E-mail:* info@greatchefs.com *Web Site:* www.greatchefs.com, pg 881

Shoup, John, Leisure Video, 747 Magazine St, New Orleans, LA 70130 *Tel:* 504-299-9000 *Toll Free Tel:* 800-432-3853 *Fax:* 504-299-9090 *E-mail:* info@dukesofdixieland.com *Web Site:* www.dukesofdixieland.com; www.leisurejazz.com, pg 918

Shreve, Paul, Goose Creek Music & Entertainment, 17723 Tranquility Rd, Purcellville, VA 20132 *Tel:* 540-751-1395 *E-mail:* info@goosecreekmusic.com *Web Site:* www.goosecreekmusic.com, pg 880

Shub, E, Cambridge Documentary Films Inc, 3099 Hidden Valley Lane, Santa Barbara, CA 93108 *Tel:* 617-484-3993 *E-mail:* info@cambridgedocumentaryfilms.org *Web Site:* www.cambridgedocumentaryfilms.org, pg 818

Shuey, Phillip N, IAAVC (International Association of Audio Visual Communicators), PO Box 270779, Flower Mound, TX 75027-0779 *Tel:* 469-464-4180 *Fax:* 469-464-4170 *Web Site:* www.iaavc.org, pg 1082

Shuey, Phillip N, International CINDY Competitions, PO Box 270779, Flower Mound, TX 75027-0779 *Tel:* 469-464-4180 *Fax:* 469-464-4170 *E-mail:* cindy@cindys.com *Web Site:* www.cindys.com, pg 1117

Shumate, Thomas, Franciscan Media, 28 W Liberty St, Cincinnati, OH 45202-6498 *Tel:* 513-241-5615 *Toll Free Tel:* 800-488-0488 *Fax:* 513-241-0399 *Web Site:* www.americancatholic.org, pg 872

Shupper, Robert, Calrad Electronics, 819 N Highland Ave, Los Angeles, CA 90038 *Tel:* 323-465-2131 *Toll Free Tel:* 800-821-8536 *Fax:* 323-465-3504 *E-mail:* calradelectronics@calrad.com *Web Site:* www.calrad.com, pg 817

Shute, Jonathan, Broadcasters General Store Inc, 2480 SE 52 St, Ocala, FL 34480 *Tel:* 352-622-7700 *Fax:* 352-629-7000 *E-mail:* sales@bgs.cc (orders) *Web Site:* www.bgs.cc, pg 813

Sibley, Ellen, Barron's Educational Series Inc, 250 Wireless Blvd, Hauppauge, NY 11788 *Tel:* 631-434-3311 *Toll Free Tel:* 800-645-3476 *Fax:* 631-434-3723 *E-mail:* barrons@barronseduc.com *Web Site:* www.barronseduc.com, pg 803

Sibley, Tadd, DTC Lighting & Grip, 1280 65 St, Emeryville, CA 94608 *Tel:* 510-595-0770 *Toll Free Tel:* 877-382-3456 *Fax:* 510-595-0772 *E-mail:* sales@dtcgrip.com; rentals@dtcgrip.com *Web Site:* www.dtcgrip.com, pg 853

Sickels, Tony, Soundfold International, 9200 N State Rte 48, Centerville, OH 45458 *Tel:* 937-885-5100 *Toll Free Tel:* 800-782-8018 *Fax:* 937-885-5115 *Web Site:* www.soundfold.com, pg 1018

Sicklick, Robert, AVFX Inc, 96 Holton St, Boston, MA 02135 *Tel:* 617-254-0770 *Toll Free Tel:* 888-254-0770 *E-mail:* info@avfx.com *Web Site:* www.avfx.com, pg 798

Siddhananda, Rev Swami, Chinmaya Publications, 560 Bridgetown Pike, Langhorne, PA 19053-7210 *Tel:* 215-396-0390 *Toll Free Tel:* 888-CMW-READ (269-7323) *Fax:* 215-396-9710 *E-mail:* publications@chinmayamission.org *Web Site:* www.chinmayamission.org; www.chinmayapublications.org, pg 825

Sidles, Curt, Yamaha Electronics Corp, 6660 Orangethorpe Ave, Buena Park, CA 90620 *Tel:* 714-522-9105 *Toll Free Tel:* 800-292-2982 (cust support) *Toll Free Fax:* 800-782-8484 *Web Site:* www.yamaha.com, pg 1071

Siebert, Scott, USMotivation, 7840 Roswell Rd, USM Bldg 100, 3rd fl, Atlanta, GA 30350 *Tel:* 770-290-4700 *Toll Free Tel:* 800-476-0496 *Fax:* 770-290-4701 *E-mail:* information@usmotivation.com *Web Site:* www.usmotivation.com, pg 1051

Siebrecht, Karl, Colorado Studios, 8269 E 23 Ave, Denver, CO 80238 *Fax:* 303-388-9600 *E-mail:* info@coloradostudios.com *Web Site:* www.coloradostudios.com, pg 832

Siegel, Betty, VSA, 2700 "F" St NW, Washington, DC 20566 *Tel:* 202-416-8898 *Fax:* 202-416-4840 *E-mail:* vsainfo@kennedy-center.org *Web Site:* www.vsarts.org, pg 1061

Siegel, Frank, VCSvideo, 2807 Hunterdon Dr, Cinnaminson, NJ 08077 *Tel:* 856-273-8800 *Toll Free Tel:* 877-VCS-VIDEO (827-8433) *Web Site:* www.vcsvideo.com, pg 1052

Siegel, Joel R, Edison Price Lighting, 41-50 22 St, Long Island City, NY 11101 *Tel:* 718-685-0700 *Fax:* 718-786-8530 *E-mail:* info@epl.com *Web Site:* www.epl.com, pg 857

Siegel, Minette, The Studio of David Inocencio/Minette Siegel, 41 Fairlawn Ave, Daly City, CA 94015 *Tel:* 415-716-2791 *Fax:* 415-716-2796 *Web Site:* www.ino-sieg.com, pg 1027

Siegel, Sheila, Noteworthy Enterprises, 3829 NE 167 St, North Miami Beach, FL 33160 *Tel:* 305-949-9192 *E-mail:* shenote@comcast.net, pg 959

Sierra, Andres, Video Technology Services Inc, 5 Ariel Way, Suite 300, Syosset, NY 11791 *Tel:* 516-937-9700 *Fax:* 516-937-9704 *E-mail:* vts1@optonline.net *Web Site:* www.videotechnologyservices.com, pg 1056

Sifuentes, Jerry, Allied Artists International Inc, Production Services Ctr, 15810 E Gale Ave, Suite 133, Hacienda Heights, CA 91745 *Tel:* 626-330-0600 *Fax:* 626-961-0411 *E-mail:* info@alliedartists.net *Web Site:* us.alliedartists.com, pg 781

Sigal, M A, Solutek Corp, 94 Shirley St, Boston, MA 02119 *Tel:* 617-445-5335 *Toll Free Tel:* 800-403-0770 *Fax:* 617-445-9623 *E-mail:* bflanagan@solutek.com *Web Site:* www.solutekphotochemicals.com, pg 1015

Siko, Tom, Lex Products Corp, 15 Progress Dr, Shelton, CT 06484 *Tel:* 203-363-3738 *Toll Free Tel:* 800-643-4460 *Fax:* 203-363-3742 *E-mail:* info@lexproducts.com *Web Site:* www.lexproducts.com, pg 919

Silber, Milos, Hayden 5 Media LLC, 22 W 27 St, 6th fl, New York, NY 10001 *Tel:* 212-871-9316 *E-mail:* info@hayden5.com *Web Site:* www.hayden5.com, pg 886

Silberberg, David, Les Blank Films Inc, 10341 San Pablo Ave, El Cerrito, CA 94530-3123 *Tel:* 510-525-0942 *Toll Free Tel:* 800-572-7618 *Fax:* 510-525-1204 *E-mail:* lesblankfilmsinc@gmail.com, pg 809

Silberman, Dan, A&E Television Networks LLC, 235 E 45 St, New York, NY 10017 *Tel:* 212-210-1400 *Web Site:* www.aetv.com, pg 771

Silberman, Louis, Illuma Studios, 16601 N 90 St, Scottsdale, AZ 85260 *Tel:* 480-222-4396 *E-mail:* info@illumastudios.com *Web Site:* www.illumastudios.com, pg 894

Sills, Steven, Kaboom Productions, 1465 Illinois St, San Francisco, CA 94107 *Tel:* 415-434-2666 *Fax:* 415-970-8548 *E-mail:* updates@kaboomproductions.com *Web Site:* kaboomproductions.com, pg 907

Silva, John, Vantage Point Products Corp, PO Box 2485, Santa Fe Springs, CA 90670 *Tel:* 562-946-1718 *Toll Free Tel:* 888-886-6868 *Fax:* 562-946-3898 *Web Site:* www.thinkvp.com, pg 1051

Silva, Phil, Balboa Capital Corp, 2010 Main St, Suite 1100, Irvine, CA 92614 *Tel:* 949-756-0800 *Toll Free Tel:* 888-BALBOA1 (225-2621) *Fax:* 949-756-2565 *E-mail:* customerservice@balboacapital.com *Web Site:* www.balboacapital.com, pg 802

Silver, Don, Colortone Audio Visual, 75 Virginia Rd, White Plains, NY 10603 *Tel:* 914-592-4151 *Fax:* 914-592-2833 *Web Site:* www.colortone-av.com, pg 832

Silver, Joseph, Designomotion, 67 E 11 St, Suite 324, New York, NY 10003 *Tel:* 917-532-0738 *E-mail:* info@designomotion.com *Web Site:* designomotion.com, pg 846

Silver, Leonard, Amherst Records Inc, 1762 Main St, Suite A, Buffalo, NY 14208 *Tel:* 716-883-9520 *Toll Free Tel:* 800-836-0751 *Fax:* 716-884-1432 *E-mail:* info@amherstrecords.com *Web Site:* www.amherstrecords.com, pg 785

Silverman, Joel, Millennia Media FPC, 4600 Missouri Flat Rd, Suite 11, Placerville, CA 95667 *Tel:* 530-647-0750 *Fax:* 530-647-9921 *E-mail:* sales@mil-media.com *Web Site:* www.mil-media.com, pg 943

Silvers, Howard, Increase Video/Silver Mine Video, 5776 D Lindero Canyon Rd, Westlake Village, CA 91362 *Tel:* 805-480-0303 *Fax:* 805-375-1606, pg 897

Silvers, Stefan, Increase Video/Silver Mine Video, 5776 D Lindero Canyon Rd, Westlake Village, CA 91362 *Tel:* 805-480-0303 *Fax:* 805-375-1606, pg 897

Sim, Rob, SIM Digital, One Atlantic Ave, Suite 110, Toronto, ON M6K 3E7, Canada *Tel:* 416-979-9958 *Fax:* 416-979-7770 *E-mail:* info@simdigital.com *Web Site:* www.simdigital.com, pg 1011

Simard, Melanie, STIL Casing Solution, 76 Saint Paul, Suite 301, Quebec City, QC G1K 3V9, Canada *Tel:* 418-694-0449 (ext 10); 418-694-0449 (ext 11, sales & cust serv); 418-694-0449 (ext 12, admin) *Toll Free Tel:* 888-414-0449 (CN & US) *Fax:* 418-694-1621 *E-mail:* info@stilcasing.com; sales@stilcasing.com; admin@stilcasing.com *Web Site:* www.stilcasing.com, pg 1025

Simard, Monique, SODEC, 215 rue Saint-Jacques St, Rm 800, Montreal, QC H2Y 1M6, Canada *Tel:* 514-841-2200 *Toll Free Tel:* 800-363-0401 (CN only) *Fax:* 514-841-8606 *E-mail:* info@sodec.gouv.qc.ca *Web Site:* www.sodec.gouv.qc.ca, pg 1089

Simmons, Katie, Chico Chamber of Commerce/Butte County Film Commission, 441 Main St, Suite 150, Chico, CA 95928 *Tel:* 530-891-5556 *Toll Free Tel:* 800-852-8570 *Fax:* 530-891-3613 *E-mail:* info@chicochamber.com *Web Site:* chicochamber.com, pg 1092

Simmons, Michael, Directed Electronics, One Viper Way, Vista, CA 92081 *Tel:* 760-598-6200 *Toll Free Tel:* 800-876-0800 *Fax:* 760-598-6400 *E-mail:* customerfeedback@directed.com *Web Site:* www.directed.com, pg 848

Simon, Arlene, Real Cool TV Productions, 800 S Main St, Suite 203, Mansfield, MA 02048 *Tel:* 508-337-8520 *E-mail:* info@realcooltv.com *Web Site:* www.realcooltv.com, pg 992

Simon, Douglas, D S Simon Productions, 229 W 36 St, 9th fl, New York, NY 10018 *Tel:* 212-736-2727 *Toll Free Tel:* 800-377-4666 *Fax:* 212-736-7040 *E-mail:* news@dssimon.com *Web Site:* dssimon.com, pg 1011

Simon, Eric, TimeLogic Corp, 1914 Palomar Oaks Way, Suite 150, Carlsbad, CA 92008 *Tel:* 760-431-1263 *Toll Free Tel:* 877-222-9543 *Fax:* 760-431-1351 *Web Site:* www.timelogic.com, pg 1041

Simon, Mike, Image Video Teleproductions Inc, 6755 Freedom Ave NW, North Canton, OH 44720 *Tel:* 330-494-9303 *Fax:* 330-966-1792 *E-mail:* info@image-video.com *Web Site:* www.image-video.com, pg 895

Simon, Richard A, Simon - Kaloi Engineering, 31192 La Baya Dr, Unit G, Westlake Village, CA 91362 *Tel:* 818-707-8400 *Fax:* 818-707-8401, pg 1011

Simonello, Lorraine, Morehouse Publishing, 4775 Linglestown Rd, Harrisburg, PA 17112 *Tel:* 212-592-1800 (intl) *Toll Free Tel:* 800-242-1918 *Fax:* 717-541-8136 *E-mail:* churchpublishing@cpg.org *Web Site:* www.morehousepublishing.com; churchpublishing.org, pg 946

Simonion, Nicole, Horizon Film + Video Productions, 808 E 34 St, Austin, TX 78705 *Tel:* 512-459-3100 *Toll Free Tel:* 800-540-2785 *Fax:* 512-459-3477 *Web Site:* www.horizonvideo.com, pg 891

Simpson, Craig, Microtran Manufacturing, 1040 S Andreasen Dr, Suite 100, Escondido, CA 92029 *Tel:* 951-699-1270 *Toll Free Tel:* 800-472-6624 *Fax:* 951-676-9482 *Web Site:* www.tamuracorp.com, pg 942

Simpson, Jill, Oklahoma Film Commission & Music Office, 120 N Robinson, Suite 600, Oklahoma City, OK 73102 *Tel:* 405-230-8440 *Toll Free Tel:* 800-766-3456 *Fax:* 405-230-8640 *Web Site:* www.oklahomafilm.org; thebuffalolounge.com, pg 1101

Simpson, Neil, Chapman Recording & Mastering, 8805 Monrovia, Lenexa, KS 66215 *Tel:* 913-894-6854 *Fax:* 913-894-6857 *Web Site:* www.chapmanrecording.com, pg 824

Simpson, Sam, YAP Films, 96 Spadina Ave, Suite 205, Toronto, ON M5V 2J6, Canada *Tel:* 416-504-3662 *Fax:* 416-504-3667 *E-mail:* thedog@yapfilms.com *Web Site:* www.yapfilms.com, pg 1072

Simpson, Stephen, Southwest Sound & Electronics Inc, 2323 Loop 410 NW, San Antonio, TX 78230-5348 *Tel:* 210-341-4411 *Fax:* 210-349-8300 *Web Site:* www.swsoundinc.com, pg 1019

Sims, Jane, Graftek Imaging Inc, 8900 Shoal Creek Blvd, Bldg 300, Suite B, Austin, TX 78757 *Tel:* 512-416-1099 *Toll Free Tel:* 800-441-2118 *Fax:* 512-416-1014 *E-mail:* graftek@graftek.com *Web Site:* www.graftek.com, pg 881

Simsovic, Diane, Niagara Region-Economic Development, Campbell East, 3rd fl, 2201 Saint David's Rd, Thorold, ON L2V 4T7, Canada *Tel:* 905-685-4225 *Toll Free Tel:* 800-263-7215 *Fax:* 905-688-5907 *E-mail:* info@niagaracanada.com *Web Site:* www.niagaracanada.com, pg 1105

Sin, Andy, SLI Manufacturing Inc, 550 McNicholl Ave, Toronto, ON M2H 2E1, Canada *Tel:* 416-493-8900 *Toll Free Tel:* 888-216-2382 *Fax:* 416-493-8901 *E-mail:* salesinfo@slicanada.com *Web Site:* www.slicanada.com, pg 1013

Sinasac, Joseph, Novalis, 10 Lower Spadina Ave, Suite 400, Toronto, ON M5V 2Z2, Canada *Tel:* 416-363-3303 *Toll Free Tel:* 877-702-7773; 800-387-7164 (US & CN only) *Fax:* 416-363-9409 *Toll Free Fax:* 877-702-7775; 800-204-4140 (cust serv) *E-mail:* books@novalis.ca; resources@novalis.ca *Web Site:* www.novalis.ca, pg 959

Sinauer, Andrew D, Sinauer Associates Inc, 23 Plumtree Rd, Sunderland, MA 01375 *Tel:* 413-549-4300 *Fax:* 413-549-1118 *E-mail:* orders@sinauer.com (orders); custserv@sinauer.com (cust serv); publish@sinauer.com (general edit correspondence) *Web Site:* www.sinauer.com, pg 1012

Singer, Alan, Hollywood Center Studios, 1040 N Las Palmas, Los Angeles, CA 90038 *Tel:* 323-860-0000 *E-mail:* info@hollywoodcenter.com *Web Site:* www.hollywoodcenter.com, pg 890

Singer, Andrew, Sound by Singer Ltd, 242 W 27 St, 2nd fl, New York, NY 10001 *Tel:* 212-924-8600 *Fax:* 212-366-6351 *E-mail:* info@soundbysinger.com *Web Site:* www.soundbysinger.com, pg 1017

Singer, Barbara, Barbara Singer Productions, 319 E 24 St, No 3-A, New York, NY 10010 *Tel:* 212-689-0395 *Fax:* 212-686-4890 *E-mail:* barbara@barbarasinger.com *Web Site:* www.barbarasinger.com, pg 1012

Singer, J L, Hollywood Center Studios, 1040 N Las Palmas, Los Angeles, CA 90038 *Tel:* 323-860-0000 *E-mail:* info@hollywoodcenter.com *Web Site:* www.hollywoodcenter.com, pg 890

Singletary, Jon, AV Metro Inc, 5401 Etta Burke Ct, Raleigh, NC 27606 *Tel:* 919-233-1901 *Fax:* 919-233-1804 *E-mail:* info@avmetro.com *Web Site:* www.avmetro.com, pg 797

Singleton, John A, Sun Entertainment Corp, 3106 Belmont Blvd, Nashville, TN 37212 *Tel:* 615-385-1960 *E-mail:* info@sunrecords.com *Web Site:* www.sunrecords.com, pg 1028

Singleton, Sidney S, Sun Entertainment Corp, 3106 Belmont Blvd, Nashville, TN 37212 *Tel:* 615-385-1960 *E-mail:* info@sunrecords.com *Web Site:* www.sunrecords.com, pg 1028

Singleton, Tammy, National Religious Broadcasters (NRB), 9510 Technology Dr, Manassas, VA 20110 *Tel:* 703-330-7000 *Fax:* 703-330-7100 *E-mail:* info@nrb.org *Web Site:* www.nrb.org, pg 1086

Sinkler, Scott, Public Eye Productions, 409 Meeker St, South Orange, NJ 07079 *Tel:* 917-446-8977 *Web Site:* www.publiceyeproductions.com, pg 987

Sinkoff, Howard L, Vutec Corp, Video Products Division, 11711 W Sample Rd, Coral Springs, FL 33065-3155 *Tel:* 954-545-9000 *Toll Free Tel:* 800-770-4700 *Fax:* 954-545-9011 *Toll Free Fax:* 800-548-5885 *E-mail:* info@vutec.com; sales@vutec.com *Web Site:* www.vutec.com, pg 1061

Sipes, Michael, KAKE-TV, 1500 N West St, Wichita, KS 67203-1323 *Tel:* 316-943-4221; 316-946-1314 (sales) *Fax:* 316-943-5493 *Web Site:* kake.com, pg 907

Siporen, Jaromy, Big Door, 114 Sheldon St, El Segundo, CA 90245 *Tel:* 310-546-6100 *Fax:* 310-906-4585 *E-mail:* sales@bigdoor.tv *Web Site:* www.bigdoor.tv; www.bigdoorstudio.tv, pg 807

Sippola, Carlene, Whole Person Associates Inc, 101 W Second St, Suite 203, Duluth, MN 55802-5004 *Tel:* 218-727-0500 *Toll Free Tel:* 800-247-6789 *Fax:* 218-727-0505 *E-mail:* books@wholeperson.com *Web Site:* www.wholeperson.com, pg 1066

Sirah, Kiran, International Storytelling Center, 116 W Main St, Jonesborough, TN 37659 *Tel:* 423-753-2171 *Toll Free Tel:* 800-952-8392 *Fax:* 423-913-8219 *E-mail:* customerservice@storytellingcenter.net *Web Site:* www.storytellingcenter.net, pg 1084

Sirah, Kiran, National Storytelling Festival, 116 W Main St, Jonesborough, TN 37659 *Tel:* 423-753-2171 *Toll Free Tel:* 800-952-8392 *Fax:* 423-913-8219 *E-mail:* customerservice@storytellingcenter.net *Web Site:* www.storytellingfestival.net; www.storytellingcenter.net, pg 1121

Sirkin, Adam, Liberty Uplink, 2547 Yellow Springs Rd, Malvern, PA 19355 *Tel:* 215-964-5222; 917-254-0155 *E-mail:* info@libertyuplink.com *Web Site:* www.libertyuplink.com, pg 919

Sirotin, Jason, ECG Productions, 120 Interstate N Pkwy SE, Suite 435, Atlanta, GA 30339 *Tel:* 678-855-5169 *E-mail:* info@ecgprod.com *Web Site:* www.ecgprod.com, pg 856

Siteman, Frank, Frank Siteman Photography, 136 Pond St, Winchester, MA 01890 *Tel:* 781-729-3747 *Fax:* 781-729-2549 *Web Site:* www.franksiteman.com, pg 1012

Sitkin, Judith, Allegro Productions Inc, 1000 Clint Moore Rd, Suite 108, Boca Raton, FL 33487 *Tel:* 561-994-9111 *Toll Free Tel:* 800-232-2133 (ext 201) *Fax:* 561-241-0707 *Web Site:* www.allegrovideo.com, pg 781

Sitler, Linn, The Memphis & Shelby County Film & TV Commission, 496 S Main St, Suite 101, Memphis, TN 38103 *Tel:* 901-527-8300 (ext 2) *Fax:* 901-527-8326 *E-mail:* info@memphisfilmcomm.org *Web Site:* www.filmmemphis.org, pg 1102

Sitler, Penny R, Draper Inc, 411 S Pearl St, Spiceland, IN 47385 *Tel:* 765-987-7999 *Toll Free Tel:* 800-238-7999 *Fax:* 765-987-7142 *Web Site:* www.draperinc.com; blog.draperinc.com, pg 852

Sittnick, Patrick, Kozmic Lazer Show LLC, PO Box 140197, Nashville, TN 37214-0197 *Tel:* 615-391-3226 *Toll Free Tel:* 800-MRLASER (675-2737) *Fax:* 615-391-3265 *E-mail:* mrlaser800@aol.com *Web Site:* www.kozmiclazershow.com, pg 913

Siwolop, Halina, Set Decorators Society of America (SDSA), 7100 Tujunga Ave, Suite A, North Hollywood, CA 91605 *Tel:* 818-255-2425 *Fax:* 818-982-8597 *E-mail:* sdsa@setdecorators.org *Web Site:* www.setdecorators.org, pg 1088

Size, Dennis M, Lighting Design Group, 49 W 27 St, Suite 920, New York, NY 10001 *Tel:* 212-685-4940 *Fax:* 212-685-4927 *E-mail:* lighting@ldg.com *Web Site:* www.ldg.com, pg 920

Skaf, Rashid, AMX, 3000 Research Dr, Richardson, TX 75082 *Tel:* 469-624-8000 *Toll Free Tel:* 800-222-0193 *Fax:* 469-624-7153 *E-mail:* service@amx.com *Web Site:* www.amx.com, pg 786

Skaggs, Ken, 3008, 3008 Ross Ave, Suite 100, Dallas, TX 75204 *Tel:* 214-922-9232 *Fax:* 214-922-8861 *Web Site:* www.3008.com, pg 1040

Skarka, Danny, MediaOne Services, 901 Battery St, Suite 220, San Francisco, CA 94111 *Tel:* 415-262-4222 *E-mail:* sales@mediaoneservices.com *Web Site:* mediaoneservices.com, pg 938

Skaw, Jerry, Vexcel Corp, 5775 Flatiron Pkwy, Suite 220, Boulder, CO 80301 *Tel:* 303-415-6000 *Fax:* 303-442-2956 *E-mail:* vexcel@microsoft.com *Web Site:* www.vexcel.com, pg 1053

Skeel, Joe, Sigma Delta Chi Awards in Journalism, Eugene S Pulliam National Journalism Ctr, 3909 N Meridian St, Indianapolis, IN 46208 *Tel:* 317-927-8000 *Fax:* 317-920-4789 *E-mail:* awards@spj.org *Web Site:* www.spj.org, pg 1127

Skelton, Todd, Palardo Productions, 1807 Taft Ave, Suite 4, Hollywood, CA 90028 *Tel:* 323-469-8991 *E-mail:* palardo2@msn.com, pg 968

Skerbelis, Monika, Big Bear Lake International Film Festival, PO Box 1981, Big Bear Lake, CA 92315 *Tel:* 909-547-4019 *E-mail:* info@bigbearfilmfestival.com *Web Site:* www.bigbearfilmfestival.com, pg 1109

Skibitzky, Clinton, daCapo Productions, 516 Hargrave St, Winnipeg, MB R3A 0X8, Canada *Tel:* 204-956-2867 *Fax:* 204-956-2869 *Web Site:* www.dacapo.ca, pg 842

Skiles, Denny, USDA/FSA Aerial Photography Field Office, 2222 W 2300 S, Salt Lake City, UT 84119-2020 *Tel:* 801-844-2922 *Toll Free Fax:* 855-415-2014 *E-mail:* apfo.sales@slc.usda.gov *Web Site:* www.apfo.usda.gov, pg 1051

Skinner, Georja, State of Hawaii Film Office, 250 S Hotel St, Suite 510-A, Honolulu, HI 96813 *Tel:* 808-586-2570 *Fax:* 808-586-2572 *E-mail:* info@hawaiifilmoffice.com *Web Site:* www.filmoffice.hawaii.gov, pg 1097

Skjekkeland, Atle, Association for Information and Image Management (AIIM), 1100 Wayne Ave, Suite 1100, Silver Spring, MD 20910 *Tel:* 301-587-8202 *Toll Free Tel:* 800-477-2446 *Fax:* 301-587-2711 *E-mail:* aiim@aiim.org *Web Site:* www.aiim.org, pg 1078

Skjonberg, Knut, Skjonberg Controls Inc, 1363 Donlon St, Suite 6, Ventura, CA 93003 *Tel:* 805-650-0877 *Toll Free Fax:* 800-650-0360 *E-mail:* sales@skjonberg.com *Web Site:* www.skjonberg.com, pg 1012

Skora, Jerry, On Site Video, PO Box 1865, Palatine, IL 60078-1865 *Tel:* 847-980-9808 *Fax:* 847-358-8697 *E-mail:* producersvideo@hotmail.com, pg 963

Skunes, Timothy, CyberOptics, 5900 Golden Hills Dr, Minneapolis, MN 55416 *Tel:* 763-542-5000 *Fax:* 763-542-5100 *E-mail:* info@cyberoptics.com *Web Site:* cyberoptics.com, pg 841

Skuranskis, B, Sound Physics Labs Inc, PO Box 319, Glenview, IL 60025 *Tel:* 847-380-9390 *E-mail:* sales@soundphysics.com; info@soundphysics.com *Web Site:* www.soundphysics.com, pg 1017

Sky, Bob, Audio Mechanics, 1200 W Magnolia Blvd, Burbank, CA 91506 *Tel:* 818-846-5525 *Fax:* 818-846-5501 *E-mail:* info@audiomechanics.com *Web Site:* audiomechanics.com, pg 794

Slattery, Catherine, Filmdex Inc, 14016 Sullyfield Circle, Chantilly, VA 20151 *Tel:* 703-631-0600 *Toll Free Tel:* 888-FILMDEX (345-6339) *Fax:* 703-818-0237 *E-mail:* webinquiry@filmdex.com *Web Site:* www.filmdex.com, pg 867

Slechter, Richard J Sr, RJS Productions, PO Box 739, Westminster, MD 21158 *Tel:* 410-876-6300 *Fax:* 410-857-0608, pg 997

Slepicoff, Jodi, SANYO Fisher Co, 2055 Sanyo Ave, San Diego, CA 92154 *Tel:* 619-661-1134 *Fax:* 619-661-6795 *Web Site:* us.sanyo.com; www.fisherav.com, pg 1002

Slinger, Farrah, Event Essentials, 6485 Blanchar's Crossing, Windsor, WI 53598 *Tel:* 608-846-5004 *Toll Free Tel:* 800-220-4991 *Fax:* 608-222-5063 *Web Site:* www.eventessentials.com, pg 863

Slinger, Penny, Blue Lotus Temple Studio, PO Box 888, Boulder Creek, CA 95006 *Tel:* 831-338-2544 *E-mail:* info@bluelotustemple.com *Web Site:* www.bluelotustemple.com, pg 809

Slivinskas, Todd, TVO/Ontario Educational Communications Authority (OECA), 2180 Yonge St, Toronto, ON M4S 2B9, Canada *Tel:* 416-484-2600; 416-484-2665 (cust rel) *Toll Free Tel:* 800-613-0513; 800-INFO-TVO (463-6886) *E-mail:* asktvo@tvo.org *Web Site:* tvo.org, pg 1046

Sloan, Amanda, B&H Publishing Group, One Lifeway Plaza, Nashville, TN 37234 *Toll Free Tel:* 800-251-3225 (retailers); 800-448-8032 (consumers); 800-458-2772 (churches) *Fax:* 615-251-3914 (consumers); 615-251-5933 (churches) *Toll Free Fax:* 800-296-4036 (retailers) *Web Site:* www.bhpublishinggroup.com, pg 802

Sloan, Douglas, Icontent, 149 Fifth Ave, New York, NY 10010 *Tel:* 212-462-0022 *E-mail:* info@icontent.tv; tania@icontent.tv *Web Site:* www.icontent.tv, pg 893

Sloan, Lauren Grimshaw, Colorado Office of Film, Television & Media, 1625 Broadway, Suite 2700, Denver, CO 80202 *Tel:* 303-892-3840 *Fax:* 303-892-3848 *E-mail:* info@coloradofilm.org *Web Site:* www.coloradofilm.org, pg 1095

Slomovits, Sandor, Gemini, 2000 Penncraft Ct, Ann Arbor, MI 48103 *Tel:* 734-665-0165 *Toll Free Tel:* 800-317-9929 *Fax:* 734-786-4007 *E-mail:* info@geminichildrensmusic.com *Web Site:* www.geminichildrensmusic.com, pg 876

Slovarp, Jeremiah, Jereco Studios Inc, 627 E Peach St, Suite E, Bozeman, MT 59715 *Tel:* 406-586-5262 *Fax:* 406-586-5262 *Web Site:* www.jerecostudios.com, pg 905

Sluijter, Jaap, Krishnamurti Foundation of America, 1070 McAndrew Rd, Ojai, CA 93023 *Tel:* 805-646-2726 (ext 10) *Fax:* 805-646-6674 *E-mail:* kfa@kfa.org *Web Site:* www.kfa.org, pg 913

Small, Eric, Modulation Sciences Inc, 14 Worlds Fair Dr, Suite K, Somerset, NJ 08873 *Tel:* 732-302-3090 *Toll Free Tel:* 800-826-2603 *Fax:* 732-302-0206 *E-mail:* info@modsci.com; sales@modsci.com *Web Site:* www.modsci.com, pg 945

Smallman, Peter, Image Zone Inc, 11 W 69 St, Suite 10A, New York, NY 10023 *Tel:* 212-924-8804 *Web Site:* www.imagezone.com, pg 896

Smallwood, Lawrence L Jr, Philadelphia International Film Festival & Market, PO Box 48134, Philadelphia, PA 19144 *Tel:* 215-849-2716 (festival) *Toll Free Tel:* 877-347-FILM (347-3456) *E-mail:* info@philafilm.org *Web Site:* www.philafilm.org, pg 1124

Smart, Gordon, API, 8301 Patuxent Range Rd, Jessup, MD 20794 *Tel:* 301-776-7879 *Fax:* 301-776-8117 *E-mail:* service@apiaudio.com *Web Site:* www.apiaudio.com, pg 788

Smart, Robert J, RJ Video Productions, 15585 Tilden St, San Leandro, CA 94579-2316 *Tel:* 510-357-6535 *Fax:* 510-357-6535 *E-mail:* tuffnut56@att.net, pg 997

Smerekanich, Ilona, Cochise County Arizona, Queen Mine Tour Bldg, 478 Dart Rd, Bisbee, AZ 85603 *Tel:* 520-432-3554 *Toll Free Tel:* 866-2BISBEE (224-7233) *E-mail:* ilona@discoverbisbee.com *Web Site:* www.explorecochise.com, pg 1091

Smidt, James A, Metropolitan Audio-Visual Inc, 35333 N 27 Lane, Phoenix, AZ 85086 *Tel:* 480-948-9008 *Fax:* 480-948-9130 *Web Site:* www.metroav.tv, pg 940

Smisek, Anita, Alliance Publications Inc (API)/Sinsinawa Studios Productions, 585 County Rd Z, Sinsinawa, WI 53824-0157 *Tel:* 608-748-4411 (ext 124) *Fax:* 608-748-4491 *E-mail:* api@apimusic.org *Web Site:* www.apimusic.org, pg 781

Smith, Amanda, Celebration of Service to America Awards, 1771 "N" St NW, Washington, DC 20036-2891 *Tel:* 202-421-3191 *E-mail:* nabef@nab.org *Web Site:* www.nabef.org, pg 1111

Smith, Amanda, Illuma Studios, 16601 N 90 St, Scottsdale, AZ 85260 *Tel:* 480-222-4396 *E-mail:* info@illumastudios.com *Web Site:* www.illumastudios.com, pg 894

Smith, Andrew, Boyce Nemec Designs, PO Box 566, Norfolk, CT 06058-0566 *Tel:* 860-542-5937 *Web Site:* www.boycenemec.com, pg 811

Smith, Barry, Emerson Radio Corp, 3 University Plaza, Suite 405, Hackensack, NJ 07601 *Tel:* 973-884-5800 *Toll Free Tel:* 800-909-1240 (cust serv) *Fax:* 973-428-2067 *E-mail:* internet@emersonradio.com *Web Site:* www.emersonradio.com, pg 860

Smith, Bill, ICL Imaging Inc, 51 Mellen St, Framingham, MA 01702 *Tel:* 508-872-3280 *Toll Free Tel:* 800-660-3280 *Fax:* 508-872-7364 *E-mail:* csr@icl-imaging.com *Web Site:* www.icl-imaging.com, pg 893

Smith, Brad E, Shure Manufacturing Corp, 1901 W Main St, Washington, MO 63090 *Tel:* 636-390-7100 *Toll Free Tel:* 800-227-4873 *Fax:* 636-390-7171 *E-mail:* sales@shureusa.com *Web Site:* www.shureusa.com, pg 1010

Smith, Chauncey, The Wyland Group, 101 W Cochran St, Simi Valley, CA 93065 *Tel:* 805-955-7680 *Fax:* 805-522-1082 *Web Site:* www.adventistmediacenter.com, pg 1071

Smith, Christopher, University of Florida, Warrington College of Business Administration, 100 BRY, Gainesville, FL 32611 *Tel:* 352-392-2397 *Fax:* 352-392-2086 *E-mail:* ufwcba@warrington.ufl.edu *Web Site:* www.cba.ufl.edu, pg 1049

Smith, Craig, OSV Studios, 29605 Lorain Rd N, Olmsted, OH 44070 *Tel:* 440-779-1900 *Web Site:* www.osvstudios.com, pg 966

Smith, Curt, Sascom Marketing Group Inc, 34 Nelson St, Oakville, ON L6L 3H6, Canada *Tel:* 905-469-8080 *Fax:* 647-439-1510 *Web Site:* www.sascom.com, pg 1003

Smith, Daniel, Fuller Street Productions, 10702 Hathaway Dr, No 2, Santa Fe Springs, CA 90670 *Toll Free Tel:* 877-637-8733 *Toll Free Fax:* 877-637-8733 *E-mail:* contact@fullerstreet.com *Web Site:* www.fullerstreet.com, pg 874

Smith, Daniel J, ooLite Media, 1702 Nelson Rd, Bozeman, MT 59718 *Tel:* 406-587-1456 *Toll Free Tel:* 800-798-9980 *Fax:* 406-587-1459 *Web Site:* www.oolitemedia.com/earthtalk, pg 964

Smith, Deb, Bulb Direct, 7911 Rae Blvd, Victor, NY 14564 *Tel:* 585-385-3540 *Toll Free Tel:* 800-772-5267 *Fax:* 585-385-4976 *Toll Free Fax:* 800-257-0760 *E-mail:* info@bulbdirect.com *Web Site:* www.bulbdirect.com, pg 815

Smith, Donna, Chester F Carlson Award, 7003 Kilworth Lane, Springfield, VA 22151 *Tel:* 703-642-9090 *Fax:* 703-642-9094 *E-mail:* info@imaging.org *Web Site:* www.imaging.org, pg 1111

Smith, Donna, Society for Imaging Science and Technology (IS&T), 7003 Kilworth Lane, Springfield, VA 22151 *Tel:* 703-642-9090 *Fax:* 703-642-9094 *E-mail:* info@imaging.org *Web Site:* www.imaging.org, pg 1089

Smith, E L, Ellison Educational Equipment Inc, 25862 Commercentre Dr, Lake Forest, CA 92630-8804 *Tel:* 949-598-8822 *Toll Free Tel:* 800-253-2238 *Fax:* 949-598-8840 *Toll Free Fax:* 800-253-2240 *E-mail:* customersupport@ellison.com *Web Site:* www.ellison.com, pg 859

Smith, Edgar, Geomatrix Productions, 270 Amity Rd, Woodbridge, CT 06525-2267 *Tel:* 203-389-0001 *Web Site:* www.geomatrixproductions.com, pg 877

Smith, Eric, Auralex Acoustics Inc, 9955 Westpoint Dr, Suite 101, Indianapolis, IN 46256 *Tel:* 317-842-2600 *Toll Free Tel:* 800-95-WEDGE (959-3343, orders) *Fax:* 317-842-2760 *E-mail:* info@auralex.com *Web Site:* www.auralex.com, pg 796

Smith, Eric M, CMI Communications, 400 Mile Crossing Blvd, Rochester, NY 14624 *Tel:* 585-424-1900 *Toll Free Tel:* 888-736-8264 *Fax:* 585-424-1913 *E-mail:* info@cmiav.com *Web Site:* www.cmiav.com, pg 830

Smith, Frank, Franklin Video Inc, 931 Marilyn Dr, Raleigh, NC 27607 *Tel:* 919-833-8888 *Web Site:* www.franklinvideo.com, pg 872

Smith, George C, Smithall Electronics Inc, 2001 Vine St, Cincinnati, OH 45202 *Tel:* 513-381-2828 *Fax:* 513-381-5160 *Web Site:* www.smithall.com, pg 1014

Smith, Glenn, Mouser Electronics, 1000 N Main St, Mansfield, TX 76063-1514 *Tel:* 817-804-3888 *Toll Free Tel:* 800-346-6873 *Fax:* 817-804-3899 *Web Site:* www.mouser.com, pg 947

Smith, Gordon H, National Association of Broadcasters (NAB), 1771 "N" St NW, Washington, DC 20036 *Tel:* 202-429-5300 *Fax:* 202-429-4199 *E-mail:* nab@nab.org *Web Site:* www.nab.org, pg 1085

Smith, Greg, Arc Light Efx Inc, 9338 San Fernando Rd, Sun Valley, CA 91352 *Tel:* 818-394-6330 *Fax:* 818-252-3486 *E-mail:* gaslights@arclightefx.com *Web Site:* www.arclightefx.com, pg 789

Smith, Greg, Navigator Systems US, 1312 W Main St, Suite E, Lebanon, TN 37087 *Tel:* 615-547-1895 *Fax:* 615-547-1897 *E-mail:* sales@hiretrack.com *Web Site:* www.hiretrack.com, pg 953

Smith, Gregory Allgire, Residency Fellowship, 154 San Angelo Dr, Amherst, VA 24521 *Tel:* 434-946-7236 *Fax:* 434-946-7239 *E-mail:* vcca@vcca.com *Web Site:* www.vcca.com, pg 1125

Smith, Harry, Har-Ken Specialties, PO Box 37, Parkesburg, PA 19365-0037 *Tel:* 610-384-2161 *Fax:* 610-384-8258 *E-mail:* harken1@comcast.net *Web Site:* www.har-kenspecialties.com; www.har-ken.com, pg 884

Smith, Jamie L, Avatar Award, 550 W Frontage Rd, Suite 3600, Northfield, IL 60093 *Tel:* 847-716-7000 *Fax:* 847-716-7004 *E-mail:* info@mediafinance.org *Web Site:* www.mediafinance.org, pg 1108

Smith, Jamie L, Media Financial Management Association (MFM), 550 W Frontage Rd, Suite 3600, Northfield, IL 60093 *Tel:* 847-716-7000 *Fax:* 847-716-7004 *E-mail:* info@mediafinance.org *Web Site:* www.mediafinance.org, pg 1084

Smith, Jeff, Blonder Tongue Laboratories Inc, One Jake Brown Rd, Old Bridge, NJ 08857 *Tel:* 732-679-4000 *Toll Free Tel:* 800-523-6049 *Fax:* 732-679-4353 *E-mail:* custsvc@blondertongue.com; btglobalsales@blondertongue.com (other than US & CN) *Web Site:* www.blondertongue.com, pg 809

Smith, Jennifer, Avid Technology Inc, 65-75 Network Dr, Burlington, MA 01830 *Tel:* 978-640-6789 *Fax:* 978-640-3366 *Web Site:* www.avid.com, pg 799

Smith, Jennifer J, Xplor® International, 24156 State Rd 54, Suite 4, Lutz, FL 33559 *Tel:* 813-949-6170 *Toll Free Tel:* 800-669-7567 *Fax:* 813-949-9977 *E-mail:* info@xplor.org *Web Site:* www.xplor.org, pg 1090

Smith, Joseph, Bisk Education, 9417 Princess Palm Ave, Tampa, FL 33619 *Toll Free Tel:* 800-280-9718 *E-mail:* customerservice@bisk.com *Web Site:* www.bisk.com, pg 808

Smith, Judy, Waterfront Film Festival (WFF), PO Box 387, Saugatuck, MI 49453-0387 *Tel:* 269-857-8351 *Fax:* 269-857-1072 *E-mail:* info@waterfrontfilm.org *Web Site:* www.waterfrontfilm.org, pg 1129

Smith, Julie, Strand Lighting Inc, 10911 Petal St, Dallas, TX 75238 *Tel:* 214-647-7880 *Fax:* 214-647-8031 *E-mail:* sales@strandlighting.com *Web Site:* www.strandlighting.com, pg 1025

Smith, Kary, Arc Light Efx Inc, 9338 San Fernando Rd, Sun Valley, CA 91352 *Tel:* 818-394-6330 *Fax:* 818-252-3486 *E-mail:* gaslights@arclightefx.com *Web Site:* www.arclightefx.com, pg 789

Smith, Kathleen, Holbrook Film Commission, 465 N First Ave, Holbrook, AZ 86025 *Tel:* 928-524-6227 *Toll Free Tel:* 800-524-2459 *Fax:* 928-524-1719 *E-mail:* holbrook@gotouraz.com *Web Site:* www.gotouraz.com, pg 1091

Smith, Kelly, OSV Studios, 29605 Lorain Rd N, Olmsted, OH 44070 *Tel:* 440-779-1900 *Web Site:* www.osvstudios.com, pg 966

Smith, Linda W, National Religious Broadcasters (NRB), 9510 Technology Dr, Manassas, VA 20110 *Tel:* 703-330-7000 *Fax:* 703-330-7100 *E-mail:* info@nrb.org *Web Site:* www.nrb.org, pg 1086

Smith, Mark, T & M Digital Services, 54 Flint Ridge Rd, Monroe, CT 06468 *Tel:* 203-268-5290 *Fax:* 203-268-5290, pg 1031

Smith, Mary, Spot Media Production Group, 2745 Locust St, St Louis, MO 63103 *Tel:* 314-667-5915 *E-mail:* info@spotmpg.com *Web Site:* www.spotmpg.com, pg 1022

Smith, Matt, A/S Custom Furniture, 364-C Valley Rd, Warrington, PA 18976 *Tel:* 215-491-3100 *Fax:* 215-491-3107 *E-mail:* sales@ascustom.com *Web Site:* www.ascustom.com, pg 771

Smith, Matt, Jameco Electronics, 1355 Shoreway Rd, Belmont, CA 94002-4105 *Tel:* 650-592-8097 *Toll Free Tel:* 800-831-4242 (orders); 800-536-4316 (cust serv) *Fax:* 650-592-2503 *Toll Free Fax:* 800-237-6948 *E-mail:* info@jameco.com; sales@jameco.com *Web Site:* www.jameco.com, pg 904

Smith, Michael, Cinema Equipment Sales of California Inc, 24881 Alicia Pkwy, Suite E-326, Laguna Hills, CA 92653 *Tel:* 949-470-0298 *Fax:* 949-470-0835 *E-mail:* cinemadealer@cinemadealer.com *Web Site:* www.cinema-equip.com, pg 827

Smith, Mike, United Scenic Artists Local 829, 29 W 38 St, 15th fl, New York, NY 10018 *Tel:* 212-581-0300 *Fax:* 212-977-2011 *E-mail:* businessoffice@usa829.org *Web Site:* www.usa829.org; vfx.usa829.org, pg 1090

Smith, Nick, AV Concepts, 1917 W First St, Tempe, AZ 85281 *Tel:* 480-557-6000 *Toll Free Tel:* 866-927-7590 *Fax:* 480-894-8376 *E-mail:* info@avconcepts.com *Web Site:* www.avconcepts.com, pg 797

Smith, Paula, Cinema Equipment Sales of California Inc, 24881 Alicia Pkwy, Suite E-326, Laguna Hills, CA 92653 *Tel:* 949-470-0298 *Fax:* 949-470-0835 *E-mail:* cinemadealer@cinemadealer.com *Web Site:* www.cinema-equip.com, pg 827

Smith, Pete, Specialized Products Co, 1100 S Kimball Ave, Southlake, TX 76092 *Tel:* 817-329-6647 *Toll Free Tel:* 800-866-5353 *Fax:* 817-329-6195 *Toll Free Fax:* 800-234-8286 *E-mail:* info@specialized.net *Web Site:* www.specialized.net, pg 1020

Smith, R Bob III, Psychological Assessment Resources Inc (PAR), 16204 N Florida Ave, Lutz, FL 33549 *Tel:* 813-968-3003; 813-449-4065 (cust serv) *Toll Free Tel:* 800-331-8378 (tech support) *Fax:* 813-968-2598 *Toll Free Fax:* 800-727-9329 *Web Site:* www4.parinc.com, pg 987

Smith, Randy, PromaxBDA, 1522e Cloverfield Blvd, Santa Monica, CA 90404 *Tel:* 310-788-7600 *Fax:* 310-788-7616 *Web Site:* www.promaxbda.org, pg 1087

Smith, Randy, Winsted Corp, 10901 Hampshire Ave S, Minneapolis, MN 55438 *Tel:* 952-944-9050 *Toll Free Tel:* 800-447-2257 *Fax:* 952-944-1546 *Toll Free Fax:* 800-421-3839 *E-mail:* info@winsted.com *Web Site:* www.winsted.com, pg 1068

Smith, Robert, Zhone Technologies Inc, 7195 Oakport St, Oakland, CA 94621 *Tel:* 510-777-7000 *Toll Free Tel:* 877-ZHONE-20 (946-6320, US & CN) *Fax:* 510-777-7001 *E-mail:* info@zhone.com; sales@zhone.com *Web Site:* www.zhone.com, pg 1073

Smith, Ron, Martel Electronics Sales Inc, Yorba Linda Hills Business Park, 23221 E La Palma Ave, Yorba Linda, CA 92887 *Tel:* 714-692-6690 *Toll Free Tel:* 800-553-5536 *Fax:* 714-692-1799 *E-mail:* martelsales@marteldirect.com *Web Site:* www.martelelectronics.com, pg 932

Smith, Roy Sr, A/S Custom Furniture, 364-C Valley Rd, Warrington, PA 18976 *Tel:* 215-491-3100 *Fax:* 215-491-3107 *E-mail:* sales@ascustom.com *Web Site:* www.ascustom.com, pg 771

Smith, Ryan, Pogo Pictures, 114 E Ponce de Leon Ave, Suite B, Decatur, GA 30030 *Tel:* 404-892-9490 *Fax:* 404-892-9491 *E-mail:* info@pogopictures.com *Web Site:* www.pogopictures.com, pg 977

Smith, Sara, RingSide Creative, 13320 Northend, Suite 3000, Oak Park, MI 48237 *Tel:* 248-548-2500 *E-mail:* info@ringsidecreative.eom; newbiz@ringsidecreative.com *Web Site:* www.ringsidecreative.com, pg 997

Smith, Stephen M, John Wiley & Sons Inc, 111 River St, Hoboken, NJ 07030 *Tel:* 201-748-6000 *Toll Free Tel:* 800-225-5945 *Fax:* 201-748-6088 *E-mail:* info@wiley.com *Web Site:* www.wiley.com, pg 1066

Smith, Steve, Oasis Audio, 289 S Main Place, Carol Stream, IL 60188-2425 *Toll Free Tel:* 800-323-2500 *E-mail:* questions@oasisaudio.com *Web Site:* www.oasisaudio.com, pg 960

Smith, Steve, Revels Records, 80 Mount Auburn St, Watertown, MA 02472 *Tel:* 617-972-8300 *E-mail:* info@revels.org *Web Site:* www.revels.org, pg 995

Smith, Steve, Turner Broadcasting System Inc, One CNN Ctr, Atlanta, GA 30303 *Tel:* 404-827-1700 *Web Site:* www.turner.com, pg 1046

Smith, Steven T, Videosmith Inc, 200 Spring Garden St, Suite C, Philadelphia, PA 19123 *Tel:* 215-238-5070 *Fax:* 215-238-5075 *E-mail:* info@videosmith.com *Web Site:* videosmith.com, pg 1057

Smith, Tyson, HEC Reading Horizons, 60 N Cutler Dr, Suite 101, North Salt Lake, UT 84054 *Tel:* 801-295-7054 *Toll Free Tel:* 800-333-0054 *Fax:* 801-295-7088 *E-mail:* info@readinghorizons.com *Web Site:* www.readinghorizons.com, pg 887

Smith, Wendy, National Board of Review (of Motion Pictures), 40 W 37 St, Suite 501, New York, NY 10018 *Tel:* 212-465-9166 *Fax:* 212-465-9168 *E-mail:* nbr@nbrmp.org *Web Site:* www.nationalboardofreview.org, pg 1085

Smither, Jonathan, Tarpley Media Systems, 3737 50 St, Lubbock, TX 79413 *Tel:* 806-797-5833 *Toll Free Tel:* 800-600-5833 *Fax:* 806-797-5139 *E-mail:* tms@tarpleymedia.com *Web Site:* www.tarpleymedia.com, pg 1032

Smolian, Steven, Smolian Sound Studios, One Worman's Mill Ct, Frederick, MD 21701 *Tel:* 301-694-5134 *E-mail:* smolians@erols.com *Web Site:* www.soundsaver.com, pg 1014

Smolin, Rachel, Sennheiser Electronic Corp, One Enterprise Dr, Old Lyme, CT 06371 *Tel:* 860-434-9190 *Toll Free Tel:* 877-SENNHEISER (736-6434) *Fax:* 860-434-1759 *E-mail:* info@sennheiserusa.com *Web Site:* en-us.sennheiser.com, pg 1006

Smoote, Cydney, MAM-A Inc, 4250 Buckingham Dr, Suite 100, Colorado Springs, CO 80907 *Toll Free Tel:* 888-626-3472 *Fax:* 719-592-0057 *Toll Free Fax:* 888-923-7203 *E-mail:* info@mam-a.com *Web Site:* www.mam-a.com, pg 929

Smoots, Todd, Westworks Studios, 4100 E Dry Creek Rd, Littleton, CO 80122 *Toll Free Tel:* 800-491-1947 *E-mail:* info@westworksstudios.com *Web Site:* westworksstudios.com, pg 1064

Smylie, Bob, Bowie Audio Visual Enterprises Inc, 290 Highpoint Dr, Ridgeland, MS 39157 *Tel:* 601-957-6566 *Toll Free Tel:* 800-748-9030 *Fax:* 601-957-7042 *E-mail:* sales@bowieav.com *Web Site:* www.bowieav.com, pg 811

Smyth, Robert, Yellow Moon Press, PO Box 381316, Cambridge, MA 02238-1316 *Tel:* 617-776-2230 *Toll Free Tel:* 800-497-4385 *Fax:* 617-776-8246 *E-mail:* story@yellowmoon.com *Web Site:* www.yellowmoon.com, pg 1072

Smythe, William K Jr, NPES The Association for Suppliers of Printing, Publishing & Converting Technologies, 1899 Preston White Dr, Reston, VA 20191 *Tel:* 703-264-7200 *Fax:* 703-620-0994 *E-mail:* npes@npes.org *Web Site:* www.npes.org, pg 1087

Snavely, David, Association of Federal Communications Consulting Engineers (AFCCE), PO Box 19333, Washington, DC 20036-0333 *E-mail:* secretary@afcce.org *Web Site:* www.afcce.org, pg 1079

Snead, Paul, Sound/Video Impressions Inc, 110 S River Rd, Des Plaines, IL 60016 *Tel:* 847-297-4360 *Fax:* 847-297-6870 *E-mail:* info@soundvideoimpressions.com *Web Site:* www.soundvideoimpressions.com, pg 1018

Snell, David A, ATTO Technology Inc, 155 CrossPoint Pkwy, Amherst, NY 14068 *Tel:* 716-691-1999 *Fax:* 716-691-9353 *Web Site:* www.attotech.com, pg 793

Sneve, Shirley K, Vision Maker Media, 1800 N 33 St, Lincoln, NE 68503 *Tel:* 402-472-3522 *Fax:* 402-472-8675 *E-mail:* visionmaker@unl.edu *Web Site:* www.visionmakermedia.org, pg 1058

Snider, Dick, Innovative Electronic Designs LLC, 9701 Taylorsville Rd, Louisville, KY 40299 *Tel:* 502-267-7436 *Fax:* 502-267-9070 *E-mail:* info@iedaudio.com *Web Site:* www.iedaudio.com, pg 898

Snider, Kris, Pacific Radio Electronics, 3031 Thornton Ave, Burbank, CA 91504 *Tel:* 818-556-4177 *Toll Free Tel:* 800-634-9476 *Fax:* 818-556-4185 *E-mail:* sales@pacrad.com *Web Site:* www.pacrad.com, pg 967

Snipes, Kenneth, L'AIR International, 117 Vacek St, Fort Worth, TX 76107 *Tel:* 817-237-9390 *Toll Free Tel:* 844-243-8574 *Fax:* 817-237-9407 *E-mail:* info@lairfloors.com *Web Site:* www.lairfloors.com, pg 914

Snow, Dennis, Image Technologies Corp, 523 Hanley Industrial Ct, St Louis, MO 63144 *Tel:* 314-646-1800 *Toll Free Tel:* 800-962-2344 *Fax:* 314-646-1818 *Web Site:* www.imagetechnologies.com, pg 895

Snow, Sheila M, Monroe-West Monroe Convention & Visitors Bureau, 601 Constitution Dr, West Monroe, LA 71292 *Tel:* 318-387-5691 *Toll Free Tel:* 800-843-1872 *Fax:* 318-324-1752 *E-mail:* mwmcvb@monroe-westmonroe.org *Web Site:* www.monroe-westmonroe.org, pg 1098

Snyder, Daniel R, Audio Visions Inc, 1501 N George St, York, PA 17404 *Tel:* 717-843-1561 *Fax:* 717-848-3289 *Web Site:* www.audiovisionsinc.com, pg 795

Snyder, Frank PhD, Developmental Studies Center, 1250 53 St, Suite 3, Emeryville, CA 94608 *Tel:* 510-533-0213 *Toll Free Tel:* 800-666-7270 *Fax:* 510-464-3670 *E-mail:* info@devstu.org; customer_service@devstu.org *Web Site:* www.devstu.org, pg 846

Snyder, Jim, WETA Production Center, 3620 S 27 St, Arlington, VA 22206 *Tel:* 703-998-2054 *Fax:* 703-998-2706 *Web Site:* www.weta.org/tv/productioncenter, pg 1064

Snyder, Rick, Interactive Multimedia & Collaborative Communications Alliance (IMCCA), PO Box 756, Syosset, NY 11791 *Web Site:* www.imcca.org, pg 1083

Soares, Paul, Evertz Microsystems Ltd, 5292 John Lucas Dr, Burlington, ON L7L 5Z9, Canada *Tel:* 905-335-3700 *Toll Free Tel:* 877-995-3700 *Fax:* 905-335-3573 *E-mail:* sales@evertz.com *Web Site:* www.evertz.com, pg 863

Sobkowska, Anja, YAP Films, 96 Spadina Ave, Suite 205, Toronto, ON M5V 2J6, Canada *Tel:* 416-504-3662 *Fax:* 416-504-3667 *E-mail:* thedog@yapfilms.com *Web Site:* www.yapfilms.com, pg 1072

Sobrito, June Marie, The Citation of Outstanding Service to the Society Award, 3 Barker Ave, 5th fl, White Plains, NY 10601 *Tel:* 914-761-1100 *Fax:* 914-761-3115 *E-mail:* smpte@smpte.org *Web Site:* www.smpte.org, pg 1112

Sobrito, June Marie, The Journal Award & SMPTE Journal Certificate of Merit, 3 Barker Ave, 5th fl, White Plains, NY 10601 *Tel:* 914-761-1100 *Fax:* 914-761-3115 *E-mail:* smpte@smpte.org *Web Site:* www.smpte.org, pg 1118

Sobrito, June Marie, The Presidential Proclamation Award, 3 Barker Ave, 5th fl, White Plains, NY 10601 *Tel:* 914-761-1100 *Fax:* 914-761-3115 *E-mail:* smpte@smpte.org *Web Site:* www.smpte.org, pg 1124

Sobrito, June Marie, The Progress Medal Award, 3 Barker Ave, 5th fl, White Plains, NY 10601 *Tel:* 914-761-1100 *Fax:* 914-761-3115 *E-mail:* smpte@smpte.org *Web Site:* www.smpte.org, pg 1124

Sobrito, June Marie, Society of Motion Picture & Television Engineers (SMPTE), 3 Barker Ave, 5th fl, White Plains, NY 10601 *Tel:* 914-761-1100 *Fax:* 914-761-3115 *E-mail:* membership@smpte.org *Web Site:* www.smpte.org, pg 1089

Sobrito, June Marie, Technicolor-Herbert T Kalmus Gold Medal Award, 3 Barker Ave, 5th fl, White Plains, NY 10601 *Tel:* 914-761-1100 *Fax:* 914-761-3115 *E-mail:* smpte@smpte.org *Web Site:* www.smpte.org, pg 1128

Sobrito, June Marie, The Samuel L Warner Memorial Award, 3 Barker Ave, 5th fl, White Plains, NY 10601 *Tel:* 914-761-1100 *Fax:* 914-761-3115 *E-mail:* smpte@smpte.org *Web Site:* www.smpte.org, pg 1129

Socher, Jeff, Love Shack Recording Studios, 909 18 Ave S, Nashville, TN 37212 *Tel:* 615-843-0019 *E-mail:* book@loveshackstudios.com *Web Site:* loveshackstudios.com, pg 925

Soell, Alan, ABS Enterprises, PO Box 5127, Evanston, IL 60204-5127 *Tel:* 847-982-1414, pg 772

Sohrabkani, Azarin, Ottawa International Animation Festival, 2 Daly Ave, Suite 120, Ottawa, ON K1N 6E2, Canada *Tel:* 613-232-8769 *Fax:* 613-232-6315 *E-mail:* info@animationfestival.ca *Web Site:* www.animationfestival.ca, pg 1123

Soifer, Tyler, Side 3 Studios, 725 Mariposa St, Denver, CO 80204 *Tel:* 720-515-2649 *E-mail:* info@side3.com *Web Site:* www.side3.com, pg 1010

Soileau, Chris, Maison de Soul Records, 238 E Main St, Ville Platte, LA 70586 *Tel:* 337-363-2177 *Fax:* 337-363-2094 *E-mail:* info@flattownmusic.com *Web Site:* www.flattownmusic.com, pg 929

Soileau, Floyd, Flat Town Music Co, 238 E Main St, Ville Platte, LA 70856 *Tel:* 337-363-2177 *Fax:* 337-363-2094 *E-mail:* info@flattownmusic.com *Web Site:* www.flattownmusic.com, pg 869

Soileau, Floyd, Jin, 238 E Main St, Ville Platte, LA 70586 *Tel:* 337-363-2177 *Fax:* 337-363-2094 *E-mail:* info@flattownmusic.com *Web Site:* www.flattownmusic.com, pg 905

Soileau, Floyd, Maison de Soul Records, 238 E Main St, Ville Platte, LA 70586 *Tel:* 337-363-2177 *Fax:* 337-363-2094 *E-mail:* info@flattownmusic.com *Web Site:* www.flattownmusic.com, pg 929

Soileau, Floyd, Swallow, 238 E Main St, Drawer 10, Ville Platte, LA 70586 *Tel:* 337-363-2177 *Fax:* 337-363-2094 *E-mail:* info@flattownmusic.com *Web Site:* www.flattownmusic.com, pg 1029

Sokolov, Elliot, Elliot Sokolov Music, 149 Mountainview Rd, Patterson, NY 12563 *Tel:* 917-690-5487 *E-mail:* elliotsoko@aol.com *Web Site:* www.elliotsokolov.com, pg 1015

Sokolowsky, Leah, Film Florida, c/o Jennifer Parramore, St Petersburg-Clearwater Film Commission, 13805 58 St N, Suite 2-200, Clearwater, FL 33760 *E-mail:* info@filmflorida.org *Web Site:* www.filmflorida.org, pg 1081

Solin, Mike, Benchmark Media, 72 N State Rd, Suite 415, Briarcliff Manor, NY 10510 *Tel:* 914-762-3838 *Fax:* 914-762-3895 *E-mail:* benchmarkmedia.info@gmail.com *Web Site:* www.benchmarkmedia.info, pg 805

Solis, Amber, Mobilized Tech Systems, 4015 Blackthorn Dr, Vacaville, CA 95688 *Tel:* 707-602-5548 *Toll Free Tel:* 888-293-0869 *Fax:* 707-602-5549 *E-mail:* info@bigfootmobilecarts.com *Web Site:* www.bigfootmobilecarts.com, pg 944

Solis, Doug, Mobilized Tech Systems, 4015 Blackthorn Dr, Vacaville, CA 95688 *Tel:* 707-602-5548 *Toll Free Tel:* 888-293-0869 *Fax:* 707-602-5549 *E-mail:* info@bigfootmobilecarts.com *Web Site:* www.bigfootmobilecarts.com, pg 944

Solit, Adele, Celebrities Productions, c/o Clayton-Davis & Associates, 230 S Bemiston Ave, Suite 1400, St Louis, MO 63105 *Tel:* 314-862-7800 *Fax:* 314-721-5171 *E-mail:* idcda@aol.com *Web Site:* www.claytondavis.com, pg 822

Solomon, David, Lightspeed Technologies Inc, 11509 SW Herman Rd, Tualatin, OR 97062 *Tel:* 503-684-5538 *Toll Free Tel:* 800-732-8999 *Fax:* 503-684-3197 *Web Site:* www.lightspeed-tek.com, pg 921

Solomon, Leslie, VRSim Inc, 222 Pitkin St, Suite 119, East Hartford, CT 06108-3220 *Tel:* 860-893-0080 *E-mail:* info@vrsim.net *Web Site:* www.vrsim.net, pg 1061

Solomon, Melanie, Film & Creative Industries Nova Scotia, Historic Properties, Collins Bank Bldg, 3rd fl, 1883 Upper Water St, Suite 302, Halifax, NS B3J 1S9, Canada *Tel:* 902-424-7177 *Toll Free Tel:* 888-360-2111 *Fax:* 902-424-0617 *E-mail:* filmandcreativens@gov.ns.ca *Web Site:* www.filmandcreativens.ca, pg 1105

Solomon, Micah, Oasis CD Manufacturing, 7905 N Crescent Blvd, Delair, NJ 08110 *Toll Free Tel:* 888-296-2747 *Fax:* 540-987-8812 *Toll Free Fax:* 866-929-8402 *E-mail:* info@oasisrecording.com *Web Site:* www.oasisrecording.com, pg 961

Solotoff, Rocky, Toon Makers, 17333 Ludlow St, Granada Hills, CA 91344 *Tel:* 818-832-8666 *E-mail:* info@toonmakers.com *Web Site:* toonmakers.com, pg 1042

Sommers, David A, Photo Technicians Inc, 3664 N River Rd, Freeland, MI 48623 *Tel:* 989-751-8517 *Web Site:* www.phototechnicians.com, pg 974

Somo, Darren, GVISION USA Inc, 20532 Crescent Bay Dr, Lake Forest, CA 92630 *Tel:* 949-586-3338 *Fax:* 949-586-3398 *E-mail:* info@gvision-usa.com; gsales@gvision-usa.com *Web Site:* www.gvision-usa.com, pg 883

Sonder, Mark, Mark Sonder Productions Inc, 2479 Freezeland Rd, Linden, VA 22642 *Tel:* 540-636-1640 *E-mail:* inquiry@marksonderproductions.com *Web Site:* www.marksonderproductions.com, pg 931

Sonheim, Bill, Gaiam Inc, 833 W South Boulder Rd, PO Box 3095, Boulder, CO 80307-3095 *Tel:* 303-222-3600 *Toll Free Tel:* 877-989-6321 (cust serv) *Fax:* 303-222-3700 *E-mail:* customerservice@gaiam.com *Web Site:* www.gaiam.com, pg 875

Sonneborn, Jon, Really Good Stuff, 448 Pepper St, Monroe, CT 06468 *Tel:* 203-261-1920 *Toll Free Tel:* 800-366-1920 (orders); 877-867-1920 (cust serv) *Fax:* 203-268-1796 *Web Site:* www.reallygoodstuff.com, pg 992

Sooley, Ray, American Fibertek Inc, 120 Belmont Dr, Somerset, NJ 08873-4243 *Tel:* 732-302-0660 *Toll Free Tel:* 877-234-7200 *Fax:* 732-302-0667 *E-mail:* sales@americanfibertek.com; techinfo@americanfibertek.com *Web Site:* www.americanfibertek.com, pg 784

Soran, David, Audio Consultant Services Inc, 2133 S Bellair, Suite 5, Denver, CO 80222 *Tel:* 303-296-1885 *Web Site:* www.audio-consultants.com, pg 794

Sorensen, Robert, Wisconsin Technical College System Foundation Inc, One Foundation Circle, Waunakee, WI 53597-8914 *Tel:* 608-849-2424; 608-849-2400 *Toll Free Tel:* 800-821-6313 *Fax:* 608-849-2468 *E-mail:* foundation@wtcsf.tec.wi.us *Web Site:* www.wtcsf.tec.wi.us, pg 1068

Sorenson, L R "Skip", GatesAir, 5300 Kings Island Dr, Suite 101, Mason, OH 45040 *Tel:* 513-459-3400 *Fax:* 513-459-3796 *E-mail:* information@gatesair.com; orders@gatesair.com; support@gatesair.com *Web Site:* www.gatesair.com, pg 875

Sorenson, L R "Skip", Imagine Communications Corp, 3001 Dallas Pkwy, Suite 300, Frisco, TX 75034 *Tel:* 469-803-4900 *Toll Free Tel:* 866-4-IMAGINE (446-2446) *Fax:* 469-803-4899 *E-mail:* insidesales@imaginecommunications.com *Web Site:* www.imaginecommunications.com, pg 896

Soria, Lorenzo, Golden Globe Awards, 646 N Robertson Blvd, West Hollywood, CA 90069 *Tel:* 310-657-1731 *Fax:* 310-657-5576 *E-mail:* info@hfpa.org *Web Site:* www.hfpa.org, pg 1115

Sosa, Edward, Lux Mundi Production House, 1405 16 St, Racine, WI 53403 *Tel:* 262-619-1622 *E-mail:* producer@luxmundistudio.com *Web Site:* www.luxmundistudio.com, pg 926

Sosa, Richard, Lux Mundi Production House, 1405 16 St, Racine, WI 53403 *Tel:* 262-619-1622 *E-mail:* producer@luxmundistudio.com *Web Site:* www.luxmundistudio.com, pg 926

Sosenko, John, Bill Quinn Productions, PO Box 213, Ocean Gate, NJ 08740 *Tel:* 732-237-0525, pg 989

Soss, Martin, Raven Screen Corp, PO Box 691, Harriman, NY 10926 *Tel:* 845-782-1844 *Toll Free Tel:* 800-847-6906 *Fax:* 845-782-1840 *E-mail:* info@ravenscreen.com *Web Site:* www.ravenscreen.com, pg 992

Sotelo, Janine, VidCAD by Commsys Design LLC, 2010 E Lohman Ave, Suite 2, Las Cruces, NM 88001 *Tel:* 575-522-0003 *Toll Free Tel:* 800-VIDCAD-6 (843-2236 sales); 888-4-VIDTEC (484-3832 tech support) *Fax:* 575-635-4518 *E-mail:* sales@vidcad.com *Web Site:* www.vidcad.com, pg 1054

Sotelo, Jesse, The Video Project, 145 Ninth St, Suite 102, San Francisco, CA 94103 *Tel:* 415-981-9710 *Toll Free Tel:* 800-475-2638 *Toll Free Fax:* 888-562-9012 *E-mail:* orders@videoproject.com; support@videoproject.com *Web Site:* www.videoproject.com, pg 1056

Soudan, Debra Ann, Broadcast Video Productions LLC, 61 Briarwood Dr, Old Saybrook, CT 06475 *Tel:* 860-575-7247 *Fax:* 860-395-2036 *E-mail:* bvpusa@comcast.net, pg 813

Soudan, Kenneth, Broadcast Video Productions LLC, 61 Briarwood Dr, Old Saybrook, CT 06475 *Tel:* 860-575-7247 *Fax:* 860-395-2036 *E-mail:* bvpusa@comcast.net, pg 813

Soussan, Phil, The Recording Academy, 3030 Olympic Blvd, Santa Monica, CA 90404 *Tel:* 310-392-3777 *Fax:* 310-392-2306 *E-mail:* losangeles@grammy.com *Web Site:* www.grammy.org/recording-academy, pg 1088

Souto, Gerson, SES World Skies, 4 Research Way, Princeton, NJ 08540 *Tel:* 609-987-4000; 609-987-4200 *Fax:* 609-987-4517 *E-mail:* info@ses.com *Web Site:* www.ses.com, pg 1007

Souza, James, Pyro Spectaculars, 3196 N Locust Ave, Rialto, CA 92377 *Tel:* 909-355-8120 *Toll Free Tel:* 888-477-7976 *Fax:* 909-355-9813 *E-mail:* info@pyrospectaculars.com *Web Site:* www.pyrospectaculars.com, pg 988

Sowle, Michael, Astronomical Society of the Pacific, 390 Ashton Ave, San Francisco, CA 94112 *Tel:* 415-337-1100 *Toll Free Tel:* 800-335-2624 *Fax:* 415-337-5205 *E-mail:* service@astrosociety.org *Web Site:* astrosociety.org, pg 792

Spain, Jay, The Communications Group Inc, 502 S West St, Raleigh, NC 27601 *Tel:* 919-828-4086 *Toll Free Tel:* 800-595-2937 *E-mail:* info@cgfilm.com *Web Site:* www.cgfilm.com, pg 833

Spain, John J, On Location North Carolina, 2121 Atlantic Ave, Suite 106, Raleigh, NC 27604 *Tel:* 919-755-9488 *Toll Free Tel:* 888-469-4747 *Fax:* 919-832-7797 *E-mail:* info@onlocation-nc.com *Web Site:* www.onlocation-nc.com, pg 963

Spallone, Nicholas F, Morefield Communications Inc, 35 N 35 St, Camp Hill, PA 17011-2707 *Tel:* 717-761-6170 *Toll Free Tel:* 800-382-1266 *E-mail:* info@morefield.com *Web Site:* www.morefield.com, pg 946

Spani, Stuart, Norlynn Audio Visual Services, 1858 Beaulynn Place, North Vancouver, BC V7J 2T1, Canada *Tel:* 604-988-4996 *Fax:* 604-988-4996 *E-mail:* sales@norlynn.ca *Web Site:* www.norlynn.ca; www.reason-for-hope.com, pg 958

Spanier, Larry, WESCAM Inc, 649 N Service Rd W, Burlington, ON L7P 5B9, Canada *Tel:* 905-633-4000 *Toll Free Tel:* 800-668-4355 *Fax:* 905-633-4100 *E-mail:* sales.wescam@l-3com.com *Web Site:* www.wescam.com, pg 1063

Sparacio, Joseph, IMAX Corp, 2525 Speakman Dr, Mississauga, ON L5K 1B1, Canada *Tel:* 905-403-6500 *Fax:* 905-403-6450 *E-mail:* info@imax.com *Web Site:* www.imax.com, pg 896

Speaks, Valerie, Palace Costume & Prop Co, 835 N Fairfax Ave, Hollywood, CA 90046 *Tel:* 323-651-5458 *Fax:* 323-658-7133 *E-mail:* rentals@palacecostume.com *Web Site:* www.palacecostume.com, pg 967

Spear, Ty, Roconex Corp, 20 Marybill Dr S, Troy, OH 45373 *Tel:* 937-339-2616 *Fax:* 937-339-1470 *E-mail:* info@roconex.com *Web Site:* www.roconex.com, pg 998

Spears, Ross, James Agee Film Project, PO Box 73, Riverdale, MD 20738-0073 *Tel:* 301-277-3880 *E-mail:* jagee@cstone.net *Web Site:* www.ageefilms.org, pg 904

Spears, Scott, Production Partners Media, 520 Enterprise Dr, Suite C, Lewis Center, OH 43035 *Tel:* 614-888-4888 *Web Site:* productionpartnersmedia.com, pg 984

Speckels, Larry, One Touch Systems Inc, 2346 Bering Dr, San Jose, CA 95131 *Tel:* 408-660-8435 *Fax:* 408-436-4699 *E-mail:* info@onetouchsys.com *Web Site:* www.onetouchsys.com, pg 963

Spellisey, Tim, Global Television Station, 5325 Allard Way, Edmonton, AB T6H 5B8, Canada *Tel:* 780-436-1250; 780-989-4683 *Fax:* 780-989-4686 *E-mail:* globalnews.ed@globaltv.com *Web Site:* www.globaltv.com, pg 879

Spence, Carl, Golden Space Needle Awards, 305 Harrison St, Seattle, WA 98109 *Tel:* 206-464-5830 *Fax:* 206-264-7919 *E-mail:* info@siff.net *Web Site:* www.siff.net, pg 1116

Spence, Carl, Seattle International Film Festival (SIFF), 305 Harrison St, Seattle, WA 98109 *Tel:* 206-464-5830 *Fax:* 206-264-7919 *E-mail:* info@siff.net *Web Site:* www.siff.net, pg 1127

Spence, Susan, Television Academy, 5220 Lankershim Blvd, North Hollywood, CA 91601-3109 *Tel:* 818-754-2800 *Fax:* 818-761-2827 *Web Site:* www.emmys.com, pg 1089

Spence-Thomas, Richard, Spence-Thomas Audio Post, 70 Richmond St E, Suite 300, Toronto, ON M5C 1N8, Canada *Tel:* 416-361-6383 *Toll Free Tel:* 866-547-2617 *Fax:* 416-361-2970 *E-mail:* info@spence-thomas.com; bookings@spence-thomas.com *Web Site:* www.spence-thomas.com, pg 1021

Spencer, Charity, NuMynd Studios, 915 Twin Elms Ct, Nashville, TN 37210 *Tel:* 615-259-1143 *Fax:* 615-259-1141 *E-mail:* hello@numyndstudios.com *Web Site:* www.numyndstudios.com, pg 960

Spencer, Geoff, Sonance, 212 Avenida Fabricante, San Clemente, CA 92672-7531 *Tel:* 949-492-7777 *Toll Free Tel:* 800-592-4644; 800-582-0772 (tech support); 800-582-7777 *Toll Free Fax:* 800-538-5151 *E-mail:* customerservice@sonance.com *Web Site:* www.sonance.com, pg 1015

Spencer, Greg, Blue Wave Records, 3221 Perryville Rd, Baldwinsville, NY 13027 *Tel:* 315-638-4286 *Fax:* 315-635-4757 *E-mail:* bluewave@localnet.com *Web Site:* www.bluewaverecords.com, pg 810

Spencer, James R, Video Learning Library, 15838 N 62 St, Scottsdale, AZ 85254-1988 *Tel:* 480-596-9970 *Toll Free Tel:* 800-383-8811 (orders) *E-mail:* videos@videolearning.com *Web Site:* www.videolearning.com, pg 1055

Spencer, Kellie, Roundabout Entertainment Inc, 217 S Lake St, Burbank, CA 91502 *Tel:* 818-842-9300 *Fax:* 818-842-9301 *E-mail:* info@roundabout.com *Web Site:* www.roundabout.com, pg 1000

Spenneberg, Joe, Magick Lantern, 750 Ralph McGill Blvd, Atlanta, GA 30312 *Tel:* 404-688-3348 *Fax:* 404-584-5247 *E-mail:* info@magicklantern.com *Web Site:* magicklantern.com, pg 928

Sperling, Ehud, Inner Traditions International, One Park St, Rochester, VT 05767 *Tel:* 802-767-3174 *Toll Free Tel:* 800-246-8648 *Fax:* 802-767-3726 *E-mail:* customerservice@innertraditions.com *Web Site:* www.innertraditions.com, pg 898

Sperry, Mary E, USCCB Publishing, 3211 Fourth St NE, Washington, DC 20017 *Tel:* 202-541-3090 *Toll Free Tel:* 800-235-8722 (cust serv) *Fax:* 202-722-8709 (cust serv) *E-mail:* publications@usccb.org *Web Site:* www.usccbpublishing.org, pg 1051

Spezialetti, Gary, J E Foss Co, 3328-B Industrial Blvd, Bethel Park, PA 15102 *Tel:* 412-564-5644 *Toll Free Tel:* 800-245-6240 *Fax:* 412-564-5646 *E-mail:* jefoss@earthlink.net *Web Site:* www.jefoss.com, pg 871

Spica, Tony, RGB Spectrum, 950 Marina Village Pkwy, Alameda, CA 94501 *Tel:* 510-814-7000 *Fax:* 510-814-7026 *E-mail:* sales@rgb.com *Web Site:* www.rgb.com, pg 996

Spichtig, Alexandra, Taylor Associates, 110 W Canal St, Suite 301, Winooski, VT 05404 *Tel:* 802-735-1942 *Toll Free Tel:* 800-READ-PLUS (732-3758) *Fax:* 802-419-4786 *E-mail:* info@readingplus.com *Web Site:* www.readingplus.com, pg 1032

Spiegal, Ron, Astoria Communications Inc, 12054 Miramar Pkwy, Miami, FL 33025 *Tel:* 305-728-4280 *Toll Free Tel:* 877-GETMEAV (438-6328) *Fax:* 305-728-4285 *Web Site:* www.getmeav.com, pg 792

Spier, Ed, WGVU TV, 301 Fulton St W, Grand Rapids, MI 49504-6492 *Tel:* 616-331-6666 *Toll Free Tel:* 800-442-2771 *E-mail:* wgvu@gvsu.edu *Web Site:* www.wgvu.org, pg 1065

Spiersch, Sue, Latham Foundation Publications, Latham Plaza Bldg, 1826 Clement Ave, Alameda, CA 94501 *Tel:* 510-521-0920 *Fax:* 510-521-9861 *E-mail:* info@latham.org *Web Site:* www.latham.org, pg 916

Spillman, Seth, Oklahoma City Convention & Visitors Bureau, 123 Park Ave, Oklahoma City, OK 73102 *Tel:* 405-297-8912 *Toll Free Tel:* 800-225-5652 *Fax:* 405-297-8888 *E-mail:* contact@visitokc.com *Web Site:* www.visitokc.org, pg 1101

Spire, Joanne, Spire Audio Visual Co Inc, 12170 SW 128 Ct, Unit 105, Miami, FL 33186 *Tel:* 305-378-5334; 786-367-3408 (cell) *Fax:* 786-397-7462 *Web Site:* www.spireav.com, pg 1021

Spire, John, Spire Audio Visual Co Inc, 12170 SW 128 Ct, Unit 105, Miami, FL 33186 *Tel:* 305-378-5334; 786-367-3408 (cell) *Fax:* 786-397-7462 *Web Site:* www.spireav.com, pg 1021

Spitzmiller, Don, CFP Video Productions Inc, PO Box 86, Caldwell, NJ 07006-0086 *Tel:* 973-226-2481 *Fax:* 973-226-2480 *Web Site:* cfpvideo.com, pg 823

Spizzirri, Linda, Spizzirri Press Inc, PO Box 9397, Rapid City, SD 57709-9397 *Tel:* 605-348-2749 *Toll Free Tel:* 800-325-9819 *Fax:* 605-348-6251 *Toll Free Fax:* 800-322-9819 *E-mail:* spizzpub@aol.com *Web Site:* www.spizzirri.com, pg 1021

Spizzirri, Peter, Spizzirri Press Inc, PO Box 9397, Rapid City, SD 57709-9397 *Tel:* 605-348-2749 *Toll Free Tel:* 800-325-9819 *Fax:* 605-348-6251 *Toll Free Fax:* 800-322-9819 *E-mail:* spizzpub@aol.com *Web Site:* www.spizzirri.com, pg 1021

Spollen, Dan, Aydin Displays Inc, One Riga Lane, Birdsboro, PA 19508 *Tel:* 610-404-7400; 610-404-5353 (sales) *Toll Free Tel:* 866-367-2934 *Fax:* 610-404-8190 *E-mail:* sales1@aydindisplays.com; orders@aydindisplays.com *Web Site:* www.aydindisplays.com, pg 800

Spooner, Becky, Video West Inc, 570 W Southern Ave, Tempe, AZ 85282 *Tel:* 480-222-3180 *Fax:* 480-222-3191 *E-mail:* info@videowestinc.com *Web Site:* www.videowestinc.com, pg 1056

Sporcic, Andrea, Missouri Film Commission, 301 W High St, Suite 720, Jefferson City, MO 65101 *Tel:* 573-526-3566 *E-mail:* mofilm@ded.mo.gov *Web Site:* www.mofilm.org, pg 1099

Spoto, Ashley, Crossroads Audio Inc, 2623 Myrtle Springs Ave, Dallas, TX 75220 *Tel:* 214-358-2623 *Toll Free Tel:* 800-287-0436 *Fax:* 214-358-0185 *E-mail:* mail@crossroadsaudio.com *Web Site:* www.crossroadsaudio.com, pg 840

Spoto, Charles, Satellite Technology Systems Inc, 4702 State Rte 176, Unit F, Crystal Lake, IL 60014 *Tel:* 815-482-0224 *Toll Free Tel:* 800-838-1472 *Fax:* 815-568-8478 *E-mail:* sts@mc.net *Web Site:* www.satellitetechsys.com, pg 1003

Spoto, Ed, Crossroads Audio Inc, 2623 Myrtle Springs Ave, Dallas, TX 75220 *Tel:* 214-358-2623 *Toll Free Tel:* 800-287-0436 *Fax:* 214-358-0185 *E-mail:* mail@crossroadsaudio.com *Web Site:* www.crossroadsaudio.com, pg 840

Sprague, Jennifer, Warner/Chappell Production Music, 1030 16 Ave S, Nashville, TN 37212 *Toll Free Tel:* 888-615-8729 *Fax:* 615-242-2455 *E-mail:* info@warnerchappellpm.com *Web Site:* www.warnerchappellpm.com/615-music, pg 1062

Spratt, Andy, Family Health Media, PO Box 5832, Charlottesville, VA 22905-5832 *Tel:* 434-566-0123 *Toll Free Tel:* 800-366-3641 *Toll Free Fax:* 888-234-2579 *E-mail:* support@familyhealthmedia.com *Web Site:* www.familyhealthmedia.com, pg 865

Sprei, Doug, Learning Ally, 20 Roszel Rd, Princeton, NJ 08540 *Tel:* 609-750-1830 *Toll Free Tel:* 800-221-4792 (memb support) *E-mail:* custserv@learningally.org *Web Site:* www.learningally.org, pg 917

Spring, Steven L, Aspen Systems Inc, 3900 Youngfield St, Wheat Ridge, CO 80033-3865 *Tel:* 303-431-4606 *Toll Free Tel:* 800-992-9242 *Fax:* 303-431-7196 *E-mail:* sales@aspsys.com *Web Site:* www.aspsys.com, pg 792

Springer, Jim, Capital Communications Inc, 2357-3, S Tamiami Trail, Venice, FL 34293 *Tel:* 941-539-6741 *E-mail:* cap5678@isp.com, pg 819

Springs, Cliff, Genesis Creative, 1006 Hafely Ct, Cayce, SC 29033 *Tel:* 803-796-9666 *E-mail:* geninfo@gencreative.com *Web Site:* genesisstudiossc.com, pg 877

Sprinkle, Marilyn J, Trance Formations Unlimited, 1425 Steele St, Laramie, WY 82070 *Tel:* 307-745-7897, pg 1043

Sprinkle, R Leo, Trance Formations Unlimited, 1425 Steele St, Laramie, WY 82070 *Tel:* 307-745-7897, pg 1043

Sprows, Marybeth, Paulist Productions, 17575 Pacific Coast Hwy, Pacific Palisades, CA 90272-4128 *Tel:* 310-454-0688 *Toll Free Tel:* 800-624-8613 *Fax:* 310-459-6549 *E-mail:* paulistmail@paulistproductions.org *Web Site:* www.paulistproductions.org, pg 970

Spruill, Vicki, Council on Foundations, 2121 Crystal Dr, Suite 700, Arlington, VA 22202 *Toll Free Tel:* 800-673-9036 *Web Site:* www.cof.org, pg 837

Sprumont, Joseph, American Thermoplastic Co, 106 Gamma Dr, Pittsburgh, PA 15238 *Tel:* 412-967-0900 *Toll Free Tel:* 800-245-6600 *Fax:* 412-967-9990 *E-mail:* atc@binders.com *Web Site:* www.binders.com, pg 785

Squair, Juliette, Audio Network US Inc, 48 W 25 St, 10th fl, New York, NY 10010 *Tel:* 646-688-4320 *E-mail:* nyoffice@audionetwork.com *Web Site:* us.audionetwork.com, pg 794

St George, Cassandra, Bond Street Studio, 235 Bond St, Brooklyn, NY 11217 *Tel:* 718-858-2238 *Fax:* 718-858-2239 *E-mail:* info@bondstreetstudio.com *Web Site:* www.bondstreetstudio.com, pg 810

St Germain, Norm, APS Lighting-Sound-AV, 901 Columbia Circle, Merrimack, NH 03054 *Tel:* 603-424-9198 *Toll Free Tel:* 800-837-0005 *Fax:* 603-423-9816 *E-mail:* info@apslightingnh.com *Web Site:* www.apslightingnh.com, pg 789

St John, Lorna, Hamilton Studio, 1427 W Dean Ave, Spokane, WA 99201 *Tel:* 509-327-9501 *Web Site:* www.hamiltonstudio.com, pg 884

St Lifer, Evan, Scholastic Library Publishing, 90 Sherman Tpke, Danbury, CT 06816 *Toll Free Tel:* 800-621-1115 (cust serv) *Toll Free Fax:* 866-783-4361 *Web Site:* www.scholastic.com/aboutscholastic/librarypublishing.htm, pg 1004

St Louis, Tim, Sharp's Audio-Visual Ltd, 3636 Seventh St SE, Calgary, AB T2G 2Y8, Canada *Tel:* 403-255-4123 *Toll Free Tel:* 800-491-1121 *Fax:* 403-255-3478 *E-mail:* sales@sharpsav.com *Web Site:* www.sharpsav.com, pg 1008

Stabenau, Jeff, Giant Interactive, 88 Tenth Ave, Suite 6-W, New York, NY 10011 *Tel:* 212-675-7300 *Fax:* 212-765-9336 *E-mail:* info@giant-interactive.com *Web Site:* www.giant-interactive.com, pg 878

Stables, LeeAnne, Paramount Pictures Corporation, 5555 Melrose Ave, Los Angeles, CA 90038 *Tel:* 323-956-8398 *Web Site:* www.paramount.com, pg 969

Stack, Therisa, Tom Stack & Associates Inc, 154 Tequesta St, Tavernier, FL 33070 *Tel:* 305-852-5520 *E-mail:* tomstack@earthlink.net *Web Site:* tomstackassociates.photoshelter.com, pg 1022

Stack, Tom, Tom Stack & Associates Inc, 154 Tequesta St, Tavernier, FL 33070 *Tel:* 305-852-5520 *E-mail:* tomstack@earthlink.net *Web Site:* tomstackassociates.photoshelter.com, pg 1022

Stadin, Richard, Mastervision Inc, 969 Park Ave, New York, NY 10028 *Tel:* 212-879-0448 *Toll Free Tel:* 800-876-0091 (order info) *Fax:* 212-744-3560 *Web Site:* www.mastervision.com, pg 933

Stadulis, Emily, Hollywood Lights Inc, 5251 SE McLoughlin Blvd, Portland, OR 97202-4836 *Tel:* 503-232-9001; 503-232-8855 *Toll Free Tel:* 800-826-9881 *Fax:* 503-517-8686 *E-mail:* portland@hollywoodlights.biz *Web Site:* www.hollywoodlights.biz, pg 890

Stafford, Clay, American Blackguard Inc, PO Box 680686, Franklin, TN 37068-0686 *Tel:* 615-599-4032 *E-mail:* contact@americanblackguard.com *Web Site:* www.americanblackguard.com, pg 784

Stafford, David, McGraw-Hill School Education Group, 8787 Orion Place, Columbus, OH 43240-4027 *Tel:* 614-430-4000 *Toll Free Tel:* 800-334-7734 *Fax:* 614-755-5682 *E-mail:* customer.service@mcgraw-hill.com *Web Site:* www.mcgraw-hill.com, pg 935

Staggs, Deny, Montana Film Office, 301 S Park Ave, Helena, MT 59620 *Tel:* 406-841-2876 *Toll Free Tel:* 800-553-4563 *Fax:* 406-841-2877 *E-mail:* montanafilm@mt.gov *Web Site:* www.montanafilm.com, pg 1099

Staley, Steve, Kentucky Grip & Lighting, 1340 Connor Station Rd, Simpsonville, KY 40067 *Tel:* 502-548-5833 *E-mail:* sstaley@iglou.com *Web Site:* www.kentuckyvideo.net; www.kentuckygrip.com, pg 909

Stalkfleet, Rick, Rauland-Borg Corp, 1802 W Central Rd, Mount Prospect, IL 60056 *Tel:* 847-590-7100 *Toll Free Tel:* 800-752-7725 *Web Site:* www.rauland.com, pg 991

Stall, Mark A, Pro Studio Supply, 140 S Park St, Oconomowoc, WI 53066 *Tel:* 262-567-8047 *Toll Free Tel:* 800-558-0114 *Fax:* 262-567-8479 *E-mail:* mail2@prostudiousa.com; sales@prostudiousa.com *Web Site:* www.prostudiousa.com, pg 983

Stall, Sean E, Ironik Design & Post, 56 E Main St, Suite 203, Avon, CT 06001 *Tel:* 860-404-2386 *Fax:* 860-404-2735 *E-mail:* info@ironikdesign.com *Web Site:* www.ironikdesign.com, pg 902

Stallsmith, Mark, Audio Visual Media, 1141 Lexington Ave, Mansfield, OH 44907 *Tel:* 419-756-2698 *Fax:* 419-756-1560 *E-mail:* avm2698@aol.com *Web Site:* audiovisualmedia.net, pg 795

Stamatopoulos, Dino, Starburns Industries, 1700 W Burbank Blvd, Burbank, CA 91506 *Tel:* 818-433-3300 *Fax:* 818-433-3383 *Web Site:* www.starburnsindustries.com, pg 1024

Stamm, Alan, 30 Second Films, 3019 Pico Blvd, Santa Monica, CA 90405 *Tel:* 310-315-1750 *Fax:* 310-315-1757 *E-mail:* sales@30secondfilms.com *Web Site:* www.30secondfilms.com, pg 1039

Stamper, Steven, Canvys™, 40W267 Keslinger Rd, La Fox, IL 60147-0393 *Toll Free Tel:* 888-735-7373 *Fax:* 630-208-2830 *Web Site:* www.canvys.com, pg 819

Stampone, Enzo, Entel Systems Inc, 230 W Parkway, Pompton Plains, NJ 07444 *Tel:* 201-447-2000 *Toll Free Tel:* 888-914-7100 *Fax:* 201-447-2880 *E-mail:* service@entelsystems.com *Web Site:* www.entelsystems.com, pg 861

Stancil, John, Technomedia Solutions, 4545 36 St, Orlando, FL 32811 *Tel:* 407-351-0909 *Fax:* 407-248-9484 *E-mail:* sales@gotechnomedia.com *Web Site:* www.gotechnomedia.com, pg 1035

Standard, Gary, WorldStage, 259 W 30 St, 12th fl, New York, NY 10001-2863 *Tel:* 212-582-2345 *Fax:* 718-610-1750 *E-mail:* info@worldstage.com *Web Site:* www.worldstage.com, pg 1070

Standing, Dean, Rane, 10802 47 Ave W, Mukilteo, WA 98275-5000 *Tel:* 425-355-6000 *E-mail:* info@rane.com *Web Site:* www.rane.com, pg 991

Stanek, Stan, Alpha Video & Audio Inc, 7711 Computer Ave, Edina, MN 55435 *Tel:* 952-896-9898 *Toll Free Tel:* 800-388-0008 *Fax:* 952-896-9899 *E-mail:* info@alphavideo.com *Web Site:* www.alphavideo.com, pg 782

Stanfield, Colin, Nantucket Film Festival (NFF), 68 Jay St, Suite 319, Brooklyn, NY 11201 *Tel:* 646-480-1900; 508-325-6274 *Fax:* 646-365-3367 *E-mail:* info@nantucketfilmfestival.org *Web Site:* www.nantucketfilmfestival.org, pg 1121

Stanfield, James EdD, James Stanfield Co Inc, 129 S Quarantina St, Santa Barbara, CA 93103 *Tel:* 805-897-1185 *Toll Free Tel:* 800-421-6534 *Fax:* 805-897-1187 *E-mail:* maindesk@stanfield.com *Web Site:* www.stanfield.com, pg 1023

Stango, Mike, RTS Inc, 40-11 Burt Dr, Deer Park, NY 11729 *Tel:* 631-242-6801 *Fax:* 631-242-6808 *E-mail:* rtsinc@rcn.com *Web Site:* www.rtsphoto.com, pg 1000

Stankoski, Michael, JungleTV, 571 NW Mercantile Place, Port St Lucie, FL 34986 *Tel:* 772-370-0043 *E-mail:* info@jungletv.com *Web Site:* www.jungletv.com, pg 907

Stanley, Jay S, Jay S Stanley & Associates Inc, 5313 McClanahan Dr, Suite G-5, North Little Rock, AR 72116 *Tel:* 501-758-8029 *Toll Free Tel:* 888-758-4728 *Fax:* 501-758-8037 *E-mail:* info@jaystanley.com *Web Site:* www.jaystanley.com, pg 1023

Stansky, Hyman, Harbor House Studios, 2525 Florence Rd, Suite B, Keller, TX 76262 *Tel:* 817-379-1500 *Fax:* 817-337-5104 *E-mail:* info@harborhousestudios.com *Web Site:* www.harborhousestudios.com, pg 884

Stanton, Andrew, Clever Devices Ltd, 300 Crossways Park Dr, Woodburg, NY 11797 *Tel:* 516-433-6100 *Toll Free Tel:* 800-872-6129 *Web Site:* www.cleverdevices.com, pg 830

Stanton, William, Main Point Productions, 295 Lobachsville Rd, Oley, PA 19547 *Tel:* 610-987-9320 *E-mail:* mainpoint@dejazzd.com, pg 929

Staples, Michael, Opterna AM, 44901 Falcon Place, Suite 116, Sterling, VA 20166-9531 *Tel:* 703-653-1130 *Toll Free Tel:* 800-248-9004 *Fax:* 703-803-8313 *Web Site:* www.opterna-am.com, pg 964

Stark, Chris D, Ballantyne Strong Inc, 13710 FNB Pkwy, Suite 400, Omaha, NE 68154 *Tel:* 402-453-4444 *Toll Free Tel:* 800-424-1215 *Fax:* 402-453-7238 *E-mail:* info@btn-inc.com *Web Site:* ballantynestrong.com, pg 802

Stark, Christopher, Trans-Lux Multimedia Corp, 950 Third Ave, Suite 2804, New York, NY 10022 *Tel:* 203-853-4321 *Toll Free Tel:* 800-243-5544; 800-462-2716 *Fax:* 203-229-0691 *Web Site:* www.trans-lux.com, pg 1043

Starks, Shirley, Set Decorators Society of America (SDSA), 7100 Tujunga Ave, Suite A, North Hollywood, CA 91605 *Tel:* 818-255-2425 *Fax:* 818-982-8597 *E-mail:* sdsa@setdecorators.org *Web Site:* www.setdecorators.org, pg 1088

Starner, Barbara Kazmark, Kart-A-Bag Manufacturing Inc, 510 Manhattan Rd, Joliet, IL 60433 *Tel:* 815-723-1940 *Toll Free Tel:* 800-423-9328 *Fax:* 815-723-2495 *E-mail:* bks@kart-a-bag.com *Web Site:* www.kart-a-bag.com, pg 908

Starns, Rod, Running Pony Productions LLC, 1770 Kirby Pkwy, Suite 118, Memphis, TN 38138 *Tel:* 901-683-6693 *Toll Free Tel:* 877-891-7669 *Fax:* 901-683-3093 *E-mail:* info@runningpony.com *Web Site:* www.runningpony.com, pg 1001

Starobin, Becky, Bridge Records Inc, 200 Clinton Ave, New Rochelle, NY 10801 *Tel:* 914-654-9270 *E-mail:* bridgerec@bridgerecords.com *Web Site:* www.bridgerecords.com, pg 812

Starobin, David, Bridge Records Inc, 200 Clinton Ave, New Rochelle, NY 10801 *Tel:* 914-654-9270 *E-mail:* bridgerec@bridgerecords.com *Web Site:* www.bridgerecords.com, pg 812

Starobin, Robert, Bridge Records Inc, 200 Clinton Ave, New Rochelle, NY 10801 *Tel:* 914-654-9270 *E-mail:* bridgerec@bridgerecords.com *Web Site:* www.bridgerecords.com, pg 812

Staropoli, James, Sentry Industries Inc, One Bridge St, Hillburn, NY 10931-0885 *Tel:* 845-753-2910 *Fax:* 845-753-2920 *E-mail:* techsupport@sentryindustries.com *Web Site:* www.sentryindustries.com, pg 1007

Starr, Charlie, Audio & Light, 2209 Randleman Rd, Greensboro, NC 27406 *Tel:* 336-274-1234 *Fax:* 336-274-4022 *E-mail:* info@audio-light.com *Web Site:* www.audio-light.com, pg 794

Stasio, Megan, Data Projections Inc, 3700 W Sam Houston Pkwy S, Suite 525, Houston, TX 77042 *Tel:* 713-781-1999 *Toll Free Tel:* 866-225-5374 *Fax:* 713-781-3338 *Web Site:* www.dataprojections.com, pg 843

Stauber, Barry, Oklahoma Sound Corp, 149 Entin Rd, Clifton, NJ 07014 *Tel:* 973-594-9000 *Toll Free Tel:* 800-261-4112 *Fax:* 201-322-2104 *E-mail:* info@oklahomasound.com *Web Site:* www.oklahomasound.com, pg 961

Stauffer, Jim, HOThead, 56 W 45 St, 17th fl, New York, NY 10036 *Tel:* 212-575-5566 *Fax:* 212-575-1070 *E-mail:* info@hothead.tv *Web Site:* www.hothead.tv, pg 891

Staverman, Heather, ASPRS: The Imaging and Geospatial Information Society, 5410 Grosvenor Lane, Suite 210, Bethesda, MD 20814-2160 *Tel:* 301-493-0290 *Fax:* 301-493-0208 *E-mail:* asprs@asprs.org *Web Site:* www.asprs.org, pg 1078

Stavrev, Jordan, Cinema Entertainment Inc, 1779 NW 79 Ave, Doral, FL 33126 *Tel:* 561-899-0721 *E-mail:* info@cinemaent.com *Web Site:* cinemaent.com, pg 827

Staylor, Anne Farrell, Staylor-Made Communications Inc, 11835 Carmel Mountain Rd, Suite 1304-365, San Diego, CA 92128-4609 *Tel:* 858-779-4266 *Toll Free Tel:* 800-711-6699 *E-mail:* info@staylor-made.com *Web Site:* staylor-made.com, pg 1024

Staylor, Jim, Staylor-Made Communications Inc, 11835 Carmel Mountain Rd, Suite 1304-365, San Diego, CA 92128-4609 *Tel:* 858-779-4266 *Toll Free Tel:* 800-711-6699 *E-mail:* info@staylor-made.com *Web Site:* staylor-made.com, pg 1024

Stearn, Lynn, POP TV, 5069 Maureen Lane, Moorpark, CA 93021-7127 *Tel:* 805-499-8513 *Toll Free Tel:* 800-331-4626 *Fax:* 805-499-8206 *E-mail:* sales@mpo-video.com *Web Site:* www.mpo-video.com, pg 978

Stechly, Paul, Applied Electronics Ltd, 1260 Kamato Rd, Mississauga, ON L4W 1Y1, Canada *Tel:* 905-625-4321 *Fax:* 905-625-4333 *E-mail:* ael.toronto@appliedelectronics.com *Web Site:* www.appliedelectronics.com, pg 789

Steeb, Christian, Arkwright Advanced Coating Inc, 538 Main St, Fiskeville, RI 02823 *Tel:* 401-821-1000 *Toll Free Tel:* 800-556-6866 *Web Site:* www.sihlusa.com, pg 790

Steele, Andrew, TVO/Ontario Educational Communications Authority (OECA), 2180 Yonge St, Toronto, ON M4S 2B9, Canada *Tel:* 416-484-2600; 416-484-2665 (cust rel) *Toll Free Tel:* 800-613-0513; 800-INFO-TVO (463-6886) *E-mail:* asktvo@tvo.org *Web Site:* tvo.org, pg 1046

Steenson, Keeley, Cine Las Americas International Film Festival (CLAIFF), 81 San Marcos St, Austin, TX 78702 *Tel:* 512-535-0765 *Fax:* 512-535-6268 *E-mail:* cine@cinelasamericas.org *Web Site:* www.cinelasamericas.org; www.facebook.com/cinelasamericasaustin, pg 1112

Steffens, Lucy, Sacramento Film Commission, 1608 "I" St, Sacramento, CA 95814-2042 *Tel:* 916-808-7777 *Fax:* 916-808-7788 *Web Site:* www.filmsacramento.com, pg 1094

Steger, Harry, Docter Optics Inc, 1425 W Elliot Rd, Suite A-105, Gilbert, AZ 85233 *Tel:* 480-844-7585 *Fax:* 480-844-7826 *E-mail:* doi@docteroptics.com *Web Site:* www.docteroptics.com, pg 850

Stehlik, Milos, Facets Multi-Media Inc, 1517 W Fullerton Ave, Chicago, IL 60614 *Tel:* 773-281-9075 (ext 3011) *Toll Free Tel:* 800-331-6197 *Fax:* 773-929-5437 *E-mail:* sales@facets.org *Web Site:* www.facets.org, pg 865

Stehlin, David, MRV Communications Inc, 20415 Nordhoff St, Chatsworth, CA 91311 *Tel:* 818-773-0900 *Toll Free Tel:* 800-338-5316 *Fax:* 818-773-0906 *E-mail:* info@mrv.com *Web Site:* www.mrv-corporate.com, pg 948

Stein, Charlie, InJoy Birth & Parenting Education, 7107 La Vista Place, Longmont, CO 80503 *Tel:* 303-447-2082 (ext 2) *Toll Free Tel:* 800-326-2082 (ext 2) *Fax:* 303-449-8788 *E-mail:* custserv@injoyvideos.com *Web Site:* www.injoyvideos.com, pg 898

Stein, Evan, SDI Technologies Inc, 1299 Main St, Rahway, NJ 07065 *Tel:* 732-574-9000 *Toll Free Tel:* 800-333-3092; 800-888-4491 (cust serv) *Web Site:* www.sditechnologies.com; www.ihomeaudio.com, pg 1005

Stein, Kevin, HAVE Inc, 309 Power Ave, Hudson, NY 12534 *Tel:* 518-828-2000 *Toll Free Tel:* 888-999-HAVE (999-4283) *Fax:* 518-828-2008 *E-mail:* pro_sales@haveinc.com; have@haveinc.com *Web Site:* www.haveinc.com, pg 886

Stein, Lonny, Barron's Educational Series Inc, 250 Wireless Blvd, Hauppauge, NY 11788 *Tel:* 631-434-3311 *Toll Free Tel:* 800-645-3476 *Fax:* 631-434-3723 *E-mail:* barrons@barronseduc.com *Web Site:* www.barronseduc.com, pg 803

Stein, Robert, Criterion Collection, 215 Park Ave S, 5th fl, New York, NY 10003 *Tel:* 212-756-8822 *E-mail:* orders@criterion.com *Web Site:* www.criterion.com, pg 839

Steinbach, James, Wisconsin Public Television, 821 University Ave, Madison, WI 53706 *Tel:* 608-263-2121 *Toll Free Tel:* 800-422-9707 *Fax:* 608-263-9763 *E-mail:* comments@wpt.org *Web Site:* www.wpt.org, pg 1068

Steinberg, Betsy, Illinois Film Office, James R Thompson Ctr, Suite 3-400, 100 W Randolph, Chicago, IL 60601 *Tel:* 312-814-3600 *Fax:* 312-814-8874 *E-mail:* film@illinois.gov *Web Site:* www.illinoisfilm.biz, pg 1097

Steinberg, Jay, Major Media Inc, PO Box 209, Deerfield, IL 60015 *Tel:* 847-433-1682 *E-mail:* webmaster@major-media.com *Web Site:* www.major-media.com, pg 929

Steinberg, Jay, Major Media Productions Inc, PO Box 209, Deerfield, IL 60015 *Tel:* 847-433-1682 *E-mail:* webmaster@major-media.com *Web Site:* www.major-media.com, pg 929

Steinberg, Jay, Major Reproductions Equipment Co, PO Box 209, Deerfield, IL 60015 *Tel:* 847-433-1682 *E-mail:* webmaster@major-media.com *Web Site:* www.major-media.com, pg 929

Steinberg, Neil, Synaptic Digital, 79 Fifth Ave, 14th fl, New York, NY 10003 *Tel:* 212-682-8300 *Toll Free Tel:* 800-843-0677 *Fax:* 212-682-5260 *E-mail:* learnmore@synapticdigital.com *Web Site:* www.synapticdigital.com, pg 1030

Steinberg, Ron, RC Communications, 3900 N River Rd, Schiller Park, IL 60176-2345 *Tel:* 847-678-7000 *Fax:* 847-678-9378 *E-mail:* rccsales@rentcom.com; rent@rentcom.com *Web Site:* www.rentcom.com; www.rc-communications.com, pg 992

Steinbroner, Paul J, CNS Productions Inc, 11 Almond St, Medford, OR 97504 *Tel:* 541-779-3361 *Toll Free Tel:* 800-888-0617 *Fax:* 541-773-5905 *E-mail:* info@cnsproductions.com *Web Site:* www.cnsproductions.com, pg 830

Steiner, Henry, Northeast Video Productions Inc, Box 8425, Sleepy Hollow, NY 10591 *Tel:* 914-714-0703, pg 959

Steiner, Michael, Sounds Unique, 1721-A Little Orchard St, San Jose, CA 95125 *Tel:* 408-287-3002 *Web Site:* www.soundsunique.com, pg 1018

Stelly, Christopher, Louisiana Entertainment, Off of Entertainment Indus Devt, Capital Annex Bldg, 1051 N Third St, Baton Rouge, LA 70802 *Tel:* 225-342-5403 *Fax:* 225-342-5554 *E-mail:* led-entertainment@la.gov *Web Site:* louisianaentertainment.gov, pg 1098

Stelmack, Joe, Baron Stage Curtain & Equipment Co Inc, 3218 Noble St, Baltimore, MD 21224 *Tel:* 410-327-6962 *Fax:* 410-327-7077 *E-mail:* curtains@baronstage.com *Web Site:* www.baronstage.com, pg 803

Stelmakowich, Ken, Majortech Inc, 8464 Ninth Line RR-1, Norval, ON L0P 1K0, Canada *Tel:* 905-873-0778 *Fax:* 905-873-1244 *Web Site:* www.majortech.com, pg 929

Stelmaschuk, Scott, Yorkton Film Festival (YFF), 49 Smith St E, Yorkton, SK S3N 0H4, Canada *Tel:* 306-782-7077 *Fax:* 306-782-1550 *E-mail:* info@yorktonfilm.com *Web Site:* yorktonfilm.com, pg 1130

Stemen, Jeremy, Blue Water Film Award, PO Box 611109, Port Huron, MI 48061 *E-mail:* bwff@bluewaterfilmfestival.com *Web Site:* bluewaterfilmfestival.com, pg 1110

Stemler, Arthur W, Viking Cases, 10480 Oak St NE, St Petersburg, FL 33716 *Tel:* 727-577-1216 *Toll Free Tel:* 800-237-8560 *Fax:* 727-577-2082 *E-mail:* sales@vikingcases.com *Web Site:* www.vikingcases.com, pg 1058

Stemler, Bruce S, Viking Cases, 10480 Oak St NE, St Petersburg, FL 33716 *Tel:* 727-577-1216 *Toll Free Tel:* 800-237-8560 *Fax:* 727-577-2082 *E-mail:* sales@vikingcases.com *Web Site:* www.vikingcases.com, pg 1058

Stengel, Mike, Swank Audio Visuals, 639-E Gravois Bluffs, St Louis, MO 63026 *Tel:* 636-680-9000 *Toll Free Tel:* 877-792-6528 *Fax:* 636-680-2853 *Web Site:* www.swankav.com, pg 1029

Stepaneko, Maria, Express Media Inc, 2225 Palou Ave, San Francisco, CA 94124 *Tel:* 415-255-9883 *Fax:* 415-255-0139 *Web Site:* www.expressmedia.tv, pg 864

Stephan, Egon Jr, CineVideotech Inc, 7330 NE Fourth Ct, Miami, FL 33138 *Tel:* 305-754-2611 *Fax:* 305-759-2463 *Web Site:* www.cinevideotech.com, pg 828

Stephens, Jody, Ardent Music LLC, 2000 Madison Ave, Memphis, TN 38104 *Tel:* 901-725-0855 *Fax:* 901-725-7011 *E-mail:* info@ardentmusic.com *Web Site:* www.ardentmusic.com, pg 789

Stephens, Jody, Ardent Studios Inc, 2000 Madison Ave, Memphis, TN 38104 *Tel:* 901-725-0855 *Fax:* 901-725-7011 *E-mail:* info@ardentstudios.com *Web Site:* www.ardentstudios.com, pg 789

Stephenson, Greg, Dallas Prompter, PO Box 571233, Dallas, TX 75357 *Tel:* 214-275-9000 *Web Site:* www.dallasprompter.com, pg 842

Stephenson, Helga, Canadian Screen Awards, 49 Ontario St, Suite 501, Toronto, ON M5A 2V1, Canada *Tel:* 416-366-2227 *Toll Free Tel:* 800-644-5194 *Fax:* 416-366-8454 *E-mail:* academie@acct.ca *Web Site:* www.acct.ca/prixgemeaux; www.academy.ca/awards, pg 1111

Sterling, LeeAnn, Greeley/Weld Film Commission, 902 Seventh Ave, Greeley, CO 80631 *Tel:* 970-352-3567 *Toll Free Tel:* 800-449-3866 *Fax:* 970-352-3572 *E-mail:* info@greeleycvb.com *Web Site:* www.greeleychamber.com, pg 1095

Stern, Peter C, Time Warner Cable, 60 Columbus Circle, 17th fl, New York, NY 10023 *Tel:* 212-364-8200 *Web Site:* www.timewarnercable.com, pg 1040

Stern, Robert, Projects in Knowledge Inc, 290 W Mount Pleasant Ave, Suite 2350, Livingston, NJ 07039 *Tel:* 973-890-8988 *Toll Free Tel:* 800-772-8277 *Fax:* 973-992-5810 *E-mail:* info@projectsinknowledge.com *Web Site:* www.projectsinknowledge.com, pg 986

Steuerwald, Jane, Black Maria Film/Video Festival, c/o New Jersey City University, Dept of Media Arts, 2039 Kennedy Blvd, Jersey City, NJ 07305 *Tel:* 201-200-2043 *Fax:* 201-200-3490 *E-mail:* info@blackmariafilmfestival.org *Web Site:* www.blackmariafilmfestival.org, pg 1109

Stevens, Dean W, Vide-O-Go/That's Infotainment!, 206 Winding Ridge Dr, Cary, NC 27518-8934 *Tel:* 919-363-7920 *E-mail:* videogo@aol.com *Web Site:* www.videogo.com, pg 1054

Stevens, Joe, Kaboom Productions, 1465 Illinois St, San Francisco, CA 94107 *Tel:* 415-434-2666 *Fax:* 415-970-8548 *E-mail:* updates@kaboomproductions.com *Web Site:* kaboomproductions.com, pg 907

Stevens, Kris Erik, Kris Stevens Enterprises, 22362 Dardenne St, Calabasas, CA 91302 *Tel:* 818-225-7585 *E-mail:* inquiry@kriserikstevens.com *Web Site:* www.kriserikstevens.com, pg 1024

Stevens, Mark, RLJ Entertainment Inc, 8515 Georgia Ave, Suite 650, Silver Spring, MD 20910 *Tel:* 301-608-2115 *Toll Free Tel:* 800-999-0212 *Fax:* 301-608-9312 *E-mail:* inquiries@rljentertainment.com *Web Site:* www.us.rljentertainment.com, pg 997

Stevens, Rob, Mother West, 37 W 20 St, Suite 1006, New York, NY 10011 *Tel:* 212-807-0405 *E-mail:* info@motherwest.com *Web Site:* www.motherwest.com, pg 947

Stevens, Tim, Stevens Design & Animation LLC, 3405 Calle Cuervo NW, Unit 912, Albuquerque, NM 87114 *Tel:* 505-200-2042 *Web Site:* stevensanimation.com, pg 1024

Stevenson, Cameron, Stevenson Photography, 530 E Erie Dr, Tempe, AZ 85282 *Tel:* 480-967-6312 *E-mail:* info@stevensonphotography.com *Web Site:* www.stevensonphotography.com, pg 1025

Stevenson, Don B, Stevenson Photography, 530 E Erie Dr, Tempe, AZ 85282 *Tel:* 480-967-6312 *E-mail:* info@stevensonphotography.com *Web Site:* www.stevensonphotography.com, pg 1025

Stevenson, Noelle, Greater Fort Lauderdale/Broward Office of Film & Entertainment, 110 E Broward, Suite 1990, Fort Lauderdale, FL 33301 *Tel:* 954-524-3113 *Toll Free Tel:* 800-741-1420 *Fax:* 954-524-3167 *E-mail:* info@browardalliance.org *Web Site:* www.browardalliance.org/film; www.sunny.org, pg 1095

Stevenson, Ryan, Stevenson Photography, 530 E Erie Dr, Tempe, AZ 85282 *Tel:* 480-967-6312 *E-mail:* info@stevensonphotography.com *Web Site:* www.stevensonphotography.com, pg 1025

Stewart, Amy, Big Shoulders Digital Video Productions, 875 N Michigan Ave, Suite 3750, Chicago, IL 60611 *Tel:* 312-540-5400 *E-mail:* info@bigshoulders.com; sales@bigshoulders.com *Web Site:* www.bigshoulders.com, pg 807

Stewart, Cathy, Garcia Marketing Inc, 400 Ninth St, Conway, PA 15027-1663 *Tel:* 724-869-0100 *Toll Free Tel:* 800-683-1925 *Fax:* 724-869-1925 *E-mail:* gmavfoto@verizon.net, pg 875

Stewart, Grant, Stewart Filmscreen Corp, 1161 Sepulveda Blvd, Torrance, CA 90502-2754 *Tel:* 310-784-5300 *Toll Free Tel:* 800-762-4999 (North America only) *Fax:* 310-326-6870 *E-mail:* request@stewartfilmscreen.com *Web Site:* www.stewartfilmscreen.com, pg 1025

Stewart, Ken, GAPC (General Assembly Production Centre), 1550 Laperriere Ave, Suite 102, Ottawa, ON K1Z 7T2, Canada *Tel:* 613-723-3316 *Fax:* 613-723-8583 *Web Site:* www.gapc.com, pg 875

Stewart, Lamont, Image Innovations Inc, 8607 Wurzbach Rd, San Antonio, TX 78240 *Tel:* 210-696-5900 *Web Site:* www.slidescribe.com, pg 895

Stewart, Linda, Wisconsin Technical College System Foundation Inc, One Foundation Circle, Waunakee, WI 53597-8914 *Tel:* 608-849-2424; 608-849-2400 *Toll Free Tel:* 800-821-6313 *Fax:* 608-849-2468 *E-mail:* foundation@wtcsf.tec.wi.us *Web Site:* www.wtcsf.tec.wi.us, pg 1068

Stewart, Noral D PhD, Stewart Acoustical Consultants, 7330 Chapel Hill Rd, Suite 101, Raleigh, NC 27607 *Tel:* 919-858-0899 *Fax:* 919-858-0878 *Web Site:* www.sacnc.com, pg 1025

Stewart, Peter, Leprecon®, 10087 Industrial Dr, Hamburg, MI 48139 *Tel:* 810-852-4300 *Toll Free Tel:* 888-422-3537 *Fax:* 810-231-1631 *E-mail:* lepsls@leprecon.com *Web Site:* www.leprecon.com, pg 919

Stewart, Rick, piXvfm, 1805 E Dyer, Suite 107, Santa Ana, CA 92705-5701 *Tel:* 949-250-1749 *Fax:* 949-419-3485 *E-mail:* infoweb@pixvfm.com *Web Site:* www.pixvfm.com, pg 976

Stiener, Jim, ProVideo, 2302 W Badger Rd, Madison, WI 53713-2322 *Tel:* 608-271-1226 *Toll Free Tel:* 800-569-6810 *Fax:* 608-271-2737 *E-mail:* info@provideo.com *Web Site:* www.provideo.com, pg 986

Stiles, Diane, Castillo Theater, 543 W 42 St, New York, NY 10036 *Tel:* 212-941-5800 *Toll Free Tel:* 800-435-7453 *E-mail:* castillo@allstars.org *Web Site:* www.castillo.org, pg 821

Stillman, Joseph C, La Paloma Films, 719 Dorr Edson Rd, Suite 1, Oneonta, NY 13820 *Tel:* 607-287-5175 *E-mail:* lapalomafilms@yahoo.com *Web Site:* www.lapalomafilms.net, pg 915

Stillwaugh, Bob, Graham-Patten, 119 E McKnight Way, Unit A, Grass Valley, CA 95949 *Tel:* 530-477-2984 *Fax:* 530-477-2986 *E-mail:* support@isis-group.com *Web Site:* www.gpsys.com, pg 881

Stillwaugh, Kay, Graham-Patten, 119 E McKnight Way, Unit A, Grass Valley, CA 95949 *Tel:* 530-477-2984 *Fax:* 530-477-2986 *E-mail:* support@isis-group.com *Web Site:* www.gpsys.com, pg 881

Stillwell, Karen, Rough House, 550 Bryant St, San Francisco, CA 94107-1217 *Tel:* 415-561-4544 *Fax:* 415-543-8390 *E-mail:* info@roughhouse.com *Web Site:* www.roughhouse.com, pg 1000

Stimler, Ian, Zeitgeist Films Ltd, 247 Centre St, 2nd fl, New York, NY 10013 *Tel:* 212-274-1989 *Fax:* 212-274-1644 *E-mail:* mail@zeitgeistfilms.com *Web Site:* www.zeitgeistfilms.com, pg 1073

Stimler, Mike, Water Bearer Films Inc, 3239 Gateway Circle, Charlottesville, VA 22911 *Tel:* 434-923-8686 *Toll Free Tel:* 800-551-8304 *E-mail:* sales@waterbearerfilms.com *Web Site:* store.waterbearerfilms.com, pg 1062

Stingley, Thomas, Sencore Inc, 3200 Sencore Dr, Sioux Falls, SD 57107 *Tel:* 605-978-4600 *Toll Free Tel:* 800-SENCORE (736-2673) *Fax:* 605-335-6379 *E-mail:* info@sencore.com *Web Site:* www.sencore.com, pg 1006

Stinson, Becky, Dallas Learning Solutions, 9596 Walnut St, Dallas, TX 75243-2112 *Tel:* 972-669-6650 *Toll Free Tel:* 866-DISTLRN (347-8576) *Fax:* 972-669-6668 *E-mail:* tlearn@dcccd.edu *Web Site:* dls.dcccd.edu, pg 842

Stitt, Dena, FIDM Productions, 919 S Grand Ave, Los Angeles, CA 90015-1421 *Tel:* 213-624-1201 *Toll Free Tel:* 800-624-1200 *Fax:* 213-624-4799 *Toll Free Fax:* 800-624-1200 *Web Site:* fidm.edu, pg 866

Stobaugh, Clay, John Wiley & Sons Inc, 111 River St, Hoboken, NJ 07030 *Tel:* 201-748-6000 *Toll Free Tel:* 800-225-5945 *Fax:* 201-748-6088 *E-mail:* info@wiley.com *Web Site:* www.wiley.com, pg 1066

Stockman, Gary, Computer Sciences Corp, 3170 Fairview Park Dr, Falls Church, VA 22042 *Tel:* 703-876-1000 *Web Site:* www.csc.com, pg 834

Stocks, Joey, The Dramatists Guild of America, 1501 Broadway, Suite 701, New York, NY 10036 *Tel:* 212-398-9366 *Fax:* 212-944-0420 *E-mail:* info@dramatistsguild.com *Web Site:* www.dramatistsguild.com, pg 1081

Stocks, John C, National Education Association (NEA), 1201 16 St NW, Washington, DC 20036-3290 *Tel:* 202-833-4000 *Fax:* 202-822-7974 *Web Site:* www.nea.org, pg 952

Stockton, Dick, Cinema Xenon International Inc, 261 Valley Vista Dr, Camarillo, CA 93010-1655 *Tel:* 805-383-5548 *Toll Free Tel:* 888-669-7271 *Fax:* 805-389-9611 *E-mail:* info@cxilamps.com *Web Site:* www.cxilamps.com, pg 827

Stockwell-Nicholas, Shelley PhD, Creativity Unlimited Press®, 30819 Casilina Dr, Rancho Palos Verdes, CA 90275 *Tel:* 310-541-4844 *Fax:* 310-377-7946 *E-mail:* ihf@cox.net *Web Site:* drshelleynicholas.com; hypnosisfederation.com, pg 839

Stoddard, Zane, NASCAR Media Group LLC, 550 S Caldwell St, Suite 2000, Charlotte, NC 28202 *Tel:* 704-348-7100 *Web Site:* www.nascarmediagroup.com, pg 952

Stoebner, Jeff, AVI Systems, 9675 W 76 St, Suite 200, Eden Prairie, MN 55344 *Tel:* 952-949-3700 *Toll Free Tel:* 800-488-4954 *Fax:* 952-949-6000 *E-mail:* info@avisystems.com *Web Site:* www.avisystems.com, pg 799

Stoebner, Joe, AVI Systems, 9675 W 76 St, Suite 200, Eden Prairie, MN 55344 *Tel:* 952-949-3700 *Toll Free Tel:* 800-488-4954 *Fax:* 952-949-6000 *E-mail:* info@avisystems.com *Web Site:* www.avisystems.com, pg 799

Stofan, Ronald A, Garner Products Inc, 10620 Industrial Ave, Suite 100, Roseville, CA 95678 *Tel:* 916-784-0200 *Toll Free Tel:* 800-624-1903 *Fax:* 916-784-1425 *E-mail:* info@garner-products.com *Web Site:* www.garner-products.com, pg 875

Stoffan, Michael, Tranquil Technology Music, PO Box 20463, Oakland, CA 94620-0463 *Tel:* 510-658-2560 *Web Site:* michaelmantra.com, pg 1043

Stohn, Stephen, Epitome Pictures Inc, 220 Bartley Dr, Toronto, ON M4A 1G1, Canada *Tel:* 416-752-7627 *Fax:* 416-752-7837 *E-mail:* info@epitomepictures.com *Web Site:* www.epitomepictures.com, pg 862

Stokes, Andrea, Canamedia Inc, 1540 Cornwall Rd, Suite 216, Oakville, ON L6J 7W5, Canada *Tel:* 416-363-6765 *Toll Free Tel:* 866-999-5292 *Fax:* 416-363-7834 *Web Site:* www.canamedia.com, pg 818

Stokes, Chuck, Stages Video Productions, 514 29 Ave N, Myrtle Beach, SC 29577 *Tel:* 843-626-7466 *E-mail:* info@stagesvideo.com *Web Site:* www.stagesvideo.com, pg 1023

Stokes, Justine, University of Wisconsin-Oshkosh Radio-TV-Film Dept, Arts & Communications Bldg, W-112, 800 Algoma Blvd, Oshkosh, WI 54901 *Tel:* 920-424-3131 *Fax:* 920-424-7041 *E-mail:* rtf@uwosh.edu *Web Site:* www.uwosh.edu/rtf, pg 1050

Stollier, Bill, GrooveWorx, 1418 Second St, Santa Monica, CA 90401 *Tel:* 310-260-2626 *Toll Free Tel:* 800-400-6767 *Fax:* 310-260-2662 *E-mail:* contact@grooveworx.com *Web Site:* www.grooveworx.com, pg 882

Stoltz, David, Sports Cinematography Group, 73 Market St, Venice, CA 90291-3606 *Tel:* 310-785-9100 *Fax:* 310-564-7500 *E-mail:* sportscinema@earthlink.net *Web Site:* www.sportscinematographygroup.com, pg 1021

Stolzar, Karen, SmartPros Ltd, 12 Skyline Dr, Hawthorne, NY 10532-2133 *Tel:* 914-345-2620 *Fax:* 914-345-2603 *E-mail:* admin@smartpros.com *Web Site:* www.smartpros.com, pg 1014

Stone, Ben, Sonoma County Film Office, 141 Stony Circle, Suite 110, Santa Rosa, CA 95401-4154 *Tel:* 707-565-7170 *Fax:* 707-565-7231 *E-mail:* film@sonoma-county.org *Web Site:* www.sonoma-county.org/film, pg 1094

Stone, David M, Photographic Solutions Inc, 430-G Ansin Blvd, Hallendale, FL 33009 *Tel:* 954-458-4744 *Toll Free Tel:* 800-637-3212 *Fax:* 954-458-4745 *E-mail:* orders@photosol.com *Web Site:* www.photosol.com, pg 975

Stone, Gary, Gold Standard Productions, 12952 Miriam Place, Santa Ana, CA 92705-1334 *Tel:* 714-544-7000 *Fax:* 714-544-7010 *Web Site:* www.goldstandardproductions.com, pg 880

Stone, Kevin, Stewart Audio, 14397 Cuesta Ct, Suite D1, Sonora, CA 95370 *Tel:* 209-588-8111 *Fax:* 209-588-8113 *E-mail:* sales@stewartaudio.com; support@stewartaudio.com *Web Site:* www.stewartaudio.com, pg 1025

Stoneman, Rebecca, San Juan School District Heritage Language Resource Center, 28 W 200 N, Blanding, UT 84511 *Tel:* 435-678-1230; 435-678-1229 *Fax:* 435-678-1283 *Web Site:* media.sjsd.org, pg 1002

Storey, Jeff, Level 3 Communications Inc, 1025 Eldorado Blvd, Broomfield, CO 80021 *Tel:* 720-888-1000 *Toll Free Tel:* 877-2LEVEL3 (253-8357) *Web Site:* www.level3.com, pg 919

Storm, Melody, Bel-Air Film Festival (BAFF), 5900 Wilshire Blvd, 10th fl, Los Angeles, CA 90036 *Tel:* 323-801-0100 *E-mail:* info@belairfilmfestival.com *Web Site:* www.belairfilmfestival.com, pg 1109

Storyk, John, Walters-Storyk Design Group Inc (WSDG), 262 Martin Ave, Highland, NY 12528 *Tel:* 845-691-9300 *Fax:* 845-691-9361 *E-mail:* info@wsdg.com *Web Site:* www.wsdg.com, pg 1062

Stosich, Michael, Esoteric Sound, 1608 Hemstock Ave, Wheaton, IL 60189 *Tel:* 630-933-9801 *Fax:* 630-933-9801 *E-mail:* esotericTT@aol.com *Web Site:* www.esotericsound.com, pg 862

Stoughton, Lynn, A T Products Inc, 1600 S Division St, Harvard, IL 60033 *Tel:* 815-943-3590 *Toll Free Tel:* 800-848-2205 *Fax:* 815-943-3604 *E-mail:* atprod@mc.net *Web Site:* atproducts.com, pg 771

Stoughton-Jackson, Kerri, Outfest, 3470 Wilshire Blvd, Suite 935, Los Angeles, CA 90010 *Tel:* 213-480-7088 *Fax:* 213-480-7099 *E-mail:* outfest@outfest.org *Web Site:* www.outfest.org, pg 1123

Stout, Bob, Moxie Media, 1301 Dealers Ave, New Orleans, LA 70123 *Tel:* 504-733-6907 *Toll Free Tel:* 800-346-6943 *Fax:* 504-733-9493 *E-mail:* info@moxiemedia.com *Web Site:* www.moxiemedia.com; www.moxietraining.com, pg 948

Stover, Carol L, Adventure Productions LLC, 5910 York Rd, Lower Level, Baltimore, MD 21212 *Tel:* 410-878-1261; 410-961-5942 (cell) *Fax:* 410-878-1263 *Web Site:* www.adventureproductions.com, pg 778

Stover, George A III, Adventure Productions LLC, 5910 York Rd, Lower Level, Baltimore, MD 21212 *Tel:* 410-878-1261; 410-961-5942 (cell) *Fax:* 410-878-1263 *Web Site:* www.adventureproductions.com, pg 778

Strain, Mike Jr, Fantasy Creations FX, 2060 E McDaniel St, Springfield, MO 65802 *Tel:* 417-619-1138 *E-mail:* fcfxmike@yahoo.com *Web Site:* www.fantasycreationsfx.com, pg 865

Strand, Diane, JDS Video & Media Productions Inc, 39870 Camden Ct, Temecula, CA 92591 *Tel:* 951-296-6715 *Toll Free Fax:* 866-737-2239 *E-mail:* info@jds-productions.com *Web Site:* www.jds-productions.com, pg 905

Strasser, Samuel, Pak-Wik Corp, 128 Tivoli St, Albany, NY 12207 *Tel:* 518-465-4556 *Toll Free Tel:* 800-372-5945 *Fax:* 518-465-4559 *E-mail:* sales@pakwik.com *Web Site:* www.pakwik.com, pg 967

Strassner, Bunnie, Flashback Media Productions, 510 E Sutton Circle, Lafayette, CO 80026 *Tel:* 303-545-9955 *Fax:* 303-545-6658 *E-mail:* info@flashback.tv *Web Site:* www.flashback.tv, pg 869

Strassner, Norman, Flashback Media Productions, 510 E Sutton Circle, Lafayette, CO 80026 *Tel:* 303-545-9955 *Fax:* 303-545-6658 *E-mail:* info@flashback.tv *Web Site:* www.flashback.tv, pg 869

Straus, Sam, Old Dominion Broadcasting, 9505 Lakewater Ct, Richmond, VA 23229 *Tel:* 804-740-4717 *Fax:* 804-740-4717, pg 961

Strauss, Fred, Communications Corporation of America, PO Box 14262, Chicago, IL 60614-0262 *Tel:* 773-348-0001 *E-mail:* comcorp30@aol.com, pg 833

Street, Rita, Women In Animation, PO Box 17706, Encino, CA 91416-7706 *Tel:* 818-759-9596 *E-mail:* wia@womeninanimation.org; info@womeninanimation.org *Web Site:* www.womeninanimation.org, pg 1090

Streeter, Jerry, Bear Creek Studio & Music Production Inc, 6313 Maltby Rd, Woodinville, WA 98072 *Tel:* 425-481-4100 *Fax:* 425-486-2718 *E-mail:* bearcreek@seanet.com *Web Site:* bearcreekstudio.com, pg 804

Streich, Nina, Global Peace Film Festival (GPFF), 1000 Universal Studios Plaza, Bldg 22-A, Orlando, FL 32819 *Tel:* 407-224-6625 *E-mail:* info@peacefilmfest.org *Web Site:* www.peacefilmfest.org, pg 1115

Streicher, Ron, Pacific Audio-Visual Enterprises, 3807 E Green St, Pasadena, CA 91107-3904 *Tel:* 626-449-9353 *Toll Free Tel:* 888-240-8012 *Fax:* 626-395-9793 *Web Site:* www.stereosoundbook.com, pg 967

Streichler, Robin, Tatum Video, 103 S Davis St, Telluride, CO 81435 *Tel:* 213-999-5970 (cell); 970-728-4892 *Fax:* 970-728-4892 *E-mail:* utemtn@aol.com, pg 1032

Streitfeld, Andy, AMS Pictures, 16986 N Dallas Pkwy, Dallas, TX 75248 *Tel:* 972-818-7400 *Toll Free Tel:* 866-691-3660 *Fax:* 972-818-1257 *Web Site:* www.amspictures.com, pg 786

Stricker, Diane, Stricker Books, 8 Main St N, Unit C, Acton, ON L7J 1W1, Canada *Tel:* 519-853-2780 *Toll Free Tel:* 800-924-3966 *Fax:* 519-853-2847 *E-mail:* stricker@strickerbooks.com *Web Site:* www.strickerbooks.com, pg 1026

Stricker, Joseph, Stricker Books, 8 Main St N, Unit C, Acton, ON L7J 1W1, Canada *Tel:* 519-853-2780 *Toll Free Tel:* 800-924-3966 *Fax:* 519-853-2847 *E-mail:* stricker@strickerbooks.com *Web Site:* www.strickerbooks.com, pg 1026

Stricker, Sue, Stricker Books, 8 Main St N, Unit C, Acton, ON L7J 1W1, Canada *Tel:* 519-853-2780 *Toll Free Tel:* 800-924-3966 *Fax:* 519-853-2847 *E-mail:* stricker@strickerbooks.com *Web Site:* www.strickerbooks.com, pg 1026

Stricklin, Colin, Wyoming Film Office, 5611 High Plains Rd, Cheyenne, WY 82007 *Tel:* 307-777-3400 *Toll Free Tel:* 800-458-6657 *Fax:* 307-777-2877 *E-mail:* info@filmwyoming.com *Web Site:* www.filmwyoming.com, pg 1104

Strock, Anne, 3008, 3008 Ross Ave, Suite 100, Dallas, TX 75204 *Tel:* 214-922-9232 *Fax:* 214-922-8861 *Web Site:* www.3008.com, pg 1040

Strollo, Tom, Sand Box Studio, 555 Minnesota St, San Francisco, CA 94107 *Tel:* 415-550-8732 *E-mail:* inquiries@sandboxstudio.com *Web Site:* www.sandboxstudio.com, pg 1002

Strong, Bob, Intermed Video Technologies Inc, 18 Commerce Rd, Newtown, CT 06470 *Tel:* 203-270-0677; 203-270-9100 *Fax:* 203-270-9619 *E-mail:* sales@intermedvideo.com *Web Site:* www.intermedvideo.com, pg 900

Stroup, Stewart, Grassland Media Inc, 5944 Seminole Centre Ct, Suite 120, Fitchburg, WI 53711-5019 *Tel:* 608-238-7575 *Toll Free Tel:* 800-236-7575 *Fax:* 608-270-9301 *Web Site:* www.grasslandmedia.com, pg 881

Struhs, Steve, TBC Consoles Inc, 170 Rodeo Dr, Edgewood, NY 11717 *Tel:* 631-293-4068 *Toll Free Tel:* 888-CONSOLE (266-7653) *Fax:* 631-293-4075 *E-mail:* info@tbcconsoles.com; sales@tbcconsoles.com; support@tbcconsoles.com *Web Site:* www.tbcconsoles.com, pg 1033

Strum, Alison, Art Resource, 536 Broadway, 5th fl, New York, NY 10012 *Tel:* 212-505-8700 *Fax:* 212-505-2053 *E-mail:* requests@artres.com *Web Site:* www.artres.com, pg 791

Struthers, Scott, Sonance, 212 Avenida Fabricante, San Clemente, CA 92672-7531 *Tel:* 949-492-7777 *Toll Free Tel:* 800-592-4644; 800-582-0772 (tech support); 800-582-7777 *Toll Free Fax:* 800-538-5151 *E-mail:* customerservice@sonance.com *Web Site:* www.sonance.com, pg 1015

Struwe, Sara, Spina Bifida Association, 4590 MacArthur Blvd NW, Suite 250, Washington, DC 20007 *Tel:* 202-944-3285 *Toll Free Tel:* 800-621-3141 (outside DC) *Fax:* 202-944-3295 *E-mail:* sbaa@sbaa.org *Web Site:* www.sbaa.org, pg 1021

Stubbs, Chris, Redco Audio Inc, 1701 Stratford Ave, Stratford, CT 06615 *Tel:* 203-502-7600 *Toll Free Tel:* 800-572-7280 *Fax:* 203-502-7610 *E-mail:* orders@redco.com *Web Site:* www.redco.com, pg 993

Stubenvoll, Karin, Banff Mountain Film & Book Festival, 107 Tunnel Mountain Dr, Banff, AB T1L 1H5, Canada *Tel:* 403-762-6347 *Fax:* 403-762-6277 *E-mail:* banffmountainfestival@banffcentre.ca *Web Site:* www.banffcentre.ca/mountainfestival, pg 1109

Stuckey, Jason, Birns & Sawyer Inc, 5275 Craner Ave, North Hollywood, CA 91601 *Tel:* 323-466-8211 *Fax:* 323-466-1868; 818-358-4395 (rental) *E-mail:* info@birnsandsawyer.com *Web Site:* www.birnsandsawyer.com, pg 808

Studley, Jeff, CPR MultiMedia Solutions, 7812 Cessna Ave, Gaithersburg, MD 20879 *Tel:* 301-590-9400 *Fax:* 301-590-9402 *E-mail:* info@cprmms.com *Web Site:* www.cprmms.com, pg 837

Stull, Margie, Cape Girardeau Convention & Visitors Bureau, 400 Broadway St, Suite 100, Cape Girardeau, MO 63701 *Tel:* 573-335-1631 *Toll Free Tel:* 800-777-0068 *Fax:* 573-334-6702 *E-mail:* info@visitcape.com *Web Site:* visitcape.com, pg 1099

Stull, Victoria, Dynamic Digital Depth Inc (DDD), 6100 Center Dr W, Suite 1100, Los Angeles, CA 90045 *Tel:* 310-566-3340 *Toll Free Tel:* 877-884-4333 *Fax:* 310-566-3380 *E-mail:* info@ddd.com *Web Site:* www.ddd.com, pg 854

Stum, Andrew D, Raymond Entertainment Direct (RED), 3450 Cahuenga Blvd W, Suite 410, Los Angeles, CA 90068 *Tel:* 323-785-4700 *Fax:* 323-785-4701 *E-mail:* info@raymondentertainment.com *Web Site:* www.raymondentertainment.com, pg 992

Sturgeon, Russ, Russ Sturgeon Productions/RSVP, 916 Third Ave S, Nashville, TN 37210 *Tel:* 615-255-7787 *Fax:* 615-254-7788 *Web Site:* www.rsvpnashville.com, pg 1027

Sturges, Keith, SirsiDynix, 3300 N Ashton Blvd, Suite 500, Lehi, UT 84043-5340 *Tel:* 801-223-5200 *Toll Free Tel:* 800-288-8020 *Fax:* 801-223-5202 *E-mail:* info@sirsidynix.com; sales@sirsidynix.com *Web Site:* www.sirsidynix.com, pg 1012

Suapaia, Jason, 1013 Integrated, 1013 Kawaiahao St, Honolulu, HI 96814 *Tel:* 808-593-8848 *Fax:* 808-593-9427 *E-mail:* info@1013integrated.com *Web Site:* www.1013i.com, pg 1037

Suarez, Raul, Third Ear Sound Co, 30965 San Benito St, Hayward, CA 94544 *Tel:* 510-429-1000 *Toll Free Tel:* 800-587-1115 *Fax:* 510-429-1001 *E-mail:* raul@thirdearsound.com *Web Site:* www.thirdearsound.com, pg 1039

Subramanian, Subu, ALOM Technologies Corp, 48105 Warm Springs Blvd, Fremont, CA 94539-7498 *Tel:* 510-360-3600 *Toll Free Tel:* 800-500-9991 *Fax:* 510-226-7617 *E-mail:* customerservice@alom.com *Web Site:* www.alom.com, pg 782

Suddreth, Sherwin, Thinking Maps Inc, 401 Cascade Pointe Lane, Cary, NC 27513-5780 *Tel:* 919-678-8778 *Toll Free Tel:* 800-243-9169 *Fax:* 919-678-8782 *E-mail:* office@thinkingmaps.com *Web Site:* thinkingmaps.com, pg 1038

Suede, Bob, Suede Interactive, 693 Main St, Hackensack, NJ 07601-4713 *Tel:* 201-646-0416 *E-mail:* suede@suede.tv *Web Site:* www.suede.tv, pg 1028

Sufranski, Bruce, American Society of Safety Engineers (ASSE), 1800 E Oakton St, Des Plaines, IL 60018 *Tel:* 847-699-2929 *E-mail:* customerservice@asse.org *Web Site:* www.asse.org, pg 1077

Suga, Yasu, THK Photo Products Inc, 7642 Woodwind Dr, Huntington Beach, CA 92647 *Tel:* 714-849-5700 *Toll Free Tel:* 800-421-1141 *Fax:* 714-849-5677 *E-mail:* support@thkphoto.com *Web Site:* www.thkphoto.com, pg 1039

Suggs, Jeanne, Suggs Media Productions Inc, 156 W 44 St, New York, NY 10036 *Tel:* 212-398-4200 *Fax:* 212-382-0922, pg 1028

Sukhdeo, Dolores, Comtel Inc, 14901 NE 20 Ave, Miami, FL 33181 *Tel:* 305-948-9116 *Fax:* 305-947-9306 *E-mail:* info@comtelinc.com *Web Site:* www.comtelinc.com, pg 834

Sullivan, Barbara, California Language Laboratories, 6170 Palmero Circle, Cameron Park, CA 95682 *Toll Free Tel:* 800-327-1147 *Fax:* 530-350-8072 *E-mail:* info@esltapes.com *Web Site:* www.esltapes.com, pg 817

Sullivan, Jerry, Precision Camera & Video, 2438 W Anderson Lane, Suite B-4, Austin, TX 78757 *Tel:* 512-467-7676 *Toll Free Tel:* 800-677-1023 *Fax:* 512-467-0607 *Web Site:* www.precision-camera.com, pg 980

Sullivan, Joe, Duxbury Systems Inc, 270 Littleton Rd, Unit 6, Westford, MA 01886-3523 *Tel:* 978-692-3000 *Fax:* 978-692-7912 *E-mail:* info@duxsys.com *Web Site:* www.duxburysystems.com, pg 854

Sullivan, John, Covid Inc, 1723 W Fourth St, Tempe, AZ 85281 *Tel:* 480-966-2221 *Toll Free Tel:* 800-638-6104 *Fax:* 480-966-6728 *E-mail:* sales@covid.com *Web Site:* www.covid.com, pg 837

Sullivan, Kevin, Sullivan Home Entertainment, 110 Davenport Rd, Toronto, ON M5R 3R3, Canada *Tel:* 416-921-7177 *Fax:* 416-921-7538 *E-mail:* inquire@sullivan-ent.com *Web Site:* www.sullivanmovies.com, pg 1028

Sullivan, Peter, Duxbury Systems Inc, 270 Littleton Rd, Unit 6, Westford, MA 01886-3523 *Tel:* 978-692-3000 *Fax:* 978-692-7912 *E-mail:* info@duxsys.com *Web Site:* www.duxburysystems.com, pg 854

Sullivan, Scott, Jupiter Systems, 31015 Huntwood Ave, Hayward, CA 94544 *Tel:* 510-675-1000 *Fax:* 510-675-1001 *E-mail:* sales@jupiter.com *Web Site:* www.jupiter.com, pg 907

Sullivano, Joseph, Video Production Associates Inc, 525 Bridgeport Ave, Shelton, CT 06484-1397 *Tel:* 203-929-8869 *Toll Free Tel:* 800-394-8869 *Fax:* 203-925-0344 *Web Site:* www.vpa-inc.com, pg 1056

Sullivant, Wayne, PeopleVisionFX, 311 E First Ave, Bldg A, Roselle, NJ 07203 *Tel:* 973-509-2056 *Web Site:* peoplevisionfx.com, pg 972

Summerland, Jon, Okanagan Film Commission, 1450 KLO Rd, Kelowna, BC V1W 3Z4, Canada *Tel:* 250-717-0087 *Fax:* 250-868-0512 *E-mail:* info@okanaganfilm.com *Web Site:* www.okanaganfilm.com, pg 1104

Summers, Todd A PhD, SoftWright LLC, PO Box 7205, Charlotte, VA 22906 *Tel:* 303-344-5486 *Toll Free Tel:* 800-728-4033 *Fax:* 303-265-9399 *E-mail:* sales@softwright.com *Web Site:* www.softwright.com, pg 1015

Sunnucks, Andrew, Audio Network US Inc, 48 W 25 St, 10th fl, New York, NY 10010 *Tel:* 646-688-4320 *E-mail:* nyoffice@audionetwork.com *Web Site:* us.audionetwork.com, pg 794

Sunshine, Jaqueline, Chapman/Leonard Studios & Production Center, 12950 Raymer St, North Hollywood, CA 91605 *Tel:* 818-764-6726 *Toll Free Tel:* 888-883-6559 *Fax:* 818-764-6730 *Web Site:* www.chapman-leonard.com, pg 824

Sunshine, Robert H, International Cinema Technology Association (ICTA), 770 Broadway, 5th fl, New York, NY 10003-9595 *Tel:* 212-493-4097; 212-493-4058 *Fax:* 212-257-6428 *E-mail:* info@itea.com *Web Site:* www.internationalcinematechnologyassociation.com, pg 1083

Suppes, Kurt, Caption Colorado LLC, 5690 DTC Blvd, Suite 500W, Greenwood Village, CO 80111 *Tel:* 720-489-5662 *Toll Free Tel:* 800-775-7838 *Fax:* 720-489-5664 *Web Site:* www.captioncolorado.com, pg 820

Surack, Chuck, Sweetwater Sound Inc, 5501 US Hwy 30 W, Fort Wayne, IN 46818 *Tel:* 260-432-8176 *Toll Free Tel:* 800-222-4700 *Fax:* 260-432-1758 *Web Site:* www.sweetwater.com, pg 1029

Surico, Joanne, Intellidyne LLC, 5203 Leesburg Pike, Suite 400, 2 Skyline Place, Falls Church, VA 22041 *Tel:* 703-575-9715 *Fax:* 703-575-9718 *Web Site:* www.intellidyne-llc.com, pg 899

Suriyakumar, K, ARC Document Solutions, 1981 N Broadway, Suite 385, Walnut Creek, CA 94596 *Tel:* 925-949-5100 *Fax:* 925-949-5101 *E-mail:* info@e-arc.com *Web Site:* www.e-arc.com, pg 789

Susco, Ed, Audio Visual Associates, One Stewart Ct, Denville, NJ 07834 *Toll Free Tel:* 888-435-6678 *Fax:* 973-442-0888 *E-mail:* sales@avaonline.com; info@avaonline.com *Web Site:* www.avaonline.com, pg 795

Susser, Cheryl, Phase Technology, 6400 Youngerman Circle, Jacksonville, FL 32244 *Tel:* 913-663-5600 *Toll Free Tel:* 800-874-7076; 888-PHASE-TK (742-7385) *Fax:* 913-663-3200 *E-mail:* sales@phasetech.com *Web Site:* www.phasetech.com, pg 973

Sutardja, Dr Sehat, Marvell Semiconductor Inc, 5488 Marvell Lane, Santa Clara, CA 95054 *Tel:* 408-222-2500 *Fax:* 408-988-8279 *Web Site:* www.marvell.com, pg 932

Suter, Ron, Universal Studios Canada Inc, 2450 Victoria Park Ave, Willowdale, ON M2J 4A2, Canada *Tel:* 416-491-3000 *Web Site:* www.universalpictures.ca, pg 1049

Sutherland, Linda, GTI (Graphic Technology Inc), PO Box 3138, Newburgh, NY 12550-0651 *Tel:* 845-562-7066 *Toll Free Tel:* 888-562-7066 *Fax:* 845-562-2543 *E-mail:* sales@gtilite.com *Web Site:* www.gtilite.com, pg 883

Sutphen, Richard, Valley of the Sun Publishing Co, PO Box 2053, Sedona, AZ 86339 *Tel:* 928-554-1333 *E-mail:* info@dicksutphen.com *Web Site:* www.dicksutphen.com, pg 1051

Sutton, Elizabeth, Ashgate Publishing Co, 110 Cherry St, Suite 3-1, Burlington, VT 05401-3818 *Tel:* 802-865-7641 *Toll Free Tel:* 800-535-9544 (distribution) *Fax:* 802-865-7847 *E-mail:* info@ashgate.com *Web Site:* www.ashgate.com, pg 792

Sutton, Howard G, PESA, 103 Quality Circle, Suite 210, Huntsville, AL 35806 *Tel:* 256-726-9200 *Toll Free Tel:* 800-323-7372 *E-mail:* sales@pesa.com *Web Site:* www.pesa.com, pg 973

Sutton, Mike, Rule Broadcast Systems, 1284 Soldier's Field Rd, Boston, MA 02135 *Tel:* 617-277-2200 *Toll Free Tel:* 800-785-3266 *Fax:* 617-277-6800 *E-mail:* answers@rule.com *Web Site:* www.rule.com, pg 1000

Svitil, Gregory, Art Museum of the Americas, 201 18 St, Washington, DC 20006 *Tel:* 202-370-0147 *E-mail:* artmus@oas.org *Web Site:* www.amamuseum.org, pg 791

Swan, Doug, Audio-Technica US Inc, 1221 Commerce Dr, Stow, OH 44224 *Tel:* 330-686-2600 *Fax:* 330-686-0719 *E-mail:* pro@atus.com *Web Site:* www.audio-technica.com, pg 795

Swanson, Donna, Regal Photo Products Inc/Arkay Corp, 2769 S 34 St, Milwaukee, WI 53215-3541 *Tel:* 414-645-2050 *Toll Free Tel:* 800-695-2055 (sales) *Fax:* 414-645-9515, pg 994

Swarr, John, Bang Pictures, 78 Graterford Rd, Schwenksville, PA 19473 *Tel:* 610-357-1015 *Web Site:* www.bangpictures.com, pg 802

Swarth, Kelvin J, DSan Corp, 142 Mineola Ave, Roslyn Heights, NY 11577 *Tel:* 516-625-5608 *Fax:* 516-625-0878 *E-mail:* sales@dsan.com *Web Site:* www.dsan.com, pg 852

Swarth, Rodger, DSan Corp, 142 Mineola Ave, Roslyn Heights, NY 11577 *Tel:* 516-625-5608 *Fax:* 516-625-0878 *E-mail:* sales@dsan.com *Web Site:* www.dsan.com, pg 852

Swartz, Randy, Stagestep Inc, 4701 Bath St, No 46, Philadelphia, PA 19137 *Tel:* 215-636-9000 *Toll Free Tel:* 800-523-0960 (US & CN) *Fax:* 267-672-2912 *E-mail:* stagestep@stagestep.com; info@stagestep.com *Web Site:* www.stagestep.com, pg 1023

Sweany, Debbie, WhisperRoom™ Inc, 116 S Sugar Hollow Rd, Morristown, TN 37813 *Tel:* 423-585-5827 *Toll Free Tel:* 800-200-8168 *Fax:* 423-585-5831 *E-mail:* info@whisperroom.com *Web Site:* www.whisperroom.com, pg 1065

Swearingen, Roger, Tri-Digital Software Inc, 8424 154 Ave NE, Redmond, WA 98052 *Tel:* 425-284-3888 *Toll Free Tel:* 800-206-2547 *Fax:* 425-883-3887 *E-mail:* tdp@tri-digital.com *Web Site:* www.tri-digital.com, pg 1044

Swedenburg, Paul, HAVE Inc, 309 Power Ave, Hudson, NY 12534 *Tel:* 518-828-2000 *Toll Free Tel:* 888-999-HAVE (999-4283) *Fax:* 518-828-2008 *E-mail:* pro_sales@haveinc.com; have@haveinc.com *Web Site:* www.haveinc.com, pg 886

Sweet, Freddy, Live Wire Media, PO Box 848, Mill Valley, CA 94942 *Tel:* 415-564-9500 *Toll Free Tel:* 800-359-KIDS (359-5437) *Fax:* 415-552-4087 *E-mail:* sales@livewiremedia.com *Web Site:* www.livewiremedia.com, pg 923

Sweetow, Stuart, Audio Visual Consultants, 3640 Grand Ave, Suite 105, Oakland, CA 94610 *Tel:* 510-839-2020 *Fax:* 510-839-6464 *E-mail:* info@avconsultants.com *Web Site:* www.avconsultants.com, pg 795

Swenson, Chris, Seattle Mayor's Office of Film & Music, 700 Fifth Ave, Suite 5752, Seattle, WA 98104 *Tel:* 206-684-8090 *Fax:* 206-684-0379 *E-mail:* filmandmusicoffice@seattle.gov *Web Site:* www.seattle.gov/filmandmusic, pg 1103

Swenson, Eric, GMI Productions, One General Mills Blvd, Minneapolis, MN 55426 *Tel:* 763-764-7600 *Toll Free Tel:* 800-248-7310 *Fax:* 763-764-2739 *Web Site:* www.generalmills.com, pg 879

Swenson, Lora, MAM-A Inc, 4250 Buckingham Dr, Suite 100, Colorado Springs, CO 80907 *Toll Free Tel:* 888-626-3472 *Fax:* 719-592-0057 *Toll Free Fax:* 888-923-7203 *E-mail:* info@mam-a.com *Web Site:* www.mam-a.com, pg 929

Swerdlin, Hallie, Modulation Sciences Inc, 14 Worlds Fair Dr, Suite K, Somerset, NJ 08873 *Tel:* 732-302-3090 *Toll Free Tel:* 800-826-2603 *Fax:* 732-302-0206 *E-mail:* info@modsci.com; sales@modsci.com *Web Site:* www.modsci.com, pg 945

Swift, Janet, Telestream Inc, 848 Gold Flat Rd, Nevada City, CA 95959 *Tel:* 530-470-1300 *Toll Free Tel:* 877-257-6245 *Fax:* 530-470-1301 *E-mail:* info@telestream.net *Web Site:* www.telestream.net, pg 1036

Swift, Mike, Bell & Howell LLC, 760 S Wolf Rd, Wheeling, IL 60090 *Tel:* 847-675-7600 *Toll Free Tel:* 800-220-3030 (cust serv) *E-mail:* marketing@bhemail.com *Web Site:* www.bellhowell.net, pg 804

Swihart, John, Sonic Gravy, 2515 Laurel Path, Los Angeles, CA 90046 *Tel:* 323-650-2751 *Fax:* 323-822-1003 *Web Site:* www.johnswihart.tumblr.com, pg 1015

Switchenko, Katie, RTDNA Edward R Murrow Awards, The National Press Bldg, 529 14 St NW, Suite 425, Washington, DC 20045 *Tel:* 202-659-6510 *Fax:* 202-223-4007 *E-mail:* awards@rtdna.org *Web Site:* www.rtdna.org, pg 1126

Sykes, Phil, Phil Sykes & Associates Inc, 692 Sunset Ct, Shoreview, MN 55126 *Tel:* 651-481-4940 *Fax:* 651-481-3290 *E-mail:* mail@sykesnet.com *Web Site:* www.sykesnet.com, pg 974

Sylvester, Marcia, Dance Horizons Video, 614 Rte 130, Hightstown, NJ 08520 *Tel:* 609-426-0602 *Toll Free Tel:* 800-220-7149 *Fax:* 609-426-1344 *E-mail:* pbc@dancehorizons.com *Web Site:* www.dancehorizons.com, pg 842

Symmes, Ed, Symmes Systems, 3977 Briarcliff Rd NE, Atlanta, GA 30345 *Tel:* 404-320-1012 *Fax:* 404-320-3465, pg 1030

Symonds, Timothy J, Audio Accessories Inc, 25 Mill St, Marlow, NH 03456 *Tel:* 603-446-3335 *Fax:* 603-446-7543 *E-mail:* audioacc@patchbays.com *Web Site:* www.patchbays.com, pg 794

Syrett, Aaron, North Carolina Film Office, 301 N Wilmington St, Raleigh, NC 27601 *Tel:* 919-733-9900 *Toll Free Tel:* 866-468-2273 *Fax:* 919-715-0151 *Web Site:* www.ncfilm.com, pg 1101

Szczerba, Mark, D A Sound, 12932 SE Kent Kangley Rd, Box 460, Kent, WA 98030 *Tel:* 206-632-7773 *Toll Free Tel:* 855-DASOUND (327-6863) *Toll Free Fax:* 866-859-8650 *E-mail:* info@dasound.biz *Web Site:* www.dasound.biz, pg 842

Szepesi, Walter, Televersions, 747 N May St, Chicago, IL 60642 *Tel:* 312-642-9488 *Toll Free Tel:* 800-942-9488 *Fax:* 312-642-9491 *E-mail:* convert@televersions.com *Web Site:* www.televersions.com, pg 1036

Szew, Fernando, MarVista Entertainment Inc, 10277 W Olympic Blvd, 3rd fl, Los Angeles, CA 90067 *Tel:* 424-274-3000 *Fax:* 424-274-3050 *E-mail:* info@marvista.net *Web Site:* www.marvista.net, pg 933

Szew, Joseph, MarVista Entertainment Inc, 10277 W Olympic Blvd, 3rd fl, Los Angeles, CA 90067 *Tel:* 424-274-3000 *Fax:* 424-274-3050 *E-mail:* info@marvista.net *Web Site:* www.marvista.net, pg 933

Szewc, Adam, Agfa Graphics, 611 River Dr, Ctr 3, Elmwood Park, NJ 07407 *Tel:* 201-440-2500 *Toll Free Tel:* 800-540-2432 *Web Site:* www.agfagraphics.com; www.agfa.com, pg 778

Szymczak, Melodi, Vital Learning LLC, 1675 Larimer St, No 410, Denver, CO 80202 *Tel:* 402-592-1602 *Toll Free Tel:* 800-243-5858 *Fax:* 402-592-7142 *E-mail:* sales@vital-learning.com; info@vital-learning.com *Web Site:* www.vital-learning.com, pg 1060

Tabbot, Milton, Independent Film Week, 68 Jay St, Rm 425, Brooklyn, NY 11201-8361 *Tel:* 212-465-8200 *Fax:* 212-465-8525 *Web Site:* www.ifp.org/programs/independent-film-week, pg 1117

Tabbot, Milton, The Independent Filmmaker Project (IFP), 68 Jay St, Rm 425, Brooklyn, NY 11201-8361 *Tel:* 212-465-8200 *Fax:* 212-465-8525 *Web Site:* www.ifp.org, pg 1083

Tadross, Michael, East of Hollywood NY, 140 53 St, Brooklyn, NY 11232 *Tel:* 718-492-7400 *Fax:* 718-439-3930 *E-mail:* info@eastofhollywoodny.com *Web Site:* www.eastofhollywoodny.com, pg 855

Tadzynski, Steven, Laurel Video Productions, 1999 Marlton Pike, Suite 11, Cherry Hill, NJ 08003 *Tel:* 856-424-3300 *E-mail:* inquiries@laurelvideo.net *Web Site:* www.laurelvideo.net, pg 917

Tafese, Henok, Opticomm-EMCORE, 2015 Chestnut St, Alhambra, CA 91803 *Tel:* 626-293-3400; 626-293-3670 (west coast team); 540-626-3381 (east coast team) *Toll Free Tel:* 800-8OPTICOMM (867-8426) *Fax:* 626-293-3427 *E-mail:* video-sales@emcore.com *Web Site:* www.opticomm.com, pg 964

Tager, Joshua, Crystal Pictures Inc, 2000 Riverside Dr, Asheville, NC 28804 *Tel:* 828-285-9995 *Toll Free Tel:* 800-669-4057 *Fax:* 828-285-9997 *E-mail:* cryspic@aol.com *Web Site:* www.ivyvideo.com, pg 840

Tagler, John, Association of American Publishers (AAP), 71 Fifth Ave, 2nd fl, New York, NY 10003-3004 *Tel:* 212-255-0200 *Fax:* 212-255-7007 *E-mail:* info@publishers.org *Web Site:* www.publishers.org, pg 1078

Taiko, Tom, Konica Minolta Business Solutions, 100 Williams Dr, Ramsey, NJ 07446 *Tel:* 201-825-4000 *Fax:* 201-825-7567 *Web Site:* kmbs.konicaminolta.us, pg 913

Taing, Denny, Keslow Camera Inc, 11260 Playa Ct, Culver City, CA 90230 *Tel:* 310-636-4600 *Fax:* 310-915-5335 *E-mail:* info@keslowcamera.com *Web Site:* www.keslowcamera.com, pg 910

Tait, Larry, Close Up Foundation, 1330 Braddock Place, Suite 400, Alexandria, VA 22314 *Tel:* 703-706-3300 *Toll Free Tel:* 800-CLOSEUP (256-7387) *E-mail:* info@closeup.org *Web Site:* www.closeup.org, pg 830

Takac, Mike, Warner Home Video Inc, 4000 Warner Blvd, Bldg 160, Burbank, CA 91522 *Tel:* 818-954-6000 *Fax:* 818-954-6480 *Web Site:* www.warnerbros.com, pg 1062

Talbert, Beth, Sunset Bronson Studios, 1438 N Gower St, Box 88, Hollywood, CA 90028 *Tel:* 323-460-5858 *Fax:* 323-460-3844 *E-mail:* sbs.reception@sgsandsbs.com *Web Site:* sgsandsbs.com, pg 1028

Talley, Terry, Rocky Mountain Audio/Video Productions Inc, 7950 S Lincoln St, Littleton, CO 80122 *Tel:* 303-730-1100 *Toll Free Tel:* 877-856-4644 *Fax:* 303-468-9811 *E-mail:* sales@rmavp.com *Web Site:* www.rmavp.com, pg 998

Tamargo, Angel, Global Video Distributors Inc, 8181 NW 91 Terr, Suite 7, Medley, FL 33166 *Tel:* 305-887-2000 *Fax:* 305-887-2000 *Web Site:* global.myvideostore.com, pg 879

Tamburelli, Misty, Argyle Post, 2633 N San Fernando Blvd, Burbank, CA 91504 *Tel:* 818-845-5555; 310-560-2373 *Fax:* 818-842-8115 *E-mail:* info@argylepost.com *Web Site:* www.argylepost.com, pg 789

Tan, Kathy, Films for the Humanities & Sciences, 132 W 31 St, 17th fl, New York, NY 10001 *Toll Free Tel:* 800-257-5126 *Fax:* 609-671-0266 *E-mail:* custserv@films.com *Web Site:* ffh.films.com, pg 868

Tanke, Peter, Xytech Systems Corp, 15451 San Fernando Mission Blvd, Suite 400, Mission Hills, CA 91345 *Tel:* 818-698-4900 *Fax:* 818-698-4901 *E-mail:* sales@xytechsystems.com *Web Site:* www.xytechsystems.com, pg 1071

Tankersley, Jay, Vital Learning LLC, 1675 Larimer St, No 410, Denver, CO 80202 *Tel:* 402-592-1602 *Toll Free Tel:* 800-243-5858 *Fax:* 402-592-7142 *E-mail:* sales@vital-learning.com; info@vital-learning.com *Web Site:* www.vital-learning.com, pg 1060

Tannen, Steve, Illuminate Post/Digital Finishing, 3575 Cahuenga Blvd W, 4th fl, Hollywood, CA 90068 *Tel:* 323-969-8822 *Fax:* 323-969-8860 *Web Site:* illuminatehollywood.com, pg 894

Tannen, Steve, Illuminate Studios, 10900 Ventura Blvd, Studio City, CA 90068 *Tel:* 818-769-4500 *Fax:* 818-769-7150 *Web Site:* illuminatehollywood.com, pg 894

Tanner, Dave, North-by-Northwest Productions, 903 W Broadway Ave, Spokane, WA 99201 *Tel:* 509-324-2949 *Fax:* 509-324-2959 *E-mail:* contact@nxnw.net *Web Site:* www.nxnw.net, pg 958

Tanner, James, Bryston Ltd, 677 Neal Dr, Peterborough, ON K9J 6X7, Canada *Tel:* 705-742-5325 *Fax:* 705-742-0882 *Web Site:* bryston.com, pg 814

Tanoue, Mr Hiro, For-A Corp of America, 11155 Knott Ave, Suite G & H, Cypress, CA 90630 *Tel:* 714-894-3311 *Fax:* 714-894-5399 *E-mail:* info@for-a.com *Web Site:* www.for-a.com, pg 871

Tarabino, Joe, Trinidad Film Commission, 136 W Main St, Trinidad, CO 81082 *Tel:* 719-846-7324 *Toll Free Tel:* 866-480-4750 *Fax:* 719-846-3545 *Web Site:* www.trinidadchamber.com, pg 1095

Tarde, Jerry, Golf Digest, 20 Westport Rd, Wilton, CT 06897 *Tel:* 203-761-5100 *Toll Free Tel:* 800-727-4653 *Fax:* 203-761-5129 *Web Site:* www.golfdigest.com, pg 880

Tarpley, David, Tarpley Media Systems, 3737 50 St, Lubbock, TX 79413 *Tel:* 806-797-5833 *Toll Free Tel:* 800-600-5833 *Fax:* 806-797-5139 *E-mail:* tms@tarpleymedia.com *Web Site:* www.tarpleymedia.com, pg 1032

Tarsio, Bob, Broadcast Devices Inc, Westchester Industrial Complex, 3199 Albany Post Rd, Suite 122, Buchanan, NY 10511-1639 *Tel:* 914-737-5032 *Fax:* 914-736-6916 *E-mail:* sales@broadcast-devices.com *Web Site:* www.broadcast-devices.com, pg 813

Tart, David, Kendall/Hunt Publishing Co, 4050 Westmark Dr, Dubuque, IA 52002 *Tel:* 563-589-1000 *Toll Free Tel:* 800-228-0810 *Fax:* 563-589-1237 *Toll Free Fax:* 800-772-9165 *E-mail:* orders@kendallhunt.com *Web Site:* www.kendallhunt.com, pg 909

Tatham, Ron C, SpaceCam, 31111 Via Colinas, Suite 202, Westlake Village, CA 91362 *Tel:* 818-889-6060 *Fax:* 818-889-6062 *E-mail:* rentals@spacecam.com *Web Site:* spacecam.com, pg 1019

Tatsumi, Takahito, DNP Photo Imaging America Corp, 101 Uhland Rd, Suite 210, San Marcos, TX 78666 *Tel:* 512-753-7280 *Toll Free Tel:* 800-467-4935 *Fax:* 512-753-7299 *E-mail:* info@pixelmagic.com; sales@pixelmagic.com; customercare@pixelmagic.com *Web Site:* www.dnpphoto.com; www.pixelmagic.com; www.pmimaging.com, pg 849

Tatum, Tom, Tatum Video, 103 S Davis St, Telluride, CO 81435 *Tel:* 213-999-5970 (cell); 970-728-4892 *Fax:* 970-728-4892 *E-mail:* utemtn@aol.com, pg 1032

Tatz, Carl, Carl Tatz Design, 6666 Brookmont Terr, Suite 1109, Nashville, TN 37205 *Tel:* 615-354-6242 *Fax:* 615-356-4791 *E-mail:* carl@carltatzdesign.com *Web Site:* www.carltatzdesign.com, pg 1032

Taubin, Dawn, DreamWorks Animation SKG Inc, 1000 Flower St, Glendale, CA 91201 *Tel:* 818-695-5000 *Fax:* 818-695-4190 *Web Site:* www.dreamworksanimation.com, pg 852

Taunton, Connie, Natchez Film Commission, 640 S Canal St, Box C, Natchez, MS 39120 *Tel:* 601-446-6345 *Toll Free Tel:* 800-647-6724 *Fax:* 601-442-0814 *E-mail:* info@visitnatchez.org *Web Site:* www.visitnatchez.org, pg 1099

Taylor, Adam, Associated Production Music LLC, 6255 Sunset Blvd, Suite 900, Hollywood, CA 90028 *Tel:* 323-461-3211 *Fax:* 323-461-9102 *E-mail:* info@apmmusic.com *Web Site:* www.apmmusic.com, pg 792

Taylor, Betty Jo, The Communications Department Inc, 3724 Amherst Ave, Dallas, TX 75225-7201 *Tel:* 214-369-1281, pg 833

Taylor, Bill Jr, Video Express, 181 Newbury St, 5th fl, Boston, MA 02116 *Tel:* 617-267-7900 *Fax:* 617-267-6306 *E-mail:* information@evideoexpress.com *Web Site:* www.evideoexpress.com, pg 1055

Taylor, Brian, Evolve Inc, 1210 E Arlington Blvd, Greenville, NC 27858 *Tel:* 252-754-2957 *Fax:* 252-754-2832 *Web Site:* www.evolveinc.com, pg 863

Taylor, Chip, Chip Taylor Communications LLC, 2 East View Dr, Derry, NH 03038 *Tel:* 603-434-9262 *Toll Free Tel:* 800-876-CHIP (876-2447) *Fax:* 603-432-2723 *E-mail:* chip.taylor@chiptaylor.com *Web Site:* www.chiptaylor.com, pg 1032

Taylor, Connie, Bulb Direct, 7911 Rae Blvd, Victor, NY 14564 *Tel:* 585-385-3540 *Toll Free Tel:* 800-772-5267 *Fax:* 585-385-4976 *Toll Free Fax:* 800-257-0760 *E-mail:* info@bulbdirect.com *Web Site:* www.bulbdirect.com, pg 815

Taylor, Dan, Inland Empire Film Commission (IEFC), 1601 E Third St, Suite 102, San Bernardino, CA 92408 *Fax:* 909-382-6060 *E-mail:* info@filminlandempire.com *Web Site:* www.filminlandempire.com, pg 1094

Taylor, Jeremy, ADI Systems Inc, 3144 Thunderbird Crescent, Burnaby, BC V5A 3G4, Canada *Tel:* 604-291-1839 *Toll Free Tel:* 800-663-1042 *Fax:* 604-294-5782 *E-mail:* burnaby.ca@adiglobal.com *Web Site:* www.adiglobal.ca, pg 776

Taylor, Jessica, Antenna International, 383 Main Ave, Norwalk, CT 06851 *Tel:* 203-523-0320 *Fax:* 203-354-5519 *E-mail:* inquiry@antennainternational.com *Web Site:* www.antennainternational.com, pg 787

Taylor, Joe, Panasonic Corp, One Panasonic Way, Secaucus, NJ 07094 *Tel:* 201-348-7000 *Toll Free Tel:* 800-211-7262; 888-275-2595 *Fax:* 201-348-7807 *Web Site:* www.panasonic.com, pg 968

Taylor, Dr John, ADD Plus, 488 Glacier Way S, Monmouth, OR 97361 *Toll Free Tel:* 800-847-1233 *Fax:* 503-838-1608 *Web Site:* www.add-plus.com, pg 776

Taylor, John, MicroImage Video Systems, PO Box 331, Boyertown, PA 19512-0331 *Tel:* 610-754-6800 *Fax:* 610-754-9766 *E-mail:* sales@mivs.com *Web Site:* www.mivs.com, pg 941

Taylor, John, World Video Sales Co Inc, PO Box 117, Boyertown, PA 19512-0117 *Tel:* 610-754-6800 *Fax:* 610-754-9766 *E-mail:* sales@mivs.com *Web Site:* www.mivs.com, pg 1070

Taylor, Liz, SmackDab Media, 1033 Third Ave S, Nashville, TN 37210 *Toll Free Tel:* 888-248-8197 *Web Site:* smackdabmedia.com, pg 1013

Taylor, Mark, Taylor Associates, 110 W Canal St, Suite 301, Winooski, VT 05404 *Tel:* 802-735-1942 *Toll Free Tel:* 800-READ-PLUS (732-3758) *Fax:* 802-419-4786 *E-mail:* info@readingplus.com *Web Site:* www.readingplus.com, pg 1032

Taylor, Mary C, Library & Information Technology Association (LITA), c/o American Library Association, 50 E Huron St, Chicago, IL 60611-2795 *Toll Free Tel:* 800-545-2433 (ext 4270) *Fax:* 312-280-3257 *E-mail:* lita@ala.org *Web Site:* www.ala.org/lita, pg 1084

Taylor, Mel, Production Garden Music, 510 E Ramsey, Suite 4, San Antonio, TX 78216 *Tel:* 210-530-5200 *Toll Free Tel:* 800-247-5317 *Fax:* 210-530-5230 *E-mail:* sales@productiongarden.com *Web Site:* www.productiongarden.com, pg 984

Taylor, Paul S, ChristianAnswers.Net™, PO Box 1167, Marysville, WA 98270-1167 *Tel:* 480-507-3621 *Toll Free Tel:* 800-332-2261 (orders only) *Fax:* 480-507-3623 *E-mail:* mail@eden.org *Web Site:* www.christiananswers.net; www.christiananswers.net/eden/home.html, pg 825

Taylor, Rebecca, Strata™, 3013 Santa Clara Dr, Santa Clara, UT 84765 *Tel:* 435-628-5218 *Toll Free Tel:* 800-STRATA-3D (787-2823); 800-6-STRATA (678-7282) *Fax:* 435-628-9756 *E-mail:* sales@strata.com *Web Site:* www.strata.com, pg 1025

Taylor, Stanford E, Taylor Associates, 110 W Canal St, Suite 301, Winooski, VT 05404 *Tel:* 802-735-1942 *Toll Free Tel:* 800-READ-PLUS (732-3758) *Fax:* 802-419-4786 *E-mail:* info@readingplus.com *Web Site:* www.readingplus.com, pg 1032

Taylor, Tess, National Association of Record Industry Professionals (NARIP), PO Box 2446, Toluca Lake, CA 91610-2446 *Tel:* 818-769-7007; 559-271-7900 (Pollstar Live!) *Fax:* 818-769-6191 *E-mail:* info@narip.com *Web Site:* www.narip.com, pg 1085

Teachworth, Dan, Satellite Center, 2535 Williams Blvd, Kenner, LA 70062 *Tel:* 504-466-3474 *Toll Free Tel:* 800-256-4010 *Web Site:* satctr.com, pg 1003

Tebault, Hugh III, Latham Foundation Publications, Latham Plaza Bldg, 1826 Clement Ave, Alameda, CA 94501 *Tel:* 510-521-0920 *Fax:* 510-521-9861 *E-mail:* info@latham.org *Web Site:* www.latham.org, pg 916

Tedesco, John, Phoebus Lighting, 2800 Third St, San Francisco, CA 94107 *Tel:* 415-550-0770 *Fax:* 415-550-2655 *Web Site:* www.phoebus.com, pg 974

Tedesco, John, Phoebus Manufacturing, 2800 Third St, San Francisco, CA 94107 *Tel:* 415-550-0770 *Fax:* 415-550-2655 *Web Site:* www.phoebus.com/phoebusmanufactu.html; www.phoebus.com, pg 974

Tedford, Thomas W, ACCO Brands Corp, 4 Corporate Dr, Lake Zurick, IL 60047-8997 *Toll Free Tel:* 800-541-0094 *Toll Free Fax:* 800-941-4463 *E-mail:* contactus@gbc.com *Web Site:* www.accobrands.com, pg 773

Tedo, Kunihiko, Canon USA Inc, One Canon Park, Melville, NY 11747 *Tel:* 613-330-5000 *E-mail:* pr@cusa.canon.com *Web Site:* www.usa.canon.com, pg 819

Teeters, Roger, Veetronix Inc, 1311 W Pacific St, Lexington, NE 68850 *Tel:* 308-324-6661 *Toll Free Tel:* 800-445-0007 *Fax:* 308-324-4985 *E-mail:* sales@veetronix.com *Web Site:* www.veetronix.com, pg 1052

Teiper, James, Available Light, 5251 Dixon Rd, Oceanside, CA 92056-2319 *Tel:* 760-505-1605; 760-505-1600 *E-mail:* availablelight@jtservices.com *Web Site:* www.jtservices.com, pg 798

Teissler, Scott, Turner Broadcasting System Inc, One CNN Ctr, Atlanta, GA 30303 *Tel:* 404-827-1700 *Web Site:* www.turner.com, pg 1046

Teitelbaum, Matthew, Art Gallery of Ontario, 317 Dundas St W, Toronto, ON M5T 1G4, Canada *Tel:* 416-979-6660 *Toll Free Tel:* 877-225-4246 *Fax:* 416-979-6674 *E-mail:* danny_winchester@ago.net *Web Site:* www.ago.net, pg 791

Tejani, Reeshma, BBC Worldwide Canada Ltd, 409 King St W, 5th fl, Toronto, ON M5V 1K1, Canada *Tel:* 416-204-0500 *Web Site:* www.bbcworldwide.com, pg 803

Teltschik, Theresa, Romar Learning, 6700 Woodlands Pkwy, Suite 230-292, Woodlands, TX 77382 *Tel:* 281-292-5508 *Fax:* 281-363-2309 *E-mail:* info@romarlearning.com *Web Site:* www.romarlearning.com, pg 999

Temen, Mark, Audio Video Resources, 4323 E Cotton Center Blvd, Phoenix, AZ 85040 *Tel:* 602-643-4200; 602-643-4300 (rentals) *Toll Free Tel:* 877-643-4204 *Fax:* 602-643-4270 *E-mail:* sales@avrinc.com; rentals@avrinc.com *Web Site:* www.avrinc.com, pg 795

Temple, Ginny, Direct Current Video Productions, 1928 E Highland, Suite F-104-448, Phoenix, AZ 85016 *Tel:* 602-263-7717 *Fax:* 602-263-7719 *Web Site:* www.directcurrentproductions.com, pg 848

Temple, Nancy Ellen, IV Media Resources, 910 Redwing Dr, Geneva, IL 60134 *Tel:* 630-389-0000 *Fax:* 630-389-0208 *E-mail:* info@infinitevideo.com *Web Site:* www.infinitevideo.com, pg 903

Templeman-Holmes, Katy, Soundcraft USA, 8500 Balboa Blvd, North Ridge, CA 91329 *Tel:* 818-920-3212 *Fax:* 818-920-3209 *E-mail:* soundcraft-usa@harman.com *Web Site:* usa.soundcraft.com, pg 1018

TenEyck, Peter, blue onion, 940 Wadsworth Blvd, 3rd fl, Lakewood, CO 80214 *Tel:* 303-232-1100 *Fax:* 303-232-2241 *E-mail:* info@digourideas.com *Web Site:* www.digourideas.com, pg 810

Teng, Vivian, Chicago International Film Festival, 30 E Adams St, Suite 800, Chicago, IL 60603 *Tel:* 312-683-0121 *Fax:* 312-683-0122 *E-mail:* info@chicagofilmfestival.com *Web Site:* www.chicagofilmfestival.com, pg 1111

Teng, Vivian, INTERCOM, 30 E Adams St, Suite 800, Chicago, IL 60603 *Tel:* 312-683-0121 *Fax:* 312-683-0122 *E-mail:* info@chicagofilmfestival.com *Web Site:* www.chicagofilmfestival.com, pg 1117

Tennyson, Erica, Big Bear Lake International Film Festival, PO Box 1981, Big Bear Lake, CA 92315 *Tel:* 909-547-4019 *E-mail:* info@bigbearfilmfestival.com *Web Site:* www.bigbearfilmfestival.com, pg 1109

Tepper, Paul, Dedotec USA Inc, 48 Sheffield Business Park, Ashley Falls, MA 01222 *Tel:* 413-229-2550 *Fax:* 413-229-2556 *E-mail:* info@dedolight.com *Web Site:* www.dedolight.com, pg 844

Terry, David C, Artist Fellowships, 20 Jay St, 7th fl, Suite 740, Brooklyn, NY 11201 *Tel:* 212-366-6900 *Fax:* 212-366-1778 *E-mail:* fellowships@nyfa.org *Web Site:* nyfa.org, pg 1108

Terry, Terry N, MessageMakers, 1217 Turner St, Lansing, MI 48906 *Tel:* 517-482-3333 *Toll Free Tel:* 888-482-6688 *E-mail:* info@messagemakers.com *Web Site:* www.messagemakers.com, pg 939

Terwilliger, Connie, Annual MCA-I Media Festival, PO Box 5135, Madison, WI 53705-0135 *Tel:* 608-836-0722 *Toll Free Tel:* 888-899-MCAI (899-6224) *Toll Free Fax:* 888-862-8150 *E-mail:* info@mca-i.org; mcaimediafestival@gmail.com *Web Site:* www.mca-i.org, pg 1119

Terwilliger, Connie, Media Communications Association-International (MCA-I), PO Box 5135, Madison, WI 53705-0135 *Tel:* 608-836-0722 *Toll Free Tel:* 888-899-MCAI (899-6224) *Fax:* 608-443-2474; 608-443-2478 *Toll Free Fax:* 888-862-8150 *E-mail:* info@mca-i.org *Web Site:* www.mca-i.org, pg 936, 1084

Tessmar, Jim, Pro Power Products Inc, 913 S Victory Blvd, Burbank, CA 91502-2430 *Tel:* 818-558-6222 *Toll Free Tel:* 800-395-8466 *Fax:* 818-558-3999 *Web Site:* propowerproducts.com, pg 983

Testa, Bruce, Chromavision Corp, The Radio Wave Bldg, 8th fl, 49 W 27 St, New York, NY 10001 *Tel:* 212-686-7366 *E-mail:* info@chromavision.net *Web Site:* www.chromavision.net, pg 826

Teti, Nick, HDrental.com, 16129 Covello St, Van Nuys, CA 91406 *Tel:* 818-994-3461 *Fax:* 818-994-3471 *Web Site:* hdrental.com, pg 886

Tetlow, W James, Nautilus Entertainment Design Inc (NED), 1010 Turquoise St, Suite 215, San Diego, CA 92109 *Tel:* 858-456-6395 *E-mail:* info@n-e-d.com *Web Site:* www.n-e-d.com, pg 953

Tews, Jason, Kelmscott Communications, 1665 Mallette Rd, Aurora, IL 60505-1354 *Tel:* 630-898-0800 *Fax:* 630-898-2183 *Web Site:* kelmscottcommunications.com, pg 909

Tham, Sean, WAC Lighting Co, 44 Harbor Park Dr, Port Washington, NY 11050 *Tel:* 516-515-5000 *Toll Free Tel:* 800-526-2588 *Fax:* 516-515-5050 *Toll Free Fax:* 800-526-2585 *E-mail:* sales@waclighting.com *Web Site:* www.waclighting.com, pg 1061

Thames, Joel, Sound Service Co, 6630 Morella Ave, North Hollywood, CA 91606-1651 *Tel:* 818-503-4440, pg 1017

Thaw, Bruce R, Bulbtronics Inc, 45 Banfi Plaza N, Farmingdale, NY 11735 *Tel:* 631-249-2272 *Toll Free Tel:* 800-654-8542 (sales); 800-588-2852 *Fax:* 631-249-6066 *E-mail:* marketing@bulbtronics.com *Web Site:* www.bulbtronics.com, pg 815

Thayer, Rev George Allan, Christian TV Services of Ellicottville, NY, 6490 Pine Tree Rd, Bldg 5, Apt 315, Ellicottville, NY 14731-9603 *Tel:* 716-699-2549 (off & home); 716-257-2096 (cell); 716-397-9825 (cell) *Web Site:* www.christiantvservices.com; www.angelfire.com/ny/christiantvservices; home.sbu.edu/christ; www.christiantvservices.net; www.sauen.com/george/adm; www.christiantvservices.us; www.christiantvservices.info, pg 825

Thayer, Peter W, Thayer Birding Software, 12650 Colliers Reserve Dr, Naples, FL 34110 *Tel:* 239-596-1637 *Toll Free Tel:* 800-865-2473 *Fax:* 239-596-0232 *Web Site:* www.thayerbirding.com, pg 1038

Thel, Christine, Banff Mountain Film & Book Festival, 107 Tunnel Mountain Dr, Banff, AB T1L 1H5, Canada *Tel:* 403-762-6347 *Fax:* 403-762-6277 *E-mail:* banffmountainfestival@banffcentre.ca *Web Site:* www.banffcentre.ca/mountainfestival, pg 1109

Thelemaque, Jacques, Filmmakers Alliance (FA), 1317 N San Fernando Blvd, Unit 366, Burbank, CA 91504 *Tel:* 310-568-0633 *Fax:* 818-301-2257 *E-mail:* info@filmmakersalliance.org *Web Site:* filmmakersalliance.org, pg 1082

Theriult, Bruce, Edward R Murrow Award, 401 Ninth St NW, Washington, DC 20004-2129 *Tel:* 202-879-9600 *Toll Free Tel:* 800-272-2190 *Fax:* 202-879-9700 *E-mail:* comments@cpb.org *Web Site:* www.cpb.org, pg 1121

Theron, Diana, Cibola Systems, 180 S Cypress St, Orange, CA 92866 *Tel:* 714-480-0272 *Fax:* 714-480-0768 *E-mail:* info@cibolasystems.com *Web Site:* cibolasystems.com, pg 826

Therrien, Lucie, French American Music Enterprises, 5 Junkins Ave, Suite 106, Portsmouth, NH 03801 *Tel:* 603-430-9524 *Web Site:* www.luciet.com, pg 873

Thielking, Eric, AMV/Unitel, 515 W 57 St, New York, NY 10019 *Tel:* 212-265-3600 (studios); 212-586-8616 (sales) *Fax:* 212-246-5059 *E-mail:* hdsales@allmobilevideo.com *Web Site:* www.allmobilevideo.com, pg 786

Thielman, Gary, Harrison Consoles, 1024 Firestone Pkwy, La Vergne, TN 37086-3505 *Tel:* 615-641-7200 *Fax:* 615-641-7224 *E-mail:* info@harrisonconsoles.com *Web Site:* www.harrisonconsoles.com, pg 885

Thigpen, Dorothy, Third World Newsreel/Camera News Inc, 545 Eighth Ave, Suite 550, New York, NY 10018 *Tel:* 212-947-9277 *Fax:* 212-594-6417 *E-mail:* twn@twn.org *Web Site:* www.twn.org, pg 1039

Thil, Diane, MultiMedia, 333 Washington Ave N, Suite 212, Minneapolis, MN 55401 *Tel:* 612-767-1660 *Fax:* 612-339-5121 *E-mail:* info@multimedia-inc.com *Web Site:* www.multimedia-inc.com, pg 950

Thoman, Brad, Jeppesen, 55 Inverness Dr E, Englewood, CO 80112 *Tel:* 303-799-9090 *Toll Free Tel:* 800-621-5377; 800-353-2107 *Fax:* 303-328-4153 *Web Site:* www.jeppesen.com, pg 905

Thomas, Alisha, HEC Reading Horizons, 60 N Cutler Dr, Suite 101, North Salt Lake, UT 84054 *Tel:* 801-295-7054 *Toll Free Tel:* 800-333-0054 *Fax:* 801-295-7088 *E-mail:* info@readinghorizons.com *Web Site:* www.readinghorizons.com, pg 887

Thomas, Brad, Progressive AE, 1811 Four Mile Rd NE, Grand Rapids, MI 49525 *Tel:* 616-361-2664 *Fax:* 616-361-1493 *E-mail:* info@progressiveae.com *Web Site:* www.progressiveae.com, pg 985

Thomas, Bryan, Thomas Reprographics, 801 Second Ave N, Minneapolis, MN 55405 *Tel:* 612-374-1120 *Toll Free Tel:* 800-328-7154 *Fax:* 612-374-1129 *E-mail:* orders501@thomasrepro.com *Web Site:* thomasrepro.com, pg 1039

Thomas, Colette, Sonoma County Film Office, 141 Stony Circle, Suite 110, Santa Rosa, CA 95401-4154 *Tel:* 707-565-7170 *Fax:* 707-565-7231 *E-mail:* film@sonoma-county.org *Web Site:* www.sonoma-county.org/film, pg 1094

Thomas, Cristin, Dallas Learning Solutions, 9596 Walnut St, Dallas, TX 75243-2112 *Tel:* 972-669-6650 *Toll Free Tel:* 866-DISTLRN (347-8576) *Fax:* 972-669-6668 *E-mail:* tlearn@dcccd.edu *Web Site:* dls.dcccd.edu, pg 842

Thomas, Dave, Animax, 6627 Valjean Ave, Van Nuys, CA 91406 *Tel:* 818-787-4444 *E-mail:* hello@animaxent.com *Web Site:* www.animaxent.com, pg 787

Thomas, Douglas, Spectra Film & Video, 5626 Vineland Ave, North Hollywood, CA 91601 *Tel:* 818-762-4545 *Fax:* 818-762-5454 *E-mail:* sales@spectrafilmandvideo.com *Web Site:* www.spectrafilmandvideo.com, pg 1020

Thomas, Gary, Videssence, 10768 Lower Azusa Rd, El Monte, CA 91731 *Tel:* 626-579-0943 *Fax:* 626-579-6803 *E-mail:* contact@videssence.tv *Web Site:* www.videssence.tv, pg 1057

Thomas, John A, Liturgy Training Publications, 3949 S Racine Ave, Chicago, IL 60609-2523 *Tel:* 773-579-4900 *Toll Free Tel:* 800-933-1800 (orders) *Fax:* 773-579-4929 *E-mail:* orders@ltp.org *Web Site:* www.ltp.org, pg 923

Thomas, Lee, Georgia Film, Music & Digital Entertainment Office, 75 Fifth St W, Suite 1200, Atlanta, GA 30308 *Tel:* 404-962-4052 *Toll Free Tel:* 877-SHOOTGA (746-6842) *Fax:* 404-962-4053 *E-mail:* film@georgia.org *Web Site:* www.georgia.org, pg 1096

Thomas, Robert, Peppers Ghost HD®, c/o Bob Thomas Productions Inc, 2 Franklin Ct, Montville, NJ 07045 *Tel:* 973-335-9100 *Web Site:* www.peppersghosthd.com, pg 973

Thomas, Scott, Victory Studios, 2247 15 Ave W, Seattle, WA 98119 *Tel:* 206-282-1776 *Toll Free Tel:* 888-282-1776 *Fax:* 206-282-3535 *Toll Free Fax:* 888-765-9563 *E-mail:* info@victorystudios.com *Web Site:* www.victorystudios.com, pg 1054

Thomas, Terry, Captions & Subtitle Services Ltd, 101 Hempstead Place, Suite 1A, Joliet, IL 60433 *Tel:* 815-740-1009 *Toll Free Tel:* 866-230-1009 *E-mail:* info@capsubservices.com; quote@capsubservices.com *Web Site:* www.capsubservices.com, pg 820

Thomas, William Tyler, Bright Ideas Creative Services, 107 W Maple St, Suite 206, Jeffersonville, IN 47130 *Tel:* 812-282-9900; 502-693-9900 (cell) *Toll Free Fax:* 866-593-5753 *Web Site:* www.brightideascreative.com, pg 812

Thomas-Matson, Val, North-by-Northwest Productions, 903 W Broadway Ave, Spokane, WA 99201 *Tel:* 509-324-2949 *Fax:* 509-324-2959 *E-mail:* contact@nxnw.net *Web Site:* www.nxnw.net, pg 959

Thommes, Jeff, Staging Resources Inc, 257 E Helen Rd, Palatine, IL 60067 *Tel:* 847-963-6600 *Toll Free Tel:* 877-963-6600 *Fax:* 847-963-6601 *E-mail:* info@stagingresources.com *Web Site:* www.stagingresources.com, pg 1023

Thompson, Alim, New Leaf Distributing Co, 401 Thornton Rd, Lithia Springs, GA 30122-1557 *Tel:* 770-948-7845 *Toll Free Tel:* 800-326-2665 (orders) *Fax:* 770-944-2313 *E-mail:* newleaf@newleaf-dist.com *Web Site:* www.newleaf-dist.com, pg 956

Thompson, Dennis, TAPPI, 15 Technology Pkwy S, Norcross, GA 30092 *Tel:* 770-446-1400 *Toll Free Tel:* 800-332-8686 (US); 800-446-9431 (CN) *Fax:* 770-446-6947 *E-mail:* memberconnection@tappi.org *Web Site:* www.tappi.org, pg 1032

Thompson, Don, Finale Editworks, 2339 Columbia, Suite 100, Vancouver, BC V5Y 3V5, Canada *Tel:* 604-876-7678 *Fax:* 604-876-3299 *E-mail:* info@finale.tv *Web Site:* www.finale.tv, pg 868

Thompson, Frank, AV Metro Inc, 5401 Etta Burke Ct, Raleigh, NC 27606 *Tel:* 919-233-1901 *Fax:* 919-233-1804 *E-mail:* info@avmetro.com *Web Site:* www.avmetro.com, pg 797

Thompson, Harry H III, Thompson-Mitchell & Associates Inc, 1205 Johnson Ferry Rd, No 136, Marietta, GA 30068 *Tel:* 404-233-5435 *Toll Free Tel:* 800-554-1389 *Fax:* 404-521-4643, pg 1039

Thompson, Jim, Broadcasters Foundation Awards, 125 W 55 St, 3rd fl, New York, NY 10019-5366 *Tel:* 212-373-8250 *Fax:* 212-373-8254 *E-mail:* info@thebfoa.org *Web Site:* www.broadcastersfoundation.org, pg 1110

Thompson, Jim, Broadcasters Foundation of America, 125 W 55 St, 3rd fl, New York, NY 10019-5366 *Tel:* 212-373-8250 *Fax:* 212-373-8254 *E-mail:* info@thebfoa.org *Web Site:* www.broadcastersfoundation.org, pg 1080

Thompson, Jim, Golden Mike Award, 125 W 55 St, 3rd fl, New York, NY 10019-5366 *Tel:* 212-373-8250 *Fax:* 212-373-8254 *E-mail:* info@thebfoa.org *Web Site:* www.broadcastersfoundation.org, pg 1115

Thompson, Joseph B III, Berry & Homer, 2035 Richmond St, Philadelphia, PA 19125 *Tel:* 215-425-0888 *Fax:* 215-425-2701 *E-mail:* info@berryandhomer.com *Web Site:* www.berryandhomer.com, pg 805

Thompson, Kim Mitzo, Twin Sisters Productions LLC, 4710 Hudson Dr, Stow, OH 44224 *Toll Free Tel:* 800-248-TWIN (248-8946) *Toll Free Fax:* 800-480-TWIN (480-8946) *E-mail:* twinsisters@twinsisters.com *Web Site:* www.twinsisters.com, pg 1047

Thompson, Kirsten, Alpine Texas Chamber of Commerce, 106 N Third St, Alpine, TX 79830 *Tel:* 432-837-2326 *Toll Free Tel:* 800-561-3712 *Fax:* 432-837-1259 *E-mail:* info@alpinetexas.com *Web Site:* www.alpinetexas.com, pg 1102

Thompson, Lacy Jr, LT Sound Inc, 7980 LT Pkwy, Lithonia, GA 30058 *Tel:* 770-482-4836 *E-mail:* info3@ltsound.com *Web Site:* www.ltsound.com, pg 925

Thompson, Lonna, Association of Public Television Stations (APTS), 2100 Crystal Dr, Suite 700, Arlington, VA 22202 *Tel:* 202-654-4200 *Fax:* 202-654-4236 *Web Site:* www.apts.org, pg 1079

Thompson, Mike, Strategic Connections, 2721 Spring Forest Rd, Raleigh, NC 27616 *Tel:* 919-878-0550 *Fax:* 919-875-8712 *E-mail:* info@strategicmail.net *Web Site:* www.strategicconnections.net, pg 1026

Thompson, Shawn, PolyPhaser Corp, 10701 Airport Rd, Hayden, ID 83835 *Tel:* 208-772-8515 *Toll Free Tel:* 800-882-9110 *Fax:* 208-762-6117 *Web Site:* www.smithspower.com/brands/polyphaser, pg 978

Thompson, Tonya, Professional Photographers of Canada –Ontario (PPOC-ON), 209 Light St, Woodstock, ON N4S 6H6, Canada *Tel:* 519-537-2555 *Toll Free Tel:* 888-643-7762 *Toll Free Fax:* 888-831-4036 *E-mail:* info@ppocontario.com *Web Site:* www.ppocontario.com, pg 1087

Thompson, Trent, Moog Music Inc, 160 Broadway St, Asheville, NC 28801 *Tel:* 828-251-0090 *Toll Free Tel:* 800-948-1990 *Fax:* 828-254-6233 *E-mail:* info@moogmusic.com *Web Site:* www.moogmusic.com, pg 946

Thomson, Daniel, Image Video Services & Productions, 1210 Southview Dr, Sudbury, ON P3E 2L6, Canada *Tel:* 705-698-1212 *Fax:* 705-805-0110 *E-mail:* info@imagevideo.ca *Web Site:* www.imagevideo.ca, pg 895

Thomson, Ryan, Captain Fiddle Music & Publications, 94 Wiswall Rd, Lee, NH 03861 *Tel:* 603-659-2658 *E-mail:* cfiddle@tiac.net *Web Site:* captainfiddle.com, pg 820

Thomson, Steve, AirBrands Event & Marketing Group, 6470 Wyoming St, Dearborn, MI 48126 *Tel:* 519-254-9563 *Toll Free Tel:* 800-411-6200 (ext 26) *E-mail:* service@airbrandsmarketing.com *Web Site:* www.airbrandsmarketing.com, pg 779

Thomson, Susan, Image Video Services & Productions, 1210 Southview Dr, Sudbury, ON P3E 2L6, Canada *Tel:* 705-698-1212 *Fax:* 705-805-0110 *E-mail:* info@imagevideo.ca *Web Site:* www.imagevideo.ca, pg 895

Thomson, Tawni, Bishop Area Chamber of Commerce & Visitors Bureau, 690 N Main St, Bishop, CA 93514 *Tel:* 760-873-8405 *Toll Free Tel:* 888-395-3952 *Fax:* 760-873-6999 *Web Site:* www.bishopvisitor.com, pg 1092

Thor, Glen, Strong Entertainment Lighting, 13710 FNB Pkwy, Suite 400, Omaha, NE 68154 *Tel:* 402-453-4444 *Toll Free Tel:* 800-424-1215 *Fax:* 402-453-7238 *E-mail:* info@btn-inc.com *Web Site:* www.strong-world.com, pg 1026

Thorburn, Lisa A, Thorburn Associates, Acoustic, Technology, Lighting Design, 20880 Baker St, Castro Valley, CA 94546 *Tel:* 510-886-7826 *Fax:* 510-886-7828 *E-mail:* ta@ta-inc.com *Web Site:* www.ta-inc.com, pg 1039

Thorburn, Steven J, Thorburn Associates, Acoustic, Technology, Lighting Design, 20880 Baker St, Castro Valley, CA 94546 *Tel:* 510-886-7826 *Fax:* 510-886-7828 *E-mail:* ta@ta-inc.com *Web Site:* www.ta-inc.com, pg 1039

Thornberg, Linda, Audacity Creative, 2734 Polk St, Suite B, Hollywood, FL 33020 *Tel:* 954-920-4418 *Toll Free Fax:* 877-229-6298 *E-mail:* info@audacitycreative.com; audacityrecording@mac.com *Web Site:* audacitycreative.com; audacityrecording.com, pg 793

Thorne-Stone, Karen, Ontario Media Development Corp, South Tower, Suite 501, 175 Bloor St E, Toronto, ON M4W 3R8, Canada *Tel:* 416-314-6858 *Fax:* 416-314-6876 *E-mail:* reception@omdc.on.ca *Web Site:* www.omdc.on.ca, pg 1105

Thorpe, Robert, Earl Girls Inc, 1648 White Horse Pike, Egg Harbor City, NJ 08215 *Tel:* 609-965-6900 *Toll Free Tel:* 888-777-EARL (777-3275) *Fax:* 609-965-3330 *E-mail:* sales@earlgirlsinc.com *Web Site:* earlgirlsinc.com, pg 855

Thrasher, Charlotte, Opti-Case Inc, 1175 CR 481 W, Henderson, TX 75654 *Tel:* 903-657-5666 *Toll Free Tel:* 800-637-6635 *Fax:* 903-657-6030 *E-mail:* sales@opti-case.net *Web Site:* www.opti-case.net, pg 964

Throop, Darren, Entertainment One Distribution, 70 Driver Rd, Unit 1, Brampton, ON L6T 5V2, Canada *Tel:* 905-624-7337 *Toll Free Tel:* 800-387-0184 *Fax:* 905-624-7310; 905-463-9755 (cust serv) *E-mail:* info@entertainmentone.ca *Web Site:* entertainmentone.com; ca.eonedistribution.com, pg 861

Thuillot, Dominique, Editions Hurtubise HMH Ltee, 1815 Avenue De Lorimier, Montreal, QC H2K 3W6, Canada *Tel:* 514-523-1523 *Toll Free Tel:* 800-361-1664 *Fax:* 514-523-9969 *Web Site:* www.editionshurtubise.com, pg 892

Thuot, Stephanie, International Film Festival in Abitibi-Teiscamingue/Festival du cinema international en Abitibi-Temiscamingue, 215 Ave Mercier, Rouyn-Noranda, QC J9X 5W8, Canada *Tel:* 819-762-6212 *Fax:* 819-762-6762 *E-mail:* info@festivalcinema.ca *Web Site:* www.festivalcinema.ca, pg 1117

Thurman, Doug, StageSound, 2240 Shenandoah Ave NW, Roanoke, VA 24017 *Tel:* 540-342-2040 *Toll Free Tel:* 800-778-9839 *Fax:* 540-345-5158 *Web Site:* stagesound.com, pg 1023

Tibodeau, Mike, Guerrilla Film Fest, 1421 Massachusetts Ave NW, Suite 202, Washington, DC 20005 *Tel:* 202-234-2889 *E-mail:* gfilmfest@yahoo.com *Web Site:* www.gfilmfest.com, pg 1116

Tierney, Jim, Tierney Brothers Inc, 3300 University Ave SE, Minneapolis, MN 55414-3326 *Tel:* 612-331-5500 *Toll Free Tel:* 866-557-6062 *Fax:* 612-331-3424 *E-mail:* contactform@tierneybrothers.com *Web Site:* www.tierneybrothers.com, pg 1040

Tierney, Paula, Tierney Brothers Inc, 3300 University Ave SE, Minneapolis, MN 55414-3326 *Tel:* 612-331-5500 *Toll Free Tel:* 866-557-6062 *Fax:* 612-331-3424 *E-mail:* contactform@tierneybrothers.com *Web Site:* www.tierneybrothers.com, pg 1040

Tierney, Tom, Tierney Brothers Inc, 3300 University Ave SE, Minneapolis, MN 55414-3326 *Tel:* 612-331-5500 *Toll Free Tel:* 866-557-6062 *Fax:* 612-331-3424 *E-mail:* contactform@tierneybrothers.com *Web Site:* www.tierneybrothers.com, pg 1040

Tiffen, Steven, The Tiffen Co LLC, 90 Oser Ave, Hauppauge, NY 11788-3886 *Tel:* 631-273-2500 *Toll Free Tel:* 800-989-6013; 800-645-8500; 800-645-2522 *Fax:* 631-273-2557 *E-mail:* techsupport@tiffen.com *Web Site:* www.tiffen.com, pg 1040

Tigar, Michael, Tigar Hare Studios, 4485 Matilija Ave, Sherman Oaks, CA 91423 *Tel:* 818-907-6663 *Fax:* 818-907-0693 *E-mail:* info@tigarhare.com *Web Site:* www.tigarhare.com, pg 1040

Tilghman, Isabelle, Celebration of Service to America Awards, 1771 "N" St NW, Washington, DC 20036-2891 *Tel:* 202-421-3191 *E-mail:* nabef@nab.org *Web Site:* www.nabef.org, pg 1111

Till, Rod, WESCAM Inc, 649 N Service Rd W, Burlington, ON L7P 5B9, Canada *Tel:* 905-633-4000 *Toll Free Tel:* 800-668-4355 *Fax:* 905-633-4100 *E-mail:* sales.wescam@l-3com.com *Web Site:* www.wescam.com, pg 1063

Tillett, Chuck D, PESA, 103 Quality Circle, Suite 210, Huntsville, AL 35806 *Tel:* 256-726-9200 *Toll Free Tel:* 800-323-7372 *E-mail:* sales@pesa.com *Web Site:* www.pesa.com, pg 973

Tillman, Paul, L Acoustics US, 2201 Celsius Ave, Unit E, Oxnard, CA 93030 *Tel:* 805-604-0577 *Fax:* 805-604-0858 *E-mail:* info@l-acoustics-us.com *Web Site:* www.l-acoustics.com, pg 914

Tilly, Steve, Telestream Inc, 848 Gold Flat Rd, Nevada City, CA 95959 *Tel:* 530-470-1300 *Toll Free Tel:* 877-257-6245 *Fax:* 530-470-1301 *E-mail:* info@telestream.net *Web Site:* www.telestream.net, pg 1036

Timms, Daniel Glen, Mellow Hollow Studio, 3030 River Rd, Ashland City, TN 37015 *Tel:* 615-971-0146 *Fax:* 615-792-1787 *Web Site:* www.mellowhollow.com, pg 938

Tinnon, Robert S, Wilson McLeran Inc, 41 Corey Hill Rd, Saxtons River, VT 05154 *Tel:* 802-869-3111 *Toll Free Tel:* 800-562-9646 *Fax:* 802-869-3111 *Web Site:* www.job-bridge.com, pg 1067

Tippmann, Vince, Advanced Media Integration, 2300 Meyer Rd, Fort Wayne, IN 46805 *Tel:* 260-428-2698 *Toll Free Tel:* 877-428-2610 *Fax:* 260-428-2699 *E-mail:* info@advancedmediaintegration.com *Web Site:* www.advancedmediaintegration.com, pg 777

Titen, Andrew, Bisk Education, 9417 Princess Palm Ave, Tampa, FL 33619 *Toll Free Tel:* 800-280-9718 *E-mail:* customerservice@bisk.com *Web Site:* www.bisk.com, pg 808

Titus, Dick, ETC, 3031 Pleasant View Rd, Middleton, WI 53562-4809 *Tel:* 608-831-4116 *Toll Free Tel:* 800-688-4116 *Fax:* 608-836-1736 *E-mail:* mail@etcconnect.com; americas@etcconnect.com *Web Site:* www.etcconnect.com, pg 862

Titus, Lawrence, Titus Technological Laboratories (TTL), 77 Kreiger Lane, Glastonbury, CT 06033 *Tel:* 860-633-5472 *Toll Free Tel:* 800-806-TTL1 (806-8851) *Fax:* 860-633-8244 *E-mail:* sales1@tituslabs.com *Web Site:* www.tituslabs.com, pg 1041

Tjaden, Teresa, American Color Imaging (ACI), 715 E 18 St, Cedar Falls, IA 50613 *Tel:* 319-277-3655 *Toll Free Tel:* 800-728-2722 *Fax:* 319-277-6522 *E-mail:* sales@acilab.com *Web Site:* www.acilab.com, pg 784

Tkach, Alex, North West Digital Ltd, 400-116 W Sixth Ave, Vancouver, BC V5Y 1K6, Canada *Tel:* 604-709-3444 *Fax:* 604-687-7600 *Web Site:* www.nwdigi.com, pg 959

Toback, Dan, Digital Film Studios, 11800 Sheldon St, Unit C/D, Sun Valley, CA 91352 *Tel:* 818-771-0019 *Fax:* 818-351-1155 *E-mail:* info@digitalfilmstudios.com *Web Site:* www.digitalfilmstudios.com, pg 847

Tobias, Eric M, Tobias Associates Inc, 50 Industrial Dr, Warminster, PA 18974-1433 *Tel:* 215-322-1500 *Toll Free Tel:* 800-877-3367 *Fax:* 215-322-1504 *E-mail:* sales@tobiasinc.com *Web Site:* www.densitometers.net, pg 1041

Tobin, Clive, Tobin Cinema Systems Inc, 6116 N Ormond Rd, Otis Orchards, WA 99027 *Tel:* 509-621-0323 *E-mail:* filmstodvd@comcast.net *Web Site:* www.tobincinemasystems.com, pg 1041

Tobin, Dwight B, Tobin Productions Inc, 630 Ninth Ave, Suite 215, New York, NY 10036 *Tel:* 212-727-1500 *Toll Free Tel:* 800-877-8273 *Fax:* 212-727-1766 *E-mail:* info@tobinproductions.com *Web Site:* www.tobinproductions.com, pg 1041

Tochilin, Jerry, General Production Services, 883 S East St, Anaheim, CA 92805 *Tel:* 714-535-2271 *Fax:* 714-535-0952 *E-mail:* lensclens@yahoo.com *Web Site:* www.lensclens.com, pg 877

Tocidlowski, Steve, Television Equipment Associates Inc (TEA), 16 Mount Ebo Rd S, Suite 6, Brewster, NY 10509 *Tel:* 845-278-0960 *Fax:* 845-278-0964 *E-mail:* info@swatheadsets.com *Web Site:* www.swatheadsets.com, pg 1037

Tod, Dorothy, Dorothy Tod Films, 41 Hazel Brown Rd, Warren, VT 05674 *Tel:* 802-496-5280 *Fax:* 802-496-5280, pg 1041

Todd, Hunter, WorldFest-Houston, 9898 Bissonnet St, Suite 650, Houston, TX 77036 *Tel:* 713-965-9955 *Toll Free Tel:* 866-965-9955 *Fax:* 713-965-9960 *E-mail:* mail@worldfest.org; entry@worldfest.org *Web Site:* www.worldfest.org, pg 1130

Todd, Jean, Independent Audio Inc, 43 Deerfield Rd, Portland, ME 04101 *Tel:* 207-773-2424 *Fax:* 207-773-2422 *E-mail:* info@independentaudio.com *Web Site:* www.independentaudio.com, pg 897

Toland, Shelby, The Brainwash Movie Festival, 1675 Seventh St, No 23302, Oakland, CA 94623-6009 *Tel:* 510-836-3210 *Web Site:* www.brainwashm.com, pg 1110

Tolchin, Talc, Forte Productions, PO Box 17, San Geronimo, CA 94963-0325 *Tel:* 415-488-9446 *Fax:* 415-488-9446 *Web Site:* www.pianovideos.com, pg 871

Toledano, Gabrielle, Electronic Arts, 209 Redwood Shores Pkwy, Redwood City, CA 94065 *Tel:* 650-628-1500 *Web Site:* www.ea.com, pg 859

Tomkin, Michael, Production Resource Group LLC (PRG), 539 Temple Hill Rd, New Windsor, NY 12553-5533 *Tel:* 845-567-5700 *Fax:* 845-567-5800 *E-mail:* info@prg.com *Web Site:* www.prg.com, pg 984

Toms, Mark, Quantel Inc, 25 W 43 St, Suite 1118, New York, NY 10036-7406 *Tel:* 212-944-6820 *Toll Free Tel:* 800-331-8327 (cust serv) *Fax:* 212-944-6813 *Web Site:* www.quantel.com, pg 989

Tomwil, Jim Rokas, Tatum Video, 103 S Davis St, Telluride, CO 81435 *Tel:* 213-999-5970 (cell); 970-728-4892 *Fax:* 970-728-4892 *E-mail:* utemtn@aol.com, pg 1032

Tonges, Michael A, Image Video Teleproductions Inc, 6755 Freedom Ave NW, North Canton, OH 44720 *Tel:* 330-494-9303 *Fax:* 330-966-1792 *E-mail:* info@image-video.com *Web Site:* www.image-video.com, pg 895

Topjian, Lori, Spirig Advanced Technologies Inc (SAT), 144 Oakland St, Springfield, MA 01108 *Tel:* 413-788-6191 *Toll Free Tel:* 866-977-4744 *Fax:* 413-788-0490 *E-mail:* sat@spirig.com; order@spirig.com *Web Site:* www.spirig.com, pg 1021

Topscher, Thomas, Media Dimensions Inc, 2212 Autumn Glow Ct, Bel Air, MD 21015 *Tel:* 410-561-4550 *Fax:* 410-561-4550 *E-mail:* info@mediadimensions.com *Web Site:* www.mediadimensions.com, pg 936

Torjman, Kathy, 4 Wall Entertainment, 3325 W Sunset Rd, Suite F, Las Vegas, NV 89118 *Tel:* 702-263-3858 *Toll Free Tel:* 877-789-8167 (Western US); 866-492-5540 (Eastern US) *Fax:* 702-263-3863 *E-mail:* info@4wall.com *Web Site:* www.4wall.com; www.usedlighting.com, pg 872

Tornek, Alexandra, So Smart Productions, 701 Sharpley Rd, Wilmington, DE 19803 *Tel:* 484-753-1520 *E-mail:* info@sosmart.com *Web Site:* store.sosmart.com, pg 1015

Tornek, Scott, So Smart Productions, 701 Sharpley Rd, Wilmington, DE 19803 *Tel:* 484-753-1520 *E-mail:* info@sosmart.com *Web Site:* store.sosmart.com, pg 1015

Torno, Earl, Wanted! Sound + Picture, 409 King St W, Suite 300, Toronto, ON M5V 1K1, Canada *Tel:* 416-596-1101 *Fax:* 416-596-0690 *E-mail:* info@wantedsp.com *Web Site:* www.wantedsp.com, pg 1062

Torno, Tim, eInstruction Corp, 14400 N 87 St, Suite 250, Scottsdale, AZ 85260 *Tel:* 480-948-6540 *Toll Free Tel:* 800-856-0732 *Fax:* 480-948-5508 *Web Site:* www.einstruction.com, pg 858

Tornquist, Duane, American Audio Visual Center, 7434 E Monte Cristo Ave, Scottsdale, AZ 85260 *Tel:* 480-596-9880 *Fax:* 480-596-0942 *Web Site:* www.americanavc.com, pg 783

Torok, George, Hallel Communications, Hallel Institute, 175 Rte 340, Sparkill, NY 10976-1047 *Tel:* 845-365-2277 *Toll Free Tel:* 800-445-7477 *Fax:* 845-365-2279 *E-mail:* hallel@hallel.net *Web Site:* www.hallelvideos.com, pg 884

Torra, Veronica, Cayman Islands Department of Tourism, Empire State Bldg, 350 Fifth Ave, Suite 2720, New York, NY 10018 *Tel:* 212-889-9009 *Toll Free Tel:* 877-4-CAYMAN (422-9626) *Fax:* 212-889-9125 *Web Site:* www.caymanislands.ky; www.divecayman.ky, pg 1100

Torres, Mark, Pacifica Radio Archives, 3729 Cahuenga Blvd W, North Hollywood, CA 91604 *Tel:* 818-506-1077 *Toll Free Tel:* 800-735-0230 *Fax:* 818-506-1084 *E-mail:* pacarchive@aol.com *Web Site:* www.pacificaradioarchives.org, pg 967

Torres, Ray, Checkers Industrial Products LLC, 620 Compton St, Broomfield, CO 80020 *Tel:* 720-890-1187 *Toll Free Tel:* 800-438-9336 *Fax:* 720-890-1191 *E-mail:* sales@checkersindustrial.com *Web Site:* www.checkersindustrial.com, pg 824

Torres Rojas, Roselly, Third World Newsreel/Camera News Inc, 545 Eighth Ave, Suite 550, New York, NY 10018 *Tel:* 212-947-9277 *Fax:* 212-594-6417 *E-mail:* twn@twn.org *Web Site:* www.twn.org, pg 1039

Torrey, David, DRT Mastering, 20 Vine St, Peterborough, NH 03458 *Tel:* 603-924-2277 *Web Site:* www.drtmastering.com, pg 852

Torroija, Diego, Two Door Productions, 416 N Harper Ave, Los Angeles, CA 90048 *E-mail:* shoot@usphotograph.com *Web Site:* www.twodoorfx.com, pg 1047

Tosterud, Dominic, Creative Technology, 1455 Estes Ave, Elk Grove Village, IL 60007 *Tel:* 847-671-9670 *Toll Free Tel:* 800-826-4761 *Fax:* 847-640-6559 *E-mail:* info@ctchicago.com *Web Site:* us.ct-group.com, pg 838

Totaro, Matt, Event Tech, 7601 Brandon Woods Blvd, Baltimore, MD 21226 *Tel:* 410-360-5006 *Toll Free Tel:* 866-950-8343 *Fax:* 410-360-5002 *E-mail:* info@eventtech.com *Web Site:* www.eventtech.com, pg 863

Toth, John E D, ARC Document Solutions, 1981 N Broadway, Suite 385, Walnut Creek, CA 94596 *Tel:* 925-949-5100 *Fax:* 925-949-5101 *E-mail:* info@e-arc.com *Web Site:* www.e-arc.com, pg 789

Touhill, Nancy, Personal Communications Industry Association (PCIA), 500 Montgomery St, Suite 500, Alexandria, VA 22314 *Tel:* 703-739-0300 *Toll Free Tel:* 800-759-0300 *Fax:* 703-836-1608 *Web Site:* www.pcia.com, pg 1087

Touma, Dara, Griffiths Broadcast Co Inc, 2981 Le Conte St, Viera, FL 32940 *Tel:* 321-622-4619 *Fax:* 321-622-4619 *E-mail:* griffiths.broadcast@usa.net *Web Site:* www.griffithsbroadcast.com, pg 882

Tourlitis, Shari, Evolve Inc, 1210 E Arlington Blvd, Greenville, NC 27858 *Tel:* 252-754-2957 *Fax:* 252-754-2832 *Web Site:* www.evolveinc.com, pg 863

Toutoungi, Nick, DocMiami International Film Festival, 8770 Sunset Dr, No 274, Miami, FL 33173-3512 *Tel:* 786-493-8308 *E-mail:* info@docmiami.org *Web Site:* www.docmiami.org, pg 1114

Towell, Dennis, Iron Ring Communications Ltd, 431 Brookmill Rd, Unit 1, Oakville, ON L6J 5K6, Canada *Tel:* 905-849-5922 *Fax:* 905-849-6188 *Web Site:* www.ironringltd.com, pg 902

Towey, Brian, Microboards Technology LLC, 8150 Mallory Ct, Chanhassen, MN 55317 *Tel:* 952-556-1600 *Toll Free Tel:* 800-646-8881; 800-290-9012 *Fax:* 952-556-1620 *E-mail:* sales@microboards.com *Web Site:* www.microboards.com, pg 941

Towne, Victoria, Preston Productions Inc, 128 Bartlett St, Marlborough, MA 01752 *Toll Free Tel:* 800-822-2299 *E-mail:* ideas@prestonevents.com *Web Site:* www.prestonproductions.com; www.prestonevents.com, pg 981

Towner, John, Solid Sound Recording Studio, 2400 Hassell Rd, Suite 430, Hoffman Estates, IL 60169 *Tel:* 847-490-2101 *E-mail:* solidsoundrecordingstudios@gmail.com, pg 1015

Townley, Shannon, SurgeX, 800 Knightdale Blvd, Suite 121, Knightdale, NC 27545 *Toll Free Tel:* 800-645-9721 (tech & cust support) *Fax:* 919-269-0454 *Web Site:* www.surgex.com, pg 1029

Townsend, Joanne, H Wilson Co, 2245 Delany Rd, Waukegan, IL 60087 *Tel:* 847-244-1800 *Toll Free Tel:* 800-245-7224; 800-323-4656 (sales) *Fax:* 708-210-2069; 847-244-1818 (sales) *Toll Free Fax:* 800-245-8224; 800-327-1698 (sales) *E-mail:* sales@hwilson.com; info@wilson.com; customerservice@wilson.com *Web Site:* www.hwilson.com, pg 1067

Towry, Jimi, Tropikal Productions, 137 Sequoia Rd, Rockwall, TX 75032 *Tel:* 972-771-3797 *Fax:* 972-771-0853 *E-mail:* tropikalproductions@gmail.com *Web Site:* www.tropikalproductions.com, pg 1045

Towry, Jimi, World Beat Studio, 137 Sequoia Rd, Rockwall, TX 75032 *Tel:* 972-771-3797 *Fax:* 972-771-0853 *E-mail:* tropikalproductions@gmail.com *Web Site:* www.tropikalproductions.com, pg 1069

Towstego, Anthony J, Thomega Entertainment Inc, 3027 Miller Ave, Bay D, Saskatoon, SK S7K 6G5, Canada *Tel:* 306-373-3765 *Fax:* 306-242-5845 *E-mail:* thomega@sasktel.net *Web Site:* www.thomega.com, pg 1039

Tracey, Robin, RingSide Creative, 13320 Northend, Suite 3000, Oak Park, MI 48237 *Tel:* 248-548-2500 *E-mail:* info@ringsidecreative.com; newbiz@ringsidecreative.com *Web Site:* www.ringsidecreative.com, pg 997

Tracton, Peter, Patco Resources Inc, 9 Washington Circle, Suffern, NY 10901 *Tel:* 845-357-5300 *Fax:* 845-357-6427 *E-mail:* musicinfo@patcoresources.com *Web Site:* www.patcoresources.com, pg 970

Tracy, Doug, Computer Sciences Corp, 3170 Fairview Park Dr, Falls Church, VA 22042 *Tel:* 703-876-1000 *Web Site:* www.csc.com, pg 834

Tracy, Reid, Hay House Inc, PO Box 5100, Carlsbad, CA 92018-5100 *Tel:* 760-431-7695 (ext 2, intl) *Toll Free Tel:* 800-654-5126 (ext 2, US); 800-650-5115 *Fax:* 760-431-6948 *Web Site:* www.hayhouse.com, pg 886

Tracy, Sue, The DubHouse, 404 SE 15 St, Fort Lauderdale, FL 33316 *Tel:* 954-524-3658 *Toll Free Tel:* 877-900-DUBS (900-3827) *Fax:* 954-522-1905 *Web Site:* www.thedubhouse.net, pg 853

Trainor, Julia, Musikvergnuegen, 1545 Wilcox Ave, Suite 202, Hollywood, CA 90028 *Tel:* 323-856-5900 *Fax:* 323-856-5917 *E-mail:* info@musikv.com *Web Site:* www.musikvergnuegen.com, pg 951

Tramantano, Michelle, Photoimaging Manufacturers & Distributors Association Inc, 7600 Jericho Tpke, Suite 301, Woodbury, NY 11797 *Tel:* 516-802-0895 *Fax:* 516-364-0140 *Web Site:* www.pmda.com, pg 1087

Trapani, Jim, JT Communications, 579 NE 44 Ave, Ocala, FL 34470-1421 *Tel:* 352-236-0744 *Fax:* 352-236-5130 *E-mail:* general_info@jtcomms.com *Web Site:* www.jtcomms.com, pg 906

Traubner, Andrea, Filmakers Library, 3212 Duke St, Alexandria, VA 22314 *Tel:* 703-212-8520 *E-mail:* sales@alexanderstreet.com; orders@alexanderstreet.com *Web Site:* www.academicvideostore.com/filmakers; www.academicvideostore.com, pg 867

Traum, Happy, Homespun Video, 1610 Rte 212, Saugerties, NY 12477 *Tel:* 845-246-2550 *Toll Free Tel:* 800-338-2737 (orders-US & CN) *Fax:* 845-246-5282 *E-mail:* info@homespuntapes.com *Web Site:* www.homespuntapes.com, pg 890

Traum, Jane, Homespun Video, 1610 Rte 212, Saugerties, NY 12477 *Tel:* 845-246-2550 *Toll Free Tel:* 800-338-2737 (orders-US & CN) *Fax:* 845-246-5282 *E-mail:* info@homespuntapes.com *Web Site:* www.homespuntapes.com, pg 890

Travers, Scott, CamTec Motion Picture Cameras, 4221 W Magnolia Blvd, Burbank, CA 91505 *Tel:* 818-841-8700 *Fax:* 818-841-8777 *Web Site:* www.camtec.tv, pg 818

Traverso, Mark, SCI Television Productions LLC, 160 E Grand Ave, Suite 5W, Chicago, IL 60611 *Tel:* 312-643-2080 *E-mail:* info@scitvproductions.com *Web Site:* www.scitvproductions.com, pg 1005

Traversy, Pete, Graphx Inc, 400 W Cummings Park, Suite 3900, Woburn, MA 01801 *Tel:* 781-932-0430 *Fax:* 781-932-0855 *E-mail:* info@graphx.com *Web Site:* www.graphx.com, pg 881

Treadway, Toni, Brodsky & Treadway, 69 Warehouse Lane, Rowley, MA 01969 *Tel:* 978-948-7985 *Web Site:* www.LittleFilm.com, pg 813

Trebswether, Sue, American Society of Safety Engineers (ASSE), 1800 E Oakton St, Des Plaines, IL 60018 *Tel:* 847-699-2929 *E-mail:* customerservice@asse.org *Web Site:* www.asse.org, pg 1077

Treesuwan, Kate, Instrumentation Marketing Corp, 820 S Mariposa St, Burbank, CA 91506-3196 *Tel:* 818-842-2141 *Fax:* 818-842-2610 *E-mail:* mail@photosonics.com *Web Site:* www.photosonics.com/imc.htm, pg 899

Treffiletti, Carmen, DME Studios, 1025 Greenwood Blvd, Suite 191, Lake Mary, FL 32746 *Tel:* 407-585-7500 *E-mail:* creativeteam@dmestudios.com *Web Site:* www.dmestudios.com, pg 849

Treibitz, Alan, Z-Axis Corp, 4600 S Ulster St, Suite 270, Denver, CO 80237 *Tel:* 303-713-0200 *Toll Free Tel:* 800-827-2947 *E-mail:* info@zaxis.com *Web Site:* www.zaxis.com, pg 1073

Tremblay, Robert, Group PVP, 296 Saint Pierre St, Matane, QC G4W 2B9, Canada *Tel:* 418-566-2040 *Toll Free Tel:* 877-320-2040 *Fax:* 418-562-4643 *E-mail:* info@pvp.ca *Web Site:* www.pvp.ca, pg 883

Tremble, Mike, Cinema Concepts, 2030 Powers Ferry Rd, Suite 214, Atlanta, GA 30339 *Tel:* 770-956-7460 *Toll Free Tel:* 800-SHOWADS (746-9237) *Fax:* 770-956-8358 *E-mail:* info@cinemaconcepts.com *Web Site:* www.cinemaconcepts.com, pg 827

Trendler, Meg, Eugene, Cascades & Coast-Travel Lane County, 754 Olive St, Eugene, OR 97401 *Tel:* 541-484-5307 *Toll Free Tel:* 800-547-5445 *Fax:* 541-343-6335 *E-mail:* film@eugenecascadescoast.org *Web Site:* www.eugenecascadescoast.org, pg 1101

Trent, Michael, Dances With Films, Formosa Bldg, 2nd fl, 1041 N Formosa Ave, West Hollywood, CA 90046 *Tel:* 323-850-2929 *E-mail:* info@danceswithfilms.com *Web Site:* www.danceswithfilms.com, pg 1113

Treutler, Theresa, The Bessies Awards, 160 Bloor St E, Suite 1005, Toronto, ON M4W 1B9, Canada *Tel:* 416-923-8813 *Toll Free Tel:* 800-231-0051 (CN only) *Fax:* 416-413-3879 *E-mail:* tvb@tvb.ca *Web Site:* www.tvb.ca/pages/thebessies.htm; thebessies.ca, pg 1109

Trien, Ooana, Sunrise Media LLC, 200 Central Park S, Suite 12F, New York, NY 10019 *Tel:* 212-221-6310 *Fax:* 212-302-1854 *E-mail:* info@ipfmedia.org *Web Site:* www.ipfmedia.org/vetc.htm, pg 1028

Tritchew, Steve, WESCAM Inc, 649 N Service Rd W, Burlington, ON L7P 5B9, Canada *Tel:* 905-633-4000 *Toll Free Tel:* 800-668-4355 *Fax:* 905-633-4100 *E-mail:* sales.wescam@l-3com.com *Web Site:* www.wescam.com, pg 1063

Troiano, Kenneth, Modernage Photographic Services Inc, 555 Eighth Ave, New York, NY 10018 *Tel:* 212-997-1800 *Toll Free Tel:* 800-997-2510 *Fax:* 212-869-4796 *E-mail:* info@modernage.com *Web Site:* www.modernage.com, pg 944

Trojian, Elizabeth, YAP Films, 96 Spadina Ave, Suite 205, Toronto, ON M5V 2J6, Canada *Tel:* 416-504-3662 *Fax:* 416-504-3667 *E-mail:* thedog@yapfilms.com *Web Site:* www.yapfilms.com, pg 1072

Tronolone, James, PatchAmp, 20 E Kennedy St, Hackensack, NJ 07601 *Tel:* 201-457-1504 *Fax:* 201-457-1507 *E-mail:* sales@patchamp.com *Web Site:* www.patchamp.com, pg 970

Trost, Mark, FILM Archives Inc, 35 W 35 St, Suite 904, New York, NY 10001-2238 *Tel:* 212-696-2616 *Fax:* 503-210-9927 *E-mail:* info@filmarchives.com *Web Site:* www.filmarchivesonline.com, pg 867

Trotter, Elaine G, InVision Productions, 821 Las Colindas Rd, San Rafael, CA 94903 *Tel:* 415-492-0414 *E-mail:* invision@goinvision.com *Web Site:* www.goinvision.com, pg 902

Troupe, Phil, Rainbow Video Productions Inc, 23803 S 162 St, Adams, NE 68301 *Tel:* 402-430-7343 *Web Site:* www.rainbowvideo.com, pg 991

Troy, Robert, JR Media Services, 2501 W Burbank Blvd, Suite 200, Burbank, CA 91505 *Tel:* 818-557-0200 *Fax:* 818-557-0201 *E-mail:* info@jrmediaservices.com *Web Site:* www.jrmediaservices.com, pg 906

True, Karen, Portland Models & Talent LLC, PO Box 4727, Portland, ME 04112-4727 *Tel:* 207-741-2850; 207-799-9758 *E-mail:* PortlandModels@aol.com *Web Site:* www.portlandmodels.com, pg 979

Trufant, Michael, Launch Media, Celtic Media Ctr, 10000 Celtic Dr, Baton Rouge, LA 70809 *Tel:* 225-612-2112 *E-mail:* contactus@launchmedia.tv *Web Site:* www.launchmedia.tv, pg 916

Truley, Ellen Bligh, SESAC Inc, 55 Music Sq E, Nashville, TN 37203 *Tel:* 615-320-0055 *Fax:* 615-963-3527 *Web Site:* www.sesac.com, pg 1088

Truong, Thao, Educational Insights, 380 N Fairway Dr, Vernon Hills, IL 60061 *Toll Free Tel:* 888-591-9334 (cust serv) *Toll Free Fax:* 888-995-0506 (cust serv) *E-mail:* info@edin.com; cs@educationalinsights.com *Web Site:* www.educationalinsights.com, pg 857

Trupp, Scott, MCCOM Inc, 383 Rte 206, Chester, NJ 07930 *Tel:* 908-879-9590 *Fax:* 908-879-9679 *E-mail:* info@mccominc.com *Web Site:* www.mccom.tv, pg 935

Ts'o, Pauline, Rhythm & Hues, 2100 E Grand Ave, Suite A, El Segundo, CA 90245-5024 *Tel:* 310-448-7500 *Fax:* 310-448-7600 *E-mail:* info-la@rhythm.com *Web Site:* www.rhythm.com, pg 996

Tschohl, John, Service Quality Institute, 9201 E Bloomington Fwy, Minneapolis, MN 55420-3437 *Tel:* 952-884-3311 *Toll Free Tel:* 800-548-0538 *Fax:* 952-884-8901 *E-mail:* quality@servicequality.com *Web Site:* www.customer-service.com, pg 1007

Tsinberg, Mike, Key Digital Systems, 521 E Third St, Mount Vernon, NY 10553 *Tel:* 914-667-9700 *Fax:* 914-668-8666 *E-mail:* info@keydigital.com *Web Site:* www.keydigital.com, pg 910

Tsuno, Keiko, Downtown Community Television Center (DCTV), 87 Lafayette St, New York, NY 10013 *Tel:* 212-966-4510 *Fax:* 212-226-3053 *E-mail:* info@dctvny.org *Web Site:* www.dctvny.org, pg 851

Tu, Laura, TVA Productions, 3950 Vantage Ave, Studio City, CA 91604 *Tel:* 818-505-8300 *Toll Free Tel:* 888-322-4296 *E-mail:* info@tvaproductions.com *Web Site:* www.tvaproductions.com, pg 1046

Tuck, Jack, Communications Specialists Inc, 7272 Jackson Ave, Mechanicsville, VA 23111 *Tel:* 804-559-4274 *Fax:* 804-559-4479 *E-mail:* info@csisystems.net *Web Site:* www.csisystems.net, pg 833

Tucker, Allan, Foothill Digital Inc, 217 Storer Ave, New Rochelle, NY 10801 *Tel:* 914-235-5670 *E-mail:* info@foothilldigital.com *Web Site:* www.foothilldigital.com; www.tuckersound.com, pg 871

Tucker, Darria, Refinery, 16 W 46 St, 12th fl, New York, NY 10036 *Tel:* 212-391-8166 *Fax:* 212-391-8783 *Web Site:* refinerynyc.com, pg 994

Tucker, Ron, Grace Church - St Louis, 2695 Creve Coeur Mill Rd, Maryland Heights, MO 63043 *Tel:* 314-292-8300 *Fax:* 314-291-0918 *E-mail:* info@gracestl.org *Web Site:* www.gracestl.org, pg 881

Tucker, Scott, Sure Shot Transmissions Inc, 10314 Main St, New Middletown, OH 44442 *Tel:* 330-542-0900 *Fax:* 330-542-1020 *Web Site:* www.sureshotsat.com, pg 1029

Tucker, Tomas, Videofax, 1750 Cesar Chavez St, Unit G, San Francisco, CA 94124 *Tel:* 415-641-0100 *E-mail:* rentals@videofax.com *Web Site:* www.videofax.com, pg 1057

Tudor, Dawn, Verilux® - The Healthy Lighting Co, 340 Mad River Park, Suite 1, Waitsfield, VT 05673 *Tel:* 802-496-3101 *Toll Free Tel:* 888-544-4865 (cust support); 800-454-4408 (orders) *Fax:* 802-496-3105 (orders) *E-mail:* info@verilux.com *Web Site:* www.verilux.com, pg 1053

Tudryn, Joyce M, International Radio & Television Society Foundation (IRTS), 1697 Broadway, 10th fl, New York, NY 10019 *Tel:* 212-867-6650 *Web Site:* irtsfoundation.org, pg 1083

Tuffs, Jim, Harnel Case Co, 1600 Marshall Ave SE, Grand Rapids, MI 49507 *Tel:* 616-452-4522 *Fax:* 616-452-5514 *E-mail:* info@harnelcase.com *Web Site:* www.harnelcase.com, pg 885

Tufty, Chris, Society of Camera Operators, PO Box 2006, Toluca Lake, CA 91610-0006 *Tel:* 818-382-7070 *E-mail:* info@soc.org *Web Site:* www.soc.org, pg 1089

Tull, Danette, Nevada Film Office, 6655 W Sahara, Suite C106, Las Vegas, NV 89146 *Tel:* 702-486-2711 *Toll Free Tel:* 877-638-3456 *Fax:* 702-486-2712 *E-mail:* lvnfo@nevadafilm.com *Web Site:* www.nevadafilm.com, pg 1100

Tull, Thomas, Legendary Pictures LLC, 2900 W Alameda Ave, 15th fl, Burbank, CA 91505 *Tel:* 818-688-7003 *E-mail:* info@legendary.com *Web Site:* www.legendary.com, pg 918

Tullis, Jay W, Rees Associates, Rees Plaza at East Wharf, Suite 300, 9211 Lake Hefner Pkwy, Oklahoma City, OK 73120 *Tel:* 405-942-7337 *Fax:* 405-948-1261 *E-mail:* rees@rees-associates.com *Web Site:* www.rees.com, pg 994

Tullo, Jamie, Face Digital Post, 9753 Via Roma, Burbank, CA 91504 *Tel:* 818-842-9081 *Fax:* 818-768-6313 *E-mail:* face@facedigitalpost.com *Web Site:* www.facedigitalpost.com, pg 865

Turchyn, Roman, WESCAM Inc, 649 N Service Rd W, Burlington, ON L7P 5B9, Canada *Tel:* 905-633-4000 *Toll Free Tel:* 800-668-4355 *Fax:* 905-633-4100 *E-mail:* sales.wescam@l-3com.com *Web Site:* www.wescam.com, pg 1063

Turell, Jonathan, Criterion Collection, 215 Park Ave S, 5th fl, New York, NY 10003 *Tel:* 212-756-8822 *E-mail:* orders@criterion.com *Web Site:* www.criterion.com, pg 839

Turlick, Paul, Big Foot Productions Inc, 37-09 36 Ave, Long Island City, NY 11101 *Tel:* 718-729-1900 *Fax:* 718-729-8638 *E-mail:* info@bigfootnyc.com *Web Site:* www.bigfootnyc.com, pg 807

Turner, Carolyn A, Stanislaus Audio Video Inc, 1431 Kansas Ave, Modesto, CA 95351 *Tel:* 209-529-2700 *Fax:* 209-529-7355 *E-mail:* info@stanav.com *Web Site:* www.stanav.com, pg 1023

Turner, George E, Stanislaus Audio Video Inc, 1431 Kansas Ave, Modesto, CA 95351 *Tel:* 209-529-2700 *Fax:* 209-529-7355 *E-mail:* info@stanav.com *Web Site:* www.stanav.com, pg 1023

Turner, Jean, Pinewood Sound, 555 Brooksbank Ave, Stage S, North Vancouver, BC V7J 3S5, Canada *Tel:* 604-669-6900; 604-983-5200 *Fax:* 604-983-5204 *E-mail:* info@pinewoodsound.com; sales@pinewoodsound.com *Web Site:* www.pinewoodsound.com, pg 975

Turner, Jim, Moviola, 1135 N Mansfield Ave, Hollywood, CA 90038 *Tel:* 323-467-3107 *Toll Free Tel:* 877-MOVIOLA (668-4652) *Fax:* 323-464-1518 *Web Site:* www.moviola.com, pg 948

Turner, John J Jr, Turner Engineering Inc, 14 Morris Ave, Mountain Lakes, NJ 07046-1433 *Tel:* 973-263-1000 *Fax:* 973-334-1620 *E-mail:* adair@turnereng.com *Web Site:* www.turnereng.com, pg 1046

Turner, Marsha L, Lighting Industry Resource Council, 440 N Wells St, Suite 210, Chicago, IL 60654 *Tel:* 312-527-3677 *Fax:* 312-527-3680 *E-mail:* iald@iald.org *Web Site:* www.iald.org/council, pg 920

Turner, Mike, The Pocket Studios, 920 Eastern Ave, Top fl, Toronto, ON M4L 1A4, Canada *Tel:* 416-466-0029 *E-mail:* info@thepocketstudios.com *Web Site:* www.thepocketstudios.com, pg 977

Turner, Randy, Memphis Communications Corp, 4771 Summer Ave, Memphis, TN 38122 *Tel:* 901-725-9271 *Fax:* 901-272-3577, pg 938

Turner, Robby, Data Projections Inc, 3700 W Sam Houston Pkwy S, Suite 525, Houston, TX 77042 *Tel:* 713-781-1999 *Toll Free Tel:* 866-225-5374 *Fax:* 713-781-3338 *Web Site:* www.dataprojections.com, pg 843

Tuscany-Wines, Pamela, Universal Studios Florida® Production Group, 1000 Universal Studios Plaza, Bldg 22-A, Orlando, FL 32819 *Tel:* 407-363-8400 *Toll Free Tel:* 877-612-3737 (outside FL) *Fax:* 407-363-8869 *E-mail:* productiongroup@universalorlando.com *Web Site:* www.universalstudios.com/studio/florida, pg 1049

Tuthill, Ted, Sear Sound, 353 W 48 St, 6th fl, New York, NY 10036 *Tel:* 212-582-5380 *Fax:* 212-581-2731 *E-mail:* waltersear@aol.com *Web Site:* www.searsound.com, pg 1005

Tuttle, Guy H, Special Projects, 345 Glen Iris Dr NE, Atlanta, GA 30312-1445 *Tel:* 404-588-2800 *Toll Free Tel:* 888-588-2800 *Fax:* 678-904-6629 *E-mail:* info@specialprojects.tv *Web Site:* www.specialprojects.tv, pg 1020

Tuttle, Paige, ACS Technologies, 180 N Dunbarton Dr, Florence, SC 29501 *Tel:* 843-662-1681 *Toll Free Tel:* 800-736-7425 *Fax:* 843-669-3198 *E-mail:* info@acstechnologies.com *Web Site:* www.acstechnologies.com, pg 775

Twersky, Alex, Kinetic Arts, 306 Gold St, No 5-I, Brooklyn, NY 11201 *Tel:* 917-439-4008 *E-mail:* info@kineticarts.tv *Web Site:* www.kineticarts.tv, pg 911

Twetten, James, Iowa State University-Information Technology Services, 1200 Communications Bldg, Ames, IA 50011-3243 *Tel:* 515-294-6014 (multimedia & streaming prodn) *Fax:* 515-294-8089 *Web Site:* www.it.iastate.edu, pg 902

Tyler, Jay, Wheatstone Corp, 600 Industrial Dr, New Bern, NC 28562 *Tel:* 252-638-7000 *Fax:* 252-635-1285 *E-mail:* sales@wheatstone.com *Web Site:* www.wheatstone.com, pg 1065

Tyndell, Allan, Lacquer-Mat Inc, 13035 Wayne Rd, Livonia, MI 48150 *Toll Free Tel:* 800-942-2223 (cust serv) *Fax:* 734-422-4205 (orders) *Web Site:* www.lacquer-mat.com, pg 915

Tyson, Alex, Billings Film Liaison Office, 815 S 27 St, Billings, MT 59101 *Tel:* 406-245-4111 *Toll Free Tel:* 800-711-2630 *Fax:* 406-245-7333 *Web Site:* www.visitbillings.com, pg 1099

Tyson, Brian, Upstage Video, 212 Shoemaker Rd, Pottstown, PA 19464 *Tel:* 610-323-7200 *Toll Free Tel:* 877-484-3887 *Fax:* 484-727-9056 *E-mail:* info@upstagevideo.com *Web Site:* www.upstagevideo.com, pg 1050

Uchiyama, Teruhisa, MetroSonic Recording Studio, 143 Roebling St, 3rd fl, Brooklyn, NY 11211 *Tel:* 718-782-1872 *E-mail:* manager@metrosonic.net *Web Site:* www.metrosonic.net, pg 940

Ucik, Martin, Plus 24, 1155 N La Brea Ave, West Hollywood, CA 90038 *Tel:* 323-845-1171; 323-845-1168 (support) *Toll Free Tel:* 800-330-7753 (orders) *Fax:* 323-845-1170 *E-mail:* info@plus24.net; sales@plus24.net *Web Site:* www.plus24.net, pg 977

Ugie, Heather, Chico Chamber of Commerce/Butte County Film Commission, 441 Main St, Suite 150, Chico, CA 95928 *Tel:* 530-891-5556 *Toll Free Tel:* 800-852-8570 *Fax:* 530-891-3613 *E-mail:* info@chicochamber.com *Web Site:* chicochamber.com, pg 1092

Uhl, Mike, RF Specialties of California Inc, PO Box 16655, San Diego, CA 92176 *Tel:* 619-501-3936 *Fax:* 619-342-8511 *Web Site:* www.rfspec.com, pg 995

Ulm, Margie, Renkus-Heinz Inc, 19201 Cook St, Foothill Ranch, CA 92610-3501 *Tel:* 949-588-9997 *Fax:* 949-588-9514 *E-mail:* sales@renkus-heinz.com *Web Site:* www.renkus-heinz.com, pg 994

Ulrich, Phyllis, Interactive Products, 101 Commerce Dr, Montgomeryville, PA 18936 *Tel:* 215-362-2766 *Toll Free Tel:* 800-523-6716 *Fax:* 215-361-0167 *E-mail:* numonics@numonics.com *Web Site:* www.numonics.com, pg 900

Underwood, Jeff, Big Bear Lake International Film Festival, PO Box 1981, Big Bear Lake, CA 92315 *Tel:* 909-547-4019 *E-mail:* info@bigbearfilmfestival.com *Web Site:* www.bigbearfilmfestival.com, pg 1109

Ungar, Donald, Ungar Video & Film, 1001 Guilford, Medina, OH 44256 *Tel:* 216-661-5090 *E-mail:* donungarvideo@yahoo.com, pg 1048

Updegraff, Will, Associated Sound, 1417 Del Paso Blvd, Sacramento, CA 95815 *Tel:* 916-649-8040 *Toll Free Tel:* 800-492-6800 *Fax:* 916-649-0243 *E-mail:* sales@associatedsound.com *Web Site:* www.associatedsound.com, pg 792

Urasaki, Debbie, ATTCO Inc, 825 Ilaniwai St, Honolulu, HI 96813 *Tel:* 808-836-1191 *Fax:* 808-834-1046 *E-mail:* information@attcoinc.com *Web Site:* www.attcoinc.com, pg 793

Urbanski, Larry, Moviecraft Inc, PO Box 438, Orland Park, IL 60462-0438 *Tel:* 708-460-9082 *Fax:* 708-460-9099 *E-mail:* stock@moviecraft.com *Web Site:* www.moviecraft.com, pg 947

Urbanski, Larry, Urbanski Film, PO Box 438, Orland Park, IL 60462-0438 *Tel:* 708-460-9082 *Fax:* 708-460-9099 *E-mail:* info@urbanskifilm.com *Web Site:* www.urbanskifilm.com, pg 1050

Urena, Teresa, Renkus-Heinz Inc, 19201 Cook St, Foothill Ranch, CA 92610-3501 *Tel:* 949-588-9997 *Fax:* 949-588-9514 *E-mail:* sales@renkus-heinz.com *Web Site:* www.renkus-heinz.com, pg 994

Urick, Natalie, Videorama Industries LLC, 1119 N Hudson Ave, Hollywood, CA 90038 *Tel:* 323-466-7232 *Fax:* 323-466-7228 *Web Site:* www.videorama.com, pg 1057

Ursino, Marco, Brooklyn Film Festival (BiFF), 180 S Fourth St, Suite 2-S, Brooklyn, NY 11211 *Tel:* 718-388-4306 *Fax:* 718-599-5039 *E-mail:* festival@wbff.org *Web Site:* www.brooklynfilmfestival.org, pg 1110

Usdin, Bob, Showman Fabricators Inc, 47-22 Pearson Place, Long Island City, NY 11101 *Tel:* 718-935-9899 *Fax:* 718-855-9823 *E-mail:* info@showfab.com *Web Site:* www.showfab.com, pg 1010

Vaccher, L J, Orvac Electronics, 1645 E Orangethorpe Ave, Fullerton, CA 92831 *Tel:* 714-871-1020 *Fax:* 714-871-1951 *E-mail:* myorvac@orvac.com *Web Site:* www.orvac.com, pg 965

Vachna, Lisa, Griffiths Broadcast Co Inc, 2981 Le Conte St, Viera, FL 32940 *Tel:* 321-622-4619 *Fax:* 321-622-4619 *E-mail:* griffiths.broadcast@usa.net *Web Site:* www.griffithsbroadcast.com, pg 882

Vachon, Chris, Sigma Delta Chi Awards in Journalism, Eugene S Pulliam National Journalism Ctr, 3909 N Meridian St, Indianapolis, IN 46208 *Tel:* 317-927-8000 *Fax:* 317-920-4789 *E-mail:* awards@spj.org *Web Site:* www.spj.org, pg 1127

Vagnini, Alfred, Powerstation Events, 1486 Highland Ave, Bldg 2, Suite 6, Cheshire, CT 06410 *Tel:* 203-250-8500 *Toll Free Tel:* 800-423-7835 *Fax:* 203-250-8575 *E-mail:* sales@powerstationevents.com *Web Site:* www.powerstationevents.com, pg 979

Vail, Natalie, Audio & Light, 2209 Randleman Rd, Greensboro, NC 27406 *Tel:* 336-274-1234 *Fax:* 336-274-4022 *E-mail:* info@audio-light.com *Web Site:* www.audio-light.com, pg 794

Vala, Houshang, Velodyne Acoustics Inc, 345 Digital Dr, Morgan Hill, CA 95037 *Tel:* 408-465-2800 *Toll Free Tel:* 866-243-0789 *Fax:* 408-779-9227; 408-779-9208 (cust serv); 408-779-9377 (orders) *E-mail:* service@velodyne.com; orders@velodyne.com *Web Site:* www.velodyne.com, pg 1052

Valdez, Dr Jude, Institute of Texan Cultures, UTSA HemisFair Park Campus, 801 E Cesar E Chavez Blvd, San Antonio, TX 78205-3296 *Tel:* 210-458-2300 *Toll Free Tel:* 800-776-7651 *Fax:* 210-458-2205 *Web Site:* www.texancultures.com, pg 899

Valdez, Tony, Lumeni Productions Inc, 1632 Flower St, Glendale, CA 91201 *Tel:* 818-956-2200 *Fax:* 818-956-3298 *E-mail:* info@lumeni.com *Web Site:* www.lumeni.com, pg 926

Valent, Susan, Simco-Ion, 2257 N Penn Rd, Hatfield, PA 19440 *Tel:* 215-822-6401 *Toll Free Tel:* 800-203-3419 *Fax:* 215-822-3795 *E-mail:* customerservice@simco-ion.com *Web Site:* www.simco-ion.com, pg 1011

Valenti, James, Northern Lights, 25 Burlingham Rd, Pine Bush, NY 12566 *Tel:* 845-361-4356 *Toll Free Tel:* 888-353-5134 *Fax:* 845-361-4900, pg 959

Valenti, Robert, Northern Lights, 25 Burlingham Rd, Pine Bush, NY 12566 *Tel:* 845-361-4356 *Toll Free Tel:* 888-353-5134 *Fax:* 845-361-4900, pg 959

Valentine, John, AudioImage Recording, 110 N Jefferson St, Richmond, VA 23220-5022 *Tel:* 804-644-7700 *Fax:* 804-644-8801 *E-mail:* info@audioimagerecording.com *Web Site:* www.audioimagerecording.com, pg 796

Valentine, John, Miranda Telecast Fiber Systems Inc, 102 Grove St, Worcester, MA 01605 *Tel:* 508-754-4858 *Fax:* 508-752-1520 *E-mail:* telecast.sales@belden.com *Web Site:* www.miranda.com; www.belden.com, pg 944

Valenza, Stacey, Hearst Entertainment & Syndication, 300 W 57 St, New York, NY 10019-5238 *Tel:* 212-969-7553 *Toll Free Tel:* 800-526-5464 *Fax:* 646-280-1553 *E-mail:* hearstentertainment@hearst.com *Web Site:* www.hearst.com, pg 887

Valenzuela, Pamela, The Association for Women in Communications (AWC), 3337 Duke St, Alexandria, VA 22314 *Tel:* 703-370-7436 *Fax:* 703-342-4311 *E-mail:* info@womcom.org *Web Site:* www.womcom.org, pg 1078

Valenzuela, Pamela, Clarion Awards, 3337 Duke St, Alexandria, VA 22314 *Tel:* 703-370-7436 *Fax:* 703-342-4311 *E-mail:* clarion@womcom.org *Web Site:* www.womcom.org, pg 1112

Vallerand, Genevieve, Arts Grants, 350 Albert St, Ottawa, ON K2P 1L4, Canada *Tel:* 613-566-4414 *Toll Free Tel:* 800-263-5588 *Fax:* 613-566-4390 *E-mail:* info@canadacouncil.ca *Web Site:* www.canadacouncil.ca; www.conseildesarts.ca, pg 1108

Van Citters, Darrell, Renegade Animation, 111 E Broadway, Suite 208, Glendale, CA 91205 *Tel:* 818-551-2351 *Fax:* 818-551-2350 *Web Site:* www.renegadeanimation.com, pg 994

Van Der Bosch, Karen, MakeMusic® Inc, 7615 Golden Triangle Dr, Suite M, Eden Prairie, MN 55344 *Tel:* 952-937-9611 *Toll Free Tel:* 800-843-2066 (cust serv) *Fax:* 952-937-9760 *Web Site:* www.makemusic.com, pg 929

Van Dine, Mike, Power & Light, 1313 Mound St, Alameda, CA 94501 *Tel:* 510-205-4101 (cell) *Web Site:* www.powerlight.net, pg 979

Van Dommelen, Brad, Traverse City Convention & Visitors Bureau, 101 W Grandview Pkwy, Traverse City, MI 49684 *Tel:* 231-947-1120 *Toll Free Tel:* 800-940-1120 *Fax:* 231-947-2621 *Web Site:* www.visittraversecity.com, pg 1098

Van Dyke, Greg, PSAV® Presentation Services, 111 W Ocean Blvd, Suite 1110, Long Beach, CA 90802-4688 *Tel:* 562-366-0620 *Toll Free Tel:* 877-430-7728 *Fax:* 562-366-0628 *Web Site:* www.psav.com, pg 987

Van Emden, Howard L, Videorama Industries LLC, 1119 N Hudson Ave, Hollywood, CA 90038 *Tel:* 323-466-7232 *Fax:* 323-466-7228 *Web Site:* www.videorama.com, pg 1057

Van Engelen, Nicole, Carr McLean Ltd, 461 Horner Ave, Toronto, ON M8W 4X2, Canada *Tel:* 416-252-3371 *Toll Free Tel:* 800-268-2123 (CN) *Fax:* 416-252-9203 *Toll Free Fax:* 800-871-2397 *E-mail:* sales@carrmclean.ca *Web Site:* www.carrmclean.ca, pg 820

Van Gorp, Mark, Bell & Howell LLC, 760 S Wolf Rd, Wheeling, IL 60090 *Tel:* 847-675-7600 *Toll Free Tel:* 800-220-3030 (cust serv) *E-mail:* marketing@bhemail.com *Web Site:* www.bellhowell.net, pg 804

van Haaften-Schick, Lauren, Artist Fellowships, 20 Jay St, 7th fl, Suite 740, Brooklyn, NY 11201 *Tel:* 212-366-6900 *Fax:* 212-366-1778 *E-mail:* fellowships@nyfa.org *Web Site:* nyfa.org, pg 1108

Van Horne, Richard "Vance", Sheffield Audio/Video Productions, 13816 Sunnybrook Rd, Phoenix, MD 21131 *Tel:* 410-628-7260 *Toll Free Tel:* 800-355-6613 *Fax:* 410-628-1977 *E-mail:* info@sheffieldav.com *Web Site:* www.sheffieldav.com/production, pg 1008

Van Hoy, Dave, Advanced Systems Group LLC, 1226 Powell St, Emeryville, CA 94608-2618 *Tel:* 510-654-8300 *Fax:* 510-654-8370 *Web Site:* www.asgllc.com, pg 778

Van Hoy, David, Diaquest, 5808 Vallejo St, Emeryville, CA 94608 *Tel:* 510-547-4544 *Fax:* 510-654-8370 *E-mail:* sales@diaquest.com; support@diaquest.com *Web Site:* www.diaquest.com, pg 846

Van Impe, Dr Jack, Jack Van Impe Ministries International, 1718 Northfield Dr, Rochester Hills, MI 48309 *Tel:* 248-852-2244; 248-852-5225 (orders) *Fax:* 248-852-2692 *E-mail:* jvimi@jvim.com *Web Site:* www.jvim.com, pg 1051

Van Mecl, Alex, Big Bear Lake International Film Festival, PO Box 1981, Big Bear Lake, CA 92315 *Tel:* 909-547-4019 *E-mail:* info@bigbearfilmfestival.com *Web Site:* www.bigbearfilmfestival.com, pg 1109

Van Meter, Dan, NOR-COM Inc, 2126 Petersburg Rd, Hebron, KY 41048 *Tel:* 859-689-7451 *Toll Free Tel:* 800-689-6889 *Fax:* 859-689-7483 *E-mail:* norcom@nor-com.com *Web Site:* www.nor-com.com, pg 958

Van Nostran, Bill, Petra Productions Ltd, 52 Sycamore Rd, Mahopac, NY 10541 *E-mail:* information@petraproductions.org *Web Site:* www.petraproductions.org, pg 973

Van Ost, Betsy, Janson Media, 118 Main St, Tappan, NY 10983 *Tel:* 845-359-8488 *E-mail:* info@janson.com *Web Site:* www.janson.com, pg 904

Van Petten, Vance, Producers Guild of America Inc (PGA), 8530 Wilshire Blvd, Suite 400, Beverly Hills, CA 90211 *Tel:* 310-358-9020 *E-mail:* info@producersguild.org *Web Site:* www.producersguild.org, pg 1087

Van Roekel, Dennis, National Education Association (NEA), 1201 16 St NW, Washington, DC 20036-3290 *Tel:* 202-833-4000 *Fax:* 202-822-7974 *Web Site:* www.nea.org, pg 952

Van Syckle, Richard, Stage Post, 255 French Landing Dr, Nashville, TN 37228 *Tel:* 615-248-1978 *Toll Free Tel:* 877-250-1839 *Fax:* 615-242-8861 *E-mail:* mail@stagepost.com *Web Site:* www.stagepost.com, pg 1022

Van Tine, Mark, Jeppesen, 55 Inverness Dr E, Englewood, CO 80112 *Tel:* 303-799-9090 *Toll Free Tel:* 800-621-5377; 800-353-2107 *Fax:* 303-328-4153 *Web Site:* www.jeppesen.com, pg 905

Van Waay, Brian, TeachLogic Inc, 1688 Ord Way, Oceanside, CA 92056 *Tel:* 760-631-7800 *Toll Free Tel:* 800-588-0018 *Fax:* 760-631-1283 *E-mail:* sales@teachlogic.com; info@teachlogic.com *Web Site:* www.teachlogic.com, pg 1033

Van Winkle, Vernon, 21st Century Video Productions, 890 S Higley Rd, Pahrump, NV 89048 *Tel:* 775-727-9400 *Fax:* 775-727-8750 *Web Site:* www.kpvm.tv, pg 1047

Vandal, Luc, Max Films Inc, 1751 Richardson St, Suite 5101, Montreal, QC H3K 1G6, Canada *Tel:* 514-282-8444 *Fax:* 514-282-9222 *E-mail:* info@maxfilms.ca *Web Site:* www.maxfilms.ca, pg 934

VanDenBosch, Betty, ART (Applied Research & Technology Inc), 4625 Witmer Industrial Estate, Niagara Falls, NY 14305 *Tel:* 716-297-2920 *Fax:* 716-297-3689 *E-mail:* usa@yorkville.com *Web Site:* www.artproaudio.com; www.yorkville.com, pg 791

Vanderveen, Arthur, Compass Learning Inc, 203 Colorado St, Austin, TX 78701 *Tel:* 512-478-9600 *Toll Free Tel:* 866-586-7387 (sales); 800-678-1412 (cust support) *Web Site:* www.compasslearning.com, pg 833

Vandever, Lesley, Parlights Inc, One Wormans Mill Ct, Suite 7, Frederick, MD 21701 *Tel:* 301-698-9242 *Fax:* 301-846-0369 *E-mail:* sales@parlights.com *Web Site:* www.parlights.com, pg 969

Vandevrie, Ken, ADS Media, 620 Trinity Church Rd, Hamilton, ON L0R 1P0, Canada *Tel:* 905-692-2960 *Fax:* 905-692-2961 *E-mail:* info@adsmedia.ca *Web Site:* www.adsmedia.ca, pg 777

Vangas, Arunas, Optikinetics Ltd - The Americas, 11211 Air Park Rd, Suite 1, Ashland, VA 23005 *Tel:* 804-752-2570 *Toll Free Tel:* 800-575-6784 *Fax:* 804-752-2888 *E-mail:* optius@optikinetics.com *Web Site:* www.optikinetics.com, pg 964

Vanjani, Bob, Gingerbread Productions, 1323 Shepard Dr, Unit I, Sterling, VA 20164 *Tel:* 703-450-7722; 571-432-6920 *Toll Free Tel:* 877-219-3562 *Fax:* 703-450-6836 *E-mail:* bakegingerbread@aol.com *Web Site:* www.gingerbreadproductions.com, pg 878

Vanni, Steve, Technet® Systems Group, PO Box 422, Auburn, NH 03032-0422 *Tel:* 603-483-5365 *Toll Free Tel:* 888-TECHNET (832-4638) *Fax:* 603-483-0512 *E-mail:* sales@technetsystems.com *Web Site:* www.technetsystems.com, pg 1033

Vapour, Mel, Berkeley Video & Film Festival, 1939 Addison St, Berkeley, CA 94704 *Tel:* 510-843-3699 *Fax:* 510-843-3379 *E-mail:* maketv@aol.com *Web Site:* www.berkeleyvideofilmfest.org, pg 1109

Varela, Rodrigo Diaz, ReelWorld Film Festival, 438 Parliament St, Suite 300, Toronto, ON M5A 3A2, Canada *Tel:* 416-598-7933 *E-mail:* info@reelworld.ca; events@reelworld.ca *Web Site:* www.reelworld.ca, pg 1125

Varga, Dana, CohuHD, 12367 Crosthwaite Circle, Poway, CA 92064 *Tel:* 858-391-1800 *E-mail:* info@cohuhd.com *Web Site:* www.cohuhd.com, pg 831

Vargas, Berenice, Chicago Latino Film Festival, 676 N La Salle Dr, Suite 520, Chicago, IL 60654 *Tel:* 312-431-1330 *Fax:* 312-786-0126 *E-mail:* info@latinoculturalcenter.org *Web Site:* www.chicagolatinofilmfestival.org, pg 1111

Vargas, Diana, Havana Film Festival New York (HFFNY), 4 W 43 St, Suite 304, New York, NY 10036 *Tel:* 212-687-2146 *Fax:* 212-681-8037 *E-mail:* info@hffny.com; info@aflfc.org *Web Site:* www.hffny.com, pg 1116

Vargas, Joe, MediaMix Inc, 4 Pearl Ct, Allendale, NJ 07401 *Tel:* 201-262-3700 (day); 201-378-3035 (nights/weekends) *Fax:* 201-262-3798 *E-mail:* info@mmix.net *Web Site:* www.mmix.net, pg 938

Vargas, Pepe, Chicago Latino Film Festival, 676 N La Salle Dr, Suite 520, Chicago, IL 60654 *Tel:* 312-431-1330 *Fax:* 312-786-0126 *E-mail:* info@latinoculturalcenter.org *Web Site:* www.chicagolatinofilmfestival.org, pg 1111

Varnell, Kevin, The Kitchen, 4119 W Burbank Blvd, Burbank, CA 91505 *Tel:* 818-306-5300 *Fax:* 305-415-6201 *E-mail:* info@thekitchen.tv *Web Site:* www.thekitchen.tv, pg 911

Varness, Eric, Novell Inc, 1800 S Novell Place, Provo, UT 84606 *Tel:* 801-861-4272 *Toll Free Tel:* 888-321-4272 (sales); 800-858-4000 (support) *E-mail:* crc@novell.com *Web Site:* www.novell.com, pg 959

Vasconi, Eugene, Communication Arts Multimedia Inc, 1618 Williams Dr, No 5, Georgetown, TX 78628 *Tel:* 512-868-0548 *Toll Free Tel:* 888-742-0074 *Fax:* 512-868-0548 *E-mail:* mail@commartsmultimedia.com *Web Site:* commartsmultimedia.com, pg 832

Vasquez, Janet, San Antonio Film Commission, 203 S Saint Mary's St, Suite 360, San Antonio, TX 78205 *Tel:* 210-207-6730 *Toll Free Tel:* 800-447-3372 *Fax:* 210-207-4526 *E-mail:* filmsa@filmsanantonio.com *Web Site:* www.filmsanantonio.com, pg 1103

Vassallo, Mark, ETC, 3031 Pleasant View Rd, Middleton, WI 53562-4809 *Tel:* 608-831-4116 *Toll Free Tel:* 800-688-4116 *Fax:* 608-836-1736 *E-mail:* mail@etcconnect.com; americas@etcconnect.com *Web Site:* www.etcconnect.com, pg 862

Vassar, Bill, EUE/Screen Gems Studios, 1223 N 23 St, Wilmington, NC 28405 *Tel:* 910-343-3500 *Fax:* 910-343-3574 *E-mail:* info@euescreengems.com *Web Site:* euescreengems.com, pg 863

Vaughn, Holt, Eastco Multimedia Solutions Inc, 3646 California Rd, Orchard Park, NY 14127 *Tel:* 716-662-0536 *Toll Free Tel:* 800-365-8273 (orders) *Fax:* 716-662-3360 *E-mail:* info@eastcomultimedia.com *Web Site:* www.eastcomultimedia.com, pg 856

Vedock, Tray, SKC Communication Products Inc, 8320 Hedge Lane Terr, Shawnee Mission, KS 66227 *Tel:* 913-422-4222 *Toll Free Tel:* 800-882-7779 *Toll Free Fax:* 800-454-4752 *E-mail:* contact.us@skccom.com *Web Site:* www.skccom.com, pg 1012

Veening, Kelli, Allsop Inc, PO Box 23, Bellingham, WA 98227-0023 *Tel:* 360-734-9090 *Toll Free Tel:* 800-426-4303 *Fax:* 360-734-9858 (sales); 360-733-4302 (corp) *E-mail:* info@allsop.com *Web Site:* www.allsop.com, pg 781

Veenstra, John, Tekskil Industries Inc, 102-998 Harbourside Dr, North Vancouver, BC V7P 3T2, Canada *Tel:* 604-985-2250 *Toll Free Tel:* 877-835-7545 *Toll Free Fax:* 877-576-8361 *E-mail:* tekskilprompters2012@tekskil.com *Web Site:* www.tekskil.com, pg 1035

Veenstra, Ken, Progressive Media & Music, 2116 Southview Ave, Tampa, FL 33606 *Tel:* 813-251-8093 *Fax:* 813-251-6050 *E-mail:* info@progressivecds.com *Web Site:* www.progressivecds.com/index.html, pg 985

Vegso, Peter, Health Communications Inc, 3201 SW 15 St, Deerfield Beach, FL 33442-8124 *Tel:* 954-360-0909 *Toll Free Tel:* 800-441-5569 *Fax:* 954-360-0034 *Web Site:* www.hcibooks.com, pg 887

Vekil, Erol, Gesturetek, 317 Adelaide St W, Suite 903, Toronto, ON M5V 1P9, Canada *Tel:* 416-340-9290 *Toll Free Tel:* 800-315-1189 *Fax:* 416-348-9809 *E-mail:* info@gesturetek.com *Web Site:* www.gesturetek.com, pg 877

Vela, William, Miami short Film Festival (MsFF), 247 SW Eighth St, Suite 44, Miami, FL 33130 *E-mail:* info@miamishortfilmfestival.com *Web Site:* www.miamishortfilmfestival.com, pg 1120

Velazquez, Aram, ACT Productions, 407 Lincoln Rd, Suite 302, Miami Beach, FL 33139 *Tel:* 305-538-3809 *Fax:* 305-538-3814 *E-mail:* info@actproductions.com *Web Site:* www.actproductions.com, pg 775

Veldey, Mark, ETC, 3031 Pleasant View Rd, Middleton, WI 53562-4809 *Tel:* 608-831-4116 *Toll Free Tel:* 800-688-4116 *Fax:* 608-836-1736 *E-mail:* mail@etcconnect.com; americas@etcconnect.com *Web Site:* www.etcconnect.com, pg 862

Vellequette, Dave, Avaya Inc, 211 Mount Airy Rd, Basking Ridge, NJ 07920 *Tel:* 908-953-6000 *Toll Free Tel:* 866-GO-AVAYA (462-8292 US & CN) *Web Site:* www.avaya.com, pg 798

Veloso, Ruben, CCI Digital, 2921 W Alameda Ave, Burbank, CA 91505 *Tel:* 818-562-6300 *Fax:* 818-562-8222 *E-mail:* info@ccidigital.com *Web Site:* www.ccidigital.com, pg 821

Veltze, Roxanna, 360 Systems, 3281 Grande Vista Dr, Newbury Park, CA 91320-1193 *Tel:* 818-991-0360 *Fax:* 818-991-1360 *E-mail:* info@360systems.com; sales@360systems.com *Web Site:* www.360systems.com, pg 1039

Ventress, Connie, JFW Industries Inc, 5134 Commerce Square Dr, Indianapolis, IN 46237 *Tel:* 317-887-1340 *Toll Free Tel:* 877-887-4539 *Fax:* 317-881-6790 *E-mail:* sales@jfwindustries.com; jfwengr@jfwindustries.com *Web Site:* www.jfwindustries.com, pg 905

Ventura, Kristi, Creative Technology, 1455 Estes Ave, Elk Grove Village, IL 60007 *Tel:* 847-671-9670 *Toll Free Tel:* 800-826-4761 *Fax:* 847-640-6559 *E-mail:* info@ctchicago.com *Web Site:* us.ct-group.com, pg 838

Venturella, Frank, Magna Visual Inc, 9400 Watson Rd, St Louis, MO 63126-1596 *Tel:* 314-843-9000 *Toll Free Tel:* 800-843-3399 *Fax:* 314-843-0000 *E-mail:* magna@magnavisual.com *Web Site:* www.magnavisual.com, pg 928

Verbitsky, Irra, Polestar Films & Associated Arts Ltd, PO Box 20104, West Village Sta, New York, NY 10014-0708 *Tel:* 212-352-1375, pg 978

Vernerey, Laurent, MGE UPS Systems, 1660 Scenic Ave, Costa Mesa, CA 92626 *Tel:* 714-557-1636 *Toll Free Tel:* 800-344-0570 *Web Site:* www.apc.com, pg 940

Vernetti, Rick, L-3 GCS, 7640 Omnitech Place, Victor, NY 14564 *Tel:* 585-742-9100 *Toll Free Tel:* 888-SAT1USA (728-1872); 877-247-1207 (tech support) *Fax:* 585-742-1914 *E-mail:* gcs.info@l-3com.com *Web Site:* www.globalcoms.com, pg 915

Vernon, Larry, Association for Educational Communications & Technology (AECT), 320 W Eighth St, Suite 101, Bloomington, IN 47404-3745 *Tel:* 812-335-7675 *Toll Free Tel:* 877-677-AECT (677-2328) *Fax:* 812-335-7678 *E-mail:* aect@aect.org *Web Site:* www.aect.org, pg 1078

Verson, Mindy, Audio Producers Group, 200 N Dearborn St, Suite 2705, Chicago, IL 60601 *Tel:* 312-977-9400 *Fax:* 312-977-9494 *E-mail:* info@apgaudio.com *Web Site:* www.audioproducersgroup.com, pg 794

Verwey, Bert, Broadcast Video Systems Corp, 25 Forest Ridge Rd, Richmond Hill, ON L4E 3L8, Canada *E-mail:* broadcastvideosystems@gmail.com *Web Site:* www.bvs.ca, pg 813

Verwey, Jill, Broadcast Video Systems Corp, 25 Forest Ridge Rd, Richmond Hill, ON L4E 3L8, Canada *E-mail:* broadcastvideosystems@gmail.com *Web Site:* www.bvs.ca, pg 813

Vesely, Kevin, Vista Color Imaging Inc, 2048 Fulton Rd, Cleveland, OH 44113 *Tel:* 216-651-2830 *Toll Free Tel:* 800-890-0062 *Fax:* 216-651-5004 *E-mail:* info@vistacolorimaging.com *Web Site:* www.vistacolorimaging.com, pg 1059

Vespico, Carrie, Society for Applied Learning Technology (SALT®), 50 Culpeper St, Warrenton, VA 20186 *Tel:* 540-347-0055 *Fax:* 540-349-3169 *E-mail:* info@lti.org *Web Site:* www.salt.org, pg 1089

Vetkos, Jim, Intel-A-Jib™, 409 Calle San Pablo, No 108, Camarillo, CA 93012 *Web Site:* www.intel-a-jib.com, pg 899

Vexler, Laurence, LHV Audio Services, 3417 Lake Breeze Rd, Orlando, FL 32808 *Tel:* 407-295-3565 *E-mail:* service@lhvaudio.com *Web Site:* www.lhvaudio.com, pg 919

Vianello, Lili, Visionworks Design Services Inc, 204 Peach Way, Suite H, Columbia, MO 65203 *Tel:* 573-449-8567 *Fax:* 573-449-6714 *E-mail:* info@visionworksgroup.com *Web Site:* visionworksgroup.com, pg 1059

Viau, Catherine, Les Productions Via Le Monde (Daniel Bertolino) Inc, 1222 rue MacKay, Suite 201, Montreal, QC H3G 2H4, Canada *Tel:* 514-285-1658 *Fax:* 514-285-1970 *Web Site:* www.vialemonde.com, pg 985

Vicente, Joana, Independent Film Week, 68 Jay St, Rm 425, Brooklyn, NY 11201-8361 *Tel:* 212-465-8200 *Fax:* 212-465-8525 *Web Site:* www.ifp.org/programs/independent-film-week, pg 1117

Vicente, Joana, The Independent Filmmaker Project (IFP), 68 Jay St, Rm 425, Brooklyn, NY 11201-8361 *Tel:* 212-465-8200 *Fax:* 212-465-8525 *Web Site:* www.ifp.org, pg 1083

Vick, Laura, Nutmeg Post, 45 W 45 St, New York, NY 10036 *Tel:* 212-921-8005 *Fax:* 212-921-7728 *E-mail:* info@nutmegpost.com *Web Site:* www.nutmegpost.com, pg 960

Viegas, Victor, Immersion Corp, 310 Rio Robles, San Jose, CA 95134 *Tel:* 408-467-1900 *Fax:* 408-467-1901 *E-mail:* info@immersion.com *Web Site:* www.immersion.com, pg 896

Viering, Holly, World Media Group Inc, 6737 E 30 St, Indianapolis, IN 46219 *Tel:* 317-549-8484 *Toll Free Tel:* 800-400-4964 *Fax:* 317-549-8480 *E-mail:* getstarted@worldmediagroup.com *Web Site:* www.worldmediagroup.com, pg 1069

Vigeant, Philip, Pro8mm, 2805 W Magnolia Blvd, Burbank, CA 91505-3037 *Tel:* 818-848-5522 *Fax:* 818-848-5956 *E-mail:* sales@pro8mm.com; info@pro8mm.com *Web Site:* www.pro8mm.com, pg 983

Vigeant, Rhonda, Pro8mm, 2805 W Magnolia Blvd, Burbank, CA 91505-3037 *Tel:* 818-848-5522 *Fax:* 818-848-5956 *E-mail:* sales@pro8mm.com; info@pro8mm.com *Web Site:* www.pro8mm.com, pg 983

Villano, Stephanie, Pearson Education Canada, 26 Prince Andrew Place, North York, ON M3C 2T8, Canada *Tel:* 416-447-5101 *Toll Free Tel:* 800-361-6128 *Fax:* 416-447-2551 *Toll Free Fax:* 800-563-9196 *Web Site:* www.pearsonschoolcanada.ca, pg 970

Villareal, Ben, ECS Inc, 5665 Tremont Ave, Davenport, IA 52807-2658 *Tel:* 563-322-1525 *Fax:* 563-322-5920 *Web Site:* www.ecsdav.com, pg 856

Villayne, Zander, Z-Ville Productions, 34710 Lancaster Rd, Gorman, CA 93536 *Tel:* 310-422-9590 *Fax:* 310-422-9590 *E-mail:* info@zvpro.com *Web Site:* www.z-ville.com, pg 1073

Villegas, Jaime, D A S Audio of America Inc, Sunset Palmetto Park, 6900 NW 52 St, Miami, FL 33166 *Tel:* 305-436-0521 *Fax:* 305-436-0528 *E-mail:* sales@dasaudio.com *Web Site:* www.dasaudio.com, pg 842

Villoria, Stephen, MediaPOINTE, 667 Rancho Conejo Blvd, Newbury Park, CA 91320 *Tel:* 805-480-3700 *Fax:* 805-480-3770 *E-mail:* info@mediapointe.com; sales@mediapointe.com *Web Site:* www.mediapointe.com, pg 938

Vince, Robert, Keystone Entertainment, 23410 Civic Ctr Way, Suite E-9, Malibu, CA 90265 *Tel:* 310-317-4883 *Fax:* 310-317-4903 *E-mail:* films@keypics.com *Web Site:* www.keypics.com, pg 910

Vincent, Carolyn, Sally Mountain Park Bluegrass Festival, Rte 2, Box 15, Greentop, MO 63546 *Tel:* 660-949-2345 *E-mail:* festival@marktwain.net *Web Site:* www.sallymountainshow.com, pg 1126

Vincent, Greg T, Communications Design Associates, 437 Turnpike St, Canton, MA 02021 *Tel:* 339-502-6551 *Fax:* 339-502-6595 *E-mail:* information@cdaconsultants.com *Web Site:* www.cdaconsultants.com, pg 833

Vincent, John, Gesturetek, 317 Adelaide St W, Suite 903, Toronto, ON M5V 1P9, Canada *Tel:* 416-340-9290 *Toll Free Tel:* 800-315-1189 *Fax:* 416-348-9809 *E-mail:* info@gesturetek.com *Web Site:* www.gesturetek.com, pg 877

Vincent, Johnny, Sally Mountain Park Bluegrass Festival, Rte 2, Box 15, Greentop, MO 63546 *Tel:* 660-949-2345 *E-mail:* festival@marktwain.net *Web Site:* www.sallymountainshow.com, pg 1126

Vincent, Paul, Vincent Lighting Systems, 6161 Cochran Rd, Suite D, Solon, OH 44139 *Tel:* 216-475-7600 *Toll Free Tel:* 800-922-5356 *Fax:* 216-475-6376 *E-mail:* info@vls.com *Web Site:* www.vincentlighting.com, pg 1058

Vincent, Robert A, David Clark Co Inc, 360 Franklin St, Worcester, MA 01604 *Tel:* 508-751-5800 *Toll Free Tel:* 800-900-3434 *Fax:* 508-753-5827 *E-mail:* sales@davidclark.com *Web Site:* www.davidclark.com, pg 843

Vincent, Sister Mary Clare, St Bede's Publications, 271 N Main St, Petersham, MA 01366-9503 *Tel:* 978-724-3213, pg 1001

Vining, Earlene, Executive Development Systems, 3818 Vinecrest Dr, Dallas, TX 75229 *Tel:* 214-351-0055 *Toll Free Tel:* 800-955-7353 *Fax:* 214-351-5024 *Web Site:* www.edforeman.com, pg 864

Vinson, Kathryn, Tatum Video, 103 S Davis St, Telluride, CO 81435 *Tel:* 213-999-5970 (cell); 970-728-4892 *Fax:* 970-728-4892 *E-mail:* utemtn@aol.com, pg 1032

Vinterfeld, Yan, Final Draft Inc, 26707 W Agoura Rd, Suite 205, Calabasas, CA 91302 *Tel:* 818-995-8995; 818-906-8930 (tech support) *Toll Free Tel:* 800-231-4055 *Fax:* 818-995-4422 *E-mail:* info@finaldraft.com *Web Site:* www.finaldraft.com, pg 868

Viola, Mark, Showman Fabricators Inc, 47-22 Pearson Place, Long Island City, NY 11101 *Tel:* 718-935-9899 *Fax:* 718-855-9823 *E-mail:* info@showfab.com *Web Site:* www.showfab.com, pg 1010

Virant, John, Rounder Records, 1209 Pine St, Suite 100, Nashville, TN 37203 *Web Site:* www.rounder.com, pg 1000

Virta, Ellen, Associated Bag Co, 400 W Boden St, Milwaukee, WI 53207 *Tel:* 414-769-1000 *Toll Free Tel:* 800-926-6100 *Fax:* 414-769-6530 *Toll Free Fax:* 800-926-4610 *E-mail:* customerservice@associatedbag.com *Web Site:* www.associatedbag.com, pg 792

Visco, Franklin J, Lucerne Media, 37 Ground Pine Rd, Morris Plains, NJ 07950 *Tel:* 973-538-1401 *Fax:* 973-538-0855 *E-mail:* lucernemedia@optonline.net, pg 925

Vitale, Charles, Sound & Vision Media, 372 Squire Rd, Revere, MA 02151 *Tel:* 781-284-9707 *Web Site:* www.soundandvisionmedia.com, pg 1017

Vitale, Joe, Mackenzie Laboratories Inc, 1163 Nicole Ct, Glendora, CA 91740 *Tel:* 909-394-9007 *Fax:* 909-394-9411 *E-mail:* info@macklabs.com *Web Site:* www.macklabs.com, pg 927

Vitola, Lindsay, Morrisound Recording, 12111 N 56 St, Tampa, FL 33617 *Tel:* 813-989-2108 *Fax:* 813-980-6950 *E-mail:* info@morrisound.com *Web Site:* morrisound.com, pg 946

Vivier, Carole, Manitoba Film & Music, 410-93 Lombard Ave, Suite 410, Winnipeg, MB R3B 3B1, Canada *Tel:* 204-947-2040 *Fax:* 204-956-5261 *E-mail:* info@mbfilmmusic.ca *Web Site:* www.mbfilmmusic.ca, pg 930, 1105

Vlahos, Paul, Ultimatte Corp, 20945 Plummer St, Chatsworth, CA 91311 *Tel:* 818-993-8007 *Fax:* 818-993-3762 *E-mail:* sales@ultimatte.com *Web Site:* www.ultimatte.com, pg 1047

Voakes, Peggy, Dialect Accent Specialists Inc, PO Box 44, Lyndonville, VT 05851-0044 *Toll Free Tel:* 800-753-1016 *E-mail:* dasinc@kingcon.com; info@dialectaccentspecialists.com *Web Site:* www.dialectaccentspecialists.com; www.learnaccent.com, pg 846

Vogel, Giselle, Videofilm Systems Inc, 7 Islandbrook Ave, Unit D-1, Bridgeport, CT 06606 *Tel:* 203-870-6013 *Web Site:* www.videofilmsystems.com, pg 1057

Vogeney, Rick, LightCraft Graphics Inc, 1269 Rand Rd, Des Plaines, IL 60016 *Tel:* 847-759-8500 *Fax:* 847-759-8540 *Web Site:* www.lightcraft.com, pg 920

Vogt, Charlie, Imagine Communications Corp, 3001 Dallas Pkwy, Suite 300, Frisco, TX 75034 *Tel:* 469-803-4900 *Toll Free Tel:* 866-4-IMAGINE (446-2446) *Fax:* 469-803-4899 *E-mail:* insidesales@imaginecommunications.com *Web Site:* www.imaginecommunications.com, pg 896

Vogt, Edward, EAR Professional Audio/Video, 2641 E McDowell Rd, Phoenix, AZ 85008 *Tel:* 602-267-0600 *Toll Free Tel:* 800-473-6914 *Fax:* 602-275-3277 *E-mail:* info@ear.net *Web Site:* www.ear.net, pg 855

Voigt, Gina, Sony Pro Audio (Broadcast & Professional Systems Division), One Sony Dr, Park Ridge, NJ 07656 *Tel:* 201-930-1000 *Web Site:* pro.sony.com/bbsc/ssr/home.do, pg 1016

Volk, Patrick, Geomatrix Productions, 270 Amity Rd, Woodbridge, CT 06525-2267 *Tel:* 203-389-0001 *Web Site:* www.geomatrixproductions.com, pg 877

Von Fange, Eric, The Light Source, 3935 Westinghouse Blvd, Charlotte, NC 28273 *Tel:* 704-504-8399 *Fax:* 704-588-4693 (acctg); 704-588-4637 (orders) *E-mail:* mail@thelightsource.com; sales@thelightsource.com *Web Site:* www.thelightsource.com, pg 920

von Olenhusen, Cuno Goetz, Hannecke Display Systems Inc, 91 Fulton St, Boonton, NJ 07005 *Tel:* 973-335-0434 *Toll Free Tel:* 800-345-8631 *Fax:* 973-335-1274 *E-mail:* info.usa@hannecke.com *Web Site:* www.hannecke.com, pg 884

Voorhies, Robert, Projector Protector Inc, 131 SW 35 Terr, Cape Coral, FL 33914 *Tel:* 239-945-0792 *Fax:* 239-945-0792 *E-mail:* projectorprotector@excite.com *Web Site:* www.projectorprotector.com, pg 986

Vosburgh, Jack M, JCS Video Productions, 4617 Sequoia Park Ave, Las Vegas, NV 89139 *Tel:* 702-596-9291 (cell); 702-546-0150 *Toll Free Tel:* 800-791-8671 *Fax:* 702-546-0150 *E-mail:* jcsvideo@cox.net *Web Site:* www.jcsvideo.com, pg 904

Vosteen, William E, Monroe Electronics Inc, 100 Housel Ave, Lyndonville, NY 14098 *Tel:* 585-765-2254 *Fax:* 585-765-9330 *Web Site:* www.monroe-electronics.com, pg 945

Voth, Karla, Bronze Anvil Awards, 33 Maiden Lane, 11th fl, New York, NY 10038-5150 *Tel:* 212-460-1400 *Toll Free Tel:* 800-350-0111 *Fax:* 212-995-0757 *E-mail:* awards@prsa.org *Web Site:* www.prsa.org, pg 1110

Voth, Karla, Silver Anvil Awards, 33 Maiden Lane, 11th fl, New York, NY 10038-5150 *Tel:* 212-460-1400 *Toll Free Tel:* 800-350-0111 *Fax:* 212-995-0757 *E-mail:* awards@prsa.org *Web Site:* www.prsa.org, pg 1127

Vrettas, Peter T, EDR Media LLC, 23330 Commerce Park, Beachwood, OH 44122-5811 *Tel:* 216-292-7300 *Web Site:* www.edrmedia.com; www.beachwoodstudios.com, pg 857

Vroom, Steven, 911 Media Arts Center, 909 NE 43 St, Suite 206, Seattle, WA 98105 *Tel:* 206-682-6552 *E-mail:* info@911media.org *Web Site:* www.911media.org, pg 957

Wachtler, Randy, Warner/Chappell Production Music, 1030 16 Ave S, Nashville, TN 37212 *Toll Free Tel:* 888-615-8729 *Fax:* 615-242-2455 *E-mail:* info@warnerchappellpm.com *Web Site:* www.warnerchappellpm.com/615-music, pg 1062

Wacker, Erica, Explore Minnesota Tourism, Metro Sq, Suite 100, 121 E Seventh Place, St Paul, MN 55101-2112 *Tel:* 651-757-1870 *Toll Free Tel:* 800-657-3638 *Fax:* 651-296-7095 *E-mail:* explore@state.mn.us *Web Site:* www.exploreminnesota.com, pg 1099

Wade, Donal, BitFlow Inc, 400 W Cummings Park, Suite 5050, Woburn, MA 01801 *Tel:* 781-932-2900 *Fax:* 781-933-9965 *E-mail:* sales@bitflow.com *Web Site:* www.bitflow.com, pg 808

Wade, Jeff, RIA Corp, 1615 W 2200 S, Suite B, Salt Lake City, UT 84119 *Tel:* 801-486-8822 *Fax:* 801-486-2741 *E-mail:* sales@riacorp.com *Web Site:* www.riacorp.com, pg 996

Wade, Wyatt, Davis Art Images, 50 Portland St, Worcester, MA 01608 *Tel:* 508-754-7201 *Toll Free Tel:* 800-533-2847 *Fax:* 508-753-3834 *E-mail:* das@davisart.com *Web Site:* www.davisartimages.com, pg 843

Wadsworth, Bill, Mind Over Eye Inc, 2221 Rosecrans Ave, Suite 195, El Segundo, CA 90245 *Tel:* 310-396-4663 *Fax:* 310-297-9526 *E-mail:* info@mindovereye.com *Web Site:* www.mindovereye.com, pg 943

Waechter, Thomas, JDSU, 430 N McCarthy Blvd, Milpitas, CA 95035 *Tel:* 408-546-5000 *Fax:* 408-546-4300 *Web Site:* www.jdsu.com, pg 905

Waganer, Richard, Cre-a-tv Studios, 1332 Londontown Blvd, Suite 102, Eldesburg, MD 21784 *Toll Free Tel:* 800-628-0112 *E-mail:* production@cre-a-tv.com *Web Site:* cre-a-tv.com, pg 839

Waganer, Tina Apellaniz, Cre-a-tv Studios, 1332 Londontown Blvd, Suite 102, Eldesburg, MD 21784 *Toll Free Tel:* 800-628-0112 *E-mail:* production@cre-a-tv.com *Web Site:* cre-a-tv.com, pg 839

Waggoner, Bruce E, Adrienne Electronics Corp (AEC), 901 American Pacific Dr, Suite 170, Henderson, NV 89014 *Tel:* 702-896-1858 *Toll Free Tel:* 800-782-2321 *Fax:* 702-896-3034 *E-mail:* info@adrielec.com; orders@adrielec.com; support@adrielec.com *Web Site:* www.adrielec.com, pg 777

Wagner, Adrianne, Yuma Film Commission, 180 W First St, Suite D, Yuma, AZ 85364 *Tel:* 928-314-9247 *Fax:* 928-373-0133 *Web Site:* www.filmyuma.com, pg 1092

Wagner, Erin Jackson, Greater Philadelphia Film Office, One Parkway Bldg, 11th fl, 1515 Arch St, Philadelphia, PA 19102 *Tel:* 215-686-2668 *Fax:* 215-686-3659 *E-mail:* mail@film.org *Web Site:* www.film.org, pg 1102

Wagner, Sam B, Video I-D Teleproductions Inc, 105 Muller Rd, Washington, IL 61571 *Tel:* 309-444-4323 *Toll Free Tel:* 800-333-9123 *Fax:* 309-444-4333 *Web Site:* www.videoid.com, pg 1055

Wagnon, Stan, Lubbock Audio Visual Inc, 2120 Ave "Q", Lubbock, TX 79405 *Tel:* 806-744-2559 *Toll Free Tel:* 800-850-2559 *Fax:* 806-747-6939 *E-mail:* sales@lav.com *Web Site:* www.lav.com, pg 925

Wahab, Haitham, CMI Media Management, 100 Business Park Dr, Armonk, NY 10504-1750 *Tel:* 914-273-7500 *Toll Free Tel:* 800-431-1102 *Fax:* 914-273-7575 *Web Site:* www.cinemagnetics.com, pg 830

Wais, Ed, AVS Group, 3120 South Ave, La Crosse, WI 54601 *Tel:* 608-787-1010 *Fax:* 608-787-0012 *E-mail:* info@avsgroup.com *Web Site:* www.avsgroup.com, pg 800

Waitkus, Jack, Video West Inc, 570 W Southern Ave, Tempe, AZ 85282 *Tel:* 480-222-3180 *Fax:* 480-222-3191 *E-mail:* info@videowestinc.com *Web Site:* www.videowestinc.com, pg 1056

Wakefield, Jennifer, Metro Orlando Film Commission, 301 E Pine St, Suite 900, Orlando, FL 32801 *Tel:* 407-422-7159 *Fax:* 407-425-6428 *E-mail:* info@filmorlando.com *Web Site:* www.filmorlando.com, pg 1096

Waldenmaier, Jack, The Music Bakery, 7522 Campbell Rd, Suite 113, Dallas, TX 75248 *Tel:* 972-578-7863 *Toll Free Tel:* 800-229-0313 *Fax:* 214-884-6068 *E-mail:* helpnow@musicbakery.com *Web Site:* www.musicbakery.com, pg 950

Walenta, Michael T, WGVU TV, 301 Fulton St W, Grand Rapids, MI 49504-6492 *Tel:* 616-331-6666 *Toll Free Tel:* 800-442-2771 *E-mail:* wgvu@gvsu.edu *Web Site:* www.wgvu.org, pg 1065

Wales, Dirk, Rainbow International Inc/Rainbow Productions Inc, 1103 Canyon Rd, Santa Fe, NM 87501 *Tel:* 773-505-6264 *Fax:* 773-525-6278 *Web Site:* www.rainbowplace.com, pg 991

Waligora, Jack, C-Ducer/C T Audio, 54 Old Lakeside Rd S, Hewitt, NJ 07421 *Tel:* 973-728-1743 *Toll Free Tel:* 800-282-8346 *Toll Free Fax:* 866-548-7683 *E-mail:* meow54@rocketmail.com *Web Site:* www.c-ducer.com, pg 816

Walker, Ashley, FLIR Systems Inc, 27700 SW Parkway Ave, Wilsonville, OR 97070 *Tel:* 503-498-3547 *Toll Free Tel:* 800-322-3731 *Fax:* 503-498-3904 *E-mail:* marketing@flir.com *Web Site:* www.flir.com, pg 870

Walker, Bill, MCS Recording Studios, 550 Queen St E, Suite G100, Toronto, ON M5A 1V2, Canada *Tel:* 416-361-1688 *Toll Free Tel:* 866-322-8555 *Fax:* 416-361-5088 *E-mail:* info@mcsrecording.com *Web Site:* www.mcsrecording.com, pg 936

Walker, Cheryl, General Projection Systems Inc, 707 Platinum Point, Lake Mary, FL 32746-5702 *Tel:* 407-260-5511 *Toll Free Tel:* 888-GENPROJ (436-7765) *Fax:* 407-833-4990 *E-mail:* solutions@genproj.com *Web Site:* www.genproj.com, pg 877

Walker, Chris, SoundTech, 1000 Corporate Grove Dr, Buffalo Grove, IL 60089 *Tel:* 847-949-0444 *Toll Free Tel:* 800-US-SOUND (877-6863) *Fax:* 847-949-8444; 775-898-4891 *E-mail:* soundtech@soundtech.com *Web Site:* www.usmusiccorp.com; www.soundtech.com, pg 1018

Walker, Christopher, WalkerVision Interarts, PO Box 22533, San Diego, CA 92192-2533 *Tel:* 858-458-9038 *Fax:* 858-458-9104 *Web Site:* www.walkervisioninterarts.com, pg 1061

Walker, Fred, JFW Industries Inc, 5134 Commerce Square Dr, Indianapolis, IN 46237 *Tel:* 317-887-1340 *Toll Free Tel:* 877-887-4539 *Fax:* 317-881-6790 *E-mail:* sales@jfwindustries.com; jfwengr@jfwindustries.com *Web Site:* www.jfwindustries.com, pg 905

Walker, Jeff, Alliance Entertainment Corp (AEC) LLC, 4250 Coral Ridge Dr, Coral Springs, FL 33065 *Tel:* 954-346-4024 *Toll Free Tel:* 800-356-2049 (ext 4600) *Web Site:* www.aent.com, pg 781

Walker, John, Tickets.com, 555 Anton Blvd, Costa Mesa, CA 92626 *Tel:* 714-327-5400 *Toll Free Tel:* 800-352-0212 (cust serv) *Fax:* 714-327-5410 *E-mail:* sales@tickets.com *Web Site:* www.tickets.com, pg 1040

Walker, Julie A, American Association of School Librarians (AASL), 50 E Huron St, Chicago, IL 60611 *Tel:* 312-280-4382 *Toll Free Tel:* 800-545-2433 (ext 4382) *Fax:* 312-280-5276 *E-mail:* aasl@ala.org *Web Site:* www.aasl.org, pg 1076

Walker, Lea Ann, WalkerVision Interarts, PO Box 22533, San Diego, CA 92192-2533 *Tel:* 858-458-9038 *Fax:* 858-458-9104 *Web Site:* www.walkervisioninterarts.com, pg 1061

Walker, Matt, Doug Fleenor Design Inc, 396 Corbett Canyon Rd, Arroyo Grande, CA 93420 *Tel:* 805-481-9599 *Toll Free Tel:* 888-436-9512 *Fax:* 805-481-9599 *E-mail:* info@dfd.com *Web Site:* www.dfd.com, pg 869

Walker, Melissa, WalkerVision Interarts, PO Box 22533, San Diego, CA 92192-2533 *Tel:* 858-458-9038 *Fax:* 858-458-9104 *Web Site:* www.walkervisioninterarts.com, pg 1061

Walker, Patrick E, WalkerVision Interarts, PO Box 22533, San Diego, CA 92192-2533 *Tel:* 858-458-9038 *Fax:* 858-458-9104 *Web Site:* www.walkervisioninterarts.com, pg 1061

Walker, Paul, Artaflex Inc, 96 Steelcase Rd W, Markham, ON L3R 1B5, Canada *Tel:* 905-470-0109 *Toll Free Tel:* 866-502-3378 *Fax:* 905-470-0621 *Web Site:* www.artaflex.com, pg 791

Walker, Virgil, Auton Motorized Systems, 29102 Hancock Pkwy, Valencia, CA 91355 *Tel:* 661-257-9282 *Fax:* 661-295-5638 *E-mail:* tvlifts@auton.com *Web Site:* www.auton.com, pg 797

Walko, Diana Sole, MotionMasters, 2288 Roxalana Rd, Dunbar, WV 25064 *Tel:* 304-345-8800 *Fax:* 304-345-8809 *E-mail:* storytellers@motionmasters.com *Web Site:* motionmasters.com, pg 947

Walkowiak, Tad, Inter-Media Electronics, 192 Willard St, Quincy, MA 02169 *Tel:* 617-773-9688 *Fax:* 617-696-6327 *E-mail:* intermedia.ex@verizon.net; info@ime-imaging.com *Web Site:* www.viapolonia.net/IME, pg 899

Wallace, Chris, AV Metro Inc, 5401 Etta Burke Ct, Raleigh, NC 27606 *Tel:* 919-233-1901 *Fax:* 919-233-1804 *E-mail:* info@avmetro.com *Web Site:* www.avmetro.com, pg 797

Wallace, Donald, Wallace Creative Inc, 1705 NW 25 Ave, Portland, OR 97210 *Tel:* 503-224-9660 *E-mail:* info@wallyhood.com *Web Site:* www.wallyhood.com, pg 1061

Wallace, Earl, Unilux Inc, 59 N Fifth St, Saddle Brook, NJ 07663 *Tel:* 201-712-1266 *Toll Free Tel:* 800-522-0801 (US only) *Fax:* 201-712-1366 *Web Site:* www.unilux.com, pg 1048

Wallace, Frances, Frameline Completion Fund, 145 Ninth St, Suite 300, San Francisco, CA 94103 *Tel:* 415-703-8650 *Fax:* 415-861-1404 *E-mail:* info@frameline.org *Web Site:* www.frameline.org, pg 1114

Wallace, Frances, San Francisco International LGBT Film Festival, 145 Ninth St, Suite 300, San Francisco, CA 94103 *Tel:* 415-703-8650 *Fax:* 415-861-1404 *E-mail:* info@frameline.org *Web Site:* www.frameline.org, pg 1126

Wallace, Judy, KPHO-TV5, 4016 N Black Canyon Hwy, Phoenix, AZ 85017 *Tel:* 602-264-1000 *Fax:* 602-274-1596 *E-mail:* cbs5news@kpho.com *Web Site:* www.news5.tv, pg 913

Wallace, Matthew, VRSim Inc, 222 Pitkin St, Suite 119, East Hartford, CT 06108-3220 *Tel:* 860-893-0080 *E-mail:* info@vrsim.net *Web Site:* www.vrsim.net, pg 1061

Wallace, Nick, Optikinetics Ltd - The Americas, 11211 Air Park Rd, Suite 1, Ashland, VA 23005 *Tel:* 804-752-2570 *Toll Free Tel:* 800-575-6784 *Fax:* 804-752-2888 *E-mail:* optius@optikinetics.com *Web Site:* www.optikinetics.com, pg 964

Wallach, George, Wallach Entertainment, 1400 Braeridge Dr, Beverly Hills, CA 90210 *Tel:* 310-278-4574 *Fax:* 310-273-0548 *E-mail:* gwallach@roadrunner.com, pg 1061

Waller, Heather, Fleetwood Group Inc, 11832 James St, Holland, MI 49424 *Tel:* 616-396-1142 *Toll Free Tel:* 800-257-6390 *Fax:* 616-820-8301 *E-mail:* sales@fleetwoodgroup.com *Web Site:* www.fleetwoodgroup.com; www.replysystems.com (electronics div), pg 870

Waller-Stults, Nancy, Merestone, 7232 E First St, Scottsdale, AZ 85251 *Tel:* 480-945-4631 *Fax:* 480-945-0590 *Web Site:* www.merestone.com, pg 938

Wallis, Stephen, modprop.com, 1044 Madison Ave, New York, NY 10021 *Tel:* 212-628-7582 *E-mail:* info@modprop.com *Web Site:* www.modprop.com, pg 945

Walpole, Alton, Mountainair Films, 1623 Camino De Cruz Blanca, Santa Fe, NM 87505 *Tel:* 505-471-9293 *Fax:* 505-438-0294 *E-mail:* produce@mountainairfilms.com *Web Site:* mountainairfilms.com, pg 947

Walpuck, John, Creative Realities Inc, 55 Broadway, 9th fl, New York, NY 10006 *Tel:* 212-324-6660 *Toll Free Tel:* 888-432-7328 *E-mail:* info@cri.com *Web Site:* www.cri.com, pg 838

Walsh, Declan, Transistor Devices Inc, 36 Newburgh Rd, Hackettstown, NJ 07840 *Tel:* 908-850-5088 *Fax:* 908-850-1607 *E-mail:* info@tdipower.com *Web Site:* www.tdipower.com, pg 1043

Walsh, John, Catholic Books & Tapes, PO Box 350333, Fort Lauderdale, FL 33335-0333 *Tel:* 954-583-5108 *Fax:* 954-583-5108 *E-mail:* mascmen7@yahoo.com *Web Site:* www.catholicbook.com, pg 821

Walsh, John R, Children of Mary, PO Box 350333, Fort Lauderdale, FL 33335-0333 *Tel:* 954-583-5108 *Fax:* 954-583-5108 *E-mail:* mascmen7@yahoo.com *Web Site:* www.catholicbook.com, pg 825

Walsh, Michael S, VMS Inc, 805 Airway Dr, Allegan, MI 49101-8516 *Tel:* 269-673-2200 *Toll Free Tel:* 800-343-6430 *Fax:* 269-673-9509 *E-mail:* sales@vms-online.com *Web Site:* www.vms-online.com, pg 1060

Walsh, Ray, Metro Productions, 8570 Magellan Pkwy, Suite 400, Richmond, VA 23227 *Tel:* 804-261-1172 *Toll Free Tel:* 877-669-4687 *Fax:* 804-261-1885 *E-mail:* contactmetro@metro-productions.com *Web Site:* www.metro-productions.com, pg 939

Walsh, Thomas, Media Control Systems LLC, 1050 Pioneer Way, Suite Q, El Cajon, CA 92020 *Tel:* 619-599-1050 *Fax:* 619-599-1051 *Web Site:* www.mediacontrolsystems.com, pg 936

Walsh, Timothy, Laser Spectacles Inc, PO Box 1535, San Marcos, TX 78667 *Tel:* 512-392-4600 *Fax:* 512-392-4601 *E-mail:* laserinfo@laserspectacles.com *Web Site:* www.laserspectacles.com, pg 916

Walter, Ruth, SYMCO Inc, 29 Poplar Dr, Stirling, NJ 07980 *Tel:* 908-647-6262 *Fax:* 908-647-4904 *E-mail:* orders@symcoinc.com *Web Site:* www.symcoinc.com, pg 1030

Walters, Beth, Walters-Storyk Design Group Inc (WSDG), 262 Martin Ave, Highland, NY 12528 *Tel:* 845-691-9300 *Fax:* 845-691-9361 *E-mail:* info@wsdg.com *Web Site:* www.wsdg.com, pg 1062

Walters, Betsy, CINE Golden Eagle Awards, 1003 "K" St NW, Suite 208, Washington, DC 20001 *Tel:* 507-400-CINE (400-2463) *E-mail:* info@cine.org *Web Site:* www.cine.org, pg 1112

Walters, Betsy, Council on International Nontheatrical Events (CINE), 1003 "K" St NW, Suite 208, Washington, DC 20001 *Tel:* 507-400-CINE (400-2463) *E-mail:* info@cine.org *Web Site:* www.cine.org, pg 1081

Walters, Darlene, Warner Home Video Inc, 4000 Warner Blvd, Bldg 160, Burbank, CA 91522 *Tel:* 818-954-6000 *Fax:* 818-954-6480 *Web Site:* www.warnerbros.com, pg 1062

Walters, David, iVideo Technologies, 14885 Sprague Rd, Cleveland, OH 44136 *Tel:* 440-891-9440 *Toll Free Tel:* 800-352-6150 *Fax:* 440-891-9450 *E-mail:* info@ivideo.com *Web Site:* www.ivideo.com, pg 903

Walters, Ed, WFRV-TV 5 CBS, 1181 E Mason St, Green Bay, WI 54301 *Tel:* 920-437-5411 *Fax:* 920-437-4576 *E-mail:* mailbox@wfrv.com *Web Site:* www.wfrv.com, pg 1064

Walton, Bill, ITC Learning LLC, 1616 Anderson Rd, Suite 109, McLean, VA 22102 *Toll Free Tel:* 800-638-3757 *E-mail:* sales@itclearning.com *Web Site:* www.itclearning.com, pg 903

Walton, Erik, Mitsubishi Electric Visual Solutions America Inc (MEVSA), 10833 Valley View St, Suite 300, Cypress, CA 90630 *Toll Free Tel:* 800-332-2119 *E-mail:* tvsupport@mevsa.com *Web Site:* www.mitsubishi-tv.com, pg 944

Wandolowski, Ray, Pres-On Merchandising Corp, 2600 E 107 St, Bolingbrook, IL 60440 *Toll Free Tel:* 800-323-7467 *Fax:* 630-628-8025 *Web Site:* www.pres-on.com, pg 981

Wang, Joseph, Biway Media, 5803 Sovereign, Suite 204, Houston, TX 77036 *Tel:* 713-271-4036 *Toll Free Tel:* 877-BIWAY DV (249-2938) *Fax:* 713-271-4240 *E-mail:* info@biwaymedia.com; sales@biwaymedia.com; audiosales@biwaymedia.com *Web Site:* www.biwaymedia.com, pg 808

Wang, Kim E, Digital Art Video Inc, 8506 60 Ave, 3rd fl, Middle Village, NY 11379-5430 *Tel:* 718-457-5388 *Web Site:* www.digital-art.com, pg 847

Wang, Tony, WAC Lighting Co, 44 Harbor Park Dr, Port Washington, NY 11050 *Tel:* 516-515-5000 *Toll Free Tel:* 800-526-2588 *Fax:* 516-515-5050 *Toll Free Fax:* 800-526-2585 *E-mail:* sales@waclighting.com *Web Site:* www.waclighting.com, pg 1061

Wang, Vork PhD, York Telecom, 81 Corbett Way, Eatontown, NJ 07724 *Tel:* 732-413-6000 *Toll Free Tel:* 866-836-8463 *Fax:* 732-413-6060 *E-mail:* knowmore@yorktel.com *Web Site:* yorktel.com, pg 1072

Wanlass, Gordon, PowerPhysics Inc, 877 Production Place, Newport Beach, CA 92663-2809 *Tel:* 949-371-6202 *Fax:* 815-572-8936 *E-mail:* contact@powerphysics.com *Web Site:* www.powerphysics.com, pg 979

Wantman, Charles D, Audio Vistas LLC, 170 N Woods Dr, South Orange, NJ 07079 *Tel:* 212-586-2177 *E-mail:* info@audiovistas.com *Web Site:* www.audiovistas.com, pg 795

Ward, Al, Award Productions, 164 Great Rd, Acton, MA 01720 *Tel:* 978-667-3335 *E-mail:* web@awardproductions.com *Web Site:* www.awardproductions.com, pg 800

Ward, Fern, Intellidyne LLC, 5203 Leesburg Pike, Suite 400, 2 Skyline Place, Falls Church, VA 22041 *Tel:* 703-575-9715 *Fax:* 703-575-9718 *Web Site:* www.intellidyne-llc.com, pg 899

Ward, Ray, POP TV, 5069 Maureen Lane, Moorpark, CA 93021-7127 *Tel:* 805-499-8513 *Toll Free Tel:* 800-331-4626 *Fax:* 805-499-8206 *E-mail:* sales@mpo-video.com *Web Site:* www.mpo-video.com, pg 978

Ward, Steve, WSI, 400 Minuteman Rd, Andover, MA 01810 *Tel:* 978-983-6300 *Fax:* 978-983-6400 *Web Site:* www.wsi.com, pg 1070

Ward, Tom, Saturn Productions Inc, 305 E 86 St, Suite 14-JW, New York, NY 10028 *Tel:* 212-348-7300 *Fax:* 212-426-7907 *E-mail:* saturnnyc@aol.com, pg 1003

Warden, Linda C, LCW Productions LLC, 3019 Hayden Dr, Wilmington, NC 28411-9625 *Tel:* 910-681-0835 *Fax:* 910-524-2736 *Web Site:* www.lcwproductions.com, pg 917

Ware, John David, 168 Film Festival, 100 E Cedar, Burbank, CA 91502 *Tel:* 818-557-8507 *Fax:* 818-942-6076 *E-mail:* info@168project.com *Web Site:* www.168project.com, pg 1123

Warhola, Karen Carberry, Maine Film Office, 59 State House Sta, Augusta, ME 04333 *Tel:* 207-624-9828 *Fax:* 207-287-8070 *E-mail:* film@maine.gov *Web Site:* www.filminmaine.com, pg 1098

Waring, Tom, Trailblazer Studios®, 1610 Midtown Place, Raleigh, NC 27609 *Tel:* 919-645-6600 *Fax:* 919-645-6601 *Web Site:* www.trailblazerstudios.com, pg 1043

Warman, S David, RGB Technology Inc, 590 Herndon Pkwy, Suite 500, Herndon, VA 20170-5267 *Tel:* 703-834-1500 *Fax:* 703-834-1506 *Web Site:* www.rgbtec.com, pg 996

Warner, Michael, Air Sea Land Productions Inc (ASL), 19-69 Steinway St, Astoria, NY 11105-1108 *Tel:* 718-626-2646 *Toll Free Tel:* 888-ASL-LENS (275-5367) *Fax:* 718-626-1493 *E-mail:* sales@airsealand.com *Web Site:* www.airsealand.com, pg 779

Warnock, Dr John E, Adobe Systems Inc, 345 Park Ave, San Jose, CA 95110-2704 *Tel:* 408-536-6000 *Fax:* 408-537-6000 *Web Site:* www.adobe.com, pg 776

Warot, Andy, Inter-Media Electronics, 192 Willard St, Quincy, MA 02169 *Tel:* 617-773-9688 *Fax:* 617-696-6327 *E-mail:* intermedia.ex@verizon.net; info@ime-imaging.com *Web Site:* www.viapolonia.net/IME, pg 899

Warr, Jr, Jeff PhD, Zachry Associates Inc, 500 Chestnut St, Suite 2000, Abilene, TX 79602 *Tel:* 325-677-1342 *Fax:* 325-672-2001 *E-mail:* info@zachryinc.com *Web Site:* zachryinc.com, pg 1073

Warren, Ashley, Metro Productions, 8570 Magellan Pkwy, Suite 400, Richmond, VA 23227 *Tel:* 804-261-1172 *Toll Free Tel:* 877-669-4687 *Fax:* 804-261-1885 *E-mail:* contactmetro@metro-productions.com *Web Site:* www.metro-productions.com, pg 939

Warren, Galen, SNL Kagan Media & Communications, One SNL Plaza, 212 Seventh St NE, Charlottesville, VA 22902 *Tel:* 434-977-1600 *Toll Free Tel:* 866-296-3743 *Fax:* 434-977-4466 *E-mail:* snlkagansales@snl.com *Web Site:* www.snl.com, pg 1014

Warren, Joseph G, Canon USA Inc, One Canon Park, Melville, NY 11747 *Tel:* 613-330-5000 *E-mail:* pr@cusa.canon.com *Web Site:* www.usa.canon.com, pg 819

Warring, Michael, National Teaching Aids Inc, 401 Hickory St, Fort Collins, CO 80524 *Tel:* 970-484-7445 *Toll Free Tel:* 800-289-9299 *Fax:* 970-484-1198 *E-mail:* custserv@amep.com *Web Site:* www.amep.com, pg 953

Warring, Michael, Scott Resources Inc, 401 Hickory St, Fort Collins, CO 80524-1125 *Tel:* 970-484-7445 *Toll Free Tel:* 800-289-9299 *Fax:* 970-484-1198 *E-mail:* custserv@amep.com *Web Site:* amep.com, pg 1005

Warsaw, Michael P, Eternal Word Television Network (EWTN), 5817 Old Leeds Rd, Irondale, AL 35210-2164 *Tel:* 205-271-2900 *Fax:* 205-271-2920 *E-mail:* viewer@ewtn.com *Web Site:* www.ewtn.com, pg 862

Warzak, Frank, FJW Optical Systems Inc, 322 N Woodwork Lane, Palatine, IL 60067-4933 *Tel:* 847-358-2500 *Toll Free Tel:* 800-355-4FJW (355-4359) *Fax:* 847-358-2533 *E-mail:* irsales@findrscope.com *Web Site:* www.findrscope.com, pg 869

Warzer, Peter L, Long Island Video Enterprises Live Inc, 110 Pratt Oval, Glen Cove, NY 11542 *Tel:* 516-759-5483 *Fax:* 516-671-5874 *E-mail:* info@longislandvideo.com *Web Site:* www.longislandvideo.com, pg 924

Wasaman, Melissa, High-Tech Special Effects Inc, PO Box 193, Eads, TN 38028-0193 *Tel:* 901-850-5522 *Fax:* 901-850-8317 *Web Site:* www.hightechspecialeffects.com, pg 889

Wasch, Kenneth, Software & Information Industry Association (SIIA), 1090 Vermont Ave NW, 6th fl, Washington, DC 20005-4095 *Tel:* 202-289-7442 *Fax:* 202-289-7097 *Web Site:* www.siia.net, pg 1089

Wasco, Sonia S, Grant Heilman Photography Inc, 506 W Lincoln Ave, Lititz, PA 17543 *Tel:* 717-626-0296 *Toll Free Tel:* 800-622-2046 *Fax:* 717-626-0971 *E-mail:* info@heilmanphoto.com *Web Site:* www.heilmanphoto.com, pg 887

Washington, Kiko, Warner Bros Entertainment Inc, 4000 Warner Blvd, Burbank, CA 91522 *Tel:* 818-954-3000 *Fax:* 818-954-4918 *E-mail:* wbsf@warnerbros.com *Web Site:* www.warnerbros.com; studiofacilities.warnerbros.com, pg 1062

Washington, Paul, The Denver Office of Economic Development, Wellington E Webb Municipal Bldg, 2nd fl, 201 W Colfax Ave, Dept 1005, Denver, CO 80202 *Tel:* 720-913-1999 *Fax:* 720-913-1802 *E-mail:* oed@denvergov.org *Web Site:* www.milehigh.com, pg 1095

Waskey, Bill, A&S Case Co Inc, 5260 Vineland Ave, North Hollywood, CA 91601 *Tel:* 818-509-5920 *Toll Free Tel:* 800-394-6181 *Fax:* 818-509-1397 *E-mail:* info@ascase.com *Web Site:* www.ascase.com, pg 772

Wasser, Eric, Compass Learning Inc, 203 Colorado St, Austin, TX 78701 *Tel:* 512-478-9600 *Toll Free Tel:* 866-586-7387 (sales); 800-678-1412 (cust support) *Web Site:* www.compasslearning.com, pg 833

Waterhouse, Lloyd G, McGraw-Hill School Education Group, 8787 Orion Place, Columbus, OH 43240-4027 *Tel:* 614-430-4000 *Toll Free Tel:* 800-334-7734 *Fax:* 614-755-5682 *E-mail:* customer.service@mcgraw-hill.com *Web Site:* www.mcgraw-hill.com, pg 935

Waters, Buck, Broadcasters General Store Inc, 2480 SE 52 St, Ocala, FL 34480 *Tel:* 352-622-7700 *Fax:* 352-629-7000 *E-mail:* sales@bgs.cc (orders) *Web Site:* www.bgs.cc, pg 813

Waters, Mitch, The ADS Group, 2155 Niagara Lane N, Suite 120, Plymouth, MN 55447 *Tel:* 763-449-5500 *Toll Free Tel:* 800-759-0992 *Fax:* 763-449-5555 *E-mail:* sales@theadsgroup.com *Web Site:* www.theadsgroup.com, pg 777

Watier, Penny, AC Lighting Inc, 88 Horner Ave, Toronto, ON M8Z 5Y3, Canada *Tel:* 416-255-9494 *Fax:* 416-255-3514 *E-mail:* northamerica@aclighting.com *Web Site:* www.aclighting.com, pg 772

Watkins, Glenn, Acoustic Systems, 1301 Arrow Point Dr, Cedar Park, TX 78613 *Tel:* 512-531-6400 *Toll Free Tel:* 800-749-1460 *Fax:* 512-531-6500 *E-mail:* sales@ets-lindgren.com *Web Site:* www.ets-lindgren.com, pg 774

Watkins, Matt, MultiDyne Video & Fiber Optics Systems, 191 Forest Ave, Locust Valley, NY 11560 *Tel:* 516-671-7278 *Toll Free Tel:* 877-MULTIDYNE (685-8439) *Fax:* 516-671-3362 *E-mail:* sales@multidyne.com *Web Site:* www.multidyne.com, pg 950

Watson, Don, Walltalkers, 3875 Embassy Pkwy, Fairlawn, OH 44333 *Tel:* 330-668-7600 *Toll Free Tel:* 800-820-9255 *Fax:* 330-668-7703 *E-mail:* customerservice@koroseal.com *Web Site:* www.walltalkers.com, pg 1061

Watson, Justin, Trod Nossel Productions & Recording Studios, 10 George St, Wallingford, CT 06492 *Tel:* 203-269-4465 *Toll Free Tel:* 800-800-HITS (800-4487) *Fax:* 203-294-1745 *E-mail:* info@trodnossel.com *Web Site:* www.trodnossel.com, pg 1045

Watt, Jim, Bennett-Watt HD Productions Inc, 13021 244 Ave SE, Issaquah, WA 98027 *Tel:* 425-392-3935 *Toll Free Tel:* 800-327-2893 *Fax:* 425-526-5851 *E-mail:* info@bennett-watt.com *Web Site:* www.bennett-watt.com, pg 805

Watt, Kelly, Bennett-Watt HD Productions Inc, 13021 244 Ave SE, Issaquah, WA 98027 *Tel:* 425-392-3935 *Toll Free Tel:* 800-327-2893 *Fax:* 425-526-5851 *E-mail:* info@bennett-watt.com *Web Site:* www.bennett-watt.com, pg 805

Watts, Dylis, Videografix LLC, 2530 Berryessa Rd, Suite 314, San Jose, CA 95132-2903 *Tel:* 408-499-1280 *Fax:* 408-583-4018 *E-mail:* info@videografix.com *Web Site:* www.videografix.com, pg 1057

Watts, Jeff, JWP Inc, PO Box 14867, Fort Worth, TX 76117 *Tel:* 817-233-6462 *Fax:* 817-439-2353 *Web Site:* www.jwproductions.org, pg 907

Watts, Jeff, Watts Communications Inc, 149 N 120 St, Wauwatosa, WI 53226 *Tel:* 414-727-9505 *Fax:* 414-727-9506 *E-mail:* sales@wattscom.com *Web Site:* www.wattscom.com, pg 1062

Watts, Keith, Watts Communications Inc, 149 N 120 St, Wauwatosa, WI 53226 *Tel:* 414-727-9505 *Fax:* 414-727-9506 *E-mail:* sales@wattscom.com *Web Site:* www.wattscom.com, pg 1062

Way, Brian, ESE, 142 Sierra St, El Segundo, CA 90245 *Tel:* 310-322-2136 *Fax:* 310-322-8127 *E-mail:* ese@ese-web.com *Web Site:* www.ese-web.com, pg 862

Way, Steven F, Advanced Lighting & Production Services Inc (ALPS), 65 Teed Dr, Randolph, MA 02368 *Tel:* 781-961-3066 *Toll Free Tel:* 866-961-3066 *Fax:* 781-961-3256 *E-mail:* info@alpsweb.com *Web Site:* www.alpsweb.com, pg 777

Wayne, Don, Don Wayne Magic Inc, 10907 Magnolia Blvd, Suite 467, North Hollywood, CA 91601 *Tel:* 818-763-3192 *E-mail:* info@donwaynemagic.com *Web Site:* www.donwaynemagic.com, pg 1063

Wayne, Robert C, Sunburst Recording, 10313 Jefferson Blvd, Culver City, CA 90232 *Tel:* 310-204-2222 *E-mail:* info@sunburstrecording.com *Web Site:* sunburstrecording.com, pg 1028

Weatherford, Elizabeth, Smithsonian National Museum of the American Indian, c/o Film & Video Ctr, Natl Museum of the American Indian, One Bowling Green, New York, NY 10004-1415 *Tel:* 212-514-3700 *Fax:* 212-514-3725 *E-mail:* fvc@si.edu *Web Site:* www.nmai.si.edu, pg 1014

Weaver, Avery, Emery-Pratt Co, 1966 W M-21, Owosso, MI 48867-1379 *Tel:* 989-723-5291 *Toll Free Tel:* 800-248-3887 *Fax:* 989-723-4677 *Toll Free Fax:* 800-523-6379 *E-mail:* mail@emery-pratt.com *Web Site:* www.emery-pratt.com, pg 860

Webb, Bob, Ingram Entertainment Inc, 2 Ingram Blvd, La Vergne, TN 37089-7006 *Tel:* 615-287-4000 (corp) *Toll Free Tel:* 800-621-1333 (sales & cust serv) *Fax:* 615-287-4982 *Web Site:* www.ingramentertainment.com, pg 898

Webb, J Thomas, GlobalStreams™ Corp, 20353 W 108 St, Olathe, KS 66061 *Tel:* 314-423-6700 *Toll Free Tel:* 800-788-7205; 866-558-7830 (cust support) *Fax:* 314-423-6705 *E-mail:* gsinfo@globalstreams.com; support@globalstreams.com; sales@globalstreams.com *Web Site:* www.globalstreams.com, pg 879

Webb, Scott T, Webb Audio Visual Communication, 3020 S West Temple, Salt Lake City, UT 84115 *Tel:* 801-484-8567 (installation) *Toll Free Tel:* 877-909-8567 *Fax:* 801-484-8589 *Web Site:* www.webbav.com, pg 1063

Webb, Steven M, Webb Audio Visual Communication, 3020 S West Temple, Salt Lake City, UT 84115 *Tel:* 801-484-8567 (installation) *Toll Free Tel:* 877-909-8567 *Fax:* 801-484-8589 *Web Site:* www.webbav.com, pg 1063

Weber, Dave, PicturePhone Inc, 200 Commerce Dr, Rochester, NY 14623 *Tel:* 585-334-9040 *Toll Free Tel:* 800-521-5454 *Fax:* 585-486-1919 *E-mail:* info@picturephone.com *Web Site:* www.picturephone.com, pg 975

Weber, Doug, Theatre Effects, 1810 Airport Exchange Blvd, Suite 400, Erlanger, KY 41018-3184 *Tel:* 513-772-7646 (intl) *Toll Free Tel:* 800-791-7646 *Fax:* 513-772-3579 *E-mail:* service@theatrefx.com *Web Site:* www.theatrefx.com, pg 1038

Weber, Mark, Noontide Press, PO Box 2719, Newport Beach, CA 92759 *Tel:* 714-593-9725 *E-mail:* orders@noontidepress.com *Web Site:* www.noontidepress.com, pg 958

Weber, William J, WHYY Inc, Independence Mall West, 150 N Sixth St, Philadelphia, PA 19106 *Tel:* 215-351-1200 *Fax:* 215-351-0398 *E-mail:* talkback@whyy.org *Web Site:* www.whyy.org, pg 1066

Weberman, Alisa S, Listen & Live Audio Inc, 1700 Manhattan Ave, Union City, NJ 07068 *Tel:* 201-558-9000 *Toll Free Tel:* 800-653-9400 (orders) *Fax:* 201-558-9800 *Web Site:* www.listenandlive.com, pg 923

Webley, Scott, ShowBiz Studios, 15521 Lanark St, Van Nuys, CA 91406 *Tel:* 818-989-7007 *Fax:* 818-989-8272 *Web Site:* www.showbizstudios.com, pg 1009

Webster, James L, Continental Film, 1466 Riverside Dr, Suite E, Chattanooga, TN 37406 *Tel:* 423-622-1193 *Toll Free Tel:* 888-909-3456 *Fax:* 423-629-0853 *Web Site:* www.continentalfilm.com, pg 835

Webster, Kathy L, The Miller Group, Multiplex Division, 1610 Design Way, Dupo, IL 62239-1820 *Tel:* 636-343-5700 *Toll Free Tel:* 800-325-3350 *Fax:* 618-286-6202 *E-mail:* info@miller-group.com *Web Site:* www.multiplexdisplays.com, pg 943

Webster, Van, Webster Communications, 607 N Avenue 64, Los Angeles, CA 90042 *Tel:* 323-258-6741 *E-mail:* info@vanwebster.com *Web Site:* www.vanwebster.com, pg 1063

Wechsler, Bradley J, IMAX Corp, 2525 Speakman Dr, Mississauga, ON L5K 1B1, Canada *Tel:* 905-403-6500 *Fax:* 905-403-6450 *E-mail:* info@imax.com *Web Site:* www.imax.com, pg 896

Weckel, Matt, Blue Barn Pictures Inc, 68 Jay St, Suite 311, Brooklyn, NY 11201 *Tel:* 718-852-1403 *Web Site:* www.bluebarnpictures.com, pg 809

Wedel, Terry, VO2 Mix Studios, 116 Spadina Ave, Suite 208, Toronto, ON M5V 2K6, Canada *Tel:* 416-603-3954 *Fax:* 416-603-3957 *E-mail:* info@vo2mix.ca *Web Site:* www.vo2mix.ca, pg 1060

Weidenaar, Reynold, Magnetic Music Publishing Co, 20 Jane St, Suite 2-C, New York, NY 10014-1945 *Tel:* 212-255-8527 *Fax:* 212-595-2067 *E-mail:* info@magneticmusic.ws *Web Site:* magneticmusic.ws, pg 928

Weigert, Marc, Method Studios, 730 Arizona Ave, Santa Monica, CA 90401 *Tel:* 310-434-6500 *Web Site:* www.methodstudios.com, pg 939

Weigl, Linda A, Weigl Publishers Inc, 350 Fifth Ave, 59th fl, New York, NY 10118 *Toll Free Tel:* 866-649-3445 *Toll Free Fax:* 866-449-3445 *Web Site:* www.weigl.com, pg 1063

Weiland, Maggie, San Francisco Film Commission, City Hall, Rm 473, One Dr Carlton B Goodlett Place, San Francisco, CA 94102-4649 *Tel:* 415-554-6241 *Fax:* 415-554-6503 *E-mail:* film@sfgov.org *Web Site:* www.filmsf.org, pg 1094

Weiler, Clint, MVD Entertainment Group, 203 Windsor Rd, Pottstown, PA 19464 *Tel:* 610-650-8200 *Toll Free Tel:* 800-888-0486 *Fax:* 610-650-9102 *Toll Free Fax:* 888-536-7998 *Web Site:* mvdb2b.com, pg 951

Weiman, Mark, Regent Press Publishers & Printers, 2747 Regent St, Berkeley, CA 94705 *Tel:* 510-845-1196 *E-mail:* regentpress@mindspring.com *Web Site:* www.regentpress.net, pg 994

Wein, David, Mind Over Eye Inc, 2221 Rosecrans Ave, Suite 195, El Segundo, CA 90245 *Tel:* 310-396-4663 *Fax:* 310-297-9526 *E-mail:* info@mindovereye.com *Web Site:* www.mindovereye.com, pg 943

Wein, Garrett, Dot Hill Systems Corp, 1351 S Sunset St, Longmont, CO 80501-6533 *Tel:* 303-845-3200 *Toll Free Tel:* 800-872-2783 *Fax:* 303-845-3655 *E-mail:* support@dothill.com; websales@dothill.com *Web Site:* www.dothill.com, pg 851

Weinberg, Felicia, Alden Films, PO Box 449, Clarksburg, NJ 08510-0449 *Tel:* 732-462-3522 *Toll Free Tel:* 800-832-0980 *Fax:* 732-294-0330 *E-mail:* info@aldenfilms.com *Web Site:* www.aldenfilms.com, pg 780

Weinberg, Felicia, Business Education Films, PO Box 449, Clarksburg, NJ 08510-0449 *Tel:* 732-462-3522 *Fax:* 732-294-0330 *E-mail:* info@aldenfilms.com *Web Site:* www.aldenfilms.com, pg 815

Weinberg, Felicia, Films of the Nations, PO Box 449, Clarksburg, NJ 08510-0449 *Tel:* 732-462-3522 *Toll Free Tel:* 800-832-0980 *Fax:* 732-294-0330 *E-mail:* info@aldenfilms.com *Web Site:* www.aldenfilms.com, pg 868

Weinberg, Paul, Alden Films, PO Box 449, Clarksburg, NJ 08510-0449 *Tel:* 732-462-3522 *Toll Free Tel:* 800-832-0980 *Fax:* 732-294-0330 *E-mail:* info@aldenfilms.com *Web Site:* www.aldenfilms.com, pg 780

Weinberg, Paul, Business Education Films, PO Box 449, Clarksburg, NJ 08510-0449 *Tel:* 732-462-3522 *Fax:* 732-294-0330 *E-mail:* info@aldenfilms.com *Web Site:* www.aldenfilms.com, pg 815

Weinberg, Paul, Films of the Nations, PO Box 449, Clarksburg, NJ 08510-0449 *Tel:* 732-462-3522 *Toll Free Tel:* 800-832-0980 *Fax:* 732-294-0330 *E-mail:* info@aldenfilms.com *Web Site:* www.aldenfilms.com, pg 868

Weiner, David, Health Education Services, 10200 Jefferson Blvd, Culver City, CA 90232 *Tel:* 310-839-2436 *Toll Free Tel:* 800-421-4246 *Fax:* 310-839-2249 *Toll Free Fax:* 800-944-5432 *E-mail:* access@socialstudies.com *Web Site:* www.socialstudies.com, pg 887

Weiner, David, Social Studies School Service, 10200 Jefferson Blvd, Culver City, CA 90232 *Tel:* 310-839-2436 *Toll Free Tel:* 800-421-4246 *Fax:* 310-839-2249 *Toll Free Fax:* 800-944-5432 *E-mail:* access@socialstudies.com *Web Site:* www.socialstudies.com, pg 1015

Weiner, Glenn, Mole-Richardson Co, 937 N Sycamore Ave, Hollywood, CA 90038-2384 *Tel:* 323-851-0111 *Fax:* 323-851-5593 *E-mail:* info@mole.com *Web Site:* www.mole.com, pg 945

Weiner, Kay, Eastman Corp, 7447 Via de Fortuna, Carlsbad, CA 92009 *Tel:* 760-603-8646 *Web Site:* www.kbwfoundation.com, pg 856

Weiner, Michael J, The Image Generators, 18156 Darnell Dr, Olney, MD 20832 *Tel:* 301-924-5700 *Fax:* 240-363-0062 *E-mail:* info@imagegenerators.com *Web Site:* www.imagegenerators.com, pg 895

Weiner, Sanford, The Writing Co, 10200 Jefferson Blvd, Culver City, CA 90232 *Tel:* 310-839-2436 *Toll Free Tel:* 800-421-4246 *Fax:* 310-839-2249 *Toll Free Fax:* 800-944-5432 *E-mail:* access@writingco.com; access@socialstudies.com *Web Site:* www.socialstudies.com; www.writingco.com, pg 1070

Weingarden, Marshall, Ever-Ready Media Packaging, 8192 Gatherly Circle, Easton, MD 21601 *Tel:* 973-566-9333 *Fax:* 201-387-1530 *E-mail:* packages@erpack.com *Web Site:* www.erpack.com, pg 863

Weingart, Daniel, Three D Graphics Inc, 11340 W Olympic Blvd, Suite 352, Los Angeles, CA 90064-1613 *Tel:* 310-231-3330 *Toll Free Tel:* 800-913-0008 *Fax:* 310-231-3303 *E-mail:* info@threedgraphics.com *Web Site:* www.threedgraphics.com, pg 1039

Weingarten, Jeff, Interface Media Group, 1233 20 St NW, Washington, DC 20036 *Tel:* 202-861-0500 *E-mail:* info@interfacevideo.com *Web Site:* www.interfacevideo.com, pg 900

Weingarten, Lisa, Bestwell Optical Instrument Corp, 46 Henry St, Merrick, NY 11566 *Tel:* 516-379-2280 *Fax:* 516-706-1744 *Web Site:* www.bestwelloptical.com, pg 806

Weingert, Alex, Otto Nemenz International Inc, 870 N Vine St, Los Angeles, CA 90038 *Tel:* 323-469-2774 *Fax:* 323-469-1217 *E-mail:* info@ottonemenz.com *Web Site:* www.ottonemenz.com, pg 954

Weinrich, Howard, SLD Lighting, 36-05 Broadway, Fair Lawn, NJ 07410 *Tel:* 201-373-2700 *Toll Free Tel:* 800-245-6630 *Fax:* 201-793-7618 *E-mail:* sales@sldlighting.com *Web Site:* www.sldlighting.com, pg 1013

Weinschreider, Cindy, Bretford Manufacturing Inc, 11000 Seymour Ave, Franklin Park, IL 60131 *Tel:* 847-678-2545 *Toll Free Tel:* 800-521-9614 *Fax:* 847-678-0852 *Toll Free Fax:* 800-343-1779 *E-mail:* customerservice@bretford.com *Web Site:* bretford.com, pg 812

Weinstein, Chuck, Design Audio Visual Inc, 195-A Central Ave, Farmingdale, NY 11735 *Tel:* 631-694-3334 *Toll Free Tel:* 800-886-1328 *Fax:* 631-694-3549 *Web Site:* www.design-av.com, pg 845

Weinstein, Dana, US Holocaust Memorial Museum, 100 Raoul Wallenberg Place SW, Washington, DC 20024-2126 *Tel:* 202-488-0400 *Fax:* 202-488-2695 *E-mail:* membership@ushmm.org *Web Site:* www.ushmm.org, pg 1050

Weir, Jacqueline, The Big House Group, 17 Waller Ave, Ossining, NY 10562 *Tel:* 914-944-4011 *Fax:* 914-944-8044 *Web Site:* www.bighousetv.com, pg 807

Weir, Robert L, Metro Video Systems Inc, 1220 E Imperial Ave, El Segundo, CA 90245 *Tel:* 310-640-9250 *Fax:* 310-640-9347 *E-mail:* sales@metrovideosystems.com *Web Site:* www.metrovideosystems.com, pg 940

Weisbart, Steve, Get Smart Products, 30 S Highland Ave, Ossining, NY 10562 *Tel:* 914-762-3500 *Toll Free Tel:* 800-827-0673 *Fax:* 914-923-5818 *Toll Free Fax:* 866-827-0673 *E-mail:* getsmart@pfile.com *Web Site:* www.pfile.com, pg 877

Weisberg, Josh, WorldStage, 259 W 30 St, 12th fl, New York, NY 10001-2863 *Tel:* 212-582-2345 *Fax:* 718-610-1750 *E-mail:* info@worldstage.com *Web Site:* www.worldstage.com, pg 1070

Weisberg, Larry, Backstage Pass Entertainment Inc, 7438 Shoshone Ave, Lake Balboa, CA 91406-2340 *Tel:* 818-881-9888 *Toll Free Tel:* 800-664-6555 *Fax:* 818-881-0555 *E-mail:* blowinsmokeband@ktb.net, pg 801

Weisen, Bob, Duplication Depot Inc, 7 Brookstan Rd, Nesconset, NY 11767 *Tel:* 631-752-0608 *E-mail:* copymydisc@gmail.com *Web Site:* www.duplicationdepot.com, pg 853

Weisenberg, Beverly, Landmark Media Inc, 3450 Slade Run Dr, Falls Church, VA 22042 *Tel:* 703-241-2030 *Toll Free Tel:* 800-342-4336 *Fax:* 703-536-9540 *E-mail:* info@landmarkmedia.com; landmrkmed@aol.com *Web Site:* www.landmarkmedia.com, pg 915

Weiser, Don, Salina Film Commission, 120 W Ash St, Salina, KS 67402 *Tel:* 785-827-9301 *Fax:* 785-827-9758 *E-mail:* info@salinakansas.org *Web Site:* www.salinakansas.org, pg 1097

Weiskoff, Marty, Hunt's Photo, Video & Digital, 100 Main St, Melrose, MA 02176-6104 *Tel:* 781-662-8822 (retail sales) *Toll Free Tel:* 800-924-8682 (retail sales); 800-221-1830 (ext 2340, corp sales) *Fax:* 781-662-6524 *E-mail:* ecommerce@wbhunt.com (retail online sales) *Web Site:* www.huntsphotoandvideo.com, pg 892

Weiss, Alan, Alan Weiss Productions, 270 White Plains Rd, Suite 2N, East Chester, NY 10709 *Tel:* 212-974-0606 *E-mail:* awpinfo@awptv.com *Web Site:* www.awptv.com, pg 1063

Weiss, Bart, Dallas Video Festival, 1405 Woodlawn Ave, Dallas, TX 75208 *E-mail:* info@videofest.org *Web Site:* www.videofest.org, pg 1113

Weiss, Chanan, SintecMedia, 425 Madison Ave, Suite 1602, New York, NY 10017 *Tel:* 917-606-5310 *Fax:* 917-606-5311 *E-mail:* sales@sintecmedia.com *Web Site:* www.sintecmedia.com, pg 1012

Weiss, Ed, Movies Unlimited, 3015 Darnell Rd, Philadelphia, PA 19154 *Tel:* 215-637-4444 *Toll Free Tel:* 800-4-MOVIES (466-8437) *Fax:* 215-637-2350 *E-mail:* movies@moviesunlimited.com *Web Site:* www.moviesunlimited.com, pg 947

Weiss, George, Electronic Service Dealers Association, 4925 W Irving Park Rd, Chicago, IL 60641 *Tel:* 773-282-9400, pg 1081

Weiss, Matt, Havas Worldwide, 200 Hudson St, New York, NY 10013 *Tel:* 212-886-2000 *Fax:* 212-886-5013 *Web Site:* havasworldwide.com, pg 886

Weiss, Michael, Video Labs, 15237 Display Ct, Rockville, MD 20850 *Tel:* 301-217-0000 *Toll Free Tel:* 800-800-8240 *Fax:* 301-217-0044 *E-mail:* sales@videolabs.net *Web Site:* www.videolabs.net, pg 1055

Weiss, Paul, Techni-Tool Inc, 1547 N Trooper Rd, Worcester, PA 19490 *Tel:* 610-941-2400 *Toll Free Tel:* 800-832-4866 *Fax:* 610-828-5623 *Toll Free Fax:* 800-854-8665 *E-mail:* sales@techni-tool.com *Web Site:* www.techni-tool.com, pg 1033

Welge, Niki, The Florida Office of Film & Entertainment, 107 E Madison St, MSC 80, Tallahassee, FL 32399 *Tel:* 850-717-8990; 818-508-7772 *Toll Free Tel:* 877-FLA-FILM (352-3456) *Fax:* 850-410-4770 *Web Site:* www.filminflorida.com, pg 1096

Weller, Victoria (Vicci), Thompson-Nicola Film Commission, 300-465 Victoria St, Kamloops, BC V2C 2A9, Canada *Tel:* 250-377-8673 *Toll Free Tel:* 877-377-8673 (BC only) *Fax:* 250-372-5048 *E-mail:* admin@tnrd.bc.ca *Web Site:* www.tnrdfilm.com, pg 1104

Welles, Doug, Frey Scientific, 80 Northwest Blvd, Nashua, NH 03063-4067 *Toll Free Tel:* 800-225-3739 *Toll Free Fax:* 877-256-3739 *E-mail:* customercare@freyscientific.com *Web Site:* www.freyscientific.com, pg 873

Wells, Andy, Music 2 Hues, 54 Hazard Ave, Suite 315, Enfield, CT 06082 *Tel:* 860-745-1312 *Fax:* 860-745-1312 (orders) *E-mail:* info@music2hues.com *Web Site:* www.music2hues.com, pg 951

Wells, David, Moving Picture, 748 N Victoria Park Rd, Fort Lauderdale, FL 33304 *Tel:* 954-522-1361 *Toll Free Tel:* 800-800-1361 *Fax:* 954-523-1361 *E-mail:* info@movingpicture.com *Web Site:* www.movingpicture.com, pg 947

Wells, Faith, San Luis Obispo County Film Commission, 811 El Capitan, Suite 200, San Luis Obispo, CA 93401 *Tel:* 805-541-8000 *Fax:* 805-543-9498 *Web Site:* www.sanluisobispocounty.com, pg 1094

Wells, Frank, Audio Engineering Society Inc (AES), 60 E 42 St, Rm 2520, New York, NY 10165-2520 *Tel:* 212-661-8528 *Fax:* 212-682-0477 *Web Site:* www.aes.org, pg 1079

Wells, Kevin, Corporate Color Graphics Inc, 3525 Lousma Dr SE, Grand Rapids, MI 49548 *Tel:* 616-774-9583 *Toll Free Tel:* 800-776-9583 *Fax:* 616-774-8235 *E-mail:* production@corpcolor.com *Web Site:* www.corpcolor.com, pg 836

Welsh, Daniel M, Spoken Arts Inc, 195 S White Rock Rd, Holmes, NY 12531 *Tel:* 845-878-9600 *Toll Free Tel:* 800-326-4090 *Fax:* 845-878-9009 *E-mail:* sales@spokenartsmedia.com *Web Site:* www.spokenartsmedia.com, pg 1021

Welsh, Leah, Trailblazer Studios®, 1610 Midtown Place, Raleigh, NC 27609 *Tel:* 919-645-6600 *Fax:* 919-645-6601 *Web Site:* www.trailblazerstudios.com, pg 1043

Welsh, Susan, Spoken Arts Inc, 195 S White Rock Rd, Holmes, NY 12531 *Tel:* 845-878-9600 *Toll Free Tel:* 800-326-4090 *Fax:* 845-878-9009 *E-mail:* sales@spokenartsmedia.com *Web Site:* www.spokenartsmedia.com, pg 1021

Welz, Gary, Science Television Co, 460 W 24 St, Unit 3A, New York, NY 10011 *Tel:* 917-593-2537 *E-mail:* admin@scitv.com *Web Site:* www.scitv.com, pg 1005

Welz, Joey, Canadian American Records, PO Box 808, Lititz, PA 17543-0538 *Tel:* 717-627-4800 *Fax:* 717-627-4800 *E-mail:* canadianamerican@dejazzd.com *Web Site:* www.canadianamericanrecords.net; www.joeywelz.com, pg 818

Wendorf, Bryan, Chicago Underground Film Festival, 2044 W Chicago Ave, PMB 155, Chicago, IL 60622 *Tel:* 773-341-6727 *E-mail:* info@cuff.org *Web Site:* www.cuff.org, pg 1112

Wendt, Ryan, American Recordable Media, 110 Dewey Dr, Suite A, Nicholasville, KY 40356 *Toll Free Tel:* 800-598-8273 *E-mail:* info@americanrecordablemedia.com *Web Site:* www.americanrecordablemedia.com, pg 785

Wennberg, Jeff, Caption Colorado LLC, 5690 DTC Blvd, Suite 500W, Greenwood Village, CO 80111 *Tel:* 720-489-5662 *Toll Free Tel:* 800-775-7838 *Fax:* 720-489-5664 *Web Site:* www.captioncolorado.com, pg 820

Wensley, Brad, Quantel Inc, 25 W 43 St, Suite 1118, New York, NY 10036-7406 *Tel:* 212-944-6820 *Toll Free Tel:* 800-331-8327 (cust serv) *Fax:* 212-944-6813 *Web Site:* www.quantel.com, pg 989

Wentling, Mark, Ashly Audio Inc, 847 Holt Rd, Webster, NY 14580-9103 *Tel:* 585-872-0010 *Toll Free Tel:* 800-828-6308 *Fax:* 585-872-0739 *E-mail:* info@ashly.com; sales@ashly.com *Web Site:* www.ashly.com, pg 792

Wentz, Eric, Alpha Technologies, 3767 Alpha Way, Bellingham, WA 98226 *Tel:* 360-647-2360 *Fax:* 360-671-4936 *E-mail:* alpha@alpha.com *Web Site:* www.alpha.com, pg 782

Werbin, Phil, Ahead Stereo Inc, 7428 Beverly Blvd, Los Angeles, CA 90036 *Tel:* 323-931-8873 *Fax:* 323-937-7285 *E-mail:* mrstereo@pacbell.net *Web Site:* www.aheadstereo.com, pg 778

Werbowski, Kim E, Inland Audio Visual Ltd, 422 Lucas Ave, Box 102, Group 200, RR 2, Winnipeg, MB R3C 2E6, Canada *Tel:* 204-786-6521 *Toll Free Tel:* 800-933-6006 *Fax:* 204-783-6281 *E-mail:* winnipeg@inlandav.ca *Web Site:* www.inlandav.ca, pg 898

Werby, Doug, Kaboom Productions, 1465 Illinois St, San Francisco, CA 94107 *Tel:* 415-434-2666 *Fax:* 415-970-8548 *E-mail:* updates@kaboomproductions.com *Web Site:* kaboomproductions.com, pg 907

Werd, Randy, Nelson Enterprises Theatrical Supply Co, 1014 Rte 173 E, Bloomsbury, NJ 08804 *Tel:* 908-479-6902 *Fax:* 908-479-6903 *E-mail:* sales@nelson-enterprises.com; rentals@nelson-enterprises.com *Web Site:* www.nelson-enterprises.com, pg 954

Werk, David M, Videowerks, 3435 Ocean Park Blvd, Suite 107, Santa Monica, CA 90405 *Tel:* 310-393-8754; 310-780-4156 (cell) *Fax:* 310-399-1829 *E-mail:* videowerks@earthlink.net *Web Site:* www.videowerks.com, pg 1057

Werner, Jeffrey, Audio Visual Resources LLC, 1000 N Division St, Suite 2F, Peekskill, NY 10566 *Tel:* 914-526-2698 *Fax:* 914-526-3060 *E-mail:* info@avrny.com *Web Site:* www.avrny.com, pg 796

Wershba, Don, Solid State Logic Inc, 320 W 46 St, 2nd fl, New York, NY 10036-8398 *Tel:* 212-315-1111 *E-mail:* sales@solidstatelogic.com *Web Site:* www.solid-state-logic.com, pg 1015

Weschcke, Carl L, Llewellyn Publications, 2143 Wooddale Dr, Woodbury, MN 55125-2989 *Tel:* 651-291-1970 *Toll Free Tel:* 877-NEWWRLD (639-9753) *Fax:* 651-291-1908 *E-mail:* publicity@llewellyn.com; customerservice@llewellyn.com *Web Site:* www.llewellyn.com, pg 923

Weschcke, Sandra K, Llewellyn Publications, 2143 Wooddale Dr, Woodbury, MN 55125-2989 *Tel:* 651-291-1970 *Toll Free Tel:* 877-NEWWRLD (639-9753) *Fax:* 651-291-1908 *E-mail:* publicity@llewellyn.com; customerservice@llewellyn.com *Web Site:* www.llewellyn.com, pg 923

Wesolowski, Cindy, OmegaBrandess Distribution, 626 Hanover Pike, Suite 102, Hampstead, MD 21074-2036 *Tel:* 410-374-3250 *Fax:* 410-374-3184 *E-mail:* customerservice@omegabrandess.com *Web Site:* www.omegabrandess.com, pg 962

Wesselhoff, Jennifer, Sedona Film Office, 45 Sunset Dr, Sedona, AZ 86336 *Tel:* 928-204-1123 ext 130 *Fax:* 928-204-1064 *E-mail:* pr@sedonachamber.com *Web Site:* www.sedonafilmoffice.com, pg 1091

Wesson, Donald, Veritech Corp, 80 Denslow Rd, East Longmeadow, MA 01028 *Tel:* 413-525-3368 *Toll Free Tel:* 800-525-5912 *Fax:* 413-525-7449 *E-mail:* info@veritechmedia.com *Web Site:* www.veritechmedia.com, pg 1053

West, Garry, Green Linnet Records, 916 19 Ave S, Nashville, TN 37212 *Tel:* 615-320-7672 *Toll Free Tel:* 800-468-6644 *Fax:* 615-320-7378 *E-mail:* info@compassrecords.com *Web Site:* greenlinnet.com; www.compassrecords.com, pg 882

West, Jo-Ann, Producers Guild of America Inc (PGA), 8530 Wilshire Blvd, Suite 400, Beverly Hills, CA 90211 *Tel:* 310-358-9020 *E-mail:* info@producersguild.org *Web Site:* www.producersguild.org, pg 1087

West, Judith, AudioTransitions, 6429 N Talman Ave, Chicago, IL 60645 *Tel:* 773-338-8813 *Fax:* 773-338-8813 *Web Site:* www.judithwest.com, pg 796

West, Kim, Simco-Ion, 2257 N Penn Rd, Hatfield, PA 19440 *Tel:* 215-822-6401 *Toll Free Tel:* 800-203-3419 *Fax:* 215-822-3795 *E-mail:* customerservice@simco-ion.com *Web Site:* www.simco-ion.com, pg 1011

West, Sue, Gabriel Awards, 1645 Brook Lynn Dr, Suite 2, Dayton, OH 45432-1944 *Tel:* 937-458-0265 *Fax:* 937-458-0263 *E-mail:* admin@catholicacademy.org *Web Site:* www.catholicacademy.org; www.gabrielawards.com, pg 1115

West, Tyler, Barco Inc, 3059 Premiere Pkwy, Suite 400, Duluth, GA 30097 *Tel:* 916-859-2500; 678-475-8000 *Toll Free Tel:* 888-414-7226 *E-mail:* sales.events.us@barco.com *Web Site:* www.barco.com, pg 803

West-Snipes, Serena, L'AIR International, 117 Vacek St, Fort Worth, TX 76107 *Tel:* 817-237-9390 *Toll Free Tel:* 844-243-8574 *Fax:* 817-237-9407 *E-mail:* info@lairfloors.com *Web Site:* www.lairfloors.com, pg 914

Westerman, Chris, Horizon Film + Video Productions, 808 E 34 St, Austin, TX 78705 *Tel:* 512-459-3100 *Toll Free Tel:* 800-540-2785 *Fax:* 512-459-3477 *Web Site:* www.horizonvideo.com, pg 891

Westmorland, Stuart, Stuart Westmorland Photography, 14128 11 Dr SE, Mill Creek, WA 98012 *Tel:* 425-225-5733 *Fax:* 425-225-5733 *E-mail:* info@stuartwestmorland.com *Web Site:* stuartwestmorland.com, pg 1064

Weston, Brian, EDCOR Electronics Corp, 7130 National Parks Hwy, Carlsbad, NM 88220 *Tel:* 575-887-6790 *Toll Free Tel:* 800-854-0259 *Fax:* 575-887-6880 *E-mail:* sales@edcorusa.com *Web Site:* www.edcorusa.com, pg 856

Weston, Greg, National Student Production Awards, Hershey Square Ctr, 1152 Mae St, Hummelstown, PA 17036 *Toll Free Tel:* 855-ASK-4CBI (275-4224) *Web Site:* www.askcbi.org, pg 1121

Weston, Phyllis, EDCOR Electronics Corp, 7130 National Parks Hwy, Carlsbad, NM 88220 *Tel:* 575-887-6790 *Toll Free Tel:* 800-854-0259 *Fax:* 575-887-6880 *E-mail:* sales@edcorusa.com *Web Site:* www.edcorusa.com, pg 856

Weterrings, Frans, Red Sky Studios, 184 Everett St, Allston, MA 02134 *Tel:* 617-903-3373 *E-mail:* mail@redsky-studios.com *Web Site:* redsky-studios.com, pg 993

Wetsch, Maureen, Timeless Books, Box 9, Kootenay Bay, BC V0B 1X0, Canada *Tel:* 250-227-9224 *Toll Free Tel:* 800-661-8711 *Fax:* 250-227-9494 *E-mail:* contact@timeless.org *Web Site:* www.timeless.org, pg 1040

Wetzel, Arren C, Central Lighting & Equipment Inc (CLE), 4103 E 16 St, Des Moines, IA 50313 *Tel:* 515-277-4190 *Toll Free Tel:* 877-977-4190 *Fax:* 515-277-2295 *E-mail:* info@cleproductions.com *Web Site:* www.cleproductions.com, pg 823

Wexler, B R, David Wexler & Co, 7807 E Greenway Rd, Suite 8, Scottsdale, AZ 85260-1717 *Tel:* 480-675-8888 *Fax:* 480-675-8900 *E-mail:* wexlermusic@aol.com *Web Site:* www.wexlermusic.com, pg 1064

Wexler, David, Hollywood Vaults Inc, 742 N Seward St, Hollywood, CA 90038-3504 *Tel:* 323-461-6464 *Toll Free Tel:* 800-569-5336 *Fax:* 323-461-6479 *E-mail:* vault@hollywoodvaults.com *Web Site:* www.hollywoodvaults.com, pg 890

Wexler, Julie, Hollywood Vaults Inc, 742 N Seward St, Hollywood, CA 90038-3504 *Tel:* 323-461-6464 *Toll Free Tel:* 800-569-5336 *Fax:* 323-461-6479 *E-mail:* vault@hollywoodvaults.com *Web Site:* www.hollywoodvaults.com, pg 890

Weynand, Diana, Rev Up Transmedia, 20929 Ventura Blvd, Suite 47-212, Woodland Hills, CA 91364 *Tel:* 818-995-1719 *Toll Free Tel:* 877-372-0005 *Fax:* 818-979-9599 *E-mail:* info@revuptransmedia.com *Web Site:* revuptransmedia.com, pg 995

Whang, Julie, Women Make Movies Inc, 115 W 29 St, Suite 1200, New York, NY 10001 *Tel:* 212-925-0606 *Fax:* 212-925-2052 *E-mail:* info@wmm.com *Web Site:* www.wmm.com, pg 1069

Wheat-James, Sandy, Camarillo Chamber of Commerce, 2400 E Ventura Blvd, Camarillo, CA 93010 *Tel:* 805-484-4383 *Fax:* 805-484-1395 *E-mail:* info@camarillochamber.org *Web Site:* www.camarillochamber.org, pg 1092

Wheatley, Luana, US Virgin Islands Film Promotion Office, PO Box 6400, St Thomas, VI 00804-6400 *Tel:* 340-775-1444 (ext 2243) *Fax:* 340-774-4390 *E-mail:* info@filmusvi.com *Web Site:* www.filmusvi.com, pg 1104

Wheeler, David M, Hughie's Event Production Services, 1260 E 38 St, Cleveland, OH 44114 *Tel:* 216-361-4600 *Toll Free Tel:* 800-449-4115 *Fax:* 216-361-2570 *Web Site:* www.hughies.com, pg 892

Wheelock, Martha, Ishtar Films, 12400 Moorpark St, Suite 2, Studio City, CA 91604 *Toll Free Tel:* 800-428-7136 *Fax:* 818-985-0567 *E-mail:* ishtarfilms2@sbcglobal.net *Web Site:* www.ishtarfilms.com, pg 902

Whelan, Mary Beth, Globe Photos Inc, 24 Edmore Lane S, West Islip, NY 11795 *Tel:* 631-661-3131 *Fax:* 631-321-4063 *E-mail:* info@globephotos.com *Web Site:* www.globephotos.com, pg 879

Whelan, Raymond F, Globe Photos Inc, 24 Edmore Lane S, West Islip, NY 11795 *Tel:* 631-661-3131 *Fax:* 631-321-4063 *E-mail:* info@globephotos.com *Web Site:* www.globephotos.com, pg 879

Whipple, Richard, Gordon Visual Solutions, 504 Reiman St, Buffalo, NY 14212-2250 *Tel:* 716-894-5930 *Fax:* 630-839-5930 *E-mail:* info@gordonvisualsolutions.com; service@gordonvisualsolutions.com *Web Site:* www.gordonvisualsolutions.com, pg 880

Whitaker, John, Anchor Distributors, 1030 Hunt Valley Circle, New Kensington, PA 15068 *Tel:* 724-334-7000 *Toll Free Tel:* 800-444-4484 *Fax:* 724-334-1200 *Toll Free Fax:* 800-765-1960 *E-mail:* marketing@anchordistributors.com *Web Site:* www.anchordistributors.com; www.whitakerhouse.com, pg 786

Whitaker, Robert Sr, Anchor Distributors, 1030 Hunt Valley Circle, New Kensington, PA 15068 *Tel:* 724-334-7000 *Toll Free Tel:* 800-444-4484 *Fax:* 724-334-1200 *Toll Free Fax:* 800-765-1960 *E-mail:* marketing@anchordistributors.com *Web Site:* www.anchordistributors.com; www.whitakerhouse.com, pg 786

Whitcomb, Laurel, Television Academy, 5220 Lankershim Blvd, North Hollywood, CA 91601-3109 *Tel:* 818-754-2800 *Fax:* 818-761-2827 *Web Site:* www.emmys.com, pg 1089

White, Bill, Instructional Resources Corp, 1819 Bay Ridge Ave, Annapolis, MD 21403 *Tel:* 410-263-0025 *Toll Free Tel:* 800-922-1711 *Fax:* 410-268-8320 *Web Site:* www.historypictures.com, pg 899

White, David, Screen Actors Guild & American Federation of Television & Radio Artists (SAG-AFTRA), 5757 Wilshire Blvd, 7th fl, Los Angeles, CA 90036-3600 *Tel:* 323-954-1600 (former SAG); 323-634-8100 (former AFTRA) *Toll Free Tel:* 855-SAG-AFTRA (724-2387) *Fax:* 323-634-8194 *E-mail:* sagaftrainfo@sagaftra.org *Web Site:* www.sagaftra.org/ny, pg 1088

White, Ellie, Ann Arbor Film Festival, 217 N First St, Ann Arbor, MI 48104 *Tel:* 734-995-5356 *Fax:* 734-995-5396 *E-mail:* info@aafilmfest.org *Web Site:* www.aafilmfest.org, pg 1107

White, Mr Ganga, White Lotus Foundation, 2500 San Marcos Pass, Santa Barbara, CA 93105 *Tel:* 805-964-1944 *Fax:* 805-964-9617 *E-mail:* info@whitelotus.org *Web Site:* www.whitelotus.org, pg 1065

White, Helene B, HBW Entertainment Inc, 62 Massey Place, SW, T2V 2G5 Calgary, AB T2H 2H1, Canada *Tel:* 403-228-1900 *Fax:* 403-259-3860, pg 886

White, Mark, Swank Audio Visuals, 639-E Gravois Bluffs, St Louis, MO 63026 *Tel:* 636-680-9000 *Toll Free Tel:* 877-792-6528 *Fax:* 636-680-2853 *Web Site:* www.swankav.com, pg 1029

White, Pattie, ACS Technologies, 180 N Dunbarton Dr, Florence, SC 29501 *Tel:* 843-662-1681 *Toll Free Tel:* 800-736-7425 *Fax:* 843-669-3198 *E-mail:* info@acstechnologies.com *Web Site:* www.acstechnologies.com, pg 775

White, Red, Broadview Media, 4455 W 77 St, Minneapolis, MN 55435 *Tel:* 952-835-4455; 612-280-6947 *Fax:* 952-835-0971 *E-mail:* sales@broadviewmedia.com; corporate@broadviewmedia.com *Web Site:* www.broadviewmedia.com, pg 813

White, Ruth S, Rhythms Productions (Tom Thumb Music), PO Box 786, Malibu, CA 90265-0786 *Tel:* 310-836-4678, pg 996

White, Sara, Associated Press Television News, 450 W 33 St, New York, NY 10001 *Tel:* 212-621-1500 *Fax:* 212-621-7419 *Web Site:* www.aptn.com, pg 792

White, Sharon, WhisperRoom™ Inc, 116 S Sugar Hollow Rd, Morristown, TN 37813 *Tel:* 423-585-5827 *Toll Free Tel:* 800-200-8168 *Fax:* 423-585-5831 *E-mail:* info@whisperroom.com *Web Site:* www.whisperroom.com, pg 1065

Whiteman, Michael E, Morefield Communications Inc, 35 N 35 St, Camp Hill, PA 17011-2707 *Tel:* 717-761-6170 *Toll Free Tel:* 800-382-1266 *E-mail:* info@morefield.com *Web Site:* www.morefield.com, pg 946

Whiteside, Joe, Hoppmann Audio Visual, 4170 Lafayette Center Dr, Suite 100, Chantilly, VA 20151-1255 *Tel:* 703-502-4080 *Toll Free Tel:* 800-220-3038 *Fax:* 703-222-0038 *E-mail:* info@hoppmann-av.com; sales@hoppmann-av.com *Web Site:* www.hoppmann-av.net, pg 891

Whiting, Amanda, Clark Wire & Cable, 408 Washington Blvd, Mundelein, IL 60060-3102 *Tel:* 847-949-9944 *Toll Free Tel:* 800-222-5348 *Fax:* 847-949-9595 *E-mail:* sales@clarkwire.com *Web Site:* www.clarkwire.com, pg 829

Whitley, Alisha, Raincoast Books, 2440 Viking Way, Richmond, BC V6V 1N2, Canada *Tel:* 604-323-7100 *Toll Free Tel:* 800-663-5714 (cust serv & book orders) *Fax:* 604-270-7161 *Toll Free Fax:* 800-565-3770 (cust serv & book orders) *E-mail:* info@raincoast.com; customerservice@raincoast.com *Web Site:* www.raincoast.com, pg 991

Whitlock, Bill, Jensen Transformers Inc, 9304 Deering Ave, Chatsworth, CA 91311 *Tel:* 818-374-5857 *Toll Free Tel:* 866-476-6291 *Fax:* 818-374-5856 *E-mail:* sales@jensen-transformers.com *Web Site:* www.jensen-transformers.com, pg 905

Whitlock, John, The Whitlock Group, 12820 West Creek Pkwy, Richmond, VA 23238 *Tel:* 804-273-9100 *Toll Free Tel:* 800-726-9843 *Fax:* 804-273-9380 *E-mail:* information@whitlock.com *Web Site:* www.whitlock.com, pg 1065

Whitlock, William, WTL Productions, 345 E 52 St, Suite 1, New York, NY 10022 *Tel:* 212-355-1893 *E-mail:* wtlvideo@aol.com, pg 1071

Whitman, Meg, Hewlett-Packard Co, 3000 Hanover St, Palo Alto, CA 94304-1185 *Tel:* 650-857-1501 *Toll Free Tel:* 800-752-0900 *Fax:* 650-857-5518 *Web Site:* www.hp.com, pg 888

Whitmire, Dewey, American Society of Safety Engineers (ASSE), 1800 E Oakton St, Des Plaines, IL 60018 *Tel:* 847-699-2929 *E-mail:* customerservice@asse.org *Web Site:* www.asse.org, pg 1077

Whitney, Jeffrey, Kenexa, 650 E Swedesford Rd, 2nd fl, Wayne, PA 19087 *Tel:* 407-548-1444 *Fax:* 610-971-9181 *E-mail:* kenexa_learn_sales@kenexa.com *Web Site:* www.outstart.com, pg 909

Whitney, Jim, Western Connecticut Convention & Visitors Bureau, PO Box 968, Litchfield, CT 06759-0968 *Tel:* 860-567-4506 *Toll Free Tel:* 800-663-1273 *Fax:* 860-567-5214 *E-mail:* info@litchfieldhills.com *Web Site:* www.visitwesternct.com; www.litchfieldhills.com; www.visitfairfieldcountyct.com, pg 1095

Whyte, Kirby, Creative Video of Washington Inc, 1410 Spring Hill Rd, Suite 100, McLean, VA 22102 *Tel:* 703-891-2620 *Fax:* 703-891-2625 *Web Site:* www.creativevideo.com, pg 839

Whyte, Peter, McIntyre Media Inc, 203-75 First St, Orangeville, ON L9W 5B6, Canada *Tel:* 519-942-9640 *Toll Free Tel:* 800-565-3036 *Fax:* 519-942-8489 *E-mail:* info@mcintyre.ca *Web Site:* www.mcintyre.ca, pg 935

Wick, Michael, Institute on Religious Life Inc, PO Box 7500, Libertyville, IL 60048-7500 *Tel:* 847-573-8975 *Fax:* 847-573-8960 *Web Site:* www.religiouslife.com, pg 899

Wickenhiser, Sister Mary Mark, Pauline Books & Media, 50 St Paul's Ave, Boston, MA 02130-3491 *Tel:* 617-522-8911 *Toll Free Tel:* 800-876-4463 (orders); 800-836-9723 (cust serv) *Fax:* 617-541-9805 *E-mail:* records@pauline.org *Web Site:* www.pauline.org, pg 970

Wicks, Erin, HarperAudio, 10 E 53 St, New York, NY 10022 *Tel:* 212-207-7000 *Toll Free Tel:* 800-242-7737 *Fax:* 212-207-2582 *Toll Free Fax:* 800-822-4090 *Web Site:* www.harpercollins.com, pg 885

Widoff, Joseph, Satellite Broadcasting & Communications Association, 1100 17 St NW, Suite 1150, Washington, DC 20036 *Tel:* 202-349-3620 *Toll Free Tel:* 800-541-5981 *Fax:* 202-349-3621 *E-mail:* info@sbca.org *Web Site:* www.sbca.com, pg 1088

Wiedman, Charles, RuffHouse LLC, 2823 Lariat Trail, Austin, TX 78734 *Tel:* 512-965-2957 *E-mail:* info@ruffhousin.com *Web Site:* www.ruffhousin.com, pg 1000

Wieland, Tim, C2 Imaging LLC, 423 W 55 St, New York, NY 10019 *Tel:* 646-557-6300 *Fax:* 646-557-6400 *Web Site:* www.vomela.com/locations/c2_imaging, pg 841

Wiener, David, Aphex LLC, PO Box 711674, Salt Lake City, UT 84171 *Tel:* 818-767-2929 *E-mail:* sales@aphex.com *Web Site:* www.aphex.com, pg 788

Wiens, Mark, Eye & I Productions, 1250 Kay Lane, Oakley, CA 94561 *Tel:* 925-625-7888 *Toll Free Tel:* 800-720-9014 *E-mail:* contact@voicecrystal.com *Web Site:* www.voicecrystal.com, pg 864

Wiersema, Roger, Polarity Post Production, 69 Green St, San Francisco, CA 94111 *Tel:* 415-421-6622 *Fax:* 415-391-4995 *E-mail:* info@polaritypost.com *Web Site:* www.polaritypost.com, pg 978

Wiesbrock, Michael, Santa Barbara International Film Festival, 1528 Chapala St, Suite 203, Santa Barbara, CA 93101 *Tel:* 805-963-0023 *Fax:* 805-962-2524 *E-mail:* generalinfo@sbfilmfestival.org *Web Site:* sbiff.org, pg 1126

Wieser, Franz, ARRI Inc, 600 N Victory Blvd, Burbank, CA 91502-1639 *Tel:* 818-841-7070 *Fax:* 818-848-4028 *E-mail:* info@arri.com *Web Site:* www.arri.com, pg 790

Wightman, David, Dow-Key Microwave Corp, 4822 McGrath St, Ventura, CA 93003 *Tel:* 805-650-0260 *Toll Free Tel:* 800-266-3695 *Fax:* 805-650-1734 *E-mail:* askdk@dowkey.com *Web Site:* www.dowkey.com, pg 851

Wignot, Jack, Mind Over Eye Inc, 2221 Rosecrans Ave, Suite 195, El Segundo, CA 90245 *Tel:* 310-396-4663 *Fax:* 310-297-9526 *E-mail:* info@mindovereye.com *Web Site:* www.mindovereye.com, pg 943

Wihtol, Arn S, Pacific International Enterprises Inc (PIE), 401 Crater Lake Ave, Suite 2, Medford, OR 97504 *Tel:* 541-779-0990 *Toll Free Tel:* 800-547-2316 *Fax:* 541-779-0880 *E-mail:* info@family-films.com *Web Site:* www.family-films.com, pg 967

Wijesuriya, Dilantha, ARC Document Solutions, 1981 N Broadway, Suite 385, Walnut Creek, CA 94596 *Tel:* 925-949-5100 *Fax:* 925-949-5101 *E-mail:* info@e-arc.com *Web Site:* www.e-arc.com, pg 789

Wiland, Ava, RAVA Films, 67 West St, Suite 604, Brooklyn, NY 11222 *Web Site:* www.ravafilms.com, pg 991

Wilbur, Adriana, Musikvergnuegen, 1545 Wilcox Ave, Suite 202, Hollywood, CA 90028 *Tel:* 323-856-5900 *Fax:* 323-856-5917 *E-mail:* info@musikv.com *Web Site:* www.musikvergnuegen.com, pg 951

Wilby, Ted, Ted The Fiddler Music, 103 S Main St, Spring City, PA 19475-1820 *Tel:* 610-948-0345 *Web Site:* www.tfiddler.com, pg 1035

Wilcox, Dwight, Wiltronix, 16850 Oakmont Ave, Washington Grove, MD 20880 *Tel:* 301-258-7676 *Toll Free Tel:* 800-848-7870 *Fax:* 301-854-3434 *E-mail:* equipsales@wiltronix.com *Web Site:* www.wiltronix.com, pg 1067

Wilcox, Peter, Beachwood Productions, 1500 Mill Creek Ct SW, Marietta, GA 30008 *Tel:* 770-432-6563; 404-324-7271 (cell) *Web Site:* www.beachwoodproductions.com, pg 804

Wilcoxen, John, PicturePhone Inc, 200 Commerce Dr, Rochester, NY 14623 *Tel:* 585-334-9040 *Toll Free Tel:* 800-521-5454 *Fax:* 585-486-1919 *E-mail:* info@picturephone.com *Web Site:* www.picturephone.com, pg 975

Wild, Katy, Freeman, 1600 Viceroy, Suite 100, Dallas, TX 75235 *Tel:* 214-445-1000 *Fax:* 214-445-0200 *Web Site:* www.freemanco.com, pg 872

Wild, Steve, RingSide Creative, 13320 Northend, Suite 3000, Oak Park, MI 48237 *Tel:* 248-548-2500 *E-mail:* info@ringsidecreative.com; newbiz@ringsidecreative.com *Web Site:* www.ringsidecreative.com, pg 997

Wilder, Thomas, Nelson White Systems Inc, 8725-A Loch Raven Blvd, Baltimore, MD 21286 *Tel:* 410-668-9628 *Toll Free Tel:* 800-296-7555 *Fax:* 410-668-9629 *E-mail:* sales@nelsonwhite.com; service@nelsonwhite.com; rentals@nelsonwhite.com *Web Site:* www.nelsonwhite.com, pg 954

Wildman, Dr Frank PhD, Feldenkrais® Movement Institute, 721 The Alameda, Berkeley, CA 94707 *Tel:* 510-527-2634 *Toll Free Tel:* 800-342-3424 *Fax:* 510-528-1332 *E-mail:* info@feldenkraisinstitute.org *Web Site:* www.feldenkraisinstitute.org, pg 866

Wilken, Jim, The Trinity Recording Studio, PO Box 1417, Corpus Christi, TX 78403 *Tel:* 361-854-7464 *E-mail:* info@trinitystudio.com *Web Site:* www.trinitystudio.com, pg 1045

Wilken, Rachel Whitefield, The Trinity Recording Studio, PO Box 1417, Corpus Christi, TX 78403 *Tel:* 361-854-7464 *E-mail:* info@trinitystudio.com *Web Site:* www.trinitystudio.com, pg 1045

Wilkerson, Dave, Right Coast Recording Inc, 349 Chestnut St, Columbia, PA 17512-1259 *Tel:* 717-681-9801 *Fax:* 717-681-9801 *E-mail:* rightcoastrecording@gmail.com *Web Site:* www.rightcoastrecording.com, pg 997

Wilkes, Dave, Novell Inc, 1800 S Novell Place, Provo, UT 84606 *Tel:* 801-861-4272 *Toll Free Tel:* 888-321-4272 (sales); 800-858-4000 (support) *E-mail:* crc@novell.com *Web Site:* www.novell.com, pg 959

Wilkes, Peter, Lions Gate Entertainment Corp, 2700 Colorado Ave, Santa Monica, CA 90404 *Tel:* 310-449-9200 *Fax:* 310-255-3870 *E-mail:* general-inquiries@lionsgate.com *Web Site:* www.lionsgate.com; corporate.lionsgate.com, pg 922

Wilkins, Carolyn, NAB Distinguished Service Award, 1771 "N" St NW, Washington, DC 20036 *Tel:* 202-429-5300 *Fax:* 202-775-3516 *E-mail:* nab@nab.org *Web Site:* www.nab.org, pg 1121

Wilkins, David, Metropolitan Audio Visual Co LLC, 2862 Hartland Rd, Falls Church, VA 22043 *Tel:* 703-834-0004 *Toll Free Tel:* 800-966-4333 *Fax:* 703-834-0866 *E-mail:* sales@metroav.com *Web Site:* www.metroav.com, pg 940

Wilkinson, Bob, One Touch Systems Inc, 2346 Bering Dr, San Jose, CA 95131 *Tel:* 408-660-8435 *Fax:* 408-436-4699 *E-mail:* info@onetouchsys.com *Web Site:* www.onetouchsys.com, pg 963

Wilkinson, Richard, ODC Nimbus Inc, 490 E Princeland Ct, Suites 3 & 4, Corona, CA 92879 *Tel:* 951-372-9800 *Fax:* 951-372-9119 *E-mail:* sales@odc-nimbus.com *Web Site:* www.optical-disc.com, pg 961

Wilkinson, Timothy, Selco Products Co, 8780 Technology Way, Reno, NV 89521-5908 *Toll Free Tel:* 877-807-5426 *Fax:* 775-674-5111 *E-mail:* sales@selcoproducts.com *Web Site:* www.selcoproducts.com, pg 1006

Wille, Cindy, DH Satellite, 600 N Marquette Rd, Prairie du Chien, WI 53821 *Tel:* 608-326-8406 *Toll Free Tel:* 800-627-9443 *Fax:* 608-326-4233 *E-mail:* dhsat@mhtc.net *Web Site:* www.dhsatellite.com, pg 846

Wille, Michelle, Marshall Furniture Inc, 999 Anita Ave, Antioch, IL 60002 *Tel:* 847-395-9350 *Fax:* 847-395-9351 *E-mail:* info@marshallfurniture.com *Web Site:* www.marshallfurniture.com, pg 932

Willemin, Christy, High End Systems Inc, 2105 Gracy Farms Lane, Austin, TX 78758 *Tel:* 512-836-2242 *Toll Free Tel:* 800-890-8989 *Fax:* 512-837-5290 *E-mail:* info@highend.com *Web Site:* www.highend.com, pg 888

William, Martin, Gateways, PO Box 1706, Ojai, CA 93024-1706 *Tel:* 805-649-5367 *Toll Free Tel:* 800-477-8908 *Fax:* 805-649-5302 *E-mail:* gwgateways@sbcglobal.net, pg 876

Williams, Bill, A Cut Above Video Productions Inc, 4450 W Eau Gallie Blvd, Suite 220, Melbourne, FL 32934 *Tel:* 321-253-5677 *Fax:* 321-253-5611 *Web Site:* www.acutabovevideo.com, pg 771

Williams, Bradford, On-Trax Inc, 3052 Vine St, Riverside, CA 92507 *Tel:* 951-786-3921 *Fax:* 951-786-3922 *Web Site:* www.on-trax.com, pg 963

Williams, Chaaz, LW Media Group, 107 W Valencia Ave, Burbank, CA 91502 *Tel:* 818-439-2989 *E-mail:* lwmgbooking@gmail.com *Web Site:* www.lwmgstudios.com, pg 926

Williams, Darnell, Elektrashock, 1320 Main St, Venice, CA 90291 *Tel:* 310-399-4985 *Fax:* 310-399-4972 *E-mail:* info@elektrashock.com *Web Site:* www.elektrashock.com, pg 859

Williams, Glenn, Citizens Systems America Corp, 363 Van Ness Way, Suite 404, Torrance, CA 90501 *Tel:* 310-781-1460 *Toll Free Tel:* 800-421-6516 *Fax:* 310-781-9152 *Web Site:* www.citizen-systems.com, pg 828

Williams, Jackie, National Council of Acoustical Consultants (NCAC), 9100 Purdue Rd, Suite 200, Indianapolis, IN 46268 *Tel:* 317-328-0642 *Fax:* 317-328-4629 *E-mail:* info@ncac.com *Web Site:* www.ncac.com, pg 1085

Williams, Jacob, Refinery, 16 W 46 St, 12th fl, New York, NY 10036 *Tel:* 212-391-8166 *Fax:* 212-391-8783 *Web Site:* refinerynyc.com, pg 994

Williams, Jeff, CBM Metal, High Point Business Park, 8750 Holgate Cresent, Milton, ON L9T 0K3, Canada *Tel:* 905-878-0648 *Toll Free Tel:* 800-387-

4834 *Fax:* 905-878-6748 *Toll Free Fax:* 888-554-5501 *E-mail:* sales@cbmmetal.com *Web Site:* www.cbmmetal.com, pg 821

Williams, Jim, Audio Upgrades, 6982 Mimosa Dr, Carlsbad, CA 92011 *Tel:* 818-780-1222 *Web Site:* www.audioupgrades.com, pg 795

Williams, Larry J, Wireworks Corp, 380 Hillside Ave, Hillside, NJ 07205 *Tel:* 908-686-7400 *Toll Free Tel:* 800-642-9473 *Fax:* 908-686-0483 *E-mail:* sales@wireworks.com; info@wireworks.com *Web Site:* www.wireworks.com, pg 1068

Williams, Lisa, The RapcoHorizon Co, 3581 Larch Lane, Jackson, MO 63755 *Tel:* 573-243-1433 *Toll Free Tel:* 800-325-0266 *Fax:* 573-243-4913 *E-mail:* info@rapcohorizon.com *Web Site:* www.rapcohorizon.com, pg 991

Williams, Marilyn, Richmond Sound Design Ltd, 5264 Ross St, Vancouver, BC V5W 3K7, Canada *Web Site:* www.richmondsounddesign.com, pg 996

Williams, Marvin, Manhattan Center Studios Inc, 311 W 34 St, New York, NY 10001 *Tel:* 212-279-7740 *Fax:* 212-564-1072 *E-mail:* info@mcstudios.com *Web Site:* www.mcstudios.com, pg 930

Williams, Matt, BMI Supply, 571 Queensbury Ave, Queensbury, NY 12804 *Tel:* 518-793-6706 *Toll Free Tel:* 800-836-0524 *Fax:* 518-793-6181 *E-mail:* bminy@bmisupply.com *Web Site:* www.bmisupply.com, pg 810

Williams, Michael, McBain Audio Visual Ltd, 10805 107 Ave, Edmonton, AB T5H 0W9, Canada *Tel:* 780-420-0404 *Toll Free Tel:* 800-661-6980 *Fax:* 780-421-1188 *Web Site:* www.mcbaincamera.com, pg 935

Williams, Roger, Image Media Farm, 1090 E Georgia St, Vancouver, BC V6A 2A7, Canada *Tel:* 604-874-7513 *Toll Free Tel:* 800-352-1454 (prodn rentals); 800-567-0037 (equip rentals) *Fax:* 604-874-7516 *E-mail:* info@imagemediafarm.com *Web Site:* www.imagemediafarm.com, pg 895

Williams, Scott, Quince Imaging Inc, 2810 Towerview Rd, Herndon, VA 20171-3206 *Tel:* 703-742-7520 *Toll Free Tel:* 888-252-4960 *Fax:* 703-742-7586 *E-mail:* info@quinceimaging.com; sales@quinceimaging.com; operations@quinceimaging.com *Web Site:* www.quinceimaging.com, pg 989

Williams, Ted C, Professional Marketing Services Inc, 105 S Southgate Dr, Chandler, AZ 85226 *Tel:* 480-940-5400 *Fax:* 480-940-5488 *E-mail:* pmsi@promarketinc.com *Web Site:* www.promarketinc.com, pg 985

Williams, Tony, Midwest Uplink Inc, 911 N East St, Indianapolis, IN 46202 *Tel:* 317-423-8684 *Toll Free Tel:* 866-886-6247 *Fax:* 317-423-3061 *Web Site:* midwestuplink.com, pg 942

Williams, Tonya Lee, ReelWorld Film Festival, 438 Parliament St, Suite 300, Toronto, ON M5A 3A2, Canada *Tel:* 416-598-7933 *E-mail:* info@reelworld.ca; events@reelworld.ca *Web Site:* www.reelworld.ca, pg 1125

Williams, Vivian T, Voyager Recordings & Publications, 424 35 Ave, Seattle, WA 98122 *Tel:* 206-323-1112 *E-mail:* info@voyagerrecords.com *Web Site:* www.voyagerrecords.com, pg 1060

Williams, Wayne E, Telect Inc, 23321 E Knox Ave, Liberty Lake, WA 99019 *Tel:* 509-926-6000 *Toll Free Tel:* 800-551-4567 *E-mail:* getinfo@telect.com *Web Site:* www.telect.com, pg 1036

Williams, William, Aliso Creek Productions Inc, 4106 W Burbank Blvd, Burbank, CA 91510 *Tel:* 818-954-9931 *Web Site:* www.alisocreek.net, pg 780

Williamson, Kent, National Council of Teachers of English (NCTE), 1111 W Kenyon Rd, Urbana, IL 61801-1096 *Tel:* 217-328-3870 *Toll Free Tel:* 877-369-6283 *Fax:* 217-328-9645 *Web Site:* www.ncte.org, pg 1086

Willis, Dr Aaron, Health Education Services, 10200 Jefferson Blvd, Culver City, CA 90232 *Tel:* 310-839-2436 *Toll Free Tel:* 800-421-4246 *Fax:* 310-839-2249 *Toll Free Fax:* 800-944-5432 *E-mail:* access@socialstudies.com *Web Site:* www.socialstudies.com, pg 887

Willis, Barry, University of Idaho Engineering Outreach, 875 Perimeter Dr MS 1014, Moscow, ID 83844-1014 *Tel:* 208-885-6373 *Toll Free Tel:* 800-824-2889 *Fax:* 208-885-9249 *E-mail:* outreach@uidaho.edu *Web Site:* eo.uidaho.edu, pg 1049

Willis, Katherine, RuffHouse LLC, 2823 Lariat Trail, Austin, TX 78734 *Tel:* 512-965-2957 *E-mail:* info@ruffhousin.com *Web Site:* www.ruffhousin.com, pg 1000

Willson, Frank, BSW Records, PO Box 2297, Universal City, TX 78148-1297 *Tel:* 210-653-3989 *Fax:* 210-653-3989 *E-mail:* bswr18@att.net *Web Site:* www.bsw-records.com, pg 814

Willson, Regina, BSW Records, PO Box 2297, Universal City, TX 78148-1297 *Tel:* 210-653-3989 *Fax:* 210-653-3989 *E-mail:* bswr18@att.net *Web Site:* www.bsw-records.com, pg 814

Wilson, Abbie, P&P Studios Inc, 110 Lenox Ave, Suite 210, Stamford, CT 06906 *Tel:* 203-359-9292 *Toll Free Tel:* 888-WEPRODUCE (937-7638) *E-mail:* ppstudios@weproduce.com *Web Site:* www.weproduce.com, pg 968

Wilson, Andrew, Electronic Arts, 209 Redwood Shores Pkwy, Redwood City, CA 94065 *Tel:* 650-628-1500 *Web Site:* www.ea.com, pg 859

Wilson, Charles, Agency for Instructional Technology (AIT), 8111 N Lee Paul Rd, Bloomington, IN 47404-7916 *Tel:* 812-339-2203 *Toll Free Tel:* 800-457-4509 *Fax:* 812-333-4218 *E-mail:* info@ait.net *Web Site:* www.ait.net, pg 778, 1075

Wilson, Christopher, Moving Pictures, 655-H Pressley Rd, Charlotte, NC 28217 *Tel:* 704-676-0868 *Fax:* 704-676-0813 *E-mail:* info@mpicts.com *Web Site:* www.mpicts.com, pg 948

Wilson, Chuck, National Systems Contractors Association (NSCA), 3950 River Ridge Dr NE, Cedar Rapids, IA 52402 *Tel:* 319-366-6722 *Toll Free Tel:* 800-446-6722 *Fax:* 319-366-4164 *E-mail:* nsca@nsca.org *Web Site:* www.nsca.org, pg 1086

Wilson, Chuck, Studio 637, 637 Cypress Ave, Hermosa Beach, CA 90254 *Tel:* 310-372-8218 *Web Site:* studio-637.com, pg 1027

Wilson, Dave, MISCO, 2637 32 Ave S, Minneapolis, MN 55406-1641 *Tel:* 612-825-1010 *Toll Free Tel:* 800-276-9955 *Fax:* 612-825-7010 *E-mail:* info@miscospeakers.com *Web Site:* www.miscospeakers.com, pg 944

Wilson, Debbie, Power Integrity Corporation, PO Box 9682, Greensboro, NC 27429-0682 *Tel:* 336-379-9773 *Toll Free Tel:* 800-237-6260 (tech support) *E-mail:* info@powerintegritycorp.com *Web Site:* www.powerintegritycorp.com, pg 979

Wilson, Donna, MeshTel-Intelite, PO Box 747, Genoa, NV 89411 *Tel:* 775-267-5959 *Fax:* 775-267-5958 *E-mail:* info@meshtel.com *Web Site:* www.meshtel.com, pg 939

Wilson, Jim, National Undergraduate Student Electronic Media Competition, PO Box 4206, Chesterfield, MO 63006 *Tel:* 636-536-1943 *Fax:* 636-898-6920 *E-mail:* national-office@nbs-aerho.org *Web Site:* www.nbs-aerho.org, pg 1121

Wilson, Jon, WoodenBoat Publications, 41 WoodenBoat Lane, Brooklin, ME 04616 *Tel:* 207-359-4651 *Toll Free Tel:* 800-877-5284 (subns); 800-487-2084 (subns) *Fax:* 207-359-8920; 818-487-4550 (subns) *E-mail:* woodenboat@woodenboat.com *Web Site:* www.woodenboat.com, pg 1069

Wilson, Ken, Sportsmen on Film Inc, 231 Earl Garrett, Suite 300, Kerrville, TX 78028 *Tel:* 830-792-4200 *Toll Free Tel:* 800-910-HUNT (910-4868) *Fax:* 830-792-4224 *Web Site:* www.sportsmenonfilm.com, pg 1022

Wilson, Laura, Macmillan Audio, 175 Fifth Ave, New York, NY 10010 *Tel:* 646-600-7856; 646-307-5742 *Toll Free Tel:* 888-330-8477 (orders); 800-221-7945 *Toll Free Fax:* 800-672-7703 (orders) *E-mail:* macmillan.audio@macmillanusa.com *Web Site:* us.macmillan.com/audio.aspx, pg 927

Wilson, Lynn, Photographers' Formulary Inc, 7079 Hwy 83 N, Condon, MT 59826 *Tel:* 406-754-2891 *Toll Free Tel:* 800-922-5255 *Fax:* 406-754-2896 *E-mail:* formulary@blackfoot.net *Web Site:* www.photoformulary.com, pg 975

Wilson, Nandy, Slamdance Film Festival, 5634 Melrose Ave, Los Angeles, CA 90038 *Tel:* 323-466-1786 *Fax:* 323-466-1784 *E-mail:* submissions@slamdance.com *Web Site:* www.slamdance.com, pg 1127

Wilson, Robert F, Wilson McLeran Inc, 41 Corey Hill Rd, Saxtons River, VT 05154 *Tel:* 802-869-3111 *Toll Free Tel:* 800-562-9646 *Fax:* 802-869-3111 *Web Site:* www.job-bridge.com, pg 1067

Wilson, Sharon, Ontario Media Development Corp, South Tower, Suite 501, 175 Bloor St E, Toronto, ON M4W 3R8, Canada *Tel:* 416-314-6858 *Fax:* 416-314-6876 *E-mail:* reception@omdc.on.ca *Web Site:* www.omdc.on.ca, pg 1105

Wilson, Tom, Duke Media Services, 0052 Bryan Ctr, Durham, NC 27708 *Tel:* 919-660-1740 *Fax:* 919-660-1719 *Web Site:* sites.duke.edu/mediaservices, pg 853

Wilson, William "Bud" G, Photographers' Formulary Inc, 7079 Hwy 83 N, Condon, MT 59826 *Tel:* 406-754-2891 *Toll Free Tel:* 800-922-5255 *Fax:* 406-754-2896 *E-mail:* formulary@blackfoot.net *Web Site:* www.photoformulary.com, pg 975

Winberg, Wynn, Aries Productions, 1110 Avenue "H" E, Suite 200, Arlington, TX 76011 *Tel:* 817-640-9955; 817-300-5255 (cell) *Fax:* 817-649-2529 *E-mail:* inform@aries-prods.com *Web Site:* www.aries-prods.com, pg 789

Winchowky, Larry, Christie Lites, 6990 Lake Ellenor Dr, Orlando, FL 32809 *Tel:* 407-856-0016 *Fax:* 407-856-0765 *Web Site:* www.christielites.com, pg 825

Winey, Mark, Magnepan Inc, 1645 Ninth St, White Bear Lake, MN 55110 *Tel:* 651-426-1645 *Toll Free Tel:* 800-474-1646 *Fax:* 651-426-0441 *Web Site:* www.magnepan.com, pg 928

Winkelman, Babe, Babe Winkelman Productions Inc, 7119 Forthun Rd S, Baxter, MN 56425 *Tel:* 218-822-4424 *Toll Free Tel:* 800-333-0471 *Fax:* 218-822-7436 *Web Site:* www.winkelman.com, pg 1068

Winkelmann, Rich, Gettysburg Bluegrass Festival, 3340 Fairfield Rd, Gettysburg, PA 17325 *Tel:* 717-642-8749 *E-mail:* bluegrass@granitehillcampingresort.com *Web Site:* www.gettysburgbluegrass.com, pg 1115

Winkler, Jeff, American Audio Visual Center, 7434 E Monte Cristo Ave, Scottsdale, AZ 85260 *Tel:* 480-596-9880 *Fax:* 480-596-0942 *Web Site:* www.americanavc.com, pg 783

Winn, Kate, A&E Home Video, 235 E 45 St, New York, NY 10017 *Tel:* 212-210-1400 *Toll Free Tel:* 877-447-4253 *Fax:* 212-907-9418 *Web Site:* www.aetv.com, pg 771

Winship, Chad, Advanced Lighting & Production Services Inc (ALPS), 65 Teed Dr, Randolph, MA 02368 *Tel:* 781-961-3066 *Toll Free Tel:* 866-961-3066 *Fax:* 781-961-3256 *E-mail:* info@alpsweb.com *Web Site:* www.alpsweb.com, pg 777

Winter, Don, Winter Productions, 10625 S Hoyne, Chicago, IL 60643 *E-mail:* winterpr@aol.com *Web Site:* www.winterproductions.com, pg 1068

Winter, Greg, Blue 60 Pictures, 555 First Ave NE, Suite 200, Minneapolis, MN 55413 *Tel:* 612-871-6800 *E-mail:* info@blue-60.com *Web Site:* www.blue-60.com, pg 810

Winter, Lucinda, Minnesota Film & TV, 401 N Third St, Suite 245, Minneapolis, MN 55401 *Tel:* 612-767-0095 *Fax:* 612-767-2425 *Web Site:* www.mnfilmtv.org, pg 1098

Winterhalter, Andrea, QCA, 2832 Spring Grove Ave, Cincinnati, OH 45225 *Tel:* 513-681-8400 *Toll Free Tel:* 800-859-8401 *E-mail:* info@go-qca.com *Web Site:* www.go-qca.com, pg 988

Winters, Greg, Kino Mountain Productions LLC, 307 S Salem St, No 311, Apex, NC 27502 *Tel:* 919-210-1379 *Web Site:* www.kinomountain.com, pg 911

Winters, Walt, ImageWorks Communications, 10155 High Point Lane, Suite 100, Sandy, UT 84092 *Tel:* 801-231-7234 (cell) *Web Site:* www.imageworkscommunications.com, pg 896

Winton, Peggy, Association for Information and Image Management (AIIM), 1100 Wayne Ave, Suite 1100, Silver Spring, MD 20910 *Tel:* 301-587-8202 *Toll Free Tel:* 800-477-2446 *Fax:* 301-587-2711 *E-mail:* aiim@aiim.org *Web Site:* www.aiim.org, pg 1078

Wiott, Kevin, RGB Technology Inc, 590 Herndon Pkwy, Suite 500, Herndon, VA 20170-5267 *Tel:* 703-834-1500 *Fax:* 703-834-1506 *Web Site:* www.rgbtec.com, pg 996

Wirt, Kathleen, 4th Street Recording, 1211 Fourth St, Santa Monica, CA 90401 *Tel:* 310-395-9114 *E-mail:* info@4thstreetrecording.com *Web Site:* www.4thstreetrecording.com, pg 872

Wischmeyer, Jim, Bag End Loudspeakers, 1201 Armstrong St, Algonquin, IL 60102 *Tel:* 847-658-8888 *Fax:* 847-658-5008 *E-mail:* info@bagend.com; usedcars@bagend.com (sales) *Web Site:* www.bagend.com, pg 801

Wise, Pamela, Rebirth/Wenha Records, 81 Chandler St, Detroit, MI 48202 *Tel:* 313-875-0289, pg 993

Wise, Tomas, Music Sales Corp, 180 Madison Ave, 24th fl, New York, NY 10016 *Tel:* 212-254-2100 *Fax:* 212-254-2013 *E-mail:* info@musicsales.com *Web Site:* www.musicsales.com, pg 951

Wiseman, Todd Jr, Hayden 5 Media LLC, 22 W 27 St, 6th fl, New York, NY 10001 *Tel:* 212-871-9316 *E-mail:* info@hayden5.com *Web Site:* www.hayden5.com, pg 886

Wiser, Brian, Bosch Security Systems North America, 130 Perinton Pkwy, Fairport, NY 14450 *Tel:* 585-223-4060 *Toll Free Tel:* 800-289-0096 *Fax:* 585-223-9180 *Web Site:* us.boschsecurity.com, pg 811

Wishman, Seymour, First Run Features, The Film Center Bldg, Suite 1213, 630 Ninth Ave, New York, NY 10036-3708 *Tel:* 212-243-0600 *Fax:* 212-989-7649 *E-mail:* info@firstrunfeatures.com *Web Site:* www.firstrunfeatures.com, pg 869

Wislen, William, Pro Image, 1716 Terrace Ave, Snohomish, WA 98290 *Tel:* 206-284-5000 *Toll Free Tel:* 888-284-6400, pg 983

Wislocki, Stash, Mountainfilm in Telluride, 109 E Colorado Ave, Suite 1, Telluride, CO 81435 *Tel:* 970-728-4123 *Fax:* 970-728-6458 *E-mail:* contact@mountainfilm.org *Web Site:* www.mountainfilm.org, pg 1121

Witcher, Brenna, Marsh Media, 200 Avila Circle, Kansas City, MO 64114 *Tel:* 816-523-1059 *Toll Free Tel:* 800-821-3303 *Fax:* 816-333-7421 *Toll Free Fax:* 866-333-7421 *E-mail:* order@marshmedia.com; info@marshmedia.com *Web Site:* www.marshmedia.com, pg 931

Witcher, Dan, Marsh Media, 200 Avila Circle, Kansas City, MO 64114 *Tel:* 816-523-1059 *Toll Free Tel:* 800-821-3303 *Fax:* 816-333-7421 *Toll Free Fax:* 866-333-7421 *E-mail:* order@marshmedia.com; info@marshmedia.com *Web Site:* www.marshmedia.com, pg 931

Withers, Gary, EiKO Ltd, 23220 W 84 St, Shawnee Mission, KS 66227 *Tel:* 913-441-8500 *Toll Free Tel:* 800-852-2217 *Fax:* 913-441-6679 *E-mail:* eiko@eiko.com *Web Site:* www.eiko-ltd.com, pg 858

Withey, Brit, Denver Film Society, 1510 York St, 3rd fl, Denver, CO 80206 *Tel:* 303-595-3456 *Fax:* 303-595-0956 *E-mail:* info@denverfilm.org *Web Site:* www.denverfilm.org, pg 1081

Withey, Brit, Starz Denver Film Festival, 1510 York St, 3rd fl, Denver, CO 80206 *Tel:* 303-595-3456 *Fax:* 303-595-0956 *E-mail:* info@denverfilm.org *Web Site:* www.denverfilm.org/festival, pg 1127

Witmer, Melinda C, Time Warner Cable, 60 Columbus Circle, 17th fl, New York, NY 10023 *Tel:* 212-364-8200 *Web Site:* www.timewarnercable.com, pg 1040

Witsoe, Craig, Elo TouchSystems, 1033 McCarthy Blvd, Milpitas, CA 95035 *Toll Free Tel:* 800-356-8682; 800-557-1458 *Fax:* 650-361-4722 *E-mail:* eloinfo@elotouch.com; customerservice@elotouch.com *Web Site:* www.elotouch.com, pg 859

Witte, Steve, Wavemaker Media Design, PO Box 226, Duncans Mills, CA 95430 *Tel:* 707-788-6040 *Fax:* 707-788-6040 *E-mail:* sales@wavemakermediadesign.com *Web Site:* www.wavemakermediadesign.com, pg 1062

Wiwchar, Corey, Thompson Rivers University Open Learning, BC Centre for Open Learning, 4th fl, 900 McGill Rd, Kamloops, BC V2C 0C8, Canada *Tel:* 250-852-7000 *Toll Free Tel:* 800-663-9711 *E-mail:* student@tru.ca; olmarketing@tru.ca *Web Site:* www.tru.ca/distance, pg 1039

Woessner, Steve, Brilliance Audio, 1704 Eaton Dr, Grand Haven, MI 49417 *Tel:* 616-846-5256 *Toll Free Tel:* 800-648-2312 (orders) *Fax:* 616-846-0630 *E-mail:* customerservice@brillianceaudio.com *Web Site:* www.brillianceaudio.com, pg 812

Wogsberg, Eric, Jupiter Systems, 31015 Huntwood Ave, Hayward, CA 94544 *Tel:* 510-675-1000 *Fax:* 510-675-1001 *E-mail:* sales@jupiter.com *Web Site:* www.jupiter.com, pg 907

Wohlmut, Thomas A, WMS Media Inc, 555 Bryant St, Suite 361, Palo Alto, CA 94301 *Toll Free Tel:* 800-487-1073 *Fax:* 510-796-0924 *E-mail:* info@wmsmedia.com *Web Site:* www.wmsmedia.com, pg 1069

Wojcich, Joe, Tempe Camera, 606 W University, Tempe, AZ 85281 *Tel:* 480-966-6954 *Toll Free Tel:* 800-836-7374 *E-mail:* rent@tempecamera.com; sales@tempecamera.com *Web Site:* www.tempecamera.biz, pg 1037

Wojdyla, Cindy, The Pepper Group, 220 N Smith St, Suite 406, Palatine, IL 60067 *Tel:* 847-963-0333 *Fax:* 847-963-0888 *E-mail:* pepper@peppergroup.com *Web Site:* www.peppergroup.com, pg 973

Wolavka, Bill, Research Technology International (RTI), 4700 Chase Ave, Lincolnwood, IL 60712-1689 *Tel:* 847-677-3000 *Toll Free Tel:* 800-323-7520 *Fax:* 847-677-1311 *Toll Free Fax:* 800-784-6733 *E-mail:* sales@rtico.com *Web Site:* www.rtico.com, pg 995

Wolf, Daniel, Videobotics, 220 N Palisade Dr, Santa Maria, CA 93454 *Tel:* 805-349-1104 *E-mail:* videobotics@megagem.com; megagem@megagem.com *Web Site:* www.videobotics.com; camrobot.com, pg 1056

Wolf, David, Herman Pro AV, 10110 USA Today Way, Miramar, FL 33025 *Tel:* 305-477-0063 *Toll Free Tel:* 888-736-6888 *Fax:* 305-392-3377 *E-mail:* sales@hermanproav.com; info@hermanproav.com *Web Site:* www.hermanproav.com, pg 888

Wolf, Jeffrey, Herman Pro AV, 10110 USA Today Way, Miramar, FL 33025 *Tel:* 305-477-0063 *Toll Free Tel:* 888-736-6888 *Fax:* 305-392-3377 *E-mail:* sales@hermanproav.com; info@hermanproav.com *Web Site:* www.hermanproav.com, pg 888

Wolf, Joe, JoeAudio, 10850 John Galt Blvd, Omaha, NE 68137 *Tel:* 402-341-9153 *Toll Free Tel:* 866-JOE-AUDIO (563-2834) *Web Site:* www.joeaudioproductions.com, pg 905

Wolf, Jonathan, Independent Film & Television Alliance® (IFTA), 10850 Wilshire Blvd, 9th fl, Los Angeles, CA 90024-4311 *Tel:* 310-446-1000 *Fax:* 310-446-1600 *E-mail:* info@ifta-online.org *Web Site:* www.ifta-online.org, pg 1083

Wolf, Joseph, WolfVision Inc, 1601 Bayshore Hwy, Suite 168, Burlingame, CA 94010 *Tel:* 650-648-0002 *Toll Free Tel:* 800-356-9653 *Fax:* 650-648-0009 *E-mail:* sales@wolfvision.us; support@wolfvision.us *Web Site:* www.wolfvision.com, pg 1069

Wolf, Phil, Trio Video, 915 Sherwood Dr, Lake Bluff, IL 60044 *Tel:* 312-421-7060 *Fax:* 312-421-0361 *Web Site:* www.triovideo.com, pg 1045

Wolf, Steve, Theatrical Services Inc, 128 S Washington St, Wichita, KS 67202 *Tel:* 316-263-4415 *Toll Free Tel:* 888-874-2649 *Fax:* 316-263-9927 *Web Site:* www.theatricalservices.com, pg 1038

Wolfe, Bob, Starlite Productions, 9 Whittendale Dr, Moorestown, NJ 08057 *Tel:* 856-780-8000 *Toll Free Tel:* 800-738-7400 *Fax:* 856-780-8001 *E-mail:* info@starlite.com *Web Site:* www.starlite.com, pg 1024

Wolfe, Gianna, Radiant Images, 4125 W Jefferson Blvd, Los Angeles, CA 90016 *Tel:* 323-737-1314 *Fax:* 310-861-0163 *E-mail:* info@radiantimages.com *Web Site:* www.radiantimages.com, pg 990

Wolfenberg, Todd, Himalayan Institute Audio/Video, 952 Bethany Tpke, Honesdale, PA 18431 *Tel:* 570-253-5551 *Toll Free Tel:* 800-822-4547 *Fax:* 570-253-9078 *E-mail:* info@himalayaninstitute.org *Web Site:* www.himalayaninstitute.org, pg 889

Wolff, Liz, Dance on Camera Festival, 252 Java St, Suite 333, Brooklyn, NY 11222 *Tel:* 347-505-8649 *E-mail:* info@dancefilms.org *Web Site:* www.dancefilms.org, pg 1113

Wolfrum, Edward J, Audio Graphic Services, 1516 Ferris Ave, Royal Oak, MI 48067 *Tel:* 248-544-1793 *E-mail:* netmail@audiographicservices.com *Web Site:* www.audiographicservices.com, pg 794

Wolfrum, Susan E, Audio Graphic Services, 1516 Ferris Ave, Royal Oak, MI 48067 *Tel:* 248-544-1793 *E-mail:* netmail@audiographicservices.com *Web Site:* www.audiographicservices.com, pg 794

Wolin, Dave, Madera County Film Commission, PO Box 3690, Oakhurst, CA 93644 *Tel:* 559-760-1143 *Fax:* 559-658-2851 *Web Site:* www.yosemite-sierra.com; www.filmcalifornia.com/yosemite.html, pg 1093

Wolpert, Raymond, Union Connector Co Inc, 8182 Baymeadow Way W, Jacksonville, FL 32256 *Tel:* 631-753-9550 *Fax:* 631-753-9560 *E-mail:* sales@unionconnector.com *Web Site:* www.unionconnector.com, pg 1048

Wong, Gloria, Tripp Lite, 1111 W 35 St, Chicago, IL 60609 *Tel:* 773-869-1111; 773-869-1234 *Fax:* 773-869-1935 *E-mail:* av@tripplite.com *Web Site:* www.tripplite.com, pg 1045

Wong, Henry, Banff World Media Festival, 102 Boulder Crescent, Suite 202, Canmore, AB T1W 1L2, Canada *Tel:* 403-678-1216 *Toll Free Tel:* 888-287-2279 *Fax:* 403-678-3357 *E-mail:* info@achillesmedia.com *Web Site:* banffmediafestival.com, pg 1109

Wong, Henry, Rockie Awards, 21 St Clair Ave E, Suite 700, Toronto, ON M4T 1L9, Canada *Tel:* 416-921-3171 *E-mail:* info@achillesmedia.com *Web Site:* www.banffmediafestival.com, pg 1125

Wong, Nelson, SoundByte Productions Inc, 353 W 48 St, 6th fl, New York, NY 10036 *Tel:* 212-675-0600 *Fax:* 212-675-3724 *E-mail:* info@soundbyte.com *Web Site:* www.soundbyte.com, pg 1018

Wong, Robert, Creative BC (CrBC), 2225 W Broadway, Vancouver, BC V6K 2E4, Canada *Tel:* 604-730-2732 *Fax:* 604-736-7290 *E-mail:* info@creativebc.com *Web Site:* www.creativebc.com, pg 1104

Wong, Stan, Videssence, 10768 Lower Azusa Rd, El Monte, CA 91731 *Tel:* 626-579-0943 *Fax:* 626-579-6803 *E-mail:* contact@videssence.tv *Web Site:* www.videssence.tv, pg 1057

Wong, Whei, Denver Media Center, 3853 S Broadway, Englewood, CO 80113 *Tel:* 303-872-9993 *Web Site:* denvermediacenter.com, pg 845

Woo, Carolyn, SANYO Fisher Co, 2055 Sanyo Ave, San Diego, CA 92154 *Tel:* 619-661-1134 *Fax:* 619-661-6795 *Web Site:* us.sanyo.com; www.fisherav.com, pg 1002

Woo, John C, Asian American International Film Festival (AAIFF), 115 W 30 St, Suite 708, New York, NY 10001-4068 *Tel:* 212-989-1422 *Fax:* 212-727-3584 *E-mail:* festival@asiancinevision.org; info@asiancinevision.org *Web Site:* aaiff.org; www.asiancinevision.org, pg 1108

Wood, Brian, Supercircuits, 11000 N Mopac Expwy, Bldg 300, Austin, TX 78759 *Toll Free Tel:* 877-995-2288 *E-mail:* operations@supercircuits.com; customercare@supercircuits.com *Web Site:* www.supercircuits.com, pg 1029

Wood, David, Ensemble Designs Inc, 870 Gold Flat Rd, Nevada City, CA 95959 *Tel:* 530-478-1830 *Fax:* 530-478-1832 *E-mail:* info@ensembledesigns.com *Web Site:* www.ensembledesigns.com, pg 861

Wood, Doug, Omnimusic, 52 Main St, Port Washington, NY 11050 *Tel:* 516-883-0121 *Toll Free Tel:* 800-828-6664 *Fax:* 516-883-0271 *E-mail:* omni@omnimusic.com *Web Site:* www.omnimusic.com, pg 963

Wood, James B, IATSE, 207 W 25 St, 4th fl, New York, NY 10001 *Tel:* 212-730-1770 *Fax:* 212-730-7809 *Web Site:* www.iatse-intl.org, pg 1082

Wood, Jeffrey, Fantasy Studios, 2600 Tenth St, Berkeley, CA 94710 *Tel:* 510-486-2038 *Fax:* 510-486-2248 *Web Site:* www.fantasystudios.com, pg 865

Wood, Rob, SurgeX, 800 Knightdale Blvd, Suite 121, Knightdale, NC 27545 *Toll Free Tel:* 800-645-9721 (tech & cust support) *Fax:* 919-269-0454 *Web Site:* www.surgex.com, pg 1029

Woodburn, Robin, Hollywood Lights Inc, 5251 SE McLoughlin Blvd, Portland, OR 97202-4836 *Tel:* 503-232-9001; 503-232-8855 *Toll Free Tel:* 800-826-9881 *Fax:* 503-517-8686 *E-mail:* portland@hollywoodlights.biz *Web Site:* www.hollywoodlights.biz, pg 890

Woodbury, Troy, Wegener Communications, Technology Park, 11350 Technology Circle, Johns Creek, GA 30097 *Tel:* 770-814-4000; 770-814-4021 (sales); 770-814-4057 (cust serv) *Toll Free Tel:* 800-848-9467 (cust serv) *Fax:* 770-623-0698; 770-232-0621 (cust serv) *E-mail:* info@wegener.com; globalsales@wegener.com; service@wegener.com *Web Site:* www.wegener.com, pg 1063

Woodford, Charles H, Dance Horizons Video, 614 Rte 130, Hightstown, NJ 08520 *Tel:* 609-426-0602 *Toll Free Tel:* 800-220-7149 *Fax:* 609-426-1344 *E-mail:* pbc@dancehorizons.com *Web Site:* www.dancehorizons.com, pg 842

Woodford, Charles H, Princeton Book Company, Publishers, 614 Rte 130, Hightstown, NJ 08520 *Tel:* 609-426-0602 *Toll Free Tel:* 800-220-7149 *Fax:* 609-426-1344 *E-mail:* pbc@dancehorizons.com *Web Site:* www.dancehorizons.com, pg 982

Woodring, Suzie, Crest Electronics Inc, 3706 Alliance Dr, Greensboro, NC 27407 *Tel:* 336-855-6422 *Toll Free Tel:* 888-502-7378 *Fax:* 336-855-6676 *E-mail:* info@crestelectronics.com; custserv@crestelectronics.com *Web Site:* www.crestelectronics.com, pg 839

Woodroffe, Steve, Kits & Expendables, 45-27 37 St, Long Island, NY 11101 *Tel:* 718-482-1824; 718-482-1993; 917-842-8394 (emergencies after hrs) *Fax:* 718-482-1853 *E-mail:* orders@kitsandexpendables.com *Web Site:* www.kitsandexpendables.com, pg 911

Woods, Susan W, East Lansing Film Festival (ELFF), 210 Abbot Rd, Suite 48, East Lansing, MI 48823-4348 *Tel:* 517-980-5802 *Web Site:* elff.com, pg 1114

Woodward, Terry, WaxWorks VideoWorks, 325 E Third St, Owensboro, KY 42303 *Tel:* 270-926-0008 *Toll Free Tel:* 800-825-8558 *Fax:* 270-663-0737 *Web Site:* www.waxworksonline.com, pg 1063

Woodworth, Amy, Crystal Productions, 5320 Carpinteria Ave, Suite K, Carpinteria, CA 93013-2107 *Tel:* 847-657-8144 *Toll Free Tel:* 800-255-8629 *Fax:* 847-657-8149 *Toll Free Fax:* 800-657-8149 *E-mail:* custserv@crystalproductions.com *Web Site:* www.crystalproductions.com, pg 840

Woolf, Ellen, Connecticut Office of Film, Television & Digital Media, c/o Dept of Economic & Community Development, 505 Hudson St, Hartford, CT 06106 *Tel:* 860-270-8198 *Web Site:* www.ctfilm.com, pg 1095

Woolf, Richard, Xtech Inc, 241 Rock Creek Lane, Suite B, Scarsdale, NY 10583 *Tel:* 718-543-1222 *Toll Free Fax:* 888-528-6511 *E-mail:* info@xtechsystems.com *Web Site:* www.xtechsystems.com, pg 1071

Woolum, Sue, Conquest Sound Co Inc, 26113 S Ridgeland Ave, Monee, IL 60449 *Tel:* 708-534-0390 *Toll Free Tel:* 800-323-7671 *Fax:* 708-534-0398 *E-mail:* info@conquestsound.com; customerservice@conquestsound.com *Web Site:* www.conquestsound.com, pg 835

Worrell, Greg, Scholastic Library Publishing, 90 Sherman Tpke, Danbury, CT 06816 *Toll Free Tel:* 800-621-1115 (cust serv) *Toll Free Fax:* 866-783-4361 *Web Site:* www.scholastic.com/aboutscholastic/librarypublishing.htm, pg 1004

Worthington, Bob, Jupiter Systems, 31015 Huntwood Ave, Hayward, CA 94544 *Tel:* 510-675-1000 *Fax:* 510-675-1001 *E-mail:* sales@jupiter.com *Web Site:* www.jupiter.com, pg 907

Woydziak, Jon, Dogma Studios, 10559 Jefferson Blvd, Culver City, CA 90232 *Tel:* 310-838-2973 *Fax:* 310-838-2975 *E-mail:* info@dogmastudios.com *Web Site:* www.dogmastudios.com, pg 850

Woznow, Ken, Eagle Camera Support Systems Ltd, 1783 Draycott Rd, North Vancouver, BC V7J 1W5, Canada *Tel:* 604-649-6350 *Web Site:* eaglecss.com, pg 855

Wright, Eddie, Sound & Images Inc, 104 Corporate Blvd, Suite 411, West Columbia, SC 29169 *Tel:* 803-791-3925 *E-mail:* marketing@s-and-i.com *Web Site:* www.s-and-i.com, pg 1016

Wright, James, Primacoustic, 1588 Kebet Way, Port Coquitlam, BC V3C 5M5, Canada *Tel:* 604-942-1001 *Fax:* 604-942-1010 *E-mail:* info@primacoustic.com *Web Site:* www.primacoustic.com, pg 982

Wright, Keith, Reel Picture, 5330 Eastgate Mall, San Diego, CA 92121 *Tel:* 858-587-0301 *Toll Free Tel:* 866 502-3472 (US & CN) *Fax:* 858-587-8838 *Web Site:* www.reelpicture.com, pg 994

Wright, Randolph, Pyramid Media, 3200 Airport Ave, No 19, Santa Monica, CA 90405 *Tel:* 310-398-6149 *Toll Free Tel:* 800-421-2304 *Fax:* 310-398-7869 *E-mail:* info@pyramidmedia.com; sales@pyramidmedia.com *Web Site:* www.pyramidmedia.com, pg 987

Wright, Ray, IPRO, 34157 W 9 Mile Rd, Farmington Hills, MI 48335 *Tel:* 248-474-0522 *Toll Free Tel:* 800-420-4268 *Web Site:* www.avreps.org, pg 1084

Wright, Sandy Sanchez, Palardo Productions, 1807 Taft Ave, Suite 4, Hollywood, CA 90028 *Tel:* 323-469-8991 *E-mail:* palardo2@msn.com, pg 968

Wright, Wm M, DW Electrochemicals Ltd, 3-97 Newkirk Rd N, Richmond Hill, ON L4C 3G4, Canada *Tel:* 905-508-7500 *Fax:* 905-508-7502 *E-mail:* dwel@stabilant.com *Web Site:* www.stabilant.com, pg 854

Wu, Dan, Orevox USA Corp, 240 N Puente Ave, City of Industry, CA 91746-2303 *Tel:* 626-336-0516 *Toll Free Tel:* 800-237-0700 *Fax:* 626-336-3748 *Web Site:* www.dynavox.com, pg 965

Wuertz, William J, Dot Hill Systems Corp, 1351 S Sunset St, Longmont, CO 80501-6533 *Tel:* 303-845-3200 *Toll Free Tel:* 800-872-2783 *Fax:* 303-845-3655 *E-mail:* support@dothill.com; websales@dothill.com *Web Site:* www.dothill.com, pg 851

Wunderlich, R, Cambridge Documentary Films Inc, 3099 Hidden Valley Lane, Santa Barbara, CA 93108 *Tel:* 617-484-3993 *E-mail:* info@cambridgedocumentaryfilms.org *Web Site:* www.cambridgedocumentaryfilms.org, pg 818

Wurm, Jim, Exhibit & Event Marketers Association (E2MA), 2214 NW Fifth St, Bend, OR 97701 *Tel:* 541-317-8768 *Fax:* 541-317-8749 *Web Site:* www.e2ma.org, pg 1081

Wussow, George, Recortec Inc, 3329 Kifer Rd, Santa Clara, CA 95051-0719 *Tel:* 408-928-1480 *Toll Free Tel:* 800-729-7654 *Fax:* 408-928-1489 *E-mail:* info@recortec.com; support@recortec.com; sales@recortec.com *Web Site:* www.recortec.com, pg 993

Wuthrich, Kim, Warner Home Video Inc, 4000 Warner Blvd, Bldg 160, Burbank, CA 91522 *Tel:* 818-954-6000 *Fax:* 818-954-6480 *Web Site:* www.warnerbros.com, pg 1062

Wyatt, Mindy, Rafik, 812 Broadway, Suite 4, New York, NY 10003 *Tel:* 212-475-7884 *E-mail:* info@rafikvideo.com; sales@rafikvideo.com *Web Site:* www.rafikvideo.com, pg 990

Wyler, Max, Accord Productions, 2140 S Dixie Hwy, Suite 301, Miami, FL 33133 *Tel:* 305-856-1245 *Toll Free Tel:* 800-833-1245 *Fax:* 305-856-9101 *Web Site:* www.accordvideo.com, pg 773

Wyler, Rocky, Accord Productions, 2140 S Dixie Hwy, Suite 301, Miami, FL 33133 *Tel:* 305-856-1245 *Toll Free Tel:* 800-833-1245 *Fax:* 305-856-9101 *Web Site:* www.accordvideo.com, pg 773

Wyler, William, Accord Productions, 2140 S Dixie Hwy, Suite 301, Miami, FL 33133 *Tel:* 305-856-1245 *Toll Free Tel:* 800-833-1245 *Fax:* 305-856-9101 *Web Site:* www.accordvideo.com, pg 773

Wylie, Kimberly, Publishers Group West Inc, 1700 Fourth St, Berkeley, CA 94710 *Tel:* 510-809-3700 *Toll Free Tel:* 800-788-3123 (cust serv) *Fax:* 510-809-3777 *E-mail:* info@pgw.com *Web Site:* www.pgw.com, pg 987

Wyllie, Chris, Theatre Effects, 1810 Airport Exchange Blvd, Suite 400, Erlanger, KY 41018-3184 *Tel:* 513-772-7646 (intl) *Toll Free Tel:* 800-791-7646 *Fax:* 513-772-3579 *E-mail:* service@theatrefx.com *Web Site:* www.theatrefx.com, pg 1038

Wyne, David, Schiller's Audio-Visual, 9240 Manchester Rd, St Louis, MO 63144-2636 *Tel:* 314-968-3650 *Toll Free Tel:* 800-366-7244 *Fax:* 314-968-1184 *E-mail:* sales@schillers.com; av@schillers.com *Web Site:* www.schillersav.com, pg 1004

Wyner, Jonathan, M Works Mastering Studios, 1035 Cambridge St, Suite 17-B, Cambridge, MA 02141 *Tel:* 617-577-0089 *Fax:* 617-577-0098 *E-mail:* studio@m-works.com *Web Site:* www.m-works.com, pg 927

Wynn, Peter, Animotion Inc, 501 W Fayette St, Syracuse, NY 13204 *Tel:* 315-471-3533 *Fax:* 315-471-2730 *E-mail:* info@animotioninc.com *Web Site:* animotioninc.com, pg 787

Wynne, Dan, Sharp Electronics Corp, Professional Display Division, One Sharp Plaza, Mahwah, NJ 07495-1163 *Tel:* 201-529-8200 *Fax:* 201-529-8425 *E-mail:* prolcd@sharpsec.com *Web Site:* www.sharpusa.com, pg 1008

Wynne, Kenneth, CMI Media Management, 100 Business Park Dr, Armonk, NY 10504-1750 *Tel:* 914-273-7500 *Toll Free Tel:* 800-431-1102 *Fax:* 914-273-7575 *Web Site:* www.cinemagnetics.com, pg 830

Yablon, Gilbert, Lumeni Productions Inc, 1632 Flower St, Glendale, CA 91201 *Tel:* 818-956-2200 *Fax:* 818-956-3298 *E-mail:* info@lumeni.com *Web Site:* www.lumeni.com, pg 926

Yacoub, Marilou, Alan Weiss Productions, 270 White Plains Rd, Suite 2N, East Chester, NY 10709 *Tel:* 212-974-0606 *E-mail:* awpinfo@awptv.com *Web Site:* www.awptv.com, pg 1063

Yada, Michael, Yada/Levine Video Productions, 1253 Vine St, Suite 21-A, Hollywood, CA 90038 *Tel:* 323-461-1616 *Fax:* 323-461-2288 *E-mail:* video@yadalevine.com *Web Site:* www.yadalevine.com, pg 1071

Yadin, Orly, Vermont International Film Festival, 230 College St, Burlington, VT 05401 *Tel:* 802-660-2600 *Fax:* 802-860-9555 *E-mail:* info@vtiff.org *Web Site:* www.vtiff.org, pg 1129

Yaetes, Barbara, Charleston International Film Festival (CIFF), 915 Folly Rd, No 78, Charleston, SC 29412 *Tel:* 843-817-1617 *E-mail:* info@charlestoniff.org *Web Site:* charlestoniff.org, pg 1111

Yale, Martin, Sonic Science Inc, 79 Denlow Blvd, Toronto, ON M3B 1P8, Canada *Tel:* 416-383-0260 *Toll Free Tel:* 800-267-6642 *Fax:* 416-383-0261 *E-mail:* sales@sonicscience.com *Web Site:* www.sonicscience.com, pg 1016

Yamada, Kevin, Studio 637, 637 Cypress Ave, Hermosa Beach, CA 90254 *Tel:* 310-372-8218 *Web Site:* studio-637.com, pg 1027

Yancey, Mark, Satellite Digital Teleproductions (SDTV), 4004 La Salle St, San Diego, CA 92110-5124 *Tel:* 619-293-7777 *Toll Free Tel:* 800-SKY-PROD (759-7763 US) *Fax:* 619-223-3626 *E-mail:* info@sdtv.com *Web Site:* www.sdtv.com, pg 1003

Yanchar, Carl J, Yanchar Design & Consulting Group, 26741 Portola Pkwy, Suite 1-E, Foothill Ranch, CA 92610-1763 *Tel:* 949-770-6601 *Fax:* 949-770-6575 *E-mail:* info@yanchardesign.com *Web Site:* www.yanchardesign.com, pg 1072

Yanes, Vince, Ver Sales Inc, 2509 N Naomi St, Burbank, CA 91504 *Tel:* 818-567-3000 *Toll Free Tel:* 800-229-0518; 800-300-WIRE (300-9479, CA only) *Fax:* 818-567-3018 *E-mail:* sales@versales.com *Web Site:* www.versales.com, pg 1052

Yaney, Martha, Vista Group International Inc, 25 Van Zant St, Unit 8-D, Norwalk, CT 06855 *Tel:* 203-852-5557 *Toll Free Tel:* 800-866-2113 *Fax:* 203-852-5559 *E-mail:* info@vistagroupinternational.com *Web Site:* www.vistagroupinternational.com, pg 1059

Yankovich, Jennifer, Sonoma Valley Chamber of Commerce, 651-A Broadway, Sonoma, CA 95476-7041 *Tel:* 707-996-1033 *Fax:* 707-996-9402 *E-mail:* info@sonomachamber.com *Web Site:* sonomachamber.org, pg 1016, 1094

Yates, Bunny, SBS Productions, 1646 Livonia Ave, Los Angeles, CA 90035 *Tel:* 310-557-1545 *E-mail:* eindigo2@pacbell.net, pg 1003

Yates, Mark, New England Keyboard Inc, One Princeton Rd, Fitchburg, MA 01420 *Tel:* 978-345-8332 *Fax:* 978-345-4329 *E-mail:* info@newenglandkeyboard.com *Web Site:* www.newenglandkeyboard.com, pg 955

Yaung, Bruce, Avid Technology Inc, 65-75 Network Dr, Burlington, MA 01830 *Tel:* 978-640-6789 *Fax:* 978-640-3366 *Web Site:* www.avid.com, pg 799

Yeaman, Evan, Virtual Research Systems Inc, 3824 Vienna Dr, Aptos, CA 95003 *Tel:* 408-748-8712 *Fax:* 408-748-8714 *Web Site:* www.virtualresearch.com, pg 1058

Yeaman, Kevin, Dolby Labs Inc, 100 Potrero Ave, San Francisco, CA 94103-4813 *Tel:* 415-558-0200 *Fax:* 415-645-4000 *E-mail:* info@dolby.com *Web Site:* www.dolby.com, pg 850

Yeko, Bruce, Original Cast Records, PO Box 496, Georgetown, CT 06829-0496 *Tel:* 203-544-8288 *Fax:* 203-544-8288 *E-mail:* originalcast@aol.com *Web Site:* www.originalcastrecords.com; footlight.com, pg 965

Yep, Richard, American Counseling Association, 6101 Stevenson Ave, Alexandria, VA 22304 *Tel:* 703-823-9800 (ext 222) *Toll Free Tel:* 800-422-2648 (ext 222) *Fax:* 703-370-4833 *Toll Free Fax:* 800-473-2329 *E-mail:* membership@counseling.org *Web Site:* www.counseling.org, pg 784

Yessian, Brian, Yessian, 137 Fifth Ave, 3rd fl, New York, NY 10010 *Tel:* 212-533-3443 *E-mail:* info-ny@yessian.com *Web Site:* www.yessian.com, pg 1072

Yessian, Michael, Yessian, 137 Fifth Ave, 3rd fl, New York, NY 10010 *Tel:* 212-533-3443 *E-mail:* info-ny@yessian.com *Web Site:* www.yessian.com, pg 1072

Yessios, Chris, AutoDesSys Inc, 3518 Riverside Dr, Suite 102, Columbus, OH 43221 *Tel:* 614-488-8838 *Fax:* 614-488-0848 *E-mail:* formz@formz.com; sales@formz.com; sales@autodessys.com *Web Site:* www.formz.com, pg 797

Yewdall, Christopher, Dynamic Digital Depth Inc (DDD), 6100 Center Dr W, Suite 1100, Los Angeles, CA 90045 *Tel:* 310-566-3340 *Toll Free Tel:* 877-884-4333 *Fax:* 310-566-3380 *E-mail:* info@ddd.com *Web Site:* www.ddd.com, pg 854

Yewell, Julia, Welocalize, 241 E Fourth St, Suite 207, Frederick, MD 21701 *Tel:* 301-668-0330 *Toll Free Tel:* 800-370-9515 *Fax:* 301-668-0335 *E-mail:* info@welocalize.com *Web Site:* www.welocalize.com, pg 1063

Yewell, Smith, Welocalize, 241 E Fourth St, Suite 207, Frederick, MD 21701 *Tel:* 301-668-0330 *Toll Free Tel:* 800-370-9515 *Fax:* 301-668-0335 *E-mail:* info@welocalize.com *Web Site:* www.welocalize.com, pg 1063

Yoder, Phil, Icom Multimedia, 294 E Long St, Columbus, OH 43215-1829 *Tel:* 614-224-4400 *Fax:* 614-457-8050 *Web Site:* www.icommultimedia.com, pg 893

Yoffe, Max, Big Door, 114 Sheldon St, El Segundo, CA 90245 *Tel:* 310-546-6100 *Fax:* 310-906-4585 *E-mail:* sales@bigdoor.tv *Web Site:* www.bigdoor.tv; www.bigdoorstudio.tv, pg 807

Yoosufani, Zahid, University of Texas at Austin - Petroleum Extension Service, J J Pickle Research Campus, Petroleum Extension Service, Bldg 2, 10100 Burnet Rd, Austin, TX 78758-4445 *Tel:* 512-471-5940 *Toll Free Tel:* 800-687-4132 *Fax:* 512-471-9410 *Toll Free Fax:* 800-687-7839 *E-mail:* petex@www.utexas.edu *Web Site:* www.utexas.edu/ce/petex, pg 1050

York, Kerry L, Ed Ethridge Productions Inc, 1215 E Broward Blvd, Suite 200, Fort Lauderdale, FL 33301 *Tel:* 954-533-7100 *Fax:* 954-306-3261 *Web Site:* www.ethridgeproductions.com, pg 863

Yoshida, Ron, Hello World Communications, 118 W 22 St, 2nd fl, New York, NY 10011 *Tel:* 212-243-8800 *Fax:* 212-691-6961 *E-mail:* excitable01@gmail.com *Web Site:* www.hwc.tv, pg 888

Yoshitake, Junichi, Canon USA Inc, One Canon Park, Melville, NY 11747 *Tel:* 613-330-5000 *E-mail:* pr@cusa.canon.com *Web Site:* www.usa.canon.com, pg 819

Yost, Dave, WPHL-TV, 5001 Wynnefield Ave, Philadelphia, PA 19131 *Tel:* 215-878-1700 *Fax:* 215-879-7683; 215-877-4912 *E-mail:* feedback@phl17.com *Web Site:* www.phl17.com, pg 1070

Yost, Kelly, Channel Productions, 1964 Filer Ave E, Twin Falls, ID 83301 *Fax:* 208-734-6550 *E-mail:* chanpro@mindspring.com, pg 823

Young, Andrew, Young Minds Inc, 1014 E Cooley Dr, Suite H, Colton, CA 92324 *Tel:* 909-426-4860 *Fax:* 909-426-4866 *E-mail:* info@ymi.com; sales@ymi.com *Web Site:* www.ymi.com, pg 1072

Young, Christian, Leader Instruments Corp, 6484 Commerce Dr, Cypress, CA 90630 *Tel:* 714-527-9300 *Toll Free Tel:* 800-645-5104 *Fax:* 714-527-7490 *E-mail:* sales@leaderusa.com *Web Site:* www.leaderusa.com, pg 917

Young, Deborah M, National Association of Elementary School Principals (NAESP), 1615 Duke St, Alexandria, VA 22314 *Tel:* 703-684-3345 *Toll Free Tel:* 800-386-2377 *Fax:* 703-549-5568 *Toll Free Fax:* 800-396-2377 *E-mail:* naesp@naesp.org *Web Site:* www.naesp.org, pg 952

Young, Joanne, Audio Visual Imagineering Inc, 6565 Hazeltine National Dr, Suite 2, Orlando, FL 32822 *Tel:* 407-859-8166 *Fax:* 407-859-8254 *Web Site:* www.av-imagineering.com, pg 795

Young, Rick, Bitcentral Inc, 4340 Von Karman Ave, Suite 400, Newport Beach, CA 92660 *Tel:* 949-253-9000 *E-mail:* sales@bitcentral.com; support@bitcentral.com *Web Site:* www.bitcentral.com, pg 808

Young, Star, E Video Productions, 17 Washington St, Toms River, NJ 08753 *Tel:* 732-349-4762 *Toll Free Tel:* 877-384-3365 *Web Site:* www.evideoproductions.net, pg 855

Young, Steve, Videografix LLC, 2530 Berryessa Rd, Suite 314, San Jose, CA 95132-2903 *Tel:* 408-499-1280 *Fax:* 408-583-4018 *E-mail:* info@videografix.com *Web Site:* www.videografix.com, pg 1057

Young, Susan, MarVista Entertainment Inc, 10277 W Olympic Blvd, 3rd fl, Los Angeles, CA 90067 *Tel:* 424-274-3000 *Fax:* 424-274-3050 *E-mail:* info@marvista.net *Web Site:* www.marvista.net, pg 933

Young, Will, Whirlwind Music Distributors Inc, 99 Ling Rd, Rochester, NY 14612 *Tel:* 585-663-8820 *Toll Free Tel:* 800-733-9473 (US only) *Fax:* 585-865-8930 *E-mail:* sales@whirlwindusa.com; techsupport@whirlwindusa.com; darylg@whirlwindusa.com (Canadian inquiries) *Web Site:* whirlwindusa.com, pg 1065

Younger, Alex, Cinema Equipment & Supplies Inc, 12457 SW 130 St, Miami, FL 33186 *Tel:* 305-232-8182 *Toll Free Tel:* 800-759-5905 *E-mail:* sales@cinemaequip.com *Web Site:* www.cinemaequip.com, pg 827

Youngs, Ross O, Univenture Inc, 13311 Industrial Pkwy, Marysville, OH 43040 *Tel:* 937-645-4600 *Toll Free Tel:* 877-831-9428 *Fax:* 937-645-4700 *E-mail:* sales@univenture.com; orders@univenture.com *Web Site:* www.univenture.com, pg 1049

Youngson, Steve, Innovative Electronic Designs LLC, 9701 Taylorsville Rd, Louisville, KY 40299 *Tel:* 502-267-7436 *Fax:* 502-267-9070 *E-mail:* info@iedaudio.com *Web Site:* www.iedaudio.com, pg 898

Yu, Raymond, InFocus Corp, 13190 SW 68 Pkwy, Suite 200, Portland, OR 97223-8368 *Tel:* 503-207-4700 *Toll Free Tel:* 877-388-8385 *Fax:* 503-207-4707 *E-mail:* sales@infocus.com *Web Site:* www.infocus.com, pg 898

Yu, Tricia, Uncharted Country Publishing, PO Box 756, Taos, NM 87571 *Tel:* 575-776-3470 *Toll Free Tel:* 800-488-4940 *E-mail:* ucp@taichihealth.com *Web Site:* www.taichihealth.com, pg 1048

Yurish, Pete, Spectrum Audio Visual Services, 351 W 45 Ave, Denver, CO 80216 *Tel:* 303-477-4456 *Toll Free Tel:* 800-477-4752 *Fax:* 303-477-0114 *E-mail:* info@spectrumav.com *Web Site:* www.spectrumav.com, pg 1020

Yurkiw, Mark, Think 3-D.com, 180 Cross Hwy, Westport, CT 06880 *Tel:* 646-732-9197 *Web Site:* www.think3-d.com, pg 1038

Yuvminina, Victoria, Canamedia Inc, 1540 Cornwall Rd, Suite 216, Oakville, ON L6J 7W5, Canada *Tel:* 416-363-6765 *Toll Free Tel:* 866-999-5292 *Fax:* 416-363-7834 *Web Site:* www.canamedia.com, pg 818

Zacchi, Dawn T, Rosco Laboratories Inc, 52 Harbor View, Stamford, CT 06902 *Tel:* 203-708-8900 *Toll Free Tel:* 800-ROSCO NY (767-2669) *Fax:* 203-708-8919 *E-mail:* info@rosco.com *Web Site:* www.rosco.com, pg 999

Zachry, H C, Zachry Associates Inc, 500 Chestnut St, Suite 2000, Abilene, TX 79602 *Tel:* 325-677-1342 *Fax:* 325-672-2001 *E-mail:* info@zachryinc.com *Web Site:* zachryinc.com, pg 1073

Zagrobelny, Jim, Crispin Corp, 600 Wade Ave, Raleigh, NC 27605 *Tel:* 919-845-7744 *Fax:* 919-845-7766 *E-mail:* welisten@crispincorp.com *Web Site:* www.crispincorp.com, pg 839

Zagryn, Jim, SYMCO Inc, 29 Poplar Dr, Stirling, NJ 07980 *Tel:* 908-647-6262 *Fax:* 908-647-4904 *E-mail:* orders@symcoinc.com *Web Site:* www.symcoinc.com, pg 1030

Zaidi, Nasir, Spectra Cine Inc, 3607 W Magnolia Blvd, Burbank, CA 91505 *Tel:* 818-954-9222 *Fax:* 818-954-0016 *E-mail:* info@spectracine.com *Web Site:* www.spectracine.com, pg 1020

Zajaczkiwsky, Steve, HD Source, 1333 Matheson Blvd E, Mississauga, ON L4W 1R1, Canada *Tel:* 416-449-3030; 905-890-6905 *Fax:* 416-449-5230 *Web Site:* www.hdsource.ca, pg 886

Zajaczkiwsky, Steve, ZTV Broadcast Services Inc, 1333 Matheson Blvd E, Mississauga, ON L4W 1R1, Canada *Tel:* 905-290-4430 *Fax:* 905-290-3370 *Web Site:* ztvbroadcast.com, pg 1074

Zajde, Lionel, VITEC Multimedia, 931 Benecia, Sunnyvale, CA 94085 *Tel:* 650-230-2400 *Toll Free Tel:* 800-451-5101 *Fax:* 404-320-3132 *E-mail:* info@vitec.com *Web Site:* www.vitec.com, pg 1060

Zakrzewski, Frank, Fox Connecticut, 285 Broad St, Hartford, CT 06115 *Tel:* 860-527-6161 *Fax:* 860-727-0158 *Web Site:* www.ctnow.com, pg 872

Zakrzewski, Paul, Manfrotto Distribution Inc, 10 Mountainview Rd, Suite 320 S, Upper Saddle River, NJ 07458 *Tel:* 201-818-9500 *Fax:* 201-818-9177 *E-mail:* info@manfrottodistribution.us *Web Site:* www.manfrottodistribution.us, pg 930

Zalacain, Francois, Sunnyside Communications Inc, 348 W 38 St, Suite 12-B, New York, NY 10018 *Tel:* 212-564-4606 *Fax:* 212-967-2968 *Web Site:* www.sunnysiderecords.com, pg 1028

Zaleski, Billy, Data Projections Inc, 3700 W Sam Houston Pkwy S, Suite 525, Houston, TX 77042 *Tel:* 713-781-1999 *Toll Free Tel:* 866-225-5374 *Fax:* 713-781-3338 *Web Site:* www.dataprojections.com, pg 843

Zaleski, Jeff, Parabola Audio/Video, 20 W 20 St, 2nd fl, New York, NY 10011 *Tel:* 212-822-8806 (edit & publg); 201-656-7220 (ad) *Toll Free Tel:* 800-560-MYTH (560-6984); 877-593-2521 (subns) *Fax:* 212-822-8823 *E-mail:* info@parabola.org *Web Site:* www.parabola.org, pg 969

Zaleski, Linda C, Data Projections Inc, 3700 W Sam Houston Pkwy S, Suite 525, Houston, TX 77042 *Tel:* 713-781-1999 *Toll Free Tel:* 866-225-5374 *Fax:* 713-781-3338 *Web Site:* www.dataprojections.com, pg 843

Zaleski, Matthew, Data Projections Inc, 3700 W Sam Houston Pkwy S, Suite 525, Houston, TX 77042 *Tel:* 713-781-1999 *Toll Free Tel:* 866-225-5374 *Fax:* 713-781-3338 *Web Site:* www.dataprojections.com, pg 843

Zalud, Becky, A T Products Inc, 1600 S Division St, Harvard, IL 60033 *Tel:* 815-943-3590 *Toll Free Tel:* 800-848-2205 *Fax:* 815-943-3604 *E-mail:* atprod@mc.net *Web Site:* atproducts.com, pg 771

Zamacona, Frank, Zamacona Productions, 2600 Tenth St, Suite 302, Berkeley, CA 94710 *Tel:* 510-704-4011 *Fax:* 510-704-4013 *E-mail:* admin@zamacona-productions.com *Web Site:* www.zamacona-productions.com, pg 1073

Zammit, Joe, L A Management Co LLC, 8131 Bay Pointe Dr, Denver, NC 28037 *Tel:* 704-560-6274 *Toll Free Tel:* 800-651-7818 *Fax:* 704-973-7968 *E-mail:* info@managementco.com *Web Site:* lamanagementco.com, pg 914

Zampas, Jerry, Quality Clones, 3940 Laurel Canyon Blvd, Suite 405, Studio City, CA 91604 *Tel:* 323-464-5853 *E-mail:* info@qualityclones.com *Web Site:* www.qualityclones.com, pg 988

Zapel, Mark, Meriwether Publishing Ltd, 885 Elkton Dr, Colorado Springs, CO 80907-3522 *Tel:* 719-594-4422 *Toll Free Tel:* 800-937-5297 *Fax:* 719-594-9916 *Toll Free Fax:* 888-594-4436 *E-mail:* customerservice@meriwether.com; orders@meriwether.com *Web Site:* www.meriwether.com, pg 939

Zapel, Ted, Meriwether Publishing Ltd, 885 Elkton Dr, Colorado Springs, CO 80907-3522 *Tel:* 719-594-4422 *Toll Free Tel:* 800-937-5297 *Fax:* 719-594-9916 *Toll Free Fax:* 888-594-4436 *E-mail:* customerservice@meriwether.com; orders@meriwether.com *Web Site:* www.meriwether.com, pg 939

Zaransky, Steve, Airways Digital Media, 4055 W Peterson Ave, Chicago, IL 60646 *Tel:* 773-539-8400 *E-mail:* info@airwaysdigital.com *Web Site:* www.airwaysdigital.com, pg 779

Zargharmi, Ms Syma, Nickelodeon, 1515 Broadway, 44th fl, New York, NY 10036 *Tel:* 212-258-8000 *Fax:* 212-258-1822 *Web Site:* www.nick.com, pg 957

Zarrabian, Massood, Kenexa, 650 E Swedesford Rd, 2nd fl, Wayne, PA 19087 *Tel:* 407-548-1444 *Fax:* 610-971-9181 *E-mail:* kenexa_learn_sales@kenexa.com *Web Site:* www.outstart.com, pg 909

Zboray, David, VRSim Inc, 222 Pitkin St, Suite 119, East Hartford, CT 06108-3220 *Tel:* 860-893-0080 *E-mail:* info@vrsim.net *Web Site:* www.vrsim.net, pg 1061

Zelkin, Carol, Interactive Multimedia & Collaborative Communications Alliance (IMCCA), PO Box 756, Syosset, NY 11791 *Web Site:* www.imcca.org, pg 1083

Zellan, Les, ZGC Inc, 264 Morris Ave, Mountain Lakes, NJ 07046 *Tel:* 973-335-4460 *Fax:* 973-335-4560 *E-mail:* sales@zgc.com *Web Site:* www.zgc.com, pg 1073

Zelle, Carolyn, Odyssey Productions Inc, 2800 NW Thurman, Portland, OR 97210 *Tel:* 503-223-3480 *Fax:* 503-223-3493 *E-mail:* info@odysseypro.com *Web Site:* www.odysseypro.com, pg 961

Zeller, Paul R, Imation Corp, One Imation Way, Oakdale, MN 55128-3421 *Tel:* 651-704-4000 *Toll Free Tel:* 888-466-3456 *Fax:* 651-704-3444 *Toll Free Fax:* 888-704-4200 *E-mail:* info@imation.com *Web Site:* www.imation.com, pg 896

Zelman, D'vora, Zelman Studios Ltd, 623 Cortelyou Rd, Brooklyn, NY 11218 *Tel:* 718-941-5500 *E-mail:* kaforce@yahoo.com, pg 1073

Zelman, Sidney M, Zelman Studios Ltd, 623 Cortelyou Rd, Brooklyn, NY 11218 *Tel:* 718-941-5500 *E-mail:* kaforce@yahoo.com, pg 1073

Zelnikel, Glenn, Z-Systems Audio Engineering, 1325 NW 53 Ave, Suite B, Gainesville, FL 32609 *Tel:* 352-371-0990 *E-mail:* z-sys@z-sys.com *Web Site:* www.z-sys.com, pg 1073

Zemke, Ryan, AVL Systems Design LLC, 14901 Bristol Park Blvd, Edmond, OK 73013 *Tel:* 405-749-1866 *Fax:* 405-749-1851 *E-mail:* dnix@avl1.com *Web Site:* www.avl1.com, pg 800

Zemniakova, Iana, RGB Spectrum, 950 Marina Village Pkwy, Alameda, CA 94501 *Tel:* 510-814-7000 *Fax:* 510-814-7026 *E-mail:* sales@rgb.com *Web Site:* www.rgb.com, pg 996

Zemrak, Derek, California Independent Film Festival (CAIFF), 350 Park St, Moraga, CA 94566 *Tel:* 925-388-0752; 310-879-9188 (Los Angeles off) *E-mail:* info@caiff.org *Web Site:* caiff.org, pg 1110

Zeno, Amy, Advanced Systems Group LLC, 1226 Powell St, Emeryville, CA 94608-2618 *Tel:* 510-654-8300 *Fax:* 510-654-8370 *Web Site:* www.asgllc.com, pg 778

Zerone, Tim, The Music Place, 844 Rte 73, West Berlin, NJ 08091 *Tel:* 856-768-2226 *Fax:* 856-768-7135 *E-mail:* zeronemusic@aol.com, pg 951

Zetien, Zeke, Tel-Test, 605 NW 53 Ave, Suite A-17, Gainesville, FL 32609 *Tel:* 352-335-0901 *Fax:* 352-376-3260, pg 1035

Zettel, John, AVI-SPL, 6301 Benjamin Rd, Suite 101, Tampa, FL 33634 *Tel:* 813-884-7168 *Toll Free Tel:* 866-708-5034; 800-282-6733; 866-925-8298 (cust serv); 866-559-8197 (sales) *Fax:* 813-882-9508 *E-mail:* questions@avispl.com; sales@avispl.com; customerservice@avispl.com *Web Site:* www.avispl.com, pg 798

Ziegerbein, Tim, Lumalaser, 84777 Charlottes Way, Eugene, OR 97405 *Tel:* 541-687-1414 *Toll Free Tel:* 800-606-2597 *Fax:* 541-687-1438 *E-mail:* info@lumalaser.com *Web Site:* www.lumalaser.com, pg 926

Ziegler, Diana, Steven Halpern's Inner Peace Music, PO Box 2644, San Anselmo, CA 94979-2644 *Tel:* 541-488-7870 *Toll Free Tel:* 888-765-9697 (shipping); 800-909-0707 (orders) *Fax:* 541-488-7870 *E-mail:* info@innerpeacemusic.com *Web Site:* www.innerpeacemusic.com, pg 884

Ziegler, Liz, Tyler Camera Systems, 14218 Aetna St, Van Nuys, CA 91401 *Tel:* 818-989-4420 *Toll Free Tel:* 800-390-6070 *Fax:* 818-989-0423 *E-mail:* info@tylermount.com *Web Site:* www.tylermount.com, pg 1047

Zieman, Nancy, Nancy's Notions, 333 Beichl Ave, Beaver Dam, WI 53916 *Tel:* 920-887-0391 *Toll Free Tel:* 800-833-0690 (orders) *Fax:* 920-887-2133 *Toll Free Fax:* 800-255-8119 (orders) *E-mail:* custserv@nancysnotions.com *Web Site:* www.nancysnotions.com, pg 952

Zimbelman, Dan, API, 8301 Patuxent Range Rd, Jessup, MD 20794 *Tel:* 301-776-7879 *Fax:* 301-776-8117 *E-mail:* service@apiaudio.com *Web Site:* www.apiaudio.com, pg 788

Zimmer, Lydia, Art Directors Guild (ADG), 11969 Ventura Blvd, 2nd fl, Studio City, CA 91604 *Tel:* 818-762-9995 *Fax:* 818-762-9997 *Web Site:* www.adg.org, pg 1078

Zimmerman, Arthur, Zim Records, 18 Ivy Dr, Jericho, NY 11753 *Tel:* 516-681-7102 *E-mail:* zimrecords@msn.com, pg 1074

Zimmerman, Barbara, BZ/Rights & Permissions Inc, 145 W 86 St, New York, NY 10024 *Tel:* 212-924-3000 *Fax:* 212-924-2525 *E-mail:* info@bzrights.com *Web Site:* www.bzrights.com; www.thepublicdomainsite.com, pg 816

Zimmerman, Bill, Canadian American Records, PO Box 808, Lititz, PA 17543-0538 *Tel:* 717-627-4800 *Fax:* 717-627-4800 *E-mail:* canadianamerican@dejazzd.com *Web Site:* www.canadianamericanrecords.net; www.joeywelz.com, pg 818

Zimmerman, Debra, Women Make Movies Inc, 115 W 29 St, Suite 1200, New York, NY 10001 *Tel:* 212-925-0606 *Fax:* 212-925-2052 *E-mail:* info@wmm.com *Web Site:* www.wmm.com, pg 1069

Zimmerman, Jeffery, Sound-Craft Systems Inc, 1584 Petit Jean Mountain Rd, Morrilton, AR 72110 *Tel:* 501-727-5476 *Toll Free Tel:* 800-643-8747 *Fax:* 501-727-5402 *E-mail:* sales@sound-craft.com *Web Site:* www.sound-craft.com, pg 1017

Zimmerman, Mark, Newton Instrument Co Inc, 111 E "A" St, Butner, NC 27509-2426 *Tel:* 919-575-6426 *Fax:* 919-575-4708 *Web Site:* www.enewton.com, pg 957

Zimmerman, Otto, March Manufacturing Inc, 1819 Pickwick Ave, Glenview, IL 60026 *Tel:* 847-729-5300 *Fax:* 847-729-7062 *E-mail:* sales@marchpump.com *Web Site:* www.marchpump.com, pg 930

Zinar, Raymond J, Anchor Bay Entertainment LLC, 9242 Beverly Blvd, Suite 201, Beverly Hills, CA 90210 *Tel:* 424-204-4166 *E-mail:* questions@anchorbayent.com *Web Site:* www.anchorbayentertainment.com, pg 786

Zinman, Paul, SoundByte Productions Inc, 353 W 48 St, 6th fl, New York, NY 10036 *Tel:* 212-675-0600 *Fax:* 212-675-3724 *E-mail:* info@soundbyte.com *Web Site:* www.soundbyte.com, pg 1018

Zinn, Roland C, Tufnut Theft Protection, 2910 San Isidro Ct, Santa Fe, NM 87501 *Tel:* 505-424-1954 *Toll Free Tel:* 800-227-0949 *Fax:* 505-424-1956 *E-mail:* tufnut@tufnut.com *Web Site:* www.tufnut.com, pg 1046

Zinno, Joyce A, The New Film Company Inc, 7 Scott St, Cambridge, MA 02138 *Tel:* 617-520-5005 *Fax:* 617-491-9201 *E-mail:* newfilmco@aol.com *Web Site:* www.newfilmco.com, pg 955

Ziobro, Robert J, Advance Audiovisual Presentation Ltd, 5 Rothschild Ct, Gaithersburg, MD 20878 *Tel:* 301-937-0900 *Fax:* 301-330-2937 *E-mail:* aaplav@outlook.com *Web Site:* aaplav.com, pg 777

Zipper, Todd, The Learning House Inc, 427 S Fourth St, Suite 300, Louisville, KY 40202 *Tel:* 502-589-9878 *Fax:* 502-589-9825 *E-mail:* sales@learninghouse.com *Web Site:* www.learninghouse.com, pg 917

Zipursky, Arnie, Cambium Catalyst International (CCI), 18 Dupont St, Toronto, ON M5R 1V2, Canada *Tel:* 416-964-8750 *Fax:* 416-964-1980 *E-mail:* info@ccientertainment.com *Web Site:* www.ccientertainment.com, pg 817

Zittell, Philip, Omnirax, PO Box 1792, Sausalito, CA 94966-1792 *Tel:* 415-332-3392 *Toll Free Tel:* 800-332-3393 *Fax:* 415-332-2607 *E-mail:* info@omnirax.com *Web Site:* www.omnirax.com, pg 963

Zogas, Pete, National Instruments Corp, 11500 N Mopac Expwy, Austin, TX 78759-3504 *Toll Free Tel:* 888-280-7645 (sales); 800-531-5066 (cust serv) *Fax:* 512-683-8411 *Web Site:* www.ni.com, pg 953

Zogby, Drew, Alpha Technologies, 3767 Alpha Way, Bellingham, WA 98226 *Tel:* 360-647-2360 *Fax:* 360-671-4936 *E-mail:* alpha@alpha.com *Web Site:* www.alpha.com, pg 782

Zoll, Keith, Ray Supply Inc, 871 Rte 9, Queensbury, NY 12804 *Tel:* 518-792-5848 *Toll Free Tel:* 800-347-5851 (orders) *Fax:* 518-792-1727 *E-mail:* sales@raysupply.com *Web Site:* www.raysupply.com, pg 992

Zollo, Caden, Specialty Bulb Co Inc, 80 Orville Dr, Bohemia, NY 11716 *Tel:* 631-589-3393 *Toll Free Tel:* 800-331-BULB (331-2852) *Fax:* 631-563-3089 *E-mail:* info@bulbspecialists.com *Web Site:* www.bulbspecialists.com, pg 1020

Zoltan, Laszlo "Les", Computer Modules Inc, 11409 W Bernardo Ct, San Diego, CA 92127 *Tel:* 858-613-1818 *Fax:* 858-613-1815 *E-mail:* info@computermodules.com *Web Site:* www.dveo.com, pg 834

Zoradi, Mark, DreamWorks Animation SKG Inc, 1000 Flower St, Glendale, CA 91201 *Tel:* 818-695-5000 *Fax:* 818-695-4190 *Web Site:* www.dreamworksanimation.com, pg 852

Zoradi, Michael, Medcom Inc, 6060 Phyllis Dr, Cypress, CA 90630-5243 *Tel:* 714-891-1443 *Toll Free Tel:* 800-877-1443; 800-541-0253 *Fax:* 714-891-3140 *E-mail:* customerservice@medcominc.com *Web Site:* www.medcominc.com, pg 936

Zorba, V, Zelo Productions Inc, 3 S Newton St, Denver, CO 80219 *Tel:* 303-936-8995; 303-898-0911 (cell) *Fax:* 303-936-0799 *E-mail:* zelo@earthlink.net *Web Site:* www.zeloproductions.com, pg 1073

Zorich, Stefan, FilmNation Entertainment, 150 W 22 St, 9th fl, New York, NY 10011 *Web Site:* www.filmnation.com, pg 867

Zubko, Scott, Cine Audio Visual Sales & Service Ltd, 10251 106 St, Edmonton, AB T5J 1H5, Canada *Tel:* 780-423-5081 *Toll Free Tel:* 877-423-5081 *Fax:* 780-424-0309 *E-mail:* cineav@cineav.com; sales@cineav.com; info@cineav.com *Web Site:* www.cineav.com, pg 826

Zuchlinski, Donna, Ontario Media Development Corp, South Tower, Suite 501, 175 Bloor St E, Toronto, ON M4W 3R8, Canada *Tel:* 416-314-6858 *Fax:* 416-314-6876 *E-mail:* reception@omdc.on.ca *Web Site:* www.omdc.on.ca, pg 1105

Zuckerman, David, Easy Edit Video Inc, 8431 Baymeadows Way, Jacksonville, FL 32256 *Tel:* 904-730-9999 *Fax:* 904-730-0412 *Web Site:* www.easyeditvideo.com, pg 856

Zuckerman, Donald, Colorado Office of Film, Television & Media, 1625 Broadway, Suite 2700, Denver, CO 80202 *Tel:* 303-892-3840 *Fax:* 303-892-3848 *E-mail:* info@coloradofilm.org *Web Site:* www.coloradofilm.org, pg 1095

Zwaal, Mike, Brown United, PO Box 362, Monrovia, CA 91017-0362 *Tel:* 626-357-1161 *Toll Free Tel:* 800-44-BROWN (442-7696) *Fax:* 626-358-3064 *Toll Free Fax:* 800-26-BROWN (262-7696) *E-mail:* info@brownunited.com *Web Site:* www.brownunited.com, pg 814

Zylstra, Nadine, Sesame Workshop, 1900 Broadway, 4th fl, New York, NY 10023 *Tel:* 212-595-3456 *Fax:* 212-875-6113 *Web Site:* www.sesameworkshop.org, pg 1088